The
College
Blue Book®
44th Edition

Degrees Offered
by College
and Subject

The College Blue Book®

44th Edition

Degrees Offered by College and Subject

MACMILLAN REFERENCE USA
A part of Gale, Cengage Learning

GALE
CENGAGE Learning®

Farmington Hills, Mich • San Francisco • New York • Waterville, Maine
Meriden, Conn • Mason, Ohio • Chicago

**The College Blue Book, 44th Edition
Volume 3**

Project Editor: Bohdan Romaniuk

Editorial Support Services: Wayne Fong

Composition and Electronic Prepress: Gary
  Leach

Manufacturing: Rita Wimberley

For product information and technology assistance, contact us at
Gale Customer Support, 1-800-877-4253.
For permission to use material from this text or product,
submit all requests online at **www.cengage.com/permissions.**
Further permissions questions can be emailed to
permissionrequest@cengage.com

Gale
27500 Drake Rd.
Farmington Hills, MI, 48331-3535

ISBN-13: 978-0-02-866306-7 (6 vol. set)
ISBN-13: 978-0-02-866309-8 (vol. 3)

ISSN 1082-7048

This title is also available as an e-book.
ISBN-13: 978-0-02-866314-2 (set)
Contact your Gale sales representative for ordering information.

Printed in the United States of America
1 2 3 4 5 6 7 20 19 18 17 16

Contents

The College Blue Book® has been a standard, professional reference on higher education since it was first published in 1923. New features have been added during the intervening years to keep pace with the changing needs for information about our educational facilities. The information, especially in the areas of tuition, room and board, enrollment figures, library holdings, is constantly changing. It is difficult to maintain up-to-date figures in these areas, as many schools change tuition and related costs on an ongoing basis. We therefore urge our readers to check directly with the schools for the most current cost information.

CONTENTS OF EACH VOLUME

Volume 1: Narrative Descriptions

More than 4,300 colleges in the United States and Canada are fully described. Entrance requirements are detailed and campus facilities and costs are described. A map of each U.S. state and Canadian province is included and each college has a grid index for easy location. Web sites are also listed.

Volume 2: Tabular Data

Colleges are listed alphabetically by state or province. Information about costs, accreditation, enrollment figures, faculty, and names of the chief administrative officers are given for each school.

Volume 3: Degrees Offered by College and Subject

In Part I, the name of each college is listed alphabetically by state or province, with a list of the subject areas for which degrees are offered. Part II includes an alphabetical listing of subject areas for which degrees are granted by one or more institutions of higher education.

Volume 4: Occupational Education

More than 6,500 schools in the United States that provide occupational or technical training are fully described, offering such information as tuition costs, enrollment figures, and entrance requirements. Two indexes are provided: an alphabetical listing of schools in the "Index of Occupational Education Schools," in addition to the "Curricula and Areas of Instruction" index.

Volume 5: Scholarships, Fellowships, Grants, and Loans

This volume provides a listing of more than 6,000 sources of financial aid for students wishing to further their education. Split alphabetically into eight broad subject areas (each containing several more specialized concentrations of study), as well as a general section, each listing provides basic information about a specific award, including eligibility requirements, amount of award, and application deadlines.

Volume 6: Distance Learning Programs

Responding to this rapidly growing trend in postsecondary education, this volume features comprehensive profiles of nearly 1,000 institutions offering distance learning programs within the United States and Canada.

FOR MORE INFORMATION

We are always open to suggestions and recommendations for improvement of *The College Blue Book®* from our readers and from the educational professions. Please contact: Editor, *The College Blue Book*

Macmillan Reference USA

27500 Drake Rd.

Farmington Hills, MI 48331-3535

Phone: (248)699-4253

Toll-free: 800-877-4253

Fax: (248)699-8075

Email: bob.romaniukl@cengage.com

Web site: www.gale.cengage.com

The decision to continue education beyond high school years, the selection of a collegiate institution, and the area of study to be pursued are some of the essential experiences necessary for students to determine their futures. Alternatives of choice institutions, work selection, job opportunities, professional training, or even discontinuing any further education are all selective decisions open to the students.

Nearly all students today have opportunities to continue education beyond high school. There are more schools accepting wider ranges of student ability and interest than ever before. This means more effort, more planning, and more personal study in making the college choice.

Self Appraisal

The best place to begin is with oneself. An appraisal with objective, honest answers is necessary. What are the personal potentials as a student? Where has the best performance been? What are the probabilities for improvement? What are the reasons for really wanting to go to college; is it for intellectual development, vocational preparation, or simply to satisfy a desire for status? What are the personal ideas of college? What is expected from the college experience? Have career plans been made? Where are the academic abilities? What subjects are preferred? What is the quality of performance in the preferred areas of study? What is the overall grade average? What is the class rank in high school? In what subject areas is there the greatest interest? What is the quality of work in these areas? Are interests and performance generally consistent? Are the expressed and recorded interests truly and accurately reflecting the inward wishes? What was liked best about the high school experience? Has the college preparatory program been followed in high school? What were the social and cultural experiences during high school years that were most meaningful? What was considered, if anything, to be lacking?

Well-thought-out answers to these and similar questions are helpful. Discussions of such topics with counselors, parents, and teachers increases the probability of success in college selection, attendance, and completion.

The counselor today is an extremely valued resource person available to assist the student. When an effective working team of counselor-student-parent actually exists, the probabilities for the student making selective choices that prove to be the "right" ones are unquestionably the greatest. The better the student and the counselor know one another, the more effective the guidance and counseling program will be. For this to occur, the opportunity for face-to-face student-counselor discussion needs to start in the latter elementary school years and continue through high school and college.

College Appraisals

Research is continuing in the areas of college admissions and student success. The identification and understanding of causes of success and failure need professional study. However, one thing is apparent: the more careful the preparations and planning by the student, the better the chances of college admission and success.

Systemized planning should begin early. The more self-understanding and knowledge about available colleges one has, the better one can plan with corresponding success. Certainly, early in the high school career, students should be reviewing detailed information on colleges and universities with the counselor, noting academic requirements such as scholastic performance, course requirements, costs and other particular qualities of individual collegiate institutions. There is no single one-and-only college for the student. Colleges have personalities just as the students do. There are always several colleges with academic and social climates compatible and acceptable to each student.

Entrance requirements, courses available, costs, size of student body, academic pressure, special programs, geographical location, and specialty schools are some of the considerations of every student in appraising available colleges.

The College Blue Book® is dedicated to providing detailed information regarding collegiate institutions throughout the United States and Canada. Students and counselors should browse through The College Blue Book® and become familiar with the colleges of our country and neighboring Canada. As interest sharpens and narrows, a more selective and in-depth study of institutions should be made.

Where feasible, students should plan visits to college campuses. Campus visiting may begin during the summer between the sophomore and junior years of high school. The best time to be on a college campus, however, is during the regular term with a carefully planned visit in the spring semester of the junior year. Preparatory plans should be made with the high school counselor, reviewing discussions of earlier personal conferences. Advance arrangements should be made with admission officers of the colleges the student expects to visit. The admission officer's name and telephone number will be found in most instances in *The College Blue Book®* volume entitled *Tabular Data*. The admissions officer in many cases will want to know whether the student has actually applied for admission and probably the areas the student may plan to major in or other special interests the student has in the particular institution. The student should have prepared a summary of personal data. If possible, high school students should also talk to students of the colleges they wish to attend.

The growth of community colleges has opened up another avenue for students, especially those of limited finances or those who have not decided on their ultimate educational goals. Students will find many of these community colleges offer an excellent opportunity to gain a solid college background. Then one can choose a four-year institution to complete an undergraduate degree.

Any regular high school graduate can find a school that will accept him. Many students need to be encouraged to consider the smaller, private and public colleges of good standing.

Students entering professional training such as engineering or law might consider small schools that have cooperative programs with major universities. A knowledgeable student, through planning and guidance, can avoid unnecessary disappointment. A college career can be quite beneficial to the student who spends three to four years on a small campus and one, two, or three additional years of graduate work on another, larger campus.

Costs

Costs are continuing to rise. Tuition charges as listed herein should only be used as a guide. It would be wise to check with the institution of interest to be sure of having the most up-to-date information available.

Should the need for financial aid be a factor in selecting a college, a college-bound student should be aware that the best single source of financial assistance and information is the financial aid officer or admission director at the college. It is most important for the student to contact the finance office as early as possible during the student's senior year in high school. A principal source of financial assistance is the major federal undergraduate aid programs. Applications can be obtained from the college. Most colleges and universities also offer financial assistance in several forms including academic and general scholarships, grants-in-aid, student loans, and part-time work. For more information, see volume 5 of *The College Blue Book®*: *Scholarships, Fellowships, Grants, and Loans*.

Two-Year Colleges

Two-year colleges, referred to as junior colleges or community colleges, both public and private, offer programs that prepare students for technical and semiprofessional careers in business and technology fields, and for transfer to senior colleges. There are hundreds of two-year colleges providing comprehensive programs meeting the lower division requirements of virtually all four-year colleges and universities.

There are decided advantages for some students to enroll in a two-year college. Some of these are: less cost, home residence, availability of highly specialized programs, opportunity for the student to mature, a smaller student body, and generally a closer relationship to the faculty. The development of two-year colleges across the nation is one of the most vital forces in education today. The two-year college is neither an extension of high school, nor a little senior college. It has its own identity, sphere of service, and contribution to make to American education. The comprehensive community college is considered one of the best means of accommodating the demands of higher education, embracing the increasing variety of abilities of students graduating from high schools, preparing students in the technological and semiprofessional occupations, and all in an economical manner.

One very important caution needs to be heeded by students enrolling in two-year colleges who are planning to continue their work through a bachelor's program. Students expecting to transfer should very carefully study the requirements of the institution they ultimately plan to attend. In conference with the junior college counselor, a careful review of the planned program should be made to be sure the contemplated courses at the junior college will satisfy the requirements of the senior institution. Students who depart from prescribed courses stated by the senior institution or fail in any of these courses may experience difficulty with admission or normal progress toward the bachelor degree.

Liberal Arts Colleges

The liberal arts colleges offer four years of college and award the Bachelor of Arts and the Bachelor of Science degrees. The curriculum for the first two years is usually broad with an emphasis in the humanities, natural sciences, and cultural history of our society. The last two years may provide a concentration of specific programs such as premedicine or pre-law leading to graduate professional training.

Students considering professional training at the graduate level should keep this in mind as they plan their work at the liberal arts college. Graduate schools in some cases have strict preparatory requirements. Familiarity with these requirements can greatly assist in making the transfer to graduate level without loss of credit or time.

Specialized Institutions

Four-year institutions of technology are examples of the more specialized schools where concentration in a specialty is intensively pursued throughout the college career. Most of these institutions are quite selective in admission practice and may require more high school mathematics and science than most other schools for entrance. These programs lead to engineering degrees in many fields emphasizing technology and science. Recently there has been a broadening of the program of the first two years, but, in general, such a program is not nearly as comprehensive and varied as the liberal arts college. The demand for engineers and scientists with specially developed skills creates great competition for entrance into schools of technology.

There are other specialized institutions such as conservatories of music, seminaries, medical and law schools, institutions specializing in teacher training, or schools of the fine arts, most of which require specialized preparation for entrance.

Universities

The university is generally composed of a number of degree-granting colleges and schools where both bachelor and graduate degrees are grouped under one administrative head. Bachelor degrees at the university may be earned in liberal arts or one of the professions such as engineering or the physical sciences. The university, to some extent, combines what is available at the liberal arts college with the specialized institution. Complete professional training in such areas as law, medicine, and science is available on the university campus.

As a rule, universities have much larger student bodies than colleges. In order to meet the demand, most state universities have established several campuses. Many state universities are very selective in admitting students. This is particularly true for a student who is applying for admission from out-of-state.

Entrance Examinations

There are more applicants than there is room for students on many campuses. As this demand increases, colleges and universities attempt to identify those applicants who are most likely to succeed on their campuses. A quality scholastic record has more influence on acceptance and admission than any other single factor. High school grades predict with better accuracy than any other single measurement what college grades and success will be. The more selective colleges and universities may choose students who come out highest on quantitative criteria, that is, high school scholastic averages combined with test scores. Some institutions have far more applicants (whose scholastic records and test scores are of a maximum quality) than they can accept. In such cases, applicants are sometimes screened and accepted on the basis of categories according to residence in the state or region, special talents, minority groups, or relationship to alumni. Such procedures are used in an attempt to influence the makeup of the enrollment.

When investigating several schools, one of the most accurate ways for evaluation of an institution is to consider test scores and the high school rank order of the students actually on campus. In many instances this is more informative than the announced admission policies.

College testing is required by many colleges and universities for entering students; some have developed their own tests and over the years have established norms for such tests. Most institutions requiring tests for entrance, however, now use either the test of the American College Testing Program (ACT) or the examinations of the College Entrance Examination Board. The College Entrance Examination Board offers the Preliminary Scholastic Assessment Test/National Merit Scholarship Qualifying Test (PSAT/ NMSQT), the Scholastic Assessment Test I: Reasoning Test (Verbal and Math), and the SAT II: Subject Tests.

Coaching, tutoring, drill, and memorization of facts can do little to improve the scores of the standardized examinations. It is recommended that students not invest time and money in cramming in hopes of improving test scores. Students can do their best preparation in general reading, completing their school assignments, and arriving on the proper day of the test rested and refreshed.

American College Testing Assessment (ACT)

The ACT Assessment provided by the American College Testing Program covers four subject areas: English, mathematics, reading, and science reasoning. The ACT test is scored on a range of 1 to 36. The ACT is administered at various test sites in the United States and other countries on specified dates throughout the year. Many colleges and universities recommend that prospective students take the examination early in the senior year.

The tests provide estimates of the students' current level of educational development in knowledge skill areas often required in college work. The ACT college testing program was founded in 1959. It is a nonprofit educational service offering programs in testing and financial need analysis.

Scholastic Assessment Tests (SAT)

The SAT I: Reasoning Test is an examination to measure the verbal and mathematics abilities students have developed both in and out of school. The SAT II: Subject Tests, which some colleges require for admission or placement purposes, consist of 22 separate tests that cover subjects such as literature, history, math, languages, chemistry, biology, and physics. Unlike the SAT I, which measures more general abilities, the SAT II tests measure the students' knowledge of a particular subject and their ability to apply that knowledge. Because of this, students should try to take a SAT II Test as soon as possible after completion of their last course in that subject.

The SAT I and II tests are given on certain dates throughout the year at various test centers in the United States and foreign countries. The combination of the student's academic record and the SAT scores, along with other pertinent secondary information enables admissions officers to estimate how well the student will perform on a particular college campus. The SAT is scored on a scale of 200 minimum to 800 maximum.

Admission Policies

One of the most important considerations in planning is to note when colleges and universities request applications, and to be sure that the applications are complete and forwarded during the appropriate periods. Failure in any way in this procedure will usually automatically disqualify a student from acceptance.

Counselors can provide students with freshman profiles on many of the institutions. Studying *The College Blue Book*®, particularly the volume *Tabular Data,* provides a great amount of information on the kind of student bodies found on the campuses of American institutions. There are four general classifications of admission policies. An understanding of these provides valuable guidelines in identifying colleges for consideration.

Most Selective: Many more students apply who meet the announced admission requirements than the college could possibly accept. In addition to requiring outstanding academic records, personal recommendations are required from the high school, and identification of any special qualities of the student should be made known. In this regard, the high school recommendation made to the collegiate institution requires special attention.

Many times, particularly at selective institutions, the high school recommendation actually provides the necessary edge for admission. The recommendation should be on time, carefully providing all information called for, and finally, be precise and detailed in citing personal qualities of the applicant.

All these qualities, however, do not guarantee acceptance. It is strongly recommended that qualified students apply to more than one institution of this type, and that not all applicationss should be made to the same type of institution.

Very Selective: Colleges having a very selective procedure in accepting students require ACT scores of 23 or over, or an SAT I score of 600 or more. Students should rank in the top 10 to 12 percent of their high school graduating classes. In addition, strong recommendations stressing particular talents and achievements are necessary. Applications should be made to several institutions of this type.

Selective: An ACT of 20 or over, or an SAT I score of 550 or more is generally necessary. Applications for admission to selective colleges and universities are usually called for in the spring prior to fall entry. In many situations, applications may be submitted in the fall of the senior year with final confirmation to be made after all grades are recorded and confirmed upon graduation from high school.

Least Selective: The fourth classification represents those institutions that will accept students with a C average on their high school work. In certain unusual instances, and

under special situations, even the selective institutions may accept students who are in this category, particularly if the scores on the ACT are in the mid-20's or are in excess of 500 on the SAT I. Generally, for acceptance in the less selective schools, students should have an ACT composite score of 17 or a SAT I score of 450.

Entrance examinations may or may not be required. Occasionally, if examinations are required, the results are used for student placement rather than admission. Most high school graduates can meet the requirements for entry and will be accepted. It should be pointed out, however, that in some cases an institution may be liberal in acceptance but carefully screens candidates for graduation. In such an institution, a high attrition rate may occur.

Open Enrollment Policy: This is becoming more common, particularly with the public community colleges. Many students will find this privilege most helpful in continuing their formal education beyond high school. Such a policy enables those students to have a second chance who have failed to perform up to their ability during their high school years. Enrollment and attendance may enable the student to complete a most rewarding vocational program or to later transfer and complete the Bachelor degree, which otherwise might not have been possible because of the deficiency in the high school scholastic record.

A number of colleges and universities, particularly the publicly supported ones, have adopted the open enrollment policy. In response to a feeling of community responsibility, they accept any student who has a diploma (or G.E.D. equivalency certificate) from an accredited high school. This procedure allows students from disadvantaged and minority backgrounds, who might otherwise be denied such an opportunity, to acquire a college education and prepare for a meaningful occupation. These institutions have not lowered their graduation requirements; they have, instead, created opportunities for more students to satisfy these requirements.

Do not assume the erroneous generality that the tougher it is to get into an institution, the better the quality; or the easier to enter, the poorer the school. In fact, there is research evidence available indicating that it may be wise to re-examine some of our traditional notions and attitudes regarding admissions. Not all degree programs on any particular campus are equally outstanding. Every institution has its particular strengths in programs available. Certain institutions are excellent places for some kinds of students in some kinds of programs, but no institution is the one most suited for everyone.

Degrees Offered by College and Subject provides guidance counselors and high school students with a means to identify those institutions most suitable to their curricular needs.

Part I, *Degrees Offered by College,* tabulates degree programs offered by more than 4,300 two-year colleges, colleges, and universities in the United States, Canada and U.S. Territories. These programs are arranged by college in alphabetical order within states and provinces.

The subject areas are arranged alphabetically in Part II, *Degrees Offered by Subject,* and within each subject arranged alphabetically by state and province and within each state and province by college.

In collecting these data, it became evident that the traditional progression of students in their pursuit of a college education is no longer limited to a choice of a four-year college and perhaps the usual steps toward an advanced degree. Alternatives exist everywhere within the scope of postsecondary education. For example, the phenomenal growth of community colleges alone has provided the student with a vast number of options within the framework of a two-year program. One can decide whether one wants a transfer, a parallel, or a terminal program; an Arts Degree, a Science Degree, or a Certificate; a full-time, a part-time, or a cooperative program; whether to pursue a technical, trade, professional, paraprofessional, or liberal arts program.

Similar alternatives can be found in other institutions as well, making it possible for entire educational programs to be constructed on an individual basis for each student.

Structuring a volume such as this presents many problems. To list each course of study within every institution not only makes for an unwieldy collection of facts, but is in itself a distortion since there is no way the user can be provided with criteria by which to discriminate among programs with similar titles. Also, many colleges list the same course in a different manner (e.g. Speech and Drama and then Drama and Speech).

For this reason an attempt was made to establish some sort of standardized curriculum listing. However, rigidity of subject headings can be just as much of a distortion as too

much flexibility, and therefore compromises had to be made. These compromises came about from lengthy study of questionnaires and catalogs in an effort to weigh each school's programs and to make a comparative assessment. (It must be emphasized that no value judgments were or even could be made as to the quality of these programs.)

Users of this volume must bear in mind that degrees are listed for junior and/or community colleges only if a valid curriculum was detailed within the school catalog, but it must also be recognized that these colleges, in most cases, provide a satisfactory basic liberal arts program which will enable the student to transfer without difficulty to an upper level college to gain a degree in the major of choice.

Another evaluation that had to be made was in the curriculum headings themselves. Since there is a great deal of varying terminology among schools, the rule of thumb decided upon was to be reasonably general in listing curricula for two- and four-year degrees, and very specific for graduate degrees.

Users of this volume also must be made aware of the very specific and limited use given here of the word "Education." It must be emphasized that it is used only in the sense of teacher training. If a school has indicated to us either in a catalog or questionnaire that they offer, for example, Business Education, and their meaning of the term indicates this is a program for students interested in the business world, then the word "Education" was dropped. Business Education is used only for programs involving students whose eventual goal is to teach business subjects. Similarly, Education, Music; Education, Home Economics; Education, Art are all programs for future teachers of these subjects. An attempt was made to eliminate confusing terminology among schools.

With regard to the degrees themselves, no effort is made to distinguish between the different types of the same degree, such as Bachelor of Arts or Bachelor of Science. Other refers to post-baccalaureate degrees other than master's or doctoral (e.g., Certificate, Diploma, Engineer, Specialist).

Those postsecondary institutions that grant certificates only, such as many of the vocational/technical schools or nursing schools, are not listed in this volume. Only those that grant Associate degrees and beyond are included. The number of programs offered by most of these schools is just too numerous for consideration here. More information can be found in the companion volume to this one, *Occupational Education,* which was designed to provide the necessary detail.

A	Associate Degree		M	Master's Degree
B	Bachelor Degree		O	Other Advanced Degree
D	Doctorate Degree			

U.S. COLLEGES

Alabama

ALABAMA AGRICULTURAL AND MECHANICAL UNIVERSITY

Accounting, B
Agribusiness, D
Agricultural Economics, B
Agricultural Sciences, MD
Agronomy and Soil Sciences, MD
Animal Sciences, B
Art Education, M
Biological and Biomedical Sciences, MD
Biology/Biological Sciences, B
Business Administration and Management, B
Business Administration, Management and Operations, MD
Business Education, MO
Business Statistics, B
Business/Commerce, B
Business/Managerial Economics, B
Chemistry, B
Child and Family Studies, M
City/Urban, Community and Regional Planning, B
Civil Engineering, B
Civil Engineering Technology/Technician, B
Clinical Psychology, M
Clothing and Textiles, M
Communication Disorders, M
Computer Science, M
Computer and Information Sciences, B
Construction Management, M
Counseling Psychology, M
Counselor Education/School Counseling and Guidance Services, MO
Early Childhood Education and Teaching, MDO
Economics, B
Education, MO
Education/Teaching of Individuals with Speech or Language Impairments, B
Educational Media/Instructional Technology, M
Electrical, Electronics and Communications Engineering, B
Elementary Education and Teaching, BMDO
Engineering and Applied Sciences, MD
English Education, M
English Language and Literature, B
Family and Consumer Economics and Related Services, B
Finance, B
Food Science, B
Food Science and Technology, MD
Home Economics, M
Home Economics Education, MO
Hospitality Administration/Management, M
Human Development, M
Industrial Education, M
Kindergarten/PreSchool Education and Teaching, B
Logistics and Materials Management, M
Marketing, MD
Marketing/Marketing Management, B
Materials Engineering, M

Materials Sciences, D
Mathematics, B
Mathematics Teacher Education, MO
Mechanical Engineering, B
Mechanical Engineering/Mechanical Technology/Technician, B
Music Teacher Education, BM
Nutritional Sciences, M
Optics/Optical Sciences, D
Physical Education Teaching and Coaching, BM
Physics, BMD
Planetary Astronomy and Science, D
Plant Sciences, MD
Political Science and Government, B
Psychology, BMO
Radio and Television Broadcasting Technology/Technician, B
Reading Teacher Education, D
Rehabilitation Counseling, M
School Psychology, M
Science Teacher Education/General Science Teacher Education, MO
Secondary Education and Teaching, BMO
Social Studies Teacher Education, M
Social Work, BM
Sociology, B
Special Education and Teaching, BMO
Supply Chain Management, M
Urban and Regional Planning, M

ALABAMA SOUTHERN COMMUNITY COLLEGE

Agricultural Business and Management, A
Agriculture, A
Art/Art Studies, General, A
Biology/Biological Sciences, A
Biomedical Technology/Technician, A
Chemistry, A
Computer Science, A
Criminal Justice/Law Enforcement Administration, A
Drama and Dramatics/Theatre Arts, A
Early Childhood Education and Teaching, A
Elementary Education and Teaching, A
Forestry Technology/Technician, A
Health Information/Medical Records Administration/Administrator, A
Health Services/Allied Health/Health Sciences, A
Kindergarten/PreSchool Education and Teaching, A
Liberal Arts and Sciences Studies and Humanities, A
Mathematics, A
Music, A
Physical Education Teaching and Coaching, A
Pre-Dentistry Studies, A
Pre-Law Studies, A
Pre-Medicine/Pre-Medical Studies, A
Pre-Pharmacy Studies, A
Pre-Veterinary Studies, A
Secondary Education and Teaching, A
Social Sciences, A

Special Education and Teaching, A

ALABAMA STATE UNIVERSITY

Accounting, BM
Allied Health and Medical Assisting Services, MD
Art/Art Studies, General, B
Biological and Biomedical Sciences, MD
Biology/Biological Sciences, B
Biomedical/Medical Engineering, B
Business Administration and Management, B
Business Administration, Management and Operations, M
Chemistry, B
Communication Studies/Speech Communication and Rhetoric, B
Computer Science, B
Counselor Education/School Counseling and Guidance Services, MO
Criminal Justice/Safety Studies, B
Criminalistics and Criminal Science, B
Dance, B
Drama and Dramatics/Theatre Arts, B
Early Childhood Education and Teaching, BMO
Education, MDO
Educational Administration and Supervision, MDO
Educational Leadership and Administration, MDO
Educational Media/Instructional Technology, MO
Educational Policy, D
Elementary Education and Teaching, BMO
English Education, M
English Language and Literature, B
Finance, B
Forensic Science and Technology, M
Health Education, M
Health Information/Medical Records Administration/Administrator, B
History, B
Information Science/Studies, B
Marine Biology and Biological Oceanography, B
Marketing/Marketing Management, B
Mathematics, BM
Mathematics Teacher Education, MO
Music, B
Music Teacher Education, BM
Occupational Therapy/Therapist, BM
Physical Education Teaching and Coaching, BM
Physical Therapy/Therapist, D
Physics, B
Political Science and Government, B
Psychology, B
Reading Teacher Education, M
Rehabilitation Counseling, M
Rehabilitation Sciences, M
Rehabilitation and Therapeutic Professions, B
Science Teacher Education/General Science Teacher Education, MO
Secondary Education and Teaching, BMO
Social Studies Teacher Education, MO
Special Education and Teaching, BM

AMRIDGE UNIVERSITY

Bible/Biblical Studies, B
Business Administration and Management, B

Computer and Information Sciences and Support
  Services, B
Counseling Psychology, M
Counselor Education/School Counseling and Guid-
  ance Services, D
Liberal Arts and Sciences Studies and Humani-
  ties, AB
Marriage and Family Therapy/Counseling, MD
Organizational Behavior Studies, M
Organizational Management, M
Pastoral Studies/Counseling, M
Religion/Religious Studies, M
Theology and Religious Vocations, MD

ATHENS STATE UNIVERSITY

Accounting, B
Art/Art Studies, General, B
Behavioral Sciences, B
Biology/Biological Sciences, B
Business Administration and Management, B
Business, Management, Marketing, and Related
  Support Services, B
Chemistry, B
Computer Science, B
Computer and Information Sciences, B
Criminal Justice/Law Enforcement Administration, B
Criminal Justice/Safety Studies, B
Elementary Education and Teaching, B
English Language and Literature, B
Fire Protection and Safety Technology/Technician, B
Health Professions and Related Clinical Sciences, B
History, B
Human Resources Management/Personnel Adminis-
  tration, B
Humanities/Humanistic Studies, B
Information Resources Management/CIO Training, B
Kindergarten/PreSchool Education and Teaching, B
Liberal Arts and Sciences Studies and Humani-
  ties, B
Logistics and Materials Management, B
Mathematics, B
Multi-/Interdisciplinary Studies, B
Natural Sciences, B
Physical Education Teaching and Coaching, B
Political Science and Government, B
Psychology, B
Purchasing, Procurement/Acquisitions and Con-
  tracts Management, B
Religion/Religious Studies, B
Social Sciences, B
Sociology, B
Special Education and Teaching, B
Sport and Fitness Administration/Management, B
Technical Teacher Education, B

AUBURN UNIVERSITY

Accounting, BM
Adult and Continuing Education and Teaching, BMD
Aerospace, Aeronautical and Astronautical Engi-
  neering, BMD
Agricultural Communication/Journalism, B
Agricultural Economics, BM
Agricultural Sciences, MD
Agricultural Teacher Education, B
Agricultural/Biological Engineering and Bioengineer-
  ing, B
Agriculture, B
Agronomy and Crop Science, B
Agronomy and Soil Sciences, MD
Airline/Commercial/Professional Pilot and Flight
  Crew, B
Analytical Chemistry, MD
Anatomy, M
Animal Sciences, BMD
Anthropology, B
Apparel and Textile Marketing Management, B
Apparel and Textiles, B
Applied Behavior Analysis, M
Applied Economics, D
Applied Mathematics, BM
Aquaculture, BMD
Architectural Engineering, B
Architecture, BM
Audiology/Audiologist and Speech-Language
  Pathology/Pathologist, B
Aviation/Airway Management and Operations, B

Biochemistry, BMD
Biological and Biomedical Sciences, MD
Biology/Biological Sciences, B
Biomedical Sciences, B
Biosystems Engineering, MD
Botany/Plant Biology, BM
Broadcast Journalism, B
Building Science, M
Business Administration and Management, B
Business Administration, Management and Opera-
  tions, M
Business Education, MD
Business Teacher Education, B
Business/Managerial Economics, B
Cell Biology and Anatomy, D
Chemical Engineering, BMD
Chemistry, BMD
Child Development, B
Child and Family Studies, MD
Civil Engineering, BMD
Clinical Laboratory Science/Medical
  Technology/Technologist, B
Clinical/Medical Laboratory Science and Allied Pro-
  fessions, B
Clinical/Medical Laboratory Technician, B
Clothing and Textiles, MD
Communication Disorders, BMD
Communication and Media Studies, BMO
Communication, Journalism and Related Pro-
  grams, B
Computer Engineering, BMD
Computer Hardware Engineering, B
Computer Science, MD
Computer Software Engineering, B
Computer and Information Sciences, B
Construction Engineering and Management, MD
Construction Management, M
Criminology, B
Curriculum and Instruction, MDO
Design and Visual Communications, B
Drama and Dramatics/Theatre Arts, B
Early Childhood Education and Teaching, BMDO
Economics, BM
Education, BMDO
Educational Administration and Supervision, MDO
Educational Media/Instructional Technology, M
Educational Psychology, D
Electrical Engineering, MD
Electrical, Electronics and Communications Engi-
  neering, B
Elementary Education and Teaching, BMDO
Engineering, B
Engineering and Applied Sciences, MDO
English, MDO
English Education, MDO
English Language and Literature, B
English/Language Arts Teacher Education, B
Entomology, MD
Environmental Design/Architecture, B
Environmental Engineering
  Technology/Environmental Technology, MD
Environmental Sciences, B
Exercise Physiology, B
Exercise and Sports Science, MD
Experimental Psychology, D
Family and Consumer Sciences/Human Sciences, B
Finance, B
Finance and Banking, M
Fine/Studio Arts, B
Fish, Game and Wildlife Management, MD
Food Science, B
Food Science and Technology, MDO
Foods, Nutrition, and Wellness Studies, B
Foreign Language Teacher Education, BM
Foreign Languages and Literatures, B
Forest Sciences and Biology, B
Forestry, MD
French Language Teacher Education, B
French Language and Literature, B
Geography, BM
Geology/Earth Science, BM
Geotechnical Engineering, MD
German Language Teacher Education, B
German Language and Literature, B
Graphic Design, B
Health Education, MDO

Health Promotion, M
Health Teacher Education, B
Health/Health Care Administration/Management, B
Higher Education/Higher Education Administra-
  tion, MDO
History, BMDO
History Teacher Education, B
Horticultural Science, BMD
Hospitality Administration/Management, BO
Hotel/Motel Administration/Management, B
Human Development, MD
Human Development and Family Studies, B
Human Resources Management and Services, D
Human Resources Management/Personnel Adminis-
  tration, B
Hydraulics and Fluid Power Technology, MD
Hydrology and Water Resources Science, MD
Industrial Design, BM
Industrial Engineering, B
Industrial and Organizational Psychology, D
Industrial/Management Engineering, MDO
Inorganic Chemistry, MD
Interior Architecture, B
Interior Design, B
International Business/Trade/Commerce, B
Journalism, B
Kinesiology and Movement Studies, D
Landscape Architecture, M
Liberal Arts and Sciences Studies and Humani-
  ties, B
Logistics and Materials Management, B
Management, MD
Management Information Systems and Ser-
  vices, BMD
Management Science, B
Marine Biology and Biological Oceanography, B
Marketing/Marketing Management, B
Mass Communication/Media Studies, BM
Materials Engineering, BMD
Mathematics, BMD
Mathematics Teacher Education, BMDO
Mechanical Engineering, BMD
Medical Microbiology and Bacteriology, B
Microbiology, B
Molecular Biology, BD
Music, B
Music Teacher Education, BMDO
Natural Resources Management/Development and
  Policy, B
Natural Resources and Conservation, M
Nursing, M
Nursing Education, M
Nutritional Sciences, BMDO
Operations Management and Supervision, B
Organic Chemistry, D
Pathobiology, M
Pharmaceutical Sciences, MD
Pharmacology, M
Pharmacy, D
Philosophy, B
Physical Chemistry, MD
Physical Education Teaching and Coaching, BMDO
Physics, BMD
Physics Teacher Education, B
Plant Pathology/Phytopathology, MD
Plant Sciences, B
Political Science and Government, BMDO
Polymer/Plastics Engineering, BMD
Poultry Science, BMD
Pre-Dentistry Studies, B
Pre-Law Studies, B
Pre-Medicine/Pre-Medical Studies, B
Pre-Pharmacy Studies, B
Pre-Veterinary Studies, B
Psychology, BMD
Public Administration, BMDO
Public Relations/Image Management, B
Radiation Biology/Radiobiology, M
Radio and Television, B
Reading Teacher Education, DO
Real Estate, M
Rehabilitation Counseling, MD
Rural Sociology, M
Science Teacher Education/General Science
  Teacher Education, BMDO
Secondary Education and Teaching, BMDO

Social Science Teacher Education, B
Social Studies Teacher Education, MDO
Social Work, B
Sociology, BM
Software Engineering, MD
Spanish Language Teacher Education, B
Spanish Language and Literature, BM
Special Education and Teaching, BMD
Statistics, M
Structural Engineering, MD
Systems Engineering, MDO
Technical Communication, MDO
Technical Teacher Education, B
Textile Sciences and Engineering, B
Trade and Industrial Teacher Education, B
Transportation and Highway Engineering, MD
Urban and Regional Planning, M
Veterinary Medicine, D
Veterinary Sciences, MD
Wildlife and Wildlands Science and Management, B
Zoology/Animal Biology, BM

AUBURN UNIVERSITY AT MONTGOMERY

Accounting, B
Art Education, M
Art/Art Studies, General, B
Biology/Biological Sciences, B
Business Administration and Management, B
Business Administration, Management and Operations, M
Business/Commerce, B
Business/Managerial Economics, B
Cartography, B
Chemistry, B
Clinical Laboratory Science/Medical Technology/Technologist, B
Clinical Psychology, M
Clinical/Medical Laboratory Technician, B
Communication Studies/Speech Communication and Rhetoric, B
Computer Science, B
Computer and Information Systems Security, M
Counselor Education/School Counseling and Guidance Services, MO
Criminal Justice/Safety Studies, B
Criminology, MO
Early Childhood Education and Teaching, MO
Economics, B
Education, MO
Educational Leadership and Administration, O
Educational Media/Instructional Technology, M
Elementary Education and Teaching, BMO
Emergency Management, M
English Education, M
English Language and Literature, B
Environmental Sciences, B
Exercise and Sports Science, MO
Finance, B
Foreign Languages and Literatures, B
Health Services Administration, O
History, B
Homeland Security, M
Human Resources Management/Personnel Administration, B
Information Science/Studies, M
International Affairs, M
International Business/Trade/Commerce, B
International/Global Studies, B
Kinesiology and Exercise Science, B
Legal and Justice Studies, MO
Liberal Arts and Sciences Studies and Humanities, B
Liberal Studies, MDO
Management Information Systems and Services, BM
Marketing/Marketing Management, B
Mathematics, B
Mathematics Teacher Education, M
Non-Profit/Public/Organizational Management, O
Nursing, M
Nursing Education, M
Organizational Management, M
Physical Education Teaching and Coaching, MO
Physical Sciences, B
Political Science and Government, BMDO

Psychology, BM
Public Administration, MDO
Public Health, O
Public Policy Analysis, D
Science Teacher Education/General Science Teacher Education, M
Secondary Education and Teaching, MO
Social Studies Teacher Education, M
Sociology, BM
Spanish Language and Literature, B
Special Education and Teaching, BMO

BEVILL STATE COMMUNITY COLLEGE

Administrative Assistant and Secretarial Science, A
Child Care and Support Services Management, A
Computer and Information Sciences, A
Drafting and Design Technology/Technician, A
Electrician, A
Emergency Medical Technology/Technician (EMT Paramedic), A
General Studies, A
Heating, Air Conditioning and Refrigeration Technology/Technician, A
Industrial Electronics Technology/Technician, A
Legal Assistant/Paralegal, A
Liberal Arts and Sciences Studies and Humanities, A
Tool and Die Technology/Technician, A

BIRMINGHAM-SOUTHERN COLLEGE

Art History, Criticism and Conservation, B
Art Teacher Education, B
Art/Art Studies, General, B
Asian Studies/Civilization, B
Biology/Biological Sciences, B
Business Administration and Management, B
Chemistry, B
Drama and Dramatics/Theatre Arts, B
Drawing, B
Economics, B
Education, B
Elementary Education and Teaching, B
English Language and Literature, B
Environmental Studies, B
Film/Video and Photographic Arts, B
Fine Arts and Art Studies, B
Fine/Studio Arts, B
History, B
International Business/Trade/Commerce, B
Mathematics, B
Music, B
Music History, Literature, and Theory, B
Music Teacher Education, B
Music Theory and Composition, B
Painting, B
Philosophy, B
Physics, B
Piano and Organ, B
Political Science and Government, B
Pre-Dentistry Studies, B
Pre-Law Studies, B
Pre-Medicine/Pre-Medical Studies, B
Printmaking, B
Psychology, B
Religion/Religious Studies, B
Sculpture, B
Secondary Education and Teaching, B
Sociology, B
Spanish Language and Literature, B
Teacher Education, Multiple Levels, B
Voice and Opera, B

BISHOP STATE COMMUNITY COLLEGE

Accounting Technology/Technician and Bookkeeping, A
Administrative Assistant and Secretarial Science, A
Child Care and Support Services Management, A
Civil Engineering Technology/Technician, A
Computer and Information Sciences, A
Drafting and Design Technology/Technician, A
Electrical, Electronic and Communications Engineering Technology/Technician, A
Emergency Medical Technology/Technician (EMT Paramedic), A
Foodservice Systems Administration/Management, A

Funeral Service and Mortuary Science, A
General Studies, A
Graphic Communications, A
Health Information/Medical Records Technology/Technician, A
Multi-/Interdisciplinary Studies, A
Physical Therapist Assistant, A

CALHOUN COMMUNITY COLLEGE

Aeronautical/Aerospace Engineering Technology/Technician, A
Allied Health Diagnostic, Intervention, and Treatment Professions, A
Business Administration and Management, A
Chemical Technology/Technician, A
Child Care and Support Services Management, A
Clinical/Medical Laboratory Technician, A
Computer and Information Sciences, A
Dental Assisting/Assistant, A
Design and Visual Communications, A
Drafting and Design Technology/Technician, A
Electrical and Electronic Engineering Technologies/Technicians, A
Electrical, Electronic and Communications Engineering Technology/Technician, A
Electrician, A
Emergency Medical Technology/Technician (EMT Paramedic), A
Fire Protection and Safety Technology/Technician, A
General Studies, A
Health Professions and Related Clinical Sciences, A
Heating, Air Conditioning, Ventilation and Refrigeration Maintenance Technology/Technician, A
Industrial Mechanics and Maintenance Technology, A
Industrial Production Technologies/Technicians, A
Legal Assistant/Paralegal, A
Liberal Arts and Sciences Studies and Humanities, A
Manufacturing Technology/Technician, A
Music, A
Opticianry/Ophthalmic Dispensing Optician, A
Photographic and Film/Video Technology/Technician and Assistant, A
Real Estate, A
Respiratory Care Therapy/Therapist, A
Surgical Technology/Technologist, A
Tool and Die Technology/Technician, A

CENTRAL ALABAMA COMMUNITY COLLEGE

Administrative Assistant and Secretarial Science, A
Apparel and Textiles, A
Business Administration and Management, A
Computer Programming/Programmer, A
Computer Science, A
Drafting and Design Technology/Technician, A
Electrical, Electronic and Communications Engineering Technology/Technician, A
Environmental Engineering Technology/Environmental Technology, A
Information Science/Studies, A
Liberal Arts and Sciences Studies and Humanities, A

CHATTAHOOCHEE VALLEY COMMUNITY COLLEGE

Accounting, A
Administrative Assistant and Secretarial Science, A
Business Administration and Management, A
Computer and Information Sciences, A
Criminal Justice/Police Science, A
Design and Visual Communications, A
Fire Services Administration, A
General Studies, A
Liberal Arts and Sciences Studies and Humanities, A
Medical/Clinical Assistant, A
Music History, Literature, and Theory, A
Security and Protective Services, A

COLUMBIA SOUTHERN UNIVERSITY

Business Administration and Management, AB
Business Administration, Management and Operations, MD

Computer and Information Systems Security, B
Criminal Justice/Police Science, AB
Criminology, M
Emergency Management, M
Emergency Medical Technology/Technician (EMT
  Paramedic), B
Environmental Studies, B
Environmental and Occupational Health, M
Finance and Banking, M
Fire Science/Firefighting, AB
Fire Services Administration, B
General Studies, A
Health Services Administration, M
Health/Health Care Administration/Management, B
Hospitality Administration/Management, B
Human Resources Management and Services, M
Human Resources Management/Personnel Adminis-
  tration, B
Information Technology, B
Management, M
Marketing, M
Marketing/Marketing Management, B
Medical Insurance Coding Specialist/Coder, A
Occupational Safety and Health
  Technology/Technician, AB
Organizational Management, M
Psychiatric/Mental Health Services Technician, B

COMMUNITY COLLEGE OF THE AIR FORCE

Aeronautics/Aviation/Aerospace Science and Tech-
  nology, A
Air Traffic Controller, A
Airframe Mechanics and Aircraft Maintenance
  Technology/Technician, A
Apparel and Textile Marketing Management, A
Atmospheric Sciences and Meteorology, A
Automobile/Automotive Mechanics
  Technology/Technician, A
Avionics Maintenance Technology/Technician, A
Biomedical Technology/Technician, A
Cardiovascular Technology/Technologist, A
Clinical/Medical Laboratory Technician, A
Commercial and Advertising Art, A
Communications Technology/Technician, A
Construction Engineering Technology/Technician, A
Criminal Justice/Law Enforcement Administration, A
Dental Assisting/Assistant, A
Dental Laboratory Technology/Technician, A
Dietetics/Dieticians, A
Educational Leadership and Administration, A
Educational/Instructional Media Design, A
Electrical, Electronic and Communications Engineer-
  ing Technology/Technician, A
Environmental Health, A
Environmental Studies, A
Finance, A
Fire Science/Firefighting, A
Health/Health Care Administration/Management, A
Hematology Technology/Technician, A
Hotel/Motel Administration/Management, A
Human Resources Management/Personnel Adminis-
  tration, A
Industrial Technology/Technician, A
Legal Assistant/Paralegal, A
Logistics and Materials Management, A
Management Information Systems and Services, A
Medical Radiologic Technology/Science - Radiation
  Therapist, A
Mental Health Counseling/Counselor, A
Metallurgical Technology/Technician, A
Music Performance, A
Nuclear Medical Technology/Technologist, A
Occupational Safety and Health
  Technology/Technician, A
Office Management and Supervision, A
Ophthalmic Laboratory Technology/Technician, A
Parks, Recreation, Leisure and Fitness Studies, A
Pharmacy Technician/Assistant, A
Physical Therapist Assistant, A
Physiology, A
Public Relations/Image Management, A
Purchasing, Procurement/Acquisitions and Con-
  tracts Management, A
Security and Loss Prevention Services, A
Social Work, A

Surgical Technology/Technologist, A

CONCORDIA COLLEGE ALABAMA

Business Administration and Management, B
Early Childhood Education and Teaching, B
Elementary Education and Teaching, B
General Studies, A

ENTERPRISE STATE COMMUNITY COLLEGE

Administrative Assistant and Secretarial Science, A
Aircraft Powerplant Technology/Technician, A
Airframe Mechanics and Aircraft Maintenance
  Technology/Technician, A
Avionics Maintenance Technology/Technician, A
Business Administration and Management, A
Child Care and Support Services Management, A
Computer Technology/Computer Systems Technol-
  ogy, A
Computer and Information Sciences, A
Emergency Medical Technology/Technician (EMT
  Paramedic), A
General Studies, A
Health Information/Medical Records
  Administration/Administrator, A
Legal Assistant/Paralegal, A
Liberal Arts and Sciences Studies and Humani-
  ties, A
Multi-/Interdisciplinary Studies, A

FAULKNER UNIVERSITY

Accounting, B
Bible/Biblical Studies, B
Biology/Biological Sciences, B
Business Administration and Management, AB
Business Administration, Management and Opera-
  tions, M
Counselor Education/School Counseling and Guid-
  ance Services, M
Criminology, M
Drama and Dramatics/Theatre Arts, B
Education, M
Elementary Education and Teaching, B
English Language and Literature, B
History, BM
Human Resources Management/Personnel Adminis-
  tration, B
Humanities/Humanistic Studies, B
Law and Legal Studies, D
Liberal Arts and Sciences Studies and Humani-
  ties, AB
Liberal Studies, M
Missions/Missionary Studies and Missiology, M
Pastoral Studies/Counseling, M
Physical Education Teaching and Coaching, B
Social Sciences, B
Sport and Fitness Administration/Management, B
Theology and Religious Vocations, M

GADSDEN STATE COMMUNITY COLLEGE

Accounting Technology/Technician and Bookkeep-
  ing, A
Administrative Assistant and Secretarial Science, A
Child Care and Support Services Management, A
Civil Engineering Technology/Technician, A
Clinical/Medical Laboratory Technician, A
Communication, Journalism and Related Pro-
  grams, A
Computer and Information Sciences, A
Court Reporting/Court Reporter, A
Criminal Justice/Police Science, A
Drafting and Design Technology/Technician, A
Electrical, Electronic and Communications Engineer-
  ing Technology/Technician, A
Emergency Medical Technology/Technician (EMT
  Paramedic), A
General Studies, A
Heating, Air Conditioning and Refrigeration
  Technology/Technician, A
Industrial Mechanics and Maintenance Technol-
  ogy, A
Legal Assistant/Paralegal, A
Liberal Arts and Sciences Studies and Humani-
  ties, A

Manufacturing Technology/Technician, A
Radiologic Technology/Science - Radiographer, A
Sales, Distribution and Marketing Operations, A
Substance Abuse/Addiction Counseling, A
Tool and Die Technology/Technician, A

GEORGE C. WALLACE COMMUNITY COLLEGE

Accounting, A
Administrative Assistant and Secretarial Science, A
Autobody/Collision and Repair
  Technology/Technician, A
Automobile/Automotive Mechanics
  Technology/Technician, A
Business Administration and Management, A
Cabinetmaking and Millwork/Millwright, A
Carpentry/Carpenter, A
Clinical/Medical Laboratory Technician, A
Computer Science, A
Computer and Information Sciences, A
Criminal Justice/Police Science, A
Drafting and Design Technology/Technician, A
Electrical, Electronic and Communications Engineer-
  ing Technology/Technician, A
Electrician, A
Emergency Medical Technology/Technician (EMT
  Paramedic), A
Heating, Air Conditioning and Refrigeration
  Technology/Technician, A
Heating, Air Conditioning, Ventilation and Refrigera-
  tion Maintenance Technology/Technician, A
Industrial Mechanics and Maintenance Technol-
  ogy, A
Machine Tool Technology/Machinist, A
Medical Radiologic Technology/Science - Radiation
  Therapist, A
Medical/Clinical Assistant, A
Physical Therapist Assistant, A
Radiologic Technology/Science - Radiographer, A
Respiratory Care Therapy/Therapist, A
Tool and Die Technology/Technician, A
Welding Technology/Welder, A

GEORGE CORLEY WALLACE STATE COMMUNITY COLLEGE

Administrative Assistant and Secretarial Science, A
Business Administration and Management, A
Computer Science, A
Drafting and Design Technology/Technician, A
Electrician, A
General Studies, A
Liberal Arts and Sciences Studies and Humani-
  ties, A
Tool and Die Technology/Technician, A

H. COUNCILL TRENHOLM STATE COMMUNITY COLLEGE

Accounting Technology/Technician and Bookkeep-
  ing, A
Administrative Assistant and Secretarial Science, A
Automotive Engineering Technology/Technician, A
Child Care and Support Services Management, A
Computer and Information Sciences, A
Culinary Arts/Chef Training, A
Dental Assisting/Assistant, A
Diagnostic Medical Sonography/Sonographer and
  Ultrasound Technician, A
Drafting and Design Technology/Technician, A
Electrician, A
Emergency Medical Technology/Technician (EMT
  Paramedic), A
Graphic Communications, A
Heating, Air Conditioning and Refrigeration
  Technology/Technician, A
Industrial Mechanics and Maintenance Technol-
  ogy, A
Machine Tool Technology/Machinist, A
Manufacturing Technology/Technician, A
Medical/Clinical Assistant, A
Radiologic Technology/Science - Radiographer, A

HERITAGE CHRISTIAN UNIVERSITY

Bible/Biblical Studies, AB
Classics and Classical Languages, Literatures, and Linguistics, M

Pastoral Studies/Counseling, M
Religion/Religious Studies, M

HUNTINGDON COLLEGE

Accounting, B
Biochemistry, B
Biology Teacher Education, B
Biology/Biological Sciences, B
Business Administration and Management, B
Business Administration, Management and Operations, B
Business/Commerce, B
Cell Biology and Anatomy, B
Chemistry, B
Chemistry Teacher Education, B
Criminal Justice/Law Enforcement Administration, B
Elementary Education and Teaching, B
English Language and Literature, B
English/Language Arts Teacher Education, B
Fine Arts and Art Studies, B
Fine/Studio Arts, B
History, B
History Teacher Education, B
Kinesiology and Exercise Science, B
Mathematics, B
Mathematics Teacher Education, B
Music, B
Music Performance, B
Music Teacher Education, B
Physical Education Teaching and Coaching, B
Political Science and Government, B
Psychology, B
Religion/Religious Studies, B
Science Teacher Education/General Science Teacher Education, B
Social Studies Teacher Education, B
Sport and Fitness Administration/Management, B

J. F. DRAKE STATE COMMUNITY AND TECHNICAL COLLEGE

Automotive Engineering Technology/Technician, A
Business Administration and Management, A
Computer and Information Sciences, A
Culinary Arts/Chef Training, A
Drafting and Design Technology/Technician, A
Electrical, Electronic and Communications Engineering Technology/Technician, A
Electrician, A
Heating, Air Conditioning and Refrigeration Technology/Technician, A
Industrial Electronics Technology/Technician, A
Medical/Clinical Assistant, A
Salon/Beauty Salon Management/Manager, A
Tool and Die Technology/Technician, A

JACKSONVILLE STATE UNIVERSITY

Accounting, B
Animal Genetics, B
Anthropology, B
Apparel and Textiles, B
Army JROTC/ROTC, B
Art/Art Studies, General, B
Biological and Biomedical Sciences, M
Biology/Biological Sciences, B
Business Administration and Management, B
Business Administration, Management and Operations, M
Chemistry, B
Communication Studies/Speech Communication and Rhetoric, B
Computer Science, M
Computer and Information Sciences, B
Corrections, B
Counselor Education/School Counseling and Guidance Services, M
Criminal Justice/Law Enforcement Administration, B
Criminal Justice/Police Science, B
Criminology, M
Dietetics/Dieticians, B
Drama and Dramatics/Theatre Arts, B
Early Childhood Education and Teaching, M
Ecology, B
Economics, B
Education, BMO
Educational Administration and Supervision, MO
Educational Leadership and Administration, B

Educational Media/Instructional Technology, M
Educational/Instructional Media Design, B
Electrical, Electronic and Communications Engineering Technology/Technician, B
Elementary Education and Teaching, BM
Emergency Management, MD
English, M
English Language and Literature, B
Environmental Biology, B
Family and Consumer Sciences/Home Economics Teacher Education, B
Family and Consumer Sciences/Human Sciences, B
Finance, B
Foods, Nutrition, and Wellness Studies, B
Forensic Science and Technology, B
French Language and Literature, B
Geography, B
Geology/Earth Science, B
German Language and Literature, B
Health Teacher Education, B
Health and Physical Education, B
History, BM
Industrial Technology/Technician, B
Junior High/Intermediate/Middle School Education and Teaching, B
Kindergarten/PreSchool Education and Teaching, B
Kinesiology and Exercise Science, B
Liberal Studies, M
Marine Biology and Biological Oceanography, B
Marketing/Marketing Management, B
Mathematics, BM
Music, BM
Music Teacher Education, B
Nursing, M
Occupational Safety and Health Technology/Technician, B
Parks, Recreation, Leisure and Fitness Studies, B
Physical Education Teaching and Coaching, BMO
Physics, B
Political Science and Government, BM
Psychology, BM
Public Administration and Social Service Professions, B
Reading Teacher Education, M
Secondary Education and Teaching, BM
Social Work, B
Sociology, B
Software Engineering, M
Spanish Language and Literature, B
Special Education and Teaching, BM
Sport and Fitness Administration/Management, B

JAMES H. FAULKNER STATE COMMUNITY COLLEGE

Administrative Assistant and Secretarial Science, A
Agricultural Economics, A
Business Administration and Management, A
Commercial and Advertising Art, A
Computer and Information Sciences, A
Criminal Justice/Law Enforcement Administration, A
Dental Assisting/Assistant, A
Environmental Engineering Technology/Environmental Technology, A
General Studies, A
Hospitality Administration/Management, A
Landscaping and Groundskeeping, A
Legal Assistant/Paralegal, A
Liberal Arts and Sciences Studies and Humanities, A
Mass Communication/Media Studies, A
Parks, Recreation and Leisure Facilities Management, A
Surgical Technology/Technologist, A

JEFFERSON DAVIS COMMUNITY COLLEGE

Administrative Assistant and Secretarial Science, A
Drafting and Design Technology/Technician, A
General Studies, A

Liberal Arts and Sciences Studies and Humanities, A

JEFFERSON STATE COMMUNITY COLLEGE

Accounting Technology/Technician and Bookkeeping, A
Administrative Assistant and Secretarial Science, A
Child Care and Support Services Management, A
Clinical/Medical Laboratory Technician, A
Computer and Information Sciences, A
Construction Engineering Technology/Technician, A
Criminal Justice/Police Science, A
Emergency Medical Technology/Technician (EMT Paramedic), A
Engineering Technology, A
Fire Services Administration, A
Funeral Service and Mortuary Science, A
General Studies, A
Hospitality Administration/Management, A
Liberal Arts and Sciences Studies and Humanities, A
Office Management and Supervision, A
Physical Therapist Assistant, A
Radiologic Technology/Science - Radiographer, A
Veterinary/Animal Health Technology/Technician and Veterinary Assistant, A

JUDSON COLLEGE

Art/Art Studies, General, B
Biology/Biological Sciences, B
Business/Commerce, B
Chemistry, B
Criminal Justice/Law Enforcement Administration, B
Elementary Education and Teaching, B
English Language and Literature, B
English/Language Arts Teacher Education, B
Equestrian/Equine Studies, B
History, B
Mathematics, B
Mathematics Teacher Education, B
Music, B
Music Teacher Education, B
Psychology, B
Religion/Religious Studies, B
Science Teacher Education/General Science Teacher Education, B
Social Science Teacher Education, B
Social Work, B
Spanish Language and Literature, B

LAWSON STATE COMMUNITY COLLEGE

Accounting Technology/Technician and Bookkeeping, A
Administrative Assistant and Secretarial Science, A
Automotive Engineering Technology/Technician, A
Building/Construction Finishing, Management, and Inspection, A
Business Administration and Management, A
Child Care and Support Services Management, A
Computer and Information Sciences, A
Criminal Justice/Police Science, A
Drafting and Design Technology/Technician, A
General Studies, A
Industrial Electronics Technology/Technician, A
Liberal Arts and Sciences Studies and Humanities, A
Manufacturing Technology/Technician, A
Social Work, A

LURLEEN B. WALLACE COMMUNITY COLLEGE

Administrative Assistant and Secretarial Science, A
Child Care and Support Services Management, A
Computer and Information Sciences, A
Diagnostic Medical Sonography/Sonographer and Ultrasound Technician, A
Emergency Medical Technology/Technician (EMT Paramedic), A
Forestry Technology/Technician, A
General Studies, A
Industrial Electronics Technology/Technician, A

Liberal Arts and Sciences Studies and Humanities, A

MARION MILITARY INSTITUTE

Biological and Physical Sciences, A
Engineering, A
General Studies, A
Liberal Arts and Sciences Studies and Humanities, A

MILES COLLEGE

Accounting and Business/Management, B
African Studies, B
Behavioral Sciences, B
Biology/Biological Sciences, B
Business Administration and Management, B
Chemistry, B
Communication and Media Studies, B
Computer and Information Sciences, B
Criminal Justice/Law Enforcement Administration, B
Early Childhood Education and Teaching, B
Education, B
Elementary Education and Teaching, B
English Language and Literature, B
English/Language Arts Teacher Education, B
Environmental Sciences, B
History, B
Mass Communication/Media Studies, B
Mathematics, B
Mathematics Teacher Education, B
Physics, B
Political Science and Government, B
Religion/Religious Studies, B
Secondary Education and Teaching, B
Social Sciences, B
Social Work, B

NORTHEAST ALABAMA COMMUNITY COLLEGE

Administrative Assistant and Secretarial Science, A
Business Administration and Management, A
Business/Commerce, A
Child Care and Support Services Management, A
Computer and Information Sciences, A
Drafting and Design Technology/Technician, A
Emergency Medical Technology/Technician (EMT Paramedic), A
Industrial Electronics Technology/Technician, A
Industrial Mechanics and Maintenance Technology, A
Medical/Clinical Assistant, A

NORTHWEST-SHOALS COMMUNITY COLLEGE

Administrative Assistant and Secretarial Science, A
Child Care and Support Services Management, A
Child Development, A
Computer and Information Sciences, A
Criminal Justice/Police Science, A
Drafting and Design Technology/Technician, A
Emergency Medical Technology/Technician (EMT Paramedic), A
Environmental Engineering Technology/Environmental Technology, A
General Studies, A
Industrial Electronics Technology/Technician, A
Industrial Mechanics and Maintenance Technology, A
Liberal Arts and Sciences Studies and Humanities, A
Medical/Clinical Assistant, A
Multi-/Interdisciplinary Studies, A
Salon/Beauty Salon Management/Manager, A

OAKWOOD UNIVERSITY

Accounting, AB
Administrative Assistant and Secretarial Science, AB
Applied Mathematics, B
Bible/Biblical Studies, A
Biochemistry, B
Biology/Biological Sciences, B
Business Administration and Management, B
Business Teacher Education, B
Chemistry, B

Clinical Laboratory Science/Medical Technology/Technologist, B
Commercial and Advertising Art, A
Computer Science, B
Dietetics/Dieticians, AB
Economics, B
Elementary Education and Teaching, B
Engineering, B
English Language and Literature, B
Family and Consumer Sciences/Home Economics Teacher Education, B
Family and Consumer Sciences/Human Sciences, B
French Language and Literature, B
History, B
Information Science/Studies, AB
Mass Communication/Media Studies, B
Mathematics, B
Music, B
Music Teacher Education, B
Natural Sciences, B
Occupational Therapy/Therapist, A
Pastoral Studies/Counseling, AM
Physical Education Teaching and Coaching, B
Physical Therapy/Therapist, A
Psychology, B
Religion/Religious Studies, A
Religious Education, B
Science Teacher Education/General Science Teacher Education, B
Social Sciences, B
Social Work, B
Spanish Language and Literature, B
Theology/Theological Studies, B

REID STATE TECHNICAL COLLEGE

Administrative Assistant and Secretarial Science, A
Child Care and Support Services Management, A
Computer and Information Sciences, A
Electrical, Electronic and Communications Engineering Technology/Technician, A

REMINGTON COLLEGE–MOBILE CAMPUS

Computer Systems Networking and Telecommunications, A
Criminal Justice/Law Enforcement Administration, A
Electrical, Electronics and Communications Engineering, A
Operations Management and Supervision, B

SAMFORD UNIVERSITY

Accounting, B
Ancient/Classical Greek Language and Literature, B
Art/Art Studies, General, B
Athletic Training and Sports Medicine, B
Biochemistry, B
Biology/Biological Sciences, B
Business Administration and Management, B
Business Administration, Management and Operations, M
Business/Managerial Economics, B
Chemistry, B
Classics and Classical Languages, Literatures, and Linguistics, B
Communication Disorders, B
Communication Studies/Speech Communication and Rhetoric, B
Computer Science, B
Criminal Justice/Safety Studies, B
Early Childhood Education and Teaching, M
Education, MDO
Education/Teaching of the Gifted and Talented, M
Educational Leadership and Administration, MDO
Elementary Education and Teaching, BM
Energy Management and Policy, M
Engineering Physics, B
English Language and Literature, B
English/Language Arts Teacher Education, B
Entrepreneurship/Entrepreneurial Studies, B
Environmental Policy and Resource Management, M
Environmental Sciences, B
Finance, B
Foods, Nutrition, and Related Services, B
Foods, Nutrition, and Wellness Studies, B
Foreign Languages and Literatures, B

French Language and Literature, B
General Studies, B
Geography, B
German Language and Literature, B
Graphic Design, B
Health Professions and Related Clinical Sciences, B
History, B
History Teacher Education, B
Human Development and Family Studies, B
Interior Design, B
International Business/Trade/Commerce, B
International Relations and Affairs, B
International/Global Studies, B
Journalism, B
Kinesiology and Exercise Science, B
Latin American Studies, B
Latin Language and Literature, B
Law and Legal Studies, BMD
Legal Assistant/Paralegal, B
Marine Biology and Biological Oceanography, B
Marketing/Marketing Management, B
Mathematics, B
Multi-/Interdisciplinary Studies, B
Music, BM
Music Pedagogy, B
Music Performance, B
Music Teacher Education, BM
Music Theory and Composition, B
Nurse Anesthetist, M
Nursing, MD
Nursing - Advanced Practice, M
Nursing Administration, D
Nursing Education, M
Performance, M
Pharmacy, BD
Philosophy, B
Philosophy and Religious Studies, B
Physics, B
Piano and Organ, B
Political Science and Government, B
Pre-Medicine/Pre-Medical Studies, B
Psychology, B
Public Administration, B
Public Health (MPH, DPH), B
Religion/Religious Studies, B
Religious/Sacred Music, B
Sacred Music, M
Secondary Education and Teaching, M
Sociology, B
Spanish Language and Literature, B
Special Education and Teaching, M
Sport and Fitness Administration/Management, B
Teacher Education, Multiple Levels, B
Theology and Religious Vocations, MD
Visual and Performing Arts, B
Voice and Opera, B
Youth Services/Administration, B

SELMA UNIVERSITY

Bible/Biblical Studies, AB
Biology/Biological Sciences, B
Business Administration and Management, B
General Studies, B
Health and Physical Education, B
Liberal Arts and Sciences Studies and Humanities, B

SHELTON STATE COMMUNITY COLLEGE

Administrative Assistant and Secretarial Science, A
Business/Commerce, A
Culinary Arts/Chef Training, A
Diesel Mechanics Technology/Technician, A
Drafting and Design Technology/Technician, A
Electrical, Electronic and Communications Engineering Technology/Technician, A
Electrician, A
General Studies, A
Heating, Air Conditioning and Refrigeration Technology/Technician, A
Industrial Electronics Technology/Technician, A
Liberal Arts and Sciences Studies and Humanities, A
Machine Tool Technology/Machinist, A
Medical Administrative Assistant/Secretary, A
Precision Metal Working, A

Respiratory Care Therapy/Therapist, A
Tool and Die Technology/Technician, A
Welding Technology/Welder, A

SNEAD STATE COMMUNITY COLLEGE

Business Administration and Management, A
Child Care and Support Services Management, A
Computer and Information Sciences, A
Engineering Technology, A
General Studies, A

SOUTH UNIVERSITY

Business Administration and Management, B
Business Administration, Management and Operations, M
Counseling Psychology, M
Criminal Justice/Law Enforcement Administration, B
Criminology, M
Health Services Administration, M
Health/Health Care Administration/Management, B
Health/Medical Preparatory Programs, B
Information Science/Studies, B
Legal Assistant/Paralegal, AB
Management Information Systems and Services, M
Medical/Clinical Assistant, A
Nursing, M
Physical Therapist Assistant, A
Psychology, B
Public Administration, M
Public Relations/Image Management, B

SOUTHEASTERN BIBLE COLLEGE

Bible/Biblical Studies, AB

SOUTHERN UNION STATE COMMUNITY COLLEGE

Administrative Assistant and Secretarial Science, A
Autobody/Collision and Repair
   Technology/Technician, A
Automobile/Automotive Mechanics
   Technology/Technician, A
Business/Commerce, A
Child Care and Support Services Management, A
Computer and Information Sciences, A
Cosmetology/Cosmetologist, A
Electrical, Electronic and Communications Engineering Technology/Technician, A
Emergency Medical Technology/Technician (EMT
   Paramedic), A
General Studies, A
Health Information/Medical Records
   Technology/Technician, A
Heating, Air Conditioning, Ventilation and Refrigeration Maintenance Technology/Technician, A
Industrial Electronics Technology/Technician, A
Industrial Mechanics and Maintenance Technology, A
Liberal Arts and Sciences Studies and Humanities, A
Machine Shop Technology/Assistant, A
Medical Radiologic Technology/Science - Radiation
   Therapist, A
Multi-/Interdisciplinary Studies, A
Welding Technology/Welder, A

SPRING HILL COLLEGE

Accounting, B
Biochemistry, B
Biology Teacher Education, B
Biology/Biological Sciences, B
Biopsychology, B
Business Administration and Management, B
Business Administration, Management and Operations, M
Business/Managerial Economics, B
Chemistry, B
Computer and Information Sciences, B
Criminology, B
Drama and Dramatics/Theatre Arts, B
Early Childhood Education and Teaching, BM
Education, M
Elementary Education and Teaching, BM
English, M
English Language and Literature, B
English/Language Arts Teacher Education, B

Ethics, MO
Fine Arts and Art Studies, MO
Fine/Studio Arts, B
Foundations and Philosophy of Education, M
General Studies, B
Graphic Design, B
Health Services/Allied Health/Health Sciences, B
History, BM
History Teacher Education, B
International Business/Trade/Commerce, B
International Relations and Affairs, B
Journalism, B
Liberal Studies, MO
Marine Biology and Biological Oceanography, B
Marketing/Marketing Management, B
Mathematics, B
Mathematics Teacher Education, B
Nursing, MO
Nursing Administration, MO
Pastoral Studies/Counseling, MO
Philosophy, B
Political Science and Government, B
Psychology, B
Public Relations, Advertising, and Applied Communication, B
Radio, Television, and Digital Communication, B
Religion/Religious Studies, B
Secondary Education and Teaching, BM
Social Sciences, B
Social Studies Teacher Education, BM
Sociology, B
Spanish Language Teacher Education, B
Spanish Language and Literature, B
Theology and Religious Vocations, MO

STILLMAN COLLEGE

Art/Art Studies, General, B
Biology/Biological Sciences, B
Business Administration and Management, B
Elementary Education and Teaching, B
English Language and Literature, B
General Studies, B
History, B
Journalism, B
Mathematics, B
Music, B
Philosophy and Religious Studies, B
Physical Education Teaching and Coaching, B
Psychology, B

STRAYER UNIVERSITY–BIRMINGHAM CAMPUS

Accounting, B
Business Administration and Management, B
Criminal Justice/Law Enforcement Administration, B
Economics, B
International Business/Trade/Commerce, B
Management Information Systems and Services, B

STRAYER UNIVERSITY–HUNTSVILLE CAMPUS

Accounting, B
Business Administration and Management, B
Criminal Justice/Law Enforcement Administration, B
Economics, B
International Business/Trade/Commerce, B
Management Information Systems and Services, B

TALLADEGA COLLEGE

Accounting, B
African-American/Black Studies, B
Biology Teacher Education, B
Biology/Biological Sciences, B
Business Administration and Management, B
Chemistry, B
Chemistry Teacher Education, B
Computer Science, B
Economics, B
Education, B
English Language and Literature, B
English/Language Arts Teacher Education, B
Finance, B
Fine/Studio Arts, B
French Language Teacher Education, B
History, B

History Teacher Education, B
Journalism, B
Marketing/Marketing Management, B
Mass Communication/Media Studies, B
Mathematics, B
Mathematics Teacher Education, B
Music, B
Music Performance, B
Music Teacher Education, B
Pre-Law Studies, B
Psychology, B
Public Administration, B
Science Teacher Education/General Science
   Teacher Education, B
Social Work, B
Sociology, B
Voice and Opera, B

TROY UNIVERSITY

Accounting, BM
Adult and Continuing Education and Teaching, M
Anthropology, M
Art Education, M
Art/Art Studies, General, B
Athletic Training and Sports Medicine, B
Biological and Biomedical Sciences, MO
Biological and Physical Sciences, B
Biology/Biological Sciences, B
Biomedical Sciences, B
Business Administration and Management, B
Business Administration, Management and Operations, M
Business, Management, Marketing, and Related
   Support Services, B
Business/Managerial Economics, B
Chemistry, B
Clinical Psychology, M
Communication Studies/Speech Communication
   and Rhetoric, B
Communication and Media Studies, M
Community Psychology, O
Computer Education, M
Computer Science, M
Computer and Information Sciences, AB
Corporate and Organizational Communication, M
Corrections, M
Counselor Education/School Counseling and Guidance Services, MO
Criminal Justice/Safety Studies, B
Criminology, M
Dance, B
Early Childhood Education and Teaching, MO
Economic Development, M
Economics, B
Education, MO
Education/Teaching of the Gifted and Talented, M
Educational Administration and Supervision, MO
Educational Leadership and Administration, MO
Electrical, Electronic and Communications Engineering Technology/Technician, B
Elementary Education and Teaching, BMO
English Language and Literature, B
Environmental Policy and Resource Management, M
Environmental Sciences, BM
Finance and Banking, M
Health Services Administration, M
Health Teacher Education, B
History, BM
Hospitality Administration/Management, M
Human Resources Management and Services, M
International Affairs, M
International Business/Trade/Commerce, M
Journalism, B
Kinesiology and Exercise Science, B
Liberal Arts and Sciences Studies and Humanities, AB
Management, M
Management Information Systems and Services, M
Marine Biology and Biological Oceanography, B
Maternal and Child Health, MD
Mathematics, B
Mathematics Teacher Education, M
Music, B
Music Teacher Education, M
National Security, M

Non-Profit/Public/Organizational Management, M
Nursing, MDO
Nursing - Adult, MD
Nursing - Advanced Practice, MDO
Nursing Informatics, M
Organizational Management, M
Physical Education Teaching and Coaching, M
Physics, B
Political Science and Government, B
Psychology, B
Public Administration, M
Public Administration and Social Service Professions, B
Radio and Television, B
Reading Teacher Education, M
Rehabilitation Counseling, M
Rehabilitation and Therapeutic Professions, B
School Psychology, MO
Science Teacher Education/General Science Teacher Education, M
Secondary Education and Teaching, BM
Sign Language Interpretation and Translation, B
Social Sciences, BM
Social Studies Teacher Education, M
Social Work, BM
Sociology, B
Spanish Language and Literature, B
Sport and Fitness Administration/Management, BM
Substance Abuse/Addiction Counseling, M
Survey Technology/Surveying, B
Taxation, MO
Teacher Education, Multiple Levels, B

TUSKEGEE UNIVERSITY

Accounting, B
Aerospace, Aeronautical and Astronautical Engineering, B
Agricultural Business and Management, B
Agricultural Economics, M
Agriculture, B
Agronomy and Crop Science, B
Agronomy and Soil Sciences, M
Animal Sciences, BM
Architecture, B
Biological and Biomedical Sciences, MD
Biology/Biological Sciences, B
Building/Home/Construction Inspection/Inspector, B
Business Administration and Management, B
Chemical Engineering, B
Chemistry, BM
Clinical Laboratory Science/Medical Technology/Technologist, B
Computer Science, B
Computer and Information Systems Security, M
Construction Engineering Technology/Technician, B
Dietetics/Dieticians, B
Economics, B
Electrical Engineering, M
Electrical, Electronics and Communications Engineering, B
Elementary Education and Teaching, B
Engineering Technology, B
Engineering and Applied Sciences, MD
English Language and Literature, B
Environmental Sciences, M
Environmental Studies, B
Finance, B
Food Science, B
Food Science and Technology, M
Foods, Nutrition, and Wellness Studies, B
History, B
Hospitality Administration/Management, B
Hospitality and Recreation Marketing Operations, B
Management Information Systems and Services, M
Management Science, B
Marketing/Marketing Management, B
Materials Engineering, D
Mathematics, B
Mechanical Engineering, BM
Natural Resources Management/Development and Policy, B
Nutritional Sciences, M
Occupational Therapy/Therapist, BM
Physics, B
Plant Sciences, BM
Political Science and Government, B

Poultry Science, BM
Psychology, B
Sales, Distribution and Marketing Operations, B
Social Work, B
Sociology, B
Veterinary Medicine, MD
Veterinary Sciences, MD

UNITED STATES SPORTS ACADEMY

Exercise and Sports Science, M
Kinesiology and Exercise Science, B
Physical Education Teaching and Coaching, BM
Sport and Fitness Administration/Management, BMD
Sports Medicine, M

THE UNIVERSITY OF ALABAMA

Accounting, BMD
Advertising, B
Advertising and Public Relations, M
Aerospace, Aeronautical and Astronautical Engineering, BMD
African-American/Black Studies, B
American/United States Studies/Civilization, BM
Anthropology, BMD
Apparel and Textiles, B
Applied Mathematics, D
Applied Statistics, MD
Architectural Engineering, B
Art History, Criticism and Conservation, BM
Athletic Training and Sports Medicine, B
Audiology/Audiologist and Speech-Language Pathology/Pathologist, B
Biological and Biomedical Sciences, MD
Biology/Biological Sciences, B
Business Administration and Management, B
Business Administration, Management and Operations, M
Business/Managerial Economics, B
Ceramic Arts and Ceramics, M
Chemical Engineering, BMD
Chemistry, BMD
Child and Family Studies, M
Civil Engineering, BMD
Clinical Psychology, D
Clothing and Textiles, M
Communication Disorders, M
Communication Studies/Speech Communication and Rhetoric, B
Communication and Media Studies, MD
Community Health and Preventive Medicine, M
Composition, MD
Computer Engineering, MD
Computer Science, MD
Computer and Information Sciences, B
Construction Engineering, B
Construction Engineering and Management, MD
Consumer Economics, M
Counselor Education/School Counseling and Guidance Services, MDO
Criminal Justice/Safety Studies, B
Criminology, M
Dance, B
Dietetics/Dieticians, B
Drama and Dramatics/Theatre Arts, B
Early Childhood Education and Teaching, B
Economics, B
Education/Teaching of the Gifted and Talented, MO
Educational Administration and Supervision, MD
Educational Leadership and Administration, MDO
Electrical Engineering, MD
Electrical, Electronics and Communications Engineering, B
Elementary Education and Teaching, BMDO
Engineering and Applied Sciences, MD
English, MD
English Language and Literature, B
English as a Second Language, M
Environmental Engineering Technology/Environmental Technology, MD
Environmental Sciences, B
Environmental/Environmental Health Engineering, B
Ergonomics and Human Factors, M
Exercise and Sports Science, MD
Experimental Psychology, D
Family Resource Management Studies, B
Family and Consumer Sciences/Human Sciences, B

Film, Television, and Video Production, M
Finance, B
Finance and Banking, MD
Fine Arts and Art Studies, M
Fine/Studio Arts, B
Foreign Languages and Literatures, B
French Language and Literature, MD
Geographic Information Systems, M
Geography, BM
Geology/Earth Science, BMD
Geosciences, M
German Language and Literature, M
Health Education, MD
Health Professions and Related Clinical Sciences, B
Health Promotion, MD
Higher Education/Higher Education Administration, MD
History, BMD
Home Economics, MD
Hospital and Health Care Facilities Administration/Management, B
Hospitality Administration/Management, M
Human Development, M
Human Development and Family Studies, B
Industrial and Manufacturing Management, MD
Information Science/Studies, MD
Interdisciplinary Studies, D
Interior Design, B
International Relations and Affairs, B
Journalism, BM
Kinesiology and Movement Studies, MD
Latin American Studies, B
Law and Legal Studies, MD
Library Science, MD
Linguistics, D
Management, MD
Management Information Systems and Services, B
Management Science, B
Marine Biology and Biological Oceanography, B
Marketing, MD
Marketing/Marketing Management, B
Mass Communication/Media Studies, D
Materials Engineering, MD
Materials Sciences, D
Mathematics, BMD
Mechanical Engineering, BMD
Mechanics, MD
Media Studies, M
Metallurgical Engineering, BMD
Microbiology, B
Music, BMD
Music Teacher Education, BMDO
Music Theory and Composition, M
Musicology and Ethnomusicology, M
Nursing, MD
Nutritional Sciences, M
Painting, M
Performance, MD
Philosophy, B
Photography, M
Physical Education Teaching and Coaching, BMD
Physics, BMD
Political Science and Government, BMD
Printmaking, M
Psychology, BD
Public Administration, M
Public Relations/Image Management, B
Quality Management, M
Radio and Television, B
Religion/Religious Studies, B
Restaurant/Food Services Management, B
Rhetoric, MD
Romance Languages, Literatures, and Linguistics, MD
Sacred Music, M
Sculpture, M
Secondary Education and Teaching, BMDO
Social Work, BMD
Sociology, B
Spanish Language and Literature, BMD
Special Education and Teaching, BMDO
Speech and Interpersonal Communication, M
Sport and Fitness Administration/Management, M
Taxation, M
Theater, M
Urban and Regional Planning, M

Women's Studies, M
Writing, M

THE UNIVERSITY OF ALABAMA AT BIRMINGHAM

Accounting, BM
African-American/Black Studies, B
Allied Health and Medical Assisting Services, MDO
Allopathic Medicine, D
Anthropology, BM
Applied Mathematics, D
Art Education, M
Art History, Criticism and Conservation, M
Art/Art Studies, General, B
BioTechnology, M
Biochemistry, D
Bioinformatics, D
Biological and Biomedical Sciences, MD
Biological and Physical Sciences, B
Biology/Biological Sciences, B
Biomedical Engineering, MD
Biomedical/Medical Engineering, B
Biostatistics, MD
Business Administration and Management, B
Business Administration, Management and Operations, BM
Business/Managerial Economics, B
Cancer Biology/Oncology, D
Cell Biology and Anatomy, D
Chemistry, BMD
Civil Engineering, BMD
Clinical Laboratory Science/Medical Technology/Technologist, B
Clinical Laboratory Sciences, M
Clinical Psychology, D
Communication Studies/Speech Communication and Rhetoric, B
Communication and Media Studies, M
Composition, M
Computational Sciences, D
Computer Engineering, D
Computer Science, MD
Computer and Information Sciences, B
Computer and Information Systems Security, M
Construction Engineering and Management, M
Corrections and Criminal Justice, B
Counselor Education/School Counseling and Guidance Services, M
Criminology, M
Curriculum and Instruction, O
Dentistry, D
Developmental Biology and Embryology, D
Developmental Psychology, D
Drama and Dramatics/Theatre Arts, B
Early Childhood Education and Teaching, BMD
Education, MDO
Educational Leadership and Administration, MDO
Electrical Engineering, M
Electrical, Electronics and Communications Engineering, B
Elementary Education and Teaching, BM
Engineering Design, M
Engineering Management, MD
Engineering and Applied Sciences, MD
English, M
English Language and Literature, B
English as a Second Language, M
Environmental Engineering Technology/Environmental Technology, D
Environmental and Occupational Health, MD
Epidemiology, MD
Exercise and Sports Science, M
Finance, B
Finance and Banking, M
Foreign Languages and Literatures, B
Forensic Science and Technology, M
Genetic Counseling/Counselor, M
Genetics, D
Genomic Sciences, D
Health Education, MD
Health Informatics, M
Health Information/Medical Records Administration/Administrator, B
Health Promotion, D
Health Psychology, M
Health Services Administration, MD

Health Services Research, MD
Health Teacher Education, B
Health/Health Care Administration/Management, B
History, BM
Industrial Hygiene, MD
Information Science/Studies, MD
Interdisciplinary Studies, D
Kinesiology and Movement Studies, M
Management Information Systems and Services, BM
Marketing, M
Marketing/Marketing Management, B
Materials Engineering, BMD
Materials Sciences, D
Maternal and Child Health, MD
Mathematics, BM
Mechanical Engineering, BM
Microbiology, D
Molecular Biology, D
Molecular Medicine, D
Music, B
Neurobiology and Neurophysiology, D
Neuroscience, D
Nuclear Medical Technology/Technologist, B
Nurse Anesthetist, M
Nursing, MD
Nutritional Sciences, MD
Occupational Therapy/Therapist, MO
Optometry, D
Oral and Dental Sciences, M
Pathobiology, D
Pharmacology, D
Philosophy, B
Physical Education Teaching and Coaching, BM
Physical Therapy/Therapist, D
Physician Assistant, M
Physics, BMD
Political Science and Government, B
Psychology, BMD
Public Administration, M
Public Health, MD
Quantitative Analysis, M
Reading Teacher Education, M
Rehabilitation Sciences, D
Respiratory Care Therapy/Therapist, B
Rhetoric, M
Safety Engineering, M
Secondary Education and Teaching, BM
Social Sciences, B
Social Work, B
Sociology, BMD
Special Education and Teaching, M
Structural Biology, D
Toxicology, MD
Vision Science/Physiological Optics, MD
Writing, M

THE UNIVERSITY OF ALABAMA IN HUNTSVILLE

Accounting, BM
Acute Care/Critical Care Nursing, M
Aerospace, Aeronautical and Astronautical Engineering, BMD
Applied Mathematics, D
Art/Art Studies, General, B
Atmospheric Sciences and Meteorology, MD
BioTechnology, D
Biological and Biomedical Sciences, MD
Biology/Biological Sciences, B
Business Administration and Management, B
Business/Managerial Economics, B
Chemical Engineering, BMD
Chemistry, BMD
Civil Engineering, BMD
Communication Studies/Speech Communication and Rhetoric, B
Computer Engineering, BMD
Computer Science, MDO
Computer and Information Sciences, B
Computer and Information Systems Security, MO
Electrical Engineering, MD
Electrical, Electronics and Communications Engineering, B
Elementary Education and Teaching, B
Engineering, B
Engineering and Applied Sciences, MD

English, MO
English Education, M
English Language and Literature, B
Entrepreneurship/Entrepreneurial Studies, M
Environmental Engineering Technology/Environmental Technology, MD
Environmental Sciences, MD
Finance, B
Finance and Banking, M
Foreign Languages and Literatures, B
Geosciences, M
Geotechnical Engineering, M
Health Services Administration, M
History, BM
Human Resources Management and Services, M
Industrial Engineering, B
Industrial and Organizational Psychology, M
Industrial/Management Engineering, MD
Interdisciplinary Studies, MDO
Logistics and Materials Management, M
Management, MO
Management Information Systems and Services, BMO
Management of Technology, O
Marketing, M
Marketing/Marketing Management, B
Materials Sciences, MD
Mathematics, BMD
Mathematics Teacher Education, M
Mechanical Engineering, BMD
Modeling and Simulation, MDO
Multi-/Interdisciplinary Studies, B
Music, B
Nursing, MDO
Nursing - Advanced Practice, MO
Nursing Education, O
Operations Research, M
Optical Technologies, M
Optics/Optical Sciences, MD
Philosophy, B
Photonics, M
Physical Sciences, B
Physics, BMD
Political Science and Government, B
Project Management, M
Psychology, BM
Public Affairs, M
Purchasing, Procurement/Acquisitions and Contracts Management, B
Reading Teacher Education, M
Science Teacher Education/General Science Teacher Education, M
Secondary Education and Teaching, B
Securities Services Administration/Management, MO
Social Studies Teacher Education, M
Sociology, B
Software Engineering, MO
Structural Engineering, M
Supply Chain Management, MO
Systems Engineering, M
Taxation, M
Technical and Business Writing, O
Transportation and Highway Engineering, M
Water Resources Engineering, M

UNIVERSITY OF MOBILE

Accounting, B
Art/Art Studies, General, B
Athletic Training and Sports Medicine, B
Biology Teacher Education, B
Biology/Biological Sciences, B
Business Administration and Management, B
Business Administration, Management and Operations, M
Communication and Media Studies, B
Computer and Information Sciences, B
Drama and Dramatics/Theatre Arts, B
Early Childhood Education and Teaching, B
Education, M
Elementary Education and Teaching, B
English Language and Literature, B
English/Language Arts Teacher Education, B
Environmental Sciences, B
General Studies, AB
Health and Physical Education, B
History, B

History Teacher Education, B
Humanities/Humanistic Studies, B
Intercultural/Multicultural and Diversity Studies, B
Marine Biology and Biological Oceanography, B
Marriage and Family Therapy/Counseling, BM
Mathematics, B
Mathematics Teacher Education, B
Music, B
Music Teacher Education, B
Nursing, M
Physical Education Teaching and Coaching, B
Political Science and Government, B
Psychology, B
Religion/Religious Studies, B
Religious/Sacred Music, B
Social Science Teacher Education, B
Social Sciences, B
Sociology, B
Voice and Opera, B

UNIVERSITY OF MONTEVALLO

Accounting, B
Art/Art Studies, General, B
Audiology/Audiologist and Hearing Sciences, B
Biology/Biological Sciences, B
Business Administration and Management, B
Business Administration, Management and Operations, M
Chemistry, B
Communication Disorders, M
Community Psychology, M
Counselor Education/School Counseling and Guidance Services, M
Drama and Dramatics/Theatre Arts, B
Education, MO
Educational Administration and Supervision, MO
Elementary Education and Teaching, BM
English, M
English Language and Literature, B
Family and Consumer Sciences/Human Sciences, B
Finance, B
Foreign Languages and Literatures, B
Health and Physical Education, B
History, B
Marketing/Marketing Management, B
Marriage and Family Therapy/Counseling, M
Mathematics, B
Multi-/Interdisciplinary Studies, B
Music, B
Political Science and Government, B
Psychology, B
Radio and Television, B
Secondary Education and Teaching, M
Social Sciences, B
Social Work, B
Sociology, B
Speech-Language Pathology/Pathologist, B

UNIVERSITY OF NORTH ALABAMA

Accounting, BM
Art/Art Studies, General, B
Biology/Biological Sciences, B
Business Administration and Management, B
Business Administration, Management and Operations, M
Business/Managerial Economics, B
Cartography, B
Chemistry, B
Child and Family Studies, M
Communication Studies/Speech Communication and Rhetoric, B
Computer and Information Sciences, B
Counselor Education/School Counseling and Guidance Services, M
Criminal Justice/Law Enforcement Administration, B
Criminology, M
Culinary Arts and Related Services, B
Drama and Dramatics/Theatre Arts, B
Education, MO
Educational Leadership and Administration, O
Elementary Education and Teaching, BMO
Engineering Technology, B
English, M
English Language and Literature, B
Environmental and Occupational Health, M
Exercise and Sports Science, M

Family and Consumer Sciences/Human Sciences, B
Finance, B
Finance and Banking, M
Foreign Languages and Literatures, B
French Language and Literature, B
Geographic Information Systems, M
Geography, B
German Language and Literature, B
Health Promotion, M
Health Services Administration, M
History, BM
International Business/Trade/Commerce, M
Kinesiology and Movement Studies, M
Management Information Systems and Services, BM
Marine Biology and Biological Oceanography, B
Marketing/Marketing Management, B
Mass Communication/Media Studies, B
Mathematics, B
Music, B
Nursing, M
Parks, Recreation, Leisure and Fitness Studies, B
Physical Education Teaching and Coaching, M
Physical Sciences, B
Physics, B
Political Science and Government, B
Project Management, M
Psychology, B
School Psychology, M
Secondary Education and Teaching, BMO
Social Sciences, B
Social Work, B
Sociology, B
Spanish Language and Literature, B
Special Education and Teaching, M
Teacher Education, Multiple Levels, B
Urban and Regional Planning, M

UNIVERSITY OF SOUTH ALABAMA

Accounting, BM
Allied Health and Medical Assisting Services, MD
Allopathic Medicine, D
Anthropology, B
Art/Art Studies, General, B
Biological and Biomedical Sciences, MD
Biology/Biological Sciences, B
Biomedical Sciences, B
Business Administration and Management, B
Business Administration, Management and Operations, MD
Business/Commerce, B
Chemical Engineering, BM
Chemistry, B
Civil Engineering, BM
Clinical Psychology, D
Communication Disorders, BMD
Communication Studies/Speech Communication and Rhetoric, B
Communication and Media Studies, M
Community Health Nursing, M
Computer Engineering, B
Computer Science, BMD
Computer and Information Systems Security, B
Counseling Psychology, D
Criminal Justice/Law Enforcement Administration, B
Drama and Dramatics/Theatre Arts, B
Early Childhood Education and Teaching, BM
Education, BMDO
Educational Leadership and Administration, M
Electrical, Electronics and Communications Engineering, B
Elementary Education and Teaching, BM
Emergency Medical Technology/Technician (EMT Paramedic), B
Engineering and Applied Sciences, MD
English, M
English Language and Literature, B
Environmental and Occupational Health, M
Exercise and Sports Science, M
Finance, B
Foreign Languages and Literatures, B
Geography, B
Geology/Earth Science, B
Health Education, M
Health/Medical Preparatory Programs, B
History, BM

Hospitality Administration/Management, B
Information Science/Studies, B
Information Technology, B
Interdisciplinary Studies, MD
International/Global Studies, B
Leisure Studies, M
Management Information Systems and Services, M
Marine Sciences, MD
Marketing/Marketing Management, B
Maternal/Child Health and Neonatal Nurse/Nursing, M
Mathematics, M
Mechanical Engineering, BM
Medical Informatics, B
Meteorology, B
Music, BM
Music Teacher Education, M
Nursing, MDO
Nursing - Adult, M
Occupational Therapy/Therapist, M
Parks, Recreation, Leisure and Fitness Studies, B
Performance, M
Philosophy, B
Physical Education Teaching and Coaching, BM
Physical Therapy/Therapist, D
Physician Assistant, M
Physics, B
Political Science and Government, B
Psychology, B
Public Administration, M
Radiologic Technology/Science - Radiographer, B
Reading Teacher Education, M
Respiratory Care Therapy/Therapist, B
Science Teacher Education/General Science Teacher Education, M
Secondary Education and Teaching, BM
Social Work, B
Sociology, B
Special Education and Teaching, BMO
Systems Engineering, D
Toxicology, M

THE UNIVERSITY OF WEST ALABAMA

Accounting, B
Adult and Continuing Education and Teaching, M
Athletic Training and Sports Medicine, B
Biological and Physical Sciences, B
Biology/Biological Sciences, B
Business Administration and Management, B
Business Administration, Management and Operations, M
Chemistry, B
Child Development, O
Communication and Media Studies, B
Counselor Education/School Counseling and Guidance Services, MO
Curriculum and Instruction, MO
Early Childhood Education and Teaching, MO
Education, MO
Educational Leadership and Administration, MO
Educational Media/Instructional Technology, MO
Elementary Education and Teaching, MO
Emergency Medical Technology/Technician (EMT Paramedic), A
Engineering Technologies/Technicians, B
Engineering Technology, B
English Education, M
English Language and Literature, B
Finance, B
History, BM
Industrial Mechanics and Maintenance Technology, A
Kinesiology and Exercise Science, B
Management Information Systems and Services, B
Marine Biology and Biological Oceanography, B
Marketing/Marketing Management, B
Marriage and Family Therapy/Counseling, M
Mathematics, B
Mathematics Teacher Education, M
Multi-/Interdisciplinary Studies, B
Physical Education Teaching and Coaching, BM
Psychology, B
School Psychology, MO
Science Teacher Education/General Science Teacher Education, M
Secondary Education and Teaching, M

Social Studies Teacher Education, M
Sociology, B
Special Education and Teaching, BMO
Teacher Education, Multiple Levels, B

VIRGINIA COLLEGE IN BIRMINGHAM

Accounting, AB
Administrative Assistant and Secretarial Science, A
Business Administration and Management, B
Business Administration, Management and Operations, M
Computer Graphics, AB
Computer Programming/Programmer, A
Computer and Information Systems Security, B
Cooking and Related Culinary Arts, A
Criminal Justice/Law Enforcement Administration, AB
Criminology, M
Data Modeling/Warehousing and Database Administration, A
Diagnostic Medical Sonography/Sonographer and Ultrasound Technician, A
Graphic Design, A
Health Services Administration, M
Human Resources Management/Personnel Administration, A
Interior Design, AB
Legal Assistant/Paralegal, A
Management, M
Management Information Systems and Services, B
Massage Therapy/Therapeutic Massage, A
Medical Insurance Specialist/Medical Biller, A
Medical Office Assistant/Specialist, A
Medical/Health Management and Clinical Assistant/Specialist, B
Securities Services Administration/Management, M
Surgical Technology/Technologist, A
Web Page, Digital/Multimedia and Information Resources Design, A
Web/Multimedia Management and Webmaster, A

VIRGINIA COLLEGE IN HUNTSVILLE

Accounting Technology/Technician and Bookkeeping, A
Business Administration and Management, B
Computer Graphics, A
Computer Systems Networking and Telecommunications, AB
Computer and Information Sciences, A
Corrections and Criminal Justice, AB
Cosmetology/Cosmetologist, A
Design and Visual Communications, A
Health Services Administration, B
Legal Assistant/Paralegal, A
Massage Therapy/Therapeutic Massage, A
Medical Insurance Coding Specialist/Coder, A
Medical Office Management/Administration, A
Medical/Clinical Assistant, A
Office Management and Supervision, A
Web/Multimedia Management and Webmaster, B

VIRGINIA COLLEGE IN MOBILE

CAD/CADD Drafting and/or Design Technology/Technician, A
Finance, A
Health and Medical Administrative Services, A
Human Resources Management/Personnel Administration, A
Interior Design, A
Legal Assistant/Paralegal, A
Medical Insurance Specialist/Medical Biller, A
Medical Office Management/Administration, A
Office Management and Supervision, A
Orthotist/Prosthetist, A
Surgical Technology/Technologist, A

WALLACE STATE COMMUNITY COLLEGE

Accounting, A
Administrative Assistant and Secretarial Science, A
Agriculture, A
Airline/Commercial/Professional Pilot and Flight Crew, A
Art Teacher Education, A

Automobile/Automotive Mechanics Technology/Technician, A
Avionics Maintenance Technology/Technician, A
Business Administration and Management, A
Business Teacher Education, A
Carpentry/Carpenter, A
Child Development, A
Clinical/Medical Laboratory Technician, A
Computer Programming/Programmer, A
Computer Science, A
Construction Engineering Technology/Technician, A
Cosmetology/Cosmetologist, A
Criminal Justice/Law Enforcement Administration, A
Criminal Justice/Police Science, A
Dental Assisting/Assistant, A
Dental Hygiene/Hygienist, A
Drafting and Design Technology/Technician, A
Education, A
Electrical, Electronic and Communications Engineering Technology/Technician, A
Elementary Education and Teaching, A
Emergency Medical Technology/Technician (EMT Paramedic), A
Engineering, A
Farm/Farm and Ranch Management, A
Fashion Merchandising, A
Finance, A
Fire Science/Firefighting, A
Health Information/Medical Records Administration/Administrator, A
Heating, Air Conditioning, Ventilation and Refrigeration Maintenance Technology/Technician, A
Horticultural Science, A
Industrial Radiologic Technology/Technician, A
Interior Design, A
Kindergarten/PreSchool Education and Teaching, A
Labor and Industrial Relations, A
Legal Administrative Assistant/Secretary, A
Legal Assistant/Paralegal, A
Liberal Arts and Sciences Studies and Humanities, A
Library Science, A
Machine Tool Technology/Machinist, A
Marketing/Marketing Management, A
Medical Administrative Assistant/Secretary, A
Medical/Clinical Assistant, A
Mental Health Counseling/Counselor, A
Music, A
Occupational Safety and Health Technology/Technician, A
Occupational Therapy/Therapist, A
Physical Therapy/Therapist, A
Poultry Science, A
Real Estate, A
Religion/Religious Studies, A
Respiratory Care Therapy/Therapist, A
Special Products Marketing Operations, A
Welding Technology/Welder, A

Alaska

ALASKA BIBLE COLLEGE

Bible/Biblical Studies, AB

ALASKA CAREER COLLEGE

Business Administration and Management, A

ALASKA PACIFIC UNIVERSITY

Business Administration and Management, AB
Business Administration, Management and Operations, M
Counseling Psychology, M
Education, M
Elementary Education and Teaching, M
Environmental Education, M
Environmental Sciences, BM
Geology/Earth Science, B
Health Services Administration, M
Interdisciplinary Studies, M
Investment Management, O
Liberal Arts and Sciences Studies and Humanities, B
Liberal Studies, M
Marine Biology and Biological Oceanography, B
Middle School Education, M

Natural Resources Management/Development and Policy, B
Parks, Recreation, Leisure and Fitness Studies, B
Pre-Medicine/Pre-Medical Studies, B
Psychology, B
Telecommunications Management, M

CHARTER COLLEGE

Accounting, A
Business Administration and Management, A
CAD/CADD Drafting and/or Design Technology/Technician, A
Computer Systems Networking and Telecommunications, A
Computer and Information Systems Security, A
Computer/Information Technology Services Administration and Management, B
General Office Occupations and Clerical Services, A
Information Technology, B
Medical Insurance Coding Specialist/Coder, A
System, Networking, and LAN/WAN Management/Manager, A

ILISAGVIK COLLEGE

Accounting Technology/Technician and Bookkeeping, A
American Indian/Native American Studies, A
Business Administration and Management, A
Fire Science/Firefighting, A
Health Services/Allied Health/Health Sciences, A
Liberal Arts and Sciences Studies and Humanities, A
Office Management and Supervision, A

UNIVERSITY OF ALASKA ANCHORAGE

Accounting, AB
Aeronautics/Aviation/Aerospace Science and Technology, AB
Air Traffic Controller, A
Airframe Mechanics and Aircraft Maintenance Technology/Technician, A
Airline/Commercial/Professional Pilot and Flight Crew, A
Anthropology, BM
Architectural Engineering Technology/Technician, A
Art/Art Studies, General, B
Automobile/Automotive Mechanics Technology/Technician, A
Aviation/Airway Management and Operations, A
Avionics Maintenance Technology/Technician, A
Biological and Biomedical Sciences, M
Biological and Physical Sciences, B
Biology/Biological Sciences, B
Business Administration and Management, AB
Business Administration, Management and Operations, M
Business/Commerce, A
Business/Managerial Economics, B
Business/Office Automation/Technology/Data Entry, A
Chemistry, B
Child Care Provider/Assistant, A
Civil Engineering, BMO
Clinical Laboratory Science/Medical Technology/Technologist, B
Clinical Psychology, MD
Clinical/Medical Laboratory Technician, A
Community Psychology, D
Computer Engineering Technology/Technician, A
Computer Programming, Specific Applications, A
Computer Science, B
Computer Systems Networking and Telecommunications, A
Computer Technology/Computer Systems Technology, A
Computer and Information Sciences, A
Construction Management, AB
Construction/Heavy Equipment/Earthmoving Equipment Operation, A
Counselor Education/School Counseling and Guidance Services, M
Culinary Arts/Chef Training, A
Dental Assisting/Assistant, A
Dental Hygiene/Hygienist, A
Drafting and Design Technology/Technician, A
Drama and Dramatics/Theatre Arts, B

Early Childhood Education and Teaching, M
Economics, B
Education, BMO
Educational Leadership and Administration, MO
Electrical, Electronic and Communications Engineering Technology/Technician, A
Elementary Education and Teaching, B
Emergency Medical Technology/Technician (EMT Paramedic), A
Engineering, B
Engineering Management, M
Engineering Technology, A
Engineering and Applied Sciences, MO
English, M
English Language and Literature, B
Entrepreneurship/Entrepreneurial Studies, AB
Environmental Engineering Technology/Environmental Technology, M
Environmental Sciences, M
Environmental Studies, B
Family and Consumer Sciences/Human Sciences, A
Finance, B
Fine/Studio Arts, B
Fire Science/Firefighting, A
Foods, Nutrition, and Wellness Studies, B
Foreign Languages and Literatures, B
French Language and Literature, B
Geological Engineering, M
Geology/Earth Science, B
German Language and Literature, B
Health Professions and Related Clinical Sciences, B
Health Services/Allied Health/Health Sciences, B
Health and Physical Education, B
Heating, Air Conditioning, Ventilation and Refrigeration Maintenance Technology/Technician, A
Heavy Equipment Maintenance Technology/Technician, A
History, B
Human Services, A
Industrial Mechanics and Maintenance Technology, A
Industrial Technology/Technician, A
Information Science/Studies, A
Instrumentation Technology/Technician, A
Interdisciplinary Studies, M
International/Global Studies, B
Japanese Language and Literature, B
Journalism, B
Kindergarten/PreSchool Education and Teaching, B
Liberal Arts and Sciences Studies and Humanities, B
Logistics and Materials Management, ABMO
Management Information Systems and Services, B
Management Science, A
Marketing/Marketing Management, B
Mass Communication/Media Studies, B
Mathematics, B
Mathematics and Computer Science, B
Medical/Clinical Assistant, A
Music, B
Music Performance, B
Music Teacher Education, B
Natural Sciences, B
Nursing, M
Occupational Safety and Health Technology/Technician, A
Ocean Engineering, O
Petroleum Technology/Technician, A
Philosophy, B
Physical Education Teaching and Coaching, B
Political Science and Government, B
Project Management, M
Psychiatric/Mental Health Services Technician, AB
Psychology, BMD
Public Administration, BM
Public Health, M
Public Health (MPH, DPH), B
Radiologic Technology/Science - Radiographer, A
Restaurant/Food Services Management, B
Russian Language and Literature, B
Science, Technology and Society, B
Secondary Education and Teaching, B
Small Business Administration/Management, A
Social Work, BMO
Sociology, B
Spanish Language and Literature, B

Special Education and Teaching, MO
Survey Technology/Surveying, AB
Technical Theatre/Theatre Design and Technology, B
Welding Technology/Welder, A
Writing, M

UNIVERSITY OF ALASKA ANCHORAGE, KENAI PENINSULA COLLEGE

Business Administration and Management, A
Digital Communication and Media/Multimedia, A
Early Childhood Education and Teaching, A
Elementary Education and Teaching, B
Emergency Medical Technology/Technician (EMT Paramedic), A
Human Services, A
Liberal Arts and Sciences Studies and Humanities, AB
Occupational Safety and Health Technology/Technician, A
Psychology, B

UNIVERSITY OF ALASKA ANCHORAGE, KODIAK COLLEGE

Accounting, A
Accounting Technology/Technician and Bookkeeping, A
Computer Programming, Specific Applications, A
Computer Technology/Computer Systems Technology, A
Construction Management, A
Occupational Safety and Health Technology/Technician, A
Welding Technology/Welder, A

UNIVERSITY OF ALASKA ANCHORAGE, MATANUSKA-SUSITNA COLLEGE

Accounting, A
Administrative Assistant and Secretarial Science, A
Architectural Engineering Technology/Technician, A
Business Administration and Management, A
Electrical, Electronic and Communications Engineering Technology/Technician, A
Emergency Medical Technology/Technician (EMT Paramedic), A
Heating, Air Conditioning, Ventilation and Refrigeration Maintenance Technology/Technician, A
Human Services, A
Liberal Arts and Sciences Studies and Humanities, A

UNIVERSITY OF ALASKA FAIRBANKS

Accounting, B
Accounting Technology/Technician and Bookkeeping, A
Aircraft Powerplant Technology/Technician, A
Airline/Commercial/Professional Pilot and Flight Crew, A
American Indian/Native American Languages, Literatures, and Linguistics, AB
American Indian/Native American Studies, B
Anthropology, BMD
Area Studies, B
Art/Art Studies, General, B
Astrophysics, M
Atmospheric Sciences and Meteorology, MD
Biochemistry, MD
Biological and Physical Sciences, B
Biology/Biological Sciences, B
Business Administration and Management, AB
Business Administration, Management and Operations, M
Carpentry/Carpenter, A
Ceramic Arts and Ceramics, M
Chemistry, BMD
Child Development, B
Civil Engineering, BMDO
Clinical Psychology, D
Clinical/Medical Laboratory Assistant, A
Communication Studies/Speech Communication and Rhetoric, B
Communication and Media Studies, M
Community Organization and Advocacy, AB
Community Psychology, MD
Computational Sciences, M

Computer Art and Design, M
Computer Engineering, B
Computer Installation and Repair Technology/Technician, A
Computer Science, BM
Computer and Information Sciences, B
Construction Management, AO
Corporate and Organizational Communication, M
Corrections and Criminal Justice, B
Counselor Education/School Counseling and Guidance Services, MO
Criminology, M
Culinary Arts/Chef Training, A
Cultural Studies, M
Dental Assisting/Assistant, A
Dental Hygiene/Hygienist, A
Drafting and Design Technology/Technician, A
Early Childhood Education and Teaching, A
Economics, BM
Education, MO
Electrical Engineering, M
Electrical, Electronics and Communications Engineering, B
Elementary Education and Teaching, BM
Engineering Management, M
Engineering and Applied Sciences, D
English, M
English Language and Literature, B
Environmental Engineering Technology/Environmental Technology, MD
Environmental Policy, M
Environmental Policy and Resource Management, M
Environmental Sciences, M
Film/Cinema Studies, B
Finance and Banking, M
Fine Arts and Art Studies, M
Fire Science/Firefighting, A
Fishing and Fisheries Sciences and Management, B
Foreign Languages and Literatures, B
Foreign Languages, Literatures, and Linguistics, AB
Geographic Information Systems, MD
Geography, B
Geological Engineering, M
Geological/Geophysical Engineering, B
Geology/Earth Science, BMD
Geophysics and Seismology, MD
Hazardous Materials Management and Waste Technology/Technician, M
History, BM
Industrial Production Technologies/Technicians, A
Interdisciplinary Studies, MD
Japanese Language and Literature, B
Journalism, B
Legal Assistant/Paralegal, A
Liberal Arts and Sciences Studies and Humanities, AB
Limnology, MD
Linguistics, BM
Management, M
Marine Biology and Biological Oceanography, MD
Marine Sciences, MD
Mathematics, BMDO
Mechanical Engineering, BM
Medical/Clinical Assistant, A
Mental and Social Health Services and Allied Professions, M
Mineral/Mining Engineering, M
Mining and Mineral Engineering, B
Multi-/Interdisciplinary Studies, AB
Multilingual and Multicultural Education, M
Music, BM
Natural Resources Management/Development and Policy, AM
Natural Resources and Conservation, BMD
Natural Sciences, A
Neuroscience, D
Northern Studies, M
Painting, M
Petroleum Engineering, BM
Philosophy, B
Photography, M
Physics, BMD
Political Science and Government, B
Printmaking, M
Psychology, BD

Public Health (MPH, DPH), A
Rural Planning and Studies, M
Russian Studies, B
Science Technologies/Technicians, A
Sculpture, M
Secondary Education and Teaching, BM
Social Work, B
Sociology, B
Special Education and Teaching, M
Statistics, MDO
Sustainable Development, D
Technical Theatre/Theatre Design and Technology, B
Water Resources, M
Wildlife and Wildlands Science and Management, B
Writing, M

UNIVERSITY OF ALASKA, PRINCE WILLIAM SOUND COLLEGE

Administrative Assistant and Secretarial Science, A
Liberal Arts and Sciences Studies and Humanities, A
Mental Health Counseling/Counselor, A

UNIVERSITY OF ALASKA SOUTHEAST

Biology/Biological Sciences, B
Business Administration and Management, AB
Business Administration, Management and Operations, M
Carpentry/Carpenter, A
Communication Studies/Speech Communication and Rhetoric, B
Early Childhood Education and Teaching, AM
Education, BM
Educational Media/Instructional Technology, M
Electrical and Power Transmission Installation/Installer, A
Elementary Education and Teaching, ABM
Engineering-Related Technologies, A
English Language and Literature, B
Environmental Studies, B
Fishing and Fisheries Sciences and Management, A
General Studies, AB
Health Information/Medical Records Administration/Administrator, A
Health Professions and Related Clinical Sciences, A
History, B
Humanities/Humanistic Studies, AB
Law and Legal Studies, A
Liberal Arts and Sciences Studies and Humanities, AB
Management Information Systems and Services, A
Mathematics, B
Multi-/Interdisciplinary Studies, B
Natural Resources and Conservation, B
Public Administration, M
Public Health (MPH, DPH), A
Science Technologies/Technicians, A
Secondary Education and Teaching, M
Social Sciences, B

UNIVERSITY OF ALASKA SOUTHEAST, KETCHIKAN CAMPUS

Business Administration and Management, A
Computer and Information Sciences, A
Fishing and Fisheries Sciences and Management, A
Health Professions and Related Clinical Sciences, A
Liberal Arts and Sciences Studies and Humanities, A

UNIVERSITY OF ALASKA SOUTHEAST, SITKA CAMPUS

Business Administration and Management, AB
Criminal Justice/Law Enforcement Administration, A
Elementary Education and Teaching, B
Fishing and Fisheries Sciences and Management, A
General Studies, A
Health Information/Medical Records Administration/Administrator, A
Health Information/Medical Records Technology/Technician, A
Health Services/Allied Health/Health Sciences, A
Liberal Arts and Sciences Studies and Humanities, AB
Social Sciences, B

Special Education and Teaching, B

Arizona
ARGOSY UNIVERSITY, PHOENIX

Accounting, D
Adult and Continuing Education and Teaching, M
Business Administration and Management, AB
Business Administration, Management and Operations, MD
Clinical Psychology, MD
Community College Education, D
Counseling Psychology, M
Criminal Justice/Law Enforcement Administration, B
Education, MDO
Educational Administration and Supervision, MDO
Educational Leadership and Administration, M
Educational Media/Instructional Technology, D
Elementary Education and Teaching, D
Finance and Banking, M
Forensic Psychology, M
Health Services Administration, M
Higher Education/Higher Education Administration, MD
Industrial and Organizational Psychology, M
Information Technology, AB
International Business/Trade/Commerce, MD
Liberal Arts and Sciences Studies and Humanities, B
Management, MD
Management Information Systems and Services, MD
Marketing, MD
Neuroscience, D
Psychology, ABMD
Public Administration, M
Public Health, M
School Psychology, MD
Secondary Education and Teaching, D
Sport Psychology, MD
Sustainability Management, MD

ARIZONA AUTOMOTIVE INSTITUTE

Automobile/Automotive Mechanics Technology/Technician, A
Diesel Mechanics Technology/Technician, A
Heating, Air Conditioning and Refrigeration Technology/Technician, A

ARIZONA CHRISTIAN UNIVERSITY

American Government and Politics (United States), B
Bible/Biblical Studies, B
Biology Teacher Education, B
Biology/Biological Sciences, B
Business Administration and Management, B
Business Teacher Education, B
Elementary Education and Teaching, B
English/Language Arts Teacher Education, B
Liberal Arts and Sciences Studies and Humanities, A
Mathematics Teacher Education, B
Missions/Missionary Studies and Missiology, B
Psychology, B
Religious/Sacred Music, B
Science Teacher Education/General Science Teacher Education, B
Secondary Education and Teaching, B
Social Studies Teacher Education, B
Voice and Opera, B
Youth Ministry, B

ARIZONA COLLEGE

Allied Health and Medical Assisting Services, A
Health Information/Medical Records Technology/Technician, A

ARIZONA STATE UNIVERSITY AT THE DOWNTOWN PHOENIX CAMPUS

Communication Studies/Speech Communication and Rhetoric, B
Community Organization and Advocacy, B
Criminal Justice/Law Enforcement Administration, B
Foods, Nutrition, and Wellness Studies, B
Health Services Administration, B

Health and Physical Education/Fitness, B
Health/Medical Preparatory Programs, B
Journalism, B
Kinesiology and Exercise Science, B
Multi-/Interdisciplinary Studies, B
Non-Profit/Public/Organizational Management, B
Parks, Recreation, Leisure and Fitness Studies, B
Pre-Medicine/Pre-Medical Studies, B
Pre-Nursing Studies, B
Public Health (MPH, DPH), B
Public Health Education and Promotion, B
Public Policy Analysis, B
Science Technologies/Technicians, B
Social Work, B
Sport and Fitness Administration/Management, B
Tourism and Travel Services Management, B
Urban Studies/Affairs, B

ARIZONA STATE UNIVERSITY AT THE POLYTECHNIC CAMPUS

Aeronautics/Aviation/Aerospace Science and Technology, B
Agricultural Business and Management, B
Air Traffic Controller, B
Biology/Biological Sciences, B
Business Administration and Management, B
Business, Management, Marketing, and Related Support Services, B
Communication Studies/Speech Communication and Rhetoric, B
Computer Engineering Technology/Technician, B
Computer Software Engineering, B
Computer Systems Analysis/Analyst, B
Education, B
Electrical, Electronic and Communications Engineering Technology/Technician, B
Elementary Education and Teaching, B
Engineering, B
English Language and Literature, B
Environmental/Environmental Health Engineering, B
Graphic Communications, B
Health/Health Care Administration/Management, B
History, B
Liberal Arts and Sciences Studies and Humanities, B
Manufacturing Engineering, B
Manufacturing Technology/Technician, B
Mechanical Engineering/Mechanical Technology/Technician, B
Multi-/Interdisciplinary Studies, B
Operations Management and Supervision, B
Political Science and Government, B
Science Technologies/Technicians, B
Science, Technology and Society, B
Secondary Education and Teaching, B
Special Education and Teaching, B

ARIZONA STATE UNIVERSITY AT THE TEMPE CAMPUS

Accounting, BMD
Actuarial Science, B
Aerospace, Aeronautical and Astronautical Engineering, BMD
African Studies, O
African-American/Black Studies, B
Agribusiness, D
American Indian/Native American Studies, B
Animal Behavior and Ethology, D
Anthropology, BMDO
Applied Behavior Analysis, M
Applied Mathematics, BD
Applied Psychology, M
Archeology, O
Architectural History and Criticism, D
Architecture, BMD
Art Education, M
Art History, Criticism and Conservation, M
Art/Art Studies, General, B
Arts Management, M
Asian Studies/Civilization, B
Asian-American Studies, B
Astrophysics, MD
Aviation/Airway Management and Operations, M
BioTechnology, M
Biochemistry, BMD
Bioinformatics, BMD

Biological and Biomedical Sciences, MD
Biology/Biological Sciences, B
Biomedical Engineering, MD
Biomedical/Medical Engineering, B
Biophysics, B
Building Science, M
Business Administration and Management, B
Business Administration, Management and Operations, MD
Business, Management, Marketing, and Related Support Services, B
Cartography, B
Cell Biology and Anatomy, D
Ceramic Arts and Ceramics, M
Chemical Engineering, BMD
Chemistry, BMD
Child and Family Studies, M
Chinese Studies, MD
City/Urban, Community and Regional Planning, B
Civil Engineering, BMD
Clinical Psychology, D
Cognitive Sciences, D
Communication Disorders, BMD
Communication Studies/Speech Communication and Rhetoric, B
Communication and Media Studies, MD
Community Health and Preventive Medicine, O
Comparative Literature, M
Composition, MD
Computational Mathematics, B
Computer Engineering, BMD
Computer Science, BMD
Computer and Information Sciences, B
Conservation Biology, M
Construction Engineering, B
Construction Engineering and Management, M
Construction Management, BMD
Counseling Psychology, D
Counselor Education/School Counseling and Guidance Services, M
Criminology, MDO
Cultural Studies, MD
Curriculum and Instruction, M
Dance, BM
Design and Applied Arts, BMD
Developmental Psychology, D
Drama and Dramatics/Theatre Arts, B
Early Childhood Education and Teaching, B
East Asian Languages, Literatures, and Linguistics, B
Economics, BD
Education, BMDO
Educational Leadership and Administration, MD
Educational Measurement and Evaluation, D
Educational Media/Instructional Technology, MO
Educational Policy, D
Electrical Engineering, MDO
Electrical, Electronics and Communications Engineering, B
Elementary Education and Teaching, BM
Emergency Management, M
Energy and Power Engineering, M
Engineering and Applied Sciences, MDO
Engineering/Industrial Management, B
English, MDO
English Language and Literature, B
English as a Second Language, M
Entrepreneurship/Entrepreneurial Studies, BM
Environmental Design/Architecture, BD
Environmental Engineering Technology/Environmental Technology, MD
Environmental Sciences, D
Environmental Studies, BM
Ergonomics and Human Factors, M
Ethics, M
Ethnomusicology, M
Evolutionary Biology, D
Exercise and Sports Science, MD
Family Resource Management Studies, B
Film, Television, and Video Production, M
Film/Video and Photographic Arts, B
Finance, B
Finance and Banking, M
Fine Arts and Art Studies, MD
Foreign Language Teacher Education, M
Foreign Languages, Literatures, and Linguistics, B

French Language and Literature, BM
Gender Studies, DO
Geographic Information Systems, MO
Geography, BMDO
Geological Engineering, MD
Geology/Earth Science, BMD
Geosciences, MD
German Language and Literature, BM
Gerontological Nursing, O
Gerontology, O
Graphic Design, B
Health Education, D
Health Promotion, MD
Health Services Administration, M
Higher Education/Higher Education Administration, M
Hispanic-American, Puerto Rican, and Mexican-American/Chicano Studies, B
History, BMDO
History of Science and Technology, D
Homeland Security, M
Human Development, MD
Industrial Design, B
Industrial Engineering, B
Industrial/Management Engineering, MD
Information Science/Studies, M
Interdisciplinary Studies, M
Interior Design, B
International Business/Trade/Commerce, M
International Public Health/International Health, MDO
International/Global Studies, B
Italian Language and Literature, B
Japanese Studies, M
Jewelry/Metalsmithing, M
Jewish/Judaic Studies, B
Journalism, MD
Landscape Architecture, BM
Law and Legal Studies, BMD
Legal and Justice Studies, MDO
Liberal Studies, M
Linguistics, MD
Management Information Systems and Services, MD
Management Science, B
Management Strategy and Policy, D
Management of Technology, M
Manufacturing Engineering, M
Marketing, MD
Marketing/Marketing Management, B
Marriage and Family Therapy/Counseling, M
Mass Communication/Media Studies, MD
Materials Engineering, BMD
Materials Sciences, MD
Mathematics, BMDO
Mathematics Teacher Education, D
Mechanical Engineering, BMD
Media Studies, MD
Medical Informatics, MD
Medieval and Renaissance Studies, O
Microbiology, BD
Modeling and Simulation, MD
Molecular Biology, BD
Multi-/Interdisciplinary Studies, B
Museology/Museum Studies, M
Music, BMD
Music History, Literature, and Theory, M
Music Performance, B
Music Teacher Education, BMD
Music Theory and Composition, B
Music Therapy/Therapist, BM
NanoTechnology, M
Neuroscience, D
Non-Profit/Public/Organizational Management, MO
Nuclear Engineering, O
Nursing, MDO
Nursing - Advanced Practice, O
Nursing Administration, M
Nursing Education, M
Nutritional Sciences, MD
Organizational Behavior Studies, D
Painting, M
Performance, MD
Philosophy, BMD
Physical Education Teaching and Coaching, M
Physical Sciences, B

Physics, BMD
Planetary Astronomy and Science, D
Plant Biology, M
Political Science and Government, BMD
Printmaking, M
Psychiatric/Mental Health Nurse/Nursing, O
Psychology, BMD
Public Administration, MD
Public Affairs, MD
Public Health, O
Public History, M
Public Policy Analysis, M
Publishing, O
Purchasing, Procurement/Acquisitions and Contracts Management, B
Real Estate, M
Reliability Engineering, M
Religion/Religious Studies, BMD
Rhetoric, D
Russian Language and Literature, B
Sculpture, M
Secondary Education and Teaching, BM
Social Psychology, D
Social Work, MDO
Sociology, BMD
Software Engineering, M
Spanish Language and Literature, BMD
Special Education and Teaching, BMO
Statistics, MDO
Supply Chain Management, MD
Sustainable Development, MDO
Systems Engineering, M
Systems Science and Theory, MD
Technology and Public Policy, M
Textile Design, M
Theater, MD
Translation and Interpretation, O
Transportation and Highway Engineering, O
Travel and Tourism, MDO
Urban Design, M
Urban Planning, MDO
Urban Studies/Affairs, D
Urban and Regional Planning, MDO
Visual and Performing Arts, B
Women's Studies, B
Writing, M

ARIZONA STATE UNIVERSITY AT THE WEST CAMPUS

Accounting, B
American/United States Studies/Civilization, B
Applied Mathematics, B
Biology/Biological Sciences, B
Business Administration and Management, B
Business, Management, Marketing, and Related Support Services, B
Communication Studies/Speech Communication and Rhetoric, B
Computer and Information Sciences and Support Services, B
Education, B
Elementary Education and Teaching, B
English Language and Literature, B
Environmental Sciences, B
Ethnic and Cultural Studies, B
Health Services Administration, B
History, B
International Business/Trade/Commerce, B
Multi-/Interdisciplinary Studies, B
Political Science and Government, B
Psychology, B
Secondary Education and Teaching, B
Social Sciences, B
Sociology, B
Spanish Language and Literature, B
Special Education and Teaching, B
Statistics, B
Visual and Performing Arts, B
Women's Studies, B

ARIZONA WESTERN COLLEGE

Accounting, A
Agricultural Business and Management, A
Agriculture, A
American Indian/Native American Studies, A
Architectural Technology/Technician, A

Automobile/Automotive Mechanics Technology/Technician, A
Automotive Engineering Technology/Technician, A
Biology/Biological Sciences, A
Business Administration and Management, A
CAD/CADD Drafting and/or Design Technology/Technician, A
Carpentry/Carpenter, A
Chemistry, A
Civil Engineering Technology/Technician, A
Community Health and Preventive Medicine, A
Computer Graphics, A
Computer and Information Sciences, A
Construction Engineering Technology/Technician, A
Construction Management, A
Criminal Justice/Law Enforcement Administration, A
Crop Production, A
Culinary Arts/Chef Training, A
Data Entry/Microcomputer Applications, A
Drama and Dramatics/Theatre Arts, A
Early Childhood Education and Teaching, A
Electrical, Electronic and Communications Engineering Technology/Technician, A
Elementary Education and Teaching, A
Emergency Medical Technology/Technician (EMT Paramedic), A
Engineering, A
English Language and Literature, A
Environmental Sciences, A
Family and Consumer Sciences/Human Sciences, A
Fine/Studio Arts, A
Fire Science/Firefighting, A
General Studies, A
Geology/Earth Science, A
Health and Physical Education, A
Heating, Air Conditioning and Refrigeration Technology/Technician, A
Heating, Air Conditioning, Ventilation and Refrigeration Maintenance Technology/Technician, A
History, A
Hospitality Administration/Management, A
Industrial Technology/Technician, A
Legal Assistant/Paralegal, A
Logistics and Materials Management, A
Manufacturing Technology/Technician, A
Massage Therapy/Therapeutic Massage, A
Mathematics, A
Music, A
Parks, Recreation and Leisure Facilities Management, A
Philosophy, A
Physics, A
Plumbing Technology/Plumber, A
Political Science and Government, A
Pre-Nursing Studies, A
Psychology, A
Radio and Television Broadcasting Technology/Technician, A
Radiologic Technology/Science - Radiographer, A
Secondary Education and Teaching, A
Social Sciences, A
Solar Energy Technology/Technician, A
Spanish Language and Literature, A
Sport and Fitness Administration/Management, A
Water Quality and Wastewater Treatment Management and Recycling Technology/Technician, A

THE ART INSTITUTE OF PHOENIX

Advertising, B
Animation, Interactive Technology, Video Graphics and Special Effects, B
Apparel and Accessories Marketing Operations, B
Baking and Pastry Arts/Baker/Pastry Chef, A
Cinematography and Film/Video Production, B
Commercial Photography, B
Culinary Arts/Chef Training, A
Fashion/Apparel Design, B
Graphic Design, B
Interior Design, B
Restaurant, Culinary, and Catering Management/Manager, B

Web Page, Digital/Multimedia and Information Resources Design, B

THE ART INSTITUTE OF TUCSON

Advertising, B
Animation, Interactive Technology, Video Graphics and Special Effects, B
Apparel and Accessories Marketing Operations, B
Baking and Pastry Arts/Baker/Pastry Chef, A
Cinematography and Film/Video Production, B
Commercial Photography, B
Computer Graphics, B
Culinary Arts/Chef Training, AB
Fashion/Apparel Design, B
Graphic Design, A
Interior Design, B
Web Page, Digital/Multimedia and Information Resources Design, B

BROOKLINE COLLEGE (PHOENIX)

Accounting, A
Business Administration and Management, AB
Clinical/Medical Laboratory Technician, AB
Criminal Justice/Law Enforcement Administration, AB
Health/Health Care Administration/Management, AB
Legal Assistant/Paralegal, A
Physical Therapist Assistant, A

BROOKLINE COLLEGE (TEMPE)

Clinical/Medical Laboratory Technician, A
Criminal Justice/Law Enforcement Administration, A

BROOKLINE COLLEGE (TUCSON)

Business Administration and Management, A
Clinical/Medical Laboratory Technician, A
Criminal Justice/Law Enforcement Administration, A
Legal Assistant/Paralegal, A

CARRINGTON COLLEGE–MESA

Dental Hygiene/Hygienist, A
Medical Office Management/Administration, A
Physical Therapist Assistant, A
Respiratory Care Therapy/Therapist, A
Respiratory Therapy Technician/Assistant, A

CARRINGTON COLLEGE–PHOENIX NORTH

Massage Therapy/Therapeutic Massage, A
Medical Office Management/Administration, A
Occupational Therapy/Therapist, A
Radiologic Technology/Science - Radiographer, A
Respiratory Care Therapy/Therapist, A

CARRINGTON COLLEGE–PHOENIX WEST

Clinical/Medical Laboratory Technician, A
Hospital and Health Care Facilities Administration/Management, A
Medical Radiologic Technology/Science - Radiation Therapist, A
Occupational Therapist Assistant, A
Respiratory Therapy Technician/Assistant, A

CARRINGTON COLLEGE–TUCSON

Clinical/Medical Laboratory Technician, A
Medical Office Management/Administration, A

CENTRAL ARIZONA COLLEGE

Accounting, A
Administrative Assistant and Secretarial Science, A
Agricultural Business and Management, A
Agricultural Mechanics and Equipment/Machine Technology, A
Agriculture, A
Automobile/Automotive Mechanics Technology/Technician, A
Business/Commerce, A
Child Development, A
Civil Engineering Technology/Technician, A
Clinical Nutrition/Nutritionist, A
Computer Science, A
Computer and Information Sciences, A

Construction/Heavy Equipment/Earthmoving Equipment Operation, A
Corrections, A
Corrections and Criminal Justice, A
Criminal Justice/Law Enforcement Administration, A
Diesel Mechanics Technology/Technician, A
Dietetics/Dieticians, A
Elementary Education and Teaching, A
Emergency Medical Technology/Technician (EMT Paramedic), A
Fire Protection, A
General Studies, A
Health Aide, A
Hotel/Motel Administration/Management, A
Industrial Technology/Technician, A
Kindergarten/PreSchool Education and Teaching, A
Legal Administrative Assistant/Secretary, A
Liberal Arts and Sciences Studies and Humanities, A
Manufacturing Engineering, A
Massage Therapy/Therapeutic Massage, A
Medical Administrative Assistant/Secretary, A
Medical Transcription/Transcriptionist, A

CHANDLER-GILBERT COMMUNITY COLLEGE

Accounting, A
Accounting Technology/Technician and Bookkeeping, A
Airline/Commercial/Professional Pilot and Flight Crew, A
Business Administration and Management, A
Business Administration, Management and Operations, A
Business, Management, Marketing, and Related Support Services, A
Business/Commerce, A
Computer Programming, Vendor/Product Certification, A
Computer Programming/Programmer, A
Computer Systems Analysis/Analyst, A
Computer Systems Networking and Telecommunications, A
Computer and Information Sciences, A
Computer and Information Sciences and Support Services, A
Criminal Justice/Safety Studies, A
Data Entry/Microcomputer Applications, A
Data Modeling/Warehousing and Database Administration, A
Dietetic Technician (DTR), A
Dietician Assistant, A
Drama and Dramatics/Theatre Arts, A
Electromechanical Technology/Electromechanical Engineering Technology, A
Elementary Education and Teaching, A
Fine/Studio Arts, A
General Studies, A
Information Technology, A
Kinesiology and Exercise Science, A
Liberal Arts and Sciences Studies and Humanities, A
Lineworker, A
Massage Therapy/Therapeutic Massage, A
Mechanic and Repair Technologies/Technicians, A
Organizational Behavior Studies, A
Physical Sciences, A
Psychology, A
Social Work, A
Visual and Performing Arts, A

COCHISE COUNTY COMMUNITY COLLEGE DISTRICT

Administrative Assistant and Secretarial Science, A
Adult and Continuing Education and Teaching, A
Agricultural Business and Management, A
Air Transportation, A
Airline/Commercial/Professional Pilot and Flight Crew, A
Art/Art Studies, General, A
Automobile/Automotive Mechanics Technology/Technician, A
Avionics Maintenance Technology/Technician, A
Biology/Biological Sciences, A
Business Administration and Management, A
Chemistry, A

Communication Studies/Speech Communication and Rhetoric, A
Computer Programming/Programmer, A
Computer Science, A
Computer Systems Networking and Telecommunications, A
Computer and Information Systems Security, A
Criminal Justice/Police Science, A
Culinary Arts/Chef Training, A
Digital Communication and Media/Multimedia, A
Drama and Dramatics/Theatre Arts, A
Early Childhood Education and Teaching, A
Economics, A
Electrical, Electronic and Communications Engineering Technology/Technician, A
Elementary Education and Teaching, A
Emergency Medical Technology/Technician (EMT Paramedic), A
Engineering, A
English Language and Literature, A
Equestrian/Equine Studies, A
Fire Science/Firefighting, A
General Studies, A
Health and Physical Education, A
Humanities/Humanistic Studies, A
Information Science/Studies, A
Journalism, A
Logistics and Materials Management, A
Mathematics, A
Military Studies, A
Music, A
Philosophy, A
Physics, A
Psychology, A
Respiratory Care Therapy/Therapist, A
Social Sciences, A
Social Work, A
Transportation and Materials Moving, A
Welding Technology/Welder, A

COCONINO COMMUNITY COLLEGE

Accounting Technology/Technician and Bookkeeping, A
Anthropology, A
Architectural Drafting and Architectural CAD/CADD, A
Architectural Engineering Technology/Technician, A
Architectural Technology/Technician, A
Area Studies, A
Business Administration and Management, A
Business/Commerce, A
Carpentry/Carpenter, A
Computer Software Technology/Technician, A
Computer Technology/Computer Systems Technology, A
Construction Management, A
Construction Trades, A
Corrections, A
Corrections and Criminal Justice, A
Criminal Justice/Law Enforcement Administration, A
Early Childhood Education and Teaching, A
Electrical, Electronic and Communications Engineering Technology/Technician, A
Elementary Education and Teaching, A
Emergency Care Attendant (EMT Ambulance), A
Environmental Sciences, A
Fine/Studio Arts, A
Fire Science/Firefighting, A
Forensic Science and Technology, A
General Studies, A
Hospitality Administration/Management, A
Medical Insurance Specialist/Medical Biller, A
Medical Office Assistant/Specialist, A
Phlebotomy/Phlebotomist, A
Prepress/Desktop Publishing and Digital Imaging Design, A
Psychology, A
Sheet Metal Technology/Sheetworking, A
Sign Language Interpretation and Translation, A
Sociology, A
Solar Energy Technology/Technician, A
Visual and Performing Arts, A

COLLEGEAMERICA–FLAGSTAFF

Business Administration and Management, A
Computer Science, B

Computer Systems Networking and Telecommunications, A
Health/Health Care Administration/Management, B
Medical/Health Management and Clinical Assistant/Specialist, A

DEVRY UNIVERSITY (MESA)

Accounting, B
Business Administration and Management, B
Business Administration, Management and Operations, BMO
Business/Commerce, B
Computer Systems Analysis/Analyst, B
Electrical, Electronic and Communications Engineering Technology/Technician, A

DEVRY UNIVERSITY (PHOENIX)

Accounting, B
Biomedical Technology/Technician, B
Business Administration and Management, B
Business Administration, Management and Operations, BM
Business/Commerce, B
Clinical Laboratory Science/Medical Technology/Technologist, B
Computer Engineering Technology/Technician, B
Computer Software Engineering, B
Computer Systems Analysis/Analyst, B
Computer Systems Networking and Telecommunications, AB
Criminal Justice/Law Enforcement Administration, B
Electrical, Electronic and Communications Engineering Technology/Technician, AB
Web Page, Digital/Multimedia and Information Resources Design, AB

DINÉ COLLEGE

Administrative Assistant and Secretarial Science, A
American Indian/Native American Studies, A
Art/Art Studies, General, A
Business Administration and Management, A
Computer Science, A
Early Childhood Education and Teaching, A
Elementary Education and Teaching, A
Fine/Studio Arts, A
Health Professions and Related Clinical Sciences, A
Kinesiology and Exercise Science, A
Liberal Arts and Sciences Studies and Humanities, A
Social Sciences, A
Social Work, A

DUNLAP-STONE UNIVERSITY

International Business/Trade/Commerce, B

EASTERN ARIZONA COLLEGE

Anthropology, A
Art Teacher Education, A
Art/Art Studies, General, A
Automobile/Automotive Mechanics Technology/Technician, A
Biology/Biological Sciences, A
Business Administration and Management, A
Business Operations Support and Secretarial Services, A
Business Teacher Education, A
Business, Management, Marketing, and Related Support Services, A
Chemistry, A
Civil Engineering Technology/Technician, A
Commercial and Advertising Art, A
Cosmetology/Cosmetologist, A
Criminal Justice/Law Enforcement Administration, A
Criminal Justice/Police Science, A
Diesel Mechanics Technology/Technician, A
Drafting and Design Technology/Technician, A
Drama and Dramatics/Theatre Arts, A
Early Childhood Education and Teaching, A
Elementary Education and Teaching, A
Emergency Medical Technology/Technician (EMT Paramedic), A
English Language and Literature, A
Entrepreneurship/Entrepreneurial Studies, A
Environmental Biology, A
Fire Science/Firefighting, A

Foreign Languages and Literatures, A
Forestry, A
Geology/Earth Science, A
Health and Physical Education, A
Health/Medical Preparatory Programs, A
History, A
Industrial Electronics Technology/Technician, A
Industrial Mechanics and Maintenance Technology, A
Information Science/Studies, A
Liberal Arts and Sciences Studies and Humanities, A
Machine Shop Technology/Assistant, A
Mathematics, A
Mining Technology/Technician, A
Multi-/Interdisciplinary Studies, A
Music, A
Pharmacy Technician/Assistant, A
Physics, A
Political Science and Government, A
Pre-Medicine/Pre-Medical Studies, A
Pre-Pharmacy Studies, A
Psychology, A
Secondary Education and Teaching, A
Sociology, A
Technology Teacher Education/Industrial Arts Teacher Education, A
Welding Technology/Welder, A
Wildlife Biology, A

EMBRY-RIDDLE AERONAUTICAL UNIVERSITY–PRESCOTT

Aeronautics/Aviation/Aerospace Science and Technology, B
Aerospace, Aeronautical and Astronautical Engineering, B
Air Traffic Controller, B
Airline/Commercial/Professional Pilot and Flight Crew, B
Astronomy, B
Atmospheric Sciences and Meteorology, B
Aviation/Airway Management and Operations, B
Business Administration, Management and Operations, B
Computer Engineering, B
Computer Science, B
Computer Software Engineering, B
Electrical and Electronic Engineering Technologies/Technicians, B
Electrical, Electronics and Communications Engineering, B
Engineering Technologies/Technicians, B
Forensic Science and Technology, B
International Business/Trade/Commerce, B
International Relations and Affairs, B
Mechanical Engineering, B
Military and Defense Studies, M
Multi-/Interdisciplinary Studies, B
Physics, B
Safety Engineering, M

ESTRELLA MOUNTAIN COMMUNITY COLLEGE

General Studies, A
Liberal Arts and Sciences Studies and Humanities, A

GATEWAY COMMUNITY COLLEGE

Accounting, A
Accounting Technology/Technician and Bookkeeping, A
Accounting and Computer Science, A
Administrative Assistant and Secretarial Science, A
Aeronautical/Aerospace Engineering Technology/Technician, A
Automobile/Automotive Mechanics Technology/Technician, A
BioTechnology, A
Business Administration and Management, A
Business Administration, Management and Operations, A
Business/Commerce, A
Business/Office Automation/Technology/Data Entry, A
Cabinetmaking and Millwork/Millwright, A
Carpentry/Carpenter, A

Clinical Laboratory Science/Medical Technology/Technologist, A
Computer Systems Networking and Telecommunications, A
Computer and Information Sciences, A
Construction/Heavy Equipment/Earthmoving Equipment Operation, A
Court Reporting/Court Reporter, A
Diagnostic Medical Sonography/Sonographer and Ultrasound Technician, A
Electrician, A
Electromechanical Technology/Electromechanical Engineering Technology, A
Elementary Education and Teaching, A
Energy Management and Systems Technology/Technician, A
General Studies, A
Health and Medical Administrative Services, A
Health/Health Care Administration/Management, A
Heating, Air Conditioning and Refrigeration Technology/Technician, A
Heating, Air Conditioning, Ventilation and Refrigeration Maintenance Technology/Technician, A
Industrial Design, A
Ironworking/Ironworker, A
Liberal Arts and Sciences Studies and Humanities, A
Lineworker, A
Management Information Systems and Services, A
Manufacturing Technology/Technician, A
Marketing/Marketing Management, A
Mason/Masonry, A
Medical Radiologic Technology/Science - Radiation Therapist, A
Medical Transcription/Transcriptionist, A
Nuclear Medical Technology/Technologist, A
Occupational Safety and Health Technology/Technician, A
Organizational Behavior Studies, A
Painting/Painter and Wall Coverer, A
Personal and Culinary Services, A
Physical Sciences, A
Physical Therapist Assistant, A
Pipefitting/Pipefitter and Sprinkler Fitter, A
Plumbing Technology/Plumber, A
Radiologic Technology/Science - Radiographer, A
Respiratory Care Therapy/Therapist, A
Sheet Metal Technology/Sheetworking, A
Surgical Technology/Technologist, A
Water Quality and Wastewater Treatment Management and Recycling Technology/Technician, A
Web Page, Digital/Multimedia and Information Resources Design, A

GLENDALE COMMUNITY COLLEGE

Accounting Technology/Technician and Bookkeeping, A
Administrative Assistant and Secretarial Science, A
Architectural Drafting and Architectural CAD/CADD, A
Automobile/Automotive Mechanics Technology/Technician, A
Behavioral Sciences, A
BioTechnology, A
Business Administration and Management, A
Business/Commerce, A
CAD/CADD Drafting and/or Design Technology/Technician, A
Cinematography and Film/Video Production, A
Commercial and Advertising Art, A
Computer Systems Analysis/Analyst, A
Computer Systems Networking and Telecommunications, A
Computer and Information Sciences, A
Computer and Information Systems Security, A
Criminal Justice/Safety Studies, A
Data Entry/Microcomputer Applications, A
Early Childhood Education and Teaching, A
Educational Leadership and Administration, A
Emergency Medical Technology/Technician (EMT Paramedic), A
Engineering Technology, A
Family and Community Services, A
Fire Science/Firefighting, A
Graphic Design, A
Kinesiology and Exercise Science, A

Marketing/Marketing Management, A
Public Relations/Image Management, A
Recording Arts Technology/Technician, A
Security and Protective Services, A
Web Page, Digital/Multimedia and Information Resources Design, A

GRAND CANYON UNIVERSITY

Accounting, BM
Acute Care/Critical Care Nursing, MO
Athletic Training and Sports Medicine, B
Bible/Biblical Studies, B
Biology Teacher Education, B
Biology/Biological Sciences, B
Business Administration and Management, B
Business Administration, Management and Operations, MD
Chemistry Teacher Education, B
Christian Studies, B
Cinematography and Film/Video Production, B
Cognitive Sciences, D
Counseling Psychology, M
Criminal Justice/Safety Studies, B
Curriculum and Instruction, M
Dance, B
Drama and Dramatics/Theatre Arts, B
Dramatic/Theatre Arts and Stagecraft, B
Education, MD
Educational Administration and Supervision, M
Educational Leadership and Administration, D
Elementary Education and Teaching, BM
Emergency Management, M
English/Language Arts Teacher Education, B
Entrepreneurship/Entrepreneurial Studies, M
Exercise Physiology, B
Finance and Banking, M
General Studies, B
Health Education, D
Health Informatics, M
Health Professions and Related Clinical Sciences, B
Health Services Administration, M
Health/Health Care Administration/Management, B
Higher Education/Higher Education Administration, D
History, B
Human Resources Management and Services, BM
Industrial and Organizational Psychology, D
Management, M
Management Information Systems and Services, M
Marketing, M
Marketing/Marketing Management, B
Marriage and Family Therapy/Counseling, M
Mathematics Teacher Education, B
Multi-/Interdisciplinary Studies, B
Nursing, MO
Nursing - Advanced Practice, M
Nursing Education, MO
Organizational Management, D
Parks, Recreation, Leisure and Fitness Studies, B
Physical Education Teaching and Coaching, B
Piano and Organ, B
Psychology, BD
Public Administration, M
Public Health, M
Religion/Religious Studies, B
Secondary Education and Teaching, BM
Sociology, B
Special Education and Teaching, BM
Sport and Fitness Administration/Management, B
Substance Abuse/Addiction Counseling, M
Teaching English as a Second or Foreign Language/ESL Language Instructor, B

HARRISON MIDDLETON UNIVERSITY

Comparative Literature, BM
Education, BMD
Humanities/Humanistic Studies, ABM
Interdisciplinary Studies, D
Legal and Justice Studies, M
Natural Sciences, B
Philosophy, M
Philosophy and Religious Studies, B
Religion/Religious Studies, M
Science Teacher Education/General Science Teacher Education, M

Social Sciences, BM

INTERNATIONAL BAPTIST COLLEGE AND SEMINARY

Bible/Biblical Studies, AB
Education, M
Pastoral Studies/Counseling, MD
Teacher Education, Multiple Levels, B
Theology and Religious Vocations, M

MESA COMMUNITY COLLEGE

Accounting, A
Administrative Assistant and Secretarial Science, A
Agricultural Business and Management, A
Agricultural Mechanization, A
Agronomy and Crop Science, A
Art/Art Studies, General, A
Automobile/Automotive Mechanics Technology/Technician, A
Biology/Biological Sciences, A
Business Administration and Management, A
Child Development, A
Criminal Justice/Law Enforcement Administration, A
Data Processing and Data Processing Technology/Technician, A
Drafting and Design Technology/Technician, A
Electrical, Electronic and Communications Engineering Technology/Technician, A
Engineering Technology, A
Family and Consumer Sciences/Human Sciences, A
Fashion Merchandising, A
Finance, A
Fire Science/Firefighting, A
Heavy Equipment Maintenance Technology/Technician, A
Horticultural Science, A
Industrial Technology/Technician, A
Insurance, A
Interior Design, A
Liberal Arts and Sciences Studies and Humanities, A
Library Science, A
Marketing/Marketing Management, A
Mathematics, A
Medical Administrative Assistant/Secretary, A
Music, A
Ornamental Horticulture, A
Quality Control Technology/Technician, A
Real Estate, A
Teacher Assistant/Aide, A

MOHAVE COMMUNITY COLLEGE

Accounting, A
Art/Art Studies, General, A
Automobile/Automotive Mechanics Technology/Technician, A
Building/Construction Finishing, Management, and Inspection, A
Business Administration and Management, A
Computer Programming, Specific Applications, A
Computer Science, A
Computer and Information Sciences, A
Criminal Justice/Police Science, A
Culinary Arts/Chef Training, A
Dental Assisting/Assistant, A
Dental Hygiene/Hygienist, A
Drafting and Design Technology/Technician, A
Education, A
Emergency Medical Technology/Technician (EMT Paramedic), A
English Language and Literature, A
Fire Science/Firefighting, A
Heating, Air Conditioning, Ventilation and Refrigeration Maintenance Technology/Technician, A
History, A
Information Technology, A
Legal Assistant/Paralegal, A
Liberal Arts and Sciences Studies and Humanities, A
Mathematics, A
Medical/Clinical Assistant, A
Personal and Culinary Services, A
Pharmacy Technician/Assistant, A
Physical Therapist Assistant, A
Psychology, A
Sociology, A

Substance Abuse/Addiction Counseling, A
Surgical Technology/Technologist, A
Truck and Bus Driver/Commercial Vehicle Operation, A
Welding Technology/Welder, A

NATIONAL PARALEGAL COLLEGE

Law and Legal Studies, B
Legal Assistant/Paralegal, A
Legal and Justice Studies, M
Taxation, M

NORTHCENTRAL UNIVERSITY

Accounting and Business/Management, B
Business Administration and Management, B
Business Administration, Management and Operations, MDO
Computer Science, B
Criminal Justice/Law Enforcement Administration, B
Education, MDO
Elementary Education and Teaching, B
Human Resources Management/Personnel Administration, B
Marketing/Marketing Management, B
Marriage and Family Therapy/Counseling, MDO
Psychology, BMDO
Secondary Education and Teaching, B

NORTHERN ARIZONA UNIVERSITY

Accounting, B
Allied Health and Medical Assisting Services, MDO
American Indian/Native American Studies, B
Anthropology, BM
Applied Physics, M
Applied Statistics, O
Archeology, M
Astronomy, B
Atmospheric Sciences and Meteorology, M
Biological and Biomedical Sciences, MD
Biology/Biological Sciences, B
Biomedical Sciences, B
Business Administration and Management, B
Business Administration, Management and Operations, M
Business/Managerial Economics, B
Chemistry, BM
Civil Engineering, BM
Clinical Psychology, M
Communication Disorders, M
Communication Studies/Speech Communication and Rhetoric, B
Communication and Media Studies, M
Community College Education, M
Composition, M
Computer Science, BM
Computer Systems Analysis/Analyst, B
Construction Management, B
Counseling Psychology, D
Counselor Education/School Counseling and Guidance Services, M
Criminology, BM
Cultural Anthropology, M
Dental Hygiene/Hygienist, B
Design and Visual Communications, B
Drama and Dramatics/Theatre Arts, B
Early Childhood Education and Teaching, BM
Education, MDO
Educational Leadership and Administration, MDO
Educational Media/Instructional Technology, MO
Educational Psychology, MDO
Electrical Engineering, M
Electrical, Electronics and Communications Engineering, B
Elementary Education and Teaching, BM
Engineering and Applied Sciences, MDO
English, MDO
English Education, M
English Language and Literature, B
English as a Second Language, MO
Environmental Engineering Technology/Environmental Technology, M
Environmental Policy, M
Environmental Sciences, BM
Environmental Studies, B
Environmental/Environmental Health Engineering, B
Ethnic and Cultural Studies, O

Finance, B
Fine/Studio Arts, B
Foreign Language Teacher Education, M
Foreign Languages and Literatures, B
Forest Sciences and Biology, B
Forestry, MD
Foundations and Philosophy of Education, M
Gender Studies, O
Geographic Information Systems, MO
Geography, BMO
Geology/Earth Science, BM
Health Services Administration, O
Higher Education/Higher Education Administration, M
History, BM
Hospitality Administration/Management, B
Human Development, O
Interior Design, B
International Relations and Affairs, B
Journalism, B
Kinesiology and Exercise Science, B
Liberal Arts and Sciences Studies and Humanities, B
Liberal Studies, M
Linguistics, D
Management Information Systems and Services, B
Marketing/Marketing Management, B
Mathematics, BMO
Mathematics Teacher Education, MO
Mechanical Engineering, BM
Meteorology, MD
Microbiology, B
Multilingual and Multicultural Education, M
Music, BMO
Music Performance, B
Music Teacher Education, B
Music Theory and Composition, M
Musicology and Ethnomusicology, M
Nursing, MDO
Nursing - Advanced Practice, MO
Parks, Recreation, Leisure and Fitness Studies, B
Performance, M
Philosophy, B
Photography, B
Physical Therapy/Therapist, D
Physician Assistant, M
Physics, BM
Political Science and Government, BMDO
Pre-Law Studies, B
Psychology, BM
Public Administration, BMO
Public Health, O
Public Health (MPH, DPH), B
Public Relations, Advertising, and Applied Communication, B
Radio and Television, B
Rhetoric, M
School Psychology, DO
Science Teacher Education/General Science Teacher Education, MO
Science Technologies/Technicians, B
Secondary Education and Teaching, M
Social Sciences, B
Social Work, B
Sociology, BM
Spanish Language and Literature, BM
Special Education and Teaching, BM
Statistics, M
Student Personnel Services, M
Sustainable Development, M
Urban and Regional Planning, MO
Vocational and Technical Education, MO
Women's Studies, BO
Writing, MO

NORTHLAND PIONEER COLLEGE

Accounting Technology/Technician and Bookkeeping, A
Administrative Assistant and Secretarial Science, A
Agriculture, A
Apparel and Textiles, A
Biological and Physical Sciences, A
Building/Property Maintenance and Management, A
Business Administration and Management, A
Business and Personal/Financial Services Marketing Operations, A

Business/Commerce, A
Business/Office Automation/Technology/Data Entry, A
Carpentry/Carpenter, A
Child Care Provider/Assistant, A
Child Care and Support Services Management, A
Child Development, A
Computer Graphics, A
Computer Installation and Repair Technology/Technician, A
Computer Systems Networking and Telecommunications, A
Computer and Information Sciences, A
Corrections, A
Cosmetology/Cosmetologist, A
Court Reporting/Court Reporter, A
Data Modeling/Warehousing and Database Administration, A
Drafting and Design Technology/Technician, A
Early Childhood Education and Teaching, A
Education/Teaching of Individuals in Early Childhood Special Education Programs, A
Electrical, Electronic and Communications Engineering Technology/Technician, A
Electrician, A
Elementary Education and Teaching, A
Emergency Medical Technology/Technician (EMT Paramedic), A
Entrepreneurial and Small Business Operations, A
Fire Science/Firefighting, A
General Studies, A
Health Information/Medical Records Administration/Administrator, A
Industrial Mechanics and Maintenance Technology, A
Industrial Technology/Technician, A
Information Science/Studies, A
Kindergarten/PreSchool Education and Teaching, A
Legal Administrative Assistant/Secretary, A
Legal Assistant/Paralegal, A
Legal Professions and Studies, A
Liberal Arts and Sciences Studies and Humanities, A
Library Assistant/Technician, A
Management Information Systems and Services, A
Massage Therapy/Therapeutic Massage, A
Medical Transcription/Transcriptionist, A
Museology/Museum Studies, A
Parks, Recreation and Leisure Facilities Management, A
Photography, A
Restaurant, Culinary, and Catering Management/Manager, A
Small Business Administration/Management, A
Teacher Assistant/Aide, A
Teaching Assistants/Aides, A
Turf and Turfgrass Management, A
Welding Technology/Welder, A

PARADISE VALLEY COMMUNITY COLLEGE

Accounting, A
Accounting Technology/Technician and Bookkeeping, A
Administrative Assistant and Secretarial Science, A
Business Administration and Management, A
Business/Commerce, A
Business/Office Automation/Technology/Data Entry, A
Commercial and Advertising Art, A
Computer Installation and Repair Technology/Technician, A
Computer Programming, Vendor/Product Certification, A
Computer Systems Networking and Telecommunications, A
Computer Typography and Composition Equipment Operator, A
Criminal Justice/Safety Studies, A
Early Childhood Education and Teaching, A
Elementary Education and Teaching, A
Emergency Medical Technology/Technician (EMT Paramedic), A
Fine/Studio Arts, A
Fire Science/Firefighting, A
General Studies, A

International Business/Trade/Commerce, A
Journalism, A
Kinesiology and Exercise Science, A
Liberal Arts and Sciences Studies and Humanities, A
Natural Sciences, A
Occupational Safety and Health Technology/Technician, A
Physical Sciences, A
Recording Arts Technology/Technician, A
Visual and Performing Arts, A
Web Page, Digital/Multimedia and Information Resources Design, A

THE PARALEGAL INSTITUTE AT BRIGHTON COLLEGE

Criminal Justice/Law Enforcement Administration, A
Legal Assistant/Paralegal, A

PENN FOSTER COLLEGE

Accounting, A
Business Administration and Management, AB
Computer Installation and Repair Technology/Technician, A
Computer and Information Sciences, A
Criminal Justice/Law Enforcement Administration, AB
Early Childhood Education and Teaching, A
Engineering Technology, A
Fashion Merchandising, A
Finance, A
Graphic Design, A
Health Information/Medical Records Technology/Technician, A
Health/Health Care Administration/Management, A
Hospitality Administration/Management, A
Human Resources Management/Personnel Administration, A
Industrial Electronics Technology/Technician, A
Legal Assistant/Paralegal, A
Marketing Research, A
Marketing/Marketing Management, A
Medical/Clinical Assistant, A
Roofer, A
Veterinary/Animal Health Technology/Technician and Veterinary Assistant, A

PHOENIX COLLEGE

Accounting, A
Administrative Assistant and Secretarial Science, A
Architectural Drafting and Architectural CAD/CADD, A
Art/Art Studies, General, A
Banking and Financial Support Services, A
Building/Home/Construction Inspection/Inspector, A
Business Administration and Management, A
Business/Commerce, A
Child Care and Support Services Management, A
Civil Engineering Technology/Technician, A
Clinical/Medical Laboratory Technician, A
Commercial Photography, A
Commercial and Advertising Art, A
Computer Graphics, A
Computer Systems Analysis/Analyst, A
Computer and Information Sciences, A
Construction Management, A
Criminal Justice/Safety Studies, A
Culinary Arts/Chef Training, A
Dental Assisting/Assistant, A
Dental Hygiene/Hygienist, A
Drama and Dramatics/Theatre Arts, A
Elementary Education and Teaching, A
Emergency Medical Technology/Technician (EMT Paramedic), A
Family and Community Services, A
Family and Consumer Sciences/Human Sciences, A
Fashion Merchandising, A
Fashion/Apparel Design, A
Fine/Studio Arts, A
Fire Science/Firefighting, A
Foodservice Systems Administration/Management, A
Forensic Science and Technology, A
General Studies, A
Graphic Design, A

Health Information/Medical Records Technology/Technician, A
Histologic Technology/Histotechnologist, A
Human Services, A
Interior Design, A
Legal Assistant/Paralegal, A
Liberal Arts and Sciences Studies and Humanities, A
Marketing/Marketing Management, A
Massage Therapy/Therapeutic Massage, A
Medical Office Assistant/Specialist, A
Medical/Clinical Assistant, A
Natural Sciences, A
Organizational Behavior Studies, A
Parks, Recreation, Leisure and Fitness Studies, A
Physical Sciences, A
Recording Arts Technology/Technician, A
Sign Language Interpretation and Translation, A
Survey Technology/Surveying, A
Teacher Assistant/Aide, A
Visual and Performing Arts, A
Web Page, Digital/Multimedia and Information Resources Design, A

PIMA COMMUNITY COLLEGE

Accounting, A
Administrative Assistant and Secretarial Science, A
Airframe Mechanics and Aircraft Maintenance Technology/Technician, A
American Indian/Native American Studies, A
American Sign Language (ASL), A
Anthropology, A
Automobile/Automotive Mechanics Technology/Technician, A
Building/Property Maintenance and Management, A
Business/Commerce, A
CAD/CADD Drafting and/or Design Technology/Technician, A
Cinematography and Film/Video Production, A
Clinical/Medical Laboratory Assistant, A
Clinical/Medical Laboratory Technician, A
Clinical/Medical Social Work, A
Computer Systems Analysis/Analyst, A
Computer Systems Networking and Telecommunications, A
Criminal Justice/Police Science, A
Criminal Justice/Safety Studies, A
Dental Hygiene/Hygienist, A
Dental Laboratory Technology/Technician, A
Design and Visual Communications, A
Digital Communication and Media/Multimedia, A
Early Childhood Education and Teaching, A
Education, A
Electrical/Electronics Equipment Installation and Repair, A
Electrical/Electronics Maintenance and Repair Technology, A
Elementary Education and Teaching, A
Emergency Medical Technology/Technician (EMT Paramedic), A
Executive Assistant/Executive Secretary, A
Fashion Merchandising, A
Fashion/Apparel Design, A
Fire Science/Firefighting, A
General Studies, A
Health Information/Medical Records Technology/Technician, A
Hospitality Administration/Management, A
Interior Design, A
Language Interpretation and Translation, A
Legal Assistant/Paralegal, A
Liberal Arts and Sciences Studies and Humanities, A
Logistics and Materials Management, A
Machine Tool Technology/Machinist, A
Massage Therapy/Therapeutic Massage, A
Mining and Petroleum Technologies/Technicians, A
Pharmacy Technician/Assistant, A
Political Science and Government, A
Psychology, A
Radiologic Technology/Science - Radiographer, A
Respiratory Care Therapy/Therapist, A
Restaurant, Culinary, and Catering Management/Manager, A
Social Work, A
Sociology, A

Substance Abuse/Addiction Counseling, A
Veterinary/Animal Health Technology/Technician and Veterinary Assistant, A
Visual and Performing Arts, A
Welding Technology/Welder, A
Youth Services/Administration, A

PIMA MEDICAL INSTITUTE (MESA)

Health/Health Care Administration/Management, A
Veterinary/Animal Health Technology/Technician and Veterinary Assistant, A

PIMA MEDICAL INSTITUTE (MESA)

Health/Health Care Administration/Management, A
Occupational Therapist Assistant, A
Physical Therapist Assistant, A
Radiologic Technology/Science - Radiographer, A
Respiratory Therapy Technician/Assistant, A

PIMA MEDICAL INSTITUTE (TUCSON)

Health/Health Care Administration/Management, A
Occupational Therapist Assistant, A
Physical Therapist Assistant, A
Radiologic Technology/Science - Radiographer, A
Respiratory Therapy Technician/Assistant, A
Veterinary/Animal Health Technology/Technician and Veterinary Assistant, A

PRESCOTT COLLEGE

Art Therapy/Therapist, BM
Business Administration, Management and Operations, B
Conservation Biology, B
Counseling Psychology, M
Counselor Education/School Counseling and Guidance Services, M
Early Childhood Education and Teaching, BM
Ecology, B
Education, BMD
Education/Teaching of Individuals in Early Childhood Special Education Programs, B
Education/Teaching of Individuals with Specific Learning Disabilities, B
Educational Leadership and Administration, M
Elementary Education and Teaching, BM
Environmental Education, B
Environmental Studies, BM
Fine/Studio Arts, B
Health Psychology, M
Humanities/Humanistic Studies, M
Latin American Studies, B
Legal and Justice Studies, M
Leisure Studies, M
Liberal Arts and Sciences Studies and Humanities, B
Marine Biology and Biological Oceanography, B
Multi-/Interdisciplinary Studies, B
Natural Resources and Conservation, B
Psychoanalysis and Psychotherapy, M
Psychology, B
Public Administration and Social Service Professions, B
Regional Studies (U.S., Canadian, Foreign), B
Rehabilitation and Therapeutic Professions, B
Secondary Education and Teaching, BM
Social Sciences, B
Special Education and Teaching, M
Visual and Performing Arts, B
Women's Studies, B

THE REFRIGERATION SCHOOL

Electromechanical Technology/Electromechanical Engineering Technology, A
Energy Management and Systems Technology/Technician, A
Heating, Air Conditioning and Refrigeration Technology/Technician, A

RIO SALADO COLLEGE

Business Administration and Management, A
Computer Programming, A
Computer Science, A
Computer and Information Sciences, A
Computer and Information Sciences and Support Services, A

Consumer Services and Advocacy, A
Data Entry/Microcomputer Applications, A
Dental Hygiene/Hygienist, A
Information Science/Studies, A
Information Technology, A
Public Administration, A
Substance Abuse/Addiction Counseling, A
System Administration/Administrator, A
Web Page, Digital/Multimedia and Information Resources Design, A
Web/Multimedia Management and Webmaster, A

SCOTTSDALE COMMUNITY COLLEGE

Accounting, A
Administrative Assistant and Secretarial Science, A
Business Administration and Management, A
Criminal Justice/Law Enforcement Administration, A
Culinary Arts/Chef Training, A
Drama and Dramatics/Theatre Arts, A
Electrical, Electronic and Communications Engineering Technology/Technician, A
Environmental Design/Architecture, A
Equestrian/Equine Studies, A
Fashion Merchandising, A
Finance, A
Hospitality Administration/Management, A
Hotel/Motel Administration/Management, A
Information Science/Studies, A
Interior Design, A
Mathematics, A
Medical Administrative Assistant/Secretary, A
Photography, A
Public Administration, A
Real Estate, A
Special Products Marketing Operations, A

SESSIONS COLLEGE FOR PROFESSIONAL DESIGN

Animation, Interactive Technology, Video Graphics and Special Effects, A
Graphic Design, A
Illustration, A
Web Page, Digital/Multimedia and Information Resources Design, A

SOUTH MOUNTAIN COMMUNITY COLLEGE

Adult and Continuing Education and Teaching, A
Behavioral Sciences, A
Business Administration and Management, A
Business Administration, Management and Operations, A
Business/Commerce, A
Child Care and Support Services Management, A
Child Development, A
Computer Systems Networking and Telecommunications, A
Computer and Information Sciences, A
Computer and Information Sciences and Support Services, A
Computer and Information Systems Security, A
Drama and Dramatics/Theatre Arts, A
Early Childhood Education and Teaching, A
Education, A
Elementary Education and Teaching, A
General Studies, A
Liberal Arts and Sciences Studies and Humanities, A
Management Information Systems and Services, A
Multi-/Interdisciplinary Studies, A
Physical Sciences, A
Radio and Television Broadcasting Technology/Technician, A

SOUTHWEST INSTITUTE OF HEALING ARTS

Alternative and Complementary Medical Support Services, A

SOUTHWEST UNIVERSITY OF VISUAL ARTS

Advertising, B
Animation, Interactive Technology, Video Graphics and Special Effects, B
Fine Arts and Art Studies, M

Fine/Studio Arts, B
Graphic Design, B
Illustration, B
Interior Design, B
Landscape Architecture, B
Painting, M
Photography, BM

TOHONO O'ODHAM COMMUNITY COLLEGE

Business Administration and Management, A
Child Development, A
Computer Systems Analysis/Analyst, A
Early Childhood Education and Teaching, A
Human Services, A
Liberal Arts and Sciences Studies and Humanities, A

UNIVERSAL TECHNICAL INSTITUTE

Automobile/Automotive Mechanics Technology/Technician, A
Diesel Mechanics Technology/Technician, A

UNIVERSITY OF ADVANCING TECHNOLOGY

Artificial Intelligence and Robotics, B
Cinematography and Film/Video Production, AB
Commercial and Advertising Art, AB
Computer Graphics, AB
Computer Hardware Technology/Technician, B
Computer Programming/Programmer, AB
Computer Science, BM
Computer Software Technology/Technician, B
Computer Systems Analysis/Analyst, AB
Computer and Information Systems Security, BM
Data Processing and Data Processing Technology/Technician, AB
Design and Visual Communications, AB
Digital Communication and Media/Multimedia, B
Game Design and Development, M
Internet and Interactive Multimedia, M
Management of Technology, M
Radio, Television, and Digital Communication, B
Robotics Technology/Technician, B
Web Page, Digital/Multimedia and Information Resources Design, B

THE UNIVERSITY OF ARIZONA

Accounting, BMD
Aerospace, Aeronautical and Astronautical Engineering, BMD
African-American/Black Studies, B
Agricultural Business Technology, B
Agricultural Business and Management, B
Agricultural Economics, M
Agricultural Education, M
Agricultural Engineering, MD
Agricultural Sciences, MD
Agriculture, Agriculture Operations and Related Sciences, B
Agronomy and Soil Sciences, MD
Allopathic Medicine, MD
American Indian/Native American Studies, BMD
Animal Sciences, BMD
Anthropology, BMD
Applied Economics, B
Applied Mathematics, MD
Architecture, BM
Architecture and Related Services, B
Art Education, MD
Art History, Criticism and Conservation, BMD
Art Teacher Education, B
Astronomy, BMD
Atmospheric Sciences and Meteorology, MD
Biochemistry, BD
Bioinformatics, B
Biological and Biomedical Sciences, M
Biology/Biological Sciences, B
Biomedical Engineering, MD
Biomedical/Medical Engineering, B
Biostatistics, D
Biosystems Engineering, MD
Business Administration, Management and Operations, MD
Business/Commerce, B

Business/Managerial Economics, B
Cancer Biology/Oncology, D
Cartography, B
Cell Biology and Anatomy, MD
Cell/Cellular and Molecular Biology, B
Chemical Engineering, BMD
Chemistry, BD
Child and Family Studies, M
City/Urban, Community and Regional Planning, B
Civil Engineering, B
Classics and Classical Languages, Literatures, and Linguistics, BM
Communication Disorders, BMD
Communication Studies/Speech Communication and Rhetoric, B
Communication and Media Studies, MD
Community Health Services/Liaison/Counseling, B
Composition, MD
Computer Engineering, MD
Computer Science, BMD
Computer and Information Sciences, B
Counseling Psychology, M
Counselor Education/School Counseling and Guidance Services, M
Dance, BM
Drama and Dramatics/Theatre Arts, B
East Asian Studies, BMD
Ecology, MD
Economics, BMD
Education, MDO
Educational Leadership and Administration, MDO
Educational Psychology, MDO
Electrical Engineering, MD
Elementary Education and Teaching, BMD
Engineering and Applied Sciences, MDO
Engineering/Industrial Management, B
English, MD
English Education, MD
English Language and Literature, B
English as a Second Language, MD
Entomology, MD
Entrepreneurship/Entrepreneurial Studies, B
Environmental Engineering Technology/Environmental Technology, MD
Environmental Policy, M
Environmental Sciences, BMD
Environmental Studies, B
Epidemiology, MD
Ethnomusicology, M
Evolutionary Biology, MD
Film/Cinema Studies, B
Finance, B
Finance and Banking, MD
Fine Arts and Art Studies, M
Fine/Studio Arts, B
Fish, Game and Wildlife Management, MD
Forestry, MD
French Language and Literature, BM
Gender Studies, MDO
Genetics, MD
Geographic Information Systems, MO
Geography, BMDO
Geological Engineering, M
Geology/Earth Science, B
Geosciences, MD
German Language and Literature, BMD
Higher Education/Higher Education Administration, MD
Hispanic-American, Puerto Rican, and Mexican-American/Chicano Studies, B
History, BMD
Home Economics, MD
Human Development, M
Human Development and Family Studies, B
Human Resources Management/Personnel Administration, B
Hydrology and Water Resources Science, BMD
Immunology, MD
Industrial Engineering, B
Industrial/Management Engineering, MD
Information Science/Studies, MD
Interdisciplinary Studies, MD
International/Global Studies, B
Italian Language and Literature, B
Jewish/Judaic Studies, B
Journalism, BM

Kindergarten/PreSchool Education and Teaching, B
Landscape Architecture, M
Latin American Studies, BM
Law and Legal Studies, MD
Legal Professions and Studies, B
Library Science, MD
Linguistics, BMD
Management Information Systems and Services, BM
Management Strategy and Policy, D
Marketing, MD
Marketing/Marketing Management, B
Materials Engineering, MD
Materials Sciences, MD
Mathematics, BMD
Mathematics Teacher Education, M
Mechanical Engineering, BMD
Medical Informatics, O
Medical Physics, M
Meteorology, MD
Microbiology, BMD
Middle School Education, M
Mineral/Mining Engineering, MO
Mining and Mineral Engineering, B
Molecular Biology, MD
Molecular Medicine, MDO
Multilingual and Multicultural Education, MDO
Music, BMD
Music Performance, B
Music Teacher Education, BMD
Music Theory and Composition, MD
Musicology and Ethnomusicology, M
Natural Resources and Conservation, BMD
Near and Middle Eastern Studies, BMD
Neuroscience, D
Nursing, MDO
Nursing - Advanced Practice, MO
Nutritional Sciences, BMD
Operations Management and Supervision, B
Optics/Optical Sciences, BMD
Performance, MD
Perfusion Technology/Perfusionist, M
Pharmaceutical Sciences, MD
Pharmacology, MD
Pharmacy, D
Philosophy, BMD
Physics, BMD
Physiology, BMD
Planetary Astronomy and Science, MD
Plant Pathology/Phytopathology, MD
Plant Sciences, BMD
Political Science and Government, BMD
Pre-Veterinary Studies, B
Psychology, BMD
Public Administration, BMD
Public Health, MD
Public Health (MPH, DPH), B
Public Policy Analysis, D
Range Science and Management, MD
Reading Teacher Education, MDO
Rehabilitation Counseling, MD
Religion/Religious Studies, B
Rhetoric, MD
Russian Language and Literature, BM
School Psychology, DO
Science Technologies/Technicians, B
Secondary Education and Teaching, MD
Sociology, BD
Spanish Language and Literature, BMD
Special Education and Teaching, BMD
Statistics, MD
Systems Engineering, BMD
Technical Theatre/Theatre Design and Technology, B
Theater, M
Urban Planning, M
Visual and Performing Arts, B
Water Resources, MD
Web Page, Digital/Multimedia and Information Resources Design, B
Women's Studies, BMDO

Writing, M

UNIVERSITY OF PHOENIX–ONLINE CAMPUS

Accounting, BMO
Adult and Continuing Education Administration, AB
Adult and Continuing Education and Teaching, M
Business Administration and Management, B
Business Administration, Management and Operations, MDO
Computer Education, M
Computer Programming/Programmer, B
Conflict Resolution and Mediation/Peace Studies, O
Consumer Merchandising/Retailing Management, AB
Corrections and Criminal Justice, B
Criminology, M
Curriculum and Instruction, MD
Early Childhood Education and Teaching, M
Education, MO
Educational Administration and Supervision, MO
Educational Leadership and Administration, MD
Educational Media/Instructional Technology, D
Elementary Education and Teaching, MO
Energy Management and Policy, M
English Education, M
English as a Second Language, MO
Finance, B
General Studies, B
Health Education, O
Health Informatics, MO
Health Services Administration, MD
Health/Health Care Administration/Management, B
Higher Education/Higher Education Administration, D
Homeland Security, M
Human Resources Management and Services, MO
Industrial and Organizational Psychology, MD
International Business/Trade/Commerce, M
Management Information Systems and Services, M
Management Science, B
Management of Technology, M
Marketing, MO
Mathematics Teacher Education, M
Middle School Education, M
Nursing, MDO
Nursing - Advanced Practice, O
Nursing Education, M
Organizational Management, D
Project Management, MO
Psychology, M
Public Administration, M
Reading Teacher Education, M
Science Teacher Education/General Science Teacher Education, M
Secondary Education and Teaching, MO
Securities Services Administration/Management, M
Security and Protective Services, AB
Special Education and Teaching, MO

UNIVERSITY OF PHOENIX–PHOENIX CAMPUS

Accounting, BMO
Adult and Continuing Education and Teaching, M
Business Administration and Management, B
Business Administration, Management and Operations, MO
Business/Corporate Communications, B
Clinical Psychology, M
Community Psychology, M
Computer Software Engineering, B
Computer and Information Systems Security, B
Consumer Merchandising/Retailing Management, B
Counseling Psychology, M
Counselor Education/School Counseling and Guidance Services, M
Criminal Justice/Law Enforcement Administration, B
Criminology, M
Curriculum and Instruction, M
Digital Communication and Media/Multimedia, B
E-Commerce/Electronic Commerce, B
Early Childhood Education and Teaching, M
Education, M
Educational Administration and Supervision, M
Educational Leadership and Administration, M
Elementary Education and Teaching, M

Energy Management and Policy, M
Finance, B
Gerontological Nursing, O
Health Services Administration, BM
Health/Health Care Administration/Management, B
Homeland Security, M
Hospitality Administration/Management, B
Human Resources Management and Services, MO
Human Services, B
Information Technology, B
International Business/Trade/Commerce, BM
Law Enforcement, M
Management, B
Management Information Systems and Services, B
Management Science, B
Management of Technology, M
Marketing, M
Marketing/Marketing Management, B
Marriage and Family Therapy/Counseling, M
Medical Informatics, O
Nursing, MO
Nursing - Advanced Practice, MO
Nursing Education, MO
Nursing Informatics, M
Operations Management and Supervision, B
Organizational Behavior Studies, B
Project Management, M
Psychology, BM
Public Administration, BM
Reading Teacher Education, M
Secondary Education and Teaching, M
Special Education and Teaching, M
Vocational and Technical Education, M

UNIVERSITY OF PHOENIX–SOUTHERN ARIZONA CAMPUS

Accounting, BM
Adult and Continuing Education and Teaching, M
Business Administration and Management, B
Business Administration, Management and Operations, M
Corrections and Criminal Justice, B
Counselor Education/School Counseling and Guidance Services, M
Curriculum and Instruction, M
Education, MO
Educational Administration and Supervision, M
Educational Psychology, M
Elementary Education and Teaching, M
Finance, B
Health/Health Care Administration/Management, B
Human Resources Management and Services, M
Information Technology, B
International Business/Trade/Commerce, M
Management, M
Management Information Systems and Services, BM
Management Science, B
Management of Technology, M
Marketing, M
Marketing/Marketing Management, B
Psychology, M
Public Administration and Social Service Professions, B
Secondary Education and Teaching, M
Special Education and Teaching, MO

WESTERN INTERNATIONAL UNIVERSITY

Accounting, B
Behavioral Sciences, B
Business Administration and Management, AB
Business Administration, Management and Operations, M
Business/Commerce, B
Business/Corporate Communications, B
Criminal Justice/Law Enforcement Administration, B
Finance and Banking, M
Human Resources Management/Personnel Administration, B
Information Technology, B
International Business/Trade/Commerce, M
Law and Legal Studies, B
Management, M
Management Information Systems and Services, M
Management Strategy and Policy, M

Marketing, M
Marketing/Marketing Management, B
Organizational Behavior Studies, M
Organizational Management, M
Public Administration, M
Systems Engineering, M

YAVAPAI COLLEGE

Accounting, A
Administrative Assistant and Secretarial Science, A
Agribusiness, A
Agricultural Business and Management, A
Agriculture, A
Aquaculture, A
Architectural Drafting and Architectural CAD/CADD, A
Automobile/Automotive Mechanics Technology/Technician, A
Business Administration and Management, A
Commercial and Advertising Art, A
Construction Engineering Technology/Technician, A
Criminal Justice/Police Science, A
Education, A
Equestrian/Equine Studies, A
Film/Cinema Studies, A
Fine Arts and Art Studies, A
Fire Science/Firefighting, A
Graphic Design, A
Gunsmithing/Gunsmith, A
Horse Husbandry/Equine Science and Management, A
Information Science/Studies, A
Legal Administrative Assistant/Secretary, A
Legal Assistant/Paralegal, A
Liberal Arts and Sciences Studies and Humanities, A

Arkansas

ARKANSAS BAPTIST COLLEGE

Adult and Continuing Education and Teaching, B
Business Administration and Management, AB
Elementary Education and Teaching, B
Liberal Arts and Sciences Studies and Humanities, AB
Religion/Religious Studies, AB
Secondary Education and Teaching, B
Social Work, B

ARKANSAS NORTHEASTERN COLLEGE

Business/Commerce, A
Criminal Justice/Police Science, A
General Studies, A
Industrial Mechanics and Maintenance Technology, A
Industrial Production Technologies/Technicians, A
Industrial Technology/Technician, A
Junior High/Intermediate/Middle School Education and Teaching, A
Marketing/Marketing Management, A
Metallurgical Technology/Technician, A
Multi-/Interdisciplinary Studies, A

ARKANSAS STATE UNIVERSITY

Accounting, BM
Agribusiness, B
Agricultural Education, O
Agricultural Sciences, MO
Animal Sciences, B
Art/Art Studies, General, B
Athletic Training and Sports Medicine, B
Audiology/Audiologist and Speech-Language Pathology/Pathologist, B
BioTechnology, M
Biological and Biomedical Sciences, MO
Biology Teacher Education, B
Biology/Biological Sciences, B
Business Administration and Management, B
Business Administration, Management and Operations, M
Business Education, O
Business Teacher Education, B
Business/Managerial Economics, B
Chemistry, BMO

Chemistry Teacher Education, B
Civil Engineering, B
Clinical Laboratory Science/Medical Technology/Technologist, AB
Clinical Psychology, O
Commercial and Advertising Art, B
Communication Disorders, M
Communication and Media Studies, MO
Community College Education, O
Computer Science, M
Computer and Information Sciences, B
Counseling Psychology, O
Counselor Education/School Counseling and Guidance Services, MO
Criminal Justice/Law Enforcement Administration, A
Criminal Justice/Police Science, A
Criminology, B
Data Processing and Data Processing Technology/Technician, B
Dietetics/Dieticians, B
Drama and Dramatics/Theatre Arts, B
Early Childhood Education and Teaching, BM
Economics, B
Education, MDO
Education/Teaching of the Gifted and Talented, M
Educational Administration and Supervision, O
Educational Leadership and Administration, MDO
Electrical, Electronics and Communications Engineering, B
Elementary Education and Teaching, MDO
Emergency Management, MO
Engineering, B
Engineering Management, M
Engineering Technologies/Technicians, AB
Engineering and Applied Sciences, M
English, MO
English Education, MO
English Language and Literature, B
English/Language Arts Teacher Education, B
Environmental Sciences, MD
Exercise and Sports Science, M
Finance, B
Foreign Language Teacher Education, B
Foreign Languages and Literatures, B
Forensic Science and Technology, A
Foundations and Philosophy of Education, M
General Studies, AB
Gerontology, O
Health Education, O
Health Services Administration, O
Health and Physical Education, B
Historic Preservation and Conservation, MD
History, BMO
International Business/Trade/Commerce, B
Journalism, BM
Junior High/Intermediate/Middle School Education and Teaching, B
Kinesiology and Exercise Science, B
Liberal Arts and Sciences Studies and Humanities, A
Logistics and Materials Management, B
Management Information Systems and Services, AO
Marketing/Marketing Management, B
Mathematics, BM
Mathematics Teacher Education, BM
Mechanical Engineering, B
Media Studies, M
Medical Radiologic Technology/Science - Radiation Therapist, B
Middle School Education, M
Molecular Biology, MD
Multi-/Interdisciplinary Studies, B
Music, BMO
Music Performance, B
Music Teacher Education, BMO
Nurse Anesthetist, M
Nursing, MDO
Occupational Therapist Assistant, A
Performance, M
Philosophy, B
Physical Education Teaching and Coaching, BMO
Physical Therapist Assistant, A
Physical Therapy/Therapist, D
Physics, B
Physics Teacher Education, B
Plant Sciences, B

Political Science and Government, BMO
Psychology, B
Public Administration, M
Public Relations, Advertising, and Applied Communication, B
Radio, Television, and Digital Communication, B
Reading Teacher Education, MO
Rehabilitation Counseling, M
School Psychology, M
Science Teacher Education/General Science Teacher Education, MO
Social Science Teacher Education, B
Social Studies Teacher Education, MO
Social Work, BMO
Sociology, BMO
Special Education and Teaching, BM
Speech and Interpersonal Communication, B
Sport and Fitness Administration/Management, BM
Student Personnel Services, MO
Substance Abuse/Addiction Counseling, O
Wildlife and Wildlands Science and Management, B

ARKANSAS STATE UNIVERSITY MID-SOUTH

Computer and Information Sciences, A
Liberal Arts and Sciences Studies and Humanities, A
Management Information Systems and Services, A
Manufacturing Technology/Technician, A
Multi-/Interdisciplinary Studies, A
Teacher Education, Multiple Levels, A
Web/Multimedia Management and Webmaster, A

ARKANSAS STATE UNIVERSITY-BEEBE

Agriculture, A
Animal Sciences, A
Business Administration and Management, A
Clinical/Medical Laboratory Technician, A
Computer Programming, Vendor/Product Certification, A
Computer Systems Networking and Telecommunications, A
Computer Technology/Computer Systems Technology, A
Drafting and Design Technology/Technician, A
Electrical, Electronic and Communications Engineering Technology/Technician, A
General Studies, A
Health/Medical Preparatory Programs, A
Industrial Mechanics and Maintenance Technology, A
Information Technology, A
Liberal Arts and Sciences Studies and Humanities, A
Quality Control Technology/Technician, A
Vehicle Maintenance and Repair Technologies, A

ARKANSAS STATE UNIVERSITY-MOUNTAIN HOME

Administrative Assistant and Secretarial Science, A
Business/Commerce, A
Criminal Justice/Law Enforcement Administration, A
Criminal Justice/Police Science, A
Early Childhood Education and Teaching, A
Emergency Medical Technology/Technician (EMT Paramedic), A
Forensic Science and Technology, A
Funeral Service and Mortuary Science, A
Information Science/Studies, A
Junior High/Intermediate/Middle School Education and Teaching, A
Liberal Arts and Sciences Studies and Humanities, A
Respiratory Care Therapy/Therapist, A
Teacher Education, Multiple Levels, A
Welding Technology/Welder, A

ARKANSAS STATE UNIVERSITY-NEWPORT

Autobody/Collision and Repair Technology/Technician, A
Automobile/Automotive Mechanics Technology/Technician, A
Business/Commerce, A

Computer Technology/Computer Systems Technology, A
Criminal Justice/Law Enforcement Administration, A
Early Childhood Education and Teaching, A
Emergency Medical Technology/Technician (EMT Paramedic), A
Forensic Science and Technology, A
General Studies, A
Health/Medical Preparatory Programs, A
Heating, Air Conditioning and Refrigeration Technology/Technician, A
Liberal Arts and Sciences Studies and Humanities, A
Management Information Systems and Services, A
Multi-/Interdisciplinary Studies, A
Teacher Education, Multiple Levels, A

ARKANSAS TECH UNIVERSITY

Accounting, B
Administrative Assistant and Secretarial Science, A
Agribusiness, B
Agricultural Teacher Education, B
Art Teacher Education, B
Art/Art Studies, General, B
Biology Teacher Education, B
Biology/Biological Sciences, B
Business Administration and Management, B
Business Administration, Management and Operations, M
Business Teacher Education, B
Business/Managerial Economics, B
Cardiovascular Technology/Technologist, A
Chemistry, B
Child Development, A
Clinical Laboratory Science/Medical Technology/Technologist, B
Communication Studies/Speech Communication and Rhetoric, B
Computer Systems Analysis/Analyst, B
Computer and Information Sciences, B
Counselor Education/School Counseling and Guidance Services, M
Criminal Justice/Safety Studies, A
Curriculum and Instruction, M
Early Childhood Education and Teaching, B
Education, M
Educational Leadership and Administration, MO
Educational Media/Instructional Technology, M
Electrical, Electronics and Communications Engineering, B
Elementary Education and Teaching, BM
Emergency Management, M
Emergency Medical Technology/Technician (EMT Paramedic), A
Engineering Physics, B
Engineering and Applied Sciences, M
English, M
English Education, M
English Language and Literature, B
English as a Second Language, M
English/Language Arts Teacher Education, B
Fish, Game and Wildlife Management, M
Foreign Language Teacher Education, B
Foreign Languages and Literatures, B
General Studies, A
Geography, B
Geology/Earth Science, B
Graphic Design, B
Health Informatics, M
Health Information/Medical Records Administration/Administrator, B
History, BM
Hospitality Administration/Management, B
Human Services, A
Industrial Technology/Technician, A
Information Science/Studies, M
Information Technology, AB
International/Global Studies, B
Journalism, BM
Junior High/Intermediate/Middle School Education and Teaching, B
Liberal Studies, M
Logistics and Materials Management, A
Management Sciences and Quantitative Methods, B
Mathematics, B
Mathematics Teacher Education, B

Mechanical Engineering, B
Medical Administrative Assistant/Secretary, A
Medical/Clinical Assistant, A
Multi-/Interdisciplinary Studies, AB
Music, B
Music Teacher Education, B
Nuclear Engineering Technology/Technician, A
Nuclear Physics, B
Nursing, M
Occupational Therapist Assistant, A
Parks, Recreation and Leisure Facilities Management, B
Physical Education Teaching and Coaching, B
Physical Sciences, B
Physical Therapist Assistant, A
Physics, B
Political Science and Government, B
Psychology, BM
Public/Applied History and Archival Administration, B
Regional Studies (U.S., Canadian, Foreign), A
Restaurant, Culinary, and Catering Management/Manager, A
Science Teacher Education/General Science Teacher Education, B
Social Studies Teacher Education, B
Sociology, B
Speech Teacher Education, B
Student Personnel Services, M
Wildlife and Wildlands Science and Management, B

BLACK RIVER TECHNICAL COLLEGE

Administrative Assistant and Secretarial Science, A
Aircraft Powerplant Technology/Technician, A
Criminal Justice/Law Enforcement Administration, A
Criminal Justice/Police Science, A
Dietetics/Dieticians, A
Early Childhood Education and Teaching, A
Emergency Medical Technology/Technician (EMT Paramedic), A
Fire Science/Firefighting, A
Forensic Science and Technology, A
Industrial Mechanics and Maintenance Technology, A
Junior High/Intermediate/Middle School Education and Teaching, A
Liberal Arts and Sciences Studies and Humanities, A
Multi-/Interdisciplinary Studies, A

CENTRAL BAPTIST COLLEGE

Accounting, B
Bible/Biblical Studies, B
BioTechnology, B
Biology/Biological Sciences, B
Business Administration and Management, AB
Business, Management, Marketing, and Related Support Services, B
Data Processing and Data Processing Technology/Technician, B
Early Childhood Education and Teaching, B
Education, M
English Language and Literature, B
General Studies, A
Health Services/Allied Health/Health Sciences, B
History, B
Human Resources Management/Personnel Administration, B
Kinesiology and Exercise Science, B
Liberal Arts and Sciences Studies and Humanities, AB
Management Information Systems and Services, B
Marketing/Marketing Management, B
Missions/Missionary Studies and Missiology, B
Music, B
Organizational Behavior Studies, B
Physical Education Teaching and Coaching, B
Psychology, B
Religious/Sacred Music, B
Secondary Education and Teaching, B
Social Work, B

COLLEGE OF THE OUACHITAS

Accounting, A
Administrative Assistant and Secretarial Science, A
Automobile/Automotive Mechanics Technology/Technician, A

Business Administration and Management, A
Child Care and Support Services Management, A
Computer and Information Sciences, A
Electromechanical Technology/Electromechanical Engineering Technology, A
Industrial Technology/Technician, A
Legal Administrative Assistant/Secretary, A
Legal Assistant/Paralegal, A
Liberal Arts and Sciences Studies and Humanities, A
Machine Tool Technology/Machinist, A
Management Information Systems and Services, A
Marketing/Marketing Management, A
Medical Administrative Assistant/Secretary, A

COSSATOT COMMUNITY COLLEGE OF THE UNIVERSITY OF ARKANSAS

Aeronautics/Aviation/Aerospace Science and Technology, A
Agricultural Business and Management, A
Automobile/Automotive Mechanics Technology/Technician, A
Business Administration and Management, A
Business/Commerce, A
Criminal Justice/Law Enforcement Administration, A
Criminal Justice/Safety Studies, A
Early Childhood Education and Teaching, A
Forensic Science and Technology, A
General Studies, A
Junior High/Intermediate/Middle School Education and Teaching, A
Liberal Arts and Sciences Studies and Humanities, A
Management Information Systems and Services, A
Medical/Clinical Assistant, A
Multi-/Interdisciplinary Studies, A
Physical Education Teaching and Coaching, A
Psychology, A

CROWLEY'S RIDGE COLLEGE

Bible/Biblical Studies, A
General Studies, A

EAST ARKANSAS COMMUNITY COLLEGE

Administrative Assistant and Secretarial Science, A
Business Administration and Management, A
Child Care and Support Services Management, A
Computer Engineering Technology/Technician, A
Criminal Justice/Law Enforcement Administration, A
Criminal Justice/Police Science, A
Drafting and Design Technology/Technician, A
Electrical, Electronic and Communications Engineering Technology/Technician, A
Emergency Medical Technology/Technician (EMT Paramedic), A
Engineering Technology, A
Environmental Engineering Technology/Environmental Technology, A
Industrial Mechanics and Maintenance Technology, A
Liberal Arts and Sciences Studies and Humanities, A
Manufacturing Technology/Technician, A
Medical Radiologic Technology/Science - Radiation Therapist, A
Medical/Clinical Assistant, A

ECCLESIA COLLEGE

Bible/Biblical Studies, AB
Business Administration and Management, B
Divinity/Ministry (BD, MDiv.), B
Liberal Arts and Sciences Studies and Humanities, A
Pastoral Studies/Counseling, B
Sport and Fitness Administration/Management, B

HARDING UNIVERSITY

Accounting, B
Advertising, B
Allied Health and Medical Assisting Services, MD
Art Education, M
Art Teacher Education, B
Art Therapy/Therapist, B
Athletic Training and Sports Medicine, B

Bible/Biblical Studies, B
Biochemistry, B
Biochemistry, Biophysics and Molecular Biology, B
Biology Teacher Education, B
Biology/Biological Sciences, B
Biomedical/Medical Engineering, B
Broadcast Journalism, B
Business Administration and Management, B
Business Administration, Management and Operations, M
Chemistry, B
Child Development, B
Communication Disorders, BM
Communication Studies/Speech Communication and Rhetoric, B
Computer Engineering, B
Computer Science, B
Counseling Psychology, M
Counselor Education/School Counseling and Guidance Services, MO
Criminal Justice/Safety Studies, B
Design and Applied Arts, B
Dietetics/Dieticians, B
Digital Communication and Media/Multimedia, B
Drama and Dramatics/Theatre Arts, B
Early Childhood Education and Teaching, BM
Economics, B
Education, MO
Education/Teaching of Individuals in Early Childhood Special Education Programs, B
Educational Leadership and Administration, MO
Electrical, Electronics and Communications Engineering, B
Elementary Education and Teaching, BM
English Education, M
English Language and Literature, B
English as a Second Language, M
English/Language Arts Teacher Education, B
Family and Community Services, B
Family and Consumer Sciences/Home Economics Teacher Education, B
Family and Consumer Sciences/Human Sciences, B
Fashion Merchandising, B
Finance, B
Fine/Studio Arts, B
Foreign Language Teacher Education, M
French Language Teacher Education, B
French Language and Literature, B
General Studies, B
Graphic Design, B
Health Education, M
Health Services Administration, M
Health Teacher Education, B
Health/Health Care Administration/Management, B
History, B
Housing and Human Environments, B
Human Development and Family Studies, B
Humanities/Humanistic Studies, B
Information Technology, B
Interior Design, B
International Business/Trade/Commerce, BM
International/Global Studies, B
Journalism, B
Junior High/Intermediate/Middle School Education and Teaching, B
Kinesiology and Exercise Science, B
Law and Legal Studies, B
Management of Technology, M
Marketing/Marketing Management, B
Marriage and Family Therapy/Counseling, M
Mathematics, B
Mathematics Teacher Education, BM
Mechanical Engineering, B
Missions/Missionary Studies and Missiology, B
Music, B
Music Teacher Education, B
Organizational Management, M
Painting, B
Pastoral Studies/Counseling, M
Pharmacy, D
Physical Therapy/Therapist, D
Physician Assistant, M
Physics, B
Political Science and Government, B
Psychology, B
Public Administration, B

Public Relations/Image Management, B
Reading Teacher Education, BM
Religious Education, B
Sales, Distribution and Marketing Operations, B
Science Teacher Education/General Science Teacher Education, B
Secondary Education and Teaching, BM
Social Sciences, B
Social Studies Teacher Education, BM
Social Work, B
Spanish Language Teacher Education, B
Spanish Language and Literature, B
Special Education and Teaching, M
Speech Teacher Education, B
Speech-Language Pathology/Pathologist, B
Sport and Fitness Administration/Management, B
Teacher Education, Multiple Levels, B
Web Page, Digital/Multimedia and Information Resources Design, B
Youth Ministry, B

HENDERSON STATE UNIVERSITY

Accounting, B
Airline/Commercial/Professional Pilot and Flight Crew, B
Art Teacher Education, B
Art/Art Studies, General, B
Athletic Training and Sports Medicine, B
Biology/Biological Sciences, B
Business Administration, Management and Operations, M
Business/Commerce, B
Chemistry, B
Child Development, B
Clinical Laboratory Science/Medical Technology/Technologist, B
Computer and Information Sciences, B
Counseling Psychology, M
Counselor Education/School Counseling and Guidance Services, MO
Criminal Justice/Safety Studies, B
Curriculum and Instruction, MO
Drama and Dramatics/Theatre Arts, B
Early Childhood Education and Teaching, M
Education, MO
Educational Leadership and Administration, MO
Engineering Physics, B
English Language and Literature, B
English as a Second Language, O
Family and Consumer Sciences/Human Sciences, B
General Studies, B
History, B
Journalism, B
Junior High/Intermediate/Middle School Education and Teaching, B
Liberal Studies, M
Management Information Systems and Services, B
Mathematics, B
Middle School Education, M
Music, B
Music Performance, B
Parks, Recreation and Leisure Facilities Management, B
Physical Education Teaching and Coaching, BM
Physics, B
Political Science and Government, B
Psychology, B
Public Administration, B
Radiologic Technology/Science - Radiographer, B
Reading Teacher Education, M
Social Science Teacher Education, B
Social Work, B
Sociology, B
Spanish Language and Literature, B
Special Education and Teaching, M
Sport and Fitness Administration/Management, M

HENDRIX COLLEGE

Accounting, BM
American/United States Studies/Civilization, B
Anthropology, B
Art/Art Studies, General, B
Biochemistry, Biophysics and Molecular Biology, B
Biology/Biological Sciences, B
Chemical Physics, B
Chemistry, B

Classics and Classical Languages, Literatures, and Linguistics, B
Computer Science, B
Drama and Dramatics/Theatre Arts, B
Economics, B
English Language and Literature, B
Environmental Studies, B
French Language and Literature, B
German Language and Literature, B
Health Services/Allied Health/Health Sciences, B
History, B
International Relations and Affairs, B
Mathematics, B
Music, B
Philosophy, B
Philosophy and Religious Studies, B
Physics, B
Political Science and Government, B
Psychology, B
Religion/Religious Studies, B
Sociology, B
Spanish Language and Literature, B

JOHN BROWN UNIVERSITY

Accounting, B
Bible/Biblical Studies, B
Biochemistry, B
Biological and Physical Sciences, B
Biology/Biological Sciences, B
Broadcast Journalism, B
Building/Construction Finishing, Management, and Inspection, AB
Business Administration and Management, B
Business Administration, Management and Operations, BM
Business Teacher Education, B
Chemistry, B
Cinematography and Film/Video Production, B
Clinical Psychology, M
Communication Studies/Speech Communication and Rhetoric, B
Computer Graphics, B
Construction Engineering, B
Construction Engineering Technology/Technician, B
Construction Management, B
Construction Trades, AB
Counseling Psychology, M
Counselor Education/School Counseling and Guidance Services, BMO
Curriculum and Instruction, M
Development Economics and International Development, B
Digital Communication and Media/Multimedia, B
Divinity/Ministry (BD, MDiv.), B
Early Childhood Education and Teaching, B
Economics, B
Education, BM
Educational Leadership and Administration, M
Electrical, Electronics and Communications Engineering, B
Electromechanical Technology/Electromechanical Engineering Technology, AB
Elementary Education and Teaching, B
Engineering, B
Engineering/Industrial Management, B
English Language and Literature, B
Environmental Sciences, B
Environmental Studies, B
Ethics, M
Family Systems, B
Family and Community Services, B
Film/Cinema Studies, B
General Studies, AB
Graphic Design, B
Health Teacher Education, B
Health and Physical Education, B
Health and Physical Education/Fitness, B
Higher Education/Higher Education Administration, M
History, B
Illustration, B
International Business/Trade/Commerce, BM
International Relations and Affairs, B
International/Global Studies, B
Journalism, AB
Kindergarten/PreSchool Education and Teaching, B

Kinesiology and Exercise Science, B
Management Information Systems and Services, B
Management Science, B
Marketing/Marketing Management, B
Marriage and Family Therapy/Counseling, BM
Mass Communication/Media Studies, B
Mathematics, B
Mathematics Teacher Education, B
Mechanical Engineering, B
Multi-/Interdisciplinary Studies, B
Music, B
Music Performance, B
Music Teacher Education, B
Organizational Behavior Studies, B
Parks, Recreation and Leisure Facilities Management, B
Pastoral Counseling and Specialized Ministries, B
Pastoral Studies/Counseling, B
Philosophy and Religious Studies, B
Photography, B
Physical Sciences, B
Political Science and Government, B
Pre-Theology/Pre-Ministerial Studies, B
Psychology, B
Public Relations, Advertising, and Applied Communication, AB
Public Relations/Image Management, AB
Radio and Television, B
Radio, Television, and Digital Communication, B
Religion/Religious Studies, B
Religious/Sacred Music, B
Secondary Education and Teaching, BM
Social Studies Teacher Education, B
Spanish Language and Literature, B
Special Education and Teaching, B
Sport and Fitness Administration/Management, B
Teacher Education and Professional Development, Specific Levels and Methods, B
Theological and Ministerial Studies, B
Theology/Theological Studies, B
Youth Ministry, B

LYON COLLEGE

Art/Art Studies, General, B
Biology/Biological Sciences, B
Business Administration and Management, B
Chemistry, B
Drama and Dramatics/Theatre Arts, B
Economics, B
English Language and Literature, B
History, B
Mathematics, B
Music, B
Philosophy and Religious Studies, B
Political Science and Government, B
Psychology, B
Spanish Language and Literature, B

NATIONAL PARK COLLEGE

Accounting, A
Administrative Assistant and Secretarial Science, A
Art/Art Studies, General, A
Business Administration and Management, A
Child Development, A
Clinical Laboratory Science/Medical Technology/Technologist, A
Clinical/Medical Laboratory Technician, A
Commercial and Advertising Art, A
Computer Graphics, A
Criminal Justice/Law Enforcement Administration, A
Data Processing and Data Processing Technology/Technician, A
Education, A
Electrical, Electronic and Communications Engineering Technology/Technician, A
Elementary Education and Teaching, A
Emergency Medical Technology/Technician (EMT Paramedic), A
Finance, A
Fire Science/Firefighting, A
Health Information/Medical Records Administration/Administrator, A
Health Professions and Related Clinical Sciences, A
Health/Health Care Administration/Management, A
Industrial Radiologic Technology/Technician, A
Information Science/Studies, A

Liberal Arts and Sciences Studies and Humanities, A
Medical Administrative Assistant/Secretary, A
Parks, Recreation and Leisure Facilities Management, A
Parks, Recreation, Leisure and Fitness Studies, A
Physical Sciences, A
Public Administration, A
Radiologic Technology/Science - Radiographer, A
Trade and Industrial Teacher Education, A

NORTH ARKANSAS COLLEGE

Biomedical Technology/Technician, A
Business/Commerce, A
Clinical/Medical Laboratory Technician, A
Computer and Information Sciences, A
Criminal Justice/Law Enforcement Administration, A
Electrical, Electronic and Communications Engineering Technology/Technician, A
Emergency Medical Technology/Technician (EMT Paramedic), A
Forensic Science and Technology, A
General Studies, A
Liberal Arts and Sciences Studies and Humanities, A
Medical Radiologic Technology/Science - Radiation Therapist, A
Multi-/Interdisciplinary Studies, A
Surgical Technology/Technologist, A
Teacher Education, Multiple Levels, A

NORTHWEST ARKANSAS COMMUNITY COLLEGE

Accounting, A
Business Administration and Management, A
Commercial and Advertising Art, A
Computer Programming/Programmer, A
Criminal Justice/Law Enforcement Administration, A
Criminal Justice/Safety Studies, A
Culinary Arts/Chef Training, A
Data Processing and Data Processing Technology/Technician, A
Drafting and Design Technology/Technician, A
Early Childhood Education and Teaching, A
Education, A
Electrical, Electronic and Communications Engineering Technology/Technician, A
Emergency Medical Technology/Technician (EMT Paramedic), A
Environmental Sciences, A
Finance, A
Fire Services Administration, A
Health Information/Medical Records Technology/Technician, A
Legal Assistant/Paralegal, A
Liberal Arts and Sciences Studies and Humanities, A
Occupational Safety and Health Technology/Technician, A
Physical Therapy/Therapist, A
Respiratory Care Therapy/Therapist, A
Security and Protective Services, A

OUACHITA BAPTIST UNIVERSITY

Accounting, B
Art Teacher Education, B
Bible/Biblical Studies, B
Biology/Biological Sciences, B
Business Administration and Management, B
Chemistry, B
Christian Studies, AB
Communication Disorders Sciences and Services, B
Communication Studies/Speech Communication and Rhetoric, B
Computer Science, B
Dietetics/Dieticians, B
Drama and Dramatics/Theatre Arts, B
Early Childhood Education and Teaching, B
English Language and Literature, B
Fine/Studio Arts, B
General Studies, A
Graphic Design, B
History, B
Junior High/Intermediate/Middle School Education and Teaching, B
Kinesiology and Exercise Science, B

Mass Communication/Media Studies, B
Mathematics, B
Missions/Missionary Studies and Missiology, B
Music, B
Music History, Literature, and Theory, B
Music Performance, B
Music Teacher Education, B
Music Theory and Composition, B
Pastoral Counseling and Specialized Ministries, B
Pastoral Studies/Counseling, B
Philosophy, B
Philosophy and Religious Studies, B
Physical Education Teaching and Coaching, B
Physics, B
Piano and Organ, B
Political Science and Government, B
Pre-Dentistry Studies, B
Pre-Law Studies, B
Pre-Medicine/Pre-Medical Studies, B
Pre-Nursing Studies, B
Pre-Pharmacy Studies, B
Pre-Veterinary Studies, B
Psychology, B
Religious/Sacred Music, B
Science Teacher Education/General Science Teacher Education, B
Secondary Education and Teaching, B
Social Studies Teacher Education, B
Sociology, B
Spanish Language and Literature, B
Theology and Religious Vocations, B
Theology/Theological Studies, B
Voice and Opera, B

OZARKA COLLEGE

Automobile/Automotive Mechanics Technology/Technician, A
Business/Office Automation/Technology/Data Entry, A
Criminal Justice/Law Enforcement Administration, A
Culinary Arts/Chef Training, A
Health Information/Medical Records Technology/Technician, A
Information Science/Studies, A
Junior High/Intermediate/Middle School Education and Teaching, A
Liberal Arts and Sciences Studies and Humanities, A

PHILANDER SMITH COLLEGE

Biological and Physical Sciences, B
Biology/Biological Sciences, B
Business Administration and Management, B
Chemistry, B
Computer Science, B
Educational Administration and Supervision, B
Elementary and Middle School Administration/Principalship, B
English Language and Literature, B
Health and Physical Education, B
Hospitality Administration/Management, B
Kindergarten/PreSchool Education and Teaching, B
Mathematics, B
Organizational Behavior Studies, B
Political Science and Government, B
Psychology, B
Religion/Religious Studies, B
Social Work, B
Sociology, B

PHILLIPS COMMUNITY COLLEGE OF THE UNIVERSITY OF ARKANSAS

Administrative Assistant and Secretarial Science, A
Building/Construction Finishing, Management, and Inspection, A
Computer Systems Networking and Telecommunications, A
Early Childhood Education and Teaching, A
Industrial Technology/Technician, A
Instrumentation Technology/Technician, A
Liberal Arts and Sciences Studies and Humanities, A
Management Information Systems and Services, A
Platemaker/Imager, A
Sales, Distribution and Marketing Operations, A
Social Work, A

Welding Technology/Welder, A

PULASKI TECHNICAL COLLEGE

Administrative Assistant and Secretarial Science, A
Aircraft Powerplant Technology/Technician, A
Airline/Commercial/Professional Pilot and Flight
  Crew, A
Business Operations Support and Secretarial Ser-
  vices, A
Child Development, A
Computer Technology/Computer Systems Technol-
  ogy, A
Construction Trades, A
Culinary Arts/Chef Training, A
Drafting and Design Technology/Technician, A
Electromechanical Technology/Electromechanical
  Engineering Technology, A
Environmental Engineering
  Technology/Environmental Technology, A
Heating, Air Conditioning, Ventilation and Refrigera-
  tion Maintenance Technology/Technician, A
Hospitality Administration/Management, A
Industrial Technology/Technician, A
Liberal Arts and Sciences Studies and Humani-
  ties, A
Management Information Systems and Services, A
Occupational Therapist Assistant, A
Respiratory Care Therapy/Therapist, A

REMINGTON COLLEGE–LITTLE ROCK CAMPUS

Computer Systems Networking and Telecommunications, A
Criminal Justice/Law Enforcement Administration, A

RICH MOUNTAIN COMMUNITY COLLEGE

Administrative Assistant and Secretarial Science, A
Computer Systems Analysis/Analyst, A
General Studies, A
Information Science/Studies, A
Junior High/Intermediate/Middle School Education
  and Teaching, A
Liberal Arts and Sciences Studies and Humani-
  ties, A
Multi-/Interdisciplinary Studies, A
Sales, Distribution and Marketing Operations, A

SHORTER COLLEGE

Administrative Assistant and Secretarial Science, A
Behavioral Sciences, A
Biological and Physical Sciences, A
Business Administration and Management, A
Business Teacher Education, A
Clinical/Medical Laboratory Technician, A
Computer Programming/Programmer, A
Computer Science, A
Education, A
Fire Science/Firefighting, A
Health Professions and Related Clinical Sciences, A
Kindergarten/PreSchool Education and Teaching, A
Legal Assistant/Paralegal, A
Liberal Arts and Sciences Studies and Humani-
  ties, A
Social Sciences, A
Social Work, A

SOUTH ARKANSAS COMMUNITY COLLEGE

Administrative Assistant and Secretarial Science, A
Business/Commerce, A
Clinical/Medical Laboratory Technician, A
Criminal Justice/Police Science, A
Emergency Medical Technology/Technician (EMT
  Paramedic), A
General Studies, A
Industrial Technology/Technician, A
Management Information Systems and Services, A
Medical Radiologic Technology/Science - Radiation
  Therapist, A
Physical Therapist Assistant, A

SOUTHEAST ARKANSAS COLLEGE

Business/Commerce, A
Cardiovascular Technology/Technologist, A

Child Care Provider/Assistant, A
Computer Systems Networking and Telecommunica-
  tions, A
Criminal Justice/Law Enforcement Administration, A
Criminal Justice/Safety Studies, A
Drafting and Design Technology/Technician, A
Emergency Medical Technology/Technician (EMT
  Paramedic), A
Forensic Science and Technology, A
General Studies, A
Industrial Electronics Technology/Technician, A
Industrial Mechanics and Maintenance Technol-
  ogy, A
Legal Assistant/Paralegal, A
Liberal Arts and Sciences Studies and Humani-
  ties, A
Management Information Systems and Services, A
Medical Radiologic Technology/Science - Radiation
  Therapist, A
Multi-/Interdisciplinary Studies, A
Respiratory Care Therapy/Therapist, A
Science, Technology and Society, A
Security and Protective Services, A
Surgical Technology/Technologist, A

SOUTHERN ARKANSAS UNIVERSITY TECH

Aircraft Powerplant Technology/Technician, A
Business Administration and Management, A
Child Care Provider/Assistant, A
Computer Science, A
Computer Software and Media Applications, A
Computer Technology/Computer Systems Technol-
  ogy, A
Engineering Technologies/Technicians, A
Environmental Engineering
  Technology/Environmental Technology, A
Fire Science/Firefighting, A
Fire Services Administration, A
General Studies, A
Industrial Technology/Technician, A
Junior High/Intermediate/Middle School Education
  and Teaching, A
Multi-/Interdisciplinary Studies, A
Office Management and Supervision, A
Teacher Education, Multiple Levels, A

SOUTHERN ARKANSAS UNIVERSITY–MAGNOLIA

Accounting, B
Agribusiness, A
Agricultural Business and Management, B
Agricultural Sciences, M
Agricultural Teacher Education, B
Agriculture, B
Art Teacher Education, B
Art/Art Studies, General, B
Athletic Training and Sports Medicine, B
Biological and Physical Sciences, B
Biology/Biological Sciences, B
Business Administration and Management, B
Business Administration, Management and Opera-
  tions, M
Business Teacher Education, B
Business/Commerce, AB
Chemistry, AB
Clinical Laboratory Science/Medical
  Technology/Technologist, B
Community Organization and Advocacy, B
Computer Science, M
Computer and Information Sciences, B
Counselor Education/School Counseling and Guid-
  ance Services, M
Criminal Justice/Safety Studies, B
Curriculum and Instruction, M
Drama and Dramatics/Theatre Arts, B
Early Childhood Education and Teaching, B
Education, M
Educational Administration and Supervision, M
Elementary Education and Teaching, M
English Language and Literature, B
English as a Second Language, M
Fine/Studio Arts, B
General Studies, AB
History, B
Industrial Technology/Technician, AB

Journalism, B
Junior High/Intermediate/Middle School Education
  and Teaching, B
Kinesiology and Exercise Science, B
Kinesiology and Movement Studies, M
Library Science, M
Mathematics, B
Multi-/Interdisciplinary Studies, B
Music, B
Music Teacher Education, B
Physical Education Teaching and Coaching, B
Physics, B
Political Science and Government, B
Psychiatric/Mental Health Nurse/Nursing, M
Psychology, B
Public Administration, M
Reading Teacher Education, M
Secondary Education and Teaching, M
Social Sciences, B
Social Work, B
Spanish Language and Literature, B

STRAYER UNIVERSITY–LITTLE ROCK CAMPUS

Accounting, B
Business Administration and Management, B
Criminal Justice/Law Enforcement Administration, B
Management Information Systems and Services, B

UNIVERSITY OF ARKANSAS

Accounting, BM
Agribusiness, B
Agricultural Economics, M
Agricultural Education, M
Agricultural Engineering, MD
Agricultural Sciences, MD
Agricultural Teacher Education, B
Agricultural and Extension Education Services, B
Agricultural/Biological Engineering and Bioengineer-
  ing, B
Agronomy and Crop Science, B
Agronomy and Soil Sciences, MD
American/United States Studies/Civilization, B
Animal Sciences, BMD
Anthropology, BMD
Apparel and Textiles, B
Applied Physics, M
Architecture, B
Art/Art Studies, General, B
Athletic Training and Sports Medicine, M
Audiology/Audiologist and Speech-Language
  Pathology/Pathologist, B
Bioengineering, M
Biological and Biomedical Sciences, MD
Biology/Biological Sciences, B
Biomedical Engineering, M
Biomedical/Medical Engineering, B
Business Administration and Management, B
Business Administration, Management and Opera-
  tions, MD
Business/Commerce, B
Business/Managerial Economics, B
Cell Biology and Anatomy, MD
Chemical Engineering, BMD
Chemistry, BMD
Civil Engineering, BMD
Classics and Classical Languages, Litera-
  tures, and Linguistics, B
Communication Disorders, M
Communication Studies/Speech Communication
  and Rhetoric, B
Communication and Media Studies, M
Community Health and Preventive Medicine, MD
Comparative Literature, MD
Computer Engineering, BMD
Computer Science, MD
Computer and Information Sciences, B
Counselor Education/School Counseling and Guid-
  ance Services, MDO
Criminal Justice/Safety Studies, B
Curriculum and Instruction, D
Data Processing and Data Processing
  Technology/Technician, B
Drama and Dramatics/Theatre Arts, B
Early Childhood Education and Teaching, BM
Economics, BMD

Education, BMDO
Educational Leadership and Administration, MDO
Educational Measurement and Evaluation, MD
Educational Media/Instructional Technology, M
Educational Policy, D
Electrical Engineering, MD
Electrical, Electronics and Communications Engineering, B
Electronic Materials, MD
Elementary Education and Teaching, B
Engineering and Applied Sciences, MD
English, MD
English Language and Literature, B
Entomology, MD
Environmental Engineering Technology/Environmental Technology, M
Environmental Sciences, B
Family and Consumer Sciences/Human Sciences, BM
Finance, B
Fine Arts and Art Studies, M
Food Science, B
Food Science and Technology, MD
Foods, Nutrition, and Wellness Studies, B
French Language and Literature, BM
Geography, BM
Geology/Earth Science, BM
German Language and Literature, BM
Health Education, MD
Health Promotion, MD
Health and Physical Education, B
Higher Education/Higher Education Administration, MDO
History, BMD
Horticultural Science, M
Human Development and Family Studies, B
Human Resources Development, BMD
Industrial Engineering, B
Industrial and Manufacturing Management, M
Industrial/Management Engineering, MD
Interdisciplinary Studies, MD
Interior Design, B
International Business/Trade/Commerce, B
International Relations and Affairs, B
Journalism, BM
Kindergarten/PreSchool Education and Teaching, B
Kinesiology and Movement Studies, MD
Landscape Architecture, B
Law and Legal Studies, MD
Logistics and Materials Management, B
Management Information Systems and Services, BM
Management Science, B
Marketing/Marketing Management, B
Mathematics, BMD
Mathematics Teacher Education, M
Mechanical Engineering, BMD
Middle School Education, M
Molecular Biology, MD
Music, M
Music Performance, B
Nursing, M
Operations Research, M
Ornamental Horticulture, B
Parks, Recreation, Leisure and Fitness Studies, B
Philosophy, BMD
Photonics, MD
Physical Education Teaching and Coaching, M
Physics, BMD
Planetary Astronomy and Science, MD
Plant Pathology/Phytopathology, M
Plant Sciences, D
Political Science and Government, BM
Poultry Science, BMD
Pre-Medicine/Pre-Medical Studies, B
Psychology, BMD
Public Administration, M
Public Health (MPH, DPH), B
Public Health Education and Promotion, B
Public Policy Analysis, D
Recreation and Park Management, MD
Rehabilitation Counseling, MD
Secondary Education and Teaching, MO
Social Work, BM
Sociology, BM
Spanish Language and Literature, BM

Special Education and Teaching, BM
Sport and Fitness Administration/Management, MD
Statistics, M
Technical Teacher Education, B
Telecommunications, M
Theater, M
Transportation and Highway Engineering, M
Vocational and Technical Education, MD
Writing, M

UNIVERSITY OF ARKANSAS COMMUNITY COLLEGE AT BATESVILLE

Aircraft Powerplant Technology/Technician, A
Business/Commerce, A
Criminal Justice/Safety Studies, A
Early Childhood Education and Teaching, A
Electrical/Electronics Equipment Installation and Repair, A
Emergency Medical Technology/Technician (EMT Paramedic), A
Liberal Arts and Sciences Studies and Humanities, A
Medical Office Management/Administration, A
Multi-/Interdisciplinary Studies, A

UNIVERSITY OF ARKANSAS COMMUNITY COLLEGE AT HOPE

Business/Commerce, A
Child Care and Support Services Management, A
Computer and Information Sciences, A
Electrical, Electronic and Communications Engineering Technology/Technician, A
Emergency Medical Technology/Technician (EMT Paramedic), A
Funeral Service and Mortuary Science, A
General Studies, A
Human Services, A
Liberal Arts and Sciences Studies and Humanities, A
Medical Office Management/Administration, A
Multi-/Interdisciplinary Studies, A
Teacher Education, Multiple Levels, A

UNIVERSITY OF ARKANSAS COMMUNITY COLLEGE AT MORRILTON

Autobody/Collision and Repair Technology/Technician, A
Automobile/Automotive Mechanics Technology/Technician, A
Business/Commerce, A
Child Development, A
Commercial and Advertising Art, A
Computer Technology/Computer Systems Technology, A
Computer and Information Sciences, A
Criminal Justice/Law Enforcement Administration, A
Drafting and Design Technology/Technician, A
Forensic Science and Technology, A
General Studies, A
Heating, Air Conditioning, Ventilation and Refrigeration Maintenance Technology/Technician, A
Industrial Mechanics and Maintenance Technology, A
Liberal Arts and Sciences Studies and Humanities, A
Petroleum Technology/Technician, A
Survey Technology/Surveying, A
Teacher Education, Multiple Levels, A

UNIVERSITY OF ARKANSAS AT LITTLE ROCK

Accounting, B
Adult and Continuing Education and Teaching, M
Anthropology, B
Applied Mathematics, MO
Applied Psychology, M
Applied Science and Technology, MD
Applied Statistics, O
Art Education, M
Art History, Criticism and Conservation, M
Art/Art Studies, General, B
Audiology/Audiologist and Speech-Language Pathology/Pathologist, B
Bioinformatics, MD
Biological and Biomedical Sciences, M

Biology/Biological Sciences, B
Business Administration and Management, B
Business Administration, Management and Operations, MO
Business/Commerce, B
Chemistry, BM
Communication Studies/Speech Communication and Rhetoric, B
Community College Education, M
Computer Engineering Technology/Technician, B
Computer Programming/Programmer, A
Computer Science, BMD
Conflict Resolution and Mediation/Peace Studies, O
Construction Engineering, B
Construction Engineering Technology/Technician, B
Construction Management, M
Counselor Education/School Counseling and Guidance Services, M
Criminal Justice/Police Science, A
Criminal Justice/Safety Studies, B
Criminology, MD
Curriculum and Instruction, M
Dance, B
Drama and Dramatics/Theatre Arts, B
Early Childhood Education and Teaching, B
Education, BMDO
Education/Teaching of the Gifted and Talented, MO
Educational Administration and Supervision, MDO
Educational Media/Instructional Technology, M
Electrical, Electronic and Communications Engineering Technology/Technician, AB
Elementary Education and Teaching, B
English Language and Literature, B
English as a Second Language, M
Entrepreneurship/Entrepreneurial Studies, O
Environmental Health, B
Exercise and Sports Science, M
Film/Cinema Studies, B
Finance, B
Fine Arts and Art Studies, M
Fine/Studio Arts, B
Foreign Language Teacher Education, M
Foreign Languages and Literatures, B
French Language and Literature, B
General Studies, A
Geology/Earth Science, B
Geosciences, O
Gerontology, O
Health Education, M
Health Professions and Related Clinical Sciences, B
Higher Education/Higher Education Administration, MD
History, B
Humanities/Humanistic Studies, B
Information Science/Studies, BMDO
Interdisciplinary Studies, M
International Business/Trade/Commerce, B
Journalism, B
Law and Legal Studies, D
Liberal Arts and Sciences Studies and Humanities, B
Management, O
Management Information Systems and Services, BMO
Marketing/Marketing Management, B
Mass Communication/Media Studies, M
Mathematics, BM
Mechanical Engineering/Mechanical Technology/Technician, AB
Middle School Education, M
Multi-/Interdisciplinary Studies, B
Music, B
Non-Profit/Public/Organizational Management, O
Philosophy, B
Physics, B
Political Science and Government, B
Psychology, BM
Public Administration, M
Public Affairs, MO
Public History, M
Radio and Television, B
Reading Teacher Education, MDO
Rehabilitation Counseling, MO
Rhetoric, M
Secondary Education and Teaching, M
Sign Language Interpretation and Translation, AB

Social Work, BM
Sociology, B
Spanish Language and Literature, B
Special Education and Teaching, MO
Speech and Interpersonal Communication, M
Sport and Fitness Administration/Management, M
Student Personnel Services, M
Systems Engineering, BMDO
Technical and Business Writing, M
Writing, M

UNIVERSITY OF ARKANSAS FOR MEDICAL SCIENCES

Allied Health Diagnostic, Intervention, and Treatment Professions, B
Allopathic Medicine, D
Biochemistry, MD
Bioinformatics, MD
Biological and Biomedical Sciences, MDO
Biomedical Technology/Technician, A
Biostatistics, M
Clinical Laboratory Science/Medical Technology/Technologist, B
Communication Disorders, MD
CytoTechnology/Cytotechnologist, B
Dental Hygiene/Hygienist, AB
Diagnostic Medical Sonography/Sonographer and Ultrasound Technician, AB
Emergency Medical Technology/Technician (EMT Paramedic), AB
Environmental and Occupational Health, MO
Epidemiology, MD
Genetic Counseling/Counselor, M
Health Education, M
Health Information/Medical Records Administration/Administrator, B
Health Information/Medical Records Technology/Technician, A
Health Physics/Radiological Health, M
Health Promotion, D
Health Services Administration, M
Health Services Research, D
Immunology, D
Medical Radiologic Technology/Science - Radiation Therapist, AB
Microbiology, D
Molecular Biology, MD
Molecular Biophysics, MD
Neurobiology and Neurophysiology, D
Nuclear Medical Technology/Technologist, B
Nursing, D
Nutritional Sciences, M
Ophthalmic Technician/Technologist, B
Pharmacology, D
Pharmacy, MD
Physician Assistant, M
Physiology, MD
Public Health, MDO
Respiratory Care Therapy/Therapist, A
Surgical Technology/Technologist, A
Toxicology, M

UNIVERSITY OF ARKANSAS AT MONTICELLO

Accounting, B
Agricultural Production Operations, A
Agriculture, B
Art/Art Studies, General, B
Biological and Physical Sciences, B
Biology/Biological Sciences, B
Business Administration and Management, B
Chemistry, B
Communication Studies/Speech Communication and Rhetoric, B
Criminal Justice/Law Enforcement Administration, A
Criminal Justice/Safety Studies, B
Education, BM
Educational Leadership and Administration, M
English Language and Literature, B
Foreign Languages and Literatures, B
Forensic Science and Technology, A
Forestry, BM
General Studies, A
Health and Physical Education, B
History, B

Industrial Mechanics and Maintenance Technology, A
Junior High/Intermediate/Middle School Education and Teaching, B
Kindergarten/PreSchool Education and Teaching, B
Management Information Systems and Services, B
Mathematics, B
Multi-/Interdisciplinary Studies, AB
Music, B
Music Teacher Education, B
Natural Resources and Conservation, M
Physical Education Teaching and Coaching, B
Political Science and Government, B
Psychology, B
Social Sciences, B
Social Work, B
Survey Technology/Surveying, AB
Wildlife and Wildlands Science and Management, B

UNIVERSITY OF ARKANSAS AT PINE BLUFF

Accounting, B
Agricultural Economics, B
Agricultural Teacher Education, B
Agriculture, B
Aquaculture, B
Art/Art Studies, General, B
Biology/Biological Sciences, B
Business Administration and Management, B
Business Teacher Education, B
Chemistry, B
Computer Science, B
Corrections, B
Criminal Justice/Law Enforcement Administration, A
Criminal Justice/Police Science, A
Early Childhood Education and Teaching, M
Education, M
English Education, M
English Language and Literature, B
Family and Consumer Sciences/Home Economics Teacher Education, B
Family and Consumer Sciences/Human Sciences, B
Fish, Game and Wildlife Management, M
Fishing and Fisheries Sciences and Management, B
History, B
Industrial Technology/Technician, AB
Junior High/Intermediate/Middle School Education and Teaching, B
Kindergarten/PreSchool Education and Teaching, B
Mathematics, B
Mathematics Teacher Education, M
Music, B
Parks, Recreation, Leisure and Fitness Studies, B
Physical Education Teaching and Coaching, BM
Physics, B
Political Science and Government, B
Psychology, B
Rehabilitation and Therapeutic Professions, B
Science Teacher Education/General Science Teacher Education, M
Secondary Education and Teaching, BM
Social Sciences, B
Social Studies Teacher Education, M
Social Work, B
Sociology, B
Special Education and Teaching, B
Substance Abuse/Addiction Counseling, M

UNIVERSITY OF ARKANSAS–FORT SMITH

Animation, Interactive Technology, Video Graphics and Special Effects, B
Art/Art Studies, General, B
Biology Teacher Education, B
Biology/Biological Sciences, B
Business Administration and Management, AB
CAD/CADD Drafting and/or Design Technology/Technician, A
Chemistry, B
Chemistry Teacher Education, B
Computer and Information Sciences, B
Criminal Justice/Law Enforcement Administration, AB
Dental Hygiene/Hygienist, A
Drama and Dramatics/Theatre Arts, B
Early Childhood Education and Teaching, AB

Electrical/Electronics Equipment Installation and Repair, A
English Language and Literature, B
English/Language Arts Teacher Education, B
Executive Assistant/Executive Secretary, A
Forensic Science and Technology, A
General Studies, AB
Graphic Design, B
History, B
History Teacher Education, B
Junior High/Intermediate/Middle School Education and Teaching, B
Legal Assistant/Paralegal, A
Liberal Arts and Sciences Studies and Humanities, A
Mathematics, B
Mathematics Teacher Education, B
Multi-/Interdisciplinary Studies, AB
Music, B
Music Teacher Education, B
Political Science and Government, B
Psychology, B
Radiologic Technology/Science - Radiographer, AB
Spanish Language Teacher Education, B
Spanish Language and Literature, B
Surgical Technology/Technologist, A

UNIVERSITY OF CENTRAL ARKANSAS

Accounting, BM
Adult and Continuing Education and Teaching, O
African-American/Black Studies, B
Applied Mathematics, M
Art/Art Studies, General, B
Athletic Training and Sports Medicine, B
Audiology/Audiologist and Speech-Language Pathology/Pathologist, B
Biological and Biomedical Sciences, M
Biological and Physical Sciences, B
Biology/Biological Sciences, B
Business Administration and Management, B
Business Administration, Management and Operations, M
Business Teacher Education, B
Business/Commerce, B
Chemistry, B
Cinematography and Film/Video Production, B
Clinical Laboratory Science/Medical Technology/Technologist, B
Communication Disorders, MD
Community Health Services/Liaison/Counseling, B
Community Psychology, M
Computer Art and Design, M
Computer Science, M
Computer and Information Sciences, B
Counseling Psychology, M
Counselor Education/School Counseling and Guidance Services, M
Curriculum and Instruction, O
Drama and Dramatics/Theatre Arts, B
Economic Development, MO
Economics, BMO
Education, MO
Education/Teaching of the Gifted and Talented, O
Educational Administration and Supervision, O
Educational Leadership and Administration, MO
Educational Media/Instructional Technology, M
English, M
English Language and Literature, B
Entrepreneurship/Entrepreneurial Studies, B
Environmental Studies, B
Family and Consumer Sciences/Home Economics Teacher Education, B
Family and Consumer Sciences/Human Sciences, B
Film, Television, and Video Production, M
Finance, B
Foods, Nutrition, and Wellness Studies, B
Foreign Language Teacher Education, M
French Language and Literature, B
General Studies, A
Geographic Information Systems, MO
Geography, BMO
Health Education, M
Health Professions and Related Clinical Sciences, B
History, BM
Home Economics, M
Insurance, B

Interior Design, B
International/Global Studies, B
Journalism, B
Junior High/Intermediate/Middle School Education and Teaching, B
Kindergarten/PreSchool Education and Teaching, B
Kinesiology and Exercise Science, B
Kinesiology and Movement Studies, M
Liberal Arts and Sciences Studies and Humanities, B
Library Science, M
Management Information Systems and Services, B
Marketing/Marketing Management, B
Mathematics, BM
Mathematics Teacher Education, BM
Medical Radiologic Technology/Science - Radiation Therapist, B
Multi-/Interdisciplinary Studies, B
Music, BMO
Music Performance, B
Music Teacher Education, M
Music Theory and Composition, M
Nuclear Medical Technology/Technologist, B
Nursing, MO
Nursing - Adult, O
Nursing - Advanced Practice, MO
Nursing Administration, O
Nursing Education, O
Occupational Therapy/Therapist, M
Organizational Management, D
Performance, M
Philosophy, B
Physical Education Teaching and Coaching, B
Physical Therapy/Therapist, D
Physics, B
Political Science and Government, B
Psychology, BMDO
Public Administration, B
Public Relations, Advertising, and Applied Communication, B
Reading Teacher Education, M
Religion/Religious Studies, B
School Psychology, MDO
Science Teacher Education/General Science Teacher Education, B
Social Studies Teacher Education, B
Sociology, B
Spanish Language and Literature, B
Special Education and Teaching, MO
Student Personnel Services, M
Substance Abuse/Addiction Counseling, B
Urban and Regional Planning, M
Writing, M

UNIVERSITY OF THE OZARKS

Accounting, B
Biology/Biological Sciences, B
Broadcast Journalism, B
Business Administration and Management, B
Chemistry, B
Drama and Dramatics/Theatre Arts, B
Economics, B
Elementary Education and Teaching, B
English Language and Literature, B
Environmental Studies, B
Fine/Studio Arts, B
General Studies, B
Health Services/Allied Health/Health Sciences, B
History, B
Humanities/Humanistic Studies, B
International Business/Trade/Commerce, B
Junior High/Intermediate/Middle School Education and Teaching, B
Marketing/Marketing Management, B
Mass Communication/Media Studies, B
Mathematics, B
Music, B
Philosophy, B
Philosophy and Religious Studies, B
Physical Education Teaching and Coaching, B
Physical Sciences, B
Political Science and Government, B
Psychology, B
Religion/Religious Studies, B
Secondary Education and Teaching, B
Sociology, B

Spanish Language and Literature, B
Technology Teacher Education/Industrial Arts Teacher Education, B

WILLIAMS BAPTIST COLLEGE

Administrative Assistant and Secretarial Science, A
Art Teacher Education, B
Art/Art Studies, General, B
Biology/Biological Sciences, B
Business Administration and Management, AB
Computer and Information Sciences, B
Divinity/Ministry (BD, MDiv.), B
Education, B
Elementary Education and Teaching, B
English Language and Literature, B
Fine/Studio Arts, B
History, B
Kindergarten/PreSchool Education and Teaching, B
Liberal Arts and Sciences Studies and Humanities, AB
Music, B
Music Teacher Education, B
Pastoral Studies/Counseling, B
Physical Education Teaching and Coaching, B
Pre-Dentistry Studies, B
Pre-Law Studies, B
Pre-Medicine/Pre-Medical Studies, B
Psychology, B
Religion/Religious Studies, B
Religious Education, B
Religious/Sacred Music, B
Theology/Theological Studies, AB

California

ACADEMY OF ART UNIVERSITY

Acting, AB
Advertising, AB
Advertising and Public Relations, M
Animation, Interactive Technology, Video Graphics and Special Effects, AB
Apparel and Textile Manufacture, AB
Apparel and Textile Marketing Management, AB
Applied Arts and Design, M
Architecture, BM
Art Education, M
Art History, Criticism and Conservation, BM
Art Teacher Education, B
Arts Journalism, M
Autobody/Collision and Repair Technology/Technician, A
Cinematography and Film/Video Production, AB
Clothing and Textiles, M
Commercial and Advertising Art, AB
Communication and Media Studies, B
Computer Art and Design, M
Computer Programming, Specific Applications, AB
Consumer Merchandising/Retailing Management, AB
Fashion Merchandising, AB
Fashion and Fabric Consultant, AB
Fashion/Apparel Design, AB
Film, Television, and Video Production, M
Fine Arts and Art Studies, ABM
Fine/Studio Arts, AB
Game Design and Development, M
Graphic Design, ABM
Illustration, ABM
Industrial Design, ABM
Interior Design, ABM
Internet and Interactive Multimedia, M
Jewelry/Metalsmithing, M
Journalism, AB
Landscape Architecture, ABM
Metal and Jewelry Arts, AB
Modeling and Simulation, M
Music, ABM
Painting, M
Photography, M
Playwriting and Screenwriting, B
Printmaking, M
Sculpture, M
Textile Design, M
Theater, M

Web Page, Digital/Multimedia and Information Resources Design, AB
Writing, M

ACADEMY OF COUTURE ART

Apparel and Textile Manufacture, AB
Fashion/Apparel Design, AB

ALLAN HANCOCK COLLEGE

Accounting, A
Administrative Assistant and Secretarial Science, A
Aerospace, Aeronautical and Astronautical Engineering, A
Agribusiness, A
Architectural Engineering Technology/Technician, A
Art/Art Studies, General, A
Automobile/Automotive Mechanics Technology/Technician, A
Biology/Biological Sciences, A
Business Administration and Management, A
Chemistry, A
Civil Engineering Technology/Technician, A
Commercial and Advertising Art, A
Computer Engineering Technology/Technician, A
Computer Science, A
Cosmetology/Cosmetologist, A
Criminal Justice/Police Science, A
Dance, A
Dental Assisting/Assistant, A
Design and Applied Arts, A
Dietetics/Dieticians, A
Electrical, Electronic and Communications Engineering Technology/Technician, A
Engineering, A
Engineering Technology, A
English Language and Literature, A
Environmental Engineering Technology/Environmental Technology, A
Family and Consumer Economics and Related Services, A
Fashion/Apparel Design, A
Film/Cinema Studies, A
Fire Science/Firefighting, A
Heavy Equipment Maintenance Technology/Technician, A
Human Services, A
Information Science/Studies, A
Interior Design, A
International Relations and Affairs, A
Kindergarten/PreSchool Education and Teaching, A
Legal Administrative Assistant/Secretary, A
Liberal Arts and Sciences Studies and Humanities, A
Machine Tool Technology/Machinist, A
Medical/Clinical Assistant, A
Music, A
Parks, Recreation, Leisure and Fitness Studies, A
Photography, A
Physical Education Teaching and Coaching, A
Physical Therapy/Therapist, A
Physics, A
Social Sciences, A
Spanish Language and Literature, A
Welding Technology/Welder, A

ALLIANT INTERNATIONAL UNIVERSITY–SAN DIEGO

Business Administration and Management, B
Child Development, B
Criminal Justice/Law Enforcement Administration, B
Psychology, B

ALLIED AMERICAN UNIVERSITY

Business Administration and Management, AB
Computer and Information Sciences, AB
Criminal Justice/Law Enforcement Administration, AB

Liberal Arts and Sciences Studies and Humanities, AB

AMERICAN ACADEMY OF DRAMATIC ARTS–LOS ANGELES

Drama and Dramatics/Theatre Arts, A

AMERICAN CAREER COLLEGE (ANAHEIM)

Health Information/Medical Records Technology/Technician, A
Respiratory Therapy Technician/Assistant, A
Surgical Technology/Technologist, A

AMERICAN CAREER COLLEGE (LOS ANGELES)

Respiratory Therapy Technician/Assistant, A
Surgical Technology/Technologist, A

AMERICAN CAREER COLLEGE (ONTARIO)

Surgical Technology/Technologist, A

AMERICAN JEWISH UNIVERSITY

American Government and Politics (United States), B
Bioethics/Medical Ethics, B
Business Administration, Management and Operations, M
Business/Commerce, B
Education, M
Jewish/Judaic Studies, BM
Liberal Arts and Sciences Studies and Humanities, B
Mass Communication/Media Studies, B
Non-Profit/Public/Organizational Management, M
Political Science and Government, B
Psychology, B
Social Work, M
Theology and Religious Vocations, M

AMERICAN MUSICAL AND DRAMATIC ACADEMY, LOS ANGELES

Acting, B
Dance, B
Drama and Dramatics/Theatre Arts, B
Visual and Performing Arts, B

AMERICAN RIVER COLLEGE

Accounting, A
Administrative Assistant and Secretarial Science, A
Adult Development and Aging, A
Advertising, A
American Sign Language (ASL), A
Anthropology, A
Apparel and Textile Marketing Management, A
Art/Art Studies, General, A
Autobody/Collision and Repair Technology/Technician, A
Automobile/Automotive Mechanics Technology/Technician, A
Biological and Physical Sciences, A
Biology Technician/BioTechnology Laboratory Technician, A
Business Administration and Management, A
Business/Commerce, A
Carpentry/Carpenter, A
Child Development, A
Computer Programming/Programmer, A
Computer Science, A
Computer Systems Networking and Telecommunications, A
Culinary Arts/Chef Training, A
Data Entry/Microcomputer Applications, A
Data Modeling/Warehousing and Database Administration, A
Diesel Mechanics Technology/Technician, A
Drafting and Design Technology/Technician, A
Drama and Dramatics/Theatre Arts, A
Drywall Installation/Drywaller, A
Electrical, Electronic and Communications Engineering Technology/Technician, A
Electrician, A

Emergency Medical Technology/Technician (EMT Paramedic), A
Engineering, A
Engineering Technology, A
English Language and Literature, A
Family Systems, A
Fashion/Apparel Design, A
Fire Science/Firefighting, A
Foodservice Systems Administration/Management, A
Funeral Service and Mortuary Science, A
Geography, A
Home Health Aide/Home Attendant, A
Human Services, A
Industrial Electronics Technology/Technician, A
Interior Design, A
International Relations and Affairs, A
Journalism, A
Landscaping and Groundskeeping, A
Legal Assistant/Paralegal, A
Liberal Arts and Sciences Studies and Humanities, A
Mathematics, A
Music, A
Natural Resources Management/Development and Policy, A
Parks, Recreation, Leisure and Fitness Studies, A
Photography, A
Physical Sciences, A
Plant Nursery Operations and Management, A
Psychology, A
Radio, Television, and Digital Communication, A
Real Estate, A
Respiratory Care Therapy/Therapist, A
Restaurant, Culinary, and Catering Management/Manager, A
Retailing and Retail Operations, A
Sales, Distribution and Marketing Operations, A
Sheet Metal Technology/Sheetworking, A
Sign Language Interpretation and Translation, A
Small Business Administration/Management, A
Social Sciences, A
Sport and Fitness Administration/Management, A
Substance Abuse/Addiction Counseling, A
System Administration/Administrator, A
Technical Theatre/Theatre Design and Technology, A
Welding Technology/Welder, A

AMERICAN UNIVERSITY OF HEALTH SCIENCES

Clinical Research, M
Pharmacy, Pharmaceutical Sciences, and Administration, B

ANTELOPE VALLEY COLLEGE

Accounting Technology/Technician and Bookkeeping, A
Administrative Assistant and Secretarial Science, A
Aircraft Powerplant Technology/Technician, A
Airframe Mechanics and Aircraft Maintenance Technology/Technician, A
American Sign Language (ASL), A
Animation, Interactive Technology, Video Graphics and Special Effects, A
Anthropology, A
Apparel and Textiles, A
Applied Horticulture/Horticultural Operations, A
Art/Art Studies, General, A
Autobody/Collision and Repair Technology/Technician, A
Automobile/Automotive Mechanics Technology/Technician, A
Biological and Physical Sciences, A
Business Administration and Management, A
Business/Commerce, A
Child Care Provider/Assistant, A
Communication Studies/Speech Communication and Rhetoric, A
Computer Graphics, A
Computer Programming/Programmer, A
Computer Systems Networking and Telecommunications, A
Criminal Justice/Police Science, A
Data Entry/Microcomputer Applications, A
Drafting and Design Technology/Technician, A

Electrical/Electronics Equipment Installation and Repair, A
Electrician, A
Engineering Technology, A
English Language and Literature, A
Family and Consumer Sciences/Human Sciences, A
Fire Protection and Safety Technology/Technician, A
Geography, A
Geology/Earth Science, A
Health and Physical Education, A
Heating, Air Conditioning and Refrigeration Technology/Technician, A
Heating, Air Conditioning, Ventilation and Refrigeration Maintenance Technology/Technician, A
History, A
Humanities/Humanistic Studies, A
Industrial Production Technologies/Technicians, A
Information Technology, A
Interior Design, A
Kinesiology and Exercise Science, A
Landscaping and Groundskeeping, A
Liberal Arts and Sciences Studies and Humanities, A
Mathematics, A
Medical/Clinical Assistant, A
Music, A
Philosophy, A
Photographic and Film/Video Technology/Technician and Assistant, A
Photography, A
Physical Sciences, A
Physics, A
Political Science and Government, A
Prepress/Desktop Publishing and Digital Imaging Design, A
Radiologic Technology/Science - Radiographer, A
Real Estate, A
Respiratory Care Therapy/Therapist, A
Sales, Distribution and Marketing Operations, A
Sign Language Interpretation and Translation, A
Small Business Administration/Management, A
Social Sciences, A
Sociology, A
Teacher Assistant/Aide, A
Visual and Performing Arts, A
Welding Technology/Welder, A

ANTIOCH UNIVERSITY LOS ANGELES

Business Administration and Management, B
Clinical Psychology, M
Criminal Justice/Safety Studies, B
Design and Applied Arts, B
Education, M
Human Resources Development, M
Liberal Arts and Sciences Studies and Humanities, B
Management, M
Non-Profit/Public/Organizational Management, M
Organizational Management, M
Psychology, M
Sustainable Development, M
Urban Studies/Affairs, B
Writing, MO

ANTIOCH UNIVERSITY SANTA BARBARA

Business Administration, Management and Operations, M
Clinical Psychology, MD
Education, M
Liberal Arts and Sciences Studies and Humanities, B
Management Strategy and Policy, M
Non-Profit/Public/Organizational Management, M

APT COLLEGE

Electrical and Power Transmission Installation/Installer, A
Telecommunications Technology/Technician, A

ARGOSY UNIVERSITY, INLAND EMPIRE

Accounting, D
Business Administration and Management, AB
Business Administration, Management and Operations, MD

Clinical Psychology, M
Community College Education, D
Counseling Psychology, D
Criminal Justice/Law Enforcement Administration, B
Education, MD
Educational Administration and Supervision, D
Educational Leadership and Administration, MD
Elementary Education and Teaching, D
Finance and Banking, M
Forensic Psychology, M
Health Services Administration, M
Health/Health Care Administration/Management, B
Higher Education/Higher Education Administration, D
Industrial and Organizational Psychology, M
Information Technology, AB
International Business/Trade/Commerce, MD
Liberal Arts and Sciences Studies and Humanities, B
Management, MD
Management Information Systems and Services, MD
Marketing, MD
Marriage and Family Therapy/Counseling, M
Organizational Management, D
Psychology, ABMD
Public Administration, M
Public Health, M
Secondary Education and Teaching, D
Sport Psychology, M
Sustainability Management, MD

ARGOSY UNIVERSITY, LOS ANGELES

Accounting, D
Business Administration and Management, AB
Business Administration, Management and Operations, MD
Clinical Psychology, M
Community College Education, D
Counseling Psychology, MD
Criminal Justice/Law Enforcement Administration, B
Education, MD
Educational Administration and Supervision, D
Educational Leadership and Administration, MD
Elementary Education and Teaching, D
Finance and Banking, M
Forensic Psychology, M
Health Services Administration, M
Health/Health Care Administration/Management, B
Higher Education/Higher Education Administration, D
Information Technology, AB
International Business/Trade/Commerce, MD
Liberal Arts and Sciences Studies and Humanities, B
Management, M
Management Information Systems and Services, MD
Marketing, MD
Marriage and Family Therapy/Counseling, M
Organizational Management, D
Psychology, BMD
Public Administration, M
Public Health, M
Secondary Education and Teaching, D
Sustainability Management, M

ARGOSY UNIVERSITY, ORANGE COUNTY

Accounting, DO
Business Administration and Management, AB
Business Administration, Management and Operations, MDO
Clinical Psychology, MD
Community College Education, D
Counseling Psychology, MD
Criminal Justice/Law Enforcement Administration, B
Education, MD
Educational Administration and Supervision, D
Educational Leadership and Administration, MD
Educational Media/Instructional Technology, D
Elementary Education and Teaching, D
Finance and Banking, MO
Forensic Psychology, M
Health Services Administration, MO
Health/Health Care Administration/Management, B

Higher Education/Higher Education Administration, D
Information Technology, AB
International Business/Trade/Commerce, MDO
Liberal Arts and Sciences Studies and Humanities, B
Management, MDO
Management Information Systems and Services, MDO
Marketing, MDO
Marriage and Family Therapy/Counseling, M
Organizational Management, D
Psychology, ABMD
Public Administration, MO
Public Health, M
Secondary Education and Teaching, D
Sport Psychology, M
Sustainability Management, MD

ARGOSY UNIVERSITY, SAN DIEGO

Accounting, D
Business Administration and Management, AB
Business Administration, Management and Operations, MD
Clinical Psychology, M
Community College Education, D
Counseling Psychology, MD
Criminal Justice/Law Enforcement Administration, B
Education, MD
Educational Administration and Supervision, D
Educational Leadership and Administration, MD
Elementary Education and Teaching, D
Finance and Banking, M
Forensic Psychology, M
Health/Health Care Administration/Management, B
Higher Education/Higher Education Administration, D
Information Technology, AB
International Business/Trade/Commerce, MD
Liberal Arts and Sciences Studies and Humanities, B
Management, MD
Management Information Systems and Services, MD
Marketing, MD
Marriage and Family Therapy/Counseling, M
Organizational Management, D
Psychology, ABMD
Public Administration, M
Public Health, M
Secondary Education and Teaching, D

ARGOSY UNIVERSITY, SAN FRANCISCO BAY AREA

Accounting, D
Business Administration and Management, AB
Business Administration, Management and Operations, MD
Clinical Psychology, MD
Community College Education, D
Counseling Psychology, MD
Criminal Justice/Law Enforcement Administration, B
Education, MD
Educational Administration and Supervision, D
Educational Leadership and Administration, MD
Educational Media/Instructional Technology, D
Elementary Education and Teaching, D
Finance and Banking, M
Forensic Psychology, M
Health Services Administration, M
Health/Health Care Administration/Management, B
Higher Education/Higher Education Administration, D
Information Technology, AB
International Business/Trade/Commerce, MD
Liberal Arts and Sciences Studies and Humanities, B
Management, MD
Management Information Systems and Services, MD
Marketing, MD
Organizational Management, D
Psychology, ABMD
Public Administration, M
Public Health, M
Secondary Education and Teaching, D

Sport Psychology, M
Sustainability Management, MD

ART CENTER COLLEGE OF DESIGN

Advertising, B
Animation, Interactive Technology, Video Graphics and Special Effects, B
Automotive Engineering Technology/Technician, B
Cinematography and Film/Video Production, B
Commercial and Advertising Art, B
Computer Art and Design, M
Computer Software and Media Applications, B
Environmental Design/Architecture, BM
Film, Television, and Video Production, M
Fine Arts and Art Studies, BM
Graphic Design, B
Illustration, B
Industrial Design, BM
Interior Design, B
Intermedia/Multimedia, B
Photography, B
Transportation and Highway Engineering, M

THE ART INSTITUTE OF CALIFORNIA–HOLLYWOOD, A CAMPUS OF ARGOSY UNIVERSITY

Advertising, B
Animation, Interactive Technology, Video Graphics and Special Effects, B
Apparel and Accessories Marketing Operations, AB
Baking and Pastry Arts/Baker/Pastry Chef, A
CAD/CADD Drafting and/or Design Technology/Technician, B
Commercial Photography, AB
Computer Graphics, B
Culinary Arts/Chef Training, A
Design and Applied Arts, B
Fashion/Apparel Design, AB
Graphic Design, A
Industrial Design, B
Interior Design, B
Recording Arts Technology/Technician, AB
Restaurant, Culinary, and Catering Management/Manager, B
Web Page, Digital/Multimedia and Information Resources Design, AB

THE ART INSTITUTE OF CALIFORNIA–INLAND EMPIRE, A CAMPUS OF ARGOSY UNIVERSITY

Advertising, B
Apparel and Accessories Marketing Operations, AB
Baking and Pastry Arts/Baker/Pastry Chef, A
CAD/CADD Drafting and/or Design Technology/Technician, B
Cinematography and Film/Video Production, B
Commercial Photography, AB
Culinary Arts/Chef Training, A
Digital Communication and Media/Multimedia, B
Fashion/Apparel Design, B
Graphic Design, AB
Interior Design, B
Recording Arts Technology/Technician, AB
Restaurant, Culinary, and Catering Management/Manager, B
Web Page, Digital/Multimedia and Information Resources Design, B

THE ART INSTITUTE OF CALIFORNIA–LOS ANGELES, A CAMPUS OF ARGOSY UNIVERSITY

Advertising, B
Animation, Interactive Technology, Video Graphics and Special Effects, B
Apparel and Accessories Marketing Operations, B
Baking and Pastry Arts/Baker/Pastry Chef, A
CAD/CADD Drafting and/or Design Technology/Technician, B
Commercial Photography, AB
Culinary Arts/Chef Training, A
Fashion/Apparel Design, B
Graphic Design, A
Interior Design, B
Recording Arts Technology/Technician, AB

Restaurant, Culinary, and Catering
   Management/Manager, B
Web Page, Digital/Multimedia and Information Re-
   sources Design, AB

THE ART INSTITUTE OF CALIFORNIA–ORANGE COUNTY, A CAMPUS OF ARGOSY UNIVERSITY

Advertising, B
Animation, Interactive Technology, Video Graphics
   and Special Effects, B
Apparel and Accessories Marketing Operations, AB
Baking and Pastry Arts/Baker/Pastry Chef, A
CAD/CADD Drafting and/or Design
   Technology/Technician, B
Cinematography and Film/Video Production, B
Commercial Photography, AB
Computer Graphics, B
Culinary Arts/Chef Training, A
Digital Communication and Media/Multimedia, B
Fashion Merchandising, B
Fashion/Apparel Design, B
Graphic Design, A
Industrial Design, B
Interior Design, B
Photography, A
Restaurant, Culinary, and Catering
   Management/Manager, B
Web Page, Digital/Multimedia and Information Re-
   sources Design, AB

THE ART INSTITUTE OF CALIFORNIA–SACRAMENTO, A CAMPUS OF ARGOSY UNIVERSITY

Advertising, B
Animation, Interactive Technology, Video Graphics
   and Special Effects, B
Apparel and Accessories Marketing Operations, B
Baking and Pastry Arts/Baker/Pastry Chef, A
Cinematography and Film/Video Production, B
Computer Graphics, B
Culinary Arts/Chef Training, A
Fashion/Apparel Design, B
Graphic Design, A
Interior Design, B
Photography, A
Restaurant, Culinary, and Catering
   Management/Manager, B
Web Page, Digital/Multimedia and Information Re-
   sources Design, AB

THE ART INSTITUTE OF CALIFORNIA–SAN DIEGO, A CAMPUS OF ARGOSY UNIVERSITY

Advertising, AB
Apparel and Accessories Marketing Operations, B
Baking and Pastry Arts/Baker/Pastry Chef, A
CAD/CADD Drafting and/or Design
   Technology/Technician, B
Commercial Photography, B
Computer Graphics, B
Culinary Arts/Chef Training, A
Fashion/Apparel Design, B
Graphic Design, AB
Interior Design, B
Photography, A
Recording Arts Technology/Technician, AB
Restaurant, Culinary, and Catering
   Management/Manager, B
Web Page, Digital/Multimedia and Information Re-
   sources Design, B

THE ART INSTITUTE OF CALIFORNIA–SAN FRANCISCO, A CAMPUS OF ARGOSY UNIVERSITY

Advertising, B
Animation, Interactive Technology, Video Graphics
   and Special Effects, B
Baking and Pastry Arts/Baker/Pastry Chef, A
Cinematography and Film/Video Production, B
Commercial Photography, AB
Computer Art and Design, M

Computer Graphics, B
Culinary Arts/Chef Training, A
Fashion/Apparel Design, AB
Film, Television, and Video Production, M
Graphic Design, B
Interior Design, B
Recording Arts Technology/Technician, B
Restaurant, Culinary, and Catering
   Management/Manager, B
Web Page, Digital/Multimedia and Information Re-
   sources Design, AB

ASHFORD UNIVERSITY

Accounting, B
Athletic Training and Sports Medicine, B
Biology/Biological Sciences, B
Business Administration and Management, B
Business Teacher Education, B
Communication, Journalism and Related Pro-
   grams, B
Computer and Information Sciences, B
Criminal Justice/Safety Studies, B
CytoTechnology/Cytotechnologist, B
Education, B
Elementary Education and Teaching, B
English Language and Literature, B
General Studies, B
Health/Health Care Administration/Management, B
History, B
Human Services, B
Humanities/Humanistic Studies, B
Journalism, B
Junior High/Intermediate/Middle School Education
   and Teaching, B
Kindergarten/PreSchool Education and Teaching, B
Liberal Arts and Sciences Studies and Humani-
   ties, AB
Multi-/Interdisciplinary Studies, B
Music, B
Music Teacher Education, B
Pre-Law Studies, B
Pre-Medicine/Pre-Medical Studies, B
Psychology, B
Religion/Religious Studies, B
Science Teacher Education/General Science
   Teacher Education, B
Secondary Education and Teaching, B
Social Sciences, B
Visual and Performing Arts, B

AVIATION & ELECTRONIC SCHOOLS OF AMERICA

Computer Science, A

AZUSA PACIFIC UNIVERSITY

Accounting, B
Athletic Training and Sports Medicine, B
Bible/Biblical Studies, B
Biochemistry, B
Biology/Biological Sciences, B
Business Administration and Management, B
Business Administration, Management and Opera-
   tions, M
Chemistry, B
Clinical Psychology, MD
Communication Studies/Speech Communication
   and Rhetoric, B
Computer Science, B
Counselor Education/School Counseling and Guid-
   ance Services, M
Curriculum and Instruction, M
Design and Applied Arts, B
Divinity/Ministry (BD, MDiv.), B
Education, MDO
Educational Administration and Supervision, M
Educational Leadership and Administration, D
Educational Media/Instructional Technology, M
English Language and Literature, B
English as a Second Language, M
Entrepreneurship/Entrepreneurial Studies, M
Ethics, M
Finance and Banking, M
Fine Arts and Art Studies, M
Foundations and Philosophy of Education, M
Health Professions and Related Clinical Sciences, B

Higher Education/Higher Education Administra-
   tion, MD
History, B
Human Resources Development, M
Human Resources Management and Services, M
International Affairs, M
International Business/Trade/Commerce, M
International Relations and Affairs, B
Liberal Arts and Sciences Studies and Humani-
   ties, B
Library Science, MO
Management Information Systems and Services, B
Management Strategy and Policy, M
Marketing, M
Marketing/Marketing Management, B
Marriage and Family Therapy/Counseling, M
Mathematics, B
Multilingual and Multicultural Education, M
Music, BM
Music Teacher Education, M
Natural Sciences, B
Non-Profit/Public/Organizational Management, M
Nursing, MD
Nursing Education, D
Organizational Management, M
Pastoral Studies/Counseling, M
Philosophy, B
Physical Education Teaching and Coaching, BM
Physical Therapy/Therapist, D
Physics, B
Political Science and Government, B
Pre-Law Studies, B
Psychology, BMD
Public Administration, M
Religion/Religious Studies, B
Religious Education, M
School Psychology, M
Social Sciences, B
Social Work, BM
Sociology, B
Spanish Language and Literature, B
Special Education and Teaching, M
Student Personnel Services, M
Theology and Religious Vocations, MD
Theology/Theological Studies, B
Urban Studies/Affairs, M
Web Page, Digital/Multimedia and Information Re-
   sources Design, B

BAKERSFIELD COLLEGE

Accounting, A
Administrative Assistant and Secretarial Science, A
Agricultural Business and Management, A
Agriculture, A
Animal Sciences, A
Anthropology, A
Architectural Engineering Technology/Technician, A
Art Teacher Education, A
Art/Art Studies, General, A
Automobile/Automotive Mechanics
   Technology/Technician, A
Biology/Biological Sciences, A
Broadcast Journalism, A
Business Administration and Management, A
Carpentry/Carpenter, A
Chemistry, A
Child Development, A
Computer Science, A
Corrections, A
Cosmetology/Cosmetologist, A
Criminal Justice/Law Enforcement Administration, A
Criminal Justice/Police Science, A
Culinary Arts/Chef Training, A
Data Processing and Data Processing
   Technology/Technician, A
Dental Hygiene/Hygienist, A
Dietetics/Dieticians, A
Drafting and Design Technology/Technician, A
Drama and Dramatics/Theatre Arts, A
Economics, A
Electrical, Electronic and Communications Engineer-
   ing Technology/Technician, A
Emergency Medical Technology/Technician (EMT
   Paramedic), A
Engineering, A
English Language and Literature, A

Environmental Engineering Technology/Environmental Technology, A
Family and Consumer Economics and Related Services, A
Finance, A
Fire Science/Firefighting, A
Foods, Nutrition, and Wellness Studies, A
Forestry, A
French Language and Literature, A
Geography, A
Geology/Earth Science, A
German Language and Literature, A
History, A
Horticultural Science, A
Hotel/Motel Administration/Management, A
Human Services, A
Industrial Radiologic Technology/Technician, A
Industrial Technology/Technician, A
Information Science/Studies, A
Interior Design, A
Journalism, A
Legal Administrative Assistant/Secretary, A
Liberal Arts and Sciences Studies and Humanities, A
Machine Tool Technology/Machinist, A
Marketing/Marketing Management, A
Mathematics, A
Music, A
Ornamental Horticulture, A
Parks, Recreation, Leisure and Fitness Studies, A
Petroleum Technology/Technician, A
Philosophy, A
Photography, A
Physical Education Teaching and Coaching, A
Physics, A
Pipefitting/Pipefitter and Sprinkler Fitter, A
Political Science and Government, A
Psychology, A
Real Estate, A
Sociology, A
Spanish Language and Literature, A
Survey Technology/Surveying, A
Welding Technology/Welder, A
Wood Science and Wood Products/Pulp and Paper Technology, A

BARSTOW COMMUNITY COLLEGE

Accounting Technology/Technician and Bookkeeping, A
Automobile/Automotive Mechanics Technology/Technician, A
Biological and Physical Sciences, A
Business Administration and Management, A
Business/Commerce, A
Child Care Provider/Assistant, A
Cosmetology/Cosmetologist, A
Criminal Justice/Police Science, A
Diesel Mechanics Technology/Technician, A
Electrical/Electronics Equipment Installation and Repair, A
Electrician, A
Emergency Medical Technology/Technician (EMT Paramedic), A
Fire Science/Firefighting, A
Health and Physical Education, A
Humanities/Humanistic Studies, A
Information Technology, A
Medical/Clinical Assistant, A
Photography, A
Social Sciences, A
Welding Technology/Welder, A

BERGIN UNIVERSITY OF CANINE STUDIES

Animal Sciences, M

BERKELEY CITY COLLEGE

Accounting, A
Accounting and Business/Management, A
American Sign Language (ASL), A
Art/Art Studies, General, A
Biology Technician/BioTechnology Laboratory Technician, A
Business Administration and Management, A
Business Administration, Management and Operations, A

Business, Management, Marketing, and Related Support Services, A
Business/Commerce, A
Computer Graphics, A
Computer Software and Media Applications, A
Computer and Information Sciences, A
Computer and Information Systems Security, A
Data Entry/Microcomputer Applications, A
English Language and Literature, A
Fine/Studio Arts, A
General Studies, A
Liberal Arts and Sciences Studies and Humanities, A
Medical Administrative Assistant/Secretary, A
Office Management and Supervision, A
Psychology, A
Public Health, A
Public Health Education and Promotion, A
Sign Language Interpretation and Translation, A
Social Sciences, A
Social Work, A
Sociology, A
Spanish Language and Literature, A
Web Page, Digital/Multimedia and Information Resources Design, A

BETHESDA UNIVERSITY

Bible/Biblical Studies, B
Design and Visual Communications, B
Divinity/Ministry (BD, MDiv.), B
Early Childhood Education and Teaching, B
Information Technology, B
Metal and Jewelry Arts, B
Missions/Missionary Studies and Missiology, B
Music, B
Pastoral Studies/Counseling, B
Religion/Religious Studies, M
Religious Education, B
Sacred Music, M
Theology and Religious Vocations, M

BIOLA UNIVERSITY

Accounting, B
Anthropology, BM
Applied Mathematics, B
Archeology, B
Art/Art Studies, General, B
Audiology/Audiologist and Hearing Sciences, B
Audiology/Audiologist and Speech-Language Pathology/Pathologist, B
Bible/Biblical Studies, B
Biochemistry, B
Biological and Biomedical Sciences, B
Biology Teacher Education, B
Biology/Biological Sciences, B
Broadcast Journalism, B
Business Administration and Management, B
Business Administration, Management and Operations, M
Chemistry, B
Cinematography and Film/Video Production, B
Clinical Psychology, D
Commercial and Advertising Art, B
Communication Disorders, B
Communication Studies/Speech Communication and Rhetoric, B
Communication and Media Studies, B
Computer Science, B
Criminology, B
Cultural Studies, MDO
Curriculum and Instruction, O
Design and Visual Communications, B
Divinity/Ministry (BD, MDiv.), B
Drama and Dramatics/Theatre Arts, B
Drawing, B
Early Childhood Education and Teaching, M
Education, BMO
Elementary Education and Teaching, B
Engineering, B
Engineering Physics, B
English Language and Literature, B
English as a Second Language, MO
Environmental Sciences, B
Exercise Physiology, B
Film/Cinema Studies, B
Fine/Studio Arts, B

Health Services/Allied Health/Health Sciences, B
Health and Physical Education, B
History, B
History Teacher Education, B
Humanities/Humanistic Studies, B
Intercultural/Multicultural and Diversity Studies, B
Intermedia/Multimedia, B
International Business/Trade/Commerce, B
Jewish/Judaic Studies, MO
Journalism, B
Kinesiology and Exercise Science, B
Liberal Arts and Sciences Studies and Humanities, B
Linguistics, BMO
Management Information Systems and Services, B
Marketing/Marketing Management, B
Mathematics, B
Mathematics Teacher Education, B
Mathematics and Computer Science, B
Missions/Missionary Studies and Missiology, BM
Music, B
Music Performance, B
Music Teacher Education, B
Music Theory and Composition, B
Painting, B
Parks, Recreation, Leisure and Fitness Studies, B
Pastoral Studies/Counseling, BMO
Philosophy, B
Physical Education Teaching and Coaching, B
Physical Sciences, B
Physical Therapy/Therapist, B
Physics, B
Political Science and Government, B
Pre-Law Studies, B
Pre-Nursing Studies, B
Psychology, BD
Public Administration, B
Public Relations/Image Management, B
Radio and Television, B
Religion/Religious Studies, BMO
Religious Education, BMD
Science Teacher Education/General Science Teacher Education, BMO
Sculpture, B
Secondary Education and Teaching, B
Social Science Teacher Education, B
Social Sciences, B
Social Studies Teacher Education, B
Social Work, B
Sociology, B
Spanish Language and Literature, B
Special Education and Teaching, MO
Speech-Language Pathology/Pathologist, B
Teacher Education, Multiple Levels, A
Technical Theatre/Theatre Design and Technology, B
Theology and Religious Vocations, MDO
Theology/Theological Studies, B
Voice and Opera, B

BRANDMAN UNIVERSITY

Business Administration and Management, B
Business Administration, Management and Operations, M
Counseling Psychology, M
Counselor Education/School Counseling and Guidance Services, M
Criminal Justice/Safety Studies, B
Early Childhood Education and Teaching, B
Education, M
Educational Leadership and Administration, M
Emergency Management, M
Foods, Nutrition, and Wellness Studies, B
General Studies, A
Health Communication, M
Health Services Administration, M
Human Resources Management and Services, M
Information Technology, B
Law and Legal Studies, B
Liberal Arts and Sciences Studies and Humanities, B
Marriage and Family Therapy/Counseling, M
Organizational Management, M
Psychology, BM
Public Administration, M
Social Sciences, B

Social Work, B
Sociology, B
Special Education and Teaching, M

BRIGHTWOOD COLLEGE, BAKERSFIELD CAMPUS

Criminal Justice/Law Enforcement Administration, A

BRIGHTWOOD COLLEGE, CHULA VISTA CAMPUS

Criminal Justice/Law Enforcement Administration, A

BRIGHTWOOD COLLEGE, FRESNO CAMPUS

Criminal Justice/Law Enforcement Administration, A

BRIGHTWOOD COLLEGE, MODESTO CAMPUS

Criminal Justice/Law Enforcement Administration, A
Respiratory Therapy Technician/Assistant, A

BRIGHTWOOD COLLEGE, NORTH HOLLYWOOD CAMPUS

Medical Radiologic Technology/Science - Radiation Therapist, A

BRIGHTWOOD COLLEGE, PALM SPRINGS CAMPUS

Criminal Justice/Law Enforcement Administration, A

BRIGHTWOOD COLLEGE, RIVERSIDE CAMPUS

Criminal Justice/Law Enforcement Administration, A
Health Information/Medical Records Technology/Technician, A

BRIGHTWOOD COLLEGE, SACRAMENTO CAMPUS

Criminal Justice/Law Enforcement Administration, A

BRIGHTWOOD COLLEGE, SAN DIEGO CAMPUS

Criminal Justice/Law Enforcement Administration, A
Health Information/Medical Records Technology/Technician, A

BRIGHTWOOD COLLEGE, VISTA CAMPUS

Criminal Justice/Law Enforcement Administration, A

BRISTOL UNIVERSITY

Business Administration, Management and Operations, M
International Business/Trade/Commerce, M
Marketing, M
Sport and Fitness Administration/Management, M

BROOKS INSTITUTE

Cinematography and Film/Video Production, B
Graphic Design, B
Photography, BM
Photojournalism, AB

BRYAN COLLEGE

Court Reporting/Court Reporter, A
Health and Physical Education/Fitness, A
Massage Therapy/Therapeutic Massage, A
Medical Insurance Coding Specialist/Coder, A

BUTTE COLLEGE

Accounting, A
Administrative Assistant and Secretarial Science, A
Agribusiness, A
Agricultural Mechanics and Equipment/Machine Technology, A
Agriculture, A
Art/Art Studies, General, A
Automobile/Automotive Mechanics Technology/Technician, A
Biology/Biological Sciences, A
Business Administration and Management, A
Ceramic Arts and Ceramics, A

Chemistry, A
Child Development, A
Computer Science, A
Cosmetology/Cosmetologist, A
Criminal Justice/Police Science, A
Data Entry/Microcomputer Applications, A
Digital Communication and Media/Multimedia, A
Drafting and Design Technology/Technician, A
Emergency Medical Technology/Technician (EMT Paramedic), A
Engineering, A
Engineering Technologies/Technicians, A
English Language and Literature, A
Environmental Sciences, A
Family and Consumer Sciences/Human Sciences, A
Fire Science/Firefighting, A
Foods, Nutrition, and Wellness Studies, A
Graphic Design, A
Hazardous Materials Management and Waste Technology/Technician, A
Health and Physical Education, A
Horticultural Science, A
Information Technology, A
Interior Design, A
Journalism, A
Legal Administrative Assistant/Secretary, A
Liberal Arts and Sciences Studies and Humanities, A
Mathematics, A
Medical Administrative Assistant/Secretary, A
Natural Resources Management/Development and Policy, A
Parks, Recreation and Leisure Facilities Management, A
Photography, A
Physical Sciences, A
Physics, A
Radio and Television, A
Real Estate, A
Respiratory Care Therapy/Therapist, A
Retailing and Retail Operations, A
Sales, Distribution and Marketing Operations, A
Small Business Administration/Management, A
Social Sciences, A
Substance Abuse/Addiction Counseling, A
System Administration/Administrator, A
Tourism and Travel Services Management, A
Welding Technology/Welder, A

CABRILLO COLLEGE

Accounting Technology/Technician and Bookkeeping, A
Administrative Assistant and Secretarial Science, A
American/United States Studies/Civilization, A
Anthropology, A
Applied Horticulture/Horticultural Operations, A
Archeology, A
Area Studies, A
Art/Art Studies, General, A
Astronomy, A
Biological and Physical Sciences, A
Biology/Biological Sciences, A
Building/Construction Site Management/Manager, A
Building/Home/Construction Inspection/Inspector, A
Business/Commerce, A
Chemistry, A
Child Care Provider/Assistant, A
Communication Studies/Speech Communication and Rhetoric, A
Computer Science, A
Computer Systems Networking and Telecommunications, A
Cooking and Related Culinary Arts, A
Corrections, A
Criminal Justice/Police Science, A
Dance, A
Dental Hygiene/Hygienist, A
Drama and Dramatics/Theatre Arts, A
Economics, A
Engineering, A
Engineering Technology, A
English Language and Literature, A
Ethnic, Cultural Minority, and Gender Studies, A
Fire Science/Firefighting, A
French Language and Literature, A
Geography, A

Geology/Earth Science, A
German Language and Literature, A
Health Teacher Education, A
Health and Physical Education, A
History, A
Human Services, A
Humanities/Humanistic Studies, A
International Relations and Affairs, A
Journalism, A
Landscaping and Groundskeeping, A
Mathematics, A
Medical Administrative Assistant/Secretary, A
Medical/Clinical Assistant, A
Music, A
Philosophy, A
Photography, A
Physics, A
Political Science and Government, A
Prepress/Desktop Publishing and Digital Imaging Design, A
Psychology, A
Radiologic Technology/Science - Radiographer, A
Real Estate, A
Social Sciences, A
Sociology, A
Spanish Language and Literature, A
System Administration/Administrator, A
Web Page, Digital/Multimedia and Information Resources Design, A
Women's Studies, A

CALIFORNIA BAPTIST UNIVERSITY

Accounting, BM
Actuarial Science, B
Adult and Continuing Education and Teaching, M
Advertising and Public Relations, M
Air Transportation, B
Airline/Commercial/Professional Pilot and Flight Crew, B
Anthropology, B
Architecture, BM
Athletic Training and Sports Medicine, M
Aviation/Airway Management and Operations, B
Behavioral Sciences, B
Bible/Biblical Studies, B
Biochemistry, Biophysics and Molecular Biology, B
Biology/Biological Sciences, B
Biomedical/Medical Engineering, B
Business Administration, Management and Operations, M
Business/Commerce, B
Chemical Engineering, B
Chemistry, B
Christian Studies, B
Civil Engineering, B
Communication Disorders, B
Communication Studies/Speech Communication and Rhetoric, B
Communication and Media Studies, M
Computer Engineering, B
Computer Science, B
Computer Software Engineering, B
Construction Engineering Technology/Technician, B
Construction Management, M
Counseling Psychology, M
Counselor Education/School Counseling and Guidance Services, M
Criminal Justice/Law Enforcement Administration, B
Curriculum and Instruction, M
Disability Studies, M
Distance Education Development, M
Drama and Dramatics/Theatre Arts, B
Early Childhood Education and Teaching, B
Education, M
Educational Leadership and Administration, M
Educational Media/Instructional Technology, M
Engineering, B
English, M
English Education, M
English Language and Literature, B
English as a Second Language, M
Entrepreneurship/Entrepreneurial Studies, M
Environmental Sciences, B
Exercise Physiology, B
Exercise and Sports Science, M
Film/Cinema Studies, B

Forensic Psychology, M
Health Promotion, M
Health Services Administration, M
Health Services/Allied Health/Health Sciences, B
Health/Health Care Administration/Management, B
Higher Education/Higher Education Administration, M
History, B
Industrial Engineering, B
Information Technology, B
International Public Health/International Health, B
International and Comparative Education, M
International/Global Studies, B
Journalism, B
Kinesiology and Exercise Science, B
Liberal Arts and Sciences Studies and Humanities, B
Management, M
Marketing/Marketing Management, B
Mathematics, B
Mathematics Teacher Education, B
Mechanical Engineering, B
Missions/Missionary Studies and Missiology, B
Multi-/Interdisciplinary Studies, B
Music, BM
Music Performance, B
Music Teacher Education, BM
Music Theory and Composition, B
Non-Profit/Public/Organizational Management, M
Nursing, MD
Nursing - Adult, M
Nursing - Advanced Practice, M
Nursing Education, M
Nutritional Sciences, BM
Organizational Management, M
Pastoral Studies/Counseling, M
Performance, M
Philosophy, B
Photography, B
Physical Education Teaching and Coaching, M
Piano and Organ, B
Political Science and Government, B
Prepress/Desktop Publishing and Digital Imaging Design, B
Psychology, B
Public Administration, BM
Public Health, M
Public Health Education and Promotion, B
Reading Teacher Education, M
School Psychology, M
Science Teacher Education/General Science Teacher Education, M
Sociology, B
Spanish Language and Literature, B
Special Education and Teaching, M
Sport and Fitness Administration/Management, M
Statistics, B
Visual and Performing Arts, B
Vocational and Technical Education, M
Voice and Opera, B

CALIFORNIA CHRISTIAN COLLEGE

General Studies, A
Theological and Ministerial Studies, AB

CALIFORNIA COAST UNIVERSITY

Business Administration and Management, AB
Business Administration, Management and Operations, M
Criminal Justice/Law Enforcement Administration, AB
Criminology, M
Curriculum and Instruction, M
Education, MD
Educational Administration and Supervision, MD
Educational Psychology, D
General Studies, AB
Health Services Administration, M
Health/Health Care Administration/Management, AB
Human Resources Management and Services, M
Human Resources Management/Personnel Administration, B
Management, M
Management Science, B
Marketing, M
Marketing/Marketing Management, AB

Organizational Management, D
Psychology, ABM

CALIFORNIA COLLEGE OF THE ARTS

Animation, Interactive Technology, Video Graphics and Special Effects, B
Architecture, BM
Art/Art Studies, General, B
Ceramic Arts and Ceramics, BM
Commercial and Advertising Art, B
Computer Art and Design, M
Crafts, M
Design and Applied Arts, BM
Design and Visual Communications, B
Digital Communication and Media/Multimedia, B
Drawing, B
Fashion/Apparel Design, B
Fiber, Textile and Weaving Arts, B
Film, Television, and Video Production, M
Film, Television, and Video Theory and Criticism, M
Film/Cinema Studies, B
Finance and Banking, M
Fine Arts and Art Studies, M
Fine/Studio Arts, B
Graphic Design, M
Illustration, B
Industrial Design, BM
Interdisciplinary Studies, M
Interior Architecture, B
Jewelry/Metalsmithing, M
Media Studies, M
Metal and Jewelry Arts, B
Museology/Museum Studies, M
Organizational Management, M
Painting, BM
Photography, BM
Printmaking, BM
Sculpture, BM
Textile Design, M
Writing, M

CALIFORNIA COLLEGE SAN DIEGO

Accounting, B
Business Administration and Management, B
Business, Management, Marketing, and Related Support Services, A
Computer Programming/Programmer, A
Computer Science, B
Computer Technology/Computer Systems Technology, A
Health/Health Care Administration/Management, B
Medical/Clinical Assistant, A
Respiratory Therapy Technician/Assistant, AB

CALIFORNIA INSTITUTE OF THE ARTS

Applied Arts and Design, MO
Cinematography and Film/Video Production, B
Composition, MO
Dance, BMO
Design and Visual Communications, B
Directing and Theatrical Production, B
Film, Television, and Video Production, MO
Fine Arts and Art Studies, MO
Fine/Studio Arts, B
Graphic Design, MO
Music, MO
Music Performance, B
Music Theory and Composition, B
Performance, MO
Photography, BMO
Technical Theatre/Theatre Design and Technology, B
Theater, MO
Visual and Performing Arts, B
Writing, MO

CALIFORNIA INSTITUTE OF INTEGRAL STUDIES

Art Therapy/Therapist, M
Asian Studies/Civilization, MD
Clinical Psychology, D
Community Psychology, M
Counseling Psychology, M
Cultural Anthropology, MD

Drama Therapy, M
Ecology, MD
Health Psychology, M
Humanities/Humanistic Studies, MD
Interdisciplinary Studies, M
Multi-/Interdisciplinary Studies, B
Philosophy, MD
Psychology, MD
Religion/Religious Studies, MD
Theology and Religious Vocations, M
Women's Studies, MD
Writing, M

CALIFORNIA INSTITUTE OF TECHNOLOGY

Aerospace, Aeronautical and Astronautical Engineering, MDO
Applied Mathematics, MD
Applied Physics, MD
Astronomy, D
Astrophysics, B
Biochemistry, MD
Bioengineering, MD
Biological and Biomedical Sciences, D
Biology/Biological Sciences, B
Biomedical/Medical Engineering, B
Biophysics, D
Business/Managerial Economics, B
Cell Biology and Anatomy, D
Chemical Engineering, BMD
Chemistry, BMD
Civil Engineering, MDO
Computational Mathematics, B
Computational Sciences, MD
Computer Engineering, B
Computer Science, MD
Developmental Biology and Embryology, D
Economics, B
Electrical Engineering, MDO
Electrical, Electronics and Communications Engineering, B
Engineering, B
Engineering Physics, B
Engineering and Applied Sciences, MDO
English Language and Literature, B
Environmental Engineering Technology/Environmental Technology, MD
Environmental Sciences, MD
Genetics, D
Geochemistry, BMD
Geology/Earth Science, BMD
Geophysics and Seismology, BMD
History, B
History and Philosophy of Science and Technology, B
Immunology, D
Materials Sciences, MD
Mathematics, BD
Mechanical Engineering, BMDO
Mechanics, MD
Molecular Biology, D
Molecular Biophysics, MD
Multi-/Interdisciplinary Studies, B
Neurobiology and Neurophysiology, D
Neuroscience, MD
Philosophy, B
Physics, BD
Planetary Astronomy and Science, BMD
Political Science and Government, B
Social Sciences, MD
Systems Engineering, MD

CALIFORNIA INTERCONTINENTAL UNIVERSITY

Business Administration and Management, B
Business Administration, Management and Operations, MD
Entertainment Management, M
Entrepreneurship/Entrepreneurial Studies, D
Finance and Banking, M
Health Services Administration, MD
Human Resources Management and Services, M
Information Technology, M
International Business/Trade/Commerce, MD
Management Information Systems and Services, BMD

Marketing, M
Organizational Management, M
Project Management, M
Quality Management, M

CALIFORNIA LUTHERAN UNIVERSITY

Accounting, B
Art Teacher Education, B
Art/Art Studies, General, B
Biochemistry, B
Biology/Biological Sciences, B
Business Administration and Management, B
Business Administration, Management and Operations, MO
Chemistry, B
Clinical Psychology, MD
Communication, Journalism and Related Programs, B
Computer Science, B
Computer and Information Sciences, B
Counselor Education/School Counseling and Guidance Services, M
Criminal Justice/Law Enforcement Administration, B
Digital Communication and Media/Multimedia, B
Drama and Dramatics/Theatre Arts, B
Economics, BM
Education, MD
Educational Administration and Supervision, M
Educational Leadership and Administration, MD
Elementary Education and Teaching, D
English Language and Literature, B
Entrepreneurship/Entrepreneurial Studies, MO
Environmental Sciences, B
Finance and Banking, MO
French Language Teacher Education, B
French Language and Literature, B
Geology/Earth Science, B
German Language Teacher Education, B
German Language and Literature, B
Higher Education/Higher Education Administration, D
History, B
Information Science/Studies, B
International Business/Trade/Commerce, MO
International Relations and Affairs, B
Journalism, B
Kinesiology and Exercise Science, B
Liberal Arts and Sciences Studies and Humanities, B
Management Information Systems and Services, MO
Management of Technology, MO
Marketing, MO
Marketing/Marketing Management, B
Marriage and Family Therapy/Counseling, M
Mass Communication/Media Studies, B
Mathematics, B
Mathematics Teacher Education, B
Middle School Education, D
Molecular Biology, B
Multi-/Interdisciplinary Studies, B
Music, B
Music Teacher Education, B
Non-Profit/Public/Organizational Management, M
Organizational Behavior Studies, MO
Philosophy, B
Physical Education Teaching and Coaching, B
Physics, B
Political Science and Government, B
Psychology, BMD
Psychology Teacher Education, B
Public Administration, BM
Public Policy Analysis, M
Public Relations, Advertising, and Applied Communication, B
Public Relations/Image Management, B
Religion/Religious Studies, B
Science Teacher Education/General Science Teacher Education, B
Social Science Teacher Education, B
Social Sciences, B
Sociology, B
Spanish Language Teacher Education, B
Spanish Language and Literature, B
Special Education and Teaching, M

Theology and Religious Vocations, MDO

CALIFORNIA MARITIME ACADEMY

Business Administration and Management, B
Emergency Management, M
Engineering Management, M
Engineering Technologies/Technicians, B
Marine Maintenance/Fitter and Ship Repair Technology/Technician, B
Mechanical Engineering, B
Transportation/Transportation Management, M

CALIFORNIA MIRAMAR UNIVERSITY

Business Administration and Management, AB
Business Administration, Management and Operations, M
Management Strategy and Policy, M
Public Administration, B
Taxation, M
Telecommunications, M
Telecommunications Management, M

CALIFORNIA NATIONAL UNIVERSITY FOR ADVANCED STUDIES

Business Administration and Management, B
Business Administration, Management and Operations, M
Computer Science, B
Engineering, B
Engineering Management, M
Engineering and Applied Sciences, M
Quality Control Technology/Technician, B

CALIFORNIA POLYTECHNIC STATE UNIVERSITY, SAN LUIS OBISPO

Aerospace, Aeronautical and Astronautical Engineering, BM
Agribusiness, M
Agricultural Business and Management, B
Agricultural Communication/Journalism, B
Agricultural Education, M
Agricultural Mechanization, B
Agricultural Sciences, M
Agricultural Teacher Education, B
Agricultural/Biological Engineering and Bioengineering, B
Agronomy and Crop Science, B
Animal Sciences, B
Architectural Engineering, B
Architecture, BM
Biochemistry, BM
Biological and Biomedical Sciences, M
Biology/Biological Sciences, B
Biomedical/Medical Engineering, B
Business Administration and Management, B
Business Administration, Management and Operations, M
Chemistry, BM
City/Urban, Community and Regional Planning, B
Civil Engineering, BM
Communication Studies/Speech Communication and Rhetoric, B
Computer Engineering, B
Computer Science, BM
Computer Systems Analysis/Analyst, B
Dairy Science, B
Dietetics/Dieticians, B
Drama and Dramatics/Theatre Arts, B
Economics, B
Education, M
Electrical Engineering, M
Electrical, Electronics and Communications Engineering, B
Engineering Science, B
Engineering and Applied Sciences, M
English, M
English Language and Literature, B
Environmental Engineering Technology/Environmental Technology, M
Environmental/Environmental Health Engineering, B
Ethnic, Cultural Minority, and Gender Studies, B
Fine/Studio Arts, B
Food Science, B
Foreign Languages and Literatures, B
Forestry, BM

Geology/Earth Science, B
Graphic Communications, B
Health and Physical Education, B
History, BM
Industrial Engineering, B
Industrial Technology/Technician, B
Industrial and Manufacturing Management, M
Industrial/Management Engineering, M
Journalism, B
Kindergarten/PreSchool Education and Teaching, B
Kinesiology and Movement Studies, M
Landscape Architecture, B
Liberal Arts and Sciences Studies and Humanities, B
Manufacturing Engineering, B
Materials Engineering, B
Mathematics, BM
Mechanical Engineering, BM
Medical Microbiology and Bacteriology, B
Multi-/Interdisciplinary Studies, B
Music, B
Natural Resources Management/Development and Policy, M
Natural Resources and Conservation, B
Parks, Recreation, Leisure and Fitness Studies, B
Philosophy, B
Physics, B
Political Science and Government, BM
Polymer/Plastics Engineering, M
Psychology, BM
Social Sciences, B
Sociology, B
Soil Science and Agronomy, B
Statistics, B
Taxation, M
Urban and Regional Planning, M

CALIFORNIA STATE POLYTECHNIC UNIVERSITY, POMONA

Accounting, M
Aerospace, Aeronautical and Astronautical Engineering, BM
Agricultural Business and Management, B
Agricultural Sciences, M
Agricultural Teacher Education, B
American/United States Studies/Civilization, B
Animal Sciences, B
Anthropology, B
Apparel and Textiles, B
Applied Mathematics, M
Architecture, BM
Art History, Criticism and Conservation, B
Art/Art Studies, General, B
BioTechnology, BM
Biological and Biomedical Sciences, M
Biology/Biological Sciences, B
Business Administration and Management, B
Business Administration, Management and Operations, M
Chemical Engineering, B
Chemistry, BM
City/Urban, Community and Regional Planning, B
Civil Engineering, BM
Communication Studies/Speech Communication and Rhetoric, B
Computer Engineering, B
Computer Science, BM
Construction Engineering Technology/Technician, B
Curriculum and Instruction, M
Dietetics/Dieticians, B
Drama and Dramatics/Theatre Arts, B
Economics, BM
Education, B
Educational Leadership and Administration, MD
Educational Media/Instructional Technology, M
Electrical Engineering, B
Electrical, Electronic and Communications Engineering Technology/Technician, B
Electrical, Electronics and Communications Engineering, B
Engineering, B
Engineering Management, M
Engineering Technology, B
English, M
English Language and Literature, B
Environmental Biology, B

Environmental Sciences, M
Ethnic, Cultural Minority, and Gender Studies, B
Food Science, B
Geography, B
Geology/Earth Science, BM
Graphic Design, B
Health and Physical Education, B
History, BM
Hospitality Administration/Management, BM
Humanities/Humanistic Studies, B
Industrial Engineering, B
Interior Design, M
Kinesiology and Movement Studies, M
Landscape Architecture, BM
Liberal Arts and Sciences Studies and Humanities, B
Management Information Systems and Services, M
Manufacturing Engineering, B
Mathematics, BM
Mechanical Engineering, BM
Music, B
Philosophy, B
Physics, B
Plant Protection and Integrated Pest Management, B
Political Science and Government, B
Psychology, BM
Public Administration, M
Science, Technology and Society, B
Sociology, B
Spanish Language and Literature, B
Special Education and Teaching, M
Urban and Regional Planning, M

CALIFORNIA STATE UNIVERSITY, BAKERSFIELD

Anthropology, BM
Art/Art Studies, General, B
Biological and Biomedical Sciences, M
Biology/Biological Sciences, B
Business Administration and Management, B
Business Administration, Management and Operations, M
Chemistry, B
Computer Science, B
Counseling Psychology, M
Counselor Education/School Counseling and Guidance Services, M
Criminal Justice/Law Enforcement Administration, B
Curriculum and Instruction, M
Drama and Dramatics/Theatre Arts, B
Economics, B
Education, M
Educational Administration and Supervision, M
English, M
English Language and Literature, B
Finance, B
Geology/Earth Science, BM
Health Services Administration, M
History, BM
Hydrology and Water Resources Science, M
Interdisciplinary Studies, M
Land Use Planning and Management/Development, B
Liberal Arts and Sciences Studies and Humanities, B
Mass Communication/Media Studies, B
Mathematics, B
Mathematics Teacher Education, M
Middle School Education, M
Music, B
Philosophy, B
Physical Education Teaching and Coaching, B
Physics, B
Political Science and Government, B
Psychology, B
Public Administration, BM
Religion/Religious Studies, B
Science Teacher Education/General Science Teacher Education, M
Secondary Education and Teaching, M
Social Work, M
Sociology, BM
Spanish Language and Literature, BM
Special Education and Teaching, M

Student Personnel Services, M

CALIFORNIA STATE UNIVERSITY CHANNEL ISLANDS

Art/Art Studies, General, B
BioTechnology, M
Bioinformatics, M
Biology/Biological Sciences, B
Business Administration and Management, B
Business Administration, Management and Operations, M
Cell/Cellular and Molecular Biology, B
Chemistry, B
Computer Science, BM
Economics, B
Education, B
English Language and Literature, B
Environmental Sciences, B
History, B
Information Technology, B
Liberal Arts and Sciences Studies and Humanities, B
Mathematics, BM
Political Science and Government, B
Psychology, B
Sociology, B
Spanish Language and Literature, B
Visual and Performing Arts, B

CALIFORNIA STATE UNIVERSITY, CHICO

Agricultural Business and Management, B
Animal Sciences, B
Anthropology, BM
Applied Psychology, M
Art History, Criticism and Conservation, M
Art/Art Studies, General, B
Asian Studies/Civilization, B
Biochemistry, B
Biological and Biomedical Sciences, M
Biology/Biological Sciences, B
Botany/Plant Biology, M
Business Administration and Management, B
Business Administration, Management and Operations, M
Chemistry, B
Civil Engineering, B
Communication Disorders, BM
Communication and Media Studies, M
Computer Engineering, BM
Computer Graphics, B
Computer Science, BM
Construction Engineering Technology/Technician, B
Criminal Justice/Safety Studies, B
Curriculum and Instruction, M
Design and Visual Communications, B
Dietetics/Dieticians, B
Early Childhood Education and Teaching, B
Economics, B
Electrical Engineering, M
Electrical, Electronics and Communications Engineering, B
Engineering, B
Engineering and Applied Sciences, M
English, M
English Language and Literature, B
English as a Second Language, M
Environmental Policy, M
Environmental Policy and Resource Management, M
Environmental Sciences, M
Ethnic, Cultural Minority, and Gender Studies, B
Fine Arts and Art Studies, M
Fine/Studio Arts, B
French Language and Literature, B
Geography, B
Geological and Earth Sciences/Geosciences, B
Geology/Earth Science, BM
Geosciences, M
German Language and Literature, B
Health Services Administration, M
Health Services/Allied Health/Health Sciences, B
Health and Physical Education, B
History, B
Humanities/Humanistic Studies, B
Hydrogeology, M

Hydrology and Water Resources Science, M
Information Technology, B
International Relations and Affairs, B
Journalism, B
Kinesiology and Exercise Science, B
Kinesiology and Movement Studies, M
Latin American Studies, B
Liberal Arts and Sciences Studies and Humanities, B
Management, M
Marriage and Family Therapy/Counseling, M
Mathematics, B
Mathematics Teacher Education, M
Mechanical Engineering, B
Microbiology, B
Museology/Museum Studies, M
Music, B
Nursing, M
Nutritional Sciences, M
Parks, Recreation, Leisure and Fitness Studies, B
Philosophy, B
Physical Education Teaching and Coaching, B
Physics, B
Political Science and Government, BM
Psychology, BM
Public Administration, BM
Recreation and Park Management, M
Rural Planning and Studies, M
Social Sciences, M
Social Studies Teacher Education, M
Social Work, M
Special Education and Teaching, M
Urban and Regional Planning, M

CALIFORNIA STATE UNIVERSITY, DOMINGUEZ HILLS

Accounting, B
African-American/Black Studies, B
Anthropology, B
Applied Social Research, O
Art History, Criticism and Conservation, B
Art/Art Studies, General, B
Behavioral Sciences, B
Biochemistry, B
Bioinformatics, B
Biological and Biomedical Sciences, M
Biology/Biological Sciences, B
Business Administration and Management, B
Business Administration, Management and Operations, M
Business Teacher Education, B
Business, Management, Marketing, and Related Support Services, B
Business/Commerce, B
Cell/Cellular Biology and Histology, B
Chemistry, B
Clinical Laboratory Science/Medical Technology/Technologist, B
Clinical Psychology, M
Communication Studies/Speech Communication and Rhetoric, B
Computer Education, MO
Computer Science, BM
Computer and Information Sciences, B
Conflict Resolution and Mediation/Peace Studies, M
Counselor Education/School Counseling and Guidance Services, M
Criminal Justice/Safety Studies, B
Cultural Resource Management and Policy Analysis, B
Curriculum and Instruction, M
Digital Communication and Media/Multimedia, B
Drama and Dramatics/Theatre Arts, B
Early Childhood Education and Teaching, B
Ecology, B
Education, MO
Educational Leadership and Administration, M
Educational Media/Instructional Technology, MO
English, MO
English Language and Literature, B
English as a Second Language, O
Entrepreneurship/Entrepreneurial Studies, B
Environmental Sciences, M
Finance, B
Geography, B
Geological and Earth Sciences/Geosciences, B

Graphic Design, B
Health Services/Allied Health/Health Sciences, B
Health and Physical Education, B
Health/Health Care Administration/Management, B
Health/Medical Physics, B
Hispanic-American, Puerto Rican, and Mexican-American/Chicano Studies, B
History, B
Hospitality Administration/Management, B
Human Services, B
Humanities/Humanistic Studies, M
Information Technology, B
International Business/Trade/Commerce, B
International and Comparative Education, M
Journalism, B
Labor Studies, B
Liberal Arts and Sciences Studies and Humanities, B
Linguistics, B
Logistics and Materials Management, B
Marketing/Marketing Management, B
Marriage and Family Therapy/Counseling, M
Mathematics, B
Mathematics Teacher Education, M
Microbiology, B
Multi-/Interdisciplinary Studies, B
Multilingual and Multicultural Education, M
Music, B
Natural Sciences, B
Nursing, M
Occupational Therapy/Therapist, M
Operations Management and Supervision, B
Peace Studies and Conflict Resolution, B
Philosophy, B
Physical Education Teaching and Coaching, M
Physics, B
Political Science and Government, B
Pre-Law Studies, B
Psychology, BM
Public Administration, BM
Public Relations/Image Management, B
Quality Control Technology/Technician, B
Quality Management, M
Real Estate, B
Rhetoric, O
Science Teacher Education/General Science Teacher Education, M
Social Work, M
Sociology, BMO
Spanish Language and Literature, B
Special Education and Teaching, M
Urban Studies/Affairs, B

CALIFORNIA STATE UNIVERSITY, EAST BAY

Accounting, B
Actuarial Science, M
Advertising, B
African-American/Black Studies, B
American Indian/Native American Studies, B
Anthropology, BM
Applied Mathematics, BM
Applied Statistics, M
Art History, Criticism and Conservation, B
Asian-American Studies, B
Athletic Training and Sports Medicine, B
Audiology/Audiologist and Speech-Language Pathology/Pathologist, B
Biochemistry, BM
Biological and Biomedical Sciences, M
Biology/Biological Sciences, B
Biomedical Technology/Technician, B
Biostatistics, M
Broadcast Journalism, B
Business Administration and Management, B
Business Administration, Management and Operations, M
Business/Managerial Economics, B
Ceramic Arts and Ceramics, B
Chemistry, BM
Child Development, B
Child and Family Studies, M
Clinical/Medical Laboratory Technician, B
Commercial and Advertising Art, B
Communication Disorders, M
Communication and Media Studies, M

Community Psychology, M
Computer Graphics, B
Computer Science, BM
Computer Systems Networking and Telecommunications, B
Construction Management, M
Corrections, B
Counselor Education/School Counseling and Guidance Services, M
Criminal Justice/Law Enforcement Administration, B
Criminal Justice/Police Science, B
Dance, B
Drama and Dramatics/Theatre Arts, B
Drawing, B
Early Childhood Education and Teaching, M
Ecology, B
Economics, BM
Education, M
Educational Leadership and Administration, MD
Educational Media/Instructional Technology, M
Engineering Management, M
Engineering and Applied Sciences, M
English, M
English Language and Literature, B
English as a Second Language, M
Entrepreneurship/Entrepreneurial Studies, M
Environmental Sciences, M
Environmental Studies, B
Family and Consumer Sciences/Human Sciences, B
Finance, B
Finance and Banking, M
Fine/Studio Arts, B
French Language and Literature, B
Geography, BM
Geology/Earth Science, BM
Gerontology, B
Health Professions and Related Clinical Sciences, B
Health Services Administration, M
Hispanic-American, Puerto Rican, and Mexican-American/Chicano Studies, B
History, BM
Human Development and Family Studies, B
Human Resources Management and Services, M
Human Resources Management/Personnel Administration, B
Industrial Engineering, B
Industrial and Manufacturing Management, M
Industrial/Management Engineering, M
Information Science/Studies, B
Interdisciplinary Studies, M
International Business/Trade/Commerce, M
International Relations and Affairs, B
Internet and Interactive Multimedia, M
Journalism, B
Kinesiology and Exercise Science, B
Latin American Studies, B
Liberal Arts and Sciences Studies and Humanities, B
Management Information Systems and Services, BM
Management Strategy and Policy, M
Marine Sciences, M
Marketing, M
Marketing/Marketing Management, B
Marriage and Family Therapy/Counseling, M
Mass Communication/Media Studies, B
Mathematics, BM
Mathematics Teacher Education, M
Music, BM
Organizational Management, M
Painting, B
Parks, Recreation, Leisure and Fitness Studies, B
Philosophy, B
Photography, B
Physical Education Teaching and Coaching, BM
Physical Sciences, B
Physics, B
Political Science and Government, B
Pre-Dentistry Studies, B
Pre-Medicine/Pre-Medical Studies, B
Pre-Veterinary Studies, B
Printmaking, B
Psychology, B
Public Administration, BM
Public History, M
Public Policy Analysis, M

Public Relations/Image Management, B
Purchasing, Procurement/Acquisitions and Contracts Management, B
Reading Teacher Education, M
Real Estate, B
Recreation and Park Management, M
Religion/Religious Studies, B
School Psychology, M
Sculpture, B
Social Studies Teacher Education, M
Social Work, BM
Sociology, B
Spanish Language and Literature, B
Special Education and Teaching, M
Statistics, BM
Supply Chain Management, M
Telecommunications Technology/Technician, B
Therapeutic Recreation/Recreational Therapy, B
Travel and Tourism, B
Writing, M

CALIFORNIA STATE UNIVERSITY, FRESNO

Accounting, BM
African-American/Black Studies, B
Agricultural Business and Management, B
Agricultural Teacher Education, B
Agronomy and Crop Science, B
Animal Physiology, B
Animal Sciences, BM
Anthropology, B
Art/Art Studies, General, B
Audiology/Audiologist and Speech-Language Pathology/Pathologist, B
Biological and Biomedical Sciences, M
Biological and Physical Sciences, B
Biology/Biological Sciences, B
Business Administration and Management, B
Business Administration, Management and Operations, M
Cell/Cellular Biology and Histology, B
Chemistry, BM
Child Development, B
Civil Engineering, BM
Cognitive Sciences, B
Commercial and Advertising Art, B
Communication Disorders, BM
Communication Studies/Speech Communication and Rhetoric, B
Communication and Media Studies, M
Computer Engineering, B
Computer Science, BM
Computer and Information Sciences, B
Construction Engineering Technology/Technician, B
Construction Management, B
Counselor Education/School Counseling and Guidance Services, M
Criminal Justice/Safety Studies, B
Criminology, BM
Curriculum and Instruction, M
Dance, B
Design and Applied Arts, M
Dietetics/Dieticians, B
Drama and Dramatics/Theatre Arts, B
Early Childhood Education and Teaching, M
Ecology, B
Economics, B
Education, MD
Educational Administration and Supervision, M
Educational Leadership and Administration, D
Electrical Engineering, M
Electrical, Electronics and Communications Engineering, B
Engineering and Applied Sciences, M
English, M
English Language and Literature, B
English as a Second Language, M
Environmental Sciences, B
Exercise and Sports Science, M
Family and Consumer Economics and Related Services, B
Family and Consumer Sciences/Human Sciences, M
Finance, B
Fine Arts and Art Studies, M
Food Science and Technology, M

Foods, Nutrition, and Wellness Studies, B
French Language and Literature, B
Geography, B
Geology/Earth Science, BM
Graphic Design, B
Health Professions and Related Clinical Sciences, B
Health Promotion, M
Health Services Administration, M
Hispanic-American, Puerto Rican, and Mexican-American/Chicano Studies, B
History, BM
Horticultural Science, B
Human Resources Management/Personnel Administration, B
Industrial Technology/Technician, B
Industrial/Management Engineering, M
Interior Design, B
International Affairs, M
International Business/Trade/Commerce, B
Journalism, BM
Kinesiology and Movement Studies, M
Liberal Arts and Sciences Studies and Humanities, B
Linguistics, BM
Management Information Systems and Services, B
Marine Sciences, M
Marketing/Marketing Management, B
Marriage and Family Therapy/Counseling, M
Mass Communication/Media Studies, BM
Mathematics, BM
Mathematics Teacher Education, M
Mechanical Engineering, BM
Molecular Biology, B
Music, BM
Music Teacher Education, BM
Natural Sciences, B
Nursing, M
Nursing - Advanced Practice, M
Nursing Education, M
Occupational Health and Industrial Hygiene, B
Occupational Safety and Health Technology/Technician, B
Ornamental Horticulture, B
Parks, Recreation and Leisure Facilities Management, B
Parks, Recreation, Leisure and Fitness Studies, B
Performance, M
Philosophy, B
Physical Education Teaching and Coaching, B
Physical Therapy/Therapist, BMD
Physics, BM
Plant Sciences, BM
Political Science and Government, B
Pre-Law Studies, B
Psychology, BM
Public Administration, BM
Public Health, M
Public Relations/Image Management, B
Radio and Television, B
Reading Teacher Education, M
Real Estate, B
Rehabilitation Counseling, M
Religion/Religious Studies, B
Social Studies Teacher Education, M
Social Work, BM
Sociology, B
Spanish Language and Literature, BM
Special Education and Teaching, M
Sport Psychology, M
Viticulture and Enology, M
Women's Studies, B
Writing, M

CALIFORNIA STATE UNIVERSITY, FULLERTON

Accounting, BM
Advertising, B
Advertising and Public Relations, M
African-American/Black Studies, B
American/United States Studies/Civilization, BM
Anthropology, BM
Applied Mathematics, BM
Art History, Criticism and Conservation, BM
Art/Art Studies, General, B
Asian-American Studies, B
Athletic Training and Sports Medicine, B

BioTechnology, M
Biochemistry, B
Biological and Biomedical Sciences, M
Biology/Biological Sciences, B
Business Administration and Management, B
Business Administration, Management and Operations, M
Business/Managerial Economics, B
Ceramic Arts and Ceramics, M
Chemistry, BM
Civil Engineering, M
Clinical Psychology, M
Communication Disorders, BM
Communication Studies/Speech Communication and Rhetoric, B
Communication and Media Studies, M
Community College Education, D
Community Psychology, M
Comparative Literature, B
Composition, M
Computer Engineering, B
Computer Science, BM
Counselor Education/School Counseling and Guidance Services, M
Crafts, M
Criminal Justice/Safety Studies, B
Dance, BM
Design and Applied Arts, M
Drama and Dramatics/Theatre Arts, B
Economics, BM
Educational Administration and Supervision, M
Educational Leadership and Administration, MD
Educational Media/Instructional Technology, M
Electrical Engineering, M
Electrical, Electronics and Communications Engineering, M
Electronic Commerce, M
Elementary Education and Teaching, M
Engineering and Applied Sciences, M
English, M
English Language and Literature, B
English as a Second Language, M
Entertainment Management, M
Entrepreneurship/Entrepreneurial Studies, BM
Environmental Engineering Technology/Environmental Technology, M
Environmental Studies, M
Film, Television, and Video Production, M
Finance and Banking, M
Fine Arts and Art Studies, M
Fine/Studio Arts, B
French Language and Literature, BM
Geochemistry, M
Geography, BM
Geological and Earth Sciences/Geosciences, B
Geology/Earth Science, BM
German Language and Literature, M
Gerontology, M
Graphic Design, M
Health Services/Allied Health/Health Sciences, B
Health and Physical Education, B
Higher Education/Higher Education Administration, M
Hispanic-American, Puerto Rican, and Mexican-American/Chicano Studies, B
History, BM
Hospitality Administration/Management, B
Human Services, B
Illustration, M
Information Science/Studies, M
Information Technology, B
Insurance, M
International Business/Trade/Commerce, BM
Japanese Language and Literature, B
Journalism, B
Latin American Studies, B
Liberal Arts and Sciences Studies and Humanities, B
Linguistics, BM
Management, M
Management Information Systems and Services, M
Marketing, M
Marketing/Marketing Management, B
Mass Communication/Media Studies, M
Mathematics, BM
Mathematics Teacher Education, M

Mechanical Engineering, BM
Multilingual and Multicultural Education, M
Museology/Museum Studies, M
Music, BM
Music History, Literature, and Theory, M
Music Performance, B
Music Teacher Education, BM
Music Theory and Composition, M
Nurse Anesthetist, M
Nursing, MD
Nursing Administration, M
Nursing Education, M
Operations Research, B
Organizational Management, M
Performance, M
Philosophy, B
Photography, M
Physical Education Teaching and Coaching, M
Physics, BM
Political Science and Government, BM
Pre-Nursing Studies, B
Psychology, BM
Public Administration, BM
Public Health, M
Public Relations/Image Management, B
Radio and Television, B
Reading Teacher Education, M
Religion/Religious Studies, B
Science Teacher Education/General Science Teacher Education, M
Sculpture, M
Secondary Education and Teaching, M
Social Work, M
Sociology, BM
Software Engineering, M
Spanish Language and Literature, BM
Special Education and Teaching, M
Speech and Interpersonal Communication, M
Statistics, B
Systems Engineering, M
Taxation, M
Theater, M
Travel and Tourism, M
Women's Health Nursing, M
Women's Studies, B

CALIFORNIA STATE UNIVERSITY, LONG BEACH

Accounting, B
Acting, B
Aerospace, Aeronautical and Astronautical Engineering, BM
African Studies, M
African-American/Black Studies, B
American/United States Studies/Civilization, BM
Ancient/Classical Greek Language and Literature, B
Anthropology, BM
Apparel and Textiles, B
Applied Mathematics, BMD
Applied Statistics, M
Art Education, M
Art History, Criticism and Conservation, BM
Art Teacher Education, B
Art/Art Studies, General, B
Asian Studies/Civilization, BM
Asian-American Studies, BM
Athletic Training and Sports Medicine, B
Audiology/Audiologist and Hearing Sciences, B
Audiology/Audiologist and Speech-Language Pathology/Pathologist, B
Biochemistry, BM
Biochemistry, Biophysics and Molecular Biology, B
Biological and Biomedical Sciences, M
Biology Teacher Education, B
Biology/Biological Sciences, B
Biomedical/Medical Engineering, B
Botany/Plant Biology, B
Broadcast Journalism, B
Building/Construction Finishing, Management, and Inspection, B
Business Administration and Management, B
Business Administration, Management and Operations, M
Business/Managerial Economics, B
Cell/Cellular Biology and Histology, B
Ceramic Arts and Ceramics, B

Chemical Engineering, BM
Chemistry, BM
Child Development, B
Chinese Language and Literature, B
Cinematography and Film/Video Production, B
Civil Engineering, BM
Classics and Classical Languages, Literatures, and Linguistics, B
Commercial and Advertising Art, B
Communication Disorders, BM
Comparative Literature, B
Composition, B
Computer Engineering, BM
Computer Engineering Technology/Technician, B
Computer Science, BM
Construction Engineering, B
Construction Engineering Technology/Technician, B
Consumer Economics, M
Counselor Education/School Counseling and Guidance Services, M
Criminal Justice/Law Enforcement Administration, B
Criminology, M
Dance, BM
Dietetics/Dieticians, B
Directing and Theatrical Production, B
Drama and Dramatics/Theatre Arts, B
Drawing, B
Ecology, B
Economics, BM
Education, MD
Educational Administration and Supervision, MD
Educational Psychology, M
Electrical Engineering, M
Electrical, Electronic and Communications Engineering Technology/Technician, B
Electrical, Electronics and Communications Engineering, B
Elementary Education and Teaching, M
Emergency Management, M
Engineering, B
Engineering Management, M
Engineering Technology, B
Engineering/Industrial Management, B
English, M
English Language and Literature, B
English as a Second Language, M
English/Language Arts Teacher Education, B
Environmental Engineering Technology/Environmental Technology, B
Environmental Sciences, B
Ergonomics and Human Factors, M
Exercise and Sports Science, M
Family and Consumer Sciences/Human Sciences, B
Fashion Merchandising, B
Fiber, Textile and Weaving Arts, B
Film/Cinema Studies, B
Finance, B
Fine Arts and Art Studies, BM
Fine/Studio Arts, B
Food Science and Technology, M
Foods, Nutrition, and Related Services, M
French Language and Literature, BM
Geography, BM
Geology/Earth Science, BM
Geophysics and Seismology, M
German Language and Literature, BM
Gerontology, M
Graphic Design, B
Health Education, M
Health Professions and Related Clinical Sciences, B
Health Services Administration, M
Health and Physical Education/Fitness, B
Health/Health Care Administration/Management, B
Higher Education/Higher Education Administration, M
Hispanic-American, Puerto Rican, and Mexican-American/Chicano Studies, B
History, BM
Home Economics, M
Hospitality Administration/Management, M
Hotel/Motel Administration/Management, B
Human Development and Family Studies, B
Human Resources Management/Personnel Administration, B
Illustration, B

Industrial Design, B
Industrial Engineering, B
Industrial Technology/Technician, B
Industrial and Organizational Psychology, M
Interdisciplinary Studies, M
Interior Design, B
International Business/Trade/Commerce, B
International Relations and Affairs, B
Italian Language and Literature, B
Japanese Language and Literature, B
Journalism, B
Kinesiology and Exercise Science, B
Kinesiology and Movement Studies, M
Kinesiotherapy/Kinesiotherapist, B
Latin American Studies, M
Leisure Studies, M
Liberal Arts and Sciences Studies and Humanities, B
Linguistics, M
Logistics and Materials Management, B
Management Information Systems and Services, B
Manufacturing Technology/Technician, B
Marine Biology and Biological Oceanography, B
Marketing/Marketing Management, B
Marriage and Family Therapy/Counseling, M
Mass Communication/Media Studies, B
Materials Engineering, B
Mathematics, BM
Mathematics Teacher Education, BM
Mechanical Engineering, BMD
Mechanical Engineering/Mechanical Technology/Technician, B
Medical Radiologic Technology/Science - Radiation Therapist, B
Medieval and Renaissance Studies, M
Metal and Jewelry Arts, B
Microbiology, BM
Multi-/Interdisciplinary Studies, B
Music, BM
Music History, Literature, and Theory, B
Music Performance, B
Music Theory and Composition, B
Near and Middle Eastern Studies, M
Nursing, MD
Nutritional Sciences, M
Ocean Engineering, B
Operations Management and Supervision, B
Painting, B
Parks, Recreation, Leisure and Fitness Studies, B
Performance, M
Philosophy, BM
Photography, B
Physical Education Teaching and Coaching, BM
Physical Therapy/Therapist, D
Physics, BM
Physiology, B
Political Science and Government, BM
Printmaking, B
Psychology, BM
Public Administration, M
Public Health (MPH, DPH), B
Public Health Education and Promotion, B
Public Policy Analysis, M
Public Relations/Image Management, B
Quality Control Technology/Technician, B
Radio and Television, B
Recreation and Park Management, M
Religion/Religious Studies, BM
Science Teacher Education/General Science Teacher Education, M
Sculpture, B
Secondary Education and Teaching, M
Social Work, BM
Sociology, B
Spanish Language and Literature, BM
Special Education and Teaching, M
Sport Psychology, M
Sport and Fitness Administration/Management, M
Sports Medicine, B
Statistics, B
Student Personnel Services, M
Theater, M
Trade and Industrial Teacher Education, B
Voice and Opera, B
Western European Studies, M
Women's Studies, B

Writing, M
Zoology/Animal Biology, B

CALIFORNIA STATE UNIVERSITY, LOS ANGELES

Accounting, M
African-American/Black Studies, B
Analytical Chemistry, M
Anthropology, BM
Applied Arts and Design, M
Applied Mathematics, M
Art Education, M
Art History, Criticism and Conservation, M
Art Therapy/Therapist, M
Art/Art Studies, General, B
Asian Studies/Civilization, B
Asian-American Studies, B
Aviation/Airway Management and Operations, B
Biochemistry, M
Biological and Biomedical Sciences, M
Biology/Biological Sciences, B
Business Administration and Management, B
Ceramic Arts and Ceramics, M
Chemistry, BM
Child Development, M
Child and Family Studies, M
Chinese Language and Literature, B
Civil Engineering, BM
Communication Disorders, BM
Communication Studies/Speech Communication and Rhetoric, B
Communication and Media Studies, M
Composition, M
Computer Science, BM
Computer and Information Sciences, B
Computer and Information Sciences and Support Services, B
Counselor Education/School Counseling and Guidance Services, MD
Crafts, M
Criminal Justice/Safety Studies, B
Criminology, M
Dance, B
Design and Applied Arts, M
Dietetics/Dieticians, B
Drama and Dramatics/Theatre Arts, B
Early Childhood Education and Teaching, B
Economics, BM
Education, MD
Electrical Engineering, M
Electrical, Electronics and Communications Engineering, B
Elementary Education and Teaching, M
Engineering, B
Engineering and Applied Sciences, M
English, M
English Language and Literature, B
Finance and Banking, M
Fine Arts and Art Studies, M
Fire Services Administration, B
Foods, Nutrition, and Wellness Studies, B
French Language and Literature, BM
Geography, BM
Geology/Earth Science, BM
Graphic Design, M
Health Education, M
Health Professions and Related Clinical Sciences, B
Health Services Administration, M
Hispanic Studies, M
Hispanic-American, Puerto Rican, and Mexican-American/Chicano Studies, B
History, BM
Industrial Technology/Technician, B
Information Technology, B
Inorganic Chemistry, M
International Business/Trade/Commerce, M
Japanese Language and Literature, B
Kinesiology and Exercise Science, B
Kinesiology and Movement Studies, M
Latin American Studies, BM
Liberal Arts and Sciences Studies and Humanities, B
Management, M
Management Information Systems and Services, M
Management of Technology, M
Marketing, M

Mathematics, BM
Mechanical Engineering, BM
Microbiology, B
Multi-/Interdisciplinary Studies, B
Music, BM
Music Performance, B
Music Teacher Education, M
Musicology and Ethnomusicology, M
Natural Sciences, B
Nursing, M
Nutritional Sciences, BM
Organic Chemistry, M
Painting, M
Performance, M
Philosophy, BM
Photography, M
Physical Chemistry, M
Physical Education Teaching and Coaching, M
Physics, BM
Political Science and Government, BM
Psychology, BM
Public Administration, M
Radio and Television, B
Reading Teacher Education, M
Rehabilitation Counseling, M
Rehabilitation and Therapeutic Professions, B
School Psychology, M
Secondary Education and Teaching, M
Social Sciences, B
Social Work, BM
Sociology, BM
Spanish Language and Literature, BM
Special Education and Teaching, MD
Taxation, M
Textile Design, M
Theater, M

CALIFORNIA STATE UNIVERSITY, MONTEREY BAY

Art/Art Studies, General, B
Biology/Biological Sciences, B
Business Administration and Management, B
Business Administration, Management and Operations, M
Computer and Information Sciences, B
Design and Visual Communications, B
Education, M
Environmental Sciences, B
Environmental Studies, B
Health and Physical Education, B
Human Services, B
Humanities/Humanistic Studies, B
International Relations and Affairs, B
Japanese Language and Literature, B
Liberal Arts and Sciences Studies and Humanities, B
Linguistics, B
Management Information Systems and Services, M
Marine Sciences, M
Mathematics, B
Multi-/Interdisciplinary Studies, B
Music, B
Psychology, B
Radio and Television, B
Social Sciences, B
Social Work, M
Spanish Language and Literature, B
Water Resources, M

CALIFORNIA STATE UNIVERSITY, NORTHRIDGE

Accounting, B
African-American/Black Studies, B
Anthropology, BM
Applied Mathematics, M
Archeology, M
Art Education, M
Art History, Criticism and Conservation, M
Art/Art Studies, General, B
Artificial Intelligence and Robotics, M
Asian-American Studies, M
Athletic Training and Sports Medicine, B
Biochemistry, BM
Biological and Biomedical Sciences, M
Biology/Biological Sciences, B
Business Administration and Management, B

Business Administration, Management and Operations, MO
Chemistry, BM
Child Development, B
Cinematography and Film/Video Production, B
Civil Engineering, BM
Clinical Psychology, M
Communication Disorders, BM
Communication and Media Studies, M
Comparative Literature, M
Composition, M
Computer Engineering, B
Computer Science, BM
Construction Management, B
Counselor Education/School Counseling and Guidance Services, M
Curriculum and Instruction, M
Drama and Dramatics/Theatre Arts, B
Early Childhood Education and Teaching, M
Economics, B
Education, MD
Educational Administration and Supervision, M
Educational Leadership and Administration, MD
Educational Media/Instructional Technology, M
Educational Psychology, M
Electrical Engineering, M
Electrical, Electronics and Communications Engineering, B
Elementary Education and Teaching, M
Engineering Management, M
Engineering and Applied Sciences, M
English, M
English Education, M
English Language and Literature, B
Entertainment Management, M
Environmental Health, B
Environmental Sciences, M
Environmental and Occupational Health, M
Experimental Psychology, M
Family and Consumer Sciences/Human Sciences, BM
Film, Television, and Video Production, M
Film/Cinema Studies, B
Finance, B
Fine Arts and Art Studies, M
French Language and Literature, B
Geography, BM
Geology/Earth Science, BM
Health Education, M
Health Services Administration, M
Health Services/Allied Health/Health Sciences, B
Health/Medical Physics, B
Hispanic Studies, M
Hispanic-American, Puerto Rican, and Mexican-American/Chicano Studies, B
History, BM
Hospitality Administration/Management, M
Humanities/Humanistic Studies, B
Industrial Hygiene, M
Industrial/Management Engineering, M
Information Science/Studies, B
Jewish/Judaic Studies, B
Journalism, BM
Kinesiology and Exercise Science, B
Kinesiology and Movement Studies, M
Latin American Studies, B
Liberal Arts and Sciences Studies and Humanities, B
Linguistics, BM
Management, M
Management Science, B
Manufacturing Engineering, BM
Marketing/Marketing Management, B
Marriage and Family Therapy/Counseling, M
Mass Communication/Media Studies, M
Materials Engineering, M
Mathematics, BM
Mathematics Teacher Education, M
Mechanical Engineering, BM
Multilingual and Multicultural Education, M
Music, BM
Music Teacher Education, M
Non-Profit/Public/Organizational Management, O
Parks, Recreation, Leisure and Fitness Studies, B
Performance, M
Philosophy, B

Physical Therapy/Therapist, M
Physics, BM
Political Science and Government, BM
Psychology, BM
Public Administration, M
Public Health, M
Reading Teacher Education, M
Recreation and Park Management, M
Religion/Religious Studies, B
Rhetoric, M
School Psychology, M
Science Teacher Education/General Science Teacher Education, M
Secondary Education and Teaching, M
Social Work, M
Sociology, BM
Software Engineering, M
Spanish Language and Literature, BM
Special Education and Teaching, M
Speech and Rhetorical Studies, M
Structural Engineering, M
Systems Engineering, M
Taxation, M
Theater, M
Travel and Tourism, M
Urban Studies/Affairs, B
Women's Studies, B
Writing, M

CALIFORNIA STATE UNIVERSITY, SACRAMENTO

Accounting, M
American Sign Language (ASL), B
Anthropology, BM
Applied Behavior Analysis, M
Art/Art Studies, General, B
Asian Studies/Civilization, B
Audiology/Audiologist and Speech-Language Pathology/Pathologist, B
Biological and Biomedical Sciences, M
Biology/Biological Sciences, B
Business Administration and Management, B
Business Administration, Management and Operations, M
Cell Biology and Anatomy, M
Chemistry, BM
Child Development, B
Civil Engineering, BM
Communication Disorders, M
Communication Studies/Speech Communication and Rhetoric, B
Communication and Media Studies, M
Composition, M
Computer Engineering, B
Computer Science, BM
Conservation Biology, M
Construction Engineering Technology/Technician, B
Counseling Psychology, M
Counselor Education/School Counseling and Guidance Services, M
Criminal Justice/Law Enforcement Administration, B
Criminology, M
Curriculum and Instruction, M
Dance, B
Developmental Biology and Embryology, M
Drama and Dramatics/Theatre Arts, B
Economics, B
Education, M
Educational Leadership and Administration, M
Educational Media/Instructional Technology, M
Electrical Engineering, M
Electrical, Electronics and Communications Engineering, B
Engineering and Applied Sciences, M
English, M
English Language and Literature, B
English as a Second Language, M
Environmental Studies, B
Family and Consumer Economics and Related Services, B
Film/Cinema Studies, B
Fine Arts and Art Studies, M
Foreign Language Teacher Education, M
French Language and Literature, B
Gender Studies, M
Geography, B

Geology/Earth Science, B
Gerontology, B
Graphic Design, B
Health Professions and Related Clinical Sciences, B
Higher Education/Higher Education Administration, M
History, B
Human Resources Development, M
Human Resources Management and Services, M
Human Services, M
Humanities/Humanistic Studies, B
Industrial and Organizational Psychology, M
Interior Design, B
Journalism, B
Kinesiology and Exercise Science, B
Liberal Arts and Sciences Studies and Humanities, B
Marketing/Marketing Management, B
Marriage and Family Therapy/Counseling, M
Mass Communication/Media Studies, B
Mathematics, BM
Mechanical Engineering, BM
Mechanical Engineering/Mechanical Technology/Technician, B
Molecular Biology, M
Multilingual and Multicultural Education, M
Music, BM
Nursing, M
Parks, Recreation and Leisure Facilities Management, B
Parks, Recreation, Leisure and Fitness Studies, B
Philosophy, B
Photography, B
Physical Education Teaching and Coaching, M
Physical Sciences, B
Physics, B
Political Science and Government, BM
Psychology, BM
Public Administration, M
Public History, MD
Public Policy Analysis, M
Reading Teacher Education, M
Real Estate, M
Recreation and Park Management, M
Religion/Religious Studies, B
School Psychology, M
Social Sciences, B
Social Work, BM
Sociology, BM
Software Engineering, M
Spanish Language and Literature, B
Special Education and Teaching, M
Vocational and Technical Education, M
Writing, M

CALIFORNIA STATE UNIVERSITY, SAN BERNARDINO

Accounting, BM
American/United States Studies/Civilization, B
Anthropology, B
Art Education, M
Art/Art Studies, General, B
Bioinformatics, B
Biological and Biomedical Sciences, M
Biology/Biological Sciences, B
Business Administration and Management, B
Business Administration, Management and Operations, BM
Chemistry, BM
Child Development, M
Clinical Psychology, M
Communication and Media Studies, M
Composition, M
Computer Engineering, B
Computer Science, BM
Computer and Information Systems Security, M
Corporate and Organizational Communication, M
Counseling Psychology, M
Counselor Education/School Counseling and Guidance Services, M
Criminal Justice/Safety Studies, B
Criminology, M
Curriculum and Instruction, M
Dietetics/Dieticians, B
Drama and Dramatics/Theatre Arts, B
Early Childhood Education and Teaching, B

Economics, B
Education, MD
Educational Administration and Supervision, M
Educational Leadership and Administration, D
Educational Media/Instructional Technology, M
English, M
English Language and Literature, B
Entrepreneurship/Entrepreneurial Studies, M
Environmental Sciences, M
Experimental Psychology, M
Finance and Banking, M
Fine Arts and Art Studies, M
French Language and Literature, B
General Studies, B
Geography, B
Geology/Earth Science, B
Health Education, M
Health Services Administration, M
Health Services/Allied Health/Health Sciences, B
Health and Physical Education, B
History, B
Human Development and Family Studies, B
Human Services, B
Humanities/Humanistic Studies, B
Industrial and Organizational Psychology, M
Information Technology, B
Interdisciplinary Studies, M
International Business/Trade/Commerce, M
Liberal Arts and Sciences Studies and Humanities, B
Management, M
Management Information Systems and Services, M
Marketing, M
Mathematics, BM
Mathematics Teacher Education, M
Multi-/Interdisciplinary Studies, B
Multilingual and Multicultural Education, M
Music, B
National Security, M
Nursing, M
Philosophy, B
Physics, B
Political Science and Government, B
Psychology, BM
Public Administration, M
Public Health, M
Reading Teacher Education, M
Rehabilitation Counseling, M
Science Teacher Education/General Science Teacher Education, M
Social Sciences, BM
Social Work, BM
Sociology, B
Spanish Language and Literature, BM
Supply Chain Management, M
Theater, M
Trade and Industrial Teacher Education, B
Vocational and Technical Education, M
Writing, M

CALIFORNIA STATE UNIVERSITY, SAN MARCOS

Accounting, B
Anthropology, B
BioTechnology, B
Biochemistry, B
Biological and Biomedical Sciences, M
Biology/Biological Sciences, B
Business Administration and Management, B
Business Administration, Management and Operations, M
Cell/Cellular Biology and Histology, B
Chemistry, B
Child and Family Studies, M
Communication Disorders, M
Communication Studies/Speech Communication and Rhetoric, B
Computer Science, BM
Criminology, B
Data Processing and Data Processing Technology/Technician, B
Early Childhood Education and Teaching, B
Ecology, B
Economics, B
Education, MD
Educational Administration and Supervision, M

Educational Leadership and Administration, D
English, M
English Language and Literature, B
Environmental Studies, B
Finance, B
General Studies, B
Health Education, M
Health and Physical Education, B
Hispanic Studies, M
Hispanic and Latin American Languages, M
History, BM
Human Development and Family Studies, B
International Business/Trade/Commerce, B
International Relations and Affairs, B
Kinesiology and Exercise Science, B
Liberal Arts and Sciences Studies and Humanities, B
Marketing/Marketing Management, B
Mass Communication/Media Studies, B
Mathematics, BM
Multi-/Interdisciplinary Studies, B
Music, B
Physics, B
Physiology, B
Political Science and Government, B
Psychology, BM
Reading Teacher Education, M
Social Sciences, B
Social Work, M
Sociology, BM
Spanish Language and Literature, BM
Special Education and Teaching, M
Visual and Performing Arts, B
Women's Studies, B
Writing, M

CALIFORNIA STATE UNIVERSITY, STANISLAUS

Accounting, B
Agriculture, B
Agriculture, Agriculture Operations and Related Sciences, B
Anthropology, B
Applied Behavior Analysis, M
Art History, Criticism and Conservation, B
Art/Art Studies, General, B
Bilingual and Multilingual Education, B
Biology/Biological Sciences, B
Business Administration and Management, B
Business Administration, Management and Operations, M
Chemistry, B
Cognitive Sciences, B
Communication Studies/Speech Communication and Rhetoric, B
Community College Education, D
Computer Science, B
Conservation Biology, M
Corrections, B
Counseling Psychology, M
Counselor Education/School Counseling and Guidance Services, M
Criminal Justice/Safety Studies, B
Criminology, BM
Curriculum and Instruction, M
Drama and Dramatics/Theatre Arts, B
Early Childhood Education and Teaching, B
Ecology, M
Economics, B
Education, MDO
Educational Administration and Supervision, M
Educational Leadership and Administration, D
Educational Media/Instructional Technology, M
Elementary Education and Teaching, M
English, MO
English Language and Literature, B
English as a Second Language, M
Ethnic, Cultural Minority, and Gender Studies, B
Finance, B
Fine/Studio Arts, B
Genetic Counseling/Counselor, M
Geography, B
Geology/Earth Science, B
Gerontological Nursing, M
Health Teacher Education, B
Health and Physical Education, B

History, BM
Information Science/Studies, B
Information Technology, B
Interdisciplinary Studies, M
International Affairs, M
Liberal Arts and Sciences Studies and Humanities, B
Marketing/Marketing Management, B
Mathematics, B
Multi-/Interdisciplinary Studies, B
Multilingual and Multicultural Education, M
Music, B
Music Performance, B
Nursing, M
Nursing Education, M
Operations Management and Supervision, B
Philosophy, B
Physical Education Teaching and Coaching, BM
Physical Sciences, B
Physics, B
Political Science and Government, B
Psychology, BM
Public Administration, M
Reading Teacher Education, M
Rhetoric, M
Secondary Education and Teaching, M
Social Sciences, B
Social Work, M
Sociology, B
Spanish Language and Literature, B
Special Education and Teaching, M
Sustainable Development, M
Teaching English as a Second or Foreign Language/ESL Language Instructor, B
Urban Studies/Affairs, B
Writing, M

CALIFORNIA UNIVERSITY OF MANAGEMENT AND SCIENCES

Business Administration and Management, B
Business Administration, Management and Operations, MD
Computer and Information Systems Security, B
Economics, BM
Health/Health Care Administration/Management, A
International Business/Trade/Commerce, BM
Legal Assistant/Paralegal, A
Management Information Systems and Services, M
Sport and Fitness Administration/Management, BM
Veterinary/Animal Health Technology/Technician and Veterinary Assistant, A

CAMBRIDGE JUNIOR COLLEGE

Accounting, A
Accounting and Business/Management, A

CAÑADA COLLEGE

Accounting Technology/Technician and Bookkeeping, A
Administrative Assistant and Secretarial Science, A
Animation, Interactive Technology, Video Graphics and Special Effects, A
Anthropology, A
Apparel and Textile Manufacture, A
Archeology, A
Art/Art Studies, General, A
Biological and Physical Sciences, A
Biology/Biological Sciences, A
Business Administration and Management, A
Chemistry, A
Child Care Provider/Assistant, A
Communication Studies/Speech Communication and Rhetoric, A
Computer Science, A
Computer Systems Networking and Telecommunications, A
Drama and Dramatics/Theatre Arts, A
Economics, A
Education, A
Engineering, A
English Language and Literature, A
Fashion/Apparel Design, A
Geography, A
Health and Physical Education, A
History, A
Human Services, A

Humanities/Humanistic Studies, A
Interior Design, A
International Relations and Affairs, A
Legal Assistant/Paralegal, A
Liberal Arts and Sciences Studies and Humanities, A
Linguistics, A
Mathematics, A
Medical/Clinical Assistant, A
Music, A
Philosophy, A
Physics, A
Political Science and Government, A
Psychology, A
Radiologic Technology/Science - Radiographer, A
Retailing and Retail Operations, A
Small Business Administration/Management, A
Sociology, A
Spanish Language and Literature, A
Sport and Fitness Administration/Management, A
System Administration/Administrator, A

CARRINGTON COLLEGE–CITRUS HEIGHTS

Accounting Technology/Technician and Bookkeeping, A
Business Administration and Management, A
Criminal Justice/Safety Studies, A
Dental Assisting/Assistant, A
Health/Health Care Administration/Management, A
Medical Insurance Specialist/Medical Biller, A
Medical/Clinical Assistant, A
Pharmacy Technician/Assistant, A
Surgical Technology/Technologist, A
Veterinary/Animal Health Technology/Technician and Veterinary Assistant, A

CARRINGTON COLLEGE–PLEASANT HILL

Criminal Justice/Police Science, A
Dental Assisting/Assistant, A
Health Information/Medical Records Technology/Technician, A
Health and Medical Administrative Services, A
Health/Health Care Administration/Management, A
Massage Therapy/Therapeutic Massage, A
Medical Insurance Specialist/Medical Biller, A
Medical/Clinical Assistant, A
Pharmacy Technician/Assistant, A
Physical Therapist Assistant, A
Respiratory Therapy Technician/Assistant, A
Security and Loss Prevention Services, A
Veterinary/Animal Health Technology/Technician and Veterinary Assistant, A

CARRINGTON COLLEGE–POMONA

Dental Assisting/Assistant, A
Medical Insurance Specialist/Medical Biller, A
Medical/Clinical Assistant, A
Pharmacy Technician/Assistant, A
Veterinary/Animal Health Technology/Technician and Veterinary Assistant, A

CARRINGTON COLLEGE–SACRAMENTO

Dental Assisting/Assistant, A
Dental Hygiene/Hygienist, A
Health/Health Care Administration/Management, A
Medical Administrative Assistant/Secretary, A
Medical Insurance Specialist/Medical Biller, A
Medical Office Management/Administration, A
Medical/Clinical Assistant, A
Pharmacy Technician/Assistant, A
Veterinary/Animal Health Technology/Technician and Veterinary Assistant, A

CARRINGTON COLLEGE–SAN JOSE

Allied Health and Medical Assisting Services, A
Criminal Justice/Safety Studies, A
Dental Assisting/Assistant, A
Dental Hygiene/Hygienist, A
Health/Health Care Administration/Management, A
Medical Insurance Specialist/Medical Biller, A
Medical Office Management/Administration, A
Medical/Clinical Assistant, A

Pharmacy Technician/Assistant, A
Security and Loss Prevention Services, A
Surgical Technology/Technologist, A
Veterinary/Animal Health Technology/Technician and Veterinary Assistant, A

CARRINGTON COLLEGE–SAN LEANDRO

Dental Assisting/Assistant, A
Health and Medical Administrative Services, A
Health/Health Care Administration/Management, A
Medical Insurance Specialist/Medical Biller, A
Medical/Clinical Assistant, A
Pharmacy Technician/Assistant, A
Security and Loss Prevention Services, A
Veterinary/Animal Health Technology/Technician and Veterinary Assistant, A

CARRINGTON COLLEGE–STOCKTON

Veterinary/Animal Health Technology/Technician and Veterinary Assistant, A

CERRITOS COLLEGE

Accounting, A
Administrative Assistant and Secretarial Science, A
Alternative Fuel Vehicle Technology/Technician, A
Animation, Interactive Technology, Video Graphics and Special Effects, A
Anthropology, A
Architectural Engineering Technology/Technician, A
Art/Art Studies, General, A
Audiology/Audiologist and Speech-Language Pathology/Pathologist, A
Autobody/Collision and Repair Technology/Technician, A
Automobile/Automotive Mechanics Technology/Technician, A
Biological and Physical Sciences, A
Biology/Biological Sciences, A
Biomedical Technology/Technician, A
Broadcast Journalism, A
Business Administration and Management, A
Cabinetmaking and Millwork/Millwright, A
Chemistry, A
Cinematography and Film/Video Production, A
Communication Studies/Speech Communication and Rhetoric, A
Computer Programming/Programmer, A
Computer Science, A
Computer Systems Analysis/Analyst, A
Computer Systems Networking and Telecommunications, A
Cooking and Related Culinary Arts, A
Cosmetology/Cosmetologist, A
Court Reporting/Court Reporter, A
Criminal Justice/Police Science, A
Dance, A
Data Entry/Microcomputer Applications, A
Dental Hygiene/Hygienist, A
Drafting and Design Technology/Technician, A
Drama and Dramatics/Theatre Arts, A
Economics, A
Electrical, Electronic and Communications Engineering Technology/Technician, A
English Language and Literature, A
Fashion/Apparel Design, A
Food Technology and Processing, A
French Language and Literature, A
Geography, A
Geology/Earth Science, A
German Language and Literature, A
Hispanic-American, Puerto Rican, and Mexican-American/Chicano Studies, A
History, A
Human Services, A
Industrial Technology/Technician, A
Insurance, A
International Relations and Affairs, A
Journalism, A
Kindergarten/PreSchool Education and Teaching, A
Kinesiology and Exercise Science, A
Legal Administrative Assistant/Secretary, A
Legal Assistant/Paralegal, A
Liberal Arts and Sciences Studies and Humanities, A
Machine Tool Technology/Machinist, A

Manufacturing Technology/Technician, A
Marketing/Marketing Management, A
Mathematics, A
Medical/Clinical Assistant, A
Music, A
Pharmacy, A
Philosophy, A
Photography, A
Physical Education Teaching and Coaching, A
Physical Sciences, A
Physical Therapy/Therapist, A
Physics, A
Plastics Engineering Technology/Technician, A
Political Science and Government, A
Psychology, A
Real Estate, A
Religion/Religious Studies, A
Small Business Administration/Management, A
Sociology, A
Spanish Language and Literature, A
Sport and Fitness Administration/Management, A
Technology Teacher Education/Industrial Arts
    Teacher Education, A
Visual and Performing Arts, A
Welding Technology/Welder, A
Women's Studies, A
Zoology/Animal Biology, A

CERRO COSO COMMUNITY COLLEGE

Administrative Assistant and Secretarial Science, A
Animation, Interactive Technology, Video Graphics
    and Special Effects, A
Art/Art Studies, General, A
Automobile/Automotive Mechanics
    Technology/Technician, A
Biological and Physical Sciences, A
Business Administration and Management, A
Business/Commerce, A
Chemical Technology/Technician, A
Child Development, A
Computer Science, A
Criminal Justice/Law Enforcement Administration, A
Drafting and Design Technology/Technician, A
Drama and Dramatics/Theatre Arts, A
Electrical/Electronics Equipment Installation and Re-
    pair, A
Emergency Medical Technology/Technician (EMT
    Paramedic), A
Engineering, A
Engineering Technology, A
Fire Science/Firefighting, A
Health and Physical Education, A
Humanities/Humanistic Studies, A
Information Technology, A
Legal Assistant/Paralegal, A
Liberal Arts and Sciences Studies and Humani-
    ties, A
Machine Tool Technology/Machinist, A
Medical/Clinical Assistant, A
Natural Resources Management/Development and
    Policy, A
Resort Management, A
Small Business Administration/Management, A
Social Sciences, A
Visual and Performing Arts, A
Web Page, Digital/Multimedia and Information Re-
    sources Design, A
Welding Technology/Welder, A

CHABOT COLLEGE

Accounting, A
Administrative Assistant and Secretarial Science, A
Adult Development and Aging, A
Architectural Engineering Technology/Technician, A
Architectural Technology/Technician, A
Art/Art Studies, General, A
Automobile/Automotive Mechanics
    Technology/Technician, A
Biology/Biological Sciences, A
Building/Home/Construction Inspection/Inspector, A
Business/Commerce, A
Ceramic Arts and Ceramics, A
Chemistry, A
Child Development, A
Commercial Photography, A
Commercial and Advertising Art, A

Communications Systems Installation and Repair
    Technology, A
Computer Installation and Repair
    Technology/Technician, A
Computer Programming/Programmer, A
Computer Science, A
Computer and Information Sciences, A
Criminal Justice/Police Science, A
Data Entry/Microcomputer Applications, A
Dental Hygiene/Hygienist, A
Drawing, A
Electrical/Electronics Drafting and
    Electrical/Electronics CAD/CADD, A
Electrical/Electronics Equipment Installation and Re-
    pair, A
Electrician, A
English Language and Literature, A
Fire Science/Firefighting, A
French Language and Literature, A
Geography, A
Graphic Design, A
Health Information/Medical Records
    Administration/Administrator, A
Health and Physical Education, A
Human Services, A
Humanities/Humanistic Studies, A
Illustration, A
Industrial Electronics Technology/Technician, A
Information Technology, A
Interior Design, A
International Relations and Affairs, A
Journalism, A
Legal Administrative Assistant/Secretary, A
Liberal Arts and Sciences Studies and Humani-
    ties, A
Machine Tool Technology/Machinist, A
Manufacturing Technology/Technician, A
Mass Communication/Media Studies, A
Mathematics, A
Medical Insurance Coding Specialist/Coder, A
Medical/Clinical Assistant, A
Music, A
Office Management and Supervision, A
Parks, Recreation, Leisure and Fitness Studies, A
Psychology, A
Radio and Television, A
Real Estate, A
Retailing and Retail Operations, A
Roofer, A
Sales, Distribution and Marketing Operations, A
Sculpture, A
Sheet Metal Technology/Sheetworking, A
Small Business Administration/Management, A
Social Sciences, A
Spanish Language and Literature, A
Sport and Fitness Administration/Management, A
System Administration/Administrator, A
Welding Technology/Welder, A

CHAFFEY COLLEGE

Accounting Technology/Technician and Bookkeep-
    ing, A
Administrative Assistant and Secretarial Science, A
Adult Development and Aging, A
Aircraft Powerplant Technology/Technician, A
Airframe Mechanics and Aircraft Maintenance
    Technology/Technician, A
Animation, Interactive Technology, Video Graphics
    and Special Effects, A
Anthropology, A
Apparel and Textile Marketing Management, A
Architectural Drafting and Architectural
    CAD/CADD, A
Art/Art Studies, General, A
Autobody/Collision and Repair
    Technology/Technician, A
Automobile/Automotive Mechanics
    Technology/Technician, A
Biological and Physical Sciences, A
Biology/Biological Sciences, A
Business Administration and Management, A
Business Family and Consumer Sciences/Human
    Sciences, A
Ceramic Arts and Ceramics, A
Chemistry, A
Child Care Provider/Assistant, A

Commercial and Advertising Art, A
Computer Graphics, A
Corrections, A
Criminal Justice/Police Science, A
Dance, A
Dental Assisting/Assistant, A
Dietetic Technician (DTR), A
Drama and Dramatics/Theatre Arts, A
Drawing, A
Economics, A
Electrical and Power Transmission
    Installation/Installer, A
Electromechanical and Instrumentation and Mainte-
    nance Technologies/Technicians, A
Engineering, A
English Language and Literature, A
Family and Consumer Sciences/Human Sciences, A
Fashion/Apparel Design, A
Fire Science/Firefighting, A
Foods, Nutrition, and Wellness Studies, A
French Language and Literature, A
Geography, A
Geology/Earth Science, A
Health and Physical Education, A
History, A
Hotel/Motel Administration/Management, A
Humanities/Humanistic Studies, A
Information Technology, A
Instrumentation Technology/Technician, A
Interior Design, A
Liberal Arts and Sciences Studies and Humani-
    ties, A
Logistics and Materials Management, A
Mathematics, A
Mechanical Drafting and Mechanical Drafting
    CAD/CADD, A
Medical Administrative Assistant/Secretary, A
Multi-/Interdisciplinary Studies, A
Music, A
Office Management and Supervision, A
Philosophy, A
Photographic and Film/Video Technology/Technician
    and Assistant, A
Physical Sciences, A
Physics, A
Political Science and Government, A
Psychology, A
Radio and Television, A
Radiologic Technology/Science - Radiographer, A
Real Estate, A
Recording Arts Technology/Technician, A
Religion/Religious Studies, A
Restaurant, Culinary, and Catering
    Management/Manager, A
Retailing and Retail Operations, A
Social Sciences, A
Sociology, A
Spanish Language and Literature, A
Teacher Assistant/Aide, A
Visual and Performing Arts, A
Web Page, Digital/Multimedia and Information Re-
    sources Design, A

CHAPMAN UNIVERSITY

Accounting, B
Acting, B
Art History, Criticism and Conservation, B
Art/Art Studies, General, B
Athletic Training and Sports Medicine, B
Biochemistry, B
Biology/Biological Sciences, B
Broadcast Journalism, B
Business Administration and Management, B
Business Administration, Management and Opera-
    tions, M
Business/Managerial Economics, B
Chemistry, B
Cinematography and Film/Video Production, B
Communication Disorders, MO
Communication Studies/Speech Communication
    and Rhetoric, B
Computational Sciences, MD
Computer Science, B
Computer and Information Sciences, B
Conducting, B

Counselor Education/School Counseling and Guidance Services, MO
Cultural Studies, D
Curriculum and Instruction, D
Dance, B
Disability Studies, D
Drama and Dramatics/Theatre Arts, B
Education, BMDO
Educational Leadership and Administration, MD
Educational Psychology, M
Elementary Education and Teaching, M
English, M
English Language and Literature, B
Environmental Law, D
Film, Television, and Video Production, M
Film/Cinema Studies, B
Fine/Studio Arts, B
Food Science and Technology, M
French Language and Literature, B
Graphic Design, B
Health Communication, M
Health Services Administration, B
History, B
Holocaust Studies, M
International Affairs, M
Law and Legal Studies, MD
Liberal Arts and Sciences Studies and Humanities, B
Marriage and Family Therapy/Counseling, M
Mathematics, B
Music, B
Music Performance, B
Music Teacher Education, B
Music Theory and Composition, B
Nutritional Sciences, M
Peace Studies and Conflict Resolution, B
Pharmaceutical Sciences, M
Pharmacy, MD
Philosophy, B
Physical Therapy/Therapist, D
Piano and Organ, B
Playwriting and Screenwriting, B
Political Science and Government, B
Pre-Dentistry Studies, B
Pre-Medicine/Pre-Medical Studies, B
Pre-Veterinary Studies, B
Psychology, B
Public Relations/Image Management, B
Religion/Religious Studies, B
School Psychology, MDO
Secondary Education and Teaching, M
Social Work, B
Sociology, B
Spanish Language and Literature, B
Special Education and Teaching, MO
Taxation, MD
Theoretical and Mathematical Physics, B
Voice and Opera, B
Writing, M

CHARLES R. DREW UNIVERSITY OF MEDICINE AND SCIENCE

Allopathic Medicine, D
Biomedical Sciences, B
Diagnostic Medical Sonography/Sonographer and Ultrasound Technician, B
Health Information/Medical Records Administration/Administrator, A
Health Information/Medical Records Technology/Technician, A
Health/Medical Preparatory Programs, B
Medical Radiologic Technology/Science - Radiation Therapist, AB
Nuclear Medical Technology/Technologist, B
Pharmacy Technician/Assistant, A
Physician Assistant, B
Public Health, M
Substance Abuse/Addiction Counseling, A

CITRUS COLLEGE

Administrative Assistant and Secretarial Science, A
Art/Art Studies, General, A
Automobile/Automotive Mechanics Technology/Technician, A
Behavioral Sciences, A
Biological and Physical Sciences, A

Biology/Biological Sciences, A
Business Administration and Management, A
Business/Commerce, A
Child Development, A
Communication Studies/Speech Communication and Rhetoric, A
Computer Graphics, A
Computer Science, A
Computer and Information Sciences, A
Construction Trades, A
Cosmetology/Cosmetologist, A
Criminal Justice/Law Enforcement Administration, A
Criminal Justice/Police Science, A
Dance, A
Data Processing and Data Processing Technology/Technician, A
Dental Assisting/Assistant, A
Diesel Mechanics Technology/Technician, A
Drafting and Design Technology/Technician, A
Drama and Dramatics/Theatre Arts, A
Electrical, Electronic and Communications Engineering Technology/Technician, A
Engineering, A
Engineering Technology, A
English Language and Literature, A
French Language and Literature, A
German Language and Literature, A
Health and Physical Education, A
History, A
Hydrology and Water Resources Science, A
Japanese Language and Literature, A
Journalism, A
Liberal Arts and Sciences Studies and Humanities, A
Library Assistant/Technician, A
Library Science, A
Mathematics, A
Mechanical Engineering/Mechanical Technology/Technician, A
Modern Languages, A
Music, A
Natural Sciences, A
Photography, A
Physical Education Teaching and Coaching, A
Physical Sciences, A
Psychology, A
Public Administration, A
Real Estate, A
Recording Arts Technology/Technician, A
Security and Loss Prevention Services, A
Social Sciences, A
Sociology, A
Spanish Language and Literature, A
Visual and Performing Arts, A
Water Quality and Wastewater Treatment Management and Recycling Technology/Technician, A

CITY COLLEGE OF SAN FRANCISCO

Accounting Technology/Technician and Bookkeeping, A
Administrative Assistant and Secretarial Science, A
Aircraft Powerplant Technology/Technician, A
Airframe Mechanics and Aircraft Maintenance Technology/Technician, A
Apparel and Textile Marketing Management, A
Architectural Technology/Technician, A
Automobile/Automotive Mechanics Technology/Technician, A
Avionics Maintenance Technology/Technician, A
Banking and Financial Support Services, A
Biological and Physical Sciences, A
Biomedical Technology/Technician, A
Building/Construction Site Management/Manager, A
Business/Commerce, A
Child Care Provider/Assistant, A
Chinese Language and Literature, A
Cinematography and Film/Video Production, A
Computer Science, A
Cooking and Related Culinary Arts, A
Criminal Justice/Police Science, A
Dental Assisting/Assistant, A
Electrical/Electronics Equipment Installation and Repair, A
Emergency Medical Technology/Technician (EMT Paramedic), A
Engineering, A

Engineering Technology, A
English Language and Literature, A
Fire Science/Firefighting, A
Floriculture/Floristry Operations and Management, A
French Language and Literature, A
Graphic Design, A
Graphic and Printing Equipment Operator Production, A
Health Information/Medical Records Technology/Technician, A
Hotel/Motel Administration/Management, A
Humanities/Humanistic Studies, A
Information Technology, A
Interior Design, A
Italian Language and Literature, A
Japanese Language and Literature, A
Journalism, A
Labor and Industrial Relations, A
Landscaping and Groundskeeping, A
Legal Assistant/Paralegal, A
Liberal Arts and Sciences Studies and Humanities, A
Library Science, A
Medical Radiologic Technology/Science - Radiation Therapist, A
Medical/Clinical Assistant, A
Photography, A
Plant Nursery Operations and Management, A
Radiologic Technology/Science - Radiographer, A
Real Estate, A
Restaurant, Culinary, and Catering Management/Manager, A
Sales, Distribution and Marketing Operations, A
Small Engine Mechanics and Repair Technology/Technician, A
Social Sciences, A
Spanish Language and Literature, A
System Administration/Administrator, A
Teacher Assistant/Aide, A
Tourism and Travel Services Marketing Operations, A

CLAREMONT MCKENNA COLLEGE

Accounting, B
African-American/Black Studies, B
American/United States Studies/Civilization, B
Asian Studies/Civilization, B
Biochemistry, B
Biology/Biological Sciences, B
Biophysics, B
Chemistry, B
Classics and Classical Languages, Literatures, and Linguistics, B
Drama and Dramatics/Theatre Arts, B
Economics, B
Engineering, B
Engineering/Industrial Management, B
English Language and Literature, B
Environmental Studies, B
Film/Cinema Studies, B
Finance and Banking, M
French Language and Literature, B
Hispanic-American, Puerto Rican, and Mexican-American/Chicano Studies, B
History, B
International Relations and Affairs, B
Law and Legal Studies, B
Mathematics, B
Molecular Biology, B
Multi-/Interdisciplinary Studies, B
Near and Middle Eastern Studies, B
Philosophy, B
Physics, B
Political Science and Government, B
Psychology, B
Religion/Religious Studies, B
Science, Technology and Society, B

Spanish Language and Literature, B

COASTLINE COMMUNITY COLLEGE

Liberal Arts and Sciences Studies and Humanities, A

COGSWELL POLYTECHNICAL COLLEGE

Animation, Interactive Technology, Video Graphics and Special Effects, B
Computer Programming/Programmer, B
Computer Software Technology/Technician, B
Entrepreneurship/Entrepreneurial Studies, ABM

THE COLBURN SCHOOL CONSERVATORY OF MUSIC

Music Performance, B
Piano and Organ, B
Violin, Viola, Guitar and Other Stringed Instruments, B

COLEMAN UNIVERSITY

Bioinformatics, A
Computer Graphics, AB
Computer Systems Networking and Telecommunications, AB
Computer and Information Sciences, AB
Information Science/Studies, M
Management of Technology, M

COLLEGE OF ALAMEDA

Accounting Technology/Technician and Bookkeeping, A
Administrative Assistant and Secretarial Science, A
Aircraft Powerplant Technology/Technician, A
Airframe Mechanics and Aircraft Maintenance Technology/Technician, A
Anthropology, A
Apparel and Textiles, A
Art/Art Studies, General, A
Autobody/Collision and Repair Technology/Technician, A
Automobile/Automotive Mechanics Technology/Technician, A
Biology/Biological Sciences, A
Business Administration and Management, A
Dental Assisting/Assistant, A
Diesel Mechanics Technology/Technician, A
English Language and Literature, A
Ethnic, Cultural Minority, and Gender Studies, A
Geography, A
History, A
Humanities/Humanistic Studies, A
Information Technology, A
Liberal Arts and Sciences Studies and Humanities, A
Mathematics, A
Philosophy, A
Political Science and Government, A
Psychology, A
Public Administration and Social Service Professions, A
Social Sciences, A
Sociology, A
Spanish Language and Literature, A

COLLEGE OF THE CANYONS

Accounting Technology/Technician and Bookkeeping, A
Administrative Assistant and Secretarial Science, A
Animation, Interactive Technology, Video Graphics and Special Effects, A
Architectural Drafting and Architectural CAD/CADD, A
Art/Art Studies, General, A
Athletic Training and Sports Medicine, A
Automobile/Automotive Mechanics Technology/Technician, A
Biological and Physical Sciences, A
Building/Construction Site Management/Manager, A
Business Administration and Management, A
Child Care Provider/Assistant, A
Cinematography and Film/Video Production, A
Clinical/Medical Laboratory Technician, A

Communication Studies/Speech Communication and Rhetoric, A
Computer Science, A
Computer Systems Networking and Telecommunications, A
Criminal Justice/Police Science, A
Drama and Dramatics/Theatre Arts, A
English Language and Literature, A
Fire Protection and Safety Technology/Technician, A
French Language and Literature, A
Geography, A
Geology/Earth Science, A
Graphic Design, A
Health and Physical Education, A
History, A
Hospitality Administration/Management, A
Hotel/Motel Administration/Management, A
Humanities/Humanistic Studies, A
Interior Design, A
Journalism, A
Legal Assistant/Paralegal, A
Liberal Arts and Sciences Studies and Humanities, A
Manufacturing Technology/Technician, A
Mathematics, A
Music, A
Parks, Recreation, Leisure and Fitness Studies, A
Philosophy, A
Photography, A
Physics, A
Political Science and Government, A
Psychology, A
Real Estate, A
Restaurant, Culinary, and Catering Management/Manager, A
Sales, Distribution and Marketing Operations, A
Sign Language Interpretation and Translation, A
Small Business Administration/Management, A
Social Sciences, A
Sociology, A
Spanish Language and Literature, A
Survey Technology/Surveying, A
Water Quality and Wastewater Treatment Management and Recycling Technology/Technician, A
Welding Technology/Welder, A

COLLEGE OF THE DESERT

Agribusiness, A
Agriculture, A
Anthropology, A
Applied Horticulture/Horticultural Operations, A
Architectural Technology/Technician, A
Art/Art Studies, General, A
Automobile/Automotive Mechanics Technology/Technician, A
Biological and Physical Sciences, A
Biology/Biological Sciences, A
Building/Construction Site Management/Manager, A
Business Administration and Management, A
Business/Commerce, A
Chemistry, A
Child Care and Support Services Management, A
Communication Studies/Speech Communication and Rhetoric, A
Computer Graphics, A
Computer Science, A
Criminal Justice/Police Science, A
Crop Production, A
Culinary Arts/Chef Training, A
Dietetic Technician (DTR), A
Drafting and Design Technology/Technician, A
Drama and Dramatics/Theatre Arts, A
Economics, A
English Language and Literature, A
Environmental Sciences, A
Environmental Studies, A
Fire Science/Firefighting, A
French Language and Literature, A
Geography, A
Geology/Earth Science, A
Health and Physical Education, A
Heating, Air Conditioning, Ventilation and Refrigeration Maintenance Technology/Technician, A
History, A
Hospitality Administration/Management, A
Humanities/Humanistic Studies, A

Information Technology, A
Italian Language and Literature, A
Journalism, A
Liberal Arts and Sciences Studies and Humanities, A
Mass Communication/Media Studies, A
Mathematics, A
Multi-/Interdisciplinary Studies, A
Music, A
Natural Resources and Conservation, A
Office Management and Supervision, A
Parks, Recreation and Leisure Facilities Management, A
Philosophy, A
Physics, A
Political Science and Government, A
Psychology, A
Resort Management, A
Social Sciences, A
Sociology, A
Spanish Language and Literature, A
Substance Abuse/Addiction Counseling, A
Turf and Turfgrass Management, A

COLLEGE OF MARIN

Accounting Technology/Technician and Bookkeeping, A
Animation, Interactive Technology, Video Graphics and Special Effects, A
Architectural Technology/Technician, A
Art/Art Studies, General, A
Autobody/Collision and Repair Technology/Technician, A
Automobile/Automotive Mechanics Technology/Technician, A
Biological and Physical Sciences, A
Biology/Biological Sciences, A
Business Administration and Management, A
Business/Commerce, A
Chemistry, A
Child Care Provider/Assistant, A
Cinematography and Film/Video Production, A
Communication Studies/Speech Communication and Rhetoric, A
Computer Science, A
Computer Systems Networking and Telecommunications, A
Court Reporting/Court Reporter, A
Criminal Justice/Police Science, A
Dance, A
Data Modeling/Warehousing and Database Administration, A
Dental Assisting/Assistant, A
Design and Visual Communications, A
Drama and Dramatics/Theatre Arts, A
Engineering, A
Engineering Technology, A
English Language and Literature, A
Ethnic, Cultural Minority, and Gender Studies, A
Film/Cinema Studies, A
Foreign Languages and Literatures, A
French Language and Literature, A
Geography, A
Geology/Earth Science, A
Health and Physical Education, A
History, A
Humanities/Humanistic Studies, A
Interior Design, A
International Relations and Affairs, A
Landscaping and Groundskeeping, A
Liberal Arts and Sciences Studies and Humanities, A
Machine Tool Technology/Machinist, A
Mass Communication/Media Studies, A
Mathematics, A
Medical Administrative Assistant/Secretary, A
Medical/Clinical Assistant, A
Music, A
Office Management and Supervision, A
Physical Sciences, A
Physics, A
Plant Nursery Operations and Management, A
Political Science and Government, A
Psychology, A
Real Estate, A
Social Sciences, A

Spanish Language and Literature, A

COLLEGE OF THE REDWOODS

Administrative Assistant and Secretarial Science, A
Agribusiness, A
Agriculture, A
Animation, Interactive Technology, Video Graphics
and Special Effects, A
Architectural Drafting and Architectural
CAD/CADD, A
Automobile/Automotive Mechanics
Technology/Technician, A
Biological and Physical Sciences, A
Business/Commerce, A
Child Care Provider/Assistant, A
Child Development, A
Civil Drafting and Civil Engineering CAD/CADD, A
Computer Programming/Programmer, A
Computer Systems Networking and Telecommunica-
tions, A
Construction Trades, A
Corrections, A
Criminal Justice/Police Science, A
Crop Production, A
Data Entry/Microcomputer Applications, A
Dental Assisting/Assistant, A
Diesel Mechanics Technology/Technician, A
Digital Communication and Media/Multimedia, A
Electrical/Electronics Equipment Installation and Re-
pair, A
Forestry, A
Graphic Design, A
Hospitality Administration/Management, A
Humanities/Humanistic Studies, A
Legal Administrative Assistant/Secretary, A
Legal Assistant/Paralegal, A
Liberal Arts and Sciences Studies and Humani-
ties, A
Machine Tool Technology/Machinist, A
Manufacturing Technology/Technician, A
Mechanical Drafting and Mechanical Drafting
CAD/CADD, A
Medical/Clinical Assistant, A
Multi-/Interdisciplinary Studies, A
Science Technologies/Technicians, A

COLLEGE OF SAN MATEO

Accounting Technology/Technician and Bookkeep-
ing, A
Administrative Assistant and Secretarial Science, A
Architectural Technology/Technician, A
Art/Art Studies, General, A
Avionics Maintenance Technology/Technician, A
Biological and Physical Sciences, A
Biology/Biological Sciences, A
Biomedical Technology/Technician, A
Building/Home/Construction Inspection/Inspector, A
Business Administration and Management, A
Business/Commerce, A
Chemistry, A
Cinematography and Film/Video Production, A
Commercial and Advertising Art, A
Computer Graphics, A
Computer Programming/Programmer, A
Computer Science, A
Computer Systems Networking and Telecommunica-
tions, A
Cosmetology/Cosmetologist, A
Criminal Justice/Police Science, A
Dental Assisting/Assistant, A
Dental Hygiene/Hygienist, A
Drafting and Design Technology/Technician, A
Drawing, A
Electrical, Electronic and Communications Engineer-
ing Technology/Technician, A
Electrician, A
Engineering, A
Engineering Technology, A
English Language and Literature, A
Ethnic, Cultural Minority, and Gender Studies, A
Fire Science/Firefighting, A
Floriculture/Floristry Operations and Management, A
French Language and Literature, A
Geology/Earth Science, A
German Language and Literature, A
Graphic Design, A

Health/Medical Preparatory Programs, A
Heating, Air Conditioning, Ventilation and Refrigera-
tion Maintenance Technology/Technician, A
Human Services, A
Humanities/Humanistic Studies, A
Insurance, A
Journalism, A
Landscaping and Groundskeeping, A
Liberal Arts and Sciences Studies and Humani-
ties, A
Mathematics, A
Music, A
Photography, A
Physical Sciences, A
Physics, A
Plant Nursery Operations and Management, A
Plumbing Technology/Plumber, A
Prepress/Desktop Publishing and Digital Imaging
Design, A
Radio and Television, A
Real Estate, A
Retailing and Retail Operations, A
Sales, Distribution and Marketing Operations, A
Selling Skills and Sales Operations, A
Social Sciences, A
Spanish Language and Literature, A
Substance Abuse/Addiction Counseling, A
System Administration/Administrator, A
Web Page, Digital/Multimedia and Information Re-
sources Design, A
Welding Technology/Welder, A

COLLEGE OF THE SEQUOIAS

Accounting, A
Administrative Assistant and Secretarial Science, A
Agricultural Business and Management, A
Agricultural Mechanization, A
Agricultural Teacher Education, A
Agriculture, A
Animal Sciences, A
Architectural Engineering Technology/Technician, A
Art/Art Studies, General, A
Athletic Training and Sports Medicine, A
Automobile/Automotive Mechanics
Technology/Technician, A
Biological and Physical Sciences, A
Biology/Biological Sciences, A
Business Administration and Management, A
Carpentry/Carpenter, A
Chemistry, A
Commercial and Advertising Art, A
Community Organization and Advocacy, A
Computer Engineering Technology/Technician, A
Computer Graphics, A
Computer Programming/Programmer, A
Computer Science, A
Computer Software and Media Applications, A
Computer Typography and Composition Equipment
Operator, A
Construction Engineering Technology/Technician, A
Corrections, A
Cosmetology/Cosmetologist, A
Criminal Justice/Law Enforcement Administration, A
Criminal Justice/Police Science, A
Culinary Arts/Chef Training, A
Dairy Science, A
Data Modeling/Warehousing and Database Adminis-
tration, A
Drafting and Design Technology/Technician, A
Drama and Dramatics/Theatre Arts, A
Electrical, Electronic and Communications Engineer-
ing Technology/Technician, A
Engineering, A
English Language and Literature, A
Family and Consumer Sciences/Home Economics
Teacher Education, A
Family and Consumer Sciences/Human Sciences, A
Fashion Merchandising, A
Fashion/Apparel Design, A
Fire Science/Firefighting, A
French Language and Literature, A
Health Teacher Education, A
Heating, Air Conditioning, Ventilation and Refrigera-
tion Maintenance Technology/Technician, A
History, A
Horticultural Science, A

Humanities/Humanistic Studies, A
Information Science/Studies, A
Interior Design, A
Journalism, A
Kindergarten/PreSchool Education and Teaching, A
Legal Assistant/Paralegal, A
Liberal Arts and Sciences Studies and Humani-
ties, A
Marketing/Marketing Management, A
Mass Communication/Media Studies, A
Mathematics, A
Modern Languages, A
Music, A
Ornamental Horticulture, A
Physical Education Teaching and Coaching, A
Real Estate, A
Sign Language Interpretation and Translation, A
Social Sciences, A
Sociology, A
Spanish Language and Literature, A
Web Page, Digital/Multimedia and Information Re-
sources Design, A
Welding Technology/Welder, A
Word Processing, A

COLLEGE OF THE SISKIYOUS

Accounting Technology/Technician and Bookkeep-
ing, A
Administrative Assistant and Secretarial Science, A
Anthropology, A
Art/Art Studies, General, A
Biological and Physical Sciences, A
Biology/Biological Sciences, A
Business Administration and Management, A
Chemistry, A
Child Care Provider/Assistant, A
Communication Studies/Speech Communication
and Rhetoric, A
Computer Science, A
Criminal Justice/Police Science, A
Drama and Dramatics/Theatre Arts, A
Emergency Medical Technology/Technician (EMT
Paramedic), A
Engineering, A
English Language and Literature, A
Ethnic, Cultural Minority, and Gender Studies, A
Fire Science/Firefighting, A
Health and Physical Education, A
History, A
Human Services, A
Humanities/Humanistic Studies, A
Liberal Arts and Sciences Studies and Humani-
ties, A
Mass Communication/Media Studies, A
Mathematics, A
Music, A
Physics, A
Political Science and Government, A
Psychology, A
Social Sciences, A
Spanish Language and Literature, A
Substance Abuse/Addiction Counseling, A
Technical Teacher Education, A
Welding Technology/Welder, A

COLUMBIA COLLEGE

Administrative Assistant and Secretarial Science, A
Art/Art Studies, General, A
Automobile/Automotive Mechanics
Technology/Technician, A
Biological and Physical Sciences, A
Biology/Biological Sciences, A
Business Administration and Management, A
Business/Commerce, A
Child Care Provider/Assistant, A
Communication Studies/Speech Communication
and Rhetoric, A
Computer Science, A
Cooking and Related Culinary Arts, A
Emergency Medical Technology/Technician (EMT
Paramedic), A
English Language and Literature, A
Environmental Sciences, A
Fire Science/Firefighting, A
Forestry, A
Geography, A

Geology/Earth Science, A
Health Services/Allied Health/Health Sciences, A
Health and Physical Education, A
Hotel/Motel Administration/Management, A
Human Services, A
Humanities/Humanistic Studies, A
Information Technology, A
Liberal Arts and Sciences Studies and Humanities, A
Mathematics, A
Medical Administrative Assistant/Secretary, A
Music, A
Natural Resources and Conservation, A
Photography, A
Physical Sciences, A
Restaurant, Culinary, and Catering Management/Manager, A

COLUMBIA COLLEGE HOLLYWOOD

Broadcast Journalism, B
Cinematography and Film/Video Production, B
Film/Cinema Studies, B
Radio and Television, B
Telecommunications Technology/Technician, AB

COMMUNITY CHRISTIAN COLLEGE

Liberal Arts and Sciences Studies and Humanities, A

CONCORDE CAREER COLLEGE (GARDEN GROVE)

Respiratory Care Therapy/Therapist, A

CONCORDE CAREER COLLEGE (NORTH HOLLYWOOD)

Respiratory Care Therapy/Therapist, A

CONCORDE CAREER COLLEGE (SAN DIEGO)

Respiratory Care Therapy/Therapist, A

CONCORDIA UNIVERSITY IRVINE

Ancient Near Eastern and Biblical Languages, Literatures, and Linguistics, B
Applied Social Research, M
Art/Art Studies, General, B
Athletic Training and Sports Medicine, B
Behavioral Sciences, B
Biology/Biological Sciences, B
Business Administration and Management, B
Business Administration, Management and Operations, M
Chemistry, B
Counselor Education/School Counseling and Guidance Services, M
Cultural Studies, M
Curriculum and Instruction, M
Drama and Dramatics/Theatre Arts, B
Economics, B
Education, M
Educational Administration and Supervision, M
Educational Media/Instructional Technology, M
English Language and Literature, B
Graphic Design, B
Health and Physical Education, B
Health/Health Care Administration/Management, B
History, B
Humanities/Humanistic Studies, B
International Affairs, M
International/Global Studies, B
Liberal Arts and Sciences Studies and Humanities, AB
Mathematics, B
Music, B
Physical Education Teaching and Coaching, M
Physics, B
Political Science and Government, B
Psychology, B
Religion/Religious Studies, BM
Religious Education, B
Sport and Fitness Administration/Management, M
Theology and Religious Vocations, M

Theology/Theological Studies, B

CONTRA COSTA COLLEGE

Administrative Assistant and Secretarial Science, A
Anthropology, A
Architectural Technology/Technician, A
Art/Art Studies, General, A
Autobody/Collision and Repair Technology/Technician, A
Automobile/Automotive Mechanics Technology/Technician, A
Biology/Biological Sciences, A
Biomedical Technology/Technician, A
Business Administration and Management, A
Chemistry, A
Child Care Provider/Assistant, A
Computer Programming/Programmer, A
Computer Science, A
Computer Systems Networking and Telecommunications, A
Computer and Information Sciences and Support Services, A
Cooking and Related Culinary Arts, A
Corrections, A
Criminal Justice/Police Science, A
Data Entry/Microcomputer Applications, A
Dental Assisting/Assistant, A
Drafting and Design Technology/Technician, A
Economics, A
Electrical/Electronics Equipment Installation and Repair, A
Engineering, A
English Language and Literature, A
Ethnic, Cultural Minority, and Gender Studies, A
French Language and Literature, A
Geography, A
Geology/Earth Science, A
Health and Physical Education, A
History, A
Human Services, A
Humanities/Humanistic Studies, A
Journalism, A
Liberal Arts and Sciences Studies and Humanities, A
Mathematics, A
Medical/Clinical Assistant, A
Music, A
Physics, A
Political Science and Government, A
Psychology, A
Radiologic Technology/Science - Radiographer, A
Real Estate, A
Sociology, A
Spanish Language and Literature, A

COPPER MOUNTAIN COLLEGE

Anthropology, A
Art/Art Studies, General, A
Automobile/Automotive Mechanics Technology/Technician, A
Business Administration and Management, A
Business/Commerce, A
Computer Science, A
Criminal Justice/Police Science, A
Drawing, A
Economics, A
English Language and Literature, A
Environmental Sciences, A
Fire Science/Firefighting, A
History, A
Information Technology, A
Liberal Arts and Sciences Studies and Humanities, A
Mathematics, A
Philosophy, A
Political Science and Government, A
Psychology, A
Social Sciences, A
Spanish Language and Literature, A

COSUMNES RIVER COLLEGE

Accounting Technology/Technician and Bookkeeping, A
Administrative Assistant and Secretarial Science, A
Agribusiness, A
Agriculture, A

Architectural Drafting and Architectural CAD/CADD, A
Architectural Technology/Technician, A
Art/Art Studies, General, A
Automobile/Automotive Mechanics Technology/Technician, A
Banking and Financial Support Services, A
Biological and Physical Sciences, A
Broadcast Journalism, A
Building/Construction Site Management/Manager, A
Building/Home/Construction Inspection/Inspector, A
Business Administration and Management, A
Business/Commerce, A
Chemistry, A
Child Care Provider/Assistant, A
Child Care and Support Services Management, A
Communication Studies/Speech Communication and Rhetoric, A
Computer Programming/Programmer, A
Computer Science, A
Computer Systems Networking and Telecommunications, A
Construction Trades, A
Dietetic Technician (DTR), A
Drama and Dramatics/Theatre Arts, A
Engineering, A
English Language and Literature, A
Environmental Studies, A
Ethnic, Cultural Minority, and Gender Studies, A
Film/Cinema Studies, A
Fire Science/Firefighting, A
Geography, A
Geology/Earth Science, A
Graphic Design, A
Health Information/Medical Records Technology/Technician, A
Health Teacher Education, A
Health and Physical Education, A
Horse Husbandry/Equine Science and Management, A
Human Services, A
Humanities/Humanistic Studies, A
Information Technology, A
Journalism, A
Liberal Arts and Sciences Studies and Humanities, A
Mathematics, A
Medical/Clinical Assistant, A
Music, A
Pharmacy Technician/Assistant, A
Photographic and Film/Video Technology/Technician and Assistant, A
Physics, A
Plant Nursery Operations and Management, A
Public Relations/Image Management, A
Radio and Television, A
Real Estate, A
Restaurant, Culinary, and Catering Management/Manager, A
Sales, Distribution and Marketing Operations, A
Small Business Administration/Management, A
Social Sciences, A
Spanish Language and Literature, A
System Administration/Administrator, A
Veterinary/Animal Health Technology/Technician and Veterinary Assistant, A

CRAFTON HILLS COLLEGE

Accounting Technology/Technician and Bookkeeping, A
Anthropology, A
Art/Art Studies, General, A
Biological and Physical Sciences, A
Business Administration and Management, A
Chemistry, A
Child Care Provider/Assistant, A
Communication Studies/Speech Communication and Rhetoric, A
Criminal Justice/Police Science, A
Drama and Dramatics/Theatre Arts, A
Economics, A
Emergency Medical Technology/Technician (EMT Paramedic), A
English Language and Literature, A
Environmental Sciences, A
Fire Science/Firefighting, A

Geography, A
Geology/Earth Science, A
Humanities/Humanistic Studies, A
Information Technology, A
Liberal Arts and Sciences Studies and Humanities, A
Mathematics, A
Microbiology, A
Music, A
Philosophy, A
Photographic and Film/Video Technology/Technician and Assistant, A
Physics, A
Physiology, A
Political Science and Government, A
Psychology, A
Radiologic Technology/Science - Radiographer, A
Religion/Religious Studies, A
Respiratory Care Therapy/Therapist, A
Retailing and Retail Operations, A
Social Sciences, A
Sociology, A
Spanish Language and Literature, A
Visual and Performing Arts, A

CUESTA COLLEGE

Administrative Assistant and Secretarial Science, A
Agriculture, Agriculture Operations and Related Sciences, A
Animal/Livestock Husbandry and Production, A
Apparel and Textile Manufacture, A
Applied Horticulture/Horticultural Operations, A
Architectural Technology/Technician, A
Art/Art Studies, General, A
Autobody/Collision and Repair Technology/Technician, A
Automobile/Automotive Mechanics Technology/Technician, A
Biological and Physical Sciences, A
Biology/Biological Sciences, A
Business Administration and Management, A
Chemistry, A
Child Care Provider/Assistant, A
Communications Technology/Technician, A
Computer Programming/Programmer, A
Computer Science, A
Construction Trades, A
Cooking and Related Culinary Arts, A
Criminal Justice/Police Science, A
Dairy Husbandry and Production, A
Dance, A
Data Modeling/Warehousing and Database Administration, A
Drama and Dramatics/Theatre Arts, A
Drawing, A
Electrical/Electronics Equipment Installation and Repair, A
Electromechanical and Instrumentation and Maintenance Technologies/Technicians, A
Engineering, A
English Language and Literature, A
Fashion/Apparel Design, A
Floriculture/Floristry Operations and Management, A
Food Technology and Processing, A
Health and Physical Education, A
History, A
Hospitality Administration/Management, A
Human Development and Family Studies, A
Humanities/Humanistic Studies, A
Interior Design, A
International Business/Trade/Commerce, A
International Relations and Affairs, A
Journalism, A
Law and Legal Studies, A
Legal Assistant/Paralegal, A
Liberal Arts and Sciences Studies and Humanities, A
Library Science, A
Mathematics, A
Mechanical Engineering/Mechanical Technology/Technician, A
Medical/Clinical Assistant, A
Music, A
Parks, Recreation, Leisure and Fitness Studies, A
Physical Sciences, A
Physics, A

Political Science and Government, A
Psychiatric/Mental Health Services Technician, A
Psychology, A
Radio and Television, A
Real Estate, A
Sales, Distribution and Marketing Operations, A
Sculpture, A
Sociology, A
System Administration/Administrator, A
Welding Technology/Welder, A

CUYAMACA COLLEGE

Accounting, A
Accounting Technology/Technician and Bookkeeping, A
Automobile/Automotive Mechanics Technology/Technician, A
Biological and Physical Sciences, A
Business Administration and Management, A
Business/Commerce, A
Chemistry, A
Child Development, A
Commercial and Advertising Art, A
Drafting and Design Technology/Technician, A
Drafting/Design Engineering Technologies/Technicians, A
Drawing, A
Elementary Education and Teaching, A
English Language and Literature, A
Entrepreneurship/Entrepreneurial Studies, A
Environmental Engineering Technology/Environmental Technology, A
General Studies, A
History, A
Information Science/Studies, A
Landscaping and Groundskeeping, A
Legal Assistant/Paralegal, A
Liberal Arts and Sciences Studies and Humanities, A
Occupational Safety and Health Technology/Technician, A
Office Management and Supervision, A
Ornamental Horticulture, A
Painting, A
Physics, A
Plant Nursery Operations and Management, A
Real Estate, A
Special Products Marketing Operations, A
Survey Technology/Surveying, A
Turf and Turfgrass Management, A

CYPRESS COLLEGE

Accounting Technology/Technician and Bookkeeping, A
Administrative Assistant and Secretarial Science, A
Airline Flight Attendant, A
Airline/Commercial/Professional Pilot and Flight Crew, A
Anthropology, A
Art/Art Studies, General, A
Autobody/Collision and Repair Technology/Technician, A
Automobile/Automotive Mechanics Technology/Technician, A
Aviation/Airway Management and Operations, A
Biological and Physical Sciences, A
Business Administration and Management, A
Business/Commerce, A
Commercial and Advertising Art, A
Computer Programming/Programmer, A
Cooking and Related Culinary Arts, A
Court Reporting/Court Reporter, A
Dance, A
Data Entry/Microcomputer Applications, A
Dental Assisting/Assistant, A
Dental Hygiene/Hygienist, A
Diagnostic Medical Sonography/Sonographer and Ultrasound Technician, A
Drafting and Design Technology/Technician, A
Drama and Dramatics/Theatre Arts, A
Engineering, A
Ethnic, Cultural Minority, and Gender Studies, A
Funeral Service and Mortuary Science, A
Health Information/Medical Records Technology/Technician, A
Health and Physical Education, A

Heating, Air Conditioning, Ventilation and Refrigeration Maintenance Technology/Technician, A
Hospital and Health Care Facilities Administration/Management, A
Hotel/Motel Administration/Management, A
Human Services, A
Humanities/Humanistic Studies, A
Information Technology, A
Insurance, A
Legal Administrative Assistant/Secretary, A
Liberal Arts and Sciences Studies and Humanities, A
Music, A
Philosophy, A
Photographic and Film/Video Technology/Technician and Assistant, A
Psychiatric/Mental Health Services Technician, A
Psychology, A
Radiologic Technology/Science - Radiographer, A
Restaurant, Culinary, and Catering Management/Manager, A
Retailing and Retail Operations, A
Sales, Distribution and Marketing Operations, A
Selling Skills and Sales Operations, A
Small Business Administration/Management, A
Sociology, A
Teacher Assistant/Aide, A
Tourism and Travel Services Marketing Operations, A
Visual and Performing Arts, A

DE ANZA COLLEGE

Accounting, A
Administrative Assistant and Secretarial Science, A
Art History, Criticism and Conservation, A
Art/Art Studies, General, A
Automobile/Automotive Mechanics Technology/Technician, A
Behavioral Sciences, A
Biology/Biological Sciences, A
Business Administration and Management, A
Business Machine Repairer, A
Ceramic Arts and Ceramics, A
Child Development, A
Commercial and Advertising Art, A
Computer Graphics, A
Computer Programming/Programmer, A
Computer Science, A
Construction Engineering Technology/Technician, A
Corrections, A
Criminal Justice/Law Enforcement Administration, A
Criminal Justice/Police Science, A
Drafting/Design Engineering Technologies/Technicians, A
Drama and Dramatics/Theatre Arts, A
Drawing, A
Economics, A
Engineering, A
Engineering Technology, A
English Language and Literature, A
Environmental Studies, A
Film/Cinema Studies, A
History, A
Humanities/Humanistic Studies, A
Industrial Technology/Technician, A
Information Science/Studies, A
International Relations and Affairs, A
Journalism, A
Legal Assistant/Paralegal, A
Liberal Arts and Sciences Studies and Humanities, A
Machine Tool Technology/Machinist, A
Marketing/Marketing Management, A
Mass Communication/Media Studies, A
Mathematics, A
Medical/Clinical Assistant, A
Music, A
Philosophy, A
Photography, A
Physical Education Teaching and Coaching, A
Physical Therapy/Therapist, A
Physics, A
Political Science and Government, A
Printmaking, A
Psychology, A

Purchasing, Procurement/Acquisitions and Contracts Management, A
Radio and Television, A
Real Estate, A
Sculpture, A
Social Sciences, A
Sociology, A
Spanish Language and Literature, A

DEEP SPRINGS COLLEGE

Liberal Arts and Sciences Studies and Humanities, A

DESIGN INSTITUTE OF SAN DIEGO

Interior Design, B

DEVRY UNIVERSITY (ALHAMBRA)

Accounting, B
Business Administration and Management, B
Business Administration, Management and Operations, BM
Business/Commerce, B
Computer Software Engineering, B
Computer Systems Analysis/Analyst, B
Computer Systems Networking and Telecommunications, AB
Criminal Justice/Law Enforcement Administration, B
Electrical, Electronic and Communications Engineering Technology/Technician, A
Health/Health Care Administration/Management, B
Web Page, Digital/Multimedia and Information Resources Design, AB

DEVRY UNIVERSITY (ANAHEIM)

Accounting, B
Business Administration and Management, B
Business Administration, Management and Operations, BM
Computer Software Engineering, B
Computer Systems Analysis/Analyst, B
Computer Systems Networking and Telecommunications, AB
Criminal Justice/Law Enforcement Administration, B
Electrical, Electronic and Communications Engineering Technology/Technician, A
Health/Health Care Administration/Management, B
Web Page, Digital/Multimedia and Information Resources Design, AB

DEVRY UNIVERSITY (BAKERSFIELD)

Accounting, AB
Business Administration and Management, B
Business Administration, Management and Operations, B
Business/Commerce, B
Computer Systems Analysis/Analyst, B
Computer Systems Networking and Telecommunications, AB
Criminal Justice/Law Enforcement Administration, B
Electrical, Electronic and Communications Engineering Technology/Technician, A
Health/Health Care Administration/Management, B
Web Page, Digital/Multimedia and Information Resources Design, AB

DEVRY UNIVERSITY (FREMONT)

Accounting, A
Biomedical Technology/Technician, B
Business Administration and Management, B
Business Administration, Management and Operations, BM
Business/Commerce, B
Computer Engineering Technology/Technician, B
Computer Software Engineering, B
Computer Systems Analysis/Analyst, B
Computer Systems Networking and Telecommunications, AB
Criminal Justice/Law Enforcement Administration, B
Electrical, Electronic and Communications Engineering Technology/Technician, AB
Health/Health Care Administration/Management, B

Web Page, Digital/Multimedia and Information Resources Design, AB

DEVRY UNIVERSITY (LONG BEACH)

Accounting, B
Business Administration and Management, B
Business Administration, Management and Operations, BM
Business/Commerce, B
Computer Engineering Technology/Technician, B
Computer Software Engineering, B
Computer Systems Analysis/Analyst, B
Computer Systems Networking and Telecommunications, AB
Criminal Justice/Law Enforcement Administration, B
Electrical, Electronic and Communications Engineering Technology/Technician, AB
Health/Health Care Administration/Management, B
Web Page, Digital/Multimedia and Information Resources Design, AB

DEVRY UNIVERSITY (OAKLAND)

Accounting, B
Business Administration and Management, B
Business Administration, Management and Operations, BM
Business/Commerce, B
Computer Systems Analysis/Analyst, B
Computer Systems Networking and Telecommunications, AB
Criminal Justice/Law Enforcement Administration, B
Health/Health Care Administration/Management, B
Web Page, Digital/Multimedia and Information Resources Design, AB

DEVRY UNIVERSITY (OXNARD)

Accounting, B
Business Administration and Management, B
Business Administration, Management and Operations, BMO
Business/Commerce, B
Computer Systems Analysis/Analyst, B
Computer Systems Networking and Telecommunications, AB
Criminal Justice/Law Enforcement Administration, B
Electrical, Electronic and Communications Engineering Technology/Technician, A
Health/Health Care Administration/Management, B
Web Page, Digital/Multimedia and Information Resources Design, AB

DEVRY UNIVERSITY (PALMDALE)

Accounting, B
Business Administration and Management, B
Business Administration, Management and Operations, BMO
Business/Commerce, B
Computer Software Engineering, B
Computer Systems Analysis/Analyst, B
Computer Systems Networking and Telecommunications, AB
Criminal Justice/Law Enforcement Administration, B
Electrical, Electronic and Communications Engineering Technology/Technician, A
Health/Health Care Administration/Management, B
Web Page, Digital/Multimedia and Information Resources Design, AB

DEVRY UNIVERSITY (POMONA)

Accounting, B
Accounting Technology/Technician and Bookkeeping, A
Business Administration and Management, B
Business Administration, Management and Operations, BM
Business/Commerce, B
Computer Engineering Technology/Technician, B
Computer Software Engineering, B
Computer Systems Analysis/Analyst, B
Computer Systems Networking and Telecommunications, AB
Criminal Justice/Law Enforcement Administration, B
Education, M
Electrical, Electronic and Communications Engineering Technology/Technician, AB

Health Information/Medical Records Technology/Technician, A
Health/Health Care Administration/Management, B
Web Page, Digital/Multimedia and Information Resources Design, AB

DEVRY UNIVERSITY (SAN DIEGO)

Business Administration and Management, B
Business Administration, Management and Operations, BMO
Business/Commerce, B
Computer Software Engineering, B
Computer Systems Analysis/Analyst, B
Computer Systems Networking and Telecommunications, AB
Criminal Justice/Law Enforcement Administration, B
Electrical, Electronic and Communications Engineering Technology/Technician, A
Health/Health Care Administration/Management, B
Web Page, Digital/Multimedia and Information Resources Design, AB

DEVRY UNIVERSITY (SHERMAN OAKS)

Accounting, B
Business Administration and Management, B
Business Administration, Management and Operations, B
Business/Commerce, B
Computer Engineering Technology/Technician, B
Computer Software Engineering, B
Computer Systems Analysis/Analyst, B
Computer Systems Networking and Telecommunications, AB
Criminal Justice/Law Enforcement Administration, B
Electrical, Electronic and Communications Engineering Technology/Technician, AB
Health/Health Care Administration/Management, B
Web Page, Digital/Multimedia and Information Resources Design, AB

DIABLO VALLEY COLLEGE

Atmospheric Sciences and Meteorology, A
Electrical/Electronics Equipment Installation and Repair, A
English Language and Literature, A
Geography, A
Humanities/Humanistic Studies, A
Liberal Arts and Sciences Studies and Humanities, A
Political Science and Government, A
Psychology, A

DOMINICAN UNIVERSITY OF CALIFORNIA

Art History, Criticism and Conservation, BM
Art/Art Studies, General, B
Biological and Biomedical Sciences, M
Biology/Biological Sciences, B
Business Administration and Management, B
Business Administration, Management and Operations, BM
Chemistry, B
Clinical Laboratory Sciences, M
Communication, Journalism and Related Programs, B
Counseling Psychology, M
Dance, B
Education, M
English, M
English Language and Literature, B
Gender Studies, M
Graphic Design, B
History, BM
Humanities/Humanistic Studies, BM
International Business/Trade/Commerce, M
International/Global Studies, B
Liberal Arts and Sciences Studies and Humanities, B
Management Strategy and Policy, M
Marriage and Family Therapy/Counseling, M
Music, BM
Natural Resources Management/Development and Policy, B
Occupational Therapy/Therapist, BM
Philosophy, M

Political Science and Government, BM
Psychology, B
Public Health (MPH, DPH), B
Religion/Religious Studies, BM
Special Education and Teaching, M
Sustainability Management, M
Women's Studies, BM
Writing, M

EAST LOS ANGELES COLLEGE

Accounting, A
Administrative Assistant and Secretarial Science, A
Anthropology, A
Architectural Engineering Technology/Technician, A
Art/Art Studies, General, A
Asian Studies/Civilization, A
Automobile/Automotive Mechanics Technology/Technician, A
Biology/Biological Sciences, A
Business Administration and Management, A
Chemistry, A
Child Development, A
Civil Engineering Technology/Technician, A
Computer Engineering Technology/Technician, A
Computer Programming/Programmer, A
Counselor Education/School Counseling and Guidance Services, A
Criminal Justice/Law Enforcement Administration, A
Criminal Justice/Police Science, A
Data Processing and Data Processing Technology/Technician, A
Drafting and Design Technology/Technician, A
Drama and Dramatics/Theatre Arts, A
Electrical, Electronic and Communications Engineering Technology/Technician, A
Emergency Medical Technology/Technician (EMT Paramedic), A
Engineering, A
English Language and Literature, A
Environmental Studies, A
Family and Consumer Sciences/Human Sciences, A
Finance, A
Fire Science/Firefighting, A
French Language and Literature, A
Geography, A
Geology/Earth Science, A
Health Information/Medical Records Administration/Administrator, A
Hispanic-American, Puerto Rican, and Mexican-American/Chicano Studies, A
History, A
Japanese Language and Literature, A
Journalism, A
Legal Administrative Assistant/Secretary, A
Liberal Arts and Sciences Studies and Humanities, A
Marketing/Marketing Management, A
Mathematics, A
Medical Administrative Assistant/Secretary, A
Medical/Clinical Assistant, A
Music, A
Philosophy, A
Photography, A
Physical Education Teaching and Coaching, A
Political Science and Government, A
Psychology, A
Public Administration, A
Real Estate, A
Respiratory Care Therapy/Therapist, A
Social Work, A
Sociology, A
Spanish Language and Literature, A
Trade and Industrial Teacher Education, A

EL CAMINO COLLEGE

Accounting, A
Administrative Assistant and Secretarial Science, A
Advertising, A
African-American/Black Studies, A
American/United States Studies/Civilization, A
Anthropology, A
Architectural Engineering Technology/Technician, A
Art History, Criticism and Conservation, A
Art/Art Studies, General, A
Asian Studies/Civilization, A
Astronomy, A

Automobile/Automotive Mechanics Technology/Technician, A
Biology/Biological Sciences, A
Botany/Plant Biology, A
Business Administration and Management, A
Chemistry, A
Construction Engineering Technology/Technician, A
Cosmetology/Cosmetologist, A
Criminal Justice/Police Science, A
Culinary Arts/Chef Training, A
Data Processing and Data Processing Technology/Technician, A
Drafting and Design Technology/Technician, A
Drama and Dramatics/Theatre Arts, A
Economics, A
Electrical, Electronic and Communications Engineering Technology/Technician, A
Engineering, A
English Language and Literature, A
Family and Consumer Sciences/Human Sciences, A
Fashion/Apparel Design, A
Finance, A
Fire Science/Firefighting, A
Forestry Technology/Technician, A
Geography, A
Geology/Earth Science, A
German Language and Literature, A
Gerontology, A
Heating, Air Conditioning, Ventilation and Refrigeration Maintenance Technology/Technician, A
History, A
Horticultural Science, A
Interior Design, A
Italian Language and Literature, A
Japanese Language and Literature, A
Journalism, A
Kindergarten/PreSchool Education and Teaching, A
Labor and Industrial Relations, A
Legal Assistant/Paralegal, A
Liberal Arts and Sciences Studies and Humanities, A
Marketing/Marketing Management, A
Mathematics, A
Medical/Clinical Assistant, A
Music, A
Ornamental Horticulture, A
Philosophy, A
Photography, A
Physical Education Teaching and Coaching, A
Physical Sciences, A
Physics, A
Political Science and Government, A
Psychology, A
Real Estate, A
Respiratory Care Therapy/Therapist, A
Russian Language and Literature, A
Social Work, A
Sociology, A
Spanish Language and Literature, A
Special Products Marketing Operations, A
Welding Technology/Welder, A
Zoology/Animal Biology, A

EMPIRE COLLEGE

Accounting, A
Administrative Assistant and Secretarial Science, A
Computer and Information Sciences, A
Legal Administrative Assistant/Secretary, A
Medical/Clinical Assistant, A

EPIC BIBLE COLLEGE

Christian Studies, A
Divinity/Ministry (BD, MDiv.), AB

EVERGREEN VALLEY COLLEGE

Accounting Technology/Technician and Bookkeeping, A
Administrative Assistant and Secretarial Science, A
Art/Art Studies, General, A
Automobile/Automotive Mechanics Technology/Technician, A
Biological and Physical Sciences, A
Biology/Biological Sciences, A
Business Administration and Management, A
Chemistry, A
Criminal Justice/Police Science, A

Drafting and Design Technology/Technician, A
Drawing, A
Engineering, A
English Language and Literature, A
Humanities/Humanistic Studies, A
Information Technology, A
Legal Assistant/Paralegal, A
Liberal Arts and Sciences Studies and Humanities, A
Psychology, A
Retailing and Retail Operations, A
Sculpture, A

EX'PRESSION COLLEGE FOR DIGITAL ARTS

Animation, Interactive Technology, Video Graphics and Special Effects, B

FEATHER RIVER COLLEGE

Accounting Technology/Technician and Bookkeeping, A
Administrative Assistant and Secretarial Science, A
Agriculture, A
Anthropology, A
Biology/Biological Sciences, A
Business/Commerce, A
Child Care Provider/Assistant, A
Computer Programming/Programmer, A
Cooking and Related Culinary Arts, A
Corrections and Criminal Justice, A
English Language and Literature, A
Environmental Studies, A
Foods, Nutrition, and Wellness Studies, A
Health and Physical Education, A
History, A
Horse Husbandry/Equine Science and Management, A
Humanities/Humanistic Studies, A
Kinesiology and Exercise Science, A
Liberal Arts and Sciences Studies and Humanities, A
Mathematics, A
Natural Resources and Conservation, A
Parks, Recreation, Leisure and Fitness Studies, A
Physical Sciences, A
Political Science and Government, A
Social Sciences, A
Sociology, A
Visual and Performing Arts, A
Wildlife and Wildlands Science and Management, A

FIDM/FASHION INSTITUTE OF DESIGN & MERCHANDISING, LOS ANGELES CAMPUS

Apparel and Textile Manufacture, B
Apparel and Textile Marketing Management, A
Business, Management, Marketing, and Related Support Services, B
Cinematography and Film/Video Production, AB
Design and Visual Communications, A
Fashion Merchandising, A
Fashion/Apparel Design, A
Graphic Design, AB
Industrial Design, B
Interior Design, AB
Logistics and Materials Management, A
Marketing/Marketing Management, AB
Metal and Jewelry Arts, A

FIDM/FASHION INSTITUTE OF DESIGN & MERCHANDISING, ORANGE COUNTY CAMPUS

Apparel and Textile Marketing Management, A
Design and Visual Communications, A
Fashion Merchandising, A
Fashion/Apparel Design, A
Graphic Design, A
Interior Design, A

FIDM/FASHION INSTITUTE OF DESIGN & MERCHANDISING, SAN DIEGO CAMPUS

Design and Visual Communications, A
Fashion Merchandising, A

FIDM/FASHION INSTITUTE OF DESIGN & MERCHANDISING, SAN FRANCISCO CAMPUS

Apparel and Textile Marketing Management, A
Business, Management, Marketing, and Related
 Support Services, B
Design and Visual Communications, A
Fashion Merchandising, A
Fashion/Apparel Design, A
Graphic Design, A
Interior Design, A

FOLSOM LAKE COLLEGE

Accounting, A
Art/Art Studies, General, A
Biology/Biological Sciences, A
Business Administration and Management, A
Communication, Journalism and Related Pro-
 grams, A
Computer and Information Sciences, A
Criminal Justice/Law Enforcement Administration, A
Early Childhood Education and Teaching, A
Education, A
English Language and Literature, A
Finance, A
Geology/Earth Science, A
Human Services, A
Liberal Arts and Sciences Studies and Humani-
 ties, A
Marketing/Marketing Management, A
Mathematics, A
Physical Sciences, A
Psychology, A
Real Estate, A
Social Sciences, A

FOOTHILL COLLEGE

Accounting, A
Administration of Special Education, A
American/United States Studies/Civilization, A
Anthropology, A
Art History, Criticism and Conservation, A
Art/Art Studies, General, A
Athletic Training and Sports Medicine, A
Biology/Biological Sciences, A
Business Administration and Management, A
Chemistry, A
Child Development, A
Classics and Classical Languages, Litera-
 tures, and Linguistics, A
Comparative Literature, A
Computer Science, A
Dental Assisting/Assistant, A
Dental Hygiene/Hygienist, A
Diagnostic Medical Sonography/Sonographer and
 Ultrasound Technician, A
Drama and Dramatics/Theatre Arts, A
Economics, A
Electrical, Electronic and Communications Engineer-
 ing Technology/Technician, A
Emergency Medical Technology/Technician (EMT
 Paramedic), A
English Language and Literature, A
Fine/Studio Arts, A
Geography, A
Graphic Design, A
History, A
International Business/Trade/Commerce, A
Japanese Language and Literature, A
Liberal Arts and Sciences Studies and Humani-
 ties, A
Mathematics, A
Medical Radiologic Technology/Science - Radiation
 Therapist, A
Music, A
Natural Sciences, A
Ornamental Horticulture, A
Pharmacy Technician/Assistant, A
Philosophy, A
Photography, A
Physical Education Teaching and Coaching, A
Physician Assistant, A
Physics, A
Political Science and Government, A

Pre-Law Studies, A
Psychology, A
Radiologic Technology/Science - Radiographer, A
Real Estate, A
Respiratory Care Therapy/Therapist, A
Social Sciences, A
Sociology, A
Spanish Language and Literature, A
Technical Theatre/Theatre Design and Technol-
 ogy, A
Veterinary/Animal Health Technology/Technician and
 Veterinary Assistant, A
Women's Studies, A

FREMONT COLLEGE (CERRITOS)

Legal Assistant/Paralegal, A

FRESNO CITY COLLEGE

Accounting Technology/Technician and Bookkeep-
 ing, A
Administrative Assistant and Secretarial Science, A
Apparel and Textile Marketing Management, A
Architectural Technology/Technician, A
Art/Art Studies, General, A
Autobody/Collision and Repair
 Technology/Technician, A
Automobile/Automotive Mechanics
 Technology/Technician, A
Biological and Physical Sciences, A
Biology/Biological Sciences, A
Building/Construction Site Management/Manager, A
Building/Home/Construction Inspection/Inspector, A
Business Administration and Management, A
Carpentry/Carpenter, A
Child Care Provider/Assistant, A
Communication Studies/Speech Communication
 and Rhetoric, A
Computer Systems Networking and Telecommunica-
 tions, A
Construction Trades, A
Corrections, A
Criminal Justice/Police Science, A
Customer Service Support/Call Center/Teleservice
 Operation, A
Dance, A
Dental Hygiene/Hygienist, A
Drafting and Design Technology/Technician, A
Drama and Dramatics/Theatre Arts, A
Education/Teaching of Individuals in Early Childhood
 Special Education Programs, A
Electrical/Electronics Equipment Installation and Re-
 pair, A
Engineering, A
English Language and Literature, A
Ethnic, Cultural Minority, and Gender Studies, A
Family and Consumer Sciences/Human Sciences, A
Fire Science/Firefighting, A
Foods, Nutrition, and Wellness Studies, A
Foreign Languages and Literatures, A
Forensic Science and Technology, A
Graphic Design, A
Graphic and Printing Equipment Operator Produc-
 tion, A
Hazardous Materials Management and Waste
 Technology/Technician, A
Health Information/Medical Records
 Administration/Administrator, A
Heating, Air Conditioning, Ventilation and Refrigera-
 tion Maintenance Technology/Technician, A
Human Services, A
Humanities/Humanistic Studies, A
Information Technology, A
Legal Administrative Assistant/Secretary, A
Legal Assistant/Paralegal, A
Liberal Arts and Sciences Studies and Humani-
 ties, A
Library Science, A
Mathematics, A
Medical Administrative Assistant/Secretary, A
Medical/Clinical Assistant, A
Modern Greek Language and Literature, A
Music, A
Parks, Recreation, Leisure and Fitness Studies, A
Philosophy, A
Photographic and Film/Video Technology/Technician
 and Assistant, A

Physical Sciences, A
Radiologic Technology/Science - Radiographer, A
Real Estate, A
Recording Arts Technology/Technician, A
Respiratory Care Therapy/Therapist, A
Restaurant, Culinary, and Catering
 Management/Manager, A
Retailing and Retail Operations, A
Sales, Distribution and Marketing Operations, A
Social Sciences, A
Sociology, A
Spanish Language and Literature, A
Substance Abuse/Addiction Counseling, A
Surgical Technology/Technologist, A
Teacher Assistant/Aide, A
Technical Theatre/Theatre Design and Technol-
 ogy, A
Technology Teacher Education/Industrial Arts
 Teacher Education, A
Web/Multimedia Management and Webmaster, A
Welding Technology/Welder, A
Women's Studies, A

FRESNO PACIFIC UNIVERSITY

Accounting, B
Applied Mathematics, B
Bible/Biblical Studies, B
Biology/Biological Sciences, B
Business Administration, Management and Opera-
 tions, M
Chemistry, B
Conflict Resolution and Mediation/Peace Stud-
 ies, MO
Counselor Education/School Counseling and Guid-
 ance Services, M
Curriculum and Instruction, M
Education, MO
Educational Administration and Supervision, M
Educational Media/Instructional Technology, M
English Language and Literature, B
English as a Second Language, M
History, B
Humanities/Humanistic Studies, B
Interdisciplinary Studies, M
International Business/Trade/Commerce, B
Kinesiology and Movement Studies, M
Marketing/Marketing Management, B
Marriage and Family Therapy/Counseling, M
Mathematics, B
Mathematics Teacher Education, M
Missions/Missionary Studies and Missiology, M
Music, B
Music Teacher Education, B
Natural Sciences, AB
Non-Profit/Public/Organizational Management, B
Nursing, M
Nursing - Advanced Practice, M
Pastoral Studies/Counseling, M
Physical Education Teaching and Coaching, AB
Pre-Law Studies, B
Pre-Medicine/Pre-Medical Studies, B
Psychology, AB
Reading Teacher Education, MO
School Psychology, M
Science Teacher Education/General Science
 Teacher Education, M
Social Work, B
Sociology, A
Spanish Language and Literature, AB
Special Education and Teaching, M
Sport and Fitness Administration/Management, B
Student Personnel Services, MO
Theology and Religious Vocations, M

FULLERTON COLLEGE

Accounting Technology/Technician and Bookkeep-
 ing, A
Administrative Assistant and Secretarial Science, A
Anthropology, A
Apparel and Textile Marketing Management, A
Apparel and Textiles, A
Applied Horticulture/Horticultural Operations, A
Architectural Technology/Technician, A
Area Studies, A
Art/Art Studies, General, A
Astronomy, A

Automobile/Automotive Mechanics
Technology/Technician, A
Biological and Physical Sciences, A
Biology/Biological Sciences, A
Biomedical Technology/Technician, A
Building/Construction Site Management/Manager, A
Building/Home/Construction Inspection/Inspector, A
Business Administration and Management, A
Carpentry/Carpenter, A
Chemical Technology/Technician, A
Chemistry, A
Child Care Provider/Assistant, A
Communication Studies/Speech Communication
and Rhetoric, A
Computer Science, A
Construction Trades, A
Cosmetology/Cosmetologist, A
Criminal Justice/Police Science, A
Dance, A
Drafting and Design Technology/Technician, A
Drama and Dramatics/Theatre Arts, A
Economics, A
Electrical/Electronics Equipment Installation and Re-
pair, A
Engineering, A
English Language and Literature, A
Environmental Studies, A
Ethnic, Cultural Minority, and Gender Studies, A
Fashion/Apparel Design, A
Foods, Nutrition, and Wellness Studies, A
Foreign Languages and Literatures, A
Geography, A
Geology/Earth Science, A
Graphic Design, A
Graphic and Printing Equipment Operator Produc-
tion, A
Hazardous Materials Management and Waste
Technology/Technician, A
Health and Physical Education, A
Health/Medical Preparatory Programs, A
History, A
Humanities/Humanistic Studies, A
Information Technology, A
Interior Design, A
International Business/Trade/Commerce, A
Journalism, A
Landscaping and Groundskeeping, A
Legal Administrative Assistant/Secretary, A
Legal Assistant/Paralegal, A
Liberal Arts and Sciences Studies and Humani-
ties, A
Mass Communication/Media Studies, A
Mathematics, A
Mechanical Engineering/Mechanical
Technology/Technician, A
Microbiology, A
Music, A
Parks, Recreation, Leisure and Fitness Studies, A
Philosophy, A
Physics, A
Plant Nursery Operations and Management, A
Political Science and Government, A
Psychology, A
Radio and Television, A
Real Estate, A
Recording Arts Technology/Technician, A
Religion/Religious Studies, A
Sales, Distribution and Marketing Operations, A
Small Business Administration/Management, A
Sociology, A
Sport and Fitness Administration/Management, A
Technology Teacher Education/Industrial Arts
Teacher Education, A

GAVILAN COLLEGE

Accounting Technology/Technician and Bookkeep-
ing, A
Administrative Assistant and Secretarial Science, A
Airframe Mechanics and Aircraft Maintenance
Technology/Technician, A
Art/Art Studies, General, A
Biological and Physical Sciences, A
Biology/Biological Sciences, A
Business Administration and Management, A
Business/Commerce, A
Carpentry/Carpenter, A

Child Care Provider/Assistant, A
Cinematography and Film/Video Production, A
Computer Graphics, A
Computer Programming/Programmer, A
Computer Science, A
Computer Systems Networking and Telecommunica-
tions, A
Corrections, A
Cosmetology/Cosmetologist, A
Criminal Justice/Police Science, A
Data Entry/Microcomputer Applications, A
Drafting and Design Technology/Technician, A
Drama and Dramatics/Theatre Arts, A
Engineering, A
English Language and Literature, A
Family Resource Management Studies, A
General Studies, A
Health and Physical Education, A
Health/Medical Preparatory Programs, A
Liberal Arts and Sciences Studies and Humani-
ties, A
Mathematics, A
Medical Administrative Assistant/Secretary, A
Music, A
Physical Sciences, A
Prepress/Desktop Publishing and Digital Imaging
Design, A
Real Estate, A
Social Sciences, A
Spanish Language and Literature, A
System Administration/Administrator, A
Technical Theatre/Theatre Design and Technol-
ogy, A
Visual and Performing Arts, A

GLENDALE COMMUNITY COLLEGE

Accounting, A
Accounting Technology/Technician and Bookkeep-
ing, A
Administrative Assistant and Secretarial Science, A
Airline Flight Attendant, A
Airline/Commercial/Professional Pilot and Flight
Crew, A
Animation, Interactive Technology, Video Graphics
and Special Effects, A
Art/Art Studies, General, A
Aviation/Airway Management and Operations, A
Behavioral Sciences, A
Biology/Biological Sciences, A
Business Administration and Management, A
Ceramic Arts and Ceramics, A
Commercial and Advertising Art, A
Communication Studies/Speech Communication
and Rhetoric, A
Computer Engineering Technology/Technician, A
Computer Programming, Specific Applications, A
Computer Programming/Programmer, A
Computer Science, A
Computer Software Technology/Technician, A
Computer and Information Sciences, A
Consumer Merchandising/Retailing Management, A
Criminal Justice/Law Enforcement Administration, A
Dance, A
Design and Visual Communications, A
Dietetics/Dieticians, A
Drama and Dance Teacher Education, A
Drama and Dramatics/Theatre Arts, A
Early Childhood Education and Teaching, A
Electrical, Electronic and Communications Engineer-
ing Technology/Technician, A
Elementary Education and Teaching, A
Engine Machinist, A
English Language and Literature, A
Entrepreneurship/Entrepreneurial Studies, A
Financial Planning and Services, A
Fire Protection and Safety Technology/Technician, A
Foreign Languages and Literatures, A
Health and Physical Education, A
Insurance, A
International Business/Trade/Commerce, A
Legal Administrative Assistant/Secretary, A
Liberal Arts and Sciences Studies and Humani-
ties, A
Management Science, A
Marketing/Marketing Management, A
Mass Communication/Media Studies, A

Mathematics, A
Medical Administrative Assistant/Secretary, A
Medical Office Assistant/Specialist, A
Medical Transcription/Transcriptionist, A
Multi-/Interdisciplinary Studies, A
Music, A
Office Management and Supervision, A
Parks, Recreation, Leisure and Fitness Studies, A
Photography, A
Physical Sciences, A
Radio and Television, A
Real Estate, A
Restaurant/Food Services Management, A
Social Sciences, A
Sport and Fitness Administration/Management, A
Substance Abuse/Addiction Counseling, A
Technical Theatre/Theatre Design and Technol-
ogy, A
Web/Multimedia Management and Webmaster, A
Welding Technology/Welder, A

GOLDEN GATE UNIVERSITY

Accounting, BMO
Advertising and Public Relations, MO
Business Administration and Management, B
Business Administration, Management and Opera-
tions, MDO
Corporate and Organizational Communication, MO
Environmental Law, M
Finance, B
Finance and Banking, MO
Forensic Science and Technology, M
Health Informatics, O
Human Resources Management and Services, MO
Human Resources Management/Personnel Adminis-
tration, B
Information Technology, B
Intellectual Property Law, M
International Business/Trade/Commerce, BM
Law and Legal Studies, MD
Legal and Justice Studies, MD
Management, M
Management Information Systems and Ser-
vices, MO
Management of Technology, O
Marketing, MO
Marketing/Marketing Management, B
Operations Management and Supervision, B
Psychology, MO
Public Administration, M
Supply Chain Management, O
Taxation, MO

GOLDEN WEST COLLEGE

Accounting, A
Administrative Assistant and Secretarial Science, A
Architectural Engineering Technology/Technician, A
Art/Art Studies, General, A
Automobile/Automotive Mechanics
Technology/Technician, A
Biological and Physical Sciences, A
Biology/Biological Sciences, A
Business Administration and Management, A
Commercial and Advertising Art, A
Consumer Merchandising/Retailing Management, A
Cosmetology/Cosmetologist, A
Criminal Justice/Law Enforcement Administration, A
Criminal Justice/Police Science, A
Drafting and Design Technology/Technician, A
Electrical, Electronic and Communications Engineer-
ing Technology/Technician, A
Engineering Technology, A
Graphic and Printing Equipment Operator Produc-
tion, A
Humanities/Humanistic Studies, A
Journalism, A
Legal Administrative Assistant/Secretary, A
Liberal Arts and Sciences Studies and Humani-
ties, A
Marketing/Marketing Management, A
Mathematics, A
Music, A
Natural Sciences, A
Ornamental Horticulture, A
Physical Sciences, A
Radio and Television, A

Real Estate, A
Sign Language Interpretation and Translation, A

GOLF ACADEMY OF AMERICA

Business Administration, Management and Operations, A

GROSSMONT COLLEGE

Administrative Assistant and Secretarial Science, A
American Sign Language (ASL), A
Animation, Interactive Technology, Video Graphics
   and Special Effects, A
Arabic Language and Literature, A
Art/Art Studies, General, A
Audiology/Audiologist and Speech-Language
   Pathology/Pathologist, A
Biology/Biological Sciences, A
Business Administration and Management, A
Business/Commerce, A
Cardiovascular Technology/Technologist, A
Ceramic Arts and Ceramics, A
Chemistry, A
Child Care and Support Services Management, A
Clinical/Medical Laboratory Science and Allied Professions, A
Communication Studies/Speech Communication
   and Rhetoric, A
Computer Programming/Programmer, A
Computer Systems Networking and Telecommunications, A
Cooking and Related Culinary Arts, A
Corrections, A
Criminal Justice/Police Science, A
Dance, A
Data Entry/Microcomputer Applications, A
Drama and Dramatics/Theatre Arts, A
Drawing, A
Economics, A
English Language and Literature, A
Ethnic, Cultural Minority, and Gender Studies, A
Family Systems, A
Forensic Science and Technology, A
French Language and Literature, A
Geography, A
Geology/Earth Science, A
German Language and Literature, A
Health and Physical Education, A
History, A
Hospitality Administration/Management, A
International Business/Trade/Commerce, A
Japanese Language and Literature, A
Journalism, A
Liberal Arts and Sciences Studies and Humanities, A
Mathematics, A
Music, A
Occupational Therapy/Therapist, A
Oceanography, Chemical and Physical, A
Philosophy, A
Photography, A
Physics, A
Political Science and Government, A
Public Administration and Social Service Professions, A
Radio and Television, A
Respiratory Care Therapy/Therapist, A
Restaurant, Culinary, and Catering
   Management/Manager, A
Retailing and Retail Operations, A
Sculpture, A
Security and Loss Prevention Services, A
Slavic Languages, Literatures, and Linguistics, A
Spanish Language and Literature, A
Technical Theatre/Theatre Design and Technology, A
Visual and Performing Arts, A
Web/Multimedia Management and Webmaster, A

HARTNELL COLLEGE

Administrative Assistant and Secretarial Science, A
Agricultural Business and Management, A
Agriculture, A
Animation, Interactive Technology, Video Graphics
   and Special Effects, A
Art/Art Studies, General, A

Autobody/Collision and Repair
   Technology/Technician, A
Automobile/Automotive Mechanics
   Technology/Technician, A
Banking and Financial Support Services, A
Biology/Biological Sciences, A
Building/Construction Site Management/Manager, A
Business Administration and Management, A
Chemistry, A
Child Care Provider/Assistant, A
Clinical/Medical Laboratory Technician, A
Communication Studies/Speech Communication
   and Rhetoric, A
Computer Programming/Programmer, A
Corrections, A
Criminal Justice/Police Science, A
Dental Assisting/Assistant, A
Diesel Mechanics Technology/Technician, A
Drafting and Design Technology/Technician, A
Drama and Dramatics/Theatre Arts, A
English Language and Literature, A
Fire Protection and Safety Technology/Technician, A
Geology/Earth Science, A
Health and Physical Education, A
History, A
Human Services, A
Liberal Arts and Sciences Studies and Humanities, A
Library Science, A
Mathematics, A
Mechanical Engineering/Mechanical
   Technology/Technician, A
Music, A
Photography, A
Physics, A
Psychology, A
Real Estate, A
Social Sciences, A
Spanish Language and Literature, A
Substance Abuse/Addiction Counseling, A
Teacher Assistant/Aide, A
Veterinary/Animal Health Technology/Technician and
   Veterinary Assistant, A
Water Quality and Wastewater Treatment Management and Recycling Technology/Technician, A
Web Page, Digital/Multimedia and Information Resources Design, A
Welding Technology/Welder, A

HARVEY MUDD COLLEGE

Biology/Biological Sciences, B
Biomathematics and Bioinformatics, B
Chemistry, B
Computer Science, B
Engineering, B
Mathematics, B
Physics, B

HENLEY-PUTNAM UNIVERSITY

Conflict Resolution and Mediation/Peace Studies, M
Homeland Security, M
Military Studies, B
Military and Defense Studies, M
National Security, D
Securities Services Administration/Management, B

HOLY NAMES UNIVERSITY

Accounting, B
Biological and Biomedical Sciences, B
Biology/Biological Sciences, B
Business Administration and Management, B
Business Administration, Management and Operations, M
Business/Corporate Communications, B
Community Health Nursing, M
Computer Software and Media Applications, B
Computer/Information Technology Services Administration and Management, B
Counseling Psychology, M
Education, MO
Educational Psychology, MO
Energy Management and Policy, M
English Language and Literature, B
English as a Second Language, M
Finance and Banking, M
Forensic Psychology, MO

History, B
Human Resources Management/Personnel Administration, B
Human Services, B
Humanities/Humanistic Studies, B
International Relations and Affairs, B
Liberal Arts and Sciences Studies and Humanities, B
Management, M
Marketing, M
Marketing/Marketing Management, B
Music, BMO
Music Pedagogy, B
Music Performance, B
Music Teacher Education, MO
Nursing, MO
Nursing - Advanced Practice, MO
Nursing Administration, MO
Nursing Education, MO
Pastoral Studies/Counseling, MO
Philosophy, B
Philosophy and Religious Studies, B
Psychology, B
Religion/Religious Studies, BMO
Sociology, B
Spanish Language and Literature, B
Special Education and Teaching, MO
Sport and Fitness Administration/Management, M
Urban Education and Leadership, M
Writing, M

HOPE INTERNATIONAL UNIVERSITY

Bible/Biblical Studies, B
Business Administration and Management, B
Education, M
Educational Administration and Supervision, M
Elementary Education and Teaching, BM
English Language and Literature, B
General Studies, A
Human Development and Family Studies, B
International Business/Trade/Commerce, M
International Development, M
Liberal Arts and Sciences Studies and Humanities, B
Marketing, M
Marriage and Family Therapy/Counseling, M
Missions/Missionary Studies and Missiology, BM
Non-Profit/Public/Organizational Management, M
Psychology, B
Religion/Religious Studies, BM
Religious/Sacred Music, B
Sacred Music, M
Secondary Education and Teaching, M
Social Sciences, B
Social and Philosophical Foundations of Education, M
Theological and Ministerial Studies, B
Youth Ministry, B

HORIZON UNIVERSITY

Bible/Biblical Studies, A
Theological and Ministerial Studies, B

HUMBOLDT STATE UNIVERSITY

American Indian/Native American Studies, B
Anthropology, BM
Applied Mathematics, B
Art History, Criticism and Conservation, B
Art Teacher Education, B
Art/Art Studies, General, B
Athletic Training and Sports Medicine, M
Biochemistry, B
Biological and Biomedical Sciences, M
Biology/Biological Sciences, B
Botany/Plant Biology, B
Broadcast Journalism, B
Business Administration and Management, B
Business Administration, Management and Operations, M
Cell/Cellular Biology and Histology, B
Chemistry, B
Child Development, B
Computer Science, B
Counseling Psychology, M
Drama and Dramatics/Theatre Arts, B
Economics, B

Education, BM
Elementary Education and Teaching, B
English, M
English Language and Literature, B
English as a Second Language, M
Environmental Biology, B
Environmental Sciences, BM
Environmental Studies, BM
Environmental/Environmental Health Engineering, B
Exercise and Sports Science, M
Fine/Studio Arts, B
Fish, Game and Wildlife Management, M
Fishing and Fisheries Sciences and Management, B
Forestry, BM
French Language and Literature, B
Geography, B
Geology/Earth Science, BM
Hazardous Materials Management and Waste Technology/Technician, M
History, B
Hydrology and Water Resources Science, B
Information Technology, B
Journalism, B
Kindergarten/PreSchool Education and Teaching, B
Kinesiology and Exercise Science, B
Kinesiology and Movement Studies, M
Liberal Arts and Sciences Studies and Humanities, B
Marine Biology and Biological Oceanography, B
Mathematics, B
Medical Microbiology and Bacteriology, B
Molecular Biology, B
Multi-/Interdisciplinary Studies, B
Music, B
Music Teacher Education, B
Natural Resources Management/Development and Policy, B
Natural Resources and Conservation, BM
Natural Sciences, B
Oceanography, Chemical and Physical, B
Parks, Recreation and Leisure Facilities Management, B
Parks, Recreation, Leisure and Fitness Studies, B
Philosophy, B
Physical Education Teaching and Coaching, BM
Physical Therapy/Therapist, M
Physics, B
Political Science and Government, B
Psychology, BM
Range Science and Management, B
Religion/Religious Studies, B
School Psychology, M
Secondary Education and Teaching, B
Social Sciences, BM
Social Work, BM
Sociology, BM
Spanish Language and Literature, B
Water Resources, M
Wildlife and Wildlands Science and Management, B
Zoology/Animal Biology, B

HUMPHREYS COLLEGE

Accounting, AB
Administrative Assistant and Secretarial Science, AB
Business Administration and Management, AB
Community Organization and Advocacy, B
Computer Programming/Programmer, AB
Computer Science, AB
Court Reporting/Court Reporter, A
Data Processing and Data Processing Technology/Technician, AB
Information Science/Studies, AB
Law and Legal Studies, D
Legal Assistant/Paralegal, B
Liberal Arts and Sciences Studies and Humanities, AB

IMPERIAL VALLEY COLLEGE

Accounting, A
Administrative Assistant and Secretarial Science, A
Agricultural Business and Management, A
Agricultural Mechanization, A
Agriculture, A
Anthropology, A
Art/Art Studies, General, A

Automobile/Automotive Mechanics Technology/Technician, A
Behavioral Sciences, A
Biological and Physical Sciences, A
Business Administration and Management, A
Criminal Justice/Law Enforcement Administration, A
English Language and Literature, A
Fire Science/Firefighting, A
French Language and Literature, A
Human Development and Family Studies, A
Humanities/Humanistic Studies, A
Hydrology and Water Resources Science, A
Information Science/Studies, A
Journalism, A
Kindergarten/PreSchool Education and Teaching, A
Liberal Arts and Sciences Studies and Humanities, A
Marketing/Marketing Management, A
Mathematics, A
Modern Languages, A
Music, A
Physical Education Teaching and Coaching, A
Physical Sciences, A
Psychology, A
Social Sciences, A
Spanish Language and Literature, A
Welding Technology/Welder, A

INTERIOR DESIGNERS INSTITUTE

Interior Design, ABM

IRVINE VALLEY COLLEGE

Accounting, A
Administrative Assistant and Secretarial Science, A
Art/Art Studies, General, A
Behavioral Sciences, A
Biological and Physical Sciences, A
Biology/Biological Sciences, A
Business Administration and Management, A
Business Machine Repairer, A
Comparative Literature, A
Computer Engineering Technology/Technician, A
Criminal Justice/Law Enforcement Administration, A
Data Processing and Data Processing Technology/Technician, A
Electromechanical Technology/Electromechanical Engineering Technology, A
English Language and Literature, A
History, A
Humanities/Humanistic Studies, A
Liberal Arts and Sciences Studies and Humanities, A
Mathematics, A
Social Sciences, A

JOHN F. KENNEDY UNIVERSITY

Business Administration and Management, B
Business Administration, Management and Operations, MO
Comparative and Interdisciplinary Arts, M
Counseling Psychology, M
Education, M
Fine Arts and Art Studies, M
Fine/Studio Arts, B
Health Education, M
Health Psychology, M
Human Resources Development, MO
Industrial and Organizational Psychology, MO
Law and Legal Studies, D
Legal Assistant/Paralegal, B
Liberal Arts and Sciences Studies and Humanities, B
Museology/Museum Studies, MO
Organizational Management, O
Philosophy and Religious Studies, B
Psychology, BMDO
Sport Psychology, M
Systems Science and Theory, B
Transpersonal and Humanistic Psychology, M

JOHN PAUL THE GREAT CATHOLIC UNIVERSITY

Cinematography and Film/Video Production, B
Entrepreneurship/Entrepreneurial Studies, B

Theology and Religious Vocations, M

LA SIERRA UNIVERSITY

Accounting, BM
Advertising and Public Relations, M
Art/Art Studies, General, B
Biochemistry, B
Biology/Biological Sciences, B
Biophysics, B
Business Administration and Management, B
Business Administration, Management and Operations, MO
Business/Commerce, B
Chemistry, B
Cinematography and Film/Video Production, B
Communication Studies/Speech Communication and Rhetoric, B
Communication Theory, M
Computer Science, B
Counselor Education/School Counseling and Guidance Services, MO
Criminal Justice/Safety Studies, B
Curriculum and Instruction, MDO
Economics, B
Education, MDO
Educational Administration and Supervision, MDO
Educational Psychology, MO
English, M
English Language and Literature, B
Environmental Sciences, B
Film/Cinema Studies, B
Finance, B
Finance and Banking, M
Fine/Studio Arts, B
Health and Physical Education, B
History, B
Human Resources Management and Services, M
Human Resources Management/Personnel Administration, B
Information Science/Studies, B
International/Global Studies, B
Kinesiology and Exercise Science, B
Liberal Arts and Sciences Studies and Humanities, B
Management, M
Marketing, M
Marketing/Marketing Management, B
Mathematics, B
Music, B
Music Teacher Education, B
Pastoral Studies/Counseling, M
Physical Sciences, B
Physics, B
Psychology, B
Religion/Religious Studies, BM
Religious Education, M
School Psychology, O
Social Work, B
Sociology, B
Spanish Language and Literature, B
Writing, M

LAGUNA COLLEGE OF ART & DESIGN

Animation, Interactive Technology, Video Graphics and Special Effects, B
Art/Art Studies, General, B
Commercial and Advertising Art, B
Design and Applied Arts, B
Design and Visual Communications, B
Drawing, B
Fine/Studio Arts, B
Graphic Design, B
Illustration, B
Intermedia/Multimedia, B
Painting, BM
Printmaking, B
Sculpture, B

LAKE TAHOE COMMUNITY COLLEGE

Accounting, A
Administrative Assistant and Secretarial Science, A
Art/Art Studies, General, A
Biological and Physical Sciences, A
Business Administration and Management, A
Computer Science, A
Criminal Justice/Law Enforcement Administration, A

Criminal Justice/Police Science, A
Drama and Dramatics/Theatre Arts, A
Finance, A
Fire Science/Firefighting, A
Geography, A
Geology/Earth Science, A
Humanities/Humanistic Studies, A
Kindergarten/PreSchool Education and Teaching, A
Liberal Arts and Sciences Studies and Humanities, A
Marketing/Marketing Management, A
Mathematics, A
Medical Administrative Assistant/Secretary, A
Medical/Clinical Assistant, A
Music, A
Natural Sciences, A
Physical Education Teaching and Coaching, A
Psychology, A
Real Estate, A
Social Sciences, A
Spanish Language and Literature, A

LANEY COLLEGE

Accounting, A
Administrative Assistant and Secretarial Science, A
African-American/Black Studies, A
Architectural Engineering Technology/Technician, A
Art/Art Studies, General, A
Asian Studies/Civilization, A
Biological and Physical Sciences, A
Broadcast Journalism, A
Building/Construction Finishing, Management, and Inspection, A
Business Administration and Management, A
Carpentry/Carpenter, A
Ceramic Arts and Ceramics, A
Commercial and Advertising Art, A
Computer Programming/Programmer, A
Computer Typography and Composition Equipment Operator, A
Cosmetology/Cosmetologist, A
Culinary Arts/Chef Training, A
Dance, A
Drama and Dramatics/Theatre Arts, A
Engineering, A
Engineering Technology, A
Finance, A
Graphic and Printing Equipment Operator Production, A
Heating, Air Conditioning, Ventilation and Refrigeration Maintenance Technology/Technician, A
Hispanic-American, Puerto Rican, and Mexican-American/Chicano Studies, A
Humanities/Humanistic Studies, A
Information Science/Studies, A
Journalism, A
Labor and Industrial Relations, A
Liberal Arts and Sciences Studies and Humanities, A
Machine Tool Technology/Machinist, A
Management Information Systems and Services, A
Marketing/Marketing Management, A
Mathematics, A
Music, A
Photography, A
Radio and Television, A
Reading Teacher Education, A
Social Sciences, A
Welding Technology/Welder, A
Wood Science and Wood Products/Pulp and Paper Technology, A

LAS POSITAS COLLEGE

Accounting, A
Administrative Assistant and Secretarial Science, A
Automobile/Automotive Mechanics Technology/Technician, A
Business Administration and Management, A
Computer Science, A
Criminal Justice/Police Science, A
Drafting and Design Technology/Technician, A
Education, A
Electrical, Electronic and Communications Engineering Technology/Technician, A
Environmental Studies, A
Fashion Merchandising, A

Fire Science/Firefighting, A
Horticultural Science, A
Industrial Design, A
Industrial Radiologic Technology/Technician, A
Information Science/Studies, A
Interior Design, A
Kindergarten/PreSchool Education and Teaching, A
Liberal Arts and Sciences Studies and Humanities, A
Marketing/Marketing Management, A
Occupational Safety and Health Technology/Technician, A
Real Estate, A
Welding Technology/Welder, A

LASSEN COMMUNITY COLLEGE DISTRICT

Accounting, A
Administrative Assistant and Secretarial Science, A
Agricultural Business and Management, A
Agricultural Economics, A
Agricultural Mechanization, A
Agriculture, A
Agronomy and Crop Science, A
Art/Art Studies, General, A
Automobile/Automotive Mechanics Technology/Technician, A
Biological and Physical Sciences, A
Biology/Biological Sciences, A
Botany/Plant Biology, A
Business Administration and Management, A
Business Machine Repairer, A
Carpentry/Carpenter, A
Ceramic Arts and Ceramics, A
Chemistry, A
Child Development, A
Commercial and Advertising Art, A
Communications Technology/Technician, A
Computer Science, A
Construction Engineering Technology/Technician, A
Construction Trades, A
Corrections, A
Cosmetology/Cosmetologist, A
Criminal Justice/Police Science, A
Design and Applied Arts, A
Drafting and Design Technology/Technician, A
Drawing, A
Energy Management and Systems Technology/Technician, A
Engineering Technology, A
Farm/Farm and Ranch Management, A
Health and Physical Education, A
History, A
Human Services, A
Humanities/Humanistic Studies, A
Information Technology, A
Journalism, A
Kindergarten/PreSchool Education and Teaching, A
Legal Administrative Assistant/Secretary, A
Liberal Arts and Sciences Studies and Humanities, A
Mass Communication/Media Studies, A
Mathematics, A
Mechanical Engineering/Mechanical Technology/Technician, A
Medical Administrative Assistant/Secretary, A
Natural Sciences, A
Photography, A
Physical Education Teaching and Coaching, A
Physical Sciences, A
Psychology, A
Radio and Television, A
Real Estate, A
Social Sciences, A
Substance Abuse/Addiction Counseling, A
Welding Technology/Welder, A

LIFE PACIFIC COLLEGE

Bible/Biblical Studies, AB
Pastoral Studies/Counseling, B
Theology/Theological Studies, B

LINCOLN UNIVERSITY

Business Administration and Management, B
Business Administration, Management and Operations, MD

Diagnostic Medical Sonography/Sonographer and Ultrasound Technician, A
Economics, B
Finance and Banking, MD
Health Services/Allied Health/Health Sciences, B
Human Resources Management and Services, MD
International Business/Trade/Commerce, BM
Investment Management, MD
Management Information Systems and Services, BM
Small Business Administration/Management, B

LOMA LINDA UNIVERSITY

Allied Health and Medical Assisting Services, MD
Allopathic Medicine, MD
Anatomy, MD
Audiology/Audiologist and Speech-Language Pathology/Pathologist, AB
Biochemistry, MD
Bioethics/Medical Ethics, MO
Biological and Biomedical Sciences, MD
Biostatistics, MDO
Child and Family Studies, MDO
Clinical Laboratory Science/Medical Technology/Technologist, AB
Communication Disorders, M
Counselor Education/School Counseling and Guidance Services, MDO
CytoTechnology/Cytotechnologist, B
Dental Hygiene/Hygienist, B
Dental and Oral Surgery, MO
Dentistry, MDO
Emergency Medical Technology/Technician (EMT Paramedic), B
Environmental and Occupational Health, M
Epidemiology, MDO
Geology/Earth Science, B
Geosciences, MD
Gerontological Nursing, M
Health Education, MD
Health Information/Medical Records Administration/Administrator, B
Health Promotion, MD
Health Services Administration, M
International Public Health/International Health, M
Medical Radiologic Technology/Science - Radiation Therapist, AB
Microbiology, MD
Nursing, M
Nursing - Adult, M
Nursing Administration, M
Nutritional Sciences, MD
Occupational Therapist Assistant, A
Occupational Therapy/Therapist, MD
Oral and Dental Sciences, MO
Orthodontics, MO
Pastoral Studies/Counseling, MO
Pathology/Experimental Pathology, MD
Pediatric Nurse/Nursing, M
Periodontics, M
Pharmacology, MD
Pharmacy, D
Physical Therapist Assistant, A
Physical Therapy/Therapist, MD
Physician Assistant, M
Physiology, MD
Psychology, D
Public Health, MDO
Religion/Religious Studies, M
Respiratory Care Therapy/Therapist, AB
Social Work, MD
Spanish and Iberian Studies, A

LONG BEACH CITY COLLEGE

Accounting Technology/Technician and Bookkeeping, A
Administrative Assistant and Secretarial Science, A
Airframe Mechanics and Aircraft Maintenance Technology/Technician, A
Airline/Commercial/Professional Pilot and Flight Crew, A
Alternative Fuel Vehicle Technology/Technician, A
Apparel and Textile Marketing Management, A
Applied Horticulture/Horticultural Operations, A
Architectural Drafting and Architectural CAD/CADD, A

Architectural Technology/Technician, A
Art/Art Studies, General, A
Autobody/Collision and Repair
  Technology/Technician, A
Automobile/Automotive Mechanics
  Technology/Technician, A
Aviation/Airway Management and Operations, A
Biology/Biological Sciences, A
Broadcast Journalism, A
Business Administration and Management, A
Business Family and Consumer Sciences/Human
  Sciences, A
Business/Commerce, A
Cabinetmaking and Millwork/Millwright, A
Carpentry/Carpenter, A
Child Care Provider/Assistant, A
Communications Technology/Technician, A
Computer Graphics, A
Computer Programming/Programmer, A
Computer Systems Networking and Telecommunica-
  tions, A
Cooking and Related Culinary Arts, A
Criminal Justice/Police Science, A
Customer Service Support/Call Center/Teleservice
  Operation, A
Dance, A
Design and Visual Communications, A
Diesel Mechanics Technology/Technician, A
Dietetic Technician (DTR), A
Drama and Dramatics/Theatre Arts, A
Drawing, A
Electrical/Electronics Equipment Installation and Re-
  pair, A
Engineering, A
English Language and Literature, A
Fashion/Apparel Design, A
Film/Cinema Studies, A
Fire Science/Firefighting, A
Floriculture/Floristry Operations and Management, A
Foodservice Systems
  Administration/Management, A
Foreign Languages and Literatures, A
Graphic Design, A
Health and Physical Education, A
Heating, Air Conditioning and Refrigeration
  Technology/Technician, A
Hotel/Motel Administration/Management, A
Human Services, A
Information Technology, A
Interior Design, A
International Business/Trade/Commerce, A
Journalism, A
Legal Administrative Assistant/Secretary, A
Liberal Arts and Sciences Studies and Humani-
  ties, A
Library Assistant/Technician, A
Machine Tool Technology/Machinist, A
Manufacturing Technology/Technician, A
Mathematics, A
Mechanical Drafting and Mechanical Drafting
  CAD/CADD, A
Mechanical Engineering/Mechanical
  Technology/Technician, A
Medical Administrative Assistant/Secretary, A
Medical/Clinical Assistant, A
Music, A
Physical Sciences, A
Prepress/Desktop Publishing and Digital Imaging
  Design, A
Public Relations/Image Management, A
Radio and Television, A
Radiologic Technology/Science - Radiographer, A
Real Estate, A
Recording Arts Technology/Technician, A
Restaurant, Culinary, and Catering
  Management/Manager, A
Sales, Distribution and Marketing Operations, A
Sculpture, A
Sheet Metal Technology/Sheetworking, A
Social Sciences, A
Spanish Language and Literature, A
Special Education and Teaching, A
Substance Abuse/Addiction Counseling, A
System Administration/Administrator, A
Technical Theatre/Theatre Design and Technol-
  ogy, A

Tourism and Travel Services Marketing Opera-
  tions, A
Visual and Performing Arts, A
Welding Technology/Welder, A

LOS ANGELES CITY COLLEGE

Accounting, A
Administrative Assistant and Secretarial Science, A
Advertising, A
African-American/Black Studies, A
American/United States Studies/Civilization, A
Apparel and Textiles, A
Architectural Engineering Technology/Technician, A
Art/Art Studies, General, A
Biological and Physical Sciences, A
Biology/Biological Sciences, A
Broadcast Journalism, A
Business Administration and Management, A
Ceramic Arts and Ceramics, A
Chemistry, A
Child Development, A
Computer Engineering Technology/Technician, A
Computer Programming, A
Computer Programming, Specific Applications, A
Computer Programming, Vendor/Product Certifica-
  tion, A
Computer Programming/Programmer, A
Computer Software and Media Applications, A
Computer Systems Networking and Telecommunica-
  tions, A
Computer and Information Sciences, A
Computer and Information Sciences and Support
  Services, A
Computer and Information Systems Security, A
Computer/Information Technology Services Adminis-
  tration and Management, A
Consumer Merchandising/Retailing Management, A
Corrections, A
Criminal Justice/Law Enforcement Administration, A
Criminal Justice/Police Science, A
Data Entry/Microcomputer Applications, A
Data Processing and Data Processing
  Technology/Technician, A
Dental Hygiene/Hygienist, A
Design and Applied Arts, A
Dietetics/Dieticians, A
Drafting and Design Technology/Technician, A
Drama and Dramatics/Theatre Arts, A
Electrical, Electronic and Communications Engineer-
  ing Technology/Technician, A
Engineering, A
English Language and Literature, A
Family and Consumer Economics and Related Ser-
  vices, A
Family and Consumer Sciences/Human Sciences, A
Finance, A
Food Science, A
Food Technology and Processing, A
French Language and Literature, A
German Language and Literature, A
Hispanic-American, Puerto Rican, and Mexican-
  American/Chicano Studies, A
History, A
Human Services, A
Industrial Radiologic Technology/Technician, A
Information Technology, A
Journalism, A
Legal Administrative Assistant/Secretary, A
Liberal Arts and Sciences Studies and Humani-
  ties, A
Marketing/Marketing Management, A
Mass Communication/Media Studies, A
Mathematics, A
Medical Administrative Assistant/Secretary, A
Mental Health Counseling/Counselor, A
Music, A
Nuclear Medical Technology/Technologist, A
Ophthalmic Laboratory Technology/Technician, A
Photography, A
Physics, A
Psychology, A
Public Administration, A
Public Relations/Image Management, A
Radio and Television, A
Radiologic Technology/Science - Radiographer, A
Real Estate, A

Sociology, A
Spanish Language and Literature, A
Special Products Marketing Operations, A
System Administration/Administrator, A
Teacher Assistant/Aide, A
Telecommunications Technology/Technician, A
Tourism and Travel Services Management, A
Web Page, Digital/Multimedia and Information Re-
  sources Design, A
Web/Multimedia Management and Webmaster, A
Word Processing, A

LOS ANGELES FILM SCHOOL

Computer Graphics, B
Film/Cinema Studies, A
Recording Arts Technology/Technician, A

LOS ANGELES HARBOR COLLEGE

Accounting, A
Administrative Assistant and Secretarial Science, A
Architectural Engineering Technology/Technician, A
Automobile/Automotive Mechanics
  Technology/Technician, A
Biology/Biological Sciences, A
Business Administration and Management, A
Computer Engineering Technology/Technician, A
Criminal Justice/Police Science, A
Data Processing and Data Processing
  Technology/Technician, A
Drafting and Design Technology/Technician, A
Electrical, Electronic and Communications Engineer-
  ing Technology/Technician, A
Electromechanical Technology/Electromechanical
  Engineering Technology, A
Engineering Technology, A
Fire Science/Firefighting, A
Information Science/Studies, A
Legal Administrative Assistant/Secretary, A
Liberal Arts and Sciences Studies and Humani-
  ties, A
Medical Administrative Assistant/Secretary, A
Physics, A
Real Estate, A

LOS ANGELES MISSION COLLEGE

Accounting, A
Administrative Assistant and Secretarial Science, A
Biology/Biological Sciences, A
Business Administration and Management, A
Computer Programming/Programmer, A
Criminal Justice/Police Science, A
Culinary Arts/Chef Training, A
Drama and Dramatics/Theatre Arts, A
English Language and Literature, A
Family and Consumer Economics and Related Ser-
  vices, A
Finance, A
Geography, A
History, A
Humanities/Humanistic Studies, A
Liberal Arts and Sciences Studies and Humani-
  ties, A
Mathematics, A
Music, A
Philosophy, A
Physical Sciences, A
Psychology, A
Social Sciences, A
Sociology, A
Spanish Language and Literature, A

LOS ANGELES PIERCE COLLEGE

Accounting, A
Agriculture, A
Animal Sciences, A
Architectural Engineering Technology/Technician, A
Art/Art Studies, General, A
Automobile/Automotive Mechanics
  Technology/Technician, A
Computer Engineering Technology/Technician, A
Computer Programming/Programmer, A
Computer Science, A
Construction Engineering Technology/Technician, A
Data Processing and Data Processing
  Technology/Technician, A
Drafting and Design Technology/Technician, A

Drama and Dramatics/Theatre Arts, A
Electrical, Electronic and Communications Engineering Technology/Technician, A
Equestrian/Equine Studies, A
Horticultural Science, A
Industrial Technology/Technician, A
Journalism, A
Landscape Architecture, A
Landscaping and Groundskeeping, A
Liberal Arts and Sciences Studies and Humanities, A
Machine Tool Technology/Machinist, A
Music, A
Ornamental Horticulture, A
Photography, A
Plant Protection and Integrated Pest Management, A
Quality Control Technology/Technician, A
Real Estate, A
Sign Language Interpretation and Translation, A
Veterinary/Animal Health Technology/Technician and Veterinary Assistant, A
Welding Technology/Welder, A

LOS ANGELES SOUTHWEST COLLEGE

Accounting, A
Administrative Assistant and Secretarial Science, A
African Studies, A
Anthropology, A
Behavioral Sciences, A
Biology/Biological Sciences, A
Business Administration and Management, A
Child Development, A
Computer Science, A
Criminal Justice/Law Enforcement Administration, A
Criminal Justice/Police Science, A
Data Processing and Data Processing Technology/Technician, A
Drafting and Design Technology/Technician, A
Drama and Dramatics/Theatre Arts, A
Economics, A
Education, A
Electrical, Electronic and Communications Engineering Technology/Technician, A
Engineering, A
English Language and Literature, A
Family and Consumer Economics and Related Services, A
Finance, A
Humanities/Humanistic Studies, A
Kindergarten/PreSchool Education and Teaching, A
Marketing/Marketing Management, A
Music, A
Quality Control Technology/Technician, A
Radio and Television, A
Real Estate, A
Sign Language Interpretation and Translation, A
Social Sciences, A
Spanish Language and Literature, A
Teacher Assistant/Aide, A

LOS ANGELES TRADE-TECHNICAL COLLEGE

Accounting, A
Architectural Engineering Technology/Technician, A
Automobile/Automotive Mechanics Technology/Technician, A
Business Administration and Management, A
Carpentry/Carpenter, A
Chemical Engineering, A
Commercial and Advertising Art, A
Computer Engineering Technology/Technician, A
Computer Programming/Programmer, A
Construction Engineering Technology/Technician, A
Cosmetology/Cosmetologist, A
Culinary Arts/Chef Training, A
Drafting and Design Technology/Technician, A
Electrical, Electronic and Communications Engineering Technology/Technician, A
Engineering, A
Fashion Merchandising, A
Fashion/Apparel Design, A
Heating, Air Conditioning, Ventilation and Refrigeration Maintenance Technology/Technician, A
Heavy Equipment Maintenance Technology/Technician, A

Hydrology and Water Resources Science, A
Industrial Technology/Technician, A
Information Science/Studies, A
Labor and Industrial Relations, A
Liberal Arts and Sciences Studies and Humanities, A
Pipefitting/Pipefitter and Sprinkler Fitter, A
Real Estate, A
Transportation and Materials Moving, A
Welding Technology/Welder, A

LOS ANGELES VALLEY COLLEGE

Accounting, A
Administrative Assistant and Secretarial Science, A
Art/Art Studies, General, A
Banking and Financial Support Services, A
Biology/Biological Sciences, A
Biomedical Technology/Technician, A
Chemistry, A
Child Development, A
Cinematography and Film/Video Production, A
Commercial and Advertising Art, A
Computer Installation and Repair Technology/Technician, A
Computer Programming/Programmer, A
Criminal Justice/Police Science, A
Drama and Dramatics/Theatre Arts, A
Drawing, A
Economics, A
Education/Teaching of Individuals in Early Childhood Special Education Programs, A
Electrical/Electronics Equipment Installation and Repair, A
Engineering, A
English Language and Literature, A
Ethnic, Cultural Minority, and Gender Studies, A
Fire Science/Firefighting, A
Foreign Languages and Literatures, A
French Language and Literature, A
Geography, A
Geology/Earth Science, A
German Language and Literature, A
Health and Physical Education, A
Hebrew Language and Literature, A
History, A
Industrial Electronics Technology/Technician, A
Italian Language and Literature, A
Journalism, A
Kindergarten/PreSchool Education and Teaching, A
Liberal Arts and Sciences Studies and Humanities, A
Machine Tool Technology/Machinist, A
Manufacturing Technology/Technician, A
Mass Communication/Media Studies, A
Mathematics, A
Mechanical Drafting and Mechanical Drafting CAD/CADD, A
Music, A
Office Management and Supervision, A
Philosophy, A
Physics, A
Political Science and Government, A
Psychology, A
Radio and Television, A
Real Estate, A
Respiratory Care Therapy/Therapist, A
Sales, Distribution and Marketing Operations, A
Sculpture, A
Sociology, A
Spanish Language and Literature, A
Technical Theatre/Theatre Design and Technology, A

LOS MEDANOS COLLEGE

Accounting, A
Administrative Assistant and Secretarial Science, A
Anthropology, A
Art/Art Studies, General, A
Automobile/Automotive Mechanics Technology/Technician, A
Behavioral Sciences, A
Biology/Biological Sciences, A
Business Administration and Management, A
Business/Managerial Economics, A
Chemistry, A
Commercial and Advertising Art, A

Drafting and Design Technology/Technician, A
Electrical, Electronic and Communications Engineering Technology/Technician, A
Emergency Medical Technology/Technician (EMT Paramedic), A
Fire Science/Firefighting, A
Heating, Air Conditioning, Ventilation and Refrigeration Maintenance Technology/Technician, A
Journalism, A
Liberal Arts and Sciences Studies and Humanities, A
Mathematics, A
Music, A
Psychology, A
Real Estate, A
Small Engine Mechanics and Repair Technology/Technician, A
Sociology, A
Tourism and Travel Services Management, A
Welding Technology/Welder, A

LOYOLA MARYMOUNT UNIVERSITY

Accounting, BM
African-American/Black Studies, B
Ancient Studies/Civilization, B
Animation, Interactive Technology, Video Graphics and Special Effects, B
Applied Mathematics, B
Art History, Criticism and Conservation, B
Asian Studies/Civilization, B
Biochemistry, B
Bioethics/Medical Ethics, M
Biology/Biological Sciences, B
Business Administration, Management and Operations, M
Chemistry, B
Cinematography and Film/Video Production, B
Civil Engineering, BM
Communication Studies/Speech Communication and Rhetoric, B
Computer and Information Sciences, B
Counselor Education/School Counseling and Guidance Services, M
Dance, B
Drama and Dramatics/Theatre Arts, B
Early Childhood Education and Teaching, M
Economics, B
Education, MD
Educational Administration and Supervision, M
Educational Leadership and Administration, D
Electrical, Electronics and Communications Engineering, B
Elementary Education and Teaching, M
Engineering Physics, B
English, M
English Language and Literature, B
Entrepreneurship/Entrepreneurial Studies, B
Environmental Sciences, BM
European Studies/Civilization, B
Film, Television, and Video Production, M
Finance, B
Fine/Studio Arts, B
French Language and Literature, B
Hispanic-American, Puerto Rican, and Mexican-American/Chicano Studies, B
History, B
Humanities/Humanistic Studies, B
Law and Legal Studies, MD
Liberal Arts and Sciences Studies and Humanities, B
Management Information Systems and Services, B
Marketing/Marketing Management, B
Marriage and Family Therapy/Counseling, M
Mathematics, B
Mathematics Teacher Education, M
Mechanical Engineering, BM
Multi-/Interdisciplinary Studies, B
Multilingual and Multicultural Education, M
Music, B
Natural Sciences, B
Pastoral Studies/Counseling, M
Philosophy, BM
Physics, B
Playwriting and Screenwriting, B
Political Science and Government, B
Psychology, B

Reading Teacher Education, M
Recording Arts Technology/Technician, B
Religious Education, M
Romance Languages, Literatures, and Linguistics, B
School Psychology, M
Secondary Education and Teaching, M
Sociology, B
Spanish Language and Literature, B
Special Education and Teaching, M
Systems Engineering, M
Taxation, M
Theology and Religious Vocations, M
Theology/Theological Studies, B
Therapeutic Recreation, M
Urban Education and Leadership, M
Urban Studies/Affairs, B
Women's Studies, B
Writing, M

MARYMOUNT CALIFORNIA UNIVERSITY

Business Administration and Management, B
Business Administration, Management and Operations, M
Community Psychology, M
Criminal Justice/Law Enforcement Administration, B
International Development, M
Liberal Arts and Sciences Studies and Humanities, AB
Psychology, B

THE MASTER'S COLLEGE AND SEMINARY

Accounting, B
American Government and Politics (United States), B
Ancient Near Eastern and Biblical Languages, Literatures, and Linguistics, B
Applied Mathematics, B
Bible/Biblical Studies, B
Biological and Physical Sciences, B
Biology/Biological Sciences, B
Business Administration and Management, B
Computer and Information Sciences, B
Divinity/Ministry (BD, MDiv.), B
Education, B
Elementary Education and Teaching, B
English Language and Literature, B
Environmental Biology, B
Family and Consumer Sciences/Human Sciences, B
Finance, B
Health and Physical Education, B
History, B
Junior High/Intermediate/Middle School Education and Teaching, B
Kinesiology and Exercise Science, B
Liberal Arts and Sciences Studies and Humanities, B
Management Information Systems and Services, B
Mass Communication/Media Studies, B
Mathematics, B
Music, B
Music Teacher Education, B
Natural Sciences, B
Pastoral Studies/Counseling, BMD
Physical Education Teaching and Coaching, B
Physical Sciences, B
Piano and Organ, B
Political Science and Government, B
Pre-Law Studies, B
Pre-Medicine/Pre-Medical Studies, B
Public Relations/Image Management, B
Radio and Television, B
Religion/Religious Studies, B
Religious Education, B
Religious/Sacred Music, B
Science Teacher Education/General Science Teacher Education, B
Secondary Education and Teaching, B
Theology and Religious Vocations, MD
Theology/Theological Studies, B
Voice and Opera, B

MENDOCINO COLLEGE

Accounting, A
Administrative Assistant and Secretarial Science, A

Agriculture, A
Art/Art Studies, General, A
Automobile/Automotive Mechanics Technology/Technician, A
Biology/Biological Sciences, A
Business Administration and Management, A
Chemistry, A
Child Development, A
Criminal Justice/Law Enforcement Administration, A
Criminal Justice/Police Science, A
Data Processing and Data Processing Technology/Technician, A
Drama and Dramatics/Theatre Arts, A
English Language and Literature, A
Fiber, Textile and Weaving Arts, A
Finance, A
French Language and Literature, A
Health Professions and Related Clinical Sciences, A
Human Services, A
Information Science/Studies, A
Kindergarten/PreSchool Education and Teaching, A
Liberal Arts and Sciences Studies and Humanities, A
Mathematics, A
Music, A
Ornamental Horticulture, A
Physical Education Teaching and Coaching, A
Physical Sciences, A
Psychology, A
Real Estate, A
Social Sciences, A
Spanish Language and Literature, A
Substance Abuse/Addiction Counseling, A

MENLO COLLEGE

Accounting, B
Entrepreneurship/Entrepreneurial Studies, B
Finance, B
Human Resources Management and Services, B
International Business/Trade/Commerce, B
Management Information Systems and Services, B
Marketing/Marketing Management, B
Psychology, B
Real Estate, B
Sport and Fitness Administration/Management, B

MERCED COLLEGE

Accounting, A
Administrative Assistant and Secretarial Science, A
Agricultural Business and Management, A
Agriculture, A
Agronomy and Crop Science, A
Airframe Mechanics and Aircraft Maintenance Technology/Technician, A
Animal Sciences, A
Art/Art Studies, General, A
Automobile/Automotive Mechanics Technology/Technician, A
Biological and Physical Sciences, A
Business Administration and Management, A
Carpentry/Carpenter, A
Computer Engineering Technology/Technician, A
Computer Science, A
Construction Engineering Technology/Technician, A
Consumer Merchandising/Retailing Management, A
Criminal Justice/Police Science, A
Data Processing and Data Processing Technology/Technician, A
Dental Hygiene/Hygienist, A
Design and Applied Arts, A
Dietetics/Dieticians, A
Drama and Dramatics/Theatre Arts, A
Electrical, Electronic and Communications Engineering Technology/Technician, A
Environmental Engineering Technology/Environmental Technology, A
Family and Consumer Sciences/Human Sciences, A
Fashion Merchandising, A
Fashion/Apparel Design, A
Finance, A
Fire Science/Firefighting, A
Human Services, A
Humanities/Humanistic Studies, A
Industrial Radiologic Technology/Technician, A
Insurance, A
Kindergarten/PreSchool Education and Teaching, A

Landscape Architecture, A
Legal Administrative Assistant/Secretary, A
Liberal Arts and Sciences Studies and Humanities, A
Library Science, A
Management Information Systems and Services, A
Marketing/Marketing Management, A
Mathematics, A
Medical Administrative Assistant/Secretary, A
Medical/Clinical Assistant, A
Music, A
Natural Sciences, A
Ornamental Horticulture, A
Physical Education Teaching and Coaching, A
Physical Sciences, A
Political Science and Government, A
Real Estate, A
Social Sciences, A
Special Products Marketing Operations, A
Teacher Assistant/Aide, A

MERRITT COLLEGE

Accounting, A
Administrative Assistant and Secretarial Science, A
Anthropology, A
Biological and Physical Sciences, A
Business Administration and Management, A
Business/Commerce, A
Child Development, A
Computer Programming/Programmer, A
Computer Systems Networking and Telecommunications, A
Corrections, A
Criminal Justice/Police Science, A
Dietetic Technician (DTR), A
Economics, A
Energy Management and Systems Technology/Technician, A
English Language and Literature, A
Environmental Studies, A
Ethnic, Cultural Minority, and Gender Studies, A
French Language and Literature, A
Hazardous Materials Management and Waste Technology/Technician, A
Health/Medical Preparatory Programs, A
Human Services, A
Humanities/Humanistic Studies, A
Landscaping and Groundskeeping, A
Legal Assistant/Paralegal, A
Liberal Arts and Sciences Studies and Humanities, A
Mathematics, A
Parks, Recreation, Leisure and Fitness Studies, A
Plant Nursery Operations and Management, A
Radiologic Technology/Science - Radiographer, A
Real Estate, A
Social Sciences, A
Spanish Language and Literature, A
Substance Abuse/Addiction Counseling, A

MILLS COLLEGE

American/United States Studies/Civilization, B
Anthropology, B
Art Education, M
Art History, Criticism and Conservation, B
Biochemistry, B
Biological and Biomedical Sciences, O
Biology/Biological Sciences, B
Business Administration, Management and Operations, M
Business/Managerial Economics, B
Ceramic Arts and Ceramics, M
Chemistry, B
Comparative Literature, B
Composition, M
Computer Science, BMO
Curriculum and Instruction, M
Dance, BM
Drama and Dramatics/Theatre Arts, B
Early Childhood Education and Teaching, M
Economics, B
Education, MD
Educational Administration and Supervision, MD
Elementary Education and Teaching, M
Engineering, B
English, M

English Education, M
English Language and Literature, B
Environmental Sciences, B
Environmental Studies, B
Ethnic, Cultural Minority, and Gender Studies, B
Fine Arts and Art Studies, M
Fine/Studio Arts, B
Foreign Language Teacher Education, M
French Language and Literature, B
French Studies, B
Gay/Lesbian Studies, B
Health Education, M
Hispanic-American, Puerto Rican, and Mexican-American/Chicano Studies, B
History, B
Illustration, M
Interdisciplinary Studies, M
Intermedia/Multimedia, B
International Relations and Affairs, B
Mathematics, B
Mathematics Teacher Education, M
Music, BM
Painting, M
Performance, M
Philosophy, B
Photography, M
Political Science and Government, B
Psychology, B
Public Policy Analysis, BM
Science Teacher Education/General Science Teacher Education, M
Sculpture, M
Secondary Education and Teaching, M
Social Studies Teacher Education, M
Sociology, B
Spanish Language and Literature, B
Writing, M

MIRACOSTA COLLEGE

Accounting Technology/Technician and Bookkeeping, A
Administrative Assistant and Secretarial Science, A
Adult Development and Aging, A
Architectural Technology/Technician, A
Art/Art Studies, General, A
Biological and Physical Sciences, A
Biomedical Technology/Technician, A
Business Administration and Management, A
Child Care Provider/Assistant, A
Child Care and Support Services Management, A
Computer Programming/Programmer, A
Computer Science, A
Computer Systems Networking and Telecommunications, A
Criminal Justice/Police Science, A
Dance, A
Data Entry/Microcomputer Applications, A
Drafting and Design Technology/Technician, A
History, A
Hospitality Administration/Management, A
Liberal Arts and Sciences Studies and Humanities, A
Mathematics, A
Medical/Clinical Assistant, A
Music, A
Office Management and Supervision, A
Photographic and Film/Video Technology/Technician and Assistant, A
Plant Nursery Operations and Management, A
Psychology, A
Real Estate, A
Recording Arts Technology/Technician, A
Restaurant, Culinary, and Catering Management/Manager, A
Sales, Distribution and Marketing Operations, A
Small Business Administration/Management, A
Sociology, A
Surgical Technology/Technologist, A
Technical Theatre/Theatre Design and Technology, A
Web/Multimedia Management and Webmaster, A

MISSION COLLEGE

Accounting, A
Administrative Assistant and Secretarial Science, A
Art/Art Studies, General, A

Business Administration and Management, A
Commercial and Advertising Art, A
Computer Engineering Technology/Technician, A
Computer Programming/Programmer, A
Data Processing and Data Processing Technology/Technician, A
Drafting and Design Technology/Technician, A
Electrical, Electronic and Communications Engineering Technology/Technician, A
Electrical/Electronics Drafting and Electrical/Electronics CAD/CADD, A
Fire Science/Firefighting, A
Food Technology and Processing, A
Graphic and Printing Equipment Operator Production, A
Health Professions and Related Clinical Sciences, A
Information Science/Studies, A
Liberal Arts and Sciences Studies and Humanities, A
Marketing/Marketing Management, A
Mathematics, A
Real Estate, A
Social Sciences, A
Special Products Marketing Operations, A

MODESTO JUNIOR COLLEGE

Accounting, A
Accounting Technology/Technician and Bookkeeping, A
Administrative Assistant and Secretarial Science, A
Agricultural Business and Management, A
Agricultural Mechanization, A
Agricultural Production Operations, A
Agricultural/Farm Supplies Retailing and Wholesaling, A
Agriculture, A
Agronomy and Crop Science, A
Animal Sciences, A
Apparel and Textiles, A
Architectural Drafting and Architectural CAD/CADD, A
Architectural Engineering Technology/Technician, A
Art/Art Studies, General, A
Athletic Training and Sports Medicine, A
Autobody/Collision and Repair Technology/Technician, A
Automobile/Automotive Mechanics Technology/Technician, A
Banking and Financial Support Services, A
Behavioral Sciences, A
Building/Construction Finishing, Management, and Inspection, A
Building/Home/Construction Inspection/Inspector, A
Business Administration and Management, A
Child Care Provider/Assistant, A
Child Care and Support Services Management, A
Child Development, A
City/Urban, Community and Regional Planning, A
Commercial and Advertising Art, A
Communications Systems Installation and Repair Technology, A
Computer Graphics, A
Computer Installation and Repair Technology/Technician, A
Computer Science, A
Computer/Information Technology Services Administration and Management, A
Corrections, A
Criminal Justice/Law Enforcement Administration, A
Criminal Justice/Police Science, A
Culinary Arts/Chef Training, A
Dairy Science, A
Data Entry/Microcomputer Applications, A
Dental Assisting/Assistant, A
Drafting and Design Technology/Technician, A
Drama and Dramatics/Theatre Arts, A
Electrical, Electronic and Communications Engineering Technology/Technician, A
Electrical/Electronics Equipment Installation and Repair, A
Emergency Medical Technology/Technician (EMT Paramedic), A
Engineering, A
Engineering Technology, A
English Language and Literature, A

Family and Consumer Economics and Related Services, A
Fashion Merchandising, A
Finance, A
Fire Science/Firefighting, A
Food Science, A
Food Technology and Processing, A
Foreign Languages and Literatures, A
Forestry, A
Forestry Technology/Technician, A
General Office Occupations and Clerical Services, A
General Studies, A
Graphic and Printing Equipment Operator Production, A
Heating, Air Conditioning, Ventilation and Refrigeration Maintenance Technology/Technician, A
Horticultural Science, A
Housing and Human Environments, A
Human Services, A
Humanities/Humanistic Studies, A
Industrial Electronics Technology/Technician, A
Interior Design, A
Journalism, A
Kindergarten/PreSchool Education and Teaching, A
Landscape Architecture, A
Machine Shop Technology/Assistant, A
Machine Tool Technology/Machinist, A
Management Information Systems and Services, A
Marketing/Marketing Management, A
Mass Communication/Media Studies, A
Mathematics, A
Medical/Clinical Assistant, A
Music, A
Office Management and Supervision, A
Ornamental Horticulture, A
Parks, Recreation and Leisure Facilities Management, A
Photography, A
Physical Education Teaching and Coaching, A
Plant Nursery Operations and Management, A
Poultry Science, A
Radio and Television, A
Real Estate, A
Respiratory Care Therapy/Therapist, A
Social Sciences, A
Spanish Language and Literature, A
Special Products Marketing Operations, A
Substance Abuse/Addiction Counseling, A
Welding Technology/Welder, A
Word Processing, A

MONTEREY PENINSULA COLLEGE

Accounting, A
Administrative Assistant and Secretarial Science, A
Anthropology, A
Apparel and Textiles, A
Art History, Criticism and Conservation, A
Art/Art Studies, General, A
Automobile/Automotive Mechanics Technology/Technician, A
Biology/Biological Sciences, A
Business Administration and Management, A
Ceramic Arts and Ceramics, A
Chemistry, A
Child Development, A
Commercial and Advertising Art, A
Computer Engineering Technology/Technician, A
Computer Science, A
Computer Typography and Composition Equipment Operator, A
Criminal Justice/Law Enforcement Administration, A
Criminal Justice/Police Science, A
Dance, A
Data Processing and Data Processing Technology/Technician, A
Dental Hygiene/Hygienist, A
Drama and Dramatics/Theatre Arts, A
Drawing, A
Economics, A
Engineering, A
English Language and Literature, A
Family and Consumer Economics and Related Services, A
Fashion Merchandising, A
Fiber, Textile and Weaving Arts, A
Fine/Studio Arts, A

Fire Science/Firefighting, A
Fishing and Fisheries Sciences and Management, A
French Language and Literature, A
Geology/Earth Science, A
German Language and Literature, A
History, A
Hospitality Administration/Management, A
Hotel/Motel Administration/Management, A
Information Science/Studies, A
Interior Design, A
International Business/Trade/Commerce, A
Kindergarten/PreSchool Education and Teaching, A
Kinesiology and Exercise Science, A
Legal Administrative Assistant/Secretary, A
Liberal Arts and Sciences Studies and Humanities, A
Marketing/Marketing Management, A
Mass Communication/Media Studies, A
Mathematics, A
Medical Administrative Assistant/Secretary, A
Medical/Clinical Assistant, A
Metal and Jewelry Arts, A
Music, A
Occupational Therapy/Therapist, A
Ornamental Horticulture, A
Parks, Recreation and Leisure Facilities Management, A
Philosophy, A
Photography, A
Physical Education Teaching and Coaching, A
Physical Therapy/Therapist, A
Physics, A
Political Science and Government, A
Psychology, A
Real Estate, A
Sculpture, A
Sociology, A
Spanish Language and Literature, A
Wildlife and Wildlands Science and Management, A
Women's Studies, A

MOORPARK COLLEGE

Accounting, A
Animal Sciences, A
Anthropology, A
Art/Art Studies, General, A
Behavioral Sciences, A
Biology/Biological Sciences, A
Broadcast Journalism, A
Business Administration and Management, A
Business Machine Repairer, A
Chemistry, A
Commercial and Advertising Art, A
Computer Science, A
Corrections, A
Criminal Justice/Law Enforcement Administration, A
Criminal Justice/Police Science, A
Data Processing and Data Processing Technology/Technician, A
Drama and Dramatics/Theatre Arts, A
Electrical, Electronic and Communications Engineering Technology/Technician, A
Engineering, A
Engineering Technology, A
Fashion/Apparel Design, A
Film/Cinema Studies, A
Geology/Earth Science, A
Graphic and Printing Equipment Operator Production, A
Information Science/Studies, A
Journalism, A
Kindergarten/PreSchool Education and Teaching, A
Laser and Optical Technology/Technician, A
Liberal Arts and Sciences Studies and Humanities, A
Marketing/Marketing Management, A
Mathematics, A
Music, A
Natural Sciences, A
Photography, A
Teacher Assistant/Aide, A
Telecommunications Technology/Technician, A

Wildlife and Wildlands Science and Management, A

MORENO VALLEY COLLEGE

Accounting, A
Computer Programming/Programmer, A
Dental Hygiene/Hygienist, A
Early Childhood Education and Teaching, A
Fire Science/Firefighting, A
Health and Physical Education, A
Medical/Clinical Assistant, A
Physician Assistant, A

MOUNT SAINT MARY'S UNIVERSITY

Accounting, B
American/United States Studies/Civilization, B
Art/Art Studies, General, B
Biochemistry, B
Biology/Biological Sciences, B
Business Administration and Management, AB
Business Administration, Management and Operations, M
Chemistry, B
Child Development, B
Cinematography and Film/Video Production, B
Commercial and Advertising Art, A
Counseling Psychology, M
Criminology, B
Early Childhood Education and Teaching, A
Education, BMO
Elementary Education and Teaching, B
English, M
English Language and Literature, B
Film, Television, and Video Production, M
Film/Video and Photographic Arts, B
French Language and Literature, B
Gerontology, B
Health Services Administration, M
Health/Health Care Administration/Management, A
Health/Medical Preparatory Programs, A
History, B
Human Services, A
Humanities/Humanistic Studies, M
International Business/Trade/Commerce, B
Journalism, B
Kindergarten/PreSchool Education and Teaching, A
Liberal Arts and Sciences Studies and Humanities, AB
Marketing/Marketing Management, B
Mathematics, B
Music, B
Nursing, MO
Philosophy, B
Physical Therapy/Therapist, D
Political Science and Government, B
Psychology, B
Religion/Religious Studies, BM
Secondary Education and Teaching, B
Social Sciences, B
Social Work, B
Sociology, B
Spanish Language and Literature, B
Writing, M

MT. SAN ANTONIO COLLEGE

Accounting, A
Administrative Assistant and Secretarial Science, A
Advertising, A
Agricultural Business and Management, A
Agriculture, A
Air Traffic Controller, A
Airframe Mechanics and Aircraft Maintenance Technology/Technician, A
Airline/Commercial/Professional Pilot and Flight Crew, A
Animal Sciences, A
Apparel and Textiles, A
Architectural Engineering Technology/Technician, A
Avionics Maintenance Technology/Technician, A
Biological and Physical Sciences, A
Building/Construction Finishing, Management, and Inspection, A
Business Administration and Management, A
Business Teacher Education, A
Child Development, A
Civil Engineering Technology/Technician, A
Commercial and Advertising Art, A

Computer Engineering Technology/Technician, A
Computer Graphics, A
Computer Science, A
Computer and Information Sciences, A
Corrections, A
Criminal Justice/Police Science, A
Dairy Science, A
Data Processing and Data Processing Technology/Technician, A
Drafting and Design Technology/Technician, A
Drafting/Design Engineering Technologies/Technicians, A
Electrical, Electronic and Communications Engineering Technology/Technician, A
Emergency Medical Technology/Technician (EMT Paramedic), A
Engineering Technology, A
English Language and Literature, A
Family and Consumer Sciences/Human Sciences, A
Fashion Merchandising, A
Finance, A
Fire Science/Firefighting, A
Forestry Technology/Technician, A
Health and Physical Education, A
Heating, Air Conditioning, Ventilation and Refrigeration Maintenance Technology/Technician, A
Horticultural Science, A
Hotel/Motel Administration/Management, A
Humanities/Humanistic Studies, A
Industrial Design, A
Industrial Radiologic Technology/Technician, A
Interior Design, A
Journalism, A
Kindergarten/PreSchool Education and Teaching, A
Landscape Architecture, A
Legal Administrative Assistant/Secretary, A
Legal Assistant/Paralegal, A
Machine Tool Technology/Machinist, A
Marketing/Marketing Management, A
Mathematics, A
Medical Administrative Assistant/Secretary, A
Mental Health Counseling/Counselor, A
Music, A
Occupational Safety and Health Technology/Technician, A
Ornamental Horticulture, A
Parks, Recreation and Leisure Facilities Management, A
Parks, Recreation, Leisure and Fitness Studies, A
Photography, A
Physical Sciences, A
Quality Control Technology/Technician, A
Radio and Television, A
Real Estate, A
Respiratory Care Therapy/Therapist, A
Sign Language Interpretation and Translation, A
Social Sciences, A
Survey Technology/Surveying, A
Transportation and Materials Moving, A
Visual and Performing Arts, A
Welding Technology/Welder, A
Wildlife and Wildlands Science and Management, A

MT. SAN JACINTO COLLEGE

Administrative Assistant and Secretarial Science, A
Adult Development and Aging, A
Art/Art Studies, General, A
Automobile/Automotive Mechanics Technology/Technician, A
Biological and Physical Sciences, A
Business Administration and Management, A
Child Development, A
Criminal Justice/Police Science, A
Dance, A
Design and Visual Communications, A
Diagnostic Medical Sonography/Sonographer and Ultrasound Technician, A
Digital Communication and Media/Multimedia, A
Drafting and Design Technology/Technician, A
Drama and Dramatics/Theatre Arts, A
Fire Science/Firefighting, A
Geography, A
Health and Physical Education, A
Humanities/Humanistic Studies, A
Information Technology, A
Legal Assistant/Paralegal, A

Liberal Arts and Sciences Studies and Humanities, A
Mathematics, A
Medical/Clinical Assistant, A
Music, A
Photography, A
Real Estate, A
Social Sciences, A
Substance Abuse/Addiction Counseling, A
Turf and Turfgrass Management, A
Visual and Performing Arts, A
Water Quality and Wastewater Treatment Management and Recycling Technology/Technician, A

MT. SIERRA COLLEGE

Animation, Interactive Technology, Video Graphics and Special Effects, B
Business Administration and Management, B
Computer Systems Networking and Telecommunications, B
Computer and Information Sciences, B
Computer and Information Sciences and Support Services, B
Computer and Information Systems Security, B
Design and Visual Communications, B
E-Commerce/Electronic Commerce, B
Graphic Design, B
Intermedia/Multimedia, B

MTI COLLEGE

Business Administration and Management, A
Legal Assistant/Paralegal, A
System, Networking, and LAN/WAN Management/Manager, A

MUSICIANS INSTITUTE

Music, AB
Music Performance, AB

NAPA VALLEY COLLEGE

Accounting, A
Administrative Assistant and Secretarial Science, A
Agriculture, A
Art/Art Studies, General, A
Behavioral Sciences, A
Biological and Physical Sciences, A
Biomedical Technology/Technician, A
Business Administration and Management, A
Child Development, A
Communications Technology/Technician, A
Computer Science, A
Corrections, A
Cosmetology/Cosmetologist, A
Criminal Justice/Law Enforcement Administration, A
Criminal Justice/Police Science, A
Data Processing and Data Processing Technology/Technician, A
Drafting and Design Technology/Technician, A
Electrical, Electronic and Communications Engineering Technology/Technician, A
Emergency Medical Technology/Technician (EMT Paramedic), A
Engineering, A
Environmental Engineering Technology/Environmental Technology, A
Environmental Studies, A
Humanities/Humanistic Studies, A
Kindergarten/PreSchool Education and Teaching, A
Legal Administrative Assistant/Secretary, A
Legal Assistant/Paralegal, A
Machine Tool Technology/Machinist, A
Management Information Systems and Services, A
Marketing/Marketing Management, A
Music, A
Photography, A
Radio and Television, A
Real Estate, A
Respiratory Care Therapy/Therapist, A
Telecommunications Technology/Technician, A
Welding Technology/Welder, A

NATIONAL UNIVERSITY

Accounting, BM
Accounting and Business/Management, B
Allied Health and Medical Assisting Services, A

Applied Behavior Analysis, MO
Arabic Language and Literature, B
Art/Art Studies, General, B
Biological and Biomedical Sciences, M
Biological and Physical Sciences, B
Biology/Biological Sciences, B
Biomedical/Medical Engineering, B
Biostatistics, B
Business Administration and Management, AB
Business Administration, Management and Operations, MO
Business/Corporate Communications, B
Cell/Cellular Biology and Anatomical Sciences, A
Child Development, B
Chinese Language and Literature, B
Clinical Laboratory Science/Medical Technology/Technologist, B
Clinical Psychology, M
Clinical/Medical Laboratory Assistant, B
Communication Disorders, M
Communication, Journalism and Related Programs, B
Community Health and Preventive Medicine, AB
Comparative Literature, B
Computer Science, BM
Computer Software Engineering, B
Computer and Information Sciences, AB
Computer and Information Sciences and Support Services, B
Computer and Information Systems Security, M
Computer/Information Technology Services Administration and Management, B
Construction Engineering, B
Construction Management, B
Construction Trades, B
Corporate and Organizational Communication, M
Counseling Psychology, M
Counselor Education/School Counseling and Guidance Services, M
Criminal Justice/Law Enforcement Administration, B
Criminal Justice/Safety Studies, B
Criminology, M
Database Systems, M
Digital Communication and Media/Multimedia, AB
Distance Education Development, MO
Drafting/Design Engineering Technologies/Technicians, B
Early Childhood Education and Teaching, ABMO
Education, AMO
Educational Administration and Supervision, M
Educational Leadership and Administration, MO
Educational Media/Instructional Technology, MO
Educational/Instructional Media Design, B
Electrical, Electronics and Communications Engineering, B
Elementary Education and Teaching, B
Emergency Management, M
Engineering Management, M
Engineering Science, A
Engineering Technology, A
Engineering/Industrial Management, B
English, M
English Language and Literature, B
English/Language Arts Teacher Education, B
Environmental Engineering Technology/Environmental Technology, M
Environmental Sciences, B
Environmental Studies, B
Film, Television, and Video Production, M
Film, Television, and Video Theory and Criticism, M
Film/Cinema Studies, B
Finance, B
Finance and Banking, M
Finance and Financial Management Services, B
Forensic Nursing, M
Forensic Science and Technology, MO
General Studies, AB
Geology/Earth Science, B
Health Aide, A
Health Informatics, M
Health Information/Medical Records Technology/Technician, A
Health Occupations Teacher Education, B
Health Promotion, MO
Health Services Administration, M
Health Services/Allied Health/Health Sciences, B

Health Teacher Education, B
Health and Medical Administrative Services, A
Health/Health Care Administration/Management, AB
History, BM
Homeland Security, M
Hospitality Administration/Management, A
Human Resources Management and Services, M
Human Services, MDO
Information Science/Studies, B
International Business/Trade/Commerce, M
International and Comparative Education, M
International/Global Studies, B
Internet and Interactive Multimedia, M
Iranian/Persian Languages, Literatures, and Linguistics, B
Journalism, ABM
Law and Legal Studies, B
Legal Assistant/Paralegal, AB
Legal Professions and Studies, B
Legal and Justice Studies, M
Liberal Arts and Sciences Studies and Humanities, B
Linguistics, M
Management Information Systems and Services, BM
Management Science, B
Management of Technology, M
Manufacturing Engineering, B
Marketing, M
Marketing Research, B
Marketing/Marketing Management, B
Marriage and Family Therapy/Counseling, M
Mathematics, B
Mathematics Teacher Education, BMO
Medical Informatics, AO
Medical Insurance Coding Specialist/Coder, A
Medical Radiologic Technology/Science - Radiation Therapist, B
Multi-/Interdisciplinary Studies, B
Natural Sciences, B
Nurse Anesthetist, M
Nursing, MD
Nursing Administration, MO
Nursing Informatics, MO
Office Management and Supervision, B
Organizational Behavior Studies, B
Organizational Management, M
Physical Education Teaching and Coaching, B
Political Science and Government, B
Pre-Law Studies, B
Pre-Nursing Studies, AB
Project Management, MO
Psychology, BM
Public Administration, BM
Public Health, M
Public Health (MPH, DPH), B
Radiologic Technology/Science - Radiographer, B
Reading Teacher Education, MO
Real Estate, A
Rehabilitation and Therapeutic Professions, A
Rhetoric, M
School Psychology, M
Secondary Education and Teaching, B
Security and Loss Prevention Services, B
Social Sciences, B
Social and Philosophical Foundations of Education, B
Sociology, B
Software Engineering, M
Spanish Language and Literature, B
Special Education and Teaching, BMO
Sport Psychology, M
Sport and Fitness Administration/Management, AM
Substance Abuse/Addiction Counseling, A
Sustainability Management, M
Systems Engineering, M
Teacher Assistant/Aide, A
Teacher Education and Professional Development, Specific Subject Areas, A
Telecommunications, M
Web Page, Digital/Multimedia and Information Resources Design, B

Writing, M

NEW CHARTER UNIVERSITY

Business Administration, Management and Operations, M
Business/Commerce, AB
Communication Studies/Speech Communication and Rhetoric, AB
Criminal Justice/Safety Studies, AB
Criminology, M
Finance and Banking, M
Health Services Administration, M
Management, M
Public Administration, M

NEW YORK FILM ACADEMY

Acting, A
Cinematography and Film/Video Production, AB
Film, Television, and Video Production, M
Photography, M

NEWSCHOOL OF ARCHITECTURE AND DESIGN

Animation, Interactive Technology, Video Graphics and Special Effects, B
Architecture, BM
Building/Construction Site Management/Manager, B
Construction Management, BM
Environmental Design/Architecture, B
Industrial Design, B
Interior Design, B

NORCO COLLEGE

Accounting, A
Business/Commerce, A
Computer Programming/Programmer, A
Early Childhood Education and Teaching, A
Engineering Technology, A
Marketing/Marketing Management, A
Real Estate, A

NORTHWESTERN POLYTECHNIC UNIVERSITY

Business Administration and Management, B
Business Administration, Management and Operations, M
Computer Engineering, BM
Computer Science, BM
Electrical Engineering, M
Electrical, Electronics and Communications Engineering, B
Engineering and Applied Sciences, M

NOTRE DAME DE NAMUR UNIVERSITY

Art Therapy/Therapist, MD
Art/Art Studies, General, B
Biochemistry, B
Biological and Biomedical Sciences, O
Biology/Biological Sciences, B
Business Administration and Management, B
Business Administration, Management and Operations, M
Clinical Psychology, M
Communication Studies/Speech Communication and Rhetoric, B
Communication, Journalism and Related Programs, B
Computer Science, M
Computer and Information Sciences, B
Curriculum and Instruction, M
Drama and Dramatics/Theatre Arts, B
Education, MO
Educational Administration and Supervision, MO
Educational Media/Instructional Technology, M
English, MO
English Language and Literature, B
English as a Second Language, O
Entrepreneurship/Entrepreneurial Studies, M
Finance and Banking, M
Fine/Studio Arts, B
History, B
Human Resources Management and Services, M
Human Services, B
Industrial and Manufacturing Management, M
Information Science/Studies, M

Kinesiology and Exercise Science, B
Liberal Arts and Sciences Studies and Humanities, B
Management, M
Management of Technology, M
Marketing, M
Marriage and Family Therapy/Counseling, M
Music, B
Music Performance, B
Performance, MO
Philosophy, B
Political Science and Government, B
Pre-Law Studies, B
Pre-Medicine/Pre-Medical Studies, B
Psychology, BM
Public Administration, M
Public Affairs, M
Religion/Religious Studies, B
Social Sciences, B
Sociology, B
Special Education and Teaching, MO
Voice and Opera, B

OCCIDENTAL COLLEGE

American/United States Studies/Civilization, B
Art/Art Studies, General, B
Biochemistry, B
Biological and Biomedical Sciences, M
Biology/Biological Sciences, B
Chemistry, B
Chinese Language and Literature, B
Cognitive Sciences, B
Drama and Dramatics/Theatre Arts, B
East Asian Studies, B
Economics, B
Education, M
Elementary Education and Teaching, M
English Education, M
English Language and Literature, B
Environmental Studies, B
Foreign Language Teacher Education, M
Foreign Languages, Literatures, and Linguistics, B
French Language and Literature, B
Geology/Earth Science, B
History, B
International Relations and Affairs, B
Japanese Language and Literature, B
Kinesiology and Exercise Science, B
Latin American Studies, B
Liberal Studies, M
Mathematics, B
Mathematics Teacher Education, M
Music, B
Philosophy, B
Physics, B
Political Science and Government, B
Psychology, B
Religion/Religious Studies, B
Science Teacher Education/General Science Teacher Education, M
Secondary Education and Teaching, M
Social Studies Teacher Education, M
Sociology, B
Spanish Language and Literature, B
Visual and Performing Arts, B

OHLONE COLLEGE

Accounting, A
Administrative Assistant and Secretarial Science, A
American Sign Language (ASL), A
Anthropology, A
Art/Art Studies, General, A
BioTechnology, A
Biology/Biological Sciences, A
Broadcast Journalism, A
Business Administration and Management, A
Child Development, A
Commercial and Advertising Art, A
Computer Engineering, A
Computer Programming/Programmer, A
Computer Science, A
Computer Systems Networking and Telecommunications, A
Computer Typography and Composition Equipment Operator, A
Computer and Information Sciences, A

Computer and Information Systems Security, A
Consumer Services and Advocacy, A
Criminal Justice/Law Enforcement Administration, A
Criminal Justice/Police Science, A
Drafting and Design Technology/Technician, A
Early Childhood Education and Teaching, A
Economics, A
Electrical, Electronic and Communications Engineering Technology/Technician, A
Engineering, A
English Language and Literature, A
Environmental Sciences, A
Environmental Studies, A
Family and Consumer Sciences/Human Sciences, A
Fine Arts and Art Studies, A
Foods, Nutrition, and Wellness Studies, A
Geography, A
Geology/Earth Science, A
Health Professions and Related Clinical Sciences, A
History, A
Human Development and Family Studies, A
Interior Design, A
Journalism, A
Kindergarten/PreSchool Education and Teaching, A
Kinesiology and Exercise Science, A
Liberal Arts and Sciences Studies and Humanities, A
Marketing/Marketing Management, A
Mass Communication/Media Studies, A
Mathematics, A
Medical Administrative Assistant/Secretary, A
Medical/Clinical Assistant, A
Music, A
Music History, Literature, and Theory, A
Music Performance, A
Music Theory and Composition, A
Natural Sciences, A
Philosophy, A
Physical Sciences, A
Physical Therapist Assistant, A
Physical Therapy/Therapist, A
Physics, A
Psychology, A
Radio and Television, A
Radio and Television Broadcasting Technology/Technician, A
Real Estate, A
Respiratory Care Therapy/Therapist, A
Sign Language Interpretation and Translation, A
Social Sciences, A
Sociology, A
Spanish Language and Literature, A
System Administration/Administrator, A
Technical Theatre/Theatre Design and Technology, A

ORANGE COAST COLLEGE

Accounting, A
Accounting Technology/Technician and Bookkeeping, A
Aircraft Powerplant Technology/Technician, A
Airframe Mechanics and Aircraft Maintenance Technology/Technician, A
Airline Flight Attendant, A
Animation, Interactive Technology, Video Graphics and Special Effects, A
Anthropology, A
Apparel and Textile Manufacture, A
Apparel and Textile Marketing Management, A
Applied Horticulture/Horticultural Operations, A
Architectural Technology/Technician, A
Art/Art Studies, General, A
Audiology/Audiologist and Speech-Language Pathology/Pathologist, A
Aviation/Airway Management and Operations, A
Biology/Biological Sciences, A
Business Administration and Management, A
Business/Commerce, A
Cardiovascular Technology/Technologist, A
Chemistry, A
Child Care Provider/Assistant, A
Child Care and Support Services Management, A
Cinematography and Film/Video Production, A
Clinical/Medical Laboratory Technician, A
Commercial and Advertising Art, A

Communication Studies/Speech Communication and Rhetoric, A
Computer Graphics, A
Computer Installation and Repair Technology/Technician, A
Computer Programming/Programmer, A
Computer Science, A
Construction Trades, A
Cooking and Related Culinary Arts, A
Culinary Arts/Chef Training, A
Dance, A
Dental Assisting/Assistant, A
Diagnostic Medical Sonography/Sonographer and Ultrasound Technician, A
Dietetic Technician (DTR), A
Drama and Dramatics/Theatre Arts, A
Economics, A
Education/Teaching of Individuals in Early Childhood Special Education Programs, A
Electrical/Electronics Equipment Installation and Repair, A
Electrocardiograph Technology/Technician, A
Electroneurodiagnostic/Electroencephalographic Technology/Technologist, A
Elementary Education and Teaching, A
Engineering Technologies/Technicians, A
Family and Consumer Sciences/Human Sciences, A
Fashion/Apparel Design, A
Foods, Nutrition, and Wellness Studies, A
Foreign Languages and Literatures, A
General Merchandising, Sales, and Related Marketing Operations, A
Geography, A
Geology/Earth Science, A
Health Services/Allied Health/Health Sciences, A
Health and Physical Education, A
History, A
Hotel/Motel Administration/Management, A
Humanities/Humanistic Studies, A
Interior Design, A
International Business/Trade/Commerce, A
Journalism, A
Kinesiology and Exercise Science, A
Liberal Arts and Sciences Studies and Humanities, A
Machine Tool Technology/Machinist, A
Marine Transportation, A
Mass Communication/Media Studies, A
Mathematics, A
Medical/Clinical Assistant, A
Mental Health Counseling/Counselor, A
Music, A
Philosophy, A
Photographic and Film/Video Technology/Technician and Assistant, A
Photography, A
Physics, A
Political Science and Government, A
Psychology, A
Real Estate, A
Recording Arts Technology/Technician, A
Religion/Religious Studies, A
Respiratory Care Therapy/Therapist, A
Restaurant, Culinary, and Catering Management/Manager, A
Sales, Distribution and Marketing Operations, A
Social Sciences, A
Sociology, A
Spanish Language and Literature, A
Tourism and Travel Services Marketing Operations, A
Welding Technology/Welder, A

OTIS COLLEGE OF ART AND DESIGN

Art/Art Studies, General, B
Commercial and Advertising Art, B
Design and Applied Arts, B
Drawing, B
Environmental Design/Architecture, B
Fashion/Apparel Design, B
Fine Arts and Art Studies, M
Fine/Studio Arts, B
Graphic Design, M
Interior Design, B
Painting, M
Photography, BM

Sculpture, BM
Writing, M

OXNARD COLLEGE

Administrative Assistant and Secretarial Science, A
Anthropology, A
Art/Art Studies, General, A
Autobody/Collision and Repair Technology/Technician, A
Automobile/Automotive Mechanics Technology/Technician, A
Biology/Biological Sciences, A
Business Administration and Management, A
Child Development, A
Communication Studies/Speech Communication and Rhetoric, A
Computer Systems Networking and Telecommunications, A
Computer and Information Systems Security, A
Culinary Arts/Chef Training, A
Dental Hygiene/Hygienist, A
Economics, A
English Language and Literature, A
Environmental Engineering Technology/Environmental Technology, A
Environmental Studies, A
Family and Community Services, A
Fine/Studio Arts, A
Fire Protection and Safety Technology/Technician, A
Fire Science/Firefighting, A
Fire Services Administration, A
Heating, Air Conditioning, Ventilation and Refrigeration Maintenance Technology/Technician, A
History, A
Hotel/Motel Administration/Management, A
Legal Assistant/Paralegal, A
Marketing/Marketing Management, A
Mathematics, A
Philosophy, A
Political Science and Government, A
Psychology, A
Radio and Television, A
Restaurant/Food Services Management, A
Sociology, A
Spanish Language and Literature, A
Substance Abuse/Addiction Counseling, A
Web Page, Digital/Multimedia and Information Resources Design, A

PACIFIC OAKS COLLEGE

Child Development, B
Early Childhood Education and Teaching, M
Education, M
Elementary Education and Teaching, B
Human Development, M
Human Development and Family Studies, B
Human Services, B
Kindergarten/PreSchool Education and Teaching, B
Marriage and Family Therapy/Counseling, M
Special Education and Teaching, BM

PACIFIC STATES UNIVERSITY

Accounting, M
Business Administration and Management, B
Business Administration, Management and Operations, MD
Computer Science, BM
Finance and Banking, M
International Business/Trade/Commerce, MD
Management Information Systems and Services, M
Management of Technology, M
Real Estate, M

PACIFIC UNION COLLEGE

Acting, A
Aeronautics/Aviation/Aerospace Science and Technology, AB
Biochemistry, B
Bioinformatics, B
Biology/Biological Sciences, B
Biophysics, B
Business/Commerce, AB
Chemistry, B
Cinematography and Film/Video Production, AB
Computer Science, B
Early Childhood Education and Teaching, AB

Education, M
Elementary Education and Teaching, BM
Emergency Medical Technology/Technician (EMT Paramedic), A
English Language and Literature, B
Environmental Studies, B
Fine/Studio Arts, B
General Studies, AB
Graphic Design, AB
Health and Physical Education, B
History, B
Kinesiology and Exercise Science, B
Mathematics, B
Music, AB
Music Performance, B
Music Teacher Education, B
Natural Sciences, B
Photography, AB
Physical Education Teaching and Coaching, B
Physics, B
Playwriting and Screenwriting, A
Pre-Law Studies, B
Psychology, B
Religion/Religious Studies, B
Secondary Education and Teaching, M
Social Science Teacher Education, B
Social Work, B
Spanish Language and Literature, B
Theology/Theological Studies, B

PALO ALTO UNIVERSITY

Biopsychology, D
Clinical Psychology, D
Counseling Psychology, M
Psychology, BMD

PALO VERDE COLLEGE

Accounting Technology/Technician and Bookkeeping, A
Administrative Assistant and Secretarial Science, A
Automotive Engineering Technology/Technician, A
Biological and Physical Sciences, A
Business Administration and Management, A
Child Care Provider/Assistant, A
Construction Trades, A
Criminal Justice/Police Science, A
Hazardous Materials Management and Waste Technology/Technician, A
Humanities/Humanistic Studies, A
Information Technology, A
Liberal Arts and Sciences Studies and Humanities, A
Multi-/Interdisciplinary Studies, A

PALOMAR COLLEGE

Accounting Technology/Technician and Bookkeeping, A
Administrative Assistant and Secretarial Science, A
Advertising, A
Airline/Commercial/Professional Pilot and Flight Crew, A
Animation, Interactive Technology, Video Graphics and Special Effects, A
Apparel and Textile Marketing Management, A
Archeology, A
Architectural Drafting and Architectural CAD/CADD, A
Architectural Technology/Technician, A
Art/Art Studies, General, A
Astronomy, A
Autobody/Collision and Repair Technology/Technician, A
Automobile/Automotive Mechanics Technology/Technician, A
Aviation/Airway Management and Operations, A
Biological and Physical Sciences, A
Biology/Biological Sciences, A
Broadcast Journalism, A
Building/Home/Construction Inspection/Inspector, A
Business Administration and Management, A
Business/Commerce, A
Cabinetmaking and Millwork/Millwright, A
Carpentry/Carpenter, A
Ceramic Arts and Ceramics, A
Chemistry, A
Child Care Provider/Assistant, A

Child Care and Support Services Management, A
Commercial and Advertising Art, A
Communication Studies/Speech Communication
and Rhetoric, A
Computer Graphics, A
Computer Programming/Programmer, A
Computer Systems Networking and Telecommunications, A
Construction Trades, A
Dance, A
Dental Assisting/Assistant, A
Design and Visual Communications, A
Diesel Mechanics Technology/Technician, A
Drafting and Design Technology/Technician, A
Drama and Dramatics/Theatre Arts, A
Drawing, A
Drywall Installation/Drywaller, A
Economics, A
Education, A
Education/Teaching of Individuals in Early Childhood
Special Education Programs, A
Electrical/Electronics Drafting and
Electrical/Electronics CAD/CADD, A
Electrician, A
Emergency Medical Technology/Technician (EMT
Paramedic), A
English Language and Literature, A
Family and Community Services, A
Family and Consumer Sciences/Human Sciences, A
Fashion/Apparel Design, A
Film/Cinema Studies, A
Fire Protection and Safety Technology/Technician, A
Foreign Languages and Literatures, A
Forensic Science and Technology, A
French Language and Literature, A
Geography, A
Geology/Earth Science, A
Graphic Design, A
Graphic and Printing Equipment Operator Production, A
Humanities/Humanistic Studies, A
Information Technology, A
Insurance, A
Interior Design, A
International Business/Trade/Commerce, A
Journalism, A
Kinesiology and Exercise Science, A
Law and Legal Studies, A
Liberal Arts and Sciences Studies and Humanities, A
Library Assistant/Technician, A
Mason/Masonry, A
Mathematics, A
Medical Administrative Assistant/Secretary, A
Metal and Jewelry Arts, A
Music, A
Parks, Recreation, Leisure and Fitness Studies, A
Photographic and Film/Video Technology/Technician
and Assistant, A
Prepress/Desktop Publishing and Digital Imaging
Design, A
Psychology, A
Public Administration, A
Radio and Television, A
Real Estate, A
Sculpture, A
Sheet Metal Technology/Sheetworking, A
Sign Language Interpretation and Translation, A
Social Sciences, A
Sociology, A
Substance Abuse/Addiction Counseling, A
Water Quality and Wastewater Treatment Management and Recycling Technology/Technician, A
Web Page, Digital/Multimedia and Information Resources Design, A
Welding Technology/Welder, A
Women's Studies, A

PASADENA CITY COLLEGE

Accounting, A
Accounting Technology/Technician and Bookkeeping, A
Administrative Assistant and Secretarial Science, A
Animation, Interactive Technology, Video Graphics
and Special Effects, A
Anthropology, A

Architecture, A
Art/Art Studies, General, A
Audiology/Audiologist and Speech-Language
Pathology/Pathologist, A
Automobile/Automotive Mechanics
Technology/Technician, A
Biochemistry, A
Biological and Physical Sciences, A
Biology/Biological Sciences, A
Broadcast Journalism, A
Building/Home/Construction Inspection/Inspector, A
Business Administration and Management, A
Business/Office Automation/Technology/Data Entry, A
Chemistry, A
Child Development, A
Cinematography and Film/Video Production, A
Classics and Classical Languages, Literatures, and Linguistics, A
Communication Studies/Speech Communication
and Rhetoric, A
Computer Science, A
Computer Technology/Computer Systems Technology, A
Computer/Information Technology Services Administration and Management, A
Construction Trades, A
Cosmetology, Barber/Styling, and Nail Instructor, A
Cosmetology/Cosmetologist, A
Criminal Justice/Law Enforcement Administration, A
Dance, A
Data Entry/Microcomputer Applications, A
Dental Assisting/Assistant, A
Dental Hygiene/Hygienist, A
Dental Laboratory Technology/Technician, A
Digital Communication and Media/Multimedia, A
Drafting and Design Technology/Technician, A
Drama and Dramatics/Theatre Arts, A
Electrical and Electronic Engineering
Technologies/Technicians, A
Electrical, Electronics and Communications Engineering, A
Engineering Technology, A
Fashion Merchandising, A
Fashion/Apparel Design, A
Fire Protection and Safety Technology/Technician, A
Food Service, Waiter/Waitress, and Dining Room
Management/Manager, A
Graphic Design, A
Graphic and Printing Equipment Operator Production, A
History, A
Hospitality Administration/Management, A
Humanities/Humanistic Studies, A
Industrial Electronics Technology/Technician, A
International Business/Trade/Commerce, A
International/Global Studies, A
Legal Assistant/Paralegal, A
Liberal Arts and Sciences Studies and Humanities, A
Library Science, A
Machine Shop Technology/Assistant, A
Marketing/Marketing Management, A
Mathematics, A
Mechanical Engineering, A
Medical Insurance Specialist/Medical Biller, A
Medical Office Assistant/Specialist, A
Medical/Clinical Assistant, A
Photography, A
Photojournalism, A
Prepress/Desktop Publishing and Digital Imaging
Design, A
Psychology, A
Radio and Television, A
Radio and Television Broadcasting
Technology/Technician, A
Radiologic Technology/Science - Radiographer, A
Sociology, A
Spanish Language and Literature, A
Technical Theatre/Theatre Design and Technology, A
Welding Technology/Welder, A

PATTEN UNIVERSITY

Bible/Biblical Studies, AB
Business Administration and Management, B

Divinity/Ministry (BD, MDiv.), B
Kindergarten/PreSchool Education and Teaching, A
Liberal Arts and Sciences Studies and Humanities, AB
Pastoral Studies/Counseling, B
Religious/Sacred Music, B

PEPPERDINE UNIVERSITY

Accounting, B
Acting, B
Advertising, B
American/United States Studies/Civilization, M
Art History, Criticism and Conservation, B
Art/Art Studies, General, A
Asian Studies/Civilization, B
Biology/Biological Sciences, B
Business Administration and Management, B
Business Administration, Management and Operations, M
Chemistry, B
Chemistry Teacher Education, B
Clinical Psychology, M
Communication Studies/Speech Communication
and Rhetoric, B
Communication and Media Studies, M
Conflict Resolution and Mediation/Peace Studies, M
Directing and Theatrical Production, B
Dramatic/Theatre Arts and Stagecraft, B
Economics, BM
Education, M
Educational Administration and Supervision, MD
Educational Leadership and Administration, D
Educational Media/Instructional Technology, MD
English Language and Literature, B
English/Language Arts Teacher Education, B
Entrepreneurship/Entrepreneurial Studies, M
European Studies/Civilization, B
Film, Television, and Video Production, M
Film/Cinema Studies, B
Finance, B
Finance and Banking, M
French Language and Literature, B
General Studies, B
German Language and Literature, B
Health and Physical Education, B
Hispanic-American, Puerto Rican, and Mexican-
American/Chicano Studies, B
History, B
International Affairs, M
International Business/Trade/Commerce, BM
International/Global Studies, B
Italian Language and Literature, B
Journalism, B
Kinesiology and Exercise Science, B
Latin American Studies, B
Law and Legal Studies, D
Liberal Arts and Sciences Studies and Humanities, B
Marriage and Family Therapy/Counseling, M
Mathematics, B
Mathematics Teacher Education, B
Mathematics and Computer Science, B
Media Studies, M
Multi-/Interdisciplinary Studies, B
Music, B
Music Teacher Education, B
Music Theory and Composition, B
Natural Sciences, B
Nutritional Sciences, B
Organizational Communication, B
Organizational Management, M
Pastoral Studies/Counseling, M
Philosophy, B
Physics, B
Political Science and Government, BM
Psychology, BMD
Public Administration, M
Public Policy Analysis, M
Public Relations, Advertising, and Applied Communication, B
Radio and Television, B
Religion/Religious Studies, BM
Semitic Languages, Literatures, and Linguistics, B
Sociology, B
Spanish Language and Literature, B
Sport and Fitness Administration/Management, B

Technical Theatre/Theatre Design and Technology, B
Theology and Religious Vocations, M
Web/Multimedia Management and Webmaster, B
Writing, M

PIMA MEDICAL INSTITUTE

Health/Health Care Administration/Management, A
Radiologic Technology/Science - Radiographer, A
Respiratory Therapy Technician/Assistant, A
Veterinary/Animal Health Technology/Technician and Veterinary Assistant, A

PITZER COLLEGE

African-American/Black Studies, B
American/United States Studies/Civilization, B
Anthropology, B
Art History, Criticism and Conservation, B
Art/Art Studies, General, B
Asian Studies/Civilization, B
Asian-American Studies, B
Biochemistry, B
Biology/Biological Sciences, B
Chemistry, B
Classics and Classical Languages, Literatures, and Linguistics, B
Dance, B
Drama and Dramatics/Theatre Arts, B
Economics, B
English Language and Literature, B
Environmental Sciences, B
Film/Cinema Studies, B
Fine/Studio Arts, B
Foreign Languages and Literatures, B
Hispanic-American, Puerto Rican, and Mexican-American/Chicano Studies, B
History, B
International/Global Studies, B
Linguistics, B
Mathematics, B
Molecular Biology, B
Music, B
Organizational Behavior Studies, B
Philosophy, B
Physics, B
Political Science and Government, B
Psychology, B
Religion/Religious Studies, B
Science, Technology and Society, B
Sociology, B
Spanish Language and Literature, B
Women's Studies, B

PLATT COLLEGE (ALHAMBRA)

Allied Health and Medical Assisting Services, A
Design and Visual Communications, B
Legal Assistant/Paralegal, A

PLATT COLLEGE (ONTARIO)

Allied Health and Medical Assisting Services, A
Design and Visual Communications, B
Legal Assistant/Paralegal, A

PLATT COLLEGE SAN DIEGO

Animation, Interactive Technology, Video Graphics and Special Effects, B
Computer Software and Media Applications, A
Digital Communication and Media/Multimedia, A
Graphic Design, A
Intermedia/Multimedia, AB
Photographic and Film/Video Technology/Technician and Assistant, B
Prepress/Desktop Publishing and Digital Imaging Design, A
Web Page, Digital/Multimedia and Information Resources Design, B

POINT LOMA NAZARENE UNIVERSITY

Accounting, B
Allied Health Diagnostic, Intervention, and Treatment Professions, B
Art Teacher Education, B
Athletic Training and Sports Medicine, B
Bible/Biblical Studies, B
Biochemistry, B

Biological and Biomedical Sciences, M
Biology/Biological Sciences, B
Broadcast Journalism, B
Business Administration and Management, B
Business Administration, Management and Operations, M
Business/Corporate Communications, B
Business/Managerial Economics, B
Chemistry, B
Child Development, B
Communication Studies/Speech Communication and Rhetoric, B
Computer Software Engineering, B
Computer Technology/Computer Systems Technology, B
Counselor Education/School Counseling and Guidance Services, M
Development Economics and International Development, B
Dietetics/Dieticians, B
Education, M
Educational Leadership and Administration, M
Elementary Education and Teaching, B
Engineering Physics, B
English Language and Literature, B
Entrepreneurship/Entrepreneurial Studies, B
Environmental Sciences, B
Finance, B
Foods, Nutrition, and Wellness Studies, B
Foodservice Systems Administration/Management, B
French Language and Literature, B
Gerontological Nursing, M
Graphic Design, B
Health Services Administration, M
Health and Physical Education, B
History, B
Interior Design, B
International/Global Studies, B
Journalism, B
Kinesiology and Exercise Science, B
Liberal Arts and Sciences Studies and Humanities, B
Management Information Systems and Services, B
Management Science, B
Marketing/Marketing Management, B
Mass Communication/Media Studies, B
Maternal/Child Health and Neonatal Nurse/Nursing, M
Mathematics, B
Music, B
Music Performance, B
Music Teacher Education, B
Music Theory and Composition, B
Non-Profit/Public/Organizational Management, BM
Nursing, MO
Nursing - Advanced Practice, M
Office Management and Supervision, B
Organizational Management, M
Pastoral Studies/Counseling, M
Philosophy, B
Physics, B
Piano and Organ, B
Political Science and Government, B
Pre-Theology/Pre-Ministerial Studies, B
Psychiatric/Mental Health Nurse/Nursing, M
Psychology, B
Religion/Religious Studies, M
Religious/Sacred Music, B
Social Sciences, B
Social Work, B
Sociology, B
Spanish Language and Literature, B
Special Education and Teaching, M
Sustainability Management, M
Visual and Performing Arts, B
Voice and Opera, B

POMONA COLLEGE

African-American/Black Studies, B
American/United States Studies/Civilization, B
Anthropology, B
Art History, Criticism and Conservation, B
Art/Art Studies, General, B
Asian Studies/Civilization, B
Asian-American Studies, B

Astronomy, B
Biology/Biological Sciences, B
Central/Middle and Eastern European Studies, B
Chemistry, B
Chinese Language and Literature, B
Classics and Classical Languages, Literatures, and Linguistics, B
Cognitive Sciences, B
Computer Science, B
Dance, B
Drama and Dramatics/Theatre Arts, B
Economics, B
English Language and Literature, B
Environmental Studies, B
French Language and Literature, B
Geology/Earth Science, B
German Language and Literature, B
German Studies, B
Hispanic-American, Puerto Rican, and Mexican-American/Chicano Studies, B
History, B
International Relations and Affairs, B
Japanese Language and Literature, B
Latin American Studies, B
Linguistics, B
Mass Communication/Media Studies, B
Mathematics, B
Medieval and Renaissance Studies, B
Molecular Biology, B
Music, B
Near and Middle Eastern Studies, B
Philosophy, B
Physics, B
Political Science and Government, B
Psychology, B
Public Policy Analysis, B
Religion/Religious Studies, B
Romance Languages, Literatures, and Linguistics, B
Russian Language and Literature, B
Science, Technology and Society, B
Sociology, B
Spanish Language and Literature, B
Women's Studies, B

PORTERVILLE COLLEGE

Administrative Assistant and Secretarial Science, A
Agricultural Business and Management, A
Art/Art Studies, General, A
Automobile/Automotive Mechanics Technology/Technician, A
Biological and Physical Sciences, A
Biology/Biological Sciences, A
Business Administration and Management, A
Business Teacher Education, A
Carpentry/Carpenter, A
Child Development, A
Commercial and Advertising Art, A
Computer Science, A
Criminal Justice/Law Enforcement Administration, A
Criminal Justice/Police Science, A
Design and Applied Arts, A
Drafting and Design Technology/Technician, A
Education, A
English Language and Literature, A
Finance, A
Fire Science/Firefighting, A
History, A
Human Services, A
Liberal Arts and Sciences Studies and Humanities, A
Mathematics, A
Mental Health Counseling/Counselor, A
Music, A
Natural Sciences, A
Photography, A
Physical Education Teaching and Coaching, A
Social Sciences, A

Welding Technology/Welder, A

PROFESSIONAL GOLFERS CAREER COLLEGE

Parks, Recreation and Leisure Facilities Management, A

REEDLEY COLLEGE

Accounting, A
Administrative Assistant and Secretarial Science, A
Agricultural Business and Management, A
Agricultural Mechanization, A
Agriculture, A
Animal Sciences, A
Art/Art Studies, General, A
Automobile/Automotive Mechanics Technology/Technician, A
Avionics Maintenance Technology/Technician, A
Biology/Biological Sciences, A
Business/Commerce, A
Child Care and Support Services Management, A
Commercial and Advertising Art, A
Computer and Information Sciences, A
Corrections and Criminal Justice, A
Criminal Justice/Police Science, A
Dental Assisting/Assistant, A
English Language and Literature, A
Entrepreneurship/Entrepreneurial Studies, A
Fine Arts and Art Studies, A
Foreign Languages and Literatures, A
General Office Occupations and Clerical Services, A
General Studies, A
Health and Physical Education, A
Horticultural Science, A
Hospitality Administration/Management, A
Information Science/Studies, A
Liberal Arts and Sciences Studies and Humanities, A
Machine Tool Technology/Machinist, A
Management Science, A
Mathematics, A
Music Performance, A
Natural Resources Management/Development and Policy, A
Physical Sciences, A
Plant Sciences, A
Precision Metal Working, A
Social Sciences, A
Voice and Opera, A
Welding Technology/Welder, A

RIO HONDO COLLEGE

Business Teacher Education, A
Criminal Justice/Law Enforcement Administration, A
Liberal Arts and Sciences Studies and Humanities, A

RIVERSIDE CITY COLLEGE

Accounting, A
Autobody/Collision and Repair Technology/Technician, A
Automobile/Automotive Mechanics Technology/Technician, A
Business Administration and Management, A
Computer Programming/Programmer, A
Cosmetology/Cosmetologist, A
Culinary Arts/Chef Training, A
Early Childhood Education and Teaching, A
Graphic and Printing Equipment Operator Production, A
Heating, Air Conditioning, Ventilation and Refrigeration Maintenance Technology/Technician, A
Human Services, A
Marketing/Marketing Management, A
Office Management and Supervision, A
Real Estate, A
Sign Language Interpretation and Translation, A
Welding Technology/Welder, A

SACRAMENTO CITY COLLEGE

Accounting, A
Administrative Assistant and Secretarial Science, A
Advertising, A
Airframe Mechanics and Aircraft Maintenance Technology/Technician, A

Army JROTC/ROTC, A
Art/Art Studies, General, A
Avionics Maintenance Technology/Technician, A
Biological and Physical Sciences, A
Business Administration and Management, A
Comparative Literature, A
Computer Science, A
Cosmetology/Cosmetologist, A
Criminal Justice/Law Enforcement Administration, A
Data Processing and Data Processing Technology/Technician, A
Dental Assisting/Assistant, A
Dental Hygiene/Hygienist, A
Drafting and Design Technology/Technician, A
Drama and Dramatics/Theatre Arts, A
Electrical, Electronic and Communications Engineering Technology/Technician, A
Engineering, A
Family and Consumer Economics and Related Services, A
Graphic and Printing Equipment Operator Production, A
Human Services, A
Humanities/Humanistic Studies, A
Kindergarten/PreSchool Education and Teaching, A
Legal Administrative Assistant/Secretary, A
Liberal Arts and Sciences Studies and Humanities, A
Library Science, A
Mass Communication/Media Studies, A
Mathematics, A
Medical Administrative Assistant/Secretary, A
Music, A
Natural Resources Management/Development and Policy, A
Natural Sciences, A
Occupational Therapy/Therapist, A
Physical Education Teaching and Coaching, A
Physical Sciences, A
Physical Therapist Assistant, A
Psychology, A
Real Estate, A
Social Sciences, A
Social Work, A
Survey Technology/Surveying, A
Transportation and Materials Moving, A
Women's Studies, A

SADDLEBACK COLLEGE

Accounting, A
Administrative Assistant and Secretarial Science, A
American/United States Studies/Civilization, A
Anthropology, A
Architectural Engineering Technology/Technician, A
Art/Art Studies, General, A
Astronomy, A
Automobile/Automotive Mechanics Technology/Technician, A
Biology/Biological Sciences, A
Business Administration and Management, A
Carpentry/Carpenter, A
Chemical Engineering, A
Chemistry, A
Child Development, A
Cinematography and Film/Video Production, A
Commercial and Advertising Art, A
Comparative Literature, A
Computer Programming/Programmer, A
Computer Science, A
Computer Typography and Composition Equipment Operator, A
Computer and Information Sciences, A
Construction Engineering Technology/Technician, A
Consumer Merchandising/Retailing Management, A
Consumer Services and Advocacy, A
Cosmetology/Cosmetologist, A
Drafting and Design Technology/Technician, A
Drama and Dramatics/Theatre Arts, A
Economics, A
Electrical, Electronic and Communications Engineering Technology/Technician, A
Emergency Medical Technology/Technician (EMT Paramedic), A
Engineering, A
Environmental Studies, A
Family and Community Services, A

Family and Consumer Sciences/Human Sciences, A
Fashion Merchandising, A
Fashion/Apparel Design, A
Food Science, A
Food Technology and Processing, A
Foods, Nutrition, and Wellness Studies, A
Geography, A
Geology/Earth Science, A
Gerontology, A
History, A
Horticultural Science, A
Human Development and Family Studies, A
Human Services, A
Humanities/Humanistic Studies, A
Information Science/Studies, A
Interior Design, A
Journalism, A
Kindergarten/PreSchool Education and Teaching, A
Landscape Architecture, A
Law and Legal Studies, A
Legal Administrative Assistant/Secretary, A
Legal Assistant/Paralegal, A
Liberal Arts and Sciences Studies and Humanities, A
Marine Maintenance/Fitter and Ship Repair Technology/Technician, A
Marine Science/Merchant Marine Officer, A
Mathematics, A
Medical/Clinical Assistant, A
Music, A
Natural Sciences, A
Ornamental Horticulture, A
Philosophy, A
Photography, A
Physical Education Teaching and Coaching, A
Physical Sciences, A
Physics, A
Political Science and Government, A
Psychology, A
Radio and Television, A
Real Estate, A
Social Sciences, A
Sociology, A
Special Products Marketing Operations, A
Substance Abuse/Addiction Counseling, A
Teacher Assistant/Aide, A
Tourism and Travel Services Management, A
Women's Studies, A

SAGE COLLEGE

Court Reporting/Court Reporter, A
Legal Administrative Assistant/Secretary, A

SAINT KATHERINE COLLEGE

Art/Art Studies, General, B
Biochemistry, B
Biology/Biological Sciences, B
Business Administration and Management, B
English Language and Literature, B
Exercise Physiology, B
History, B
Kinesiology and Exercise Science, B
Music, B
Theology/Theological Studies, B

SAINT MARY'S COLLEGE OF CALIFORNIA

Accounting, B
Accounting and Related Services, B
American/United States Studies/Civilization, B
Anthropology, B
Archeology, B
Art History, Criticism and Conservation, B
Art/Art Studies, General, B
Biochemistry, B
Biological and Biomedical Sciences, B
Biology/Biological Sciences, B
Business Administration and Management, B
Business Administration, Management and Operations, M
Business/Commerce, B
Chemistry, B
Communication Studies/Speech Communication and Rhetoric, B
Communication, Journalism and Related Programs, B

Comparative Literature, B
Counselor Education/School Counseling and Guidance Services, M
Curriculum and Instruction, M
Dance, BM
Drama and Dramatics/Theatre Arts, B
Early Childhood Education and Teaching, M
Economics, B
Education, MD
Educational Administration and Supervision, MD
Educational Leadership and Administration, M
Engineering, B
English Language and Literature, B
European Studies/Civilization, B
Exercise and Sports Science, M
Finance and Banking, M
Finance and Financial Management Services, B
Foreign Languages, Literatures, and Linguistics, B
French Language and Literature, B
German Language and Literature, B
Health and Physical Education, B
Health and Physical Education/Fitness, B
Historic Preservation and Conservation, B
History, B
International Business/Trade/Commerce, B
International Relations and Affairs, B
Investment Management, M
Italian Language and Literature, B
Kinesiology and Exercise Science, B
Kinesiology and Movement Studies, M
Latin American Studies, B
Latin Language and Literature, B
Liberal Arts and Sciences Studies and Humanities, B
Management, M
Marriage and Family Therapy/Counseling, M
Mathematics, B
Mathematics and Computer Science, B
Mathematics and Statistics, B
Modern Greek Language and Literature, B
Modern Languages, B
Multi-/Interdisciplinary Studies, B
Music, B
Philosophy, B
Physics, B
Political Science and Government, B
Psychology, B
Reading Teacher Education, M
Religion/Religious Studies, B
Social Sciences, B
Sociology, B
Spanish Language and Literature, B
Special Education and Teaching, M
Sport and Fitness Administration/Management, BM
Theatre Literature, History and Criticism, B
Theology/Theological Studies, B
Visual and Performing Arts, B
Women's Studies, B
Writing, M

THE SALVATION ARMY COLLEGE FOR OFFICER TRAINING AT CRESTMONT

Divinity/Ministry (BD, MDiv.), A

SAMUEL MERRITT UNIVERSITY

Nurse Anesthetist, MO
Nursing, MDO
Nursing - Advanced Practice, MO
Nursing Administration, M
Occupational Therapy/Therapist, M
Physical Therapy/Therapist, D
Physician Assistant, M

SAN BERNARDINO VALLEY COLLEGE

Accounting, A
Administrative Assistant and Secretarial Science, A
Aeronautics/Aviation/Aerospace Science and Technology, A
Anthropology, A
Architectural Engineering Technology/Technician, A
Art/Art Studies, General, A
Astronomy, A
Automobile/Automotive Mechanics Technology/Technician, A
Biology/Biological Sciences, A
Botany/Plant Biology, A

Business Administration and Management, A
Chemical Engineering, A
Chemistry, A
Civil Engineering Technology/Technician, A
Clinical/Medical Laboratory Technician, A
Commercial and Advertising Art, A
Computer Engineering Technology/Technician, A
Computer Science, A
Corrections, A
Criminal Justice/Police Science, A
Data Processing and Data Processing Technology/Technician, A
Dental Hygiene/Hygienist, A
Drafting and Design Technology/Technician, A
Economics, A
Electrical, Electronic and Communications Engineering Technology/Technician, A
English Language and Literature, A
Environmental Studies, A
Family and Consumer Economics and Related Services, A
Finance, A
French Language and Literature, A
Geography, A
Geology/Earth Science, A
German Language and Literature, A
Heating, Air Conditioning, Ventilation and Refrigeration Maintenance Technology/Technician, A
History, A
Hotel/Motel Administration/Management, A
Human Services, A
Interior Design, A
Journalism, A
Liberal Arts and Sciences Studies and Humanities, A
Machine Tool Technology/Machinist, A
Marketing/Marketing Management, A
Mathematics, A
Mental Health Counseling/Counselor, A
Music, A
Parks, Recreation, Leisure and Fitness Studies, A
Philosophy, A
Photography, A
Physical Education Teaching and Coaching, A
Physical Sciences, A
Physics, A
Political Science and Government, A
Psychology, A
Radio and Television, A
Real Estate, A
Religion/Religious Studies, A
Sociology, A
Spanish Language and Literature, A
Telecommunications Technology/Technician, A
Welding Technology/Welder, A
Zoology/Animal Biology, A

SAN DIEGO CHRISTIAN COLLEGE

Aeronautics/Aviation/Aerospace Science and Technology, B
Bible/Biblical Studies, B
Biology/Biological Sciences, B
Business Administration and Management, B
Communication Studies/Speech Communication and Rhetoric, B
Criminal Justice/Law Enforcement Administration, B
Divinity/Ministry (BD, MDiv.), B
Education, B
Elementary Education and Teaching, B
English Language and Literature, B
History, B
Human Development and Family Studies, B
Kinesiology and Exercise Science, B
Liberal Arts and Sciences Studies and Humanities, AB
Multi-/Interdisciplinary Studies, B
Music, B
Music Performance, B
Pastoral Studies/Counseling, B
Physical Education Teaching and Coaching, B
Political Science and Government, B
Psychology, B
Religious/Sacred Music, B
Secondary Education and Teaching, B

Teacher Education, Multiple Levels, B

SAN DIEGO CITY COLLEGE

Accounting, A
Administrative Assistant and Secretarial Science, A
African-American/Black Studies, A
Anthropology, A
Art/Art Studies, General, A
Artificial Intelligence and Robotics, A
Automobile/Automotive Mechanics Technology/Technician, A
Behavioral Sciences, A
Biology/Biological Sciences, A
Business Administration and Management, A
Carpentry/Carpenter, A
Commercial and Advertising Art, A
Computer Engineering Technology/Technician, A
Consumer Services and Advocacy, A
Cosmetology/Cosmetologist, A
Court Reporting/Court Reporter, A
Data Processing and Data Processing Technology/Technician, A
Drafting and Design Technology/Technician, A
Drama and Dramatics/Theatre Arts, A
Electrical, Electronic and Communications Engineering Technology/Technician, A
Emergency Medical Technology/Technician (EMT Paramedic), A
Engineering Technology, A
English Language and Literature, A
Environmental Engineering Technology/Environmental Technology, A
Fashion Merchandising, A
Finance, A
Graphic and Printing Equipment Operator Production, A
Hispanic-American, Puerto Rican, and Mexican-American/Chicano Studies, A
Hospitality Administration/Management, A
Industrial Technology/Technician, A
Insurance, A
Interior Design, A
Journalism, A
Labor and Industrial Relations, A
Latin American Studies, A
Legal Administrative Assistant/Secretary, A
Legal Assistant/Paralegal, A
Liberal Arts and Sciences Studies and Humanities, A
Machine Tool Technology/Machinist, A
Marketing/Marketing Management, A
Mathematics, A
Modern Languages, A
Music, A
Occupational Safety and Health Technology/Technician, A
Parks, Recreation, Leisure and Fitness Studies, A
Photography, A
Physical Education Teaching and Coaching, A
Physical Sciences, A
Political Science and Government, A
Psychology, A
Radio and Television, A
Real Estate, A
Social Sciences, A
Social Work, A
Sociology, A
Special Products Marketing Operations, A
Teacher Assistant/Aide, A
Telecommunications Technology/Technician, A
Tourism and Travel Services Management, A
Transportation and Materials Moving, A
Welding Technology/Welder, A

SAN DIEGO MESA COLLEGE

Accounting, A
Administrative Assistant and Secretarial Science, A
African-American/Black Studies, A
Architectural Engineering Technology/Technician, A
Architecture, A
Art/Art Studies, General, A
Biology/Biological Sciences, A
Business Administration and Management, A
Chemistry, A
Child Care Provider/Assistant, A
Clinical/Medical Laboratory Technician, A

Computer Programming, A
Computer Programming, Specific Applications, A
Computer Science, A
Computer Software and Media Applications, A
Computer and Information Sciences, A
Construction Engineering Technology/Technician, A
Data Entry/Microcomputer Applications, A
Dental Assisting/Assistant, A
Engineering, A
English Language and Literature, A
Fashion Merchandising, A
Fashion/Apparel Design, A
Foods, Nutrition, and Related Services, A
Foods, Nutrition, and Wellness Studies, A
French Language and Literature, A
Geography, A
Health Information/Medical Records
    Administration/Administrator, A
Hispanic-American, Puerto Rican, and Mexican-
    American/Chicano Studies, A
Hospitality and Recreation Marketing Operations, A
Hotel/Motel Administration/Management, A
Industrial Radiologic Technology/Technician, A
Interior Design, A
Intermedia/Multimedia, A
Landscape Architecture, A
Legal Administrative Assistant/Secretary, A
Liberal Arts and Sciences Studies and Humani-
    ties, A
Marketing Research, A
Marketing/Marketing Management, A
Mathematics, A
Medical/Clinical Assistant, A
Music, A
Physical Education Teaching and Coaching, A
Physical Sciences, A
Physical Therapist Assistant, A
Physics, A
Psychology, A
Real Estate, A
Social Sciences, A
Sociology, A
Spanish Language and Literature, A
Tourism and Travel Services Management, A
Tourism and Travel Services Marketing Opera-
    tions, A
Veterinary/Animal Health Technology/Technician and
    Veterinary Assistant, A

SAN DIEGO MIRAMAR COLLEGE

Accounting, A
Administrative Assistant and Secretarial Science, A
Airframe Mechanics and Aircraft Maintenance
    Technology/Technician, A
Anthropology, A
Applied Mathematics, A
Art/Art Studies, General, A
Automobile/Automotive Mechanics
    Technology/Technician, A
Avionics Maintenance Technology/Technician, A
Biology/Biological Sciences, A
Business Administration and Management, A
Chemistry, A
Corrections, A
Criminal Justice/Law Enforcement Administration, A
Criminal Justice/Police Science, A
Emergency Medical Technology/Technician (EMT
    Paramedic), A
English Language and Literature, A
Fine/Studio Arts, A
Fire Science/Firefighting, A
Geography, A
Humanities/Humanistic Studies, A
Information Science/Studies, A
Legal Assistant/Paralegal, A
Liberal Arts and Sciences Studies and Humani-
    ties, A
Mathematics, A
Occupational Safety and Health
    Technology/Technician, A
Philosophy, A
Physical Education Teaching and Coaching, A
Physical Sciences, A
Physics, A
Psychology, A
Social Sciences, A

Sociology, A
Spanish Language and Literature, A
Transportation and Materials Moving, A

SAN DIEGO STATE UNIVERSITY

Accounting, BM
Advertising, B
Advertising and Public Relations, M
Aerospace, Aeronautical and Astronautical Engi-
    neering, BMD
African-American/Black Studies, B
American Indian/Native American Studies, B
Anthropology, BM
Applied Arts and Design, M
Applied Mathematics, BM
Art History, Criticism and Conservation, BM
Art/Art Studies, General, B
Asian Studies/Civilization, BM
Astronomy, BM
Athletic Training and Sports Medicine, B
Atomic/Molecular Physics, B
Biochemistry, MD
Biological and Biomedical Sciences, MD
Biology/Biological Sciences, B
Biometry/Biometrics, M
Biostatistics, M
Business Administration and Management, B
Business Administration, Management and Opera-
    tions, M
Cell Biology and Anatomy, D
Central/Middle and Eastern European Studies, B
Chemistry, BMD
Child Development, M
Child and Family Studies, M
Civil Engineering, BM
Classics and Classical Languages, Litera-
    tures, and Linguistics, B
Clinical Psychology, MD
Communication Disorders, BMD
Communication Studies/Speech Communication
    and Rhetoric, B
Communication and Media Studies, M
Comparative Literature, B
Composition, M
Computational Sciences, MD
Computer Engineering, B
Computer Science, BM
Construction Engineering Technology/Technician, B
Counselor Education/School Counseling and Guid-
    ance Services, M
Criminal Justice/Safety Studies, B
Criminology, M
Curriculum and Instruction, M
Dance, B
Design and Applied Arts, M
Dietetics/Dieticians, B
Digital Communication and Media/Multimedia, B
Drama and Dramatics/Theatre Arts, B
Early Childhood Education and Teaching, B
Ecology, BMD
Economics, BM
Education, MD
Educational Leadership and Administration, M
Educational Media/Instructional Technology, MD
Electrical Engineering, M
Electrical, Electronics and Communications Engi-
    neering, B
Elementary Education and Teaching, M
Emergency Management, M
Emergency Medical Services, M
Engineering, B
Engineering Design, M
Engineering and Applied Sciences, MD
English, M
English Language and Literature, B
English as a Second Language, MO
Entrepreneurship/Entrepreneurial Studies, M
Environmental Design/Architecture, M
Environmental Sciences, B
Environmental Studies, B
Environmental and Occupational Health, M
Environmental/Environmental Health Engineering, B
Epidemiology, MD
Ethnic, Cultural Minority, and Gender Studies, B
Ethnomusicology, M
European Studies/Civilization, B

Exercise and Sports Science, M
Film, Television, and Video Production, M
Finance, B
Finance and Banking, M
Financial Planning and Services, B
Fine Arts and Art Studies, M
Fine/Studio Arts, B
French Language and Literature, B
Gender Studies, O
General Studies, B
Geography, BMD
Geology/Earth Science, BM
German Language and Literature, B
Gerontology, M
Graphic Design, BM
Health Communication, B
Health Physics/Radiological Health, M
Health Promotion, M
Health Psychology, D
Health Services Administration, M
Health Services/Allied Health/Health Sciences, B
Health and Physical Education, B
Higher Education/Higher Education Administra-
    tion, M
Hispanic-American, Puerto Rican, and Mexican-
    American/Chicano Studies, B
History, BM
Hospitality Administration/Management, B
Human Resources Management and Services, M
Human Resources Management/Personnel Adminis-
    tration, B
Humanities/Humanistic Studies, B
Industrial and Organizational Psychology, M
Information Technology, B
Interdisciplinary Studies, M
Interior Design, BM
International Business/Trade/Commerce, B
International Public Health/International Health, D
International Relations and Affairs, B
Internet and Interactive Multimedia, M
Japanese Language and Literature, B
Jewish/Judaic Studies, B
Journalism, B
Kinesiology and Exercise Science, B
Kinesiology and Movement Studies, M
Latin American Studies, BM
Liberal Arts and Sciences Studies and Humani-
    ties, B
Liberal Studies, M
Linguistics, BMO
Management, M
Management Information Systems and Services, M
Marketing, M
Marketing/Marketing Management, B
Mathematics, BMD
Mathematics Teacher Education, D
Mechanical Engineering, BMD
Mechanics, MD
Media Studies, M
Microbiology, BM
Molecular Biology, D
Multi-/Interdisciplinary Studies, B
Multilingual and Multicultural Education, MD
Music, BM
Music Performance, B
Music Teacher Education, BM
Music Theory and Composition, M
Musicology and Ethnomusicology, M
Nursing, M
Nutritional Sciences, M
Operations Management and Supervision, B
Painting, M
Parks, Recreation, Leisure and Fitness Studies, B
Performance, M
Pharmaceutical Administration, M
Philosophy, BM
Physical Sciences, B
Physical Therapy/Therapist, D
Physics, BM
Political Science and Government, BM
Printmaking, M
Psychology, BMD
Public Administration, BM
Public Administration and Social Service Profes-
    sions, B
Public Health, MD

Public Relations/Image Management, B
Radio and Television, B
Reading Teacher Education, M
Real Estate, B
Rehabilitation Counseling, M
Religion/Religious Studies, B
Rhetoric, M
Romance Languages, Literatures, and Linguistics, M
Russian Language and Literature, B
School Psychology, M
Science Teacher Education/General Science Teacher Education, D
Sculpture, M
Secondary Education and Teaching, M
Social Sciences, B
Social Work, BM
Sociology, BM
Spanish Language and Literature, BM
Special Education and Teaching, M
Speech-Language Pathology/Pathologist, B
Sport and Fitness Administration/Management, M
Statistics, BM
Telecommunications Management, M
Theater, M
Toxicology, M
Urban Studies/Affairs, B
Urban and Regional Planning, M
Western European Studies, M
Women's Studies, BM
Writing, M
Zoology/Animal Biology, B

SAN DIEGO STATE UNIVERSITY–IMPERIAL VALLEY CAMPUS

Computer Science, B
Criminal Justice/Law Enforcement Administration, B
English Language and Literature, B
History, B
International Business/Trade/Commerce, B
Latin American Studies, B
Liberal Arts and Sciences Studies and Humanities, B
Mathematics, B
Psychology, B
Public Administration, B
Social Sciences, B
Spanish Language and Literature, B

SAN FRANCISCO ART INSTITUTE

Art History, Criticism and Conservation, BM
Cinematography and Film/Video Production, B
Fine Arts and Art Studies, MO
Museology/Museum Studies, M
Painting, B
Photography, B
Printmaking, B
Sculpture, B
Visual and Performing Arts, B

SAN FRANCISCO CONSERVATORY OF MUSIC

Composition, M
Music, M
Music Theory and Composition, B
Performance, M
Piano and Organ, B
Violin, Viola, Guitar and Other Stringed Instruments, B
Voice and Opera, B

SAN FRANCISCO STATE UNIVERSITY

Accounting, BM
Acute Care/Critical Care Nursing, M
Adult and Continuing Education and Teaching, M
African-American/Black Studies, B
American Indian/Native American Studies, B
American/United States Studies/Civilization, B
Anthropology, BM
Applied Mathematics, B
Archeology, M
Art History, Criticism and Conservation, M
Art/Art Studies, General, B
Asian-American Studies, BM
Astronomy, BM

Astrophysics, B
BioTechnology, M
Biochemistry, BM
Biological and Biomedical Sciences, M
Biological and Physical Sciences, B
Biology/Biological Sciences, B
Botany/Plant Biology, B
Business Administration and Management, B
Business Administration, Management and Operations, M
Cell Biology and Anatomy, M
Cell/Cellular Biology and Histology, B
Chemistry, BM
Chinese Language and Literature, B
Chinese Studies, M
Civil Engineering, B
Classics and Classical Languages, Literatures, and Linguistics, B
Communication Disorders, BM
Communication Studies/Speech Communication and Rhetoric, B
Community Health Nursing, M
Comparative Literature, BM
Composition, M
Computer Engineering, B
Computer Science, BM
Consumer Merchandising/Retailing Management, B
Counseling Psychology, M
Counselor Education/School Counseling and Guidance Services, O
Criminal Justice/Law Enforcement Administration, B
Criminology, M
Cultural Anthropology, M
Cultural Studies, M
Dance, B
Design and Visual Communications, B
Developmental Biology and Embryology, M
Dietetics/Dieticians, B
Drama and Dramatics/Theatre Arts, B
Early Childhood Education and Teaching, BMO
Ecology, B
Economics, BM
Education, MDO
Educational Administration and Supervision, MO
Educational Leadership and Administration, D
Educational Media/Instructional Technology, M
Electrical, Electronics and Communications Engineering, B
Elementary Education and Teaching, M
Energy and Power Engineering, M
Engineering and Applied Sciences, M
English, MO
English Education, MO
English Language and Literature, B
English as a Second Language, M
Entrepreneurship/Entrepreneurial Studies, M
Environmental Policy, M
Environmental Policy and Resource Management, M
Environmental Studies, B
Ethnic and Cultural Studies, M
Family and Consumer Sciences/Human Sciences, BM
Film, Television, and Video Production, M
Film, Television, and Video Theory and Criticism, M
Film/Cinema Studies, B
Finance, B
Finance and Banking, M
Fine Arts and Art Studies, M
French Language and Literature, BM
Geography, BM
Geology/Earth Science, B
Geosciences, M
German Language and Literature, BM
Gerontology, M
Health Education, M
Health Professions and Related Clinical Sciences, B
Hispanic-American, Puerto Rican, and Mexican-American/Chicano Studies, B
History, BM
Hospitality Administration/Management, B
Humanities/Humanistic Studies, BM
Industrial Design, BM
Industrial and Manufacturing Management, M
Industrial and Organizational Psychology, M
Information Science/Studies, B

Interior Design, B
International Affairs, M
International Business/Trade/Commerce, BM
International Relations and Affairs, B
Italian Language and Literature, BM
Japanese Language and Literature, B
Japanese Studies, M
Jewish/Judaic Studies, B
Journalism, B
Kinesiology and Exercise Science, B
Kinesiology and Movement Studies, M
Labor and Industrial Relations, B
Legal and Justice Studies, M
Leisure Studies, M
Liberal Arts and Sciences Studies and Humanities, B
Linguistics, M
Management Information Systems and Services, M
Marine Biology and Biological Oceanography, BM
Marine Sciences, M
Marketing, M
Marketing/Marketing Management, B
Marriage and Family Therapy/Counseling, M
Mathematics, BM
Mathematics Teacher Education, M
Mechanical Engineering, B
Media Studies, M
Medical Microbiology and Bacteriology, B
Microbiology, M
Molecular Biology, BM
Multi-/Interdisciplinary Studies, B
Museology/Museum Studies, M
Music, BM
Music History, Literature, and Theory, M
Music Performance, B
Music Teacher Education, M
Non-Profit/Public/Organizational Management, M
Nursing, MO
Nursing - Advanced Practice, MO
Nursing Administration, M
Parks, Recreation, Leisure and Fitness Studies, B
Pediatric Nurse/Nursing, M
Performance, M
Philosophy, BM
Philosophy and Religious Studies, B
Physical Education Teaching and Coaching, B
Physical Sciences, B
Physical Therapy/Therapist, D
Physics, BM
Physiology, M
Political Science and Government, BM
Psychology, BMO
Public Administration, M
Public Health, M
Public Policy Analysis, M
Quantitative Analysis, M
Radio and Television, B
Radio, Television, and Digital Communication, B
Reading Teacher Education, MO
Recreation and Park Management, M
Rehabilitation Counseling, M
School Psychology, O
Secondary Education and Teaching, MO
Social Psychology, M
Social Work, BM
Sociology, B
Spanish Language and Literature, BM
Special Education and Teaching, MDO
Speech and Rhetorical Studies, M
Statistics, B
Sustainability Management, M
Theater, M
Travel and Tourism, M
Urban Studies/Affairs, B
Women's Health Nursing, M
Women's Studies, BM
Writing, M
Zoology/Animal Biology, B

SAN JOAQUIN DELTA COLLEGE

Accounting, A
Agricultural Business and Management, A
Agricultural Mechanization, A
Agriculture, A
Animal Sciences, A
Anthropology, A

Art/Art Studies, General, A
Automobile/Automotive Mechanics
　Technology/Technician, A
Biology/Biological Sciences, A
Broadcast Journalism, A
Business Administration and Management, A
Chemistry, A
Civil Engineering Technology/Technician, A
Commercial and Advertising Art, A
Comparative Literature, A
Computer Science, A
Construction Engineering Technology/Technician, A
Corrections, A
Criminal Justice/Police Science, A
Crop Production, A
Culinary Arts/Chef Training, A
Dance, A
Drama and Dramatics/Theatre Arts, A
Economics, A
Electrical, Electronic and Communications Engineer-
　ing Technology/Technician, A
Engineering, A
Engineering Technology, A
English Language and Literature, A
Family and Consumer Sciences/Human Sciences, A
Fashion Merchandising, A
Fire Science/Firefighting, A
Geology/Earth Science, A
Heating, Air Conditioning, Ventilation and Refrigera-
　tion Maintenance Technology/Technician, A
History, A
Humanities/Humanistic Studies, A
Journalism, A
Liberal Arts and Sciences Studies and Humani-
　ties, A
Machine Tool Technology/Machinist, A
Mathematics, A
Mechanical Engineering/Mechanical
　Technology/Technician, A
Music, A
Natural Resources Management/Development and
　Policy, A
Natural Sciences, A
Ornamental Horticulture, A
Philosophy, A
Photography, A
Physical Education Teaching and Coaching, A
Physical Sciences, A
Political Science and Government, A
Psychology, A
Religion/Religious Studies, A
Social Sciences, A
Sociology, A

SAN JOAQUIN VALLEY COLLEGE (BA-KERSFIELD)

Business Administration and Management, A
Corrections, A
Heating, Air Conditioning and Refrigeration
　Technology/Technician, A
Medical Insurance Specialist/Medical Biller, A
Medical/Clinical Assistant, A
Pharmacy Technician/Assistant, A
Respiratory Care Therapy/Therapist, A
Security and Protective Services, A
Surgical Technology/Technologist, A

SAN JOAQUIN VALLEY COLLEGE (CHULA VISTA)

Dental Hygiene/Hygienist, A

SAN JOAQUIN VALLEY COLLEGE (FRESNO)

Corrections, A
General Office Occupations and Clerical Services, A
Heating, Air Conditioning and Refrigeration
　Technology/Technician, A
Medical Office Assistant/Specialist, A
Medical/Clinical Assistant, A
Pharmacy Technician/Assistant, A
Surgical Technology/Technologist, A

Veterinary/Animal Health Technology/Technician and
　Veterinary Assistant, A

SAN JOAQUIN VALLEY COLLEGE (HANFORD)

Criminal Justice/Law Enforcement Administration, A
General Office Occupations and Clerical Services, A
Medical Insurance Specialist/Medical Biller, A
Medical/Clinical Assistant, A

SAN JOAQUIN VALLEY COLLEGE (HESPERIA)

Criminal Justice/Law Enforcement Administration, A
General Office Occupations and Clerical Services, A
Heating, Air Conditioning, Ventilation and Refrigera-
　tion Maintenance Technology/Technician, A
Industrial Technology/Technician, A
Medical Insurance Specialist/Medical Biller, A
Medical/Clinical Assistant, A
Pharmacy Technician/Assistant, A

SAN JOAQUIN VALLEY COLLEGE (LANCASTER)

Corrections, A
General Office Occupations and Clerical Services, A
Heating, Air Conditioning, Ventilation and Refrigera-
　tion Maintenance Technology/Technician, A
Industrial Mechanics and Maintenance Technol-
　ogy, A
Medical Office Assistant/Specialist, A
Medical/Clinical Assistant, A
Pharmacy Technician/Assistant, A

SAN JOAQUIN VALLEY COLLEGE (ON-TARIO)

Construction Management, A
Corrections, A
Dental Hygiene/Hygienist, A
General Office Occupations and Clerical Services, A
Heating, Air Conditioning, Ventilation and Refrigera-
　tion Maintenance Technology/Technician, A
Industrial Mechanics and Maintenance Technol-
　ogy, A
Medical Office Assistant/Specialist, A
Medical/Clinical Assistant, A
Pharmacy Technician/Assistant, A
Respiratory Care Therapy/Therapist, A

SAN JOAQUIN VALLEY COLLEGE (RANCHO CORDOVA)

Respiratory Therapy Technician/Assistant, A

SAN JOAQUIN VALLEY COLLEGE (SALIDA)

General Office Occupations and Clerical Services, A
Industrial Technology/Technician, A
Massage Therapy/Therapeutic Massage, A
Medical Office Assistant/Specialist, A
Medical/Clinical Assistant, A
Pharmacy Technician/Assistant, A

SAN JOAQUIN VALLEY COLLEGE (TEMECULA)

General Office Occupations and Clerical Services, A
Heating, Air Conditioning, Ventilation and Refrigera-
　tion Maintenance Technology/Technician, A
Medical Office Assistant/Specialist, A
Medical/Clinical Assistant, A
Pharmacy Technician/Assistant, A
Respiratory Care Therapy/Therapist, A

SAN JOAQUIN VALLEY COLLEGE (VISALIA)

Business/Commerce, A
Computer and Information Sciences and Support
　Services, A
Corrections, A
Dental Hygiene/Hygienist, A
Health and Medical Administrative Services, A
Heating, Air Conditioning and Refrigeration
　Technology/Technician, A
Human Resources Management/Personnel Adminis-
　tration, A
Industrial Technology/Technician, A

Medical Administrative Assistant/Secretary, A
Medical Office Assistant/Specialist, A
Medical/Clinical Assistant, A
Pharmacy Technician/Assistant, A
Physician Assistant, A
Respiratory Care Therapy/Therapist, A

SAN JOAQUIN VALLEY COL-LEGE–FRESNO AVIATION CAMPUS

Airframe Mechanics and Aircraft Maintenance
　Technology/Technician, A

SAN JOAQUIN VALLEY COL-LEGE–ONLINE

Business Administration and Management, A
Construction Management, A
General Office Occupations and Clerical Services, A
Human Resources Management/Personnel Adminis-
　tration, A
Information Technology, A
Medical Insurance Coding Specialist/Coder, A
Medical Office Management/Administration, A
Medical/Clinical Assistant, A

SAN JOSE CITY COLLEGE

Accounting, A
Administrative Assistant and Secretarial Science, A
Art/Art Studies, General, A
Biology/Biological Sciences, A
Business Administration and Management, A
Business/Commerce, A
Chemistry, A
Child Development, A
Communication, Journalism and Related Pro-
　grams, A
Communications Systems Installation and Repair
　Technology, A
Computer Programming/Programmer, A
Computer Science, A
Computer Systems Networking and Telecommunica-
　tions, A
Construction Trades, A
Cosmetology/Cosmetologist, A
Criminal Justice/Police Science, A
Dental Assisting/Assistant, A
Digital Communication and Media/Multimedia, A
Drama and Dramatics/Theatre Arts, A
E-Commerce/Electronic Commerce, A
Electrical/Electronics Equipment Installation and Re-
　pair, A
English Language and Literature, A
Ethnic, Cultural Minority, and Gender Studies, A
Family and Consumer Sciences/Human Sciences, A
Foreign Languages and Literatures, A
Heating, Air Conditioning, Ventilation and Refrigera-
　tion Maintenance Technology/Technician, A
Humanities/Humanistic Studies, A
Labor and Industrial Relations, A
Laser and Optical Technology/Technician, A
Liberal Arts and Sciences Studies and Humani-
　ties, A
Machine Tool Technology/Machinist, A
Manufacturing Technology/Technician, A
Mathematics, A
Mechanical Engineering/Mechanical
　Technology/Technician, A
Music, A
Philosophy, A
Photography, A
Physical Sciences, A
Psychology, A
Real Estate, A
Sales, Distribution and Marketing Operations, A
Small Business Administration/Management, A
Social Sciences, A
Substance Abuse/Addiction Counseling, A
Web Page, Digital/Multimedia and Information Re-
　sources Design, A
Web/Multimedia Management and Webmaster, A

SAN JOSE STATE UNIVERSITY

Accounting, BM
Advertising, B
Aeronautics/Aviation/Aerospace Science and Tech-
　nology, B

Aerospace, Aeronautical and Astronautical Engineering, BM
African-American/Black Studies, B
Anthropology, BM
Applied Arts and Design, M
Applied Economics, M
Applied Mathematics, BM
Art History, Criticism and Conservation, BM
Art/Art Studies, General, B
Atmospheric Sciences and Meteorology, B
Behavioral Sciences, B
Biochemistry, B
Biological and Biomedical Sciences, BM
Biology/Biological Sciences, B
Business Administration and Management, B
Business Administration, Management and Operations, BM
Chemical Engineering, BM
Chemistry, BM
Child and Family Studies, M
Chinese Language and Literature, B
Civil Engineering, BM
Clinical Psychology, M
Communication Disorders, BM
Communication and Media Studies, M
Comparative Literature, M
Computer Art and Design, M
Computer Engineering, BM
Computer Science, BM
Counselor Education/School Counseling and Guidance Services, M
Criminal Justice/Safety Studies, B
Criminology, M
Curriculum and Instruction, M
Dance, B
Dietetics/Dieticians, B
Drama and Dramatics/Theatre Arts, B
Early Childhood Education and Teaching, B
Ecology, M
Economics, BM
Education, MDO
Educational Administration and Supervision, MD
Electrical Engineering, M
Electrical, Electronics and Communications Engineering, B
Elementary Education and Teaching, MO
Engineering, B
Engineering and Applied Sciences, M
English, M
English Language and Literature, B
English as a Second Language, MO
Environmental Studies, BM
Experimental Psychology, M
Film, Television, and Video Production, M
Finance, B
Finance and Financial Management Services, B
Fine Arts and Art Studies, M
Fine/Studio Arts, B
Food Science, B
French Language and Literature, BM
Geographic Information Systems, O
Geography, BMO
Geological and Earth Sciences/Geosciences, B
Geology/Earth Science, BM
German Language and Literature, B
Gerontological Nursing, M
Gerontology, O
Graphic Design, B
Health Education, M
Health Services/Allied Health/Health Sciences, B
Health and Physical Education, B
Health/Health Care Administration/Management, B
Higher Education/Higher Education Administration, MD
Hispanic Studies, M
History, BM
Hospitality Administration/Management, B
Human Resources Management/Personnel Administration, B
Humanities/Humanistic Studies, B
Illustration, M
Industrial Design, B
Industrial Engineering, B
Industrial and Manufacturing Management, M
Industrial and Organizational Psychology, M
Industrial/Management Engineering, M

Information Science/Studies, MD
Information Technology, B
Interdisciplinary Studies, M
Interior Design, B
International Business/Trade/Commerce, B
Japanese Language and Literature, B
Journalism, B
Kinesiology and Movement Studies, M
Liberal Arts and Sciences Studies and Humanities, B
Library Science, MD
Linguistics, BMO
Management Information Systems and Services, M
Marine Biology and Biological Oceanography, B
Marine Sciences, M
Marketing/Marketing Management, B
Mass Communication/Media Studies, M
Materials Engineering, BM
Mathematics, BM
Mathematics Teacher Education, M
Mechanical Engineering, BM
Meteorology, M
Microbiology, M
Molecular Biology, BM
Multi-/Interdisciplinary Studies, B
Music, BM
Music Performance, B
Natural Sciences, B
Nursing, MO
Nursing Administration, M
Nursing Education, M
Nutritional Sciences, M
Occupational Therapy/Therapist, BM
Painting, M
Parks, Recreation, Leisure and Fitness Studies, B
Philosophy, BM
Photography, M
Physics, BM
Physiology, M
Political Science and Government, B
Psychology, BM
Public Administration, M
Public Health, MO
Public Relations/Image Management, B
Quality Control Technology/Technician, B
Quality Management, M
Radio and Television, B
Reading Teacher Education, O
Recreation and Park Management, M
Religion/Religious Studies, B
Science Teacher Education/General Science Teacher Education, M
Secondary Education and Teaching, O
Social Sciences, B
Social Work, BMO
Sociology, BM
Software Engineering, M
Spanish Language and Literature, BM
Special Education and Teaching, BM
Speech and Rhetorical Studies, M
Statistics, M
Student Personnel Services, M
Systems Engineering, M
Taxation, M
Theater, M
Transportation/Transportation Management, M
Urban and Regional Planning, MO
Visual and Performing Arts, B

SANTA ANA COLLEGE

Accounting, A
Administrative Assistant and Secretarial Science, A
African-American/Black Studies, A
Anthropology, A
Art/Art Studies, General, A
Automobile/Automotive Mechanics Technology/Technician, A
Biological and Physical Sciences, A
Biology/Biological Sciences, A
Business Administration and Management, A
Chemistry, A
Commercial and Advertising Art, A
Communication Studies/Speech Communication and Rhetoric, A
Computer Programming, A
Computer Science, A

Computer and Information Sciences, A
Cosmetology/Cosmetologist, A
Criminal Justice/Law Enforcement Administration, A
Criminal Justice/Police Science, A
Dance, A
Data Entry/Microcomputer Applications, A
Diesel Mechanics Technology/Technician, A
Drafting and Design Technology/Technician, A
Drama and Dramatics/Theatre Arts, A
Economics, A
Electrical, Electronic and Communications Engineering Technology/Technician, A
Engineering, A
Engineering Technology, A
English Language and Literature, A
Environmental Studies, A
Family and Consumer Economics and Related Services, A
Fashion Merchandising, A
Fashion/Apparel Design, A
Fire Science/Firefighting, A
Foods, Nutrition, and Wellness Studies, A
Geography, A
Geology/Earth Science, A
Hispanic-American, Puerto Rican, and Mexican-American/Chicano Studies, A
History, A
Industrial Technology/Technician, A
Information Science/Studies, A
Information Technology, A
Journalism, A
Kindergarten/PreSchool Education and Teaching, A
Kinesiology and Exercise Science, A
Law and Legal Studies, A
Liberal Arts and Sciences Studies and Humanities, A
Library Science, A
Management Science, A
Marketing/Marketing Management, A
Mathematics, A
Medical/Clinical Assistant, A
Modern Languages, A
Music, A
Occupational Therapy/Therapist, A
Pharmacy Technician/Assistant, A
Philosophy, A
Photography, A
Physics, A
Political Science and Government, A
Psychology, A
Quality Control Technology/Technician, A
Real Estate, A
Sales, Distribution and Marketing Operations, A
Social Sciences, A
Sociology, A
Telecommunications Technology/Technician, A
Tourism and Travel Services Management, A
Water Resources Engineering, A
Welding Technology/Welder, A
Women's Studies, A
Word Processing, A

SANTA BARBARA CITY COLLEGE

Accounting, A
Acting, A
Administrative Assistant and Secretarial Science, A
African-American/Black Studies, A
American Indian/Native American Studies, A
Anthropology, A
Applied Horticulture/Horticultural Operations, A
Art History, Criticism and Conservation, A
Athletic Training and Sports Medicine, A
Automobile/Automotive Mechanics Technology/Technician, A
BioTechnology, A
Biology/Biological Sciences, A
Biomedical Technology/Technician, A
Business Administration and Management, A
Chemistry, A
Child Care and Support Services Management, A
Commercial and Advertising Art, A
Communication Studies/Speech Communication and Rhetoric, A
Computer Engineering, A
Computer Science, A
Cosmetology/Cosmetologist, A

Criminal Justice/Law Enforcement Administration, A
Culinary Arts and Related Services, A
Drafting and Design Technology/Technician, A
Drama and Dramatics/Theatre Arts, A
Economics, A
Electrical, Electronic and Communications Engineering Technology/Technician, A
Electrical/Electronics Equipment Installation and Repair, A
Engineering, A
Engineering Technology, A
English Language and Literature, A
Environmental Studies, A
Environmental/Environmental Health Engineering, A
Film/Cinema Studies, A
Finance, A
Fine/Studio Arts, A
Foodservice Systems Administration/Management, A
French Language and Literature, A
Geography, A
Geology/Earth Science, A
Health Information/Medical Records Technology/Technician, A
Hispanic-American, Puerto Rican, and Mexican-American/Chicano Studies, A
History, A
Hotel/Motel Administration/Management, A
Industrial Engineering, A
Industrial Technology/Technician, A
Information Science/Studies, A
Information Technology, A
Institutional Food Workers, A
Interior Design, A
International Relations and Affairs, A
Kindergarten/PreSchool Education and Teaching, A
Kinesiology and Exercise Science, A
Landscaping and Groundskeeping, A
Law and Legal Studies, A
Liberal Arts and Sciences Studies and Humanities, A
Marine Maintenance/Fitter and Ship Repair Technology/Technician, A
Marketing/Marketing Management, A
Mathematics, A
Medical Radiologic Technology/Science - Radiation Therapist, A
Music, A
Ornamental Horticulture, A
Parks, Recreation, Leisure and Fitness Studies, A
Philosophy, A
Physical Education Teaching and Coaching, A
Physics, A
Political Science and Government, A
Psychology, A
Real Estate, A
Sales, Distribution and Marketing Operations, A
Selling Skills and Sales Operations, A
Sociology, A
Spanish Language and Literature, A
System Administration/Administrator, A
Technical Theatre/Theatre Design and Technology, A
Therapeutic Recreation/Recreational Therapy, A

SANTA CLARA UNIVERSITY

Accounting, B
Accounting and Business/Management, B
Ancient Studies/Civilization, B
Ancient/Classical Greek Language and Literature, B
Anthropology, B
Applied Mathematics, M
Art History, Criticism and Conservation, B
Biochemistry, B
Bioengineering, M
Biology/Biological Sciences, B
Biomedical/Medical Engineering, B
Business Administration, Management and Operations, M
Chemistry, B
Civil Engineering, BM
Classics and Classical Languages, Literatures, and Linguistics, B
Communication Studies/Speech Communication and Rhetoric, B
Computer Engineering, BMDO

Computer Science, MDO
Computer and Information Systems Security, O
Counseling Psychology, M
Counselor Education/School Counseling and Guidance Services, M
Drama and Dramatics/Theatre Arts, B
Economics, B
Education, MO
Educational Administration and Supervision, M
Electrical Engineering, MDO
Electrical, Electronics and Communications Engineering, B
Energy Management and Policy, O
Energy and Power Engineering, MO
Engineering Design, O
Engineering Management, M
Engineering Physics, B
Engineering and Applied Sciences, MDO
English Language and Literature, B
Entrepreneurship/Entrepreneurial Studies, M
Environmental Sciences, B
Environmental Studies, B
Ethnic, Cultural Minority, and Gender Studies, B
Finance, B
Finance and Banking, M
Fine/Studio Arts, B
French Language and Literature, B
German Language and Literature, B
History, B
Intellectual Property Law, M
Interdisciplinary Studies, M
Italian Language and Literature, B
Latin Language and Literature, B
Law and Legal Studies, MDO
Liberal Arts and Sciences Studies and Humanities, B
Management Information Systems and Services, BM
Marketing/Marketing Management, B
Materials Engineering, O
Mathematics, B
Mathematics and Computer Science, B
Mechanical Engineering, BMDO
Music, B
Organizational Behavior Studies, B
Pastoral Studies/Counseling, M
Philosophy, B
Physics, B
Political Science and Government, B
Psychology, B
Public Health (MPH, DPH), B
Religion/Religious Studies, B
Sociology, B
Software Engineering, O
Spanish Language and Literature, B
Theology and Religious Vocations, MDO
Web Page, Digital/Multimedia and Information Resources Design, B
Women's Studies, B

SANTA MONICA COLLEGE

Accounting, A
Administrative Assistant and Secretarial Science, A
Animation, Interactive Technology, Video Graphics and Special Effects, A
Anthropology, A
Apparel and Textile Marketing Management, A
Art/Art Studies, General, A
Biological and Physical Sciences, A
Business Administration and Management, A
Child Development, A
Commercial Photography, A
Computer Programming/Programmer, A
Computer Science, A
Cosmetology/Cosmetologist, A
Dance, A
Data Entry/Microcomputer Applications, A
Data Modeling/Warehousing and Database Administration, A
Digital Communication and Media/Multimedia, A
Drama and Dramatics/Theatre Arts, A
Education/Teaching of Individuals in Early Childhood Special Education Programs, A
Fashion/Apparel Design, A
Film/Cinema Studies, A
Graphic Design, A

Health and Physical Education, A
Interior Design, A
Journalism, A
Legal Administrative Assistant/Secretary, A
Liberal Arts and Sciences Studies and Humanities, A
Music, A
Office Management and Supervision, A
Radio and Television, A
Respiratory Care Therapy/Therapist, A
Sales, Distribution and Marketing Operations, A
Selling Skills and Sales Operations, A
Women's Studies, A

SANTA ROSA JUNIOR COLLEGE

Agricultural Business and Management, A
Agricultural Communication/Journalism, A
American Sign Language (ASL), A
Animal Sciences, A
Anthropology, A
Art History, Criticism and Conservation, A
Art/Art Studies, General, A
Automobile/Automotive Mechanics Technology/Technician, A
Behavioral Sciences, A
Biology/Biological Sciences, A
Business Administration and Management, A
Chemistry, A
Child Development, A
Civil Engineering Technology/Technician, A
Community Health Services/Liaison/Counseling, A
Computer Science, A
Criminal Justice/Law Enforcement Administration, A
Culinary Arts/Chef Training, A
Dance, A
Dental Hygiene/Hygienist, A
Diesel Mechanics Technology/Technician, A
Dietetic Technician (DTR), A
Digital Communication and Media/Multimedia, A
Drama and Dramatics/Theatre Arts, A
Early Childhood Education and Teaching, A
Economics, A
Electrical, Electronic and Communications Engineering Technology/Technician, A
Emergency Medical Technology/Technician (EMT Paramedic), A
Engineering, A
English Language and Literature, A
Environmental Studies, A
Fashion Merchandising, A
Fashion/Apparel Design, A
Fire Science/Firefighting, A
Floriculture/Floristry Operations and Management, A
French Language and Literature, A
Graphic Design, A
Health and Physical Education, A
History, A
Horse Husbandry/Equine Science and Management, A
Human Resources Management/Personnel Administration, A
Human Services, A
Humanities/Humanistic Studies, A
Interior Design, A
Jazz/Jazz Studies, A
Kinesiology and Exercise Science, A
Landscaping and Groundskeeping, A
Latin American Studies, A
Legal Assistant/Paralegal, A
Liberal Arts and Sciences Studies and Humanities, A
Mathematics, A
Medical/Clinical Assistant, A
Music, A
Natural Resources and Conservation, A
Natural Sciences, A
Nutritional Sciences, A
Parks, Recreation and Leisure Facilities Management, A
Pharmacy Technician/Assistant, A
Philosophy, A
Physics, A
Political Science and Government, A
Psychology, A
Radiologic Technology/Science - Radiographer, A
Real Estate, A

Religion/Religious Studies, A
Restaurant/Food Services Management, A
Social Sciences, A
Sociology, A
Spanish Language and Literature, A
Survey Technology/Surveying, A
Women's Studies, A

SANTIAGO CANYON COLLEGE

Accounting, A
Anthropology, A
Art/Art Studies, General, A
Biology/Biological Sciences, A
Business Administration and Management, A
Business Administration, Management and Operations, A
Business/Office Automation/Technology/Data Entry, A
Carpentry/Carpenter, A
Cartography, A
Chemistry, A
Communication Studies/Speech Communication and Rhetoric, A
Computer Science, A
Computer and Information Sciences, A
Cosmetology/Cosmetologist, A
Drama and Dramatics/Theatre Arts, A
Economics, A
Electrician, A
English Language and Literature, A
Geography, A
Geology/Earth Science, A
History, A
Human Development and Family Studies, A
Kinesiology and Exercise Science, A
Liberal Arts and Sciences Studies and Humanities, A
Management Science, A
Marketing/Marketing Management, A
Mathematics, A
Modern Languages, A
Music, A
Natural Sciences, A
Philosophy, A
Physics, A
Political Science and Government, A
Psychology, A
Public Administration, A
Radio, Television, and Digital Communication, A
Real Estate, A
Sheet Metal Technology/Sheetworking, A
Social Sciences, A
Sociology, A
Survey Technology/Surveying, A
Tourism and Travel Services Management, A
Water Quality and Wastewater Treatment Management and Recycling Technology/Technician, A
Women's Studies, A

SCRIPPS COLLEGE

Accounting, B
African-American/Black Studies, B
American/United States Studies/Civilization, B
Anthropology, B
Art History, Criticism and Conservation, B
Art/Art Studies, General, B
Asian Studies/Civilization, B
Asian-American Studies, B
Biochemistry, B
Biology/Biological Sciences, B
Biophysics, B
Chemistry, B
Chinese Language and Literature, B
Classics and Classical Languages, Literatures, and Linguistics, B
Computer Science, B
Dance, B
Drama and Dramatics/Theatre Arts, B
Econometrics and Quantitative Economics, B
Economics, B
English Language and Literature, B
Environmental Sciences, B
European Studies/Civilization, B
Film/Video and Photographic Arts, B
Fine/Studio Arts, B
Foreign Languages and Literatures, B

French Language and Literature, B
Geology/Earth Science, B
German Language and Literature, B
Hispanic-American, Puerto Rican, and Mexican-American/Chicano Studies, B
History, B
Humanities/Humanistic Studies, B
International/Global Studies, B
Italian Language and Literature, B
Italian Studies, B
Japanese Language and Literature, B
Jewish/Judaic Studies, B
Latin American Studies, B
Law and Legal Studies, B
Linguistics, B
Mass Communication/Media Studies, B
Mathematics, B
Molecular Biology, B
Multi-/Interdisciplinary Studies, B
Music, B
Near and Middle Eastern Studies, B
Organizational Behavior Studies, B
Philosophy, B
Physics, B
Political Science and Government, B
Psychology, B
Public Policy Analysis, B
Religion/Religious Studies, B
Russian Language and Literature, B
Russian Studies, B
Science, Technology and Society, B
Sociology, B
Spanish Language and Literature, B
Women's Studies, B

SHASTA BIBLE COLLEGE

Bible/Biblical Studies, AB
Early Childhood Education and Teaching, A
Education, B
Educational Administration and Supervision, M
Pastoral Studies/Counseling, M
Religious Education, M

SHASTA COLLEGE

Accounting, A
Administrative Assistant and Secretarial Science, A
Agricultural Business and Management, A
Animal Sciences, A
Art/Art Studies, General, A
Automobile/Automotive Mechanics Technology/Technician, A
Avionics Maintenance Technology/Technician, A
Business Administration and Management, A
Civil Engineering Technology/Technician, A
Construction Engineering Technology/Technician, A
Criminal Justice/Law Enforcement Administration, A
Culinary Arts/Chef Training, A
Dental Hygiene/Hygienist, A
Design and Visual Communications, A
Diesel Mechanics Technology/Technician, A
Drafting and Design Technology/Technician, A
Drama and Dramatics/Theatre Arts, A
Electrical, Electronic and Communications Engineering Technology/Technician, A
Family and Consumer Sciences/Human Sciences, A
Fire Science/Firefighting, A
Horticultural Science, A
Journalism, A
Kindergarten/PreSchool Education and Teaching, A
Legal Administrative Assistant/Secretary, A
Legal Assistant/Paralegal, A
Management Information Systems and Services, A
Medical Administrative Assistant/Secretary, A
Medical/Clinical Assistant, A
Music, A
Natural Resources Management/Development and Policy, A
Ornamental Horticulture, A
Real Estate, A
Welding Technology/Welder, A

SHEPHERD UNIVERSITY

Computer Art and Design, M
Game Design and Development, M
Management Information Systems and Services, M
Music, M

Theology and Religious Vocations, MD

SIERRA COLLEGE

Accounting, A
Administrative Assistant and Secretarial Science, A
Agriculture, A
American Sign Language (ASL), A
Animal/Livestock Husbandry and Production, A
Apparel and Textile Manufacture, A
Apparel and Textile Marketing Management, A
Applied Horticulture/Horticultural Operations, A
Architectural Drafting and Architectural CAD/CADD, A
Art/Art Studies, General, A
Automobile/Automotive Mechanics Technology/Technician, A
Biological and Physical Sciences, A
Biology/Biological Sciences, A
Business Administration and Management, A
Business/Commerce, A
Cabinetmaking and Millwork/Millwright, A
Chemistry, A
Child Development, A
Commercial Photography, A
Computer Installation and Repair Technology/Technician, A
Computer Programming/Programmer, A
Computer Systems Networking and Telecommunications, A
Computer and Information Sciences and Support Services, A
Construction Trades, A
Corrections, A
Criminal Justice/Police Science, A
Data Entry/Microcomputer Applications, A
Digital Communication and Media/Multimedia, A
Electrical/Electronics Equipment Installation and Repair, A
Engineering, A
English Language and Literature, A
Equestrian/Equine Studies, A
Fire Science/Firefighting, A
Forestry, A
General Studies, A
Geology/Earth Science, A
Graphic Design, A
Hazardous Materials Management and Waste Technology/Technician, A
Health and Physical Education, A
Industrial Electronics Technology/Technician, A
Information Technology, A
Liberal Arts and Sciences Studies and Humanities, A
Manufacturing Technology/Technician, A
Mathematics, A
Mechanical Drafting and Mechanical Drafting CAD/CADD, A
Music, A
Parks, Recreation, Leisure and Fitness Studies, A
Philosophy, A
Physics, A
Psychology, A
Real Estate, A
Sales, Distribution and Marketing Operations, A
Small Business Administration/Management, A
Social Sciences, A
System Administration/Administrator, A
Visual and Performing Arts, A
Web Page, Digital/Multimedia and Information Resources Design, A
Women's Studies, A

SILICON VALLEY UNIVERSITY

Business Administration and Management, B
Business Administration, Management and Operations, M
Computer Engineering, BM
Computer Science, BM

SIMPSON UNIVERSITY

Accounting, B
Bible/Biblical Studies, AB
Biology/Biological Sciences, B
Business Administration and Management, B
Christian Studies, B

Communication Studies/Speech Communication and Rhetoric, B
Counseling Psychology, M
Curriculum and Instruction, M
Education, M
Educational Administration and Supervision, M
Educational Leadership and Administration, M
English Language and Literature, B
English/Language Arts Teacher Education, B
General Studies, A
Health/Health Care Administration/Management, B
History, B
Human Resources Management and Services, B
Human Resources Management/Personnel Administration, B
Liberal Arts and Sciences Studies and Humanities, B
Mathematics, B
Mathematics Teacher Education, B
Missions/Missionary Studies and Missiology, BM
Music, B
Music Teacher Education, B
Organizational Behavior Studies, B
Organizational Management, M
Parks, Recreation, Leisure and Fitness Studies, B
Pastoral Studies/Counseling, B
Psychology, B
Religious Education, B
Social Science Teacher Education, B
Spanish Language and Literature, B
Theology and Religious Vocations, B
Youth Ministry, B

SKYLINE COLLEGE

Accounting, A
Administrative Assistant and Secretarial Science, A
Anthropology, A
Art History, Criticism and Conservation, A
Art/Art Studies, General, A
Automobile/Automotive Mechanics Technology/Technician, A
Biological and Physical Sciences, A
Biology/Biological Sciences, A
Business Administration and Management, A
Chemistry, A
Comparative Literature, A
Computer Programming/Programmer, A
Computer Science, A
Cosmetology/Cosmetologist, A
Criminal Justice/Law Enforcement Administration, A
Data Processing and Data Processing Technology/Technician, A
Design and Applied Arts, A
Economics, A
Emergency Medical Technology/Technician (EMT Paramedic), A
English Language and Literature, A
Family and Consumer Sciences/Human Sciences, A
Fashion Merchandising, A
Finance, A
Fine/Studio Arts, A
History, A
Journalism, A
Legal Administrative Assistant/Secretary, A
Legal Assistant/Paralegal, A
Liberal Arts and Sciences Studies and Humanities, A
Mathematics, A
Music, A
Physical Education Teaching and Coaching, A
Physics, A
Political Science and Government, A
Psychology, A
Respiratory Care Therapy/Therapist, A
Social Sciences, A
Sociology, A
Surgical Technology/Technologist, A

Telecommunications Technology/Technician, A

SOKA UNIVERSITY OF AMERICA

Educational Leadership and Administration, M
Liberal Arts and Sciences Studies and Humanities, B

SOLANO COMMUNITY COLLEGE

Accounting, A
African Studies, A
African-American/Black Studies, A
Airframe Mechanics and Aircraft Maintenance Technology/Technician, A
Art/Art Studies, General, A
Automobile/Automotive Mechanics Technology/Technician, A
Avionics Maintenance Technology/Technician, A
Biological and Physical Sciences, A
Biology/Biological Sciences, A
Business Administration and Management, A
Business Machine Repairer, A
Chemistry, A
Commercial and Advertising Art, A
Computer Programming/Programmer, A
Cosmetology/Cosmetologist, A
Criminal Justice/Law Enforcement Administration, A
Drafting and Design Technology/Technician, A
Electrical, Electronic and Communications Engineering Technology/Technician, A
English Language and Literature, A
Family and Consumer Sciences/Human Sciences, A
Fashion Merchandising, A
Finance, A
Fire Science/Firefighting, A
French Language and Literature, A
German Language and Literature, A
Hispanic-American, Puerto Rican, and Mexican-American/Chicano Studies, A
History, A
Journalism, A
Kindergarten/PreSchool Education and Teaching, A
Legal Administrative Assistant/Secretary, A
Liberal Arts and Sciences Studies and Humanities, A
Machine Tool Technology/Machinist, A
Marketing/Marketing Management, A
Mathematics, A
Music, A
Ornamental Horticulture, A
Photography, A
Physical Education Teaching and Coaching, A
Physics, A
Political Science and Government, A
Psychology, A
Public Administration, A
Social Sciences, A
Spanish Language and Literature, A
Telecommunications Technology/Technician, A
Welding Technology/Welder, A

SONOMA STATE UNIVERSITY

African-American/Black Studies, B
American Indian/Native American Studies, B
American/United States Studies/Civilization, B
Animal Physiology, B
Anthropology, BM
Applied History, M
Applied Mathematics, B
Art History, Criticism and Conservation, B
Art/Art Studies, General, B
Biochemistry, M
Biological and Biomedical Sciences, M
Biology/Biological Sciences, B
Botany/Plant Biology, B
Business Administration and Management, B
Business Administration, Management and Operations, M
Business/Managerial Economics, B
Cell Biology and Anatomy, M
Cell/Cellular Biology and Histology, B
Chemistry, B
Clinical Psychology, M
Clinical/Medical Laboratory Technician, B
Communication Studies/Speech Communication and Rhetoric, B
Comparative Literature, B

Computer Science, B
Counseling Psychology, M
Counselor Education/School Counseling and Guidance Services, M
Criminal Justice/Law Enforcement Administration, B
Curriculum and Instruction, M
Drama and Dramatics/Theatre Arts, B
Drawing, B
Early Childhood Education and Teaching, M
Ecology, BM
Economics, B
Education, MDO
Educational Leadership and Administration, M
Engineering Science, B
English, M
English Language and Literature, B
Environmental Biology, M
Environmental Studies, B
Ethics, M
Evolutionary Biology, M
Fine/Studio Arts, B
French Language and Literature, B
Geography, B
Geology/Earth Science, B
Health Professions and Related Clinical Sciences, B
Health Promotion, M
Hispanic-American, Puerto Rican, and Mexican-American/Chicano Studies, B
History, BM
Interdisciplinary Studies, M
International Business/Trade/Commerce, M
International Relations and Affairs, B
Kinesiology and Exercise Science, B
Kinesiology and Movement Studies, M
Liberal Arts and Sciences Studies and Humanities, B
Marine Biology and Biological Oceanography, B
Marriage and Family Therapy/Counseling, M
Mass Communication/Media Studies, B
Mathematics, B
Medical Microbiology and Bacteriology, B
Molecular Biology, M
Multi-/Interdisciplinary Studies, B
Music, B
Music Teacher Education, B
Non-Profit/Public/Organizational Management, O
Nursing, M
Nursing - Advanced Practice, M
Occupational Therapy/Therapist, M
Philosophy, B
Physical Education Teaching and Coaching, BM
Physical Therapy/Therapist, M
Physics, B
Political Science and Government, BMO
Pre-Dentistry Studies, B
Pre-Law Studies, B
Pre-Medicine/Pre-Medical Studies, B
Pre-Veterinary Studies, B
Printmaking, B
Psychology, B
Public Administration, M
Reading Teacher Education, M
Sculpture, B
Sociology, B
Spanish Language and Literature, B
Special Education and Teaching, MO
Sport and Fitness Administration/Management, M
Statistics, B
Women's Studies, B
Writing, M
Zoology/Animal Biology, B

SOUTH COAST COLLEGE

Medical Transcription/Transcriptionist, A

SOUTHERN CALIFORNIA INSTITUTE OF ARCHITECTURE

Architecture, BM

SOUTHERN CALIFORNIA INSTITUTE OF TECHNOLOGY

Accounting, B
Biomedical/Medical Engineering, B
Business Administration and Management, A
Business, Management, Marketing, and Related Support Services, B

Computer Science, AB
Electrical, Electronics and Communications Engineering, AB

SOUTHERN CALIFORNIA SEMINARY

Bible/Biblical Studies, AB
Counseling Psychology, M
Marriage and Family Therapy/Counseling, M
Psychology, D
Religion/Religious Studies, M
Theology and Religious Vocations, MD

SOUTHWESTERN COLLEGE

Accounting, A
Administrative Assistant and Secretarial Science, A
Animation, Interactive Technology, Video Graphics and Special Effects, A
Anthropology, A
Architectural Technology/Technician, A
Art/Art Studies, General, A
Astronomy, A
Automobile/Automotive Mechanics Technology/Technician, A
Banking and Financial Support Services, A
Biology Technician/BioTechnology Laboratory Technician, A
Biology/Biological Sciences, A
Building/Construction Site Management/Manager, A
Building/Home/Construction Inspection/Inspector, A
Business Administration and Management, A
Chemical Technology/Technician, A
Chemistry, A
Child Development, A
Communications Systems Installation and Repair Technology, A
Computer Installation and Repair Technology/Technician, A
Computer Programming/Programmer, A
Computer Science, A
Computer Systems Networking and Telecommunications, A
Computer and Information Sciences, A
Cooking and Related Culinary Arts, A
Crafts/Craft Design, Folk Art and Artisanry, A
Criminal Justice/Police Science, A
Dance, A
Data Entry/Microcomputer Applications, A
Dental Hygiene/Hygienist, A
Drafting and Design Technology/Technician, A
E-Commerce/Electronic Commerce, A
Economics, A
Electrical/Electronics Equipment Installation and Repair, A
Emergency Medical Technology/Technician (EMT Paramedic), A
Engineering, A
English Language and Literature, A
Ethnic, Cultural Minority, and Gender Studies, A
Fire Science/Firefighting, A
Floriculture/Floristry Operations and Management, A
Forensic Science and Technology, A
French Language and Literature, A
General Studies, A
Geography, A
Geology/Earth Science, A
Graphic Design, A
Hazardous Materials Management and Waste Technology/Technician, A
Health and Physical Education, A
Health/Medical Preparatory Programs, A
History, A
Hospitality Administration/Management, A
Hotel/Motel Administration/Management, A
Human Services, A
Industrial Safety Technology/Technician, A
Information Technology, A
Insurance, A
International Business/Trade/Commerce, A
Journalism, A
Landscaping and Groundskeeping, A
Language Interpretation and Translation, A
Legal Administrative Assistant/Secretary, A
Legal Assistant/Paralegal, A
Liberal Arts and Sciences Studies and Humanities, A
Logistics and Materials Management, A

Mathematics, A
Medical Insurance Coding Specialist/Coder, A
Medical/Clinical Assistant, A
Music, A
Ornamental Horticulture, A
Parks, Recreation, Leisure and Fitness Studies, A
Philosophy, A
Photography, A
Physical Sciences, A
Physics, A
Plant Nursery Operations and Management, A
Political Science and Government, A
Psychology, A
Public Administration, A
Public Administration and Social Service Professions, A
Radio and Television, A
Real Estate, A
Restaurant, Culinary, and Catering Management/Manager, A
Sales, Distribution and Marketing Operations, A
Small Engine Mechanics and Repair Technology/Technician, A
Sociology, A
Spanish Language and Literature, A
Surgical Technology/Technologist, A
System Administration/Administrator, A
Tourism and Travel Services Marketing Operations, A
Transportation and Materials Moving, A
Turf and Turfgrass Management, A
Web Page, Digital/Multimedia and Information Resources Design, A
Web/Multimedia Management and Webmaster, A
Women's Studies, A

SPARTAN COLLEGE OF AERONAUTICS AND TECHNOLOGY

Airframe Mechanics and Aircraft Maintenance Technology/Technician, A

STANBRIDGE COLLEGE

Computer and Information Systems Security, A

STANFORD UNIVERSITY

Aerospace, Aeronautical and Astronautical Engineering, B
African-American/Black Studies, B
Allopathic Medicine, D
American Indian/Native American Studies, B
American/United States Studies/Civilization, B
Ancient/Classical Greek Language and Literature, B
Anthropology, BMD
Applied Physics, MD
Archeology, BD
Area Studies, B
Art History, Criticism and Conservation, B
Art/Art Studies, General, B
Asian Languages, MD
Asian-American Studies, B
Biochemistry, D
Bioengineering, MD
Biological and Biomedical Sciences, MD
Biology/Biological Sciences, B
Biomedical Engineering, M
Biomedical/Medical Engineering, B
Biometry/Biometrics, B
Biophysics, D
Biostatistics, D
Business Administration, Management and Operations, MD
Chemical Engineering, BMD
Chemistry, BD
Chinese Language and Literature, B
Chinese Studies, MD
Cinematography and Film/Video Production, B
Civil Engineering, BMDO
Classics and Classical Languages, Literatures, and Linguistics, BMD
Clinical Research, MD
Communication Theory, D
Communication and Media Studies, BMD
Comparative Literature, BD
Composition, D
Computational Sciences, MD
Computer Science, BMD

Construction Engineering and Management, M
Cultural Studies, D
Curriculum and Instruction, M
Design and Applied Arts, M
Developmental Biology and Embryology, MD
Drama and Dramatics/Theatre Arts, B
East Asian Studies, BM
East European and Russian Studies, M
Ecology, D
Economics, BD
Education, MD
Educational Leadership and Administration, M
Educational Media/Instructional Technology, M
Educational Policy, M
Electrical Engineering, MD
Electrical, Electronics and Communications Engineering, B
Elementary Education and Teaching, M
Energy and Power Engineering, MDO
Engineering, B
Engineering Design, M
Engineering Management, MD
Engineering Physics, M
Engineering and Applied Sciences, MDO
Engineering/Industrial Management, B
English, MD
English Language and Literature, B
Environmental Engineering Technology/Environmental Technology, MDO
Environmental Law, M
Environmental Sciences, MDO
Environmental Studies, B
Environmental/Environmental Health Engineering, B
Epidemiology, MD
Ethnic, Cultural Minority, and Gender Studies, B
Film, Television, and Video Production, M
Film/Cinema Studies, B
Fine Arts and Art Studies, MD
Fine/Studio Arts, B
Foreign Languages and Literatures, B
French Language and Literature, BMD
Genetics, D
Geological and Earth Sciences/Geosciences, B
Geology/Earth Science, B
Geophysics and Seismology, BMD
Geosciences, MDO
Geotechnical Engineering, M
German Language and Literature, MD
German Studies, B
Health Services Research, MD
Hispanic-American, Puerto Rican, and Mexican-American/Chicano Studies, B
History, BMD
Hydrology and Water Resources Science, D
Immunology, D
Industrial Design, B
Industrial Engineering, B
Industrial/Management Engineering, MD
International Relations and Affairs, B
International and Comparative Education, MD
Italian Language and Literature, BMD
Japanese Language and Literature, B
Japanese Studies, MD
Journalism, M
Latin American Studies, B
Law and Legal Studies, MD
Legal and Justice Studies, M
Linguistics, BMD
Materials Engineering, MDO
Materials Sciences, MDO
Mathematics, BMD
Mathematics and Computer Science, B
Mechanical Engineering, BMDO
Mechanics, D
Media Studies, M
Medical Informatics, MD
Microbiology, D
Music, BMD
Music Theory and Composition, D
Musicology and Ethnomusicology, D
Natural Resources Conservation and Research, B
Petroleum Engineering, B
Philosophy, BMD
Physics, BD
Physiology, D
Political Science and Government, BMD

Psychology, BD
Public Policy Analysis, B
Religion/Religious Studies, BD
Science, Technology and Society, B
Secondary Education and Teaching, M
Slavic Languages, Literatures, and Linguistics, BD
Sociology, BD
Spanish Language and Literature, BMD
Statistics, MD
Structural Biology, D
Structural Engineering, M
Sustainable Development, M
Systematic Biology/Biological Systematics, D
Systems Engineering, B
Systems Science and Theory, B
Theater, D
Urban Studies/Affairs, B
Women's Studies, B

SUM BIBLE COLLEGE & THEOLOGICAL SEMINARY

Bible/Biblical Studies, AB

TAFT COLLEGE

Accounting, A
Administrative Assistant and Secretarial Science, A
Art/Art Studies, General, A
Automobile/Automotive Mechanics Technology/Technician, A
Biology/Biological Sciences, A
Business Administration and Management, A
Computer Science, A
Criminal Justice/Law Enforcement Administration, A
Data Processing and Data Processing Technology/Technician, A
Dental Hygiene/Hygienist, A
Drafting and Design Technology/Technician, A
Electrical, Electronic and Communications Engineering Technology/Technician, A
English Language and Literature, A
General Studies, A
Journalism, A
Kindergarten/PreSchool Education and Teaching, A
Liberal Arts and Sciences Studies and Humanities, A
Mathematics, A
Parks, Recreation, Leisure and Fitness Studies, A
Physical Education Teaching and Coaching, A
Physical Sciences, A
Social Sciences, A

THOMAS AQUINAS COLLEGE

Liberal Arts and Sciences Studies and Humanities, B

TOURO COLLEGE LOS ANGELES

Business Administration and Management, B
Jewish/Judaic Studies, B
Psychology, B

TRIDENT UNIVERSITY INTERNATIONAL

Adult and Continuing Education and Teaching, M
Business Administration and Management, B
Business Administration, Management and Operations, MD
Business/Commerce, B
Clinical Research, MO
Computer and Information Systems Security, M
Conflict Resolution and Mediation/Peace Studies, M
Criminology, M
Early Childhood Education and Teaching, M
Education, MD
Educational Leadership and Administration, MD
Educational Media/Instructional Technology, D
Emergency Management, MO
Environmental and Occupational Health, O
Finance and Banking, M
Health Education, MO
Health Informatics, MO
Health Services Administration, MDO
Health Services/Allied Health/Health Sciences, B
Health Teacher Education, B
Health/Health Care Administration/Management, B
Higher Education/Higher Education Administration, MD

Hospitality Administration/Management, B
Human Resources Management and Services, M
Information Technology, B
International Business/Trade/Commerce, M
International Public Health/International Health, MD
Legal and Justice Studies, M
Logistics and Materials Management, M
Management Information Systems and Services, BMO
Marketing, M
Nursing Administration, D
Project Management, M
Public Administration, M
Public Health, MDO
Public Health (MPH, DPH), B
Quality Management, MO
Reading Teacher Education, M

UNITED STATES UNIVERSITY

Biology/Biological Sciences, B
General Studies, B
Liberal Arts and Sciences Studies and Humanities, B
Management Science, B
Natural Sciences, B
Nursing - Advanced Practice, M
Spanish Language and Literature, B

UNIVERSITY OF ANTELOPE VALLEY

Allied Health and Medical Assisting Services, A
Business Administration and Management, AB
Business Administration, Management and Operations, M
Criminal Justice/Police Science, AB
Criminology, M
Fire Science/Firefighting, A
Health/Health Care Administration/Management, A
Hospitality Administration/Management, A
Legal Assistant/Paralegal, A

UNIVERSITY OF CALIFORNIA, BERKELEY

Accounting, DO
African-American Studies, D
African-American/Black Studies, B
Agricultural Economics, D
American Indian/Native American Studies, B
American/United States Studies/Civilization, B
Ancient/Classical Greek Language and Literature, B
Anthropology, BD
Applied Mathematics, BD
Applied Science and Technology, D
Archeology, MD
Architectural History and Criticism, MD
Architecture, BMD
Art History, Criticism and Conservation, BD
Art/Art Studies, General, B
Asian Languages, MD
Asian Studies/Civilization, BMD
Asian-American Studies, B
Astrophysics, BD
Atmospheric Sciences and Meteorology, B
Biochemistry, D
Bioengineering, D
Biological and Biomedical Sciences, D
Biology/Biological Sciences, B
Biomedical/Medical Engineering, B
Biophysics, D
Biostatistics, MD
Botany/Plant Biology, B
Building Science, D
Business Administration and Management, B
Business Administration, Management and Operations, MDO
Cell Biology and Anatomy, D
Cell/Cellular and Molecular Biology, B
Celtic Languages, Literatures, and Linguistics, B
Chemical Engineering, BMD
Chemistry, BD
Chinese Language and Literature, B
Chinese Studies, D
Civil Engineering, BMD
Classical, Ancient Mediterranean and Near Eastern Studies and Archaeology, B
Classics and Classical Languages, Literatures, and Linguistics, BMD

Clinical Research, O
Cognitive Sciences, B
Comparative Literature, BD
Computer Science, BMD
Construction Management, O
Counseling Psychology, O
Dance, B
Demography, MD
Design and Applied Arts, MO
Drama and Dramatics/Theatre Arts, B
Dutch/Flemish Language and Literature, B
East Asian Studies, M
Economics, BD
Education, MDO
Electrical Engineering, MD
Electrical, Electronics and Communications Engineering, B
Energy Management and Policy, MD
Engineering Management, MD
Engineering Physics, B
Engineering Science, B
Engineering and Applied Sciences, MDO
English, D
English Language and Literature, B
English as a Second Language, O
Environmental Design/Architecture, MD
Environmental Engineering Technology/Environmental Technology, MD
Environmental Policy and Resource Management, MDO
Environmental Sciences, MD
Environmental and Occupational Health, MD
Environmental/Environmental Health Engineering, B
Epidemiology, MD
Ethnic and Cultural Studies, D
Ethnic, Cultural Minority, and Gender Studies, B
Facilities Planning and Management, O
Film/Cinema Studies, B
Finance and Banking, DO
Financial Engineering, M
Fine Arts and Art Studies, MO
Folklore, M
Foreign Languages, Literatures, and Linguistics, B
Forest Management/Forest Resources Management, B
Forestry, BM
French Language and Literature, BD
Geography, BD
Geological/Geophysical Engineering, B
Geology/Earth Science, BMD
Geophysics and Seismology, MD
Geotechnical Engineering, MD
German Language and Literature, BD
Health Services Administration, D
Hispanic and Latin American Languages, D
Hispanic-American, Puerto Rican, and Mexican-American/Chicano Studies, B
History, BMD
History of Science and Technology, D
Human Development, MD
Human Resources Management and Services, O
Immunology, D
Industrial and Labor Relations, D
Industrial/Management Engineering, MD
Infectious Diseases, MD
Information Science/Studies, MD
Interior Design, O
International Affairs, MD
International Business/Trade/Commerce, O
Italian Language and Literature, BD
Japanese Language and Literature, B
Japanese Studies, D
Jewish/Judaic Studies, D
Journalism, M
Landscape Architecture, BMO
Latin American Studies, BM
Latin Language and Literature, B
Law and Legal Studies, BMD
Legal and Justice Studies, D
Linguistics, BD
Management, O
Management Information Systems and Services, O
Manufacturing Engineering, B
Marketing, DO
Mass Communication/Media Studies, B
Materials Engineering, MD

Materials Sciences, MD
Mathematics, BMD
Mathematics Teacher Education, MD
Mechanical Engineering, BMD
Mechanics, MD
Microbiology, BD
Molecular Biology, D
Molecular Toxicology, D
Multi-/Interdisciplinary Studies, B
Music, BD
Natural Resources Management/Development and
    Policy, BMD
Natural Resources and Conservation, B
Near and Middle Eastern Studies, BMD
Neuroscience, D
Nuclear Engineering, BMD
Nutritional Sciences, BD
Operations Research, BMD
Optometry, DO
Organizational Behavior Studies, D
Peace Studies and Conflict Resolution, B
Philosophy, BD
Physics, BD
Physiology, MD
Plant Biology, D
Political Science and Government, BD
Project Management, O
Psychology, BD
Public Health, BMD
Public Policy Analysis, MD
Range Science and Management, M
Real Estate, D
Religion/Religious Studies, BD
Rhetoric, D
Romance Languages, Literatures, and Linguistics, D
Russian Language and Literature, D
Scandinavian Languages, Literatures, and Linguis-
    tics, BD
Science Teacher Education/General Science
    Teacher Education, MD
Slavic Languages, Literatures, and Linguistics, BD
Social Sciences, B
Social Work, BMD
Sociology, BD
South and Southeast Asian Studies, M
Southeast Asian Studies, B
Spanish Language and Literature, BD
Special Education and Teaching, D
Statistics, BMD
Structural Engineering, MD
Substance Abuse/Addiction Counseling, O
Sustainability Management, O
Sustainable Development, O
Theater, D
Toxicology, B
Transportation and Highway Engineering, MD
Urban Design, MD
Urban Studies/Affairs, B
Urban and Regional Planning, MD
Vision Science/Physiological Optics, MD
Water Resources Engineering, MD
Women's Studies, B
Writing, O

UNIVERSITY OF CALIFORNIA, DAVIS

Accounting, M
Aerospace, Aeronautical and Astronautical Engi-
    neering, BMDO
African-American/Black Studies, B
Agricultural Business and Management, B
Agricultural Economics, MD
Agricultural Sciences, M
Agriculture, Agriculture Operations and Related Sci-
    ences, B
Agronomy and Soil Sciences, MD
Allopathic Medicine, D
American Indian/Native American Studies, BMD
American/United States Studies/Civilization, B
Animal Behavior and Ethology, D
Animal Sciences, BMD
Anthropology, BMD
Apparel and Textiles, B
Applied Mathematics, BMD
Applied Science and Technology, MD
Art History, Criticism and Conservation, BM
Asian-American Studies, B

Atmospheric Sciences and Meteorology, BMD
BioTechnology, B
Biochemistry, MD
Bioengineering, MD
Biology/Biological Sciences, B
Biomedical Engineering, MD
Biomedical/Medical Engineering, B
Biophysics, MD
Biostatistics, MD
Botany/Plant Biology, B
Business Administration, Management and Opera-
    tions, M
Cell Biology and Anatomy, MD
Cell/Cellular Biology and Histology, B
Chemical Engineering, BMD
Chemistry, BMD
Child Development, M
Chinese Language and Literature, B
City/Urban, Community and Regional Planning, B
Civil Engineering, BMDO
Classical, Ancient Mediterranean and Near Eastern
    Studies and Archaeology, B
Clinical Research, M
Clothing and Textiles, M
Communication Studies/Speech Communication
    and Rhetoric, B
Communication and Media Studies, M
Comparative Literature, BD
Composition, MD
Computational Mathematics, B
Computer Engineering, MD
Computer Science, MD
Cultural Studies, MD
Curriculum and Instruction, D
Developmental Biology and Embryology, MD
East Asian Studies, B
Ecology, MD
Ecology, Evolution, Systematics and Population Bi-
    ology, B
Economics, BMD
Education, MD
Educational Psychology, D
Electrical Engineering, MD
Electrical, Electronics and Communications Engi-
    neering, B
Engineering, B
Engineering and Applied Sciences, MDO
English, MD
English Language and Literature, B
Entomology, BMD
Environmental Engineering
    Technology/Environmental Technology, MDO
Environmental Sciences, MD
Environmental Studies, B
Environmental Toxicology, B
Epidemiology, MD
Exercise Physiology, B
Exercise and Sports Science, M
Film/Cinema Studies, B
Fine Arts and Art Studies, M
Fine/Studio Arts, B
Food Science, B
Food Science and Technology, MD
Forensic Science and Technology, M
French Language and Literature, BD
Genetics, BMD
Geography, MD
Geology/Earth Science, BMD
German Language and Literature, BMD
Hispanic-American, Puerto Rican, and Mexican-
    American/Chicano Studies, B
History, BMD
Horticultural Science, M
Human Development, M
Human Development and Family Studies, B
Hydrology and Water Resources Science, BMD
Immunology, MD
International Agriculture, B
International Relations and Affairs, B
Italian Language and Literature, B
Japanese Language and Literature, B
Landscape Architecture, B
Law and Legal Studies, MD
Linguistics, BMD
Materials Engineering, BMD
Materials Sciences, MD

Maternal and Child Health, M
Mathematics, BMD
Mechanical Engineering, BMDO
Medical Informatics, M
Microbiology, BMD
Molecular Biochemistry, MD
Molecular Biology, MD
Multi-/Interdisciplinary Studies, B
Music, BMD
Musicology and Ethnomusicology, D
Natural Resources and Conservation, B
Neuroscience, D
Nutritional Sciences, BMD
Pathology/Experimental Pathology, MD
Performance, MD
Pharmacology, MD
Philosophy, BMD
Physical Sciences, B
Physics, BMD
Physiology, MD
Plant Biology, M
Plant Pathology/Phytopathology, MD
Political Science and Government, BMD
Psychology, BD
Religion/Religious Studies, B
Russian Language and Literature, B
Sociobiology, D
Sociology, BMD
Soil Science and Agronomy, B
Spanish Language and Literature, BMD
Statistics, BMD
Textile Design, M
Theater, B
Toxicology, MD
Transportation and Highway Engineering, MD
Transportation/Transportation Management, MD
Urban Forestry, M
Urban and Regional Planning, M
Veterinary Medicine, D
Veterinary Sciences, MO
Visual and Performing Arts, B
Viticulture and Enology, MD
Women's Studies, B
Writing, M
Zoology/Animal Biology, BM

UNIVERSITY OF CALIFORNIA, IRVINE

Accounting, M
Aerospace, Aeronautical and Astronautical Engi-
    neering, BMD
African-American/Black Studies, B
Allopathic Medicine, D
Anatomy, MD
Anthropology, BMD
Applied Mathematics, MD
Art History, Criticism and Conservation, B
Asian Languages, MD
Asian-American Studies, B
BioTechnology, M
Biochemical Engineering, MD
Biochemistry, MD
Biochemistry, Biophysics and Molecular Biology, B
Bioinformatics, B
Biological and Biomedical Sciences, MD
Biology Teacher Education, B
Biology/Biological Sciences, B
Biomedical Engineering, MD
Biomedical/Medical Engineering, B
Biophysics, D
Botany/Plant Biology, B
Business Administration and Management, B
Business Administration, Management and Opera-
    tions, MD
Business/Managerial Economics, B
Cell Biology and Anatomy, MD
Cell/Cellular and Molecular Biology, B
Chemical Engineering, BMD
Chemistry, BMD
Chinese Studies, BMD
Civil Engineering, BMD
Classical, Ancient Mediterranean and Near Eastern
    Studies and Archaeology, B
Classics and Classical Languages, Litera-
    tures, and Linguistics, BMD
Cognitive Sciences, B
Comparative Literature, BMD

Computational Biology, D
Computer Engineering, B
Computer Science, BMD
Computer Software Engineering, B
Computer and Information Sciences, B
Criminology, BMD
Cultural Studies, D
Dance, BM
Demography and Population Studies, M
Developmental Biology and Embryology, MD
Drama and Dramatics/Theatre Arts, B
East Asian Studies, B
Ecology, MD
Econometrics and Quantitative Economics, B
Economics, BMD
Education, BMD
Educational Administration and Supervision, D
Educational Media/Instructional Technology, M
Electrical Engineering, MD
Electrical, Electronics and Communications Engineering, B
Elementary Education and Teaching, M
Engineering, B
Engineering Management, M
Engineering and Applied Sciences, MD
English, MD
English Language and Literature, B
Environmental Design/Architecture, D
Environmental Engineering Technology/Environmental Technology, MD
Environmental Sciences, B
Environmental Studies, B
Environmental/Environmental Health Engineering, B
Epidemiology, MD
Ethnic, Cultural Minority, and Gender Studies, B
European Studies/Civilization, B
Evolutionary Biology, MD
Exercise Physiology, B
Film/Cinema Studies, B
Fine Arts and Art Studies, MD
Fine/Studio Arts, B
Foreign Language Teacher Education, M
French Language and Literature, BMD
Genetic Counseling/Counselor, M
Genetics, BD
Geology/Earth Science, B
Geosciences, MD
German Language and Literature, MD
German Studies, B
Health Services Administration, M
Hispanic-American, Puerto Rican, and Mexican-American/Chicano Studies, B
History, BMD
Humanities/Humanistic Studies, B
Information Resources Management/CIO Training, B
Information Science/Studies, MD
International/Global Studies, B
Japanese Language and Literature, B
Japanese Studies, MD
Journalism, B
Korean Language and Literature, B
Law and Legal Studies, D
Manufacturing Engineering, MD
Materials Engineering, BMD
Materials Sciences, MD
Mathematics, BMD
Mechanical Engineering, BMD
Medicinal and Pharmaceutical Chemistry, D
Microbiology, MD
Molecular Biology, MD
Molecular Genetics, MD
Multi-/Interdisciplinary Studies, B
Music, BM
Music Performance, B
Neurobiology and Neurophysiology, MD
Neuroscience, D
Nursing, M
Pathology/Experimental Pathology, D
Performance, M
Philosophy, BMD
Physics, BMD
Physiology, D
Political Science and Government, BD
Psychology, BD
Public Health, BMD
Religion/Religious Studies, B

Secondary Education and Teaching, M
Social Sciences, B
Sociology, BD
Spanish Language and Literature, BMD
Statistics, MD
Systematic Biology/Biological Systematics, D
Theater, MD
Toxicology, MD
Translational Biology, M
Transportation and Highway Engineering, MD
Urban Studies/Affairs, BMD
Urban and Regional Planning, MD
Visual and Performing Arts, B
Writing, M

UNIVERSITY OF CALIFORNIA, LOS ANGELES

Accounting, D
Aerospace, Aeronautical and Astronautical Engineering, BMD
African Languages, Literatures, and Linguistics, B
African Studies, M
African-American Studies, M
African-American/Black Studies, B
Allopathic Medicine, D
American Indian/Native American Studies, BM
Anatomy, MD
Ancient/Classical Greek Language and Literature, B
Anthropology, BMD
Applied Mathematics, B
Applied Social Research, MD
Arabic Language and Literature, B
Archeology, MD
Architecture, BMD
Archives/Archival Administration, M
Art History, Criticism and Conservation, BMD
Art/Art Studies, General, B
Asian Languages, MD
Asian Studies/Civilization, MD
Asian-American Studies, BM
Astronomy, MD
Astrophysics, BMD
Atmospheric Sciences and Meteorology, BMD
Biochemistry, BMD
Bioengineering, MD
Bioinformatics, MD
Biological and Biomedical Sciences, MD
Biology/Biological Sciences, B
Biomathematics and Bioinformatics, BMD
Biomedical Engineering, MD
Biophysics, B
Biostatistics, MD
Business Administration, Management and Operations, MD
Business/Managerial Economics, B
Cell Biology and Anatomy, MD
Cell/Cellular and Molecular Biology, B
Chemical Engineering, BMD
Chemistry, BMD
Chinese Language and Literature, B
Civil Engineering, BMD
Classical, Ancient Mediterranean and Near Eastern Studies and Archaeology, B
Classics and Classical Languages, Literatures, and Linguistics, BMD
Clinical Research, M
Cognitive Sciences, B
Community Health and Preventive Medicine, MD
Comparative Literature, BMD
Computational Mathematics, B
Computer Engineering, B
Computer Science, MD
Computer and Information Sciences, B
Dance, BMD
Dentistry, DO
Design and Applied Arts, BM
Development Economics and International Development, B
Developmental Biology and Embryology, MD
Drama and Dramatics/Theatre Arts, B
East Asian Studies, M
Ecology, BMD
Economics, BMD
Education, MD
Educational Leadership and Administration, D
Electrical Engineering, MD

Electrical, Electronics and Communications Engineering, B
Engineering and Applied Sciences, MD
English, MD
English Language and Literature, B
English as a Second Language, MDO
Environmental Engineering Technology/Environmental Technology, MD
Environmental Sciences, BD
Environmental and Occupational Health, MD
Epidemiology, MD
Ethnic, Cultural Minority, and Gender Studies, B
Ethnomusicology, MD
European Studies/Civilization, B
Evolutionary Biology, MD
Film, Television, and Video Production, MD
Film/Cinema Studies, B
Finance and Banking, D
Financial Engineering, M
Fine Arts and Art Studies, BM
Foreign Languages, Literatures, and Linguistics, B
French Language and Literature, BMD
Gender Studies, MD
Geochemistry, MD
Geography, BMD
Geological and Earth Sciences/Geosciences, B
Geological/Geophysical Engineering, B
Geology/Earth Science, BMD
Geophysics and Seismology, BMD
Geosciences, MD
German Language and Literature, BMD
Health Services Administration, MD
Hispanic and Latin American Languages, D
Hispanic-American, Puerto Rican, and Mexican-American/Chicano Studies, B
Historic Preservation and Conservation, M
History, BMD
Human Genetics, MD
Human Resources Development, D
Immunology, MD
Industrial and Manufacturing Management, D
Information Science/Studies, MDO
International Business/Trade/Commerce, MD
International Economics, B
International/Global Studies, B
Italian Language and Literature, BMD
Japanese Language and Literature, B
Jewish/Judaic Studies, B
Korean Language and Literature, B
Latin American Studies, BM
Latin Language and Literature, B
Law and Legal Studies, MD
Liberal Arts and Sciences Studies and Humanities, B
Library Science, MDO
Linguistic, Comparative, and Related Language Studies and Services, B
Linguistics, MD
Management Information Systems and Services, D
Management Strategy and Policy, D
Manufacturing Engineering, M
Marine Biology and Biological Oceanography, B
Marketing, D
Materials Engineering, BMD
Materials Sciences, MD
Mathematics, BMD
Mechanical Engineering, BMD
Media Studies, MD
Medical Physics, MD
Microbiological Sciences and Immunology, B
Microbiology, MD
Molecular Biology, MD
Molecular Genetics, MD
Molecular Physiology, D
Molecular Toxicology, D
Multi-/Interdisciplinary Studies, B
Music, BMD
Music History, Literature, and Theory, B
Musicology and Ethnomusicology, BMD
Near and Middle Eastern Languages, MD
Near and Middle Eastern Studies, BMD
Neurobiology and Neurophysiology, MD
Neuroscience, D
Nursing, MD
Oceanography, Chemical and Physical, MD
Oral Biology, MD

Organizational Behavior Studies, D
Pathology/Experimental Pathology, MD
Pharmacology, MD
Philosophy, BMD
Physics, BMD
Physiology, BMD
Planetary Astronomy and Science, MD
Political Science and Government, BMD
Portuguese Language and Literature, BM
Psychology, BMD
Public Health, MD
Public Policy Analysis, M
Religion/Religious Studies, B
Russian Language and Literature, B
Russian Studies, B
Scandinavian Languages, Literatures, and Linguistics, BM
Scandinavian Studies, B
Slavic Languages, Literatures, and Linguistics, BMD
Social Work, MD
Sociology, BMD
Southeast Asian Studies, B
Spanish Language and Literature, BM
Special Education and Teaching, D
Statistics, BMD
Theater, MD
Toxicology, D
Urban Design, MD
Urban Planning, MD
Visual and Performing Arts, B

UNIVERSITY OF CALIFORNIA, MERCED

Anthropology, B
Applied Mathematics, BMD
Biochemistry, MD
Bioengineering, MD
Biological and Biomedical Sciences, MD
Biology/Biological Sciences, B
Biomedical/Medical Engineering, B
Business Administration and Management, B
Chemistry, BMD
Cognitive Sciences, BMD
Comparative Literature, B
Computer Engineering, B
Computer Science, MD
Cultural Studies, MD
Economics, B
Electrical Engineering, MD
Engineering and Applied Sciences, MD
English Language and Literature, B
Environmental Engineering Technology/Environmental Technology, MD
Environmental/Environmental Health Engineering, B
Geology/Earth Science, B
History, B
Information Science/Studies, MD
Management Science, B
Materials Engineering, B
Mechanical Engineering, BMD
Mechanics, D
Multi-/Interdisciplinary Studies, B
Physics, BMD
Political Science and Government, B
Psychology, BMD
Public Health (MPH, DPH), B
Social Sciences, MD
Sociology, B
Systematic Biology/Biological Systematics, MD
Systems Engineering, MD

UNIVERSITY OF CALIFORNIA, RIVERSIDE

Accounting, M
African-American/Black Studies, B
Agronomy and Soil Sciences, MD
American Indian/Native American Studies, B
Anthropology, BMD
Applied Statistics, D
Archives/Archival Administration, M
Art History, Criticism and Conservation, BM
Art/Art Studies, General, B
Artificial Intelligence and Robotics, MD
Asian Studies/Civilization, B
Asian-American Studies, B
Biochemistry, BMD

Bioengineering, MD
Bioinformatics, D
Biological and Biomedical Sciences, MD
Biology/Biological Sciences, B
Biomedical Sciences, B
Biomedical/Medical Engineering, B
Botany/Plant Biology, BMD
Business Administration and Management, B
Business Administration, Management and Operations, MD
Business/Managerial Economics, B
Cell Biology and Anatomy, MD
Chemical Engineering, BMD
Chemistry, BMD
Classics and Classical Languages, Literatures, and Linguistics, D
Comparative Literature, MD
Composition, D
Computer Engineering, BM
Computer Science, BMD
Cultural Studies, D
Dance, MD
Developmental Biology and Embryology, MD
Drama and Dramatics/Theatre Arts, B
Ecology, D
Economics, BMD
Education, MDO
Educational Administration and Supervision, MD
Educational Psychology, MD
Electrical Engineering, MD
Electrical, Electronics and Communications Engineering, B
English, MD
English Language and Literature, B
English as a Second Language, M
Entomology, BMD
Environmental Engineering Technology/Environmental Technology, MD
Environmental Sciences, BMD
Environmental/Environmental Health Engineering, B
Ethnic and Cultural Studies, D
Ethnomusicology, MD
Evolutionary Biology, MD
Finance and Banking, M
Fine Arts and Art Studies, M
Fine/Studio Arts, B
Foreign Languages and Literatures, B
Foundations and Philosophy of Education, MD
French Language and Literature, B
Genetics, D
Genomic Sciences, D
Geology/Earth Science, BMD
Geophysics and Seismology, B
German Studies, B
Higher Education/Higher Education Administration, MD
Hispanic Studies, MD
Hispanic-American, Puerto Rican, and Mexican-American/Chicano Studies, B
Historic Preservation and Conservation, M
History, BMD
Humanities/Humanistic Studies, B
International/Global Studies, B
Latin American Studies, B
Legal and Justice Studies, D
Liberal Arts and Sciences Studies and Humanities, B
Linguistics, B
Materials Engineering, MD
Materials Sciences, MD
Mathematics, BMD
Mechanical Engineering, BMD
Microbiology, MD
Molecular Biology, MD
Multilingual and Multicultural Education, M
Museology/Museum Studies, M
Music, BMD
Musicology and Ethnomusicology, D
NanoTechnology, MD
Neuroscience, D
Philosophy, BMD
Physical Sciences, B
Physics, BMD
Plant Biology, MD
Plant Molecular Biology, D
Plant Pathology/Phytopathology, MD

Plant Sciences, MD
Political Science and Government, BMD
Psychology, BMD
Public Policy Analysis, B
Reading Teacher Education, M
Religion/Religious Studies, BD
Russian Studies, B
School Psychology, D
Sociology, BMD
South and Southeast Asian Studies, M
Spanish Language and Literature, BMD
Special Education and Teaching, MD
Statistics, BMD
Toxicology, MD
Water Resources, MD
Women's Studies, B
Writing, M

UNIVERSITY OF CALIFORNIA, SAN DIEGO

Aerospace, Aeronautical and Astronautical Engineering, BMD
Allopathic Medicine, D
Anthropology, BD
Applied Mathematics, BM
Applied Physics, MD
Architectural Engineering, M
Art History, Criticism and Conservation, BMD
Art/Art Studies, General, B
Artificial Intelligence and Robotics, MD
BioTechnology, B
Biochemistry, BMD
Bioengineering, MD
Bioinformatics, D
Biological and Biomedical Sciences, D
Biology/Biological Sciences, B
Biomedical/Medical Engineering, B
Biophysics, BD
Business Administration, Management and Operations, MD
Cell/Cellular Biology and Histology, B
Chemical Engineering, BMD
Chemistry, BMD
Chemistry Teacher Education, B
Chinese Language and Literature, B
Classics and Classical Languages, Literatures, and Linguistics, B
Clinical Psychology, D
Clinical Research, M
Cognitive Sciences, D
Communication Disorders, D
Communication and Media Studies, D
Comparative Literature, B
Computational Sciences, MD
Computer Engineering, BMD
Computer Science, BMD
Curriculum and Instruction, M
Dance, BMD
Drama and Dramatics/Theatre Arts, B
Ecology, B
Economics, BD
Education, MD
Educational Leadership and Administration, D
Electrical Engineering, MD
Electrical, Electronics and Communications Engineering, B
Engineering, B
Engineering Physics, BMD
Engineering Science, B
English, MD
English Language and Literature, B
Environmental Studies, B
Epidemiology, D
Ethnic and Cultural Studies, D
Family and Consumer Sciences/Human Sciences, B
Film/Cinema Studies, B
Finance and Banking, M
Fine Arts and Art Studies, MD
Fine/Studio Arts, B
Foreign Languages and Literatures, B
French Language and Literature, B
Geology/Earth Science, B
Geophysics and Seismology, D
Geosciences, MD
German Language and Literature, B
Health Law, M

Health Services Administration, M
History, BMD
History of Science and Technology, D
International Affairs, MD
International Public Health/International Health, D
Italian Language and Literature, B
Japanese Language and Literature, B
Jewish/Judaic Studies, BM
Latin American Studies, BM
Law and Legal Studies, M
Legal and Justice Studies, M
Linguistics, BD
Management, D
Management Science, B
Marine Biology and Biological Oceanography, MD
Marine Sciences, M
Mass Communication/Media Studies, B
Materials Sciences, MD
Mathematics, BMD
Mathematics Teacher Education, BD
Mechanical Engineering, BMD
Mechanics, MD
Medical Microbiology and Bacteriology, B
Medical Technology, MD
Medicinal and Pharmaceutical Chemistry, B
Meteorology, M
Modeling and Simulation, M
Molecular Biology, B
Multilingual and Multicultural Education, M
Music, BMD
Music History, Literature, and Theory, B
NanoTechnology, MD
Neuroscience, D
Ocean Engineering, MD
Oceanography, Chemical and Physical, MD
Performance, D
Pharmacy, D
Philosophy, BD
Photonics, MD
Physics, BD
Physics Teacher Education, B
Political Science and Government, BD
Psychology, BD
Public Health, D
Public Policy Analysis, M
Religion/Religious Studies, B
Russian Language and Literature, B
Russian Studies, B
Science Teacher Education/General Science
   Teacher Education, D
Sociology, BD
Spanish Language and Literature, B
Statistics, MD
Structural Engineering, BMD
Systematic Biology/Biological Systematics, D
Telecommunications, MD
Theater, MD
Urban Studies/Affairs, B
Women's Studies, B
Writing, M

UNIVERSITY OF CALIFOR-
NIA, SANTA BARBARA

Actuarial Science, B
African-American Studies, D
African-American/Black Studies, B
Agricultural Economics, MD
Anthropology, BMD
Applied Mathematics, BM
Applied Statistics, M
Archeology, MD
Area Studies, B
Art History, Criticism and Conservation, BD
Asian Languages, MD
Asian Studies/Civilization, B
Asian-American Studies, B
BioTechnology, M
Biochemistry, D
Bioengineering, MD
Biology/Biological Sciences, B
Biophysics, D
Biopsychology, B
Cell Biology and Anatomy, MD
Chemical Engineering, BMD
Chemistry, BMD
Chinese Language and Literature, B

Classics and Classical Languages, Litera-
   tures, and Linguistics, BMD
Clinical Psychology, MDO
Cognitive Sciences, D
Communication and Media Studies, D
Comparative Literature, BD
Composition, MD
Computational Sciences, MD
Computer Engineering, BMD
Computer Science, BMD
Counseling Psychology, MDO
Cultural Anthropology, MD
Cultural Studies, MD
Dance, B
Developmental Biology and Embryology, BMD
Drama and Dramatics/Theatre Arts, B
East Asian Studies, MD
Ecology, BMD
Econometrics and Quantitative Economics, B
Economics, BMD
Education, MDO
Electrical Engineering, MD
Electrical, Electronics and Communications Engi-
   neering, B
Engineering and Applied Sciences, MD
English, D
English Language and Literature, B
Environmental Policy and Resource Manage-
   ment, MD
Environmental Sciences, MD
Environmental Studies, BMD
Ethnomusicology, MD
Evolutionary Biology, MD
Film, Television, and Video Production, D
Film/Cinema Studies, B
Finance and Banking, D
Fine Arts and Art Studies, M
Fine/Studio Arts, B
French Language and Literature, BD
Geography, BMD
Geology/Earth Science, B
Geophysics and Seismology, B
Geosciences, MD
German Language and Literature, B
Hispanic Studies, D
Hispanic and Latin American Languages, MD
Hispanic-American, Puerto Rican, and Mexican-
   American/Chicano Studies, B
History, BD
Hydrology and Water Resources Science, B
Industrial and Labor Relations, D
Interdisciplinary Studies, D
International Affairs, MD
International/Global Studies, B
Italian Studies, B
Japanese Language and Literature, B
Latin American Studies, M
Liberal Arts and Sciences Studies and Humani-
   ties, B
Linguistic, Comparative, and Related Language
   Studies and Services, B
Linguistics, BD
Management of Technology, M
Marine Biology and Biological Oceanography, BMD
Marine Sciences, MD
Materials Engineering, MD
Materials Sciences, MD
Mathematical and Computational Finance, D
Mathematics, BMD
Mechanical Engineering, BMD
Media Studies, MD
Medieval and Renaissance Studies, BD
Microbiology, B
Molecular Biology, BMD
Multi-/Interdisciplinary Studies, B
Music, BMD
Music Theory and Composition, BMD
Musicology and Ethnomusicology, MD
Near and Middle Eastern Studies, B
Neuroscience, D
Organic Chemistry, B
Performance, MD
Pharmacology, BM
Philosophy, BD
Photonics, MD
Physics, BD

Physiology, B
Political Science and Government, BMD
Portuguese Language and Literature, BMD
Psychology, BD
Public History, D
Quantitative Analysis, D
Religion/Religious Studies, BMD
School Psychology, DO
Slavic Languages, Literatures, and Linguistics, B
Social Sciences, D
Sociology, BD
Spanish Language and Literature, BMD
Speech and Interpersonal Communication, D
Statistics, BMD
Sustainable Development, MD
Theater, MD
Translation and Interpretation, D
Transportation/Transportation Management, D
Women's Studies, BMD
Writing, D
Zoology/Animal Biology, B

UNIVERSITY OF CALIFOR-
NIA, SANTA CRUZ

American/United States Studies/Civilization, B
Anthropology, BD
Applied Economics, M
Applied Mathematics, MD
Art History, Criticism and Conservation, B
Art/Art Studies, General, B
Astronomy, BD
Astrophysics, BD
Biochemistry, BMD
Bioinformatics, BMD
Biology/Biological Sciences, B
Biomedical/Medical Engineering, B
Business/Managerial Economics, B
Cell Biology and Anatomy, MD
Cell/Cellular Biology and Histology, B
Chemistry, BMD
Classics and Classical Languages, Litera-
   tures, and Linguistics, B
Communication and Media Studies, O
Comparative Literature, BMD
Composition, MD
Computer Art and Design, MD
Computer Engineering, BMD
Computer Graphics, B
Computer Science, BMD
Cultural Anthropology, D
Developmental Biology and Embryology, MD
Drama and Dramatics/Theatre Arts, B
Ecology, BMD
Economics, BD
Education, BMD
Electrical Engineering, MD
Electrical, Electronics and Communications Engi-
   neering, B
Engineering and Applied Sciences, MD
English, MD
Environmental Biology, MD
Environmental Studies, BD
Ethnomusicology, M
Evolutionary Biology, MD
Family and Community Services, B
Film, Television, and Video Theory and Criticism, D
Film/Cinema Studies, B
Finance and Banking, M
Fine Arts and Art Studies, MD
Foreign Languages and Literatures, B
Geology/Earth Science, B
Geosciences, MD
German Language and Literature, B
Health Professions and Related Clinical Sciences, B
Hispanic-American, Puerto Rican, and Mexican-
   American/Chicano Studies, B
History, BMD
Humanities/Humanistic Studies, D
Information Science/Studies, B
Interdisciplinary Studies, D
International Affairs, D
International Economics, B
Italian Studies, B
Latin American Studies, B
Law and Legal Studies, B
Linguistics, BMD

Management Information Systems and Services, MD
Management of Technology, MD
Marine Biology and Biological Oceanography, B
Marine Sciences, MD
Mathematics, BMD
Molecular Biology, BMD
Music, BMD
Performance, M
Philosophy, BMD
Physics, BMD
Planetary Astronomy and Science, MD
Plant Sciences, B
Political Science and Government, BD
Pre-Law Studies, B
Pre-Medicine/Pre-Medical Studies, B
Psychology, BD
Russian Studies, B
Social Sciences, D
Social Studies Teacher Education, M
Sociology, BD
Spanish Language and Literature, B
Statistics, MD
Systems Engineering, B
Telecommunications, M
Theater, O
Toxicology, MD
Women's Studies, B
Writing, M

UNIVERSITY OF LA VERNE

Accounting, BM
Anthropology, B
Art History, Criticism and Conservation, B
Art/Art Studies, General, B
Athletic Training and Sports Medicine, B
Behavioral Sciences, B
Biology/Biological Sciences, B
Broadcast Journalism, B
Business Administration and Management, B
Business Administration, Management and Operations, M
Chemistry, B
Child Development, BM
Child and Family Studies, M
Clinical Psychology, D
Communication Studies/Speech Communication and Rhetoric, B
Comparative Literature, B
Computer Engineering, B
Computer Science, B
Counselor Education/School Counseling and Guidance Services, MO
Criminology, B
Drama and Dramatics/Theatre Arts, B
E-Commerce/Electronic Commerce, B
Economics, B
Education, MO
Educational Administration and Supervision, O
Educational Leadership and Administration, MD
Elementary Education and Teaching, O
English Language and Literature, B
Environmental Biology, B
Finance and Banking, M
French Language and Literature, B
Gerontology, MO
Health Services Administration, M
Health Services Research, M
Health/Health Care Administration/Management, B
History, B
Human Resources Management and Services, M
International Business/Trade/Commerce, BM
International Relations and Affairs, B
International/Global Studies, B
Journalism, B
Kinesiology and Exercise Science, B
Law and Legal Studies, D
Legal Assistant/Paralegal, B
Liberal Arts and Sciences Studies and Humanities, B
Management, MO
Management Information Systems and Services, M
Marketing, M
Marketing/Marketing Management, B
Marriage and Family Therapy/Counseling, M
Mathematics, B

Music, B
Natural Resources Management/Development and Policy, B
Natural Sciences, B
Non-Profit/Public/Organizational Management, MO
Organizational Management, MDO
Philosophy, B
Photography, B
Physics, B
Political Science and Government, B
Psychology, BMD
Public Administration, BMD
Reading Teacher Education, MO
Religion/Religious Studies, B
School Psychology, M
Secondary Education and Teaching, O
Social Sciences, B
Sociology, B
Spanish Language and Literature, B
Special Education and Teaching, MO
Supply Chain Management, M

UNIVERSITY OF THE PACIFIC

Art History, Criticism and Conservation, B
Art/Art Studies, General, B
Audiology/Audiologist and Speech-Language Pathology/Pathologist, B
Biochemistry, B
Biological and Biomedical Sciences, M
Biology/Biological Sciences, B
Biomedical/Medical Engineering, B
Business Administration and Management, B
Business Administration, Management and Operations, M
Chemistry, B
Civil Engineering, B
Classics and Classical Languages, Literatures, and Linguistics, B
Commercial and Advertising Art, B
Communication Disorders, B
Communication Studies/Speech Communication and Rhetoric, B
Communication and Media Studies, M
Computer Engineering, B
Computer Science, B
Curriculum and Instruction, MD
Dentistry, MDO
Drama and Dramatics/Theatre Arts, B
Economics, B
Education, BMDO
Educational Administration and Supervision, MD
Educational Psychology, MDO
Electrical, Electronics and Communications Engineering, B
Engineering Physics, B
Engineering and Applied Sciences, M
Engineering/Industrial Management, B
English Language and Literature, B
Environmental Studies, B
Exercise and Sports Science, M
Fine/Studio Arts, B
French Language and Literature, B
Geology/Earth Science, B
German Language and Literature, B
History, B
Information Science/Studies, B
International Affairs, D
International Relations and Affairs, B
Japanese Language and Literature, B
Kinesiology and Exercise Science, B
Law and Legal Studies, MD
Mathematics, B
Mechanical Engineering, B
Music, BM
Music History, Literature, and Theory, B
Music Teacher Education, BM
Music Theory and Composition, B
Music Therapy/Therapist, BM
Pharmaceutical Sciences, MD
Pharmacy, BD
Philosophy, B
Physical Sciences, B
Physical Therapy/Therapist, MD
Physics, B
Piano and Organ, B
Political Science and Government, B

Psychology, BM
Public Policy Analysis, M
Religion/Religious Studies, B
School Psychology, MDO
Social Sciences, B
Sociology, B
Spanish Language and Literature, B
Special Education and Teaching, BM
Voice and Opera, B
Water Resources, D

UNIVERSITY OF PHOENIX–BAY AREA CAMPUS

Accounting, BM
Adult and Continuing Education and Teaching, M
Business Administration and Management, B
Business Administration, Management and Operations, MD
Business/Corporate Communications, B
Computer Software Engineering, B
Computer and Information Systems Security, B
Consumer Merchandising/Retailing Management, B
Corrections and Criminal Justice, B
Criminal Justice/Law Enforcement Administration, B
Criminology, M
Digital Communication and Media/Multimedia, B
E-Commerce/Electronic Commerce, B
Early Childhood Education and Teaching, M
Education, MDO
Educational Administration and Supervision, MD
Educational Leadership and Administration, MD
Elementary Education and Teaching, M
Energy Management and Policy, M
Gerontological Nursing, M
Health Services Administration, BM
Health/Health Care Administration/Management, B
Higher Education/Higher Education Administration, D
Hospitality Administration/Management, B
Human Resources Management and Services, M
Human Services, B
Information Technology, B
International Business/Trade/Commerce, BM
Management Information Systems and Services, BMD
Management Science, B
Management of Technology, M
Marketing, M
Marketing/Marketing Management, B
Marriage and Family Therapy/Counseling, M
Nursing, MD
Nursing Administration, MD
Nursing Education, M
Nursing Informatics, M
Operations Management and Supervision, B
Organizational Behavior Studies, B
Organizational Management, D
Project Management, M
Psychology, B
Public Administration, BM
Secondary Education and Teaching, M
Securities Services Administration/Management, M
Special Education and Teaching, M

UNIVERSITY OF PHOENIX–CENTRAL VALLEY CAMPUS

Accounting, BM
Business Administration and Management, B
Business Administration, Management and Operations, M
Community Health and Preventive Medicine, M
Computer Education, M
Corrections and Criminal Justice, B
Curriculum and Instruction, M
Education, M
Elementary Education and Teaching, M
Gerontology, M
Health Services Administration, M
Health/Health Care Administration/Management, B
Human Resources Management and Services, M
International Business/Trade/Commerce, M
Management Information Systems and Services, BM
Management of Technology, M
Marketing, M
Marketing/Marketing Management, B

Marriage and Family Therapy/Counseling, M
Nursing, M
Public Administration, M
Public Administration and Social Service Professions, B
Secondary Education and Teaching, M

UNIVERSITY OF PHOENIX–SACRAMENTO VALLEY CAMPUS

Accounting, BM
Adult and Continuing Education and Teaching, M
Business Administration and Management, B
Business Administration, Management and Operations, M
Business/Corporate Communications, B
Computer Software Engineering, B
Computer and Information Systems Security, B
Consumer Merchandising/Retailing Management, B
Corrections and Criminal Justice, B
Criminal Justice/Law Enforcement Administration, B
Curriculum and Instruction, M
Digital Communication and Media/Multimedia, B
E-Commerce/Electronic Commerce, B
Education, MO
Elementary Education and Teaching, M
Finance, B
Health Services Administration, BM
Health/Health Care Administration/Management, B
Hospitality Administration/Management, B
Human Resources Management and Services, M
Human Services, B
Information Technology, B
International Business/Trade/Commerce, BM
Management, M
Management Information Systems and Services, BM
Management Science, B
Management of Technology, M
Marketing, M
Marketing/Marketing Management, B
Nursing, M
Nursing - Advanced Practice, M
Nursing Education, M
Operations Management and Supervision, B
Organizational Behavior Studies, B
Psychology, B
Public Administration, BM
Public Administration and Social Service Professions, B
Secondary Education and Teaching, M

UNIVERSITY OF PHOENIX–SAN DIEGO CAMPUS

Accounting, BM
Business Administration and Management, B
Business Administration, Management and Operations, M
Business/Commerce, B
Business/Corporate Communications, B
Computer Education, M
Criminal Justice/Law Enforcement Administration, B
Curriculum and Instruction, M
Education, M
Elementary Education and Teaching, M
English as a Second Language, M
Health Services Administration, B
Health/Health Care Administration/Management, B
Human Resources Management and Services, M
Human Services, B
Information Technology, B
International Business/Trade/Commerce, M
Management, M
Management Information Systems and Services, BM
Management of Technology, M
Marketing, M
Marketing/Marketing Management, B
Nursing, M
Nursing Education, M
Public Administration, M

Secondary Education and Teaching, M

UNIVERSITY OF PHOENIX–SOUTHERN CALIFORNIA CAMPUS

Accounting, BM
Adult and Continuing Education and Teaching, M
Business Administration and Management, B
Computer and Information Systems Security, B
Counselor Education/School Counseling and Guidance Services, M
Criminal Justice/Law Enforcement Administration, B
Criminology, M
Digital Communication and Media/Multimedia, B
Education, MO
Educational Administration and Supervision, MO
Educational Leadership and Administration, M
Elementary Education and Teaching, M
Energy Management and Policy, M
English as a Second Language, O
Health Services Administration, BM
Homeland Security, M
Human Resources Management and Services, M
Human Services, B
Information Technology, B
International Business/Trade/Commerce, M
Management, M
Management of Technology, M
Marketing, M
Marriage and Family Therapy/Counseling, M
Nursing, MO
Nursing - Advanced Practice, MO
Nursing Education, MO
Nursing Informatics, M
Project Management, M
Psychology, M
Public Administration, BM
Secondary Education and Teaching, M
Security and Protective Services, B

UNIVERSITY OF REDLANDS

Accounting, B
Anthropology, B
Art History, Criticism and Conservation, B
Asian Studies/Civilization, B
Audiology/Audiologist and Speech-Language Pathology/Pathologist, B
Biology/Biological Sciences, B
Business Administration and Management, B
Business Administration, Management and Operations, M
Business/Commerce, B
Chemistry, B
Communication Disorders, BM
Comparative Literature, B
Computer Science, B
Design and Visual Communications, B
Economics, B
Education, BMDO
Elementary Education and Teaching, B
English Language and Literature, B
Environmental Studies, B
Fine/Studio Arts, B
French Language and Literature, B
Geographic Information Systems, M
Geography, B
German Language and Literature, B
History, B
International Relations and Affairs, B
Liberal Arts and Sciences Studies and Humanities, B
Management, M
Management Information Systems and Services, BM
Mathematics, B
Music, BM
Music History, Literature, and Theory, B
Music Performance, B
Music Teacher Education, B
Music Theory and Composition, B
Philosophy, B
Physics, B
Piano and Organ, B
Political Science and Government, B
Psychology, B
Public Policy Analysis, B
Religion/Religious Studies, B

Secondary Education and Teaching, B
Sociology, B
Spanish Language and Literature, B
Voice and Opera, B

UNIVERSITY OF SAN DIEGO

Accounting, BM
Anthropology, B
Architectural History and Criticism, B
Art History, Criticism and Conservation, B
Art/Art Studies, General, B
Biochemistry, B
Biology/Biological Sciences, B
Biophysics, B
Business Administration and Management, B
Business Administration, Management and Operations, M
Business/Managerial Economics, B
Chemistry, B
Communication Disorders, M
Computer Science, B
Conflict Resolution and Mediation/Peace Studies, M
Counseling Psychology, M
Counselor Education/School Counseling and Guidance Services, M
Curriculum and Instruction, M
Drama and Dramatics/Theatre Arts, B
Economics, B
Education, MDO
Educational Leadership and Administration, MDO
Electrical, Electronics and Communications Engineering, B
English Language and Literature, B
English as a Second Language, M
Environmental Studies, B
Ethnic and Cultural Studies, B
Finance, B
French Language and Literature, B
Gerontological Nursing, M
Health Informatics, M
Higher Education/Higher Education Administration, M
History, BM
Humanities/Humanistic Studies, B
Industrial Engineering, B
International Affairs, M
International Business/Trade/Commerce, BM
International Relations and Affairs, B
Italian Studies, B
Law and Legal Studies, MDO
Legal and Justice Studies, M
Liberal Arts and Sciences Studies and Humanities, B
Management, M
Marine Affairs, M
Marine Biology and Biological Oceanography, B
Marine Sciences, M
Marketing/Marketing Management, B
Mathematics, B
Mechanical Engineering, B
Music, B
Non-Profit/Public/Organizational Management, M
Nursing, MD
Nursing - Adult, M
Nursing - Advanced Practice, M
Nursing Administration, M
Philosophy, B
Physics, B
Political Science and Government, B
Psychiatric/Mental Health Nurse/Nursing, M
Psychology, B
Reading Teacher Education, M
Real Estate, BM
Religion/Religious Studies, B
Sociology, B
Spanish Language and Literature, B
Special Education and Teaching, M
Supply Chain Management, MO
Taxation, MO
Theater, M

UNIVERSITY OF SAN FRANCISCO

Accounting, B
Adult and Continuing Education and Teaching, B
Advertising, B
American/United States Studies/Civilization, B

Applied Economics, B
Architecture, B
Art History, Criticism and Conservation, B
Art/Art Studies, General, B
Asian Studies/Civilization, BM
Bilingual and Multilingual Education, B
BioTechnology, M
Biological and Biomedical Sciences, M
Biology/Biological Sciences, B
Business Administration and Management, B
Business Administration, Management and Operations, M
Business/Commerce, B
Business/Managerial Economics, B
Chemistry, BM
City/Urban, Community and Regional Planning, B
Commercial and Advertising Art, B
Communication Studies/Speech Communication and Rhetoric, B
Comparative Literature, B
Computer Science, BM
Computer and Information Sciences, B
Counseling Psychology, M
Counselor Education/School Counseling and Guidance Services, M
Curriculum and Instruction, MD
Database Systems, M
Design and Visual Communications, B
Development Economics and International Development, B
Drawing, B
Economics, BM
Education, BMD
Educational Administration and Supervision, MD
Educational Leadership and Administration, B
Educational Media/Instructional Technology, M
Elementary Education and Teaching, B
English Language and Literature, B
English as a Second Language, M
Entrepreneurship/Entrepreneurial Studies, BM
Environmental Sciences, B
Environmental Studies, B
Finance, B
Finance and Banking, M
Fine/Studio Arts, B
French Language and Literature, B
Graphic Design, B
Health Education, M
Health Services Administration, BM
Health Services/Allied Health/Health Sciences, B
Health and Physical Education, B
History, B
Hospitality Administration/Management, B
Hotel/Motel Administration/Management, B
Illustration, B
Information Science/Studies, B
Information Technology, B
Intellectual Property Law, M
International Affairs, M
International Business/Trade/Commerce, BM
International Development, M
International Relations and Affairs, B
International and Comparative Education, MD
Internet Engineering, M
Internet and Interactive Multimedia, M
Investment Management, M
Japanese Language and Literature, B
Japanese Studies, B
Kinesiology and Exercise Science, B
Latin American Studies, B
Law and Legal Studies, MD
Liberal Arts and Sciences Studies and Humanities, B
Management Information Systems and Services, BM
Marketing, M
Marketing/Marketing Management, B
Marriage and Family Therapy/Counseling, M
Mass Communication/Media Studies, B
Mathematics, B
Multilingual and Multicultural Education, MD
Museology/Museum Studies, M
Natural Resources Management/Development and Policy, M
Non-Profit/Public/Organizational Management, M
Nursing, MD

Nursing - Advanced Practice, D
Nursing Administration, MD
Organizational Behavior Studies, B
Organizational Management, M
Pacific Area/Pacific Rim Studies, M
Painting, B
Philosophy, B
Physical Education Teaching and Coaching, B
Physics, B
Political Science and Government, B
Pre-Dentistry Studies, B
Pre-Medicine/Pre-Medical Studies, B
Pre-Veterinary Studies, B
Printmaking, B
Psychiatric/Mental Health Nurse/Nursing, D
Psychology, B
Public Administration, BM
Public Affairs, M
Public Health, M
Reading Teacher Education, M
Religion/Religious Studies, B
Religious Education, MD
Restaurant/Food Services Management, B
Secondary Education and Teaching, B
Sociology, B
Spanish Language and Literature, B
Special Education and Teaching, MD
Sport and Fitness Administration/Management, M
Taxation, M
Theology/Theological Studies, B
Urban Education and Leadership, M
Urban Studies/Affairs, M
Visual and Performing Arts, B
Writing, M

UNIVERSITY OF SOUTHERN CALIFORNIA

Accounting, BM
Acting, B
Advertising and Public Relations, M
Aerospace, Aeronautical and Astronautical Engineering, BMDO
African-American/Black Studies, B
Allopathic Medicine, D
American/United States Studies/Civilization, BD
Anthropology, B
Applied Mathematics, MD
Archeology, B
Architecture, BMD
Art History, Criticism and Conservation, BMDO
Art/Art Studies, General, B
Artificial Intelligence and Robotics, M
Arts Management, M
Asian Languages, MD
Asian-American Studies, B
Astronomy, B
Biochemistry, BM
Bioinformatics, D
Biological and Biomedical Sciences, MDO
Biology/Biological Sciences, B
Biomedical Engineering, MD
Biomedical/Medical Engineering, B
Biophysics, BM
Biostatistics, MD
Broadcast Journalism, B
Business Administration and Management, B
Business Administration, Management and Operations, MD
Cancer Biology/Oncology, D
Cell Biology and Anatomy, MD
Chemical Engineering, BMDO
Chemistry, BD
Child and Family Studies, M
Cinematography and Film/Video Production, B
Civil Engineering, BMD
Classics and Classical Languages, Literatures, and Linguistics, BMD
Clinical Psychology, D
Clinical Research, O
Cognitive Sciences, BD
Communication Studies/Speech Communication and Rhetoric, B
Communication Theory, D
Communication and Media Studies, M
Comparative Literature, BD
Composition, MD

Computational Biology, MD
Computer Art and Design, M
Computer Engineering, BMD
Computer Science, BMD
Computer and Information Systems Security, M
Construction Management, M
Corporate and Organizational Communication, M
Counselor Education/School Counseling and Guidance Services, M
Cultural Studies, D
Dance, B
Dental Hygiene/Hygienist, B
Dentistry, D
Developmental Biology and Embryology, D
Developmental Psychology, D
Drama and Dramatics/Theatre Arts, B
Dramatic/Theatre Arts and Stagecraft, B
East Asian Languages, Literatures, and Linguistics, B
East Asian Studies, BMD
Economic Development, MD
Economics, BMD
Education, MD
Educational Administration and Supervision, D
Educational Leadership and Administration, D
Educational Policy, D
Educational Psychology, D
Electrical Engineering, DO
Electrical, Electronics and Communications Engineering, B
Engineering Management, M
Engineering and Applied Sciences, MDO
English, MD
English Language and Literature, B
English as a Second Language, M
Entrepreneurship/Entrepreneurial Studies, M
Environmental Biology, M
Environmental Engineering Technology/Environmental Technology, MD
Environmental Sciences, B
Environmental Studies, B
Environmental and Occupational Health, M
Environmental/Environmental Health Engineering, B
Epidemiology, MD
Ethnic, Cultural Minority, and Gender Studies, B
Evolutionary Biology, D
Film, Television, and Video Production, M
Film, Television, and Video Theory and Criticism, MD
Film/Cinema Studies, B
Fine Arts and Art Studies, MO
Fine/Studio Arts, B
Food Science and Technology, O
French Language and Literature, B
Game Design and Development, M
Genomic Sciences, D
Geographic Information Systems, MO
Geography, BMO
Geology/Earth Science, B
Geosciences, MD
Geotechnical Engineering, M
Gerontology, BMDO
Hazardous Materials Management and Waste Technology/Technician, M
Health Communication, MD
Health Education, M
Health Promotion, M
Health Services Administration, MO
Health Services Research, D
Health Services/Allied Health/Health Sciences, B
Higher Education/Higher Education Administration, D
Hispanic-American, Puerto Rican, and Mexican-American/Chicano Studies, B
History, BD
Homeland Security, O
Immunology, M
Industrial Engineering, B
Industrial/Management Engineering, MDO
International Affairs, MD
International Business/Trade/Commerce, B
International Public Health/International Health, BMO
International Relations and Affairs, B
International/Global Studies, B
Internet and Interactive Multimedia, M

Italian Language and Literature, B
Jazz/Jazz Studies, B
Jewish/Judaic Studies, B
Journalism, BM
Kinesiology and Movement Studies, MD
Latin American Studies, D
Law and Legal Studies, MD
Linguistic, Comparative, and Related Language
   Studies and Services, B
Linguistics, BMD
Manufacturing Engineering, M
Marine Biology and Biological Oceanography, MD
Marine Sciences, MD
Marriage and Family Therapy/Counseling, M
Materials Engineering, M
Materials Sciences, MDO
Mathematical and Computational Finance, M
Mathematics, BMD
Mechanical Engineering, BMDO
Mechanics, M
Media Studies, MD
Medical Imaging, M
Medical Microbiology and Bacteriology, D
Microbiology, M
Modeling and Simulation, M
Molecular Biology, MD
Molecular Pharmacology, MD
Multi-/Interdisciplinary Studies, B
Multilingual and Multicultural Education, D
Music, BMDO
Music History, Literature, and Theory, D
Music Performance, B
Music Teacher Education, MD
Music Theory and Composition, B
Musicology and Ethnomusicology, D
Neurobiology and Neurophysiology, D
Neuroscience, MD
Non-Profit/Public/Organizational Management, O
Occupational Therapy/Therapist, BMD
Oceanography, Chemical and Physical, MD
Operations Research, M
Oral and Dental Sciences, MDO
Organizational Management, M
Painting, M
Pathobiology, D
Pathology/Experimental Pathology, MD
Performance, MDO
Petroleum Engineering, MDO
Pharmaceutical Administration, M
Pharmaceutical Sciences, MDO
Pharmacy, D
Philosophy, BMD
Photography, M
Physical Chemistry, D
Physical Sciences, B
Physical Therapy/Therapist, D
Physician Assistant, M
Physics, BMD
Physiology, M
Piano and Organ, B
Playwriting and Screenwriting, B
Political Science and Government, BMD
Psychology, BMD
Public Administration, MO
Public Health, MD
Public Policy Analysis, MDO
Public Relations/Image Management, B
Quantitative Analysis, D
Real Estate, BM
Religion/Religious Studies, B
Rhetoric, D
Russian Language and Literature, B
Sacred Music, MD
Safety Engineering, MO
Sculpture, M
Slavic Languages, Literatures, and Linguistics, MD
Social Psychology, D
Social Sciences, B
Social Work, MD
Sociology, BD
Software Engineering, M
Spanish Language and Literature, BD
Statistics, M
Structural Engineering, B
Student Personnel Services, M
Supply Chain Management, MO

Sustainable Development, O
Systems Engineering, MDO
Taxation, M
Technical Theatre/Theatre Design and Technol-
   ogy, B
Telecommunications, MO
Theater, M
Toxicology, MD
Transportation and Highway Engineering, MO
Urban Education and Leadership, D
Urban Planning, MDO
Urban and Regional Planning, D
Violin, Viola, Guitar and Other Stringed Instru-
   ments, B
Visual and Performing Arts, B
Voice and Opera, B
Water Resources, M
Writing, MD

UNIVERSITY OF THE WEST

Asian History, B
Buddhist Studies, B
Business Administration and Management, B
Business Administration, Management and Opera-
   tions, M
English Language and Literature, B
Finance and Banking, M
General Studies, B
International Business/Trade/Commerce, M
Management Information Systems and Services, M
Non-Profit/Public/Organizational Management, M
Psychology, BM
Religion/Religious Studies, BMD
Theology and Religious Vocations, M

VANGUARD UNIVERSITY OF SOUTH-ERN CALIFORNIA

Accounting, B
Anthropology, B
Athletic Training and Sports Medicine, B
Bible/Biblical Studies, B
Biochemistry, B
Biological and Physical Sciences, B
Biology/Biological Sciences, B
Business Administration and Management, B
Chemistry, B
Cinematography and Film/Video Production, B
Clinical Psychology, M
Communication Studies/Speech Communication
   and Rhetoric, B
Drama and Dramatics/Theatre Arts, B
Education, BM
Elementary Education and Teaching, B
English Language and Literature, B
Finance, B
Health and Physical Education, B
History, B
Human Development and Family Studies, B
Information Technology, B
Intercultural/Multicultural and Diversity Studies, B
International Business/Trade/Commerce, B
Kinesiology and Exercise Science, B
Marketing/Marketing Management, B
Mathematics, B
Missions/Missionary Studies and Missiology, B
Music, B
Music Performance, B
Music Teacher Education, B
Nursing, M
Pastoral Studies/Counseling, B
Physical Education Teaching and Coaching, B
Physical Therapy/Therapist, B
Political Science and Government, B
Pre-Law Studies, B
Pre-Medicine/Pre-Medical Studies, B
Psychology, B
Radio and Television, B
Religion/Religious Studies, BM
Religious Education, B
Secondary Education and Teaching, B
Sociology, B
Technical Theatre/Theatre Design and Technol-
   ogy, B
Theology and Religious Vocations, M
Theology/Theological Studies, B

Youth Ministry, B

VENTURA COLLEGE

Accounting, A
Agriculture, A
Automobile/Automotive Mechanics
   Technology/Technician, A
Biology/Biological Sciences, A
Business Administration and Management, A
Ceramic Arts and Ceramics, A
Commercial and Advertising Art, A
Computer and Information Sciences, A
Construction Engineering Technology/Technician, A
Criminal Justice/Law Enforcement Administration, A
Drama and Dramatics/Theatre Arts, A
Engineering, A
Fashion/Apparel Design, A
Fine/Studio Arts, A
Hydrology and Water Resources Science, A
Journalism, A
Liberal Arts and Sciences Studies and Humani-
   ties, A
Machine Tool Technology/Machinist, A
Medical Transcription/Transcriptionist, A
Medical/Clinical Assistant, A
Music, A
Natural Resources Management/Development and
   Policy, A
Parks, Recreation, Leisure and Fitness Studies, A
Physical Sciences, A
Plant Sciences, A
Real Estate, A
Tool and Die Technology/Technician, A
Welding Technology/Welder, A

VICTOR VALLEY COLLEGE

Administrative Assistant and Secretarial Science, A
Agricultural Teacher Education, A
Art/Art Studies, General, A
Automobile/Automotive Mechanics
   Technology/Technician, A
Biological and Physical Sciences, A
Biology/Biological Sciences, A
Building/Construction Finishing, Manage-
   ment, and Inspection, A
Business Administration and Management, A
Business/Commerce, A
Child Care and Support Services Management, A
Child Development, A
Computer Programming, Specific Applications, A
Computer Science, A
Computer and Information Sciences, A
Construction Engineering Technology/Technician, A
Criminal Justice/Police Science, A
Drama and Dramatics/Theatre Arts, A
Electrical, Electronic and Communications Engineer-
   ing Technology/Technician, A
Fire Protection and Safety Technology/Technician, A
Fire Science/Firefighting, A
Food Technology and Processing, A
Horticultural Science, A
Humanities/Humanistic Studies, A
Information Science/Studies, A
Kindergarten/PreSchool Education and Teaching, A
Liberal Arts and Sciences Studies and Humani-
   ties, A
Management Information Systems and Services, A
Mathematics, A
Music, A
Natural Sciences, A
Ornamental Horticulture, A
Physical Sciences, A
Real Estate, A
Respiratory Care Therapy/Therapist, A
Science Technologies/Technicians, A
Social Sciences, A
Teacher Assistant/Aide, A
Trade and Industrial Teacher Education, A
Vehicle Maintenance and Repair Technologies, A

Welding Technology/Welder, A

WEST COAST UNIVERSITY (ANAHEIM)

Dental Hygiene/Hygienist, B

WEST COAST UNIVERSITY (NORTH HOLLYWOOD)

Health/Health Care Administration/Management, B

WEST COAST UNIVERSITY (ONTARIO)

Dental Hygiene/Hygienist, B

WEST HILLS COMMUNITY COLLEGE

Accounting, A
Administrative Assistant and Secretarial Science, A
Agricultural Business and Management, A
Agricultural Mechanization, A
Agronomy and Crop Science, A
Animal Sciences, A
Art/Art Studies, General, A
Automobile/Automotive Mechanics
   Technology/Technician, A
Biology/Biological Sciences, A
Business Administration and Management, A
Chemistry, A
Child Development, A
Criminal Justice/Law Enforcement Administration, A
Equestrian/Equine Studies, A
Geography, A
Geology/Earth Science, A
Health Professions and Related Clinical Sciences, A
Humanities/Humanistic Studies, A
Information Science/Studies, A
Kindergarten/PreSchool Education and Teaching, A
Liberal Arts and Sciences Studies and Humani-
   ties, A
Mathematics, A
Physical Education Teaching and Coaching, A
Physics, A
Psychology, A
Social Sciences, A
Transportation and Materials Moving, A
Welding Technology/Welder, A

WEST LOS ANGELES COLLEGE

Accounting, A
Administrative Assistant and Secretarial Science, A
Airframe Mechanics and Aircraft Maintenance
   Technology/Technician, A
Anthropology, A
Art/Art Studies, General, A
Avionics Maintenance Technology/Technician, A
Biology/Biological Sciences, A
Business Administration and Management, A
Chemistry, A
Computer Programming/Programmer, A
Consumer Merchandising/Retailing Management, A
Criminal Justice/Law Enforcement Administration, A
Criminal Justice/Police Science, A
Data Processing and Data Processing
   Technology/Technician, A
Dental Hygiene/Hygienist, A
Drafting and Design Technology/Technician, A
Economics, A
Education, A
Electrical, Electronic and Communications Engineer-
   ing Technology/Technician, A
Engineering, A
English Language and Literature, A
Family and Consumer Economics and Related Ser-
   vices, A
French Language and Literature, A
Geography, A
Geology/Earth Science, A
History, A
Journalism, A
Legal Administrative Assistant/Secretary, A
Legal Assistant/Paralegal, A
Liberal Arts and Sciences Studies and Humani-
   ties, A
Marketing/Marketing Management, A
Mathematics, A
Medical Administrative Assistant/Secretary, A
Music, A
Philosophy, A

Physical Education Teaching and Coaching, A
Physics, A
Political Science and Government, A
Psychology, A
Real Estate, A
Sociology, A
Spanish Language and Literature, A
Tourism and Travel Services Management, A

WEST VALLEY COLLEGE

Accounting, A
Administrative Assistant and Secretarial Science, A
Art/Art Studies, General, A
Biology/Biological Sciences, A
Business Administration and Management, A
Chemistry, A
Court Reporting/Court Reporter, A
Criminal Justice/Law Enforcement Administration, A
Criminal Justice/Police Science, A
Data Processing and Data Processing
   Technology/Technician, A
Drafting and Design Technology/Technician, A
Drama and Dramatics/Theatre Arts, A
Economics, A
English Language and Literature, A
Fashion/Apparel Design, A
French Language and Literature, A
German Language and Literature, A
Health Information/Medical Records
   Administration/Administrator, A
History, A
Information Science/Studies, A
Interior Design, A
Italian Language and Literature, A
Kindergarten/PreSchool Education and Teaching, A
Landscape Architecture, A
Legal Administrative Assistant/Secretary, A
Liberal Arts and Sciences Studies and Humani-
   ties, A
Marketing/Marketing Management, A
Mathematics, A
Medical Administrative Assistant/Secretary, A
Medical/Clinical Assistant, A
Music, A
Parks, Recreation and Leisure Facilities Manage-
   ment, A
Physical Education Teaching and Coaching, A
Physics, A
Psychology, A
Social Sciences, A
Sociology, A
Spanish Language and Literature, A
Women's Studies, A

WESTMONT COLLEGE

Anthropology, B
Art Teacher Education, B
Art/Art Studies, General, B
Biology/Biological Sciences, B
Business/Commerce, B
Business/Managerial Economics, B
Chemistry, B
Communication Studies/Speech Communication
   and Rhetoric, B
Computer Science, B
Drama and Dramatics/Theatre Arts, B
Economics, B
Education, B
Elementary Education and Teaching, B
Engineering Physics, B
English Language and Literature, B
English/Language Arts Teacher Education, B
French Language and Literature, B
History, B
Kinesiology and Exercise Science, B
Liberal Arts and Sciences Studies and Humani-
   ties, B
Mathematics, B
Mathematics Teacher Education, B
Modern Languages, B
Music, B
Philosophy, B
Physical Education Teaching and Coaching, B
Physics, B
Political Science and Government, B
Pre-Dentistry Studies, B

Pre-Law Studies, B
Pre-Medicine/Pre-Medical Studies, B
Pre-Pharmacy Studies, B
Pre-Theology/Pre-Ministerial Studies, B
Pre-Veterinary Studies, B
Psychology, B
Religion/Religious Studies, B
Secondary Education and Teaching, B
Social Science Teacher Education, B
Social Sciences, B
Sociology, B
Spanish Language and Literature, B

WHITTIER COLLEGE

Anthropology, B
Art/Art Studies, General, B
Biochemistry, B
Biology/Biological Sciences, B
Business Administration and Management, B
Chemistry, B
Child Development, BM
Chinese Language and Literature, B
Drama and Dramatics/Theatre Arts, B
Economics, B
Education, M
Educational Administration and Supervision, M
Elementary Education and Teaching, M
Engineering Physics, B
English Language and Literature, B
Environmental Sciences, B
Environmental Studies, B
French Language and Literature, B
Health and Physical Education, B
History, B
International/Global Studies, B
Kinesiology and Exercise Science, B
Latin American Studies, B
Law and Legal Studies, D
Liberal Arts and Sciences Studies and Humani-
   ties, B
Mathematics, B
Music, B
Philosophy, B
Physics, B
Political Science and Government, B
Pre-Law Studies, B
Pre-Medicine/Pre-Medical Studies, B
Psychology, B
Religion/Religious Studies, B
Secondary Education and Teaching, M
Social Sciences, B
Social Work, B
Sociology, B
Spanish Language and Literature, B

WILLIAM JESSUP UNIVERSITY

Art/Art Studies, General, B
Biology/Biological Sciences, B
Business Administration and Management, B
Computer and Information Sciences, B
Drama and Dramatics/Theatre Arts, B
Education, BM
English Education, M
English Language and Literature, B
Environmental Sciences, B
History, B
Kinesiology and Exercise Science, B
Mathematics, B
Mathematics Teacher Education, M
Missions/Missionary Studies and Missiology, B
Music, B
Pastoral Studies/Counseling, AB
Political Science and Government, B
Psychology, B
Religious Education, B
Theology/Theological Studies, AB
Youth Ministry, B

WOODBURY UNIVERSITY

Accounting, B
Apparel and Accessories Marketing Operations, B
Architecture, BM
Business Administration and Management, B
Business Administration, Management and Opera-
   tions, BM
Commercial and Advertising Art, B

Communication Studies/Speech Communication
and Rhetoric, B
Fashion Merchandising, B
Fashion/Apparel Design, B
Film/Video and Photographic Arts, B
History, B
Interior Architecture, B
Marketing/Marketing Management, B
Multi-/Interdisciplinary Studies, B
Organizational Management, M
Psychology, B

WOODLAND COMMUNITY COLLEGE

Agriculture, A
English Language and Literature, A
Ethnic and Cultural Studies, A
History, A
Psychology, A
Sociology, A

YESHIVA OHR ELCHONON CHABAD/WEST COAST TALMUDICAL SEMINARY

Talmudic Studies, B

YUBA COLLEGE

Accounting, A
Administrative Assistant and Secretarial Science, A
Advertising, A
African-American/Black Studies, A
Agricultural Business and Management, A
Agricultural Mechanization, A
Agriculture, A
Agronomy and Crop Science, A
Animal Sciences, A
Art/Art Studies, General, A
Automobile/Automotive Mechanics
Technology/Technician, A
Biological and Physical Sciences, A
Biology/Biological Sciences, A
Business Administration and Management, A
Chemistry, A
Child Development, A
Communication Studies/Speech Communication
and Rhetoric, A
Computer Science, A
Computer and Information Sciences, A
Corrections, A
Cosmetology/Cosmetologist, A
Criminal Justice/Law Enforcement Administration, A
Criminal Justice/Police Science, A
Drama and Dramatics/Theatre Arts, A
Education, A
Electrical, Electronic and Communications Engineer-
ing Technology/Technician, A
Elementary Education and Teaching, A
English Language and Literature, A
Family and Consumer Economics and Related Ser-
vices, A
Family and Consumer Sciences/Human Sciences, A
Fire Science/Firefighting, A
Health Teacher Education, A
Hispanic-American, Puerto Rican, and Mexican-
American/Chicano Studies, A
History, A
Human Services, A
Industrial Radiologic Technology/Technician, A
Industrial Technology/Technician, A
Kindergarten/PreSchool Education and Teaching, A
Machine Tool Technology/Machinist, A
Mass Communication/Media Studies, A
Mathematics, A
Music, A
Philosophy, A
Photography, A
Physical Education Teaching and Coaching, A
Psychiatric/Mental Health Services Technician, A
Psychology, A
Robotics Technology/Technician, A
Social Sciences, A
Substance Abuse/Addiction Counseling, A
Veterinary/Animal Health Technology/Technician and
Veterinary Assistant, A
Welding Technology/Welder, A
Women's Studies, A

Word Processing, A

Colorado

ADAMS STATE UNIVERSITY

Accounting, B
Advertising, B
Agribusiness, B
Art History, Criticism and Conservation, B
Art Teacher Education, B
Biochemistry, B
Biology Teacher Education, B
Biology/Biological Sciences, B
Business Administration and Management, B
Business Administration, Management and Opera-
tions, B
Business Teacher Education, B
Business/Commerce, AB
Cell/Cellular and Molecular Biology, B
Ceramic Arts and Ceramics, B
Chemical Physics, B
Chemistry, B
Chemistry Teacher Education, B
Computer Science, B
Corrections, B
Counselor Education/School Counseling and Guid-
ance Services, M
Criminal Justice/Law Enforcement Administration, B
Criminology, B
Drama and Dance Teacher Education, B
Drama and Dramatics/Theatre Arts, A
Dramatic/Theatre Arts and Stagecraft, B
Drawing, B
Early Childhood Education and Teaching, AB
Economics, B
Education, M
Elementary Education and Teaching, A
Engineering Physics, B
English Language and Literature, B
English/Language Arts Teacher Education, B
Fiber, Textile and Weaving Arts, B
Finance, B
Fine Arts and Art Studies, M
Fine/Studio Arts, A
Geography, B
Geology/Earth Science, B
Graphic Design, B
Health/Health Care Administration/Management, B
History, BM
International Business/Trade/Commerce, B
Journalism, A
Kinesiology and Exercise Science, B
Law and Legal Studies, B
Liberal Arts and Sciences Studies and Humani-
ties, AB
Management Information Systems and Services, B
Marketing/Marketing Management, B
Mass Communication/Media Studies, AB
Mathematics, B
Mathematics Teacher Education, B
Medical Microbiology and Bacteriology, B
Metal and Jewelry Arts, B
Multi-/Interdisciplinary Studies, B
Music, B
Music Performance, B
Music Teacher Education, B
Music Theory and Composition, B
Office Management and Supervision, B
Painting, B
Photography, B
Physical Education Teaching and Coaching, BM
Physics, B
Political Science and Government, A
Printmaking, B
Psychology, B
Science Teacher Education/General Science
Teacher Education, B
Small Business Administration/Management, B
Social Studies Teacher Education, B
Social Work, B
Spanish Language Teacher Education, B
Spanish Language and Literature, B
Special Education and Teaching, BM
Teacher Education, Multiple Levels, B

Wildlife Biology, B

AIMS COMMUNITY COLLEGE

Accounting Technology/Technician and Bookkeep-
ing, A
Administrative Assistant and Secretarial Science, A
Air Transportation, A
Airline/Commercial/Professional Pilot and Flight
Crew, A
Animation, Interactive Technology, Video Graphics
and Special Effects, A
Autobody/Collision and Repair
Technology/Technician, A
Automobile/Automotive Mechanics
Technology/Technician, A
Biomedical Technology/Technician, A
Broadcast Journalism, A
Building/Construction Site Management/Manager, A
Business/Office Automation/Technology/Data En-
try, A
Child Care and Support Services Management, A
Child Development, A
Communications Technology/Technician, A
Criminal Justice/Law Enforcement Administration, A
Digital Communication and Media/Multimedia, A
Electrical, Electronic and Communications Engineer-
ing Technology/Technician, A
Emergency Medical Technology/Technician (EMT
Paramedic), A
Engineering Technology, A
Entrepreneurship/Entrepreneurial Studies, A
Fire Protection, A
Fire Protection and Safety Technology/Technician, A
Graphic Communications, A
Liberal Arts and Sciences Studies and Humani-
ties, A
Management Information Systems and Services, A
Marketing/Marketing Management, A
Medical Office Management/Administration, A
Medical/Health Management and Clinical
Assistant/Specialist, A
Pharmacy Technician/Assistant, A
Photographic and Film/Video Technology/Technician
and Assistant, A
Radio and Television, A
Radio and Television Broadcasting
Technology/Technician, A
Radiologic Technology/Science - Radiographer, A
Recording Arts Technology/Technician, A
Science Technologies/Technicians, A
Surgical Technology/Technologist, A
Welding Technology/Welder, A

AMERICAN SENTINEL UNIVERSITY

Business Administration and Management, AB
Business Administration, Management and Opera-
tions, M
Computer Science, ABM
Computer and Information Systems Security, B
Data Processing and Data Processing
Technology/Technician, B
Finance, B
Health Informatics, M
Health Services Administration, M
Health/Health Care Administration/Management, B
Human Resources Management/Personnel Adminis-
tration, B
Information Science/Studies, AB
Information Technology, B
Management Information Systems and Ser-
vices, BM
Management Science, B
Marketing/Marketing Management, B
Medical Informatics, B
Nursing, M
Web/Multimedia Management and Webmaster, B

ARAPAHOE COMMUNITY COLLEGE

Accounting Technology/Technician and Bookkeep-
ing, A
Architectural Engineering Technology/Technician, A
Automobile/Automotive Mechanics
Technology/Technician, A
Building/Construction Site Management/Manager, A
Business Administration and Management, A
Clinical/Medical Laboratory Technician, A

Computer Systems Networking and Telecommunications, A
Computer and Information Sciences, A
Criminal Justice/Law Enforcement Administration, A
Emergency Medical Technology/Technician (EMT Paramedic), A
Engineering Technology, A
Funeral Service and Mortuary Science, A
General Studies, A
Graphic Design, A
Health Information/Medical Records Technology/Technician, A
Health and Physical Education, A
Interior Design, A
Journalism, A
Legal Assistant/Paralegal, A
Liberal Arts and Sciences Studies and Humanities, A
Physical Therapist Assistant, A
Retailing and Retail Operations, A
Science Technologies/Technicians, A
Telecommunications Technology/Technician, A

ARGOSY UNIVERSITY, DENVER

Accounting, D
Business Administration and Management, AB
Business Administration, Management and Operations, MD
Clinical Psychology, MD
Community College Education, D
Counseling Psychology, MD
Counselor Education/School Counseling and Guidance Services, D
Criminal Justice/Law Enforcement Administration, B
Education, MD
Educational Administration and Supervision, D
Educational Leadership and Administration, MD
Educational Media/Instructional Technology, D
Elementary Education and Teaching, D
Finance and Banking, M
Forensic Psychology, M
Health Services Administration, M
Higher Education/Higher Education Administration, D
Industrial and Organizational Psychology, M
Information Technology, AB
International Business/Trade/Commerce, MD
Liberal Arts and Sciences Studies and Humanities, B
Management, MD
Management Information Systems and Services, MD
Marketing, MD
Marriage and Family Therapy/Counseling, MD
Organizational Management, D
Psychology, ABMD
Public Administration, M
Public Health, M
Sustainability Management, MD

THE ART INSTITUTE OF COLORADO

Animation, Interactive Technology, Video Graphics and Special Effects, B
Apparel and Accessories Marketing Operations, B
Baking and Pastry Arts/Baker/Pastry Chef, A
CAD/CADD Drafting and/or Design Technology/Technician, B
Cinematography and Film/Video Production, AB
Commercial Photography, AB
Computer Graphics, B
Culinary Arts/Chef Training, A
Fashion/Apparel Design, B
Graphic Design, B
Interior Design, B
Recording Arts Technology/Technician, B
Restaurant, Culinary, and Catering Management/Manager, B
Web Page, Digital/Multimedia and Information Resources Design, AB

ASPEN UNIVERSITY

Business Administration and Management, B
Business Administration, Management and Operations, MO
Criminal Justice/Law Enforcement Administration, B
Early Childhood Education and Teaching, B

Finance and Banking, M
Information Science/Studies, MO
Management Information Systems and Services, MO
Project Management, MO

BEL–REA INSTITUTE OF ANIMAL TECHNOLOGY

Veterinary/Animal Health Technology/Technician and Veterinary Assistant, A

COLLEGEAMERICA–COLORADO SPRINGS

Accounting, B
Allied Health and Medical Assisting Services, A
Business Administration and Management, AB
Computer and Information Sciences, AB
Hospital and Health Care Facilities Administration/Management, B

COLLEGEAMERICA–DENVER

Accounting, B
Accounting and Business/Management, A
Computer Technology/Computer Systems Technology, A
Health/Health Care Administration/Management, B
Medical/Health Management and Clinical Assistant/Specialist, A

COLLEGEAMERICA–FORT COLLINS

Accounting, B
Accounting Technology/Technician and Bookkeeping, A
Allied Health and Medical Assisting Services, A
Business Administration and Management, B
Computer Graphics, A
Computer Programming/Programmer, A
Computer Science, B
Computer Technology/Computer Systems Technology, A
Health/Health Care Administration/Management, B

COLORADO CHRISTIAN UNIVERSITY

Accounting, B
Biological and Physical Sciences, B
Biology/Biological Sciences, B
Business Administration and Management, B
Business Administration, Management and Operations, BM
Business Education, M
Computer and Information Sciences, B
Computer and Information Systems Security, M
Counseling Psychology, M
Curriculum and Instruction, M
Distance Education Development, M
Early Childhood Education and Teaching, M
Economics, B
Education, ABM
Educational Media/Instructional Technology, M
Elementary Education and Teaching, BM
English Language and Literature, B
English/Language Arts Teacher Education, B
Finance, B
General Studies, AB
Health Services/Allied Health/Health Sciences, B
History Teacher Education, B
International/Global Studies, B
Liberal Arts and Sciences Studies and Humanities, B
Management Information Systems and Services, B
Marketing, B
Marketing/Marketing Management, B
Music, B
Music Performance, B
Music Teacher Education, B
Political Science and Government, B
Pre-Law Studies, B
Pre-Medicine/Pre-Medical Studies, B
Project Management, M
Psychology, B
Religion/Religious Studies, B
Social Sciences, B
Special Education and Teaching, BM
Theology/Theological Studies, B

Youth Ministry, B

THE COLORADO COLLEGE

American/United States Studies/Civilization, M
Anthropology, B
Art Education, M
Art History, Criticism and Conservation, B
Asian Studies/Civilization, B
Biochemistry, B
Biology/Biological Sciences, B
Cell/Cellular and Molecular Biology, B
Chemistry, B
Classics and Classical Languages, Literatures, and Linguistics, B
Comparative Literature, B
Computer and Information Sciences, B
Dance, B
Drama and Dramatics/Theatre Arts, B
Econometrics and Quantitative Economics, B
Economics, B
Education, BM
Elementary Education and Teaching, M
English Education, M
English Language and Literature, B
Environmental Sciences, B
Environmental Studies, B
Ethnic, Cultural Minority, and Gender Studies, B
Film/Cinema Studies, B
Fine/Studio Arts, B
Foreign Language Teacher Education, M
French Language and Literature, B
French Studies, B
Geology/Earth Science, B
German Language and Literature, B
Hispanic-American, Puerto Rican, and Mexican-American/Chicano Studies, B
History, B
Humanities/Humanistic Studies, M
International Economics, B
Italian Language and Literature, B
Italian Studies, B
Liberal Arts and Sciences Studies and Humanities, B
Liberal Studies, M
Mathematics, B
Mathematics Teacher Education, M
Mathematics and Computer Science, B
Multi-/Interdisciplinary Studies, B
Music, B
Music Teacher Education, M
Philosophy, B
Physics, B
Political Science and Government, B
Psychology, B
Regional Studies (U.S., Canadian, Foreign), B
Religion/Religious Studies, B
Russian Studies, B
Science Teacher Education/General Science Teacher Education, M
Secondary Education and Teaching, M
Social Studies Teacher Education, M
Sociology, B
Spanish Language and Literature, B
Women's Studies, B

COLORADO HEIGHTS UNIVERSITY

Accounting, M
Environmental Policy and Resource Management, M
Finance and Banking, M
Health Services Administration, M
Intercultural/Multicultural and Diversity Studies, B
International Business/Trade/Commerce, BM

COLORADO MESA UNIVERSITY

Accounting, B
Agricultural Business and Management, AB
Animation, Interactive Technology, Video Graphics and Special Effects, A
Art/Art Studies, General, B
Athletic Training and Sports Medicine, B
Automobile/Automotive Mechanics Technology/Technician, A
Baking and Pastry Arts/Baker/Pastry Chef, A
Biology/Biological Sciences, B

Business Administration, Management and Operations, BM
Business/Commerce, B
Business/Office Automation/Technology/Data Entry, A
Chemistry, B
Clinical/Medical Laboratory Technician, A
Communications Technology/Technician, A
Computer Systems Networking and Telecommunications, A
Computer and Information Sciences, B
Construction Engineering Technology/Technician, B
Construction Trades, A
Cooking and Related Culinary Arts, A
Criminal Justice/Law Enforcement Administration, A
Criminal Justice/Police Science, B
Criminal Justice/Safety Studies, B
Drama and Dramatics/Theatre Arts, B
Education, M
Education/Teaching of the Gifted and Talented, M
Educational Leadership and Administration, M
Emergency Medical Technology/Technician (EMT Paramedic), A
English Language and Literature, B
English as a Second Language, M
Environmental Sciences, B
Geology/Earth Science, B
Graphic Design, B
History, B
Hospitality Administration/Management, AB
Kinesiology and Exercise Science, B
Liberal Arts and Sciences Studies and Humanities, AB
Machine Tool Technology/Machinist, A
Management Information Systems and Services, B
Manufacturing Technology/Technician, A
Mass Communication/Media Studies, B
Mathematics, B
Mechanical Engineering/Mechanical Technology/Technician, B
Medical/Clinical Assistant, A
Music, B
Physical Sciences, B
Physics, B
Political Science and Government, B
Psychology, B
Public Administration, B
Radiologic Technology/Science - Radiographer, AB
Social Sciences, B
Social Work, B
Sociology, B
Spanish Language and Literature, B
Special Education and Teaching, M
Sport and Fitness Administration/Management, B
Water Quality and Wastewater Treatment Management and Recycling Technology/Technician, A

COLORADO MOUNTAIN COLLEGE (GLENWOOD SPRINGS)

Accounting, A
Behavioral Sciences, A
Biological and Physical Sciences, A
Biology/Biological Sciences, A
Business Administration and Management, AB
Commercial and Advertising Art, A
Computer Engineering Technology/Technician, A
Computer Systems Networking and Telecommunications, A
Computer and Information Sciences and Support Services, A
Criminal Justice/Law Enforcement Administration, A
Data Entry/Microcomputer Applications, A
Digital Communication and Media/Multimedia, A
Drama and Dramatics/Theatre Arts, A
English Language and Literature, A
Humanities/Humanistic Studies, A
Liberal Arts and Sciences Studies and Humanities, A
Mathematics, A
Natural Sciences, A
Photography, A
Psychology, A
Social Sciences, A
Therapeutic Recreation/Recreational Therapy, A

Veterinary/Animal Health Technology/Technician and Veterinary Assistant, A

COLORADO MOUNTAIN COLLEGE (LEADVILLE)

Accounting, A
Business Administration and Management, B
Business/Commerce, A
Corrections, A
Criminal Justice/Law Enforcement Administration, A
Early Childhood Education and Teaching, A
Emergency Medical Technology/Technician (EMT Paramedic), A
Entrepreneurship/Entrepreneurial Studies, A
Environmental Studies, AB
Finance, A
Fire Protection and Safety Technology/Technician, A
General Studies, A
Historic Preservation and Conservation, A
Hospitality Administration/Management, A
Land Use Planning and Management/Development, A
Liberal Arts and Sciences Studies and Humanities, A
Natural Resources and Conservation, A
Parks, Recreation and Leisure Facilities Management, A
Parks, Recreation, Leisure and Fitness Studies, A

COLORADO MOUNTAIN COLLEGE (STEAMBOAT SPRINGS)

Accounting, A
Behavioral Sciences, A
Biological and Physical Sciences, A
Biology/Biological Sciences, A
Business Administration and Management, AB
Computer Engineering Technology/Technician, A
Consumer Merchandising/Retailing Management, A
Data Entry/Microcomputer Applications, A
E-Commerce/Electronic Commerce, A
Early Childhood Education and Teaching, A
English Language and Literature, A
Fine/Studio Arts, A
Geology/Earth Science, A
Hospitality Administration/Management, A
Hotel/Motel Administration/Management, A
Humanities/Humanistic Studies, A
Liberal Arts and Sciences Studies and Humanities, A
Marketing/Marketing Management, A
Mathematics, A
Parks, Recreation and Leisure Facilities Management, A
Physical Sciences, A
Real Estate, A
Restaurant, Culinary, and Catering Management/Manager, A
Social Sciences, A
Tourism and Travel Services Management, A

COLORADO NORTHWESTERN COMMUNITY COLLEGE

Accounting, A
Aircraft Powerplant Technology/Technician, A
Airline/Commercial/Professional Pilot and Flight Crew, A
Banking and Financial Support Services, A
Cosmetology/Cosmetologist, A
Dental Hygiene/Hygienist, A
Early Childhood Education and Teaching, A
Emergency Medical Technology/Technician (EMT Paramedic), A
Equestrian/Equine Studies, A
General Studies, A
Liberal Arts and Sciences Studies and Humanities, A
Natural Resources and Conservation, A

Small Business Administration/Management, A

COLORADO SCHOOL OF HEALING ARTS

Massage Therapy/Therapeutic Massage, A

COLORADO SCHOOL OF MINES

Applied Mathematics, MD
Applied Physics, MD
Bioengineering, MD
Biomedical/Medical Engineering, B
Chemical Engineering, BMD
Chemistry, BMD
Civil Engineering, BMD
Computer Science, BMD
Construction Engineering and Management, MD
Economics, B
Electrical Engineering, MD
Electrical, Electronics and Communications Engineering, B
Electronic Materials, M
Engineering, B
Engineering Management, M
Engineering Physics, B
Engineering and Applied Sciences, MDO
Environmental Engineering Technology/Environmental Technology, MD
Environmental/Environmental Health Engineering, B
Geochemistry, MD
Geological Engineering, MD
Geological/Geophysical Engineering, B
Geology/Earth Science, MD
Geophysics Engineering, MD
Geophysics and Seismology, MD
Hydrology and Water Resources Science, MD
International Affairs, O
Management of Technology, M
Materials Engineering, MD
Materials Sciences, MD
Mathematics, BMD
Mechanical Engineering, BMD
Metallurgical Engineering, BMD
Mineral Economics, D
Mineral/Mining Engineering, MD
Mining and Mineral Engineering, B
Nuclear Engineering, M
Operations Research, D
Petroleum Engineering, BMD
Physics, MD
Statistics, B

COLORADO SCHOOL OF TRADES

Gunsmithing/Gunsmith, A

COLORADO STATE UNIVERSITY

Accounting, BM
Adult and Continuing Education and Teaching, M
Advertising and Public Relations, MD
Agribusiness, B
Agricultural Economics, BMD
Agricultural Sciences, MD
Agricultural Teacher Education, B
Agronomy and Crop Science, B
Agronomy and Soil Sciences, MD
Animal Sciences, BMD
Anthropology, BM
Apparel and Textile Marketing Management, B
Applied Horticulture/Horticultural Operations, B
Art Teacher Education, B
Atmospheric Sciences and Meteorology, MD
BioTechnology, B
Biochemistry, BMD
Biological and Biomedical Sciences, MD
Biology Teacher Education, B
Biology/Biological Sciences, B
Biomedical Engineering, MD
Biomedical Sciences, B
Biomedical/Medical Engineering, B
Botany/Plant Biology, BMD
Business Administration and Management, B
Business Administration, Management and Operations, M
Cell Biology and Anatomy, MD
Chemical Engineering, BMD
Chemistry, BMD

Chemistry Teacher Education, B
Child and Family Studies, MD
Civil Engineering, BMD
Communication Studies/Speech Communication and Rhetoric, B
Community College Education, D
Computer Engineering, B
Computer Science, MD
Computer Teacher Education, B
Computer Technology/Computer Systems Technology, B
Computer and Information Sciences, B
Conservation Biology, MD
Construction Management, BM
Consumer Economics, M
Counselor Education/School Counseling and Guidance Services, M
Dance, B
Drama and Dramatics/Theatre Arts, B
Drawing, B
Early Childhood Education and Teaching, B
Ecology, BMD
Economics, BMD
Education, MD
Educational Leadership and Administration, MD
Electrical Engineering, MD
Electrical, Electronics and Communications Engineering, B
Engineering Physics, B
Engineering Science, B
Engineering and Applied Sciences, MD
English, M
English Language and Literature, B
English/Language Arts Teacher Education, B
Entomology, MD
Environmental Health, B
Environmental and Occupational Health, MD
Environmental/Environmental Health Engineering, B
Equestrian/Equine Studies, B
Ethnic and Cultural Studies, B
Exercise and Sports Science, MD
Family and Consumer Sciences/Home Economics Teacher Education, B
Family and Consumer Sciences/Human Sciences, B
Fiber, Textile and Weaving Arts, B
Finance, B
Finance and Banking, M
Fine Arts and Art Studies, M
Fine/Studio Arts, B
Fire Services Administration, B
Fish, Game and Wildlife Management, MD
Fishing and Fisheries Sciences and Management, B
Food Science and Technology, MD
Foreign Language Teacher Education, M
Foreign Languages and Literatures, B
Forest Sciences and Biology, B
Forestry, MD
French Language Teacher Education, B
French Language and Literature, B
Geology/Earth Science, B
Geosciences, MD
German Language Teacher Education, B
German Language and Literature, B
Graphic Design, B
History, BM
Horticultural Science, BMD
Human Development, MD
Human Development and Family Studies, B
Human Nutrition, B
Hydrology and Water Resources Science, M
Immunology, MD
Information Science/Studies, B
Interior Design, B
International/Global Studies, B
Journalism, B
Kinesiology and Exercise Science, B
Landscape Architecture, BMD
Liberal Arts and Sciences Studies and Humanities, B
Management Information Systems and Services, BM
Marketing/Marketing Management, B
Mass Communication/Media Studies, MD
Mathematics, BMD
Mathematics Teacher Education, B
Mechanical Engineering, BMD

Metal and Jewelry Arts, B
Microbiology, BMD
Molecular Biology, MD
Music, BM
Music Performance, B
Music Teacher Education, B
Music Theory and Composition, B
Music Therapy/Therapist, B
Natural Resources Management/Development and Policy, B
Natural Resources and Conservation, B
Natural Sciences, B
Neuroscience, D
Nutritional Sciences, MD
Occupational Therapy/Therapist, MD
Organizational Management, M
Painting, B
Parks, Recreation and Leisure Facilities Management, B
Pathology/Experimental Pathology, MD
Philosophy, BM
Photography, B
Physics, BMD
Physics Teacher Education, B
Plant Nursery Operations and Management, B
Plant Pathology/Phytopathology, MD
Plant Sciences, MD
Political Science and Government, BMD
Psychology, BMD
Radiation Biology/Radiobiology, MD
Range Science and Management, BMD
Real Estate, B
Recreation and Park Management, MD
Resource Management, MD
Restaurant/Food Services Management, B
Science Teacher Education/General Science Teacher Education, B
Sculpture, B
Social Studies Teacher Education, B
Social Work, BMD
Sociology, BMD
Soil Science and Agronomy, B
Spanish Language Teacher Education, B
Spanish Language and Literature, B
Speech Teacher Education, B
Speech and Interpersonal Communication, M
Statistics, BMD
Student Personnel Services, M
Sustainability Management, M
Technical Communication, MD
Technical and Business Writing, M
Technology Teacher Education/Industrial Arts Teacher Education, B
Veterinary Medicine, D
Veterinary Sciences, MD
Vocational and Technical Education, MD
Water Resources, M
Water, Wetlands, and Marine Resources Management, B
Wildlife Biology, B
Writing, M
Zoology/Animal Biology, BMD

COLORADO STATE UNIVERSITY–GLOBAL CAMPUS

Accounting, M
Business Administration, Management and Operations, M
Criminology, M
Education, M
Educational Leadership and Administration, M
Finance and Banking, M
Health Services Administration, M
Human Resources Management and Services, M
International Business/Trade/Commerce, M
Management Information Systems and Services, M
Organizational Management, M
Project Management, M

COLORADO STATE UNIVERSITY–PUEBLO

Accounting, B
Applied Science and Technology, M
Art Education, M
Automotive Engineering Technology/Technician, B
Biochemistry, M

Biological and Biomedical Sciences, M
Biology/Biological Sciences, B
Business Administration, Management and Operations, M
Business/Commerce, B
Business/Managerial Economics, B
Chemistry, BM
Civil Engineering Technology/Technician, B
Education, M
Educational Media/Instructional Technology, M
Engineering, B
Engineering and Applied Sciences, M
English Language and Literature, B
Fine/Studio Arts, B
Foreign Language Teacher Education, M
Foreign Languages and Literatures, B
Health Education, M
History, B
Industrial/Management Engineering, M
Information Science/Studies, B
Kinesiology and Exercise Science, B
Liberal Arts and Sciences Studies and Humanities, B
Mass Communication/Media Studies, B
Mathematics, B
Mechanic and Repair Technologies/Technicians, B
Music, B
Music Teacher Education, M
Nursing, B
Physical Education Teaching and Coaching, M
Physics, B
Political Science and Government, B
Psychology, B
Social Sciences, B
Social Work, B
Sociology, B
Special Education and Teaching, M
Systems Engineering, M

COLORADO TECHNICAL UNIVERSITY COLORADO SPRINGS

Accounting, ABM
Business Administration and Management, AB
Business Administration, Management and Operations, MD
Computer Engineering, BM
Computer Science, ABMD
Computer and Information Systems Security, M
Conflict Resolution and Mediation/Peace Studies, M
Criminal Justice/Law Enforcement Administration, AB
Criminology, M
Database Systems, M
E-Commerce/Electronic Commerce, AB
Electrical Engineering, M
Electrical, Electronic and Communications Engineering Technology/Technician, AB
Electrical, Electronics and Communications Engineering, B
Finance and Banking, M
General Studies, A
Graphic Design, AB
Human Resources Management and Services, M
Industrial and Manufacturing Management, M
Information Science/Studies, AB
Logistics and Materials Management, M
Management Information Systems and Services, B
Management of Technology, M
Marketing, M
Project Management, M
Software Engineering, M
Surgical Technology/Technologist, A
Systems Engineering, M

COLORADO TECHNICAL UNIVERSITY DENVER SOUTH

Accounting, ABM
Business Administration and Management, AB
Business Administration, Management and Operations, M
Computer Engineering, M
Computer Science, ABM
Computer and Information Systems Security, M
Conflict Resolution and Mediation/Peace Studies, M
Criminal Justice/Law Enforcement Administration, AB

Database Systems, M
Electrical Engineering, M
Finance and Banking, M
Graphic Design, AB
Health Information/Medical Records
    Technology/Technician, A
Human Resources Management and Services, M
Industrial and Manufacturing Management, M
Information Science/Studies, AB
Management Information Systems and Services, B
Management of Technology, M
Marketing, M
Project Management, M
Securities Services Administration/Management, M
Software Engineering, M
Surgical Technology/Technologist, A
Systems Engineering, M

COLORADO TECHNICAL UNIVERSITY ONLINE

Accounting, AB
Accounting and Finance, B
Business Administration and Management, AB
Court Reporting/Court Reporter, B
Criminal Justice/Law Enforcement Administra-
    tion, AB
General Studies, A
Health/Health Care Administration/Management, B
Human Resources Management/Personnel Adminis-
    tration, B
Information Technology, B
International Business/Trade/Commerce, B
Legal Assistant/Paralegal, A
Marketing/Marketing Management, B
Medical Insurance Coding Specialist/Coder, A
Real Estate, B

COMMUNITY COLLEGE OF AURORA

Accounting Technology/Technician and Bookkeep-
    ing, A
Child Development, A
Cinematography and Film/Video Production, A
Criminal Justice/Law Enforcement Administration, A
Emergency Medical Technology/Technician (EMT
    Paramedic), A
Fire Science/Firefighting, A
General Studies, A
Heavy Equipment Maintenance
    Technology/Technician, A
Liberal Arts and Sciences Studies and Humani-
    ties, A
Management Information Systems and Services, A
Office Management and Supervision, A
Science Technologies/Technicians, A

COMMUNITY COLLEGE OF DENVER

Accounting, A
Accounting Technology/Technician and Bookkeep-
    ing, A
Administrative Assistant and Secretarial Science, A
Business Administration and Management, A
Child Development, A
Computer and Information Sciences, A
Dental Hygiene/Hygienist, A
Drafting and Design Technology/Technician, A
Electroneurodiagnostic/Electroencephalographic
    Technology/Technologist, A
General Studies, A
Graphic Design, A
Human Services, A
Legal Assistant/Paralegal, A
Liberal Arts and Sciences Studies and Humani-
    ties, A
Machine Shop Technology/Assistant, A
Management Information Systems and Services, A
Mental Health Counseling/Counselor, A
Office Management and Supervision, A
Quality Control and Safety
    Technologies/Technicians, A
Radiologic Technology/Science - Radiographer, A
Science Technologies/Technicians, A
Teacher Assistant/Aide, A
Teaching Assistants/Aides, A
Veterinary/Animal Health Technology/Technician and
    Veterinary Assistant, A

Welding Technology/Welder, A

DEVRY UNIVERSITY (COLORADO SPRINGS)

Accounting, AB
Business Administration and Management, B
Business Administration, Management and Opera-
    tions, BMO
Business/Commerce, B
Computer Systems Analysis/Analyst, B
Computer Systems Networking and Telecommunica-
    tions, AB
Electrical, Electronic and Communications Engineer-
    ing Technology/Technician, A
Health/Health Care Administration/Management, B
Web Page, Digital/Multimedia and Information Re-
    sources Design, AB

DEVRY UNIVERSITY (WESTMINSTER)

Accounting, B
Accounting Technology/Technician and Bookkeep-
    ing, A
Business Administration and Management, B
Business Administration, Management and Opera-
    tions, B
Business/Commerce, B
Computer Engineering Technology/Technician, B
Computer Software Engineering, B
Computer Systems Analysis/Analyst, B
Computer Systems Networking and Telecommunica-
    tions, AB
Criminal Justice/Law Enforcement Administration, B
Electrical, Electronic and Communications Engineer-
    ing Technology/Technician, B
Health Information/Medical Records
    Technology/Technician, A
Health/Health Care Administration/Management, B
Web Page, Digital/Multimedia and Information Re-
    sources Design, AB

EVEREST COLLEGE (COLORADO SPRINGS)

Accounting, A
Administrative Assistant and Secretarial Science, A
Business Administration and Management, A
Computer Programming/Programmer, A
Computer Systems Networking and Telecommunica-
    tions, A
Criminal Justice/Law Enforcement Administration, A
Legal Assistant/Paralegal, A
Medical/Clinical Assistant, A

EVEREST COLLEGE (THORNTON)

Accounting, A
Accounting and Related Services, A
Allied Health and Medical Assisting Services, A
Business Administration and Management, A
Computer Science, A
Criminal Justice/Safety Studies, A
Legal Assistant/Paralegal, A
Surgical Technology/Technologist, A

FORT LEWIS COLLEGE

Accounting, B
American Indian/Native American Studies, B
Anthropology, B
Art/Art Studies, General, B
Athletic Training and Sports Medicine, B
Biochemistry, B
Biology Teacher Education, B
Business Administration and Management, B
Business/Managerial Economics, B
Cell/Cellular and Molecular Biology, B
Chemistry, B
Chemistry Teacher Education, B
Drama and Dramatics/Theatre Arts, B
Early Childhood Education and Teaching, B
Ecology, B
Economics, B
Educational Leadership and Administration, MO
Elementary Education and Teaching, B
Engineering Physics, B
Engineering/Industrial Management, B
English Language and Literature, B
English/Language Arts Teacher Education, B

Environmental Biology, B
Environmental Studies, B
European Studies/Civilization, B
Finance, B
General Studies, B
Geology/Earth Science, B
History, B
Humanities/Humanistic Studies, B
International Business/Trade/Commerce, B
Liberal Arts and Sciences Studies and Humani-
    ties, B
Marketing/Marketing Management, B
Mathematics, B
Multilingual and Multicultural Education, B
Music, B
Music Performance, B
Music Teacher Education, B
Operations Management and Supervision, B
Parks, Recreation, Leisure and Fitness Studies, B
Philosophy, B
Physical Education Teaching and Coaching, B
Physics, B
Political Science and Government, B
Psychology, B
Public Health (MPH, DPH), B
Secondary Education and Teaching, B
Sociology, B
Spanish Language and Literature, B
Sport and Fitness Administration/Management, B
Tourism and Travel Services Management, B
Women's Studies, B

FRONT RANGE COMMUNITY COLLEGE

Accounting Technology/Technician and Bookkeep-
    ing, A
Animation, Interactive Technology, Video Graphics
    and Special Effects, A
Applied Horticulture/Horticultural Operations, A
Architectural Engineering Technology/Technician, A
Automobile/Automotive Mechanics
    Technology/Technician, A
Business Administration and Management, A
CAD/CADD Drafting and/or Design
    Technology/Technician, A
Computer Systems Networking and Telecommunica-
    tions, A
Computer and Information Sciences, A
Early Childhood Education and Teaching, A
Energy Management and Systems
    Technology/Technician, A
General Studies, A
Health Information/Medical Records
    Technology/Technician, A
Heating, Air Conditioning and Refrigeration
    Technology/Technician, A
Hospitality Administration/Management, A
Interior Design, A
Legal Assistant/Paralegal, A
Liberal Arts and Sciences Studies and Humani-
    ties, A
Medical Office Assistant/Specialist, A
Science Technologies/Technicians, A
Sign Language Interpretation and Translation, A
Veterinary/Animal Health Technology/Technician and
    Veterinary Assistant, A
Welding Technology/Welder, A
Wildlife and Wildlands Science and Management, A

HERITAGE COLLEGE

Allied Health and Medical Assisting Services, A
Massage Therapy/Therapeutic Massage, A
Rehabilitation and Therapeutic Professions, A

IBMC COLLEGE (COLORADO SPRINGS)

Clinical/Medical Laboratory Technician, A
Massage Therapy/Therapeutic Massage, A
Medical Administrative Assistant/Secretary, A
Medical/Clinical Assistant, A

IBMC COLLEGE (FORT COLLINS)

Accounting Technology/Technician and Bookkeep-
    ing, A
Aesthetician/Esthetician and Skin Care Specialist, A
Business Administration and Management, A

Cosmetology, Barber/Styling, and Nail Instructor, A
Dental Assisting/Assistant, A
General Office Occupations and Clerical Services, A
Hair Styling/Stylist and Hair Design, A
Legal Administrative Assistant/Secretary, A
Legal Assistant/Paralegal, A
Massage Therapy/Therapeutic Massage, A
Medical Administrative Assistant/Secretary, A
Medical/Clinical Assistant, A
Nail Technician/Specialist and Manicurist, A

INTELLITEC COLLEGE (COLORADO SPRINGS)

Architectural Drafting and Architectural
    CAD/CADD, A
Automobile/Automotive Mechanics
    Technology/Technician, A
Computer Systems Networking and Telecommunications, A
Heating, Air Conditioning and Refrigeration
    Technology/Technician, A
Mechanical Drafting and Mechanical Drafting
    CAD/CADD, A

INTELLITEC COLLEGE (GRAND JUNCTION)

Accounting and Business/Management, A
Automotive Engineering Technology/Technician, A
Clinical/Medical Laboratory Assistant, A
Environmental Engineering
    Technology/Environmental Technology, A

JOHNSON & WALES UNIVERSITY

Baking and Pastry Arts/Baker/Pastry Chef, B
Business Administration and Management, B
Criminal Justice/Law Enforcement Administration, B
Culinary Arts and Related Services, AB
Culinary Arts/Chef Training, AB
Entrepreneurship/Entrepreneurial Studies, B
Fashion Merchandising, B
Food Service, Waiter/Waitress, and Dining Room
    Management/Manager, B
Hospitality Administration/Management, B
Hotel/Motel Administration/Management, B
International Business/Trade/Commerce, B
Marketing/Marketing Management, B
Nutritional Sciences, B
Parks, Recreation and Leisure Facilities Management, B
Restaurant/Food Services Management, B
Sport and Fitness Administration/Management, B

LAMAR COMMUNITY COLLEGE

Accounting, A
Agricultural Business and Management, A
Agriculture, A
Agronomy and Crop Science, A
Animal Sciences, A
Animal Training, A
Biological and Physical Sciences, A
Biology/Biological Sciences, A
Business Administration and Management, A
Computer Programming/Programmer, A
Computer Science, A
Computer Typography and Composition Equipment
    Operator, A
Construction Trades, A
Cosmetology/Cosmetologist, A
Criminal Justice/Safety Studies, A
Data Processing and Data Processing
    Technology/Technician, A
Emergency Medical Technology/Technician (EMT
    Paramedic), A
Entrepreneurship/Entrepreneurial Studies, A
Equestrian/Equine Studies, A
Farm/Farm and Ranch Management, A
History, A
Information Science/Studies, A
Liberal Arts and Sciences Studies and Humanities, A
Management Information Systems and Services, A
Marketing/Marketing Management, A

Medical Office Computer Specialist/Assistant, A

LINCOLN COLLEGE OF TECHNOLOGY

Automobile/Automotive Mechanics
    Technology/Technician, A
Diesel Mechanics Technology/Technician, A

METROPOLITAN STATE UNIVERSITY OF DENVER

Accounting, BM
Aeronautics/Aviation/Aerospace Science and Technology, B
African-American/Black Studies, B
Anthropology, B
Art/Art Studies, General, B
Aviation/Airway Management and Operations, B
Behavioral Sciences, B
Biology/Biological Sciences, B
Business Administration and Management, B
Chemistry, B
Civil Engineering Technology/Technician, B
Computer Science, B
Computer and Information Sciences, B
Criminal Justice/Safety Studies, B
Drama and Dramatics/Theatre Arts, B
Economics, B
Education, M
Electrical, Electronic and Communications Engineering Technology/Technician, B
Elementary Education and Teaching, M
English Language and Literature, B
Environmental Sciences, B
Finance, B
Health/Health Care Administration/Management, B
Hispanic-American, Puerto Rican, and Mexican-American/Chicano Studies, B
History, B
Hospitality Administration/Management, B
Human Nutrition, B
Human Services, B
Industrial Design, B
Journalism, B
Land Use Planning and
    Management/Development, B
Marketing/Marketing Management, B
Mathematics, B
Mechanical Engineering/Mechanical
    Technology/Technician, B
Meteorology, B
Modern Languages, B
Music, B
Music Teacher Education, B
Parks, Recreation, Leisure and Fitness Studies, B
Philosophy, B
Physics, B
Political Science and Government, B
Psychology, B
Public Relations, Advertising, and Applied Communication, B
Social Work, BM
Sociology, B
Special Education and Teaching, BM
Survey Technology/Surveying, B

MORGAN COMMUNITY COLLEGE

Agribusiness, B
Agricultural Business Technology, B
Agricultural/Farm Supplies Retailing and Wholesaling, B
Airline/Commercial/Professional Pilot and Flight
    Crew, AB
Animation, Interactive Technology, Video Graphics
    and Special Effects, AB
Autobody/Collision and Repair
    Technology/Technician, AB
Automobile/Automotive Mechanics
    Technology/Technician, AB
Business Administration and Management, AB
Child Care Provider/Assistant, AB
Emergency Medical Technology/Technician (EMT
    Paramedic), B
Farm/Farm and Ranch Management, B
General Studies, A
Health Aide, B
Liberal Arts and Sciences Studies and Humanities, A

Manufacturing Technology/Technician, AB
Massage Therapy/Therapeutic Massage, B
Medical Office Assistant/Specialist, B
Medical/Clinical Assistant, AB
Phlebotomy/Phlebotomist, B
Physical Therapist Assistant, A
Science Technologies/Technicians, A
Welding Technology/Welder, AB

NAROPA UNIVERSITY

Art Therapy/Therapist, BM
Asian Languages, M
Counseling Psychology, M
Counselor Education/School Counseling and Guidance Services, M
Dance Therapy/Therapist, M
Drama and Dramatics/Theatre Arts, B
Early Childhood Education and Teaching, B
Education, M
English Language and Literature, B
Environmental Policy and Resource Management, M
Environmental Studies, B
Fine/Studio Arts, B
Health and Physical Education/Fitness, B
Multi-/Interdisciplinary Studies, B
Music, B
Music Performance, B
Peace Studies and Conflict Resolution, B
Psychoanalysis and Psychotherapy, M
Psychology, B
Religion/Religious Studies, BM
Social Psychology, M
Theater, B
Theology and Religious Vocations, M
Therapeutic Recreation, M
Transpersonal and Humanistic Psychology, M
Visual and Performing Arts, B
Writing, M

NATIONAL AMERICAN UNIVERSITY (COLORADO SPRINGS)

Accounting, AB
Allied Health and Medical Assisting Services, A
Business Administration and Management, AB
Computer and Information Sciences, A
Health/Health Care Administration/Management, B
Information Technology, B
Liberal Arts and Sciences Studies and Humanities, A
System Administration/Administrator, B

NATIONAL AMERICAN UNIVERSITY (DENVER)

Accounting, AB
Business Administration and Management, AB
Computer Programming, AB
Computer Programming, Specific Applications, AB
Computer Programming/Programmer, AB
Computer Systems Networking and Telecommunications, AB
Computer and Information Sciences, AB
Computer/Information Technology Services Administration and Management, AB
Data Entry/Microcomputer Applications, AB
Health Services/Allied Health/Health Sciences, A
Health/Health Care Administration/Management, AB
Information Science/Studies, AB
Information Technology, AB
Management Information Systems and Services, B
Medical/Clinical Assistant, A
Medical/Health Management and Clinical
    Assistant/Specialist, A
System Administration/Administrator, AB
System, Networking, and LAN/WAN
    Management/Manager, AB
Web Page, Digital/Multimedia and Information Resources Design, AB

NAZARENE BIBLE COLLEGE

Bible/Biblical Studies, B
Divinity/Ministry (BD, MDiv.), B
Early Childhood Education and Teaching, A
Education, B
Pastoral Counseling and Specialized Ministries, B

Pre-Theology/Pre-Ministerial Studies, A
Religious Education, AB
Religious/Sacred Music, AB

NORTHEASTERN JUNIOR COLLEGE

Accounting, A
Agricultural Business and Management, A
Agricultural Teacher Education, A
Agriculture, A
Agronomy and Crop Science, A
Animal Sciences, A
Anthropology, A
Art History, Criticism and Conservation, A
Art/Art Studies, General, A
Automobile/Automotive Mechanics
    Technology/Technician, A
Biology/Biological Sciences, A
Business Administration and Management, A
Chemistry, A
Child Development, A
Cosmetology/Cosmetologist, A
Criminal Justice/Police Science, A
Drama and Dramatics/Theatre Arts, A
Economics, A
Elementary Education and Teaching, A
Emergency Medical Technology/Technician (EMT
    Paramedic), A
English Language and Literature, A
Equestrian/Equine Studies, A
Farm/Farm and Ranch Management, A
Fine/Studio Arts, A
Geography, A
Geology/Earth Science, A
History, A
Journalism, A
Liberal Arts and Sciences Studies and Humani-
    ties, A
Marketing/Marketing Management, A
Mathematics, A
Music, A
Natural Sciences, A
Philosophy, A
Physical Education Teaching and Coaching, A
Physical Sciences, A
Political Science and Government, A
Psychology, A
Social Sciences, A
Sociology, A

OTERO JUNIOR COLLEGE

Administrative Assistant and Secretarial Science, A
Agricultural Business and Management, A
Automobile/Automotive Mechanics
    Technology/Technician, A
Biological and Physical Sciences, A
Biology/Biological Sciences, A
Business Administration and Management, A
Child Development, A
Comparative Literature, A
Data Processing and Data Processing
    Technology/Technician, A
Drama and Dramatics/Theatre Arts, A
Elementary Education and Teaching, A
History, A
Humanities/Humanistic Studies, A
Kindergarten/PreSchool Education and Teaching, A
Legal Administrative Assistant/Secretary, A
Liberal Arts and Sciences Studies and Humani-
    ties, A
Mathematics, A
Medical Administrative Assistant/Secretary, A
Modern Languages, A
Political Science and Government, A
Psychology, A
Social Sciences, A

PIKES PEAK COMMUNITY COLLEGE

Accounting Technology/Technician and Bookkeep-
    ing, A
Animation, Interactive Technology, Video Graphics
    and Special Effects, A
Architectural Engineering Technology/Technician, A
Autobody/Collision and Repair
    Technology/Technician, A
Automobile/Automotive Mechanics
    Technology/Technician, A

Building/Construction Finishing, Manage-
    ment, and Inspection, A
Business Administration and Management, A
CAD/CADD Drafting and/or Design
    Technology/Technician, A
Child Development, A
Cooking and Related Culinary Arts, A
Criminal Justice/Law Enforcement Administration, A
Dental Assisting/Assistant, A
Educational/Instructional Media Design, A
Electrical, Electronic and Communications Engineer-
    ing Technology/Technician, A
Emergency Medical Technology/Technician (EMT
    Paramedic), A
Fire Protection and Safety Technology/Technician, A
General Studies, A
Interior Design, A
Legal Assistant/Paralegal, A
Liberal Arts and Sciences Studies and Humani-
    ties, A
Management Information Systems and Services, A
Medical Office Management/Administration, A
Natural Resources Management/Development and
    Policy, A
Psychiatric/Mental Health Services Technician, A
Radio and Television Broadcasting
    Technology/Technician, A
Security and Protective Services, A
Sign Language Interpretation and Translation, A
Welding Technology/Welder, A

PIMA MEDICAL INSTITUTE (COLO-RADO SPRINGS)

Health/Health Care Administration/Management, A
Veterinary/Animal Health Technology/Technician and
    Veterinary Assistant, A

PIMA MEDICAL INSTITUTE (DENVER)

Health/Health Care Administration/Management, A
Occupational Therapist Assistant, A
Ophthalmic Technician/Technologist, A
Physical Therapist Assistant, A
Radiologic Technology/Science - Radiographer, A
Respiratory Therapy Technician/Assistant, A

PLATT COLLEGE

Design and Visual Communications, AB

PUEBLO COMMUNITY COLLEGE

Accounting Technology/Technician and Bookkeep-
    ing, A
Animation, Interactive Technology, Video Graphics
    and Special Effects, A
Autobody/Collision and Repair
    Technology/Technician, A
Automobile/Automotive Mechanics
    Technology/Technician, A
Business Administration and Management, A
Business/Office Automation/Technology/Data En-
    try, A
Communications Technology/Technician, A
Computer and Information Sciences, A
Cooking and Related Culinary Arts, A
Cosmetology/Cosmetologist, A
Criminal Justice/Law Enforcement Administration, A
Dental Assisting/Assistant, A
Dental Hygiene/Hygienist, A
Early Childhood Education and Teaching, A
Electrical, Electronic and Communications Engineer-
    ing Technology/Technician, A
Electromechanical and Instrumentation and Mainte-
    nance Technologies/Technicians, A
Emergency Medical Technology/Technician (EMT
    Paramedic), A
Engineering Technology, A
Fire Science/Firefighting, A
General Studies, A
Liberal Arts and Sciences Studies and Humani-
    ties, A
Library Assistant/Technician, A
Machine Shop Technology/Assistant, A
Manufacturing Technology/Technician, A
Medical Office Management/Administration, A
Occupational Therapist Assistant, A
Physical Therapist Assistant, A

Psychiatric/Mental Health Services Technician, A
Radiologic Technology/Science - Radiographer, A
Respiratory Care Therapy/Therapist, A
Science Technologies/Technicians, A
Surgical Technology/Technologist, A
Web Page, Digital/Multimedia and Information Re-
    sources Design, A
Welding Technology/Welder, A

RED ROCKS COMMUNITY COLLEGE

Accounting Technology/Technician and Bookkeep-
    ing, A
Animation, Interactive Technology, Video Graphics
    and Special Effects, A
Autobody/Collision and Repair
    Technology/Technician, A
Automobile/Automotive Mechanics
    Technology/Technician, A
Business Administration and Management, A
Business Administration, Management and Opera-
    tions, A
Cinematography and Film/Video Production, A
Computer Programming/Programmer, A
Computer Systems Networking and Telecommunica-
    tions, A
Construction Trades, A
Cosmetology/Cosmetologist, A
Criminal Justice/Police Science, A
Culinary Arts/Chef Training, A
Data Modeling/Warehousing and Database Adminis-
    tration, A
Diagnostic Medical Sonography/Sonographer and
    Ultrasound Technician, A
Digital Communication and Media/Multimedia, A
Drafting and Design Technology/Technician, A
Early Childhood Education and Teaching, A
Educational/Instructional Media Design, A
Electrician, A
Electromechanical and Instrumentation and Mainte-
    nance Technologies/Technicians, A
Emergency Medical Technology/Technician (EMT
    Paramedic), A
Energy Management and Systems
    Technology/Technician, A
Fire Science/Firefighting, A
General Studies, A
Industrial Technology/Technician, A
Interior Design, A
Liberal Arts and Sciences Studies and Humani-
    ties, A
Machine Shop Technology/Assistant, A
Management Information Systems and Services, A
Manufacturing Technology/Technician, A
Medical Office Management/Administration, A
Motorcycle Maintenance and Repair
    Technology/Technician, A
Parks, Recreation, Leisure and Fitness Studies, A
Parts and Warehousing Operations and Mainte-
    nance Technology/Technician, A
Photography, A
Radiologic Technology/Science - Radiographer, A
Real Estate, A
Science Technologies/Technicians, A
Security and Protective Services, A
Technical Theatre/Theatre Design and Technol-
    ogy, A
Water Quality and Wastewater Treatment Manage-
    ment and Recycling Technology/Technician, A
Web Page, Digital/Multimedia and Information Re-
    sources Design, A
Web/Multimedia Management and Webmaster, A
Welding Technology/Welder, A
Woodworking, A

REDSTONE COLLEGE–DENVER

Avionics Maintenance Technology/Technician, A
Construction Management, A

REGIS UNIVERSITY

Accounting, BM
Adult and Continuing Education and Teaching, MO
Allied Health and Medical Assisting Services, MDO
Art History, Criticism and Conservation, B
Art/Art Studies, General, B
Biochemistry, B
Biological and Biomedical Sciences, M

Biology/Biological Sciences, B
Business Administration and Management, B
Business Administration, Management and Operations, M
Chemistry, B
Communication Studies/Speech Communication and Rhetoric, B
Computer Science, BMO
Computer and Information Sciences, B
Computer and Information Systems Security, M
Counseling Psychology, MO
Criminology, BM
Curriculum and Instruction, M
Database Systems, MO
Economics, B
Education, BMO
Education/Teaching of the Gifted and Talented, O
Educational Leadership and Administration, MO
Educational Media/Instructional Technology, O
Elementary Education and Teaching, B
English Language and Literature, B
Environmental Sciences, B
Environmental Studies, B
Finance, B
Finance and Banking, M
French Language and Literature, B
Health Informatics, MO
Health Information/Medical Records Administration/Administrator, B
Health Services Administration, MO
Health/Health Care Administration/Management, B
History, B
Human Resources Management and Services, O
Human Resources Management/Personnel Administration, B
Information Science/Studies, MO
Kinesiology and Exercise Science, B
Liberal Arts and Sciences Studies and Humanities, B
Liberal Studies, M
Management Information Systems and Services, O
Management Strategy and Policy, M
Marketing, M
Marketing/Marketing Management, B
Marriage and Family Therapy/Counseling, MO
Mathematics, B
Multi-/Interdisciplinary Studies, B
Multilingual and Multicultural Education, M
Music, B
Non-Profit/Public/Organizational Management, MO
Nursing, MD
Nursing - Advanced Practice, M
Nursing Administration, MD
Nursing Education, M
Organizational Management, MO
Peace Studies and Conflict Resolution, B
Pharmacy, D
Philosophy, B
Physical Therapy/Therapist, D
Physics, B
Political Science and Government, B
Project Management, O
Psychology, B
Public Administration, B
Reading Teacher Education, MO
Religion/Religious Studies, B
Social Sciences, B
Sociology, B
Software Engineering, MO
Spanish Language and Literature, B
Special Education and Teaching, O
System Administration/Administrator, B
Systems Engineering, M
Women's Studies, B

ROCKY MOUNTAIN COLLEGE OF ART + DESIGN

Animation, Interactive Technology, Video Graphics and Special Effects, B
Art Education, M
Art Teacher Education, B
Arts Management, M
Commercial Photography, B
Computer Graphics, B
Fashion/Apparel Design, B
Fine/Studio Arts, B

Graphic Design, B
Illustration, B
Interior Design, B
Internet and Interactive Multimedia, M

TRINIDAD STATE JUNIOR COLLEGE

Agricultural Business and Management, A
Aquaculture, A
Automobile/Automotive Mechanics Technology/Technician, A
Biological and Physical Sciences, A
Biology/Biological Sciences, A
Business Administration and Management, A
Business/Office Automation/Technology/Data Entry, A
Chemistry, A
Construction Trades, A
Construction/Heavy Equipment/Earthmoving Equipment Operation, A
Criminal Justice/Law Enforcement Administration, A
Diesel Mechanics Technology/Technician, A
Drama and Dramatics/Theatre Arts, A
Early Childhood Education and Teaching, A
Education, A
Emergency Medical Technology/Technician (EMT Paramedic), A
English Language and Literature, A
Environmental Engineering Technology/Environmental Technology, A
Fire Science/Firefighting, A
General Studies, A
Gunsmithing/Gunsmith, A
Heavy Equipment Maintenance Technology/Technician, A
Liberal Arts and Sciences Studies and Humanities, A
Lineworker, A
Manufacturing Technology/Technician, A
Massage Therapy/Therapeutic Massage, A
Medical Office Assistant/Specialist, A
Natural Resources Management/Development and Policy, A
Occupational Safety and Health Technology/Technician, A
Physical Education Teaching and Coaching, A
Psychology, A
Science Technologies/Technicians, A
Welding Technology/Welder, A

UNITED STATES AIR FORCE ACADEMY

Aerospace, Aeronautical and Astronautical Engineering, B
Atmospheric Sciences and Meteorology, B
Behavioral Sciences, B
Biochemistry, B
Biological and Physical Sciences, B
Biology/Biological Sciences, B
Business Administration and Management, B
Chemistry, B
Civil Engineering, B
Computer Science, B
Economics, B
Electrical, Electronics and Communications Engineering, B
Engineering, B
Engineering Mechanics, B
Engineering Science, B
English Language and Literature, B
Environmental/Environmental Health Engineering, B
Geography, B
History, B
Humanities/Humanistic Studies, B
International/Global Studies, B
Law and Legal Studies, B
Mathematics, B
Mechanical Engineering, B
Operations Research, B
Philosophy, B
Physics, B
Political Science and Government, B

Social Sciences, B

UNIVERSITY OF COLORADO BOULDER

Accounting, BMD
Aerospace, Aeronautical and Astronautical Engineering, BMD
Animal Behavior and Ethology, M
Anthropology, BMD
Applied Mathematics, BMD
Architectural Engineering, BMD
Art History, Criticism and Conservation, BM
Asian Studies/Civilization, B
Astronomy, B
Astrophysics, MD
Atmospheric Sciences and Meteorology, MD
Biochemistry, BMD
Business Administration and Management, B
Business Administration, Management and Operations, M
Cell Biology and Anatomy, MD
Cell/Cellular and Molecular Biology, B
Ceramic Arts and Ceramics, M
Chemical Engineering, BMD
Chemical Physics, D
Chemistry, BMD
Chinese Language and Literature, B
Chinese Studies, MD
Civil Engineering, BMD
Classics and Classical Languages, Literatures, and Linguistics, BMD
Communication Disorders, BMD
Communication Studies/Speech Communication and Rhetoric, B
Communication and Media Studies, BMD
Comparative Literature, MD
Composition, MD
Computer Engineering, BMD
Computer Science, BMD
Construction Engineering and Management, MD
Curriculum and Instruction, MD
Dance, BMD
Developmental Biology and Embryology, MD
Drama and Dramatics/Theatre Arts, B
East Asian Studies, MD
Ecology, MD
Ecology, Evolution, Systematics and Population Biology, B
Economics, BMD
Education, MD
Educational Measurement and Evaluation, D
Educational Policy, MD
Educational Psychology, MD
Electrical Engineering, MD
Electrical, Electronics and Communications Engineering, B
Engineering, B
Engineering Management, M
Engineering Physics, B
Engineering and Applied Sciences, MD
English, MD
English Language and Literature, B
Entrepreneurship/Entrepreneurial Studies, D
Environmental Design/Architecture, B
Environmental Engineering Technology/Environmental Technology, MD
Environmental Studies, BMD
Environmental/Environmental Health Engineering, B
Ethnic and Cultural Studies, BD
Evolutionary Biology, MD
Film/Cinema Studies, B
Finance, B
Finance and Banking, D
Fine Arts and Art Studies, M
Fine/Studio Arts, B
French Language and Literature, BMD
Genetics, D
Geography, BMD
Geology/Earth Science, BMD
Geophysics and Seismology, D
Geotechnical Engineering, MD
German Language and Literature, M
Germanic Languages, Literatures, and Linguistics, B
Hispanic and Latin American Languages, D
History, BMD
Humanities/Humanistic Studies, B

Hydrology and Water Resources Science, MD
Information Science/Studies, B
International Affairs, M
International/Global Studies, B
Italian Language and Literature, B
Japanese Language and Literature, B
Japanese Studies, MD
Jewish/Judaic Studies, B
Journalism, BMD
Kinesiology and Movement Studies, MD
Law and Legal Studies, D
Linguistics, BMD
Management Information Systems and Services, BD
Marine Biology and Biological Oceanography, MD
Marketing, D
Marketing/Marketing Management, B
Mass Communication/Media Studies, BMD
Mathematical Physics, D
Mathematics, BMD
Mechanical Engineering, BMD
Media Studies, MD
Medical Physics, D
Microbiology, MD
Molecular Biology, MD
Multi-/Interdisciplinary Studies, B
Multilingual and Multicultural Education, MD
Museology/Museum Studies, M
Music, BMD
Music Performance, B
Music Teacher Education, BMD
Music Theory and Composition, M
Musicology and Ethnomusicology, D
Neurobiology and Neurophysiology, M
Oceanography, Chemical and Physical, MD
Operations Research, M
Optics/Optical Sciences, D
Organizational Management, D
Painting, M
Performance, MD
Philosophy, BMD
Photography, M
Physics, BMD
Physiology, BMD
Plasma and High-Temperature Physics, MD
Political Science and Government, BMD
Printmaking, M
Psychology, BMD
Public Policy Analysis, M
Religion/Religious Studies, BM
Russian Studies, B
Sculpture, M
Sociology, BD
Spanish Language and Literature, BMD
Structural Engineering, MD
Telecommunications, M
Telecommunications Management, M
Theater, MD
Water Resources Engineering, MD
Women's Studies, B
Writing, M

UNIVERSITY OF COLORADO COLORADO SPRINGS

Aerospace, Aeronautical and Astronautical Engineering, M
Anthropology, B
Applied Mathematics, M
Biochemistry, B
Biology/Biological Sciences, B
Business Administration and Management, B
Business Administration, Management and Operations, M
Chemistry, B
Communication and Media Studies, M
Computer Engineering, B
Computer Science, BM
Computer and Information Systems Security, BM
Counselor Education/School Counseling and Guidance Services, M
Criminal Justice/Law Enforcement Administration, B
Criminology, M
Curriculum and Instruction, M
Early Childhood Education and Teaching, B
Economics, B
Education, MD
Educational Leadership and Administration, MD

Electrical Engineering, M
Electrical, Electronics and Communications Engineering, B
Energy and Power Engineering, M
Engineering, B
Engineering Management, MD
Engineering and Applied Sciences, MD
English Language and Literature, B
Environmental Sciences, M
Ethnic, Cultural Minority, and Gender Studies, B
Exercise Physiology, B
Geography, BM
Gerontological Nursing, M
Health Services/Allied Health/Health Sciences, B
History, BM
Human Services, M
Interdisciplinary Studies, M
Mathematics, B
Mechanical Engineering, BM
Nursing, MD
Nursing - Adult, M
Nursing Education, M
Philosophy, B
Physics, B
Political Science and Government, B
Psychology, BMD
Public Administration, M
Public Affairs, M
Sociology, BM
Software Engineering, M
Spanish Language and Literature, B
Special Education and Teaching, M
Systems Engineering, M
Visual and Performing Arts, B

UNIVERSITY OF COLORADO DENVER

Accounting, M
Adult and Continuing Education and Teaching, M
Allopathic Medicine, D
American/United States Studies/Civilization, M
Anatomy, M
Anesthesiologist Assistant, M
Animal Behavior and Ethology, M
Anthropology, BM
Applied Mathematics, MD
Applied Science and Technology, M
Applied Statistics, M
Archeology, M
Architectural History and Criticism, D
Architecture, BM
Biochemistry, D
Bioengineering, MD
Bioinformatics, D
Biological and Biomedical Sciences, MD
Biology/Biological Sciences, B
Biomedical Sciences, B
Biomedical/Medical Engineering, B
Biophysics, MD
Biostatistics, MD
Business Administration and Management, B
Business Administration, Management and Operations, M
Cancer Biology/Oncology, D
Cell Biology and Anatomy, MD
Chemistry, BM
Civil Engineering, BMD
Clinical Laboratory Sciences, MD
Clinical Psychology, MD
Clinical Research, D
Communication Studies/Speech Communication and Rhetoric, B
Communication and Media Studies, M
Community Health and Preventive Medicine, MD
Computational Biology, MD
Computational Sciences, D
Computer Science, MD
Computer and Information Sciences, B
Corporate and Organizational Communication, M
Counseling Psychology, M
Counselor Education/School Counseling and Guidance Services, M
Criminal Justice/Law Enforcement Administration, B
Criminology, M
Dentistry, MD
Developmental Biology and Embryology, MD
Distance Education Development, M

Drama and Dramatics/Theatre Arts, B
Early Childhood Education and Teaching, MD
Ecology, M
Economic Development, M
Economics, BM
Education, BMDO
Educational Administration and Supervision, MO
Educational Leadership and Administration, D
Educational Measurement and Evaluation, MD
Educational Media/Instructional Technology, M
Educational Policy, D
Educational Psychology, MO
Electrical Engineering, D
Electrical, Electronics and Communications Engineering, B
Elementary Education and Teaching, M
Emergency Management, M
Energy Management and Policy, M
Engineering and Applied Sciences, MD
English, M
English Education, M
English Language and Literature, B
Entertainment Management, M
Entrepreneurship/Entrepreneurial Studies, M
Environmental Education, M
Environmental Engineering Technology/Environmental Technology, MD
Environmental Law, M
Environmental Policy and Resource Management, M
Environmental Sciences, M
Environmental Studies, M
Environmental and Occupational Health, M
Epidemiology, MD
Ethnic and Cultural Studies, B
Evolutionary Biology, M
Finance and Banking, M
Fine Arts and Art Studies, M
Fine/Studio Arts, B
Forensic Science and Technology, M
French Language and Literature, B
Gender Studies, M
Genetic Counseling/Counselor, MD
Genetics, MD
Geographic Information Systems, M
Geography, B
Geotechnical Engineering, MD
Hazardous Materials Management and Waste Technology/Technician, M
Health Education, MD
Health Psychology, D
Health Services Administration, M
Health Services Research, D
Historic Preservation and Conservation, M
History, BM
Homeland Security, M
Human Development, M
Human Resources Management and Services, M
Humanities/Humanistic Studies, M
Hydraulics and Fluid Power Technology, MD
Hydrology and Water Resources Science, MD
Immunology, D
Information Science/Studies, D
Insurance, M
International Affairs, M
International Business/Trade/Commerce, M
International Public Health/International Health, M
International/Global Studies, B
Investment Management, M
Landscape Architecture, M
Linguistics, M
Management, M
Management Information Systems and Services, MD
Management Strategy and Policy, M
Management of Technology, M
Marketing, M
Marketing Research, M
Marriage and Family Therapy/Counseling, M
Mathematics, BMD
Mathematics Teacher Education, MD
Mechanical Engineering, BM
Mechanics, M
Medical Informatics, M
Microbiology, MD
Military and Defense Studies, M

Molecular Biology, MD
Molecular Genetics, D
Multi-/Interdisciplinary Studies, B
Multilingual and Multicultural Education, M
Music, BM
Neurobiology and Neurophysiology, M
Neuroscience, D
Non-Profit/Public/Organizational Management, M
Nurse Midwife/Nursing Midwifery, M
Nursing, MD
Nursing - Adult, M
Nursing - Advanced Practice, M
Nursing Administration, M
Operations Research, MD
Orthodontics, M
Pediatric Nurse/Nursing, M
Periodontics, M
Pharmaceutical Sciences, D
Pharmacology, D
Philosophy, B
Physical Therapy/Therapist, D
Physician Assistant, M
Physics, B
Physiology, D
Political Science and Government, BM
Psychiatric/Mental Health Nurse/Nursing, M
Psychology, B
Public Administration, MD
Public Affairs, MD
Public Health, MD
Public Health (MPH, DPH), B
Public History, M
Quantitative Analysis, M
Reading Teacher Education, M
Rehabilitation Sciences, D
Rhetoric, M
School Psychology, MO
Science Teacher Education/General Science
    Teacher Education, MD
Secondary Education and Teaching, M
Sociology, BM
Spanish Language and Literature, BM
Special Education and Teaching, M
Sport and Fitness Administration/Management, M
Statistics, MD
Structural Engineering, MD
Sustainability Management, M
Sustainable Development, MD
Taxation, M
Toxicology, D
Transportation and Highway Engineering, MD
Urban Design, MD
Urban and Regional Planning, MD
Water Resources, M
Western European Studies, M
Women's Health Nursing, M
Women's Studies, M
Writing, M

UNIVERSITY OF DENVER

Accounting, BM
Advertising and Public Relations, M
Animal Sciences, B
Anthropology, BM
Applied Physics, MD
Archeology, M
Art History, Criticism and Conservation, BM
Art Teacher Education, B
Art/Art Studies, General, B
Asian-American Studies, B
Astronomy, MD
Biochemistry, B
Bioengineering, M
Bioinformatics, B
Biological and Biomedical Sciences, MD
Biological and Physical Sciences, B
Biology/Biological Sciences, B
Business Administration and Management, B
Business Administration, Management and Opera-
    tions, M
Business Statistics, B
Business/Commerce, B
Business/Managerial Economics, B
Cell Biology and Anatomy, M
Chemistry, BMD
Child and Family Studies, M

Clinical Psychology, MD
Cognitive Sciences, D
Communication Studies/Speech Communication
    and Rhetoric, B
Computer Art and Design, M
Computer Engineering, BMD
Computer Science, BMD
Computer Software and Media Applications, B
Computer Systems Analysis/Analyst, B
Computer and Information Systems Security, M
Conflict Resolution and Mediation/Peace Studies, M
Construction Management, M
Corporate and Organizational Communication, M
Counseling Psychology, D
Criminology, B
Cultural Anthropology, M
Cultural Studies, MO
Curriculum and Instruction, MDO
Developmental Psychology, D
Digital Communication and Media/Multimedia, B
Drama and Dramatics/Theatre Arts, B
Ecology, BD
Economics, BM
Education, MDO
Educational Leadership and Administration, MD
Educational Policy, MD
Electrical Engineering, MD
Electrical, Electronics and Communications Engi-
    neering, M
Emergency Management, MO
Engineering, B
Engineering Management, M
Engineering and Applied Sciences, MD
English, MD
English Language and Literature, B
Environmental Policy and Resource Manage-
    ment, MO
Environmental Sciences, B
Ethnic, Cultural Minority, and Gender Studies, B
Evolutionary Biology, D
Film, Television, and Video Production, M
Film/Cinema Studies, B
Finance, B
Finance and Banking, M
Fine Arts and Art Studies, M
Forensic Psychology, M
French Language and Literature, B
Geographic Information Systems, MO
Geography, BMD
German Language and Literature, B
Graphic Design, B
History, BO
Hospitality Administration/Management, B
Hotel/Motel Administration/Management, B
Information Technology, B
International Affairs, MDO
International Business/Trade/Commerce, BM
International Relations and Affairs, B
Internet Engineering, M
Internet and Interactive Multimedia, M
Italian Language and Literature, B
Journalism, B
Latin American Studies, B
Law and Legal Studies, BMDO
Legal and Justice Studies, MO
Library Science, M
Management Information Systems and Ser-
    vices, BM
Management Strategy and Policy, M
Management of Technology, M
Marketing, M
Marketing/Marketing Management, B
Mass Communication/Media Studies, BM
Materials Engineering, MD
Materials Sciences, M
Mathematics, BMD
Mechanical Engineering, BMD
Molecular Biology, BM
Multi-/Interdisciplinary Studies, B
Museology/Museum Studies, M
Music, BMO
Music Performance, B
Music Theory and Composition, B
Musicology and Ethnomusicology, B
Organizational Management, MO
Philosophy, B

Physics, BMD
Political Science and Government, B
Project Management, MO
Psychology, BMD
Public Policy Analysis, BM
Real Estate, BM
Religion/Religious Studies, BMD
Russian Language and Literature, B
School Psychology, O
Securities Services Administration/Management, MO
Social Psychology, D
Social Sciences, B
Social Work, MDO
Sociology, B
Software Engineering, M
Spanish Language and Literature, B
Speech and Interpersonal Communication, MD
Sport Psychology, M
Statistics, M
Taxation, M
Telecommunications, M
Theology and Religious Vocations, D
Translation and Interpretation, O
Writing, D

UNIVERSITY OF NORTHERN COLO-RADO

Accounting, M
African-American/Black Studies, B
Anthropology, B
Applied Statistics, MD
Asian Studies/Civilization, B
Athletic Training and Sports Medicine, B
Audiology/Audiologist and Speech-Language
    Pathology/Pathologist, B
Biological and Biomedical Sciences, M
Biology/Biological Sciences, B
Business Administration and Management, B
Chemistry, BMD
Communication Disorders, MD
Communication Studies/Speech Communication
    and Rhetoric, B
Communication Theory, M
Composition, MD
Computer Software Engineering, B
Counselor Education/School Counseling and Guid-
    ance Services, MD
Criminal Justice/Safety Studies, B
Criminology, M
Dietetics/Dieticians, B
Drama and Dramatics/Theatre Arts, B
Dramatic/Theatre Arts and Stagecraft, B
Early Childhood Education and Teaching, BM
Economics, B
Education, MDO
Education/Teaching of the Gifted and Talented, M
Educational Leadership and Administration, MDO
Educational Measurement and Evaluation, MD
Educational Media/Instructional Technology, MD
Educational Psychology, MD
Elementary Education and Teaching, B
English, M
English Language and Literature, B
Exercise and Sports Science, MD
Fine Arts and Art Studies, M
Fine/Studio Arts, B
Foreign Language Teacher Education, M
Foreign Languages and Literatures, B
Geography, B
Geology/Earth Science, B
Geosciences, B
Gerontology, M
Health Education, M
Health Services/Allied Health/Health Sciences, B
Higher Education/Higher Education Administra-
    tion, D
Hispanic-American, Puerto Rican, and Mexican-
    American/Chicano Studies, B
History, BM
International/Global Studies, B
Journalism, B
Kinesiology and Exercise Science, B
Library Science, M
Mathematics, BMD
Mathematics Teacher Education, MD
Multi-/Interdisciplinary Studies, B

Music, BMD
Music History, Literature, and Theory, MD
Music Teacher Education, BMD
Music Theory and Composition, MD
Nursing, MD
Nursing - Advanced Practice, M
Nursing Education, MD
Nutritional Sciences, B
Parks, Recreation and Leisure Facilities Management, B
Performance, MD
Philosophy, B
Physical Education Teaching and Coaching, MD
Physics, B
Political Science and Government, B
Psychology, BMD
Public Health, M
Reading Teacher Education, M
Rehabilitation Counseling, MD
School Psychology, DO
Science Teacher Education/General Science Teacher Education, MD
Sign Language Interpretation and Translation, B
Social Sciences, B
Social Studies Teacher Education, B
Sociology, BM
Spanish Language and Literature, BM
Special Education and Teaching, BMD
Sport and Fitness Administration/Management, MD
Student Personnel Services, D

UNIVERSITY OF PHOENIX–COLORADO CAMPUS

Accounting, BM
Business Administration and Management, B
Business Administration, Management and Operations, M
Business/Corporate Communications, B
Computer Software Engineering, B
Computer Software and Media Applications, B
Computer and Information Systems Security, B
Criminal Justice/Law Enforcement Administration, B
Curriculum and Instruction, M
Digital Communication and Media/Multimedia, B
E-Commerce/Electronic Commerce, B
Education, M
Educational Administration and Supervision, M
Electronic Commerce, M
Elementary Education and Teaching, M
Finance, B
Health Services Administration, M
Health/Health Care Administration/Management, B
Hospitality Administration/Management, B
Human Resources Management and Services, M
Human Services, B
Information Technology, B
International Business/Trade/Commerce, M
Management, M
Management Information Systems and Services, BM
Management Science, B
Management of Technology, M
Marketing, M
Marketing/Marketing Management, B
Nursing, M
Operations Management and Supervision, B
Psychology, B
Public Administration, M
Public Administration and Social Service Professions, B
School Psychology, M
Secondary Education and Teaching, M

UNIVERSITY OF PHOENIX–COLORADO SPRINGS DOWNTOWN CAMPUS

Accounting, BM
Business Administration and Management, B
Business Administration, Management and Operations, M
Business/Corporate Communications, B
Computer Software Engineering, B
Consumer Merchandising/Retailing Management, B
Corrections and Criminal Justice, B
Curriculum and Instruction, M
Education, MO
Educational Administration and Supervision, MO

Elementary Education and Teaching, M
Finance, B
Gerontology, M
Health Education, M
Health Services Administration, BM
Human Resources Management and Services, M
Human Services, B
Information Technology, B
International Business/Trade/Commerce, M
Management, M
Management Information Systems and Services, BM
Management Science, B
Management of Technology, M
Marketing, M
Marketing/Marketing Management, B
Nursing, M
Operations Management and Supervision, B
Psychology, B
Public Administration, BM
School Psychology, M
Secondary Education and Teaching, M
Security and Protective Services, B

WESTERN STATE COLORADO UNIVERSITY

Accounting, B
Accounting and Business/Management, B
Accounting and Finance, B
Anthropology, B
Art Teacher Education, B
Art/Art Studies, General, B
Biochemistry, B
Biological and Biomedical Sciences, B
Biology Teacher Education, B
Biology/Biological Sciences, B
Business Administration and Management, B
Business, Management, Marketing, and Related Support Services, B
Business/Managerial Economics, B
Cell Biology and Anatomy, B
Ceramic Arts and Ceramics, B
Chemistry, B
Chemistry Teacher Education, B
Computer Science, B
Computer Systems Networking and Telecommunications, B
Criminology, B
Drama and Dramatics/Theatre Arts, B
Economics, B
Education, M
Educational Administration and Supervision, M
Educational Leadership and Administration, M
English Language and Literature, B
English/Language Arts Teacher Education, B
Entrepreneurship/Entrepreneurial Studies, B
Environmental Biology, B
Environmental Policy and Resource Management, M
Environmental Studies, B
Film, Television, and Video Production, M
Fine/Studio Arts, B
Geological and Earth Sciences/Geosciences, B
Geology/Earth Science, B
Graphic Design, B
History, B
History Teacher Education, B
Kinesiology and Exercise Science, B
Management Information Systems and Services, B
Marketing/Marketing Management, B
Mathematics, B
Mathematics Teacher Education, B
Mathematics and Statistics, B
Metal and Jewelry Arts, B
Music, B
Music Teacher Education, B
Painting, B
Parks, Recreation and Leisure Facilities Management, B
Parks, Recreation, Leisure and Fitness Studies, B
Photography, B
Physical Education Teaching and Coaching, B
Physics, B
Political Science and Government, B
Pre-Law Studies, B
Printmaking, B

Psychology, B
Reading Teacher Education, M
Science Teacher Education/General Science Teacher Education, B
Sculpture, B
Social Science Teacher Education, B
Sociology, B
Spanish Language Teacher Education, B
Spanish Language and Literature, B
Sport and Fitness Administration/Management, B
Technical Theatre/Theatre Design and Technology, B
Visual and Performing Arts, B
Water, Wetlands, and Marine Resources Management, B
Writing, M

YESHIVA TORAS CHAIM TALMUDICAL SEMINARY

Talmudic Studies, B

Connecticut
ALBERTUS MAGNUS COLLEGE

Accounting, BM
Art History, Criticism and Conservation, B
Art Therapy/Therapist, BM
Art/Art Studies, General, B
Biology/Biological Sciences, B
Business Administration and Management, AB
Business Administration, Management and Operations, M
Chemistry, B
Child Development, B
Communication Studies/Speech Communication and Rhetoric, B
Criminal Justice/Law Enforcement Administration, B
Criminology, M
Curriculum and Instruction, B
Drama and Dramatics/Theatre Arts, B
Education, BM
English Language and Literature, B
Finance, B
Fine/Studio Arts, B
General Studies, B
Graphic Design, B
History, B
Human Resources Management and Services, B
Human Services, BM
Humanities/Humanistic Studies, B
Information Science/Studies, B
International Business/Trade/Commerce, B
International/Global Studies, B
Junior High/Intermediate/Middle School Education and Teaching, B
Liberal Studies, M
Management, M
Marketing/Marketing Management, B
Mathematics, B
Organizational Management, M
Philosophy, B
Photography, B
Political Science and Government, B
Pre-Dentistry Studies, B
Pre-Law Studies, B
Pre-Medicine/Pre-Medical Studies, B
Pre-Veterinary Studies, B
Psychology, B
Religion/Religious Studies, B
Secondary Education and Teaching, B
Social Sciences, B
Social Work, B
Sociology, B
Spanish Language and Literature, B
Sport and Fitness Administration/Management, B
Theatre Literature, History and Criticism, B
Urban Studies/Affairs, B
Writing, M

ASNUNTUCK COMMUNITY COLLEGE

Accounting Technology/Technician and Bookkeeping, A
Banking and Financial Support Services, A
Criminal Justice/Police Science, A
Engineering Science, A

Engineering Technology, A
General Studies, A
Liberal Arts and Sciences Studies and Humanities, A
Management Information Systems and Services, A
Psychiatric/Mental Health Services Technician, A

BAIS BINYOMIN ACADEMY

Talmudic Studies, B

CAPITAL COMMUNITY COLLEGE

Accounting Technology/Technician and Bookkeeping, A
Administrative Assistant and Secretarial Science, A
Architectural Engineering Technology/Technician, A
Banking and Financial Support Services, A
Business, Management, Marketing, and Related Support Services, A
Child Care and Support Services Management, A
Communication Studies/Speech Communication and Rhetoric, A
Computer and Information Sciences and Support Services, A
Criminal Justice/Police Science, A
Emergency Medical Technology/Technician (EMT Paramedic), A
Engineering Science, A
Engineering Technology, A
Engineering-Related Technologies, A
Financial Planning and Services, A
Fire Services Administration, A
General Studies, A
Liberal Arts and Sciences Studies and Humanities, A
Management Information Systems and Services, A
Medical Radiologic Technology/Science - Radiation Therapist, A
Medical/Clinical Assistant, A
Physical Therapist Assistant, A
Social Work, A

CENTRAL CONNECTICUT STATE UNIVERSITY

Accounting, B
Actuarial Science, M
Advertising and Public Relations, O
Anthropology, B
Art Education, MO
Art Teacher Education, B
Art/Art Studies, General, B
Athletic Training and Sports Medicine, B
Biochemistry, BO
Biological and Biomedical Sciences, MO
Biology/Biological Sciences, B
Chemistry, BO
Civil Engineering, B
Communication and Media Studies, MO
Community Psychology, M
Computer Engineering Technology/Technician, B
Computer Science, M
Computer and Information Sciences, B
Construction Management, BMO
Corporate and Organizational Communication, M
Counselor Education/School Counseling and Guidance Services, MO
Criminology, BM
Design and Visual Communications, B
Early Childhood Education and Teaching, M
Economics, B
Education, MDO
Educational Leadership and Administration, MDO
Educational Media/Instructional Technology, M
Electrical, Electronic and Communications Engineering Technology/Technician, B
Elementary Education and Teaching, BMO
Engineering and Applied Sciences, MO
English, MO
English Language and Literature, B
English as a Second Language, MO
Exercise and Sports Science, MO
Finance, B
Foreign Language Teacher Education, MO
Foundations and Philosophy of Education, M
French Language and Literature, BMO
Geography, BM
Geology/Earth Science, B

Geosciences, MO
German Language and Literature, BO
Health Psychology, M
Hispanic and Latin American Languages, M
History, BMO
Industrial Technology/Technician, B
Industrial and Manufacturing Management, O
Information Science/Studies, M
International Affairs, M
International/Global Studies, B
Italian Language and Literature, BO
Journalism, B
Logistics and Materials Management, O
Management Information Systems and Services, B
Management of Technology, MO
Manufacturing Technology/Technician, B
Marketing/Marketing Management, B
Marriage and Family Therapy/Counseling, M
Mathematics, BMO
Mechanical Engineering/Mechanical Technology/Technician, B
Molecular Biology, MO
Multi-/Interdisciplinary Studies, B
Music, B
Music Teacher Education, BMO
Nurse Anesthetist, M
Philosophy, B
Physical Education Teaching and Coaching, BMO
Physics, BMO
Political Science and Government, B
Psychology, BM
Reading Teacher Education, MO
Rehabilitation Counseling, MO
School Psychology, M
Science Teacher Education/General Science Teacher Education, MO
Secondary Education and Teaching, M
Social Sciences, B
Social Work, B
Sociology, B
Spanish Language and Literature, BMO
Special Education and Teaching, MO
Statistics, MO
Supply Chain Management, O
Technology Teacher Education/Industrial Arts Teacher Education, B
Vocational and Technical Education, MO

CHARTER OAK STATE COLLEGE

Business Administration and Management, B
Computer and Information Systems Security, B
Health Information/Medical Records Administration/Administrator, B
Health/Health Care Administration/Management, B
Liberal Arts and Sciences Studies and Humanities, AB
Psychology, B

CONNECTICUT COLLEGE

African Studies, B
American/United States Studies/Civilization, B
Anthropology, B
Architecture and Related Services, B
Art History, Criticism and Conservation, B
Biochemistry, B
Biology/Biological Sciences, B
Biopsychology, M
Botany/Plant Biology, B
Cell/Cellular and Molecular Biology, B
Chemistry, B
Classics and Classical Languages, Literatures, and Linguistics, B
Clinical Psychology, M
Computer Science, B
Dance, B
Drama and Dramatics/Theatre Arts, B
East Asian Studies, B
Ecology, B
Economics, B
English Language and Literature, B
Film/Cinema Studies, B
Fine/Studio Arts, B
French Language and Literature, B
German Language and Literature, B
Health Psychology, M
History, B

Human Development and Family Studies, B
International Relations and Affairs, B
Islamic Studies, B
Italian Studies, B
Latin American Studies, B
Mathematics, B
Molecular Biology, B
Multi-/Interdisciplinary Studies, B
Music, B
Neuroscience, M
Philosophy, B
Physics, B
Political Science and Government, B
Psychology, BM
Religion/Religious Studies, B
Slavic Studies, B
Social Psychology, M
Sociology, B
Spanish Language and Literature, B
Women's Studies, B

EASTERN CONNECTICUT STATE UNIVERSITY

Accounting, B
Biochemistry, B
Biology/Biological Sciences, B
Business Administration and Management, B
Communication Studies/Speech Communication and Rhetoric, B
Computer and Information Sciences, B
Drama and Dramatics/Theatre Arts, B
Early Childhood Education and Teaching, M
Economics, B
Education, M
Educational Media/Instructional Technology, M
Elementary Education and Teaching, BM
English Language and Literature, B
Finance, B
Fine/Studio Arts, B
General Studies, AB
Health Services/Allied Health/Health Sciences, B
History, B
Information Science/Studies, B
Kindergarten/PreSchool Education and Teaching, B
Labor Studies, B
Liberal Arts and Sciences Studies and Humanities, B
Mathematics, B
Music, B
Organizational Management, M
Philosophy, B
Physical Education Teaching and Coaching, B
Political Science and Government, B
Psychology, B
Reading Teacher Education, M
Science Teacher Education/General Science Teacher Education, M
Secondary Education and Teaching, M
Social Work, B
Sociology, B
Spanish Language and Literature, B
Sport and Fitness Administration/Management, B
Women's Studies, B

FAIRFIELD UNIVERSITY

Accounting, BMO
American/United States Studies/Civilization, BM
Applied Behavior Analysis, O
Applied Psychology, M
Art History, Criticism and Conservation, B
Biochemistry, B
Biology/Biological Sciences, B
Business Administration and Management, B
Business Administration, Management and Operations, MO
Chemistry, B
Child and Family Studies, M
Clinical Psychology, MO
Communication Studies/Speech Communication and Rhetoric, B
Communication and Media Studies, M
Computer Engineering, BM
Computer Software Engineering, B
Computer and Information Sciences, B
Computer and Information Systems Security, O
Counseling Psychology, MO

Counselor Education/School Counseling and Guidance Services, M
Database Systems, O
Drama and Dramatics/Theatre Arts, B
Early Childhood Education and Teaching, O
Economics, B
Education, MO
Educational Media/Instructional Technology, M
Electrical Engineering, M
Electrical, Electronics and Communications Engineering, B
Elementary Education and Teaching, MO
Engineering and Applied Sciences, MO
English Language and Literature, B
English as a Second Language, MO
Entrepreneurship/Entrepreneurial Studies, MO
Film/Video and Photographic Arts, B
Finance, B
Finance and Banking, MO
Fine/Studio Arts, B
Foundations and Philosophy of Education, MO
French Language and Literature, B
General Studies, B
German Language and Literature, B
History, B
Human Resources Management and Services, MO
International Relations and Affairs, B
Internet and Interactive Multimedia, O
Italian Language and Literature, B
Liberal Arts and Sciences Studies and Humanities, B
Management, MO
Management Information Systems and Services, BMO
Management of Technology, M
Manufacturing Engineering, O
Marketing, MO
Marketing/Marketing Management, B
Marriage and Family Therapy/Counseling, MO
Mathematics, BM
Mechanical Engineering, BM
Multilingual and Multicultural Education, MO
Music, B
Nurse Anesthetist, D
Nursing, MD
Nursing - Advanced Practice, MD
Nursing Administration, MD
Pastoral Studies/Counseling, O
Philosophy, B
Physics, B
Political Science and Government, B
Psychiatric/Mental Health Nurse/Nursing, MD
Psychology, B
Public Administration, M
Religion/Religious Studies, B
School Psychology, MO
Secondary Education and Teaching, M
Software Engineering, M
Spanish Language and Literature, B
Special Education and Teaching, MO
Substance Abuse/Addiction Counseling, O
Taxation, MO
Telecommunications, O
Writing, M

GATEWAY COMMUNITY COLLEGE

Accounting, A
Automobile/Automotive Mechanics Technology/Technician, A
Avionics Maintenance Technology/Technician, A
Biomedical Technology/Technician, A
Business Administration and Management, A
Computer Engineering, A
Computer Engineering Technology/Technician, A
Computer Graphics, A
Computer Typography and Composition Equipment Operator, A
Computer and Information Sciences, A
Consumer Merchandising/Retailing Management, A
Data Entry/Microcomputer Applications, A
Data Processing and Data Processing Technology/Technician, A
Dietetics/Dieticians, A
Electrical, Electronic and Communications Engineering Technology/Technician, A
Engineering Technology, A

Engineering-Related Technologies, A
Fashion Merchandising, A
Fire Science/Firefighting, A
Gerontology, A
Hotel/Motel Administration/Management, A
Human Services, A
Industrial Radiologic Technology/Technician, A
Industrial Technology/Technician, A
Kindergarten/PreSchool Education and Teaching, A
Legal Administrative Assistant/Secretary, A
Liberal Arts and Sciences Studies and Humanities, A
Mechanical Engineering/Mechanical Technology/Technician, A
Medical Administrative Assistant/Secretary, A
Mental Health Counseling/Counselor, A
Nuclear Medical Technology/Technologist, A
Special Products Marketing Operations, A
Substance Abuse/Addiction Counseling, A
Word Processing, A

GOODWIN COLLEGE

Business Administration and Management, AB
Business/Commerce, A
Child Care and Support Services Management, A
Child Development, AB
Criminal Justice/Law Enforcement Administration, A
Criminal Justice/Safety Studies, B
Dental Hygiene/Hygienist, A
Environmental Studies, AB
Family Systems, AB
Health Services/Allied Health/Health Sciences, AB
Histologic Technician, A
Human Services, A
Liberal Arts and Sciences Studies and Humanities, A
Logistics and Materials Management, A
Medical Insurance Coding Specialist/Coder, A
Medical Insurance Specialist/Medical Biller, A
Medical/Clinical Assistant, A
Non-Profit/Public/Organizational Management, A
Occupational Therapist Assistant, A
Office Management and Supervision, A
Operations Management and Supervision, B
Opticianry/Ophthalmic Dispensing Optician, A
Organizational Behavior Studies, B
Quality Control Technology/Technician, A
Respiratory Care Therapy/Therapist, A
Security and Protective Services, A

HOLY APOSTLES COLLEGE AND SEMINARY

Humanities/Humanistic Studies, B
Philosophy, B
Religion/Religious Studies, AB
Social Sciences, B
Theology and Religious Vocations, MO

HOUSATONIC COMMUNITY COLLEGE

Accounting, A
Administrative Assistant and Secretarial Science, A
Art/Art Studies, General, A
Avionics Maintenance Technology/Technician, A
Business Administration and Management, A
Child Development, A
Clinical/Medical Laboratory Technician, A
Commercial and Advertising Art, A
Computer Typography and Composition Equipment Operator, A
Criminal Justice/Law Enforcement Administration, A
Data Processing and Data Processing Technology/Technician, A
Environmental Studies, A
Human Services, A
Humanities/Humanistic Studies, A
Journalism, A
Liberal Arts and Sciences Studies and Humanities, A
Mathematics, A
Mental Health Counseling/Counselor, A
Physical Therapy/Therapist, A
Public Administration, A
Social Sciences, A

Substance Abuse/Addiction Counseling, A

LINCOLN COLLEGE OF NEW ENGLAND

Business Administration and Management, A
Business Administration, Management and Operations, B
Communication Studies/Speech Communication and Rhetoric, A
Criminal Justice/Law Enforcement Administration, AB
Dental Assisting/Assistant, A
Foodservice Systems Administration/Management, A
Funeral Service and Mortuary Science, AB
Health Information/Medical Records Administration/Administrator, A
Health Information/Medical Records Technology/Technician, A
Human Services, A
Medical Administrative Assistant/Secretary, A
Medical/Clinical Assistant, A
Occupational Therapist Assistant, A
Radio and Television Broadcasting Technology/Technician, A

MANCHESTER COMMUNITY COLLEGE

Accounting, A
Administrative Assistant and Secretarial Science, A
Business Administration and Management, A
Clinical/Medical Laboratory Technician, A
Commercial and Advertising Art, A
Communication Studies/Speech Communication and Rhetoric, A
Criminal Justice/Law Enforcement Administration, A
Drama and Dramatics/Theatre Arts, A
Engineering Science, A
Fine/Studio Arts, A
General Studies, A
Hotel/Motel Administration/Management, A
Human Services, A
Industrial Engineering, A
Industrial Technology/Technician, A
Information Science/Studies, A
Journalism, A
Kindergarten/PreSchool Education and Teaching, A
Legal Administrative Assistant/Secretary, A
Legal Assistant/Paralegal, A
Liberal Arts and Sciences Studies and Humanities, A
Management Information Systems and Services, A
Marketing/Marketing Management, A
Medical Administrative Assistant/Secretary, A
Music, A
Occupational Therapist Assistant, A
Physical Therapist Assistant, A
Respiratory Care Therapy/Therapist, A
Social Work, A
Surgical Technology/Technologist, A
Teacher Assistant/Aide, A

MIDDLESEX COMMUNITY COLLEGE

Accounting, A
Administrative Assistant and Secretarial Science, A
Biological and Physical Sciences, A
Biology Technician/BioTechnology Laboratory Technician, A
Broadcast Journalism, A
Business Administration and Management, A
Commercial and Advertising Art, A
Computer Programming/Programmer, A
Criminal Justice/Police Science, A
Engineering Science, A
Engineering Technology, A
Environmental Studies, A
Fine/Studio Arts, A
Human Services, A
Industrial Radiologic Technology/Technician, A
Intermedia/Multimedia, A
Legal Administrative Assistant/Secretary, A
Liberal Arts and Sciences Studies and Humanities, A
Marketing/Marketing Management, A
Mass Communication/Media Studies, A
Medical Administrative Assistant/Secretary, A

Medical Radiologic Technology/Science - Radiation
  Therapist, A
Mental Health Counseling/Counselor, A
Ophthalmic Laboratory Technology/Technician, A
Substance Abuse/Addiction Counseling, A

MITCHELL COLLEGE

Business Administration and Management, B
Commercial and Advertising Art, A
Communication and Media Studies, B
Criminal Justice/Safety Studies, B
Early Childhood Education and Teaching, B
Elementary Education and Teaching, B
Environmental Studies, B
Hospitality Administration/Management, B
Human Development and Family Studies, B
Kindergarten/PreSchool Education and Teaching, A
Liberal Arts and Sciences Studies and Humani-
  ties, AB
Psychology, B
Security and Protective Services, B
Sport and Fitness Administration/Management, B

NAUGATUCK VALLEY COMMUNITY COLLEGE

Accounting Technology/Technician and Bookkeep-
  ing, A
Aeronautics/Aviation/Aerospace Science and Tech-
  nology, A
Art/Art Studies, General, A
Automobile/Automotive Mechanics
  Technology/Technician, A
Behavioral Sciences, A
Business Administration and Management, A
Business/Commerce, A
Computer Engineering Technology/Technician, A
Criminal Justice/Police Science, A
Digital Communication and Media/Multimedia, A
Early Childhood Education and Teaching, A
Electrical, Electronic and Communications Engineer-
  ing Technology/Technician, A
Engineering Science, A
Engineering Technology, A
Environmental Engineering
  Technology/Environmental Technology, A
Finance, A
Fire Services Administration, A
General Studies, A
Horticultural Science, A
Hospitality Administration/Management, A
Hotel/Motel Administration/Management, A
Legal Assistant/Paralegal, A
Liberal Arts and Sciences Studies and Humani-
  ties, A
Marketing/Marketing Management, A
Medical Radiologic Technology/Science - Radiation
  Therapist, A
Physical Sciences, A
Physical Therapist Assistant, A
Psychiatric/Mental Health Services Technician, A
Respiratory Care Therapy/Therapist, A
Restaurant/Food Services Management, A
Substance Abuse/Addiction Counseling, A

NORTHWESTERN CONNECTICUT COMMUNITY COLLEGE

Accounting, A
Administrative Assistant and Secretarial Science, A
Art/Art Studies, General, A
Behavioral Sciences, A
Biology/Biological Sciences, A
Business Administration and Management, A
Child Development, A
Commercial and Advertising Art, A
Communications Technology/Technician, A
Computer Engineering Technology/Technician, A
Computer Graphics, A
Computer Programming/Programmer, A
Computer Science, A
Criminal Justice/Law Enforcement Administration, A
Criminal Justice/Police Science, A
Electrical, Electronic and Communications Engineer-
  ing Technology/Technician, A
Engineering, A
English Language and Literature, A
Health Professions and Related Clinical Sciences, A

Human Services, A
Information Science/Studies, A
Kindergarten/PreSchool Education and Teaching, A
Legal Assistant/Paralegal, A
Liberal Arts and Sciences Studies and Humani-
  ties, A
Mathematics, A
Medical/Clinical Assistant, A
Parks, Recreation and Leisure Facilities Manage-
  ment, A
Parks, Recreation, Leisure and Fitness Studies, A
Physical Sciences, A
Sign Language Interpretation and Translation, A
Social Sciences, A
Substance Abuse/Addiction Counseling, A
Therapeutic Recreation/Recreational Therapy, A
Veterinary/Animal Health Technology/Technician and
  Veterinary Assistant, A

NORWALK COMMUNITY COLLEGE

Accounting, A
Administrative Assistant and Secretarial Science, A
Architectural Engineering Technology/Technician, A
Art/Art Studies, General, A
Business Administration and Management, A
Commercial and Advertising Art, A
Communication Studies/Speech Communication
  and Rhetoric, A
Computer Systems Networking and Telecommunica-
  tions, A
Computer and Information Systems Security, A
Construction Engineering Technology/Technician, A
Criminal Justice/Law Enforcement Administration, A
Early Childhood Education and Teaching, A
Engineering Science, A
Finance, A
Fine/Studio Arts, A
Fire Science/Firefighting, A
General Studies, A
Graphic Design, A
Hotel/Motel Administration/Management, A
Human Services, A
Information Science/Studies, A
Information Technology, A
Interior Design, A
Kinesiology and Exercise Science, A
Legal Assistant/Paralegal, A
Liberal Arts and Sciences Studies and Humani-
  ties, A
Marketing/Marketing Management, A
Medical Office Management/Administration, A
Parks, Recreation, Leisure and Fitness Studies, A
Psychology, A
Respiratory Care Therapy/Therapist, A
Restaurant/Food Services Management, A
Web Page, Digital/Multimedia and Information Re-
  sources Design, A

PAIER COLLEGE OF ART, INC.

Fine/Studio Arts, B
Graphic Design, B
Illustration, B
Interior Design, B
Photography, AB

POST UNIVERSITY

Accounting, ABM
Biology/Biological Sciences, B
Business Administration and Management, AB
Business Administration, Management and Opera-
  tions, M
Child Care and Support Services Management, A
Child Development, B
Criminal Justice/Safety Studies, AB
Distance Education Development, M
Education, M
Educational Administration and Supervision, M
Educational Media/Instructional Technology, M
English as a Second Language, M
Entrepreneurship/Entrepreneurial Studies, M
Environmental Sciences, B
Equestrian/Equine Studies, B
Finance, B
Finance and Banking, M
Health Services Administration, M
Human Services, BM

International Business/Trade/Commerce, B
Kindergarten/PreSchool Education and Teaching, B
Law and Legal Studies, AB
Management Information Systems and Services, B
Marketing, M
Marketing/Marketing Management, AB
Non-Profit/Public/Organizational Management, M
Project Management, M
Psychology, B
Public Administration, M
Sociology, B
Sport and Fitness Administration/Management, B
Substance Abuse/Addiction Counseling, M

QUINEBAUG VALLEY COMMUNITY COLLEGE

Accounting, A
Administrative Assistant and Secretarial Science, A
Art/Art Studies, General, A
Avionics Maintenance Technology/Technician, A
Business Administration and Management, A
Computer Graphics, A
Computer Systems Networking and Telecommunica-
  tions, A
Computer and Information Sciences, A
Data Entry/Microcomputer Applications, A
Engineering Technology, A
Human Services, A
Liberal Arts and Sciences Studies and Humani-
  ties, A
Medical/Clinical Assistant, A
Plastics Engineering Technology/Technician, A
Substance Abuse/Addiction Counseling, A
System Administration/Administrator, A
Word Processing, A

QUINNIPIAC UNIVERSITY

Accounting, B
Advertising, B
Advertising and Public Relations, M
Allied Health and Medical Assisting Services, MD
Allopathic Medicine, D
Anesthesiologist Assistant, M
Applied Mathematics, B
Athletic Training and Sports Medicine, B
Biochemistry, B
Biological and Physical Sciences, B
Biology/Biological Sciences, B
Broadcast Journalism, BM
Business Administration and Management, B
Business Administration, Management and Opera-
  tions, M
Business/Managerial Economics, B
Cardiovascular Sciences, M
Cell Biology and Anatomy, M
Chemistry, B
Child Development, B
Cinematography and Film/Video Production, B
Civil Engineering, B
Clinical Laboratory Sciences, M
Communication and Media Studies, M
Communication, Journalism and Related Pro-
  grams, B
Community Health and Preventive Medicine, D
Comparative Literature, B
Computer Science, B
Computer Software Engineering, B
Criminal Justice/Safety Studies, B
Drama and Dramatics/Theatre Arts, B
Economics, B
Education, BMO
Educational Leadership and Administration, MO
Educational Media/Instructional Technology, M
Elementary Education and Teaching, M
Engineering, B
English Education, M
English Language and Literature, B
Entrepreneurship/Entrepreneurial Studies, B
Film, Television, and Video Production, M
Film/Cinema Studies, B
Finance, B
Foreign Language Teacher Education, M
Gerontology, B
Health Physics/Radiological Health, M
Health Services/Allied Health/Health Sciences, B
History, B

Human Resources Management/Personnel Administration, B
Human Services, B
Industrial Engineering, B
Information Science/Studies, B
International Business/Trade/Commerce, B
International Relations and Affairs, B
Internet and Interactive Multimedia, M
Journalism, BM
Law and Legal Studies, BMD
Legal Assistant/Paralegal, B
Liberal Arts and Sciences Studies and Humanities, B
Management Information Systems and Services, M
Marketing/Marketing Management, B
Mass Communication/Media Studies, B
Mathematics, B
Mathematics Teacher Education, M
Mechanical Engineering, B
Medical Microbiology and Bacteriology, B
Middle School Education, M
Molecular Biology, M
Nurse Anesthetist, D
Nursing, MD
Nursing - Adult, MD
Nursing - Advanced Practice, MD
Nursing Administration, D
Occupational Therapy/Therapist, BM
Organizational Management, M
Pathology/Experimental Pathology, M
Perfusion Technology/Perfusionist, M
Philosophy, B
Physical Therapy/Therapist, BD
Physician Assistant, BM
Political Science and Government, B
Pre-Dentistry Studies, B
Pre-Law Studies, B
Pre-Medicine/Pre-Medical Studies, B
Pre-Veterinary Studies, B
Psychology, B
Public Relations/Image Management, B
Radiologic Technology/Science - Radiographer, B
Sales, Distribution and Marketing Operations, B
Science Teacher Education/General Science Teacher Education, M
Secondary Education and Teaching, M
Social Sciences, B
Social Studies Teacher Education, M
Social Work, M
Sociology, B
Spanish Language and Literature, B
Supply Chain Management, M
Web Page, Digital/Multimedia and Information Resources Design, B

SACRED HEART UNIVERSITY

Accounting, BMO
Advertising and Public Relations, M
Allied Health Diagnostic, Intervention, and Treatment Professions, B
Applied Psychology, M
Art/Art Studies, General, B
Athletic Training and Sports Medicine, B
Biology/Biological Sciences, B
Business Administration and Management, B
Business Administration, Management and Operations, MDO
Chemistry, BM
Communication Disorders, M
Communication Studies/Speech Communication and Rhetoric, B
Communication and Media Studies, M
Communication, Journalism and Related Programs, B
Computer Science, MO
Computer and Information Sciences, B
Computer and Information Systems Security, MO
Corporate and Organizational Communication, M
Criminal Justice/Law Enforcement Administration, B
Criminal Justice/Safety Studies, B
Criminology, M
Database Systems, O
Drama and Dramatics/Theatre Arts, B
Economics, B
Education, BMO
Educational Administration and Supervision, O

Educational Media/Instructional Technology, O
Elementary Education and Teaching, B
English Language and Literature, B
English as a Second Language, M
Environmental Policy and Resource Management, M
Exercise and Sports Science, M
Film, Television, and Video Production, M
Finance, B
Finance and Banking, MDO
Game Design and Development, M
General Studies, AB
Health Informatics, M
History, B
Human Resources Management and Services, M
Information Science/Studies, O
International/Global Studies, A
Internet and Interactive Multimedia, O
Journalism, M
Liberal Arts and Sciences Studies and Humanities, B
Management Information Systems and Services, MO
Marketing, MO
Marketing/Marketing Management, B
Mathematics, B
Media Studies, M
Nursing, MDO
Nursing - Advanced Practice, MO
Nursing Administration, MD
Nursing Education, M
Occupational Therapy/Therapist, BM
Philosophy, M
Physical Therapy/Therapist, BDO
Political Science and Government, B
Psychology, B
Reading Teacher Education, O
Religion/Religious Studies, BM
Social Work, B
Sociology, B
Spanish Language and Literature, B
Women's Studies, B

ST. VINCENT'S COLLEGE

General Studies, A
Health/Health Care Administration/Management, B
Medical/Clinical Assistant, A
Radiologic Technology/Science - Radiographer, AB

SOUTHERN CONNECTICUT STATE UNIVERSITY

Accounting, B
Anthropology, B
Art Education, M
Art History, Criticism and Conservation, B
Art Teacher Education, B
Athletic Training and Sports Medicine, B
Audiology/Audiologist and Speech-Language Pathology/Pathologist, B
Biological and Biomedical Sciences, M
Biology/Biological Sciences, B
Business Administration and Management, B
Business Administration, Management and Operations, M
Business/Managerial Economics, B
Chemistry, BM
Communication Disorders, M
Communication Studies/Speech Communication and Rhetoric, B
Computer Science, BM
Counselor Education/School Counseling and Guidance Services, MO
Drama and Dramatics/Theatre Arts, B
Early Childhood Education and Teaching, B
Economics, B
Education, MDO
Educational Leadership and Administration, MDO
Educational Measurement and Evaluation, M
Elementary Education and Teaching, BMO
English, M
English Language and Literature, B
English as a Second Language, M
Environmental Education, MO
Exercise and Sports Science, M
Finance, B
Fine/Studio Arts, B

Foreign Language Teacher Education, M
Foundations and Philosophy of Education, O
French Language and Literature, B
Geography, B
Geology/Earth Science, B
German Language and Literature, B
Health Education, M
History, BM
Information Science/Studies, O
Italian Language and Literature, B
Journalism, B
Leisure Studies, M
Liberal Arts and Sciences Studies and Humanities, B
Library Science, BMO
Marketing/Marketing Management, B
Mathematics, BM
Multilingual and Multicultural Education, M
Music, B
Nursing, M
Nursing Administration, M
Nursing Education, M
Parks, Recreation, Leisure and Fitness Studies, B
Philosophy, B
Physical Education Teaching and Coaching, M
Physics, B
Political Science and Government, BM
Psychology, BM
Public Health, M
Public Health (MPH, DPH), B
Reading Teacher Education, MO
Recreation and Park Management, M
School Psychology, MO
Science Teacher Education/General Science Teacher Education, MO
Secondary Education and Teaching, B
Social Work, BM
Sociology, BM
Spanish Language and Literature, B
Special Education and Teaching, BM
Sport Psychology, M
Women's Studies, M

THREE RIVERS COMMUNITY COLLEGE

Accounting, A
Accounting Technology/Technician and Bookkeeping, A
Airframe Mechanics and Aircraft Maintenance Technology/Technician, A
Architectural Drafting and Architectural CAD/CADD, A
Architectural Engineering Technology/Technician, A
Banking and Financial Support Services, A
Business/Commerce, A
Child Care and Support Services Management, A
Civil Engineering Technology/Technician, A
Computer Engineering Technology/Technician, A
Construction Management, A
Criminal Justice/Police Science, A
E-Commerce/Electronic Commerce, A
Education, A
Electrical, Electronic and Communications Engineering Technology/Technician, A
Engineering Science, A
Engineering Technology, A
Entrepreneurship/Entrepreneurial Studies, A
Environmental Engineering Technology/Environmental Technology, A
Fine/Studio Arts, A
Fire Services Administration, A
General Studies, A
Graphic Design, A
Hospitality Administration/Management, A
Kinesiology and Exercise Science, A
Laser and Optical Technology/Technician, A
Liberal Arts and Sciences Studies and Humanities, A
Management Information Systems and Services, A
Manufacturing Technology/Technician, A
Marketing/Marketing Management, A
Mechanical Engineering/Mechanical Technology/Technician, A
Nuclear/Nuclear Power Technology/Technician, A
Psychiatric/Mental Health Services Technician, A

Sport and Fitness Administration/Management, A

TRINITY COLLEGE

American/United States Studies/Civilization, BM
Anthropology, B
Art History, Criticism and Conservation, B
Art/Art Studies, General, B
Biochemistry, B
Biology/Biological Sciences, B
Biomedical/Medical Engineering, B
Chemistry, B
Chinese Language and Literature, B
Classics and Classical Languages, Litera-
   tures, and Linguistics, B
Comparative Literature, B
Computer Engineering, B
Computer Science, B
Cultural Studies, M
Dance, B
Drama and Dramatics/Theatre Arts, B
Economics, B
Education, B
Electrical, Electronics and Communications Engi-
   neering, B
Engineering, B
English, M
English Language and Literature, B
Environmental Sciences, B
Fine/Studio Arts, B
French Language and Literature, B
Gay/Lesbian Studies, B
German Language and Literature, B
History, B
International Relations and Affairs, B
Italian Language and Literature, B
Japanese Language and Literature, B
Jewish/Judaic Studies, B
Mathematics, B
Mechanical Engineering, B
Media Studies, M
Modern Languages, B
Museology/Museum Studies, M
Music, B
Philosophy, B
Physics, B
Political Science and Government, B
Psychology, B
Public Policy Analysis, BM
Religion/Religious Studies, B
Russian Language and Literature, B
Sociology, B
Spanish Language and Literature, B
Urban Studies/Affairs, B
Women's Studies, B
Writing, M

TUNXIS COMMUNITY COLLEGE

Accounting, A
Administrative Assistant and Secretarial Science, A
Art/Art Studies, General, A
Business Administration and Management, A
Commercial and Advertising Art, A
Corrections, A
Criminal Justice/Law Enforcement Administration, A
Data Processing and Data Processing
   Technology/Technician, A
Dental Hygiene/Hygienist, A
Design and Applied Arts, A
Engineering, A
Engineering Technology, A
Forensic Science and Technology, A
Human Services, A
Information Science/Studies, A
Kindergarten/PreSchool Education and Teaching, A
Liberal Arts and Sciences Studies and Humani-
   ties, A
Marketing/Marketing Management, A
Medical Administrative Assistant/Secretary, A

UNITED STATES COAST GUARD ACADEMY

Civil Engineering, B
Electrical, Electronics and Communications Engi-
   neering, B
Management Science, B
Mechanical Engineering, B

Naval Architecture and Marine Engineering, B
Oceanography, Chemical and Physical, B
Operations Research, B
Political Science and Government, B

UNIVERSITY OF BRIDGEPORT

Accounting, BM
Acupuncture and Oriental Medicine, M
Biology/Biological Sciences, B
Biomedical Engineering, M
Business Administration, Management and Opera-
   tions, M
Business/Commerce, AB
Chiropractic, D
Clinical Laboratory Science/Medical
   Technology/Technologist, B
Clinical Psychology, M
Communication and Media Studies, M
Community Psychology, M
Computer Education, O
Computer Engineering, BMD
Computer Science, BMD
Conflict Resolution and Mediation/Peace Studies, M
Counseling Psychology, M
Criminal Justice/Safety Studies, B
Dental Hygiene/Hygienist, ABM
Design and Applied Arts, M
Early Childhood Education and Teaching, MO
East Asian Studies, BM
Education, MDO
Educational Administration and Supervision, DO
Electrical Engineering, M
Electrical, Electronics and Communications Engi-
   neering, B
Elementary Education and Teaching, MO
Engineering and Applied Sciences, MD
English Language and Literature, B
Entrepreneurship/Entrepreneurial Studies, M
Fashion Merchandising, AB
Finance, B
Finance and Banking, M
General Studies, AB
Graphic Design, B
Health Professions and Related Clinical Sciences, B
Human Resources Development, M
Human Resources Management and Services, M
Human Services, BM
Humanities/Humanistic Studies, B
Industrial Design, B
Industrial and Manufacturing Management, M
Interior Design, B
International Affairs, M
International Business/Trade/Commerce, BM
International Relations and Affairs, B
International and Comparative Education, O
Journalism, B
Labor and Industrial Relations, B
Liberal Arts and Sciences Studies and Humani-
   ties, B
Management, M
Management Information Systems and Ser-
   vices, BM
Management of Technology, M
Marketing, M
Marketing/Marketing Management, B
Mass Communication/Media Studies, B
Mathematics, B
Mechanical Engineering, M
Media Studies, M
Middle School Education, M
Music, B
Music Teacher Education, M
Naturopathic Medicine/Naturopathy, D
Nutritional Sciences, M
Physician Assistant, M
Pre-Dentistry Studies, B
Pre-Law Studies, B
Pre-Medicine/Pre-Medical Studies, B
Pre-Veterinary Studies, B
Psychology, B
Reading Teacher Education, MO
Religion/Religious Studies, B
Secondary Education and Teaching, MO
Social Sciences, B

Student Personnel Services, M

UNIVERSITY OF CONNECTICUT

Accounting, BMD
Acting, B
Actuarial Science, BMD
Adult and Continuing Education and Teaching, MD
African Studies, M
African-American/Black Studies, B
Agricultural Economics, BMD
Agricultural Education, MDO
Agricultural Sciences, MD
Agricultural Teacher Education, B
Agriculture, B
Agronomy and Crop Science, B
Agronomy and Soil Sciences, MD
Allied Health and Medical Assisting Services, BM
American/United States Studies/Civilization, B
Animal Physiology, B
Animal Sciences, ABMD
Animal/Livestock Husbandry and Production, A
Anthropology, BMD
Applied Horticulture/Horticultural Operations, A
Applied Mathematics, BM
Art History, Criticism and Conservation, BM
Athletic Training and Sports Medicine, B
Biochemistry, MD
Biology/Biological Sciences, B
Biomedical Engineering, MD
Biomedical/Medical Engineering, B
Biophysics, BMD
Biopsychology, D
Botany/Plant Biology, MD
Business Administration and Management, B
Business Administration, Management and Opera-
   tions, MD
Business/Commerce, B
Cell Biology and Anatomy, MD
Cell/Cellular and Molecular Biology, B
Chemical Engineering, BMD
Chemistry, BMD
Child and Family Studies, MDO
Chinese Language and Literature, B
Civil Engineering, BMD
Classics and Classical Languages, Litera-
   tures, and Linguistics, B
Clinical Laboratory Science/Medical
   Technology/Technologist, B
Clinical Psychology, MD
Cognitive Sciences, MDO
Communication Disorders, MD
Communication Studies/Speech Communication
   and Rhetoric, B
Communication and Media Studies, M
Comparative Literature, MD
Computer Engineering, B
Computer Science, BMD
Corporate and Organizational Communication, D
Counseling Psychology, MDO
Counselor Education/School Counseling and Guid-
   ance Services, MO
CytoTechnology/Cytotechnologist, B
Developmental Biology and Embryology, MD
Developmental Psychology, MD
Dietetics/Dieticians, B
Digital Communication and Media/Multimedia, B
Drama and Dramatics/Theatre Arts, B
Dramatic/Theatre Arts and Stagecraft, B
Ecology, BMD
Economics, BMD
Education, MDO
Education/Teaching of the Gifted and Tal-
   ented, MDO
Educational Administration and Supervision, DO
Educational Measurement and Evaluation, MDO
Educational Media/Instructional Technology, MDO
Educational Psychology, MDO
Electrical Engineering, MD
Electrical, Electronics and Communications Engi-
   neering, B
Elementary Education and Teaching, BMDO
Engineering Physics, B
Engineering and Applied Sciences, MD
English, MD
English Education, MDO
English Language and Literature, B

Entomology, MD
Environmental Engineering Technology/Environmental Technology, MD
Environmental Sciences, B
Environmental Studies, B
Environmental and Occupational Health, M
Environmental/Environmental Health Engineering, B
Exercise and Sports Science, MD
Experimental Psychology, D
Finance, B
Finance and Banking, DO
Financial Planning and Services, B
Fine Arts and Art Studies, M
Fine/Studio Arts, B
Foreign Language Teacher Education, MDO
Foundations and Philosophy of Education, D
French Language and Literature, BMD
Gene/Genetic Therapy, B
General Studies, B
Genetics, MD
Genomic Sciences, M
Geographic Information Systems, O
Geography, BMD
Geology/Earth Science, BMD
German Language and Literature, BMD
Health Psychology, O
Health Services Administration, M
Health/Health Care Administration/Management, B
Higher Education/Higher Education Administration, M
History, BMD
Homeland Security, M
Horticultural Science, AB
Human Development, MDO
Human Development and Family Studies, B
Human Resources Development, M
Human Resources Management and Services, M
Industrial Engineering, B
Industrial and Organizational Psychology, D
Insurance, B
International Affairs, M
Italian Language and Literature, BMD
Jewish/Judaic Studies, M
Journalism, B
Landscape Architecture, B
Latin American Studies, BM
Law and Legal Studies, D
Leisure Studies, MD
Liberal Arts and Sciences Studies and Humanities, B
Linguistics, BMD
Management Information Systems and Services, B
Marine Biology and Biological Oceanography, B
Marine Sciences, MD
Marketing, MD
Marketing/Marketing Management, B
Materials Engineering, BMD
Materials Sciences, MD
Mathematical and Computational Finance, M
Mathematics, BMD
Mathematics Teacher Education, MDO
Mechanical Engineering, BMD
Medicinal and Pharmaceutical Chemistry, MD
Medieval and Renaissance Studies, MD
Metallurgy, MD
Microbiology, MD
Molecular Biology, M
Multi-/Interdisciplinary Studies, B
Multilingual and Multicultural Education, MDO
Music, BMDO
Music History, Literature, and Theory, D
Music Teacher Education, BMD
Music Theory and Composition, MD
Musicology and Ethnomusicology, M
Natural Resources Management/Development and Policy, MD
Natural Resources and Conservation, BMD
Neurobiology and Neurophysiology, MD
Neuroscience, D
Non-Profit/Public/Organizational Management, O
Nursing, MDO
Nutritional Sciences, BMD
Oceanography, Chemical and Physical, MD
Pathobiology, MD
Pathology/Experimental Pathology, B
Performance, MD

Pharmaceutical Sciences, MD
Pharmacology, MD
Pharmacy, BD
Philosophy, BMD
Physical Education Teaching and Coaching, B
Physical Therapy/Therapist, D
Physics, BMD
Physiology, MD
Plant Biology, MD
Plant Molecular Biology, MD
Plant Sciences, MD
Political Science and Government, BMD
Polymer/Plastics Engineering, MD
Psychology, BMDO
Public Administration, MO
Quantitative Analysis, O
Reading Teacher Education, MDO
Real Estate, B
School Psychology, MDO
Science Teacher Education/General Science Teacher Education, BMD
Secondary Education and Teaching, MDO
Social Psychology, MD
Social Studies Teacher Education, MDO
Sociology, BMD
Software Engineering, MD
Spanish Language and Literature, BMD
Special Education and Teaching, BMDO
Sport and Fitness Administration/Management, B
Statistics, BMD
Structural Biology, MD
Sustainable Development, M
Technical Theatre/Theatre Design and Technology, B
Theater, M
Theatre Literature, History and Criticism, B
Toxicology, MD
Urban Studies/Affairs, B
Western European Studies, M
Women's Studies, B
Zoology/Animal Biology, MD

UNIVERSITY OF HARTFORD

Accounting, BMO
Acting, B
Architectural Engineering Technology/Technician, B
Architecture, M
Art History, Criticism and Conservation, B
Biological and Biomedical Sciences, M
Biology/Biological Sciences, B
Business Administration and Management, B
Business Administration, Management and Operations, M
Ceramic Arts and Ceramics, B
Chemistry, B
Civil Engineering, B
Clinical Laboratory Science/Medical Technology/Technologist, B
Clinical Psychology, MD
Communication Studies/Speech Communication and Rhetoric, B
Communication and Media Studies, M
Community Health Nursing, M
Community Organization and Advocacy, B
Composition, MDO
Computer Engineering, B
Computer Engineering Technology/Technician, AB
Computer and Information Sciences, B
Counselor Education/School Counseling and Guidance Services, MO
Criminal Justice/Police Science, B
Dance, B
Design and Visual Communications, B
Drawing, B
Early Childhood Education and Teaching, BM
Economics, B
Education, MDO
Educational Leadership and Administration, DO
Educational Media/Instructional Technology, M
Electrical, Electronic and Communications Engineering Technology/Technician, AB
Electrical, Electronics and Communications Engineering, B
Elementary Education and Teaching, BM
Engineering, B
Engineering Technologies/Technicians, B

Engineering Technology, B
Engineering and Applied Sciences, M
English Language and Literature, B
Entrepreneurship/Entrepreneurial Studies, B
Experimental Psychology, M
Film/Cinema Studies, B
Finance, B
Fine Arts and Art Studies, BM
Foreign Languages and Literatures, B
General Merchandising, Sales, and Related Marketing Operations, B
General Studies, AB
Graphic Design, B
Health Professions and Related Clinical Sciences, AB
Health Services/Allied Health/Health Sciences, AB
History, B
Human Services, B
Illustration, B
Information Science/Studies, B
Insurance, B
Intermedia/Multimedia, B
International Relations and Affairs, B
Jazz/Jazz Studies, B
Jewish/Judaic Studies, B
Law and Legal Studies, AB
Legal Assistant/Paralegal, AB
Liberal Arts and Sciences Studies and Humanities, AB
Management, M
Mathematics, B
Mathematics Teacher Education, B
Mechanical Engineering, B
Mechanical Engineering/Mechanical Technology/Technician, B
Medical Radiologic Technology/Science - Radiation Therapist, B
Music, BMDO
Music History, Literature, and Theory, BM
Music Performance, B
Music Teacher Education, BMD
Music Theory and Composition, M
Neuroscience, M
Nursing, M
Nursing Education, M
Organizational Behavior Studies, M
Painting, B
Performance, MDO
Philosophy, B
Photography, B
Physical Therapy/Therapist, BMD
Physics, B
Political Science and Government, B
Pre-Medicine/Pre-Medical Studies, B
Printmaking, B
Psychology, BMD
Religious/Sacred Music, B
Respiratory Care Therapy/Therapist, B
School Psychology, M
Sculpture, B
Secondary Education and Teaching, B
Sociology, B
Special Education and Teaching, B
Taxation, MO
Women's Studies, B

UNIVERSITY OF NEW HAVEN

Accounting, BMO
Applied Mathematics, B
Biochemistry, B
Biology Technician/BioTechnology Laboratory Technician, B
Biology/Biological Sciences, B
Business Administration and Management, AB
Business Administration, Management and Operations, MO
Cell Biology and Anatomy, MO
Chemical Engineering, B
Chemistry, B
Civil Engineering, B
Commercial and Advertising Art, B
Communication Studies/Speech Communication and Rhetoric, B
Community Psychology, MO
Computer Engineering, BM
Computer Science, ABMO

Computer and Information Sciences, B
Computer and Information Systems Security, MO
Conflict Resolution and Mediation/Peace Studies, MO
Criminal Justice/Law Enforcement Administration, B
Criminal Justice/Police Science, A
Criminology, MDO
Database Systems, M
Dental Hygiene/Hygienist, AB
Dietetics/Dieticians, B
Drama and Dramatics/Theatre Arts, B
Drawing, B
Ecology, M
Economics, B
Education, M
Electrical Engineering, M
Electrical, Electronics and Communications Engineering, B
Emergency Management, MO
Emergency Medical Technology/Technician (EMT Paramedic), AB
Engineering, B
Engineering Management, MO
Engineering and Applied Sciences, MO
English Language and Literature, B
Environmental Engineering Technology/Environmental Technology, M
Environmental Policy and Resource Management, M
Environmental Sciences, BMO
Environmental Studies, B
Environmental and Occupational Health, M
Facilities Planning and Management, M
Finance, B
Finance and Banking, MO
Fine/Studio Arts, B
Fire Protection Engineering, MO
Fire Protection and Safety Technology/Technician, AB
Fire Science/Firefighting, AB
Forensic Psychology, M
Forensic Science and Technology, BMO
Geographic Information Systems, MO
Geosciences, M
Graphic Design, B
Hazardous Materials Management and Waste Technology/Technician, M
Health Services Administration, MO
Higher Education/Higher Education Administration, M
History, B
Homeland Security, MO
Hospitality Administration/Management, B
Hotel/Motel Administration/Management, B
Human Resources Management and Services, MO
Illustration, B
Industrial Engineering, B
Industrial and Labor Relations, M
Industrial and Manufacturing Management, MO
Industrial and Organizational Psychology, MO
Industrial/Management Engineering, MO
Information Science/Studies, BMO
Interior Architecture, B
International Business/Trade/Commerce, MO
International/Global Studies, B
Law and Legal Studies, AB
Liberal Arts and Sciences Studies and Humanities, B
Management Strategy and Policy, M
Marine Biology and Biological Oceanography, B
Marketing, MO
Marketing/Marketing Management, B
Mathematics, B
Mechanical Engineering, BM
Molecular Biology, MO
Music, B
National Security, MO
Nutritional Sciences, M
Organizational Management, M
Painting, B
Political Science and Government, B
Psychology, B
Public Administration, BMO
Science Teacher Education/General Science Teacher Education, M
Sculpture, B

Software Engineering, M
Sport and Fitness Administration/Management, BMO
Systems Engineering, M
Taxation, MO
Urban and Regional Planning, M
Visual and Performing Arts, B
Water Resources Engineering, M

UNIVERSITY OF SAINT JOSEPH

Accounting, B
Applied Behavior Analysis, MO
Art History, Criticism and Conservation, B
Biochemistry, BM
Biological and Biomedical Sciences, M
Biology/Biological Sciences, B
Business Administration and Management, B
Chemistry, BM
Child Development, B
Clinical Psychology, M
Corrections and Criminal Justice, B
Counseling Psychology, M
Counselor Education/School Counseling and Guidance Services, M
Curriculum and Instruction, M
Education, M
Educational Media/Instructional Technology, M
English Language and Literature, B
Family and Consumer Sciences/Human Sciences, B
Foods, Nutrition, and Wellness Studies, B
Gerontology, O
History, B
International/Global Studies, B
Management, M
Marriage and Family Therapy/Counseling, M
Mathematics, B
Multi-/Interdisciplinary Studies, B
Nursing, MD
Nursing - Advanced Practice, M
Nursing Education, M
Nutritional Sciences, M
Pharmacy, D
Philosophy, B
Psychiatric/Mental Health Nurse/Nursing, M
Psychology, B
Public Health (MPH, DPH), B
Public Policy Analysis, B
Reading Teacher Education, M
Religion/Religious Studies, B
Social Work, B
Spanish Language and Literature, B
Special Education and Teaching, BMO
Women's Studies, B

WESLEYAN UNIVERSITY

African-American/Black Studies, B
American/United States Studies/Civilization, B
Ancient Studies/Civilization, B
Anthropology, B
Archeology, B
Art History, Criticism and Conservation, B
Astronomy, BM
Biochemistry, D
Biological and Biomedical Sciences, D
Biological and Physical Sciences, B
Biology/Biological Sciences, B
Chemical Physics, D
Chemistry, BD
Classics and Classical Languages, Literatures, and Linguistics, B
Composition, M
Computer Science, BMD
Dance, B
Developmental Biology and Embryology, D
Drama and Dramatics/Theatre Arts, B
East Asian Studies, B
Ecology, D
Economics, B
English Language and Literature, B
Environmental Sciences, M
Environmental Studies, B
Ethnic, Cultural Minority, and Gender Studies, B
Ethnomusicology, MD
Evolutionary Biology, D
Film/Cinema Studies, B
Fine/Studio Arts, B

French Studies, B
Genetics, D
Geosciences, M
German Studies, B
History, B
Humanities/Humanistic Studies, B
Inorganic Chemistry, D
Italian Studies, B
Latin American Studies, B
Liberal Arts and Sciences Studies and Humanities, B
Liberal Studies, M
Mathematics, BMD
Molecular Biochemistry, B
Molecular Biology, D
Molecular Biophysics, D
Molecular Genetics, D
Music, BMD
Neurobiology and Neurophysiology, D
Organic Chemistry, D
Philosophy, B
Physical Sciences, B
Physics, BD
Political Science and Government, B
Psychology, B
Religion/Religious Studies, B
Romance Languages, Literatures, and Linguistics, B
Russian Studies, B
Science, Technology and Society, B
Social Sciences, B
Sociology, B
Spanish and Iberian Studies, B
Theoretical Chemistry, D

WESTERN CONNECTICUT STATE UNIVERSITY

Accounting, BM
American/United States Studies/Civilization, B
Anthropology, B
Art/Art Studies, General, B
Atmospheric Sciences and Meteorology, B
Biological and Biomedical Sciences, M
Biology/Biological Sciences, B
Business Administration and Management, B
Business Administration, Management and Operations, M
Chemistry, B
Clinical Laboratory Science/Medical Technology/Technologist, B
Clinical Psychology, M
Communication Studies/Speech Communication and Rhetoric, B
Community Health Services/Liaison/Counseling, B
Computer Science, B
Counselor Education/School Counseling and Guidance Services, M
Criminal Justice/Police Science, B
Criminology, M
Curriculum and Instruction, M
Drama and Dramatics/Theatre Arts, B
Economics, B
Education, MD
Educational Leadership and Administration, D
Educational Media/Instructional Technology, M
Elementary Education and Teaching, B
English, M
English Language and Literature, B
Environmental Sciences, M
Finance, B
Fine Arts and Art Studies, M
Geology/Earth Science, B
Geosciences, M
Gerontological Nursing, M
Health Services Administration, M
Health Teacher Education, B
History, BM
Illustration, M
Liberal Arts and Sciences Studies and Humanities, AB
Management Information Systems and Services, B
Marketing/Marketing Management, B
Mathematics, BM
Music, B
Music Performance, B
Music Teacher Education, BM
Music Theory and Composition, B

Nursing, MD
Nursing - Adult, M
Nursing Education, D
Painting, M
Planetary Astronomy and Science, M
Political Science and Government, B
Psychology, B
Reading Teacher Education, M
Secondary Education and Teaching, B
Social Sciences, B
Social Work, B
Sociology, B
Spanish Language and Literature, B
Special Education and Teaching, M
Writing, M

YALE UNIVERSITY

Accounting, D
African Studies, BM
African-American Studies, D
African-American/Black Studies, B
Allopathic Medicine, D
American/United States Studies/Civilization, BD
Ancient/Classical Greek Language and Literature, B
Anthropology, BMD
Applied Arts and Design, M
Applied Mathematics, BMD
Applied Physics, MD
Archeology, BMD
Architecture, BMD
Art History, Criticism and Conservation, BD
Art/Art Studies, General, B
Asian Languages, D
Astronomy, BMD
Astrophysics, BD
Atmospheric Sciences and Meteorology, D
Biochemistry, D
Bioinformatics, D
Biological and Biomedical Sciences, D
Biology/Biological Sciences, B
Biomedical Engineering, MD
Biomedical/Medical Engineering, B
Biophysics, D
Biostatistics, MD
Business Administration, Management and Operations, MD
Cancer Biology/Oncology, D
Cell Biology and Anatomy, D
Cell/Cellular Biology and Anatomical Sciences, B
Chemical Engineering, BMD
Chemistry, BD
Chinese Language and Literature, B
Classics and Classical Languages, Literatures, and Linguistics, BMD
Clinical Psychology, D
Cognitive Sciences, D
Comparative Literature, BD
Computational Biology, D
Computer Programming, Specific Applications, B
Computer Science, MD
Computer and Information Sciences, B
Developmental Biology and Embryology, D
Developmental Psychology, D
Drama and Dramatics/Theatre Arts, B
East Asian Studies, BM
East European and Russian Studies, MD
Ecology, BD
Economic Development, M
Economics, BMD
Electrical Engineering, MD
Electrical, Electronics and Communications Engineering, B
Engineering Physics, BMD
Engineering Science, B
Engineering and Applied Sciences, MD
English, MD
English Language and Literature, B
Environmental Design/Architecture, MD
Environmental Engineering Technology/Environmental Technology, MD
Environmental Policy and Resource Management, MD
Environmental Sciences, MD
Environmental Studies, B
Environmental and Occupational Health, MD
Environmental/Environmental Health Engineering, B

Epidemiology, MD
Ethnic, Cultural Minority, and Gender Studies, B
Evolutionary Biology, BD
Film, Television, and Video Theory and Criticism, D
Film/Cinema Studies, B
Finance and Banking, D
Fine Arts and Art Studies, M
Foreign Languages, Literatures, and Linguistics, B
Forestry, MD
French Language and Literature, BMD
Genetics, D
Genomic Sciences, D
Geochemistry, D
Geological and Earth Sciences/Geosciences, B
Geology/Earth Science, D
Geophysics and Seismology, D
Geosciences, D
German Language and Literature, BD
Graphic Design, M
Health Services Administration, MD
History, BMD
History of Medicine, MD
History of Science and Technology, MD
Humanities/Humanistic Studies, B
Immunology, D
Infectious Diseases, D
Inorganic Chemistry, D
International Affairs, M
International Economics, M
International Public Health/International Health, M
International Relations and Affairs, B
Italian Language and Literature, BD
Japanese Language and Literature, B
Jewish/Judaic Studies, B
Latin American Studies, BD
Latin Language and Literature, B
Law and Legal Studies, MD
Linguistics, BD
Marketing, D
Mathematics, BMD
Mechanical Engineering, BMD
Medieval and Renaissance Studies, MD
Meteorology, D
Microbiology, D
Molecular Biology, BD
Molecular Biophysics, D
Molecular Medicine, D
Molecular Pathology, D
Molecular Physiology, D
Multi-/Interdisciplinary Studies, B
Music, BMDO
Music History, Literature, and Theory, M
Music Theory and Composition, M
Near and Middle Eastern Languages, MD
Near and Middle Eastern Studies, BMD
Neurobiology and Neurophysiology, D
Neuroscience, D
Nursing, MDO
Oceanography, Chemical and Physical, D
Organic Chemistry, D
Organizational Management, D
Painting, M
Paleontology, D
Pathobiology, D
Pathology/Experimental Pathology, MD
Pharmacology, D
Philosophy, BD
Photography, M
Physical Chemistry, D
Physician Assistant, M
Physics, BD
Physiology, D
Planetary Astronomy and Science, D
Plant Biology, D
Political Science and Government, BD
Portuguese Language and Literature, BD
Printmaking, M
Psychology, BD
Public Health, MD
Religion/Religious Studies, BD
Russian Language and Literature, BD
Russian Studies, B
Sculpture, M
Slavic Languages, Literatures, and Linguistics, D
Social Psychology, D
Social Sciences, M

Sociology, BD
South Asian Languages, Literatures, and Linguistics, B
Spanish Language and Literature, BD
Statistics, BMD
Systems Science and Theory, B
Theater, MDO
Theology and Religious Vocations, M
Theoretical Chemistry, D
Virology, D
Women's Studies, B
Writing, MO

Delaware

DELAWARE COLLEGE OF ART AND DESIGN

Animation, Interactive Technology, Video Graphics and Special Effects, A
Fine/Studio Arts, A
Graphic Design, A
Illustration, A
Interior Design, A
Photography, A

DELAWARE STATE UNIVERSITY

Accounting, B
Adult and Continuing Education and Teaching, M
Aeronautics/Aviation/Aerospace Science and Technology, B
Agricultural Business and Management, B
Agricultural Teacher Education, B
Agricultural and Horticultural Plant Breeding, B
Agriculture, B
Agronomy and Crop Science, B
Airline/Commercial/Professional Pilot and Flight Crew, B
Animal Sciences, B
Apparel and Textiles, B
Applied Mathematics, MD
Architectural Engineering Technology/Technician, B
Art Education, M
Art Teacher Education, B
Art/Art Studies, General, B
Aviation/Airway Management and Operations, B
Banking and Financial Support Services, B
BioTechnology, B
Biological and Biomedical Sciences, BM
Biology Teacher Education, B
Biology Technician/BioTechnology Laboratory Technician, B
Biology/Biological Sciences, B
Biomedical/Medical Engineering, B
Broadcast Journalism, B
Business Administration and Management, B
Business Administration, Management and Operations, BM
Business Operations Support and Secretarial Services, B
Business Teacher Education, B
Business/Managerial Economics, B
Chemistry, BMD
Chemistry Teacher Education, B
Child Development, B
Civil Engineering, B
Civil Engineering Technology/Technician, B
Clinical/Medical Laboratory Technician, B
Community Health Services/Liaison/Counseling, B
Computer Science, B
Computer and Information Sciences, B
Consumer Economics, B
Corrections and Criminal Justice, B
Criminal Justice/Law Enforcement Administration, B
Criminology, B
Curriculum and Instruction, M
Data Processing and Data Processing Technology/Technician, B
Dental Assisting/Assistant, B
Dental Services and Allied Professions, B
Dietetics/Dieticians, B
E-Commerce/Electronic Commerce, B
Early Childhood Education and Teaching, B
Education, BMD
Education/Teaching of Individuals in Early Childhood Special Education Programs, B

Education/Teaching of the Gifted and Talented, B
Educational Leadership and Administration, MD
Electrical, Electronic and Communications Engineering Technology/Technician, B
Electrical, Electronics and Communications Engineering, B
Elementary Education and Teaching, B
Engineering Physics, B
English Language and Literature, B
English/Language Arts Teacher Education, B
Environmental Control Technologies/Technicians, B
Environmental Sciences, B
Exercise and Sports Science, M
Family and Consumer Sciences/Human Sciences, B
Fashion Merchandising, B
Finance, B
Fire Protection and Safety Technology/Technician, B
Fishing and Fisheries Sciences and Management, B
Foods, Nutrition, and Wellness Studies, B
Foreign Language Teacher Education, M
Forensic Science and Technology, B
Forestry, B
French Language Teacher Education, B
French Language and Literature, B
German Language Teacher Education, B
German Language and Literature, B
Health Teacher Education, B
Health and Physical Education, B
Historic Preservation and Conservation, BM
History, B
Hospitality Administration/Management, B
Human Resources Management/Personnel Administration, B
Industrial Production Technologies/Technicians, B
Information Science/Studies, B
Journalism, B
Junior High/Intermediate/Middle School Education and Teaching, B
Kindergarten/PreSchool Education and Teaching, B
Library Science, B
Marketing, B
Marketing/Marketing Management, B
Mathematics, BM
Mathematics Teacher Education, BM
Mathematics and Computer Science, B
Mathematics and Statistics, B
Mechanical Engineering, B
Mechanical Engineering Related Technologies/Technicians, B
Mechanical Engineering/Mechanical Technology/Technician, B
Music, B
Music Teacher Education, B
Musical Instrument Fabrication and Repair, B
Natural Resources Management/Development and Policy, B
Natural Resources and Conservation, M
Neuroscience, MD
Nursing, M
Optics/Optical Sciences, MD
Parks, Recreation and Leisure Facilities Management, B
Philosophy, B
Physical Education Teaching and Coaching, B
Physical Science Technologies/Technicians, B
Physics, BMD
Physics Teacher Education, B
Plant Sciences, M
Political Science and Government, B
Poultry Science, B
Pre-Nursing Studies, B
Pre-Veterinary Studies, B
Psychology, B
Public Administration and Social Service Professions, B
Public Health (MPH, DPH), B
Public Relations/Image Management, B
Radio and Television, B
Reading Teacher Education, M
Science Teacher Education/General Science Teacher Education, BM
Secondary Education and Teaching, B
Social Work, BM
Sociology, B
Spanish Language Teacher Education, B
Spanish Language and Literature, B

Special Education and Teaching, BM
Sport and Fitness Administration/Management, B
Systems Engineering, B
Teacher Education and Professional Development, Specific Levels and Methods, B
Theoretical Physics, D
Tourism and Travel Services Management, B
Trade and Industrial Teacher Education, B
Urban Studies/Affairs, B
Voice and Opera, B
Wildlife and Wildlands Science and Management, B

DELAWARE TECHNICAL & COMMUNITY COLLEGE, JACK F. OWENS CAMPUS

Accounting, A
Aeronautical/Aerospace Engineering Technology/Technician, A
Agricultural Business and Management, A
Agricultural Production Operations, A
Applied Horticulture/Horticultural Operations, A
Architectural Engineering Technology/Technician, A
Automobile/Automotive Mechanics Technology/Technician, A
Biology Technician/BioTechnology Laboratory Technician, A
Biology/Biological Sciences, A
Business/Commerce, A
Business/Office Automation/Technology/Data Entry, A
Civil Engineering Technology/Technician, A
Clinical/Medical Laboratory Assistant, A
Computer Technology/Computer Systems Technology, A
Computer and Information Sciences, A
Construction Management, A
Criminal Justice/Law Enforcement Administration, A
Criminal Justice/Police Science, A
Customer Service Support/Call Center/Teleservice Operation, A
Diagnostic Medical Sonography/Sonographer and Ultrasound Technician, A
Drafting and Design Technology/Technician, A
E-Commerce/Electronic Commerce, A
Early Childhood Education and Teaching, A
Electrical, Electronic and Communications Engineering Technology/Technician, A
Elementary Education and Teaching, A
Emergency Medical Technology/Technician (EMT Paramedic), A
Energy Management and Systems Technology/Technician, A
Entrepreneurship/Entrepreneurial Studies, A
Heating, Air Conditioning, Ventilation and Refrigeration Maintenance Technology/Technician, A
Human Services, A
Junior High/Intermediate/Middle School Education and Teaching, A
Kindergarten/PreSchool Education and Teaching, A
Legal Administrative Assistant/Secretary, A
Management Information Systems and Services, A
Marketing/Marketing Management, A
Mathematics Teacher Education, A
Mechanical Drafting and Mechanical Drafting CAD/CADD, A
Medical/Clinical Assistant, A
Nuclear Engineering Technology/Technician, A
Occupational Therapist Assistant, A
Office Management and Supervision, A
Physical Therapist Assistant, A
Poultry Science, A
Radiologic Technology/Science - Radiographer, A
Respiratory Therapy Technician/Assistant, A
Survey Technology/Surveying, A
Teacher Education, Multiple Levels, A
Turf and Turfgrass Management, A
Veterinary/Animal Health Technology/Technician and Veterinary Assistant, A

Water Quality and Wastewater Treatment Management and Recycling Technology/Technician, A

DELAWARE TECHNICAL & COMMUNITY COLLEGE, STANTON/WILMINGTON CAMPUS

Accounting, A
Agricultural Business and Management, A
Architectural Engineering Technology/Technician, A
Automobile/Automotive Mechanics Technology/Technician, A
Biology Technician/BioTechnology Laboratory Technician, A
Biology/Biological Sciences, A
Business Administration and Management, A
Business/Commerce, A
Business/Office Automation/Technology/Data Entry, A
CAD/CADD Drafting and/or Design Technology/Technician, A
Cardiovascular Technology/Technologist, A
Chemical Technology/Technician, A
Civil Drafting and Civil Engineering CAD/CADD, A
Computer Engineering Technology/Technician, A
Computer Systems Networking and Telecommunications, A
Computer and Information Sciences, A
Construction Management, A
Criminal Justice/Law Enforcement Administration, A
Criminal Justice/Police Science, A
Culinary Arts/Chef Training, A
Customer Service Management, A
Customer Service Support/Call Center/Teleservice Operation, A
Dental Hygiene/Hygienist, A
Diagnostic Medical Sonography/Sonographer and Ultrasound Technician, A
Drafting and Design Technology/Technician, A
Early Childhood Education and Teaching, A
Electrical, Electronic and Communications Engineering Technology/Technician, A
Electrocardiograph Technology/Technician, A
Elementary Education and Teaching, A
Emergency Care Attendant (EMT Ambulance), A
Emergency Medical Technology/Technician (EMT Paramedic), A
Energy Management and Systems Technology/Technician, A
Engineering/Industrial Management, A
Fire Protection and Safety Technology/Technician, A
Fire Science/Firefighting, A
Fire Services Administration, A
Heating, Air Conditioning and Refrigeration Technology/Technician, A
Histologic Technology/Histotechnologist, A
Hotel/Motel Administration/Management, A
Human Services, A
Junior High/Intermediate/Middle School Education and Teaching, A
Kindergarten/PreSchool Education and Teaching, A
Kinesiology and Exercise Science, A
Management Information Systems and Services, A
Management Science, A
Manufacturing Technology/Technician, A
Marketing/Marketing Management, A
Mathematics Teacher Education, A
Mechanical Engineering/Mechanical Technology/Technician, A
Medical/Clinical Assistant, A
Nuclear Engineering Technology/Technician, A
Nuclear Medical Technology/Technologist, A
Occupational Therapist Assistant, A
Office Management and Supervision, A
Operations Research, A
Physical Therapist Assistant, A
Radiologic Technology/Science - Radiographer, A
Respiratory Therapy Technician/Assistant, A
Restaurant, Culinary, and Catering Management/Manager, A
Science Technologies/Technicians, A
Substance Abuse/Addiction Counseling, A
Survey Technology/Surveying, A

Teacher Education, Multiple Levels, A

DELAWARE TECHNICAL & COMMUNITY COLLEGE, TERRY CAMPUS

Accounting, A
Agricultural Business and Management, A
Architectural Engineering Technology/Technician, A
Bilingual and Multilingual Education, A
Biomedical Technology/Technician, A
Business Administration and Management, A
Business/Commerce, A
Business/Office Automation/Technology/Data Entry, A
Civil Engineering Technology/Technician, A
Commercial and Advertising Art, A
Computer Engineering Technology/Technician, A
Computer Systems Networking and Telecommunications, A
Computer Technology/Computer Systems Technology, A
Computer and Information Sciences, A
Construction Management, A
Criminal Justice/Law Enforcement Administration, A
Criminal Justice/Police Science, A
Culinary Arts/Chef Training, A
Digital Communication and Media/Multimedia, A
Drafting and Design Technology/Technician, A
E-Commerce/Electronic Commerce, A
Early Childhood Education and Teaching, A
Electrical, Electronic and Communications Engineering Technology/Technician, A
Electromechanical Technology/Electromechanical Engineering Technology, A
Elementary Education and Teaching, A
Emergency Medical Technology/Technician (EMT Paramedic), A
Energy Management and Systems Technology/Technician, A
Entrepreneurship/Entrepreneurial Studies, A
Hotel/Motel Administration/Management, A
Human Resources Management/Personnel Administration, A
Human Services, A
Interior Design, A
Junior High/Intermediate/Middle School Education and Teaching, A
Kindergarten/PreSchool Education and Teaching, A
Legal Administrative Assistant/Secretary, A
Management Information Systems and Services, A
Marketing/Marketing Management, A
Mathematics Teacher Education, A
Medical/Clinical Assistant, A
Office Management and Supervision, A
Photography, A
Substance Abuse/Addiction Counseling, A
Teacher Education, Multiple Levels, A

GOLDEY-BEACOM COLLEGE

Accounting, AB
Accounting and Computer Science, B
Business Administration and Management, AB
Business Administration, Management and Operations, M
Corrections and Criminal Justice, B
Economics, B
English Language and Literature, B
Finance, B
Finance and Banking, M
Finance and Financial Management Services, B
Health Services Administration, M
Health/Health Care Administration/Management, B
Human Resources Management and Services, M
Human Resources Management/Personnel Administration, B
Information Science/Studies, AB
International Business/Trade/Commerce, BM
Law and Legal Studies, B
Management, M
Management Information Systems and Services, BM
Marketing, M
Marketing/Marketing Management, B
Psychology, B
Sport and Fitness Administration/Management, B

Taxation, M

STRAYER UNIVERSITY–CHRISTIANA CAMPUS

Accounting, B
Business Administration and Management, B
Criminal Justice/Law Enforcement Administration, B
Economics, B
International Business/Trade/Commerce, B
Management Information Systems and Services, B

UNIVERSITY OF DELAWARE

Accounting, BM
African-American/Black Studies, B
Agribusiness, B
Agricultural Business and Management, B
Agricultural Economics, M
Agricultural Education, M
Agricultural Sciences, MD
Agricultural Teacher Education, B
Agriculture, AB
Agronomy and Soil Sciences, MD
American/United States Studies/Civilization, M
Animal Sciences, BMD
Anthropology, B
Apparel and Textiles, B
Applied Mathematics, MD
Art History, Criticism and Conservation, BMD
Art/Art Studies, General, B
Asian Studies/Civilization, B
Astronomy, MD
Athletic Training and Sports Medicine, B
Bilingual and Multilingual Education, B
BioTechnology, M
Biochemistry, BMD
Biological and Biomedical Sciences, MD
Biology Teacher Education, B
Biology/Biological Sciences, B
Biomedical/Medical Engineering, B
Biometry/Biometrics, B
Business Administration, Management and Operations, M
Business Education, M
Business/Commerce, B
Cancer Biology/Oncology, MD
Cell Biology and Anatomy, MD
Chemical Engineering, BMD
Chemistry, BMD
Chemistry Teacher Education, B
Child and Family Studies, MD
Chinese Studies, M
Civil Engineering, BMD
Clinical Laboratory Science/Medical Technology/Technologist, B
Clinical Psychology, D
Clothing and Textiles, M
Cognitive Sciences, BMD
Communication Studies/Speech Communication and Rhetoric, B
Communication and Media Studies, M
Comparative Literature, B
Composition, M
Computer Engineering, BMD
Computer Science, BMD
Computer and Information Sciences, B
Criminology, BMD
Curriculum and Instruction, M
Design and Applied Arts, M
Developmental Biology and Embryology, MD
Dietetics/Dieticians, B
Early Childhood Education and Teaching, B
Ecology, BMD
Economics, BMD
Education, MDO
Educational Administration and Supervision, M
Educational Leadership and Administration, MD
Electrical Engineering, MD
Electrical, Electronics and Communications Engineering, B
Elementary Education and Teaching, B
Emergency Management, MD
Energy Management and Policy, MD
Engineering, B
Engineering Technology, B
Engineering and Applied Sciences, MD
English, MD

English Language and Literature, B
English as a Second Language, M
English/Language Arts Teacher Education, B
Entomology, BMD
Entrepreneurship/Entrepreneurial Studies, M
Environmental Engineering Technology/Environmental Technology, MD
Environmental Policy and Resource Management, MD
Environmental Sciences, B
Environmental Studies, B
Environmental/Environmental Health Engineering, B
European Studies/Civilization, B
Evolutionary Biology, MD
Exercise Physiology, B
Fashion/Apparel Design, B
Finance, B
Finance and Banking, M
Fine Arts and Art Studies, M
Fine/Studio Arts, B
Fish, Game and Wildlife Management, M
Food Science, B
Food Science and Technology, MD
Foods, Nutrition, and Wellness Studies, B
Foreign Language Teacher Education, M
Foreign Languages and Literatures, B
Foreign Languages, Literatures, and Linguistics, B
French Language Teacher Education, B
French Language and Literature, M
General Studies, B
Genetics, MD
Geography, BMD
Geography Teacher Education, B
Geology/Earth Science, BMD
Geotechnical Engineering, MD
German Language Teacher Education, B
German Language and Literature, M
Gerontological Nursing, MO
HIV/AIDS Nursing, MO
Health Professions and Related Clinical Sciences, B
Health Promotion, M
Health and Physical Education, B
Higher Education/Higher Education Administration, M
Historic Preservation and Conservation, BMD
History, BMD
History Teacher Education, B
History of Science and Technology, MD
Horticultural Science, M
Hospitality Administration/Management, BM
Hotel/Motel Administration/Management, B
Human Development, MD
Human Services, B
Information Science/Studies, MD
International Affairs, MD
International Business/Trade/Commerce, B
International Relations and Affairs, B
Italian Language and Literature, B
Kinesiology and Exercise Science, B
Kinesiology and Movement Studies, MD
Landscape Architecture, B
Latin American Studies, B
Latin Teacher Education, B
Liberal Arts and Sciences Studies and Humanities, AB
Liberal Studies, M
Linguistics, BMD
Management, D
Management Information Systems and Services, BMD
Management Science, B
Management of Technology, M
Marine Affairs, MD
Marine Biology and Biological Oceanography, B
Marine Geology, MD
Marine Sciences, MD
Marketing/Marketing Management, B
Materials Engineering, MD
Materials Sciences, MD
Maternal/Child Health and Neonatal Nurse/Nursing, MO
Mathematics, BMD
Mathematics Teacher Education, B
Mechanical Engineering, BMD
Medical Microbiology and Bacteriology, B
Microbiology, MD

Molecular Biology, MD
Multilingual and Multicultural Education, M
Music, BM
Music History, Literature, and Theory, B
Music Performance, B
Music Teacher Education, BM
Music Theory and Composition, B
Natural Resources Management/Development and
 Policy, B
Natural Resources and Conservation, M
Neuroscience, D
Nursing, MO
Nursing - Adult, MO
Nursing - Advanced Practice, MO
Nursing Administration, MO
Nutritional Sciences, BM
Ocean Engineering, MD
Oceanography, Chemical and Physical, MD
Oncology Nursing, MO
Operations Management and Supervision, B
Operations Research, M
Parks, Recreation and Leisure Facilities Manage-
 ment, B
Pediatric Nurse/Nursing, MO
Performance, M
Pharmacy, B
Philosophy, B
Physical Therapy/Therapist, D
Physics, BMD
Physics Teacher Education, B
Physiology, MD
Piano and Organ, B
Plant Protection and Integrated Pest Manage-
 ment, B
Plant Sciences, BMD
Political Science and Government, BMD
Pre-Veterinary Studies, B
Psychiatric/Mental Health Nurse/Nursing, MO
Psychology, BD
Psychology Teacher Education, B
Public Administration, M
Public Policy Analysis, BMD
Russian Studies, B
School Psychology, MO
Social Psychology, D
Social Science Teacher Education, B
Social Studies Teacher Education, B
Sociology, BMD
Spanish Language Teacher Education, B
Spanish Language and Literature, BM
Special Education and Teaching, B
Sport and Fitness Administration/Management, B
Statistics, BM
Structural Engineering, MD
Theater, M
Translation and Interpretation, M
Transportation and Highway Engineering, MD
Urban Education and Leadership, B
Urban Studies/Affairs, MD
Voice and Opera, B
Water Resources Engineering, MD
Wildlife and Wildlands Science and Management, B
Women's Health Nursing, MO
Women's Studies, B

WESLEY COLLEGE

Accounting, B
American/United States Studies/Civilization, B
Biology/Biological Sciences, B
Business Administration and Management, AB
Business Administration, Management and Opera-
 tions, M
Clinical Laboratory Science/Medical
 Technology/Technologist, B
Communication and Media Studies, B
Education, BM
English Language and Literature, B
Environmental Policy and Resource Manage-
 ment, M
Environmental Studies, BM
History, B
Legal Assistant/Paralegal, B
Liberal Arts and Sciences Studies and Humani-
 ties, AB
Marketing/Marketing Management, B
Mass Communication/Media Studies, B

Mathematics and Statistics, B
Nursing, M
Parks, Recreation, Leisure and Fitness Studies, B
Physical Education Teaching and Coaching, B
Political Science and Government, B
Psychology, B

WILMINGTON UNIVERSITY

Accounting, BM
Aviation/Airway Management and Operations, B
Behavioral Sciences, B
Business Administration and Management, B
Business Administration, Management and Opera-
 tions, MD
Cinematography and Film/Video Production, B
Clinical Psychology, M
Computer Graphics, B
Computer and Information Systems Security, BM
Counseling Psychology, M
Counselor Education/School Counseling and Guid-
 ance Services, M
Criminal Justice/Law Enforcement Administration, B
Criminology, M
Design and Visual Communications, B
Early Childhood Education and Teaching, AB
Education, MD
Education/Teaching of the Gifted and Talented, M
Educational Leadership and Administration, MD
Educational Media/Instructional Technology, M
Educational/Instructional Media Design, M
Elementary Education and Teaching, BM
English as a Second Language, M
English/Language Arts Teacher Education, B
Environmental Policy and Resource Manage-
 ment, M
Finance, B
Finance and Banking, M
General Studies, AB
Geographic Information Systems, M
Gerontological Nursing, M
Health Services Administration, M
Health Services/Allied Health/Health Sciences, B
Higher Education/Higher Education Administra-
 tion, D
Homeland Security, M
Human Resources Management and Services, M
Human Resources Management/Personnel Adminis-
 tration, B
Human Services, M
Information Resources Management/CIO Training, B
Internet Engineering, M
Internet and Interactive Multimedia, M
Junior High/Intermediate/Middle School Education
 and Teaching, B
Law and Legal Studies, B
Management Information Systems and Services, M
Marketing, M
Marketing/Marketing Management, B
Mathematics Teacher Education, B
Nursing, MD
Nursing - Adult, M
Nursing - Advanced Practice, M
Nursing Administration, M
Organizational Behavior Studies, B
Organizational Management, M
Photographic and Film/Video Technology/Technician
 and Assistant, B
Political Science and Government, B
Prepress/Desktop Publishing and Digital Imaging
 Design, B
Psychology, B
Public Administration, M
Radio and Television Broadcasting
 Technology/Technician, B
Reading Teacher Education, M
Science Teacher Education/General Science
 Teacher Education, B
Secondary Education and Teaching, M
Social Science Teacher Education, B
Special Education and Teaching, M
Sport and Fitness Administration/Management, B
Vocational and Technical Education, M

Web Page, Digital/Multimedia and Information Resources Design, A

District of Columbia

AMERICAN UNIVERSITY

Accounting, B
American/United States Studies/Civilization, BO
Anthropology, B
Applied Mathematics, B
Arabic Language and Literature, B
Art History, Criticism and Conservation, B
Biochemistry, B
Biology/Biological Sciences, B
Business Administration and Management, B
Business, Management, Marketing, and Related
 Support Services, B
Chemistry, B
Cinematography and Film/Video Production, B
Communication Studies/Speech Communication
 and Rhetoric, B
Communication and Media Studies, MD
Computer and Information Sciences, B
Conflict Resolution and Mediation/Peace Stud-
 ies, MO
Criminal Justice/Safety Studies, B
Cultural Studies, O
Design and Visual Communications, B
Drama and Dramatics/Theatre Arts, B
Economics, BM
Elementary Education and Teaching, B
Entrepreneurship/Entrepreneurial Studies, M
Environmental Policy, MO
Environmental Sciences, B
Environmental Studies, B
Ethics, M
Ethnic, Cultural Minority, and Gender Studies, B
Film, Television, and Video Production, M
Finance, B
Fine/Studio Arts, B
French Language and Literature, B
French Studies, B
Gender Studies, O
German Language and Literature, B
German Studies, B
Graphic Design, B
Health Education, MO
History, B
International Affairs, MDO
International Development, MO
International Public Health/International Health, B
International Relations and Affairs, B
Jewish/Judaic Studies, B
Journalism, BM
Latin American Studies, B
Law and Legal Studies, BMD
Legal and Justice Studies, MD
Liberal Arts and Sciences Studies and Humani-
 ties, AB
Management Information Systems and Services, O
Mass Communication/Media Studies, BM
Mathematics, B
Media Studies, MD
Multi-/Interdisciplinary Studies, B
Music, B
Music History, Literature, and Theory, B
Natural Resources and Conservation, M
Near and Middle Eastern Studies, B
Nutritional Sciences, MO
Philosophy, B
Physics, B
Political Science and Government, BMO
Pre-Dentistry Studies, B
Pre-Medicine/Pre-Medical Studies, B
Pre-Veterinary Studies, B
Project Management, O
Psychology, B
Public Affairs, M
Public Health (MPH, DPH), B
Public Health Education and Promotion, B
Recording Arts Technology/Technician, B
Russian Language and Literature, B
Russian Studies, B
Scandinavian Studies, B
Secondary Education and Teaching, B
Social Sciences, B

Sociology, B
Spanish Language and Literature, B
Statistics, B
Sustainable Development, M
Teaching English as a Second or Foreign
   Language/ESL Language Instructor, B
Western European Studies, O
Women's Studies, BO

THE CATHOLIC UNIVERSITY OF AMERICA

Accounting, BM
Anthropology, BM
Applied Psychology, D
Arabic Language and Literature, D
Architecture, BM
Art History, Criticism and Conservation, B
Art/Art Studies, General, B
Biochemistry, B
Biological and Biomedical Sciences, MD
Biology/Biological Sciences, B
Biomedical Engineering, MD
Biomedical/Medical Engineering, B
Business Administration and Management, B
Business Administration, Management and Opera-
   tions, M
Business/Commerce, B
Cell Biology and Anatomy, MD
Chemistry, B
Civil Engineering, BMD
Classics and Classical Languages, Litera-
   tures, and Linguistics, BMDO
Clinical Laboratory Science/Medical
   Technology/Technologist, B
Clinical Laboratory Sciences, MD
Clinical Psychology, D
Communication Studies/Speech Communication
   and Rhetoric, B
Computer Science, BMD
Computer and Information Sciences, B
Drama and Dramatics/Theatre Arts, B
Early Childhood Education and Teaching, B
Economic Development, M
Economics, BM
Education, BMDO
Educational Leadership and Administration, MD
Educational Policy, D
Educational Psychology, D
Electrical Engineering, MD
Electrical, Electronics and Communications Engi-
   neering, B
Elementary Education and Teaching, B
Engineering, B
Engineering Management, MO
Engineering and Applied Sciences, MDO
English, MDO
English Language and Literature, B
English/Language Arts Teacher Education, B
Environmental Engineering
   Technology/Environmental Technology, D
Ergonomics and Human Factors, M
Experimental Psychology, D
Finance, B
French Language Teacher Education, B
French Language and Literature, B
General Studies, B
German Language Teacher Education, B
German Language and Literature, B
Hebrew Language and Literature, MD
History, BMD
History Teacher Education, B
Human Resources Management and Services, M
Human Resources Management/Personnel Adminis-
   tration, B
Human Services, A
Information Science/Studies, M
International Affairs, M
International Business/Trade/Commerce, B
International Finance, M
Latin Language and Literature, B
Law and Legal Studies, D
Legal and Justice Studies, DO
Liberal Arts and Sciences Studies and Humani-
   ties, B
Library Science, M
Management, M

Management Science, B
Marketing/Marketing Management, B
Materials Engineering, M
Materials Sciences, M
Mathematics, B
Mathematics Teacher Education, B
Mechanical Engineering, BMD
Medieval and Renaissance Studies, BMDO
Microbiology, MD
Music, BMDO
Music History, Literature, and Theory, B
Music Performance, B
Music Theory and Composition, B
Near and Middle Eastern Languages, MD
Near and Middle Eastern Studies, MD
Nursing, MDO
Operations Research, M
Pastoral Studies/Counseling, MDO
Philosophy, BMDO
Physics, BMD
Piano and Organ, B
Political Science and Government, BMD
Psychology, BMD
Religion/Religious Studies, BMDO
Rhetoric, O
Secondary Education and Teaching, BM
Social Work, BMD
Sociology, BM
Spanish Language Teacher Education, B
Spanish Language and Literature, BMD
Special Education and Teaching, M
Teaching English as a Second or Foreign
   Language/ESL Language Instructor, B
Theater, M
Theology and Religious Vocations, MDO
Urban and Regional Planning, M
Voice and Opera, B
Western European Studies, M

GALLAUDET UNIVERSITY

Accounting, B
American Government and Politics (United
   States), B
Art History, Criticism and Conservation, B
Art Teacher Education, B
Biology/Biological Sciences, B
Business Administration and Management, B
Chemistry, B
Clinical Psychology, D
Communication Disorders, MDO
Communication Studies/Speech Communication
   and Rhetoric, B
Computer and Information Sciences, B
Counseling Psychology, M
Counselor Education/School Counseling and Guid-
   ance Services, M
Early Childhood Education and Teaching, MO
Education, BM
Elementary Education and Teaching, M
English Language and Literature, B
Fine/Studio Arts, B
Information Science/Studies, B
Insurance, B
International and Comparative Education, M
Linguistics, MD
Mathematics, B
Multilingual and Multicultural Education, O
Neuroscience, D
Philosophy, B
Photography, B
Physical Education Teaching and Coaching, B
Psychology, B
Public Administration, M
School Psychology, O
Secondary Education and Teaching, M
Sign Language Interpretation and Translation, B
Social Work, M
Sociology, B
Spanish Language and Literature, B
Special Education and Teaching, MDO
Translation and Interpretation, MD

THE GEORGE WASHINGTON UNIVERSITY

Accounting, BM
Adult and Continuing Education and Teaching, O

Aerospace, Aeronautical and Astronautical Engi-
   neering, MDO
Allopathic Medicine, D
American/United States Studies/Civilization, BMD
Analytical Chemistry, MD
Anthropology, BMD
Applied Mathematics, BM
Applied Psychology, D
Archeology, B
Art Education, M
Art History, Criticism and Conservation, BM
Art Therapy/Therapist, MO
Art/Art Studies, General, B
Asian Studies/Civilization, BM
Audiology/Audiologist and Speech-Language
   Pathology/Pathologist, B
BioTechnology, M
Biochemistry, MD
Bioinformatics, M
Biological and Biomedical Sciences, MD
Biology/Biological Sciences, B
Biostatistics, MD
Business Administration and Management, B
Business Administration, Management and Opera-
   tions, MD
Business/Managerial Economics, B
Ceramic Arts and Ceramics, M
Chemistry, BMD
Chinese Language and Literature, B
Civil Engineering, BMDO
Classics and Classical Languages, Litera-
   tures, and Linguistics, B
Clinical Laboratory Science/Medical
   Technology/Technologist, B
Clinical Psychology, MD
Clinical/Medical Laboratory Technician, A
Cognitive Sciences, D
Communication Disorders, M
Communication and Media Studies, M
Community Health and Preventive Medicine, MD
Computer Engineering, BMDO
Computer Science, BMDO
Computer and Information Sciences, B
Computer and Information Systems Security, M
Counselor Education/School Counseling and Guid-
   ance Services, MDO
Criminal Justice/Law Enforcement Administration, B
Criminology, M
Curriculum and Instruction, MDO
Dance, BMO
Diagnostic Medical Sonography/Sonographer and
   Ultrasound Technician, B
Distance Education Development, O
Drama and Dramatics/Theatre Arts, B
Early Childhood Education and Teaching, M
East Asian Studies, BM
East European and Russian Studies, M
Economics, BMD
Education, MDO
Educational Administration and Supervision, MDO
Educational Leadership and Administration, MO
Educational Media/Instructional Technology, MO
Educational Policy, MDO
Electrical Engineering, MDO
Electrical, Electronics and Communications Engi-
   neering, B
Elementary Education and Teaching, M
Emergency Management, M
Emergency Medical Technology/Technician (EMT
   Paramedic), B
Engineering, B
Engineering Management, MDO
Engineering and Applied Sciences, MDO
English, MD
English Language and Literature, B
Environmental Engineering
   Technology/Environmental Technology, MDO
Environmental Policy and Resource Manage-
   ment, M
Environmental Studies, B
Environmental and Occupational Health, D
Environmental/Environmental Health Engineering, B
Epidemiology, M
European Studies/Civilization, B
Exercise and Sports Science, M
Finance, B

Finance and Banking, MD
Fine/Studio Arts, B
Folklore, M
Foreign Language Teacher Education, M
Forensic Psychology, O
Forensic Science and Technology, MO
Foundations and Philosophy of Education, O
French Language and Literature, B
Gender Studies, O
Genetics, B
Geography, BMO
Geology/Earth Science, B
German Language and Literature, B
Health Communication, M
Health Services Administration, MO
Health Services Research, M
Higher Education/Higher Education Administration, MDO
Historic Preservation and Conservation, M
History, BMD
Hospitality Administration/Management, M
Human Development, M
Human Resources Development, MDO
Human Resources Management and Services, M
Human Resources Management/Personnel Administration, B
Human Services, B
Humanities/Humanistic Studies, B
Immunology, D
Industrial Radiologic Technology/Technician, A
Infectious Diseases, M
Inorganic Chemistry, MD
Interior Design, M
International Affairs, M
International Business/Trade/Commerce, BD
International Development, M
International Public Health/International Health, MD
International Relations and Affairs, B
International Trade, M
International Trade Policy, M
International and Comparative Education, MO
Investment Management, M
Jewish/Judaic Studies, B
Journalism, B
Kinesiology and Exercise Science, B
Latin American Studies, BM
Law and Legal Studies, MD
Legal and Justice Studies, MDO
Liberal Arts and Sciences Studies and Humanities, B
Management Information Systems and Services, MD
Management Strategy and Policy, MDO
Management of Technology, MD
Marketing, MD
Marketing/Marketing Management, B
Mass Communication/Media Studies, BMO
Materials Sciences, MD
Mathematical and Computational Finance, O
Mathematics, BMDO
Mathematics Teacher Education, M
Mechanical Engineering, BMDO
Microbiology, MD
Military and Defense Studies, M
Molecular Medicine, D
Multilingual and Multicultural Education, MO
Museology/Museum Studies, MO
Museum Education, M
Music, B
National Security, M
Near and Middle Eastern Studies, BM
Non-Profit/Public/Organizational Management, O
Nuclear Medical Technology/Technologist, A
Nursing, MDO
Nursing - Adult, MDO
Nursing - Advanced Practice, MDO
Nursing Administration, M
Nursing Education, D
Organic Chemistry, MD
Organizational Management, MO
Painting, M
Pharmacology and Toxicology, B
Philosophy, BM
Photography, M
Physical Chemistry, MD
Physical Therapy/Therapist, D

Physician Assistant, BM
Physics, BMD
Political Science and Government, BMD
Pre-Dentistry Studies, B
Pre-Law Studies, B
Pre-Medicine/Pre-Medical Studies, B
Project Management, MO
Psychology, BMDO
Public Administration, MD
Public Affairs, MO
Public Health, MD
Public Policy Analysis, BMD
Publishing, M
Radio and Television, B
Radiologic Technology/Science - Radiographer, B
Reading Teacher Education, O
Real Estate, O
Rehabilitation Counseling, M
Religion/Religious Studies, BM
Russian Language and Literature, B
Russian Studies, B
Science Teacher Education/General Science Teacher Education, M
Sculpture, M
Secondary Education and Teaching, M
Securities Services Administration/Management, M
Social Psychology, D
Sociology, BM
Spanish Language and Literature, B
Special Education and Teaching, MDO
Sport and Fitness Administration/Management, M
Statistics, BMDO
Student Personnel Services, MO
Substance Abuse/Addiction Counseling, M
Systematic Biology/Biological Systematics, D
Systems Engineering, BMDO
Technology and Public Policy, MO
Telecommunications, M
Theater, MO
Toxicology, M
Travel and Tourism, MO
Vocational and Technical Education, O
Western European Studies, M
Women's Studies, MO

GEORGETOWN UNIVERSITY

Accounting, B
Acute Care/Critical Care Nursing, M
Advertising and Public Relations, M
Allopathic Medicine, D
American/United States Studies/Civilization, BM
Analytical Chemistry, D
Anthropology, B
Arabic Language and Literature, BMO
Art History, Criticism and Conservation, B
Asian Studies/Civilization, M
Biochemistry, BMD
Bioinformatics, M
Biological and Biomedical Sciences, MD
Biology/Biological Sciences, B
Biostatistics, MO
Business Administration and Management, B
Business Administration, Management and Operations, M
Chemistry, BD
Chinese Language and Literature, B
Classics and Classical Languages, Literatures, and Linguistics, B
Communication and Media Studies, M
Comparative Literature, BM
Computer Science, BMD
Conflict Resolution and Mediation/Peace Studies, M
East European and Russian Studies, M
Economic Development, D
Economics, BD
Emergency Management, M
English, M
English Language and Literature, B
Environmental Law, M
Environmental Studies, B
Epidemiology, MO
Ethics, M
Finance, B
Finance and Banking, MD
Fine/Studio Arts, B
French Language and Literature, B

German Language and Literature, BMD
Health Law, M
Health Physics/Radiological Health, M
Health Professions and Related Clinical Sciences, B
Health Promotion, M
History, BMD
Hospitality Administration/Management, M
Human Development, M
Human Resources Management and Services, M
Humanities/Humanistic Studies, M
Immunology, M
Industrial and Labor Relations, D
Industrial and Manufacturing Management, D
Infectious Diseases, MD
Inorganic Chemistry, D
Interdisciplinary Studies, M
International Affairs, M
International Business/Trade/Commerce, BMD
International Economics, B
International Public Health/International Health, M
International Relations and Affairs, B
International Trade, D
Internet and Interactive Multimedia, M
Italian Language and Literature, B
Japanese Language and Literature, B
Journalism, M
Latin American Studies, M
Law and Legal Studies, MD
Liberal Arts and Sciences Studies and Humanities, B
Liberal Studies, MD
Linguistics, BMD
Management of Technology, M
Marketing/Marketing Management, B
Materials Sciences, D
Mathematics, BM
Media Studies, M
Medieval and Renaissance Studies, BM
Microbiology, MD
Molecular Biology, MD
Multi-/Interdisciplinary Studies, B
Near and Middle Eastern Studies, MO
Neuroscience, D
Nurse Anesthetist, M
Nurse Midwife/Nursing Midwifery, M
Nursing, MD
Nursing - Advanced Practice, M
Nursing Education, M
Organic Chemistry, D
Pharmacology, MD
Philosophy, BMD
Physics, M
Physiology, MD
Political Science and Government, BMD
Portuguese Language and Literature, B
Psychology, BD
Public Health, M
Public Policy Analysis, M
Radiation Biology/Radiobiology, M
Real Estate, M
Religion/Religious Studies, M
Russian Language and Literature, B
Science, Technology and Society, B
Social Sciences, B
Sociology, B
Spanish Language and Literature, BMD
Sport and Fitness Administration/Management, M
Statistics, M
Systems Engineering, M
Taxation, M
Theology and Religious Vocations, D
Theology/Theological Studies, B
Theoretical Chemistry, D
Urban and Regional Planning, M
Western European Studies, M
Women's Studies, B

HOWARD UNIVERSITY

Accounting, BM
African Studies, MD
African-American/Black Studies, B
Allopathic Medicine, D
Analytical Chemistry, MD
Anatomy, BMD
Anthropology, B
Applied Mathematics, MD

Architecture, B
Art History, Criticism and Conservation, M
Art Therapy/Therapist, B
Art/Art Studies, General, B
Atmospheric Sciences and Meteorology, MD
BioTechnology, M
Biochemistry, MD
Biological and Biomedical Sciences, MD
Biology/Biological Sciences, B
Biophysics, D
Biopsychology, D
Broadcast Journalism, B
Business Administration and Management, B
Business Administration, Management and Operations, M
Ceramic Arts and Ceramics, BM
Chemical Engineering, BM
Chemistry, BMD
Civil Engineering, BM
Classics and Classical Languages, Literatures, and Linguistics, B
Clinical Laboratory Science/Medical Technology/Technologist, B
Clinical Psychology, D
Communication Disorders, MD
Communication and Media Studies, MD
Computer Engineering, B
Computer Science, BM
Corporate and Organizational Communication, MD
Counseling Psychology, D
Counselor Education/School Counseling and Guidance Services, BM
Criminal Justice/Police Science, B
Dental Hygiene/Hygienist, B
Dental and Oral Surgery, O
Dentistry, DO
Design and Applied Arts, BM
Developmental Psychology, D
Drama Therapy, B
Drama and Dramatics/Theatre Arts, B
Economics, BMD
Education, BMDO
Educational Administration and Supervision, MDO
Educational Leadership and Administration, MDO
Educational Policy, MDO
Educational Psychology, D
Electrical Engineering, MD
Electrical, Electronics and Communications Engineering, B
Elementary Education and Teaching, M
Engineering and Applied Sciences, MD
English, MD
English Language and Literature, B
Environmental Sciences, MD
Exercise and Sports Science, M
Experimental Psychology, D
Family and Consumer Economics and Related Services, B
Fashion/Apparel Design, B
Film, Television, and Video Production, M
Film/Cinema Studies, B
Finance, B
Finance and Banking, M
Fine Arts and Art Studies, M
Foods, Nutrition, and Wellness Studies, B
French Language and Literature, BM
German Language and Literature, B
Health Education, M
History, BMD
Hotel/Motel Administration/Management, B
Human Resources Management and Services, M
Industrial Radiologic Technology/Technician, B
Information Science/Studies, B
Inorganic Chemistry, MD
Insurance, B
Interior Design, B
International Business/Trade/Commerce, BM
International Economics, B
Journalism, B
Kindergarten/PreSchool Education and Teaching, B
Law and Legal Studies, MD
Leisure Studies, M
Management, M
Management Information Systems and Services, M
Marketing, M
Marketing/Marketing Management, B

Mass Communication/Media Studies, BMD
Mathematics, BMD
Mechanical Engineering, BMD
Media Studies, MD
Microbiology, D
Molecular Biology, MD
Multilingual and Multicultural Education, MD
Music, BM
Music Teacher Education, M
Nursing, MO
Nursing - Advanced Practice, O
Nutritional Sciences, MD
Occupational Therapy/Therapist, B
Organic Chemistry, MD
Orthodontics, O
Painting, M
Pedodontics, O
Pharmacology, MD
Pharmacy, BD
Philosophy, BM
Photography, M
Physical Chemistry, MD
Physical Education Teaching and Coaching, BM
Physical Therapy/Therapist, B
Physician Assistant, B
Physics, BMD
Physiology, D
Political Science and Government, BMD
Psychology, BMD
Public Administration, M
Public Health, M
Radio and Television, B
Russian Language and Literature, B
School Psychology, MD
Sculpture, M
Secondary Education and Teaching, M
Social Psychology, D
Social Work, BMD
Sociology, BMD
Spanish Language and Literature, BM
Special Education and Teaching, M
Sport and Fitness Administration/Management, M
Supply Chain Management, M
Theology and Religious Vocations, MD

STRAYER UNIVERSITY–TAKOMA PARK CAMPUS

Accounting, B
Business Administration and Management, B
Criminal Justice/Law Enforcement Administration, B
Economics, B
International Business/Trade/Commerce, B
Management Information Systems and Services, B

STRAYER UNIVERSITY–WASHINGTON CAMPUS

Accounting, B
Business Administration and Management, B
Criminal Justice/Law Enforcement Administration, B
Economics, B
International Business/Trade/Commerce, B
Management Information Systems and Services, B

TRINITY WASHINGTON UNIVERSITY

Biochemistry, B
Biology/Biological Sciences, B
Business Administration and Management, B
Business Administration, Management and Operations, M
Chemistry, B
Clinical Psychology, M
Communication Studies/Speech Communication and Rhetoric, B
Communication and Media Studies, M
Counseling Psychology, M
Counselor Education/School Counseling and Guidance Services, M
Criminal Justice/Law Enforcement Administration, B
Curriculum and Instruction, M
Early Childhood Education and Teaching, M
Economics, B
Education, BM
Educational Administration and Supervision, M
Elementary Education and Teaching, M
English Education, M
English Language and Literature, B

Fine/Studio Arts, B
History, B
Human Development and Family Studies, B
Human Resources Management and Services, M
International Relations and Affairs, B
Mathematics, B
Music, B
National Security, M
Non-Profit/Public/Organizational Management, M
Organizational Management, M
Philosophy, B
Political Science and Government, B
Psychology, B
Public Health, M
Reading Teacher Education, M
Religion/Religious Studies, B
Secondary Education and Teaching, M
Social Studies Teacher Education, M
Sociology, B
Special Education and Teaching, M
Statistics, B
Women's Studies, B

UNIVERSITY OF THE DISTRICT OF COLUMBIA

Accounting, B
Accounting Technology/Technician and Bookkeeping, A
Administrative Assistant and Secretarial Science, A
Adult and Continuing Education Administration, B
Adult and Continuing Education and Teaching, M
Aeronautical/Aerospace Engineering Technology/Technician, A
Aeronautics/Aviation/Aerospace Science and Technology, A
Anthropology, B
Applied Mathematics, B
Applied Statistics, M
Architectural Engineering Technology/Technician, A
Architecture, BM
Art Teacher Education, B
Art/Art Studies, General, B
Audiology/Audiologist and Speech-Language Pathology/Pathologist, B
Automobile/Automotive Mechanics Technology/Technician, A
Aviation/Airway Management and Operations, A
Biology/Biological Sciences, B
Building/Construction Finishing, Management, and Inspection, B
Business Administration and Management, B
Business Administration, Management and Operations, BM
Business/Office Automation/Technology/Data Entry, A
Cancer Biology/Oncology, M
Chemistry, B
Civil Engineering, B
Communication Disorders, M
Computer Engineering Technology/Technician, A
Computer Science, BM
Construction Management, A
Corrections, A
Counseling Psychology, M
Drama and Dramatics/Theatre Arts, B
Early Childhood Education and Teaching, BM
Economics, B
Education, A
Electrical Engineering, M
Electrical and Electronic Engineering Technologies/Technicians, B
Electrical, Electronic and Communications Engineering Technology/Technician, A
Electrical, Electronics and Communications Engineering, B
Elementary Education and Teaching, BM
Engineering and Applied Sciences, M
English Education, M
English Language and Literature, B
Environmental Sciences, B
Environmental Studies, B
Fashion Merchandising, A
Finance, B
Fine/Studio Arts, B
Fire Science/Firefighting, A
Fire Services Administration, B

Funeral Service and Mortuary Science, A
Graphic Communications, A
Graphic Design, AB
Health Services Administration, B
Health Teacher Education, B
History, B
Homeland Security, M
Hospitality Administration/Management, A
Human Development and Family Studies, B
Information Science/Studies, B
Information Technology, B
Kindergarten/PreSchool Education and Teaching, B
Law and Legal Studies, BMD
Legal Administrative Assistant/Secretary, A
Legal Professions and Studies, A
Legal and Justice Studies, MD
Liberal Arts and Sciences Studies and Humanities, A
Management Information Systems and Services, B
Marketing, B
Mass Communication/Media Studies, B
Mathematics, B
Mathematics Teacher Education, M
Mechanical Engineering, B
Mechanical Engineering/Mechanical Technology/Technician, B
Middle School Education, M
Mortuary Science and Embalming/Embalmer, A
Music, AB
Nutritional Sciences, BM
Office Management and Supervision, B
Ornamental Horticulture, B
Physics, B
Political Science and Government, B
Psychology, B
Public Administration, M
Purchasing, Procurement/Acquisitions and Contracts Management, B
Rehabilitation Counseling, M
Respiratory Care Therapy/Therapist, A
Respiratory Therapy Technician/Assistant, A
Secondary Education and Teaching, M
Social Studies Teacher Education, M
Social Work, B
Sociology, B
Spanish Language and Literature, B
Special Education and Teaching, B
Speech-Language Pathology/Pathologist, B
Trade and Industrial Teacher Education, B
Urban Studies/Affairs, B
Water Resources, M

UNIVERSITY OF PHOENIX–WASHINGTON D.C. CAMPUS

Accounting, BM
Adult and Continuing Education and Teaching, M
Business Administration and Management, B
Business Administration, Management and Operations, MD
Computer Education, M
Consumer Merchandising/Retailing Management, B
Criminology, M
Curriculum and Instruction, MD
E-Commerce/Electronic Commerce, B
Early Childhood Education and Teaching, M
Education, MDO
Educational Administration and Supervision, MD
Educational Leadership and Administration, MD
Educational Media/Instructional Technology, D
Elementary Education and Teaching, M
English Education, M
English as a Second Language, M
Finance, B
Gerontology, M
Health Education, M
Health Informatics, M
Health Services Administration, MD
Higher Education/Higher Education Administration, D
Human Resources Management and Services, M
Industrial and Organizational Psychology, D
Management Information Systems and Services, BMD
Marketing/Marketing Management, B
Mathematics Teacher Education, M
Nursing, MD

Nursing Administration, M
Nursing Education, M
Nursing Informatics, M
Organizational Management, D
Psychology, MD
Public Administration, BM
Secondary Education and Teaching, M
Special Education and Teaching, M

UNIVERSITY OF THE POTOMAC

Accounting, AB
Business Administration and Management, AB
Business Administration, Management and Operations, M
Computer and Information Sciences and Support Services, AB
Computer and Information Systems Security, AB
Health/Health Care Administration/Management, B
International Business/Trade/Commerce, AB
Purchasing, Procurement/Acquisitions and Contracts Management, B

Florida

ADVENTIST UNIVERSITY OF HEALTH SCIENCES

Biomedical Sciences, B
Diagnostic Medical Sonography/Sonographer and Ultrasound Technician, AB
Education/Teaching of Individuals with Multiple Disabilities, B
General Studies, A
Health Services/Allied Health/Health Sciences, B
Health/Health Care Administration/Management, B
Nuclear Medical Technology/Technologist, B
Nurse Anesthetist, M
Occupational Therapist Assistant, A
Radiologic Technology/Science - Radiographer, AB

ARGOSY UNIVERSITY, SARASOTA

Accounting, DO
Business Administration and Management, AB
Business Administration, Management and Operations, MDO
Community Psychology, M
Counseling Psychology, MD
Counselor Education/School Counseling and Guidance Services, MDO
Criminal Justice/Law Enforcement Administration, B
Education, MDO
Educational Administration and Supervision, D
Educational Leadership and Administration, MDO
Educational Media/Instructional Technology, D
Elementary Education and Teaching, D
Finance and Banking, MO
Forensic Psychology, M
Health Services Administration, MO
Health/Health Care Administration/Management, B
Higher Education/Higher Education Administration, D
Information Technology, AB
International Business/Trade/Commerce, MDO
Liberal Arts and Sciences Studies and Humanities, B
Management, MDO
Management Information Systems and Services, MDO
Marketing, MDO
Marriage and Family Therapy/Counseling, M
Organizational Management, D
Pastoral Studies/Counseling, D
Psychology, ABMD
Public Administration, MO
Public Health, M
School Psychology, M
Secondary Education and Teaching, D
Sustainability Management, MDO

ARGOSY UNIVERSITY, TAMPA

Accounting, D
Business Administration and Management, AB
Business Administration, Management and Operations, MD
Clinical Psychology, MD
Community College Education, D

Counseling Psychology, M
Counselor Education/School Counseling and Guidance Services, MD
Criminal Justice/Law Enforcement Administration, B
Education, MDO
Educational Administration and Supervision, D
Educational Leadership and Administration, MDO
Elementary Education and Teaching, D
Finance and Banking, M
Health Services Administration, M
Higher Education/Higher Education Administration, D
Industrial and Organizational Psychology, M
Information Technology, AB
International Business/Trade/Commerce, MD
Liberal Arts and Sciences Studies and Humanities, B
Management, MD
Management Information Systems and Services, MD
Marketing, MD
Marriage and Family Therapy/Counseling, MD
Neuroscience, D
Organizational Management, D
Psychology, ABMD
Public Administration, M
Public Health, M
Secondary Education and Teaching, D
Sustainability Management, MD

THE ART INSTITUTE OF FORT LAUDERDALE

Advertising, B
Animation, Interactive Technology, Video Graphics and Special Effects, B
Baking and Pastry Arts/Baker/Pastry Chef, A
Cinematography and Film/Video Production, AB
Computer Graphics, B
Culinary Arts/Chef Training, A
Fashion Merchandising, B
Fashion/Apparel Design, AB
Graphic Design, AB
Illustration, B
Industrial Design, B
Interior Design, AB
Photography, AB
Recording Arts Technology/Technician, B
Restaurant, Culinary, and Catering Management/Manager, A
Web Page, Digital/Multimedia and Information Resources Design, AB

THE ART INSTITUTE OF TAMPA, A BRANCH OF MIAMI INTERNATIONAL UNIVERSITY OF ART & DESIGN

Animation, Interactive Technology, Video Graphics and Special Effects, B
Apparel and Accessories Marketing Operations, B
Baking and Pastry Arts/Baker/Pastry Chef, A
Cinematography and Film/Video Production, B
Commercial Photography, B
Computer Graphics, B
Culinary Arts/Chef Training, A
Graphic Design, AB
Interior Design, B
Restaurant, Culinary, and Catering Management/Manager, B
Web Page, Digital/Multimedia and Information Resources Design, B

AVE MARIA UNIVERSITY

Accounting, B
American Government and Politics (United States), B
American/United States Studies/Civilization, B
Biochemistry, B
Biology/Biological Sciences, B
Business/Commerce, B
Classics and Classical Languages, Literatures, and Linguistics, B
Comparative Literature, B
Economics, B
English Language and Literature, B
Environmental Sciences, B

Exercise Physiology, B
Finance, B
Health and Medical Administrative Services, B
History, B
Humanities/Humanistic Studies, B
International Business/Trade/Commerce, B
Mathematics, B
Pastoral Studies/Counseling, M
Philosophy, B
Physics, B
Pre-Theology/Pre-Ministerial Studies, B
Psychology, B
Religion/Religious Studies, B
Religious/Sacred Music, B
Teacher Education and Professional Development, Specific Levels and Methods, B
Theology and Religious Vocations, BMD
Theology/Theological Studies, B

THE BAPTIST COLLEGE OF FLORIDA

Bible/Biblical Studies, B
Business Administration and Management, B
Education, B
Elementary Education and Teaching, B
English/Language Arts Teacher Education, B
Music Teacher Education, B
Pastoral Studies/Counseling, B
Sacred Music, M
Social Studies Teacher Education, B
Theology and Religious Vocations, M
Visual and Performing Arts, B

BARRY UNIVERSITY

Accounting, BM
Acting, B
Acute Care/Critical Care Nursing, M
Advertising, B
Anatomy, M
Athletic Training and Sports Medicine, M
Biological and Biomedical Sciences, M
Biology/Biological Sciences, B
Broadcast Journalism, B
Business Administration and Management, B
Business Administration, Management and Operations, M
Chemistry, B
Clinical Laboratory Science/Medical Technology/Technologist, B
Clinical Psychology, M
Clinical/Medical Laboratory Technician, B
Communication Disorders, M
Communication Studies/Speech Communication and Rhetoric, B
Communication and Media Studies, MO
Comparative Literature, B
Computer Science, B
Corporate and Organizational Communication, M
Counselor Education/School Counseling and Guidance Services, MDO
Criminology, B
Curriculum and Instruction, DO
CytoTechnology/Cytotechnologist, B
Distance Education Development, O
Drama and Dramatics/Theatre Arts, B
Early Childhood Education and Teaching, MDO
Ecology, B
Economics, B
Education, BMDO
Education/Teaching of the Gifted and Talented, MDO
Educational Administration and Supervision, MD
Educational Leadership and Administration, MDO
Educational Media/Instructional Technology, MDO
Elementary Education and Teaching, BMDO
Engineering, B
English Language and Literature, B
English as a Second Language, M
English/Language Arts Teacher Education, B
Exercise and Sports Science, M
Finance, B
Finance and Banking, O
Fine Arts and Art Studies, M
French Language and Literature, B
Health Informatics, O
Health Services Administration, MO

Higher Education/Higher Education Administration, MD
History, B
Human Resources Development, MD
Human Resources Management and Services, O
Information Science/Studies, BM
International Business/Trade/Commerce, BO
International Relations and Affairs, B
Journalism, B
Kindergarten/PreSchool Education and Teaching, B
Kinesiology and Exercise Science, B
Kinesiology and Movement Studies, M
Law and Legal Studies, D
Liberal Arts and Sciences Studies and Humanities, B
Liberal Studies, M
Management, O
Management Information Systems and Services, BO
Marine Biology and Biological Oceanography, B
Marketing, O
Marketing/Marketing Management, B
Marriage and Family Therapy/Counseling, MO
Mass Communication/Media Studies, B
Mathematics, B
Nuclear Medical Technology/Technologist, B
Nurse Anesthetist, M
Nursing, MDO
Nursing - Advanced Practice, MO
Nursing Administration, MDO
Nursing Education, MO
Occupational Therapy/Therapist, M
Pastoral Studies/Counseling, MD
Philosophy, B
Photography, BM
Physical Education Teaching and Coaching, B
Physician Assistant, M
Piano and Organ, B
Podiatric Medicine, D
Political Science and Government, B
Pre-Dentistry Studies, B
Pre-Law Studies, B
Pre-Medicine/Pre-Medical Studies, B
Pre-Pharmacy Studies, B
Pre-Veterinary Studies, B
Psychology, BMO
Public Administration, M
Public Relations/Image Management, B
Radio and Television, B
Reading Teacher Education, MO
Rehabilitation Counseling, MO
School Psychology, MO
Social Work, MD
Sociology, B
Spanish Language and Literature, B
Special Education and Teaching, BMDO
Sport Psychology, M
Sport and Fitness Administration/Management, BM
Theology and Religious Vocations, MD
Theology/Theological Studies, B
Voice and Opera, B

BEACON COLLEGE

Business Administration and Management, AB
Computer and Information Sciences, AB
Fine/Studio Arts, AB
Hospitality Administration/Management, B
Human Services, AB
Liberal Arts and Sciences Studies and Humanities, AB
Psychology, AB

BELHAVEN UNIVERSITY

Bible/Biblical Studies, A
Business Administration and Management, B
Health Services Administration, B
Liberal Arts and Sciences Studies and Humanities, A
Management Science, B
Missions/Missionary Studies and Missiology, AB
Social Work, B

BETHUNE-COOKMAN UNIVERSITY

Accounting, B
Biology Teacher Education, B
Biology/Biological Sciences, B

Business Administration and Management, B
Business Teacher Education, B
Chemistry, B
Chemistry Teacher Education, B
Clinical Laboratory Science/Medical Technology/Technologist, B
Communication Studies/Speech Communication and Rhetoric, B
Computer Engineering, B
Computer Science, B
Corrections and Criminal Justice, B
Education, B
Education/Teaching of Individuals with Specific Learning Disabilities, B
Elementary Education and Teaching, B
English Language and Literature, B
English/Language Arts Teacher Education, B
Environmental Sciences, B
Gerontology, B
Hotel/Motel Administration/Management, B
Information Science/Studies, B
International Business/Trade/Commerce, B
International Relations and Affairs, B
Liberal Arts and Sciences Studies and Humanities, B
Mass Communication/Media Studies, B
Mathematics, B
Music Performance, B
Music Teacher Education, B
Parks, Recreation, Leisure and Fitness Studies, B
Philosophy and Religious Studies, B
Physical Education Teaching and Coaching, B
Political Science and Government, B
Psychology, B
Social Studies Teacher Education, B
Sociology, B
Theology and Religious Vocations, M

BROWARD COLLEGE

Accounting, A
Accounting Technology/Technician and Bookkeeping, A
Actuarial Science, A
Advertising, A
Aeronautical/Aerospace Engineering Technology/Technician, A
African-American/Black Studies, A
Air Traffic Controller, A
Airline/Commercial/Professional Pilot and Flight Crew, A
Anthropology, A
Applied Mathematics, A
Architecture, A
Art History, Criticism and Conservation, A
Art Teacher Education, A
Art/Art Studies, General, A
Astronomy, A
Audiology/Audiologist and Speech-Language Pathology/Pathologist, A
Automobile/Automotive Mechanics Technology/Technician, A
Aviation/Airway Management and Operations, A
Biochemistry, A
Biology Teacher Education, B
Biology/Biological Sciences, A
Biomedical Technology/Technician, A
Botany/Plant Biology, A
Business Administration and Management, A
Chemical Engineering, A
Chemistry, A
Chemistry Teacher Education, A
City/Urban, Community and Regional Planning, A
Civil Engineering, A
Computer Engineering, A
Computer Programming/Programmer, A
Computer Systems Analysis/Analyst, A
Computer and Information Sciences, A
Criminal Justice/Law Enforcement Administration, A
Dance, A
Data Modeling/Warehousing and Database Administration, A
Dental Hygiene/Hygienist, A
Diagnostic Medical Sonography/Sonographer and Ultrasound Technician, A
Dietetics/Dieticians, A
Drama and Dramatics/Theatre Arts, A

Early Childhood Education and Teaching, A
Ecology, A
Economics, A
Education/Teaching of Individuals with Emotional
 Disturbances, A
Education/Teaching of Individuals with Mental Retar-
 dation, A
Education/Teaching of Individuals with Specific
 Learning Disabilities, A
Education/Teaching of Individuals with Vision Impair-
 ments, Including Blindness, A
Electrical, Electronics and Communications Engi-
 neering, A
Elementary Education and Teaching, A
Emergency Medical Technology/Technician (EMT
 Paramedic), A
Engineering, A
Engineering Science, A
English Language and Literature, A
English/Language Arts Teacher Education, A
Entomology, A
Environmental Sciences, A
Finance, A
Fire Science/Firefighting, A
Food Science, A
Foreign Language Teacher Education, A
Forensic Science and Technology, A
Forest Management/Forest Resources Manage-
 ment, A
French Language and Literature, A
Geography, A
Geology/Earth Science, A
German Language and Literature, A
Graphic Design, A
Health Information/Medical Records
 Administration/Administrator, A
Health Services Administration, A
Health Teacher Education, A
History, A
Horticultural Science, A
Hospitality Administration/Management, A
Human Nutrition, A
Human Resources Management/Personnel Adminis-
 tration, A
Humanities/Humanistic Studies, A
Information Science/Studies, A
Information Technology, B
Insurance, A
Interior Design, A
International Business/Trade/Commerce, A
International Relations and Affairs, A
Italian Language and Literature, A
Jewish/Judaic Studies, A
Journalism, A
Kinesiology and Exercise Science, A
Latin American Studies, A
Law and Legal Studies, A
Legal Administrative Assistant/Secretary, A
Legal Assistant/Paralegal, A
Liberal Arts and Sciences Studies and Humani-
 ties, A
Management Information Systems and Services, A
Management Science, B
Manufacturing Engineering, A
Marine Biology and Biological Oceanography, A
Marketing/Marketing Management, A
Mass Communication/Media Studies, A
Mathematics, A
Mathematics Teacher Education, B
Mechanical Engineering, A
Mechanical Engineering Related
 Technologies/Technicians, A
Medical Office Assistant/Specialist, A
Medical Radiologic Technology/Science - Radiation
 Therapist, A
Music, A
Music Teacher Education, A
Nuclear Engineering, A
Nuclear Medical Technology/Technologist, A
Nutritional Sciences, A
Ocean Engineering, A
Opticianry/Ophthalmic Dispensing Optician, A
Parks, Recreation and Leisure Facilities Manage-
 ment, A
Pharmacy, A
Philosophy, A

Physical Education Teaching and Coaching, A
Physical Therapy/Therapist, A
Physics, A
Physics Teacher Education, A
Playwriting and Screenwriting, A
Political Science and Government, A
Portuguese Language and Literature, A
Pre-Medicine/Pre-Medical Studies, A
Pre-Veterinary Studies, A
Psychology, A
Public Administration, A
Radio and Television, A
Real Estate, A
Religion/Religious Studies, A
Respiratory Care Therapy/Therapist, A
Restaurant, Culinary, and Catering
 Management/Manager, A
Restaurant/Food Services Management, A
Sales and Marketing Operations/Marketing and Dis-
 tribution Teacher Education, A
Science Teacher Education/General Science
 Teacher Education, B
Social Sciences, A
Social Studies Teacher Education, A
Social Work, A
Sociology, A
Spanish Language and Literature, A
Special Education and Teaching, AB
Statistics, A
System Administration/Administrator, A
Systems Engineering, A
Technical Theatre/Theatre Design and Technol-
 ogy, A
Therapeutic Recreation/Recreational Therapy, A
Tourism and Travel Services Management, A
Trade and Industrial Teacher Education, A
Women's Studies, A
Zoology/Animal Biology, A

CAMBRIDGE INSTITUTE OF ALLIED HEALTH AND TECHNOLOGY

Diagnostic Medical Sonography/Sonographer and
 Ultrasound Technician, A
Radiation Protection/Health Physics Technician, A
Radiologic Technology/Science - Radiographer, A

CARLOS ALBIZU UNIVERSITY, MI- AMI CAMPUS

Business Administration and Management, B
Business Administration, Management and Opera-
 tions, BMD
Clinical Psychology, D
Counseling Psychology, M
Criminal Justice/Safety Studies, B
Education/Teaching of the Gifted and Talented, M
Elementary Education and Teaching, B
English as a Second Language, M
Entrepreneurship/Entrepreneurial Studies, M
Human Services, D
Industrial and Organizational Psychology, M
Marriage and Family Therapy/Counseling, M
Non-Profit/Public/Organizational Management, M
Organizational Management, M
Psychology, BMD
School Psychology, M
Special Education and Teaching, BM

CHIPOLA COLLEGE

Accounting, A
Agriculture, A
Agronomy and Crop Science, A
Art/Art Studies, General, A
Biological and Physical Sciences, A
Business Administration and Management, AB
Clinical Laboratory Science/Medical
 Technology/Technologist, A
Computer Science, A
Computer and Information Sciences, A
Education, AB
Finance, A
Liberal Arts and Sciences Studies and Humani-
 ties, A
Mass Communication/Media Studies, A
Mathematics Teacher Education, B
Science Teacher Education/General Science
 Teacher Education, B

Secondary Education and Teaching, B
Social Work, A

CITY COLLEGE (ALTAMONTE SPRINGS)

Business Administration and Management, AB
Legal Assistant/Paralegal, A
Medical Insurance Coding Specialist/Coder, A
Medical Insurance Specialist/Medical Biller, A
Medical/Clinical Assistant, A
Psychiatric/Mental Health Services Technician, A

CITY COLLEGE (FORT LAUDERDALE)

Accounting, AB
Business Administration and Management, AB
Criminal Justice/Law Enforcement Administration, A
Emergency Medical Technology/Technician (EMT
 Paramedic), A
Legal Assistant/Paralegal, A
Medical Insurance Coding Specialist/Coder, A
Medical/Clinical Assistant, A
Radio and Television, A

CITY COLLEGE (GAINESVILLE)

Accounting and Business/Management, A
Allied Health and Medical Assisting Services, A
Blood Bank Technology Specialist, A
Business Administration and Management, AB
Data Entry/Microcomputer Applications, A
Hospitality Administration/Management, A
Legal Assistant/Paralegal, A
Legal Professions and Studies, A
Medical Insurance Coding Specialist/Coder, A
Medical Office Management/Administration, A
Substance Abuse/Addiction Counseling, A

CITY COLLEGE (MIAMI)

Accounting, AB
Business Administration and Management, AB
Criminal Justice/Law Enforcement Administration, A
Data Entry/Microcomputer Applications, A
Emergency Medical Technology/Technician (EMT
 Paramedic), A
Hospitality Administration/Management, A
Legal Assistant/Paralegal, A
Medical Insurance Coding Specialist/Coder, A
Medical/Clinical Assistant, A

COLLEGE OF BUSINESS AND TECHNOLOGY–CUTLER BAY CAMPUS

Accounting, A
Business Administration and Management, A
Electrical/Electronics Maintenance and Repair Tech-
 nology, A
Health Information/Medical Records
 Technology/Technician, A
Medical/Clinical Assistant, A

COLLEGE OF BUSINESS AND TECHNOLOGY–FLAGLER CAMPUS

Accounting, A
Business Administration and Management, A
Computer Systems Networking and Telecommunica-
 tions, A
Electrical/Electronics Maintenance and Repair Tech-
 nology, A
Heating, Air Conditioning and Refrigeration
 Technology/Technician, A

COLLEGE OF BUSINESS AND TECHNOLOGY–HIALEAH CAMPUS

Electrical/Electronics Maintenance and Repair Tech-
 nology, A
Heating, Air Conditioning and Refrigeration
 Technology/Technician, A

COLLEGE OF BUSINESS AND TECHNOLOGY–MAIN CAMPUS

Accounting, A
Business Administration and Management, AB
Computer Graphics, A
Computer Systems Networking and Telecommunica-
 tions, A
Graphic Design, A

Heating, Air Conditioning, Ventilation and Refrigeration Maintenance Technology/Technician, A
Medical/Clinical Assistant, A
System, Networking, and LAN/WAN Management/Manager, A

COLLEGE OF BUSINESS AND TECHNOLOGY–MIAMI GARDENS

Business Administration and Management, AB
Computer Systems Networking and Telecommunications, A
Electrical/Electronics Maintenance and Repair Technology, A
Graphic Design, A
Medical/Clinical Assistant, A

COLLEGE OF CENTRAL FLORIDA

Accounting Technology/Technician and Bookkeeping, A
Advertising, A
Agribusiness, A
Agriculture, A
Animal Sciences, A
Architecture, A
Art/Art Studies, General, A
Biology/Biological Sciences, A
Business Administration and Management, A
Business Administration, Management and Operations, AB
Business/Commerce, AB
Chemistry, A
Clinical Laboratory Science/Medical Technology/Technologist, A
Computer and Information Sciences, A
Construction Engineering Technology/Technician, A
Criminal Justice/Law Enforcement Administration, A
Criminology, A
Dental Assisting/Assistant, A
Drafting and Design Technology/Technician, A
Drama and Dramatics/Theatre Arts, A
Early Childhood Education and Teaching, AB
Economics, A
Elementary Education and Teaching, A
Emergency Medical Technology/Technician (EMT Paramedic), A
Engineering, A
Engineering Technology, A
English Language and Literature, A
Environmental Studies, A
Equestrian/Equine Studies, A
Family and Consumer Sciences/Human Sciences, A
Fire Science/Firefighting, A
Foreign Languages and Literatures, A
Forestry, A
Health Information/Medical Records Technology/Technician, A
Health Services/Allied Health/Health Sciences, A
Health/Medical Preparatory Programs, A
History, A
Human Services, A
Humanities/Humanistic Studies, A
Information Technology, A
Interior Architecture, A
Journalism, A
Landscaping and Groundskeeping, A
Legal Assistant/Paralegal, A
Liberal Arts and Sciences Studies and Humanities, A
Library Science, A
Marketing/Marketing Management, A
Mathematics, A
Medical Radiologic Technology/Science - Radiation Therapist, A
Music, A
Music Teacher Education, A
Occupational Therapy/Therapist, A
Office Management and Supervision, A
Parks, Recreation, Leisure and Fitness Studies, A
Philosophy, A
Physical Education Teaching and Coaching, A
Physical Therapist Assistant, A
Physical Therapy/Therapist, A
Physics, A
Pre-Law Studies, A
Pre-Medicine/Pre-Medical Studies, A
Pre-Pharmacy Studies, A

Pre-Veterinary Studies, A
Psychology, A
Religion/Religious Studies, A
Restaurant, Culinary, and Catering Management/Manager, A
Secondary Education and Teaching, A
Social Sciences, A
Social Work, A
Sociology, A
Special Education and Teaching, A
Statistics, A
Veterinary/Animal Health Technology/Technician and Veterinary Assistant, A

DAYTONA STATE COLLEGE

Accounting, A
Administrative Assistant and Secretarial Science, A
Architectural Engineering Technology/Technician, A
Automobile/Automotive Mechanics Technology/Technician, A
Biology Teacher Education, B
Business Administration and Management, AB
Child Development, A
Communications Technology/Technician, A
Computer Engineering, A
Computer Graphics, A
Computer Programming, Specific Applications, A
Computer Programming/Programmer, A
Computer Science, A
Computer Systems Networking and Telecommunications, A
Computer Technology/Computer Systems Technology, AB
Computer and Information Sciences, A
Computer/Information Technology Services Administration and Management, A
Criminal Justice/Law Enforcement Administration, A
Criminal Justice/Police Science, A
Culinary Arts/Chef Training, A
Dental Hygiene/Hygienist, A
Drafting and Design Technology/Technician, A
Education/Teaching of Individuals in Early Childhood Special Education Programs, B
Electrical, Electronic and Communications Engineering Technology/Technician, AB
Elementary Education and Teaching, B
Emergency Medical Technology/Technician (EMT Paramedic), A
Engineering, AB
Fire Science/Firefighting, A
Health Information/Medical Records Administration/Administrator, A
Hospitality Administration/Management, A
Hotel/Motel Administration/Management, A
Human Services, A
Industrial Radiologic Technology/Technician, A
Industrial Technology/Technician, A
Information Technology, AB
Interior Design, A
Kindergarten/PreSchool Education and Teaching, A
Legal Assistant/Paralegal, A
Machine Shop Technology/Assistant, A
Mathematics Teacher Education, B
Medical Administrative Assistant/Secretary, A
Occupational Therapist Assistant, A
Photographic and Film/Video Technology/Technician and Assistant, A
Physical Therapy/Therapist, A
Plastics Engineering Technology/Technician, A
Radio and Television, A
Respiratory Care Therapy/Therapist, A
Robotics Technology/Technician, A
Secondary Education and Teaching, B
Tourism and Travel Services Management, A

DEVRY UNIVERSITY (JACKSONVILLE)

Accounting, AB
Business Administration and Management, B
Business Administration, Management and Operations, BM
Business/Commerce, B
Computer Systems Analysis/Analyst, B
Computer Systems Networking and Telecommunications, AB
Criminal Justice/Law Enforcement Administration, B
Health/Health Care Administration/Management, B

Web Page, Digital/Multimedia and Information Resources Design, AB

DEVRY UNIVERSITY (MIRAMAR)

Accounting, B
Accounting Technology/Technician and Bookkeeping, A
Biomedical Technology/Technician, B
Business Administration and Management, B
Business Administration, Management and Operations, BM
Business/Commerce, B
Computer Engineering Technology/Technician, B
Computer Systems Analysis/Analyst, B
Computer Systems Networking and Telecommunications, AB
Criminal Justice/Law Enforcement Administration, B
Education, M
Electrical, Electronic and Communications Engineering Technology/Technician, AB
Health/Health Care Administration/Management, B
Web Page, Digital/Multimedia and Information Resources Design, AB

DEVRY UNIVERSITY (ORLANDO)

Accounting, B
Accounting Technology/Technician and Bookkeeping, A
Biomedical Technology/Technician, B
Business Administration and Management, B
Business Administration, Management and Operations, BM
Business/Commerce, B
Computer Engineering Technology/Technician, B
Computer Software Engineering, B
Computer Systems Analysis/Analyst, B
Computer Systems Networking and Telecommunications, AB
Criminal Justice/Law Enforcement Administration, B
Education, M
Electrical, Electronic and Communications Engineering Technology/Technician, AB
Health/Health Care Administration/Management, B
Web Page, Digital/Multimedia and Information Resources Design, AB

DIGITAL MEDIA ARTS COLLEGE

Animation, Interactive Technology, Video Graphics and Special Effects, B
Computer Art and Design, M
Graphic Design, BM
Media Studies, M

EASTERN FLORIDA STATE COLLEGE

Aeronautics/Aviation/Aerospace Science and Technology, A
Art/Art Studies, General, A
Business Administration and Management, A
Chemical Technology/Technician, A
Clinical/Medical Laboratory Technician, A
Computer Programming/Programmer, A
Computer Systems Networking and Telecommunications, A
Criminal Justice/Law Enforcement Administration, A
Dance, A
Dental Assisting/Assistant, A
Dental Hygiene/Hygienist, A
Digital Communication and Media/Multimedia, A
Drafting and Design Technology/Technician, A
Drama and Dramatics/Theatre Arts, A
Early Childhood Education and Teaching, A
Emergency Medical Technology/Technician (EMT Paramedic), A
Engineering Technology, A
Fire Science/Firefighting, A
Graphic Communications, A
Information Technology, A
Legal Assistant/Paralegal, A
Medical Radiologic Technology/Science - Radiation Therapist, A
Music, A
Office Management and Supervision, A

Veterinary/Animal Health Technology/Technician and Veterinary Assistant, A

ECKERD COLLEGE

American/United States Studies/Civilization, B
Ancient Studies/Civilization, B
Anthropology, B
Biochemistry, B
Biology/Biological Sciences, B
Business Administration and Management, B
Chemistry, B
Classics and Classical Languages, Literatures, and Linguistics, B
Communication Studies/Speech Communication and Rhetoric, B
Comparative Literature, B
Computer Science, B
Drama and Dramatics/Theatre Arts, B
East Asian Languages, Literatures, and Linguistics, B
Economics, B
English Language and Literature, B
Environmental Studies, B
Film/Cinema Studies, B
French Language and Literature, B
Geological and Earth Sciences/Geosciences, B
History, B
Human Development and Family Studies, B
Humanities/Humanistic Studies, B
International Business/Trade/Commerce, B
International Relations and Affairs, B
Marine Biology and Biological Oceanography, B
Mathematics, B
Music, B
Philosophy, B
Physics, B
Political Science and Government, B
Psychology, B
Religion/Religious Studies, B
Sociology, B
Spanish Language and Literature, B
Visual and Performing Arts, B
Women's Studies, B

EDWARD WATERS COLLEGE

Biology/Biological Sciences, B
Business Administration and Management, B
Chemistry, B
Criminal Justice/Law Enforcement Administration, B
Education, B
Elementary Education and Teaching, B
English Language and Literature, B
History, B
Information Science/Studies, B
Journalism, B
Kindergarten/PreSchool Education and Teaching, B
Mathematics, B
Physical Education Teaching and Coaching, B
Psychology, B
Public Administration, B
Secondary Education and Teaching, B
Social Sciences, B
Social Work, B
Sociology, B

EMBRY-RIDDLE AERONAUTICAL UNIVERSITY–DAYTONA

Aeronautics/Aviation/Aerospace Science and Technology, B
Aerospace, Aeronautical and Astronautical Engineering, BMD
Air Traffic Controller, B
Aircraft Powerplant Technology/Technician, AB
Airline/Commercial/Professional Pilot and Flight Crew, B
Atmospheric Sciences and Meteorology, B
Aviation/Airway Management and Operations, MD
Business Administration, Management and Operations, BMD
Civil Engineering, B
Communication Studies/Speech Communication and Rhetoric, B
Computational Mathematics, B
Computer Engineering, BM
Computer Science, B
Computer Software Engineering, B

Computer and Information Systems Security, M
Electrical Engineering, M
Electrical, Electronics and Communications Engineering, B
Engineering, B
Engineering Physics, BMD
Ergonomics and Human Factors, MD
Finance and Banking, MD
International Affairs, M
Mechanical Engineering, BMD
Multi-/Interdisciplinary Studies, B
Occupational Safety and Health Technology/Technician, B
Physics, B
Software Engineering, M
Systems Engineering, MD

EMBRY-RIDDLE AERONAUTICAL UNIVERSITY–WORLDWIDE

Aeronautical/Aerospace Engineering Technology/Technician, B
Aeronautics/Aviation/Aerospace Science and Technology, AB
Aerospace, Aeronautical and Astronautical Engineering, AM
Aircraft Powerplant Technology/Technician, AB
Aviation/Airway Management and Operations, ABM
Business Administration and Management, AB
Business Administration, Management and Operations, ABM
Communication Studies/Speech Communication and Rhetoric, B
Engineering Management, M
Environmental and Occupational Health, M
Fire Science/Firefighting, B
International Affairs, M
Logistics and Materials Management, ABM
Occupational Safety and Health Technology/Technician, B
Project Management, M
Supply Chain Management, M
Systems Engineering, M
Transportation/Transportation Management, B

EVEREST UNIVERSITY (LARGO)

Accounting, ABM
Business Administration, Management and Operations, ABM
Computer and Information Sciences, AB
Criminal Justice/Safety Studies, AB
Health/Health Care Administration/Management, B
Human Resources Management and Services, M
International Business/Trade/Commerce, M
Legal Assistant/Paralegal, A
Medical/Clinical Assistant, A

EVEREST UNIVERSITY (ORANGE PARK)

Business Administration and Management, AB
Criminal Justice/Law Enforcement Administration, AB
Criminalistics and Criminal Science, A
Medical Insurance Coding Specialist/Coder, A
Medical/Clinical Assistant, A

EVEREST UNIVERSITY (ORLANDO)

Accounting, ABM
Business Administration and Management, AB
Business Administration, Management and Operations, M
Computer Science, AB
Computer and Information Sciences, A
Computer and Information Sciences and Support Services, A
Criminal Justice/Law Enforcement Administration, AB
Criminal Justice/Safety Studies, A
Health/Health Care Administration/Management, B
Human Resources Management and Services, M
International Business/Trade/Commerce, M
Legal Assistant/Paralegal, AB
Management, M
Marketing/Marketing Management, AB
Medical Insurance Specialist/Medical Biller, A

Medical/Clinical Assistant, A

EVEREST UNIVERSITY (TAMPA)

Accounting, ABM
Business Administration and Management, AB
Business Administration, Management and Operations, M
Computer Programming/Programmer, AB
Computer Science, A
Criminal Justice/Law Enforcement Administration, AB
Human Resources Management and Services, M
International Business/Trade/Commerce, M
Legal Assistant/Paralegal, A
Medical Insurance Specialist/Medical Biller, A
Medical/Clinical Assistant, A
Pharmacy Technician/Assistant, A

EVERGLADES UNIVERSITY (BOCA RATON)

Aeronautics/Aviation/Aerospace Science and Technology, B
Alternative and Complementary Medicine and Medical Systems, B
Aviation, M
Business Administration and Management, B
Business Administration, Management and Operations, M
Construction Management, B
Hospitality Administration/Management, B
Information Science/Studies, M
International Business/Trade/Commerce, B
Land Use Planning and Management/Development, B
Natural Resources Management/Development and Policy, B
Natural Resources and Conservation, B
Public Administration, B
Survey Technology/Surveying, B

EVERGLADES UNIVERSITY (MAITLAND)

Aeronautics/Aviation/Aerospace Science and Technology, B
Alternative and Complementary Medicine and Medical Systems, B
Business Administration and Management, B
Construction Management, B
Hospitality Administration/Management, B
International Business/Trade/Commerce, B
Land Use Planning and Management/Development, B
Natural Resources Management/Development and Policy, B
Natural Resources and Conservation, B
Public Administration, B
Survey Technology/Surveying, B

EVERGLADES UNIVERSITY (SARASOTA)

Aeronautics/Aviation/Aerospace Science and Technology, B
Alternative and Complementary Medicine and Medical Systems, B
Business Administration and Management, B
Construction Management, B
Hospitality Administration/Management, B
International Business/Trade/Commerce, B
Land Use Planning and Management/Development, B
Natural Resources Management/Development and Policy, B
Natural Resources and Conservation, B
Public Administration, B
Survey Technology/Surveying, B

FLAGLER COLLEGE

Accounting, B
Art History, Criticism and Conservation, B
Art Teacher Education, B
Business Administration and Management, B
Criminology, B
Drama and Dramatics/Theatre Arts, B
Economics, B

Education/Teaching of Individuals with Hearing Impairments, Including Deafness, B
Elementary Education and Teaching, B
English Language and Literature, B
English/Language Arts Teacher Education, B
Environmental Sciences, B
Fine/Studio Arts, B
Graphic Design, B
History, B
Hospitality Administration/Management, B
International/Global Studies, B
Journalism, B
Latin American Studies, B
Liberal Arts and Sciences Studies and Humanities, B
Mass Communication/Media Studies, B
Political Science and Government, B
Psychology, B
Public Administration, B
Social Science Teacher Education, B
Sociology, B
Spanish Language and Literature, B
Special Education and Teaching, B
Sport and Fitness Administration/Management, B

FLORIDA AGRICULTURAL AND MECHANICAL UNIVERSITY

Accounting, BM
Adult and Continuing Education and Teaching, M
African-American/Black Studies, B
Agribusiness, B
Agricultural/Biological Engineering and Bioengineering, B
Agriculture, B
Allied Health and Medical Assisting Services, MD
Architecture, BM
Biology/Biological Sciences, B
Biomedical Engineering, MD
Business Administration and Management, B
Business Administration, Management and Operations, M
Business Education, M
Chemical Engineering, BMD
Chemistry, BM
Civil Engineering, BMD
Community Psychology, M
Computer Engineering, B
Computer and Information Sciences, B
Construction Engineering Technology/Technician, B
Counselor Education/School Counseling and Guidance Services, M
Criminal Justice/Safety Studies, B
Criminology, M
Drama and Dramatics/Theatre Arts, B
Early Childhood Education and Teaching, B
Economics, B
Education, MD
Educational Administration and Supervision, MD
Educational Leadership and Administration, D
Electrical Engineering, MD
Electrical, Electronic and Communications Engineering Technology/Technician, B
Electrical, Electronics and Communications Engineering, B
Elementary Education and Teaching, BM
Engineering and Applied Sciences, MD
English Education, M
English Language and Literature, B
English/Language Arts Teacher Education, B
Environmental Sciences, BMD
Environmental Studies, M
Finance and Banking, M
Fine/Studio Arts, B
Graphic Design, B
Health Information/Medical Records Administration/Administrator, B
Health Services Research, D
Health Services/Allied Health/Health Sciences, B
Health and Physical Education, B
Health/Health Care Administration/Management, B
History, BM
Industrial Education, M
Industrial Engineering, B
Industrial/Management Engineering, MD
Information Technology, B
Journalism, BM

Landscape Architecture, M
Law and Legal Studies, D
Liberal Arts and Sciences Studies and Humanities, A
Management Information Systems and Services, M
Marketing, M
Mathematics, B
Mathematics Teacher Education, BM
Mechanical Engineering, BMD
Medicinal and Pharmaceutical Chemistry, MD
Music, B
Music Teacher Education, B
Nursing, MD
Nursing Administration, M
Occupational Therapy/Therapist, M
Pharmaceutical Administration, M
Pharmaceutical Sciences, MD
Pharmacology, MD
Pharmacy, D
Philosophy and Religious Studies, B
Physical Education Teaching and Coaching, BM
Physical Therapy/Therapist, D
Physics, BMD
Political Science and Government, BM
Psychology, BM
Public Administration, M
Public Health, MD
Public Relations/Image Management, B
Respiratory Care Therapy/Therapist, B
Science Teacher Education/General Science Teacher Education, BM
Secondary Education and Teaching, M
Social Science Teacher Education, B
Social Sciences, M
Social Studies Teacher Education, M
Social Work, BM
Sociology, B
Software Engineering, M
Sport and Fitness Administration/Management, M
Toxicology, MD
Trade and Industrial Teacher Education, B
Vocational and Technical Education, M

FLORIDA ATLANTIC UNIVERSITY

Accounting, BMD
Adult and Continuing Education and Teaching, MDO
Allopathic Medicine, D
Anthropology, BM
Applied Arts and Design, M
Applied Mathematics, M
Architecture, B
Art Education, M
Art/Art Studies, General, B
BioTechnology, M
Bioengineering, M
Biological and Biomedical Sciences, MD
Biology/Biological Sciences, B
Business Administration and Management, B
Business Administration, Management and Operations, M
Ceramic Arts and Ceramics, M
Chemistry, BMD
City/Urban, Community and Regional Planning, B
Civil Engineering, BM
Communication Disorders, M
Communication Studies/Speech Communication and Rhetoric, B
Communication and Media Studies, MO
Comparative Literature, M
Comparative and Interdisciplinary Arts, D
Composition, M
Computer Engineering, BMD
Computer Science, MD
Computer Technology/Computer Systems Technology, B
Computer and Information Sciences, B
Counseling Psychology, MO
Counselor Education/School Counseling and Guidance Services, MDO
Criminal Justice/Safety Studies, B
Criminology, M
Curriculum and Instruction, MDO
Digital Communication and Media/Multimedia, B
Drama and Dramatics/Theatre Arts, B
Early Childhood Education and Teaching, BM
Economic Development, O

Economics, BM
Education, MDO
Educational Administration and Supervision, D
Educational Leadership and Administration, MDO
Educational Media/Instructional Technology, M
Educational Psychology, M
Electrical Engineering, MD
Electrical, Electronics and Communications Engineering, B
Elementary Education and Teaching, BM
Engineering and Applied Sciences, MD
English, M
English Education, M
English Language and Literature, B
English as a Second Language, M
English/Language Arts Teacher Education, B
Entrepreneurship/Entrepreneurial Studies, M
Environmental Design/Architecture, BO
Environmental Education, M
Environmental Engineering Technology/Environmental Technology, M
Environmental Sciences, M
Environmental Studies, O
Exercise and Sports Science, M
Experimental Psychology, D
Film, Television, and Video Production, O
Finance, B
Finance and Banking, D
Forensic Science and Technology, M
Foundations and Philosophy of Education, M
French Language and Literature, BM
Geography, BM
Geology/Earth Science, BM
Geosciences, D
German Language and Literature, M
Gerontological Nursing, O
Graphic Design, M
Health Promotion, M
Health Services Administration, M
Health/Health Care Administration/Management, B
Higher Education/Higher Education Administration, M
History, BMO
Hospitality Administration/Management, B
International Business/Trade/Commerce, BM
Jewish/Judaic Studies, B
Kinesiology and Exercise Science, B
Liberal Arts and Sciences Studies and Humanities, AB
Liberal Studies, M
Linguistics, BM
Management Information Systems and Services, BMD
Marketing, D
Marketing/Marketing Management, B
Marriage and Family Therapy/Counseling, O
Mathematics, BMD
Mathematics Teacher Education, BM
Mechanical Engineering, BMD
Media Studies, M
Medical Physics, M
Multilingual and Multicultural Education, M
Music, BM
Music History, Literature, and Theory, M
Music Teacher Education, BM
Neuroscience, D
Non-Profit/Public/Organizational Management, MD
Nursing, MDO
Nursing - Adult, O
Nursing - Advanced Practice, MO
Nursing Administration, MO
Nursing Education, MO
Ocean Engineering, BMD
Performance, M
Philosophy, B
Physics, BMD
Political Science and Government, BM
Psychology, BMD
Public Administration, BMD
Reading Teacher Education, M
Real Estate, B
Rehabilitation Counseling, M
Rhetoric, M
Science Teacher Education/General Science Teacher Education, BM
Security and Protective Services, B

Social Science Teacher Education, B
Social Sciences, B
Social Studies Teacher Education, M
Social Work, BM
Sociology, BM
Spanish Language and Literature, BM
Special Education and Teaching, BMD
Sport and Fitness Administration/Management, M
Statistics, M
Surveying Engineering, B
Sustainable Development, O
Taxation, M
Theater, M
Travel and Tourism, O
Urban and Regional Planning, MO
Women's Studies, MO
Writing, M

FLORIDA CAREER COLLEGE

Allied Health and Medical Assisting Services, A
Computer Engineering, A
Computer Programming/Programmer, A
Massage Therapy/Therapeutic Massage, A
Web/Multimedia Management and Webmaster, A

FLORIDA COLLEGE

American History (United States), B
Bible/Biblical Studies, B
Business Administration and Management, B
Elementary Education and Teaching, B
History, B
Liberal Arts and Sciences Studies and Humanities, AB
Music, B
Organizational Communication, B
Religious Education, B

FLORIDA COLLEGE OF NATURAL HEALTH (MAITLAND)

Aesthetician/Esthetician and Skin Care Specialist, A
Massage Therapy/Therapeutic Massage, A

FLORIDA COLLEGE OF NATURAL HEALTH (MIAMI)

Aesthetician/Esthetician and Skin Care Specialist, A
Massage Therapy/Therapeutic Massage, A

FLORIDA COLLEGE OF NATURAL HEALTH (POMPANO BEACH)

Aesthetician/Esthetician and Skin Care Specialist, A
Massage Therapy/Therapeutic Massage, A

FLORIDA GATEWAY COLLEGE

Computer Programming/Programmer, A
Computer and Information Sciences, A
Corrections, A
Criminal Justice/Law Enforcement Administration, A
Early Childhood Education and Teaching, AB
Emergency Medical Technology/Technician (EMT Paramedic), A
Engineering Technology, A
Graphic Design, A
Health Information/Medical Records Administration/Administrator, A
Health Services Administration, A
Information Technology, A
Liberal Arts and Sciences Studies and Humanities, A
Logistics and Materials Management, A
Natural Resources and Conservation, A
Office Management and Supervision, A
Physical Therapist Assistant, A
Veterinary/Animal Health Technology/Technician and Veterinary Assistant, A

FLORIDA GULF COAST UNIVERSITY

Accounting, BM
Allied Health and Medical Assisting Services, MD
Anthropology, B
Art/Art Studies, General, B
Athletic Training and Sports Medicine, B
BioTechnology, B
Biology/Biological Sciences, B
Biomedical/Medical Engineering, B

Business Administration, Management and Operations, M
Chemistry, B
Civil Engineering, B
Clinical Laboratory Science/Medical Technology/Technologist, B
Community Health and Preventive Medicine, B
Computer Science, M
Computer and Information Sciences, B
Counselor Education/School Counseling and Guidance Services, BM
Criminal Justice/Safety Studies, B
Criminalistics and Criminal Science, B
Criminology, M
Curriculum and Instruction, MDO
Drama and Dramatics/Theatre Arts, B
Early Childhood Education and Teaching, B
Economics, B
Education, BMDO
Educational Leadership and Administration, MDO
Educational Media/Instructional Technology, M
Elementary Education and Teaching, B
English, M
English Education, M
English Language and Literature, B
Environmental Policy, M
Environmental Sciences, M
Environmental/Environmental Health Engineering, B
Finance, B
Forensic Science and Technology, M
Health Services/Allied Health/Health Sciences, B
History, BM
Information Science/Studies, M
Interdisciplinary Studies, M
Kinesiology and Exercise Science, B
Legal Assistant/Paralegal, B
Liberal Arts and Sciences Studies and Humanities, B
Marketing/Marketing Management, B
Mass Communication/Media Studies, B
Mathematics, BM
Music Performance, B
Nurse Anesthetist, M
Occupational Therapy/Therapist, M
Philosophy, B
Physical Therapy/Therapist, MD
Political Science and Government, B
Psychology, B
Public Administration, M
Reading Teacher Education, M
Resort Management, B
Secondary Education and Teaching, B
Social Work, BM
Sociology, B
Spanish Language and Literature, B
Special Education and Teaching, BM
Taxation, M
Water, Wetlands, and Marine Resources Management, B

FLORIDA INSTITUTE OF TECHNOLOGY

Aeronautics/Aviation/Aerospace Science and Technology, B
Aerospace, Aeronautical and Astronautical Engineering, BMD
Air Transportation, B
Applied Behavior Analysis, MD
Applied Mathematics, B
Aquatic Biology/Limnology, B
Astronomy and Astrophysics, B
Aviation, MD
Aviation/Airway Management and Operations, BM
BioTechnology, M
Biochemistry, BM
Biological and Biomedical Sciences, MD
Biology Teacher Education, B
Biology/Biological Sciences, B
Biomathematics and Bioinformatics, B
Biomedical Engineering, MD
Biomedical Sciences, B
Biomedical/Medical Engineering, B
Business Administration and Management, B
Business Administration, Management and Operations, BMD
Cell Biology and Anatomy, M
Chemical Engineering, BMD

Chemistry, BMD
Chemistry Teacher Education, B
Civil Engineering, BMD
Communication and Media Studies, M
Communication, Journalism and Related Programs, B
Computer Education, M
Computer Engineering, B
Computer Science, BMD
Computer Software Engineering, B
Computer and Information Systems Security, M
Conservation Biology, BM
Construction Engineering Technology/Technician, B
Ecology, M
Education, M
Educational Media/Instructional Technology, M
Electrical Engineering, MD
Electrical, Electronics and Communications Engineering, B
Electronic Commerce, M
Elementary Education and Teaching, M
Emergency Management, M
Engineering, B
Engineering Management, M
Engineering and Applied Sciences, MD
Entrepreneurship/Entrepreneurial Studies, M
Environmental Education, M
Environmental Sciences, B
Ergonomics and Human Factors, MD
General Studies, B
Geosciences, M
Health Services Administration, M
Human Resources Management and Services, M
Human-Computer Interaction, M
Humanities/Humanistic Studies, B
Interdisciplinary Studies, M
International Business/Trade/Commerce, B
Junior High/Intermediate/Middle School Education and Teaching, B
Logistics and Materials Management, BM
Management, M
Management Information Systems and Services, BM
Management of Technology, M
Marine Biology and Biological Oceanography, BM
Marine Sciences, M
Marketing/Marketing Management, B
Mathematics, B
Mathematics Teacher Education, BMDO
Mechanical Engineering, BMD
Meteorology, BM
Molecular Biology, BM
Multi-/Interdisciplinary Studies, B
Ocean Engineering, BMD
Oceanography, Chemical and Physical, BMD
Operations Research, M
Organizational Behavior Studies, M
Organizational Management, M
Physical Sciences, B
Physics, B
Physics Teacher Education, B
Planetary Astronomy and Science, B
Pre-Law Studies, B
Project Management, M
Psychology, BMD
Public Administration, M
Quality Management, M
Safety Engineering, M
Science Teacher Education/General Science Teacher Education, BMDO
Small Business Administration/Management, B
Software Engineering, M
Sport and Fitness Administration/Management, B
Supply Chain Management, M
System Management, M
Systems Engineering, MD
Teacher Education and Professional Development, Specific Subject Areas, M
Transportation/Transportation Management, M

FLORIDA INTERNATIONAL UNIVERSITY

Accounting, BM
Adult and Continuing Education and Teaching, MD
African Studies, M
Allopathic Medicine, MD
Applied Behavior Analysis, M

Architecture, MO
Art Education, M
Art History, Criticism and Conservation, B
Art Teacher Education, B
Art/Art Studies, General, B
Asian Studies/Civilization, BM
Athletic Training and Sports Medicine, M
Biological and Biomedical Sciences, MD
Biology/Biological Sciences, B
Biomedical Engineering, MD
Biomedical/Medical Engineering, B
Biostatistics, M
Business Administration and Management, B
Business Administration, Management and Operations, MD
Chemistry, BMD
Civil Engineering, BMD
Clinical Psychology, MD
Communication Disorders, M
Communication Studies/Speech Communication and Rhetoric, B
Communication and Media Studies, M
Computer Engineering, BM
Computer Science, MD
Computer and Information Sciences, B
Construction Engineering Technology/Technician, B
Construction Management, M
Counseling Psychology, M
Counselor Education/School Counseling and Guidance Services, M
Criminal Justice/Safety Studies, B
Criminology, M
Curriculum and Instruction, MDO
Developmental Psychology, MD
Dietetics/Dieticians, B
Drama and Dramatics/Theatre Arts, B
Early Childhood Education and Teaching, BM
Economics, BMD
Education, MDO
Educational Administration and Supervision, MD
Educational Leadership and Administration, MO
Educational Media/Instructional Technology, MD
Electrical Engineering, MD
Electrical, Electronics and Communications Engineering, B
Elementary Education and Teaching, BM
Engineering and Applied Sciences, MD
English, M
English Education, M
English Language and Literature, B
English as a Second Language, M
Environmental Engineering Technology/Environmental Technology, M
Environmental Sciences, M
Environmental Studies, BM
Environmental and Occupational Health, MD
Environmental/Environmental Health Engineering, B
Epidemiology, MD
Finance, B
Finance and Banking, M
Fine Arts and Art Studies, MO
Fine/Studio Arts, B
Foreign Language Teacher Education, M
Forensic Science and Technology, MD
French Language and Literature, B
Geography, B
Geology/Earth Science, B
Geosciences, MD
Health Promotion, MD
Health Services Administration, M
Health/Health Care Administration/Management, B
Higher Education/Higher Education Administration, D
History, BMD
Hospitality Administration/Management, BM
Human Resources Development, MD
Human Resources Management and Services, M
Human Resources Management/Personnel Administration, B
Industrial and Organizational Psychology, MD
Information Science/Studies, MD
Information Technology, B
Interior Design, BMO
International Affairs, MD
International Business/Trade/Commerce, BMD
International Relations and Affairs, B

International and Comparative Education, M
Italian Language and Literature, B
Journalism, M
Landscape Architecture, M
Latin American Studies, M
Law and Legal Studies, D
Liberal Arts and Sciences Studies and Humanities, B
Liberal Studies, M
Linguistics, M
Management Information Systems and Services, BMD
Marine Biology and Biological Oceanography, B
Marketing/Marketing Management, B
Mass Communication/Media Studies, BM
Materials Engineering, MD
Materials Sciences, MD
Mathematics, BM
Mathematics Teacher Education, M
Mechanical Engineering, BMD
Multi-/Interdisciplinary Studies, B
Multilingual and Multicultural Education, M
Museology/Museum Studies, O
Music, BM
Music Teacher Education, M
Nursing, MD
Nutritional Sciences, MD
Occupational Therapy/Therapist, M
Parks, Recreation and Leisure Facilities Management, B
Philosophy, B
Physical Education Teaching and Coaching, BM
Physical Therapy/Therapist, D
Physics, BMD
Political Science and Government, BMD
Portuguese Language and Literature, B
Psychology, BMD
Public Administration, BMD
Public Affairs, D
Public Health, MD
Reading Teacher Education, MD
Real Estate, BM
Recreation and Park Management, M
Rehabilitation Counseling, M
Religion/Religious Studies, BM
School Psychology, MO
Science Teacher Education/General Science Teacher Education, M
Social Studies Teacher Education, M
Social Work, BMD
Sociology, BMD
Spanish Language and Literature, BMD
Special Education and Teaching, BMD
Sport and Fitness Administration/Management, M
Statistics, BM
Taxation, M
Telecommunications, M
Therapeutic Recreation, M
Urban Education and Leadership, M
Women's Studies, B
Writing, M

FLORIDA KEYS COMMUNITY COLLEGE

Business Administration and Management, A
Cinematography and Film/Video Production, A
Commercial and Advertising Art, A
Computer Programming/Programmer, A
Computer Systems Analysis/Analyst, A
Criminal Justice/Law Enforcement Administration, A
Fishing and Fisheries Sciences and Management, A
Legal Assistant/Paralegal, A
Liberal Arts and Sciences Studies and Humanities, A
Mechanical Engineering Related Technologies/Technicians, A
Parks, Recreation, Leisure and Fitness Studies, A

FLORIDA MEMORIAL UNIVERSITY

Accounting, B
Air Traffic Controller, B
Aviation/Airway Management and Operations, B
Biology/Biological Sciences, B
Business Administration and Management, B
Business Administration, Management and Operations, M

Clinical Laboratory Science/Medical Technology/Technologist, B
Computer Science, B
Criminal Justice/Law Enforcement Administration, B
Data Processing and Data Processing Technology/Technician, B
Education, M
Elementary Education and Teaching, BM
English Language and Literature, B
Mathematics, B
Modern Languages, B
Music Teacher Education, B
Physical Education Teaching and Coaching, B
Political Science and Government, B
Psychology, B
Public Administration, B
Reading Teacher Education, M
Religion/Religious Studies, B
Secondary Education and Teaching, B
Sociology, B
Special Education and Teaching, M
Urban Studies/Affairs, B

FLORIDA NATIONAL UNIVERSITY

Accounting, B
Accounting Technology/Technician and Bookkeeping, A
Accounting and Related Services, A
Allied Health and Medical Assisting Services, A
Business Administration and Management, AB
Business Administration, Management and Operations, M
Business, Management, Marketing, and Related Support Services, A
Computer Science, A
Computer Systems Networking and Telecommunications, A
Criminal Justice/Law Enforcement Administration, B
Criminal Justice/Safety Studies, A
Dental Hygiene/Hygienist, A
Dental Laboratory Technology/Technician, A
Diagnostic Medical Sonography/Sonographer and Ultrasound Technician, A
Digital Communication and Media/Multimedia, A
Education, A
Finance and Banking, M
Health Services Administration, AB
Hospitality Administration/Management, A
Information Technology, A
Law and Legal Studies, B
Legal Assistant/Paralegal, A
Liberal Arts and Sciences Studies and Humanities, B
Marketing, M
Medical Administrative Assistant/Secretary, A
Medical Microbiology and Bacteriology, A
Medical/Clinical Assistant, A
Medical/Health Management and Clinical Assistant/Specialist, A
Pre-Law Studies, A
Psychology, B
Public Administration, A
Radiologic Technology/Science - Radiographer, A
Respiratory Therapy Technician/Assistant, A
System Administration/Administrator, A
Web Page, Digital/Multimedia and Information Resources Design, A

THE FLORIDA SCHOOL OF TRADITIONAL MIDWIFERY

Direct Entry Midwifery (LM, CPM), A

FLORIDA SOUTHERN COLLEGE

Accounting, B
Acting, B
Agricultural Business and Management, B
Art History, Criticism and Conservation, B
Art Teacher Education, B
Athletic Training and Sports Medicine, B
BioTechnology, B
Biochemistry, Biophysics and Molecular Biology, B
Biology Teacher Education, B
Biology/Biological Sciences, B
Business Administration and Management, B
Business Administration, Management and Operations, M

Chemistry, B
Computer Science, B
Criminology, B
Dance, B
Drama and Dramatics/Theatre Arts, B
Economics, B
Education, M
Elementary Education and Teaching, B
English/Language Arts Teacher Education, B
Environmental Studies, B
Exercise Physiology, B
Fine/Studio Arts, B
Foreign Language Teacher Education, B
Gerontological Nursing, M
Health/Health Care Administration/Management, B
History, B
History Teacher Education, B
Humanities/Humanistic Studies, B
Marine Biology and Biological Oceanography, B
Mass Communication/Media Studies, B
Mathematics, B
Mathematics Teacher Education, B
Multi-/Interdisciplinary Studies, B
Music, B
Music Performance, B
Music Teacher Education, B
Nursing, M
Nursing - Adult, M
Nursing Administration, M
Nursing Education, M
Organizational Communication, B
Philosophy, B
Political Communication, B
Political Science and Government, B
Pre-Dentistry Studies, B
Pre-Law Studies, B
Pre-Medicine/Pre-Medical Studies, B
Pre-Veterinary Studies, B
Psychology, B
Religion/Religious Studies, B
Small Business Administration/Management, B
Social Science Teacher Education, B
Social Sciences, B
Spanish Language and Literature, B
Sport and Fitness Administration/Management, B
Teacher Education, Multiple Levels, B
Technical Theatre/Theatre Design and Technology, B
Youth Ministry, B

FLORIDA SOUTHWESTERN STATE COLLEGE

Accounting Technology/Technician and Bookkeeping, A
Architectural Technology/Technician, A
Biology Teacher Education, B
Biology Technician/BioTechnology Laboratory Technician, A
Business Administration and Management, A
Business Administration, Management and Operations, B
Cardiovascular Technology/Technologist, A
Child Care Provider/Assistant, A
Civil Engineering Technology/Technician, A
Community Health Services/Liaison/Counseling, A
Computer Programming/Programmer, A
Computer Systems Networking and Telecommunications, A
Criminal Justice/Law Enforcement Administration, AB
Dental Hygiene/Hygienist, A
Drafting and Design Technology/Technician, A
Early Childhood Education and Teaching, A
Elementary Education and Teaching, B
Emergency Medical Technology/Technician (EMT Paramedic), A
English/Language Arts Teacher Education, B
Fire Protection and Safety Technology/Technician, A
Forensic Science and Technology, A
Health Information/Medical Records Technology/Technician, A
Information Technology, A
Legal Assistant/Paralegal, A
Liberal Arts and Sciences Studies and Humanities, A
Management Information Systems and Services, A

Mathematics Teacher Education, B
Medical Radiologic Technology/Science - Radiation Therapist, A
Operations Management and Supervision, B
Opticianry/Ophthalmic Dispensing Optician, A
Physical Therapist Assistant, A
Respiratory Care Therapy/Therapist, AB
Respiratory Therapy Technician/Assistant, A
Science Teacher Education/General Science Teacher Education, B
Security and Protective Services, B
Substance Abuse/Addiction Counseling, A
System Administration/Administrator, A
Turf and Turfgrass Management, A
Web Page, Digital/Multimedia and Information Resources Design, A

FLORIDA STATE COLLEGE AT JACKSONVILLE

Airframe Mechanics and Aircraft Maintenance Technology/Technician, A
Airline/Commercial/Professional Pilot and Flight Crew, A
Animation, Interactive Technology, Video Graphics and Special Effects, B
Architectural Technology/Technician, A
Autobody/Collision and Repair Technology/Technician, A
Automobile/Automotive Mechanics Technology/Technician, A
Automotive Engineering Technology/Technician, A
Aviation/Airway Management and Operations, A
Biology Technician/BioTechnology Laboratory Technician, A
Biomedical Sciences, B
Biomedical Technology/Technician, A
Business Administration and Management, A
Business Administration, Management and Operations, B
Cardiovascular Technology/Technologist, A
Child Care Provider/Assistant, A
Child Care and Support Services Management, A
Clinical/Medical Laboratory Technician, A
Computer Graphics, A
Computer Systems Networking and Telecommunications, B
Computer/Information Technology Services Administration and Management, B
Criminal Justice/Law Enforcement Administration, A
Criminal Justice/Police Science, A
Culinary Arts/Chef Training, A
Dental Hygiene/Hygienist, A
Drafting and Design Technology/Technician, A
Early Childhood Education and Teaching, B
Education/Teaching of Individuals with Hearing Impairments, Including Deafness, A
Emergency Medical Technology/Technician (EMT Paramedic), A
Engineering Technology, A
Environmental Sciences, A
Finance, B
Fire Protection and Safety Technology/Technician, A
Fire Science/Firefighting, A
Fire Services Administration, A
Funeral Service and Mortuary Science, A
Health Information/Medical Records Technology/Technician, A
Histologic Technician, A
Hotel/Motel Administration/Management, A
Information Technology, A
Interior Design, A
Legal Assistant/Paralegal, A
Liberal Arts and Sciences Studies and Humanities, A
Logistics and Materials Management, B
Marketing/Marketing Management, A
Mass Communication/Media Studies, B
Medical Radiologic Technology/Science - Radiation Therapist, A
Occupational Therapist Assistant, A
Office Management and Supervision, A
Operations Management and Supervision, A
Ophthalmic Technician/Technologist, A
Physical Therapist Assistant, A
Real Estate, A
Respiratory Care Therapy/Therapist, A

Restaurant, Culinary, and Catering Management/Manager, A
Security and Protective Services, B
System Administration/Administrator, A
Technical Theatre/Theatre Design and Technology, A
Transportation/Transportation Management, A
Web Page, Digital/Multimedia and Information Resources Design, A

FLORIDA STATE UNIVERSITY

Accounting, BMD
Acting, B
American/United States Studies/Civilization, M
Analytical Chemistry, MD
Applied Behavior Analysis, M
Applied Mathematics, MD
Applied Statistics, M
Archeology, M
Art Education, MDO
Art History, Criticism and Conservation, BMDO
Arts Management, M
Asian Studies/Civilization, M
Athletic Training and Sports Medicine, B
Atmospheric Sciences and Meteorology, BD
Biochemistry, BMD
Bioinformatics, M
Biological and Biomedical Sciences, MD
Biomathematics and Bioinformatics, B
Biomedical Engineering, MD
Biostatistics, MD
Business Administration and Management, B
Business Administration, Management and Operations, MD
Business/Commerce, B
Cell Biology and Anatomy, MD
Cell/Cellular and Molecular Biology, B
Chemical Engineering, MD
Chemistry, BMD
Child and Family Studies, MD
Civil Engineering, MD
Classics and Classical Languages, Literatures, and Linguistics, MD
Clinical Psychology, D
Cognitive Sciences, D
Communication Disorders, MD
Communication Theory, D
Communication and Media Studies, BMD
Community College Education, M
Composition, MD
Computational Biology, D
Computational Sciences, MD
Computer Science, MD
Computer Software and Media Applications, B
Computer and Information Systems Security, M
Corporate and Organizational Communication, M
Counseling Psychology, D
Criminology, BMD
Cultural Studies, M
Curriculum and Instruction, MDO
Dance, BM
Demography and Population Studies, M
Developmental Psychology, D
Distance Education Development, M
Drama and Dramatics/Theatre Arts, B
Early Childhood Education and Teaching, BMDO
East European and Russian Studies, M
Ecology, MD
Economics, BMD
Education, MDO
Educational Administration and Supervision, MDO
Educational Leadership and Administration, MDO
Educational Measurement and Evaluation, MDO
Educational Media/Instructional Technology, MDO
Educational Policy, MDO
Educational Psychology, MDO
Electrical Engineering, MD
Elementary Education and Teaching, MDO
Energy and Power Engineering, M
Engineering and Applied Sciences, MD
English, MD
English Education, MDO
English Language and Literature, B
Entrepreneurial and Small Business Operations, B
Environmental Engineering Technology/Environmental Technology, MD

Environmental Law, M
Environmental Sciences, M
Ethnomusicology, MD
Evolutionary Biology, MD
Exercise and Sports Science, MD
Family and Consumer Sciences/Human Sciences, MD
Film, Television, and Video Production, M
Film/Cinema Studies, B
Finance, B
Finance and Banking, MD
Fine Arts and Art Studies, M
Fine/Studio Arts, B
Food Science and Technology, MD
Foreign Language Teacher Education, MDO
French Language and Literature, MD
Geographic Information Systems, M
Geography, BMD
Geology/Earth Science, BMD
Geophysics and Seismology, D
Geosciences, D
German Language and Literature, M
Graphic Design, B
Health Education, M
Higher Education/Higher Education Administration, MDO
History, BMD
Hospitality Administration/Management, B
Human Development and Family Studies, B
Human Resources Management and Services, D
Humanities/Humanistic Studies, B
Industrial Design, M
Industrial/Management Engineering, MD
Information Science/Studies, MDO
Inorganic Chemistry, MD
Insurance, MD
Interior Design, BM
International Affairs, M
International Business/Trade/Commerce, M
International Relations and Affairs, B
International and Comparative Education, MD
Italian Language and Literature, M
Jazz/Jazz Studies, B
Kinesiology and Exercise Science, B
Law and Legal Studies, MD
Library Science, MDO
Management Information Systems and Services, MD
Management Strategy and Policy, D
Manufacturing Engineering, MD
Marine Sciences, M
Marketing, MD
Marriage and Family Therapy/Counseling, D
Materials Engineering, MD
Materials Sciences, MD
Mathematical and Computational Finance, MD
Mathematics, BMD
Mathematics Teacher Education, MDO
Mechanical Engineering, MD
Media Studies, M
Meteorology, BMD
Molecular Biology, MD
Molecular Biophysics, D
Museology/Museum Studies, MO
Music, BMD
Music History, Literature, and Theory, MD
Music Teacher Education, MD
Music Theory and Composition, BMD
Music Therapy/Therapist, BM
Musicology and Ethnomusicology, MD
Neuroscience, MD
Nursing, MDO
Nursing - Advanced Practice, D
Nursing Administration, MO
Nursing Education, MO
Nutritional Sciences, MD
Oceanography, Chemical and Physical, MD
Organic Chemistry, MD
Organizational Behavior Studies, D
Performance, MD
Philosophy, BMD
Physical Chemistry, MD
Physical Education Teaching and Coaching, MDO
Physics, BMD
Plant Biology, MD

Political Science and Government, BMD
Psychology, BMD
Public Administration, MDO
Public Health, M
Public History, M
Public Policy Analysis, MDO
Reading Teacher Education, MDO
Recreation and Park Management, MDO
Religion/Religious Studies, MD
Rhetoric, MD
School Psychology, D
Science Teacher Education/General Science Teacher Education, MDO
Secondary Education and Teaching, M
Slavic Languages, Literatures, and Linguistics, M
Social Psychology, D
Social Sciences, B
Social Studies Teacher Education, MDO
Social Work, BMD
Sociology, BMD
Spanish Language and Literature, MD
Special Education and Teaching, MDO
Sport Psychology, MD
Sport and Fitness Administration/Management, MDO
Statistics, BMD
Structural Biology, MD
Taxation, M
Theater, MD
Urban and Regional Planning, MD
Writing, MD

FLORIDA TECHNICAL COLLEGE (DELAND)

CAD/CADD Drafting and/or Design Technology/Technician, A
Computer Science, A
Criminal Justice/Safety Studies, A
Legal Assistant/Paralegal, A
Medical Administrative Assistant/Secretary, A
Medical/Clinical Assistant, A
Web Page, Digital/Multimedia and Information Resources Design, A

FLORIDA TECHNICAL COLLEGE (ORLANDO)

Business Administration and Management, A
CAD/CADD Drafting and/or Design Technology/Technician, A
Computer Programming, Vendor/Product Certification, A
Computer Systems Networking and Telecommunications, A
Criminal Justice/Law Enforcement Administration, A
Electrical and Electronic Engineering Technologies/Technicians, A
Legal Assistant/Paralegal, A
Medical Administrative Assistant/Secretary, A
Medical/Clinical Assistant, A
Web Page, Digital/Multimedia and Information Resources Design, A

FORTIS COLLEGE (LARGO)

Medical/Clinical Assistant, A

FORTIS COLLEGE (ORANGE PARK)

Accounting, A
Business Administration and Management, A
Business Administration, Management and Operations, A
Business/Office Automation/Technology/Data Entry, A
Criminal Justice/Law Enforcement Administration, A
Health and Medical Administrative Services, A
Medical/Clinical Assistant, A
Pharmacy Technician/Assistant, A
Surgical Technology/Technologist, A

FORTIS COLLEGE (WINTER PARK)

Accounting Technology/Technician and Bookkeeping, A
Business Administration and Management, A
Business/Commerce, A
Criminal Justice/Safety Studies, A
Entrepreneurship/Entrepreneurial Studies, A

Health Information/Medical Records Technology/Technician, A
Medical Insurance Coding Specialist/Coder, A
Medical Insurance Specialist/Medical Biller, A
Medical Office Assistant/Specialist, A
Medical/Clinical Assistant, A
Pharmacy Technician/Assistant, A

FORTIS INSTITUTE (PALM SPRINGS)

Clinical/Medical Laboratory Technician, A
Computer Technology/Computer Systems Technology, A
Medical Radiologic Technology/Science - Radiation Therapist, A

FULL SAIL UNIVERSITY

Animation, Interactive Technology, Video Graphics and Special Effects, B
Audiovisual Communications Technologies/Technicians, B
Business Administration, Management and Operations, M
Business, Management, Marketing, and Related Support Services, B
Cinematography and Film/Video Production, B
Communication and Media Studies, B
Computer Art and Design, M
Computer Graphics, B
Computer Programming, Specific Applications, B
Computer Teacher Education, A
Design and Applied Arts, B
Design and Visual Communications, B
E-Commerce/Electronic Commerce, B
Educational Media/Instructional Technology, M
Entertainment Management, M
Film/Cinema Studies, B
Film/Video and Photographic Arts, B
Fine Arts and Art Studies, M
Game Design and Development, M
Graphic Communications, B
Graphic Design, BM
Internet and Interactive Multimedia, M
Journalism, M
Marketing, M
Media Studies, M
Music Theory and Composition, B
Recording Arts Technology/Technician, B
Web Page, Digital/Multimedia and Information Resources Design, B
Writing, M

GULF COAST STATE COLLEGE

Accounting Technology/Technician and Bookkeeping, A
Animation, Interactive Technology, Video Graphics and Special Effects, B
Business Administration and Management, A
Business Administration, Management and Operations, B
CAD/CADD Drafting and/or Design Technology/Technician, A
Child Care Provider/Assistant, A
Civil Engineering Technology/Technician, A
Communications Technology/Technician, A
Computer Programming, Vendor/Product Certification, A
Computer Programming/Programmer, A
Computer Systems Networking and Telecommunications, A
Computer/Information Technology Services Administration and Management, B
Construction Engineering Technology/Technician, A
Criminal Justice/Law Enforcement Administration, A
Dental Hygiene/Hygienist, A
Diagnostic Medical Sonography/Sonographer and Ultrasound Technician, A
Digital Communication and Media/Multimedia, A
Early Childhood Education and Teaching, A
Electrical, Electronic and Communications Engineering Technology/Technician, A
Emergency Medical Technology/Technician (EMT Paramedic), A
Engineering Technology, A
Fire Protection and Safety Technology/Technician, A
Forensic Science and Technology, A
Health Services/Allied Health/Health Sciences, A

Hospitality Administration/Management, A
Liberal Arts and Sciences Studies and Humanities, A
Management Information Systems and Services, A
Manufacturing Technology/Technician, A
Medical Administrative Assistant/Secretary, A
Medical Radiologic Technology/Science - Radiation Therapist, A
Nuclear Medical Technology/Technologist, A
Office Management and Supervision, A
Physical Therapist Assistant, A
Respiratory Care Therapy/Therapist, A
Restaurant, Culinary, and Catering Management/Manager, A
Surgical Technology/Technologist, A
System Administration/Administrator, A
Transportation/Transportation Management, A
Web Page, Digital/Multimedia and Information Resources Design, A

HILLSBOROUGH COMMUNITY COLLEGE

Accounting Technology/Technician and Bookkeeping, A
Aquaculture, A
Architectural Engineering Technology/Technician, A
Biology Technician/BioTechnology Laboratory Technician, A
Business Administration and Management, A
Child Care and Support Services Management, A
Cinematography and Film/Video Production, A
Computer Programming, Specific Applications, A
Computer Systems Analysis/Analyst, A
Computer Technology/Computer Systems Technology, A
Criminal Justice/Law Enforcement Administration, A
Dental Hygiene/Hygienist, A
Diagnostic Medical Sonography/Sonographer and Ultrasound Technician, A
Dietician Assistant, A
Education/Teaching of Individuals with Hearing Impairments, Including Deafness, A
Electrical, Electronic and Communications Engineering Technology/Technician, A
Emergency Medical Technology/Technician (EMT Paramedic), A
Engineering Technology, A
Environmental Control Technologies/Technicians, A
Executive Assistant/Executive Secretary, A
Fire Protection and Safety Technology/Technician, A
Hospitality Administration/Management, A
Legal Assistant/Paralegal, A
Liberal Arts and Sciences Studies and Humanities, A
Management Information Systems and Services, A
Medical Radiologic Technology/Science - Radiation Therapist, A
Nuclear Medical Technology/Technologist, A
Operations Management and Supervision, A
Opticianry/Ophthalmic Dispensing Optician, A
Optometric Technician/Assistant, A
Psychiatric/Mental Health Services Technician, A
Respiratory Care Therapy/Therapist, A
Restaurant, Culinary, and Catering Management/Manager, A
Restaurant/Food Services Management, A
Veterinary/Animal Health Technology/Technician and Veterinary Assistant, A

HOBE SOUND BIBLE COLLEGE

Accounting, A
Administrative Assistant and Secretarial Science, A
Bible/Biblical Studies, B
Computer Software and Media Applications, A
Elementary Education and Teaching, B
English/Language Arts Teacher Education, B
History Teacher Education, B
Liberal Arts and Sciences Studies and Humanities, AB
Mathematics Teacher Education, B
Missions/Missionary Studies and Missiology, AB
Music, B
Music Teacher Education, B
Science Teacher Education/General Science Teacher Education, B

Theology and Religious Vocations, B

HODGES UNIVERSITY

Accounting, M
Business Administration, Management and Operations, BM
Clinical Psychology, M
Computer/Information Technology Services Administration and Management, B
Counseling Psychology, M
Health Information/Medical Records Technology/Technician, A
Health Services Administration, M
Health/Health Care Administration/Management, B
Health/Medical Preparatory Programs, B
Legal Assistant/Paralegal, A
Legal Professions and Studies, B
Legal and Justice Studies, M
Management, M
Management Information Systems and Services, M
Medical/Clinical Assistant, A

INDIAN RIVER STATE COLLEGE

Accounting, A
Administrative Assistant and Secretarial Science, A
Agricultural Business and Management, A
Airline/Commercial/Professional Pilot and Flight Crew, A
Anthropology, A
Apparel and Textiles, A
Architectural Drafting and Architectural CAD/CADD, A
Art Teacher Education, A
Automobile/Automotive Mechanics Technology/Technician, A
Banking and Financial Support Services, A
Biology Teacher Education, B
Biology/Biological Sciences, A
Business Administration and Management, A
Carpentry/Carpenter, A
Chemistry, A
Child Development, A
Civil Engineering Technology/Technician, A
Clinical/Medical Laboratory Technician, A
Computer Engineering Technology/Technician, A
Computer Programming/Programmer, A
Computer Science, A
Computer Typography and Composition Equipment Operator, A
Consumer Merchandising/Retailing Management, A
Corrections, A
Cosmetology/Cosmetologist, A
Criminal Justice/Law Enforcement Administration, A
Criminal Justice/Police Science, A
Criminal Justice/Safety Studies, B
Culinary Arts/Chef Training, A
Dental Hygiene/Hygienist, A
Drafting and Design Technology/Technician, A
Drama and Dramatics/Theatre Arts, A
Economics, A
Education, A
Electrical, Electronic and Communications Engineering Technology/Technician, A
Emergency Medical Technology/Technician (EMT Paramedic), A
Engineering, A
Engineering Technology, A
English Language and Literature, A
Family and Consumer Sciences/Human Sciences, A
Fashion Merchandising, A
Finance, A
Fire Science/Firefighting, A
Foods, Nutrition, and Wellness Studies, A
Forestry, A
French Language and Literature, A
Health Information/Medical Records Administration/Administrator, A
Health/Health Care Administration/Management, B
Heating, Air Conditioning, Ventilation and Refrigeration Maintenance Technology/Technician, A
History, A
Hotel/Motel Administration/Management, A
Human Services, A
Humanities/Humanistic Studies, A
Hydrology and Water Resources Science, A
Industrial Radiologic Technology/Technician, A

Information Science/Studies, A
Interior Design, A
Journalism, A
Kindergarten/PreSchool Education and Teaching, A
Language Interpretation and Translation, A
Legal Assistant/Paralegal, A
Liberal Arts and Sciences Studies and Humanities, A
Library Science, A
Marine Science/Merchant Marine Officer, A
Marketing/Marketing Management, A
Mathematics, A
Mathematics Teacher Education, B
Medical Administrative Assistant/Secretary, A
Music, A
Organizational Behavior Studies, B
Pharmacy, A
Philosophy, A
Physical Education Teaching and Coaching, A
Physical Therapist Assistant, A
Physical Therapy/Therapist, A
Physics, A
Political Science and Government, A
Psychology, A
Respiratory Care Therapy/Therapist, A
Science Teacher Education/General Science Teacher Education, B
Social Sciences, A
Social Work, A
Sociology, A
Spanish Language and Literature, A
Special Education and Teaching, B
Special Products Marketing Operations, A
Survey Technology/Surveying, A
Teacher Assistant/Aide, A

JACKSONVILLE UNIVERSITY

Accounting, BM
Airline/Commercial/Professional Pilot and Flight Crew, B
Army JROTC/ROTC, B
Art History, Criticism and Conservation, B
Art Teacher Education, B
Art/Art Studies, General, B
Aviation/Airway Management and Operations, B
Biology/Biological Sciences, B
Business Administration and Management, B
Business Administration, Management and Operations, BM
Business/Commerce, B
Business/Managerial Economics, B
Chemistry, B
Clinical Laboratory Science/Medical Technology/Technologist, B
Commercial and Advertising Art, B
Communication Disorders, B
Communication Studies/Speech Communication and Rhetoric, B
Computer and Information Sciences, B
Dance, BM
Design and Visual Communications, B
Drama and Dance Teacher Education, B
Drama and Dramatics/Theatre Arts, B
Economics, B
Education, M
Educational Leadership and Administration, M
Electrical, Electronics and Communications Engineering, B
Elementary Education and Teaching, B
Engineering, B
Engineering Physics, B
English Language and Literature, B
Entrepreneurship/Entrepreneurial Studies, B
Fashion/Apparel Design, B
Film/Cinema Studies, B
Finance, B
Finance and Banking, M
Fine Arts and Art Studies, B
Fine/Studio Arts, B
French Language and Literature, B
General Studies, B
Geography, B
Germanic Languages, Literatures, and Linguistics, B
Health and Physical Education, B
History, B
Humanities/Humanistic Studies, B

Information Science/Studies, B
Intermedia/Multimedia, B
International Business/Trade/Commerce, B
International Relations and Affairs, B
Jazz/Jazz Studies, B
Kinesiology and Exercise Science, B
Liberal Arts and Sciences Studies and Humanities, B
Management Information Systems and Services, B
Management Science, B
Marine Biology and Biological Oceanography, B
Marine Science/Merchant Marine Officer, B
Marine Sciences, M
Marketing/Marketing Management, B
Mass Communication/Media Studies, B
Mathematics, B
Mechanical Engineering, B
Multi-/Interdisciplinary Studies, B
Music, B
Music History, Literature, and Theory, B
Music Performance, B
Music Teacher Education, B
Music Theory and Composition, B
Navy/Marine Corps JROTC/ROTC, B
Nursing, MD
Organizational Management, M
Orthodontics, O
Philosophy, B
Physical Education Teaching and Coaching, B
Physics, B
Piano and Organ, B
Political Science and Government, B
Pre-Dentistry Studies, B
Pre-Law Studies, B
Pre-Medicine/Pre-Medical Studies, B
Pre-Nursing Studies, B
Pre-Veterinary Studies, B
Psychology, B
Public Policy Analysis, B
Religious/Sacred Music, B
Secondary Education and Teaching, B
Social Sciences, B
Sociology, B
Spanish Language and Literature, B
Special Education and Teaching, B
Sport and Fitness Administration/Management, BM
Visual and Performing Arts, B
Voice and Opera, B

JOHNSON UNIVERSITY FLORIDA

Bible/Biblical Studies, AB
Divinity/Ministry (BD, MDiv.), AB
Humanities/Humanistic Studies, B
Religious Education, B

JOHNSON & WALES UNIVERSITY

Baking and Pastry Arts/Baker/Pastry Chef, AB
Business Administration and Management, B
Criminal Justice/Law Enforcement Administration, B
Culinary Arts and Related Services, AB
Culinary Arts/Chef Training, AB
Fashion Merchandising, B
Food Service, Waiter/Waitress, and Dining Room
    Management/Manager, A
Hospitality Administration/Management, B
Hotel/Motel Administration/Management, B
Marketing/Marketing Management, B
Parks, Recreation and Leisure Facilities Management, B
Restaurant, Culinary, and Catering
    Management/Manager, B
Sport and Fitness Administration/Management, B
Tourism and Travel Services Management, B

JONES COLLEGE

Allied Health and Medical Assisting Services, AB
Business Administration and Management, AB
Computer and Information Sciences, AB
Elementary Education and Teaching, B
Legal Assistant/Paralegal, AB

JOSE MARIA VARGAS UNIVERSITY

Accounting, A
Business Administration and Management, B
Early Childhood Education and Teaching, ABM

Graphic Design, B

KEISER UNIVERSITY

Accounting, ABM
Baking and Pastry Arts/Baker/Pastry Chef, A
BioTechnology, AB
Biomedical Sciences, B
Business Administration and Management, AB
Business Administration, Management and Operations, MD
CAD/CADD Drafting and/or Design
    Technology/Technician, A
Clinical/Medical Laboratory Technician, A
Computer Software Engineering, B
Computer Systems Networking and Telecommunications, B
Computer and Information Systems Security, M
Criminal Justice/Law Enforcement Administration, AB
Criminal Justice/Safety Studies, B
Criminalistics and Criminal Science, A
Criminology, M
Culinary Arts/Chef Training, A
Design and Visual Communications, A
Diagnostic Medical Sonography/Sonographer and
    Ultrasound Technician, A
Dietetics/Dieticians, B
Distance Education Development, M
Education, M
Educational Administration and Supervision, M
Educational Leadership and Administration, MDO
Educational Media/Instructional Technology, DO
Elementary Education and Teaching, B
Finance, B
Fire Science/Firefighting, A
Forensic Science and Technology, B
Health Education, M
Health Information/Medical Records
    Administration/Administrator, AB
Health Information/Medical Records
    Technology/Technician, AB
Health Services Administration, ABM
Health Services/Allied Health/Health Sciences, B
Histologic Technology/Histotechnologist, A
Homeland Security, M
Hospitality Administration/Management, A
Human Resources Management/Personnel Administration, B
Industrial and Organizational Psychology, MD
Information Technology, AB
International Business/Trade/Commerce, BMD
Kinesiology and Exercise Science, B
Law and Legal Studies, B
Legal Assistant/Paralegal, A
Management, M
Management Information Systems and Services, BM
Management Science, B
Marketing, MD
Marketing/Marketing Management, B
Massage Therapy/Therapeutic Massage, A
Medical Radiologic Technology/Science - Radiation
    Therapist, A
Medical/Clinical Assistant, A
Nuclear Medical Technology/Technologist, A
Nursing, M
Nutritional Sciences, B
Occupational Therapist Assistant, A
Organizational Management, D
Physical Therapist Assistant, A
Physician Assistant, M
Political Science and Government, B
Psychology, BMD
Public Administration, B
Radiation Protection/Health Physics Technician, A
Respiratory Care Therapy/Therapist, A
Respiratory Therapy Technician/Assistant, A
Sport and Fitness Administration/Management, A
Surgical Technology/Technologist, A

KEY COLLEGE

Court Reporting/Court Reporter, A
Drafting and Design Technology/Technician, A
Legal Assistant/Paralegal, A

Medical Office Management/Administration, A

LAKE-SUMTER STATE COLLEGE

Business Administration and Management, A
Child Care Provider/Assistant, A
Commercial and Advertising Art, A
Computer Science, A
Computer Technology/Computer Systems Technology, A
Computer and Information Sciences, A
Criminal Justice/Law Enforcement Administration, A
Early Childhood Education and Teaching, A
Electrical, Electronic and Communications Engineering Technology/Technician, A
Emergency Medical Technology/Technician (EMT
    Paramedic), A
Fire Science/Firefighting, A
Health Information/Medical Records
    Administration/Administrator, A
Legal Assistant/Paralegal, A
Liberal Arts and Sciences Studies and Humanities, A
Mathematics, A
Office Management and Supervision, A
Sport and Fitness Administration/Management, A

LINCOLN COLLEGE OF TECHNOLOGY

Administrative Assistant and Secretarial Science, A
Architectural Drafting and Architectural
    CAD/CADD, A
Automobile/Automotive Mechanics
    Technology/Technician, A
Baking and Pastry Arts/Baker/Pastry Chef, A
Computer Systems Networking and Telecommunications, A
Culinary Arts/Chef Training, A
Electrical/Electronics Equipment Installation and Repair, A
Health and Physical Education, A
Heating, Air Conditioning and Refrigeration
    Technology/Technician, A
Legal Assistant/Paralegal, A
Medical Office Management/Administration, A
Restaurant, Culinary, and Catering
    Management/Manager, AB
Salon/Beauty Salon Management/Manager, A

LINCOLN CULINARY INSTITUTE

Baking and Pastry Arts/Baker/Pastry Chef, A
Culinary Arts/Chef Training, A
Restaurant, Culinary, and Catering
    Management/Manager, A

LYNN UNIVERSITY

Applied Psychology, M
Aviation/Airway Management and Operations, B
Biology/Biological Sciences, B
Business Administration and Management, B
Business Administration, Management and Operations, M
Cinematography and Film/Video Production, B
Communication and Media Studies, B
Composition, M
Criminal Justice/Law Enforcement Administration, B
Criminology, M
Drama and Dramatics/Theatre Arts, B
Education, MD
Education/Teaching of the Gifted and Talented, M
Educational Leadership and Administration, MD
Elementary Education and Teaching, B
Emergency Management, M
Entrepreneurship/Entrepreneurial Studies, B
Environmental Studies, B
Fashion Merchandising, B
Forensic Science and Technology, B
Hospitality Administration/Management, BM
International Business/Trade/Commerce, BM
Internet and Interactive Multimedia, MO
Investment Management, M
Investments and Securities, B
Journalism, B
Marketing, M
Marketing/Marketing Management, B
Mass Communication/Media Studies, BMO
Media Studies, M
Music Performance, B

Music Theory and Composition, B
Performance, MO
Political Science and Government, B
Psychology, B
Special Education and Teaching, M
Sport and Fitness Administration/Management, BM

MARCONI INTERNATIONAL UNIVERSITY

Business Administration, Management and Operations, MD
Educational Leadership and Administration, MD
Educational Media/Instructional Technology, M
International Business/Trade/Commerce, M

MERIDIAN COLLEGE

Business Administration and Management, A
Diagnostic Medical Sonography/Sonographer and Ultrasound Technician, A
Medical Office Management/Administration, A
Medical/Clinical Assistant, A

MIAMI DADE COLLEGE

Accounting Technology/Technician and Bookkeeping, A
Administrative Assistant and Secretarial Science, A
Aeronautics/Aviation/Aerospace Science and Technology, A
Agriculture, A
Air Traffic Controller, A
Airline/Commercial/Professional Pilot and Flight Crew, A
American/United States Studies/Civilization, A
Anthropology, A
Architectural Drafting and Architectural CAD/CADD, A
Architectural Engineering Technology/Technician, A
Architectural Technology/Technician, A
Art/Art Studies, General, A
Asian Studies/Civilization, A
Audiology/Audiologist and Speech-Language Pathology/Pathologist, A
Aviation/Airway Management and Operations, A
Banking and Financial Support Services, A
Behavioral Sciences, A
BioTechnology, A
Biology Teacher Education, B
Biology/Biological Sciences, AB
Biomedical Technology/Technician, A
Business Administration and Management, A
Business Administration, Management and Operations, B
Business/Office Automation/Technology/Data Entry, A
CAD/CADD Drafting and/or Design Technology/Technician, A
Chemistry, A
Chemistry Teacher Education, B
Child Care Provider/Assistant, A
Child Development, A
Cinematography and Film/Video Production, AB
Civil Engineering Technology/Technician, A
Clinical/Medical Laboratory Technician, A
Commercial and Advertising Art, A
Community Health Services/Liaison/Counseling, A
Comparative Literature, A
Computer Engineering Technology/Technician, A
Computer Graphics, A
Computer Installation and Repair Technology/Technician, A
Computer Programming, Specific Applications, A
Computer Programming, Vendor/Product Certification, A
Computer Programming/Programmer, A
Computer Science, A
Computer Software Technology/Technician, A
Computer Systems Networking and Telecommunications, A
Computer Technology/Computer Systems Technology, A
Construction Engineering Technology/Technician, A
Cooking and Related Culinary Arts, A
Corrections, A
Corrections and Criminal Justice, A
Court Reporting/Court Reporter, A
Criminal Justice/Law Enforcement Administration, A

Criminal Justice/Police Science, A
Culinary Arts/Chef Training, A
Customer Service Support/Call Center/Teleservice Operation, A
Dance, A
Dental Hygiene/Hygienist, A
Diagnostic Medical Sonography/Sonographer and Ultrasound Technician, A
Dietetic Technician (DTR), A
Dietetics/Dieticians, A
Drafting and Design Technology/Technician, A
Drama and Dramatics/Theatre Arts, A
Early Childhood Education and Teaching, AB
Economics, A
Education, AB
Education/Teaching of Individuals with Hearing Impairments, Including Deafness, A
Electrical and Electronic Engineering Technologies/Technicians, A
Electrical, Electronic and Communications Engineering Technology/Technician, AB
Electrician, A
Elementary Education and Teaching, A
Emergency Medical Technology/Technician (EMT Paramedic), A
Engineering, A
Engineering Technology, A
English Language and Literature, A
Entrepreneurship/Entrepreneurial Studies, A
Environmental Engineering Technology/Environmental Technology, A
Environmental Sciences, A
Finance, A
Fire Protection and Safety Technology/Technician, A
Fire Science/Firefighting, A
Food Science, A
Forensic Science and Technology, A
Forestry, A
French Language and Literature, A
Funeral Service and Mortuary Science, A
General Studies, A
Geology/Earth Science, A
German Language and Literature, A
Health Information/Medical Records Administration/Administrator, A
Health Information/Medical Records Technology/Technician, A
Health Professions and Related Clinical Sciences, A
Health Services/Allied Health/Health Sciences, AB
Health/Medical Preparatory Programs, A
Heating, Air Conditioning and Refrigeration Technology/Technician, A
Heating, Air Conditioning, Ventilation and Refrigeration Maintenance Technology/Technician, A
Histologic Technician, A
Histologic Technology/Histotechnologist, A
History, A
Horticultural Science, A
Hospitality Administration/Management, A
Hotel/Motel Administration/Management, A
Human Services, A
Humanities/Humanistic Studies, A
Industrial Technology/Technician, A
Information Science/Studies, A
Information Technology, AB
Interior Design, A
International Relations and Affairs, A
Italian Language and Literature, A
Journalism, A
Junior High/Intermediate/Middle School Education and Teaching, A
Kindergarten/PreSchool Education and Teaching, A
Landscaping and Groundskeeping, A
Latin American Studies, A
Legal Administrative Assistant/Secretary, A
Legal Assistant/Paralegal, A
Liberal Arts and Sciences Studies and Humanities, A
Logistics and Materials Management, AB
Management Information Systems and Services, A
Manufacturing Technology/Technician, A
Marketing/Marketing Management, A
Mass Communication/Media Studies, A
Massage Therapy/Therapeutic Massage, A
Mathematics, A
Mathematics Teacher Education, B

Medical Radiologic Technology/Science - Radiation Therapist, A
Medical/Clinical Assistant, A
Music, A
Music Performance, A
Music Teacher Education, A
Natural Sciences, A
Non-Profit/Public/Organizational Management, A
Nuclear Medical Technology/Technologist, A
Office Management and Supervision, A
Operations Management and Supervision, A
Ophthalmic Technician/Technologist, A
Opticianry/Ophthalmic Dispensing Optician, A
Ornamental Horticulture, A
Parks, Recreation, Leisure and Fitness Studies, A
Pharmacy Technician/Assistant, A
Philosophy, A
Phlebotomy/Phlebotomist, A
Photographic and Film/Video Technology/Technician and Assistant, A
Photography, A
Physical Education Teaching and Coaching, A
Physical Sciences, A
Physical Therapist Assistant, A
Physician Assistant, A
Physics, A
Physics Teacher Education, B
Pipefitting/Pipefitter and Sprinkler Fitter, A
Plant Nursery Operations and Management, A
Plumbing Technology/Plumber, A
Political Science and Government, A
Portuguese Language and Literature, A
Psychology, A
Public Administration, A
Radio and Television, A
Radio and Television Broadcasting Technology/Technician, A
Radiologic Technology/Science - Radiographer, A
Real Estate, A
Recording Arts Technology/Technician, A
Respiratory Care Therapy/Therapist, A
Respiratory Therapy Technician/Assistant, A
Restaurant, Culinary, and Catering Management/Manager, A
Restaurant/Food Services Management, A
Science Teacher Education/General Science Teacher Education, B
Security and Loss Prevention Services, A
Security and Protective Services, B
Sheet Metal Technology/Sheetworking, A
Sign Language Interpretation and Translation, A
Social Sciences, A
Social Work, A
Sociology, A
Spanish Language and Literature, A
Special Education and Teaching, AB
Substance Abuse/Addiction Counseling, A
System Administration/Administrator, A
Teacher Assistant/Aide, A
Teacher Education and Professional Development, Specific Levels and Methods, A
Technical Theatre/Theatre Design and Technology, A
Telecommunications Technology/Technician, A
Tourism and Travel Services Management, A
Veterinary/Animal Health Technology/Technician and Veterinary Assistant, A
Web Page, Digital/Multimedia and Information Resources Design, A

MIAMI INTERNATIONAL UNIVERSITY OF ART & DESIGN

Advertising, B
Animation, Interactive Technology, Video Graphics and Special Effects, B
Cinematography and Film/Video Production, B
Commercial Photography, B
Design and Applied Arts, M
Design and Visual Communications, B
Fashion Merchandising, AB
Fashion/Apparel Design, AB
Film, Television, and Video Production, M
Graphic Design, B
Interior Design, B
Recording Arts Technology/Technician, B

Web Page, Digital/Multimedia and Information Resources Design, B

MILLENNIA ATLANTIC UNIVERSITY

Accounting, ABM
Business Administration and Management, AB
Business Administration, Management and Operations, M
Health Informatics, M
Health Information/Medical Records Administration/Administrator, B
Health Information/Medical Records Technology/Technician, A
Health/Health Care Administration/Management, A
Human Resources Management and Services, M
Human Resources Management/Personnel Administration, B
Legal Assistant/Paralegal, AB
Office Management and Supervision, A

NEW COLLEGE OF FLORIDA

Anthropology, B
Applied Mathematics, B
Art History, Criticism and Conservation, B
Biochemistry, B
Biology/Biological Sciences, B
Chemistry, B
Chinese Language and Literature, B
Classics and Classical Languages, Literatures, and Linguistics, B
Comparative Literature, B
Economics, B
English Language and Literature, B
Environmental Studies, B
European Studies/Civilization, B
Fine/Studio Arts, B
French Language and Literature, B
French Studies, B
General Studies, B
German Language and Literature, B
Germanic Languages, Literatures, and Linguistics, B
History, B
Humanities/Humanistic Studies, B
International/Global Studies, B
Latin American Studies, B
Liberal Arts and Sciences Studies and Humanities, B
Marine Biology and Biological Oceanography, B
Mathematics, B
Medieval and Renaissance Studies, B
Music, B
Music History, Literature, and Theory, B
Natural Sciences, B
Philosophy, B
Physics, B
Political Science and Government, B
Psychology, B
Public Policy Analysis, B
Religion/Religious Studies, B
Russian Language and Literature, B
Social Sciences, B
Sociology, B
Spanish Language and Literature, B
Urban Studies/Affairs, B

NEW WORLD SCHOOL OF THE ARTS

Acting, B
Dance, B
Drama and Dramatics/Theatre Arts, B
Music Performance, B

NORTH FLORIDA COMMUNITY COLLEGE

Accounting Technology/Technician and Bookkeeping, A
Architectural Drafting and Architectural CAD/CADD, A
Business Administration and Management, A
Business and Personal/Financial Services Marketing Operations, A
Criminal Justice/Safety Studies, A
Education/Teaching of Individuals with Hearing Impairments, Including Deafness, A
Industrial Technology/Technician, A

Liberal Arts and Sciences Studies and Humanities, A
Mechanical Drafting and Mechanical Drafting CAD/CADD, A

NORTHWEST FLORIDA STATE COLLEGE

Accounting Technology/Technician and Bookkeeping, A
Accounting and Related Services, A
Architectural Engineering Technology/Technician, A
Business Administration and Management, A
Business, Management, Marketing, and Related Support Services, A
Child Care Provider/Assistant, A
Commercial and Advertising Art, A
Computer Programming, Specific Applications, A
Computer Systems Analysis/Analyst, A
Computer Technology/Computer Systems Technology, A
Computer/Information Technology Services Administration and Management, A
Criminal Justice/Law Enforcement Administration, A
Criminal Justice/Police Science, A
Dental Assisting/Assistant, A
Drafting and Design Technology/Technician, A
Electrical, Electronic and Communications Engineering Technology/Technician, A
Elementary Education and Teaching, B
Emergency Medical Technology/Technician (EMT Paramedic), A
Entrepreneurship/Entrepreneurial Studies, A
Executive Assistant/Executive Secretary, A
General Merchandising, Sales, and Related Marketing Operations, A
Health Information/Medical Records Technology/Technician, A
Health/Health Care Administration/Management, A
Legal Assistant/Paralegal, A
Liberal Arts and Sciences Studies and Humanities, A
Management Information Systems and Services, A
Manufacturing Technology/Technician, A
Marketing/Marketing Management, A
Mathematics Teacher Education, B
Medical Radiologic Technology/Science - Radiation Therapist, A
Music, A
Occupational Safety and Health Technology/Technician, A
Office Management and Supervision, A
Operations Management and Supervision, A
Public Administration, A
Purchasing, Procurement/Acquisitions and Contracts Management, B
Science Teacher Education/General Science Teacher Education, B
Selling Skills and Sales Operations, A
Surgical Technology/Technologist, A
Visual and Performing Arts, A
Welding Technology/Welder, A

NOVA SOUTHEASTERN UNIVERSITY

Accounting, B
Allied Health and Medical Assisting Services, MD
Anesthesiologist Assistant, M
Art Teacher Education, B
Atmospheric Sciences and Meteorology, O
Behavioral Sciences, B
Bioinformatics, MO
Biological and Biomedical Sciences, M
Biology/Biological Sciences, B
Business Administration and Management, B
Chemistry, B
Clinical Psychology, D
Communication Disorders, MD
Communication Studies/Speech Communication and Rhetoric, B
Computer Science, BMD
Computer Software Engineering, B
Computer and Information Sciences, B
Computer and Information Systems Security, MD
Conflict Resolution and Mediation/Peace Studies, MDO
Counseling Psychology, M

Counselor Education/School Counseling and Guidance Services, M
Criminal Justice/Safety Studies, B
Dance, B
Dentistry, MDO
Diagnostic Medical Sonography/Sonographer and Ultrasound Technician, B
Distance Education Development, M
Drama and Dramatics/Theatre Arts, B
Early Childhood Education and Teaching, A
Education, BMDO
Educational Media/Instructional Technology, M
Elementary Education and Teaching, B
Emergency Management, M
English Language and Literature, B
English/Language Arts Teacher Education, B
Environmental Sciences, BM
Experimental Psychology, M
Finance, B
Fine/Studio Arts, B
General Studies, B
Health Informatics, O
Health Professions and Related Clinical Sciences, B
History, B
Human Development and Family Studies, B
Human Services, B
Humanities/Humanistic Studies, B
Information Science/Studies, MD
Interdisciplinary Studies, M
International Relations and Affairs, B
Kinesiology and Exercise Science, B
Law and Legal Studies, MD
Legal Assistant/Paralegal, B
Legal and Justice Studies, MD
Management, M
Management Information Systems and Services, MD
Marine Affairs, M
Marine Biology and Biological Oceanography, BMD
Marine Sciences, MO
Marketing/Marketing Management, B
Marriage and Family Therapy/Counseling, MD
Mathematics Teacher Education, B
Medical Informatics, MO
Music, B
Nursing, MD
Nursing Education, D
Occupational Therapy/Therapist, MD
Oceanography, Chemical and Physical, MDO
Optometry, MD
Osteopathic Medicine, MDO
Pharmaceutical Administration, D
Pharmacy, D
Philosophy, B
Physical Education Teaching and Coaching, B
Physical Therapy/Therapist, D
Physician Assistant, M
Political Science and Government, B
Pre-Law Studies, B
Psychology, BMDO
Public Administration, BM
Public Health, M
Respiratory Care Therapy/Therapist, B
School Psychology, M
Secondary Education and Teaching, B
Social Studies Teacher Education, B
Sociology, B
Software Engineering, M
Speech-Language Pathology/Pathologist, B
Sport and Fitness Administration/Management, B
Student Personnel Services, M
Taxation, M
Writing, M

PALM BEACH ATLANTIC UNIVERSITY

Accounting, B
Art Teacher Education, B
Athletic Training and Sports Medicine, B
Bible/Biblical Studies, B
Biology Teacher Education, B
Biology/Biological Sciences, B
Business Administration and Management, B
Business Administration, Management and Operations, M
Chemistry, B
Cinematography and Film/Video Production, B

Communication Studies/Speech Communication and Rhetoric, B
Computer Science, B
Counseling Psychology, M
Counselor Education/School Counseling and Guidance Services, M
Dance, B
Drama and Dramatics/Theatre Arts, B
Education, M
Elementary Education and Teaching, B
English Language and Literature, B
English/Language Arts Teacher Education, B
Finance, B
Fine/Studio Arts, B
General Studies, B
Graphic Design, B
History, B
International Business/Trade/Commerce, B
Journalism, B
Marketing/Marketing Management, B
Marriage and Family Therapy/Counseling, M
Mass Communication/Media Studies, B
Mathematics, B
Mathematics Teacher Education, B
Mathematics and Computer Science, B
Missions/Missionary Studies and Missiology, B
Multi-/Interdisciplinary Studies, B
Music, B
Music Performance, B
Music Teacher Education, B
Music Theory and Composition, B
Organizational Behavior Studies, B
Organizational Management, M
Pharmacy, D
Philosophy, B
Physical Education Teaching and Coaching, B
Piano and Organ, B
Political Science and Government, B
Pre-Law Studies, B
Psychology, B
Public Relations/Image Management, B
Substance Abuse/Addiction Counseling, M
Theology and Religious Vocations, M
Theology/Theological Studies, B
Voice and Opera, B

PALM BEACH STATE COLLEGE

Accounting, A
Administrative Assistant and Secretarial Science, A
Airline/Commercial/Professional Pilot and Flight Crew, A
Apparel and Textiles, A
Art History, Criticism and Conservation, A
Art/Art Studies, General, A
Biology/Biological Sciences, A
Botany/Plant Biology, A
Building/Construction Finishing, Management, and Inspection, A
Business Administration and Management, B
Ceramic Arts and Ceramics, A
Chemistry, A
Commercial and Advertising Art, A
Comparative Literature, A
Computer Programming, Specific Applications, A
Computer Programming/Programmer, A
Computer Science, A
Computer and Information Sciences and Support Services, A
Criminal Justice/Law Enforcement Administration, A
Criminal Justice/Police Science, A
Data Processing and Data Processing Technology/Technician, A
Dental Hygiene/Hygienist, A
Drafting and Design Technology/Technician, A
Drama and Dramatics/Theatre Arts, A
Economics, A
Education, A
Electrical, Electronic and Communications Engineering Technology/Technician, A
Elementary Education and Teaching, A
English Language and Literature, A
Family and Consumer Sciences/Human Sciences, A
Fashion Merchandising, A
Fashion/Apparel Design, A
Finance, A
Fire Science/Firefighting, A

Foods, Nutrition, and Wellness Studies, A
Health Teacher Education, A
History, A
Hotel/Motel Administration/Management, A
Industrial Radiologic Technology/Technician, A
Interior Design, A
Journalism, A
Kindergarten/PreSchool Education and Teaching, A
Legal Administrative Assistant/Secretary, A
Liberal Arts and Sciences Studies and Humanities, A
Marketing/Marketing Management, A
Mass Communication/Media Studies, A
Mathematics, A
Music, A
Occupational Therapy/Therapist, A
Philosophy, A
Photography, A
Physical Education Teaching and Coaching, A
Physical Sciences, A
Physical Therapy/Therapist, A
Political Science and Government, A
Psychology, A
Religion/Religious Studies, A
Social Sciences, A
Social Work, A
Special Products Marketing Operations, A
Survey Technology/Surveying, A
System Administration/Administrator, A
Web Page, Digital/Multimedia and Information Resources Design, A
Word Processing, A
Zoology/Animal Biology, A

PASCO-HERNANDO STATE COLLEGE

Business Administration and Management, A
Computer Programming, A
Computer Programming, Specific Applications, A
Computer Systems Networking and Telecommunications, A
Computer Technology/Computer Systems Technology, A
Criminal Justice/Law Enforcement Administration, A
Dental Hygiene/Hygienist, A
Drafting and Design Technology/Technician, A
E-Commerce/Electronic Commerce, A
Emergency Medical Technology/Technician (EMT Paramedic), A
Human Services, A
Information Technology, A
Legal Assistant/Paralegal, A
Liberal Arts and Sciences Studies and Humanities, A
Marketing/Marketing Management, A
Radiologic Technology/Science - Radiographer, A
Web Page, Digital/Multimedia and Information Resources Design, A

PENSACOLA STATE COLLEGE

Accounting, A
Accounting Technology/Technician and Bookkeeping, A
Administrative Assistant and Secretarial Science, A
Agricultural Business and Management, A
Agriculture, A
Art Teacher Education, A
Art/Art Studies, General, A
Biochemistry, A
Biology/Biological Sciences, A
Botany/Plant Biology, A
Building/Property Maintenance and Management, A
Business Administration and Management, A
Business Administration, Management and Operations, AB
Business/Commerce, A
Chemical Technology/Technician, A
Chemistry, A
Child Care Provider/Assistant, A
Child Care and Support Services Management, A
Civil Engineering Technology/Technician, A
Commercial and Advertising Art, A
Communications Technology/Technician, A
Computer Engineering, A
Computer Programming, Specific Applications, A
Computer Programming, Vendor/Product Certification, A

Computer Programming/Programmer, A
Computer Science, A
Computer Systems Analysis/Analyst, A
Computer and Information Sciences, A
Computer and Information Systems Security, A
Construction Engineering Technology/Technician, A
Consumer Services and Advocacy, A
Cooking and Related Culinary Arts, A
Criminal Justice/Law Enforcement Administration, A
Dental Hygiene/Hygienist, A
Diagnostic Medical Sonography/Sonographer and Ultrasound Technician, A
Dietetics/Dieticians, A
Drafting and Design Technology/Technician, A
Drama and Dramatics/Theatre Arts, A
Early Childhood Education and Teaching, A
Education, A
Electrical, Electronic and Communications Engineering Technology/Technician, A
Elementary Education and Teaching, A
Emergency Medical Technology/Technician (EMT Paramedic), A
Engineering, A
Engineering Technology, A
English Language and Literature, A
Executive Assistant/Executive Secretary, A
Foods, Nutrition, and Wellness Studies, A
Foodservice Systems Administration/Management, A
Forensic Science and Technology, A
Geology/Earth Science, A
Graphic Design, AB
Hazardous Materials Management and Waste Technology/Technician, A
Health Information/Medical Records Administration/Administrator, A
Health Information/Medical Records Technology/Technician, A
Health/Health Care Administration/Management, A
History, A
Hospitality Administration/Management, A
Hotel/Motel Administration/Management, A
Information Science/Studies, A
Journalism, A
Landscaping and Groundskeeping, A
Legal Administrative Assistant/Secretary, A
Legal Assistant/Paralegal, A
Liberal Arts and Sciences Studies and Humanities, A
Management Information Systems and Services, A
Management Science, A
Mathematics, A
Medical Radiologic Technology/Science - Radiation Therapist, A
Music, A
Music Teacher Education, A
Natural Resources Management/Development and Policy, A
Ornamental Horticulture, A
Pharmacy Technician/Assistant, A
Philosophy, A
Photography, A
Physical Therapist Assistant, A
Physics, A
Pre-Dentistry Studies, A
Pre-Law Studies, A
Pre-Medicine/Pre-Medical Studies, A
Pre-Nursing Studies, A
Pre-Pharmacy Studies, A
Pre-Veterinary Studies, A
Psychology, A
Restaurant, Culinary, and Catering Management/Manager, A
Sociology, A
Special Education and Teaching, A
Telecommunications Technology/Technician, A
Veterinary/Animal Health Technology/Technician and Veterinary Assistant, A

POLK STATE COLLEGE

Accounting Technology/Technician and Bookkeeping, A
Aeronautics/Aviation/Aerospace Science and Technology, B
Airline/Commercial/Professional Pilot and Flight Crew, A

Aviation/Airway Management and Operations, A
Business Administration and Management, B
Business Administration, Management and Operations, B
Cardiovascular Technology/Technologist, A
Child Care and Support Services Management, A
Child Development, A
Computer Engineering Technology/Technician, A
Computer Programming/Programmer, A
Criminal Justice/Law Enforcement Administration, AB
Diagnostic Medical Sonography/Sonographer and Ultrasound Technician, A
Electrical and Power Transmission Installation/Installer, A
Emergency Medical Technology/Technician (EMT Paramedic), A
Engineering Technology, A
Fire Protection and Safety Technology/Technician, A
Fire Science/Firefighting, A
Liberal Arts and Sciences Studies and Humanities, A
Medical Radiologic Technology/Science - Radiation Therapist, A
Occupational Therapist Assistant, A
Operations Management and Supervision, A
Physical Therapist Assistant, A
Respiratory Care Therapy/Therapist, A
System Administration/Administrator, A
Transportation/Transportation Management, A
Web Page, Digital/Multimedia and Information Resources Design, A

POLYTECHNIC UNIVERSITY OF PUERTO RICO, MIAMI CAMPUS

Accounting, M
Business Administration and Management, B
Business Administration, Management and Operations, M
Computer and Information Sciences, B
Construction Management, M
Environmental Engineering Technology/Environmental Technology, M
Environmental Policy and Resource Management, M
Finance and Banking, M
Human Resources Management and Services, M
Industrial and Manufacturing Management, M
International Business/Trade/Commerce, M
Logistics and Materials Management, M
Marketing, M
Non-Profit/Public/Organizational Management, B
Project Management, M
Supply Chain Management, M

POLYTECHNIC UNIVERSITY OF PUERTO RICO, ORLANDO CAMPUS

Accounting, M
Business Administration and Management, B
Business Administration, Management and Operations, M
Civil Engineering, B
Computer Engineering, B
Construction Management, M
Electrical, Electronics and Communications Engineering, B
Engineering Management, M
Environmental Engineering Technology/Environmental Technology, M
Environmental Policy and Resource Management, M
Finance and Banking, M
Human Resources Management and Services, M
Industrial and Manufacturing Management, M
International Business/Trade/Commerce, M
Management of Technology, M

RASMUSSEN COLLEGE FORT MYERS

Accounting, AB
Accounting and Business/Management, B
Business Administration and Management, AB
Computer Science, B
Computer Software Engineering, A
Computer and Information Systems Security, B
Corrections and Criminal Justice, AB
Early Childhood Education and Teaching, A

Graphic Communications, B
Health Information/Medical Records Administration/Administrator, B
Health Information/Medical Records Technology/Technician, A
Health/Health Care Administration/Management, B
Human Resources Management/Personnel Administration, AB
Human Services, A
Information Resources Management/CIO Training, A
Legal Assistant/Paralegal, A
Management Information Systems and Services, A
Marketing/Marketing Management, AB
Medical Administrative Assistant/Secretary, A
Medical/Clinical Assistant, A
Pharmacy Technician/Assistant, A
Web Page, Digital/Multimedia and Information Resources Design, AB

RASMUSSEN COLLEGE LAND O' LAKES

Accounting, AB
Accounting and Business/Management, B
Business Administration and Management, AB
Computer Science, B
Computer Software Engineering, A
Computer and Information Systems Security, B
Corrections and Criminal Justice, AB
Early Childhood Education and Teaching, A
Graphic Communications, B
Health Information/Medical Records Administration/Administrator, B
Health Information/Medical Records Technology/Technician, A
Health/Health Care Administration/Management, B
Human Resources Management/Personnel Administration, AB
Human Services, A
Information Resources Management/CIO Training, AB
Legal Assistant/Paralegal, A
Management Information Systems and Services, A
Marketing/Marketing Management, AB
Medical Administrative Assistant/Secretary, A
Medical/Clinical Assistant, A
Pharmacy Technician/Assistant, A
Web Page, Digital/Multimedia and Information Resources Design, AB

RASMUSSEN COLLEGE NEW PORT RICHEY

Accounting, AB
Accounting and Business/Management, B
Business Administration and Management, AB
Computer Science, B
Computer Software Engineering, A
Computer and Information Systems Security, B
Corrections and Criminal Justice, AB
Early Childhood Education and Teaching, A
Graphic Communications, B
Health Information/Medical Records Administration/Administrator, B
Health Information/Medical Records Technology/Technician, A
Health/Health Care Administration/Management, B
Human Resources Management/Personnel Administration, AB
Human Services, A
Information Resources Management/CIO Training, AB
Legal Assistant/Paralegal, A
Management Information Systems and Services, A
Marketing/Marketing Management, AB
Medical Administrative Assistant/Secretary, A
Medical/Clinical Assistant, A
Pharmacy Technician/Assistant, A
Web Page, Digital/Multimedia and Information Resources Design, AB

RASMUSSEN COLLEGE OCALA

Accounting, AB
Accounting and Business/Management, B
Business Administration and Management, AB
Computer Science, B
Computer Software Engineering, A
Computer and Information Systems Security, B

Corrections and Criminal Justice, AB
Early Childhood Education and Teaching, A
Graphic Communications, B
Health Information/Medical Records Administration/Administrator, B
Health Information/Medical Records Technology/Technician, A
Health/Health Care Administration/Management, B
Human Resources Management/Personnel Administration, AB
Human Services, A
Information Resources Management/CIO Training, AB
Legal Assistant/Paralegal, A
Management Information Systems and Services, A
Marketing/Marketing Management, AB
Medical Administrative Assistant/Secretary, A
Medical/Clinical Assistant, A
Pharmacy Technician/Assistant, A
Web Page, Digital/Multimedia and Information Resources Design, AB

RASMUSSEN COLLEGE TAMPA/BRANDON

Accounting, AB
Accounting and Business/Management, B
Business Administration and Management, AB
Computer Science, B
Computer Software Engineering, A
Computer and Information Systems Security, B
Corrections and Criminal Justice, AB
Early Childhood Education and Teaching, A
Graphic Communications, B
Health Information/Medical Records Administration/Administrator, B
Health Information/Medical Records Technology/Technician, A
Health/Health Care Administration/Management, B
Human Resources Management/Personnel Administration, AB
Human Services, A
Information Resources Management/CIO Training, AB
Legal Assistant/Paralegal, A
Management Information Systems and Services, A
Marketing/Marketing Management, AB
Medical Administrative Assistant/Secretary, A
Medical/Clinical Assistant, A
Pharmacy Technician/Assistant, A
Web Page, Digital/Multimedia and Information Resources Design, AB

RINGLING COLLEGE OF ART AND DESIGN

Advertising, B
Animation, Interactive Technology, Video Graphics and Special Effects, B
Cinematography and Film/Video Production, B
Commercial and Advertising Art, B
Fine/Studio Arts, B
Graphic Design, B
Illustration, B
Interior Design, B
Photography, B

ROLLINS COLLEGE

Anthropology, B
Art History, Criticism and Conservation, B
Art/Art Studies, General, B
Biochemistry, B
Biology/Biological Sciences, B
Business Administration, Management and Operations, MD
Chemistry, B
Classics and Classical Languages, Literatures, and Linguistics, B
Communication and Media Studies, B
Computer and Information Sciences, B
Counselor Education/School Counseling and Guidance Services, M
Drama and Dramatics/Theatre Arts, B
Economics, B
Education, M
Elementary Education and Teaching, BM
English Language and Literature, B
Entrepreneurship/Entrepreneurial Studies, M

Environmental Studies, B
Finance and Banking, M
French Language and Literature, B
History, B
Human Resources Development, M
Human Resources Management and Services, M
Humanities/Humanistic Studies, B
International Business/Trade/Commerce, BM
International Relations and Affairs, B
Liberal Studies, B
Management, M
Management of Technology, M
Marine Biology and Biological Oceanography, B
Marketing, M
Mathematics, B
Molecular Biology, B
Multi-/Interdisciplinary Studies, B
Music, B
Philosophy, B
Physics, B
Political Science and Government, B
Psychology, B
Religion/Religious Studies, B
Sociology, B
Spanish Language and Literature, B

ST. JOHN VIANNEY COLLEGE SEMINARY

Philosophy, B
Theology/Theological Studies, B

ST. JOHNS RIVER STATE COLLEGE

Accounting Technology/Technician and Bookkeeping, A
Administrative Assistant and Secretarial Science, A
Architectural Drafting and Architectural CAD/CADD, A
Art/Art Studies, General, A
Business Administration and Management, A
Chemical Technology/Technician, A
Commercial and Advertising Art, A
Computer Engineering Technology/Technician, A
Computer Programming/Programmer, A
Computer Typography and Composition Equipment Operator, A
Computer and Information Sciences, A
Criminal Justice/Law Enforcement Administration, A
Dance, A
Design and Applied Arts, A
Drama and Dramatics/Theatre Arts, A
Electrical, Electronic and Communications Engineering Technology/Technician, A
Emergency Medical Technology/Technician (EMT Paramedic), A
Fire Science/Firefighting, A
Health Information/Medical Records Administration/Administrator, A
Industrial Technology/Technician, A
Liberal Arts and Sciences Studies and Humanities, A
Marketing/Marketing Management, A
Radiologic Technology/Science - Radiographer, A
Respiratory Care Therapy/Therapist, A
System, Networking, and LAN/WAN Management/Manager, A

SAINT LEO UNIVERSITY

Accounting, BM
Biology/Biological Sciences, B
Biomedical Sciences, B
Business Administration and Management, AB
Business Administration, Management and Operations, BM
Business/Commerce, B
Business/Corporate Communications, B
Clinical Laboratory Science/Medical Technology/Technologist, B
Computer and Information Sciences, B
Computer and Information Systems Security, M
Corrections, M
Criminal Justice/Safety Studies, B
Criminalistics and Criminal Science, B
Criminology, M
Ecology, B
Economics, B
Education, M

Elementary Education and Teaching, B
English Language and Literature, B
Forensic Science and Technology, M
Health Services Administration, M
Health/Health Care Administration/Management, B
History, B
Hospitality Administration/Management, B
Human Resources Management and Services, M
Human Resources Management/Personnel Administration, B
International/Global Studies, B
Junior High/Intermediate/Middle School Education and Teaching, B
Legal and Justice Studies, M
Liberal Arts and Sciences Studies and Humanities, A
Management Science, B
Marketing, M
Marketing Research, M
Marketing/Marketing Management, B
Mathematics, B
Pastoral Studies/Counseling, M
Political Science and Government, B
Project Management, M
Psychology, B
Religion/Religious Studies, B
Secondary Education and Teaching, B
Social Work, BM
Sociology, B
Sport and Fitness Administration/Management, BM

ST. PETERSBURG COLLEGE

Airframe Mechanics and Aircraft Maintenance Technology/Technician, A
Banking and Financial Support Services, A
Biology Teacher Education, B
Biology/Biological Sciences, B
Business Administration and Management, AB
Business Administration, Management and Operations, B
Business Teacher Education, B
Clinical/Medical Laboratory Technician, A
Computer Engineering Technology/Technician, A
Computer Programming/Programmer, A
Computer/Information Technology Services Administration and Management, AB
Criminal Justice/Law Enforcement Administration, A
Dental Hygiene/Hygienist, AB
Early Childhood Education and Teaching, A
Education, B
Elementary Education and Teaching, B
Emergency Medical Technology/Technician (EMT Paramedic), A
Engineering Technology, A
Fire Science/Firefighting, A
Forensic Science and Technology, A
Funeral Service and Mortuary Science, A
Health Information/Medical Records Administration/Administrator, A
Health Services Administration, B
Hospitality Administration/Management, A
Industrial Technology/Technician, A
International Business/Trade/Commerce, B
Legal Assistant/Paralegal, AB
Liberal Arts and Sciences Studies and Humanities, A
Mathematics Teacher Education, B
Music, A
Natural Resources Management/Development and Policy, B
Natural Sciences, A
Orthotist/Prosthetist, B
Parks, Recreation, Leisure and Fitness Studies, A
Photography, A
Physical Therapist Assistant, A
Radiologic Technology/Science - Radiographer, A
Respiratory Care Therapy/Therapist, A
Restaurant, Culinary, and Catering Management/Manager, A
Science Teacher Education/General Science Teacher Education, B
Security and Protective Services, AB
Special Education and Teaching, B
Substance Abuse/Addiction Counseling, A
Technology Teacher Education/Industrial Arts Teacher Education, B

Veterinary/Animal Health Technology/Technician and Veterinary Assistant, AB
Web Page, Digital/Multimedia and Information Resources Design, A
Web/Multimedia Management and Webmaster, A

ST. THOMAS UNIVERSITY

Accounting, BMO
Arts Management, M
Biology/Biological Sciences, B
Business Administration and Management, B
Business Administration, Management and Operations, BMO
Business/Commerce, B
Chemistry, B
Communication and Media Studies, BMDO
Computer Science, B
Computer and Information Sciences, B
Counseling Psychology, M
Counselor Education/School Counseling and Guidance Services, MO
Criminal Justice/Law Enforcement Administration, B
Criminal Justice/Safety Studies, B
Criminology, MO
Economics, B
Education, MDO
Education/Teaching of the Gifted and Talented, O
Educational Administration and Supervision, MO
Educational Leadership and Administration, D
Educational Media/Instructional Technology, MO
Elementary Education and Teaching, BM
Engineering, A
English Language and Literature, B
English as a Second Language, O
Environmental Studies, B
Film, Television, and Video Production, M
Finance, B
Fire Services Administration, B
Geosciences, O
Health Services Administration, MO
Health/Health Care Administration/Management, B
Hispanic Studies, MO
History, B
Hospitality Administration/Management, B
Hotel/Motel Administration/Management, B
Human Resources Management and Services, MO
Human Services, B
Information Science/Studies, B
International Business/Trade/Commerce, BMO
International/Global Studies, B
Law and Legal Studies, MD
Liberal Arts and Sciences Studies and Humanities, B
Logistics and Materials Management, B
Management, MO
Marketing/Marketing Management, B
Marriage and Family Therapy/Counseling, MO
Mass Communication/Media Studies, B
Mathematics, B
Pastoral Studies/Counseling, BMDO
Physics, B
Planetary Astronomy and Science, O
Political Science and Government, B
Pre-Dentistry Studies, B
Pre-Law Studies, B
Pre-Medicine/Pre-Medical Studies, B
Pre-Nursing Studies, B
Psychology, B
Public Administration, BMO
Reading Teacher Education, MO
Religion/Religious Studies, B
Secondary Education and Teaching, B
Social Studies Teacher Education, B
Special Education and Teaching, M
Sport and Fitness Administration/Management, BM
Taxation, M
Theology and Religious Vocations, D
Theology/Theological Studies, B
Tourism and Travel Services Management, B

SANTA FE COLLEGE

Airline/Commercial/Professional Pilot and Flight Crew, A
Animal Sciences, A
Automotive Engineering Technology/Technician, A
Aviation/Airway Management and Operations, A

BioTechnology, B
Biology Technician/BioTechnology Laboratory Technician, A
Biomedical Technology/Technician, A
Business Administration and Management, A
Business Administration, Management and Operations, B
Cardiovascular Technology/Technologist, A
Child Care Provider/Assistant, A
Cinematography and Film/Video Production, B
Clinical Laboratory Science/Medical Technology/Technologist, B
Commercial and Advertising Art, A
Computer Systems Analysis/Analyst, A
Construction Engineering Technology/Technician, A
Criminal Justice/Law Enforcement Administration, A
Dental Hygiene/Hygienist, A
Diagnostic Medical Sonography/Sonographer and Ultrasound Technician, A
Early Childhood Education and Teaching, B
Emergency Medical Technology/Technician (EMT Paramedic), A
Executive Assistant/Executive Secretary, A
Fire Protection and Safety Technology/Technician, A
Health Information/Medical Records Administration/Administrator, A
Health Information/Medical Records Technology/Technician, A
Health/Health Care Administration/Management, B
Heating, Air Conditioning, Ventilation and Refrigeration Maintenance Technology/Technician, A
Legal Assistant/Paralegal, A
Liberal Arts and Sciences Studies and Humanities, A
Management Information Systems and Services, A
Medical Radiologic Technology/Science - Radiation Therapist, A
Nuclear Medical Technology/Technologist, A
Respiratory Care Therapy/Therapist, A

SCHILLER INTERNATIONAL UNIVERSITY

Business Administration, Management and Operations, M
Finance and Banking, M
Hospitality Administration/Management, M
International Business/Trade/Commerce, ABM
International Relations and Affairs, B
Liberal Arts and Sciences Studies and Humanities, A
Management Information Systems and Services, M
Tourism and Travel Services Management, B
Travel and Tourism, M

SEMINOLE STATE COLLEGE OF FLORIDA

Accounting, A
Administrative Assistant and Secretarial Science, A
Architectural Engineering Technology/Technician, AB
Automobile/Automotive Mechanics Technology/Technician, A
Banking and Financial Support Services, A
Building/Construction Finishing, Management, and Inspection, A
Business Administration and Management, AB
Child Development, A
Civil Engineering Technology/Technician, A
Computer Engineering, A
Computer Engineering Technology/Technician, A
Computer Graphics, A
Computer Hardware Engineering, A
Computer Programming, A
Computer Programming, Specific Applications, A
Computer Programming, Vendor/Product Certification, A
Computer Programming/Programmer, A
Computer Software Engineering, A
Computer Software and Media Applications, A
Computer Systems Networking and Telecommunications, A
Computer and Information Sciences, A
Computer and Information Sciences and Support Services, A
Computer and Information Systems Security, A
Computer/Information Technology Services Administration and Management, A

Construction Engineering Technology/Technician, AB
Criminal Justice/Law Enforcement Administration, A
Data Entry/Microcomputer Applications, A
Data Modeling/Warehousing and Database Administration, A
Data Processing and Data Processing Technology/Technician, A
Drafting and Design Technology/Technician, A
Electrical, Electronic and Communications Engineering Technology/Technician, A
Emergency Medical Technology/Technician (EMT Paramedic), A
Finance, A
Fire Science/Firefighting, A
Industrial Technology/Technician, A
Information Science/Studies, A
Information Technology, AB
Interior Design, AB
Legal Assistant/Paralegal, A
Liberal Arts and Sciences Studies and Humanities, A
Marketing/Marketing Management, A
Physical Therapy/Therapist, A
Respiratory Care Therapy/Therapist, A
System Administration/Administrator, A
Telecommunications Technology/Technician, A
Web Page, Digital/Multimedia and Information Resources Design, A
Web/Multimedia Management and Webmaster, A
Word Processing, A

SOUTH FLORIDA STATE COLLEGE

Accounting, A
Accounting Technology/Technician and Bookkeeping, A
Actuarial Science, A
Advertising, A
Aerospace, Aeronautical and Astronautical Engineering, A
Agribusiness, A
Agricultural Economics, A
Agricultural Teacher Education, A
Agricultural/Biological Engineering and Bioengineering, A
Agriculture, A
American/United States Studies/Civilization, A
Animal Sciences, A
Anthropology, A
Applied Mathematics, A
Architecture, A
Art History, Criticism and Conservation, A
Art Teacher Education, A
Art/Art Studies, General, A
Astronomy, A
Atmospheric Sciences and Meteorology, A
Audiology/Audiologist and Speech-Language Pathology/Pathologist, A
Banking and Financial Support Services, A
Biochemistry, A
Biological and Physical Sciences, A
Biology/Biological Sciences, A
Biomedical Technology/Technician, A
Botany/Plant Biology, A
Business Administration and Management, A
Business Administration, Management and Operations, B
Business Teacher Education, A
Business/Commerce, A
Business/Managerial Economics, A
Chemical Engineering, A
Chemistry, A
City/Urban, Community and Regional Planning, A
Civil Engineering, A
Civil Engineering Technology/Technician, A
Clinical Laboratory Science/Medical Technology/Technologist, A
Communication Studies/Speech Communication and Rhetoric, A
Computer Engineering, A
Computer Engineering Technology/Technician, A
Computer Programming/Programmer, A
Computer and Information Sciences, A
Construction Engineering Technology/Technician, A
Criminal Justice/Law Enforcement Administration, A
Criminal Justice/Safety Studies, A
Dental Hygiene/Hygienist, A

Dietetics/Dieticians, A
Drama and Dramatics/Theatre Arts, A
Early Childhood Education and Teaching, A
Economics, A
Education/Teaching of Individuals with Emotional Disturbances, A
Education/Teaching of Individuals with Mental Retardation, A
Education/Teaching of Individuals with Specific Learning Disabilities, A
Education/Teaching of Individuals with Vision Impairments, Including Blindness, A
Electrical, Electronic and Communications Engineering Technology/Technician, A
Electrical, Electronics and Communications Engineering, A
Elementary Education and Teaching, AB
Emergency Medical Technology/Technician (EMT Paramedic), A
Engineering, A
Engineering Science, A
Engineering Technology, A
English Language and Literature, A
English/Language Arts Teacher Education, A
Entomology, A
Environmental Sciences, A
Environmental/Environmental Health Engineering, A
Family and Consumer Sciences/Home Economics Teacher Education, A
Finance, A
Fine/Studio Arts, A
Fire Protection and Safety Technology/Technician, A
Food Science, A
Foreign Language Teacher Education, A
Foreign Languages and Literatures, A
Forensic Science and Technology, A
Forestry, A
French Language and Literature, A
General Studies, A
Geography, A
Geology/Earth Science, A
Gerontology, A
Graphic Design, A
Health Information/Medical Records Administration/Administrator, A
Health Services/Allied Health/Health Sciences, A
Health Teacher Education, A
Health/Health Care Administration/Management, A
History, A
Horticultural Science, A
Hospitality Administration/Management, A
Human Resources Management/Personnel Administration, A
Humanities/Humanistic Studies, A
Industrial Engineering, A
Information Science/Studies, A
Insurance, A
International Business/Trade/Commerce, A
International Relations and Affairs, A
Jazz/Jazz Studies, A
Journalism, A
Junior High/Intermediate/Middle School Education and Teaching, A
Kinesiology and Exercise Science, A
Landscaping and Groundskeeping, A
Legal Assistant/Paralegal, A
Liberal Arts and Sciences Studies and Humanities, A
Linguistics, A
Management Information Systems and Services, A
Management Science, A
Manufacturing Technology/Technician, A
Marine Biology and Biological Oceanography, A
Marketing/Marketing Management, A
Materials Engineering, A
Mathematics, A
Mathematics Teacher Education, A
Mechanical Engineering, A
Medical Microbiology and Bacteriology, A
Medical Radiologic Technology/Science - Radiation Therapist, A
Multi-/Interdisciplinary Studies, A
Music, A
Music History, Literature, and Theory, A
Music Performance, A
Music Teacher Education, A

Music Theory and Composition, A
Music Therapy/Therapist, A
Nuclear Engineering, A
Occupational Therapy/Therapist, A
Ocean Engineering, A
Office Management and Supervision, A
Operations Management and Supervision, A
Parks, Recreation and Leisure Facilities Management, A
Pharmacy, A
Philosophy, A
Philosophy and Religious Studies, A
Physics, A
Plant Sciences, A
Political Science and Government, A
Psychology, A
Public Administration, A
Public Relations/Image Management, A
Radio and Television, A
Real Estate, A
Religion/Religious Studies, A
Respiratory Care Therapy/Therapist, A
Science Teacher Education/General Science
    Teacher Education, A
Secondary Education and Teaching, A
Social Science Teacher Education, A
Social Sciences, A
Social Work, A
Sociology, A
Soil Science and Agronomy, A
Spanish Language and Literature, A
Special Education and Teaching, A
Statistics, A
Survey Technology/Surveying, A
System Administration/Administrator, A
Systems Engineering, A
Trade and Industrial Teacher Education, A
Transportation/Transportation Management, A
Vocational Rehabilitation Counseling/Counselor, A
Water, Wetlands, and Marine Resources Management, A
Zoology/Animal Biology, A

SOUTH UNIVERSITY (ROYAL PALM BEACH)

Business Administration and Management, B
Business Administration, Management and Operations, M
Counseling Psychology, M
Criminal Justice/Law Enforcement Administration, B
Criminology, M
Health Services Administration, M
Health/Health Care Administration/Management, B
Health/Medical Preparatory Programs, B
Information Technology, B
Legal Assistant/Paralegal, AB
Management Information Systems and Services, M
Nursing, M
Nursing - Advanced Practice, M
Occupational Therapist Assistant, A
Occupational Therapy/Therapist, D
Physical Therapist Assistant, A
Psychology, B
Public Administration, M

SOUTH UNIVERSITY (TAMPA)

Business Administration and Management, B
Business Administration, Management and Operations, M
Criminal Justice/Law Enforcement Administration, B
Criminology, M
Health Services Administration, M
Health/Health Care Administration/Management, B
Health/Medical Preparatory Programs, B
Information Science/Studies, B
Management Information Systems and Services, M
Nursing, M
Nursing - Adult, M
Nursing - Advanced Practice, M
Nursing Education, M
Occupational Therapist Assistant, A
Physical Therapist Assistant, A
Physician Assistant, M

Psychology, B

SOUTHEASTERN COLLEGE–WEST PALM BEACH

Aesthetician/Esthetician and Skin Care Specialist, A
Business, Management, Marketing, and Related
    Support Services, A
Computer Systems Networking and Telecommunications, A
Computer and Information Sciences and Support
    Services, A
Emergency Medical Technology/Technician (EMT
    Paramedic), A
Health Professions and Related Clinical Sciences, A
Massage Therapy/Therapeutic Massage, A
Medical Insurance Coding Specialist/Coder, A
Medical Insurance Specialist/Medical Biller, A
Medical/Clinical Assistant, A
Parks, Recreation and Leisure Facilities Management, A
Pharmacy Technician/Assistant, A
Salon/Beauty Salon Management/Manager, A
Surgical Technology/Technologist, A

SOUTHEASTERN UNIVERSITY

Accounting, B
American Government and Politics (United
    States), B
Biology Teacher Education, B
Biology/Biological Sciences, B
Business Administration and Management, B
Business Administration, Management and Operations, M
Business, Management, Marketing, and Related
    Support Services, B
Counseling Psychology, M
Counselor Education/School Counseling and Guidance Services, M
Criminal Justice/Law Enforcement Administration, B
Drama and Dramatics/Theatre Arts, B
Education, M
Educational Leadership and Administration, M
Elementary Education and Teaching, BM
English Language and Literature, B
English/Language Arts Teacher Education, B
Film/Cinema Studies, B
Finance, B
History, B
Human Services, BM
International Business/Trade/Commerce, B
Journalism, B
Management Information Systems and Services, B
Marketing/Marketing Management, B
Mathematics, B
Mathematics Teacher Education, B
Missions/Missionary Studies and Missiology, B
Music, B
Music Performance, B
Music Teacher Education, B
Organizational Communication, B
Pastoral Studies/Counseling, M
Piano and Organ, B
Pre-Medicine/Pre-Medical Studies, B
Pre-Theology/Pre-Ministerial Studies, B
Psychology, B
Public Policy Analysis, B
Radio and Television, B
Religious/Sacred Music, B
Science Teacher Education/General Science
    Teacher Education, B
Social Science Teacher Education, B
Social Work, B
Special Education and Teaching, B
Sport and Fitness Administration/Management, B
Theology and Religious Vocations, AB
Voice and Opera, B

SOUTHERN TECHNICAL COLLEGE (FORT MYERS)

Accounting, AB
Business Administration and Management, B
Computer Software and Media Applications, A
Computer Systems Networking and Telecommunications, A
Criminal Justice/Law Enforcement Administration, A

Diagnostic Medical Sonography/Sonographer and
    Ultrasound Technician, A
Early Childhood Education and Teaching, AB
Health/Health Care Administration/Management, A
Information Technology, B
Interior Design, AB
Medical Staff Services Technology/Technician, A
Medical/Clinical Assistant, A
Public Administration, B
Surgical Technology/Technologist, A

SOUTHERN TECHNICAL COLLEGE (ORLANDO)

Electrical, Electronics and Communications Engineering, A
Electrical/Electronics Maintenance and Repair Technology, A
Medical Insurance Specialist/Medical Biller, A
Medical/Clinical Assistant, A

SOUTHERN TECHNICAL COLLEGE (TAMPA)

Animation, Interactive Technology, Video Graphics
    and Special Effects, A
CAD/CADD Drafting and/or Design
    Technology/Technician, A
Computer Programming/Programmer, A
Criminal Justice/Law Enforcement Administration, AB
Early Childhood Education and Teaching, AB
Graphic Design, A
Health Information/Medical Records
    Technology/Technician, A
Health/Health Care Administration/Management, B
Management Science, B
Marketing/Marketing Management, A
Medical/Clinical Assistant, A
Surgical Technology/Technologist, A
System Administration/Administrator, A

STATE COLLEGE OF FLORIDA MANATEE-SARASOTA

Accounting, A
Administrative Assistant and Secretarial Science, A
Advertising, A
African-American/Black Studies, A
American Government and Politics (United
    States), A
American/United States Studies/Civilization, A
Art History, Criticism and Conservation, A
Art/Art Studies, General, A
Asian Studies/Civilization, A
Astronomy, A
Biology Teacher Education, A
Biology/Biological Sciences, A
Business Administration and Management, A
Business/Commerce, A
Business/Managerial Economics, A
Central/Middle and Eastern European Studies, A
Chemistry, A
Chemistry Teacher Education, A
Child Development, A
Civil Engineering Technology/Technician, A
Commercial and Advertising Art, A
Community Health Services/Liaison/Counseling, A
Computer Engineering Technology/Technician, A
Computer Graphics, A
Computer Programming, A
Computer Programming/Programmer, A
Computer and Information Sciences, A
Construction Engineering Technology/Technician, A
Criminal Justice/Safety Studies, A
Dietetics/Dieticians, A
Drafting and Design Technology/Technician, A
Drama and Dramatics/Theatre Arts, A
Early Childhood Education and Teaching, B
Economics, A
Electrical, Electronic and Communications Engineering Technology/Technician, A
Energy Management and Systems
    Technology/Technician, B
Engineering, A
English Language and Literature, A
English/Language Arts Teacher Education, A

Family and Consumer Sciences/Home Economics
Teacher Education, A
Finance, A
Fine/Studio Arts, A
Fire Science/Firefighting, A
Foreign Language Teacher Education, A
French Language and Literature, A
German Language and Literature, A
Gerontology, B
Health Services Administration, B
Health Teacher Education, A
Health/Health Care Administration/Management, A
History, A
Hospital and Health Care Facilities
Administration/Management, A
Human Nutrition, B
Humanities/Humanistic Studies, A
Information Science/Studies, A
International Business/Trade/Commerce, B
Jazz/Jazz Studies, A
Jewish/Judaic Studies, A
Journalism, A
Kindergarten/PreSchool Education and Teaching, A
Latin American Studies, A
Legal Assistant/Paralegal, A
Liberal Arts and Sciences Studies and Humani-
ties, A
Mass Communication/Media Studies, A
Mathematics Teacher Education, A
Medical Radiologic Technology/Science - Radiation
Therapist, A
Music, A
Music Performance, A
Music Teacher Education, A
Music Theory and Composition, A
Occupational Therapist Assistant, A
Occupational Therapy/Therapist, A
Philosophy, A
Physical Education Teaching and Coaching, A
Physical Therapist Assistant, A
Physical Therapy/Therapist, A
Physician Assistant, A
Physics, A
Physics Teacher Education, A
Pre-Pharmacy Studies, A
Psychology, A
Public Administration, A
Radio and Television, A
Radio and Television Broadcasting
Technology/Technician, A
Radiologic Technology/Science - Radiographer, A
Religion/Religious Studies, A
Respiratory Care Therapy/Therapist, A
Russian Studies, A
Science Teacher Education/General Science
Teacher Education, A
Social Sciences, A
Social Studies Teacher Education, A
Social Work, A
Spanish Language and Literature, A
Statistics, A
Technology Teacher Education/Industrial Arts
Teacher Education, A
Trade and Industrial Teacher Education, A
Vocational Rehabilitation Counseling/Counselor, A
Women's Studies, A

STETSON UNIVERSITY

Accounting, BM
American/United States Studies/Civilization, B
Aquatic Biology/Limnology, B
Art History, Criticism and Conservation, B
Art/Art Studies, General, B
Biochemistry, B
Biology/Biological Sciences, B
Business Administration and Management, B
Business Administration, Management and Opera-
tions, M
Business/Managerial Economics, B
Chemistry, B
Computer Science, B
Computer and Information Sciences, B
Counselor Education/School Counseling and Guid-
ance Services, M
Curriculum and Instruction, O
Drama and Dramatics/Theatre Arts, B

Economics, B
Education, BMO
Educational Leadership and Administration, M
Elementary Education and Teaching, B
English Language and Literature, B
Entrepreneurship/Entrepreneurial Studies, B
Environmental Sciences, B
Finance, B
French Language and Literature, B
Geography, B
German Language and Literature, B
Health Services/Allied Health/Health Sciences, B
History, B
International Business/Trade/Commerce, B
International Relations and Affairs, B
Law and Legal Studies, MD
Management Information Systems and Services, B
Marketing/Marketing Management, B
Marriage and Family Therapy/Counseling, M
Mathematics, B
Molecular Biology, B
Music, B
Music Performance, B
Music Teacher Education, B
Music Theory and Composition, B
Philosophy, B
Physics, B
Piano and Organ, B
Political Science and Government, B
Pre-Dentistry Studies, B
Pre-Law Studies, B
Pre-Medicine/Pre-Medical Studies, B
Pre-Veterinary Studies, B
Psychology, B
Religion/Religious Studies, B
Russian Studies, B
Social Sciences, B
Sociology, B
Spanish Language and Literature, B
Sport and Fitness Administration/Management, B
Violin, Viola, Guitar and Other Stringed Instru-
ments, B
Voice and Opera, B

STRAYER UNIVERSITY–BAYMEADOWS CAMPUS

Accounting, B
Business Administration and Management, B
Criminal Justice/Law Enforcement Administration, B
Economics, B
International Business/Trade/Commerce, B
Management Information Systems and Services, B

STRAYER UNIVERSITY–BRICKELL CAMPUS

Accounting, B
Business Administration and Management, B
Criminal Justice/Law Enforcement Administration, B
Economics, B
International Business/Trade/Commerce, B
Management Information Systems and Services, B

STRAYER UNIVERSITY–CORAL SPRINGS CAMPUS

Accounting, B
Business Administration and Management, B
Criminal Justice/Law Enforcement Administration, B
Economics, B
International Business/Trade/Commerce, B
Management Information Systems and Services, B

STRAYER UNIVERSITY–DORAL CAM-PUS

Accounting, B
Business Administration and Management, B
Criminal Justice/Law Enforcement Administration, B
Economics, B
International Business/Trade/Commerce, B
Management Information Systems and Services, B

STRAYER UNIVERSITY–FORT LAUDER-DALE CAMPUS

Accounting, B
Business Administration and Management, B
Criminal Justice/Law Enforcement Administration, B

Economics, B
International Business/Trade/Commerce, B
Management Information Systems and Services, B

STRAYER UNIVERSITY–MAITLAND CAMPUS

Accounting, B
Business Administration and Management, B
Criminal Justice/Law Enforcement Administration, B
Economics, B
International Business/Trade/Commerce, B
Management Information Systems and Services, B

STRAYER UNIVERSITY–MIRAMAR CAMPUS

Accounting, B
Business Administration and Management, B
Criminal Justice/Law Enforcement Administration, B
Economics, B
International Business/Trade/Commerce, B
Management Information Systems and Services, B

STRAYER UNIVERSITY–ORLANDO EAST CAMPUS

Accounting, B
Business Administration and Management, B
Criminal Justice/Law Enforcement Administration, B
Economics, B
International Business/Trade/Commerce, B
Management Information Systems and Services, B

STRAYER UNIVERSITY–PALM BEACH GARDENS CAMPUS

Accounting, B
Business Administration and Management, B
Criminal Justice/Law Enforcement Administration, B
Economics, B
International Business/Trade/Commerce, B
Management Information Systems and Services, B

STRAYER UNIVERSITY–SAND LAKE CAMPUS

Accounting, B
Business Administration and Management, B
Criminal Justice/Law Enforcement Administration, B
Economics, B
International Business/Trade/Commerce, B
Management Information Systems and Services, B

STRAYER UNIVERSITY–TAMPA EAST CAMPUS

Accounting, B
Business Administration and Management, B
Criminal Justice/Law Enforcement Administration, B
Economics, B
International Business/Trade/Commerce, B
Management Information Systems and Services, B

STRAYER UNIVERSITY–TAMPA WESTSHORE CAMPUS

Accounting, B
Business Administration and Management, B
Criminal Justice/Law Enforcement Administration, B
Economics, B
International Business/Trade/Commerce, B
Management Information Systems and Services, B

TALLAHASSEE COMMUNITY COLLEGE

Accounting Technology/Technician and Bookkeep-
ing, A
CAD/CADD Drafting and/or Design
Technology/Technician, A
Commercial and Advertising Art, A
Computer Graphics, A
Computer Programming, Specific Applications, A
Computer Programming/Programmer, A
Computer Systems Networking and Telecommunica-
tions, A
Construction Engineering Technology/Technician, A
Corrections, A
Criminal Justice/Law Enforcement Administration, A
Criminal Justice/Police Science, A
Dental Assisting/Assistant, A
Dental Hygiene/Hygienist, A

Diagnostic Medical Sonography/Sonographer and Ultrasound Technician, A
Drafting and Design Technology/Technician, A
Early Childhood Education and Teaching, A
Emergency Medical Technology/Technician (EMT Paramedic), A
Entrepreneurship/Entrepreneurial Studies, A
Environmental Sciences, A
Fire Science/Firefighting, A
Health Information/Medical Records Technology/Technician, A
Information Technology, A
Legal Assistant/Paralegal, A
Liberal Arts and Sciences Studies and Humanities, A
Manufacturing Technology/Technician, A
Mason/Masonry, A
Medical Radiologic Technology/Science - Radiation Therapist, A
Office Management and Supervision, A
Pharmacy Technician/Assistant, A
Respiratory Care Therapy/Therapist, A
Security and Loss Prevention Services, A
Surgical Technology/Technologist, A
Web Page, Digital/Multimedia and Information Resources Design, A
Welding Technology/Welder, A

TALMUDIC UNIVERSITY

Bible/Biblical Studies, B
Jewish/Judaic Studies, B
Rabbinical Studies, B
Religious Education, B
Talmudic Studies, B
Theology and Religious Vocations, M

TRINITY BAPTIST COLLEGE

Administrative Assistant and Secretarial Science, A
Bible/Biblical Studies, B
Educational Leadership and Administration, M
Elementary Education and Teaching, B
Missions/Missionary Studies and Missiology, B
Music, B
Pastoral Studies/Counseling, B
Secondary Education and Teaching, B
Special Education and Teaching, BM

TRINITY COLLEGE OF FLORIDA

Bible/Biblical Studies, A
Business/Commerce, B
Elementary Education and Teaching, B
General Studies, AB
Missions/Missionary Studies and Missiology, B
Pastoral Studies/Counseling, B
Pre-Theology/Pre-Ministerial Studies, B
Psychology, B
Theological and Ministerial Studies, B
Youth Ministry, B

ULTIMATE MEDICAL ACADEMY CLEARWATER

Health Services/Allied Health/Health Sciences, A

ULTIMATE MEDICAL ACADEMY ON-LINE

Health Information/Medical Records Technology/Technician, A
Health Services/Allied Health/Health Sciences, A
Health/Health Care Administration/Management, A
Human Services, A
Medical Administrative Assistant/Secretary, A
Medical Insurance Specialist/Medical Biller, A
Pharmacy Technician/Assistant, A

ULTIMATE MEDICAL ACADEMY TAMPA

Health Services/Allied Health/Health Sciences, A

UNIVERSITY OF CENTRAL FLORIDA

Accounting, BM
Actuarial Science, MO
Advertising, B
Aerospace, Aeronautical and Astronautical Engineering, BM
Allopathic Medicine, MD
Anthropology, BMO

Applied Psychology, MD
Architecture, B
Art Education, M
Art Teacher Education, B
Art/Art Studies, General, B
Athletic Training and Sports Medicine, B
Audiology/Audiologist and Speech-Language Pathology/Pathologist, B
BioTechnology, BM
Biological and Biomedical Sciences, MD
Biology/Biological Sciences, B
Biomedical Sciences, B
Business Administration and Management, B
Business Administration, Management and Operations, MD
Business/Commerce, B
Business/Managerial Economics, B
Chemistry, BMDO
Cinematography and Film/Video Production, B
Civil Engineering, BMDO
Clinical Laboratory Science/Medical Technology/Technologist, B
Clinical Psychology, MD
Communication Disorders, MDO
Communication Studies/Speech Communication and Rhetoric, B
Communication and Media Studies, MO
Community College Education, M
Computer Art and Design, M
Computer Engineering, BMD
Computer Science, MD
Computer and Information Sciences, B
Conservation Biology, MDO
Construction Engineering and Management, O
Corrections, O
Counselor Education/School Counseling and Guidance Services, MO
Criminal Justice/Safety Studies, B
Criminology, MDO
Drama and Dramatics/Theatre Arts, B
Early Childhood Education and Teaching, BD
Economics, B
Educational Leadership and Administration, MDO
Educational Media/Instructional Technology, MDO
Electrical Engineering, MDO
Electrical, Electronics and Communications Engineering, B
Elementary Education and Teaching, BMD
Emergency Management, O
Engineering and Applied Sciences, MDO
English, MDO
English Education, M
English Language and Literature, B
English as a Second Language, MDO
English/Language Arts Teacher Education, B
Entrepreneurship/Entrepreneurial Studies, MO
Environmental Engineering Technology/Environmental Technology, MD
Environmental/Environmental Health Engineering, B
Exercise and Sports Science, MD
Experimental Psychology, MD
Film, Television, and Video Production, M
Finance, B
Fine Arts and Art Studies, M
Fine/Studio Arts, B
Foreign Language Teacher Education, B
Forensic Science and Technology, BM
French Language and Literature, B
Game Design and Development, M
Gender Studies, O
General Studies, B
Health Informatics, M
Health Information/Medical Records Administration/Administrator, B
Health Services Administration, MO
Health Services/Allied Health/Health Sciences, B
Health/Health Care Administration/Management, B
Higher Education/Higher Education Administration, D
History, BM
Homeland Security, O
Hospitality Administration/Management, BMDO
Humanities/Humanistic Studies, B
Industrial Engineering, B
Industrial and Organizational Psychology, MD
Industrial/Management Engineering, MDO

Information Technology, B
Interdisciplinary Studies, MO
International/Global Studies, B
Journalism, B
Latin American Studies, B
Law Enforcement, O
Legal Assistant/Paralegal, B
Management, MO
Marketing/Marketing Management, B
Marriage and Family Therapy/Counseling, MO
Materials Engineering, MD
Materials Sciences, MD
Mathematics, B
Mathematics Teacher Education, BMDO
Mechanical Engineering, BMD
Modeling and Simulation, MDO
Music, M
Music Performance, B
Music Teacher Education, B
National Security, D
Non-Profit/Public/Organizational Management, MO
Nursing, MDO
Nursing Education, O
Optical Technologies, MD
Optics/Optical Sciences, MD
Philosophy, B
Photography, B
Photonics, MD
Physical Education Teaching and Coaching, B
Physical Therapy/Therapist, D
Physics, BMD
Political Science and Government, BMD
Psychology, BMD
Public Administration, BMO
Public Affairs, MDO
Radio and Television, B
Reading Teacher Education, MO
Real Estate, B
Religion/Religious Studies, B
Restaurant/Food Services Management, B
School Psychology, O
Science Teacher Education/General Science Teacher Education, BMDO
Social Science Teacher Education, B
Social Sciences, B
Social Studies Teacher Education, MD
Social Work, BMO
Sociology, BMD
Spanish Language and Literature, BM
Special Education and Teaching, MDO
Sport and Fitness Administration/Management, M
Statistics, BMO
Structural Engineering, BO
Student Personnel Services, M
Taxation, M
Theater, M
Trade and Industrial Teacher Education, B
Transportation and Highway Engineering, O
Travel and Tourism, B
Urban and Regional Planning, M
Vocational and Technical Education, M

UNIVERSITY OF FLORIDA

Accounting, BMD
Advertising, B
Advertising and Public Relations, M
Aerospace, Aeronautical and Astronautical Engineering, BMD
African Studies, O
African-American/Black Studies, B
Agricultural Economics, BMD
Agricultural Education, MD
Agricultural Engineering, MDO
Agricultural Sciences, MDO
Agricultural Teacher Education, B
Agricultural and Food Products Processing, B
Agronomy and Soil Sciences, MD
Allied Health and Medical Assisting Services, MDO
Allopathic Medicine, D
Animal Sciences, BMD
Anthropology, BMD
Aquaculture, MD
Architecture, BMD
Art Education, M
Art History, Criticism and Conservation, BMD
Art Teacher Education, B

Astronomy, BMD
Athletic Training and Sports Medicine, BM
Audiology/Audiologist and Speech-Language
 Pathology/Pathologist, B
Biochemistry, D
Bioengineering, MDO
Biological and Biomedical Sciences, MD
Biology/Biological Sciences, B
Biomedical Engineering, MDO
Biomedical/Medical Engineering, B
Biostatistics, MD
Botany/Plant Biology, BMD
Business Administration and Management, B
Business Administration, Management and Opera-
 tions, MD
Cell Biology and Anatomy, MD
Chemical Engineering, BMDO
Chemistry, BMD
Child Development, M
Civil Engineering, BMD
Classics and Classical Languages, Litera-
 tures, and Linguistics, BMD
Clinical Laboratory Sciences, MD
Clinical Psychology, MD
Clinical Research, MD
Communication Disorders, MD
Communication and Media Studies, MD
Community Health and Preventive Medicine, B
Composition, M
Computer Art and Design, M
Computer Engineering, BMD
Computer Science, MD
Computer and Information Sciences, B
Construction Engineering Technology/Technician, B
Construction Management, MD
Counseling Psychology, D
Counselor Education/School Counseling and Guid-
 ance Services, MDO
Criminology, BMD
Curriculum and Instruction, MDO
Dance, B
Dentistry, DO
Dietetics/Dieticians, B
Drama and Dramatics/Theatre Arts, B
Early Childhood Education and Teaching, M
East Asian Languages, Literatures, and Linguis-
 tics, B
Ecology, MDO
Economics, BMD
Education, MDO
Educational Administration and Supervision, D
Educational Leadership and Administration, MDO
Educational Measurement and Evaluation, MD
Educational Policy, D
Electrical Engineering, MD
Electrical, Electronics and Communications Engi-
 neering, B
Elementary Education and Teaching, BM
Emergency Management, M
Engineering and Applied Sciences, MDO
English, MD
English Education, M
English Language and Literature, B
English as a Second Language, O
Entomology, BMD
Entrepreneurship/Entrepreneurial Studies, M
Environmental Education, O
Environmental Engineering
 Technology/Environmental Technology, MDO
Environmental Law, M
Environmental Sciences, B
Environmental and Occupational Health, MD
Environmental/Environmental Health Engineering, B
Epidemiology, MD
Ethnomusicology, M
Exercise Physiology, B
Exercise and Sports Science, MD
Family and Community Services, B
Family and Consumer Sciences/Human Sci-
 ences, M
Finance, B
Finance and Banking, MDO
Fine Arts and Art Studies, MD
Fine/Studio Arts, B
Fire Science/Firefighting, B
Fish, Game and Wildlife Management, MDO

Food Science, B
Food Science and Technology, MD
Foreign Language Teacher Education, MD
Forensic Science and Technology, MO
Forestry, BMD
French Language and Literature, BMD
Gender Studies, MO
Genetics, D
Geographic Information Systems, MD
Geography, BMD
Geology/Earth Science, BMD
Geosciences, MD
German Language and Literature, BMD
Graphic Design, B
Health Communication, MO
Health Education, MDO
Health Psychology, MD
Health Services Administration, MD
Health Services Research, D
Health Services/Allied Health/Health Sciences, B
Higher Education/Higher Education Administra-
 tion, MD
Historic Preservation and Conservation, MD
History, BMD
Horticultural Science, BMD
Human Resources Management and Services, M
Hydrology and Water Resources Science, MD
Immunology, D
Industrial/Management Engineering, MDO
Information Science/Studies, MD
Insurance, D
Interdisciplinary Studies, M
Interior Design, BMD
International Affairs, M
International Business/Trade/Commerce, M
International Development, MO
International Public Health/International Health, MD
International/Global Studies, B
Jewish/Judaic Studies, BM
Journalism, BM
Kinesiology and Movement Studies, MD
Landscape Architecture, BMD
Latin American Studies, MO
Law and Legal Studies, MD
Limnology, MD
Linguistics, BMDO
Management, MD
Management Information Systems and Ser-
 vices, MDO
Management Science, B
Marine Sciences, MD
Marketing, MD
Marketing/Marketing Management, B
Marriage and Family Therapy/Counseling, MDO
Mass Communication/Media Studies, MD
Materials Engineering, BMD
Materials Sciences, MD
Mathematics, BMD
Mathematics Teacher Education, M
Mechanical Engineering, BMD
Media Studies, M
Medical Microbiology and Bacteriology, B
Medical Physics, MD
Medicinal and Pharmaceutical Chemistry, MD
Microbiology, MD
Molecular Biology, MD
Molecular Genetics, M
Multi-/Interdisciplinary Studies, B
Museology/Museum Studies, M
Music, BMD
Music History, Literature, and Theory, MD
Music Teacher Education, BMD
Music Theory and Composition, M
Natural Resources and Conservation, MD
Neuroscience, D
Non-Profit/Public/Organizational Management, M
Nuclear Engineering, BMD
Nursing, MD
Nutritional Sciences, BMD
Occupational Therapy/Therapist, M
Ocean Engineering, MD
Oral Biology, D
Oral and Dental Sciences, MO
Orthodontics, MO
Parks, Recreation and Leisure Facilities Manage-
 ment, B

Performance, M
Periodontics, MO
Pharmaceutical Administration, MD
Pharmaceutical Sciences, MD
Pharmacology, MD
Pharmacy, MD
Philosophy, BMD
Physical Education Teaching and Coaching, M
Physical Therapy/Therapist, D
Physician Assistant, M
Physics, BMD
Physiology, MD
Plant Biology, MD
Plant Molecular Biology, MD
Plant Pathology/Phytopathology, MD
Plant Sciences, BD
Political Science and Government, BMDO
Portuguese Language and Literature, B
Psychology, BMD
Public Affairs, M
Public Health, MDO
Public Relations/Image Management, B
Quantitative Analysis, D
Radio and Television, B
Reading Teacher Education, M
Real Estate, BMDO
Recreation and Park Management, MD
Rehabilitation Sciences, D
Religion/Religious Studies, BMD
Russian Language and Literature, B
Sacred Music, M
School Psychology, MDO
Science Teacher Education/General Science
 Teacher Education, M
Social Sciences, M
Social Studies Teacher Education, M
Sociology, BMD
Soil Science and Agronomy, B
Spanish Language and Literature, BMD
Special Education and Teaching, BMDO
Sport and Fitness Administration/Management, BMD
Sports Medicine, M
Statistics, BMD
Student Personnel Services, M
Supply Chain Management, O
Survey Technology/Surveying, B
Sustainable Development, M
Systems Engineering, BMDO
Taxation, MD
Telecommunications, M
Theater, M
Therapeutic Recreation, M
Toxicology, MO
Travel and Tourism, MD
Urban and Regional Planning, MD
Veterinary Medicine, D
Veterinary Sciences, MDO
Water Resources, MD
Wildlife and Wildlands Science and Management, B
Women's Studies, BMO
Writing, M
Zoology/Animal Biology, BMD

UNIVERSITY OF FORT LAUDERDALE

Accounting, B
Business Administration and Management, AB
Divinity/Ministry (BD, MDiv.), AB
Pastoral Studies/Counseling, M

UNIVERSITY OF MIAMI

Accounting, BM
Acting, B
Acute Care/Critical Care Nursing, M
Advertising, B
Advertising and Public Relations, M
Aerospace, Aeronautical and Astronautical Engi-
 neering, BMD
African-American/Black Studies, B
Allopathic Medicine, D
American/United States Studies/Civilization, B
Ancient Studies/Civilization, B
Ancient/Classical Greek Language and Literature, B
Anthropology, B
Applied Mathematics, B
Architectural Engineering, BMD
Architectural History and Criticism, B

Architecture, BM
Art History, Criticism and Conservation, BM
Art/Art Studies, General, B
Athletic Training and Sports Medicine, BM
Atmospheric Sciences and Meteorology, B
Biochemistry, BD
Biochemistry, Biophysics and Molecular Biology, B
Bioethics/Medical Ethics, B
Biological and Biomedical Sciences, MD
Biology/Biological Sciences, B
Biomedical Engineering, MD
Biomedical/Medical Engineering, B
Biophysics, D
Broadcast Journalism, BM
Business Administration and Management, B
Business Administration, Management and Operations, BM
Business/Managerial Economics, B
Cancer Biology/Oncology, D
Cell Biology and Anatomy, D
Ceramic Arts and Ceramics, BM
Chemistry, BMD
Cinematography and Film/Video Production, B
Civil Engineering, BMD
Classics and Classical Languages, Literatures, and Linguistics, B
Clinical Psychology, D
Communication Studies/Speech Communication and Rhetoric, B
Communication and Media Studies, BMD
Communication, Journalism and Related Programs, B
Community Health and Preventive Medicine, D
Composition, MD
Computer Engineering, BMD
Computer Graphics, B
Computer Science, BMD
Computer Software Engineering, B
Computer and Information Systems Security, B
Counseling Psychology, D
Counselor Education/School Counseling and Guidance Services, MO
Criminology, B
Developmental Biology and Embryology, D
Developmental Psychology, D
Digital Communication and Media/Multimedia, B
Directing and Theatrical Production, B
Drama and Dramatics/Theatre Arts, B
Dramatic/Theatre Arts and Stagecraft, B
Early Childhood Education and Teaching, MO
Economic Development, MD
Economics, BMD
Education, BMDO
Educational Measurement and Evaluation, MD
Electrical Engineering, MD
Electrical, Electronics and Communications Engineering, B
Elementary Education and Teaching, B
Engineering, B
Engineering Science, B
Engineering and Applied Sciences, MD
English, MD
English Language and Literature, B
Entrepreneurship/Entrepreneurial Studies, B
Environmental Policy and Resource Management, D
Environmental and Occupational Health, M
Environmental/Environmental Health Engineering, B
Epidemiology, MD
Ergonomics and Human Factors, MD
Evolutionary Biology, MD
Exercise Physiology, B
Exercise and Sports Science, MD
Family and Community Services, B
Film, Television, and Video Production, M
Film, Television, and Video Theory and Criticism, MD
Finance, B
Finance and Banking, M
Fine Arts and Art Studies, M
Fine/Studio Arts, B
Fish, Game and Wildlife Management, MD
French Language and Literature, BD
General Studies, B
Genetics, MD
Geography, BM
Geological and Earth Sciences/Geosciences, B

Geology/Earth Science, B
Geophysics and Seismology, MD
German Language and Literature, B
Graphic Design, BM
Health Services/Allied Health/Health Sciences, B
Health/Health Care Administration/Management, B
Higher Education/Higher Education Administration, MDO
History, BMD
Human Resources Management/Personnel Administration, B
Immunology, D
Industrial Engineering, B
Industrial and Labor Relations, D
Industrial/Management Engineering, MD
Information Science/Studies, B
Inorganic Chemistry, D
International Affairs, MD
International Business/Trade/Commerce, BM
International Economics, MD
International Relations and Affairs, B
Internet and Interactive Multimedia, M
Jazz/Jazz Studies, B
Jewish/Judaic Studies, B
Journalism, BM
Latin American Studies, BM
Latin Language and Literature, B
Law and Legal Studies, BMDO
Liberal Studies, M
Management, M
Management Information Systems and Services, M
Management Science, B
Management of Technology, M
Marine Affairs, M
Marine Biology and Biological Oceanography, BMD
Marine Geology, MD
Marine Sciences, MD
Marketing, M
Marketing/Marketing Management, B
Marriage and Family Therapy/Counseling, M
Mass Communication/Media Studies, B
Mathematical Statistics and Probability, B
Mathematics, BMD
Mathematics Teacher Education, D
Mechanical Engineering, BMD
Meteorology, BMD
Microbiology, D
Molecular Biology, D
Multilingual and Multicultural Education, D
Music, BM
Music Performance, B
Music Teacher Education, BMDO
Music Theory and Composition, BMD
Music Therapy/Therapist, BMDO
Musicology and Ethnomusicology, M
Natural Resources Management/Development and Policy, B
Neuroscience, D
Nurse Anesthetist, M
Nurse Midwife/Nursing Midwifery, M
Nursing, MD
Nursing - Adult, M
Nursing - Advanced Practice, M
Nutritional Sciences, M
Oceanography, Chemical and Physical, BMD
Organic Chemistry, D
Painting, BM
Performance, MDO
Pharmacology, D
Philosophy, BMD
Photography, BM
Photojournalism, B
Physical Chemistry, D
Physical Sciences, B
Physical Therapy/Therapist, D
Physics, BMD
Physiology, D
Piano and Organ, B
Political Science and Government, BM
Printmaking, BM
Psychology, BMD
Public Health, MD
Public Health (MPH, DPH), B
Public Relations/Image Management, B
Radio and Television, B
Reading Teacher Education, D

Real Estate, BM
Religion/Religious Studies, B
Romance Languages, Literatures, and Linguistics, D
Science Teacher Education/General Science Teacher Education, D
Sculpture, BM
Sociology, BMD
Spanish Language and Literature, BMD
Special Education and Teaching, MDO
Sport and Fitness Administration/Management, BM
Sports Medicine, M
Taxation, M
Technical Theatre/Theatre Design and Technology, B
Urban Design, M
Voice and Opera, B
Women's Studies, B
Writing, M

UNIVERSITY OF NORTH FLORIDA

Accounting, BM
Adult and Continuing Education and Teaching, M
Allied Health and Medical Assisting Services, MDO
Anthropology, B
Applied Behavior Analysis, M
Applied Mathematics, B
Art Teacher Education, B
Art/Art Studies, General, B
Athletic Training and Sports Medicine, B
Banking and Financial Support Services, B
Biological and Biomedical Sciences, M
Biology/Biological Sciences, B
Business Administration and Management, B
Business Administration, Management and Operations, M
Business/Managerial Economics, B
Chemistry, B
Civil Engineering, BM
Communication Disorders, M
Community Health and Preventive Medicine, M
Computer Science, M
Computer and Information Sciences, B
Construction Engineering Technology/Technician, B
Construction Management, M
Counseling Psychology, M
Counselor Education/School Counseling and Guidance Services, M
Criminal Justice/Safety Studies, B
Criminology, M
Early Childhood Education and Teaching, B
Economics, BM
Education, MD
Educational Leadership and Administration, MD
Educational Media/Instructional Technology, M
Electrical Engineering, M
Electrical, Electronics and Communications Engineering, B
Electronic Commerce, M
Elementary Education and Teaching, BM
English, M
English Language and Literature, B
English as a Second Language, M
Ethics, MO
Exercise and Sports Science, MD
Finance, B
Finance and Banking, M
Fine/Studio Arts, B
French Studies, B
Gerontology, M
Health Services Administration, M
Health Services/Allied Health/Health Sciences, B
Health/Health Care Administration/Management, B
History, BM
Human Resources Management and Services, M
International Business/Trade/Commerce, BM
International/Global Studies, B
Jazz/Jazz Studies, B
Junior High/Intermediate/Middle School Education and Teaching, B
Logistics and Materials Management, M
Management, M
Management Information Systems and Services, M
Marketing/Marketing Management, B
Mass Communication/Media Studies, B
Mathematics, BM
Mathematics Teacher Education, B

Mechanical Engineering, BM
Music Performance, B
Music Teacher Education, B
Non-Profit/Public/Organizational Management, O
Nurse Anesthetist, M
Nursing, MDO
Nursing - Adult, M
Nursing - Advanced Practice, O
Nursing Administration, M
Nutritional Sciences, M
Philosophy, BMO
Physical Education Teaching and Coaching, B
Physical Therapy/Therapist, MD
Physics, B
Political Science and Government, B
Psychology, BM
Public Administration, MO
Public Health, MO
Reading Teacher Education, M
Rehabilitation Counseling, M
Religion/Religious Studies, B
Science Teacher Education/General Science
  Teacher Education, B
Secondary Education and Teaching, BM
Sign Language Interpretation and Translation, B
Social Work, B
Sociology, B
Software Engineering, M
Spanish Language and Literature, B
Special Education and Teaching, BM
Sport and Fitness Administration/Management, BM
Statistics, BM
Translation and Interpretation, M
Transportation/Transportation Management, B
Writing, M

UNIVERSITY OF PHOENIX–CENTRAL FLORIDA CAMPUS

Accounting, B
Business Administration and Management, B
Corrections and Criminal Justice, B
Criminal Justice/Law Enforcement Administration, B
Digital Communication and Media/Multimedia, B
E-Commerce/Electronic Commerce, B
Elementary Education and Teaching, B
Health Services Administration, B
Information Technology, B
International Business/Trade/Commerce, B
Management Information Systems and Services, B
Management Science, B
Marketing/Marketing Management, B

UNIVERSITY OF PHOENIX–NORTH FLORIDA CAMPUS

Accounting, BM
Business Administration and Management, B
Business Administration, Management and Opera-
  tions, M
Computer Education, M
Criminal Justice/Law Enforcement Administration, B
Curriculum and Instruction, M
E-Commerce/Electronic Commerce, B
Early Childhood Education and Teaching, M
Education, M
Educational Administration and Supervision, M
Elementary Education and Teaching, BM
Entrepreneurship/Entrepreneurial Studies, B
Health Services Administration, BM
Health/Health Care Administration/Management, B
Human Resources Management and Services, M
Information Science/Studies, B
Information Technology, B
International Business/Trade/Commerce, BM
Management, M
Management Information Systems and Ser-
  vices, BM
Management Science, B
Marketing, M
Marketing/Marketing Management, B
Mathematics Teacher Education, M
Nursing, M
Nursing Education, M
Public Administration, M

Secondary Education and Teaching, M

UNIVERSITY OF PHOENIX–SOUTH FLORIDA CAMPUS

Accounting, BM
Business Administration and Management, B
Business Administration, Management and Opera-
  tions, M
Computer Education, M
Criminal Justice/Law Enforcement Administration, B
Curriculum and Instruction, M
Digital Communication and Media/Multimedia, B
Early Childhood Education and Teaching, M
Education, M
Educational Administration and Supervision, M
Elementary Education and Teaching, BM
Health Services Administration, BM
Health/Health Care Administration/Management, B
Human Resources Management and Services, M
Information Technology, B
International Business/Trade/Commerce, BM
Management, M
Management Information Systems and Ser-
  vices, BM
Management Science, B
Marketing, M
Marketing/Marketing Management, B
Mathematics Teacher Education, M
Nursing, M
Nursing Education, M
Public Administration, M
Secondary Education and Teaching, M

UNIVERSITY OF SOUTH FLORIDA

Accounting, BMD
Acute Care/Critical Care Nursing, MD
Adult and Continuing Education and Teaching, MDO
African Studies, MO
African-American/Black Studies, B
Allopathic Medicine, MD
American/United States Studies/Civilization, BM
Anatomy, MD
Anthropology, BMDO
Applied Behavior Analysis, MD
Applied Mathematics, MD
Applied Physics, MD
Archeology, MD
Architecture, M
Art History, Criticism and Conservation, BM
Art/Art Studies, General, B
Athletic Training and Sports Medicine, M
Atmospheric Sciences and Meteorology, M
Audiology/Audiologist and Speech-Language
  Pathology/Pathologist, B
BioTechnology, MO
Bioethics/Medical Ethics, O
Bioinformatics, MO
Biological and Biomedical Sciences, MD
Biological and Physical Sciences, B
Biology/Biological Sciences, B
Biomedical Engineering, MDO
Biomedical Sciences, B
Biophysics, D
Biostatistics, MDO
Business Administration and Management, B
Business Administration, Management and Opera-
  tions, M
Business/Commerce, B
Cancer Biology/Oncology, MD
Cardiovascular Sciences, O
Cell Biology and Anatomy, MD
Chemical Engineering, BMDO
Chemistry, BMD
Child and Family Studies, MDO
Civil Engineering, BMDO
Classics and Classical Languages, Litera-
  tures, and Linguistics, B
Clinical Laboratory Science/Medical
  Technology/Technologist, B
Clinical Psychology, D
Clinical Research, MDO
Cognitive Sciences, D
Communication Disorders, MDO
Communication Studies/Speech Communication
  and Rhetoric, B
Communication and Media Studies, MD

Community College Education, MD
Community Health and Preventive Medicine, MDO
Comparative Literature, O
Composition, MD
Computational Biology, M
Computer Engineering, BMD
Computer Science, MD
Computer and Information Sciences, B
Corporate and Organizational Communication, MO
Counseling Psychology, O
Counselor Education/School Counseling and Guid-
  ance Services, MDO
Criminology, BMDO
Cultural Anthropology, MD
Curriculum and Instruction, D
Dance, B
Distance Education Development, O
Drama and Dramatics/Theatre Arts, B
Early Childhood Education and Teaching, BMDO
Ecology, MD
Economics, BMD
Education, MDO
Education/Teaching of the Gifted and Talented, M
Educational Leadership and Administration, MDO
Educational Measurement and Evaluation, MDO
Educational Media/Instructional Technology, MDO
Electrical Engineering, MDO
Electrical, Electronics and Communications Engi-
  neering, B
Elementary Education and Teaching, BMDO
Emergency Management, O
Engineering Management, MD
Engineering and Applied Sciences, MD
English, MDO
English Education, MD
English Language and Literature, B
English as a Second Language, MO
English/Language Arts Teacher Education, B
Entrepreneurship/Entrepreneurial Studies, MO
Environmental Biology, MD
Environmental Engineering
  Technology/Environmental Technology, MD
Environmental Policy, MD
Environmental Policy and Resource Manage-
  ment, O
Environmental Sciences, BMD
Environmental and Occupational Health, MDO
Epidemiology, MDO
Evolutionary Biology, MD
Exercise and Sports Science, M
Film, Television, and Video Theory and Criticism, M
Finance, B
Finance and Banking, MD
Fine Arts and Art Studies, M
Fine/Studio Arts, B
Foreign Language Teacher Education, BMO
French Language and Literature, BM
Gender Studies, MO
General Studies, B
Geographic Information Systems, MO
Geography, BDO
Geology/Earth Science, BMD
Geosciences, MD
Geotechnical Engineering, MD
German Language and Literature, B
Gerontological Nursing, MD
Gerontology, BMDO
Health Informatics, MO
Health Services Administration, MDO
Health Services/Allied Health/Health Sciences, B
Health/Health Care Administration/Management, B
Higher Education/Higher Education Administra-
  tion, MDO
History, BMD
Hospitality Administration/Management, B
Human Resources Development, O
Human Services, B
Humanities/Humanistic Studies, BM
Hydrogeology, O
Immunology, M
Industrial Engineering, B
Industrial and Organizational Psychology, D
Industrial/Management Engineering, MDO
Information Science/Studies, BMO
Information Technology, B
Interdisciplinary Studies, M

International Affairs, MDO
International Business/Trade/Commerce, B
International Public Health/International
    Health, MDO
International Relations and Affairs, B
Internet and Interactive Multimedia, MO
Italian Language and Literature, B
Journalism, MO
Latin American Studies, O
Legal and Justice Studies, O
Liberal Studies, M
Management, M
Management Information Systems and Ser-
    vices, BMDO
Management Strategy and Policy, O
Management of Technology, O
Marine Sciences, MD
Marketing, BMD
Marketing/Marketing Management, B
Marriage and Family Therapy/Counseling, MO
Mass Communication/Media Studies, BMO
Materials Engineering, MDO
Materials Sciences, MDO
Maternal and Child Health, O
Mathematics, BMDO
Mathematics Teacher Education, BMDO
Mechanical Engineering, BMD
Media Studies, M
Medical Microbiology and Bacteriology, BM
Medical Physics, M
Microbiology, MD
Molecular Biology, MD
Molecular Medicine, MD
Molecular Pharmacology, D
Museology/Museum Studies, O
Music, MD
Music Performance, B
Music Teacher Education, BMD
Music Theory and Composition, M
Neuroscience, MDO
Non-Profit/Public/Organizational Management, O
Nurse Anesthetist, M
Nursing, MD
Nursing - Adult, MD
Nursing - Advanced Practice, MD
Nursing Administration, M
Nursing Education, MD
Nutritional Sciences, MO
Occupational Health Nursing, MD
Oceanography, Chemical and Physical, MD
Oncology Nursing, MD
Pathology/Experimental Pathology, D
Pediatric Nurse/Nursing, MD
Performance, M
Pharmacology, D
Pharmacy, DO
Philosophy, BMD
Physical Education Teaching and Coaching, BM
Physical Therapy/Therapist, D
Physics, BMD
Physiology, MD
Political Science and Government, BMDO
Psychology, BD
Public Administration, O
Public Affairs, O
Public Health, MDO
Public Health (MPH, DPH), B
Public Policy Analysis, M
Reading Teacher Education, MDO
Real Estate, M
Rehabilitation Counseling, MO
Religion/Religious Studies, BMD
Rhetoric, MD
Russian Language and Literature, B
School Psychology, DO
Science Teacher Education/General Science
    Teacher Education, BMD
Secondary Education and Teaching, MDO
Social Science Teacher Education, B
Social Sciences, B
Social Studies Teacher Education, M
Social Work, BMDO
Sociology, BMD
Spanish Language and Literature, BM
Special Education and Teaching, BMDO
Sport and Fitness Administration/Management, M

Statistics, BMD
Structural Engineering, MD
Student Personnel Services, M
Substance Abuse/Addiction Counseling, M
Sustainability Management, M
Sustainable Development, MO
Systems Engineering, O
Taxation, M
Technical Communication, O
Transportation and Highway Engineering, MDO
Travel and Tourism, M
Urban and Regional Planning, MO
Visual and Performing Arts, B
Vocational and Technical Education, MDO
Water Resources Engineering, MDO
Women's Studies, BM
Writing, MO

UNIVERSITY OF SOUTH FLORIDA, ST. PETERSBURG

Accounting, B
Anthropology, B
Art/Art Studies, General, B
Biology/Biological Sciences, B
Business Administration, Management and Opera-
    tions, M
Business/Managerial Economics, B
Computer Art and Design, M
Criminology, B
Education, M
Educational Leadership and Administration, M
Elementary Education and Teaching, M
English Education, M
English Language and Literature, B
Entrepreneurship/Entrepreneurial Studies, B
Environmental Policy, M
Environmental Sciences, BM
Finance, B
Foreign Languages and Literatures, B
Health Services/Allied Health/Health Sciences, B
History, B
Journalism, M
Liberal Arts and Sciences Studies and Humani-
    ties, A
Liberal Studies, M
Management Information Systems and Services, B
Marketing/Marketing Management, B
Mass Communication/Media Studies, B
Mathematics Teacher Education, M
Media Studies, M
Middle School Education, M
Political Science and Government, B
Psychology, BM
Reading Teacher Education, M
Science Teacher Education/General Science
    Teacher Education, M
Social Sciences, M
Teacher Education, Multiple Levels, B
Visual and Performing Arts, B

UNIVERSITY OF SOUTH FLORIDA SARASOTA-MANATEE

Accounting, B
Biology/Biological Sciences, B
Business Administration and Management, B
Business Administration, Management and Opera-
    tions, M
Business/Commerce, B
Communication Disorders, B
Criminology, BM
Curriculum and Instruction, M
Education, M
Educational Leadership and Administration, M
Elementary Education and Teaching, BM
English Education, M
English Language and Literature, B
Finance, B
General Studies, AB
History, B
Hospitality Administration/Management, BM
Information Technology, B
Marketing/Marketing Management, B
Psychology, B

Social Sciences, B

THE UNIVERSITY OF TAMPA

Accounting, BM
Art/Art Studies, General, B
Athletic Training and Sports Medicine, B
Biochemistry, B
Biology/Biological Sciences, B
Business Administration and Management, B
Business Administration, Management and Opera-
    tions, M
Chemistry, B
Computer and Information Sciences, B
Criminology, B
Digital Communication and Media/Multimedia, B
Drama and Dramatics/Theatre Arts, B
Economics, B
Education, M
Educational Media/Instructional Technology, M
Elementary Education and Teaching, B
English Language and Literature, B
Entrepreneurship/Entrepreneurial Studies, BM
Environmental Studies, B
Exercise and Sports Science, M
Film/Cinema Studies, B
Finance, B
Finance and Banking, M
Finance and Financial Management Services, B
Forensic Science and Technology, B
Graphic Design, B
Health and Physical Education, B
History, B
International Business/Trade/Commerce, BM
Liberal Arts and Sciences Studies and Humani-
    ties, B
Management Information Systems and Services, M
Marine Biology and Biological Oceanography, B
Marketing, M
Marketing/Marketing Management, B
Mathematics, B
Mathematics and Computer Science, B
Music, B
Music Performance, B
Music Teacher Education, B
Non-Profit/Public/Organizational Management, M
Nursing, M
Nutritional Sciences, M
Philosophy, B
Political Science and Government, B
Psychology, B
Public Health (MPH, DPH), B
Public Relations, Advertising, and Applied Commu-
    nication, B
Secondary Education and Teaching, B
Sociology, B
Spanish Language and Literature, B
Sport and Fitness Administration/Management, B
Writing, M

UNIVERSITY OF WEST FLORIDA

Accounting, BM
Anthropology, BM
Applied Statistics, M
Archeology, M
Art History, Criticism and Conservation, B
Art/Art Studies, General, B
BioTechnology, M
Biochemistry, M
Biological and Biomedical Sciences, M
Biological and Physical Sciences, B
Biology/Biological Sciences, B
Business Administration and Management, B
Business Administration, Management and Opera-
    tions, M
Business/Commerce, B
Business/Managerial Economics, B
Chemistry, B
Clinical Laboratory Science/Medical
    Technology/Technologist, B
Communication and Media Studies, M
Community Health Services/Liaison/Counseling, B
Community Health and Preventive Medicine, M
Computer Engineering, B
Computer Science, M
Computer and Information Sciences, B
Counseling Psychology, M

Counselor Education/School Counseling and Guidance Services, M
Criminal Justice/Safety Studies, B
Criminology, M
Curriculum and Instruction, MO
Database Systems, M
Drama and Dramatics/Theatre Arts, B
Early Childhood Education and Teaching, BM
Economics, B
Education, D
Educational Administration and Supervision, D
Educational Leadership and Administration, MO
Educational Media/Instructional Technology, MD
Electrical, Electronics and Communications Engineering, B
Elementary Education and Teaching, BM
Engineering Technology, B
English, M
English Language and Literature, B
Environmental Biology, M
Environmental Sciences, BM
Environmental and Occupational Health, M
Exercise and Sports Science, M
Finance, B
Fine/Studio Arts, B
French Language and Literature, B
Geosciences, M
Gerontology, M
Health Education, M
Health Services/Allied Health/Health Sciences, B
Health and Physical Education, B
History, BM
Hospitality Administration/Management, B
Humanities/Humanistic Studies, B
Industrial and Organizational Psychology, M
Information Technology, B
International Relations and Affairs, B
Junior High/Intermediate/Middle School Education and Teaching, B
Legal Assistant/Paralegal, B
Leisure Studies, M
Liberal Arts and Sciences Studies and Humanities, A
Management, M
Management Information Systems and Services, B
Management Strategy and Policy, M
Marine Affairs, M
Marine Biology and Biological Oceanography, B
Marketing/Marketing Management, B
Mass Communication/Media Studies, B
Mathematics, BM
Middle School Education, M
Military and Defense Studies, M
Multilingual and Multicultural Education, D
Music Performance, B
Music Teacher Education, B
Nursing, M
Nursing Administration, M
Oceanography, Chemical and Physical, B
Philosophy, B
Physical Education Teaching and Coaching, MD
Physics, B
Political Science and Government, BM
Psychology, BM
Public Administration, M
Public Health, M
Public History, M
Reading Teacher Education, M
Science Teacher Education/General Science Teacher Education, MD
Secondary Education and Teaching, M
Social Sciences, B
Social Studies Teacher Education, D
Social Work, BM
Sociology, BM
Software Engineering, M
Spanish Language and Literature, B
Special Education and Teaching, BM
Student Personnel Services, M
Trade and Industrial Teacher Education, B
Vocational and Technical Education, M
Writing, M

VALENCIA COLLEGE

Accounting Technology/Technician and Bookkeeping, A

Baking and Pastry Arts/Baker/Pastry Chef, A
Business Administration and Management, A
Cardiovascular Technology/Technologist, A
Cinematography and Film/Video Production, A
Civil Engineering Technology/Technician, A
Computer Engineering Technology/Technician, A
Computer Programming, Specific Applications, A
Construction Engineering Technology/Technician, A
Criminal Justice/Law Enforcement Administration, A
Culinary Arts/Chef Training, A
Dental Hygiene/Hygienist, A
Diagnostic Medical Sonography/Sonographer and Ultrasound Technician, A
Drafting and Design Technology/Technician, A
Emergency Medical Technology/Technician (EMT Paramedic), A
Hospitality Administration/Management, A
Hotel/Motel Administration/Management, A
Landscaping and Groundskeeping, A
Legal Assistant/Paralegal, A
Liberal Arts and Sciences Studies and Humanities, A
Medical Radiologic Technology/Science - Radiation Therapist, AB
Respiratory Care Therapy/Therapist, A
Restaurant/Food Services Management, A

VIRGINIA COLLEGE IN PENSACOLA

Criminal Justice/Safety Studies, A
Finance, A
Human Resources Management/Personnel Administration, A
Legal Assistant/Paralegal, A
Medical Insurance Specialist/Medical Biller, A
Office Management and Supervision, A
Pharmacy, Pharmaceutical Sciences, and Administration, A
Surgical Technology/Technologist, A

WARNER UNIVERSITY

Bible/Biblical Studies, B
Biology/Biological Sciences, B
Business Administration and Management, B
Business Administration, Management and Operations, M
Business/Commerce, B
Communication Studies/Speech Communication and Rhetoric, B
Comparative Literature, B
Divinity/Ministry (BD, MDiv.), AB
Education, M
Education/Teaching of the Gifted and Talented, B
Elementary Education and Teaching, B
English Language and Literature, B
General Studies, A
History, B
Human Resources Management/Personnel Administration, B
Kinesiology and Exercise Science, B
Music Teacher Education, B
Physical Education Teaching and Coaching, B
Psychology, B
Religious/Sacred Music, B
Science Teacher Education/General Science Teacher Education, B
Secondary Education and Teaching, B
Social Science Teacher Education, B
Social Work, B
Special Education and Teaching, B

WEBBER INTERNATIONAL UNIVERSITY

Accounting, ABM
Business Administration and Management, AB
Business Administration, Management and Operations, M
Business/Commerce, B
Communication Studies/Speech Communication and Rhetoric, B
Computer and Information Sciences, AB
Criminal Justice/Law Enforcement Administration, AB
Criminology, M
Finance, B
Hospitality Administration/Management, AB
Management, M

Marketing/Marketing Management, AB
Parks, Recreation and Leisure Facilities Management, AB
Pre-Law Studies, B
Securities Services Administration/Management, BM
Sport and Fitness Administration/Management, ABM

YESHIVA GEDOLAH RABBINICAL COLLEGE

Talmudic Studies, B

Georgia

ABRAHAM BALDWIN AGRICULTURAL COLLEGE

Accounting, A
Agricultural Business and Management, A
Agricultural Economics, A
Agriculture, AB
Animal Sciences, A
Art/Art Studies, General, A
Biological and Physical Sciences, A
Biology/Biological Sciences, A
Business Administration and Management, A
Chemistry, A
Child Development, A
Computer Engineering Technology/Technician, A
Computer Science, A
Criminal Justice/Law Enforcement Administration, A
Criminal Justice/Police Science, A
Education, A
Elementary Education and Teaching, A
English Language and Literature, A
Family and Consumer Sciences/Human Sciences, A
Farm/Farm and Ranch Management, A
Fashion Merchandising, A
Fishing and Fisheries Sciences and Management, A
Forestry, A
Forestry Technology/Technician, A
History, A
Horticultural Science, A
Humanities/Humanistic Studies, A
Journalism, A
Kindergarten/PreSchool Education and Teaching, A
Landscaping and Groundskeeping, A
Liberal Arts and Sciences Studies and Humanities, A
Marketing/Marketing Management, A
Mathematics, A
Music, A
Ornamental Horticulture, A
Pharmacy Technician/Assistant, A
Physical Education Teaching and Coaching, A
Physical Sciences, A
Political Science and Government, A
Poultry Science, A
Psychology, A
Social Sciences, A
Social Work, A
Sociology, A
Wildlife and Wildlands Science and Management, A

AGNES SCOTT COLLEGE

African Studies, B
Anthropology, B
Art History, Criticism and Conservation, B
Astrophysics, B
Biochemistry, B
Biology/Biological Sciences, B
Business Administration and Management, B
Chemistry, B
Classics and Classical Languages, Literatures, and Linguistics, B
Dance, B
Drama and Dramatics/Theatre Arts, B
Economics, B
Engineering, B
English Language and Literature, B
Fine/Studio Arts, B
French Language and Literature, B
German Language and Literature, B
History, B
International Relations and Affairs, B
Mathematics, B
Multi-/Interdisciplinary Studies, B

Music, B
Philosophy, B
Physics, B
Political Science and Government, B
Psychology, B
Public Health (MPH, DPH), B
Religion/Religious Studies, B
Sociology, B
Spanish Language and Literature, B
Women's Studies, B

ALBANY STATE UNIVERSITY

Accounting, BM
Art/Art Studies, General, B
Biology/Biological Sciences, B
Business Administration and Management, B
Business Administration, Management and Operations, BM
Chemistry, B
Computer and Information Sciences, B
Corrections, M
Corrections and Criminal Justice, B
Counselor Education/School Counseling and Guidance Services, M
Criminal Justice/Safety Studies, B
Criminology, M
Drawing, B
Early Childhood Education and Teaching, BM
Economic Development, M
Economics, M
Education, BMO
Educational Administration and Supervision, M
Educational Leadership and Administration, M
English Education, M
English Language and Literature, B
Fire Services Administration, B
Forensic Science and Technology, M
Health Education, M
Health Services Administration, M
History, B
Human Resources Management and Services, M
Information Science/Studies, B
Junior High/Intermediate/Middle School Education and Teaching, B
Law Enforcement, M
Logistics and Materials Management, B
Management Information Systems and Services, B
Marketing/Marketing Management, B
Mass Communication/Media Studies, B
Mathematics, B
Mathematics Teacher Education, M
Middle School Education, M
Music, B
Music Teacher Education, B
Nursing, M
Nursing - Advanced Practice, M
Nursing Education, M
Physical Education Teaching and Coaching, BM
Political Science and Government, B
Psychology, B
Public Administration, M
Public Policy Analysis, M
Science Teacher Education/General Science Teacher Education, BM
Social Work, BM
Sociology, B
Spanish Language and Literature, B
Special Education and Teaching, BM
Water Resources, M

ALBANY TECHNICAL COLLEGE

Accounting, A
Adult Development and Aging, A
Child Development, A
Computer and Information Sciences, A
Corrections and Criminal Justice, A
Culinary Arts/Chef Training, A
Drafting and Design Technology/Technician, A
Electrical and Electronic Engineering Technologies/Technicians, A
Forestry Technology/Technician, A
Hotel/Motel Administration/Management, A
Human Development and Family Studies, A
Industrial Technology/Technician, A
Manufacturing Technology/Technician, A
Marketing/Marketing Management, A

Medical Radiologic Technology/Science - Radiation Therapist, A
Pharmacy Technician/Assistant, A
Tourism and Travel Services Management, A

AMERICAN INTERCONTINENTAL UNIVERSITY ATLANTA

Animation, Interactive Technology, Video Graphics and Special Effects, B
Audiovisual Communications Technologies/Technicians, B
Business Administration and Management, AB
Criminal Justice/Law Enforcement Administration, AB
Design and Visual Communications, AB
Fashion Merchandising, B
Fashion/Apparel Design, B
Information Science/Studies, M
Information Technology, B
Interior Design, B
International Business/Trade/Commerce, M
Management Information Systems and Services, M

ANDREW COLLEGE

Agriculture, A
Athletic Training and Sports Medicine, A
Biological and Physical Sciences, A
Biology/Biological Sciences, A
Business Administration and Management, A
Clinical Laboratory Science/Medical Technology/Technologist, A
Comparative Literature, A
Computer and Information Sciences, A
Criminal Justice/Safety Studies, A
Dental Hygiene/Hygienist, A
Education, A
English Language and Literature, A
Environmental Sciences, A
Health Information/Medical Records Technology/Technician, A
Health and Physical Education, A
History, A
Humanities/Humanistic Studies, A
International/Global Studies, A
Kinesiology and Exercise Science, A
Mass Communication/Media Studies, A
Mathematics, A
Music, A
Occupational Therapy/Therapist, A
Parks, Recreation and Leisure Facilities Management, A
Physical Therapy/Therapist, A
Physician Assistant, A
Pre-Dentistry Studies, A
Pre-Law Studies, A
Pre-Medicine/Pre-Medical Studies, A
Pre-Nursing Studies, A
Pre-Pharmacy Studies, A
Pre-Theology/Pre-Ministerial Studies, A
Pre-Veterinary Studies, A
Psychology, A
Radiologic Technology/Science - Radiographer, A
Social Sciences, A
Social Work, A
Sociology, A
Sport and Fitness Administration/Management, A
Visual and Performing Arts, A

ARGOSY UNIVERSITY, ATLANTA

Accounting, D
Biopsychology, D
Business Administration and Management, A
Business Administration, Management and Operations, MD
Business/Commerce, B
Clinical Psychology, MDO
Community Psychology, M
Counselor Education/School Counseling and Guidance Services, D
Criminal Justice/Law Enforcement Administration, B
Education, MDO
Educational Administration and Supervision, D
Educational Leadership and Administration, MDO
Educational Media/Instructional Technology, D
Elementary Education and Teaching, D
Finance and Banking, M

Forensic Psychology, M
Health Psychology, D
Health Services Administration, M
Higher Education/Higher Education Administration, D
Industrial and Organizational Psychology, M
Information Technology, AB
International Business/Trade/Commerce, MD
Liberal Arts and Sciences Studies and Humanities, B
Management, MD
Management Information Systems and Services, MD
Marketing, MD
Marriage and Family Therapy/Counseling, MDO
Psychology, ABMDO
Public Health, M
Secondary Education and Teaching, D
Sport Psychology, M

ARMSTRONG STATE UNIVERSITY

Acute Care/Critical Care Nursing, M
Adult and Continuing Education and Teaching, MO
American/United States Studies/Civilization, M
Art Teacher Education, B
Art/Art Studies, General, B
Biochemistry, B
Biology/Biological Sciences, B
Business/Managerial Economics, B
Chemistry, B
Clinical Laboratory Science/Medical Technology/Technologist, B
Communication Disorders, M
Computer Science, M
Computer and Information Sciences, B
Computer and Information Systems Security, O
Corporate and Organizational Communication, MO
Criminal Justice/Police Science, AB
Criminology, MO
Curriculum and Instruction, M
Drama and Dramatics/Theatre Arts, B
Early Childhood Education and Teaching, BM
Economics, B
Education, MO
Education/Teaching of Individuals with Speech or Language Impairments, B
English Language and Literature, B
English/Language Arts Teacher Education, B
Exercise and Sports Science, M
French Language and Literature, B
Gerontological Nursing, M
Health Professions and Related Clinical Sciences, B
Health Services Administration, MO
History, BM
History Teacher Education, B
Information Science/Studies, B
Junior High/Intermediate/Middle School Education and Teaching, B
Legal Professions and Studies, B
Liberal Arts and Sciences Studies and Humanities, AB
Management, MO
Mathematics, B
Mathematics Teacher Education, B
Medical Informatics, O
Medical Radiologic Technology/Science - Radiation Therapist, B
Music, B
Music Teacher Education, B
Nursing, M
Nursing - Adult, M
Physical Education Teaching and Coaching, B
Physical Therapy/Therapist, BD
Physics, B
Political Science and Government, B
Psychology, B
Public Health, M
Public History, M
Reading Teacher Education, O
Respiratory Care Therapy/Therapist, B
Science Teacher Education/General Science Teacher Education, B
Secondary Education and Teaching, M
Spanish Language and Literature, B
Special Education and Teaching, BM
Sports Medicine, MO

Western European Studies, M
Women's Studies, B
Writing, MO

THE ART INSTITUTE OF ATLANTA

Advertising, B
Animation, Interactive Technology, Video Graphics and Special Effects, B
Apparel and Accessories Marketing Operations, B
Baking and Pastry Arts/Baker/Pastry Chef, A
Cinematography and Film/Video Production, AB
Commercial Photography, AB
Computer Graphics, B
Culinary Arts/Chef Training, A
Illustration, B
Interior Design, B
Recording Arts Technology/Technician, B
Restaurant, Culinary, and Catering Management/Manager, AB
Web Page, Digital/Multimedia and Information Resources Design, AB

ASHWORTH COLLEGE

Accounting, A
Business Administration and Management, AB
Business Administration, Management and Operations, M
Computer and Information Sciences, A
Construction Management, A
Criminal Justice/Law Enforcement Administration, AB
Criminology, M
E-Commerce/Electronic Commerce, B
Early Childhood Education and Teaching, AB
Finance, A
Health Services Administration, AM
Human Resources Management and Services, M
Human Resources Management/Personnel Administration, A
International Business/Trade/Commerce, M
Legal Assistant/Paralegal, A
Management, M
Management Science, B
Marketing, M
Marketing/Marketing Management, AB
Psychology, A
Security and Loss Prevention Services, A

ATHENS TECHNICAL COLLEGE

Accounting, A
Administrative Assistant and Secretarial Science, A
Biology Technician/BioTechnology Laboratory Technician, A
Child Development, A
Clinical Laboratory Science/Medical Technology/Technologist, A
Communications Technology/Technician, A
Computer Programming/Programmer, A
Computer Systems Networking and Telecommunications, A
Criminal Justice/Law Enforcement Administration, A
Dental Assisting/Assistant, A
Dental Hygiene/Hygienist, A
Diagnostic Medical Sonography/Sonographer and Ultrasound Technician, A
Electrical, Electronic and Communications Engineering Technology/Technician, A
Emergency Medical Technology/Technician (EMT Paramedic), A
Hotel/Motel Administration/Management, A
Information Science/Studies, A
Legal Assistant/Paralegal, A
Logistics and Materials Management, A
Marketing/Marketing Management, A
Medical Radiologic Technology/Science - Radiation Therapist, A
Physical Therapy/Therapist, A
Respiratory Care Therapy/Therapist, A
Surgical Technology/Technologist, A
Tourism and Travel Services Management, A

Veterinary/Animal Health Technology/Technician and Veterinary Assistant, A

ATLANTA METROPOLITAN STATE COLLEGE

English Language and Literature, A
Liberal Arts and Sciences Studies and Humanities, A

ATLANTA TECHNICAL COLLEGE

Accounting, A
Child Development, A
Computer Programming/Programmer, A
Culinary Arts/Chef Training, A
Dental Hygiene/Hygienist, A
Health Information/Medical Records Technology/Technician, A
Hotel/Motel Administration/Management, A
Information Technology, A
Legal Assistant/Paralegal, A
Marketing/Marketing Management, A
Tourism and Travel Services Management, A

AUGUSTA TECHNICAL COLLEGE

Accounting, A
Administrative Assistant and Secretarial Science, A
BioTechnology, A
Business Administration and Management, A
Cardiovascular Technology/Technologist, A
Child Development, A
Computer Programming/Programmer, A
Computer Systems Networking and Telecommunications, A
Criminal Justice/Safety Studies, A
Culinary Arts/Chef Training, A
E-Commerce/Electronic Commerce, A
Electrical, Electronic and Communications Engineering Technology/Technician, A
Emergency Medical Technology/Technician (EMT Paramedic), A
Fire Science/Firefighting, A
Information Science/Studies, A
Marketing/Marketing Management, A
Mechanical Engineering/Mechanical Technology/Technician, A
Medical Radiologic Technology/Science - Radiation Therapist, A
Occupational Therapist Assistant, A
Parks, Recreation and Leisure Facilities Management, A
Pharmacy Technician/Assistant, A
Respiratory Care Therapy/Therapist, A
Respiratory Therapy Technician/Assistant, A
Surgical Technology/Technologist, A

AUGUSTA UNIVERSITY

Accounting, B
Allopathic Medicine, D
Anatomy, MD
Anthropology, B
Biochemistry, MD
Biology/Biological Sciences, B
Biostatistics, MD
Business Administration and Management, B
Business Administration, Management and Operations, M
Cardiovascular Sciences, MD
Cell Biology and Anatomy, MD
Cell/Cellular and Molecular Biology, B
Chemistry, B
Clinical Laboratory Science/Medical Technology/Technologist, B
Clinical Research, MO
Communication Studies/Speech Communication and Rhetoric, B
Computer and Information Sciences, B
Counselor Education/School Counseling and Guidance Services, MO
Criminal Justice/Safety Studies, AB
Curriculum and Instruction, M
Dental Hygiene/Hygienist, B
Dentistry, D
Early Childhood Education and Teaching, B
Ecology, B
Education, MO

Educational Leadership and Administration, MO
English Language and Literature, B
Finance, B
Foreign Languages, Literatures, and Linguistics, B
Genomic Sciences, MD
Health Informatics, M
Health Information/Medical Records Administration/Administrator, B
History, B
Information Technology, B
Intermedia/Multimedia, B
Junior High/Intermediate/Middle School Education and Teaching, B
Kinesiology and Exercise Science, B
Liberal Arts and Sciences Studies and Humanities, A
Management Information Systems and Services, B
Marketing/Marketing Management, B
Mathematics, B
Medical Illustration and Informatics, M
Medical Radiologic Technology/Science - Radiation Therapist, B
Molecular Biology, MD
Molecular Medicine, MD
Music, B
Music Performance, B
Music Teacher Education, B
Neuroscience, MD
Nuclear Medical Technology/Technologist, B
Nurse Anesthetist, M
Nursing, D
Nursing - Advanced Practice, MO
Nursing Administration, M
Oral Biology, MD
Pediatric Nurse/Nursing, MO
Pharmacology, MD
Physical Education Teaching and Coaching, B
Physics, B
Physiology, MD
Political Science and Government, BM
Psychology, BM
Public Health, M
Respiratory Care Therapy/Therapist, B
Social Work, B
Sociology, B
Special Education and Teaching, B

BAINBRIDGE STATE COLLEGE

Accounting, A
Administrative Assistant and Secretarial Science, A
Agribusiness, A
Agriculture, A
Art/Art Studies, General, A
Biology/Biological Sciences, A
Business Administration and Management, B
Business Teacher Education, A
Chemistry, A
Criminal Justice/Law Enforcement Administration, A
Data Processing and Data Processing Technology/Technician, A
Drafting and Design Technology/Technician, A
Drama and Dramatics/Theatre Arts, A
Education, A
Electrical, Electronic and Communications Engineering Technology/Technician, A
Elementary Education and Teaching, A
English Language and Literature, A
Family and Consumer Sciences/Human Sciences, A
Health Information/Medical Records Technology/Technician, A
Health Teacher Education, A
History, A
Information Science/Studies, A
Kindergarten/PreSchool Education and Teaching, A
Liberal Arts and Sciences Studies and Humanities, A
Marketing/Marketing Management, A
Mathematics, A
Political Science and Government, A
Psychology, A
Sociology, A
Welding Technology/Welder, A

BERRY COLLEGE

Accounting, B
Animal Sciences, B

Art Teacher Education, B
Art/Art Studies, General, B
Biochemistry, B
Biology/Biological Sciences, B
Business Administration, Management and Operations, M
Business/Managerial Economics, B
Chemistry, B
Communication, Journalism and Related Programs, B
Curriculum and Instruction, MO
Early Childhood Education and Teaching, BM
Education, MO
Educational Leadership and Administration, O
Engineering Technology, B
English Language and Literature, B
Environmental Sciences, B
Finance, B
French Language and Literature, B
German Language and Literature, B
History, B
International Business/Trade/Commerce, B
International Relations and Affairs, B
Junior High/Intermediate/Middle School Education and Teaching, B
Kinesiology and Exercise Science, B
Marketing/Marketing Management, B
Mathematics, B
Mathematics Teacher Education, B
Middle School Education, M
Multi-/Interdisciplinary Studies, B
Music, B
Music Teacher Education, B
Philosophy and Religious Studies, B
Physics, B
Political Science and Government, B
Pre-Nursing Studies, B
Psychology, B
Reading Teacher Education, M
Secondary Education and Teaching, BM
Social Sciences, B
Spanish Language and Literature, B

BEULAH HEIGHTS UNIVERSITY

Bible/Biblical Studies, AB
Business Administration and Management, AB
Religion/Religious Studies, ABM

BRENAU UNIVERSITY

Accounting, BM
Art Teacher Education, B
Biology/Biological Sciences, B
Business Administration, Management and Operations, BM
Business/Commerce, B
Dance, B
Drama and Dance Teacher Education, B
Early Childhood Education and Teaching, MO
Education, BMO
Education/Teaching of Individuals with Mental Retardation, B
Elementary Education and Teaching, B
English Language and Literature, B
Fashion Merchandising, B
Fashion/Apparel Design, B
Finance and Financial Management Services, B
Fine/Studio Arts, B
General Studies, B
Health Services Administration, M
Health Services/Allied Health/Health Sciences, B
Health and Medical Administrative Services, B
History, B
Human Resources Management/Personnel Administration, B
Interior Design, BM
International Relations and Affairs, B
Junior High/Intermediate/Middle School Education and Teaching, B
Law and Legal Studies, B
Legal Professions and Studies, B
Marketing/Marketing Management, B
Mass Communication/Media Studies, B
Middle School Education, MO
Music, B
Music Performance, B
Music Teacher Education, B

Nursing - Advanced Practice, M
Nursing Administration, M
Nursing Education, M
Occupational Therapy/Therapist, BM
Organizational Management, M
Project Management, M
Psychology, M
Secondary Education and Teaching, M
Small Business Administration/Management, B
Special Education and Teaching, M
Sport and Fitness Administration/Management, B

BREWTON-PARKER COLLEGE

Accounting, B
Biology Teacher Education, B
Biology/Biological Sciences, AB
Business Administration and Management, AB
Communication Studies/Speech Communication and Rhetoric, B
Computer and Information Sciences, B
Early Childhood Education and Teaching, B
Education, B
English Language and Literature, B
English/Language Arts Teacher Education, B
General Studies, AB
Health and Physical Education/Fitness, B
History, B
History Teacher Education, B
Information Science/Studies, B
Junior High/Intermediate/Middle School Education and Teaching, B
Physical Education Teaching and Coaching, B
Political Science and Government, B
Psychology, B
Religion/Religious Studies, AB
Science Teacher Education/General Science Teacher Education, B
Secondary Education and Teaching, B
Social Sciences, B
Sociology, B
Theology/Theological Studies, B

CARVER COLLEGE

Accounting and Business/Management, B
Behavioral Sciences, B
Bible/Biblical Studies, AB

CENTRAL GEORGIA TECHNICAL COLLEGE

Accounting, A
Administrative Assistant and Secretarial Science, A
Adult Development and Aging, A
Banking and Financial Support Services, A
Business Administration and Management, A
Cabinetmaking and Millwork/Millwright, A
Cardiovascular Technology/Technologist, A
Carpentry/Carpenter, A
Child Care and Support Services Management, A
Child Development, A
Clinical/Medical Laboratory Technician, A
Computer Programming/Programmer, A
Computer Systems Networking and Telecommunications, A
Criminal Justice/Safety Studies, A
Dental Hygiene/Hygienist, A
Drafting and Design Technology/Technician, A
E-Commerce/Electronic Commerce, A
Electrical, Electronic and Communications Engineering Technology/Technician, A
Hotel/Motel Administration/Management, A
Industrial Technology/Technician, A
Information Science/Studies, A
Legal Assistant/Paralegal, A
Marketing/Marketing Management, A
Medical Radiologic Technology/Science - Radiation Therapist, A
Tourism and Travel Services Management, A
Veterinary/Animal Health Technology/Technician and Veterinary Assistant, A

Web Page, Digital/Multimedia and Information Resources Design, A

CHATTAHOOCHEE TECHNICAL COLLEGE

Accounting, A
Administrative Assistant and Secretarial Science, A
Automobile/Automotive Mechanics Technology/Technician, A
Biomedical Technology/Technician, A
Business Administration and Management, A
Child Development, A
Civil Engineering Technology/Technician, A
Computer Programming/Programmer, A
Computer Systems Networking and Telecommunications, A
Computer and Information Systems Security, A
Criminal Justice/Safety Studies, A
Culinary Arts/Chef Training, A
Drafting and Design Technology/Technician, A
Electrical, Electronic and Communications Engineering Technology/Technician, A
Fire Science/Firefighting, A
Horticultural Science, A
Information Science/Studies, A
Logistics and Materials Management, A
Marketing/Marketing Management, A
Medical Radiologic Technology/Science - Radiation Therapist, A
Parks, Recreation and Leisure Facilities Management, A
Web Page, Digital/Multimedia and Information Resources Design, A

CLARK ATLANTA UNIVERSITY

Accounting, BM
African-American Studies, MD
Art/Art Studies, General, B
Biological and Biomedical Sciences, MD
Biology/Biological Sciences, B
Business Administration and Management, B
Business Administration, Management and Operations, M
Business/Managerial Economics, B
Chemistry, BMD
Computer Science, BM
Computer and Information Sciences, B
Counselor Education/School Counseling and Guidance Services, M
Criminal Justice/Safety Studies, B
Criminology, M
Curriculum and Instruction, M
Early Childhood Education and Teaching, B
Economics, M
Education, BMDO
Educational Leadership and Administration, MDO
Educational Psychology, M
English, MD
English Language and Literature, B
Fashion/Apparel Design, B
French Language and Literature, B
History, BMD
Information Science/Studies, M
Mathematics, BM
Mathematics Teacher Education, M
Music, B
Philosophy, B
Physics, BM
Political Science and Government, BMD
Psychology, B
Public Administration, M
Radio, Television, and Digital Communication, B
Religion/Religious Studies, B
Romance Languages, Literatures, and Linguistics, MD
Science Teacher Education/General Science Teacher Education, M
Social Work, BMD
Sociology, BM
Spanish Language and Literature, B
Special Education and Teaching, M
Theatre Literature, History and Criticism, B

Women's Studies, MD

CLAYTON STATE UNIVERSITY

Accounting, BM
Administrative Assistant and Secretarial Science, A
Applied Psychology, M
Archives/Archival Administration, M
Biology/Biological Sciences, B
Business Administration and Management, B
Business Administration, Management and Operations, BM
Business/Commerce, B
Chemistry, B
Cinematography and Film/Video Production, AB
Clinical Psychology, M
Communication Studies/Speech Communication and Rhetoric, B
Computer Science, B
Computer Systems Networking and Telecommunications, A
Criminal Justice/Safety Studies, B
Dental Hygiene/Hygienist, B
Developmental Psychology, M
Drama and Dramatics/Theatre Arts, B
Education, M
English Education, M
English Language and Literature, B
Health Services Administration, M
Health and Medical Administrative Services, B
History, B
Hospital and Health Care Facilities Administration/Management, B
Information Science/Studies, B
Information Technology, B
International Business/Trade/Commerce, M
Junior High/Intermediate/Middle School Education and Teaching, B
Legal Assistant/Paralegal, AB
Liberal Arts and Sciences Studies and Humanities, AB
Liberal Studies, M
Logistics and Materials Management, B
Marketing/Marketing Management, B
Mathematics, B
Mathematics Teacher Education, M
Music, AB
Nursing, M
Office Management and Supervision, B
Philosophy, B
Political Science and Government, B
Psychology, M
Sociology, B
Sport and Fitness Administration/Management, B
Supply Chain Management, M

COASTAL PINES TECHNICAL COLLEGE

Administrative Assistant and Secretarial Science, A
Child Development, A
Clinical/Medical Laboratory Technician, A
Computer Systems Networking and Telecommunications, A
Computer Technology/Computer Systems Technology, A
Criminal Justice/Police Science, A
Forestry Technology/Technician, A
Information Science/Studies, A
Occupational Safety and Health Technology/Technician, A
Respiratory Therapy Technician/Assistant, A
Surgical Technology/Technologist, A

COLLEGE OF COASTAL GEORGIA

Agricultural Business and Management, A
American/United States Studies/Civilization, B
Art/Art Studies, General, A
Biology/Biological Sciences, AB
Business Administration and Management, AB
Chemistry, A
Clinical/Medical Laboratory Technician, A
Computer Science, A
Criminal Justice/Law Enforcement Administration, AB
Dental Hygiene/Hygienist, A
English Language and Literature, A
Foreign Languages and Literatures, B

Forestry, A
Geology/Earth Science, A
Health Information/Medical Records Administration/Administrator, B
Health and Physical Education, A
History, A
Mathematics, AB
Medical Radiologic Technology/Science - Radiation Therapist, A
Occupational Therapy/Therapist, A
Parks, Recreation and Leisure Facilities Management, A
Philosophy, A
Physical Therapy/Therapist, A
Physician Assistant, A
Physics, A
Political Science and Government, A
Pre-Dentistry Studies, A
Pre-Medicine/Pre-Medical Studies, A
Pre-Pharmacy Studies, A
Pre-Veterinary Studies, A
Psychology, AB
Public Administration and Social Service Professions, B
Respiratory Care Therapy/Therapist, A
Sociology, A
Teacher Education, Multiple Levels, AB
Wildlife and Wildlands Science and Management, A

COLUMBUS STATE UNIVERSITY

Accounting, B
Art Education, M
Art Teacher Education, B
Biology/Biological Sciences, B
Business Administration and Management, B
Business Administration, Management and Operations, MO
Business/Commerce, B
Chemistry, B
Computer Science, MO
Computer and Information Sciences, B
Computer and Information Systems Security, O
Counseling Psychology, M
Counselor Education/School Counseling and Guidance Services, MDO
Criminal Justice/Safety Studies, AB
Curriculum and Instruction, D
Drama and Dance Teacher Education, B
Drama and Dramatics/Theatre Arts, B
Drawing, B
Early Childhood Education and Teaching, BMO
Education, MDO
Educational Leadership and Administration, MDO
English Education, MO
English Language and Literature, B
English as a Second Language, O
English/Language Arts Teacher Education, B
Environmental Sciences, M
Exercise and Sports Science, M
Finance, B
French Language and Literature, B
Geology/Earth Science, B
Health Education, M
Health Services/Allied Health/Health Sciences, B
Higher Education/Higher Education Administration, M
History, BM
Homeland Security, M
Information Technology, B
Junior High/Intermediate/Middle School Education and Teaching, B
Kinesiology and Exercise Science, B
Liberal Arts and Sciences Studies and Humanities, AB
Management Information Systems and Services, B
Marketing/Marketing Management, B
Mathematics, B
Mathematics Teacher Education, BMO
Middle School Education, MO
Modeling and Simulation, O
Music, B
Music Performance, B
Music Teacher Education, BMO
Nursing, M
Organizational Management, M
Performance, M

Physical Education Teaching and Coaching, BM
Political Science and Government, B
Psychology, B
Public Administration, M
Science Teacher Education/General Science Teacher Education, BMO
Secondary Education and Teaching, MO
Social Studies Teacher Education, BMO
Sociology, B
Spanish Language and Literature, B
Special Education and Teaching, BMO
Theater, M

COLUMBUS TECHNICAL COLLEGE

Accounting, A
Administrative Assistant and Secretarial Science, A
Automobile/Automotive Mechanics Technology/Technician, A
Child Development, A
Computer Engineering, A
Computer Systems Networking and Telecommunications, A
Dental Hygiene/Hygienist, A
Diagnostic Medical Sonography/Sonographer and Ultrasound Technician, A
Drafting and Design Technology/Technician, A
Electrical, Electronic and Communications Engineering Technology/Technician, A
Emergency Medical Technology/Technician (EMT Paramedic), A
Health Information/Medical Records Technology/Technician, A
Horticultural Science, A
Industrial Technology/Technician, A
Information Science/Studies, A
Machine Tool Technology/Machinist, A
Mechanical Engineering/Mechanical Technology/Technician, A
Medical Office Management/Administration, A
Medical Radiologic Technology/Science - Radiation Therapist, A
Pharmacy Technician/Assistant, A
Respiratory Therapy Technician/Assistant, A
Surgical Technology/Technologist, A
Web Page, Digital/Multimedia and Information Resources Design, A

COVENANT COLLEGE

Bible/Biblical Studies, AB
Biological and Physical Sciences, B
Biology/Biological Sciences, B
Business/Commerce, B
Chemistry, B
Computer and Information Sciences, B
Drama and Dramatics/Theatre Arts, B
Education, M
Elementary Education and Teaching, B
English Language and Literature, B
English/Language Arts Teacher Education, B
Fine Arts and Art Studies, B
Foreign Languages and Literatures, B
History, B
History Teacher Education, B
Mathematics, B
Mathematics Teacher Education, B
Multi-/Interdisciplinary Studies, B
Music, B
Music Performance, B
Philosophy, B
Philosophy and Religious Studies, B
Physical Sciences, B
Physics, B
Psychology, B
Science Teacher Education/General Science Teacher Education, B
Social Sciences, B
Sociology, B

DALTON STATE COLLEGE

Accounting, B
Biology/Biological Sciences, AB
Business Administration and Management, AB
Chemistry, AB
Clinical Laboratory Science/Medical Technology/Technologist, A
Clinical/Medical Laboratory Technician, A

Computer Engineering Technology/Technician, A
Computer Installation and Repair Technology/Technician, A
Computer Science, A
Computer Technology/Computer Systems Technology, A
Criminal Justice/Law Enforcement Administration, AB
Criminal Justice/Police Science, A
Dental Hygiene/Hygienist, A
Drafting and Design Technology/Technician, A
Education, A
Electrical, Electronic and Communications Engineering Technology/Technician, A
Elementary Education and Teaching, AB
English Language and Literature, AB
General Studies, A
Health Information/Medical Records Administration/Administrator, A
History, AB
Industrial Electronics Technology/Technician, A
Industrial Technology/Technician, A
Liberal Arts and Sciences Studies and Humanities, A
Management Information Systems and Services, B
Marketing/Marketing Management, AB
Mathematics, AB
Medical Office Management/Administration, A
Office Management and Supervision, A
Operations Management and Supervision, B
Physics, A
Political Science and Government, A
Pre-Pharmacy Studies, A
Psychology, A
Radiologic Technology/Science - Radiographer, A
Respiratory Therapy Technician/Assistant, A
Sales, Distribution and Marketing Operations, AB
Social Work, B

DARTON STATE COLLEGE

Accounting, A
Agriculture, A
Anthropology, A
Art Teacher Education, A
Art/Art Studies, General, A
Biological and Biomedical Sciences, A
Biology/Biological Sciences, A
Business Administration and Management, A
Business Teacher Education, A
Cardiovascular Technology/Technologist, A
Chemistry, A
Clinical Laboratory Science/Medical Technology/Technologist, A
Computer Science, A
Computer and Information Sciences, A
Computer and Information Sciences and Support Services, A
Criminal Justice/Law Enforcement Administration, A
Dance, A
Dental Hygiene/Hygienist, A
Diagnostic Medical Sonography/Sonographer and Ultrasound Technician, A
Drama and Dance Teacher Education, A
Drama and Dramatics/Theatre Arts, A
Economics, A
Emergency Medical Technology/Technician (EMT Paramedic), A
Engineering Technology, A
English Language and Literature, A
English/Language Arts Teacher Education, A
Environmental Studies, A
Foreign Languages and Literatures, A
Forensic Science and Technology, A
Forestry, A
General Studies, A
Geography, A
Health Information/Medical Records Administration/Administrator, A
Health Information/Medical Records Technology/Technician, A
Health and Physical Education, A
Health/Medical Preparatory Programs, A
Histologic Technician, A
History, A
History Teacher Education, A
Journalism, A

Junior High/Intermediate/Middle School Education and Teaching, A
Mathematics, A
Mathematics Teacher Education, A
Music, A
Music Teacher Education, A
Nuclear Medical Technology/Technologist, A
Occupational Therapist Assistant, A
Philosophy, A
Physical Therapist Assistant, A
Physics, A
Political Science and Government, A
Pre-Dentistry Studies, A
Pre-Law Studies, A
Pre-Medicine/Pre-Medical Studies, A
Pre-Pharmacy Studies, A
Pre-Veterinary Studies, A
Psychology, A
Respiratory Care Therapy/Therapist, A
Science Teacher Education/General Science Teacher Education, A
Social Work, A
Sociology, A
Special Education and Teaching, A
Speech Teacher Education, A
Trade and Industrial Teacher Education, A

DEVRY UNIVERSITY (ALPHARETTA)

Accounting, B
Business Administration and Management, B
Business Administration, Management and Operations, BM
Business/Commerce, B
Computer Engineering Technology/Technician, B
Computer Software Engineering, B
Computer Systems Analysis/Analyst, B
Computer Systems Networking and Telecommunications, AB
Criminal Justice/Law Enforcement Administration, B
Electrical, Electronic and Communications Engineering Technology/Technician, B
Web Page, Digital/Multimedia and Information Resources Design, AB

DEVRY UNIVERSITY (ATLANTA)

Business Administration and Management, B
Computer and Information Sciences, B
Electrical, Electronic and Communications Engineering Technology/Technician, A
Health Information/Medical Records Technology/Technician, A

DEVRY UNIVERSITY (DECATUR)

Accounting, B
Accounting Technology/Technician and Bookkeeping, A
Biomedical Technology/Technician, B
Business Administration and Management, B
Business Administration, Management and Operations, BM
Business/Commerce, B
Computer Engineering Technology/Technician, B
Computer Software Engineering, B
Computer Systems Analysis/Analyst, B
Computer Systems Networking and Telecommunications, AB
Criminal Justice/Law Enforcement Administration, B
Electrical, Electronic and Communications Engineering Technology/Technician, AB
Health Information/Medical Records Technology/Technician, A
Health/Health Care Administration/Management, B
Web Page, Digital/Multimedia and Information Resources Design, AB

DEVRY UNIVERSITY (DULUTH)

Accounting, B
Business Administration and Management, B
Business Administration, Management and Operations, BMO
Business/Commerce, B
Computer Systems Analysis/Analyst, B
Computer Systems Networking and Telecommunications, AB
Criminal Justice/Law Enforcement Administration, B

Web Page, Digital/Multimedia and Information Resources Design, AB

EAST GEORGIA STATE COLLEGE

Liberal Arts and Sciences Studies and Humanities, A
Medical/Clinical Assistant, A

EMMANUEL COLLEGE

Biology/Biological Sciences, B
Business Teacher Education, B
Computer and Information Sciences, B
Criminal Justice/Law Enforcement Administration, B
Elementary Education and Teaching, B
English Language and Literature, B
English/Language Arts Teacher Education, B
Junior High/Intermediate/Middle School Education and Teaching, B
Kinesiology and Exercise Science, B
Liberal Arts and Sciences Studies and Humanities, A
Mass Communication/Media Studies, B
Mathematics, B
Mathematics Teacher Education, B
Music, B
Music Teacher Education, B
Office Management and Supervision, A
Organizational Communication, B
Pastoral Studies/Counseling, B
Pre-Law Studies, B
Pre-Pharmacy Studies, B
Psychology, B
Religious/Sacred Music, B
Social Science Teacher Education, B
Sport and Fitness Administration/Management, B

EMORY UNIVERSITY

Accounting, D
African Studies, B
African-American/Black Studies, B
Allied Health and Medical Assisting Services, MD
Allopathic Medicine, D
American/United States Studies/Civilization, B
Ancient Studies/Civilization, B
Ancient/Classical Greek Language and Literature, B
Anesthesiologist Assistant, M
Animal Behavior and Ethology, D
Anthropology, BD
Applied Mathematics, B
Arabic Language and Literature, B
Art History, Criticism and Conservation, BD
Astronomy and Astrophysics, B
Biochemistry, D
Bioethics/Medical Ethics, M
Bioinformatics, MD
Biological and Biomedical Sciences, D
Biological and Physical Sciences, B
Biology/Biological Sciences, B
Biophysics, BD
Biostatistics, MD
Business Administration and Management, B
Business Administration, Management and Operations, MD
Cancer Biology/Oncology, D
Cell Biology and Anatomy, D
Chemistry, BD
Chinese Language and Literature, B
Classical, Ancient Mediterranean and Near Eastern Studies and Archaeology, B
Classics and Classical Languages, Literatures, and Linguistics, B
Clinical Psychology, D
Clinical Research, M
Cognitive Sciences, D
Communication and Media Studies, B
Comparative Literature, BDO
Computational Sciences, D
Computer Science, BMD
Dance, B
Developmental Biology and Embryology, D
Developmental Psychology, D
Drama and Dramatics/Theatre Arts, B
East Asian Studies, B
Ecology, D
Economics, BD
Education, BMD

Engineering Science, B
English, DO
English Language and Literature, B
Environmental Studies, B
Environmental and Occupational Health, MD
Epidemiology, MD
Ethics, M
Evolutionary Biology, D
Film, Television, and Video Theory and Criticism, MO
Film/Cinema Studies, B
Finance and Banking, D
Fine/Studio Arts, B
French Language and Literature, D
French Studies, B
Genetic Counseling/Counselor, M
Genetics, D
German Studies, B
Health Education, MD
Health Informatics, M
Health Promotion, M
Health Services Administration, MD
Health Services Research, M
Health and Physical Education, B
History, BD
Human Genetics, M
Humanities/Humanistic Studies, B
Immunology, D
Interdisciplinary Studies, D
International Public Health/International Health, M
International Relations and Affairs, B
Italian Studies, B
Japanese Language and Literature, B
Jewish/Judaic Studies, B
Latin American Studies, B
Latin Language and Literature, B
Law and Legal Studies, MDO
Liberal Arts and Sciences Studies and Humanities, B
Linguistics, B
Management Information Systems and Services, D
Marketing, D
Mathematics, BMD
Mathematics and Computer Science, B
Medieval and Renaissance Studies, B
Microbiology, D
Middle School Education, M
Molecular Biology, D
Molecular Genetics, D
Molecular Pathogenesis, D
Multi-/Interdisciplinary Studies, B
Music, BM
Near and Middle Eastern Studies, B
Neuroscience, D
Nurse Midwife/Nursing Midwifery, M
Nursing, MD
Nursing - Adult, M
Nursing - Advanced Practice, M
Nursing Administration, M
Nutritional Sciences, MD
Organizational Management, D
Pastoral Studies/Counseling, D
Pediatric Nurse/Nursing, M
Performance, M
Pharmacology, D
Philosophy, BDO
Physical Therapy/Therapist, D
Physician Assistant, M
Physics, BD
Playwriting and Screenwriting, B
Political Science and Government, BD
Portuguese Language and Literature, DO
Psychology, BD
Public Health, MD
Religion/Religious Studies, BD
Romance Languages, Literatures, and Linguistics, B
Russian Language and Literature, B
Russian Studies, B
Secondary Education and Teaching, M
Sociology, BD
Spanish Language and Literature, BDO
Sustainable Development, M
Theology and Religious Vocations, MD
Theoretical Physics, D
Visual and Performing Arts, B
Women's Health Nursing, M

Women's Studies, BDO

EMORY UNIVERSITY, OXFORD COLLEGE

Liberal Arts and Sciences Studies and Humanities, AB

FORT VALLEY STATE UNIVERSITY

Accounting, B
Administrative Assistant and Secretarial Science, AB
African Studies, B
Agricultural Economics, B
Agricultural/Biological Engineering and Bioengineering, B
Agronomy and Crop Science, B
Animal Sciences, BM
Biology/Biological Sciences, B
Botany/Plant Biology, B
Business Administration and Management, B
Chemistry, B
Computer Science, B
Counseling Psychology, M
Counselor Education/School Counseling and Guidance Services, O
Criminal Justice/Law Enforcement Administration, AB
Economics, B
Electrical, Electronic and Communications Engineering Technology/Technician, AB
Environmental and Occupational Health, M
Family and Consumer Sciences/Home Economics Teacher Education, B
Foods, Nutrition, and Wellness Studies, B
French Language and Literature, B
Health Teacher Education, B
Kindergarten/PreSchool Education and Teaching, B
Liberal Arts and Sciences Studies and Humanities, B
Marketing/Marketing Management, B
Mass Communication/Media Studies, B
Mathematics, B
Ornamental Horticulture, B
Physical Education Teaching and Coaching, B
Political Science and Government, B
Psychology, B
Public Health, M
Rehabilitation Counseling, M
Social Sciences, B
Social Work, B
Sociology, B
Veterinary/Animal Health Technology/Technician and Veterinary Assistant, A
Zoology/Animal Biology, B

GEORGIA CHRISTIAN UNIVERSITY

Business Administration, Management and Operations, M
Missions/Missionary Studies and Missiology, M
Music, M
Pastoral Studies/Counseling, D
Theology and Religious Vocations, MD

GEORGIA COLLEGE & STATE UNIVERSITY

Accounting, BM
American/United States Studies/Civilization, M
Art Therapy/Therapist, M
Art/Art Studies, General, B
Athletic Training and Sports Medicine, B
Biological and Biomedical Sciences, M
Biology/Biological Sciences, B
Business Administration and Management, B
Business Administration, Management and Operations, M
Business/Managerial Economics, B
Chemistry, B
Community Health and Preventive Medicine, B
Computer Science, B
Criminal Justice/Law Enforcement Administration, B
Criminology, M
Curriculum and Instruction, O
Drama and Dramatics/Theatre Arts, B
Early Childhood Education and Teaching, BMO
Education, MO
Educational Leadership and Administration, O

Educational Media/Instructional Technology, M
English, M
English Language and Literature, B
Environmental Sciences, B
Exercise and Sports Science, M
French Language and Literature, B
Geography, B
Health Education, M
Health Promotion, M
History, BM
Journalism, B
Junior High/Intermediate/Middle School Education and Teaching, B
Kinesiology and Exercise Science, B
Kinesiology and Movement Studies, M
Liberal Arts and Sciences Studies and Humanities, B
Logistics and Materials Management, M
Management Information Systems and Services, M
Marketing/Marketing Management, B
Mathematics, B
Middle School Education, M
Music, B
Music Teacher Education, BM
Music Therapy/Therapist, BM
Nursing, MD
Parks, Recreation, Leisure and Fitness Studies, B
Philosophy, B
Physical Education Teaching and Coaching, M
Physics, B
Political Science and Government, B
Public Administration, M
Public History, M
Reading Teacher Education, M
Recreation and Park Management, M
Secondary Education and Teaching, MO
Sociology, B
Spanish Language and Literature, B
Special Education and Teaching, BMO
Web/Multimedia Management and Webmaster, B
Western European Studies, M
Writing, M

GEORGIA GWINNETT COLLEGE

Biology/Biological Sciences, B
Business/Commerce, B
Chemistry, B
Criminal Justice/Safety Studies, B
Early Childhood Education and Teaching, B
English Language and Literature, B
Environmental Sciences, AB
History, B
Information Technology, B
Kinesiology and Exercise Science, B
Mathematics, B
Political Science and Government, B
Psychology, B
Special Education and Teaching, B

GEORGIA HIGHLANDS COLLEGE

Agriculture, A
Art/Art Studies, General, A
Biology/Biological Sciences, A
Business Administration and Management, A
Chemistry, A
Clinical Laboratory Science/Medical Technology/Technologist, A
Communication Studies/Speech Communication and Rhetoric, A
Computer and Information Sciences, A
Criminal Justice/Police Science, A
Dental Hygiene/Hygienist, AB
Economics, A
Education, A
English Language and Literature, A
Foreign Languages and Literatures, A
General Studies, A
Geology/Earth Science, A
Health Information/Medical Records Administration/Administrator, A
History, A
Human Services, A
Information Science/Studies, A
Journalism, A
Liberal Arts and Sciences Studies and Humanities, A

Mathematics, A
Music, A
Philosophy, A
Physician Assistant, A
Physics, A
Political Science and Government, A
Pre-Pharmacy Studies, A
Psychology, A
Respiratory Therapy Technician/Assistant, A
Sociology, A

GEORGIA INSTITUTE OF TECHNOLOGY

Aerospace, Aeronautical and Astronautical Engineering, BMD
Applied Mathematics, B
Architecture, BMD
Artificial Intelligence and Robotics, D
Atmospheric Sciences and Meteorology, MD
Biochemistry, B
Bioengineering, MD
Bioinformatics, MD
Biological and Biomedical Sciences, MD
Biology/Biological Sciences, B
Biomedical Engineering, MD
Biomedical/Medical Engineering, B
Building Science, MD
Business Administration and Management, B
Business Administration, Management and Operations, M
Business/Managerial Economics, B
Chemical Engineering, BMD
Chemistry, BMD
Civil Engineering, BMD
Computational Sciences, MD
Computer Art and Design, MD
Computer Engineering, BMD
Computer Science, MD
Computer and Information Sciences, B
Computer and Information Systems Security, M
Digital Communication and Media/Multimedia, B
Economic Development, M
Economics, MD
Electrical Engineering, MD
Electrical, Electronics and Communications Engineering, B
Engineering and Applied Sciences, MD
Environmental Engineering Technology/Environmental Technology, MD
Environmental Policy, M
Environmental/Environmental Health Engineering, B
Ergonomics and Human Factors, D
Foreign Languages and Literatures, B
Geographic Information Systems, M
Geological and Earth Sciences/Geosciences, B
Geosciences, MD
Health Physics/Radiological Health, MD
Health Services Administration, M
History and Philosophy of Science and Technology, B
History of Science and Technology, MD
Human-Computer Interaction, M
Industrial Design, BM
Industrial Engineering, B
Industrial/Management Engineering, MD
International Affairs, MD
International Business/Trade/Commerce, M
International Relations and Affairs, B
International/Global Studies, B
Internet and Interactive Multimedia, MD
Logistics and Materials Management, M
Management, D
Management Information Systems and Services, M
Materials Engineering, BMD
Mathematical and Computational Finance, M
Mathematics, MD
Mechanical Engineering, BMD
Mechanics, MD
Multi-/Interdisciplinary Studies, B
Musicology and Ethnomusicology, MD
Nuclear Engineering, BMD
Operations Research, MD
Physics, BMD
Physiology, MD
Psychology, MD
Public Policy Analysis, BMD

Science, Technology and Society, B
Statistics, M
Systems Engineering, M
Textile Sciences and Engineering, B
Urban Design, M
Urban and Regional Planning, MD

GEORGIA MILITARY COLLEGE

Biology/Biological Sciences, A
Business Administration and Management, B
Business/Commerce, A
Computer Science, A
Computer and Information Systems Security, A
Criminal Justice/Law Enforcement Administration, A
Early Childhood Education and Teaching, A
English Language and Literature, A
General Studies, A
Health Services/Allied Health/Health Sciences, A
Health Teacher Education, A
History, A
Information Technology, A
Junior High/Intermediate/Middle School Education and Teaching, A
Legal Assistant/Paralegal, A
Logistics and Materials Management, A
Management Information Systems and Services, A
Mass Communication/Media Studies, A
Mathematics, A
Political Science and Government, A
Pre-Nursing Studies, A
Psychology, A
Secondary Education and Teaching, A
Social Work, A
Sociology, A

GEORGIA NORTHWESTERN TECHNICAL COLLEGE

Accounting, A
Child Development, A
Computer Programming/Programmer, A
Criminal Justice/Safety Studies, A
Environmental Engineering Technology/Environmental Technology, A
Fire Science/Firefighting, A
Information Science/Studies, A
Legal Assistant/Paralegal, A
Marketing/Marketing Management, A
Medical Office Management/Administration, A
Respiratory Therapy Technician/Assistant, A
Surgical Technology/Technologist, A
Web Page, Digital/Multimedia and Information Resources Design, A

GEORGIA PIEDMONT TECHNICAL COLLEGE

Accounting, A
Administrative Assistant and Secretarial Science, A
Automobile/Automotive Mechanics Technology/Technician, A
Business/Commerce, A
Clinical/Medical Laboratory Technician, A
Computer Engineering Technology/Technician, A
Computer Programming/Programmer, A
Computer Systems Networking and Telecommunications, A
Criminal Justice/Safety Studies, A
Drafting and Design Technology/Technician, A
Electrical, Electronic and Communications Engineering Technology/Technician, A
Electromechanical Technology/Electromechanical Engineering Technology, A
Engineering Technology, A
Heating, Air Conditioning and Refrigeration Technology/Technician, A
Industrial Technology/Technician, A
Information Science/Studies, A
Instrumentation Technology/Technician, A
Legal Administrative Assistant/Secretary, A
Legal Assistant/Paralegal, A
Machine Tool Technology/Machinist, A
Marketing/Marketing Management, A
Medical/Clinical Assistant, A
Operations Management and Supervision, A
Ophthalmic Laboratory Technology/Technician, A
Opticianry/Ophthalmic Dispensing Optician, A
Surgical Technology/Technologist, A

Telecommunications Technology/Technician, A

GEORGIA SOUTHERN UNIVERSITY

Accounting, BM
Allied Health and Medical Assisting Services, MDO
Anthropology, B
Apparel and Textiles, B
Applied Economics, MO
Applied Physics, M
Art/Art Studies, General, B
Athletic Training and Sports Medicine, B
Biological and Biomedical Sciences, M
Biology/Biological Sciences, B
Biostatistics, MD
Business Administration and Management, B
Business Administration, Management and Operations, M
Business/Managerial Economics, B
Chemistry, B
Civil Engineering, B
Civil Engineering Technology/Technician, B
Communication Studies/Speech Communication and Rhetoric, B
Community Health and Preventive Medicine, MD
Computer Science, M
Computer and Information Sciences, B
Construction Engineering Technology/Technician, B
Counselor Education/School Counseling and Guidance Services, MO
Criminal Justice/Safety Studies, B
Curriculum and Instruction, MD
Development Economics and International Development, B
Digital Communication and Media/Multimedia, B
Drama and Dramatics/Theatre Arts, B
Early Childhood Education and Teaching, MO
Economics, B
Education, BMDO
Educational Administration and Supervision, MD
Educational Leadership and Administration, MDO
Educational Media/Instructional Technology, MO
Electrical Engineering, M
Electrical, Electronic and Communications Engineering Technology/Technician, B
Electrical, Electronics and Communications Engineering, B
Elementary Education and Teaching, BM
Energy and Power Engineering, M
Engineering Management, M
Engineering and Applied Sciences, MO
English, M
English Education, M
English Language and Literature, B
Environmental and Occupational Health, MO
Epidemiology, M
Family and Consumer Sciences/Home Economics Teacher Education, B
Finance, B
Fine Arts and Art Studies, M
Foods, Nutrition, and Wellness Studies, B
Foreign Languages, Literatures, and Linguistics, B
Forestry, B
French Language and Literature, B
General Studies, B
Geography, B
Geology/Earth Science, B
German Language and Literature, B
Graphic Design, BM
Graphic and Printing Equipment Operator Production, B
Health Education, MD
Health Services Administration, MD
Health and Physical Education, B
Higher Education/Higher Education Administration, M
History, BMO
Hotel/Motel Administration/Management, B
Human Development and Family Studies, B
Industrial Production Technologies/Technicians, B
Information Science/Studies, B
Interior Design, B
International Business/Trade/Commerce, B
International Relations and Affairs, B
Journalism, B
Junior High/Intermediate/Middle School Education and Teaching, B

Kinesiology and Exercise Science, B
Kinesiology and Movement Studies, M
Logistics and Materials Management, BD
Management Information Systems and Services, BMO
Manufacturing Engineering, BO
Marketing/Marketing Management, B
Mathematics, BM
Mathematics Teacher Education, M
Mechanical Engineering, BM
Mechanical Engineering/Mechanical Technology/Technician, B
Middle School Education, MO
Music, BM
Music Performance, B
Music Teacher Education, B
Music Theory and Composition, B
Non-Profit/Public/Organizational Management, O
Nursing, D
Nursing - Advanced Practice, M
Nursing Education, O
Nutritional Sciences, O
Parks, Recreation, Leisure and Fitness Studies, B
Pharmacology, B
Philosophy, B
Physical Education Teaching and Coaching, B
Physics, B
Political Science and Government, B
Pre-Dentistry Studies, B
Pre-Medicine/Pre-Medical Studies, B
Pre-Pharmacy Studies, B
Pre-Veterinary Studies, B
Psychology, BMD
Public Administration, M
Public Health, MD
Public Health Education and Promotion, B
Public Relations/Image Management, B
Radio and Television, B
Reading Teacher Education, MO
School Psychology, MO
Secondary Education and Teaching, MO
Social Studies Teacher Education, M
Sociology, BM
Spanish Language Teacher Education, B
Spanish Language and Literature, M
Special Education and Teaching, BMO
Sport and Fitness Administration/Management, BM
Supply Chain Management, D
Systems Engineering, M
Technology Teacher Education/Industrial Arts Teacher Education, B

GEORGIA SOUTHWESTERN STATE UNIVERSITY

Accounting, B
Art/Art Studies, General, B
Biology/Biological Sciences, B
Business Administration and Management, B
Business Administration, Management and Operations, M
Chemistry, B
Computer Science, BMO
Criminal Justice/Law Enforcement Administration, B
Drama and Dramatics/Theatre Arts, B
Early Childhood Education and Teaching, MO
Education, MO
Elementary Education and Teaching, B
English Language and Literature, B
Geology/Earth Science, B
History, B
Human Resources Management/Personnel Administration, B
Information Technology, B
Junior High/Intermediate/Middle School Education and Teaching, B
Marketing/Marketing Management, B
Mathematics, B
Middle School Education, O
Music, B
Physical Education Teaching and Coaching, B
Political Science and Government, B
Psychology, B
Sociology, B

Special Education and Teaching, BM

GEORGIA STATE UNIVERSITY

Accounting, BM
Actuarial Science, BM
African-American Studies, M
African-American/Black Studies, B
Allied Health and Medical Assisting Services, M
Analytical Chemistry, MD
Anthropology, BM
Art Education, M
Art History, Criticism and Conservation, M
Art Teacher Education, B
Astronomy, D
Biochemistry, MD
Bioinformatics, MD
Biological and Biomedical Sciences, MD
Biology/Biological Sciences, B
Biostatistics, MD
Business Administration and Management, B
Business Administration, Management and Operations, MD
Business/Managerial Economics, B
Cell Biology and Anatomy, MD
Ceramic Arts and Ceramics, M
Chemistry, BMD
Clinical Psychology, D
Clothing and Textiles, M
Cognitive Sciences, D
Communication Disorders, MD
Communication Studies/Speech Communication and Rhetoric, B
Communication and Media Studies, MD
Community Psychology, D
Composition, M
Computer Science, BMD
Computer and Information Sciences, B
Counseling Psychology, MO
Counselor Education/School Counseling and Guidance Services, MO
Criminal Justice/Safety Studies, B
Criminology, MD
Curriculum and Instruction, D
Developmental Psychology, D
Dietetics/Dieticians, B
Drawing, B
Early Childhood Education and Teaching, MDO
Economic Development, MDO
Economics, BMD
Education, MDO
Education/Teaching of Individuals with Multiple Disabilities, M
Educational Administration and Supervision, MDO
Educational Measurement and Evaluation, MD
Educational Media/Instructional Technology, MD
Educational Policy, MDO
Educational Psychology, MD
Elementary Education and Teaching, D
Emergency Management, MO
English, MD
English Education, M
English Language and Literature, B
Entrepreneurship/Entrepreneurial Studies, M
Environmental Biology, MD
Environmental Policy, D
Exercise and Sports Science, M
Film, Television, and Video Production, MD
Film/Cinema Studies, B
Finance, B
Finance and Banking, MD
Fine Arts and Art Studies, M
Foreign Language Teacher Education, M
Forensic Science and Technology, O
Foundations and Philosophy of Education, MD
French Language and Literature, BMO
General Merchandising, Sales, and Related Marketing Operations, B
Geochemistry, D
Geographic Information Systems, O
Geography, M
Geology/Earth Science, BM
Geosciences, MO
German Language and Literature, BO
Gerontology, MO
Graphic Design, M
Health Education, M

Health Informatics, M
Health Services Administration, MD
Historic Preservation and Conservation, M
History, BMD
Hospitality Administration/Management, B
Human Resources Management and Services, MD
Human Services, M
Industrial and Labor Relations, D
Information Science/Studies, MDO
Insurance, BMDO
Interior Design, M
International Business/Trade/Commerce, M
International Economics, B
Journalism, B
Kindergarten/PreSchool Education and Teaching, B
Kinesiology and Movement Studies, D
Latin American Studies, O
Law and Legal Studies, D
Linguistics, BMD
Management, MD
Management Information Systems and Services, MDO
Management Strategy and Policy, D
Marketing, MD
Marketing/Marketing Management, B
Mass Communication/Media Studies, MD
Mathematics, BMD
Mathematics Teacher Education, MD
Media Studies, D
Microbiology, MD
Middle School Education, MD
Molecular Biology, MD
Molecular Genetics, MD
Multi-/Interdisciplinary Studies, B
Music, MDO
Music Performance, B
Music Teacher Education, MD
Neurobiology and Neurophysiology, MD
Neuroscience, D
Non-Profit/Public/Organizational Management, MDO
Nursing, MDO
Nursing - Adult, MO
Nursing - Advanced Practice, MO
Nursing Administration, M
Nursing Informatics, M
Nutritional Sciences, M
Operations Research, M
Organic Chemistry, M
Organizational Management, MD
Painting, M
Pediatric Nurse/Nursing, MO
Performance, MDO
Philosophy, BM
Photography, M
Physical Chemistry, MD
Physical Education Teaching and Coaching, BM
Physical Therapy/Therapist, D
Physics, BMD
Physiology, MD
Political Science and Government, BMD
Printmaking, M
Psychiatric/Mental Health Nurse/Nursing, MO
Psychology, BD
Public Administration, M
Public Health, MDO
Public History, M
Public Policy Analysis, BM
Reading Teacher Education, MD
Real Estate, BMDO
Rehabilitation Counseling, M
Religion/Religious Studies, BM
Respiratory Care Therapy/Therapist, B
Rhetoric, MD
School Psychology, MDO
Science Teacher Education/General Science Teacher Education, MD
Sculpture, M
Secondary Education and Teaching, MD
Social Studies Teacher Education, MD
Social Work, BMO
Sociology, BMD
Spanish Language and Literature, BMO
Special Education and Teaching, MD
Speech and Interpersonal Communication, M
Sport and Fitness Administration/Management, M
Sports Medicine, M

Statistics, MD
Taxation, M
Translation and Interpretation, O
Urban Education and Leadership, M
Urban and Regional Planning, MDO
Women's Health Nursing, MO
Women's Studies, BMO
Writing, MD

GORDON STATE COLLEGE

Art/Art Studies, General, A
Astronomy, A
Biological and Biomedical Sciences, AB
Biology Teacher Education, B
Business Administration and Management, A
Chemistry, A
Computer Science, A
Criminal Justice/Safety Studies, A
Dental Services and Allied Professions, A
Drama and Dramatics/Theatre Arts, A
Early Childhood Education and Teaching, AB
Elementary Education and Teaching, B
English Language and Literature, AB
English/Language Arts Teacher Education, B
Environmental Sciences, A
Foreign Languages and Literatures, A
Forestry, A
General Studies, A
Health Information/Medical Records
   Administration/Administrator, B
Health and Physical Education, A
Health/Medical Preparatory Programs, A
History, AB
History Teacher Education, B
Human Services, B
Information Technology, A
Junior High/Intermediate/Middle School Education
   and Teaching, A
Liberal Arts and Sciences Studies and Humani-
   ties, A
Mathematics, AB
Mathematics Teacher Education, B
Music, A
Physics, A
Political Science and Government, A
Pre-Pharmacy Studies, A
Psychology, A
Radiologic Technology/Science - Radiographer, A
Secondary Education and Teaching, A
Social Work, A
Sociology, A
Teaching English as a Second or Foreign
   Language/ESL Language Instructor, A

GUPTON-JONES COLLEGE OF FU-NERAL SERVICE

Mortuary Science and Embalming/Embalmer, A

GWINNETT TECHNICAL COLLEGE

Accounting, A
Administrative Assistant and Secretarial Science, A
Automobile/Automotive Mechanics
   Technology/Technician, A
Building/Construction Finishing, Manage-
   ment, and Inspection, A
Business Administration and Management, A
Computer Programming/Programmer, A
Computer Science, A
Computer Systems Networking and Telecommunica-
   tions, A
Drafting and Design Technology/Technician, A
Electrical, Electronic and Communications Engineer-
   ing Technology/Technician, A
Emergency Medical Technology/Technician (EMT
   Paramedic), A
Horticultural Science, A
Hotel/Motel Administration/Management, A
Information Science/Studies, A
Interior Design, A
Machine Tool Technology/Machinist, A
Management Information Systems and Services, A
Marketing/Marketing Management, A
Medical Radiologic Technology/Science - Radiation
   Therapist, A
Medical/Clinical Assistant, A
Ornamental Horticulture, A

Photography, A
Physical Therapist Assistant, A
Physical Therapy/Therapist, A
Respiratory Care Therapy/Therapist, A
Tourism and Travel Services Management, A
Veterinary/Animal Health Technology/Technician and
   Veterinary Assistant, A

INTERACTIVE COLLEGE OF TECHNOL-OGY (CHAMBLEE)

Accounting Technology/Technician and Bookkeep-
   ing, A
Administrative Assistant and Secretarial Science, A
Computer and Information Sciences, A
Computer and Information Sciences and Support
   Services, A
Management Information Systems and Services, A

KENNESAW STATE UNIVERSITY

Accounting, BM
African Studies, B
American/United States Studies/Civilization, M
Anthropology, B
Applied Mathematics, B
Applied Statistics, M
Architecture, BM
Art Education, M
Art History, Criticism and Conservation, B
Art Teacher Education, B
Art/Art Studies, General, B
BioTechnology, B
Biochemistry, BM
Biological and Biomedical Sciences, M
Biology Teacher Education, B
Biology/Biological Sciences, B
Business Administration and Management, B
Business Administration, Management and Opera-
   tions, MD
Business/Managerial Economics, B
Cartography, B
Chemistry, BM
Civil Engineering, B
Civil Engineering Technology/Technician, B
Communication Studies/Speech Communication
   and Rhetoric, B
Communication and Media Studies, BM
Computer Engineering, M
Computer Engineering Technology/Technician, B
Computer Programming, Specific Applications, B
Computer Science, BM
Computer Software Engineering, B
Computer and Information Sciences, B
Computer and Information Systems Security, BO
Conflict Resolution and Mediation/Peace Stud-
   ies, MD
Construction Engineering, B
Construction Management, BM
Criminal Justice/Safety Studies, B
Criminology, M
Dance, B
Drama and Dramatics/Theatre Arts, B
Early Childhood Education and Teaching, BM
Education, MDO
Educational Leadership and Administration, MDO
Educational Media/Instructional Technology, M
Electrical Engineering, M
Electrical, Electronic and Communications Engineer-
   ing Technology/Technician, B
Electrical, Electronics and Communications Engi-
   neering, B
Elementary Education and Teaching, BM
Engineering Technology, B
Engineering and Applied Sciences, MO
Engineering/Industrial Management, B
English Education, M
English Language and Literature, B
English as a Second Language, M
English/Language Arts Teacher Education, B
Environmental Engineering
   Technology/Environmental Technology, B
Environmental Sciences, B
Environmental/Environmental Health Engineering, B
Ethics, O
Exercise and Sports Science, M
Finance, B
Foreign Language Teacher Education, M

Foreign Languages, Literatures, and Linguistics, B
Geography, B
Health Informatics, O
Health Services Administration, M
History, B
Human Services, B
Industrial Production Technologies/Technicians, B
Information Science/Studies, BMO
Information Technology, B
International Affairs, M
International Business/Trade/Commerce, B
International Relations and Affairs, B
Journalism, B
Junior High/Intermediate/Middle School Education
   and Teaching, B
Kinesiology and Exercise Science, B
Logistics and Materials Management, B
Marketing/Marketing Management, B
Mathematics, B
Mathematics Teacher Education, BM
Mechanical Engineering, B
Mechanical Engineering/Mechanical
   Technology/Technician, B
Middle School Education, M
Multi-/Interdisciplinary Studies, B
Music, B
Music Performance, B
Music Teacher Education, B
Nursing, MD
Philosophy, B
Physical Education Teaching and Coaching, B
Physics, BM
Political Science and Government, B
Psychology, B
Public Administration, M
Public Health Education and Promotion, B
Reading Teacher Education, M
Restaurant/Food Services Management, B
Sales, Distribution and Marketing Operations, B
Secondary Education and Teaching, M
Social Studies Teacher Education, B
Social Work, M
Sociology, B
Software Engineering, MO
Special Education and Teaching, M
Sport and Fitness Administration/Management, B
Survey Technology/Surveying, B
Systems Engineering, BMO
Telecommunications Technology/Technician, B
Visual and Performing Arts, B
Writing, M

LAGRANGE COLLEGE

Accounting, B
Biochemistry, B
Biology/Biological Sciences, B
Business Administration and Management, B
Chemistry, B
Computer and Information Sciences, B
Curriculum and Instruction, MO
Drama and Dramatics/Theatre Arts, B
Early Childhood Education and Teaching, B
Education, MO
Engineering, B
English Language and Literature, B
General Studies, B
History, B
Human Development and Family Studies, B
Kinesiology and Exercise Science, B
Mathematics, B
Mathematics Teacher Education, B
Middle School Education, M
Music, B
Music Performance, B
Non-Profit/Public/Organizational Management, B
Organizational Management, M
Political Science and Government, B
Psychology, B
Religion/Religious Studies, B
Secondary Education and Teaching, M
Social Studies Teacher Education, B
Sociology, B
Spanish Language and Literature, B

Visual and Performing Arts, B

LANIER TECHNICAL COLLEGE

Accounting, A
Administrative Assistant and Secretarial Science, A
Banking and Financial Support Services, A
Child Development, A
Computer Programming/Programmer, A
Computer Science, A
Computer Systems Networking and Telecommunications, A
Computer and Information Systems Security, A
Criminal Justice/Safety Studies, A
Drafting and Design Technology/Technician, A
Electrical, Electronic and Communications Engineering Technology/Technician, A
Fire Science/Firefighting, A
Health Professions and Related Clinical Sciences, A
Industrial Technology/Technician, A
Information Science/Studies, A
Interior Design, A
Marketing/Marketing Management, A
Medical Radiologic Technology/Science - Radiation Therapist, A
Occupational Safety and Health Technology/Technician, A
Surgical Technology/Technologist, A
Web Page, Digital/Multimedia and Information Resources Design, A

LIFE UNIVERSITY

Biology/Biological Sciences, B
Biopsychology, B
Business Administration and Management, B
Chiropractic, D
Clinical Nutrition/Nutritionist, B
Dietetics/Dieticians, B
Exercise and Sports Science, M
Foods, Nutrition, and Wellness Studies, B
Human Nutrition, B
Information Technology, AB
Kinesiology and Exercise Science, B
Liberal Arts and Sciences Studies and Humanities, B
Nutritional Sciences, M
Psychology, AB

LUTHER RICE COLLEGE & SEMINARY

Bible/Biblical Studies, B
Christian Studies, B
Clinical Pastoral Counseling/Patient Counseling, B
Divinity/Ministry (BD, MDiv.), B
Pastoral Studies/Counseling, MD
Religion/Religious Studies, M
Theology and Religious Vocations, MD

MERCER UNIVERSITY

Accounting, BM
African-American/Black Studies, B
Allopathic Medicine, MD
Art/Art Studies, General, B
Biochemistry, B
Biology/Biological Sciences, B
Biomedical Engineering, M
Business Administration, Management and Operations, BM
Business/Commerce, B
Chemistry, B
Christian Studies, B
Classics and Classical Languages, Literatures, and Linguistics, B
Clinical Psychology, M
Communication Studies/Speech Communication and Rhetoric, B
Communication, Journalism and Related Programs, B
Community Organization and Advocacy, B
Computer Engineering, M
Computer Science, B
Computer and Information Sciences, B
Counselor Education/School Counseling and Guidance Services, D
Criminal Justice/Safety Studies, B
Curriculum and Instruction, D
Drama and Dramatics/Theatre Arts, B
Early Childhood Education and Teaching, MO

Economics, B
Education, BMDO
Educational Leadership and Administration, MDO
Electrical Engineering, M
Elementary Education and Teaching, B
Engineering, B
Engineering Management, M
Engineering and Applied Sciences, M
English Language and Literature, B
Environmental Engineering Technology/Environmental Technology, M
Environmental Sciences, M
Environmental and Occupational Health, M
Finance, B
French Language and Literature, B
German Language and Literature, B
Graphic Design, B
Health/Medical Preparatory Programs, B
Higher Education/Higher Education Administration, M
History, B
Human Services, B
Information Science/Studies, B
International Business/Trade/Commerce, B
International Public Health/International Health, B
International Relations and Affairs, B
Journalism, B
Junior High/Intermediate/Middle School Education and Teaching, B
Latin Language and Literature, B
Law and Legal Studies, D
Management Information Systems and Services, B
Management Sciences and Quantitative Methods, B
Management of Technology, M
Marketing/Marketing Management, B
Mass Communication/Media Studies, B
Mathematics, B
Mechanical Engineering, M
Middle School Education, M
Multi-/Interdisciplinary Studies, B
Music, B
Music Performance, B
Music Teacher Education, B
Nursing, MDO
Organizational Management, M
Pastoral Studies/Counseling, M
Performance, M
Pharmaceutical Sciences, D
Pharmacy, D
Philosophy, B
Physical Therapy/Therapist, D
Physician Assistant, M
Physics, B
Political Science and Government, B
Pre-Medicine/Pre-Medical Studies, B
Psychology, B
Public Health, M
Public Health (MPH, DPH), B
Reading Teacher Education, M
Regional Studies (U.S., Canadian, Foreign), B
Rehabilitation Counseling, M
Sacred Music, M
School Psychology, M
Secondary Education and Teaching, M
Sociology, B
Software Engineering, M
Spanish Language and Literature, B
Theology and Religious Vocations, MD

MIDDLE GEORGIA STATE UNIVERSITY

Air Traffic Controller, A
Aircraft Powerplant Technology/Technician, A
Airline/Commercial/Professional Pilot and Flight Crew, A
Art/Art Studies, General, A
Aviation/Airway Management and Operations, B
Avionics Maintenance Technology/Technician, A
Biology Teacher Education, B
Biology/Biological Sciences, B
Business Administration, Management and Operations, B
Communication and Media Studies, B
Criminal Justice/Law Enforcement Administration, A
Criminal Justice/Safety Studies, B
Early Childhood Education and Teaching, B
English Language and Literature, B

Health Information/Medical Records Administration/Administrator, B
Health Information/Medical Records Technology/Technician, A
Health Services Administration, B
Health/Health Care Administration/Management, B
History, B
History Teacher Education, B
Human Services, B
Information Technology, B
Liberal Arts and Sciences Studies and Humanities, AB
Mathematics, B
Mathematics Teacher Education, B
Music, A
Occupational Therapist Assistant, A
Political Science and Government, A
Psychology, B
Respiratory Care Therapy/Therapist, AB
Social Work, A
Sociology, A

MOREHOUSE COLLEGE

African-American/Black Studies, B
Art/Art Studies, General, B
Biology/Biological Sciences, B
Business Administration and Management, B
Chemistry, B
Computer and Information Sciences, B
Drama and Dramatics/Theatre Arts, B
Early Childhood Education and Teaching, B
Economics, B
Engineering Physics, B
Engineering Science, B
English Language and Literature, B
Film/Cinema Studies, B
French Language and Literature, B
Health and Physical Education, B
History, B
Mathematics, B
Music, B
Philosophy, B
Physics, B
Political Science and Government, B
Psychology, B
Religion/Religious Studies, B
Sociology, B
Spanish Language and Literature, B
Urban Studies/Affairs, B

NORTH GEORGIA TECHNICAL COLLEGE

Administrative Assistant and Secretarial Science, A
Computer Systems Networking and Telecommunications, A
Criminal Justice/Safety Studies, A
Culinary Arts/Chef Training, A
Heating, Air Conditioning and Refrigeration Technology/Technician, A
Horticultural Science, A
Industrial Technology/Technician, A
Parks, Recreation and Leisure Facilities Management, A
Turf and Turfgrass Management, A
Web Page, Digital/Multimedia and Information Resources Design, A

OCONEE FALL LINE TECHNICAL COLLEGE

Accounting, A
Administrative Assistant and Secretarial Science, A
Child Development, A
Computer Systems Networking and Telecommunications, A
Information Science/Studies, A

OGEECHEE TECHNICAL COLLEGE

Accounting, A
Administrative Assistant and Secretarial Science, A
Agribusiness, A
Automobile/Automotive Mechanics Technology/Technician, A
Banking and Financial Support Services, A
Child Development, A

Computer Systems Networking and Telecommunications, A
Construction Trades, A
Culinary Arts/Chef Training, A
Dental Hygiene/Hygienist, A
Forestry Technology/Technician, A
Funeral Service and Mortuary Science, A
Health Information/Medical Records Technology/Technician, A
Hotel/Motel Administration/Management, A
Information Science/Studies, A
Interior Design, A
Legal Assistant/Paralegal, A
Marketing/Marketing Management, A
Opticianry/Ophthalmic Dispensing Optician, A
Tourism and Travel Services Management, A
Veterinary/Animal Health Technology/Technician and Veterinary Assistant, A
Water Quality and Wastewater Treatment Management and Recycling Technology/Technician, A
Wildlife and Wildlands Science and Management, A
Wood Science and Wood Products/Pulp and Paper Technology, A

OGLETHORPE UNIVERSITY

Accounting, B
American/United States Studies/Civilization, B
Art History, Criticism and Conservation, B
Art/Art Studies, General, B
Biology/Biological Sciences, B
Biopsychology, B
Business Administration and Management, B
Business/Managerial Economics, B
Chemistry, B
Communication Studies/Speech Communication and Rhetoric, B
Economics, B
Engineering, B
English Language and Literature, B
French Language and Literature, B
History, B
International Relations and Affairs, B
Mathematics, B
Philosophy, B
Physics, B
Political Science and Government, B
Pre-Dentistry Studies, B
Pre-Law Studies, B
Pre-Medicine/Pre-Medical Studies, B
Pre-Veterinary Studies, B
Psychology, B
Social Work, B
Sociology, B
Spanish Language and Literature, B
Urban Studies/Affairs, B

PAINE COLLEGE

Biology Teacher Education, B
Biology/Biological Sciences, B
Business Administration and Management, B
Chemistry, B
Elementary Education and Teaching, B
English Language and Literature, B
English/Language Arts Teacher Education, B
History, B
History Teacher Education, B
Junior High/Intermediate/Middle School Education and Teaching, B
Mathematics, B
Mathematics Teacher Education, B
Philosophy, B
Physics, B
Psychology, B
Religion/Religious Studies, B
Sociology, B

PIEDMONT COLLEGE

Art Education, M
Art Teacher Education, B
Art/Art Studies, General, B
Athletic Training and Sports Medicine, B
Biology/Biological Sciences, B
Business Administration and Management, B
Business Administration, Management and Operations, M
Chemistry, B

Criminal Justice/Law Enforcement Administration, B
Curriculum and Instruction, O
Drama and Dance Teacher Education, B
Drama and Dramatics/Theatre Arts, B
Early Childhood Education and Teaching, BM
Education, BMO
Educational Media/Instructional Technology, M
English Language and Literature, B
English/Language Arts Teacher Education, B
Environmental Sciences, B
Fine/Studio Arts, B
Foreign Language Teacher Education, B
Foreign Languages and Literatures, B
Forensic Science and Technology, B
Geology/Earth Science, B
History, B
History Teacher Education, B
Junior High/Intermediate/Middle School Education and Teaching, B
Kindergarten/PreSchool Education and Teaching, B
Mass Communication/Media Studies, B
Mathematics, B
Mathematics Teacher Education, B
Middle School Education, M
Music, B
Music Performance, B
Music Teacher Education, BM
Nursing, B
Nursing Administration, M
Nursing Education, M
Philosophy, B
Physics, B
Political Science and Government, B
Psychology, B
Religion/Religious Studies, B
Science Teacher Education/General Science Teacher Education, B
Secondary Education and Teaching, BM
Social Sciences, B
Sociology, B
Spanish Language Teacher Education, B
Spanish Language and Literature, B
Special Education and Teaching, M
Teacher Education and Professional Development, Specific Subject Areas, B
Teacher Education, Multiple Levels, B
Technical Theatre/Theatre Design and Technology, B

POINT UNIVERSITY

Accounting, B
Bible/Biblical Studies, AB
Biology/Biological Sciences, B
Business Administration and Management, AB
Child Development, AB
Criminal Justice/Safety Studies, AB
Early Childhood Education and Teaching, B
English Language and Literature, B
General Studies, A
History, B
Humanities/Humanistic Studies, B
Junior High/Intermediate/Middle School Education and Teaching, B
Kinesiology and Exercise Science, B
Marketing/Marketing Management, B
Music, B
Pre-Theology/Pre-Ministerial Studies, B
Psychology, AB
Social Sciences, B
Sociology, B

REINHARDT UNIVERSITY

Accounting, B
Art/Art Studies, General, B
Biology/Biological Sciences, B
Business Administration and Management, B
Business Administration, Management and Operations, M
Business/Commerce, B
Communication and Media Studies, B
Communication, Journalism and Related Programs, B
Criminal Justice/Law Enforcement Administration, A
Design and Applied Arts, B
Early Childhood Education and Teaching, BM
Education, BM

English Language and Literature, B
English/Language Arts Teacher Education, B
Entrepreneurship/Entrepreneurial Studies, B
Health and Physical Education/Fitness, B
History, B
Information Science/Studies, B
International/Global Studies, B
Junior High/Intermediate/Middle School Education and Teaching, B
Liberal Arts and Sciences Studies and Humanities, AB
Mathematics, B
Music, BM
Music Teacher Education, M
Performance, M
Physical Education Teaching and Coaching, B
Political Science and Government, B
Pre-Nursing Studies, A
Psychology, B
Religion/Religious Studies, B
Sociology, B
Sport and Fitness Administration/Management, B

SAVANNAH COLLEGE OF ART AND DESIGN

Advertising and Public Relations, M
Animation, Interactive Technology, Video Graphics and Special Effects, B
Apparel and Textile Marketing Management, B
Apparel and Textiles, B
Applied Arts and Design, MO
Architectural History and Criticism, BM
Architecture, M
Art History, Criticism and Conservation, BM
Arts Management, M
Cinematography and Film/Video Production, B
Clothing and Textiles, M
Computer Art and Design, MO
Consumer Merchandising/Retailing Management, B
Crafts, M
Design and Visual Communications, B
Digital Communication and Media/Multimedia, B
Drama and Dramatics/Theatre Arts, B
Equestrian/Equine Studies, B
Fashion/Apparel Design, B
Fiber, Textile and Weaving Arts, B
Film, Television, and Video Production, M
Film, Television, and Video Theory and Criticism, M
Fine Arts and Art Studies, M
Game Design and Development, MO
Graphic Design, M
Historic Preservation and Conservation, BMO
Illustration, BM
Industrial Design, BM
Interior Design, BM
Internet and Interactive Multimedia, MO
Jewelry/Metalsmithing, M
Manufacturing Engineering, B
Media Studies, M
Metal and Jewelry Arts, B
Painting, BM
Performance, M
Photography, BM
Printmaking, BM
Radio and Television, B
Recording Arts Technology/Technician, B
Sculpture, BM
Sustainable Development, M
Technical Theatre/Theatre Design and Technology, B
Textile Design, M
Theater, M
Travel and Tourism, M
Urban Design, M
Writing, M

SAVANNAH STATE UNIVERSITY

Accounting, B
Biology/Biological Sciences, B
Business Administration and Management, B
Business Administration, Management and Operations, M
Business/Commerce, B
Chemistry, B
Civil Engineering Technology/Technician, B
Computer Engineering Technology/Technician, B

Corrections and Criminal Justice, B
Electrical, Electronic and Communications Engineering Technology/Technician, B
English Language and Literature, B
Ethnic, Cultural Minority, and Gender Studies, B
Forensic Science and Technology, B
General Studies, B
Geology/Earth Science, B
History, B
Human Resources Management and Services, M
Information Science/Studies, B
International Business/Trade/Commerce, B
Journalism, B
Liberal Arts and Sciences Studies and Humanities, A
Marine Biology and Biological Oceanography, AB
Marine Sciences, M
Marketing/Marketing Management, B
Mathematics, B
Political Science and Government, B
Public Administration, M
Security and Protective Services, B
Social Work, BM
Sociology, B
Urban Studies/Affairs, M
Urban and Regional Planning, M
Visual and Performing Arts, B

SAVANNAH TECHNICAL COLLEGE

Accounting, A
Administrative Assistant and Secretarial Science, A
Automobile/Automotive Mechanics Technology/Technician, A
Child Development, A
Computer Systems Networking and Telecommunications, A
Criminal Justice/Safety Studies, A
Culinary Arts/Chef Training, A
Electrical, Electronic and Communications Engineering Technology/Technician, A
Fire Science/Firefighting, A
Heating, Air Conditioning and Refrigeration Technology/Technician, A
Hotel/Motel Administration/Management, A
Industrial Technology/Technician, A
Information Technology, A
Marketing/Marketing Management, A
Surgical Technology/Technologist, A
Tourism and Travel Services Management, A

SHORTER UNIVERSITY

Accounting, BM
Art/Art Studies, General, B
Biology/Biological Sciences, B
Business Administration and Management, AB
Business Administration, Management and Operations, M
Business/Managerial Economics, B
Chemistry, B
Computer and Information Sciences, B
Curriculum and Instruction, M
Divinity/Ministry (BD, MDiv.), B
Drama and Dramatics/Theatre Arts, B
Economics, B
Elementary Education and Teaching, B
English Language and Literature, B
Environmental Studies, B
Fine/Studio Arts, B
General Studies, B
History, B
Junior High/Intermediate/Middle School Education and Teaching, B
Liberal Arts and Sciences Studies and Humanities, B
Mathematics, B
Mathematics Teacher Education, B
Music, B
Music Teacher Education, B
Natural Sciences, B
Organizational Communication, B
Parks, Recreation, Leisure and Fitness Studies, B
Piano and Organ, B
Pre-Theology/Pre-Ministerial Studies, B
Psychology, B
Religion/Religious Studies, B
Religious/Sacred Music, B

Social Sciences, B
Sociology, B
Spanish Language and Literature, B
Voice and Opera, B

SOUTH GEORGIA STATE COLLEGE

Biology/Biological Sciences, AB
Business Administration and Management, A
Chemistry, A
Computer Science, A
Criminal Justice/Law Enforcement Administration, A
Drama and Dramatics/Theatre Arts, A
English Language and Literature, A
Foreign Languages and Literatures, A
General Studies, A
Health/Medical Preparatory Programs, A
History, A
Journalism, A
Kinesiology and Exercise Science, A
Logistics and Materials Management, A
Mathematics, A
Parks, Recreation, Leisure and Fitness Studies, A
Philosophy, A
Physics, A
Political Science and Government, A
Psychology, A
Sociology, A
Teacher Education, Multiple Levels, A

SOUTH GEORGIA TECHNICAL COLLEGE

Accounting, A
Administrative Assistant and Secretarial Science, A
Child Development, A
Computer Systems Networking and Telecommunications, A
Criminal Justice/Safety Studies, A
Culinary Arts/Chef Training, A
Drafting and Design Technology/Technician, A
Electrical, Electronic and Communications Engineering Technology/Technician, A
Heating, Air Conditioning and Refrigeration Technology/Technician, A
Horticultural Science, A
Industrial Technology/Technician, A
Information Science/Studies, A
Legal Assistant/Paralegal, A
Manufacturing Technology/Technician, A
Marketing/Marketing Management, A

SOUTH UNIVERSITY

Anesthesiologist Assistant, M
Business Administration and Management, B
Business Administration, Management and Operations, M
Corrections, M
Counseling Psychology, M
Criminal Justice/Law Enforcement Administration, B
Criminology, M
Entrepreneurship/Entrepreneurial Studies, M
Environmental Studies, B
Health Services Administration, M
Health/Health Care Administration/Management, B
Hospitality Administration/Management, M
Information Science/Studies, B
Legal Assistant/Paralegal, AB
Medical/Clinical Assistant, A
Nursing, M
Nursing Education, M
Organizational Management, M
Pastoral Studies/Counseling, D
Physical Therapist Assistant, A
Physician Assistant, M
Psychology, B
Public Administration, M
Public Relations/Image Management, B
Sustainability Management, M

SOUTHEASTERN TECHNICAL COLLEGE

Accounting, A
Administrative Assistant and Secretarial Science, A
Child Development, A
Computer Systems Networking and Telecommunications, A

Criminal Justice/Safety Studies, A
Dental Hygiene/Hygienist, A
Design and Visual Communications, A
Electrical, Electronic and Communications Engineering Technology/Technician, A
Information Science/Studies, A
Marketing/Marketing Management, A
Medical Radiologic Technology/Science - Radiation Therapist, A
Respiratory Therapy Technician/Assistant, A
Web Page, Digital/Multimedia and Information Resources Design, A

SOUTHERN CRESCENT TECHNICAL COLLEGE

Accounting, A
Administrative Assistant and Secretarial Science, A
Automobile/Automotive Mechanics Technology/Technician, A
Business Administration and Management, A
Child Development, A
Computer Programming/Programmer, A
Computer Systems Networking and Telecommunications, A
Computer and Information Systems Security, A
Criminal Justice/Safety Studies, A
Drafting and Design Technology/Technician, A
Electrical, Electronic and Communications Engineering Technology/Technician, A
Emergency Medical Technology/Technician (EMT Paramedic), A
Heating, Air Conditioning and Refrigeration Technology/Technician, A
Horticultural Science, A
Industrial Technology/Technician, A
Legal Assistant/Paralegal, A
Manufacturing Technology/Technician, A
Marketing/Marketing Management, A
Medical Radiologic Technology/Science - Radiation Therapist, A
Pharmacy Technician/Assistant, A
Respiratory Therapy Technician/Assistant, A
Surgical Technology/Technologist, A
Web Page, Digital/Multimedia and Information Resources Design, A

SOUTHERN REGIONAL TECHNICAL COLLEGE

Accounting, A
Administrative Assistant and Secretarial Science, A
Agricultural Mechanization, A
Child Development, A
Computer Systems Networking and Telecommunications, A
Criminal Justice/Safety Studies, A
Information Science/Studies, A
Medical Radiologic Technology/Science - Radiation Therapist, A
Respiratory Care Therapy/Therapist, A
Surgical Technology/Technologist, A

SPELMAN COLLEGE

Art/Art Studies, General, B
Biochemistry, B
Biology/Biological Sciences, B
Chemistry, B
Computer Science, B
Drama and Dramatics/Theatre Arts, B
Economics, B
Engineering, B
English Language and Literature, B
Environmental Studies, B
French Language and Literature, B
Health Services/Allied Health/Health Sciences, B
History, B
Human Services, B
International Relations and Affairs, B
Mathematics, B
Multi-/Interdisciplinary Studies, B
Music, B
Philosophy, B
Physics, B
Political Science and Government, B
Psychology, B
Religion/Religious Studies, B
Sociology, B

Spanish Language and Literature, B
Teacher Education, Multiple Levels, B
Women's Studies, B

STRAYER UNIVERSITY–AUGUSTA CAMPUS

Accounting, B
Business Administration and Management, B
Criminal Justice/Law Enforcement Administration, B
Economics, B
International Business/Trade/Commerce, B
Management Information Systems and Services, B

STRAYER UNIVERSITY–CHAMBLEE CAMPUS

Accounting, B
Business Administration and Management, B
Criminal Justice/Law Enforcement Administration, B
Economics, B
International Business/Trade/Commerce, B
Management Information Systems and Services, B

STRAYER UNIVERSITY–COBB COUNTY CAMPUS

Accounting, B
Business Administration and Management, B
Criminal Justice/Law Enforcement Administration, B
Economics, B
International Business/Trade/Commerce, B
Management Information Systems and Services, B

STRAYER UNIVERSITY–COLUMBUS CAMPUS

Accounting, B
Business Administration and Management, B
Criminal Justice/Law Enforcement Administration, B
Economics, B
International Business/Trade/Commerce, B
Management Information Systems and Services, B

STRAYER UNIVERSITY–DOUGLASVILLE CAMPUS

Accounting, B
Business Administration and Management, B
Criminal Justice/Law Enforcement Administration, B
Economics, B
International Business/Trade/Commerce, B
Management Information Systems and Services, B

STRAYER UNIVERSITY–LITHONIA CAMPUS

Accounting, B
Business Administration and Management, B
Criminal Justice/Law Enforcement Administration, B
Economics, B
International Business/Trade/Commerce, B
Management Information Systems and Services, B

STRAYER UNIVERSITY–MORROW CAMPUS

Accounting, B
Business Administration and Management, B
Criminal Justice/Law Enforcement Administration, B
Economics, B
International Business/Trade/Commerce, B
Management Information Systems and Services, B

STRAYER UNIVERSITY–ROSWELL CAMPUS

Accounting, B
Business Administration and Management, B
Criminal Justice/Law Enforcement Administration, B
Economics, B
International Business/Trade/Commerce, B
Management Information Systems and Services, B

STRAYER UNIVERSITY–SAVANNAH CAMPUS

Accounting, B
Business Administration and Management, B
Criminal Justice/Law Enforcement Administration, B
Economics, B
International Business/Trade/Commerce, B

Management Information Systems and Services, B

THOMAS UNIVERSITY

Accounting, B
Biology/Biological Sciences, B
Business Administration and Management, B
Business Administration, Management and Operations, M
Business/Commerce, A
Communication Studies/Speech Communication and Rhetoric, B
Community Psychology, M
Criminal Justice/Law Enforcement Administration, AB
Criminology, B
Early Childhood Education and Teaching, B
Education, M
English Language and Literature, B
Human Services, M
Humanities/Humanistic Studies, B
Junior High/Intermediate/Middle School Education and Teaching, B
Kindergarten/PreSchool Education and Teaching, B
Liberal Arts and Sciences Studies and Humanities, AB
Mathematics, A
Nursing, M
Parks, Recreation and Leisure Facilities Management, B
Political Science and Government, B
Psychology, B
Rehabilitation Counseling, M
Rehabilitation and Therapeutic Professions, B
Secondary Education and Teaching, B
Social Sciences, B
Social Work, B
Sociology, B

TOCCOA FALLS COLLEGE

Ancient Near Eastern and Biblical Languages, Literatures, and Linguistics, B
Bible/Biblical Studies, B
Biology/Biological Sciences, B
Business Administration and Management, AB
Christian Studies, B
Divinity/Ministry (BD, MDiv.), B
Elementary Education and Teaching, B
English Language and Literature, B
English/Language Arts Teacher Education, B
Family and Community Services, B
General Studies, AB
History, B
History Teacher Education, B
Junior High/Intermediate/Middle School Education and Teaching, B
Missions/Missionary Studies and Missiology, B
Music, B
Music Performance, B
Music Teacher Education, B
Non-Profit/Public/Organizational Management, B
Philosophy, B
Religious Education, B
Secondary Education and Teaching, B
Sport and Fitness Administration/Management, B
Youth Ministry, B

TRUETT-MCCONNELL COLLEGE

Bible/Biblical Studies, B
Biology/Biological Sciences, B
Business Administration and Management, B
Christian Studies, B
Criminal Justice/Safety Studies, B
Elementary Education and Teaching, B
English Language and Literature, B
History, B
Junior High/Intermediate/Middle School Education and Teaching, B
Kinesiology and Exercise Science, B
Missions/Missionary Studies and Missiology, B
Multi-/Interdisciplinary Studies, B
Music, B
Music Teacher Education, B

Psychology, B

UNIVERSITY OF GEORGIA

Accounting, BM
Adult and Continuing Education and Teaching, MDO
Advertising, B
African-American/Black Studies, B
Agribusiness, B
Agricultural Communication/Journalism, B
Agricultural Economics, BMD
Agricultural Education, M
Agricultural Engineering, MD
Agricultural Sciences, MD
Agricultural Teacher Education, B
Agricultural/Biological Engineering and Bioengineering, B
Agriculture, B
Agronomy and Soil Sciences, MD
Analytical Chemistry, MD
Anatomy, M
Ancient/Classical Greek Language and Literature, B
Animal Health, B
Animal Sciences, BMD
Anthropology, BMD
Applied Economics, MD
Applied Horticulture/Horticultural Operations, B
Applied Mathematics, M
Arabic Language and Literature, B
Archeology, M
Art Education, MDO
Art History, Criticism and Conservation, BM
Art/Art Studies, General, B
Artificial Intelligence and Robotics, M
Astronomy, B
Athletic Training and Sports Medicine, B
BioTechnology, B
Biochemical Engineering, M
Biochemistry, MD
Biochemistry, Biophysics and Molecular Biology, B
Bioengineering, MD
Bioinformatics, MDO
Biological and Biomedical Sciences, D
Biological and Physical Sciences, B
Biology/Biological Sciences, B
Botany/Plant Biology, B
Broadcast Journalism, B
Business Administration and Management, B
Business Administration, Management and Operations, MD
Business Education, M
Business/Commerce, B
Business/Managerial Economics, B
Cell Biology and Anatomy, MD
Cell/Cellular Biology and Histology, B
Chemistry, BMD
Child and Family Studies, MD
Chinese Language and Literature, B
Civil Engineering, B
Classics and Classical Languages, Literatures, and Linguistics, BM
Clothing and Textiles, MD
Cognitive Sciences, B
Communication Disorders, BMDO
Communication Studies/Speech Communication and Rhetoric, B
Communication and Media Studies, MD
Comparative Literature, BMD
Computer Engineering, B
Computer Science, BMD
Consumer Economics, BMD
Counselor Education/School Counseling and Guidance Services, MDO
Criminal Justice/Law Enforcement Administration, B
Dairy Science, BM
Dance, B
Dietetics/Dieticians, B
Digital Communication and Media/Multimedia, B
Drama and Dramatics/Theatre Arts, B
Early Childhood Education and Teaching, BMDO
Ecology, BMD
Economics, MD
Education, MDO
Educational Administration and Supervision, MDO
Educational Leadership and Administration, D
Educational Media/Instructional Technology, MDO
Educational Policy, MDO

Educational Psychology, MDO
Elementary Education and Teaching, MDO
English, MD
English Education, MDO
English Language and Literature, B
English/Language Arts Teacher Education, B
Entomology, BMD
Environmental Design/Architecture, M
Environmental Engineering
 Technology/Environmental Technology, M
Environmental Health, B
Environmental Sciences, B
Environmental and Occupational Health, M
Environmental/Environmental Health Engineering, B
Family Resource Management Studies, B
Family and Consumer Sciences/Home Economics
 Teacher Education, B
Family and Consumer Sciences/Human Sci-
 ences, MD
Family and Consumer Sciences/Human Sciences
 Communication, B
Fashion Merchandising, B
Film/Cinema Studies, B
Finance, B
Fine Arts and Art Studies, MD
Fine/Studio Arts, B
Food Science, B
Food Science and Technology, MD
Foods, Nutrition, and Wellness Studies, B
Foreign Language Teacher Education, BMO
Forestry, BMD
French Language and Literature, BM
Genetics, BMD
Genomic Sciences, MD
Geography, BMD
Geology/Earth Science, BMD
German Language and Literature, BM
Gerontology, O
Health Education, MD
Health Promotion, MD
Health Services Administration, M
Health and Physical Education, B
Higher Education/Higher Education Administra-
 tion, D
Historic Preservation and Conservation, M
History, BMD
Home Economics Education, M
Horticultural Science, MD
Housing and Human Environments, B
Human Development and Family Studies, B
Human Resources Management and Services, M
Infectious Diseases, MD
Inorganic Chemistry, MD
Insurance, B
Interior Design, MD
International Affairs, MD
International Business/Trade/Commerce, B
International Relations and Affairs, B
Internet Engineering, M
Internet and Interactive Multimedia, M
Italian Language and Literature, B
Japanese Language and Literature, B
Journalism, MD
Junior High/Intermediate/Middle School Education
 and Teaching, B
Kindergarten/PreSchool Education and Teaching, B
Kinesiology and Movement Studies, MD
Landscape Architecture, BM
Latin Language and Literature, B
Law and Legal Studies, MD
Leisure Studies, MD
Liberal Arts and Sciences Studies and Humani-
 ties, B
Linguistics, BMD
Management Information Systems and Services, BD
Marine Sciences, MD
Marketing/Marketing Management, B
Mass Communication/Media Studies, MD
Mathematics, BMD
Mathematics Teacher Education, BMDO
Microbiology, BMD
Middle School Education, MDO
Molecular Biology, MD
Music, BMD
Music Performance, B
Music Teacher Education, BMDO

Music Theory and Composition, B
Music Therapy/Therapist, B
Natural Resources and Conservation, MD
Neuroscience, D
Non-Profit/Public/Organizational Management, MDO
Nutritional Sciences, BMD
Organic Chemistry, MD
Pathology/Experimental Pathology, MD
Pharmaceutical Administration, D
Pharmaceutical Sciences, D
Pharmacology, MD
Pharmacy, MDO
Philosophy, BMD
Physical Chemistry, MD
Physical Education Teaching and Coaching, MD
Physics, BMD
Physiology, MD
Plant Biology, MD
Plant Pathology/Phytopathology, MD
Plant Sciences, MD
Political Science and Government, BMD
Poultry Science, BMD
Psychology, BMD
Public Administration, MD
Public Health, D
Public Health Education and Promotion, B
Public Policy Analysis, MD
Public Relations/Image Management, B
Reading Teacher Education, MDO
Real Estate, B
Religion/Religious Studies, BM
Romance Languages, Literatures, and Linguis-
 tics, BMD
Russian Language and Literature, B
Science Teacher Education/General Science
 Teacher Education, BMDO
Social Studies Teacher Education, BMDO
Social Work, BMDO
Sociology, BMD
Soil Science and Agronomy, B
Spanish Language and Literature, BM
Special Education and Teaching, BMDO
Speech and Interpersonal Communication, MD
Statistics, BMD
Student Personnel Services, MD
Sustainable Development, M
Theater, MD
Turf and Turfgrass Management, B
Veterinary Medicine, MD
Veterinary Sciences, M
Vocational and Technical Education, MDO
Wildlife and Wildlands Science and Management, B
Women's Studies, BO
Writing, MD

UNIVERSITY OF NORTH GEORGIA

Accounting, B
Art Education, M
Art Teacher Education, B
Art/Art Studies, General, B
Athletic Training and Sports Medicine, B
Biology/Biological Sciences, B
Business Administration and Management, B
Business Administration, Management and Opera-
 tions, BM
Chemistry, B
Chinese Language and Literature, B
Clinical Psychology, M
Commercial and Advertising Art, B
Computer and Information Sciences, B
Counseling Psychology, M
Criminal Justice/Safety Studies, B
Criminology, M
Early Childhood Education and Teaching, BM
Education, MO
Educational Administration and Supervision, O
English Education, M
English Language and Literature, B
Finance, B
Fine/Studio Arts, B
French Language and Literature, B
General Studies, B
History, BM
Human Services, B
Information Science/Studies, B
International Affairs, M

International Relations and Affairs, B
Junior High/Intermediate/Middle School Education
 and Teaching, B
Liberal Arts and Sciences Studies and Humani-
 ties, A
Marketing/Marketing Management, B
Mathematics, B
Mathematics Teacher Education, M
Middle School Education, M
Music, BM
Music Performance, B
Music Teacher Education, B
Nursing - Advanced Practice, M
Nursing Education, M
Physical Education Teaching and Coaching, BM
Physical Therapy/Therapist, D
Physics, B
Political Science and Government, B
Psychology, B
Public Administration, M
Secondary Education and Teaching, M
Social Sciences, B
Social Studies Teacher Education, M
Sociology, B
Spanish Language and Literature, B
Special Education and Teaching, B
Technical Theatre/Theatre Design and Technol-
 ogy, B

UNIVERSITY OF PHOENIX–ATLANTA CAMPUS

Accounting, BM
Business Administration and Management, B
Business Administration, Management and Opera-
 tions, M
Business/Corporate Communications, B
Computer Software Engineering, B
Computer and Information Systems Security, B
Consumer Merchandising/Retailing Management, B
Criminal Justice/Law Enforcement Administration, B
E-Commerce/Electronic Commerce, B
Elementary Education and Teaching, B
Finance, B
Health Services Administration, BM
Hospitality Administration/Management, B
Human Resources Management and Services, M
Information Technology, B
International Business/Trade/Commerce, BM
Management Information Systems and Ser-
 vices, BM
Management Science, B
Management of Technology, M
Marketing, M
Marketing/Marketing Management, B
Nursing, M
Nursing Education, M
Operations Management and Supervision, B
Psychology, B
Public Administration, BM
Security and Protective Services, B

UNIVERSITY OF PHOENIX–AUGUSTA CAMPUS

Accounting, ABM
Business Administration and Management, B
Business Administration, Management and Opera-
 tions, M
Business/Commerce, A
Business/Corporate Communications, B
Computer Software Engineering, B
Computer and Information Systems Security, B
Consumer Merchandising/Retailing Management, B
Criminal Justice/Law Enforcement Administra-
 tion, AB
Criminology, M
E-Commerce/Electronic Commerce, B
Finance, B
General Studies, A
Graphic Communications, A
Health Services Administration, ABM
Hospitality Administration/Management, B
Human Resources Management and Services, M
Human Services, B
Information Technology, AB
International Business/Trade/Commerce, BM

Management Information Systems and Services, BM
Management Science, B
Management of Technology, M
Marketing, M
Marketing/Marketing Management, B
Nursing, M
Nursing Education, M
Psychology, B
Public Administration, BM
Security and Protective Services, B
System, Networking, and LAN/WAN Management/Manager, A
Taxation, B
Teacher Assistant/Aide, A

UNIVERSITY OF PHOENIX–COLUMBUS GEORGIA CAMPUS

Accounting, M
Business Administration and Management, AB
Business Administration, Management and Operations, M
Business/Corporate Communications, B
Computer and Information Sciences, B
Consumer Merchandising/Retailing Management, AB
Criminal Justice/Law Enforcement Administration, AB
E-Commerce/Electronic Commerce, AB
Electronic Commerce, M
Finance, AB
Health Services Administration, AB
Health/Health Care Administration/Management, AB
Hospitality Administration/Management, AB
Human Resources Management and Services, M
Human Services, AB
International Business/Trade/Commerce, ABM
Management Information Systems and Services, ABM
Management Science, B
Management of Technology, M
Marketing, M
Marketing/Marketing Management, B
Nursing, M
Operations Management and Supervision, AB
Psychology, AB
Public Administration, BM

UNIVERSITY OF WEST GEORGIA

Accounting, BM
Anthropology, B
Applied Mathematics, M
Art/Art Studies, General, B
Biological and Biomedical Sciences, M
Biology/Biological Sciences, B
Business Administration and Management, B
Business Administration, Management and Operations, M
Business/Managerial Economics, B
Chemistry, B
Communication Disorders, M
Computer Science, M
Computer and Information Sciences, B
Counselor Education/School Counseling and Guidance Services, MDO
Criminology, BM
Drama and Dramatics/Theatre Arts, B
Early Childhood Education and Teaching, MO
Economics, B
Education, MDO
Educational Leadership and Administration, MO
Educational Measurement and Evaluation, D
Educational Media/Instructional Technology, MO
Elementary Education and Teaching, B
English, M
English Language and Literature, B
Finance, B
Foreign Languages, Literatures, and Linguistics, B
Foundations and Philosophy of Education, MO
Geographic Information Systems, O
Geography, B
Geology/Earth Science, B
Health Services Administration, O
History, BM
International Economics, B
International Relations and Affairs, B

Journalism, B
Management Information Systems and Services, B
Marketing/Marketing Management, B
Mathematics, BM
Mathematics Teacher Education, M
Museology/Museum Studies, O
Music Performance, B
Music Teacher Education, BM
Music Theory and Composition, B
Nursing, MDO
Nursing Education, DO
Parks, Recreation and Leisure Facilities Management, B
Performance, M
Philosophy, B
Physical Education Teaching and Coaching, B
Physics, B
Political Science and Government, B
Psychology, BMDO
Public Administration, MO
Public History, O
Reading Teacher Education, M
Real Estate, B
Secondary Education and Teaching, M
Sociology, BMO
Special Education and Teaching, BMO
Speech-Language Pathology/Pathologist, B

VALDOSTA STATE UNIVERSITY

Accounting, B
Administrative Assistant and Secretarial Science, B
Applied Mathematics, B
Art Teacher Education, B
Art/Art Studies, General, B
Astronomy, B
Athletic Training and Sports Medicine, B
Biology/Biological Sciences, B
Business Administration and Management, B
Business Administration, Management and Operations, M
Business/Managerial Economics, B
Chemistry, B
Communication Studies/Speech Communication and Rhetoric, B
Composition, M
Computer and Information Sciences, B
Counselor Education/School Counseling and Guidance Services, MO
Criminal Justice/Safety Studies, B
Criminology, M
Dance, B
Dental Services and Allied Professions, A
Drama and Dramatics/Theatre Arts, B
Early Childhood Education and Teaching, BMO
Educational Leadership and Administration, M
English, M
English Education, M
English Language and Literature, B
Finance, B
French Language and Literature, B
Geology/Earth Science, B
Health Services Administration, M
Health and Physical Education/Fitness, B
Health/Health Care Administration/Management, B
History, BM
Industrial Production Technologies/Technicians, B
Information Science/Studies, BM
Interior Design, B
International Business/Trade/Commerce, B
Junior High/Intermediate/Middle School Education and Teaching, B
Legal Assistant/Paralegal, B
Liberal Arts and Sciences Studies and Humanities, AB
Library Science, M
Marketing/Marketing Management, B
Mass Communication/Media Studies, B
Mathematics, B
Music, B
Music Performance, B
Physical Education Teaching and Coaching, B
Physics, B
Political Science and Government, B
Psychology, BMO
Rhetoric, M
Sign Language Interpretation and Translation, B

Social Work, M
Sociology, M
Spanish Language and Literature, B
Special Education and Teaching, BMO
Speech-Language Pathology/Pathologist, B
Trade and Industrial Teacher Education, B

VIRGINIA COLLEGE IN MACON

Business Administration and Management, A
Medical Office Management/Administration, A
Medical/Clinical Assistant, A
Office Management and Supervision, A
Surgical Technology/Technologist, A

WESLEYAN COLLEGE

Accounting, B
Advertising, B
American/United States Studies/Civilization, B
Art History, Criticism and Conservation, B
Biology/Biological Sciences, B
Business Administration and Management, B
Business Administration, Management and Operations, M
Chemistry, B
Communication Studies/Speech Communication and Rhetoric, B
Early Childhood Education and Teaching, BM
Economics, B
Education, M
English Language and Literature, B
Environmental Sciences, B
Fine/Studio Arts, B
French Language and Literature, B
History, B
Human Services, B
Humanities/Humanistic Studies, B
International Business/Trade/Commerce, B
International Relations and Affairs, B
Mathematics, B
Music, B
Philosophy, B
Physical Sciences, B
Political Science and Government, B
Psychology, B
Religion/Religious Studies, B
Social Sciences, B
Spanish Language and Literature, B
Women's Studies, B

WEST GEORGIA TECHNICAL COLLEGE

Accounting, A
Administrative Assistant and Secretarial Science, A
Automobile/Automotive Mechanics Technology/Technician, A
Child Development, A
Computer Systems Networking and Telecommunications, A
Criminal Justice/Safety Studies, A
Electrical, Electronic and Communications Engineering Technology/Technician, A
Fire Science/Firefighting, A
Health Information/Medical Records Technology/Technician, A
Industrial Technology/Technician, A
Information Science/Studies, A
Marketing/Marketing Management, A
Medical Radiologic Technology/Science - Radiation Therapist, A
Pharmacy Technician/Assistant, A
Plastics Engineering Technology/Technician, A
Social Work, A
Web Page, Digital/Multimedia and Information Resources Design, A

WIREGRASS GEORGIA TECHNICAL COLLEGE

Accounting, A
Administrative Assistant and Secretarial Science, A
Banking and Financial Support Services, A
Child Development, A
Computer Programming/Programmer, A
Computer Systems Networking and Telecommunications, A
Computer and Information Systems Security, A

Criminal Justice/Safety Studies, A
Drafting and Design Technology/Technician, A
E-Commerce/Electronic Commerce, A
Fire Science/Firefighting, A
Machine Tool Technology/Machinist, A
Marketing/Marketing Management, A
Medical Radiologic Technology/Science - Radiation Therapist, A
Web Page, Digital/Multimedia and Information Resources Design, A

YOUNG HARRIS COLLEGE

Accounting and Business/Management, B
Art/Art Studies, General, B
Biological and Physical Sciences, B
Biology/Biological Sciences, B
Business Administration and Management, B
Business, Management, Marketing, and Related Support Services, B
Communication and Media Studies, B
Communication, Journalism and Related Programs, B
Drama and Dramatics/Theatre Arts, B
Early Childhood Education and Teaching, B
Education, B
English Language and Literature, B
History, B
Junior High/Intermediate/Middle School Education and Teaching, B
Mathematics, B
Music, B
Music Teacher Education, B
Political Science and Government, B
Pre-Dentistry Studies, B
Pre-Law Studies, B
Pre-Medicine/Pre-Medical Studies, B
Pre-Pharmacy Studies, B
Pre-Veterinary Studies, B
Psychology, B
Religion/Religious Studies, B
Secondary Education and Teaching, B
Spanish Language and Literature, B

Hawaii
ARGOSY UNIVERSITY, HAWAI'I

Accounting, D
Adult and Continuing Education and Teaching, M
Business Administration and Management, AB
Business Administration, Management and Operations, MDO
Clinical Psychology, MDO
Counseling Psychology, D
Education, MD
Educational Administration and Supervision, D
Educational Leadership and Administration, D
Elementary Education and Teaching, D
Finance and Banking, MO
Forensic Psychology, M
Health Services Administration, MO
Health/Health Care Administration/Management, B
Higher Education/Higher Education Administration, D
Information Technology, AB
International Business/Trade/Commerce, MDO
Liberal Arts and Sciences Studies and Humanities, B
Management, MD
Management Information Systems and Services, MDO
Marketing, MDO
Marriage and Family Therapy/Counseling, M
Organizational Management, D
Pharmacology, MO
Psychology, ABMDO
Public Health, M
School Psychology, M
Secondary Education and Teaching, D
Substance Abuse/Addiction Counseling, O
Sustainability Management, MD

BRIGHAM YOUNG UNIVERSITY–HAWAII

Accounting, B
Anthropology, B

Art Teacher Education, B
Art/Art Studies, General, B
Biochemistry, B
Biology Teacher Education, B
Biology/Biological Sciences, B
Business Administration and Management, B
Business Teacher Education, B
Chemistry, B
Chemistry Teacher Education, B
Communication Studies/Speech Communication and Rhetoric, B
Communication, Journalism and Related Programs, B
Computer Programming/Programmer, B
Computer Science, B
Drama and Dramatics/Theatre Arts, A
Education, B
Elementary Education and Teaching, B
English Language and Literature, B
English/Language Arts Teacher Education, B
Health and Physical Education, B
History, B
Hotel/Motel Administration/Management, B
Humanities/Humanistic Studies, B
Information Science/Studies, B
International Business/Trade/Commerce, B
Kinesiology and Exercise Science, B
Mathematics, B
Mathematics Teacher Education, B
Multi-/Interdisciplinary Studies, B
Music, B
Music Performance, B
Music Teacher Education, B
Pacific Area/Pacific Rim Studies, B
Physical Education Teaching and Coaching, B
Physical Sciences, B
Physics Teacher Education, B
Piano and Organ, B
Political Science and Government, B
Psychology, B
Science Teacher Education/General Science Teacher Education, B
Secondary Education and Teaching, B
Social Science Teacher Education, B
Social Work, B
Special Education and Teaching, B
Teaching English as a Second or Foreign Language/ESL Language Instructor, B
Tourism and Travel Services Management, B
Voice and Opera, B

CHAMINADE UNIVERSITY OF HONOLULU

Accounting, M
Accounting and Business/Management, B
Behavioral Sciences, B
Biochemistry, B
Biology/Biological Sciences, B
Business Administration and Management, AB
Business Administration, Management and Operations, M
Child Development, M
Communication Studies/Speech Communication and Rhetoric, B
Counseling Psychology, M
Criminal Justice/Safety Studies, AB
Criminology, MO
Early Childhood Education and Teaching, ABM
Education, M
Educational Leadership and Administration, M
Elementary Education and Teaching, BM
English Education, M
English Language and Literature, B
Environmental Studies, B
Forensic Science and Technology, BMO
General Studies, A
History, B
Homeland Security, MO
Humanities/Humanistic Studies, B
Interior Design, AB
International Business/Trade/Commerce, B
International Relations and Affairs, B
Marketing/Marketing Management, B
Marriage and Family Therapy/Counseling, M
Mathematics Teacher Education, M
Non-Profit/Public/Organizational Management, M

Pastoral Studies/Counseling, M
Psychology, B
Religion/Religious Studies, B
School Psychology, M
Science Teacher Education/General Science Teacher Education, M
Secondary Education and Teaching, BM
Social Sciences, B
Social Studies Teacher Education, M
Special Education and Teaching, BM
Theology and Religious Vocations, M

HAWAII COMMUNITY COLLEGE

Accounting, A
Administrative Assistant and Secretarial Science, A
Agricultural Production Operations, A
American Indian/Native American Studies, A
Architectural Drafting and Architectural CAD/CADD, A
Autobody/Collision and Repair Technology/Technician, A
Automobile/Automotive Mechanics Technology/Technician, A
Carpentry/Carpenter, A
Cooking and Related Culinary Arts, A
Criminal Justice/Law Enforcement Administration, A
Diesel Mechanics Technology/Technician, A
Early Childhood Education and Teaching, A
Electrical, Electronic and Communications Engineering Technology/Technician, A
Electrical/Electronics Equipment Installation and Repair, A
Forestry, A
Hotel/Motel Administration/Management, A
Information Technology, A
Liberal Arts and Sciences Studies and Humanities, A
Marketing/Marketing Management, A
Welding Technology/Welder, A

HAWAI'I PACIFIC UNIVERSITY

Accounting, ABM
Advertising, B
Anthropology, B
Applied Mathematics, B
Banking and Financial Support Services, B
Behavioral Sciences, B
Biology/Biological Sciences, B
Business Administration and Management, AB
Business Administration, Management and Operations, M
Business/Commerce, B
Business/Corporate Communications, B
Business/Managerial Economics, AB
Clinical Psychology, M
Communication Studies/Speech Communication and Rhetoric, B
Communication and Media Studies, M
Comparative Literature, B
Computer Science, AB
Computer and Information Sciences, B
Criminal Justice/Law Enforcement Administration, A
Digital Communication and Media/Multimedia, B
Economics, BM
Elementary Education and Teaching, BM
English Language and Literature, B
English as a Second Language, M
Entrepreneurship/Entrepreneurial Studies, B
Environmental Sciences, B
Environmental Studies, B
Finance, AB
Finance and Banking, M
General Studies, A
Health Services/Allied Health/Health Sciences, B
History, B
Hospitality Administration/Management, M
Human Development and Family Studies, B
Human Resources Management and Services, M
Human Resources Management/Personnel Administration, B
Human Services, B
Humanities/Humanistic Studies, B
International Business/Trade/Commerce, BM
International Finance, B
International Relations and Affairs, B

International/Global Studies, B
Journalism, B
Liberal Arts and Sciences Studies and Humanities, B
Management Information Systems and Services, BM
Marine Biology and Biological Oceanography, B
Marine Sciences, M
Marketing, M
Marketing/Marketing Management, B
Mass Communication/Media Studies, B
Mathematics, A
Military and Defense Studies, M
Nursing, M
Oceanography, Chemical and Physical, B
Organizational Management, M
Political Science and Government, B
Pre-Medicine/Pre-Medical Studies, B
Psychology, B
Public Administration, B
Public Relations/Image Management, B
Secondary Education and Teaching, M
Social Sciences, B
Social Work, BM
Sociology, B
Sustainable Development, M
Teaching English as a Second or Foreign Language/ESL Language Instructor, B
Tourism and Travel Services Management, B

HAWAII TOKAI INTERNATIONAL COLLEGE

Liberal Arts and Sciences Studies and Humanities, A

HONOLULU COMMUNITY COLLEGE

Architectural Engineering Technology/Technician, A
Automobile/Automotive Mechanics Technology/Technician, A
Avionics Maintenance Technology/Technician, A
Carpentry/Carpenter, A
Commercial and Advertising Art, A
Community Organization and Advocacy, A
Cosmetology/Cosmetologist, A
Criminal Justice/Police Science, A
Drafting and Design Technology/Technician, A
Electrical, Electronic and Communications Engineering Technology/Technician, A
Engineering Technology, A
Fashion/Apparel Design, A
Fire Science/Firefighting, A
Food Technology and Processing, A
Heating, Air Conditioning, Ventilation and Refrigeration Maintenance Technology/Technician, A
Human Services, A
Kindergarten/PreSchool Education and Teaching, A
Liberal Arts and Sciences Studies and Humanities, A
Marine Maintenance/Fitter and Ship Repair Technology/Technician, A
Occupational Safety and Health Technology/Technician, A
Welding Technology/Welder, A

KAPIOLANI COMMUNITY COLLEGE

Accounting, A
Clinical/Medical Laboratory Technician, A
Cooking and Related Culinary Arts, A
E-Commerce/Electronic Commerce, A
Emergency Medical Technology/Technician (EMT Paramedic), A
Graphic Communications, A
Hotel/Motel Administration/Management, A
Information Technology, A
Kinesiology and Exercise Science, A
Language Interpretation and Translation, A
Legal Assistant/Paralegal, A
Liberal Arts and Sciences Studies and Humanities, A
Marketing/Marketing Management, A
Medical Radiologic Technology/Science - Radiation Therapist, A
Medical/Clinical Assistant, A
Natural Sciences, A
Occupational Therapist Assistant, A
Physical Therapist Assistant, A

Respiratory Care Therapy/Therapist, A
Teacher Assistant/Aide, A
Tourism and Travel Services Management, A

KAUAI COMMUNITY COLLEGE

Accounting, A
Administrative Assistant and Secretarial Science, A
Autobody/Collision and Repair Technology/Technician, A
Automobile/Automotive Mechanics Technology/Technician, A
Carpentry/Carpenter, A
Culinary Arts/Chef Training, A
Electrical, Electronic and Communications Engineering Technology/Technician, A
Hospitality Administration/Management, A
Kindergarten/PreSchool Education and Teaching, A
Liberal Arts and Sciences Studies and Humanities, A

LEEWARD COMMUNITY COLLEGE

Accounting, A
Administrative Assistant and Secretarial Science, A
American Indian/Native American Studies, A
Automobile/Automotive Mechanics Technology/Technician, A
Business Administration and Management, A
Computer and Information Sciences, A
Cooking and Related Culinary Arts, A
Health Information/Medical Records Technology/Technician, A
Liberal Arts and Sciences Studies and Humanities, A
Natural Sciences, A
Plant Sciences, A
Prepress/Desktop Publishing and Digital Imaging Design, A
Radio and Television Broadcasting Technology/Technician, A
Teacher Education and Professional Development, Specific Levels and Methods, A

REMINGTON COLLEGE–HONOLULU CAMPUS

Computer Systems Networking and Telecommunications, A
Criminal Justice/Law Enforcement Administration, AB
International Business/Trade/Commerce, A
Medical Office Assistant/Specialist, A
Operations Management and Supervision, B

UNIVERSITY OF HAWAII AT HILO

Accounting, B
Agricultural Business and Management, B
Agriculture, B
American Indian/Native American Studies, B
Animal Sciences, B
Anthropology, B
Art/Art Studies, General, B
Astronomy, B
Biology/Biological Sciences, B
Business Administration and Management, B
Chemistry, B
Computer Science, B
Conservation Biology, M
Counseling Psychology, M
Criminal Justice/Safety Studies, B
Cultural Studies, MD
Economics, B
Education, M
Elementary Education and Teaching, B
Engineering, B
English Language and Literature, B
Environmental Sciences, BM
Environmental Studies, B
Foreign Language Teacher Education, MD
Geography, B
Geology/Earth Science, B
History, B
Horticultural Science, B
Japanese Language and Literature, B
Japanese Studies, B
Kinesiology and Exercise Science, B

Liberal Arts and Sciences Studies and Humanities, B
Linguistics, B
Marine Biology and Biological Oceanography, BM
Mathematics, B
Music, B
Natural Sciences, B
Nursing, D
Pharmaceutical Sciences, D
Pharmacology, M
Pharmacy, D

UNIVERSITY OF HAWAII AT MANOA

Accounting, BMD
Agricultural Sciences, MD
Agricultural/Biological Engineering and Bioengineering, B
Allopathic Medicine, D
American Indian/Native American Studies, B
American/United States Studies/Civilization, BMDO
Animal Sciences, BM
Anthropology, BMD
Apparel and Textiles, B
Architecture, BD
Art History, Criticism and Conservation, M
Art/Art Studies, General, B
Asian Languages, MD
Asian Studies/Civilization, B
Astronomy, BMD
Astrophysics, B
BioTechnology, B
Biochemistry, B
Bioengineering, M
Biological and Biomedical Sciences, MD
Biology/Biological Sciences, B
Botany/Plant Biology, BMD
Business Administration and Management, B
Business Administration, Management and Operations, M
Business/Commerce, B
Cell/Cellular and Molecular Biology, B
Chemistry, BMD
Chinese Language and Literature, B
Chinese Studies, MDO
Civil Engineering, BMD
Classics and Classical Languages, Literatures, and Linguistics, B
Clinical Laboratory Science/Medical Technology/Technologist, B
Clinical Psychology, D
Communication Disorders, M
Communication Studies/Speech Communication and Rhetoric, B
Communication and Media Studies, M
Community Health Nursing, M
Community Psychology, D
Computer Science, BD
Computer and Information Sciences, B
Conflict Resolution and Mediation/Peace Studies, O
Conservation Biology, MD
Cultural Studies, O
Curriculum and Instruction, MD
Dance, BMD
Demography and Population Studies, O
Dental Hygiene/Hygienist, B
Developmental Biology and Embryology, MD
Disability Studies, O
Drama and Dramatics/Theatre Arts, B
Early Childhood Education and Teaching, BM
East Asian Studies, O
Ecology, MD
Economics, BMD
Education, BMDO
Educational Administration and Supervision, MD
Educational Leadership and Administration, D
Educational Media/Instructional Technology, MD
Educational Policy, D
Educational Psychology, MD
Electrical Engineering, MD
Electrical, Electronics and Communications Engineering, B
Elementary Education and Teaching, B
Emergency Management, O
Engineering, B
Engineering and Applied Sciences, MD
English, MD

English Language and Literature, B
English as a Second Language, MDO
Entomology, MD
Entrepreneurship/Entrepreneurial Studies, BMO
Environmental Design/Architecture, B
Environmental Engineering
 Technology/Environmental Technology, MD
Environmental Policy and Resource Manage-
 ment, MD
Environmental Sciences, B
Epidemiology, D
Ethnic, Cultural Minority, and Gender Studies, B
Evolutionary Biology, MD
Family and Consumer Economics and Related Ser-
 vices, B
Filipino/Tagalog Language and Literature, B
Finance, B
Finance and Banking, MD
Financial Engineering, M
Fine Arts and Art Studies, M
Food Science and Technology, M
Foreign Language Teacher Education, MD
Foreign Languages, Literatures, and Linguistics, B
Foundations and Philosophy of Education, MD
French Language and Literature, BM
Genetics, MD
Geochemistry, MD
Geography, BMDO
Geological Engineering, MD
Geology/Earth Science, BMD
Geophysics and Seismology, MD
German Language and Literature, B
Gerontology, O
Health and Physical Education, B
Historic Preservation and Conservation, O
History, BMD
Horticultural Science, MD
Human Resources Management and Services, M
Human Resources Management/Personnel Adminis-
 tration, B
Hydrogeology, MD
Information Science/Studies, MDO
International Affairs, O
International Business/Trade/Commerce, BMD
Japanese Language and Literature, B
Japanese Studies, MDO
Journalism, B
Kinesiology and Exercise Science, B
Kinesiology and Movement Studies, MD
Korean Language and Literature, B
Law and Legal Studies, MDO
Liberal Arts and Sciences Studies and Humani-
 ties, B
Library Science, MO
Linguistics, MD
Management Information Systems and Ser-
 vices, BMDO
Marine Biology and Biological Oceanography, BMD
Marine Geology, MD
Marine Sciences, O
Marketing, MD
Marketing/Marketing Management, B
Mathematics, BMD
Mechanical Engineering, BMD
Medical Microbiology and Bacteriology, MD
Meteorology, BMD
Microbiology, BMD
Molecular Biology, MD
Museology/Museum Studies, O
Music, BMD
Natural Resources Management/Development and
 Policy, B
Natural Resources and Conservation, MD
Nursing, MDO
Nursing - Adult, M
Nursing - Advanced Practice, M
Nursing Administration, M
Nutritional Sciences, BMD
Ocean Engineering, MD
Oceanography, Chemical and Physical, MD
Organizational Behavior Studies, M
Organizational Management, MD
Pacific Area/Pacific Rim Studies, BMO
Philosophy, BMD
Physics, BMD
Physiology, MD

Planetary Astronomy and Science, MD
Plant Pathology/Phytopathology, MD
Plant Protection and Integrated Pest Manage-
 ment, B
Plant Sciences, BMD
Political Science and Government, BMD
Psychology, BMDO
Public Administration, MO
Public Health, MD
Public Health (MPH, DPH), B
Public Policy Analysis, O
Real Estate, M
Religion/Religious Studies, BM
Reproductive Biology, MD
Russian Language and Literature, B
Secondary Education and Teaching, B
Social Work, BMD
Sociology, BMD
Soil Sciences, B
South and Southeast Asian Studies, O
Spanish Language and Literature, BM
Special Education and Teaching, BMD
Speech and Rhetorical Studies, M
Taxation, M
Teaching English as a Second or Foreign
 Language/ESL Language Instructor, B
Telecommunications, O
Theater, MD
Tourism and Travel Services Management, B
Travel and Tourism, M
Urban and Regional Planning, MDO
Women's Studies, BO
Zoology/Animal Biology, BMD

UNIVERSITY OF HAWAII MAUI COLLEGE

Accounting, A
Administrative Assistant and Secretarial Science, A
Agricultural Mechanization, A
Automobile/Automotive Mechanics
 Technology/Technician, A
Business Administration and Management, B
Carpentry/Carpenter, A
Construction Engineering Technology/Technician, A
Criminal Justice/Law Enforcement Administration, A
Fashion/Apparel Design, A
Food Technology and Processing, A
Horticultural Science, A
Hotel/Motel Administration/Management, A
Human Services, A
Liberal Arts and Sciences Studies and Humani-
 ties, A
Marketing/Marketing Management, A
Welding Technology/Welder, A

UNIVERSITY OF HAWAII–WEST OAHU

Accounting, B
Anthropology, B
Australian/Oceanic/Pacific Languages, Litera-
 tures, and Linguistics, B
Business Administration and Management, B
Criminal Justice/Law Enforcement Administration, B
Early Childhood Education and Teaching, B
Economics, B
Elementary Education and Teaching, B
English Language and Literature, B
Health/Health Care Administration/Management, B
History, B
Humanities/Humanistic Studies, B
Pacific Area/Pacific Rim Studies, B
Philosophy, B
Political Science and Government, B
Psychology, B
Public Administration, B
Restaurant, Culinary, and Catering
 Management/Manager, B
Social Sciences, B
Sociology, B
System, Networking, and LAN/WAN
 Management/Manager, B

UNIVERSITY OF PHOENIX–HAWAII CAMPUS

Accounting, BM
Business Administration and Management, B

Business Administration, Management and Opera-
 tions, M
Business/Corporate Communications, B
Community Health and Preventive Medicine, M
Computer and Information Systems Security, B
Consumer Merchandising/Retailing Management, B
Criminal Justice/Law Enforcement Administration, B
Curriculum and Instruction, M
Digital Communication and Media/Multimedia, B
E-Commerce/Electronic Commerce, B
Education, M
Educational Administration and Supervision, M
Elementary Education and Teaching, M
Finance, M
Gerontology, M
Health Information/Medical Records
 Technology/Technician, B
Health Services Administration, BM
Health/Health Care Administration/Management, B
Hospital and Health Care Facilities
 Administration/Management, B
Hospitality Administration/Management, B
Human Resources Management and Services, M
Human Services, B
Information Technology, B
International Business/Trade/Commerce, BM
Management, M
Management Information Systems and Ser-
 vices, BM
Management Science, B
Management of Technology, M
Marketing, M
Marketing/Marketing Management, B
Nursing, M
Nursing - Advanced Practice, M
Nursing Education, M
Operations Management and Supervision, B
Organizational Behavior Studies, B
Psychology, B
Public Administration, BM
Public Administration and Social Service Profes-
 sions, B
Secondary Education and Teaching, M
Security and Protective Services, B
Special Education and Teaching, M

WINDWARD COMMUNITY COLLEGE

Liberal Arts and Sciences Studies and Humanities, A

Idaho

BOISE BIBLE COLLEGE

Bible/Biblical Studies, AB
Missions/Missionary Studies and Missiology, AB
Pastoral Counseling and Specialized Ministries, B
Pastoral Studies/Counseling, AB
Religious Education, AB
Youth Ministry, B

BOISE STATE UNIVERSITY

Accounting, BM
Accounting and Finance, B
Animal Sciences, M
Anthropology, BM
Applied Mathematics, B
Art Education, M
Art History, Criticism and Conservation, B
Art Teacher Education, B
Bilingual and Multilingual Education, B
Biological and Biomedical Sciences, M
Biology Teacher Education, B
Biology/Biological Sciences, B
Business Administration and Management, B
Business Administration, Management and Opera-
 tions, M
Business/Commerce, B
Business/Managerial Economics, B
Chemistry, BMD
Civil Engineering, BM
Commercial and Advertising Art, B
Communication Studies/Speech Communication
 and Rhetoric, B
Communication and Media Studies, M
Computer Engineering, MD

Computer Science, BM
Computer Systems Networking and Telecommunications, B
Construction Management, B
Counselor Education/School Counseling and Guidance Services, MO
Criminal Justice/Law Enforcement Administration, AB
Criminology, MO
Curriculum and Instruction, MD
Design and Visual Communications, B
Drama and Dance Teacher Education, B
Drama and Dramatics/Theatre Arts, B
Early Childhood Education and Teaching, ABM
Economics, B
Education, MDO
Educational Leadership and Administration, M
Educational Media/Instructional Technology, MDO
Electrical Engineering, MD
Electrical, Electronics and Communications Engineering, B
Elementary Education and Teaching, B
Engineering and Applied Sciences, MDO
English, M
English Language and Literature, B
English/Language Arts Teacher Education, B
Environmental Health, B
Environmental Policy and Resource Management, M
Environmental Studies, B
Environmental and Occupational Health, M
Ethnic, Cultural Minority, and Gender Studies, B
Exercise and Sports Science, M
Finance, B
Fine Arts and Art Studies, M
French Language Teacher Education, B
French Language and Literature, B
General Studies, B
Geology/Earth Science, BMD
Geophysics and Seismology, BMD
German Language Teacher Education, B
German Language and Literature, B
Graphic Design, B
Health Information/Medical Records Administration/Administrator, B
Health Information/Medical Records Technology/Technician, A
Health Professions and Related Clinical Sciences, B
Health Promotion, M
Health Services Administration, M
Health Services Research, M
Health and Physical Education, B
History, BM
History Teacher Education, B
Hydrology and Water Resources Science, M
Illustration, B
Information Science/Studies, B
Information Technology, B
Interdisciplinary Studies, M
International Business/Trade/Commerce, B
Kinesiology and Exercise Science, B
Kinesiology and Movement Studies, M
Liberal Arts and Sciences Studies and Humanities, A
Logistics and Materials Management, B
Marketing/Marketing Management, B
Mass Communication/Media Studies, B
Materials Engineering, BMD
Mathematics, BM
Mathematics Teacher Education, BM
Mechanical Engineering, BM
Medical Radiologic Technology/Science - Radiation Therapist, B
Molecular Biology, D
Multi-/Interdisciplinary Studies, B
Music, BM
Music Performance, B
Music Teacher Education, BM
Music Theory and Composition, B
Nursing, MO
Operations Management and Supervision, B
Organizational Management, MO
Performance, M
Philosophy, B
Physical Education Teaching and Coaching, BM
Physics, B

Political Science and Government, B
Pre-Dentistry Studies, B
Pre-Medicine/Pre-Medical Studies, B
Pre-Veterinary Studies, B
Psychology, B
Psychology Teacher Education, B
Public Administration, MO
Public Health, MO
Public Policy Analysis, MO
Reading Teacher Education, M
Respiratory Care Therapy/Therapist, AB
Science Teacher Education/General Science Teacher Education, M
Social Science Teacher Education, B
Social Sciences, B
Social Work, BM
Sociology, B
Spanish Language Teacher Education, B
Spanish Language and Literature, B
Special Education and Teaching, BM
Speech Teacher Education, B
Taxation, M
Technical Communication, M
Writing, M

BRIGHAM YOUNG UNIVERSITY–IDAHO

Accounting, B
Agricultural Business Technology, B
Agricultural Business and Management, B
Agricultural Economics, B
Agriculture, B
Agronomy and Crop Science, B
Animal Health, B
Animal Sciences, B
Applied Mathematics, B
Architectural Engineering Technology/Technician, A
Army JROTC/ROTC, A
Art Teacher Education, B
Art/Art Studies, General, B
Automobile/Automotive Mechanics Technology/Technician, AB
Biology Teacher Education, B
Biology/Biological Sciences, B
Business Administration and Management, B
Chemical Engineering, A
Chemistry, B
Chemistry Teacher Education, B
Child Development, B
Chinese Language and Literature, A
Clinical/Medical Laboratory Assistant, A
Computer Engineering, B
Computer Science, B
Construction Management, B
Dance, B
Drama and Dramatics/Theatre Arts, B
Early Childhood Education and Teaching, B
Ecology, B
Economics, B
Electrical, Electronic and Communications Engineering Technology/Technician, AB
Elementary Education and Teaching, B
Emergency Medical Technology/Technician (EMT Paramedic), B
Engineering, A
Engineering Technology, A
English Language and Literature, B
English/Language Arts Teacher Education, B
Exercise Physiology, B
Family and Consumer Sciences/Human Sciences, B
Finance, B
Fine/Studio Arts, B
Geology/Earth Science, B
Health Services/Allied Health/Health Sciences, B
Health/Health Care Administration/Management, B
History, B
History Teacher Education, B
Horticultural Science, B
Humanities/Humanistic Studies, B
Information Technology, B
Interior Design, B
International/Global Studies, B
Kindergarten/PreSchool Education and Teaching, A
Liberal Arts and Sciences Studies and Humanities, AB
Management Science, B
Mathematics Teacher Education, B

Mechanical Engineering/Mechanical Technology/Technician, A
Medical/Clinical Assistant, A
Music, B
Music Teacher Education, B
Parks, Recreation and Leisure Facilities Management, B
Physics, B
Physics Teacher Education, B
Political Science and Government, B
Psychology, B
Social Studies Teacher Education, B
Social Work, B
Sociology, B
Spanish Language Teacher Education, B
Veterinary/Animal Health Technology/Technician and Veterinary Assistant, A
Web Page, Digital/Multimedia and Information Resources Design, B
Welding Technology/Welder, AB

BROADVIEW UNIVERSITY–BOISE

Accounting, AB
Business Administration and Management, AB
Computer Programming, Specific Applications, AB
Computer Systems Networking and Telecommunications, A
Criminal Justice/Law Enforcement Administration, AB
Information Technology, B
Legal Assistant/Paralegal, AB
Marketing/Marketing Management, A
Massage Therapy/Therapeutic Massage, A
Medical Administrative Assistant/Secretary, A
Medical/Clinical Assistant, A
Veterinary/Animal Health Technology/Technician and Veterinary Assistant, A

CARRINGTON COLLEGE–BOISE

Dental Assisting/Assistant, A
Dental Hygiene/Hygienist, A
Massage Therapy/Therapeutic Massage, A
Medical Insurance Specialist/Medical Biller, A
Medical Office Management/Administration, A
Medical/Clinical Assistant, A
Pharmacy Technician/Assistant, A
Physical Therapist Assistant, A

THE COLLEGE OF IDAHO

Accounting, B
Anthropology, B
Applied Mathematics, B
Art/Art Studies, General, B
Audiology/Audiologist and Speech-Language Pathology/Pathologist, B
Biology/Biological Sciences, B
Business Administration and Management, B
Chemistry, B
Clinical/Medical Laboratory Science and Allied Professions, B
Curriculum and Instruction, M
Drama and Dramatics/Theatre Arts, B
Education, M
Engineering, B
English Language and Literature, B
Environmental Studies, B
Fine/Studio Arts, B
Health Services/Allied Health/Health Sciences, B
History, B
International Business/Trade/Commerce, B
International Economics, B
International Relations and Affairs, B
Kinesiology and Exercise Science, B
Mathematics, B
Multi-/Interdisciplinary Studies, B
Music, B
Pharmacy, B
Philosophy, B
Physical Education Teaching and Coaching, B
Physics, B
Political Science and Government, B
Pre-Nursing Studies, B
Psychology, B
Religion/Religious Studies, B
Social Sciences, B
Spanish Language and Literature, B

Sport and Fitness Administration/Management, B

COLLEGE OF SOUTHERN IDAHO

Accounting, A
Administrative Assistant and Secretarial Science, A
Agricultural Business and Management, A
Agriculture, A
American Sign Language (ASL), A
Animal Sciences, A
Anthropology, A
Applied Horticulture/Horticultural Operations, A
Aquaculture, A
Art/Art Studies, General, A
Autobody/Collision and Repair
    Technology/Technician, A
Automobile/Automotive Mechanics
    Technology/Technician, A
Bilingual and Multilingual Education, A
Biology/Biological Sciences, A
Building/Construction Finishing, Manage-
    ment, and Inspection, A
Business Administration and Management, A
Cabinetmaking and Millwork/Millwright, A
Chemistry, A
Child Care and Support Services Management, A
Clinical Laboratory Science/Medical
    Technology/Technologist, A
Commercial and Advertising Art, A
Communication Studies/Speech Communication
    and Rhetoric, A
Computer Science, A
Computer Systems Networking and Telecommunica-
    tions, A
Criminal Justice/Law Enforcement Administration, A
Culinary Arts/Chef Training, A
Dental Assisting/Assistant, A
Diesel Mechanics Technology/Technician, A
Drafting and Design Technology/Technician, A
Drama and Dramatics/Theatre Arts, A
Education, A
Elementary Education and Teaching, A
Emergency Medical Technology/Technician (EMT
    Paramedic), A
Engineering, A
English Language and Literature, A
Entrepreneurship/Entrepreneurial Studies, A
Equestrian/Equine Studies, A
Foreign Languages and Literatures, A
Forestry, A
Geography, A
Geology/Earth Science, A
History, A
Hotel/Motel Administration/Management, A
Human Services, A
Hydrology and Water Resources Science, A
Liberal Arts and Sciences Studies and Humani-
    ties, A
Library Science, A
Manufacturing Technology/Technician, A
Mathematics, A
Medical Radiologic Technology/Science - Radiation
    Therapist, A
Music, A
Photography, A
Physical Education Teaching and Coaching, A
Physics, A
Political Science and Government, A
Pre-Law Studies, A
Pre-Pharmacy Studies, A
Psychiatric/Mental Health Services Technician, A
Psychology, A
Public Health Education and Promotion, A
Real Estate, A
Social Sciences, A
Sociology, A
Surgical Technology/Technologist, A
Teacher Assistant/Aide, A
Veterinary/Animal Health Technology/Technician and
    Veterinary Assistant, A
Water Quality and Wastewater Treatment Manage-
    ment and Recycling Technology/Technician, A
Web Page, Digital/Multimedia and Information Re-
    sources Design, A

Welding Technology/Welder, A

COLLEGE OF WESTERN IDAHO

Administrative Assistant and Secretarial Science, A
Agriculture, A
Anthropology, A
Autobody/Collision and Repair
    Technology/Technician, A
Automobile/Automotive Mechanics
    Technology/Technician, A
Baking and Pastry Arts/Baker/Pastry Chef, A
Biology/Biological Sciences, A
Biomedical Sciences, A
Business, Management, Marketing, and Related
    Support Services, A
Criminal Justice/Police Science, A
Culinary Arts/Chef Training, A
Dental Assisting/Assistant, A
Drafting and Design Technology/Technician, A
Early Childhood Education and Teaching, A
Elementary Education and Teaching, A
English Language and Literature, A
Geography, A
Geology/Earth Science, A
Heavy Equipment Maintenance
    Technology/Technician, A
History, A
Horticultural Science, A
Liberal Arts and Sciences Studies and Humani-
    ties, A
Machine Tool Technology/Machinist, A
Marketing/Marketing Management, A
Medical Administrative Assistant/Secretary, A
Physical Education Teaching and Coaching, A
Political Science and Government, A
Psychology, A
Small Engine Mechanics and Repair
    Technology/Technician, A
Sociology, A
Surgical Technology/Technologist, A
System Administration/Administrator, A
Web Page, Digital/Multimedia and Information Re-
    sources Design, A

EASTERN IDAHO TECHNICAL COL-
LEGE

Accounting, A
Administrative Assistant and Secretarial Science, A
Automobile/Automotive Mechanics
    Technology/Technician, A
Computer Systems Networking and Telecommunica-
    tions, A
Diesel Mechanics Technology/Technician, A
Electrician, A
Fire Science/Firefighting, A
Legal Assistant/Paralegal, A
Marketing/Marketing Management, A
Medical/Clinical Assistant, A
Surgical Technology/Technologist, A
Web Page, Digital/Multimedia and Information Re-
    sources Design, A
Welding Technology/Welder, A

IDAHO STATE UNIVERSITY

Accounting, B
Administrative Assistant and Secretarial Science, AB
Aircraft Powerplant Technology/Technician, AB
Allied Health and Medical Assisting Services, MDO
American Indian/Native American Languages, Lit-
    eratures, and Linguistics, A
American Sign Language (ASL), A
Anthropology, BM
Applied Physics, D
Art/Art Studies, General, B
Audiology/Audiologist and Speech-Language
    Pathology/Pathologist, A
Autobody/Collision and Repair
    Technology/Technician, AB
Automobile/Automotive Mechanics
    Technology/Technician, AB
Biochemistry, B
Biological and Biomedical Sciences, MD
Biology/Biological Sciences, B
Business Administration and Management, B
Business Administration, Management and Opera-
    tions, MO

Business/Commerce, AB
CAD/CADD Drafting and/or Design
    Technology/Technician, AB
Chemistry, BM
Civil Engineering, BM
Civil Engineering Technology/Technician, AB
Clinical Laboratory Science/Medical
    Technology/Technologist, B
Clinical Microbiology, M
Clinical Psychology, D
Communication Disorders, MDO
Communication Studies/Speech Communication
    and Rhetoric, B
Community Health and Preventive Medicine, O
Computer Systems Networking and Telecommunica-
    tions, AB
Computer and Information Sciences, B
Counseling Psychology, M
Counselor Education/School Counseling and Guid-
    ance Services, MDO
Criminal Justice/Police Science, AB
Criminal Justice/Safety Studies, A
Curriculum and Instruction, M
Dental Hygiene/Hygienist, BM
Dentistry, O
Diesel Mechanics Technology/Technician, AB
Dietetics/Dieticians, B
Drama and Dramatics/Theatre Arts, B
Early Childhood Education and Teaching, B
Economics, B
Education, MDO
Educational Administration and Supervision, MDO
Educational Leadership and Administration, MDO
Educational Media/Instructional Technology, MD
Electrical, Electronic and Communications Engineer-
    ing Technology/Technician, AB
Electrical, Electronics and Communications Engi-
    neering, B
Elementary Education and Teaching, BM
Emergency Medical Technology/Technician (EMT
    Paramedic), A
Energy Management and Systems
    Technology/Technician, AB
Engineering and Applied Sciences, MDO
English, MDO
English Language and Literature, B
English as a Second Language, O
Environmental Engineering
    Technology/Environmental Technology, M
Environmental Policy and Resource Manage-
    ment, M
Environmental Sciences, BM
Experimental Psychology, D
Family and Consumer Sciences/Human Sciences, B
Finance, B
Fine Arts and Art Studies, M
Fire Science/Firefighting, AB
French Language and Literature, B
General Studies, AB
Geographic Information Systems, M
Geology/Earth Science, BMO
Geophysics and Seismology, M
Geosciences, MO
German Language and Literature, B
Hazardous Materials Management and Waste
    Technology/Technician, M
Health Education, M
Health Information/Medical Records
    Technology/Technician, AB
Health Physics/Radiological Health, M
Health Services/Allied Health/Health Sciences, B
Health Teacher Education, B
Health/Health Care Administration/Management, B
History, BM
Human Resources Management/Personnel Adminis-
    tration, B
Hydrology and Water Resources Science, M
Industrial Education, M
Information Science/Studies, B
Instrumentation Technology/Technician, AB
Insurance, B
Interdisciplinary Studies, M
International Relations and Affairs, B
Legal Assistant/Paralegal, AB
Machine Tool Technology/Machinist, AB

Management Information Systems and Services, MO
Management of Technology, M
Marketing/Marketing Management, AB
Marriage and Family Therapy/Counseling, M
Mass Communication/Media Studies, B
Massage Therapy/Therapeutic Massage, AB
Mathematics, ABMD
Mathematics Teacher Education, M
Mechanical Engineering, BM
Mechanical Engineering/Mechanical Technology/Technician, AB
Mechanics and Repairers, AB
Medical Radiologic Technology/Science - Radiation Therapist, AB
Medical/Clinical Assistant, AB
Medicinal and Pharmaceutical Chemistry, D
Microbiology, BM
Music, B
Music Performance, B
Music Teacher Education, B
Nuclear Engineering, BMD
Nuclear Engineering Technology/Technician, AB
Nursing, MO
Nutritional Sciences, O
Occupational Therapy/Therapist, M
Operations Research, M
Oral and Dental Sciences, O
Pharmaceutical Administration, MD
Pharmaceutical Sciences, MD
Pharmacology, D
Pharmacy, MD
Philosophy, B
Physical Education Teaching and Coaching, BM
Physical Therapist Assistant, AB
Physical Therapy/Therapist, D
Physician Assistant, M
Physics, ABMD
Political Science and Government, BMD
Psychology, BD
Public Administration, M
Public Health, M
Reading Teacher Education, M
Respiratory Care Therapy/Therapist, A
Rhetoric, M
Robotics Technology/Technician, AB
Russian Language and Literature, A
School Psychology, MO
Secondary Education and Teaching, BM
Security and Protective Services, AB
Sign Language Interpretation and Translation, B
Social Work, B
Sociology, BM
Spanish Language and Literature, B
Special Education and Teaching, BMO
Speech and Interpersonal Communication, M
Statistics, B
Survey Technology/Surveying, B
Theater, M
Vocational and Technical Education, M
Welding Technology/Welder, AB

LEWIS-CLARK STATE COLLEGE

Accounting Technology/Technician and Bookkeeping, AB
Administrative Assistant and Secretarial Science, AB
Autobody/Collision and Repair Technology/Technician, AB
Automobile/Automotive Mechanics Technology/Technician, AB
Behavioral Sciences, A
Biology/Biological Sciences, B
Business Administration and Management, B
Chemistry, B
Child Development, AB
Communication Studies/Speech Communication and Rhetoric, B
Computer Science, B
Computer and Information Sciences, AB
Corrections, B
Diesel Mechanics Technology/Technician, AB
Drafting and Design Technology/Technician, AB
Electrical/Electronics Equipment Installation and Repair, AB
Elementary Education and Teaching, B
English Language and Literature, B

English/Language Arts Teacher Education, B
Fire Science/Firefighting, AB
Graphic and Printing Equipment Operator Production, AB
Heating, Air Conditioning, Ventilation and Refrigeration Maintenance Technology/Technician, AB
Hospitality Administration/Management, AB
Industrial Electronics Technology/Technician, AB
Kinesiology and Exercise Science, B
Legal Administrative Assistant/Secretary, AB
Legal Assistant/Paralegal, AB
Liberal Arts and Sciences Studies and Humanities, A
Manufacturing Technology/Technician, AB
Mathematics, B
Mathematics Teacher Education, B
Mechanics and Repairers, AB
Medical Office Assistant/Specialist, AB
Medical/Health Management and Clinical Assistant/Specialist, AB
Multi-/Interdisciplinary Studies, B
Natural Sciences, B
Physical Education Teaching and Coaching, B
Psychology, B
Radiologic Technology/Science - Radiographer, A
Science Teacher Education/General Science Teacher Education, B
Small Business Administration/Management, AB
Social Science Teacher Education, B
Social Sciences, B
Social Work, B
Web/Multimedia Management and Webmaster, AB
Welding Technology/Welder, AB

NEW SAINT ANDREWS COLLEGE

Liberal Arts and Sciences Studies and Humanities, AB
Religion/Religious Studies, O
Theology and Religious Vocations, MO

NORTH IDAHO COLLEGE

Administrative Assistant and Secretarial Science, A
Agriculture, A
American Indian/Native American Studies, A
Anthropology, A
Art/Art Studies, General, A
Astronomy, A
Athletic Training and Sports Medicine, A
Automobile/Automotive Mechanics Technology/Technician, A
Biological and Physical Sciences, A
Biology/Biological Sciences, A
Botany/Plant Biology, A
Business Administration and Management, A
Business Teacher Education, A
Carpentry/Carpenter, A
Chemistry, A
Clinical Laboratory Science/Medical Technology/Technologist, A
Commercial and Advertising Art, A
Computer Programming/Programmer, A
Computer Science, A
Computer and Information Sciences, A
Computer and Information Sciences and Support Services, A
Criminal Justice/Law Enforcement Administration, A
Criminal Justice/Police Science, A
Culinary Arts/Chef Training, A
Drafting and Design Technology/Technician, A
Drama and Dramatics/Theatre Arts, A
Education, A
Electrical, Electronic and Communications Engineering Technology/Technician, A
Elementary Education and Teaching, A
Engineering, A
English Language and Literature, A
Environmental Health, A
Fishing and Fisheries Sciences and Management, A
Forestry, A
French Language and Literature, A
Geology/Earth Science, A
German Language and Literature, A
Health/Health Care Administration/Management, A
Heating, Air Conditioning, Ventilation and Refrigeration Maintenance Technology/Technician, A

Heavy Equipment Maintenance Technology/Technician, A
History, A
Hospitality Administration/Management, A
Human Services, A
Journalism, A
Legal Administrative Assistant/Secretary, A
Legal Assistant/Paralegal, A
Liberal Arts and Sciences Studies and Humanities, A
Machine Tool Technology/Machinist, A
Marine Maintenance/Fitter and Ship Repair Technology/Technician, A
Mass Communication/Media Studies, A
Mathematics, A
Medical Administrative Assistant/Secretary, A
Music, A
Music Teacher Education, A
Physical Sciences, A
Physics, A
Political Science and Government, A
Psychology, A
Social Sciences, A
Sociology, A
Spanish Language and Literature, A
Welding Technology/Welder, A
Wildlife Biology, A
Wildlife and Wildlands Science and Management, A
Zoology/Animal Biology, A

NORTHWEST NAZARENE UNIVERSITY

Accounting, B
Ancient Near Eastern and Biblical Languages, Literatures, and Linguistics, B
Art Teacher Education, B
Art/Art Studies, General, B
Athletic Training and Sports Medicine, B
Bible/Biblical Studies, B
Biochemistry, B
Biology Teacher Education, B
Biology/Biological Sciences, B
Business Administration and Management, B
Business Administration, Management and Operations, M
Cell/Cellular and Molecular Biology, B
Ceramic Arts and Ceramics, B
Chemistry, B
Chemistry Teacher Education, B
Clinical Psychology, M
Commercial and Advertising Art, B
Communication Studies/Speech Communication and Rhetoric, B
Computer Science, B
Counselor Education/School Counseling and Guidance Services, M
Criminal Justice/Law Enforcement Administration, B
Curriculum and Instruction, M
Divinity/Ministry (BD, MDiv.), B
Education, BMDO
Educational Leadership and Administration, MDO
Elementary Education and Teaching, B
Engineering Physics, B
English Language and Literature, B
English/Language Arts Teacher Education, B
Finance, B
Forensic Science and Technology, B
Graphic Design, B
Health Services Administration, M
Health and Physical Education, B
History, B
History Teacher Education, B
Humanities/Humanistic Studies, B
International Business/Trade/Commerce, B
International Relations and Affairs, B
Kinesiology and Exercise Science, B
Liberal Arts and Sciences Studies and Humanities, B
Marketing/Marketing Management, B
Marriage and Family Therapy/Counseling, M
Mass Communication/Media Studies, B
Mathematics, B
Mathematics Teacher Education, B
Missions/Missionary Studies and Missiology, BM
Music, B
Music Performance, B
Music Teacher Education, B

Music Theory and Composition, B
Nursing Administration, M
Painting, B
Parks, Recreation, Leisure and Fitness Studies, B
Pastoral Studies/Counseling, BM
Philosophy, B
Physical Education Teaching and Coaching, B
Physical Therapy/Therapist, B
Physics, B
Political Science and Government, B
Pre-Dentistry Studies, B
Pre-Law Studies, B
Pre-Medicine/Pre-Medical Studies, B
Pre-Pharmacy Studies, B
Pre-Veterinary Studies, B
Printmaking, B
Psychology, B
Radio and Television Broadcasting
  Technology/Technician, B
Religion/Religious Studies, BM
Religious Education, B
Religious/Sacred Music, B
School Psychology, M
Sculpture, B
Secondary Education and Teaching, B
Social Work, BM
Spanish Language Teacher Education, B
Spanish Language and Literature, B
Substance Abuse/Addiction Counseling, M
Theology and Religious Vocations, M
Theology/Theological Studies, B
Urban and Regional Planning, M

STEVENS-HENAGER COLLEGE (BOISE)

Accounting, B
Accounting and Business/Management, A
Business Administration and Management, B
Computer Programming/Programmer, A
Computer Science, B
Computer Systems Networking and Telecommunications, A
Graphic Design, AB
Health/Health Care Administration/Management, B
Respiratory Care Therapy/Therapist, AB
Surgical Technology/Technologist, A

UNIVERSITY OF IDAHO

Accounting, BM
Advertising, B
Agribusiness, BM
Agricultural Business and Management, B
Agricultural Communication/Journalism, B
Agricultural Economics, BM
Agricultural Education, M
Agricultural Engineering, MD
Agricultural Mechanization, B
Agricultural Teacher Education, B
Agronomy and Soil Sciences, MD
American Indian/Native American Studies, D
Animal Sciences, BMD
Anthropology, BM
Apparel and Textiles, B
Applied Economics, M
Applied Mathematics, B
Architecture, BM
Art Education, B
Art Teacher Education, B
Art/Art Studies, General, B
Athletic Training and Sports Medicine, BMD
Biochemistry, BD
Bioengineering, MD
Bioinformatics, MD
Biological and Biomedical Sciences, MD
Biology/Biological Sciences, B
Business Administration and Management, B
Business Administration, Management and Operations, MD
Business/Managerial Economics, B
Chemical Engineering, BMD
Chemistry, BMD
Civil Engineering, BMD
Computational Biology, MD
Computer Engineering, BM
Computer Science, BMD
Conflict Resolution and Mediation/Peace Studies, D

Conservation Biology, B
Consumer Economics, M
Counselor Education/School Counseling and Guidance Services, M
Curriculum and Instruction, MO
Dance, B
Digital Communication and Media/Multimedia, B
Drama and Dramatics/Theatre Arts, B
Economics, B
Education, MDO
Educational Leadership and Administration, MO
Electrical Engineering, MD
Electrical, Electronics and Communications Engineering, D
Elementary Education and Teaching, B
Engineering Management, M
Engineering and Applied Sciences, MD
English, M
English Language and Literature, B
English as a Second Language, M
English/Language Arts Teacher Education, B
Entomology, MD
Entrepreneurship/Entrepreneurial Studies, D
Environmental Engineering
  Technology/Environmental Technology, M
Environmental Law, D
Environmental Policy and Resource Management, M
Environmental Sciences, BMD
Family Resource Management Studies, B
Finance, B
Fine Arts and Art Studies, M
Fine/Studio Arts, B
Fishing and Fisheries Sciences and Management, B
Food Science, B
Food Science and Technology, MD
Foods, Nutrition, and Wellness Studies, B
Foreign Languages and Literatures, B
Forest Management/Forest Resources Management, B
Forest Sciences and Biology, B
French Language and Literature, B
General Studies, B
Geography, BMD
Geological Engineering, M
Geology/Earth Science, BMD
History, BMD
Horticultural Science, B
Human Development and Family Studies, B
Human Resources Management/Personnel Administration, B
Human Services, M
Hydrology and Water Resources Science, M
Industrial Technology/Technician, B
Interdisciplinary Studies, M
Interior Design, B
International Relations and Affairs, B
Journalism, B
Landscape Architecture, BM
Latin American Studies, B
Law and Legal Studies, D
Management Information Systems and Services, B
Management of Technology, M
Marketing/Marketing Management, B
Materials Engineering, B
Materials Sciences, D
Mathematics, BMD
Mechanical Engineering, BMD
Microbiology, BMD
Molecular Biology, BM
Multi-/Interdisciplinary Studies, B
Music, BM
Music History, Literature, and Theory, B
Music Performance, B
Music Teacher Education, B
Music Theory and Composition, B
Natural Resources and Conservation, MD
Neuroscience, MD
Nuclear Engineering, MD
Organizational Communication, B
Parks, Recreation and Leisure Facilities Management, B
Philosophy, BM
Physical Education Teaching and Coaching, BM
Physics, BMD
Plant Sciences, MD

Political Science and Government, BMD
Psychology, BM
Public Administration, M
Public Relations/Image Management, B
Range Science and Management, B
Recreation and Park Management, M
Rehabilitation Counseling, M
Secondary Education and Teaching, B
Sociology, B
Spanish Language and Literature, B
Special Education and Teaching, BM
Statistics, M
Technical Teacher Education, B
Theater, M
Urban and Regional Planning, M
Veterinary Sciences, MD
Vocational and Technical Education, M
Water Resources, MD
Water Resources Engineering, MD
Wildlife and Wildlands Science and Management, B
Wood Science and Wood Products/Pulp and Paper Technology, B
Writing, M

Illinois

AMERICAN ACADEMY OF ART

Animation, Interactive Technology, Video Graphics and Special Effects, B
Art/Art Studies, General, B
Commercial and Advertising Art, B
Drawing, B
Graphic Design, B
Illustration, B
Painting, B
Photography, B
Web Page, Digital/Multimedia and Information Resources Design, B

AMERICAN INTERCONTINENTAL UNIVERSITY ONLINE

Accounting, M
Business Administration and Management, AB
Business Administration, Management and Operations, M
Computer and Information Systems Security, M
Criminal Justice/Safety Studies, B
Curriculum and Instruction, M
Design and Visual Communications, B
Education, M
Educational Leadership and Administration, M
Educational Measurement and Evaluation, M
Educational Media/Instructional Technology, M
Educational/Instructional Media Design, B
Finance and Banking, M
Health Services Administration, M
Human Resources Management and Services, M
Industrial and Manufacturing Management, M
Industrial and Organizational Psychology, M
Information Science/Studies, M
Information Technology, B
International Business/Trade/Commerce, M
Management, M
Marketing, M
Project Management, M

ARGOSY UNIVERSITY, CHICAGO

Accounting, D
Adult and Continuing Education and Teaching, M
Business Administration and Management, B
Business Administration, Management and Operations, MD
Clinical Psychology, MD
Community College Education, D
Community Psychology, M
Counseling Psychology, D
Counselor Education/School Counseling and Guidance Services, D
Criminal Justice/Law Enforcement Administration, B
Education, MDO
Educational Administration and Supervision, D
Educational Leadership and Administration, MDO
Elementary Education and Teaching, D
Finance and Banking, M
Forensic Psychology, D

Health Psychology, D
Health Services Administration, M
Higher Education/Higher Education Administration, D
Human Development, D
Industrial and Organizational Psychology, M
International Business/Trade/Commerce, MD
Liberal Arts and Sciences Studies and Humanities, B
Management, MD
Management Information Systems and Services, MD
Marketing, MD
Marriage and Family Therapy/Counseling, D
Neuroscience, D
Organizational Behavior Studies, D
Organizational Management, D
Psychoanalysis and Psychotherapy, D
Psychology, BMD
Public Administration, M
Public Health, M
Secondary Education and Teaching, D
Sustainability Management, MD

ARGOSY UNIVERSITY, SCHAUMBURG

Accounting, DO
Business Administration and Management, B
Business Administration, Management and Operations, MDO
Clinical Psychology, MD
Corporate and Organizational Communication, D
Counseling Psychology, M
Criminal Justice/Law Enforcement Administration, B
Finance and Banking, MO
Forensic Psychology, MO
Health Services Administration, MO
Human Resources Management and Services, M
Industrial and Organizational Psychology, M
International Business/Trade/Commerce, MDO
Liberal Arts and Sciences Studies and Humanities, B
Management, MDO
Management Information Systems and Services, MO
Marketing, MDO
Organizational Management, M
Psychology, BMO
Public Administration, M
Public Health, M
Sport Psychology, M
Sustainability Management, M

AUGUSTANA COLLEGE

Accounting, B
African Studies, B
Ancient/Classical Greek Language and Literature, B
Anthropology, B
Applied Mathematics, B
Art History, Criticism and Conservation, B
Art Teacher Education, B
Art/Art Studies, General, B
Asian Studies/Civilization, B
Biochemistry, B
Biology Teacher Education, B
Biology/Biological Sciences, B
Business Administration and Management, B
Chemistry, B
Chemistry Teacher Education, B
Classics and Classical Languages, Literatures, and Linguistics, B
Communication Disorders, B
Communication, Journalism and Related Programs, B
Computer Science, B
Drama and Dramatics/Theatre Arts, B
Economics, B
Elementary Education and Teaching, B
Engineering Physics, B
English Language and Literature, B
English/Language Arts Teacher Education, B
Environmental Studies, B
French Language Teacher Education, B
French Language and Literature, B
Geography, B
Geology/Earth Science, B
German Language Teacher Education, B

German Language and Literature, B
Graphic Design, B
History, B
History Teacher Education, B
International Business/Trade/Commerce, B
Latin Language and Literature, B
Liberal Arts and Sciences Studies and Humanities, B
Mass Communication/Media Studies, B
Mathematics, B
Mathematics Teacher Education, B
Music, B
Music Performance, B
Music Teacher Education, B
Music Theory and Composition, B
Philosophy, B
Physics, B
Physics Teacher Education, B
Political Science and Government, B
Pre-Medicine/Pre-Medical Studies, B
Psychology, B
Public Administration, B
Public Health (MPH, DPH), B
Religion/Religious Studies, B
Scandinavian Languages, Literatures, and Linguistics, B
Sociology, B
Spanish Language Teacher Education, B
Spanish Language and Literature, B
Women's Studies, B

AURORA UNIVERSITY

Accounting, B
Actuarial Science, B
Art/Art Studies, General, B
Athletic Training and Sports Medicine, B
Bilingual and Multilingual Education, B
Biology/Biological Sciences, B
Business Administration and Management, B
Business Administration, Management and Operations, M
Business/Commerce, B
Communication Studies/Speech Communication and Rhetoric, B
Computer Science, B
Criminal Justice/Safety Studies, B
Criminology, M
Curriculum and Instruction, MD
Drama and Dramatics/Theatre Arts, B
Early Childhood Education and Teaching, M
Education, MD
Educational Administration and Supervision, D
Educational Leadership and Administration, M
Educational Media/Instructional Technology, M
Elementary Education and Teaching, BM
English Language and Literature, B
Finance, B
Health/Medical Preparatory Programs, B
History, B
Liberal Arts and Sciences Studies and Humanities, B
Management Information Systems and Services, B
Management Science, B
Marketing/Marketing Management, B
Mathematics, BM
Mathematics Teacher Education, M
Music, B
Nursing, M
Parks, Recreation, Leisure and Fitness Studies, B
Philosophy, B
Physical Education Teaching and Coaching, B
Political Science and Government, B
Pre-Law Studies, B
Psychology, B
Reading Teacher Education, M
Recreation and Park Management, M
Religion/Religious Studies, B
Science Teacher Education/General Science Teacher Education, M
Secondary Education and Teaching, B
Social Work, BMD
Sociology, B
Spanish Language and Literature, B
Special Education and Teaching, BM

Sport and Fitness Administration/Management, B

BENEDICTINE UNIVERSITY

Accounting, BM
Biochemistry, Biophysics and Molecular Biology, B
Biology/Biological Sciences, B
Business Administration and Management, A
Business Administration, Management and Operations, BM
Business, Management, Marketing, and Related Support Services, B
Business/Managerial Economics, B
Chemistry, B
Clinical Laboratory Science/Medical Technology/Technologist, B
Clinical Psychology, M
Communication Studies/Speech Communication and Rhetoric, B
Communication, Journalism and Related Programs, B
Computer Science, B
Computer and Information Systems Security, M
Criminal Justice/Safety Studies, B
Curriculum and Instruction, M
Diagnostic Medical Sonography/Sonographer and Ultrasound Technician, B
Economics, B
Education, M
Educational Administration and Supervision, MD
Educational Leadership and Administration, M
Elementary Education and Teaching, BM
Emergency Management, M
Engineering Science, B
English Language and Literature, B
Entrepreneurship/Entrepreneurial Studies, M
Environmental Sciences, B
Exercise and Sports Science, M
Finance, B
Finance and Banking, M
Fine Arts and Art Studies, B
Fine/Studio Arts, B
Foods, Nutrition, and Wellness Studies, B
Graphic Design, B
Health Education, M
Health Informatics, M
Health Promotion, M
Health Services Administration, M
Health/Health Care Administration/Management, B
Health/Medical Preparatory Programs, B
Higher Education/Higher Education Administration, D
History, B
Human Resources Management and Services, M
Humanities/Humanistic Studies, B
Information Science/Studies, B
International Business/Trade/Commerce, BM
International Relations and Affairs, B
International/Global Studies, B
Journalism, B
Logistics and Materials Management, M
Management, M
Management Information Systems and Services, M
Marketing, M
Marketing/Marketing Management, B
Mathematics, B
Music, B
Music Teacher Education, B
Nuclear Medical Technology/Technologist, B
Nursing, M
Nutritional Sciences, M
Organizational Behavior Studies, BM
Organizational Management, MD
Philosophy, B
Physical Education Teaching and Coaching, B
Physics, B
Political Science and Government, B
Pre-Pharmacy Studies, B
Psychology, B
Public Health, M
Reading Teacher Education, M
Science Teacher Education/General Science Teacher Education, M
Secondary Education and Teaching, M
Social Sciences, B
Sociology, B
Spanish Language and Literature, B

Special Education and Teaching, BM
Theology/Theological Studies, B
Women's Studies, M

BLACK HAWK COLLEGE

Accounting, A
Administrative Assistant and Secretarial Science, A
Agricultural Business and Management, A
Agricultural Mechanics and Equipment/Machine Technology, A
Agricultural Production Operations, A
Applied Horticulture/Horticultural Operations, A
Art/Art Studies, General, A
Automobile/Automotive Mechanics Technology/Technician, A
Banking and Financial Support Services, A
Biological and Physical Sciences, A
Business/Office Automation/Technology/Data Entry, A
Carpentry/Carpenter, A
Child Care Provider/Assistant, A
Concrete Finishing/Concrete Finisher, A
Criminal Justice/Police Science, A
Crop Production, A
Design and Visual Communications, A
Electrician, A
Emergency Medical Technology/Technician (EMT Paramedic), A
Environmental Engineering Technology/Environmental Technology, A
Equestrian/Equine Studies, A
Fire Services Administration, A
General Studies, A
Horse Husbandry/Equine Science and Management, A
Legal Administrative Assistant/Secretary, A
Liberal Arts and Sciences Studies and Humanities, A
Manufacturing Technology/Technician, A
Physical Therapist Assistant, A
Pipefitting/Pipefitter and Sprinkler Fitter, A
Radiologic Technology/Science - Radiographer, A
Retailing and Retail Operations, A
Small Business Administration/Management, A

BLACKBURN COLLEGE

Accounting, B
Art Teacher Education, B
Art/Art Studies, General, B
Biochemistry, Biophysics and Molecular Biology, B
Biology Teacher Education, B
Biology/Biological Sciences, B
Business Administration, Management and Operations, B
Chemistry, B
Clinical Laboratory Science/Medical Technology/Technologist, B
Communication Studies/Speech Communication and Rhetoric, B
Computer Science, B
Criminal Justice/Law Enforcement Administration, B
Drama and Dramatics/Theatre Arts, B
Education, B
Educational Assessment, Evaluation, and Research, B
Elementary Education and Teaching, B
English Language and Literature, B
English/Language Arts Teacher Education, B
Environmental Biology, B
Environmental Sciences, B
Health and Physical Education, B
Health/Medical Preparatory Programs, B
History, B
Human Resources Development, B
Law and Legal Studies, B
Marketing/Marketing Management, B
Mathematics, B
Mathematics Teacher Education, B
Molecular Biology, B
Music, B
Physical Education Teaching and Coaching, B
Political Science and Government, B
Psychology, B
Public Administration, B
Secondary Education and Teaching, B
Social Science Teacher Education, B

Spanish Language and Literature, B
Sport and Fitness Administration/Management, B
Teacher Assistant/Aide, B
Visual and Performing Arts, B

BLESSING-RIEMAN COLLEGE OF NURSING

Nursing, M

BRADLEY UNIVERSITY

Accounting, BM
Acting, B
Actuarial Science, B
Advertising, B
Animation, Interactive Technology, Video Graphics and Special Effects, B
Art History, Criticism and Conservation, B
Art Teacher Education, B
Art/Art Studies, General, B
Auditing, B
Biochemistry, BM
Biological and Biomedical Sciences, M
Biology Teacher Education, B
Biology/Biological Sciences, B
Biomedical Sciences, B
Business Administration and Management, B
Business Administration, Management and Operations, M
Business/Managerial Economics, B
Cell/Cellular and Molecular Biology, B
Ceramic Arts and Ceramics, BM
Chemistry, BM
Chemistry Teacher Education, B
Civil Engineering, BM
Clinical Laboratory Science/Medical Technology/Technologist, B
Clinical Psychology, M
Comparative and Interdisciplinary Arts, M
Computer Engineering, B
Computer Science, BM
Computer and Information Sciences, B
Construction Engineering, B
Construction Engineering Technology/Technician, B
Construction Engineering and Management, M
Construction Management, B
Consumer Merchandising/Retailing Management, B
Counseling Psychology, M
Counselor Education/School Counseling and Guidance Services, BM
Criminal Justice/Law Enforcement Administration, B
Curriculum and Instruction, MO
Dietetics/Dieticians, B
Digital Communication and Media/Multimedia, B
Directing and Theatrical Production, B
Drama and Dance Teacher Education, B
Drama and Dramatics/Theatre Arts, B
Drawing, B
Early Childhood Education and Teaching, B
Economics, B
Education, BMDO
Education/Teaching of Individuals with Mental Retardation, B
Education/Teaching of Individuals with Multiple Disabilities, B
Education/Teaching of Individuals with Specific Learning Disabilities, B
Educational Leadership and Administration, M
Electrical Engineering, M
Electrical, Electronics and Communications Engineering, B
Elementary Education and Teaching, B
Engineering Physics, B
Engineering and Applied Sciences, M
English, M
English Language and Literature, B
English/Language Arts Teacher Education, B
Entrepreneurship/Entrepreneurial Studies, B
Environmental Sciences, B
Family and Consumer Sciences/Home Economics Teacher Education, B
Family and Consumer Sciences/Human Sciences, B
Finance, B
Fine Arts and Art Studies, M
Fine/Studio Arts, B
Foods, Nutrition, and Wellness Studies, B
French Language Teacher Education, B

French Language and Literature, B
Graphic Communications, B
Graphic Design, B
Health Professions and Related Clinical Sciences, B
History, B
History Teacher Education, B
Hospitality Administration/Management, B
Human Development, M
Human Resources Management/Personnel Administration, B
Humanities/Humanistic Studies, B
Industrial Engineering, B
Industrial/Management Engineering, M
Information Science/Studies, BM
Information Technology, B
Insurance, B
International Business/Trade/Commerce, B
International Relations and Affairs, B
Journalism, B
Liberal Arts and Sciences Studies and Humanities, B
Logistics and Materials Management, B
Management Information Systems and Services, B
Manufacturing Engineering, BM
Manufacturing Technology/Technician, B
Marketing/Marketing Management, B
Mathematics, B
Mathematics Teacher Education, B
Mechanical Engineering, BM
Music, B
Music Performance, B
Music Teacher Education, B
Music Theory and Composition, B
Non-Profit/Public/Organizational Management, M
Nursing, MO
Nursing Administration, M
Nursing Education, M
Organizational Communication, B
Painting, BM
Philosophy, B
Photography, BM
Photojournalism, B
Physical Therapy/Therapist, D
Physics, B
Physics Teacher Education, B
Political Science and Government, B
Pre-Dentistry Studies, B
Pre-Medicine/Pre-Medical Studies, B
Pre-Veterinary Studies, B
Printmaking, BM
Psychology, B
Psychology Teacher Education, B
Public Relations, Advertising, and Applied Communication, B
Public Relations/Image Management, B
Radio and Television, B
Religion/Religious Studies, B
Science Teacher Education/General Science Teacher Education, B
Sculpture, BM
Selling Skills and Sales Operations, B
Small Business Administration/Management, B
Social Science Teacher Education, B
Social Studies Teacher Education, B
Social Work, B
Sociology, B
Spanish Language Teacher Education, B
Spanish Language and Literature, B
Speech Teacher Education, B
Voice and Opera, B

CARL SANDBURG COLLEGE

Accounting, A
Administrative Assistant and Secretarial Science, A
Autobody/Collision and Repair Technology/Technician, A
Automobile/Automotive Mechanics Technology/Technician, A
Biological and Physical Sciences, A
Child Care Provider/Assistant, A
Computer Programming/Programmer, A
Computer Systems Networking and Telecommunications, A
Criminal Justice/Police Science, A
Dental Hygiene/Hygienist, A
Diesel Mechanics Technology/Technician, A

Electrical, Electronic and Communications Engineering Technology/Technician, A
Human Resources Management/Personnel Administration, A
Industrial Technology/Technician, A
Liberal Arts and Sciences Studies and Humanities, A
Management Information Systems and Services, A
Mechanical Engineering Related Technologies/Technicians, A
Mortuary Science and Embalming/Embalmer, A
Music, A
Music Teacher Education, A
Radiologic Technology/Science - Radiographer, A
Selling Skills and Sales Operations, A
Substance Abuse/Addiction Counseling, A

CHICAGO STATE UNIVERSITY

African-American/Black Studies, B
Art/Art Studies, General, B
Bilingual and Multilingual Education, B
Biological and Biomedical Sciences, M
Biology/Biological Sciences, B
Business Administration and Management, B
Chemistry, B
Computer Science, BM
Counselor Education/School Counseling and Guidance Services, M
Criminal Justice/Safety Studies, B
Criminology, M
Early Childhood Education and Teaching, BM
Economics, B
Education, MD
Educational Administration and Supervision, MD
Educational Leadership and Administration, D
Educational Media/Instructional Technology, M
Elementary Education and Teaching, BM
English, M
English Language and Literature, B
Foundations and Philosophy of Education, M
General Studies, B
Geographic Information Systems, M
Geography, BM
Health Information/Medical Records Administration/Administrator, B
Health Services/Allied Health/Health Sciences, B
Higher Education/Higher Education Administration, M
History, BM
International/Global Studies, B
Liberal Arts and Sciences Studies and Humanities, B
Library Science, M
Mathematics, BM
Middle School Education, M
Multilingual and Multicultural Education, M
Music, B
Music Teacher Education, B
Nursing, M
Occupational Therapy/Therapist, M
Parks, Recreation and Leisure Facilities Management, B
Pharmacy, D
Physical Education Teaching and Coaching, BM
Physical Therapy/Therapist, B
Physics, B
Political Science and Government, B
Psychology, B
Public Health, M
Public Health Education and Promotion, B
Radio and Television, B
Reading Teacher Education, M
Secondary Education and Teaching, M
Social Work, M
Sociology, B
Spanish Language and Literature, B
Special Education and Teaching, M
Technology Teacher Education/Industrial Arts Teacher Education, B
Vocational and Technical Education, M

Writing, M

CHRISTIAN LIFE COLLEGE

Divinity/Ministry (BD, MDiv.), AB

CITY COLLEGES OF CHICAGO, HAROLD WASHINGTON COLLEGE

Accounting, A
Animation, Interactive Technology, Video Graphics and Special Effects, A
Architectural Drafting and Architectural CAD/CADD, A
Art Teacher Education, A
Biological and Physical Sciences, A
Business Administration and Management, A
Child Care Provider/Assistant, A
Crafts/Craft Design, Folk Art and Artisanry, A
Criminal Justice/Safety Studies, A
Engineering, A
Fire Science/Firefighting, A
General Studies, A
Information Technology, A
Liberal Arts and Sciences Studies and Humanities, A
Social Work, A
Substance Abuse/Addiction Counseling, A

CITY COLLEGES OF CHICAGO, HARRY S. TRUMAN COLLEGE

Accounting, A
Automobile/Automotive Mechanics Technology/Technician, A
Biological and Physical Sciences, A
Business Administration and Management, A
Child Care Provider/Assistant, A
Computer Systems Networking and Telecommunications, A
Criminal Justice/Safety Studies, A
General Studies, A
Information Technology, A
Liberal Arts and Sciences Studies and Humanities, A
Mechanical Drafting and Mechanical Drafting CAD/CADD, A

CITY COLLEGES OF CHICAGO, KENNEDY-KING COLLEGE

Automobile/Automotive Mechanics Technology/Technician, A
Biological and Physical Sciences, A
Business Administration and Management, A
Child Care Provider/Assistant, A
Criminal Justice/Safety Studies, A
Culinary Arts/Chef Training, A
Data Processing and Data Processing Technology/Technician, A
Dental Hygiene/Hygienist, A
General Studies, A
Heating, Air Conditioning, Ventilation and Refrigeration Maintenance Technology/Technician, A
Information Technology, A
Liberal Arts and Sciences Studies and Humanities, A
Radio and Television, A
Social Work, A
Substance Abuse/Addiction Counseling, A

CITY COLLEGES OF CHICAGO, MALCOLM X COLLEGE

Accounting, A
Administrative Assistant and Secretarial Science, A
Art/Art Studies, General, A
Child Care Provider/Assistant, A
Clinical/Medical Laboratory Technician, A
Computer Programming, Specific Applications, A
Dietician Assistant, A
Elementary Education and Teaching, A
Emergency Medical Technology/Technician (EMT Paramedic), A
Funeral Service and Mortuary Science, A
General Studies, A
Hospital and Health Care Facilities Administration/Management, A
Liberal Arts and Sciences Studies and Humanities, A

Medical Radiologic Technology/Science - Radiation Therapist, A
Medical/Clinical Assistant, A
Music, A
Physical Education Teaching and Coaching, A
Physician Assistant, A
Pre-Medicine/Pre-Medical Studies, A
Pre-Pharmacy Studies, A
Respiratory Care Therapy/Therapist, A
Restaurant, Culinary, and Catering Management/Manager, A
Secondary Education and Teaching, A
Surgical Technology/Technologist, A
Teacher Assistant/Aide, A

CITY COLLEGES OF CHICAGO, OLIVE-HARVEY COLLEGE

Accounting, A
Biological and Physical Sciences, A
Business Administration and Management, A
Child Care Provider/Assistant, A
Diesel Mechanics Technology/Technician, A
Engineering Science, A
Fine/Studio Arts, A
General Studies, A
Human Development and Family Studies, A
Information Technology, A
Liberal Arts and Sciences Studies and Humanities, A
Logistics and Materials Management, A
Manufacturing Technology/Technician, A
Respiratory Care Therapy/Therapist, A
Web Page, Digital/Multimedia and Information Resources Design, A

CITY COLLEGES OF CHICAGO, RICHARD J. DALEY COLLEGE

Accounting, A
Architectural Engineering Technology/Technician, A
Business Administration and Management, A
Child Development, A
Clinical Laboratory Science/Medical Technology/Technologist, A
Criminal Justice/Police Science, A
Electrical, Electronic and Communications Engineering Technology/Technician, A
Horticultural Science, A
Humanities/Humanistic Studies, A
Liberal Arts and Sciences Studies and Humanities, A
Marketing/Marketing Management, A
Medical Administrative Assistant/Secretary, A
Transportation and Materials Moving, A

CITY COLLEGES OF CHICAGO, WILBUR WRIGHT COLLEGE

Accounting, A
Architectural Engineering Technology/Technician, A
Architectural Technology/Technician, A
Art/Art Studies, General, A
Biological and Physical Sciences, A
Business Administration and Management, A
Computer and Information Sciences, A
Computer and Information Systems Security, A
Criminal Justice/Police Science, A
Data Processing and Data Processing Technology/Technician, A
Elementary Education and Teaching, A
Engineering, A
English Language and Literature, A
Environmental Engineering Technology/Environmental Technology, A
Environmental Sciences, A
General Studies, A
Gerontology, A
Hispanic-American, Puerto Rican, and Mexican-American/Chicano Studies, A
Journalism, A
Liberal Arts and Sciences Studies and Humanities, A
Library Science, A
Machine Tool Technology/Machinist, A
Marketing/Marketing Management, A
Medical Radiologic Technology/Science - Radiation Therapist, A

Modern Languages, A
Music, A
Occupational Therapy/Therapist, A
Physical Sciences, A

COLLEGE OF DUPAGE

Accounting, A
Administrative Assistant and Secretarial Science, A
Automobile/Automotive Mechanics
  Technology/Technician, A
Baking and Pastry Arts/Baker/Pastry Chef, A
Biological and Physical Sciences, A
Building/Property Maintenance and Management, A
Business Administration and Management, A
Child Care Provider/Assistant, A
Child Care and Support Services Management, A
Child Development, A
Cinematography and Film/Video Production, A
Commercial and Advertising Art, A
Communications Systems Installation and Repair
  Technology, A
Communications Technology/Technician, A
Computer Installation and Repair
  Technology/Technician, A
Computer Programming, Specific Applications, A
Computer Typography and Composition Equipment
  Operator, A
Corrections, A
Criminal Justice/Law Enforcement Administration, A
Criminal Justice/Police Science, A
Culinary Arts/Chef Training, A
Data Entry/Microcomputer Applications, A
Dental Hygiene/Hygienist, A
Design and Visual Communications, A
Drafting and Design Technology/Technician, A
Drafting/Design Engineering
  Technologies/Technicians, A
Electrical, Electronic and Communications Engineer-
  ing Technology/Technician, A
Electrical/Electronics Equipment Installation and Re-
  pair, A
Electromechanical Technology/Electromechanical
  Engineering Technology, A
Emergency Medical Technology/Technician (EMT
  Paramedic), A
Engineering, A
Fashion Merchandising, A
Fashion and Fabric Consultant, A
Fashion/Apparel Design, A
Fire Science/Firefighting, A
Graphic and Printing Equipment Operator Produc-
  tion, A
Health Information/Medical Records
  Administration/Administrator, A
Health Information/Medical Records
  Technology/Technician, A
Health/Health Care Administration/Management, A
Heating, Air Conditioning, Ventilation and Refrigera-
  tion Maintenance Technology/Technician, A
Hospital and Health Care Facilities
  Administration/Management, A
Hospitality Administration/Management, A
Hotel/Motel Administration/Management, A
Human Services, A
Industrial Electronics Technology/Technician, A
Industrial Technology/Technician, A
Interior Design, A
Landscaping and Groundskeeping, A
Legal Administrative Assistant/Secretary, A
Liberal Arts and Sciences Studies and Humani-
  ties, A
Library Assistant/Technician, A
Library Science, A
Machine Tool Technology/Machinist, A
Manufacturing Technology/Technician, A
Marketing/Marketing Management, A
Massage Therapy/Therapeutic Massage, A
Medical Radiologic Technology/Science - Radiation
  Therapist, A
Merchandising and Buying Operations, A
Nuclear Medical Technology/Technologist, A
Occupational Therapist Assistant, A
Occupational Therapy/Therapist, A
Office Management and Supervision, A
Ornamental Horticulture, A
Photography, A

Physical Therapist Assistant, A
Plastics Engineering Technology/Technician, A
Precision Production Trades, A
Prepress/Desktop Publishing and Digital Imaging
  Design, A
Real Estate, A
Respiratory Care Therapy/Therapist, A
Restaurant, Culinary, and Catering
  Management/Manager, A
Retailing and Retail Operations, A
Robotics Technology/Technician, A
Sales, Distribution and Marketing Operations, A
Selling Skills and Sales Operations, A
Speech-Language Pathology/Pathologist, A
Substance Abuse/Addiction Counseling, A
Surgical Technology/Technologist, A
Tourism Promotion Operations, A
Tourism and Travel Services Management, A
Tourism and Travel Services Marketing Opera-
  tions, A
Transportation and Materials Moving, A
Welding Technology/Welder, A

COLLEGE OF LAKE COUNTY

Accounting Technology/Technician and Bookkeep-
  ing, A
Administrative Assistant and Secretarial Science, A
Architectural Drafting and Architectural
  CAD/CADD, A
Art/Art Studies, General, A
Automobile/Automotive Mechanics
  Technology/Technician, A
Biological and Physical Sciences, A
Business Administration and Management, A
Business/Office Automation/Technology/Data En-
  try, A
Chemical Technology/Technician, A
Child Care Provider/Assistant, A
Civil Engineering Technology/Technician, A
Computer Installation and Repair
  Technology/Technician, A
Computer Programming, Specific Applications, A
Computer Systems Networking and Telecommunica-
  tions, A
Construction Engineering Technology/Technician, A
Criminal Justice/Police Science, A
Dental Hygiene/Hygienist, A
Electrical, Electronic and Communications Engineer-
  ing Technology/Technician, A
Electrician, A
Engineering, A
Fire Protection and Safety Technology/Technician, A
Heating, Air Conditioning, Ventilation and Refrigera-
  tion Maintenance Technology/Technician, A
Industrial Mechanics and Maintenance Technol-
  ogy, A
Landscaping and Groundskeeping, A
Liberal Arts and Sciences Studies and Humani-
  ties, A
Machine Shop Technology/Assistant, A
Mechanical Engineering/Mechanical
  Technology/Technician, A
Medical Office Management/Administration, A
Medical Radiologic Technology/Science - Radiation
  Therapist, A
Music, A
Music Teacher Education, A
Natural Resources Management/Development and
  Policy, A
Ornamental Horticulture, A
Restaurant, Culinary, and Catering
  Management/Manager, A
Selling Skills and Sales Operations, A
Social Work, A
Substance Abuse/Addiction Counseling, A
Turf and Turfgrass Management, A

COLUMBIA COLLEGE CHICAGO

Acoustics, B
Acting, B
Advertising, B
Animation, Interactive Technology, Video Graphics
  and Special Effects, B
Art History, Criticism and Conservation, B
Arts Management, M
Cinematography and Film/Video Production, B

Commercial and Advertising Art, B
Comparative and Interdisciplinary Arts, M
Composition, M
Computer and Information Sciences and Support
  Services, B
Dance, B
Dance Therapy/Therapist, BMO
Digital Communication and Media/Multimedia, B
Directing and Theatrical Production, B
Drama Therapy, MO
Drama and Dramatics/Theatre Arts, B
Dramatic/Theatre Arts and Stagecraft, B
Early Childhood Education and Teaching, B
Entertainment Management, M
Ethnic, Cultural Minority, and Gender Studies, B
Fashion/Apparel Design, B
Film, Television, and Video Production, M
Film/Cinema Studies, B
Fine/Studio Arts, B
Graphic Design, B
Illustration, B
Industrial Design, B
Interior Design, B
Intermedia/Multimedia, B
Journalism, BM
Kindergarten/PreSchool Education and Teaching, B
Liberal Arts and Sciences Studies and Humani-
  ties, B
Marketing/Marketing Management, B
Multi-/Interdisciplinary Studies, B
Music, B
Music Performance, B
Music Theory and Composition, B
Photography, BM
Photojournalism, B
Playwriting and Screenwriting, B
Public Relations/Image Management, B
Radio and Television, B
Recording Arts Technology/Technician, B
Sign Language Interpretation and Translation, B
Sport and Fitness Administration/Management, B
Teacher Education and Professional Develop-
  ment, Specific Levels and Methods, B
Teacher Education and Professional Develop-
  ment, Specific Subject Areas, B
Technical Theatre/Theatre Design and Technol-
  ogy, B
Web Page, Digital/Multimedia and Information Re-
  sources Design, B
Writing, M

CONCORDIA UNIVERSITY CHICAGO

Accounting, B
Ancient Near Eastern and Biblical Languages, Lit-
  eratures, and Linguistics, B
Art Teacher Education, B
Art/Art Studies, General, B
Biology Teacher Education, B
Biology/Biological Sciences, B
Business Administration and Management, B
Business Administration, Management and Opera-
  tions, M
Business/Corporate Communications, B
Chemistry, B
Chemistry Teacher Education, B
Commercial and Advertising Art, B
Communication Studies/Speech Communication
  and Rhetoric, B
Computer Teacher Education, B
Computer and Information Sciences, B
Counseling Psychology, M
Counselor Education/School Counseling and Guid-
  ance Services, MO
Curriculum and Instruction, M
Drama and Dramatics/Theatre Arts, B
Early Childhood Education and Teaching, BMD
Education, BM
Educational Administration and Supervision, MDO
Educational Media/Instructional Technology, M
Elementary Education and Teaching, BM
Emergency Medical Technology/Technician (EMT
  Paramedic), B
English Language and Literature, B
English/Language Arts Teacher Education, B
Environmental Sciences, B
Exercise and Sports Science, M

Geography, B
Geology/Earth Science, B
Gerontology, M
History, B
History Teacher Education, B
Human Services, M
Journalism, B
Kinesiology and Exercise Science, B
Liberal Studies, M
Marketing/Marketing Management, B
Mathematics, B
Mathematics Teacher Education, B
Music, BM
Music Performance, B
Music Teacher Education, B
Music Theory and Composition, B
Natural Sciences, B
Non-Profit/Public/Organizational Management, B
Philosophy, B
Physical Education Teaching and Coaching, B
Physical Sciences, B
Political Science and Government, B
Pre-Dentistry Studies, B
Pre-Law Studies, B
Pre-Medicine/Pre-Medical Studies, B
Pre-Theology/Pre-Ministerial Studies, B
Psychology, BM
Reading Teacher Education, BM
Religion/Religious Studies, BM
Religious Education, BM
Religious/Sacred Music, B
Sacred Music, M
Science Teacher Education/General Science
  Teacher Education, B
Secondary Education and Teaching, BM
Social Science Teacher Education, B
Social Work, B
Sociology, B
Spanish Language and Literature, B
Special Education and Teaching, B
Sport and Fitness Administration/Management, B
Teacher Education, Multiple Levels, B
Theology/Theological Studies, B
Women's Studies, B

DANVILLE AREA COMMUNITY COLLEGE

Accounting Technology/Technician and Bookkeeping, A
Agricultural Business and Management, A
Autobody/Collision and Repair
  Technology/Technician, A
Automobile/Automotive Mechanics
  Technology/Technician, A
Business/Office Automation/Technology/Data Entry, A
CAD/CADD Drafting and/or Design
  Technology/Technician, A
Child Care Provider/Assistant, A
Computer Programming, Specific Applications, A
Computer Systems Networking and Telecommunications, A
Corrections, A
Criminal Justice/Police Science, A
Electrician, A
Energy Management and Systems
  Technology/Technician, A
Engineering, A
Executive Assistant/Executive Secretary, A
Fire Science/Firefighting, A
Floriculture/Floristry Operations and Management, A
General Studies, A
Health Information/Medical Records
  Technology/Technician, A
Industrial Electronics Technology/Technician, A
Industrial Mechanics and Maintenance Technology, A
Juvenile Corrections, A
Landscaping and Groundskeeping, A
Liberal Arts and Sciences Studies and Humanities, A
Manufacturing Technology/Technician, A
Medical Administrative Assistant/Secretary, A
Radiologic Technology/Science - Radiographer, A
Selling Skills and Sales Operations, A
Teacher Assistant/Aide, A

Turf and Turfgrass Management, A

DEPAUL UNIVERSITY

Accounting, BM
Acting, B
Adult and Continuing Education and Teaching, M
Advertising and Public Relations, M
African-American/Black Studies, B
American/United States Studies/Civilization, B
Animation, Interactive Technology, Video Graphics
  and Special Effects, B
Anthropology, B
Applied Economics, M
Applied Mathematics, BM
Applied Statistics, M
Arabic Language and Literature, BM
Architectural History and Criticism, B
Art History, Criticism and Conservation, B
Art Teacher Education, B
Art Therapy/Therapist, B
Art/Art Studies, General, B
Biological and Biomedical Sciences, M
Biological and Physical Sciences, B
Biology/Biological Sciences, B
Business Administration and Management, B
Business Administration, Management and Operations, BM
Business/Managerial Economics, B
Chemistry, BM
Chinese Studies, BM
Cinematography and Film/Video Production, B
Clinical Laboratory Science/Medical
  Technology/Technologist, B
Clinical Psychology, M
Communication Studies/Speech Communication
  and Rhetoric, B
Communication and Media Studies, BM
Community Organization and Advocacy, B
Composition, M
Computer Art and Design, M
Computer Graphics, B
Computer Programming, Specific Applications, B
Computer Programming/Programmer, B
Computer Science, BMD
Computer Software and Media Applications, B
Computer Systems Networking and Telecommunications, B
Computer and Information Sciences and Support
  Services, B
Computer and Information Systems Security, BM
Corporate and Organizational Communication, M
Counseling Psychology, M
Counselor Education/School Counseling and Guidance Services, M
Curriculum and Instruction, MD
Drama and Dramatics/Theatre Arts, B
Dramatic/Theatre Arts and Stagecraft, B
E-Commerce/Electronic Commerce, B
Early Childhood Education and Teaching, BMD
East Asian Studies, B
Economics, BM
Education, BMD
Educational Administration and Supervision, M
Educational Leadership and Administration, BMD
Electronic Commerce, M
Elementary Education and Teaching, BM
English, M
English Language and Literature, B
Entrepreneurship/Entrepreneurial Studies, M
Environmental Sciences, B
Film, Television, and Video Production, M
Film, Television, and Video Theory and Criticism, M
Finance, B
Finance and Banking, B
Foreign Language Teacher Education, M
Foundations and Philosophy of Education, M
French Language and Literature, BM
Game Design and Development, M
General Studies, B
Geography, B
German Language and Literature, BM
Graphic Design, B
Health Communication, M
Health Informatics, M
Health Law, M
Health Professions and Related Clinical Sciences, B

Health Services Administration, M
Health Services/Allied Health/Health Sciences, B
Health Teacher Education, B
Health and Physical Education, B
History, BM
Hospitality Administration/Management, BM
Human Resources Management and Services, M
Human Resources Management/Personnel Administration, B
Human-Computer Interaction, M
Humanities/Humanistic Studies, B
Industrial and Manufacturing Management, M
Information Science/Studies, BMD
Information Technology, B
Intellectual Property Law, M
Interdisciplinary Studies, M
International Affairs, M
International Relations and Affairs, B
Internet and Interactive Multimedia, M
Investment Management, M
Islamic Studies, M
Italian Language and Literature, BM
Japanese Studies, M
Jazz/Jazz Studies, B
Jewish/Judaic Studies, B
Journalism, BM
Kinesiology and Exercise Science, B
Latin American Studies, B
Law and Legal Studies, MD
Liberal Studies, M
Management Information Systems and Services, BM
Management Science, B
Management Strategy and Policy, M
Management of Technology, M
Marketing, M
Marketing/Marketing Management, B
Mass Communication/Media Studies, B
Mathematical and Computational Finance, M
Mathematics, BM
Mathematics Teacher Education, M
Mathematics and Computer Science, B
Media Studies, M
Multilingual and Multicultural Education, M
Music, BMO
Music Performance, B
Music Teacher Education, BM
Music Theory and Composition, B
Non-Profit/Public/Organizational Management, M
Nursing, M
Nursing - Advanced Practice, D
Organizational Behavior Studies, B
Organizational Management, M
Peace Studies and Conflict Resolution, B
Performance, MO
Philosophy, B
Physical Education Teaching and Coaching, B
Physics, BM
Playwriting and Screenwriting, B
Political Science and Government, B
Psychology, BM
Public Administration, M
Public Health, M
Public Policy Analysis, BM
Public Relations, Advertising, and Applied Communication, B
Publishing, M
Reading Teacher Education, M
Real Estate, BM
Religion/Religious Studies, B
Rhetoric, M
School Psychology, M
Science Teacher Education/General Science
  Teacher Education, M
Secondary Education and Teaching, BM
Social Sciences, B
Social Work, M
Sociology, BM
Software Engineering, M
Spanish Language and Literature, BM
Special Education and Teaching, BM
Sport and Fitness Administration/Management, M
Student Personnel Services, M
Sustainability Management, M
Sustainable Development, M
Taxation, M

Teacher Education, Multiple Levels, B
Technical Theatre/Theatre Design and Technology, B
Theater, M
Theatre Literature, History and Criticism, B
Urban Design, M
Urban Studies/Affairs, B
Web Page, Digital/Multimedia and Information Resources Design, B
Women's Studies, BM
Writing, M

DEVRY UNIVERSITY (ADDISON)

Biomedical Technology/Technician, B
Business Administration and Management, B
Business Administration, Management and Operations, B
Business/Commerce, B
Computer Engineering Technology/Technician, B
Computer Software Engineering, B
Computer Systems Analysis/Analyst, B
Computer Systems Networking and Telecommunications, AB
Criminal Justice/Law Enforcement Administration, B
Electrical, Electronic and Communications Engineering Technology/Technician, B
Health/Health Care Administration/Management, B
Web Page, Digital/Multimedia and Information Resources Design, AB

DEVRY UNIVERSITY (CHICAGO)

Biomedical Technology/Technician, B
Business Administration and Management, B
Business Administration, Management and Operations, BM
Business/Commerce, B
Computer Engineering Technology/Technician, B
Computer Systems Analysis/Analyst, B
Computer Systems Networking and Telecommunications, AB
Criminal Justice/Law Enforcement Administration, B
Education, M
Electrical, Electronic and Communications Engineering Technology/Technician, AB
Health Information/Medical Records Technology/Technician, A
Web Page, Digital/Multimedia and Information Resources Design, AB

DEVRY UNIVERSITY (DOWNERS GROVE)

Accounting, M
Business Administration and Management, B
Business Administration, Management and Operations, BM
Business/Commerce, B
Communication and Media Studies, M
Computer Systems Analysis/Analyst, B
Criminal Justice/Law Enforcement Administration, B
Education, M
Educational Media/Instructional Technology, M
Electrical Engineering, M
Finance and Banking, M
Health/Health Care Administration/Management, B
Human Resources Management and Services, M
Management Information Systems and Services, M
Project Management, M
Public Administration, M

DEVRY UNIVERSITY (ELGIN)

Business Administration and Management, B
Business Administration, Management and Operations, BMO
Business/Commerce, B
Computer Systems Analysis/Analyst, B
Criminal Justice/Law Enforcement Administration, B
Health/Health Care Administration/Management, B

DEVRY UNIVERSITY (GURNEE)

Business Administration and Management, B
Business Administration, Management and Operations, BMO
Business/Commerce, B
Computer Systems Analysis/Analyst, B

Web Page, Digital/Multimedia and Information Resources Design, AB

DEVRY UNIVERSITY (NAPERVILLE)

Business Administration and Management, B
Business Administration, Management and Operations, BMO
Business/Commerce, B
Computer Systems Analysis/Analyst, B
Criminal Justice/Law Enforcement Administration, B
Health/Health Care Administration/Management, B

DEVRY UNIVERSITY (TINLEY PARK)

Biomedical Technology/Technician, B
Business Administration and Management, B
Business Administration, Management and Operations, BM
Business/Commerce, B
Computer Engineering Technology/Technician, B
Computer Software Engineering, B
Computer Systems Analysis/Analyst, B
Computer Systems Networking and Telecommunications, AB
Criminal Justice/Law Enforcement Administration, B
Electrical, Electronic and Communications Engineering Technology/Technician, AB
Health/Health Care Administration/Management, B
Web Page, Digital/Multimedia and Information Resources Design, AB

DEVRY UNIVERSITY ONLINE

Accounting Technology/Technician and Bookkeeping, A
Business Administration and Management, B
Business Administration, Management and Operations, BM
Business/Commerce, B
Computer Engineering Technology/Technician, B
Computer Software Engineering, B
Computer Systems Analysis/Analyst, B
Computer Systems Networking and Telecommunications, AB
Criminal Justice/Law Enforcement Administration, B
Electrical, Electronic and Communications Engineering Technology/Technician, AB
Health Information/Medical Records Technology/Technician, A
Health/Health Care Administration/Management, B
Web Page, Digital/Multimedia and Information Resources Design, AB

DOMINICAN UNIVERSITY

Accounting, BM
African-American/Black Studies, B
American/United States Studies/Civilization, B
Art History, Criticism and Conservation, B
Biochemistry, B
Biological and Physical Sciences, B
Biology/Biological Sciences, B
Business Administration and Management, B
Business Administration, Management and Operations, M
Chemistry, B
Commercial and Advertising Art, B
Communication Studies/Speech Communication and Rhetoric, B
Computer Science, B
Conflict Resolution and Mediation/Peace Studies, M
Criminology, B
Curriculum and Instruction, M
Dietetics/Dieticians, B
Drama and Dramatics/Theatre Arts, B
Early Childhood Education and Teaching, BM
Economics, B
Education, M
Educational Administration and Supervision, M
Electrical, Electronics and Communications Engineering, B
Elementary Education and Teaching, BM
Engineering, B
English Language and Literature, B
English as a Second Language, M
Environmental Sciences, B
Fashion Merchandising, B
Fashion/Apparel Design, B
Film/Cinema Studies, B

Finance, B
Fine/Studio Arts, B
Food Science, B
Foods, Nutrition, and Wellness Studies, B
Foodservice Systems Administration/Management, B
French Language and Literature, B
History, B
History Teacher Education, B
Human Services, B
Information Science/Studies, MDO
International Business/Trade/Commerce, B
International Relations and Affairs, B
Italian Language and Literature, B
Journalism, B
Law and Legal Studies, B
Library Science, MDO
Marketing/Marketing Management, B
Mathematics, B
Mathematics and Computer Science, B
Music, B
Natural Sciences, B
Pastoral Studies/Counseling, B
Philosophy, B
Photography, B
Physical Therapy/Therapist, B
Political Science and Government, B
Pre-Law Studies, B
Pre-Medicine/Pre-Medical Studies, B
Pre-Pharmacy Studies, B
Psychology, B
Public Relations/Image Management, B
Reading Teacher Education, M
Sculpture, B
Secondary Education and Teaching, B
Social Work, M
Sociology, B
Spanish Language and Literature, B
Special Education and Teaching, M
Special Products Marketing Operations, B
Teacher Education, Multiple Levels, B
Theology/Theological Studies, B
Women's Studies, B

EAST-WEST UNIVERSITY

Behavioral Sciences, B
Biology/Biological Sciences, A
Business Administration and Management, AB
Computer Science, B
English Language and Literature, B
Liberal Arts and Sciences Studies and Humanities, A
Mathematics, B

EASTERN ILLINOIS UNIVERSITY

Accounting, BM
Adult and Continuing Education and Teaching, B
African-American/Black Studies, B
Art Education, M
Art/Art Studies, General, B
Athletic Training and Sports Medicine, B
Biological and Biomedical Sciences, M
Biology/Biological Sciences, B
Business Administration and Management, B
Business Administration, Management and Operations, M
Chemistry, BM
Clinical Laboratory Science/Medical Technology/Technologist, B
Clinical Psychology, M
Communication Disorders, BM
Community College Education, M
Computer Science, MO
Computer and Information Sciences, B
Computer and Information Systems Security, O
Counselor Education/School Counseling and Guidance Services, M
Drama and Dramatics/Theatre Arts, B
Early Childhood Education and Teaching, M
Economics, BM
Education, MO
Educational Leadership and Administration, MO
Elementary Education and Teaching, BM
Energy Management and Policy, M
Engineering, B
Engineering and Applied Sciences, MO

English, M
English Language and Literature, B
Exercise and Sports Science, M
Family and Consumer Sciences/Human Sciences, BM
Finance, B
Fine Arts and Art Studies, M
Foreign Languages and Literatures, B
Geographic Information Systems, M
Geography, B
Geology/Earth Science, B
Gerontology, M
Health Teacher Education, B
History, BM
Industrial Technology/Technician, B
Journalism, B
Junior High/Intermediate/Middle School Education and Teaching, B
Kindergarten/PreSchool Education and Teaching, B
Kinesiology and Exercise Science, B
Kinesiology and Movement Studies, M
Liberal Arts and Sciences Studies and Humanities, B
Management, M
Management Science, B
Marketing/Marketing Management, B
Mathematics, BM
Mathematics Teacher Education, M
Mathematics and Computer Science, B
Middle School Education, M
Multi-/Interdisciplinary Studies, B
Music, BM
Nutritional Sciences, M
Parks, Recreation and Leisure Facilities Management, B
Philosophy, B
Physics, B
Political Science and Government, BM
Psychology, BMO
Public History, M
School Psychology, O
Science Teacher Education/General Science Teacher Education, B
Social Science Teacher Education, B
Sociology, B
Special Education and Teaching, BM
Speech and Interpersonal Communication, M
Student Personnel Services, M
Sustainable Development, M
Systems Science and Theory, O
Technical Teacher Education, B

ELGIN COMMUNITY COLLEGE

Accounting, A
Administrative Assistant and Secretarial Science, A
Animation, Interactive Technology, Video Graphics and Special Effects, A
Automobile/Automotive Mechanics Technology/Technician, A
Baking and Pastry Arts/Baker/Pastry Chef, A
Biological and Physical Sciences, A
Biology Technician/BioTechnology Laboratory Technician, A
Business Administration and Management, A
CAD/CADD Drafting and/or Design Technology/Technician, A
Clinical/Medical Laboratory Technician, A
Computer and Information Systems Security, A
Criminal Justice/Police Science, A
Culinary Arts/Chef Training, A
Data Entry/Microcomputer Applications, A
Design and Visual Communications, A
Engineering, A
Entrepreneurship/Entrepreneurial Studies, A
Executive Assistant/Executive Secretary, A
Fine/Studio Arts, A
Fire Science/Firefighting, A
Graphic Design, A
Health and Physical Education, A
Heating, Air Conditioning, Ventilation and Refrigeration Maintenance Technology/Technician, A
Industrial Mechanics and Maintenance Technology, A
Legal Assistant/Paralegal, A
Liberal Arts and Sciences Studies and Humanities, A

Machine Tool Technology/Machinist, A
Marketing/Marketing Management, A
Music, A
Physical Therapist Assistant, A
Radiologic Technology/Science - Radiographer, A
Restaurant, Culinary, and Catering Management/Manager, A
Retailing and Retail Operations, A
Social Work, A

ELLIS UNIVERSITY

Accounting, ABM
Accounting and Business/Management, B
Business Administration and Management, AB
Business Administration, Management and Operations, M
Business/Commerce, B
Child Development, AB
Corrections, B
Criminal Justice/Law Enforcement Administration, B
Early Childhood Education and Teaching, M
Education, M
Educational Leadership and Administration, M
Educational Media/Instructional Technology, M
Electronic Commerce, M
Entrepreneurship/Entrepreneurial Studies, B
Finance, AB
Finance and Banking, M
Forensic Science and Technology, B
Health Services Administration, M
Human Resources Management/Personnel Administration, B
International Business/Trade/Commerce, M
Legal Assistant/Paralegal, AB
Management, M
Management Information Systems and Services, BM
Management Science, AB
Marketing, M
Marketing/Marketing Management, AB
Project Management, M

ELMHURST COLLEGE

Accounting, BM
Actuarial Science, B
American/United States Studies/Civilization, B
Animation, Interactive Technology, Video Graphics and Special Effects, B
Art Teacher Education, B
Art/Art Studies, General, B
Audiology/Audiologist and Speech-Language Pathology/Pathologist, B
Biochemistry, B
Biology Teacher Education, B
Biology/Biological Sciences, B
Business Administration and Management, B
Business Administration, Management and Operations, M
Chemistry, B
Chemistry Teacher Education, B
Clinical Laboratory Science/Medical Technology/Technologist, B
Communication Disorders, M
Communication Studies/Speech Communication and Rhetoric, B
Criminology, B
CytoTechnology/Cytotechnologist, B
Database Systems, M
Drama and Dramatics/Theatre Arts, B
Economics, B
Education, B
Educational Leadership and Administration, M
Elementary Education and Teaching, B
English Language and Literature, B
English/Language Arts Teacher Education, B
Environmental Studies, B
Finance, B
French Language Teacher Education, B
French Language and Literature, B
Geographic Information Systems, M
Geography, B
German Language Teacher Education, B
German Language and Literature, B
Graphic Design, B
Health and Physical Education, B
History, B

History Teacher Education, B
Industrial and Organizational Psychology, M
Information Science/Studies, B
International Business/Trade/Commerce, B
Kindergarten/PreSchool Education and Teaching, B
Kinesiology and Exercise Science, B
Logistics and Materials Management, B
Management Information Systems and Services, BM
Marketing/Marketing Management, B
Mathematics, B
Mathematics Teacher Education, B
Music, B
Music Performance, B
Music Teacher Education, B
Nursing, M
Nutritional Sciences, B
Occupational Therapy/Therapist, B
Philosophy, B
Physical Education Teaching and Coaching, B
Physical Therapy/Therapist, B
Physician Assistant, B
Physics, B
Physics Teacher Education, B
Political Science and Government, B
Pre-Dentistry Studies, B
Pre-Law Studies, B
Pre-Medicine/Pre-Medical Studies, B
Pre-Pharmacy Studies, B
Pre-Veterinary Studies, B
Psychology, B
Public Health, M
Secondary Education and Teaching, B
Sociology, B
Spanish Language Teacher Education, B
Spanish Language and Literature, B
Special Education and Teaching, BM
Sport and Fitness Administration/Management, B
Supply Chain Management, M
Theology/Theological Studies, B
Urban Studies/Affairs, B

EUREKA COLLEGE

Accounting, B
Art/Art Studies, General, B
Athletic Training and Sports Medicine, B
Biological and Physical Sciences, B
Biology/Biological Sciences, B
Business Administration and Management, B
Chemistry, B
Clinical Laboratory Science/Medical Technology/Technologist, B
Communication Studies/Speech Communication and Rhetoric, B
Comparative Literature, B
Computer Science, B
Computer and Information Sciences, B
Corrections and Criminal Justice, B
Drama and Dramatics/Theatre Arts, B
Education, B
Elementary Education and Teaching, B
English Language and Literature, B
Environmental Sciences, B
Environmental Studies, B
History, B
Kinesiology and Exercise Science, B
Liberal Arts and Sciences Studies and Humanities, B
Management Information Systems and Services, B
Philosophy and Religious Studies, B

FOX COLLEGE

Accounting Technology/Technician and Bookkeeping, A
Administrative Assistant and Secretarial Science, A
Dental Hygiene/Hygienist, A
Medical/Clinical Assistant, A
Occupational Therapist Assistant, A
Physical Therapist Assistant, A
Veterinary/Animal Health Technology/Technician and Veterinary Assistant, A

GOVERNORS STATE UNIVERSITY

Accounting, BM
Analytical Chemistry, M
Art/Art Studies, General, B

Biology/Biological Sciences, B
Business Administration and Management, B
Business Administration, Management and Operations, M
Chemistry, B
Communication Disorders, BM
Communication Studies/Speech Communication and Rhetoric, B
Communication and Media Studies, M
Community Health and Preventive Medicine, B
Computer Science, BM
Counseling Psychology, M
Criminal Justice/Safety Studies, B
Drama and Dramatics/Theatre Arts, B
Early Childhood Education and Teaching, BM
Economics, B
Education, M
Educational Administration and Supervision, M
Educational Media/Instructional Technology, M
Elementary Education and Teaching, B
English, M
English Language and Literature, B
Entrepreneurship/Entrepreneurial Studies, B
Environmental Biology, M
Fine Arts and Art Studies, M
Health Services Administration, M
History, B
Hospital and Health Care Facilities Administration/Management, B
Information Technology, B
Legal and Justice Studies, M
Liberal Arts and Sciences Studies and Humanities, B
Management Information Systems and Services, BM
Mass Communication/Media Studies, B
Mathematics, B
Media Studies, M
Nursing, M
Occupational Therapy/Therapist, M
Operations Management and Supervision, B
Physical Therapy/Therapist, MD
Political Science and Government, BM
Psychology, BM
Public Administration, M
Reading Teacher Education, M
Social Sciences, B
Social Work, BM
Special Education and Teaching, M
Substance Abuse/Addiction Counseling, M

GREENVILLE COLLEGE

Accounting, B
Art/Art Studies, General, B
Biology Teacher Education, B
Biology/Biological Sciences, B
Business Administration and Management, B
Chemistry, B
Chemistry Teacher Education, B
Communication Studies/Speech Communication and Rhetoric, B
Communication and Media Studies, B
Computer and Information Sciences, B
Criminal Justice/Law Enforcement Administration, B
Drama and Dramatics/Theatre Arts, B
Education, M
Elementary Education and Teaching, BM
English Language and Literature, B
English/Language Arts Teacher Education, B
Environmental Biology, B
History, B
History Teacher Education, B
International/Global Studies, B
Kinesiology and Exercise Science, B
Liberal Arts and Sciences Studies and Humanities, B
Management Information Systems and Services, B
Marketing/Marketing Management, B
Mass Communication/Media Studies, B
Mathematics, B
Mathematics Teacher Education, B
Multi-/Interdisciplinary Studies, B
Music, B
Music Teacher Education, B
Organizational Behavior Studies, B
Pastoral Studies/Counseling, BM

Philosophy, B
Physical Education Teaching and Coaching, B
Physics, B
Physics Teacher Education, B
Psychology, B
Public Relations/Image Management, B
Recording Arts Technology/Technician, B
Religion/Religious Studies, B
Religious/Sacred Music, B
Secondary Education and Teaching, M
Social Work, B
Sociology, B
Spanish Language Teacher Education, B
Spanish Language and Literature, B
Special Education and Teaching, B
Sport and Fitness Administration/Management, B
Youth Ministry, B

HARPER COLLEGE

Accounting, A
Administrative Assistant and Secretarial Science, A
Architectural Drafting and Architectural CAD/CADD, A
Architectural Engineering Technology/Technician, A
Art/Art Studies, General, A
Banking and Financial Support Services, A
Biology/Biological Sciences, A
Business Administration and Management, A
Cardiovascular Technology/Technologist, A
Chemistry, A
Child Care Provider/Assistant, A
Communication Studies/Speech Communication and Rhetoric, A
Computer Programming, Specific Applications, A
Computer Programming/Programmer, A
Computer Science, A
Computer and Information Sciences, A
Criminal Justice/Law Enforcement Administration, A
Dental Hygiene/Hygienist, A
Diagnostic Medical Sonography/Sonographer and Ultrasound Technician, A
Dietetic Technician (DTR), A
Dietetics/Dieticians, A
Early Childhood Education and Teaching, A
Electrical, Electronic and Communications Engineering Technology/Technician, A
Elementary Education and Teaching, A
Emergency Medical Technology/Technician (EMT Paramedic), A
Engineering, A
English Language and Literature, A
Environmental Studies, A
Fashion Merchandising, A
Fashion and Fabric Consultant, A
Fashion/Apparel Design, A
Finance, A
Fine/Studio Arts, A
Fire Science/Firefighting, A
Foodservice Systems Administration/Management, A
Health Teacher Education, A
Heating, Air Conditioning, Ventilation and Refrigeration Maintenance Technology/Technician, A
History, A
Hospitality Administration/Management, A
Human Services, A
Humanities/Humanistic Studies, A
Interior Design, A
International Business/Trade/Commerce, A
Legal Administrative Assistant/Secretary, A
Legal Assistant/Paralegal, A
Liberal Arts and Sciences Studies and Humanities, A
Marketing/Marketing Management, A
Mathematics, A
Medical Administrative Assistant/Secretary, A
Medical/Clinical Assistant, A
Music, A
Philosophy, A
Physical Education Teaching and Coaching, A
Physical Sciences, A
Psychology, A
Public Relations, Advertising, and Applied Communication, A
Radiologic Technology/Science - Radiographer, A
Sales, Distribution and Marketing Operations, A

Small Business Administration/Management, A
Web Page, Digital/Multimedia and Information Resources Design, A

HEARTLAND COMMUNITY COLLEGE

Administrative Assistant and Secretarial Science, A
Biological and Physical Sciences, A
Building/Construction Finishing, Management, and Inspection, A
Business Administration and Management, A
Business and Personal/Financial Services Marketing Operations, A
CAD/CADD Drafting and/or Design Technology/Technician, A
Child Care Provider/Assistant, A
Computer Engineering Technology/Technician, A
Computer Programming, Specific Applications, A
Computer Programming, Vendor/Product Certification, A
Computer Programming/Programmer, A
Computer Science, A
Computer Systems Networking and Telecommunications, A
Computer and Information Sciences, A
Computer and Information Sciences and Support Services, A
Corrections, A
Criminal Justice/Safety Studies, A
Data Entry/Microcomputer Applications, A
Design and Visual Communications, A
Drafting and Design Technology/Technician, A
Electrical, Electronic and Communications Engineering Technology/Technician, A
Electrician, A
Engineering, A
Heating, Air Conditioning, Ventilation and Refrigeration Maintenance Technology/Technician, A
Industrial Mechanics and Maintenance Technology, A
Industrial Technology/Technician, A
Information Science/Studies, A
Information Technology, A
Liberal Arts and Sciences Studies and Humanities, A
Machine Tool Technology/Machinist, A
Mathematics Teacher Education, A
Quality Control Technology/Technician, A
Radiologic Technology/Science - Radiographer, A
System Administration/Administrator, A
Teacher Assistant/Aide, A
Web Page, Digital/Multimedia and Information Resources Design, A
Welding Technology/Welder, A

HEBREW THEOLOGICAL COLLEGE

Jewish/Judaic Studies, B

HIGHLAND COMMUNITY COLLEGE

Accounting, A
Administrative Assistant and Secretarial Science, A
Autobody/Collision and Repair Technology/Technician, A
Automobile/Automotive Mechanics Technology/Technician, A
Biological and Physical Sciences, A
Business Administration and Management, A
Child Care Provider/Assistant, A
Early Childhood Education and Teaching, A
Emergency Medical Technology/Technician (EMT Paramedic), A
Engineering, A
Equestrian/Equine Studies, A
General Studies, A
Graphic Design, A
Health Information/Medical Records Technology/Technician, A
Heavy Equipment Maintenance Technology/Technician, A
Hospitality Administration/Management, A
Industrial Technology/Technician, A
Information Technology, A
Liberal Arts and Sciences Studies and Humanities, A
Mathematics Teacher Education, A
Medical/Clinical Assistant, A
Special Education and Teaching, A

Teacher Assistant/Aide, A

Web Page, Digital/Multimedia and Information Resources Design, A

Welding Technology/Welder, A

ILLINOIS CENTRAL COLLEGE

Accounting, A

Accounting Technology/Technician and Bookkeeping, A

Administrative Assistant and Secretarial Science, A

Agricultural Business and Management, A

Agricultural Mechanics and Equipment/Machine Technology, A

Agricultural Production Operations, A

Agricultural/Farm Supplies Retailing and Wholesaling, A

Animal/Livestock Husbandry and Production, A

Animation, Interactive Technology, Video Graphics and Special Effects, A

Applied Horticulture/Horticultural Operations, A

Automobile/Automotive Mechanics Technology/Technician, A

Banking and Financial Support Services, A

Business Administration and Management, A

Child Care Provider/Assistant, A

Clinical/Medical Laboratory Technician, A

Community Health Services/Liaison/Counseling, A

Computer Programming/Programmer, A

Computer Systems Networking and Telecommunications, A

Construction Engineering Technology/Technician, A

Corrections, A

Criminal Justice/Police Science, A

Crop Production, A

Culinary Arts/Chef Training, A

Data Entry/Microcomputer Applications, A

Dental Hygiene/Hygienist, A

Diesel Mechanics Technology/Technician, A

Electrical, Electronic and Communications Engineering Technology/Technician, A

Emergency Medical Technology/Technician (EMT Paramedic), A

Energy Management and Systems Technology/Technician, A

Engineering, A

Fire Science/Firefighting, A

Forensic Science and Technology, A

General Studies, A

Graphic Design, A

Health and Physical Education, A

Heating, Air Conditioning, Ventilation and Refrigeration Maintenance Technology/Technician, A

Industrial Technology/Technician, A

Juvenile Corrections, A

Legal Assistant/Paralegal, A

Liberal Arts and Sciences Studies and Humanities, A

Library Assistant/Technician, A

Manufacturing Technology/Technician, A

Mechanical Engineering/Mechanical Technology/Technician, A

Mental Health Counseling/Counselor, A

Occupational Therapist Assistant, A

Physical Therapist Assistant, A

Platemaker/Imager, A

Psychiatric/Mental Health Services Technician, A

Radiologic Technology/Science - Radiographer, A

Real Estate, A

Respiratory Care Therapy/Therapist, A

Retailing and Retail Operations, A

Robotics Technology/Technician, A

Security and Loss Prevention Services, A

Sign Language Interpretation and Translation, A

Substance Abuse/Addiction Counseling, A

Surgical Technology/Technologist, A

Teacher Assistant/Aide, A

Web Page, Digital/Multimedia and Information Resources Design, A

Web/Multimedia Management and Webmaster, A

Welding Technology/Welder, A

ILLINOIS COLLEGE

Accounting, B

Art/Art Studies, General, B

Biology/Biological Sciences, B

Business Administration and Management, B

Business/Managerial Economics, B

Chemistry, B

Clinical Laboratory Science/Medical Technology/Technologist, B

Computer Science, B

CytoTechnology/Cytotechnologist, B

Drama and Dramatics/Theatre Arts, B

Early Childhood Education and Teaching, B

Economics, B

Education, BM

Elementary Education and Teaching, B

English Language and Literature, B

Environmental Studies, B

Finance, B

French Language and Literature, B

German Language and Literature, B

History, B

Information Science/Studies, B

International Relations and Affairs, B

Liberal Arts and Sciences Studies and Humanities, B

Management Information Systems and Services, B

Mass Communication/Media Studies, B

Mathematics, B

Music, B

Occupational Therapy/Therapist, B

Philosophy, B

Physical Education Teaching and Coaching, B

Physics, B

Political Science and Government, B

Pre-Dentistry Studies, B

Pre-Law Studies, B

Pre-Medicine/Pre-Medical Studies, B

Pre-Veterinary Studies, B

Psychology, B

Religion/Religious Studies, B

Secondary Education and Teaching, B

Sociology, B

Spanish Language and Literature, B

Teacher Education, Multiple Levels, B

ILLINOIS EASTERN COMMUNITY COLLEGES, FRONTIER COMMUNITY COLLEGE

Automobile/Automotive Mechanics Technology/Technician, A

Biological and Physical Sciences, A

Business/Office Automation/Technology/Data Entry, A

Construction Trades, A

Corrections, A

Emergency Care Attendant (EMT Ambulance), A

Engineering, A

Executive Assistant/Executive Secretary, A

Fire Science/Firefighting, A

General Studies, A

Health Information/Medical Records Technology/Technician, A

Liberal Arts and Sciences Studies and Humanities, A

Quality Control Technology/Technician, A

Sport and Fitness Administration/Management, A

ILLINOIS EASTERN COMMUNITY COLLEGES, LINCOLN TRAIL COLLEGE

Biological and Physical Sciences, A

Business/Office Automation/Technology/Data Entry, A

Computer Systems Networking and Telecommunications, A

Construction Trades, A

Corrections, A

General Studies, A

Health Information/Medical Records Administration/Administrator, A

Liberal Arts and Sciences Studies and Humanities, A

Mechanical Engineering/Mechanical Technology/Technician, A

Medical/Clinical Assistant, A

Quality Control Technology/Technician, A

Sport and Fitness Administration/Management, A

Teacher Assistant/Aide, A

Telecommunications Technology/Technician, A

ILLINOIS EASTERN COMMUNITY COLLEGES, OLNEY CENTRAL COLLEGE

Accounting, A

Autobody/Collision and Repair Technology/Technician, A

Automobile/Automotive Mechanics Technology/Technician, A

Biological and Physical Sciences, A

Business Administration and Management, A

Business/Office Automation/Technology/Data Entry, A

Culinary Arts/Chef Training, A

Engineering, A

General Studies, A

Human Resources Management/Personnel Administration, A

Industrial Mechanics and Maintenance Technology, A

Information Technology, A

Liberal Arts and Sciences Studies and Humanities, A

Medical Administrative Assistant/Secretary, A

Medical Radiologic Technology/Science - Radiation Therapist, A

ILLINOIS EASTERN COMMUNITY COLLEGES, WABASH VALLEY COLLEGE

Agricultural Business and Management, A

Agricultural Production Operations, A

Biological and Physical Sciences, A

Business Administration and Management, A

Business/Office Automation/Technology/Data Entry, A

Child Development, A

Diesel Mechanics Technology/Technician, A

Energy Management and Systems Technology/Technician, A

Engineering, A

Executive Assistant/Executive Secretary, A

General Studies, A

Industrial Technology/Technician, A

Legal Assistant/Paralegal, A

Liberal Arts and Sciences Studies and Humanities, A

Machine Tool Technology/Machinist, A

Manufacturing Technology/Technician, A

Mining Technology/Technician, A

Radio and Television, A

Social Work, A

Sport and Fitness Administration/Management, A

THE ILLINOIS INSTITUTE OF ART–CHICAGO

Advertising, B

Apparel and Accessories Marketing Operations, B

Cinematography and Film/Video Production, B

Commercial Photography, B

Computer Graphics, B

Culinary Arts/Chef Training, A

Fashion Merchandising, A

Fashion/Apparel Design, B

Graphic Design, AB

Illustration, B

Interior Design, B

Recording Arts Technology/Technician, B

Restaurant, Culinary, and Catering Management/Manager, AB

THE ILLINOIS INSTITUTE OF ART–SCHAUMBURG

Advertising, B

Animation, Interactive Technology, Video Graphics and Special Effects, B

Apparel and Accessories Marketing Operations, B

Cinematography and Film/Video Production, B

Commercial Photography, B

Computer Graphics, B

Design and Visual Communications, B

Fashion Merchandising, A

Fashion/Apparel Design, B

Graphic Design, AB

Interior Design, B

Recording Arts Technology/Technician, B

Restaurant, Culinary, and Catering
  Management/Manager, AB
Web Page, Digital/Multimedia and Information Re-
  sources Design, AB

ILLINOIS INSTITUTE OF TECHNOLOGY

Aerospace, Aeronautical and Astronautical Engi-
  neering, BMD
Analytical Chemistry, M
Applied Arts and Design, MD
Applied Economics, B
Applied Mathematics, BMD
Applied Physics, M
Architectural Engineering, BMD
Architecture, BMD
Artificial Intelligence and Robotics, M
Astrophysics, B
Biochemistry, M
Bioengineering, M
Biological and Biomedical Sciences, MD
Biology/Biological Sciences, B
Biomedical Engineering, MD
Biomedical/Medical Engineering, B
Biophysics, B
Business Administration and Management, B
Business Administration, Management and Opera-
  tions, M
Cell Biology and Anatomy, M
Chemical Engineering, BMD
Chemistry, BMD
Civil Engineering, BMD
Clinical Psychology, D
Communication and Media Studies, MD
Computer Education, M
Computer Engineering, BMD
Computer Science, BMD
Computer and Information Sciences, B
Computer and Information Systems Security, M
Construction Engineering and Management, M
Construction Management, M
Corporate and Organizational Communication, M
Database Systems, M
Development Economics and International Develop-
  ment, B
Electrical Engineering, MD
Electrical, Electronics and Communications Engi-
  neering, B
Engineering, B
Engineering Physics, B
Engineering and Applied Sciences, MD
Engineering/Industrial Management, B
Environmental Engineering
  Technology/Environmental Technology, MD
Environmental Policy and Resource Manage-
  ment, M
Finance and Banking, M
Food Engineering, M
Food Science and Technology, M
Geotechnical Engineering, M
Health Physics/Radiological Health, M
Human Resources Development, M
Humanities/Humanistic Studies, MD
Industrial and Manufacturing Management, M
Industrial and Organizational Psychology, D
Information Technology, B
Inorganic Chemistry, M
Landscape Architecture, MD
Law and Legal Studies, MD
Legal and Justice Studies, D
Liberal Arts and Sciences Studies and Humani-
  ties, B
Management, D
Management Information Systems and Services, M
Manufacturing Engineering, M
Marketing, M
Materials Engineering, BMD
Materials Sciences, MD
Mathematical and Computational Finance, M
Mathematics Teacher Education, MD
Mechanical Engineering, BMD
Medical Imaging, M
Microbiology, M
Molecular Biology, MD
Molecular Biophysics, MD
Pharmacy, B
Physics, BMD

Political Science and Government, B
Psychology, BMD
Public Administration, M
Rehabilitation Counseling, MD
Science Teacher Education/General Science
  Teacher Education, MD
Social Sciences, B
Sociology, B
Software Engineering, M
Structural Engineering, M
Sustainability Management, M
Taxation, M
Technical and Business Writing, MD
Telecommunications, M
Transportation and Highway Engineering, M

ILLINOIS STATE UNIVERSITY

Accounting, BM
Agribusiness, M
Agricultural Sciences, M
Agriculture, B
Animal Behavior and Ethology, M
Anthropology, B
Archeology, M
Art History, Criticism and Conservation, M
Art/Art Studies, General, B
Athletic Training and Sports Medicine, B
Audiology/Audiologist and Speech-Language
  Pathology/Pathologist, B
Bacteriology, M
BioTechnology, M
Biochemistry, BM
Biological and Biomedical Sciences, MD
Biology Teacher Education, B
Biology/Biological Sciences, B
Biophysics, M
Botany/Plant Biology, MD
Business Administration and Management, B
Business Administration, Management and Opera-
  tions, M
Business Teacher Education, B
Cell Biology and Anatomy, M
Cell/Cellular and Molecular Biology, B
Ceramic Arts and Ceramics, M
Chemistry, BM
Clinical Laboratory Science/Medical
  Technology/Technologist, B
Clinical Psychology, M
Communication Disorders, M
Communication Studies/Speech Communication
  and Rhetoric, B
Communication and Media Studies, M
Computer Science, B
Computer Systems Networking and Telecommunica-
  tions, B
Conservation Biology, M
Construction Management, B
Counseling Psychology, M
Criminal Justice/Safety Studies, B
Criminology, M
Curriculum and Instruction, MD
Developmental Biology and Embryology, M
Developmental Psychology, M
Drama and Dramatics/Theatre Arts, B
Early Childhood Education and Teaching, B
Ecology, MD
Economics, BM
Education, MD
Educational Administration and Supervision, MD
Educational Policy, D
Educational Psychology, M
Elementary Education and Teaching, B
Energy Management and Systems
  Technology/Technician, B
Engineering Technology, B
English, MD
English Language and Literature, B
Entomology, M
Environmental Health, B
Evolutionary Biology, M
Experimental Psychology, M
Family and Consumer Sciences/Human Sci-
  ences, BM
Finance, B
Fine Arts and Art Studies, M
Fine/Studio Arts, B

French Language and Literature, BM
General Studies, B
Genetics, MD
Geography, B
Geology/Earth Science, B
German Language and Literature, BM
Graphic Communications, B
Graphic Design, M
Health Education, M
Health Information/Medical Records
  Administration/Administrator, B
Health Teacher Education, B
Higher Education/Higher Education Administra-
  tion, D
History, BM
Hydrogeology, M
Hydrology and Water Resources Science, M
Immunology, M
Industrial Technology/Technician, B
Industrial and Organizational Psychology, M
Industrial/Management Engineering, M
Information Technology, B
Insurance, B
International Business/Trade/Commerce, B
Jewelry/Metalsmithing, M
Journalism, B
Junior High/Intermediate/Middle School Education
  and Teaching, B
Kindergarten/PreSchool Education and Teaching, B
Kinesiology and Exercise Science, B
Law and Legal Studies, B
Legal Assistant/Paralegal, B
Liberal Arts and Sciences Studies and Humani-
  ties, B
Management Information Systems and Ser-
  vices, BM
Management Science, B
Management of Technology, M
Marketing/Marketing Management, B
Mass Communication/Media Studies, B
Mathematics, B
Mathematics Teacher Education, D
Microbiology, MD
Molecular Biology, M
Molecular Genetics, M
Music, BM
Music Performance, B
Music Teacher Education, B
Neurobiology and Neurophysiology, M
Neuroscience, M
Nursing, MDO
Nursing - Advanced Practice, O
Occupational Health and Industrial Hygiene, B
Painting, M
Parasitology, M
Parks, Recreation and Leisure Facilities Manage-
  ment, B
Philosophy, B
Photography, M
Physical Education Teaching and Coaching, BM
Physics, B
Physiology, MD
Plant Biology, M
Plant Molecular Biology, M
Plant Sciences, M
Political Science and Government, BM
Printmaking, M
Psychology, BMDO
Public Relations/Image Management, B
Reading Teacher Education, M
School Psychology, DO
Sculpture, M
Social Work, BM
Sociology, BM
Spanish Language and Literature, BM
Special Education and Teaching, BMD
Structural Biology, M
Student Personnel Services, M
Technology Teacher Education/Industrial Arts
  Teacher Education, B
Textile Design, M
Theater, M
Visual and Performing Arts, B
Writing, M

Zoology/Animal Biology, MD

ILLINOIS VALLEY COMMUNITY COLLEGE

Accounting, A
Automobile/Automotive Mechanics Technology/Technician, A
Biological and Physical Sciences, A
Business Administration and Management, A
Business/Office Automation/Technology/Data Entry, A
CAD/CADD Drafting and/or Design Technology/Technician, A
Child Care Provider/Assistant, A
Child Development, A
Computer Programming/Programmer, A
Computer Systems Networking and Telecommunications, A
Corrections, A
Criminal Justice/Law Enforcement Administration, A
Criminal Justice/Police Science, A
Data Processing and Data Processing Technology/Technician, A
Drafting and Design Technology/Technician, A
Drafting/Design Engineering Technologies/Technicians, A
Early Childhood Education and Teaching, A
Education, A
Electrical, Electronic and Communications Engineering Technology/Technician, A
Electrician, A
Elementary Education and Teaching, A
Engineering, A
English Language and Literature, A
Floriculture/Floristry Operations and Management, A
Forensic Science and Technology, A
General Studies, A
Graphic Design, A
Industrial Technology/Technician, A
Information Technology, A
Journalism, A
Juvenile Corrections, A
Landscaping and Groundskeeping, A
Liberal Arts and Sciences Studies and Humanities, A
Marketing/Marketing Management, A
Massage Therapy/Therapeutic Massage, A
Mechanical Engineering/Mechanical Technology/Technician, A
Selling Skills and Sales Operations, A
Social Work, A
System Administration/Administrator, A
Teacher Assistant/Aide, A

ILLINOIS WESLEYAN UNIVERSITY

Accounting, B
Acting, B
African Studies, B
American/United States Studies/Civilization, B
Anthropology, B
Area Studies, B
Art/Art Studies, General, B
Asian Studies/Civilization, B
Biology/Biological Sciences, B
Business Administration and Management, B
Chemistry, B
Classics and Classical Languages, Literatures, and Linguistics, B
Computer Science, B
Drama and Dramatics/Theatre Arts, B
Economics, B
Education, B
Elementary Education and Teaching, B
Environmental Studies, B
French Language and Literature, B
German Language and Literature, B
History, B
Insurance, B
International Business/Trade/Commerce, B
International Relations and Affairs, B
International/Global Studies, B
Latin American Studies, B
Liberal Arts and Sciences Studies and Humanities, B
Mathematics, B
Multi-/Interdisciplinary Studies, B

Music, B
Music Performance, B
Music Teacher Education, B
Music Theory and Composition, B
Philosophy, B
Physics, B
Piano and Organ, B
Political Science and Government, B
Psychology, B
Religion/Religious Studies, B
Sociology, B
Spanish Language and Literature, B
Technical Theatre/Theatre Design and Technology, B
Visual and Performing Arts, B
Voice and Opera, B
Western European Studies, B
Women's Studies, B

JOHN A. LOGAN COLLEGE

Accounting, A
Anthropology, A
Art Teacher Education, A
Art/Art Studies, General, A
Autobody/Collision and Repair Technology/Technician, A
Automobile/Automotive Mechanics Technology/Technician, A
Banking and Financial Support Services, A
Biological and Physical Sciences, A
Biology/Biological Sciences, A
Business Administration and Management, A
Business Teacher Education, A
CAD/CADD Drafting and/or Design Technology/Technician, A
Carpentry/Carpenter, A
Chemistry, A
Child Care Provider/Assistant, A
Clinical/Medical Laboratory Technician, A
Computer Engineering Technology/Technician, A
Computer Installation and Repair Technology/Technician, A
Computer and Information Sciences, A
Cosmetology/Cosmetologist, A
Court Reporting/Court Reporter, A
Criminal Justice/Police Science, A
Data Entry/Microcomputer Applications, A
Dental Hygiene/Hygienist, A
Diagnostic Medical Sonography/Sonographer and Ultrasound Technician, A
Drama and Dramatics/Theatre Arts, A
Economics, A
Electrical, Electronic and Communications Engineering Technology/Technician, A
Elementary Education and Teaching, A
Emergency Medical Technology/Technician (EMT Paramedic), A
Engineering, A
English Language and Literature, A
English/Language Arts Teacher Education, A
Executive Assistant/Executive Secretary, A
Graphic Design, A
Health Information/Medical Records Technology/Technician, A
Health Services/Allied Health/Health Sciences, A
Health/Medical Preparatory Programs, A
Heating, Air Conditioning, Ventilation and Refrigeration Maintenance Technology/Technician, A
History, A
History Teacher Education, A
Industrial Mechanics and Maintenance Technology, A
Industrial Technology/Technician, A
Information Technology, A
International Relations and Affairs, A
Journalism, A
Kindergarten/PreSchool Education and Teaching, A
Liberal Arts and Sciences Studies and Humanities, A
Mathematics, A
Mathematics Teacher Education, A
Medical Administrative Assistant/Secretary, A
Music, A
Occupational Therapist Assistant, A
Office Management and Supervision, A
Physical Education Teaching and Coaching, A

Physics, A
Political Science and Government, A
Pre-Law Studies, A
Pre-Pharmacy Studies, A
Psychology, A
Public Administration and Social Service Professions, A
Secondary Education and Teaching, A
Selling Skills and Sales Operations, A
Sign Language Interpretation and Translation, A
Social Studies Teacher Education, A
Social Work, A
Sociology, A
Special Education and Teaching, A
Teacher Assistant/Aide, A
Tool and Die Technology/Technician, A
Tourism and Travel Services Management, A
Veterinary/Animal Health Technology/Technician and Veterinary Assistant, A

JOHN WOOD COMMUNITY COLLEGE

Accounting, A
Administrative Assistant and Secretarial Science, A
Agricultural Business and Management, A
Animal Sciences, A
Applied Horticulture/Horticultural Operations, A
Biological and Physical Sciences, A
Business Administration and Management, A
CAD/CADD Drafting and/or Design Technology/Technician, A
Carpentry/Carpenter, A
Child Care Provider/Assistant, A
Clinical/Medical Laboratory Technician, A
Criminal Justice/Police Science, A
Electrician, A
Emergency Medical Technology/Technician (EMT Paramedic), A
Executive Assistant/Executive Secretary, A
Fire Science/Firefighting, A
General Studies, A
Graphic Design, A
Legal Administrative Assistant/Secretary, A
Liberal Arts and Sciences Studies and Humanities, A
Management Information Systems and Services, A
Manufacturing Technology/Technician, A
Medical Staff Services Technology/Technician, A
Office Management and Supervision, A
Radiologic Technology/Science - Radiographer, A
Restaurant, Culinary, and Catering Management/Manager, A
Selling Skills and Sales Operations, A

JOLIET JUNIOR COLLEGE

Accounting, A
Administrative Assistant and Secretarial Science, A
Agricultural Economics, A
Agricultural Production Operations, A
Animation, Interactive Technology, Video Graphics and Special Effects, A
Automobile/Automotive Mechanics Technology/Technician, A
Biological and Physical Sciences, A
Biomedical Technology/Technician, A
Child Care Provider/Assistant, A
Computer Programming/Programmer, A
Computer Systems Networking and Telecommunications, A
Construction Engineering Technology/Technician, A
Corrections, A
Criminal Justice/Safety Studies, A
Culinary Arts/Chef Training, A
Electrical, Electronic and Communications Engineering Technology/Technician, A
Emergency Medical Technology/Technician (EMT Paramedic), A
Fashion Merchandising, A
Fire Science/Firefighting, A
General Studies, A
Health Information/Medical Records Administration/Administrator, A
Heating, Air Conditioning, Ventilation and Refrigeration Maintenance Technology/Technician, A
Hospitality Administration/Management, A
Industrial Electronics Technology/Technician, A

Industrial Mechanics and Maintenance Technology, A
Interior Design, A
Liberal Arts and Sciences Studies and Humanities, A
Massage Therapy/Therapeutic Massage, A
Mechanical Engineering/Mechanical Technology/Technician, A
Medical Office Assistant/Specialist, A
Operations Management and Supervision, A
Plant Nursery Operations and Management, A
Radiologic Technology/Science - Radiographer, A
Selling Skills and Sales Operations, A
Teacher Assistant/Aide, A
Turf and Turfgrass Management, A
Veterinary/Animal Health Technology/Technician and Veterinary Assistant, A
Web/Multimedia Management and Webmaster, A

JUDSON UNIVERSITY

Accounting, B
Architecture, BM
Art/Art Studies, General, B
Bible/Biblical Studies, B
Biochemistry, B
Biology/Biological Sciences, B
Business Administration and Management, B
Business Administration, Management and Operations, BM
Chemistry, B
Communication Studies/Speech Communication and Rhetoric, B
Communication and Media Studies, B
Criminal Justice/Safety Studies, B
Divinity/Ministry (BD, MDiv.), B
Early Childhood Education and Teaching, B
Education/Teaching of Individuals in Early Childhood Special Education Programs, B
Education/Teaching of Individuals with Specific Learning Disabilities, B
Elementary Education and Teaching, B
English Language and Literature, B
Environmental Studies, B
Film/Cinema Studies, B
Fine/Studio Arts, B
Graphic Design, B
History, B
Human Resources Management/Personnel Administration, B
Human Services, B
Intercultural/Multicultural and Diversity Studies, B
Interior Design, B
Liberal Arts and Sciences Studies and Humanities, A
Marketing/Marketing Management, B
Mathematics, B
Music Performance, B
Natural Sciences, B
Organizational Management, M
Pastoral Counseling and Specialized Ministries, B
Pastoral Studies/Counseling, M
Photography, B
Physical Education Teaching and Coaching, B
Playwriting and Screenwriting, B
Pre-Law Studies, B
Psychology, B
Reading Teacher Education, MD
Religious/Sacred Music, B
Secondary Education and Teaching, B
Sociology, B
Sport and Fitness Administration/Management, B
Sustainable Development, M
Urban Design, M
Youth Ministry, B

KANKAKEE COMMUNITY COLLEGE

Administrative Assistant and Secretarial Science, A
Agriculture, A
Applied Horticulture/Horticultural Operations, A
Art/Art Studies, General, A
Automobile/Automotive Mechanics Technology/Technician, A
Biology/Biological Sciences, A
Business Administration and Management, A
Chemistry, A
Clinical/Medical Laboratory Technician, A

Construction Management, A
Criminal Justice/Law Enforcement Administration, A
Criminal Justice/Police Science, A
Drafting and Design Technology/Technician, A
Early Childhood Education and Teaching, A
Education, A
Elementary Education and Teaching, A
Emergency Medical Technology/Technician (EMT Paramedic), A
Engineering, A
English Language and Literature, A
General Studies, A
Heating, Air Conditioning, Ventilation and Refrigeration Maintenance Technology/Technician, A
History, A
Industrial Electronics Technology/Technician, A
Legal Assistant/Paralegal, A
Mathematics, A
Mathematics Teacher Education, A
Medical Office Assistant/Specialist, A
Medical/Clinical Assistant, A
Physical Therapist Assistant, A
Physics, A
Political Science and Government, A
Prepress/Desktop Publishing and Digital Imaging Design, A
Psychology, A
Radiologic Technology/Science - Radiographer, A
Respiratory Care Therapy/Therapist, A
Secondary Education and Teaching, A
Sociology, A
Special Education and Teaching, A
Teacher Assistant/Aide, A
Visual and Performing Arts, A
Welding Technology/Welder, A

KASKASKIA COLLEGE

Accounting, A
Agriculture, A
Animal Sciences, A
Applied Horticulture/Horticultural Operations, A
Architectural Drafting and Architectural CAD/CADD, A
Autobody/Collision and Repair Technology/Technician, A
Automobile/Automotive Mechanics Technology/Technician, A
Biological and Physical Sciences, A
Business/Commerce, A
Business/Office Automation/Technology/Data Entry, A
Carpentry/Carpenter, A
Child Care Provider/Assistant, A
Clinical/Medical Laboratory Technician, A
Construction Management, A
Cosmetology/Cosmetologist, A
Criminal Justice/Law Enforcement Administration, A
Culinary Arts/Chef Training, A
Dental Assisting/Assistant, A
Electrical, Electronic and Communications Engineering Technology/Technician, A
Electrician, A
Emergency Medical Technology/Technician (EMT Paramedic), A
Engineering, A
Executive Assistant/Executive Secretary, A
General Studies, A
Health Information/Medical Records Technology/Technician, A
Heating, Air Conditioning, Ventilation and Refrigeration Maintenance Technology/Technician, A
Industrial Mechanics and Maintenance Technology, A
Information Science/Studies, A
Juvenile Corrections, A
Liberal Arts and Sciences Studies and Humanities, A
Mathematics Teacher Education, A
Music, A
Occupational Therapist Assistant, A
Physical Therapist Assistant, A
Radiologic Technology/Science - Radiographer, A
Respiratory Care Therapy/Therapist, A
Robotics Technology/Technician, A
System Administration/Administrator, A
Teacher Assistant/Aide, A

Veterinary/Animal Health Technology/Technician and Veterinary Assistant, A
Web/Multimedia Management and Webmaster, A
Welding Technology/Welder, A

KENDALL COLLEGE

Baking and Pastry Arts/Baker/Pastry Chef, A
Business/Commerce, B
Culinary Arts/Chef Training, AB
Early Childhood Education and Teaching, B
Hospitality Administration/Management, B

KISHWAUKEE COLLEGE

Administrative Assistant and Secretarial Science, A
Agricultural Mechanization, A
Airline/Commercial/Professional Pilot and Flight Crew, A
Applied Horticulture/Horticultural Operations, A
Art/Art Studies, General, A
Autobody/Collision and Repair Technology/Technician, A
Automobile/Automotive Mechanics Technology/Technician, A
Biological and Physical Sciences, A
Business Administration and Management, A
CAD/CADD Drafting and/or Design Technology/Technician, A
Child Care Provider/Assistant, A
Child Care and Support Services Management, A
Criminal Justice/Police Science, A
Criminal Justice/Safety Studies, A
Diesel Mechanics Technology/Technician, A
Electrical, Electronic and Communications Engineering Technology/Technician, A
Emergency Medical Technology/Technician (EMT Paramedic), A
Engineering, A
Fine/Studio Arts, A
Forensic Science and Technology, A
Information Technology, A
Landscaping and Groundskeeping, A
Liberal Arts and Sciences Studies and Humanities, A
Ornamental Horticulture, A
Radiologic Technology/Science - Radiographer, A
System Administration/Administrator, A
Teacher Assistant/Aide, A
Teacher Education, Multiple Levels, A

KNOX COLLEGE

African-American/Black Studies, B
American/United States Studies/Civilization, B
Ancient/Classical Greek Language and Literature, B
Anthropology, B
Art History, Criticism and Conservation, B
Art/Art Studies, General, B
Asian Studies/Civilization, B
Biochemistry, B
Biology/Biological Sciences, B
Chemistry, B
Classics and Classical Languages, Literatures, and Linguistics, B
Computer Science, B
Drama and Dramatics/Theatre Arts, B
Economics, B
Education, B
Elementary Education and Teaching, B
English Language and Literature, B
Environmental Studies, B
Fine/Studio Arts, B
Foreign Languages and Literatures, B
French Language and Literature, B
German Language and Literature, B
History, B
International Relations and Affairs, B
International/Global Studies, B
Latin American Studies, B
Latin Language and Literature, B
Mathematics, B
Multi-/Interdisciplinary Studies, B
Music, B
Philosophy, B
Physics, B
Political Science and Government, B
Psychology, B
Secondary Education and Teaching, B

Social Science Teacher Education, B
Sociology, B
Spanish Language and Literature, B
Women's Studies, B

LAKE FOREST COLLEGE

American/United States Studies/Civilization, BM
Anthropology, B
Area Studies, B
Art Education, M
Art History, Criticism and Conservation, B
Art/Art Studies, General, B
Asian Studies/Civilization, B
Biology/Biological Sciences, B
Business/Managerial Economics, B
Chemistry, B
Computer Science, B
Drama and Dramatics/Theatre Arts, B
Economics, B
Education, BM
Elementary Education and Teaching, M
English Education, M
English Language and Literature, B
Environmental Studies, BM
Finance, B
Fine Arts and Art Studies, M
French Language and Literature, BM
History, BM
International Relations and Affairs, B
Latin American Studies, B
Liberal Studies, M
Mathematics, B
Mathematics Teacher Education, M
Music, B
Music Teacher Education, M
Philosophy, B
Physics, B
Political Science and Government, B
Psychology, B
Religion/Religious Studies, B
Science Teacher Education/General Science
    Teacher Education, M
Secondary Education and Teaching, M
Social Studies Teacher Education, M
Sociology, B
Spanish Language and Literature, BM
Writing, M

LAKE LAND COLLEGE

Accounting Technology/Technician and Bookkeep-
    ing, A
Administrative Assistant and Secretarial Science, A
Agricultural Business and Management, A
Agricultural Mechanization, A
Agricultural Production Operations, A
Architectural Engineering Technology/Technician, A
Automobile/Automotive Mechanics
    Technology/Technician, A
Biological and Physical Sciences, A
Business Administration and Management, A
Child Care and Support Services Management, A
Civil Engineering Technology/Technician, A
Computer Programming, Specific Applications, A
Computer Systems Networking and Telecommunica-
    tions, A
Corrections, A
Criminal Justice/Police Science, A
Dental Hygiene/Hygienist, A
Drafting and Design Technology/Technician, A
Electrical, Electronic and Communications Engineer-
    ing Technology/Technician, A
Electromechanical Technology/Electromechanical
    Engineering Technology, A
Executive Assistant/Executive Secretary, A
General Studies, A
Graphic and Printing Equipment Operator Produc-
    tion, A
Human Services, A
Industrial Technology/Technician, A
Information Technology, A
Legal Administrative Assistant/Secretary, A
Liberal Arts and Sciences Studies and Humani-
    ties, A
Marketing/Marketing Management, A
Medical Administrative Assistant/Secretary, A
Office Management and Supervision, A

Physical Therapist Assistant, A
Prepress/Desktop Publishing and Digital Imaging
    Design, A
Printing Press Operator, A
Radio and Television, A
Social Work, A
Telecommunications Technology/Technician, A

LEWIS AND CLARK COMMUNITY COL-LEGE

Accounting, A
Administrative Assistant and Secretarial Science, A
Art/Art Studies, General, A
Automobile/Automotive Mechanics
    Technology/Technician, A
Biological and Physical Sciences, A
Business Administration and Management, A
CAD/CADD Drafting and/or Design
    Technology/Technician, A
Child Care Provider/Assistant, A
Computer Graphics, A
Computer Programming/Programmer, A
Computer Systems Networking and Telecommunica-
    tions, A
Criminal Justice/Law Enforcement Administration, A
Dental Hygiene/Hygienist, A
Engineering, A
Fire Science/Firefighting, A
General Studies, A
Kinesiology and Exercise Science, A
Legal Administrative Assistant/Secretary, A
Legal Assistant/Paralegal, A
Liberal Arts and Sciences Studies and Humani-
    ties, A
Library Assistant/Technician, A
Manufacturing Technology/Technician, A
Massage Therapy/Therapeutic Massage, A
Medical Administrative Assistant/Secretary, A
Occupational Therapist Assistant, A
Radio and Television, A
Web Page, Digital/Multimedia and Information Re-
    sources Design, A

LEWIS UNIVERSITY

Accounting, BM
Aeronautics/Aviation/Aerospace Science and Tech-
    nology, B
Air Traffic Controller, AB
Airframe Mechanics and Aircraft Maintenance
    Technology/Technician, A
Airline/Commercial/Professional Pilot and Flight
    Crew, A
Art/Art Studies, General, B
Athletic Training and Sports Medicine, B
Aviation, M
Aviation/Airway Management and Operations, BM
Avionics Maintenance Technology/Technician, B
Biochemistry, B
Biology/Biological Sciences, B
Biomedical Sciences, B
Business Administration and Management, B
Business Administration, Management and Opera-
    tions, M
Business/Commerce, B
Business/Managerial Economics, B
Chemical Physics, B
Chemistry, B
Clinical Psychology, M
Commercial and Advertising Art, B
Communication Studies/Speech Communication
    and Rhetoric, B
Communications Technologies/Technicians and Sup-
    port Services, B
Community Organization and Advocacy, B
Computer Engineering, B
Computer Science, B
Computer and Information Systems Security, BM
Counseling Psychology, M
Counselor Education/School Counseling and Guid-
    ance Services, M
Criminal Justice/Safety Studies, B
Criminology, M
Database Systems, M
Dental Hygiene/Hygienist, B
Design and Visual Communications, B

Diagnostic Medical Sonography/Sonographer and
    Ultrasound Technician, B
Digital Communication and Media/Multimedia, B
Drama and Dramatics/Theatre Arts, B
Drawing, B
E-Commerce/Electronic Commerce, B
Early Childhood Education and Teaching, M
Education, MDO
Education/Teaching of Individuals in Early Childhood
    Special Education Programs, B
Educational Administration and Supervision, O
Educational Leadership and Administration, MD
Educational Media/Instructional Technology, M
Electronic Commerce, M
Elementary Education and Teaching, BM
English Language and Literature, B
English as a Second Language, M
Environmental Sciences, B
Environmental and Occupational Health, M
Finance, B
Finance and Banking, M
Fire Services Administration, B
Forensic Science and Technology, B
General Studies, B
Health Services Administration, M
Health/Health Care Administration/Management, B
Higher Education/Higher Education Administra-
    tion, M
History, B
Human Resources Management and Services, M
Human Resources Management/Personnel Adminis-
    tration, B
Information Resources Management/CIO Training, B
Information Science/Studies, B
International Business/Trade/Commerce, BM
International Relations and Affairs, B
Journalism, B
Junior High/Intermediate/Middle School Education
    and Teaching, B
Kinesiology and Exercise Science, B
Legal Assistant/Paralegal, B
Liberal Arts and Sciences Studies and Humani-
    ties, B
Management Information Systems and Ser-
    vices, BM
Management of Technology, M
Marketing, M
Marketing/Marketing Management, B
Mass Communication/Media Studies, B
Mathematics, B
Mathematics Teacher Education, M
Multi-/Interdisciplinary Studies, B
Music, B
Non-Profit/Public/Organizational Management, M
Nuclear Medical Technology/Technologist, B
Nursing, MD
Nursing - Adult, M
Nursing Administration, M
Nursing Education, M
Organizational Communication, B
Organizational Management, M
Painting, B
Philosophy, B
Physics, B
Political Science and Government, B
Project Management, M
Psychology, B
Public Administration, B
Public Relations/Image Management, B
Radiation Protection/Health Physics Technician, B
Radio and Television, B
Radiologic Technology/Science - Radiographer, B
Reading Teacher Education, M
Religion/Religious Studies, B
Science Teacher Education/General Science
    Teacher Education, M
Secondary Education and Teaching, BM
Security and Loss Prevention Services, B
Security and Protective Services, B
Social Studies Teacher Education, M
Social Work, B
Sociology, B
Spanish Language Teacher Education, M
Spanish Language and Literature, B
Special Education and Teaching, BM
Sport and Fitness Administration/Management, BM

Student Personnel Services, M
Transportation and Materials Moving, B

LINCOLN CHRISTIAN UNIVERSITY

Bible/Biblical Studies, AB
Business Administration, Management and Operations, B
Cultural Studies, M
Education, A
English as a Second Language, M
General Studies, AB
Human Services, B
Marriage and Family Therapy/Counseling, M
Missions/Missionary Studies and Missiology, B
Organizational Management, M
Pastoral Studies/Counseling, B
Philosophy, B
Pre-Nursing Studies, A
Psychology, B
Theological and Ministerial Studies, AB
Theology and Religious Vocations, M
Youth Ministry, B

LINCOLN COLLEGE

Business Administration and Management, A
Criminal Justice/Law Enforcement Administration, A
English Language and Literature, A
General Studies, A
Health and Physical Education, A
History, A
Mathematics, A
Music, A
Pre-Nursing Studies, A
Radio and Television Broadcasting
Technology/Technician, A

LINCOLN COLLEGE–NORMAL

Aesthetician/Esthetician and Skin Care Specialist, A
Business Administration and Management, B
Corrections, B
Cosmetology/Cosmetologist, A
Criminal Justice/Law Enforcement Administration, B
Liberal Arts and Sciences Studies and Humanities, AB
Nail Technician/Specialist and Manicurist, A
Sport and Fitness Administration/Management, B

LINCOLN LAND COMMUNITY COLLEGE

Accounting, A
Administrative Assistant and Secretarial Science, A
Agricultural Production Operations, A
Airframe Mechanics and Aircraft Maintenance Technology/Technician, A
Architectural Drafting and Architectural CAD/CADD, A
Autobody/Collision and Repair Technology/Technician, A
Automobile/Automotive Mechanics Technology/Technician, A
Aviation/Airway Management and Operations, A
Biological and Physical Sciences, A
Building/Property Maintenance and Management, A
Business/Commerce, A
Business/Office Automation/Technology/Data Entry, A
Child Care Provider/Assistant, A
Computer Programming, Specific Applications, A
Computer Programming/Programmer, A
Computer Systems Networking and Telecommunications, A
Construction Engineering Technology/Technician, A
Criminal Justice/Police Science, A
Culinary Arts/Chef Training, A
Early Childhood Education and Teaching, A
Electrical, Electronic and Communications Engineering Technology/Technician, A
Electroneurodiagnostic/Electroencephalographic Technology/Technologist, A
Emergency Medical Technology/Technician (EMT Paramedic), A
Engineering, A
Fine/Studio Arts, A
Fire Science/Firefighting, A
General Studies, A

Graphic Design, A
Hospitality Administration/Management, A
Industrial Electronics Technology/Technician, A
Industrial Technology/Technician, A
Landscaping and Groundskeeping, A
Legal Administrative Assistant/Secretary, A
Liberal Arts and Sciences Studies and Humanities, A
Music, A
Occupational Therapist Assistant, A
Radiologic Technology/Science - Radiographer, A
Respiratory Care Therapy/Therapist, A
Special Education and Teaching, A
Surgical Technology/Technologist, A
Teacher Assistant/Aide, A

LOYOLA UNIVERSITY CHICAGO

Accounting, BM
Acute Care/Critical Care Nursing, MO
Advertising, B
African-American/Black Studies, B
Allopathic Medicine, D
Anatomy, MD
Ancient/Classical Greek Language and Literature, B
Anthropology, B
Applied Psychology, MD
Applied Statistics, M
Art History, Criticism and Conservation, B
Behavioral Sciences, A
Bilingual and Multilingual Education, B
Biochemistry, BMD
Bioethics/Medical Ethics, DO
Bioinformatics, B
Biological and Biomedical Sciences, MD
Biology/Biological Sciences, B
Biomedical/Medical Engineering, B
Business Administration and Management, A
Business Administration, Management and Operations, M
Business, Management, Marketing, and Related Support Services, B
Business/Managerial Economics, B
Cardiovascular Sciences, O
Cell Biology and Anatomy, MD
Chemistry, BMD
Classics and Classical Languages, Literatures, and Linguistics, B
Clinical Psychology, MD
Clinical Research, M
Communication Studies/Speech Communication and Rhetoric, B
Communication and Media Studies, B
Community Psychology, MO
Computer Engineering, B
Computer Science, M
Computer Software and Media Applications, B
Computer and Information Sciences, B
Computer and Information Systems Security, B
Corporate and Organizational Communication, M
Counseling Psychology, D
Counselor Education/School Counseling and Guidance Services, MO
Criminal Justice/Safety Studies, B
Criminology, M
Curriculum and Instruction, MD
Dance, B
Design and Visual Communications, B
Developmental Psychology, MD
Digital Communication and Media/Multimedia, B
Drama and Dramatics/Theatre Arts, B
Early Childhood Education and Teaching, B
Economics, M
Education, MDO
Educational Administration and Supervision, MDO
Educational Measurement and Evaluation, MD
Educational Policy, MD
Educational Psychology, M
Elementary Education and Teaching, BM
English, MD
English Language and Literature, B
English as a Second Language, O
Entrepreneurial and Small Business Operations, B
Entrepreneurship/Entrepreneurial Studies, M
Environmental Sciences, B
Environmental Studies, B
Environmental and Occupational Health, MO

Environmental/Environmental Health Engineering, B
Ethics, M
Finance, B
Finance and Banking, M
Fine/Studio Arts, B
Forensic Science and Technology, B
French Language and Literature, B
General Studies, B
Health Law, MD
Health Services Administration, MDO
Health/Health Care Administration/Management, B
Higher Education/Higher Education Administration, MD
History, BMD
Human Resources Management and Services, M
Human Resources Management/Personnel Administration, B
Human Services, B
Humanities/Humanistic Studies, M
Immunology, MD
Industrial and Labor Relations, M
Infectious Diseases, MO
Information Science/Studies, M
Information Technology, B
International Business/Trade/Commerce, BM
International Relations and Affairs, B
Italian Language and Literature, B
Journalism, B
Latin Language and Literature, B
Law and Legal Studies, MD
Legal Assistant/Paralegal, B
Legal and Justice Studies, M
Liberal Arts and Sciences Studies and Humanities, A
Management Information Systems and Services, BM
Marketing, M
Marketing/Marketing Management, B
Mathematics, BM
Mathematics Teacher Education, B
Mathematics and Computer Science, B
Microbiology, MD
Molecular Biology, MD
Molecular Pharmacology, MD
Molecular Physiology, D
Multi-/Interdisciplinary Studies, B
Music, B
Neurobiology and Neurophysiology, MD
Neuroscience, MD
Nursing, MD
Nursing - Adult, MO
Nursing - Advanced Practice, M
Nursing Administration, M
Nursing Informatics, D
Nutritional Sciences, MO
Office Management and Supervision, B
Oncology Nursing, MO
Operations Management and Supervision, B
Pastoral Studies/Counseling, BM
Philosophy, BMD
Physical Therapy/Therapist, B
Physics, B
Physiology, M
Political Science and Government, BMD
Psychology, BMD
Public Health, M
Public History, M
Public Policy Analysis, M
Public Relations, Advertising, and Applied Communication, B
Reading Teacher Education, MO
Religious Education, BM
School Psychology, DO
Science Teacher Education/General Science Teacher Education, B
Secondary Education and Teaching, BM
Social Psychology, MD
Social Work, BMDO
Sociology, BMD
Software Engineering, M
Spanish Language and Literature, BM
Special Education and Teaching, BMO
Statistics, BM
Supply Chain Management, M
Taxation, M
Theology and Religious Vocations, MDO

Theology/Theological Studies, B
Urban Studies/Affairs, B
Urban and Regional Planning, M
Women's Health Nursing, MO
Women's Studies, B

MACCORMAC COLLEGE

Accounting, A
Administrative Assistant and Secretarial Science, A
Business Administration and Management, A
Computer Typography and Composition Equipment
   Operator, A
Computer and Information Sciences, A
Consumer Merchandising/Retailing Management, A
Court Reporting/Court Reporter, A
Hotel/Motel Administration/Management, A
International Business/Trade/Commerce, A
Law and Legal Studies, A
Legal Administrative Assistant/Secretary, A
Legal Assistant/Paralegal, A
Marketing/Marketing Management, A
Medical Administrative Assistant/Secretary, A
Tourism and Travel Services Management, A

MACMURRAY COLLEGE

Accounting, B
Art/Art Studies, General, B
Biology/Biological Sciences, B
Business Administration and Management, B
Criminal Justice/Law Enforcement Administration, AB
Criminal Justice/Police Science, AB
Education/Teaching of Individuals with Hearing Impairments, Including Deafness, B
English Language and Literature, B
Liberal Arts and Sciences Studies and Humanities, B
Marketing/Marketing Management, B
Pre-Dentistry Studies, B
Pre-Law Studies, B
Pre-Medicine/Pre-Medical Studies, B
Pre-Veterinary Studies, B
Psychology, B
Sign Language Interpretation and Translation, B
Social Work, B
Special Education and Teaching, B
Sport and Fitness Administration/Management, B

MCHENRY COUNTY COLLEGE

Accounting, A
Administrative Assistant and Secretarial Science, A
Animation, Interactive Technology, Video Graphics
   and Special Effects, A
Applied Horticulture/Horticultural Operations, A
Biological and Physical Sciences, A
Business Administration and Management, A
Child Care Provider/Assistant, A
Commercial Photography, A
Computer Systems Networking and Telecommunications, A
Construction Management, A
Criminal Justice/Police Science, A
Emergency Medical Technology/Technician (EMT
   Paramedic), A
Engineering, A
Fine/Studio Arts, A
Fire Science/Firefighting, A
General Studies, A
Health and Physical Education, A
Information Technology, A
Liberal Arts and Sciences Studies and Humanities, A
Music, A
Occupational Therapist Assistant, A
Operations Management and Supervision, A
Restaurant, Culinary, and Catering
   Management/Manager, A
Robotics Technology/Technician, A
Selling Skills and Sales Operations, A
Special Education and Teaching, A

MCKENDREE UNIVERSITY

Accounting, B
Art Teacher Education, B
Art/Art Studies, General, B
Athletic Training and Sports Medicine, B

Biology Teacher Education, B
Biology/Biological Sciences, B
Business Administration and Management, AB
Business Administration, Management and Operations, M
Business Teacher Education, B
Chemistry, B
Clinical Psychology, M
Communication Studies/Speech Communication
   and Rhetoric, B
Computational Mathematics, B
Computer Science, B
Computer Software and Media Applications, B
Computer and Information Sciences, B
Counseling Psychology, M
Curriculum and Instruction, DO
Economics, B
Education, MDO
Educational Administration and Supervision, M
Educational Leadership and Administration, M
Elementary Education and Teaching, B
Engineering, B
English Language and Literature, B
English/Language Arts Teacher Education, B
Environmental Studies, B
Finance, B
Health Services/Allied Health/Health Sciences, B
Health Teacher Education, B
Higher Education/Higher Education Administration, M
History, B
History Teacher Education, B
Human Resources Management and Services, M
Human Resources Management/Personnel Administration, B
Information Science/Studies, B
Information Technology, B
International Business/Trade/Commerce, M
International Relations and Affairs, B
International/Global Studies, B
Junior High/Intermediate/Middle School Education
   and Teaching, B
Kinesiology and Exercise Science, B
Management Science, B
Marketing/Marketing Management, B
Mathematics, B
Mathematics Teacher Education, B
Music, B
Music Teacher Education, BM
Nursing, M
Nursing Administration, M
Nursing Education, M
Occupational Therapy/Therapist, B
Organizational Communication, B
Philosophy, B
Physical Education Teaching and Coaching, B
Political Science and Government, B
Pre-Dentistry Studies, B
Pre-Law Studies, B
Pre-Medicine/Pre-Medical Studies, B
Pre-Veterinary Studies, B
Psychology, B
Reading Teacher Education, M
Religion/Religious Studies, B
Sales, Distribution and Marketing Operations, B
Science Teacher Education/General Science
   Teacher Education, B
Secondary Education and Teaching, B
Social Science Teacher Education, B
Social Sciences, B
Social Work, B
Sociology, B
Spanish Language and Literature, B
Special Education and Teaching, M
Speech Teacher Education, B
Sport and Fitness Administration/Management, B
Teacher Education, Multiple Levels, B

MIDSTATE COLLEGE

Accounting, B
Accounting Technology/Technician and Bookkeeping, A
Administrative Assistant and Secretarial Science, A
Business Administration and Management, AB
Computer and Information Sciences, A
Court Reporting/Court Reporter, A

Health Information/Medical Records
   Technology/Technician, A
Health/Health Care Administration/Management, B
Information Science/Studies, A
Legal Assistant/Paralegal, A
Legal Support Services, A
Medical/Clinical Assistant, A

MILLIKIN UNIVERSITY

Accounting, B
Art Teacher Education, B
Art Therapy/Therapist, B
Athletic Training and Sports Medicine, B
Biology Teacher Education, B
Biology/Biological Sciences, B
Business Administration and Management, B
Business Administration, Management and Operations, BM
Chemistry, B
Chemistry Teacher Education, B
Commercial and Advertising Art, B
Communication Studies/Speech Communication
   and Rhetoric, B
Drama and Dramatics/Theatre Arts, B
Early Childhood Education and Teaching, B
Elementary Education and Teaching, B
English Language and Literature, B
English/Language Arts Teacher Education, B
Entrepreneurship/Entrepreneurial Studies, B
Fine/Studio Arts, B
History, B
International Business/Trade/Commerce, B
Management Information Systems and Services, B
Marketing/Marketing Management, B
Mathematics, B
Mathematics Teacher Education, B
Molecular Biology, B
Multi-/Interdisciplinary Studies, B
Music, B
Music Performance, B
Music Teacher Education, B
Nurse Anesthetist, D
Nursing, MD
Nursing Administration, M
Nursing Education, M
Philosophy, B
Physical Education Teaching and Coaching, B
Physics, B
Political Science and Government, B
Pre-Dentistry Studies, B
Pre-Law Studies, B
Pre-Medicine/Pre-Medical Studies, B
Pre-Pharmacy Studies, B
Pre-Veterinary Studies, B
Psychology, B
Social Science Teacher Education, B
Social Work, B
Sociology, B
Spanish Language and Literature, B
Sport and Fitness Administration/Management, B
Technical Theatre/Theatre Design and Technology, B
Visual and Performing Arts, B

MONMOUTH COLLEGE

Accounting, B
Ancient/Classical Greek Language and Literature, B
Anthropology, B
Art/Art Studies, General, B
Biochemistry, B
Biology/Biological Sciences, B
Biopsychology, B
Business Administration and Management, B
Chemistry, B
Classics and Classical Languages, Literatures, and Linguistics, B
Communication Studies/Speech Communication
   and Rhetoric, B
Computer Science, B
Drama and Dramatics/Theatre Arts, B
Economics, B
Elementary Education and Teaching, B
English Language and Literature, B
Environmental Sciences, B
French Language and Literature, B
Health and Physical Education, B

History, B
International Business/Trade/Commerce, B
International/Global Studies, B
Kinesiology and Exercise Science, B
Latin Language and Literature, B
Liberal Arts and Sciences Studies and Humanities, B
Mathematics, B
Music, B
Philosophy, B
Physical Education Teaching and Coaching, B
Physics, B
Political Science and Government, B
Psychology, B
Public Relations/Image Management, B
Religion/Religious Studies, B
Sociology, B
Spanish Language and Literature, B

MOODY BIBLE INSTITUTE

Bible/Biblical Studies, B
Communication Studies/Speech Communication and Rhetoric, B
Divinity/Ministry (BD, MDiv.), B
Missions/Missionary Studies and Missiology, B
Pastoral Studies/Counseling, BMO
Religious Education, B
Religious/Sacred Music, B
Theology and Religious Vocations, MO
Theology/Theological Studies, B
Urban Studies/Affairs, MO

MORAINE VALLEY COMMUNITY COLLEGE

Administrative Assistant and Secretarial Science, A
Automobile/Automotive Mechanics Technology/Technician, A
Baking and Pastry Arts/Baker/Pastry Chef, A
Biological and Physical Sciences, A
Biology/Biological Sciences, A
Business Administration and Management, A
Business/Commerce, A
Child Care Provider/Assistant, A
Computer Graphics, A
Computer Science, A
Computer and Information Sciences, A
Computer and Information Systems Security, A
Criminal Justice/Law Enforcement Administration, A
Criminal Justice/Police Science, A
Design and Visual Communications, A
Early Childhood Education and Teaching, A
Elementary Education and Teaching, A
Emergency Medical Technology/Technician (EMT Paramedic), A
Engineering, A
English Language and Literature, A
Fire Protection and Safety Technology/Technician, A
Fire Science/Firefighting, A
Health Information/Medical Records Technology/Technician, A
Heating, Air Conditioning, Ventilation and Refrigeration Maintenance Technology/Technician, A
History, A
Hospitality Administration/Management, A
Human Resources Management/Personnel Administration, A
Industrial Electronics Technology/Technician, A
Instrumentation Technology/Technician, A
Liberal Arts and Sciences Studies and Humanities, A
Management Information Systems and Services, A
Manufacturing Technology/Technician, A
Mathematics, A
Mathematics Teacher Education, A
Mechanical Engineering/Mechanical Technology/Technician, A
Movement and Mind-Body Therapies and Education, A
Music, A
Parks, Recreation and Leisure Facilities Management, A
Physics, A
Political Science and Government, A
Psychology, A
Radiologic Technology/Science - Radiographer, A
Respiratory Care Therapy/Therapist, A

Restaurant, Culinary, and Catering Management/Manager, A
Retailing and Retail Operations, A
Science Teacher Education/General Science Teacher Education, A
Small Business Administration/Management, A
Sociology, A
Special Education and Teaching, A
Substance Abuse/Addiction Counseling, A
Survey Technology/Surveying, A
System, Networking, and LAN/WAN Management/Manager, A
Teacher Assistant/Aide, A
Tourism and Travel Services Management, A
Visual and Performing Arts, A
Web/Multimedia Management and Webmaster, A

MORRISON INSTITUTE OF TECHNOLOGY

CAD/CADD Drafting and/or Design Technology/Technician, A
Construction Engineering Technology/Technician, A
Drafting and Design Technology/Technician, A
Engineering Technology, A
Mechanical Drafting and Mechanical Drafting CAD/CADD, A
Survey Technology/Surveying, A

MORTON COLLEGE

Accounting, A
Administrative Assistant and Secretarial Science, A
Art/Art Studies, General, A
Automobile/Automotive Mechanics Technology/Technician, A
Biological and Physical Sciences, A
Business Administration and Management, A
Criminal Justice/Police Science, A
Data Processing and Data Processing Technology/Technician, A
Drafting and Design Technology/Technician, A
Finance, A
Fine/Studio Arts, A
Heating, Air Conditioning, Ventilation and Refrigeration Maintenance Technology/Technician, A
Legal Administrative Assistant/Secretary, A
Liberal Arts and Sciences Studies and Humanities, A
Marketing/Marketing Management, A
Medical Administrative Assistant/Secretary, A
Music, A
Physical Therapy/Therapist, A
Real Estate, A

NATIONAL LOUIS UNIVERSITY

Adult and Continuing Education and Teaching, MDO
Biology/Biological Sciences, B
Business Administration and Management, B
Business Administration, Management and Operations, M
Child Care and Support Services Management, B
Counselor Education/School Counseling and Guidance Services, M
Curriculum and Instruction, MO
Developmental Education, MO
Early Childhood Education and Teaching, BMO
Education, MDO
Educational Administration and Supervision, MO
Educational Media/Instructional Technology, MO
Educational Psychology, MO
Elementary Education and Teaching, BM
English Education, MO
English Language and Literature, B
Health and Medical Administrative Services, B
Human Development, MO
Human Resources Development, M
Human Resources Management and Services, M
Human Services, M
Information Science/Studies, B
Liberal Arts and Sciences Studies and Humanities, B
Management, M
Management Information Systems and Services, B
Management Science, B
Mathematics, B
Mathematics Teacher Education, MO
Multi-/Interdisciplinary Studies, B

Political Science and Government, B
Psychology, BMDO
Public Administration and Social Service Professions, B
Public Policy Analysis, M
Reading Teacher Education, MO
School Psychology, MO
Science Teacher Education/General Science Teacher Education, MO
Secondary Education and Teaching, M
Social Sciences, B
Special Education and Teaching, MO
Writing, MO

NORTH CENTRAL COLLEGE

Accounting, B
Actuarial Science, B
Analytical Chemistry, B
Animation, Interactive Technology, Video Graphics and Special Effects, B
Anthropology, B
Applied Mathematics, B
Art History, Criticism and Conservation, B
Art Teacher Education, B
Art/Art Studies, General, B
Athletic Training and Sports Medicine, B
Biochemistry, B
Biological and Physical Sciences, B
Biology/Biological Sciences, B
Business Administration and Management, B
Business Administration, Management and Operations, M
Chemistry, B
Chinese Language and Literature, B
Classics and Classical Languages, Literatures, and Linguistics, B
Communication Studies/Speech Communication and Rhetoric, B
Computer Science, BM
Cultural Studies, M
Curriculum and Instruction, M
Drama and Dramatics/Theatre Arts, B
East Asian Studies, B
Economics, B
Education, BM
Educational Administration and Supervision, M
Educational Leadership and Administration, M
Elementary Education and Teaching, B
English Language and Literature, B
Ethics, M
Finance, B
Finance and Banking, M
French Language and Literature, B
German Language and Literature, B
Graphic Design, B
History, B
Human Resources Management and Services, M
Human Resources Management/Personnel Administration, B
Humanities/Humanistic Studies, B
International Business/Trade/Commerce, BM
International/Global Studies, B
Internet and Interactive Multimedia, M
Japanese Language and Literature, B
Jazz/Jazz Studies, B
Journalism, B
Kinesiology and Exercise Science, B
Liberal Arts and Sciences Studies and Humanities, B
Liberal Studies, M
Management, M
Management Information Systems and Services, M
Management Strategy and Policy, M
Marketing, M
Marketing/Marketing Management, B
Mathematics, B
Medical Radiologic Technology/Science - Radiation Therapist, B
Multi-/Interdisciplinary Studies, B
Music, B
Music Teacher Education, B
Nuclear Medical Technology/Technologist, B
Organizational Communication, B
Organizational Management, M
Philosophy, B
Physical Education Teaching and Coaching, B

Physics, B
Political Science and Government, B
Pre-Dentistry Studies, B
Pre-Law Studies, B
Pre-Medicine/Pre-Medical Studies, B
Pre-Veterinary Studies, B
Psychology, B
Publishing, M
Radio and Television, B
Religion/Religious Studies, B
Secondary Education and Teaching, B
Small Business Administration/Management, B
Social Sciences, B
Sociology, B
Spanish Language and Literature, B
Sport and Fitness Administration/Management, BM
Technical Communication, M
Technical Theatre/Theatre Design and Technology, B
Writing, M

NORTH PARK UNIVERSITY

Accounting, B
Advertising, B
African Studies, B
Art/Art Studies, General, B
Athletic Training and Sports Medicine, B
Bible/Biblical Studies, B
Biology/Biological Sciences, B
Business Administration and Management, B
Business Administration, Management and Operations, M
Chemistry, B
Communication Studies/Speech Communication and Rhetoric, B
Comparative Literature, B
Computer Science, B
Criminal Justice/Law Enforcement Administration, B
Drama and Dramatics/Theatre Arts, B
Early Childhood Education and Teaching, B
Economics, B
Education, M
Elementary Education and Teaching, B
Engineering, B
English Language and Literature, B
Environmental Studies, B
Finance, B
French Language and Literature, B
French Studies, B
History, B
Information Technology, B
International Business/Trade/Commerce, B
International/Global Studies, B
Kinesiology and Exercise Science, B
Management Science, B
Marketing/Marketing Management, B
Mass Communication/Media Studies, B
Mathematics, B
Music, BM
Music Teacher Education, B
Non-Profit/Public/Organizational Management, BM
Nursing, M
Nursing - Adult, M
Nursing Administration, M
Philosophy, B
Physical Education Teaching and Coaching, B
Physics, B
Political Science and Government, B
Pre-Dentistry Studies, B
Pre-Law Studies, B
Pre-Medicine/Pre-Medical Studies, B
Pre-Veterinary Studies, B
Psychology, B
Religious/Sacred Music, B
Scandinavian Languages, Literatures, and Linguistics, B
Scandinavian Studies, B
Secondary Education and Teaching, B
Sociology, B
Spanish Language and Literature, B
Youth Ministry, B

NORTHEASTERN ILLINOIS UNIVERSITY

Accounting, BM
Anthropology, B

Applied Mathematics, M
Art/Art Studies, General, B
Bilingual and Multilingual Education, B
Biological and Biomedical Sciences, M
Biology/Biological Sciences, B
Business Administration and Management, B
Business Administration, Management and Operations, M
Business/Commerce, B
Chemistry, BM
Communication and Media Studies, B
Community Health Services/Liaison/Counseling, B
Community Psychology, M
Computer Science, BM
Counselor Education/School Counseling and Guidance Services, M
Criminal Justice/Safety Studies, B
Early Childhood Education and Teaching, BM
Economics, B
Education, M
Education/Teaching of the Gifted and Talented, M
Educational Administration and Supervision, M
Educational Leadership and Administration, M
Elementary Education and Teaching, BM
English, M
English Language and Literature, B
English as a Second Language, M
Environmental Studies, BM
Ethnic, Cultural Minority, and Gender Studies, B
Exercise and Sports Science, M
Finance, B
Finance and Banking, M
French Language and Literature, B
Geography, BM
Geology/Earth Science, B
Gerontology, M
History, BM
Human Resources Development, M
Human Resources Management/Personnel Administration, B
Latin American Studies, M
Liberal Arts and Sciences Studies and Humanities, B
Linguistics, M
Management, M
Marketing, M
Marketing/Marketing Management, B
Marriage and Family Therapy/Counseling, M
Mathematics, BM
Mathematics Teacher Education, M
Multilingual and Multicultural Education, M
Music, BM
Philosophy, B
Physical Education Teaching and Coaching, B
Physics, B
Political Science and Government, BM
Psychology, B
Public Administration and Social Service Professions, B
Reading Teacher Education, M
Rehabilitation Counseling, M
Secondary Education and Teaching, M
Social Work, B
Sociology, B
Spanish Language and Literature, B
Special Education and Teaching, BM
Speech and Rhetorical Studies, M
Urban Education and Leadership, M
Urban Studies/Affairs, B
Women's Studies, B
Writing, M

NORTHERN ILLINOIS UNIVERSITY

Accounting, BM
Adult and Continuing Education and Teaching, MD
Anthropology, BM
Apparel and Textiles, B
Applied Mathematics, B
Art History, Criticism and Conservation, B
Art Teacher Education, B
Art/Art Studies, General, B
Athletic Training and Sports Medicine, B
Atmospheric Sciences and Meteorology, B
Biological and Biomedical Sciences, MD
Biology/Biological Sciences, B
Business Administration and Management, B

Business Administration, Management and Operations, M
Business/Commerce, B
Chemistry, BMD
Child and Family Studies, M
Clinical Laboratory Science/Medical Technology/Technologist, B
Communication Disorders, BMD
Communication Studies/Speech Communication and Rhetoric, B
Communication and Media Studies, M
Community Health Services/Liaison/Counseling, B
Computer Science, BM
Counselor Education/School Counseling and Guidance Services, MD
Curriculum and Instruction, MD
Dance, M
Dietetics/Dieticians, B
Drama and Dramatics/Theatre Arts, B
Early Childhood Education and Teaching, BM
Economics, BMD
Education, BMDO
Educational Administration and Supervision, MDO
Educational Leadership and Administration, D
Educational Media/Instructional Technology, MD
Educational Psychology, MDO
Electrical Engineering, M
Electrical, Electronics and Communications Engineering, A
Elementary Education and Teaching, BMD
Engineering Technology, B
Engineering and Applied Sciences, M
English, MD
English Language and Literature, B
Environmental Studies, B
Family and Consumer Sciences/Home Economics Teacher Education, B
Finance, B
Fine Arts and Art Studies, M
Fine/Studio Arts, B
Foods, Nutrition, and Wellness Studies, B
Foundations and Philosophy of Education, M
French Language and Literature, BM
Geography, BMD
Geology/Earth Science, BMD
German Language and Literature, B
Health Professions and Related Clinical Sciences, B
Health Teacher Education, B
Health and Physical Education, B
Health/Medical Preparatory Programs, B
Higher Education/Higher Education Administration, MD
History, BMD
Human Development and Family Studies, B
Industrial Engineering, B
Industrial Technology/Technician, B
Industrial and Manufacturing Management, M
Industrial/Management Engineering, M
Journalism, B
Kindergarten/PreSchool Education and Teaching, B
Law and Legal Studies, D
Liberal Arts and Sciences Studies and Humanities, B
Management Information Systems and Services, BM
Management Science, B
Marketing/Marketing Management, B
Mathematics, BMD
Mechanical Engineering, BM
Multi-/Interdisciplinary Studies, B
Music, BMO
Music Teacher Education, B
Nursing, M
Nutritional Sciences, M
Operations Management and Supervision, B
Philosophy, BM
Physical Education Teaching and Coaching, BM
Physical Therapy/Therapist, BMD
Physics, BMD
Political Science and Government, BMD
Psychology, BMD
Public Administration, M
Public Health, M
Reading Teacher Education, MD
Romance Languages, Literatures, and Linguistics, M

Secondary Education and Teaching, D
Sociology, BM
Spanish Language and Literature, BM
Special Education and Teaching, M
Sport and Fitness Administration/Management, M
Statistics, M
Taxation, M
Theater, M

NORTHWESTERN COL- LEGE–BRIDGEVIEW CAMPUS

Accounting and Related Services, A
Administrative Assistant and Secretarial Science, A
Business Administration and Management, A
Computer Programming, Specific Applications, A
Computer Software and Media Applications, A
Computer and Information Sciences and Support
  Services, A
Computer and Information Systems Security, A
Computer/Information Technology Services Adminis-
  tration and Management, A
Criminal Justice/Law Enforcement Administration, A
Health Information/Medical Records
  Technology/Technician, A
Hospitality Administration/Management, A
Human Resources Management/Personnel Adminis-
  tration, A
Information Technology, A
Legal Assistant/Paralegal, A
Management Information Systems and Services, A
Massage Therapy/Therapeutic Massage, A
Medical Office Assistant/Specialist, A
Medical/Clinical Assistant, A
Prepress/Desktop Publishing and Digital Imaging
  Design, A
Real Estate, A
Tourism and Travel Services Management, A
Web Page, Digital/Multimedia and Information Re-
  sources Design, A

NORTHWESTERN COLLEGE–CHICAGO CAMPUS

Accounting Technology/Technician and Bookkeep-
  ing, A
Business Administration and Management, A
Criminal Justice/Law Enforcement Administration, A
Diagnostic Medical Sonography/Sonographer and
  Ultrasound Technician, A
Health Information/Medical Records
  Technology/Technician, A
Legal Assistant/Paralegal, A
Massage Therapy/Therapeutic Massage, A
Medical/Clinical Assistant, A
Radiologic Technology/Science - Radiographer, A

NORTHWESTERN UNIVERSITY

Accounting, MD
African Studies, BO
African-American Studies, D
African-American/Black Studies, B
American/United States Studies/Civilization, BM
Anthropology, BD
Applied Mathematics, BMD
Applied Physics, D
Area Studies, B
Art History, Criticism and Conservation, BD
Art/Art Studies, General, B
Arts Management, M
Asian Studies/Civilization, B
Astronomy, BD
Audiology/Audiologist and Hearing Sciences, B
Audiology/Audiologist and Speech-Language
  Pathology/Pathologist, B
BioTechnology, MD
Biochemistry, BD
Bioengineering, D
Biological and Biomedical Sciences, D
Biological and Physical Sciences, B
Biology/Biological Sciences, B
Biomedical Engineering, MD
Biomedical/Medical Engineering, B
Biophysics, D
Biopsychology, D
Biostatistics, D
Broadcast Journalism, M

Business Administration, Management and Opera-
  tions, MD
Caribbean Studies, B
Cell Biology and Anatomy, D
Cell/Cellular Biology and Histology, B
Chemical Engineering, BMD
Chemistry, BD
Civil Engineering, BMD
Classics and Classical Languages, Litera-
  tures, and Linguistics, B
Clinical Laboratory Sciences, M
Clinical Psychology, D
Clinical Research, MO
Cognitive Sciences, D
Communication Disorders, BMD
Communication Studies/Speech Communication
  and Rhetoric, B
Communication and Media Studies, BMD
Community Organization and Advocacy, B
Comparative Literature, BMD
Composition, D
Computer Engineering, BMD
Computer Science, BMD
Computer and Information Sciences, B
Computer and Information Systems Security, M
Corporate and Organizational Communication, M
Dance, B
Database Systems, M
Developmental Biology and Embryology, D
Drama and Dramatics/Theatre Arts, B
East Asian Languages, Literatures, and Linguis-
  tics, B
Ecology, B
Economics, BD
Education, BMD
Education/Teaching of Individuals with Specific
  Learning Disabilities, B
Educational Leadership and Administration, M
Educational Media/Instructional Technology, MD
Electrical Engineering, MD
Electrical, Electronics and Communications Engi-
  neering, D
Electronic Commerce, M
Elementary Education and Teaching, M
Engineering, B
Engineering Design, M
Engineering Management, MD
Engineering Science, B
Engineering and Applied Sciences, MDO
English, MD
English Language and Literature, B
Entrepreneurship/Entrepreneurial Studies, M
Environmental Engineering
  Technology/Environmental Technology, MD
Environmental Sciences, B
Environmental Studies, B
Environmental/Environmental Health Engineering, B
Epidemiology, D
Ethics, M
Ethnomusicology, M
Film, Television, and Video Production, MD
Film/Cinema Studies, B
Finance and Banking, MD
Fine Arts and Art Studies, M
French Language and Literature, BDO
Gender Studies, O
General Studies, B
Genetic Counseling/Counselor, M
Geography, B
Geology/Earth Science, BD
Geosciences, D
Geotechnical Engineering, MD
German Language and Literature, BD
Health Informatics, D
Health Services Administration, MD
Health Services Research, D
History, BMD
Human Development, D
Human Resources Management and Services, M
Humanities/Humanistic Studies, B
Industrial Engineering, B
Industrial and Manufacturing Management, MD
Industrial/Management Engineering, MD
Information Science/Studies, BM
International Affairs, MO
International Business/Trade/Commerce, M

International Public Health/International Health, M
International Relations and Affairs, B
Internet and Interactive Multimedia, M
Italian Language and Literature, BDO
Jazz/Jazz Studies, B
Journalism, BM
Kinesiology and Movement Studies, D
Law and Legal Studies, BMD
Liberal Arts and Sciences Studies and Humani-
  ties, B
Liberal Studies, M
Linguistics, BD
Management, M
Management Information Systems and Services, M
Management Strategy and Policy, MD
Manufacturing Engineering, B
Marketing, MD
Marriage and Family Therapy/Counseling, M
Materials Engineering, BMDO
Materials Sciences, MDO
Mathematics, BD
Mathematics Teacher Education, B
Mechanical Engineering, BMD
Mechanics, MD
Media Studies, MD
Medical Informatics, MD
Molecular Biology, BD
Multi-/Interdisciplinary Studies, B
Music, BMD
Music History, Literature, and Theory, B
Music Performance, B
Music Teacher Education, BMD
Music Theory and Composition, BMD
Musicology and Ethnomusicology, BD
Neurobiology and Neurophysiology, MD
Neuroscience, D
Organizational Behavior Studies, BM
Organizational Management, MD
Performance, MD
Philosophy, BD
Physical Therapy/Therapist, D
Physics, BD
Physiology, M
Piano and Organ, B
Plant Biology, MD
Political Science and Government, BD
Portuguese Language and Literature, D
Pre-Medicine/Pre-Medical Studies, B
Project Management, MD
Psychology, BD
Public Administration, M
Public Health, M
Public Policy Analysis, BMD
Publishing, M
Quality Management, M
Quantitative Analysis, M
Radio and Television, B
Real Estate, M
Rehabilitation Sciences, D
Religion/Religious Studies, BMD
Rhetoric, D
Science, Technology and Society, B
Secondary Education and Teaching, BM
Slavic Languages, Literatures, and Linguistics, BD
Slavic Studies, B
Social Psychology, D
Social Sciences, B
Social and Philosophical Foundations of Educa-
  tion, B
Sociology, BD
Software Engineering, M
South Asian Languages, Literatures, and Linguis-
  tics, B
Spanish Language and Literature, BD
Speech and Interpersonal Communication, MD
Speech-Language Pathology/Pathologist, B
Sport and Fitness Administration/Management, M
Statistics, BMD
Structural Biology, D
Structural Engineering, MD
Systematic Biology/Biological Systematics, D
Taxation, M
Theater, MD
Theatre Literature, History and Criticism, B
Transportation and Highway Engineering, MD
Urban Studies/Affairs, B

Violin, Viola, Guitar and Other Stringed Instruments, B
Visual and Performing Arts, B
Voice and Opera, B
Women's Studies, B
Writing, M

OAKTON COMMUNITY COLLEGE

Accounting Technology/Technician and Bookkeeping, A
Administrative Assistant and Secretarial Science, A
Architectural Drafting and Architectural CAD/CADD, A
Automobile/Automotive Mechanics Technology/Technician, A
Banking and Financial Support Services, A
Biological and Physical Sciences, A
Building/Construction Finishing, Management, and Inspection, A
Child Care Provider/Assistant, A
Clinical/Medical Laboratory Technician, A
Computer Programming/Programmer, A
Criminal Justice/Police Science, A
Electrical, Electronic and Communications Engineering Technology/Technician, A
Engineering, A
Fire Science/Firefighting, A
Graphic Design, A
Health Information/Medical Records Administration/Administrator, A
Heating, Air Conditioning and Refrigeration Technology/Technician, A
Information Technology, A
Liberal Arts and Sciences Studies and Humanities, A
Manufacturing Technology/Technician, A
Marketing/Marketing Management, A
Mechanical Engineering/Mechanical Technology/Technician, A
Music, A
Operations Management and Supervision, A
Physical Therapist Assistant, A
Real Estate, A
Sales, Distribution and Marketing Operations, A
Social Work, A
Substance Abuse/Addiction Counseling, A

OLIVET NAZARENE UNIVERSITY

Accounting, B
Art/Art Studies, General, B
Athletic Training and Sports Medicine, B
Biology/Biological Sciences, B
Business Administration and Management, B
Business Administration, Management and Operations, BM
Business/Commerce, A
Chemistry, B
Child Development, B
Communication Studies/Speech Communication and Rhetoric, B
Computer Science, B
Criminal Justice/Law Enforcement Administration, B
Curriculum and Instruction, M
Dietetics/Dieticians, B
Economics, B
Education, M
Educational Leadership and Administration, M
Elementary Education and Teaching, BM
Engineering, B
English Language and Literature, B
Environmental Design/Architecture, B
Family and Consumer Sciences/Human Sciences, B
Fashion Merchandising, B
Geography, B
Geology/Earth Science, B
History, B
Information Science/Studies, B
International Business/Trade/Commerce, B
Kindergarten/PreSchool Education and Teaching, B
Kinesiology and Exercise Science, B
Liberal Arts and Sciences Studies and Humanities, B
Library Science, M
Management Information Systems and Services, B
Marketing/Marketing Management, B
Mass Communication/Media Studies, B

Mathematics, B
Missions/Missionary Studies and Missiology, B
Music, B
Music Performance, B
Music Teacher Education, B
Music Theory and Composition, B
Organizational Management, M
Pastoral Studies/Counseling, B
Philosophy, B
Physical Education Teaching and Coaching, B
Physical Sciences, B
Political Science and Government, B
Psychology, B
Public Policy Analysis, B
Reading Teacher Education, M
Religion/Religious Studies, BM
Religious Education, B
Religious/Sacred Music, B
Science Teacher Education/General Science Teacher Education, B
Secondary Education and Teaching, M
Social Sciences, B
Social Work, B
Sociology, B
Spanish Language and Literature, B
Sport and Fitness Administration/Management, B
Theology and Religious Vocations, M
Theology/Theological Studies, B
Youth Ministry, B
Zoology/Animal Biology, B

PARKLAND COLLEGE

Accounting Technology/Technician and Bookkeeping, A
Administrative Assistant and Secretarial Science, A
Advertising, A
Agricultural Business and Management, A
Agricultural Mechanization, A
Art Teacher Education, A
Art/Art Studies, General, A
Autobody/Collision and Repair Technology/Technician, A
Automobile/Automotive Mechanics Technology/Technician, A
Biological and Physical Sciences, A
Biomedical Technology/Technician, A
Building/Construction Finishing, Management, and Inspection, A
Business Administration and Management, A
Business/Office Automation/Technology/Data Entry, A
Child Care Provider/Assistant, A
Computer Graphics, A
Computer Programming, Specific Applications, A
Computer Programming, Vendor/Product Certification, A
Computer Programming/Programmer, A
Computer Science, A
Computer Software and Media Applications, A
Computer Systems Networking and Telecommunications, A
Computer and Information Sciences, A
Computer and Information Sciences and Support Services, A
Computer/Information Technology Services Administration and Management, A
Consumer Merchandising/Retailing Management, A
Criminal Justice/Safety Studies, A
Data Entry/Microcomputer Applications, A
Dental Hygiene/Hygienist, A
Design and Visual Communications, A
Electroneurodiagnostic/Electroencephalographic Technology/Technologist, A
Elementary Education and Teaching, A
Engineering Science, A
English Language and Literature, A
General Studies, A
Graphic Design, A
History, A
Human Services, A
Industrial Technology/Technician, A
Information Science/Studies, A
Kindergarten/PreSchool Education and Teaching, A
Landscaping and Groundskeeping, A
Liberal Arts and Sciences Studies and Humanities, A

Mass Communication/Media Studies, A
Medical Radiologic Technology/Science - Radiation Therapist, A
Music Performance, A
Music Teacher Education, A
Occupational Therapist Assistant, A
Radio and Television, A
Radio and Television Broadcasting Technology/Technician, A
Respiratory Care Therapy/Therapist, A
Sales and Marketing Operations/Marketing and Distribution Teacher Education, A
Secondary Education and Teaching, A
Speech-Language Pathology/Pathologist, A
Surgical Technology/Technologist, A
System Administration/Administrator, A
Veterinary/Animal Health Technology/Technician and Veterinary Assistant, A
Web Page, Digital/Multimedia and Information Resources Design, A

PRAIRIE STATE COLLEGE

Automobile/Automotive Mechanics Technology/Technician, A
Biological and Physical Sciences, A
Child Care Provider/Assistant, A
Commercial Photography, A
Criminal Justice/Police Science, A
Dental Hygiene/Hygienist, A
Electrical, Electronic and Communications Engineering Technology/Technician, A
Electrician, A
Fine/Studio Arts, A
Fire Science/Firefighting, A
General Studies, A
Graphic Communications, A
Information Technology, A
Kinesiology and Exercise Science, A
Liberal Arts and Sciences Studies and Humanities, A
Manufacturing Technology/Technician, A
Mechanical Engineering/Mechanical Technology/Technician, A
Operations Management and Supervision, A
Teacher Assistant/Aide, A

PRINCIPIA COLLEGE

Art History, Criticism and Conservation, B
Biology/Biological Sciences, B
Business Administration and Management, B
Chemistry, B
Computer and Information Sciences, B
Drama and Dramatics/Theatre Arts, B
Economics, B
Engineering, B
English Language and Literature, B
Environmental Studies, B
Fine/Studio Arts, B
Foreign Languages and Literatures, B
French Language and Literature, B
History, B
Mass Communication/Media Studies, B
Mathematics, B
Music, B
Philosophy, B
Physics, B
Political Science and Government, B
Religion/Religious Studies, B
Spanish Language and Literature, B

QUINCY UNIVERSITY

Accounting, B
Airline/Commercial/Professional Pilot and Flight Crew, B
Aviation/Airway Management and Operations, B
Biology/Biological Sciences, B
Business Administration and Management, B
Business Administration, Management and Operations, M
Chemistry, B
Clinical Laboratory Science/Medical Technology/Technologist, B
Communication and Media Studies, M
Communication, Journalism and Related Programs, B
Computer Science, B

Counselor Education/School Counseling and Guidance Services, M
Criminal Justice/Safety Studies, B
Curriculum and Instruction, M
Education, BM
Educational Leadership and Administration, M
Elementary Education and Teaching, B
English Language and Literature, B
English as a Second Language, M
Finance, B
Forensic Science and Technology, B
General Studies, B
Graphic Design, B
Health and Physical Education, B
History, B
Human Services, B
Humanities/Humanistic Studies, B
Information Science/Studies, B
Liberal Arts and Sciences Studies and Humanities, AB
Management Science, B
Marketing/Marketing Management, B
Mathematics, B
Multilingual and Multicultural Education, M
Music, B
Music Teacher Education, B
Philosophy and Religious Studies, B
Physical Education Teaching and Coaching, B
Political Science and Government, B
Psychology, B
Reading Teacher Education, M
Religious/Sacred Music, B
School Psychology, M
Sign Language Interpretation and Translation, B
Special Education and Teaching, BM
Sport and Fitness Administration/Management, B
Teacher Education, Multiple Levels, B
Web/Multimedia Management and Webmaster, B

RASMUSSEN COLLEGE AURORA

Accounting, A
Business Administration and Management, A
Corrections and Criminal Justice, A
Early Childhood Education and Teaching, A
Graphic Communications, B
Health Information/Medical Records Administration/Administrator, B
Health Information/Medical Records Technology/Technician, A
Health/Health Care Administration/Management, B
Legal Assistant/Paralegal, A
Management Information Systems and Services, A
Medical Administrative Assistant/Secretary, A
Medical/Clinical Assistant, A
Pharmacy Technician/Assistant, A
Web Page, Digital/Multimedia and Information Resources Design, A

RASMUSSEN COLLEGE MOKENA/TINLEY PARK

Accounting, A
Business Administration and Management, A
Corrections and Criminal Justice, A
Early Childhood Education and Teaching, A
Graphic Communications, B
Health Information/Medical Records Administration/Administrator, B
Health Information/Medical Records Technology/Technician, A
Health/Health Care Administration/Management, B
Legal Assistant/Paralegal, A
Management Information Systems and Services, A
Medical Administrative Assistant/Secretary, A
Medical/Clinical Assistant, A
Pharmacy Technician/Assistant, A
Web Page, Digital/Multimedia and Information Resources Design, A

RASMUSSEN COLLEGE ROCKFORD

Accounting, B
Business Administration and Management, B
Corrections and Criminal Justice, A
Early Childhood Education and Teaching, A
Graphic Communications, B
Health Information/Medical Records Administration/Administrator, B

Health Information/Medical Records Technology/Technician, A
Health/Health Care Administration/Management, B
Legal Assistant/Paralegal, A
Management Information Systems and Services, A
Medical Administrative Assistant/Secretary, A
Medical/Clinical Assistant, A
Pharmacy Technician/Assistant, A
Web Page, Digital/Multimedia and Information Resources Design, B

RASMUSSEN COLLEGE ROMEOVILLE/JOLIET

Accounting, A
Business Administration and Management, A
Corrections and Criminal Justice, A
Early Childhood Education and Teaching, A
Graphic Communications, A
Health Information/Medical Records Administration/Administrator, B
Health Information/Medical Records Technology/Technician, A
Health/Health Care Administration/Management, B
Legal Assistant/Paralegal, A
Management Information Systems and Services, A
Medical Administrative Assistant/Secretary, A
Medical/Clinical Assistant, A
Pharmacy Technician/Assistant, A
Web Page, Digital/Multimedia and Information Resources Design, A

REND LAKE COLLEGE

Administrative Assistant and Secretarial Science, A
Agricultural Mechanics and Equipment/Machine Technology, A
Agricultural Mechanization, A
Agricultural Production Operations, A
Applied Horticulture/Horticultural Operations, A
Architectural Drafting and Architectural CAD/CADD, A
Automobile/Automotive Mechanics Technology/Technician, A
Barbering/Barber, A
Biological and Physical Sciences, A
Child Care Provider/Assistant, A
Clinical/Medical Laboratory Technician, A
Computer Technology/Computer Systems Technology, A
Cosmetology/Cosmetologist, A
Criminal Justice/Police Science, A
Culinary Arts/Chef Training, A
Drafting and Design Technology/Technician, A
E-Commerce/Electronic Commerce, A
Electrical, Electronic and Communications Engineering Technology/Technician, A
Electrician, A
Emergency Medical Technology/Technician (EMT Paramedic), A
Engineering, A
Fine/Studio Arts, A
Graphic Design, A
Health Information/Medical Records Technology/Technician, A
Heavy Equipment Maintenance Technology/Technician, A
Industrial Mechanics and Maintenance Technology, A
Liberal Arts and Sciences Studies and Humanities, A
Manufacturing Technology/Technician, A
Medical Radiologic Technology/Science - Radiation Therapist, A
Medical Staff Services Technology/Technician, A
Mining Technology/Technician, A
Occupational Therapist Assistant, A
Petroleum Technology/Technician, A
Plant Sciences, A
Special Education and Teaching, A
Veterinary/Animal Health Technology/Technician and Veterinary Assistant, A
Welding Technology/Welder, A

RESURRECTION UNIVERSITY

Health Information/Medical Records Technology/Technician, B

Nursing, M

RICHLAND COMMUNITY COLLEGE

Accounting, A
Administrative Assistant and Secretarial Science, A
Agricultural Business and Management, A
Automobile/Automotive Mechanics Technology/Technician, A
Biological and Physical Sciences, A
Business Administration and Management, A
Child Development, A
Computer Graphics, A
Computer Programming, Specific Applications, A
Computer and Information Sciences, A
Construction Engineering Technology/Technician, A
Criminal Justice/Police Science, A
Data Entry/Microcomputer Applications, A
Drafting and Design Technology/Technician, A
Electrical, Electronic and Communications Engineering Technology/Technician, A
Fire Science/Firefighting, A
Food Technology and Processing, A
Industrial Technology/Technician, A
Information Science/Studies, A
Insurance, A
Legal Administrative Assistant/Secretary, A
Liberal Arts and Sciences Studies and Humanities, A
Medical Administrative Assistant/Secretary, A
Surgical Technology/Technologist, A
Word Processing, A

ROBERT MORRIS UNIVERSITY ILLINOIS

Accounting, BM
Arts Management, M
Business Administration and Management, AB
Business Administration, Management and Operations, M
Commercial and Advertising Art, A
Computer Systems Networking and Telecommunications, A
Computer and Information Systems Security, M
Culinary Arts/Chef Training, A
Educational Administration and Supervision, M
Educational Media/Instructional Technology, M
Finance and Banking, M
Graphic Design, B
Health Services Administration, M
Health and Physical Education, A
Higher Education/Higher Education Administration, M
Human Resources Management and Services, M
Information Technology, B
Interior Design, A
Law Enforcement, M
Legal Assistant/Paralegal, A
Management, M
Management Information Systems and Services, M
Management Strategy and Policy, M
Media Studies, M
Medical/Clinical Assistant, A
Multi-/Interdisciplinary Studies, B
Pharmacy Technician/Assistant, A
Sport and Fitness Administration/Management, M
Surgical Technology/Technologist, A

ROCK VALLEY COLLEGE

Accounting, A
Administrative Assistant and Secretarial Science, A
Automobile/Automotive Mechanics Technology/Technician, A
Avionics Maintenance Technology/Technician, A
Business Administration and Management, A
Child Development, A
Computer Engineering Technology/Technician, A
Computer Science, A
Computer Systems Networking and Telecommunications, A
Construction Engineering Technology/Technician, A
Criminal Justice/Law Enforcement Administration, A
Dental Hygiene/Hygienist, A
Drafting/Design Engineering Technologies/Technicians, A
Electrical, Electronic and Communications Engineering Technology/Technician, A

Electrician, A
Energy Management and Systems Technology/Technician, A
Fire Science/Firefighting, A
Graphic and Printing Equipment Operator Production, A
Human Services, A
Industrial Design, A
Industrial Technology/Technician, A
Liberal Arts and Sciences Studies and Humanities, A
Marketing/Marketing Management, A
Quality Control Technology/Technician, A
Respiratory Care Therapy/Therapist, A
Sheet Metal Technology/Sheetworking, A
Sport and Fitness Administration/Management, A
Surgical Technology/Technologist, A
Tool and Die Technology/Technician, A
Welding Technology/Welder, A

ROCKFORD CAREER COLLEGE

Accounting, A
Business Administration and Management, A
Computer and Information Sciences, A
Executive Assistant/Executive Secretary, A
Legal Administrative Assistant/Secretary, A
Legal Assistant/Paralegal, A
Marketing/Marketing Management, A
Medical Transcription/Transcriptionist, A
Medical/Clinical Assistant, A

ROCKFORD UNIVERSITY

Accounting, B
Anthropology, B
Art History, Criticism and Conservation, B
Art/Art Studies, General, B
Biochemistry, B
Biological and Physical Sciences, B
Biology/Biological Sciences, B
Business Administration and Management, B
Business Administration, Management and Operations, M
Chemistry, B
Classics and Classical Languages, Literatures, and Linguistics, B
Comparative Literature, B
Computer Science, B
Dance, B
Drama and Dramatics/Theatre Arts, B
Early Childhood Education and Teaching, BM
Economics, B
Education, BM
Elementary Education and Teaching, BM
English Language and Literature, B
Finance, B
French Language and Literature, B
History, B
Human Development and Family Studies, B
Humanities/Humanistic Studies, B
International Economics, B
International/Global Studies, B
Latin Language and Literature, B
Management Information Systems and Services, B
Marketing/Marketing Management, B
Mathematics, B
Music, B
Music Performance, B
Philosophy, B
Physical Education Teaching and Coaching, B
Political Science and Government, B
Pre-Dentistry Studies, B
Pre-Law Studies, B
Pre-Medicine/Pre-Medical Studies, B
Pre-Veterinary Studies, B
Psychology, B
Reading Teacher Education, M
Romance Languages, Literatures, and Linguistics, B
Secondary Education and Teaching, BM
Social Sciences, B
Social Work, B
Sociology, B
Spanish Language and Literature, B
Special Education and Teaching, BM

Sport and Fitness Administration/Management, B

ROOSEVELT UNIVERSITY

Accounting, BM
Acting, B
Actuarial Science, BM
African-American/Black Studies, B
Anthropology, M
Applied Economics, M
BioTechnology, BM
Biochemistry, B
Biology/Biological Sciences, B
Business Administration, Management and Operations, BM
Business/Commerce, B
Business/Corporate Communications, B
Chemistry, BM
Clinical Laboratory Science/Medical Technology/Technologist, B
Clinical Psychology, M
Clinical/Medical Laboratory Science and Allied Professions, B
Communication Studies/Speech Communication and Rhetoric, B
Communication and Media Studies, M
Computer Science, BM
Computer Systems Networking and Telecommunications, B
Corporate and Organizational Communication, M
Counselor Education/School Counseling and Guidance Services, M
Criminal Justice/Safety Studies, B
Diagnostic Medical Sonography/Sonographer and Ultrasound Technician, B
Drama and Dramatics/Theatre Arts, B
Early Childhood Education and Teaching, BM
Economics, BM
Education, MD
Educational Leadership and Administration, M
Elementary Education and Teaching, BM
English, M
English Language and Literature, B
Finance, B
Gender Studies, MO
Histologic Technology/Histotechnologist, B
History, BM
Hospitality Administration/Management, BM
Human Resources Development, M
Human Resources Management and Services, M
Human Resources Management/Personnel Administration, B
Industrial and Organizational Psychology, MD
International Business/Trade/Commerce, M
International Relations and Affairs, B
Jazz/Jazz Studies, B
Journalism, BM
Legal Assistant/Paralegal, B
Liberal Arts and Sciences Studies and Humanities, B
Management Information Systems and Services, M
Management Science, B
Marketing, M
Marketing/Marketing Management, B
Mathematics, BM
Medical Radiologic Technology/Science - Radiation Therapist, B
Music, BMO
Music Performance, B
Music Teacher Education, BO
Music Theory and Composition, B
Nuclear Medical Technology/Technologist, B
Office Management and Supervision, B
Organizational Behavior Studies, B
Organizational Communication, B
Organizational Management, MD
Pharmacy, D
Philosophy, B
Piano and Organ, B
Political Science and Government, BM
Psychology, BMD
Public Administration, BM
Public Relations/Image Management, B
Reading Teacher Education, M
Real Estate, MO
Secondary Education and Teaching, M
Social Sciences, B

Sociology, BM
Spanish Language and Literature, M
Special Education and Teaching, BM
Telecommunications, M
Theater, M
Violin, Viola, Guitar and Other Stringed Instruments, B
Voice and Opera, B
Women's Studies, MO
Writing, M

RUSH UNIVERSITY

Allopathic Medicine, D
Anatomy, MD
Biochemistry, MD
Cell Biology and Anatomy, MD
Clinical Laboratory Science/Medical Technology/Technologist, B
Clinical Laboratory Sciences, M
Communication Disorders, MD
Community Health Nursing, D
Diagnostic Medical Sonography/Sonographer and Ultrasound Technician, B
Gerontological Nursing, D
Health Services Administration, MD
Immunology, MD
Maternal/Child Health and Neonatal Nurse/Nursing, DO
Medical Physics, MD
Medical Technology, M
Microbiology, D
Neuroscience, MD
Nurse Anesthetist, D
Nursing, MDO
Nursing - Adult, D
Nursing - Advanced Practice, D
Nursing Administration, M
Nutritional Sciences, M
Occupational Therapy/Therapist, M
Pediatric Nurse/Nursing, DO
Perfusion Technology/Perfusionist, M
Pharmaceutical Sciences, M
Pharmacology, MD
Physical Therapy/Therapist, M
Physician Assistant, M
Physiology, D
Psychiatric/Mental Health Nurse/Nursing, D
Virology, MD

SAINT ANTHONY COLLEGE OF NURSING

Nursing, M

ST. AUGUSTINE COLLEGE

Accounting Technology/Technician and Bookkeeping, A
Administrative Assistant and Secretarial Science, A
Business Administration and Management, A
Business Administration, Management and Operations, A
Computer and Information Sciences, A
Culinary Arts/Chef Training, A
Early Childhood Education and Teaching, A
General Studies, A
Liberal Arts and Sciences Studies and Humanities, A
Management Information Systems and Services, A
Respiratory Care Therapy/Therapist, A
Social Work, B
Substance Abuse/Addiction Counseling, A

SAINT FRANCIS MEDICAL CENTER COLLEGE OF NURSING

Gerontological Nursing, M
Maternal/Child Health and Neonatal Nurse/Nursing, M
Medical/Surgical Nursing, MDO
Nursing, MDO
Nursing - Advanced Practice, M
Nursing Administration, M
Nursing Education, MDO

Psychiatric/Mental Health Nurse/Nursing, M

SAINT XAVIER UNIVERSITY

Accounting, B
Art Teacher Education, B
Art/Art Studies, General, B
Biological and Physical Sciences, B
Biology Teacher Education, B
Biology/Biological Sciences, B
Botany/Plant Biology, B
Business Administration, Management and Operations, MO
Business/Commerce, B
Chemistry, B
Communication Disorders, M
Communication Studies/Speech Communication and Rhetoric, B
Computer Science, BM
Computer and Information Sciences, B
Counselor Education/School Counseling and Guidance Services, M
Criminal Justice/Safety Studies, B
Curriculum and Instruction, M
Early Childhood Education and Teaching, M
Education, M
Educational Administration and Supervision, M
Educational Leadership and Administration, M
Educational Media/Instructional Technology, M
Elementary Education and Teaching, BM
English Language and Literature, B
English as a Second Language, M
English/Language Arts Teacher Education, B
Finance and Banking, MO
Foreign Language Teacher Education, M
Health Services Administration, MO
History, B
History Teacher Education, B
International Business/Trade/Commerce, B
International Relations and Affairs, B
Kindergarten/PreSchool Education and Teaching, B
Liberal Arts and Sciences Studies and Humanities, B
Management, M
Marketing, M
Mathematics, B
Mathematics Teacher Education, B
Music, B
Music Performance, B
Music Teacher Education, BM
Nursing, MO
Philosophy, B
Political Science and Government, B
Project Management, MO
Psychology, B
Reading Teacher Education, M
Religion/Religious Studies, B
Science Teacher Education/General Science Teacher Education, M
Secondary Education and Teaching, M
Social Sciences, B
Sociology, B
Spanish Language Teacher Education, B
Spanish Language and Literature, BM
Special Education and Teaching, M
Speech-Language Pathology/Pathologist, B

SAUK VALLEY COMMUNITY COLLEGE

Accounting, A
Administrative Assistant and Secretarial Science, A
Agricultural Business and Management, A
Agriculture, A
Art/Art Studies, General, A
Athletic Training and Sports Medicine, A
Biology/Biological Sciences, A
Business Administration and Management, A
Chemistry, A
Communication Studies/Speech Communication and Rhetoric, A
Computer and Information Sciences, A
Corrections, A
Criminal Justice/Law Enforcement Administration, A
Criminal Justice/Police Science, A
Drama and Dramatics/Theatre Arts, A
Early Childhood Education and Teaching, A
Economics, A
Education, A

Electrical, Electronic and Communications Engineering Technology/Technician, A
Elementary Education and Teaching, A
English Language and Literature, A
Fire Science/Firefighting, A
Foreign Languages, Literatures, and Linguistics, A
Heating, Air Conditioning, Ventilation and Refrigeration Maintenance Technology/Technician, A
History, A
Legal Administrative Assistant/Secretary, A
Management Science, A
Marketing/Marketing Management, A
Mathematics, A
Medical Office Assistant/Specialist, A
Music, A
Occupational Therapy/Therapist, A
Physical Education Teaching and Coaching, A
Physics, A
Political Science and Government, A
Pre-Medicine/Pre-Medical Studies, A
Psychology, A
Radiologic Technology/Science - Radiographer, A
Secondary Education and Teaching, A
Social Work, A
Sociology, A
Special Education and Teaching, A

SCHOOL OF THE ART INSTITUTE OF CHICAGO

Animation, Interactive Technology, Video Graphics and Special Effects, B
Architecture, M
Architecture and Related Services, B
Art Education, M
Art History, Criticism and Conservation, BM
Art Teacher Education, M
Art Therapy/Therapist, M
Art/Art Studies, General, B
Arts Journalism, M
Arts Management, M
Ceramic Arts and Ceramics, BM
Cinematography and Film/Video Production, B
Computer Graphics, B
Design and Applied Arts, BM
Design and Visual Communications, B
Digital Communication and Media/Multimedia, B
Drawing, B
Fashion/Apparel Design, B
Fiber, Textile and Weaving Arts, B
Film, Television, and Video Production, M
Film/Cinema Studies, B
Film/Video and Photographic Arts, B
Fine Arts and Art Studies, BM
Fine/Studio Arts, B
Graphic Communications, B
Graphic Design, BM
Historic Preservation and Conservation, M
Illustration, B
Interior Architecture, B
Interior Design, M
Intermedia/Multimedia, B
Journalism, M
Materials Sciences, M
Metal and Jewelry Arts, B
Music, B
Performance, M
Photography, BM
Printmaking, BM
Sculpture, BM
Textile Design, MO
Visual and Performing Arts, B
Web Page, Digital/Multimedia and Information Resources Design, B
Writing, MO

SHAWNEE COMMUNITY COLLEGE

Accounting, A
Administrative Assistant and Secretarial Science, A
Agricultural Business and Management, A
Agriculture, A
Agronomy and Crop Science, A
Animal Sciences, A
Automobile/Automotive Mechanics Technology/Technician, A
Biological and Physical Sciences, A

Business Administration and Management, A
Business/Office Automation/Technology/Data Entry, A
Child Development, A
Clinical/Medical Laboratory Technician, A
Computer Graphics, A
Computer Systems Networking and Telecommunications, A
Cosmetology/Cosmetologist, A
Criminal Justice/Police Science, A
Electrical, Electronic and Communications Engineering Technology/Technician, A
Health Information/Medical Records Technology/Technician, A
Human Services, A
Information Science/Studies, A
Legal Administrative Assistant/Secretary, A
Liberal Arts and Sciences Studies and Humanities, A
Medical Administrative Assistant/Secretary, A
Occupational Therapist Assistant, A
Sheet Metal Technology/Sheetworking, A
Social Work, A
Veterinary/Animal Health Technology/Technician and Veterinary Assistant, A
Welding Technology/Welder, A
Wildlife and Wildlands Science and Management, A

SHIMER COLLEGE

Comparative Literature, B
General Studies, B
Humanities/Humanistic Studies, B
Liberal Arts and Sciences Studies and Humanities, B
Natural Sciences, B
Social Sciences, B

SOLEX COLLEGE

Accounting, A

SOUTH SUBURBAN COLLEGE

Accounting, A
Accounting Technology/Technician and Bookkeeping, A
Architectural Drafting and Architectural CAD/CADD, A
Biological and Physical Sciences, A
Building/Home/Construction Inspection/Inspector, A
CAD/CADD Drafting and/or Design Technology/Technician, A
Child Care Provider/Assistant, A
Construction Engineering Technology/Technician, A
Court Reporting/Court Reporter, A
Criminal Justice/Safety Studies, A
Electrical, Electronic and Communications Engineering Technology/Technician, A
Executive Assistant/Executive Secretary, A
Fine/Studio Arts, A
Information Technology, A
Kinesiology and Exercise Science, A
Legal Assistant/Paralegal, A
Liberal Arts and Sciences Studies and Humanities, A
Occupational Therapist Assistant, A
Office Management and Supervision, A
Radiologic Technology/Science - Radiographer, A
Small Business Administration/Management, A
Social Work, A

SOUTHEASTERN ILLINOIS COLLEGE

Accounting, A
Administrative Assistant and Secretarial Science, A
Agricultural Mechanization, A
Automobile/Automotive Mechanics Technology/Technician, A
Business Administration and Management, A
Child Development, A
Clinical/Medical Laboratory Technician, A
Corrections, A
Criminal Justice/Police Science, A
Electrical, Electronic and Communications Engineering Technology/Technician, A
Emergency Medical Technology/Technician (EMT Paramedic), A
Fire Science/Firefighting, A
Forestry Technology/Technician, A

Health Information/Medical Records Administration/Administrator, A
Human Services, A
Hydrology and Water Resources Science, A
Information Science/Studies, A
Mining Technology/Technician, A
Occupational Therapy/Therapist, A
Real Estate, A
Surgical Technology/Technologist, A
Welding Technology/Welder, A
Wildlife and Wildlands Science and Management, A

SOUTHERN ILLINOIS UNIVERSITY CARBONDALE

Accounting, BMD
African-American/Black Studies, B
Agricultural Economics, BM
Agricultural Sciences, M
Agriculture, B
Agronomy and Soil Sciences, M
Airline/Commercial/Professional Pilot and Flight Crew, A
Animal Sciences, BM
Anthropology, BMD
Apparel and Textiles, B
Applied Arts and Design, M
Applied Physics, MD
Architecture, BM
Art/Art Studies, General, B
Automotive Engineering Technology/Technician, B
Aviation/Airway Management and Operations, B
Avionics Maintenance Technology/Technician, B
Biochemistry, MD
Biological and Biomedical Sciences, MD
Biology/Biological Sciences, B
Biomedical Engineering, M
Botany/Plant Biology, B
Business Administration and Management, B
Business Administration, Management and Operations, MD
Business/Managerial Economics, B
Ceramic Arts and Ceramics, M
Chemistry, BMD
Cinematography and Film/Video Production, B
Civil Engineering, BM
Clinical Psychology, D
Communication Disorders, BM
Communication and Media Studies, MD
Community Health and Preventive Medicine, M
Computer Engineering, BMD
Computer Science, BMD
Counseling Psychology, D
Crafts, M
Criminology, M
Cultural Studies, M
Curriculum and Instruction, MD
Dental Hygiene/Hygienist, B
Design and Visual Communications, B
Drama and Dramatics/Theatre Arts, B
Dramatic/Theatre Arts and Stagecraft, B
Early Childhood Education and Teaching, B
Economics, BMD
Education, MD
Educational Administration and Supervision, MD
Educational Psychology, MD
Electrical Engineering, MD
Electrical and Electronic Engineering Technologies/Technicians, B
Electrical, Electronics and Communications Engineering, B
Elementary Education and Teaching, B
Engineering Management, M
Engineering Technology, B
Engineering and Applied Sciences, MD
English, MD
English Language and Literature, B
English as a Second Language, M
Environmental Policy and Resource Management, MD
Environmental Sciences, D
Experimental Psychology, M
Finance, B
Fine Arts and Art Studies, M
Fine/Studio Arts, B
Fire Services Administration, B
Foreign Languages and Literatures, B

Forestry, BM
Funeral Service and Mortuary Science, B
Geography, BMD
Geology/Earth Science, BMD
Health Education, MD
Health Law, M
Health Services Administration, M
Health/Health Care Administration/Management, B
Higher Education/Higher Education Administration, M
History, BMD
Homeland Security, M
Hospitality Administration/Management, B
Industrial Technology/Technician, B
Information Science/Studies, B
Interior Design, B
Jewelry/Metalsmithing, M
Journalism, BD
Kinesiology and Exercise Science, B
Kinesiology and Movement Studies, M
Law and Legal Studies, MD
Legal Assistant/Paralegal, B
Legal and Justice Studies, M
Liberal Arts and Sciences Studies and Humanities, B
Linguistics, BM
Management Science, B
Marketing/Marketing Management, B
Mass Communication/Media Studies, M
Mathematics, BMD
Mechanical Engineering, BM
Mechanics, M
Media Studies, M
Medical Physics, M
Medical Radiologic Technology/Science - Radiation Therapist, B
Microbiology, BMD
Mineral/Mining Engineering, M
Mining and Mineral Engineering, B
Molecular Biology, MD
Multi-/Interdisciplinary Studies, B
Music, BM
Nutritional Sciences, BM
Painting, M
Parks, Recreation, Leisure and Fitness Studies, B
Pharmacology, MD
Philosophy, BMD
Physical Education Teaching and Coaching, M
Physical Therapist Assistant, A
Physician Assistant, BM
Physics, BMD
Physiology, BMD
Plant Biology, MD
Plant Sciences, BM
Political Science and Government, BMD
Psychology, BMD
Public Administration, M
Radio and Television, B
Recreation and Park Management, M
Rehabilitation and Therapeutic Professions, B
Rhetoric, MD
Social Sciences, B
Social Work, BM
Sociology, BMD
Special Education and Teaching, BM
Speech and Interpersonal Communication, MD
Sport and Fitness Administration/Management, B
Theater, MD
Trade and Industrial Teacher Education, B
Vocational and Technical Education, MD
Writing, M
Zoology/Animal Biology, BMD

SOUTHERN ILLINOIS UNIVERSITY EDWARDSVILLE

Accounting, BM
Advertising and Public Relations, M
Anthropology, B
Applied Mathematics, M
Art Therapy/Therapist, M
Art/Art Studies, General, B
Audiology/Audiologist and Speech-Language Pathology/Pathologist, B
Biological and Biomedical Sciences, M
Biology/Biological Sciences, B
Business Administration and Management, B

Business Administration, Management and Operations, M
Business/Managerial Economics, B
Chemistry, BM
Civil Engineering, BM
Clinical Nutrition/Nutritionist, B
Clinical Psychology, M
Communication Disorders, M
Communication Studies/Speech Communication and Rhetoric, B
Computational Sciences, M
Computer Engineering, B
Computer Science, BM
Computer and Information Sciences, B
Construction Engineering Technology/Technician, B
Corporate and Organizational Communication, M
Criminal Justice/Safety Studies, B
Curriculum and Instruction, M
Dentistry, D
Drama and Dramatics/Theatre Arts, B
Early Childhood Education and Teaching, B
Economics, BM
Education, MDO
Educational Administration and Supervision, MO
Educational Leadership and Administration, D
Educational Media/Instructional Technology, MO
Electrical Engineering, M
Electrical, Electronics and Communications Engineering, B
Elementary Education and Teaching, B
Engineering and Applied Sciences, M
English, MO
English Education, MO
English Language and Literature, B
English as a Second Language, MO
Environmental Engineering Technology/Environmental Technology, M
Environmental Policy and Resource Management, M
Environmental Sciences, BM
Exercise and Sports Science, M
Finance and Banking, M
Fine Arts and Art Studies, M
Fine/Studio Arts, B
Foreign Languages and Literatures, B
Foundations and Philosophy of Education, M
Geography, M
Geotechnical Engineering, M
Health Communication, M
Health Education, MDO
Health Informatics, M
Health Teacher Education, B
Higher Education/Higher Education Administration, M
History, BM
Industrial Engineering, B
Industrial and Organizational Psychology, M
Industrial/Management Engineering, M
Junior High/Intermediate/Middle School Education and Teaching, M
Kinesiology and Exercise Science, B
Kinesiology and Movement Studies, M
Liberal Arts and Sciences Studies and Humanities, B
Management Information Systems and Services, BM
Manufacturing Engineering, B
Marketing Research, M
Mass Communication/Media Studies, BM
Mathematics, BM
Mathematics Teacher Education, M
Mechanical Engineering, BM
Media Studies, O
Museology/Museum Studies, O
Music, BM
Music Teacher Education, MO
Nurse Anesthetist, D
Nursing, MDO
Nursing - Advanced Practice, MDO
Nursing Administration, MO
Nursing Education, MO
Operations Research, M
Performance, M
Pharmacy, D
Philosophy, B
Physical Education Teaching and Coaching, M

Physics, B
Political Science and Government, B
Project Management, M
Psychology, BMO
Public Administration, M
Reading Teacher Education, MO
School Psychology, O
Science Teacher Education/General Science
   Teacher Education, B
Social Work, BM
Sociology, BM
Special Education and Teaching, BMO
Speech and Interpersonal Communication, M
Sport Psychology, M
Statistics, M
Structural Engineering, M
Student Personnel Services, M
Taxation, M
Transportation and Highway Engineering, M
Writing, M

SOUTHWESTERN ILLINOIS COLLEGE

Accounting, A
Administrative Assistant and Secretarial Science, A
Airframe Mechanics and Aircraft Maintenance
   Technology/Technician, A
Airline/Commercial/Professional Pilot and Flight
   Crew, A
Applied Horticulture/Horticultural Operations, A
Autobody/Collision and Repair
   Technology/Technician, A
Aviation/Airway Management and Operations, A
Biological and Physical Sciences, A
Carpentry/Carpenter, A
Child Care Provider/Assistant, A
Clinical/Medical Laboratory Technician, A
Computer Programming/Programmer, A
Computer and Information Sciences, A
Computer/Information Technology Services Adminis-
   tration and Management, A
Concrete Finishing/Concrete Finisher, A
Construction Trades, A
Criminal Justice/Law Enforcement Administration, A
Data Modeling/Warehousing and Database Adminis-
   tration, A
Electrical and Power Transmission
   Installation/Installer, A
Electrical, Electronic and Communications Engineer-
   ing Technology/Technician, A
Electrician, A
Emergency Medical Technology/Technician (EMT
   Paramedic), A
Fine/Studio Arts, A
Fire Science/Firefighting, A
General Studies, A
Health Information/Medical Records
   Technology/Technician, A
Heating, Air Conditioning, Ventilation and Refrigera-
   tion Maintenance Technology/Technician, A
Industrial Mechanics and Maintenance Technol-
   ogy, A
Information Technology, A
Ironworking/Ironworker, A
Legal Administrative Assistant/Secretary, A
Legal Assistant/Paralegal, A
Liberal Arts and Sciences Studies and Humani-
   ties, A
Machine Tool Technology/Machinist, A
Manufacturing Technology/Technician, A
Mason/Masonry, A
Massage Therapy/Therapeutic Massage, A
Mathematics Teacher Education, A
Mechanical Drafting and Mechanical Drafting
   CAD/CADD, A
Medical Office Assistant/Specialist, A
Medical/Clinical Assistant, A
Music, A
Music Teacher Education, A
Painting/Painter and Wall Coverer, A
Physical Therapist Assistant, A
Pipefitting/Pipefitter and Sprinkler Fitter, A
Prepress/Desktop Publishing and Digital Imaging
   Design, A
Radiologic Technology/Science - Radiographer, A
Respiratory Care Therapy/Therapist, A

Restaurant, Culinary, and Catering
   Management/Manager, A
Selling Skills and Sales Operations, A
Sheet Metal Technology/Sheetworking, A
Sign Language Interpretation and Translation, A
Small Business Administration/Management, A
Social Work, A
System Administration/Administrator, A
Teacher Assistant/Aide, A
Web/Multimedia Management and Webmaster, A
Welding Technology/Welder, A

SPOON RIVER COLLEGE

Accounting, A
Administrative Assistant and Secretarial Science, A
Agricultural Business and Management, A
Agricultural Mechanics and Equipment/Machine
   Technology, A
Agricultural Mechanization, A
Agricultural Teacher Education, A
Art/Art Studies, General, A
Biological and Physical Sciences, A
Biology/Biological Sciences, A
Botany/Plant Biology, A
Business Administration and Management, A
Business Teacher Education, A
Chemistry, A
Child Development, A
Computer Programming, Specific Applications, A
Computer and Information Systems Security, A
Criminal Justice/Law Enforcement Administration, A
Criminal Justice/Police Science, A
Drama and Dramatics/Theatre Arts, A
Education, A
Electrical, Electronic and Communications Engineer-
   ing Technology/Technician, A
English Language and Literature, A
Finance, A
General Studies, A
Graphic Design, A
Health Professions and Related Clinical Sciences, A
History, A
Industrial Technology/Technician, A
Information Science/Studies, A
Kindergarten/PreSchool Education and Teaching, A
Legal Administrative Assistant/Secretary, A
Liberal Arts and Sciences Studies and Humani-
   ties, A
Mass Communication/Media Studies, A
Mathematics, A
Medical Administrative Assistant/Secretary, A
Physical Education Teaching and Coaching, A
Physical Sciences, A
Physics, A
Political Science and Government, A
Psychology, A
Social Sciences, A
Sociology, A
Truck and Bus Driver/Commercial Vehicle Opera-
   tion, A
Web Page, Digital/Multimedia and Information Re-
   sources Design, A

TAYLOR BUSINESS INSTITUTE

Accounting Technology/Technician and Bookkeep-
   ing, A
Criminal Justice/Law Enforcement Administration, A
Electrical, Electronic and Communications Engineer-
   ing Technology/Technician, A
Health Information/Medical Records
   Technology/Technician, A
Medical Insurance Specialist/Medical Biller, A

TELSHE YESHIVA–CHICAGO

Jewish/Judaic Studies, O
Talmudic Studies, B

TRIBECA FLASHPOINT COLLEGE

Animation, Interactive Technology, Video Graphics
   and Special Effects, A
Cinematography and Film/Video Production, A
Recording Arts Technology/Technician, A

Web Page, Digital/Multimedia and Information Resources Design, A

TRINITY CHRISTIAN COLLEGE

Accounting, B
Art Teacher Education, B
Biochemistry, B
Bioinformatics, B
Biology Teacher Education, B
Biology/Biological Sciences, B
Business Administration and Management, B
Business Teacher Education, B
Business/Corporate Communications, B
Chemistry, B
Chemistry Teacher Education, B
Communication Studies/Speech Communication
   and Rhetoric, B
Computer Science, B
Computer and Information Sciences, B
Counseling Psychology, M
Criminal Justice/Law Enforcement Administration, B
Education, B
Elementary Education and Teaching, B
English Language and Literature, B
English/Language Arts Teacher Education, B
Entrepreneurship/Entrepreneurial Studies, B
Environmental Sciences, B
Finance, B
Fine/Studio Arts, B
Graphic Design, B
History, B
History Teacher Education, B
Junior High/Intermediate/Middle School Education
   and Teaching, B
Kinesiology and Exercise Science, B
Marketing/Marketing Management, B
Mathematics, B
Mathematics Teacher Education, B
Music, B
Music Teacher Education, B
Parks, Recreation, Leisure and Fitness Studies, B
Philosophy, B
Physical Education Teaching and Coaching, B
Psychology, B
Social Work, B
Spanish Language Teacher Education, B
Spanish Language and Literature, B
Special Education and Teaching, BM
Speech-Language Pathology/Pathologist, B
Theology and Religious Vocations, B
Theology/Theological Studies, B

TRINITY COLLEGE OF NURSING AND HEALTH SCIENCES

Emergency Care Attendant (EMT Ambulance), A
Emergency Medical Technology/Technician (EMT
   Paramedic), A
Medical Radiologic Technology/Science - Radiation
   Therapist, A
Radiologic Technology/Science - Radiographer, A
Respiratory Care Therapy/Therapist, A
Surgical Technology/Technologist, A

TRINITY INTERNATIONAL UNIVERSITY

Accounting, B
Archeology, M
Athletic Training and Sports Medicine, B
Bible/Biblical Studies, B
Bioethics/Medical Ethics, M
Biology/Biological Sciences, B
Business Administration and Management, B
Chemistry, B
Communication and Media Studies, BM
Computer Science, B
Counseling Psychology, M
Education, BM
Educational Leadership and Administration, M
Elementary Education and Teaching, B
English Language and Literature, B
History, B
Human Resources Development, B
Human Resources Management/Personnel Adminis-
   tration, B
Humanities/Humanistic Studies, B
International Business/Trade/Commerce, B
Law and Legal Studies, D

Liberal Arts and Sciences Studies and Humanities, B
Management, D
Management Science, B
Marketing/Marketing Management, B
Mathematics, B
Missions/Missionary Studies and Missiology, MD
Music, B
Music History, Literature, and Theory, B
Music Pedagogy, B
Music Teacher Education, B
Music Theory and Composition, B
Non-Profit/Public/Organizational Management, B
Pastoral Counseling and Specialized Ministries, B
Pastoral Studies/Counseling, MD
Philosophy, B
Physical Education Teaching and Coaching, B
Pre-Medicine/Pre-Medical Studies, B
Pre-Nursing Studies, B
Pre-Theology/Pre-Ministerial Studies, B
Psychology, B
Religious Education, D
Religious/Sacred Music, B
Secondary Education and Teaching, B
Social Sciences, B
Teacher Education, Multiple Levels, B
Theology and Religious Vocations, MDO
Youth Ministry, B

TRITON COLLEGE

Accounting, A
Anthropology, A
Architectural Drafting and Architectural CAD/CADD, A
Art/Art Studies, General, A
Automobile/Automotive Mechanics Technology/Technician, A
Biological and Physical Sciences, A
Biology/Biological Sciences, A
Business Administration and Management, A
CAD/CADD Drafting and/or Design Technology/Technician, A
Chemistry, A
Child Care Provider/Assistant, A
Communication Studies/Speech Communication and Rhetoric, A
Computer Science, A
Computer Systems Networking and Telecommunications, A
Computer and Information Sciences, A
Construction Management, A
Criminal Justice/Law Enforcement Administration, A
Culinary Arts/Chef Training, A
Design and Visual Communications, A
Diagnostic Medical Sonography/Sonographer and Ultrasound Technician, A
Early Childhood Education and Teaching, A
Economics, A
Education, A
Educational/Instructional Media Design, A
Emergency Medical Technology/Technician (EMT Paramedic), A
English Language and Literature, A
Financial Planning and Services, A
Fine/Studio Arts, A
Fire Science/Firefighting, A
French Language and Literature, A
Geography, A
Geology/Earth Science, A
Health and Physical Education, A
Heating, Air Conditioning, Ventilation and Refrigeration Maintenance Technology/Technician, A
History, A
Home Furnishings and Equipment Installers, A
Hotel/Motel Administration/Management, A
Human Resources Management/Personnel Administration, A
Information Science/Studies, A
Intercultural/Multicultural and Diversity Studies, A
International Business/Trade/Commerce, A
Italian Language and Literature, A
Liberal Arts and Sciences Studies and Humanities, A
Mathematics, A
Mathematics Teacher Education, A
Mechanic and Repair Technologies/Technicians, A

Mechanical Engineering/Mechanical Technology/Technician, A
Multi-/Interdisciplinary Studies, A
Music, A
Nuclear Medical Technology/Technologist, A
Ophthalmic Technician/Technologist, A
Ornamental Horticulture, A
Philosophy, A
Physics, A
Political Science and Government, A
Psychology, A
Radiologic Technology/Science - Radiographer, A
Respiratory Care Therapy/Therapist, A
Restaurant/Food Services Management, A
Selling Skills and Sales Operations, A
Sociology, A
Spanish Language and Literature, A
Substance Abuse/Addiction Counseling, A
Survey Technology/Surveying, A
Welding Technology/Welder, A
Women's Studies, A

UNIVERSITY OF CHICAGO

Accounting, M
African Studies, B
Allopathic Medicine, D
Anatomy, D
Ancient Near Eastern and Biblical Languages, Literatures, and Linguistics, B
Anthropology, BD
Applied Mathematics, D
Applied Statistics, M
Archeology, D
Art History, Criticism and Conservation, BMD
Asian Languages, D
Astronomy, D
Astrophysics, D
Atmospheric Sciences and Meteorology, D
Biochemistry, D
Bioengineering, D
Biological and Biomedical Sciences, D
Biology/Biological Sciences, B
Biophysics, D
Business Administration, Management and Operations, MDO
Cancer Biology/Oncology, D
Cell Biology and Anatomy, D
Chemistry, BD
Classics and Classical Languages, Literatures, and Linguistics, BMD
Comparative Literature, BMD
Computational Sciences, M
Computer Science, BMD
Developmental Biology and Embryology, D
Directing and Theatrical Production, B
East Asian Languages, Literatures, and Linguistics, B
East Asian Studies, D
Ecology, D
Economics, BMD
Emergency Management, M
English, MD
English Language and Literature, B
Entrepreneurship/Entrepreneurial Studies, M
Environmental Policy and Resource Management, M
Environmental Sciences, M
Environmental Studies, B
Ethics, D
Ethnic, Cultural Minority, and Gender Studies, B
Evolutionary Biology, D
Film, Television, and Video Theory and Criticism, D
Film/Cinema Studies, B
Finance and Banking, M
Fine Arts and Art Studies, M
French Language and Literature, D
Genetics, D
Genomic Sciences, D
Geochemistry, D
Geography, B
Geophysics and Seismology, BD
Geosciences, D
German Language and Literature, BMD
Health Promotion, MD
Health Services Administration, O
History, BD

History and Philosophy of Science and Technology, B
Human Development, D
Human Genetics, D
Human Resources Management and Services, M
Humanities/Humanistic Studies, BM
Immunology, D
Interdisciplinary Studies, D
International Affairs, M
International Business/Trade/Commerce, M
International Relations and Affairs, B
Italian Language and Literature, D
Jewish/Judaic Studies, B
Latin American Studies, BM
Law and Legal Studies, MD
Liberal Arts and Sciences Studies and Humanities, B
Liberal Studies, M
Linguistics, BMD
Management Strategy and Policy, M
Marketing, M
Mathematical and Computational Finance, M
Mathematics, BD
Media Studies, D
Medical Physics, D
Medieval and Renaissance Studies, B
Microbiology, D
Middle/Near Eastern and Semitic Languages, Literatures, and Linguistics, B
Molecular Biology, D
Molecular Biophysics, D
Molecular Medicine, D
Molecular Pathogenesis, D
Music, BMD
Near and Middle Eastern Languages, D
Near and Middle Eastern Studies, MD
Neurobiology and Neurophysiology, D
Neuroscience, D
Nutritional Sciences, D
Organizational Behavior Studies, M
Paleontology, D
Pastoral Studies/Counseling, M
Philosophy, BMD
Physics, BMD
Planetary Astronomy and Science, D
Political Science and Government, BD
Psychology, BD
Public Policy Analysis, BMD
Religion/Religious Studies, MD
Romance Languages, Literatures, and Linguistics, BMD
Russian Studies, B
Science Teacher Education/General Science Teacher Education, D
Slavic Languages, Literatures, and Linguistics, B
Social Sciences, BMD
Social Work, MD
Sociology, BD
South Asian Languages, Literatures, and Linguistics, B
South Asian Studies, B
South and Southeast Asian Studies, MD
Spanish Language and Literature, D
Statistics, BMD
Systematic Biology/Biological Systematics, D
Theology and Religious Vocations, D
Theology/Theological Studies, B
Urban Education and Leadership, M
Visual and Performing Arts, B
Writing, M
Zoology/Animal Biology, D

UNIVERSITY OF ILLINOIS AT CHICAGO

Accounting, BM
Acute Care/Critical Care Nursing, M
African-American/Black Studies, B
Allied Health and Medical Assisting Services, MDO
Allopathic Medicine, D
Anatomy, M
Anthropology, BMD
Architecture, BM
Architecture and Related Services, B
Art History, Criticism and Conservation, BMD
Art Teacher Education, B
BioTechnology, MD
Biochemistry, BD

Bioengineering, MD
Bioinformatics, MD
Biological and Biomedical Sciences, MD
Biology Teacher Education, B
Biology/Biological Sciences, B
Biomedical/Medical Engineering, B
Biophysics, MD
Biostatistics, MD
Business Administration and Management, B
Business Administration, Management and Operations, MD
Cell Biology and Anatomy, MD
Chemical Engineering, BMD
Chemistry, BMD
Chemistry Teacher Education, B
Cinematography and Film/Video Production, B
Civil Engineering, BMD
Classical, Ancient Mediterranean and Near Eastern Studies and Archaeology, B
Classics and Classical Languages, Literatures, and Linguistics, B
Communication Studies/Speech Communication and Rhetoric, B
Communication and Media Studies, MD
Community Health Nursing, M
Community Health and Preventive Medicine, MD
Computer Education, D
Computer Engineering, B
Computer Science, BMD
Criminal Justice/Safety Studies, B
Criminology, MD
Curriculum and Instruction, MD
Dentistry, D
Design and Applied Arts, BM
Developmental Psychology, M
Dietetics/Dieticians, B
Disability Studies, MD
Drama and Dramatics/Theatre Arts, B
Early Childhood Education and Teaching, M
East European and Russian Studies, MD
Economics, BMD
Education, MD
Educational Leadership and Administration, D
Educational Measurement and Evaluation, M
Educational Policy, MD
Educational Psychology, MD
Electrical, Electronics and Communications Engineering, B
Elementary Education and Teaching, BM
Engineering Physics, B
Engineering and Applied Sciences, MD
Engineering/Industrial Management, B
English, MD
English Language and Literature, B
English as a Second Language, M
English/Language Arts Teacher Education, B
Entrepreneurship/Entrepreneurial Studies, B
Environmental Sciences, B
Environmental and Occupational Health, MD
Epidemiology, MD
Ethnic, Cultural Minority, and Gender Studies, B
Film/Video and Photographic Arts, B
Finance, B
Finance and Banking, M
Fine Arts and Art Studies, MD
Fine/Studio Arts, B
Foreign Language Teacher Education, M
Forensic Science and Technology, M
French Language Teacher Education, B
French Language and Literature, BM
Genetics, D
Geography, M
Geology/Earth Science, BMD
Geosciences, MD
German Language Teacher Education, B
German Language and Literature, MD
German Studies, B
Gerontological Nursing, M
Graphic Design, BM
Health Education, M
Health Informatics, MO
Health Information/Medical Records Administration/Administrator, B
Health Services Administration, MD
Health Services Research, D
Hispanic Studies, MD

Hispanic and Latin American Languages, D
History, BMD
History Teacher Education, B
Human Development, MD
Immunology, D
Industrial Design, B
Industrial Engineering, B
Industrial/Management Engineering, MD
Information Science/Studies, B
Interdisciplinary Studies, D
Italian Language and Literature, B
Kinesiology and Exercise Science, B
Kinesiology and Movement Studies, MD
Latin American Studies, BM
Linguistics, M
Management Information Systems and Services, MD
Management Science, B
Marketing/Marketing Management, B
Materials Engineering, MD
Maternal/Child Health and Neonatal Nurse/Nursing, M
Mathematics, BMD
Mathematics Teacher Education, BMD
Mathematics and Computer Science, B
Mechanical Engineering, BMD
Medical Illustration and Informatics, M
Microbiology, D
Molecular Biology, D
Molecular Genetics, D
Museology/Museum Studies, M
Music, B
Neuroscience, MD
Nurse Midwife/Nursing Midwifery, M
Nursing, MDO
Nursing - Adult, M
Nursing - Advanced Practice, M
Nursing Administration, O
Nutritional Sciences, BMD
Occupational Health Nursing, M
Occupational Therapy/Therapist, MD
Operations Research, MD
Oral and Dental Sciences, MD
Painting, B
Pediatric Nurse/Nursing, M
Pharmaceutical Administration, MD
Pharmaceutical Sciences, MD
Pharmacognosy, MD
Pharmacology, D
Pharmacy, MD
Philosophy, BMD
Photography, B
Physical Therapy/Therapist, MD
Physics, BMD
Physics Teacher Education, B
Physiology, MD
Polish Language and Literature, B
Political Science and Government, BMD
Pre-Dentistry Studies, B
Pre-Veterinary Studies, B
Psychology, BMD
Public Administration, MD
Public Health, MD
Real Estate, M
Romance Languages, Literatures, and Linguistics, B
Russian Language and Literature, B
School Nursing, M
Science Teacher Education/General Science Teacher Education, D
Secondary Education and Teaching, M
Slavic Languages, Literatures, and Linguistics, BMD
Social Studies Teacher Education, D
Social Work, BMDO
Sociology, BMD
Spanish Language Teacher Education, B
Spanish Language and Literature, BMD
Special Education and Teaching, MD
Statistics, BMD
Toxicology, M
Urban Education and Leadership, D
Urban Studies/Affairs, B
Urban and Regional Planning, MD
Women's Health Nursing, M

Women's Studies, B

UNIVERSITY OF ILLINOIS AT SPRINGFIELD

Accounting, BM
Biological and Biomedical Sciences, M
Biology/Biological Sciences, B
Business Administration and Management, B
Business Administration, Management and Operations, BM
Chemistry, B
Child and Family Studies, M
Clinical Laboratory Science/Medical Technology/Technologist, B
Communication and Media Studies, M
Community Health and Preventive Medicine, O
Computer Science, BM
Computer Systems Analysis/Analyst, B
Computer and Information Systems Security, B
Criminal Justice/Safety Studies, B
Economics, B
Education, MO
Educational Leadership and Administration, MO
Emergency Management, O
English, MO
English Education, O
English Language and Literature, B
Environmental Sciences, M
Environmental Studies, BM
Epidemiology, O
Fine/Studio Arts, B
Gerontology, M
Health Education, O
History, BM
Homeland Security, O
Human Development, M
Human Services, MO
Interdisciplinary Studies, M
International/Global Studies, B
Journalism, M
Legal Professions and Studies, B
Legal and Justice Studies, M
Liberal Arts and Sciences Studies and Humanities, B
Management Information Systems and Services, M
Mathematics, B
Philosophy, B
Political Science and Government, BM
Psychology, B
Public Administration, MDO
Public Health, MO
Public History, M
Social Sciences, M
Social Work, B
Substance Abuse/Addiction Counseling, MO

UNIVERSITY OF ILLINOIS AT URBANA–CHAMPAIGN

Accounting, BMD
Accounting and Business/Management, B
Actuarial Science, BM
Advertising, B
Advertising and Public Relations, M
Aerospace, Aeronautical and Astronautical Engineering, BMD
African Studies, M
Agricultural Business and Management, B
Agricultural Communication/Journalism, B
Agricultural Economics, BMD
Agricultural Education, M
Agricultural Engineering, MD
Agricultural Mechanization, B
Agricultural Public Services, B
Agricultural Sciences, M
Agricultural Teacher Education, M
Agricultural and Extension Education Services, B
Agricultural/Biological Engineering and Bioengineering, B
Agronomy and Crop Science, B
Agronomy and Soil Sciences, MD
Airline/Commercial/Professional Pilot and Flight Crew, B
Animal Sciences, BMD
Animal/Livestock Husbandry and Production, B
Anthropology, BMD
Applied Arts and Design, MD

Applied Economics, MD
Applied Horticulture/Horticultural Operations, B
Applied Mathematics, M
Applied Statistics, M
Architecture, BMD
Architecture and Related Services, B
Area Studies, B
Art Education, MD
Art History, Criticism and Conservation, BMD
Art Teacher Education, B
Asian Languages, MD
Astronomy, BMD
Athletic Training and Sports Medicine, B
Atmospheric Sciences and Meteorology, BMD
Audiology/Audiologist and Hearing Sciences, B
Audiology/Audiologist and Speech-Language
   Pathology/Pathologist, B
Auditing, B
Aviation/Airway Management and Operations, B
Banking and Financial Support Services, B
BioTechnology, B
Biochemistry, BMD
Bioengineering, MD
Bioinformatics, M
Biological and Biomedical Sciences, BMD
Biology/Biological Sciences, B
Biomedical/Medical Engineering, B
Biophysics, BMD
Botany/Plant Biology, B
Broadcast Journalism, B
Business Administration and Management, B
Business Administration, Management and Opera-
   tions, MD
Business Teacher Education, B
Business/Commerce, B
Cell Biology and Anatomy, D
Cell/Cellular Biology and Histology, B
Cell/Cellular and Molecular Biology, B
Ceramic Sciences and Engineering, B
Chemical Engineering, BMD
Chemical Physics, D
Chemistry, BMD
Chemistry Teacher Education, B
Child Development, B
City/Urban, Community and Regional Planning, B
Civil Engineering, BMD
Classics and Classical Languages, Litera-
   tures, and Linguistics, BMD
Communication Disorders, MD
Communication Studies/Speech Communication
   and Rhetoric, B
Communication and Media Studies, MD
Communication, Journalism and Related Pro-
   grams, B
Community Health and Preventive Medicine, BMD
Comparative Literature, BMD
Computational Biology, MD
Computational Mathematics, B
Computer Engineering, BMD
Computer Programming/Programmer, B
Computer Science, BMD
Computer Software Engineering, B
Computer and Information Sciences, B
Computer and Information Systems Security, B
Conservation Biology, MD
Construction Engineering, B
Consumer Economics, BMD
Counselor Education/School Counseling and Guid-
   ance Services, MDO
Crafts, M
Crafts/Craft Design, Folk Art and Artisanry, B
Curriculum and Instruction, MDO
Dance, BM
Developmental Biology and Embryology, D
Dietetics/Dieticians, B
Directing and Theatrical Production, B
Drama and Dramatics/Theatre Arts, B
Early Childhood Education and Teaching, B
East Asian Languages, Literatures, and Linguis-
   tics, B
East Asian Studies, BMD
East European and Russian Studies, M
Ecology, BMD
Economics, BMD
Education, MDO

Education/Teaching of Individuals in Early Childhood
   Special Education Programs, B
Education/Teaching of Individuals with Multiple Dis-
   abilities, BMDO
Educational Administration and Supervision, O
Educational Leadership and Administration, MDO
Educational Policy, MDO
Educational Psychology, MDO
Electrical Engineering, MD
Electrical, Electronics and Communications Engi-
   neering, B
Elementary Education and Teaching, B
Energy Management and Policy, M
Energy and Power Engineering, M
Engineering, B
Engineering Mechanics, B
Engineering Physics, B
Engineering and Applied Sciences, MD
English, MD
English Language and Literature, B
English as a Second Language, M
English/Language Arts Teacher Education, B
Entomology, BMD
Entrepreneurship/Entrepreneurial Studies, B
Environmental Engineering
   Technology/Environmental Technology, MD
Environmental Health, B
Environmental Sciences, BMD
Environmental/Environmental Health Engineering, B
Evolutionary Biology, MD
Family and Consumer Sciences/Human Sciences
   Business Services, B
Farm/Farm and Ranch Management, B
Fashion Merchandising, B
Film/Cinema Studies, B
Finance, B
Finance and Banking, MD
Financial Engineering, M
Financial Planning and Services, B
Fine Arts and Art Studies, M
Food Science, B
Food Science and Technology, BMD
Food Technology and Processing, B
Foreign Language Teacher Education, BMD
Forest Sciences and Biology, B
Forestry, B
French Language Teacher Education, B
French Language and Literature, BMD
General Studies, B
Geography, BMD
Geological and Earth Sciences/Geosciences, B
Geology/Earth Science, BMD
Geosciences, M
Geotechnical Engineering, B
German Language Teacher Education, B
German Language and Literature, BMD
Graphic Design, BM
Health Informatics, MDO
Health Services Administration, BM
Hebrew Language and Literature, B
History, BMD
History Teacher Education, B
Horticultural Science, B
Hospitality Administration/Management, B
Human Development, MD
Human Development and Family Studies, B
Human Nutrition, B
Human Resources Management and Ser-
   vices, MDO
Human Resources Management/Personnel Adminis-
   tration, B
Human Services, M
Human-Computer Interaction, MDO
Humanities/Humanistic Studies, B
Industrial Design, BM
Industrial Engineering, B
Industrial and Labor Relations, MD
Industrial/Management Engineering, MD
Information Science/Studies, MDO
Insurance, B
Interdisciplinary Studies, D
International Agriculture, B
International/Global Studies, B
Italian Language and Literature, BMD
Jazz/Jazz Studies, B
Jewelry/Metalsmithing, M

Journalism, BM
Kindergarten/PreSchool Education and Teaching, B
Kinesiology and Exercise Science, B
Kinesiology and Movement Studies, MD
Landscape Architecture, BMD
Latin American Studies, BM
Latin Teacher Education, B
Law and Legal Studies, MD
Leisure Studies, MD
Liberal Arts and Sciences Studies and Humani-
   ties, B
Library Science, MDO
Linguistics, BMD
Logistics and Materials Management, B
Management Information Systems and Services, B
Management Science, B
Management Strategy and Policy, M
Management of Technology, M
Manufacturing Engineering, B
Marketing Research, B
Marketing/Marketing Management, B
Mass Communication/Media Studies, B
Materials Engineering, BMD
Materials Sciences, MD
Mathematics, BMD
Mathematics Teacher Education, BM
Mathematics and Computer Science, B
Mechanical Engineering, BMD
Mechanics, MD
Media Studies, MD
Medical Informatics, MDO
Metallurgical Engineering, B
Microbiology, BMD
Molecular Physiology, MD
Music, BMD
Music History, Literature, and Theory, B
Music Performance, B
Music Teacher Education, BMD
Music Theory and Composition, B
Musicology and Ethnomusicology, D
Natural Resources Conservation and Research, B
Natural Resources Management/Development and
   Policy, B
Natural Resources and Conservation, BMD
Near and Middle Eastern Studies, M
Neuroscience, D
Nuclear Engineering, BMD
Nutritional Sciences, MD
Operations Management and Supervision, B
Operations Research, B
Organizational Behavior Studies, B
Organizational Communication, B
Ornamental Horticulture, B
Painting, BM
Parks, Recreation, Leisure and Fitness Studies, B
Pathobiology, MD
Philosophy, BMD
Photography, BM
Physical Education Teaching and Coaching, B
Physics, BMD
Physics Teacher Education, B
Physiology, BMD
Plant Biology, MD
Plant Molecular Biology, B
Plant Protection and Integrated Pest Manage-
   ment, B
Political Science and Government, BMD
Polymer/Plastics Engineering, B
Portuguese Language and Literature, BMD
Pre-Law Studies, B
Pre-Veterinary Studies, B
Psychology, BMD
Public Health, BM
Purchasing, Procurement/Acquisitions and Con-
   tracts Management, B
Real Estate, B
Rehabilitation Sciences, M
Religion/Religious Studies, BMD
Restaurant, Culinary, and Catering
   Management/Manager, B
Romance Languages, Literatures, and Linguistics, D
Russian Language and Literature, B
Russian Studies, B
Sales, Distribution and Marketing Operations, B
Science Teacher Education/General Science
   Teacher Education, BM

Sculpture, BM
Secondary Education and Teaching, B
Slavic Languages, Literatures, and Linguistics, BMD
Social Science Teacher Education, B
Social Studies Teacher Education, B
Social Work, MD
Sociology, BMD
South and Southeast Asian Studies, M
Spanish Language Teacher Education, B
Spanish Language and Literature, BMD
Special Education and Teaching, BMDO
Sport and Fitness Administration/Management, B
Statistics, BMD
Structural Engineering, B
Systems Engineering, MD
Taxation, M
Teacher Education, Multiple Levels, B
Technical Teacher Education, B
Theater, MD
Theatre Literature, History and Criticism, B
Translation and Interpretation, M
Urban Forestry, B
Urban and Regional Planning, MD
Veterinary Medicine, D
Veterinary Sciences, MD
Vocational Rehabilitation Counseling/Counselor, B
Voice and Opera, B
Water Resources Engineering, B
Western European Studies, M
Wildlife and Wildlands Science and Management, B
Women's Studies, B
Writing, M
Zoology/Animal Biology, MD

UNIVERSITY OF ST. FRANCIS

Accounting, BO
Art Education, M
Art Teacher Education, B
Biology/Biological Sciences, B
Business Administration and Management, B
Business Administration, Management and Operations, MO
Business Education, MO
Clinical Laboratory Science/Medical Technology/Technologist, B
Computer Science, B
Criminal Justice/Law Enforcement Administration, B
Curriculum and Instruction, M
Education, MDO
Educational Leadership and Administration, MD
Educational Media/Instructional Technology, O
Elementary Education and Teaching, BM
English Education, M
English Language and Literature, B
English as a Second Language, O
English/Language Arts Teacher Education, B
Entrepreneurship/Entrepreneurial Studies, B
Environmental Sciences, B
Finance, B
Finance and Banking, O
Forensic Science and Technology, O
Health Services Administration, M
Health/Health Care Administration/Management, B
Higher Education/Higher Education Administration, M
History, B
Hospital and Health Care Facilities Administration/Management, B
Human Resources Management/Personnel Administration, B
Information Technology, B
International Business/Trade/Commerce, B
Liberal Arts and Sciences Studies and Humanities, B
Logistics and Materials Management, BO
Management Science, B
Management Strategy and Policy, O
Marketing/Marketing Management, B
Mass Communication/Media Studies, B
Mathematics, B
Mathematics Teacher Education, BM
Mathematics and Computer Science, B
Medical Radiologic Technology/Science - Radiation Therapist, B
Multi-/Interdisciplinary Studies, B
Music, B

Music Performance, B
Music Teacher Education, B
Nuclear Medical Technology/Technologist, B
Nursing, MDO
Nursing - Advanced Practice, MO
Nursing Administration, M
Nursing Education, MO
Organizational Behavior Studies, B
Parks, Recreation and Leisure Facilities Management, B
Physician Assistant, M
Political Science and Government, B
Pre-Dentistry Studies, B
Pre-Law Studies, B
Pre-Medicine/Pre-Medical Studies, B
Pre-Pharmacy Studies, B
Pre-Veterinary Studies, B
Psychiatric/Mental Health Nurse/Nursing, MO
Psychology, B
Radiologic Technology/Science - Radiographer, B
Reading Teacher Education, M
Science Teacher Education/General Science Teacher Education, BM
Secondary Education and Teaching, M
Social Studies Teacher Education, BM
Social Work, BMO
Special Education and Teaching, BM
Substance Abuse/Addiction Counseling, B
Theology/Theological Studies, B
Visual and Performing Arts, B
Web/Multimedia Management and Webmaster, B

VANDERCOOK COLLEGE OF MUSIC

Music Teacher Education, BM

VET TECH INSTITUTE AT FOX COLLEGE

Veterinary/Animal Health Technology/Technician and Veterinary Assistant, A

WAUBONSEE COMMUNITY COLLEGE

Accounting, A
Autobody/Collision and Repair Technology/Technician, A
Automobile/Automotive Mechanics Technology/Technician, A
Biological and Physical Sciences, A
Business Administration and Management, A
Business/Office Automation/Technology/Data Entry, A
CAD/CADD Drafting and/or Design Technology/Technician, A
Child Care Provider/Assistant, A
Community Health Services/Liaison/Counseling, A
Computer Programming/Programmer, A
Construction Management, A
Criminal Justice/Police Science, A
Electrical, Electronic and Communications Engineering Technology/Technician, A
Electrician, A
Emergency Care Attendant (EMT Ambulance), A
Engineering, A
Executive Assistant/Executive Secretary, A
Fine/Studio Arts, A
Fire Science/Firefighting, A
General Studies, A
Graphic Design, A
Health Information/Medical Records Technology/Technician, A
Health and Physical Education, A
Heating, Air Conditioning, Ventilation and Refrigeration Maintenance Technology/Technician, A
Human Resources Management/Personnel Administration, A
Liberal Arts and Sciences Studies and Humanities, A
Library Assistant/Technician, A
Manufacturing Technology/Technician, A
Music, A
Radio and Television Broadcasting Technology/Technician, A
Sign Language Interpretation and Translation, A
Small Business Administration/Management, A
Social Work, A
Survey Technology/Surveying, A
Teacher Assistant/Aide, A

Web Page, Digital/Multimedia and Information Resources Design, A
Welding Technology/Welder, A

WESTERN ILLINOIS UNIVERSITY

Accounting, BM
African-American/Black Studies, B
Agriculture, B
Anthropology, B
Applied Mathematics, O
Art/Art Studies, General, B
Athletic Training and Sports Medicine, B
Bilingual and Multilingual Education, B
Biological and Biomedical Sciences, MO
Biology/Biological Sciences, B
Business Administration and Management, B
Business Administration, Management and Operations, MO
Business/Managerial Economics, B
Chemistry, BM
Clinical Laboratory Science/Medical Technology/Technologist, B
Clinical Psychology, M
Communication Disorders, BM
Communication Studies/Speech Communication and Rhetoric, B
Communication and Media Studies, M
Community Psychology, M
Computer Science, M
Computer Systems Networking and Telecommunications, B
Computer and Information Sciences, B
Construction Management, B
Counselor Education/School Counseling and Guidance Services, M
Criminal Justice/Law Enforcement Administration, B
Design and Applied Arts, M
Dietetics/Dieticians, B
Distance Education Development, O
Drama and Dramatics/Theatre Arts, B
Ecology, D
Economic Development, O
Economics, BMO
Education, MDO
Educational Leadership and Administration, MDO
Educational Media/Instructional Technology, MO
Educational/Instructional Media Design, B
Elementary Education and Teaching, BM
Engineering, B
Engineering Technology, B
English, MO
English Language and Literature, B
English as a Second Language, O
Environmental Sciences, D
Family and Consumer Sciences/Human Sciences, B
Fashion Merchandising, B
Finance, B
Fine/Studio Arts, B
Fire Services Administration, B
Foods, Nutrition, and Wellness Studies, B
Foreign Languages and Literatures, B
Foundations and Philosophy of Education, MO
French Language Teacher Education, B
French Language and Literature, B
Geographic Information Systems, O
Geography, BMO
Geology/Earth Science, B
Graphic Design, O
Graphic and Printing Equipment Operator Production, B
Health Education, MO
Health Services Administration, O
Health Teacher Education, B
Health/Health Care Administration/Management, B
History, BM
Hospitality Administration/Management, B
Human Resources Management/Personnel Administration, B
Information Technology, B
Internet and Interactive Multimedia, O
Journalism, B
Kinesiology and Exercise Science, B
Kinesiology and Movement Studies, M
Law Enforcement, MO
Liberal Arts and Sciences Studies and Humanities, B

Liberal Studies, M
Logistics and Materials Management, B
Manufacturing Engineering, M
Marine Biology and Biological Oceanography, O
Marketing/Marketing Management, B
Mathematics, BMO
Meteorology, B
Museology/Museum Studies, MO
Music, BM
Music Performance, B
Parks, Recreation and Leisure Facilities Management, B
Philosophy, B
Physical Education Teaching and Coaching, B
Physics, BM
Political Science and Government, BM
Psychology, BMO
Public Health Education and Promotion, B
Radio and Television, B
Reading Teacher Education, M
Recreation and Park Management, M
Religion/Religious Studies, B
School Psychology, O
Security and Protective Services, B
Social Work, B
Sociology, BM
Spanish Language Teacher Education, B
Spanish Language and Literature, B
Special Education and Teaching, BM
Sport and Fitness Administration/Management, M
Student Personnel Services, M
Supply Chain Management, O
Sustainable Development, O
Theater, M
Travel and Tourism, M
Women's Studies, B
Writing, O
Zoology/Animal Biology, O

WHEATON COLLEGE

Anthropology, B
Applied Mathematics, B
Archeology, BM
Art/Art Studies, General, B
Bible/Biblical Studies, B
Biology/Biological Sciences, B
Business/Managerial Economics, B
Chemistry, B
Classics and Classical Languages, Literatures, and Linguistics, B
Clinical Psychology, MD
Communication Studies/Speech Communication and Rhetoric, B
Computer Science, B
Counseling Psychology, M
Cultural Studies, MO
Economics, B
Education, M
Elementary Education and Teaching, BM
Engineering, B
English Language and Literature, B
English as a Second Language, MO
Environmental Sciences, B
French Language and Literature, B
Geology/Earth Science, B
German Language and Literature, B
Health Services/Allied Health/Health Sciences, B
History, B
International Relations and Affairs, B
Marriage and Family Therapy/Counseling, M
Mathematics, B
Missions/Missionary Studies and Missiology, MO
Multi-/Interdisciplinary Studies, B
Music, B
Music History, Literature, and Theory, B
Music Pedagogy, B
Music Performance, B
Music Teacher Education, B
Music Theory and Composition, B
Pastoral Studies/Counseling, M
Philosophy, B
Physics, B
Political Science and Government, B
Psychology, BMD
Religious Education, BM
Secondary Education and Teaching, BM

Sociology, B
Spanish Language and Literature, B
Theology and Religious Vocations, MD
Urban Studies/Affairs, B

WORSHAM COLLEGE OF MORTUARY SCIENCE

Funeral Service and Mortuary Science, A

Indiana

ANCILLA COLLEGE

Agriculture, A
Behavioral Sciences, A
Biological and Physical Sciences, A
Business Administration and Management, A
Business Administration, Management and Operations, A
Communication Studies/Speech Communication and Rhetoric, A
Computer and Information Sciences, A
Criminal Justice/Safety Studies, A
Culinary Arts and Related Services, A
Data Processing and Data Processing Technology/Technician, A
Early Childhood Education and Teaching, A
Elementary Education and Teaching, A
English Language and Literature, A
Environmental Studies, A
General Studies, A
Health Services/Allied Health/Health Sciences, A
History, A
Hospitality Administration/Management, A
Kinesiology and Exercise Science, A
Logistics and Materials Management, A
Mass Communication/Media Studies, A
Religion/Religious Studies, A
Secondary Education and Teaching, A
Theology and Religious Vocations, A

ANDERSON UNIVERSITY

Accounting, BM
Athletic Training and Sports Medicine, B
Bible/Biblical Studies, B
Biochemistry, B
Biology/Biological Sciences, B
Business Administration and Management, AB
Business Administration, Management and Operations, MD
Business/Managerial Economics, B
Chemistry, B
Cinematography and Film/Video Production, B
Clinical Laboratory Science/Medical Technology/Technologist, B
Computer Science, B
Criminal Justice/Law Enforcement Administration, AB
Dance, B
Design and Visual Communications, B
Education, BM
Electrical, Electronics and Communications Engineering, B
Elementary Education and Teaching, B
English Language and Literature, B
English/Language Arts Teacher Education, B
Entrepreneurship/Entrepreneurial Studies, B
Family Systems, B
Finance, B
History, B
Information Science/Studies, B
International Business/Trade/Commerce, B
Liberal Arts and Sciences Studies and Humanities, AB
Marketing/Marketing Management, B
Mathematics, B
Mathematics Teacher Education, B
Mathematics and Computer Science, B
Mathematics and Statistics, B
Mechanical Engineering, B
Missions/Missionary Studies and Missiology, M
Multi-/Interdisciplinary Studies, B
Music Performance, B
Music Teacher Education, B
Music Theory and Composition, B
Physical Education Teaching and Coaching, B

Physical Sciences, B
Physics, B
Physics Teacher Education, B
Political Science and Government, B
Pre-Dentistry Studies, B
Pre-Law Studies, B
Pre-Medicine/Pre-Medical Studies, B
Pre-Veterinary Studies, B
Psychology, B
Religion/Religious Studies, B
Religious/Sacred Music, B
Social Studies Teacher Education, B
Social Work, B
Sociology, B
Spanish Language Teacher Education, B
Spanish Language and Literature, B
Speech Teacher Education, B
Theology and Religious Vocations, AMD
Theology/Theological Studies, B
Youth Ministry, B

THE ART INSTITUTE OF INDIANAPOLIS

Apparel and Accessories Marketing Operations, B
Baking and Pastry Arts/Baker/Pastry Chef, A
Commercial Photography, AB
Computer Graphics, B
Culinary Arts/Chef Training, A
Fashion/Apparel Design, B
Graphic Design, AB
Interior Design, B
Restaurant, Culinary, and Catering Management/Manager, B
Web Page, Digital/Multimedia and Information Resources Design, B

BALL STATE UNIVERSITY

Accounting, BM
Actuarial Science, BM
Administrative Assistant and Secretarial Science, A
Adult and Continuing Education and Teaching, MD
Advertising, B
Advertising and Public Relations, M
Allied Health Diagnostic, Intervention, and Treatment Professions, A
Anthropology, BM
Applied Behavior Analysis, M
Architecture, BM
Art/Art Studies, General, B
Astronomy, B
Athletic Training and Sports Medicine, B
Audiology/Audiologist and Speech-Language Pathology/Pathologist, B
Biological and Biomedical Sciences, MD
Biology Teacher Education, B
Biology/Biological Sciences, B
Business Administration, Management and Operations, MO
Business Education, M
Business Teacher Education, B
Business, Management, Marketing, and Related Support Services, A
Business/Commerce, B
Business/Managerial Economics, B
Chemical Technology/Technician, A
Chemistry, BM
Chemistry Teacher Education, B
City/Urban, Community and Regional Planning, B
Classics and Classical Languages, Literatures, and Linguistics, B
Clinical Laboratory Science/Medical Technology/Technologist, B
Clinical Psychology, M
Cognitive Sciences, M
Communication Disorders, MD
Communication Studies/Speech Communication and Rhetoric, B
Communication and Media Studies, M
Community Health and Preventive Medicine, B
Computer Science, M
Computer and Information Sciences, B
Construction Management, B
Counseling Psychology, MD
Criminal Justice/Safety Studies, AB
Criminology, M
Curriculum and Instruction, MO
Dance, B

Dental Hygiene/Hygienist, B
Dietetics/Dieticians, B
Drama and Dramatics/Theatre Arts, B
Early Childhood Education and Teaching, B
Education, MDO
Education/Teaching of Individuals with Multiple Disabilities, B
Educational Administration and Supervision, MDO
Educational Psychology, MDO
Elementary Education and Teaching, BMD
Engineering, B
Engineering Technologies/Technicians, B
English, MD
English Language and Literature, B
English as a Second Language, M
Entrepreneurship/Entrepreneurial Studies, B
Environmental Design/Architecture, B
Environmental Sciences, D
Exercise and Sports Science, MD
Family and Consumer Sciences/Human Sciences, BM
Finance, B
Fine Arts and Art Studies, BM
Foundations and Philosophy of Education, D
French Language and Literature, B
General Studies, AB
Geography, BM
Geology/Earth Science, BM
German Language and Literature, B
Gerontology, M
Health Promotion, M
Higher Education/Higher Education Administration, MD
Historic Preservation and Conservation, M
History, BM
Human Development and Family Studies, B
Human Resources Management/Personnel Administration, B
Industrial Technology/Technician, B
Information Science/Studies, M
Insurance, B
International Business/Trade/Commerce, B
Japanese Language and Literature, B
Journalism, BM
Kinesiology and Exercise Science, B
Landscape Architecture, BM
Legal Professions and Studies, B
Liberal Arts and Sciences Studies and Humanities, AB
Linguistics, MD
Management Information Systems and Services, B
Management Science, B
Manufacturing Technology/Technician, B
Marketing/Marketing Management, B
Mathematics, BM
Mathematics Teacher Education, M
Medical Radiologic Technology/Science - Radiation Therapist, A
Multi-/Interdisciplinary Studies, B
Music, B
Music Teacher Education, BMD
Natural Resources and Conservation, BMD
Nuclear Medical Technology/Technologist, A
Nursing, MD
Nutritional Sciences, M
Operations Management and Supervision, B
Philosophy, B
Physical Education Teaching and Coaching, BM
Physics, BM
Physics Teacher Education, B
Physiology, M
Political Science and Government, BM
Pre-Dentistry Studies, B
Pre-Medicine/Pre-Medical Studies, B
Psychology, BM
Public Administration, M
Radio and Television, B
Religion/Religious Studies, B
Respiratory Care Therapy/Therapist, B
Rhetoric, M
School Psychology, MDO
Science Teacher Education/General Science Teacher Education, BMD
Secondary Education and Teaching, M
Selling Skills and Sales Operations, B
Social Psychology, M

Social Sciences, B
Social Studies Teacher Education, B
Social Work, B
Sociology, BM
Spanish Language and Literature, B
Special Education and Teaching, MDO
Speech and Interpersonal Communication, M
Sport and Fitness Administration/Management, B
Statistics, M
Technology Teacher Education/Industrial Arts Teacher Education, B
Telecommunications, M
Urban Design, M
Urban Planning, M
Vocational and Technical Education, M
Women's Studies, B
Writing, MD

BETHEL COLLEGE

Accounting, B
American Sign Language (ASL), A
Art/Art Studies, General, B
Bible/Biblical Studies, AB
Biology/Biological Sciences, B
Business Administration and Management, AB
Business Administration, Management and Operations, M
Business/Commerce, AB
Cell/Cellular and Molecular Biology, B
Chemistry, B
Christian Studies, B
Communication Studies/Speech Communication and Rhetoric, B
Criminal Justice/Safety Studies, AB
Design and Visual Communications, B
Divinity/Ministry (BD, MDiv.), B
Drama and Dramatics/Theatre Arts, B
Early Childhood Education and Teaching, AB
Education, BM
Elementary Education and Teaching, B
Engineering, B
English Language and Literature, B
English/Language Arts Teacher Education, B
Financial Planning and Services, B
Fine/Studio Arts, B
General Studies, AB
Health and Physical Education, B
History, B
Human Services, AB
International Business/Trade/Commerce, B
International Public Health/International Health, B
Junior High/Intermediate/Middle School Education and Teaching, B
Kinesiology and Exercise Science, B
Liberal Arts and Sciences Studies and Humanities, AB
Mathematics, B
Mathematics Teacher Education, B
Missions/Missionary Studies and Missiology, B
Music, B
Music Performance, B
Music Teacher Education, B
Nursing, M
Pastoral Studies/Counseling, BM
Philosophy, B
Physical Education Teaching and Coaching, B
Political Science and Government, B
Psychology, B
Science Teacher Education/General Science Teacher Education, B
Secondary Education and Teaching, B
Sign Language Interpretation and Translation, B
Social Sciences, B
Social Studies Teacher Education, B
Sociology, B
Sport and Fitness Administration/Management, B
Theology and Religious Vocations, M

BRIGHTWOOD COLLEGE, HAMMOND CAMPUS

Computer Systems Networking and Telecommunications, A
Massage Therapy/Therapeutic Massage, A

Medical/Clinical Assistant, A

BRIGHTWOOD COLLEGE, INDIANAPOLIS CAMPUS

Criminal Justice/Law Enforcement Administration, A

BUTLER UNIVERSITY

Accounting, BM
Actuarial Science, B
Anthropology, B
Astronomy and Astrophysics, B
Biology/Biological Sciences, B
Business Administration, Management and Operations, M
Chemistry, B
Classical, Ancient Mediterranean and Near Eastern Studies and Archaeology, B
Communication Disorders, B
Communication and Media Studies, B
Computer and Information Sciences, B
Counselor Education/School Counseling and Guidance Services, M
Criminology, B
Dance, B
Design and Applied Arts, B
Digital Communication and Media/Multimedia, B
Drama and Dramatics/Theatre Arts, B
Early Childhood Education and Teaching, B
Economics, B
Education, M
Educational Administration and Supervision, M
Educational Leadership and Administration, M
Elementary Education and Teaching, B
English, M
English Language and Literature, B
Entrepreneurship/Entrepreneurial Studies, B
Finance, B
French Language and Literature, B
German Language and Literature, B
Health Services/Allied Health/Health Sciences, B
Health/Health Care Administration/Management, B
History, BM
Insurance, B
International Business/Trade/Commerce, B
International Relations and Affairs, B
Jazz/Jazz Studies, B
Journalism, B
Liberal Arts and Sciences Studies and Humanities, B
Management Information Systems and Services, B
Marketing/Marketing Management, B
Mathematics, B
Music, BM
Music Performance, B
Music Teacher Education, B
Music Theory and Composition, B
Organizational Communication, B
Peace Studies and Conflict Resolution, B
Pharmaceutical Sciences, MD
Pharmacy, BMD
Philosophy, B
Philosophy and Religious Studies, B
Physician Assistant, BM
Physics, B
Political Science and Government, B
Pre-Pharmacy Studies, B
Psychology, B
Public Relations, Advertising, and Applied Communication, B
Radio and Television, B
Recording Arts Technology/Technician, B
Religion/Religious Studies, B
Science, Technology and Society, B
Secondary Education and Teaching, B
Sociology, B
Spanish Language and Literature, B
Women's Studies, B
Writing, M

CALUMET COLLEGE OF SAINT JOSEPH

Accounting, AB
Biological and Physical Sciences, B
Business Administration and Management, AB
Business Administration, Management and Operations, B

Computer and Information Sciences, AB
Criminal Justice/Safety Studies, AB
Educational Leadership and Administration, M
Elementary Education and Teaching, B
English Language and Literature, AB
General Studies, AB
Human Services, AB
Intermedia/Multimedia, B
Law Enforcement, M
Legal Assistant/Paralegal, AB
Liberal Arts and Sciences Studies and Humanities, AB
Psychology, AB
Quality Management, M
Religion/Religious Studies, AB
Social Sciences, B

COLLEGE OF COURT REPORTING

Court Reporting/Court Reporter, A

CROSSROADS BIBLE COLLEGE

Bible/Biblical Studies, B
Christian Studies, B
Pastoral Counseling and Specialized Ministries, B
Pastoral Studies/Counseling, B
Religious Education, B
Teacher Education, Multiple Levels, B
Youth Ministry, B

DEPAUW UNIVERSITY

African-American/Black Studies, B
Ancient/Classical Greek Language and Literature, B
Anthropology, B
Art History, Criticism and Conservation, B
Athletic Training and Sports Medicine, B
Biochemistry, B
Biology/Biological Sciences, B
Chemistry, B
Classics and Classical Languages, Literatures, and Linguistics, B
Computer Science, B
Drama and Dramatics/Theatre Arts, B
East Asian Studies, B
Economics, B
Elementary Education and Teaching, B
English Language and Literature, B
Environmental Studies, B
Fine/Studio Arts, B
French Language and Literature, B
Geology/Earth Science, B
German Language and Literature, B
History, B
Kinesiology and Exercise Science, B
Latin Language and Literature, B
Mass Communication/Media Studies, B
Mathematics, B
Multi-/Interdisciplinary Studies, B
Music, B
Music Performance, B
Music Teacher Education, B
Music Theory and Composition, B
Peace Studies and Conflict Resolution, B
Philosophy, B
Physical Education Teaching and Coaching, B
Physics, B
Political Science and Government, B
Psychology, B
Religion/Religious Studies, B
Romance Languages, Literatures, and Linguistics, B
Russian Studies, B
Sociology, B
Spanish Language and Literature, B
Women's Studies, B

DEVRY UNIVERSITY

Business Administration and Management, B
Business Administration, Management and Operations, BMO
Business/Commerce, B
Computer Systems Analysis/Analyst, B
Criminal Justice/Law Enforcement Administration, B
Health/Health Care Administration/Management, B

Web Page, Digital/Multimedia and Information Resources Design, AB

EARLHAM COLLEGE

African-American/Black Studies, B
Anthropology, B
Art/Art Studies, General, B
Biochemistry, B
Biology/Biological Sciences, B
Business/Commerce, B
Chemistry, B
Classics and Classical Languages, Literatures, and Linguistics, B
Comparative Literature, B
Computer and Information Sciences, B
Drama and Dramatics/Theatre Arts, B
Economics, B
Education, M
English Language and Literature, B
Environmental Sciences, B
Environmental Studies, B
French Language and Literature, B
Geological and Earth Sciences/Geosciences, B
German Language and Literature, B
History, B
Japanese Studies, B
Latin American Studies, B
Mathematics, B
Multi-/Interdisciplinary Studies, B
Music, B
Peace Studies and Conflict Resolution, B
Philosophy, B
Physics, B
Political Science and Government, B
Pre-Medicine/Pre-Medical Studies, B
Psychology, B
Religion/Religious Studies, B
Sociology, B
Spanish Language and Literature, B
Women's Studies, B

FRANKLIN COLLEGE

Accounting, B
Athletic Training and Sports Medicine, B
Biology Teacher Education, B
Biology/Biological Sciences, B
Business/Commerce, B
Chemistry, B
Chemistry Teacher Education, B
Computer Science, B
Computer and Information Sciences, B
Drama and Dramatics/Theatre Arts, B
Economics, B
Elementary Education and Teaching, B
English Language and Literature, B
English/Language Arts Teacher Education, B
French Language Teacher Education, B
French Language and Literature, B
History, B
Journalism, B
Kinesiology and Exercise Science, B
Mathematics, B
Mathematics Teacher Education, B
Philosophy, B
Physical Education Teaching and Coaching, B
Political Science and Government, B
Psychology, B
Religion/Religious Studies, B
Social Studies Teacher Education, B
Sociology, B
Spanish Language Teacher Education, B
Spanish Language and Literature, B

GOSHEN COLLEGE

Accounting, B
American Sign Language (ASL), B
Art Teacher Education, B
Art/Art Studies, General, B
Bible/Biblical Studies, B
Biology Teacher Education, B
Biology/Biological Sciences, B
Broadcast Journalism, B
Business Administration and Management, B
Business Teacher Education, B
Business/Commerce, B
Chemistry, B

Chemistry Teacher Education, B
Cinematography and Film/Video Production, B
Computer Science, B
Drama and Dramatics/Theatre Arts, B
Education, B
Elementary Education and Teaching, B
English Language and Literature, B
English/Language Arts Teacher Education, B
Environmental Education, M
Environmental Sciences, B
History, B
Information Science/Studies, B
Journalism, B
Kinesiology and Exercise Science, B
Marketing/Marketing Management, B
Mathematics, B
Mathematics Teacher Education, B
Molecular Biology, B
Music, B
Music Teacher Education, B
Nursing, M
Peace Studies and Conflict Resolution, B
Physical Education Teaching and Coaching, B
Physics, B
Physics Teacher Education, B
Psychology, B
Public/Applied History and Archival Administration, B
Religion/Religious Studies, B
Science Teacher Education/General Science Teacher Education, B
Secondary Education and Teaching, B
Sign Language Interpretation and Translation, B
Social Studies Teacher Education, B
Social Work, B
Sociology, B
Spanish Language Teacher Education, B
Spanish Language and Literature, B
Special Education and Teaching, B
Teaching English as a Second or Foreign Language/ESL Language Instructor, B

GRACE COLLEGE

Accounting, B
Actuarial Science, B
Art Teacher Education, B
Art/Art Studies, General, B
Bible/Biblical Studies, AB
Biological and Physical Sciences, B
Biology Teacher Education, B
Biology/Biological Sciences, B
Business Administration and Management, B
Business Administration, Management and Operations, B
Business Teacher Education, B
Business/Commerce, B
Clinical Psychology, M
Communication Studies/Speech Communication and Rhetoric, B
Counseling Psychology, M
Criminal Justice/Safety Studies, B
Drama and Dramatics/Theatre Arts, B
Drawing, B
Education, B
Elementary Education and Teaching, B
Engineering Physics, B
English Language and Literature, B
English/Language Arts Teacher Education, B
Entrepreneurship/Entrepreneurial Studies, B
Environmental Biology, B
Environmental Sciences, B
Environmental Studies, B
Film/Cinema Studies, B
Finance, B
Foreign Languages and Literatures, B
French Language Teacher Education, B
French Language and Literature, B
Graphic Design, B
Health/Medical Preparatory Programs, B
History, B
Hospitality and Recreation Marketing Operations, B
Illustration, B
Information Technology, B
Journalism, B
Kinesiology and Exercise Science, B
Language Interpretation and Translation, B
Management Information Systems and Services, B

Marketing/Marketing Management, B
Mathematics, B
Mathematics Teacher Education, B
Mathematics and Computer Science, B
Missions/Missionary Studies and Missiology, B
Non-Profit/Public/Organizational Management, B
Photography, B
Political Science and Government, B
Psychology, B
Public Relations, Advertising, and Applied Communication, B
Social Studies Teacher Education, B
Sociology, B
Spanish Language Teacher Education, B
Spanish Language and Literature, B
Special Education and Teaching, B
Sport and Fitness Administration/Management, B
Web Page, Digital/Multimedia and Information Resources Design, B
Youth Ministry, B

HANOVER COLLEGE

Anthropology, B
Art History, Criticism and Conservation, B
Art/Art Studies, General, B
Biochemistry, B
Biology/Biological Sciences, B
Chemistry, B
Classical, Ancient Mediterranean and Near Eastern Studies and Archaeology, B
Classics and Classical Languages, Literatures, and Linguistics, B
Computer Science, B
Drama and Dramatics/Theatre Arts, B
Economics, B
Elementary Education and Teaching, B
English Language and Literature, B
French Language and Literature, B
Geology/Earth Science, B
German Language and Literature, B
Health and Physical Education, B
History, B
International/Global Studies, B
Kinesiology and Exercise Science, B
Mass Communication/Media Studies, B
Mathematics, B
Medieval and Renaissance Studies, B
Music, B
Philosophy, B
Physics, B
Political Science and Government, B
Psychology, B
Sociology, B
Spanish Language and Literature, B
Theology/Theological Studies, B

HARRISON COLLEGE

Accounting, AB
Administrative Assistant and Secretarial Science, A
Baking and Pastry Arts/Baker/Pastry Chef, A
Banking and Financial Support Services, A
Business Administration and Management, AB
Clinical Laboratory Science/Medical Technology/Technologist, A
Computer Systems Networking and Telecommunications, A
Computer Technology/Computer Systems Technology, A
Cooking and Related Culinary Arts, A
Criminal Justice/Law Enforcement Administration, AB
Criminal Justice/Safety Studies, AB
Culinary Arts/Chef Training, A
Fashion Merchandising, AB
Finance, A
Fire Protection and Safety Technology/Technician, A
Health/Health Care Administration/Management, B
Hospitality Administration/Management, B
Hotel/Motel Administration/Management, B
Human Resources Management/Personnel Administration, AB
Information Technology, B
Legal Assistant/Paralegal, A
Management Information Systems and Services, A
Manufacturing Technology/Technician, A
Marketing/Marketing Management, A

Massage Therapy/Therapeutic Massage, A
Medical Insurance Specialist/Medical Biller, A
Medical/Clinical Assistant, A
Surgical Technology/Technologist, A
System Administration/Administrator, A
Veterinary/Animal Health Technology/Technician and Veterinary Assistant, A
Web Page, Digital/Multimedia and Information Resources Design, B

HOLY CROSS COLLEGE

Art/Art Studies, General, B
Business Administration and Management, B
Business Administration, Management and Operations, B
Design and Visual Communications, B
Elementary Education and Teaching, B
English Language and Literature, B
Gerontology, A
History, B
International/Global Studies, A
Liberal Arts and Sciences Studies and Humanities, AB
Political Science and Government, A
Pre-Medicine/Pre-Medical Studies, B
Psychology, B
Sociology, A
Spanish Language and Literature, A
Theology/Theological Studies, B

HUNTINGTON UNIVERSITY

Accounting, B
Animation, Interactive Technology, Video Graphics and Special Effects, B
Art Teacher Education, B
Art/Art Studies, General, B
Athletic Training and Sports Medicine, B
Bible/Biblical Studies, B
Biological and Physical Sciences, B
Biology Teacher Education, B
Biology/Biological Sciences, B
Broadcast Journalism, B
Business Administration and Management, B
Business/Managerial Economics, B
Chemistry, B
Chemistry Teacher Education, B
Christian Studies, A
Communication Studies/Speech Communication and Rhetoric, B
Computer Science, B
Digital Communication and Media/Multimedia, B
Divinity/Ministry (BD, MDiv.), B
Drama and Dramatics/Theatre Arts, B
Economics, B
Education, BM
Elementary Education and Teaching, B
English Language and Literature, B
English as a Second Language, M
English/Language Arts Teacher Education, B
Film/Cinema Studies, B
Fine/Studio Arts, B
Graphic Design, B
History, B
Human Resources Management/Personnel Administration, B
Journalism, B
Junior High/Intermediate/Middle School Education and Teaching, B
Kinesiology and Exercise Science, B
Liberal Arts and Sciences Studies and Humanities, B
Marketing/Marketing Management, B
Mass Communication/Media Studies, B
Mathematics, B
Mathematics Teacher Education, B
Middle School Education, M
Missions/Missionary Studies and Missiology, BM
Music, B
Music Pedagogy, B
Music Performance, B
Music Teacher Education, B
Non-Profit/Public/Organizational Management, B
Parks, Recreation, Leisure and Fitness Studies, B
Pastoral Studies/Counseling, MD
Philosophy, B
Physical Education Teaching and Coaching, B

Political Science and Government, B
Pre-Law Studies, B
Pre-Medicine/Pre-Medical Studies, B
Pre-Pharmacy Studies, B
Psychology, B
Public Relations/Image Management, B
Religion/Religious Studies, AB
Religious/Sacred Music, B
Science Teacher Education/General Science Teacher Education, B
Secondary Education and Teaching, B
Small Business Administration/Management, B
Social Studies Teacher Education, B
Social Work, B
Sociology, B
Special Education and Teaching, B
Sport and Fitness Administration/Management, B
Teaching English as a Second or Foreign Language/ESL Language Instructor, B
Technical Theatre/Theatre Design and Technology, B
Theological and Ministerial Studies, B
Theology/Theological Studies, B
Youth Ministry, B

INDIANA STATE UNIVERSITY

Accounting, B
Aeronautics/Aviation/Aerospace Science and Technology, B
African-American/Black Studies, B
Airline/Commercial/Professional Pilot and Flight Crew, B
Anthropology, B
Apparel and Textiles, B
Architectural Technology/Technician, B
Art Teacher Education, B
Art/Art Studies, General, B
Athletic Training and Sports Medicine, BMD
Audiology/Audiologist and Speech-Language Pathology/Pathologist, B
Automotive Engineering Technology/Technician, B
Aviation/Airway Management and Operations, B
Biological and Biomedical Sciences, MD
Biology/Biological Sciences, B
Business Administration and Management, B
Business Administration, Management and Operations, M
Business Teacher Education, B
Cell Biology and Anatomy, D
Ceramic Arts and Ceramics, M
Chemistry, B
Civil Engineering Technology/Technician, B
Clinical Laboratory Science/Medical Technology/Technologist, B
Clinical Psychology, MD
Communication Disorders, MDO
Communication Studies/Speech Communication and Rhetoric, B
Communication and Media Studies, M
Community Health Services/Liaison/Counseling, B
Computer Engineering, M
Computer Engineering Technology/Technician, B
Computer Science, M
Computer and Information Sciences, B
Construction Management, B
Counselor Education/School Counseling and Guidance Services, M
Criminology, BM
Curriculum and Instruction, MD
Drama and Dramatics/Theatre Arts, B
Ecology, D
Economics, B
Education, MDO
Educational Administration and Supervision, MDO
Educational Media/Instructional Technology, MD
Electrical, Electronic and Communications Engineering Technology/Technician, B
Elementary Education and Teaching, B
Engineering Technology, B
Engineering and Applied Sciences, M
English, M
English Language and Literature, B
English as a Second Language, MO
Environmental and Occupational Health, M
Evolutionary Biology, D
Family and Consumer Sciences/Human Sciences, B

Finance, B
Fine Arts and Art Studies, M
Fine/Studio Arts, B
Foods, Nutrition, and Wellness Studies, B
Foreign Language Teacher Education, D
Foreign Languages, Literatures, and Linguistics, B
Geography, B
Geology/Earth Science, B
Graphic Design, M
Higher Education/Higher Education Administration, MD
History, BM
Human Development and Family Studies, B
Human Resources Development, M
Human Resources Management/Personnel Administration, B
Industrial Technology/Technician, B
Information Technology, B
Insurance, B
Interior Architecture, B
Kinesiology and Exercise Science, B
Liberal Arts and Sciences Studies and Humanities, B
Linguistics, M
Management Information Systems and Services, B
Management Sciences and Quantitative Methods, B
Management of Technology, MD
Manufacturing Technology/Technician, B
Marketing/Marketing Management, B
Mathematics, BM
Mechanical Engineering Related Technologies/Technicians, B
Media Studies, M
Molecular Biology, D
Multi-/Interdisciplinary Studies, B
Multilingual and Multicultural Education, O
Music, BM
Music Performance, B
Music Teacher Education, M
Nursing, MD
Nursing - Advanced Practice, M
Nursing Administration, M
Nursing Education, M
Occupational Safety and Health Technology/Technician, B
Occupational Therapy/Therapist, M
Office Management and Supervision, B
Painting, M
Parks, Recreation and Leisure Facilities Management, B
Philosophy, B
Photography, M
Physical Education Teaching and Coaching, BM
Physical Therapy/Therapist, D
Physician Assistant, M
Physics, B
Physiology, D
Political Science and Government, B
Printmaking, M
Psychology, BMD
Public Administration, M
Recreation and Park Management, MD
Robotics Technology/Technician, B
School Psychology, DO
Science Teacher Education/General Science Teacher Education, BM
Sculpture, M
Social Studies Teacher Education, B
Social Work, BM
Spanish Language and Literature, M
Special Education and Teaching, B
Sport and Fitness Administration/Management, MD
Student Personnel Services, M
Technology Teacher Education/Industrial Arts Teacher Education, B
Trade and Industrial Teacher Education, B
Vocational and Technical Education, M
Writing, M

INDIANA TECH

Accounting, ABM
Apparel and Textile Marketing Management, B
Biomedical/Medical Engineering, B
Business Administration and Management, AB
Business Administration, Management and Operations, M

Communication Studies/Speech Communication and Rhetoric, B
Computer Engineering, B
Computer Graphics, A
Computer Science, B
Computer Software Engineering, B
Computer Systems Networking and Telecommunications, AB
Computer and Information Sciences and Support Services, B
Computer and Information Systems Security, B
Corrections and Criminal Justice, B
Criminal Justice/Law Enforcement Administration, B
Criminal Justice/Safety Studies, A
Criminalistics and Criminal Science, B
Electrical, Electronics and Communications Engineering, B
Elementary Education and Teaching, B
Environmental/Environmental Health Engineering, B
General Studies, A
Health Services Administration, M
Human Resources Development, M
Human Resources Management and Services, M
Human Services, B
Industrial Engineering, AB
International Business/Trade/Commerce, D
Management, M
Marketing, M
Mechanical Engineering, B
Organizational Management, M
Parks, Recreation and Leisure Facilities Management, AB
Physical Education Teaching and Coaching, B
Pre-Law Studies, B
Psychology, B
Science Teacher Education/General Science Teacher Education, M
Sport and Fitness Administration/Management, B
Therapeutic Recreation/Recreational Therapy, B
Web/Multimedia Management and Webmaster, AB

INDIANA UNIVERSITY BLOOMINGTON

African Studies, M
African-American Studies, M
African-American/Black Studies, B
American/United States Studies/Civilization, B
Analytical Chemistry, D
Ancient/Classical Greek Language and Literature, B
Animal Behavior and Ethology, B
Anthropology, BMD
Apparel and Textiles, B
Applied Mathematics, M
Applied Statistics, M
Art Education, MD
Art History, Criticism and Conservation, BMD
Art Teacher Education, B
Art/Art Studies, General, B
Artificial Intelligence and Robotics, D
Arts Management, M
Asian Languages, MD
Asian Studies/Civilization, MD
Astronomy, BMD
Astrophysics, D
Athletic Training and Sports Medicine, BM
Audiology/Audiologist and Speech-Language Pathology/Pathologist, B
Ballet, B
BioTechnology, BM
Biochemistry, BD
Bioinformatics, MD
Biological and Biomedical Sciences, BMD
Biology Teacher Education, B
Biology/Biological Sciences, B
Biostatistics, MD
Business Administration, Management and Operations, MD
Business/Commerce, B
Cell Biology and Anatomy, D
Chemistry, BMD
Chemistry Teacher Education, B
Chinese Studies, MD
Classics and Classical Languages, Literatures, and Linguistics, BMD
Cognitive Sciences, BD
Communication Disorders, MD

Communication Studies/Speech Communication and Rhetoric, B
Communication and Media Studies, MD
Community Health and Preventive Medicine, BM
Comparative Literature, BMD
Computer Art and Design, M
Computer Science, BMD
Computer and Information Systems Security, MD
Counselor Education/School Counseling and Guidance Services, MDO
Criminal Justice/Safety Studies, B
Criminology, MD
Curriculum and Instruction, MDO
Dance, B
Database Systems, MO
Developmental Psychology, D
Digital Communication and Media/Multimedia, B
Drama and Dramatics/Theatre Arts, B
Early Childhood Education and Teaching, B
East Asian Languages, Literatures, and Linguistics, B
East Asian Studies, BMD
East European and Russian Studies, MO
Ecology, MD
Economic Development, M
Economics, BD
Education, MDO
Educational Administration and Supervision, M
Educational Leadership and Administration, MDO
Educational Measurement and Evaluation, D
Educational Media/Instructional Technology, MD
Educational Policy, MDO
Educational Psychology, MDO
Elementary Education and Teaching, BMDO
Energy Management and Policy, M
Engineering, B
English, MD
English Language and Literature, B
English as a Second Language, M
English/Language Arts Teacher Education, B
Environmental Policy, D
Environmental Policy and Resource Management, M
Environmental Sciences, BMDO
Environmental Studies, B
Environmental and Occupational Health, MD
Epidemiology, MD
Ergonomics and Human Factors, M
Ethnic, Cultural Minority, and Gender Studies, B
Ethnomusicology, MD
Evolutionary Biology, MD
Exercise and Sports Science, MD
Fashion/Apparel Design, B
Film, Television, and Video Theory and Criticism, D
Finance and Banking, MDO
Fine Arts and Art Studies, MD
Fine/Studio Arts, B
Folklore, MD
Foreign Language Teacher Education, BM
Foundations and Philosophy of Education, MD
French Language Teacher Education, B
French Language and Literature, BMD
Gender Studies, D
Genetics, D
Geochemistry, MD
Geography, BMD
Geology/Earth Science, BMD
Geophysics and Seismology, M
Geosciences, MD
German Language Teacher Education, B
German Language and Literature, MD
Germanic Languages, Literatures, and Linguistics, B
Health Education, M
Health Informatics, D
Health Promotion, B
Health Services Administration, M
Health Teacher Education, B
Higher Education/Higher Education Administration, MD
Hispanic and Latin American Languages, MD
History, BMD
History of Science and Technology, MD
Human-Computer Interaction, MD
Hydrogeology, D
Information Science/Studies, MDO
Inorganic Chemistry, D

Interior Design, B
International Development, M
International Relations and Affairs, B
International and Comparative Education, MD
Italian Language and Literature, BMD
Japanese Studies, MD
Jewish/Judaic Studies, BM
Journalism, BMD
Kinesiology and Exercise Science, B
Kinesiology and Movement Studies, MD
Labor Studies, AB
Latin American Studies, M
Latin Teacher Education, B
Law and Legal Studies, MDO
Leisure Studies, D
Liberal Arts and Sciences Studies and Humanities, B
Library Science, MDO
Linguistic, Comparative, and Related Language Studies and Services, B
Linguistics, BMD
Management Information Systems and Services, M
Mass Communication/Media Studies, BD
Materials Sciences, D
Mathematical Physics, D
Mathematics, BMD
Mathematics Teacher Education, BMD
Media Studies, D
Medical Physics, M
Medieval and Renaissance Studies, D
Microbiology, BMD
Mineralogy, MD
Molecular Biology, D
Multilingual and Multicultural Education, MD
Music, BMDO
Music Performance, B
Music Teacher Education, B
Musical Instrument Fabrication and Repair, A
Near and Middle Eastern Languages, MD
Neuroscience, D
Non-Profit/Public/Organizational Management, MO
Nutritional Sciences, M
Optometric Technician/Assistant, A
Optometry, MD
Organic Chemistry, D
Organizational Management, O
Parks, Recreation, Leisure and Fitness Studies, B
Performance, D
Philosophy, BMD
Physical Chemistry, D
Physical Education Teaching and Coaching, MD
Physics, BMD
Physics Teacher Education, B
Plant Biology, MD
Political Science and Government, BMD
Portuguese Language and Literature, BMD
Psychology, BD
Public Administration, BMDO
Public Affairs, MDO
Public Health, BMD
Public Policy Analysis, MD
Reading Teacher Education, MDO
Recording Arts Technology/Technician, AB
Recreation and Park Management, MD
Religion/Religious Studies, BMD
Rhetoric, D
Safety Engineering, M
School Psychology, MDO
Science Teacher Education/General Science Teacher Education, MD
Secondary Education and Teaching, BMD
Semitic Languages, Literatures, and Linguistics, B
Slavic Languages, Literatures, and Linguistics, BMD
Social Psychology, D
Social Sciences, D
Social Studies Teacher Education, BMD
Social Work, B
Sociology, BMD
South Asian Studies, B
Spanish Language Teacher Education, B
Spanish Language and Literature, BMD
Special Education and Teaching, BDO
Speech and Interpersonal Communication, MD
Sport and Fitness Administration/Management, MD
Statistics, BMD
Sustainability Management, M

Teacher Education and Professional Development, Specific Subject Areas, B
Telecommunications, M
Theater, MD
Therapeutic Recreation, M
Toxicology, M
Travel and Tourism, M
Ural-Altaic and Central Asian Studies, B
Vision Science/Physiological Optics, B
Water Resources Engineering, M
Western European Studies, M
Writing, M
Zoology/Animal Biology, MD

INDIANA UNIVERSITY EAST

Art/Art Studies, General, B
BioTechnology, B
Biochemistry, B
Biological and Biomedical Sciences, B
Biology/Biological Sciences, B
Business/Commerce, B
Communication Studies/Speech Communication and Rhetoric, B
Criminal Justice/Law Enforcement Administration, B
Education, M
Elementary Education and Teaching, B
English Language and Literature, B
History, B
Humanities/Humanistic Studies, B
Liberal Arts and Sciences Studies and Humanities, B
Mathematics, B
Natural Sciences, B
Nursing, M
Political Science and Government, B
Psychology, B
Secondary Education and Teaching, B
Social Work, BM
Sociology, B

INDIANA UNIVERSITY KOKOMO

Art/Art Studies, General, B
Biochemistry, B
Biochemistry, Biophysics and Molecular Biology, B
Biological and Physical Sciences, B
Biology/Biological Sciences, B
Business Administration, Management and Operations, M
Business/Commerce, B
Chemistry, B
Communication Studies/Speech Communication and Rhetoric, B
Criminal Justice/Safety Studies, B
Digital Communication and Media/Multimedia, B
Early Childhood Education and Teaching, B
Elementary Education and Teaching, B
English Language and Literature, B
Fine/Studio Arts, B
Health Services Administration, MO
History, B
Hospitality Administration/Management, B
Humanities/Humanistic Studies, B
Liberal Arts and Sciences Studies and Humanities, B
Mathematics, B
Medical Radiologic Technology/Science - Radiation Therapist, B
Nursing, M
Nursing Administration, M
Nursing Education, M
Psychology, B
Public Administration, BMO
Radiologic Technology/Science - Radiographer, A
Secondary Education and Teaching, B
Sociology, B

INDIANA UNIVERSITY NORTHWEST

Actuarial Science, B
African-American/Black Studies, B
Anthropology, B
Biology Teacher Education, B
Biology/Biological Sciences, B
Business Administration, Management and Operations, MO
Business/Commerce, B
Chemistry, B

Chemistry Teacher Education, B
Communication Studies/Speech Communication and Rhetoric, B
Computer Science, B
Counseling Psychology, M
Criminal Justice/Safety Studies, B
Criminology, M
Dental Hygiene/Hygienist, B
Drama and Dramatics/Theatre Arts, B
Economics, B
Education, M
Educational Leadership and Administration, M
Elementary Education and Teaching, BM
English Language and Literature, B
English/Language Arts Teacher Education, B
Environmental Policy and Resource Management, O
Fine/Studio Arts, B
French Language and Literature, B
Geology/Earth Science, B
Health Information/Medical Records Technology/Technician, A
Health Services Administration, BM
History, B
Labor Studies, AB
Liberal Arts and Sciences Studies and Humanities, B
Liberal Studies, M
Management, MO
Mathematics, B
Mathematics Teacher Education, B
Non-Profit/Public/Organizational Management, O
Philosophy, B
Political Science and Government, B
Psychology, B
Public Administration, BM
Public Affairs, MO
Radiologic Technology/Science - Radiographer, AB
Secondary Education and Teaching, BM
Social Studies Teacher Education, B
Social Work, BM
Sociology, B
Spanish Language and Literature, B
Substance Abuse/Addiction Counseling, M

INDIANA UNIVERSITY SOUTH BEND

Accounting, M
Actuarial Science, B
Anthropology, B
Applied Mathematics, BM
Art Education, M
Art Teacher Education, B
Art/Art Studies, General, B
Biochemistry, B
Biology Teacher Education, B
Biology/Biological Sciences, B
Business Administration, Management and Operations, M
Business/Commerce, B
Chemistry, B
Chemistry Teacher Education, B
Communication Studies/Speech Communication and Rhetoric, B
Computer Programming, Specific Applications, A
Computer Science, BM
Counselor Education/School Counseling and Guidance Services, M
Criminal Justice/Safety Studies, B
Dental Hygiene/Hygienist, AB
Digital Communication and Media/Multimedia, B
Drama and Dramatics/Theatre Arts, B
Dramatic/Theatre Arts and Stagecraft, B
Economics, B
Education, M
Elementary Education and Teaching, BM
English, M
English Language and Literature, B
English/Language Arts Teacher Education, B
Environmental Studies, B
Ethnic, Cultural Minority, and Gender Studies, B
Fine/Studio Arts, B
French Language Teacher Education, B
French Language and Literature, B
General Studies, AB
German Language Teacher Education, B
German Language and Literature, B

History, B
Labor Studies, B
Liberal Arts and Sciences Studies and Humanities, B
Liberal Studies, M
Management Information Systems and Services, M
Mathematics, B
Mathematics Teacher Education, B
Medical Radiologic Technology/Science - Radiation Therapist, B
Music, BM
Music Performance, B
Music Teacher Education, B
Nursing, M
Nursing - Advanced Practice, M
Philosophy, B
Physics, B
Physics Teacher Education, B
Political Science and Government, B
Psychology, B
Public Affairs, M
Radiologic Technology/Science - Radiographer, A
Science Teacher Education/General Science Teacher Education, B
Secondary Education and Teaching, BM
Social Studies Teacher Education, B
Social Work, BM
Sociology, B
Spanish Language Teacher Education, B
Spanish Language and Literature, B
Special Education and Teaching, BM

INDIANA UNIVERSITY SOUTHEAST

Art/Art Studies, General, B
Biology Teacher Education, B
Biology/Biological Sciences, B
Business Administration, Management and Operations, M
Business/Commerce, B
Chemistry, B
Clinical Laboratory Science/Medical Technology/Technologist, B
Communication Studies/Speech Communication and Rhetoric, B
Computer Science, B
Counselor Education/School Counseling and Guidance Services, M
Criminal Justice/Safety Studies, B
Economics, B
Education, M
Elementary Education and Teaching, BM
English Language and Literature, B
English/Language Arts Teacher Education, B
Finance and Banking, M
Fine/Studio Arts, B
French Language and Literature, B
Geography, B
German Language and Literature, B
Health Information/Medical Records Administration/Administrator, B
History, B
Interdisciplinary Studies, MO
International Relations and Affairs, B
Journalism, B
Liberal Arts and Sciences Studies and Humanities, B
Mathematics, B
Mathematics Teacher Education, B
Music, B
Philosophy, B
Physics, B
Political Science and Government, B
Psychology, B
Secondary Education and Teaching, BM
Social Studies Teacher Education, B
Sociology, B
Spanish Language and Literature, B
Special Education and Teaching, B

INDIANA UNIVERSITY–PURDUE UNIVERSITY FORT WAYNE

Accounting, B
Anthropology, B
Applied Mathematics, M
Applied Statistics, O
Architectural Engineering Technology/Technician, A

Art Teacher Education, B
Art/Art Studies, General, B
Audiology/Audiologist and Speech-Language Pathology/Pathologist, B
Biological and Biomedical Sciences, M
Biology Teacher Education, B
Biology/Biological Sciences, B
Business Administration and Management, B
Business Administration, Management and Operations, M
Business/Commerce, B
Business/Managerial Economics, B
Chemical Technology/Technician, A
Chemistry, B
Chemistry Teacher Education, B
Civil Engineering, BM
Civil Engineering Technology/Technician, A
Clinical Laboratory Science/Medical Technology/Technologist, B
Clinical/Medical Laboratory Technician, B
Commercial and Advertising Art, B
Communication Disorders, M
Communication Studies/Speech Communication and Rhetoric, B
Communication and Media Studies, M
Community Health Services/Liaison/Counseling, B
Computational Mathematics, B
Computer Engineering, BM
Computer Engineering Technology/Technician, B
Computer Science, M
Computer and Information Sciences, B
Construction Engineering Technology/Technician, B
Counselor Education/School Counseling and Guidance Services, M
Crafts/Craft Design, Folk Art and Artisanry, B
Dental Hygiene/Hygienist, A
Dental Laboratory Technology/Technician, A
Drama and Dramatics/Theatre Arts, B
Drawing, B
Economics, B
Education, BMO
Educational Leadership and Administration, MO
Electrical Engineering, M
Electrical, Electronic and Communications Engineering Technology/Technician, AB
Electrical, Electronics and Communications Engineering, B
Elementary Education and Teaching, BM
Engineering and Applied Sciences, MO
English, MO
English Education, M
English Language and Literature, B
English as a Second Language, O
English/Language Arts Teacher Education, B
Finance, B
Fine/Studio Arts, B
French Language Teacher Education, B
French Language and Literature, B
General Studies, B
Geology/Earth Science, B
German Language Teacher Education, B
German Language and Literature, B
Gerontological Nursing, M
Graphic Design, B
Health Services Administration, B
Health/Health Care Administration/Management, B
History, B
History Teacher Education, B
Hospitality Administration/Management, B
Hotel/Motel Administration/Management, B
Industrial Technology/Technician, AB
Industrial/Management Engineering, M
Information Science/Studies, ABM
Information Technology, AB
Interior Design, AB
Labor and Industrial Relations, AB
Liberal Studies, M
Marketing/Marketing Management, B
Marriage and Family Therapy/Counseling, M
Mass Communication/Media Studies, B
Mathematics, BMO
Mathematics Teacher Education, BM
Mathematics and Computer Science, B
Mechanical Engineering, BM
Mechanical Engineering/Mechanical Technology/Technician, AB

Medical Radiologic Technology/Science - Radiation Therapist, A
Music, B
Music Performance, B
Music Teacher Education, B
Music Therapy/Therapist, B
Nursing, MO
Nursing - Adult, M
Nursing Administration, MO
Nursing Education, M
Operations Management and Supervision, AB
Operations Research, M
Organizational Communication, B
Organizational Management, MO
Painting, B
Philosophy, B
Photography, B
Physics, B
Physics Teacher Education, B
Piano and Organ, B
Political Science and Government, B
Pre-Dentistry Studies, B
Pre-Medicine/Pre-Medical Studies, B
Pre-Veterinary Studies, B
Printmaking, B
Psychiatric/Mental Health Services Technician, B
Psychology, B
Public Administration, B
Public Policy Analysis, BMO
Science Teacher Education/General Science Teacher Education, B
Sculpture, B
Secondary Education and Teaching, BM
Social Studies Teacher Education, B
Sociology, BM
Spanish Language Teacher Education, B
Spanish Language and Literature, B
Special Education and Teaching, MO
Speech Teacher Education, B
Statistics, B
Substance Abuse/Addiction Counseling, B
Systems Engineering, M
Voice and Opera, B
Women's Health Nursing, M
Women's Studies, AB

INDIANA UNIVERSITY–PURDUE UNIVERSITY INDIANAPOLIS

Accounting, M
African-American/Black Studies, B
Allopathic Medicine, MD
Anatomy, MD
Anthropology, B
Applied Mathematics, MD
Applied Statistics, M
Architectural Engineering Technology/Technician, B
Art Education, M
Art History, Criticism and Conservation, B
Art Teacher Education, B
Art Therapy/Therapist, M
BioTechnology, B
Biochemistry, MD
Bioethics/Medical Ethics, O
Bioinformatics, MD
Biological and Biomedical Sciences, MD
Biological and Physical Sciences, B
Biology/Biological Sciences, B
Biomedical Engineering, MD
Biomedical Technology/Technician, AB
Biomedical/Medical Engineering, B
Biopsychology, D
Biostatistics, MD
Business Administration, Management and Operations, M
Business/Commerce, B
Cell Biology and Anatomy, MD
Chemistry, BMD
Child and Family Studies, M
Clinical Laboratory Science/Medical Technology/Technologist, B
Clinical Psychology, M
Communication Studies/Speech Communication and Rhetoric, B
Communication and Media Studies, MD
Community Health and Preventive Medicine, M
Computer Education, O

Computer Engineering, BMD
Computer Engineering Technology/Technician, B
Computer Science, BMDO
Computer and Information Sciences and Support
   Services, B
Counselor Education/School Counseling and Guid-
   ance Services, M
Crafts, M
Criminal Justice/Safety Studies, B
Criminology, M
Curriculum and Instruction, M
CytoTechnology/Cytotechnologist, B
Dental Hygiene/Hygienist, A
Dental Services and Allied Professions, B
Dentistry, MDO
Design and Applied Arts, M
Digital Communication and Media/Multimedia, AB
Early Childhood Education and Teaching, MO
Economics, BM
Education, MO
Educational Leadership and Administration, MO
Electrical Engineering, MD
Electrical, Electronic and Communications Engineer-
   ing Technology/Technician, B
Electrical, Electronics and Communications Engi-
   neering, B
Elementary Education and Teaching, B
Emergency Management, O
Emergency Medical Technology/Technician (EMT
   Paramedic), A
Engineering, B
English, MO
English Language and Literature, B
English as a Second Language, O
English/Language Arts Teacher Education, B
Environmental Sciences, B
Environmental and Occupational Health, M
Epidemiology, MD
Fine Arts and Art Studies, M
Fine/Studio Arts, B
Foreign Language Teacher Education, M
Forensic Science and Technology, BM
French Language and Literature, B
Gender Studies, M
Geographic Information Systems, MO
Geography, B
Geology/Earth Science, BM
Geosciences, MD
German Language and Literature, B
Health Communication, MD
Health Education, M
Health Informatics, MD
Health Information/Medical Records
   Administration/Administrator, B
Health Services Administration, BMD
Health/Health Care Administration/Management, B
Higher Education/Higher Education Administra-
   tion, M
Histologic Technician, A
History, BM
Homeland Security, O
Human-Computer Interaction, MD
Immunology, MD
Industrial and Organizational Psychology, M
Information Science/Studies, M
Interior Design, AB
International Relations and Affairs, B
Internet and Interactive Multimedia, MD
Journalism, B
Kinesiology and Exercise Science, B
Labor Studies, AB
Law and Legal Studies, MD
Legal Assistant/Paralegal, B
Liberal Arts and Sciences Studies and Humani-
   ties, B
Liberal Studies, MDO
Library Science, MO
Mathematics, BMD
Mathematics Teacher Education, M
Mechanical Drafting and Mechanical Drafting
   CAD/CADD, B
Mechanical Engineering, BMDO
Mechanical Engineering Related
   Technologies/Technicians, B
Medical Radiologic Technology/Science - Radiation
   Therapist, B

Microbiology, MD
Molecular Biology, MD
Molecular Genetics, MD
Multi-/Interdisciplinary Studies, B
Museology/Museum Studies, MO
Music, M
Music Therapy/Therapist, M
Neurobiology and Neurophysiology, D
Non-Profit/Public/Organizational Management, O
Nuclear Medical Technology/Technologist, B
Nursing, MDO
Nursing Administration, M
Nursing Education, M
Nutritional Sciences, M
Occupational Therapy/Therapist, M
Operations Management and Supervision, B
Organizational Management, O
Pathology/Experimental Pathology, MD
Pharmacology, MD
Philanthropic Studies, MD
Philosophy, BMO
Physical Education Teaching and Coaching, M
Physical Therapy/Therapist, D
Physics, BMD
Political Science and Government, BMO
Pre-Medicine/Pre-Medical Studies, B
Pre-Pharmacy Studies, B
Pre-Veterinary Studies, B
Printmaking, M
Psychology, BMD
Public Administration, BO
Public Affairs, MO
Public Health, MD
Public Health (MPH, DPH), B
Public History, M
Radiation Protection/Health Physics Technician, B
Radiologic Technology/Science - Radiographer, A
Reading Teacher Education, O
Rehabilitation Sciences, MD
Religion/Religious Studies, M
Respiratory Care Therapy/Therapist, B
Robotics Technology/Technician, B
Sculpture, M
Sign Language Interpretation and Translation, B
Social Sciences, M
Social Studies Teacher Education, B
Social Work, BMDO
Sociology, BM
Spanish Language Teacher Education, B
Spanish Language and Literature, B
Special Education and Teaching, MO
Statistics, D
Student Personnel Services, M
Substance Abuse/Addiction Counseling, D
Tourism and Travel Services Management, B
Toxicology, MD
Writing, O

INDIANA WESLEYAN UNIVERSITY

Accounting, ABMO
Art Teacher Education, B
Art Therapy/Therapist, B
Art/Art Studies, General, AB
Athletic Training and Sports Medicine, B
Bible/Biblical Studies, B
Biochemistry, B
Biology Teacher Education, B
Biology/Biological Sciences, AB
Business Administration and Management, AB
Business Administration, Management and Opera-
   tions, M
Ceramic Arts and Ceramics, B
Chemistry, AB
Chemistry Teacher Education, B
Clinical Laboratory Science/Medical
   Technology/Technologist, B
Communication Studies/Speech Communication
   and Rhetoric, AB
Community Organization and Advocacy, B
Community Psychology, M
Computer Graphics, B
Computer Software Engineering, B
Computer and Information Sciences, AB
Counseling Psychology, M
Counselor Education/School Counseling and Guid-
   ance Services, M

Criminal Justice/Safety Studies, AB
Divinity/Ministry (BD, MDiv.), B
Economics, B
Education, B
Educational Leadership and Administration, MO
Elementary Education and Teaching, B
English Language and Literature, AB
English/Language Arts Teacher Education, B
Entrepreneurship/Entrepreneurial Studies, B
Finance, AB
Fine Arts and Art Studies, B
General Studies, AB
Health Services Administration, O
Higher Education/Higher Education Administra-
   tion, M
History, AB
Human Resources Management and Services, MO
Illustration, B
Intercultural/Multicultural and Diversity Studies, B
Interior Design, B
International Relations and Affairs, B
Journalism, B
Junior High/Intermediate/Middle School Education
   and Teaching, B
Kinesiology and Exercise Science, B
Management, M
Marketing/Marketing Management, B
Marriage and Family Therapy/Counseling, M
Mass Communication/Media Studies, B
Mathematics, AB
Mathematics Teacher Education, B
Missions/Missionary Studies and Missiology, B
Multilingual and Multicultural Education, B
Music Performance, B
Music Teacher Education, B
Music Theory and Composition, B
Nursing, M
Nursing Administration, M
Nursing Education, M
Organizational Management, MD
Painting, B
Parks, Recreation and Leisure Facilities Manage-
   ment, B
Pastoral Studies/Counseling, ABM
Philosophy, B
Photography, B
Physical Education Teaching and Coaching, B
Political Science and Government, B
Pre-Dentistry Studies, B
Pre-Law Studies, B
Pre-Medicine/Pre-Medical Studies, B
Pre-Veterinary Studies, B
Printmaking, B
Psychology, B
Public Policy Analysis, B
Public Relations/Image Management, B
Religious Education, B
Religious/Sacred Music, AB
Science Teacher Education/General Science
   Teacher Education, B
Secondary Education and Teaching, B
Social Studies Teacher Education, B
Social Work, B
Sociology, B
Spanish Language Teacher Education, B
Spanish Language and Literature, B
Special Education and Teaching, B
Sport and Fitness Administration/Management, B
Substance Abuse/Addiction Counseling, ABM
Teacher Education, Multiple Levels, B
Teaching English as a Second or Foreign
   Language/ESL Language Instructor, B
Theology and Religious Vocations, M
Theology/Theological Studies, B
Web Page, Digital/Multimedia and Information Re-
   sources Design, B
Youth Ministry, B

INTERNATIONAL BUSINESS COLLEGE (FORT WAYNE)

Accounting Technology/Technician and Bookkeep-
   ing, AB
Administrative Assistant and Secretarial Science, AB
Business Administration and Management, B
Computer Programming/Programmer, AB

Computer Systems Networking and Telecommunications, A
Graphic Design, AB
Hotel/Motel Administration/Management, AB
Legal Administrative Assistant/Secretary, AB
Legal Assistant/Paralegal, AB
Medical/Clinical Assistant, AB
Retailing and Retail Operations, AB
Veterinary/Animal Health Technology/Technician and Veterinary Assistant, A

INTERNATIONAL BUSINESS COLLEGE (INDIANAPOLIS)

Accounting Technology/Technician and Bookkeeping, A
Administrative Assistant and Secretarial Science, A
Computer Programming/Programmer, A
Computer Systems Networking and Telecommunications, A
Dental Assisting/Assistant, A
Graphic Design, A
Hotel/Motel Administration/Management, A
Legal Administrative Assistant/Secretary, A
Legal Assistant/Paralegal, A
Medical/Clinical Assistant, A
Veterinary/Animal Health Technology/Technician and Veterinary Assistant, A

IVY TECH COMMUNITY COLLEGE–BLOOMINGTON

Accounting Technology/Technician and Bookkeeping, A
Administrative Assistant and Secretarial Science, A
BioTechnology, A
Building/Property Maintenance and Management, A
Business Administration and Management, A
Business/Office Automation/Technology/Data Entry, A
Cabinetmaking and Millwork/Millwright, A
Child Care and Support Services Management, A
Computer Science, A
Computer Systems Networking and Telecommunications, A
Computer and Information Sciences, A
Criminal Justice/Safety Studies, A
Data Modeling/Warehousing and Database Administration, A
Drafting and Design Technology/Technician, A
Early Childhood Education and Teaching, A
Education, A
Electrical, Electronic and Communications Engineering Technology/Technician, A
Electrician, A
Emergency Medical Technology/Technician (EMT Paramedic), A
Engineering Technology, A
Executive Assistant/Executive Secretary, A
Fine/Studio Arts, A
General Studies, A
Heating, Air Conditioning, Ventilation and Refrigeration Maintenance Technology/Technician, A
Hospitality Administration/Management, A
Human Services, A
Industrial Technology/Technician, A
Information Science/Studies, A
Information Technology, A
Legal Assistant/Paralegal, A
Liberal Arts and Sciences Studies and Humanities, A
Library Assistant/Technician, A
Logistics and Materials Management, A
Machine Tool Technology/Machinist, A
Manufacturing Technology/Technician, A
Mechanic and Repair Technologies/Technicians, A
Mechanics and Repairers, A
Medical Radiologic Technology/Science - Radiation Therapist, A
Medical/Health Management and Clinical Assistant/Specialist, A
Pipefitting/Pipefitter and Sprinkler Fitter, A
Psychiatric/Mental Health Services Technician, A
Respiratory Care Therapy/Therapist, A
System Administration/Administrator, A

Tool and Die Technology/Technician, A

IVY TECH COMMUNITY COLLEGE–CENTRAL INDIANA

Accounting Technology/Technician and Bookkeeping, A
Automobile/Automotive Mechanics Technology/Technician, A
BioTechnology, A
Building/Property Maintenance and Management, A
Business Administration and Management, A
Business/Office Automation/Technology/Data Entry, A
Cabinetmaking and Millwork/Millwright, A
Carpentry/Carpenter, A
Child Care and Support Services Management, A
Child Development, A
Computer Science, A
Computer and Information Sciences, A
Criminal Justice/Safety Studies, A
Data Modeling/Warehousing and Database Administration, A
Design and Visual Communications, A
Drafting and Design Technology/Technician, A
Early Childhood Education and Teaching, A
Education, A
Electrical, Electronic and Communications Engineering Technology/Technician, A
Electrician, A
Executive Assistant/Executive Secretary, A
General Studies, A
Health Information/Medical Records Technology/Technician, A
Heating, Air Conditioning, Ventilation and Refrigeration Maintenance Technology/Technician, A
Hospitality Administration/Management, A
Human Services, A
Industrial Production Technologies/Technicians, A
Industrial Technology/Technician, A
Information Science/Studies, A
Information Technology, A
Legal Assistant/Paralegal, A
Liberal Arts and Sciences Studies and Humanities, A
Logistics and Materials Management, A
Machine Shop Technology/Assistant, A
Machine Tool Technology/Machinist, A
Manufacturing Technology/Technician, A
Mason/Masonry, A
Mechanics and Repairers, A
Medical Radiologic Technology/Science - Radiation Therapist, A
Medical/Clinical Assistant, A
Medical/Health Management and Clinical Assistant/Specialist, A
Occupational Safety and Health Technology/Technician, A
Occupational Therapist Assistant, A
Painting/Painter and Wall Coverer, A
Pipefitting/Pipefitter and Sprinkler Fitter, A
Psychiatric/Mental Health Services Technician, A
Respiratory Care Therapy/Therapist, A
Sheet Metal Technology/Sheetworking, A
Surgical Technology/Technologist, A
System Administration/Administrator, A
Tool and Die Technology/Technician, A
Transportation/Transportation Management, A

IVY TECH COMMUNITY COLLEGE–COLUMBUS

Accounting Technology/Technician and Bookkeeping, A
Administrative Assistant and Secretarial Science, A
Agriculture, A
Automobile/Automotive Mechanics Technology/Technician, A
Building/Property Maintenance and Management, A
Business Administration and Management, A
Business/Office Automation/Technology/Data Entry, A
Cabinetmaking and Millwork/Millwright, A
Child Care and Support Services Management, A
Computer Science, A
Computer and Information Sciences, A
Criminal Justice/Safety Studies, A

Data Modeling/Warehousing and Database Administration, A
Dental Assisting/Assistant, A
Design and Visual Communications, A
Drafting and Design Technology/Technician, A
Early Childhood Education and Teaching, A
Education, A
Electrical and Power Transmission Installation/Installer, A
Electrical, Electronic and Communications Engineering Technology/Technician, A
Emergency Medical Technology/Technician (EMT Paramedic), A
Engineering Technology, A
Executive Assistant/Executive Secretary, A
General Studies, A
Heating, Air Conditioning, Ventilation and Refrigeration Maintenance Technology/Technician, A
Hospitality Administration/Management, A
Human Services, A
Industrial Technology/Technician, A
Information Science/Studies, A
Information Technology, A
Interior Design, A
Legal Assistant/Paralegal, A
Liberal Arts and Sciences Studies and Humanities, A
Library Assistant/Technician, A
Logistics and Materials Management, A
Machine Tool Technology/Machinist, A
Manufacturing Technology/Technician, A
Mason/Masonry, A
Mechanic and Repair Technologies/Technicians, A
Mechanics and Repairers, A
Medical Radiologic Technology/Science - Radiation Therapist, A
Medical/Clinical Assistant, A
Medical/Health Management and Clinical Assistant/Specialist, A
Pipefitting/Pipefitter and Sprinkler Fitter, A
Psychiatric/Mental Health Services Technician, A
Robotics Technology/Technician, A
Surgical Technology/Technologist, A
Tool and Die Technology/Technician, A

IVY TECH COMMUNITY COLLEGE–EAST CENTRAL

Accounting Technology/Technician and Bookkeeping, A
Administrative Assistant and Secretarial Science, A
Agriculture, A
Automobile/Automotive Mechanics Technology/Technician, A
Building/Property Maintenance and Management, A
Business Administration and Management, A
Carpentry/Carpenter, A
Computer Science, A
Computer Systems Networking and Telecommunications, A
Computer and Information Sciences, A
Construction Trades, A
Criminal Justice/Safety Studies, A
Data Modeling/Warehousing and Database Administration, A
Dental Assisting/Assistant, A
Dental Hygiene/Hygienist, A
Drafting and Design Technology/Technician, A
Early Childhood Education and Teaching, A
Education, A
Electrical, Electronic and Communications Engineering Technology/Technician, A
Electrician, A
Energy Management and Systems Technology/Technician, A
Engineering Technology, A
Executive Assistant/Executive Secretary, A
General Studies, A
Health Information/Medical Records Technology/Technician, A
Heating, Air Conditioning, Ventilation and Refrigeration Maintenance Technology/Technician, A
Hospitality Administration/Management, A
Human Services, A
Industrial Mechanics and Maintenance Technology, A
Industrial Production Technologies/Technicians, A

Industrial Technology/Technician, A
Information Science/Studies, A
Information Technology, A
Interior Design, A
Kinesiology and Exercise Science, A
Legal Assistant/Paralegal, A
Liberal Arts and Sciences Studies and Humanities, A
Library Assistant/Technician, A
Logistics and Materials Management, A
Machine Shop Technology/Assistant, A
Machine Tool Technology/Machinist, A
Manufacturing Technology/Technician, A
Mason/Masonry, A
Medical Radiologic Technology/Science - Radiation Therapist, A
Medical/Clinical Assistant, A
Medical/Health Management and Clinical Assistant/Specialist, A
Painting/Painter and Wall Coverer, A
Physical Therapist Assistant, A
Pipefitting/Pipefitter and Sprinkler Fitter, A
Surgical Technology/Technologist, A
System Administration/Administrator, A
Tool and Die Technology/Technician, A

IVY TECH COMMUNITY COLLEGE–KOKOMO

Accounting Technology/Technician and Bookkeeping, A
Administrative Assistant and Secretarial Science, A
Agriculture, A
Automobile/Automotive Mechanics Technology/Technician, A
Building/Construction Site Management/Manager, A
Building/Property Maintenance and Management, A
Business Administration and Management, A
Communication, Journalism and Related Programs, A
Computer Science, A
Computer Systems Networking and Telecommunications, A
Computer and Information Sciences, A
Construction Trades, A
Criminal Justice/Safety Studies, A
Data Modeling/Warehousing and Database Administration, A
Dental Assisting/Assistant, A
Dental Hygiene/Hygienist, A
Design and Visual Communications, A
Drafting and Design Technology/Technician, A
Early Childhood Education and Teaching, A
Education, A
Electrical, Electronic and Communications Engineering Technology/Technician, A
Electrician, A
Emergency Medical Technology/Technician (EMT Paramedic), A
Engineering Technology, A
Executive Assistant/Executive Secretary, A
General Studies, A
Health Aide, A
Health Information/Medical Records Technology/Technician, A
Heating, Air Conditioning, Ventilation and Refrigeration Maintenance Technology/Technician, A
Human Services, A
Industrial Production Technologies/Technicians, A
Industrial Technology/Technician, A
Information Science/Studies, A
Information Technology, A
Legal Assistant/Paralegal, A
Liberal Arts and Sciences Studies and Humanities, A
Library Assistant/Technician, A
Machine Shop Technology/Assistant, A
Machine Tool Technology/Machinist, A
Manufacturing Technology/Technician, A
Mechanic and Repair Technologies/Technicians, A
Mechanics and Repairers, A
Medical/Clinical Assistant, A
Physical Therapist Assistant, A
Surgical Technology/Technologist, A
System Administration/Administrator, A

Tool and Die Technology/Technician, A

IVY TECH COMMUNITY COLLEGE–LAFAYETTE

Accounting, A
Accounting Technology/Technician and Bookkeeping, A
Agriculture, A
Automobile/Automotive Mechanics Technology/Technician, A
BioTechnology, A
Building/Property Maintenance and Management, A
Business Administration and Management, A
Business/Office Automation/Technology/Data Entry, A
Cabinetmaking and Millwork/Millwright, A
Carpentry/Carpenter, A
Chemical Technology/Technician, A
Child Care and Support Services Management, A
Clinical/Medical Laboratory Technician, A
Computer Science, A
Computer Systems Networking and Telecommunications, A
Computer and Information Sciences, A
Criminal Justice/Safety Studies, A
Data Modeling/Warehousing and Database Administration, A
Dental Assisting/Assistant, A
Drafting and Design Technology/Technician, A
Early Childhood Education and Teaching, A
Education, A
Electrical, Electronic and Communications Engineering Technology/Technician, A
Electrician, A
Executive Assistant/Executive Secretary, A
General Studies, A
Health Aide, A
Health Information/Medical Records Technology/Technician, A
Heating, Air Conditioning, Ventilation and Refrigeration Maintenance Technology/Technician, A
Human Services, A
Industrial Production Technologies/Technicians, A
Industrial Technology/Technician, A
Information Science/Studies, A
Information Technology, A
Ironworking/Ironworker, A
Legal Assistant/Paralegal, A
Liberal Arts and Sciences Studies and Humanities, A
Library Assistant/Technician, A
Lineworker, A
Machine Tool Technology/Machinist, A
Manufacturing Technology/Technician, A
Mason/Masonry, A
Mechanic and Repair Technologies/Technicians, A
Mechanical Engineering/Mechanical Technology/Technician, A
Mechanics and Repairers, A
Medical/Clinical Assistant, A
Medical/Health Management and Clinical Assistant/Specialist, A
Painting/Painter and Wall Coverer, A
Pipefitting/Pipefitter and Sprinkler Fitter, A
Psychiatric/Mental Health Services Technician, A
Quality Control Technology/Technician, A
Quality Control and Safety Technologies/Technicians, A
Respiratory Care Therapy/Therapist, A
Robotics Technology/Technician, A
Sheet Metal Technology/Sheetworking, A
Surgical Technology/Technologist, A
Telecommunications Technology/Technician, A
Tool and Die Technology/Technician, A

IVY TECH COMMUNITY COLLEGE–NORTH CENTRAL

Accounting Technology/Technician and Bookkeeping, A
Automobile/Automotive Mechanics Technology/Technician, A
BioTechnology, A
Building/Property Maintenance and Management, A
Business Administration and Management, A
Business/Office Automation/Technology/Data Entry, A

Cabinetmaking and Millwork/Millwright, A
Carpentry/Carpenter, A
Child Care and Support Services Management, A
Clinical/Medical Laboratory Technician, A
Computer and Information Sciences, A
Criminal Justice/Safety Studies, A
Design and Visual Communications, A
Early Childhood Education and Teaching, A
Educational/Instructional Media Design, A
Electrical, Electronic and Communications Engineering Technology/Technician, A
Electrician, A
Emergency Medical Technology/Technician (EMT Paramedic), A
Executive Assistant/Executive Secretary, A
General Studies, A
Heating, Air Conditioning, Ventilation and Refrigeration Maintenance Technology/Technician, A
Hospitality Administration/Management, A
Human Services, A
Industrial Production Technologies/Technicians, A
Industrial Technology/Technician, A
Interior Design, A
Ironworking/Ironworker, A
Legal Assistant/Paralegal, A
Liberal Arts and Sciences Studies and Humanities, A
Library Assistant/Technician, A
Machine Tool Technology/Machinist, A
Mason/Masonry, A
Mechanic and Repair Technologies/Technicians, A
Mechanics and Repairers, A
Medical/Clinical Assistant, A
Painting/Painter and Wall Coverer, A
Pipefitting/Pipefitter and Sprinkler Fitter, A
Robotics Technology/Technician, A
Sheet Metal Technology/Sheetworking, A
Telecommunications Technology/Technician, A
Tool and Die Technology/Technician, A

IVY TECH COMMUNITY COLLEGE–NORTHEAST

Accounting Technology/Technician and Bookkeeping, A
Agriculture, A
Automobile/Automotive Mechanics Technology/Technician, A
Building/Property Maintenance and Management, A
Business Administration and Management, A
Business/Office Automation/Technology/Data Entry, A
Cabinetmaking and Millwork/Millwright, A
Child Care and Support Services Management, A
Computer Science, A
Computer and Information Sciences, A
Construction Trades, A
Criminal Justice/Safety Studies, A
Data Modeling/Warehousing and Database Administration, A
Drafting and Design Technology/Technician, A
Early Childhood Education and Teaching, A
Electrical, Electronic and Communications Engineering Technology/Technician, A
Electrician, A
Executive Assistant/Executive Secretary, A
Heating, Air Conditioning, Ventilation and Refrigeration Maintenance Technology/Technician, A
Hospitality Administration/Management, A
Human Services, A
Industrial Production Technologies/Technicians, A
Industrial Technology/Technician, A
Ironworking/Ironworker, A
Legal Assistant/Paralegal, A
Liberal Arts and Sciences Studies and Humanities, A
Library Assistant/Technician, A
Machine Tool Technology/Machinist, A
Manufacturing Technology/Technician, A
Mason/Masonry, A
Massage Therapy/Therapeutic Massage, A
Mechanics and Repairers, A
Medical/Clinical Assistant, A
Occupational Safety and Health Technology/Technician, A
Painting/Painter and Wall Coverer, A
Pipefitting/Pipefitter and Sprinkler Fitter, A

Psychiatric/Mental Health Services Technician, A
Respiratory Care Therapy/Therapist, A
Robotics Technology/Technician, A
Sheet Metal Technology/Sheetworking, A
Tool and Die Technology/Technician, A

IVY TECH COMMUNITY COLLEGE–NORTHWEST

Accounting Technology/Technician and Bookkeeping, A
Automobile/Automotive Mechanics Technology/Technician, A
Building/Construction Finishing, Management, and Inspection, A
Building/Property Maintenance and Management, A
Business Administration and Management, A
Business/Office Automation/Technology/Data Entry, A
Cabinetmaking and Millwork/Millwright, A
Carpentry/Carpenter, A
Child Care and Support Services Management, A
Computer and Information Sciences, A
Construction Trades, A
Criminal Justice/Safety Studies, A
Drafting and Design Technology/Technician, A
Early Childhood Education and Teaching, A
Electrical, Electronic and Communications Engineering Technology/Technician, A
Electrician, A
Executive Assistant/Executive Secretary, A
Funeral Service and Mortuary Science, A
General Studies, A
Heating, Air Conditioning, Ventilation and Refrigeration Maintenance Technology/Technician, A
Hospitality Administration/Management, A
Human Services, A
Industrial Technology/Technician, A
Ironworking/Ironworker, A
Legal Assistant/Paralegal, A
Liberal Arts and Sciences Studies and Humanities, A
Library Assistant/Technician, A
Machine Tool Technology/Machinist, A
Mason/Masonry, A
Mechanic and Repair Technologies/Technicians, A
Mechanics and Repairers, A
Medical/Clinical Assistant, A
Occupational Safety and Health Technology/Technician, A
Painting/Painter and Wall Coverer, A
Pipefitting/Pipefitter and Sprinkler Fitter, A
Psychiatric/Mental Health Services Technician, A
Respiratory Care Therapy/Therapist, A
Sheet Metal Technology/Sheetworking, A
Surgical Technology/Technologist, A
Telecommunications Technology/Technician, A
Tool and Die Technology/Technician, A

IVY TECH COMMUNITY COLLEGE–RICHMOND

Accounting Technology/Technician and Bookkeeping, A
Agriculture, A
Automobile/Automotive Mechanics Technology/Technician, A
Building/Property Maintenance and Management, A
Business Administration and Management, A
Business/Office Automation/Technology/Data Entry, A
Cabinetmaking and Millwork/Millwright, A
Child Care and Support Services Management, A
Computer Science, A
Computer and Information Sciences, A
Construction Trades, A
Criminal Justice/Safety Studies, A
Data Modeling/Warehousing and Database Administration, A
Early Childhood Education and Teaching, A
Education, A
Electrical, Electronic and Communications Engineering Technology/Technician, A
Electrician, A
Emergency Medical Technology/Technician (EMT Paramedic), A
Engineering Technology, A
Executive Assistant/Executive Secretary, A

General Studies, A
Heating, Air Conditioning, Ventilation and Refrigeration Maintenance Technology/Technician, A
Human Services, A
Industrial Production Technologies/Technicians, A
Industrial Technology/Technician, A
Information Science/Studies, A
Information Technology, A
Legal Assistant/Paralegal, A
Liberal Arts and Sciences Studies and Humanities, A
Library Assistant/Technician, A
Logistics and Materials Management, A
Machine Shop Technology/Assistant, A
Machine Tool Technology/Machinist, A
Manufacturing Technology/Technician, A
Mechanics and Repairers, A
Medical Radiologic Technology/Science - Radiation Therapist, A
Medical/Clinical Assistant, A
Medical/Health Management and Clinical Assistant/Specialist, A
Pipefitting/Pipefitter and Sprinkler Fitter, A
Psychiatric/Mental Health Services Technician, A
Respiratory Care Therapy/Therapist, A
Robotics Technology/Technician, A
System Administration/Administrator, A
Tool and Die Technology/Technician, A

IVY TECH COMMUNITY COLLEGE–SOUTHEAST

Accounting Technology/Technician and Bookkeeping, A
Administrative Assistant and Secretarial Science, A
Business Administration and Management, A
Business/Office Automation/Technology/Data Entry, A
Child Care and Support Services Management, A
Computer Science, A
Computer and Information Sciences, A
Criminal Justice/Safety Studies, A
Data Modeling/Warehousing and Database Administration, A
Drafting and Design Technology/Technician, A
Early Childhood Education and Teaching, A
Education, A
Electrical, Electronic and Communications Engineering Technology/Technician, A
Executive Assistant/Executive Secretary, A
General Studies, A
Human Services, A
Industrial Technology/Technician, A
Information Science/Studies, A
Information Technology, A
Legal Assistant/Paralegal, A
Liberal Arts and Sciences Studies and Humanities, A
Library Assistant/Technician, A
Logistics and Materials Management, A
Manufacturing Technology/Technician, A
Medical Radiologic Technology/Science - Radiation Therapist, A
Medical/Clinical Assistant, A
Medical/Health Management and Clinical Assistant/Specialist, A
Psychiatric/Mental Health Services Technician, A
System Administration/Administrator, A

IVY TECH COMMUNITY COLLEGE–SOUTHERN INDIANA

Accounting Technology/Technician and Bookkeeping, A
Administrative Assistant and Secretarial Science, A
Automobile/Automotive Mechanics Technology/Technician, A
Building/Property Maintenance and Management, A
Business Administration and Management, A
Business/Office Automation/Technology/Data Entry, A
Cabinetmaking and Millwork/Millwright, A
Carpentry/Carpenter, A
Child Care and Support Services Management, A
Clinical/Medical Laboratory Technician, A
Computer Science, A
Computer Systems Networking and Telecommunications, A

Computer and Information Sciences, A
Data Modeling/Warehousing and Database Administration, A
Design and Visual Communications, A
Drafting and Design Technology/Technician, A
Early Childhood Education and Teaching, A
Education, A
Electrical, Electronic and Communications Engineering Technology/Technician, A
Electrician, A
Energy Management and Systems Technology/Technician, A
Engineering Technology, A
Executive Assistant/Executive Secretary, A
General Studies, A
Heating, Air Conditioning, Ventilation and Refrigeration Maintenance Technology/Technician, A
Human Services, A
Industrial Technology/Technician, A
Information Science/Studies, A
Information Technology, A
Kinesiology and Exercise Science, A
Legal Assistant/Paralegal, A
Liberal Arts and Sciences Studies and Humanities, A
Library Assistant/Technician, A
Logistics and Materials Management, A
Machine Tool Technology/Machinist, A
Manufacturing Technology/Technician, A
Mason/Masonry, A
Mechanics and Repairers, A
Medical/Clinical Assistant, A
Medical/Health Management and Clinical Assistant/Specialist, A
Physical Therapist Assistant, A
Pipefitting/Pipefitter and Sprinkler Fitter, A
Psychiatric/Mental Health Services Technician, A
Respiratory Care Therapy/Therapist, A
Sheet Metal Technology/Sheetworking, A
System Administration/Administrator, A
Telecommunications Technology/Technician, A
Tool and Die Technology/Technician, A

IVY TECH COMMUNITY COLLEGE–SOUTHWEST

Accounting Technology/Technician and Bookkeeping, A
Administrative Assistant and Secretarial Science, A
Agriculture, A
Automobile/Automotive Mechanics Technology/Technician, A
BioTechnology, A
Boilermaking/Boilermaker, A
Building/Property Maintenance and Management, A
Business Administration and Management, A
Business/Office Automation/Technology/Data Entry, A
Cabinetmaking and Millwork/Millwright, A
Carpentry/Carpenter, A
Child Care and Support Services Management, A
Computer Science, A
Computer and Information Sciences, A
Construction/Heavy Equipment/Earthmoving Equipment Operation, A
Criminal Justice/Safety Studies, A
Data Modeling/Warehousing and Database Administration, A
Design and Visual Communications, A
Drafting and Design Technology/Technician, A
Early Childhood Education and Teaching, A
Education, A
Electrical, Electronic and Communications Engineering Technology/Technician, A
Electrician, A
Emergency Medical Technology/Technician (EMT Paramedic), A
Energy Management and Systems Technology/Technician, A
Engineering Technology, A
Executive Assistant/Executive Secretary, A
General Studies, A
Graphic Design, A
Heating, Air Conditioning, Ventilation and Refrigeration Maintenance Technology/Technician, A
Hospitality Administration/Management, A
Human Services, A

Industrial Production Technologies/Technicians, A
Industrial Technology/Technician, A
Information Science/Studies, A
Information Technology, A
Interior Design, A
Ironworking/Ironworker, A
Legal Assistant/Paralegal, A
Liberal Arts and Sciences Studies and Humanities, A
Library Assistant/Technician, A
Logistics and Materials Management, A
Machine Tool Technology/Machinist, A
Manufacturing Technology/Technician, A
Mason/Masonry, A
Mechanic and Repair Technologies/Technicians, A
Mechanics and Repairers, A
Medical/Clinical Assistant, A
Medical/Health Management and Clinical Assistant/Specialist, A
Painting/Painter and Wall Coverer, A
Pipefitting/Pipefitter and Sprinkler Fitter, A
Psychiatric/Mental Health Services Technician, A
Robotics Technology/Technician, A
Sheet Metal Technology/Sheetworking, A
Surgical Technology/Technologist, A
System Administration/Administrator, A
Telecommunications Technology/Technician, A
Tool and Die Technology/Technician, A

IVY TECH COMMUNITY COLLEGE–WABASH VALLEY

Accounting Technology/Technician and Bookkeeping, A
Agricultural Mechanization, A
Agriculture, A
Airframe Mechanics and Aircraft Maintenance Technology/Technician, A
Automobile/Automotive Mechanics Technology/Technician, A
Biomedical Sciences, A
Building/Property Maintenance and Management, A
Business Administration and Management, A
Cabinetmaking and Millwork/Millwright, A
Carpentry/Carpenter, A
Chemical Technology/Technician, A
Clinical/Medical Laboratory Technician, A
Computer Science, A
Computer Systems Networking and Telecommunications, A
Computer and Information Sciences, A
Construction/Heavy Equipment/Earthmoving Equipment Operation, A
Criminal Justice/Safety Studies, A
Data Modeling/Warehousing and Database Administration, A
Design and Visual Communications, A
Drafting and Design Technology/Technician, A
Early Childhood Education and Teaching, A
Education, A
Electrical, Electronic and Communications Engineering Technology/Technician, A
Electrician, A
Emergency Medical Technology/Technician (EMT Paramedic), A
Energy Management and Systems Technology/Technician, A
Engineering Technology, A
Executive Assistant/Executive Secretary, A
General Studies, A
Health Aide, A
Health Information/Medical Records Technology/Technician, A
Heating, Air Conditioning, Ventilation and Refrigeration Maintenance Technology/Technician, A
Human Services, A
Industrial Production Technologies/Technicians, A
Industrial Technology/Technician, A
Information Science/Studies, A
Information Technology, A
Ironworking/Ironworker, A
Legal Assistant/Paralegal, A
Liberal Arts and Sciences Studies and Humanities, A
Library Assistant/Technician, A
Logistics and Materials Management, A
Machine Shop Technology/Assistant, A

Machine Tool Technology/Machinist, A
Manufacturing Technology/Technician, A
Mason/Masonry, A
Mechanics and Repairers, A
Medical Radiologic Technology/Science - Radiation Therapist, A
Medical/Clinical Assistant, A
Medical/Health Management and Clinical Assistant/Specialist, A
Occupational Safety and Health Technology/Technician, A
Office Management and Supervision, A
Painting/Painter and Wall Coverer, A
Pipefitting/Pipefitter and Sprinkler Fitter, A
Quality Control and Safety Technologies/Technicians, A
Respiratory Care Therapy/Therapist, A
Sheet Metal Technology/Sheetworking, A
Surgical Technology/Technologist, A
System Administration/Administrator, A
Tool and Die Technology/Technician, A

LINCOLN COLLEGE OF TECHNOLOGY

Architectural Drafting and Architectural CAD/CADD, A
Automobile/Automotive Mechanics Technology/Technician, A
Diesel Mechanics Technology/Technician, A
Mechanical Drafting and Mechanical Drafting CAD/CADD, A

MANCHESTER UNIVERSITY

Accounting, B
Art Teacher Education, B
Art/Art Studies, General, B
Athletic Training and Sports Medicine, BM
Biochemistry, B
Biology Teacher Education, B
Biology/Biological Sciences, B
Broadcast Journalism, B
Business Administration and Management, B
Business/Commerce, B
Chemistry, B
Chemistry Teacher Education, B
Clinical Laboratory Science/Medical Technology/Technologist, B
Communication Studies/Speech Communication and Rhetoric, B
Comparative Literature, B
Computer Science, B
Computer and Information Sciences, A
Criminal Justice/Safety Studies, AB
Drama and Dramatics/Theatre Arts, B
Early Childhood Education and Teaching, A
Ecology, B
Economics, B
Education, B
Education/Teaching of Individuals with Mental Retardation, B
Elementary Education and Teaching, B
Engineering, B
English Language and Literature, B
English/Language Arts Teacher Education, B
Environmental Biology, B
Environmental Studies, B
Finance, B
Fine/Studio Arts, B
Foreign Language Teacher Education, B
Foreign Languages and Literatures, B
French Language Teacher Education, B
French Language and Literature, B
Gerontology, A
Health Professions and Related Clinical Sciences, B
History, B
History Teacher Education, B
International/Global Studies, B
Journalism, A
Junior High/Intermediate/Middle School Education and Teaching, B
Kinesiology and Exercise Science, B
Liberal Arts and Sciences Studies and Humanities, B
Marketing/Marketing Management, B
Mass Communication/Media Studies, B
Mathematics, B
Mathematics Teacher Education, B

Mathematics and Computer Science, B
Multi-/Interdisciplinary Studies, B
Music, B
Music Performance, B
Music Teacher Education, B
Music Theory and Composition, B
Natural Resources and Conservation, B
Parks, Recreation, Leisure and Fitness Studies, B
Peace Studies and Conflict Resolution, B
Pharmacy, BD
Philosophy, B
Physical Education Teaching and Coaching, B
Physics, B
Physics Teacher Education, B
Political Science and Government, B
Pre-Dentistry Studies, B
Pre-Law Studies, B
Pre-Medicine/Pre-Medical Studies, B
Pre-Pharmacy Studies, B
Pre-Theology/Pre-Ministerial Studies, B
Pre-Veterinary Studies, B
Psychology, B
Religion/Religious Studies, B
Science Teacher Education/General Science Teacher Education, B
Secondary Education and Teaching, B
Social Science Teacher Education, B
Social Sciences, B
Social Studies Teacher Education, B
Social Work, B
Sociology, B
Spanish Language Teacher Education, B
Spanish Language and Literature, B
Special Education and Teaching, B
Sport and Fitness Administration/Management, B
Teacher Education, Multiple Levels, B
Women's Studies, B

MARIAN UNIVERSITY

Accounting, B
Art History, Criticism and Conservation, B
Biology/Biological Sciences, B
Business Administration and Management, AB
Chemistry, B
Christian Studies, B
Clinical Laboratory Science/Medical Technology/Technologist, B
Communication Studies/Speech Communication and Rhetoric, B
Economics, B
Education, BM
Elementary Education and Teaching, B
English Language and Literature, B
Finance, B
Fine/Studio Arts, B
French Language and Literature, B
Graphic Design, B
Health and Physical Education, B
History, B
Kinesiology and Exercise Science, B
Legal Assistant/Paralegal, A
Liberal Arts and Sciences Studies and Humanities, A
Marketing/Marketing Management, B
Mathematics, B
Music, AB
Music Performance, B
Music Teacher Education, B
Osteopathic Medicine, D
Pastoral Studies/Counseling, AB
Philosophy, B
Photography, B
Physical Education Teaching and Coaching, B
Political Science and Government, B
Psychology, B
Religious Education, AB
Religious/Sacred Music, B
Secondary Education and Teaching, B
Sociology, B
Spanish Language and Literature, B
Special Education and Teaching, B
Sport and Fitness Administration/Management, B

Theology/Theological Studies, AB

MARTIN UNIVERSITY

Accounting, B
Biology/Biological Sciences, B
Business Administration and Management, B
Chemistry, B
Community Psychology, M
Criminal Justice/Safety Studies, B
Early Childhood Education and Teaching, B
Environmental Sciences, B
Gerontology, B
Insurance, B
Liberal Arts and Sciences Studies and Humanities, B
Pastoral Studies/Counseling, M
Psychology, BM
Religion/Religious Studies, B
Sociology, B
Substance Abuse/Addiction Counseling, B

MID-AMERICA COLLEGE OF FUNERAL SERVICE

Funeral Service and Mortuary Science, A

OAKLAND CITY UNIVERSITY

Accounting, A
Art/Art Studies, General, AB
Biology Teacher Education, B
Biology/Biological Sciences, B
Business Administration and Management, AB
Business Administration, Management and Operations, M
Business Teacher Education, B
Criminal Justice/Safety Studies, AB
Early Childhood Education and Teaching, AB
Education, MD
Educational Leadership and Administration, D
Elementary Education and Teaching, B
English Language and Literature, B
English/Language Arts Teacher Education, B
General Studies, AB
Health and Physical Education, B
Human Resources Management and Services, AB
Humanities/Humanistic Studies, B
Mathematics, B
Mathematics Teacher Education, B
Music, B
Operations Management and Supervision, B
Physical Education Teaching and Coaching, B
Psychology, B
Religion/Religious Studies, AB
Religious/Sacred Music, B
Social Sciences, B
Social Studies Teacher Education, B
Special Education and Teaching, B
Theology and Religious Vocations, MD

PURDUE UNIVERSITY

Accounting, B
Acting, B
Actuarial Science, B
Aeronautics/Aviation/Aerospace Science and Technology, AB
Aerospace, Aeronautical and Astronautical Engineering, BMD
African-American/Black Studies, B
Agricultural Business and Management, B
Agricultural Communication/Journalism, B
Agricultural Economics, BMD
Agricultural Education, MDO
Agricultural Engineering, MD
Agricultural Mechanization, B
Agricultural Sciences, MD
Agricultural Teacher Education, B
Agricultural/Biological Engineering and Bioengineering, B
Agriculture, B
Agronomy and Crop Science, B
Agronomy and Soil Sciences, MD
Allied Health and Medical Assisting Services, D
American/United States Studies/Civilization, BMD
Analytical Chemistry, MD
Anatomy, MD
Ancient Studies/Civilization, B

Animal Sciences, BMD
Anthropology, BMD
Applied Mathematics, B
Aquaculture, MD
Architectural Engineering Technology/Technician, B
Art Education, D
Art History, Criticism and Conservation, B
Art Teacher Education, B
Asian Studies/Civilization, B
Atmospheric Sciences and Meteorology, BMD
Audiology/Audiologist and Speech-Language Pathology/Pathologist, B
Aviation/Airway Management and Operations, M
BioTechnology, D
Biochemistry, BMD
Biochemistry, Biophysics and Molecular Biology, B
Biological and Biomedical Sciences, MD
Biological and Physical Sciences, B
Biology/Biological Sciences, B
Biomedical Engineering, MD
Biomedical/Medical Engineering, B
Biophysics, D
Botany/Plant Biology, BMD
Business Administration and Management, B
Business Administration, Management and Operations, M
Cancer Biology/Oncology, D
Cell Biology and Anatomy, D
Cell/Cellular and Molecular Biology, B
Chemical Engineering, BMD
Chemistry, BMD
Child Development, MD
Child and Family Studies, MD
Civil Engineering, BMD
Clinical Laboratory Science/Medical Technology/Technologist, B
Clinical Psychology, D
Cognitive Sciences, D
Communication Disorders, MD
Communication and Media Studies, MD
Comparative Literature, BMD
Computational Sciences, D
Computer Art and Design, MD
Computer Engineering, BMD
Computer Graphics, AB
Computer Science, BMD
Computer and Information Systems Security, M
Construction Engineering, B
Construction Management, M
Consumer Economics, MD
Consumer Merchandising/Retailing Management, B
Counselor Education/School Counseling and Guidance Services, MD
Curriculum and Instruction, MDO
Design and Applied Arts, M
Design and Visual Communications, B
Developmental Biology and Embryology, D
Dietetics/Dieticians, B
Drama and Dramatics/Theatre Arts, B
Early Childhood Education and Teaching, B
Ecology, MD
Economics, BD
Education, BMDO
Education/Teaching of the Gifted and Talented, M
Educational Administration and Supervision, MDO
Educational Media/Instructional Technology, MDO
Educational Psychology, MD
Electrical Engineering, MD
Electrical, Electronic and Communications Engineering Technology/Technician, AB
Electrical, Electronics and Communications Engineering, B
Elementary Education and Teaching, BM
Engineering, B
Engineering and Applied Sciences, MDO
English, MD
English Education, MDO
English/Language Arts Teacher Education, B
Entomology, MD
Environmental Policy and Resource Management, MD
Environmental Sciences, B
Environmental and Occupational Health, M
Environmental/Environmental Health Engineering, B
Epidemiology, MD
Ergonomics and Human Factors, MD

Evolutionary Biology, MD
Exercise and Sports Science, MD
Family and Consumer Sciences/Human Sciences, B
Farm/Farm and Ranch Management, B
Fashion/Apparel Design, B
Film/Cinema Studies, B
Finance and Banking, M
Financial Planning and Services, B
Fine Arts and Art Studies, M
Fine/Studio Arts, B
Fish, Game and Wildlife Management, MD
Fishing and Fisheries Sciences and Management, B
Food Science, B
Food Science and Technology, MD
Food Technology and Processing, B
Foreign Language Teacher Education, MDO
Forestry, BMD
Foundations and Philosophy of Education, MD
French Language and Literature, BMD
Genetics, BMD
Genomic Sciences, D
Geology/Earth Science, B
Geosciences, MD
German Language and Literature, BMD
Health Education, MD
Health Physics/Radiological Health, MD
Health Professions and Related Clinical Sciences, B
Health Teacher Education, B
Higher Education/Higher Education Administration, MD
History, BMD
Home Economics, MD
Home Economics Education, MDO
Horticultural Science, BMD
Hospitality Administration/Management, MD
Hotel/Motel Administration/Management, B
Human Development, MD
Human Development and Family Studies, B
Human Resources Management and Services, MD
Humanities/Humanistic Studies, B
Immunology, MD
Industrial Design, B
Industrial Engineering, B
Industrial and Manufacturing Management, M
Industrial and Organizational Psychology, D
Industrial/Management Engineering, MD
Information Technology, AB
Inorganic Chemistry, MD
International Business/Trade/Commerce, M
Italian Studies, B
Japanese Language and Literature, B
Japanese Studies, M
Jewish/Judaic Studies, B
Kinesiology and Exercise Science, B
Kinesiology and Movement Studies, MD
Landscape Architecture, B
Linguistics, BMD
Management, D
Management Information Systems and Services, M
Management of Technology, MD
Manufacturing Technology/Technician, AB
Marriage and Family Therapy/Counseling, MD
Materials Engineering, BMD
Mathematical Statistics and Probability, B
Mathematics, BMD
Mathematics Teacher Education, MDO
Mathematics and Computer Science, B
Mechanical Engineering, BMDO
Mechanical Engineering/Mechanical Technology/Technician, AB
Medical Physics, MD
Medicinal and Pharmaceutical Chemistry, D
Medieval and Renaissance Studies, B
Microbiology, MD
Molecular Biology, D
Molecular Pharmacology, D
Natural Resources and Conservation, BMD
Neurobiology and Neurophysiology, MD
Neuroscience, D
Nuclear Engineering, BMD
Nutritional Sciences, MD
Organic Chemistry, MD
Organizational Behavior Studies, D
Pathobiology, MD
Pathology/Experimental Pathology, M
Pharmaceutical Administration, MO

Pharmaceutical Sciences, MD
Pharmaceutics and Drug Design, B
Pharmacology, MD
Pharmacy, D
Philosophy, BMD
Photography, B
Physical Chemistry, MD
Physical Education Teaching and Coaching, BMD
Physics, BMD
Physiology, MD
Plant Genetics, B
Plant Pathology/Phytopathology, MD
Plant Physiology, D
Plant Sciences, D
Political Science and Government, BMD
Psychology, BD
Public Health, MD
Public Health Education and Promotion, B
Quantitative Analysis, MD
Reading Teacher Education, MDO
Recreation and Park Management, MD
Religion/Religious Studies, B
Russian Language and Literature, B
Science Teacher Education/General Science
  Teacher Education, MDO
Selling Skills and Sales Operations, B
Social Studies Teacher Education, BMDO
Sociology, BMD
Soil Science and Agronomy, B
Spanish Language and Literature, MD
Special Education and Teaching, BMD
Sport Psychology, MD
Sport and Fitness Administration/Management, MD
Statistics, MD
Systematic Biology/Biological Systematics, D
Technical Theatre/Theatre Design and Technol-
  ogy, B
Technology Teacher Education/Industrial Arts
  Teacher Education, B
Theater, M
Toxicology, MD
Travel and Tourism, MD
Veterinary Medicine, D
Veterinary Sciences, MD
Veterinary/Animal Health Technology/Technician and
  Veterinary Assistant, AB
Virology, D
Vocational and Technical Education, MDO
Women's Studies, B
Wood Science and Wood Products/Pulp and Paper
  Technology, B
Writing, M

PURDUE UNIVERSITY NORTHWEST (HAMMOND)

Accounting, BM
Acute Care/Critical Care Nursing, M
Behavioral Sciences, B
BioTechnology, M
Biological and Biomedical Sciences, M
Biology/Biological Sciences, B
Business Administration and Management, B
Business Administration, Management and Opera-
  tions, M
Business/Commerce, B
Chemistry, B
Child Care and Support Services Management, B
Child Development, M
Child and Family Studies, M
Civil Engineering, B
Clinical Laboratory Science/Medical
  Technology/Technologist, B
Communication Studies/Speech Communication
  and Rhetoric, B
Communication and Media Studies, M
Computer Engineering, BM
Computer Graphics, B
Computer Science, BM
Computer and Information Sciences and Support
  Services, B
Counseling Psychology, M
Counselor Education/School Counseling and Guid-
  ance Services, M
Economics, B
Education, M
Educational Administration and Supervision, M

Educational Media/Instructional Technology, M
Electrical Engineering, M
Electrical, Electronic and Communications Engineer-
  ing Technology/Technician, B
Electrical, Electronics and Communications Engi-
  neering, B
Elementary Education and Teaching, B
Emergency Medical Technology/Technician (EMT
  Paramedic), A
Engineering, B
Engineering and Applied Sciences, M
Engineering/Industrial Management, B
English, M
English Language and Literature, B
Foreign Languages and Literatures, B
History, BM
Hospitality Administration/Management, B
Human Development and Family Studies, B
Human Services, M
Industrial Technology/Technician, B
Liberal Arts and Sciences Studies and Humani-
  ties, B
Management, M
Management Information Systems and Services, B
Marriage and Family Therapy/Counseling, M
Mathematics, BM
Mathematics Teacher Education, M
Mechanical Engineering, BM
Mechanical Engineering/Mechanical
  Technology/Technician, B
Nursing, M
Nursing - Adult, M
Nursing - Advanced Practice, M
Nursing Administration, M
Philosophy, B
Physical Sciences, B
Physics, B
Political Science and Government, B
Pre-Veterinary Studies, B
Psychology, B
School Psychology, M
Science Teacher Education/General Science
  Teacher Education, M
Sociology, B
Special Education and Teaching, M
Survey Technology/Surveying, B

PURDUE UNIVERSITY NORTHWEST (WESTVILLE)

Behavioral Sciences, B
Biology/Biological Sciences, B
Business, Management, Marketing, and Related
  Support Services, AB
Communication Studies/Speech Communication
  and Rhetoric, B
Computer and Information Sciences and Support
  Services, B
Early Childhood Education and Teaching, B
Education, M
Electrical, Electronic and Communications Engineer-
  ing Technology/Technician, A
Electrical, Electronics and Communications Engi-
  neering, B
Elementary Education and Teaching, BM
Engineering, A
English Language and Literature, B
History, B
Human Resources Management/Personnel Adminis-
  tration, B
Industrial Production Technologies/Technicians, B
Liberal Arts and Sciences Studies and Humani-
  ties, B
Management Information Systems and Services, A
Mechanical Engineering, B
Mechanical Engineering Related
  Technologies/Technicians, AB
Operations Management and Supervision, B
Psychology, B
Secondary Education and Teaching, B
Social Work, B

ROSE-HULMAN INSTITUTE OF TECHNOLOGY

Biochemistry, B
Biology/Biological Sciences, B
Biomedical Engineering, M

Biomedical/Medical Engineering, B
Chemical Engineering, BM
Chemistry, B
Civil Engineering, BM
Computer Engineering, BM
Computer Science, B
Computer Software Engineering, B
Economics, B
Electrical Engineering, M
Electrical, Electronics and Communications Engi-
  neering, B
Engineering, B
Engineering Management, M
Engineering Physics, B
Engineering and Applied Sciences, M
Environmental Engineering
  Technology/Environmental Technology, M
Mathematics, B
Mechanical Engineering, BM
Optics/Optical Sciences, M
Physics, B
Software Engineering, M
System Management, M
Systems Engineering, M

SAINT JOSEPH'S COLLEGE

Accounting, B
Art Teacher Education, B
Athletic Training and Sports Medicine, B
Biochemistry, AB
Biology/Biological Sciences, B
Business/Commerce, B
Chemistry, B
Clinical Laboratory Science/Medical
  Technology/Technologist, B
Communication Studies/Speech Communication
  and Rhetoric, B
Computer and Information Sciences, B
Criminal Justice/Safety Studies, B
Digital Communication and Media/Multimedia, B
Directing and Theatrical Production, B
Economics, B
Elementary Education and Teaching, B
Emergency Medical Technology/Technician (EMT
  Paramedic), A
English Language and Literature, B
Fine/Studio Arts, B
Health and Physical Education, B
History, B
International Relations and Affairs, B
Mathematics, B
Music History, Literature, and Theory, B
Pastoral Studies/Counseling, B
Philosophy, B
Philosophy and Religious Studies, B
Political Science and Government, B
Psychology, B
Sacred Music, MO
Sociology, B
Sport and Fitness Administration/Management, B

SAINT MARY-OF-THE-WOODS COL-LEGE

Accounting, AB
Accounting and Computer Science, B
Agricultural and Domestic Animals Services, B
Art Teacher Education, B
Art Therapy/Therapist, MO
Biology/Biological Sciences, B
Business Administration and Management, B
Business/Commerce, A
Clinical Laboratory Science/Medical
  Technology/Technologist, B
Computer and Information Sciences, B
Criminology, B
Design and Visual Communications, B
Education, B
Education/Teaching of Individuals Who are Develop-
  mentally Delayed, AB
Elementary Education and Teaching, AB
English Language and Literature, B
Equestrian/Equine Studies, AB
Health Professions and Related Clinical Sciences, B
Health/Health Care Administration/Management, B
Horse Husbandry/Equine Science and Manage-
  ment, B

Human Resources Management/Personnel Administration, B
Human Services, B
Humanities/Humanistic Studies, AB
Legal Assistant/Paralegal, AB
Liberal Arts and Sciences Studies and Humanities, B
Management Strategy and Policy, M
Marketing/Marketing Management, B
Mass Communication/Media Studies, B
Mathematics, B
Music, B
Music Therapy/Therapist, BM
Pastoral Studies/Counseling, O
Psychology, B
Social Studies Teacher Education, B
Special Education and Teaching, B
Teacher Assistant/Aide, A
Teacher Education, Multiple Levels, B
Theological and Ministerial Studies, B
Theology and Religious Vocations, MO

SAINT MARY'S COLLEGE

Accounting, B
Art Teacher Education, B
Art/Art Studies, General, B
Biology/Biological Sciences, B
Business Administration and Management, B
Business Teacher Education, B
Chemistry, B
Communication Disorders, B
Communication Studies/Speech Communication and Rhetoric, B
Drama and Dramatics/Theatre Arts, B
Economics, B
Elementary Education and Teaching, B
English Language and Literature, B
History, B
Humanities/Humanistic Studies, B
International/Global Studies, B
Management Information Systems and Services, B
Mathematics, B
Mathematics and Computer Science, B
Music, B
Music Teacher Education, B
Philosophy, B
Political Science and Government, B
Psychology, B
Religion/Religious Studies, B
Social Work, B
Sociology, B
Spanish Language and Literature, B
Statistics, B
Women's Studies, B

TAYLOR UNIVERSITY

Accounting, B
Applied Mathematics, B
Art Teacher Education, B
Art/Art Studies, General, B
Bible/Biblical Studies, B
Biochemistry, B
Biology/Biological Sciences, B
Business Administration and Management, AB
Business Administration, Management and Operations, M
Business/Commerce, B
Business/Managerial Economics, B
Chemistry, B
Cinematography and Film/Video Production, B
Communication and Media Studies, B
Computer Engineering, B
Computer Science, B
Computer Systems Analysis/Analyst, B
Computer and Information Sciences, B
Design and Applied Arts, B
Development Economics and International Development, B
Digital Communication and Media/Multimedia, B
Early Childhood Education and Teaching, A
Economics, B
Education, B
Engineering Physics, B
English Language and Literature, B
English/Language Arts Teacher Education, B
Environmental Sciences, B

Environmental Studies, B
Environmental/Environmental Health Engineering, B
Finance, B
Geography, B
Geology/Earth Science, B
Higher Education/Higher Education Administration, M
History, B
International Business/Trade/Commerce, BM
International Relations and Affairs, B
Liberal Arts and Sciences Studies and Humanities, A
Management Strategy and Policy, M
Marketing/Marketing Management, B
Mathematics, B
Mathematics Teacher Education, B
Multi-/Interdisciplinary Studies, B
Music, B
Music Performance, B
Music Teacher Education, B
Music Theory and Composition, B
Natural Sciences, B
Philosophy, B
Physical Education Teaching and Coaching, B
Physics, B
Political Science and Government, B
Psychology, B
Public Relations/Image Management, B
Religious Education, B
Science Teacher Education/General Science Teacher Education, B
Secondary Education and Teaching, B
Social Studies Teacher Education, B
Social Work, B
Sociology, B
Spanish Language Teacher Education, B
Spanish Language and Literature, B
Sport and Fitness Administration/Management, B
Systems Engineering, B
Teacher Education and Professional Development, Specific Subject Areas, B

TRINE UNIVERSITY

Accounting, AB
Biological and Physical Sciences, A
Biology/Biological Sciences, B
Business Administration and Management, AB
Chemical Engineering, B
Chemistry, B
Civil Engineering, BM
Communication Studies/Speech Communication and Rhetoric, AB
Computer Engineering, B
Computer Science, B
Criminal Justice/Law Enforcement Administration, AB
Criminology, M
Drafting and Design Technology/Technician, B
Education, B
Electrical, Electronics and Communications Engineering, B
Elementary Education and Teaching, B
Emergency Management, M
Engineering Management, M
Engineering and Applied Sciences, M
Entrepreneurship/Entrepreneurial Studies, B
Environmental Studies, B
Forensic Psychology, M
Forensic Science and Technology, B
Law and Legal Studies, M
Liberal Arts and Sciences Studies and Humanities, AB
Marketing/Marketing Management, B
Mathematics, AB
Mathematics Teacher Education, B
Mechanical Engineering, B
Operations Management and Supervision, B
Parks, Recreation and Leisure Facilities Management, B
Physical Education Teaching and Coaching, B
Physical Sciences, B
Pre-Law Studies, B
Pre-Medicine/Pre-Medical Studies, B
Psychology, B
Public Administration, M

Science Teacher Education/General Science Teacher Education, B
Secondary Education and Teaching, B
Social Sciences, AB
Social Studies Teacher Education, B
Sport and Fitness Administration/Management, B

UNIVERSITY OF EVANSVILLE

Accounting, B
Archeology, B
Art History, Criticism and Conservation, B
Art Teacher Education, B
Art/Art Studies, General, B
Athletic Training and Sports Medicine, B
Biochemistry, B
Biology Teacher Education, B
Biology/Biological Sciences, B
Business Administration and Management, B
Chemistry, B
Chemistry Teacher Education, B
Civil Engineering, B
Classics and Classical Languages, Literatures, and Linguistics, B
Clinical Laboratory Science/Medical Technology/Technologist, B
Cognitive Sciences, B
Computer Engineering, B
Computer Science, B
Criminal Justice/Safety Studies, B
Design and Visual Communications, B
Drama and Dance Teacher Education, B
Drama and Dramatics/Theatre Arts, B
Economics, B
Electrical, Electronics and Communications Engineering, B
Elementary Education and Teaching, B
English Language and Literature, B
English/Language Arts Teacher Education, B
Environmental Sciences, B
Environmental Studies, B
Finance, B
French Language Teacher Education, B
French Language and Literature, B
German Language Teacher Education, B
German Language and Literature, B
Health Services Administration, M
Health/Health Care Administration/Management, B
History, B
International Business/Trade/Commerce, B
International Relations and Affairs, B
Kinesiology and Exercise Science, B
Liberal Arts and Sciences Studies and Humanities, B
Marketing/Marketing Management, B
Mathematics, B
Mathematics Teacher Education, B
Mechanical Engineering, B
Music, B
Music Performance, B
Music Teacher Education, B
Music Therapy/Therapist, B
Philosophy, B
Physical Therapist Assistant, A
Physical Therapy/Therapist, D
Physics, B
Physics Teacher Education, B
Political Science and Government, B
Psychology, B
Public Administration, M
Public Health (MPH, DPH), B
Social Studies Teacher Education, B
Sociology, B
Spanish Language Teacher Education, B
Spanish Language and Literature, B
Special Education and Teaching, B

UNIVERSITY OF INDIANAPOLIS

Accounting, B
Anthropology, BM
Archeology, B
Art Education, M
Art Teacher Education, B
Art Therapy/Therapist, B
Art/Art Studies, General, B
Athletic Training and Sports Medicine, B
Biological and Biomedical Sciences, M

Biology/Biological Sciences, B
Business Administration, Management and Operations, MO
Business Teacher Education, B
Business/Managerial Economics, B
Clinical Laboratory Science/Medical Technology/Technologist, B
Clinical Psychology, MD
Commercial and Advertising Art, B
Communication Studies/Speech Communication and Rhetoric, B
Computer Engineering, B
Computer Science, B
Counseling Psychology, M
Curriculum and Instruction, M
Drama and Dramatics/Theatre Arts, B
Education, BM
Educational Administration and Supervision, M
Elementary Education and Teaching, BM
English, M
English Education, M
English Language and Literature, B
English/Language Arts Teacher Education, B
Entrepreneurship/Entrepreneurial Studies, B
Environmental Studies, B
Fine Arts and Art Studies, M
Fine/Studio Arts, B
Foreign Language Teacher Education, M
French Language Teacher Education, B
French Language and Literature, B
Geology/Earth Science, B
German Language and Literature, B
Gerontology, MO
History, BM
International Affairs, M
International Business/Trade/Commerce, B
International Relations and Affairs, B
Kinesiology and Exercise Science, B
Marketing/Marketing Management, B
Maternal/Child Health and Neonatal Nurse/Nursing, M
Mathematics, B
Mathematics Teacher Education, BM
Mechanical Engineering, B
Music, B
Music Performance, B
Music Teacher Education, B
Nurse Midwife/Nursing Midwifery, M
Nursing, MD
Nursing - Advanced Practice, M
Nursing Administration, M
Nursing Education, M
Occupational Therapy/Therapist, MD
Operations Management and Supervision, B
Philosophy, B
Physical Education Teaching and Coaching, BM
Physical Therapist Assistant, A
Physical Therapy/Therapist, MD
Physics, B
Political Science and Government, B
Pre-Dentistry Studies, B
Pre-Law Studies, B
Pre-Medicine/Pre-Medical Studies, B
Pre-Theology/Pre-Ministerial Studies, B
Pre-Veterinary Studies, B
Psychology, BMD
Public Health, M
Religion/Religious Studies, B
Respiratory Care Therapy/Therapist, B
Science Teacher Education/General Science Teacher Education, BM
Secondary Education and Teaching, BM
Social Studies Teacher Education, BM
Social Work, B
Sociology, BM
Spanish Language Teacher Education, B
Spanish Language and Literature, B
Speech Teacher Education, B
Sport and Fitness Administration/Management, BM
Women's Health Nursing, M
Youth Ministry, B

UNIVERSITY OF NOTRE DAME

Accounting, BM
Aerospace, Aeronautical and Astronautical Engineering, BMD

African-American/Black Studies, B
American/United States Studies/Civilization, B
Ancient/Classical Greek Language and Literature, B
Anthropology, B
Applied Mathematics, M
Applied Statistics, M
Arabic Language and Literature, B
Architecture, BM
Art History, Criticism and Conservation, BM
Biochemistry, BMD
Bioengineering, M
Biological and Biomedical Sciences, MD
Biology/Biological Sciences, B
Business Administration, Management and Operations, M
Business/Commerce, B
Cell Biology and Anatomy, MD
Ceramic Arts and Ceramics, M
Chemical Engineering, BMD
Chemistry, BMD
Chinese Language and Literature, B
Civil Engineering, BMD
Classics and Classical Languages, Literatures, and Linguistics, B
Cognitive Sciences, B
Comparative Literature, D
Computational Sciences, MD
Computer Engineering, BMD
Computer Science, MD
Computer and Information Sciences, B
Computer and Information Sciences and Support Services, B
Conflict Resolution and Mediation/Peace Studies, MD
Counseling Psychology, D
Database Systems, M
Design and Applied Arts, M
Design and Visual Communications, B
Developmental Psychology, D
Drama and Dramatics/Theatre Arts, B
Ecology, MD
Economics, BMD
Education, M
Electrical Engineering, MD
Electrical, Electronics and Communications Engineering, B
Engineering and Applied Sciences, MD
English, MD
English Language and Literature, B
Entrepreneurship/Entrepreneurial Studies, B
Environmental Engineering Technology/Environmental Technology, M
Environmental Sciences, B
Environmental/Environmental Health Engineering, B
Evolutionary Biology, MD
Finance, B
Finance and Banking, M
Fine Arts and Art Studies, M
Fine/Studio Arts, B
French Language and Literature, BM
Genetics, MD
Geosciences, MD
German Language and Literature, B
Graphic Design, M
History, BMD
History of Science and Technology, MD
Industrial Design, M
Inorganic Chemistry, MD
Italian Language and Literature, BM
Japanese Language and Literature, B
Latin American Studies, M
Law and Legal Studies, MD
Liberal Arts and Sciences Studies and Humanities, B
Management Information Systems and Services, B
Marketing/Marketing Management, B
Mathematical and Computational Finance, M
Mathematics, BMD
Mechanical Engineering, BMD
Medieval and Renaissance Studies, BMD
Molecular Biology, MD
Music, B
Non-Profit/Public/Organizational Management, M
Organic Chemistry, MD
Painting, M
Parasitology, MD

Philosophy, BD
Philosophy and Religious Studies, B
Photography, M
Physical Chemistry, MD
Physics, BMD
Physiology, MD
Political Science and Government, BD
Pre-Medicine/Pre-Medical Studies, B
Printmaking, M
Psychology, BD
Religion/Religious Studies, M
Romance Languages, Literatures, and Linguistics, BM
Russian Language and Literature, B
Science Teacher Education/General Science Teacher Education, B
Sculpture, M
Sociology, BD
Spanish Language and Literature, BM
Statistics, MD
Taxation, M
Theology and Religious Vocations, MD
Theology/Theological Studies, B
Writing, M

UNIVERSITY OF SAINT FRANCIS

Accounting, B
Art History, Criticism and Conservation, B
Art Teacher Education, B
Art Therapy/Therapist, B
Biology Teacher Education, B
Biology/Biological Sciences, B
Business Administration and Management, B
Business Administration, Management and Operations, M
Business Teacher Education, B
Business/Commerce, B
Chemistry, AB
Chemistry Teacher Education, B
Clinical Laboratory Science/Medical Technology/Technologist, B
Clinical Psychology, O
Clinical/Medical Laboratory Technician, A
Counseling Psychology, MO
Counselor Education/School Counseling and Guidance Services, M
Criminal Justice/Safety Studies, AB
Dance, AB
Design and Visual Communications, AB
Education, BMO
Elementary Education and Teaching, B
English Language and Literature, B
English/Language Arts Teacher Education, B
Environmental Sciences, AB
Environmental and Occupational Health, M
Finance, B
Fine Arts and Art Studies, M
Fine/Studio Arts, AB
General Studies, A
Health Services Administration, M
Health Teacher Education, B
Health/Health Care Administration/Management, B
History, B
Insurance, B
Liberal Arts and Sciences Studies and Humanities, AB
Marketing/Marketing Management, B
Mathematics, B
Mathematics Teacher Education, B
Nursing, MO
Nursing - Advanced Practice, MO
Nutritional Sciences, B
Pastoral Studies/Counseling, MO
Philosophy, B
Physical Therapist Assistant, A
Physician Assistant, M
Political Science and Government, B
Psychology, MO
Radiologic Technology/Science - Radiographer, A
Rehabilitation Counseling, MO
Social Studies Teacher Education, B
Social Work, B
Sociology, B
Special Education and Teaching, BMO
Surgical Technology/Technologist, A
Sustainability Management, M

Theology and Religious Vocations, M
Theology/Theological Studies, B

UNIVERSITY OF SOUTHERN INDIANA

Accounting, B
Advertising, B
Anthropology, B
Art/Art Studies, General, B
Biochemistry, B
Biological and Physical Sciences, B
Biology/Biological Sciences, B
Biophysics, B
Business Administration and Management, B
Business Administration, Management and Operations, M
Business Teacher Education, B
Business/Commerce, AB
Chemistry, B
Communication and Media Studies, M
Computer Science, B
Computer and Information Sciences, B
Criminal Justice/Safety Studies, B
Dental Assisting/Assistant, A
Dental Hygiene/Hygienist, B
Drama and Dramatics/Theatre Arts, B
Early Childhood Education and Teaching, AB
Economics, B
Education, M
Elementary Education and Teaching, BM
Engineering, B
Engineering and Applied Sciences, M
English, M
English Language and Literature, B
Entrepreneurship/Entrepreneurial Studies, B
Environmental Studies, B
Finance, B
French Language and Literature, B
Geology/Earth Science, B
German Language and Literature, B
Health Services Administration, M
Health/Health Care Administration/Management, B
History, B
Industrial and Manufacturing Management, M
International Relations and Affairs, B
Journalism, B
Kinesiology and Exercise Science, B
Liberal Arts and Sciences Studies and Humanities, B
Liberal Studies, M
Manufacturing Technology/Technician, B
Marketing/Marketing Management, B
Mass Communication/Media Studies, B
Mathematics, B
Medical Radiologic Technology/Science - Radiation Therapist, B
Nursing, MD
Nutritional Sciences, B
Occupational Therapist Assistant, A
Occupational Therapy/Therapist, BM
Office Management and Supervision, B
Operations Management and Supervision, B
Philosophy, B
Physical Education Teaching and Coaching, B
Political Science and Government, B
Psychology, B
Public Administration, M
Radio and Television, B
Respiratory Care Therapy/Therapist, A
Secondary Education and Teaching, M
Social Sciences, AB
Social Work, BM
Sociology, B
Spanish Language and Literature, B
Special Education and Teaching, B
Sport and Fitness Administration/Management, B

VALPARAISO UNIVERSITY

Accounting, B
Actuarial Science, B
American/United States Studies/Civilization, B
Art Teacher Education, B
Art/Art Studies, General, B
Arts Management, M
Asian Studies/Civilization, M
Astronomy, B
Atmospheric Sciences and Meteorology, B

Biochemistry, B
Biological and Physical Sciences, A
Biology Teacher Education, B
Biology/Biological Sciences, B
Business Administration, Management and Operations, MO
Chemistry, B
Chemistry Teacher Education, B
Civil Engineering, B
Classics and Classical Languages, Literatures, and Linguistics, B
Clinical Psychology, M
Communication Studies/Speech Communication and Rhetoric, B
Communication and Media Studies, MO
Communication, Journalism and Related Programs, A
Computational Sciences, M
Computer Engineering, B
Computer Science, B
Computer and Information Systems Security, M
Counselor Education/School Counseling and Guidance Services, M
Criminology, B
Digital Communication and Media/Multimedia, B
Drama and Dance Teacher Education, B
Drama and Dramatics/Theatre Arts, B
East Asian Studies, B
Economics, B
Education, M
Educational Leadership and Administration, M
Electrical, Electronics and Communications Engineering, B
Elementary Education and Teaching, B
Engineering Management, O
English, MO
English Language and Literature, B
English as a Second Language, MO
English/Language Arts Teacher Education, B
Entertainment Management, M
Entrepreneurship/Entrepreneurial Studies, O
Environmental Sciences, B
Ethics, MO
Finance, B
Finance and Banking, MO
Foreign Language Teacher Education, B
French Language Teacher Education, B
French Language and Literature, B
Geography, B
Geography Teacher Education, B
Geology/Earth Science, B
German Language Teacher Education, B
German Language and Literature, B
Gerontology, MO
Health Services Administration, M
Health Services/Allied Health/Health Sciences, B
Health and Physical Education, B
Health/Health Care Administration/Management, B
History, BMO
History Teacher Education, B
Humanities/Humanistic Studies, AB
International Business/Trade/Commerce, BM
International Economics, BM
International Relations and Affairs, B
International and Comparative Education, M
International/Global Studies, B
Kinesiology and Exercise Science, B
Law and Legal Studies, MD
Legal and Justice Studies, O
Liberal Studies, MO
Management Information Systems and Services, M
Management Science, B
Management Strategy and Policy, O
Marketing, O
Marketing/Marketing Management, B
Mathematics, B
Mathematics Teacher Education, B
Mechanical Engineering, B
Media Studies, MO
Multi-/Interdisciplinary Studies, B
Music, B
Music Performance, B
Music Teacher Education, B
Music Theory and Composition, B
Nursing, MDO
Nursing Education, MO

Pastoral Studies/Counseling, M
Philosophy, B
Physical Education Teaching and Coaching, B
Physics, B
Physics Teacher Education, B
Piano and Organ, B
Political Science and Government, B
Psychology, BM
Psychology Teacher Education, B
Public Health, M
Public Health (MPH, DPH), B
Science Teacher Education/General Science Teacher Education, B
Secondary Education and Teaching, B
Social Science Teacher Education, B
Social Sciences, AB
Social Work, B
Sociology, B
Spanish Language Teacher Education, B
Spanish Language and Literature, B
Sport and Fitness Administration/Management, BM
Sustainability Management, O
Teacher Assistant/Aide, A
Theology and Religious Vocations, MO
Theology/Theological Studies, B
Voice and Opera, B

VET TECH INSTITUTE AT INTERNATIONAL BUSINESS COLLEGE (FORT WAYNE)

Veterinary/Animal Health Technology/Technician and Veterinary Assistant, A

VET TECH INSTITUTE AT INTERNATIONAL BUSINESS COLLEGE (INDIANAPOLIS)

Veterinary/Animal Health Technology/Technician and Veterinary Assistant, A

VINCENNES UNIVERSITY

Accounting Technology/Technician and Bookkeeping, A
Administrative Assistant and Secretarial Science, A
Agricultural Business and Management, A
Agricultural/Biological Engineering and Bioengineering, A
Agriculture, A
Aircraft Powerplant Technology/Technician, A
Airline/Commercial/Professional Pilot and Flight Crew, A
American Sign Language (ASL), A
Anthropology, A
Applied Horticulture/Horticultural Operations, A
Architectural Drafting and Architectural CAD/CADD, A
Art Teacher Education, A
Art Therapy/Therapist, A
Art/Art Studies, General, A
Autobody/Collision and Repair Technology/Technician, A
Automobile/Automotive Mechanics Technology/Technician, A
Behavioral Sciences, A
BioTechnology, A
Biochemistry, A
Biological and Biomedical Sciences, A
Biological and Physical Sciences, A
Biology/Biological Sciences, A
Building/Home/Construction Inspection/Inspector, A
Business Administration and Management, A
Business/Commerce, A
Chemistry, A
Chemistry Teacher Education, A
Child Care Provider/Assistant, A
Child Care and Support Services Management, A
Civil Engineering, A
Commercial and Advertising Art, A
Communications Technology/Technician, A
Computer Programming/Programmer, A
Computer Science, A
Computer Systems Networking and Telecommunications, A
Computer and Information Sciences, A
Computer/Information Technology Services Administration and Management, A

Construction Trades, A
Corrections and Criminal Justice, B
Cosmetology/Cosmetologist, A
Criminal Justice/Police Science, A
Culinary Arts/Chef Training, A
Design and Applied Arts, A
Diesel Mechanics Technology/Technician, A
Dietetics/Dieticians, A
Drama and Dramatics/Theatre Arts, A
Early Childhood Education and Teaching, A
Economics, A
Education, A
Electrical, Electronic and Communications Engineering Technology/Technician, A
Elementary Education and Teaching, A
Emergency Medical Technology/Technician (EMT Paramedic), A
Engineering Technology, A
English Language and Literature, A
English/Language Arts Teacher Education, A
Family and Consumer Sciences/Home Economics Teacher Education, A
Family and Consumer Sciences/Human Sciences, A
Fashion Merchandising, A
Finance, A
Fire Science/Firefighting, A
Food Science, A
Foreign Languages and Literatures, A
Foreign Languages, Literatures, and Linguistics, A
Funeral Service and Mortuary Science, A
Geology/Earth Science, A
Graphic and Printing Equipment Operator Production, A
Health Information/Medical Records Technology/Technician, A
Health and Physical Education, A
History, A
Hospitality Administration/Management, A
Hotel/Motel Administration/Management, A
Industrial Technology/Technician, B
Journalism, A
Legal Assistant/Paralegal, A
Liberal Arts and Sciences Studies and Humanities, A
Manufacturing Technology/Technician, A
Marketing/Marketing Management, A
Massage Therapy/Therapeutic Massage, A
Mathematics, A
Mathematics Teacher Education, AB
Mechanical Drafting and Mechanical Drafting CAD/CADD, A
Mechanical Engineering/Mechanical Technology/Technician, A
Medical Radiologic Technology/Science - Radiation Therapist, A
Music, A
Music Teacher Education, A
Natural Resources and Conservation, A
Nuclear Medical Technology/Technologist, A
Ophthalmic and Optometric Support Services and Allied Professions, A
Parks, Recreation, Leisure and Fitness Studies, A
Pharmacy Technician/Assistant, A
Philosophy, A
Photojournalism, A
Physical Education Teaching and Coaching, A
Physical Sciences, A
Physical Therapist Assistant, A
Political Science and Government, A
Pre-Dentistry Studies, A
Pre-Medicine/Pre-Medical Studies, A
Pre-Pharmacy Studies, A
Pre-Veterinary Studies, A
Psychology, A
Public Relations/Image Management, A
Radio and Television Broadcasting Technology/Technician, A
Recording Arts Technology/Technician, A
Restaurant, Culinary, and Catering Management/Manager, A
Robotics Technology/Technician, A
Science Teacher Education/General Science Teacher Education, AB
Secondary Education and Teaching, A
Securities Services Administration/Management, A
Security and Loss Prevention Services, A

Sheet Metal Technology/Sheetworking, A
Social Work, A
Sociology, A
Special Education and Teaching, AB
Sport and Fitness Administration/Management, A
Surgical Technology/Technologist, A
Survey Technology/Surveying, A
Teacher Assistant/Aide, A
Technical Theatre/Theatre Design and Technology, A
Tool and Die Technology/Technician, A
Web/Multimedia Management and Webmaster, A
Woodworking, A

WABASH COLLEGE

Ancient/Classical Greek Language and Literature, B
Applied Economics, B
Art/Art Studies, General, B
Biochemistry, B
Biology/Biological Sciences, B
Chemistry, B
Classics and Classical Languages, Literatures, and Linguistics, B
Drama and Dramatics/Theatre Arts, B
Economics, B
English Language and Literature, B
French Language and Literature, B
German Language and Literature, B
History, B
Humanities/Humanistic Studies, B
Latin Language and Literature, B
Mathematics, B
Music, B
Philosophy, B
Physics, B
Political Science and Government, B
Psychology, B
Religion/Religious Studies, B
Spanish Language and Literature, B
Spanish and Iberian Studies, B

Iowa

ALLEN COLLEGE

Acute Care/Critical Care Nursing, O
Clinical/Medical Laboratory Science and Allied Professions, B
Community Health Nursing, MO
Dental Hygiene/Hygienist, B
Gerontological Nursing, MO
Nuclear Medical Technology/Technologist, B
Nursing, MDO
Nursing - Adult, MO
Nursing - Advanced Practice, MO
Nursing Administration, MO
Psychiatric/Mental Health Nurse/Nursing, O
Public Health, MO
Public Health (MPH, DPH), B
Radiologic Technology/Science - Radiographer, A

BRIAR CLIFF UNIVERSITY

Accounting, B
Art/Art Studies, General, B
Biology/Biological Sciences, B
Business Administration and Management, B
Chemistry, B
Criminal Justice/Law Enforcement Administration, B
Drama and Dramatics/Theatre Arts, B
Education, B
Elementary Education and Teaching, B
English Language and Literature, B
Environmental Sciences, B
Graphic Design, B
History, B
Human Resources Management and Services, M
Human Resources Management/Personnel Administration, B
Industrial Radiologic Technology/Technician, B
Liberal Arts and Sciences Studies and Humanities, A
Management Information Systems and Services, B
Mass Communication/Media Studies, B
Mathematics, B
Music, B
Nursing, M

Physical Education Teaching and Coaching, B
Political Science and Government, B
Psychology, B
Secondary Education and Teaching, B
Social Work, B
Spanish Language and Literature, B
Theology/Theological Studies, AB

BROWN MACKIE COLLEGE–QUAD CITIES

Business Administration and Management, A
Criminal Justice/Safety Studies, A
Medical Office Management/Administration, A
Occupational Therapist Assistant, A

BUENA VISTA UNIVERSITY

Accounting, B
Art Teacher Education, B
Art/Art Studies, General, B
Athletic Training and Sports Medicine, B
Banking and Financial Support Services, B
Biological and Physical Sciences, B
Biology Teacher Education, B
Biology/Biological Sciences, B
Business Administration and Management, B
Business Teacher Education, B
Business/Managerial Economics, B
Chemistry, B
Chemistry Teacher Education, B
Commercial and Advertising Art, B
Communication Studies/Speech Communication and Rhetoric, B
Computer Science, B
Computer Teacher Education, B
Counselor Education/School Counseling and Guidance Services, BM
Criminal Justice/Safety Studies, B
Curriculum and Instruction, M
Education, M
Elementary Education and Teaching, B
English Language and Literature, B
English as a Second Language, M
English/Language Arts Teacher Education, B
Entrepreneurship/Entrepreneurial Studies, B
Environmental Sciences, B
History, B
History Teacher Education, B
Human Resources Management/Personnel Administration, B
International Business/Trade/Commerce, B
Management Information Systems and Services, B
Marketing/Marketing Management, B
Mass Communication/Media Studies, B
Mathematics, B
Mathematics Teacher Education, B
Multi-/Interdisciplinary Studies, B
Music Performance, B
Music Teacher Education, B
Organizational Communication, B
Philosophy and Religious Studies, B
Physical Education Teaching and Coaching, B
Physics, B
Physics Teacher Education, B
Political Science and Government, B
Psychology, B
Public Administration, B
Public Relations, Advertising, and Applied Communication, B
Science Teacher Education/General Science Teacher Education, B
Social Science Teacher Education, B
Social Work, B
Sociology, B
Spanish Language Teacher Education, B
Spanish Language and Literature, B
Special Education and Teaching, B
Speech Teacher Education, B
Sport and Fitness Administration/Management, B
Theatre Literature, History and Criticism, B

CENTRAL COLLEGE

Accounting, B
Actuarial Science, B
Anthropology, B
Art/Art Studies, General, B
Athletic Training and Sports Medicine, B

Biochemistry, B
Biology/Biological Sciences, B
Business Administration and Management, B
Chemistry, B
Communication Studies/Speech Communication and Rhetoric, B
Computer Science, B
Drama and Dramatics/Theatre Arts, B
Economics, B
Elementary Education and Teaching, B
Engineering, B
English Language and Literature, B
Environmental Studies, B
Exercise Physiology, B
French Language and Literature, B
German Studies, B
History, B
Information Science/Studies, B
International Business/Trade/Commerce, B
International/Global Studies, B
Linguistics, B
Mathematics, B
Multi-/Interdisciplinary Studies, B
Music, B
Music Teacher Education, B
Natural Sciences, B
Philosophy, B
Physics, B
Political Science and Government, B
Psychology, B
Religion/Religious Studies, B
Social Sciences, B
Sociology, B
Spanish Language and Literature, B

CLARKE UNIVERSITY

Accounting, B
Art History, Criticism and Conservation, B
Art Teacher Education, B
Athletic Training and Sports Medicine, B
Biochemistry, B
Biology/Biological Sciences, B
Business Administration and Management, B
Business Administration, Management and Operations, M
Chemistry, B
Communication, Journalism and Related Programs, B
Computer and Information Sciences, B
Drama and Dramatics/Theatre Arts, B
Early Childhood Education and Teaching, M
Education, M
Educational Administration and Supervision, M
Educational Media/Instructional Technology, M
Elementary Education and Teaching, B
English Language and Literature, B
Environmental Studies, B
Fine/Studio Arts, B
Food Science, B
Graphic Design, B
History, B
Liberal Arts and Sciences Studies and Humanities, AB
Mathematics, B
Music Performance, B
Music Teacher Education, B
Nursing, MDO
Nursing - Advanced Practice, MO
Nursing Administration, M
Nursing Education, M
Philosophy, B
Physical Therapy/Therapist, D
Psychology, B
Reading Teacher Education, M
Religion/Religious Studies, B
Secondary Education and Teaching, B
Social Work, BM
Spanish Language and Literature, B
Special Education and Teaching, M
Sport and Fitness Administration/Management, B

CLINTON COMMUNITY COLLEGE

Administrative Assistant and Secretarial Science, A
Architectural Drafting and Architectural CAD/CADD, A
Business Administration and Management, A

Computer/Information Technology Services Administration and Management, A
Electrical, Electronic and Communications Engineering Technology/Technician, A
Emergency Medical Technology/Technician (EMT Paramedic), A
Environmental Engineering Technology/Environmental Technology, A
Graphic and Printing Equipment Operator Production, A
Liberal Arts and Sciences Studies and Humanities, A
Occupational Safety and Health Technology/Technician, A
Physical Therapy/Therapist, A
Respiratory Care Therapy/Therapist, A

COE COLLEGE

Accounting, B
African-American/Black Studies, B
American/United States Studies/Civilization, B
Art History, Criticism and Conservation, B
Art Teacher Education, B
Art/Art Studies, General, B
Asian Studies/Civilization, B
Athletic Training and Sports Medicine, B
Biochemistry, B
Biology/Biological Sciences, B
Business Administration and Management, B
Chemistry, B
Classics and Classical Languages, Literatures, and Linguistics, B
Communication Studies/Speech Communication and Rhetoric, B
Computer Science, B
Drama and Dramatics/Theatre Arts, B
Economics, B
Education, B
Elementary Education and Teaching, B
English Language and Literature, B
Environmental Sciences, B
Environmental Studies, B
Film/Cinema Studies, B
Film/Video and Photographic Arts, B
Fine/Studio Arts, B
French Language and Literature, B
French Studies, B
German Language and Literature, B
German Studies, B
Health and Physical Education/Fitness, B
History, B
Liberal Arts and Sciences Studies and Humanities, B
Mathematics, B
Molecular Biology, B
Music, B
Music Performance, B
Music Teacher Education, B
Music Theory and Composition, B
Organizational Behavior Studies, B
Painting, B
Philosophy, B
Photography, B
Physical Education Teaching and Coaching, B
Physical Sciences, B
Physics, B
Political Science and Government, B
Pre-Dentistry Studies, B
Pre-Law Studies, B
Pre-Medicine/Pre-Medical Studies, B
Pre-Veterinary Studies, B
Psychology, B
Public Relations/Image Management, B
Religion/Religious Studies, B
Science Teacher Education/General Science Teacher Education, B
Secondary Education and Teaching, B
Sociology, B
Spanish Language and Literature, B
Spanish and Iberian Studies, B
Technical Theatre/Theatre Design and Technology, B

Women's Studies, B

CORNELL COLLEGE

Anthropology, B
Archeology, B
Architecture, B
Art History, Criticism and Conservation, B
Art/Art Studies, General, B
Biochemistry, B
Biology/Biological Sciences, B
Chemistry, B
Classics and Classical Languages, Literatures, and Linguistics, B
Computer Science, B
Drama and Dramatics/Theatre Arts, B
Economics, B
Elementary Education and Teaching, B
English Language and Literature, B
Environmental Studies, B
Ethnic, Cultural Minority, and Gender Studies, B
French Language and Literature, B
Geology/Earth Science, B
German Language and Literature, B
Health and Physical Education/Fitness, B
History, B
International Business/Trade/Commerce, B
International Relations and Affairs, B
Kinesiology and Exercise Science, B
Latin American Studies, B
Liberal Arts and Sciences Studies and Humanities, B
Mathematics, B
Medieval and Renaissance Studies, B
Modern Languages, B
Multi-/Interdisciplinary Studies, B
Music, B
Music Teacher Education, B
Philosophy, B
Physical Education Teaching and Coaching, B
Physics, B
Political Science and Government, B
Psychology, B
Religion/Religious Studies, B
Russian Language and Literature, B
Russian Studies, B
Secondary Education and Teaching, B
Sociology, B
Spanish Language and Literature, B
Women's Studies, B

DES MOINES AREA COMMUNITY COLLEGE

Accounting, A
Accounting Technology/Technician and Bookkeeping, A
Accounting and Business/Management, A
Agricultural/Farm Supplies Retailing and Wholesaling, A
Apparel and Accessories Marketing Operations, A
Applied Horticulture/Horticultural Business Services, A
Architectural Drafting and Architectural CAD/CADD, A
Autobody/Collision and Repair Technology/Technician, A
Automobile/Automotive Mechanics Technology/Technician, A
Biomedical Technology/Technician, A
Business Administration and Management, A
Child Care Provider/Assistant, A
Civil Engineering Technology/Technician, A
Clinical/Medical Laboratory Technician, A
Commercial and Advertising Art, A
Communications Systems Installation and Repair Technology, A
Computer Engineering Technology/Technician, A
Computer Programming, Specific Applications, A
Computer and Information Sciences and Support Services, A
Criminal Justice/Law Enforcement Administration, A
Culinary Arts/Chef Training, A
Dental Hygiene/Hygienist, A
Diesel Mechanics Technology/Technician, A
Electrical, Electronic and Communications Engineering Technology/Technician, A
Fire Protection and Safety Technology/Technician, A

Funeral Service and Mortuary Science, A
Health/Health Care Administration/Management, A
Heating, Air Conditioning, Ventilation and Refrigeration Maintenance Technology/Technician, A
Hospitality Administration/Management, A
Industrial Electronics Technology/Technician, A
Industrial Mechanics and Maintenance Technology, A
Information Technology, A
Language Interpretation and Translation, A
Legal Assistant/Paralegal, A
Liberal Arts and Sciences Studies and Humanities, A
Machine Tool Technology/Machinist, A
Marketing/Marketing Management, A
Mechanical Drafting and Mechanical Drafting CAD/CADD, A
Medical Administrative Assistant/Secretary, A
Medical/Clinical Assistant, A
Office Management and Supervision, A
Prepress/Desktop Publishing and Digital Imaging Design, A
Respiratory Care Therapy/Therapist, A
Sales, Distribution and Marketing Operations, A
Sport and Fitness Administration/Management, A
Surveying Engineering, A
Tool and Die Technology/Technician, A
Veterinary/Animal Health Technology/Technician and Veterinary Assistant, A

DIVINE WORD COLLEGE

Philosophy, B
Social Sciences, AB

DORDT COLLEGE

Accounting, B
Actuarial Science, B
Administrative Assistant and Secretarial Science, A
Agricultural Teacher Education, B
Agricultural/Biological Engineering and Bioengineering, B
Agriculture, B
Animal Sciences, B
Animal/Livestock Husbandry and Production, B
Biology Teacher Education, B
Biology/Biological Sciences, B
Business Administration and Management, B
Business Teacher Education, B
Chemistry, B
Chemistry Teacher Education, B
Civil Engineering, B
Clinical Laboratory Science/Medical Technology/Technologist, B
Commercial and Advertising Art, B
Computer Engineering, B
Computer Programming/Programmer, B
Computer Science, B
Computer Teacher Education, B
Computer/Information Technology Services Administration and Management, B
Data Processing and Data Processing Technology/Technician, A
Digital Communication and Media/Multimedia, B
Drama and Dance Teacher Education, B
Drama and Dramatics/Theatre Arts, B
Education, BM
Electrical, Electronics and Communications Engineering, B
Elementary Education and Teaching, B
Engineering, B
Engineering Mechanics, B
Engineering Technology, B
English Language and Literature, B
Environmental Studies, B
General Studies, B
Graphic Design, B
Health and Physical Education, B
History, B
History Teacher Education, B
Journalism, B
Kinesiology and Exercise Science, B
Legal Administrative Assistant/Secretary, A
Management Information Systems and Services, B
Mass Communication/Media Studies, B
Mathematics, B

Mechanical Engineering, B
Missions/Missionary Studies and Missiology, B
Music, B
Music Performance, B
Music Teacher Education, B
Natural Sciences, B
Parks, Recreation, Leisure and Fitness Studies, B
Philosophy, B
Physical Education Teaching and Coaching, B
Physics, B
Piano and Organ, B
Political Science and Government, B
Pre-Dentistry Studies, B
Pre-Law Studies, B
Pre-Medicine/Pre-Medical Studies, B
Pre-Pharmacy Studies, B
Pre-Veterinary Studies, B
Psychology, B
Reading Teacher Education, B
Religion/Religious Studies, B
Science Teacher Education/General Science Teacher Education, B
Secondary Education and Teaching, B
Social Science Teacher Education, B
Social Sciences, B
Social Studies Teacher Education, B
Social Work, B
Sociology, B
Spanish Language Teacher Education, B
Spanish Language and Literature, B
Speech Teacher Education, B
Sport and Fitness Administration/Management, B
Statistics, B
Superintendency and Educational System Administration, B
System Administration/Administrator, B
Teacher Assistant/Aide, A
Teacher Education, Multiple Levels, B
Theology/Theological Studies, B
Voice and Opera, B
Youth Ministry, B

DRAKE UNIVERSITY

Accounting, B
Accounting and Finance, B
Acting, B
Actuarial Science, B
Advertising, B
Anthropology, B
Art History, Criticism and Conservation, B
Art/Art Studies, General, B
Astronomy, B
Biochemistry, B
Biology/Biological Sciences, B
Broadcast Journalism, B
Business Administration and Management, B
Business Administration, Management and Operations, M
Business/Commerce, B
Chemistry, B
Commercial and Advertising Art, B
Communication and Media Studies, M
Computer Science, B
Directing and Theatrical Production, B
Drama and Dramatics/Theatre Arts, B
Dramatic/Theatre Arts and Stagecraft, B
Drawing, B
Education, MDO
Elementary Education and Teaching, B
English Language and Literature, B
Environmental Sciences, B
Environmental Studies, B
Ethics, B
Finance, B
Fine/Studio Arts, B
Graphic Design, B
History, B
International Business/Trade/Commerce, B
International Relations and Affairs, B
Jazz/Jazz Studies, B
Journalism, B
Law and Legal Studies, MD
Marketing/Marketing Management, B
Mass Communication/Media Studies, B
Mathematics, B
Music, B

Music Performance, B
Music Teacher Education, B
Painting, B
Pharmacy, BD
Pharmacy Administration and Pharmacy Policy and Regulatory Affairs, B
Philosophy, B
Physics, B
Piano and Organ, B
Political Science and Government, B
Pre-Dentistry Studies, B
Pre-Law Studies, B
Pre-Medicine/Pre-Medical Studies, B
Pre-Veterinary Studies, B
Printmaking, B
Psychology, B
Public Administration, M
Public Relations/Image Management, B
Radio and Television, B
Radio, Television, and Digital Communication, B
Religion/Religious Studies, B
Religious/Sacred Music, B
Sculpture, B
Secondary Education and Teaching, B
Sociology, B
Voice and Opera, B

ELLSWORTH COMMUNITY COLLEGE

Accounting, A
Administrative Assistant and Secretarial Science, A
Agricultural Business and Management, A
BioTechnology, A
Business Administration and Management, A
Computer Systems Networking and Telecommunications, A
Construction Trades, A
Criminal Justice/Law Enforcement Administration, A
Fashion Merchandising, A
Horse Husbandry/Equine Science and Management, A
Liberal Arts and Sciences Studies and Humanities, A
Natural Resources and Conservation, A
Selling Skills and Sales Operations, A

EMMAUS BIBLE COLLEGE

Bible/Biblical Studies, AB
Business Administration and Management, B
Computer and Information Sciences, B
Elementary Education and Teaching, B
Missions/Missionary Studies and Missiology, B
Music Teacher Education, B
Pre-Theology/Pre-Ministerial Studies, B
Secondary Education and Teaching, B
Youth Ministry, B

FAITH BAPTIST BIBLE COLLEGE AND THEOLOGICAL SEMINARY

Administrative Assistant and Secretarial Science, AB
Bible/Biblical Studies, AB
Divinity/Ministry (BD, MDiv.), B
Elementary Education and Teaching, B
English/Language Arts Teacher Education, B
Missions/Missionary Studies and Missiology, AB
Music Teacher Education, B
Pastoral Studies/Counseling, BM
Religion/Religious Studies, M
Religious Education, B
Religious/Sacred Music, B
Theology and Religious Vocations, M

GRACELAND UNIVERSITY

Accounting, B
Art Teacher Education, B
Art/Art Studies, General, B
Athletic Training and Sports Medicine, B
Biology/Biological Sciences, B
Business Administration and Management, B
Chemistry, B
Clinical Laboratory Science/Medical Technology/Technologist, B
Commercial and Advertising Art, B
Comparative Literature, B
Computer Science, B
Criminal Justice/Law Enforcement Administration, B

Drama and Dramatics/Theatre Arts, B
Economics, B
Education, BM
Educational Administration and Supervision, M
Educational Media/Instructional Technology, M
Elementary Education and Teaching, B
English Language and Literature, B
Fine/Studio Arts, B
Health Services/Allied Health/Health Sciences, B
Health Teacher Education, B
History, B
Human Services, B
International Business/Trade/Commerce, B
International Relations and Affairs, B
Liberal Arts and Sciences Studies and Humanities, B
Management Information Systems and Services, B
Mathematics, B
Music, B
Music Teacher Education, B
Nursing, MDO
Nursing - Advanced Practice, MO
Nursing Education, MO
Organizational Management, D
Parks, Recreation, Leisure and Fitness Studies, B
Philosophy and Religious Studies, B
Physical Education Teaching and Coaching, B
Physical Sciences, B
Pre-Dentistry Studies, B
Pre-Medicine/Pre-Medical Studies, B
Psychology, B
Publishing, B
Reading Teacher Education, M
Religion/Religious Studies, BM
Science Teacher Education/General Science Teacher Education, B
Secondary Education and Teaching, B
Social Work, B
Spanish Language and Literature, B
Special Education and Teaching, M
Teacher Education and Professional Development, Specific Subject Areas, B
Theology and Religious Vocations, M

GRAND VIEW UNIVERSITY

Accounting, B
Applied Mathematics, B
BioTechnology, B
Biochemistry, B
Biology/Biological Sciences, B
Broadcast Journalism, B
Business Administration and Management, B
Business Administration, Management and Operations, M
Computer Science, B
Criminal Justice/Law Enforcement Administration, B
Drama and Dramatics/Theatre Arts, B
Education, M
Elementary Education and Teaching, B
English Language and Literature, B
English/Language Arts Teacher Education, B
Fine Arts and Art Studies, B
Fine/Studio Arts, B
Graphic Communications, B
Graphic Design, B
Health and Physical Education, B
History, B
Human Services, B
Information Science/Studies, B
Journalism, B
Kinesiology and Exercise Science, B
Liberal Arts and Sciences Studies and Humanities, B
Management Information Systems and Services, B
Marketing/Marketing Management, B
Mass Communication/Media Studies, B
Music, B
Music Teacher Education, B
Nursing, M
Organizational Management, M
Photography, B
Physical Education Teaching and Coaching, B
Political Science and Government, B
Pre-Law Studies, B
Psychology, B
Religion/Religious Studies, B

Secondary Education and Teaching, B
Spanish Language and Literature, B
Sport and Fitness Administration/Management, B

GRINNELL COLLEGE

Anthropology, B
Art/Art Studies, General, B
Biochemistry, B
Biology/Biological Sciences, B
Chemistry, B
Chinese Language and Literature, B
Classics and Classical Languages, Literatures, and Linguistics, B
Computer Science, B
Drama and Dramatics/Theatre Arts, B
Economics, B
English Language and Literature, B
Ethnic, Cultural Minority, and Gender Studies, B
Fine/Studio Arts, B
French Language and Literature, B
German Language and Literature, B
History, B
Mathematics, B
Music, B
Philosophy, B
Physics, B
Political Science and Government, B
Psychology, B
Religion/Religious Studies, B
Russian Language and Literature, B
Sociology, B
Spanish Language and Literature, B

HAMILTON TECHNICAL COLLEGE

Electrical, Electronic and Communications Engineering Technology/Technician, AB

HAWKEYE COMMUNITY COLLEGE

Accounting, A
Agricultural Power Machinery Operation, A
Agricultural/Farm Supplies Retailing and Wholesaling, A
Animal/Livestock Husbandry and Production, A
Autobody/Collision and Repair Technology/Technician, A
Automobile/Automotive Mechanics Technology/Technician, A
Carpentry/Carpenter, A
Child Care Provider/Assistant, A
Civil Engineering Technology/Technician, A
Clinical/Medical Laboratory Technician, A
Commercial Photography, A
Computer Systems Networking and Telecommunications, A
Computer/Information Technology Services Administration and Management, A
Criminal Justice/Police Science, A
Dental Hygiene/Hygienist, A
Diesel Mechanics Technology/Technician, A
Digital Communication and Media/Multimedia, A
Electrical, Electronic and Communications Engineering Technology/Technician, A
Electromechanical Technology/Electromechanical Engineering Technology, A
Emergency Medical Technology/Technician (EMT Paramedic), A
Energy Management and Systems Technology/Technician, A
Executive Assistant/Executive Secretary, A
Fire Science/Firefighting, A
Hospitality Administration/Management, A
Human Resources Management/Personnel Administration, A
Interior Design, A
Landscaping and Groundskeeping, A
Liberal Arts and Sciences Studies and Humanities, A
Machine Tool Technology/Machinist, A
Medical Administrative Assistant/Secretary, A
Medical Insurance Coding Specialist/Coder, A
Multi-/Interdisciplinary Studies, A
Natural Resources Management/Development and Policy, A
Occupational Therapist Assistant, A
Physical Therapist Assistant, A

Prepress/Desktop Publishing and Digital Imaging Design, A
Respiratory Care Therapy/Therapist, A
Sales, Distribution and Marketing Operations, A
Web Page, Digital/Multimedia and Information Resources Design, A

INDIAN HILLS COMMUNITY COLLEGE

Airline/Commercial/Professional Pilot and Flight Crew, A
Autobody/Collision and Repair Technology/Technician, A
Automobile/Automotive Mechanics Technology/Technician, A
Avionics Maintenance Technology/Technician, A
Biology Technician/BioTechnology Laboratory Technician, A
Business Administration and Management, A
Child Care Provider/Assistant, A
Computer Programming/Programmer, A
Computer Systems Networking and Telecommunications, A
Computer and Information Systems Security, A
Construction Trades, A
Criminal Justice/Law Enforcement Administration, A
Culinary Arts/Chef Training, A
Diesel Mechanics Technology/Technician, A
Electrical, Electronic and Communications Engineering Technology/Technician, A
Emergency Medical Technology/Technician (EMT Paramedic), A
Laser and Optical Technology/Technician, A
Liberal Arts and Sciences Studies and Humanities, A
Machine Tool Technology/Machinist, A
Mechanical Drafting and Mechanical Drafting CAD/CADD, A
Nuclear Engineering Technology/Technician, A
Physical Therapy/Therapist, A
Radiologic Technology/Science - Radiographer, A

INSTE BIBLE COLLEGE

Bible/Biblical Studies, B

IOWA CENTRAL COMMUNITY COLLEGE

Accounting, A
Administrative Assistant and Secretarial Science, A
Airline/Commercial/Professional Pilot and Flight Crew, A
Automobile/Automotive Mechanics Technology/Technician, A
Aviation/Airway Management and Operations, A
Biological and Physical Sciences, A
Broadcast Journalism, A
Business Administration and Management, A
Business Teacher Education, A
Carpentry/Carpenter, A
Clinical/Medical Laboratory Technician, A
Community Organization and Advocacy, A
Computer Engineering Technology/Technician, A
Criminal Justice/Police Science, A
Data Processing and Data Processing Technology/Technician, A
Drafting and Design Technology/Technician, A
Education, A
Electrical, Electronic and Communications Engineering Technology/Technician, A
Hospitality and Recreation Marketing Operations, A
Industrial Radiologic Technology/Technician, A
Journalism, A
Liberal Arts and Sciences Studies and Humanities, A
Machine Tool Technology/Machinist, A
Mass Communication/Media Studies, A
Medical/Clinical Assistant, A
Occupational Therapy/Therapist, A
Physical Therapy/Therapist, A
Radio and Television, A
Science Teacher Education/General Science Teacher Education, A
Social Work, A
Sociology, A
Telecommunications Technology/Technician, A

Welding Technology/Welder, A

IOWA LAKES COMMUNITY COLLEGE

Accounting, A
Accounting Technology/Technician and Bookkeeping, A
Administrative Assistant and Secretarial Science, A
Agribusiness, A
Agricultural Business Technology, A
Agricultural Business and Management, A
Agricultural Economics, A
Agricultural Mechanics and Equipment/Machine Technology, A
Agricultural Mechanization, A
Agricultural Power Machinery Operation, A
Agricultural Production Operations, A
Agricultural Teacher Education, A
Agricultural/Farm Supplies Retailing and Wholesaling, A
Agriculture, A
Agronomy and Crop Science, A
Airline/Commercial/Professional Pilot and Flight Crew, A
Animal Sciences, A
Animal/Livestock Husbandry and Production, A
Art Teacher Education, A
Astronomy, A
Athletic Training and Sports Medicine, A
Autobody/Collision and Repair Technology/Technician, A
Automobile/Automotive Mechanics Technology/Technician, A
Aviation/Airway Management and Operations, A
Behavioral Sciences, A
Biological and Physical Sciences, A
Biology/Biological Sciences, A
Botany/Plant Biology, A
Business Administration and Management, A
Business Machine Repairer, A
Business Teacher Education, A
Business/Office Automation/Technology/Data Entry, A
Carpentry/Carpenter, A
Chemistry, A
Child Care Provider/Assistant, A
Child Development, A
Commercial and Advertising Art, A
Communication, Journalism and Related Programs, A
Comparative Literature, A
Computer Graphics, A
Computer Programming/Programmer, A
Computer Science, A
Computer Software Technology/Technician, A
Computer Systems Networking and Telecommunications, A
Computer and Information Sciences, A
Computer/Information Technology Services Administration and Management, A
Construction Engineering Technology/Technician, A
Construction Management, A
Construction Trades, A
Consumer Merchandising/Retailing Management, A
Corrections, A
Criminal Justice/Law Enforcement Administration, A
Criminal Justice/Police Science, A
Crop Production, A
Culinary Arts and Related Services, A
Data Entry/Microcomputer Applications, A
Data Processing and Data Processing Technology/Technician, A
Design and Applied Arts, A
Early Childhood Education and Teaching, A
Ecology, A
Economics, A
Education, A
Electrical, Electronic and Communications Engineering Technology/Technician, A
Electrical/Electronics Equipment Installation and Repair, A
Elementary Education and Teaching, A
Emergency Care Attendant (EMT Ambulance), A
Energy Management and Systems Technology/Technician, A
Engineering Technology, A
Environmental Design/Architecture, A

Environmental Engineering Technology/Environmental Technology, A
Environmental Studies, A
Family and Consumer Sciences/Human Sciences, A
Farm/Farm and Ranch Management, A
Fashion Merchandising, A
Finance, A
Fine/Studio Arts, A
Fishing and Fisheries Sciences and Management, A
Flight Instructor, A
Food Preparation/Professional Cooking/Kitchen Assistant, A
Food Service, Waiter/Waitress, and Dining Room Management/Manager, A
Foods, Nutrition, and Related Services, A
Foreign Languages and Literatures, A
Forestry, A
General Merchandising, Sales, and Related Marketing Operations, A
General Office Occupations and Clerical Services, A
General Studies, A
Geology/Earth Science, A
Graphic Communications, A
Graphic Design, A
Graphic and Printing Equipment Operator Production, A
Health and Physical Education, A
Health/Health Care Administration/Management, A
Heating, Air Conditioning and Refrigeration Technology/Technician, A
Heating, Air Conditioning, Ventilation and Refrigeration Maintenance Technology/Technician, A
History, A
Hospitality Administration/Management, A
Hotel/Motel Administration/Management, A
Human Resources Management and Services, A
Humanities/Humanistic Studies, A
Hydrology and Water Resources Science, A
Information Technology, A
Institutional Food Workers, A
Jazz/Jazz Studies, A
Journalism, A
Kindergarten/PreSchool Education and Teaching, A
Landscaping and Groundskeeping, A
Law and Legal Studies, A
Legal Administrative Assistant/Secretary, A
Legal Assistant/Paralegal, A
Liberal Arts and Sciences Studies and Humanities, A
Marine Maintenance/Fitter and Ship Repair Technology/Technician, A
Marketing/Marketing Management, A
Mass Communication/Media Studies, A
Massage Therapy/Therapeutic Massage, A
Mathematics, A
Medical Administrative Assistant/Secretary, A
Medical Office Assistant/Specialist, A
Medical Office Computer Specialist/Assistant, A
Medical Reception/Receptionist, A
Medical Transcription/Transcriptionist, A
Medical/Clinical Assistant, A
Motorcycle Maintenance and Repair Technology/Technician, A
Music, A
Music Teacher Education, A
Natural Resources and Conservation, A
Natural Sciences, A
Office Management and Supervision, A
Parks, Recreation, Leisure and Fitness Studies, A
Pharmacy, A
Philosophy, A
Photography, A
Physical Education Teaching and Coaching, A
Physical Sciences, A
Piano and Organ, A
Political Science and Government, A
Pre-Dentistry Studies, A
Pre-Law Studies, A
Pre-Medicine/Pre-Medical Studies, A
Pre-Nursing Studies, A
Pre-Pharmacy Studies, A
Pre-Veterinary Studies, A
Prepress/Desktop Publishing and Digital Imaging Design, A
Psychology, A
Radio and Television, A

Radio and Television Broadcasting Technology/Technician, A
Real Estate, A
Receptionist, A
Rehabilitation and Therapeutic Professions, A
Restaurant, Culinary, and Catering Management/Manager, A
Restaurant/Food Services Management, A
Retailing and Retail Operations, A
Sales, Distribution and Marketing Operations, A
Science Teacher Education/General Science Teacher Education, A
Selling Skills and Sales Operations, A
Small Business Administration/Management, A
Small Engine Mechanics and Repair Technology/Technician, A
Social Sciences, A
Social Work, A
Sociology, A
Soil Science and Agronomy, A
Spanish Language and Literature, A
Sport and Fitness Administration/Management, A
Surgical Technology/Technologist, A
System, Networking, and LAN/WAN Management/Manager, A
Technology Teacher Education/Industrial Arts Teacher Education, A
Trade and Industrial Teacher Education, A
Turf and Turfgrass Management, A
Voice and Opera, A
Water, Wetlands, and Marine Resources Management, A
Welding Technology/Welder, A
Wildlife Biology, A
Wildlife and Wildlands Science and Management, A
Word Processing, A

IOWA STATE UNIVERSITY OF SCIENCE AND TECHNOLOGY

Accounting, BM
Advertising, B
Aerospace, Aeronautical and Astronautical Engineering, BMD
Agribusiness, M
Agricultural Business and Management, B
Agricultural Economics, MD
Agricultural Education, MD
Agricultural Engineering, MD
Agricultural Mechanization, B
Agricultural Sciences, MD
Agricultural Teacher Education, B
Agricultural/Biological Engineering and Bioengineering, B
Agriculture, B
Agronomy and Crop Science, B
Agronomy and Soil Sciences, MD
Analytical Chemistry, D
Animal Sciences, BMD
Anthropology, BM
Apparel and Textiles, B
Applied Mathematics, MD
Applied Physics, MD
Architecture, BM
Art/Art Studies, General, B
Astrophysics, MD
Athletic Training and Sports Medicine, B
Atmospheric Sciences and Meteorology, B
Biochemistry, B
Bioinformatics, BMD
Biological and Biomedical Sciences, MD
Biology/Biological Sciences, B
Biophysics, BMD
Biostatistics, MD
Botany/Plant Biology, B
Business Administration and Management, B
Cell Biology and Anatomy, MD
Chemical Engineering, BMD
Chemistry, BMD
Child and Family Studies, MD
City/Urban, Community and Regional Planning, B
Civil Engineering, BMD
Clothing and Textiles, MD
Cognitive Sciences, D
Commercial and Advertising Art, B
Computational Biology, MD
Computer Engineering, BMD

Computer Science, MD
Computer Software Engineering, B
Condensed Matter Physics, MD
Construction Engineering, B
Construction Engineering and Management, MD
Consumer Economics, MD
Corporate and Organizational Communication, MD
Counseling Psychology, D
Counselor Education/School Counseling and Guidance Services, M
Curriculum and Instruction, MD
Dairy Science, B
Design and Visual Communications, B
Developmental Biology and Embryology, MD
Dietetics/Dieticians, B
Drama and Dramatics/Theatre Arts, B
Early Childhood Education and Teaching, B
Ecology, BMD
Economics, BMD
Education, B
Educational Administration and Supervision, M
Educational Leadership and Administration, MD
Educational Measurement and Evaluation, M
Educational Media/Instructional Technology, MD
Electrical Engineering, MD
Electrical, Electronics and Communications Engineering, B
Elementary Education and Teaching, BM
English, MD
English Language and Literature, B
English as a Second Language, M
Entomology, MD
Environmental Engineering Technology/Environmental Technology, MD
Environmental Sciences, MD
Environmental Studies, B
Evolutionary Biology, MD
Exercise and Sports Science, M
Family Resource Management Studies, B
Family and Community Services, B
Family and Consumer Sciences/Home Economics Teacher Education, B
Family and Consumer Sciences/Human Sciences, BM
Fashion/Apparel Design, B
Finance, B
Finance and Banking, M
Fine Arts and Art Studies, M
Fish, Game and Wildlife Management, MD
Fishing and Fisheries Sciences and Management, B
Food Science, B
Food Science and Technology, MD
Food Technology and Processing, B
Foods, Nutrition, and Wellness Studies, B
Forestry, BMD
Foundations and Philosophy of Education, M
French Language and Literature, B
Genetics, BMD
Geology/Earth Science, BMD
Geosciences, MD
Geotechnical Engineering, MD
German Language and Literature, B
Graphic Design, BM
Health Teacher Education, B
Health and Physical Education, B
Higher Education/Higher Education Administration, M
History, BMD
History of Science and Technology, MD
Home Economics Education, MD
Horticultural Science, BMD
Hospitality Administration/Management, BMD
Human Development, MD
Human Resources Development, M
Human-Computer Interaction, MD
Immunology, MD
Industrial Design, BM
Industrial Engineering, B
Industrial/Management Engineering, MD
Information Science/Studies, M
Inorganic Chemistry, MD
Interdisciplinary Studies, M
Interior Design, BM
International Agriculture, B
International Business/Trade/Commerce, B
International Relations and Affairs, B

Journalism, BM
Kinesiology and Exercise Science, B
Kinesiology and Movement Studies, MD
Landscape Architecture, BM
Liberal Arts and Sciences Studies and Humanities, B
Linguistic, Comparative, and Related Language Studies and Services, B
Linguistics, BMD
Logistics and Materials Management, B
Management Information Systems and Services, BMD
Marketing/Marketing Management, B
Mass Communication/Media Studies, BM
Materials Engineering, BMD
Materials Sciences, MD
Mathematics, BMD
Mathematics Teacher Education, M
Mechanical Engineering, BMD
Mechanics, MD
Medical Illustration/Medical Illustrator, B
Meteorology, MD
Microbiology, BMD
Molecular Biology, MD
Molecular Genetics, D
Multi-/Interdisciplinary Studies, B
Music, B
Music Teacher Education, B
Natural Resources Management/Development and Policy, B
Natural Resources and Conservation, MD
Neuroscience, M
Nutritional Sciences, BMD
Operations Research, M
Organic Chemistry, MD
Pathology/Experimental Pathology, MD
Philosophy, B
Physical Chemistry, MD
Physics, BMD
Plant Biology, MD
Plant Pathology/Phytopathology, MD
Plant Protection and Integrated Pest Management, B
Plant Sciences, MD
Political Science and Government, BM
Pre-Dentistry Studies, B
Pre-Law Studies, B
Pre-Medicine/Pre-Medical Studies, B
Pre-Veterinary Studies, B
Psychology, BD
Public Administration, M
Public Relations/Image Management, B
Religion/Religious Studies, B
Rhetoric, MD
Rural Planning and Studies, D
Rural Sociology, MD
Science Teacher Education/General Science Teacher Education, M
Secondary Education and Teaching, B
Social Psychology, D
Sociology, BMD
Spanish Language and Literature, B
Special Education and Teaching, MD
Statistics, BMD
Structural Biology, MD
Structural Engineering, MD
Student Personnel Services, M
Sustainable Development, MD
Systems Engineering, M
Toxicology, MD
Transportation and Highway Engineering, MD
Transportation/Transportation Management, M
Urban and Regional Planning, M
Veterinary Medicine, M
Veterinary Sciences, MD
Visual and Performing Arts, B
Vocational and Technical Education, MD
Women's Studies, B
Writing, M

IOWA WESLEYAN UNIVERSITY

Art/Art Studies, General, B
Biological and Physical Sciences, B
Biology/Biological Sciences, B
Business Administration and Management, B
Business/Commerce, B

Christian Studies, B
Criminal Justice/Safety Studies, B
Design and Visual Communications, B
Early Childhood Education and Teaching, B
Education, B
Elementary Education and Teaching, B
English Language and Literature, B
Health Teacher Education, B
Health and Physical Education, B
Human Services, B
Kinesiology and Exercise Science, B
Music, B
Philosophy and Religious Studies, B
Physical Education Teaching and Coaching, B
Pre-Dentistry Studies, B
Pre-Medicine/Pre-Medical Studies, B
Pre-Veterinary Studies, B
Psychology, B
Reading Teacher Education, B
Web Page, Digital/Multimedia and Information Resources Design, B

IOWA WESTERN COMMUNITY COLLEGE

Accounting, A
Administrative Assistant and Secretarial Science, A
Agricultural Business and Management, A
Architectural Drafting and Architectural CAD/CADD, A
Automobile/Automotive Mechanics Technology/Technician, A
Avionics Maintenance Technology/Technician, A
Business Administration and Management, A
Child Care Provider/Assistant, A
Civil Engineering Technology/Technician, A
Computer Programming, Specific Applications, A
Computer and Information Sciences and Support Services, A
Computer/Information Technology Services Administration and Management, A
Construction Trades, A
Dental Hygiene/Hygienist, A
Diesel Mechanics Technology/Technician, A
Electrical, Electronic and Communications Engineering Technology/Technician, A
Emergency Medical Technology/Technician (EMT Paramedic), A
Food Service, Waiter/Waitress, and Dining Room Management/Manager, A
Graphic Communications, A
Human Resources Management/Personnel Administration, A
Landscaping and Groundskeeping, A
Liberal Arts and Sciences Studies and Humanities, A
Machine Tool Technology/Machinist, A
Manufacturing Technology/Technician, A
Multi-/Interdisciplinary Studies, A
Radio and Television Broadcasting Technology/Technician, A
Sales, Distribution and Marketing Operations, A
Sign Language Interpretation and Translation, A
Veterinary/Animal Health Technology/Technician and Veterinary Assistant, A

KAPLAN UNIVERSITY, CEDAR RAPIDS

Accounting, AB
Business Administration and Management, AB
Computer and Information Sciences, A
Criminal Justice/Law Enforcement Administration, AB
Information Technology, B
Medical/Clinical Assistant, A

KAPLAN UNIVERSITY, DAVENPORT CAMPUS

Accounting, A
Business Administration and Management, AB
Business Administration, Management and Operations, M
Communication Studies/Speech Communication and Rhetoric, B
Computer and Information Systems Security, M
Corrections, M
Criminal Justice/Safety Studies, AB
Criminology, M

Education, M
Educational Administration and Supervision, M
Educational Leadership and Administration, M
Educational Media/Instructional Technology, M
Entrepreneurship/Entrepreneurial Studies, M
Finance and Banking, M
Health Services Administration, M
Higher Education/Higher Education Administration, M
Hospitality Administration/Management, A
Human Resources Management and Services, M
Information Technology, AB
International Business/Trade/Commerce, M
Law Enforcement, M
Law and Legal Studies, BM
Legal Assistant/Paralegal, AB
Legal and Justice Studies, MO
Logistics and Materials Management, M
Management, M
Management Information Systems and Services, M
Marketing, M
Mathematics Teacher Education, M
Medical Office Management/Administration, A
Medical Transcription/Transcriptionist, A
Medical/Clinical Assistant, A
Nursing, M
Nursing Administration, M
Nursing Education, M
Organizational Management, M
Political Science and Government, M
Project Management, M
Reading Teacher Education, M
Science Teacher Education/General Science Teacher Education, M
Secondary Education and Teaching, M
Securities Services Administration/Management, M
Special Education and Teaching, M
Student Personnel Services, M
Supply Chain Management, M

KAPLAN UNIVERSITY, DES MOINES

Accounting, AB
Business Administration and Management, AB
Criminal Justice/Police Science, A
Health Services/Allied Health/Health Sciences, B
Health/Health Care Administration/Management, B
Human Services, AB
Information Technology, AB
Legal Assistant/Paralegal, A
Medical Administrative Assistant/Secretary, A
Medical Office Management/Administration, A

KAPLAN UNIVERSITY, MASON CITY CAMPUS

Accounting, A
Business Administration and Management, AB
Criminal Justice/Law Enforcement Administration, A
Information Technology, A
Legal Assistant/Paralegal, A
Medical/Clinical Assistant, A

KIRKWOOD COMMUNITY COLLEGE

Accounting, A
Administrative Assistant and Secretarial Science, A
Agricultural Business and Management, A
Agricultural Power Machinery Operation, A
Agricultural Production Operations, A
Agricultural/Farm Supplies Retailing and Wholesaling, A
Agriculture, A
Apparel and Accessories Marketing Operations, A
Applied Horticulture/Horticultural Business Services, A
Architectural Drafting and Architectural CAD/CADD, A
Automobile/Automotive Mechanics Technology/Technician, A
BioTechnology, A
Business Administration and Management, A
Child Care Provider/Assistant, A
Community Organization and Advocacy, A
Computer Programming, Specific Applications, A
Computer and Information Sciences and Support Services, A
Computer/Information Technology Services Administration and Management, A

Construction Trades, A
Corrections, A
Criminal Justice/Police Science, A
Culinary Arts/Chef Training, A
Dental Assisting/Assistant, A
Dental Hygiene/Hygienist, A
Dental Laboratory Technology/Technician, A
Diesel Mechanics Technology/Technician, A
Education, A
Electrical, Electronic and Communications Engineering Technology/Technician, A
Electroneurodiagnostic/Electroencephalographic Technology/Technologist, A
Emergency Medical Technology/Technician (EMT Paramedic), A
Finance, A
Fire Protection and Safety Technology/Technician, A
Fire Science/Firefighting, A
Graphic Communications, A
Health Information/Medical Records Technology/Technician, A
Horse Husbandry/Equine Science and Management, A
Hospitality Administration/Management, A
Industrial Electronics Technology/Technician, A
Landscaping and Groundskeeping, A
Legal Assistant/Paralegal, A
Liberal Arts and Sciences Studies and Humanities, A
Machine Tool Technology/Machinist, A
Marketing/Marketing Management, A
Mechanical Drafting and Mechanical Drafting CAD/CADD, A
Medical/Clinical Assistant, A
Natural Resources and Conservation, A
Occupational Therapist Assistant, A
Physical Therapist Assistant, A
Radio and Television Broadcasting Technology/Technician, A
Respiratory Care Therapy/Therapist, A
Restaurant, Culinary, and Catering Management/Manager, A
Sheet Metal Technology/Sheetworking, A
Sign Language Interpretation and Translation, A
Social Work, A
Surgical Technology/Technologist, A
Surveying Engineering, A
System Administration/Administrator, A
Telecommunications Technology/Technician, A
Turf and Turfgrass Management, A
Veterinary/Animal Health Technology/Technician and Veterinary Assistant, A
Water Quality and Wastewater Treatment Management and Recycling Technology/Technician, A
Web Page, Digital/Multimedia and Information Resources Design, A
Welding Technology/Welder, A

LORAS COLLEGE

Accounting, B
Applied Psychology, M
Athletic Training and Sports Medicine, B
Biochemistry, B
Biology/Biological Sciences, B
Business Administration and Management, B
Chemistry, B
Computer Science, B
Criminal Justice/Safety Studies, B
Economics, B
Educational Leadership and Administration, M
Elementary Education and Teaching, B
Engineering Physics, B
English Language and Literature, B
Finance, B
History, B
International Relations and Affairs, B
Kinesiology and Exercise Science, B
Liberal Arts and Sciences Studies and Humanities, AB
Management Information Systems and Services, B
Management Science, B
Marketing/Marketing Management, B
Mass Communication/Media Studies, B
Mathematics, B
Music, B
Music Teacher Education, B

Pastoral Studies/Counseling, M
Philosophy, B
Political Science and Government, B
Psychology, B
Public Relations/Image Management, B
Religion/Religious Studies, B
Social Work, B
Sociology, B
Spanish Language and Literature, B
Special Education and Teaching, M
Sport and Fitness Administration/Management, B
Theology and Religious Vocations, M

LUTHER COLLEGE

Accounting, B
African-American/Black Studies, B
Ancient Near Eastern and Biblical Languages, Literatures, and Linguistics, B
Anthropology, B
Art/Art Studies, General, B
Athletic Training and Sports Medicine, B
Biology/Biological Sciences, B
Business Administration and Management, B
Chemistry, B
Classics and Classical Languages, Literatures, and Linguistics, B
Communication Studies/Speech Communication and Rhetoric, B
Computer Science, B
Drama and Dramatics/Theatre Arts, B
Economics, B
Elementary Education and Teaching, B
English Language and Literature, B
Environmental Studies, B
French Language and Literature, B
German Language and Literature, B
Health and Physical Education, B
History, B
Information Science/Studies, B
Intermedia/Multimedia, B
International/Global Studies, B
Management Information Systems and Services, B
Mathematics, B
Multi-/Interdisciplinary Studies, B
Music, B
Philosophy, B
Physics, B
Political Science and Government, B
Psychology, B
Religion/Religious Studies, B
Russian Language and Literature, B
Scandinavian Languages, Literatures, and Linguistics, B
Social Work, B
Sociology, B
Spanish Language and Literature, B
Women's Studies, B

MAHARISHI UNIVERSITY OF MANAGEMENT

Accounting, M
Asian Studies/Civilization, MD
Ayurvedic Medicine/Ayurveda, B
Business Administration and Management, B
Business Administration, Management and Operations, MD
Cinematography and Film/Video Production, B
Computer Science, BM
Elementary Education and Teaching, B
English Language and Literature, B
Environmental Studies, B
Fine/Studio Arts, B
Mathematics, B
Secondary Education and Teaching, B
Sustainability Management, M

MARSHALLTOWN COMMUNITY COLLEGE

Accounting, A
Administrative Assistant and Secretarial Science, A
Apparel and Accessories Marketing Operations, A
Business Administration and Management, A
Child Care Provider/Assistant, A
Computer Programming, Specific Applications, A
Computer Systems Networking and Telecommunications, A

Construction Trades, A
Criminal Justice/Police Science, A
Dental Assisting/Assistant, A
Industrial Mechanics and Maintenance Technology, A
Liberal Arts and Sciences Studies and Humanities, A
Manufacturing Technology/Technician, A
Mechanical Drafting and Mechanical Drafting CAD/CADD, A
Radio and Television Broadcasting Technology/Technician, A
Sales, Distribution and Marketing Operations, A
Tool and Die Technology/Technician, A

MERCY COLLEGE OF HEALTH SCIENCES

Diagnostic Medical Sonography/Sonographer and Ultrasound Technician, A
Emergency Medical Technology/Technician (EMT Paramedic), A
Health Services/Allied Health/Health Sciences, B
Health/Health Care Administration/Management, B
Liberal Arts and Sciences Studies and Humanities, AB
Medical/Clinical Assistant, A
Physical Therapist Assistant, A
Pre-Medicine/Pre-Medical Studies, B
Radiologic Technology/Science - Radiographer, A
Surgical Technology/Technologist, A

MORNINGSIDE COLLEGE

Agricultural and Food Products Processing, B
American History (United States), B
Art Teacher Education, B
Biology Teacher Education, B
Biology/Biological Sciences, B
Biopsychology, B
Business Administration and Management, B
Business/Corporate Communications, B
Chemistry, B
Chemistry Teacher Education, B
Clinical Laboratory Science/Medical Technology/Technologist, B
Drama and Dramatics/Theatre Arts, B
Education, M
Education/Teaching of Individuals with Emotional Disturbances, B
Education/Teaching of Individuals with Mental Retardation, B
Elementary Education and Teaching, B
Engineering Physics, B
English Language and Literature, B
English/Language Arts Teacher Education, B
Fine/Studio Arts, B
Graphic Design, B
History, B
History Teacher Education, B
International Relations and Affairs, B
International/Global Studies, B
Mathematics, B
Mathematics Teacher Education, B
Music, B
Music Performance, B
Music Teacher Education, B
Philosophy, B
Photography, B
Physics, B
Physics Teacher Education, B
Political Science and Government, B
Psychology, B
Religion/Religious Studies, B
Science Teacher Education/General Science Teacher Education, B
Spanish Language Teacher Education, B
Spanish Language and Literature, B
Special Education and Teaching, BM

MOUNT MERCY UNIVERSITY

Accounting, B
Actuarial Science, B
Art Teacher Education, B
Art/Art Studies, General, B
Biochemistry, B
Biology/Biological Sciences, B
Business Administration and Management, B

Business Administration, Management and Operations, M
Business/Commerce, B
Chemistry, B
Clinical Laboratory Science/Medical Technology/Technologist, B
Communication Studies/Speech Communication and Rhetoric, B
Criminal Justice/Law Enforcement Administration, B
Criminology, M
Digital Communication and Media/Multimedia, B
Education, M
Educational Leadership and Administration, M
Elementary Education and Teaching, B
English Language and Literature, B
Finance, B
Graphic Design, B
Health and Medical Administrative Services, B
Health/Health Care Administration/Management, B
History, B
Human Resources Management and Services, M
Human Resources Management/Personnel Administration, B
International Business/Trade/Commerce, B
International Relations and Affairs, B
Journalism, B
Junior High/Intermediate/Middle School Education and Teaching, B
Management Information Systems and Services, B
Management Strategy and Policy, M
Marketing, B
Marketing/Marketing Management, B
Marriage and Family Therapy/Counseling, M
Mathematics, B
Multi-/Interdisciplinary Studies, B
Music, B
Music Teacher Education, B
Natural Resources and Conservation, B
Nursing, M
Nursing Administration, M
Nursing Education, M
Operations Management and Supervision, B
Philosophy, B
Political Science and Government, B
Pre-Dentistry Studies, B
Pre-Law Studies, B
Pre-Medicine/Pre-Medical Studies, B
Pre-Veterinary Studies, B
Psychology, B
Public Relations/Image Management, B
Quality Management, M
Reading Teacher Education, M
Religion/Religious Studies, B
Science Teacher Education/General Science Teacher Education, B
Secondary Education and Teaching, B
Social Work, B
Sociology, B
Special Education and Teaching, M

MUSCATINE COMMUNITY COLLEGE

Accounting, A
Administrative Assistant and Secretarial Science, A
Agricultural Production Operations, A
Agricultural/Farm Supplies Retailing and Wholesaling, A
Business Administration and Management, A
Child Care and Support Services Management, A
Computer/Information Technology Services Administration and Management, A
Dental Hygiene/Hygienist, A
Emergency Medical Technology/Technician (EMT Paramedic), A
Environmental Engineering Technology/Environmental Technology, A
Liberal Arts and Sciences Studies and Humanities, A
Machine Tool Technology/Machinist, A
Massage Therapy/Therapeutic Massage, A
Multi-/Interdisciplinary Studies, A
Natural Resources and Conservation, A

Physical Therapist Assistant, A

NORTH IOWA AREA COMMUNITY COLLEGE

Accounting, A
Accounting Technology/Technician and Bookkeeping, A
Administrative Assistant and Secretarial Science, A
Agricultural Economics, A
Agricultural Production Operations, A
Agricultural/Farm Supplies Retailing and Wholesaling, A
Automobile/Automotive Mechanics Technology/Technician, A
Business Administration and Management, A
Carpentry/Carpenter, A
Clinical/Medical Laboratory Technician, A
Computer Systems Networking and Telecommunications, A
Criminal Justice/Police Science, A
Early Childhood Education and Teaching, A
Electrical, Electronic and Communications Engineering Technology/Technician, A
Emergency Medical Technology/Technician (EMT Paramedic), A
Entrepreneurship/Entrepreneurial Studies, A
Fire Protection and Safety Technology/Technician, A
Health and Medical Administrative Services, A
Heating, Air Conditioning, Ventilation and Refrigeration Maintenance Technology/Technician, A
Hospitality Administration/Management, A
Insurance, A
Legal Administrative Assistant/Secretary, A
Liberal Arts and Sciences Studies and Humanities, A
Manufacturing Technology/Technician, A
Mechanical Drafting and Mechanical Drafting CAD/CADD, A
Medical Administrative Assistant/Secretary, A
Medical/Clinical Assistant, A
Multi-/Interdisciplinary Studies, A
Physical Education Teaching and Coaching, A
Physical Therapist Assistant, A
Prepress/Desktop Publishing and Digital Imaging Design, A
Sales, Distribution and Marketing Operations, A
Sport and Fitness Administration/Management, A
System Administration/Administrator, A
Tool and Die Technology/Technician, A
Web Page, Digital/Multimedia and Information Resources Design, A
Welding Technology/Welder, A

NORTHEAST IOWA COMMUNITY COLLEGE

Accounting, A
Administrative Assistant and Secretarial Science, A
Agribusiness, A
Agricultural Power Machinery Operation, A
Agricultural Production Operations, A
Agricultural and Food Products Processing, A
Automobile/Automotive Mechanics Technology/Technician, A
Business Administration and Management, A
Business/Office Automation/Technology/Data Entry, A
Clinical/Medical Laboratory Technician, A
Computer Programming, Specific Applications, A
Construction Trades, A
Cosmetology/Cosmetologist, A
Crop Production, A
Dairy Husbandry and Production, A
Electrical, Electronic and Communications Engineering Technology/Technician, A
Electrician, A
Emergency Medical Technology/Technician (EMT Paramedic), A
Energy Management and Systems Technology/Technician, A
Fire Science/Firefighting, A
Health Information/Medical Records Technology/Technician, A
Liberal Arts and Sciences Studies and Humanities, A
Plumbing Technology/Plumber, A

Prepress/Desktop Publishing and Digital Imaging
 Design, A
Radiologic Technology/Science - Radiographer, A
Respiratory Care Therapy/Therapist, A
Sales, Distribution and Marketing Operations, A
Social Work, A

NORTHWEST IOWA COMMUNITY COL-LEGE

Accounting, A
Administrative Assistant and Secretarial Science, A
Agriculture, A
Autobody/Collision and Repair
 Technology/Technician, A
Automobile/Automotive Mechanics
 Technology/Technician, A
BioTechnology, A
Business Administration and Management, A
Computer Programming/Programmer, A
Computer Systems Networking and Telecommunica-
 tions, A
Construction Trades, A
Diesel Mechanics Technology/Technician, A
Electrical, Electronic and Communications Engineer-
 ing Technology/Technician, A
Emergency Medical Technology/Technician (EMT
 Paramedic), A
Health Information/Medical Records
 Technology/Technician, A
Industrial Electronics Technology/Technician, A
Liberal Arts and Sciences Studies and Humani-
 ties, A
Lineworker, A
Manufacturing Technology/Technician, A
Radiologic Technology/Science - Radiographer, A

NORTHWESTERN COLLEGE

Accounting, B
Actuarial Science, B
Art Teacher Education, B
Art/Art Studies, General, B
Athletic Training and Sports Medicine, B
Biochemistry, B
Biology Teacher Education, B
Biology/Biological Sciences, B
Business Administration and Management, B
Business Teacher Education, B
Chemistry, B
Clinical Laboratory Science/Medical
 Technology/Technologist, B
Computer Science, B
Corrections and Criminal Justice, B
Drama and Dramatics/Theatre Arts, B
Economics, B
Elementary Education and Teaching, B
English Language and Literature, B
English/Language Arts Teacher Education, B
Environmental Biology, B
Graphic Design, B
History, B
Humanities/Humanistic Studies, B
Information Science/Studies, B
Journalism, B
Kinesiology and Exercise Science, B
Language Interpretation and Translation, B
Liberal Arts and Sciences Studies and Humani-
 ties, B
Mathematics, B
Music, B
Music Teacher Education, B
Philosophy, B
Physical Education Teaching and Coaching, B
Political Science and Government, B
Psychology, B
Public Relations/Image Management, B
Religion/Religious Studies, B
Religious Education, B
Secondary Education and Teaching, B
Social Work, B
Sociology, B
Spanish Language and Literature, B
Speech Teacher Education, B
Sport and Fitness Administration/Management, B
Teacher Education, Multiple Levels, B

Visual and Performing Arts, B

PALMER COLLEGE OF CHIROPRACTIC

Anatomy, M
Biological and Physical Sciences, B
Chiropractic, AD
Clinical Research, M
Medical/Clinical Assistant, A

ST. AMBROSE UNIVERSITY

Accounting, BM
Art Teacher Education, B
Art/Art Studies, General, B
Biology/Biological Sciences, B
Business Administration, Management and Opera-
 tions, MD
Chemistry, B
Communication Disorders, M
Computer Science, B
Computer Systems Analysis/Analyst, B
Computer and Information Systems Security, B
Criminal Justice/Safety Studies, B
Criminology, M
Drama and Dramatics/Theatre Arts, B
Early Childhood Education and Teaching, B
Economics, B
Education, BM
Educational Administration and Supervision, M
Elementary Education and Teaching, B
Engineering Physics, B
English Language and Literature, B
English/Language Arts Teacher Education, B
Finance, B
Fine/Studio Arts, B
French Language and Literature, B
Health Services Administration, M
History, B
History Teacher Education, B
Human Resources Management and Services, M
Industrial Engineering, B
International Business/Trade/Commerce, B
Journalism, B
Management Science, B
Management of Technology, M
Marketing/Marketing Management, B
Mathematics, B
Mathematics Teacher Education, B
Music, B
Music Teacher Education, B
Nursing, M
Occupational Therapy/Therapist, M
Organizational Communication, B
Organizational Management, M
Painting, B
Pastoral Studies/Counseling, M
Philosophy, B
Physical Therapy/Therapist, D
Political Science and Government, B
Psychology, B
Public Relations/Image Management, B
Radio and Television, B
Secondary Education and Teaching, B
Social Science Teacher Education, B
Social Work, M
Sociology, B
Spanish Language Teacher Education, B
Spanish Language and Literature, B
Special Education and Teaching, M
Speech Teacher Education, B
Sport and Fitness Administration/Management, B
Theology/Theological Studies, B

ST. LUKE'S COLLEGE

Health Services/Allied Health/Health Sciences, B
Radiologic Technology/Science - Radiographer, A
Respiratory Care Therapy/Therapist, A

SCOTT COMMUNITY COLLEGE

Accounting, A
Administrative Assistant and Secretarial Science, A
Airline/Commercial/Professional Pilot and Flight
 Crew, A
Autobody/Collision and Repair
 Technology/Technician, A
Automobile/Automotive Mechanics
 Technology/Technician, A

Business Administration and Management, A
Child Care and Support Services Management, A
Computer and Information Sciences, A
Criminal Justice/Police Science, A
Culinary Arts/Chef Training, A
Dental Assisting/Assistant, A
Dental Hygiene/Hygienist, A
Diesel Mechanics Technology/Technician, A
Drafting and Design Technology/Technician, A
Electroneurodiagnostic/Electroencephalographic
 Technology/Technologist, A
Emergency Medical Technology/Technician (EMT
 Paramedic), A
Energy Management and Systems
 Technology/Technician, A
Environmental Engineering
 Technology/Environmental Technology, A
Equestrian/Equine Studies, A
Fire Science/Firefighting, A
Health Information/Medical Records
 Technology/Technician, A
Heating, Air Conditioning, Ventilation and Refrigera-
 tion Maintenance Technology/Technician, A
Hospitality Administration/Management, A
Industrial Mechanics and Maintenance Technol-
 ogy, A
Interior Design, A
Liberal Arts and Sciences Studies and Humani-
 ties, A
Logistics and Materials Management, A
Machine Tool Technology/Machinist, A
Manufacturing Technology/Technician, A
Massage Therapy/Therapeutic Massage, A
Mechanical Drafting and Mechanical Drafting
 CAD/CADD, A
Medical Radiologic Technology/Science - Radiation
 Therapist, A
Multi-/Interdisciplinary Studies, A
Occupational Therapist Assistant, A
Physical Therapist Assistant, A
Physical Therapy/Therapist, A
Respiratory Care Therapy/Therapist, A
Sign Language Interpretation and Translation, A
Truck and Bus Driver/Commercial Vehicle Opera-
 tion, A
Welding Technology/Welder, A

SHILOH UNIVERSITY

Bible/Biblical Studies, B
Liberal Arts and Sciences Studies and Humani-
 ties, A
Pastoral Studies/Counseling, BM
Theology and Religious Vocations, M

SIMPSON COLLEGE

Accounting, B
Actuarial Science, B
Art Teacher Education, B
Art/Art Studies, General, B
Athletic Training and Sports Medicine, B
Biochemistry, B
Biology/Biological Sciences, B
Business Administration and Management, B
Chemistry, B
Computer Science, B
Computer and Information Sciences, B
Criminal Justice/Law Enforcement Administration, B
Criminology, M
Digital Communication and Media/Multimedia, B
Drama and Dramatics/Theatre Arts, B
Economics, B
Education, BM
Elementary Education and Teaching, B
English Language and Literature, B
Environmental Sciences, B
Fine/Studio Arts, B
Forensic Science and Technology, B
French Language and Literature, B
German Language and Literature, B
Graphic Design, B
Health/Health Care Administration/Management, B
History, B
International Business/Trade/Commerce, B
International Relations and Affairs, B
Journalism, B
Kinesiology and Exercise Science, B

Management Information Systems and Services, B
Marketing/Marketing Management, B
Mathematics, B
Music, B
Music Performance, B
Music Teacher Education, B
Philosophy, B
Physical Education Teaching and Coaching, B
Physics, B
Political Science and Government, B
Pre-Dentistry Studies, B
Pre-Law Studies, B
Pre-Medicine/Pre-Medical Studies, B
Pre-Nursing Studies, B
Pre-Pharmacy Studies, B
Pre-Theology/Pre-Ministerial Studies, B
Pre-Veterinary Studies, B
Psychology, B
Religion/Religious Studies, B
Secondary Education and Teaching, BM
Sociology, B
Spanish Language and Literature, B
Sport and Fitness Administration/Management, B

SOUTHEASTERN COMMUNITY COLLEGE

Accounting, A
Administrative Assistant and Secretarial Science, A
Agricultural Business and Management, A
Agronomy and Crop Science, A
Artificial Intelligence and Robotics, A
Automobile/Automotive Mechanics Technology/Technician, A
Biomedical Technology/Technician, A
Business Administration and Management, A
Child Development, A
Computer Programming/Programmer, A
Construction Engineering Technology/Technician, A
Cosmetology/Cosmetologist, A
Criminal Justice/Law Enforcement Administration, A
Drafting and Design Technology/Technician, A
Electrical, Electronic and Communications Engineering Technology/Technician, A
Emergency Medical Technology/Technician (EMT Paramedic), A
Engineering, A
Industrial Radiologic Technology/Technician, A
Information Science/Studies, A
Liberal Arts and Sciences Studies and Humanities, A
Machine Tool Technology/Machinist, A
Mechanical Engineering/Mechanical Technology/Technician, A
Medical/Clinical Assistant, A
Respiratory Care Therapy/Therapist, A
Substance Abuse/Addiction Counseling, A
Trade and Industrial Teacher Education, A
Welding Technology/Welder, A

SOUTHWESTERN COMMUNITY COLLEGE

Accounting Technology/Technician and Bookkeeping, A
Agribusiness, A
Autobody/Collision and Repair Technology/Technician, A
Automobile/Automotive Mechanics Technology/Technician, A
Business Administration and Management, A
Carpentry/Carpenter, A
Civil Drafting and Civil Engineering CAD/CADD, A
Computer Systems Networking and Telecommunications, A
Liberal Arts and Sciences Studies and Humanities, A
Library Science, A
Medical Transcription/Transcriptionist, A
Music, A
Web Page, Digital/Multimedia and Information Resources Design, A

UNIVERSITY OF DUBUQUE

Accounting, B
Airline/Commercial/Professional Pilot and Flight Crew, B

Animation, Interactive Technology, Video Graphics and Special Effects, B
Aviation/Airway Management and Operations, B
Biological and Physical Sciences, B
Biology Teacher Education, B
Biology/Biological Sciences, B
Business Administration and Management, B
Business Administration, Management and Operations, M
Communication and Media Studies, M
Computer Graphics, B
Computer Science, B
Computer and Information Sciences, B
Criminal Justice/Law Enforcement Administration, B
Elementary Education and Teaching, B
English Language and Literature, B
English/Language Arts Teacher Education, B
Environmental Biology, B
Environmental Sciences, B
Environmental Studies, B
Mass Communication/Media Studies, B
Mathematics, B
Parks, Recreation, Leisure and Fitness Studies, B
Philosophy, B
Physical Education Teaching and Coaching, B
Psychology, B
Religion/Religious Studies, B
Secondary Education and Teaching, B
Sociology, B
Theology and Religious Vocations, MD
Theology/Theological Studies, B
Web Page, Digital/Multimedia and Information Resources Design, B
Web/Multimedia Management and Webmaster, B

THE UNIVERSITY OF IOWA

Accounting, BMD
Actuarial Science, BMD
African Studies, B
African-American/Black Studies, B
Agricultural Sciences, MD
Air Force JROTC/ROTC, B
Allopathic Medicine, D
American/United States Studies/Civilization, BMD
Anatomy, D
Ancient Studies/Civilization, B
Ancient/Classical Greek Language and Literature, B
Anthropology, BMD
Applied Mathematics, BD
Army JROTC/ROTC, B
Art Education, M
Art History, Criticism and Conservation, BMD
Art Teacher Education, B
Art/Art Studies, General, B
Asian Languages, M
Asian Studies/Civilization, BM
Astronomy, BM
Athletic Training and Sports Medicine, BM
Audiology/Audiologist and Speech-Language Pathology/Pathologist, B
Bacteriology, MD
Biochemical Engineering, MD
Biochemistry, BMD
Bioinformatics, MD
Biological and Biomedical Sciences, MD
Biology Teacher Education, B
Biology/Biological Sciences, B
Biomedical Engineering, MD
Biomedical/Medical Engineering, B
Biophysics, MD
Biostatistics, MDO
Business Administration and Management, B
Business Administration, Management and Operations, MD
Business/Managerial Economics, B
Cell Biology and Anatomy, MD
Ceramic Arts and Ceramics, B
Chemical Engineering, BMD
Chemistry, BD
Chemistry Teacher Education, B
Chinese Language and Literature, B
Chinese Studies, M
Cinematography and Film/Video Production, B
Civil Engineering, BMD
Classics and Classical Languages, Literatures, and Linguistics, BMD

Clinical Laboratory Science/Medical Technology/Technologist, B
Clinical Research, M
Communication Disorders, MD
Communication Studies/Speech Communication and Rhetoric, B
Communication and Media Studies, MD
Community Health and Preventive Medicine, MD
Comparative Literature, B
Computational Biology, O
Computational Sciences, D
Computer Engineering, MD
Computer Science, BMD
Counseling Psychology, MD
Counselor Education/School Counseling and Guidance Services, MD
Dance, BM
Dental and Oral Surgery, MDO
Dentistry, MDO
Developmental Education, M
Drama and Dance Teacher Education, B
Drama and Dramatics/Theatre Arts, B
Drawing, B
Economics, BD
Education, MDO
Educational Leadership and Administration, MDO
Educational Measurement and Evaluation, MD
Educational Policy, MDO
Educational Psychology, MD
Electrical Engineering, MD
Electrical, Electronics and Communications Engineering, B
Elementary Education and Teaching, BM
Energy and Power Engineering, MD
Engineering, B
Engineering and Applied Sciences, MD
English, MD
English Education, M
English Language and Literature, B
English as a Second Language, M
Environmental Engineering Technology/Environmental Technology, MD
Environmental Sciences, B
Environmental Studies, B
Environmental and Occupational Health, MDO
Epidemiology, MD
Ergonomics and Human Factors, MD
Evolutionary Biology, MD
Exercise and Sports Science, MD
Film, Television, and Video Production, M
Film, Television, and Video Theory and Criticism, MD
Film/Cinema Studies, B
Finance, B
Finance and Banking, MD
Fine Arts and Art Studies, M
Foreign Language Teacher Education, MD
Foundations and Philosophy of Education, MDO
French Language Teacher Education, B
French Language and Literature, BMD
Genetics, MD
Geographic Information Systems, MDO
Geography, BMDO
Geology/Earth Science, B
Geosciences, MD
German Language Teacher Education, B
German Language and Literature, B
Health Informatics, MDO
Health Services Administration, MD
Health and Physical Education, B
Health and Physical Education/Fitness, B
Higher Education/Higher Education Administration, MD
History, BMD
History Teacher Education, B
Human Resources Management/Personnel Administration, B
Immunology, MD
Industrial Engineering, B
Industrial Hygiene, MD
Industrial/Management Engineering, MD
Information Science/Studies, BMDO
International Public Health/International Health, B
International/Global Studies, B
Investment Management, M
Italian Language and Literature, B

Japanese Language and Literature, B
Jazz/Jazz Studies, B
Journalism, BMD
Kinesiology and Exercise Science, B
Labor and Industrial Relations, B
Latin American Studies, B
Law and Legal Studies, MD
Leisure Studies, MD
Liberal Arts and Sciences Studies and Humanities, B
Library Science, MD
Linguistics, BMD
Management, D
Management Information Systems and Services, B
Management Science, B
Management Sciences and Quantitative Methods, B
Management Strategy and Policy, M
Manufacturing Engineering, MD
Marketing, BMD
Marketing/Marketing Management, B
Marriage and Family Therapy/Counseling, D
Mass Communication/Media Studies, BMD
Materials Engineering, MD
Mathematics, BMD
Mathematics Teacher Education, BMD
Mechanical Engineering, BMD
Media Studies, MD
Medicinal and Pharmaceutical Chemistry, D
Medieval and Renaissance Studies, B
Metal and Jewelry Arts, B
Microbiology, BMD
Molecular Biology, D
Museology/Museum Studies, B
Music, BMD
Music Performance, B
Music Teacher Education, BMD
Music Theory and Composition, B
Music Therapy/Therapist, B
Neurobiology and Neurophysiology, MD
Neuroscience, D
Nuclear Medical Technology/Technologist, B
Nursing, MD
Operations Research, MD
Oral and Dental Sciences, MDO
Orthodontics, MO
Painting, B
Parks, Recreation and Leisure Facilities Management, B
Parks, Recreation, Leisure and Fitness Studies, B
Pathology/Experimental Pathology, M
Pedodontics, O
Periodontics, MO
Pharmaceutical Sciences, MD
Pharmacology, MD
Pharmacy, BMD
Philosophy, BD
Photography, B
Physical Therapy/Therapist, MD
Physician Assistant, M
Physics, BMD
Physiology, MD
Piano and Organ, B
Political Science and Government, BD
Portuguese Language and Literature, B
Pre-Dentistry Studies, B
Pre-Law Studies, B
Pre-Medicine/Pre-Medical Studies, B
Pre-Nursing Studies, B
Pre-Pharmacy Studies, B
Pre-Veterinary Studies, B
Printmaking, B
Psychology, BMDO
Public Health, MDO
Public Health Education and Promotion, B
Quantitative Analysis, M
Radiation Biology/Radiobiology, M
Radiologic Technology/Science - Radiographer, B
Recreation and Park Management, D
Rehabilitation Counseling, MD
Rehabilitation Sciences, MD
Religion/Religious Studies, BMD
Rhetoric, MD
Russian Language and Literature, B
Russian Studies, B
Sanskrit and Classical Indian Languages, Literatures, and Linguistics, B

School Psychology, DO
Science Teacher Education/General Science Teacher Education, BM
Sculpture, B
Secondary Education and Teaching, M
Social Studies Teacher Education, BMD
Social Work, BMD
Sociology, BMD
South and Southeast Asian Studies, M
Spanish Language Teacher Education, B
Spanish Language and Literature, BMD
Special Education and Teaching, MD
Speech Teacher Education, B
Speech and Interpersonal Communication, MD
Sport and Fitness Administration/Management, BD
Statistics, BMD
Student Personnel Services, MD
Supply Chain Management, M
Theater, M
Therapeutic Recreation, M
Therapeutic Recreation/Recreational Therapy, B
Toxicology, MD
Translational Biology, MD
Urban and Regional Planning, M
Violin, Viola, Guitar and Other Stringed Instruments, B
Virology, MD
Voice and Opera, B
Women's Studies, BO
Writing, M

UNIVERSITY OF NORTHERN IOWA

Accounting, BM
Acting, B
Anthropology, B
Apparel and Textiles, B
Applied Economics, B
Applied Mathematics, BM
Art Education, M
Art History, Criticism and Conservation, B
Art Teacher Education, B
Art/Art Studies, General, B
Athletic Training and Sports Medicine, BM
BioTechnology, B
Biochemistry, B
Bioinformatics, B
Biological and Biomedical Sciences, M
Biological and Physical Sciences, B
Biology/Biological Sciences, B
Business Administration and Management, B
Business Administration, Management and Operations, M
Business Teacher Education, B
Chemistry, B
Communication Disorders, M
Communication Studies/Speech Communication and Rhetoric, B
Communication and Media Studies, M
Community College Education, M
Community Health Services/Liaison/Counseling, B
Community Health and Preventive Medicine, M
Composition, M
Computer Science, B
Computer and Information Sciences and Support Services, B
Construction Management, B
Counseling Psychology, M
Counselor Education/School Counseling and Guidance Services, M
Criminology, B
Digital Communication and Media/Multimedia, B
Drama and Dramatics/Theatre Arts, B
Early Childhood Education and Teaching, M
Ecology, B
Economics, B
Education, MDO
Educational Leadership and Administration, M
Educational Measurement and Evaluation, M
Educational Media/Instructional Technology, M
Educational Psychology, M
Electromechanical Technology/Electromechanical Engineering Technology, B
Elementary Education and Teaching, BM
Engineering Physics, B
English, M
English Education, M

English Language and Literature, B
English as a Second Language, M
Environmental Sciences, B
Family and Community Services, B
Family and Consumer Economics and Related Services, B
Finance, B
Fine Arts and Art Studies, M
Fine/Studio Arts, B
Foods, Nutrition, and Wellness Studies, B
Foreign Language Teacher Education, BM
Gender Studies, M
Geography, BM
Geological and Earth Sciences/Geosciences, B
Geology/Earth Science, B
Geosciences, M
Gerontology, B
Graphic Communications, B
Health Education, M
Health Professions and Related Clinical Sciences, B
Health Promotion, M
Health Teacher Education, B
Health and Physical Education, B
Higher Education/Higher Education Administration, M
History, BM
Housing and Human Environments, B
Human Services, M
Humanities/Humanistic Studies, B
Industrial Technology/Technician, B
Interior Design, B
Junior High/Intermediate/Middle School Education and Teaching, B
Kindergarten/PreSchool Education and Teaching, B
Kinesiology and Movement Studies, M
Liberal Arts and Sciences Studies and Humanities, B
Management Information Systems and Services, B
Manufacturing Technology/Technician, B
Marketing/Marketing Management, B
Mathematics, BM
Mathematics Teacher Education, BM
Microbiology, B
Middle School Education, M
Music, BM
Music History, Literature, and Theory, M
Music Performance, B
Music Teacher Education, BM
Music Theory and Composition, B
Non-Profit/Public/Organizational Management, M
Organizational Communication, B
Parks, Recreation, Leisure and Fitness Studies, B
Performance, M
Philosophy, B
Physical Education Teaching and Coaching, BM
Physics, BM
Political Science and Government, B
Psychology, BM
Public Administration, B
Public History, M
Public Policy Analysis, M
Public Relations/Image Management, B
Reading Teacher Education, BM
Real Estate, B
Religion/Religious Studies, B
School Psychology, MO
Science Teacher Education/General Science Teacher Education, BM
Secondary Education and Teaching, M
Social Science Teacher Education, M
Social Sciences, M
Social Work, BM
Sociology, B
Spanish Language and Literature, BM
Special Education and Teaching, BM
Speech Teacher Education, B
Speech-Language Pathology/Pathologist, B
Sport and Fitness Administration/Management, M
Student Personnel Services, M
Teaching English as a Second or Foreign Language/ESL Language Instructor, B
Technology Teacher Education/Industrial Arts Teacher Education, B
Vocational and Technical Education, MD
Women's Studies, M

Writing, M

UPPER IOWA UNIVERSITY

Accounting, BM
Agricultural Business and Management, B
Art Teacher Education, B
Art/Art Studies, General, B
Athletic Training and Sports Medicine, B
Biological and Physical Sciences, B
Biology/Biological Sciences, B
Business Administration and Management, AB
Business Administration, Management and Operations, M
Business Teacher Education, B
Chemistry, B
Commercial and Advertising Art, B
Criminology, BM
Education, BM
Educational Administration and Supervision, M
Elementary Education and Teaching, B
English Language and Literature, B
Environmental Sciences, B
Finance and Banking, M
Health/Health Care Administration/Management, B
Higher Education/Higher Education Administration, M
Homeland Security, M
Human Resources Management and Services, M
Human Services, BM
International Business/Trade/Commerce, M
Kinesiology and Exercise Science, B
Liberal Arts and Sciences Studies and Humanities, A
Management Information Systems and Services, B
Marketing/Marketing Management, B
Mass Communication/Media Studies, B
Mathematics, B
Natural Resources and Conservation, B
Organizational Management, M
Parks, Recreation, Leisure and Fitness Studies, B
Physical Education Teaching and Coaching, B
Pre-Dentistry Studies, B
Pre-Medicine/Pre-Medical Studies, B
Pre-Veterinary Studies, B
Psychology, B
Public Administration, BM
Quality Management, M
Reading Teacher Education, B
Science Teacher Education/General Science Teacher Education, B
Social Science Teacher Education, B
Social Sciences, B
Sociology, B
Trade and Industrial Teacher Education, B

VATTEROTT COLLEGE

CAD/CADD Drafting and/or Design Technology/Technician, A
Computer Technology/Computer Systems Technology, AB
Dental Assisting/Assistant, A
Medical Office Management/Administration, A
Medical/Clinical Assistant, A

WALDORF COLLEGE

Biology/Biological Sciences, B
Business Administration and Management, B
Business/Commerce, B
Communication and Media Studies, B
Criminal Justice/Law Enforcement Administration, B
Drama and Dramatics/Theatre Arts, B
Education, B
Elementary Education and Teaching, B
English Language and Literature, B
Fire Services Administration, B
Foods, Nutrition, and Wellness Studies, B
History, B
International Business/Trade/Commerce, B
Liberal Arts and Sciences Studies and Humanities, A
Music, B
Music Teacher Education, B
Organizational Behavior Studies, B
Physical Education Teaching and Coaching, B
Psychology, B
Secondary Education and Teaching, B

Sport and Fitness Administration/Management, B

WARTBURG COLLEGE

Accounting, B
Art Teacher Education, B
Art/Art Studies, General, B
Biochemistry, B
Biology/Biological Sciences, B
Broadcast Journalism, B
Business Administration and Management, B
Chemistry, B
Clinical Laboratory Science/Medical Technology/Technologist, B
Commercial and Advertising Art, B
Communication Studies/Speech Communication and Rhetoric, B
Computer Science, B
Computer and Information Sciences, B
Drama and Dramatics/Theatre Arts, B
Economics, B
Elementary Education and Teaching, B
Engineering, B
Engineering Science, B
English Language and Literature, B
Environmental Sciences, B
Finance, B
French Language and Literature, B
German Language and Literature, B
History, B
History Teacher Education, B
International Business/Trade/Commerce, B
International Relations and Affairs, B
Journalism, B
Kindergarten/PreSchool Education and Teaching, B
Marketing/Marketing Management, B
Mass Communication/Media Studies, B
Mathematics, B
Mathematics Teacher Education, B
Music, B
Music Performance, B
Music Teacher Education, B
Music Theory and Composition, B
Music Therapy/Therapist, B
Occupational Therapy/Therapist, B
Peace Studies and Conflict Resolution, B
Philosophy, B
Physical Education Teaching and Coaching, B
Physics, B
Political Science and Government, B
Psychology, B
Public Relations/Image Management, B
Radio and Television, B
Religion/Religious Studies, B
Religious/Sacred Music, B
Secondary Education and Teaching, B
Social Science Teacher Education, B
Social Work, B
Sociology, B
Spanish Language and Literature, B
Speech Teacher Education, B
Sport and Fitness Administration/Management, B

WESTERN IOWA TECH COMMUNITY COLLEGE

Accounting, A
Accounting Technology/Technician and Bookkeeping, A
Administrative Assistant and Secretarial Science, A
Agricultural/Farm Supplies Retailing and Wholesaling, A
Animation, Interactive Technology, Video Graphics and Special Effects, A
Architectural Engineering Technology/Technician, A
Autobody/Collision and Repair Technology/Technician, A
Automobile/Automotive Mechanics Technology/Technician, A
Biomedical Technology/Technician, A
Business Administration and Management, A
Business/Office Automation/Technology/Data Entry, A
Carpentry/Carpenter, A
Child Care Provider/Assistant, A
Cinematography and Film/Video Production, A
Commercial Photography, A
Computer Programming, Specific Applications, A

Computer/Information Technology Services Administration and Management, A
Criminal Justice/Police Science, A
Dental Assisting/Assistant, A
Electrician, A
Emergency Medical Technology/Technician (EMT Paramedic), A
Energy Management and Systems Technology/Technician, A
Finance, A
Fire Science/Firefighting, A
Heating, Air Conditioning, Ventilation and Refrigeration Maintenance Technology/Technician, A
Human Resources Management/Personnel Administration, A
Industrial Mechanics and Maintenance Technology, A
Interior Design, A
Legal Assistant/Paralegal, A
Liberal Arts and Sciences Studies and Humanities, A
Mechanical Drafting and Mechanical Drafting CAD/CADD, A
Medical Administrative Assistant/Secretary, A
Medical Office Management/Administration, A
Medical/Clinical Assistant, A
Motorcycle Maintenance and Repair Technology/Technician, A
Multi-/Interdisciplinary Studies, A
Musical Instrument Fabrication and Repair, A
Pharmacy Technician/Assistant, A
Physical Therapist Assistant, A
Prepress/Desktop Publishing and Digital Imaging Design, A
Recording Arts Technology/Technician, A
Retailing and Retail Operations, A
Sales, Distribution and Marketing Operations, A
Securities Services Administration/Management, A
Surgical Technology/Technologist, A
Teacher Assistant/Aide, A
Telecommunications Technology/Technician, A
Veterinary/Animal Health Technology/Technician and Veterinary Assistant, A
Web Page, Digital/Multimedia and Information Resources Design, A
Welding Technology/Welder, A

WILLIAM PENN UNIVERSITY

Accounting, B
Applied Mathematics, B
Biology/Biological Sciences, B
Broadcast Journalism, B
Business/Commerce, B
Communication, Journalism and Related Programs, B
Computer Science, B
Computer Software Engineering, B
Computer and Information Sciences, B
Criminal Justice/Safety Studies, B
Criminology, B
Education, B
Elementary Education and Teaching, B
Engineering Technology, B
English Language and Literature, B
Environmental Biology, B
Family and Community Services, B
Health Teacher Education, B
Health and Physical Education, B
History, B
Human Resources Management and Services, B
Human Resources Management/Personnel Administration, B
Human Services, B
Industrial Technology/Technician, B
Information Technology, B
Insurance, B
Kinesiology and Exercise Science, B
Liberal Arts and Sciences Studies and Humanities, A
Mass Communication/Media Studies, B
Mathematics, B
Mechanical Engineering, B
Music Performance, B
Organizational Management, M
Parks, Recreation, Leisure and Fitness Studies, B
Physical Education Teaching and Coaching, B

Political Science and Government, B
Pre-Dentistry Studies, B
Pre-Law Studies, B
Pre-Medicine/Pre-Medical Studies, B
Psychology, B
Public Relations/Image Management, B
Radio and Television, B
Radio, Television, and Digital Communication, B
Reading Teacher Education, B
Science Teacher Education/General Science
   Teacher Education, B
Secondary Education and Teaching, B
Social Science Teacher Education, B
Sociology, B
Special Education and Teaching, B
Sport and Fitness Administration/Management, B

Kansas

ALLEN COMMUNITY COLLEGE

Accounting, A
Administrative Assistant and Secretarial Science, A
Agricultural Production Operations, A
Architecture, A
Art/Art Studies, General, A
Athletic Training and Sports Medicine, A
Banking and Financial Support Services, A
Biology/Biological Sciences, A
Business Administration and Management, A
Business Teacher Education, A
Business/Commerce, A
Chemistry, A
Child Development, A
Computer Science, A
Computer Systems Networking and Telecommunica-
   tions, A
Criminal Justice/Law Enforcement Administration, A
Data Processing and Data Processing
   Technology/Technician, A
Drafting and Design Technology/Technician, A
Drama and Dramatics/Theatre Arts, A
Economics, A
Electrical, Electronic and Communications Engineer-
   ing Technology/Technician, A
Electrical, Electronics and Communications Engi-
   neering, A
Elementary Education and Teaching, A
Emergency Medical Technology/Technician (EMT
   Paramedic), A
Engineering, A
Engineering Technology, A
Equestrian/Equine Studies, A
Family and Consumer Sciences/Human Sciences, A
Farm/Farm and Ranch Management, A
Forestry, A
General Studies, A
Geography, A
Health Aide, A
Health and Physical Education, A
History, A
Home Health Aide/Home Attendant, A
Hospital and Health Care Facilities
   Administration/Management, A
Humanities/Humanistic Studies, A
Industrial Technology/Technician, A
Information Science/Studies, A
Journalism, A
Language Interpretation and Translation, A
Library Science, A
Mathematics, A
Music, A
Nuclear/Nuclear Power Technology/Technician, A
Parks, Recreation and Leisure Facilities Manage-
   ment, A
Philosophy, A
Physical Therapy/Therapist, A
Physics, A
Political Science and Government, A
Pre-Dentistry Studies, A
Pre-Law Studies, A
Pre-Medicine/Pre-Medical Studies, A
Pre-Pharmacy Studies, A
Pre-Veterinary Studies, A
Psychology, A
Religion/Religious Studies, A
Secondary Education and Teaching, A

Social Work, A
Sociology, A
Technology Teacher Education/Industrial Arts
   Teacher Education, A

BAKER UNIVERSITY

Accounting, B
Art History, Criticism and Conservation, B
Art Teacher Education, B
Biology/Biological Sciences, B
Business Administration, Management and Opera-
   tions, M
Business/Commerce, B
Chemistry, B
Computer Science, B
Drama and Dramatics/Theatre Arts, B
Economics, B
Education, MD
Elementary Education and Teaching, B
English Language and Literature, B
Fine/Studio Arts, B
French Language and Literature, B
German Language and Literature, B
Graphic Design, B
Health and Physical Education, B
History, B
International Business/Trade/Commerce, B
International/Global Studies, B
Junior High/Intermediate/Middle School Education
   and Teaching, B
Kinesiology and Exercise Science, B
Liberal Studies, M
Mass Communication/Media Studies, B
Mathematics, B
Music, B
Music Teacher Education, B
Organizational Management, M
Philosophy, B
Physics, B
Psychology, B
Religion/Religious Studies, B
Secondary Education and Teaching, B
Sociology, B
Spanish Language and Literature, B
Sport and Fitness Administration/Management, B

BARCLAY COLLEGE

Bible/Biblical Studies, AB
Business Administration and Management, B
Divinity/Ministry (BD, MDiv.), B
Elementary Education and Teaching, B
General Studies, A
Pastoral Studies/Counseling, B
Psychology, B
Religious Education, B
Religious/Sacred Music, B
Theology and Religious Vocations, M

BARTON COUNTY COMMUNITY COL-
LEGE

Accounting, A
Administrative Assistant and Secretarial Science, A
Agricultural Business and Management, A
Agriculture, A
Anthropology, A
Architecture, A
Art/Art Studies, General, A
Athletic Training and Sports Medicine, A
Automobile/Automotive Mechanics
   Technology/Technician, A
Banking and Financial Support Services, A
Biology/Biological Sciences, A
Business Administration and Management, A
Chemistry, A
Child Care and Support Services Management, A
Chiropractic, A
Clinical/Medical Laboratory Technician, A
Communication Studies/Speech Communication
   and Rhetoric, A
Computer Programming, Specific Applications, A
Computer Science, A
Computer Systems Networking and Telecommunica-
   tions, A
Computer/Information Technology Services Adminis-
   tration and Management, A
Corrections, A

Criminal Justice/Police Science, A
Crop Production, A
CytoTechnology/Cytotechnologist, A
Dance, A
Dental Hygiene/Hygienist, A
Dietician Assistant, A
Drama and Dramatics/Theatre Arts, A
Early Childhood Education and Teaching, A
Economics, A
Elementary Education and Teaching, A
Emergency Care Attendant (EMT Ambulance), A
Emergency Medical Technology/Technician (EMT
   Paramedic), A
Engineering Technology, A
English Language and Literature, A
Financial Planning and Services, A
Fire Science/Firefighting, A
Forestry, A
Funeral Service and Mortuary Science, A
General Studies, A
Geology/Earth Science, A
Graphic Design, A
Hazardous Materials Management and Waste
   Technology/Technician, A
Health Aides/Attendants/Orderlies, A
Health Information/Medical Records
   Administration/Administrator, A
Health and Medical Administrative Services, A
History, A
Home Health Aide/Home Attendant, A
Human Resources Management and Services, A
Human Resources Management/Personnel Adminis-
   tration, A
Industrial Production Technologies/Technicians, A
Information Science/Studies, A
Journalism, A
Kinesiology and Exercise Science, A
Liberal Arts and Sciences Studies and Humani-
   ties, A
Livestock Management, A
Logistics and Materials Management, A
Marketing/Marketing Management, A
Mathematics, A
Medical Administrative Assistant/Secretary, A
Medical Insurance Coding Specialist/Coder, A
Medical Office Assistant/Specialist, A
Medical Transcription/Transcriptionist, A
Medical/Clinical Assistant, A
Medication Aide, A
Modern Languages, A
Music, A
Occupational Therapy/Therapist, A
Optometric Technician/Assistant, A
Pharmacy, A
Pharmacy Technician/Assistant, A
Philosophy, A
Phlebotomy/Phlebotomist, A
Physical Education Teaching and Coaching, A
Physical Sciences, A
Physical Therapist Assistant, A
Physical Therapy/Therapist, A
Physician Assistant, A
Physics, A
Political Science and Government, A
Pre-Dentistry Studies, A
Pre-Law Studies, A
Pre-Medicine/Pre-Medical Studies, A
Pre-Veterinary Studies, A
Psychology, A
Public Administration, A
Radiologic Technology/Science - Radiographer, A
Religion/Religious Studies, A
Respiratory Care Therapy/Therapist, A
Secondary Education and Teaching, A
Security and Protective Services, A
Social Work, A
Sociology, A
Sport and Fitness Administration/Management, A
Wildlife and Wildlands Science and Management, A

BENEDICTINE COLLEGE

Accounting, B
Art Teacher Education, B
Art/Art Studies, General, B
Astronomy, B
Athletic Training and Sports Medicine, B

Biochemistry, B
Biology/Biological Sciences, B
Business Administration and Management, B
Business Administration, Management and Operations, M
Chemistry, B
Computer Science, B
Criminology, B
Drama and Dramatics/Theatre Arts, B
Dramatic/Theatre Arts and Stagecraft, B
Economics, B
Educational Leadership and Administration, M
Elementary Education and Teaching, B
Engineering, B
English Language and Literature, B
Finance, B
Foreign Languages and Literatures, B
French Language and Literature, B
History, B
International Business/Trade/Commerce, B
International/Global Studies, B
Journalism, B
Liberal Arts and Sciences Studies and Humanities, B
Marketing/Marketing Management, B
Mass Communication/Media Studies, B
Mathematics, B
Mechanical Engineering, B
Music, B
Music Teacher Education, B
Natural Sciences, B
Philosophy, B
Physical Education Teaching and Coaching, B
Physics, B
Political Science and Government, B
Psychology, B
Religious Education, B
Secondary Education and Teaching, B
Social Sciences, B
Sociology, B
Spanish Language and Literature, B
Special Education and Teaching, B
Theology/Theological Studies, B

BETHANY COLLEGE

Accounting, B
Art Teacher Education, B
Art Therapy/Therapist, B
Athletic Training and Sports Medicine, B
Biology Teacher Education, B
Biology/Biological Sciences, B
Business Administration and Management, B
Business Teacher Education, B
Business/Managerial Economics, B
Ceramic Arts and Ceramics, B
Chemistry, B
Chemistry Teacher Education, B
Christian Studies, B
Communication Studies/Speech Communication and Rhetoric, B
Criminal Justice/Safety Studies, B
Drawing, B
Education, B
Elementary Education and Teaching, B
English Language and Literature, B
English/Language Arts Teacher Education, B
Finance, B
Financial Planning and Services, B
Forensic Science and Technology, B
Health and Physical Education/Fitness, B
History, B
International Business/Trade/Commerce, B
Marketing/Marketing Management, B
Mathematics, B
Mathematics Teacher Education, B
Music, B
Music Teacher Education, B
Operations Management and Supervision, B
Painting, B
Philosophy, B
Physical Education Teaching and Coaching, B
Political Science and Government, B
Psychology, B
Religion/Religious Studies, B
Sculpture, B
Social Studies Teacher Education, B

Sociology, B
Sport and Fitness Administration/Management, B

BETHEL COLLEGE

Athletic Training and Sports Medicine, B
Biology/Biological Sciences, B
Business/Commerce, B
Chemistry, B
Elementary Education and Teaching, B
English Language and Literature, B
Fine/Studio Arts, B
Health and Physical Education, B
History, B
Mass Communication/Media Studies, B
Mathematics, B
Music, B
Natural Sciences, B
Psychology, B
Religion/Religious Studies, B
Social Work, B

BUTLER COMMUNITY COLLEGE

Accounting, A
Administrative Assistant and Secretarial Science, A
Agricultural Business and Management, A
Art/Art Studies, General, A
Automobile/Automotive Mechanics Technology/Technician, A
Biology/Biological Sciences, A
Business Administration and Management, A
Chemistry, A
Child Development, A
Computer Science, A
Computer and Information Sciences, A
Criminal Justice/Police Science, A
Data Processing and Data Processing Technology/Technician, A
Drafting and Design Technology/Technician, A
Drama and Dramatics/Theatre Arts, A
Electrical, Electronic and Communications Engineering Technology/Technician, A
English Language and Literature, A
Farm/Farm and Ranch Management, A
Fire Science/Firefighting, A
Health Information/Medical Records Administration/Administrator, A
History, A
Hotel/Motel Administration/Management, A
Journalism, A
Kindergarten/PreSchool Education and Teaching, A
Liberal Arts and Sciences Studies and Humanities, A
Marketing/Marketing Management, A
Mass Communication/Media Studies, A
Mathematics, A
Medical Administrative Assistant/Secretary, A
Music, A
Music Performance, A
Physical Education Teaching and Coaching, A
Physical Therapy/Therapist, A
Physics, A
Political Science and Government, A
Psychology, A
Sociology, A
Substance Abuse/Addiction Counseling, A
Welding Technology/Welder, A

CENTRAL CHRISTIAN COLLEGE OF KANSAS

Accounting, B
Accounting and Finance, AB
Acting, AB
Airline/Commercial/Professional Pilot and Flight Crew, A
Art Teacher Education, AB
Art/Art Studies, General, AB
Athletic Training and Sports Medicine, AB
Bible/Biblical Studies, AB
Biological and Physical Sciences, A
Biology Teacher Education, A
Business Teacher Education, A
Business/Commerce, B
Business/Corporate Communications, A
Business/Managerial Economics, A
Chemistry Teacher Education, A
Computer Science, A

Computer Teacher Education, A
Criminal Justice/Law Enforcement Administration, A
Criminal Justice/Safety Studies, A
Divinity/Ministry (BD, MDiv.), B
Drama and Dance Teacher Education, A
Economics, A
Elementary Education and Teaching, AB
Engineering, A
English Language and Literature, B
Environmental Studies, A
Family and Community Services, A
Finance, A
Health Teacher Education, AB
Health and Physical Education, AB
History, AB
History Teacher Education, AB
Human Resources Management/Personnel Administration, AB
Kindergarten/PreSchool Education and Teaching, AB
Kinesiology and Exercise Science, AB
Law and Legal Studies, A
Liberal Arts and Sciences Studies and Humanities, B
Marketing/Marketing Management, A
Mathematics, AB
Mathematics Teacher Education, A
Missions/Missionary Studies and Missiology, AB
Music, AB
Music History, Literature, and Theory, A
Music Performance, AB
Music Teacher Education, AB
Natural Sciences, AB
Pastoral Studies/Counseling, AB
Photography, A
Physical Education Teaching and Coaching, AB
Physician Assistant, A
Pre-Dentistry Studies, B
Pre-Law Studies, AB
Pre-Medicine/Pre-Medical Studies, B
Pre-Pharmacy Studies, B
Pre-Theology/Pre-Ministerial Studies, B
Pre-Veterinary Studies, B
Psychology, B
Psychology Teacher Education, A
Religion/Religious Studies, AB
Religious/Sacred Music, AB
Sales and Marketing Operations/Marketing and Distribution Teacher Education, A
Science Teacher Education/General Science Teacher Education, A
Secondary Education and Teaching, AB
Social Science Teacher Education, A
Social Sciences, AB
Social Studies Teacher Education, AB
Social Work, A
Sociology, AB
Speech Teacher Education, A
Sport and Fitness Administration/Management, AB
Theology/Theological Studies, A
Wildlife Biology, A
Youth Ministry, AB
Zoology/Animal Biology, AB

CLEVELAND UNIVERSITY–KANSAS CITY

Biology/Biological Sciences, AB
Chiropractic, D
Health Promotion, M

CLOUD COUNTY COMMUNITY COLLEGE

Administrative Assistant and Secretarial Science, A
Agricultural Business and Management, A
Agricultural/Farm Supplies Retailing and Wholesaling, A
Business Administration and Management, A
Business, Management, Marketing, and Related Support Services, A
Child Care and Support Services Management, A
Child Development, A
Criminal Justice/Police Science, A
General Office Occupations and Clerical Services, A
Graphic Design, A
Journalism, A
Legal Assistant/Paralegal, A

Liberal Arts and Sciences Studies and Humanities, A
Mechanic and Repair Technologies/Technicians, A
Radio and Television Broadcasting Technology/Technician, A
System, Networking, and LAN/WAN Management/Manager, A
Teacher Assistant/Aide, A
Web Page, Digital/Multimedia and Information Resources Design, A

COFFEYVILLE COMMUNITY COLLEGE

Administrative Assistant and Secretarial Science, A
Agriculture, A
Applied Horticulture/Horticultural Operations, A
Autobody/Collision and Repair Technology/Technician, A
Automobile/Automotive Mechanics Technology/Technician, A
Business Administration and Management, A
Carpentry/Carpenter, A
Communications Technologies/Technicians and Support Services, A
Computer Systems Networking and Telecommunications, A
Computer and Information Sciences, A
Education, A
Electrician, A
Emergency Medical Technology/Technician (EMT Paramedic), A
Liberal Arts and Sciences Studies and Humanities, A
Medical/Clinical Assistant, A
Music, A
Psychology, A
Welding Technology/Welder, A

COLBY COMMUNITY COLLEGE

Administrative Assistant and Secretarial Science, A
Agribusiness, A
Agricultural Business and Management, A
Agricultural Teacher Education, A
Agronomy and Crop Science, A
Broadcast Journalism, A
Business Administration and Management, A
Child Care and Support Services Management, A
Child Development, A
Computer and Information Sciences, A
Criminal Justice/Law Enforcement Administration, A
Criminal Justice/Police Science, A
Dental Hygiene/Hygienist, A
Engineering, A
Farm/Farm and Ranch Management, A
Horse Husbandry/Equine Science and Management, A
Liberal Arts and Sciences Studies and Humanities, A
Physical Therapist Assistant, A
Radio and Television, A
Substance Abuse/Addiction Counseling, A
Veterinary/Animal Health Technology/Technician and Veterinary Assistant, A

COWLEY COUNTY COMMUNITY COLLEGE AND AREA VOCATIONAL–TECHNICAL SCHOOL

Accounting, A
Administrative Assistant and Secretarial Science, A
Agriculture, A
Art/Art Studies, General, A
Automobile/Automotive Mechanics Technology/Technician, A
Biology/Biological Sciences, A
Business Administration and Management, A
Chemistry, A
Child Care and Support Services Management, A
Child Development, A
Computer Graphics, A
Computer Programming, Specific Applications, A
Computer Science, A
Computer and Information Sciences, A
Computer and Information Systems Security, A
Cosmetology/Cosmetologist, A
Criminal Justice/Law Enforcement Administration, A
Criminal Justice/Police Science, A
Dietetics and Clinical Nutrition Services, A

Drafting and Design Technology/Technician, A
Drama and Dramatics/Theatre Arts, A
Education, A
Electromechanical and Instrumentation and Maintenance Technologies/Technicians, A
Elementary Education and Teaching, A
Emergency Medical Technology/Technician (EMT Paramedic), A
Engineering Technology, A
Entrepreneurship/Entrepreneurial Studies, A
Hotel/Motel Administration/Management, A
Industrial Radiologic Technology/Technician, A
Journalism, A
Legal Administrative Assistant/Secretary, A
Liberal Arts and Sciences Studies and Humanities, A
Machine Tool Technology/Machinist, A
Marketing/Marketing Management, A
Medical Insurance Coding Specialist/Coder, A
Medical Transcription/Transcriptionist, A
Music, A
Physical Anthropology, A
Religion/Religious Studies, A
Social Work, A
Technology Teacher Education/Industrial Arts Teacher Education, A
Welding Technology/Welder, A

DODGE CITY COMMUNITY COLLEGE

Accounting, A
Administrative Assistant and Secretarial Science, A
Agricultural Business and Management, A
Agricultural Economics, A
Agricultural Mechanization, A
Agronomy and Crop Science, A
Animal Sciences, A
Art/Art Studies, General, A
Athletic Training and Sports Medicine, A
Automobile/Automotive Mechanics Technology/Technician, A
Behavioral Sciences, A
Biological and Physical Sciences, A
Biology/Biological Sciences, A
Broadcast Journalism, A
Business Administration and Management, A
Chemistry, A
Child Development, A
Clinical Laboratory Science/Medical Technology/Technologist, A
Communications Technology/Technician, A
Computer Programming/Programmer, A
Computer Science, A
Construction Engineering Technology/Technician, A
Cosmetology/Cosmetologist, A
Criminal Justice/Law Enforcement Administration, A
Data Processing and Data Processing Technology/Technician, A
Drama and Dramatics/Theatre Arts, A
Education, A
Electrical, Electronic and Communications Engineering Technology/Technician, A
Elementary Education and Teaching, A
Engineering, A
Engineering Technology, A
English Language and Literature, A
Equestrian/Equine Studies, A
Farm/Farm and Ranch Management, A
Finance, A
Fire Science/Firefighting, A
Forestry, A
Health Information/Medical Records Administration/Administrator, A
History, A
Humanities/Humanistic Studies, A
Hydrology and Water Resources Science, A
Industrial Technology/Technician, A
Information Science/Studies, A
Journalism, A
Legal Administrative Assistant/Secretary, A
Liberal Arts and Sciences Studies and Humanities, A
Marketing/Marketing Management, A
Mass Communication/Media Studies, A
Mathematics, A
Medical Administrative Assistant/Secretary, A
Music, A

Music Teacher Education, A
Physical Education Teaching and Coaching, A
Physical Sciences, A
Physical Therapy/Therapist, A
Physics, A
Political Science and Government, A
Pre-Pharmacy Studies, A
Psychology, A
Radio and Television, A
Real Estate, A
Respiratory Care Therapy/Therapist, A
Social Sciences, A
Social Work, A
Welding Technology/Welder, A
Wildlife Biology, A

DONNELLY COLLEGE

Computer and Information Systems Security, B
Elementary Education and Teaching, B
Liberal Arts and Sciences Studies and Humanities, A
Non-Profit/Public/Organizational Management, B

EMPORIA STATE UNIVERSITY

Accounting, B
Art Therapy/Therapist, M
Art/Art Studies, General, B
Athletic Training and Sports Medicine, B
Biological and Biomedical Sciences, M
Biology/Biological Sciences, B
Botany/Plant Biology, M
Business Administration and Management, B
Business Administration, Management and Operations, M
Business Education, M
Cell Biology and Anatomy, M
Chemistry, B
Clinical Psychology, M
Communication Studies/Speech Communication and Rhetoric, B
Computer and Information Sciences, B
Corrections and Criminal Justice, B
Counseling Psychology, M
Counselor Education/School Counseling and Guidance Services, M
Curriculum and Instruction, M
Drama and Dramatics/Theatre Arts, B
Early Childhood Education and Teaching, M
Economics, B
Education, M
Education/Teaching of the Gifted and Talented, M
Educational Administration and Supervision, M
Educational Leadership and Administration, M
Educational Media/Instructional Technology, M
Elementary Education and Teaching, BM
English, M
English Language and Literature, B
English as a Second Language, M
Environmental Biology, M
Foreign Languages and Literatures, B
General Studies, B
Geology/Earth Science, B
Geosciences, MO
History, BM
Industrial and Organizational Psychology, M
Information Science/Studies, B
Marketing/Marketing Management, B
Mathematics, BM
Microbiology, M
Multi-/Interdisciplinary Studies, B
Music, BM
Music Teacher Education, B
Parks, Recreation, Leisure and Fitness Studies, B
Physical Education Teaching and Coaching, M
Physical Sciences, B
Physics, B
Political Science and Government, B
Psychology, BM
Reading Teacher Education, M
Rehabilitation Counseling, M
School Psychology, MO
Secondary Education and Teaching, B
Social Science Teacher Education, B
Social Sciences, B
Social Studies Teacher Education, M
Sociology, B

Special Education and Teaching, M
Vocational Rehabilitation Counseling/Counselor, B
Zoology/Animal Biology, M

FLINT HILLS TECHNICAL COLLEGE

Administrative Assistant and Secretarial Science, A
Automobile/Automotive Mechanics
  Technology/Technician, A
Building/Property Maintenance and Management, A
Carpentry/Carpenter, A
Computer Programming/Programmer, A
Computer Systems Networking and Telecommunications, A
Dental Assisting/Assistant, A
Emergency Medical Technology/Technician (EMT
  Paramedic), A
Foodservice Systems
  Administration/Management, A
Graphic and Printing Equipment Operator Production, A
Manufacturing Technology/Technician, A
Nuclear Engineering Technology/Technician, A

FORT HAYS STATE UNIVERSITY

Accounting, B
Administrative Assistant and Secretarial Science, A
Agricultural Business and Management, B
Agriculture, B
Agronomy and Crop Science, B
Animal Sciences, B
Art History, Criticism and Conservation, B
Art Teacher Education, B
Art/Art Studies, General, B
Audiology/Audiologist and Speech-Language
  Pathology/Pathologist, B
Biological and Biomedical Sciences, M
Biological and Physical Sciences, B
Biology/Biological Sciences, B
Business Administration and Management, B
Business Administration, Management and Operations, M
Business Teacher Education, B
Business/Corporate Communications, B
Business/Managerial Economics, B
Chemistry, B
Clinical Laboratory Science/Medical
  Technology/Technologist, B
Communication Disorders, M
Communication and Media Studies, M
Computer Science, B
Counselor Education/School Counseling and Guidance Services, M
Criminal Justice/Safety Studies, B
Drama and Dramatics/Theatre Arts, B
Economics, B
Education, MO
Educational Administration and Supervision, MO
Educational Media/Instructional Technology, M
Elementary Education and Teaching, B
English, M
English Language and Literature, B
Finance, B
Fine Arts and Art Studies, M
Fine/Studio Arts, B
French Language and Literature, B
General Studies, AB
Geography, BM
Geology/Earth Science, BM
Geosciences, M
German Language and Literature, B
Graphic Design, B
Health Education, M
History, BM
Human Resources Management/Personnel Administration, B
Industrial Technology/Technician, B
Information Science/Studies, B
Interior Design, B
Journalism, B
Kindergarten/PreSchool Education and Teaching, B
Liberal Arts and Sciences Studies and Humanities, B
Liberal Studies, M
Livestock Management, B
Management Information Systems and Services, B
Marketing/Marketing Management, B

Mathematics, B
Music, B
Music Performance, B
Music Teacher Education, B
Natural Resources Management/Development and
  Policy, B
Nursing, M
Philosophy, B
Physical Education Teaching and Coaching, BM
Physical Sciences, B
Physics, B
Political Science and Government, B
Pre-Law Studies, B
Psychology, BMO
Public Relations/Image Management, B
Radiologic Technology/Science - Radiographer, AB
Range Science and Management, B
School Psychology, O
Science Teacher Education/General Science
  Teacher Education, B
Social Work, B
Sociology, B
Spanish Language and Literature, B
Special Education and Teaching, M
Tourism and Travel Services Management, B
Wildlife and Wildlands Science and Management, B

FORT SCOTT COMMUNITY COLLEGE

Administrative Assistant and Secretarial Science, A
Agricultural Mechanization, A
Cosmetology/Cosmetologist, A
Criminal Justice/Law Enforcement Administration, A
Dental Hygiene/Hygienist, A
Farm/Farm and Ranch Management, A
Graphic Communications, A
Heating, Air Conditioning, Ventilation and Refrigeration Maintenance Technology/Technician, A
Journalism, A
Liberal Arts and Sciences Studies and Humanities, A
Motorcycle Maintenance and Repair
  Technology/Technician, A
Retailing and Retail Operations, A
Teacher Assistant/Aide, A
Water Quality and Wastewater Treatment Management and Recycling Technology/Technician, A

FRIENDS UNIVERSITY

Accounting, BM
Art Teacher Education, B
Art/Art Studies, General, B
Ballet, B
Biology Teacher Education, B
Biology/Biological Sciences, B
Business Administration and Management, B
Business Teacher Education, B
Chemistry, B
Communication, Journalism and Related Programs, B
Computer and Information Sciences, B
Computer/Information Technology Services Administration and Management, B
Criminal Justice/Safety Studies, B
Drama and Dramatics/Theatre Arts, B
Elementary Education and Teaching, B
English Language and Literature, B
English/Language Arts Teacher Education, B
Environmental Biology, B
Finance, B
Forensic Science and Technology, B
General Studies, A
Health Services Administration, M
Health Services/Allied Health/Health Sciences, B
Health and Physical Education, B
History, B
History Teacher Education, B
Human Resources Management/Personnel Administration, B
Information Science/Studies, B
International Business/Trade/Commerce, B
Law and Legal Studies, M
Liberal Arts and Sciences Studies and Humanities, B
Logistics and Materials Management, M
Management Information Systems and Services, M
Management Strategy and Policy, M

Marketing/Marketing Management, B
Marriage and Family Therapy/Counseling, M
Mathematics, B
Mathematics Teacher Education, B
Music, B
Music Performance, B
Music Teacher Education, B
Non-Profit/Public/Organizational Management, B
Philosophy and Religious Studies, B
Physical Education Teaching and Coaching, B
Political Science and Government, B
Psychology, B
Radiologic Technology/Science - Radiographer, B
Sociology, B
Spanish Language Teacher Education, B
Spanish Language and Literature, B
Speech Teacher Education, B
Sport and Fitness Administration/Management, B
Supply Chain Management, M
Wildlife Biology, B

GARDEN CITY COMMUNITY COLLEGE

Administrative Assistant and Secretarial Science, A
Agricultural Mechanization, A
Agricultural Production Operations, A
Agricultural and Food Products Processing, A
Architecture and Related Services, A
Automobile/Automotive Mechanics
  Technology/Technician, A
Biology/Biological Sciences, A
Business Administration and Management, A
Communication Studies/Speech Communication
  and Rhetoric, A
Computer Science, A
Computer Systems Networking and Telecommunications, A
Cosmetology/Cosmetologist, A
Criminal Justice/Police Science, A
Drafting and Design Technology/Technician, A
Education, A
Emergency Medical Technology/Technician (EMT
  Paramedic), A
Engineering, A
English Language and Literature, A
Family and Consumer Sciences/Human Sciences, A
Fire Science/Firefighting, A
General Studies, A
Health Services/Allied Health/Health Sciences, A
Health and Physical Education/Fitness, A
Humanities/Humanistic Studies, A
Liberal Arts and Sciences Studies and Humanities, A
Manufacturing Technology/Technician, A
Mathematics, A
Physical Sciences, A
Pre-Law Studies, A
Pre-Medicine/Pre-Medical Studies, A
Pre-Nursing Studies, A
Pre-Pharmacy Studies, A
Pre-Veterinary Studies, A
Psychology, A
Retailing and Retail Operations, A
Social Sciences, A
Social Work, A
Substance Abuse/Addiction Counseling, A
Visual and Performing Arts, A
Welding Technology/Welder, A
Zoology/Animal Biology, A

GRANTHAM UNIVERSITY

Accounting, B
Business Administration and Management, AB
Business Administration, Management and Operations, M
Computer Engineering Technology/Technician, B
Computer Science, AB
Computer Systems Networking and Telecommunications, AB
Criminal Justice/Law Enforcement Administration, AB
Electrical, Electronic and Communications Engineering Technology/Technician, AB
Engineering/Industrial Management, AB
General Studies, AB
Health Services Administration, M
Human Resources Development, BM

Information Resources Management/CIO Training, B
Management Information Systems and Services, M
Management Strategy and Policy, M
Medical Insurance Coding Specialist/Coder, A
Multi-/Interdisciplinary Studies, AB
Nursing Administration, M
Nursing Education, M
Nursing Informatics, M
Organizational Management, M
Project Management, M

HASKELL INDIAN NATIONS UNIVERSITY

American Indian/Native American Studies, B
Art/Art Studies, General, A
Business Administration and Management, AB
Elementary Education and Teaching, B
Environmental Sciences, B
Health and Physical Education, A
Liberal Arts and Sciences Studies and Humanities, A
Mass Communication/Media Studies, A
Natural Resources and Conservation, A
Natural Sciences, A
Social Work, A

HESSTON COLLEGE

Aeronautics/Aviation/Aerospace Science and Technology, A
Air Traffic Controller, A
Airline/Commercial/Professional Pilot and Flight Crew, A
Bible/Biblical Studies, A
Business Administration and Management, A
Computer/Information Technology Services Administration and Management, A
Early Childhood Education and Teaching, A
General Studies, A
Kindergarten/PreSchool Education and Teaching, A
Liberal Arts and Sciences Studies and Humanities, A
Pastoral Studies/Counseling, A
Youth Ministry, A

HIGHLAND COMMUNITY COLLEGE

Administrative Assistant and Secretarial Science, A
Agriculture, A
Biology/Biological Sciences, A
Business/Commerce, A
Child Care and Support Services Management, A
Communication Studies/Speech Communication and Rhetoric, A
Computer and Information Sciences, A
Criminal Justice/Police Science, A
Education, A
Engineering, A
Liberal Arts and Sciences Studies and Humanities, A
Mathematics, A
Movement and Mind-Body Therapies and Education, A
Physical Sciences, A
Psychology, A
Security and Loss Prevention Services, A
Social Sciences, A
Teacher Assistant/Aide, A
Visual and Performing Arts, A

HUTCHINSON COMMUNITY COLLEGE

Administrative Assistant and Secretarial Science, A
Agricultural Mechanics and Equipment/Machine Technology, A
Agriculture, A
Architectural Drafting and Architectural CAD/CADD, A
Autobody/Collision and Repair Technology/Technician, A
Automobile/Automotive Mechanics Technology/Technician, A
Biology Technician/BioTechnology Laboratory Technician, A
Biology/Biological Sciences, A
Business and Personal/Financial Services Marketing Operations, A
Business/Commerce, A

Carpentry/Carpenter, A
Child Care and Support Services Management, A
Clinical/Medical Laboratory Technician, A
Communication Studies/Speech Communication and Rhetoric, A
Communications Technology/Technician, A
Computer Systems Analysis/Analyst, A
Computer Systems Networking and Telecommunications, A
Computer and Information Sciences, A
Criminal Justice/Police Science, A
Design and Visual Communications, A
Drafting and Design Technology/Technician, A
Drama and Dance Teacher Education, A
Education, A
Electrical, Electronic and Communications Engineering Technology/Technician, A
Electrical/Electronics Equipment Installation and Repair, A
Emergency Medical Technology/Technician (EMT Paramedic), A
Engineering, A
English Language and Literature, A
Family and Consumer Sciences/Human Sciences, A
Farm/Farm and Ranch Management, A
Fire Science/Firefighting, A
Foreign Languages and Literatures, A
Graphic Communications, A
Health Information/Medical Records Technology/Technician, A
Legal Assistant/Paralegal, A
Liberal Arts and Sciences Studies and Humanities, A
Machine Tool Technology/Machinist, A
Manufacturing Technology/Technician, A
Mathematics, A
Mechanical Drafting and Mechanical Drafting CAD/CADD, A
Medical Radiologic Technology/Science - Radiation Therapist, A
Natural Resources Management/Development and Policy, A
Pharmacy Technician/Assistant, A
Physical Sciences, A
Physical Therapist Assistant, A
Psychology, A
Radio and Television Broadcasting Technology/Technician, A
Radiologic Technology/Science - Radiographer, A
Respiratory Care Therapy/Therapist, A
Respiratory Therapy Technician/Assistant, A
Retailing and Retail Operations, A
Social Sciences, A
Sport and Fitness Administration/Management, A
Surgical Technology/Technologist, A
Visual and Performing Arts, A
Web Page, Digital/Multimedia and Information Resources Design, A
Welding Technology/Welder, A

INDEPENDENCE COMMUNITY COLLEGE

Accounting, A
Administrative Assistant and Secretarial Science, A
Architectural Engineering Technology/Technician, A
Art/Art Studies, General, A
Athletic Training and Sports Medicine, A
Biology/Biological Sciences, A
Business Administration and Management, A
Child Care and Support Services Management, A
Communication Studies/Speech Communication and Rhetoric, A
Computer Programming/Programmer, A
Computer Science, A
Computer Systems Networking and Telecommunications, A
Computer and Information Sciences, A
Cosmetology/Cosmetologist, A
Drafting and Design Technology/Technician, A
Drama and Dramatics/Theatre Arts, A
Education, A
English Language and Literature, A
Entrepreneurship/Entrepreneurial Studies, A
Foreign Languages and Literatures, A
History, A

Liberal Arts and Sciences Studies and Humanities, A
Mathematics, A
Music, A
Physical Sciences, A
Small Business Administration/Management, A
Social Sciences, A
Veterinary/Animal Health Technology/Technician and Veterinary Assistant, A
Web Page, Digital/Multimedia and Information Resources Design, A

JOHNSON COUNTY COMMUNITY COLLEGE

Accounting Technology/Technician and Bookkeeping, A
Administrative Assistant and Secretarial Science, A
Automobile/Automotive Mechanics Technology/Technician, A
Biology Technician/BioTechnology Laboratory Technician, A
Business Administration and Management, A
CAD/CADD Drafting and/or Design Technology/Technician, A
Child Care and Support Services Management, A
Civil Engineering Technology/Technician, A
Computer Programming, Specific Applications, A
Computer Programming/Programmer, A
Computer Systems Networking and Telecommunications, A
Cosmetology/Cosmetologist, A
Criminal Justice/Police Science, A
Culinary Arts/Chef Training, A
Dental Hygiene/Hygienist, A
Electrical/Electronics Equipment Installation and Repair, A
Electrician, A
Emergency Medical Technology/Technician (EMT Paramedic), A
Entrepreneurship/Entrepreneurial Studies, A
Fashion Merchandising, A
Fashion/Apparel Design, A
Fire Science/Firefighting, A
Graphic Design, A
Ground Transportation, A
Heating, Air Conditioning and Refrigeration Technology/Technician, A
Hotel/Motel Administration/Management, A
Industrial Mechanics and Maintenance Technology, A
Interior Design, A
Legal Administrative Assistant/Secretary, A
Legal Assistant/Paralegal, A
Liberal Arts and Sciences Studies and Humanities, A
Marketing/Marketing Management, A
Mechanic and Repair Technologies/Technicians, A
Medical Office Assistant/Specialist, A
Respiratory Care Therapy/Therapist, A
Restaurant, Culinary, and Catering Management/Manager, A
Sales, Distribution and Marketing Operations, A
Sign Language Interpretation and Translation, A
Web Page, Digital/Multimedia and Information Resources Design, A
Welding Technology/Welder, A

KANSAS CITY KANSAS COMMUNITY COLLEGE

Accounting, A
Accounting and Business/Management, A
Administrative Assistant and Secretarial Science, A
Business Administration and Management, A
CAD/CADD Drafting and/or Design Technology/Technician, A
Child Care and Support Services Management, A
Computer Engineering Technology/Technician, A
Computer Software Technology/Technician, A
Computer Systems Networking and Telecommunications, A
Corrections, A
Corrections and Criminal Justice, A
Criminal Justice/Police Science, A
Early Childhood Education and Teaching, A
Emergency Medical Technology/Technician (EMT Paramedic), A

Fire Protection, A
Fire Science/Firefighting, A
Funeral Service and Mortuary Science, A
Hazardous Materials Management and Waste Technology/Technician, A
Legal Assistant/Paralegal, A
Liberal Arts and Sciences Studies and Humanities, A
Marketing/Marketing Management, A
Prepress/Desktop Publishing and Digital Imaging Design, A
Recording Arts Technology/Technician, A
Respiratory Care Therapy/Therapist, A
Respiratory Therapy Technician/Assistant, A
Substance Abuse/Addiction Counseling, A

KANSAS STATE UNIVERSITY

Accounting, BM
Accounting and Business/Management, A
Advertising and Public Relations, M
Aeronautics/Aviation/Aerospace Science and Technology, B
Agricultural Business and Management, B
Agricultural Communication/Journalism, B
Agricultural Economics, BMD
Agricultural Education, M
Agricultural Engineering, MD
Agricultural Mechanization, B
Agricultural Sciences, MDO
Agricultural Teacher Education, B
Agricultural and Food Products Processing, B
Agricultural/Biological Engineering and Bioengineering, B
Agronomy and Crop Science, B
Agronomy and Soil Sciences, MDO
Airframe Mechanics and Aircraft Maintenance Technology/Technician, A
Airline/Commercial/Professional Pilot and Flight Crew, B
American/United States Studies/Civilization, B
Analytical Chemistry, M
Animal Sciences, BMD
Anthropology, B
Apparel and Textiles, B
Architectural Engineering, BM
Architecture, M
Art Teacher Education, B
Art/Art Studies, General, B
Athletic Training and Sports Medicine, B
Biochemistry, BMD
Bioengineering, MD
Biological and Biomedical Sciences, MD
Biology/Biological Sciences, B
Business Administration and Management, B
Business Administration, Management and Operations, MO
Business/Commerce, B
Chemical Engineering, BMDO
Chemistry, BMD
Child Development, BMO
Child and Family Studies, MDO
Civil Engineering, BMD
Clinical Laboratory Science/Medical Technology/Technologist, B
Clothing and Textiles, MD
Communication Disorders, BM
Communication Studies/Speech Communication and Rhetoric, B
Communication and Media Studies, M
Computer Engineering, BM
Computer Science, MD
Computer Systems Networking and Telecommunications, B
Computer and Information Sciences, B
Conflict Resolution and Mediation/Peace Studies, O
Construction Engineering Technology/Technician, B
Consumer Economics, D
Counselor Education/School Counseling and Guidance Services, MD
Curriculum and Instruction, MD
Design and Applied Arts, M
Dietetics/Dieticians, B
Drama and Dramatics/Theatre Arts, B
Early Childhood Education and Teaching, M
Economics, BMD
Education, MD

Educational Leadership and Administration, MD
Educational Media/Instructional Technology, M
Electrical Engineering, MD
Electrical, Electronics and Communications Engineering, B
Elementary Education and Teaching, BM
Energy Management and Policy, M
Energy and Power Engineering, M
Engineering Management, M
Engineering Technology, AB
Engineering and Applied Sciences, MDO
Engineering/Industrial Management, B
English, MO
English Education, M
English Language and Literature, B
Entomology, MD
Entrepreneurship/Entrepreneurial Studies, B
Environmental Design/Architecture, D
Environmental Engineering Technology/Environmental Technology, MD
Environmental Sciences, D
Ethnic and Cultural Studies, B
Family and Consumer Sciences/Human Sciences, BMDO
Finance, B
Finance and Banking, MO
Financial Planning and Services, B
Fine Arts and Art Studies, M
Fine/Studio Arts, B
Food Engineering, MD
Food Science, B
Food Science and Technology, MD
Foreign Languages and Literatures, B
Genetics, MD
Geography, BMDO
Geology/Earth Science, BM
Geotechnical Engineering, MD
Gerontology, MO
Health Communication, M
History, BMD
Horticultural Science, BMD
Hospitality Administration/Management, BMD
Hotel/Motel Administration/Management, B
Human Development, MD
Human Development and Family Studies, B
Human Nutrition, B
Human Services, MO
Humanities/Humanistic Studies, B
Industrial Engineering, B
Industrial and Manufacturing Management, M
Industrial/Management Engineering, MD
Information Science/Studies, BMD
Inorganic Chemistry, M
Interior Design, B
International Affairs, M
Journalism, BM
Kinesiology and Exercise Science, B
Kinesiology and Movement Studies, MD
Landscape Architecture, M
Management, M
Management of Technology, M
Manufacturing Engineering, MD
Marketing, M
Marketing/Marketing Management, B
Marriage and Family Therapy/Counseling, MD
Mass Communication/Media Studies, M
Mathematics, BMDO
Mechanical Engineering, BMD
Microbiology, B
Middle School Education, M
Music, BM
Music Teacher Education, B
National Security, MD
Natural Resources Management/Development and Policy, B
Natural Sciences, B
Nuclear Engineering, MD
Nutritional Sciences, MD
Operations Research, M
Organic Chemistry, M
Parks, Recreation and Leisure Facilities Management, B
Pathobiology, MD
Philosophy, B
Physical Chemistry, M
Physical Sciences, B

Physics, BMD
Physiology, D
Plant Pathology/Phytopathology, MD
Plant Sciences, M
Political Science and Government, BM
Psychology, BMD
Public Administration, M
Public Health, MDO
Range Science and Management, MD
Reading Teacher Education, M
Secondary Education and Teaching, B
Social Sciences, B
Social Work, B
Sociology, BMD
Special Education and Teaching, MD
Statistics, BMDO
Structural Engineering, MD
Student Personnel Services, M
Supply Chain Management, M
Theater, M
Transportation and Highway Engineering, MD
Urban and Regional Planning, M
Veterinary Medicine, D
Veterinary Sciences, MO
Water Resources Engineering, MD
Wildlife Biology, B
Women's Studies, BO

KANSAS WESLEYAN UNIVERSITY

Accounting, B
Art Teacher Education, B
Biology Teacher Education, B
Biology/Biological Sciences, B
Business Administration and Management, AB
Business Administration, Management and Operations, BM
Chemistry, B
Chemistry Teacher Education, B
Communication Studies/Speech Communication and Rhetoric, B
Computer and Information Sciences, B
Criminal Justice/Law Enforcement Administration, B
Divinity/Ministry (BD, MDiv.), B
Drama and Dramatics/Theatre Arts, B
Drawing, B
Elementary Education and Teaching, B
Engineering Physics, B
English Language and Literature, B
English/Language Arts Teacher Education, B
Environmental Studies, B
General Studies, B
Graphic Design, B
Health Teacher Education, B
History, B
History Teacher Education, B
Human Resources Management/Personnel Administration, B
Kinesiology and Exercise Science, B
Liberal Arts and Sciences Studies and Humanities, B
Marketing/Marketing Management, B
Mathematics, B
Mathematics Teacher Education, B
Music, B
Music Performance, B
Music Teacher Education, B
Painting, B
Philosophy, B
Photography, B
Physics Teacher Education, B
Pre-Dentistry Studies, B
Pre-Law Studies, B
Pre-Medicine/Pre-Medical Studies, B
Pre-Veterinary Studies, B
Psychology, B
Religion/Religious Studies, B
Secondary Education and Teaching, B
Sociology, B
Special Education and Teaching, B
Speech Teacher Education, B
Sport and Fitness Administration/Management, BM
Substance Abuse/Addiction Counseling, B

Visual and Performing Arts, B

LABETTE COMMUNITY COLLEGE

Accounting, A
Administrative Assistant and Secretarial Science, A
Art/Art Studies, General, A
Behavioral Sciences, A
Biology/Biological Sciences, A
Business Administration and Management, A
Chemistry, A
Child Development, A
Commercial and Advertising Art, A
Computer Science, A
Criminal Justice/Law Enforcement Administration, A
Criminal Justice/Police Science, A
Data Processing and Data Processing
    Technology/Technician, A
Drafting and Design Technology/Technician, A
Education, A
Elementary Education and Teaching, A
English Language and Literature, A
Fire Science/Firefighting, A
Heating, Air Conditioning, Ventilation and Refrigera-
    tion Maintenance Technology/Technician, A
History, A
Industrial Radiologic Technology/Technician, A
Industrial Technology/Technician, A
Kindergarten/PreSchool Education and Teaching, A
Legal Administrative Assistant/Secretary, A
Liberal Arts and Sciences Studies and Humani-
    ties, A
Mathematics, A
Medical Administrative Assistant/Secretary, A
Music, A
Physical Education Teaching and Coaching, A
Respiratory Care Therapy/Therapist, A
Social Sciences, A

MANHATTAN AREA TECHNICAL COL-LEGE

Accounting Technology/Technician and Bookkeep-
    ing, A
Administrative Assistant and Secretarial Science, A
Autobody/Collision and Repair
    Technology/Technician, A
Automobile/Automotive Mechanics
    Technology/Technician, A
Biology Technician/BioTechnology Laboratory Tech-
    nician, A
Building/Construction Finishing, Manage-
    ment, and Inspection, A
Building/Property Maintenance and Management, A
CAD/CADD Drafting and/or Design
    Technology/Technician, A
Carpentry/Carpenter, A
Clinical/Medical Laboratory Technician, A
Computer Systems Networking and Telecommunica-
    tions, A
Computer Technology/Computer Systems Technol-
    ogy, A
Drafting and Design Technology/Technician, A
Electrical and Power Transmission
    Installation/Installer, A
Electrical and Power Transmission Installers, A
Heating, Air Conditioning and Refrigeration
    Technology/Technician, A
Heating, Air Conditioning, Ventilation and Refrigera-
    tion Maintenance Technology/Technician, A
Management Information Systems and Services, A
Medical Office Assistant/Specialist, A
Multi-/Interdisciplinary Studies, A
System Administration/Administrator, A
Welding Technology/Welder, A

MANHATTAN CHRISTIAN COLLEGE

Bible/Biblical Studies, AB
Missions/Missionary Studies and Missiology, AB
Pastoral Studies/Counseling, B
Religion/Religious Studies, B
Religious Education, AB
Religious/Sacred Music, AB
Theological and Ministerial Studies, AB
Theology/Theological Studies, B

Youth Ministry, B

MCPHERSON COLLEGE

Accounting, B
Art/Art Studies, General, B
Automobile/Automotive Mechanics
    Technology/Technician, B
Biochemistry, B
Biology/Biological Sciences, B
Business Administration and Management, B
Chemistry, B
Communication Studies/Speech Communication
    and Rhetoric, B
Drama and Dramatics/Theatre Arts, B
Education, M
English Language and Literature, B
Finance, B
History, B
Industrial Production Technologies/Technicians, B
Interior Design, B
International Business/Trade/Commerce, B
Kindergarten/PreSchool Education and Teaching, B
Mathematics, B
Music, B
Natural Sciences, B
Philosophy, B
Physical Education Teaching and Coaching, B
Psychology, B
Public Relations/Image Management, B
Sociology, B
Spanish Language and Literature, B
Special Education and Teaching, B
Vehicle Maintenance and Repair Technologies, B

MIDAMERICA NAZARENE UNIVERSITY

Accounting, B
Athletic Training and Sports Medicine, B
Bible/Biblical Studies, B
Biology Teacher Education, B
Biology/Biological Sciences, B
Business Administration and Management, B
Business Administration, Management and Opera-
    tions, M
Business/Corporate Communications, B
Chemistry, B
Counseling Psychology, MO
Criminal Justice/Law Enforcement Administration, B
Drama and Dramatics/Theatre Arts, B
Education, M
Educational Media/Instructional Technology, M
Elementary Education and Teaching, B
English Language and Literature, B
English as a Second Language, M
English/Language Arts Teacher Education, B
Finance and Banking, M
Graphic Design, B
History, B
History Teacher Education, B
International Business/Trade/Commerce, M
Junior High/Intermediate/Middle School Education
    and Teaching, B
Kinesiology and Exercise Science, B
Liberal Arts and Sciences Studies and Humani-
    ties, A
Marketing/Marketing Management, B
Mass Communication/Media Studies, B
Mathematics, B
Mathematics Teacher Education, B
Missions/Missionary Studies and Missiology, B
Music Performance, B
Music Teacher Education, B
Non-Profit/Public/Organizational Management, M
Organizational Management, M
Physical Education Teaching and Coaching, B
Physics, B
Psychology, B
Religion/Religious Studies, B
Secondary Education and Teaching, B
Social Studies Teacher Education, B
Sociology, B
Spanish Language Teacher Education, B
Spanish Language and Literature, B
Special Education and Teaching, M
Sport and Fitness Administration/Management, B
Theology/Theological Studies, B
Voice and Opera, B

Youth Ministry, B

NATIONAL AMERICAN UNIVERSITY

Business Administration, Management and Opera-
    tions, A
Computer and Information Sciences, A
Information Technology, A
Legal Assistant/Paralegal, A

NEOSHO COUNTY COMMUNITY COL-LEGE

Accounting, A
Administrative Assistant and Secretarial Science, A
Athletic Training and Sports Medicine, A
Biological and Physical Sciences, A
Business Administration and Management, A
Business Machine Repairer, A
Carpentry/Carpenter, A
Computer Science, A
Construction Engineering Technology/Technician, A
Criminal Justice/Law Enforcement Administration, A
Criminal Justice/Police Science, A
Electrical, Electronic and Communications Engineer-
    ing Technology/Technician, A
Finance, A
Information Science/Studies, A
Liberal Arts and Sciences Studies and Humani-
    ties, A
Marketing/Marketing Management, A
Physical Sciences, A
Teacher Assistant/Aide, A
Trade and Industrial Teacher Education, A
Welding Technology/Welder, A

NEWMAN UNIVERSITY

Accounting, B
Art/Art Studies, General, B
Biochemistry, B
Biology/Biological Sciences, B
Business Administration and Management, AB
Business Administration, Management and Opera-
    tions, M
Chemistry, B
Criminal Justice/Law Enforcement Administration, B
Curriculum and Instruction, M
Diagnostic Medical Sonography/Sonographer and
    Ultrasound Technician, B
Early Childhood Education and Teaching, B
Education, BM
Educational Leadership and Administration, M
Elementary Education and Teaching, B
English Language and Literature, B
English as a Second Language, M
Finance and Banking, M
Forensic Science and Technology, B
Health Professions and Related Clinical Sci-
    ences, AB
History, B
Hospital and Health Care Facilities
    Administration/Management, B
Information Science/Studies, AB
International Business/Trade/Commerce, M
Legal Assistant/Paralegal, A
Liberal Arts and Sciences Studies and Humani-
    ties, AB
Management, M
Management Information Systems and Ser-
    vices, BM
Mass Communication/Media Studies, B
Mathematics, B
Medical Radiologic Technology/Science - Radiation
    Therapist, A
Multi-/Interdisciplinary Studies, B
Nurse Anesthetist, M
Occupational Therapist Assistant, A
Organizational Management, M
Pastoral Studies/Counseling, B
Philosophy, B
Pre-Dentistry Studies, B
Pre-Law Studies, B
Pre-Medicine/Pre-Medical Studies, B
Pre-Veterinary Studies, B
Psychology, B
Radiologic Technology/Science - Radiographer, A
Reading Teacher Education, M
Respiratory Care Therapy/Therapist, A

Secondary Education and Teaching, B
Social Work, M
Sociology, B
Substance Abuse/Addiction Counseling, B
Theology and Religious Vocations, BM
Theology/Theological Studies, B

NORTH CENTRAL KANSAS TECHNI-CAL COLLEGE

Administrative Assistant and Secretarial Science, A
Agricultural Power Machinery Operation, A
Automobile/Automotive Mechanics
  Technology/Technician, A
Communications Systems Installation and Repair
  Technology, A
Diesel Mechanics Technology/Technician, A
Electrical, Electronic and Communications Engineer-
  ing Technology/Technician, A
Electrician, A

NORTHWEST KANSAS TECHNICAL COLLEGE

Administrative Assistant and Secretarial Science, A
Autobody/Collision and Repair
  Technology/Technician, A
Automobile/Automotive Mechanics
  Technology/Technician, A
Carpentry/Carpenter, A
Civil Engineering Technology/Technician, A
Communications Systems Installation and Repair
  Technology, A
Cosmetology/Cosmetologist, A
Diesel Mechanics Technology/Technician, A
Electrical/Electronics Equipment Installation and Re-
  pair, A
Electrician, A
Heating, Air Conditioning, Ventilation and Refrigera-
  tion Maintenance Technology/Technician, A
Industrial Electronics Technology/Technician, A
Medical/Clinical Assistant, A
Prepress/Desktop Publishing and Digital Imaging
  Design, A
Welding Technology/Welder, A

OTTAWA UNIVERSITY

Accounting, B
Art Therapy/Therapist, M
Art/Art Studies, General, B
Biology/Biological Sciences, B
Business Administration and Management, B
Business Administration, Management and Opera-
  tions, M
Communication Studies/Speech Communication
  and Rhetoric, B
Counseling Psychology, M
Counselor Education/School Counseling and Guid-
  ance Services, M
Curriculum and Instruction, M
Drama and Dramatics/Theatre Arts, B
Early Childhood Education and Teaching, M
Education, M
Educational Leadership and Administration, M
Educational Media/Instructional Technology, M
Elementary Education and Teaching, BM
English Language and Literature, B
Finance and Banking, M
History, B
Human Resources Development, M
Human Resources Management and Services, M
Human Services, B
Information Science/Studies, B
Information Technology, B
Kinesiology and Exercise Science, B
Marketing, M
Marriage and Family Therapy/Counseling, M
Mass Communication/Media Studies, B
Mathematics, B
Music, B
Parks, Recreation, Leisure and Fitness Studies, B
Pastoral Studies/Counseling, M
Psychology, B
Religion/Religious Studies, B
School Psychology, M
Sociology, B

Special Education and Teaching, M

PITTSBURG STATE UNIVERSITY

Accounting, BM
Applied Physics, M
Art Education, M
Art/Art Studies, General, B
Automobile/Automotive Mechanics
  Technology/Technician, A
Automotive Engineering Technology/Technician, B
Biological and Biomedical Sciences, M
Biology Teacher Education, B
Biology/Biological Sciences, B
Business Administration, Management and Opera-
  tions, M
Business/Commerce, B
Chemistry, BM
Chemistry Teacher Education, B
Clinical Laboratory Science/Medical
  Technology/Technologist, B
Communication Studies/Speech Communication
  and Rhetoric, B
Communication and Media Studies, M
Community College Education, O
Community Psychology, M
Computer Systems Analysis/Analyst, B
Computer and Information Sciences, B
Construction Engineering Technology/Technician, B
Construction Engineering and Management, M
Construction Management, B
Counselor Education/School Counseling and Guid-
  ance Services, M
Criminal Justice/Safety Studies, B
Early Childhood Education and Teaching, M
Economics, B
Education, MO
Educational Administration and Supervision, O
Educational Leadership and Administration, M
Educational Media/Instructional Technology, M
Electrical, Electronic and Communications Engineer-
  ing Technology/Technician, B
Electrical/Electronics Equipment Installation and Re-
  pair, A
Elementary Education and Teaching, BM
Engineering Technologies/Technicians, B
Engineering and Applied Sciences, M
Engineering/Industrial Management, B
English, M
English Language and Literature, B
English/Language Arts Teacher Education, B
Family and Consumer Sciences/Home Economics
  Teacher Education, B
Family and Consumer Sciences/Human Sciences, B
Finance, B
Fine Arts and Art Studies, M
French Language Teacher Education, B
French Language and Literature, B
Geography, B
Graphic Design, M
Higher Education/Higher Education Administra-
  tion, O
History, BM
History Teacher Education, B
Human Resources Development, M
Industrial Technology/Technician, AB
International Business/Trade/Commerce, B
Kinesiology and Exercise Science, B
Liberal Arts and Sciences Studies and Humani-
  ties, B
Manufacturing Technology/Technician, B
Marketing/Marketing Management, B
Mathematics, BM
Mathematics Teacher Education, B
Mechanical Engineering/Mechanical
  Technology/Technician, B
Multi-/Interdisciplinary Studies, B
Music, M
Music History, Literature, and Theory, M
Music Performance, B
Music Teacher Education, BM
Music Theory and Composition, M
Nursing, M
Occupational Safety and Health
  Technology/Technician, B
Parks, Recreation, Leisure and Fitness Studies, B
Performance, M

Physical Education Teaching and Coaching, BM
Physics, BM
Physics Teacher Education, B
Plastics Engineering Technology/Technician, B
Political Science and Government, B
Polymer Chemistry, B
Polymer/Plastics Engineering, M
Printing Management, B
Psychology, BM
Psychology Teacher Education, B
Reading Teacher Education, M
School Psychology, O
Secondary Education and Teaching, M
Social Work, B
Sociology, B
Spanish Language Teacher Education, B
Spanish Language and Literature, B
Special Education and Teaching, M
Teacher Education and Professional Develop-
  ment, Specific Subject Areas, B
Technology Teacher Education/Industrial Arts
  Teacher Education, B
Theater, M
Vocational and Technical Education, MO

PRATT COMMUNITY COLLEGE

Accounting, A
Administrative Assistant and Secretarial Science, A
Agricultural Business and Management, A
Agricultural Economics, A
Agricultural Mechanization, A
Agricultural Teacher Education, A
Agriculture, A
Animal Sciences, A
Animal/Livestock Husbandry and Production, A
Art Teacher Education, A
Art/Art Studies, General, A
Athletic Training and Sports Medicine, A
Automobile/Automotive Mechanics
  Technology/Technician, A
Biological and Physical Sciences, A
Biology/Biological Sciences, A
Business Administration and Management, A
Business Teacher Education, A
Chemistry, A
Child Development, A
Commercial and Advertising Art, A
Comparative Literature, A
Computer Systems Networking and Telecommunica-
  tions, A
Computer Typography and Composition Equipment
  Operator, A
Computer and Information Sciences and Support
  Services, A
Counselor Education/School Counseling and Guid-
  ance Services, A
Data Entry/Microcomputer Applications, A
Design and Applied Arts, A
Elementary Education and Teaching, A
Energy Management and Systems
  Technology/Technician, A
English Language and Literature, A
Family and Consumer Sciences/Human Sciences, A
Farm/Farm and Ranch Management, A
Fine/Studio Arts, A
Health Teacher Education, A
History, A
Human Services, A
Humanities/Humanistic Studies, A
Kindergarten/PreSchool Education and Teaching, A
Liberal Arts and Sciences Studies and Humani-
  ties, A
Mass Communication/Media Studies, A
Mathematics, A
Music, A
Physical Education Teaching and Coaching, A
Psychology, A
Social Sciences, A
Social Work, A
Sociology, A
Speech Teacher Education, A
Teacher Education, Multiple Levels, A
Trade and Industrial Teacher Education, A
Welding Technology/Welder, A
Wildlife Biology, A

Word Processing, A

RASMUSSEN COLLEGE KANSAS CITY/OVERLAND PARK

Accounting, AB
Business Administration and Management, AB
Computer Software Engineering, A
Computer and Information Systems Security, B
Corrections and Criminal Justice, AB
Early Childhood Education and Teaching, A
Health Information/Medical Records Administration/Administrator, B
Health Information/Medical Records Technology/Technician, A
Health/Health Care Administration/Management, B
Human Resources Management/Personnel Administration, AB
Human Services, A
Legal Assistant/Paralegal, A
Management Information Systems and Services, A
Marketing/Marketing Management, AB
Medical Administrative Assistant/Secretary, A
Medical/Clinical Assistant, A
Pharmacy Technician/Assistant, A
Web Page, Digital/Multimedia and Information Resources Design, AB

RASMUSSEN COLLEGE TOPEKA

Accounting, AB
Business Administration and Management, AB
Computer Science, B
Computer Software Engineering, A
Computer and Information Systems Security, B
Corrections and Criminal Justice, AB
Early Childhood Education and Teaching, A
Health Information/Medical Records Administration/Administrator, B
Health Information/Medical Records Technology/Technician, A
Health/Health Care Administration/Management, B
Human Resources Management/Personnel Administration, AB
Human Services, A
Legal Assistant/Paralegal, A
Marketing/Marketing Management, AB
Medical/Clinical Assistant, A
Pharmacy Technician/Assistant, A
Web Page, Digital/Multimedia and Information Resources Design, AB

SEWARD COUNTY COMMUNITY COLLEGE AND AREA TECHNICAL SCHOOL

Accounting, A
Administrative Assistant and Secretarial Science, A
Agricultural Business and Management, A
Agricultural/Biological Engineering and Bioengineering, A
Automobile/Automotive Mechanics Technology/Technician, A
Biology/Biological Sciences, A
Business Administration and Management, A
Business Operations Support and Secretarial Services, A
Business, Management, Marketing, and Related Support Services, A
Business/Commerce, A
Chemistry, A
Clinical/Medical Laboratory Technician, A
Commercial and Advertising Art, A
Communication Studies/Speech Communication and Rhetoric, A
Communications Technologies/Technicians and Support Services, A
Computer and Information Sciences, A
Corrections and Criminal Justice, A
Cosmetology/Cosmetologist, A
Data Processing and Data Processing Technology/Technician, A
Design and Applied Arts, A
Diesel Mechanics Technology/Technician, A
Drafting and Design Technology/Technician, A
Education, A
Elementary Education and Teaching, A
Engineering, A
English Language and Literature, A
Finance, A

General Studies, A
Health Teacher Education, A
Heating, Air Conditioning, Ventilation and Refrigeration Maintenance Technology/Technician, A
History, A
Journalism, A
Liberal Arts and Sciences Studies and Humanities, A
Mathematics, A
Mechanics and Repairers, A
Medical/Clinical Assistant, A
Music, A
Occupational Health and Industrial Hygiene, A
Office Management and Supervision, A
Physical Education Teaching and Coaching, A
Physical Sciences, A
Physical Therapist Assistant, A
Physician Assistant, A
Political Science and Government, A
Pre-Law Studies, A
Pre-Medicine/Pre-Medical Studies, A
Pre-Pharmacy Studies, A
Pre-Veterinary Studies, A
Psychology, A
Respiratory Care Therapy/Therapist, A
Science, Technology and Society, A
Surgical Technology/Technologist, A
Visual and Performing Arts, A

SOUTHWESTERN COLLEGE

Accounting, BM
Athletic Training and Sports Medicine, B
Biochemistry, B
Biology/Biological Sciences, B
Business Administration and Management, B
Business Administration, Management and Operations, M
Business, Management, Marketing, and Related Support Services, B
Chemistry, B
Christian Studies, B
Communication Studies/Speech Communication and Rhetoric, B
Communication and Media Studies, B
Computer Programming/Programmer, B
Computer Science, B
Computer and Information Sciences and Support Services, B
Criminal Justice/Safety Studies, B
Curriculum and Instruction, M
Digital Communication and Media/Multimedia, B
Drama and Dramatics/Theatre Arts, B
Dramatic/Theatre Arts and Stagecraft, B
Early Childhood Education and Teaching, BM
Education, MD
Educational Leadership and Administration, D
Elementary Education and Teaching, B
English/Language Arts Teacher Education, B
Film/Cinema Studies, B
Finance, B
General Studies, AB
Health/Health Care Administration/Management, B
History, B
Human Resources Development, B
Journalism, B
Liberal Arts and Sciences Studies and Humanities, B
Management, M
Management Information Systems and Services, B
Marine Biology and Biological Oceanography, B
Marketing/Marketing Management, B
Mathematics, B
Mathematics Teacher Education, B
Music, B
Music Performance, B
Music Teacher Education, B
Operations Management and Supervision, B
Pastoral Studies/Counseling, B
Physical Education Teaching and Coaching, B
Psychology, B
Radio and Television, B
Securities Services Administration/Management, BM
Special Education and Teaching, M
Speech Teacher Education, B
Sport and Fitness Administration/Management, B

Technical Theatre/Theatre Design and Technology, B
Theology and Religious Vocations, M
Youth Ministry, B

STERLING COLLEGE

Art/Art Studies, General, B
Athletic Training and Sports Medicine, B
Behavioral Sciences, B
Biology/Biological Sciences, B
Business Administration and Management, B
Communication, Journalism and Related Programs, B
Computer and Information Sciences, B
Criminal Justice/Law Enforcement Administration, B
Drama and Dramatics/Theatre Arts, B
Elementary Education and Teaching, B
English Language and Literature, B
Health and Physical Education, B
History, B
Mathematics, B
Music, B
Music Teacher Education, B
Philosophy and Religious Studies, B
Physical Education Teaching and Coaching, B
Religious Education, B

TABOR COLLEGE

Accounting, M
Accounting and Finance, B
Agricultural Business and Management, B
Athletic Training and Sports Medicine, B
Behavioral Sciences, B
Biochemistry, B
Biology Teacher Education, B
Biology/Biological Sciences, B
Business Administration and Management, B
Business Administration, Management and Operations, M
Business Teacher Education, B
Business/Commerce, B
Chemistry, B
Chemistry Teacher Education, B
Christian Studies, B
Communication Studies/Speech Communication and Rhetoric, B
Criminology, B
Drama and Dramatics/Theatre Arts, B
Education, D
Elementary Education and Teaching, B
English Language and Literature, B
English/Language Arts Teacher Education, B
Fine/Studio Arts, B
General Studies, B
Graphic Design, B
Health Teacher Education, B
Health and Physical Education, B
History, B
History Teacher Education, B
International/Global Studies, B
Liberal Arts and Sciences Studies and Humanities, A
Marketing/Marketing Management, B
Mathematics, B
Mathematics Teacher Education, B
Missions/Missionary Studies and Missiology, B
Music, B
Music Performance, B
Music Teacher Education, B
Natural Resources Management/Development and Policy, B
Natural Sciences, B
Painting, B
Physical Education Teaching and Coaching, B
Pre-Dentistry Studies, B
Pre-Law Studies, B
Pre-Medicine/Pre-Medical Studies, B
Pre-Nursing Studies, B
Pre-Pharmacy Studies, B
Pre-Theology/Pre-Ministerial Studies, B
Pre-Veterinary Studies, B
Psychology, B
Religion/Religious Studies, B
Science Teacher Education/General Science Teacher Education, B
Secondary Education and Teaching, B

Social Science Teacher Education, B
Social Work, B
Sport and Fitness Administration/Management, B
Youth Ministry, B

THE UNIVERSITY OF KANSAS

Accounting, BM
Aerospace, Aeronautical and Astronautical Engineering, BMD
African Studies, BMO
African-American Studies, MO
African-American/Black Studies, B
Allied Health and Medical Assisting Services, MDO
Allopathic Medicine, D
American Indian/Native American Studies, MO
American/United States Studies/Civilization, BMD
Anatomy, MD
Ancient Studies/Civilization, B
Anthropology, BMD
Applied Behavior Analysis, MD
Architectural Engineering, BM
Architectural History and Criticism, B
Architecture, BMDO
Art Education, M
Art History, Criticism and Conservation, BMD
Art Teacher Education, B
Asian Languages, M
Astronomy, BMD
Athletic Training and Sports Medicine, B
Atmospheric Sciences and Meteorology, BM
Behavioral Sciences, B
BioTechnology, M
Biochemistry, BMD
Bioengineering, MD
Biological and Biomedical Sciences, MD
Biology/Biological Sciences, B
Biophysics, MD
Biostatistics, MDO
Botany/Plant Biology, MD
Business Administration and Management, B
Business Administration, Management and Operations, MD
Business/Commerce, B
Cell Biology and Anatomy, MD
Ceramic Arts and Ceramics, BM
Chemical Engineering, BMD
Chemistry, BMD
Civil Engineering, BMD
Classics and Classical Languages, Literatures, and Linguistics, BM
Clinical Laboratory Science/Medical Technology/Technologist, B
Clinical Psychology, MD
Clinical Research, M
Cognitive Sciences, D
Communication Disorders, BMD
Communication Studies/Speech Communication and Rhetoric, B
Communication and Media Studies, MD
Community Health Nursing, O
Community Health Services/Liaison/Counseling, B
Computational Biology, D
Computational Sciences, M
Computer Art and Design, M
Computer Engineering, BM
Computer Science, MD
Computer and Information Sciences, B
Construction Management, M
Counseling Psychology, MD
Curriculum and Instruction, MD
Dance, B
Design and Applied Arts, M
Design and Visual Communications, B
Developmental Biology and Embryology, MD
Developmental Psychology, D
Drama and Dramatics/Theatre Arts, B
Early Childhood Education and Teaching, B
East Asian Languages, Literatures, and Linguistics, B
East Asian Studies, M
East European and Russian Studies, MO
Ecology, MD
Economics, BMD
Education, MDO
Educational Administration and Supervision, MD
Educational Leadership and Administration, D

Educational Measurement and Evaluation, MD
Educational Media/Instructional Technology, MD
Educational Policy, D
Educational Psychology, MD
Electrical Engineering, MD
Electrical, Electronics and Communications Engineering, B
Elementary Education and Teaching, B
Engineering Management, M
Engineering Physics, B
Engineering and Applied Sciences, MD
English, MD
English Language and Literature, B
Entomology, MD
Environmental Engineering Technology/Environmental Technology, MD
Environmental Sciences, MD
Environmental Studies, B
Environmental and Occupational Health, M
Epidemiology, M
European Studies/Civilization, B
Evolutionary Biology, MD
Facilities Planning and Management, O
Fiber, Textile and Weaving Arts, B
Film, Television, and Video Theory and Criticism, MD
Film/Cinema Studies, B
Finance, B
Fine Arts and Art Studies, M
Fine/Studio Arts, B
Foundations and Philosophy of Education, D
French Language and Literature, BMD
Geography, BMD
Geology/Earth Science, BMD
German Language and Literature, MD
Germanic Languages, Literatures, and Linguistics, B
Gerontological Nursing, O
Gerontology, MDO
Graphic Design, B
Health Education, MDO
Health Informatics, M
Health Information/Medical Records Administration/Administrator, B
Health Services Administration, MD
Health and Physical Education, B
Higher Education/Higher Education Administration, MD
History, BMD
Humanities/Humanistic Studies, B
Illustration, B
Industrial Design, B
Information Technology, B
Interdisciplinary Studies, MD
International Affairs, M
International/Global Studies, B
Jewelry/Metalsmithing, M
Journalism, BM
Junior High/Intermediate/Middle School Education and Teaching, B
Kinesiology and Exercise Science, B
Latin American Studies, BMO
Law and Legal Studies, D
Liberal Arts and Sciences Studies and Humanities, B
Linguistics, BMD
Logistics and Materials Management, B
Management Information Systems and Services, BM
Marketing/Marketing Management, B
Mathematics, BMD
Mechanical Engineering, BMD
Media Studies, MD
Medical Informatics, O
Medicinal and Pharmaceutical Chemistry, MD
Metal and Jewelry Arts, B
Microbiology, BMD
Molecular Biology, BMD
Museology/Museum Studies, MO
Music, BMD
Music Performance, B
Music Teacher Education, BMD
Music Theory and Composition, B
Music Therapy/Therapist, BM
Musicology and Ethnomusicology, B
Near and Middle Eastern Studies, MO
Neuroscience, MD

Nurse Anesthetist, MD
Nurse Midwife/Nursing Midwifery, O
Nursing, MDO
Nursing - Adult, O
Nursing Administration, O
Nutritional Sciences, MDO
Occupational Therapy/Therapist, BMD
Organizational Management, O
Painting, BM
Pathology/Experimental Pathology, MD
Petroleum Engineering, BMD
Pharmaceutical Sciences, M
Pharmacology, MD
Pharmacy, BM
Philosophy, BMD
Physical Education Teaching and Coaching, BMD
Physical Therapy/Therapist, D
Physics, BMD
Physiology, MD
Piano and Organ, B
Political Science and Government, BMD
Printmaking, BM
Project Management, M
Psychiatric/Mental Health Nurse/Nursing, O
Psychology, BMD
Public Administration, BMD
Public Health, M
Rehabilitation Counseling, D
Rehabilitation Sciences, D
Religion/Religious Studies, BM
Respiratory Care Therapy/Therapist, B
Russian Studies, B
School Psychology, DO
Sculpture, BM
Secondary Education and Teaching, B
Slavic Languages, Literatures, and Linguistics, BMD
Social Psychology, D
Social Work, BMD
Sociology, BMD
Spanish Language and Literature, BMD
Special Education and Teaching, MD
Sport and Fitness Administration/Management, B
Statistics, MDO
Technical Theatre/Theatre Design and Technology, B
Textile Design, M
Theater, MD
Toxicology, MD
Urban and Regional Planning, M
Violin, Viola, Guitar and Other Stringed Instruments, B
Voice and Opera, B
Women's Studies, B
Writing, M

UNIVERSITY OF SAINT MARY

Accounting, B
Advertising and Public Relations, M
Art/Art Studies, General, B
Biology/Biological Sciences, B
Business Administration and Management, B
Business Administration, Management and Operations, M
Chemistry, B
Child Development, B
Community Organization and Advocacy, B
Computer and Information Sciences, B
Counseling Psychology, M
Criminology, B
Drama and Dramatics/Theatre Arts, B
Education, BM
Elementary Education and Teaching, BM
English Language and Literature, B
Health Information/Medical Records Technology/Technician, B
Health Services Administration, M
History, B
Human Resources Management and Services, M
Information Technology, B
Liberal Arts and Sciences Studies and Humanities, B
Management, M
Marketing, M
Mathematics, B
Multi-/Interdisciplinary Studies, B
Nursing, M

Nursing Administration, M
Nursing Education, M
Pastoral Studies/Counseling, B
Physical Therapy/Therapist, D
Political Science and Government, B
Psychology, BM
Special Education and Teaching, M
Sport and Fitness Administration/Management, B
Theology/Theological Studies, B
Visual and Performing Arts, B

WASHBURN UNIVERSITY

Accounting, BM
Administrative Assistant and Secretarial Science, A
Anthropology, B
Art History, Criticism and Conservation, B
Art Teacher Education, B
Art/Art Studies, General, B
Athletic Training and Sports Medicine, B
Biochemistry, B
Biology Teacher Education, B
Biology Technician/BioTechnology Laboratory Technician, B
Biology/Biological Sciences, B
Business Administration and Management, B
Business Administration, Management and Operations, M
Business/Commerce, B
Business/Managerial Economics, B
Chemistry, B
Chemistry Teacher Education, B
Clinical Laboratory Science/Medical Technology/Technologist, B
Clinical Psychology, M
Communication Studies/Speech Communication and Rhetoric, B
Computer and Information Sciences, AB
Corrections, B
Criminal Justice/Law Enforcement Administration, AB
Criminology, M
Curriculum and Instruction, M
Design and Applied Arts, A
Diagnostic Medical Sonography/Sonographer and Ultrasound Technician, A
Drama and Dramatics/Theatre Arts, B
Early Childhood Education and Teaching, A
Economics, B
Education, BM
Educational Administration and Supervision, M
Elementary Education and Teaching, B
Engineering/Industrial Management, B
English Language and Literature, B
English/Language Arts Teacher Education, B
Finance, B
Food Preparation/Professional Cooking/Kitchen Assistant, A
Forensic Science and Technology, B
French Language Teacher Education, B
French Language and Literature, B
German Language Teacher Education, B
German Language and Literature, B
Health Management, M
Health Information/Medical Records Technology/Technician, A
Health and Medical Administrative Services, B
Health/Health Care Administration/Management, A
History, B
History Teacher Education, B
Human Services, M
Humanities/Humanistic Studies, A
Industrial Technology/Technician, A
Law and Legal Studies, MD
Legal Administrative Assistant/Secretary, A
Legal Assistant/Paralegal, AB
Legal and Justice Studies, MD
Liberal Arts and Sciences Studies and Humanities, AB
Liberal Studies, M
Marketing/Marketing Management, B
Mass Communication/Media Studies, B
Mathematics, B
Mathematics Teacher Education, B
Mechanic and Repair Technologies/Technicians, A
Mental and Social Health Services and Allied Professions, AB

Multi-/Interdisciplinary Studies, AB
Music, B
Music Performance, B
Music Teacher Education, B
Natural Sciences, A
Nursing, MD
Nursing Administration, M
Occupational Therapist Assistant, A
Philosophy, B
Physical Education Teaching and Coaching, B
Physical Sciences, B
Physical Therapist Assistant, A
Physics, B
Political Science and Government, B
Pre-Dentistry Studies, B
Pre-Law Studies, B
Pre-Medicine/Pre-Medical Studies, B
Pre-Pharmacy Studies, B
Pre-Theology/Pre-Ministerial Studies, B
Pre-Veterinary Studies, B
Psychology, BM
Public Administration, B
Radiologic Technology/Science - Radiographer, A
Reading Teacher Education, M
Religion/Religious Studies, B
Respiratory Care Therapy/Therapist, A
Securities Services Administration/Management, B
Security and Protective Services, B
Social Work, BM
Sociology, B
Spanish Language Teacher Education, B
Spanish Language and Literature, B
Special Education and Teaching, M
Substance Abuse/Addiction Counseling, ABM
Surgical Technology/Technologist, A

WICHITA AREA TECHNICAL COLLEGE

Aeronautical/Aerospace Engineering Technology/Technician, A
Airframe Mechanics and Aircraft Maintenance Technology/Technician, A
Autobody/Collision and Repair Technology/Technician, A
Automobile/Automotive Mechanics Technology/Technician, A
Avionics Maintenance Technology/Technician, A
Business Administration and Management, A
Clinical/Medical Laboratory Technician, A
Criminal Justice/Police Science, A
Dental Assisting/Assistant, A
Drafting and Design Technology/Technician, A
Entrepreneurship/Entrepreneurial Studies, A
General Office Occupations and Clerical Services, A
Health and Medical Administrative Services, A
Heating, Air Conditioning, Ventilation and Refrigeration Maintenance Technology/Technician, A
Industrial Mechanics and Maintenance Technology, A
Industrial Radiologic Technology/Technician, A
Interior Design, A
Machine Tool Technology/Machinist, A
Mechanical Drafting and Mechanical Drafting CAD/CADD, A
Mechanical Engineering/Mechanical Technology/Technician, A
Medical/Clinical Assistant, A
Plastics Engineering Technology/Technician, A
Precision Production, A
Robotics Technology/Technician, A
Surgical Technology/Technologist, A
Welding Technology/Welder, A

WICHITA STATE UNIVERSITY

Accounting, BM
Aerospace, Aeronautical and Astronautical Engineering, BMD
Allied Health and Medical Assisting Services, MD
Anthropology, BM
Applied Mathematics, D
Athletic Training and Sports Medicine, B
Biological and Biomedical Sciences, M
Biology/Biological Sciences, B
Biomedical/Medical Engineering, B
Business Administration and Management, B
Business Administration, Management and Operations, M

Ceramic Arts and Ceramics, M
Chemistry, BMD
Clinical Laboratory Science/Medical Technology/Technologist, B
Clinical Psychology, D
Communication Disorders, BMD
Communication Studies/Speech Communication and Rhetoric, B
Communication and Media Studies, M
Community Psychology, D
Computer Engineering, BM
Computer Science, MD
Computer Software Engineering, B
Counselor Education/School Counseling and Guidance Services, M
Criminal Justice/Safety Studies, B
Criminology, M
Curriculum and Instruction, M
Dental Hygiene/Hygienist, B
Drama and Dramatics/Theatre Arts, B
Early Childhood Education and Teaching, M
Economics, BM
Education, MDO
Education/Teaching of the Gifted and Talented, M
Educational Administration and Supervision, MDO
Educational Leadership and Administration, MD
Educational Psychology, M
Electrical Engineering, M
Electrical, Electronics and Communications Engineering, B
Elementary Education and Teaching, B
Engineering Management, M
Engineering Technology, B
Engineering and Applied Sciences, MD
English, M
English Language and Literature, B
Entrepreneurship/Entrepreneurial Studies, B
Environmental Sciences, M
Exercise and Sports Science, M
Finance, B
Fine Arts and Art Studies, M
Foreign Languages and Literatures, B
Forensic Science and Technology, B
French Language and Literature, B
General Studies, B
Geology/Earth Science, BM
Gerontology, BMD
Graphic Design, B
Health/Health Care Administration/Management, B
History, BM
Human Resources Management/Personnel Administration, B
Human Services, M
Industrial Engineering, B
Industrial/Management Engineering, MD
International Business/Trade/Commerce, B
Kinesiology and Exercise Science, B
Liberal Arts and Sciences Studies and Humanities, AB
Liberal Studies, M
Management Information Systems and Services, B
Manufacturing Engineering, BMD
Marketing/Marketing Management, B
Mathematics, BMD
Mechanical Engineering, BMD
Middle School Education, M
Multi-/Interdisciplinary Studies, B
Music, BM
Music Teacher Education, BM
Nursing, MD
Painting, M
Philosophy, B
Physical Therapy/Therapist, D
Physician Assistant, M
Physics, B
Political Science and Government, B
Printmaking, M
Psychology, BD
Public Administration, M
School Psychology, O
Sculpture, M
Secondary Education and Teaching, BM
Social Work, BM
Sociology, BM
Spanish Language and Literature, M
Special Education and Teaching, M

Sport and Fitness Administration/Management, M
Visual and Performing Arts, B
Women's Studies, B
Writing, M

Kentucky

ALICE LLOYD COLLEGE

Biological and Physical Sciences, B
Biology/Biological Sciences, B
Business Administration and Management, B
Business/Commerce, B
Elementary Education and Teaching, B
English Language and Literature, B
English/Language Arts Teacher Education, B
History, B
Junior High/Intermediate/Middle School Education
   and Teaching, B
Mathematics Teacher Education, B
Physical Education Teaching and Coaching, B
Science Teacher Education/General Science
   Teacher Education, B
Secondary Education and Teaching, B
Social Studies Teacher Education, B
Sport and Fitness Administration/Management, B

AMERICAN NATIONAL UNIVERSITY
(DANVILLE)

Accounting, A
Administrative Assistant and Secretarial Science, A
Business Administration and Management, A
Computer and Information Sciences, A
Medical/Clinical Assistant, A

AMERICAN NATIONAL UNIVERSITY
(FLORENCE)

Accounting, A
Administrative Assistant and Secretarial Science, A
Business Administration and Management, A
Computer and Information Sciences, A
Medical/Clinical Assistant, A
Surgical Technology/Technologist, A

AMERICAN NATIONAL UNIVERSITY
(LEXINGTON)

Accounting, AB
Administrative Assistant and Secretarial Science, A
Business Administration and Management, AB
Computer and Information Sciences, A
Information Science/Studies, A
Medical/Clinical Assistant, A
Radio and Television, A
Surgical Technology/Technologist, A

AMERICAN NATIONAL UNIVERSITY
(LOUISVILLE)

Accounting, AB
Administrative Assistant and Secretarial Science, A
Business Administration and Management, AB
Computer and Information Sciences, A
Data Modeling/Warehousing and Database Adminis-
   tration, B
Health Information/Medical Records
   Technology/Technician, A
Health/Health Care Administration/Management, B
Information Science/Studies, A
Medical/Clinical Assistant, A
Surgical Technology/Technologist, A

AMERICAN NATIONAL UNIVERSITY
(PIKEVILLE)

Accounting, A
Administrative Assistant and Secretarial Science, A
Business Administration and Management, A
Computer and Information Sciences, A
Medical/Clinical Assistant, A

AMERICAN NATIONAL UNIVERSITY
(RICHMOND)

Accounting, A
Administrative Assistant and Secretarial Science, A
Business Administration and Management, A
Computer and Information Sciences, A

Medical/Clinical Assistant, A

ASBURY UNIVERSITY

Accounting, B
Art Teacher Education, B
Bible/Biblical Studies, B
Biochemistry, B
Biology/Biological Sciences, B
Business/Commerce, B
Chemistry, B
Child and Family Studies, M
Classics and Classical Languages, Litera-
   tures, and Linguistics, BM
Computational Mathematics, B
Design and Applied Arts, B
Drama and Dramatics/Theatre Arts, B
Educational Leadership and Administration, M
Elementary Education and Teaching, B
English, M
English Language and Literature, B
English as a Second Language, M
Equestrian/Equine Studies, B
Fine/Studio Arts, B
French Language and Literature, BM
General Studies, A
Health and Physical Education, B
Health/Medical Preparatory Programs, B
History, B
Journalism, B
Junior High/Intermediate/Middle School Education
   and Teaching, B
Marketing/Marketing Management, B
Mathematics, B
Mathematics Teacher Education, M
Missions/Missionary Studies and Missiology, B
Music, B
Music Teacher Education, B
Parks, Recreation and Leisure Facilities Manage-
   ment, B
Philosophy, B
Physical Education Teaching and Coaching, B
Political Science and Government, B
Psychology, B
Radio, Television, and Digital Communication, B
Reading Teacher Education, M
Religious Education, B
Religious/Sacred Music, B
Science Teacher Education/General Science
   Teacher Education, M
Social Sciences, B
Social Studies Teacher Education, M
Social Work, BM
Sociology, B
Spanish Language and Literature, BM
Special Education and Teaching, BM
Sport and Fitness Administration/Management, B
Writing, M
Youth Ministry, B

ASHLAND COMMUNITY AND TECHNI-
CAL COLLEGE

Business Administration and Management, A
Chemical Technology/Technician, A
Child Care Provider/Assistant, A
Computer and Information Sciences, A
Criminal Justice/Law Enforcement Administration, A
Culinary Arts/Chef Training, A
Executive Assistant/Executive Secretary, A
Fire Science/Firefighting, A
Liberal Arts and Sciences Studies and Humani-
   ties, A
Medical Radiologic Technology/Science - Radiation
   Therapist, A
Multi-/Interdisciplinary Studies, A
Respiratory Therapy Technician/Assistant, A

ATA COLLEGE

Health Information/Medical Records
   Technology/Technician, A
Medical Office Assistant/Specialist, A

BECKFIELD COLLEGE

Business Administration and Management, AB
Computer Systems Networking and Telecommunications, A

Legal Assistant/Paralegal, AB
Medical Office Management/Administration, A

BELLARMINE UNIVERSITY

Accounting, B
Actuarial Science, B
Biochemistry, Biophysics and Molecular Biology, B
Biology/Biological Sciences, B
Business Administration, Management and Opera-
   tions, M
Business/Commerce, B
Chemistry, B
Clinical Laboratory Science/Medical
   Technology/Technologist, B
Communication Studies/Speech Communication
   and Rhetoric, B
Communication and Media Studies, M
Computer Engineering, B
Computer and Information Sciences, B
Criminal Justice/Safety Studies, B
Design and Visual Communications, B
Drama and Dramatics/Theatre Arts, B
Economics, B
Education, MDO
Educational Administration and Supervision, O
Educational Leadership and Administration, MO
Elementary Education and Teaching, BM
English Language and Literature, B
Environmental Sciences, B
Environmental Studies, B
Finance, B
Fine/Studio Arts, B
History, B
Junior High/Intermediate/Middle School Education
   and Teaching, B
Kinesiology and Exercise Science, B
Liberal Arts and Sciences Studies and Humani-
   ties, B
Management Strategy and Policy, M
Mathematics, B
Middle School Education, M
Multi-/Interdisciplinary Studies, B
Music, B
Nursing, MD
Nursing - Advanced Practice, M
Nursing Administration, M
Nursing Education, M
Philosophy, B
Physical Therapy/Therapist, BD
Physics, B
Political Science and Government, B
Psychology, B
Reading Teacher Education, M
Religion/Religious Studies, M
Respiratory Care Therapy/Therapist, B
Secondary Education and Teaching, BM
Sociology, B
Spanish Language and Literature, B
Special Education and Teaching, BM
Sport and Fitness Administration/Management, B
Theology/Theological Studies, B

BEREA COLLEGE

African-American/Black Studies, B
Agriculture, B
Applied Mathematics, B
Art Teacher Education, B
Art/Art Studies, General, B
Asian Studies/Civilization, B
Biology/Biological Sciences, B
Business Administration and Management, B
Chemistry, B
Computer and Information Sciences, B
Drama and Dramatics/Theatre Arts, B
Economics, B
Education, B
Elementary and Middle School
   Administration/Principalship, B
English Language and Literature, B
Family and Consumer Sciences/Human Sciences, B
French Language and Literature, B
German Language and Literature, B
Health and Physical Education, B
History, B
Junior High/Intermediate/Middle School Education
   and Teaching, B

Kinesiology and Exercise Science, B
Manufacturing Technology/Technician, B
Mass Communication/Media Studies, B
Mathematics, B
Multi-/Interdisciplinary Studies, B
Music, B
Music Teacher Education, B
Philosophy, B
Physics, B
Political Science and Government, B
Psychology, B
Religion/Religious Studies, B
Sociology, B
Spanish Language and Literature, B
Technology Teacher Education/Industrial Arts
    Teacher Education, B
Women's Studies, B

BIG SANDY COMMUNITY AND TECHNI-CAL COLLEGE

Business Administration and Management, A
Computer and Information Sciences, A
Criminal Justice/Law Enforcement Administration, A
Dental Hygiene/Hygienist, A
Drafting and Design Technology/Technician, A
Heating, Air Conditioning, Ventilation and Refrigera-
    tion Maintenance Technology/Technician, A
Medical Administrative Assistant/Secretary, A
Social Work, A
Survey Technology/Surveying, A

BLUEGRASS COMMUNITY AND TECH-NICAL COLLEGE

Architectural Drafting and Architectural
    CAD/CADD, A
Automobile/Automotive Mechanics
    Technology/Technician, A
Business Administration and Management, A
Carpentry/Carpenter, A
Child Care Provider/Assistant, A
Civil Engineering Technology/Technician, A
Computer and Information Sciences, A
Data Processing and Data Processing
    Technology/Technician, A
Dental Hygiene/Hygienist, A
Dental Laboratory Technology/Technician, A
Electrical, Electronic and Communications Engineer-
    ing Technology/Technician, A
Electrician, A
Engineering Technology, A
Environmental Engineering
    Technology/Environmental Technology, A
Executive Assistant/Executive Secretary, A
Fire Science/Firefighting, A
Heating, Air Conditioning, Ventilation and Refrigera-
    tion Maintenance Technology/Technician, A
Industrial Electronics Technology/Technician, A
Industrial Mechanics and Maintenance Technol-
    ogy, A
Liberal Arts and Sciences Studies and Humani-
    ties, A
Machine Shop Technology/Assistant, A
Medical Administrative Assistant/Secretary, A
Medical Radiologic Technology/Science - Radiation
    Therapist, A
Medical/Clinical Assistant, A
Multi-/Interdisciplinary Studies, A
Nuclear Medical Technology/Technologist, A
Respiratory Care Therapy/Therapist, A
Surgical Technology/Technologist, A
Teacher Assistant/Aide, A
Welding Technology/Welder, A

BRESCIA UNIVERSITY

Accounting, B
Applied Mathematics, B
Art Teacher Education, B
Art/Art Studies, General, B
Audiology/Audiologist and Speech-Language
    Pathology/Pathologist, B
Banking and Financial Support Services, AB
Biology/Biological Sciences, B
Business Administration, Management and Opera-
    tions, M
Business/Commerce, AB
Chemistry, B

Clinical Laboratory Science/Medical
    Technology/Technologist, B
Curriculum and Instruction, M
Elementary Education and Teaching, B
Engineering, A
Engineering Technology, A
English Language and Literature, B
Finance, B
Graphic Design, B
History, B
Human Resources Management/Personnel Adminis-
    tration, B
Human Services, A
Junior High/Intermediate/Middle School Education
    and Teaching, B
Liberal Arts and Sciences Studies and Humani-
    ties, AB
Management, M
Mathematics and Computer Science, B
Pastoral Counseling and Specialized Ministries, AB
Political Science and Government, B
Psychology, B
Social Sciences, B
Social Work, B
Spanish Language and Literature, B
Special Education and Teaching, B
Theology/Theological Studies, B

BROWN MACKIE COL-LEGE–HOPKINSVILLE

Business/Commerce, A
Criminal Justice/Safety Studies, A
Medical Office Management/Administration, A
Occupational Therapist Assistant, A

CAMPBELLSVILLE UNIVERSITY

Accounting, B
Administrative Assistant and Secretarial Science, AB
Art Teacher Education, B
Art/Art Studies, General, B
Bible/Biblical Studies, AB
Biology Teacher Education, B
Biology/Biological Sciences, B
Business Administration and Management, AB
Business Administration, Management and Opera-
    tions, M
Business Teacher Education, B
Business/Managerial Economics, AB
Chemistry, B
Chemistry Teacher Education, B
Clinical Laboratory Science/Medical
    Technology/Technologist, B
Counselor Education/School Counseling and Guid-
    ance Services, M
Criminal Justice/Law Enforcement Administra-
    tion, AB
Curriculum and Instruction, M
Data Processing and Data Processing
    Technology/Technician, A
Divinity/Ministry (BD, MDiv.), B
Economics, B
Education, M
Elementary Education and Teaching, B
English Language and Literature, B
English/Language Arts Teacher Education, B
Health Teacher Education, B
History, B
History Teacher Education, B
Information Science/Studies, AB
Journalism, B
Marketing/Marketing Management, B
Mass Communication/Media Studies, B
Mathematics, B
Mathematics Teacher Education, B
Music, BM
Music Teacher Education, BM
Organizational Management, M
Parks, Recreation, Leisure and Fitness Studies, B
Pastoral Studies/Counseling, B
Performance, M
Physical Education Teaching and Coaching, B
Piano and Organ, B
Political Science and Government, B
Pre-Dentistry Studies, B
Pre-Law Studies, B
Pre-Medicine/Pre-Medical Studies, B

Pre-Veterinary Studies, B
Psychology, B
Psychology Teacher Education, B
Religion/Religious Studies, B
Religious Education, B
Religious/Sacred Music, B
Sacred Music, M
Science Teacher Education/General Science
    Teacher Education, B
Secondary Education and Teaching, B
Social Science Teacher Education, B
Social Sciences, ABM
Social Studies Teacher Education, B
Social Work, BM
Sociology, B
Special Education and Teaching, M
Theology and Religious Vocations, M
Voice and Opera, B

CENTRE COLLEGE

Art History, Criticism and Conservation, B
Biochemistry, Biophysics and Molecular Biology, B
Biology/Biological Sciences, B
Chemical Physics, B
Chemistry, B
Classics and Classical Languages, Litera-
    tures, and Linguistics, B
Computer Science, B
Drama and Dramatics/Theatre Arts, B
Economics, B
English Language and Literature, B
Environmental Studies, B
Fine/Studio Arts, B
French Language and Literature, B
German Language and Literature, B
History, B
International/Global Studies, B
Liberal Arts and Sciences Studies and Humani-
    ties, B
Mathematics, B
Music, B
Philosophy, B
Physics, B
Political Science and Government, B
Psychology, B
Religion/Religious Studies, B
Spanish Language and Literature, B

CLEAR CREEK BAPTIST BIBLE COL-LEGE

Bible/Biblical Studies, AB
Divinity/Ministry (BD, MDiv.), AB

DAYMAR COLLEGE (BELLEVUE)

Business Administration and Management, A
Computer Systems Networking and Telecommunica-
    tions, A
E-Commerce/Electronic Commerce, A
Legal Assistant/Paralegal, A
Medical Insurance Coding Specialist/Coder, A
Medical Office Assistant/Specialist, A

DAYMAR COLLEGE (BOWLING GREEN)

Accounting, A
Business Administration, Management and Opera-
    tions, A
Cardiovascular Technology/Technologist, A
Computer Science, A
Criminal Justice/Safety Studies, A
E-Commerce/Electronic Commerce, A
Health Information/Medical Records
    Technology/Technician, A
Legal Assistant/Paralegal, A
Medical/Clinical Assistant, A
Pharmacy Technician/Assistant, A

DAYMAR COLLEGE (OWENSBORO)

Business/Office Automation/Technology/Data En-
    try, A
Computer Programming/Programmer, A
Computer Systems Networking and Telecommunica-
    tions, A
Criminal Justice/Safety Studies, A
Legal Assistant/Paralegal, A

Medical Insurance Specialist/Medical Biller, A
Medical/Clinical Assistant, A
Office Management and Supervision, A
Pharmacy Technician/Assistant, A

EASTERN KENTUCKY UNIVERSITY

Accounting, B
Administrative Assistant and Secretarial Science, A
Agricultural Education, M
Agricultural Production Operations, B
Airline/Commercial/Professional Pilot and Flight Crew, B
Allied Health and Medical Assisting Services, M
American Sign Language, B
Anthropology, B
Art Education, M
Art/Art Studies, General, B
Athletic Training and Sports Medicine, B
Audiology/Audiologist and Speech-Language Pathology/Pathologist, B
Biological and Biomedical Sciences, M
Biology Teacher Education, B
Biology/Biological Sciences, B
Business Administration and Management, B
Business Administration, Management and Operations, M
Business Education, M
Business Teacher Education, B
Chemistry, BM
Child Care Provider/Assistant, A
Clinical Laboratory Science/Medical Technology/Technologist, B
Clinical Psychology, M
Clinical/Medical Laboratory Technician, A
Communication Disorders, M
Communication Studies/Speech Communication and Rhetoric, B
Community Health and Preventive Medicine, M
Composition, M
Computer Engineering Technologies/Technicians, B
Computer Engineering Technology/Technician, A
Computer Science, B
Computer and Information Sciences, B
Construction Management, B
Corrections, BM
Counselor Education/School Counseling and Guidance Services, M
Criminal Justice/Law Enforcement Administration, B
Criminal Justice/Police Science, AB
Criminology, M
Curriculum and Instruction, M
Ecology, M
Economics, B
Education, M
Education/Teaching of Individuals in Early Childhood Special Education Programs, B
Education/Teaching of Individuals with Hearing Impairments, Including Deafness, B
Education/Teaching of the Gifted and Talented, B
Educational Administration and Supervision, M
Educational Leadership and Administration, M
Elementary Education and Teaching, BM
Emergency Medical Technology/Technician (EMT Paramedic), AB
Engineering, A
Engineering/Industrial Management, B
English, M
English Education, M
English Language and Literature, B
English/Language Arts Teacher Education, B
Environmental Health, B
Environmental Studies, B
Environmental and Occupational Health, M
Family and Consumer Sciences/Home Economics Teacher Education, B
Fashion Merchandising, B
Finance, B
Fine/Studio Arts, B
Fire Protection and Safety Technology/Technician, B
Fire Services Administration, B
Foods, Nutrition, and Wellness Studies, B
Forensic Science and Technology, B
French Language Teacher Education, B
French Language and Literature, B
General Studies, AB
Geography, B

Geology/Earth Science, BMD
Health Education, M
Health Information/Medical Records Administration/Administrator, B
Health Promotion, M
Health Services Administration, M
Health/Health Care Administration/Management, B
Health/Medical Preparatory Programs, B
Higher Education/Higher Education Administration, M
History, BM
History Teacher Education, B
Home Economics Education, M
Human Development and Family Studies, B
Humanities/Humanistic Studies, B
Industrial Education, M
Industrial Safety Technology/Technician, B
Industrial Technology/Technician, A
Industrial and Organizational Psychology, M
Industrial/Management Engineering, M
International/Global Studies, B
Journalism, B
Junior High/Intermediate/Middle School Education and Teaching, B
Law Enforcement, M
Legal Assistant/Paralegal, AB
Library Science, M
Management Information Systems and Services, B
Manufacturing Engineering, M
Marketing/Marketing Management, B
Mathematics, BM
Mathematics Teacher Education, BM
Multi-/Interdisciplinary Studies, B
Music, BM
Music Teacher Education, BM
Music Theory and Composition, M
Nursing, M
Nursing - Advanced Practice, M
Nutritional Sciences, M
Occupational Therapy/Therapist, BM
Office Management and Supervision, B
Ornamental Horticulture, B
Parks, Recreation and Leisure Facilities Management, B
Performance, M
Philosophy, B
Physical Education Teaching and Coaching, BM
Physics, B
Physics Teacher Education, B
Political Science and Government, BM
Pre-Nursing Studies, B
Printing Management, B
Psychology, BMO
Public Administration, M
Public Health Education and Promotion, B
Public Relations/Image Management, B
Radio and Television, B
Recreation and Park Management, M
School Psychology, O
Science Teacher Education/General Science Teacher Education, M
Secondary Education and Teaching, M
Securities Services Administration/Management, M
Sign Language Interpretation and Translation, B
Social Studies Teacher Education, M
Social Work, B
Sociology, B
Spanish Language Teacher Education, B
Spanish Language and Literature, B
Special Education and Teaching, BM
Sport and Fitness Administration/Management, BM
Statistics, B
Teacher Education and Professional Development, Specific Subject Areas, B
Trade and Industrial Teacher Education, AB
Urban and Regional Planning, M
Wildlife and Wildlands Science and Management, B
Writing, M

ELIZABETHTOWN COMMUNITY AND TECHNICAL COLLEGE

Automobile/Automotive Mechanics Technology/Technician, A
Business Administration and Management, A
Child Care Provider/Assistant, A
Computer and Information Sciences, A

Criminal Justice/Law Enforcement Administration, A
Data Processing and Data Processing Technology/Technician, A
Dental Hygiene/Hygienist, A
Diesel Mechanics Technology/Technician, A
Electrician, A
Engineering Technology, A
Executive Assistant/Executive Secretary, A
Fire Science/Firefighting, A
Industrial Electronics Technology/Technician, A
Industrial Mechanics and Maintenance Technology, A
Liberal Arts and Sciences Studies and Humanities, A
Medical Administrative Assistant/Secretary, A
Medical Radiologic Technology/Science - Radiation Therapist, A
Quality Control and Safety Technologies/Technicians, A
Respiratory Care Therapy/Therapist, A
Social Work, A
Teacher Assistant/Aide, A
Welding Technology/Welder, A

GATEWAY COMMUNITY AND TECHNICAL COLLEGE

Business Administration and Management, A
CAD/CADD Drafting and/or Design Technology/Technician, A
Computer and Information Sciences, A
Criminal Justice/Law Enforcement Administration, A
Early Childhood Education and Teaching, A
Educational/Instructional Media Design, A
Engineering Technology, A
Fire Science/Firefighting, A
General Office Occupations and Clerical Services, A
General Studies, A
Health Professions and Related Clinical Sciences, A
Industrial Technology/Technician, A
Manufacturing Technology/Technician, A
Teacher Assistant/Aide, A

GEORGETOWN COLLEGE

Accounting, B
American/United States Studies/Civilization, B
Athletic Training and Sports Medicine, B
Biochemistry, B
Biology/Biological Sciences, B
Business Administration and Management, B
Business/Managerial Economics, B
Chemistry, B
Communication and Media Studies, B
Computer and Information Sciences, B
Drama and Dramatics/Theatre Arts, B
Ecology, B
Economics, B
Education, M
Elementary Education and Teaching, B
English Language and Literature, B
European Studies/Civilization, B
Finance, B
Fine/Studio Arts, B
French Language and Literature, B
History, B
Junior High/Intermediate/Middle School Education and Teaching, B
Kinesiology and Exercise Science, B
Marketing/Marketing Management, B
Mathematics, B
Multi-/Interdisciplinary Studies, B
Philosophy, B
Physics, B
Political Science and Government, B
Psychology, B
Reading Teacher Education, M
Religion/Religious Studies, B
Sociology, B
Spanish Language and Literature, B
Special Education and Teaching, M
Sport and Fitness Administration/Management, B

HAZARD COMMUNITY AND TECHNICAL COLLEGE

Business Administration and Management, A
Child Care Provider/Assistant, A
Computer and Information Sciences, A

Crafts/Craft Design, Folk Art and Artisanry, A
Liberal Arts and Sciences Studies and Humanities, A
Medical Administrative Assistant/Secretary, A
Medical Radiologic Technology/Science - Radiation Therapist, A
Multi-/Interdisciplinary Studies, A
Physical Therapist Assistant, A

HENDERSON COMMUNITY COLLEGE

Agricultural Production Operations, A
Business Administration and Management, A
Child Care Provider/Assistant, A
Clinical/Medical Laboratory Technician, A
Computer and Information Sciences, A
Electromechanical Technology/Electromechanical Engineering Technology, A
Liberal Arts and Sciences Studies and Humanities, A
Medical/Clinical Assistant, A
Social Work, A

HOPKINSVILLE COMMUNITY COLLEGE

Administrative Assistant and Secretarial Science, A
Agricultural Production Operations, A
Business Administration and Management, A
Child Care Provider/Assistant, A
Computer and Information Sciences, A
Criminal Justice/Law Enforcement Administration, A
Electrical, Electronic and Communications Engineering Technology/Technician, A
Executive Assistant/Executive Secretary, A
Human Services, A
Industrial Technology/Technician, A
Liberal Arts and Sciences Studies and Humanities, A
Multi-/Interdisciplinary Studies, A
Social Work, A

JEFFERSON COMMUNITY AND TECHNICAL COLLEGE

Accounting Technology/Technician and Bookkeeping, A
Aeronautics/Aviation/Aerospace Science and Technology, A
Audiovisual Communications Technologies/Technicians, A
Automobile/Automotive Mechanics Technology/Technician, A
Business Administration and Management, A
Chemical Technology/Technician, A
Communications Technology/Technician, A
Computer and Information Sciences, A
Criminal Justice/Law Enforcement Administration, A
Culinary Arts/Chef Training, A
Diagnostic Medical Sonography/Sonographer and Ultrasound Technician, A
Early Childhood Education and Teaching, A
Education, A
Electrical, Electronic and Communications Engineering Technology/Technician, A
Electrical, Electronics and Communications Engineering, A
Engineering Technology, A
Fire Science/Firefighting, A
Health Information/Medical Records Technology/Technician, A
Human Services, A
Information Technology, A
International/Global Studies, A
Nuclear Medical Technology/Technologist, A
Occupational Therapist Assistant, A
Office Management and Supervision, A
Physical Therapist Assistant, A
Radiologic Technology/Science - Radiographer, A
Real Estate, A
Respiratory Care Therapy/Therapist, A
Surgical Technology/Technologist, A
Welding Technology/Welder, A

KENTUCKY CHRISTIAN UNIVERSITY

Bible/Biblical Studies, B
Biology/Biological Sciences, B
Business Administration and Management, B
Elementary Education and Teaching, B

English/Language Arts Teacher Education, B
History, B
Humanities/Humanistic Studies, B
Junior High/Intermediate/Middle School Education and Teaching, B
Mathematics Teacher Education, B
Multi-/Interdisciplinary Studies, B
Music Performance, B
Pastoral Studies/Counseling, B
Psychology, B
Religion/Religious Studies, M
Religious/Sacred Music, B
Social Studies Teacher Education, B
Social Work, B
Theology and Religious Vocations, M

KENTUCKY MOUNTAIN BIBLE COLLEGE

Bible/Biblical Studies, AB
Elementary Education and Teaching, B
Missions/Missionary Studies and Missiology, B
Pastoral Studies/Counseling, B
Religious Education, B
Religious/Sacred Music, B
Theology and Religious Vocations, B
Theology/Theological Studies, B
Youth Ministry, B

KENTUCKY STATE UNIVERSITY

African Studies, B
Agriculture, B
Aquaculture, M
Biology/Biological Sciences, B
Business Administration, Management and Operations, M
Business/Commerce, B
Chemistry, B
Computer Science, M
Computer and Information Sciences, B
Criminal Justice/Safety Studies, B
Elementary Education and Teaching, B
English Language and Literature, B
Environmental Studies, M
Fine/Studio Arts, B
Human Development and Family Studies, B
Human Resources Development, M
Information Technology, B
International Development, M
Journalism, B
Liberal Arts and Sciences Studies and Humanities, AB
Management Information Systems and Services, M
Mathematics, B
Music, B
Non-Profit/Public/Organizational Management, M
Nursing, D
Physical Education Teaching and Coaching, B
Political Science and Government, B
Psychology, B
Public Administration, BM
Social Sciences, B
Social Work, B
Spanish Language and Literature, B
Special Education and Teaching, M

KENTUCKY WESLEYAN COLLEGE

Accounting, B
American/United States Studies/Civilization, B
Art Teacher Education, B
Art/Art Studies, General, B
Biology/Biological Sciences, B
Business Administration and Management, B
Business/Managerial Economics, B
Chemistry, B
Communication Studies/Speech Communication and Rhetoric, B
Computer and Information Sciences, B
Criminal Justice/Safety Studies, B
Drama and Dramatics/Theatre Arts, B
Elementary Education and Teaching, B
English Language and Literature, B
Fine Arts and Art Studies, B
General Studies, B
Graphic Design, B
Health Services/Allied Health/Health Sciences, B
History, B

Human Services, B
Junior High/Intermediate/Middle School Education and Teaching, B
Kinesiology and Exercise Science, B
Law and Legal Studies, B
Mathematics, B
Multi-/Interdisciplinary Studies, B
Music Performance, B
Music Teacher Education, B
Physical Education Teaching and Coaching, B
Physics, B
Political Science and Government, B
Psychology, B
Religion/Religious Studies, B
Religious/Sacred Music, B
Sociology, B
Spanish Language Teacher Education, B
Spanish Language and Literature, B
Sport and Fitness Administration/Management, B
Zoology/Animal Biology, B

LINDSEY WILSON COLLEGE

American/United States Studies/Civilization, B
Art Teacher Education, B
Biology Teacher Education, B
Biology/Biological Sciences, B
Business Administration and Management, B
Chemistry, A
Computer and Information Sciences, A
Counseling Psychology, MD
Counselor Education/School Counseling and Guidance Services, D
Criminal Justice/Law Enforcement Administration, B
Early Childhood Education and Teaching, A
Education, B
Educational Leadership and Administration, M
Elementary Education and Teaching, B
Engineering, A
English Language and Literature, B
Fine/Studio Arts, AB
Health Services/Allied Health/Health Sciences, A
History, AB
Human Development, M
Human Services, B
Internet and Interactive Multimedia, M
Junior High/Intermediate/Middle School Education and Teaching, B
Management Information Systems and Services, A
Mass Communication/Media Studies, B
Mathematics Teacher Education, B
Parks, Recreation, Leisure and Fitness Studies, B
Physical Education Teaching and Coaching, B
Pre-Dentistry Studies, B
Pre-Law Studies, B
Pre-Medicine/Pre-Medical Studies, B
Pre-Pharmacy Studies, B
Pre-Veterinary Studies, B
Psychology, B
Religious Education, B
Secondary Education and Teaching, B
Social Science Teacher Education, B

MADISONVILLE COMMUNITY COLLEGE

Accounting, A
Accounting Technology/Technician and Bookkeeping, A
Administrative Assistant and Secretarial Science, A
Banking and Financial Support Services, A
Biomedical Technology/Technician, A
Business Administration and Management, A
Computer Technology/Computer Systems Technology, A
Consumer Merchandising/Retailing Management, A
Criminal Justice/Police Science, A
Electrical, Electronic and Communications Engineering Technology/Technician, A
Information Science/Studies, A
Mechanical Engineering/Mechanical Technology/Technician, A
Occupational Therapist Assistant, A
Physical Therapist Assistant, A
Radiologic Technology/Science - Radiographer, A
Real Estate, A

Respiratory Care Therapy/Therapist, A

MAYSVILLE COMMUNITY AND TECHNICAL COLLEGE (MAYSVILLE)

Business Administration and Management, A
Computer and Information Sciences, A
Electromechanical Technology/Electromechanical Engineering Technology, A
Engineering Technology, A
Executive Assistant/Executive Secretary, A
Family Systems, A
Liberal Arts and Sciences Studies and Humanities, A
Machine Shop Technology/Assistant, A
Respiratory Care Therapy/Therapist, A
Welding Technology/Welder, A

MAYSVILLE COMMUNITY AND TECHNICAL COLLEGE (MOREHEAD)

Business Administration and Management, A
Business/Office Automation/Technology/Data Entry, A
Engineering Technology, A
Fire Protection and Safety Technology/Technician, A
General Studies, A
Information Technology, A
Machine Tool Technology/Machinist, A
Respiratory Care Therapy/Therapist, A

MIDWAY UNIVERSITY

Accounting, B
Biology/Biological Sciences, B
Business Administration and Management, AB
Business Administration, Management and Operations, M
Business/Commerce, AB
Computer and Information Sciences, AB
Data Processing and Data Processing Technology/Technician, B
Education, BM
Elementary Education and Teaching, B
English Language and Literature, B
Environmental Biology, B
Equestrian/Equine Studies, AB
Health/Health Care Administration/Management, B
Horse Husbandry/Equine Science and Management, B
Human Resources Management/Personnel Administration, B
Junior High/Intermediate/Middle School Education and Teaching, B
Liberal Arts and Sciences Studies and Humanities, B
Mathematics, B
Multi-/Interdisciplinary Studies, B
Organizational Behavior Studies, B
Organizational Management, M
Psychology, B
Secondary Education and Teaching, B
Security and Protective Services, B
Special Education and Teaching, B
Sport and Fitness Administration/Management, B

MOREHEAD STATE UNIVERSITY

Accounting, B
Adult and Continuing Education and Teaching, MO
Agricultural Sciences, M
Agriculture, B
Art Education, M
Biological and Biomedical Sciences, M
Biology/Biological Sciences, B
Biomedical Sciences, B
Business Administration and Management, B
Business Administration, Management and Operations, M
Business Education, M
Business Teacher Education, B
Business/Commerce, B
Business/Managerial Economics, B
Chemistry, B
Clinical Psychology, M
Communication and Media Studies, BM
Communication, Journalism and Related Programs, B
Computer and Information Sciences, B

Counseling Psychology, M
Counselor Education/School Counseling and Guidance Services, MO
Criminology, M
Curriculum and Instruction, O
Drama and Dramatics/Theatre Arts, B
Early Childhood Education and Teaching, B
Education, MO
Education/Teaching of the Gifted and Talented, M
Educational Administration and Supervision, M
Educational Leadership and Administration, MO
Educational Media/Instructional Technology, M
Elementary Education and Teaching, BM
Engineering, B
Engineering Technology, AB
Engineering/Industrial Management, B
English, M
English Education, M
English Language and Literature, B
Environmental Policy, M
Exercise and Sports Science, M
Experimental Psychology, M
Finance, B
Fine Arts and Art Studies, M
Fine/Studio Arts, B
Foreign Language Teacher Education, M
French Language and Literature, B
General Studies, AB
Geology/Earth Science, B
Gerontology, M
Graphic Design, M
Health Education, M
Health Teacher Education, B
Health and Physical Education, B
Higher Education/Higher Education Administration, MO
History, B
Industrial/Management Engineering, M
International and Comparative Education, M
International/Global Studies, B
Junior High/Intermediate/Middle School Education and Teaching, B
Kinesiology and Exercise Science, B
Law and Legal Studies, B
Legal Assistant/Paralegal, B
Management Information Systems and Services, ABM
Manufacturing Technology/Technician, AB
Marketing/Marketing Management, B
Mathematics, B
Mathematics Teacher Education, M
Medical Radiologic Technology/Science - Radiation Therapist, AB
Middle School Education, M
Music, B
Music Teacher Education, M
Performance, M
Philosophy, B
Physical Education Teaching and Coaching, BM
Physics, B
Political Science and Government, B
Psychology, BM
Public Administration, M
Public Policy Analysis, BM
Reading Teacher Education, M
Respiratory Care Therapy/Therapist, A
Science Teacher Education/General Science Teacher Education, M
Secondary Education and Teaching, M
Social Sciences, B
Social Studies Teacher Education, M
Social Work, B
Sociology, BM
Spanish Language and Literature, B
Special Education and Teaching, BM
Sport and Fitness Administration/Management, BM
Veterinary/Animal Health Technology/Technician and Veterinary Assistant, AB
Vocational and Technical Education, M

MURRAY STATE UNIVERSITY

Accounting, BM
Advertising, B
Agricultural Education, M
Agricultural Sciences, M

Agriculture, Agriculture Operations and Related Sciences, AB
Athletic Training and Sports Medicine, B
Audiology/Audiologist and Speech-Language Pathology/Pathologist, B
Biological and Biomedical Sciences, MD
Biology/Biological Sciences, B
Business Administration and Management, B
Business Administration, Management and Operations, M
Business/Commerce, AB
CAD/CADD Drafting and/or Design Technology/Technician, B
Chemistry, BM
Civil Engineering Technology/Technician, AB
Clinical Psychology, M
Communication Disorders, M
Community Health and Preventive Medicine, B
Computer Science, B
Corporate and Organizational Communication, M
Counselor Education/School Counseling and Guidance Services, MO
Criminal Justice/Safety Studies, B
Drama and Dramatics/Theatre Arts, B
Early Childhood Education and Teaching, BM
Economics, BM
Education, MDO
Educational Administration and Supervision, MO
Electromechanical Technology/Electromechanical Engineering Technology, B
Elementary Education and Teaching, BMO
Engineering Physics, B
English, M
English Language and Literature, B
English as a Second Language, M
Environmental Sciences, M
Environmental and Occupational Health, M
Exercise and Sports Science, M
Finance, B
Fine/Studio Arts, B
Foods, Nutrition, and Wellness Studies, B
French Language and Literature, B
General Studies, B
Geology/Earth Science, B
Geosciences, M
German Language and Literature, B
Graphic Communications, B
Health Information/Medical Records Administration/Administrator, B
Health Teacher Education, B
History, BM
Human Services, M
Hydrology and Water Resources Science, M
Industrial Hygiene, M
Industrial Technology/Technician, A
Information Science/Studies, B
Information Technology, B
International Business/Trade/Commerce, B
International Relations and Affairs, B
Japanese Language and Literature, B
Journalism, B
Junior High/Intermediate/Middle School Education and Teaching, B
Kinesiology and Exercise Science, B
Leisure Studies, M
Liberal Arts and Sciences Studies and Humanities, AB
Logistics and Materials Management, B
Management of Technology, M
Manufacturing Technology/Technician, B
Marketing/Marketing Management, B
Mass Communication/Media Studies, M
Mathematics, BM
Middle School Education, MO
Music, BM
Music Teacher Education, M
Nurse Anesthetist, M
Nursing, M
Nursing - Advanced Practice, M
Occupational Safety and Health Technology/Technician, B
Organizational Communication, B
Philosophy, B
Physical Education Teaching and Coaching, M
Physics, B
Political Science and Government, B

Psychology, BM
Public Administration, B
Public Affairs, M
Public Relations/Image Management, B
Radio and Television, B
Reading Teacher Education, MO
Safety Engineering, M
Secondary Education and Teaching, MO
Social Work, B
Sociology, B
Spanish Language and Literature, B
Special Education and Teaching, BM
Statistics, M
Teacher Education and Professional Development, Specific Subject Areas, B
Telecommunications Management, M
Trade and Industrial Teacher Education, AB
Veterinary/Animal Health Technology/Technician and Veterinary Assistant, B
Vocational and Technical Education, M
Wildlife and Wildlands Science and Management, B
Writing, M
Youth Services/Administration, B

NORTHERN KENTUCKY UNIVERSITY

Accounting, BMO
Advertising and Public Relations, O
Allied Health and Medical Assisting Services, M
Anthropology, B
Architectural Engineering Technology/Technician, B
Athletic Training and Sports Medicine, B
Biology/Biological Sciences, B
Broadcast Journalism, B
Business Administration and Management, B
Business Administration, Management and Operations, MO
Business Teacher Education, B
Business/Commerce, B
Business/Managerial Economics, B
Chemistry, B
Clinical Psychology, M
Commercial and Advertising Art, B
Communication Studies/Speech Communication and Rhetoric, B
Communication and Media Studies, MO
Composition, O
Computer Science, MO
Computer and Information Sciences, B
Computer and Information Sciences and Support Services, B
Computer and Information Systems Security, O
Construction Management, B
Counseling Psychology, M
Counselor Education/School Counseling and Guidance Services, M
Criminal Justice/Safety Studies, B
Cultural Studies, O
Drama and Dramatics/Theatre Arts, B
Education, MDO
Educational Leadership and Administration, MDO
Electrical, Electronic and Communications Engineering Technology/Technician, B
Elementary Education and Teaching, B
English, MO
English Language and Literature, B
Entrepreneurship/Entrepreneurial Studies, B
Environmental Sciences, B
Finance, B
Fine/Studio Arts, B
Foreign Language Teacher Education, B
French Language and Literature, B
General Studies, AB
Geographic Information Systems, O
Geography, B
Geology/Earth Science, B
German Language and Literature, B
Health Informatics, MO
Health Psychology, O
Health Services/Allied Health/Health Sciences, B
History, B
Human Resources Development, B
Industrial and Organizational Psychology, MO
Information Science/Studies, BMO
Information Technology, B
International Relations and Affairs, B
Journalism, B

Junior High/Intermediate/Middle School Education and Teaching, B
Kindergarten/PreSchool Education and Teaching, B
Law and Legal Studies, D
Liberal Arts and Sciences Studies and Humanities, AB
Liberal Studies, M
Management, M
Management Information Systems and Services, B
Management of Technology, M
Manufacturing Technology/Technician, B
Marketing/Marketing Management, B
Marriage and Family Therapy/Counseling, O
Mathematics, B
Media Studies, O
Mental and Social Health Services and Allied Professions, B
Music, B
Music Teacher Education, B
Non-Profit/Public/Organizational Management, O
Nursing, MDO
Organizational Behavior Studies, B
Organizational Management, M
Philosophy, B
Physical Education Teaching and Coaching, B
Physics, B
Political Science and Government, B
Psychology, B
Public Administration, MO
Public History, M
Public Relations/Image Management, B
Radiologic Technology/Science - Radiographer, B
Respiratory Care Therapy/Therapist, B
Rhetoric, O
Secondary Education and Teaching, B
Social Sciences, B
Social Work, BM
Sociology, B
Software Engineering, O
Spanish Language and Literature, B
Special Education and Teaching, BO
Sport and Fitness Administration/Management, B
Statistics, B
Taxation, O
Writing, O

OWENSBORO COMMUNITY AND TECHNICAL COLLEGE

Agricultural Production Operations, A
Applied Horticulture/Horticultural Operations, A
Automobile/Automotive Mechanics Technology/Technician, A
Business Administration and Management, A
Child Care Provider/Assistant, A
Computer and Information Sciences, A
Construction Trades, A
Criminal Justice/Law Enforcement Administration, A
Diesel Mechanics Technology/Technician, A
Drama and Dramatics/Theatre Arts, A
Electrical and Electronic Engineering Technologies/Technicians, A
Electrician, A
Emergency Medical Technology/Technician (EMT Paramedic), A
Executive Assistant/Executive Secretary, A
Fine/Studio Arts, A
Fire Science/Firefighting, A
Health and Medical Administrative Services, A
Human Services, A
Liberal Arts and Sciences Studies and Humanities, A
Machine Shop Technology/Assistant, A
Mechanics and Repairers, A
Medical Administrative Assistant/Secretary, A
Multi-/Interdisciplinary Studies, A
Precision Production Trades, A
Radiologic Technology/Science - Radiographer, A
Surgical Technology/Technologist, A
Veterinary/Animal Health Technology/Technician and Veterinary Assistant, A

SOMERSET COMMUNITY COLLEGE

Aircraft Powerplant Technology/Technician, A
Business Administration and Management, A
Child Care Provider/Assistant, A
Clinical/Medical Laboratory Assistant, A

Computer and Information Sciences, A
Criminal Justice/Law Enforcement Administration, A
Engineering Technology, A
Executive Assistant/Executive Secretary, A
Industrial Mechanics and Maintenance Technology, A
Liberal Arts and Sciences Studies and Humanities, A
Medical Administrative Assistant/Secretary, A
Medical Radiologic Technology/Science - Radiation Therapist, A
Multi-/Interdisciplinary Studies, A
Physical Therapist Assistant, A
Respiratory Care Therapy/Therapist, A
Surgical Technology/Technologist, A
Teacher Assistant/Aide, A

SOUTHCENTRAL KENTUCKY COMMUNITY AND TECHNICAL COLLEGE

Automobile/Automotive Mechanics Technology/Technician, A
Computer and Information Sciences, A
Culinary Arts/Chef Training, A
Electromechanical Technology/Electromechanical Engineering Technology, A
Engineering Technology, A
Fire Science/Firefighting, A
Industrial Mechanics and Maintenance Technology, A
Medical Radiologic Technology/Science - Radiation Therapist, A
Multi-/Interdisciplinary Studies, A
Respiratory Therapy Technician/Assistant, A

SOUTHEAST KENTUCKY COMMUNITY AND TECHNICAL COLLEGE

Administrative Assistant and Secretarial Science, A
Business Administration and Management, A
Clinical/Medical Laboratory Technician, A
Computer Engineering Technology/Technician, A
Computer/Information Technology Services Administration and Management, A
Criminal Justice/Police Science, A
Data Processing and Data Processing Technology/Technician, A
Information Technology, A
Liberal Arts and Sciences Studies and Humanities, A
Management Information Systems and Services, A
Medical Radiologic Technology/Science - Radiation Therapist, A
Physical Therapist Assistant, A
Respiratory Care Therapy/Therapist, A

THE SOUTHERN BAPTIST THEOLOGICAL SEMINARY

Bible/Biblical Studies, B
Christian Studies, B
Divinity/Ministry (BD, MDiv.), B
Missions/Missionary Studies and Missiology, BMD
Pastoral Studies/Counseling, BMD
Philosophy, M
Religion/Religious Studies, M
Theology and Religious Vocations, MD
Youth Ministry, B

SPALDING UNIVERSITY

Accounting, B
Accounting and Business/Management, B
Applied Behavior Analysis, M
Art Education, M
Athletic Training and Sports Medicine, M
Biological and Physical Sciences, B
Business Education, M
Business/Commerce, AB
Clinical Psychology, MD
Communication Studies/Speech Communication and Rhetoric, B
Corporate and Organizational Communication, M
Counselor Education/School Counseling and Guidance Services, M
Early Childhood Education and Teaching, B
Education, BMD
Educational Administration and Supervision, M
Educational Leadership and Administration, D

Elementary Education and Teaching, BM
Emergency Medical Technology/Technician (EMT Paramedic), A
Fine/Studio Arts, B
Foreign Language Teacher Education, M
General Studies, B
Health Services/Allied Health/Health Sciences, B
Humanities/Humanistic Studies, B
Junior High/Intermediate/Middle School Education and Teaching, B
Liberal Arts and Sciences Studies and Humanities, B
Mass Communication/Media Studies, B
Middle School Education, M
Nursing, MDO
Nursing - Adult, MO
Nursing - Advanced Practice, MO
Nursing Administration, M
Occupational Therapy/Therapist, BM
Pediatric Nurse/Nursing, MO
Psychology, BMD
Secondary Education and Teaching, BM
Social Sciences, B
Social Work, BM
Special Education and Teaching, BM
Teacher Education, Multiple Levels, B
Writing, M

SPENCERIAN COLLEGE

Clinical Laboratory Science/Medical Technology/Technologist, B
Clinical/Medical Laboratory Technician, A
Massage Therapy/Therapeutic Massage, A
Medical Insurance Coding Specialist/Coder, A
Radiologic Technology/Science - Radiographer, AB
Respiratory Care Therapy/Therapist, A
Surgical Technology/Technologist, A

SPENCERIAN COLLEGE–LEXINGTON

Clinical/Medical Laboratory Technician, A
Medical Office Management/Administration, A
Radiologic Technology/Science - Radiographer, A

SULLIVAN COLLEGE OF TECHNOLOGY AND DESIGN

Animation, Interactive Technology, Video Graphics and Special Effects, AB
Architectural Drafting and Architectural CAD/CADD, A
Architectural Engineering Technology/Technician, A
Architecture and Related Services, A
Artificial Intelligence and Robotics, AB
CAD/CADD Drafting and/or Design Technology/Technician, A
Civil Drafting and Civil Engineering CAD/CADD, A
Computer Engineering Technology/Technician, A
Computer Graphics, AB
Computer Hardware Engineering, A
Computer Hardware Technology/Technician, A
Computer Installation and Repair Technology/Technician, A
Computer Programming, Vendor/Product Certification, A
Computer Systems Networking and Telecommunications, A
Computer Technology/Computer Systems Technology, A
Computer and Information Sciences, A
Computer and Information Sciences and Support Services, A
Computer and Information Systems Security, AB
Digital Communication and Media/Multimedia, AB
Drafting and Design Technology/Technician, A
Drafting/Design Engineering Technologies/Technicians, A
Electrical and Electronic Engineering Technologies/Technicians, A
Electrical, Electronic and Communications Engineering Technology/Technician, A
Electrical/Electronics Equipment Installation and Repair, A
Electrical/Electronics Maintenance and Repair Technology, AB
Electromechanical and Instrumentation and Maintenance Technologies/Technicians, AB
Engineering Technologies/Technicians, A

Engineering Technology, A
Graphic Communications, AB
Graphic Design, AB
Graphic and Printing Equipment Operator Production, A
Heating, Air Conditioning and Refrigeration Technology/Technician, A
Housing and Human Environments, A
Industrial Electronics Technology/Technician, AB
Industrial Mechanics and Maintenance Technology, AB
Information Technology, AB
Interior Design, AB
Manufacturing Technology/Technician, AB
Mechanical Drafting and Mechanical Drafting CAD/CADD, A
Mechanical Engineering/Mechanical Technology/Technician, A
Prepress/Desktop Publishing and Digital Imaging Design, AB
Robotics Technology/Technician, AB
System Administration/Administrator, AB
Web Page, Digital/Multimedia and Information Resources Design, AB

SULLIVAN UNIVERSITY

Accounting, B
Accounting Technology/Technician and Bookkeeping, A
Baking and Pastry Arts/Baker/Pastry Chef, A
Business Administration and Management, AB
Business Administration, Management and Operations, MD
Business/Commerce, B
Criminal Justice/Police Science, A
Criminal Justice/Safety Studies, B
Culinary Arts/Chef Training, A
Early Childhood Education and Teaching, A
Executive Assistant/Executive Secretary, A
Health Information/Medical Records Administration/Administrator, B
Health Information/Medical Records Technology/Technician, A
Hospitality Administration/Management, B
Human Resources Management/Personnel Administration, B
Information Technology, B
Legal Administrative Assistant/Secretary, A
Legal Assistant/Paralegal, AB
Logistics and Materials Management, A
Medical Office Assistant/Specialist, A
Medical/Clinical Assistant, A
Pharmacy Technician/Assistant, A
Sales, Distribution and Marketing Operations, A

THOMAS MORE COLLEGE

Accounting, AB
Art History, Criticism and Conservation, AB
Art Teacher Education, B
Athletic Training and Sports Medicine, B
Biochemistry, B
Biology/Biological Sciences, AB
Business Administration and Management, AB
Business Administration, Management and Operations, M
Business Teacher Education, B
Business/Commerce, A
Chemistry, AB
Clinical Laboratory Science/Medical Technology/Technologist, B
Criminal Justice/Safety Studies, AB
Drama and Dramatics/Theatre Arts, AB
Economics, AB
Education, BM
Educational Leadership and Administration, M
Elementary Education and Teaching, B
English Language and Literature, AB
Environmental Sciences, B
Fine/Studio Arts, AB
Forensic Science and Technology, B
French Language and Literature, A
Gerontology, A
Health/Health Care Administration/Management, B
History, AB
Humanities/Humanistic Studies, AB
Information Technology, AB

International/Global Studies, AB
Junior High/Intermediate/Middle School Education and Teaching, B
Law and Legal Studies, B
Liberal Arts and Sciences Studies and Humanities, AB
Mathematics, AB
Multi-/Interdisciplinary Studies, B
Music, A
Philosophy, AB
Physics, AB
Political Science and Government, AB
Pre-Law Studies, A
Psychology, AB
Public Administration and Social Service Professions, A
Religion/Religious Studies, AB
Secondary Education and Teaching, B
Sociology, AB
Spanish Language and Literature, AB
Sport and Fitness Administration/Management, B
Web Page, Digital/Multimedia and Information Resources Design, AB

TRANSYLVANIA UNIVERSITY

Accounting, B
Anthropology, B
Art History, Criticism and Conservation, B
Art Teacher Education, B
Art/Art Studies, General, B
Biology/Biological Sciences, B
Business/Commerce, B
Chemistry, B
Chemistry Teacher Education, B
Classics and Classical Languages, Literatures, and Linguistics, B
Computer and Information Sciences, B
Drama and Dramatics/Theatre Arts, B
Economics, B
Elementary Education and Teaching, B
English Language and Literature, B
French Language and Literature, B
German Language and Literature, B
History, B
Junior High/Intermediate/Middle School Education and Teaching, B
Kinesiology and Exercise Science, B
Mathematics, B
Music Performance, B
Music Teacher Education, B
Philosophy, B
Physical Education Teaching and Coaching, B
Physics, B
Political Science and Government, B
Psychology, B
Religion/Religious Studies, B
Social and Philosophical Foundations of Education, B
Sociology, B
Spanish Language and Literature, B

UNION COLLEGE

Accounting, B
Athletic Training and Sports Medicine, B
Biology/Biological Sciences, B
Business Administration and Management, B
Chemistry, B
Clinical Psychology, M
Counseling Psychology, M
Criminal Justice/Law Enforcement Administration, B
Education, BM
Educational Administration and Supervision, M
Educational Leadership and Administration, M
Elementary Education and Teaching, BM
English Language and Literature, B
Health Education, M
Health Teacher Education, B
History, B
Information Technology, B
Junior High/Intermediate/Middle School Education and Teaching, B
Kinesiology and Exercise Science, B
Marketing/Marketing Management, B
Mass Communication/Media Studies, B
Mathematics, B
Middle School Education, M

Music Teacher Education, M
Office Management and Supervision, B
Parks, Recreation and Leisure Facilities Management, B
Physical Education Teaching and Coaching, BM
Psychology, BM
Reading Teacher Education, M
Religion/Religious Studies, B
School Psychology, M
Science Teacher Education/General Science Teacher Education, B
Secondary Education and Teaching, M
Social Studies Teacher Education, B
Social Work, B
Sociology, B
Special Education and Teaching, M
Sport and Fitness Administration/Management, B
Visual and Performing Arts, B

UNIVERSITY OF THE CUMBERLANDS

Accounting, BM
Art Teacher Education, B
Biology/Biological Sciences, B
Business Administration and Management, AB
Business Administration, Management and Operations, M
Business Education, M
Chemistry, B
Christian Studies, B
Clinical Psychology, D
Communication Studies/Speech Communication and Rhetoric, B
Counseling Psychology, M
Counselor Education/School Counseling and Guidance Services, MD
Criminal Justice/Safety Studies, AB
Drama and Dramatics/Theatre Arts, B
Education, MDO
Educational Administration and Supervision, O
Educational Leadership and Administration, MDO
Elementary Education and Teaching, BM
English Language and Literature, B
Fine/Studio Arts, B
French Language Teacher Education, B
French Language and Literature, B
General Studies, B
Health Teacher Education, B
Health and Physical Education, B
History, B
Human Services, AB
Journalism, B
Junior High/Intermediate/Middle School Education and Teaching, B
Management Information Systems and Services, B
Marketing, M
Mathematics, B
Middle School Education, M
Missions/Missionary Studies and Missiology, AB
Music, B
Music Teacher Education, B
Physical Education Teaching and Coaching, B
Physician Assistant, M
Physics, B
Political Science and Government, B
Psychology, AB
Public Health (MPH, DPH), B
Reading Teacher Education, M
Religion/Religious Studies, M
Religious/Sacred Music, B
Secondary Education and Teaching, BM
Social Studies Teacher Education, B
Spanish Language Teacher Education, B
Spanish Language and Literature, B
Special Education and Teaching, BMO
Speech Teacher Education, B
Sport and Fitness Administration/Management, B
Student Personnel Services, O
Theater, M

UNIVERSITY OF KENTUCKY

Accounting, BM
Agricultural Economics, BMD
Agricultural Engineering, MD
Agricultural Public Services, B
Agricultural Sciences, MD

Agricultural/Biological Engineering and Bioengineering, B
Agriculture, Agriculture Operations and Related Sciences, B
Agronomy and Crop Science, B
Agronomy and Soil Sciences, MD
Allied Health and Medical Assisting Services, MD
Allopathic Medicine, D
Anatomy, D
Animal Sciences, BMD
Anthropology, BMD
Apparel and Textiles, B
Applied Mathematics, M
Architecture, BM
Art Education, M
Art History, Criticism and Conservation, BM
Art Teacher Education, B
Arts Management, M
Astronomy, MD
Athletic Training and Sports Medicine, M
Audiology/Audiologist and Speech-Language Pathology/Pathologist, B
BioTechnology, B
Biochemistry, D
Biological and Biomedical Sciences, MD
Biology/Biological Sciences, B
Biomedical Engineering, MD
Biostatistics, D
Business Administration, Management and Operations, MD
Business/Commerce, B
Business/Managerial Economics, B
Chemical Engineering, BMD
Chemistry, BMD
Child and Family Studies, MD
Chinese Language and Literature, B
Civil Engineering, BMD
Classics and Classical Languages, Literatures, and Linguistics, BM
Clinical Laboratory Science/Medical Technology/Technologist, B
Clinical Research, M
Communication Disorders, M
Communication Studies/Speech Communication and Rhetoric, B
Communication and Media Studies, MD
Composition, MD
Computer Engineering, B
Computer Science, MD
Computer and Information Sciences, B
Consumer Economics, B
Counseling Psychology, MDO
Curriculum and Instruction, MD
Dentistry, D
Design and Applied Arts, M
Drama and Dramatics/Theatre Arts, B
Early Childhood Education and Teaching, BM
Economics, BMD
Education, MDO
Educational Leadership and Administration, MDO
Educational Measurement and Evaluation, MD
Educational Media/Instructional Technology, M
Educational Policy, MD
Educational Psychology, MDO
Electrical Engineering, MD
Electrical, Electronics and Communications Engineering, B
Elementary Education and Teaching, BM
Engineering and Applied Sciences, MD
English, MD
English Language and Literature, B
Entomology, MD
Environmental Studies, B
Epidemiology, D
Ethnic, Cultural Minority, and Gender Studies, B
Exercise and Sports Science, MD
Family and Consumer Sciences/Human Sciences, B
Finance, B
Fine Arts and Art Studies, M
Fine/Studio Arts, B
Food Science, B
Food Science and Technology, MD
Foods, Nutrition, and Wellness Studies, B
Foreign Language Teacher Education, M
Forest Sciences and Biology, B
Forestry, M

French Language and Literature, B
General Studies, B
Geography, BMD
Geology/Earth Science, BMD
German Language and Literature, BM
Gerontology, DO
Health Physics/Radiological Health, M
Health Promotion, MD
Health Services Administration, M
Health Services/Allied Health/Health Sciences, B
Health Teacher Education, B
Health/Health Care Administration/Management, B
Higher Education/Higher Education Administration, MD
Hispanic Studies, MD
Historic Preservation and Conservation, M
History, BMD
Horse Husbandry/Equine Science and Management, B
Hospitality Administration/Management, BM
Human Development and Family Studies, B
Human Nutrition, B
Immunology, D
Information Science/Studies, BM
Interior Design, BM
International Affairs, M
International Business/Trade/Commerce, M
International/Global Studies, B
Japanese Language and Literature, B
Journalism, B
Junior High/Intermediate/Middle School Education and Teaching, B
Kinesiology and Movement Studies, MD
Landscape Architecture, B
Latin American Studies, B
Law and Legal Studies, D
Library Science, M
Linguistic, Comparative, and Related Language Studies and Services, B
Linguistics, B
Management Science, B
Manufacturing Engineering, M
Marketing/Marketing Management, B
Materials Engineering, BMD
Materials Sciences, MD
Mathematics, BMD
Mechanical Engineering, BMD
Medical Microbiology and Bacteriology, B
Medical Physics, M
Microbiology, D
Middle School Education, M
Mineral/Mining Engineering, MD
Mining and Mineral Engineering, B
Multi-/Interdisciplinary Studies, B
Music, MD
Music History, Literature, and Theory, B
Music Performance, B
Music Teacher Education, BMD
Music Theory and Composition, MD
Music Therapy/Therapist, M
Musicology and Ethnomusicology, MD
Natural Resources and Conservation, B
Neurobiology and Neurophysiology, D
Nursing, D
Nutritional Sciences, MD
Oral and Dental Sciences, M
Performance, MD
Pharmaceutical Sciences, MD
Pharmacology, D
Pharmacy, BD
Philosophy, BMD
Physical Education Teaching and Coaching, BMD
Physical Therapy/Therapist, D
Physician Assistant, BM
Physics, BMD
Physiology, D
Plant Pathology/Phytopathology, MD
Plant Sciences, MD
Political Science and Government, BMD
Psychology, BMD
Public Administration, MD
Public Health, MD
Public Health (MPH, DPH), B
Public Policy Analysis, MD
Radio and Television, B
Reading Teacher Education, M

Rehabilitation Counseling, MD
Rehabilitation Sciences, D
Russian Language and Literature, B
Sacred Music, M
School Psychology, DO
Science Teacher Education/General Science
  Teacher Education, B
Secondary Education and Teaching, M
Social Studies Teacher Education, B
Social Work, BMD
Sociology, BMD
Spanish Language and Literature, B
Special Education and Teaching, BMD
Statistics, MD
Teacher Education and Professional Develop-
  ment, Specific Subject Areas, B
Technical Teacher Education, B
Toxicology, MD
Veterinary Sciences, MD

UNIVERSITY OF LOUISVILLE

Accounting, BM
African Studies, M
African-American Studies, M
African-American/Black Studies, B
Allopathic Medicine, D
Analytical Chemistry, MD
Anatomy, MD
Anthropology, BM
Applied Mathematics, D
Art Education, M
Art History, Criticism and Conservation, BMD
Asian Studies/Civilization, BO
Atmospheric Sciences and Meteorology, B
Biochemistry, MD
Bioengineering, M
Biological and Biomedical Sciences, M
Biology/Biological Sciences, B
Biomedical/Medical Engineering, B
Biophysics, MD
Biostatistics, MD
Business Administration, Management and Opera-
  tions, BM
Business/Managerial Economics, B
Chemical Engineering, BMD
Chemical Physics, D
Chemistry, BMD
Civil Engineering, BMDO
Clinical Psychology, D
Clinical Research, MO
Communication Disorders, MD
Communication Studies/Speech Communication
  and Rhetoric, B
Communication and Media Studies, M
Community Health and Preventive Medicine, M
Composition, M
Computer Engineering, BMDO
Computer Science, MDO
Computer and Information Systems Security, O
Counselor Education/School Counseling and Guid-
  ance Services, MD
Criminal Justice/Law Enforcement Administration, B
Criminology, MD
Curriculum and Instruction, D
Dental Hygiene/Hygienist, B
Dentistry, MD
Drama and Dramatics/Theatre Arts, B
Early Childhood Education and Teaching, M
Economics, B
Education, MDO
Educational Administration and Supervision, MO
Educational Leadership and Administration, MD
Educational Psychology, MD
Electrical Engineering, MD
Electrical, Electronics and Communications Engi-
  neering, B
Elementary Education and Teaching, BM
Engineering Management, M
Engineering and Applied Sciences, MDO
English, MD
English Language and Literature, B
Entrepreneurship/Entrepreneurial Studies, MD
Environmental Biology, D
Environmental Engineering
  Technology/Environmental Technology, MDO
Environmental and Occupational Health, MD

Epidemiology, MD
Exercise and Sports Science, M
Experimental Psychology, D
Finance, B
Fine Arts and Art Studies, M
Fine/Studio Arts, B
French Language and Literature, BM
Geography, BM
Gerontology, M
Health Education, M
Health Promotion, D
Health Services Administration, MD
Health and Physical Education, B
Higher Education/Higher Education Administra-
  tion, M
History, BMO
Human Resources Development, M
Human Resources Management and Services, M
Humanities/Humanistic Studies, BMD
Immunology, MD
Industrial Engineering, B
Industrial/Management Engineering, MD
Inorganic Chemistry, MD
Interdisciplinary Studies, MD
International Business/Trade/Commerce, M
Latin American Studies, B
Law and Legal Studies, D
Legal Assistant/Paralegal, A
Liberal Arts and Sciences Studies and Humani-
  ties, B
Logistics and Materials Management, O
Management Information Systems and Services, B
Marketing/Marketing Management, B
Marriage and Family Therapy/Counseling, DO
Maternal/Child Health and Neonatal
  Nurse/Nursing, M
Mathematics, BMD
Mechanical Engineering, BMD
Microbiology, MD
Middle School Education, M
Molecular Biology, MD
Museology/Museum Studies, M
Music, B
Music History, Literature, and Theory, M
Music Teacher Education, BM
Music Theory and Composition, M
Music Therapy/Therapist, B
Neurobiology and Neurophysiology, MD
Non-Profit/Public/Organizational Management, M
Nursing, MD
Nursing - Adult, M
Nursing - Advanced Practice, M
Oral Biology, M
Organic Chemistry, MD
Pharmacology, MD
Philosophy, BM
Physical Chemistry, MD
Physical Education Teaching and Coaching, M
Physics, BMD
Physiology, MD
Political Science and Government, BM
Psychiatric/Mental Health Nurse/Nursing, M
Psychology, BD
Public Administration, M
Public Affairs, D
Public Health, D
Public Health (MPH, DPH), B
Public History, O
Public Policy Analysis, M
Rhetoric, MD
Secondary Education and Teaching, M
Sign Language Interpretation and Translation, B
Social Work, BMDO
Sociology, BMD
Spanish Language and Literature, BM
Special Education and Teaching, M
Sport and Fitness Administration/Management, BM
Student Personnel Services, M
Substance Abuse/Addiction Counseling, M
Supply Chain Management, O
Teacher Education, Multiple Levels, B
Theater, M
Toxicology, MD
Trade and Industrial Teacher Education, B
Urban Planning, M
Urban Studies/Affairs, D

Veterinary Sciences, O
Women's Studies, BMO
Writing, M

UNIVERSITY OF PIKEVILLE

Art/Art Studies, General, B
Biology/Biological Sciences, B
Business Administration and Management, AB
Business Administration, Management and Opera-
  tions, M
Chemistry, B
Communication Studies/Speech Communication
  and Rhetoric, B
Computer and Information Sciences, B
Criminal Justice/Safety Studies, AB
Elementary Education and Teaching, B
English Language and Literature, B
Film/Cinema Studies, B
History, B
Junior High/Intermediate/Middle School Education
  and Teaching, B
Mathematics, B
Multi-/Interdisciplinary Studies, B
Osteopathic Medicine, D
Psychology, B
Religion/Religious Studies, B
Social Work, B
Sociology, B
Spanish Language and Literature, B

WEST KENTUCKY COMMUNITY AND TECHNICAL COLLEGE

Accounting, A
Business Administration and Management, A
Computer and Information Sciences, A
Court Reporting/Court Reporter, A
Criminal Justice/Law Enforcement Administration, A
Culinary Arts/Chef Training, A
Diagnostic Medical Sonography/Sonographer and
  Ultrasound Technician, A
Electrician, A
Fire Science/Firefighting, A
Machine Shop Technology/Assistant, A
Physical Therapist Assistant, A
Respiratory Care Therapy/Therapist, A
Surgical Technology/Technologist, A

WESTERN KENTUCKY UNIVERSITY

Accounting, B
Adult and Continuing Education and Teaching, M
Advertising, B
Agricultural Production Operations, A
Agricultural Sciences, M
Agriculture, B
Anthropology, BM
Apparel and Textiles, B
Applied Economics, M
Arabic Language and Literature, B
Architectural Technology/Technician, B
Art Education, M
Art History, Criticism and Conservation, B
Asian Studies/Civilization, B
Biochemistry, B
Biological and Biomedical Sciences, M
Biology/Biological Sciences, B
Broadcast Journalism, B
Business Administration and Management, AB
Business Administration, Management and Opera-
  tions, M
Business Teacher Education, B
Business/Managerial Economics, B
Cartography, B
Chemistry, BM
Chinese Language and Literature, B
Civil Engineering, B
Clinical Laboratory Science/Medical
  Technology/Technologist, B
Clinical Psychology, M
Communication Disorders, BM
Communication Studies/Speech Communication
  and Rhetoric, B
Communication and Media Studies, MO
Community Health and Preventive Medicine, B
Comparative Literature, B
Computational Sciences, M
Computer Science, M

Computer and Information Sciences, B
Construction Engineering Technology/Technician, B
Corporate and Organizational Communication, O
Counseling Psychology, M
Counselor Education/School Counseling and Guidance Services, M
Criminology, BM
Dance, B
Dental Hygiene/Hygienist, AB
Drama and Dramatics/Theatre Arts, B
Dramatic/Theatre Arts and Stagecraft, B
Early Childhood Education and Teaching, ABM
Econometrics and Quantitative Economics, B
Economics, B
Educational Administration and Supervision, MDO
Educational Media/Instructional Technology, M
Electrical, Electronics and Communications Engineering, B
Elementary Education and Teaching, BMO
Emergency Medical Technology/Technician (EMT Paramedic), A
English, M
English Education, M
English Language and Literature, B
English as a Second Language, M
Entrepreneurship/Entrepreneurial Studies, B
Environmental Health, B
Ethnic, Cultural Minority, and Gender Studies, B
Experimental Psychology, M
Family and Consumer Sciences/Home Economics Teacher Education, B
Finance, B
Fine/Studio Arts, B
Foreign Language Teacher Education, M
French Language and Literature, BM
General Studies, AB
Geography, B
Geology/Earth Science, BM
Geosciences, M
German Language and Literature, BM
Health Information/Medical Records Administration/Administrator, B
Health Information/Medical Records Technology/Technician, A
Health Services Administration, M
Health Services/Allied Health/Health Sciences, B
Health/Health Care Administration/Management, B
Higher Education/Higher Education Administration, M
History, BM
Homeland Security, M
Hospitality Administration/Management, B
Industrial Technology/Technician, B
Industrial and Organizational Psychology, M
Information Technology, B
Interdisciplinary Studies, M
International Business/Trade/Commerce, B
International Relations and Affairs, B
Journalism, B
Junior High/Intermediate/Middle School Education and Teaching, B
Kinesiology and Exercise Science, B
Legal Assistant/Paralegal, AB
Management Information Systems and Services, B
Management Science, B
Management of Technology, M
Manufacturing Technology/Technician, B
Marketing/Marketing Management, B
Marriage and Family Therapy/Counseling, M
Mathematics, BM
Mechanical Engineering, B
Meteorology, B
Middle School Education, M
Multi-/Interdisciplinary Studies, B
Music, B
Music Performance, B
Music Teacher Education, M
Nursing, M
Organizational Communication, B
Parks, Recreation and Leisure Facilities Management, B
Photojournalism, B
Physical Education Teaching and Coaching, BM
Physical Sciences, B
Physical Therapy/Therapist, D
Physics, BM

Political Science and Government, BM
Psychology, BMO
Public Administration, M
Public Health, M
Public Relations/Image Management, B
Radio and Television, B
Reading Teacher Education, M
Recreation and Park Management, M
Religion/Religious Studies, B
School Psychology, O
Secondary Education and Teaching, MO
Social Sciences, B
Social Work, BM
Sociology, BM
Spanish Language and Literature, BM
Special Education and Teaching, BM
Sport and Fitness Administration/Management, M
Student Personnel Services, M
Teacher Education, Multiple Levels, B
Technical Teacher Education, A
Trade and Industrial Teacher Education, B
Water Quality and Wastewater Treatment Management and Recycling Technology/Technician, A
Writing, M

Louisiana

BATON ROUGE COMMUNITY COLLEGE

Business/Commerce, A
Cinematography and Film/Video Production, A
Education, A
General Studies, A
Industrial Production Technologies/Technicians, A
Liberal Arts and Sciences Studies and Humanities, A
Science Technologies/Technicians, A
Security and Protective Services, A

BATON ROUGE SCHOOL OF COMPUTERS

Computer Systems Networking and Telecommunications, A
Computer and Information Sciences, A

BLUE CLIFF COLLEGE–SHREVEPORT

Criminal Justice/Law Enforcement Administration, A
Massage Therapy/Therapeutic Massage, A
Medical Administrative Assistant/Secretary, A

BOSSIER PARISH COMMUNITY COLLEGE

Administrative Assistant and Secretarial Science, A
Audiovisual Communications Technologies/Technicians, A
Business/Commerce, A
Child Care Provider/Assistant, A
Computer/Information Technology Services Administration and Management, A
Construction Engineering, A
Construction Engineering Technology/Technician, A
Criminal Justice/Safety Studies, A
Culinary Arts/Chef Training, A
Drafting and Design Technology/Technician, A
Drama and Dramatics/Theatre Arts, A
Education, A
Educational/Instructional Media Design, A
Emergency Medical Technology/Technician (EMT Paramedic), A
Engineering, A
Foods, Nutrition, and Wellness Studies, A
General Studies, A
Hospital and Health Care Facilities Administration/Management, A
Industrial Mechanics and Maintenance Technology, A
Industrial Technology/Technician, A
Information Science/Studies, A
Liberal Arts and Sciences Studies and Humanities, A
Medical/Clinical Assistant, A
Music, A
Natural Sciences, A
Occupational Therapist Assistant, A
Petroleum Technology/Technician, A
Pharmacy Technician/Assistant, A

Physical Therapist Assistant, A
Physical Therapy/Therapist, A
Recording Arts Technology/Technician, A
Respiratory Care Therapy/Therapist, A
Visual and Performing Arts, A

CAMERON COLLEGE

Medical/Clinical Assistant, A

CENTENARY COLLEGE OF LOUISIANA

Art/Art Studies, General, B
Biochemistry, B
Biology/Biological Sciences, B
Business Administration and Management, B
Business Administration, Management and Operations, M
Chemistry, B
Drama and Dramatics/Theatre Arts, B
Economics, B
Education, M
Elementary Education and Teaching, M
English Language and Literature, B
Fine/Studio Arts, B
French Language and Literature, B
Geology/Earth Science, B
History, B
Mathematics, B
Music, B
Philosophy, B
Political Science and Government, B
Psychology, B
Religion/Religious Studies, B
Secondary Education and Teaching, M
Sociology, B
Visual and Performing Arts, B

DELGADO COMMUNITY COLLEGE

Accounting, A
Architectural Engineering Technology/Technician, A
Automobile/Automotive Mechanics Technology/Technician, A
Biological and Physical Sciences, A
Biomedical Technology/Technician, A
Building/Construction Finishing, Management, and Inspection, A
Building/Property Maintenance and Management, A
Business Administration and Management, A
Civil Engineering Technology/Technician, A
Clinical/Medical Laboratory Technician, A
Commercial and Advertising Art, A
Communication, Journalism and Related Programs, A
Computer Engineering Technology/Technician, A
Computer Installation and Repair Technology/Technician, A
Criminal Justice/Police Science, A
Data Processing and Data Processing Technology/Technician, A
Dental Hygiene/Hygienist, A
Dental Laboratory Technology/Technician, A
Dietetics/Dieticians, A
Drafting and Design Technology/Technician, A
Electrical, Electronic and Communications Engineering Technology/Technician, A
Electrical/Electronics Equipment Installation and Repair, A
Emergency Medical Technology/Technician (EMT Paramedic), A
Fire Protection and Safety Technology/Technician, A
Funeral Service and Mortuary Science, A
General Studies, A
Health Information/Medical Records Technology/Technician, A
Hospitality Administration/Management, A
Interior Architecture, A
Kindergarten/PreSchool Education and Teaching, A
Medical Radiologic Technology/Science - Radiation Therapist, A
Occupational Safety and Health Technology/Technician, A
Occupational Therapist Assistant, A
Physical Therapist Assistant, A
Respiratory Care Therapy/Therapist, A

Sign Language Interpretation and Translation, A

DELTA SCHOOL OF BUSINESS AND TECHNOLOGY

Accounting, A
Administrative Assistant and Secretarial Science, A
Business Administration and Management, A
CAD/CADD Drafting and/or Design
    Technology/Technician, A
Information Technology, A
Medical Office Assistant/Specialist, A

DILLARD UNIVERSITY

Accounting, B
Art/Art Studies, General, B
Biology/Biological Sciences, B
Business Administration and Management, B
Chemistry, B
Computer Science, B
Drama and Dramatics/Theatre Arts, B
Economics, B
English Language and Literature, B
Health/Health Care Administration/Management, B
History, B
International Business/Trade/Commerce, B
Mass Communication/Media Studies, B
Mathematics, B
Music, B
Music Performance, B
Physics, B
Political Science and Government, B
Psychology, B
Public Health (MPH, DPH), B
Sociology, B
Urban Studies/Affairs, B

FLETCHER TECHNICAL COMMUNITY COLLEGE

Accounting, A
Automobile/Automotive Mechanics
    Technology/Technician, A
Cardiopulmonary Technology/Technologist, A
Criminal Justice/Police Science, A
Drafting and Design Technology/Technician, A
Electrician, A
Emergency Medical Technology/Technician (EMT
    Paramedic), A
General Office Occupations and Clerical Services, A
General Studies, A
Heating, Air Conditioning, Ventilation and Refrigera-
    tion Maintenance Technology/Technician, A
Machine Tool Technology/Machinist, A
Marine Maintenance/Fitter and Ship Repair
    Technology/Technician, A
Petroleum Technology/Technician, A
Phlebotomy/Phlebotomist, A

FORTIS COLLEGE

Clinical/Medical Laboratory Technician, A
Radiologic Technology/Science - Radiographer, A

GRAMBLING STATE UNIVERSITY

Accounting, B
Biology/Biological Sciences, B
Business Administration and Management, B
Business/Managerial Economics, B
Chemistry, B
Computer Science, B
Counselor Education/School Counseling and Guid-
    ance Services, M
Criminal Justice/Safety Studies, B
Criminology, M
Curriculum and Instruction, MD
Developmental Education, MDO
Education, MDO
Educational Administration and Supervision, D
Educational Leadership and Administration, MDO
Educational Media/Instructional Technology, D
Elementary Education and Teaching, B
Engineering Technology, B
English, M
English Language and Literature, B
English/Language Arts Teacher Education, B
Health Services Administration, M

Higher Education/Higher Education Administra-
    tion, D
History, B
Human Resources Management and Services, M
Information Science/Studies, B
Marketing/Marketing Management, B
Mass Communication/Media Studies, BM
Mathematics, B
Mathematics Teacher Education, BM
Music, B
Nursing, MO
Nursing - Advanced Practice, O
Parks, Recreation, Leisure and Fitness Studies, B
Physical Education Teaching and Coaching, B
Political Science and Government, BM
Psychology, B
Public Administration, M
Reading Teacher Education, M
Science Teacher Education/General Science
    Teacher Education, M
Secondary Education and Teaching, B
Social Studies Teacher Education, BM
Social Work, BM
Sociology, B
Special Education and Teaching, M
Sport and Fitness Administration/Management, M
Student Personnel Services, D
Visual and Performing Arts, B

ITI TECHNICAL COLLEGE

Computer Technology/Computer Systems Technol-
    ogy, A
Drafting and Design Technology/Technician, A
Electrical, Electronic and Communications Engineer-
    ing Technology/Technician, A
General Office Occupations and Clerical Services, A
Information Science/Studies, A
Information Technology, A
Instrumentation Technology/Technician, A
Manufacturing Technology/Technician, A

LOUISIANA COLLEGE

Accounting, B
Adult and Continuing Education and Teaching, B
Advertising, B
Art Teacher Education, B
Art/Art Studies, General, B
Athletic Training and Sports Medicine, B
Biology/Biological Sciences, B
Broadcast Journalism, B
Business Administration and Management, B
Business Teacher Education, B
Chemistry, B
Clinical Laboratory Science/Medical
    Technology/Technologist, B
Commercial and Advertising Art, B
Criminal Justice/Police Science, B
Drama and Dramatics/Theatre Arts, B
Economics, B
Education, M
Elementary Education and Teaching, B
English Language and Literature, B
Family and Consumer Economics and Related Ser-
    vices, B
Finance, B
Fine/Studio Arts, B
French Language and Literature, B
Health Teacher Education, B
History, B
Journalism, B
Kindergarten/PreSchool Education and Teaching, B
Kinesiology and Exercise Science, B
Liberal Arts and Sciences Studies and Humani-
    ties, B
Marketing/Marketing Management, B
Mass Communication/Media Studies, B
Mathematics, B
Modern Languages, B
Music, B
Music Teacher Education, B
Pastoral Studies/Counseling, M
Philosophy, B
Physical Education Teaching and Coaching, B
Physical Therapist Assistant, A
Physics, B
Piano and Organ, B

Pre-Law Studies, B
Psychology, B
Public Administration, B
Religion/Religious Studies, B
Religious Education, B
Religious/Sacred Music, B
Science Teacher Education/General Science
    Teacher Education, B
Secondary Education and Teaching, B
Social Work, B
Spanish Language and Literature, B
Special Education and Teaching, B
Theology and Religious Vocations, M
Theology/Theological Studies, B
Voice and Opera, B

LOUISIANA DELTA COMMUNITY COL-LEGE

Administrative Assistant and Secretarial Science, A
Business/Commerce, A
Child Care Provider/Assistant, A
Drafting and Design Technology/Technician, A
Education, A
Forensic Science and Technology, A
General Studies, A
Heating, Air Conditioning, Ventilation and Refrigera-
    tion Maintenance Technology/Technician, A
Industrial Electronics Technology/Technician, A
Industrial Production Technologies/Technicians, A
Instrumentation Technology/Technician, A
Liberal Arts and Sciences Studies and Humani-
    ties, A
System Administration/Administrator, A

LOUISIANA STATE UNIVERSITY AND AGRICULTURAL & MECHANICAL COL-LEGE

Accounting, BMD
Adult and Continuing Education and Teaching, B
Agricultural Business and Management, B
Agricultural Economics, MD
Agricultural Education, MD
Agricultural Engineering, MD
Agricultural Sciences, MD
Agricultural Teacher Education, B
Agricultural and Extension Education Services, B
Animal Sciences, BMD
Anthropology, BMD
Applied Science and Technology, M
Applied Statistics, M
Architecture, BM
Art History, Criticism and Conservation, M
Astronomy, MD
Astrophysics, D
Athletic Training and Sports Medicine, B
Audiology/Audiologist and Speech-Language
    Pathology/Pathologist, B
Biochemistry, BMD
Bioengineering, MD
Biological and Biomedical Sciences, MD
Biology/Biological Sciences, B
Biomedical/Medical Engineering, B
Biopsychology, MD
Business Administration and Management, B
Business Administration, Management and Opera-
    tions, MD
Business Education, M
Business/Managerial Economics, B
Ceramic Arts and Ceramics, M
Chemical Engineering, BMD
Chemistry, BMD
Civil Engineering, BMD
Clinical Psychology, MD
Cognitive Sciences, MD
Communication Disorders, MD
Communication Studies/Speech Communication
    and Rhetoric, B
Communication and Media Studies, MD
Comparative Literature, MD
Computer Engineering, BMD
Computer Science, BMD
Construction Management, BMD
Counselor Education/School Counseling and Guid-
    ance Services, MO
Design and Applied Arts, M
Developmental Psychology, MD

Drama and Dramatics/Theatre Arts, B
Early Childhood Education and Teaching, B
Economics, BMD
Education, MDO
Educational Administration and Supervision, MDO
Educational Leadership and Administration, MDO
Educational Measurement and Evaluation, D
Educational Media/Instructional Technology, M
Electrical Engineering, MD
Electrical, Electronics and Communications Engineering, B
Elementary Education and Teaching, BM
Engineering and Applied Sciences, MD
English, MD
English Language and Literature, B
Entomology, MD
Environmental Engineering Technology/Environmental Technology, MD
Environmental Policy and Resource Management, M
Environmental Sciences, BMD
Environmental/Environmental Health Engineering, B
Family and Consumer Sciences/Human Sciences, BMD
Fashion Merchandising, B
Finance, B
Finance and Banking, MD
Fine Arts and Art Studies, M
Fine/Studio Arts, B
Fish, Game and Wildlife Management, MD
Food Science and Technology, MD
Forestry, MD
French Language and Literature, BMD
Geography, BMD
Geology/Earth Science, BMD
Geophysics and Seismology, MD
Geotechnical Engineering, MD
Graphic Design, M
Higher Education/Higher Education Administration, D
Hispanic Studies, M
History, BMD
Home Economics Education, M
Human Resources Development, MD
Industrial Education, M
Industrial Engineering, B
Information Science/Studies, M
Interior Architecture, B
International Business/Trade/Commerce, B
International and Comparative Education, MD
International/Global Studies, B
Kinesiology and Movement Studies, MD
Landscape Architecture, BM
Law and Legal Studies, MD
Liberal Arts and Sciences Studies and Humanities, B
Liberal Studies, M
Library Science, M
Management Information Systems and Services, MD
Management Science, B
Marine Affairs, MD
Marketing/Marketing Management, B
Mass Communication/Media Studies, BMD
Mathematics, BMD
Mechanical Engineering, BMD
Mechanics, MD
Media Studies, MD
Medical Physics, M
Microbiology, B
Multi-/Interdisciplinary Studies, B
Music, BMD
Music Performance, B
Music Teacher Education, BD
Natural Resources Management/Development and Policy, B
Natural Resources and Conservation, MD
Nutritional Sciences, B
Oceanography, Chemical and Physical, BMD
Painting, M
Petroleum Engineering, BMD
Philosophy, BM
Photography, M
Physical Education Teaching and Coaching, B
Physics, BMD
Plant Pathology/Phytopathology, MD

Plant Sciences, B
Political Science and Government, BMD
Printmaking, M
Psychology, BMD
Public Administration, MD
School Psychology, MD
Sculpture, M
Secondary Education and Teaching, M
Social Work, MD
Sociology, BMD
Spanish Language and Literature, B
Sport and Fitness Administration/Management, B
Statistics, M
Structural Engineering, MD
Systems Science and Theory, M
Theater, MD
Toxicology, M
Transportation and Highway Engineering, MD
Veterinary Medicine, D
Veterinary Sciences, MD
Vocational and Technical Education, MD
Water Resources Engineering, MD
Writing, M

LOUISIANA STATE UNIVERSITY AT ALEXANDRIA

Biology/Biological Sciences, B
Business Administration and Management, B
Child Care Provider/Assistant, A
Clinical Laboratory Science/Medical Technology/Technologist, B
Clinical/Medical Laboratory Technician, A
Criminal Justice/Safety Studies, B
Elementary Education and Teaching, B
English Language and Literature, B
History, B
Liberal Arts and Sciences Studies and Humanities, AB
Mass Communication/Media Studies, B
Mathematics, B
Psychology, B
Radiologic Technology/Science - Radiographer, A

LOUISIANA STATE UNIVERSITY AT EUNICE

Administrative Assistant and Secretarial Science, A
Business Administration and Management, A
Computer Programming/Programmer, A
Criminal Justice/Police Science, A
Criminal Justice/Safety Studies, A
Fire Science/Firefighting, A
General Studies, A
Legal Assistant/Paralegal, A
Radiologic Technology/Science - Radiographer, A
Respiratory Care Therapy/Therapist, A

LOUISIANA STATE UNIVERSITY HEALTH SCIENCES CENTER

Allopathic Medicine, MD
Anatomy, MD
Biological and Biomedical Sciences, MD
Biostatistics, MD
Cardiovascular Technology/Technologist, B
Cell Biology and Anatomy, MD
Clinical Laboratory Science/Medical Technology/Technologist, B
Communication Disorders, MD
Community Health Nursing, M
Community Health and Preventive Medicine, MD
Dental Hygiene/Hygienist, B
Dental Laboratory Technology/Technician, A
Dentistry, D
Developmental Biology and Embryology, MD
Environmental and Occupational Health, M
Epidemiology, MD
Health Services Administration, M
Human Genetics, MD
Immunology, MD
Microbiology, MD
Neurobiology and Neurophysiology, MD
Neuroscience, MD
Nurse Anesthetist, M
Nursing, MD
Nursing - Adult, M
Occupational Therapy/Therapist, M

Parasitology, MD
Pharmacology, MD
Physical Therapy/Therapist, D
Physician Assistant, M
Physiology, MD
Public Health, MD
Rehabilitation Counseling, M

LOUISIANA STATE UNIVERSITY IN SHREVEPORT

Accounting, B
Art Teacher Education, B
Art/Art Studies, General, B
Biological and Biomedical Sciences, BM
Biological and Physical Sciences, B
Biology Teacher Education, B
Biology/Biological Sciences, B
Business Administration and Management, B
Business Administration, Management and Operations, M
Business/Managerial Economics, B
Chemistry, B
Chemistry Teacher Education, B
Computer Science, BM
Counseling Psychology, M
Counselor Education/School Counseling and Guidance Services, M
Criminal Justice/Safety Studies, B
Curriculum and Instruction, M
Education, M
Educational Leadership and Administration, M
Elementary Education and Teaching, B
English Language and Literature, B
English/Language Arts Teacher Education, B
Finance, B
French Language Teacher Education, B
General Studies, B
Health Services Administration, M
History, B
Information Science/Studies, B
Liberal Studies, M
Marketing/Marketing Management, B
Mass Communication/Media Studies, B
Mathematics, B
Mathematics Teacher Education, B
Non-Profit/Public/Organizational Management, M
Physics, B
Physics Teacher Education, B
Psychology, B
Public Health, M
Public Health Education and Promotion, B
School Psychology, O
Social Studies Teacher Education, B
Sociology, B
Systems Science and Theory, M

LOUISIANA TECH UNIVERSITY

Accounting, BM
Adult and Continuing Education and Teaching, M
Aeronautics/Aviation/Aerospace Science and Technology, B
Agricultural Business and Management, B
Agricultural Teacher Education, B
Animal Sciences, B
Applied Arts and Design, M
Applied Physics, M
Architecture, BMD
Art Teacher Education, B
Art/Art Studies, General, B
Audiology/Audiologist and Speech-Language Pathology/Pathologist, B
Aviation/Airway Management and Operations, B
Biological and Biomedical Sciences, MD
Biology Teacher Education, B
Biology/Biological Sciences, B
Biomedical Engineering, MD
Biomedical/Medical Engineering, B
Business Administration and Management, B
Business Administration, Management and Operations, MD
Business Teacher Education, B
Business/Managerial Economics, B
Chemical Engineering, BMD
Chemistry, BM
Chemistry Teacher Education, B
Child Development, B

Civil Engineering, BMD
Clinical Laboratory Science/Medical
  Technology/Technologist, B
Commercial and Advertising Art, B
Communication Disorders, M
Computer Science, BMD
Construction Engineering Technology/Technician, B
Consumer Economics, B
Counseling Psychology, D
Counselor Education/School Counseling and Guid-
  ance Services, M
Curriculum and Instruction, MD
Dietetics/Dieticians, B
Early Childhood Education and Teaching, BM
Economics, MD
Education, MD
Education/Teaching of Individuals with Speech or
  Language Impairments, B
Educational Leadership and Administration, MD
Electrical Engineering, MD
Electrical, Electronic and Communications Engineer-
  ing Technology/Technician, B
Electrical, Electronics and Communications Engi-
  neering, B
Elementary Education and Teaching, B
Engineering Physics, D
Engineering and Applied Sciences, MD
English, MO
English Education, M
English Language and Literature, B
English/Language Arts Teacher Education, B
Environmental Studies, B
Exercise and Sports Science, M
Family and Consumer Sciences/Home Economics
  Teacher Education, B
Family and Consumer Sciences/Human Sci-
  ences, M
Finance, B
Finance and Banking, MD
Fine Arts and Art Studies, M
Forestry, B
French Language Teacher Education, B
French Language and Literature, B
General Studies, AB
Geography, B
Geology/Earth Science, B
Graphic Design, M
Health Informatics, M
Health Information/Medical Records
  Administration/Administrator, B
Health Information/Medical Records
  Technology/Technician, A
Health and Physical Education, B
Higher Education/Higher Education Administra-
  tion, D
History, BM
Human Resources Management/Personnel Adminis-
  tration, B
Industrial Engineering, B
Industrial and Organizational Psychology, MD
Industrial/Management Engineering, M
Interior Architecture, B
Journalism, B
Junior High/Intermediate/Middle School Education
  and Teaching, B
Kindergarten/PreSchool Education and Teaching, B
Management Information Systems and Services, B
Management Science, B
Marketing/Marketing Management, B
Mathematics, BMD
Mathematics Teacher Education, BM
Mechanical Engineering, BMD
Molecular Biology, M
Music, B
Music Performance, B
Music Teacher Education, B
Natural Resources and Conservation, B
Nutritional Sciences, M
Operations Management and Supervision, B
Photography, BM
Physical Education Teaching and Coaching, BM
Physics, BMD
Physics Teacher Education, B
Plant Sciences, B
Political Science and Government, B
Psychology, BMD

Science Teacher Education/General Science
  Teacher Education, B
Social Studies Teacher Education, BM
Sociology, B
Spanish Language and Literature, B
Special Education and Teaching, BM
Speech Teacher Education, B
Speech and Rhetorical Studies, MD
Statistics, MD
Teacher Education and Professional Develop-
  ment, Specific Subject Areas, B
Technical and Business Writing, MO
Theater, M

LOYOLA UNIVERSITY NEW ORLEANS

Accounting, B
Ancient/Classical Greek Language and Literature, B
Biochemistry, B
Biology/Biological Sciences, B
Business Administration and Management, B
Business Administration, Management and Opera-
  tions, M
Business Statistics, B
Business/Managerial Economics, B
Christian Studies, B
Cinematography and Film/Video Production, B
Classics and Classical Languages, Litera-
  tures, and Linguistics, B
Clinical Psychology, M
Computational Mathematics, B
Computer and Information Sciences, B
Criminology, BM
Design and Visual Communications, B
Drama and Dramatics/Theatre Arts, B
Economics, B
English Language and Literature, B
Entrepreneurship/Entrepreneurial Studies, M
Environmental Sciences, B
Environmental Studies, B
Finance, B
Fine/Studio Arts, B
French Language and Literature, B
Health Services Administration, M
History, B
International Business/Trade/Commerce, B
Jazz/Jazz Studies, B
Journalism, B
Latin Language and Literature, B
Law and Legal Studies, MD
Liberal Arts and Sciences Studies and Humani-
  ties, B
Marketing, M
Marketing/Marketing Management, B
Mathematics, B
Music, BM
Music Performance, B
Music Teacher Education, B
Music Theory and Composition, B
Music Therapy/Therapist, BM
Nursing, MD
Organizational Management, M
Performance, M
Philosophy, B
Physics, B
Political Science and Government, B
Religion/Religious Studies, B
Religious Education, B
Social Sciences, B
Sociology, B
Spanish Language and Literature, B
Theology and Religious Vocations, MO
Voice and Opera, B

MCCANN SCHOOL OF BUSINESS & TECHNOLOGY (MONROE)

Administrative Assistant and Secretarial Science, A
Business Administration and Management, A
Computer and Information Sciences and Support
  Services, A
Corrections and Criminal Justice, A
Legal Administrative Assistant/Secretary, A
Management Science, A
Massage Therapy/Therapeutic Massage, A
Medical Office Management/Administration, A
Medical/Clinical Assistant, A
Radiologic Technology/Science - Radiographer, A

Respiratory Therapy Technician/Assistant, A
Surgical Technology/Technologist, A

MCNEESE STATE UNIVERSITY

Accounting, B
Agricultural Sciences, M
Agriculture, B
Applied Behavior Analysis, M
Art/Art Studies, General, B
Athletic Training and Sports Medicine, B
Biology/Biological Sciences, B
Business Administration and Management, B
Business Administration, Management and Opera-
  tions, M
Chemical Engineering, M
Chemistry, BM
Civil Engineering, M
Clinical Laboratory Science/Medical
  Technology/Technologist, B
Computer Science, BM
Counseling Psychology, M
Counselor Education/School Counseling and Guid-
  ance Services, MO
Criminal Justice/Safety Studies, B
Criminology, M
Curriculum and Instruction, M
Early Childhood Education and Teaching, BMO
Education, O
Educational Leadership and Administration, MO
Educational Measurement and Evaluation, MO
Educational Media/Instructional Technology, MO
Electrical Engineering, M
Elementary Education and Teaching, BMO
Engineering, B
Engineering Management, M
Engineering and Applied Sciences, MO
English, M
English Language and Literature, B
Environmental Sciences, M
Exercise and Sports Science, M
Experimental Psychology, M
Finance, B
Foreign Languages and Literatures, B
General Studies, AB
Health Promotion, M
Health Services Administration, B
History, B
Kinesiology and Exercise Science, B
Legal Assistant/Paralegal, A
Liberal Arts and Sciences Studies and Humani-
  ties, B
Library Science, O
Marketing/Marketing Management, B
Mass Communication/Media Studies, B
Mathematics, BM
Mechanical Engineering, MO
Middle School Education, O
Music Performance, B
Music Teacher Education, O
Nursing, MO
Nursing - Advanced Practice, MO
Nursing Administration, MO
Nursing Education, M
Nutritional Sciences, BM
Physical Education Teaching and Coaching, B
Political Science and Government, B
Psychiatric/Mental Health Nurse/Nursing, MO
Psychology, BM
Radiologic Technology/Science - Radiographer, B
Reading Teacher Education, MO
School Psychology, M
Science Teacher Education/General Science
  Teacher Education, M
Secondary Education and Teaching, BMO
Sociology, B
Special Education and Teaching, MO
Statistics, M
Substance Abuse/Addiction Counseling, M
Wildlife and Wildlands Science and Management, B
Writing, M

NEW ORLEANS BAPTIST THEOLOGI-CAL SEMINARY

Divinity/Ministry (BD, MDiv.), AB
Pastoral Studies/Counseling, MD
Religion/Religious Studies, AB

Religious Education, MD
Religious/Sacred Music, AB
Sacred Music, MD
Theology and Religious Vocations, MD
Youth Ministry, A

NICHOLLS STATE UNIVERSITY

Art Teacher Education, B
Art/Art Studies, General, B
Audiology/Audiologist and Speech-Language
    Pathology/Pathologist, B
Biology/Biological Sciences, B
Business Administration and Management, B
Business Administration, Management and Opera-
    tions, M
Business Teacher Education, B
Chemistry, B
Child Care and Support Services Management, A
Clinical Psychology, M
Counselor Education/School Counseling and Guid-
    ance Services, M
Culinary Arts/Chef Training, AB
Curriculum and Instruction, M
Dietetics/Dieticians, B
Early Childhood Education and Teaching, B
Education, M
Educational Administration and Supervision, M
Elementary Education and Teaching, BM
English Language and Literature, B
English/Language Arts Teacher Education, B
Environmental Biology, M
Family and Consumer Sciences/Human Sciences, B
Finance, B
General Studies, AB
Health Education, M
Health Services/Allied Health/Health Sciences, B
History, B
Junior High/Intermediate/Middle School Education
    and Teaching, B
Management Information Systems and Services, B
Marine Biology and Biological Oceanography, M
Marketing/Marketing Management, B
Mass Communication/Media Studies, B
Mathematics, B
Mathematics Teacher Education, BM
Mechanical Engineering/Mechanical
    Technology/Technician, B
Middle School Education, M
Music, B
Music Teacher Education, B
Nursing, M
Nursing - Advanced Practice, M
Nursing Administration, M
Nursing Education, M
Petroleum Technology/Technician, AB
Physical Education Teaching and Coaching, B
Political Science and Government, B
Psychiatric/Mental Health Nurse/Nursing, M
Psychology, B
School Psychology, MO
Science Teacher Education/General Science
    Teacher Education, B
Secondary Education and Teaching, M
Social Studies Teacher Education, B
Sociology, B
Survey Technology/Surveying, B

NORTHWEST LOUISIANA TECHNICAL COLLEGE

Accounting Technology/Technician and Bookkeep-
    ing, A
Computer Science, A
Hotel/Motel Administration/Management, A
Instrumentation Technology/Technician, A
Management Information Systems and Services, A

NORTHWESTERN STATE UNIVERSITY OF LOUISIANA

Accounting, B
Adult and Continuing Education and Teaching, M
Biology/Biological Sciences, B
Business Administration and Management, B
Clinical Psychology, M
Communication Studies/Speech Communication
    and Rhetoric, B

Counselor Education/School Counseling and Guid-
    ance Services, MO
Criminal Justice/Safety Studies, B
Curriculum and Instruction, M
Drama and Dramatics/Theatre Arts, B
Early Childhood Education and Teaching, BM
Education, MO
Educational Leadership and Administration, MO
Educational Media/Instructional Technology, MO
Electrical, Electronic and Communications Engineer-
    ing Technology/Technician, AB
Elementary Education and Teaching, BMO
English, M
English Language and Literature, B
Family and Consumer Sciences/Human Sciences, B
Fine Arts and Art Studies, M
Fine/Studio Arts, B
General Studies, AB
Health Education, M
Health Physics/Radiological Health, M
Health Services/Allied Health/Health Sciences, B
Health and Physical Education, B
History, B
Homeland Security, M
Hospitality Administration/Management, B
Industrial Technology/Technician, B
Information Science/Studies, B
Liberal Arts and Sciences Studies and Humani-
    ties, A
Mathematics, B
Middle School Education, M
Multi-/Interdisciplinary Studies, B
Music, M
Music Performance, B
Music Teacher Education, B
Nursing, B
Physical Education Teaching and Coaching, B
Physical Sciences, B
Psychology, BM
Radiologic Technology/Science - Radiographer, B
Reading Teacher Education, O
Secondary Education and Teaching, BMO
Social Work, B
Special Education and Teaching, MO
Student Personnel Services, M
Substance Abuse/Addiction Counseling, B
Veterinary/Animal Health Technology/Technician and
    Veterinary Assistant, A

NUNEZ COMMUNITY COLLEGE

Business/Commerce, A
Child Care Provider/Assistant, A
Culinary Arts/Chef Training, A
Education, A
General Studies, A
Industrial Technology/Technician, A
Kindergarten/PreSchool Education and Teaching, A
Legal Assistant/Paralegal, A
Liberal Arts and Sciences Studies and Humani-
    ties, A

OUR LADY OF THE LAKE COLLEGE

Biological and Biomedical Sciences, B
Biology/Biological Sciences, B
Biomedical Sciences, B
Clinical Laboratory Science/Medical
    Technology/Technologist, B
Clinical/Medical Laboratory Technician, AB
General Studies, A
Health Services Administration, M
Health/Health Care Administration/Management, B
Humanities/Humanistic Studies, B
Industrial Radiologic Technology/Technician, A
Nurse Anesthetist, M
Nursing, M
Nursing Administration, M
Nursing Education, M
Physical Therapist Assistant, A
Physician Assistant, M

REMINGTON COLLEGE–BATON ROUGE CAMPUS

Business Administration and Management, A
Computer Systems Networking and Telecommunica-
    tions, A

Criminal Justice/Law Enforcement Administration, A

REMINGTON COLLEGE–LAFAYETTE CAMPUS

Business Administration and Management, A
Computer Systems Networking and Telecommunica-
    tions, A
Criminal Justice/Law Enforcement Administration, A

REMINGTON COLLEGE–SHREVEPORT

Business Administration and Management, A
Criminal Justice/Law Enforcement Administration, A

RIVER PARISHES COMMUNITY COLLEGE

Education, A
General Studies, A
Humanities/Humanistic Studies, A
Liberal Arts and Sciences Studies and Humani-
    ties, A

SAINT JOSEPH SEMINARY COLLEGE

Liberal Arts and Sciences Studies and Humani-
    ties, B

SOUTH CENTRAL LOUISIANA TECHNICAL COLLEGE

Accounting Technology/Technician and Bookkeep-
    ing, A
Management Information Systems and Services, A

SOUTH LOUISIANA COMMUNITY COLLEGE

Administrative Assistant and Secretarial Science, A
Aircraft Powerplant Technology/Technician, A
Automobile/Automotive Mechanics
    Technology/Technician, A
Business/Commerce, A
Carpentry/Carpenter, A
Clinical/Medical Laboratory Technician, A
Computer Systems Networking and Telecommunica-
    tions, A
Criminal Justice/Safety Studies, A
Culinary Arts/Chef Training, A
Diesel Mechanics Technology/Technician, A
Drafting and Design Technology/Technician, A
Education, A
Electrician, A
Emergency Medical Technology/Technician (EMT
    Paramedic), A
Energy Management and Systems
    Technology/Technician, A
General Studies, A
Heating, Air Conditioning, Ventilation and Refrigera-
    tion Maintenance Technology/Technician, A
Industrial Electronics Technology/Technician, A
Industrial Mechanics and Maintenance Technol-
    ogy, A
Industrial Radiologic Technology/Technician, A
Industrial Technology/Technician, A
Machine Tool Technology/Machinist, A
Prepress/Desktop Publishing and Digital Imaging
    Design, A
Surgical Technology/Technologist, A
Survey Technology/Surveying, A
Web Page, Digital/Multimedia and Information Re-
    sources Design, A
Welding Technology/Welder, A

SOUTHEASTERN LOUISIANA UNIVERSITY

Accounting, B
Applied Science and Technology, M
Art/Art Studies, General, B
Athletic Training and Sports Medicine, B
Audiology/Audiologist and Speech-Language
    Pathology/Pathologist, B
Biological and Biomedical Sciences, M
Biology/Biological Sciences, B
Business Administration and Management, B
Business Administration, Management and Opera-
    tions, M
Chemistry, B
Communication Disorders, M

Communication Studies/Speech Communication and Rhetoric, B
Communication and Media Studies, M
Computer Science, B
Counselor Education/School Counseling and Guidance Services, M
Criminal Justice/Safety Studies, B
Curriculum and Instruction, M
Early Childhood Education and Teaching, B
Education, MD
Educational Administration and Supervision, MD
Educational Media/Instructional Technology, M
Elementary Education and Teaching, BM
Engineering Technology, B
English, M
English Education, M
English Language and Literature, B
English/Language Arts Teacher Education, B
Family and Consumer Sciences/Human Sciences, B
Finance, B
General Studies, B
Health Education, M
History, BM
Industrial Technology/Technician, AB
Junior High/Intermediate/Middle School Education and Teaching, B
Kinesiology and Movement Studies, M
Logistics and Materials Management, B
Marketing/Marketing Management, B
Mathematics, B
Music, M
Music Performance, B
Occupational Safety and Health Technology/Technician, B
Performance, M
Physical Education Teaching and Coaching, B
Physics, B
Political Science and Government, B
Psychology, BM
Public Health Education and Promotion, B
Reading Teacher Education, M
Social Studies Teacher Education, B
Social Work, B
Sociology, BM
Spanish Language and Literature, B
Special Education and Teaching, M
Sport and Fitness Administration/Management, B
Writing, M

SOUTHERN UNIVERSITY AND AGRICULTURAL AND MECHANICAL COLLEGE

Accounting, B
Agricultural Economics, B
Agricultural Sciences, M
Agricultural Teacher Education, B
Analytical Chemistry, M
Animal Sciences, B
Architecture, B
Art Teacher Education, B
Audiology/Audiologist and Speech-Language Pathology/Pathologist, B
Biochemistry, M
Biological and Biomedical Sciences, M
Biology Teacher Education, B
Biology/Biological Sciences, B
Business Administration and Management, B
Business Administration, Management and Operations, M
Business/Managerial Economics, B
Chemistry, BM
Chemistry Teacher Education, B
Civil Engineering, B
Communication Studies/Speech Communication and Rhetoric, B
Computer Science, BM
Computer Teacher Education, B
Counselor Education/School Counseling and Guidance Services, M
Criminal Justice/Police Science, A
Criminal Justice/Safety Studies, B
Criminology, M
Drama and Dramatics/Theatre Arts, B
E-Commerce/Electronic Commerce, B
Early Childhood Education and Teaching, B
Education, MD

Educational Administration and Supervision, M
Educational Leadership and Administration, M
Educational Media/Instructional Technology, M
Electrical, Electronic and Communications Engineering Technology/Technician, B
Electrical, Electronics and Communications Engineering, B
Elementary Education and Teaching, BM
Engineering and Applied Sciences, M
English Language and Literature, B
English/Language Arts Teacher Education, B
Environmental Sciences, M
Family and Consumer Sciences/Human Sciences, B
Finance, B
Fine/Studio Arts, B
Forestry, M
French Language Teacher Education, B
French Language and Literature, B
Gerontological Nursing, D
History, BM
Inorganic Chemistry, M
Junior High/Intermediate/Middle School Education and Teaching, B
Law and Legal Studies, D
Marketing/Marketing Management, B
Mass Communication/Media Studies, BM
Mathematics, BM
Mathematics Teacher Education, BD
Mechanical Engineering, B
Music Performance, B
Music Teacher Education, B
Nursing, MDO
Nursing - Advanced Practice, O
Nursing Administration, D
Nursing Education, D
Organic Chemistry, M
Physical Chemistry, M
Physical Education Teaching and Coaching, B
Physics, BM
Physics Teacher Education, B
Political Science and Government, BM
Psychology, BM
Public Administration, M
Public Policy Analysis, D
Rehabilitation Counseling, M
Rehabilitation and Therapeutic Professions, B
Science Teacher Education/General Science Teacher Education, BD
Secondary Education and Teaching, BM
Social Sciences, M
Social Studies Teacher Education, B
Social Work, B
Sociology, B
Spanish Language Teacher Education, B
Spanish Language and Literature, B
Special Education and Teaching, BMD
Therapeutic Recreation, M
Therapeutic Recreation/Recreational Therapy, B
Urban Forestry, B
Vocational Rehabilitation Counseling/Counselor, B

SOUTHERN UNIVERSITY AT NEW ORLEANS

Biology/Biological Sciences, B
Criminal Justice/Safety Studies, B
Criminology, M
Early Childhood Education and Teaching, B
Elementary Education and Teaching, B
English Language and Literature, B
Entrepreneurship/Entrepreneurial Studies, B
Family and Community Services, B
General Studies, B
Health Information/Medical Records Administration/Administrator, B
History, B
Management Information Systems and Services, BM
Mathematics, B
Museology/Museum Studies, M
Psychology, B
Public Administration, B
Social Work, BM

Sociology, B

SOUTHERN UNIVERSITY AT SHREVEPORT

Accounting, A
Accounting Technology/Technician and Bookkeeping, A
Avionics Maintenance Technology/Technician, A
Banking and Financial Support Services, A
Biology/Biological Sciences, A
Business/Commerce, A
Cardiovascular Technology/Technologist, A
Chemistry, A
Clinical/Medical Laboratory Technician, A
Computer Science, A
Criminal Justice/Law Enforcement Administration, A
Dental Hygiene/Hygienist, A
Electrical, Electronic and Communications Engineering Technology/Technician, A
General Studies, A
Health Information/Medical Records Administration/Administrator, A
Health Information/Medical Records Technology/Technician, A
Hospitality Administration/Management, A
Hotel/Motel Administration/Management, A
Human Services, A
Kindergarten/PreSchool Education and Teaching, A
Legal Assistant/Paralegal, A
Liberal Arts and Sciences Studies and Humanities, A
Mathematics, A
Mechanical Engineering/Mechanical Technology/Technician, A
Medical Radiologic Technology/Science - Radiation Therapist, A
Mental Health Counseling/Counselor, A
Physical Therapist Assistant, A
Public Administration, A
Radiologic Technology/Science - Radiographer, A
Respiratory Care Therapy/Therapist, A
Robotics Technology/Technician, A
Sociology, A
Surgical Technology/Technologist, A
Teacher Assistant/Aide, A
Tourism and Travel Services Management, A

SOUTHWEST UNIVERSITY

Business Administration and Management, AB
Business Administration, Management and Operations, M
Business Statistics, B
Criminal Justice/Law Enforcement Administration, AB
Criminology, M
Human Resources Management/Personnel Administration, A
International Business/Trade/Commerce, B
Management, M
Management Science, B
Marketing/Marketing Management, B
Organizational Management, M

SOWELA TECHNICAL COMMUNITY COLLEGE

Accounting Technology/Technician and Bookkeeping, A
Administrative Assistant and Secretarial Science, A
Aircraft Powerplant Technology/Technician, A
Commercial and Advertising Art, A
Computer Programming/Programmer, A
Computer Systems Networking and Telecommunications, A
Criminal Justice/Safety Studies, A
Culinary Arts/Chef Training, A
Drafting and Design Technology/Technician, A
General Studies, A
Instrumentation Technology/Technician, A
Liberal Arts and Sciences Studies and Humanities, A

TULANE UNIVERSITY

Accounting, BM
African Studies, B
Allopathic Medicine, D

American/United States Studies/Civilization, B
Anatomy, B
Anthropology, BMD
Applied Mathematics, M
Architecture, BM
Art History, Criticism and Conservation, BM
Art/Art Studies, General, B
Asian Studies/Civilization, B
Biochemistry, BMD
Biological and Biomedical Sciences, MD
Biology/Biological Sciences, B
Biomedical Engineering, MD
Biomedical/Medical Engineering, B
Biostatistics, BMD
Business Administration and Management, AB
Business Administration, Management and Operations, MD
Business/Commerce, A
Cell Biology and Anatomy, MD
Cell/Cellular Biology and Anatomical Sciences, B
Cell/Cellular Biology and Histology, B
Chemical Engineering, BD
Chemistry, BMD
Classics and Classical Languages, Literatures, and Linguistics, BM
Communication Studies/Speech Communication and Rhetoric, A
Communication, Journalism and Related Programs, A
Community Health and Preventive Medicine, MD
Computer Science, B
Computer and Information Sciences, AB
Corrections, B
Dance, BM
Drama and Dramatics/Theatre Arts, B
Ecology, BMD
Economics, BMD
Electrical, Electronics and Communications Engineering, B
Emergency Management, M
Energy Management and Policy, M
Engineering Science, B
English, MD
English Language and Literature, B
Entrepreneurship/Entrepreneurial Studies, M
Environmental Biology, B
Environmental Studies, B
Environmental and Occupational Health, MD
Environmental/Environmental Health Engineering, B
Epidemiology, MD
Evolutionary Biology, BMD
Finance, B
Finance and Banking, MD
Fine Arts and Art Studies, MD
Fine/Studio Arts, B
Foreign Languages and Literatures, B
French Language and Literature, BMD
Geology/Earth Science, B
German Language and Literature, B
Health Communication, M
Health Education, M
Health Services Administration, MD
Hispanic-American, Puerto Rican, and Mexican-American/Chicano Studies, B
History, BMD
Human Genetics, MD
Immunology, MD
Information Science/Studies, AB
Interdisciplinary Studies, D
International Business/Trade/Commerce, M
International Development, MD
International Public Health/International Health, MD
International Relations and Affairs, B
Italian Language and Literature, B
Italian Studies, B
Jewish/Judaic Studies, B
Latin American Studies, BMD
Latin Language and Literature, B
Law and Legal Studies, MD
Legal Assistant/Paralegal, A
Legal Professions and Studies, B
Liberal Arts and Sciences Studies and Humanities, B
Liberal Studies, M
Linguistics, B
Management Strategy and Policy, M

Marketing, M
Marketing/Marketing Management, AB
Mass Communication/Media Studies, B
Maternal and Child Health, M
Mathematics, BMD
Mathematics and Statistics, B
Medieval and Renaissance Studies, B
Microbiology, MD
Modern Greek Language and Literature, B
Molecular Biology, BMD
Multi-/Interdisciplinary Studies, B
Music, BM
Music Performance, B
Music Theory and Composition, B
Neuroscience, MD
Nutritional Sciences, M
Parasitology, D
Pharmacology, MD
Philosophy, BMD
Physics, BD
Physiology, MD
Political Science and Government, BD
Portuguese Language and Literature, BMD
Psychology, BMD
Public Health, MDO
Religion/Religious Studies, B
Russian Language and Literature, B
Russian Studies, B
Social Work, MD
Sociology, BD
Spanish Language and Literature, BMD
Statistics, M
Structural Biology, MD
Theater, M
Women's Studies, B

UNIVERSITY OF HOLY CROSS

Accounting, B
Biology/Biological Sciences, B
Business Administration and Management, B
Computer and Information Sciences, B
Counselor Education/School Counseling and Guidance Services, M
Criminology, B
Curriculum and Instruction, M
Education, BM
Educational Administration and Supervision, M
English Language and Literature, B
General Studies, B
History, B
Humanities/Humanistic Studies, B
Marketing/Marketing Management, B
Marriage and Family Therapy/Counseling, M
Social Sciences, B
Teacher Education, Multiple Levels, B
Theology/Theological Studies, B
Tourism and Travel Services Management, B

UNIVERSITY OF LOUISIANA AT LAFAYETTE

Accounting, B
American/United States Studies/Civilization, D
Anthropology, B
Architectural Engineering, M
Architecture, B
Architecture and Related Services, B
Art/Art Studies, General, B
Athletic Training and Sports Medicine, B
Audiology/Audiologist and Speech-Language Pathology/Pathologist, B
Biological and Biomedical Sciences, MD
Biology/Biological Sciences, B
Business Administration and Management, B
Business Administration, Management and Operations, M
Business, Management, Marketing, and Related Support Services, B
Business/Managerial Economics, B
Chemical Engineering, BM
Chemistry, B
Civil Engineering, BM
Cognitive Sciences, D
Communication Disorders, MD
Communication Studies/Speech Communication and Rhetoric, B
Communication and Media Studies, M

Computer Engineering, BMD
Computer Science, BMD
Computer Systems Analysis/Analyst, B
Computer and Information Sciences, B
Counselor Education/School Counseling and Guidance Services, B
Criminal Justice/Safety Studies, B
Curriculum and Instruction, M
Dietetics/Dieticians, B
Early Childhood Education and Teaching, B
Education, MD
Education/Teaching of the Gifted and Talented, M
Educational Administration and Supervision, M
Educational Leadership and Administration, MD
Electrical, Electronics and Communications Engineering, B
Elementary Education and Teaching, B
Engineering Management, M
English, MD
English Language and Literature, B
Environmental Biology, D
Environmental Sciences, B
Evolutionary Biology, D
Film/Cinema Studies, B
Finance, B
Folklore, M
Foreign Languages and Literatures, B
French Language and Literature, MD
General Studies, B
Geology/Earth Science, BM
Health Information/Medical Records Administration/Administrator, B
Health/Health Care Administration/Management, B
History, BM
Hospitality Administration/Management, B
Human Development and Family Studies, B
Industrial Design, B
Industrial Technology/Technician, B
Insurance, B
Interior Architecture, B
Junior High/Intermediate/Middle School Education and Teaching, B
Marketing/Marketing Management, B
Mass Communication/Media Studies, BM
Mathematics, BMD
Mechanical Engineering, BM
Music, BM
Music Performance, B
Music Teacher Education, M
Natural Resources and Conservation, B
Nursing, M
Performance, M
Petroleum Engineering, BM
Physical Education Teaching and Coaching, B
Physics, BM
Political Science and Government, B
Psychology, BM
Public Relations/Image Management, B
Rehabilitation Counseling, M
Rhetoric, MD
Secondary Education and Teaching, B
Sociology, B
Teacher Education, Multiple Levels, B
Telecommunications, M
Visual and Performing Arts, B
Writing, MD

UNIVERSITY OF LOUISIANA AT MONROE

Accounting, B
Agricultural Business and Management, B
Airline/Commercial/Professional Pilot and Flight Crew, B
Art Education, M
Atmospheric Sciences and Meteorology, B
Audiology/Audiologist and Speech-Language Pathology/Pathologist, B
Biological and Biomedical Sciences, M
Biology Teacher Education, B
Biology/Biological Sciences, B
Business Administration and Management, B
Business Administration, Management and Operations, M
Chemistry Teacher Education, B
Clinical Laboratory Science/Medical Technology/Technologist, B

Clinical Psychology, M
Communication Disorders, M
Communication and Media Studies, M
Computer Science, B
Construction Management, B
Counseling Psychology, M
Counselor Education/School Counseling and Guidance Services, M
Criminal Justice/Safety Studies, B
Criminology, M
Curriculum and Instruction, MD
Dental Hygiene/Hygienist, B
Early Childhood Education and Teaching, M
Education/Teaching of the Gifted and Talented, M
Educational Leadership and Administration, M
Educational Measurement and Evaluation, M
Elementary Education and Teaching, BM
English, M
English Education, M
English Language and Literature, B
English as a Second Language, M
English/Language Arts Teacher Education, B
Exercise and Sports Science, M
Family and Consumer Sciences/Human Sciences, M
Finance, B
Fine/Studio Arts, B
Foreign Language Teacher Education, M
Foreign Languages and Literatures, B
Forensic Psychology, M
General Studies, AB
Gerontology, MO
Health Professions and Related Clinical Sciences, B
History, BM
Insurance, B
Kinesiology and Exercise Science, B
Management Information Systems and Services, B
Marketing/Marketing Management, B
Marriage and Family Therapy/Counseling, MD
Mass Communication/Media Studies, B
Mathematics, B
Mathematics Teacher Education, BM
Middle School Education, M
Music Performance, B
Music Teacher Education, M
Occupational Therapist Assistant, A
Occupational Therapy/Therapist, M
Pharmacy, BD
Physical Education Teaching and Coaching, B
Political Science and Government, B
Psychology, BM
Radiologic Technology/Science - Radiographer, B
Reading Teacher Education, M
Science Teacher Education/General Science Teacher Education, M
Secondary Education and Teaching, BM
Social Studies Teacher Education, BM
Social Work, B
Sociology, B
Special Education and Teaching, M
Speech and Interpersonal Communication, M
Toxicology, BD

UNIVERSITY OF NEW ORLEANS

Accounting, BM
Anthropology, B
Art History, Criticism and Conservation, B
Arts Management, M
Biological and Biomedical Sciences, MD
Biology/Biological Sciences, B
Business Administration and Management, B
Business Administration, Management and Operations, M
Chemistry, BMD
Civil Engineering, B
Computer Science, BM
Counselor Education/School Counseling and Guidance Services, MD
Curriculum and Instruction, MD
Drama and Dramatics/Theatre Arts, B
Economics, MD
Education, MD
Educational Leadership and Administration, MD
Electrical, Electronics and Communications Engineering, B
Elementary Education and Teaching, B

Engineering Management, M
Engineering and Applied Sciences, MD
English, M
English Language and Literature, B
Environmental Sciences, M
Film, Television, and Video Production, M
Finance, B
Finance and Banking, M
Fine Arts and Art Studies, M
Fine/Studio Arts, B
Foreign Languages and Literatures, B
Geography, M
Geology/Earth Science, B
Geosciences, M
Health Services Administration, BM
Health and Physical Education, B
History, BM
Hospitality Administration/Management, BM
International/Global Studies, B
Marketing/Marketing Management, B
Mathematics, BM
Mechanical Engineering, BM
Multi-/Interdisciplinary Studies, B
Music, BM
Naval Architecture and Marine Engineering, B
Philosophy, B
Physics, BMD
Political Science and Government, BMD
Psychology, BMD
Public Administration, M
Romance Languages, Literatures, and Linguistics, M
Secondary Education and Teaching, B
Sociology, BM
Special Education and Teaching, MD
Taxation, M
Theater, M
Transportation/Transportation Management, M
Travel and Tourism, M
Urban Studies/Affairs, BMD
Urban and Regional Planning, M

VIRGINIA COLLEGE IN BATON ROUGE

Business Administration and Management, A
Medical Office Management/Administration, A
Medical/Clinical Assistant, A
Office Management and Supervision, A
Surgical Technology/Technologist, A

XAVIER UNIVERSITY OF LOUISIANA

Accounting, B
Art Teacher Education, B
Art/Art Studies, General, B
Biochemistry, B
Biology Teacher Education, B
Biology/Biological Sciences, B
Business Administration and Management, B
Chemistry, B
Chemistry Teacher Education, B
Communication Disorders, B
Computer Engineering, B
Computer Science, B
Computer and Information Sciences, B
Counselor Education/School Counseling and Guidance Services, M
Curriculum and Instruction, M
Early Childhood Education and Teaching, B
Education, BM
Educational Administration and Supervision, M
Elementary Education and Teaching, B
English Language and Literature, B
French Language Teacher Education, B
French Language and Literature, B
History, B
History Teacher Education, B
Junior High/Intermediate/Middle School Education and Teaching, B
Marketing/Marketing Management, B
Mass Communication/Media Studies, B
Mathematics, B
Medical Microbiology and Bacteriology, B
Music, B
Music Performance, B
Music Teacher Education, B
Pastoral Studies/Counseling, M
Pharmacy, D

Philosophy, B
Physical Education Teaching and Coaching, B
Physics, B
Piano and Organ, B
Political Science and Government, B
Pre-Law Studies, B
Pre-Medicine/Pre-Medical Studies, B
Psychology, B
Science Teacher Education/General Science Teacher Education, B
Secondary Education and Teaching, B
Social Studies Teacher Education, B
Sociology, B
Spanish Language Teacher Education, B
Spanish Language and Literature, B
Speech-Language Pathology/Pathologist, B
Statistics, B
Theology and Religious Vocations, M
Theology/Theological Studies, B
Violin, Viola, Guitar and Other Stringed Instruments, B

Maine

BATES COLLEGE

African-American/Black Studies, B
American/United States Studies/Civilization, B
Ancient Studies/Civilization, B
Anthropology, B
Art/Art Studies, General, B
Biochemistry, B
Biology/Biological Sciences, B
Chemistry, B
Chinese Language and Literature, B
Dance, B
Drama and Dramatics/Theatre Arts, B
East Asian Studies, B
Economics, B
Engineering, B
English Language and Literature, B
Environmental Studies, B
French Language and Literature, B
Geology/Earth Science, B
German Language and Literature, B
History, B
Japanese Language and Literature, B
Latin American Studies, B
Mathematics, B
Multi-/Interdisciplinary Studies, B
Music, B
Philosophy, B
Physics, B
Political Science and Government, B
Psychology, B
Religion/Religious Studies, B
Sociology, B
Spanish Language and Literature, B
Western European Studies, B
Women's Studies, B

BEAL COLLEGE

Accounting, A
Administrative Assistant and Secretarial Science, A
Business Administration and Management, A
Criminal Justice/Law Enforcement Administration, A
Health Information/Medical Records Technology/Technician, A
Human Resources Management/Personnel Administration, A
Human Services, A
Medical Office Assistant/Specialist, A
Medical/Clinical Assistant, A
Substance Abuse/Addiction Counseling, A
Welding Technology/Welder, A

BOWDOIN COLLEGE

African Studies, B
Ancient Studies/Civilization, B
Anthropology, B
Archeology, B
Art History, Criticism and Conservation, B
Asian Studies/Civilization, B
Biochemistry, B
Biology/Biological Sciences, B
Central/Middle and Eastern European Studies, B

Chemical Physics, B
Chemistry, B
Classical, Ancient Mediterranean and Near Eastern Studies and Archaeology, B
Classics and Classical Languages, Literatures, and Linguistics, B
Computer Science, B
Econometrics and Quantitative Economics, B
Economics, B
English Language and Literature, B
Environmental Studies, B
Fine Arts and Art Studies, B
Fine/Studio Arts, B
French Language and Literature, B
French Studies, B
Geology/Earth Science, B
German Language and Literature, B
History, B
Italian Studies, B
Latin American Studies, B
Mathematics, B
Mathematics Teacher Education, B
Mathematics and Computer Science, B
Multi-/Interdisciplinary Studies, B
Music, B
Philosophy, B
Physics, B
Political Science and Government, B
Psychology, B
Religion/Religious Studies, B
Romance Languages, Literatures, and Linguistics, B
Russian Language and Literature, B
Sociology, B
Spanish Language and Literature, B
Spanish and Iberian Studies, B
Theatre Literature, History and Criticism, B
Women's Studies, B

CENTRAL MAINE COMMUNITY COLLEGE

Accounting, A
Administrative Assistant and Secretarial Science, A
Automobile/Automotive Mechanics Technology/Technician, A
Biology/Biological Sciences, A
Business Administration and Management, A
Civil Engineering Technology/Technician, A
Construction Trades, A
Criminal Justice/Law Enforcement Administration, A
Criminal Justice/Safety Studies, A
Early Childhood Education and Teaching, A
Electromechanical Technology/Electromechanical Engineering Technology, A
Graphic Communications, A
Graphic and Printing Equipment Operator Production, A
Human Services, A
Liberal Arts and Sciences Studies and Humanities, A
Machine Tool Technology/Machinist, A
Medical/Clinical Assistant, A
Multi-/Interdisciplinary Studies, A
System Administration/Administrator, A

COLBY COLLEGE

African-American/Black Studies, B
American/United States Studies/Civilization, B
Ancient Studies/Civilization, B
Anthropology, B
Art History, Criticism and Conservation, B
Art/Art Studies, General, B
Biochemistry, B
Biology/Biological Sciences, B
Chemistry, B
Classics and Classical Languages, Literatures, and Linguistics, B
Computer Science, B
Drama and Dramatics/Theatre Arts, B
East Asian Studies, B
Economics, B
Education, B
English Language and Literature, B
Environmental Biology, B
Environmental Sciences, B
Environmental Studies, B
Fine/Studio Arts, B

French Language and Literature, B
Geology/Earth Science, B
German Language and Literature, B
History, B
International/Global Studies, B
Latin American Studies, B
Mathematics, B
Molecular Biology, B
Multi-/Interdisciplinary Studies, B
Music, B
Natural Resources Conservation and Research, B
Philosophy, B
Physics, B
Political Science and Government, B
Psychology, B
Religion/Religious Studies, B
Russian Studies, B
Science, Technology and Society, B
Sociology, B
Spanish Language and Literature, B
Women's Studies, B

COLLEGE OF THE ATLANTIC

Agriculture, Agriculture Operations and Related Sciences, B
Animation, Interactive Technology, Video Graphics and Special Effects, B
Art/Art Studies, General, B
Biological and Physical Sciences, B
Biology/Biological Sciences, B
Botany/Plant Biology, B
Ceramic Arts and Ceramics, B
Comparative Literature, B
Computer Graphics, B
Drawing, B
Economics, B
Education, B
Elementary Education and Teaching, B
English Language and Literature, B
Entrepreneurship/Entrepreneurial Studies, B
Environmental Biology, B
Environmental Design/Architecture, B
Environmental Studies, BM
Evolutionary Biology, B
Family and Consumer Sciences/Human Sciences, B
Film/Video and Photographic Arts, B
Junior High/Intermediate/Middle School Education and Teaching, B
Landscape Architecture, B
Law and Legal Studies, B
Liberal Arts and Sciences Studies and Humanities, B
Marine Biology and Biological Oceanography, B
Museology/Museum Studies, B
Music, B
Natural Sciences, B
Oceanography, Chemical and Physical, B
Philosophy, B
Pre-Veterinary Studies, B
Psychology, B
Public Policy Analysis, B
Science Teacher Education/General Science Teacher Education, B
Secondary Education and Teaching, B
Wildlife Biology, B
Zoology/Animal Biology, B

EASTERN MAINE COMMUNITY COLLEGE

Administrative Assistant and Secretarial Science, A
Automobile/Automotive Mechanics Technology/Technician, A
Banking and Financial Support Services, A
Business Administration and Management, A
CAD/CADD Drafting and/or Design Technology/Technician, A
Civil Engineering Technology/Technician, A
Computer Technology/Computer Systems Technology, A
Construction Engineering Technology/Technician, A
Culinary Arts/Chef Training, A
Early Childhood Education and Teaching, A
Electrical, Electronic and Communications Engineering Technology/Technician, A
Emergency Medical Technology/Technician (EMT Paramedic), A

Heating, Air Conditioning, Ventilation and Refrigeration Maintenance Technology/Technician, A
Heavy Equipment Maintenance Technology/Technician, A
Liberal Arts and Sciences Studies and Humanities, A
Machine Tool Technology/Machinist, A
Medical Radiologic Technology/Science - Radiation Therapist, A
Medical Transcription/Transcriptionist, A
Multi-/Interdisciplinary Studies, A
Restaurant, Culinary, and Catering Management/Manager, A
Surgical Technology/Technologist, A
Teacher Assistant/Aide, A
Telecommunications Technology/Technician, A
Welding Technology/Welder, A

HUSSON UNIVERSITY

Accounting, AB
Accounting and Business/Management, B
Audiovisual Communications Technologies/Technicians, B
Banking and Financial Support Services, B
Biology Teacher Education, B
Biology/Biological Sciences, B
Business Administration and Management, AB
Business Administration, Management and Operations, M
Business/Commerce, B
Business/Managerial Economics, B
Chemistry, B
Clinical Psychology, M
Community Health Nursing, MO
Computer Programming/Programmer, B
Computer and Information Sciences, AB
Counseling Psychology, M
Counselor Education/School Counseling and Guidance Services, M
Criminal Justice/Law Enforcement Administration, AB
Criminal Justice/Safety Studies, AB
Criminology, BM
Elementary Education and Teaching, B
English Language and Literature, B
English/Language Arts Teacher Education, B
Entrepreneurship/Entrepreneurial Studies, B
Environmental Sciences, B
Finance, B
Forensic Science and Technology, B
Health Services Administration, M
Health Services/Allied Health/Health Sciences, B
Health and Physical Education, B
Hospitality Administration/Management, BM
Hospitality and Recreation Marketing Operations, B
Hotel/Motel Administration/Management, B
International Business/Trade/Commerce, B
International Marketing, B
Kinesiology and Exercise Science, B
Legal Assistant/Paralegal, AB
Liberal Arts and Sciences Studies and Humanities, B
Management Information Systems and Services, B
Marketing Research, B
Marketing/Marketing Management, B
Non-Profit/Public/Organizational Management, M
Nursing, MO
Nursing - Advanced Practice, MO
Nursing Education, MO
Occupational Therapy/Therapist, M
Parks, Recreation and Leisure Facilities Management, B
Pastoral Studies/Counseling, M
Pharmacy, D
Photographic and Film/Video Technology/Technician and Assistant, B
Physical Education Teaching and Coaching, B
Physical Therapy/Therapist, D
Pre-Pharmacy Studies, B
Psychiatric/Mental Health Nurse/Nursing, MO
Psychology, B
Public Finance, B
Recording Arts Technology/Technician, B
Sales, Distribution and Marketing Operations, B
School Psychology, M
Secondary Education and Teaching, B

Small Business Administration/Management, B
Social Psychology, M
Sport and Fitness Administration/Management, B
Technical Theatre/Theatre Design and Technology, B

KAPLAN UNIVERSITY, SOUTH PORT-LAND

Accounting, A
Administrative Assistant and Secretarial Science, A
Business Administration and Management, A
Child Care and Support Services Management, A
Criminal Justice/Law Enforcement Administration, A
Legal Assistant/Paralegal, A
Management Information Systems and Services, A
Medical/Clinical Assistant, A
Tourism and Travel Services Management, A

KENNEBEC VALLEY COMMUNITY COL-LEGE

Accounting Technology/Technician and Bookkeeping, A
Biology Technician/BioTechnology Laboratory Technician, A
Child Development, A
Cooking and Related Culinary Arts, A
Diagnostic Medical Sonography/Sonographer and Ultrasound Technician, A
Drafting/Design Engineering Technologies/Technicians, A
Electrical, Electronic and Communications Engineering Technology/Technician, A
Electrical/Electronics Maintenance and Repair Technology, A
Electrician, A
Emergency Medical Technology/Technician (EMT Paramedic), A
Health Information/Medical Records Technology/Technician, A
Heating, Air Conditioning and Refrigeration Technology/Technician, A
Industrial Mechanics and Maintenance Technology, A
Liberal Arts and Sciences Studies and Humanities, A
Lineworker, A
Machine Tool Technology/Machinist, A
Management Information Systems and Services, A
Marketing/Marketing Management, A
Medical Administrative Assistant/Secretary, A
Medical/Clinical Assistant, A
Mental and Social Health Services and Allied Professions, A
Multi-/Interdisciplinary Studies, A
Occupational Therapist Assistant, A
Physical Therapist Assistant, A
Radiologic Technology/Science - Radiographer, A
Respiratory Care Therapy/Therapist, A
Welding Technology/Welder, A
Wood Science and Wood Products/Pulp and Paper Technology, A

THE LANDING SCHOOL

Marine Maintenance/Fitter and Ship Repair Technology/Technician, A

MAINE COLLEGE OF ART

Ceramic Arts and Ceramics, B
Crafts/Craft Design, Folk Art and Artisanry, B
Fine Arts and Art Studies, M
Graphic Design, B
Illustration, B
Intermedia/Multimedia, B
Metal and Jewelry Arts, B
Painting, B
Photography, B
Printmaking, B
Sculpture, B

Visual and Performing Arts, B

MAINE COLLEGE OF HEALTH PRO-FESSIONS

Nuclear Medical Technology/Technologist, A
Radiologic Technology/Science - Radiographer, A

MAINE MARITIME ACADEMY

Business Administration and Management, B
Engineering, B
Engineering Technology, B
International Business/Trade/Commerce, BM
Logistics and Materials Management, B
Marine Biology and Biological Oceanography, B
Marine Science/Merchant Marine Officer, B
Naval Architecture and Marine Engineering, B
Oceanography, Chemical and Physical, B
Supply Chain Management, M
Systems Engineering, B
Transportation and Materials Moving, B
Transportation/Transportation Management, M

NORTHERN MAINE COMMUNITY COL-LEGE

Accounting, A
Administrative Assistant and Secretarial Science, A
Automobile/Automotive Mechanics Technology/Technician, A
Business Administration and Management, A
Carpentry/Carpenter, A
Computer Programming/Programmer, A
Computer Systems Networking and Telecommunications, A
Construction Trades, A
Drafting and Design Technology/Technician, A
Electrical, Electronic and Communications Engineering Technology/Technician, A
Emergency Medical Technology/Technician (EMT Paramedic), A
General Studies, A
Heating, Air Conditioning, Ventilation and Refrigeration Maintenance Technology/Technician, A
Kindergarten/PreSchool Education and Teaching, A
Legal Administrative Assistant/Secretary, A
Liberal Arts and Sciences Studies and Humanities, A
Medical Administrative Assistant/Secretary, A
Pipefitting/Pipefitter and Sprinkler Fitter, A

SAINT JOSEPH'S COLLEGE OF MAINE

Accounting, BM
Adult and Continuing Education and Teaching, M
Biology Teacher Education, B
Biology/Biological Sciences, B
Business Administration and Management, B
Business Administration, Management and Operations, M
Chemistry, B
Chemistry Teacher Education, B
Classics and Classical Languages, Literatures, and Linguistics, B
Criminal Justice/Safety Studies, B
Digital Communication and Media/Multimedia, B
Education, BM
Educational Leadership and Administration, M
Elementary Education and Teaching, B
English Language and Literature, B
English/Language Arts Teacher Education, B
Environmental Sciences, B
Environmental Studies, B
Finance, B
General Studies, B
Health Education, M
Health Services Administration, M
History, B
History Teacher Education, B
Human Resources Management/Personnel Administration, B
International Business/Trade/Commerce, B
Journalism, B
Kinesiology and Exercise Science, B
Liberal Arts and Sciences Studies and Humanities, B
Management Science, B
Marine Biology and Biological Oceanography, B

Marketing/Marketing Management, B
Mass Communication/Media Studies, B
Mathematics, B
Mathematics Teacher Education, B
Nursing, MO
Nursing - Advanced Practice, M
Nursing Administration, MO
Nursing Education, MO
Ophthalmic and Optometric Support Services and Allied Professions, B
Pastoral Studies/Counseling, M
Philosophy, B
Physical Education Teaching and Coaching, B
Physician Assistant, B
Political Science and Government, B
Pre-Dentistry Studies, B
Pre-Medicine/Pre-Medical Studies, B
Pre-Pharmacy Studies, B
Pre-Veterinary Studies, B
Psychology, B
Public Relations/Image Management, B
Religion/Religious Studies, B
Social Work, B
Sociology, B
Special Education and Teaching, B
Sport and Fitness Administration/Management, B
Theology/Theological Studies, B

SOUTHERN MAINE COMMUNITY COL-LEGE

Automobile/Automotive Mechanics Technology/Technician, A
BioTechnology, A
Business Administration and Management, A
Cardiovascular Technology/Technologist, A
Computer Engineering Technology/Technician, A
Computer Science, A
Culinary Arts/Chef Training, A
Dietetic Technician (DTR), A
Digital Communication and Media/Multimedia, A
Drafting and Design Technology/Technician, A
Early Childhood Education and Teaching, A
Electrical, Electronic and Communications Engineering Technology/Technician, A
Emergency Medical Technology/Technician (EMT Paramedic), A
Fire Science/Firefighting, A
Health Information/Medical Records Technology/Technician, A
Heating, Air Conditioning, Ventilation and Refrigeration Maintenance Technology/Technician, A
Liberal Arts and Sciences Studies and Humanities, A
Machine Tool Technology/Machinist, A
Marine Biology and Biological Oceanography, A
Materials Engineering, A
Medical/Clinical Assistant, A
Plumbing Technology/Plumber, A
Radiologic Technology/Science - Radiographer, A
Respiratory Care Therapy/Therapist, A
Surgical Technology/Technologist, A

THOMAS COLLEGE

Accounting, AB
American Government and Politics (United States), B
Business Administration and Management, AB
Business Administration, Management and Operations, M
Business Education, M
Business/Commerce, A
Computer Education, M
Computer Science, B
Computer/Information Technology Services Administration and Management, B
Criminal Justice/Law Enforcement Administration, B
Early Childhood Education and Teaching, B
Elementary Education and Teaching, B
English Language and Literature, B
Finance, B
General Studies, B
Hotel/Motel Administration/Management, B
Human Resources Management and Services, M
Human Resources Management/Personnel Administration, B
International Business/Trade/Commerce, B

Liberal Arts and Sciences Studies and Humanities, A
Management Information Systems and Services, B
Marketing/Marketing Management, B
Psychology, B
Public Relations, Advertising, and Applied Communication, B
Secondary Education and Teaching, B
Sport and Fitness Administration/Management, B

UNITY COLLEGE

Communication and Media Studies, B
Energy Management and Systems Technology/Technician, B
Environmental Biology, B
Environmental Sciences, B
Fine/Studio Arts, B
Liberal Arts and Sciences Studies and Humanities, A
Marine Biology and Biological Oceanography, B
Secondary Education and Teaching, B
Therapeutic Recreation/Recreational Therapy, B
Wildlife Biology, B
Wildlife and Wildlands Science and Management, B

UNIVERSITY OF MAINE

Accounting, BM
Agricultural Economics, M
Agricultural Sciences, MDO
Agricultural/Biological Engineering and Bioengineering, B
Animal Sciences, BM
Anthropology, BD
Applied Horticulture/Horticultural Operations, B
Art History, Criticism and Conservation, B
Art Teacher Education, B
Athletic Training and Sports Medicine, B
Biochemistry, B
Bioinformatics, M
Biological and Biomedical Sciences, MD
Biology Teacher Education, B
Biology/Biological Sciences, B
Biomedical Engineering, D
Biomedical/Medical Engineering, B
Botany/Plant Biology, BM
Business Administration and Management, B
Business Administration, Management and Operations, MO
Canadian Studies, M
Chemical Engineering, BMD
Chemistry, BMD
Chemistry Teacher Education, B
Civil Engineering, BMD
Civil Engineering Technology/Technician, B
Clinical Laboratory Science/Medical Technology/Technologist, B
Communication Disorders, BM
Communication and Media Studies, MD
Composition, M
Computer Engineering, BMD
Computer Science, BMDO
Counselor Education/School Counseling and Guidance Services, MDO
Digital Communication and Media/Multimedia, B
Drama and Dramatics/Theatre Arts, B
Early Childhood Education and Teaching, O
East Asian Studies, M
Ecology, MD
Economics, BM
Education, MDO
Educational Leadership and Administration, MDO
Educational Media/Instructional Technology, O
Electrical Engineering, MD
Electrical, Electronic and Communications Engineering Technology/Technician, B
Electrical, Electronics and Communications Engineering, B
Elementary Education and Teaching, BMDO
Engineering Physics, BM
Engineering and Applied Sciences, MD
English, M
English Education, M
English Language and Literature, B
English/Language Arts Teacher Education, B
Entomology, M
Environmental Policy and Resource Management, D

Environmental Sciences, BMD
Exercise and Sports Science, MDO
Finance, B
Finance and Banking, M
Fine Arts and Art Studies, M
Fine/Studio Arts, B
Fish, Game and Wildlife Management, MD
Food Science, B
Food Science and Technology, MD
Foreign Language Teacher Education, B
Foreign Languages and Literatures, B
Forest Sciences and Biology, B
Forestry, BMD
French Language Teacher Education, B
French Language and Literature, B
Gender Studies, M
Geographic Information Systems, MDO
Geology/Earth Science, BMO
Geosciences, MD
German Language and Literature, B
Higher Education/Higher Education Administration, MDO
History, BMD
History Teacher Education, B
Horticultural Science, M
Human Development, MDO
Human Development and Family Studies, B
Information Science/Studies, MDO
Interdisciplinary Studies, MD
International Affairs, M
International Business/Trade/Commerce, M
International Relations and Affairs, B
Journalism, B
Kinesiology and Movement Studies, M
Latin Language and Literature, B
Liberal Arts and Sciences Studies and Humanities, B
Management, M
Management Information Systems and Services, M
Marine Affairs, M
Marine Biology and Biological Oceanography, MD
Marine Sciences, MD
Marketing/Marketing Management, B
Mass Communication/Media Studies, BM
Mathematics, B
Mathematics Teacher Education, BMDO
Mechanical Engineering, BMD
Mechanical Engineering/Mechanical Technology/Technician, B
Microbiology, BD
Molecular Biology, BMD
Multi-/Interdisciplinary Studies, B
Music, BM
Music Performance, B
Music Teacher Education, B
Natural Resources and Conservation, MD
Nursing, MO
Nursing - Advanced Practice, MO
Nursing Education, O
Nutritional Sciences, MD
Oceanography, Chemical and Physical, MD
Parks, Recreation and Leisure Facilities Management, B
Performance, M
Philosophy, B
Physical Education Teaching and Coaching, BM
Physics, BMD
Plant Pathology/Phytopathology, M
Plant Sciences, D
Political Science and Government, B
Psychology, BMD
Reading Teacher Education, DO
Romance Languages, Literatures, and Linguistics, B
Science Teacher Education/General Science Teacher Education, BMDO
Secondary Education and Teaching, BMDO
Social Studies Teacher Education, BM
Social Work, BMO
Sociology, B
Spanish Language Teacher Education, B
Spanish Language and Literature, B
Special Education and Teaching, M
Survey Technology/Surveying, B
Sustainability Management, M
Water Resources, MD
Western European Studies, M

Wildlife and Wildlands Science and Management, B
Women's Studies, B
Wood Science and Wood Products/Pulp and Paper Technology, B
Zoology/Animal Biology, BMD

UNIVERSITY OF MAINE AT AUGUSTA

Accounting, B
Architectural Technology/Technician, B
Architecture, B
Biology/Biological Sciences, B
Business Administration and Management, AB
Clinical/Medical Laboratory Assistant, A
Computer and Information Systems Security, B
Criminal Justice/Law Enforcement Administration, B
Criminal Justice/Safety Studies, A
Dental Assisting/Assistant, A
Dental Hygiene/Hygienist, AB
English Language and Literature, B
Financial Planning and Services, B
Fine/Studio Arts, AB
Flight Instructor, B
Information Technology, AB
Jazz/Jazz Studies, AB
Liberal Arts and Sciences Studies and Humanities, AB
Library Assistant/Technician, A
Library Science, B
Mental and Social Health Services and Allied Professions, AB
Psychiatric/Mental Health Services Technician, AB
Public Administration, AB
Social Sciences, B
Veterinary/Animal Health Technology/Technician and Veterinary Assistant, AB

UNIVERSITY OF MAINE AT FARMINGTON

Actuarial Science, B
Art/Art Studies, General, B
Biology Teacher Education, B
Biology/Biological Sciences, B
Business Administration, Management and Operations, B
Business/Managerial Economics, B
Chemistry Teacher Education, B
Community Health Services/Liaison/Counseling, B
Computer Science, B
Early Childhood Education and Teaching, BM
Education, M
Education/Teaching of Individuals in Early Childhood Special Education Programs, B
Educational Leadership and Administration, M
Elementary Education and Teaching, B
English Language and Literature, B
English/Language Arts Teacher Education, B
Environmental Sciences, B
Environmental Studies, B
Geography, B
Geology/Earth Science, B
Health Information/Medical Records Administration/Administrator, B
Health Teacher Education, B
History, B
Intermedia/Multimedia, B
International/Global Studies, B
Kindergarten/PreSchool Education and Teaching, B
Liberal Arts and Sciences Studies and Humanities, B
Mathematics, B
Mathematics Teacher Education, B
Multi-/Interdisciplinary Studies, B
Music, B
Physics Teacher Education, B
Political Science and Government, B
Psychology, B
Secondary Education and Teaching, B
Social Science Teacher Education, B
Special Education and Teaching, B
Visual and Performing Arts, B

UNIVERSITY OF MAINE AT FORT KENT

Behavioral Sciences, B
Biology/Biological Sciences, B
Business Administration and Management, AB
Business/Commerce, AB

Computer Science, AB
Computer and Information Systems Security, A
Criminal Justice/Law Enforcement Administration, A
English Language and Literature, B
Environmental Studies, B
Forestry Technology/Technician, A
French Language and Literature, B
General Studies, A
Health Services/Allied Health/Health Sciences, A
Human Services, B
Liberal Arts and Sciences Studies and Humanities, AB
Public Administration, B
Social Sciences, B
Teacher Education, Multiple Levels, B

UNIVERSITY OF MAINE AT MACHIAS

Accounting, B
Art/Art Studies, General, B
Behavioral Sciences, B
Biology Teacher Education, B
Biology/Biological Sciences, B
Business Administration and Management, B
Business Teacher Education, B
Conservation Biology, B
Drama and Dramatics/Theatre Arts, B
Ecology, B
Education, B
Elementary Education and Teaching, B
English Language and Literature, B
English/Language Arts Teacher Education, B
Entrepreneurship/Entrepreneurial Studies, B
Environmental Studies, B
Family and Community Services, B
General Studies, B
History, B
History Teacher Education, B
Hotel/Motel Administration/Management, B
Human Services, B
Marine Biology and Biological Oceanography, B
Marketing/Marketing Management, B
Mathematics Teacher Education, B
Music, B
Parks, Recreation and Leisure Facilities Management, B
Parks, Recreation, Leisure and Fitness Studies, B
Pre-Medicine/Pre-Medical Studies, B
Psychology, B
Public Administration, B
Science Teacher Education/General Science Teacher Education, B
Social Science Teacher Education, B
Tourism and Travel Services Management, B
Visual and Performing Arts, B

UNIVERSITY OF MAINE AT PRESQUE ISLE

Art/Art Studies, General, B
Athletic Training and Sports Medicine, B
Biology/Biological Sciences, B
Business Administration and Management, A
Clinical/Medical Laboratory Assistant, A
Clinical/Medical Laboratory Technician, A
Criminal Justice/Law Enforcement Administration, AB
Design and Applied Arts, A
Education, B
Elementary Education and Teaching, B
English Language and Literature, B
Environmental Sciences, B
Environmental Studies, B
Fine/Studio Arts, B
History, B
Liberal Arts and Sciences Studies and Humanities, AB
Mathematics, B
Physical Education Teaching and Coaching, B
Physical Therapist Assistant, A
Political Science and Government, B
Psychology, B
Public Relations, Advertising, and Applied Communication, A
Secondary Education and Teaching, B
Social Sciences, B
Social Work, B
Special Education and Teaching, A

Teacher Assistant/Aide, A

UNIVERSITY OF NEW ENGLAND

Animal Behavior and Ethology, B
Aquaculture, B
Athletic Training and Sports Medicine, B
Biochemistry, B
Biological and Biomedical Sciences, M
Biology/Biological Sciences, B
Biomedical Sciences, B
Business Administration and Management, B
Business/Corporate Communications, B
Chemistry, B
Clinical Laboratory Science/Medical Technology/Technologist, B
Curriculum and Instruction, MO
Dental Hygiene/Hygienist, B
Dentistry, D
Education, MO
Educational Leadership and Administration, MDO
Educational Measurement and Evaluation, M
Elementary Education and Teaching, B
English Language and Literature, B
Environmental Sciences, B
Environmental Studies, B
Ethics, O
Health Education, MO
Health Professions and Related Clinical Sciences, B
Health Services/Allied Health/Health Sciences, B
Health and Physical Education/Fitness, B
Health/Health Care Administration/Management, B
History, B
Kinesiology and Exercise Science, B
Liberal Arts and Sciences Studies and Humanities, B
Marine Biology and Biological Oceanography, B
Marine Sciences, M
Mathematics, B
Nurse Anesthetist, M
Occupational Therapy/Therapist, BM
Osteopathic Medicine, D
Pharmacy, D
Physical Therapy/Therapist, D
Physician Assistant, M
Political Science and Government, B
Pre-Medicine/Pre-Medical Studies, B
Pre-Pharmacy Studies, B
Psychology, B
Public Health, MO
Public Health (MPH, DPH), B
Reading Teacher Education, MO
Social Sciences, B
Social Work, BM
Sociology, B
Special Education and Teaching, M
Sport and Fitness Administration/Management, B
Vocational and Technical Education, MO

UNIVERSITY OF SOUTHERN MAINE

Accounting, BM
Accounting and Finance, B
Adult and Continuing Education and Teaching, MO
American/United States Studies/Civilization, MO
Applied Behavior Analysis, MO
Art Teacher Education, B
Athletic Training and Sports Medicine, B
Biological and Biomedical Sciences, M
Biology/Biological Sciences, B
Business Administration and Management, B
Business Administration, Management and Operations, BM
Chemistry, B
Communication Studies/Speech Communication and Rhetoric, B
Composition, M
Computer Science, BMO
Counseling Psychology, M
Counselor Education/School Counseling and Guidance Services, MO
Criminology, B
Cultural Studies, O
Drama and Dramatics/Theatre Arts, B
Economics, B
Education, MDO
Education/Teaching of the Gifted and Talented, O
Educational Administration and Supervision, O

Educational Leadership and Administration, MO
Educational Psychology, MO
Electrical, Electronics and Communications Engineering, B
English Language and Literature, B
English as a Second Language, MO
Environmental Sciences, B
Environmental Studies, B
Exercise Physiology, B
Finance, B
Finance and Banking, M
Fine/Studio Arts, B
French Language and Literature, B
Geology/Earth Science, B
Gerontological Nursing, MO
Health Services Administration, M
Health and Physical Education, B
Higher Education/Higher Education Administration, M
History, B
Humanities/Humanistic Studies, B
Immunology, M
Industrial Technology/Technician, B
Law and Legal Studies, D
Liberal Arts and Sciences Studies and Humanities, B
Linguistics, B
Management, MO
Marketing/Marketing Management, B
Mass Communication/Media Studies, B
Mathematics, B
Mathematics Teacher Education, B
Mechanical Engineering, B
Molecular Biology, M
Music, BM
Music Performance, M
Music Teacher Education, BM
Nursing, MDO
Nursing - Adult, MO
Nursing - Advanced Practice, MO
Nursing Administration, M
Nursing Education, M
Occupational Therapy/Therapist, M
Performance, M
Philosophy, B
Physical Sciences, B
Physics, B
Political Science and Government, B
Psychiatric/Mental Health Nurse/Nursing, O
Psychology, B
Public Health, MO
Public Policy Analysis, M
Reading Teacher Education, MO
Rehabilitation Counseling, M
School Psychology, MD
Social Sciences, B
Social Work, BM
Sociology, B
Software Engineering, O
Special Education and Teaching, MO
Statistics, MO
Substance Abuse/Addiction Counseling, O
Sustainability Management, M
Therapeutic Recreation/Recreational Therapy, B
Trade and Industrial Teacher Education, B
Urban and Regional Planning, MO
Women's Studies, B
Writing, M

WASHINGTON COUNTY COMMUNITY COLLEGE

Automobile/Automotive Mechanics Technology/Technician, A
Business Administration and Management, A
Child Development, A
Computer Installation and Repair Technology/Technician, A
Construction Engineering Technology/Technician, A
Engineering Technology, A
Marine Maintenance/Fitter and Ship Repair Technology/Technician, A
Mechanic and Repair Technologies/Technicians, A
Medical/Clinical Assistant, A
Multi-/Interdisciplinary Studies, A
Parks, Recreation, Leisure and Fitness Studies, A

Teacher Assistant/Aide, A

YORK COUNTY COMMUNITY COLLEGE

Accounting, A
Animation, Interactive Technology, Video Graphics and Special Effects, A
Architectural Drafting and Architectural CAD/CADD, A
Business Administration and Management, A
Computer Science, A
Construction Trades, A
Criminal Justice/Safety Studies, A
Culinary Arts/Chef Training, A
Drafting and Design Technology/Technician, A
Early Childhood Education and Teaching, A
Education, A
Health Information/Medical Records Technology/Technician, A
Health Services/Allied Health/Health Sciences, A
Human Services, A
Liberal Arts and Sciences Studies and Humanities, A
Machine Tool Technology/Machinist, A
Medical/Clinical Assistant, A
Multi-/Interdisciplinary Studies, A
System Administration/Administrator, A
Veterinary/Animal Health Technology/Technician and Veterinary Assistant, A

Maryland

ALLEGANY COLLEGE OF MARYLAND

Accounting Technology/Technician and Bookkeeping, A
Administrative Assistant and Secretarial Science, A
Automobile/Automotive Mechanics Technology/Technician, A
Business Administration and Management, A
Clinical/Medical Laboratory Assistant, A
Clinical/Medical Laboratory Technician, A
Communications Technology/Technician, A
Computer Engineering Technology/Technician, A
Cosmetology and Related Personal Grooming Arts, A
Criminal Justice/Police Science, A
Culinary Arts/Chef Training, A
Dental Hygiene/Hygienist, A
Forest Management/Forest Resources Management, A
Health Professions and Related Clinical Sciences, A
Hospitality Administration/Management, A
Legal Assistant/Paralegal, A
Liberal Arts and Sciences Studies and Humanities, A
Management Information Systems and Services, A
Marketing/Marketing Management, A
Medical Radiologic Technology/Science - Radiation Therapist, A
Occupational Therapist Assistant, A
Occupational Therapy/Therapist, A
Physical Therapist Assistant, A
Psychiatric/Mental Health Services Technician, A
Respiratory Care Therapy/Therapist, A

ANNE ARUNDEL COMMUNITY COLLEGE

Accounting Technology/Technician and Bookkeeping, A
Architectural Drafting and Architectural CAD/CADD, A
Business Administration and Management, A
Business Administration, Management and Operations, A
Business/Commerce, A
Chemistry Teacher Education, A
Child Care and Support Services Management, A
Clinical/Medical Laboratory Technician, A
Communications Technologies/Technicians and Support Services, A
Computer Systems Networking and Telecommunications, A
Computer and Information Sciences, A
Computer and Information Systems Security, A
Criminal Justice/Law Enforcement Administration, A
Criminal Justice/Police Science, A

Early Childhood Education and Teaching, A
Electrical, Electronic and Communications Engineering Technology/Technician, A
Electrical, Electronics and Communications Engineering, A
Engineering, A
English/Language Arts Teacher Education, A
Entrepreneurship/Entrepreneurial Studies, A
Fire Protection and Safety Technology/Technician, A
Gerontology, A
Graphic Design, A
Health Information/Medical Records Technology/Technician, A
Health and Physical Education, A
Hotel/Motel Administration/Management, A
Legal Assistant/Paralegal, A
Liberal Arts and Sciences Studies and Humanities, A
Management Information Systems and Services, A
Mathematics, A
Mathematics Teacher Education, A
Medical Administrative Assistant/Secretary, A
Medical Radiologic Technology/Science - Radiation Therapist, A
Multi-/Interdisciplinary Studies, A
Occupational Safety and Health Technology/Technician, A
Physical Therapist Assistant, A
Physics Teacher Education, A
Pre-Law Studies, A
Psychiatric/Mental Health Services Technician, A
Public Health (MPH, DPH), A
Spanish Language Teacher Education, A
Substance Abuse/Addiction Counseling, A
Surgical Technology/Technologist, A

BALTIMORE CITY COMMUNITY COLLEGE

Accounting Technology/Technician and Bookkeeping, A
Administrative Assistant and Secretarial Science, A
Building/Construction Finishing, Management, and Inspection, A
Business Administration and Management, A
Business/Commerce, A
Child Care and Support Services Management, A
Computer Programming, Specific Applications, A
Computer and Information Sciences, A
Criminal Justice/Police Science, A
Dental Hygiene/Hygienist, A
Dietetic Technician (DTR), A
Drafting and Design Technology/Technician, A
Drama and Dramatics/Theatre Arts, A
Education, A
Electrical, Electronic and Communications Engineering Technology/Technician, A
Elementary Education and Teaching, A
Emergency Medical Technology/Technician (EMT Paramedic), A
Engineering, A
Environmental Sciences, A
Fashion/Apparel Design, A
Fire Protection and Safety Technology/Technician, A
General Studies, A
Health Information/Medical Records Technology/Technician, A
Hotel/Motel Administration/Management, A
Legal Assistant/Paralegal, A
Liberal Arts and Sciences Studies and Humanities, A
Machine Tool Technology/Machinist, A
Mental and Social Health Services and Allied Professions, A
Physical Therapist Assistant, A
Respiratory Care Therapy/Therapist, A
Science Technologies/Technicians, A
Surgical Technology/Technologist, A

BOWIE STATE UNIVERSITY

Accounting, B
Applied Mathematics, BM
Art/Art Studies, General, B
Biology/Biological Sciences, B
Broadcast Journalism, B
Business Administration and Management, B

Business Administration, Management and Operations, M
Computer Graphics, B
Computer Science, MD
Computer and Information Sciences, B
Corporate and Organizational Communication, MO
Counseling Psychology, M
Counselor Education/School Counseling and Guidance Services, M
Criminal Justice/Law Enforcement Administration, B
Economics, B
Education, BM
Educational Administration and Supervision, M
Educational Leadership and Administration, D
Elementary Education and Teaching, BM
English, M
English Language and Literature, B
History, B
Human Resources Development, M
Kindergarten/PreSchool Education and Teaching, B
Management Information Systems and Services, MO
Marketing/Marketing Management, B
Mass Communication/Media Studies, B
Mathematics, B
Mathematics Teacher Education, B
Nursing, M
Nursing - Advanced Practice, M
Nursing Administration, M
Nursing Education, M
Political Science and Government, B
Psychology, B
Public Administration, M
Public Relations/Image Management, B
Reading Teacher Education, M
Science Teacher Education/General Science Teacher Education, M
Secondary Education and Teaching, BM
Social Work, B
Sociology, B
Special Education and Teaching, BM

BRIGHTWOOD COLLEGE, BALTIMORE CAMPUS

Computer Systems Networking and Telecommunications, A

BRIGHTWOOD COLLEGE, BELTSVILLE CAMPUS

Computer Systems Networking and Telecommunications, A
Criminal Justice/Safety Studies, A
Health Information/Medical Records Technology/Technician, A

BRIGHTWOOD COLLEGE, TOWSON CAMPUS

Computer Systems Networking and Telecommunications, A
Criminal Justice/Safety Studies, A

CAPITOL TECHNOLOGY UNIVERSITY

Aerospace, Aeronautical and Astronautical Engineering, B
Business Administration and Management, B
Business Administration, Management and Operations, M
Computer Engineering, B
Computer Engineering Technology/Technician, B
Computer Programming/Programmer, B
Computer Science, M
Computer Technology/Computer Systems Technology, A
Computer and Information Sciences, B
Computer and Information Sciences and Support Services, B
Computer and Information Systems Security, M
Electrical Engineering, M
Electrical and Electronic Engineering Technologies/Technicians, AB
Electrical, Electronic and Communications Engineering Technology/Technician, A
Electrical, Electronics and Communications Engineering, B
Engineering Technologies/Technicians, B

Information Science/Studies, M
Management Information Systems and Services, M
Operations Management and Supervision, B
Telecommunications Management, M

CARROLL COMMUNITY COLLEGE

Accounting Technology/Technician and Bookkeeping, A
Administrative Assistant and Secretarial Science, A
Architectural Drafting and Architectural CAD/CADD, A
Art/Art Studies, General, A
Business Administration and Management, A
Chemistry Teacher Education, A
Child Care and Support Services Management, A
Computer Engineering, A
Computer Graphics, A
Criminal Justice/Police Science, A
Early Childhood Education and Teaching, A
Education, A
Electrical, Electronics and Communications Engineering, A
Elementary Education and Teaching, A
Emergency Medical Technology/Technician (EMT Paramedic), A
English/Language Arts Teacher Education, A
Forensic Science and Technology, A
General Studies, A
Health Information/Medical Records Technology/Technician, A
Health Professions and Related Clinical Sciences, A
Kinesiology and Exercise Science, A
Law and Legal Studies, A
Liberal Arts and Sciences Studies and Humanities, A
Management Information Systems and Services, A
Mathematics Teacher Education, A
Multi-/Interdisciplinary Studies, A
Music, A
Physical Therapist Assistant, A
Psychology, A
Spanish Language Teacher Education, A
Technical Theatre/Theatre Design and Technology, A

CECIL COLLEGE

Administrative Assistant and Secretarial Science, A
Aeronautics/Aviation/Aerospace Science and Technology, A
Air Traffic Controller, A
Animation, Interactive Technology, Video Graphics and Special Effects, A
Applied Horticulture/Horticultural Operations, A
BioTechnology, A
Biology/Biological Sciences, A
Business Administration and Management, A
Business/Commerce, A
Business/Corporate Communications, A
Chemistry, A
Child Care and Support Services Management, A
Commercial Photography, A
Criminal Justice/Police Science, A
Design and Visual Communications, A
Drawing, A
Education, A
Electrical, Electronic and Communications Engineering Technology/Technician, A
Elementary Education and Teaching, A
Emergency Medical Technology/Technician (EMT Paramedic), A
English/Language Arts Teacher Education, A
Financial Planning and Services, A
Fine/Studio Arts, A
Fire Science/Firefighting, A
General Studies, A
Health Services/Allied Health/Health Sciences, A
Horse Husbandry/Equine Science and Management, A
Human Resources Management/Personnel Administration, A
Liberal Arts and Sciences Studies and Humanities, A
Logistics and Materials Management, A
Management Information Systems and Services, A
Marketing/Marketing Management, A
Mathematics, A

Office Management and Supervision, A
Photography, A
Physics, A
Purchasing, Procurement/Acquisitions and Contracts Management, A
Secondary Education and Teaching, A
Transportation and Materials Moving, A
Transportation/Transportation Management, A
Web Page, Digital/Multimedia and Information Resources Design, A

CHESAPEAKE COLLEGE

Accounting Technology/Technician and Bookkeeping, A
Business Administration and Management, A
Business/Commerce, A
Child Care and Support Services Management, A
Computer Science, A
Computer and Information Sciences and Support Services, A
Computer and Information Systems Security, A
Corrections and Criminal Justice, A
Early Childhood Education and Teaching, A
Education, A
Elementary Education and Teaching, A
Emergency Medical Technology/Technician (EMT Paramedic), A
Engineering-Related Technologies, A
General Studies, A
Hospitality Administration/Management, A
Legal Assistant/Paralegal, A
Liberal Arts and Sciences Studies and Humanities, A
Mathematics Teacher Education, A
Medical Radiologic Technology/Science - Radiation Therapist, A
Mental and Social Health Services and Allied Professions, A
Physical Therapy/Therapist, A
Physics Teacher Education, A

COLLEGE OF SOUTHERN MARYLAND

Accounting Technology/Technician and Bookkeeping, A
Building/Construction Finishing, Management, and Inspection, A
Business Administration and Management, A
Business/Commerce, A
Child Care and Support Services Management, A
Clinical/Medical Laboratory Technician, A
Communication and Media Studies, A
Computer Engineering, A
Computer Programming/Programmer, A
Computer and Information Sciences, A
Computer and Information Systems Security, A
Criminal Justice/Law Enforcement Administration, A
Digital Communication and Media/Multimedia, A
Early Childhood Education and Teaching, A
Education, A
Electrical, Electronics and Communications Engineering, A
Electrician, A
Elementary Education and Teaching, A
Emergency Medical Technology/Technician (EMT Paramedic), A
Engineering, A
Engineering Technologies/Technicians, A
Fire Science/Firefighting, A
Health Information/Medical Records Technology/Technician, A
Health and Physical Education/Fitness, A
Hospitality Administration/Management, A
Information Technology, A
Law and Legal Studies, A
Liberal Arts and Sciences Studies and Humanities, A
Lineworker, A
Massage Therapy/Therapeutic Massage, A
Mental and Social Health Services and Allied Professions, A
Multi-/Interdisciplinary Studies, A
Nuclear Engineering Technology/Technician, A

Physical Therapist Assistant, A

COMMUNITY COLLEGE OF BALTIMORE COUNTY

Accounting Technology/Technician and Bookkeeping, A
Administrative Assistant and Secretarial Science, A
Aeronautics/Aviation/Aerospace Science and Technology, A
Applied Horticulture/Horticultural Operations, A
Architectural Drafting and Architectural CAD/CADD, A
Automobile/Automotive Mechanics Technology/Technician, A
Biological and Physical Sciences, A
Building/Construction Finishing, Management, and Inspection, A
Building/Construction Site Management/Manager, A
Business Administration and Management, A
Business/Commerce, A
Chemistry Teacher Education, A
Child Care and Support Services Management, A
Clinical/Medical Laboratory Technician, A
Commercial and Advertising Art, A
Computer Engineering, A
Computer Systems Networking and Telecommunications, A
Computer and Information Sciences, A
Computer and Information Systems Security, A
Criminal Justice/Police Science, A
Dental Hygiene/Hygienist, A
Early Childhood Education and Teaching, A
Education, A
Electrical, Electronics and Communications Engineering, A
Elementary Education and Teaching, A
Emergency Medical Technology/Technician (EMT Paramedic), A
Engineering, A
Engineering Technologies/Technicians, A
Funeral Service and Mortuary Science, A
Geography, A
Heating, Air Conditioning and Refrigeration Technology/Technician, A
Hotel/Motel Administration/Management, A
Hydraulics and Fluid Power Technology, A
Legal Assistant/Paralegal, A
Liberal Arts and Sciences Studies and Humanities, A
Management Information Systems and Services, A
Massage Therapy/Therapeutic Massage, A
Mathematics Teacher Education, A
Medical Administrative Assistant/Secretary, A
Medical Informatics, A
Medical Radiologic Technology/Science - Radiation Therapist, A
Occupational Safety and Health Technology/Technician, A
Occupational Therapy/Therapist, A
Parks, Recreation, Leisure and Fitness Studies, A
Physics Teacher Education, A
Psychiatric/Mental Health Services Technician, A
Respiratory Care Therapy/Therapist, A
Sign Language Interpretation and Translation, A
Spanish Language Teacher Education, A
Substance Abuse/Addiction Counseling, A
Survey Technology/Surveying, A
Veterinary/Animal Health Technology/Technician and Veterinary Assistant, A
Visual and Performing Arts, A

COPPIN STATE UNIVERSITY

Adult and Continuing Education and Teaching, M
Biology/Biological Sciences, B
Chemistry, B
Computer Science, B
Criminal Justice/Law Enforcement Administration, B
Criminology, M
Curriculum and Instruction, M
Early Childhood Education and Teaching, B
Education, M
Elementary Education and Teaching, B
English Language and Literature, B
Health Information/Medical Records Administration/Administrator, B
History, B

Human Services, M
International/Global Studies, B
Liberal Arts and Sciences Studies and Humani-
ties, B
Management Science, B
Mathematics, B
Nursing, MO
Nursing - Advanced Practice, O
Psychology, B
Reading Teacher Education, M
Rehabilitation Counseling, M
Social Sciences, B
Social Work, B
Special Education and Teaching, BM
Sport and Fitness Administration/Management, B
Substance Abuse/Addiction Counseling, M
Urban Studies/Affairs, B

FAITH THEOLOGICAL SEMINARY

Theological and Ministerial Studies, B
Theology and Religious Vocations, MD

FREDERICK COMMUNITY COLLEGE

Accounting, A
Art/Art Studies, General, A
Biology/Biological Sciences, A
Building/Construction Finishing, Manage-
ment, and Inspection, A
Business Administration and Management, A
Chemistry, A
Child Development, A
Computer Science, A
Criminal Justice/Law Enforcement Administration, A
Drafting and Design Technology/Technician, A
Early Childhood Education and Teaching, A
Education, A
Elementary Education and Teaching, A
Emergency Medical Technology/Technician (EMT
Paramedic), A
Engineering, A
Fire Science/Firefighting, A
General Studies, A
Human Services, A
Information Technology, A
Legal Assistant/Paralegal, A
Liberal Arts and Sciences Studies and Humani-
ties, A
Mathematics, A
Mathematics Teacher Education, A
Medical Administrative Assistant/Secretary, A
Medical/Clinical Assistant, A
Nuclear Medical Technology/Technologist, A
Political Science and Government, A
Psychology, A
Respiratory Care Therapy/Therapist, A
Spanish Language Teacher Education, A
Surgical Technology/Technologist, A

FROSTBURG STATE UNIVERSITY

Accounting, B
Athletic Training and Sports Medicine, B
Biological and Biomedical Sciences, M
Biology/Biological Sciences, B
Botany/Plant Biology, B
Business Administration and Management, B
Business Administration, Management and Opera-
tions, M
Chemistry, B
City/Urban, Community and Regional Planning, B
Computer Science, BM
Computer and Information Systems Security, B
Computer/Information Technology Services Adminis-
tration and Management, B
Conservation Biology, M
Counseling Psychology, M
Counselor Education/School Counseling and Guid-
ance Services, M
Criminal Justice/Law Enforcement Administration, B
Criminal Justice/Safety Studies, B
Curriculum and Instruction, M
Drama and Dramatics/Theatre Arts, B
Early Childhood Education and Teaching, B
Ecology, M
Economics, B
Education, M
Educational Administration and Supervision, M

Educational Media/Instructional Technology, M
Elementary Education and Teaching, BM
Engineering, B
English Language and Literature, B
Environmental Sciences, B
Fine/Studio Arts, B
Fish, Game and Wildlife Management, M
Foreign Languages and Literatures, B
Geography, B
Geology/Earth Science, B
Health/Health Care Administration/Management, B
History, B
Information Science/Studies, B
Information Technology, B
Interdisciplinary Studies, M
International/Global Studies, B
Kinesiology and Exercise Science, B
Liberal Arts and Sciences Studies and Humani-
ties, B
Mass Communication/Media Studies, B
Mathematics, B
Music, B
Nursing, M
Nursing Administration, M
Nursing Education, M
Parks, Recreation, Leisure and Fitness Studies, B
Philosophy, B
Physical Education Teaching and Coaching, B
Physics, B
Political Science and Government, B
Psychology, BM
Reading Teacher Education, M
Recreation and Park Management, M
Secondary Education and Teaching, M
Social Sciences, B
Social Work, B
Sociology, B
Special Education and Teaching, M
Teacher Education, Multiple Levels, B
Wildlife Biology, B
Wildlife and Wildlands Science and Management, B

GARRETT COLLEGE

Business Administration and Management, A
Business/Commerce, A
Business/Office Automation/Technology/Data En-
try, A
Corrections, A
Early Childhood Education and Teaching, A
Education, A
Electrical, Electronics and Communications Engi-
neering, A
Elementary Education and Teaching, A
Liberal Arts and Sciences Studies and Humani-
ties, A
Management Information Systems and Services, A
Sport and Fitness Administration/Management, A
Wildlife and Wildlands Science and Management, A

GOUCHER COLLEGE

American/United States Studies/Civilization, B
Art History, Criticism and Conservation, B
Arts Management, M
Biochemistry, Biophysics and Molecular Biology, B
Biological and Biomedical Sciences, O
Biology/Biological Sciences, B
Business Administration and Management, B
Chemistry, B
Computer Art and Design, M
Computer Science, B
Cultural Studies, M
Dance, B
Drama and Dramatics/Theatre Arts, B
Economics, B
Education, MO
Educational Leadership and Administration, MO
Educational Media/Instructional Technology, MO
Elementary Education and Teaching, BM
English Language and Literature, B
Environmental Studies, BM
Fine/Studio Arts, B
French Language and Literature, B
Historic Preservation and Conservation, M
History, B
International Relations and Affairs, B
Management, M

Mass Communication/Media Studies, B
Mathematics, B
Middle School Education, MO
Multi-/Interdisciplinary Studies, B
Music, B
Peace Studies and Conflict Resolution, B
Philosophy, B
Physical Education Teaching and Coaching, MO
Physics, B
Political Science and Government, B
Psychology, B
Reading Teacher Education, MO
Religion/Religious Studies, B
Russian Language and Literature, B
Secondary Education and Teaching, M
Sociology, B
Spanish Language and Literature, B
Special Education and Teaching, BMO
Women's Studies, B
Writing, M

HAGERSTOWN COMMUNITY COLLEGE

Accounting Technology/Technician and Bookkeep-
ing, A
Animation, Interactive Technology, Video Graphics
and Special Effects, A
Biology Technician/BioTechnology Laboratory Tech-
nician, A
Business Administration and Management, A
Business/Commerce, A
Child Care and Support Services Management, A
Commercial and Advertising Art, A
Computer and Information Sciences, A
Computer and Information Systems Security, A
Criminal Justice/Police Science, A
Dental Hygiene/Hygienist, A
Early Childhood Education and Teaching, A
Education, A
Elementary Education and Teaching, A
Emergency Medical Technology/Technician (EMT
Paramedic), A
Engineering, A
Engineering Technologies/Technicians, A
English/Language Arts Teacher Education, A
Industrial Technology/Technician, A
Instrumentation Technology/Technician, A
Liberal Arts and Sciences Studies and Humani-
ties, A
Management Information Systems and Services, A
Mechanical Engineering/Mechanical
Technology/Technician, A
Medical Radiologic Technology/Science - Radiation
Therapist, A
Psychiatric/Mental Health Services Technician, A
Transportation/Transportation Management, A
Web Page, Digital/Multimedia and Information Re-
sources Design, A

HARFORD COMMUNITY COLLEGE

Accounting, A
Administrative Assistant and Secretarial Science, A
Advertising, A
Agribusiness, A
Agriculture, A
Anthropology, A
Biology/Biological Sciences, A
Business Administration and Management, A
Chemistry, A
Chemistry Teacher Education, A
Civil Drafting and Civil Engineering CAD/CADD, A
Computer Science, A
Computer and Information Sciences, A
Criminal Justice/Police Science, A
Early Childhood Education and Teaching, A
Education, A
Education/Teaching of Individuals in Early Childhood
Special Education Programs, A
Electroneurodiagnostic/Electroencephalographic
Technology/Technologist, A
Elementary Education and Teaching, A
Engineering, A
Engineering Technology, A
English Language and Literature, A
English/Language Arts Teacher Education, A
Entrepreneurship/Entrepreneurial Studies, A

Environmental Engineering
    Technology/Environmental Technology, A
Environmental Sciences, A
Fine/Studio Arts, A
General Studies, A
Graphic Design, A
History, A
Human Resources Management/Personnel Adminis-
    tration, A
Information Science/Studies, A
Interior Design, A
International Relations and Affairs, A
Legal Assistant/Paralegal, A
Marketing/Marketing Management, A
Mass Communication/Media Studies, A
Mathematics, A
Mathematics Teacher Education, A
Medical Office Assistant/Specialist, A
Music, A
Philosophy, A
Photography, A
Physics, A
Physics Teacher Education, A
Political Science and Government, A
Psychology, A
Social Work, A
Sociology, A
Spanish Language Teacher Education, A
Special Education and Teaching, A
Teacher Assistant/Aide, A
Teacher Education and Professional Develop-
    ment, Specific Levels and Methods, A
Teacher Education and Professional Develop-
    ment, Specific Subject Areas, A
Technical Theatre/Theatre Design and Technol-
    ogy, A

HOOD COLLEGE

Accounting, BM
Art/Art Studies, General, B
BioTechnology, M
Biochemistry, B
Bioinformatics, O
Biological and Biomedical Sciences, MO
Biology/Biological Sciences, B
Business Administration and Management, B
Business Administration, Management and Opera-
    tions, M
Ceramic Arts and Ceramics, MO
Chemistry, B
Communication and Media Studies, B
Computer Science, BMO
Computer and Information Systems Security, O
Criminal Justice/Safety Studies, B
Curriculum and Instruction, M
Early Childhood Education and Teaching, BM
Economics, B
Education, MO
Educational Leadership and Administration, MO
Elementary Education and Teaching, M
English Language and Literature, B
Environmental Biology, M
Environmental Sciences, B
Environmental Studies, B
Finance and Banking, M
Fine Arts and Art Studies, B
Foreign Languages, Literatures, and Linguistics, B
French Language and Literature, B
German Language and Literature, B
History, B
Human Development, M
Human Resources Management and Services, M
Humanities/Humanistic Studies, M
Immunology, M
Information Science/Studies, MO
International/Global Studies, B
Latin American Studies, B
Management Information Systems and Services, M
Marketing, M
Mathematics, B
Mathematics Teacher Education, MO
Microbiology, M
Middle School Education, M
Molecular Biology, M
Multi-/Interdisciplinary Studies, B
Music, B

Near and Middle Eastern Studies, B
Philosophy, B
Political Science and Government, B
Psychology, BMO
Public Administration, M
Public Relations/Image Management, B
Reading Teacher Education, M
Religion/Religious Studies, B
Romance Languages, Literatures, and Linguistics, B
Science Teacher Education/General Science
    Teacher Education, M
Secondary Education and Teaching, M
Social Work, B
Sociology, B
Spanish Language and Literature, B
Special Education and Teaching, BM
Systems Science and Theory, M
Thanatology, MO

HOWARD COMMUNITY COLLEGE

Accounting, A
Art/Art Studies, General, A
BioTechnology, A
Biological and Physical Sciences, A
Biomedical Technology/Technician, A
Business Administration and Management, A
Cardiovascular Technology/Technologist, A
Child Development, A
Clinical Laboratory Science/Medical
    Technology/Technologist, A
Computer Graphics, A
Computer Science, A
Computer Systems Networking and Telecommunica-
    tions, A
Computer and Information Sciences, A
Computer/Information Technology Services Adminis-
    tration and Management, A
Criminal Justice/Law Enforcement Administration, A
Design and Applied Arts, A
Diagnostic Medical Sonography/Sonographer and
    Ultrasound Technician, A
Drama and Dramatics/Theatre Arts, A
Electrical, Electronic and Communications Engineer-
    ing Technology/Technician, A
Elementary Education and Teaching, A
Emergency Medical Technology/Technician (EMT
    Paramedic), A
Engineering, A
Environmental Studies, A
Financial Planning and Services, A
General Studies, A
Health Teacher Education, A
Information Science/Studies, A
Information Technology, A
Kindergarten/PreSchool Education and Teaching, A
Legal Administrative Assistant/Secretary, A
Liberal Arts and Sciences Studies and Humani-
    ties, A
Medical Administrative Assistant/Secretary, A
Music, A
Nuclear Medical Technology/Technologist, A
Office Management and Supervision, A
Photography, A
Physical Sciences, A
Physical Therapist Assistant, A
Pre-Medicine/Pre-Medical Studies, A
Pre-Pharmacy Studies, A
Secondary Education and Teaching, A
Social Sciences, A
Sport and Fitness Administration/Management, A
Substance Abuse/Addiction Counseling, A
Technical Theatre/Theatre Design and Technol-
    ogy, A
Telecommunications Technology/Technician, A

JOHNS HOPKINS UNIVERSITY

Aerospace, Aeronautical and Astronautical Engi-
    neering, MO
African-American/Black Studies, B
Allopathic Medicine, D
Anatomy, D
Anthropology, BD
Applied Behavior Analysis, O
Applied Economics, M
Applied Mathematics, BMDO
Applied Physics, MO

Archeology, BD
Art History, Criticism and Conservation, BMD
Artificial Intelligence and Robotics, M
Asian Studies/Civilization, M
Astronomy, D
Behavioral Sciences, B
BioTechnology, M
Biochemistry, MD
Bioengineering, MD
Bioethics/Medical Ethics, D
Bioinformatics, MO
Biological and Biomedical Sciences, MD
Biological and Physical Sciences, B
Biology/Biological Sciences, B
Biomedical Engineering, MDO
Biomedical/Medical Engineering, B
Biophysics, BD
Biostatistics, MD
Business Administration, Management and Opera-
    tions, M
Business/Commerce, B
Cardiovascular Sciences, MD
Cell Biology and Anatomy, D
Cell/Cellular Biology and Histology, B
Cell/Cellular and Molecular Biology, B
Chemical Engineering, BMD
Chemistry, BD
Civil Engineering, BMD
Classics and Classical Languages, Litera-
    tures, and Linguistics, BD
Clinical Psychology, MD
Clinical Research, MD
Cognitive Sciences, BD
Communication and Media Studies, M
Community Health and Preventive Medicine, D
Comparative Literature, D
Computer Engineering, BMDO
Computer Science, MDO
Computer Systems Networking and Telecommunica-
    tions, B
Computer and Information Sciences, B
Computer and Information Systems Security, MO
Counseling Psychology, MO
Counselor Education/School Counseling and Guid-
    ance Services, MO
Demography, M
Developmental Biology and Embryology, D
Early Childhood Education and Teaching, MO
East Asian Studies, B
Economics, BD
Education, MDO
Education/Teaching of the Gifted and Talented, MO
Educational Administration and Supervision, MO
Educational Leadership and Administration, MDO
Educational Media/Instructional Technology, MO
Educational Policy, D
Electrical Engineering, MDO
Electrical, Electronics and Communications Engi-
    neering, B
Elementary Education and Teaching, M
Energy Management and Policy, M
Engineering, B
Engineering Management, M
Engineering Mechanics, B
Engineering and Applied Sciences, MDO
English, D
English Language and Literature, B
Environmental Engineering
    Technology/Environmental Technology, MDO
Environmental Policy, MO
Environmental Policy and Resource Manage-
    ment, MO
Environmental Sciences, BMO
Environmental Studies, B
Environmental and Occupational Health, D
Environmental/Environmental Health Engineering, B
Epidemiology, MD
Evolutionary Biology, D
Film/Cinema Studies, B
Finance and Banking, MO
French Language and Literature, BD
Genetic Counseling/Counselor, M
Genetics, MD
Geographic Information Systems, MO
Geography, BMD
Geology/Earth Science, B

Geosciences, MD
German Language and Literature, BD
Health Communication, M
Health Education, MO
Health Informatics, MDO
Health Services Administration, MDO
Health Services Research, M
Hebrew Language and Literature, D
History, BD
History and Philosophy of Science and Technology, B
History of Science and Technology, MD
Homeland Security, O
Human Genetics, D
Immunology, MD
Infectious Diseases, MD
Information Science/Studies, M
International Affairs, MDO
International Development, MO
International Economics, M
International Public Health/International Health, MD
International Relations and Affairs, B
Investment Management, O
Italian Language and Literature, BD
Latin American Studies, B
Liberal Arts and Sciences Studies and Humanities, B
Liberal Studies, MO
Management, M
Management Information Systems and Services, MO
Management of Technology, MO
Marketing, M
Materials Engineering, BMD
Materials Sciences, MD
Mathematical and Computational Finance, M
Mathematics, BD
Mathematics Teacher Education, O
Mechanical Engineering, BMD
Mechanics, M
Medical Illustration and Informatics, M
Medical Informatics, MDO
Microbiology, MD
Military and Defense Studies, M
Molecular Biology, BMD
Molecular Medicine, D
Museology/Museum Studies, MO
Music, BMDO
NanoTechnology, M
Natural Sciences, B
Near and Middle Eastern Studies, BD
Neuroscience, D
Non-Profit/Public/Organizational Management, O
Nursing, MDO
Nutritional Sciences, MD
Operations Research, MD
Pathobiology, D
Pathology/Experimental Pathology, D
Pharmaceutical Sciences, M
Pharmacology, D
Philosophy, BMD
Physics, BD
Physiology, D
Political Science and Government, BMDO
Psychology, BD
Public Administration, BM
Public Health, MD
Public Health (MPH, DPH), B
Public Policy Analysis, BM
Reading Teacher Education, M
Real Estate, M
Romance Languages, Literatures, and Linguistics, BD
Secondary Education and Teaching, M
Social Sciences, BD
Sociology, BMD
South and Southeast Asian Studies, M
Spanish Language and Literature, BD
Special Education and Teaching, MO
Statistics, MD
Substance Abuse/Addiction Counseling, D
Systems Engineering, MO
Technical and Business Writing, MO
Telecommunications, M
Toxicology, D
Urban Education and Leadership, O

Writing, MO

KAPLAN UNIVERSITY, HAGERSTOWN CAMPUS

Accounting, A
Administrative Assistant and Secretarial Science, A
Business Administration and Management, A
Computer and Information Systems Security, A
Criminal Justice/Law Enforcement Administration, A
Data Processing and Data Processing Technology/Technician, A
Health Information/Medical Records Administration/Administrator, A
Information Science/Studies, A
Legal Administrative Assistant/Secretary, A
Legal Assistant/Paralegal, A
Marketing/Marketing Management, A
Medical Administrative Assistant/Secretary, A
Medical/Clinical Assistant, A

LOYOLA UNIVERSITY MARYLAND

Accounting, BMO
Applied Mathematics, B
Art History, Criticism and Conservation, B
Art/Art Studies, General, B
Biology/Biological Sciences, B
Business Administration, Management and Operations, M
Business/Commerce, B
Chemistry, B
Classics and Classical Languages, Literatures, and Linguistics, B
Clinical Psychology, MDO
Communication Disorders, M
Communication Studies/Speech Communication and Rhetoric, B
Computer Science, BM
Computer and Information Systems Security, O
Counseling Psychology, MO
Counselor Education/School Counseling and Guidance Services, MO
Curriculum and Instruction, MO
Early Childhood Education and Teaching, MO
Economics, B
Education, BMO
Educational Leadership and Administration, MO
Educational Media/Instructional Technology, M
Elementary Education and Teaching, BMO
Engineering, B
English Education, M
English Language and Literature, B
Finance, B
Finance and Banking, M
Fine Arts and Art Studies, B
French Language and Literature, B
German Language and Literature, B
History, B
International Business/Trade/Commerce, M
Latin Language and Literature, B
Liberal Studies, M
Management Information Systems and Services, M
Marketing, M
Mathematics, B
Mathematics Teacher Education, M
Media Studies, M
Middle School Education, MO
Multi-/Interdisciplinary Studies, B
Music Teacher Education, M
Pastoral Studies/Counseling, MDO
Philosophy, B
Physics, B
Political Science and Government, B
Psychology, BMDO
Reading Teacher Education, MO
Religion/Religious Studies, B
Science Teacher Education/General Science Teacher Education, M
Secondary Education and Teaching, MO
Social Sciences, B
Sociology, B
Software Engineering, M
Spanish Language and Literature, B
Special Education and Teaching, BMO
Speech-Language Pathology/Pathologist, B
Statistics, B

Theology and Religious Vocations, M

MAPLE SPRINGS BAPTIST BIBLE COLLEGE AND SEMINARY

Bible/Biblical Studies, AB
Pastoral Studies/Counseling, BM
Religious Education, M
Theology and Religious Vocations, MDO

MARYLAND INSTITUTE COLLEGE OF ART

Applied Arts and Design, M
Art Education, M
Art History, Criticism and Conservation, B
Art Teacher Education, B
Art/Art Studies, General, B
Business Administration, Management and Operations, M
Ceramic Arts and Ceramics, B
Design and Applied Arts, BM
Drawing, B
Fiber, Textile and Weaving Arts, B
Film, Television, and Video Production, M
Film/Video and Photographic Arts, B
Fine Arts and Art Studies, BMO
Fine/Studio Arts, B
Graphic Design, BMO
Illustration, BM
Interior Design, B
Intermedia/Multimedia, B
Media Studies, M
Museology/Museum Studies, M
Painting, BM
Photography, BM
Printmaking, B
Sculpture, BM
Visual and Performing Arts, B

MCDANIEL COLLEGE

Accounting and Related Services, B
Art History, Criticism and Conservation, B
Art/Art Studies, General, B
Asian Studies/Civilization, B
Biology/Biological Sciences, B
Business Administration and Management, B
Chemistry, B
Communication Studies/Speech Communication and Rhetoric, B
Computer and Information Sciences, B
Counselor Education/School Counseling and Guidance Services, M
Curriculum and Instruction, M
Drama and Dramatics/Theatre Arts, B
Economics, B
Educational Leadership and Administration, M
Educational Media/Instructional Technology, M
Elementary Education and Teaching, B
English Language and Literature, B
English as a Second Language, M
Environmental Biology, B
Environmental Sciences, B
Environmental Studies, B
Exercise and Sports Science, M
Film/Cinema Studies, B
French Language and Literature, B
German Language and Literature, B
Gerontology, MO
Health and Physical Education, B
History, B
Human Resources Development, M
Human Services, M
Kinesiology and Exercise Science, B
Liberal Studies, M
Library Science, M
Mathematics, B
Multi-/Interdisciplinary Studies, B
Music, B
Near and Middle Eastern Studies, B
Philosophy, B
Physical Education Teaching and Coaching, M
Physics, B
Political Science and Government, B
Psychology, B
Reading Teacher Education, M
Religion/Religious Studies, B
Secondary Education and Teaching, M

Social Work, B
Sociology, B
Spanish Language and Literature, B
Special Education and Teaching, M

MONTGOMERY COLLEGE

Accounting Technology/Technician and Bookkeeping, A
American Sign Language (ASL), A
Animation, Interactive Technology, Video Graphics and Special Effects, A
Applied Horticulture/Horticultural Operations, A
Architectural Drafting and Architectural CAD/CADD, A
Art/Art Studies, General, A
Automobile/Automotive Mechanics Technology/Technician, A
Biology Technician/BioTechnology Laboratory Technician, A
Building/Construction Finishing, Management, and Inspection, A
Business/Commerce, A
Chemistry Teacher Education, A
Child Care Provider/Assistant, A
Commercial Photography, A
Commercial and Advertising Art, A
Communication Studies/Speech Communication and Rhetoric, A
Communications Technologies/Technicians and Support Services, A
Computer Technology/Computer Systems Technology, A
Computer and Information Sciences, A
Computer and Information Systems Security, A
Criminal Justice/Police Science, A
Data Entry/Microcomputer Applications, A
Diagnostic Medical Sonography/Sonographer and Ultrasound Technician, A
Early Childhood Education and Teaching, A
Elementary Education and Teaching, A
Engineering, A
English/Language Arts Teacher Education, A
Fire Protection and Safety Technology/Technician, A
Geography, A
Health Information/Medical Records Technology/Technician, A
Hotel/Motel Administration/Management, A
Interior Design, A
Legal Assistant/Paralegal, A
Liberal Arts and Sciences Studies and Humanities, A
Mathematics Teacher Education, A
Medical Radiologic Technology/Science - Radiation Therapist, A
Physical Therapist Assistant, A
Physics Teacher Education, A
Psychiatric/Mental Health Services Technician, A
Spanish Language Teacher Education, A
Surgical Technology/Technologist, A
Web Page, Digital/Multimedia and Information Resources Design, A

MORGAN STATE UNIVERSITY

Accounting, B
African Studies, B
African-American Studies, M
African-American/Black Studies, B
Architecture, M
Art History, Criticism and Conservation, B
Art/Art Studies, General, B
Behavioral Sciences, B
Bioinformatics, M
Biological and Biomedical Sciences, MD
Biology/Biological Sciences, B
Business Administration and Management, B
Business Administration, Management and Operations, D
Business Teacher Education, B
Business/Managerial Economics, B
Chemistry, BM
Civil Engineering, BMD
Clinical Laboratory Science/Medical Technology/Technologist, B
Clinical/Medical Laboratory Technician, B
Community College Education, D
Computer Science, B

Dietetics/Dieticians, B
Drama and Dramatics/Theatre Arts, B
Economics, BM
Education, BMD
Educational Administration and Supervision, MD
Educational Leadership and Administration, D
Electrical Engineering, MD
Electrical, Electronics and Communications Engineering, B
Elementary Education and Teaching, BM
Engineering, B
Engineering Physics, B
Engineering and Applied Sciences, MD
English, MD
English Language and Literature, B
Environmental Biology, D
Family and Consumer Sciences/Human Sciences, B
Finance, B
Foods, Nutrition, and Wellness Studies, B
Health Teacher Education, B
Higher Education/Higher Education Administration, MD
Historic Preservation and Conservation, M
History, BMD
Hospitality Administration/Management, B
Hotel/Motel Administration/Management, B
Industrial Engineering, B
Industrial/Management Engineering, MD
Information Science/Studies, B
International Affairs, M
Landscape Architecture, M
Management Information Systems and Services, B
Marketing/Marketing Management, B
Mass Communication/Media Studies, B
Mathematics, BM
Mathematics Teacher Education, MD
Mental Health Counseling/Counselor, B
Middle School Education, M
Museology/Museum Studies, M
Music, BM
Nursing, M
Parks, Recreation, Leisure and Fitness Studies, B
Philosophy, B
Physical Education Teaching and Coaching, B
Physics, B
Political Science and Government, B
Pre-Dentistry Studies, B
Pre-Law Studies, B
Pre-Medicine/Pre-Medical Studies, B
Psychology, BMD
Public Health, MD
Religion/Religious Studies, B
Science Teacher Education/General Science Teacher Education, MD
Secondary Education and Teaching, BM
Social Work, BMD
Sociology, BM
Sport and Fitness Administration/Management, B
Telecommunications Technology/Technician, B
Transportation and Highway Engineering, M
Transportation/Transportation Management, M
Urban Education and Leadership, D
Urban and Regional Planning, M

MOUNT ST. MARY'S UNIVERSITY

Accounting, B
Art/Art Studies, General, B
BioTechnology, M
Biochemistry, B
Biology/Biological Sciences, B
Business Administration, Management and Operations, M
Business/Commerce, B
Chemistry, B
Communication Studies/Speech Communication and Rhetoric, B
Computer and Information Sciences, B
Criminology, B
Economics, B
Education, M
Elementary Education and Teaching, B
English Language and Literature, B
Environmental Studies, B
Family and Community Services, B
French Language and Literature, B
German Language and Literature, B

Health Professions and Related Clinical Sciences, B
Health Services Administration, M
History, B
Information Resources Management/CIO Training, B
International Relations and Affairs, B
Mathematics, B
Multi-/Interdisciplinary Studies, B
Philosophy, BM
Political Science and Government, B
Psychology, B
Social Science Teacher Education, B
Sociology, B
Spanish Language and Literature, B
Sport and Fitness Administration/Management, B
Theology and Religious Vocations, M
Theology/Theological Studies, B

NER ISRAEL RABBINICAL COLLEGE

Jewish/Judaic Studies, B
Theology and Religious Vocations, MDO

NOTRE DAME OF MARYLAND UNIVERSITY

Art/Art Studies, General, B
Biology/Biological Sciences, B
Business Administration and Management, B
Chemistry, B
Classics and Classical Languages, Literatures, and Linguistics, B
Communication Studies/Speech Communication and Rhetoric, B
Communication and Media Studies, M
Criminology, B
Digital Communication and Media/Multimedia, B
Education, BM
Educational Leadership and Administration, MD
Elementary Education and Teaching, B
English Language and Literature, B
English as a Second Language, M
Foreign Languages and Literatures, B
French Language and Literature, B
History, B
Information Science/Studies, B
International Business/Trade/Commerce, B
International Relations and Affairs, B
Liberal Arts and Sciences Studies and Humanities, B
Liberal Studies, M
Management, M
Mathematics, B
Mathematics Teacher Education, B
Medical Radiologic Technology/Science - Radiation Therapist, B
Multi-/Interdisciplinary Studies, B
Non-Profit/Public/Organizational Management, M
Philosophy, B
Physics, B
Political Science and Government, B
Psychology, B
Religion/Religious Studies, B
Science Teacher Education/General Science Teacher Education, B
Spanish Language and Literature, B

PEABODY CONSERVATORY OF THE JOHNS HOPKINS UNIVERSITY

Jazz/Jazz Studies, B
Music, B
Music Performance, B
Music Teacher Education, B
Piano and Organ, B
Recording Arts Technology/Technician, B
Violin, Viola, Guitar and Other Stringed Instruments, B
Voice and Opera, B

PRINCE GEORGE'S COMMUNITY COLLEGE

Accounting, A
Aerospace, Aeronautical and Astronautical Engineering, A
Business Administration and Management, A
Business Teacher Education, A
Computer Engineering Technology/Technician, A
Computer Programming/Programmer, A

Computer Science, A
Computer Typography and Composition Equipment
   Operator, A
Criminal Justice/Law Enforcement Administration, A
Drafting and Design Technology/Technician, A
Education, A
Electrical, Electronic and Communications Engineer-
   ing Technology/Technician, A
Elementary Education and Teaching, A
Emergency Medical Technology/Technician (EMT
   Paramedic), A
Engineering, A
Forensic Science and Technology, A
Health Information/Medical Records
   Administration/Administrator, A
Health Teacher Education, A
Information Science/Studies, A
Kindergarten/PreSchool Education and Teaching, A
Legal Assistant/Paralegal, A
Liberal Arts and Sciences Studies and Humani-
   ties, A
Marketing/Marketing Management, A
Medical Office Management/Administration, A
Nuclear Medical Technology/Technologist, A
Physical Education Teaching and Coaching, A
Radiologic Technology/Science - Radiographer, A
Respiratory Care Therapy/Therapist, A

ST. JOHN'S COLLEGE

Liberal Arts and Sciences Studies and Humanities, B
Liberal Studies, M

ST. MARY'S COLLEGE OF MARYLAND

Anthropology, B
Art History, Criticism and Conservation, B
Art/Art Studies, General, B
Asian Studies/Civilization, B
Biochemistry, B
Biological and Physical Sciences, B
Biology/Biological Sciences, B
Chemistry, B
Computer and Information Sciences, B
Drama and Dramatics/Theatre Arts, B
Economics, B
Education, M
English Language and Literature, B
Environmental Studies, B
Foreign Languages and Literatures, B
History, B
Mathematics, B
Multi-/Interdisciplinary Studies, B
Music, B
Philosophy, B
Physics, B
Political Science and Government, B
Psychology, B
Public Policy Analysis, B
Religion/Religious Studies, B
Sociology, B

SALISBURY UNIVERSITY

Accounting, B
Art/Art Studies, General, B
Athletic Training and Sports Medicine, B
Biological and Biomedical Sciences, M
Biology/Biological Sciences, B
Business Administration and Management, B
Business Administration, Management and Opera-
   tions, M
Business/Managerial Economics, B
Chemistry, B
Clinical Laboratory Science/Medical
   Technology/Technologist, B
Communication Studies/Speech Communication
   and Rhetoric, B
Composition, M
Computer and Information Sciences, B
Conflict Resolution and Mediation/Peace Studies, M
Curriculum and Instruction, M
Drama and Dramatics/Theatre Arts, B
Early Childhood Education and Teaching, B
Ecology, B
Economics, B
Educational Leadership and Administration, M
Elementary Education and Teaching, B

English, M
English Language and Literature, B
English as a Second Language, M
Environmental Sciences, B
Finance, B
Fine/Studio Arts, B
French Language and Literature, B
Geographic Information Systems, M
Geography, B
Geological and Earth Sciences/Geosciences, B
Health Teacher Education, B
History, BM
Information Science/Studies, B
International Business/Trade/Commerce, B
International/Global Studies, B
Kinesiology and Exercise Science, B
Liberal Arts and Sciences Studies and Humani-
   ties, B
Marketing/Marketing Management, B
Mathematics, B
Mathematics Teacher Education, M
Middle School Education, M
Music, B
Nursing, MD
Nursing Administration, M
Nursing Education, M
Peace Studies and Conflict Resolution, B
Philosophy, B
Physical Education Teaching and Coaching, B
Physics, B
Physiology, M
Political Science and Government, B
Psychology, B
Reading Teacher Education, MD
Respiratory Care Therapy/Therapist, B
Rhetoric, M
Secondary Education and Teaching, M
Social Work, BM
Sociology, B
Spanish Language and Literature, B
Teaching English as a Second or Foreign
   Language/ESL Language Instructor, B

STEVENSON UNIVERSITY

Accounting, B
Acting, B
Applied Mathematics, B
BioTechnology, B
Biochemistry, B
Biology/Biological Sciences, B
Business Administration and Management, B
Business/Corporate Communications, B
Chemistry, B
Cinematography and Film/Video Production, B
Clinical Laboratory Science/Medical
   Technology/Technologist, B
Communication and Media Studies, M
Computer Systems Networking and Telecommunica-
   tions, B
Computer and Information Sciences, B
Computer and Information Systems Security, M
Criminal Justice/Law Enforcement Administration, B
Design and Visual Communications, B
Digital Communication and Media/Multimedia, B
Drama and Dramatics/Theatre Arts, B
Early Childhood Education and Teaching, B
Education, M
Elementary Education and Teaching, B
English Language and Literature, B
Environmental Sciences, B
Family and Community Services, B
Fashion Merchandising, B
Fashion/Apparel Design, B
Film/Cinema Studies, B
Forensic Science and Technology, M
Health Services Administration, M
History, B
Information Science/Studies, B
Junior High/Intermediate/Middle School Education
   and Teaching, B
Law and Legal Studies, B
Legal Assistant/Paralegal, B
Management Information Systems and Services, B
Management of Technology, M
Marketing, B
Mathematics Teacher Education, M

Nursing, M
Psychology, B
Science Teacher Education/General Science
   Teacher Education, M

STRATFORD UNIVERSITY

Baking and Pastry Arts/Baker/Pastry Chef, A
Culinary Arts/Chef Training, A
Hospitality Administration/Management, ABM
Restaurant, Culinary, and Catering
   Management/Manager, A
Restaurant/Food Services Management, AB

STRAYER UNIVERSITY–ANNE ARUNDEL CAMPUS

Accounting, B
Business Administration and Management, B
Economics, B
International Business/Trade/Commerce, B
Management Information Systems and Services, B

STRAYER UNIVERSITY–OWINGS MILLS CAMPUS

Accounting, B
Business Administration and Management, B
Economics, B
International Business/Trade/Commerce, B
Management Information Systems and Services, B

STRAYER UNIVERSITY–PRINCE GEORGE'S CAMPUS

Accounting, B
Business Administration and Management, B
Economics, B
International Business/Trade/Commerce, B
Management Information Systems and Services, B

STRAYER UNIVERSITY–ROCKVILLE CAMPUS

Accounting, B
Business Administration and Management, B
Economics, B
International Business/Trade/Commerce, B
Management Information Systems and Services, B

STRAYER UNIVERSITY–WHITE MARSH CAMPUS

Accounting, B
Business Administration and Management, B
Economics, B
International Business/Trade/Commerce, B
Management Information Systems and Services, B

TOWSON UNIVERSITY

Accounting, BM
Acting, B
Allied Health and Medical Assisting Services, M
American/United States Studies/Civilization, B
Applied Mathematics, M
Applied Physics, M
Art Education, MO
Art History, Criticism and Conservation, BM
Art Teacher Education, B
Art/Art Studies, General, B
Athletic Training and Sports Medicine, B
Audiology/Audiologist and Speech-Language
   Pathology/Pathologist, B
Biochemistry, Biophysics and Molecular Biology, B
Biological and Biomedical Sciences, M
Biology/Biological Sciences, B
Business Administration and Management, B
Chemistry, B
Child and Family Studies, MO
Clinical Psychology, M
Communication Disorders, MD
Communication Studies/Speech Communication
   and Rhetoric, B
Communication and Media Studies, M
Composition, M
Computer Science, BM
Computer and Information Sciences, B
Computer and Information Systems Security, O
Corporate and Organizational Communication, M
Counseling Psychology, O

Dance, B
Database Systems, O
Drama and Dramatics/Theatre Arts, B
E-Commerce/Electronic Commerce, B
Early Childhood Education and Teaching, BMO
Economics, B
Education, BM
Educational Leadership and Administration, O
Educational Media/Instructional Technology, MD
Electronic Commerce, MO
Elementary Education and Teaching, BM
English Language and Literature, B
Environmental Sciences, MO
Environmental Studies, M
Environmental and Occupational Health, D
Family Systems, B
Fine Arts and Art Studies, M
Fine/Studio Arts, B
Foreign Languages and Literatures, B
Forensic Science and Technology, BM
Geography, BM
Geological and Earth Sciences/Geosciences, B
Geology/Earth Science, B
Gerontology, BMO
Health Professions and Related Clinical Sciences, B
Health Services Administration, MO
Health Services/Allied Health/Health Sciences, B
Health/Health Care Administration/Management, B
Hebrew Studies, MO
History, B
Homeland Security, MO
Human Resources Development, M
Human Services, B
Humanities/Humanistic Studies, M
Information Science/Studies, BMDO
Information Technology, B
International Relations and Affairs, B
Internet and Interactive Multimedia, O
Jewish/Judaic Studies, M
Junior High/Intermediate/Middle School Education
    and Teaching, B
Kinesiology and Exercise Science, B
Kinesiology and Movement Studies, M
Liberal Studies, M
Management Information Systems and Services, O
Management Strategy and Policy, O
Management of Technology, MO
Mass Communication/Media Studies, B
Mathematics, B
Mathematics Teacher Education, M
Music, B
Music Teacher Education, BMO
Natural Resources and Conservation, B
Nursing, MO
Nursing Education, O
Occupational Therapy/Therapist, BM
Organizational Behavior Studies, O
Performance, M
Philosophy, B
Physical Education Teaching and Coaching, B
Physician Assistant, M
Physics, B
Political Science and Government, B
Psychology, B
Radio and Television Broadcasting
    Technology/Technician, B
Radio, Television, and Digital Communication, B
Reading Teacher Education, MO
Religion/Religious Studies, B
Religious Education, MO
School Psychology, O
Secondary Education and Teaching, M
Social Sciences, BM
Software Engineering, O
Special Education and Teaching, BMO
Speech-Language Pathology/Pathologist, B
Sport and Fitness Administration/Management, B
Supply Chain Management, MO
Theater, M
Urban Studies/Affairs, B
Women's Studies, BMO
Writing, M

UNITED STATES NAVAL ACADEMY

Aerospace, Aeronautical and Astronautical Engi-
    neering, B

Arabic Language and Literature, B
Chemistry, B
Chinese Language and Literature, B
Computer Hardware Engineering, B
Computer Science, B
Computer and Information Sciences, B
Econometrics and Quantitative Economics, B
Economics, B
Electrical, Electronics and Communications Engi-
    neering, B
Engineering, B
English Language and Literature, B
History, B
Mathematics, B
Mechanical Engineering, B
Naval Architecture and Marine Engineering, B
Nuclear Engineering, B
Ocean Engineering, B
Oceanography, Chemical and Physical, B
Operations Research, B
Physical Sciences, B
Physics, B
Political Science and Government, B
Systems Engineering, B

UNIVERSITY OF BALTIMORE

Accounting, BMO
Applied Psychology, M
Business Administration and Management, B
Business Administration, Management and Opera-
    tions, MO
Business/Commerce, B
Community Organization and Advocacy, B
Computer and Information Sciences, B
Conflict Resolution and Mediation/Peace Studies, M
Counseling Psychology, M
Criminal Justice/Law Enforcement Administration, B
Criminology, M
Design and Applied Arts, M
Digital Communication and Media/Multimedia, B
English Language and Literature, B
Entrepreneurship/Entrepreneurial Studies, BM
Environmental Sciences, B
Ethics, M
Finance, B
Finance and Banking, M
Forensic Science and Technology, B
Graphic Design, MD
Health Services Administration, M
Health and Medical Administrative Services, B
History, B
Human Resources Management/Personnel Adminis-
    tration, B
Human Services, BM
Human-Computer Interaction, M
Information Science/Studies, B
Information Technology, B
International Business/Trade/Commerce, BM
International/Global Studies, B
Law and Legal Studies, MD
Legal and Justice Studies, M
Liberal Arts and Sciences Studies and Humani-
    ties, B
Management Information Systems and Ser-
    vices, BMO
Marketing, M
Marketing/Marketing Management, B
Political Science and Government, B
Pre-Law Studies, B
Psychology, B
Public Administration, MD
Public Affairs, MD
Publishing, M
Real Estate, B
Taxation, M
Visual and Performing Arts, B
Writing, M

UNIVERSITY OF MARYLAND, BALTI-MORE COUNTY

Acting, B
African-American/Black Studies, B
American/United States Studies/Civilization, B
Ancient Studies/Civilization, B
Anthropology, B
Applied Mathematics, MD

Applied Psychology, D
Art Education, M
Asian Studies/Civilization, B
Atmospheric Sciences and Meteorology, MD
BioTechnology, MO
Biochemical Engineering, MDO
Biochemistry, D
Biochemistry, Biophysics and Molecular Biology, B
Bioinformatics, B
Biological and Biomedical Sciences, MDO
Biology Teacher Education, B
Biology/Biological Sciences, B
Biostatistics, D
Business Administration, Management and Opera-
    tions, B
Cell Biology and Anatomy, D
Chemical Engineering, BMD
Chemistry, BMD
Chemistry Teacher Education, B
Cognitive Sciences, D
Communication and Media Studies, M
Computer Art and Design, M
Computer Engineering, BMD
Computer Science, BMD
Computer and Information Systems Security, MO
Computer/Information Technology Services Adminis-
    tration and Management, B
Dance, BM
Design and Visual Communications, B
Developmental Psychology, D
Distance Education Development, O
Drama and Dramatics/Theatre Arts, B
Early Childhood Education and Teaching, M
Economics, BMD
Education, MO
Educational Media/Instructional Technology, MO
Educational Policy, M
Electrical Engineering, MD
Elementary Education and Teaching, M
Emergency Medical Technology/Technician (EMT
    Paramedic), B
Engineering, B
Engineering Management, MO
Engineering and Applied Sciences, MDO
English, M
English Education, M
English Language and Literature, B
Environmental Engineering
    Technology/Environmental Technology, MD
Environmental Policy and Resource Manage-
    ment, MD
Environmental Sciences, BMD
Environmental Studies, B
Epidemiology, M
Fine Arts and Art Studies, B
Fine/Studio Arts, B
Foreign Language Teacher Education, M
Foreign Languages and Literatures, B
Geographic Information Systems, MO
Geography, BMD
Gerontology, MD
Health Education, M
Health Informatics, M
Health Professions and Related Clinical Sciences, B
Health Services Administration, MO
History, BM
Human Services, MD
Industrial and Organizational Psychology, M
Information Science/Studies, BMD
International/Global Studies, B
Jazz/Jazz Studies, B
Linguistics, M
Marine Sciences, MD
Mass Communication/Media Studies, B
Mathematics, B
Mathematics Teacher Education, M
Mechanical Engineering, BMDO
Molecular Biology, MD
Multi-/Interdisciplinary Studies, B
Multilingual and Multicultural Education, MD
Music, BO
Music Pedagogy, B
Music Performance, B
Music Teacher Education, M
Music Theory and Composition, B
Neuroscience, D

Non-Profit/Public/Organizational Management, O
Philosophy, B
Physics, BMD
Physics Teacher Education, B
Planetary Astronomy and Science, M
Political Science and Government, B
Psychology, BMD
Public History, D
Public Policy Analysis, MD
Science Teacher Education/General Science
  Teacher Education, M
Secondary Education and Teaching, M
Social Sciences, D
Social Studies Teacher Education, M
Social Work, B
Sociology, BM
Statistics, BMD
Systems Engineering, MO
Theater, M
Urban Studies/Affairs, MD
Women's Studies, BO

UNIVERSITY OF MARYLAND, COLLEGE PARK

Accounting, B
Advertising and Public Relations, MD
Aerospace, Aeronautical and Astronautical Engineering, BMD
African-American/Black Studies, B
Agricultural Economics, BMD
Agricultural Sciences, MD
Agricultural/Biological Engineering and Bioengineering, B
Agriculture, B
American/United States Studies/Civilization, BMD
Analytical Chemistry, MD
Animal Sciences, BMD
Anthropology, BM
Applied Mathematics, MD
Arabic Language and Literature, B
Architecture, BM
Art History, Criticism and Conservation, BMD
Art Teacher Education, B
Art Therapy/Therapist, M
Astronomy, BMD
Atmospheric Sciences and Meteorology, B
Biochemistry, BMD
Bioengineering, MD
Bioinformatics, D
Biological and Biomedical Sciences, MD
Biology/Biological Sciences, B
Biophysics, D
Biostatistics, MD
Broadcast Journalism, M
Business Administration, Management and Operations, M
Business/Commerce, B
Cell Biology and Anatomy, MD
Chemical Engineering, BMD
Chemical Physics, MD
Chemistry, BMD
Child and Family Studies, MD
Chinese Language and Literature, B
Civil Engineering, BMD
Classics and Classical Languages, Literatures, and Linguistics, BM
Clinical Psychology, D
Cognitive Sciences, D
Communication Disorders, BMD
Communication Studies/Speech Communication and Rhetoric, B
Communication and Media Studies, MD
Comparative Literature, MD
Computational Biology, D
Computer Engineering, BMD
Computer Science, MD
Computer and Information Sciences, B
Conservation Biology, M
Counseling Psychology, MD
Counselor Education/School Counseling and Guidance Services, MDO
Criminology, BMD
Curriculum and Instruction, MDO
Dance, BM
Developmental Psychology, D
Drama and Dramatics/Theatre Arts, B

Ecology, BMD
Economics, BMD
Education, MDO
Educational Administration and Supervision, MD
Educational Leadership and Administration, MDO
Educational Measurement and Evaluation, MD
Educational Media/Instructional Technology, MD
Electrical Engineering, MD
Electrical, Electronics and Communications Engineering, B
Elementary Education and Teaching, B
Engineering, B
Engineering and Applied Sciences, M
English, MD
English Language and Literature, B
English as a Second Language, M
Entomology, MD
Environmental Engineering Technology/Environmental Technology, MD
Environmental Sciences, BMD
Environmental and Occupational Health, M
Epidemiology, MD
Ethnomusicology, M
Evolutionary Biology, MD
Experimental Psychology, D
Family and Community Services, B
Family and Consumer Sciences/Human Sciences, MD
Film/Cinema Studies, B
Finance, B
Fine Arts and Art Studies, M
Fine/Studio Arts, B
Fire Protection Engineering, M
Food Science, B
Food Science and Technology, MD
Foreign Language Teacher Education, D
Foundations and Philosophy of Education, MDO
French Language and Literature, BMD
Genomic Sciences, D
Geography, BMD
Geology/Earth Science, BMD
German Language and Literature, BMD
Health Education, MD
Health Services Administration, MD
Health Teacher Education, B
Historic Preservation and Conservation, MO
History, BMD
Horticultural Science, MD
Human Development, MD
Industrial and Organizational Psychology, MD
Information Science/Studies, BMD
Inorganic Chemistry, MD
International Business/Trade/Commerce, B
Iranian/Persian Languages, Literatures, and Linguistics, B
Italian Language and Literature, B
Japanese Language and Literature, B
Jewish/Judaic Studies, BM
Journalism, BMD
Junior High/Intermediate/Middle School Education and Teaching, B
Kindergarten/PreSchool Education and Teaching, B
Kinesiology and Exercise Science, B
Kinesiology and Movement Studies, MD
Landscape Architecture, BM
Linguistics, BMD
Logistics and Materials Management, B
Management, MD
Management Science, B
Manufacturing Engineering, MD
Marine Sciences, MD
Marketing/Marketing Management, B
Marriage and Family Therapy/Counseling, M
Materials Engineering, BMD
Materials Sciences, MD
Maternal and Child Health, D
Mathematics, BMD
Mechanical Engineering, BMD
Mechanics, MD
Media Studies, D
Meteorology, MD
Microbiology, B
Molecular Biology, D
Molecular Genetics, MD
Multi-/Interdisciplinary Studies, B
Music, BMD

Music Performance, B
Music Teacher Education, BMD
Natural Resources and Conservation, BMD
Neuroscience, D
Nuclear Engineering, MD
Nutritional Sciences, MD
Oceanography, Chemical and Physical, MD
Organic Chemistry, MD
Philosophy, BMD
Physical Chemistry, MD
Physical Education Teaching and Coaching, B
Physical Sciences, B
Physics, BMD
Plant Biology, MD
Political Science and Government, BD
Portuguese Language and Literature, MD
Pre-Dentistry Studies, B
Pre-Law Studies, B
Pre-Veterinary Studies, B
Psychology, BMD
Public Administration, M
Public Health, BMD
Public Policy Analysis, MD
Quantitative Analysis, MD
Reading Teacher Education, MDO
Real Estate, M
Rehabilitation Counseling, M
Reliability Engineering, MD
Romance Languages, Literatures, and Linguistics, B
Russian Language and Literature, B
Russian Studies, B
School Psychology, MD
Secondary Education and Teaching, BMDO
Social Psychology, D
Sociology, BMD
Spanish Language and Literature, BMD
Special Education and Teaching, B
Speech and Interpersonal Communication, MD
Statistics, MD
Student Personnel Services, MDO
Survey Methodology, MD
Sustainable Development, M
Systems Engineering, M
Telecommunications, M
Theater, MD
Urban and Regional Planning, MD
Veterinary Medicine, D
Veterinary Sciences, MD
Women's Studies, BMD
Writing, MD

UNIVERSITY OF MARYLAND EASTERN SHORE

Accounting, B
Agricultural Business and Management, B
Agricultural Sciences, MD
Agricultural Teacher Education, B
Agriculture, B
Air Traffic Controller, B
Art Teacher Education, B
Biology/Biological Sciences, B
Building/Construction Finishing, Management, and Inspection, B
Business Administration and Management, B
Business Teacher Education, B
Chemistry, BM
Child Development, B
Clinical Laboratory Science/Medical Technology/Technologist, B
Clinical/Medical Laboratory Technician, B
Computer Science, BM
Construction Engineering Technology/Technician, B
Counselor Education/School Counseling and Guidance Services, M
Criminal Justice/Law Enforcement Administration, B
Criminology, M
Dietetics/Dieticians, B
Ecology, B
Education, BM
Educational Leadership and Administration, D
Electrical, Electronic and Communications Engineering Technology/Technician, B
Elementary Education and Teaching, B
Engineering Technology, B
English Language and Literature, B

Environmental Policy and Resource Manage-
ment, M
Environmental Sciences, MD
Environmental Studies, B
Family and Consumer Economics and Related Ser-
vices, M
Family and Consumer Sciences/Home Economics
Teacher Education, B
Family and Consumer Sciences/Human Sciences, B
Fashion Merchandising, B
Fashion/Apparel Design, B
Fish, Game and Wildlife Management, M
Food Science and Technology, MD
History, B
Hotel/Motel Administration/Management, B
Industrial Radiologic Technology/Technician, B
Kindergarten/PreSchool Education and Teaching, B
Liberal Arts and Sciences Studies and Humani-
ties, B
Marine Biology and Biological Oceanography, B
Marine Sciences, MD
Mass Communication/Media Studies, B
Mathematics, B
Music Teacher Education, B
Organizational Management, D
Physical Education Teaching and Coaching, B
Physical Therapy/Therapist, BD
Poultry Science, B
Pre-Dentistry Studies, B
Pre-Law Studies, B
Pre-Medicine/Pre-Medical Studies, B
Rehabilitation Counseling, M
Rehabilitation Sciences, M
Rehabilitation and Therapeutic Professions, B
Social Sciences, B
Social Work, B
Sociology, B
Special Education and Teaching, BM
Special Products Marketing Operations, B
Toxicology, MD
Vocational and Technical Education, M

UNIVERSITY OF MARYLAND UNIVER-SITY COLLEGE

Accounting, BMO
Asian Studies/Civilization, B
BioTechnology, MO
Biological and Biomedical Sciences, B
Business Administration and Management, B
Business Administration, Management and Opera-
tions, BMO
Communication Studies/Speech Communication
and Rhetoric, B
Computer and Information Sciences, B
Computer and Information Systems Security, BMO
Criminal Justice/Safety Studies, B
Database Systems, MO
Distance Education Development, MO
Education, MO
English Language and Literature, B
Environmental Policy and Resource Manage-
ment, MO
Finance, B
Finance and Banking, MO
Forensic Science and Technology, B
Gerontology, B
Graphic Communications, B
Health Informatics, MO
Health Services Administration, MO
Health/Health Care Administration/Management, B
History, B
Human Resources Management/Personnel Adminis-
tration, B
Information Science/Studies, BMO
International Business/Trade/Commerce, MO
Law and Legal Studies, B
Liberal Arts and Sciences Studies and Humani-
ties, AB
Management, MDO
Management Information Systems and Ser-
vices, MO
Management of Technology, MO
Marketing/Marketing Management, B
Multi-/Interdisciplinary Studies, B
Natural Resources and Conservation, B
Political Science and Government, B

Psychology, B
Public Administration, B
Social Sciences, B

WASHINGTON ADVENTIST UNIVER-SITY

Biochemistry, B
Biology/Biological Sciences, B
Broadcast Journalism, B
Business Administration and Management, B
Business Administration, Management and Opera-
tions, M
Chemistry, B
Counseling Psychology, M
Early Childhood Education and Teaching, A
Elementary Education and Teaching, B
Engineering, A
English Language and Literature, B
English/Language Arts Teacher Education, B
Health Services Administration, M
Health and Physical Education, B
Health/Health Care Administration/Management, B
History, B
Information Science/Studies, B
Journalism, B
Liberal Arts and Sciences Studies and Humani-
ties, B
Mass Communication/Media Studies, B
Mathematics, B
Mathematics Teacher Education, B
Music, B
Music Performance, B
Music Teacher Education, B
Nursing, M
Nursing Administration, M
Nursing Education, M
Political Science and Government, B
Pre-Dentistry Studies, B
Pre-Law Studies, B
Pre-Medicine/Pre-Medical Studies, B
Pre-Veterinary Studies, B
Psychology, B
Public Administration, M
Religion/Religious Studies, M
Religious Education, B
Special Education and Teaching, B
Theology/Theological Studies, B

WASHINGTON COLLEGE

American/United States Studies/Civilization, B
Anthropology, B
Art/Art Studies, General, B
Biology/Biological Sciences, B
Business Administration and Management, B
Chemistry, B
Computer Science, B
Drama and Dramatics/Theatre Arts, B
Ecology, B
Economics, B
English Language and Literature, B
Environmental Sciences, B
Environmental Studies, B
Foreign Languages and Literatures, B
French Language and Literature, B
German Language and Literature, B
History, B
Humanities/Humanistic Studies, B
International Relations and Affairs, B
Latin American Studies, B
Liberal Arts and Sciences Studies and Humani-
ties, B
Mathematics, B
Multi-/Interdisciplinary Studies, B
Music, B
Philosophy, B
Physics, B
Political Science and Government, B
Pre-Dentistry Studies, B
Pre-Law Studies, B
Pre-Medicine/Pre-Medical Studies, B
Pre-Veterinary Studies, B
Psychology, B
Sociology, B

Spanish Language and Literature, B

WOR-WIC COMMUNITY COLLEGE

Accounting Technology/Technician and Bookkeep-
ing, A
Administrative Assistant and Secretarial Science, A
Biological and Physical Sciences, A
Business Administration and Management, A
Business/Commerce, A
Child Care and Support Services Management, A
Computer Systems Analysis/Analyst, A
Computer and Information Sciences, A
Criminal Justice/Police Science, A
Early Childhood Education and Teaching, A
Education, A
Electrical, Electronic and Communications Engineer-
ing Technology/Technician, A
Elementary Education and Teaching, A
Emergency Medical Technology/Technician (EMT
Paramedic), A
Engineering Technologies/Technicians, A
Environmental Engineering
Technology/Environmental Technology, A
Hospitality Administration/Management, A
Liberal Arts and Sciences Studies and Humani-
ties, A
Medical Radiologic Technology/Science - Radiation
Therapist, A
Occupational Therapist Assistant, A
Physical Therapist Assistant, A
Substance Abuse/Addiction Counseling, A

YESHIVA COLLEGE OF THE NATION'S CAPITAL

Theology/Theological Studies, B

Massachusetts

AMERICAN INTERNATIONAL COLLEGE

Accounting, BM
Biochemistry, B
Biology/Biological Sciences, B
Business Administration and Management, B
Business Administration, Management and Opera-
tions, M
Chemistry, B
Clinical Psychology, M
Counseling Psychology, M
Counselor Education/School Counseling and Guid-
ance Services, MO
Criminal Justice/Safety Studies, B
Drama and Dramatics/Theatre Arts, B
Early Childhood Education and Teaching, MO
Economics, B
Education, MDO
Educational Administration and Supervision, MO
Educational Psychology, MD
Elementary Education and Teaching, MO
English Language and Literature, B
Forensic Psychology, M
Health Services/Allied Health/Health Sciences, B
History, B
Hospital and Health Care Facilities
Administration/Management, B
International Business/Trade/Commerce, B
International Relations and Affairs, B
Liberal Arts and Sciences Studies and Humani-
ties, AB
Management Science, B
Marketing/Marketing Management, B
Mass Communication/Media Studies, B
Middle School Education, MO
Nursing, M
Nursing Administration, M
Nursing Education, M
Occupational Therapy/Therapist, BM
Organizational Management, M
Physical Therapy/Therapist, BD
Political Science and Government, B
Psychology, BM
Public Health (MPH, DPH), B
Reading Teacher Education, MO
Secondary Education and Teaching, MO
Social Sciences, B
Sociology, B

Special Education and Teaching, MO
Sport and Fitness Administration/Management, B
Taxation, M

AMHERST COLLEGE

African-American/Black Studies, B
American/United States Studies/Civilization, B
Ancient/Classical Greek Language and Literature, B
Anthropology, B
Asian Studies/Civilization, B
Astronomy, B
Biochemistry, Biophysics and Molecular Biology, B
Biology/Biological Sciences, B
Chemistry, B
Classics and Classical Languages, Literatures, and Linguistics, B
Computer Science, B
Dance, B
Drama and Dramatics/Theatre Arts, B
Economics, B
English Language and Literature, B
Environmental Studies, B
European Studies/Civilization, B
Fine/Studio Arts, B
French Language and Literature, B
Geology/Earth Science, B
German Language and Literature, B
History, B
Latin Language and Literature, B
Law and Legal Studies, B
Mathematics, B
Music, B
Philosophy, B
Physics, B
Political Science and Government, B
Psychology, B
Religion/Religious Studies, B
Russian Language and Literature, B
Sociology, B
Spanish Language and Literature, B
Statistics, B
Women's Studies, B

ANNA MARIA COLLEGE

Art Education, M
Art Teacher Education, B
Art Therapy/Therapist, B
Biology/Biological Sciences, B
Business Administration and Management, B
Business Administration, Management and Operations, BMO
Business and Personal/Financial Services Marketing Operations, B
Computer and Information Sciences, B
Computer/Information Technology Services Administration and Management, B
Counseling Psychology, M
Criminal Justice/Law Enforcement Administration, B
Criminology, M
Drama and Dramatics/Theatre Arts, B
Early Childhood Education and Teaching, BM
Education, BMO
Elementary Education and Teaching, BM
Emergency Management, MO
Emergency Medical Technology/Technician (EMT Paramedic), B
English Education, M
English Language and Literature, B
English/Language Arts Teacher Education, B
Environmental Sciences, B
Environmental Studies, B
Environmental and Occupational Health, M
Fine Arts and Art Studies, BM
Fire Protection Engineering, M
Fire Science/Firefighting, B
General Studies, B
Graphic Design, B
Health Services/Allied Health/Health Sciences, B
History, B
Human Services, B
Humanities/Humanistic Studies, B
Junior High/Intermediate/Middle School Education and Teaching, B
Law and Legal Studies, B
Legal Assistant/Paralegal, B

Liberal Arts and Sciences Studies and Humanities, B
Management Information Systems and Services, B
Marketing/Marketing Management, B
Mass Communication/Media Studies, B
Music, B
Music Teacher Education, B
Music Therapy/Therapist, B
Pastoral Studies/Counseling, BM
Philosophy, B
Piano and Organ, B
Political Science and Government, B
Pre-Pharmacy Studies, B
Psychology, B
Public Administration, M
Public Policy Analysis, B
Secondary Education and Teaching, B
Securities Services Administration/Management, M
Security and Loss Prevention Services, B
Small Business Administration/Management, B
Social Sciences, B
Social Work, B
Sociology, B
Spanish Language and Literature, B
Sport and Fitness Administration/Management, B
Teacher Education and Professional Development, Specific Levels and Methods, B
Theology/Theological Studies, B
Voice and Opera, B

ASSUMPTION COLLEGE

Accounting, BM
Actuarial Science, B
Art History, Criticism and Conservation, B
BioTechnology, B
Biology/Biological Sciences, B
Business Administration and Management, B
Business Administration, Management and Operations, MO
Chemistry, B
Child and Family Studies, M
Classics and Classical Languages, Literatures, and Linguistics, B
Computer and Information Sciences, B
Corporate and Organizational Communication, O
Counseling Psychology, MO
Criminology, B
Economics, BM
English Language and Literature, B
Environmental Sciences, B
Finance and Banking, M
Fine/Studio Arts, B
Foreign Languages and Literatures, B
French Language and Literature, B
Graphic Design, B
Health Services Administration, MO
History, B
Human Resources Management and Services, M
International Business/Trade/Commerce, BM
International/Global Studies, B
Italian Studies, B
Latin American Studies, B
Marketing, M
Marketing/Marketing Management, B
Mathematics, B
Molecular Biology, B
Music, B
Non-Profit/Public/Organizational Management, MO
Organizational Communication, B
Philosophy, B
Political Science and Government, B
Psychology, BM
Rehabilitation Counseling, MO
Rehabilitation and Therapeutic Professions, B
School Psychology, MO
Social Work, O
Sociology, B
Spanish Language and Literature, B
Special Education and Teaching, MO
Teacher Education, Multiple Levels, B
Theology/Theological Studies, B

BABSON COLLEGE

Accounting, BM
Accounting and Business/Management, B
Accounting and Finance, B

Auditing, B
Business Administration and Management, B
Business Administration, Management and Operations, BMO
Business/Corporate Communications, B
Economics, B
Entrepreneurial and Small Business Operations, B
Entrepreneurship/Entrepreneurial Studies, BM
Finance, B
Finance and Financial Management Services, B
International Business/Trade/Commerce, B
International Finance, B
Investments and Securities, B
Management, O
Management Information Systems and Services, B
Marketing, B
Marketing/Marketing Management, B
Office Management and Supervision, B
Operations Management and Supervision, B
Operations Research, B
Pre-Law Studies, B
Sales, Distribution and Marketing Operations, B
Small Business Administration/Management, B

BARD COLLEGE AT SIMON'S ROCK

African-American/Black Studies, B
Art History, Criticism and Conservation, B
Art/Art Studies, General, B
Asian Studies/Civilization, B
Biology/Biological Sciences, B
Chemistry, B
Computer Science, B
Dance, B
Drama and Dramatics/Theatre Arts, B
Environmental Studies, B
Ethnic, Cultural Minority, and Gender Studies, B
French Language and Literature, B
French Studies, B
Geography, B
German Language and Literature, B
German Studies, B
History, B
Intercultural/Multicultural and Diversity Studies, B
Intermedia/Multimedia, B
Latin American Studies, B
Liberal Arts and Sciences Studies and Humanities, A
Linguistics, B
Mathematics, B
Music, B
Natural Sciences, B
Philosophy, B
Physics, B
Political Science and Government, B
Pre-Medicine/Pre-Medical Studies, B
Psychology, B
Social Sciences, B
Spanish Language and Literature, B
Technical Theatre/Theatre Design and Technology, B
Visual and Performing Arts, B

BAY PATH UNIVERSITY

Accounting, BM
Applied Behavior Analysis, M
BioTechnology, B
Biochemistry, B
Biology Teacher Education, B
Biology/Biological Sciences, B
Business Administration and Management, AB
Business Administration, Management and Operations, AB
Clinical Psychology, M
Computer and Information Systems Security, BM
Counseling Psychology, M
Criminal Justice/Law Enforcement Administration, B
Criminalistics and Criminal Science, B
Developmental Psychology, M
Early Childhood Education and Teaching, B
Educational Administration and Supervision, M
Educational Media/Instructional Technology, M
Elementary Education and Teaching, B
Entrepreneurship/Entrepreneurial Studies, M
Forensic Science and Technology, BM
Health Services/Allied Health/Health Sciences, B

Higher Education/Higher Education Administration, M
Interior Design, AB
Law and Legal Studies, B
Legal Assistant/Paralegal, AB
Legal Professions and Studies, B
Liberal Arts and Sciences Studies and Humanities, AB
Management Information Systems and Services, M
Management Strategy and Policy, M
Marketing/Marketing Management, B
Non-Profit/Public/Organizational Management, M
Occupational Therapy/Therapist, BM
Physician Assistant, M
Psychology, B
Special Education and Teaching, MO
Writing, M

BAY STATE COLLEGE

Accounting, A
Animation, Interactive Technology, Video Graphics and Special Effects, AB
Business Administration and Management, AB
Business/Office Automation/Technology/Data Entry, AB
Criminal Justice/Safety Studies, AB
Education, A
Fashion Merchandising, AB
Medical Office Management/Administration, A
Medical/Clinical Assistant, A
Physical Therapist Assistant, A
Specialized Merchandising, Sales, and Marketing Operations, A
Tourism and Travel Services Marketing Operations, A

BECKER COLLEGE

Animal Sciences, AB
Animal Training, A
Animation, Interactive Technology, Video Graphics and Special Effects, B
Biology/Biological Sciences, B
Business Administration and Management, B
Communications Technologies/Technicians and Support Services, B
Community Health Services/Liaison/Counseling, B
Computer and Information Sciences, B
Criminal Justice/Law Enforcement Administration, B
Dog/Pet/Animal Grooming, A
Early Childhood Education and Teaching, AB
Education, B
Elementary Education and Teaching, B
Equestrian/Equine Studies, B
Forensic Science and Technology, B
Graphic Design, B
Horse Husbandry/Equine Science and Management, B
Kinesiology and Exercise Science, B
Liberal Arts and Sciences Studies and Humanities, B
Management Science, B
Marketing/Marketing Management, B
Pre-Law Studies, B
Pre-Veterinary Studies, B
Psychology, B
Sport and Fitness Administration/Management, B
Veterinary/Animal Health Technology/Technician and Veterinary Assistant, AB

BENJAMIN FRANKLIN INSTITUTE OF TECHNOLOGY

Architectural Drafting and Architectural CAD/CADD, A
Architectural Engineering Technology/Technician, A
Automobile/Automotive Mechanics Technology/Technician, AB
Automotive Engineering Technology/Technician, AB
Biomedical Technology/Technician, A
Biomedical/Medical Engineering, A
Computer Engineering Technology/Technician, A
Computer Science, A
Computer Technology/Computer Systems Technology, A
Drafting and Design Technology/Technician, A
Electrical and Electronic Engineering Technologies/Technicians, A

Electrical and Power Transmission Installation/Installer, A
Electrical, Electronic and Communications Engineering Technology/Technician, A
Engineering Technology, A
Mechanical Engineering/Mechanical Technology/Technician, A
Opticianry/Ophthalmic Dispensing Optician, A

BENTLEY UNIVERSITY

Accounting, BMD
Accounting and Finance, B
Accounting and Related Services, B
Actuarial Science, B
Business Administration and Management, B
Business Administration, Management and Operations, MDO
Business, Management, Marketing, and Related Support Services, B
Business/Corporate Communications, B
Business/Managerial Economics, B
Computer and Information Sciences, B
English Language and Literature, B
Ergonomics and Human Factors, M
Finance, B
Finance and Banking, M
Health Services Administration, B
History, B
Information Science/Studies, M
International/Global Studies, B
Liberal Arts and Sciences Studies and Humanities, B
Management Strategy and Policy, O
Marketing, M
Marketing/Marketing Management, B
Mass Communication/Media Studies, B
Mathematics, B
Philosophy, B
Public Policy Analysis, B
Sales, Distribution and Marketing Operations, B
Spanish Language and Literature, B
Taxation, M

BERKLEE COLLEGE OF MUSIC

Composition, M
Entertainment Management, M
Jazz/Jazz Studies, B
Music, BM
Music Performance, B
Music Teacher Education, B
Music Theory and Composition, B
Music Therapy/Therapist, B
Performance, M
Piano and Organ, B
Recording Arts Technology/Technician, B
Violin, Viola, Guitar and Other Stringed Instruments, B
Voice and Opera, B

BERKSHIRE COMMUNITY COLLEGE

Business Administration and Management, A
Business/Commerce, A
Business/Office Automation/Technology/Data Entry, A
Community Organization and Advocacy, A
Computer and Information Sciences, A
Criminal Justice/Safety Studies, A
Electrical, Electronic and Communications Engineering Technology/Technician, A
Engineering, A
Environmental Studies, A
Fire Science/Firefighting, A
Health Professions and Related Clinical Sciences, A
Hospitality Administration/Management, A
Human Services, A
International/Global Studies, A
Liberal Arts and Sciences Studies and Humanities, A
Medical Insurance Coding Specialist/Coder, A
Physical Therapist Assistant, A
Respiratory Care Therapy/Therapist, A
Visual and Performing Arts, A

BOSTON ARCHITECTURAL COLLEGE

Architecture, BM
Environmental Design/Architecture, B

Historic Preservation and Conservation, M
Interior Architecture, B
Interior Design, M
Landscape Architecture, BM
Sustainable Development, M

BOSTON BAPTIST COLLEGE

Bible/Biblical Studies, AB

BOSTON COLLEGE

Accounting, BM
Applied Psychology, MD
Art History, Criticism and Conservation, B
Biochemistry, BD
Biological and Biomedical Sciences, D
Biology/Biological Sciences, B
Business Administration and Management, B
Business Administration, Management and Operations, M
Business/Managerial Economics, B
Chemistry, BMD
Classics and Classical Languages, Literatures, and Linguistics, BM
Computer Science, B
Computer and Information Sciences, B
Counseling Psychology, MD
Curriculum and Instruction, MDO
Developmental Psychology, MD
Drama and Dramatics/Theatre Arts, B
East European and Russian Studies, M
Economics, BD
Education, MDO
Educational Administration and Supervision, MDO
Educational Measurement and Evaluation, MD
Educational Psychology, MD
Elementary Education and Teaching, BM
English, MD
English Language and Literature, B
Environmental Studies, B
Film/Cinema Studies, B
Finance, B
Finance and Banking, MD
Fine/Studio Arts, B
Forensic Nursing, M
French Language and Literature, BM
Geology/Earth Science, BM
Geophysics and Seismology, BM
German Language and Literature, B
Gerontological Nursing, M
Higher Education/Higher Education Administration, MD
Hispanic-American, Puerto Rican, and Mexican-American/Chicano Studies, B
History, BMD
Human Resources Management/Personnel Administration, B
Inorganic Chemistry, D
International/Global Studies, B
Islamic Studies, B
Italian Language and Literature, BM
Law and Legal Studies, D
Linguistics, M
Management Information Systems and Services, B
Marketing/Marketing Management, B
Maternal/Child Health and Neonatal Nurse/Nursing, M
Mathematics, BD
Music, B
Nurse Anesthetist, M
Nursing, MD
Nursing - Adult, M
Operations Management and Supervision, B
Organic Chemistry, D
Organizational Behavior Studies, D
Organizational Management, D
Pastoral Studies/Counseling, MDO
Pediatric Nurse/Nursing, M
Philosophy, BMD
Physical Chemistry, D
Physics, BMD
Political Science and Government, BMD
Psychiatric/Mental Health Nurse/Nursing, M
Psychology, BMD
Reading Teacher Education, MO
Religious Education, MDO
Russian Language and Literature, BM

Russian Studies, B
Science Teacher Education/General Science
   Teacher Education, M
Secondary Education and Teaching, BM
Slavic Languages, Literatures, and Linguistics, B
Social Work, MD
Sociology, BMD
Spanish Language and Literature, BM
Special Education and Teaching, MO
Theology and Religious Vocations, MDO
Theology/Theological Studies, B
Western European Studies, M
Women's Health Nursing, M

BOSTON UNIVERSITY

Accounting, B
Acting, B
Actuarial Science, M
Advertising and Public Relations, M
African-American Studies, M
Allied Health and Medical Assisting Services, MD
Allopathic Medicine, D
American/United States Studies/Civilization, BD
Anatomy, MD
Ancient Studies/Civilization, B
Ancient/Classical Greek Language and Literature, B
Anthropology, BMD
Archeology, BMD
Art Education, M
Art History, Criticism and Conservation, MDO
Art Teacher Education, B
Arts Management, MO
Astronomy, BMD
Astrophysics, B
Athletic Training and Sports Medicine, BD
Audiology/Audiologist and Speech-Language
   Pathology/Pathologist, B
Bilingual and Multilingual Education, B
Biochemistry, MD
Biochemistry, Biophysics and Molecular Biology, B
Bioethics/Medical Ethics, M
Bioinformatics, MD
Biological and Biomedical Sciences, BMD
Biology/Biological Sciences, B
Biomedical Engineering, MD
Biomedical/Medical Engineering, B
Biophysics, MD
Biopsychology, M
Biostatistics, MD
Business Administration and Management, B
Business Administration, Management and Opera-
   tions, M
Cell Biology and Anatomy, MD
Chemistry, BMD
Chemistry Teacher Education, B
Chinese Language and Literature, B
Classics and Classical Languages, Litera-
   tures, and Linguistics, BMD
Clinical Research, M
Communication Disorders, MD
Communication and Media Studies, MD
Comparative Literature, B
Composition, MD
Computer Engineering, BMD
Computer Science, BMO
Computer and Information Systems Security, M
Conservation Biology, B
Corporate and Organizational Communication, M
Counseling Psychology, M
Criminology, M
Cultural Studies, M
Database Systems, M
Dental Hygiene/Hygienist, M
Dental and Oral Surgery, MDO
Directing and Theatrical Production, B
Drama and Dance Teacher Education, B
Drama and Dramatics/Theatre Arts, B
Early Childhood Education and Teaching, B
East Asian Studies, B
Economics, BMD
Education, MDO
Education/Teaching of Individuals with Hearing Im-
   pairments, Including Deafness, B
Electrical Engineering, MD
Electrical, Electronics and Communications Engi-
   neering, B

Elementary Education and Teaching, B
Emergency Management, M
Energy Management and Policy, M
Engineering, B
Engineering and Applied Sciences, MD
English, MD
English Language and Literature, B
English/Language Arts Teacher Education, B
Environmental Biology, B
Environmental Policy, M
Environmental Sciences, MD
Environmental and Occupational Health, MD
Epidemiology, MD
Film, Television, and Video Production, M
Finance, B
Finance and Banking, M
Fine Arts and Art Studies, M
Food Science and Technology, M
Foreign Language Teacher Education, B
Foreign Languages and Literatures, B
Forensic Science and Technology, M
French Language and Literature, BMD
Genetic Counseling/Counselor, M
Genetics, D
Genomic Sciences, M
Geographic Information Systems, M
Geography, BD
Geological and Earth Sciences/Geosciences, B
Geology/Earth Science, B
Geophysics and Seismology, B
Geosciences, MD
German Language and Literature, B
Graphic Design, BM
Health Communication, M
Health Informatics, MO
Health Law, M
Health Professions and Related Clinical Sciences, B
Health Promotion, D
Health Services Administration, MD
Health Services/Allied Health/Health Sciences, B
Hispanic and Latin American Languages, MD
Historic Preservation and Conservation, M
History, BMD
Hospitality Administration/Management, B
Immunology, D
Intellectual Property Law, M
International Affairs, M
International Business/Trade/Commerce, M
International Public Health/International Health, MD
International Relations and Affairs, B
Internet and Interactive Multimedia, M
Investment Management, M
Italian Language and Literature, B
Italian Studies, B
Japanese Language and Literature, B
Journalism, BM
Kinesiotherapy/Kinesiotherapist, B
Latin American Studies, BM
Latin Language and Literature, B
Latin Teacher Education, B
Law and Legal Studies, MD
Legal Assistant/Paralegal, B
Legal and Justice Studies, M
Linguistics, BMD
Management, MD
Management Information Systems and Services, M
Management Strategy and Policy, M
Management of Technology, M
Manufacturing Engineering, BMD
Marine Biology and Biological Oceanography, B
Marketing, M
Mass Communication/Media Studies, M
Materials Engineering, MD
Materials Sciences, MD
Maternal and Child Health, MD
Mathematical and Computational Finance, D
Mathematics, BMD
Mathematics Teacher Education, B
Mechanical Engineering, BMD
Media Studies, MD
Medical Imaging, M
Molecular Biology, BMD
Molecular Medicine, D
Multi-/Interdisciplinary Studies, B
Museology/Museum Studies, O
Music, BMDO

Music History, Literature, and Theory, D
Music Performance, B
Music Teacher Education, BMD
Music Theory and Composition, BMD
Neurobiology and Neurophysiology, MD
Neuroscience, D
Nutritional Sciences, BMD
Occupational Therapy/Therapist, MD
Oral Biology, MD
Oral and Dental Sciences, MDO
Organizational Management, M
Orthodontics, MD
Painting, BM
Pathology/Experimental Pathology, D
Pedodontics, MDO
Performance, MO
Periodontics, MDO
Pharmaceutical Sciences, MD
Pharmacology, MD
Philosophy, BMD
Photonics, M
Physical Education Teaching and Coaching, B
Physical Therapy/Therapist, D
Physician Assistant, M
Physics, BMD
Physiology, MD
Political Science and Government, BMD
Pre-Dentistry Studies, B
Project Management, MO
Psychology, BMD
Public Health, MD
Rehabilitation Sciences, D
Rehabilitation and Therapeutic Professions, B
Religion/Religious Studies, BMD
Romance Languages, Literatures, and Linguis-
   tics, MD
Russian Language and Literature, B
Science Teacher Education/General Science
   Teacher Education, B
Sculpture, BM
Social Sciences, B
Social Studies Teacher Education, B
Social Work, MD
Sociology, BMD
Spanish Language and Literature, B
Special Education and Teaching, B
Systems Engineering, MD
Systems Science and Theory, B
Taxation, M
Teacher Education and Professional Develop-
   ment, Specific Levels and Methods, M
Technical Theatre/Theatre Design and Technol-
   ogy, B
Telecommunications, M
Telecommunications Management, M
Theater, MO
Theology and Religious Vocations, MD
Urban Studies/Affairs, BM
Urban and Regional Planning, M
Voice and Opera, B
Writing, MD

BRANDEIS UNIVERSITY

African-American/Black Studies, B
American/United States Studies/Civilization, B
Anthropology, BMD
Art History, Criticism and Conservation, B
BioTechnology, B
Biochemistry, BD
Bioinformatics, M
Biological and Biomedical Sciences, DO
Biology/Biological Sciences, B
Biophysics, BD
Business Administration, Management and Opera-
   tions, M
Business/Commerce, B
Cell Biology and Anatomy, MD
Chemistry, BMD
Child and Family Studies, MD
Classics and Classical Languages, Litera-
   tures, and Linguistics, BMO
Cognitive Sciences, D
Communication and Media Studies, M
Comparative Literature, B
Composition, M
Computer Science, BM

Computer and Information Systems Security, M
Conflict Resolution and Mediation/Peace Studies, M
Developmental Psychology, D
Disability Studies, D
Distance Education Development, M
Drama and Dramatics/Theatre Arts, B
East Asian Studies, B
Economics, BMD
Education, B
Educational Measurement and Evaluation, O
Elementary Education and Teaching, M
English, MD
English Language and Literature, B
Environmental Studies, B
European Studies/Civilization, B
Film/Cinema Studies, B
Finance and Banking, MD
Fine/Studio Arts, B
French Language and Literature, B
Gender Studies, M
Genetic Counseling/Counselor, M
Genetics, D
German Language and Literature, B
Health Education, D
Health Informatics, M
Health Services Administration, M
Health/Health Care Administration/Management, B
Hebrew Language and Literature, BM
History, BMD
Human Services, M
Inorganic Chemistry, MD
International Affairs, M
International Business/Trade/Commerce, MD
International Public Health/International Health, MD
International/Global Studies, B
Jewish/Judaic Studies, MD
Latin American Studies, B
Linguistics, BM
Management Information Systems and Services, M
Management Strategy and Policy, M
Marketing, M
Mathematics, BMDO
Medical Informatics, M
Microbiology, D
Molecular Biology, MD
Multi-/Interdisciplinary Studies, B
Music, BMD
Music Theory and Composition, MD
Musicology and Ethnomusicology, MD
Near and Middle Eastern Studies, BMD
Neurobiology and Neurophysiology, D
Neuroscience, MD
Non-Profit/Public/Organizational Management, M
Organic Chemistry, MD
Philosophy, BM
Physical Chemistry, MD
Physics, BMD
Political Science and Government, BMD
Project Management, M
Psychology, BMD
Public Policy Analysis, M
Real Estate, M
Religious Education, M
Russian Language and Literature, B
Secondary Education and Teaching, M
Social Psychology, D
Sociology, BMD
Software Engineering, M
Spanish Language and Literature, B
Sustainability Management, M
Sustainable Development, M
Theater, M
Women's Studies, BM

BRIDGEWATER STATE UNIVERSITY

Accounting, BM
Accounting and Finance, B
Aeronautics/Aviation/Aerospace Science and Technology, B
Airline/Commercial/Professional Pilot and Flight Crew, B
American Government and Politics (United States), B
Anthropology, B
Archeology, B
Area Studies, B

Art Education, M
Art History, Criticism and Conservation, B
Art Teacher Education, B
Athletic Training and Sports Medicine, B
Aviation/Airway Management and Operations, B
Biochemistry, B
Biology Teacher Education, B
Biology/Biological Sciences, B
Biomedical Sciences, B
Business Administration and Management, B
Business, Management, Marketing, and Related Support Services, B
Cell/Cellular and Molecular Biology, B
Chemistry, B
City/Urban, Community and Regional Planning, B
Communication Disorders, B
Communication Studies/Speech Communication and Rhetoric, B
Computer Science, BM
Counselor Education/School Counseling and Guidance Services, MO
Crafts/Craft Design, Folk Art and Artisanry, B
Criminal Justice/Safety Studies, B
Criminology, M
Drama and Dance Teacher Education, B
Drama and Dramatics/Theatre Arts, B
Early Childhood Education and Teaching, BM
Economics, B
Education, MO
Educational Administration and Supervision, MO
Educational Media/Instructional Technology, M
Educational/Instructional Media Design, B
Elementary Education and Teaching, BM
English, M
English Language and Literature, B
English/Language Arts Teacher Education, B
Environmental Biology, B
Ethics, B
Finance, B
Finance and Banking, M
Fine/Studio Arts, B
Geochemistry, B
Geography, B
Geological and Earth Sciences/Geosciences, B
Geology/Earth Science, B
Graphic Design, B
Health Promotion, M
Health Teacher Education, B
Health and Physical Education/Fitness, B
History, B
International Business/Trade/Commerce, B
International Relations and Affairs, B
Kinesiology and Exercise Science, B
Kinesiotherapy/Kinesiotherapist, B
Law and Legal Studies, B
Management, M
Management Information Systems and Services, B
Management Science, B
Marketing/Marketing Management, B
Mathematics, B
Mathematics Teacher Education, M
Music, B
Music Teacher Education, B
Parks, Recreation, Leisure and Fitness Studies, B
Philosophy, B
Photography, B
Physical Education Teaching and Coaching, BM
Physics, B
Political Science and Government, B
Psychology, BM
Public Administration, M
Reading Teacher Education, MO
Science Teacher Education/General Science Teacher Education, M
Science Technologies/Technicians, B
Secondary Education and Teaching, M
Social Studies Teacher Education, M
Social Work, BM
Sociology, B
Spanish Language and Literature, B
Special Education and Teaching, BM
Sport and Fitness Administration/Management, B

Transportation/Transportation Management, B

BRISTOL COMMUNITY COLLEGE

Accounting, A
American Sign Language (ASL), A
Banking and Financial Support Services, A
Business Administration and Management, A
Business Operations Support and Secretarial Services, A
Business, Management, Marketing, and Related Support Services, A
Business/Commerce, A
Child Care and Support Services Management, A
Civil Engineering, A
Clinical/Medical Laboratory Technician, A
Communication Studies/Speech Communication and Rhetoric, A
Computer Programming/Programmer, A
Computer Science, A
Computer Systems Analysis/Analyst, A
Computer and Information Sciences, A
Cosmetology and Related Personal Grooming Arts, A
Criminal Justice/Safety Studies, A
Culinary Arts and Related Services, A
Data Processing and Data Processing Technology/Technician, A
Dental Hygiene/Hygienist, A
Design and Visual Communications, A
Dramatic/Theatre Arts and Stagecraft, A
Electromechanical Technology/Electromechanical Engineering Technology, A
Engineering, A
Engineering Science, A
Engineering Technologies/Technicians, A
Entrepreneurship/Entrepreneurial Studies, A
Environmental Engineering Technology/Environmental Technology, A
Environmental Studies, A
Environmental/Environmental Health Engineering, A
Finance and Financial Management Services, A
Fine/Studio Arts, A
Fire Protection and Safety Technology/Technician, A
Fire Science/Firefighting, A
General Studies, A
Graphic Design, A
Humanities/Humanistic Studies, A
Information Science/Studies, A
Intermedia/Multimedia, A
Kindergarten/PreSchool Education and Teaching, A
Legal Assistant/Paralegal, A
Legal Professions and Studies, A
Liberal Arts and Sciences Studies and Humanities, A
Manufacturing Engineering, A
Marketing/Marketing Management, A
Mathematics and Statistics, A
Mechanical Engineering, A
Medical Administrative Assistant/Secretary, A
Occupational Therapist Assistant, A
Real Estate, A
Receptionist, A
Social Sciences, A
Social Work, A
Structural Engineering, A
Water Quality and Wastewater Treatment Management and Recycling Technology/Technician, A
Water Resources Engineering, A

BUNKER HILL COMMUNITY COLLEGE

Accounting, A
Art/Art Studies, General, A
BioTechnology, A
Biology/Biological Sciences, A
Biomedical/Medical Engineering, A
Business Administration and Management, A
Business Administration, Management and Operations, A
Business Operations Support and Secretarial Services, A
Cardiovascular Technology/Technologist, A
Chemistry, A
Clinical/Medical Laboratory Technician, A
Communication Studies/Speech Communication and Rhetoric, A
Computer Programming, Specific Applications, A

Computer Programming/Programmer, A
Computer Science, A
Computer Systems Networking and Telecommunications, A
Computer and Information Sciences and Support Services, A
Computer and Information Systems Security, A
Computer/Information Technology Services Administration and Management, A
Criminal Justice/Law Enforcement Administration, A
Criminal Justice/Police Science, A
Culinary Arts/Chef Training, A
Data Entry/Microcomputer Applications, A
Design and Visual Communications, A
Diagnostic Medical Sonography/Sonographer and Ultrasound Technician, A
Drama and Dramatics/Theatre Arts, A
Early Childhood Education and Teaching, A
Education, A
Electrical/Electronics Maintenance and Repair Technology, A
Emergency Medical Technology/Technician (EMT Paramedic), A
Engineering, A
English Language and Literature, A
Entrepreneurship/Entrepreneurial Studies, A
Finance, A
Fine Arts and Art Studies, A
Fire Protection and Safety Technology/Technician, A
Foreign Languages and Literatures, A
General Studies, A
Health Information/Medical Records Administration/Administrator, A
History, A
Hospitality Administration/Management, A
Human Services, A
International Business/Trade/Commerce, A
Legal Assistant/Paralegal, A
Mass Communication/Media Studies, A
Mathematics, A
Medical Administrative Assistant/Secretary, A
Medical Radiologic Technology/Science - Radiation Therapist, A
Music, A
Operations Management and Supervision, A
Physics, A
Psychology, A
Respiratory Therapy Technician/Assistant, A
Sociology, A
Sport and Fitness Administration/Management, A
Tourism and Travel Services Management, A
Web Page, Digital/Multimedia and Information Resources Design, A

CAMBRIDGE COLLEGE

Business Administration, Management and Operations, M
Business/Commerce, B
Conflict Resolution and Mediation/Peace Studies, M
Counseling Psychology, MO
Counselor Education/School Counseling and Guidance Services, M
Curriculum and Instruction, O
Early Childhood Education and Teaching, M
Education, MDO
Educational Administration and Supervision, MO
Educational Leadership and Administration, D
Educational Measurement and Evaluation, M
Educational Media/Instructional Technology, M
Elementary Education and Teaching, M
English as a Second Language, MO
Entrepreneurship/Entrepreneurial Studies, M
Forensic Psychology, M
Health Education, MO
Health Services Administration, M
Home Economics Education, M
Interdisciplinary Studies, M
Liberal Arts and Sciences Studies and Humanities, B
Management, M
Management Science, B
Management of Technology, M
Marriage and Family Therapy/Counseling, M
Mathematics Teacher Education, MO
Medical Informatics, M
Middle School Education, M

Non-Profit/Public/Organizational Management, M
Organizational Management, M
Psychology, BM
Reading Teacher Education, M
School Nursing, M
School Psychology, M
Science Teacher Education/General Science Teacher Education, M
Social Studies Teacher Education, M
Special Education and Teaching, MO
Substance Abuse/Addiction Counseling, MO

CAPE COD COMMUNITY COLLEGE

Accounting, A
Business Administration and Management, A
Business Administration, Management and Operations, A
Commercial and Advertising Art, A
Communication Studies/Speech Communication and Rhetoric, A
Computer Programming, A
Computer Programming/Programmer, A
Computer Science, A
Computer Systems Networking and Telecommunications, A
Criminal Justice/Police Science, A
Dental Hygiene/Hygienist, A
Drama and Dramatics/Theatre Arts, A
Early Childhood Education and Teaching, A
Education, A
English Language and Literature, A
Environmental Control Technologies/Technicians, A
Environmental Studies, A
Executive Assistant/Executive Secretary, A
Fire Protection and Safety Technology/Technician, A
Health Services/Allied Health/Health Sciences, A
History, A
Hospitality Administration/Management, A
Hotel/Motel Administration/Management, A
Information Science/Studies, A
Kindergarten/PreSchool Education and Teaching, A
Liberal Arts and Sciences Studies and Humanities, A
Marketing/Marketing Management, A
Mass Communication/Media Studies, A
Medical Administrative Assistant/Secretary, A
Multi-/Interdisciplinary Studies, A
Music, A
Physical Education Teaching and Coaching, A
Political Science and Government, A
Psychology, A
Public Administration and Social Service Professions, A
Public Relations/Image Management, A
Teacher Education and Professional Development, Specific Levels and Methods, A
Visual and Performing Arts, A
Web Page, Digital/Multimedia and Information Resources Design, A

CLARK UNIVERSITY

Accounting, M
American/United States Studies/Civilization, MD
Art History, Criticism and Conservation, B
Asian Studies/Civilization, B
Biochemistry, B
Biological and Biomedical Sciences, MD
Biology/Biological Sciences, B
Business Administration and Management, B
Business Administration, Management and Operations, M
Chemistry, BMD
Classics and Classical Languages, Literatures, and Linguistics, B
Clinical Psychology, D
Commercial and Advertising Art, B
Communication and Media Studies, M
Comparative Literature, B
Computer Science, B
Development Economics and International Development, B
Developmental Psychology, D
Drama and Dramatics/Theatre Arts, B
Ecology, B
Economics, BD
Education, BM

Elementary Education and Teaching, B
Engineering, B
English, M
English Language and Literature, B
Environmental Policy and Resource Management, M
Environmental Studies, M
Film/Cinema Studies, B
Finance and Banking, M
Fine/Studio Arts, B
French Language and Literature, B
Geographic Information Systems, M
Geography, BMD
Geology/Earth Science, B
History, BMDO
Holocaust Studies, D
Information Science/Studies, M
International Business/Trade/Commerce, M
International Development, M
International Relations and Affairs, B
Jewish/Judaic Studies, B
Junior High/Intermediate/Middle School Education and Teaching, B
Management, M
Management Information Systems and Services, M
Marketing, M
Mass Communication/Media Studies, B
Mathematics, B
Modern Languages, B
Molecular Biology, B
Music, B
Natural Resources Management/Development and Policy, M
Peace Studies and Conflict Resolution, B
Philosophy, B
Physics, BD
Political Science and Government, B
Pre-Dentistry Studies, B
Pre-Law Studies, B
Pre-Medicine/Pre-Medical Studies, B
Pre-Veterinary Studies, B
Psychology, B
Public Administration, MO
Secondary Education and Teaching, B
Social Psychology, D
Sociology, B
Spanish Language and Literature, B
Sustainability Management, M
Sustainable Development, M
Urban and Regional Planning, M
Women's Studies, B

COLLEGE OF THE HOLY CROSS

Accounting, B
Anthropology, B
Architectural History and Criticism, B
Art History, Criticism and Conservation, B
Asian Studies/Civilization, B
Biology/Biological Sciences, B
Chemistry, B
Chinese Language and Literature, B
Christian Studies, B
Classics and Classical Languages, Literatures, and Linguistics, B
Comparative Literature, B
Computer Science, B
Drama and Dramatics/Theatre Arts, B
Economics, B
English Language and Literature, B
Environmental Studies, B
Fine/Studio Arts, B
French Language and Literature, B
German Language and Literature, B
History, B
International/Global Studies, B
Italian Language and Literature, B
Mathematics, B
Music, B
Philosophy, B
Physics, B
Political Science and Government, B
Psychology, B
Religion/Religious Studies, B
Russian Language and Literature, B
Sociology, B

Spanish Language and Literature, B

CURRY COLLEGE

Biochemistry, B
Biology/Biological Sciences, B
Business Administration and Management, B
Business Administration, Management and Operations, MO
Communication and Media Studies, B
Computer Programming, B
Computer and Information Sciences, B
Criminal Justice/Safety Studies, B
Criminology, M
Early Childhood Education and Teaching, B
Education, BMO
Elementary Education and Teaching, BM
English Language and Literature, B
Environmental Sciences, B
Finance and Banking, O
Fine/Studio Arts, B
Foundations and Philosophy of Education, M
Graphic Design, B
Health Professions and Related Clinical Sciences, B
Liberal Arts and Sciences Studies and Humanities, B
Multi-/Interdisciplinary Studies, B
Nursing, M
Philosophy, B
Psychology, B
Reading Teacher Education, MO
Social Sciences, B
Sociology, B
Special Education and Teaching, BM

DEAN COLLEGE

Athletic Training and Sports Medicine, A
Biology/Biological Sciences, A
Business Administration and Management, AB
Criminal Justice/Safety Studies, A
Dance, AB
Drama and Dramatics/Theatre Arts, AB
Early Childhood Education and Teaching, A
English Language and Literature, AB
Environmental Studies, A
General Studies, AB
History, AB
Liberal Arts and Sciences Studies and Humanities, B
Mass Communication/Media Studies, A
Mathematics, A
Psychology, AB
Sociology, AB
Sport and Fitness Administration/Management, A

EASTERN NAZARENE COLLEGE

Accounting, B
Accounting and Business/Management, B
Accounting and Finance, B
Accounting and Related Services, B
Advertising, B
Aerospace, Aeronautical and Astronautical Engineering, B
Biochemistry, B
Biological and Physical Sciences, B
Biology Teacher Education, B
Biology/Biological Sciences, B
Biomedical/Medical Engineering, B
Business Administration and Management, B
Business Administration, Management and Operations, M
Business Teacher Education, B
Business, Management, Marketing, and Related Support Services, B
Business/Commerce, AB
Chemistry, B
Chemistry Teacher Education, B
Communication, Journalism and Related Programs, B
Computer Engineering, B
Counseling Psychology, M
Criminal Justice/Law Enforcement Administration, B
Criminal Justice/Police Science, B
Criminal Justice/Safety Studies, AB
Divinity/Ministry (BD, MDiv.), B
Drama and Dramatics/Theatre Arts, B
Early Childhood Education and Teaching, ABMO

Education, BMO
Educational Administration and Supervision, MO
Electrical, Electronics and Communications Engineering, B
Elementary Education and Teaching, BMO
Engineering, B
Engineering Physics, B
English Language and Literature, B
English as a Second Language, O
Environmental Sciences, B
Environmental Studies, B
Forensic Science and Technology, B
General Studies, B
Health Professions and Related Clinical Sciences, B
Health/Medical Preparatory Programs, B
History, B
History Teacher Education, B
Industrial Engineering, B
Journalism, B
Junior High/Intermediate/Middle School Education and Teaching, B
Kindergarten/PreSchool Education and Teaching, AB
Liberal Arts and Sciences Studies and Humanities, B
Marketing, B
Marketing/Marketing Management, B
Marriage and Family Therapy/Counseling, M
Mass Communication/Media Studies, B
Mathematics, B
Mechanical Engineering, B
Middle School Education, MO
Movement Therapy and Movement Education, B
Music, B
Music History, Literature, and Theory, B
Music Pedagogy, B
Music Performance, B
Music Teacher Education, B
Music Theory and Composition, B
Pastoral Studies/Counseling, B
Pharmacy, B
Philosophy and Religious Studies, B
Physical Education Teaching and Coaching, B
Physical Therapy/Therapist, B
Physics, B
Physics Teacher Education, B
Piano and Organ, B
Pre-Dentistry Studies, B
Pre-Law Studies, B
Pre-Medicine/Pre-Medical Studies, B
Pre-Nursing Studies, B
Pre-Pharmacy Studies, B
Pre-Theology/Pre-Ministerial Studies, B
Pre-Veterinary Studies, B
Psychology, B
Radio and Television, B
Reading Teacher Education, MO
Religion/Religious Studies, B
Religious Education, B
Religious/Sacred Music, B
Science Teacher Education/General Science Teacher Education, B
Secondary Education and Teaching, BMO
Social Work, B
Sociology, B
Special Education and Teaching, BMO
Sport and Fitness Administration/Management, B
Systems Engineering, B
Teacher Education and Professional Development, Specific Levels and Methods, B
Teacher Education and Professional Development, Specific Subject Areas, B
Teacher Education, Multiple Levels, B
Theology and Religious Vocations, B
Theology/Theological Studies, B
Violin, Viola, Guitar and Other Stringed Instruments, B
Voice and Opera, B
Youth Ministry, B

ELMS COLLEGE

Accounting, BM
Air Force JROTC/ROTC, B
Asian Studies/Civilization, B
Biology/Biological Sciences, B
Business Administration and Management, B

Business Administration, Management and Operations, M
Chemistry, B
Communication Disorders, BMO
Computer and Information Sciences, B
Criminal Justice/Law Enforcement Administration, B
Drama and Dramatics/Theatre Arts, B
Early Childhood Education and Teaching, M
Education, BMO
Elementary Education and Teaching, M
English Education, M
English Language and Literature, B
English as a Second Language, M
Fine/Studio Arts, B
Foreign Language Teacher Education, M
Health Services Administration, M
Health/Health Care Administration/Management, B
History, B
International Business/Trade/Commerce, B
Law and Legal Studies, B
Legal Assistant/Paralegal, AB
Liberal Arts and Sciences Studies and Humanities, B
Marketing/Marketing Management, B
Mathematics, B
Music, B
Natural Sciences, B
Nursing, MD
Nursing Administration, M
Nursing Education, M
Physical Education Teaching and Coaching, B
Psychology, B
Reading Teacher Education, M
Religion/Religious Studies, BM
Science Teacher Education/General Science Teacher Education, M
Secondary Education and Teaching, M
Social Work, B
Sociology, B
Spanish Language and Literature, B
Special Education and Teaching, M
Speech-Language Pathology/Pathologist, A
Sport and Fitness Administration/Management, B

EMERSON COLLEGE

Acting, B
Advertising, B
Advertising and Public Relations, M
Audiology/Audiologist and Speech-Language Pathology/Pathologist, B
Broadcast Journalism, BM
Cinematography and Film/Video Production, B
Communication Disorders, BM
Communication Studies/Speech Communication and Rhetoric, B
Communication and Media Studies, M
Corporate and Organizational Communication, M
Drama and Dance Teacher Education, B
Drama and Dramatics/Theatre Arts, B
Education/Teaching of Individuals with Speech or Language Impairments, B
Film/Cinema Studies, B
Health Communication, M
Intermedia/Multimedia, B
International Business/Trade/Commerce, M
Journalism, BM
Marketing, M
Marketing/Marketing Management, B
Mass Communication/Media Studies, B
Media Studies, M
Playwriting and Screenwriting, B
Political Communication, B
Public Relations/Image Management, B
Publishing, BM
Radio and Television, B
Radio and Television Broadcasting Technology/Technician, B
Radio, Television, and Digital Communication, B
Speech-Language Pathology/Pathologist, B
Technical Theatre/Theatre Design and Technology, B
Theater, M
Visual and Performing Arts, B

Writing, M

EMMANUEL COLLEGE

Accounting, B
American Government and Politics (United States), B
American/United States Studies/Civilization, B
Art Therapy/Therapist, B
Biochemistry, B
Biology/Biological Sciences, B
Biostatistics, B
Business Administration and Management, B
Chemistry, B
Communication Studies/Speech Communication and Rhetoric, B
Criminology, B
Economics, B
Education, M
Elementary Education and Teaching, BM
English Language and Literature, B
Ethnic, Cultural Minority, and Gender Studies, B
Fine/Studio Arts, B
Graphic Design, B
History, B
Human Resources Management and Services, MO
International Relations and Affairs, B
International/Global Studies, B
Liberal Arts and Sciences Studies and Humanities, B
Management, MO
Mathematics, B
Multi-/Interdisciplinary Studies, B
Nursing, MO
Nursing Administration, M
Nursing Education, M
Philosophy, B
Physiology, B
Political Science and Government, B
Psychology, B
Religion/Religious Studies, B
Secondary Education and Teaching, BM
Sociology, B
Spanish Language and Literature, B
Sport and Fitness Administration/Management, B

ENDICOTT COLLEGE

Accounting, B
Applied Behavior Analysis, MD
Applied Mathematics, B
Athletic Training and Sports Medicine, B
BioTechnology, B
Biomedical/Medical Engineering, B
Business Administration and Management, B
Business Administration, Management and Operations, M
Communication, Journalism and Related Programs, B
Computer Science, B
Criminal Justice/Safety Studies, B
Design and Visual Communications, B
Digital Communication and Media/Multimedia, B
Distance Education Development, M
Early Childhood Education and Teaching, BM
Educational Leadership and Administration, D
Elementary Education and Teaching, BM
English Language and Literature, B
Entrepreneurship/Entrepreneurial Studies, B
Environmental Sciences, B
Finance, B
Fine/Studio Arts, B
Graphic Design, B
History, B
Homeland Security, M
Hospitality Administration/Management, BM
Interior Design, BM
International Business/Trade/Commerce, B
International/Global Studies, B
Kinesiology and Exercise Science, B
Liberal Arts and Sciences Studies and Humanities, AB
Management Information Systems and Services, M
Marketing/Marketing Management, B
Mass Communication/Media Studies, B
Mathematics, B
Nursing, MD
Organizational Management, M

Photography, B
Physical Education Teaching and Coaching, B
Political Science and Government, B
Psychology, B
Reading Teacher Education, M
Secondary Education and Teaching, BM
Special Education and Teaching, MD
Sport and Fitness Administration/Management, BM
Travel and Tourism, M
Visual and Performing Arts, B

FINE MORTUARY COLLEGE, LLC

Funeral Service and Mortuary Science, A

FISHER COLLEGE

Accounting, B
Business Administration and Management, AB
Computer and Information Sciences, B
Criminal Justice/Safety Studies, AB
Early Childhood Education and Teaching, A
Fashion Merchandising, AB
Finance, B
General Studies, A
Health Information/Medical Records Technology/Technician, AB
Health Professions and Related Clinical Sciences, AB
Health Services/Allied Health/Health Sciences, AB
Hospitality Administration/Management, B
Human Resources Management/Personnel Administration, B
Human Services, B
Humanities/Humanistic Studies, A
Kindergarten/PreSchool Education and Teaching, A
Liberal Arts and Sciences Studies and Humanities, AB
Marketing/Marketing Management, B
Mass Communication/Media Studies, B
Psychology, AB
Public Administration, B
Retailing and Retail Operations, B
Sport and Fitness Administration/Management, B
Tourism and Travel Services Management, B

FITCHBURG STATE UNIVERSITY

Accounting, BM
American Government and Politics (United States), B
Applied Mathematics, B
Architectural Engineering Technology/Technician, B
Art Education, MO
BioTechnology, B
Biological and Biomedical Sciences, MO
Biology Teacher Education, B
Biology/Biological Sciences, B
Biomedical Sciences, B
Business Administration and Management, B
Business Administration, Management and Operations, M
Chemistry, B
Cinematography and Film/Video Production, B
Communication Studies/Speech Communication and Rhetoric, B
Communication and Media Studies, MO
Computer Science, BM
Computer and Information Sciences, B
Construction Engineering Technology/Technician, B
Counseling Psychology, M
Counselor Education/School Counseling and Guidance Services, M
Criminal Justice/Safety Studies, B
Curriculum and Instruction, M
Digital Communication and Media/Multimedia, B
Drama and Dramatics/Theatre Arts, B
Early Childhood Education and Teaching, BM
Economics, B
Education, B
Educational Administration and Supervision, MO
Educational Media/Instructional Technology, M
Electrical, Electronic and Communications Engineering Technology/Technician, B
Elementary Education and Teaching, BM
Energy Management and Systems Technology/Technician, B
English, MO
English Education, MO

English Language and Literature, B
English/Language Arts Teacher Education, B
Environmental Biology, B
Exercise Physiology, B
Finance, B
Forensic Nursing, MO
Geography, B
Graphic Design, B
Health Communication, M
History, BMO
History Teacher Education, B
Human Resources Management and Services, M
Human Services, B
Industrial Technology/Technician, B
Interdisciplinary Studies, O
International Economics, B
International Relations and Affairs, B
Junior High/Intermediate/Middle School Education and Teaching, B
Kinesiology and Exercise Science, B
Liberal Arts and Sciences Studies and Humanities, B
Management Science, B
Manufacturing Technology/Technician, B
Marketing/Marketing Management, B
Mathematics, B
Mathematics Teacher Education, B
Middle School Education, M
Photography, B
Political Science and Government, B
Psychology, B
Science Teacher Education/General Science Teacher Education, MO
Secondary Education and Teaching, BM
Social Studies Teacher Education, MO
Sociology, B
Special Education and Teaching, BM
Sport and Fitness Administration/Management, B
Technical Theatre/Theatre Design and Technology, B
Technical and Business Writing, M
Technology Teacher Education/Industrial Arts Teacher Education, M
Trade and Industrial Teacher Education, B
Vocational and Technical Education, M

FRAMINGHAM STATE UNIVERSITY

Accounting, B
Apparel and Textiles, B
Art Teacher Education, B
Art/Art Studies, General, B
Biology/Biological Sciences, B
Business Administration, Management and Operations, M
Business/Commerce, B
Chemistry, B
Communications Technologies/Technicians and Support Services, B
Computer and Information Sciences, B
Criminology, B
Curriculum and Instruction, M
Early Childhood Education and Teaching, BM
Economics, B
Educational Leadership and Administration, M
Educational Media/Instructional Technology, M
Elementary Education and Teaching, BM
English Education, M
English Language and Literature, B
English as a Second Language, M
Environmental Sciences, B
Finance, B
Fine Arts and Art Studies, M
Food Science, B
Food Science and Technology, M
Foods, Nutrition, and Wellness Studies, B
Foreign Language Teacher Education, M
Foreign Languages and Literatures, B
Geography, B
Geology/Earth Science, B
Health Education, M
Health Services Administration, M
History, B
Human Resources Management and Services, M
International/Global Studies, B
Knowledge Management, B

Liberal Arts and Sciences Studies and Humanities, B
Marketing/Marketing Management, B
Mathematics, B
Mathematics Teacher Education, M
Nursing, M
Nursing Administration, M
Nursing Education, M
Nutritional Sciences, M
Political Science and Government, B
Psychology, BM
Public Administration, M
Reading Teacher Education, M
Sign Language Interpretation and Translation, B
Social Studies Teacher Education, M
Sociology, B
Spanish Language and Literature, BM
Special Education and Teaching, M

FRANKLIN W. OLIN COLLEGE OF ENGINEERING

Electrical, Electronics and Communications Engineering, B
Engineering, B
Mechanical Engineering, B

GORDON COLLEGE

Accounting, B
Art/Art Studies, General, B
Bible/Biblical Studies, B
Biology/Biological Sciences, B
Business Administration and Management, B
Chemistry, B
Christian Studies, B
Communication Studies/Speech Communication and Rhetoric, B
Computer Science, B
Drama and Dramatics/Theatre Arts, B
Early Childhood Education and Teaching, BM
Economics, B
Education, MO
Educational Leadership and Administration, O
Elementary Education and Teaching, B
English Language and Literature, B
English as a Second Language, O
Finance, B
Foreign Languages and Literatures, B
French Language and Literature, B
German Language and Literature, B
History, B
International Relations and Affairs, B
Junior High/Intermediate/Middle School Education and Teaching, B
Kinesiology and Exercise Science, B
Linguistics, B
Mathematics, B
Mathematics Teacher Education, O
Music, B
Music Performance, B
Music Teacher Education, BM
Parks, Recreation, Leisure and Fitness Studies, B
Philosophy, B
Physics, B
Political Science and Government, B
Psychology, B
Reading Teacher Education, O
Secondary Education and Teaching, B
Social Work, B
Sociology, B
Spanish Language and Literature, B

GREENFIELD COMMUNITY COLLEGE

Accounting Technology/Technician and Bookkeeping, A
Acting, A
Administrative Assistant and Secretarial Science, A
American/United States Studies/Civilization, A
Art/Art Studies, General, A
Business Administration and Management, A
Business/Commerce, A
Community Health Services/Liaison/Counseling, A
Computer and Information Sciences, A
Computer and Information Sciences and Support Services, A
Criminal Justice/Police Science, A
Crop Production, A

Dance, A
Early Childhood Education and Teaching, A
Economics, A
Education, A
Engineering Science, A
English Language and Literature, A
Environmental Sciences, A
Film/Video and Photographic Arts, A
Fine/Studio Arts, A
Fire Protection and Safety Technology/Technician, A
Food Science, A
Health Professions and Related Clinical Sciences, A
Hospitality Administration/Management, A
International Relations and Affairs, A
Liberal Arts and Sciences Studies and Humanities, A
Music Performance, A
Natural Resources Conservation and Research, A
Sales, Distribution and Marketing Operations, A
Social Sciences, A
Women's Studies, A

HAMPSHIRE COLLEGE

African Studies, B
African-American/Black Studies, B
Agriculture, B
American Indian/Native American Studies, B
American/United States Studies/Civilization, B
Animal Behavior and Ethology, B
Anthropology, B
Architecture, B
Art History, Criticism and Conservation, B
Astronomy, B
Biology/Biological Sciences, B
Chemistry, B
Classical, Ancient Mediterranean and Near Eastern Studies and Archaeology, B
Cognitive Sciences, B
Communication Studies/Speech Communication and Rhetoric, B
Computer Science, B
Dance, B
Design and Applied Arts, B
Drama and Dramatics/Theatre Arts, B
East Asian Studies, B
Economics, B
Education, B
English Language and Literature, B
Entrepreneurship/Entrepreneurial Studies, B
Environmental Studies, B
Ethnic, Cultural Minority, and Gender Studies, B
European Studies/Civilization, B
Film/Video and Photographic Arts, B
Fine Arts and Art Studies, B
Gay/Lesbian Studies, B
History, B
International Relations and Affairs, B
International/Global Studies, B
Latin American Studies, B
Law and Legal Studies, B
Liberal Arts and Sciences Studies and Humanities, B
Linguistics, B
Mathematics, B
Multi-/Interdisciplinary Studies, B
Music, B
Near and Middle Eastern Studies, B
Peace Studies and Conflict Resolution, B
Philosophy, B
Physical Sciences, B
Physics, B
Political Science and Government, B
Psychology, B
Public Health, B
Public Policy Analysis, B
Religion/Religious Studies, B
Sociology, B
South Asian Studies, B
Urban Studies/Affairs, B
Web Page, Digital/Multimedia and Information Resources Design, B
Women's Studies, B

HARVARD UNIVERSITY

Accounting, D
African Studies, D

African-American Studies, D
African-American/Black Studies, B
Allopathic Medicine, D
American/United States Studies/Civilization, D
Anthropology, BMD
Applied Mathematics, BMD
Applied Physics, MD
Applied Science and Technology, O
Arabic Language and Literature, MD
Archeology, MD
Architectural History and Criticism, D
Architecture, MD
Art Education, M
Art History, Criticism and Conservation, BD
Asian Languages, MD
Asian Studies/Civilization, MD
Astronomy, D
Astronomy and Astrophysics, B
Astrophysics, D
BioTechnology, M
Biochemistry, BD
Biological and Biomedical Sciences, DO
Biology/Biological Sciences, B
Biomedical Engineering, D
Biomedical/Medical Engineering, B
Biophysics, D
Biopsychology, D
Biostatistics, MD
Business Administration, Management and Operations, MDO
Cell Biology and Anatomy, D
Cell/Cellular and Molecular Biology, B
Celtic Languages, Literatures, and Linguistics, D
Chemical Physics, BD
Chemistry, BD
Chinese Studies, D
Classics and Classical Languages, Literatures, and Linguistics, BD
Cognitive Sciences, MD
Communication and Media Studies, O
Comparative Literature, BD
Composition, MD
Computer Science, BMD
Curriculum and Instruction, M
Dental and Oral Surgery, O
Dentistry, DO
Developmental Psychology, D
East Asian Studies, BM
East European and Russian Studies, M
Economics, BD
Education, MD
Educational Leadership and Administration, MD
Educational Media/Instructional Technology, MO
Educational Policy, M
Educational Psychology, M
Engineering, B
Engineering and Applied Sciences, MD
English, DO
English Language and Literature, B
Environmental Policy and Resource Management, MO
Environmental Sciences, MD
Environmental Studies, B
Environmental and Occupational Health, MD
Epidemiology, MD
Ethnomusicology, MD
Evolutionary Biology, BD
Experimental Psychology, D
Forestry, M
Foundations and Philosophy of Education, M
French Language and Literature, MD
Genetics, D
Genomic Sciences, D
Geology/Earth Science, B
Geosciences, MD
German Language and Literature, BD
Health Promotion, MD
Health Services Administration, MD
Hebrew Language and Literature, MD
History, BD
History and Philosophy of Science and Technology, B
History of Science and Technology, MD
Human Development, M
Industrial and Manufacturing Management, D
Information Science/Studies, MD

Inorganic Chemistry, D
International Affairs, D
International Development, M
International Public Health/International Health, MD
International and Comparative Education, M
Italian Language and Literature, MD
Japanese Studies, D
Jewish/Judaic Studies, MD
Journalism, M
Landscape Architecture, MD
Law and Legal Studies, MD
Legal and Justice Studies, D
Liberal Arts and Sciences Studies and Humanities, B
Liberal Studies, M
Linguistics, BD
Management, MD
Management Strategy and Policy, D
Management of Technology, D
Marketing, D
Mathematics, BD
Mathematics Teacher Education, M
Medical Physics, D
Medieval and Renaissance Studies, D
Microbiology, D
Molecular Biology, D
Molecular Genetics, D
Molecular Pharmacology, D
Museology/Museum Studies, M
Music, BMD
Music Theory and Composition, MD
Musicology and Ethnomusicology, MD
Near and Middle Eastern Languages, MD
Near and Middle Eastern Studies, BMD
Neurobiology and Neurophysiology, D
Neuroscience, D
Nutritional Sciences, D
Oral and Dental Sciences, MDO
Organic Chemistry, D
Organizational Behavior Studies, D
Orthodontics, O
Pathology/Experimental Pathology, D
Periodontics, O
Philosophy, BMD
Physical Chemistry, D
Physics, BD
Physiology, D
Planetary Astronomy and Science, MD
Political Science and Government, BMD
Population Studies, MD
Portuguese Language and Literature, MD
Psychology, BD
Public Administration, M
Public Health, MD
Public Policy Analysis, MD
Reading Teacher Education, M
Religion/Religious Studies, BD
Romance Languages, Literatures, and Linguistics, B
Russian Language and Literature, D
Sanskrit and Classical Indian Languages, Literatures, and Linguistics, B
Scandinavian Languages, Literatures, and Linguistics, D
Slavic Languages, Literatures, and Linguistics, BD
Social Psychology, D
Social Sciences, B
Sociology, BD
South and Southeast Asian Studies, M
Southeast Asian Languages, Literatures, and Linguistics, B
Spanish Language and Literature, MD
Statistics, BMD
Structural Biology, D
Systematic Biology/Biological Systematics, D
Technical Communication, M
Theology and Religious Vocations, M
Theoretical Physics, D
Urban Design, M
Urban Planning, MD
Visual and Performing Arts, B
Women's Studies, B

HELLENIC COLLEGE

Business Administration and Management, B
Classics and Classical Languages, Literatures, and Linguistics, B

Elementary Education and Teaching, B
Human Development and Family Studies, B
Religion/Religious Studies, B
Theology/Theological Studies, B

HOLYOKE COMMUNITY COLLEGE

Accounting Technology/Technician and Bookkeeping, A
Administrative Assistant and Secretarial Science, A
Art/Art Studies, General, A
BioTechnology, A
Biology/Biological Sciences, A
Business Administration and Management, A
Chemistry, A
Child Care and Support Services Management, A
Computer Programming, Specific Applications, A
Criminal Justice/Safety Studies, A
Engineering, A
Environmental Control Technologies/Technicians, A
Health Services/Allied Health/Health Sciences, A
Health and Physical Education, A
Hospitality Administration/Management, A
Liberal Arts and Sciences Studies and Humanities, A
Mathematics, A
Medical Radiologic Technology/Science - Radiation Therapist, A
Music, A
Physics, A
Social Work, A
Sport and Fitness Administration/Management, A
Veterinary/Animal Health Technology/Technician and Veterinary Assistant, A

HULT INTERNATIONAL BUSINESS SCHOOL

Business Administration and Management, B
Business Administration, Management and Operations, M
Conflict Resolution and Mediation/Peace Studies, M
Entrepreneurship/Entrepreneurial Studies, M
Finance and Banking, M
International Affairs, M
International Business/Trade/Commerce, M
Marketing, M
National Security, M
Political Science and Government, M

LABOURÉ COLLEGE

Dietetics/Dieticians, A
Electroneurodiagnostic/Electroencephalographic Technology/Technologist, A
Health Information/Medical Records Administration/Administrator, A
Medical Radiologic Technology/Science - Radiation Therapist, A

LASELL COLLEGE

Accounting, B
Advertising and Public Relations, MO
Applied Mathematics, B
Athletic Training and Sports Medicine, B
Business Administration and Management, B
Business Administration, Management and Operations, MO
Communication and Media Studies, BMO
Corporate and Organizational Communication, MO
Criminal Justice/Safety Studies, B
Criminology, BM
Curriculum and Instruction, B
Early Childhood Education and Teaching, B
Education, BM
Elementary Education and Teaching, BM
Emergency Management, M
English Language and Literature, B
Entrepreneurship/Entrepreneurial Studies, B
Environmental Studies, B
Fashion Merchandising, B
Fashion/Apparel Design, B
Finance, B
General Studies, B
Graphic Design, B
Health Communication, MO
Health Services Administration, MO
Health Services/Allied Health/Health Sciences, B

History, B
Homeland Security, M
Hospitality Administration/Management, BMO
Human Resources Management and Services, MO
Human Services, B
Humanities/Humanistic Studies, B
International Business/Trade/Commerce, B
Journalism, B
Kindergarten/PreSchool Education and Teaching, B
Kinesiology and Exercise Science, B
Law and Legal Studies, B
Liberal Arts and Sciences Studies and Humanities, B
Management, MO
Marketing, MO
Marketing/Marketing Management, B
Multi-/Interdisciplinary Studies, B
Non-Profit/Public/Organizational Management, MO
Project Management, MO
Psychology, B
Public Administration and Social Service Professions, B
Public Relations/Image Management, B
Radio and Television, B
Rehabilitation Sciences, M
Secondary Education and Teaching, B
Sociology, B
Special Education and Teaching, M
Sport and Fitness Administration/Management, BMO
Travel and Tourism, MO
Web Page, Digital/Multimedia and Information Resources Design, B

LESLEY UNIVERSITY

Adult and Continuing Education and Teaching, D
American/United States Studies/Civilization, B
Art Education, M
Art Therapy/Therapist, BMDO
Art/Art Studies, General, B
Business Administration and Management, B
Child Development, B
Clinical Psychology, M
Communications Technologies/Technicians and Support Services, B
Community Psychology, M
Computer Education, MO
Conflict Resolution and Mediation/Peace Studies, M
Counseling Psychology, MO
Curriculum and Instruction, MO
Distance Education Development, O
Early Childhood Education and Teaching, M
Ecology, M
Education, BMDO
Educational Leadership and Administration, D
Educational Media/Instructional Technology, O
Elementary Education and Teaching, BM
English Language and Literature, B
English as a Second Language, M
Environmental Studies, B
Fine Arts and Art Studies, M
Health Psychology, M
Human Development and Family Studies, B
Human Services, B
Humanities/Humanistic Studies, B
Interdisciplinary Studies, M
International Affairs, MO
Junior High/Intermediate/Middle School Education and Teaching, B
Kindergarten/PreSchool Education and Teaching, B
Liberal Arts and Sciences Studies and Humanities, B
Mathematics Teacher Education, M
Middle School Education, M
Natural Sciences, B
Photography, M
Psychology, MDO
Reading Teacher Education, MO
School Psychology, M
Science Teacher Education/General Science Teacher Education, M
Secondary Education and Teaching, BM
Social Sciences, B
Special Education and Teaching, BMO
Sustainable Development, M
Therapies--Dance, Drama, and Music, M

Urban and Regional Planning, M
Women's Studies, M
Writing, M

MASSACHUSETTS BAY COMMUNITY COLLEGE

Accounting, A
Animal Physiology, A
Automobile/Automotive Mechanics Technology/Technician, A
Bioinformatics, A
Biological and Biomedical Sciences, A
Biology Technician/BioTechnology Laboratory Technician, A
Business Administration and Management, A
Business/Commerce, A
Community Health and Preventive Medicine, A
Computer Science, A
Computer and Information Sciences and Support Services, A
Computer and Information Systems Security, A
Computer/Information Technology Services Administration and Management, A
Criminal Justice/Law Enforcement Administration, A
Early Childhood Education and Teaching, A
Electrical and Electronic Engineering Technologies/Technicians, A
Electrical, Electronic and Communications Engineering Technology/Technician, A
Elementary Education and Teaching, A
Engineering Technologies/Technicians, A
Engineering Technology, A
English Language and Literature, A
Environmental Control Technologies/Technicians, A
General Studies, A
Hospitality Administration/Management, A
Human Services, A
International Business/Trade/Commerce, A
International/Global Studies, A
Legal Assistant/Paralegal, A
Liberal Arts and Sciences Studies and Humanities, A
Mathematics, A
Mechanical Engineering/Mechanical Technology/Technician, A
Radiologic Technology/Science - Radiographer, A
Social Sciences, A
System Administration/Administrator, A

MASSACHUSETTS COLLEGE OF ART AND DESIGN

Animation, Interactive Technology, Video Graphics and Special Effects, B
Applied Arts and Design, MO
Architecture, BM
Art Education, MO
Art History, Criticism and Conservation, B
Art Teacher Education, B
Ceramic Arts and Ceramics, B
Cinematography and Film/Video Production, B
Commercial and Advertising Art, B
Design and Applied Arts, MO
Fashion/Apparel Design, B
Fiber, Textile and Weaving Arts, B
Film, Television, and Video Production, M
Fine Arts and Art Studies, MO
Fine/Studio Arts, B
Industrial Design, B
Interdisciplinary Studies, M
Intermedia/Multimedia, B
Media Studies, MO
Metal and Jewelry Arts, B
Painting, BM
Photography, BMO
Printmaking, B
Sculpture, B
Textile Design, M

MASSACHUSETTS COLLEGE OF LIBERAL ARTS

Accounting, B
Art/Art Studies, General, B
Athletic Training and Sports Medicine, B
BioTechnology, B
Biology/Biological Sciences, B

Broadcast Journalism, B
Business Administration and Management, B
Business Administration, Management and Operations, M
Chemistry, B
Computer Science, B
Computer and Information Sciences, B
Curriculum and Instruction, M
Education, BMO
Educational Administration and Supervision, M
Educational Leadership and Administration, O
Educational Media/Instructional Technology, M
English Language and Literature, B
Environmental Sciences, B
Environmental Studies, B
Health Education, M
History, B
International Business/Trade/Commerce, B
Journalism, B
Liberal Arts and Sciences Studies and Humanities, B
Management Information Systems and Services, B
Marketing/Marketing Management, B
Mathematics, B
Music, B
Philosophy, B
Physical Education Teaching and Coaching, M
Physics, B
Political Science and Government, B
Pre-Law Studies, B
Pre-Medicine/Pre-Medical Studies, B
Psychology, B
Public Policy Analysis, B
Reading Teacher Education, M
Sociology, B
Special Education and Teaching, M
Visual and Performing Arts, B

MASSACHUSETTS INSTITUTE OF TECHNOLOGY

Aerospace, Aeronautical and Astronautical Engineering, BMDO
Anthropology, B
Archeology, D
Architectural History and Criticism, D
Architecture, BMD
Art History, Criticism and Conservation, D
Atmospheric Sciences and Meteorology, MD
Biochemistry, D
Bioengineering, MD
Bioinformatics, D
Biological and Biomedical Sciences, MD
Biology/Biological Sciences, B
Biomedical Engineering, MD
Biomedical/Medical Engineering, B
Business/Commerce, B
Cell Biology and Anatomy, D
Chemical Engineering, BMD
Chemistry, BD
City/Urban, Community and Regional Planning, B
Civil Engineering, BMDO
Cognitive Sciences, BD
Communication Disorders, D
Computational Biology, D
Computational Sciences, M
Computer Engineering, D
Computer Science, BMDO
Construction Engineering and Management, D
Developmental Biology and Embryology, D
Drama and Dramatics/Theatre Arts, B
Economics, BMD
Electrical Engineering, MDO
Electrical, Electronics and Communications Engineering, B
Engineering Management, M
Engineering and Applied Sciences, MDO
English Language and Literature, B
Environmental Biology, D
Environmental Engineering Technology/Environmental Technology, MDO
Environmental Sciences, D
Environmental/Environmental Health Engineering, B
Foreign Languages and Literatures, B
Genetics, D
Genomic Sciences, D
Geochemistry, D

Geology/Earth Science, BD
Geophysics and Seismology, MD
Geosciences, MD
Geotechnical Engineering, D
History, B
History of Science and Technology, D
Hydrology and Water Resources Science, D
Immunology, D
Information Science/Studies, D
Inorganic Chemistry, D
Liberal Arts and Sciences Studies and Humanities, B
Linguistics, BD
Logistics and Materials Management, M
Management, MD
Manufacturing Engineering, M
Marine Geology, MD
Mass Communication/Media Studies, B
Materials Engineering, BMDO
Materials Sciences, MDO
Mathematics, BD
Mathematics and Computer Science, B
Mechanical Engineering, BMDO
Media Studies, MD
Medical Physics, D
Microbiology, D
Molecular Biology, D
Molecular Toxicology, D
Music, B
Neurobiology and Neurophysiology, D
Neuroscience, D
Nuclear Engineering, BMDO
Ocean Engineering, MD
Oceanography, Chemical and Physical, MD
Operations Research, MD
Organic Chemistry, D
Philosophy, BD
Physical Chemistry, D
Physics, BMD
Planetary Astronomy and Science, D
Political Science and Government, BMD
Real Estate, M
Science, Technology and Society, B
Social Sciences, D
Structural Biology, D
Structural Engineering, D
Systematic Biology/Biological Systematics, D
Systems Engineering, MD
Technical and Business Writing, M
Technology and Public Policy, MD
Toxicology, MD
Transportation and Highway Engineering, D
Urban Studies/Affairs, MD
Urban and Regional Planning, MD
Writing, M

MASSACHUSETTS MARITIME ACADEMY

Emergency Management, M
Engineering, B
Environmental Sciences, B
Facilities Planning and Management, M
International Business/Trade/Commerce, B
Marine Science/Merchant Marine Officer, B
Naval Architecture and Marine Engineering, B
Security and Protective Services, B
Systems Engineering, B

MASSASOIT COMMUNITY COLLEGE

Accounting, A
Accounting and Finance, A
Administrative Assistant and Secretarial Science, A
Architectural Engineering Technology/Technician, A
Business Administration and Management, A
Business Administration, Management and Operations, A
Business/Office Automation/Technology/Data Entry, A
Child Care Provider/Assistant, A
Child Care and Support Services Management, A
Computer Programming/Programmer, A
Computer and Information Sciences, A
Computer and Information Sciences and Support Services, A
Criminal Justice/Police Science, A
Culinary Arts/Chef Training, A

Dental Assisting/Assistant, A
Diesel Mechanics Technology/Technician, A
Drama and Dramatics/Theatre Arts, A
Electrical, Electronic and Communications Engineering Technology/Technician, A
Fine/Studio Arts, A
Fire Science/Firefighting, A
General Office Occupations and Clerical Services, A
Graphic Design, A
Heating, Air Conditioning and Refrigeration Technology/Technician, A
Hospitality Administration/Management, A
Human Services, A
Liberal Arts and Sciences Studies and Humanities, A
Mass Communication/Media Studies, A
Medical/Clinical Assistant, A
Office Management and Supervision, A
Radiologic Technology/Science - Radiographer, A
Respiratory Care Therapy/Therapist, A
Teacher Assistant/Aide, A
Telecommunications Technology/Technician, A

MCPHS UNIVERSITY

Chemistry, BMD
Dental Hygiene/Hygienist, B
Health Professions and Related Clinical Sciences, B
Health Services Administration, M
Medical Radiologic Technology/Science - Radiation Therapist, B
Nuclear Medical Technology/Technologist, B
Nursing, M
Pharmaceutical Sciences, MD
Pharmacology, MD
Pharmacology and Toxicology, B
Pharmacy, BD
Pharmacy, Pharmaceutical Sciences, and Administration, B
Physician Assistant, M
Pre-Medicine/Pre-Medical Studies, B
Radiologic Technology/Science - Radiographer, B

MERRIMACK COLLEGE

Accounting, B
Adult and Continuing Education and Teaching, M
Art History, Criticism and Conservation, B
Athletic Training and Sports Medicine, B
Biochemistry, B
Biology Teacher Education, B
Biology/Biological Sciences, B
Business Administration and Management, B
Chemistry, B
Chemistry Teacher Education, B
Civil Engineering, B
Communication, Journalism and Related Programs, B
Computer Science, B
Criminal Justice/Law Enforcement Administration, B
Curriculum and Instruction, M
Design and Applied Arts, B
Drama and Dramatics/Theatre Arts, B
Early Childhood Education and Teaching, BM
Economics, B
Education, BMO
Educational Administration and Supervision, M
Educational Leadership and Administration, MO
Electrical, Electronics and Communications Engineering, B
Elementary Education and Teaching, BM
Engineering Management, M
Engineering and Applied Sciences, M
English Language and Literature, B
English as a Second Language, M
English/Language Arts Teacher Education, B
Environmental Sciences, B
Exercise Physiology, B
Finance, B
French Language Teacher Education, B
French Language and Literature, B
Health Professions and Related Clinical Sciences, B
Health Services/Allied Health/Health Sciences, B
Higher Education/Higher Education Administration, M
History, B
History Teacher Education, B
Human Development and Family Studies, B

Information Technology, B
International Business/Trade/Commerce, B
Italian Studies, B
Junior High/Intermediate/Middle School Education and Teaching, B
Liberal Arts and Sciences Studies and Humanities, B
Management, M
Marketing/Marketing Management, B
Mathematics, B
Mathematics Teacher Education, B
Mechanical Engineering, BM
Middle School Education, M
Philosophy, B
Physics, B
Physics Teacher Education, B
Political Science and Government, B
Psychology, B
Reading Teacher Education, O
Religion/Religious Studies, B
Romance Languages, Literatures, and Linguistics, B
Science Teacher Education/General Science Teacher Education, B
Secondary Education and Teaching, BM
Social Studies Teacher Education, B
Sociology, B
Spanish Language Teacher Education, B
Spanish Language and Literature, B
Special Education and Teaching, BM
Sport and Fitness Administration/Management, B
Student Personnel Services, M
Teacher Education, Multiple Levels, B
Women's Studies, B

MIDDLESEX COMMUNITY COLLEGE

Aircraft Powerplant Technology/Technician, A
Art/Art Studies, General, A
Biology Technician/BioTechnology Laboratory Technician, A
Biology/Biological Sciences, A
Business Administration and Management, A
Commercial and Advertising Art, A
Computer Engineering Technology/Technician, A
Computer Programming/Programmer, A
Computer and Information Sciences, A
Computer and Information Sciences and Support Services, A
Criminal Justice/Law Enforcement Administration, A
Dental Assisting/Assistant, A
Dental Hygiene/Hygienist, A
Dental Laboratory Technology/Technician, A
Diagnostic Medical Sonography/Sonographer and Ultrasound Technician, A
Electrical, Electronic and Communications Engineering Technology/Technician, A
Electrical/Electronics Drafting and Electrical/Electronics CAD/CADD, A
Elementary Education and Teaching, A
Engineering Technologies/Technicians, A
Fashion Merchandising, A
Fire Science/Firefighting, A
General Office Occupations and Clerical Services, A
General Studies, A
Hotel/Motel Administration/Management, A
Kindergarten/PreSchool Education and Teaching, A
Legal Assistant/Paralegal, A
Liberal Arts and Sciences Studies and Humanities, A
Medical Radiologic Technology/Science - Radiation Therapist, A
Medical/Clinical Assistant, A
Physical Sciences, A
Psychiatric/Mental Health Services Technician, A
Web Page, Digital/Multimedia and Information Resources Design, A

MONTSERRAT COLLEGE OF ART

Animation, Interactive Technology, Video Graphics and Special Effects, B
Crafts/Craft Design, Folk Art and Artisanry, B
Drawing, B
Fine/Studio Arts, B
Graphic Design, B
Illustration, B
Intermedia/Multimedia, B
Painting, B

Photography, B
Printmaking, B
Sculpture, B

MOUNT HOLYOKE COLLEGE

African-American/Black Studies, B
Ancient Studies/Civilization, B
Ancient/Classical Greek Language and Literature, B
Anthropology, B
Architecture and Related Services, B
Art History, Criticism and Conservation, B
Asian Studies/Civilization, B
Astronomy, B
Biochemistry, B
Biology/Biological Sciences, B
Chemistry, B
Classics and Classical Languages, Literatures, and Linguistics, B
Computer Science, B
Dance, B
Drama and Dramatics/Theatre Arts, B
East Asian Studies, B
Economics, B
Education, B
English Language and Literature, B
Environmental Studies, B
Ethnic, Cultural Minority, and Gender Studies, B
Film/Cinema Studies, B
Fine/Studio Arts, B
French Language and Literature, B
Geography, B
Geology/Earth Science, B
German Studies, B
History, B
International Relations and Affairs, B
Italian Language and Literature, B
Latin Language and Literature, B
Mathematics, B
Medieval and Renaissance Studies, B
Multi-/Interdisciplinary Studies, B
Music, B
Near and Middle Eastern Studies, B
Philosophy, B
Physics, B
Political Science and Government, B
Psychology, BM
Religion/Religious Studies, B
Romance Languages, Literatures, and Linguistics, B
Russian Studies, B
Social Sciences, B
Sociology, B
South Asian Studies, B
Spanish Language and Literature, B
Statistics, B

MOUNT IDA COLLEGE

American/United States Studies/Civilization, B
Animation, Interactive Technology, Video Graphics and Special Effects, B
Biology/Biological Sciences, B
Business Administration and Management, B
Child Development, B
Criminal Justice/Law Enforcement Administration, B
Dental Hygiene/Hygienist, AB
Early Childhood Education and Teaching, B
English Language and Literature, B
Environmental Sciences, B
Equestrian/Equine Studies, B
Fashion Merchandising, B
Fashion/Apparel Design, B
Forensic Science and Technology, B
Funeral Service and Mortuary Science, AB
Graphic Design, B
Hotel/Motel Administration/Management, B
Human Services, B
Interior Design, BM
Liberal Arts and Sciences Studies and Humanities, B
Management, M
Psychology, B
Sport and Fitness Administration/Management, B

Veterinary/Animal Health Technology/Technician and Veterinary Assistant, AB

MOUNT WACHUSETT COMMUNITY COLLEGE

Allied Health and Medical Assisting Services, A
Alternative and Complementary Medical Support Services, A
Art/Art Studies, General, A
Automobile/Automotive Mechanics Technology/Technician, A
BioTechnology, A
Business Administration and Management, A
Business/Commerce, A
Child Care and Support Services Management, A
Child Development, A
Clinical/Medical Laboratory Technician, A
Computer Graphics, A
Computer and Information Sciences, A
Corrections, A
Criminal Justice/Law Enforcement Administration, A
Dental Hygiene/Hygienist, A
Energy Management and Systems Technology/Technician, A
Environmental Studies, A
Fire Protection and Safety Technology/Technician, A
General Studies, A
Health Information/Medical Records Administration/Administrator, A
Human Services, A
Legal Assistant/Paralegal, A
Liberal Arts and Sciences Studies and Humanities, A
Medical/Clinical Assistant, A
Physical Therapist Assistant, A
Plastics Engineering Technology/Technician, A
Radio and Television Broadcasting Technology/Technician, A
Web Page, Digital/Multimedia and Information Resources Design, A

NEW ENGLAND COLLEGE OF BUSINESS AND FINANCE

Accounting, A
Business Administration and Management, A
Computer Science, A
Ethics, M
Finance, A
Finance and Banking, M
Management Information Systems and Services, A
Marketing/Marketing Management, A

NEW ENGLAND CONSERVATORY OF MUSIC

Jazz/Jazz Studies, B
Music, MDO
Music History, Literature, and Theory, B
Music Performance, B
Music Theory and Composition, B
Piano and Organ, B
Violin, Viola, Guitar and Other Stringed Instruments, B
Voice and Opera, B

NEWBURY COLLEGE

Accounting, B
Baking and Pastry Arts/Baker/Pastry Chef, A
Business Administration and Management, AB
Communication, Journalism and Related Programs, B
Computer Science, B
Consumer Merchandising/Retailing Management, B
Criminal Justice/Police Science, B
Culinary Arts and Related Services, B
Culinary Arts/Chef Training, AB
Fashion Merchandising, B
General Studies, A
Graphic Design, B
Health/Health Care Administration/Management, B
Hotel/Motel Administration/Management, B
Information Technology, B
Interior Design, B
International Business/Trade/Commerce, B
Law and Legal Studies, B
Marketing, B

Marketing Research, B
Psychology, B
Sport and Fitness Administration/Management, B

NICHOLS COLLEGE

Accounting, B
Business Administration and Management, AB
Business Administration, Management and Operations, M
Business/Commerce, B
Business/Corporate Communications, B
Business/Managerial Economics, B
Criminal Justice/Safety Studies, B
Economics, B
English Language and Literature, B
Finance, B
Hospitality Administration/Management, B
Human Resources Development, B
Human Resources Management/Personnel Administration, B
International Business/Trade/Commerce, B
Marketing/Marketing Management, B
Mathematics, B
Organizational Management, M
Psychology, B
Sport and Fitness Administration/Management, B

NORTH SHORE COMMUNITY COLLEGE

Accounting, A
Administrative Assistant and Secretarial Science, A
Airline/Commercial/Professional Pilot and Flight Crew, A
Biology Technician/BioTechnology Laboratory Technician, A
Business Administration and Management, A
Child Development, A
Computer Engineering Technology/Technician, A
Computer Graphics, A
Computer Programming, Specific Applications, A
Computer Programming/Programmer, A
Computer Science, A
Computer and Information Sciences, A
Criminal Justice/Law Enforcement Administration, A
Culinary Arts/Chef Training, A
Data Entry/Microcomputer Applications, A
Engineering Science, A
Fire Science/Firefighting, A
Foods, Nutrition, and Wellness Studies, A
Gerontology, A
Health Professions and Related Clinical Sciences, A
Hospitality Administration/Management, A
Information Science/Studies, A
Kindergarten/PreSchool Education and Teaching, A
Legal Administrative Assistant/Secretary, A
Legal Assistant/Paralegal, A
Liberal Arts and Sciences Studies and Humanities, A
Marketing/Marketing Management, A
Medical Administrative Assistant/Secretary, A
Medical Radiologic Technology/Science - Radiation Therapist, A
Mental Health Counseling/Counselor, A
Occupational Therapy/Therapist, A
Physical Therapist Assistant, A
Respiratory Care Therapy/Therapist, A
Substance Abuse/Addiction Counseling, A
Tourism and Travel Services Management, A
Veterinary/Animal Health Technology/Technician and Veterinary Assistant, A
Web Page, Digital/Multimedia and Information Resources Design, A

NORTHEASTERN UNIVERSITY

Accounting, BM
Acute Care/Critical Care Nursing, M
African-American/Black Studies, B
Allied Health and Medical Assisting Services, MDO
American Sign Language (ASL), B
Animation, Interactive Technology, Video Graphics and Special Effects, M
Applied Mathematics, MD
Architecture, BM
Art/Art Studies, General, B
Asian Studies/Civilization, B
Audiology/Audiologist and Speech-Language Pathology/Pathologist, B

BioTechnology, M
Biochemistry, B
Bioengineering, D
Bioinformatics, M
Biological and Biomedical Sciences, MD
Biology/Biological Sciences, B
Biophysics, B
Business Administration and Management, B
Business Administration, Management and Operations, M
Business/Commerce, B
Chemical Engineering, BMD
Chemistry, BMD
Civil Engineering, BMD
Communication Disorders, MD
Communication Studies/Speech Communication and Rhetoric, B
Computer Engineering, BMD
Computer Science, BMD
Computer and Information Sciences, B
Computer and Information Systems Security, D
Corporate and Organizational Communication, M
Counseling Psychology, MDO
Counselor Education/School Counseling and Guidance Services, D
Criminal Justice/Safety Studies, B
Criminology, MD
Curriculum and Instruction, D
Design and Applied Arts, M
Drama and Dramatics/Theatre Arts, B
Economic Development, M
Economics, BMD
Education, MD
Educational Administration and Supervision, MD
Electrical Engineering, MD
Electrical, Electronics and Communications Engineering, D
Elementary Education and Teaching, M
Energy and Power Engineering, M
Engineering, B
Engineering Management, MO
Engineering and Applied Sciences, MDO
English, MD
English Language and Literature, B
Entrepreneurship/Entrepreneurial Studies, BM
Environmental Sciences, B
Environmental Studies, B
Exercise and Sports Science, M
Experimental Psychology, D
Film/Cinema Studies, B
Finance, B
Finance and Banking, M
Fine Arts and Art Studies, M
Fine/Studio Arts, B
Food Services Management, M
Geographic Information Systems, M
Geology/Earth Science, B
Graphic Design, B
Health Informatics, M
Health and Medical Administrative Services, B
Higher Education/Higher Education Administration, MD
History, BMD
Homeland Security, M
Human Services, BM
Illustration, B
Industrial Engineering, B
Industrial/Management Engineering, MD
Information Science/Studies, BM
Interdisciplinary Studies, D
Intermedia/Multimedia, B
International Affairs, M
International Business/Trade/Commerce, BM
International Relations and Affairs, B
Internet and Interactive Multimedia, M
Jewish/Judaic Studies, B
Journalism, BM
Landscape Architecture, B
Law and Legal Studies, MD
Legal and Justice Studies, MD
Linguistics, B
Logistics and Materials Management, B
Management Information Systems and Services, BM
Marine Biology and Biological Oceanography, BM
Marketing/Marketing Management, B

Mathematics, BMD
Mechanical Engineering, BMD
Music, B
Non-Profit/Public/Organizational Management, M
Nursing, MDO
Nursing Administration, M
Nutritional Sciences, M
Operations Research, M
Organizational Management, D
Pharmaceutical Sciences, MD
Pharmacology, M
Pharmacy, B
Philosophy, B
Physical Therapy/Therapist, BD
Physician Assistant, M
Physics, BMD
Political Science and Government, BMD
Project Management, M
Psychiatric/Mental Health Nurse/Nursing, M
Psychology, B
Public Administration, M
Public Health, M
Public History, M
Public Policy Analysis, MD
Religion/Religious Studies, B
Religious Education, D
School Psychology, DO
Secondary Education and Teaching, M
Sociology, BMD
Spanish Language and Literature, B
Special Education and Teaching, M
Systems Engineering, M
Taxation, M
Technical Communication, M
Telecommunications, M
Urban Studies/Affairs, M

NORTHERN ESSEX COMMUNITY COLLEGE

Accounting, A
Administrative Assistant and Secretarial Science, A
Biology/Biological Sciences, A
Business Administration and Management, A
Business Teacher Education, A
Business/Commerce, A
Civil Engineering Technology/Technician, A
Commercial and Advertising Art, A
Computer Engineering Technology/Technician, A
Computer Graphics, A
Computer Programming, A
Computer Programming, Specific Applications, A
Computer Programming/Programmer, A
Computer Science, A
Computer Systems Networking and Telecommunications, A
Computer Typography and Composition Equipment Operator, A
Computer and Information Sciences, A
Criminal Justice/Law Enforcement Administration, A
Dance, A
Data Processing and Data Processing Technology/Technician, A
Dental Assisting/Assistant, A
Drama and Dramatics/Theatre Arts, A
Education, A
Electrical, Electronic and Communications Engineering Technology/Technician, A
Elementary Education and Teaching, A
Emergency Medical Technology/Technician (EMT Paramedic), A
Engineering Science, A
Finance, A
General Studies, A
Health Information/Medical Records Administration/Administrator, A
History, A
Hotel/Motel Administration/Management, A
Human Services, A
Industrial Radiologic Technology/Technician, A
International Relations and Affairs, A
Journalism, A
Kindergarten/PreSchool Education and Teaching, A
Legal Assistant/Paralegal, A
Liberal Arts and Sciences Studies and Humanities, A
Logistics and Materials Management, A

Machine Tool Technology/Machinist, A
Marketing/Marketing Management, A
Medical Administrative Assistant/Secretary, A
Medical Transcription/Transcriptionist, A
Mental Health Counseling/Counselor, A
Music, A
Parks, Recreation, Leisure and Fitness Studies, A
Physical Education Teaching and Coaching, A
Political Science and Government, A
Psychology, A
Public Health (MPH, DPH), A
Radiologic Technology/Science - Radiographer, A
Real Estate, A
Respiratory Care Therapy/Therapist, A
Respiratory Therapy Technician/Assistant, A
Sign Language Interpretation and Translation, A
Sport and Fitness Administration/Management, A
Telecommunications Technology/Technician, A
Tourism and Travel Services Management, A
Web Page, Digital/Multimedia and Information Resources Design, A
Web/Multimedia Management and Webmaster, A

NORTHPOINT BIBLE COLLEGE

Bible/Biblical Studies, B

PINE MANOR COLLEGE

Biology/Biological Sciences, AB
Business Administration and Management, AB
Communication Studies/Speech Communication and Rhetoric, B
Community Health and Preventive Medicine, B
Drama and Dramatics/Theatre Arts, A
Early Childhood Education and Teaching, AB
English Language and Literature, AB
Health Services/Allied Health/Health Sciences, A
Liberal Arts and Sciences Studies and Humanities, A
Political Science and Government, B
Psychology, B
Visual and Performing Arts, AB

QUINCY COLLEGE

Accounting, A
Biology Technician/BioTechnology Laboratory Technician, A
Business Administration and Management, A
Clinical/Medical Laboratory Technician, A
Computer Science, A
Criminal Justice/Law Enforcement Administration, A
Early Childhood Education and Teaching, A
Electromechanical Technology/Electromechanical Engineering Technology, A
Elementary Education and Teaching, A
Exercise Physiology, A
Fine Arts and Art Studies, A
General Studies, A
Health Services Administration, A
Human Services, A
Legal Assistant/Paralegal, A
Liberal Arts and Sciences Studies and Humanities, A
Natural Sciences, A
Physical Therapist Assistant, A
Securities Services Administration/Management, A

QUINSIGAMOND COMMUNITY COLLEGE

Alternative and Complementary Medicine and Medical Systems, A
Automobile/Automotive Mechanics Technology/Technician, A
BioTechnology, A
Biomedical Technology/Technician, A
Biomedical/Medical Engineering, A
Business Administration and Management, A
Business/Commerce, A
Chemistry, A
Community Health and Preventive Medicine, A
Computer Engineering Technology/Technician, A
Computer Graphics, A
Computer Programming, Specific Applications, A
Computer Science, A
Computer Systems Analysis/Analyst, A
Computer and Information Sciences, A

Computer and Information Systems Security, A
Criminal Justice/Police Science, A
Data Modeling/Warehousing and Database Administration, A
Dental Hygiene/Hygienist, A
Dental Services and Allied Professions, A
Directing and Theatrical Production, A
Electrical, Electronic and Communications Engineering Technology/Technician, A
Electromechanical Technology/Electromechanical Engineering Technology, A
Elementary Education and Teaching, A
Emergency Medical Technology/Technician (EMT Paramedic), A
Energy Management and Systems Technology/Technician, A
Engineering Technologies/Technicians, A
Environmental Sciences, A
Executive Assistant/Executive Secretary, A
Fire Services Administration, A
General Studies, A
Health Information/Medical Records Technology/Technician, A
Health Services/Allied Health/Health Sciences, A
Hospitality Administration/Management, A
Human Services, A
Kindergarten/PreSchool Education and Teaching, A
Laser and Optical Technology/Technician, A
Liberal Arts and Sciences Studies and Humanities, A
Manufacturing Technology/Technician, A
Medical Administrative Assistant/Secretary, A
Music, A
Occupational Therapist Assistant, A
Pre-Pharmacy Studies, A
Psychology, A
Radiologic Technology/Science - Radiographer, A
Respiratory Care Therapy/Therapist, A
Restaurant/Food Services Management, A
Telecommunications Technology/Technician, A
Trade and Industrial Teacher Education, A
Web Page, Digital/Multimedia and Information Resources Design, A

REGIS COLLEGE

Applied Behavior Analysis, M
BioTechnology, M
Biochemistry, B
Biological and Biomedical Sciences, M
Biology/Biological Sciences, B
Business/Commerce, B
Communication Studies/Speech Communication and Rhetoric, B
Corporate and Organizational Communication, M
Criminal Justice/Safety Studies, B
Cultural Studies, B
Education, MD
Educational Leadership and Administration, D
Elementary Education and Teaching, M
English Language and Literature, B
Health Services Administration, M
Health and Physical Education/Fitness, B
Higher Education/Higher Education Administration, D
History, B
International Relations and Affairs, B
Liberal Arts and Sciences Studies and Humanities, B
Mathematics Teacher Education, B
Multi-/Interdisciplinary Studies, B
Nursing, MDO
Nursing - Advanced Practice, O
Nursing Education, O
Political Science and Government, B
Psychology, B
Public Health (MPH, DPH), B
Quality Management, M
Radiologic Technology/Science - Radiographer, AB
Reading Teacher Education, M
Social Work, B
Spanish Language and Literature, B
Special Education and Teaching, M

Writing, MO

ROXBURY COMMUNITY COLLEGE

Accounting, A
Administrative Assistant and Secretarial Science, A
Biology/Biological Sciences, A
Business Administration and Management, A
Criminal Justice/Law Enforcement Administration, A
Data Entry/Microcomputer Applications, A
English Language and Literature, A
Environmental Engineering
    Technology/Environmental Technology, A
General Studies, A
Humanities/Humanistic Studies, A
Information Science/Studies, A
International Business/Trade/Commerce, A
Kindergarten/PreSchool Education and Teaching, A
Legal Administrative Assistant/Secretary, A
Mathematics, A
Medical Administrative Assistant/Secretary, A
Music, A
Physical Sciences, A
Radio and Television Broadcasting
    Technology/Technician, A
Social Sciences, A
Visual and Performing Arts, A

SALEM STATE UNIVERSITY

Accounting, B
Accounting and Finance, B
Acting, B
Advertising, B
American History (United States), B
Art Education, M
Art History, Criticism and Conservation, B
Art Teacher Education, B
Art/Art Studies, General, B
Athletic Training and Sports Medicine, B
Aviation/Airway Management and Operations, B
Biochemistry, B
Biology/Biological Sciences, B
Business Administration and Management, B
Business Administration, Management and Opera-
    tions, M
Cartography, B
Cell/Cellular and Molecular Biology, B
Chemistry, B
Clinical Laboratory Science/Medical
    Technology/Technologist, B
Commercial and Advertising Art, B
Communication Studies/Speech Communication
    and Rhetoric, B
Computer and Information Sciences, B
Counseling Psychology, MO
Counselor Education/School Counseling and Guid-
    ance Services, M
Criminal Justice/Law Enforcement Administration, B
Criminology, M
Design and Applied Arts, B
Drama and Dramatics/Theatre Arts, B
Early Childhood Education and Teaching, BM
Economics, B
Education, B
Educational Administration and Supervision, M
Educational Media/Instructional Technology, M
Elementary Education and Teaching, BM
English, M
English Language and Literature, B
English as a Second Language, M
Entrepreneurship/Entrepreneurial Studies, B
Environmental Biology, B
European History, B
Finance, B
Fire Services Administration, B
General Studies, B
Geography, BM
Geology/Earth Science, B
Gerontological Nursing, M
Health and Physical Education, B
Higher Education/Higher Education Administra-
    tion, M
History, BM
Hospitality Administration/Management, B
Human Resources Management/Personnel Adminis-
    tration, B
International Business/Trade/Commerce, B

Journalism, B
Junior High/Intermediate/Middle School Education
    and Teaching, B
Kinesiology and Exercise Science, B
Liberal Arts and Sciences Studies and Humani-
    ties, B
Management Information Systems and Services, B
Marine Biology and Biological Oceanography, B
Marketing/Marketing Management, B
Mathematics, BM
Mathematics Teacher Education, M
Mathematics and Computer Science, B
Middle School Education, M
Music, B
Nuclear Medical Technology/Technologist, B
Nursing, M
Nursing Administration, M
Nursing Education, M
Occupational Therapy/Therapist, M
Painting, B
Parks, Recreation, Leisure and Fitness Studies, B
Photography, B
Physical Education Teaching and Coaching, BM
Political Science and Government, B
Printmaking, B
Psychology, BMO
Public Relations/Image Management, B
Public/Applied History and Archival Administration, B
Reading Teacher Education, M
Science Teacher Education/General Science
    Teacher Education, M
Sculpture, B
Secondary Education and Teaching, BM
Social Work, BM
Sociology, B
Spanish Language Teacher Education, B
Spanish Language and Literature, BM
Special Education and Teaching, M
Sport and Fitness Administration/Management, B
Technical Theatre/Theatre Design and Technol-
    ogy, B
Theatre Literature, History and Criticism, B
Tourism and Travel Services Management, B

SALTER COLLEGE (CHICOPEE)

Medical Office Management/Administration, A
Medical/Clinical Assistant, A
Office Management and Supervision, A

SCHOOL OF THE MUSEUM OF FINE ARTS, BOSTON

Art Education, M
Art/Art Studies, General, B
Ceramic Arts and Ceramics, B
Cinematography and Film/Video Production, B
Computer Graphics, B
Design and Applied Arts, B
Drawing, B
Film/Cinema Studies, B
Film/Video and Photographic Arts, B
Fine Arts and Art Studies, BMO
Fine/Studio Arts, B
Graphic Design, B
Illustration, B
Intermedia/Multimedia, B
Metal and Jewelry Arts, B
Painting, B
Photography, B
Printmaking, B
Sculpture, B
Visual and Performing Arts, B

SIMMONS COLLEGE

African Studies, B
Applied Behavior Analysis, MDO
Art/Art Studies, General, B
Biochemistry, Biophysics and Molecular Biology, B
Biology/Biological Sciences, B
Biostatistics, B
Business Administration and Management, B
Business Administration, Management and Opera-
    tions, M
Chemistry, B
Communication Studies/Speech Communication
    and Rhetoric, B
Communication and Media Studies, M

Computer and Information Sciences, B
Consumer Merchandising/Retailing Management, B
Dietetics/Dieticians, B
East Asian Studies, B
Economics, B
Education, BM
Educational Leadership and Administration, M
Elementary Education and Teaching, BMDO
English Language and Literature, B
English as a Second Language, MO
Environmental Sciences, B
Finance, B
Finance and Financial Management Services, B
Food Science, B
Foodservice Systems
    Administration/Management, B
French Language and Literature, B
Health Education, O
Health Promotion, M
History, B
Information Science/Studies, MDO
Information Technology, B
International Relations and Affairs, B
Kinesiology and Exercise Science, B
Library Science, MDO
Marketing, M
Marketing/Marketing Management, B
Mathematics, B
Medical Informatics, B
Middle School Education, M
Multi-/Interdisciplinary Studies, B
Music, B
Non-Profit/Public/Organizational Management, M
Nursing, MD
Nutritional Sciences, MO
Philosophy, B
Physical Therapy/Therapist, BD
Physics, B
Political Science and Government, B
Psychology, B
Public Health Education and Promotion, B
Public Policy Analysis, M
Reading Teacher Education, MO
Secondary Education and Teaching, BM
Social Work, BMD
Sociology, B
Spanish Language and Literature, B
Special Education and Teaching, BMO
System Administration/Administrator, B
Teaching English as a Second or Foreign
    Language/ESL Language Instructor, B
Women's Studies, B

SMITH COLLEGE

African-American/Black Studies, B
American/United States Studies/Civilization, B
Ancient/Classical Greek Language and Literature, B
Anthropology, B
Architecture, B
Art History, Criticism and Conservation, B
Art/Art Studies, General, B
Astronomy, B
Biochemistry, B
Biological and Biomedical Sciences, M
Biology/Biological Sciences, B
Chemistry, BM
Classics and Classical Languages, Litera-
    tures, and Linguistics, B
Comparative Literature, B
Computer Science, B
Dance, BM
Drama and Dramatics/Theatre Arts, B
East Asian Languages, Literatures, and Linguis-
    tics, B
East Asian Studies, B
Economics, B
Education, BM
Elementary Education and Teaching, M
Engineering Science, B
English Education, M
English Language and Literature, B
Environmental Studies, B
Exercise and Sports Science, M
Film/Cinema Studies, B
Fine/Studio Arts, B
Foreign Language Teacher Education, M

French Language and Literature, BM
French Studies, B
Geology/Earth Science, B
German Language and Literature, B
German Studies, B
History, BM
Italian Language and Literature, B
Latin American Studies, B
Latin Language and Literature, B
Mathematics, BO
Mathematics Teacher Education, M
Medieval and Renaissance Studies, B
Middle School Education, M
Music, B
Near and Middle Eastern Studies, B
Philosophy, B
Physics, B
Political Science and Government, B
Portuguese Language and Literature, B
Pre-Law Studies, B
Pre-Medicine/Pre-Medical Studies, B
Psychology, B
Religion/Religious Studies, B
Russian Language and Literature, B
Russian Studies, B
Science Teacher Education/General Science
 Teacher Education, M
Secondary Education and Teaching, M
Social Studies Teacher Education, M
Social Work, MD
Sociology, B
Spanish Language and Literature, B
Special Education and Teaching, M
Theater, M
Women's Studies, BO

SPRINGFIELD COLLEGE

American/United States Studies/Civilization, B
Art Therapy/Therapist, BMO
Art/Art Studies, General, B
Athletic Training and Sports Medicine, BM
Biology/Biological Sciences, B
Business Administration and Management, B
Business Administration, Management and Opera-
 tions, M
Child Development, B
Clinical Psychology, D
Communication Disorders, B
Communication, Journalism and Related Pro-
 grams, B
Computer Graphics, B
Computer Science, B
Computer and Information Sciences, B
Counseling Psychology, MDO
Counselor Education/School Counseling and Guid-
 ance Services, MO
Criminal Justice/Law Enforcement Administration, B
Dance, B
Early Childhood Education and Teaching, B
Education, BM
Elementary Education and Teaching, B
Emergency Medical Technology/Technician (EMT
 Paramedic), B
English Language and Literature, B
Exercise and Sports Science, MD
General Studies, B
Health Promotion, M
Health Teacher Education, B
Health/Health Care Administration/Management, B
History, B
Human Services, M
Industrial and Organizational Psychology, MO
Kinesiology and Exercise Science, B
Mathematics, B
Mathematics and Computer Science, B
Occupational Therapy/Therapist, BM
Parks, Recreation and Leisure Facilities Manage-
 ment, B
Parks, Recreation, Leisure and Fitness Studies, B
Physical Education Teaching and Coaching, BMDO
Physical Therapy/Therapist, BD
Physician Assistant, BM
Psychology, B
Recreation and Park Management, M
Rehabilitation Counseling, M
Rehabilitation and Therapeutic Professions, B

Secondary Education and Teaching, BM
Social Work, MO
Sociology, B
Special Education and Teaching, M
Sport Psychology, MO
Sport and Fitness Administration/Management, BM
Student Personnel Services, M
Substance Abuse/Addiction Counseling, M
Therapeutic Recreation/Recreational Therapy, B

SPRINGFIELD TECHNICAL COMMU-NITY COLLEGE

Accounting, A
Administrative Assistant and Secretarial Science, A
Animation, Interactive Technology, Video Graphics
 and Special Effects, A
Architectural Engineering, A
Automobile/Automotive Mechanics
 Technology/Technician, A
Automotive Engineering Technology/Technician, A
BioTechnology, A
Biology/Biological Sciences, A
Building/Construction Finishing, Manage-
 ment, and Inspection, A
Business Administration and Management, A
Business/Commerce, A
Chemistry, A
Civil Engineering Technology/Technician, A
Clinical/Medical Laboratory Technician, A
Commercial Photography, A
Commercial and Advertising Art, A
Computer Engineering Technology/Technician, A
Computer Programming, Specific Applications, A
Computer Science, A
Computer and Information Systems Security, A
Criminal Justice/Police Science, A
Dental Hygiene/Hygienist, A
Diagnostic Medical Sonography/Sonographer and
 Ultrasound Technician, A
Early Childhood Education and Teaching, A
Electrical, Electronic and Communications Engineer-
 ing Technology/Technician, A
Electromechanical Technology/Electromechanical
 Engineering Technology, A
Elementary Education and Teaching, A
Engineering, A
Fine/Studio Arts, A
Fire Protection and Safety Technology/Technician, A
Heating, Air Conditioning and Refrigeration
 Technology/Technician, A
Landscaping and Groundskeeping, A
Laser and Optical Technology/Technician, A
Liberal Arts and Sciences Studies and Humani-
 ties, A
Marketing/Marketing Management, A
Massage Therapy/Therapeutic Massage, A
Mathematics, A
Mechanical Engineering/Mechanical
 Technology/Technician, A
Medical Administrative Assistant/Secretary, A
Medical Insurance Coding Specialist/Coder, A
Medical/Clinical Assistant, A
Occupational Therapist Assistant, A
Physical Therapist Assistant, A
Physics, A
Pre-Medicine/Pre-Medical Studies, A
Radio and Television Broadcasting
 Technology/Technician, A
Radiologic Technology/Science - Radiographer, A
Recording Arts Technology/Technician, A
Respiratory Care Therapy/Therapist, A
Secondary Education and Teaching, A
Small Business Administration/Management, A
Sport and Fitness Administration/Management, A
Surgical Technology/Technologist, A
Telecommunications Technology/Technician, A

STONEHILL COLLEGE

Accounting, B
American/United States Studies/Civilization, B
Art History, Criticism and Conservation, B
Biochemistry, B
Biology/Biological Sciences, B
Business Administration and Management, B
Chemistry, B
Christian Studies, B

Communication Studies/Speech Communication
 and Rhetoric, B
Computer Science, B
Criminology, B
Early Childhood Education and Teaching, B
Economics, B
Education, B
Elementary Education and Teaching, B
English Language and Literature, B
Environmental Sciences, B
Environmental Studies, B
Ethnic, Cultural Minority, and Gender Studies, B
Finance, B
Fine/Studio Arts, B
Foreign Languages and Literatures, B
French Language and Literature, B
Graphic Design, B
Health/Health Care Administration/Management, B
History, B
International Business/Trade/Commerce, B
Marketing/Marketing Management, B
Mathematics, B
Multi-/Interdisciplinary Studies, B
Philosophy, B
Physics, B
Political Science and Government, B
Psychology, B
Religion/Religious Studies, B
Sociology, B
Spanish Language and Literature, B
Visual and Performing Arts, B

SUFFOLK UNIVERSITY

Accounting, BMO
Advertising, B
Advertising and Public Relations, M
Applied Arts and Design, M
Biology/Biological Sciences, B
Broadcast Journalism, B
Business Administration and Management, B
Business Administration, Management and Opera-
 tions, MO
Clinical Psychology, MDO
Communication Studies/Speech Communication
 and Rhetoric, B
Communication and Media Studies, M
Computer Engineering, B
Computer Science, B
Computer and Information Sciences, B
Corporate and Organizational Communication, M
Counseling Psychology, MO
Counselor Education/School Counseling and Guid-
 ance Services, MO
Criminology, M
Drama and Dramatics/Theatre Arts, B
Economics, BM
Educational Administration and Supervision, MO
Electrical, Electronics and Communications Engi-
 neering, B
English Language and Literature, B
Entrepreneurship/Entrepreneurial Studies, BM
Environmental Sciences, B
Environmental/Environmental Health Engineering, B
Ethics, MO
Finance, B
Finance and Banking, MO
Fine/Studio Arts, B
Foreign Languages and Literatures, B
French Language and Literature, B
French Studies, B
Graphic Design, M
Health Law, D
Health Services Administration, M
History, B
Humanities/Humanistic Studies, B
Information Science/Studies, B
Intellectual Property Law, D
Interior Design, BM
International Business/Trade/Commerce, BM
Journalism, B
Law and Legal Studies, MD
Legal Assistant/Paralegal, AB
Liberal Arts and Sciences Studies and Humani-
 ties, A
Management Strategy and Policy, M
Marketing, M

Marketing/Marketing Management, B
Mass Communication/Media Studies, B
Mathematics, B
Non-Profit/Public/Organizational Management, M
Organizational Behavior Studies, M
Organizational Communication, B
Philosophy, B
Physical Sciences, B
Physics, B
Political Communication, B
Political Science and Government, BMO
Psychology, BMDO
Public Administration, MO
Public Policy Analysis, BMO
Public Relations/Image Management, B
Radiation Biology/Radiobiology, B
Radio and Television Broadcasting
   Technology/Technician, B
School Psychology, O
Sociology, B
Spanish Language and Literature, B
Supply Chain Management, M
Taxation, M
Theatre Literature, History and Criticism, B
Visual and Performing Arts, B

TUFTS UNIVERSITY

African Studies, B
African-American/Black Studies, B
Allopathic Medicine, D
American/United States Studies/Civilization, B
Analytical Chemistry, MD
Ancient/Classical Greek Language and Literature, B
Animal Sciences, M
Anthropology, B
Applied Mathematics, B
Arabic Language and Literature, B
Archeology, BM
Architectural Engineering, B
Art Education, M
Art History, Criticism and Conservation, BM
Asian Studies/Civilization, B
Astronomy, B
Astrophysics, BMD
Behavioral Sciences, B
BioTechnology, BDO
Biochemistry, B
Bioengineering, MDO
Bioinformatics, M
Biological and Biomedical Sciences, MD
Biology/Biological Sciences, B
Biomedical Engineering, MD
Biomedical/Medical Engineering, B
Biopsychology, B
Biostatistics, MD
Cell Biology and Anatomy, D
Central/Middle and Eastern European Studies, B
Chemical Engineering, BMD
Chemical Physics, D
Chemistry, BMD
Child Development, BMD
Child and Family Studies, MD
Chinese Language and Literature, B
City/Urban, Community and Regional Planning, B
Civil Engineering, BMD
Classics and Classical Languages, Litera-
   tures, and Linguistics, BM
Clinical Research, MD
Cognitive Sciences, D
Community Health and Preventive Medicine, B
Comparative Literature, B
Composition, M
Computer Engineering, B
Computer Programming/Programmer, B
Computer Science, BMDO
Computer and Information Sciences, B
Conflict Resolution and Mediation/Peace Stud-
   ies, MD
Dental and Oral Surgery, O
Dentistry, D
Developmental Biology and Embryology, D
Drama and Dramatics/Theatre Arts, B
Early Childhood Education and Teaching, BM
East Asian Studies, B
Ecology, B
Economics, BM

Education, BMDO
Electrical Engineering, MDO
Electrical, Electronics and Communications Engi-
   neering, B
Elementary Education and Teaching, BM
Engineering, B
Engineering Management, M
Engineering Physics, B
Engineering Science, B
Engineering and Applied Sciences, MD
English, MD
English Language and Literature, B
Environmental Engineering
   Technology/Environmental Technology, BMD
Environmental Policy and Resource Manage-
   ment, MDO
Environmental Sciences, MD
Environmental Studies, BMO
Environmental and Occupational Health, MD
Environmental/Environmental Health Engineering, B
Epidemiology, MDO
Ergonomics and Human Factors, M
Ethnomusicology, M
European Studies/Civilization, B
Family and Consumer Sciences/Human Sci-
   ences, MD
Film/Cinema Studies, B
Fine Arts and Art Studies, M
Fine/Studio Arts, B
Foreign Languages and Literatures, B
French Language and Literature, BM
Genetics, D
Geological/Geophysical Engineering, B
Geology/Earth Science, B
Geotechnical Engineering, MD
German Language and Literature, BM
Hazardous Materials Management and Waste
   Technology/Technician, MD
Health Communication, MO
History, BMD
Human Development, MD
Human-Computer Interaction, O
Immunology, D
Infectious Diseases, D
Information Science/Studies, B
Inorganic Chemistry, MD
Interdisciplinary Studies, D
International Affairs, MD
International Business/Trade/Commerce, MD
International Development, MD
International Public Health/International Health, MD
International Relations and Affairs, B
Italian Language and Literature, B
Italian Studies, B
Japanese Language and Literature, B
Jewish/Judaic Studies, B
Kindergarten/PreSchool Education and Teaching, B
Latin American Studies, B
Latin Language and Literature, B
Law and Legal Studies, MD
Liberal Arts and Sciences Studies and Humani-
   ties, B
Management Strategy and Policy, O
Manufacturing Engineering, O
Mass Communication/Media Studies, B
Mathematics, BMD
Mathematics Teacher Education, MD
Mathematics and Computer Science, B
Mechanical Engineering, BMD
Microbiology, D
Middle School Education, M
Modern Greek Language and Literature, B
Molecular Biology, D
Museology/Museum Studies, MO
Museum Education, M
Music, BM
Music History, Literature, and Theory, BM
Music Theory and Composition, BM
Musicology and Ethnomusicology, B
Near and Middle Eastern Studies, B
Neuroscience, D
Non-Profit/Public/Organizational Management, O
Nutritional Sciences, M
Occupational Therapy/Therapist, MDO
Oral and Dental Sciences, MO
Organic Chemistry, MD

Orthodontics, O
Pathology/Experimental Pathology, D
Peace Studies and Conflict Resolution, B
Pedodontics, O
Periodontics, O
Pharmacology, MD
Philosophy, BM
Physical Chemistry, MD
Physician Assistant, M
Physics, BMD
Political Science and Government, B
Psychology, BMD
Public Administration, O
Public Health, MDO
Public Health (MPH, DPH), B
Public Policy Analysis, M
Religion/Religious Studies, B
Reproductive Biology, D
Romance Languages, Literatures, and Linguistics, B
Russian Language and Literature, B
Russian Studies, B
School Psychology, MO
Science Teacher Education/General Science
   Teacher Education, MD
Science, Technology and Society, B
Secondary Education and Teaching, M
Sociology, B
Southeast Asian Studies, B
Spanish Language and Literature, B
Structural Engineering, MD
Theater, MD
Theatre Literature, History and Criticism, B
Urban Studies/Affairs, BM
Urban and Regional Planning, M
Veterinary Medicine, MD
Water Resources Engineering, MD
Western European Studies, B
Women's Studies, B

UNIVERSITY OF MASSACHUSETTS AMHERST

Accounting, BMD
African-American Studies, MD
African-American/Black Studies, B
Agricultural Economics, BMD
American/United States Studies/Civilization, D
Animal Behavior and Ethology, D
Animal Sciences, BMD
Anthropology, BMD
Applied Horticulture/Horticultural Business Ser-
   vices, A
Applied Horticulture/Horticultural Operations, AB
Applied Mathematics, M
Architectural Engineering, MD
Architecture, BM
Art Education, M
Art History, Criticism and Conservation, BM
Astronomy, BMD
BioTechnology, MD
Biochemistry, BMD
Biochemistry, Biophysics and Molecular Biology, B
Biological and Biomedical Sciences, MD
Biological and Physical Sciences, B
Biology/Biological Sciences, B
Biostatistics, MD
Business Administration and Management, B
Cell Biology and Anatomy, MD
Chemical Engineering, BMD
Chemistry, BMD
Child and Family Studies, D
Chinese Language and Literature, B
Chinese Studies, M
Civil Engineering, BMD
Classics and Classical Languages, Litera-
   tures, and Linguistics, BM
Clinical Psychology, MD
Cognitive Sciences, MD
Communication Disorders, BMD
Communication and Media Studies, MD
Community Health Nursing, D
Community Health and Preventive Medicine, MD
Comparative Literature, BMD
Composition, MD
Computer Engineering, BMD
Computer Science, BMD

Conflict Resolution and Mediation/Peace Studies, MD
Counselor Education/School Counseling and Guidance Services, MO
Crop Production, AB
Dance, B
Developmental Biology and Embryology, D
Developmental Psychology, MD
Drama and Dramatics/Theatre Arts, B
Early Childhood Education and Teaching, M
Economics, BMD
Education, BMDO
Educational Leadership and Administration, MDO
Educational Measurement and Evaluation, D
Educational Media/Instructional Technology, MDO
Educational Policy, D
Electrical Engineering, MD
Electrical, Electronics and Communications Engineering, B
Elementary Education and Teaching, M
Engineering and Applied Sciences, MD
English, MD
English Language and Literature, B
English as a Second Language, MO
Entrepreneurship/Entrepreneurial Studies, M
Environmental Biology, MD
Environmental Design/Architecture, B
Environmental Engineering Technology/Environmental Technology, M
Environmental Policy, MD
Environmental Sciences, B
Environmental and Occupational Health, MD
Epidemiology, MD
Equestrian/Equine Studies, A
Evolutionary Biology, MD
Exercise Physiology, B
Finance, B
Finance and Banking, MD
Fine Arts and Art Studies, M
Fine/Studio Arts, B
Fish, Game and Wildlife Management, MD
Food Science, B
Food Science and Technology, MD
Foreign Language Teacher Education, M
Forestry, MD
French Language and Literature, BM
General Studies, B
Genetics, MD
Geography, BM
Geology/Earth Science, B
Geosciences, M
Geotechnical Engineering, M
German Language and Literature, MD
German Studies, B
Gerontological Nursing, D
Health Education, MD
Health Services Administration, MD
Higher Education/Higher Education Administration, M
Hispanic and Latin American Languages, MD
Historic Preservation and Conservation, M
History, BMD
Hospitality Administration/Management, BD
Humanities/Humanistic Studies, B
Industrial Engineering, B
Industrial and Labor Relations, M
Industrial/Management Engineering, MD
Interior Design, M
International and Comparative Education, M
Italian Language and Literature, BM
Japanese Language and Literature, B
Japanese Studies, M
Jewish/Judaic Studies, B
Journalism, B
Kinesiology and Movement Studies, MD
Landscape Architecture, BM
Landscaping and Groundskeeping, A
Law and Legal Studies, B
Liberal Arts and Sciences Studies and Humanities, B
Linguistics, BMD
Management, MD
Management Strategy and Policy, D
Marine Sciences, MD
Marketing, MD
Marketing/Marketing Management, B

Mathematics, BMD
Mechanical Engineering, BMD
Mechanics, M
Microbiology, BMD
Molecular Biophysics, D
Multi-/Interdisciplinary Studies, B
Multilingual and Multicultural Education, MO
Music, MD
Music History, Literature, and Theory, M
Music Performance, B
Music Teacher Education, MD
Music Theory and Composition, D
Natural Resources and Conservation, B
Near and Middle Eastern Studies, B
Neuroscience, MD
Nursing, MD
Nursing - Adult, D
Nursing - Advanced Practice, D
Nursing Administration, MD
Nutritional Sciences, BMD
Operations Management and Supervision, B
Operations Research, MD
Organizational Management, D
Performance, M
Philosophy, BMD
Physics, BMD
Physiology, MD
Plant Biology, MD
Plant Molecular Biology, MD
Plant Physiology, MD
Plant Sciences, BMD
Political Science and Government, BMD
Polymer/Plastics Engineering, MD
Portuguese Language and Literature, BMD
Pre-Dentistry Studies, B
Pre-Medicine/Pre-Medical Studies, B
Pre-Veterinary Studies, B
Psychology, BMD
Public Administration, M
Public Health, MD
Public Health (MPH, DPH), B
Public Policy Analysis, M
Reading Teacher Education, MD
Rhetoric, D
Russian Studies, B
Scandinavian Languages, Literatures, and Linguistics, MD
School Psychology, MDO
Science Teacher Education/General Science Teacher Education, O
Secondary Education and Teaching, M
Social Psychology, MD
Social Sciences, B
Sociology, BMD
Spanish Language and Literature, BMD
Special Education and Teaching, MDO
Sport and Fitness Administration/Management, BMD
Statistics, MD
Structural Engineering, M
Sustainable Development, M
Theater, M
Transportation and Highway Engineering, M
Travel and Tourism, D
Turf and Turfgrass Management, AB
Urban and Regional Planning, MD
Water Resources, MD
Water Resources Engineering, M
Women's Studies, B
Writing, M

UNIVERSITY OF MASSACHUSETTS BOSTON

Accounting, M
African-American/Black Studies, B
American/United States Studies/Civilization, BM
Anthropology, B
Applied Economics, M
Applied Physics, M
Archeology, M
Archives/Archival Administration, M
Art/Art Studies, General, B
Asian Studies/Civilization, B
BioTechnology, M
Biochemistry, B
Biological and Biomedical Sciences, MD
Biology/Biological Sciences, B

Biomedical Engineering, D
Business Administration and Management, B
Business Administration, Management and Operations, M
Chemistry, BMD
Classics and Classical Languages, Literatures, and Linguistics, BM
Clinical Psychology, D
Cognitive Sciences, M
Community Organization and Advocacy, B
Computer Engineering, B
Computer Science, MD
Computer and Information Sciences, B
Conflict Resolution and Mediation/Peace Studies, MO
Counseling Psychology, MD
Counselor Education/School Counseling and Guidance Services, M
Criminal Justice/Safety Studies, B
Drama and Dramatics/Theatre Arts, B
Early Childhood Education and Teaching, M
Economics, B
Education, BMD
Educational Media/Instructional Technology, MO
Electrical, Electronics and Communications Engineering, B
Engineering Physics, B
English, M
English Language and Literature, B
English as a Second Language, M
Environmental Sciences, MD
Exercise and Sports Science, MD
Finance and Banking, M
Foreign Language Teacher Education, M
French Language and Literature, B
Geology/Earth Science, B
Gerontology, MDO
Health and Physical Education, B
History, BM
Human Services, BM
Information Technology, B
International Affairs, M
International Business/Trade/Commerce, M
International Development, MD
Italian Language and Literature, B
Labor and Industrial Relations, B
Linguistics, M
Management Information Systems and Services, M
Marine Sciences, MD
Marriage and Family Therapy/Counseling, M
Mathematics, B
Middle School Education, M
Multi-/Interdisciplinary Studies, B
Multilingual and Multicultural Education, M
Music, B
Nursing, MD
Philosophy, B
Physics, B
Political Science and Government, B
Psychology, B
Public Affairs, M
Public Policy Analysis, MD
Quality Management, MO
Rehabilitation Counseling, M
School Psychology, MD
Social Sciences, B
Sociology, BMD
Spanish Language and Literature, B
Special Education and Teaching, B
Vision Science/Physiological Optics, M
Women's Studies, B
Writing, M

UNIVERSITY OF MASSACHUSETTS DARTMOUTH

Accounting, BO
Acoustics, O
Art Education, M
Art History, Criticism and Conservation, B
Art Teacher Education, B
BioTechnology, MD
Biochemistry, MD
Biological and Biomedical Sciences, M
Biology/Biological Sciences, B
Biomedical Engineering, MD
Biomedical/Medical Engineering, B

Business Administration and Management, B
Business Administration, Management and Operations, MO
Business/Commerce, B
Ceramic Arts and Ceramics, B
Chemistry, BMD
Civil Engineering, BM
Clinical Laboratory Science/Medical Technology/Technologist, B
Clinical Laboratory Sciences, M
Community Health Nursing, MD
Computational Sciences, D
Computer Art and Design, M
Computer Engineering, BMDO
Computer Science, MDO
Computer and Information Sciences, B
Criminology, B
CytoTechnology/Cytotechnologist, B
Design and Applied Arts, MO
Design and Visual Communications, B
Economics, B
Education, MDO
Educational Leadership and Administration, D
Electrical Engineering, MDO
Electrical, Electronics and Communications Engineering, B
Engineering and Applied Sciences, D
English Language and Literature, B
Fiber, Textile and Weaving Arts, B
Finance, B
Finance and Banking, O
Fine Arts and Art Studies, MO
French Language and Literature, B
Health/Health Care Administration/Management, B
History, B
Illustration, B
Industrial/Management Engineering, MD
Information Science/Studies, D
International Business/Trade/Commerce, O
Latin American Studies, D
Law and Legal Studies, D
Liberal Arts and Sciences Studies and Humanities, B
Management, O
Management Information Systems and Services, B
Marine Affairs, MD
Marine Sciences, MD
Marketing, O
Marketing/Marketing Management, B
Mathematics, B
Mathematics Teacher Education, D
Mathematics and Computer Science, B
Mechanical Engineering, BM
Mechanics, D
Metal and Jewelry Arts, B
Middle School Education, MO
Multi-/Interdisciplinary Studies, B
Music, B
Nursing, MD
Nursing - Adult, M
Operations Management and Supervision, B
Organizational Management, O
Painting, BO
Philosophy, B
Photography, B
Physics, BM
Political Science and Government, B
Portuguese Language and Literature, BMD
Printmaking, O
Psychology, BMO
Public Administration, O
Public Policy Analysis, MO
Sculpture, BO
Secondary Education and Teaching, MO
Sociology, B
Spanish Language and Literature, B
Supply Chain Management, O
Systems Engineering, MD
Telecommunications, O
Textile Sciences and Engineering, M
Women's Studies, B

Writing, MO

UNIVERSITY OF MASSACHUSETTS LOWELL

Accounting, M
Allied Health and Medical Assisting Services, MDO
American/United States Studies/Civilization, B
Analytical Chemistry, D
Applied Mathematics, BM
Applied Physics, M
Atmospheric Sciences and Meteorology, MD
BioTechnology, M
Biochemistry, D
Biological and Biomedical Sciences, MD
Biology/Biological Sciences, B
Business Administration and Management, B
Business Administration, Management and Operations, MDO
Business/Commerce, A
Chemical Engineering, BMD
Chemistry, BMD
Civil Engineering, BMDO
Civil Engineering Technology/Technician, AB
Clinical Laboratory Sciences, MO
Clinical/Medical Laboratory Science and Allied Professions, B
Community Health Services/Liaison/Counseling, B
Computational Sciences, D
Computer Engineering, BM
Computer Science, BMD
Conflict Resolution and Mediation/Peace Studies, MO
Criminal Justice/Law Enforcement Administration, B
Criminology, MD
Curriculum and Instruction, MO
Economic Development, MO
Economics, BMO
Education, MDO
Educational Administration and Supervision, MO
Educational Leadership and Administration, D
Electrical Engineering, MD
Electrical, Electronic and Communications Engineering Technology/Technician, AB
Electrical, Electronics and Communications Engineering, B
Energy and Power Engineering, MD
Engineering, B
Engineering and Applied Sciences, MDO
English Language and Literature, B
Entrepreneurship/Entrepreneurial Studies, BMO
Environmental Engineering Technology/Environmental Technology, MDO
Environmental Health, B
Environmental Policy, MD
Environmental Sciences, BMDO
Environmental Studies, O
Epidemiology, MD
Ergonomics and Human Factors, MDO
Finance and Banking, O
Fine Arts and Art Studies, B
Foreign Languages and Literatures, B
Gerontological Nursing, MO
Health Informatics, MO
Health Physics/Radiological Health, M
Health Promotion, D
Health Services Administration, MO
History, B
Homeland Security, M
Industrial Hygiene, MD
Industrial Technology/Technician, B
Industrial/Management Engineering, MDO
Information Science/Studies, AB
Inorganic Chemistry, D
Legal and Justice Studies, MD
Liberal Arts and Sciences Studies and Humanities, B
Materials Engineering, MO
Mathematics, BMD
Mathematics Teacher Education, D
Mechanical Engineering, BMD
Mechanical Engineering Related Technologies/Technicians, AB
Music, BM
Music Performance, B
Music Teacher Education, M
Nuclear Engineering, BMD

Nursing, MDO
Nursing - Advanced Practice, M
Nursing Administration, D
Nutritional Sciences, BO
Optics/Optical Sciences, M
Organic Chemistry, D
Pathology/Experimental Pathology, O
Peace Studies and Conflict Resolution, B
Philosophy, B
Physical Sciences, B
Physical Therapy/Therapist, D
Physics, BMD
Political Science and Government, B
Polymer/Plastics Engineering, BMDO
Psychiatric/Mental Health Nurse/Nursing, MO
Psychology, BM
Public Health, O
Public Health (MPH, DPH), B
Reading Teacher Education, MDO
Rehabilitation and Therapeutic Professions, B
Science Teacher Education/General Science Teacher Education, D
Social Psychology, M
Sociology, BMO
Supply Chain Management, O
Sustainable Development, O
Urban and Regional Planning, MO

URBAN COLLEGE OF BOSTON

Early Childhood Education and Teaching, A
Human Services, A
Liberal Arts and Sciences Studies and Humanities, A

WELLESLEY COLLEGE

African Studies, B
African-American/Black Studies, B
American/United States Studies/Civilization, B
Ancient/Classical Greek Language and Literature, B
Anthropology, B
Architecture, B
Art History, Criticism and Conservation, B
Astronomy, B
Astrophysics, B
Biochemistry, B
Biology/Biological Sciences, B
Chemistry, B
Chinese Language and Literature, B
Classics and Classical Languages, Literatures, and Linguistics, B
Comparative Literature, B
Computer Science, B
Digital Communication and Media/Multimedia, B
Drama and Dramatics/Theatre Arts, B
East Asian Studies, B
Economics, B
English Language and Literature, B
Environmental Studies, B
Ethnic, Cultural Minority, and Gender Studies, B
Film/Cinema Studies, B
Film/Video and Photographic Arts, B
Fine/Studio Arts, B
French Language and Literature, B
French Studies, B
Geology/Earth Science, B
German Language and Literature, B
German Studies, B
History, B
International Relations and Affairs, B
Islamic Studies, B
Italian Language and Literature, B
Italian Studies, B
Japanese Language and Literature, B
Jewish/Judaic Studies, B
Latin American Studies, B
Latin Language and Literature, B
Linguistics, B
Mathematics, B
Medieval and Renaissance Studies, B
Music, B
Near and Middle Eastern Studies, B
Peace Studies and Conflict Resolution, B
Philosophy, B
Physics, B
Political Science and Government, B
Psychology, B

Religion/Religious Studies, B
Russian Language and Literature, B
Russian Studies, B
Sociology, B
Spanish Language and Literature, B
Women's Studies, B

WENTWORTH INSTITUTE OF TECH-NOLOGY

Applied Mathematics, B
Architecture, BM
Biomedical/Medical Engineering, B
Building/Construction Site Management/Manager, A
Civil Engineering, B
Computer Engineering, B
Computer Science, B
Computer Systems Networking and Telecommunications, B
Construction Management, ABM
Electrical, Electronics and Communications Engineering, B
Engineering, B
Engineering Technology, AB
Facilities Planning and Management, M
Industrial Design, B
Information Science/Studies, B
Interior Design, B
Management of Technology, M
Mechanical Engineering, B
Operations Management and Supervision, B

WESTERN NEW ENGLAND UNIVERSITY

Accounting, BM
Accounting and Finance, B
Actuarial Science, B
Advertising, B
Advertising and Public Relations, M
Applied Behavior Analysis, MD
Biology/Biological Sciences, B
Biomedical/Medical Engineering, B
Business Administration and Management, B
Business Administration, Management and Operations, M
Business/Commerce, B
Chemistry, B
Civil Engineering, B
Communication Studies/Speech Communication and Rhetoric, B
Communication and Media Studies, M
Computer Engineering, B
Computer Science, B
Criminal Justice/Safety Studies, B
Curriculum and Instruction, M
Economics, B
Electrical Engineering, M
Electrical, Electronics and Communications Engineering, B
Elementary Education and Teaching, BM
Engineering Management, MD
Engineering and Applied Sciences, MD
English Education, M
English Language and Literature, B
Entrepreneurship/Entrepreneurial Studies, B
Finance, B
Forensic Science and Technology, B
Health Services/Allied Health/Health Sciences, B
History, B
Industrial Engineering, B
Information Technology, B
International Business/Trade/Commerce, B
International/Global Studies, B
Journalism, B
Law and Legal Studies, BMD
Liberal Arts and Sciences Studies and Humanities, AB
Management Information Systems and Services, B
Manufacturing Engineering, M
Marketing, B
Marketing/Marketing Management, B
Mass Communication/Media Studies, B
Mathematics, B
Mathematics Teacher Education, M
Mechanical Engineering, BM
Organizational Management, M
Pharmacy, D

Philosophy, B
Political Science and Government, B
Psychology, B
Public Relations/Image Management, B
Secondary Education and Teaching, B
Social Work, B
Sociology, B
Sport and Fitness Administration/Management, BM
Writing, M

WESTFIELD STATE UNIVERSITY

Applied Behavior Analysis, M
Art/Art Studies, General, B
Athletic Training and Sports Medicine, B
Biology/Biological Sciences, B
Business Administration and Management, B
Chemistry, B
City/Urban, Community and Regional Planning, B
Communication Studies/Speech Communication and Rhetoric, B
Computer Science, B
Counseling Psychology, M
Counselor Education/School Counseling and Guidance Services, M
Criminal Justice/Safety Studies, B
Criminology, M
Drama and Dramatics/Theatre Arts, B
Early Childhood Education and Teaching, M
Economics, B
Education, MO
Educational Administration and Supervision, MO
Educational Media/Instructional Technology, M
Elementary Education and Teaching, BM
English, M
English Language and Literature, B
Environmental Sciences, B
Ethnic, Cultural Minority, and Gender Studies, B
Health and Physical Education, B
History, BM
Information Science/Studies, B
Kindergarten/PreSchool Education and Teaching, B
Liberal Arts and Sciences Studies and Humanities, B
Mathematics, B
Music, B
Physical Education Teaching and Coaching, M
Physical Sciences, B
Political Science and Government, B
Psychology, BM
Reading Teacher Education, M
Secondary Education and Teaching, M
Social Work, B
Sociology, B
Spanish Language and Literature, B
Special Education and Teaching, BM
Technology Teacher Education/Industrial Arts Teacher Education, B
Vocational and Technical Education, MO

WHEATON COLLEGE

African-American/Black Studies, B
American/United States Studies/Civilization, B
Ancient Studies/Civilization, B
Anthropology, B
Art History, Criticism and Conservation, B
Asian Studies/Civilization, B
Biochemistry, B
Bioinformatics, B
Biology/Biological Sciences, B
Business/Commerce, B
Chemistry, B
Classics and Classical Languages, Literatures, and Linguistics, B
Computer Science, B
Dramatic/Theatre Arts and Stagecraft, B
Economics, B
English Language and Literature, B
Environmental Sciences, B
Film/Cinema Studies, B
French Studies, B
German Language and Literature, B
German Studies, B
History, B
International Relations and Affairs, B
Italian Studies, B
Latin Language and Literature, B

Mathematics, B
Mathematics and Computer Science, B
Multi-/Interdisciplinary Studies, B
Music, B
Philosophy, B
Physics, B
Political Science and Government, B
Psychology, B
Religion/Religious Studies, B
Russian Language and Literature, B
Russian Studies, B
Sociology, B
Women's Studies, B

WHEELOCK COLLEGE

American/United States Studies/Civilization, B
Child Development, B
Child and Family Studies, M
Communication and Media Studies, B
Early Childhood Education and Teaching, BM
Education, BM
Educational Leadership and Administration, M
Elementary Education and Teaching, BM
Environmental Studies, B
General Studies, B
Human Development, M
Human Development and Family Studies, B
Humanities/Humanistic Studies, B
Liberal Arts and Sciences Studies and Humanities, B
Mathematics, B
Physical Sciences, B
Political Science and Government, B
Reading Teacher Education, M
Social Work, BM
Special Education and Teaching, BM
Visual and Performing Arts, B
Youth Services/Administration, B

WILLIAMS COLLEGE

American/United States Studies/Civilization, B
Anthropology, B
Area Studies, B
Art History, Criticism and Conservation, BM
Art/Art Studies, General, B
Asian Studies/Civilization, B
Astronomy, B
Astrophysics, B
Biology/Biological Sciences, B
Chemistry, B
Chinese Language and Literature, B
Classics and Classical Languages, Literatures, and Linguistics, B
Comparative Literature, B
Computer Science, B
Drama and Dramatics/Theatre Arts, B
Economic Development, M
Economics, B
English Language and Literature, B
Environmental Sciences, B
Environmental Studies, B
Ethnic, Cultural Minority, and Gender Studies, B
French Language and Literature, B
Geology/Earth Science, B
German Language and Literature, B
History, B
Japanese Language and Literature, B
Mathematics, B
Music, B
Near and Middle Eastern Studies, B
Philosophy, B
Physics, B
Political Science and Government, B
Psychology, B
Religion/Religious Studies, B
Russian Language and Literature, B
Social Sciences, B
Sociology, B
Spanish Language and Literature, B
Statistics, B

Women's Studies, B

WORCESTER POLYTECHNIC INSTITUTE

Actuarial Science, B
Aerospace, Aeronautical and Astronautical Engineering, B
Animal Genetics, B
Applied Mathematics, BM
Applied Statistics, M
Architectural Engineering, B
Artificial Intelligence and Robotics, BMD
BioTechnology, MD
Biochemistry, BMD
Bioinformatics, MD
Biological and Biomedical Sciences, MD
Biology Technician/BioTechnology Laboratory Technician, B
Biology/Biological Sciences, B
Biomathematics and Bioinformatics, B
Biomedical Engineering, MDO
Biomedical Sciences, B
Biomedical/Medical Engineering, B
Business Administration and Management, B
Business Administration, Management and Operations, MDO
Cell/Cellular Biology and Histology, B
Chemical Engineering, BMD
Chemistry, BMD
Civil Engineering, BMDO
Computational Biology, MD
Computer Engineering, BMDO
Computer Science, BMDO
Computer and Information Sciences, B
Construction Management, M
Database Systems, MO
Economics, B
Educational Media/Instructional Technology, MD
Electrical Engineering, MDO
Electrical, Electronics and Communications Engineering, B
Energy and Power Engineering, M
Engineering, B
Engineering Design, M
Engineering Mechanics, B
Engineering Physics, B
Engineering and Applied Sciences, MDO
Engineering/Industrial Management, B
Environmental Engineering Technology/Environmental Technology, MDO
Environmental Studies, B
Environmental/Environmental Health Engineering, B
Fire Protection Engineering, MDO
Game Design and Development, M
History, B
History and Philosophy of Science and Technology, B
Humanities/Humanistic Studies, B
Industrial Engineering, B
Information Science/Studies, B
Interdisciplinary Studies, MD
Intermedia/Multimedia, B
Internet and Interactive Multimedia, M
Management, O
Management Information Systems and Services, BM
Manufacturing Engineering, MD
Marketing, M
Materials Engineering, BMD
Materials Sciences, MD
Mathematics, BMDO
Mechanical Engineering, BMDO
Medical Microbiology and Bacteriology, B
Medicinal and Pharmaceutical Chemistry, B
Modeling and Simulation, M
Molecular Biology, B
Music, B
Nuclear Engineering, B
Organizational Management, M
Philosophy, B
Physical Sciences, B
Physics, BMD
Science, Technology and Society, B
Social Sciences, BD
Systems Engineering, MO

Systems Science and Theory, MDO

WORCESTER STATE UNIVERSITY

Accounting, M
BioTechnology, BM
Biology/Biological Sciences, B
Business Administration and Management, B
Chemistry, B
Communication Disorders, BM
Communication Studies/Speech Communication and Rhetoric, B
Community Health Nursing, M
Community Health Services/Liaison/Counseling, B
Computer and Information Sciences, B
Criminal Justice/Safety Studies, B
Early Childhood Education and Teaching, BM
Economics, B
Education, MO
Educational Administration and Supervision, MO
Elementary Education and Teaching, BM
English Education, M
English Language and Literature, B
English as a Second Language, MO
Foreign Language Teacher Education, M
Geography, B
Health Education, M
Health Professions and Related Clinical Sciences, B
Health Services Administration, M
History, BM
Management, M
Mass Communication/Media Studies, B
Mathematics, B
Middle School Education, MO
Non-Profit/Public/Organizational Management, M
Nursing Education, M
Occupational Therapy/Therapist, BM
Organizational Management, M
Physical Sciences, B
Psychology, B
Reading Teacher Education, MO
School Psychology, O
Secondary Education and Teaching, MO
Social Studies Teacher Education, M
Sociology, B
Spanish Language and Literature, BM
Special Education and Teaching, MO
Urban Studies/Affairs, B
Visual and Performing Arts, B

Michigan

ADRIAN COLLEGE

Accounting, BM
Adult and Continuing Education and Teaching, B
Art History, Criticism and Conservation, B
Art Teacher Education, B
Art/Art Studies, General, B
Athletic Training and Sports Medicine, BM
Biochemistry, B
Biology Teacher Education, B
Biology/Biological Sciences, B
Business Administration and Management, B
Chemistry, B
Chemistry Teacher Education, B
Communication Studies/Speech Communication and Rhetoric, B
Corrections and Criminal Justice, B
Criminal Justice/Law Enforcement Administration, B
Criminology, M
Drama and Dramatics/Theatre Arts, B
Economics, B
Education, B
Elementary Education and Teaching, B
English Language and Literature, B
English/Language Arts Teacher Education, B
Entrepreneurship/Entrepreneurial Studies, B
Environmental Sciences, B
Environmental Studies, B
French Language Teacher Education, B
French Language and Literature, B
Geology/Earth Science, B
German Language Teacher Education, B
German Language and Literature, B
Health Teacher Education, B
Health and Physical Education, B

Health and Physical Education/Fitness, B
History, B
History Teacher Education, B
Interior Design, B
International Business/Trade/Commerce, B
International Relations and Affairs, B
International/Global Studies, B
Japanese Studies, B
Journalism, B
Kinesiology and Exercise Science, B
Marketing/Marketing Management, B
Mathematics, B
Mathematics Teacher Education, B
Music, B
Music Teacher Education, B
Philosophy, B
Physical Education Teaching and Coaching, B
Physics, B
Physics Teacher Education, B
Political Science and Government, B
Pre-Law Studies, B
Pre-Medicine/Pre-Medical Studies, B
Pre-Theology/Pre-Ministerial Studies, B
Pre-Veterinary Studies, B
Psychology, B
Religion/Religious Studies, B
Science Teacher Education/General Science Teacher Education, B
Secondary Education and Teaching, B
Social Sciences, B
Social Studies Teacher Education, B
Social Work, B
Sociology, B
Spanish Language Teacher Education, B
Spanish Language and Literature, B
Sport and Fitness Administration/Management, B
Teacher Education, Multiple Levels, B
Women's Studies, B

ALBION COLLEGE

Accounting, B
Anthropology, B
Art History, Criticism and Conservation, B
Art/Art Studies, General, B
Athletic Training and Sports Medicine, B
Biochemistry, B
Biology Teacher Education, B
Biology/Biological Sciences, B
Business Administration and Management, B
Chemistry, B
Chemistry Teacher Education, B
Communication and Media Studies, B
Drama and Dramatics/Theatre Arts, B
Economics, B
Engineering, B
English Language and Literature, B
English/Language Arts Teacher Education, B
Environmental Sciences, B
Environmental Studies, B
Ethnic, Cultural Minority, and Gender Studies, B
Finance, B
Fine/Studio Arts, B
French Language Teacher Education, B
French Language and Literature, B
Geology/Earth Science, B
German Language Teacher Education, B
German Language and Literature, B
Health Services/Allied Health/Health Sciences, B
History, B
History Teacher Education, B
International Economics, B
International/Global Studies, B
Kinesiology and Exercise Science, B
Latin American Studies, B
Liberal Arts and Sciences Studies and Humanities, B
Mass Communication/Media Studies, B
Mathematical Statistics and Probability, B
Mathematics, B
Mathematics Teacher Education, B
Multi-/Interdisciplinary Studies, B
Music, B
Music Performance, B
Music Teacher Education, B
Organizational Communication, B
Philosophy, B

Physics, B
Physics Teacher Education, B
Political Science and Government, B
Psychology, B
Psychology Teacher Education, B
Public Policy Analysis, B
Religion/Religious Studies, B
Science Teacher Education/General Science
  Teacher Education, B
Sociology, B
Spanish Language Teacher Education, B
Spanish Language and Literature, B
Speech Teacher Education, B
Women's Studies, B

ALMA COLLEGE

Accounting, B
Anthropology, B
Art Teacher Education, B
Art/Art Studies, General, B
Biochemistry, B
Biology Teacher Education, B
Biology/Biological Sciences, B
Business Administration and Management, B
Chemistry, B
Chemistry Teacher Education, B
Communication and Media Studies, B
Computer Science, B
Computer Teacher Education, B
Dance, B
Design and Visual Communications, B
Drama and Dramatics/Theatre Arts, B
Early Childhood Education and Teaching, B
Economics, B
Education, B
Elementary Education and Teaching, B
English Language and Literature, B
English/Language Arts Teacher Education, B
Finance, B
French Language Teacher Education, B
French Language and Literature, B
German Language Teacher Education, B
German Language and Literature, B
Graphic Design, B
Health Professions and Related Clinical Sciences, B
Health Teacher Education, B
History, B
History Teacher Education, B
Kindergarten/PreSchool Education and Teaching, B
Kinesiology and Exercise Science, B
Management Science, B
Marketing/Marketing Management, B
Mathematics, B
Mathematics Teacher Education, B
Modern Languages, B
Music, B
Music Teacher Education, B
Philosophy, B
Physical Education Teaching and Coaching, B
Physics, B
Physics Teacher Education, B
Political Science and Government, B
Pre-Dentistry Studies, B
Pre-Law Studies, B
Pre-Medicine/Pre-Medical Studies, B
Pre-Theology/Pre-Ministerial Studies, B
Pre-Veterinary Studies, B
Psychology, B
Psychology Teacher Education, B
Public Health (MPH, DPH), B
Religion/Religious Studies, B
Science Teacher Education/General Science
  Teacher Education, B
Secondary Education and Teaching, B
Social Studies Teacher Education, B
Sociology, B
Spanish Language Teacher Education, B
Spanish Language and Literature, B

ALPENA COMMUNITY COLLEGE

Accounting, A
Administrative Assistant and Secretarial Science, A
Automobile/Automotive Mechanics
  Technology/Technician, A
Biology/Biological Sciences, A
Business Administration and Management, A

Business/Office Automation/Technology/Data Entry, A
Chemical Engineering, A
Chemistry, A
Computer Systems Networking and Telecommunications, A
Computer and Information Sciences, A
Computer/Information Technology Services Administration and Management, A
Corrections, A
Criminal Justice/Police Science, A
Data Processing and Data Processing
  Technology/Technician, A
Drafting and Design Technology/Technician, A
Elementary Education and Teaching, A
English Language and Literature, A
General Studies, A
Information Science/Studies, A
Liberal Arts and Sciences Studies and Humanities, A
Manufacturing Technology/Technician, A
Mathematics, A
Medical Office Assistant/Specialist, A
Office Management and Supervision, A
Operations Management and Supervision, A
Secondary Education and Teaching, A

ANDREWS UNIVERSITY

Accounting, BM
Agribusiness, B
Allied Health and Medical Assisting Services, M
Anatomy, B
Architectural Engineering, B
Architecture, BM
Art Teacher Education, B
Art/Art Studies, General, B
Audiology/Audiologist and Speech-Language
  Pathology/Pathologist, B
Behavioral Sciences, B
Bible/Biblical Studies, B
Biochemistry, B
Biological and Biomedical Sciences, M
Biology/Biological Sciences, B
Biomedical Technology/Technician, B
Biophysics, B
Botany/Plant Biology, B
Business/Managerial Economics, B
Chemistry, B
Clinical Laboratory Science/Medical
  Technology/Technologist, B
Clinical Psychology, M
Communication Disorders, M
Communication and Media Studies, M
Community Psychology, M
Computer Programming/Programmer, B
Computer Science, B
Computer and Information Sciences, B
Counseling Psychology, MD
Curriculum and Instruction, MDO
Developmental Psychology, MD
Dietetics/Dieticians, B
Economics, BM
Education, BMDO
Educational Administration and Supervision, MDO
Educational Leadership and Administration, MDO
Educational Psychology, MD
Elementary Education and Teaching, BM
English, M
English Education, M
English Language and Literature, B
English as a Second Language, M
Family and Community Services, B
Family and Consumer Economics and Related Services, B
Finance and Banking, M
Foods, Nutrition, and Wellness Studies, B
Foreign Language Teacher Education, M
French Language and Literature, B
Higher Education/Higher Education Administration, MDO
History, B
Horticultural Science, A
Human Services, M
Information Science/Studies, B
International Development, M
Journalism, B

Landscaping and Groundskeeping, B
Marketing/Marketing Management, B
Mass Communication/Media Studies, B
Mathematics, B
Mechanical Engineering, B
Missions/Missionary Studies and Missiology, D
Music, BM
Music Teacher Education, B
Nursing, MD
Nutritional Sciences, M
Pastoral Studies/Counseling, MD
Physical Therapy/Therapist, BD
Physics, B
Piano and Organ, B
Political Science and Government, B
Pre-Law Studies, B
Pre-Medicine/Pre-Medical Studies, B
Pre-Veterinary Studies, B
Psychology, BMDO
Public Relations/Image Management, B
Religion/Religious Studies, B
Religious Education, BMDO
School Psychology, MO
Science Teacher Education/General Science
  Teacher Education, BM
Secondary Education and Teaching, BM
Social Sciences, B
Social Studies Teacher Education, M
Social Work, BM
Sociology, B
Spanish Language and Literature, B
Special Education and Teaching, M
Theology and Religious Vocations, MDO
Theology/Theological Studies, B
Voice and Opera, B
Youth Ministry, B
Zoology/Animal Biology, B

AQUINAS COLLEGE

Accounting, B
Art History, Criticism and Conservation, B
Art/Art Studies, General, B
Athletic Training and Sports Medicine, B
Biology/Biological Sciences, B
Business Administration and Management, B
Business/Corporate Communications, B
Ceramic Arts and Ceramics, B
Chemistry, B
Communication Studies/Speech Communication
  and Rhetoric, B
Computer and Information Sciences, B
Drama and Dramatics/Theatre Arts, B
Drawing, B
Economics, B
Education, M
Education/Teaching of Individuals with Specific
  Learning Disabilities, B
English Language and Literature, B
English/Language Arts Teacher Education, B
Environmental Studies, M
Fine/Studio Arts, B
French Language and Literature, B
General Studies, B
Geography, B
German Language and Literature, B
Health Services Administration, M
History, B
International Business/Trade/Commerce, B
International Relations and Affairs, B
Liberal Arts and Sciences Studies and Humanities, AB
Management, M
Marketing, M
Mathematics, B
Music, B
Music Performance, B
Music Teacher Education, B
Organizational Communication, B
Organizational Management, M
Painting, B
Philosophy, B
Photography, B
Physical Education Teaching and Coaching, B
Physics, B
Political Science and Government, B
Printmaking, B

Psychology, B
Reading Teacher Education, B
Religion/Religious Studies, B
Religious/Sacred Music, B
Science Teacher Education/General Science
    Teacher Education, B
Sculpture, B
Social Sciences, B
Social Studies Teacher Education, B
Sociology, B
Spanish Language and Literature, B
Sustainability Management, M
Urban Studies/Affairs, B

THE ART INSTITUTE OF MICHIGAN

Apparel and Accessories Marketing Operations, B
Commercial Photography, B
Computer Graphics, B
Culinary Arts/Chef Training, A
Fashion Merchandising, A
Graphic Design, AB
Interior Design, AB
Recording Arts Technology/Technician, B
Restaurant, Culinary, and Catering
    Management/Manager, B
Web Page, Digital/Multimedia and Information Re-
    sources Design, AB

BAKER COLLEGE

Accounting, AB
Administrative Assistant and Secretarial Science, A
Architectural Engineering Technology/Technician, A
Automobile/Automotive Mechanics
    Technology/Technician, A
Building/Construction Finishing, Manage-
    ment, and Inspection, A
Business Administration and Management, AB
Clinical/Medical Laboratory Technician, A
Commercial and Advertising Art, A
Computer Graphics, B
Computer Programming/Programmer, AB
Computer Science, AB
Computer Systems Networking and Telecommunica-
    tions, A
Construction Engineering Technology/Technician, A
Corrections, A
Culinary Arts/Chef Training, A
Data Processing and Data Processing
    Technology/Technician, A
Dental Hygiene/Hygienist, A
Diagnostic Medical Sonography/Sonographer and
    Ultrasound Technician, A
Drafting and Design Technology/Technician, A
Education, AB
Electrical, Electronic and Communications Engineer-
    ing Technology/Technician, AB
Emergency Medical Technology/Technician (EMT
    Paramedic), A
Entrepreneurship/Entrepreneurial Studies, A
Environmental Engineering
    Technology/Environmental Technology, A
Family and Community Services, A
Health Information/Medical Records
    Technology/Technician, A
Health/Health Care Administration/Management, A
Hotel/Motel Administration/Management, A
Human Resources Management/Personnel Adminis-
    tration, AB
Human Services, A
Industrial Technology/Technician, B
Interior Design, AB
Kindergarten/PreSchool Education and Teaching, A
Legal Administrative Assistant/Secretary, A
Management Information Systems and Services, B
Marketing/Marketing Management, AB
Mechanical Drafting and Mechanical Drafting
    CAD/CADD, A
Mechanical Engineering, B
Mechanical Engineering/Mechanical
    Technology/Technician, A
Medical Administrative Assistant/Secretary, A
Medical/Clinical Assistant, A
Occupational Therapist Assistant, A
Occupational Therapy/Therapist, B
Orthotist/Prosthetist, A
Pharmacy Technician/Assistant, A

Physical Therapist Assistant, A
Radiologic Technology/Science - Radiographer, A
Rehabilitation and Therapeutic Professions, B
Sales, Distribution and Marketing Operations, A
Surgical Technology/Technologist, A
System, Networking, and LAN/WAN
    Management/Manager, A
Transportation and Materials Moving, A
Veterinary/Animal Health Technology/Technician and
    Veterinary Assistant, A
Web Page, Digital/Multimedia and Information Re-
    sources Design, A

BAY MILLS COMMUNITY COLLEGE

Administrative Assistant and Secretarial Science, A
American Indian/Native American Languages, Lit-
    eratures, and Linguistics, A
American Indian/Native American Studies, A
Computer and Information Sciences, A
Construction Trades, A
Corrections and Criminal Justice, A
Early Childhood Education and Teaching, A
Education, A
General Studies, A
Health and Physical Education, A
Social Sciences, A

BAY DE NOC COMMUNITY COLLEGE

Accounting, A
Accounting Technology/Technician and Bookkeep-
    ing, A
Administrative Assistant and Secretarial Science, A
Automobile/Automotive Mechanics
    Technology/Technician, A
Business Administration and Management, A
Business/Commerce, A
CAD/CADD Drafting and/or Design
    Technology/Technician, A
Child Development, A
Computer Programming, Specific Applications, A
Computer Systems Networking and Telecommunica-
    tions, A
Computer Technology/Computer Systems Technol-
    ogy, A
Corrections, A
Criminal Justice/Safety Studies, A
Electrical, Electronic and Communications Engineer-
    ing Technology/Technician, A
Environmental Engineering
    Technology/Environmental Technology, A
General Studies, A
Legal Administrative Assistant/Secretary, A
Liberal Arts and Sciences Studies and Humani-
    ties, A
Marketing/Marketing Management, A
Medical Administrative Assistant/Secretary, A
Mental and Social Health Services and Allied Pro-
    fessions, A
Pre-Nursing Studies, A
Small Business Administration/Management, A
Water Quality and Wastewater Treatment Manage-
    ment and Recycling Technology/Technician, A

CALVIN COLLEGE

Accounting, B
Art Teacher Education, B
Art/Art Studies, General, B
Asian Studies/Civilization, B
Audiology/Audiologist and Speech-Language
    Pathology/Pathologist, B
Bible/Biblical Studies, B
Bilingual and Multilingual Education, B
BioTechnology, B
Biochemistry, B
Biological and Physical Sciences, B
Biology Teacher Education, B
Biology/Biological Sciences, B
Business Administration and Management, B
Business/Corporate Communications, B
Chemical Engineering, B
Chemistry, B
Chemistry Teacher Education, B
Chinese Language and Literature, B
Civil Engineering, B
Classical, Ancient Mediterranean and Near Eastern
    Studies and Archaeology, B

Communication Studies/Speech Communication
    and Rhetoric, B
Computer Science, B
Curriculum and Instruction, M
Development Economics and International Develop-
    ment, B
Digital Communication and Media/Multimedia, B
Early Childhood Education and Teaching, B
Economics, B
Education, M
Educational Leadership and Administration, M
Electrical, Electronics and Communications Engi-
    neering, B
Elementary Education and Teaching, B
Engineering, B
English Language and Literature, B
Environmental Sciences, B
Environmental Studies, B
Fine/Studio Arts, B
Foreign Language Teacher Education, B
French Language Teacher Education, B
French Language and Literature, B
Geography, B
Geography Teacher Education, B
Geology/Earth Science, B
German Language Teacher Education, B
German Language and Literature, B
Germanic Languages, Literatures, and Linguistics, B
Graphic Design, B
History, B
History Teacher Education, B
International Relations and Affairs, B
Japanese Language and Literature, B
Kinesiology and Exercise Science, B
Linguistics, B
Management Information Systems and Services, B
Mass Communication/Media Studies, B
Mathematics, B
Mathematics Teacher Education, B
Mechanical Engineering, B
Music, B
Music History, Literature, and Theory, B
Music Performance, B
Music Teacher Education, B
Music Theory and Composition, B
Natural Sciences, B
Occupational Therapy/Therapist, B
Organizational Communication, B
Philosophy, B
Physical Education Teaching and Coaching, B
Physical Sciences, B
Physics, B
Political Science and Government, B
Pre-Dentistry Studies, B
Pre-Law Studies, B
Pre-Medicine/Pre-Medical Studies, B
Pre-Pharmacy Studies, B
Pre-Theology/Pre-Ministerial Studies, B
Pre-Veterinary Studies, B
Psychology, B
Public Administration, B
Public Health (MPH, DPH), B
Reading Teacher Education, M
Religion/Religious Studies, B
Religious/Sacred Music, B
Science Teacher Education/General Science
    Teacher Education, B
Secondary Education and Teaching, B
Social Sciences, B
Social Studies Teacher Education, B
Social Work, B
Sociology, B
Spanish Language Teacher Education, B
Spanish Language and Literature, B
Special Education and Teaching, BM
Sport and Fitness Administration/Management, B
Teaching English as a Second or Foreign
    Language/ESL Language Instructor, B
Theology/Theological Studies, B
Therapeutic Recreation/Recreational Therapy, B
Voice and Opera, B

CENTRAL MICHIGAN UNIVERSITY

Accounting, BM
Acting, B
Actuarial Science, B

Advertising, B
American Indian/Native American Studies, M
American/United States Studies/Civilization, O
Anthropology, B
Applied Mathematics, B
Applied Psychology, D
Art Teacher Education, B
Art/Art Studies, General, B
Astronomy, B
Athletic Training and Sports Medicine, B
Biochemistry, B
Biological and Biomedical Sciences, BM
Biology Teacher Education, B
Biology/Biological Sciences, B
Biomedical Sciences, B
Biomedical/Medical Engineering, B
Business Administration and Management, B
Business Administration, Management and Operations, BMO
Cartography, B
Chemistry, BM
Chemistry Teacher Education, B
Child Development, B
Child and Family Studies, M
Clinical Psychology, D
Clothing and Textiles, M
Communication Disorders, BMD
Communication Studies/Speech Communication and Rhetoric, B
Communication and Media Studies, M
Community College Education, M
Community Health Services/Liaison/Counseling, B
Community Organization and Advocacy, B
Composition, M
Computer Engineering, B
Computer Science, BM
Computer and Information Systems Security, O
Conservation Biology, M
Construction Engineering Technology/Technician, B
Counseling Psychology, MO
Counselor Education/School Counseling and Guidance Services, M
Cultural Studies, M
Curriculum and Instruction, MD
Dietetics/Dieticians, B
Drafting/Design Engineering Technologies/Technicians, B
Early Childhood Education and Teaching, BM
Economics, BM
Education, MDO
Education/Teaching of Individuals with Emotional Disturbances, B
Education/Teaching of Individuals with Mental Retardation, B
Educational Administration and Supervision, MO
Educational Leadership and Administration, MDO
Educational Media/Instructional Technology, MDO
Electrical, Electronics and Communications Engineering, B
Elementary Education and Teaching, BMD
Engineering Management, MO
Engineering and Applied Sciences, M
English, M
English Language and Literature, B
English as a Second Language, M
English/Language Arts Teacher Education, B
Entrepreneurship/Entrepreneurial Studies, B
Environmental Health, B
Environmental Sciences, B
Environmental Studies, B
Ethnic, Cultural Minority, and Gender Studies, B
Exercise and Sports Science, M
Experimental Psychology, MD
Family Systems, B
Fashion Merchandising, B
Film, Television, and Video Production, M
Film, Television, and Video Theory and Criticism, M
Finance, B
Finance and Banking, M
Financial Planning and Services, B
Fine/Studio Arts, B
French Language Teacher Education, B
French Language and Literature, B
Gender Studies, M
Geographic Information Systems, M
Geography, B

Geology/Earth Science, B
German Language and Literature, B
Gerontology, O
Graphic Design, B
Health Psychology, D
Health Services Administration, MDO
Health Teacher Education, B
Health/Health Care Administration/Management, B
Higher Education/Higher Education Administration, DO
History, BMO
History Teacher Education, B
Home Economics, MO
Hospitality Administration/Management, B
Human Development, M
Human Resources Management and Services, MO
Human Resources Management/Personnel Administration, B
Humanities/Humanistic Studies, M
Industrial and Manufacturing Management, M
Industrial and Organizational Psychology, MD
Information Technology, B
International Affairs, MO
International Business/Trade/Commerce, BMO
International Public Health/International Health, O
International Relations and Affairs, B
Journalism, B
Kinesiology and Exercise Science, B
Land Use Planning and Management/Development, B
Law and Legal Studies, B
Liberal Arts and Sciences Studies and Humanities, B
Logistics and Materials Management, BMO
Management, MO
Management Information Systems and Services, BMO
Manufacturing Technology/Technician, B
Marketing, M
Marketing/Marketing Management, B
Materials Sciences, D
Mathematics, BMD
Mathematics Teacher Education, BD
Mechanical Engineering, B
Mechanical Engineering/Mechanical Technology/Technician, B
Media Studies, M
Meteorology, B
Music, BM
Music Teacher Education, M
Music Theory and Composition, B
Natural Resources and Conservation, B
Neuroscience, MD
Non-Profit/Public/Organizational Management, MO
Nutritional Sciences, M
Operations Management and Supervision, B
Parks, Recreation and Leisure Facilities Management, B
Parks, Recreation, Leisure and Fitness Studies, B
Performance, M
Philosophy, B
Photojournalism, B
Physical Education Teaching and Coaching, B
Physical Therapy/Therapist, D
Physician Assistant, M
Physics, BMD
Physics Teacher Education, B
Political Science and Government, BM
Psychology, BMDO
Public Administration, MO
Public Health Education and Promotion, B
Public Relations/Image Management, B
Public/Applied History and Archival Administration, B
Purchasing, Procurement/Acquisitions and Contracts Management, B
Radio, Television, and Digital Communication, B
Reading Teacher Education, M
Real Estate, B
Recreation and Park Management, M
Rehabilitation Sciences, MD
Religion/Religious Studies, B
School Psychology, DO
Science Teacher Education/General Science Teacher Education, BM
Secondary Education and Teaching, MD
Social Sciences, B

Social Studies Teacher Education, B
Social Work, B
Sociology, B
Spanish Language Teacher Education, B
Spanish Language and Literature, BM
Special Education and Teaching, MO
Speech Teacher Education, B
Sport and Fitness Administration/Management, BM
Statistics, B
Student Personnel Services, M
Therapeutic Recreation/Recreational Therapy, B
Western European Studies, O
Women's Studies, B
Writing, M

CLEARY UNIVERSITY

Accounting, ABM
Business Administration and Management, AB
Business Administration, Management and Operations, MO
Business/Corporate Communications, B
Entrepreneurship/Entrepreneurial Studies, B
Finance, B
Finance and Banking, MO
Health Services Administration, M
Health/Health Care Administration/Management, B
Hospitality Administration/Management, B
Human Resources Management/Personnel Administration, B
Management Information Systems and Services, B
Marketing/Marketing Management, AB
Non-Profit/Public/Organizational Management, MO
Organizational Management, M
Sport and Fitness Administration/Management, B
Sustainability Management, MO

COLLEGE FOR CREATIVE STUDIES

Animation, Interactive Technology, Video Graphics and Special Effects, B
Art Teacher Education, B
Automotive Engineering Technology/Technician, M
Commercial and Advertising Art, B
Crafts/Craft Design, Folk Art and Artisanry, B
Design and Applied Arts, M
Fine Arts and Art Studies, M
Fine/Studio Arts, B
Graphic Design, B
Illustration, B
Industrial Design, B
Interior Design, B
Photography, B
Transportation and Highway Engineering, M

CONCORDIA UNIVERSITY ANN ARBOR

Ancient Near Eastern and Biblical Languages, Literatures, and Linguistics, B
Art Teacher Education, B
Art/Art Studies, General, B
Biological and Physical Sciences, B
Biology Teacher Education, B
Biology/Biological Sciences, B
Business Administration and Management, B
Criminal Justice/Law Enforcement Administration, B
Curriculum and Instruction, M
Educational Leadership and Administration, M
Elementary Education and Teaching, B
English Language and Literature, B
English/Language Arts Teacher Education, B
General Studies, A
Health Teacher Education, B
Health and Physical Education, B
History, B
Human Development and Family Studies, B
Mathematics, B
Mathematics Teacher Education, B
Music, B
Music Teacher Education, B
Organizational Management, M
Philosophy, B
Physical Education Teaching and Coaching, B
Physical Sciences, B
Pre-Medicine/Pre-Medical Studies, B
Pre-Theology/Pre-Ministerial Studies, B
Psychology, B
Psychology Teacher Education, B
Religion/Religious Studies, B

Religious Education, B
Religious/Sacred Music, B
Science Teacher Education/General Science
Teacher Education, B
Secondary Education and Teaching, B
Security and Protective Services, B
Social Sciences, B
Social Studies Teacher Education, B

CORNERSTONE UNIVERSITY

Accounting, B
Ancient Near Eastern and Biblical Languages, Literatures, and Linguistics, B
Bible/Biblical Studies, B
Biology Teacher Education, B
Biology/Biological Sciences, B
Broadcast Journalism, B
Business Administration and Management, AB
Business Administration, Management and Operations, BM
Cinematography and Film/Video Production, B
Communication Studies/Speech Communication and Rhetoric, B
Community Health Services/Liaison/Counseling, B
Digital Communication and Media/Multimedia, B
Early Childhood Education and Teaching, A
Economics, B
Education, M
Education/Teaching of Individuals with Specific Learning Disabilities, B
Elementary Education and Teaching, B
English as a Second Language, MO
English/Language Arts Teacher Education, B
Environmental Biology, B
Finance, B
General Studies, B
Health Communication, B
Health/Medical Preparatory Programs, B
History, B
History Teacher Education, B
Human Development and Family Studies, B
Human Services, A
Humanities/Humanistic Studies, B
International Business/Trade/Commerce, B
Journalism, B
Kinesiology and Exercise Science, B
Management, M
Management Information Systems and Services, B
Marketing/Marketing Management, B
Mathematics, B
Mathematics Teacher Education, B
Missions/Missionary Studies and Missiology, B
Multi-/Interdisciplinary Studies, B
Music, B
Music Performance, B
Music Teacher Education, B
Non-Profit/Public/Organizational Management, B
Photography, B
Physical Education Teaching and Coaching, B
Psychology, B
Public Relations/Image Management, B
Radio and Television, B
Science Teacher Education/General Science Teacher Education, B
Social Studies Teacher Education, B
Social Work, B
Spanish Language Teacher Education, B
Spanish Language and Literature, B
Speech Teacher Education, B
Sport and Fitness Administration/Management, B
Teaching English as a Second or Foreign Language/ESL Language Instructor, A
Theological and Ministerial Studies, B
Youth Ministry, B

DAVENPORT UNIVERSITY

Accounting, ABM
Animation, Interactive Technology, Video Graphics and Special Effects, B
Bioinformatics, B
Business Administration and Management, AB
Business Administration, Management and Operations, M
Business/Commerce, B
Computer Systems Analysis/Analyst, AB

Computer Systems Networking and Telecommunications, B
Computer and Information Systems Security, ABM
Finance, AB
Finance and Banking, M
Health Information/Medical Records Administration/Administrator, B
Health Information/Medical Records Technology/Technician, AB
Health Services Administration, M
Health/Health Care Administration/Management, B
Human Resources Management and Services, M
Human Resources Management/Personnel Administration, B
International Business/Trade/Commerce, B
Legal Assistant/Paralegal, AB
Management Strategy and Policy, M
Marketing/Marketing Management, B
Medical/Clinical Assistant, A
Medical/Health Management and Clinical Assistant/Specialist, B
Public Health, M
Sport and Fitness Administration/Management, B

DELTA COLLEGE

Accounting Technology/Technician and Bookkeeping, A
Administrative Assistant and Secretarial Science, A
Architectural Engineering Technology/Technician, A
Automobile/Automotive Mechanics Technology/Technician, A
Building/Construction Finishing, Management, and Inspection, A
Building/Property Maintenance and Management, A
Business Administration and Management, A
Carpentry/Carpenter, A
Chemical Technology/Technician, A
Child Care Provider/Assistant, A
Computer Installation and Repair Technology/Technician, A
Computer Programming/Programmer, A
Computer Systems Networking and Telecommunications, A
Computer and Information Sciences, A
Computer and Information Systems Security, A
Construction Engineering Technology/Technician, A
Corrections, A
Criminal Justice/Police Science, A
Dental Assisting/Assistant, A
Dental Hygiene/Hygienist, A
Diagnostic Medical Sonography/Sonographer and Ultrasound Technician, A
Electrical and Power Transmission Installation/Installer, A
Electrician, A
Energy Management and Systems Technology/Technician, A
Environmental Engineering Technology/Environmental Technology, A
Fine/Studio Arts, A
Fire Protection and Safety Technology/Technician, A
Fire Science/Firefighting, A
Fire Services Administration, A
General Studies, A
Heating, Air Conditioning, Ventilation and Refrigeration Maintenance Technology/Technician, A
Industrial Mechanics and Maintenance Technology, A
Journalism, A
Legal Assistant/Paralegal, A
Liberal Arts and Sciences Studies and Humanities, A
Machine Shop Technology/Assistant, A
Manufacturing Technology/Technician, A
Marketing/Marketing Management, A
Mechanical Engineering/Mechanical Technology/Technician, A
Medical Administrative Assistant/Secretary, A
Medical Radiologic Technology/Science - Radiation Therapist, A
Merchandising and Buying Operations, A
Peace Studies and Conflict Resolution, A
Physical Therapist Assistant, A
Pipefitting/Pipefitter and Sprinkler Fitter, A
Plumbing Technology/Plumber, A
Precision Metal Working, A

Precision Production, A
Radio and Television, A
Respiratory Care Therapy/Therapist, A
Retailing and Retail Operations, A
Salon/Beauty Salon Management/Manager, A
Security and Loss Prevention Services, A
Sheet Metal Technology/Sheetworking, A
Small Business Administration/Management, A
Sport and Fitness Administration/Management, A
Surgical Technology/Technologist, A
Technology Teacher Education/Industrial Arts Teacher Education, A
Tool and Die Technology/Technician, A
Water Quality and Wastewater Treatment Management and Recycling Technology/Technician, A
Web/Multimedia Management and Webmaster, A
Welding Technology/Welder, A

EASTERN MICHIGAN UNIVERSITY

Accounting, BM
Accounting and Related Services, B
Actuarial Science, B
African-American Studies, O
African-American/Black Studies, B
Airline/Commercial/Professional Pilot and Flight Crew, B
American/United States Studies/Civilization, M
Animation, Interactive Technology, Video Graphics and Special Effects, B
Anthropology, B
Area Studies, B
Art Education, M
Art History, Criticism and Conservation, B
Art Teacher Education, B
Art/Art Studies, General, B
Artificial Intelligence and Robotics, O
Arts Management, M
Athletic Training and Sports Medicine, B
Aviation/Airway Management and Operations, B
Biochemistry, B
Biological and Biomedical Sciences, M
Biological and Physical Sciences, B
Biology Teacher Education, B
Biology/Biological Sciences, B
Business Administration and Management, B
Business Administration, Management and Operations, MO
Business Teacher Education, B
Business/Commerce, B
Business/Managerial Economics, B
CAD/CADD Drafting and/or Design Technology/Technician, B
Cell Biology and Anatomy, M
Chemistry, BM
Chemistry Teacher Education, B
City/Urban, Community and Regional Planning, B
Clinical Laboratory Science/Medical Technology/Technologist, B
Clinical Psychology, M
Clinical Research, MO
Clothing and Textiles, M
Communication Disorders, M
Communication Studies/Speech Communication and Rhetoric, B
Communication and Media Studies, M
Communications Technology/Technician, B
Computer Engineering Technology/Technician, B
Computer Science, BMO
Computer Teacher Education, B
Computer and Information Sciences, B
Computer and Information Systems Security, O
Construction Management, BM
Corporate and Organizational Communication, M
Counselor Education/School Counseling and Guidance Services, MO
Criminology, BM
Cultural Studies, MO
Curriculum and Instruction, M
Dance, B
Developmental Education, M
Dietetics/Dieticians, B
Drama and Dramatics/Theatre Arts, B
Early Childhood Education and Teaching, BM
Ecology, M
Economics, BMO
Education, MDO

Education/Teaching of Individuals with Emotional Disturbances, B
Education/Teaching of Individuals with Hearing Impairments, Including Deafness, B
Education/Teaching of Individuals with Mental Retardation, B
Education/Teaching of Individuals with Orthopedic and Other Physical Health Impairments, B
Education/Teaching of Individuals with Speech or Language Impairments, B
Education/Teaching of Individuals with Vision Impairments, Including Blindness, B
Educational Administration and Supervision, MO
Educational Leadership and Administration, MDO
Educational Measurement and Evaluation, O
Educational Media/Instructional Technology, MO
Educational Psychology, MO
Electrical, Electronic and Communications Engineering Technology/Technician, B
Electronic Commerce, MO
Elementary Education and Teaching, BM
Engineering Management, M
Engineering Physics, B
Engineering and Applied Sciences, M
Engineering/Industrial Management, B
English, MO
English Education, MO
English Language and Literature, B
English as a Second Language, MO
English/Language Arts Teacher Education, B
Entrepreneurship/Entrepreneurial Studies, BMO
Exercise and Sports Science, M
Facilities Planning and Management, B
Fashion Merchandising, B
Film/Cinema Studies, B
Finance, B
Finance and Banking, MO
Fine Arts and Art Studies, M
Foreign Language Teacher Education, BMO
Foundations and Philosophy of Education, M
French Language Teacher Education, B
French Language and Literature, BM
Gender Studies, MO
General Merchandising, Sales, and Related Marketing Operations, B
Geographic Information Systems, MO
Geography, BO
Geology/Earth Science, B
Geophysics and Seismology, B
Geosciences, M
German Language Teacher Education, B
German Language and Literature, BMO
Germanic Languages, Literatures, and Linguistics, B
Gerontology, O
Health Education, MO
Health Promotion, MO
Health Services Administration, MO
Health and Physical Education, B
Health/Health Care Administration/Management, B
Hispanic Studies, O
Hispanic and Latin American Languages, O
Historic Preservation and Conservation, M
History, BMO
History Teacher Education, B
Hospitality Administration/Management, BMO
Human Resources Management and Services, MO
Human Services, O
Industrial Technology/Technician, B
Interior Design, BM
International Business/Trade/Commerce, BMO
International Relations and Affairs, B
International Trade, M
Japanese Language and Literature, B
Japanese Studies, O
Journalism, B
Kinesiology and Exercise Science, B
Kinesiology and Movement Studies, M
Labor Studies, B
Legal Assistant/Paralegal, B
Linguistics, BMO
Logistics and Materials Management, B
Management, M
Management Information Systems and Services, BMO
Management of Technology, D
Manufacturing Technology/Technician, B

Marketing, MO
Marketing/Marketing Management, B
Mathematics, BM
Mathematics Teacher Education, B
Mechanical Engineering/Mechanical Technology/Technician, B
Middle School Education, M
Molecular Biology, M
Multi-/Interdisciplinary Studies, B
Museum Education, O
Music, BM
Music Performance, B
Music Teacher Education, B
Music Therapy/Therapist, B
Non-Profit/Public/Organizational Management, MO
Nursing - Adult, M
Nursing Administration, MO
Nursing Education, MO
Nutritional Sciences, M
Occupational Therapy/Therapist, BM
Office Management and Supervision, B
Organizational Management, MO
Parks, Recreation and Leisure Facilities Management, B
Philosophy, BM
Physical Education Teaching and Coaching, BM
Physical Sciences, B
Physician Assistant, M
Physics, BM
Physics Teacher Education, B
Physiology, M
Plastics Engineering Technology/Technician, B
Political Science and Government, B
Polymer/Plastics Engineering, M
Psychology, BMD
Public Administration, BMO
Public Policy Analysis, O
Public Relations/Image Management, B
Quality Management, MO
Reading Teacher Education, BM
Sales and Marketing Operations/Marketing and Distribution Teacher Education, B
Science Teacher Education/General Science Teacher Education, BM
Science, Technology and Society, B
Secondary Education and Teaching, M
Security and Protective Services, B
Social Science Teacher Education, B
Social Sciences, BMO
Social Studies Teacher Education, B
Social Work, BM
Sociology, BM
Spanish Language Teacher Education, B
Spanish Language and Literature, BM
Special Education and Teaching, M
Speech-Language Pathology/Pathologist, B
Sport and Fitness Administration/Management, BM
Sports Medicine, MO
Statistics, B
Supply Chain Management, MO
Teacher Education and Professional Development, Specific Subject Areas, B
Technical Communication, MO
Technology Teacher Education/Industrial Arts Teacher Education, B
Technology and Public Policy, M
Theater, M
Therapeutic Recreation/Recreational Therapy, B
Toxicology, B
Travel and Tourism, M
Urban Studies/Affairs, M
Urban and Regional Planning, MO
Water Resources, MO
Women's Studies, BMO
Writing, MO

FERRIS STATE UNIVERSITY

Accounting Technology/Technician and Bookkeeping, AB
Accounting and Finance, B
Advertising, B
Allied Health and Medical Assisting Services, M
Animation, Interactive Technology, Video Graphics and Special Effects, A
Applied Mathematics, B
Architectural Engineering Technology/Technician, AB

Art History, Criticism and Conservation, B
Art Teacher Education, B
Automobile/Automotive Mechanics Technology/Technician, A
Automotive Engineering Technology/Technician, B
BioTechnology, B
Biochemistry, B
Biological and Physical Sciences, A
Biology Teacher Education, B
Biology/Biological Sciences, B
Business Administration and Management, B
Business Administration, Management and Operations, M
Business/Commerce, A
CAD/CADD Drafting and/or Design Technology/Technician, AB
Chemistry, B
Chemistry Teacher Education, B
Child Care and Support Services Management, AB
Civil Engineering Technology/Technician, A
Clinical Laboratory Science/Medical Technology/Technologist, A
Clinical/Medical Laboratory Technician, A
Communication Studies/Speech Communication and Rhetoric, B
Community College Education, D
Computer Systems Networking and Telecommunications, B
Computer and Information Sciences and Support Services, B
Computer and Information Systems Security, BM
Construction Engineering Technology/Technician, A
Construction Management, B
Criminal Justice/Law Enforcement Administration, B
Criminal Justice/Police Science, AB
Criminology, M
Curriculum and Instruction, M
Database Systems, M
Dental Hygiene/Hygienist, AB
Design and Applied Arts, BM
Developmental Education, M
Diagnostic Medical Sonography/Sonographer and Ultrasound Technician, A
Dietetics/Dieticians, A
Drawing, B
Education, M
Educational Administration and Supervision, M
Educational Leadership and Administration, MD
Electrical, Electronic and Communications Engineering Technology/Technician, B
Elementary Education and Teaching, AB
Energy Management and Systems Technology/Technician, B
Engineering, A
English/Language Arts Teacher Education, B
Environmental Biology, B
Fashion/Apparel Design, B
Finance, B
Fine Arts and Art Studies, M
Fine/Studio Arts, B
Funeral Service and Mortuary Science, A
General Studies, A
Graphic Design, AB
Health Information/Medical Records Administration/Administrator, B
Health Information/Medical Records Technology/Technician, A
Health Professions and Related Clinical Sciences, AB
Health/Health Care Administration/Management, B
Heating, Air Conditioning and Refrigeration Technology/Technician, A
Heavy Equipment Maintenance Technology/Technician, AB
History, B
History Teacher Education, B
Hospitality Administration/Management, B
Hospitality and Recreation Marketing Operations, AB
Hotel/Motel Administration/Management, AB
Human Resources Management/Personnel Administration, B
Human Services, M
Illustration, B
Industrial Design, B
Industrial Electronics Technology/Technician, A

Industrial Production Technologies/Technicians, B
Industrial Technology/Technician, B
Information Technology, AB
Interior Design, B
Legal Assistant/Paralegal, A
Liberal Arts and Sciences Studies and Humanities, A
Management, M
Management Information Systems and Services, M
Marketing/Marketing Management, AB
Mathematics Teacher Education, B
Mechanical Engineering/Mechanical Technology/Technician, AB
Medical Radiologic Technology/Science - Radiation Therapist, A
Metal and Jewelry Arts, B
Nuclear Medical Technology/Technologist, B
Nursing, M
Nursing Administration, M
Nursing Education, M
Nursing Informatics, M
Operations Management and Supervision, B
Optometry, D
Painting, B
Parks, Recreation and Leisure Facilities Management, B
Pharmacy, D
Photography, B
Plastics Engineering Technology/Technician, AB
Political Science and Government, B
Pre-Law Studies, A
Pre-Pharmacy Studies, A
Printing Management, B
Project Management, M
Psychology, AB
Public Administration, A
Public Relations/Image Management, B
Radio and Television Broadcasting Technology/Technician, B
Reading Teacher Education, M
Respiratory Care Therapy/Therapist, A
Restaurant, Culinary, and Catering Management/Manager, A
Sculpture, B
Secondary Education and Teaching, A
Social Work, AB
Sociology, B
Special Education and Teaching, M
Survey Technology/Surveying, AB
Surveying Engineering, B
Systems Engineering, B
Technical Teacher Education, B
Tool and Die Technology/Technician, A
Welding Technology/Welder, A

FINLANDIA UNIVERSITY

Art/Art Studies, General, B
Business Administration and Management, B
Ceramic Arts and Ceramics, B
Criminal Justice/Law Enforcement Administration, A
Education, B
Fiber, Textile and Weaving Arts, B
Fine/Studio Arts, B
General Studies, A
Human Services, B
Industrial Design, B
International Business/Trade/Commerce, B
Liberal Arts and Sciences Studies and Humanities, B
Physical Therapist Assistant, A
Teacher Education, Multiple Levels, B

GLEN OAKS COMMUNITY COLLEGE

Business Administration and Management, A
Business, Management, Marketing, and Related Support Services, A
Child Care and Support Services Management, A
General Studies, A
Health Professions and Related Clinical Sciences, A
Mechanical Engineering Related Technologies/Technicians, A

GOGEBIC COMMUNITY COLLEGE

Accounting, A
Accounting and Computer Science, A

Automobile/Automotive Mechanics Technology/Technician, A
Business Administration and Management, A
Business/Commerce, A
Computer and Information Sciences, A
Construction Engineering Technology/Technician, A
Criminal Justice/Law Enforcement Administration, A
Drafting and Design Technology/Technician, A
Early Childhood Education and Teaching, A
Education, A
Elementary Education and Teaching, A
Graphic Communications, A
Information Technology, A
Parks, Recreation and Leisure Facilities Management, A
Psychology, A
Secondary Education and Teaching, A
Social Work, A

GRACE BIBLE COLLEGE

Accounting, B
Bible/Biblical Studies, B
Business Administration and Management, AB
Computer and Information Sciences, B
Early Childhood Education and Teaching, B
Elementary Education and Teaching, B
Finance and Financial Management Services, B
Human Services, B
Liberal Arts and Sciences Studies and Humanities, A
Management Science, B
Marketing/Marketing Management, B
Missions/Missionary Studies and Missiology, B
Multi-/Interdisciplinary Studies, B
Music, B
Pastoral Studies/Counseling, B
Secondary Education and Teaching, B
Theology/Theological Studies, B
Youth Ministry, B

GRAND RAPIDS COMMUNITY COLLEGE

Architectural Technology/Technician, A
Architecture, A
Art/Art Studies, General, A
Automobile/Automotive Mechanics Technology/Technician, A
Business Administration and Management, A
Chemistry, A
Child Care and Support Services Management, A
Computer Programming, Specific Applications, A
Computer Programming/Programmer, A
Computer Systems Networking and Telecommunications, A
Computer and Information Sciences, A
Computer and Information Systems Security, A
Corrections, A
Criminal Justice/Law Enforcement Administration, A
Criminal Justice/Police Science, A
Culinary Arts/Chef Training, A
Dental Hygiene/Hygienist, A
Electrical, Electronic and Communications Engineering Technology/Technician, A
Elementary Education and Teaching, A
Engineering, A
English Language and Literature, A
Fashion Merchandising, A
Foreign Languages and Literatures, A
Forestry, A
Geology/Earth Science, A
Heating, Air Conditioning, Ventilation and Refrigeration Maintenance Technology/Technician, A
Industrial Technology/Technician, A
Journalism, A
Landscaping and Groundskeeping, A
Liberal Arts and Sciences Studies and Humanities, A
Library Science, A
Medical Administrative Assistant/Secretary, A
Music, A
Music Teacher Education, A
Physical Education Teaching and Coaching, A
Plastics Engineering Technology/Technician, A
Quality Control Technology/Technician, A
Recording Arts Technology/Technician, A

Restaurant, Culinary, and Catering Management/Manager, A
Secondary Education and Teaching, A
Welding Technology/Welder, A

GRAND VALLEY STATE UNIVERSITY

Accounting, BM
Adult and Continuing Education and Teaching, M
Advertising, B
Allied Health and Medical Assisting Services, MD
Anthropology, B
Art History, Criticism and Conservation, B
Art Teacher Education, B
Athletic Training and Sports Medicine, B
Bioinformatics, M
Biological and Biomedical Sciences, BM
Biological and Physical Sciences, B
Biology Teacher Education, B
Biology/Biological Sciences, B
Biopsychology, B
Biostatistics, M
Business Administration, Management and Operations, M
Business/Commerce, B
Business/Managerial Economics, B
Cell Biology and Anatomy, M
Cell/Cellular and Molecular Biology, B
Chemistry, B
Chemistry Teacher Education, B
Classics and Classical Languages, Literatures, and Linguistics, B
Clinical Laboratory Science/Medical Technology/Technologist, B
Communication Disorders, M
Communication Studies/Speech Communication and Rhetoric, B
Communication and Media Studies, M
Computer Engineering, M
Computer Science, M
Computer and Information Sciences, B
Criminal Justice/Law Enforcement Administration, B
Criminology, M
Curriculum and Instruction, M
Dance, B
Drama and Dramatics/Theatre Arts, B
Early Childhood Education and Teaching, M
East Asian Studies, B
Economics, B
Education, MO
Education/Teaching of Individuals with Emotional Disturbances, B
Education/Teaching of Individuals with Hearing Impairments, Including Deafness, B
Education/Teaching of Individuals with Mental Retardation, B
Education/Teaching of Individuals with Multiple Disabilities, B
Education/Teaching of Individuals with Orthopedic and Other Physical Health Impairments, B
Education/Teaching of the Gifted and Talented, B
Educational Leadership and Administration, MO
Educational Media/Instructional Technology, M
Electrical Engineering, M
Elementary Education and Teaching, BM
Engineering, B
Engineering and Applied Sciences, M
English, M
English Education, M
English Language and Literature, B
English as a Second Language, M
English/Language Arts Teacher Education, B
Film/Cinema Studies, B
Finance, B
Fine Arts and Art Studies, B
Foreign Language Teacher Education, B
French Language Teacher Education, B
French Language and Literature, B
Geochemistry, B
Geography, B
Geography Teacher Education, B
Geology/Earth Science, B
German Language Teacher Education, B
Germanic Languages, Literatures, and Linguistics, B
Health Communication, B
Health Services Administration, M
Health Teacher Education, B

Higher Education/Higher Education Administration, M
History, B
History Teacher Education, B
Hospitality Administration/Management, B
Hotel/Motel Administration/Management, B
Human Resources Management and Services, B
Information Science/Studies, BM
International Business/Trade/Commerce, B
International Relations and Affairs, B
Journalism, B
Junior High/Intermediate/Middle School Education and Teaching, B
Legal Assistant/Paralegal, B
Liberal Arts and Sciences Studies and Humanities, B
Management Information Systems and Services, M
Management Science, B
Manufacturing Engineering, M
Marketing/Marketing Management, B
Mathematics, B
Mathematics Teacher Education, B
Mechanical Engineering, M
Medical Informatics, M
Medical Radiologic Technology/Science - Radiation Therapist, B
Middle School Education, M
Molecular Biology, M
Music, B
Music Teacher Education, B
Natural Resources and Conservation, B
Non-Profit/Public/Organizational Management, M
Nursing, MD
Nursing Administration, MD
Nursing Education, M
Occupational Health and Industrial Hygiene, B
Occupational Safety and Health Technology/Technician, B
Occupational Therapy/Therapist, BM
Philosophy, B
Photography, B
Physical Education Teaching and Coaching, B
Physical Therapy/Therapist, BD
Physician Assistant, BM
Physics, B
Physics Teacher Education, B
Political Science and Government, B
Pre-Dentistry Studies, B
Pre-Medicine/Pre-Medical Studies, B
Pre-Veterinary Studies, B
Psychology, B
Public Administration, BM
Public Health, M
Radio and Television, B
Reading Teacher Education, BM
Russian Studies, B
School Psychology, MO
Science Teacher Education/General Science Teacher Education, B
Secondary Education and Teaching, BM
Social Sciences, B
Social Studies Teacher Education, B
Social Work, BM
Sociology, B
Software Engineering, M
Spanish Language Teacher Education, B
Spanish Language and Literature, B
Special Education and Teaching, BM
Statistics, B
Taxation, BM
Therapeutic Recreation/Recreational Therapy, B
Women's Studies, B

GREAT LAKES CHRISTIAN COLLEGE

Bible/Biblical Studies, B
Communication Studies/Speech Communication and Rhetoric, B
Divinity/Ministry (BD, MDiv.), AB
Early Childhood Education and Teaching, A
Family and Consumer Sciences/Human Sciences, B
General Studies, A
History, B
Non-Profit/Public/Organizational Management, B
Religious Education, B
Religious/Sacred Music, B

Youth Ministry, B

HENRY FORD COLLEGE

Accounting and Related Services, A
Architectural Technology/Technician, A
Art/Art Studies, General, A
Automobile/Automotive Mechanics Technology/Technician, A
Biology/Biological Sciences, A
Building/Property Maintenance and Management, A
Business Administration and Management, A
Business/Commerce, A
CAD/CADD Drafting and/or Design Technology/Technician, A
Chemistry, A
Commercial and Advertising Art, A
Computer Programming, Specific Applications, A
Computer Systems Networking and Telecommunications, A
Computer and Information Sciences, A
Corrections, A
Criminal Justice/Law Enforcement Administration, A
Culinary Arts/Chef Training, A
Drama and Dramatics/Theatre Arts, A
Early Childhood Education and Teaching, A
Electrical, Electronic and Communications Engineering Technology/Technician, A
Elementary Education and Teaching, A
Emergency Medical Technology/Technician (EMT Paramedic), A
Energy Management and Systems Technology/Technician, A
Engineering, A
Environmental Studies, A
Executive Assistant/Executive Secretary, A
General Studies, A
Health and Physical Education, A
Hospitality Administration/Management, A
Industrial Mechanics and Maintenance Technology, A
Industrial Production Technologies/Technicians, A
Interior Design, A
Legal Assistant/Paralegal, A
Liberal Arts and Sciences Studies and Humanities, A
Mass Communication/Media Studies, A
Medical Office Management/Administration, A
Medical/Health Management and Clinical Assistant/Specialist, A
Music, A
Physical Therapist Assistant, A
Pre-Pharmacy Studies, A
Radiologic Technology/Science - Radiographer, A
Respiratory Care Therapy/Therapist, A
Secondary Education and Teaching, A
Special Education and Teaching, A
Surgical Technology/Technologist, A

HILLSDALE COLLEGE

Accounting, B
American/United States Studies/Civilization, B
Ancient/Classical Greek Language and Literature, B
Applied Mathematics, B
Art/Art Studies, General, B
Biochemistry, B
Biology/Biological Sciences, B
Chemistry, B
Christian Studies, B
Classics and Classical Languages, Literatures, and Linguistics, B
Communication Studies/Speech Communication and Rhetoric, B
Comparative Literature, B
Drama and Dramatics/Theatre Arts, B
Economics, B
English Language and Literature, B
European Studies/Civilization, B
Finance, B
French Language and Literature, B
German Language and Literature, B
Health and Physical Education, B
History, B
International Business/Trade/Commerce, B
Kinesiology and Exercise Science, B
Latin Language and Literature, B
Marketing/Marketing Management, B

Mathematics, B
Music, B
Philosophy, B
Physics, B
Political Science and Government, BMD
Psychology, B
Religion/Religious Studies, B
Sociology, B
Spanish Language and Literature, B
Sport and Fitness Administration/Management, B

HOPE COLLEGE

Accounting, B
Accounting and Business/Management, B
Art History, Criticism and Conservation, B
Art Teacher Education, B
Athletic Training and Sports Medicine, B
Biochemistry, Biophysics and Molecular Biology, B
Biology Teacher Education, B
Biology/Biological Sciences, B
Business Administration and Management, B
Business/Managerial Economics, B
Chemistry, B
Chemistry Teacher Education, B
Classics and Classical Languages, Literatures, and Linguistics, B
Communication Studies/Speech Communication and Rhetoric, B
Computer and Information Sciences, B
Dance, B
Drama and Dance Teacher Education, B
Drama and Dramatics/Theatre Arts, B
Economics, B
Education/Teaching of Individuals in Early Childhood Special Education Programs, B
Education/Teaching of Individuals with Emotional Disturbances, B
Education/Teaching of Individuals with Specific Learning Disabilities, B
Elementary Education and Teaching, B
Engineering, B
English Language and Literature, B
English/Language Arts Teacher Education, B
Fine/Studio Arts, B
French Language Teacher Education, B
French Language and Literature, B
Geology/Earth Science, B
German Language Teacher Education, B
German Language and Literature, B
History, B
History Teacher Education, B
International/Global Studies, B
Japanese Studies, B
Jazz/Jazz Studies, B
Kinesiology and Exercise Science, B
Mathematics, B
Mathematics Teacher Education, B
Multi-/Interdisciplinary Studies, B
Music, B
Music Performance, B
Music Teacher Education, B
Music Theory and Composition, B
Philosophy, B
Physical Education Teaching and Coaching, B
Physics, B
Physics Teacher Education, B
Piano and Organ, B
Political Science and Government, B
Psychology, B
Religion/Religious Studies, B
Science Teacher Education/General Science Teacher Education, B
Social Studies Teacher Education, B
Social Work, B
Sociology, B
Spanish Language Teacher Education, B
Spanish Language and Literature, B
Violin, Viola, Guitar and Other Stringed Instruments, B
Voice and Opera, B
Women's Studies, B

JACKSON COLLEGE

Accounting and Finance, A
Administrative Assistant and Secretarial Science, A

Airline/Commercial/Professional Pilot and Flight Crew, A
Automobile/Automotive Mechanics Technology/Technician, A
Business Administration and Management, A
Computer and Information Sciences and Support Services, A
Construction Trades, A
Corrections, A
Criminal Justice/Law Enforcement Administration, A
Data Processing and Data Processing Technology/Technician, A
Diagnostic Medical Sonography/Sonographer and Ultrasound Technician, A
Early Childhood Education and Teaching, A
Electrical, Electronic and Communications Engineering Technology/Technician, A
Emergency Medical Technology/Technician (EMT Paramedic), A
Executive Assistant/Executive Secretary, A
General Studies, A
Graphic Design, A
Heating, Air Conditioning and Refrigeration Technology/Technician, A
Liberal Arts and Sciences Studies and Humanities, A
Marketing/Marketing Management, A
Medical Insurance Specialist/Medical Biller, A
Medical Radiologic Technology/Science - Radiation Therapist, A
Medical Transcription/Transcriptionist, A
Medical/Clinical Assistant, A

KALAMAZOO COLLEGE

Ancient/Classical Greek Language and Literature, B
Art History, Criticism and Conservation, B
Art/Art Studies, General, B
Biology/Biological Sciences, B
Business/Commerce, B
Chemistry, B
Classical, Ancient Mediterranean and Near Eastern Studies and Archaeology, B
Computer and Information Sciences, B
Drama and Dramatics/Theatre Arts, B
East Asian Studies, B
Economics, B
English Language and Literature, B
French Language and Literature, B
German Language and Literature, B
History, B
Latin Language and Literature, B
Mathematics, B
Multi-/Interdisciplinary Studies, B
Music, B
Philosophy, B
Physics, B
Political Science and Government, B
Psychology, B
Religion/Religious Studies, B
Social Sciences, B
Spanish Language and Literature, B
Women's Studies, B

KALAMAZOO VALLEY COMMUNITY COLLEGE

Accounting Technology/Technician and Bookkeeping, A
Animation, Interactive Technology, Video Graphics and Special Effects, A
Automobile/Automotive Mechanics Technology/Technician, A
Business Administration and Management, A
CAD/CADD Drafting and/or Design Technology/Technician, A
Chemical Technology/Technician, A
Computer Programming/Programmer, A
Computer Systems Analysis/Analyst, A
Criminal Justice/Police Science, A
Dental Hygiene/Hygienist, A
E-Commerce/Electronic Commerce, A
Electrical, Electronic and Communications Engineering Technology/Technician, A
Elementary Education and Teaching, A
Emergency Medical Technology/Technician (EMT Paramedic), A
Engineering, A

Engineering Technology, A
Executive Assistant/Executive Secretary, A
Fire Science/Firefighting, A
General Studies, A
Graphic Design, A
Heating, Air Conditioning and Refrigeration Technology/Technician, A
Illustration, A
International/Global Studies, A
Liberal Arts and Sciences Studies and Humanities, A
Machine Tool Technology/Machinist, A
Marketing/Marketing Management, A
Mechanical Engineering/Mechanical Technology/Technician, A
Mechanics and Repairers, A
Respiratory Care Therapy/Therapist, A
Surgical Technology/Technologist, A
Web Page, Digital/Multimedia and Information Resources Design, A
Web/Multimedia Management and Webmaster, A
Welding Technology/Welder, A

KELLOGG COMMUNITY COLLEGE

Accounting, A
Accounting Technology/Technician and Bookkeeping, A
Administrative Assistant and Secretarial Science, A
Animation, Interactive Technology, Video Graphics and Special Effects, A
Business Administration and Management, A
CAD/CADD Drafting and/or Design Technology/Technician, A
Child Care and Support Services Management, A
Community Organization and Advocacy, A
Computer Engineering Technology/Technician, A
Computer Graphics, A
Computer Programming, Specific Applications, A
Computer Programming/Programmer, A
Computer Software and Media Applications, A
Computer Technology/Computer Systems Technology, A
Corrections, A
Criminal Justice/Law Enforcement Administration, A
Criminal Justice/Police Science, A
Criminal Justice/Safety Studies, A
Data Entry/Microcomputer Applications, A
Dental Hygiene/Hygienist, A
Drafting and Design Technology/Technician, A
Elementary Education and Teaching, A
Emergency Medical Technology/Technician (EMT Paramedic), A
Executive Assistant/Executive Secretary, A
General Studies, A
Heating, Air Conditioning, Ventilation and Refrigeration Maintenance Technology/Technician, A
Human Services, A
Industrial Technology/Technician, A
Legal Administrative Assistant/Secretary, A
Legal Assistant/Paralegal, A
Liberal Arts and Sciences Studies and Humanities, A
Machine Tool Technology/Machinist, A
Manufacturing Technology/Technician, A
Medical Administrative Assistant/Secretary, A
Medical Radiologic Technology/Science - Radiation Therapist, A
Physical Therapist Assistant, A
Pipefitting/Pipefitter and Sprinkler Fitter, A
Web Page, Digital/Multimedia and Information Resources Design, A
Welding Technology/Welder, A
Word Processing, A

KETTERING UNIVERSITY

Applied Mathematics, B
Biochemistry, B
Bioinformatics, B
Biology/Biological Sciences, B
Business Administration and Management, B
Business Administration, Management and Operations, B
Chemical Engineering, B
Chemistry, B
Computer Engineering, B
Computer Science, B

Electrical Engineering, M
Electrical, Electronics and Communications Engineering, B
Engineering Management, M
Engineering Physics, B
Industrial Engineering, B
Management, M
Manufacturing Engineering, M
Mechanical Engineering, BM
Physics, B

KEWEENAW BAY OJIBWA COMMUNITY COLLEGE

American Indian/Native American Studies, A
Early Childhood Education and Teaching, A
Environmental Sciences, A
Liberal Arts and Sciences Studies and Humanities, A

KIRTLAND COMMUNITY COLLEGE

Administrative Assistant and Secretarial Science, A
Art/Art Studies, General, A
Automobile/Automotive Mechanics Technology/Technician, A
Business Administration and Management, A
Cardiovascular Technology/Technologist, A
Cosmetology/Cosmetologist, A
Criminal Justice/Law Enforcement Administration, A
Criminal Justice/Police Science, A
Electrical, Electronic and Communications Engineering Technology/Technician, A
Electromechanical Technology/Electromechanical Engineering Technology, A
Emergency Medical Technology/Technician (EMT Paramedic), A
General Studies, A
Graphic Design, A
Health Information/Medical Records Technology/Technician, A
Heating, Air Conditioning, Ventilation and Refrigeration Maintenance Technology/Technician, A
Information Science/Studies, A
Liberal Arts and Sciences Studies and Humanities, A
Management Information Systems and Services, A
Medical Administrative Assistant/Secretary, A
Medical/Clinical Assistant, A
Pharmacy Technician/Assistant, A
Robotics Technology/Technician, A
Surgical Technology/Technologist, A
Welding Technology/Welder, A

KUYPER COLLEGE

Accounting, B
Administrative Assistant and Secretarial Science, A
Bible/Biblical Studies, AB
Broadcast Journalism, B
Business Administration and Management, B
Child Development, AB
Communication Studies/Speech Communication and Rhetoric, B
Computer and Information Sciences, B
Divinity/Ministry (BD, MDiv.), B
Drama and Dramatics/Theatre Arts, B
Elementary Education and Teaching, B
International Business/Trade/Commerce, B
Kinesiology and Exercise Science, B
Liberal Arts and Sciences Studies and Humanities, A
Mass Communication/Media Studies, B
Missions/Missionary Studies and Missiology, B
Pastoral Studies/Counseling, B
Pre-Theology/Pre-Ministerial Studies, B
Religious Education, AB
Religious/Sacred Music, B
Secondary Education and Teaching, B
Social Work, B
Theology/Theological Studies, B
Youth Ministry, B

LAKE MICHIGAN COLLEGE

Accounting, A
Administrative Assistant and Secretarial Science, A
Agricultural and Horticultural Plant Breeding, A
Applied Horticulture/Horticultural Operations, A

Art/Art Studies, General, A
Biology/Biological Sciences, A
Business Administration and Management, A
Chemistry, A
Computer and Information Sciences, A
Corrections, A
Criminal Justice/Law Enforcement Administration, A
Dental Assisting/Assistant, A
Diagnostic Medical Sonography/Sonographer and Ultrasound Technician, A
Drafting and Design Technology/Technician, A
Drama and Dramatics/Theatre Arts, A
Early Childhood Education and Teaching, A
Elementary Education and Teaching, A
Emergency Medical Technology/Technician (EMT Paramedic), A
Energy Management and Systems Technology/Technician, A
English Language and Literature, A
Environmental Sciences, A
Foreign Languages and Literatures, A
Forensic Science and Technology, A
General Studies, A
Geography, A
Geology/Earth Science, A
Graphic Design, A
Health and Physical Education, A
Health/Medical Preparatory Programs, A
History, A
Hospitality Administration/Management, A
Humanities/Humanistic Studies, A
Industrial Technology/Technician, A
Landscaping and Groundskeeping, A
Legal Administrative Assistant/Secretary, A
Liberal Arts and Sciences Studies and Humanities, A
Machine Tool Technology/Machinist, A
Manufacturing Engineering, A
Marketing/Marketing Management, A
Mathematics, A
Medical Administrative Assistant/Secretary, A
Medical Radiologic Technology/Science - Radiation Therapist, A
Music, A
Philosophy, A
Physical Sciences, A
Physics, A
Political Science and Government, A
Pre-Dentistry Studies, A
Pre-Law Studies, A
Pre-Medicine/Pre-Medical Studies, A
Pre-Pharmacy Studies, A
Pre-Veterinary Studies, A
Precision Production, A
Psychology, A
Radiologic Technology/Science - Radiographer, A
Secondary Education and Teaching, A
Sociology, A
Turf and Turfgrass Management, A

LAKE SUPERIOR STATE UNIVERSITY

Accounting, B
Athletic Training and Sports Medicine, B
Biochemistry, AB
Biology/Biological Sciences, B
Business Administration and Management, AB
Business/Managerial Economics, B
Chemistry, AB
Clinical Laboratory Science/Medical Technology/Technologist, AB
Communication, Journalism and Related Programs, B
Comparative Literature, B
Computer Engineering, B
Computer Engineering Technology/Technician, B
Computer Science, AB
Conservation Biology, B
Corrections, AB
Criminal Justice/Law Enforcement Administration, AB
Criminal Justice/Police Science, AB
Criminal Justice/Safety Studies, AB
Early Childhood Education and Teaching, AB
Education, B
Electrical and Electronic Engineering Technologies/Technicians, AB

Electrical, Electronic and Communications Engineering Technology/Technician, AB
Electrical, Electronics and Communications Engineering, B
Elementary Education and Teaching, B
Engineering, AB
Engineering Technology, A
Engineering/Industrial Management, B
English Language and Literature, A
Entrepreneurship/Entrepreneurial Studies, B
Environmental Studies, B
Finance, B
Fire Science/Firefighting, AB
Fishing and Fisheries Sciences and Management, B
Geology/Earth Science, B
History, B
Hydrology and Water Resources Science, A
Industrial Technology/Technician, B
International Business/Trade/Commerce, B
Junior High/Intermediate/Middle School Education and Teaching, B
Kinesiology and Exercise Science, B
Liberal Arts and Sciences Studies and Humanities, AB
Management Information Systems and Services, B
Marketing/Marketing Management, B
Mathematics, B
Mathematics and Computer Science, B
Mechanical Engineering, B
Mechanical Engineering/Mechanical Technology/Technician, AB
Natural Resources Management/Development and Policy, A
Parks, Recreation and Leisure Facilities Management, B
Parks, Recreation, Leisure and Fitness Studies, B
Physical Sciences, B
Political Science and Government, B
Pre-Dentistry Studies, B
Pre-Law Studies, B
Psychiatric/Mental Health Services Technician, A
Psychology, B
Robotics Technology/Technician, B
Secondary Education and Teaching, B
Security and Protective Services, AB
Social Sciences, B
Sociology, B
Spanish Language and Literature, B
Sport and Fitness Administration/Management, B
Teacher Education, Multiple Levels, B
Water Quality and Wastewater Treatment Management and Recycling Technology/Technician, A
Wildlife and Wildlands Science and Management, B

LANSING COMMUNITY COLLEGE

Accounting Technology/Technician and Bookkeeping, A
Accounting and Related Services, A
Administrative Assistant and Secretarial Science, A
African-American/Black Studies, A
Agricultural Business and Management, A
Aircraft Powerplant Technology/Technician, A
Airframe Mechanics and Aircraft Maintenance Technology/Technician, A
Airline/Commercial/Professional Pilot and Flight Crew, A
American/United States Studies/Civilization, A
Animation, Interactive Technology, Video Graphics and Special Effects, A
Anthropology, A
Architectural Engineering Technology/Technician, A
Architectural Technology/Technician, A
Art History, Criticism and Conservation, A
Art/Art Studies, General, A
Autobody/Collision and Repair Technology/Technician, A
Automobile/Automotive Mechanics Technology/Technician, A
Avionics Maintenance Technology/Technician, A
Banking and Financial Support Services, A
BioTechnology, A
Biology/Biological Sciences, A
Business Administration and Management, A
Business/Commerce, A
Carpentry/Carpenter, A
Chemical Technology/Technician, A

Chemistry, A
Child Care Provider/Assistant, A
Cinematography and Film/Video Production, A
Civil Engineering Technology/Technician, A
Communication Studies/Speech Communication and Rhetoric, A
Community Organization and Advocacy, A
Computer Programming, Specific Applications, A
Computer Systems Networking and Telecommunications, A
Computer Technology/Computer Systems Technology, A
Computer and Information Sciences, A
Construction Management, A
Construction/Heavy Equipment/Earthmoving Equipment Operation, A
Corrections, A
Criminal Justice/Police Science, A
Customer Service Support/Call Center/Teleservice Operation, A
Data Modeling/Warehousing and Database Administration, A
Dental Hygiene/Hygienist, A
Diagnostic Medical Sonography/Sonographer and Ultrasound Technician, A
Drama and Dramatics/Theatre Arts, A
E-Commerce/Electronic Commerce, A
Economics, A
Electrical and Power Transmission Installation/Installer, A
Electrician, A
Electromechanical Technology/Electromechanical Engineering Technology, A
Elementary Education and Teaching, A
Emergency Medical Technology/Technician (EMT Paramedic), A
Energy Management and Systems Technology/Technician, A
Engineering, A
Engineering Physics, A
English Language and Literature, A
Environmental Engineering Technology/Environmental Technology, A
Fashion Merchandising, A
Fine/Studio Arts, A
Fire Science/Firefighting, A
Foreign Languages and Literatures, A
French Language and Literature, A
Geography, A
Germanic Languages, Literatures, and Linguistics, A
Graphic Design, A
Health and Physical Education, A
Heating, Air Conditioning, Ventilation and Refrigeration Maintenance Technology/Technician, A
Higher Education/Higher Education Administration, A
Histologic Technician, A
History, A
Hotel/Motel Administration/Management, A
Human Resources Management/Personnel Administration, A
Humanities/Humanistic Studies, A
Industrial Production Technologies/Technicians, A
Interior Design, A
International Business/Trade/Commerce, A
International Relations and Affairs, A
Japanese Language and Literature, A
Juvenile Corrections, A
Legal Assistant/Paralegal, A
Liberal Arts and Sciences Studies and Humanities, A
Machine Tool Technology/Machinist, A
Management Information Systems and Services, A
Mathematics, A
Mechanical Drafting and Mechanical Drafting CAD/CADD, A
Music, A
Music Performance, A
Office Management and Supervision, A
Philosophy, A
Photography, A
Political Science and Government, A
Pre-Medicine/Pre-Medical Studies, A
Psychology, A
Radio and Television Broadcasting Technology/Technician, A

Radiologic Technology/Science - Radiographer, A
Real Estate, A
Religion/Religious Studies, A
Sales, Distribution and Marketing Operations, A
Secondary Education and Teaching, A
Selling Skills and Sales Operations, A
Sign Language Interpretation and Translation, A
Social Sciences, A
Sociology, A
Spanish Language and Literature, A
Surgical Technology/Technologist, A
Survey Technology/Surveying, A
Teacher Assistant/Aide, A
Technical Theatre/Theatre Design and Technology, A
Tourism and Travel Services Management, A
Veterinary/Animal Health Technology/Technician and Veterinary Assistant, A
Web Page, Digital/Multimedia and Information Resources Design, A
Welding Technology/Welder, A

LAWRENCE TECHNOLOGICAL UNIVERSITY

Architectural Engineering, BM
Architectural History and Criticism, B
Architectural Technology/Technician, B
Architecture, BM
Automotive Engineering Technology/Technician, M
Biochemistry, B
Biomedical Technology/Technician, B
Biomedical/Medical Engineering, B
Business Administration and Management, B
Business Administration, Management and Operations, MD
Chemical Technology/Technician, A
Chemistry, B
Civil Engineering, BMD
Communication Studies/Speech Communication and Rhetoric, B
Communications Technology/Technician, B
Computer Engineering, BM
Computer Science, BM
Construction Engineering Technology/Technician, A
Construction Engineering and Management, M
Construction Management, B
Design and Visual Communications, B
Educational Media/Instructional Technology, M
Electrical Engineering, M
Electrical and Electronic Engineering Technologies/Technicians, A
Electrical, Electronic and Communications Engineering Technology/Technician, A
Electrical, Electronics and Communications Engineering, B
Engineering Management, M
Engineering Technology, B
Engineering and Applied Sciences, MD
Engineering/Industrial Management, B
English Language and Literature, B
Environmental Design/Architecture, B
General Studies, A
Graphic Design, B
Humanities/Humanistic Studies, B
Illustration, B
Industrial Design, B
Industrial Engineering, B
Industrial Technology/Technician, B
Industrial/Management Engineering, M
Information Technology, B
Interior Architecture, B
Interior Design, M
International Business/Trade/Commerce, B
Management, D
Management Information Systems and Services, M
Manufacturing Engineering, MD
Manufacturing Technology/Technician, A
Mathematics, B
Mathematics and Computer Science, B
Mechanical Engineering, BMD
Mechanical Engineering/Mechanical Technology/Technician, A
Molecular Biology, B
Physics, B
Psychology, B
Radio and Television, A

Radio, Television, and Digital Communication, A
Science Teacher Education/General Science Teacher Education, M
Technical Communication, M
Urban Design, M

MACOMB COMMUNITY COLLEGE

Accounting, A
Administrative Assistant and Secretarial Science, A
Agriculture, A
Architectural Drafting and Architectural CAD/CADD, A
Automobile/Automotive Mechanics Technology/Technician, A
Automotive Engineering Technology/Technician, A
Biology/Biological Sciences, A
Business Administration and Management, A
Business/Commerce, A
Business/Office Automation/Technology/Data Entry, A
Cabinetmaking and Millwork/Millwright, A
Chemistry, A
Child Care and Support Services Management, A
Civil Engineering Technology/Technician, A
Commercial and Advertising Art, A
Communication Studies/Speech Communication and Rhetoric, A
Computer Programming, Specific Applications, A
Computer Programming/Programmer, A
Construction Engineering Technology/Technician, A
Criminal Justice/Law Enforcement Administration, A
Criminal Justice/Police Science, A
Culinary Arts/Chef Training, A
Drafting and Design Technology/Technician, A
Drafting/Design Engineering Technologies/Technicians, A
Electrical, Electronic and Communications Engineering Technology/Technician, A
Electrical/Electronics Equipment Installation and Repair, A
Electromechanical Technology/Electromechanical Engineering Technology, A
Emergency Medical Technology/Technician (EMT Paramedic), A
Energy Management and Systems Technology/Technician, A
Engineering, A
Finance, A
Fire Protection and Safety Technology/Technician, A
Forensic Science and Technology, A
General Studies, A
Graphic and Printing Equipment Operator Production, A
Heating, Air Conditioning and Refrigeration Technology/Technician, A
Heating, Air Conditioning, Ventilation and Refrigeration Maintenance Technology/Technician, A
Industrial Mechanics and Maintenance Technology, A
Industrial Technology/Technician, A
International/Global Studies, A
Law and Legal Studies, A
Legal Assistant/Paralegal, A
Liberal Arts and Sciences Studies and Humanities, A
Machine Tool Technology/Machinist, A
Manufacturing Technology/Technician, A
Marketing/Marketing Management, A
Mathematics, A
Mechanic and Repair Technologies/Technicians, A
Mechanical Drafting and Mechanical Drafting CAD/CADD, A
Mechanical Engineering/Mechanical Technology/Technician, A
Medical/Clinical Assistant, A
Mental Health Counseling/Counselor, A
Metallurgical Technology/Technician, A
Music Performance, A
Occupational Therapist Assistant, A
Operations Management and Supervision, A
Physical Therapist Assistant, A
Plastics Engineering Technology/Technician, A
Plumbing Technology/Plumber, A
Quality Control Technology/Technician, A
Quality Control and Safety Technologies/Technicians, A

Respiratory Care Therapy/Therapist, A
Robotics Technology/Technician, A
Sheet Metal Technology/Sheetworking, A
Surgical Technology/Technologist, A
Survey Technology/Surveying, A
Tool and Die Technology/Technician, A
Veterinary/Animal Health Technology/Technician and Veterinary Assistant, A
Welding Technology/Welder, A

MADONNA UNIVERSITY

Accounting, B
Adult Development and Aging, AB
American Sign Language (ASL), AB
Biochemistry, B
Biology Teacher Education, B
Biology/Biological Sciences, B
Biomedical Sciences, B
Business Administration and Management, AB
Business Administration, Management and Operations, M
Chemistry, B
Chemistry Teacher Education, B
Child Development, AB
Clinical Psychology, M
Communication, Journalism and Related Programs, AB
Computer Science, AB
Computer and Information Sciences, A
Criminal Justice/Safety Studies, AB
Criminology, M
Design and Visual Communications, B
Dietetics and Clinical Nutrition Services, B
Early Childhood Education and Teaching, B
Education, M
Educational Leadership and Administration, M
Elementary Education and Teaching, B
Engineering, B
English Language and Literature, AB
English as a Second Language, M
English/Language Arts Teacher Education, B
Environmental Sciences, AB
Family and Consumer Sciences/Human Sciences, B
Fine Arts and Art Studies, AB
Fire Science/Firefighting, AB
Foods, Nutrition, and Wellness Studies, AB
Forensic Science and Technology, B
General Studies, B
Gerontology, AB
Graphic Design, AB
Health Services Administration, M
Health Services/Allied Health/Health Sciences, B
Health/Health Care Administration/Management, B
Health/Medical Preparatory Programs, B
History, B
Hospice Nursing, M
Hospitality Administration/Management, B
Human Resources Management/Personnel Administration, B
International Business/Trade/Commerce, BM
Journalism, AB
Legal Assistant/Paralegal, AB
Liberal Studies, M
Management Information Systems and Services, B
Marketing/Marketing Management, AB
Mathematics, B
Mathematics Teacher Education, B
Music, B
Music Performance, B
Music Teacher Education, B
Music Theory and Composition, B
Natural Sciences, AB
Nursing, M
Nursing - Adult, M
Nursing Administration, M
Pastoral Counseling and Specialized Ministries, B
Pastoral Studies/Counseling, M
Physical Education Teaching and Coaching, B
Physics Teacher Education, B
Piano and Organ, B
Pre-Dentistry Studies, B
Pre-Law Studies, B
Pre-Medicine/Pre-Medical Studies, B
Pre-Nursing Studies, B
Pre-Pharmacy Studies, A
Pre-Veterinary Studies, B

Psychology, BM
Quality Control and Safety
  Technologies/Technicians, AB
Quality Management, M
Radio, Television, and Digital Communication, AB
Reading Teacher Education, M
Religion/Religious Studies, AB
Religious/Sacred Music, B
Science Teacher Education/General Science
  Teacher Education, B
Science Technologies/Technicians, AB
Security and Protective Services, B
Sign Language Interpretation and Translation, B
Social Studies Teacher Education, B
Social Work, B
Sociology, B
Spanish Language and Literature, B
Special Education and Teaching, M
Sport and Fitness Administration/Management, B
Teacher Education and Professional Develop-
  ment, Specific Subject Areas, B
Theology and Religious Vocations, M
Voice and Opera, B

MARYGROVE COLLEGE

Accounting, A
Art Therapy/Therapist, B
Art/Art Studies, General, B
Biological and Physical Sciences, B
Biology/Biological Sciences, B
Business Administration and Management, B
Business/Commerce, AB
Chemistry, B
Computer and Information Sciences, B
Corrections, A
Dance, B
Design and Applied Arts, B
Education, BM
Education/Teaching of Individuals with Emotional
  Disturbances, B
Educational Leadership and Administration, M
Educational Media/Instructional Technology, M
Elementary Education and Teaching, M
English, M
English Language and Literature, B
Environmental Biology, B
Environmental Studies, B
Fine/Studio Arts, B
General Studies, B
History, B
Human Resources Management and Services, M
International Business/Trade/Commerce, B
Kindergarten/PreSchool Education and Teach-
  ing, AB
Legal and Justice Studies, M
Liberal Arts and Sciences Studies and Humani-
  ties, A
Marketing/Marketing Management, B
Mathematics, B
Music, B
Music Performance, B
Political Science and Government, B
Psychology, B
Reading Teacher Education, M
Religion/Religious Studies, B
Secondary Education and Teaching, M
Social Sciences, B
Social Work, B
Translation and Interpretation, O
Urban Education and Leadership, M

MICHIGAN JEWISH INSTITUTE

Computer and Information Sciences, AB
Information Science/Studies, AB
Jewish/Judaic Studies, AB
Talmudic Studies, A

MICHIGAN STATE UNIVERSITY

Accounting, BMD
Acting, B
Actuarial Science, B
Adult and Continuing Education and Teaching, MD
Advertising, B
Advertising and Public Relations, MD
African Studies, MD
African-American Studies, MD

Agricultural Business and Management, B
Agricultural Economics, MD
Agricultural Sciences, MD
Agricultural/Biological Engineering and Bioengineer-
  ing, B
Agronomy and Soil Sciences, MD
Allopathic Medicine, D
American/United States Studies/Civilization, MD
Animal Sciences, BMD
Anthropology, BMD
Apparel and Textile Manufacture, B
Apparel and Textiles, B
Applied Mathematics, MD
Applied Statistics, M
Arabic Language and Literature, B
Art History, Criticism and Conservation, B
Art Teacher Education, B
Art/Art Studies, General, B
Astronomy, MD
Astrophysics, BM
Athletic Training and Sports Medicine, B
Biochemistry, BMD
Biochemistry, Biophysics and Molecular Biology, B
Biological and Biomedical Sciences, MD
Biological and Physical Sciences, B
Biology Teacher Education, B
Biology/Biological Sciences, B
Biosystems Engineering, MD
Botany/Plant Biology, B
Business Administration and Management, B
Business Administration, Management and Opera-
  tions, MD
Cartography, B
Cell Biology and Anatomy, MD
Chemical Engineering, BMD
Chemical Physics, BD
Chemistry, BMD
Chemistry Teacher Education, B
Child Development, BM
Child and Family Studies, MD
Chinese Language and Literature, B
City/Urban, Community and Regional Planning, B
Civil Engineering, BMD
Clinical Laboratory Science/Medical
  Technology/Technologist, B
Clinical Laboratory Sciences, M
Communication Disorders, MD
Communication Studies/Speech Communication
  and Rhetoric, B
Communication and Media Studies, MD
Composition, MD
Computational Mathematics, B
Computer Art and Design, M
Computer Engineering, B
Computer Science, MD
Computer Teacher Education, B
Computer and Information Sciences, B
Construction Engineering Technology/Technician, B
Construction Management, BMD
Counselor Education/School Counseling and Guid-
  ance Services, MD
Criminal Justice/Law Enforcement Administration, B
Criminal Justice/Safety Studies, B
Criminology, MD
Curriculum and Instruction, MDO
Dietetics/Dieticians, B
Drama and Dramatics/Theatre Arts, B
Early Childhood Education and Teaching, B
Ecology, D
Economics, BMD
Education, BMDO
Education/Teaching of Individuals with Hearing Im-
  pairments, Including Deafness, B
Education/Teaching of Individuals with Specific
  Learning Disabilities, B
Educational Administration and Supervision, MDO
Educational Measurement and Evaluation, D
Educational Media/Instructional Technology, MD
Educational Policy, D
Educational Psychology, D
Electrical Engineering, MD
Electrical, Electronics and Communications Engi-
  neering, B
Elementary Education and Teaching, B
Engineering, B
Engineering and Applied Sciences, MD

English, MD
English Language and Literature, B
English as a Second Language, M
Entomology, BMD
Environmental Biology, B
Environmental Design/Architecture, M
Environmental Engineering
  Technology/Environmental Technology, MD
Environmental Sciences, BMD
Environmental Studies, B
Epidemiology, MD
Evolutionary Biology, D
Family and Community Services, B
Fashion/Apparel Design, B
Finance, B
Finance and Banking, MD
Fine Arts and Art Studies, M
Fish, Game and Wildlife Management, MD
Fishing and Fisheries Sciences and Management, B
Food Science, B
Food Science and Technology, MD
Food Services Management, M
Foreign Language Teacher Education, D
Forensic Science and Technology, M
Forestry, BMD
French Language Teacher Education, B
French Language and Literature, BMD
Game Design and Development, M
Genetics, MD
Geography, BMD
Geography Teacher Education, B
Geology/Earth Science, B
Geosciences, MD
German Language Teacher Education, B
German Language and Literature, BMD
Graphic Design, B
Health Communication, M
Health Teacher Education, B
Higher Education/Higher Education Administra-
  tion, MD
Hispanic Studies, D
Hispanic and Latin American Languages, M
History, BMD
History Teacher Education, B
Horticultural Science, BMD
Hospitality Administration/Management, BM
Human Resources Management and Services, MD
Human Resources Management/Personnel Adminis-
  tration, B
Humanities/Humanistic Studies, M
Industrial and Labor Relations, MD
Information Resources Management/CIO Training, B
Interior Design, BM
International Relations and Affairs, B
International/Global Studies, B
Japanese Language and Literature, B
Jazz/Jazz Studies, B
Journalism, BM
Junior High/Intermediate/Middle School Education
  and Teaching, B
Kindergarten/PreSchool Education and Teaching, B
Kinesiology and Exercise Science, B
Kinesiology and Movement Studies, MD
Landscape Architecture, B
Latin American Studies, D
Law Enforcement, M
Linguistics, BMD
Logistics and Materials Management, BMD
Management Information Systems and Ser-
  vices, MD
Management Strategy and Policy, M
Manufacturing Engineering, MD
Marketing, MD
Marketing Research, M
Marketing/Marketing Management, B
Marriage and Family Therapy/Counseling, M
Mass Communication/Media Studies, B
Materials Engineering, BMD
Materials Sciences, MD
Mathematics, BMD
Mathematics Teacher Education, BMD
Mechanical Engineering, BMD
Mechanics, MD
Media Studies, MD
Microbiology, BMD
Molecular Biology, MD

Molecular Genetics, BD
Multi-/Interdisciplinary Studies, B
Music, BMD
Music Pedagogy, B
Music Performance, B
Music Teacher Education, BM
Music Theory and Composition, BM
Music Therapy/Therapist, M
Musicology and Ethnomusicology, M
Natural Resource Economics, B
Natural Resources Management/Development and
  Policy, MD
Neuroscience, MD
Nursing, MD
Nutritional Sciences, BMD
Osteopathic Medicine, D
Parks, Recreation, Leisure and Fitness Studies, B
Pathobiology, MD
Pathology/Experimental Pathology, MD
Performance, MD
Pharmacology, MD
Philosophy, BMD
Physical Education Teaching and Coaching, B
Physical Sciences, B
Physics, BMD
Physics Teacher Education, B
Physiology, BMD
Plant Biology, MD
Plant Pathology/Phytopathology, MD
Plant Sciences, MD
Political Science and Government, BMD
Portuguese Language and Literature, MD
Pre-Law Studies, B
Pre-Medicine/Pre-Medical Studies, B
Pre-Veterinary Studies, B
Psychology, BMD
Public Health, M
Public Policy Analysis, B
Reading Teacher Education, BM
Recreation and Park Management, MD
Rehabilitation Counseling, MD
Religion/Religious Studies, B
Rhetoric, MD
Romance Languages, Literatures, and Linguis-
  tics, MD
Russian Language and Literature, B
School Psychology, MDO
Science Teacher Education/General Science
  Teacher Education, BM
Secondary Education and Teaching, B
Social Science Teacher Education, B
Social Sciences, B
Social Studies Teacher Education, BM
Social Work, BMD
Sociology, BMD
Soil Science and Agronomy, B
Spanish Language Teacher Education, B
Spanish Language and Literature, BMD
Special Education and Teaching, BMD
Statistics, BMD
Structural Biology, D
Supply Chain Management, MD
Systematic Biology/Biological Systematics, D
Taxation, M
Telecommunications, M
Textile Science, B
Theater, M
Toxicology, MD
Urban and Regional Planning, M
Veterinary Medicine, D
Veterinary Sciences, MD
Veterinary/Animal Health Technology/Technician and
  Veterinary Assistant, B
Wildlife and Wildlands Science and Management, B
Women's Studies, B
Writing, MD
Zoology/Animal Biology, BMD

MICHIGAN TECHNOLOGICAL UNIVERSITY

Accounting, BM
Anthropology, B
Archeology, MD
Atmospheric Sciences and Meteorology, D
Automotive Engineering Technology/Technician, O
Biochemistry, D

Biochemistry, Biophysics and Molecular Biology, B
Bioinformatics, B
Biological and Biomedical Sciences, MD
Biology/Biological Sciences, B
Biomedical Engineering, MD
Biomedical/Medical Engineering, B
Business Administration and Management, B
Business Administration, Management and Opera-
  tions, M
Chemical Engineering, BMD
Chemistry, BMD
Civil Engineering, BMD
Clinical Laboratory Science/Medical
  Technology/Technologist, B
Cognitive Sciences, MD
Computational Sciences, D
Computer Engineering, BMDO
Computer Science, BMD
Computer Software Engineering, B
Construction Management, B
Ecology, M
Economics, B
Electrical Engineering, MDO
Electrical, Electronic and Communications Engineer-
  ing Technology/Technician, B
Electrical, Electronics and Communications Engi-
  neering, B
Energy Management and Policy, MD
Engineering, B
Engineering Physics, D
Engineering Technology, A
Engineering and Applied Sciences, MDO
Engineering/Industrial Management, B
English Language and Literature, B
Environmental Engineering
  Technology/Environmental Technology, MD
Environmental Policy, MD
Environmental Sciences, B
Environmental/Environmental Health Engineering, B
Ergonomics and Human Factors, D
Finance, B
Forestry, BMD
Geographic Information Systems, M
Geological Engineering, MD
Geological/Geophysical Engineering, B
Geology/Earth Science, BMD
Geophysics and Seismology, BMD
Historic Preservation and Conservation, D
History, B
Humanities/Humanistic Studies, A
Interdisciplinary Studies, MDO
Kinesiology and Exercise Science, B
Kinesiology and Movement Studies, M
Liberal Arts and Sciences Studies and Humani-
  ties, B
Management Information Systems and Services, B
Marketing/Marketing Management, B
Materials Engineering, BMD
Mathematics, BMD
Mechanical Engineering, BMDO
Mechanical Engineering/Mechanical
  Technology/Technician, B
Mechanics, MDO
Medicinal and Pharmaceutical Chemistry, B
Metallurgical Engineering, MD
Mineral Economics, M
Mineral/Mining Engineering, MD
Molecular Biology, D
Natural Resources Management/Development and
  Policy, B
Physics, BMD
Plant Molecular Biology, MD
Psychology, B
Recording Arts Technology/Technician, B
Rhetoric, MD
Science Teacher Education/General Science
  Teacher Education, M
Social Sciences, B
Sport and Fitness Administration/Management, B
Statistics, B
Surveying Engineering, B
System Administration/Administrator, B
Technical Communication, MD
Technical Theatre/Theatre Design and Technol-
  ogy, B
Visual and Performing Arts, B

Wildlife and Wildlands Science and Management, B

MID MICHIGAN COMMUNITY COLLEGE

Accounting, A
Administrative Assistant and Secretarial Science, A
Art/Art Studies, General, A
Automobile/Automotive Mechanics
  Technology/Technician, A
Biological and Physical Sciences, A
Biology/Biological Sciences, A
Business Administration and Management, A
Chemistry, A
Child Care Provider/Assistant, A
Child Development, A
Corrections, A
Criminal Justice/Law Enforcement Administration, A
Drafting and Design Technology/Technician, A
Drama and Dramatics/Theatre Arts, A
Elementary Education and Teaching, A
Fire Science/Firefighting, A
General Studies, A
Heating, Air Conditioning, Ventilation and Refrigera-
  tion Maintenance Technology/Technician, A
Industrial Radiologic Technology/Technician, A
Information Science/Studies, A
Legal Administrative Assistant/Secretary, A
Liberal Arts and Sciences Studies and Humani-
  ties, A
Machine Tool Technology/Machinist, A
Marketing/Marketing Management, A
Mathematics, A
Medical Administrative Assistant/Secretary, A
Medical Transcription/Transcriptionist, A
Medical/Clinical Assistant, A
Pharmacy, A
Physical Therapy/Therapist, A
Psychology, A
Secondary Education and Teaching, A
Sociology, A
Teacher Education, Multiple Levels, A

MONROE COUNTY COMMUNITY COLLEGE

Accounting, A
Administrative Assistant and Secretarial Science, A
Architectural Engineering Technology/Technician, A
Art/Art Studies, General, A
Biology/Biological Sciences, A
Business Administration and Management, A
Child Development, A
Clinical Laboratory Science/Medical
  Technology/Technologist, A
Computer Engineering Technology/Technician, A
Computer Graphics, A
Computer Programming, Specific Applications, A
Computer and Information Sciences, A
Criminal Justice/Police Science, A
Criminal Justice/Safety Studies, A
Culinary Arts/Chef Training, A
Data Processing and Data Processing
  Technology/Technician, A
Drafting and Design Technology/Technician, A
Electrical, Electronic and Communications Engineer-
  ing Technology/Technician, A
Elementary Education and Teaching, A
English Language and Literature, A
Finance, A
Funeral Service and Mortuary Science, A
Industrial Technology/Technician, A
Information Technology, A
Journalism, A
Legal Administrative Assistant/Secretary, A
Liberal Arts and Sciences Studies and Humani-
  ties, A
Marketing/Marketing Management, A
Mass Communication/Media Studies, A
Mathematics, A
Medical Administrative Assistant/Secretary, A
Physical Therapy/Therapist, A
Psychology, A
Respiratory Care Therapy/Therapist, A
Social Work, A
Web Page, Digital/Multimedia and Information Re-
  sources Design, A
Web/Multimedia Management and Webmaster, A
Welding Technology/Welder, A

Word Processing, A

MONTCALM COMMUNITY COLLEGE

Accounting, A
Administrative Assistant and Secretarial Science, A
Automobile/Automotive Mechanics
 Technology/Technician, A
Business Administration and Management, A
Child Care Provider/Assistant, A
Child Care and Support Services Management, A
Computer Installation and Repair
 Technology/Technician, A
Corrections, A
Cosmetology/Cosmetologist, A
Criminal Justice/Law Enforcement Administration, A
Data Processing and Data Processing
 Technology/Technician, A
Drafting and Design Technology/Technician, A
Electrical, Electronic and Communications Engineer-
 ing Technology/Technician, A
Emergency Medical Technology/Technician (EMT
 Paramedic), A
Entrepreneurship/Entrepreneurial Studies, A
General Studies, A
Industrial Engineering, A
Industrial Technology/Technician, A
Liberal Arts and Sciences Studies and Humani-
 ties, A
Medical Administrative Assistant/Secretary, A
Teacher Assistant/Aide, A
Welding Technology/Welder, A

MOTT COMMUNITY COLLEGE

Accounting Technology/Technician and Bookkeep-
 ing, A
Architectural Engineering Technology/Technician, A
Automobile/Automotive Mechanics
 Technology/Technician, A
Baking and Pastry Arts/Baker/Pastry Chef, A
Biology/Biological Sciences, A
Business Administration and Management, A
Business/Commerce, A
Child Care Provider/Assistant, A
Cinematography and Film/Video Production, A
Communications Technology/Technician, A
Community Health Services/Liaison/Counseling, A
Computer Programming, Specific Applications, A
Computer Programming/Programmer, A
Computer Systems Networking and Telecommunica-
 tions, A
Corrections, A
Criminal Justice/Police Science, A
Culinary Arts/Chef Training, A
Dental Assisting/Assistant, A
Dental Hygiene/Hygienist, A
Drafting and Design Technology/Technician, A
Early Childhood Education and Teaching, A
Electrical, Electronic and Communications Engineer-
 ing Technology/Technician, A
Emergency Medical Technology/Technician (EMT
 Paramedic), A
Engineering Technologies/Technicians, A
Entrepreneurship/Entrepreneurial Studies, A
Fire Protection and Safety Technology/Technician, A
Foodservice Systems
 Administration/Management, A
General Studies, A
Graphic Design, A
Heating, Air Conditioning and Refrigeration
 Technology/Technician, A
Histologic Technician, A
Liberal Arts and Sciences Studies and Humani-
 ties, A
Marketing/Marketing Management, A
Mechanical Engineering/Mechanical
 Technology/Technician, A
Medical Radiologic Technology/Science - Radiation
 Therapist, A
Occupational Therapist Assistant, A
Photography, A
Physical Therapist Assistant, A
Precision Production, A
Respiratory Care Therapy/Therapist, A
Salon/Beauty Salon Management/Manager, A
Sign Language Interpretation and Translation, A

Visual and Performing Arts, A

MUSKEGON COMMUNITY COLLEGE

Accounting, A
Administrative Assistant and Secretarial Science, A
Advertising, A
Anthropology, A
Applied Mathematics, A
Art History, Criticism and Conservation, A
Art Teacher Education, A
Art/Art Studies, General, A
Automobile/Automotive Mechanics
 Technology/Technician, A
Biology Technician/BioTechnology Laboratory Tech-
 nician, A
Biomedical Technology/Technician, A
Business Administration and Management, A
Business Machine Repairer, A
Chemical Engineering, A
Child Development, A
Commercial and Advertising Art, A
Criminal Justice/Law Enforcement Administration, A
Data Processing and Data Processing
 Technology/Technician, A
Design and Applied Arts, A
Drafting and Design Technology/Technician, A
Economics, A
Education, A
Electrical, Electronic and Communications Engineer-
 ing Technology/Technician, A
Electromechanical Technology/Electromechanical
 Engineering Technology, A
Elementary Education and Teaching, A
Engineering Technology, A
Finance, A
Hospitality Administration/Management, A
Hospitality and Recreation Marketing Operations, A
Hotel/Motel Administration/Management, A
Industrial Technology/Technician, A
Information Science/Studies, A
Legal Administrative Assistant/Secretary, A
Liberal Arts and Sciences Studies and Humani-
 ties, A
Machine Tool Technology/Machinist, A
Marketing/Marketing Management, A
Medical Administrative Assistant/Secretary, A
Parks, Recreation, Leisure and Fitness Studies, A
Special Products Marketing Operations, A
Transportation and Materials Moving, A
Welding Technology/Welder, A

NORTH CENTRAL MICHIGAN COL-LEGE

Accounting Technology/Technician and Bookkeep-
 ing, A
Administrative Assistant and Secretarial Science, A
Agricultural and Horticultural Plant Breeding, A
Business Administration and Management, A
Computer Programming/Programmer, A
Criminal Justice/Law Enforcement Administration, A
Criminal Justice/Police Science, A
Early Childhood Education and Teaching, A
Emergency Medical Technology/Technician (EMT
 Paramedic), A
General Studies, A
Hospitality Administration/Management, A
Legal Administrative Assistant/Secretary, A
Legal Assistant/Paralegal, A
Liberal Arts and Sciences Studies and Humani-
 ties, A
Medical Administrative Assistant/Secretary, A
Physical Sciences, A
Sales, Distribution and Marketing Operations, A
System, Networking, and LAN/WAN
 Management/Manager, A
Woodworking, A

NORTHERN MICHIGAN UNIVERSITY

Accounting, A
Accounting and Finance, B
Accounting and Related Services, B
Administrative Assistant and Secretarial Science, A
Airframe Mechanics and Aircraft Maintenance
 Technology/Technician, A
Allied Health Diagnostic, Intervention, and Treat-
 ment Professions, B

Applied Behavior Analysis, M
Architecture and Related Services, B
Art History, Criticism and Conservation, B
Art Teacher Education, B
Art/Art Studies, General, AB
Athletic Training and Sports Medicine, B
Automobile/Automotive Mechanics
 Technology/Technician, A
Behavioral Sciences, B
Biochemistry, BM
Biological and Biomedical Sciences, M
Biology Teacher Education, B
Biology/Biological Sciences, B
Business Administration and Management, B
Business Administration, Management and Opera-
 tions, M
Business/Commerce, A
Business/Office Automation/Technology/Data En-
 try, A
CAD/CADD Drafting and/or Design
 Technology/Technician, A
Cartography, B
Ceramic Arts and Ceramics, B
Chemistry, B
Chemistry Teacher Education, B
Child Development, A
Cinematography and Film/Video Production, B
Clinical Laboratory Science/Medical
 Technology/Technologist, B
Clinical Laboratory Sciences, M
Communication Studies/Speech Communication
 and Rhetoric, B
Community Health Services/Liaison/Counseling, B
Computer Engineering Technology/Technician, A
Computer Systems Networking and Telecommunica-
 tions, B
Computer and Information Sciences, B
Construction Engineering Technology/Technician, B
Construction Trades, A
Criminal Justice/Law Enforcement Administration, A
Criminal Justice/Safety Studies, AB
Criminology, M
Curriculum and Instruction, M
Cytogenetics/Genetics/Clinical Genetics
 Technology/Technologist, B
Digital Communication and Media/Multimedia, B
Drafting and Design Technology/Technician, B
Drama and Dramatics/Theatre Arts, B
Drawing, B
Ecology, B
Economics, B
Education, M
Education/Teaching of Individuals with Emotional
 Disturbances, B
Education/Teaching of Individuals with Mental Retar-
 dation, B
Education/Teaching of Individuals with Specific
 Learning Disabilities, B
Educational Administration and Supervision, M
Electrical and Electronic Engineering
 Technologies/Technicians, A
Electrical, Electronic and Communications Engineer-
 ing Technology/Technician, A
Electromechanical Technology/Electromechanical
 Engineering Technology, A
Elementary Education and Teaching, BM
Engineering, B
English, MO
English Language and Literature, B
English as a Second Language, O
English/Language Arts Teacher Education, B
Entrepreneurship/Entrepreneurial Studies, B
Environmental Sciences, B
Exercise and Sports Science, M
Film/Video and Photographic Arts, B
Finance, B
Financial Planning and Services, B
Fine Arts and Art Studies, B
Foodservice Systems
 Administration/Management, A
French Language Teacher Education, B
French Language and Literature, B
General Studies, A
Geography, B
Geography Teacher Education, B
Geology/Earth Science, B

German Studies, B
Graphic Design, B
Health Information/Medical Records
    Technology/Technician, A
Health Teacher Education, B
Health and Physical Education, B
Health/Medical Preparatory Programs, B
Heating, Air Conditioning and Refrigeration
    Technology/Technician, A
Higher Education/Higher Education Administra-
    tion, M
Histologic Technician, A
History, B
History Teacher Education, B
Hospitality Administration/Management, B
Human Resources Management and Services, M
Illustration, B
Industrial Mechanics and Maintenance Technol-
    ogy, A
Industrial Technology/Technician, B
Instrumentation Technology/Technician, B
Insurance, B
International Relations and Affairs, B
Kinesiology and Exercise Science, B
Legal Assistant/Paralegal, B
Liberal Arts and Sciences Studies and Humani-
    ties, B
Management Information Systems and Services, B
Marketing/Marketing Management, B
Mathematics, B
Mathematics Teacher Education, B
Mechanical Engineering/Mechanical
    Technology/Technician, B
Metal and Jewelry Arts, B
Microbiology, B
Molecular Genetics, M
Music, B
Music Teacher Education, B
Natural Resources and Conservation, B
Nursing, MD
Nursing - Advanced Practice, MD
Painting, B
Parks, Recreation, Leisure and Fitness Studies, B
Philosophy, B
Photography, B
Physical Education Teaching and Coaching, B
Physics, B
Physics Teacher Education, B
Physiology, B
Political Science and Government, B
Pre-Dentistry Studies, B
Pre-Law Studies, B
Pre-Medicine/Pre-Medical Studies, B
Pre-Pharmacy Studies, B
Pre-Veterinary Studies, B
Printmaking, B
Psychology, BMO
Public Administration, BM
Public Relations, Advertising, and Applied Commu-
    nication, B
Public Relations/Image Management, B
Radiologic Technology/Science - Radiographer, AB
Reading Teacher Education, M
Respiratory Care Therapy/Therapist, B
Respiratory Therapy Technician/Assistant, A
Science Teacher Education/General Science
    Teacher Education, BM
Sculpture, B
Secondary Education and Teaching, BM
Security and Loss Prevention Services, B
Small Business Administration/Management, B
Social Science Teacher Education, B
Social Studies Teacher Education, B
Social Work, B
Sociology, B
Spanish Language Teacher Education, B
Spanish Language and Literature, B
Special Education and Teaching, BM
Speech-Language Pathology/Pathologist, B
Sport and Fitness Administration/Management, B
Student Personnel Services, M
Surgical Technology/Technologist, A
System, Networking, and LAN/WAN
    Management/Manager, B
Teacher Education and Professional Develop-
    ment, Specific Subject Areas, B

Theater, M
Web/Multimedia Management and Webmaster, B
Writing, M
Zoology/Animal Biology, B

NORTHWESTERN MICHIGAN COLLEGE

Accounting Technology/Technician and Bookkeep-
    ing, A
Agricultural Production Operations, A
Airline/Commercial/Professional Pilot and Flight
    Crew, A
Art/Art Studies, General, A
Automobile/Automotive Mechanics
    Technology/Technician, A
Biology/Biological Sciences, A
Business Administration and Management, A
Business and Personal/Financial Services Marketing
    Operations, A
Business, Management, Marketing, and Related
    Support Services, A
Business/Office Automation/Technology/Data En-
    try, A
Child Care and Support Services Management, A
Commercial and Advertising Art, A
Communication Studies/Speech Communication
    and Rhetoric, A
Corrections and Criminal Justice, A
Crop Production, A
Culinary Arts/Chef Training, A
Dental Assisting/Assistant, A
Drafting and Design Technology/Technician, A
Drama and Dramatics/Theatre Arts, A
Education, A
Electrical, Electronic and Communications Engineer-
    ing Technology/Technician, A
Electromechanical and Instrumentation and Mainte-
    nance Technologies/Technicians, A
Engineering, A
English Language and Literature, A
Executive Assistant/Executive Secretary, A
Forest Management/Forest Resources Manage-
    ment, A
Health Professions and Related Clinical Sciences, A
Industrial Technology/Technician, A
Landscaping and Groundskeeping, A
Legal Administrative Assistant/Secretary, A
Liberal Arts and Sciences Studies and Humani-
    ties, A
Machine Shop Technology/Assistant, A
Management Information Systems and Services, A
Marine Science/Merchant Marine Officer, B
Marine Transportation, A
Marketing/Marketing Management, A
Mathematics, A
Medical/Clinical Assistant, A
Music, A
Ocean Engineering, B
Physical Sciences, A
Social Sciences, A
Turf and Turfgrass Management, A

NORTHWOOD UNIVERSITY, MICHI-GAN CAMPUS

Accounting, B
Banking and Financial Support Services, B
Business Administration and Management, AB
Business Administration, Management and Opera-
    tions, M
Computer and Information Sciences, B
Entrepreneurship/Entrepreneurial Studies, B
Fashion Merchandising, B
Finance, B
Hotel/Motel Administration/Management, B
International Business/Trade/Commerce, B
Management Information Systems and Services, B
Marketing/Marketing Management, B
Sport and Fitness Administration/Management, B
Vehicle and Vehicle Parts and Accessories Market-
    ing Operations, B

OAKLAND COMMUNITY COLLEGE

Accounting Technology/Technician and Bookkeep-
    ing, A
Accounting and Business/Management, A
Architectural Engineering Technology/Technician, A
Art/Art Studies, General, A

Automobile/Automotive Mechanics
    Technology/Technician, A
BioTechnology, A
Business Administration and Management, A
Business/Office Automation/Technology/Data En-
    try, A
Carpentry/Carpenter, A
Ceramic Arts and Ceramics, A
Child Care and Support Services Management, A
Community Health Services/Liaison/Counseling, A
Computer Programming/Programmer, A
Computer Systems Analysis/Analyst, A
Computer and Information Sciences and Support
    Services, A
Computer and Information Systems Security, A
Computer/Information Technology Services Adminis-
    tration and Management, A
Construction Management, A
Corrections, A
Cosmetology/Cosmetologist, A
Court Reporting/Court Reporter, A
Criminal Justice/Law Enforcement Administration, A
Criminal Justice/Police Science, A
Criminalistics and Criminal Science, A
Culinary Arts/Chef Training, A
Dental Hygiene/Hygienist, A
Diagnostic Medical Sonography/Sonographer and
    Ultrasound Technician, A
Drafting and Design Technology/Technician, A
Dramatic/Theatre Arts and Stagecraft, A
Electrical, Electronic and Communications Engineer-
    ing Technology/Technician, A
Electrician, A
Electromechanical Technology/Electromechanical
    Engineering Technology, A
Emergency Medical Technology/Technician (EMT
    Paramedic), A
Entrepreneurship/Entrepreneurial Studies, A
Film/Cinema Studies, A
Fire Science/Firefighting, A
General Studies, A
Graphic Design, A
Health/Health Care Administration/Management, A
Heating, Air Conditioning and Refrigeration
    Technology/Technician, A
Histologic Technology/Histotechnologist, A
Hotel/Motel Administration/Management, A
Industrial Technology/Technician, A
Interior Design, A
International/Global Studies, A
Kinesiology and Exercise Science, A
Landscaping and Groundskeeping, A
Legal Assistant/Paralegal, A
Liberal Arts and Sciences Studies and Humani-
    ties, A
Library Assistant/Technician, A
Manufacturing Technology/Technician, A
Massage Therapy/Therapeutic Massage, A
Materials Engineering, A
Mechanical Drafting and Mechanical Drafting
    CAD/CADD, A
Medical Radiologic Technology/Science - Radiation
    Therapist, A
Medical Transcription/Transcriptionist, A
Medical/Clinical Assistant, A
Music Performance, A
Music Theory and Composition, A
Nuclear Medical Technology/Technologist, A
Occupational Therapist Assistant, A
Office Management and Supervision, A
Pharmacy Technician/Assistant, A
Photography, A
Physical Therapist Assistant, A
Pipefitting/Pipefitter and Sprinkler Fitter, A
Precision Metal Working, A
Radio and Television Broadcasting
    Technology/Technician, A
Respiratory Care Therapy/Therapist, A
Restaurant/Food Services Management, A
Robotics Technology/Technician, A
Salon/Beauty Salon Management/Manager, A
Science Technologies/Technicians, A
Sign Language Interpretation and Translation, A
Surgical Technology/Technologist, A
Veterinary/Animal Health Technology/Technician and
    Veterinary Assistant, A

Voice and Opera, A
Welding Technology/Welder, A

OAKLAND UNIVERSITY

Accounting, BMO
Acting, B
Actuarial Science, B
Allied Health and Medical Assisting Services, MDO
Anthropology, B
Applied Mathematics, MD
Applied Statistics, M
Art History, Criticism and Conservation, B
Biochemistry, B
Biological and Biomedical Sciences, MD
Biology/Biological Sciences, B
Biomedical Sciences, B
Biophysics, B
Business Administration, Management and Operations, MO
Business/Commerce, B
Business/Managerial Economics, B
Chemistry, BMD
Chinese Studies, B
Clinical Laboratory Science/Medical Technology/Technologist, B
Computer Engineering, BM
Computer Science, M
Computer and Information Sciences, B
Corrections, B
Counseling Psychology, MDO
Criminal Justice/Law Enforcement Administration, B
CytoTechnology/Cytotechnologist, B
Dance, B
Drama and Dramatics/Theatre Arts, B
Drawing, B
Early Childhood Education and Teaching, MDO
Economics, BO
Education, MDO
Educational Administration and Supervision, O
Educational Leadership and Administration, MDO
Educational Media/Instructional Technology, O
Electrical Engineering, M
Electrical, Electronics and Communications Engineering, B
Elementary Education and Teaching, B
Engineering Management, M
Engineering Physics, B
Engineering and Applied Sciences, MD
English, M
English Language and Literature, B
English as a Second Language, O
Entrepreneurship/Entrepreneurial Studies, O
Environmental Health, B
Environmental Sciences, BD
Environmental and Occupational Health, M
Exercise and Sports Science, MO
Film/Cinema Studies, B
Finance, B
Finance and Banking, MO
Fine Arts and Art Studies, B
Foreign Languages and Literatures, B
Foundations and Philosophy of Education, M
French Language and Literature, B
German Language and Literature, B
Gerontological Nursing, MO
Graphic Design, B
Health Professions and Related Clinical Sciences, B
Health Promotion, O
Health/Medical Preparatory Programs, B
Higher Education/Higher Education Administration, O
Histologic Technology/Histotechnologist, B
History, BM
Human Resources Development, BM
Human Resources Management and Services, O
Human Resources Management/Personnel Administration, B
Industrial Engineering, B
Industrial and Manufacturing Management, O
Information Technology, B
International Business/Trade/Commerce, O
International Relations and Affairs, B
Japanese Language and Literature, B
Japanese Studies, B
Journalism, B
Juvenile Corrections, B

Latin American Studies, B
Law and Legal Studies, B
Liberal Arts and Sciences Studies and Humanities, B
Liberal Studies, M
Linguistics, BMO
Management Information Systems and Services, BMO
Marketing, O
Marketing/Marketing Management, B
Maternal and Child Health, O
Mathematics, BM
Mathematics Teacher Education, O
Mechanical Engineering, BMD
Medical Physics, D
Medical Radiologic Technology/Science - Radiation Therapist, B
Music, BMD
Music Performance, B
Music Teacher Education, BD
Nuclear Medical Technology/Technologist, B
Nurse Anesthetist, MO
Nursing, MDO
Nursing - Adult, M
Nursing - Advanced Practice, MO
Nursing Education, MO
Operations Management and Supervision, B
Painting, B
Philosophy, B
Photography, B
Physical Therapy/Therapist, MDO
Physics, BMD
Piano and Organ, B
Political Science and Government, B
Psychology, B
Public Administration, BM
Radiologic Technology/Science - Radiographer, B
Reading Teacher Education, MDO
Secondary Education and Teaching, M
Social Work, B
Sociology, B
Software Engineering, M
Spanish Language and Literature, B
Special Education and Teaching, MO
Statistics, BO
Systems Engineering, MD
Systems Science and Theory, M
Technical Theatre/Theatre Design and Technology, B
Voice and Opera, B
Women's Studies, B

OLIVET COLLEGE

Actuarial Science, B
Art Teacher Education, B
Art/Art Studies, General, B
Athletic Training and Sports Medicine, B
Biochemistry, B
Biological and Physical Sciences, B
Biology/Biological Sciences, B
Business Administration and Management, B
Business/Managerial Economics, B
Chemistry, B
Chemistry Teacher Education, B
Computer Teacher Education, B
Computer and Information Sciences, B
Criminal Justice/Safety Studies, B
Drama and Dramatics/Theatre Arts, B
Education, M
Education/Teaching of Individuals with Emotional Disturbances, B
English Language and Literature, B
Environmental Studies, B
Finance, B
Finance and Financial Management Services, B
Financial Planning and Services, B
Forensic Science and Technology, B
Health Services/Allied Health/Health Sciences, B
Health Teacher Education, B
Health and Physical Education, B
History, B
Information Technology, B
Insurance, B
Journalism, B
Liberal Arts and Sciences Studies and Humanities, B

Marketing/Marketing Management, B
Mathematics, B
Mathematics Teacher Education, B
Music, B
Music Teacher Education, B
Psychology, B
Science Teacher Education/General Science Teacher Education, B
Social Sciences, B
Sociology, B
Speech Teacher Education, B
Sport and Fitness Administration/Management, B

ROCHESTER COLLEGE

Accounting, B
Behavioral Sciences, B
Bible/Biblical Studies, B
Biological and Physical Sciences, B
Biology Teacher Education, B
Business Administration and Management, B
Business/Corporate Communications, B
Communication Studies/Speech Communication and Rhetoric, B
Comparative Literature, B
Early Childhood Education and Teaching, B
Elementary Education and Teaching, B
English Language and Literature, B
English/Language Arts Teacher Education, B
History, B
History Teacher Education, B
Liberal Arts and Sciences Studies and Humanities, A
Marketing/Marketing Management, B
Mass Communication/Media Studies, B
Mathematics Teacher Education, B
Missions/Missionary Studies and Missiology, BM
Multi-/Interdisciplinary Studies, B
Music, B
Psychology, B
Religious Education, M
Science Teacher Education/General Science Teacher Education, B
Secondary Education and Teaching, B
Social Studies Teacher Education, B
Sport and Fitness Administration/Management, B
Youth Ministry, B

SACRED HEART MAJOR SEMINARY

Liberal Arts and Sciences Studies and Humanities, B
Pastoral Studies/Counseling, M
Philosophy, B
Theology and Religious Vocations, M
Theology/Theological Studies, A

SAGINAW CHIPPEWA TRIBAL COLLEGE

American Indian/Native American Studies, A
Business/Commerce, A
Liberal Arts and Sciences Studies and Humanities, A

SAGINAW VALLEY STATE UNIVERSITY

Accounting, B
Applied Mathematics, B
Art Teacher Education, B
Art/Art Studies, General, B
Athletic Training and Sports Medicine, B
Biochemistry, B
Biology Teacher Education, B
Biology/Biological Sciences, B
Business Administration and Management, B
Business Administration, Management and Operations, M
Business/Commerce, B
Business/Managerial Economics, B
Chemical Physics, B
Chemistry, B
Chemistry Teacher Education, B
Clinical Laboratory Science/Medical Technology/Technologist, B
Communication Studies/Speech Communication and Rhetoric, B
Communication and Media Studies, M
Computer Science, B

Computer Systems Analysis/Analyst, B
Computer and Information Sciences, B
Criminal Justice/Safety Studies, B
Design and Visual Communications, B
Digital Communication and Media/Multimedia, B
Distance Education Development, M
Drama and Dramatics/Theatre Arts, B
Early Childhood Education and Teaching, M
Economics, B
Education, BMO
Educational Administration and Supervision, M
Educational Leadership and Administration, MO
Educational Media/Instructional Technology, M
Electrical, Electronics and Communications Engineering, B
Elementary Education and Teaching, BM
Energy and Power Engineering, M
Engineering, B
Engineering and Applied Sciences, M
Engineering/Industrial Management, B
English Language and Literature, B
English/Language Arts Teacher Education, B
Finance, B
Fine/Studio Arts, B
French Language and Literature, B
General Studies, B
Graphic Design, B
Health Services Administration, M
Health Services/Allied Health/Health Sciences, B
Health/Medical Preparatory Programs, B
History, B
History Teacher Education, B
Industrial Production Technologies/Technicians, B
International Business/Trade/Commerce, B
International Relations and Affairs, B
International/Global Studies, B
Kinesiology and Exercise Science, B
Marketing, B
Marketing/Marketing Management, B
Materials Engineering, M
Mathematics, B
Mathematics Teacher Education, B
Mechanical Engineering, B
Media Studies, M
Middle School Education, M
Multi-/Interdisciplinary Studies, B
Music, B
Music Teacher Education, B
Nursing, M
Nursing - Advanced Practice, MD
Nursing Administration, M
Occupational Therapy/Therapist, BM
Operations Management and Supervision, B
Optics/Optical Sciences, B
Physical Education Teaching and Coaching, B
Physical Sciences, B
Physics, B
Physics Teacher Education, B
Political Science and Government, B
Pre-Dentistry Studies, B
Pre-Law Studies, B
Pre-Medicine/Pre-Medical Studies, B
Psychology, B
Public Administration, BM
Reading Teacher Education, M
Science Teacher Education/General Science Teacher Education, BM
Secondary Education and Teaching, M
Social Science Teacher Education, B
Social Work, B
Sociology, B
Spanish Language Teacher Education, B
Spanish Language and Literature, B
Special Education and Teaching, BM
Speech Teacher Education, B
Sport and Fitness Administration/Management, B
Teaching French as a Second or Foreign Language, B

ST. CLAIR COUNTY COMMUNITY COLLEGE

Accounting Technology/Technician and Bookkeeping, A
Business/Commerce, A
Child Care and Support Services Management, A
Commercial and Advertising Art, A

Computer Programming/Programmer, A
Computer Systems Networking and Telecommunications, A
Corrections, A
Criminal Justice/Law Enforcement Administration, A
Data Processing and Data Processing Technology/Technician, A
Drafting and Design Technology/Technician, A
Electrical, Electronic and Communications Engineering Technology/Technician, A
Emergency Medical Technology/Technician (EMT Paramedic), A
Energy Management and Systems Technology/Technician, A
Engineering, A
Executive Assistant/Executive Secretary, A
Fire Science/Firefighting, A
Health Information/Medical Records Technology/Technician, A
Liberal Arts and Sciences Studies and Humanities, A
Manufacturing Technology/Technician, A
Marketing/Marketing Management, A
Massage Therapy/Therapeutic Massage, A
Medical Radiologic Technology/Science - Radiation Therapist, A
Office Management and Supervision, A
Web/Multimedia Management and Webmaster, A

SCHOOLCRAFT COLLEGE

Accounting Technology/Technician and Bookkeeping, A
Biomedical Technology/Technician, A
Business Administration and Management, A
Business/Commerce, A
Business/Office Automation/Technology/Data Entry, A
Child Development, A
Computer Graphics, A
Computer Programming, Specific Applications, A
Computer Programming/Programmer, A
Criminal Justice/Police Science, A
Culinary Arts/Chef Training, A
Drafting and Design Technology/Technician, A
Education, A
Electrical, Electronic and Communications Engineering Technology/Technician, A
Emergency Medical Technology/Technician (EMT Paramedic), A
Engineering, A
Environmental Engineering Technology/Environmental Technology, A
Executive Assistant/Executive Secretary, A
Fine Arts and Art Studies, A
Fire Science/Firefighting, A
Foods, Nutrition, and Related Services, B
General Studies, A
Health Information/Medical Records Technology/Technician, A
Health Services/Allied Health/Health Sciences, A
Manufacturing Technology/Technician, A
Marketing/Marketing Management, A
Massage Therapy/Therapeutic Massage, A
Metallurgical Technology/Technician, A
Pre-Pharmacy Studies, A
Radio and Television Broadcasting Technology/Technician, A
Recording Arts Technology/Technician, A
Salon/Beauty Salon Management/Manager, A
Security and Protective Services, A
Small Business Administration/Management, A
Web Page, Digital/Multimedia and Information Resources Design, A
Welding Technology/Welder, A

SIENA HEIGHTS UNIVERSITY

Accounting, AB
Applied Mathematics, B
Art History, Criticism and Conservation, B
Art Teacher Education, B
Art/Art Studies, General, B
Biology/Biological Sciences, AB
Business Administration and Management, AB
Chemistry, AB
Child Care and Support Services Management, AB
Clinical Psychology, M

Communication, Journalism and Related Programs, B
Community Organization and Advocacy, B
Computer and Information Sciences, B
Counseling Psychology, M
Criminal Justice/Safety Studies, B
Drama and Dramatics/Theatre Arts, B
Early Childhood Education and Teaching, M
Education, MO
Educational Leadership and Administration, MO
Elementary Education and Teaching, BM
English Language and Literature, B
Environmental Sciences, B
General Studies, AB
Gerontology, A
Graphic Design, B
Health Services Administration, M
Higher Education/Higher Education Administration, M
History, B
Human Services, B
Humanities/Humanistic Studies, B
Kindergarten/PreSchool Education and Teaching, B
Mathematics, B
Montessori Teacher Education, B
Natural Sciences, B
Organizational Management, M
Philosophy, B
Pre-Law Studies, B
Psychology, AB
Public Administration, B
Reading Teacher Education, M
Religion/Religious Studies, B
Secondary Education and Teaching, BM
Social Sciences, B
Social Studies Teacher Education, B
Social Work, B
Spanish Language and Literature, B
Special Education and Teaching, M
Sport and Fitness Administration/Management, B

SOUTH UNIVERSITY

Business Administration and Management, B
Business Administration, Management and Operations, M
Counseling Psychology, M
Criminal Justice/Law Enforcement Administration, B
Health/Health Care Administration/Management, B
Health/Medical Preparatory Programs, B
Information Science/Studies, B
Legal Assistant/Paralegal, B
Nursing, M
Organizational Management, M
Pastoral Studies/Counseling, D
Physical Therapist Assistant, A
Psychology, B

SOUTHWESTERN MICHIGAN COLLEGE

Accounting Technology/Technician and Bookkeeping, A
Agricultural Production Operations, A
Automobile/Automotive Mechanics Technology/Technician, A
Business Administration and Management, A
Carpentry/Carpenter, A
Computer Programming/Programmer, A
Computer Systems Networking and Telecommunications, A
Criminal Justice/Safety Studies, A
Early Childhood Education and Teaching, A
Engineering Technology, A
Fire Science/Firefighting, A
General Studies, A
Graphic Design, A
Health Information/Medical Records Technology/Technician, A
Industrial Mechanics and Maintenance Technology, A
Industrial Production Technologies/Technicians, A
Liberal Arts and Sciences Studies and Humanities, A
Machine Tool Technology/Machinist, A
Medical/Clinical Assistant, A
Pre-Nursing Studies, A
Social Work, A

Sport and Fitness Administration/Management, A

SPRING ARBOR UNIVERSITY

Accounting, B
Actuarial Science, B
Advertising, B
Art Teacher Education, B
Art/Art Studies, General, B
Bible/Biblical Studies, B
Biochemistry, B
Biology Teacher Education, B
Biology/Biological Sciences, B
Business Administration and Management, B
Chemistry, B
Chemistry Teacher Education, B
Child and Family Studies, M
Communication Studies/Speech Communication
   and Rhetoric, B
Communication and Media Studies, BM
Computer Science, B
Corrections, B
Counseling Psychology, M
Design and Visual Communications, B
Drama and Dramatics/Theatre Arts, B
Education, M
Elementary Education and Teaching, B
English Language and Literature, B
English/Language Arts Teacher Education, B
Family Systems, B
Film/Video and Photographic Arts, B
Finance, B
Graphic Design, B
Health and Physical Education, B
Health/Health Care Administration/Management, B
History, B
History Teacher Education, B
Human Resources Management/Personnel Adminis-
   tration, B
International/Global Studies, B
Kinesiology and Exercise Science, B
Liberal Arts and Sciences Studies and Humani-
   ties, A
Management, M
Management Information Systems and Services, B
Mathematics, B
Mathematics Teacher Education, B
Music, B
Music Pedagogy, B
Music Teacher Education, B
Nursing, M
Parks, Recreation, Leisure and Fitness Studies, B
Pastoral Studies/Counseling, BM
Philosophy, B
Physical Education Teaching and Coaching, B
Physics, B
Piano and Organ, B
Political Science and Government, B
Psychology, B
Public Relations, Advertising, and Applied Commu-
   nication, B
Reading Teacher Education, M
Religion/Religious Studies, B
Secondary Education and Teaching, B
Social Sciences, B
Social Studies Teacher Education, B
Social Work, B
Sociology, B
Spanish Language and Literature, B
Special Education and Teaching, BM
Sport and Fitness Administration/Management, B
Theology and Religious Vocations, M
Theology/Theological Studies, B
Visual and Performing Arts, B
Youth Ministry, B

UNIVERSITY OF DETROIT MERCY

Accounting, B
Allied Health and Medical Assisting Services, MO
Architectural Engineering, BM
Architecture, B
Biochemistry, BM
Biology/Biological Sciences, B
Business Administration and Management, B
Business Administration, Management and Opera-
   tions, M
Chemistry, BM

Civil Engineering, BMD
Clinical Psychology, MD
Communication Studies/Speech Communication
   and Rhetoric, B
Computer Education, M
Computer Engineering, MD
Computer Science, BM
Computer Software Engineering, B
Counselor Education/School Counseling and Guid-
   ance Services, M
Criminal Justice/Safety Studies, B
Criminology, M
Curriculum and Instruction, M
Dental Hygiene/Hygienist, B
Dentistry, D
Digital Communication and Media/Multimedia, B
Drama and Dramatics/Theatre Arts, B
Economics, B
Education, BM
Education/Teaching of Individuals with Emotional
   Disturbances, B
Education/Teaching of Individuals with Specific
   Learning Disabilities, B
Educational Administration and Supervision, M
Electrical Engineering, MD
Electrical, Electronics and Communications Engi-
   neering, B
Elementary Education and Teaching, B
Engineering, B
Engineering Management, M
Engineering and Applied Sciences, MD
English Language and Literature, B
Environmental Engineering
   Technology/Environmental Technology, MD
Health Information/Medical Records
   Administration/Administrator, B
Health Services Administration, BM
Health and Medical Administrative Services, B
History, B
Industrial and Organizational Psychology, M
Information Science/Studies, M
Law and Legal Studies, BD
Liberal Arts and Sciences Studies and Humani-
   ties, B
Liberal Studies, M
Management, MO
Management Information Systems and Ser-
   vices, BM
Manufacturing Engineering, B
Mathematics, B
Mathematics Teacher Education, BM
Mechanical Engineering, MD
Military and Defense Studies, M
Natural Sciences, B
Nurse Anesthetist, M
Nursing - Advanced Practice, MO
Oral and Dental Sciences, MO
Orthodontics, MO
Periodontics, MO
Philosophy, B
Physician Assistant, M
Political Science and Government, B
Psychology, BMDO
Public Administration and Social Service Profes-
   sions, B
Religion/Religious Studies, BM
School Psychology, O
Secondary Education and Teaching, B
Securities Services Administration/Management, M
Social Science Teacher Education, B
Social Sciences, B
Social Studies Teacher Education, B
Social Work, B
Sociology, B
Software Engineering, M
Special Education and Teaching, BM
Substance Abuse/Addiction Counseling, BMO

UNIVERSITY OF MICHIGAN

Accounting, M
Acute Care/Critical Care Nursing, M
Aerospace, Aeronautical and Astronautical Engi-
   neering, BMD
African-American/Black Studies, B
Allopathic Medicine, D
American/United States Studies/Civilization, BMD

Analytical Chemistry, D
Ancient Studies/Civilization, B
Ancient/Classical Greek Language and Literature, B
Anthropology, BD
Applied Economics, M
Applied Physics, D
Applied Statistics, M
Arabic Language and Literature, MD
Archeology, MD
Architecture, BMD
Archives/Archival Administration, M
Art History, Criticism and Conservation, BMD
Art/Art Studies, General, B
Artificial Intelligence and Robotics, MD
Asian Languages, D
Asian Studies/Civilization, BMD
Astronomy, BD
Astrophysics, D
Athletic Training and Sports Medicine, B
Atmospheric Sciences and Meteorology, BMD
Automotive Engineering Technology/Technician, M
Biochemistry, BMD
Bioinformatics, MD
Biological and Biomedical Sciences, BMD
Biology/Biological Sciences, B
Biomedical Engineering, MD
Biomedical/Medical Engineering, B
Biophysics, BD
Biopsychology, D
Biostatistics, MD
Business Administration and Management, B
Business Administration, Management and Opera-
   tions, MD
Cancer Biology/Oncology, MD
Cell Biology and Anatomy, MD
Cell/Cellular and Molecular Biology, B
Ceramic Arts and Ceramics, B
Chemical Engineering, BMDO
Chemistry, BD
Civil Engineering, BMDO
Classical, Ancient Mediterranean and Near Eastern
   Studies and Archaeology, B
Classics and Classical Languages, Litera-
   tures, and Linguistics, BMDO
Clinical Psychology, D
Clinical Research, M
Cognitive Sciences, BD
Communication Studies/Speech Communication
   and Rhetoric, B
Communication and Media Studies, D
Comparative Literature, BD
Composition, MD
Computer Engineering, BMD
Computer Science, MD
Computer and Information Sciences, B
Conservation Biology, M
Construction Engineering and Management, M
Cultural Anthropology, D
Dance, BM
Data Modeling/Warehousing and Database Adminis-
   tration, B
Dental Hygiene/Hygienist, BM
Dentistry, D
Design and Applied Arts, MD
Developmental Biology and Embryology, MD
Developmental Psychology, D
Drama and Dramatics/Theatre Arts, B
Drawing, B
East Asian Studies, M
East European and Russian Studies, MO
Ecology, MD
Economics, BMD
Education, MD
Electrical Engineering, MD
Electrical, Electronics and Communications Engi-
   neering, B
Elementary Education and Teaching, B
Energy and Power Engineering, M
Engineering, B
Engineering Physics, B
Engineering Science, B
Engineering and Applied Sciences, MDO
English, MD
English Education, D
English Language and Literature, B

Environmental Engineering Technology/Environmental Technology, MDO
Environmental Policy, M
Environmental Policy and Resource Management, D
Environmental Sciences, MD
Environmental Studies, B
Environmental and Occupational Health, MD
Environmental/Environmental Health Engineering, B
Epidemiology, MD
Evolutionary Biology, MD
Fiber, Textile and Weaving Arts, B
Film, Television, and Video Theory and Criticism, DO
Film/Cinema Studies, B
Financial Engineering, M
Fine Arts and Art Studies, BM
Foreign Language Teacher Education, M
French Language and Literature, BD
General Studies, B
Genetic Counseling/Counselor, M
Geological/Geophysical Engineering, B
Geology/Earth Science, B
Geosciences, MD
German Language and Literature, BMD
Gerontological Nursing, M
Graphic Design, B
Health Education, MD
Health Informatics, M
Health Physics/Radiological Health, MD
Health Promotion, MD
Health Services Administration, MD
Health and Physical Education, B
Hebrew Language and Literature, BMD
Hispanic-American, Puerto Rican, and Mexican-American/Chicano Studies, B
History, BDO
Human Genetics, MD
Humanities/Humanistic Studies, B
Illustration, B
Immunology, MD
Industrial Design, B
Industrial Engineering, B
Industrial Hygiene, M
Industrial/Management Engineering, MD
Information Science/Studies, BMD
Inorganic Chemistry, D
Interdisciplinary Studies, MD
International Public Health/International Health, M
International/Global Studies, B
Italian Language and Literature, BD
Jazz/Jazz Studies, B
Jewish/Judaic Studies, BMDO
Kinesiology and Exercise Science, B
Kinesiology and Movement Studies, MD
Landscape Architecture, MD
Latin Language and Literature, B
Law and Legal Studies, MD
Linguistics, BD
Manufacturing Engineering, MD
Marine Engineering, MDO
Marine Sciences, M
Mass Communication/Media Studies, D
Materials Engineering, BMD
Materials Sciences, MD
Mathematics, BMD
Mechanical Engineering, BMD
Media Studies, M
Medicinal and Pharmaceutical Chemistry, BD
Medieval and Renaissance Studies, B
Metal and Jewelry Arts, B
Microbiology, BMD
Middle/Near Eastern and Semitic Languages, Literatures, and Linguistics, B
Modern Greek Language and Literature, B
Molecular Biology, BMD
Molecular Pathology, D
Multi-/Interdisciplinary Studies, B
Music, B
Music History, Literature, and Theory, B
Music Performance, B
Music Teacher Education, BMDO
Music Theory and Composition, BD
Musicology and Ethnomusicology, MD
Natural Resources Management/Development and Policy, MD
Natural Resources and Conservation, B

Naval Architecture and Marine Engineering, B
Near and Middle Eastern Languages, MD
Near and Middle Eastern Studies, BMD
Neuroscience, D
Nuclear Engineering, BMDO
Nurse Midwife/Nursing Midwifery, M
Nursing, MDO
Nursing - Adult, M
Nursing - Advanced Practice, M
Nursing Administration, M
Nutritional Sciences, MD
Ocean Engineering, MDO
Oceanography, Chemical and Physical, B
Operations Research, MD
Oral and Dental Sciences, MD
Organic Chemistry, D
Organizational Behavior Studies, B
Orthodontics, M
Pathology/Experimental Pathology, D
Pediatric Nurse/Nursing, M
Pedodontics, M
Performance, MDO
Periodontics, M
Pharmaceutical Administration, D
Pharmaceutical Engineering, M
Pharmaceutical Sciences, D
Pharmacology, MD
Pharmacy, D
Pharmacy Administration and Pharmacy Policy and Regulatory Affairs, B
Philosophy, BMD
Physical Chemistry, D
Physics, BD
Physiology, MD
Planetary Astronomy and Science, MD
Polish Language and Literature, B
Political Science and Government, BD
Printmaking, B
Psychology, D
Public Health, MD
Public Policy Analysis, BMD
Religion/Religious Studies, BMD
Romance Languages, Literatures, and Linguistics, B
Russian Language and Literature, BM
Russian Studies, B
Sculpture, B
Secondary Education and Teaching, B
Slavic Languages, Literatures, and Linguistics, MD
Social Psychology, D
Social Sciences, BD
Social Work, MD
Sociology, BD
South and Southeast Asian Studies, MO
Spanish Language and Literature, BD
Sport and Fitness Administration/Management, BM
Statistics, BMD
Structural Engineering, M
Supply Chain Management, M
Survey Methodology, MDO
Sustainable Development, M
Taxation, M
Technical Theatre/Theatre Design and Technology, B
Theater, MD
Toxicology, MD
Urban Design, M
Urban and Regional Planning, MD
Visual and Performing Arts, B
Women's Studies, BDO
Writing, M

UNIVERSITY OF MICHIGAN–DEARBORN

Accounting, BM
American/United States Studies/Civilization, B
Anthropology, B
Applied Mathematics, M
Area Studies, B
Art History, Criticism and Conservation, B
Automotive Engineering Technology/Technician, MD
Biochemistry, B
Biology/Biological Sciences, B
Business Administration and Management, B
Business Administration, Management and Operations, BM
Chemistry, B

Chemistry Teacher Education, B
Clinical Psychology, M
Communication Studies/Speech Communication and Rhetoric, B
Computational Sciences, M
Computer Engineering, M
Computer Programming/Programmer, B
Computer and Information Sciences, B
Criminal Justice/Safety Studies, B
Curriculum and Instruction, DO
Database Systems, M
Early Childhood Education and Teaching, BM
Economics, B
Education, BM
Educational Leadership and Administration, MDO
Educational Media/Instructional Technology, M
Electrical Engineering, M
Electrical, Electronics and Communications Engineering, B
Elementary Education and Teaching, B
Energy and Power Engineering, M
Engineering, B
Engineering Management, M
Engineering and Applied Sciences, MD
English Language and Literature, B
Environmental Sciences, BM
Environmental Studies, B
Finance, B
Finance and Banking, M
French Language and Literature, B
General Studies, B
Geology/Earth Science, B
Health Informatics, M
Health Psychology, M
Health/Health Care Administration/Management, B
History, B
Human Resources Management/Personnel Administration, B
Humanities/Humanistic Studies, B
Industrial Engineering, B
Industrial/Management Engineering, M
Information Science/Studies, M
Liberal Arts and Sciences Studies and Humanities, B
Management Information Systems and Services, BM
Management Strategy and Policy, M
Manufacturing Engineering, BM
Marketing/Marketing Management, B
Mathematics, B
Mathematics Teacher Education, B
Mechanical Engineering, BM
Microbiology, B
Multi-/Interdisciplinary Studies, B
Philosophy, B
Physics, B
Political Science and Government, B
Project Management, M
Psychology, B
Public Administration, M
Public Policy Analysis, M
Science Teacher Education/General Science Teacher Education, BM
Secondary Education and Teaching, B
Social Sciences, B
Social Studies Teacher Education, B
Sociology, B
Software Engineering, M
Spanish Language and Literature, B
Special Education and Teaching, M
Supply Chain Management, M
Systems Engineering, MD
Urban Education and Leadership, D
Women's Studies, B

UNIVERSITY OF MICHIGAN–FLINT

Accounting, BM
Actuarial Science, B
African-American/Black Studies, B
American/United States Studies/Civilization, M
Anthropology, B
Art History, Criticism and Conservation, B
Art Teacher Education, B
Arts Management, M
Biochemistry, B
Biological and Biomedical Sciences, M

Biology/Biological Sciences, B
Biomedical Sciences, B
Business Administration and Management, B
Business Administration, Management and Operations, MO
Chemistry, B
Clinical Laboratory Science/Medical Technology/Technologist, B
Computer Science, BM
Corrections and Criminal Justice, B
Criminology, M
Dance, B
Design and Visual Communications, B
Drama and Dramatics/Theatre Arts, B
Dramatic/Theatre Arts and Stagecraft, B
Early Childhood Education and Teaching, M
Ecology, B
Economics, B
Education, MDO
Educational Administration and Supervision, M
Educational Leadership and Administration, DO
Educational Media/Instructional Technology, M
Elementary Education and Teaching, B
Engineering Science, B
English, M
English Language and Literature, B
English/Language Arts Teacher Education, B
Entrepreneurship/Entrepreneurial Studies, B
Environmental Sciences, B
Ethics, B
Finance, B
Finance and Banking, M
Fine Arts and Art Studies, M
Fine/Studio Arts, B
French Language Teacher Education, B
French Language and Literature, B
Gender Studies, M
Health Education, M
Health Services Administration, M
Health Services/Allied Health/Health Sciences, B
Health/Health Care Administration/Management, B
Health/Medical Preparatory Programs, B
History, B
History Teacher Education, B
Human Resources Management/Personnel Administration, B
Industrial and Manufacturing Management, M
Information Science/Studies, BM
International Affairs, M
International Business/Trade/Commerce, BM
Linguistics, B
Management Information Systems and Services, M
Marketing, M
Marketing/Marketing Management, B
Mathematics, BM
Mathematics Teacher Education, B
Mechanical Engineering, B
Medical Radiologic Technology/Science - Radiation Therapist, B
Molecular Biology, B
Multi-/Interdisciplinary Studies, B
Museology/Museum Studies, M
Music, B
Music Performance, B
Music Teacher Education, B
Natural Resources Conservation and Research, B
Non-Profit/Public/Organizational Management, M
Nurse Anesthetist, MD
Nursing, MDO
Nursing - Advanced Practice, MDO
Organizational Management, M
Performance, M
Philosophy, B
Physical Therapy/Therapist, DO
Physics, B
Political Science and Government, BM
Pre-Nursing Studies, B
Psychiatric/Mental Health Nurse/Nursing, O
Psychology, B
Psychology Teacher Education, B
Public Administration, BM
Public Health, BM
Reading Teacher Education, M
Rhetoric, M
Romance Languages, Literatures, and Linguistics, B

Science Teacher Education/General Science Teacher Education, B
Social Sciences, BM
Social Studies Teacher Education, B
Social Work, B
Sociology, B
Spanish Language Teacher Education, B
Spanish Language and Literature, B
Special Education and Teaching, M
Speech Teacher Education, B
Teacher Education, Multiple Levels, B
Technical Theatre/Theatre Design and Technology, B
Wildlife Biology, B
Writing, M

UNIVERSITY OF PHOENIX–DETROIT CAMPUS

Accounting, B
Business Administration and Management, B
Consumer Merchandising/Retailing Management, B
Criminal Justice/Law Enforcement Administration, B
Digital Communication and Media/Multimedia, B
Finance, B
Health Services Administration, B
Human Services, B
Information Technology, B
International Business/Trade/Commerce, B
Management Information Systems and Services, B
Management Science, B
Marketing/Marketing Management, B
Public Administration, B
Security and Protective Services, B

WALSH COLLEGE OF ACCOUNTANCY AND BUSINESS ADMINISTRATION

Accounting, BM
Business Administration and Management, B
Business Administration, Management and Operations, M
Business/Commerce, B
Computer and Information Sciences, B
Finance, B
Finance and Banking, M
Information Technology, B
Management, M
Management Information Systems and Services, M
Marketing/Marketing Management, B
Taxation, M

WASHTENAW COMMUNITY COLLEGE

Accounting Technology/Technician and Bookkeeping, A
Administrative Assistant and Secretarial Science, A
Architectural Drafting and Architectural CAD/CADD, A
Broadcast Journalism, A
Building/Construction Site Management/Manager, A
Business Administration and Management, A
CAD/CADD Drafting and/or Design Technology/Technician, A
Child Care Provider/Assistant, A
Commercial and Advertising Art, A
Computer Programming/Programmer, A
Computer Systems Analysis/Analyst, A
Computer Systems Networking and Telecommunications, A
Computer and Information Sciences, A
Computer and Information Systems Security, A
Criminal Justice/Police Science, A
Elementary Education and Teaching, A
Engineering, A
General Studies, A
Heating, Air Conditioning, Ventilation and Refrigeration Maintenance Technology/Technician, A
Human Services, A
Industrial Production Technologies/Technicians, A
Institutional Food Workers, A
International/Global Studies, A
Journalism, A
Liberal Arts and Sciences Studies and Humanities, A
Medical Radiologic Technology/Science - Radiation Therapist, A
Office Management and Supervision, A

Photographic and Film/Video Technology/Technician and Assistant, A
Pipefitting/Pipefitter and Sprinkler Fitter, A
Precision Production, A
Robotics Technology/Technician, A
Secondary Education and Teaching, A
Web Page, Digital/Multimedia and Information Resources Design, A
Welding Technology/Welder, A

WAYNE COUNTY COMMUNITY COLLEGE DISTRICT

Accounting Technology/Technician and Bookkeeping, A
Aircraft Powerplant Technology/Technician, A
Airframe Mechanics and Aircraft Maintenance Technology/Technician, A
Autobody/Collision and Repair Technology/Technician, A
Automobile/Automotive Mechanics Technology/Technician, A
Biomedical Technology/Technician, A
Building/Property Maintenance and Management, A
Business Administration and Management, A
CAD/CADD Drafting and/or Design Technology/Technician, A
Child Care and Support Services Management, A
Computer Programming/Programmer, A
Computer and Information Sciences and Support Services, A
Corrections, A
Criminal Justice/Police Science, A
Data Modeling/Warehousing and Database Administration, A
Dental Hygiene/Hygienist, A
Digital Communication and Media/Multimedia, A
E-Commerce/Electronic Commerce, A
Electrical and Electronic Engineering Technologies/Technicians, A
Electrical, Electronic and Communications Engineering Technology/Technician, A
Electromechanical Technology/Electromechanical Engineering Technology, A
Elementary Education and Teaching, A
Emergency Medical Technology/Technician (EMT Paramedic), A
Fire Protection and Safety Technology/Technician, A
Foodservice Systems Administration/Management, A
Heating, Air Conditioning, Ventilation and Refrigeration Maintenance Technology/Technician, A
Heavy/Industrial Equipment Maintenance Technologies, A
Legal Assistant/Paralegal, A
Liberal Arts and Sciences Studies and Humanities, A
Machine Tool Technology/Machinist, A
Manufacturing Technology/Technician, A
Mortuary Science and Embalming/Embalmer, A
Office Management and Supervision, A
Pharmacy Technician/Assistant, A
Physician Assistant, A
Psychiatric/Mental Health Services Technician, A
Social Work, A
Surgical Technology/Technologist, A
System Administration/Administrator, A
System, Networking, and LAN/WAN Management/Manager, A
Veterinary/Animal Health Technology/Technician and Veterinary Assistant, A
Web/Multimedia Management and Webmaster, A
Welding Technology/Welder, A

WAYNE STATE UNIVERSITY

Accounting, BMO
Acute Care/Critical Care Nursing, M
Advertising and Public Relations, M
African Studies, D
African-American/Black Studies, B
Allopathic Medicine, D
American/United States Studies/Civilization, D
Analytical Chemistry, D
Anatomy, MD
Anthropology, BMD
Apparel and Textile Marketing Management, B
Applied Mathematics, MD

Arabic Language and Literature, M
Archives/Archival Administration, O
Art Education, MD
Art History, Criticism and Conservation, BM
Art Therapy/Therapist, M
Art/Art Studies, General, B
Astronomy, B
Automotive Engineering Technology/Technician, MO
BioTechnology, D
Biochemistry, MD
Bioinformatics, D
Biological and Biomedical Sciences, MD
Biology/Biological Sciences, B
Biomedical Engineering, MDO
Biomedical/Medical Engineering, B
Biopsychology, D
Business Administration, Management and Opera-
   tions, MDO
Cancer Biology/Oncology, MD
Cell Biology and Anatomy, D
Central/Middle and Eastern European Studies, B
Ceramic Arts and Ceramics, B
Chemical Engineering, BMD
Chemistry, BMD
Cinematography and Film/Video Production, B
Civil Engineering, BMD
Classics and Classical Languages, Litera-
   tures, and Linguistics, BM
Clinical Laboratory Science/Medical
   Technology/Technologist, B
Clinical Psychology, D
Cognitive Sciences, D
Communication Disorders, BMD
Communication Studies/Speech Communication
   and Rhetoric, B
Communication and Media Studies, MDO
Community Health Nursing, MD
Comparative Literature, M
Composition, M
Computational Biology, D
Computer Engineering, MD
Computer Science, MDO
Computer Technology/Computer Systems Technol-
   ogy, B
Computer and Information Sciences, B
Conflict Resolution and Mediation/Peace Stud-
   ies, MO
Construction Engineering Technology/Technician, B
Counselor Education/School Counseling and Guid-
   ance Services, MDO
Criminal Justice/Safety Studies, B
Criminology, M
Curriculum and Instruction, MDO
Dance, B
Design and Applied Arts, M
Developmental Psychology, D
Dietetics/Dieticians, B
Distance Education Development, O
Drama and Dramatics/Theatre Arts, M
Early Childhood Education and Teaching, MDO
East Asian Studies, B
Economic Development, MO
Economics, BMD
Education, BMDO
Educational Administration and Supervision, MDO
Educational Leadership and Administration, MD
Educational Measurement and Evaluation, MD
Educational Media/Instructional Technology, MDO
Educational Policy, D
Educational Psychology, MD
Electrical Engineering, MD
Electrical and Electronic Engineering
   Technologies/Technicians, B
Electrical, Electronic and Communications Engineer-
   ing Technology/Technician, B
Electrical, Electronics and Communications Engi-
   neering, B
Electromechanical Technology/Electromechanical
   Engineering Technology, B
Elementary Education and Teaching, BMDO
Energy and Power Engineering, MO
Engineering Management, MO
Engineering and Applied Sciences, MDO
English, MD
English Education, MDO
English Language and Literature, B

English as a Second Language, DO
Environmental Sciences, B
Ethnic, Cultural Minority, and Gender Studies, B
Evolutionary Biology, D
Exercise and Sports Science, MD
Film/Cinema Studies, B
Finance, B
Finance and Banking, M
Fine Arts and Art Studies, M
Food Science and Technology, MDO
Foods, Nutrition, and Wellness Studies, B
Foreign Language Teacher Education, MD
Foreign Languages and Literatures, B
Foundations and Philosophy of Education, MDO
French Language and Literature, MD
Funeral Direction/Service, B
Gender Studies, D
Genetic Counseling/Counselor, M
Genetics, D
Geology/Earth Science, BM
German Language and Literature, BMD
Gerontological Nursing, M
Gerontology, DO
Graphic Design, M
Health Communication, O
Health Education, MDO
Health Physics/Radiological Health, MD
Health Professions and Related Clinical Sciences, B
Health Services Administration, M
Health Teacher Education, B
Hebrew Language and Literature, M
Higher Education/Higher Education Administra-
   tion, O
History, BMDO
History of Science and Technology, D
Human Resources Management and Services, MD
Immunology, MD
Industrial Design, M
Industrial Engineering, B
Industrial and Labor Relations, M
Industrial and Manufacturing Management, MD
Industrial and Organizational Psychology, M
Industrial/Management Engineering, MD
Information Science/Studies, BMO
Inorganic Chemistry, D
Interior Design, M
International Business/Trade/Commerce, B
International Economics, MD
Italian Language and Literature, M
Jewelry/Metalsmithing, M
Journalism, BM
Kinesiology and Movement Studies, MD
Labor and Industrial Relations, B
Law and Legal Studies, MD
Library Science, MO
Linguistics, BM
Management Information Systems and Ser-
   vices, BO
Manufacturing Engineering, M
Manufacturing Technology/Technician, B
Marketing/Marketing Management, B
Materials Sciences, MDO
Maternal/Child Health and Neonatal
   Nurse/Nursing, MDO
Mathematics, BMD
Mathematics Teacher Education, MDO
Mechanical Engineering, BMD
Mechanical Engineering/Mechanical
   Technology/Technician, B
Media Studies, MO
Medical Physics, D
Medical Radiologic Technology/Science - Radiation
   Therapist, B
Medicinal and Pharmaceutical Chemistry, D
Microbiology, MD
Middle/Near Eastern and Semitic Languages, Litera-
   tures, and Linguistics, B
Molecular Biology, MD
Multilingual and Multicultural Education, MDO
Music, BMO
Music Theory and Composition, M
Near and Middle Eastern Studies, M
Neurobiology and Neurophysiology, D
Neuroscience, D
Non-Profit/Public/Organizational Management, M
Nurse Anesthetist, MO

Nurse Midwife/Nursing Midwifery, M
Nursing, DO
Nursing - Adult, MDO
Nursing - Advanced Practice, D
Nursing Education, O
Nutritional Sciences, MDO
Occupational Therapy/Therapist, M
Organic Chemistry, D
Organizational Behavior Studies, BM
Organizational Management, M
Painting, M
Pathology/Experimental Pathology, D
Pathology/Pathologist Assistant, B
Pediatric Nurse/Nursing, MDO
Performance, M
Pharmaceutical Sciences, MD
Pharmacology, D
Pharmacy, MD
Philosophy, BMD
Photography, M
Physical Chemistry, D
Physical Education Teaching and Coaching, BMDO
Physical Sciences, B
Physical Therapy/Therapist, D
Physician Assistant, M
Physics, BMD
Physiology, MD
Political Science and Government, BMD
Polymer/Plastics Engineering, O
Printmaking, M
Psychiatric/Mental Health Nurse/Nursing, MDO
Psychology, BMD
Public Administration, BM
Public Health, MO
Public Health (MPH, DPH), B
Public Policy Analysis, M
Public Relations/Image Management, B
Radio and Television, B
Reading Teacher Education, MDO
Rehabilitation Counseling, M
Romance Languages, Literatures, and Linguis-
   tics, M
School Psychology, MD
Science Teacher Education/General Science
   Teacher Education, MDO
Sculpture, M
Secondary Education and Teaching, BMDO
Slavic Languages, Literatures, and Linguistics, B
Social Psychology, D
Social Studies Teacher Education, MDO
Social Work, BMDO
Sociology, BMD
Spanish Language and Literature, MD
Special Education and Teaching, BMDO
Sport and Fitness Administration/Management, M
Statistics, MD
Sustainable Development, O
Systems Engineering, O
Taxation, M
Textile Design, M
Theater, M
Toxicology, MD
Urban Planning, MO
Urban Studies/Affairs, BM
Vocational and Technical Education, MDO
Western European Studies, D
Women's Health Nursing, M
Writing, MD

WEST SHORE COMMUNITY COLLEGE

Accounting, A
Corrections, A
Criminal Justice/Police Science, A
Data Entry/Microcomputer Applications, A
Data Processing and Data Processing
   Technology/Technician, A
Electrical, Electronic and Communications Engineer-
   ing Technology/Technician, A
Emergency Medical Technology/Technician (EMT
   Paramedic), A
Information Technology, A
Liberal Arts and Sciences Studies and Humani-
   ties, A
Machine Tool Technology/Machinist, A
Marketing/Marketing Management, A

Welding Technology/Welder, A

WESTERN MICHIGAN UNIVERSITY

Accounting, BM
Acting, B
Advertising, B
Aerospace, Aeronautical and Astronautical Engineering, BMD
African-American/Black Studies, B
Airline/Commercial/Professional Pilot and Flight Crew, B
American Government and Politics (United States), B
Anthropology, BM
Applied Arts and Design, M
Applied Economics, MD
Applied Mathematics, BM
Aquatic Biology/Limnology, B
Art Education, M
Art History, Criticism and Conservation, B
Art Teacher Education, B
Art/Art Studies, General, B
Athletic Training and Sports Medicine, BM
Audiology/Audiologist and Hearing Sciences, B
Audiology/Audiologist and Speech-Language Pathology/Pathologist, B
Aviation/Airway Management and Operations, B
Avionics Maintenance Technology/Technician, B
Biochemistry, B
Biological and Biomedical Sciences, MD
Biology Teacher Education, B
Biology/Biological Sciences, B
Biomedical Sciences, B
Business Administration and Management, B
Business Administration, Management and Operations, M
Business Teacher Education, B
Business/Commerce, B
Business/Managerial Economics, B
Chemical Engineering, BMD
Chemistry, BMD
Chemistry Teacher Education, B
Child Development, B
City/Urban, Community and Regional Planning, B
Civil Engineering, BM
Clinical Psychology, D
Communication Disorders, MD
Communication Studies/Speech Communication and Rhetoric, B
Communication and Media Studies, M
Composition, M
Computational Sciences, M
Computer Engineering, BMD
Computer Science, BMD
Computer and Information Sciences, B
Counseling Psychology, MD
Counselor Education/School Counseling and Guidance Services, MD
Criminal Justice/Safety Studies, B
Dance, B
Dietetics and Clinical Nutrition Services, B
Drafting and Design Technology/Technician, B
Dramatic/Theatre Arts and Stagecraft, B
E-Commerce/Electronic Commerce, B
Early Childhood Education and Teaching, B
Economics, BMD
Education, MDO
Education/Teaching of Individuals with Emotional Disturbances, B
Education/Teaching of Individuals with Specific Learning Disabilities, B
Educational Leadership and Administration, MDO
Educational Measurement and Evaluation, MD
Educational Media/Instructional Technology, MDO
Electrical Engineering, MD
Electrical, Electronics and Communications Engineering, B
Elementary Education and Teaching, B
Engineering, B
Engineering Management, MD
Engineering and Applied Sciences, MD
Engineering/Industrial Management, B
English, MD
English Education, M
English Language and Literature, B
English/Language Arts Teacher Education, B

Entrepreneurship/Entrepreneurial Studies, B
Environmental Studies, B
Exercise and Sports Science, M
Family Systems, B
Family and Consumer Sciences/Home Economics Teacher Education, B
Family and Consumer Sciences/Human Sciences, M
Fashion Merchandising, B
Fashion/Apparel Design, B
Film/Video and Photographic Arts, B
Finance, B
Financial Planning and Services, B
Fine/Studio Arts, B
Food Science, B
Foodservice Systems Administration/Management, B
French Language Teacher Education, B
French Language and Literature, B
Geochemistry, B
Geographic Information Systems, O
Geography, BMDO
Geography Teacher Education, B
Geology/Earth Science, B
Geophysics and Seismology, B
Geosciences, MD
German Language Teacher Education, B
German Language and Literature, B
Graphic Design, B
Health Education, DO
Health Services Administration, MO
Health Teacher Education, B
Health and Medical Administrative Services, B
Higher Education/Higher Education Administration, D
History, BMD
History Teacher Education, B
Human Resources Management and Services, B
Human Services, DO
Hydrology and Water Resources Science, B
Industrial Engineering, B
Industrial and Organizational Psychology, M
Industrial/Management Engineering, MD
Information Resources Management/CIO Training, B
Interior Design, B
International Affairs, M
International/Global Studies, B
Japanese Language and Literature, B
Jazz/Jazz Studies, B
Journalism, B
Kinesiology and Exercise Science, B
Latin Language and Literature, B
Latin Teacher Education, B
Logistics and Materials Management, B
Manufacturing Engineering, M
Manufacturing Technology/Technician, B
Marketing, B
Marketing/Marketing Management, B
Mathematics, BMD
Mathematics Teacher Education, BMD
Mechanical Engineering, BMD
Medical Informatics, B
Multi-/Interdisciplinary Studies, B
Music, BMO
Music Performance, B
Music Teacher Education, BM
Music Theory and Composition, B
Music Therapy/Therapist, BM
Non-Profit/Public/Organizational Management, O
Nursing, M
Occupational Therapy/Therapist, BM
Organizational Communication, B
Paper and Pulp Engineering, MD
Parks, Recreation and Leisure Facilities Management, B
Parks, Recreation, Leisure and Fitness Studies, B
Performance, M
Philosophy, BM
Physical Education Teaching and Coaching, BM
Physician Assistant, M
Physics, BMD
Physics Teacher Education, B
Physiology, M
Piano and Organ, B
Political Science and Government, BMD
Psychology, BMD

Public Administration, MDO
Public Affairs, MDO
Public Relations, Advertising, and Applied Communication, B
Public/Applied History and Archival Administration, B
Reading Teacher Education, MD
Rehabilitation Counseling, M
Rehabilitation Sciences, M
Religion/Religious Studies, BMO
Sales and Marketing Operations/Marketing and Distribution Teacher Education, B
Science Teacher Education/General Science Teacher Education, BMDO
Social Science Teacher Education, B
Social Studies Teacher Education, B
Social Work, BM
Sociology, BMD
Spanish Language Teacher Education, B
Spanish Language and Literature, BMD
Special Education and Teaching, MD
Sport and Fitness Administration/Management, BM
Statistics, BMDO
Structural Engineering, B
Technical Theatre/Theatre Design and Technology, B
Technology Teacher Education/Industrial Arts Teacher Education, B
Theatre Literature, History and Criticism, B
Tourism and Travel Services Marketing Operations, B
Trade and Industrial Teacher Education, B
Vocational and Technical Education, M
Voice and Opera, B
Women's Studies, B
Writing, MD

YESHIVA BETH YEHUDA–YESHIVA GEDOLAH OF GREATER DETROIT

Talmudic Studies, B

Minnesota

ACADEMY COLLEGE

Accounting, A
Airline/Commercial/Professional Pilot and Flight Crew, A
Aviation/Airway Management and Operations, A
Business Administration and Management, AB
Business/Commerce, A
Commercial and Advertising Art, A
Computer Graphics, A
Computer Programming/Programmer, A
Computer Science, B
Computer Systems Networking and Telecommunications, A
Computer and Information Sciences, A
Computer and Information Sciences and Support Services, A
Computer and Information Systems Security, A
Data Processing and Data Processing Technology/Technician, A
Design and Visual Communications, A
Finance, A
Graphic Design, A
Intermedia/Multimedia, A
Management Information Systems and Services, A
Office Management and Supervision, A
Sales, Distribution and Marketing Operations, A
System Administration/Administrator, A
System, Networking, and LAN/WAN Management/Manager, A
Web Page, Digital/Multimedia and Information Resources Design, A
Web/Multimedia Management and Webmaster, A

ALEXANDRIA TECHNICAL AND COMMUNITY COLLEGE

Accounting, A
Business Administration and Management, A
Clinical/Medical Laboratory Technician, A
Commercial and Advertising Art, A
Computer Systems Networking and Telecommunications, A
Criminal Justice/Police Science, A
Diesel Mechanics Technology/Technician, A

Early Childhood Education and Teaching, A
Fashion Merchandising, A
Human Services, A
Information Science/Studies, A
Interior Design, A
Legal Administrative Assistant/Secretary, A
Legal Assistant/Paralegal, A
Liberal Arts and Sciences Studies and Humanities, A
Mechanical Drafting and Mechanical Drafting CAD/CADD, A
Medical Administrative Assistant/Secretary, A
Multi-/Interdisciplinary Studies, A
Office Management and Supervision, A
Sales, Distribution and Marketing Operations, A

ANOKA-RAMSEY COMMUNITY COLLEGE

Accounting, A
Accounting Technology/Technician and Bookkeeping, A
Biology/Biological Sciences, A
Biomedical Technology/Technician, A
Business Administration and Management, A
Business/Commerce, A
Community Health and Preventive Medicine, A
Computer Science, A
Computer Systems Networking and Telecommunications, A
Drama and Dramatics/Theatre Arts, A
Environmental Sciences, A
Fine/Studio Arts, A
Health Services/Allied Health/Health Sciences, A
Human Resources Management/Personnel Administration, A
Liberal Arts and Sciences Studies and Humanities, A
Music, A
Pharmacy Technician/Assistant, A
Physical Therapist Assistant, A
Sales, Distribution and Marketing Operations, A

ANOKA TECHNICAL COLLEGE

Accounting, A
Administrative Assistant and Secretarial Science, A
Architectural Drafting and Architectural CAD/CADD, A
Automobile/Automotive Mechanics Technology/Technician, A
Biomedical Technology/Technician, A
Computer Technology/Computer Systems Technology, A
Court Reporting/Court Reporter, A
Electrical, Electronic and Communications Engineering Technology/Technician, A
Health Information/Medical Records Technology/Technician, A
Landscaping and Groundskeeping, A
Legal Administrative Assistant/Secretary, A
Mechanical Drafting and Mechanical Drafting CAD/CADD, A
Medical Administrative Assistant/Secretary, A
Medical/Clinical Assistant, A
Occupational Therapist Assistant, A
Office Management and Supervision, A
Surgical Technology/Technologist, A
Welding Technology/Welder, A

ARGOSY UNIVERSITY, TWIN CITIES

Accounting, D
Biopsychology, D
Business Administration and Management, AB
Business Administration, Management and Operations, MD
Clinical Psychology, MD
Clinical/Medical Laboratory Technician, AB
Criminal Justice/Law Enforcement Administration, B
Dental Hygiene/Hygienist, A
Diagnostic Medical Sonography/Sonographer and Ultrasound Technician, A
Education, MDO
Educational Administration and Supervision, DO
Educational Leadership and Administration, MDO
Educational Media/Instructional Technology, D
Elementary Education and Teaching, D
Finance and Banking, M

Forensic Psychology, MDO
Health Psychology, D
Health Services Administration, M
Higher Education/Higher Education Administration, MD
Histologic Technology/Histotechnologist, A
Industrial and Organizational Psychology, M
Information Technology, AB
International Business/Trade/Commerce, MD
Liberal Arts and Sciences Studies and Humanities, B
Management, MD
Management Information Systems and Services, MD
Marketing, MD
Marriage and Family Therapy/Counseling, MD
Medical Radiologic Technology/Science - Radiation Therapist, A
Medical/Clinical Assistant, A
Organizational Management, D
Psychology, ABMDO
Public Administration, M
Public Health, M
Radiologic Technology/Science - Radiographer, A
Secondary Education and Teaching, D
Sustainability Management, MD
Veterinary/Animal Health Technology/Technician and Veterinary Assistant, A

AUGSBURG COLLEGE

Accounting, B
Acting, B
American Indian/Native American Studies, B
Applied Economics, B
Area Studies, B
Art History, Criticism and Conservation, B
Biology/Biological Sciences, B
Biophysics, B
Biopsychology, B
Business Administration and Management, B
Business Administration, Management and Operations, BM
Chemistry, B
Communication Studies/Speech Communication and Rhetoric, B
Computer Science, B
Design and Applied Arts, B
Directing and Theatrical Production, B
Drama and Dramatics/Theatre Arts, B
Economics, B
Education, BM
Elementary Education and Teaching, B
Engineering, B
English Language and Literature, B
Environmental Studies, B
Film/Cinema Studies, B
Finance, B
Fine/Studio Arts, B
French Language and Literature, B
German Language and Literature, B
Graphic Design, B
Health Teacher Education, B
History, B
International Business/Trade/Commerce, B
International Relations and Affairs, B
Kinesiology and Exercise Science, B
Liberal Arts and Sciences Studies and Humanities, B
Management Information Systems and Services, B
Marketing/Marketing Management, B
Mathematics, B
Medieval and Renaissance Studies, B
Music, B
Music Performance, B
Music Teacher Education, B
Music Therapy/Therapist, B
Nursing, MD
Nursing - Advanced Practice, MD
Organizational Management, M
Philosophy, B
Physical Education Teaching and Coaching, B
Physician Assistant, M
Physics, B
Political Science and Government, B
Psychology, B
Religion/Religious Studies, B

Secondary Education and Teaching, B
Social Work, BM
Sociology, B
Spanish Language and Literature, B
Special Education and Teaching, B
Teacher Education and Professional Development, Specific Subject Areas, B
Teaching English as a Second or Foreign Language/ESL Language Instructor, B
Transcultural Nursing, MD
Urban Studies/Affairs, B
Women's Studies, B
Youth Ministry, B

BEMIDJI STATE UNIVERSITY

Accounting, B
American Indian/Native American Languages, Literatures, and Linguistics, B
American Indian/Native American Studies, B
Art Teacher Education, B
Art/Art Studies, General, B
Behavioral Sciences, B
Biological and Biomedical Sciences, M
Biological and Physical Sciences, B
Biology/Biological Sciences, B
Broadcast Journalism, B
Business Administration and Management, B
Chemistry, B
Clinical Laboratory Science/Medical Technology/Technologist, B
Commercial and Advertising Art, B
Community Organization and Advocacy, B
Computer Science, B
Construction Engineering Technology/Technician, B
Criminal Justice/Law Enforcement Administration, AB
Criminal Justice/Police Science, B
Data Processing and Data Processing Technology/Technician, B
Design and Applied Arts, B
Drama and Dramatics/Theatre Arts, B
Ecology, B
Economics, B
Education, BM
Elementary Education and Teaching, B
Engineering Physics, B
English, M
English Language and Literature, B
Environmental Studies, BM
Fine/Studio Arts, B
Geography, B
Geology/Earth Science, B
German Language and Literature, B
Health Teacher Education, B
History, B
Humanities/Humanistic Studies, B
Industrial Technology/Technician, B
Information Science/Studies, B
Journalism, B
Liberal Arts and Sciences Studies and Humanities, AB
Marine Biology and Biological Oceanography, B
Mass Communication/Media Studies, B
Mathematics, BM
Mathematics Teacher Education, M
Modern Languages, B
Music, B
Music Teacher Education, B
Natural Sciences, B
Parks, Recreation, Leisure and Fitness Studies, B
Philosophy, B
Physical Education Teaching and Coaching, B
Physical Sciences, B
Physics, B
Political Science and Government, B
Pre-Law Studies, B
Pre-Medicine/Pre-Medical Studies, B
Pre-Veterinary Studies, B
Psychology, B
Radio and Television, B
Religion/Religious Studies, B
Science Teacher Education/General Science Teacher Education, B
Secondary Education and Teaching, B
Social Sciences, B
Social Work, B

Sociology, B
Spanish Language and Literature, B
Special Education and Teaching, M
Speech Teacher Education, B
Sport and Fitness Administration/Management, B
Technology Teacher Education/Industrial Arts
  Teacher Education, B
Trade and Industrial Teacher Education, B

BETHANY LUTHERAN COLLEGE

Art/Art Studies, General, B
Biology/Biological Sciences, B
Business Administration and Management, B
Chemistry, B
Communication Studies/Speech Communication
  and Rhetoric, B
Drama and Dramatics/Theatre Arts, B
Elementary Education and Teaching, B
Engineering, B
English Language and Literature, B
Fine/Studio Arts, B
History, B
Law and Legal Studies, B
Liberal Arts and Sciences Studies and Humani-
  ties, B
Mathematics, B
Music, B
Physical Sciences, B
Psychology, B
Religion/Religious Studies, B
Religious/Sacred Music, B
Social Sciences, B
Sociology, B

BETHEL UNIVERSITY

Accounting and Finance, B
Art Teacher Education, B
Art/Art Studies, General, B
Athletic Training and Sports Medicine, B
Bible/Biblical Studies, B
Biological and Biomedical Sciences, B
Biology/Biological Sciences, B
Business Administration and Management, B
Business Administration, Management and Opera-
  tions, M
Chemistry, B
Communication and Media Studies, M
Computer and Information Sciences, B
Counseling Psychology, M
Drama and Dramatics/Theatre Arts, B
Economics, B
Education, M
Educational Leadership and Administration, D
Elementary Education and Teaching, BM
Engineering Science, B
English Language and Literature, B
English/Language Arts Teacher Education, B
Environmental Sciences, B
Environmental Studies, B
Ethnic, Cultural Minority, and Gender Studies, B
Fine/Studio Arts, B
Gerontology, M
Graphic Design, B
Health Teacher Education, B
Higher Education/Higher Education Administra-
  tion, O
History, B
International Relations and Affairs, B
Journalism, B
Kinesiology and Exercise Science, B
Liberal Arts and Sciences Studies and Humani-
  ties, A
Linguistics, B
Mass Communication/Media Studies, B
Mathematics, B
Mathematics Teacher Education, B
Multi-/Interdisciplinary Studies, B
Music, B
Music Performance, B
Music Teacher Education, B
Nurse Midwife/Nursing Midwifery, M
Nursing, M
Nursing Administration, O
Nursing Education, O
Organizational Management, M
Peace Studies and Conflict Resolution, B

Philosophy, B
Physical Education Teaching and Coaching, B
Physician Assistant, M
Physics, B
Political Science and Government, B
Psychology, B
Reading Teacher Education, MO
Secondary Education and Teaching, M
Social Sciences, B
Social Studies Teacher Education, B
Social Work, B
Spanish Language Teacher Education, B
Spanish Language and Literature, B
Special Education and Teaching, MO
Teaching English as a Second or Foreign
  Language/ESL Language Instructor, B

CAPELLA UNIVERSITY

Accounting, BMD
Adult and Continuing Education and Teaching, MD
Applied Behavior Analysis, M
Business Administration and Management, B
Business Administration, Management and Opera-
  tions, BMD
Business Education, D
Child and Family Studies, M
Clinical Psychology, MD
Computer and Information Sciences and Support
  Services, B
Computer and Information Systems Security, BMD
Counseling Psychology, M
Counselor Education/School Counseling and Guid-
  ance Services, MD
Criminal Justice/Safety Studies, B
Criminology, MD
Curriculum and Instruction, MD
Developmental Psychology, M
Distance Education Development, MD
Early Childhood Education and Teaching, M
Education, MD
Educational Leadership and Administration, MD
Educational Media/Instructional Technology, MD
Educational Psychology, MD
Elementary Education and Teaching, MD
Emergency Management, MD
Entrepreneurship/Entrepreneurial Studies, MD
Environmental and Occupational Health, MD
Epidemiology, D
Finance, B
Finance and Banking, MD
Gerontological Nursing, M
Gerontology, M
Health Informatics, M
Health Services Administration, MD
Health/Health Care Administration/Management, B
Higher Education/Higher Education Administra-
  tion, MD
Homeland Security, M
Human Resources Management and Services, MD
Human Resources Management/Personnel Adminis-
  tration, B
Human Services, MD
Industrial Education, D
Industrial and Organizational Psychology, MD
Information Technology, B
Management Information Systems and Ser-
  vices, MD
Management Strategy and Policy, MD
Management of Technology, MD
Marketing, MD
Marketing/Marketing Management, B
Marriage and Family Therapy/Counseling, M
Medical Informatics, B
Middle School Education, MD
Non-Profit/Public/Organizational Management, D
Nursing, MD
Nursing Administration, M
Nursing Education, MD
Operations Research, M
Organizational Management, MD
Project Management, MD
Psychology, BMD
Public Administration, MD
Reading Teacher Education, MD
Retailing and Retail Operations, B
School Psychology, MD

Security and Protective Services, B
Social Work, D
Special Education and Teaching, MD
Sport Psychology, M
Substance Abuse/Addiction Counseling, MD
Supply Chain Management, MD
System, Networking, and LAN/WAN
  Management/Manager, B

CARLETON COLLEGE

African Studies, B
American/United States Studies/Civilization, B
Ancient/Classical Greek Language and Literature, B
Anthropology, B
Art History, Criticism and Conservation, B
Asian Studies/Civilization, B
Biology/Biological Sciences, B
Chemistry, B
Classics and Classical Languages, Litera-
  tures, and Linguistics, B
Computer Science, B
Drama and Dramatics/Theatre Arts, B
Economics, B
English Language and Literature, B
Environmental Studies, B
Film/Cinema Studies, B
Fine/Studio Arts, B
French Language and Literature, B
French Studies, B
Geology/Earth Science, B
German Language and Literature, B
History, B
International Relations and Affairs, B
Latin American Studies, B
Latin Language and Literature, B
Linguistics, B
Mathematics, B
Music, B
Philosophy, B
Physics, B
Political Science and Government, B
Psychology, B
Religion/Religious Studies, B
Romance Languages, Literatures, and Linguistics, B
Russian Language and Literature, B
Russian Studies, B
Sociology, B
Spanish Language and Literature, B
Women's Studies, B

CENTRAL LAKES COLLEGE

Accounting, A
Administrative Assistant and Secretarial Science, A
Applied Horticulture/Horticultural Operations, A
Business Administration and Management, A
Child Care and Support Services Management, A
Commercial and Advertising Art, A
Computer Systems Networking and Telecommunica-
  tions, A
Computer Technology/Computer Systems Technol-
  ogy, A
Conservation Biology, A
Criminal Justice/Police Science, A
Criminal Justice/Safety Studies, A
Criminalistics and Criminal Science, A
Diesel Mechanics Technology/Technician, A
Engineering, A
Horticultural Science, A
Industrial Electronics Technology/Technician, A
Industrial Engineering, A
Kindergarten/PreSchool Education and Teaching, A
Legal Administrative Assistant/Secretary, A
Liberal Arts and Sciences Studies and Humani-
  ties, A
Machine Tool Technology/Machinist, A
Marketing/Marketing Management, A
Mechanical Drafting and Mechanical Drafting
  CAD/CADD, A
Medical Administrative Assistant/Secretary, A
Natural Resources and Conservation, A
Photographic and Film/Video Technology/Technician
  and Assistant, A
Robotics Technology/Technician, A

Welding Technology/Welder, A

CENTURY COLLEGE

Accounting, A
Administrative Assistant and Secretarial Science, A
Animation, Interactive Technology, Video Graphics and Special Effects, A
Building/Property Maintenance and Management, A
Business Administration and Management, A
CAD/CADD Drafting and/or Design Technology/Technician, A
Cinematography and Film/Video Production, A
Commercial Photography, A
Computer Science, A
Computer Systems Networking and Telecommunications, A
Computer Technology/Computer Systems Technology, A
Computer and Information Systems Security, A
Cosmetology/Cosmetologist, A
Criminal Justice/Police Science, A
Criminal Justice/Safety Studies, A
Dental Assisting/Assistant, A
Dental Hygiene/Hygienist, A
E-Commerce/Electronic Commerce, A
Education, A
Emergency Medical Technology/Technician (EMT Paramedic), A
Energy Management and Systems Technology/Technician, A
Fine/Studio Arts, A
Graphic Design, A
Greenhouse Operations and Management, A
Health Services/Allied Health/Health Sciences, A
Heating, Air Conditioning, Ventilation and Refrigeration Maintenance Technology/Technician, A
Horticultural Science, A
Human Services, A
Information Science/Studies, A
Interior Design, A
Landscaping and Groundskeeping, A
Language Interpretation and Translation, A
Liberal Arts and Sciences Studies and Humanities, A
Marketing/Marketing Management, A
Medical Administrative Assistant/Secretary, A
Multi-/Interdisciplinary Studies, A
Music, A
Orthotist/Prosthetist, A
Radiologic Technology/Science - Radiographer, A
Security and Protective Services, A
Substance Abuse/Addiction Counseling, A
Teacher Assistant/Aide, A
Web Page, Digital/Multimedia and Information Resources Design, A

COLLEGE OF SAINT BENEDICT

Accounting, B
Art/Art Studies, General, B
Biochemistry, B
Biological and Physical Sciences, B
Biology/Biological Sciences, B
Business Administration and Management, B
Chemistry, B
Classics and Classical Languages, Literatures, and Linguistics, B
Computational Mathematics, B
Computer Science, B
Dietetics and Clinical Nutrition Services, B
Drama and Dramatics/Theatre Arts, B
Economics, B
Elementary Education and Teaching, B
English Language and Literature, B
Environmental Studies, B
Fine/Studio Arts, B
Forestry, B
French Language and Literature, B
German Language and Literature, B
History, B
Humanities/Humanistic Studies, B
Liberal Arts and Sciences Studies and Humanities, B
Mathematics, B
Multi-/Interdisciplinary Studies, B
Music, B
Natural Sciences, B

Nutritional Sciences, B
Occupational Therapy/Therapist, B
Peace Studies and Conflict Resolution, B
Philosophy, B
Physical Therapy/Therapist, B
Physics, B
Political Science and Government, B
Pre-Dentistry Studies, B
Pre-Law Studies, B
Pre-Medicine/Pre-Medical Studies, B
Pre-Pharmacy Studies, B
Pre-Theology/Pre-Ministerial Studies, B
Pre-Veterinary Studies, B
Psychology, B
Secondary Education and Teaching, B
Social Sciences, B
Sociology, B
Spanish Language and Literature, B
Theology/Theological Studies, B
Women's Studies, B

THE COLLEGE OF ST. SCHOLASTICA

Accounting, B
Applied Economics, B
Art/Art Studies, General, B
Athletic Training and Sports Medicine, M
Biochemistry, B
Biology/Biological Sciences, B
Business Administration and Management, B
Chemistry, B
Christian Studies, B
Communication Studies/Speech Communication and Rhetoric, B
Computer and Information Sciences, B
Education, MO
Elementary Education and Teaching, B
English Language and Literature, B
Exercise Physiology, B
Exercise and Sports Science, M
Finance, B
Health Informatics, MO
Health Information/Medical Records Administration/Administrator, B
Health Services/Allied Health/Health Sciences, B
History, B
Humanities/Humanistic Studies, B
Indian/Native American Education, B
International/Global Studies, B
Journalism, B
Management, MO
Management Information Systems and Services, MO
Marketing/Marketing Management, B
Mathematics, B
Music Performance, B
Natural Sciences, B
Nursing, MO
Occupational Therapy/Therapist, M
Organizational Behavior Studies, B
Peace Studies and Conflict Resolution, B
Philosophy, B
Physical Sciences, B
Physical Therapy/Therapist, D
Psychology, B
Public Relations, Advertising, and Applied Communication, B
Religion/Religious Studies, B
School Librarian/School Library Media Specialist, B
Social Sciences, B
Social Work, BM
Spanish Language and Literature, B
Teacher Education, Multiple Levels, B

CONCORDIA COLLEGE

Accounting, B
Art Teacher Education, B
Art/Art Studies, General, B
Biology Teacher Education, B
Biology/Biological Sciences, B
Business Administration and Management, B
Business Teacher Education, B
Chemistry, B
Chemistry Teacher Education, B
Chinese Language and Literature, B
Classics and Classical Languages, Literatures, and Linguistics, B

Communication Studies/Speech Communication and Rhetoric, B
Drama and Dramatics/Theatre Arts, B
Education, BM
Elementary Education and Teaching, B
English Language and Literature, B
Environmental Studies, B
Finance, B
Foreign Language Teacher Education, BM
French Language Teacher Education, B
French Language and Literature, B
German Language Teacher Education, B
German Language and Literature, B
Health Teacher Education, B
Health and Physical Education, B
Health and Physical Education/Fitness, B
History, B
Humanities/Humanistic Studies, B
International Business/Trade/Commerce, B
International/Global Studies, B
Journalism, B
Latin Language and Literature, B
Latin Teacher Education, B
Liberal Arts and Sciences Studies and Humanities, B
Mathematics, B
Mathematics Teacher Education, B
Museology/Museum Studies, B
Music, B
Music Performance, B
Music Teacher Education, B
Music Theory and Composition, B
Natural Sciences, B
Nutritional Sciences, B
Philosophy, B
Physical Education Teaching and Coaching, B
Physics, B
Physics Teacher Education, B
Political Science and Government, B
Psychology, B
Religion/Religious Studies, B
Scandinavian Studies, B
Social Studies Teacher Education, B
Social Work, B
Sociology, B
Spanish Language Teacher Education, B
Spanish Language and Literature, B

CONCORDIA UNIVERSITY, ST. PAUL

Accounting, B
Applied Mathematics, B
Art Teacher Education, B
Art/Art Studies, General, B
Biology Teacher Education, B
Biology/Biological Sciences, B
Business Administration and Management, B
Business Administration, Management and Operations, M
Chemistry, B
Chemistry Teacher Education, B
Child Development, B
Child and Family Studies, M
Computer Science, B
Computer/Information Technology Services Administration and Management, B
Corporate and Organizational Communication, M
Criminal Justice/Safety Studies, B
Criminology, M
Curriculum and Instruction, M
Design and Visual Communications, B
Drama and Dramatics/Theatre Arts, B
Early Childhood Education and Teaching, BM
Education, BMDO
Educational Leadership and Administration, MO
Educational Media/Instructional Technology, M
Elementary Education and Teaching, B
Engineering Science, B
English Language and Literature, B
Exercise and Sports Science, M
Finance, B
Fine/Studio Arts, B
Forensic Psychology, M
General Studies, AB
Health Services Administration, M
Health Teacher Education, B
Health and Medical Administrative Services, B

Health and Physical Education, B
Health/Health Care Administration/Management, B
History, B
Hospitality Administration/Management, B
Human Development and Family Studies, B
Human Resources Management and Services, M
Human Resources Management/Personnel Adminis-
 tration, B
Journalism, B
Junior High/Intermediate/Middle School Education
 and Teaching, B
Kinesiology and Exercise Science, B
Marketing/Marketing Management, B
Mass Communication/Media Studies, B
Mathematics, B
Mathematics Teacher Education, B
Missions/Missionary Studies and Missiology, B
Music, B
Music Teacher Education, B
Organizational Behavior Studies, M
Organizational Management, M
Orthotist/Prosthetist, B
Physical Education Teaching and Coaching, B
Physical Therapy/Therapist, D
Psychology, B
Public Policy Analysis, B
Reading Teacher Education, MO
Religious Education, B
Religious/Sacred Music, B
Respiratory Care Therapy/Therapist, B
Secondary Education and Teaching, B
Social Studies Teacher Education, B
Sociology, B
Special Education and Teaching, MO
Sport and Fitness Administration/Management, BM
Teaching English as a Second or Foreign
 Language/ESL Language Instructor, B
Theological and Ministerial Studies, B
Theology/Theological Studies, B

CROSSROADS COLLEGE

Bible/Biblical Studies, B
Business Administration and Management, B
Business Administration, Management and Opera-
 tions, B
Liberal Arts and Sciences Studies and Humani-
 ties, AB
Missions/Missionary Studies and Missiology, B
Music, B
Pre-Theology/Pre-Ministerial Studies, B
Religious Education, B
Religious/Sacred Music, B
Theology and Religious Vocations, B
Theology/Theological Studies, B
Youth Ministry, B

CROWN COLLEGE

Biology/Biological Sciences, B
Business Administration and Management, B
Business Administration, Management and Opera-
 tions, B
Business/Commerce, A
Christian Studies, AB
Communication and Media Studies, B
Education, B
Elementary Education and Teaching, B
English Language and Literature, B
English/Language Arts Teacher Education, B
Entrepreneurial and Small Business Operations, B
Entrepreneurship/Entrepreneurial Studies, B
General Studies, B
History, B
Liberal Arts and Sciences Studies and Humani-
 ties, B
Missions/Missionary Studies and Missiology, B
Music, B
Music Teacher Education, B
Pastoral Studies/Counseling, B
Physical Education Teaching and Coaching, B
Pre-Law Studies, B
Psychology, B
Religious Education, B
Religious/Sacred Music, B
Science Teacher Education/General Science
 Teacher Education, B
Social Studies Teacher Education, B

Sport and Fitness Administration/Management, B
Teaching English as a Second or Foreign
 Language/ESL Language Instructor, B
Theology and Religious Vocations, M
Theology/Theological Studies, B
Youth Ministry, B

DAKOTA COUNTY TECHNICAL COL-
LEGE

Accounting, A
Autobody/Collision and Repair
 Technology/Technician, A
Automobile/Automotive Mechanics
 Technology/Technician, A
Biomedical Technology/Technician, A
Business Administration and Management, A
Child Care Provider/Assistant, A
Commercial and Advertising Art, A
Computer Programming/Programmer, A
Computer Systems Networking and Telecommunica-
 tions, A
Dental Assisting/Assistant, A
Electrician, A
Energy Management and Systems
 Technology/Technician, A
Executive Assistant/Executive Secretary, A
Graphic Design, A
Heavy Equipment Maintenance
 Technology/Technician, A
Interior Design, A
Kinesiology and Exercise Science, A
Landscaping and Groundskeeping, A
Legal Administrative Assistant/Secretary, A
Lineworker, A
Manufacturing Technology/Technician, A
Marketing/Marketing Management, A
Mason/Masonry, A
Medical Administrative Assistant/Secretary, A
Medical/Clinical Assistant, A
Medium/Heavy Vehicle and Truck
 Technology/Technician, A
Photography, A
Real Estate, A
Tourism and Travel Services Management, A
Web Page, Digital/Multimedia and Information Re-
 sources Design, A

DULUTH BUSINESS UNIVERSITY

Accounting Technology/Technician and Bookkeep-
 ing, A
Business Administration and Management, A
Commercial and Advertising Art, A
Health Information/Medical Records
 Technology/Technician, A
Massage Therapy/Therapeutic Massage, A
Medical/Clinical Assistant, A
Phlebotomy/Phlebotomist, A
Veterinary/Animal Health Technology/Technician and
 Veterinary Assistant, A

DUNWOODY COLLEGE OF TECHNOL-
OGY

Architectural Drafting and Architectural
 CAD/CADD, A
Architectural Technology/Technician, A
Architecture, B
Autobody/Collision and Repair
 Technology/Technician, A
Automobile/Automotive Mechanics
 Technology/Technician, A
Building/Construction Site Management/Manager, A
Business Administration and Management, B
CAD/CADD Drafting and/or Design
 Technology/Technician, A
Computer Science, B
Computer Systems Networking and Telecommunica-
 tions, A
Construction Management, AB
Electrical, Electronic and Communications Engineer-
 ing Technology/Technician, A
Electrical/Electronics Drafting and
 Electrical/Electronics CAD/CADD, A
Electrician, A
Graphic Design, A
Heating, Air Conditioning and Refrigeration
 Technology/Technician, A

Heating, Air Conditioning, Ventilation and Refrigera-
 tion Maintenance Technology/Technician, A
Industrial Technology/Technician, B
Interior Design, B
Medical Radiologic Technology/Science - Radiation
 Therapist, A
Prepress/Desktop Publishing and Digital Imaging
 Design, A
Printing Press Operator, A
Robotics Technology/Technician, A
Tool and Die Technology/Technician, A
Web Page, Digital/Multimedia and Information Re-
 sources Design, A
Welding Technology/Welder, A

FOND DU LAC TRIBAL AND COMMU-
NITY COLLEGE

Cartography, A
Corrections, A
Criminal Justice/Police Science, A
Electrical and Power Transmission
 Installation/Installer, A
Environmental Sciences, A
Finance, A
Human Services, A
Liberal Arts and Sciences Studies and Humani-
 ties, A

GLOBE UNIVERSITY–MINNEAPOLIS

Accounting, AB
Business Administration and Management, AB
Computer Programming, Specific Applications, AB
Computer Systems Networking and Telecommunica-
 tions, A
Criminal Justice/Law Enforcement Administra-
 tion, AB
Information Technology, B
Legal Assistant/Paralegal, AB
Marketing/Marketing Management, A

GLOBE UNIVERSITY–WOODBURY

Accounting, AB
Animal Sciences, A
Architectural Drafting and Architectural
 CAD/CADD, A
Business Administration and Management, AB
Business Administration, Management and Opera-
 tions, M
Computer Programming, Specific Applications, AB
Computer Software Technology/Technician, A
Computer Systems Networking and Telecommunica-
 tions, A
Criminal Justice/Law Enforcement Administra-
 tion, AB
Health Services Administration, M
Health/Health Care Administration/Management, B
Information Technology, B
Legal Assistant/Paralegal, AB
Management Information Systems and Services, M
Marketing/Marketing Management, A
Massage Therapy/Therapeutic Massage, A
Mechanical Drafting and Mechanical Drafting
 CAD/CADD, A
Medical Administrative Assistant/Secretary, A
Medical/Clinical Assistant, A
Veterinary/Animal Health Technology/Technician and
 Veterinary Assistant, AB

GUSTAVUS ADOLPHUS COLLEGE

Accounting, B
Anthropology, B
Art History, Criticism and Conservation, B
Art Teacher Education, B
Art/Art Studies, General, B
Athletic Training and Sports Medicine, B
Biochemistry, B
Biology Teacher Education, B
Biology/Biological Sciences, B
Business Administration and Management, B
Business/Managerial Economics, B
Chemistry, B
Chemistry Teacher Education, B
Classics and Classical Languages, Litera-
 tures, and Linguistics, B
Computer Science, B

Criminal Justice/Law Enforcement Administration, B
Dance, B
Drama and Dramatics/Theatre Arts, B
Economics, B
Education, B
Elementary Education and Teaching, B
English Language and Literature, B
Environmental Studies, B
French Language and Literature, B
Geography, B
Geology/Earth Science, B
German Language and Literature, B
Health Teacher Education, B
Health and Physical Education/Fitness, B
History, B
International Business/Trade/Commerce, B
Japanese Language and Literature, B
Japanese Studies, B
Latin American Studies, B
Mass Communication/Media Studies, B
Mathematics, B
Mathematics Teacher Education, B
Music, B
Music Performance, B
Music Teacher Education, B
Natural Resources and Conservation, B
Philosophy, B
Physical Education Teaching and Coaching, B
Physical Therapy/Therapist, B
Physics, B
Physics Teacher Education, B
Political Science and Government, B
Pre-Dentistry Studies, B
Pre-Law Studies, B
Pre-Medicine/Pre-Medical Studies, B
Pre-Veterinary Studies, B
Psychology, B
Religion/Religious Studies, B
Religious/Sacred Music, B
Russian Language and Literature, B
Russian Studies, B
Scandinavian Languages, Literatures, and Linguistics, B
Scandinavian Studies, B
Secondary Education and Teaching, B
Social Sciences, B
Social Studies Teacher Education, B
Sociology, B
Spanish Language and Literature, B
Women's Studies, B

HAMLINE UNIVERSITY

Accounting, B
Anthropology, B
Art History, Criticism and Conservation, B
Biochemistry, B
Biology/Biological Sciences, B
Business Administration and Management, B
Business Administration, Management and Operations, M
Business, Management, Marketing, and Related Support Services, B
Chemistry, B
Communication Studies/Speech Communication and Rhetoric, B
Criminal Justice/Safety Studies, B
Drama and Dramatics/Theatre Arts, B
East Asian Studies, B
Economics, B
Education, MD
Elementary Education and Teaching, B
English Language and Literature, B
English as a Second Language, M
Environmental Education, M
Environmental Studies, B
Finance, B
Fine/Studio Arts, B
German Language and Literature, B
History, B
International Business/Trade/Commerce, B
International/Global Studies, B
Kinesiology and Exercise Science, B
Latin American Studies, B
Law and Legal Studies, B
Liberal Studies, M
Management, MD

Management Science, B
Marketing/Marketing Management, B
Mathematics, B
Multi-/Interdisciplinary Studies, B
Music, B
Music Performance, B
Non-Profit/Public/Organizational Management, M
Peace Studies and Conflict Resolution, B
Philosophy, B
Physics, B
Political Science and Government, B
Pre-Dentistry Studies, B
Pre-Law Studies, B
Pre-Medicine/Pre-Medical Studies, B
Pre-Pharmacy Studies, B
Pre-Veterinary Studies, B
Psychology, B
Public Administration, MD
Reading Teacher Education, M
Religion/Religious Studies, B
Science Teacher Education/General Science Teacher Education, M
Secondary Education and Teaching, B
Social Sciences, B
Sociology, B
Spanish Language and Literature, B
Sport and Fitness Administration/Management, B
Teacher Education, Multiple Levels, B
Women's Studies, B
Writing, M

HENNEPIN TECHNICAL COLLEGE

Accounting, A
Administrative Assistant and Secretarial Science, A
Architectural Drafting and Architectural CAD/CADD, A
Autobody/Collision and Repair Technology/Technician, A
Automobile/Automotive Mechanics Technology/Technician, A
Business Administration and Management, A
CAD/CADD Drafting and/or Design Technology/Technician, A
Carpentry/Carpenter, A
Child Development, A
Computer Programming/Programmer, A
Computer Systems Networking and Telecommunications, A
Dental Assisting/Assistant, A
Drafting/Design Engineering Technologies/Technicians, A
Electrical, Electronic and Communications Engineering Technology/Technician, A
Fire Science/Firefighting, A
Graphic Design, A
Greenhouse Operations and Management, A
Heating, Air Conditioning, Ventilation and Refrigeration Maintenance Technology/Technician, A
Hydraulics and Fluid Power Technology, A
Landscaping and Groundskeeping, A
Machine Tool Technology/Machinist, A
Management Information Systems and Services, A
Manufacturing Technology/Technician, A
Medical Administrative Assistant/Secretary, A
Medium/Heavy Vehicle and Truck Technology/Technician, A
Photography, A
Plastics Engineering Technology/Technician, A
Prepress/Desktop Publishing and Digital Imaging Design, A
Recording Arts Technology/Technician, A
Tool and Die Technology/Technician, A
Urban Forestry, A
Web Page, Digital/Multimedia and Information Resources Design, A

HERZING UNIVERSITY

Computer Systems Networking and Telecommunications, A
Computer and Information Sciences, A
Dental Assisting/Assistant, A
Dental Hygiene/Hygienist, A
Management Information Systems and Services, B
Massage Therapy/Therapeutic Massage, A
Medical Insurance Coding Specialist/Coder, A

Medical/Clinical Assistant, A

HIBBING COMMUNITY COLLEGE

Administrative Assistant and Secretarial Science, A
Business Administration and Management, A
Clinical/Medical Laboratory Technician, A
Criminal Justice/Police Science, A
Digital Communication and Media/Multimedia, A
Engineering, A
Heavy/Industrial Equipment Maintenance Technologies, A
Legal Administrative Assistant/Secretary, A
Liberal Arts and Sciences Studies and Humanities, A
Medical Administrative Assistant/Secretary, A
Restaurant, Culinary, and Catering Management/Manager, A

THE INSTITUTE OF PRODUCTION AND RECORDING

Recording Arts Technology/Technician, A

INVER HILLS COMMUNITY COLLEGE

Accounting, A
Airline/Commercial/Professional Pilot and Flight Crew, A
Aviation/Airway Management and Operations, A
Biology/Biological Sciences, A
Building/Construction Finishing, Management, and Inspection, A
Building/Construction Site Management/Manager, A
Building/Home/Construction Inspection/Inspector, A
Business Administration and Management, A
Business/Commerce, A
Computer Programming, Specific Applications, A
Computer Programming, Vendor/Product Certification, A
Computer Programming/Programmer, A
Computer Science, A
Computer Systems Networking and Telecommunications, A
Computer Technology/Computer Systems Technology, A
Computer and Information Sciences and Support Services, A
Criminal Justice/Police Science, A
Criminal Justice/Safety Studies, A
Education, A
Emergency Medical Technology/Technician (EMT Paramedic), A
Fine/Studio Arts, A
Health/Health Care Administration/Management, A
Human Services, A
Legal Administrative Assistant/Secretary, A
Legal Assistant/Paralegal, A
Liberal Arts and Sciences Studies and Humanities, A
Medical Administrative Assistant/Secretary, A
Multi-/Interdisciplinary Studies, A
Physical Education Teaching and Coaching, A
System Administration/Administrator, A

ITASCA COMMUNITY COLLEGE

Accounting, A
American Indian/Native American Studies, A
Business Administration and Management, A
Chemical Engineering, A
Civil Engineering, A
Computer Engineering, A
Education, A
Education/Teaching of Individuals in Early Childhood Special Education Programs, A
Engineering, A
Engineering Science, A
Engineering Technology, A
Environmental Studies, A
Fishing and Fisheries Sciences and Management, A
Forestry, A
Forestry Technology/Technician, A
General Studies, A
Geography, A
Human Services, A
Liberal Arts and Sciences Studies and Humanities, A
Mechanical Engineering, A

Natural Resources Management/Development and
Policy, A
Natural Resources and Conservation, A
Nuclear Engineering, A
Psychology, A
Teacher Education, Multiple Levels, A
Wildlife and Wildlands Science and Management, A

LAKE SUPERIOR COLLEGE

Accounting, A
Airline/Commercial/Professional Pilot and Flight
Crew, A
Architectural Drafting and Architectural
CAD/CADD, A
Automobile/Automotive Mechanics
Technology/Technician, A
Business Administration and Management, A
Business/Office Automation/Technology/Data En-
try, A
CAD/CADD Drafting and/or Design
Technology/Technician, A
Civil Engineering Technology/Technician, A
Clinical/Medical Laboratory Technician, A
Computer Technology/Computer Systems Technol-
ogy, A
Dental Hygiene/Hygienist, A
Electrical, Electronic and Communications Engineer-
ing Technology/Technician, A
Electrician, A
Fine/Studio Arts, A
Fire Protection and Safety Technology/Technician, A
Health Services/Allied Health/Health Sciences, A
Legal Administrative Assistant/Secretary, A
Legal Assistant/Paralegal, A
Liberal Arts and Sciences Studies and Humani-
ties, A
Management Information Systems and Services, A
Mechanical Drafting and Mechanical Drafting
CAD/CADD, A
Medical Administrative Assistant/Secretary, A
Multi-/Interdisciplinary Studies, A
Office Management and Supervision, A
Physical Therapist Assistant, A
Radiologic Technology/Science - Radiographer, A
Respiratory Care Therapy/Therapist, A
Sheet Metal Technology/Sheetworking, A
Surgical Technology/Technologist, A
System Administration/Administrator, A
Web Page, Digital/Multimedia and Information Re-
sources Design, A

LEECH LAKE TRIBAL COLLEGE

Business Administration, Management and Opera-
tions, A
Early Childhood Education and Teaching, A
Foods, Nutrition, and Wellness Studies, A
Liberal Arts and Sciences Studies and Humani-
ties, A

MACALESTER COLLEGE

Anthropology, B
Art/Art Studies, General, B
Asian Studies/Civilization, B
Biology/Biological Sciences, B
Chemistry, B
Chinese Language and Literature, B
Classics and Classical Languages, Litera-
tures, and Linguistics, B
Computer and Information Sciences, B
Drama and Dramatics/Theatre Arts, B
Economics, B
Education, B
English Language and Literature, B
Environmental Studies, B
French Language and Literature, B
Geography, B
Geology/Earth Science, B
German Language and Literature, B
History, B
Intercultural/Multicultural and Diversity Studies, B
International/Global Studies, B
Japanese Language and Literature, B
Latin American Studies, B
Linguistics, B
Mass Communication/Media Studies, B
Mathematics, B

Multi-/Interdisciplinary Studies, B
Music, B
Philosophy, B
Physics, B
Political Science and Government, B
Psychology, B
Religion/Religious Studies, B
Russian Language and Literature, B
Sociology, B
Spanish Language and Literature, B
Women's Studies, B

MARTIN LUTHER COLLEGE

Curriculum and Instruction, M
Education, M
Educational Leadership and Administration, M
Elementary Education and Teaching, B
Kindergarten/PreSchool Education and Teaching, B
Pre-Theology/Pre-Ministerial Studies, B
Special Education and Teaching, M
Teacher Education, Multiple Levels, B
Theology/Theological Studies, B

MCNALLY SMITH COLLEGE OF MUSIC

Music, B
Music Theory and Composition, B
Performance, M
Piano and Organ, AB
Violin, Viola, Guitar and Other Stringed Instru-
ments, AB
Voice and Opera, AB

MESABI RANGE COLLEGE

Administrative Assistant and Secretarial Science, A
Business/Commerce, A
Computer Graphics, A
Computer Programming, A
Computer Programming, Specific Applications, A
Computer Software and Media Applications, A
Computer Systems Networking and Telecommunica-
tions, A
Computer/Information Technology Services Adminis-
tration and Management, A
Electrical/Electronics Equipment Installation and Re-
pair, A
Human Services, A
Information Technology, A
Instrumentation Technology/Technician, A
Liberal Arts and Sciences Studies and Humani-
ties, A
Substance Abuse/Addiction Counseling, A
Web Page, Digital/Multimedia and Information Re-
sources Design, A

METROPOLITAN STATE UNIVERSITY

Accounting, B
Advertising, B
Applied Mathematics, B
Biology Teacher Education, B
Biology/Biological Sciences, B
Business Administration and Management, B
Business Administration, Management and Opera-
tions, MDO
Communication Studies/Speech Communication
and Rhetoric, B
Computer Science, BM
Computer and Information Systems Security, BO
Criminal Justice/Police Science, B
Criminal Justice/Safety Studies, B
Criminology, M
Database Systems, O
Dental Hygiene/Hygienist, B
Drama and Dramatics/Theatre Arts, B
Early Childhood Education and Teaching, B
Economics, B
Elementary Education and Teaching, B
English Language and Literature, B
English/Language Arts Teacher Education, B
Ethnic and Cultural Studies, B
Finance, B
Health Informatics, O
History, B
Hospitality Administration/Management, B
Human Resources Management/Personnel Adminis-
tration, B
Human Services, B

Information Resources Management/CIO Training, B
Information Science/Studies, BM
International Business/Trade/Commerce, B
Liberal Arts and Sciences Studies and Humani-
ties, B
Liberal Studies, M
Management Information Systems and Ser-
vices, BO
Marketing/Marketing Management, B
Mathematics Teacher Education, B
Multi-/Interdisciplinary Studies, B
Non-Profit/Public/Organizational Management, BM
Nursing, MD
Nursing Administration, M
Nursing Education, M
Operations Management and Supervision, B
Oral and Dental Sciences, M
Philosophy, B
Playwriting and Screenwriting, B
Project Management, O
Psychology, BM
Public Administration, BM
Sales, Distribution and Marketing Operations, B
Social Sciences, B
Social Studies Teacher Education, B
Social Work, B
Substance Abuse/Addiction Counseling, B
Technical and Business Writing, M
Women's Studies, B

MINNEAPOLIS BUSINESS COLLEGE

Accounting Technology/Technician and Bookkeep-
ing, A
Administrative Assistant and Secretarial Science, A
Computer Programming/Programmer, A
Computer Systems Networking and Telecommunica-
tions, A
Graphic Design, A
Hotel/Motel Administration/Management, A
Legal Administrative Assistant/Secretary, A
Legal Assistant/Paralegal, A
Medical/Clinical Assistant, A

MINNEAPOLIS COLLEGE OF ART AND DESIGN

Advertising, B
Animation, Interactive Technology, Video Graphics
and Special Effects, B
Applied Arts and Design, M
Cinematography and Film/Video Production, B
Commercial and Advertising Art, B
Computer Art and Design, O
Drawing, B
Film, Television, and Video Production, M
Fine Arts and Art Studies, MO
Fine/Studio Arts, B
Graphic Design, MO
Illustration, BM
Intermedia/Multimedia, B
Painting, BM
Photography, BM
Printmaking, B
Sculpture, BM
Sustainable Development, O

MINNEAPOLIS COMMUNITY AND TECHNICAL COLLEGE

Accounting, A
Accounting Technology/Technician and Bookkeep-
ing, A
Administrative Assistant and Secretarial Science, A
Allied Health Diagnostic, Intervention, and Treat-
ment Professions, A
Animation, Interactive Technology, Video Graphics
and Special Effects, A
Biology/Biological Sciences, A
Business Administration and Management, A
Business/Office Automation/Technology/Data En-
try, A
Chemistry, A
Child Care and Support Services Management, A
Child Development, A
Cinematography and Film/Video Production, A
Commercial Photography, A
Community Organization and Advocacy, A
Computer Programming/Programmer, A

Computer Systems Networking and Telecommunications, A
Computer and Information Systems Security, A
Criminal Justice/Police Science, A
Criminal Justice/Safety Studies, A
Dental Assisting/Assistant, A
Design and Visual Communications, A
Digital Communication and Media/Multimedia, A
Drama and Dramatics/Theatre Arts, A
Education, A
Fine/Studio Arts, A
Heating, Air Conditioning, Ventilation and Refrigeration Maintenance Technology/Technician, A
Human Services, A
Liberal Arts and Sciences Studies and Humanities, A
Library Assistant/Technician, A
Mathematics, A
Philosophy, A
Photographic and Film/Video Technology/Technician and Assistant, A
Playwriting and Screenwriting, A
Public Administration, A
Recording Arts Technology/Technician, A
Restaurant/Food Services Management, A
Substance Abuse/Addiction Counseling, A
System Administration/Administrator, A
Teacher Education, Multiple Levels, A
Web Page, Digital/Multimedia and Information Resources Design, A

MINNESOTA SCHOOL OF BUSINESS–BLAINE

Accounting, AB
Business Administration and Management, AB
Computer Programming, Specific Applications, AB
Computer Systems Networking and Telecommunications, A
Criminal Justice/Law Enforcement Administration, AB
Health/Health Care Administration/Management, B
Information Technology, B
Legal Assistant/Paralegal, AB
Marketing/Marketing Management, A
Massage Therapy/Therapeutic Massage, A
Medical Administrative Assistant/Secretary, A
Medical/Clinical Assistant, A
Veterinary/Animal Health Technology/Technician and Veterinary Assistant, A

MINNESOTA SCHOOL OF BUSINESS–BROOKLYN CENTER

Accounting, AB
Business Administration and Management, AB
Computer Programming, Specific Applications, AB
Computer Systems Networking and Telecommunications, A
Criminal Justice/Law Enforcement Administration, AB
Health/Health Care Administration/Management, B
Information Technology, B
Legal Assistant/Paralegal, AB
Marketing/Marketing Management, A
Medical Administrative Assistant/Secretary, A
Medical/Clinical Assistant, A

MINNESOTA SCHOOL OF BUSINESS– ELK RIVER

Accounting, AB
Business Administration and Management, AB
Computer Programming, Specific Applications, AB
Computer Systems Networking and Telecommunications, A
Criminal Justice/Law Enforcement Administration, AB
Health/Health Care Administration/Management, B
Information Technology, B
Legal Assistant/Paralegal, AB
Marketing/Marketing Management, A
Massage Therapy/Therapeutic Massage, A
Medical Administrative Assistant/Secretary, A
Medical/Clinical Assistant, A

Veterinary/Animal Health Technology/Technician and Veterinary Assistant, A

MINNESOTA SCHOOL OF BUSINESS–LAKEVILLE

Accounting, AB
Business Administration and Management, AB
Computer Programming, Specific Applications, AB
Computer Systems Networking and Telecommunications, A
Criminal Justice/Law Enforcement Administration, AB
Information Technology, B
Marketing/Marketing Management, A
Massage Therapy/Therapeutic Massage, A
Medical/Clinical Assistant, A
Veterinary/Animal Health Technology/Technician and Veterinary Assistant, A

MINNESOTA SCHOOL OF BUSINESS–PLYMOUTH

Accounting, AB
Business Administration and Management, AB
Computer Programming, Specific Applications, AB
Computer Systems Networking and Telecommunications, A
Health/Health Care Administration/Management, B
Information Technology, B
Marketing/Marketing Management, A
Massage Therapy/Therapeutic Massage, A
Veterinary/Animal Health Technology/Technician and Veterinary Assistant, AB

MINNESOTA SCHOOL OF BUSINESS–RICHFIELD

Accounting, AB
Animation, Interactive Technology, Video Graphics and Special Effects, A
Computer Programming, Specific Applications, AB
Computer Programming/Programmer, A
Computer Systems Networking and Telecommunications, A
Criminal Justice/Law Enforcement Administration, AB
Graphic Design, A
Health/Health Care Administration/Management, B
Information Technology, B
Legal Assistant/Paralegal, AB
Marketing/Marketing Management, A
Medical Administrative Assistant/Secretary, A
Medical/Clinical Assistant, A

MINNESOTA SCHOOL OF BUSINESS–ROCHESTER

Accounting, AB
Business Administration and Management, AB
Computer Programming, Specific Applications, AB
Computer Systems Networking and Telecommunications, A
Criminal Justice/Law Enforcement Administration, AB
Health/Health Care Administration/Management, B
Information Technology, B
Legal Assistant/Paralegal, AB
Marketing/Marketing Management, A
Massage Therapy/Therapeutic Massage, A
Medical Administrative Assistant/Secretary, A
Medical/Clinical Assistant, A
Veterinary/Animal Health Technology/Technician and Veterinary Assistant, A

MINNESOTA SCHOOL OF BUSINESS–ST. CLOUD

Accounting, AB
Business Administration and Management, AB
Computer Programming, Specific Applications, AB
Computer Systems Networking and Telecommunications, A
Criminal Justice/Law Enforcement Administration, AB
Graphic Design, A
Health/Health Care Administration/Management, B
Information Technology, B
Legal Assistant/Paralegal, AB
Marketing/Marketing Management, A

Massage Therapy/Therapeutic Massage, A
Medical Administrative Assistant/Secretary, A
Medical/Clinical Assistant, A
Veterinary/Animal Health Technology/Technician and Veterinary Assistant, A

MINNESOTA STATE COLLEGE–SOUTHEAST TECHNICAL

Accounting, A
Accounting Technology/Technician and Bookkeeping, A
Administrative Assistant and Secretarial Science, A
Autobody/Collision and Repair Technology/Technician, A
Biomedical Technology/Technician, A
Business Administration and Management, A
CAD/CADD Drafting and/or Design Technology/Technician, A
Carpentry/Carpenter, A
Computer Programming/Programmer, A
Computer Systems Networking and Telecommunications, A
Computer Technology/Computer Systems Technology, A
Cosmetology/Cosmetologist, A
Criminal Justice/Safety Studies, A
Early Childhood Education and Teaching, A
Electrical, Electronic and Communications Engineering Technology/Technician, A
Heating, Air Conditioning, Ventilation and Refrigeration Maintenance Technology/Technician, A
Industrial Mechanics and Maintenance Technology, A
Legal Administrative Assistant/Secretary, A
Massage Therapy/Therapeutic Massage, A
Medical Administrative Assistant/Secretary, A
Multi-/Interdisciplinary Studies, A
Radiologic Technology/Science - Radiographer, A
Retailing and Retail Operations, A
Sales, Distribution and Marketing Operations, A
Selling Skills and Sales Operations, A
Web Page, Digital/Multimedia and Information Resources Design, A

MINNESOTA STATE COMMUNITY AND TECHNICAL COLLEGE

Accounting, A
Administrative Assistant and Secretarial Science, A
Agricultural and Food Products Processing, A
Architectural Drafting and Architectural CAD/CADD, A
Art/Art Studies, General, A
Autobody/Collision and Repair Technology/Technician, A
Automotive Engineering Technology/Technician, A
Biochemistry, Biophysics and Molecular Biology, A
Biology/Biological Sciences, A
Building/Construction Site Management/Manager, A
Business Administration and Management, A
Business/Office Automation/Technology/Data Entry, A
Carpentry/Carpenter, A
Civil Engineering Technology/Technician, A
Clinical/Medical Laboratory Assistant, A
Clinical/Medical Laboratory Technician, A
Computer Engineering Technology/Technician, A
Computer Programming/Programmer, A
Computer Systems Networking and Telecommunications, A
Computer Technology/Computer Systems Technology, A
Computer and Information Systems Security, A
Cooking and Related Culinary Arts, A
Cosmetology/Cosmetologist, A
Criminal Justice/Safety Studies, A
Dental Assisting/Assistant, A
Dental Hygiene/Hygienist, A
Diesel Mechanics Technology/Technician, A
Electrical and Electronic Engineering Technologies/Technicians, A
Electrical, Electronic and Communications Engineering Technology/Technician, A
Environmental Studies, A
Fashion Merchandising, A
Financial Planning and Services, A
Fire Services Administration, A

General Merchandising, Sales, and Related Market-
ing Operations, A
Graphic Design, A
Health Information/Medical Records
Technology/Technician, A
Heating, Air Conditioning and Refrigeration
Technology/Technician, A
Horse Husbandry/Equine Science and Manage-
ment, A
Human Resources Management/Personnel Adminis-
tration, A
Legal Administrative Assistant/Secretary, A
Legal Assistant/Paralegal, A
Liberal Arts and Sciences Studies and Humani-
ties, A
Lineworker, A
Manufacturing Technology/Technician, A
Marine Maintenance/Fitter and Ship Repair
Technology/Technician, A
Marketing/Marketing Management, A
Mechanical Drafting and Mechanical Drafting
CAD/CADD, A
Medical Administrative Assistant/Secretary, A
Music, A
Pharmacy Technician/Assistant, A
Plumbing Technology/Plumber, A
Radiologic Technology/Science - Radiographer, A
Telecommunications Technology/Technician, A
Web Page, Digital/Multimedia and Information Re-
sources Design, A

MINNESOTA STATE COMMUNITY AND TECHNICAL COLLEGE–DETROIT LAKES

Accounting, A
Administrative Assistant and Secretarial Science, A
Architectural Technology/Technician, A
Autobody/Collision and Repair
Technology/Technician, A
Automotive Engineering Technology/Technician, A
Computer and Information Systems Security, A
Dental Assisting/Assistant, A
Early Childhood Education and Teaching, A
Engineering Technology, A
Entrepreneurship/Entrepreneurial Studies, A
Information Technology, A
Legal Assistant/Paralegal, A
Marine Maintenance/Fitter and Ship Repair
Technology/Technician, A
Marketing/Marketing Management, A
Radiologic Technology/Science - Radiographer, A
Web Page, Digital/Multimedia and Information Re-
sources Design, A

MINNESOTA STATE COMMUNITY AND TECHNICAL COLLEGE–MOORHEAD

Accounting, A
Administrative Assistant and Secretarial Science, A
Automotive Engineering Technology/Technician, A
Biology/Biological Sciences, A
Business Administration and Management, A
Carpentry/Carpenter, A
Computer Programming/Programmer, A
Construction Management, A
Criminal Justice/Law Enforcement Administration, A
Dental Assisting/Assistant, A
Dental Hygiene/Hygienist, A
Diesel Mechanics Technology/Technician, A
Engineering, A
Graphic Design, A
Human Resources Development, A
Information Technology, A
Mechanical Drafting and Mechanical Drafting
CAD/CADD, A
Medical Administrative Assistant/Secretary, A
Plumbing Technology/Plumber, A
Sign Language Interpretation and Translation, A

MINNESOTA STATE COMMUNITY AND TECHNICAL COLLEGE–WADENA

Electrical and Power Transmission Installers, A
Medical Administrative Assistant/Secretary, A

System Administration/Administrator, A

MINNESOTA STATE UNIVERSITY MANKATO

Accounting, B
Allied Health and Medical Assisting Services, MDO
Anatomy, B
Animal Physiology, B
Anthropology, BM
Army JROTC/ROTC, B
Art Education, M
Art History, Criticism and Conservation, B
Art Teacher Education, B
Art/Art Studies, General, B
Astronomy, BM
Audiology/Audiologist and Speech-Language
Pathology/Pathologist, B
Automotive Engineering Technology/Technician, BM
Aviation/Airway Management and Operations, B
Behavioral Sciences, B
Biochemistry, B
Biological and Biomedical Sciences, M
Biological and Physical Sciences, B
Biology/Biological Sciences, B
Building/Construction Finishing, Manage-
ment, and Inspection, B
Business Administration and Management, B
Business Administration, Management and Opera-
tions, M
Ceramic Arts and Ceramics, B
Chemistry, B
Child Development, B
City/Urban, Community and Regional Planning, B
Civil Engineering, B
Clinical Laboratory Science/Medical
Technology/Technologist, B
Clinical Psychology, M
Commercial and Advertising Art, B
Communication Disorders, BM
Communication and Media Studies, MO
Community Health and Preventive Medicine, M
Comparative Literature, B
Computer Engineering, B
Computer Engineering Technology/Technician, B
Corporate and Organizational Communication, O
Corrections, B
Counseling Psychology, M
Counselor Education/School Counseling and Guid-
ance Services, MDO
Criminal Justice/Police Science, B
Curriculum and Instruction, O
Database Systems, O
Dental Hygiene/Hygienist, B
Design and Applied Arts, B
Dietetics/Dieticians, B
Drama and Dramatics/Theatre Arts, B
Drawing, B
Early Childhood Education and Teaching, MO
Ecology, B
Economics, B
Education, BMDO
Educational Leadership and Administration, M
Educational Media/Instructional Technology, MO
Electrical Engineering, M
Electrical, Electronic and Communications Engineer-
ing Technology/Technician, B
Electrical, Electronics and Communications Engi-
neering, B
Elementary Education and Teaching, BMO
English, MO
English Education, M
English Language and Literature, B
English as a Second Language, MO
Environmental Biology, B
Environmental Sciences, M
Environmental Studies, B
Ethnic and Cultural Studies, MO
Family and Consumer Economics and Related Ser-
vices, B
Family and Consumer Sciences/Home Economics
Teacher Education, B
Family and Consumer Sciences/Human Sciences, B
Finance, B
Fine Arts and Art Studies, M
Fine/Studio Arts, B
Foods, Nutrition, and Wellness Studies, B

French Language and Literature, BM
Gender Studies, MO
Geographic Information Systems, O
Geography, BMO
Geology/Earth Science, B
German Language and Literature, B
Gerontology, MO
Health Education, MO
Health Professions and Related Clinical Sciences, B
Health Teacher Education, B
Higher Education/Higher Education Administra-
tion, M
History, BM
Human Services, M
Humanities/Humanistic Studies, B
Industrial and Organizational Psychology, M
Information Science/Studies, B
Interdisciplinary Studies, M
International Business/Trade/Commerce, B
International Relations and Affairs, B
Journalism, B
Kindergarten/PreSchool Education and Teaching, B
Liberal Arts and Sciences Studies and Humani-
ties, A
Management Information Systems and Ser-
vices, MO
Manufacturing Engineering, M
Marketing/Marketing Management, B
Marriage and Family Therapy/Counseling, O
Mass Communication/Media Studies, B
Mathematics, BM
Mathematics Teacher Education, M
Mechanical Engineering, B
Medical Microbiology and Bacteriology, B
Modern Languages, B
Multilingual and Multicultural Education, MO
Music, BM
Music Teacher Education, B
Natural Sciences, B
Nursing, MD
Nursing - Advanced Practice, M
Parks, Recreation and Leisure Facilities Manage-
ment, B
Parks, Recreation, Leisure and Fitness Studies, B
Philosophy, B
Physical Education Teaching and Coaching, BM
Physical Sciences, B
Physics, BM
Political Science and Government, B
Pre-Dentistry Studies, B
Pre-Law Studies, B
Pre-Medicine/Pre-Medical Studies, B
Pre-Veterinary Studies, B
Psychology, BMD
Public Administration, BM
Public Health (MPH, DPH), B
Public Relations/Image Management, B
Real Estate, B
Rehabilitation Counseling, M
School Psychology, D
Science Teacher Education/General Science
Teacher Education, BM
Sculpture, B
Secondary Education and Teaching, BMO
Social Sciences, B
Social Studies Teacher Education, BM
Social Work, BM
Sociology, BM
Spanish Language and Literature, BM
Special Education and Teaching, MO
Sport and Fitness Administration/Management, B
Statistics, M
Student Personnel Services, MDO
Technical Communication, MO
Theater, M
Therapeutic Recreation/Recreational Therapy, B
Urban Planning, MO
Urban Studies/Affairs, BMO
Voice and Opera, B
Women's Studies, BMO
Writing, M

MINNESOTA STATE UNIVERSITY MOORHEAD

Accounting, B
Advertising, B

Anthropology, B
Art Teacher Education, B
Art/Art Studies, General, B
Athletic Training and Sports Medicine, B
Audiology/Audiologist and Speech-Language
  Pathology/Pathologist, B
Biochemistry, Biophysics and Molecular Biology, B
Biology Teacher Education, B
Biology/Biological Sciences, B
Broadcast Journalism, B
Business Administration and Management, B
Chemistry, B
Chemistry Teacher Education, B
Clinical Laboratory Science/Medical
  Technology/Technologist, B
Commercial and Advertising Art, B
Communication Disorders, M
Communication Studies/Speech Communication
  and Rhetoric, B
Community Health and Preventive Medicine, B
Computer Science, B
Construction Management, B
Counselor Education/School Counseling and Guid-
  ance Services, M
Criminal Justice/Safety Studies, B
Curriculum and Instruction, M
Digital Communication and Media/Multimedia, B
Drama and Dramatics/Theatre Arts, B
Early Childhood Education and Teaching, B
East Asian Studies, B
Economics, B
Education, MO
Educational Leadership and Administration, MO
Elementary Education and Teaching, B
English Language and Literature, B
English as a Second Language, M
English/Language Arts Teacher Education, B
Environmental Studies, B
Ethnic and Cultural Studies, B
Film/Cinema Studies, B
Finance, B
Geological and Earth Sciences/Geosciences, B
Gerontology, B
Graphic Design, B
Health Services Administration, M
Health Teacher Education, B
Health and Physical Education, B
Health/Health Care Administration/Management, B
History, B
Human Services, MO
Information Science/Studies, B
International/Global Studies, B
Jazz/Jazz Studies, B
Journalism, B
Kinesiology and Exercise Science, B
Legal Assistant/Paralegal, B
Liberal Arts and Sciences Studies and Humani-
  ties, A
Mass Communication/Media Studies, B
Mathematics, B
Mathematics Teacher Education, B
Multi-/Interdisciplinary Studies, B
Music, B
Music Performance, B
Music Teacher Education, B
Music Theory and Composition, B
Nursing, M
Operations Management and Supervision, B
Philosophy, B
Photojournalism, B
Physical Education Teaching and Coaching, B
Physics, B
Physics Teacher Education, B
Political Science and Government, B
Psychology, B
Public Relations/Image Management, B
School Psychology, MO
Social Studies Teacher Education, B
Social Work, B
Sociology, B
Spanish Language Teacher Education, B
Spanish Language and Literature, B
Special Education and Teaching, BM
Speech-Language Pathology/Pathologist, B
Teaching English as a Second or Foreign
  Language/ESL Language Instructor, B

Women's Studies, B

MINNESOTA WEST COMMUNITY AND TECHNICAL COLLEGE

Accounting, A
Administrative Assistant and Secretarial Science, A
Agribusiness, A
Agricultural Production Operations, A
Agricultural and Food Products Processing, A
Agricultural/Farm Supplies Retailing and Wholesal-
  ing, A
Agriculture, A
Agronomy and Crop Science, A
Automobile/Automotive Mechanics
  Technology/Technician, A
Biology Technician/BioTechnology Laboratory Tech-
  nician, A
Business Administration and Management, A
Business/Commerce, A
Child Care and Support Services Management, A
Clinical/Medical Laboratory Technician, A
Computer Engineering Technology/Technician, A
Computer Science, A
Computer Systems Networking and Telecommunica-
  tions, A
Computer Technology/Computer Systems Technol-
  ogy, A
Computer and Information Systems Security, A
Criminal Justice/Police Science, A
Dental Assisting/Assistant, A
Diesel Mechanics Technology/Technician, A
Electrical and Power Transmission
  Installation/Installer, A
Electrical and Power Transmission Installers, A
Electrician, A
Energy Management and Systems
  Technology/Technician, A
Hospital and Health Care Facilities
  Administration/Management, A
Human Services, A
Hydraulics and Fluid Power Technology, A
Information Technology, A
Liberal Arts and Sciences Studies and Humani-
  ties, A
Lineworker, A
Manufacturing Technology/Technician, A
Medical Administrative Assistant/Secretary, A
Medical Insurance Coding Specialist/Coder, A
Medical/Clinical Assistant, A
Plumbing Technology/Plumber, A
Radiologic Technology/Science - Radiographer, A
Robotics Technology/Technician, A
Surgical Technology/Technologist, A

NATIONAL AMERICAN UNIVERSITY (BLOOMINGTON)

Accounting, A
Business Administration and Management, A
Computer and Information Sciences, A
Computer/Information Technology Services Adminis-
  tration and Management, A
Finance and Financial Management Services, A
Health/Health Care Administration/Management, A
International Business/Trade/Commerce, A
Legal Assistant/Paralegal, A
Management Science, A
Marketing/Marketing Management, A

NATIONAL AMERICAN UNIVERSITY (BROOKLYN CENTER)

Accounting, A
Business Administration and Management, A
Computer and Information Sciences, A
Computer/Information Technology Services Adminis-
  tration and Management, A
Finance and Financial Management Services, A
Health/Health Care Administration/Management, A
International Business/Trade/Commerce, A
Legal Assistant/Paralegal, A
Management Science, A

Marketing/Marketing Management, A

NATIONAL AMERICAN UNIVERSITY (ROSEVILLE)

Accounting, B
Business Administration and Management, AB
Hospitality Administration/Management, B
Information Science/Studies, AB
Management Information Systems and Services, AB

NORMANDALE COMMUNITY COLLEGE

Computer Science, A
Computer Technology/Computer Systems Technol-
  ogy, A
Criminal Justice/Police Science, A
Criminal Justice/Safety Studies, A
Dental Hygiene/Hygienist, A
Dietetic Technician (DTR), A
Drama and Dramatics/Theatre Arts, A
Elementary Education and Teaching, A
Fine/Studio Arts, A
Food Science, A
Hospitality Administration/Management, A
Liberal Arts and Sciences Studies and Humani-
  ties, A
Management Information Systems and Services, A
Manufacturing Technology/Technician, A
Marketing/Marketing Management, A
Medical Office Computer Specialist/Assistant, A
Multi-/Interdisciplinary Studies, A
Music, A
Special Education and Teaching, A
Technical Theatre/Theatre Design and Technol-
  ogy, A

NORTH CENTRAL UNIVERSITY

American Sign Language (ASL), AB
Ancient Near Eastern and Biblical Languages, Lit-
  eratures, and Linguistics, A
Bible/Biblical Studies, AB
Business Administration and Management, AB
Child Development, B
Comparative Literature, A
Divinity/Ministry (BD, MDiv.), AB
Elementary Education and Teaching, B
English Language and Literature, B
Intercultural/Multicultural and Diversity Studies, B
Journalism, AB
Mass Communication/Media Studies, AB
Missions/Missionary Studies and Missiology, AB
Music, AB
Music Performance, B
Pastoral Studies/Counseling, AB
Psychology, AB
Religion/Religious Studies, B
Religious/Sacred Music, AB
Secondary Education and Teaching, B
Sign Language Interpretation and Translation, AB
Social Work, B
Sport and Fitness Administration/Management, B
Substance Abuse/Addiction Counseling, B
Urban Studies/Affairs, B
Youth Ministry, B

NORTH HENNEPIN COMMUNITY COL-LEGE

Accounting, A
Accounting Technology/Technician and Bookkeep-
  ing, A
Biology/Biological Sciences, A
Business Administration and Management, A
Chemistry, A
Clinical/Medical Laboratory Technician, A
Computer Science, A
Construction Management, A
Criminal Justice/Police Science, A
Criminal Justice/Safety Studies, A
Drama and Dramatics/Theatre Arts, A
Education, A
Entrepreneurship/Entrepreneurial Studies, A
Finance, A
Fine/Studio Arts, A
Graphic Design, A
Health Services/Allied Health/Health Sciences, A
Health and Physical Education, A

Histologic Technician, A
Human Services, A
Legal Assistant/Paralegal, A
Liberal Arts and Sciences Studies and Humanities, A
Management Information Systems and Services, A
Marketing/Marketing Management, A
Mathematics, A
Multi-/Interdisciplinary Studies, A
Music, A
Physical Education Teaching and Coaching, A

NORTHLAND COMMUNITY AND TECHNICAL COLLEGE

Accounting, A
Accounting Technology/Technician and Bookkeeping, A
Administrative Assistant and Secretarial Science, A
Aeronautics/Aviation/Aerospace Science and Technology, A
Agricultural Economics, A
Agricultural Mechanics and Equipment/Machine Technology, A
Agriculture, A
Agronomy and Crop Science, A
Airframe Mechanics and Aircraft Maintenance Technology/Technician, A
Architectural Drafting and Architectural CAD/CADD, A
Architectural Engineering Technology/Technician, A
Autobody/Collision and Repair Technology/Technician, A
Automobile/Automotive Mechanics Technology/Technician, A
Avionics Maintenance Technology/Technician, A
Business Administration and Management, A
CAD/CADD Drafting and/or Design Technology/Technician, A
Carpentry/Carpenter, A
Child Care Provider/Assistant, A
Computer Systems Networking and Telecommunications, A
Criminal Justice/Police Science, A
Criminology, A
Customer Service Management, A
Dietetic Technician (DTR), A
Electrician, A
Emergency Medical Technology/Technician (EMT Paramedic), A
Entrepreneurship/Entrepreneurial Studies, A
Farm/Farm and Ranch Management, A
Fire Protection and Safety Technology/Technician, A
Fire Science/Firefighting, A
Health Services/Allied Health/Health Sciences, A
Heating, Air Conditioning, Ventilation and Refrigeration Maintenance Technology/Technician, A
Liberal Arts and Sciences Studies and Humanities, A
Logistics and Materials Management, A
Machine Shop Technology/Assistant, A
Manufacturing Technology/Technician, A
Marketing/Marketing Management, A
Mass Communication/Media Studies, A
Medical Administrative Assistant/Secretary, A
Medical Insurance Coding Specialist/Coder, A
Medical Office Assistant/Specialist, A
Occupational Therapist Assistant, A
Office Management and Supervision, A
Operations Management and Supervision, A
Pharmacy Technician/Assistant, A
Phlebotomy/Phlebotomist, A
Physical Therapist Assistant, A
Plumbing Technology/Plumber, A
Radiologic Technology/Science - Radiographer, A
Respiratory Care Therapy/Therapist, A
Sales, Distribution and Marketing Operations, A
Security and Protective Services, A
Special Products Marketing Operations, A
Surgical Technology/Technologist, A
Teacher Assistant/Aide, A
Truck and Bus Driver/Commercial Vehicle Operation, A
Vehicle Maintenance and Repair Technologies, A

Welding Technology/Welder, A

NORTHWEST TECHNICAL COLLEGE

Accounting, A
Administrative Assistant and Secretarial Science, A
Automobile/Automotive Mechanics Technology/Technician, A
Business Administration and Management, A
Child Care and Support Services Management, A
Computer Systems Networking and Telecommunications, A
Dental Assisting/Assistant, A
Energy Management and Systems Technology/Technician, A
Engine Machinist, A
Industrial Safety Technology/Technician, A
Industrial Technology/Technician, A
Manufacturing Technology/Technician, A
Medical Administrative Assistant/Secretary, A
Sales, Distribution and Marketing Operations, A

OAK HILLS CHRISTIAN COLLEGE

Business Administration and Management, B
Divinity/Ministry (BD, MDiv.), B
General Studies, A
Pastoral Counseling and Specialized Ministries, B
Pastoral Studies/Counseling, B
Religious Education, B
Youth Ministry, B

PINE TECHNICAL AND COMMUNITY COLLEGE

Administrative Assistant and Secretarial Science, A
Automobile/Automotive Mechanics Technology/Technician, A
Business Teacher Education, A
Human Services, A
Machine Tool Technology/Machinist, A
Quality Control and Safety Technologies/Technicians, A

RAINY RIVER COMMUNITY COLLEGE

Administrative Assistant and Secretarial Science, A
Biological and Physical Sciences, A
Business Administration and Management, A
Liberal Arts and Sciences Studies and Humanities, A

RASMUSSEN COLLEGE BLAINE

Accounting, A
Business Administration and Management, A
Computer Science, B
Computer Software Engineering, A
Computer and Information Systems Security, B
Corrections and Criminal Justice, A
Criminal Justice/Police Science, A
Early Childhood Education and Teaching, A
Graphic Communications, B
Health Information/Medical Records Administration/Administrator, B
Health Information/Medical Records Technology/Technician, A
Health/Health Care Administration/Management, B
Human Resources Management/Personnel Administration, A
Human Services, A
Legal Assistant/Paralegal, A
Management Information Systems and Services, A
Marketing/Marketing Management, A
Medical Administrative Assistant/Secretary, A
Medical/Clinical Assistant, A
Pharmacy Technician/Assistant, A
Web Page, Digital/Multimedia and Information Resources Design, A

RASMUSSEN COLLEGE BLOOMINGTON

Accounting, AB
Business Administration and Management, AB
Computer Science, B
Computer Software Engineering, A
Computer and Information Systems Security, B
Corrections and Criminal Justice, AB
Criminal Justice/Police Science, A
Early Childhood Education and Teaching, A

Graphic Communications, B
Health Information/Medical Records Administration/Administrator, B
Health Information/Medical Records Technology/Technician, A
Health/Health Care Administration/Management, B
Human Resources Management/Personnel Administration, AB
Human Services, A
Legal Assistant/Paralegal, A
Management Information Systems and Services, A
Marketing/Marketing Management, AB
Medical Administrative Assistant/Secretary, A
Medical/Clinical Assistant, A
Pharmacy Technician/Assistant, A
Web Page, Digital/Multimedia and Information Resources Design, AB

RASMUSSEN COLLEGE BROOKLYN PARK

Accounting, AB
Business Administration and Management, AB
Computer Science, B
Computer Software Engineering, A
Computer and Information Systems Security, B
Corrections and Criminal Justice, AB
Criminal Justice/Police Science, A
Early Childhood Education and Teaching, A
Graphic Communications, B
Health Information/Medical Records Administration/Administrator, B
Health Information/Medical Records Technology/Technician, A
Health/Health Care Administration/Management, B
Human Resources Management/Personnel Administration, AB
Human Services, A
Legal Assistant/Paralegal, A
Management Information Systems and Services, A
Marketing/Marketing Management, AB
Medical Administrative Assistant/Secretary, A
Medical/Clinical Assistant, A
Pharmacy Technician/Assistant, A
Surgical Technology/Technologist, A
Web Page, Digital/Multimedia and Information Resources Design, AB

RASMUSSEN COLLEGE EAGAN

Accounting, AB
Business Administration and Management, AB
Computer Science, B
Computer Software Engineering, A
Computer and Information Systems Security, B
Corrections and Criminal Justice, AB
Criminal Justice/Police Science, A
Early Childhood Education and Teaching, A
Graphic Communications, B
Health Information/Medical Records Administration/Administrator, B
Health Information/Medical Records Technology/Technician, A
Health/Health Care Administration/Management, B
Human Resources Management/Personnel Administration, AB
Human Services, A
Legal Assistant/Paralegal, A
Management Information Systems and Services, A
Marketing/Marketing Management, AB
Medical Administrative Assistant/Secretary, A
Medical/Clinical Assistant, A
Pharmacy Technician/Assistant, A
Web Page, Digital/Multimedia and Information Resources Design, AB

RASMUSSEN COLLEGE LAKE ELMO/WOODBURY

Accounting, AB
Business Administration and Management, AB
Clinical/Medical Laboratory Technician, A
Computer Science, B
Computer Software Engineering, A
Computer and Information Systems Security, B
Corrections and Criminal Justice, AB
Criminal Justice/Police Science, A
Early Childhood Education and Teaching, A
Graphic Communications, B

Health Information/Medical Records Administration/Administrator, B
Health Information/Medical Records Technology/Technician, A
Health/Health Care Administration/Management, B
Human Resources Management/Personnel Administration, AB
Human Services, A
Legal Assistant/Paralegal, A
Management Information Systems and Services, A
Marketing/Marketing Management, AB
Medical Administrative Assistant/Secretary, A
Medical/Clinical Assistant, A
Pharmacy Technician/Assistant, A
Web Page, Digital/Multimedia and Information Resources Design, AB

RASMUSSEN COLLEGE MANKATO

Accounting, AB
Business Administration and Management, AB
Clinical/Medical Laboratory Technician, A
Computer Science, B
Computer Software Engineering, A
Computer and Information Systems Security, B
Corrections and Criminal Justice, AB
Criminal Justice/Police Science, A
Early Childhood Education and Teaching, A
Graphic Communications, B
Health Information/Medical Records Administration/Administrator, B
Health Information/Medical Records Technology/Technician, A
Health/Health Care Administration/Management, B
Human Resources Management/Personnel Administration, AB
Human Services, A
Legal Assistant/Paralegal, A
Management Information Systems and Services, A
Marketing/Marketing Management, AB
Medical Administrative Assistant/Secretary, A
Medical/Clinical Assistant, A
Pharmacy Technician/Assistant, A
Web Page, Digital/Multimedia and Information Resources Design, AB

RASMUSSEN COLLEGE MOORHEAD

Accounting, AB
Business Administration and Management, AB
Clinical/Medical Laboratory Technician, A
Computer Science, B
Computer Software Engineering, A
Computer and Information Systems Security, B
Corrections and Criminal Justice, AB
Early Childhood Education and Teaching, A
Graphic Communications, B
Health Information/Medical Records Administration/Administrator, B
Health Information/Medical Records Technology/Technician, A
Health/Health Care Administration/Management, B
Human Resources Management/Personnel Administration, AB
Human Services, A
Legal Assistant/Paralegal, A
Management Information Systems and Services, A
Marketing/Marketing Management, AB
Medical Administrative Assistant/Secretary, A
Medical/Clinical Assistant, A
Pharmacy Technician/Assistant, A
Web Page, Digital/Multimedia and Information Resources Design, AB

RASMUSSEN COLLEGE ST. CLOUD

Accounting, AB
Blood Bank Technology Specialist, AB
Business Administration and Management, AB
Clinical/Medical Laboratory Technician, A
Computer Science, B
Computer Software Engineering, A
Computer and Information Systems Security, B
Corrections and Criminal Justice, AB
Criminal Justice/Police Science, A
Early Childhood Education and Teaching, A
Graphic Communications, B
Health Information/Medical Records Administration/Administrator, B

Health Information/Medical Records Technology/Technician, A
Health/Health Care Administration/Management, B
Human Services, A
Legal Assistant/Paralegal, A
Management Information Systems and Services, A
Marketing/Marketing Management, AB
Medical Administrative Assistant/Secretary, A
Medical/Clinical Assistant, A
Pharmacy Technician/Assistant, A
Surgical Technology/Technologist, A
Web Page, Digital/Multimedia and Information Resources Design, AB

RIDGEWATER COLLEGE

Accounting, A
Administrative Assistant and Secretarial Science, A
Agribusiness, A
Agricultural Production Operations, A
Agriculture, A
Agronomy and Crop Science, A
Animal/Livestock Husbandry and Production, A
Autobody/Collision and Repair Technology/Technician, A
Automobile/Automotive Mechanics Technology/Technician, A
Biology/Biological Sciences, A
Business Administration and Management, A
Carpentry/Carpenter, A
Chemistry, A
Commercial Photography, A
Computer Programming/Programmer, A
Computer Science, A
Computer Systems Networking and Telecommunications, A
Computer Technology/Computer Systems Technology, A
Cosmetology/Cosmetologist, A
Criminal Justice/Police Science, A
Crop Production, A
Dairy Husbandry and Production, A
Digital Communication and Media/Multimedia, A
Early Childhood Education and Teaching, A
Electrical, Electronic and Communications Engineering Technology/Technician, A
Electrician, A
Electromechanical Technology/Electromechanical Engineering Technology, A
Health Information/Medical Records Technology/Technician, A
Instrumentation Technology/Technician, A
Legal Administrative Assistant/Secretary, A
Liberal Arts and Sciences Studies and Humanities, A
Machine Tool Technology/Machinist, A
Marketing/Marketing Management, A
Mechanical Drafting and Mechanical Drafting CAD/CADD, A
Medical Administrative Assistant/Secretary, A
Medical/Clinical Assistant, A
Prepress/Desktop Publishing and Digital Imaging Design, A
Radiologic Technology/Science - Radiographer, A
Recording Arts Technology/Technician, A
Sales, Distribution and Marketing Operations, A
Selling Skills and Sales Operations, A
System Administration/Administrator, A
Teacher Assistant/Aide, A
Telecommunications Technology/Technician, A
Therapeutic Recreation/Recreational Therapy, A
Tool and Die Technology/Technician, A
Veterinary/Animal Health Technology/Technician and Veterinary Assistant, A
Web Page, Digital/Multimedia and Information Resources Design, A
Welding Technology/Welder, A

RIVERLAND COMMUNITY COLLEGE

Administrative Assistant and Secretarial Science, A
Autobody/Collision and Repair Technology/Technician, A
Business Administration and Management, A
Computer Installation and Repair Technology/Technician, A
Computer Programming, Specific Applications, A

Computer Programming, Vendor/Product Certification, A
Computer Software and Media Applications, A
Computer Systems Networking and Telecommunications, A
Computer and Information Sciences and Support Services, A
Computer and Information Systems Security, A
Corrections, A
Criminal Justice/Police Science, A
Data Entry/Microcomputer Applications, A
Diesel Mechanics Technology/Technician, A
Electrical/Electronics Equipment Installation and Repair, A
Health Unit Coordinator/Ward Clerk, A
Human Services, A
Industrial Mechanics and Maintenance Technology, A
Legal Administrative Assistant/Secretary, A
Liberal Arts and Sciences Studies and Humanities, A
Machine Shop Technology/Assistant, A
Medical Administrative Assistant/Secretary, A
Medical Radiologic Technology/Science - Radiation Therapist, A
Pharmacy Technician/Assistant, A
Web Page, Digital/Multimedia and Information Resources Design, A
Web/Multimedia Management and Webmaster, A
Word Processing, A

ROCHESTER COMMUNITY AND TECHNICAL COLLEGE

Accounting, A
Administrative Assistant and Secretarial Science, A
Biomedical Sciences, A
Building/Property Maintenance and Management, A
Business Administration and Management, A
CAD/CADD Drafting and/or Design Technology/Technician, A
Cardiovascular Technology/Technologist, A
Child Care and Support Services Management, A
Civil Engineering Technology/Technician, A
Computer Science, A
Criminal Justice/Police Science, A
Criminal Justice/Safety Studies, A
Customer Service Management, A
Dental Assisting/Assistant, A
Dental Hygiene/Hygienist, A
Digital Communication and Media/Multimedia, A
Electrical, Electronic and Communications Engineering Technology/Technician, A
Electroneurodiagnostic/Electroencephalographic Technology/Technologist, A
Emergency Medical Technology/Technician (EMT Paramedic), A
General Studies, A
Graphic Design, A
Greenhouse Operations and Management, A
Health Information/Medical Records Technology/Technician, A
Horse Husbandry/Equine Science and Management, A
Liberal Arts and Sciences Studies and Humanities, A
Mechanical Engineering/Mechanical Technology/Technician, A
Medical Administrative Assistant/Secretary, A
Music Theory and Composition, A
Pre-Medicine/Pre-Medical Studies, A
Psychiatric/Mental Health Services Technician, A
Radiologic Technology/Science - Radiographer, A
Retailing and Retail Operations, A
Surgical Technology/Technologist, A
System Administration/Administrator, A
Teacher Assistant/Aide, A
Turf and Turfgrass Management, A
Veterinary/Animal Health Technology/Technician and Veterinary Assistant, A
Web Page, Digital/Multimedia and Information Resources Design, A

ST. CATHERINE UNIVERSITY

Accounting, B
American Sign Language (ASL), B
Art History, Criticism and Conservation, B

Art Teacher Education, B
Art/Art Studies, General, B
Biochemistry, B
Biology Teacher Education, B
Biology/Biological Sciences, B
Business Administration and Management, B
Business Administration, Management and Operations, M
Chemistry, B
Chemistry Teacher Education, B
Clinical Laboratory Science/Medical Technology/Technologist, B
Comparative Literature, B
Computer and Information Sciences, B
Curriculum and Instruction, M
Diagnostic Medical Sonography/Sonographer and Ultrasound Technician, A
Dietetics/Dieticians, B
Drama and Dance Teacher Education, B
Drama and Dramatics/Theatre Arts, B
Early Childhood Education and Teaching, M
Economics, B
Education, BM
Elementary Education and Teaching, B
English Language and Literature, B
English/Language Arts Teacher Education, B
Family and Consumer Sciences/Home Economics Teacher Education, B
Family and Consumer Sciences/Human Sciences, B
Fashion Merchandising, B
Fashion/Apparel Design, B
Fine/Studio Arts, B
Foods, Nutrition, and Wellness Studies, B
Franchising and Franchise Operations, B
French Language Teacher Education, B
French Language and Literature, B
Gerontological Nursing, M
Health Information/Medical Records Technology/Technician, A
Health Services Administration, M
Health and Physical Education, B
History, B
Information Science/Studies, M
Intercultural/Multicultural and Diversity Studies, B
International Business/Trade/Commerce, B
International Economics, B
International Relations and Affairs, B
Journalism, B
Kindergarten/PreSchool Education and Teaching, B
Liberal Arts and Sciences Studies and Humanities, A
Library Science, M
Management Information Systems and Services, B
Marketing, M
Marketing/Marketing Management, B
Mass Communication/Media Studies, B
Maternal/Child Health and Neonatal Nurse/Nursing, M
Mathematics, B
Mathematics Teacher Education, B
Medical Radiologic Technology/Science - Radiation Therapist, A
Music, B
Music Teacher Education, B
Nursing, MD
Nursing - Adult, M
Nursing Education, M
Occupational Therapist Assistant, A
Occupational Therapy/Therapist, BMD
Organizational Management, M
Orthoptics/Orthoptist, B
Pastoral Studies/Counseling, O
Pediatric Nurse/Nursing, M
Philosophy, B
Physical Education Teaching and Coaching, B
Physical Therapist Assistant, A
Physical Therapy/Therapist, D
Physician Assistant, M
Physics, B
Political Science and Government, B
Pre-Dentistry Studies, B
Pre-Law Studies, B
Pre-Medicine/Pre-Medical Studies, B
Pre-Veterinary Studies, B
Psychology, B
Public Health, M

Respiratory Care Therapy/Therapist, B
Sales, Distribution and Marketing Operations, B
Secondary Education and Teaching, B
Selling Skills and Sales Operations, B
Sign Language Interpretation and Translation, A
Social Sciences, B
Social Studies Teacher Education, B
Social Work, BMD
Sociology, B
Spanish Language Teacher Education, B
Spanish Language and Literature, B
Speech Teacher Education, B
Theology and Religious Vocations, MO
Theology/Theological Studies, B
Women's Studies, B

ST. CLOUD STATE UNIVERSITY

Accounting, B
Advertising, B
American/United States Studies/Civilization, B
Anthropology, B
Applied Behavior Analysis, M
Applied Economics, M
Applied Statistics, M
Archeology, M
Art History, Criticism and Conservation, B
Art Teacher Education, B
Art/Art Studies, General, B
Atmospheric Sciences and Meteorology, B
Audiology/Audiologist and Speech-Language Pathology/Pathologist, B
Behavioral Sciences, B
Biological and Biomedical Sciences, M
Biology Technician/BioTechnology Laboratory Technician, B
Biology/Biological Sciences, B
Biomedical Engineering, M
Biomedical Sciences, B
Botany/Plant Biology, B
Broadcast Journalism, B
Business Administration and Management, B
Business Administration, Management and Operations, M
Chemistry, B
Chemistry Teacher Education, B
Child Development, B
Child and Family Studies, M
City/Urban, Community and Regional Planning, B
Clinical Laboratory Science/Medical Technology/Technologist, B
Communication Disorders, BM
Communication Disorders Sciences and Services, B
Community Psychology, M
Computer Engineering, B
Computer Science, BM
Computer and Information Systems Security, M
Counselor Education/School Counseling and Guidance Services, BM
Criminal Justice/Law Enforcement Administration, B
Criminology, BM
Curriculum and Instruction, M
Design and Applied Arts, B
Drama and Dramatics/Theatre Arts, B
Dramatic/Theatre Arts and Stagecraft, B
Ecology, B
Economics, BM
Education, BMD
Educational Administration and Supervision, MD
Educational Leadership and Administration, BM
Educational Media/Instructional Technology, M
Educational/Instructional Media Design, B
Electrical Engineering, M
Electrical, Electronic and Communications Engineering Technology/Technician, B
Electrical, Electronics and Communications Engineering, B
Elementary Education and Teaching, B
Engineering, B
Engineering Management, M
Engineering Technology, B
Engineering and Applied Sciences, M
English, M
English Language and Literature, B
English as a Second Language, M
Environmental Biology, B
Environmental Studies, M

Exercise and Sports Science, M
Film/Cinema Studies, B
Finance, B
Fine/Studio Arts, B
French Language and Literature, B
Geography, BM
Geology/Earth Science, B
German Language and Literature, B
Gerontology, BM
Health Services/Allied Health/Health Sciences, B
Health Teacher Education, B
Health/Medical Preparatory Programs, B
Higher Education/Higher Education Administration, MD
Historic Preservation and Conservation, M
History, BM
Industrial Engineering, B
Industrial and Organizational Psychology, M
Information Science/Studies, B
International Business/Trade/Commerce, B
International Relations and Affairs, B
Jazz/Jazz Studies, B
Journalism, B
Junior High/Intermediate/Middle School Education and Teaching, B
Kindergarten/PreSchool Education and Teaching, B
Kinesiology and Exercise Science, B
Latin American Studies, B
Liberal Arts and Sciences Studies and Humanities, AB
Library Science, B
Marketing/Marketing Management, B
Marriage and Family Therapy/Counseling, M
Mass Communication/Media Studies, BM
Mathematics, BM
Mechanical Engineering, BM
Mental Health Counseling/Counselor, B
Multi-/Interdisciplinary Studies, B
Music, BM
Music History, Literature, and Theory, B
Music Pedagogy, B
Music Performance, B
Music Teacher Education, BM
Music Theory and Composition, B
Natural Sciences, B
Non-Profit/Public/Organizational Management, M
Nuclear Medical Technology/Technologist, B
Philosophy, B
Physical Education Teaching and Coaching, B
Physical Sciences, B
Physical Therapy/Therapist, B
Physics, B
Piano and Organ, B
Political Science and Government, B
Pre-Dentistry Studies, B
Pre-Law Studies, B
Pre-Medicine/Pre-Medical Studies, B
Pre-Pharmacy Studies, B
Pre-Veterinary Studies, B
Psychology, BMD
Public Administration, B
Public Policy Analysis, B
Public Relations/Image Management, B
Radio and Television, B
Reading Teacher Education, B
Real Estate, B
Rehabilitation Counseling, M
Sales, Distribution and Marketing Operations, A
Science Teacher Education/General Science Teacher Education, B
Sculpture, B
Secondary Education and Teaching, B
Social Sciences, B
Social Work, BM
Sociology, B
Spanish Language and Literature, B
Special Education and Teaching, BM
Speech Teacher Education, B
Speech-Language Pathology/Pathologist, B
Sport and Fitness Administration/Management, M
Statistics, M
Student Personnel Services, M
Substance Abuse/Addiction Counseling, B
Teacher Education and Professional Development, Specific Levels and Methods, B
Teacher Education, Multiple Levels, AB

Technology Teacher Education/Industrial Arts Teacher Education, B
Technology and Public Policy, M
Therapeutic Recreation/Recreational Therapy, B
Tourism Promotion Operations, A
Tourism and Travel Services Management, B
Urban Studies/Affairs, B
Violin, Viola, Guitar and Other Stringed Instruments, B
Visual and Performing Arts, B
Voice and Opera, B
Wildlife Biology, B

ST. CLOUD TECHNICAL & COMMUNITY COLLEGE

Accounting, A
Administrative Assistant and Secretarial Science, A
Advertising, A
Architectural Drafting and Architectural CAD/CADD, A
Autobody/Collision and Repair Technology/Technician, A
Automobile/Automotive Mechanics Technology/Technician, A
Biomedical Technology/Technician, A
Business Administration and Management, A
Cardiovascular Technology/Technologist, A
Carpentry/Carpenter, A
Computer Programming/Programmer, A
Credit Management, A
Culinary Arts/Chef Training, A
Dental Assisting/Assistant, A
Dental Hygiene/Hygienist, A
Diagnostic Medical Sonography/Sonographer and Ultrasound Technician, A
Digital Communication and Media/Multimedia, A
Electrical, Electronic and Communications Engineering Technology/Technician, A
Electrician, A
Emergency Medical Technology/Technician (EMT Paramedic), A
Energy Management and Systems Technology/Technician, A
Health Information/Medical Records Technology/Technician, A
Health Services/Allied Health/Health Sciences, A
Heating, Air Conditioning, Ventilation and Refrigeration Maintenance Technology/Technician, A
Human Development and Family Studies, A
Instrumentation Technology/Technician, A
Legal Administrative Assistant/Secretary, A
Legal Assistant/Paralegal, A
Liberal Arts and Sciences Studies and Humanities, A
Mechanical Drafting and Mechanical Drafting CAD/CADD, A
Medical Office Computer Specialist/Assistant, A
Medium/Heavy Vehicle and Truck Technology/Technician, A
Plumbing Technology/Plumber, A
Sales, Distribution and Marketing Operations, A
Surgical Technology/Technologist, A
System Administration/Administrator, A
Teacher Assistant/Aide, A
Water Quality and Wastewater Treatment Management and Recycling Technology/Technician, A

SAINT JOHN'S UNIVERSITY

Accounting, B
Art/Art Studies, General, B
Biochemistry, B
Biological and Physical Sciences, B
Biology/Biological Sciences, B
Business Administration and Management, B
Chemistry, B
Classics and Classical Languages, Literatures, and Linguistics, B
Computational Mathematics, B
Computer Science, B
Dietetics and Clinical Nutrition Services, B
Drama and Dramatics/Theatre Arts, B
Economics, B
Elementary Education and Teaching, B
English Language and Literature, B
Environmental Studies, B
Fine/Studio Arts, B

Forestry, B
French Language and Literature, B
German Language and Literature, B
History, B
Humanities/Humanistic Studies, B
Liberal Arts and Sciences Studies and Humanities, B
Mathematics, B
Multi-/Interdisciplinary Studies, B
Music, B
Natural Sciences, B
Nutritional Sciences, B
Occupational Therapy/Therapist, B
Pastoral Studies/Counseling, B
Peace Studies and Conflict Resolution, B
Philosophy, B
Physical Therapy/Therapist, B
Physics, B
Political Science and Government, B
Pre-Dentistry Studies, B
Pre-Law Studies, B
Pre-Medicine/Pre-Medical Studies, B
Pre-Pharmacy Studies, B
Pre-Theology/Pre-Ministerial Studies, B
Pre-Veterinary Studies, B
Psychology, B
Sacred Music, M
Secondary Education and Teaching, B
Social Sciences, B
Sociology, B
Spanish Language and Literature, B
Theology and Religious Vocations, M
Theology/Theological Studies, B
Women's Studies, B

SAINT MARY'S UNIVERSITY OF MINNESOTA

Accounting, BM
Actuarial Science, B
Arts Management, M
Biochemistry, B
Biology Teacher Education, B
Biology/Biological Sciences, B
Business Administration, Management and Operations, MD
Business, Management, Marketing, and Related Support Services, B
Chemistry, B
Chemistry Teacher Education, B
Christian Studies, B
Clinical Laboratory Science/Medical Technology/Technologist, B
Computer Science, B
Corrections and Criminal Justice, B
Counseling Psychology, MDO
CytoTechnology/Cytotechnologist, B
Drama and Dramatics/Theatre Arts, B
Education, BMO
Education/Teaching of the Gifted and Talented, O
Educational Administration and Supervision, O
Educational Leadership and Administration, MD
Educational Media/Instructional Technology, M
Elementary Education and Teaching, BMO
Engineering Physics, B
English Language and Literature, B
English/Language Arts Teacher Education, B
Entrepreneurship/Entrepreneurial Studies, B
Environmental Biology, B
Environmental and Occupational Health, M
Finance, B
Fine/Studio Arts, B
Geographic Information Systems, MO
Graphic Design, B
Health Services Administration, M
History, B
Human Development, M
Human Resources Management and Services, M
Human Resources Management/Personnel Administration, B
Human Services, B
International Business/Trade/Commerce, BM
International Development, M
International/Global Studies, B
Journalism, B
Management, M
Marketing/Marketing Management, B

Marriage and Family Therapy/Counseling, MO
Mathematics, B
Mathematics Teacher Education, B
Multilingual and Multicultural Education, O
Music, B
Music Performance, B
Music Teacher Education, B
Nuclear Medical Technology/Technologist, B
Nurse Anesthetist, M
Organizational Management, M
Philanthropic Studies, M
Philosophy, B
Physics, B
Physics Teacher Education, B
Political Science and Government, B
Prepress/Desktop Publishing and Digital Imaging Design, B
Project Management, MO
Psychology, B
Public Relations, Advertising, and Applied Communication, B
Reading Teacher Education, MO
Religious Education, BM
Secondary Education and Teaching, MO
Social Science Teacher Education, B
Sociology, B
Spanish Language Teacher Education, B
Spanish Language and Literature, B
Special Education and Teaching, MO
Substance Abuse/Addiction Counseling, O
Telecommunications, M
Theology/Theological Studies, B

ST. OLAF COLLEGE

American/United States Studies/Civilization, B
Ancient Studies/Civilization, B
Ancient/Classical Greek Language and Literature, B
Art History, Criticism and Conservation, B
Art/Art Studies, General, B
Asian Studies/Civilization, B
Biology/Biological Sciences, B
Chemistry, B
Classics and Classical Languages, Literatures, and Linguistics, B
Computer Science, B
Dance, B
Drama and Dramatics/Theatre Arts, B
Economics, B
English Language and Literature, B
Environmental Studies, B
Ethnic and Cultural Studies, B
French Language and Literature, B
German Language and Literature, B
History, B
Kinesiology and Exercise Science, B
Latin American Studies, B
Latin Language and Literature, B
Liberal Arts and Sciences Studies and Humanities, B
Mathematics, B
Medieval and Renaissance Studies, B
Music, B
Music Performance, B
Music Teacher Education, B
Music Theory and Composition, B
Norwegian Language and Literature, B
Philosophy, B
Physics, B
Political Science and Government, B
Psychology, B
Religion/Religious Studies, B
Religious/Sacred Music, B
Russian Language and Literature, B
Russian Studies, B
Social Studies Teacher Education, B
Social Work, B
Spanish Language and Literature, B
Women's Studies, B

SAINT PAUL COLLEGE–A COMMUNITY & TECHNICAL COLLEGE

Accounting, A
Administrative Assistant and Secretarial Science, A
Aesthetician/Esthetician and Skin Care Specialist, A
Animation, Interactive Technology, Video Graphics and Special Effects, A

Athletic Training and Sports Medicine, A
Autobody/Collision and Repair
  Technology/Technician, A
Automobile/Automotive Mechanics
  Technology/Technician, A
Biomedical Technology/Technician, A
Building/Construction Site Management/Manager, A
Business Administration and Management, A
Chemical Technology/Technician, A
Child Care and Support Services Management, A
Clinical/Medical Laboratory Technician, A
Computer Graphics, A
Computer Programming/Programmer, A
Computer Science, A
Computer Systems Networking and Telecommunica-
  tions, A
Cosmetology/Cosmetologist, A
Culinary Arts/Chef Training, A
Electrical, Electronic and Communications Engineer-
  ing Technology/Technician, A
Entrepreneurship/Entrepreneurial Studies, A
Health Information/Medical Records
  Technology/Technician, A
Hospitality Administration/Management, A
Human Resources Management/Personnel Adminis-
  tration, A
Industrial Technology/Technician, A
International Marketing, A
Liberal Arts and Sciences Studies and Humani-
  ties, A
Logistics and Materials Management, A
Management Information Systems and Services, A
Manufacturing Technology/Technician, A
Massage Therapy/Therapeutic Massage, A
Medical Office Assistant/Specialist, A
Office Management and Supervision, A
Respiratory Care Therapy/Therapist, A
Sign Language Interpretation and Translation, A
Survey Technology/Surveying, A

SOUTH CENTRAL COLLEGE

Accounting, A
Agricultural Business Technology, A
Agricultural Business and Management, A
Agricultural Production Operations, A
Architectural Drafting and Architectural
  CAD/CADD, A
Autobody/Collision and Repair
  Technology/Technician, A
Automobile/Automotive Mechanics
  Technology/Technician, A
Business Administration and Management, A
Carpentry/Carpenter, A
Child Care and Support Services Management, A
Clinical/Medical Laboratory Technician, A
Commercial and Advertising Art, A
Computer Programming/Programmer, A
Computer Systems Networking and Telecommunica-
  tions, A
Cooking and Related Culinary Arts, A
Dental Assisting/Assistant, A
Emergency Medical Technology/Technician (EMT
  Paramedic), A
Executive Assistant/Executive Secretary, A
Graphic and Printing Equipment Operator Produc-
  tion, A
Heating, Air Conditioning, Ventilation and Refrigera-
  tion Maintenance Technology/Technician, A
Human Services, A
Industrial Safety Technology/Technician, A
Legal Administrative Assistant/Secretary, A
Liberal Arts and Sciences Studies and Humani-
  ties, A
Marketing/Marketing Management, A
Restaurant/Food Services Management, A
Telecommunications Technology/Technician, A

SOUTHWEST MINNESOTA STATE UNIVERSITY

Accounting, AB
Agribusiness, AB
Agricultural Business and Management, B
Art Teacher Education, B
Art/Art Studies, General, B
Biology Teacher Education, B
Biology/Biological Sciences, B

Business Administration and Management, AB
Business Administration, Management and Opera-
  tions, M
Chemistry, B
Chemistry Teacher Education, B
Communication Studies/Speech Communication
  and Rhetoric, B
Computer Science, B
Criminal Justice/Law Enforcement Administration, B
Criminal Justice/Safety Studies, B
Drama and Dramatics/Theatre Arts, B
Dramatic/Theatre Arts and Stagecraft, B
Early Childhood Education and Teaching, M
Education, BM
Educational Leadership and Administration, M
Elementary Education and Teaching, B
English Language and Literature, B
English as a Second Language, M
English/Language Arts Teacher Education, B
Environmental Sciences, B
Finance, B
General Studies, B
Health Teacher Education, B
Health and Physical Education, B
History, B
Hotel/Motel Administration/Management, B
Information Technology, B
Kindergarten/PreSchool Education and Teaching, B
Kinesiology and Exercise Science, B
Management Sciences and Quantitative Methods, B
Marketing, M
Marketing/Marketing Management, AB
Mathematics, B
Mathematics Teacher Education, BM
Music, B
Music Teacher Education, B
Non-Profit/Public/Organizational Management, B
Philosophy, B
Physical Education Teaching and Coaching, B
Political Science and Government, B
Pre-Dentistry Studies, B
Pre-Law Studies, B
Pre-Medicine/Pre-Medical Studies, B
Pre-Veterinary Studies, B
Psychology, B
Public Administration, B
Radio and Television, B
Reading Teacher Education, M
Restaurant/Food Services Management, B
Social Work, B
Sociology, B
Spanish Language Teacher Education, B
Spanish Language and Literature, B
Special Education and Teaching, BM
Speech Teacher Education, B

UNIVERSITY OF MINNESOTA, CROOKSTON

Accounting, B
Aeronautics/Aviation/Aerospace Science and Tech-
  nology, B
Agribusiness, B
Agricultural Business Technology, B
Agricultural Mechanization, B
Agricultural Power Machinery Operation, B
Agronomy and Crop Science, B
Airline/Commercial/Professional Pilot and Flight
  Crew, B
Animal Sciences, B
Biology/Biological Sciences, B
Business Administration and Management, B
Business, Management, Marketing, and Related
  Support Services, B
Computer Software Engineering, B
Corrections, B
Criminal Justice/Law Enforcement Administration, B
Crop Production, B
Early Childhood Education and Teaching, B
Educational Leadership and Administration, B
Elementary Education and Teaching, B
Entrepreneurship/Entrepreneurial Studies, B
Farm/Farm and Ranch Management, B
Greenhouse Operations and Management, B
Health Services/Allied Health/Health Sciences, B
Health/Health Care Administration/Management, B

Horse Husbandry/Equine Science and Manage-
  ment, B
Horticultural Science, B
Kindergarten/PreSchool Education and Teaching, B
Landscaping and Groundskeeping, B
Marketing/Marketing Management, B
Multi-/Interdisciplinary Studies, B
Natural Resources Management/Development and
  Policy, B
Natural Resources and Conservation, B
Operations Management and Supervision, B
Parks, Recreation and Leisure Facilities Manage-
  ment, B
Plant Sciences, B
Pre-Veterinary Studies, B
Sport and Fitness Administration/Management, B
Turf and Turfgrass Management, B
Urban Forestry, B
Water, Wetlands, and Marine Resources Manage-
  ment, B

UNIVERSITY OF MINNESOTA, DULUTH

Accounting, B
Allopathic Medicine, D
American Indian/Native American Studies, B
Anthropology, BM
Applied Mathematics, M
Art History, Criticism and Conservation, B
Art Teacher Education, B
Art/Art Studies, General, B
Athletic Training and Sports Medicine, B
Biochemistry, BMD
Biochemistry, Biophysics and Molecular Biology, B
Biological and Biomedical Sciences, MD
Biology/Biological Sciences, B
Biomedical Sciences, B
Biophysics, MD
Business Administration and Management, B
Business Administration, Management and Opera-
  tions, M
Cartography, B
Cell/Cellular Biology and Histology, B
Chemical Engineering, B
Chemistry, BM
Chinese Studies, B
Civil Engineering, B
Commercial and Advertising Art, B
Communication Disorders, BM
Communication Studies/Speech Communication
  and Rhetoric, B
Communication, Journalism and Related Pro-
  grams, B
Computational Sciences, M
Computer Engineering, M
Computer Science, BM
Computer Systems Networking and Telecommunica-
  tions, B
Criminology, BM
Drama and Dramatics/Theatre Arts, B
Economics, B
Education, BMD
Electrical Engineering, M
Electrical, Electronics and Communications Engi-
  neering, B
Engineering Management, M
English, M
English Language and Literature, B
Entrepreneurship/Entrepreneurial Studies, B
Environmental Sciences, B
Environmental Studies, B
Ethnic, Cultural Minority, and Gender Studies, B
Finance, B
Financial Planning and Services, B
Fine Arts and Art Studies, M
Fine/Studio Arts, B
Foreign Language Teacher Education, B
French Language and Literature, B
Geography, B
Geology/Earth Science, BMD
German Language and Literature, B
Graphic Design, M
Health/Health Care Administration/Management, B
History, B
Human Resources Management/Personnel Adminis-
  tration, B
Immunology, MD

Industrial Engineering, B
International Relations and Affairs, B
Junior High/Intermediate/Middle School Education and Teaching, B
Kindergarten/PreSchool Education and Teaching, B
Kinesiology and Exercise Science, B
Latin American Studies, B
Liberal Studies, M
Linguistics, B
Marketing, B
Marketing/Marketing Management, B
Mathematics, B
Mathematics Teacher Education, B
Mechanical Engineering, B
Medical Microbiology and Bacteriology, MD
Molecular Biology, MD
Multi-/Interdisciplinary Studies, B
Music, BM
Music Performance, B
Music Teacher Education, BM
Music Theory and Composition, B
Parks, Recreation, Leisure and Fitness Studies, B
Performance, M
Pharmacology, MD
Pharmacy, MD
Philosophy, B
Physical Education Teaching and Coaching, B
Physics, BM
Physiology, MD
Political Science and Government, B
Printing Management, B
Psychology, B
Public Health Education and Promotion, B
Safety Engineering, M
Science Teacher Education/General Science Teacher Education, B
Social Studies Teacher Education, B
Social Work, BM
Sociology, BM
Spanish Language and Literature, B
Statistics, B
Teacher Education and Professional Development, Specific Subject Areas, B
Teacher Education, Multiple Levels, B
Toxicology, MD
Urban Studies/Affairs, B
Women's Studies, B

UNIVERSITY OF MINNESOTA, MORRIS

American Indian/Native American Studies, B
Anthropology, B
Art History, Criticism and Conservation, B
Biology/Biological Sciences, B
Business Administration and Management, B
Chemistry, B
Computer Science, B
Drama and Dramatics/Theatre Arts, B
Economics, B
Elementary Education and Teaching, B
English Language and Literature, B
Environmental Studies, B
European Studies/Civilization, B
Fine/Studio Arts, B
French Language and Literature, B
Geology/Earth Science, B
History, B
Human Services, B
Latin American Studies, B
Mathematics, B
Multi-/Interdisciplinary Studies, B
Music, B
Philosophy, B
Physical Therapy/Therapist, B
Physics, B
Political Science and Government, B
Pre-Dentistry Studies, B
Pre-Law Studies, B
Pre-Medicine/Pre-Medical Studies, B
Pre-Pharmacy Studies, B
Pre-Veterinary Studies, B
Psychology, B
Secondary Education and Teaching, B
Social Sciences, B
Sociology, B
Spanish Language and Literature, B
Statistics, B

Women's Studies, B

UNIVERSITY OF MINNESOTA, TWIN CITIES CAMPUS

Accounting, BMD
Adult and Continuing Education and Teaching, MDO
Aerospace, Aeronautical and Astronautical Engineering, BMD
African-American/Black Studies, B
Agricultural Business and Management, B
Agricultural Education, MD
Agricultural Sciences, MD
Agricultural Teacher Education, B
Agricultural/Biological Engineering and Bioengineering, B
Agronomy and Soil Sciences, MD
Allopathic Medicine, MD
American Indian/Native American Studies, B
American/United States Studies/Civilization, BD
Animal Behavior and Ethology, MD
Animal Sciences, BMD
Anthropology, BMD
Apparel and Textiles, B
Applied Economics, BMD
Archeology, MD
Architecture, BM
Art Education, MD
Art History, Criticism and Conservation, BMD
Art/Art Studies, General, B
Asian Languages, D
Asian Studies/Civilization, D
Astrophysics, BMD
Audiology/Audiologist and Speech-Language Pathology/Pathologist, B
Bible/Biblical Studies, B
BioTechnology, M
Biochemistry, BD
Biological and Biomedical Sciences, M
Biology/Biological Sciences, B
Biomedical Engineering, MD
Biomedical/Medical Engineering, B
Biophysics, MD
Biopsychology, D
Biostatistics, MD
Biosystems Engineering, MD
Botany/Plant Biology, B
Building/Construction Finishing, Management, and Inspection, B
Business Administration, Management and Operations, MD
Business Education, MD
Business Teacher Education, B
Cancer Biology/Oncology, D
Cell Biology and Anatomy, MD
Cell/Cellular Biology and Histology, B
Chemical Engineering, BMD
Chemical Physics, MD
Chemistry, BMD
Child Development, MD
Child and Family Studies, MD
Civil Engineering, BMDO
Classics and Classical Languages, Literatures, and Linguistics, BMD
Clinical Psychology, D
Clinical Research, M
Clinical/Medical Laboratory Science and Allied Professions, B
Clothing and Textiles, MD
Cognitive Sciences, D
Communication Disorders, MD
Communication and Media Studies, MD
Communication, Journalism and Related Programs, B
Community Health Nursing, M
Community Health and Preventive Medicine, M
Comparative Literature, BD
Computational Sciences, MD
Computer Engineering, BMD
Computer Science, BMD
Computer Systems Analysis/Analyst, B
Computer Systems Networking and Telecommunications, B
Computer and Information Systems Security, M
Conservation Biology, MD
Counseling Psychology, D

Counselor Education/School Counseling and Guidance Services, MDO
Criminology, B
Cultural Studies, D
Curriculum and Instruction, MDO
Dance, B
Database Systems, M
Dental Hygiene/Hygienist, B
Dentistry, D
Design and Applied Arts, MDO
Developmental Biology and Embryology, MD
Drama and Dramatics/Theatre Arts, B
Early Childhood Education and Teaching, MD
East Asian Languages, Literatures, and Linguistics, B
Ecology, BMD
Econometrics and Quantitative Economics, B
Economics, BD
Education, BMDO
Education/Teaching of the Gifted and Talented, O
Educational Administration and Supervision, MD
Educational Leadership and Administration, M
Educational Measurement and Evaluation, MDO
Educational Media/Instructional Technology, MDO
Educational Policy, MDO
Educational Psychology, MDO
Electrical Engineering, MD
Electrical, Electronics and Communications Engineering, B
Elementary Education and Teaching, BMD
Engineering and Applied Sciences, MDO
English, MD
English Education, MD
English Language and Literature, B
English as a Second Language, M
Entomology, MD
Entrepreneurship/Entrepreneurial Studies, D
Environmental Design/Architecture, B
Environmental Education, M
Environmental Policy and Resource Management, MD
Environmental Sciences, B
Environmental and Occupational Health, MDO
Environmental/Environmental Health Engineering, B
Epidemiology, MD
Evolutionary Biology, MD
Exercise Physiology, B
Exercise and Sports Science, MD
Family and Consumer Economics and Related Services, B
Film/Video and Photographic Arts, B
Finance, B
Finance and Banking, MD
Fine Arts and Art Studies, M
Fish, Game and Wildlife Management, MD
Fishing and Fisheries Sciences and Management, B
Food Science, B
Food Science and Technology, MD
Foods, Nutrition, and Related Services, B
Foreign Language Teacher Education, M
Foreign Languages and Literatures, B
Forestry, BMD
Foundations and Philosophy of Education, MDO
French Language and Literature, BMD
Funeral Service and Mortuary Science, B
Genetic Counseling/Counselor, M
Genetics, MD
Geographic Information Systems, MD
Geography, BMD
Geological Engineering, M
Geological/Geophysical Engineering, B
Geology/Earth Science, BMD
Geophysics and Seismology, MD
German Language and Literature, MD
Germanic Languages, Literatures, and Linguistics, B
Gerontological Nursing, M
Graphic Design, B
Health Informatics, MD
Health Services Administration, MD
Health Services Research, MD
Health/Health Care Administration/Management, B
Higher Education/Higher Education Administration, MD
Hispanic and Latin American Languages, MD
Hispanic-American, Puerto Rican, and Mexican-American/Chicano Studies, B

U.S. COLLEGES: MINNESOTA

History, BMD
History of Medicine, MD
History of Science and Technology, MD
Housing and Human Environments, B
Human Resources Development, MDO
Human Resources Management and Services, M
Human Resources Management/Personnel Administration, B
Hydrology and Water Resources Science, MD
Immunology, D
Industrial Engineering, B
Industrial Hygiene, MD
Industrial and Labor Relations, M
Industrial and Manufacturing Management, D
Industrial and Organizational Psychology, D
Industrial/Management Engineering, MD
Infectious Diseases, MD
Insurance, B
Interdisciplinary Studies, D
Interior Design, BMDO
International Business/Trade/Commerce, B
International Development, M
International Public Health/International Health, MD
International Relations and Affairs, B
International and Comparative Education, MD
Italian Language and Literature, B
Jewish/Judaic Studies, B
Journalism, B
Kindergarten/PreSchool Education and Teaching, B
Kinesiology and Movement Studies, MD
Labor and Industrial Relations, B
Landscape Architecture, M
Law and Legal Studies, MD
Linguistics, BMD
Management Information Systems and Services, MD
Management Strategy and Policy, D
Management of Technology, M
Marketing, MD
Marketing/Marketing Management, B
Marriage and Family Therapy/Counseling, MD
Mass Communication/Media Studies, MD
Materials Engineering, BMD
Materials Sciences, MD
Maternal and Child Health, M
Mathematics, BMDO
Mathematics Teacher Education, MD
Mechanical Engineering, BMD
Mechanics, MD
Medical Microbiology and Bacteriology, B
Medical Physics, MD
Medical Technology, M
Medicinal and Pharmaceutical Chemistry, MD
Medieval and Renaissance Studies, MD
Microbiology, D
Molecular Biology, MD
Multi-/Interdisciplinary Studies, B
Multilingual and Multicultural Education, MD
Music, BMD
Music Teacher Education, B
Music Therapy/Therapist, B
Natural Resources Management/Development and Policy, MD
Neurobiology and Neurophysiology, MD
Neuroscience, MD
Non-Profit/Public/Organizational Management, B
Nurse Anesthetist, M
Nurse Midwife/Nursing Midwifery, M
Nursing, MD
Nursing - Adult, M
Nursing - Advanced Practice, M
Nursing Administration, M
Nutritional Sciences, BMD
Occupational Health Nursing, MD
Operations Management and Supervision, B
Oral Biology, MD
Oral and Dental Sciences, MO
Orthodontics, M
Paper and Pulp Engineering, MD
Parks, Recreation, Leisure and Fitness Studies, B
Pediatric Nurse/Nursing, M
Periodontics, M
Pharmaceutical Administration, MD
Pharmaceutical Sciences, MD
Pharmacology, MD
Pharmacy, D

Philosophy, BMD
Physical Education Teaching and Coaching, M
Physical Therapy/Therapist, MD
Physics, BMD
Physiology, BD
Plant Biology, MD
Plant Pathology/Phytopathology, MD
Plant Sciences, BMD
Political Science and Government, BD
Portuguese Language and Literature, MD
Psychiatric/Mental Health Nurse/Nursing, M
Psychology, BD
Public Affairs, M
Public Health, MDO
Public Policy Analysis, M
Quantitative Analysis, O
Reading Teacher Education, MD
Religion/Religious Studies, BM
Retailing and Retail Operations, B
Russian Language and Literature, B
Sales, Distribution and Marketing Operations, B
Scandinavian Languages, Literatures, and Linguistics, MD
School Psychology, MDO
Science Teacher Education/General Science Teacher Education, MD
Social Psychology, D
Social Studies Teacher Education, MD
Social Work, MD
Sociology, BMD
Software Engineering, M
Spanish Language and Literature, BMD
Special Education and Teaching, BMDO
Sport and Fitness Administration/Management, MD
Statistics, BMD
Structural Biology, D
Student Personnel Services, MDO
Supply Chain Management, M
Taxation, M
Technology and Public Policy, M
Textile Design, MDO
Theater, MD
Toxicology, MD
Travel and Tourism, MD
Urban Studies/Affairs, B
Urban and Regional Planning, M
Veterinary Medicine, D
Veterinary Sciences, MD
Virology, D
Vocational and Technical Education, MO
Water Resources, MD
Women's Health Nursing, M
Women's Studies, BD

UNIVERSITY OF NORTHWESTERN–ST. PAUL

Accounting, AB
Animation, Interactive Technology, Video Graphics and Special Effects, B
Art Teacher Education, B
Bible/Biblical Studies, B
Biochemistry, B
Biology/Biological Sciences, B
Business Administration and Management, B
Business Administration, Management and Operations, M
Communication Studies/Speech Communication and Rhetoric, B
Criminal Justice/Safety Studies, B
Drama and Dramatics/Theatre Arts, B
Early Childhood Education and Teaching, B
Education, M
Elementary Education and Teaching, B
Engineering, B
English Language and Literature, B
English/Language Arts Teacher Education, B
Family and Consumer Sciences/Human Sciences, M
Finance, B
Fine/Studio Arts, B
Graphic Design, B
Health and Physical Education, B
History, B
Human Services, M
International Business/Trade/Commerce, B
Journalism, B

Kinesiology and Exercise Science, B
Liberal Arts and Sciences Studies and Humanities, A
Management Information Systems and Services, B
Marketing/Marketing Management, B
Mathematics, B
Mathematics Teacher Education, B
Missions/Missionary Studies and Missiology, B
Multi-/Interdisciplinary Studies, B
Music, B
Music Performance, B
Music Teacher Education, B
Music Theory and Composition, B
Organizational Management, M
Pastoral Counseling and Specialized Ministries, B
Pastoral Studies/Counseling, M
Physical Education Teaching and Coaching, B
Piano and Organ, B
Pre-Nursing Studies, B
Pre-Theology/Pre-Ministerial Studies, B
Psychology, B
Public Relations/Image Management, B
Radio and Television, AB
Social Studies Teacher Education, B
Spanish Language and Literature, B
Teaching English as a Second or Foreign Language/ESL Language Instructor, B
Theological and Ministerial Studies, B
Theology and Religious Vocations, M
Violin, Viola, Guitar and Other Stringed Instruments, B
Voice and Opera, B
Youth Ministry, B

UNIVERSITY OF ST. THOMAS

Accounting, BM
Actuarial Science, B
Art History, Criticism and Conservation, BM
Biochemistry, B
Biology/Biological Sciences, B
Business Administration and Management, B
Business Administration, Management and Operations, BM
Chemistry, B
Chemistry Teacher Education, B
Classics and Classical Languages, Literatures, and Linguistics, B
Computer and Information Systems Security, O
Corporate and Organizational Communication, M
Counseling Psychology, MD
Criminology, B
Curriculum and Instruction, M
Early Childhood Education and Teaching, M
Economics, B
Education, MDO
Educational Administration and Supervision, MDO
Educational Leadership and Administration, MDO
Educational Media/Instructional Technology, M
Educational Policy, MO
Electrical Engineering, M
Electrical, Electronics and Communications Engineering, B
Elementary Education and Teaching, M
Engineering Management, M
Engineering and Applied Sciences, MO
English, B
English Language and Literature, B
English as a Second Language, M
English/Language Arts Teacher Education, B
Entrepreneurship/Entrepreneurial Studies, B
Ethics, M
Finance, B
French Language and Literature, B
Geography, B
Geology/Earth Science, B
German Language and Literature, B
Health Services Administration, M
Health Teacher Education, B
History, B
Human Development, MD
Human Resources Development, M
Human Resources Management/Personnel Administration, B
International Business/Trade/Commerce, B
International Economics, B
Journalism, B

315

Junior High/Intermediate/Middle School Education
and Teaching, B
Latin Language and Literature, B
Law and Legal Studies, MD
Management Information Systems and Services, MO
Management of Technology, MO
Manufacturing Engineering, MO
Marketing/Marketing Management, B
Marriage and Family Therapy/Counseling, O
Mathematics, B
Mathematics Teacher Education, BO
Mechanical Engineering, BM
Multi-/Interdisciplinary Studies, B
Music, BM
Music Teacher Education, BM
Operations Management and Supervision, B
Organizational Management, MD
Pastoral Studies/Counseling, M
Peace Studies and Conflict Resolution, B
Performance, M
Philosophy, B
Physical Education Teaching and Coaching, B
Physics, B
Physics Teacher Education, B
Political Science and Government, B
Psychology, BMDO
Public Administration, B
Public Health Education and Promotion, B
Reading Teacher Education, MO
Real Estate, BM
Religion/Religious Studies, BM
Religious Education, M
Science Teacher Education/General Science
Teacher Education, B
Social Sciences, B
Social Studies Teacher Education, B
Social Work, BM
Sociology, B
Software Engineering, MO
Spanish Language and Literature, B
Special Education and Teaching, MO
Speech Teacher Education, B
Student Personnel Services, MO
Systems Engineering, M
Theology and Religious Vocations, M
Women's Studies, B

VERMILION COMMUNITY COLLEGE

Accounting, A
Aeronautics/Aviation/Aerospace Science and Technology, A
Agricultural Business and Management, A
Agricultural Economics, A
Agricultural Teacher Education, A
Agronomy and Crop Science, A
Airline/Commercial/Professional Pilot and Flight
Crew, A
Architectural Engineering Technology/Technician, A
Art History, Criticism and Conservation, A
Art Teacher Education, A
Art/Art Studies, General, A
Aviation/Airway Management and Operations, A
Biological and Physical Sciences, A
Biology/Biological Sciences, A
Business Administration and Management, A
Business/Managerial Economics, A
Chemistry, A
Computer Engineering Technology/Technician, A
Computer Science, A
Criminal Justice/Law Enforcement Administration, A
Criminal Justice/Police Science, A
Criminal Justice/Safety Studies, A
Data Processing and Data Processing
Technology/Technician, A
Drama and Dramatics/Theatre Arts, A
Drawing, A
Ecology, A
Economics, A
Education, A
Elementary Education and Teaching, A
Engineering, A
Environmental Engineering
Technology/Environmental Technology, A
Environmental Studies, A

Family and Consumer Sciences/Human Sciences, A
Finance, A
Fishing and Fisheries Sciences and Management, A
Forest Management/Forest Resources Management, A
Forest Sciences and Biology, A
Forestry, A
Forestry Technology/Technician, A
Geography, A
Geology/Earth Science, A
Health Information/Medical Records
Administration/Administrator, A
Health Teacher Education, A
History, A
Hydrology and Water Resources Science, A
Industrial Technology/Technician, A
Kindergarten/PreSchool Education and Teaching, A
Land Use Planning and
Management/Development, A
Liberal Arts and Sciences Studies and Humanities, A
Mass Communication/Media Studies, A
Mathematics, A
Medical Administrative Assistant/Secretary, A
Music, A
Natural Resources Management/Development and
Policy, A
Natural Resources and Conservation, A
Parks, Recreation and Leisure Facilities Management, A
Parks, Recreation, Leisure and Fitness Studies, A
Physical Education Teaching and Coaching, A
Physical Sciences, A
Physics, A
Political Science and Government, A
Psychology, A
Range Science and Management, A
Science Teacher Education/General Science
Teacher Education, A
Sociology, A
Soil Science and Agronomy, A
Special Products Marketing Operations, A
Water Quality and Wastewater Treatment Management and Recycling Technology/Technician, A
Wildlife Biology, A
Wildlife and Wildlands Science and Management, A

WALDEN UNIVERSITY

Accounting, BMDO
Adult and Continuing Education and Teaching, MDO
Applied Psychology, M
Business Administration and Management, B
Business Administration, Management and Operations, MO
Business/Corporate Communications, B
Child and Family Studies, MD
Clinical Psychology, MD
Clinical Research, MO
Communication and Media Studies, MO
Community College Education, D
Community Health and Preventive Medicine, D
Community Psychology, M
Computer and Information Sciences, B
Computer and Information Systems Security, M
Conflict Resolution and Mediation/Peace Studies, MD
Counseling Psychology, MD
Counselor Education/School Counseling and Guidance Services, MD
Criminal Justice/Law Enforcement Administration, B
Criminology, MDO
Curriculum and Instruction, MDO
Developmental Education, MO
Distance Education Development, MO
Early Childhood Education and Teaching, MDO
Education, MDO
Educational Administration and Supervision, MDO
Educational Leadership and Administration, MDO
Educational Measurement and Evaluation, MDO
Educational Media/Instructional Technology, MDO
Educational Policy, D
Educational Psychology, MD
Elementary Education and Teaching, MO
Emergency Management, MD
English as a Second Language, MO
Entrepreneurship/Entrepreneurial Studies, MD

Epidemiology, D
Finance and Banking, MD
Forensic Psychology, MD
Forensic Science and Technology, M
Gerontological Nursing, M
Health Education, MD
Health Informatics, M
Health Promotion, MD
Health Psychology, MD
Health Services Administration, MD
Health Services/Allied Health/Health Sciences, B
Health/Health Care Administration/Management, B
Higher Education/Higher Education Administration, MDO
Homeland Security, MDO
Human Development and Family Studies, B
Human Resources Management and Services, MDO
Human Services, BMD
Industrial and Organizational Psychology, O
Interdisciplinary Studies, D
International Affairs, D
International Business/Trade/Commerce, MD
International Development, M
International and Comparative Education, MDO
Law and Legal Studies, MD
Management, MDO
Management Information Systems and Services, MDO
Marketing, MD
Marriage and Family Therapy/Counseling, M
Mathematics Teacher Education, MO
Middle School Education, M
Multilingual and Multicultural Education, M
Non-Profit/Public/Organizational Management, MDO
Nursing, MDO
Nursing - Adult, M
Nursing - Advanced Practice, M
Nursing Administration, MDO
Nursing Education, MDO
Nursing Informatics, MO
Organizational Management, MD
Project Management, MDO
Psychology, BMDO
Public Administration, BMDO
Public Health, MD
Public Health (MPH, DPH), B
Public Policy Analysis, MDO
Reading Teacher Education, MDO
Science Teacher Education/General Science
Teacher Education, MO
Social Psychology, MD
Social Work, MD
Special Education and Teaching, MDO
Substance Abuse/Addiction Counseling, MD
Supply Chain Management, D
Sustainable Development, MD

WINONA STATE UNIVERSITY

Accounting, B
Advertising, B
Art Teacher Education, B
Art/Art Studies, General, B
Athletic Training and Sports Medicine, B
Biochemistry, B
Biology Teacher Education, B
Biology/Biological Sciences, B
Business Administration and Management, B
Business Teacher Education, B
Chemistry, B
Chemistry Teacher Education, B
Clinical Laboratory Science/Medical
Technology/Technologist, B
Computer Science, B
Corrections, B
Counselor Education/School Counseling and Guidance Services, M
CytoTechnology/Cytotechnologist, B
Drama and Dramatics/Theatre Arts, B
Economics, B
Education, BM
Educational Administration and Supervision, M
Educational Leadership and Administration, MO
Elementary Education and Teaching, B
English, M
English Language and Literature, B

English/Language Arts Teacher Education, B
Finance, B
Health Teacher Education, B
History, B
Human Resources Management/Personnel Adminis-
tration, B
International/Global Studies, B
Journalism, B
Kinesiology and Exercise Science, B
Legal Assistant/Paralegal, B
Liberal Arts and Sciences Studies and Humani-
ties, A
Management Information Systems and Services, B
Marketing/Marketing Management, B
Mass Communication/Media Studies, B
Materials Engineering, B
Mathematics, B
Mathematics Teacher Education, B
Music, B
Music Teacher Education, B
Nursing, MDO
Nursing - Adult, MO
Nursing - Advanced Practice, MO
Nursing Administration, M
Nursing Education, MO
Parks, Recreation and Leisure Facilities Manage-
ment, B
Physical Education Teaching and Coaching, B
Physics, B
Physics Teacher Education, B
Political Science and Government, B
Psychology, B
Public Administration, B
Recreation and Park Management, M
Science Teacher Education/General Science
Teacher Education, B
Social Science Teacher Education, B
Social Work, B
Sociology, B
Spanish Language Teacher Education, B
Spanish Language and Literature, B
Special Education and Teaching, BM
Sport and Fitness Administration/Management, M
Statistics, B
Teaching English as a Second or Foreign
Language/ESL Language Instructor, B

Mississippi

ALCORN STATE UNIVERSITY

Accounting, B
Agricultural Business and Management, B
Agricultural Economics, BM
Agricultural Education, M
Agricultural Sciences, M
Agriculture, B
Agronomy and Soil Sciences, M
Animal Sciences, M
Biological and Biomedical Sciences, M
Biology/Biological Sciences, B
Business Administration and Management, B
Business Administration, Management and Opera-
tions, M
Chemistry, B
Child Development, B
Computer Science, M
Computer and Information Sciences, B
Counselor Education/School Counseling and Guid-
ance Services, M
Criminal Justice/Safety Studies, B
Education, MO
Elementary Education and Teaching, BMO
English Language and Literature, B
Foods, Nutrition, and Wellness Studies, B
Health Education, M
History, B
Industrial Education, M
Information Science/Studies, M
Liberal Arts and Sciences Studies and Humani-
ties, B
Mass Communication/Media Studies, B
Mathematics, B
Music, B
Music Performance, B
Nursing, M
Parks, Recreation, Leisure and Fitness Studies, B

Physical Education Teaching and Coaching, M
Political Science and Government, B
Psychology, B
Robotics Technology/Technician, B
Secondary Education and Teaching, M
Social Work, B
Sociology, B
Special Education and Teaching, M
Sport and Fitness Administration/Management, B
System, Networking, and LAN/WAN
Management/Manager, B
Vocational and Technical Education, M

ANTONELLI COLLEGE (HATTIESBURG)

Accounting Technology/Technician and Bookkeep-
ing, A
Administrative Assistant and Secretarial Science, A
Allied Health and Medical Assisting Services, A
Business/Office Automation/Technology/Data En-
try, A
Information Technology, A
Interior Design, A
Legal Administrative Assistant/Secretary, A
Massage Therapy/Therapeutic Massage, A
Medical Insurance Coding Specialist/Coder, A
Medical Transcription/Transcriptionist, A

ANTONELLI COLLEGE (JACKSON)

Accounting Technology/Technician and Bookkeep-
ing, A
Business/Office Automation/Technology/Data En-
try, A
Commercial and Advertising Art, A
Computer Systems Networking and Telecommunica-
tions, A
Interior Design, A
Legal Assistant/Paralegal, A
Massage Therapy/Therapeutic Massage, A
Medical Insurance Coding Specialist/Coder, A
Medical Transcription/Transcriptionist, A
Medical/Clinical Assistant, A

BELHAVEN UNIVERSITY

Accounting, B
Art/Art Studies, General, B
Bible/Biblical Studies, B
Biology/Biological Sciences, B
Business Administration and Management, B
Business Administration, Management and Opera-
tions, M
Chemistry, B
Communication Studies/Speech Communication
and Rhetoric, B
Computer Science, B
Criminal Justice/Law Enforcement Administration, B
Dance, B
Drama and Dramatics/Theatre Arts, B
Education, M
Educational Media/Instructional Technology, M
Elementary Education and Teaching, BM
English Language and Literature, B
General Studies, A
Graphic Design, B
Health Services Administration, M
Health/Health Care Administration/Management, B
History, B
Human Resources Management and Services, M
Human Resources Management/Personnel Adminis-
tration, B
Humanities/Humanistic Studies, B
International/Global Studies, B
Kinesiology and Exercise Science, B
Liberal Arts and Sciences Studies and Humani-
ties, B
Mathematics, B
Multilingual and Multicultural Education, M
Music, B
Parks, Recreation, Leisure and Fitness Studies, B
Philosophy, B
Political Science and Government, B
Psychology, B
Public Administration, M
Reading Teacher Education, M
Secondary Education and Teaching, M
Social Sciences, B
Social Work, B

Sport and Fitness Administration/Management, BM

BLUE MOUNTAIN COLLEGE

Bible/Biblical Studies, B
Biology Teacher Education, B
Biology/Biological Sciences, B
Business Administration and Management, B
Clinical Laboratory Science/Medical
Technology/Technologist, B
Criminal Justice/Safety Studies, B
Elementary Education and Teaching, BM
English Language and Literature, B
English/Language Arts Teacher Education, B
History, B
Kinesiology and Exercise Science, B
Liberal Arts and Sciences Studies and Humani-
ties, B
Mathematics, B
Mathematics Teacher Education, B
Music, B
Music Teacher Education, B
Physical Education Teaching and Coaching, B
Psychology, B
Reading Teacher Education, M
Religious/Sacred Music, B
Social Science Teacher Education, B
Spanish Language Teacher Education, B
Spanish Language and Literature, B
Visual and Performing Arts, B

COAHOMA COMMUNITY COLLEGE

Accounting, A
Administrative Assistant and Secretarial Science, A
Autobody/Collision and Repair
Technology/Technician, A
Barbering/Barber, A
Biology/Biological Sciences, A
Business Operations Support and Secretarial Ser-
vices, A
Business Teacher Education, A
Business/Commerce, A
Carpentry/Carpenter, A
Chemistry, A
Child Care and Support Services Management, A
Clinical Laboratory Science/Medical
Technology/Technologist, A
Computer Science, A
Computer Technology/Computer Systems Technol-
ogy, A
Computer and Information Sciences, A
Cosmetology/Cosmetologist, A
Criminal Justice/Safety Studies, A
Culinary Arts/Chef Training, A
Early Childhood Education and Teaching, A
Education, A
Elementary Education and Teaching, A
Engineering, A
English/Language Arts Teacher Education, A
General Studies, A
Health Professions and Related Clinical Sciences, A
Health and Physical Education, A
Heavy/Industrial Equipment Maintenance Technolo-
gies, A
Hotel/Motel Administration/Management, A
Intermedia/Multimedia, A
Management Information Systems and Services, A
Mathematics, A
Mathematics Teacher Education, A
Medical Administrative Assistant/Secretary, A
Occupational Therapy/Therapist, A
Physical Education Teaching and Coaching, A
Physical Therapy/Therapist, A
Pre-Dentistry Studies, A
Pre-Law Studies, A
Pre-Medicine/Pre-Medical Studies, A
Pre-Pharmacy Studies, A
Psychology, A
Radio and Television, A
Respiratory Care Therapy/Therapist, A
Secondary Education and Teaching, A
Social Science Teacher Education, A
Social Sciences, A
Social Work, A
Visual and Performing Arts, A

Welding Technology/Welder, A

COPIAH-LINCOLN COMMUNITY COLLEGE

Accounting, A
Agribusiness, A
Agricultural Business and Management, A
Agricultural Economics, A
Agricultural/Farm Supplies Retailing and Wholesaling, A
Agriculture, A
Architecture, A
Art Teacher Education, A
Biological and Physical Sciences, A
Biology/Biological Sciences, A
Business Administration and Management, A
Chemistry, A
Child Development, A
Civil Engineering Technology/Technician, A
Clinical/Medical Laboratory Technician, A
Computer Programming/Programmer, A
Cosmetology/Cosmetologist, A
Criminal Justice/Police Science, A
Data Processing and Data Processing Technology/Technician, A
Drafting and Design Technology/Technician, A
Economics, A
Education, A
Electrical, Electronic and Communications Engineering Technology/Technician, A
Elementary Education and Teaching, A
Engineering, A
English Language and Literature, A
Family and Consumer Sciences/Home Economics Teacher Education, A
Farm/Farm and Ranch Management, A
Food Technology and Processing, A
Forestry, A
Health Teacher Education, A
History, A
Industrial Radiologic Technology/Technician, A
Journalism, A
Liberal Arts and Sciences Studies and Humanities, A
Library Science, A
Music Teacher Education, A
Physical Education Teaching and Coaching, A
Special Products Marketing Operations, A
Trade and Industrial Teacher Education, A

DELTA STATE UNIVERSITY

Accounting, BM
Aeronautics/Aviation/Aerospace Science and Technology, B
Airline/Commercial/Professional Pilot and Flight Crew, B
Athletic Training and Sports Medicine, B
Audiology/Audiologist and Speech-Language Pathology/Pathologist, B
Aviation/Airway Management and Operations, M
Biological and Biomedical Sciences, M
Biological and Physical Sciences, B
Biology/Biological Sciences, B
Business Administration and Management, B
Business Administration, Management and Operations, M
Business/Commerce, B
Chemistry, B
Counselor Education/School Counseling and Guidance Services, MDO
Criminal Justice/Safety Studies, B
Criminology, M
Education, MDO
Educational Administration and Supervision, MO
Educational Leadership and Administration, D
Elementary Education and Teaching, BMDO
English Education, M
English Language and Literature, B
English/Language Arts Teacher Education, B
Exercise and Sports Science, M
Family and Consumer Sciences/Human Sciences, B
Finance, B
Foreign Languages and Literatures, B
Gender Studies, M
General Studies, B
Health Education, M

Health Services Administration, M
Higher Education/Higher Education Administration, D
History, B
Hospitality Administration/Management, B
Insurance, B
Journalism, B
Liberal Studies, M
Management Information Systems and Services, B
Marketing/Marketing Management, B
Mathematics, B
Mathematics Teacher Education, B
Multi-/Interdisciplinary Studies, B
Music, B
Music Teacher Education, B
Nursing, MD
Nursing - Advanced Practice, M
Nursing Education, M
Philosophy, M
Physical Education Teaching and Coaching, BM
Political Science and Government, B
Psychology, B
Recreation and Park Management, M
Religion/Religious Studies, M
Secondary Education and Teaching, M
Social Science Teacher Education, B
Social Sciences, B
Social Studies Teacher Education, M
Social Work, B
Special Education and Teaching, M
Urban and Regional Planning, M
Visual and Performing Arts, B

EAST CENTRAL COMMUNITY COLLEGE

Administrative Assistant and Secretarial Science, A
Agriculture, A
American Government and Politics (United States), A
Autobody/Collision and Repair Technology/Technician, A
Automobile/Automotive Mechanics Technology/Technician, A
Business Administration and Management, A
Business/Office Automation/Technology/Data Entry, A
Child Care Provider/Assistant, A
Computer Programming/Programmer, A
Computer Systems Networking and Telecommunications, A
Computer and Information Sciences, A
Drafting and Design Technology/Technician, A
Electrical, Electronic and Communications Engineering Technology/Technician, A
Electrician, A
Elementary Education and Teaching, A
Emergency Medical Technology/Technician (EMT Paramedic), A
Engineering, A
Fine/Studio Arts, A
Health and Physical Education, A
Health/Medical Preparatory Programs, A
Heating, Air Conditioning and Refrigeration Technology/Technician, A
Hospitality Administration/Management, A
Liberal Arts and Sciences Studies and Humanities, A
Machine Tool Technology/Machinist, A
Medical Administrative Assistant/Secretary, A
Physical Education Teaching and Coaching, A
Piano and Organ, A
Pre-Dentistry Studies, A
Pre-Medicine/Pre-Medical Studies, A
Pre-Nursing Studies, A
Pre-Pharmacy Studies, A
Pre-Veterinary Studies, A
Psychology, A
Secondary Education and Teaching, A
Surgical Technology/Technologist, A
Voice and Opera, A

EAST MISSISSIPPI COMMUNITY COLLEGE

Accounting, A
Administrative Assistant and Secretarial Science, A
Art/Art Studies, General, A

Automobile/Automotive Mechanics Technology/Technician, A
Banking and Financial Support Services, A
Biology/Biological Sciences, A
Business/Commerce, A
Chemistry, A
Computer Science, A
Computer Systems Networking and Telecommunications, A
Criminal Justice/Safety Studies, A
Drafting and Design Technology/Technician, A
Electrical, Electronic and Communications Engineering Technology/Technician, A
Electrician, A
Elementary Education and Teaching, A
Engineering, A
Forestry, A
Funeral Service and Mortuary Science, A
Health and Physical Education, A
History, A
Hospitality Administration/Management, A
Industrial Mechanics and Maintenance Technology, A
Liberal Arts and Sciences Studies and Humanities, A
Management Information Systems and Services, A
Manufacturing Technology/Technician, A
Marketing/Marketing Management, A
Mathematics, A
Medical Administrative Assistant/Secretary, A
Music Teacher Education, A
Operations Management and Supervision, A
Opticianry/Ophthalmic Dispensing Optician, A
Physical Therapy/Therapist, A
Pre-Law Studies, A
Pre-Medicine/Pre-Medical Studies, A
Pre-Veterinary Studies, A
Secondary Education and Teaching, A
Social Sciences, A
Welding Technology/Welder, A

HINDS COMMUNITY COLLEGE

Accounting Technology/Technician and Bookkeeping, A
Administrative Assistant and Secretarial Science, A
Aeronautics/Aviation/Aerospace Science and Technology, A
Agribusiness, A
Agricultural Mechanization, A
Airframe Mechanics and Aircraft Maintenance Technology/Technician, A
Applied Horticulture/Horticultural Business Services, A
Architectural Engineering Technology/Technician, A
Aviation/Airway Management and Operations, A
Banking and Financial Support Services, A
Cartography, A
Child Care Provider/Assistant, A
Clinical/Medical Laboratory Technician, A
Computer Installation and Repair Technology/Technician, A
Computer Programming/Programmer, A
Computer Systems Networking and Telecommunications, A
Computer and Information Systems Security, A
Corrections and Criminal Justice, A
Court Reporting/Court Reporter, A
Dental Assisting/Assistant, A
Diagnostic Medical Sonography/Sonographer and Ultrasound Technician, A
Diesel Mechanics Technology/Technician, A
Digital Communication and Media/Multimedia, A
Drafting and Design Technology/Technician, A
Electrical, Electronic and Communications Engineering Technology/Technician, A
Electrical/Electronics Equipment Installation and Repair, A
Electrician, A
Emergency Medical Technology/Technician (EMT Paramedic), A
Fashion Merchandising, A
General Studies, A
Graphic Design, A
Health Information/Medical Records Technology/Technician, A
Health and Medical Administrative Services, A

Heating, Air Conditioning, Ventilation and Refrigeration Maintenance Technology/Technician, A
Hospitality Administration/Management, A
Institutional Food Workers, A
Landscaping and Groundskeeping, A
Legal Assistant/Paralegal, A
Logistics and Materials Management, A
Marketing/Marketing Management, A
Medical/Clinical Assistant, A
Multi-/Interdisciplinary Studies, A
Photographic and Film/Video Technology/Technician and Assistant, A
Physical Therapist Assistant, A
Plant Protection and Integrated Pest Management, A
Plumbing Technology/Plumber, A
Poultry Science, A
Radio and Television Broadcasting Technology/Technician, A
Radiologic Technology/Science - Radiographer, A
Real Estate, A
Respiratory Care Therapy/Therapist, A
Sign Language Interpretation and Translation, A
Surgical Technology/Technologist, A
Telecommunications Technology/Technician, A
Tourism and Travel Services Management, A
Veterinary/Animal Health Technology/Technician and Veterinary Assistant, A

HOLMES COMMUNITY COLLEGE

Accounting and Business/Management, A
Agriculture, A
Architectural Engineering Technology/Technician, A
Art/Art Studies, General, A
Autobody/Collision and Repair Technology/Technician, A
Automobile/Automotive Mechanics Technology/Technician, A
Biology/Biological Sciences, A
Business/Office Automation/Technology/Data Entry, A
Child Development, A
Computer Programming/Programmer, A
Computer Science, A
Computer Software Technology/Technician, A
Computer Systems Networking and Telecommunications, A
Computer and Information Sciences, A
Criminal Justice/Law Enforcement Administration, A
Drafting and Design Technology/Technician, A
Electrical, Electronics and Communications Engineering, A
Elementary Education and Teaching, A
Emergency Medical Technology/Technician (EMT Paramedic), A
Engineering, A
Engineering Technologies/Technicians, A
Forestry Technology/Technician, A
Funeral Service and Mortuary Science, A
General Studies, A
Health Information/Medical Records Administration/Administrator, A
Health Professions and Related Clinical Sciences, A
Heating, Air Conditioning, Ventilation and Refrigeration Maintenance Technology/Technician, A
Industrial Technology/Technician, A
Legal Assistant/Paralegal, A
Liberal Arts and Sciences Studies and Humanities, A
Machine Tool Technology/Machinist, A
Manufacturing Technology/Technician, A
Mathematics, A
Occupational Therapist Assistant, A
Occupational Therapy/Therapist, A
Physical Therapy/Therapist, A
Pre-Dentistry Studies, A
Pre-Law Studies, A
Pre-Medicine/Pre-Medical Studies, A
Pre-Nursing Studies, A
Pre-Pharmacy Studies, A
Pre-Veterinary Studies, A
Psychology, A
Secondary School Administration/Principalship, A
Surgical Technology/Technologist, A

Wildlife and Wildlands Science and Management, A

ITAWAMBA COMMUNITY COLLEGE

Accounting, A
Administrative Assistant and Secretarial Science, A
Agricultural Business and Management, A
Art Teacher Education, A
Art/Art Studies, General, A
Biological and Physical Sciences, A
Biology/Biological Sciences, A
Business Administration and Management, A
Chemistry, A
Civil Engineering Technology/Technician, A
Computer Science, A
Computer and Information Sciences, A
Construction Engineering Technology/Technician, A
Criminal Justice/Police Science, A
Data Processing and Data Processing Technology/Technician, A
Drafting and Design Technology/Technician, A
Economics, A
Education, A
Electrical, Electronic and Communications Engineering Technology/Technician, A
Elementary Education and Teaching, A
English Language and Literature, A
Family and Consumer Sciences/Home Economics Teacher Education, A
Family and Consumer Sciences/Human Sciences, A
Fashion/Apparel Design, A
Forestry Technology/Technician, A
Health Information/Medical Records Administration/Administrator, A
History, A
Human Services, A
Journalism, A
Kindergarten/PreSchool Education and Teaching, A
Liberal Arts and Sciences Studies and Humanities, A
Library Science, A
Marketing/Marketing Management, A
Mathematics, A
Medical Radiologic Technology/Science - Radiation Therapist, A
Modern Languages, A
Music, A
Music Teacher Education, A
Physical Education Teaching and Coaching, A
Piano and Organ, A
Political Science and Government, A
Psychology, A
Public Administration, A
Respiratory Care Therapy/Therapist, A
Science Teacher Education/General Science Teacher Education, A
Social Sciences, A
Social Work, A
Sociology, A
Trade and Industrial Teacher Education, A

JACKSON STATE UNIVERSITY

Accounting, BM
Atmospheric Sciences and Meteorology, B
Biological and Biomedical Sciences, MD
Biology/Biological Sciences, B
Business Administration and Management, B
Business Administration, Management and Operations, MD
Business/Managerial Economics, B
Chemistry, BMD
Civil Engineering, B
Clinical Psychology, D
Communication Disorders, M
Computer Engineering, B
Computer Science, M
Computer and Information Sciences, B
Counselor Education/School Counseling and Guidance Services, M
Criminal Justice/Safety Studies, B
Criminology, M
Early Childhood Education and Teaching, MDO
Education, BMDO
Educational Administration and Supervision, MDO
Educational Media/Instructional Technology, M
Educational/Instructional Media Design, B

Electrical, Electronics and Communications Engineering, B
Elementary Education and Teaching, BMDO
English, M
English Education, M
English Language and Literature, B
Entrepreneurship/Entrepreneurial Studies, B
Environmental Sciences, MD
Finance, B
Foreign Languages and Literatures, B
Geology/Earth Science, B
Health Education, M
Health/Health Care Administration/Management, B
History, BM
Industrial Education, M
Industrial Technology/Technician, B
Marketing/Marketing Management, B
Mass Communication/Media Studies, BM
Materials Sciences, M
Mathematics, BM
Mathematics Teacher Education, BM
Multi-/Interdisciplinary Studies, B
Music Performance, B
Music Teacher Education, BM
Physical Education Teaching and Coaching, BM
Physics, B
Political Science and Government, BM
Psychology, BD
Public Administration, MD
Public Affairs, MD
Public Policy Analysis, MD
Rehabilitation Counseling, M
Science Teacher Education/General Science Teacher Education, M
Secondary Education and Teaching, MO
Social Science Teacher Education, B
Social Work, BMD
Sociology, BM
Special Education and Teaching, BMO
Speech-Language Pathology/Pathologist, B
Statistics, B
Technology Teacher Education/Industrial Arts Teacher Education, B
Urban Studies/Affairs, B
Urban and Regional Planning, MD
Visual and Performing Arts, B

JONES COUNTY JUNIOR COLLEGE

Accounting, A
Agriculture, A
Art Teacher Education, A
Biological and Physical Sciences, A
Biology/Biological Sciences, A
Business Administration and Management, A
Chemistry, A
Child Development, A
Criminal Justice/Police Science, A
Data Processing and Data Processing Technology/Technician, A
Design and Applied Arts, A
Drafting and Design Technology/Technician, A
Economics, A
Education, A
Electrical, Electronic and Communications Engineering Technology/Technician, A
Emergency Medical Technology/Technician (EMT Paramedic), A
Engineering Science, A
English Language and Literature, A
Family and Consumer Sciences/Home Economics Teacher Education, A
Family and Consumer Sciences/Human Sciences, A
Forestry Technology/Technician, A
Horticultural Science, A
Mathematics, A
Music, A
Music Teacher Education, A
Physical Education Teaching and Coaching, A
Physical Sciences, A
Science Teacher Education/General Science Teacher Education, A
Voice and Opera, A

MERIDIAN COMMUNITY COLLEGE

Administrative Assistant and Secretarial Science, A
Child Care Provider/Assistant, A

Clinical/Medical Laboratory Technician, A
Dental Hygiene/Hygienist, A
Drafting and Design Technology/Technician, A
Electrical, Electronic and Communications Engineering Technology/Technician, A
Emergency Medical Technology/Technician (EMT Paramedic), A
Fire Science/Firefighting, A
Machine Tool Technology/Machinist, A
Marketing/Marketing Management, A
Respiratory Care Therapy/Therapist, A
Telecommunications Technology/Technician, A

MILLSAPS COLLEGE

Accounting, BM
Applied Mathematics, B
Art History, Criticism and Conservation, B
Biochemistry, B
Biology/Biological Sciences, B
Business Administration and Management, B
Business Administration, Management and Operations, M
Chemistry, B
Classics and Classical Languages, Literatures, and Linguistics, B
Cognitive Sciences, B
Communication Studies/Speech Communication and Rhetoric, B
Computer Science, B
Economics, B
Education, B
English Language and Literature, B
European Studies/Civilization, B
Fine/Studio Arts, B
Geology/Earth Science, B
History, B
Latin American Studies, B
Mathematics, B
Multi-/Interdisciplinary Studies, B
Music, B
Philosophy, B
Philosophy and Religious Studies, B
Physics, B
Political Science and Government, B
Psychology, B
Public Administration, B
Religion/Religious Studies, B
Spanish Language and Literature, B

MISSISSIPPI COLLEGE

Accounting, BMO
Adult and Continuing Education and Teaching, B
Advertising and Public Relations, M
Art Education, M
Art Teacher Education, B
Biochemistry, BM
Biological and Biomedical Sciences, M
Biology Teacher Education, B
Biology/Biological Sciences, B
Biomedical Sciences, B
Business Administration and Management, B
Business Administration, Management and Operations, MO
Business Education, M
Ceramic Arts and Ceramics, B
Chemical Physics, B
Chemistry, BM
Chemistry Teacher Education, B
Christian Studies, B
Communication Studies/Speech Communication and Rhetoric, B
Communication and Media Studies, M
Computer Education, M
Computer Science, BM
Computer and Information Sciences, B
Corporate and Organizational Communication, M
Counseling Psychology, M
Counselor Education/School Counseling and Guidance Services, MO
Criminal Justice/Law Enforcement Administration, B
Criminology, M
Curriculum and Instruction, M
Education, MDO
Educational Administration and Supervision, M
Educational Leadership and Administration, MDO

Electrical, Electronics and Communications Engineering, B
Elementary Education and Teaching, BMO
English, M
English Education, M
English Language and Literature, B
English as a Second Language, M
English/Language Arts Teacher Education, B
Finance, B
Finance and Banking, MO
Fine Arts and Art Studies, M
Fine/Studio Arts, B
Foreign Languages, Literatures, and Linguistics, B
French Language and Literature, B
Graphic Design, B
Health Services Administration, M
Higher Education/Higher Education Administration, M
History, BM
Interior Design, B
International/Global Studies, B
Kinesiology and Exercise Science, B
Kinesiology and Movement Studies, M
Language Interpretation and Translation, B
Law and Legal Studies, DO
Legal Assistant/Paralegal, B
Legal and Justice Studies, O
Liberal Studies, M
Marketing/Marketing Management, B
Marriage and Family Therapy/Counseling, M
Mass Communication/Media Studies, B
Mathematics, BM
Mathematics Teacher Education, M
Music, BM
Music Teacher Education, BM
Music Theory and Composition, B
Painting, B
Performance, M
Physical Education Teaching and Coaching, B
Physics, B
Piano and Organ, B
Political Science and Government, BM
Psychology, B
Public Relations/Image Management, B
Science Teacher Education/General Science Teacher Education, M
Sculpture, B
Secondary Education and Teaching, M
Securities Services Administration/Management, B
Social Sciences, M
Social Studies Teacher Education, BM
Social Work, B
Sociology, B
Spanish Language and Literature, B
Special Education and Teaching, M
Sport and Fitness Administration/Management, B
Voice and Opera, B

MISSISSIPPI DELTA COMMUNITY COLLEGE

Accounting, A
Administrative Assistant and Secretarial Science, A
Advertising, A
Agricultural Business and Management, A
Agricultural Economics, A
American/United States Studies/Civilization, A
Architectural Engineering Technology/Technician, A
Art Teacher Education, A
Behavioral Sciences, A
Biology/Biological Sciences, A
Business Machine Repairer, A
Civil Engineering Technology/Technician, A
Clinical/Medical Laboratory Technician, A
Computer Engineering Technology/Technician, A
Criminal Justice/Law Enforcement Administration, A
Dental Hygiene/Hygienist, A
Design and Applied Arts, A
Drama and Dramatics/Theatre Arts, A
Economics, A
Education, A
Electrical, Electronic and Communications Engineering Technology/Technician, A
Elementary Education and Teaching, A
English Language and Literature, A
Family and Consumer Sciences/Human Sciences, A
Geography, A

Graphic and Printing Equipment Operator Production, A
Health Information/Medical Records Administration/Administrator, A
Health Teacher Education, A
History, A
Horticultural Science, A
Liberal Arts and Sciences Studies and Humanities, A
Management Information Systems and Services, A
Mason/Masonry, A
Mathematics, A
Medical Office Computer Specialist/Assistant, A
Medical Radiologic Technology/Science - Radiation Therapist, A
Music, A
Music Teacher Education, A
Physical Education Teaching and Coaching, A
Political Science and Government, A
Science Teacher Education/General Science Teacher Education, A
Social Work, A

MISSISSIPPI GULF COAST COMMUNITY COLLEGE

Accounting, A
Administrative Assistant and Secretarial Science, A
Advertising, A
Agricultural Business and Management, A
Art Teacher Education, A
Art/Art Studies, General, A
Automobile/Automotive Mechanics Technology/Technician, A
Biological and Physical Sciences, A
Business Administration and Management, A
Business Teacher Education, A
Chemical Engineering, A
Clinical/Medical Laboratory Technician, A
Computer Engineering Technology/Technician, A
Computer Graphics, A
Computer Programming, A
Computer Science, A
Computer Systems Networking and Telecommunications, A
Computer and Information Sciences, A
Court Reporting/Court Reporter, A
Criminal Justice/Law Enforcement Administration, A
Criminal Justice/Police Science, A
Data Entry/Microcomputer Applications, A
Drafting and Design Technology/Technician, A
Education, A
Electrical, Electronic and Communications Engineering Technology/Technician, A
Elementary Education and Teaching, A
Emergency Medical Technology/Technician (EMT Paramedic), A
Fashion Merchandising, A
Finance, A
Horticultural Science, A
Hotel/Motel Administration/Management, A
Human Services, A
Industrial Radiologic Technology/Technician, A
Information Technology, A
Kindergarten/PreSchool Education and Teaching, A
Legal Assistant/Paralegal, A
Liberal Arts and Sciences Studies and Humanities, A
Marketing/Marketing Management, A
Ornamental Horticulture, A
Respiratory Care Therapy/Therapist, A
Welding Technology/Welder, A
Word Processing, A

MISSISSIPPI STATE UNIVERSITY

Accounting, BMD
Aerospace, Aeronautical and Astronautical Engineering, BMD
Agribusiness, B
Agricultural Economics, BM
Agricultural Education, MD
Agricultural Sciences, MD
Agricultural Teacher Education, B
Agriculture, B
Agronomy and Crop Science, B
Agronomy and Soil Sciences, MD
American/United States Studies/Civilization, MD

Animal Sciences, BMD
Anthropology, BM
Applied Economics, D
Applied Physics, D
Architecture, B
Atmospheric Sciences and Meteorology, D
Biochemistry, BMD
Bioengineering, MD
Biological and Biomedical Sciences, MD
Biological and Physical Sciences, B
Biology/Biological Sciences, B
Biomedical/Medical Engineering, B
Business Administration and Management, B
Business Administration, Management and Operations, MD
Business Education, M
Business Teacher Education, B
Business/Managerial Economics, B
Chemical Engineering, BMD
Chemistry, BMD
Child and Family Studies, MD
Civil Engineering, BMD
Clinical Laboratory Science/Medical Technology/Technologist, B
Clinical Psychology, M
Cognitive Sciences, D
Communication Studies/Speech Communication and Rhetoric, B
Community College Education, MD
Computer Engineering, BMD
Computer Science, MD
Computer and Information Sciences, B
Construction Management, B
Counselor Education/School Counseling and Guidance Services, MDO
Criminology, B
Curriculum and Instruction, MDO
Dairy Science, MD
Early Childhood Education and Teaching, MD
Economics, BMD
Education, MDO
Educational Administration and Supervision, MO
Educational Leadership and Administration, MDO
Educational Media/Instructional Technology, MDO
Educational Psychology, MDO
Electrical Engineering, MD
Electrical, Electronics and Communications Engineering, B
Elementary Education and Teaching, BMDO
Engineering, B
Engineering and Applied Sciences, MD
English, M
English Language and Literature, B
Entomology, MD
Exercise and Sports Science, M
Experimental Psychology, M
Family and Consumer Sciences/Human Sciences, B
Finance, B
Finance and Banking, MD
Fish, Game and Wildlife Management, MD
Food Science, B
Food Science and Technology, MD
Foreign Language Teacher Education, M
Foreign Languages and Literatures, B
Forestry, BMD
French Language and Literature, M
Genetics, MD
Geography, M
Geology/Earth Science, BM
Geosciences, MD
German Language and Literature, M
Health Promotion, M
Health/Health Care Administration/Management, B
Higher Education/Higher Education Administration, M
History, BMD
Horticultural Science, BMD
Human Development, MD
Human Resources Development, MDO
Industrial Engineering, B
Industrial Production Technologies/Technicians, B
Industrial Technology/Technician, B
Industrial/Management Engineering, MD
Insurance, B
Interior Architecture, B
Kinesiology and Movement Studies, M

Landscape Architecture, BM
Landscaping and Groundskeeping, B
Liberal Arts and Sciences Studies and Humanities, B
Management, D
Management Information Systems and Services, BMD
Marketing, MD
Marketing/Marketing Management, B
Mathematics, BMD
Mechanical Engineering, BMD
Medical Microbiology and Bacteriology, B
Meteorology, M
Middle School Education, M
Molecular Biology, MD
Multi-/Interdisciplinary Studies, B
Music, B
Music Teacher Education, B
Natural Resources and Conservation, B
Nutritional Sciences, MD
Philosophy, B
Physical Education Teaching and Coaching, BM
Physics, BMD
Plant Pathology/Phytopathology, MD
Plant Sciences, MD
Political Science and Government, BMD
Poultry Science, BMD
Project Management, M
Psychology, BMD
Public Administration, MD
Public Policy Analysis, MD
Reading Teacher Education, D
Real Estate, B
Rehabilitation Counseling, M
School Psychology, DO
Science Teacher Education/General Science Teacher Education, M
Secondary Education and Teaching, BMDO
Social Work, B
Sociology, BMD
Spanish Language and Literature, M
Special Education and Teaching, BMDO
Sport and Fitness Administration/Management, M
Statistics, M
Student Personnel Services, MD
Sustainable Development, MD
Systems Engineering, MD
Taxation, M
Teacher Education and Professional Development, Specific Subject Areas, B
Veterinary Medicine, D
Veterinary Sciences, MD
Veterinary/Animal Health Technology/Technician and Veterinary Assistant, B
Visual and Performing Arts, B
Western European Studies, MD
Wildlife and Wildlands Science and Management, B

MISSISSIPPI UNIVERSITY FOR WOMEN

Accounting, B
Art Teacher Education, B
Biology/Biological Sciences, B
Business Administration and Management, B
Business/Commerce, B
Chemistry, B
Communication Disorders, M
Communication Studies/Speech Communication and Rhetoric, B
Culinary Arts and Related Services, B
Curriculum and Instruction, M
Education, M
Education/Teaching of the Gifted and Talented, M
Educational Leadership and Administration, M
Elementary Education and Teaching, B
English Language and Literature, B
Family Systems, B
Health Education, M
Health and Physical Education, B
History, B
Legal Assistant/Paralegal, B
Liberal Arts and Sciences Studies and Humanities, B
Mathematics, B
Multi-/Interdisciplinary Studies, B
Music, B
Nursing, MO

Physical Sciences, B
Political Science and Government, B
Psychology, B
Public Administration, B
Public Health Education and Promotion, B
Reading Teacher Education, M
Social Sciences, B
Spanish Language and Literature, B
Speech-Language Pathology/Pathologist, B
Visual and Performing Arts, B
Women's Studies, B

MISSISSIPPI VALLEY STATE UNIVERSITY

Accounting, B
Art/Art Studies, General, B
Bioinformatics, M
Biology/Biological Sciences, B
Business Administration and Management, B
Chemistry, B
Computer Science, B
Criminal Justice/Law Enforcement Administration, B
Criminology, M
Education, BM
Elementary Education and Teaching, BM
English Language and Literature, B
Environmental Health, B
Environmental and Occupational Health, M
History, B
Industrial Technology/Technician, B
Kindergarten/PreSchool Education and Teaching, B
Mass Communication/Media Studies, B
Mathematics, B
Music, B
Music Teacher Education, B
Office Management and Supervision, B
Physical Education Teaching and Coaching, B
Public Administration, B
Social Work, B
Sociology, B

NORTHEAST MISSISSIPPI COMMUNITY COLLEGE

Accounting, A
Administrative Assistant and Secretarial Science, A
Agricultural Teacher Education, A
Agriculture, A
Architectural Engineering Technology/Technician, A
Architecture, A
Art Teacher Education, A
Athletic Training and Sports Medicine, A
Biological and Physical Sciences, A
Biology/Biological Sciences, A
Business Administration and Management, A
Business Teacher Education, A
Chemistry, A
Child Care Provider/Assistant, A
Civil Engineering Technology/Technician, A
Clinical/Medical Laboratory Technician, A
Communication Disorders, A
Computer Programming/Programmer, A
Computer and Information Sciences, A
Criminal Justice/Police Science, A
Dental Assisting/Assistant, A
Dental Hygiene/Hygienist, A
Drafting and Design Technology/Technician, A
Electrical, Electronic and Communications Engineering Technology/Technician, A
Electrician, A
Elementary Education and Teaching, A
Engineering, A
English Language and Literature, A
English/Language Arts Teacher Education, A
Family and Consumer Sciences/Home Economics Teacher Education, A
Family and Consumer Sciences/Human Sciences, A
Fashion Merchandising, A
Fine Arts and Art Studies, A
Forestry, A
Forestry Technology/Technician, A
Health Professions and Related Clinical Sciences, A
Health/Medical Preparatory Programs, A
Heating, Air Conditioning, Ventilation and Refrigeration Maintenance Technology/Technician, A
History, A
Hospitality Administration/Management, A

Industrial Mechanics and Maintenance Technology, A
Interior Design, A
Journalism, A
Kindergarten/PreSchool Education and Teaching, A
Landscaping and Groundskeeping, A
Legal Assistant/Paralegal, A
Liberal Arts and Sciences Studies and Humanities, A
Management Information Systems and Services, A
Marketing/Marketing Management, A
Mathematics, A
Mathematics Teacher Education, A
Medical Radiologic Technology/Science - Radiation Therapist, A
Medical/Clinical Assistant, A
Music, A
Music Teacher Education, A
Occupational Therapy/Therapist, A
Ophthalmic and Optometric Support Services and Allied Professions, A
Photography, A
Physical Education Teaching and Coaching, A
Physical Therapy/Therapist, A
Physics, A
Political Science and Government, A
Pre-Dentistry Studies, A
Pre-Law Studies, A
Pre-Medicine/Pre-Medical Studies, A
Pre-Pharmacy Studies, A
Pre-Veterinary Studies, A
Psychology, A
Radio and Television, A
Respiratory Care Therapy/Therapist, A
Science Teacher Education/General Science Teacher Education, A
Social Studies Teacher Education, A
Social Work, A
Sociology, A
Special Education and Teaching, A
Theology/Theological Studies, A
Tool and Die Technology/Technician, A

NORTHWEST MISSISSIPPI COMMUNITY COLLEGE

Accounting, A
Agricultural Business and Management, A
Agricultural Economics, A
Agricultural Mechanization, A
Agriculture, A
Animal Sciences, A
Art/Art Studies, General, A
Business Administration and Management, A
Civil Engineering Technology/Technician, A
Commercial and Advertising Art, A
Computer Programming, Specific Applications, A
Computer Programming/Programmer, A
Computer and Information Sciences, A
Court Reporting/Court Reporter, A
Dairy Science, A
Data Processing and Data Processing Technology/Technician, A
Drafting and Design Technology/Technician, A
Education, A
Electrical, Electronic and Communications Engineering Technology/Technician, A
Elementary Education and Teaching, A
Family and Consumer Sciences/Home Economics Teacher Education, A
Fashion Merchandising, A
Foods, Nutrition, and Wellness Studies, A
Heating, Air Conditioning and Refrigeration Technology/Technician, A
Heating, Air Conditioning, Ventilation and Refrigeration Maintenance Technology/Technician, A
Hotel/Motel Administration/Management, A
Journalism, A
Legal Assistant/Paralegal, A
Liberal Arts and Sciences Studies and Humanities, A
Machine Tool Technology/Machinist, A
Mathematics Teacher Education, A
Medical Administrative Assistant/Secretary, A
Music Teacher Education, A
Office Management and Supervision, A
Physical Education Teaching and Coaching, A

Plant Sciences, A
Poultry Science, A
Radio and Television, A
Radio and Television Broadcasting Technology/Technician, A
Respiratory Care Therapy/Therapist, A
Sales and Marketing Operations/Marketing and Distribution Teacher Education, A
Science Teacher Education/General Science Teacher Education, A
Social Science Teacher Education, A
Social Studies Teacher Education, A
Speech Teacher Education, A
Telecommunications Technology/Technician, A

PEARL RIVER COMMUNITY COLLEGE

Administrative Assistant and Secretarial Science, A
Business Administration and Management, A
Drafting and Design Technology/Technician, A
Electrical, Electronic and Communications Engineering Technology/Technician, A
Liberal Arts and Sciences Studies and Humanities, A
Marketing/Marketing Management, A
Medical Administrative Assistant/Secretary, A
Respiratory Care Therapy/Therapist, A

RUST COLLEGE

Biology Teacher Education, B
Biology/Biological Sciences, B
Broadcast Journalism, B
Business Administration and Management, AB
Business Teacher Education, B
Chemistry, B
Child Care and Support Services Management, B
Computer Science, B
Early Childhood Education and Teaching, A
Elementary Education and Teaching, B
English Language and Literature, B
English/Language Arts Teacher Education, B
Journalism, B
Mathematics, B
Mathematics Teacher Education, B
Music, B
Political Science and Government, B
Social Science Teacher Education, B
Social Sciences, B
Social Work, B
Sociology, B

SOUTHEASTERN BAPTIST COLLEGE

Administrative Assistant and Secretarial Science, A
Bible/Biblical Studies, AB
Business Administration and Management, A
Pastoral Studies/Counseling, B
Religious/Sacred Music, A

SOUTHWEST MISSISSIPPI COMMUNITY COLLEGE

Accounting, A
Administrative Assistant and Secretarial Science, A
Advertising, A
Automobile/Automotive Mechanics Technology/Technician, A
Biological and Physical Sciences, A
Biology/Biological Sciences, A
Business Administration and Management, A
Business Teacher Education, A
Carpentry/Carpenter, A
Chemistry, A
Computer Programming, A
Computer Science, A
Computer Systems Networking and Telecommunications, A
Construction Engineering Technology/Technician, A
Cosmetology/Cosmetologist, A
Diesel Mechanics Technology/Technician, A
Early Childhood Education and Teaching, A
Education, A
Electrical, Electronic and Communications Engineering Technology/Technician, A
Elementary Education and Teaching, A
Emergency Medical Technology/Technician (EMT Paramedic), A
Engineering, A

English Language and Literature, A
Fashion Merchandising, A
Finance, A
Health Information/Medical Records Technology/Technician, A
Health Professions and Related Clinical Sciences, A
Heating, Air Conditioning, Ventilation and Refrigeration Maintenance Technology/Technician, A
History, A
Humanities/Humanistic Studies, A
Information Technology, A
Legal Administrative Assistant/Secretary, A
Liberal Arts and Sciences Studies and Humanities, A
Marketing/Marketing Management, A
Massage Therapy/Therapeutic Massage, A
Medical Insurance Specialist/Medical Biller, A
Music, A
Music Teacher Education, A
Occupational Safety and Health Technology/Technician, A
Petroleum Technology/Technician, A
Physical Education Teaching and Coaching, A
Physical Sciences, A
Social Sciences, A
System Administration/Administrator, A
Web/Multimedia Management and Webmaster, A
Welding Technology/Welder, A
Well Drilling/Driller, A

STRAYER UNIVERSITY–JACKSON CAMPUS

Accounting, B
Business Administration and Management, B
Criminal Justice/Law Enforcement Administration, B
International Business/Trade/Commerce, B
Management Information Systems and Services, B

TOUGALOO COLLEGE

Accounting, B
African-American/Black Studies, B
Art/Art Studies, General, B
Biology/Biological Sciences, B
Business Administration and Management, B
Chemistry, B
Child Development, AB
Computer Science, B
Early Childhood Education and Teaching, A
Economics, B
Education, B
Elementary Education and Teaching, B
English Language and Literature, B
History, B
Hospitality Administration/Management, A
Mass Communication/Media Studies, B
Mathematics, B
Music, B
Physics, B
Political Science and Government, B
Psychology, B
Religion/Religious Studies, AB
Secondary Education and Teaching, B
Sociology, B

UNIVERSITY OF MISSISSIPPI

Accounting, BMD
African-American/Black Studies, B
Anthropology, BM
Applied Science and Technology, MD
Art History, Criticism and Conservation, B
Audiology/Audiologist and Speech-Language Pathology/Pathologist, B
Biochemistry, B
Biological and Biomedical Sciences, MD
Biology/Biological Sciences, B
Business Administration and Management, B
Business Administration, Management and Operations, MD
Business/Managerial Economics, B
Chemical Engineering, B
Chemistry, BMD
Chinese Language and Literature, B
Civil Engineering, B
Classics and Classical Languages, Literatures, and Linguistics, B

Clinical Laboratory Science/Medical Technology/Technologist, B
Clinical Psychology, D
Communication Disorders, BM
Computer and Information Sciences, B
Criminal Justice/Law Enforcement Administration, B
Criminology, M
CytoTechnology/Cytotechnologist, B
Dental Hygiene/Hygienist, B
Dietetics/Dieticians, B
Digital Communication and Media/Multimedia, B
Drama and Dramatics/Theatre Arts, B
Economics, BMD
Education, MDO
Electrical, Electronics and Communications Engineering, B
Elementary Education and Teaching, B
Engineering, B
Engineering and Applied Sciences, MD
English, MD
English Language and Literature, B
English/Language Arts Teacher Education, B
Exercise and Sports Science, M
Experimental Psychology, D
Finance, B
Fine Arts and Art Studies, M
Fine/Studio Arts, B
Food Science and Technology, M
Foreign Language Teacher Education, M
French Language and Literature, B
General Studies, B
Geological/Geophysical Engineering, B
Geology/Earth Science, B
German Language and Literature, B
Health Information/Medical Records Administration/Administrator, B
Health Professions and Related Clinical Sciences, B
Health Promotion, M
History, BMD
Hospitality Administration/Management, B
Insurance, B
International Relations and Affairs, B
Journalism, BM
Kinesiology and Exercise Science, B
Kinesiology and Movement Studies, D
Law and Legal Studies, MD
Legal Assistant/Paralegal, B
Liberal Arts and Sciences Studies and Humanities, B
Linguistics, B
Management Information Systems and Services, B
Marketing, B
Marketing/Marketing Management, B
Mathematics, BMD
Mathematics Teacher Education, B
Mechanical Engineering, B
Music, BMD
Nutritional Sciences, M
Parks, Recreation and Leisure Facilities Management, B
Pharmacy, MD
Pharmacy, Pharmaceutical Sciences, and Administration, B
Philosophy, BM
Physics, BMD
Political Science and Government, BMD
Psychology, B
Public Policy Analysis, B
Radiologic Technology/Science - Radiographer, B
Real Estate, B
Recreation and Park Management, M
Regional Studies (U.S., Canadian, Foreign), B
Religion/Religious Studies, B
Science Teacher Education/General Science Teacher Education, B
Social Studies Teacher Education, B
Social Work, BM
Sociology, BM
Spanish Language and Literature, B
Special Education and Teaching, B
System Management, M

Taxation, M

UNIVERSITY OF MISSISSIPPI MEDICAL CENTER

Allied Health and Medical Assisting Services, M
Allopathic Medicine, D
Anatomy, MD
Biochemistry, D
Biological and Biomedical Sciences, MD
Biophysics, D
Clinical Laboratory Science/Medical Technology/Technologist, B
CytoTechnology/Cytotechnologist, B
Dental Hygiene/Hygienist, B
Dentistry, MD
Health Information/Medical Records Administration/Administrator, B
Materials Sciences, MD
Microbiology, D
Neuroscience, D
Nursing, MD
Occupational Therapy/Therapist, M
Oral and Dental Sciences, MD
Pathology/Experimental Pathology, D
Pharmacology, D
Physical Therapy/Therapist, M
Physiology, D
Toxicology, D

UNIVERSITY OF SOUTHERN MISSISSIPPI

Accounting, BM
Advertising, B
American/United States Studies/Civilization, B
Anthropology, BM
Apparel and Textiles, B
Architectural Engineering Technology/Technician, B
Athletic Training and Sports Medicine, B
Audiology/Audiologist and Speech-Language Pathology/Pathologist, B
Biochemistry, MD
Biological and Biomedical Sciences, MD
Biological and Physical Sciences, B
Biology/Biological Sciences, B
Biostatistics, M
Business Administration and Management, B
Business Administration, Management and Operations, M
Business Teacher Education, B
Business, Management, Marketing, and Related Support Services, B
Business/Managerial Economics, B
Chemistry, BMD
Child and Family Studies, M
Clinical Laboratory Science/Medical Technology/Technologist, B
Clinical Psychology, D
Communication Disorders, MD
Communication Studies/Speech Communication and Rhetoric, B
Computational Sciences, MD
Computer Engineering Technology/Technician, B
Computer Science, MD
Computer and Information Sciences, B
Construction Engineering and Management, M
Counseling Psychology, MD
Counselor Education/School Counseling and Guidance Services, MDO
Criminal Justice/Safety Studies, B
Criminology, MD
Curriculum and Instruction, MDO
Dance, B
Data Processing and Data Processing Technology/Technician, B
Dietetics/Dieticians, B
Drama and Dramatics/Theatre Arts, B
Economic Development, M
Economics, M
Education, MDO
Education/Teaching of Individuals with Hearing Impairments, Including Deafness, B
Educational Leadership and Administration, MDO
Educational Measurement and Evaluation, MD
Educational Media/Instructional Technology, MD
Electrical, Electronic and Communications Engineering Technology/Technician, B

Elementary Education and Teaching, BMDO
English, MD
English Language and Literature, B
Environmental Biology, M
Epidemiology, M
Experimental Psychology, D
Family Systems, B
Finance, B
Fine/Studio Arts, B
Food Science and Technology, MD
Foreign Language Teacher Education, M
Foreign Languages and Literatures, B
Forensic Science and Technology, BM
Geography, BMD
Geology/Earth Science, BMD
Health Education, M
Health Services Administration, M
Health Services/Allied Health/Health Sciences, B
Health and Physical Education, B
Higher Education/Higher Education Administration, MD
History, BMD
Hospitality Administration/Management, B
Hotel/Motel Administration/Management, B
Human Resources Management/Personnel Administration, B
Hydrology and Water Resources Science, M
Industrial Technology/Technician, B
Information Science/Studies, MO
Inorganic Chemistry, M
Interior Architecture, B
International Business/Trade/Commerce, B
International Development, MD
International Relations and Affairs, B
Journalism, B
Legal Assistant/Paralegal, B
Library Science, BMO
Management Information Systems and Services, B
Marine Biology and Biological Oceanography, BM
Marine Sciences, MD
Marketing, B
Marketing/Marketing Management, B
Marriage and Family Therapy/Counseling, M
Mass Communication/Media Studies, MD
Maternal/Child Health and Neonatal Nurse/Nursing, M
Mathematics, BMD
Mathematics Teacher Education, MD
Medical Technology, M
Microbiology, MD
Molecular Biology, MD
Multi-/Interdisciplinary Studies, B
Music, BMD
Music History, Literature, and Theory, M
Music Teacher Education, BMD
Music Theory and Composition, M
Nursing, MDO
Nursing - Advanced Practice, MO
Nutritional Sciences, MD
Oceanography, Chemical and Physical, B
Organic Chemistry, M
Parks, Recreation, Leisure and Fitness Studies, B
Performance, MD
Philosophy, B
Physical Chemistry, M
Physical Education Teaching and Coaching, BMD
Physics, BMD
Political Science and Government, BMD
Polymer/Plastics Engineering, BMD
Psychiatric/Mental Health Nurse/Nursing, O
Psychology, BMD
Public Health, M
Public Health (MPH, DPH), B
Religion/Religious Studies, B
School Psychology, D
Science Teacher Education/General Science Teacher Education, MD
Social Studies Teacher Education, O
Social Work, BM
Sociology, B
Special Education and Teaching, BMDO
Speech and Interpersonal Communication, MD
Sport and Fitness Administration/Management, BM
Student Personnel Services, M
Theater, M

Visual and Performing Arts, B

VIRGINIA COLLEGE IN BILOXI

Criminal Justice/Law Enforcement Administration, A
Human Resources Management/Personnel Adminis-
tration, A
Legal Assistant/Paralegal, A
Medical Office Management/Administration, A
Medical/Clinical Assistant, A
Office Management and Supervision, A
Personal and Culinary Services, A
Surgical Technology/Technologist, A

VIRGINIA COLLEGE IN JACKSON

Accounting and Related Services, A
Cosmetology/Cosmetologist, A
Criminal Justice/Safety Studies, A
Human Resources Management/Personnel Adminis-
tration, A
Information Technology, A
Legal Assistant/Paralegal, A
Massage Therapy/Therapeutic Massage, A
Office Management and Supervision, A
Salon/Beauty Salon Management/Manager, A
Surgical Technology/Technologist, A

WILLIAM CAREY UNIVERSITY

Art Education, M
Art Teacher Education, B
Art/Art Studies, General, B
Biology Teacher Education, B
Biology/Biological Sciences, B
Business Administration and Management, B
Business Administration, Management and Opera-
tions, M
Chemistry, B
Communication Studies/Speech Communication
and Rhetoric, B
Counseling Psychology, M
Drama and Dance Teacher Education, B
Drama and Dramatics/Theatre Arts, B
Education, MO
Education/Teaching of the Gifted and Talented, M
Elementary Education and Teaching, BMO
English Education, M
English Language and Literature, B
English/Language Arts Teacher Education, B
Fine/Studio Arts, B
General Studies, B
Health Professions and Related Clinical Sciences, B
Health and Physical Education, B
History, B
Journalism, B
Mathematics, B
Mathematics Teacher Education, B
Music, B
Music Performance, B
Music Teacher Education, B
Music Therapy/Therapist, B
Nursing, M
Physical Education Teaching and Coaching, B
Psychology, BM
Religion/Religious Studies, B
Religious/Sacred Music, B
Secondary Education and Teaching, M
Social Sciences, B
Social Studies Teacher Education, BM
Special Education and Teaching, M
Speech Teacher Education, B

Missouri

AMERICAN BUSINESS & TECHNOL-
OGY UNIVERSITY

Accounting, M
Business Administration, Management and Opera-
tions, M
Computer Programming/Programmer, A
Computer Systems Networking and Telecommunica-
tions, A
Criminal Justice/Law Enforcement Administration, A
Finance and Banking, M
Health Information/Medical Records
Technology/Technician, A
Information Technology, A

International Business/Trade/Commerce, M
Management Information Systems and Services, M
Marketing, M
Project Management, M
Web Page, Digital/Multimedia and Information Re-
sources Design, A

THE ART INSTITUTE OF ST. LOUIS

Apparel and Accessories Marketing Operations, B
Cinematography and Film/Video Production, B
Commercial Photography, B
Culinary Arts/Chef Training, A
Interior Design, B
Restaurant, Culinary, and Catering
Management/Manager, B
Web Page, Digital/Multimedia and Information Re-
sources Design, AB

AVILA UNIVERSITY

Accounting, BM
Art/Art Studies, General, B
Biology/Biological Sciences, B
Business Administration and Management, B
Business Administration, Management and Opera-
tions, M
Business Teacher Education, B
Business/Commerce, B
Communication Studies/Speech Communication
and Rhetoric, B
Computer and Information Sciences, B
Counseling Psychology, M
Criminology, B
Drama and Dramatics/Theatre Arts, B
Education, BMO
Educational Leadership and Administration, B
Educational Media/Instructional Technology, M
Elementary Education and Teaching, B
English Language and Literature, B
English as a Second Language, MO
Entrepreneurship/Entrepreneurial Studies, B
Finance, B
Finance and Banking, M
Health Services Administration, M
Health and Physical Education/Fitness, B
Health/Medical Preparatory Programs, B
History, B
Hospital and Health Care Facilities
Administration/Management, B
Human Resources Management and Services, M
Human Resources Management/Personnel Adminis-
tration, B
International Business/Trade/Commerce, BM
International and Comparative Education, B
Junior High/Intermediate/Middle School Education
and Teaching, B
Kinesiology and Exercise Science, B
Management, M
Management Information Systems and Ser-
vices, BM
Marketing, M
Marketing/Marketing Management, B
Mathematics, B
Medical Radiologic Technology/Science - Radiation
Therapist, B
Music, B
Music Performance, B
Operations Management and Supervision, B
Organizational Management, M
Political Science and Government, B
Pre-Medicine/Pre-Medical Studies, B
Project Management, M
Psychology, BM
Public Relations/Image Management, B
Religion/Religious Studies, B
Sales, Distribution and Marketing Operations, B
Small Business Administration/Management, B
Social Work, B
Sociology, B
Special Education and Teaching, B
Teacher Education and Professional Develop-
ment, Specific Subject Areas, B

BAPTIST BIBLE COLLEGE

Business/Office Automation/Technology/Data Entry, A
Cultural Studies, M

Divinity/Ministry (BD, MDiv.), B
Early Childhood Education and Teaching, AB
Elementary Education and Teaching, B
Music, AB
Music Teacher Education, B
Pastoral Studies/Counseling, BM
Religious Education, B
Theology and Religious Vocations, M

BRYAN UNIVERSITY (SPRINGFIELD)

Business Administration, Management and Operations, M

CALVARY BIBLE COLLEGE AND THEO-
LOGICAL SEMINARY

Art History, Criticism and Conservation, B
Bible/Biblical Studies, AB
Business Administration and Management, B
Computer Science, B
Criminal Justice/Law Enforcement Administration, B
Divinity/Ministry (BD, MDiv.), B
Drama and Dramatics/Theatre Arts, B
Elementary Education and Teaching, B
English Language and Literature, B
Film/Video and Photographic Arts, B
History, B
Intercultural/Multicultural and Diversity Studies, B
Journalism, B
Marketing/Marketing Management, B
Mass Communication/Media Studies, B
Mathematics, B
Missions/Missionary Studies and Missiology, B
Multi-/Interdisciplinary Studies, B
Music Pedagogy, B
Music Performance, B
Music Teacher Education, B
Pastoral Counseling and Specialized Ministries, B
Pastoral Studies/Counseling, BM
Photography, B
Piano and Organ, B
Political Science and Government, B
Religious/Sacred Music, AB
Secondary Education and Teaching, B
Theology and Religious Vocations, M
Theology/Theological Studies, AB
Voice and Opera, B
Youth Ministry, AB

CENTRAL CHRISTIAN COLLEGE OF
THE BIBLE

Bible/Biblical Studies, A
Religion/Religious Studies, B

CENTRAL METHODIST UNIVERSITY

Accounting, B
Applied Mathematics, A
Athletic Training and Sports Medicine, B
Biology Teacher Education, B
Biology/Biological Sciences, B
Business Administration and Management, B
Chemistry, AB
Chemistry Teacher Education, B
Communication Studies/Speech Communication
and Rhetoric, B
Computer Science, AB
Counselor Education/School Counseling and Guid-
ance Services, M
Criminal Justice/Safety Studies, B
Drama and Dramatics/Theatre Arts, B
Early Childhood Education and Teaching, B
Economics, B
Education, BM
Elementary Education and Teaching, B
English Language and Literature, AB
Environmental Biology, B
Environmental Sciences, B
Foreign Language Teacher Education, B
Foreign Languages and Literatures, B
History, B
Junior High/Intermediate/Middle School Education
and Teaching, B
Kindergarten/PreSchool Education and Teaching, B
Management Science, B
Mathematics, B
Music, B

Music Performance, B
Music Teacher Education, BM
Nursing, M
Nursing Administration, M
Nursing Education, M
Philosophy, B
Physical Education Teaching and Coaching, B
Physics, B
Physics Teacher Education, B
Political Science and Government, B
Psychology, AB
Public Administration, AB
Religion/Religious Studies, B
Science Teacher Education/General Science
    Teacher Education, B
Secondary Education and Teaching, B
Social Science Teacher Education, B
Sociology, B
Sport and Fitness Administration/Management, B

CITY VISION UNIVERSITY

Business Administration and Management, AB
Missions/Missionary Studies and Missiology, B
Non-Profit/Public/Organizational Management, B
Substance Abuse/Addiction Counseling, B

COLLEGE OF THE OZARKS

Accounting, B
Acting, B
Agricultural Business and Management, B
Agricultural Teacher Education, B
Agronomy and Crop Science, B
Animal Sciences, B
Art Teacher Education, B
Audiovisual Communications
    Technologies/Technicians, B
Bible/Biblical Studies, B
Biology Teacher Education, B
Biomedical Sciences, B
Business Administration and Management, B
Business/Managerial Economics, B
Ceramic Arts and Ceramics, B
Chemistry, B
Child Development, B
Computer Science, B
Corrections, B
Criminal Justice/Police Science, B
Culinary Arts/Chef Training, B
Dairy Husbandry and Production, B
Design and Visual Communications, B
Dietetics/Dieticians, B
Drama and Dance Teacher Education, B
Drama and Dramatics/Theatre Arts, B
Early Childhood Education and Teaching, B
Ecology, B
Elementary Education and Teaching, B
English Language and Literature, B
English/Language Arts Teacher Education, B
Family and Community Services, B
Family and Consumer Sciences/Human Sciences, B
Fiber, Textile and Weaving Arts, B
Fine/Studio Arts, B
Foods, Nutrition, and Wellness Studies, B
Graphic Design, B
Health Services/Allied Health/Health Sciences, B
Health and Physical Education, B
Health/Medical Preparatory Programs, B
History, B
History Teacher Education, B
Horticultural Science, B
Hospitality Administration/Management, B
Information Technology, B
International Business/Trade/Commerce, B
Journalism, B
Marketing/Marketing Management, B
Mathematics, B
Mathematics Teacher Education, B
Molecular Biology, B
Music, B
Music Teacher Education, B
Painting, B
Parks, Recreation and Leisure Facilities Manage-
    ment, B
Physical Education Teaching and Coaching, B
Piano and Organ, B
Printing Management, B

Psychology, B
Public Relations, Advertising, and Applied Commu-
    nication, B
Radio and Television Broadcasting
    Technology/Technician, B
Religious/Sacred Music, B
Restaurant/Food Services Management, B
Social Work, B
Sociology, B
Spanish Language Teacher Education, B
Spanish Language and Literature, B
Technical Theatre/Theatre Design and Technol-
    ogy, B
Wildlife and Wildlands Science and Management, B

COLUMBIA COLLEGE

Accounting, B
American/United States Studies/Civilization, B
Art/Art Studies, General, B
Biology/Biological Sciences, B
Business Administration and Management, B
Business Administration, Management and Opera-
    tions, M
Business/Commerce, AB
Ceramic Arts and Ceramics, B
Chemistry, B
Communication Studies/Speech Communication
    and Rhetoric, B
Computer Science, B
Computer and Information Sciences, AB
Criminal Justice/Law Enforcement Administra-
    tion, AB
Criminology, M
Education, M
Educational Leadership and Administration, M
English Language and Literature, B
Environmental Sciences, B
Environmental Studies, A
Finance, B
Fire Services Administration, A
Forensic Science and Technology, B
General Studies, AB
Graphic Design, B
Health/Health Care Administration/Management, B
History, B
Human Resources Management/Personnel Adminis-
    tration, B
Human Services, AB
International Business/Trade/Commerce, B
Liberal Arts and Sciences Studies and Humani-
    ties, A
Management Information Systems and Services, B
Marketing/Marketing Management, B
Mathematics, B
Military and Defense Studies, M
Painting, B
Philosophy, B
Photography, B
Political Science and Government, B
Printmaking, B
Psychology, B
Public Administration, B
Public Relations, Advertising, and Applied Commu-
    nication, B
Sociology, B
Sport and Fitness Administration/Management, B

CONCEPTION SEMINARY COLLEGE

Liberal Arts and Sciences Studies and Humani-
    ties, B
Philosophy, B
Philosophy and Religious Studies, B

CONCORDE CAREER COLLEGE

Dental Assisting/Assistant, A
Health and Medical Administrative Services, A
Medical/Clinical Assistant, A
Respiratory Care Therapy/Therapist, A

COTTEY COLLEGE

Business Administration and Management, B
English Language and Literature, B
Environmental Studies, B
Health Services/Allied Health/Health Sciences, B
International Business/Trade/Commerce, B
International Relations and Affairs, B

Liberal Arts and Sciences Studies and Humani-
    ties, B
Psychology, B

COURT REPORTING INSTITUTE OF ST. LOUIS

Court Reporting/Court Reporter, A

COX COLLEGE

Allied Health Diagnostic, Intervention, and Treat-
    ment Professions, AB
Medical Insurance Specialist/Medical Biller, A
Medical/Clinical Assistant, A
Nursing, M
Nursing - Advanced Practice, M
Nursing Administration, M
Nursing Education, M
Radiologic Technology/Science - Radiographer, AB

CROWDER COLLEGE

Administrative Assistant and Secretarial Science, A
Agribusiness, A
Agricultural Mechanization, A
Agriculture, A
Art/Art Studies, General, A
Autobody/Collision and Repair
    Technology/Technician, A
Automobile/Automotive Mechanics
    Technology/Technician, A
Biology/Biological Sciences, A
Business Administration and Management, A
Business/Office Automation/Technology/Data En-
    try, A
Computer Systems Analysis/Analyst, A
Computer Systems Networking and Telecommunica-
    tions, A
Construction Engineering Technology/Technician, A
Construction Trades, A
Drafting and Design Technology/Technician, A
Drama and Dramatics/Theatre Arts, A
Education, A
Electrical, Electronic and Communications Engineer-
    ing Technology/Technician, A
Elementary Education and Teaching, A
Emergency Medical Technology/Technician (EMT
    Paramedic), A
Energy Management and Systems
    Technology/Technician, A
Environmental Engineering
    Technology/Environmental Technology, A
Executive Assistant/Executive Secretary, A
Farm/Farm and Ranch Management, A
Fire Science/Firefighting, A
General Studies, A
Health Information/Medical Records
    Technology/Technician, A
Industrial Technology/Technician, A
Legal Administrative Assistant/Secretary, A
Liberal Arts and Sciences Studies and Humani-
    ties, A
Manufacturing Technology/Technician, A
Mass Communication/Media Studies, A
Mathematics, A
Mathematics and Computer Science, A
Medical Administrative Assistant/Secretary, A
Music, A
Occupational Therapist Assistant, A
Physical Education Teaching and Coaching, A
Physical Sciences, A
Psychology, A
Public Relations/Image Management, A
Solar Energy Technology/Technician, A
Veterinary/Animal Health Technology/Technician and
    Veterinary Assistant, A
Welding Technology/Welder, A

CULINARY INSTITUTE OF ST. LOUIS AT HICKEY COLLEGE

Cooking and Related Culinary Arts, A

CULVER-STOCKTON COLLEGE

Accounting, B
Art Teacher Education, B
Art/Art Studies, General, B
Athletic Training and Sports Medicine, B

Biochemistry, Biophysics and Molecular Biology, B
Biology Teacher Education, B
Biology/Biological Sciences, B
Business Administration and Management, B
Communication Studies/Speech Communication
and Rhetoric, B
Criminal Justice/Law Enforcement Administration, B
Drama and Dramatics/Theatre Arts, B
Elementary Education and Teaching, B
English Language and Literature, B
English/Language Arts Teacher Education, B
Finance, B
Fine/Studio Arts, B
Graphic Design, B
History, B
History Teacher Education, B
International/Global Studies, B
Law and Legal Studies, B
Liberal Arts and Sciences Studies and Humani-
ties, B
Marketing/Marketing Management, B
Mass Communication/Media Studies, B
Mathematics, B
Mathematics Teacher Education, B
Music, B
Music Teacher Education, B
Physical Education Teaching and Coaching, B
Political Science and Government, B
Psychology, B
Religion/Religious Studies, B
Speech Teacher Education, B
Sport and Fitness Administration/Management, B

DEVRY UNIVERSITY (KANSAS CITY)

Accounting, B
Business Administration and Management, B
Business Administration, Management and Opera-
tions, B
Business/Commerce, B
Computer Engineering Technology/Technician, B
Computer Systems Analysis/Analyst, B
Computer Systems Networking and Telecommunica-
tions, AB
Criminal Justice/Law Enforcement Administration, B
Electrical, Electronic and Communications Engineer-
ing Technology/Technician, AB
Web Page, Digital/Multimedia and Information Re-
sources Design, AB

DEVRY UNIVERSITY (KANSAS CITY)

Accounting, B
Business Administration and Management, B
Business Administration, Management and Opera-
tions, BM
Business/Commerce, B
Computer Systems Analysis/Analyst, B
Computer Systems Networking and Telecommunica-
tions, AB
Criminal Justice/Law Enforcement Administration, B
Web Page, Digital/Multimedia and Information Re-
sources Design, AB

DRURY UNIVERSITY

Accounting, B
American Government and Politics (United
States), B
Architecture, BM
Art History, Criticism and Conservation, B
Biology/Biological Sciences, B
Business Administration and Management, B
Business Administration, Management and Opera-
tions, M
Chemistry, B
Communication and Media Studies, M
Computer Science, B
Criminology, BM
Design and Visual Communications, B
Drama and Dramatics/Theatre Arts, B
Economics, B
Education, M
Education/Teaching of the Gifted and Talented, M
Educational Media/Instructional Technology, M
Elementary Education and Teaching, BM
English Language and Literature, B
Environmental Health, B
Environmental Sciences, B

Environmental Studies, B
Finance, B
Fine Arts and Art Studies, M
Fine/Studio Arts, B
French Language and Literature, B
German Language and Literature, B
History, B
Human Services, M
International Relations and Affairs, B
Journalism, B
Kinesiology and Exercise Science, B
Management Information Systems and Services, B
Marketing/Marketing Management, B
Mathematics, B
Mathematics Teacher Education, M
Middle School Education, M
Music, B
Music Therapy/Therapist, B
Philosophy, B
Physical Education Teaching and Coaching, B
Physics, B
Political Science and Government, B
Psychology, B
Reading Teacher Education, M
Religion/Religious Studies, B
Secondary Education and Teaching, M
Sociology, B
Spanish Language and Literature, B
Special Education and Teaching, M

EAST CENTRAL COLLEGE

Accounting Technology/Technician and Bookkeep-
ing, A
Administrative Assistant and Secretarial Science, A
Automobile/Automotive Mechanics
Technology/Technician, A
Biology Technician/BioTechnology Laboratory Tech-
nician, A
Business/Commerce, A
Chemical Technology/Technician, A
Child Care and Support Services Management, A
Commercial and Advertising Art, A
Computer Systems Networking and Telecommunica-
tions, A
Construction Trades, A
Culinary Arts/Chef Training, A
Drafting and Design Technology/Technician, A
Education, A
Emergency Medical Technology/Technician (EMT
Paramedic), A
Engineering, A
Fine/Studio Arts, A
Fire Science/Firefighting, A
General Studies, A
Health Information/Medical Records
Technology/Technician, A
Heating, Air Conditioning, Ventilation and Refrigera-
tion Maintenance Technology/Technician, A
Heavy/Industrial Equipment Maintenance Technolo-
gies, A
Machine Tool Technology/Machinist, A
Medical Radiologic Technology/Science - Radiation
Therapist, A
Medical/Clinical Assistant, A
Music, A
Occupational Therapist Assistant, A
Precision Production, A
Respiratory Care Therapy/Therapist, A
Technical Teacher Education, A
Welding Technology/Welder, A

EVANGEL UNIVERSITY

Art Teacher Education, B
Art/Art Studies, General, B
Behavioral Sciences, B
Bible/Biblical Studies, B
Biology Teacher Education, B
Biology/Biological Sciences, B
Broadcast Journalism, AB
Business Administration and Management, B
Business Teacher Education, B
Chemistry, B
Chemistry Teacher Education, B
Child Development, B
Clinical Laboratory Science/Medical
Technology/Technologist, B

Clinical Psychology, M
Computer Science, B
Counseling Psychology, M
Counselor Education/School Counseling and Guid-
ance Services, M
Criminal Justice/Law Enforcement Administration, B
Curriculum and Instruction, MD
Early Childhood Education and Teaching, B
Education, M
Educational Leadership and Administration, MD
Elementary Education and Teaching, B
English Language and Literature, B
Health and Physical Education, B
History, B
History Teacher Education, B
Intercultural/Multicultural and Diversity Studies, B
Junior High/Intermediate/Middle School Education
and Teaching, B
Kindergarten/PreSchool Education and Teaching, B
Marketing/Marketing Management, B
Mathematics, B
Music, BM
Music Teacher Education, BM
Organizational Management, M
Parks, Recreation, Leisure and Fitness Studies, B
Performance, M
Physical Education Teaching and Coaching, B
Political Science and Government, B
Pre-Dentistry Studies, B
Pre-Law Studies, B
Pre-Medicine/Pre-Medical Studies, B
Pre-Veterinary Studies, B
Psychology, BM
Public Administration, B
Radio and Television, B
Reading Teacher Education, M
Religious/Sacred Music, B
School Psychology, M
Science Teacher Education/General Science
Teacher Education, B
Secondary Education and Teaching, BM
Social Work, B
Sociology, B
Spanish Language Teacher Education, B
Spanish Language and Literature, B
Special Education and Teaching, B
Speech Teacher Education, B

EVEREST COLLEGE

Accounting, A
Accounting and Related Services, B
Allied Health and Medical Assisting Services, A
Business Administration and Management, AB
Computer Science, B
Computer and Information Sciences, A
Legal Assistant/Paralegal, AB

FONTBONNE UNIVERSITY

Accounting, M
Advertising, B
Art Teacher Education, B
Art/Art Studies, General, B
Audiology/Audiologist and Speech-Language
Pathology/Pathologist, B
Biology/Biological Sciences, B
Business Administration and Management, B
Business Administration, Management and Opera-
tions, M
Commercial and Advertising Art, B
Communication Disorders, BM
Communication Studies/Speech Communication
and Rhetoric, B
Computer Education, M
Computer Science, B
Consumer Merchandising/Retailing Management, B
Dietetics/Dieticians, B
Drama and Dramatics/Theatre Arts, B
Education, BM
Elementary Education and Teaching, B
English Language and Literature, B
Family and Consumer Sciences/Home Economics
Teacher Education, B
Family and Consumer Sciences/Human Sci-
ences, BM
Fashion Merchandising, B
Fine Arts and Art Studies, M

Fine/Studio Arts, B
History, B
Human Services, B
Junior High/Intermediate/Middle School Education
and Teaching, B
Kindergarten/PreSchool Education and Teaching, B
Liberal Arts and Sciences Studies and Humani-
ties, B
Management, M
Marketing/Marketing Management, B
Mathematics, B
Pre-Law Studies, B
Psychology, B
Religion/Religious Studies, B
Secondary Education and Teaching, B
Social Sciences, B
Social Work, B
Sociology, B
Special Education and Teaching, BM
Sport and Fitness Administration/Management, B
Taxation, B
Theater, M

GLOBAL UNIVERSITY

Bible/Biblical Studies, B
Divinity/Ministry (BD, MDiv.), B
Missions/Missionary Studies and Missiology, BM
Pastoral Studies/Counseling, MD
Religion/Religious Studies, A
Religious Education, BM
Theology and Religious Vocations, MD
Theology/Theological Studies, B

GOLDFARB SCHOOL OF NURSING AT
BARNES-JEWISH COLLEGE

Acute Care/Critical Care Nursing, M
Gerontological Nursing, M
Health Services Administration, M
Nurse Anesthetist, M
Nursing, M
Nursing - Adult, M
Nursing Education, M

GRACELAND UNIVERSITY

Elementary Education and Teaching, B

HANNIBAL-LAGRANGE UNIVERSITY

Accounting, B
Art Teacher Education, B
Art/Art Studies, General, AB
Bible/Biblical Studies, B
Biology/Biological Sciences, B
Broadcast Journalism, B
Business Administration and Management, B
Business Teacher Education, B
Child Development, B
Communication Studies/Speech Communication
and Rhetoric, B
Communication, Journalism and Related Pro-
grams, B
Computer and Information Sciences, B
Criminal Justice/Law Enforcement Administra-
tion, AB
Drama and Dramatics/Theatre Arts, B
Early Childhood Education and Teaching, B
Education, BM
Elementary Education and Teaching, B
English Language and Literature, AB
English/Language Arts Teacher Education, B
History, B
History Teacher Education, B
Kinesiology and Exercise Science, B
Liberal Arts and Sciences Studies and Humani-
ties, B
Marketing/Marketing Management, B
Mathematics, B
Mathematics Teacher Education, B
Music, AB
Music Teacher Education, B
Parks, Recreation and Leisure Facilities Manage-
ment, B
Physical Education Teaching and Coaching, B
Psychology, B
Reading Teacher Education, M
Religious Education, B

Science Teacher Education/General Science
Teacher Education, B
Secondary Education and Teaching, B
Social Work, B
Sociology, B

HARRIS-STOWE STATE UNIVERSITY

Accounting, B
Biology/Biological Sciences, B
Business Administration and Management, B
Criminal Justice/Law Enforcement Administration, B
Criminal Justice/Safety Studies, B
Early Childhood Education and Teaching, B
Education, B
Elementary Education and Teaching, B
Health/Health Care Administration/Management, B
Information Science/Studies, B
Junior High/Intermediate/Middle School Education
and Teaching, B
Juvenile Corrections, B
Liberal Arts and Sciences Studies and Humani-
ties, B
Management Information Systems and Services, B
Mathematics, B
Multi-/Interdisciplinary Studies, B
Political Science and Government, B
Secondary Education and Teaching, B
Sociology, B
Urban Studies/Affairs, B

HERITAGE COLLEGE

Health and Physical Education, A
Massage Therapy/Therapeutic Massage, A
Medical/Clinical Assistant, A

HICKEY COLLEGE

Accounting Technology/Technician and Bookkeep-
ing, A
Administrative Assistant and Secretarial Science, A
Business Administration and Management, B
Computer Systems Networking and Telecommunica-
tions, A
Cooking and Related Culinary Arts, A
Graphic Design, A
Legal Administrative Assistant/Secretary, A
Legal Assistant/Paralegal, A
Medical Office Assistant/Specialist, A
Veterinary/Animal Health Technology/Technician and
Veterinary Assistant, A

IHM ACADEMY OF EMS

Emergency Medical Technology/Technician (EMT
Paramedic), A

JEFFERSON COLLEGE

Accounting Technology/Technician and Bookkeep-
ing, A
Administrative Assistant and Secretarial Science, A
Automobile/Automotive Mechanics
Technology/Technician, A
Biomedical Technology/Technician, A
Business Administration and Management, A
Business/Commerce, A
CAD/CADD Drafting and/or Design
Technology/Technician, A
Child Care and Support Services Management, A
Computer Systems Networking and Telecommunica-
tions, A
Criminal Justice/Law Enforcement Administration, A
Criminal Justice/Police Science, A
Culinary Arts/Chef Training, A
Education, A
Electrical, Electronic and Communications Engineer-
ing Technology/Technician, A
Emergency Medical Technology/Technician (EMT
Paramedic), A
Engineering, A
Fire Protection and Safety Technology/Technician, A
General Office Occupations and Clerical Services, A
Health Information/Medical Records
Technology/Technician, A
Heating, Air Conditioning, Ventilation and Refrigera-
tion Maintenance Technology/Technician, A
Industrial Mechanics and Maintenance Technol-
ogy, A

Information Technology, A
Legal Administrative Assistant/Secretary, A
Liberal Arts and Sciences Studies and Humani-
ties, A
Machine Tool Technology/Machinist, A
Manufacturing Technology/Technician, A
Medical Administrative Assistant/Secretary, A
Occupational Therapist Assistant, A
Physical Therapist Assistant, A
Precision Production, A
Radiologic Technology/Science - Radiographer, A
Teacher Education and Professional Develop-
ment, Specific Levels and Methods, A
Veterinary/Animal Health Technology/Technician and
Veterinary Assistant, A
Welding Technology/Welder, A

KANSAS CITY ART INSTITUTE

Animation, Interactive Technology, Video Graphics
and Special Effects, B
Art History, Criticism and Conservation, B
Ceramic Arts and Ceramics, B
Fiber, Textile and Weaving Arts, B
Film/Video and Photographic Arts, B
Graphic Design, B
Illustration, B
Painting, B
Photography, B
Printmaking, B
Sculpture, B

LINCOLN UNIVERSITY

Accounting, BM
Agricultural Business and Management, B
Agriculture, B
Art Teacher Education, B
Biology Teacher Education, B
Biology/Biological Sciences, B
Business Administration and Management, B
Business Administration, Management and Opera-
tions, M
Business Teacher Education, B
Chemistry, B
Chemistry Teacher Education, B
Civil Engineering Technology/Technician, B
Clinical Laboratory Science/Medical
Technology/Technologist, B
Computer and Information Sciences, A
Counselor Education/School Counseling and Guid-
ance Services, M
Criminal Justice/Law Enforcement Administra-
tion, AB
Criminology, M
Drafting and Design Technology/Technician, A
Early Childhood Education and Teaching, A
Educational Administration and Supervision, MO
Educational Leadership and Administration, O
Elementary Education and Teaching, BM
Engineering Technology, A
English Language and Literature, B
English/Language Arts Teacher Education, B
Entrepreneurship/Entrepreneurial Studies, M
Environmental Sciences, B
Fine/Studio Arts, B
Foods, Nutrition, and Wellness Studies, B
General Merchandising, Sales, and Related Market-
ing Operations, B
History, BM
Information Science/Studies, B
Journalism, B
Junior High/Intermediate/Middle School Education
and Teaching, B
Liberal Arts and Sciences Studies and Humani-
ties, B
Mathematics, B
Mathematics Teacher Education, B
Music Teacher Education, B
Physical Education Teaching and Coaching, B
Physics, B
Physics Teacher Education, B
Political Science and Government, B
Psychology, B
Public Administration, BM
Public Policy Analysis, M
Religious/Sacred Music, B
Secondary Education and Teaching, MO

Social Science Teacher Education, B
Social Work, B
Sociology, BM
Spanish Language and Literature, B
Special Education and Teaching, B
Surgical Technology/Technologist, A

LINDENWOOD UNIVERSITY

Accounting, BM
Acting, B
Advertising, B
Anthropology, B
Art History, Criticism and Conservation, B
Art Teacher Education, B
Art/Art Studies, General, B
Athletic Training and Sports Medicine, B
Biology Teacher Education, B
Biology/Biological Sciences, B
Business Administration and Management, B
Business Administration, Management and Operations, M
Business Teacher Education, B
Business and Personal/Financial Services Marketing Operations, B
Chemistry, B
Chemistry Teacher Education, B
Communication and Media Studies, M
Computer Graphics, B
Computer Science, B
Computer Systems Networking and Telecommunications, B
Computer and Information Sciences, B
Computer and Information Systems Security, B
Counseling Psychology, M
Criminal Justice/Safety Studies, B
Criminology, M
Dance, B
Digital Communication and Media/Multimedia, B
Drama and Dramatics/Theatre Arts, B
Dramatic/Theatre Arts and Stagecraft, B
Drawing, B
Early Childhood Education and Teaching, B
Economics, B
Education, BMDO
Education/Teaching of Individuals in Early Childhood Special Education Programs, B
Educational Administration and Supervision, MDO
Educational Leadership and Administration, DO
Educational Media/Instructional Technology, M
Elementary Education and Teaching, B
English Language and Literature, B
English as a Second Language, M
Entrepreneurship/Entrepreneurial Studies, BM
Environmental Biology, B
Fashion/Apparel Design, B
Finance, B
Finance and Banking, M
Fine Arts and Art Studies, BM
Fine/Studio Arts, B
Fire Services Administration, B
French Language Teacher Education, B
French Language and Literature, B
General Studies, B
Gerontology, M
Health Promotion, M
Health Services Administration, M
Health/Health Care Administration/Management, B
History, B
History Teacher Education, B
Human Resources Management and Services, M
Human Resources Management/Personnel Administration, B
Human Services, M
Information Technology, B
International Business/Trade/Commerce, BM
International Relations and Affairs, B
Internet and Interactive Multimedia, M
Journalism, BM
Junior High/Intermediate/Middle School Education and Teaching, B
Kinesiology and Exercise Science, B
Liberal Arts and Sciences Studies and Humanities, B
Management, M
Management Information Systems and Services, MO

Marketing, M
Marketing/Marketing Management, B
Mass Communication/Media Studies, B
Mathematics, B
Mathematics Teacher Education, B
Music, B
Music Teacher Education, B
Non-Profit/Public/Organizational Management, M
Nursing, M
Parks, Recreation, Leisure and Fitness Studies, B
Philosophy, B
Physical Education Teaching and Coaching, B
Political Science and Government, B
Pre-Dentistry Studies, B
Pre-Law Studies, B
Pre-Medicine/Pre-Medical Studies, B
Pre-Nursing Studies, B
Pre-Veterinary Studies, B
Psychology, B
Public Administration, BM
School Psychology, M
Science Teacher Education/General Science Teacher Education, B
Social Science Teacher Education, B
Social Work, B
Sociology, B
Spanish Language Teacher Education, B
Spanish Language and Literature, B
Special Education and Teaching, B
Sport and Fitness Administration/Management, BM
Supply Chain Management, M
Teacher Education, Multiple Levels, B
Technical Theatre/Theatre Design and Technology, B
Technology Teacher Education/Industrial Arts Teacher Education, B
Textile Design, M
Theater, M
Trade and Industrial Teacher Education, B
Web Page, Digital/Multimedia and Information Resources Design, B
Writing, M

LOGAN UNIVERSITY

Biological and Biomedical Sciences, B
Biology/Biological Sciences, B
Chiropractic, MD
Exercise and Sports Science, M
Health Education, D
Health Informatics, M
Natural Sciences, B
Nutritional Sciences, M
Rehabilitation Sciences, M

MARYVILLE UNIVERSITY OF SAINT LOUIS

Accounting, BMO
Accounting and Related Services, B
Actuarial Science, BM
Acute Care/Critical Care Nursing, M
Allied Health and Medical Assisting Services, MD
Applied Mathematics, B
Art Education, M
Art Teacher Education, B
Biochemistry, B
Biological and Physical Sciences, B
Biology/Biological Sciences, B
Biomedical Sciences, B
Business Administration and Management, B
Business Administration, Management and Operations, MO
Business/Commerce, B
Chemistry, B
Clinical Laboratory Science/Medical Technology/Technologist, B
Communication Disorders, B
Criminology, B
E-Commerce/Electronic Commerce, B
Early Childhood Education and Teaching, M
Education, MD
Education/Teaching of the Gifted and Talented, M
Educational Leadership and Administration, MD
Elementary Education and Teaching, BM
Engineering, B
English Language and Literature, B
Entertainment Management, MO

Environmental Sciences, B
Environmental Studies, B
Financial Planning and Services, B
Fine/Studio Arts, B
Gerontological Nursing, M
Graphic Design, B
Health Professions and Related Clinical Sciences, B
Health/Medical Preparatory Programs, B
Higher Education/Higher Education Administration, D
History, B
Interior Design, B
International Business/Trade/Commerce, B
International/Global Studies, B
Junior High/Intermediate/Middle School Education and Teaching, B
Kinesiology and Exercise Science, B
Legal Assistant/Paralegal, B
Legal Professions and Studies, B
Liberal Arts and Sciences Studies and Humanities, B
Management, MO
Management Information Systems and Services, B
Marketing, MO
Marketing/Marketing Management, B
Marriage and Family Therapy/Counseling, M
Mass Communication/Media Studies, B
Mathematics, B
Middle School Education, M
Music Therapy/Therapist, BM
Nursing, MD
Nursing - Adult, M
Nursing - Advanced Practice, M
Occupational Therapy/Therapist, M
Organizational Management, M
Pediatric Nurse/Nursing, M
Physical Therapy/Therapist, BD
Pre-Dentistry Studies, B
Pre-Medicine/Pre-Medical Studies, B
Pre-Veterinary Studies, B
Project Management, MO
Psychology, B
Reading Teacher Education, M
Rehabilitation Counseling, M
Secondary Education and Teaching, M
Sociology, B
Sport and Fitness Administration/Management, BMO
Substance Abuse/Addiction Counseling, M
Vocational Rehabilitation Counseling/Counselor, B

METRO BUSINESS COLLEGE (CAPE GIRARDEAU)

Business/Office Automation/Technology/Data Entry, A
Medical Office Assistant/Specialist, A

METRO BUSINESS COLLEGE (JEFFERSON CITY)

Business Administration and Management, A
Computer and Information Sciences, A
Medical Administrative Assistant/Secretary, A
Medical Insurance Coding Specialist/Coder, A
Medical Office Assistant/Specialist, A

METRO BUSINESS COLLEGE (ROLLA)

Accounting Technology/Technician and Bookkeeping, A
Business/Office Automation/Technology/Data Entry, A
Medical Insurance Coding Specialist/Coder, A
Medical Office Assistant/Specialist, A

METROPOLITAN COMMUNITY COLLEGE–KANSAS CITY

Automobile/Automotive Mechanics Technology/Technician, A
Biology/Biological Sciences, A
Building/Construction Site Management/Manager, A
Business Administration and Management, A
Chemistry, A
Child Care Provider/Assistant, A
Commercial and Advertising Art, A
Computer Graphics, A
Computer Programming/Programmer, A

Computer Science, A
Computer Typography and Composition Equipment
 Operator, A
Computer and Information Sciences, A
Corrections, A
Criminal Justice/Law Enforcement Administration, A
Criminal Justice/Police Science, A
Drafting and Design Technology/Technician, A
Electrical, Electronic and Communications Engineer-
 ing Technology/Technician, A
Emergency Medical Technology/Technician (EMT
 Paramedic), A
Engineering, A
Family and Consumer Sciences/Human Sciences, A
Fashion Merchandising, A
Fashion/Apparel Design, A
Fire Science/Firefighting, A
Glazier, A
Health Information/Medical Records
 Administration/Administrator, A
Heavy Equipment Maintenance
 Technology/Technician, A
Human Services, A
Information Science/Studies, A
Information Technology, A
Legal Administrative Assistant/Secretary, A
Liberal Arts and Sciences Studies and Humani-
 ties, A
Machine Shop Technology/Assistant, A
Marketing/Marketing Management, A
Mason/Masonry, A
Medical Administrative Assistant/Secretary, A
Occupational Therapy/Therapist, A
Physical Therapy/Therapist, A
Quality Control Technology/Technician, A
Respiratory Care Therapy/Therapist, A
Special Products Marketing Operations, A
System Administration/Administrator, A
System, Networking, and LAN/WAN
 Management/Manager, A
Web Page, Digital/Multimedia and Information Re-
 sources Design, A
Web/Multimedia Management and Webmaster, A

MIDWEST INSTITUTE (FENTON)

Massage Therapy/Therapeutic Massage, A
Medical Office Management/Administration, A

MIDWEST INSTITUTE (SAINT LOUIS)

Massage Therapy/Therapeutic Massage, A
Medical Office Assistant/Specialist, A

MIDWEST UNIVERSITY

Bible/Biblical Studies, B
Religious Education, B
Religious/Sacred Music, B

MINERAL AREA COLLEGE

Administrative Assistant and Secretarial Science, A
Agribusiness, A
Applied Horticulture/Horticultural Operations, A
Autobody/Collision and Repair
 Technology/Technician, A
Automobile/Automotive Mechanics
 Technology/Technician, A
Business/Commerce, A
Carpentry/Carpenter, A
Child Care Provider/Assistant, A
Civil Engineering Technology/Technician, A
Computer Programming/Programmer, A
Criminal Justice/Police Science, A
Culinary Arts/Chef Training, A
Drafting and Design Technology/Technician, A
Electrical, Electronic and Communications Engineer-
 ing Technology/Technician, A
Emergency Medical Technology/Technician (EMT
 Paramedic), A
Engineering Technology, A
Fire Science/Firefighting, A
General Studies, A
Graphic and Printing Equipment Operator Produc-
 tion, A
Health Professions and Related Clinical Sciences, A
Heating, Air Conditioning and Refrigeration
 Technology/Technician, A

Heavy/Industrial Equipment Maintenance Technolo-
 gies, A
Industrial Technology/Technician, A
Liberal Arts and Sciences Studies and Humani-
 ties, A
Machine Tool Technology/Machinist, A
Operations Management and Supervision, A
Precision Production, A
Precision Production Trades, A
Radio and Television Broadcasting
 Technology/Technician, A
Respiratory Therapy Technician/Assistant, A
System, Networking, and LAN/WAN
 Management/Manager, A
Technical Teacher Education, A

MISSOURI BAPTIST UNIVERSITY

Accounting, B
Behavioral Sciences, B
BioTechnology, B
Biochemistry, B
Biology/Biological Sciences, B
Business Administration and Management, AB
Business Administration, Management and Opera-
 tions, BM
Business Teacher Education, B
Chemistry, B
Child Development, B
Christian Studies, B
Communication and Media Studies, B
Counselor Education/School Counseling and Guid-
 ance Services, M
Criminal Justice/Safety Studies, B
Drama and Dance Teacher Education, B
Drama and Dramatics/Theatre Arts, B
Early Childhood Education and Teaching, B
Education, BM
Education/Teaching of Individuals in Early Childhood
 Special Education Programs, B
Education/Teaching of Individuals with Multiple Dis-
 abilities, B
Educational Administration and Supervision, M
Educational Leadership and Administration, MO
Elementary Education and Teaching, B
English Language and Literature, B
General Studies, B
Health Teacher Education, B
Health/Health Care Administration/Management, B
History, B
Human Services, B
Information Technology, B
Journalism, B
Junior High/Intermediate/Middle School Education
 and Teaching, B
Kinesiology and Exercise Science, B
Liberal Arts and Sciences Studies and Humani-
 ties, B
Marketing/Marketing Management, B
Mathematics, B
Multi-/Interdisciplinary Studies, B
Music, B
Music Performance, B
Music Teacher Education, B
Pastoral Studies/Counseling, M
Physical Education Teaching and Coaching, B
Pre-Nursing Studies, B
Psychology, B
Public Relations/Image Management, B
Radio and Television, B
Religious/Sacred Music, B
Science Teacher Education/General Science
 Teacher Education, B
Secondary Education and Teaching, B
Social Sciences, B
Sport and Fitness Administration/Management, B
Teacher Education, Multiple Levels, B
Theology and Religious Vocations, B
Theology/Theological Studies, A

MISSOURI COLLEGE

Business Administration, Management and Opera-
 tions, B
Graphic Design, A
Health and Medical Administrative Services, A
Medical Insurance Coding Specialist/Coder, A
Medical Office Management/Administration, A

Small Business Administration/Management, A
System Administration/Administrator, A

MISSOURI SOUTHERN STATE UNIVER-
SITY

Accounting, B
Art/Art Studies, General, B
Biochemistry, B
Biology/Biological Sciences, B
Business Administration, Management and Opera-
 tions, M
Business/Commerce, B
Business/Managerial Economics, B
CAD/CADD Drafting and/or Design
 Technology/Technician, A
Chemistry, B
Clinical Laboratory Science/Medical
 Technology/Technologist, B
Communication Studies/Speech Communication
 and Rhetoric, B
Computer Programming/Programmer, A
Computer and Information Sciences, B
Criminal Justice/Law Enforcement Administration, B
Criminal Justice/Police Science, A
Criminology, M
Dental Hygiene/Hygienist, AM
Drama and Dramatics/Theatre Arts, B
Early Childhood Education and Teaching, M
Education, BM
Educational Media/Instructional Technology, M
Elementary Education and Teaching, B
Engineering Technologies/Technicians, A
Engineering/Industrial Management, B
English Language and Literature, B
Environmental Health, B
Fine/Studio Arts, B
French Language and Literature, B
Geography, B
German Language and Literature, B
Graphic Design, B
Health Professions and Related Clinical Sciences, B
Health and Medical Administrative Services, B
Health and Physical Education/Fitness, B
History, B
Industrial Technology/Technician, A
International Relations and Affairs, B
Juvenile Corrections, B
Legal Professions and Studies, B
Liberal Arts and Sciences Studies and Humani-
 ties, A
Logistics and Materials Management, B
Manufacturing Technology/Technician, A
Mathematics, B
Medical Radiologic Technology/Science - Radiation
 Therapist, A
Music Performance, B
Nursing, M
Physics, B
Political Science and Government, B
Psychology, B
Respiratory Care Therapy/Therapist, A
Secondary Education and Teaching, B
Social Work, B
Sociology, B
Spanish Language and Literature, B

MISSOURI STATE UNIVERSITY

Accounting, BM
Agribusiness, B
Agricultural Sciences, M
Agricultural Teacher Education, B
Agriculture, B
Agronomy and Crop Science, B
Animal Sciences, B
Anthropology, BM
Apparel and Textiles, B
Applied Science and Technology, M
Art History, Criticism and Conservation, B
Art Teacher Education, B
Art/Art Studies, General, B
Athletic Training and Sports Medicine, BM
Audiology/Audiologist and Speech-Language
 Pathology/Pathologist, B
Biological and Biomedical Sciences, M
Biology Teacher Education, B
Biology/Biological Sciences, B

Business Administration and Management, B
Business Administration, Management and Operations, BM
Business Teacher Education, B
Business/Commerce, B
Cell Biology and Anatomy, M
Cell/Cellular and Molecular Biology, B
Chemistry, BM
Chemistry Teacher Education, B
Child and Family Studies, M
City/Urban, Community and Regional Planning, B
Clinical Laboratory Science/Medical Technology/Technologist, B
Clinical Psychology, M
Communication Studies/Speech Communication and Rhetoric, B
Communication and Media Studies, M
Computer Science, BM
Computer and Information Sciences, B
Computer/Information Technology Services Administration and Management, B
Construction Management, BM
Counseling Psychology, M
Counselor Education/School Counseling and Guidance Services, M
Criminology, BMO
Design and Visual Communications, B
Dietetics/Dieticians, B
Drama and Dramatics/Theatre Arts, B
Early Childhood Education and Teaching, BM
Economics, B
Educational Administration and Supervision, MO
Educational Measurement and Evaluation, O
Educational Media/Instructional Technology, M
Elementary Education and Teaching, BM
Engineering/Industrial Management, B
English, M
English Language and Literature, B
English/Language Arts Teacher Education, B
Entrepreneurship/Entrepreneurial Studies, B
Environmental Policy and Resource Management, M
Experimental Psychology, M
Facilities Planning and Management, B
Family and Consumer Sciences/Home Economics Teacher Education, B
Finance, B
French Language Teacher Education, B
French Language and Literature, B
Geography, BM
Geology/Earth Science, BM
Geosciences, M
German Language Teacher Education, B
German Language and Literature, B
Gerontology, B
Health Services Administration, M
Higher Education/Higher Education Administration, M
History, BM
History Teacher Education, B
Homeland Security, MO
Horticultural Science, B
Hospitality Administration/Management, B
Housing and Human Environments, B
Human Development and Family Studies, B
Industrial Production Technologies/Technicians, B
Insurance, B
Intermedia/Multimedia, B
International Affairs, M
International/Global Studies, B
Journalism, B
Junior High/Intermediate/Middle School Education and Teaching, B
Kinesiology and Exercise Science, B
Kinesiology and Movement Studies, M
Latin Language and Literature, B
Latin Teacher Education, B
Logistics and Materials Management, B
Management Information Systems and Services, BM
Marketing/Marketing Management, B
Mass Communication/Media Studies, B
Materials Sciences, M
Mathematics, BM
Mathematics Teacher Education, BM
Military and Defense Studies, M

Molecular Biology, M
Music, BM
Music Performance, B
Music Teacher Education, B
Nurse Anesthetist, M
Nursing, M
Nursing - Advanced Practice, M
Nursing Education, M
Organizational Communication, B
Parks, Recreation, Leisure and Fitness Studies, B
Philosophy, B
Physical Education Teaching and Coaching, BM
Physical Therapy/Therapist, D
Physician Assistant, M
Physics, B
Physics Teacher Education, B
Plant Sciences, M
Political Science and Government, BMO
Psychology, BM
Public Administration, BM
Public Health, M
Radiologic Technology/Science - Radiographer, B
Reading Teacher Education, M
Religion/Religious Studies, BM
Respiratory Care Therapy/Therapist, B
Science Teacher Education/General Science Teacher Education, BM
Secondary Education and Teaching, BM
Social Studies Teacher Education, M
Social Work, BM
Sociology, B
Spanish Language and Literature, B
Special Education and Teaching, BM
Sport and Fitness Administration/Management, M
Student Personnel Services, M
Teacher Education and Professional Development, Specific Subject Areas, B
Theater, M
Urban and Regional Planning, M
Visual and Performing Arts, B
Wildlife and Wildlands Science and Management, B

MISSOURI STATE UNIVERSITY–WEST PLAINS

Accounting, A
Agriculture, A
Business Administration and Management, A
Business/Commerce, A
Child Care and Support Services Management, A
Computer Graphics, A
Computer Programming, Specific Applications, A
Computer and Information Sciences, A
Criminal Justice/Law Enforcement Administration, A
Criminal Justice/Police Science, A
Engineering, A
Entrepreneurship/Entrepreneurial Studies, A
Food Science, A
General Studies, A
Horticultural Science, A
Industrial Technology/Technician, A
Information Technology, A
Legal Assistant/Paralegal, A
Management Information Systems and Services, A
Respiratory Therapy Technician/Assistant, A

MISSOURI UNIVERSITY OF SCIENCE AND TECHNOLOGY

Aerospace, Aeronautical and Astronautical Engineering, BMD
Agricultural/Biological Engineering and Bioengineering, B
Applied Mathematics, BM
Architectural Engineering, B
Biological and Biomedical Sciences, M
Biology/Biological Sciences, B
Business Administration and Management, B
Business, Management, Marketing, and Related Support Services, B
Ceramic Sciences and Engineering, BMD
Chemical Engineering, BMD
Chemistry, BMD
Civil Engineering, BMD
Computer Engineering, BMD
Computer Science, BMD
Computer and Information Sciences and Support Services, B

Construction Engineering and Management, MD
Economics, B
Electrical Engineering, MD
Electrical, Electronics and Communications Engineering, B
Engineering, B
Engineering Management, MD
Engineering and Applied Sciences, MD
Engineering/Industrial Management, B
English Language and Literature, B
Environmental Biology, M
Environmental Engineering Technology/Environmental Technology, M
Environmental/Environmental Health Engineering, B
Geochemistry, MD
Geological Engineering, MD
Geological/Geophysical Engineering, B
Geology/Earth Science, BMD
Geophysics and Seismology, BMD
Geotechnical Engineering, MD
History, B
Hydraulics and Fluid Power Technology, MD
Hydrology and Water Resources Science, MD
Industrial Engineering, B
Information Science/Studies, BM
Manufacturing Engineering, M
Mathematics, MD
Mathematics Teacher Education, M
Mechanical Engineering, BMD
Mechanics, MD
Metallurgical Engineering, BMD
Mineral/Mining Engineering, MD
Mining and Mineral Engineering, B
Nuclear Engineering, BMD
Petroleum Engineering, BMD
Philosophy, B
Physics, BMD
Psychology, B
Secondary Education and Teaching, B
Statistics, D
Systems Engineering, MD
Water Resources, MD

MISSOURI VALLEY COLLEGE

Accounting, B
Art/Art Studies, General, B
Athletic Training and Sports Medicine, B
Biology/Biological Sciences, B
Computer Science, B
Criminal Justice/Law Enforcement Administration, B
Drama and Dramatics/Theatre Arts, B
Economics, B
Education, B
Elementary Education and Teaching, B
English Language and Literature, B
Health Teacher Education, B
History, B
Human Services, B
Marketing/Marketing Management, B
Mass Communication/Media Studies, B
Mathematics, B
Music, B
Parks, Recreation and Leisure Facilities Management, B
Parks, Recreation, Leisure and Fitness Studies, B
Philosophy, B
Physical Education Teaching and Coaching, B
Political Science and Government, B
Pre-Dentistry Studies, B
Pre-Law Studies, B
Pre-Medicine/Pre-Medical Studies, B
Pre-Nursing Studies, B
Pre-Pharmacy Studies, B
Pre-Veterinary Studies, B
Psychology, B
Public Administration, B
Religion/Religious Studies, B
Science Teacher Education/General Science Teacher Education, B
Secondary Education and Teaching, B
Sociology, B
Special Education and Teaching, B

Sport and Fitness Administration/Management, B

MISSOURI WESTERN STATE UNIVERSITY

Accounting, B
Animation, Interactive Technology, Video Graphics and Special Effects, B
Art Teacher Education, B
BioTechnology, B
Biochemistry, B
Biological and Biomedical Sciences, M
Biology/Biological Sciences, B
Business Administration and Management, B
Business Administration, Management and Operations, M
Chemistry, BM
Clinical Laboratory Science/Medical Technology/Technologist, B
Communication Studies/Speech Communication and Rhetoric, B
Computer Engineering Technology/Technician, B
Computer and Information Sciences, B
Computer and Information Systems Security, M
Construction Engineering Technology/Technician, B
Criminal Justice/Police Science, A
Criminal Justice/Safety Studies, B
Drama and Dramatics/Theatre Arts, B
Early Childhood Education and Teaching, B
Economics, B
Educational Measurement and Evaluation, MO
Electrical, Electronic and Communications Engineering Technology/Technician, B
Elementary Education and Teaching, B
Engineering and Applied Sciences, M
English Language and Literature, B
English as a Second Language, MO
English/Language Arts Teacher Education, B
Ergonomics and Human Factors, M
Finance, B
Fine/Studio Arts, B
Foreign Languages and Literatures, B
Forensic Science and Technology, MO
French Language Teacher Education, B
Graphic Design, B
Health Information/Medical Records Administration/Administrator, B
Health and Physical Education, B
History, B
Information Science/Studies, M
Information Technology, B
International/Global Studies, B
Legal Assistant/Paralegal, A
Management Information Systems and Services, M
Manufacturing Technology/Technician, AB
Marketing/Marketing Management, B
Mathematics, B
Media Studies, M
Multi-/Interdisciplinary Studies, B
Music, B
Music Teacher Education, B
Nursing, MO
Nursing Administration, MO
Parks, Recreation and Leisure Facilities Management, B
Philosophy, B
Physical Therapist Assistant, A
Political Science and Government, B
Psychology, B
Public Health (MPH, DPH), B
Public Relations, Advertising, and Applied Communication, B
Rhetoric, M
Social Work, B
Sociology, B
Spanish Language Teacher Education, B
Special Education and Teaching, MO
Sport and Fitness Administration/Management, M
Teacher Education and Professional Development, Specific Subject Areas, B
Technical Communication, M
Wildlife and Wildlands Science and Management, B

Writing, M

MOBERLY AREA COMMUNITY COLLEGE

Accounting Technology/Technician and Bookkeeping, A
Administrative Assistant and Secretarial Science, A
Child Care and Support Services Management, A
Clinical/Medical Laboratory Technician, A
Computer and Information Sciences, A
Criminal Justice/Police Science, A
Drafting and Design Technology/Technician, A
Electrical, Electronic and Communications Engineering Technology/Technician, A
Graphic and Printing Equipment Operator Production, A
Industrial Technology/Technician, A
Liberal Arts and Sciences Studies and Humanities, A
Marketing/Marketing Management, A
Technical Teacher Education, A
Welding Technology/Welder, A

NATIONAL AMERICAN UNIVERSITY (KANSAS CITY)

Allied Health and Medical Assisting Services, A
Business Administration and Management, AB
General Studies, A
Information Science/Studies, AB
Legal Assistant/Paralegal, AB
Management Science, AB
Pharmacy Technician/Assistant, A

NORTH CENTRAL MISSOURI COLLEGE

Accounting, A
Administrative Assistant and Secretarial Science, A
Agricultural Business and Management, A
Automobile/Automotive Mechanics Technology/Technician, A
Business Administration and Management, A
Carpentry/Carpenter, A
Computer Engineering Technology/Technician, A
Construction Engineering Technology/Technician, A
Criminal Justice/Law Enforcement Administration, A
Data Processing and Data Processing Technology/Technician, A
Drafting and Design Technology/Technician, A
E-Commerce/Electronic Commerce, A
Early Childhood Education and Teaching, A
Electrical, Electronic and Communications Engineering Technology/Technician, A
Emergency Medical Technology/Technician (EMT Paramedic), A
Farm/Farm and Ranch Management, A
Human Services, A
Liberal Arts and Sciences Studies and Humanities, A
Marketing/Marketing Management, A
Medical/Clinical Assistant, A

NORTHWEST MISSOURI STATE UNIVERSITY

Accounting, B
Advertising, B
Agribusiness, B
Agricultural Economics, M
Agricultural Education, M
Agricultural Sciences, M
Agricultural Teacher Education, B
Agriculture, B
Agronomy and Crop Science, B
Animal Sciences, B
Art Teacher Education, B
Biological and Biomedical Sciences, M
Biological and Physical Sciences, B
Biology Teacher Education, B
Biology/Biological Sciences, B
Business Administration and Management, B
Business Administration, Management and Operations, M
Business Teacher Education, B
Business/Managerial Economics, B
Cartography, B
Chemistry, B
Chemistry Teacher Education, B

Clinical Laboratory Science/Medical Technology/Technologist, B
Computer Science, M
Computer and Information Sciences, B
Counselor Education/School Counseling and Guidance Services, M
Dietetics/Dieticians, B
Drama and Dramatics/Theatre Arts, B
Early Childhood Education and Teaching, M
Economics, B
Education, BMO
Education/Teaching of Individuals with Multiple Disabilities, B
Educational Leadership and Administration, MO
Educational Media/Instructional Technology, M
Elementary Education and Teaching, BMO
English, M
English Education, M
English Language and Literature, B
English as a Second Language, M
English/Language Arts Teacher Education, B
Exercise and Sports Science, M
Finance, B
Geographic Information Systems, MO
Geography, B
Geology/Earth Science, B
Health Education, M
History, BMO
Horticultural Science, B
Humanities/Humanistic Studies, B
International Business/Trade/Commerce, B
Junior High/Intermediate/Middle School Education and Teaching, M
Management Information Systems and Services, BM
Marine Biology and Biological Oceanography, B
Marketing/Marketing Management, B
Mathematics, BM
Mathematics Teacher Education, BM
Middle School Education, M
Multi-/Interdisciplinary Studies, A
Music, B
Music Teacher Education, BM
Organizational Communication, B
Parks, Recreation and Leisure Facilities Management, B
Philosophy, B
Physical Education Teaching and Coaching, BM
Political Science and Government, B
Pre-Veterinary Studies, B
Psychology, BM
Public Administration, B
Radiologic Technology/Science - Radiographer, B
Reading Teacher Education, M
Recreation and Park Management, M
Science Teacher Education/General Science Teacher Education, BM
Secondary Education and Teaching, MO
Social Science Teacher Education, B
Social Studies Teacher Education, M
Sociology, B
Spanish Language Teacher Education, B
Spanish Language and Literature, B
Special Education and Teaching, M
Teacher Education and Professional Development, Specific Subject Areas, B
Web Page, Digital/Multimedia and Information Resources Design, B
Wildlife and Wildlands Science and Management, B

OZARK CHRISTIAN COLLEGE

Ancient Near Eastern and Biblical Languages, Literatures, and Linguistics, B
Bible/Biblical Studies, B
Elementary Education and Teaching, A
Religious Education, B
Religious/Sacred Music, B
Sign Language Interpretation and Translation, B
Theology/Theological Studies, AB

OZARKS TECHNICAL COMMUNITY COLLEGE

Accounting, A
Administrative Assistant and Secretarial Science, A
Autobody/Collision and Repair Technology/Technician, A

Automobile/Automotive Mechanics Technology/Technician, A
Business Administration and Management, A
Business Machine Repairer, A
Computer Systems Networking and Telecommunications, A
Construction Engineering Technology/Technician, A
Culinary Arts/Chef Training, A
Diesel Mechanics Technology/Technician, A
Electrical, Electronic and Communications Engineering Technology/Technician, A
Emergency Medical Technology/Technician (EMT Paramedic), A
Fire Science/Firefighting, A
Graphic and Printing Equipment Operator Production, A
Health Information/Medical Records Technology/Technician, A
Heating, Air Conditioning, Ventilation and Refrigeration Maintenance Technology/Technician, A
Heavy Equipment Maintenance Technology/Technician, A
Hotel/Motel Administration/Management, A
Industrial Technology/Technician, A
Information Science/Studies, A
Instrumentation Technology/Technician, A
Kindergarten/PreSchool Education and Teaching, A
Liberal Arts and Sciences Studies and Humanities, A
Machine Tool Technology/Machinist, A
Management Information Systems and Services, A
Mechanical Drafting and Mechanical Drafting CAD/CADD, A
Occupational Therapist Assistant, A
Occupational Therapy/Therapist, A
Physical Sciences, A
Physical Therapist Assistant, A
Radio and Television Broadcasting Technology/Technician, A
Respiratory Care Therapy/Therapist, A
Turf and Turfgrass Management, A
Welding Technology/Welder, A

PARK UNIVERSITY

Accounting, B
Athletic Training and Sports Medicine, B
Biological and Biomedical Sciences, B
Biology/Biological Sciences, B
Business Administration and Management, B
Business Administration, Management and Operations, M
Business, Management, Marketing, and Related Support Services, B
Business/Managerial Economics, B
Chemistry, B
Communication Studies/Speech Communication and Rhetoric, B
Computer Science, B
Computer and Information Sciences, B
Computer and Information Sciences and Support Services, B
Curriculum and Instruction, M
Drama and Dramatics/Theatre Arts, B
Early Childhood Education and Teaching, B
Economics, B
Education, BM
Educational Leadership and Administration, M
Elementary Education and Teaching, B
Emergency Management, MO
Engineering, B
English Language and Literature, B
Finance and Banking, MO
Fine/Studio Arts, B
Geography, B
Graphic Design, B
Health Services Administration, MO
Health/Health Care Administration/Management, A
History, B
Human Resources Development, AB
Human Resources Management and Services, B
Human Services, B
Interior Design, B
International Business/Trade/Commerce, MO
International Public Health/International Health, O
Law and Legal Studies, B

Liberal Arts and Sciences Studies and Humanities, B
Logistics and Materials Management, AB
Management Information Systems and Services, BMO
Marketing/Marketing Management, B
Mathematics, B
Multi-/Interdisciplinary Studies, B
Music, BO
Natural Sciences, B
Non-Profit/Public/Organizational Management, MO
Performance, MO
Political Science and Government, B
Psychology, B
Public Administration, BM
Public Affairs, M
Reading Teacher Education, M
Social Work, BM
Sociology, B
Spanish Language and Literature, B
Writing, O

PINNACLE CAREER INSTITUTE (KANSAS CITY)

Electrical and Electronic Engineering Technologies/Technicians, A
Executive Assistant/Executive Secretary, A

RANKEN TECHNICAL COLLEGE

Architectural Engineering Technology/Technician, AB
Autobody/Collision and Repair Technology/Technician, A
Automobile/Automotive Mechanics Technology/Technician, A
Business Administration and Management, B
Carpentry/Carpenter, A
Communications Systems Installation and Repair Technology, A
Computer Engineering Technology/Technician, A
Heating, Air Conditioning, Ventilation and Refrigeration Maintenance Technology/Technician, A
Heavy/Industrial Equipment Maintenance Technologies, A
Industrial Electronics Technology/Technician, A
Instrumentation Technology/Technician, A
Machine Tool Technology/Machinist, A

RESEARCH COLLEGE OF NURSING

Gerontological Nursing, M
Nursing, M
Nursing - Adult, M
Nursing - Advanced Practice, M
Nursing Administration, M
Nursing Education, M

ROCKHURST UNIVERSITY

Biochemistry, B
Biology/Biological Sciences, B
Business Administration and Management, B
Business/Corporate Communications, B
Chemistry, B
Civil Engineering, B
Clinical Laboratory Science/Medical Technology/Technologist, B
Communication Disorders, M
Communication Studies/Speech Communication and Rhetoric, B
Community Organization and Advocacy, B
Criminal Justice/Law Enforcement Administration, B
Economics, B
Education, M
Electrical, Electronics and Communications Engineering, B
Elementary Education and Teaching, B
English Language and Literature, B
French Language and Literature, B
History, B
International Relations and Affairs, B
Junior High/Intermediate/Middle School Education and Teaching, B
Management, MO
Mathematics, B
Mechanical Engineering, B
Occupational Therapy/Therapist, M
Philosophy, B

Physical Therapy/Therapist, D
Physics, B
Political Science and Government, B
Psychology, B
Secondary Education and Teaching, B
Spanish Language and Literature, B
Speech-Language Pathology/Pathologist, B
Sport and Fitness Administration/Management, B
Theology/Theological Studies, B

ST. CHARLES COMMUNITY COLLEGE

Accounting Technology/Technician and Bookkeeping, A
Biology/Biological Sciences, A
Chemistry, A
Child Care Provider/Assistant, A
Child Care and Support Services Management, A
Civil Engineering, A
Commercial and Advertising Art, A
Computer Programming/Programmer, A
Criminal Justice/Police Science, A
Drafting and Design Technology/Technician, A
Drama and Dramatics/Theatre Arts, A
Economics, A
Emergency Medical Technology/Technician (EMT Paramedic), A
Engineering, A
English Language and Literature, A
Fire Science/Firefighting, A
Foreign Languages and Literatures, A
French Language and Literature, A
General Studies, A
Health Information/Medical Records Technology/Technician, A
History, A
Human Services, A
Industrial Technology/Technician, A
Liberal Arts and Sciences Studies and Humanities, A
Marketing/Marketing Management, A
Mathematics, A
Mechanical Engineering, A
Music History, Literature, and Theory, A
Occupational Therapist Assistant, A
Office Management and Supervision, A
Philosophy, A
Political Science and Government, A
Pre-Pharmacy Studies, A
Precision Production, A
Psychology, A
Social Work, A
Sociology, A
Spanish Language and Literature, A
Teacher Assistant/Aide, A
Teacher Education and Professional Development, Specific Subject Areas, A
Welding Technology/Welder, A

SAINT LOUIS CHRISTIAN COLLEGE

Bible/Biblical Studies, B
Liberal Arts and Sciences Studies and Humanities, A
Religious Education, B
Religious/Sacred Music, B
Theology/Theological Studies, B

ST. LOUIS COLLEGE OF HEALTH CAREERS (SAINT LOUIS)

Allied Health and Medical Assisting Services, A
Massage Therapy/Therapeutic Massage, A
Medical Insurance Specialist/Medical Biller, A

ST. LOUIS COLLEGE OF PHARMACY

Biomedical Sciences, B
Liberal Arts and Sciences Studies and Humanities, B
Pharmacy, D

SAINT LOUIS UNIVERSITY

Accounting, BM
Aeronautics/Aviation/Aerospace Science and Technology, B
Aerospace, Aeronautical and Astronautical Engineering, B
African-American/Black Studies, B

Airline/Commercial/Professional Pilot and Flight Crew, B
Allied Health and Medical Assisting Services, MDO
Allopathic Medicine, D
American/United States Studies/Civilization, BMD
Anatomy, MD
Anthropology, B
Art History, Criticism and Conservation, B
Athletic Training and Sports Medicine, M
Atmospheric Sciences and Meteorology, B
Biochemistry, BD
Bioethics/Medical Ethics, DO
Biological and Biomedical Sciences, MD
Biology/Biological Sciences, B
Biomedical Engineering, MD
Biomedical Sciences, B
Biomedical/Medical Engineering, B
Biostatistics, B
Business Administration and Management, B
Business Administration, Management and Operations, M
Business/Managerial Economics, B
Chemistry, BMD
Civil Engineering, B
Classics and Classical Languages, Literatures, and Linguistics, B
Clinical Laboratory Science/Medical Technology/Technologist, B
Clinical Psychology, MD
Clinical/Medical Laboratory Science and Allied Professions, B
Communication Disorders, BM
Communication and Media Studies, M
Community Health and Preventive Medicine, M
Computer Engineering, B
Computer Science, B
Computer and Information Sciences, B
Counselor Education/School Counseling and Guidance Services, MDO
Criminal Justice/Safety Studies, B
Curriculum and Instruction, MD
CytoTechnology/Cytotechnologist, B
Dentistry, M
Dietetics/Dieticians, B
Drama and Dramatics/Theatre Arts, B
Education, BMD
Educational Administration and Supervision, MDO
Educational Leadership and Administration, MDO
Electrical, Electronics and Communications Engineering, B
Elementary Education and Teaching, B
Engineering, B
Engineering Physics, B
English, MD
English Language and Literature, B
English/Language Arts Teacher Education, B
Entrepreneurship/Entrepreneurial Studies, B
Environmental Sciences, B
Environmental Studies, B
Experimental Psychology, MD
Finance, B
Finance and Banking, M
Fine/Studio Arts, B
Forensic Science and Technology, B
Foundations and Philosophy of Education, MD
French Language and Literature, BM
General Studies, B
Geographic Information Systems, O
Geology/Earth Science, B
Geophysics and Seismology, D
Geosciences, MD
German Language and Literature, B
Health Information/Medical Records Administration/Administrator, B
Health Services Administration, MD
Health Services/Allied Health/Health Sciences, B
Health/Health Care Administration/Management, B
Higher Education/Higher Education Administration, MDO
History, BMD
Human Development, M
Humanities/Humanistic Studies, B
Immunology, D
Industrial and Organizational Psychology, D
International Business/Trade/Commerce, BMD
International Relations and Affairs, B

Italian Language and Literature, B
Junior High/Intermediate/Middle School Education and Teaching, B
Kinesiology and Exercise Science, B
Latin American Studies, B
Law and Legal Studies, BMD
Liberal Arts and Sciences Studies and Humanities, B
Management Information Systems and Services, B
Marketing/Marketing Management, B
Marriage and Family Therapy/Counseling, MDO
Mathematics, BMD
Mathematics Teacher Education, B
Mechanical Engineering, B
Medical Radiologic Technology/Science - Radiation Therapist, B
Meteorology, MD
Microbiology, D
Molecular Biology, D
Music, B
Nuclear Medical Technology/Technologist, B
Nursing, MDO
Nutritional Sciences, M
Occupational Therapy/Therapist, BM
Oral and Dental Sciences, M
Organizational Behavior Studies, B
Organizational Management, O
Orthodontics, M
Pathology/Experimental Pathology, D
Periodontics, M
Pharmacology, D
Philosophy, BMD
Physical Therapy/Therapist, MD
Physician Assistant, M
Physics, B
Physiology, D
Political Science and Government, BM
Psychology, BMD
Public Administration, M
Public Health, D
Public Health (MPH, DPH), B
Public Policy Analysis, MDO
Russian Language and Literature, B
Science Teacher Education/General Science Teacher Education, B
Securities Services Administration/Management, B
Social Science Teacher Education, B
Social Work, BM
Sociology, B
Spanish Language and Literature, BM
Special Education and Teaching, M
Student Personnel Services, M
Theology and Religious Vocations, MD
Theology/Theological Studies, B
Urban Studies/Affairs, BM
Women's Studies, B

SOUTHEAST MISSOURI HOSPITAL COLLEGE OF NURSING AND HEALTH SCIENCES

Medical Radiologic Technology/Science - Radiation Therapist, A

SOUTHEAST MISSOURI STATE UNIVERSITY

Accounting, BM
Agribusiness, B
Agricultural Teacher Education, B
Art Teacher Education, B
Art/Art Studies, General, B
Athletic Training and Sports Medicine, B
Biological and Biomedical Sciences, M
Biology/Biological Sciences, B
Business Administration and Management, B
Business Administration, Management and Operations, M
Chemistry, BM
Child Care and Support Services Management, A
Clinical Laboratory Science/Medical Technology/Technologist, B
Communication Disorders, BM
Communication Studies/Speech Communication and Rhetoric, B
Computer Programming/Programmer, B
Computer Technology/Computer Systems Technology, A

Computer and Information Sciences, B
Computer and Information Systems Security, B
Corrections, B
Counseling Psychology, M
Counselor Education/School Counseling and Guidance Services, MO
Criminology, M
Drama and Dramatics/Theatre Arts, B
Early Childhood Education and Teaching, B
Economics, B
Educational Administration and Supervision, MO
Educational Media/Instructional Technology, M
Elementary Education and Teaching, BM
Engineering Physics, B
Engineering Technology, B
English, M
English Language and Literature, B
English as a Second Language, M
English/Language Arts Teacher Education, B
Entrepreneurship/Entrepreneurial Studies, M
Environmental Policy and Resource Management, M
Environmental Sciences, BM
Environmental Studies, B
Exercise and Sports Science, M
Family and Consumer Sciences/Home Economics Teacher Education, B
Family and Consumer Sciences/Human Sciences, B
Finance, B
Finance and Banking, M
Foreign Language Teacher Education, B
Foundations and Philosophy of Education, M
General Studies, B
Health Communication, B
Health Services Administration, M
Health Services/Allied Health/Health Sciences, B
Health and Physical Education, B
Health/Health Care Administration/Management, B
Higher Education/Higher Education Administration, M
Historic Preservation and Conservation, BO
History, BMO
Industrial Technology/Technician, B
Industrial and Manufacturing Management, M
International Business/Trade/Commerce, BM
International/Global Studies, B
Junior High/Intermediate/Middle School Education and Teaching, B
Leisure Studies, M
Management of Technology, M
Marketing/Marketing Management, B
Mathematics, BM
Mathematics Teacher Education, B
Middle School Education, M
Multi-/Interdisciplinary Studies, B
Music, B
Music Teacher Education, B
Nursing, M
Nutritional Sciences, M
Organizational Communication, B
Organizational Management, M
Parks, Recreation, Leisure and Fitness Studies, B
Philosophy, B
Physical Education Teaching and Coaching, B
Physics, B
Political Science and Government, B
Psychology, B
Public Administration, M
Public History, M
Science Teacher Education/General Science Teacher Education, B
Secondary Education and Teaching, M
Social Sciences, B
Social Studies Teacher Education, B
Social Work, B
Special Education and Teaching, BM
Sport and Fitness Administration/Management, BM
Technology Teacher Education/Industrial Arts Teacher Education, B
Visual and Performing Arts, B
Writing, M

SOUTHWEST BAPTIST UNIVERSITY

Accounting, B
Art Teacher Education, B
Art/Art Studies, General, B

Athletic Training and Sports Medicine, B
Bible/Biblical Studies, B
Biology Teacher Education, B
Biology/Biological Sciences, B
Business Administration and Management, B
Business Administration, Management and Operations, M
Business/Commerce, A
Chemistry, B
Chemistry Teacher Education, B
Clinical Laboratory Science/Medical Technology/Technologist, B
Commercial and Advertising Art, B
Communication Studies/Speech Communication and Rhetoric, B
Computer Science, AB
Computer and Information Sciences, B
Criminal Justice/Law Enforcement Administration, B
Customer Service Management, B
Drama and Dramatics/Theatre Arts, B
Early Childhood Education and Teaching, B
Education, MO
Educational Administration and Supervision, MO
Elementary Education and Teaching, B
Emergency Medical Technology/Technician (EMT Paramedic), A
English Language and Literature, B
English/Language Arts Teacher Education, B
Finance, B
General Studies, A
Health Services Administration, M
Health Teacher Education, B
Health and Physical Education, B
History, B
Human Services, B
Junior High/Intermediate/Middle School Education and Teaching, B
Kinesiology and Exercise Science, B
Marketing/Marketing Management, B
Mathematics, B
Mathematics Teacher Education, B
Missions/Missionary Studies and Missiology, B
Music, B
Music Teacher Education, B
Occupational Safety and Health Technology/Technician, B
Office Management and Supervision, B
Parks, Recreation, Leisure and Fitness Studies, B
Pastoral Studies/Counseling, B
Physical Education Teaching and Coaching, B
Physical Therapy/Therapist, D
Political Science and Government, B
Psychology, B
Religion/Religious Studies, B
Religious Education, B
Science Teacher Education/General Science Teacher Education, B
Social Science Teacher Education, B
Social Work, B
Sociology, B
Spanish Language and Literature, B
Speech Teacher Education, B
Sport and Fitness Administration/Management, B
Theology/Theological Studies, B

STATE FAIR COMMUNITY COLLEGE

Accounting, A
Accounting and Computer Science, A
Agribusiness, A
Applied Horticulture/Horticultural Operations, A
Automobile/Automotive Mechanics Technology/Technician, A
Building/Construction Site Management/Manager, A
Business Administration and Management, A
CAD/CADD Drafting and/or Design Technology/Technician, A
Child Care and Support Services Management, A
Computer Programming, Specific Applications, A
Computer Systems Networking and Telecommunications, A
Criminal Justice/Police Science, A
Dental Hygiene/Hygienist, A
Health Information/Medical Records Technology/Technician, A
Liberal Arts and Sciences Studies and Humanities, A

Machine Tool Technology/Machinist, A
Manufacturing Technology/Technician, A
Marine Maintenance/Fitter and Ship Repair Technology/Technician, A
Mechanic and Repair Technologies/Technicians, A
Medical Administrative Assistant/Secretary, A
Occupational Therapist Assistant, A
Physical Therapist Assistant, A
Radiologic Technology/Science - Radiographer, A
Special Products Marketing Operations, A
Teacher Assistant/Aide, A
Teacher Education and Professional Development, Specific Subject Areas, A
Technical Teacher Education, A
Web Page, Digital/Multimedia and Information Resources Design, A

STATE TECHNICAL COLLEGE OF MISSOURI

Aircraft Powerplant Technology/Technician, A
Airframe Mechanics and Aircraft Maintenance Technology/Technician, A
Autobody/Collision and Repair Technology/Technician, A
Automobile/Automotive Mechanics Technology/Technician, A
Civil Engineering Technology/Technician, A
Computer Programming/Programmer, A
Computer Systems Networking and Telecommunications, A
Drafting and Design Technology/Technician, A
Electrical, Electronic and Communications Engineering Technology/Technician, A
Electrical/Electronics Equipment Installation and Repair, A
Electrician, A
Heating, Air Conditioning, Ventilation and Refrigeration Maintenance Technology/Technician, A
Heavy Equipment Maintenance Technology/Technician, A
Lineworker, A
Machine Tool Technology/Machinist, A
Management Information Systems and Services, A
Manufacturing Technology/Technician, A
Medium/Heavy Vehicle and Truck Technology/Technician, A
Motorcycle Maintenance and Repair Technology/Technician, A
Nuclear/Nuclear Power Technology/Technician, A
Physical Therapist Assistant, A
Turf and Turfgrass Management, A
Welding Technology/Welder, A

STEPHENS COLLEGE

Apparel and Accessories Marketing Operations, B
Apparel and Textiles, B
Biology/Biological Sciences, B
Business Administration, Management and Operations, M
Counseling Psychology, M
Counselor Education/School Counseling and Guidance Services, MO
Curriculum and Instruction, M
Dance, B
Drama and Dramatics/Theatre Arts, B
Early Childhood Education and Teaching, B
English Language and Literature, B
Equestrian/Equine Studies, B
Fashion/Apparel Design, B
Film/Cinema Studies, B
Graphic Design, B
Health Informatics, O
Health Information/Medical Records Administration/Administrator, B
Health Professions and Related Clinical Sciences, B
Human Development and Family Studies, B
Marketing, B
Marriage and Family Therapy/Counseling, M
Mass Communication/Media Studies, B
Multi-/Interdisciplinary Studies, B
Psychology, B
Public Relations/Image Management, B

Technical Theatre/Theatre Design and Technology, B

STEVENS—THE INSTITUTE OF BUSINESS & ARTS

Business Administration and Management, AB
Fashion Merchandising, AB
Interior Design, AB
Legal Assistant/Paralegal, AB
Retailing and Retail Operations, AB
Tourism and Travel Services Management, A

THREE RIVERS COMMUNITY COLLEGE

Accounting, A
Administrative Assistant and Secretarial Science, A
Agricultural Business and Management, A
Agricultural Mechanization, A
Business Administration and Management, A
Clinical/Medical Laboratory Technician, A
Computer Engineering Technology/Technician, A
Computer and Information Sciences, A
Computer and Information Sciences and Support Services, A
Construction Engineering Technology/Technician, A
Criminal Justice/Law Enforcement Administration, A
Criminal Justice/Police Science, A
Data Entry/Microcomputer Applications, A
Education, A
Elementary Education and Teaching, A
Engineering Technology, A
Industrial Technology/Technician, A
Information Technology, A
Liberal Arts and Sciences Studies and Humanities, A
Marketing/Marketing Management, A
Music, A
Word Processing, A

TRUMAN STATE UNIVERSITY

Accounting, BM
Agriculture, B
Art History, Criticism and Conservation, B
Art/Art Studies, General, B
Athletic Training and Sports Medicine, B
Biological and Biomedical Sciences, M
Biology/Biological Sciences, B
Business Administration and Management, B
Chemistry, B
Classics and Classical Languages, Literatures, and Linguistics, B
Communication Disorders, BM
Communication Studies/Speech Communication and Rhetoric, B
Computer and Information Sciences, B
Criminal Justice/Safety Studies, B
Drama and Dramatics/Theatre Arts, B
Economics, B
Education, M
English, M
English Language and Literature, B
Fine/Studio Arts, B
French Language and Literature, B
German Language and Literature, B
Health and Physical Education, B
History, B
Kinesiology and Exercise Science, B
Linguistics, B
Mathematics, B
Multi-/Interdisciplinary Studies, B
Music, BM
Music Performance, B
Philosophy and Religious Studies, B
Physics, B
Political Science and Government, B
Psychology, B
Romance Languages, Literatures, and Linguistics, B
Russian Language and Literature, B
Sociology, B
Spanish Language and Literature, B

UNIVERSITY OF CENTRAL MISSOURI

Accounting, M
Aerospace, Aeronautical and Astronautical Engineering, M
Agribusiness, B

Apparel and Textiles, B
Applied Mathematics, M
Art Teacher Education, B
Biological and Biomedical Sciences, M
Biology/Biological Sciences, B
Business Administration and Management, B
Business Administration, Management and Operations, M
Business Statistics, B
Business Teacher Education, B
Chemistry, B
Clinical Laboratory Science/Medical Technology/Technologist, B
Commercial and Advertising Art, B
Communication Disorders, B
Communication and Media Studies, BM
Computer Science, M
Computer and Information Sciences, B
Counseling Psychology, O
Counselor Education/School Counseling and Guidance Services, M
Criminal Justice/Law Enforcement Administration, B
Criminology, M
Dietetics/Dieticians, B
Drama and Dramatics/Theatre Arts, B
Early Childhood Education and Teaching, M
Economics, B
Education, BMO
Educational Administration and Supervision, MO
Educational Leadership and Administration, MD
Educational Media/Instructional Technology, MO
Electrical, Electronic and Communications Engineering Technology/Technician, B
Elementary Education and Teaching, BM
English, M
English Language and Literature, B
English as a Second Language, M
Environmental Studies, M
Environmental and Occupational Health, M
Family and Consumer Sciences/Human Sciences, B
Finance, B
Finance and Banking, M
Fine/Studio Arts, B
French Language and Literature, B
Geography, B
Geology/Earth Science, B
German Language and Literature, B
Gerontology, M
History, BM
Hotel/Motel Administration/Management, B
Human Services, O
Industrial Hygiene, M
Industrial and Manufacturing Management, M
Information Science/Studies, M
Interior Design, B
Journalism, B
Junior High/Intermediate/Middle School Education and Teaching, B
Kinesiology and Movement Studies, M
Library Science, M
Management Information Systems and Services, BM
Management of Technology, MD
Marketing, M
Marketing/Marketing Management, B
Mathematics, BM
Music, BM
Music Teacher Education, B
Music Theory and Composition, B
Nursing, M
Occupational Safety and Health Technology/Technician, B
Office Management and Supervision, B
Parks, Recreation, Leisure and Fitness Studies, B
Photography, B
Physical Education Teaching and Coaching, B
Physics, B
Physics Teacher Education, B
Political Science and Government, B
Pre-Dentistry Studies, B
Pre-Medicine/Pre-Medical Studies, B
Pre-Pharmacy Studies, B
Pre-Veterinary Studies, B
Psychology, BM
Public Relations/Image Management, B
Radio and Television, B

Reading Teacher Education, BM
Secondary Education and Teaching, B
Social Work, B
Sociology, BM
Spanish Language and Literature, B
Special Education and Teaching, BM
Speech-Language Pathology/Pathologist, B
Student Personnel Services, M
Theater, M
Tourism and Travel Services Marketing Operations, B
Vocational and Technical Education, M

UNIVERSITY OF MISSOURI

Accounting, BMDO
Adult and Continuing Education and Teaching, MDO
Advertising, B
Aerospace, Aeronautical and Astronautical Engineering, MD
Agricultural Business and Management, B
Agricultural Economics, BMDO
Agricultural Education, MDO
Agricultural Engineering, MD
Agricultural Mechanization, B
Agricultural Sciences, MDO
Agricultural Teacher Education, B
Agriculture, B
Agronomy and Soil Sciences, MD
Allopathic Medicine, D
Analytical Chemistry, MD
Anatomy, M
Animal Sciences, BMD
Anthropology, BMD
Apparel and Textiles, B
Applied Mathematics, M
Archeology, BMD
Architecture, M
Art Education, MDO
Art History, Criticism and Conservation, BMD
Art Teacher Education, B
Art/Art Studies, General, B
Astronomy, MD
Atmospheric Sciences and Meteorology, BMD
Behavioral Sciences, B
Biochemistry, BMD
Bioengineering, MD
Bioinformatics, D
Biological and Biomedical Sciences, MD
Biology Teacher Education, B
Biology/Biological Sciences, B
Broadcast Journalism, B
Business Administration and Management, B
Business Administration, Management and Operations, MD
Business Education, MDO
Business Teacher Education, B
Business/Managerial Economics, B
Cell Biology and Anatomy, MD
Central/Middle and Eastern European Studies, B
Chemical Engineering, BMD
Chemistry, BMD
Chemistry Teacher Education, B
Child and Family Studies, MD
Civil Engineering, BMD
Classics and Classical Languages, Literatures, and Linguistics, BMD
Clothing and Textiles, MD
Communication Disorders, MD
Communication Disorders Sciences and Services, B
Communication Studies/Speech Communication and Rhetoric, B
Communication and Media Studies, MDO
Community Health and Preventive Medicine, M
Comparative Literature, M
Computer Art and Design, M
Computer Engineering, B
Computer Science, BMD
Computer and Information Sciences, B
Conflict Resolution and Mediation/Peace Studies, MO
Conservation Biology, O
Consumer Economics, MDO
Corporate and Organizational Communication, M
Counseling Psychology, MDO
Curriculum and Instruction, MDO

Diagnostic Medical Sonography/Sonographer and Ultrasound Technician, B
Dietetics/Dieticians, B
Drama and Dramatics/Theatre Arts, B
Early Childhood Education and Teaching, BMDO
East Asian Studies, B
Ecology, MD
Economics, BMD
Education, BMDO
Education/Teaching of the Gifted and Talented, MD
Educational Administration and Supervision, MDO
Educational Media/Instructional Technology, MDO
Educational Psychology, MDO
Electrical Engineering, MD
Electrical, Electronics and Communications Engineering, B
Elementary Education and Teaching, BMDO
Engineering and Applied Sciences, MDO
English, MD
English Education, MDO
English Language and Literature, B
Entomology, MD
Environmental Design/Architecture, M
Environmental Engineering Technology/Environmental Technology, MD
Environmental Policy and Resource Management, MD
Environmental Studies, B
Ethics, O
European Studies/Civilization, B
Evolutionary Biology, MD
Exercise and Sports Science, MD
Family and Consumer Economics and Related Services, B
Finance, B
Finance and Banking, D
Fine Arts and Art Studies, M
Fish, Game and Wildlife Management, MDO
Fishing and Fisheries Sciences and Management, B
Food Science, B
Food Science and Technology, MD
Foods, Nutrition, and Wellness Studies, B
Foreign Language Teacher Education, MDO
Forestry, BMDO
French Language and Literature, BMD
General Studies, B
Genetics, MD
Geographic Information Systems, O
Geography, BMO
Geology/Earth Science, BMD
Geotechnical Engineering, MD
German Language and Literature, BM
Gerontological Nursing, DO
Gerontology, O
Health Communication, M
Health Education, MD
Health Informatics, MDO
Health Physics/Radiological Health, M
Health Promotion, M
Health Services Administration, MDO
Health/Medical Preparatory Programs, B
Higher Education/Higher Education Administration, MDO
History, BMD
Home Economics, MDO
Horticultural Science, MD
Hospitality Administration/Management, MD
Hotel/Motel Administration/Management, B
Housing and Human Environments, B
Human Development, MD
Human Development and Family Studies, B
Immunology, MD
Industrial Engineering, B
Industrial/Management Engineering, MD
Information Science/Studies, MDO
Inorganic Chemistry, MD
Interdisciplinary Studies, O
Interior Architecture, B
International Agriculture, B
International Business/Trade/Commerce, B
International Public Health/International Health, O
Internet and Interactive Multimedia, M
Journalism, BMDO
Junior High/Intermediate/Middle School Education and Teaching, B
Kindergarten/PreSchool Education and Teaching, B

Latin American Studies, B
Latin Language and Literature, B
Law and Legal Studies, MD
Library Science, MDO
Linguistics, B
Management, D
Management Information Systems and Services, B
Manufacturing Engineering, MD
Marketing, D
Marketing/Marketing Management, B
Mass Communication/Media Studies, B
Mathematics, BMD
Mathematics Teacher Education, BMDO
Mechanical Engineering, BMD
Media Studies, M
Medical Physics, M
Medical Radiologic Technology/Science - Radiation Therapist, B
Microbiology, MD
Music, BM
Music Teacher Education, BMDO
Natural Resources and Conservation, BM
Neurobiology and Neurophysiology, MD
Neuroscience, MD
Non-Profit/Public/Organizational Management, O
Nuclear Engineering, MDO
Nuclear Medical Technology/Technologist, B
Nursing, MDO
Nursing - Adult, DO
Nursing - Advanced Practice, D
Nursing Administration, D
Nutritional Sciences, MD
Occupational Therapy/Therapist, BM
Organic Chemistry, MD
Organizational Management, O
Parks, Recreation, Leisure and Fitness Studies, B
Pathobiology, MD
Pathology/Experimental Pathology, M
Peace Studies and Conflict Resolution, B
Pediatric Nurse/Nursing, DO
Pharmacology, MD
Philosophy, BMD
Photojournalism, B
Physical Chemistry, MD
Physical Therapy/Therapist, MD
Physics, BMD
Physics Teacher Education, B
Physiology, MD
Plant Biology, MD
Plant Sciences, BMD
Political Science and Government, BMD
Psychiatric/Mental Health Nurse/Nursing, D
Psychology, BMD
Public Administration, O
Public Affairs, MDO
Public Health, MO
Public Policy Analysis, O
Publishing, B
Radio and Television, B
Radiologic Technology/Science - Radiographer, B
Reading Teacher Education, MDO
Real Estate, B
Recreation and Park Management, M
Religion/Religious Studies, BM
Respiratory Care Therapy/Therapist, B
Restaurant/Food Services Management, B
Romance Languages, Literatures, and Linguistics, MD
Rural Sociology, MD
Russian Language and Literature, BM
Russian Studies, B
School Psychology, MDO
Science Teacher Education/General Science Teacher Education, BMDO
Secondary Education and Teaching, B
Social Studies Teacher Education, BMDO
Social Work, BMDO
Sociology, BMD
South Asian Studies, B
Spanish Language and Literature, BMD
Special Education and Teaching, BMD
Statistics, BMD
Structural Engineering, MD
Taxation, O
Technical Teacher Education, B
Theater, MD

Transportation and Highway Engineering, M
Veterinary Medicine, D
Veterinary Sciences, MD
Vocational and Technical Education, MDO
Water Resources, MD
Water Resources Engineering, MD
Wildlife and Wildlands Science and Management, B

UNIVERSITY OF MISSOURI–KANSAS CITY

Accounting, BM
Allopathic Medicine, MD
American/United States Studies/Civilization, B
Analytical Chemistry, MD
Anesthesiologist Assistant, M
Architecture, B
Art History, Criticism and Conservation, BMD
Art/Art Studies, General, B
Biochemistry, D
Bioinformatics, M
Biological and Biomedical Sciences, M
Biology/Biological Sciences, B
Biophysics, D
Business Administration and Management, B
Business Administration, Management and Operations, MD
Cell Biology and Anatomy, MD
Chemistry, BMD
City/Urban, Community and Regional Planning, B
Civil Engineering, BM
Clinical Psychology, D
Clinical/Medical Laboratory Technician, B
Community Psychology, D
Composition, MD
Computer Engineering, D
Computer Science, BMDO
Construction Engineering and Management, O
Counseling Psychology, MDO
Counselor Education/School Counseling and Guidance Services, O
Criminal Justice/Law Enforcement Administration, B
Criminology, BM
Curriculum and Instruction, MO
Dance, B
Dental Hygiene/Hygienist, BM
Dental and Oral Surgery, O
Dentistry, MDO
Drama and Dramatics/Theatre Arts, B
Early Childhood Education and Teaching, B
Economics, BMD
Education, MDO
Educational Administration and Supervision, MDO
Electrical Engineering, MD
Electrical, Electronics and Communications Engineering, B
Elementary Education and Teaching, B
Engineering, B
Engineering Management, O
Engineering and Applied Sciences, MDO
English, MD
English Language and Literature, B
Entrepreneurship/Entrepreneurial Studies, D
Environmental Design/Architecture, B
Environmental Studies, B
Finance and Banking, M
Fine Arts and Art Studies, MD
Fine/Studio Arts, B
Foreign Languages and Literatures, B
French Language and Literature, M
General Studies, B
Geography, B
Geology/Earth Science, BM
Geosciences, MD
Gerontological Nursing, D
Health Education, M
Health Psychology, D
Health Services/Allied Health/Health Sciences, B
Higher Education/Higher Education Administration, D
History, BMD
Information Technology, B
Inorganic Chemistry, MD
Interdisciplinary Studies, D
Jazz/Jazz Studies, B
Junior High/Intermediate/Middle School Education and Teaching, B

Law and Legal Studies, MD
Mass Communication/Media Studies, B
Maternal/Child Health and Neonatal Nurse/Nursing, M
Mathematics, BMD
Mathematics and Statistics, B
Mechanical Engineering, BM
Media Studies, M
Molecular Biology, MD
Music, BMD
Music History, Literature, and Theory, M
Music Performance, B
Music Teacher Education, BMD
Music Theory and Composition, BM
Music Therapy/Therapist, BM
Musicology and Ethnomusicology, M
Nursing, MD
Nursing - Adult, MD
Nursing - Advanced Practice, MD
Nursing Administration, M
Nursing Education, M
Oral Biology, MD
Oral and Dental Sciences, DO
Organic Chemistry, MD
Orthodontics, O
Pediatric Nurse/Nursing, MD
Performance, MD
Periodontics, O
Pharmaceutical Sciences, D
Pharmacology, D
Pharmacy, D
Philosophy, B
Physical Chemistry, MD
Physician Assistant, M
Physics, BMD
Political Science and Government, BM
Polymer/Plastics Engineering, MD
Psychology, BMD
Public Administration, MD
Public Affairs, MD
Reading Teacher Education, MO
Real Estate, M
Romance Languages, Literatures, and Linguistics, M
Secondary Education and Teaching, B
Social Work, M
Sociology, BM
Software Engineering, M
Spanish Language and Literature, M
Special Education and Teaching, M
Statistics, MD
Taxation, M
Telecommunications, MD
Theater, M
Toxicology, D
Urban Studies/Affairs, B
Women's Health Nursing, MD
Writing, M

UNIVERSITY OF MISSOURI–ST. LOUIS

Accounting, BM
American/United States Studies/Civilization, M
Anthropology, B
Applied Physics, M
Art History, Criticism and Conservation, B
Astrophysics, M
Biochemistry, BMD
Biological and Biomedical Sciences, MDO
Biology/Biological Sciences, B
Business Administration and Management, B
Business Administration, Management and Operations, MDO
Chemistry, BMD
Civil Engineering, B
Clinical Psychology, MDO
Communication and Media Studies, M
Computer Science, BMD
Counseling Psychology, M
Counselor Education/School Counseling and Guidance Services, MD
Criminology, BMD
Cultural Studies, O
Curriculum and Instruction, M
Drama and Dramatics/Theatre Arts, B
Early Childhood Education and Teaching, BM
Economics, BM

Education, BMDO
Educational Administration and Supervision, MO
Educational Measurement and Evaluation, MO
Educational Psychology, D
Electrical, Electronics and Communications Engineering, B
Elementary Education and Teaching, BM
English, M
English Language and Literature, B
English as a Second Language, MO
Finance, B
Fine/Studio Arts, B
Foreign Languages and Literatures, B
Gender Studies, O
Gerontological Nursing, O
Gerontology, MO
Health Services Administration, O
History, B
Human Resources Development, M
Human Resources Management and Services, O
Industrial and Organizational Psychology, MD
Interdisciplinary Studies, O
Liberal Arts and Sciences Studies and Humanities, B
Logistics and Materials Management, MDO
Management, M
Management Information Systems and Services, BM
Management Strategy and Policy, O
Marketing, MO
Marketing/Marketing Management, B
Mass Communication/Media Studies, B
Maternal/Child Health and Neonatal Nurse/Nursing, M
Mathematics, BMD
Mechanical Engineering, B
Middle School Education, M
Multi-/Interdisciplinary Studies, B
Museology/Museum Studies, MO
Music, B
Music Teacher Education, M
Neuroscience, MD
Non-Profit/Public/Organizational Management, MO
Nursing, MDO
Nursing - Adult, O
Nursing - Advanced Practice, O
Nursing Administration, M
Optometry, D
Organic Chemistry, D
Pediatric Nurse/Nursing, MO
Philosophy, BM
Physical Education Teaching and Coaching, B
Physics, BMD
Political Science and Government, BMD
Psychology, BMDO
Public Administration, BMO
Public Policy Analysis, MO
Reading Teacher Education, M
School Psychology, O
Secondary Education and Teaching, BM
Social Work, BMO
Sociology, B
Special Education and Teaching, MO
Supply Chain Management, DO

VATTEROTT COLLEGE (BERKELEY)

Computer Software Technology/Technician, B
Electrician, A
Heating, Air Conditioning and Refrigeration Technology/Technician, A
Medical Insurance Coding Specialist/Coder, A
Medical/Clinical Assistant, A
Plumbing Technology/Plumber, A
System Administration/Administrator, AB
Web Page, Digital/Multimedia and Information Resources Design, A
Welding Technology/Welder, A

VATTEROTT COLLEGE (KANSAS CITY)

Administrative Assistant and Secretarial Science, A
CAD/CADD Drafting and/or Design Technology/Technician, A
Computer Programming/Programmer, A
Electrician, A
Heating, Air Conditioning and Refrigeration Technology/Technician, A

Medical/Clinical Assistant, A
Pharmacy Technician/Assistant, A
Plumbing Technology/Plumber, A
System Administration/Administrator, A
System, Networking, and LAN/WAN Management/Manager, A
Web Page, Digital/Multimedia and Information Resources Design, A

VATTEROTT COLLEGE (SAINT CHARLES)

Computer Systems Networking and Telecommunications, A
Electrical/Electronics Maintenance and Repair Technology, A
Electrician, A
Heating, Air Conditioning and Refrigeration Technology/Technician, A
Medical/Clinical Assistant, A

VATTEROTT COLLEGE (SAINT JOSEPH)

Administrative Assistant and Secretarial Science, A
Computer Systems Networking and Telecommunications, A
Criminal Justice/Safety Studies, A
Medical/Clinical Assistant, A

VATTEROTT COLLEGE (SPRINGFIELD)

CAD/CADD Drafting and/or Design Technology/Technician, A
Computer Programming/Programmer, A
Medical/Clinical Assistant, A
Pharmacy Technician/Assistant, A
System, Networking, and LAN/WAN Management/Manager, A

VATTEROTT COLLEGE (SUNSET HILLS)

Building/Construction Finishing, Management, and Inspection, A
Business/Commerce, A
CAD/CADD Drafting and/or Design Technology/Technician, A
Computer Software Technology/Technician, B
Electrician, A
Fashion Merchandising, A
Heating, Air Conditioning and Refrigeration Technology/Technician, A
Human Resources Management/Personnel Administration, A
Medical/Clinical Assistant, A
System Administration/Administrator, AB
Web Page, Digital/Multimedia and Information Resources Design, A

VET TECH INSTITUTE AT HICKEY COLLEGE

Veterinary/Animal Health Technology/Technician and Veterinary Assistant, A

WASHINGTON UNIVERSITY IN ST. LOUIS

Accounting, BM
Advertising, B
Aerospace, Aeronautical and Astronautical Engineering, MD
African Studies, B
African-American/Black Studies, B
Allopathic Medicine, D
American Indian/Native American Studies, M
American/United States Studies/Civilization, B
Ancient Studies/Civilization, B
Ancient/Classical Greek Language and Literature, B
Anthropology, BD
Applied Mathematics, B
Arabic Language and Literature, B
Archeology, BMD
Architectural Engineering Technology/Technician, B
Architectural Technology/Technician, B
Architecture, BM
Architecture and Related Services, B
Area Studies, B
Art History, Criticism and Conservation, BMD

Art Teacher Education, B
Art/Art Studies, General, B
Asian Languages, MD
Asian Studies/Civilization, BM
Biochemistry, BD
Biological and Biomedical Sciences, BD
Biological and Physical Sciences, B
Biology Teacher Education, B
Biology/Biological Sciences, B
Biomathematics and Bioinformatics, B
Biomedical Engineering, MD
Biomedical/Medical Engineering, B
Biophysics, B
Biopsychology, B
Biostatistics, MO
Business Administration and Management, B
Business Administration, Management and Operations, BMD
Business/Commerce, B
Business/Managerial Economics, B
Cell Biology and Anatomy, D
Central/Middle and Eastern European Studies, B
Ceramic Arts and Ceramics, B
Chemical Engineering, BMD
Chemistry, BD
Chemistry Teacher Education, B
Child and Family Studies, M
Chinese Language and Literature, B
Chinese Studies, MD
Classics and Classical Languages, Literatures, and Linguistics, BM
Clinical Psychology, D
Clinical Research, M
Cognitive Sciences, D
Commercial and Advertising Art, B
Communication Disorders, MD
Communication Studies/Speech Communication and Rhetoric, B
Communication, Journalism and Related Programs, B
Comparative Literature, BD
Computational Biology, D
Computer Engineering, BMD
Computer Science, BMD
Computer and Information Sciences, B
Computer and Information Sciences and Support Services, B
Computer/Information Technology Services Administration and Management, B
Counseling Psychology, M
Dance, B
Database Systems, M
Design and Applied Arts, B
Design and Visual Communications, B
Developmental Biology and Embryology, D
Developmental Psychology, D
Drama and Dance Teacher Education, B
Drama and Dramatics/Theatre Arts, B
Drawing, B
East Asian Languages, Literatures, and Linguistics, B
East Asian Studies, B
Ecology, BD
Economic Development, M
Economics, BD
Education, BMD
Educational Measurement and Evaluation, D
Electrical, Electronics and Communications Engineering, B
Elementary Education and Teaching, BM
Engineering, B
Engineering and Applied Sciences, MD
English, MD
English Language and Literature, B
English/Language Arts Teacher Education, B
Entrepreneurship/Entrepreneurial Studies, B
Environmental Biology, BD
Environmental Engineering Technology/Environmental Technology, MD
Environmental Sciences, B
Environmental Studies, B
Epidemiology, M
Ethnic, Cultural Minority, and Gender Studies, B
European Studies/Civilization, B
Evolutionary Biology, D
Fashion/Apparel Design, B

Film/Cinema Studies, B
Finance, B
Finance and Banking, MD
Fine Arts and Art Studies, M
Fine/Studio Arts, B
French Language Teacher Education, B
French Language and Literature, BMD
General Merchandising, Sales, and Related Marketing Operations, B
Genetics, MD
Genomic Sciences, M
Geochemistry, B
Geology/Earth Science, B
Geophysics and Seismology, B
Geosciences, D
German Language Teacher Education, B
German Language and Literature, BD
Germanic Languages, Literatures, and Linguistics, B
Gerontology, MD
Graphic Design, B
Health Education, M
Health Professions and Related Clinical Sciences, B
Health Services Research, MO
Health Services/Allied Health/Health Sciences, B
Health/Health Care Administration/Management, B
Hebrew Language and Literature, B
History, BD
History Teacher Education, B
Human Genetics, D
Human Resources Management/Personnel Administration, B
Humanities/Humanistic Studies, B
Illustration, B
Immunology, D
International Business/Trade/Commerce, B
International Economics, B
International Finance, B
International Public Health/International Health, M
International Relations and Affairs, B
Islamic Studies, B
Italian Language and Literature, B
Japanese Language and Literature, B
Japanese Studies, MD
Jewish/Judaic Studies, BM
Journalism, B
Junior High/Intermediate/Middle School Education and Teaching, B
Kinesiology and Movement Studies, D
Latin American Studies, B
Latin Language and Literature, B
Law and Legal Studies, MD
Liberal Arts and Sciences Studies and Humanities, B
Linguistics, B
Marketing, B
Marketing/Marketing Management, B
Materials Sciences, MD
Mathematics, BMD
Mathematics Teacher Education, B
Mathematics and Computer Science, B
Mechanical Engineering, BMD
Microbiology, D
Modern Languages, B
Molecular Biology, D
Molecular Biophysics, D
Molecular Genetics, D
Molecular Pathogenesis, D
Multi-/Interdisciplinary Studies, B
Music, BMD
Music History, Literature, and Theory, B
Music Theory and Composition, B
Natural Resources Management/Development and Policy, B
Natural Resources and Conservation, B
Natural Sciences, B
Near and Middle Eastern Studies, BM
Neuroscience, D
Occupational Therapy/Therapist, MD
Operations Management and Supervision, B
Organizational Management, M
Painting, B
Philosophy, BD
Philosophy and Religious Studies, B
Photography, B
Physical Therapy/Therapist, D
Physics, BD

Physics Teacher Education, B
Planetary Astronomy and Science, D
Plant Biology, D
Political Science and Government, BMD
Pre-Dentistry Studies, B
Pre-Medicine/Pre-Medical Studies, B
Pre-Pharmacy Studies, B
Pre-Veterinary Studies, B
Printmaking, B
Psychology, BD
Public Health, MD
Public Policy Analysis, M
Regional Studies (U.S., Canadian, Foreign), B
Rehabilitation Sciences, D
Religion/Religious Studies, BM
Romance Languages, Literatures, and Linguistics, BMD
Russian Studies, B
Science Teacher Education/General Science Teacher Education, B
Science, Technology and Society, B
Sculpture, B
Secondary Education and Teaching, BM
Social Psychology, D
Social Science Teacher Education, B
Social Sciences, B
Social Studies Teacher Education, B
Social Work, MDO
Social and Philosophical Foundations of Education, B
Spanish Language Teacher Education, B
Spanish Language and Literature, BMD
Special Education and Teaching, M
Speech and Interpersonal Communication, D
Statistics, BMD
Supply Chain Management, M
Systematic Biology/Biological Systematics, D
Systems Engineering, B
Systems Science and Theory, B
Teacher Education and Professional Development, Specific Levels and Methods, B
Teacher Education, Multiple Levels, B
Theater, M
Theatre Literature, History and Criticism, B
Urban Design, M
Urban Studies/Affairs, B
Voice and Opera, B
Women's Studies, B
Writing, M

WEBSTER UNIVERSITY

Accounting, BM
Acting, B
Advertising, B
Advertising and Public Relations, M
Aerospace, Aeronautical and Astronautical Engineering, M
Animation, Interactive Technology, Video Graphics and Special Effects, B
Art History, Criticism and Conservation, BM
Art/Art Studies, General, B
Audiovisual Communications Technologies/Technicians, B
Biology/Biological Sciences, B
Business Administration and Management, B
Business Administration, Management and Operations, M
Cinematography and Film/Video Production, B
Communication Disorders, M
Communication Studies/Speech Communication and Rhetoric, B
Communication and Media Studies, M
Communication, Journalism and Related Programs, B
Composition, M
Computer Science, BM
Computer and Information Sciences, B
Corporate and Organizational Communication, M
Counseling Psychology, M
Dance, B
Digital Communication and Media/Multimedia, B
Directing and Theatrical Production, B
Drama and Dramatics/Theatre Arts, B
Dramatic/Theatre Arts and Stagecraft, B
Early Childhood Education and Teaching, B
Economics, B

Education, BMO
Educational Media/Instructional Technology, M
Educational Psychology, MO
Elementary Education and Teaching, B
Engineering Management, M
English Language and Literature, B
English/Language Arts Teacher Education, B
Environmental Policy and Resource Management, M
European Studies/Civilization, B
Film/Cinema Studies, B
Finance, B
Finance and Banking, M
Fine Arts and Art Studies, M
Fine/Studio Arts, B
Foreign Languages and Literatures, B
Forensic Science and Technology, M
French Language and Literature, B
German Language and Literature, B
Gerontology, M
Health Services Administration, M
History, B
Human Resources Development, M
Human Resources Management and Services, M
Human Resources Management/Personnel Administration, B
Human Services, M
Humanities/Humanistic Studies, B
Information Science/Studies, B
International Affairs, M
International Business/Trade/Commerce, M
International Relations and Affairs, B
International/Global Studies, B
Internet and Interactive Multimedia, M
Jazz/Jazz Studies, B
Journalism, B
Junior High/Intermediate/Middle School Education and Teaching, B
Kinesiology and Exercise Science, B
Law and Legal Studies, B
Legal and Justice Studies, M
Management, M
Management Information Systems and Services, M
Marketing, M
Marketing/Marketing Management, B
Mass Communication/Media Studies, B
Mathematics, B
Mathematics Teacher Education, M
Media Studies, M
Music, BM
Music Performance, B
Music Teacher Education, BM
Music Theory and Composition, B
Non-Profit/Public/Organizational Management, M
Nurse Anesthetist, M
Nursing, M
Nursing Administration, M
Nursing Education, M
Performance, M
Philosophy, B
Political Science and Government, B
Psychology, BM
Public Administration, M
Public Relations/Image Management, B
Reading Teacher Education, M
Religion/Religious Studies, B
Sacred Music, M
Science Teacher Education/General Science Teacher Education, B
Secondary Education and Teaching, B
Securities Services Administration/Management, M
Social Studies Teacher Education, M
Sociology, B
Spanish Language and Literature, B
Special Education and Teaching, BM
Women's Studies, B

WENTWORTH MILITARY ACADEMY AND COLLEGE

Liberal Arts and Sciences Studies and Humanities, A

WESTMINSTER COLLEGE

Accounting, B
Anthropology, B
Biochemistry, B

Biology/Biological Sciences, B
Business Administration and Management, B
Business/Corporate Communications, B
Chemistry, B
Computer Science, B
Economics, B
Elementary Education and Teaching, B
English Language and Literature, B
Environmental Sciences, B
Environmental Studies, B
French Language and Literature, B
History, B
International Business/Trade/Commerce, B
International Relations and Affairs, B
International/Global Studies, B
Junior High/Intermediate/Middle School Education
and Teaching, B
Kinesiology and Exercise Science, B
Management Information Systems and Services, B
Mathematics, B
Philosophy, B
Physical Education Teaching and Coaching, B
Physics, B
Political Science and Government, B
Pre-Law Studies, B
Psychology, B
Religion/Religious Studies, B
Secondary Education and Teaching, B
Sociology, B
Spanish Language and Literature, B
Sport and Fitness Administration/Management, B

WILLIAM JEWELL COLLEGE

Accounting, B
Art/Art Studies, General, B
Biochemistry, B
Biology/Biological Sciences, B
Business Administration and Management, B
Chemistry, B
Civil Engineering, B
Communication Studies/Speech Communication
and Rhetoric, B
Drama and Dramatics/Theatre Arts, B
Economics, B
Education, M
Elementary Education and Teaching, B
English Language and Literature, B
French Language and Literature, B
History, B
International Relations and Affairs, B
Liberal Arts and Sciences Studies and Humani-
ties, B
Mathematics, B
Molecular Biology, B
Multi-/Interdisciplinary Studies, B
Music, B
Music Performance, B
Music Teacher Education, B
Music Theory and Composition, B
Non-Profit/Public/Organizational Management, B
Parks, Recreation, Leisure and Fitness Studies, B
Philosophy, B
Philosophy and Religious Studies, B
Physical Education Teaching and Coaching, B
Physics, B
Political Science and Government, B
Psychology, B
Religion/Religious Studies, B
Religious/Sacred Music, B
Romance Languages, Literatures, and Linguistics, B
Secondary Education and Teaching, B
Spanish Language and Literature, B
Speech Teacher Education, B
Teacher Education, Multiple Levels, B
Web Page, Digital/Multimedia and Information Re-
sources Design, B

WILLIAM WOODS UNIVERSITY

Accounting, B
Advertising and Public Relations, M
American Sign Language (ASL), B
Art Teacher Education, B
Art/Art Studies, General, B
Athletic Training and Sports Medicine, B
Biology Teacher Education, B
Biology/Biological Sciences, B

Business Administration and Management, B
Communication Studies/Speech Communication
and Rhetoric, B
Criminal Justice/Safety Studies, B
Curriculum and Instruction, MO
Drama and Dramatics/Theatre Arts, B
Education, B
Educational Administration and Supervision, MO
Educational Leadership and Administration, D
Educational Media/Instructional Technology, M
Elementary Education and Teaching, B
English Language and Literature, B
English/Language Arts Teacher Education, B
Graphic Design, B
Health Services Administration, M
History, B
History Teacher Education, B
Horse Husbandry/Equine Science and Manage-
ment, B
Human Resources Development, M
Kinesiology and Exercise Science, B
Legal Assistant/Paralegal, B
Legal Professions and Studies, B
Liberal Arts and Sciences Studies and Humani-
ties, A
Management, M
Management Information Systems and Services, B
Marketing, M
Mathematics, B
Mathematics Teacher Education, B
Physical Education Teaching and Coaching, BM
Psychology, B
Secondary Education and Teaching, B
Sign Language Interpretation and Translation, B
Social Work, B
Special Education and Teaching, B
Sport and Fitness Administration/Management, B
Teacher Education and Professional Develop-
ment, Specific Subject Areas, B

Montana

AANIIIH NAKODA COLLEGE

American Indian/Native American Studies, A
Business/Commerce, A
Computer Technology/Computer Systems Technol-
ogy, A
Computer and Information Sciences, A
Early Childhood Education and Teaching, A
Elementary Education and Teaching, A
Health Services/Allied Health/Health Sciences, A
Human Services, A
Kindergarten/PreSchool Education and Teaching, A
Liberal Arts and Sciences Studies and Humani-
ties, A
Natural Resources Management/Development and
Policy, A
Psychology, A

BLACKFEET COMMUNITY COLLEGE

Business Administration and Management, A
Computer Science, A
Computer Systems Networking and Telecommunica-
tions, A
Construction Engineering Technology/Technician, A
Early Childhood Education and Teaching, A
Elementary Education and Teaching, A
Environmental Sciences, A
Forestry, A
General Studies, A
Hospitality Administration/Management, A
Human Resources Management/Personnel Adminis-
tration, A
Natural Resources Management/Development and
Policy, A
Office Management and Supervision, A
Pre-Nursing Studies, A
Small Business Administration/Management, A

CARROLL COLLEGE

Accounting, B
Applied Mathematics, B
Biochemistry, Biophysics and Molecular Biology, B
Biology Teacher Education, B
Biology/Biological Sciences, B

Business Administration and Management, AB
Chemistry, B
Chemistry Teacher Education, B
Civil Engineering, B
Classics and Classical Languages, Litera-
tures, and Linguistics, B
Community Health Services/Liaison/Counseling, B
Community Health and Preventive Medicine, B
Computer Science, AB
Computer and Information Sciences, B
Drama and Dramatics/Theatre Arts, B
Elementary Education and Teaching, B
Engineering Mechanics, B
Engineering Science, B
English Language and Literature, AB
English/Language Arts Teacher Education, B
Environmental Studies, B
Ethics, B
Finance, B
French Language and Literature, B
Health Services/Allied Health/Health Sciences, B
Health and Physical Education, B
History, B
History Teacher Education, B
International Relations and Affairs, B
Mathematics, B
Mathematics Teacher Education, B
Multi-/Interdisciplinary Studies, B
Philosophy, AB
Physical Education Teaching and Coaching, B
Physics, B
Political Science and Government, B
Psychology, B
Public Relations/Image Management, B
Secondary Education and Teaching, B
Social Science Teacher Education, B
Social Studies Teacher Education, B
Sociology, B
Spanish Language Teacher Education, B
Spanish Language and Literature, B
Speech Teacher Education, B
Teaching English as a Second or Foreign
Language/ESL Language Instructor, B
Theology/Theological Studies, B

CHIEF DULL KNIFE COLLEGE

Business Administration and Management, A
Liberal Arts and Sciences Studies and Humani-
ties, A
Office Management and Supervision, A

DAWSON COMMUNITY COLLEGE

Agricultural Business and Management, A
Business/Commerce, A
Child Care Provider/Assistant, A
Clinical/Medical Social Work, A
Computer and Information Sciences, A
Criminal Justice/Police Science, A
Liberal Arts and Sciences Studies and Humani-
ties, A
Music, A
Substance Abuse/Addiction Counseling, A
Welding Technology/Welder, A

FLATHEAD VALLEY COMMUNITY COL-LEGE

Accounting, A
Administrative Assistant and Secretarial Science, A
Business Administration and Management, A
Carpentry/Carpenter, A
Child Care and Support Services Management, A
Computer/Information Technology Services Adminis-
tration and Management, A
Criminal Justice/Law Enforcement Administration, A
Culinary Arts/Chef Training, A
Electrician, A
Emergency Medical Technology/Technician (EMT
Paramedic), A
Hospitality and Recreation Marketing Operations, A
Human Services, A
Liberal Arts and Sciences Studies and Humani-
ties, A
Medical Administrative Assistant/Secretary, A
Medical Insurance Coding Specialist/Coder, A
Medical Radiologic Technology/Science - Radiation
Therapist, A

Medical/Clinical Assistant, A
Metal and Jewelry Arts, A
Small Business Administration/Management, A
Substance Abuse/Addiction Counseling, A
Surgical Technology/Technologist, A
Survey Technology/Surveying, A
Web/Multimedia Management and Webmaster, A
Welding Technology/Welder, A
Wildlife and Wildlands Science and Management, A

FORT PECK COMMUNITY COLLEGE

Accounting, A
American Indian/Native American Studies, A
Art/Art Studies, General, A
Automobile/Automotive Mechanics
   Technology/Technician, A
Building/Construction Finishing, Manage-
   ment, and Inspection, A
Business Administration and Management, A
Business/Office Automation/Technology/Data En-
   try, A
Computer Systems Networking and Telecommunica-
   tions, A
Computer Technology/Computer Systems Technol-
   ogy, A
Early Childhood Education and Teaching, A
Education, A
Environmental Sciences, A
General Studies, A
Hazardous Materials Management and Waste
   Technology/Technician, A
Health/Medical Preparatory Programs, A
Human Services, A
Medical Insurance Coding Specialist/Coder, A
Psychology, A
Science Technologies/Technicians, A
Teacher Assistant/Aide, A

GREAT FALLS COLLEGE MONTANA STATE UNIVERSITY

Accounting Technology/Technician and Bookkeep-
   ing, A
Computer Systems Networking and Telecommunica-
   tions, A
Dental Hygiene/Hygienist, A
Emergency Medical Technology/Technician (EMT
   Paramedic), A
Entrepreneurship/Entrepreneurial Studies, A
Health Information/Medical Records
   Technology/Technician, A
Information Technology, A
Liberal Arts and Sciences Studies and Humani-
   ties, A
Medical/Clinical Assistant, A
Physical Therapist Assistant, A
Radiologic Technology/Science - Radiographer, A
Respiratory Care Therapy/Therapist, A
Surgical Technology/Technologist, A
Welding Technology/Welder, A

HELENA COLLEGE UNIVERSITY OF MONTANA

Accounting, A
Airframe Mechanics and Aircraft Maintenance
   Technology/Technician, A
Automobile/Automotive Mechanics
   Technology/Technician, A
Computer Programming/Programmer, A
Construction Engineering Technology/Technician, A
Fire Science/Firefighting, A
General Office Occupations and Clerical Services, A
General Studies, A
Legal Administrative Assistant/Secretary, A
Medical Office Assistant/Specialist, A
Small Business Administration/Management, A
Water Resources Engineering, A
Welding Technology/Welder, A

LITTLE BIG HORN COLLEGE

Biological and Physical Sciences, A
Business Administration and Management, A
Carpentry/Carpenter, A
Computer Science, A
Elementary Education and Teaching, A

Liberal Arts and Sciences Studies and Humanities, A
Mathematics, A

MILES COMMUNITY COLLEGE

Agricultural Business and Management, A
Agricultural Production Operations, A
Animal Health, A
Automotive Engineering Technology/Technician, A
Building/Property Maintenance and Management, A
Business/Commerce, A
Computer and Information Sciences, A
Computer and Information Systems Security, A
Construction Engineering Technology/Technician, A
Education, A
Electrical, Electronic and Communications Engineer-
   ing Technology/Technician, A
Elementary Education and Teaching, A
Engineering, A
Equestrian/Equine Studies, A
Insurance, A
Legal Administrative Assistant/Secretary, A
Liberal Arts and Sciences Studies and Humani-
   ties, A
Livestock Management, A
Medical Administrative Assistant/Secretary, A
Physical Education Teaching and Coaching, A
Sales, Distribution and Marketing Operations, A
Small Business Administration/Management, A
Special Education and Teaching, A
Web Page, Digital/Multimedia and Information Re-
   sources Design, A

MONTANA STATE UNIVERSITY

Accounting, M
Adult and Continuing Education and Teaching, MD
Aeronautics/Aviation/Aerospace Science and Tech-
   nology, A
Agricultural Business and Management, B
Agricultural Education, M
Agricultural Mechanization, B
Agricultural Sciences, MD
Agricultural Teacher Education, B
Agriculture, B
American Indian/Native American Studies, M
Animal Sciences, BMD
Anthropology, B
Architecture, M
Art History, Criticism and Conservation, M
Art/Art Studies, General, B
BioTechnology, B
Biochemistry, MD
Biological and Biomedical Sciences, D
Biology/Biological Sciences, B
Business/Commerce, B
Cell/Cellular Biology and Histology, B
Chemical Engineering, BMD
Chemistry, BMD
Cinematography and Film/Video Production, B
Civil Engineering, BMD
Computer Engineering, BD
Computer Science, BMD
Construction Engineering Technology/Technician, B
Construction Engineering and Management, M
Curriculum and Instruction, MD
Drafting and Design Technology/Technician, A
Ecology, MD
Economics, B
Education, MDO
Educational Leadership and Administration, MDO
Electrical Engineering, MD
Electrical, Electronics and Communications Engi-
   neering, B
Elementary Education and Teaching, B
Engineering, B
Engineering and Applied Sciences, D
English, M
English Language and Literature, B
Environmental Design/Architecture, B
Environmental Engineering
   Technology/Environmental Technology, MD
Environmental Sciences, BMD
Family and Consumer Sciences/Human Sciences, B
Film, Television, and Video Production, M
Fine Arts and Art Studies, M
Fine/Studio Arts, B

Fish, Game and Wildlife Management, MD
Foreign Languages and Literatures, B
Geology/Earth Science, B
Geosciences, MD
Health Education, M
Higher Education/Higher Education Administra-
   tion, MD
History, BMD
Home Economics Education, M
Horticultural Science, M
Human Development, M
Immunology, MD
Industrial Engineering, B
Industrial/Management Engineering, MD
Infectious Diseases, MD
Interior Design, A
Land Use Planning and
   Management/Development, B
Liberal Arts and Sciences Studies and Humani-
   ties, AB
Marketing/Marketing Management, B
Mathematics, BMD
Mathematics Teacher Education, M
Mechanical Engineering, BMD
Mechanical Engineering/Mechanical
   Technology/Technician, B
Mechanics, D
Medical Microbiology and Bacteriology, B
Microbiology, MD
Music, B
Music Teacher Education, B
Natural Resources and Conservation, BM
Neuroscience, MD
Nursing - Advanced Practice, MDO
Nursing Administration, M
Nursing Education, O
Philosophy, B
Physics, BMD
Plant Pathology/Phytopathology, M
Plant Sciences, BMD
Political Science and Government, B
Pre-Veterinary Studies, B
Psychiatric/Mental Health Nurse/Nursing, MD
Psychology, BM
Public Administration, M
Range Science and Management, MD
School Psychology, M
Science Teacher Education/General Science
   Teacher Education, B
Social Science Teacher Education, AB
Sociology, B
Sport and Fitness Administration/Management, B
Statistics, BMD
Technical Teacher Education, B
Vocational and Technical Education, M
Wildlife and Wildlands Science and Management, B

MONTANA STATE UNIVERSITY BILL-INGS

Accounting, B
Accounting Technology/Technician and Bookkeep-
   ing, A
Accounting and Related Services, A
Administrative Assistant and Secretarial Science, A
Advertising and Public Relations, M
Art Teacher Education, B
Art/Art Studies, General, B
Athletic Training and Sports Medicine, M
Autobody/Collision and Repair
   Technology/Technician, A
Automobile/Automotive Mechanics
   Technology/Technician, A
Biology Teacher Education, B
Biology/Biological Sciences, B
Business Administration and Management, AB
Business/Commerce, AB
Business/Managerial Economics, B
Business/Office Automation/Technology/Data En-
   try, A
Carpentry/Carpenter, A
Chemistry, B
Chemistry Teacher Education, B
Communication and Media Studies, M
Computer and Information Sciences, A
Computer and Information Sciences and Support
   Services, A

Counseling Psychology, M
Counselor Education/School Counseling and Guidance Services, M
Criminal Justice/Safety Studies, B
Curriculum and Instruction, M
Data Processing and Data Processing Technology/Technician, A
Diesel Mechanics Technology/Technician, A
Drafting and Design Technology/Technician, A
Drama and Dramatics/Theatre Arts, B
Education, ABMO
Educational Media/Instructional Technology, M
Elementary Education and Teaching, B
Emergency Medical Technology/Technician (EMT Paramedic), A
Energy Management and Systems Technology/Technician, A
English Language and Literature, B
English/Language Arts Teacher Education, B
Environmental Studies, B
Finance, B
Fire Protection and Safety Technology/Technician, A
General Studies, A
Health Information/Medical Records Administration/Administrator, A
Health Services Administration, M
Health Teacher Education, B
Health and Physical Education, B
Health/Health Care Administration/Management, B
Heating, Air Conditioning, Ventilation and Refrigeration Maintenance Technology/Technician, A
History, B
History Teacher Education, B
Human Resources Management/Personnel Administration, A
Interdisciplinary Studies, M
Liberal Arts and Sciences Studies and Humanities, AB
Marketing/Marketing Management, B
Mathematics, B
Mathematics Teacher Education, B
Medical Administrative Assistant/Secretary, A
Medical/Clinical Assistant, A
Multi-/Interdisciplinary Studies, B
Music, B
Music Teacher Education, B
Organizational Communication, B
Petroleum Technology/Technician, A
Physical Education Teaching and Coaching, B
Psychology, ABM
Public Administration, M
Public Relations/Image Management, B
Reading Teacher Education, M
Rehabilitation Counseling, M
Rehabilitation and Therapeutic Professions, B
Science Teacher Education/General Science Teacher Education, B
Secondary Education and Teaching, B
Sheet Metal Technology/Sheetworking, A
Social Science Teacher Education, B
Sociology, AB
Spanish Language Teacher Education, B
Spanish Language and Literature, B
Special Education and Teaching, ABM
Sport and Fitness Administration/Management, B
Surgical Technology/Technologist, A

MONTANA STATE UNIVERSITY–NORTHERN

Agricultural Mechanics and Equipment/Machine Technology, A
Agricultural Mechanization, B
Automobile/Automotive Mechanics Technology/Technician, AB
Biology/Biological Sciences, B
Business Administration and Management, B
Business Teacher Education, B
Business/Office Automation/Technology/Data Entry, A
Carpentry/Carpenter, A
Civil Engineering Technology/Technician, AB
Commercial and Advertising Art, AB
Community Organization and Advocacy, AB
Computer and Information Sciences, AB
Counselor Education/School Counseling and Guidance Services, M

Diesel Mechanics Technology/Technician, AB
Drafting and Design Technology/Technician, AB
Education, M
Elementary Education and Teaching, B
English/Language Arts Teacher Education, B
Graphic Design, AB
Health Teacher Education, B
Industrial Technology/Technician, AB
Liberal Arts and Sciences Studies and Humanities, B
Mathematics, B
Plumbing Technology/Plumber, A
Public Health Education and Promotion, B
Science Teacher Education/General Science Teacher Education, B
Social Science Teacher Education, B
Technology Teacher Education/Industrial Arts Teacher Education, B

MONTANA TECH OF THE UNIVERSITY OF MONTANA

Accounting Technology/Technician and Bookkeeping, A
Administrative Assistant and Secretarial Science, A
Automobile/Automotive Mechanics Technology/Technician, A
Biology/Biological Sciences, B
Business/Commerce, B
CAD/CADD Drafting and/or Design Technology/Technician, A
Carpentry/Carpenter, A
Chemistry, B
Civil Engineering Technology/Technician, A
Computer Science, B
Computer Software Engineering, B
Computer Systems Networking and Telecommunications, AB
Electrical Engineering, M
Electrical, Electronics and Communications Engineering, B
Engineering, B
Engineering and Applied Sciences, M
Environmental Control Technologies/Technicians, A
Environmental Engineering Technology/Environmental Technology, M
Environmental/Environmental Health Engineering, B
General Studies, B
Geochemistry, M
Geological Engineering, M
Geological/Geophysical Engineering, B
Geology/Earth Science, M
Geophysics Engineering, M
Geosciences, M
Health Informatics, O
Historic Preservation and Conservation, A
Hydrogeology, M
Industrial Hygiene, M
Industrial/Management Engineering, M
Interdisciplinary Studies, M
Liberal Arts and Sciences Studies and Humanities, B
Management Information Systems and Services, B
Materials Sciences, D
Mathematics, B
Medical Informatics, AB
Medical/Clinical Assistant, A
Metallurgical Engineering, BM
Mineral/Mining Engineering, M
Mining and Mineral Engineering, B
Multi-/Interdisciplinary Studies, A
Occupational Health and Industrial Hygiene, B
Petroleum Engineering, BM
Physical Sciences, B
Precision Metal Working, A
Project Management, M
Radiologic Technology/Science - Radiographer, A
Statistics, B
Technical Communication, M
Web/Multimedia Management and Webmaster, A

ROCKY MOUNTAIN COLLEGE

Accounting, BM
Accounting and Business/Management, B
Accounting and Related Services, B
Airline/Commercial/Professional Pilot and Flight Crew, B

Art Teacher Education, B
Art/Art Studies, General, B
Athletic Training and Sports Medicine, B
Aviation/Airway Management and Operations, B
Biology Teacher Education, B
Biology/Biological Sciences, B
Business Administration and Management, B
Chemistry, B
Communication Studies/Speech Communication and Rhetoric, B
Computer Science, B
Drama and Dramatics/Theatre Arts, B
Educational Leadership and Administration, M
Elementary Education and Teaching, B
English Language and Literature, B
English/Language Arts Teacher Education, B
Environmental Sciences, B
Environmental Studies, B
Equestrian/Equine Studies, B
Geology/Earth Science, B
Health Teacher Education, B
Health and Physical Education, B
History, B
History Teacher Education, B
Kinesiology and Exercise Science, B
Liberal Arts and Sciences Studies and Humanities, A
Management Science, B
Mathematics, B
Mathematics Teacher Education, B
Music, B
Music Performance, B
Music Teacher Education, B
Natural Resources Management/Development and Policy, B
Philosophy and Religious Studies, B
Physical Education Teaching and Coaching, B
Physician Assistant, M
Political Science and Government, B
Psychology, B
Psychology Teacher Education, B
Science Teacher Education/General Science Teacher Education, B
Secondary Education and Teaching, B
Small Business Administration/Management, B
Social Studies Teacher Education, B
Sociology, B
Sport and Fitness Administration/Management, B
Technical Theatre/Theatre Design and Technology, B

SALISH KOOTENAI COLLEGE

Administrative Assistant and Secretarial Science, A
American Indian/Native American Studies, A
Carpentry/Carpenter, A
Child Development, A
Computer Science, A
Dental Hygiene/Hygienist, A
Environmental Studies, AB
Forestry, A
Forestry Technology/Technician, A
Human Services, AB
Kindergarten/PreSchool Education and Teaching, A
Liberal Arts and Sciences Studies and Humanities, A
Natural Resources Management/Development and Policy, A
Natural Sciences, A

STONE CHILD COLLEGE

Administrative Assistant and Secretarial Science, A
Business Administration and Management, A
Computer Science, A
Human Services, A
Liberal Arts and Sciences Studies and Humanities, A

UNIVERSITY OF GREAT FALLS

Accounting, B
Accounting and Business/Management, B
Art Teacher Education, B
Art/Art Studies, General, B
Biology Teacher Education, B
Biology/Biological Sciences, B
Botany/Plant Biology, B
Business Administration and Management, B

Chemistry, B
Chemistry Teacher Education, B
Computer Graphics, B
Computer Programming/Programmer, B
Computer Science, B
Computer Software and Media Applications, B
Computer Systems Analysis/Analyst, B
Computer Systems Networking and Telecommunications, B
Computer and Information Sciences, B
Computer and Information Sciences and Support Services, B
Computer and Information Systems Security, B
Computer/Information Technology Services Administration and Management, B
Corrections, B
Corrections Administration, B
Corrections and Criminal Justice, B
Counseling Psychology, M
Criminal Justice/Law Enforcement Administration, B
Criminal Justice/Police Science, B
Criminal Justice/Safety Studies, B
Criminology, M
Early Childhood Education and Teaching, A
Education, M
Education/Teaching of the Gifted and Talented, B
Elementary Education and Teaching, B
English Language and Literature, B
English/Language Arts Teacher Education, B
Fine/Studio Arts, B
Forensic Science and Technology, B
Health Teacher Education, B
Health and Physical Education, B
Health/Health Care Administration/Management, B
History, B
History Teacher Education, B
Human Services, ABM
Information Science/Studies, B
Information Technology, B
Junior High/Intermediate/Middle School Education and Teaching, B
Kindergarten/PreSchool Education and Teaching, AB
Legal Assistant/Paralegal, AB
Library Science, B
Management Science, B
Marketing/Marketing Management, B
Mathematics, AB
Mathematics Teacher Education, B
Physical Education Teaching and Coaching, B
Political Science and Government, B
Psychology, B
Reading Teacher Education, B
Religion/Religious Studies, B
School Librarian/School Library Media Specialist, B
Science Teacher Education/General Science Teacher Education, B
Secondary Education and Teaching, BM
Social Science Teacher Education, B
Social Sciences, B
Social Studies Teacher Education, B
Sociology, B
Special Education and Teaching, B
Substance Abuse/Addiction Counseling, AB
System Administration/Administrator, B
System, Networking, and LAN/WAN Management/Manager, B
Teacher Education, Multiple Levels, B
Theology/Theological Studies, B
Web Page, Digital/Multimedia and Information Resources Design, B
Web/Multimedia Management and Webmaster, B

UNIVERSITY OF MONTANA

Accounting, BM
Accounting Technology/Technician and Bookkeeping, A
Administrative Assistant and Secretarial Science, B
African-American/Black Studies, B
American Government and Politics (United States), B
American Indian/Native American Studies, B
Analytical Chemistry, MD
Animal Behavior and Ethology, D
Anthropology, BMD
Apparel and Accessories Marketing Operations, A

Applied Mathematics, B
Art Education, M
Art History, Criticism and Conservation, BM
Art Teacher Education, B
Art/Art Studies, General, B
Asian Studies/Civilization, B
Astronomy, B
Audiology/Audiologist and Speech-Language Pathology/Pathologist, B
Biochemistry, BD
Biological and Biomedical Sciences, MD
Biology/Biological Sciences, B
Botany/Plant Biology, B
Business Administration, Management and Operations, M
Business Teacher Education, B
Business/Commerce, B
Cell Biology and Anatomy, D
Chemistry, BMD
Child and Family Studies, M
Chinese Language and Literature, B
Cinematography and Film/Video Production, B
City/Urban, Community and Regional Planning, B
Classics and Classical Languages, Literatures, and Linguistics, B
Clinical Laboratory Science/Medical Technology/Technologist, B
Clinical Psychology, MD
Clinical/Medical Laboratory Technician, B
Communication Studies/Speech Communication and Rhetoric, B
Communication and Media Studies, M
Community Health and Preventive Medicine, M
Computer Art and Design, M
Computer Science, BM
Computer and Information Sciences, B
Counseling Psychology, M
Counselor Education/School Counseling and Guidance Services, MDO
Criminology, M
Culinary Arts/Chef Training, A
Cultural Studies, M
Curriculum and Instruction, BMD
Dance, B
Developmental Biology and Embryology, D
Developmental Psychology, D
Drama and Dramatics/Theatre Arts, B
Drawing, B
East Asian Studies, B
Ecology, MD
Economics, BM
Education, BMDO
Educational Administration and Supervision, MDO
Electrical, Electronic and Communications Engineering Technology/Technician, A
Elementary Education and Teaching, B
English, M
English Education, M
English Language and Literature, B
Environmental Sciences, M
Environmental Studies, BM
Executive Assistant/Executive Secretary, A
Exercise and Sports Science, M
Experimental Psychology, D
Fashion Merchandising, B
Film, Television, and Video Production, M
Finance, B
Fine Arts and Art Studies, M
Fish, Game and Wildlife Management, MD
Foreign Languages and Literatures, B
Forest Management/Forest Resources Management, B
Forestry, BMD
French Language and Literature, BM
Geography, BM
Geology/Earth Science, BMD
Geosciences, MD
German Language and Literature, BM
Health Education, M
Health Teacher Education, B
Heavy Equipment Maintenance Technology/Technician, A
History, BMD
Immunology, D
Information Science/Studies, B
Information Technology, B

Inorganic Chemistry, MD
Interdisciplinary Studies, MD
International Business/Trade/Commerce, B
Internet and Interactive Multimedia, M
Japanese Language and Literature, B
Journalism, BM
Latin Language and Literature, B
Law and Legal Studies, ABD
Legal Administrative Assistant/Secretary, A
Legal Assistant/Paralegal, A
Legal and Justice Studies, M
Liberal Arts and Sciences Studies and Humanities, B
Linguistics, BM
Marketing/Marketing Management, B
Mathematics, BMD
Mathematics Teacher Education, BMD
Medical Administrative Assistant/Secretary, A
Medical Microbiology and Bacteriology, B
Medicinal and Pharmaceutical Chemistry, MD
Microbiology, D
Molecular Biology, D
Music, BM
Music Performance, B
Music Teacher Education, B
Natural Resources Management/Development and Policy, B
Natural Resources and Conservation, BM
Neuroscience, D
Organic Chemistry, MD
Parks, Recreation, Leisure and Fitness Studies, B
Performance, M
Pharmaceutical Sciences, MD
Pharmaceutics and Drug Design, B
Pharmacy, BMD
Pharmacy Technician/Assistant, B
Philosophy, BM
Photography, M
Physical Chemistry, MD
Physical Education Teaching and Coaching, BM
Physical Therapy/Therapist, BD
Physics, B
Political Science and Government, M
Pre-Law Studies, B
Pre-Medicine/Pre-Medical Studies, B
Pre-Pharmacy Studies, B
Psychology, BMDO
Public Administration, M
Public Health, MO
Radio and Television, B
Radiologic Technology/Science - Radiographer, A
Reading Teacher Education, B
Receptionist, A
Recreation and Park Management, M
Respiratory Care Therapy/Therapist, A
Rural Planning and Studies, M
Rural Sociology, M
Russian Language and Literature, B
Russian Studies, B
School Psychology, MDO
Science Teacher Education/General Science Teacher Education, B
Secondary Education and Teaching, B
Small Engine Mechanics and Repair Technology/Technician, A
Social Science Teacher Education, B
Social Sciences, B
Social Work, BM
Sociology, BM
Spanish Language and Literature, BM
Statistics, B
Surgical Technology/Technologist, A
Teaching English as a Second or Foreign Language/ESL Language Instructor, B
Theater, M
Toxicology, MD
Welding Technology/Welder, A
Wildlife and Wildlands Science and Management, B
Women's Studies, B
Writing, M
Zoology/Animal Biology, BMD

THE UNIVERSITY OF MONTANA WESTERN

Art Teacher Education, B
Art/Art Studies, General, B

Biology Teacher Education, B
Biology/Biological Sciences, B
Business Administration and Management, AB
Business Teacher Education, B
Early Childhood Education and Teaching, AB
Elementary Education and Teaching, B
English Language and Literature, B
English/Language Arts Teacher Education, B
Environmental Sciences, B
Equestrian/Equine Studies, AB
Health Teacher Education, B
Health and Physical Education, B
History, B
History Teacher Education, B
Liberal Arts and Sciences Studies and Humanities, AB
Mathematics, B
Mathematics Teacher Education, B
Multi-/Interdisciplinary Studies, A
Music Teacher Education, B
Physical Education Teaching and Coaching, B
Psychology, B
Science Teacher Education/General Science Teacher Education, B
Secondary Education and Teaching, B
Teacher Assistant/Aide, A
Teacher Education, Multiple Levels, B
Technology Teacher Education/Industrial Arts Teacher Education, B

Nebraska

BELLEVUE UNIVERSITY

Accounting, B
Art/Art Studies, General, B
Biology/Biological Sciences, B
Business Administration, Management and Operations, MD
Business/Commerce, B
Computer Programming/Programmer, B
Computer and Information Sciences, B
Corporate and Organizational Communication, M
Counselor Education/School Counseling and Guidance Services, M
Criminology, M
Customer Service Management, B
Education, B
Educational Media/Instructional Technology, M
Finance and Banking, M
Graphic Design, B
Health Services Administration, M
Health and Medical Administrative Services, B
History, B
Human Resources Management and Services, D
Human Resources Management/Personnel Administration, B
Human Services, M
Information Science/Studies, M
Information Technology, B
International Relations and Affairs, B
Law and Legal Studies, B
Management Information Systems and Services, BM
Military and Defense Studies, M
National Security, M
Organizational Management, M
Philosophy, B
Physical Education Teaching and Coaching, B
Project Management, M
Psychology, B
Public Administration, M
Securities Services Administration/Management, M
Selling Skills and Sales Operations, B
Social Sciences, B
Sociology, B
System Administration/Administrator, B

Web/Multimedia Management and Webmaster, B

BRYAN COLLEGE OF HEALTH SCIENCES

Nurse Anesthetist, M

CENTRAL COMMUNITY COLLEGE–COLUMBUS CAMPUS

Administrative Assistant and Secretarial Science, A
Agricultural Business and Management, A
Automobile/Automotive Mechanics Technology/Technician, A
Business Administration and Management, A
Child Care and Support Services Management, A
Commercial and Advertising Art, A
Computer and Information Sciences, A
Criminal Justice/Safety Studies, A
Drafting and Design Technology/Technician, A
Electrical, Electronic and Communications Engineering Technology/Technician, A
Liberal Arts and Sciences Studies and Humanities, A
Machine Tool Technology/Machinist, A
Marketing/Marketing Management, A
Medical/Clinical Assistant, A
Quality Control Technology/Technician, A
Welding Technology/Welder, A

CENTRAL COMMUNITY COLLEGE–GRAND ISLAND CAMPUS

Administrative Assistant and Secretarial Science, A
Automobile/Automotive Mechanics Technology/Technician, A
Business Administration and Management, A
Child Care and Support Services Management, A
Child Development, A
Clinical/Medical Social Work, A
Computer and Information Sciences, A
Criminal Justice/Safety Studies, A
Drafting and Design Technology/Technician, A
Electrical, Electronic and Communications Engineering Technology/Technician, A
Heating, Air Conditioning, Ventilation and Refrigeration Maintenance Technology/Technician, A
Legal Assistant/Paralegal, A
Liberal Arts and Sciences Studies and Humanities, A
Medical/Clinical Assistant, A
System Administration/Administrator, A
Welding Technology/Welder, A

CENTRAL COMMUNITY COLLEGE–HASTINGS CAMPUS

Administrative Assistant and Secretarial Science, A
Agricultural Business and Management, A
Applied Horticulture/Horticultural Operations, A
Autobody/Collision and Repair Technology/Technician, A
Automobile/Automotive Mechanics Technology/Technician, A
Building/Construction Finishing, Management, and Inspection, A
Business Administration and Management, A
Child Care and Support Services Management, A
Child Development, A
Clinical/Medical Laboratory Technician, A
Clinical/Medical Social Work, A
Commercial and Advertising Art, A
Construction Engineering Technology/Technician, A
Criminal Justice/Safety Studies, A
Dental Assisting/Assistant, A
Dental Hygiene/Hygienist, A
Diesel Mechanics Technology/Technician, A
Drafting and Design Technology/Technician, A
Electrical, Electronic and Communications Engineering Technology/Technician, A
Electrician, A
Graphic and Printing Equipment Operator Production, A
Health Information/Medical Records Technology/Technician, A
Heating, Air Conditioning, Ventilation and Refrigeration Maintenance Technology/Technician, A
Hotel/Motel Administration/Management, A

Industrial Mechanics and Maintenance Technology, A
Industrial Technology/Technician, A
Liberal Arts and Sciences Studies and Humanities, A
Library Assistant/Technician, A
Logistics and Materials Management, A
Machine Tool Technology/Machinist, A
Medical/Clinical Assistant, A
Quality Control Technology/Technician, A
Radio and Television Broadcasting Technology/Technician, A
Restaurant, Culinary, and Catering Management/Manager, A
Truck and Bus Driver/Commercial Vehicle Operation, A
Vehicle and Vehicle Parts and Accessories Marketing Operations, A
Welding Technology/Welder, A

CHADRON STATE COLLEGE

Art Teacher Education, B
Art/Art Studies, General, B
Biology Teacher Education, B
Biology/Biological Sciences, B
Business Administration and Management, B
Business Administration, Management and Operations, M
Business Education, M
Business Teacher Education, B
Chemistry, B
Chemistry Teacher Education, B
Communication Studies/Speech Communication and Rhetoric, B
Corrections and Criminal Justice, B
Counselor Education/School Counseling and Guidance Services, M
Drama and Dance Teacher Education, B
Drama and Dramatics/Theatre Arts, B
Early Childhood Education and Teaching, B
Education, MO
Educational Administration and Supervision, MO
Elementary Education and Teaching, BM
English Education, M
English Language and Literature, B
English/Language Arts Teacher Education, B
Family and Consumer Sciences/Home Economics Teacher Education, B
Family and Consumer Sciences/Human Sciences, B
Health/Medical Preparatory Programs, B
History, B
History Teacher Education, B
Industrial Production Technologies/Technicians, B
Information Science/Studies, B
Junior High/Intermediate/Middle School Education and Teaching, B
Kindergarten/PreSchool Education and Teaching, B
Library Science, B
Mathematics, B
Mathematics Teacher Education, B
Multi-/Interdisciplinary Studies, B
Music, B
Music Teacher Education, B
Parks, Recreation, Leisure and Fitness Studies, B
Physical Education Teaching and Coaching, B
Physical Sciences, B
Physics, B
Physics Teacher Education, B
Psychology, B
Range Science and Management, B
School Librarian/School Library Media Specialist, B
Science Teacher Education/General Science Teacher Education, B
Secondary Education and Teaching, M
Social Studies Teacher Education, BM
Social Work, B
Spanish Language Teacher Education, B
Spanish Language and Literature, B
Special Education and Teaching, B
Technology Teacher Education/Industrial Arts Teacher Education, B

CLARKSON COLLEGE

Business Administration and Management, B
Nursing, MO
Nursing - Adult, MO

Nursing - Advanced Practice, MO
Nursing Administration, MO
Nursing Education, MO
Physical Therapy/Therapist, A
Radiologic Technology/Science - Radiographer, A

COLLEGE OF SAINT MARY

Art Teacher Education, B
Art/Art Studies, General, B
Biology Teacher Education, B
Biology/Biological Sciences, B
Business Administration and Management, AB
Business Teacher Education, B
Chemistry, B
Chemistry Teacher Education, B
Clinical Laboratory Science/Medical
    Technology/Technologist, B
Early Childhood Education and Teaching, AB
Education, BM
Educational Leadership and Administration, M
Educational Measurement and Evaluation, M
Elementary Education and Teaching, B
English Language and Literature, B
English as a Second Language, M
English/Language Arts Teacher Education, B
Health Education, D
Humanities/Humanistic Studies, B
Legal Assistant/Paralegal, AB
Liberal Arts and Sciences Studies and Humani-
    ties, B
Mathematics, B
Mathematics Teacher Education, B
Natural Sciences, B
Nursing, M
Occupational Therapy/Therapist, M
Organizational Management, M
Psychology, B
Rehabilitation and Therapeutic Professions, B
Science Teacher Education/General Science
    Teacher Education, B
Secondary Education and Teaching, B
Social Science Teacher Education, B
Social Sciences, B
Spanish Language Teacher Education, B
Teacher Education, Multiple Levels, B
Theology/Theological Studies, B

CONCORDIA UNIVERSITY, NEBRASKA

Accounting, B
Art Teacher Education, B
Art/Art Studies, General, B
Behavioral Sciences, B
Biology Teacher Education, B
Biology/Biological Sciences, B
Business Administration and Management, B
Business Teacher Education, B
Business/Commerce, B
Business/Corporate Communications, B
Chemistry, B
Chemistry Teacher Education, B
Communication Studies/Speech Communication
    and Rhetoric, B
Computer Science, B
Computer and Information Sciences, B
Corrections and Criminal Justice, B
Drama and Dramatics/Theatre Arts, B
Early Childhood Education and Teaching, BM
Education, BM
Educational Administration and Supervision, M
Elementary Education and Teaching, BM
English Language and Literature, B
English/Language Arts Teacher Education, B
Environmental Sciences, B
Environmental Studies, B
Fine/Studio Arts, B
Foreign Language Teacher Education, B
Geography, B
Geography Teacher Education, B
Graphic Design, B
Health Teacher Education, B
Health and Physical Education, B
History, B
History Teacher Education, B
International/Global Studies, B
Junior High/Intermediate/Middle School Education
    and Teaching, B

Kinesiology and Exercise Science, B
Management Information Systems and Services, B
Marketing/Marketing Management, B
Mathematics, B
Mathematics Teacher Education, B
Multi-/Interdisciplinary Studies, B
Music, B
Music Teacher Education, B
Natural Sciences, B
Organizational Communication, B
Pastoral Studies/Counseling, BM
Physical Education Teaching and Coaching, B
Physical Sciences, B
Physics, B
Physics Teacher Education, B
Pre-Dentistry Studies, B
Pre-Law Studies, B
Pre-Medicine/Pre-Medical Studies, B
Pre-Nursing Studies, B
Pre-Pharmacy Studies, B
Pre-Theology/Pre-Ministerial Studies, B
Pre-Veterinary Studies, B
Psychology, B
Psychology Teacher Education, B
Reading Teacher Education, BM
Religious Education, BM
Religious/Sacred Music, B
Science Teacher Education/General Science
    Teacher Education, B
Secondary Education and Teaching, BM
Social Science Teacher Education, B
Sociology, B
Spanish Language Teacher Education, B
Spanish Language and Literature, B
Special Education and Teaching, B
Sport and Fitness Administration/Management, B
Teacher Education and Professional Develop-
    ment, Specific Subject Areas, B
Teacher Education, Multiple Levels, B
Teaching English as a Second or Foreign
    Language/ESL Language Instructor, B
Theology/Theological Studies, B
Visual and Performing Arts, B

CREATIVE CENTER

Graphic Design, AB

CREIGHTON UNIVERSITY

Accounting, B
Allied Health and Medical Assisting Services, MD
Allopathic Medicine, D
American/United States Studies/Civilization, B
Anatomy, M
Anthropology, BM
Art/Art Studies, General, B
Biological and Biomedical Sciences, MD
Biology/Biological Sciences, B
Business Administration and Management, B
Business Administration, Management and Opera-
    tions, M
Chemistry, B
Classics and Classical Languages, Litera-
    tures, and Linguistics, B
Communication Studies/Speech Communication
    and Rhetoric, B
Community Psychology, M
Computer Science, AB
Conflict Resolution and Mediation/Peace Stud-
    ies, MO
Counselor Education/School Counseling and Guid-
    ance Services, M
Dentistry, D
Drama and Dramatics/Theatre Arts, B
East Asian Studies, M
Economics, B
Education, MD
Educational Leadership and Administration, MD
Elementary Education and Teaching, BM
Emergency Medical Services, M
Emergency Medical Technology/Technician (EMT
    Paramedic), AB
Energy Management and Systems
    Technology/Technician, B
English, M
English Language and Literature, B
Environmental Sciences, B

Finance, B
Fine/Studio Arts, B
French Language and Literature, B
German Language and Literature, B
Gerontological Nursing, MD
Graphic Design, B
Health/Health Care Administration/Management, B
History, B
Immunology, MD
Information Technology, B
International Affairs, M
International Business/Trade/Commerce, B
International Relations and Affairs, B
Journalism, B
Kinesiology and Exercise Science, B
Law and Legal Studies, MDO
Marketing/Marketing Management, B
Maternal/Child Health and Neonatal
    Nurse/Nursing, MDO
Mathematics, AB
Medical Microbiology and Bacteriology, MD
Medical Radiologic Technology/Science - Radiation
    Therapist, B
Music, B
Nursing, MDO
Nursing - Adult, MDO
Nursing - Advanced Practice, MDO
Nursing Administration, MD
Occupational Therapy/Therapist, D
Organizational Communication, A
Organizational Management, M
Peace Studies and Conflict Resolution, B
Pediatric Nurse/Nursing, MDO
Pharmaceutical Sciences, B
Pharmacology, MD
Pharmacy, D
Philosophy, B
Physical Therapy/Therapist, D
Physics, BM
Political Science and Government, B
Psychology, B
Secondary Education and Teaching, BM
Social Work, B
Sociology, B
Spanish Language and Literature, B
Special Education and Teaching, M
Theology and Religious Vocations, M
Theology/Theological Studies, AB
Western European Studies, M
Writing, M

DOANE UNIVERSITY

Accounting, B
Art/Art Studies, General, B
Biochemistry, B
Biology/Biological Sciences, B
Business Administration and Management, B
Business Administration, Management and Opera-
    tions, M
Business Teacher Education, B
Chemistry, B
Computer Science, B
Computer and Information Sciences, B
Counselor Education/School Counseling and Guid-
    ance Services, M
Curriculum and Instruction, M
Economics, B
Education, M
Educational Leadership and Administration, M
Elementary Education and Teaching, B
Engineering Physics, B
English Language and Literature, B
Environmental Studies, B
French Language and Literature, B
German Language and Literature, B
Graphic Design, B
Health and Physical Education, B
History, B
Human Services, B
Information Science/Studies, B
International/Global Studies, B
Journalism, B
Law and Legal Studies, B
Mathematics, B
Music, B
Natural Sciences, B

Philosophy, B
Physical Education Teaching and Coaching, B
Physical Sciences, B
Physics, B
Political Science and Government, B
Pre-Theology/Pre-Ministerial Studies, B
Psychology, B
Public Administration, B
Religion/Religious Studies, B
Science Teacher Education/General Science
    Teacher Education, B
Social Sciences, B
Sociology, B
Spanish Language and Literature, B
Special Education and Teaching, B
Teaching English as a Second or Foreign
    Language/ESL Language Instructor, B
Technical Theatre/Theatre Design and Technol-
    ogy, B

GRACE UNIVERSITY

Accounting, B
Agricultural Business and Management, B
Bible/Biblical Studies, AB
Broadcast Journalism, B
Business Administration and Management, B
Business Teacher Education, B
Communication Studies/Speech Communication
    and Rhetoric, B
Computer Programming/Programmer, B
Computer Science, B
Computer and Information Sciences, B
Counseling Psychology, M
Divinity/Ministry (BD, MDiv.), B
Elementary Education and Teaching, B
Junior High/Intermediate/Middle School Education
    and Teaching, B
Liberal Arts and Sciences Studies and Humani-
    ties, AB
Marriage and Family Therapy/Counseling, B
Missions/Missionary Studies and Missiology, B
Music, AB
Music Teacher Education, B
Music Theory and Composition, B
Pastoral Studies/Counseling, BM
Piano and Organ, B
Pre-Theology/Pre-Ministerial Studies, B
Psychology, B
Religious Education, B
Religious/Sacred Music, B
Secondary Education and Teaching, B
Social Science Teacher Education, B
Teacher Education, Multiple Levels, B
Theology and Religious Vocations, M
Voice and Opera, B
Web/Multimedia Management and Webmaster, B
Youth Ministry, B

HASTINGS COLLEGE

Accounting, B
Advertising, B
Agricultural Business and Management, B
Art History, Criticism and Conservation, B
Art Teacher Education, B
Art/Art Studies, General, B
Biology Teacher Education, B
Biology/Biological Sciences, B
Biopsychology, B
Broadcast Journalism, B
Business Administration and Management, B
Business Teacher Education, B
Chemistry, B
Chemistry Teacher Education, B
Communication Studies/Speech Communication
    and Rhetoric, B
Communications Technology/Technician, B
Comparative Literature, B
Computer Science, B
Computer and Information Sciences, B
Construction Management, B
Corrections and Criminal Justice, B
Drama and Dance Teacher Education, B
Drama and Dramatics/Theatre Arts, B
Early Childhood Education and Teaching, B
Economics, B
Education, BM

Elementary Education and Teaching, B
English Language and Literature, B
English/Language Arts Teacher Education, B
Foreign Language Teacher Education, B
Foreign Languages and Literatures, B
German Language Teacher Education, B
German Language and Literature, B
Health and Physical Education, B
Health/Health Care Administration/Management, B
History, B
History Teacher Education, B
Human Resources Management/Personnel Adminis-
    tration, B
Human Services, B
International Relations and Affairs, B
Journalism, B
Kinesiology and Exercise Science, B
Liberal Arts and Sciences Studies and Humani-
    ties, B
Marketing/Marketing Management, B
Mass Communication/Media Studies, B
Mathematics, B
Mathematics Teacher Education, B
Music, B
Music History, Literature, and Theory, B
Music Pedagogy, B
Music Performance, B
Music Teacher Education, B
Parks, Recreation and Leisure Facilities Manage-
    ment, B
Philosophy, B
Physical Education Teaching and Coaching, B
Physics, B
Physics Teacher Education, B
Piano and Organ, B
Political Science and Government, B
Pre-Dentistry Studies, B
Pre-Law Studies, B
Pre-Medicine/Pre-Medical Studies, B
Pre-Veterinary Studies, B
Psychology, B
Public Administration, B
Public Relations/Image Management, B
Radio and Television, B
Religion/Religious Studies, B
Science Teacher Education/General Science
    Teacher Education, B
Secondary Education and Teaching, B
Social Science Teacher Education, B
Social Studies Teacher Education, B
Sociology, B
Spanish Language Teacher Education, B
Spanish Language and Literature, B
Special Education and Teaching, B
Speech Teacher Education, B
Sport and Fitness Administration/Management, B
Violin, Viola, Guitar and Other Stringed Instru-
    ments, B
Voice and Opera, B

KAPLAN UNIVERSITY, LINCOLN

Accounting, A
Business Administration and Management, AB
Computer and Information Sciences, A
Criminal Justice/Law Enforcement Administra-
    tion, AB
Information Technology, B
Legal Assistant/Paralegal, A
Medical/Clinical Assistant, A

KAPLAN UNIVERSITY, OMAHA

Accounting, AB
Business Administration and Management, AB
Computer and Information Sciences, A
Criminal Justice/Law Enforcement Administra-
    tion, AB
Information Technology, B
Legal Assistant/Paralegal, A
Medical/Clinical Assistant, A

LITTLE PRIEST TRIBAL COLLEGE

American Indian/Native American Studies, A
Business/Commerce, A
Computer and Information Sciences, A
Health Services/Allied Health/Health Sciences, A

Liberal Arts and Sciences Studies and Humani-
    ties, A

METROPOLITAN COMMUNITY COL-
LEGE

Accounting, A
Administrative Assistant and Secretarial Science, A
Architectural Engineering Technology/Technician, A
Automobile/Automotive Mechanics
    Technology/Technician, A
Business Administration and Management, A
Child Development, A
Civil Engineering Technology/Technician, A
Commercial and Advertising Art, A
Computer Programming/Programmer, A
Construction Engineering Technology/Technician, A
Criminal Justice/Police Science, A
Culinary Arts/Chef Training, A
Drafting and Design Technology/Technician, A
Electrical, Electronic and Communications Engineer-
    ing Technology/Technician, A
Graphic and Printing Equipment Operator Produc-
    tion, A
Heating, Air Conditioning, Ventilation and Refrigera-
    tion Maintenance Technology/Technician, A
Heavy Equipment Maintenance
    Technology/Technician, A
Human Services, A
Interior Design, A
Kindergarten/PreSchool Education and Teaching, A
Law and Legal Studies, A
Legal Administrative Assistant/Secretary, A
Legal Assistant/Paralegal, A
Liberal Arts and Sciences Studies and Humani-
    ties, A
Mental Health Counseling/Counselor, A
Ornamental Horticulture, A
Photography, A
Respiratory Care Therapy/Therapist, A
Surgical Technology/Technologist, A
Welding Technology/Welder, A

MID-PLAINS COMMUNITY COLLEGE

Administrative Assistant and Secretarial Science, A
Autobody/Collision and Repair
    Technology/Technician, A
Automobile/Automotive Mechanics
    Technology/Technician, A
Building/Construction Finishing, Manage-
    ment, and Inspection, A
Business Administration and Management, A
Clinical/Medical Laboratory Technician, A
Commercial and Advertising Art, A
Computer and Information Sciences, A
Construction Engineering Technology/Technician, A
Dental Assisting/Assistant, A
Diesel Mechanics Technology/Technician, A
Fire Science/Firefighting, A
Heating, Air Conditioning, Ventilation and Refrigera-
    tion Maintenance Technology/Technician, A
Liberal Arts and Sciences Studies and Humani-
    ties, A
Transportation and Materials Moving, A
Welding Technology/Welder, A

MIDLAND UNIVERSITY

Accounting, AB
Administrative Assistant and Secretarial Science, B
Art Teacher Education, B
Art/Art Studies, General, B
Athletic Training and Sports Medicine, B
Behavioral Sciences, B
Biological and Physical Sciences, B
Biology/Biological Sciences, B
Broadcast Journalism, B
Business Administration and Management, B
Business Teacher Education, B
Chemistry, B
Community Organization and Advocacy, A
Computer Programming/Programmer, AB
Computer Science, B
Criminal Justice/Law Enforcement Administration, B
Criminology, B
Drama and Dramatics/Theatre Arts, B
Economics, B
Education, B

Elementary Education and Teaching, B
English Language and Literature, B
Environmental Studies, B
History, B
Human Services, B
Humanities/Humanistic Studies, B
Journalism, B
Junior High/Intermediate/Middle School Education
    and Teaching, B
Kindergarten/PreSchool Education and Teach-
    ing, AB
Legal Administrative Assistant/Secretary, A
Liberal Arts and Sciences Studies and Humani-
    ties, B
Management Information Systems and Services, B
Marketing/Marketing Management, B
Mass Communication/Media Studies, B
Mathematics, B
Medical Administrative Assistant/Secretary, A
Music, B
Music Teacher Education, B
Natural Sciences, B
Parks, Recreation, Leisure and Fitness Studies, B
Physical Education Teaching and Coaching, B
Physical Sciences, B
Pre-Dentistry Studies, B
Pre-Law Studies, B
Pre-Medicine/Pre-Medical Studies, B
Pre-Veterinary Studies, B
Psychology, B
Religion/Religious Studies, B
Respiratory Care Therapy/Therapist, AB
Science Teacher Education/General Science
    Teacher Education, B
Secondary Education and Teaching, B
Social Sciences, B
Sociology, B
Speech Teacher Education, B
Teacher Education, Multiple Levels, B
Tourism and Travel Services Management, A

MYOTHERAPY INSTITUTE

Massage Therapy/Therapeutic Massage, A

NEBRASKA CHRISTIAN COLLEGE

Divinity/Ministry (BD, MDiv.), AB
Pastoral Studies/Counseling, B
Religion/Religious Studies, B
Religious/Sacred Music, AB
Sign Language Interpretation and Translation, B
Theology/Theological Studies, B

NEBRASKA COLLEGE OF TECHNICAL AGRICULTURE

Agricultural Business and Management, A
Agricultural Production Operations, A
Applied Horticulture/Horticultural Operations, A
Veterinary/Animal Health Technology/Technician and
    Veterinary Assistant, A

NEBRASKA INDIAN COMMUNITY COL-LEGE

American Indian/Native American Studies, A
Building/Construction Finishing, Manage-
    ment, and Inspection, A
Business Administration and Management, A
Carpentry/Carpenter, A
Child Care and Support Services Management, A
Corrections and Criminal Justice, A
Data Entry/Microcomputer Applications, A
Early Childhood Education and Teaching, A
Human Services, A
Information Technology, A
Liberal Arts and Sciences Studies and Humani-
    ties, A
Natural Resources and Conservation, A
Social Work, A

NEBRASKA METHODIST COLLEGE

Allied Health and Medical Assisting Services, A
Cardiovascular Technology/Technologist, A
Diagnostic Medical Sonography/Sonographer and
    Ultrasound Technician, A
Health Promotion, M
Health Services Administration, M

Health/Health Care Administration/Management, B
Nursing, M
Nursing Administration, M
Nursing Education, M
Physical Therapist Assistant, A
Radiologic Technology/Science - Radiographer, AB
Respiratory Care Therapy/Therapist, AB
Surgical Technology/Technologist, A

NEBRASKA WESLEYAN UNIVERSITY

Accounting, B
Acting, B
Art/Art Studies, General, B
Athletic Training and Sports Medicine, B
Biochemistry, Biophysics and Molecular Biology, B
Biology/Biological Sciences, B
Biopsychology, B
Business Administration and Management, B
Business, Management, Marketing, and Related
    Support Services, B
Chemistry, B
Chemistry Teacher Education, B
Communication Studies/Speech Communication
    and Rhetoric, B
Directing and Theatrical Production, B
Drama and Dramatics/Theatre Arts, B
Dramatic/Theatre Arts and Stagecraft, B
Economics, B
English Language and Literature, B
English/Language Arts Teacher Education, B
Forensic Science and Technology, M
French Language and Literature, B
German Language and Literature, B
History, BM
International Business/Trade/Commerce, B
International/Global Studies, B
Junior High/Intermediate/Middle School Education
    and Teaching, B
Kinesiology and Exercise Science, B
Mathematics, B
Music, B
Music Performance, B
Music Teacher Education, B
Nursing, M
Philosophy, B
Physical Education Teaching and Coaching, B
Physics, B
Political Communication, B
Political Science and Government, B
Psychology, B
Religion/Religious Studies, B
Science Teacher Education/General Science
    Teacher Education, B
Social Science Teacher Education, B
Social Work, B
Sociology, B
Spanish Language and Literature, B
Special Education and Teaching, B
Sport and Fitness Administration/Management, B

NORTHEAST COMMUNITY COLLEGE

Accounting, A
Administrative Assistant and Secretarial Science, A
Agribusiness, A
Agricultural Mechanics and Equipment/Machine
    Technology, A
Agricultural Mechanization, A
Agriculture, A
Agriculture, Agriculture Operations and Related Sci-
    ences, A
Agronomy and Crop Science, A
Animal Sciences, A
Applied Horticulture/Horticultural Business Ser-
    vices, A
Architectural Drafting and Architectural
    CAD/CADD, A
Art/Art Studies, General, A
Autobody/Collision and Repair
    Technology/Technician, A
Automobile/Automotive Mechanics
    Technology/Technician, A
Banking and Financial Support Services, A
Biology/Biological Sciences, A
Building/Construction Finishing, Manage-
    ment, and Inspection, A
Business Administration and Management, A

Business Operations Support and Secretarial Ser-
    vices, A
Chemistry, A
Computer Programming/Programmer, A
Computer Science, A
Computer and Information Sciences, A
Computer and Information Sciences and Support
    Services, A
Corrections, A
Criminal Justice/Police Science, A
Culinary Arts/Chef Training, A
Dairy Science, A
Diesel Mechanics Technology/Technician, A
Drama and Dramatics/Theatre Arts, A
Early Childhood Education and Teaching, A
Education, A
Electrician, A
Electromechanical Technology/Electromechanical
    Engineering Technology, A
Elementary Education and Teaching, A
Emergency Medical Technology/Technician (EMT
    Paramedic), A
Energy Management and Systems
    Technology/Technician, A
Engineering, A
English Language and Literature, A
Entrepreneurship/Entrepreneurial Studies, A
Farm/Farm and Ranch Management, A
Finance and Financial Management Services, A
Foodservice Systems
    Administration/Management, A
General Office Occupations and Clerical Services, A
General Studies, A
Graphic Design, A
Health Aide, A
Health and Medical Administrative Services, A
Health and Physical Education, A
Health/Medical Preparatory Programs, A
Heating, Air Conditioning, Ventilation and Refrigera-
    tion Maintenance Technology/Technician, A
Industrial Mechanics and Maintenance Technol-
    ogy, A
International Business/Trade/Commerce, A
Journalism, A
Liberal Arts and Sciences Studies and Humani-
    ties, A
Library Assistant/Technician, A
Lineworker, A
Marketing/Marketing Management, A
Mass Communication/Media Studies, A
Mathematics, A
Medical Administrative Assistant/Secretary, A
Medical Insurance Coding Specialist/Coder, A
Medical Radiologic Technology/Science - Radiation
    Therapist, A
Medium/Heavy Vehicle and Truck
    Technology/Technician, A
Merchandising and Buying Operations, A
Music Performance, A
Music Teacher Education, A
Office Management and Supervision, A
Physical Therapist Assistant, A
Physics, A
Pre-Dentistry Studies, A
Pre-Law Studies, A
Pre-Medicine/Pre-Medical Studies, A
Pre-Pharmacy Studies, A
Pre-Veterinary Studies, A
Psychology, A
Radio and Television Broadcasting
    Technology/Technician, A
Real Estate, A
Recording Arts Technology/Technician, A
Secondary Education and Teaching, A
Social Sciences, A
Surgical Technology/Technologist, A
Veterinary/Animal Health Technology/Technician and
    Veterinary Assistant, A
Welding Technology/Welder, A

PERU STATE COLLEGE

Accounting, B
Art Teacher Education, B
Art/Art Studies, General, B
Biological and Physical Sciences, B
Biology Teacher Education, B

Biology/Biological Sciences, B
Biomedical Sciences, B
Business Administration and Management, B
Business Teacher Education, B
Business, Management, Marketing, and Related
  Support Services, B
Chemistry, B
Chemistry Teacher Education, B
Clinical Laboratory Science/Medical
  Technology/Technologist, B
Commercial and Advertising Art, B
Criminal Justice/Law Enforcement Administration, B
Curriculum and Instruction, M
Design and Applied Arts, B
Early Childhood Education and Teaching, B
Economics, M
Education, BM
Elementary Education and Teaching, B
English Language and Literature, B
English/Language Arts Teacher Education, B
Entrepreneurship/Entrepreneurial Studies, M
Graphic Design, B
Health Teacher Education, B
History, B
History Teacher Education, B
Junior High/Intermediate/Middle School Education
  and Teaching, B
Kindergarten/PreSchool Education and Teaching, B
Liberal Arts and Sciences Studies and Humani-
  ties, B
Management Information Systems and Services, B
Marketing/Marketing Management, B
Mathematics, B
Mathematics Teacher Education, B
Music, B
Music Performance, B
Music Teacher Education, B
Natural Resources and Conservation, B
Natural Sciences, B
Nuclear Medical Technology/Technologist, B
Organizational Management, M
Physical Education Teaching and Coaching, B
Physician Assistant, B
Pre-Dentistry Studies, B
Pre-Law Studies, B
Pre-Medicine/Pre-Medical Studies, B
Pre-Nursing Studies, B
Pre-Pharmacy Studies, B
Pre-Veterinary Studies, B
Psychology, B
Science Teacher Education/General Science
  Teacher Education, B
Secondary Education and Teaching, B
Social Science Teacher Education, B
Social Sciences, B
Special Education and Teaching, B
Voice and Opera, B
Wildlife and Wildlands Science and Management, B

ST. GREGORY THE GREAT SEMINARY

Philosophy, B

SOUTHEAST COMMUNITY COL-
LEGE, BEATRICE CAMPUS

Agricultural Business and Management, A
Business Administration and Management, A
Criminal Justice/Law Enforcement Administration, A
General Office Occupations and Clerical Services, A
Pharmacy Technician/Assistant, A

SOUTHEAST COMMUNITY COL-
LEGE, LINCOLN CAMPUS

Administrative Assistant and Secretarial Science, A
Automobile/Automotive Mechanics
  Technology/Technician, A
Business Administration and Management, A
Child Care and Support Services Management, A
Clinical Laboratory Science/Medical
  Technology/Technologist, A
Clinical/Medical Laboratory Technician, A
Clinical/Medical Social Work, A
Commercial and Advertising Art, A
Computer and Information Sciences, A
Criminal Justice/Safety Studies, A
Drafting and Design Technology/Technician, A

Electrical, Electronic and Communications Engineer-
  ing Technology/Technician, A
Emergency Medical Technology/Technician (EMT
  Paramedic), A
Fire Science/Firefighting, A
Health/Health Care Administration/Management, A
Liberal Arts and Sciences Studies and Humani-
  ties, A
Medical Radiologic Technology/Science - Radiation
  Therapist, A
Physical Therapist Assistant, A
Respiratory Care Therapy/Therapist, A
Restaurant, Culinary, and Catering
  Management/Manager, A
Surgical Technology/Technologist, A
System Administration/Administrator, A
Welding Technology/Welder, A

SOUTHEAST COMMUNITY COL-
LEGE, MILFORD CAMPUS

Architectural Engineering Technology/Technician, A
Autobody/Collision and Repair
  Technology/Technician, A
Automobile/Automotive Mechanics
  Technology/Technician, A
Building/Construction Finishing, Manage-
  ment, and Inspection, A
Business Administration and Management, A
Civil Engineering Technology/Technician, A
Diesel Mechanics Technology/Technician, A
Electrical, Electronic and Communications Engineer-
  ing Technology/Technician, A
Energy Management and Systems
  Technology/Technician, A
Heating, Air Conditioning, Ventilation and Refrigera-
  tion Maintenance Technology/Technician, A
Machine Tool Technology/Machinist, A
Manufacturing Engineering, A
Quality Control Technology/Technician, A
System Administration/Administrator, A

UNION COLLEGE

Accounting, AB
Art Teacher Education, B
Art/Art Studies, General, B
Bible/Biblical Studies, B
Biology Teacher Education, B
Biology/Biological Sciences, B
Biomedical Sciences, B
Business Administration and Management, AB
Business Teacher Education, B
Chemistry, B
Chemistry Teacher Education, B
Clinical Laboratory Science/Medical
  Technology/Technologist, B
Computer Science, B
Computer and Information Sciences, AB
Conducting, B
Early Childhood Education and Teaching, B
Education, B
Elementary Education and Teaching, B
Engineering, A
English Language and Literature, B
English/Language Arts Teacher Education, B
Fine/Studio Arts, B
Foreign Languages and Literatures, B
French Language and Literature, B
General Studies, B
German Language and Literature, B
Graphic Design, AB
Health Services/Allied Health/Health Sciences, B
Health and Physical Education, B
Health and Physical Education/Fitness, B
History, B
History Teacher Education, B
International Business/Trade/Commerce, B
International Public Health/International Health, B
Kinesiology and Exercise Science, B
Liberal Arts and Sciences Studies and Humani-
  ties, B
Mathematics, B
Mathematics Teacher Education, B
Music, B
Music Pedagogy, B
Music Performance, B
Music Teacher Education, B

Organizational Behavior Studies, B
Physical Education Teaching and Coaching, B
Physical Therapist Assistant, B
Physician Assistant, BM
Physics, B
Physics Teacher Education, B
Pre-Dentistry Studies, B
Pre-Law Studies, B
Pre-Medicine/Pre-Medical Studies, B
Psychology, B
Science Teacher Education/General Science
  Teacher Education, B
Social Science Teacher Education, B
Social Sciences, B
Social Work, B
Spanish Language and Literature, B
Sport and Fitness Administration/Management, B
Teacher Education and Professional Develop-
  ment, Specific Subject Areas, B
Teaching English as a Second or Foreign
  Language/ESL Language Instructor, B
Technology Teacher Education/Industrial Arts
  Teacher Education, B
Theological and Ministerial Studies, B
Theology/Theological Studies, B

UNIVERSITY OF NEBRASKA AT
KEARNEY

Accounting, M
Agricultural Business and Management, B
Allied Health Diagnostic, Intervention, and Treat-
  ment Professions, B
Art Education, M
Art/Art Studies, General, B
Biological and Biomedical Sciences, M
Biology/Biological Sciences, B
Business Administration and Management, B
Business Administration, Management and Opera-
  tions, M
Business Teacher Education, B
Chemistry, B
Communication Disorders, BM
Computer and Information Sciences, B
Counseling Psychology, M
Counselor Education/School Counseling and Guid-
  ance Services, MO
Criminal Justice/Safety Studies, B
Curriculum and Instruction, M
Drama and Dramatics/Theatre Arts, B
Early Childhood Education and Teaching, M
Economics, B
Education, MO
Education/Teaching of the Gifted and Talented, M
Educational Administration and Supervision, MO
Educational Media/Instructional Technology, M
Elementary Education and Teaching, BM
English, M
English Language and Literature, B
English as a Second Language, M
Exercise and Sports Science, M
Family and Consumer Economics and Related Ser-
  vices, B
Foreign Language Teacher Education, M
French Language and Literature, B
General Studies, B
Geography, B
German Language and Literature, B
History, BM
Human Resources Management and Services, M
Human Services, M
International Relations and Affairs, B
Journalism, B
Leisure Studies, M
Library Science, M
Management Information Systems and Services, M
Marketing, M
Mass Communication/Media Studies, B
Mathematics, B
Mathematics Teacher Education, M
Music, B
Music Teacher Education, M
Operations Management and Supervision, B
Parks, Recreation, Leisure and Fitness Studies, B
Philosophy, B
Physical Education Teaching and Coaching, BM
Physics, B

Political Science and Government, B
Psychology, B
Reading Teacher Education, M
Recreation and Park Management, M
School Psychology, MO
Science Teacher Education/General Science
  Teacher Education, M
Secondary Education and Teaching, M
Social Work, B
Sociology, B
Spanish Language and Literature, B
Special Education and Teaching, BM
Sport and Fitness Administration/Management, BM
Student Personnel Services, M
Writing, M

UNIVERSITY OF NEBRASKA MEDICAL CENTER

Allied Health and Medical Assisting Services, MDO
Allopathic Medicine, DO
Anatomy, MD
Biochemistry, D
Bioinformatics, MD
Biological and Biomedical Sciences, MD
Biostatistics, D
Cancer Biology/Oncology, D
Cell Biology and Anatomy, MD
Clinical Laboratory Science/Medical
  Technology/Technologist, B
Clinical Laboratory Sciences, M
Dental Hygiene/Hygienist, B
Diagnostic Medical Sonography/Sonographer and
  Ultrasound Technician, B
Emergency Management, M
Environmental and Occupational Health, D
Epidemiology, D
Genetics, MD
Health Promotion, D
Health Services Research, D
Medical Radiologic Technology/Science - Radiation
  Therapist, B
Medical Technology, O
Microbiology, MD
Molecular Biology, D
Neuroscience, D
Nuclear Medical Technology/Technologist, B
Nursing, D
Nutritional Sciences, O
Pathology/Experimental Pathology, MD
Perfusion Technology/Perfusionist, M
Pharmaceutical Sciences, MD
Pharmacology, D
Pharmacy, D
Physical Therapy/Therapist, D
Physician Assistant, M
Physiology, MD
Radiologic Technology/Science - Radiographer, B
Toxicology, D

UNIVERSITY OF NEBRASKA AT OMAHA

Accounting, BM
Aeronautics/Aviation/Aerospace Science and Tech-
  nology, B
African-American/Black Studies, B
American Indian/Native American Studies, B
Art History, Criticism and Conservation, B
Art Teacher Education, B
Art/Art Studies, General, B
Artificial Intelligence and Robotics, O
Athletic Training and Sports Medicine, BM
Banking and Financial Support Services, B
Behavioral Sciences, B
BioTechnology, B
Bioinformatics, BM
Biological and Biomedical Sciences, MO
Biology/Biological Sciences, B
Broadcast Journalism, B
Business Administration and Management, B
Business Administration, Management and Opera-
  tions, MO
Business/Commerce, B
Business/Managerial Economics, B
Chemistry, B
Communication Disorders, M

Communication Studies/Speech Communication
  and Rhetoric, B
Communication and Media Studies, MO
Community Health Services/Liaison/Counseling, B
Computer Science, BMO
Computer and Information Sciences, B
Computer and Information Systems Security, BMDO
Counselor Education/School Counseling and Guid-
  ance Services, M
Criminal Justice/Safety Studies, B
Criminology, MD
Design and Applied Arts, B
Drama and Dramatics/Theatre Arts, B
Economics, BM
Education, MDO
Education/Teaching of Individuals with Speech or
  Language Impairments, B
Educational Administration and Supervision, MDO
Educational Leadership and Administration, MDO
Elementary Education and Teaching, BM
English, MO
English Language and Literature, B
English as a Second Language, O
Ethnic, Cultural Minority, and Gender Studies, B
Exercise and Sports Science, D
Finance, B
Fine/Studio Arts, B
Fire Services Administration, B
Foreign Language Teacher Education, M
Foreign Languages and Literatures, B
General Studies, B
Geographic Information Systems, O
Geography, BMO
Geology/Earth Science, B
Gerontology, BMO
Graphic Design, B
Health Education, MD
Health/Health Care Administration/Management, B
History, BM
Human Resources Development, O
Human Resources Management/Personnel Adminis-
  tration, B
Industrial and Organizational Psychology, M
Information Science/Studies, BD
Information Technology, B
International/Global Studies, B
Investments and Securities, B
Journalism, B
Kinesiology and Exercise Science, B
Latin American Studies, B
Legal Professions and Studies, B
Library Science, B
Management Information Systems and Ser-
  vices, MDO
Marketing/Marketing Management, B
Mathematics, BM
Medical Informatics, M
Multi-/Interdisciplinary Studies, B
Music, BM
Music Performance, B
Music Teacher Education, B
Music Theory and Composition, B
Natural Sciences, B
Organizational Behavior Studies, B
Parks, Recreation, Leisure and Fitness Studies, B
Philosophy, B
Physical Education Teaching and Coaching, MD
Piano and Organ, B
Political Science and Government, BMO
Project Management, O
Psychology, BMDO
Public Administration, BMDO
Public Health (MPH, DPH), B
Reading Teacher Education, M
Real Estate, B
Recreation and Park Management, MD
Religion/Religious Studies, B
School Librarian/School Library Media Specialist, B
School Psychology, MO
Secondary Education and Teaching, BMO
Small Business Administration/Management, B
Social Work, BM
Sociology, M
Software Engineering, O
Special Education and Teaching, BM
Systems Engineering, O

Technical Communication, O
Theater, M
Urban Education and Leadership, O
Urban Studies/Affairs, B
Violin, Viola, Guitar and Other Stringed Instru-
  ments, B
Voice and Opera, B
Writing, MO

UNIVERSITY OF NEBRASKA–LINCOLN

Accounting, BMD
Actuarial Science, BM
Adult and Continuing Education and Teaching, M
Advertising and Public Relations, MD
Agricultural Business and Management, B
Agricultural Communication/Journalism, B
Agricultural Economics, BMD
Agricultural Education, M
Agricultural Engineering, MD
Agricultural Mechanization, B
Agricultural Sciences, MD
Agricultural Teacher Education, B
Agricultural and Food Products Processing, B
Agricultural/Biological Engineering and Bioengineer-
  ing, B
Agriculture, B
Agriculture, Agriculture Operations and Related Sci-
  ences, B
Agronomy and Crop Science, B
Agronomy and Soil Sciences, MD
Analytical Chemistry, D
Ancient Studies/Civilization, B
Animal Sciences, BMD
Anthropology, BM
Apparel and Textile Marketing Management, B
Apparel and Textiles, B
Archeology, M
Architectural Engineering, BMD
Architecture, BMD
Art History, Criticism and Conservation, BM
Astronomy, MD
Athletic Training and Sports Medicine, B
Atmospheric Sciences and Meteorology, B
Banking and Financial Support Services, B
Biochemistry, BMD
Bioengineering, MD
Bioinformatics, MD
Biological and Biomedical Sciences, MD
Biology Teacher Education, B
Biology/Biological Sciences, B
Biomedical Engineering, D
Biopsychology, D
Botany/Plant Biology, B
Broadcast Journalism, B
Business Administration and Management, B
Business Administration, Management and Opera-
  tions, MD
Business Teacher Education, B
Business/Managerial Economics, B
Chemical Engineering, BMD
Chemistry, BMD
Chemistry Teacher Education, B
Child Development, MD
Child and Family Studies, MD
Civil Engineering, BMD
Classics and Classical Languages, Litera-
  tures, and Linguistics, BM
Clinical Psychology, D
Clothing and Textiles, MD
Cognitive Sciences, MD
Communication Disorders, MDO
Communication Studies/Speech Communication
  and Rhetoric, BM
Communication and Media Studies, MD
Comparative Literature, MD
Composition, MD
Computer Engineering, BMD
Computer Science, MD
Computer Teacher Education, B
Computer and Information Sciences, B
Construction Engineering, B
Construction Engineering Technology/Technician, B
Consumer Economics, MD
Corporate and Organizational Communication, MD
Counseling Psychology, MD
Curriculum and Instruction, MDO

Dance, B
Developmental Psychology, MD
Drama and Dramatics/Theatre Arts, B
Early Childhood Education and Teaching, MD
Economics, BMD
Educational Administration and Supervision, MDO
Educational Measurement and Evaluation, MD
Educational Psychology, MDO
Electrical Engineering, MD
Electrical, Electronics and Communications Engineering, B
Elementary Education and Teaching, B
Engineering, B
Engineering Management, M
Engineering and Applied Sciences, MD
English, MD
English Language and Literature, B
Entomology, BMD
Environmental Engineering Technology/Environmental Technology, MD
Environmental Studies, B
Ethnic, Cultural Minority, and Gender Studies, B
Exercise and Sports Science, M
Family and Consumer Economics and Related Services, B
Family and Consumer Sciences/Human Sciences, MD
Film/Cinema Studies, B
Finance, B
Finance and Banking, MD
Fine Arts and Art Studies, M
Fine/Studio Arts, B
Food Science, B
Food Science and Technology, MD
Foods, Nutrition, and Wellness Studies, B
Foreign Language Teacher Education, B
Forensic Science and Technology, B
French Language Teacher Education, B
French Language and Literature, BMD
Geography, BMD
Geology/Earth Science, B
Geosciences, MD
German Language Teacher Education, B
German Language and Literature, BMD
Gerontology, D
Health Promotion, M
History, BMD
Home Economics Education, MD
Horticultural Science, BMD
Hospitality Administration/Management, B
Human Development, D
Industrial/Management Engineering, MD
Information Science/Studies, D
Inorganic Chemistry, D
Interior Architecture, B
Interior Design, M
International Business/Trade/Commerce, B
International/Global Studies, B
Investments and Securities, B
Journalism, BM
Landscape Architecture, B
Landscaping and Groundskeeping, B
Latin American Studies, B
Law and Legal Studies, MD
Legal Professions and Studies, B
Legal and Justice Studies, M
Liberal Arts and Sciences Studies and Humanities, B
Logistics and Materials Management, B
Management, M
Manufacturing Engineering, M
Marketing, MD
Marketing/Marketing Management, B
Marriage and Family Therapy/Counseling, MD
Mass Communication/Media Studies, M
Materials Engineering, MD
Materials Sciences, D
Mathematics, BMD
Mathematics Teacher Education, B
Mechanical Engineering, BMD
Mechanics, MD
Medieval and Renaissance Studies, B
Metallurgical Engineering, M
Microbiology, B
Music, BMD
Music History, Literature, and Theory, M

Music Teacher Education, BMD
Music Theory and Composition, M
Natural Resources Management/Development and Policy, BM
Natural Resources and Conservation, BMD
Nutritional Sciences, MD
Organic Chemistry, D
Performance, MD
Philosophy, BMD
Physical Chemistry, D
Physical Education Teaching and Coaching, B
Physics, BMD
Physics Teacher Education, B
Political Science and Government, BMDO
Pre-Dentistry Studies, B
Pre-Medicine/Pre-Medical Studies, B
Pre-Pharmacy Studies, B
Pre-Veterinary Studies, B
Psychology, BMD
Public Policy Analysis, O
Range Science and Management, B
Rhetoric, MD
Russian Language and Literature, B
School Psychology, MDO
Science Teacher Education/General Science Teacher Education, B
Social Psychology, D
Social Science Teacher Education, B
Sociology, BMD
Soil Science and Agronomy, B
Spanish Language Teacher Education, B
Spanish Language and Literature, BMD
Special Education and Teaching, BMDO
Speech and Interpersonal Communication, MD
Speech-Language Pathology/Pathologist, B
Statistics, MD
Survey Methodology, MD
System Management, M
Teacher Education and Professional Development, Specific Subject Areas, B
Teacher Education, Multiple Levels, B
Textile Science, B
Theater, M
Toxicology, MD
Trade and Industrial Teacher Education, B
Turf and Turfgrass Management, B
Urban and Regional Planning, M
Veterinary Sciences, MD
Veterinary/Animal Health Technology/Technician and Veterinary Assistant, B
Vocational and Technical Education, M
Women's Studies, B
Writing, MD

WAYNE STATE COLLEGE

Art Teacher Education, B
Art/Art Studies, General, B
Athletic Training and Sports Medicine, B
Biology Teacher Education, B
Biology/Biological Sciences, B
Business Administration and Management, B
Business Administration, Management and Operations, M
Business Education, M
Business Teacher Education, B
Chemistry, B
Chemistry Teacher Education, B
Child Care Provider/Assistant, B
Communication Studies/Speech Communication and Rhetoric, B
Communication and Media Studies, M
Computer and Information Sciences, B
Counselor Education/School Counseling and Guidance Services, M
Criminal Justice/Safety Studies, B
Curriculum and Instruction, M
Drama and Dance Teacher Education, B
Drama and Dramatics/Theatre Arts, B
Early Childhood Education and Teaching, BM
Education, MO
Educational Administration and Supervision, MO
Elementary Education and Teaching, BM
English Education, M
English Language and Literature, B
English as a Second Language, M
English/Language Arts Teacher Education, B

Exercise and Sports Science, M
Family and Consumer Sciences/Home Economics Teacher Education, B
Family and Consumer Sciences/Human Sciences, B
Foreign Language Teacher Education, B
Foreign Languages and Literatures, B
Geography, B
Geography Teacher Education, B
Graphic Design, B
Health and Physical Education/Fitness, B
History, B
History Teacher Education, B
Home Economics Education, M
Industrial Production Technologies/Technicians, B
Information Science/Studies, B
Junior High/Intermediate/Middle School Education and Teaching, B
Mass Communication/Media Studies, B
Mathematics, B
Mathematics Teacher Education, BM
Music, B
Music Teacher Education, BM
Organizational Management, M
Physical Education Teaching and Coaching, BM
Political Science and Government, B
Psychology, B
Psychology Teacher Education, B
Science Teacher Education/General Science Teacher Education, BM
Social Science Teacher Education, B
Social Sciences, B
Social Studies Teacher Education, M
Sociology, B
Spanish Language and Literature, B
Special Education and Teaching, BM
Speech Teacher Education, B
Sport and Fitness Administration/Management, BM
Teacher Education and Professional Development, Specific Subject Areas, B
Technology Teacher Education/Industrial Arts Teacher Education, B
Vocational and Technical Education, M

WESTERN NEBRASKA COMMUNITY COLLEGE

Agriculture, A
Anthropology, A
Art Teacher Education, A
Art/Art Studies, General, A
Biology/Biological Sciences, A
Business Administration and Management, A
Chemistry, A
Clinical Laboratory Science/Medical Technology/Technologist, A
Computer and Information Sciences, A
Criminal Justice/Safety Studies, A
Dietetics/Dieticians, A
Drama and Dance Teacher Education, A
Ecology, A
Economics, A
Elementary Education and Teaching, A
English Language and Literature, A
Forest Management/Forest Resources Management, A
French Language and Literature, A
General Studies, A
Geography, A
German Language and Literature, A
Health and Physical Education, A
History, A
Information Technology, A
Journalism, A
Kindergarten/PreSchool Education and Teaching, A
Liberal Arts and Sciences Studies and Humanities, A
Mathematics, A
Music Teacher Education, A
Physical Therapist Assistant, A
Physical Therapy/Therapist, A
Physics, A
Political Science and Government, A
Pre-Dentistry Studies, A
Pre-Law Studies, A
Pre-Medicine/Pre-Medical Studies, A
Pre-Pharmacy Studies, A
Pre-Veterinary Studies, A

Psychology, A
Radiologic Technology/Science - Radiographer, A
Secondary Education and Teaching, A
Social Work, A
Sociology, A
Spanish Language and Literature, A

YORK COLLEGE

Accounting, B
Art Teacher Education, B
Bible/Biblical Studies, B
Biological and Physical Sciences, B
Biology Teacher Education, B
Biology/Biological Sciences, B
Business Administration and Management, B
Business Teacher Education, B
Criminal Justice/Law Enforcement Administration, B
Education, B
Elementary Education and Teaching, B
English Language and Literature, B
English/Language Arts Teacher Education, B
General Studies, B
History, B
History Teacher Education, B
Junior High/Intermediate/Middle School Education
  and Teaching, B
Liberal Arts and Sciences Studies and Humani-
  ties, A
Mathematics Teacher Education, B
Music, B
Music Teacher Education, B
Natural Sciences, B
Physical Education Teaching and Coaching, B
Psychology, B
Psychology Teacher Education, B
Reading Teacher Education, B
Religion/Religious Studies, B
Religious Education, B
Science Teacher Education/General Science
  Teacher Education, B
Secondary Education and Teaching, B
Social Science Teacher Education, B
Social Studies Teacher Education, B
Social Work, B
Special Education and Teaching, B
Speech Teacher Education, B
Sport and Fitness Administration/Management, B
Teacher Education, Multiple Levels, B

Nevada

THE ART INSTITUTE OF LAS VEGAS

Advertising, B
Animation, Interactive Technology, Video Graphics
  and Special Effects, B
Apparel and Accessories Marketing Operations, B
Baking and Pastry Arts/Baker/Pastry Chef, A
CAD/CADD Drafting and/or Design
  Technology/Technician, A
Cinematography and Film/Video Production, B
Commercial Photography, AB
Computer Graphics, B
Culinary Arts/Chef Training, A
Fashion/Apparel Design, B
Graphic Design, B
Interior Design, B
Recording Arts Technology/Technician, B
Restaurant, Culinary, and Catering
  Management/Manager, B
Web Page, Digital/Multimedia and Information Re-
  sources Design, B

BRIGHTWOOD COLLEGE, LAS VEGAS CAMPUS

Criminal Justice/Law Enforcement Administration, A
Health Information/Medical Records
  Technology/Technician, A
Radiologic Technology/Science - Radiographer, A

CAREER COLLEGE OF NORTHERN NEVADA

Business Administration and Management, A
Computer and Information Sciences, A
Data Processing and Data Processing
  Technology/Technician, A

Electrical, Electronic and Communications Engineer-
  ing Technology/Technician, A
Management Information Systems and Services, A
Medical/Clinical Assistant, A

CARRINGTON COLLEGE–LAS VEGAS

Physical Therapist Assistant, A
Respiratory Therapy Technician/Assistant, A

COLLEGE OF SOUTHERN NEVADA

Accounting Technology/Technician and Bookkeep-
  ing, A
Animation, Interactive Technology, Video Graphics
  and Special Effects, A
Anthropology, A
Architectural Drafting and Architectural
  CAD/CADD, A
Art/Art Studies, General, A
Automobile/Automotive Mechanics
  Technology/Technician, A
Banking and Financial Support Services, A
Biological and Physical Sciences, A
Biology/Biological Sciences, A
Building/Construction Site Management/Manager, A
Business Administration and Management, A
Business/Managerial Economics, A
CAD/CADD Drafting and/or Design
  Technology/Technician, A
Cardiovascular Technology/Technologist, A
Carpentry/Carpenter, A
Chemistry, A
Child Care Provider/Assistant, A
Civil Engineering, A
Clinical/Medical Laboratory Technician, A
Communication Studies/Speech Communication
  and Rhetoric, A
Computer Systems Networking and Telecommunica-
  tions, A
Cooking and Related Culinary Arts, A
Corrections, A
Criminal Justice/Police Science, A
Criminology, A
Culinary Arts/Chef Training, A
Dental Hygiene/Hygienist, AB
Drama and Dramatics/Theatre Arts, A
Education/Teaching of Individuals with Hearing Im-
  pairments, Including Deafness, A
Electrical and Power Transmission
  Installation/Installer, A
Electrical, Electronic and Communications Engineer-
  ing Technology/Technician, A
Electrician, A
Elementary Education and Teaching, A
Emergency Medical Technology/Technician (EMT
  Paramedic), A
Engineering/Industrial Management, A
English Language and Literature, A
Environmental Engineering
  Technology/Environmental Technology, A
Fire Science/Firefighting, A
Foreign Languages and Literatures, A
Health Information/Medical Records
  Administration/Administrator, A
Heating, Air Conditioning, Ventilation and Refrigera-
  tion Maintenance Technology/Technician, A
History, A
Hospitality Administration/Management, A
Hotel/Motel Administration/Management, A
Information Science/Studies, A
Kindergarten/PreSchool Education and Teaching, A
Landscaping and Groundskeeping, A
Legal Assistant/Paralegal, A
Liberal Arts and Sciences Studies and Humani-
  ties, A
Mathematics, A
Mechanical Engineering/Mechanical
  Technology/Technician, A
Medical Radiologic Technology/Science - Radiation
  Therapist, A
Mining Technology/Technician, A
Music, A
Ophthalmic Technician/Technologist, A
Ornamental Horticulture, A
Physical Therapist Assistant, A
Pre-Veterinary Studies, A
Respiratory Care Therapy/Therapist, A

Restaurant/Food Services Management, A
Sales, Distribution and Marketing Operations, A
Social Sciences, A
Sociology, A
Special Education and Teaching, A
Structural Engineering, A
Survey Technology/Surveying, A
Tourism and Travel Services Management, A
Water Quality and Wastewater Treatment Manage-
  ment and Recycling Technology/Technician, A
Web Page, Digital/Multimedia and Information Re-
  sources Design, A

DEVRY UNIVERSITY

Business Administration and Management, B
Business Administration, Management and Opera-
  tions, BM
Business/Commerce, B
Computer Systems Analysis/Analyst, B
Computer Systems Networking and Telecommunica-
  tions, AB
Criminal Justice/Law Enforcement Administration, B
Electrical, Electronic and Communications Engineer-
  ing Technology/Technician, A
Web Page, Digital/Multimedia and Information Re-
  sources Design, AB

EVEREST COLLEGE

Accounting and Related Services, A
Allied Health and Medical Assisting Services, A
Business, Management, Marketing, and Related
  Support Services, A
Criminal Justice/Safety Studies, A
General Office Occupations and Clerical Services, A
Medical Administrative Assistant/Secretary, A

GREAT BASIN COLLEGE

Accounting Technology/Technician and Bookkeep-
  ing, A
Biology/Biological Sciences, AB
Business Administration and Management, AB
Business/Commerce, A
Computer Graphics, AB
Computer Systems Networking and Telecommunica-
  tions, A
Computer and Information Sciences, A
Computer/Information Technology Services Adminis-
  tration and Management, B
Criminal Justice/Safety Studies, A
Data Processing and Data Processing
  Technology/Technician, A
Diesel Mechanics Technology/Technician, A
Early Childhood Education and Teaching, A
Electrical, Electronic and Communications Engineer-
  ing Technology/Technician, A
Elementary Education and Teaching, AB
Emergency Medical Technology/Technician (EMT
  Paramedic), A
English Language and Literature, B
General Office Occupations and Clerical Services, A
General Studies, A
Geological and Earth Sciences/Geosciences, A
Human Services, A
Industrial Technology/Technician, A
Instrumentation Technology/Technician, B
Liberal Arts and Sciences Studies and Humani-
  ties, A
Management Science, B
Natural Resources Management/Development and
  Policy, AB
Operations Management and Supervision, A
Radiologic Technology/Science - Radiographer, A
Secondary Education and Teaching, B
Social Sciences, B
Social Work, B
Survey Technology/Surveying, B
Welding Technology/Welder, A

NEVADA STATE COLLEGE

Animation, Interactive Technology, Video Graphics
  and Special Effects, B
Area Studies, B
Bilingual and Multilingual Education, B
Biological and Biomedical Sciences, B
Biology Teacher Education, B
Biology/Biological Sciences, B

Computer Engineering Technology/Technician, B
Criminal Justice/Law Enforcement Administration, B
Criminal Justice/Police Science, B
Design and Visual Communications, B
Economics, B
Education, B
Education/Teaching of Individuals in Early Childhood Special Education Programs, B
Education/Teaching of Individuals with Autism, B
Education/Teaching of Individuals with Hearing Impairments, Including Deafness, B
Electrical, Electronic and Communications Engineering Technology/Technician, B
Elementary Education and Teaching, B
English Language and Literature, B
English/Language Arts Teacher Education, B
Environmental Sciences, B
History Teacher Education, B
Management Science, B
Mathematics, B
Mathematics Teacher Education, B
Multi-/Interdisciplinary Studies, B
Occupational Therapy/Therapist, B
Pre-Medicine/Pre-Medical Studies, B
Psychology, B
Science Teacher Education/General Science Teacher Education, B
Secondary Education and Teaching, B
Special Education and Teaching, B
Speech-Language Pathology/Pathologist, B

PIMA MEDICAL INSTITUTE

Health/Health Care Administration/Management, A
Physical Therapist Assistant, A
Radiologic Technology/Science - Radiographer, A
Respiratory Therapy Technician/Assistant, A
Veterinary/Animal Health Technology/Technician and Veterinary Assistant, A

SIERRA NEVADA COLLEGE

Accounting and Business/Management, B
Art Therapy/Therapist, B
Art/Art Studies, General, B
Biological and Physical Sciences, B
Business Administration and Management, B
Business, Management, Marketing, and Related Support Services, B
Computer and Information Sciences, B
Ecology, B
Education, M
Educational Leadership and Administration, M
Elementary Education and Teaching, M
English Language and Literature, B
Entrepreneurship/Entrepreneurial Studies, B
Environmental Sciences, B
Finance, B
Fine/Studio Arts, B
Humanities/Humanistic Studies, B
International Business/Trade/Commerce, B
International/Global Studies, B
Natural Resources Conservation and Research, B
Photojournalism, B
Psychology, B
Resort Management, B
Secondary Education and Teaching, M

TRUCKEE MEADOWS COMMUNITY COLLEGE

Anthropology, A
Architectural Drafting and Architectural CAD/CADD, A
Architecture, A
Automobile/Automotive Mechanics Technology/Technician, A
Biology/Biological Sciences, A
Business/Commerce, A
Chemistry, A
Civil Engineering, A
Commercial and Advertising Art, A
Computer Programming, Specific Applications, A
Computer Systems Networking and Telecommunications, A
Cooking and Related Culinary Arts, A
Criminal Justice/Police Science, A
Criminal Justice/Safety Studies, A
Dental Assisting/Assistant, A

Dental Hygiene/Hygienist, A
Diesel Mechanics Technology/Technician, A
Dietetics/Dieticians, A
Drafting and Design Technology/Technician, A
Elementary Education and Teaching, A
Energy Management and Systems Technology/Technician, A
Engineering, A
Engineering Technologies/Technicians, A
English Language and Literature, A
Entrepreneurial and Small Business Operations, A
Environmental Sciences, A
Fine Arts and Art Studies, A
Fire Protection and Safety Technology/Technician, A
Foods, Nutrition, and Wellness Studies, A
General Studies, A
Geology/Earth Science, A
Heating, Air Conditioning, Ventilation and Refrigeration Maintenance Technology/Technician, A
History, A
Kindergarten/PreSchool Education and Teaching, A
Landscape Architecture, A
Legal Assistant/Paralegal, A
Liberal Arts and Sciences Studies and Humanities, A
Logistics and Materials Management, A
Management Information Systems and Services, A
Manufacturing Technology/Technician, A
Mathematics, A
Medical Radiologic Technology/Science - Radiation Therapist, A
Mental Health Counseling/Counselor, A
Music, A
Music Performance, A
Natural Resources and Conservation, A
Philosophy, A
Physics, A
Psychology, A
Science, Technology and Society, A
Veterinary/Animal Health Technology/Technician and Veterinary Assistant, A
Welding Technology/Welder, A

UNIVERSITY OF NEVADA, LAS VEGAS

Accounting, BMO
Acting, B
African-American/Black Studies, B
Allied Health and Medical Assisting Services, MDO
Anthropology, BMD
Architecture, BMO
Art History, Criticism and Conservation, B
Art/Art Studies, General, B
Asian Studies/Civilization, B
Astronomy, MD
Athletic Training and Sports Medicine, B
Biochemistry, BM
Biological and Biomedical Sciences, MD
Biology/Biological Sciences, B
Biomedical Engineering, M
Business Administration and Management, B
Business Administration, Management and Operations, M
Chemistry, BMD
Civil Engineering, BMD
Clinical Psychology, M
Communication Studies/Speech Communication and Rhetoric, B
Communication and Media Studies, M
Community Health and Preventive Medicine, MD
Computer Engineering, BMD
Computer Science, BMD
Construction Engineering Technology/Technician, B
Construction Management, B
Counseling Psychology, M
Counselor Education/School Counseling and Guidance Services, MDO
Criminal Justice/Safety Studies, B
Criminology, MD
Culinary Arts and Related Services, B
Curriculum and Instruction, MDO
Dance, B
Dentistry, MD
Drama and Dramatics/Theatre Arts, B
Early Childhood Education and Teaching, B
Economics, BM
Education, BMDO

Educational Administration and Supervision, MDO
Educational Leadership and Administration, D
Educational Media/Instructional Technology, D
Educational Psychology, MDO
Electrical Engineering, MD
Electrical, Electronics and Communications Engineering, B
Elementary Education and Teaching, B
Emergency Management, M
Engineering, B
Engineering and Applied Sciences, MDO
English, MD
English Language and Literature, B
Entrepreneurship/Entrepreneurial Studies, BO
Environmental Engineering Technology/Environmental Technology, MD
Environmental Sciences, MDO
Environmental Studies, B
Ethnic and Cultural Studies, MD
Exercise and Sports Science, M
Film, Television, and Video Production, MO
Film/Cinema Studies, B
Finance, B
Fine Arts and Art Studies, M
French Language and Literature, B
Geology/Earth Science, B
Geosciences, MD
German Language and Literature, B
Graphic Design, B
Health Physics/Radiological Health, MDO
Health Services Administration, M
Health Teacher Education, B
Health/Health Care Administration/Management, B
Health/Medical Physics, B
Higher Education/Higher Education Administration, MDO
Hispanic Studies, M
History, BMD
Hospitality Administration/Management, BMD
Human Resources Development, D
Human Services, B
Information Science/Studies, B
Interior Architecture, B
International Business/Trade/Commerce, B
Journalism, M
Kinesiology and Exercise Science, B
Kinesiology and Movement Studies, MD
Landscape Architecture, B
Latin American Studies, B
Law and Legal Studies, MD
Liberal Arts and Sciences Studies and Humanities, B
Linguistics, B
Management, O
Management Information Systems and Services, BMO
Marketing/Marketing Management, B
Marriage and Family Therapy/Counseling, M
Mass Communication/Media Studies, B
Materials Engineering, M
Mathematics, BMD
Mechanical Engineering, BMDO
Media Studies, M
Medical Radiologic Technology/Science - Radiation Therapist, B
Multi-/Interdisciplinary Studies, B
Music, BMDO
Non-Profit/Public/Organizational Management, O
Nuclear Engineering, MO
Nuclear Medical Technology/Technologist, B
Nursing, MDO
Nursing - Advanced Practice, O
Nursing Education, O
Nutritional Sciences, B
Oral Biology, M
Oral and Dental Sciences, M
Organizational Management, D
Parks, Recreation, Leisure and Fitness Studies, B
Philosophy, B
Physical Therapy/Therapist, D
Physics, BMD
Political Science and Government, BMD
Psychology, BMD
Public Administration, BMO
Public Affairs, D
Public Health, MD

Public Health (MPH, DPH), B
Real Estate, B
Restaurant/Food Services Management, B
Romance Languages, Literatures, and Linguistics, B
Science Teacher Education/General Science Teacher Education, B
Secondary Education and Teaching, B
Social Sciences, B
Social Work, BM
Sociology, BMD
Spanish Language Teacher Education, B
Spanish Language and Literature, B
Special Education and Teaching, BD
Sport and Fitness Administration/Management, B
Substance Abuse/Addiction Counseling, O
Technical Theatre/Theatre Design and Technology, B
Theater, M
Transportation and Highway Engineering, M
Water Resources, M
Women's Studies, B
Writing, M

UNIVERSITY OF NEVADA, RENO

Accounting, BM
Agricultural Economics, MD
Agricultural Sciences, MD
Agriculture, Agriculture Operations and Related Sciences, B
Animal Sciences, M
Anthropology, BMD
Applied Economics, MD
Art History, Criticism and Conservation, B
Art/Art Studies, General, B
Atmospheric Sciences and Meteorology, BMD
BioTechnology, BM
Biochemistry, BMD
Biological and Biomedical Sciences, M
Biology/Biological Sciences, B
Biomedical Engineering, MD
Business Administration and Management, B
Business Administration, Management and Operations, M
Business/Commerce, B
Business/Managerial Economics, B
Cell Biology and Anatomy, MD
Chemical Engineering, BMD
Chemical Physics, D
Chemistry, BMD
Child Development, B
Child and Family Studies, M
Civil Engineering, BMD
Clinical Psychology, MD
Cognitive Sciences, MD
Communication Disorders, MD
Communication Studies/Speech Communication and Rhetoric, B
Computer Engineering, BMD
Computer Science, BMD
Computer and Information Sciences, B
Conservation Biology, D
Counselor Education/School Counseling and Guidance Services, MDO
Criminology, BM
Curriculum and Instruction, D
Drama and Dramatics/Theatre Arts, B
Ecology, D
Economics, M
Education, BMDO
Educational Leadership and Administration, MDO
Educational Psychology, MDO
Electrical Engineering, MD
Electrical, Electronics and Communications Engineering, B
Elementary Education and Teaching, BM
Engineering Physics, B
Engineering and Applied Sciences, MD
English, MD
English Language and Literature, B
English as a Second Language, M
Environmental Policy and Resource Management, M
Environmental Sciences, MD
Environmental and Occupational Health, MD
Environmental/Environmental Health Engineering, B
Evolutionary Biology, D

Finance, B
Finance and Banking, M
Fine Arts and Art Studies, M
Foods, Nutrition, and Wellness Studies, B
Foreign Language Teacher Education, BM
Forestry, B
French Language and Literature, BM
General Studies, B
Geochemistry, MD
Geography, BMD
Geological Engineering, MD
Geological/Geophysical Engineering, B
Geology/Earth Science, BMD
Geophysics and Seismology, BMD
German Language and Literature, M
Health Professions and Related Clinical Sciences, B
History, BMD
Housing and Human Environments, B
Human Development, M
Human Development and Family Studies, B
Hydrogeology, MD
Hydrology and Water Resources Science, MD
International Business/Trade/Commerce, B
International Relations and Affairs, B
Journalism, BM
Legal and Justice Studies, MD
Management Information Systems and Services, M
Marketing/Marketing Management, B
Materials Engineering, MD
Mathematics, BM
Mathematics Teacher Education, M
Mechanical Engineering, BMD
Metallurgical Engineering, BMD
Mineral/Mining Engineering, M
Mining and Mineral Engineering, B
Molecular Biology, MD
Molecular Pharmacology, D
Music, BM
Music Performance, B
Music Teacher Education, B
Natural Resources Management/Development and Policy, B
Natural Resources and Conservation, B
Nursing, MD
Nutritional Sciences, BM
Philosophy, BM
Physics, BMD
Physiology, D
Political Science and Government, BMD
Pre-Veterinary Studies, B
Psychology, BMD
Public Administration, M
Public Health, MD
Range Science and Management, B
Reading Teacher Education, M
Secondary Education and Teaching, M
Social Psychology, D
Social Work, BM
Sociology, BM
Spanish Language and Literature, BM
Special Education and Teaching, MD
Speech and Rhetorical Studies, M
Speech-Language Pathology/Pathologist, B
Water Resources Engineering, B
Western European Studies, D
Wildlife and Wildlands Science and Management, B
Women's Studies, B

UNIVERSITY OF PHOENIX–LAS VEGAS CAMPUS

Accounting, ABM
Allied Health and Medical Assisting Services, M
Business Administration and Management, B
Business Administration, Management and Operations, M
Business, Management, Marketing, and Related Support Services, B
Business/Commerce, A
Business/Corporate Communications, B
Computer Software Engineering, B
Computer and Information Sciences, B
Computer and Information Systems Security, B
Consumer Merchandising/Retailing Management, B
Counseling Psychology, M
Counselor Education/School Counseling and Guidance Services, M

Credit Management, B
Criminal Justice/Law Enforcement Administration, B
Curriculum and Instruction, M
E-Commerce/Electronic Commerce, B
Education, M
Educational Administration and Supervision, M
Elementary Education and Teaching, BM
Health Services Administration, B
Hospitality Administration/Management, B
Human Resources Management and Services, M
Human Services, B
Information Technology, B
International Business/Trade/Commerce, BM
Management, M
Management Information Systems and Services, BM
Management Science, B
Management of Technology, M
Marketing, M
Marketing/Marketing Management, B
Marriage and Family Therapy/Counseling, M
Operations Management and Supervision, B
Organizational Behavior Studies, B
Psychology, B
Public Administration, BM
Public Administration and Social Service Professions, B
School Psychology, M
Security and Protective Services, B

WESTERN NEVADA COLLEGE

Accounting, A
Automobile/Automotive Mechanics Technology/Technician, A
Business Administration and Management, A
Business/Commerce, A
Commercial and Advertising Art, A
Computer and Information Sciences, A
Construction Management, B
Criminal Justice/Law Enforcement Administration, A
General Studies, A
Industrial Technology/Technician, A
Liberal Arts and Sciences Studies and Humanities, A
Machine Tool Technology/Machinist, A
Management Information Systems and Services, A
Manufacturing Technology/Technician, A
Physical Sciences, A
Welding Technology/Welder, A

New Hampshire

COLBY-SAWYER COLLEGE

Art History, Criticism and Conservation, B
Art Teacher Education, B
Art/Art Studies, General, B
Athletic Training and Sports Medicine, B
Biology/Biological Sciences, B
Business Administration and Management, B
Early Childhood Education and Teaching, B
English Language and Literature, B
English/Language Arts Teacher Education, B
Environmental Studies, B
Fine/Studio Arts, B
Graphic Design, B
Health Services/Allied Health/Health Sciences, B
Health/Health Care Administration/Management, B
Kinesiology and Exercise Science, B
Liberal Arts and Sciences Studies and Humanities, A
Mass Communication/Media Studies, B
Philosophy, B
Psychology, B
Public Health (MPH, DPH), B
Public Health Education and Promotion, B
Social Sciences, B
Sociology, B
Sport and Fitness Administration/Management, B

DANIEL WEBSTER COLLEGE

Accounting, B
Aerospace, Aeronautical and Astronautical Engineering, B
Air Traffic Controller, B
Aviation/Airway Management and Operations, BM

Business Administration and Management, B
Business Administration, Management and Operations, M
Computer Science, B
Computer Software and Media Applications, B
Construction Engineering, B
Health/Health Care Administration/Management, B
Management Information Systems and Services, B
Marketing/Marketing Management, B
Mechanical Engineering, B
Psychology, B
Sport and Fitness Administration/Management, B

DARTMOUTH COLLEGE

African Studies, B
African-American/Black Studies, B
Allopathic Medicine, D
American Indian/Native American Studies, B
Ancient/Classical Greek Language and Literature, B
Animal Genetics, B
Anthropology, B
Arabic Language and Literature, B
Archeology, B
Art History, Criticism and Conservation, B
Asian Studies/Civilization, B
Astronomy, BMD
BioTechnology, MD
Biochemical Engineering, MD
Biochemistry, BD
Biological and Biomedical Sciences, D
Biology/Biological Sciences, B
Biomedical Engineering, MD
Biostatistics, D
Business Administration, Management and Operations, M
Cancer Biology/Oncology, D
Cardiovascular Sciences, D
Cell Biology and Anatomy, D
Chemistry, BD
Chinese Language and Literature, B
Classics and Classical Languages, Literatures, and Linguistics, B
Cognitive Sciences, D
Comparative Literature, BM
Computer Engineering, MD
Computer Science, BMD
Drama and Dramatics/Theatre Arts, B
East Asian Languages, Literatures, and Linguistics, B
Ecology, BD
Economics, B
Engineering, B
Engineering Management, M
Engineering Physics, B
Engineering and Applied Sciences, MD
English Language and Literature, B
Entrepreneurship/Entrepreneurial Studies, D
Environmental Engineering Technology/Environmental Technology, MD
Environmental Studies, B
Evolutionary Biology, BD
Film/Cinema Studies, B
Fine/Studio Arts, B
French Language and Literature, B
Genetics, D
Geography, B
Geology/Earth Science, B
Geosciences, MD
German Language and Literature, B
Health Services Administration, MD
Health Services Research, MD
Hebrew Language and Literature, B
Hispanic-American, Puerto Rican, and Mexican-American/Chicano Studies, B
History, B
Italian Language and Literature, B
Japanese Language and Literature, B
Latin American Studies, B
Latin Language and Literature, B
Liberal Studies, M
Linguistics, B
Materials Engineering, MD
Materials Sciences, MD
Mathematics, BD
Mechanical Engineering, MD
Microbiology, D

Molecular Biology, BD
Molecular Medicine, D
Molecular Pathogenesis, D
Molecular Pharmacology, D
Multi-/Interdisciplinary Studies, B
Music, BM
Near and Middle Eastern Studies, B
Neuroscience, D
Pharmaceutical Sciences, D
Pharmacology, D
Philosophy, B
Physics, BMD
Physiology, D
Political Science and Government, B
Psychology, BD
Public Health, M
Religion/Religious Studies, B
Romance Languages, Literatures, and Linguistics, B
Russian Language and Literature, B
Russian Studies, B
Sociology, B
Spanish Language and Literature, B
Systematic Biology/Biological Systematics, D
Toxicology, D
Women's Studies, B

FRANKLIN PIERCE UNIVERSITY

Accounting, B
Advertising, B
American/United States Studies/Civilization, B
Anthropology, B
Archeology, B
Art Teacher Education, B
Art/Art Studies, General, B
Biology/Biological Sciences, B
Business Administration and Management, B
Business Administration, Management and Operations, M
Ceramic Arts and Ceramics, B
Commercial and Advertising Art, B
Comparative Literature, B
Computer Programming/Programmer, B
Computer Science, B
Criminal Justice/Law Enforcement Administration, B
Curriculum and Instruction, BM
Design and Applied Arts, B
Drama and Dramatics/Theatre Arts, B
Education, B
Elementary Education and Teaching, B
Energy Management and Policy, M
English Language and Literature, B
Environmental Biology, B
Environmental Studies, B
Finance, B
Fine/Studio Arts, B
Health Services Administration, MO
History, B
Human Resources Management and Services, MO
Journalism, B
Liberal Arts and Sciences Studies and Humanities, B
Management Information Systems and Services, M
Marketing/Marketing Management, B
Mass Communication/Media Studies, B
Mathematics, B
Music, B
Nursing, M
Parks, Recreation and Leisure Facilities Management, B
Physical Therapy/Therapist, D
Physician Assistant, M
Political Science and Government, B
Pre-Dentistry Studies, B
Pre-Law Studies, B
Pre-Medicine/Pre-Medical Studies, B
Pre-Veterinary Studies, B
Psychology, B
Public Health (MPH, DPH), B
Radio and Television, B
Secondary Education and Teaching, B
Social Work, B
Sociology, B
Special Education and Teaching, M
Sport and Fitness Administration/Management, BM
Sustainability Management, M

Telecommunications, O

GRANITE STATE COLLEGE

Accounting and Finance, B
Behavioral Sciences, A
Business Administration and Management, B
Business/Commerce, A
Communication Disorders Sciences and Services, A
Computer and Information Sciences, A
Computer/Information Technology Services Administration and Management, B
Criminal Justice/Safety Studies, B
Digital Communication and Media/Multimedia, B
Early Childhood Education and Teaching, AB
Elementary Education and Teaching, B
English Language and Literature, B
English/Language Arts Teacher Education, B
General Studies, AB
Health Information/Medical Records Administration/Administrator, B
Health Services/Allied Health/Health Sciences, B
Health/Health Care Administration/Management, B
History, B
Hospitality Administration/Management, B
Human Resources Management/Personnel Administration, B
Human Services, B
Information Technology, B
Junior High/Intermediate/Middle School Education and Teaching, B
Liberal Arts and Sciences Studies and Humanities, B
Management, M
Management Information Systems and Services, B
Management Science, B
Marketing/Marketing Management, B
Multi-/Interdisciplinary Studies, B
Non-Profit/Public/Organizational Management, B
Operations Management and Supervision, B
Organizational Management, M
Project Management, M
Psychology, B
Secondary Education and Teaching, B
Social Sciences, B
Social Studies Teacher Education, B
Teaching English as a Second or Foreign Language/ESL Language Instructor, B

GREAT BAY COMMUNITY COLLEGE

Accounting, A
Automobile/Automotive Mechanics Technology/Technician, A
Biology Technician/BioTechnology Laboratory Technician, A
Business Administration and Management, A
CAD/CADD Drafting and/or Design Technology/Technician, A
Computer Systems Networking and Telecommunications, A
Computer and Information Sciences, A
Criminal Justice/Law Enforcement Administration, A
Early Childhood Education and Teaching, A
Education, A
General Studies, A
Human Services, A
Liberal Arts and Sciences Studies and Humanities, A
Marketing/Marketing Management, A
Surgical Technology/Technologist, A
Tourism and Travel Services Management, A
Veterinary/Animal Health Technology/Technician and Veterinary Assistant, A

KEENE STATE COLLEGE

Acting, B
American History (United States), B
American/United States Studies/Civilization, B
Applied Mathematics, B
Architecture, B
Athletic Training and Sports Medicine, B
Biological and Physical Sciences, B
Biology Teacher Education, B
Biology/Biological Sciences, B
Business Administration and Management, B
Chemistry, B
Chemistry Teacher Education, B

Cinematography and Film/Video Production, B
Commercial and Advertising Art, B
Communication Studies/Speech Communication and Rhetoric, B
Computer and Information Sciences, B
Computer and Information Sciences and Support Services, B
Corrections and Criminal Justice, B
Counselor Education/School Counseling and Guidance Services, MO
Curriculum and Instruction, M
Dance, B
Dietetics/Dieticians, B
Digital Communication and Media/Multimedia, B
Directing and Theatrical Production, B
Drama and Dance Teacher Education, B
Early Childhood Education and Teaching, B
Economics, B
Education, MO
Educational Leadership and Administration, MO
Elementary Education and Teaching, B
Engineering Technologies/Technicians, B
English Language and Literature, B
English/Language Arts Teacher Education, B
Environmental Studies, B
Environmental and Occupational Health, M
European History, B
Film/Cinema Studies, B
Fine/Studio Arts, B
French Language Teacher Education, B
French Language and Literature, B
General Studies, B
Geography, B
Geology/Earth Science, B
Health and Physical Education, B
History, B
History Teacher Education, B
Holocaust and Related Studies, B
Journalism, B
Mathematics, B
Mathematics Teacher Education, B
Multi-/Interdisciplinary Studies, B
Music, B
Music Performance, B
Music Teacher Education, B
Music Theory and Composition, B
Occupational Safety and Health Technology/Technician, B
Physical Education Teaching and Coaching, B
Political Science and Government, B
Psychology, B
Public Relations/Image Management, B
School Psychology, MO
Science Teacher Education/General Science Teacher Education, B
Secondary Education and Teaching, B
Social Sciences, B
Social Studies Teacher Education, B
Sociology, B
Spanish Language Teacher Education, B
Spanish Language and Literature, B
Special Education and Teaching, M
Substance Abuse/Addiction Counseling, B
Technical Theatre/Theatre Design and Technology, B
Women's Studies, B

LAKES REGION COMMUNITY COLLEGE

Accounting, A
Animation, Interactive Technology, Video Graphics and Special Effects, A
Automobile/Automotive Mechanics Technology/Technician, A
Business/Commerce, A
Business/Office Automation/Technology/Data Entry, A
Computer and Information Sciences, A
Culinary Arts/Chef Training, A
Early Childhood Education and Teaching, A
Education, A
Electrical/Electronics Equipment Installation and Repair, A
Energy Management and Systems Technology/Technician, A
Fine/Studio Arts, A

Fire Protection and Safety Technology/Technician, A
Fire Science/Firefighting, A
General Studies, A
Gerontology, A
Graphic and Printing Equipment Operator Production, A
Hospitality Administration/Management, A
Human Services, A
Liberal Arts and Sciences Studies and Humanities, A
Marine Maintenance/Fitter and Ship Repair Technology/Technician, A
Restaurant/Food Services Management, A

MANCHESTER COMMUNITY COLLEGE

Accounting, A
Administrative Assistant and Secretarial Science, A
Athletic Training and Sports Medicine, A
Automobile/Automotive Mechanics Technology/Technician, A
Business Administration and Management, A
Child Development, A
Commercial and Advertising Art, A
Community Organization and Advocacy, A
Construction Engineering Technology/Technician, A
Drafting and Design Technology/Technician, A
Drafting/Design Engineering Technologies/Technicians, A
Heating, Air Conditioning, Ventilation and Refrigeration Maintenance Technology/Technician, A
Human Services, A
Information Science/Studies, A
Kindergarten/PreSchool Education and Teaching, A
Kinesiology and Exercise Science, A
Liberal Arts and Sciences Studies and Humanities, A
Management Information Systems and Services, A
Marketing/Marketing Management, A
Medical Administrative Assistant/Secretary, A
Physical Therapy/Therapist, A
Welding Technology/Welder, A

NASHUA COMMUNITY COLLEGE

Accounting, A
Airframe Mechanics and Aircraft Maintenance Technology/Technician, A
Autobody/Collision and Repair Technology/Technician, A
Automobile/Automotive Mechanics Technology/Technician, A
Business Administration and Management, A
Child Development, A
Computer Engineering Technology/Technician, A
Computer Science, A
Computer and Information Sciences, A
Data Processing and Data Processing Technology/Technician, A
Drafting and Design Technology/Technician, A
Electrical, Electronic and Communications Engineering Technology/Technician, A
Electromechanical Technology/Electromechanical Engineering Technology, A
Engineering Technology, A
General Studies, A
Human Services, A
Kindergarten/PreSchool Education and Teaching, A
Legal Assistant/Paralegal, A
Liberal Arts and Sciences Studies and Humanities, A
Machine Tool Technology/Machinist, A
Social Work, A

NEW ENGLAND COLLEGE

Accounting, BM
Art/Art Studies, General, B
Biology/Biological Sciences, B
Business Administration and Management, AB
Computer and Information Sciences, B
Counseling Psychology, M
Criminal Justice/Law Enforcement Administration, B
Drama and Dramatics/Theatre Arts, B
Drawing, B
Education, BMD
Educational Administration and Supervision, MD
Educational Leadership and Administration, MD
Elementary Education and Teaching, B

Environmental Sciences, B
Finance, B
Fine/Studio Arts, B
Health Services Administration, M
Health and Physical Education, B
Health/Health Care Administration/Management, B
Higher Education/Higher Education Administration, MD
History, B
Human Services, M
International Affairs, M
Journalism, B
Liberal Arts and Sciences Studies and Humanities, A
Management, M
Management Strategy and Policy, M
Marketing, M
Marketing/Marketing Management, B
Mass Communication/Media Studies, B
Non-Profit/Public/Organizational Management, M
Parks, Recreation and Leisure Facilities Management, B
Parks, Recreation, Leisure and Fitness Studies, B
Philosophy, B
Physical Education Teaching and Coaching, B
Political Science and Government, B
Pre-Law Studies, B
Project Management, M
Psychology, AB
Public Policy Analysis, M
Public Relations/Image Management, B
Recreation and Park Management, M
Secondary Education and Teaching, B
Sociology, AB
Special Education and Teaching, BM
Sport and Fitness Administration/Management, BM
Teacher Education, Multiple Levels, B
Writing, M

NEW HAMPSHIRE INSTITUTE OF ART

Art Education, M
Ceramic Arts and Ceramics, B
Design and Visual Communications, B
Fine Arts and Art Studies, M
Fine/Studio Arts, B
Illustration, B
Photography, BM
Writing, M

NHTI, CONCORD'S COMMUNITY COLLEGE

Accounting, A
Animation, Interactive Technology, Video Graphics and Special Effects, A
Architectural Engineering Technology/Technician, A
Business Administration and Management, A
Computer Engineering Technology/Technician, A
Computer Programming, Specific Applications, A
Computer Systems Networking and Telecommunications, A
Computer and Information Sciences, A
Criminal Justice/Law Enforcement Administration, A
Dental Assisting/Assistant, A
Dental Hygiene/Hygienist, A
Diagnostic Medical Sonography/Sonographer and Ultrasound Technician, A
Electrical, Electronic and Communications Engineering Technology/Technician, A
Emergency Medical Technology/Technician (EMT Paramedic), A
Engineering Technology, A
General Studies, A
Hotel/Motel Administration/Management, A
Human Resources Management/Personnel Administration, A
Human Services, A
Kindergarten/PreSchool Education and Teaching, A
Legal Assistant/Paralegal, A
Liberal Arts and Sciences Studies and Humanities, A
Marketing/Marketing Management, A
Mechanical Engineering/Mechanical Technology/Technician, A
Mental Health Counseling/Counselor, A
Real Estate, A
Sport and Fitness Administration/Management, A

Substance Abuse/Addiction Counseling, A
Teacher Assistant/Aide, A
Tourism and Travel Services Management, A
Visual and Performing Arts, A

NORTHEAST CATHOLIC COLLEGE

Liberal Arts and Sciences Studies and Humanities, AB

PLYMOUTH STATE UNIVERSITY

Accounting, B
Adult and Continuing Education and Teaching, D
Art Education, M
Art History, Criticism and Conservation, B
Art Teacher Education, B
Art/Art Studies, General, B
Athletic Training and Sports Medicine, BM
Atmospheric Sciences and Meteorology, B
BioTechnology, B
Biological and Biomedical Sciences, M
Biology/Biological Sciences, B
Business Administration and Management, B
Business Administration, Management and Operations, M
Business/Commerce, B
Chemistry, B
City/Urban, Community and Regional Planning, B
Clinical Psychology, MO
Communication Studies/Speech Communication and Rhetoric, B
Computer Science, B
Counselor Education/School Counseling and Guidance Services, M
Criminal Justice/Safety Studies, B
Cultural Studies, M
Curriculum and Instruction, M
Drama and Dramatics/Theatre Arts, B
Early Childhood Education and Teaching, B
Education, MO
Educational Leadership and Administration, MO
Educational Media/Instructional Technology, M
Elementary Education and Teaching, BM
English Education, M
English Language and Literature, B
Environmental Biology, B
Environmental Policy and Resource Management, M
Environmental Studies, B
Finance, B
Fine/Studio Arts, B
Foreign Language Teacher Education, M
Foreign Languages and Literatures, B
French Language and Literature, B
Geography, B
Graphic Design, B
Health Education, M
Health Promotion, M
Health and Physical Education, B
Higher Education/Higher Education Administration, DO
Historic Preservation and Conservation, M
History, B
Humanities/Humanistic Studies, B
Information Technology, B
Kinesiology and Exercise Science, B
Marketing/Marketing Management, B
Mathematics, B
Mathematics Teacher Education, BM
Meteorology, M
Multi-/Interdisciplinary Studies, B
Music, B
Music Teacher Education, BM
Parks, Recreation, Leisure and Fitness Studies, B
Philosophy, B
Physical Education Teaching and Coaching, M
Political Science and Government, B
Psychology, B
Public Administration, B
Public Health Education and Promotion, B
Reading Teacher Education, M
School Psychology, MO
Science Teacher Education/General Science Teacher Education, BM
Secondary Education and Teaching, M
Social Sciences, B
Social Studies Teacher Education, BM

Social Work, B
Spanish Language and Literature, B
Special Education and Teaching, M
Sport and Fitness Administration/Management, B
Teacher Education and Professional Development, Specific Subject Areas, B
Tourism and Travel Services Management, B

RIVER VALLEY COMMUNITY COLLEGE

Accounting, A
Business Administration and Management, A
Clinical/Medical Laboratory Technician, A
Computer Science, A
Computer Systems Networking and Telecommunications, A
Criminal Justice/Law Enforcement Administration, A
Early Childhood Education and Teaching, A
General Studies, A
Human Services, A
Liberal Arts and Sciences Studies and Humanities, A
Management Information Systems and Services, A
Occupational Therapist Assistant, A
Physical Therapist Assistant, A
Respiratory Care Therapy/Therapist, A
Web/Multimedia Management and Webmaster, A

RIVIER UNIVERSITY

Biology Teacher Education, B
Biology/Biological Sciences, B
Business Administration and Management, B
Business Administration, Management and Operations, M
Clinical Psychology, M
Computer Science, M
Counseling Psychology, M
Counselor Education/School Counseling and Guidance Services, M
Criminal Justice/Law Enforcement Administration, B
Criminology, B
Curriculum and Instruction, M
Early Childhood Education and Teaching, BM
Education, BMDO
Educational Administration and Supervision, M
Educational Leadership and Administration, DO
Elementary Education and Teaching, BM
English, M
English Language and Literature, B
English/Language Arts Teacher Education, B
Experimental Psychology, M
Finance, B
Foreign Language Teacher Education, M
History, B
Information Technology, B
Liberal Arts and Sciences Studies and Humanities, AB
Management Information Systems and Services, M
Marketing/Marketing Management, B
Mathematics, BM
Mathematics Teacher Education, B
Modern Languages, B
Nursing, M
Nursing - Advanced Practice, M
Nursing Education, M
Political Science and Government, B
Pre-Dentistry Studies, B
Pre-Law Studies, B
Pre-Medicine/Pre-Medical Studies, B
Pre-Veterinary Studies, B
Psychiatric/Mental Health Nurse/Nursing, M
Psychology, BM
Reading Teacher Education, M
Secondary Education and Teaching, B
Social Studies Teacher Education, BM
Sociology, B
Spanish Language and Literature, B
Special Education and Teaching, BM
Writing, M

SAINT ANSELM COLLEGE

Accounting, B
Art/Art Studies, General, B
Biochemistry, B
Biological and Physical Sciences, B
Biology/Biological Sciences, B
Business/Commerce, B

Business/Managerial Economics, B
Chemistry, B
Classical, Ancient Mediterranean and Near Eastern Studies and Archaeology, B
Classics and Classical Languages, Literatures, and Linguistics, B
Communication Studies/Speech Communication and Rhetoric, B
Computer Science, B
Criminal Justice/Safety Studies, B
Economics, B
Elementary Education and Teaching, B
Engineering, B
English Language and Literature, B
Environmental Studies, B
Finance, B
French Language and Literature, B
History, B
International Business/Trade/Commerce, B
International Relations and Affairs, B
Liberal Arts and Sciences Studies and Humanities, B
Mathematics, B
Multi-/Interdisciplinary Studies, B
Peace Studies and Conflict Resolution, B
Philosophy, B
Physics, B
Political Science and Government, B
Pre-Dentistry Studies, B
Pre-Law Studies, B
Pre-Medicine/Pre-Medical Studies, B
Psychology, B
Secondary Education and Teaching, B
Social Work, B
Sociology, B
Spanish Language and Literature, B
Theology/Theological Studies, B

SOUTHERN NEW HAMPSHIRE UNIVERSITY

Accounting, ABMO
Accounting and Finance, B
Baking and Pastry Arts/Baker/Pastry Chef, A
Business Administration and Management, AB
Business Administration, Management and Operations, MO
Business Education, M
Business, Management, Marketing, and Related Support Services, B
Child Development, M
Community Health and Preventive Medicine, MO
Computer Graphics, B
Computer and Information Sciences, AB
Conflict Resolution and Mediation/Peace Studies, M
Corrections and Criminal Justice, B
Culinary Arts/Chef Training, AB
Curriculum and Instruction, M
Early Childhood Education and Teaching, B
Economics, B
Education, BMDO
Educational Administration and Supervision, O
Educational Leadership and Administration, MD
Educational Media/Instructional Technology, M
Elementary Education and Teaching, BM
English Education, M
English Language and Literature, B
English as a Second Language, M
English/Language Arts Teacher Education, B
Entrepreneurship/Entrepreneurial Studies, M
Environmental Policy and Resource Management, M
Environmental Sciences, B
Environmental Studies, B
Ethics, M
Fashion Merchandising, AB
Finance and Banking, MO
General Studies, B
Graphic Design, B
Health Informatics, M
Health Services Administration, M
History, B
Hospitality Administration/Management, B
Human Resources Management and Services, O
Industrial and Labor Relations, M
Industrial and Manufacturing Management, MO
International Business/Trade/Commerce, BO

Internet and Interactive Multimedia, M
Investment Management, M
Legal and Justice Studies, M
Liberal Arts and Sciences Studies and Humanities, B
Management, M
Management Information Systems and Services, MO
Marketing, MO
Marketing/Marketing Management, AB
Mathematics, B
Mathematics Teacher Education, B
Music Teacher Education, B
Non-Profit/Public/Organizational Management, O
Operations Management and Supervision, B
Organizational Communication, B
Organizational Management, M
Political Science and Government, B
Project Management, MO
Psychology, BMO
Public Administration, B
Quality Management, O
Reading Teacher Education, M
Science Teacher Education/General Science Teacher Education, B
Secondary Education and Teaching, M
Social Sciences, B
Social Studies Teacher Education, B
Special Education and Teaching, BM
Sport and Fitness Administration/Management, BMO
Supply Chain Management, MO
Sustainability Management, M
Taxation, M
Writing, M

THOMAS MORE COLLEGE OF LIBERAL ARTS

Liberal Arts and Sciences Studies and Humanities, B

UNIVERSITY OF NEW HAMPSHIRE

Accounting, M
Agricultural Business and Management, A
Ancient/Classical Greek Language and Literature, B
Animal Sciences, ABMD
Anthropology, B
Applied Horticulture/Horticultural Operations, A
Applied Mathematics, B
Art/Art Studies, General, B
Biochemistry, BMD
Biochemistry, Biophysics and Molecular Biology, B
Biological and Biomedical Sciences, BMD
Biology/Biological Sciences, B
Biomedical Sciences, B
Biomedical/Medical Engineering, B
Business Administration and Management, B
Business Administration, Management and Operations, M
Business/Commerce, A
Chemical Engineering, BMD
Chemistry, BMD
Child and Family Studies, MO
City/Urban, Community and Regional Planning, B
Civil Engineering, BMD
Civil Engineering Technology/Technician, A
Classics and Classical Languages, Literatures, and Linguistics, B
Communication Disorders, M
Communication Disorders Sciences and Services, B
Communication Studies/Speech Communication and Rhetoric, B
Community Organization and Advocacy, A
Comparative Literature, M
Composition, M
Computer Engineering, B
Computer Science, MDO
Computer and Information Sciences, B
Conservation Biology, M
Counselor Education/School Counseling and Guidance Services, M
Criminology, B
Culinary Arts and Related Services, A
Drama and Dramatics/Theatre Arts, B
Early Childhood Education and Teaching, M
Economics, BMD

Education, MDO
Educational Administration and Supervision, MO
Educational Leadership and Administration, O
Electrical Engineering, MD
Electrical, Electronics and Communications Engineering, B
Elementary Education and Teaching, M
Engineering, B
English, MD
English Education, M
English Language and Literature, B
Environmental Policy and Resource Management, M
Environmental Sciences, B
Environmental/Environmental Health Engineering, B
European Studies/Civilization, B
Evolutionary Biology, D
Fine/Studio Arts, B
Fish, Game and Wildlife Management, M
Foodservice Systems Administration/Management, A
Forestry, BM
Forestry Technology/Technician, A
French Language and Literature, B
French Studies, B
Genetics, BMD
Geographic Information Systems, O
Geography, B
Geology/Earth Science, BM
Geosciences, MD
German Language and Literature, B
Health/Health Care Administration/Management, B
Higher Education/Higher Education Administration, O
History, BMD
Horse Husbandry/Equine Science and Management, B
Horticultural Science, B
Hospitality Administration/Management, B
Human Development and Family Studies, B
Humanities/Humanistic Studies, B
Hydrology and Water Resources Science, M
Information Technology, B
International Development, M
International Relations and Affairs, B
Italian Language and Literature, B
Kinesiology and Exercise Science, B
Kinesiology and Movement Studies, MO
Latin Language and Literature, B
Law and Legal Studies, MDO
Legal and Justice Studies, M
Liberal Studies, M
Linguistics, BM
Management Information Systems and Services, M
Marine Sciences, M
Marriage and Family Therapy/Counseling, M
Materials Sciences, MD
Mathematics, BMDO
Mathematics Teacher Education, B
Mathematics and Statistics, B
Mechanical Engineering, BMD
Microbiology, MD
Multi-/Interdisciplinary Studies, B
Museology/Museum Studies, M
Music, BM
Musicology and Ethnomusicology, M
Natural Resource Economics, B
Natural Resources Management/Development and Policy, M
Natural Resources and Conservation, BD
Nursing, MDO
Nursing - Advanced Practice, O
Nutritional Sciences, BMD
Occupational Therapy/Therapist, BMO
Ocean Engineering, BMDO
Oceanography, Chemical and Physical, M
Painting, M
Parks, Recreation and Leisure Facilities Management, B
Philosophy, B
Physical Education Teaching and Coaching, O
Physics, BMD
Plant Biology, MD
Political Science and Government, BMO
Psychology, BD
Public Administration, M

Public Health, MO
Recreation and Park Management, M
Resource Management, M
Russian Language and Literature, B
Science Teacher Education/General Science Teacher Education, D
Secondary Education and Teaching, M
Sign Language Interpretation and Translation, B
Social Work, BMO
Sociology, BMD
Software Engineering, O
Spanish Language and Literature, BM
Special Education and Teaching, M
Statistics, B
Sustainability Management, O
Therapeutic Recreation, M
Urban and Regional Planning, M
Veterinary/Animal Health Technology/Technician and Veterinary Assistant, A
Water Resources, M
Wildlife and Wildlands Science and Management, B
Women's Studies, B
Zoology/Animal Biology, BMD

UNIVERSITY OF NEW HAMPSHIRE AT MANCHESTER

BioTechnology, B
Biology/Biological Sciences, AB
Business Administration and Management, AB
Computer Science, B
Electrical, Electronic and Communications Engineering Technology/Technician, B
English Language and Literature, B
History, B
Humanities/Humanistic Studies, B
Information Technology, B
Liberal Arts and Sciences Studies and Humanities, A
Mass Communication/Media Studies, B
Mechanical Engineering/Mechanical Technology/Technician, B
Political Science and Government, B
Psychology, B
Sign Language Interpretation and Translation, B

WHITE MOUNTAINS COMMUNITY COLLEGE

Accounting, A
Automobile/Automotive Mechanics Technology/Technician, A
Baking and Pastry Arts/Baker/Pastry Chef, A
Business Administration and Management, A
Computer and Information Sciences, A
Criminal Justice/Safety Studies, A
Culinary Arts/Chef Training, A
Diesel Mechanics Technology/Technician, A
Early Childhood Education and Teaching, A
Education, A
Environmental Studies, A
General Studies, A
Health Services/Allied Health/Health Sciences, A
Human Services, A
Liberal Arts and Sciences Studies and Humanities, A
Medical Office Assistant/Specialist, A
Medical/Clinical Assistant, A
Office Management and Supervision, A
Resort Management, A
Welding Technology/Welder, A

New Jersey

ASSUMPTION COLLEGE FOR SISTERS

Liberal Arts and Sciences Studies and Humanities, A
Theology/Theological Studies, A

ATLANTIC CAPE COMMUNITY COLLEGE

Accounting, A
Administrative Assistant and Secretarial Science, A
Business Administration and Management, A
Computer Programming/Programmer, A
Criminal Justice/Police Science, A

Culinary Arts/Chef Training, A
Data Processing and Data Processing
  Technology/Technician, A
Engineering Technologies/Technicians, A
Hotel/Motel Administration/Management, A
Human Services, A
Institutional Food Workers, A
Legal Assistant/Paralegal, A
Liberal Arts and Sciences Studies and Humani-
  ties, A
Management Information Systems and Services, A
Multi-/Interdisciplinary Studies, A
Respiratory Care Therapy/Therapist, A

BERGEN COMMUNITY COLLEGE

Accounting, A
Acting, A
Animation, Interactive Technology, Video Graphics
  and Special Effects, A
Applied Horticulture/Horticultural Operations, A
BioTechnology, A
Biology/Biological Sciences, A
Business Administration and Management, A
Business/Office Automation/Technology/Data En-
  try, A
Chemistry, A
Child Development, A
Communications Technology/Technician, A
Corrections, A
Crafts/Craft Design, Folk Art and Artisanry, A
Criminal Justice/Law Enforcement Administration, A
Criminal Justice/Safety Studies, A
Culinary Arts/Chef Training, A
Dance, A
Dental Hygiene/Hygienist, A
Diagnostic Medical Sonography/Sonographer and
  Ultrasound Technician, A
Drafting and Design Technology/Technician, A
Early Childhood Education and Teaching, A
Economics, A
Education, A
Electrical/Electronics Maintenance and Repair Tech-
  nology, A
Engineering Science, A
Engineering Technology, A
Film/Cinema Studies, A
Finance, A
Fine/Studio Arts, A
Graphic Design, A
History, A
Hospitality Administration/Management, A
Information Technology, A
International Business/Trade/Commerce, A
Journalism, A
Kinesiology and Exercise Science, A
Labor Studies, A
Landscape Architecture, A
Legal Assistant/Paralegal, A
Liberal Arts and Sciences Studies and Humani-
  ties, A
Management Science, A
Manufacturing Technology/Technician, A
Marketing Research, A
Marketing/Marketing Management, A
Mathematics, A
Medical Informatics, A
Medical Office Assistant/Specialist, A
Music, A
Non-Profit/Public/Organizational Management, A
Philosophy, A
Physics, A
Political Science and Government, A
Psychology, A
Radio and Television Broadcasting
  Technology/Technician, A
Radiologic Technology/Science - Radiographer, A
Religion/Religious Studies, A
Respiratory Care Therapy/Therapist, A
Restaurant, Culinary, and Catering
  Management/Manager, A
Social Sciences, A
Social Work, A
Sociology, A
System Administration/Administrator, A
Technical Theatre/Theatre Design and Technol-
  ogy, A

Veterinary/Animal Health Technology/Technician and
  Veterinary Assistant, A
Web/Multimedia Management and Webmaster, A
Women's Studies, A

BERKELEY COLLEGE–WOODLAND PARK CAMPUS

Accounting, B
Business Administration and Management, AB
Computer/Information Technology Services Adminis-
  tration and Management, AB
Criminal Justice/Law Enforcement Administration, B
Criminal Justice/Police Science, A
Design and Applied Arts, B
Fashion Merchandising, B
Financial Planning and Services, AB
Graphic Design, B
Health Information/Medical Records
  Technology/Technician, A
Health Services/Allied Health/Health Sciences, A
Health/Health Care Administration/Management, AB
Interior Design, AB
International Business/Trade/Commerce, AB
Legal Professions and Studies, AB
Marketing/Marketing Management, B
Medical/Clinical Assistant, A
Surgical Technology/Technologist, A

BLOOMFIELD COLLEGE

Accounting, BM
Applied Mathematics, B
Biology/Biological Sciences, B
Business Administration and Management, B
Chemistry, B
Clinical/Medical Laboratory Science and Allied Pro-
  fessions, B
Computer Science, B
Computer Systems Networking and Telecommunica-
  tions, B
Computer and Information Sciences, B
E-Commerce/Electronic Commerce, B
Education, B
English Language and Literature, B
History, B
Logistics and Materials Management, B
Multi-/Interdisciplinary Studies, B
Philosophy, B
Political Science and Government, B
Psychology, B
Religion/Religious Studies, B
Sociology, B
Visual and Performing Arts, B

BROOKDALE COMMUNITY COLLEGE

Accounting, A
Administrative Assistant and Secretarial Science, A
Architecture, A
Automotive Engineering Technology/Technician, A
Business Administration and Management, A
Business/Commerce, A
Computer and Information Sciences, A
Criminal Justice/Police Science, A
Culinary Arts/Chef Training, A
Dental Hygiene/Hygienist, A
Drafting and Design Technology/Technician, A
Education, A
Electrical, Electronic and Communications Engineer-
  ing Technology/Technician, A
Engineering, A
Fashion Merchandising, A
Fine/Studio Arts, A
Graphic Design, A
Interior Design, A
Legal Assistant/Paralegal, A
Liberal Arts and Sciences Studies and Humani-
  ties, A
Marketing/Marketing Management, A
Medical Radiologic Technology/Science - Radiation
  Therapist, A
Multi-/Interdisciplinary Studies, A
Public Relations/Image Management, A
Radio and Television Broadcasting
  Technology/Technician, A
Respiratory Care Therapy/Therapist, A
Social Sciences, A
Social Work, A

System Administration/Administrator, A
Teacher Assistant/Aide, A

CALDWELL UNIVERSITY

Accounting, BM
Applied Behavior Analysis, MDO
Art Therapy/Therapist, M
Art/Art Studies, General, B
Biology/Biological Sciences, B
Business Administration and Management, B
Business Administration, Management and Opera-
  tions, M
Clinical Laboratory Science/Medical
  Technology/Technologist, B
Communication Studies/Speech Communication
  and Rhetoric, B
Computer and Information Sciences, B
Counseling Psychology, MO
Counselor Education/School Counseling and Guid-
  ance Services, MO
Criminal Justice/Safety Studies, B
Curriculum and Instruction, M
Economics, B
Education, MDO
Educational Administration and Supervision, MO
Elementary Education and Teaching, B
English Language and Literature, B
Fine/Studio Arts, B
Graphic Design, B
History, B
Information Technology, B
International Business/Trade/Commerce, B
Marketing/Marketing Management, B
Mathematics, B
Multi-/Interdisciplinary Studies, B
Music, B
Political Science and Government, B
Psychology, B
Reading Teacher Education, MO
School Psychology, MO
Secondary Education and Teaching, B
Social Sciences, B
Sociology, B
Spanish Language and Literature, B
Special Education and Teaching, MO
Theology/Theological Studies, B

CAMDEN COUNTY COLLEGE

Accounting Technology/Technician and Bookkeep-
  ing, A
Administrative Assistant and Secretarial Science, A
Automotive Engineering Technology/Technician, A
Biology Technician/BioTechnology Laboratory Tech-
  nician, A
Business Administration and Management, A
Cinematography and Film/Video Production, A
Clinical/Medical Laboratory Technician, A
Communication Studies/Speech Communication
  and Rhetoric, A
Computer and Information Sciences, A
Criminal Justice/Police Science, A
Dental Assisting/Assistant, A
Dental Hygiene/Hygienist, A
Dietetic Technician (DTR), A
Dietetics/Dieticians, A
Drafting and Design Technology/Technician, A
Early Childhood Education and Teaching, A
Electrical, Electronic and Communications Engineer-
  ing Technology/Technician, A
Electromechanical Technology/Electromechanical
  Engineering Technology, A
Emergency Medical Technology/Technician (EMT
  Paramedic), A
Engineering Science, A
Engineering Technologies/Technicians, A
Fine/Studio Arts, A
Fire Protection and Safety Technology/Technician, A
Fire Services Administration, A
Health Information/Medical Records
  Administration/Administrator, A
Health Services/Allied Health/Health Sciences, A
Industrial Production Technologies/Technicians, A
Legal Assistant/Paralegal, A
Liberal Arts and Sciences Studies and Humani-
  ties, A
Management Information Systems and Services, A

Marketing/Marketing Management, A
Massage Therapy/Therapeutic Massage, A
Mechanical Engineering Related
  Technologies/Technicians, A
Mechanical Engineering/Mechanical
  Technology/Technician, A
Opticianry/Ophthalmic Dispensing Optician, A
Prepress/Desktop Publishing and Digital Imaging
  Design, A
Radio and Television Broadcasting
  Technology/Technician, A
Rehabilitation and Therapeutic Professions, A
Sign Language Interpretation and Translation, A
Social Work, A
Sport and Fitness Administration/Management, A
Substance Abuse/Addiction Counseling, A
Teacher Education, Multiple Levels, A
Veterinary/Animal Health Technology/Technician and
  Veterinary Assistant, A

CENTENARY COLLEGE

Accounting, BM
Biology/Biological Sciences, B
Business Administration and Management, B
Business Administration, Management and Opera-
  tions, M
Commercial and Advertising Art, B
Counseling Psychology, M
Criminology, B
Education, BM
Educational Leadership and Administration, M
Elementary Education and Teaching, B
English Language and Literature, B
Equestrian/Equine Studies, AB
Fashion/Apparel Design, B
Finance, B
Graphic Design, B
History, B
International Relations and Affairs, B
Liberal Arts and Sciences Studies and Humani-
  ties, A
Management Science, B
Marketing/Marketing Management, B
Mass Communication/Media Studies, B
Mathematics, B
Political Science and Government, B
Psychology, B
Secondary Education and Teaching, B
Social Work, B
Sociology, B
Special Education and Teaching, BM
Sport and Fitness Administration/Management, B
Technical Theatre/Theatre Design and Technol-
  ogy, B

THE COLLEGE OF NEW JERSEY

Accounting, B
African-American/Black Studies, B
Art Teacher Education, B
Art/Art Studies, General, B
Biology Teacher Education, B
Biology/Biological Sciences, B
Biomedical/Medical Engineering, B
Business Administration and Management, B
Chemistry, B
Chemistry Teacher Education, B
Civil Engineering, B
Commercial and Advertising Art, B
Computer Engineering, B
Computer and Information Sciences, B
Counselor Education/School Counseling and Guid-
  ance Services, M
Criminal Justice/Law Enforcement Administration, B
Early Childhood Education and Teaching, BM
Economics, B
Education, MO
Education/Teaching of Individuals with Hearing Im-
  pairments, Including Deafness, B
Educational Leadership and Administration, MO
Electrical, Electronics and Communications Engi-
  neering, B
Elementary Education and Teaching, BM
Engineering Science, B
English, M
English Language and Literature, B
English as a Second Language, MO

English/Language Arts Teacher Education, B
Fine/Studio Arts, B
Gender Studies, O
Health Education, M
History, B
History Teacher Education, B
Intermedia/Multimedia, B
International Relations and Affairs, B
International and Comparative Education, MO
Journalism, B
Marriage and Family Therapy/Counseling, O
Mathematics, B
Mathematics Teacher Education, B
Mechanical Engineering, B
Multi-/Interdisciplinary Studies, B
Music, B
Music Teacher Education, B
Nursing, MO
Philosophy, B
Physical Education Teaching and Coaching, BM
Physics, B
Physics Teacher Education, B
Political Science and Government, B
Psychology, B
Public Health (MPH, DPH), B
Reading Teacher Education, MO
Secondary Education and Teaching, BM
Sociology, B
Spanish Language and Literature, B
Special Education and Teaching, BMO
Substance Abuse/Addiction Counseling, MO
Technology Teacher Education/Industrial Arts
  Teacher Education, B
Urban Education and Leadership, B
Women's Studies, B

COLLEGE OF SAINT ELIZABETH

Allied Health Diagnostic, Intervention, and Treat-
  ment Professions, B
Allied Health and Medical Assisting Services, B
American/United States Studies/Civilization, B
Art/Art Studies, General, B
Biochemistry, B
Biology/Biological Sciences, B
Business Administration and Management, B
Business Administration, Management and Opera-
  tions, M
Chemistry, B
Clinical Laboratory Science/Medical
  Technology/Technologist, B
Communication Studies/Speech Communication
  and Rhetoric, B
Computer Science, B
Computer and Information Sciences, B
Counseling Psychology, MO
Criminology, M
Dietetics and Clinical Nutrition Services, B
Dietetics/Dieticians, B
Economics, B
Education, O
Educational Leadership and Administration, MD
Educational Media/Instructional Technology, O
English Language and Literature, B
Exercise and Sports Science, O
Forensic Psychology, M
Health Services Administration, M
Higher Education/Higher Education Administra-
  tion, O
History, B
Human Resources Management and Services, M
Human Resources Management/Personnel Adminis-
  tration, B
International/Global Studies, B
Mathematics, B
Multi-/Interdisciplinary Studies, B
Music, B
Nursing, M
Nutritional Sciences, MO
Organizational Management, M
Philosophy, B
Psychology, BMO
Public Administration, M
Sociology, B
Spanish Language and Literature, B
Special Education and Teaching, M
Student Personnel Services, O

Teacher Education, Multiple Levels, B
Theology and Religious Vocations, M
Theology/Theological Studies, B
Women's Studies, B

COUNTY COLLEGE OF MORRIS

Agricultural Business and Management, A
Airline/Commercial/Professional Pilot and Flight
  Crew, A
Biology Technician/BioTechnology Laboratory Tech-
  nician, A
Business Administration and Management, A
Business, Management, Marketing, and Related
  Support Services, A
Chemical Technology/Technician, A
Clinical/Medical Laboratory Technician, A
Communication and Media Studies, A
Computer Science, A
Criminal Justice/Police Science, A
Culinary Arts/Chef Training, A
Design and Applied Arts, A
Electrical, Electronic and Communications Engineer-
  ing Technology/Technician, A
Engineering Science, A
Engineering Technologies/Technicians, A
Fine Arts and Art Studies, A
Fire Protection and Safety Technology/Technician, A
Graphic Design, A
Hospitality Administration/Management, A
Kindergarten/PreSchool Education and Teaching, A
Kinesiology and Exercise Science, A
Liberal Arts and Sciences Studies and Humani-
  ties, A
Management Information Systems and Services, A
Mechanical Engineering/Mechanical
  Technology/Technician, A
Multi-/Interdisciplinary Studies, A
Music, A
Occupational Therapist Assistant, A
Photography, A
Public Administration, A
Public Health (MPH, DPH), A
Radiologic Technology/Science - Radiographer, A
Respiratory Care Therapy/Therapist, A
Telecommunications Technology/Technician, A
Web Page, Digital/Multimedia and Information Re-
  sources Design, A

CUMBERLAND COUNTY COLLEGE

Accounting, A
Administrative Assistant and Secretarial Science, A
Aeronautical/Aerospace Engineering
  Technology/Technician, A
Building/Construction Finishing, Manage-
  ment, and Inspection, A
Business Administration and Management, A
Computer Systems Networking and Telecommunica-
  tions, A
Computer and Information Sciences, A
Criminal Justice/Police Science, A
Education, A
Fine/Studio Arts, A
Health and Medical Administrative Services, A
Horticultural Science, A
Industrial Technology/Technician, A
Legal Assistant/Paralegal, A
Liberal Arts and Sciences Studies and Humani-
  ties, A
Medical Radiologic Technology/Science - Radiation
  Therapist, A
Ornamental Horticulture, A
Respiratory Care Therapy/Therapist, A
Social Work, A

DEVRY UNIVERSITY (NORTH BRUNS-
WICK)

Biomedical Technology/Technician, B
Business Administration and Management, B
Business Administration, Management and Opera-
  tions, BM
Computer Systems Analysis/Analyst, B
Computer Systems Networking and Telecommunica-
  tions, AB
Electrical, Electronic and Communications Engineer-
  ing Technology/Technician, AB

Electroneurodiagnostic/Electroencephalographic Technology/Technologist, A
Health Information/Medical Records Technology/Technician, A
Web Page, Digital/Multimedia and Information Resources Design, AB

DEVRY UNIVERSITY (PARAMUS)

Business Administration and Management, B
Business Administration, Management and Operations, BM
Computer Systems Analysis/Analyst, B
Computer Systems Networking and Telecommunications, AB
Electrical, Electronic and Communications Engineering Technology/Technician, AB
Web Page, Digital/Multimedia and Information Resources Design, AB

DREW UNIVERSITY

African-American/Black Studies, B
Anthropology, B
Art History, Criticism and Conservation, B
Biochemistry, B
Bioethics/Medical Ethics, MDO
Biological and Biomedical Sciences, M
Biology/Biological Sciences, B
Business Administration and Management, B
Chemistry, BM
Chinese Studies, B
Classics and Classical Languages, Literatures, and Linguistics, B
Computer Science, B
Drama and Dramatics/Theatre Arts, B
Economics, B
Education, M
English, M
English Language and Literature, B
Environmental Studies, B
Foreign Language Teacher Education, M
French Language and Literature, BM
German Language and Literature, B
History, BMD
Holocaust Studies, O
Humanities/Humanistic Studies, MDO
Interdisciplinary Studies, MDO
International Relations and Affairs, B
Italian Language and Literature, M
Mathematics, B
Mathematics Teacher Education, M
Music, B
Philosophy, B
Physics, BM
Political Science and Government, B
Psychology, B
Religion/Religious Studies, B
Science Teacher Education/General Science Teacher Education, M
Social Studies Teacher Education, M
Sociology, B
Spanish Language and Literature, BM
Theater, M
Theology and Religious Vocations, MDO
Translation and Interpretation, M
Women's Studies, B
Writing, M

ESSEX COUNTY COLLEGE

Accounting, A
Accounting Technology/Technician and Bookkeeping, A
Administrative Assistant and Secretarial Science, A
Architectural Engineering Technology/Technician, A
Art/Art Studies, General, A
BioTechnology, A
Biology/Biological Sciences, A
Business Administration and Management, A
Business Teacher Education, A
Chemical Technology/Technician, A
Chemistry, A
Civil Engineering Technology/Technician, A
Communications Technology/Technician, A
Computer Programming, Specific Applications, A
Computer Programming/Programmer, A
Computer Science, A
Computer and Information Sciences, A

Criminal Justice/Police Science, A
Dental Hygiene/Hygienist, A
Education, A
Educational/Instructional Media Design, A
Electrical, Electronic and Communications Engineering Technology/Technician, A
Energy Management and Systems Technology/Technician, A
Engineering, A
Engineering Technologies/Technicians, A
Health Professions and Related Clinical Sciences, A
Health Services/Allied Health/Health Sciences, A
Health/Health Care Administration/Management, A
Health/Medical Preparatory Programs, A
Hotel/Motel Administration/Management, A
Human Services, A
Industrial Production Technologies/Technicians, A
Information Science/Studies, A
Kindergarten/PreSchool Education and Teaching, A
Legal Assistant/Paralegal, A
Liberal Arts and Sciences Studies and Humanities, A
Manufacturing Technology/Technician, A
Mathematics, A
Medical Radiologic Technology/Science - Radiation Therapist, A
Music, A
Opticianry/Ophthalmic Dispensing Optician, A
Physical Education Teaching and Coaching, A
Physical Therapist Assistant, A
Respiratory Care Therapy/Therapist, A
Social Sciences, A
Social Work, A

FAIRLEIGH DICKINSON UNIVERSITY, COLLEGE AT FLORHAM

Accounting, BM
Allied Health Diagnostic, Intervention, and Treatment Professions, B
Biochemistry, B
Biological and Biomedical Sciences, M
Biology/Biological Sciences, B
Business Administration and Management, B
Business Administration, Management and Operations, MO
Chemical Engineering, MO
Chemistry, BM
Cinematography and Film/Video Production, B
Clinical Laboratory Science/Medical Technology/Technologist, B
Clinical Psychology, M
Communication Studies/Speech Communication and Rhetoric, B
Computer Science, M
Computer and Information Sciences, B
Corporate and Organizational Communication, M
Counseling Psychology, M
Criminology, B
Drama and Dramatics/Theatre Arts, B
Economics, B
Education, MO
Educational Leadership and Administration, M
Educational Media/Instructional Technology, O
English Language and Literature, B
Entrepreneurial and Small Business Operations, B
Entrepreneurship/Entrepreneurial Studies, BMO
Finance, B
Finance and Banking, MO
French Language and Literature, B
General Studies, B
Health Services Administration, M
Health Services/Allied Health/Health Sciences, B
History, B
Hospitality Administration/Management, BM
Human Resources Management and Services, M
Humanities/Humanistic Studies, B
Industrial and Organizational Psychology, M
International Business/Trade/Commerce, MO
Management, M
Management of Technology, O
Marine Biology and Biological Oceanography, B
Marketing, MO
Marketing/Marketing Management, B
Mathematics, B
Medical Radiologic Technology/Science - Radiation Therapist, B

Organizational Behavior Studies, MO
Organizational Management, O
Pharmacology, MO
Philosophy, B
Political Science and Government, B
Psychology, BMO
Public Administration, M
Reading Teacher Education, O
Respiratory Care Therapy/Therapist, B
Sociology, B
Spanish Language and Literature, B
Sport and Fitness Administration/Management, M
Sustainability Management, O
Taxation, MO
Visual and Performing Arts, B
Writing, M

FAIRLEIGH DICKINSON UNIVERSITY, METROPOLITAN CAMPUS

Accounting, BMO
Allied Health Diagnostic, Intervention, and Treatment Professions, B
Biochemistry, B
Biological and Biomedical Sciences, M
Biological and Physical Sciences, B
Biology/Biological Sciences, B
Business Administration and Management, B
Business Administration, Management and Operations, MO
Chemistry, BM
Civil Engineering Technology/Technician, B
Clinical Laboratory Science/Medical Technology/Technologist, B
Clinical Psychology, MD
Communication and Media Studies, BM
Comparative Literature, M
Computer Engineering, M
Computer Science, BM
Construction Engineering Technology/Technician, B
Criminal Justice/Law Enforcement Administration, B
Criminology, M
Curriculum and Instruction, M
Economics, B
Education, MO
Educational Leadership and Administration, M
Educational Media/Instructional Technology, O
Electrical Engineering, M
Electrical, Electronic and Communications Engineering Technology/Technician, B
Electrical, Electronics and Communications Engineering, B
Electronic Commerce, M
Engineering and Applied Sciences, M
English, M
English Language and Literature, B
Entrepreneurial and Small Business Operations, B
Entrepreneurship/Entrepreneurial Studies, MO
Environmental Sciences, B
Experimental Psychology, MO
Finance, B
Finance and Banking, MO
Fine Arts and Art Studies, M
Forensic Psychology, M
Foundations and Philosophy of Education, M
French Language and Literature, B
General Studies, B
Health Information/Medical Records Administration/Administrator, B
Health Services Administration, M
History, BM
Homeland Security, M
Hospitality Administration/Management, BM
Human Resources Management and Services, MO
Humanities/Humanistic Studies, B
Information Technology, B
International Affairs, M
International Business/Trade/Commerce, M
International Relations and Affairs, B
Liberal Arts and Sciences Studies and Humanities, A
Management, MO
Management Information Systems and Services, MO
Marine Biology and Biological Oceanography, B
Marketing, MO
Marketing/Marketing Management, B

Mathematics, BM
Mechanical Engineering/Mechanical
   Technology/Technician, B
Media Studies, M
Medical Technology, M
Multilingual and Multicultural Education, M
Non-Profit/Public/Organizational Management, BO
Nursing, MDO
Organizational Communication, B
Pharmaceutical Administration, MO
Philosophy, B
Physics, B
Political Science and Government, BM
Psychology, BMDO
Public Administration, MO
Radiologic Technology/Science - Radiographer, A
Reading Teacher Education, O
School Psychology, MD
Science Teacher Education/General Science
   Teacher Education, M
Sociology, B
Spanish Language and Literature, B
Special Education and Teaching, MO
Sport and Fitness Administration/Management, M
Systems Science and Theory, M
Taxation, M
Visual and Performing Arts, B

FELICIAN UNIVERSITY

Accounting, B
Art/Art Studies, General, AB
Biology/Biological Sciences, B
Business Administration and Management, AB
Business Administration, Management and Opera-
   tions, M
Communication Studies/Speech Communication
   and Rhetoric, B
Computer Science, AB
Computer and Information Sciences, B
Counseling Psychology, M
Criminal Justice/Law Enforcement Administration, B
Education, BMO
Educational Administration and Supervision, MO
Elementary Education and Teaching, B
English Language and Literature, AB
Entrepreneurship/Entrepreneurial Studies, M
Gerontological Nursing, MO
Health Services Administration, M
History, B
Humanities/Humanistic Studies, B
International Business/Trade/Commerce, B
Liberal Arts and Sciences Studies and Humani-
   ties, AB
Management Information Systems and Services, B
Marketing/Marketing Management, B
Mass Communication/Media Studies, B
Mathematics, B
Mathematics Teacher Education, B
Music, B
Natural Sciences, B
Nursing, MDO
Nursing - Adult, MO
Nursing - Advanced Practice, MO
Nursing Administration, MDO
Nursing Education, MO
Philosophy, B
Political Science and Government, B
Psychology, B
Religion/Religious Studies, B
Religious Education, MO
School Nursing, MO
Secondary Education and Teaching, B
Special Education and Teaching, B
Teacher Education, Multiple Levels, B

GEORGIAN COURT UNIVERSITY

Accounting, B
Allied Health Diagnostic, Intervention, and Treat-
   ment Professions, B
Applied Behavior Analysis, M
Art/Art Studies, General, B
Biochemistry, B
Biology/Biological Sciences, B
Business Administration and Management, B
Business Administration, Management and Opera-
   tions, M

Chemistry, B
Clinical Laboratory Science/Medical
   Technology/Technologist, B
Clinical Psychology, M
Counseling Psychology, M
Counselor Education/School Counseling and Guid-
   ance Services, O
Criminal Justice/Safety Studies, B
Dance, B
Digital Communication and Media/Multimedia, B
Education, M
Educational Administration and Supervision, M
Educational Leadership and Administration, O
Elementary Education and Teaching, B
English Language and Literature, B
Health Information/Medical Records
   Administration/Administrator, B
Health Psychology, M
History, B
Homeland Security, M
Humanities/Humanistic Studies, B
International Business/Trade/Commerce, B
Kinesiology and Exercise Science, B
Mathematics, B
Multi-/Interdisciplinary Studies, B
Natural Sciences, B
Pastoral Studies/Counseling, O
Psychology, B
Religion/Religious Studies, B
Religious Education, O
School Psychology, MO
Social Work, B
Spanish Language and Literature, B
Theology and Religious Vocations, MO

HUDSON COUNTY COMMUNITY COL-
LEGE

Accounting, A
Accounting Technology/Technician and Bookkeep-
   ing, A
Baking and Pastry Arts/Baker/Pastry Chef, A
Biological and Physical Sciences, A
Business Administration and Management, A
Cartography, A
Child Care Provider/Assistant, A
Computer Engineering Technology/Technician, A
Computer Graphics, A
Computer and Information Sciences, A
Criminal Justice/Police Science, A
Culinary Arts/Chef Training, A
Dietetic Technician (DTR), A
Electrical, Electronic and Communications Engineer-
   ing Technology/Technician, A
Emergency Medical Technology/Technician (EMT
   Paramedic), A
Engineering Science, A
Engineering Technologies/Technicians, A
Environmental Studies, A
Fine/Studio Arts, A
Health Information/Medical Records
   Technology/Technician, A
Health Services/Allied Health/Health Sciences, A
Hospitality Administration/Management, A
Legal Assistant/Paralegal, A
Liberal Arts and Sciences Studies and Humani-
   ties, A
Medical Transcription/Transcriptionist, A
Medical/Clinical Assistant, A
Radiologic Technology/Science - Radiographer, A
Respiratory Care Therapy/Therapist, A
Social Work, A

KEAN UNIVERSITY

Accounting, BM
Acting, B
Adult and Continuing Education and Teaching, M
Architecture, B
Art Education, M
Art History, Criticism and Conservation, B
Art/Art Studies, General, B
Asian Studies/Civilization, B
Athletic Training and Sports Medicine, B
BioTechnology, B
Biology/Biological Sciences, B
Business Administration and Management, B

Business Administration, Management and Opera-
   tions, M
Chemistry, B
Clinical Laboratory Science/Medical
   Technology/Technologist, B
Clinical Psychology, MD
Communication Disorders, M
Communication Studies/Speech Communication
   and Rhetoric, B
Communication and Media Studies, M
Community Health Nursing, M
Computer Systems Networking and Telecommunica-
   tions, B
Computer and Information Sciences, B
Counseling Psychology, M
Counselor Education/School Counseling and Guid-
   ance Services, M
Criminal Justice/Law Enforcement Administration, B
Criminology, M
Curriculum and Instruction, M
Design and Visual Communications, B
Drama and Dramatics/Theatre Arts, B
Early Childhood Education and Teaching, M
Economics, B
Education, M
Educational Administration and Supervision, M
Educational Leadership and Administration, MD
Elementary Education and Teaching, B
English Language and Literature, B
English as a Second Language, M
Environmental Policy and Resource Manage-
   ment, M
Exercise and Sports Science, M
Finance, B
Fine Arts and Art Studies, M
Fine/Studio Arts, B
Foreign Language Teacher Education, M
Geology/Earth Science, B
Health Information/Medical Records
   Administration/Administrator, B
Health Services Administration, M
History, B
Holocaust Studies, M
Industrial Design, B
Industrial and Organizational Psychology, M
Interior Design, B
International Business/Trade/Commerce, BM
Kindergarten/PreSchool Education and Teaching, B
Management Information Systems and Services, M
Marketing/Marketing Management, B
Marriage and Family Therapy/Counseling, MO
Mathematics, B
Mathematics Teacher Education, M
Multilingual and Multicultural Education, M
Music, B
Music Performance, B
Music Teacher Education, B
Non-Profit/Public/Organizational Management, M
Nursing, M
Nursing Administration, M
Occupational Therapy/Therapist, M
Parks, Recreation and Leisure Facilities Manage-
   ment, B
Physical Education Teaching and Coaching, B
Political Science and Government, B
Psychology, BM
Public Administration, BM
Reading Teacher Education, M
School Nursing, M
School Psychology, MDO
Science Teacher Education/General Science
   Teacher Education, M
Science Technologies/Technicians, B
Social Work, M
Sociology, BM
Spanish Language and Literature, BM
Special Education and Teaching, BM
Substance Abuse/Addiction Counseling, M
Technical Theatre/Theatre Design and Technol-
   ogy, B
Writing, M

MERCER COUNTY COMMUNITY COL-
LEGE

Accounting, A
Administrative Assistant and Secretarial Science, A

Airline Flight Attendant, A
Airline/Commercial/Professional Pilot and Flight
 Crew, A
Architectural Engineering Technology/Technician, A
Art History, Criticism and Conservation, A
Art/Art Studies, General, A
Automotive Engineering Technology/Technician, A
Aviation/Airway Management and Operations, A
Biology Technician/BioTechnology Laboratory Tech-
 nician, A
Biology/Biological Sciences, A
Business Administration and Management, A
Ceramic Arts and Ceramics, A
Chemistry, A
Civil Engineering Technology/Technician, A
Clinical/Medical Laboratory Technician, A
Commercial and Advertising Art, A
Community Organization and Advocacy, A
Computer Graphics, A
Computer Science, A
Computer Systems Networking and Telecommunica-
 tions, A
Corrections, A
Criminal Justice/Police Science, A
Culinary Arts/Chef Training, A
Dance, A
Drama and Dramatics/Theatre Arts, A
Electrical, Electronic and Communications Engineer-
 ing Technology/Technician, A
Engineering Science, A
Fire Science/Firefighting, A
Funeral Service and Mortuary Science, A
Health Professions and Related Clinical Sciences, A
Heating, Air Conditioning and Refrigeration
 Technology/Technician, A
Hotel/Motel Administration/Management, A
Humanities/Humanistic Studies, A
Legal Assistant/Paralegal, A
Liberal Arts and Sciences Studies and Humani-
 ties, A
Management Information Systems and Services, A
Mass Communication/Media Studies, A
Mathematics, A
Medical Radiologic Technology/Science - Radiation
 Therapist, A
Music, A
Ornamental Horticulture, A
Photography, A
Physical Therapist Assistant, A
Physics, A
Plant Sciences, A
Radio and Television Broadcasting
 Technology/Technician, A
Respiratory Care Therapy/Therapist, A
Sculpture, A
Teacher Assistant/Aide, A

MIDDLESEX COUNTY COLLEGE

Accounting, A
Administrative Assistant and Secretarial Science, A
Automotive Engineering Technology/Technician, A
BioTechnology, A
Biology Technician/BioTechnology Laboratory Tech-
 nician, A
Business Administration and Management, A
Civil Engineering Technology/Technician, A
Clinical/Medical Laboratory Technician, A
Communications Technologies/Technicians and Sup-
 port Services, A
Computer and Information Sciences, A
Criminal Justice/Police Science, A
Dental Hygiene/Hygienist, A
Dietician Assistant, A
Electrical, Electronic and Communications Engineer-
 ing Technology/Technician, A
Energy Management and Systems
 Technology/Technician, A
Engineering Science, A
Engineering Technologies/Technicians, A
Environmental Control Technologies/Technicians, A
Fire Protection and Safety Technology/Technician, A
Geology/Earth Science, A
Graphic Communications, A
Health Professions and Related Clinical Sciences, A
Health Services/Allied Health/Health Sciences, A
Hotel/Motel Administration/Management, A

Industrial Production Technologies/Technicians, A
Legal Assistant/Paralegal, A
Liberal Arts and Sciences Studies and Humani-
 ties, A
Marketing/Marketing Management, A
Mechanical Engineering Related
 Technologies/Technicians, A
Mechanical Engineering/Mechanical
 Technology/Technician, A
Medical Radiologic Technology/Science - Radiation
 Therapist, A
Physical Sciences, A
Rehabilitation and Therapeutic Professions, A
Respiratory Care Therapy/Therapist, A
Small Business Administration/Management, A
Specialized Merchandising, Sales, and Marketing
 Operations, A
Survey Technology/Surveying, A
Teacher Assistant/Aide, A
Visual and Performing Arts, A

MONMOUTH UNIVERSITY

Accounting, MO
Advertising and Public Relations, O
American/United States Studies/Civilization, M
Anthropology, BM
Applied Behavior Analysis, O
Art/Art Studies, General, B
Biology/Biological Sciences, B
Business Administration and Management, B
Business Administration, Management and Opera-
 tions, MO
Chemistry, B
Clinical Laboratory Science/Medical
 Technology/Technologist, B
Communication Disorders, M
Communication Studies/Speech Communication
 and Rhetoric, B
Communication and Media Studies, MO
Computer Science, MO
Computer Software Engineering, B
Computer and Information Sciences, B
Corporate and Organizational Communication, MO
Counseling Psychology, MO
Criminal Justice/Safety Studies, B
Criminology, MO
Education, BMO
Educational Administration and Supervision, M
Elementary Education and Teaching, M
English, M
English Language and Literature, B
English as a Second Language, O
Environmental Biology, B
Finance and Banking, M
Fine Arts and Art Studies, B
Foreign Languages and Literatures, B
Forensic Nursing, MO
General Studies, A
Gerontological Nursing, MO
Health Services/Allied Health/Health Sciences, B
Health and Physical Education, B
History, BM
Homeland Security, MO
Human Resources Management and Services, O
International Business/Trade/Commerce, B
Management Information Systems and Services, M
Marine Biology and Biological Oceanography, B
Mathematical and Computational Finance, M
Mathematics, B
Media Studies, O
Multi-/Interdisciplinary Studies, B
Music, B
Nursing, MDO
Nursing - Adult, MO
Nursing - Advanced Practice, MO
Nursing Administration, MO
Nursing Education, MO
Physician Assistant, M
Political Science and Government, B
Psychiatric/Mental Health Nurse/Nursing, MO
Psychology, BMO
Public Policy Analysis, M
Real Estate, M
Rhetoric, M
School Nursing, MO
Secondary Education and Teaching, BM

Social Sciences, B
Social Work, BMO
Sociology, B
Software Engineering, MO
Special Education and Teaching, BMO
Student Personnel Services, M
Substance Abuse/Addiction Counseling, M
Western European Studies, M
Writing, M

MONTCLAIR STATE UNIVERSITY

Accounting, BMO
Anthropology, B
Applied Mathematics, M
Archives/Archival Administration, M
Art Education, M
Arts Management, M
Athletic Training and Sports Medicine, B
Biochemistry, BM
Biological and Biomedical Sciences, M
Biology/Biological Sciences, B
Business Administration and Management, B
Business Administration, Management and Opera-
 tions, M
Chemistry, BM
Child Development, MO
Child and Family Studies, MDO
Cinematography and Film/Video Production, B
Classics and Classical Languages, Litera-
 tures, and Linguistics, B
Clinical Psychology, M
Communication Disorders, MD
Communication Studies/Speech Communication
 and Rhetoric, B
Communication and Media Studies, B
Computer Science, MO
Computer and Information Sciences, B
Conflict Resolution and Mediation/Peace Stud-
 ies, MO
Counselor Education/School Counseling and Guid-
 ance Services, MDO
Curriculum and Instruction, M
Dance, B
Database Systems, O
Design and Applied Arts, B
Disability Studies, MDO
Drama and Dance Teacher Education, B
Drama and Dramatics/Theatre Arts, B
Ecology, M
Economics, B
Education, MDO
Educational Leadership and Administration, MD
Educational Measurement and Evaluation, O
Educational Media/Instructional Technology, O
English, M
English Education, MO
English Language and Literature, B
English as a Second Language, MO
Environmental Education, M
Environmental Law, O
Environmental Policy and Resource Management, D
Environmental Sciences, M
Environmental Studies, M
Evolutionary Biology, M
Exercise and Sports Science, MO
Family and Consumer Sciences/Human Sciences, B
Fashion/Apparel Design, B
Fine Arts and Art Studies, M
Foods, Nutrition, and Wellness Studies, B
Forensic Psychology, O
French Language and Literature, BM
Geographic Information Systems, O
Geography, B
Geology/Earth Science, B
Geosciences, B
German Language and Literature, B
Graphic Design, B
Health Education, M
Health Teacher Education, B
History, BMO
Hospitality Administration/Management, B
Humanities/Humanistic Studies, B
Industrial Design, B
Industrial and Organizational Psychology, M
Information Technology, B
Intellectual Property Law, M

Italian Language and Literature, B
Journalism, B
Kinesiology and Exercise Science, B
Latin Language and Literature, B
Law and Legal Studies, MO
Legal Professions and Studies, B
Legal and Justice Studies, O
Linguistics, BMO
Management, M
Marine Biology and Biological Oceanography, BM
Mathematics, BM
Mathematics Teacher Education, MDO
Molecular Biology, BMO
Multi-/Interdisciplinary Studies, B
Music, BMO
Music Performance, B
Music Teacher Education, M
Music Theory and Composition, M
Music Therapy/Therapist, BMO
Nutritional Sciences, MO
Performance, MO
Pharmacology, M
Philosophy, B
Physical Education Teaching and Coaching, BM
Physics, B
Physiology, M
Political Science and Government, BMO
Psychology, BM
Public Health, M
Public Health (MPH, DPH), B
Radio and Television, B
Reading Teacher Education, M
Religion/Religious Studies, B
Science Teacher Education/General Science Teacher Education, M
Social Sciences, M
Sociology, B
Spanish Language and Literature, BM
Special Education and Teaching, MD
Sport and Fitness Administration/Management, M
Statistics, M
Substance Abuse/Addiction Counseling, O
Sustainable Development, M
Theater, M
Translation and Interpretation, O
Women's Studies, B
Writing, O
Youth Services/Administration, B

NEW JERSEY CITY UNIVERSITY

Accounting, BM
Allied Health and Medical Assisting Services, M
Art Education, M
Art Teacher Education, B
Art/Art Studies, General, B
Biology/Biological Sciences, B
Business Administration and Management, B
Business Administration, Management and Operations, M
Chemistry, B
Community Health and Preventive Medicine, M
Computer and Information Sciences, B
Computer and Information Systems Security, MD
Counseling Psychology, M
Counselor Education/School Counseling and Guidance Services, M
Criminal Justice/Safety Studies, B
Criminology, M
Early Childhood Education and Teaching, BM
Economics, B
Education, MD
Educational Administration and Supervision, M
Educational Leadership and Administration, M
Educational Media/Instructional Technology, MD
Educational Psychology, MO
Elementary Education and Teaching, BM
English Language and Literature, B
Finance, B
Finance and Banking, M
Fine Arts and Art Studies, M
Fire Science/Firefighting, B
Geology/Earth Science, B
Health Education, M
Health Professions and Related Clinical Sciences, B
Health Services Administration, M
History, B

Kindergarten/PreSchool Education and Teaching, B
Mathematics, B
Mathematics Teacher Education, M
Music, BM
Music Teacher Education, BM
National Security, MD
Performance, M
Philosophy, B
Physics, B
Political Science and Government, B
Psychology, B
Reading Teacher Education, M
School Psychology, O
Secondary Education and Teaching, M
Securities Services Administration/Management, MD
Sociology, B
Spanish Language and Literature, B
Special Education and Teaching, BM
Urban Education and Leadership, M
Urban Studies/Affairs, BM
Women's Studies, B

NEW JERSEY INSTITUTE OF TECHNOLOGY

Applied Mathematics, BM
Applied Physics, MD
Applied Statistics, M
Architecture, BMD
Architecture and Related Services, B
Art/Art Studies, General, B
Biochemistry, B
Bioinformatics, BM
Biological and Biomedical Sciences, MD
Biology/Biological Sciences, B
Biomedical Engineering, MD
Biomedical/Medical Engineering, B
Biophysics, B
Biostatistics, B
Business Administration and Management, B
Business Administration, Management and Operations, M
Business, Management, Marketing, and Related Support Services, B
Chemical Engineering, BMD
Chemistry, BMD
Civil Engineering, B
Clinical/Medical Laboratory Science and Allied Professions, B
Communication and Media Studies, B
Computational Biology, M
Computer Engineering, BMD
Computer Science, BMD
Computer and Information Sciences, B
Computer and Information Systems Security, M
Electrical Engineering, MD
Electrical, Electronics and Communications Engineering, B
Emergency Management, M
Energy and Power Engineering, M
Engineering Management, M
Engineering Science, B
Engineering Technology, B
Engineering and Applied Sciences, MD
Environmental Sciences, BMD
Environmental/Environmental Health Engineering, B
General Studies, B
Geological/Geophysical Engineering, B
Health Services Administration, M
History, BM
Industrial Design, B
Industrial Engineering, B
Industrial/Management Engineering, MD
Information Science/Studies, BMD
Information Technology, B
Interior Design, B
International Business/Trade/Commerce, B
Internet Engineering, M
Legal Professions and Studies, B
Management, M
Management Information Systems and Services, MD
Manufacturing Engineering, BM
Materials Engineering, MD
Materials Sciences, MD
Mathematical and Computational Finance, M
Mathematics, BD

Mechanical Engineering, BMD
Medicinal and Pharmaceutical Chemistry, M
Pharmaceutical Administration, M
Pharmaceutical Engineering, M
Pharmacology, M
Physics, B
Safety Engineering, M
Science, Technology and Society, B
Software Engineering, M
Systems Science and Theory, M
Technical Communication, M
Technical Theatre/Theatre Design and Technology, B
Telecommunications, M
Transportation and Highway Engineering, MD
Transportation/Transportation Management, MD
Urban Studies/Affairs, D

OCEAN COUNTY COLLEGE

Broadcast Journalism, A
Business Administration and Management, A
Business/Commerce, A
Communications Technologies/Technicians and Support Services, A
Computer and Information Sciences, A
Criminal Justice/Police Science, A
Engineering, A
Engineering Technologies/Technicians, A
Environmental Sciences, A
General Studies, A
Human Services, A
International/Global Studies, A
Liberal Arts and Sciences Studies and Humanities, A
Occupational Therapist Assistant, A
Rehabilitation and Therapeutic Professions, A
Respiratory Care Therapy/Therapist, A
Security and Protective Services, A
Sign Language Interpretation and Translation, A
Visual and Performing Arts, A

PASSAIC COUNTY COMMUNITY COLLEGE

Accounting, A
Administrative Assistant and Secretarial Science, A
Biological and Physical Sciences, A
Business Administration and Management, A
Consumer Merchandising/Retailing Management, A
Criminal Justice/Law Enforcement Administration, A
Electrical, Electronic and Communications Engineering Technology/Technician, A
English Language and Literature, A
Finance, A
Fire Science/Firefighting, A
Health Information/Medical Records Administration/Administrator, A
Hotel/Motel Administration/Management, A
Human Services, A
Humanities/Humanistic Studies, A
Industrial Radiologic Technology/Technician, A
Industrial Technology/Technician, A
Information Science/Studies, A
Kindergarten/PreSchool Education and Teaching, A
Marketing/Marketing Management, A
Mathematics, A
Medical Radiologic Technology/Science - Radiation Therapist, A
Natural Sciences, A
Psychology, A
Public Administration, A
Respiratory Care Therapy/Therapist, A

PILLAR COLLEGE

Bible/Biblical Studies, AB
Business Administration, Management and Operations, B
Clinical Pastoral Counseling/Patient Counseling, B

PRINCETON UNIVERSITY

Aerospace, Aeronautical and Astronautical Engineering, MD
Anthropology, BD
Applied Mathematics, D
Archeology, D
Architecture, BMD

Art History, Criticism and Conservation, B
Asian Studies/Civilization, D
Astronomy, D
Astrophysics, BD
Atmospheric Sciences and Meteorology, D
Chemical Engineering, BMD
Chemistry, BMD
Civil Engineering, BMD
Classics and Classical Languages, Literatures, and Linguistics, BD
Comparative Literature, BD
Composition, D
Computational Biology, D
Computational Sciences, D
Computer Engineering, B
Computer Science, MD
Demography and Population Studies, DO
East Asian Studies, B
Ecology, BD
Economics, BD
Electrical Engineering, MD
Electrical, Electronics and Communications Engineering, B
Electronic Materials, D
Engineering, B
Engineering and Applied Sciences, MD
English, D
English Language and Literature, B
Environmental Engineering Technology/Environmental Technology, MD
Evolutionary Biology, D
Finance and Banking, M
Financial Engineering, MD
French Language and Literature, BD
Geological and Earth Sciences/Geosciences, B
Geosciences, D
German Language and Literature, BD
History, BD
History of Science and Technology, D
International Affairs, MD
Marine Biology and Biological Oceanography, D
Materials Sciences, D
Mathematics, BD
Mechanical Engineering, BMD
Molecular Biology, BD
Multi-/Interdisciplinary Studies, B
Music, BD
Musicology and Ethnomusicology, D
Near and Middle Eastern Studies, BMD
Neuroscience, D
Ocean Engineering, D
Oceanography, Chemical and Physical, D
Operations Research, BMD
Philosophy, BD
Photonics, D
Physics, BD
Plasma and High-Temperature Physics, D
Political Science and Government, BD
Portuguese Language and Literature, D
Psychology, BD
Public Affairs, MD
Public Policy Analysis, BM
Religion/Religious Studies, BD
Russian Language and Literature, D
Slavic Languages, Literatures, and Linguistics, BD
Sociology, BD
Spanish Language and Literature, BD

RABBI JACOB JOSEPH SCHOOL

Talmudic Studies, B

RABBINICAL COLLEGE OF AMERICA

Religion/Religious Studies, B

RAMAPO COLLEGE OF NEW JERSEY

Accounting, B
African-American/Black Studies, B
Allied Health and Medical Assisting Services, B
American/United States Studies/Civilization, B
Area Studies, B
Biochemistry, B
Bioinformatics, B
Biological and Physical Sciences, B
Biology/Biological Sciences, B
Business Administration and Management, B

Business Administration, Management and Operations, M
Chemistry, B
Clinical Laboratory Science/Medical Technology/Technologist, B
Communication Studies/Speech Communication and Rhetoric, B
Comparative Literature, B
Computer and Information Sciences, B
Drama and Dramatics/Theatre Arts, B
Economics, B
Educational Leadership and Administration, M
Educational Media/Instructional Technology, M
Environmental Sciences, B
Environmental Studies, B
History, B
Information Science/Studies, B
Intermedia/Multimedia, B
International Business/Trade/Commerce, B
Legal Professions and Studies, B
Liberal Arts and Sciences Studies and Humanities, B
Liberal Studies, M
Mathematics, B
Music, B
Nursing, M
Nursing Education, M
Physics, B
Political Science and Government, B
Psychology, B
Social Sciences, B
Social Work, B
Sociology, B
Spanish Language and Literature, B
Sustainable Development, M
Visual and Performing Arts, B

RARITAN VALLEY COMMUNITY COLLEGE

Accounting Technology/Technician and Bookkeeping, A
Accounting and Related Services, A
Administrative Assistant and Secretarial Science, A
Animation, Interactive Technology, Video Graphics and Special Effects, A
Automotive Engineering Technology/Technician, A
BioTechnology, A
Business Administration and Management, A
Business/Commerce, A
Chemical Technology/Technician, A
Child Care Provider/Assistant, A
Cinematography and Film/Video Production, A
Communication and Media Studies, A
Computer Programming, Vendor/Product Certification, A
Computer Systems Networking and Telecommunications, A
Computer and Information Sciences and Support Services, A
Construction Engineering Technology/Technician, A
Corrections, A
Criminal Justice/Law Enforcement Administration, A
Criminal Justice/Police Science, A
Dance, A
Dental Assisting/Assistant, A
Dental Hygiene/Hygienist, A
Design and Applied Arts, A
Diesel Mechanics Technology/Technician, A
Digital Communication and Media/Multimedia, A
Engineering Science, A
Engineering Technologies/Technicians, A
English Language and Literature, A
Financial Planning and Services, A
Fine/Studio Arts, A
Health Information/Medical Records Technology/Technician, A
Health Services/Allied Health/Health Sciences, A
Health and Physical Education, A
Heating, Air Conditioning and Refrigeration Technology/Technician, A
Information Technology, A
Interior Design, A
International Business/Trade/Commerce, A
Kindergarten/PreSchool Education and Teaching, A
Kinesiology and Exercise Science, A
Legal Assistant/Paralegal, A

Liberal Arts and Sciences Studies and Humanities, A
Lineworker, A
Management Information Systems and Services, A
Manufacturing Technology/Technician, A
Marketing/Marketing Management, A
Medical/Clinical Assistant, A
Multi-/Interdisciplinary Studies, A
Music, A
Opticianry/Ophthalmic Dispensing Optician, A
Optometric Technician/Assistant, A
Respiratory Care Therapy/Therapist, A
Restaurant, Culinary, and Catering Management/Manager, A
Small Business Administration/Management, A
Web Page, Digital/Multimedia and Information Resources Design, A

RIDER UNIVERSITY

Accounting, BM
Advertising, B
American/United States Studies/Civilization, B
Applied Psychology, M
Art/Art Studies, General, B
Behavioral Sciences, B
Biochemistry, B
Biology/Biological Sciences, B
Biopsychology, B
Business Administration and Management, B
Business Administration, Management and Operations, BM
Business Education, O
Business Teacher Education, B
Business/Managerial Economics, B
Chemistry, B
Communication Studies/Speech Communication and Rhetoric, B
Composition, M
Computer and Information Sciences, B
Corporate and Organizational Communication, M
Counselor Education/School Counseling and Guidance Services, MO
Criminal Justice/Safety Studies, B
Curriculum and Instruction, MO
Dance, B
Directing and Theatrical Production, B
Economics, B
Education, MO
Educational Administration and Supervision, MO
Educational Leadership and Administration, O
Elementary Education and Teaching, BO
English Education, O
English Language and Literature, B
English as a Second Language, O
Entrepreneurship/Entrepreneurial Studies, B
Environmental Studies, B
Finance, B
Foreign Language Teacher Education, O
French Language and Literature, BO
General Studies, A
Geology/Earth Science, B
German Language and Literature, BO
Graphic Design, B
Health Services Administration, B
Health Services/Allied Health/Health Sciences, B
History, B
International Business/Trade/Commerce, B
International Relations and Affairs, B
Journalism, B
Labor and Industrial Relations, B
Liberal Arts and Sciences Studies and Humanities, B
Logistics and Materials Management, B
Management Science, B
Marketing/Marketing Management, B
Mathematics, B
Mathematics Teacher Education, O
Medical/Health Management and Clinical Assistant/Specialist, B
Music, BM
Music History, Literature, and Theory, B
Music Teacher Education, BM
Music Theory and Composition, B
Oceanography, Chemical and Physical, B
Office Management and Supervision, B
Organizational Behavior Studies, B

Organizational Management, M
Performance, M
Philosophy, B
Piano and Organ, B
Political Science and Government, B
Psychology, B
Public Relations/Image Management, B
Radio and Television, B
Reading Teacher Education, MO
Religious/Sacred Music, B
Sacred Music, M
School Psychology, O
Science Teacher Education/General Science
    Teacher Education, BO
Secondary Education and Teaching, B
Social Studies Teacher Education, O
Sociology, B
Spanish Language and Literature, BO
Special Education and Teaching, MO
Sport and Fitness Administration/Management, B
Voice and Opera, B

ROWAN COLLEGE AT BURLINGTON COUNTY

Accounting, A
Agribusiness, A
American Sign Language (ASL), A
Animation, Interactive Technology, Video Graphics
    and Special Effects, A
Art/Art Studies, General, A
Automotive Engineering Technology/Technician, A
Baking and Pastry Arts/Baker/Pastry Chef, A
BioTechnology, A
Biological and Physical Sciences, A
Biology/Biological Sciences, A
Business Administration and Management, A
Chemical Engineering, A
Chemistry, A
Commercial and Advertising Art, A
Communication Disorders Sciences and Services, A
Computer Graphics, A
Computer Science, A
Construction Engineering Technology/Technician, A
Criminal Justice/Police Science, A
Culinary Arts/Chef Training, A
Dental Hygiene/Hygienist, A
Drafting and Design Technology/Technician, A
Drama and Dramatics/Theatre Arts, A
Education, A
Electrical, Electronic and Communications Engineer-
    ing Technology/Technician, A
Energy Management and Systems
    Technology/Technician, A
Engineering, A
Engineering Technologies/Technicians, A
English Language and Literature, A
Environmental Sciences, A
Fashion/Apparel Design, A
Fire Science/Firefighting, A
Foodservice Systems
    Administration/Management, A
Geological and Earth Sciences/Geosciences, A
Graphic Design, A
Graphic and Printing Equipment Operator Produc-
    tion, A
Health Information/Medical Records
    Technology/Technician, A
Health Services/Allied Health/Health Sciences, A
History, A
Hospitality Administration/Management, A
Human Services, A
Information Technology, A
International/Global Studies, A
Journalism, A
Legal Assistant/Paralegal, A
Liberal Arts and Sciences Studies and Humani-
    ties, A
Management Information Systems and Services, A
Mathematics, A
Medical Radiologic Technology/Science - Radiation
    Therapist, A
Music, A
Philosophy, A
Physics, A
Psychology, A
Respiratory Care Therapy/Therapist, A

Restaurant/Food Services Management, A
Retailing and Retail Operations, A
Sales, Distribution and Marketing Operations, A
Sign Language Interpretation and Translation, A
Social Sciences, A
Sociology, A

ROWAN COLLEGE AT GLOUCESTER COUNTY

Accounting Technology/Technician and Bookkeep-
    ing, A
Administrative Assistant and Secretarial Science, A
Automobile/Automotive Mechanics
    Technology/Technician, A
Biology/Biological Sciences, A
Business Administration and Management, A
Chemistry, A
Civil Engineering Technology/Technician, A
Computer Graphics, A
Computer Programming/Programmer, A
Computer Science, A
Computer Systems Networking and Telecommunica-
    tions, A
Computer and Information Sciences, A
Criminal Justice/Police Science, A
Data Modeling/Warehousing and Database Adminis-
    tration, A
Diagnostic Medical Sonography/Sonographer and
    Ultrasound Technician, A
Drafting and Design Technology/Technician, A
Education, A
Engineering, A
Engineering Technology, A
Food Science, A
Health Services/Allied Health/Health Sciences, A
Kinesiology and Exercise Science, A
Legal Assistant/Paralegal, A
Liberal Arts and Sciences Studies and Humani-
    ties, A
Marketing/Marketing Management, A
Nuclear Medical Technology/Technologist, A
Physical Education Teaching and Coaching, A
Respiratory Care Therapy/Therapist, A
Special Education and Teaching, A

ROWAN UNIVERSITY

Accounting Technology/Technician and Bookkeep-
    ing, B
Advertising, B
Advertising and Public Relations, M
African Studies, B
American/United States Studies/Civilization, B
Applied Behavior Analysis, MO
Art/Art Studies, General, B
Arts Management, M
Athletic Training and Sports Medicine, B
Biochemistry, B
Bioinformatics, BM
Biological and Biomedical Sciences, M
Biology/Biological Sciences, B
Biomedical Sciences, B
Biomedical/Medical Engineering, B
Business Administration and Management, B
Business Administration, Management and Opera-
    tions, MO
Cartography, B
Chemical Engineering, BM
Chemistry, B
City/Urban, Community and Regional Planning, B
Civil Engineering, BM
Clinical Psychology, MO
Computer Science, BM
Corporate and Organizational Communication, O
Counselor Education/School Counseling and Guid-
    ance Services, M
Criminal Justice/Police Science, B
Criminal Justice/Safety Studies, B
Criminology, M
Drama and Dramatics/Theatre Arts, B
Early Childhood Education and Teaching, B
Economics, B
Education, BMDO
Educational Administration and Supervision, MO
Educational Leadership and Administration, MDO
Educational Media/Instructional Technology, O
Electrical Engineering, M

Electrical, Electronics and Communications Engi-
    neering, B
Elementary Education and Teaching, BM
Engineering and Applied Sciences, M
English Education, O
English Language and Literature, B
English as a Second Language, O
Entrepreneurship/Entrepreneurial Studies, B
Environmental Studies, B
Exercise and Sports Science, M
Finance, B
Geography, B
Health Promotion, M
Health and Physical Education, B
Higher Education/Higher Education Administra-
    tion, M
History, BMO
Human Resources Management/Personnel Adminis-
    tration, B
Journalism, B
Liberal Arts and Sciences Studies and Humani-
    ties, B
Library Science, M
Management Information Systems and Services, B
Marketing, O
Marketing/Marketing Management, B
Mathematics, BM
Mathematics Teacher Education, MO
Mechanical Engineering, BM
Media Studies, O
Middle School Education, O
Multi-/Interdisciplinary Studies, O
Multilingual and Multicultural Education, O
Music, BM
Music Performance, B
Music Teacher Education, B
Music Theory and Composition, B
Osteopathic Medicine, D
Pharmaceutical Sciences, M
Philosophy and Religious Studies, B
Physical Education Teaching and Coaching, B
Physical Sciences, B
Physics, B
Political Science and Government, B
Psychology, BMO
Public Relations/Image Management, B
Publishing, O
Radio and Television, B
Reading Teacher Education, MO
Rhetoric, O
School Nursing, O
School Psychology, MO
Science Teacher Education/General Science
    Teacher Education, M
Secondary Education and Teaching, M
Sociology, B
Solid State and Low-Temperature Physics, B
Spanish Language and Literature, B
Special Education and Teaching, BMO
Teacher Education and Professional Develop-
    ment, Specific Levels and Methods, B
Theater, M
Writing, MO

RUTGERS UNIVERSITY–CAMDEN

Accounting, B
African-American/Black Studies, B
Applied Mathematics, M
Art/Art Studies, General, B
Biological and Biomedical Sciences, M
Biology/Biological Sciences, B
Biomedical Technology/Technician, B
Business Administration and Management, B
Business Administration, Management and Opera-
    tions, M
Chemistry, BM
Child Development, MD
Clinical Laboratory Science/Medical
    Technology/Technologist, B
Computational Biology, MD
Computer Science, M
Computer and Information Sciences, B
Criminal Justice/Safety Studies, B
Criminology, B
Drama and Dramatics/Theatre Arts, B
Economics, B

Educational Leadership and Administration, M
Educational Policy, M
Engineering, B
English, M
English Language and Literature, B
Finance, B
French Language and Literature, B
German Language and Literature, B
Health Services Administration, M
History, BM
Hospitality Administration/Management, B
International Affairs, M
International Development, M
Law and Legal Studies, D
Liberal Arts and Sciences Studies and Humanities, B
Liberal Studies, M
Marketing/Marketing Management, B
Mathematics, BM
Mathematics Teacher Education, M
Multi-/Interdisciplinary Studies, B
Music, B
Philosophy, B
Physical Therapy/Therapist, D
Physics, B
Political Science and Government, B
Psychology, BM
Public Administration, M
Public Health, MO
Public History, M
Public Policy Analysis, M
Social Work, B
Sociology, B
Spanish Language and Literature, B
Urban Studies/Affairs, B
Writing, M

RUTGERS UNIVERSITY–NEW BRUNSWICK

Accounting, B
Aerospace, Aeronautical and Astronautical Engineering, MD
African Studies, BD
African-American Studies, D
Agricultural Economics, M
Agricultural/Biological Engineering and Bioengineering, B
Agriculture, B
Allied Health Diagnostic, Intervention, and Treatment Professions, B
Allopathic Medicine, D
American/United States Studies/Civilization, B
Ancient/Classical Greek Language and Literature, B
Animal Genetics, B
Animal Physiology, B
Animal Sciences, BMD
Animal/Livestock Husbandry and Production, B
Anthropology, BMD
Applied Mathematics, MD
Applied Psychology, MD
Applied Statistics, M
Architectural Engineering, B
Art History, Criticism and Conservation, BMDO
Art/Art Studies, General, B
Astronomy, MD
Astrophysics, B
Atmospheric Chemistry and Climatology, B
Atmospheric Sciences and Meteorology, BMD
BioTechnology, B
Biochemical Engineering, MD
Biochemistry, BMD
Biological and Biomedical Sciences, MD
Biology/Biological Sciences, B
Biomedical Engineering, MD
Biomedical Sciences, B
Biomedical/Medical Engineering, B
Biometry/Biometrics, B
Biopsychology, D
Biostatistics, MD
Business Administration and Management, B
Cancer Biology/Oncology, MD
Cell Biology and Anatomy, MD
Cell/Cellular Biology and Anatomical Sciences, B
Cell/Cellular Biology and Histology, B
Ceramic Arts and Ceramics, B
Ceramic Sciences and Engineering, B

Chemical Engineering, BMD
Chemistry, BMD
Chinese Language and Literature, B
Civil Engineering, BMD
Classics and Classical Languages, Literatures, and Linguistics, BMD
Clinical Laboratory Science/Medical Technology/Technologist, B
Clinical Laboratory Sciences, M
Clinical Microbiology, MD
Clinical Psychology, MD
Clinical/Medical Laboratory Science and Allied Professions, B
Cognitive Sciences, D
Commercial and Advertising Art, B
Communication Studies/Speech Communication and Rhetoric, B
Communication and Media Studies, D
Comparative Literature, BMD
Computational Biology, D
Computer Engineering, BMD
Computer Science, MD
Condensed Matter Physics, MD
Counseling Psychology, M
Counselor Education/School Counseling and Guidance Services, M
Criminal Justice/Law Enforcement Administration, B
Dance, B
Dental Hygiene/Hygienist, A
Design and Applied Arts, M
Developmental Biology and Embryology, MD
Developmental Education, M
Dietetics/Dieticians, B
Drama and Dramatics/Theatre Arts, B
Drawing, B
Early Childhood Education and Teaching, MD
East Asian Studies, BMD
Ecology, BMD
Economics, BMD
Education, MD
Educational Administration and Supervision, MD
Educational Measurement and Evaluation, M
Educational Policy, D
Educational Psychology, MD
Electrical Engineering, MD
Electrical, Electronics and Communications Engineering, B
Elementary Education and Teaching, MD
Emergency Management, O
Engineering Science, B
English, D
English Education, M
English Language and Literature, B
English as a Second Language, M
Entomology, MD
Environmental Biology, MD
Environmental Design/Architecture, B
Environmental Engineering Technology/Environmental Technology, MD
Environmental Sciences, BMD
Environmental Studies, B
Environmental and Occupational Health, MDO
Epidemiology, MDO
Equestrian/Equine Studies, B
European Studies/Civilization, B
Evolutionary Biology, BMD
Family and Consumer Sciences/Human Sciences, B
Film/Cinema Studies, B
Finance, B
Fine Arts and Art Studies, M
Food Science, B
Food Science and Technology, MD
Foreign Language Teacher Education, MD
Foreign Languages and Literatures, B
Foundations and Philosophy of Education, MD
French Language and Literature, BMD
Gender Studies, MD
Genetics, MD
Geography, BMD
Geology/Earth Science, BMD
German Language and Literature, BMD
Hazardous Materials Management and Waste Technology/Technician, MD
Health Education, MD
Health Information/Medical Records Administration/Administrator, B

Health Psychology, D
Health Services Administration, MD
Hispanic-American, Puerto Rican, and Mexican-American/Chicano Studies, B
Historic Preservation and Conservation, MO
History, BD
History of Medicine, D
History of Science and Technology, D
Horticultural Science, MD
Human Resources Management and Services, MD
Human Resources Management/Personnel Administration, B
Immunology, MD
Industrial Engineering, B
Industrial and Labor Relations, MD
Industrial/Management Engineering, MD
Information Science/Studies, BMD
Inorganic Chemistry, MD
Interdisciplinary Studies, D
International Affairs, MD
Italian Language and Literature, BMD
Jazz/Jazz Studies, B
Jewish/Judaic Studies, BMO
Journalism, B
Kinesiology and Exercise Science, B
Labor and Industrial Relations, B
Landscape Architecture, B
Latin American Studies, B
Latin Language and Literature, B
Legal and Justice Studies, D
Liberal Arts and Sciences Studies and Humanities, B
Library Science, MD
Linguistics, BD
Logistics and Materials Management, B
Management Science, B
Management Sciences and Quantitative Methods, B
Marine Biology and Biological Oceanography, BMD
Marketing/Marketing Management, B
Mass Communication/Media Studies, B
Materials Engineering, MD
Materials Sciences, MD
Mathematics, BMD
Mathematics Teacher Education, MD
Mechanical Engineering, BMD
Mechanics, MD
Media Studies, D
Medical Microbiology and Bacteriology, B
Medicinal and Pharmaceutical Chemistry, MD
Medieval and Renaissance Studies, BD
Meteorology, B
Microbiology, BMD
Molecular Biology, BMD
Molecular Biophysics, D
Molecular Genetics, BMD
Molecular Pharmacology, MD
Molecular Physiology, MD
Multi-/Interdisciplinary Studies, B
Multilingual and Multicultural Education, MD
Music, BMDO
Music Performance, B
Music Teacher Education, BMD
Natural Resources Management/Development and Policy, B
Natural Resources and Conservation, B
Near and Middle Eastern Studies, B
Neuroscience, MD
Nutritional Sciences, BMD
Occupational Therapist Assistant, A
Oceanography, Chemical and Physical, MD
Operations Research, D
Organic Chemistry, MD
Painting, BM
Pharmaceutical Sciences, MD
Pharmacy, MD
Philosophy, BD
Photography, B
Physical Chemistry, MD
Physics, BMD
Physiology, MD
Plant Biology, MD
Plant Molecular Biology, MD
Plant Pathology/Phytopathology, MD
Plant Sciences, B
Political Science and Government, BMD
Portuguese Language and Literature, B

Pre-Dentistry Studies, B
Pre-Law Studies, B
Pre-Medicine/Pre-Medical Studies, B
Printmaking, B
Psychology, BD
Public Health, MD
Public Health (MPH, DPH), B
Public Policy Analysis, MD
Quality Management, M
Reading Teacher Education, MD
Rehabilitation and Therapeutic Professions, AB
Religion/Religious Studies, BMO
Reproductive Biology, MD
Respiratory Care Therapy/Therapist, A
Russian Language and Literature, B
School Psychology, MD
Science Teacher Education/General Science
    Teacher Education, MD
Sculpture, BM
Social Psychology, D
Social Sciences, B
Social Studies Teacher Education, MD
Social Work, BMD
Sociology, BMD
Spanish Language and Literature, BMD
Special Education and Teaching, MD
Statistics, BMD
Student Personnel Services, M
Systematic Biology/Biological Systematics, D
Systems Engineering, MD
Theater, M
Theoretical Physics, MD
Toxicology, MD
Translation and Interpretation, M
Translational Biology, M
Turf and Turfgrass Management, B
Urban Studies/Affairs, B
Urban and Regional Planning, MD
Virology, MD
Visual and Performing Arts, B
Water Resources, MD
Women's Studies, BMD
Writing, M

RUTGERS UNIVERSITY–NEWARK

Accounting, BD
African-American/Black Studies, B
Allied Health Diagnostic, Intervention, and Treat-
    ment Professions, B
Allied Health and Medical Assisting Services, MDO
Allopathic Medicine, D
American/United States Studies/Civilization, BMD
Analytical Chemistry, MD
Anthropology, B
Applied Mathematics, B
Applied Physics, MD
Art/Art Studies, General, B
Biochemistry, MD
Bioinformatics, MD
Biological and Biomedical Sciences, BMDO
Biology/Biological Sciences, B
Biomedical Engineering, DO
Biopsychology, D
Botany/Plant Biology, B
Business Administration and Management, B
Business Administration, Management and Opera-
    tions, M
Cancer Biology/Oncology, D
Cell Biology and Anatomy, D
Chemistry, BMD
Cinematography and Film/Video Production, B
Classics and Classical Languages, Litera-
    tures, and Linguistics, B
Clinical Laboratory Science/Medical
    Technology/Technologist, B
Clinical Laboratory Sciences, M
Clinical/Medical Laboratory Science and Allied Pro-
    fessions, B
Clothing and Textiles, M
Cognitive Sciences, D
Computational Biology, M
Computer and Information Sciences, B
Criminal Justice/Safety Studies, B
Criminology, MD
Dentistry, MDO
Developmental Biology and Embryology, O

Drama and Dramatics/Theatre Arts, B
Economics, BMD
Engineering, B
English, M
English Language and Literature, B
Environmental Sciences, MD
Epidemiology, O
Finance, B
Finance and Banking, D
Fine Arts and Art Studies, B
French Language and Literature, B
Geological/Geophysical Engineering, B
Geology/Earth Science, BM
German Language and Literature, B
Health Education, MD
Health Physics/Radiological Health, M
Health Services Administration, MO
Health Services/Allied Health/Health Sciences, B
Hispanic-American, Puerto Rican, and Mexican-
    American/Chicano Studies, B
History, BM
Human Resources Management and Services, M
Immunology, D
Infectious Diseases, D
Information Science/Studies, B
Inorganic Chemistry, MD
International Affairs, MD
International Business/Trade/Commerce, D
Italian Language and Literature, B
Journalism, B
Law and Legal Studies, D
Logistics and Materials Management, BM
Management, D
Management Information Systems and Services, BD
Management of Technology, D
Marketing, D
Marketing/Marketing Management, B
Mathematics, BD
Medical Imaging, M
Medical Informatics, MDO
Microbiology, D
Molecular Biology, MD
Molecular Genetics, D
Molecular Medicine, D
Molecular Pathology, D
Multi-/Interdisciplinary Studies, B
Music, B
Music History, Literature, and Theory, M
Neuroscience, D
Nurse Anesthetist, M
Nursing, MO
Nursing - Adult, M
Nursing - Advanced Practice, M
Nursing Informatics, M
Nutritional Sciences, MDO
Occupational Health Nursing, M
Occupational Therapist Assistant, B
Oral and Dental Sciences, MO
Organic Chemistry, MD
Organizational Management, D
Orthodontics, O
Pathology/Experimental Pathology, D
Pedodontics, O
Pharmaceutical Administration, M
Pharmacology, DO
Philosophy, B
Physical Chemistry, MD
Physical Therapy/Therapist, D
Physician Assistant, M
Physics, B
Physiology, D
Political Science and Government, BM
Psychology, BD
Public Administration, MD
Public Administration and Social Service Profes-
    sions, B
Public Health, MO
Public Policy Analysis, MO
Quantitative Analysis, M
Real Estate, M
Rehabilitation Counseling, MD
Rehabilitation and Therapeutic Professions, AB
Respiratory Care Therapy/Therapist, B
Science, Technology and Society, B
Slavic, Baltic, and Albanian Languages, Litera-
    tures, and Linguistics, B

Social Psychology, D
Social Work, B
Sociology, B
Spanish Language and Literature, B
Supply Chain Management, D
Transcultural Nursing, D
Urban Studies/Affairs, MD
Women's Health Nursing, M
Women's Studies, B
Writing, M
Zoology/Animal Biology, B

SAINT PETER'S UNIVERSITY

Accounting, BM
American/United States Studies/Civilization, B
Applied Behavior Analysis, M
Art History, Criticism and Conservation, B
Art/Art Studies, General, B
Banking and Financial Support Services, B
Biochemistry, B
Biological and Physical Sciences, B
Biology/Biological Sciences, B
Business Administration and Management, AB
Business Administration, Management and Opera-
    tions, M
Business/Managerial Economics, AB
Chemistry, B
Classics and Classical Languages, Litera-
    tures, and Linguistics, B
Communication Studies/Speech Communication
    and Rhetoric, B
Computer and Information Sciences, B
Counselor Education/School Counseling and Guid-
    ance Services, MO
Criminal Justice/Safety Studies, B
Criminology, M
Database Systems, M
Economics, B
Education, MDO
Educational Administration and Supervision, MDO
Elementary Education and Teaching, BMO
English Language and Literature, B
Finance, A
Finance and Banking, M
Fine/Studio Arts, B
Foreign Languages and Literatures, B
Health Professions and Related Clinical Sciences, A
Health Services Administration, M
Health/Health Care Administration/Management, B
Higher Education/Higher Education Administra-
    tion, D
History, B
Human Resources Management and Services, M
Humanities/Humanistic Studies, AB
Information Science/Studies, AB
International Business/Trade/Commerce, ABM
Law Enforcement, M
Liberal Arts and Sciences Studies and Humani-
    ties, B
Management, M
Management Information Systems and Services, M
Marketing, M
Marketing/Marketing Management, AB
Mathematics, B
Mathematics Teacher Education, O
Middle School Education, MO
Modern Languages, B
Natural Sciences, B
Nursing, MDO
Nursing - Adult, MO
Nursing Administration, MD
Philosophy, B
Physics, B
Political Science and Government, B
Psychology, B
Public Administration, M
Public Policy Analysis, AB
Reading Teacher Education, M
Religion/Religious Studies, B
Secondary Education and Teaching, MO
Social Sciences, AB
Sociology, B
Spanish Language and Literature, B
Special Education and Teaching, MO
Theology/Theological Studies, B
Urban Studies/Affairs, AB

Visual and Performing Arts, B

SALEM COMMUNITY COLLEGE

Administrative Assistant and Secretarial Science, A
Agricultural Business and Management, A
Allied Health Diagnostic, Intervention, and Treatment Professions, A
Biology/Biological Sciences, A
Corrections, A
Criminal Justice/Police Science, A
Culinary Arts/Chef Training, A
Education, A
Engineering Technologies/Technicians, A
Fine Arts and Art Studies, A
Fire Science/Firefighting, A
Health Information/Medical Records Administration/Administrator, A
Journalism, A
Legal Assistant/Paralegal, A
Liberal Arts and Sciences Studies and Humanities, A
Medical Insurance Coding Specialist/Coder, A
Nuclear/Nuclear Power Technology/Technician, A
Ornamental Horticulture, A
Pharmacy Technician/Assistant, A
Political Science and Government, A
Precision Production, A
Psychology, A
Respiratory Care Therapy/Therapist, A
Sculpture, A
Social Work, A
Sociology, A
Sport and Fitness Administration/Management, A

SETON HALL UNIVERSITY

Accounting, BMO
African-American/Black Studies, B
Allied Health and Medical Assisting Services, D
Analytical Chemistry, MD
Anthropology, B
Art History, Criticism and Conservation, B
Asian Studies/Civilization, BM
Athletic Training and Sports Medicine, M
Biochemistry, BMD
Biological and Biomedical Sciences, MD
Biology/Biological Sciences, B
Business Administration and Management, B
Business Administration, Management and Operations, MO
Business/Managerial Economics, B
Chemistry, BMD
Christian Studies, B
Classics and Classical Languages, Literatures, and Linguistics, B
Commercial and Advertising Art, B
Communication Disorders, M
Communication Studies/Speech Communication and Rhetoric, B
Communication and Media Studies, M
Communication, Journalism and Related Programs, B
Computer and Information Sciences, B
Corporate and Organizational Communication, M
Counseling Psychology, MD
Counselor Education/School Counseling and Guidance Services, M
Criminal Justice/Safety Studies, B
Drama and Dramatics/Theatre Arts, B
Economics, B
Education, MDO
Educational Administration and Supervision, DO
Educational Leadership and Administration, DO
Educational Measurement and Evaluation, D
Educational Media/Instructional Technology, M
Elementary Education and Teaching, B
English, M
English Language and Literature, B
Environmental Studies, B
Experimental Psychology, M
Finance, B
Finance and Banking, M
Foreign Languages and Literatures, B
French Language and Literature, B
Gerontological Nursing, MD
Health Law, MD
Health Services Administration, MDO

Higher Education/Higher Education Administration, D
History, BM
Humanities/Humanistic Studies, B
Information Resources Management/CIO Training, B
Inorganic Chemistry, MD
International Affairs, MO
International Business/Trade/Commerce, MO
International Relations and Affairs, B
Italian Language and Literature, B
Jewish/Judaic Studies, MO
Labor and Industrial Relations, B
Latin American Studies, B
Law and Legal Studies, MD
Liberal Arts and Sciences Studies and Humanities, B
Management of Technology, M
Marketing, M
Marketing/Marketing Management, B
Marriage and Family Therapy/Counseling, MO
Mathematics, B
Microbiology, M
Molecular Biology, MD
Museology/Museum Studies, M
Museum Education, M
Music Performance, B
Neuroscience, D
Non-Profit/Public/Organizational Management, MO
Nursing, MD
Nursing - Adult, MD
Nursing Administration, M
Nursing Education, M
Occupational Therapy/Therapist, M
Organic Chemistry, MD
Pastoral Studies/Counseling, MO
Pediatric Nurse/Nursing, MD
Philosophy, B
Physical Chemistry, MD
Physical Therapy/Therapist, D
Physician Assistant, M
Physics, B
Political Science and Government, B
Psychology, BMDO
Public Administration, MO
Public Policy Analysis, M
Radio, Television, and Digital Communication, B
Religion/Religious Studies, BMO
School Nursing, M
School Psychology, M
Secondary Education and Teaching, B
Social Work, B
Sociology, B
Spanish Language and Literature, B
Special Education and Teaching, BM
Speech and Interpersonal Communication, M
Sport Psychology, M
Sport and Fitness Administration/Management, BM
Student Personnel Services, M
Supply Chain Management, M
Taxation, O
Theology and Religious Vocations, MO
Theology/Theological Studies, B
Visual and Performing Arts, B

STEVENS INSTITUTE OF TECHNOLOGY

Aerospace, Aeronautical and Astronautical Engineering, MO
Analytical Chemistry, DO
Applied Mathematics, M
Applied Statistics, O
Biochemistry, BMDO
Bioinformatics, BDO
Biomedical Engineering, MO
Biomedical/Medical Engineering, B
Business Administration and Management, B
Business Administration, Management and Operations, M
Chemical Engineering, BMDO
Chemistry, BMDO
Civil Engineering, BMDO
Communication and Media Studies, MO
Computational Mathematics, B
Computer Art and Design, O
Computer Engineering, BMDO
Computer Science, BMD

Computer and Information Systems Security, MO
Construction Engineering and Management, O
Construction Management, MO
Corporate and Organizational Communication, O
Database Systems, O
Electrical Engineering, MDO
Electrical, Electronics and Communications Engineering, B
Electronic Commerce, M
Engineering Design, M
Engineering Management, MD
Engineering Physics, BMDO
Engineering and Applied Sciences, MDO
Engineering/Industrial Management, B
English Language and Literature, B
Entrepreneurship/Entrepreneurial Studies, M
Environmental Engineering Technology/Environmental Technology, MDO
Environmental/Environmental Health Engineering, B
Ethics, MO
Finance and Banking, M
Financial Engineering, M
Health Informatics, O
History, B
History and Philosophy of Science and Technology, B
Human Resources Management and Services, M
Humanities/Humanistic Studies, B
Hydrology and Water Resources Science, M
Industrial and Manufacturing Management, M
Information Science/Studies, MO
International Business/Trade/Commerce, M
Internet and Interactive Multimedia, O
Logistics and Materials Management, MO
Management, M
Management Information Systems and Services, MDO
Management Strategy and Policy, M
Management of Technology, MDO
Manufacturing Engineering, M
Marine Affairs, M
Materials Engineering, MD
Mathematics, B
Mechanical Engineering, BMDO
Modeling and Simulation, M
Naval Architecture and Marine Engineering, B
Ocean Engineering, MD
Organic Chemistry, D
Pharmaceutical Sciences, MO
Philosophy, B
Photonics, MO
Physical Chemistry, D
Physics, BMDO
Polymer/Plastics Engineering, DO
Pre-Dentistry Studies, B
Pre-Law Studies, B
Pre-Medicine/Pre-Medical Studies, B
Project Management, MO
Quality Management, O
Software Engineering, MO
Statistics, MO
Structural Engineering, MO
Systems Engineering, BMDO
Systems Science and Theory, MD
Telecommunications, M
Telecommunications Management, MDO
Water Resources Engineering, M

STOCKTON UNIVERSITY

American/United States Studies/Civilization, MO
Audiology/Audiologist and Speech-Language Pathology/Pathologist, B
Biochemistry, B
Biology/Biological Sciences, B
Business Administration and Management, B
Business Administration, Management and Operations, M
Chemistry, B
Communication Disorders, M
Communication Studies/Speech Communication and Rhetoric, B
Computational Sciences, M
Criminology, BM
Economics, B
Education, M
Educational Leadership and Administration, M

Educational Media/Instructional Technology, M
English Language and Literature, B
Environmental Sciences, M
Environmental Studies, B
Fine/Studio Arts, B
Foreign Languages and Literatures, B
Geology/Earth Science, B
Health Services/Allied Health/Health Sciences, B
History, B
Holocaust Studies, M
Hospitality Administration/Management, B
Information Science/Studies, B
Kinesiology and Exercise Science, B
Liberal Arts and Sciences Studies and Humanities, B
Marine Biology and Biological Oceanography, B
Mathematics, B
Nursing, M
Occupational Therapy/Therapist, M
Physical Therapy/Therapist, D
Physics, B
Political Science and Government, B
Psychology, B
Public Health, B
Social Work, BM
Sociology, B
Teacher Education, Multiple Levels, B
Visual and Performing Arts, B

STRAYER UNIVERSITY–CHERRY HILL CAMPUS

Accounting, B
Business Administration and Management, B
Management Information Systems and Services, B

STRAYER UNIVERSITY–LAWRENCEVILLE CAMPUS

Accounting, B
Business Administration and Management, B
Management Information Systems and Services, B

STRAYER UNIVERSITY–PISCATAWAY CAMPUS

Accounting, B
Business Administration and Management, B
Management Information Systems and Services, B

STRAYER UNIVERSITY–WILLINGBORO CAMPUS

Accounting, B
Business Administration and Management, B
Management Information Systems and Services, B

SUSSEX COUNTY COMMUNITY COLLEGE

Accounting, A
Automotive Engineering Technology/Technician, A
Biological and Physical Sciences, A
Broadcast Journalism, A
Business Administration and Management, A
Commercial and Advertising Art, A
Computer and Information Sciences, A
Corrections and Criminal Justice, A
English Language and Literature, A
Environmental Studies, A
Fine/Studio Arts, A
Fire Protection, A
Health Professions and Related Clinical Sciences, A
Human Services, A
Journalism, A
Legal Assistant/Paralegal, A
Liberal Arts and Sciences Studies and Humanities, A

TALMUDICAL ACADEMY OF NEW JERSEY

Talmudic Studies, B

THOMAS EDISON STATE UNIVERSITY

Accounting, B
Air Traffic Controller, AB
Air Transportation, AB
Aircraft Powerplant Technology/Technician, B

Airframe Mechanics and Aircraft Maintenance Technology/Technician, AB
Allied Health Diagnostic, Intervention, and Treatment Professions, AB
Allied Health and Medical Assisting Services, A
Anthropology, B
Applied Science and Technology, O
Art/Art Studies, General, B
Biology/Biological Sciences, AB
Biomedical Technology/Technician, AB
Business Administration and Management, AB
Business Operations Support and Secretarial Services, A
Clinical Laboratory Science/Medical Technology/Technologist, AB
Communication Studies/Speech Communication and Rhetoric, AB
Computer Engineering Technologies/Technicians, A
Computer Science, AB
Construction Engineering Technology/Technician, B
Criminal Justice/Law Enforcement Administration, B
Criminal Justice/Safety Studies, AB
Dental Hygiene/Hygienist, AB
Distance Education Development, O
Drafting/Design Engineering Technologies/Technicians, AB
Drama and Dramatics/Theatre Arts, B
Economics, B
Educational Leadership and Administration, M
Educational Media/Instructional Technology, O
Electrical and Electronic Engineering Technologies/Technicians, A
Electrical, Electronic and Communications Engineering Technology/Technician, AB
Engineering Technologies/Technicians, AB
English Language and Literature, B
Entrepreneurship/Entrepreneurial Studies, B
Environmental Control Technologies/Technicians, B
Environmental Sciences, AB
Environmental Studies, B
Epidemiology, O
Finance, B
Fire Protection and Safety Technology/Technician, AB
Foreign Languages and Literatures, B
Gerontology, B
Health Professions and Related Clinical Sciences, B
History, B
Homeland Security, O
Hospital and Health Care Facilities Administration/Management, B
Hospitality Administration/Management, B
Human Resources Management and Services, MO
Human Resources Management/Personnel Administration, B
Human Services, AB
Humanities/Humanistic Studies, B
International Business/Trade/Commerce, B
Journalism, B
Liberal Arts and Sciences Studies and Humanities, AB
Liberal Studies, M
Management, M
Management Information Systems and Services, B
Manufacturing Technology/Technician, AB
Marketing/Marketing Management, B
Mathematics, AB
Mechanic and Repair Technologies/Technicians, A
Medical Radiologic Technology/Science - Radiation Therapist, AB
Multi-/Interdisciplinary Studies, AB
Music, B
Natural Sciences, B
Nuclear Engineering Technology/Technician, AB
Nuclear Medical Technology/Technologist, AB
Nursing, M
Nursing Education, O
Operations Management and Supervision, B
Organizational Management, O
Philosophy, B
Photography, AB
Political Science and Government, B
Psychology, B
Public Administration, BM
Public Health Education and Promotion, B
Radiation Protection/Health Physics Technician, AB

Real Estate, B
Religion/Religious Studies, B
Respiratory Care Therapy/Therapist, AB
Security and Protective Services, B
Social Sciences, B
Sociology, B
Veterinary/Animal Health Technology/Technician and Veterinary Assistant, AB

UNION COUNTY COLLEGE

Accounting Technology/Technician and Bookkeeping, A
Allied Health Diagnostic, Intervention, and Treatment Professions, A
American Sign Language, A
American Sign Language (ASL), A
Animation, Interactive Technology, Video Graphics and Special Effects, A
Automobile/Automotive Mechanics Technology/Technician, A
Biology/Biological Sciences, A
Business Administration and Management, A
Business/Commerce, A
Chemistry, A
Civil Engineering Technology/Technician, A
Computer Science, A
Computer and Information Sciences and Support Services, A
Criminal Justice/Law Enforcement Administration, A
Criminal Justice/Police Science, A
Customer Service Support/Call Center/Teleservice Operation, A
Dental Assisting/Assistant, A
Dental Hygiene/Hygienist, A
Diagnostic Medical Sonography/Sonographer and Ultrasound Technician, A
Electromechanical Technology/Electromechanical Engineering Technology, A
Emergency Medical Technology/Technician (EMT Paramedic), A
Engineering, A
Fire Protection and Safety Technology/Technician, A
Hospitality Administration/Management, A
Hotel/Motel Administration/Management, A
Human Services, A
Information Science/Studies, A
Information Technology, A
Language Interpretation and Translation, A
Legal Assistant/Paralegal, A
Liberal Arts and Sciences Studies and Humanities, A
Management Information Systems and Services, A
Manufacturing Technology/Technician, A
Marketing/Marketing Management, A
Mass Communication/Media Studies, A
Mathematics, A
Mechanical Engineering/Mechanical Technology/Technician, A
Medical Radiologic Technology/Science - Radiation Therapist, A
Nuclear Medical Technology/Technologist, A
Physical Therapist Assistant, A
Radiologic Technology/Science - Radiographer, A
Recording Arts Technology/Technician, A
Rehabilitation and Therapeutic Professions, A
Respiratory Care Therapy/Therapist, A
Security and Loss Prevention Services, A
Sign Language Interpretation and Translation, A
Sport and Fitness Administration/Management, A
Telecommunications Technology/Technician, A

UNIVERSITY OF PHOENIX–JERSEY CITY CAMPUS

Accounting, ABM
Business Administration, Management and Operations, M
Business/Commerce, A
Business/Corporate Communications, B
Computer Software Engineering, B
Computer and Information Systems Security, B
Consumer Merchandising/Retailing Management, B
Criminal Justice/Law Enforcement Administration, AB
Criminology, M
E-Commerce/Electronic Commerce, B
Finance, B

General Studies, A
Graphic Communications, A
Health Services Administration, AB
Hospitality Administration/Management, B
Human Resources Management and Services, M
Information Technology, AB
International Business/Trade/Commerce, BM
Management Information Systems and Services, BM
Management Science, B
Management of Technology, M
Marketing, M
Marketing/Marketing Management, B
Operations Management and Supervision, B
Organizational Behavior Studies, B
Psychology, BM
Public Administration, BM
Security and Protective Services, B
System, Networking, and LAN/WAN Management/Manager, A

WARREN COUNTY COMMUNITY COLLEGE

Accounting, A
Administrative Assistant and Secretarial Science, A
Biology/Biological Sciences, A
Business Administration and Management, A
Criminal Justice/Law Enforcement Administration, A
Data Processing and Data Processing Technology/Technician, A
Education, A
Environmental Studies, A
Fine/Studio Arts, A
Information Science/Studies, A
Legal Assistant/Paralegal, A
Liberal Arts and Sciences Studies and Humanities, A
Social Sciences, A

WILLIAM PATERSON UNIVERSITY OF NEW JERSEY

Accounting, B
African-American/Black Studies, B
Anthropology, B
Art History, Criticism and Conservation, B
Art/Art Studies, General, B
Asian Studies/Civilization, B
Athletic Training and Sports Medicine, B
BioTechnology, BM
Biological and Biomedical Sciences, M
Biology/Biological Sciences, B
Business Administration and Management, B
Business Administration, Management and Operations, M
Chemistry, B
Clinical Psychology, MD
Communication Disorders, BM
Communication Studies/Speech Communication and Rhetoric, B
Communication and Media Studies, M
Community Health Services/Liaison/Counseling, B
Computer Science, B
Computer and Information Sciences, B
Counseling Psychology, M
Counselor Education/School Counseling and Guidance Services, M
Criminal Justice/Safety Studies, B
Early Childhood Education and Teaching, B
Economics, B
Education, M
Educational Leadership and Administration, M
Elementary Education and Teaching, B
English, M
English Language and Literature, B
Environmental Studies, B
Exercise and Sports Science, M
Finance, B
Financial Planning and Services, B
Fine Arts and Art Studies, M
Fine/Studio Arts, B
French Language and Literature, B
Geography, B
Geology/Earth Science, B
Health Services/Allied Health/Health Sciences, B
History, BM
International Business/Trade/Commerce, B

Kinesiology and Exercise Science, B
Latin American Studies, B
Law and Legal Studies, B
Liberal Arts and Sciences Studies and Humanities, B
Management Science, B
Marketing/Marketing Management, B
Mathematics, B
Music, BM
Music Performance, B
Nursing, MD
Philosophy, B
Physical Education Teaching and Coaching, B
Political Science and Government, B
Psychology, B
Public Health (MPH, DPH), B
Public Policy Analysis, M
Reading Teacher Education, M
Secondary Education and Teaching, BM
Selling Skills and Sales Operations, B
Sociology, BM
Spanish Language and Literature, B
Special Education and Teaching, BM
Sport and Fitness Administration/Management, B
Women's Studies, B
Writing, M

New Mexico

BROOKLINE COLLEGE

Accounting, A
Business Administration and Management, A
Criminal Justice/Law Enforcement Administration, AB
Legal Assistant/Paralegal, A

CARRINGTON COLLEGE–ALBUQUERQUE

Medical Office Management/Administration, A
Physical Therapist Assistant, A

CENTRAL NEW MEXICO COMMUNITY COLLEGE

Accounting, A
Administrative Assistant and Secretarial Science, A
Airframe Mechanics and Aircraft Maintenance Technology/Technician, A
Anthropology, A
Architectural Drafting and Architectural CAD/CADD, A
Art/Art Studies, General, A
Automobile/Automotive Mechanics Technology/Technician, A
BioTechnology, A
Biology/Biological Sciences, A
Business Administration and Management, A
Cartography, A
Chemistry, A
Clinical/Medical Laboratory Technician, A
Computer Science, A
Computer and Information Sciences, A
Construction Management, A
Cosmetology/Cosmetologist, A
Criminal Justice/Law Enforcement Administration, A
Criminology, A
Culinary Arts/Chef Training, A
Diagnostic Medical Sonography/Sonographer and Ultrasound Technician, A
Drama and Dramatics/Theatre Arts, A
Early Childhood Education and Teaching, A
Electrical, Electronic and Communications Engineering Technology/Technician, A
Electrician, A
Emergency Medical Technology/Technician (EMT Paramedic), A
English Language and Literature, A
Environmental Design/Architecture, A
Fire Science/Firefighting, A
Foods, Nutrition, and Wellness Studies, A
Foreign Languages and Literatures, A
General Studies, A
Health Information/Medical Records Administration/Administrator, A
Health Information/Medical Records Technology/Technician, A

Health Services/Allied Health/Health Sciences, A
Health and Physical Education, A
Heating, Air Conditioning, Ventilation and Refrigeration Maintenance Technology/Technician, A
History, A
Hospitality Administration/Management, A
Human Development and Family Studies, A
Latin American Studies, A
Legal Assistant/Paralegal, A
Liberal Arts and Sciences Studies and Humanities, A
Machine Tool Technology/Machinist, A
Mathematics, A
Opticianry/Ophthalmic Dispensing Optician, A
Physics, A
Plumbing Technology/Plumber, A
Political Science and Government, A
Pre-Law Studies, A
Psychology, A
Radiologic Technology/Science - Radiographer, A
Respiratory Care Therapy/Therapist, A
Sociology, A
Surgical Technology/Technologist, A
Surveying Engineering, A
Teacher Education, Multiple Levels, A
Technology Teacher Education/Industrial Arts Teacher Education, A
Vehicle Maintenance and Repair Technologies, A
Veterinary/Animal Health Technology/Technician and Veterinary Assistant, A
Welding Technology/Welder, A

CLOVIS COMMUNITY COLLEGE

Administrative Assistant and Secretarial Science, A
Automobile/Automotive Mechanics Technology/Technician, A
Business Administration and Management, A
Commercial and Advertising Art, A
Computer and Information Sciences, A
Cosmetology/Cosmetologist, A
Criminal Justice/Police Science, A
Early Childhood Education and Teaching, A
Education, A
Electrician, A
Emergency Care Attendant (EMT Ambulance), A
Executive Assistant/Executive Secretary, A
Fine/Studio Arts, A
Fire Science/Firefighting, A
General Office Occupations and Clerical Services, A
General Studies, A
Health and Physical Education, A
Heating, Air Conditioning, Ventilation and Refrigeration Maintenance Technology/Technician, A
Industrial Mechanics and Maintenance Technology, A
Information Technology, A
Legal Administrative Assistant/Secretary, A
Legal Assistant/Paralegal, A
Legal Support Services, A
Liberal Arts and Sciences Studies and Humanities, A
Library Assistant/Technician, A
Management Information Systems and Services, A
Medical/Clinical Assistant, A
Office Management and Supervision, A
Psychology, A
Sign Language Interpretation and Translation, A
System Administration/Administrator, A
Teacher Assistant/Aide, A
Web/Multimedia Management and Webmaster, A
Welding Technology/Welder, A

DOÑA ANA COMMUNITY COLLEGE

Administrative Assistant and Secretarial Science, A
Architectural Engineering Technology/Technician, A
Automobile/Automotive Mechanics Technology/Technician, A
Business Administration and Management, A
Computer Engineering Technology/Technician, A
Computer Typography and Composition Equipment Operator, A
Consumer Merchandising/Retailing Management, A
Drafting and Design Technology/Technician, A
Electrical, Electronic and Communications Engineering Technology/Technician, A

Emergency Medical Technology/Technician (EMT
Paramedic), A
Fashion Merchandising, A
Finance, A
Fire Science/Firefighting, A
Heating, Air Conditioning, Ventilation and Refrigera-
tion Maintenance Technology/Technician, A
Hospitality Administration/Management, A
Hydrology and Water Resources Science, A
Industrial Radiologic Technology/Technician, A
Legal Assistant/Paralegal, A
Library Science, A
Respiratory Care Therapy/Therapist, A
Welding Technology/Welder, A

EASTERN NEW MEXICO UNIVERSITY

Accounting, B
Agribusiness, B
Agricultural Production Operations, A
Agricultural Teacher Education, B
Agriculture, B
Analytical Chemistry, M
Anthropology, BM
Art/Art Studies, General, AB
Audiology/Audiologist and Speech-Language
Pathology/Pathologist, B
Aviation/Airway Management and Operations, B
Biochemistry, BM
Biological and Biomedical Sciences, M
Biology/Biological Sciences, B
Botany/Plant Biology, M
Business Administration and Management, B
Business Administration, Management and Opera-
tions, M
Cell Biology and Anatomy, M
Chemistry, BM
Child Care and Support Services Management, A
Cinematography and Film/Video Production, B
Clinical Laboratory Science/Medical
Technology/Technologist, B
Clinical/Medical Social Work, B
Communication Disorders, M
Communication Studies/Speech Communication
and Rhetoric, B
Communication and Media Studies, M
Computer and Information Sciences, B
Counselor Education/School Counseling and Guid-
ance Services, M
Criminal Justice/Safety Studies, B
Culinary Arts/Chef Training, A
Curriculum and Instruction, M
Dairy Science, B
Drama and Dramatics/Theatre Arts, B
Early Childhood Education and Teaching, BM
Ecology, M
Education, M
Educational Administration and Supervision, M
Educational Media/Instructional Technology, M
Elementary Education and Teaching, BM
Engineering Technology, B
English, M
English Language and Literature, B
English as a Second Language, M
Environmental Sciences, B
Exercise and Sports Science, M
Family and Consumer Sciences/Human Sciences, A
Forensic Science and Technology, B
General Studies, B
Geology/Earth Science, B
History, B
Human Services, M
Inorganic Chemistry, M
Liberal Arts and Sciences Studies and Humani-
ties, AB
Management Information Systems and Services, B
Mathematics, B
Microbiology, M
Molecular Biology, M
Multilingual and Multicultural Education, M
Music, B
Nursing, M
Organic Chemistry, M
Parks, Recreation, Leisure and Fitness Studies, A
Physical Chemistry, M
Physical Education Teaching and Coaching, BM
Political Science and Government, B

Pre-Nursing Studies, A
Psychology, AB
Reading Teacher Education, M
Religion/Religious Studies, B
Sales and Marketing Operations/Marketing and Dis-
tribution Teacher Education, B
Secondary Education and Teaching, M
Social Sciences, B
Sociology, B
Spanish Language and Literature, B
Special Education and Teaching, BM
Sport and Fitness Administration/Management, M
Vocational and Technical Education, M
Wildlife and Wildlands Science and Management, B
Zoology/Animal Biology, M

EASTERN NEW MEXICO
UNIVERSITY–ROSWELL

Accounting, A
Administrative Assistant and Secretarial Science, A
Airframe Mechanics and Aircraft Maintenance
Technology/Technician, A
Airline/Commercial/Professional Pilot and Flight
Crew, A
Autobody/Collision and Repair
Technology/Technician, A
Automobile/Automotive Mechanics
Technology/Technician, A
Business Administration and Management, A
Child Care and Support Services Management, A
Cinematography and Film/Video Production, A
Computer Installation and Repair
Technology/Technician, A
Computer and Information Sciences, A
Criminal Justice/Police Science, A
Criminal Justice/Safety Studies, A
Dental Hygiene/Hygienist, A
Design and Visual Communications, A
Drafting and Design Technology/Technician, A
Education, A
Electromechanical Technology/Electromechanical
Engineering Technology, A
Emergency Medical Technology/Technician (EMT
Paramedic), A
Fire Protection and Safety Technology/Technician, A
General Studies, A
Graphic Design, A
Heating, Air Conditioning, Ventilation and Refrigera-
tion Maintenance Technology/Technician, A
Human Development and Family Studies, A
Industrial Technology/Technician, A
Legal Assistant/Paralegal, A
Liberal Arts and Sciences Studies and Humani-
ties, A
Medical Office Management/Administration, A
Medical/Clinical Assistant, A
Occupational Therapist Assistant, A
Office Management and Supervision, A
Quality Control and Safety
Technologies/Technicians, A
Respiratory Care Therapy/Therapist, A
Sign Language Interpretation and Translation, A
Social Work, A
Veterinary/Animal Health Technology/Technician and
Veterinary Assistant, A
Welding Technology/Welder, A

EC-COUNCIL UNIVERSITY

Computer and Information Systems Security, M

INSTITUTE OF AMERICAN INDIAN
ARTS

American Indian/Native American Studies, AB
Cinematography and Film/Video Production, AB
Fine/Studio Arts, AB
Museology/Museum Studies, AB
Writing, M

LUNA COMMUNITY COLLEGE

Accounting, A
Administrative Assistant and Secretarial Science, A
Autobody/Collision and Repair
Technology/Technician, A
Business Administration and Management, A

Computer Programming, Vendor/Product Certifica-
tion, A
Criminal Justice/Safety Studies, A
Culinary Arts/Chef Training, A
Dental Assisting/Assistant, A
Drafting and Design Technology/Technician, A
Education, A
Electrical, Electronic and Communications Engineer-
ing Technology/Technician, A
General Studies, A
Kindergarten/PreSchool Education and Teaching, A
Liberal Arts and Sciences Studies and Humani-
ties, A
Office Management and Supervision, A

MESALANDS COMMUNITY COLLEGE

Accounting and Related Services, A
Agricultural Business and Management, A
Agricultural and Domestic Animals Services, A
Automobile/Automotive Mechanics
Technology/Technician, A
Business Administration and Management, A
Child Care Provider/Assistant, A
Computer and Information Sciences, A
Criminal Justice/Police Science, A
Criminal Justice/Safety Studies, A
Diesel Mechanics Technology/Technician, A
Education, A
Engineering Technologies/Technicians, A
General Office Occupations and Clerical Services, A
Liberal Arts and Sciences Studies and Humani-
ties, A
Paleontology, A
Pre-Medicine/Pre-Medical Studies, A
Public Administration, A
Sculpture, A
Social Work, A

NATIONAL AMERICAN UNIVERSITY
(ALBUQUERQUE)

Accounting, A
Business Administration, Management and Opera-
tions, A
Computer and Information Sciences, A
Education, A
Engineering, A
General Studies, A
Health/Health Care Administration/Management, A
Information Technology, A
Management Science, A

NATIONAL AMERICAN UNIVERSITY
(ALBUQUERQUE)

Accounting, AB
Business Administration and Management, AB
Computer Programming, Specific Applications, B
General Studies, A
Health/Health Care Administration/Management, B
Information Technology, AB
Organizational Behavior Studies, B
System Administration/Administrator, B
System, Networking, and LAN/WAN
Management/Manager, B
Web Page, Digital/Multimedia and Information Re-
sources Design, B

NATIONAL COLLEGE OF MIDWIFERY

Direct Entry Midwifery (LM, CPM), AB
Nurse Midwife/Nursing Midwifery, MD

NAVAJO TECHNICAL UNIVERSITY

Accounting, A
Administrative Assistant and Secretarial Science, A
American Indian/Native American Studies, M
Baking and Pastry Arts/Baker/Pastry Chef, A
CAD/CADD Drafting and/or Design
Technology/Technician, A
Culinary Arts/Chef Training, A
Early Childhood Education and Teaching, A
Environmental Sciences, A
Geography, A
Information Technology, A
Pre-Law Studies, A
Public Administration, A

Veterinary/Animal Health Technology/Technician and Veterinary Assistant, A

NEW MEXICO HIGHLANDS UNIVERSITY

Accounting, B
American/United States Studies/Civilization, M
Anthropology, M
Art/Art Studies, General, B
Biology/Biological Sciences, B
Business Administration and Management, B
Business Administration, Management and Operations, M
Chemistry, BM
Cinematography and Film/Video Production, B
Clinical Psychology, M
Clinical/Medical Social Work, B
Communication Studies/Speech Communication and Rhetoric, B
Computer Art and Design, M
Computer Science, M
Computer and Information Sciences, B
Counseling Psychology, M
Counselor Education/School Counseling and Guidance Services, M
Criminal Justice/Safety Studies, B
Curriculum and Instruction, M
Design and Visual Communications, B
Education, M
Educational Leadership and Administration, M
Electrical, Electronics and Communications Engineering, B
Elementary Education and Teaching, AB
Engineering, B
English, M
English Language and Literature, B
Environmental Studies, B
Exercise and Sports Science, M
Family and Consumer Sciences/Human Sciences, B
Finance, B
Forensic Science and Technology, B
Forestry, B
Geology/Earth Science, B
Health Education, M
Health Teacher Education, B
History, BM
Human Resources Management and Services, M
Information Science/Studies, B
International Business/Trade/Commerce, M
Internet and Interactive Multimedia, M
Kindergarten/PreSchool Education and Teaching, B
Liberal Arts and Sciences Studies and Humanities, B
Management, M
Management Information Systems and Services, B
Marketing/Marketing Management, B
Mathematics, B
Media Studies, M
Music, B
Natural Resources Management/Development and Policy, BM
Parks, Recreation and Leisure Facilities Management, B
Parks, Recreation, Leisure and Fitness Studies, B
Physical Education Teaching and Coaching, B
Physics, B
Political Science and Government, BM
Psychology, BM
Public Affairs, M
Rhetoric, M
Science Teacher Education/General Science Teacher Education, B
Social Sciences, B
Social Work, M
Sociology, M
Spanish Language and Literature, B
Special Education and Teaching, BM
Sport and Fitness Administration/Management, M
Technology Teacher Education/Industrial Arts Teacher Education, B
Visual and Performing Arts, B

Writing, M

NEW MEXICO INSTITUTE OF MINING AND TECHNOLOGY

Applied Mathematics, MD
Astrophysics, D
Atmospheric Sciences and Meteorology, D
Biological and Biomedical Sciences, M
Biology/Biological Sciences, B
Business Administration and Management, AB
Chemical Engineering, B
Chemistry, BMD
Civil Engineering, B
Computer Science, BMD
Electrical Engineering, M
Electrical, Electronics and Communications Engineering, B
Engineering Management, M
Environmental Engineering Technology/Environmental Technology, M
Environmental Studies, B
Environmental/Environmental Health Engineering, B
General Studies, AB
Geochemistry, MD
Geology/Earth Science, BMD
Geophysics and Seismology, BMD
Geosciences, MD
Hazardous Materials Management and Waste Technology/Technician, M
Hydrology and Water Resources Science, MD
Information Technology, B
Materials Engineering, BMD
Mathematical Physics, D
Mathematics, BMD
Mechanical Engineering, BM
Mechanics, M
Mineral/Mining Engineering, M
Mining and Mineral Engineering, B
Operations Research, M
Petroleum Engineering, BMD
Physical Sciences, B
Physics, BMD
Psychology, B
Science Teacher Education/General Science Teacher Education, M
Statistics, M
Systems Engineering, M
Water Resources Engineering, M

NEW MEXICO JUNIOR COLLEGE

Accounting, A
Administrative Assistant and Secretarial Science, A
Agriculture, A
Art Teacher Education, A
Art/Art Studies, General, A
Athletic Training and Sports Medicine, A
Automobile/Automotive Mechanics Technology/Technician, A
Biological and Physical Sciences, A
Biology/Biological Sciences, A
Business Administration and Management, A
Business Teacher Education, A
Carpentry/Carpenter, A
Chemistry, A
Clinical/Medical Laboratory Technician, A
Commercial and Advertising Art, A
Computer Graphics, A
Computer Programming/Programmer, A
Computer Science, A
Computer Typography and Composition Equipment Operator, A
Construction Engineering Technology/Technician, A
Cosmetology/Cosmetologist, A
Criminal Justice/Police Science, A
Data Processing and Data Processing Technology/Technician, A
Drafting and Design Technology/Technician, A
Drama and Dramatics/Theatre Arts, A
Education, A
Elementary Education and Teaching, A
Emergency Medical Technology/Technician (EMT Paramedic), A
Engineering, A
English Language and Literature, A
Environmental Studies, A
Finance, A

Fire Science/Firefighting, A
Health Professions and Related Clinical Sciences, A
History, A
Legal Administrative Assistant/Secretary, A
Liberal Arts and Sciences Studies and Humanities, A
Machine Tool Technology/Machinist, A
Marketing/Marketing Management, A
Mathematics, A
Medical Administrative Assistant/Secretary, A
Medical/Clinical Assistant, A
Music, A
Parks, Recreation, Leisure and Fitness Studies, A
Petroleum Technology/Technician, A
Physical Education Teaching and Coaching, A
Real Estate, A
Trade and Industrial Teacher Education, A
Welding Technology/Welder, A

NEW MEXICO MILITARY INSTITUTE

Accounting, A
Army JROTC/ROTC, A
Art/Art Studies, General, A
Biological and Physical Sciences, A
Biology/Biological Sciences, A
Business Administration and Management, A
Chemistry, A
Civil Engineering Technology/Technician, A
Computer Programming/Programmer, A
Computer Science, A
Criminal Justice/Law Enforcement Administration, A
Criminal Justice/Police Science, A
Economics, A
Engineering, A
English Language and Literature, A
Finance, A
French Language and Literature, A
German Language and Literature, A
History, A
Humanities/Humanistic Studies, A
Liberal Arts and Sciences Studies and Humanities, A
Mathematics, A
Physical Education Teaching and Coaching, A
Physics, A
Social Sciences, A
Spanish Language and Literature, A
Sport and Fitness Administration/Management, A

NEW MEXICO STATE UNIVERSITY

Accounting, BM
Aerospace, Aeronautical and Astronautical Engineering, BMD
Agribusiness, BM
Agricultural Economics, MD
Agricultural Education, M
Agricultural Teacher Education, B
Agricultural and Extension Education Services, B
Agriculture, B
Agronomy and Crop Science, B
Animal Sciences, BMD
Animation, Interactive Technology, Video Graphics and Special Effects, B
Anthropology, BMO
Apparel and Textiles, B
Applied Statistics, M
Art History, Criticism and Conservation, M
Astronomy, MD
Astrophysics, M
Athletic Training and Sports Medicine, B
BioTechnology, M
Biochemistry, B
Bioinformatics, M
Biological and Biomedical Sciences, MD
Biology/Biological Sciences, B
Business Administration and Management, B
Business Administration, Management and Operations, MD
Business/Commerce, AB
Chemical Engineering, BMD
Chemistry, BMD
Cinematography and Film/Video Production, B
Civil Engineering, BMD
Cognitive Sciences, D
Communication Disorders, MDO
Communication and Media Studies, M

Community Health Nursing, D
Community Health Services/Liaison/Counseling, B
Community Organization and Advocacy, B
Computer Engineering, MDO
Computer Science, MD
Computer and Information Sciences, B
Corporate and Organizational Communication, MD
Counseling Psychology, MDO
Counselor Education/School Counseling and Guidance Services, MDO
Criminal Justice/Safety Studies, B
Criminology, M
Curriculum and Instruction, MDO
Dance, BM
Dietetics/Dieticians, B
Distance Education Development, O
Drama and Dramatics/Theatre Arts, B
Early Childhood Education and Teaching, B
Ecology, B
Economic Development, D
Economics, BMDO
Education, BMDO
Education/Teaching of Individuals with Speech or Language Impairments, B
Educational Administration and Supervision, MD
Educational Measurement and Evaluation, M
Electrical Engineering, MDO
Electrical, Electronics and Communications Engineering, B
Elementary Education and Teaching, B
Engineering Physics, B
Engineering Technology, B
Engineering and Applied Sciences, MDO
English, MD
English Education, M
English Language and Literature, B
Entomology, M
Environmental Sciences, BMD
Experimental Psychology, M
Family Resource Management Studies, B
Family and Consumer Sciences/Home Economics Teacher Education, B
Family and Consumer Sciences/Human Sciences, M
Finance, B
Finance and Banking, O
Fine Arts and Art Studies, M
Fine/Studio Arts, B
Fish, Game and Wildlife Management, M
Food Science and Technology, M
Food Technology and Processing, B
Foods, Nutrition, and Wellness Studies, B
Foreign Languages and Literatures, B
General Studies, B
Genetics, B
Geography, BM
Geological Engineering, MD
Geology/Earth Science, BM
History, BM
Horticultural Science, BMD
Hospitality Administration/Management, B
Human Development and Family Studies, B
Hydrology and Water Resources Science, M
Industrial Engineering, B
Industrial/Management Engineering, MDO
Information Technology, B
Interdisciplinary Studies, MD
International Business/Trade/Commerce, B
Journalism, B
Kinesiology and Exercise Science, B
Liberal Arts and Sciences Studies and Humanities, B
Marketing, D
Marketing/Marketing Management, B
Marriage and Family Therapy/Counseling, M
Mathematics, BMD
Mechanical Engineering, BMD
Medical Microbiology and Bacteriology, B
Molecular Biology, MD
Multilingual and Multicultural Education, D
Museology/Museum Studies, O
Music, M
Music Performance, B
Music Teacher Education, BM
Natural Resource Economics, B
Nursing, MD

Nursing Administration, M
Nutritional Sciences, M
Performance, M
Philosophy, B
Physical Education Teaching and Coaching, B
Physics, BMD
Plant Pathology/Phytopathology, BM
Plant Sciences, M
Political Science and Government, BM
Psychology, BMD
Public Health, MO
Public Health Education and Promotion, B
Range Science and Management, BMD
Rhetoric, MD
School Psychology, O
Secondary Education and Teaching, B
Social Psychology, D
Social Work, BM
Sociology, BM
Soil Science and Agronomy, B
Spanish Language and Literature, M
Special Education and Teaching, BMDO
Survey Technology/Surveying, B
Systems Engineering, O
Turf and Turfgrass Management, B
Visual and Performing Arts, B
Water Resources, MD
Wildlife and Wildlands Science and Management, B
Women's Studies, B
Writing, M

NEW MEXICO STATE UNIVERSITY–ALAMOGORDO

Administrative Assistant and Secretarial Science, A
Animation, Interactive Technology, Video Graphics and Special Effects, A
Automobile/Automotive Mechanics Technology/Technician, A
Biomedical Technology/Technician, A
Business/Commerce, A
Computer Programming/Programmer, A
Criminal Justice/Safety Studies, A
Early Childhood Education and Teaching, A
Education, A
Electrical, Electronic and Communications Engineering Technology/Technician, A
Electrician, A
Ethnic, Cultural Minority, and Gender Studies, A
Fine/Studio Arts, A
General Office Occupations and Clerical Services, A
General Studies, A
Graphic Design, A
Human Services, A
Information Technology, A
Legal Assistant/Paralegal, A

NEW MEXICO STATE UNIVERSITY–CARLSBAD

Accounting, A
Administrative Assistant and Secretarial Science, A
Architectural Drafting and Architectural CAD/CADD, A
Building/Property Maintenance and Management, A
Business/Commerce, A
Carpentry/Carpenter, A
Criminal Justice/Law Enforcement Administration, A
Criminal Justice/Safety Studies, A
Digital Communication and Media/Multimedia, A
Early Childhood Education and Teaching, A
Education, A
Electrical, Electronic and Communications Engineering Technology/Technician, A
Engineering, A
General Office Occupations and Clerical Services, A
General Studies, A
Heating, Air Conditioning and Refrigeration Technology/Technician, A
Human Services, A
Industrial Electronics Technology/Technician, A
Medical Transcription/Transcriptionist, A
Multi-/Interdisciplinary Studies, A
Teacher Assistant/Aide, A
Welding Technology/Welder, A

Word Processing, A

NEW MEXICO STATE UNIVERSITY–GRANTS

Administrative Assistant and Secretarial Science, A
Business Administration and Management, A
Business/Commerce, A
Early Childhood Education and Teaching, A
Education, A
Elementary Education and Teaching, A
General Office Occupations and Clerical Services, A
Human Services, A
Liberal Arts and Sciences Studies and Humanities, A
Multi-/Interdisciplinary Studies, A
Social Work, A
Teacher Assistant/Aide, A

NORTHERN NEW MEXICO COLLEGE

BioTechnology, A
Business/Commerce, A
Computer and Information Sciences, A
Criminal Justice/Safety Studies, A
Electrical, Electronic and Communications Engineering Technology/Technician, A
Elementary Education and Teaching, A
Environmental Studies, A
Fine/Studio Arts, A
Human Services, A
Industrial Engineering, A
Industrial Radiologic Technology/Technician, A
Library Assistant/Technician, A
Medical Radiologic Technology/Science - Radiation Therapist, A

PIMA MEDICAL INSTITUTE (ALBUQUERQUE)

Health/Health Care Administration/Management, A

PIMA MEDICAL INSTITUTE (ALBUQUERQUE)

Dental Hygiene/Hygienist, A
Health/Health Care Administration/Management, A
Physical Therapist Assistant, A
Radiologic Technology/Science - Radiographer, A
Respiratory Therapy Technician/Assistant, A

ST. JOHN'S COLLEGE

Asian Languages, M
Asian Studies/Civilization, M
General Studies, B
Liberal Arts and Sciences Studies and Humanities, B
Liberal Studies, M

SAN JUAN COLLEGE

Accounting Technology/Technician and Bookkeeping, A
American Indian/Native American Studies, A
Autobody/Collision and Repair Technology/Technician, A
Automobile/Automotive Mechanics Technology/Technician, A
Biology/Biological Sciences, A
Business Administration and Management, A
Carpentry/Carpenter, A
Chemistry, A
Child Care Provider/Assistant, A
Clinical/Medical Laboratory Technician, A
Commercial and Advertising Art, A
Cosmetology/Cosmetologist, A
Criminal Justice/Police Science, A
Data Processing and Data Processing Technology/Technician, A
Dental Hygiene/Hygienist, A
Diesel Mechanics Technology/Technician, A
Drafting and Design Technology/Technician, A
Electrical, Electronic and Communications Engineering Technology/Technician, A
Elementary Education and Teaching, A
Emergency Medical Technology/Technician (EMT Paramedic), A
Engineering, A
Engineering Technology, A
Fire Science/Firefighting, A

General Studies, A
Geology/Earth Science, A
Health Information/Medical Records Technology/Technician, A
Health and Physical Education, A
Industrial Mechanics and Maintenance Technology, A
Industrial Technology/Technician, A
Instrumentation Technology/Technician, A
Landscaping and Groundskeeping, A
Legal Assistant/Paralegal, A
Liberal Arts and Sciences Studies and Humanities, A
Machine Shop Technology/Assistant, A
Mathematics, A
Occupational Safety and Health Technology/Technician, A
Occupational Therapist Assistant, A
Parks, Recreation, Leisure and Fitness Studies, A
Physical Sciences, A
Physical Therapist Assistant, A
Physics, A
Pre-Medicine/Pre-Medical Studies, A
Psychology, A
Respiratory Care Therapy/Therapist, A
Secondary Education and Teaching, A
Social Work, A
Solar Energy Technology/Technician, A
Special Education and Teaching, A
Surgical Technology/Technologist, A
Technical Theatre/Theatre Design and Technology, A
Veterinary/Animal Health Technology/Technician and Veterinary Assistant, A
Welding Technology/Welder, A

SANTA FE COMMUNITY COLLEGE

Accounting, A
Administrative Assistant and Secretarial Science, A
Architectural Drafting and Architectural CAD/CADD, A
Art History, Criticism and Conservation, A
Art/Art Studies, General, A
Banking and Financial Support Services, A
Behavioral Sciences, A
Biology/Biological Sciences, A
Business Administration and Management, A
Ceramic Arts and Ceramics, A
Cinematography and Film/Video Production, A
Commercial Photography, A
Computer Programming/Programmer, A
Computer and Information Sciences, A
Construction Engineering Technology/Technician, A
Criminal Justice/Police Science, A
Criminal Justice/Safety Studies, A
Culinary Arts/Chef Training, A
Dental Assisting/Assistant, A
Design and Visual Communications, A
Drafting and Design Technology/Technician, A
Education, A
Electrical, Electronic and Communications Engineering Technology/Technician, A
Engineering, A
Entrepreneurship/Entrepreneurial Studies, A
Environmental Studies, A
Ethnic, Cultural Minority, and Gender Studies, A
Fashion/Apparel Design, A
Film/Cinema Studies, A
General Studies, A
Health and Physical Education, A
Humanities/Humanistic Studies, A
Interior Design, A
Intermedia/Multimedia, A
Kindergarten/PreSchool Education and Teaching, A
Legal Assistant/Paralegal, A
Metal and Jewelry Arts, A
Parks, Recreation, Leisure and Fitness Studies, A
Photography, A
Physical Sciences, A
Printmaking, A
Psychology, A
Radio and Television Broadcasting Technology/Technician, A
Respiratory Care Therapy/Therapist, A
Sculpture, A
Sign Language Interpretation and Translation, A

Social Work, A
Spanish Language and Literature, A
Survey Technology/Surveying, A
Water Quality and Wastewater Treatment Management and Recycling Technology/Technician, A
Woodworking, A

SANTA FE UNIVERSITY OF ART AND DESIGN

Business Administration and Management, B
Cinematography and Film/Video Production, B
Drama and Dramatics/Theatre Arts, B
Fine/Studio Arts, B
Graphic Design, B
Music, B
Photography, B
Technical Theatre/Theatre Design and Technology, B

SOUTHWESTERN INDIAN POLYTECHNIC INSTITUTE

Accounting Technology/Technician and Bookkeeping, A
Business Administration and Management, A
Business/Commerce, A
Cartography, A
Early Childhood Education and Teaching, A
Engineering, A
Institutional Food Workers, A
Instrumentation Technology/Technician, A
Liberal Arts and Sciences Studies and Humanities, A
Natural Resources and Conservation, A
Opticianry/Ophthalmic Dispensing Optician, A
System, Networking, and LAN/WAN Management/Manager, A

UNIVERSITY OF NEW MEXICO

Accounting, M
African-American/Black Studies, B
Allied Health and Medical Assisting Services, MDO
Allopathic Medicine, D
American Indian/Native American Studies, BM
American/United States Studies/Civilization, BMD
Anthropology, BMD
Archeology, MD
Architecture, BMD
Art Education, M
Art History, Criticism and Conservation, BMD
Art Teacher Education, B
Art/Art Studies, General, B
Asian Studies/Civilization, B
Astrophysics, B
Audiology/Audiologist and Speech-Language Pathology/Pathologist, B
Biochemistry, BMD
Biological and Biomedical Sciences, MD
Biology/Biological Sciences, B
Biomedical Engineering, MD
Business Administration and Management, B
Business Administration, Management and Operations, M
Cell Biology and Anatomy, MD
Chemical Engineering, BMD
Chemistry, BMD
Child and Family Studies, MD
Civil Engineering, BMD
Classics and Classical Languages, Literatures, and Linguistics, B
Clinical Laboratory Sciences, MO
Clinical Psychology, D
Clinical/Medical Laboratory Technician, B
Cognitive Sciences, D
Communication Disorders, M
Communication and Media Studies, MD
Community Health and Preventive Medicine, M
Community Organization and Advocacy, B
Comparative Literature, BMD
Composition, M
Computational Sciences, O
Computer Engineering, BMD
Computer Science, MD
Computer and Information Sciences, B
Computer and Information Systems Security, M
Construction Engineering, B
Construction Management, M

Corrections, B
Counselor Education/School Counseling and Guidance Services, MD
Cultural Studies, MD
Dance, BM
Dental Hygiene/Hygienist, BM
Developmental Psychology, D
Drama and Dramatics/Theatre Arts, B
Early Childhood Education and Teaching, BD
Economics, BMD
Education, MDO
Educational Leadership and Administration, MDO
Educational Media/Instructional Technology, MDO
Educational Psychology, MD
Electrical Engineering, MD
Electrical, Electronics and Communications Engineering, B
Elementary Education and Teaching, BM
Emergency Medical Technology/Technician (EMT Paramedic), B
Engineering Science, B
Engineering and Applied Sciences, MDO
English, MD
English Education, MD
English Language and Literature, B
English as a Second Language, MD
Entrepreneurship/Entrepreneurial Studies, M
Environmental Design/Architecture, B
Environmental Policy and Resource Management, M
Environmental Sciences, B
Environmental Studies, M
Epidemiology, M
Ethnic and Cultural Studies, MD
European Studies/Civilization, B
Exercise and Sports Science, MD
Family and Consumer Sciences/Human Sciences, B
Film/Cinema Studies, B
Finance and Banking, M
Fine Arts and Art Studies, M
Foods, Nutrition, and Wellness Studies, B
Foreign Languages and Literatures, B
Foundations and Philosophy of Education, MD
French Language and Literature, BMD
General Studies, B
Genetics, MD
Geography, BM
Geology/Earth Science, B
Geosciences, MD
German Language and Literature, BM
Health Education, MD
Health Psychology, D
Health Services Administration, M
Health Teacher Education, B
Higher Education/Higher Education Administration, O
Hispanic-American, Puerto Rican, and Mexican-American/Chicano Studies, B
Historic Preservation and Conservation, O
History, BMD
Human Development, M
Human Development and Family Studies, B
Human Resources Management and Services, M
Humanities/Humanistic Studies, B
International Business/Trade/Commerce, M
International Development, MD
International Economics, MD
International/Global Studies, B
Journalism, B
Landscape Architecture, M
Latin American Studies, BMD
Law and Legal Studies, D
Liberal Arts and Sciences Studies and Humanities, B
Linguistics, BMD
Management Information Systems and Services, M
Management Strategy and Policy, M
Management of Technology, M
Manufacturing Engineering, M
Marketing, M
Mass Communication/Media Studies, B
Mathematics, BMD
Mechanical Engineering, BMD
Medical Radiologic Technology/Science - Radiation Therapist, AB
Microbiology, MD

Molecular Biology, MD
Multilingual and Multicultural Education, MD
Music, M
Music History, Literature, and Theory, M
Music Performance, M
Music Teacher Education, BM
Music Theory and Composition, M
NanoTechnology, MD
Natural Resources and Conservation, MD
Neuroscience, MD
Nuclear Engineering, BMD
Nursing, MD
Nutritional Sciences, M
Occupational Therapy/Therapist, M
Optical Technologies, MD
Optics/Optical Sciences, MD
Organizational Management, M
Pathology/Experimental Pathology, MD
Performance, M
Pharmaceutical Sciences, MD
Pharmacy, D
Philosophy, BMD
Photography, D
Photonics, MD
Physical Education Teaching and Coaching, BMD
Physical Therapy/Therapist, D
Physician Assistant, M
Physics, BMD
Physiology, MD
Planetary Astronomy and Science, MD
Political Science and Government, BMD
Portuguese Language and Literature, BMD
Psychology, BD
Public Administration, M
Public Health, M
Quantitative Analysis, D
Reading Teacher Education, MD
Religion/Religious Studies, B
Russian Studies, B
Science Teacher Education/General Science
    Teacher Education, O
Secondary Education and Teaching, BM
Sign Language Interpretation and Translation, B
Sociology, BMD
Spanish Language and Literature, BMD
Special Education and Teaching, BMDO
Sport and Fitness Administration/Management, MD
Statistics, BMD
Systems Engineering, MD
Taxation, M
Technical Theatre/Theatre Design and Technol-
    ogy, B
Technology Teacher Education/Industrial Arts
    Teacher Education, B
Theater, M
Toxicology, MD
Urban Design, O
Urban and Regional Planning, M
Water Resources, M
Women's Studies, BO
Writing, M

UNIVERSITY OF NEW MEXICO–GAL-LUP

Accounting, A
Administrative Assistant and Secretarial Science, A
Art/Art Studies, General, A
Automobile/Automotive Mechanics
    Technology/Technician, A
Business Administration and Management, A
Clinical/Medical Laboratory Technician, A
Community Organization and Advocacy, A
Construction Engineering Technology/Technician, A
Corrections, A
Cosmetology/Cosmetologist, A
Criminal Justice/Law Enforcement Administration, A
Education, A
Elementary Education and Teaching, AB
General Studies, AB
Kindergarten/PreSchool Education and Teaching, A
Liberal Arts and Sciences Studies and Humani-
    ties, A
Marketing/Marketing Management, A
Physical Sciences, A

Welding Technology/Welder, A

UNIVERSITY OF NEW MEXICO–LOS ALAMOS BRANCH

Accounting, A
Administrative Assistant and Secretarial Science, A
Biological and Physical Sciences, A
Business Administration and Management, A
Computer Engineering Technology/Technician, A
Computer Programming/Programmer, A
Computer Science, A
Design and Applied Arts, A
Early Childhood Education and Teaching, A
Electrical, Electronic and Communications Engineer-
    ing Technology/Technician, A
Engineering, A
Environmental Studies, A
Fine/Studio Arts, A
General Studies, A
Liberal Arts and Sciences Studies and Humani-
    ties, A
Physical Sciences, A
Sales, Distribution and Marketing Operations, A

UNIVERSITY OF NEW MEXICO–TAOS

Administrative Assistant and Secretarial Science, A
Art/Art Studies, General, A
Behavioral Sciences, A
Business Administration, Management and Opera-
    tions, A
Communication, Journalism and Related Pro-
    grams, A
Computer and Information Sciences, A
Construction Trades, A
Corrections and Criminal Justice, A
Crafts/Craft Design, Folk Art and Artisanry, A
Criminal Justice/Safety Studies, A
Early Childhood Education and Teaching, A
Education, A
General Studies, A
Human Services, A
Liberal Arts and Sciences Studies and Humani-
    ties, A
Physical Sciences, A

UNIVERSITY OF NEW MEXICO–VALENCIA CAMPUS

Administrative Assistant and Secretarial Science, A
Agriculture, A
Building/Construction Finishing, Manage-
    ment, and Inspection, A
Business Administration and Management, A
Computer Science, A
Computer Typography and Composition Equipment
    Operator, A
Construction Engineering Technology/Technician, A
Criminal Justice/Law Enforcement Administration, A
Early Childhood Education and Teaching, A
Education, A
Human Services, A
Information Science/Studies, A
Liberal Arts and Sciences Studies and Humani-
    ties, A
Real Estate, A

UNIVERSITY OF PHOENIX–NEW MEXICO CAMPUS

Accounting, BM
Business Administration and Management, B
Business Administration, Management and Opera-
    tions, M
Counselor Education/School Counseling and Guid-
    ance Services, M
Criminal Justice/Law Enforcement Administration, B
Curriculum and Instruction, M
Education, M
Educational Administration and Supervision, M
Electronic Commerce, M
Elementary Education and Teaching, M
Health Services Administration, M
Health/Health Care Administration/Management, B
Human Resources Management and Services, M
Human Services, B
Information Technology, B
International Business/Trade/Commerce, M

Management, M
Management Information Systems and Ser-
    vices, BM
Management Science, B
Management of Technology, M
Marketing, M
Marketing/Marketing Management, B
Nursing, M
Nursing Education, M
Public Administration and Social Service Profes-
    sions, B
Secondary Education and Teaching, M

UNIVERSITY OF THE SOUTHWEST

Accounting, B
Bilingual and Multilingual Education, B
Biology/Biological Sciences, B
Business Administration and Management, B
Business Administration, Management and Opera-
    tions, M
Business, Management, Marketing, and Related
    Support Services, B
Business/Commerce, B
Counseling Psychology, M
Counselor Education/School Counseling and Guid-
    ance Services, M
Criminal Justice/Law Enforcement Administration, B
Curriculum and Instruction, M
Early Childhood Education and Teaching, M
Education, M
Educational Administration and Supervision, M
Elementary Education and Teaching, B
English Language and Literature, B
English as a Second Language, M
General Studies, B
History, B
International Business/Trade/Commerce, B
Management Science, B
Multilingual and Multicultural Education, M
Physical Education Teaching and Coaching, B
Psychology, B
Secondary Education and Teaching, B
Social Sciences, B
Special Education and Teaching, BM
Sport and Fitness Administration/Management, M
Teacher Education, Multiple Levels, B
Theology/Theological Studies, B

WESTERN NEW MEXICO UNIVERSITY

Accounting, B
Art Teacher Education, B
Art/Art Studies, General, B
Biological and Physical Sciences, B
Biology/Biological Sciences, B
Botany/Plant Biology, B
Business Administration and Management, B
Business Administration, Management and Opera-
    tions, M
Business Teacher Education, B
Chemistry, B
Clinical Laboratory Science/Medical
    Technology/Technologist, B
Computer Science, B
Computer Technology/Computer Systems Technol-
    ogy, A
Criminal Justice/Law Enforcement Administra-
    tion, AB
Criminal Justice/Police Science, AB
Digital Communication and Media/Multimedia, A
E-Commerce/Electronic Commerce, A
Early Childhood Education and Teaching, AB
Education, BM
Educational Leadership and Administration, M
Electrical/Electronics Maintenance and Repair Tech-
    nology, A
Elementary Education and Teaching, BM
English Language and Literature, B
English as a Second Language, M
Financial Planning and Services, B
Geology/Earth Science, B
Graphic Design, A
Hispanic-American, Puerto Rican, and Mexican-
    American/Chicano Studies, B
History, B
Humanities/Humanistic Studies, B
Interdisciplinary Studies, M

International Business/Trade/Commerce, B
Kindergarten/PreSchool Education and Teaching, B
Kinesiology and Exercise Science, B
Liberal Arts and Sciences Studies and Humanities, AB
Marketing/Marketing Management, B
Mathematics, B
Multilingual and Multicultural Education, M
Music, B
Music Teacher Education, B
Occupational Therapist Assistant, A
Occupational Therapy/Therapist, ABM
Physical Education Teaching and Coaching, B
Physical Sciences, B
Pre-Law Studies, B
Pre-Veterinary Studies, B
Psychology, B
Public Administration, B
Reading Teacher Education, M
Science Teacher Education/General Science
   Teacher Education, B
Secondary Education and Teaching, BM
Social Sciences, B
Social Work, BM
Sociology, B
Spanish Language and Literature, B
Special Education and Teaching, BM
Special Products Marketing Operations, B
Teacher Assistant/Aide, A
Trade and Industrial Teacher Education, B
Welding Technology/Welder, A
Wildlife and Wildlands Science and Management, B
Zoology/Animal Biology, B

New York

ADELPHI UNIVERSITY

Accounting, BM
Anthropology, B
Art Education, M
Art History, Criticism and Conservation, B
Art Teacher Education, B
Audiology/Audiologist and Speech-Language
   Pathology/Pathologist, B
Biochemistry, B
Biological and Biomedical Sciences, M
Biological and Physical Sciences, B
Biology/Biological Sciences, B
Business Administration and Management, B
Business Administration, Management and Operations, M
Business, Management, Marketing, and Related
   Support Services, B
Chemistry, B
Clinical Psychology, D
Communication Disorders, MD
Communication and Media Studies, B
Community Health and Preventive Medicine, MO
Computer and Information Sciences, B
Counseling Psychology, M
Criminal Justice/Safety Studies, B
Dance, B
Drama and Dramatics/Theatre Arts, B
Economics, B
Education, MDO
Educational Leadership and Administration, MO
Educational Media/Instructional Technology, MO
Elementary Education and Teaching, M
Emergency Management, O
English Language and Literature, B
English as a Second Language, MO
Environmental Sciences, M
Environmental Studies, BM
Finance, B
Finance and Banking, M
Fine Arts and Art Studies, BM
French Language and Literature, B
Gerontology, O
Health Education, MO
Health Informatics, MO
Health Services Administration, M
Health and Physical Education/Fitness, B
History, B
Human Resources Management and Services, MO
Humanities/Humanistic Studies, B
Information Science/Studies, B

International/Global Studies, B
Latin American Studies, B
Liberal Arts and Sciences Studies and Humanities, A
Management Information Systems and Services, M
Marketing, M
Marketing/Marketing Management, B
Mathematics, B
Multi-/Interdisciplinary Studies, B
Music, B
Music Teacher Education, B
Nursing, D
Nursing - Adult, MO
Nursing Administration, MO
Nutritional Sciences, M
Philosophy, B
Physical Education Teaching and Coaching, BMO
Physics, B
Political Science and Government, B
Psychology, BMD
Public Administration, O
Public Health, MO
Reading Teacher Education, M
School Psychology, M
Secondary Education and Teaching, M
Social Sciences, B
Social Work, BMD
Sociology, B
Spanish Language and Literature, B
Special Education and Teaching, MO
Sport and Fitness Administration/Management, BM
Visual and Performing Arts, B
Writing, M

ADIRONDACK COMMUNITY COLLEGE

Accounting, A
Accounting Technology/Technician and Bookkeeping, A
Business Administration and Management, A
Communication Studies/Speech Communication
   and Rhetoric, A
Computer Science, A
Computer Systems Networking and Telecommunications, A
Cooking and Related Culinary Arts, A
Criminal Justice/Police Science, A
Design and Visual Communications, A
Electrical, Electronic and Communications Engineering Technology/Technician, A
Electrician, A
Engineering, A
Food Technology and Processing, A
Hospitality Administration/Management, A
Information Technology, A
Liberal Arts and Sciences Studies and Humanities, A
Marketing/Marketing Management, A
Music, A
Music Performance, A
Parks, Recreation and Leisure Facilities Management, A
Radio and Television Broadcasting
   Technology/Technician, A
Radiologic Technology/Science - Radiographer, A
Sport and Fitness Administration/Management, A
Substance Abuse/Addiction Counseling, A
Tourism and Travel Services Management, A

ALBANY COLLEGE OF PHARMACY AND HEALTH SCIENCES

Cell Biology and Anatomy, M
Chemistry, B
Clinical Laboratory Science/Medical
   Technology/Technologist, B
Clinical Laboratory Sciences, M
Health Services Research, M
Health Services/Allied Health/Health Sciences, B
Microbiology, B
Molecular Biology, M
Pharmaceutical Sciences, M
Pharmacology, M
Pharmacy, MD

Pharmacy, Pharmaceutical Sciences, and Administration, B

ALFRED UNIVERSITY

Accounting, BM
Applied Arts and Design, M
Art Teacher Education, B
Art/Art Studies, General, B
Athletic Training and Sports Medicine, B
Bioengineering, M
Biological and Physical Sciences, B
Biology/Biological Sciences, B
Biomedical/Medical Engineering, B
Business Administration and Management, B
Business Administration, Management and Operations, M
Business Teacher Education, B
Ceramic Arts and Ceramics, BMD
Ceramic Sciences and Engineering, BMD
Chemistry, B
Communication Studies/Speech Communication
   and Rhetoric, B
Computer Art and Design, M
Counseling Psychology, M
Counselor Education/School Counseling and Guidance Services, MO
Criminal Justice/Law Enforcement Administration, B
Drama and Dramatics/Theatre Arts, B
Education, M
Electrical Engineering, M
Elementary Education and Teaching, B
Engineering, B
Engineering and Applied Sciences, MD
English Language and Literature, B
Environmental Studies, B
Finance, B
Fine/Studio Arts, B
General Studies, B
Geology/Earth Science, B
Gerontology, B
History, B
International/Global Studies, B
Internet and Interactive Multimedia, M
Marketing/Marketing Management, B
Materials Engineering, B
Materials Sciences, MD
Mathematics, B
Mechanical Engineering, BM
Philosophy, B
Physics, B
Political Science and Government, B
Psychology, B
Public Administration, B
Reading Teacher Education, M
School Psychology, MDO
Science Teacher Education/General Science
   Teacher Education, B
Sculpture, M
Secondary Education and Teaching, B
Sociology, B
Spanish Language and Literature, B

AMERICAN ACADEMY OF DRAMATIC ARTS–NEW YORK

Drama and Dramatics/Theatre Arts, A

AMERICAN ACADEMY MCALLISTER INSTITUTE OF FUNERAL SERVICE

Funeral Service and Mortuary Science, A

ASA COLLEGE

Accounting, A
Business/Office Automation/Technology/Data Entry, A
Computer and Information Systems Security, A
Criminal Justice/Law Enforcement Administration, A
Health Information/Medical Records
   Technology/Technician, A
Medical Office Management/Administration, A
Medical/Clinical Assistant, A
Pharmacy Technician/Assistant, A

BARD COLLEGE

African Studies, B
American/United States Studies/Civilization, B

Ancient/Classical Greek Language and Literature, B
Anthropology, B
Arabic Language and Literature, B
Art History, Criticism and Conservation, B
Asian Studies/Civilization, B
Atmospheric Sciences and Meteorology, MO
Biology/Biological Sciences, B
Business/Managerial Economics, B
Chemistry, B
Chinese Language and Literature, B
Classical, Ancient Mediterranean and Near Eastern
    Studies and Archaeology, B
Composition, M
Computer Science, B
Dance, B
Drama and Dramatics/Theatre Arts, B
Economics, BM
Education, M
English Language and Literature, B
Environmental Policy, MO
Environmental Studies, B
Film/Cinema Studies, B
Fine Arts and Art Studies, M
Fine/Studio Arts, B
French Language and Literature, B
French Studies, B
German Language and Literature, B
German Studies, B
History, B
History and Philosophy of Science and Technol-
    ogy, B
Humanities/Humanistic Studies, B
International/Global Studies, B
Italian Language and Literature, B
Italian Studies, B
Japanese Language and Literature, B
Jazz/Jazz Studies, B
Jewish/Judaic Studies, B
Latin American Studies, B
Latin Language and Literature, B
Liberal Arts and Sciences Studies and Humani-
    ties, A
Mathematics, B
Medieval and Renaissance Studies, B
Museology/Museum Studies, M
Music, BMO
Near and Middle Eastern Studies, B
Performance, MO
Philosophy, B
Photography, BM
Physics, B
Political Science and Government, B
Pre-Law Studies, B
Pre-Medicine/Pre-Medical Studies, B
Psychology, B
Religion/Religious Studies, B
Russian Language and Literature, B
Russian Studies, B
Sociology, B
Spanish Language and Literature, B
Spanish and Iberian Studies, B
Sustainability Management, M
Theology/Theological Studies, B

BARNARD COLLEGE

African Studies, B
American/United States Studies/Civilization, B
Ancient/Classical Greek Language and Literature, B
Anthropology, B
Architecture, B
Art History, Criticism and Conservation, B
Asian Studies/Civilization, B
Astronomy, B
Astrophysics, B
Biochemistry, B
Biology/Biological Sciences, B
Chemistry, B
Classics and Classical Languages, Litera-
    tures, and Linguistics, B
Comparative Literature, B
Computer and Information Sciences, B
Dance, B
Drama and Dramatics/Theatre Arts, B
Economics, B
Education, B
English Language and Literature, B

Environmental Biology, B
Environmental Sciences, B
European Studies/Civilization, B
Film/Cinema Studies, B
French Language and Literature, B
French Studies, B
German Language and Literature, B
German Studies, B
History, B
Italian Language and Literature, B
Jewish/Judaic Studies, B
Latin American Studies, B
Latin Language and Literature, B
Mathematics, B
Medieval and Renaissance Studies, B
Music, B
Philosophy, B
Physics, B
Political Science and Government, B
Psychology, B
Religion/Religious Studies, B
Russian Language and Literature, B
Slavic Studies, B
Sociology, B
Spanish Language and Literature, B
Statistics, B
Urban Studies/Affairs, B
Visual and Performing Arts, B
Women's Studies, B

BARUCH COLLEGE OF THE CITY UNI-VERSITY OF NEW YORK

Accounting, BMD
Actuarial Science, B
Arts Management, M
Business Administration and Management, B
Business Administration, Management and Opera-
    tions, MDO
Business/Managerial Economics, B
Corporate and Organizational Communication, M
Counseling Psychology, M
Economics, BM
Educational Administration and Supervision, M
Educational Leadership and Administration, MO
English Language and Literature, B
Entrepreneurship/Entrepreneurial Studies, M
Finance, B
Finance and Banking, MD
Financial Engineering, M
Health Services Administration, M
Hebrew Language and Literature, B
Higher Education/Higher Education Administra-
    tion, M
History, B
Human Resources Management and Services, M
Industrial and Labor Relations, M
Industrial and Manufacturing Management, M
Industrial and Organizational Psychology, MD
Information Science/Studies, B
International Business/Trade/Commerce, BMD
Journalism, B
Liberal Arts and Sciences Studies and Humani-
    ties, B
Management Information Systems and Ser-
    vices, MD
Marketing, MD
Mathematics, B
Music, B
Non-Profit/Public/Organizational Management, M
Organizational Behavior Studies, M
Philosophy, B
Political Science and Government, B
Psychology, B
Public Administration, BM
Public Policy Analysis, M
Quantitative Analysis, M
Real Estate, BM
Religion/Religious Studies, B
Sociology, B
Spanish Language and Literature, B
Statistics, BM
Sustainability Management, M

Taxation, M

BEIS MEDRASH HEICHAL DOVID

Talmudic Studies, B

BERKELEY COLLEGE–NEW YORK CITY CAMPUS

Accounting, AB
Business Administration and Management, AB
Computer/Information Technology Services Adminis-
    tration and Management, AB
Criminal Justice/Law Enforcement Administration, B
Criminal Justice/Police Science, A
Fashion Merchandising, AB
Financial Planning and Services, AB
Health Information/Medical Records
    Technology/Technician, A
Health/Health Care Administration/Management, AB
International Business/Trade/Commerce, AB
Legal Professions and Studies, AB
Marketing/Marketing Management, AB

BERKELEY COLLEGE–WHITE PLAINS CAMPUS

Business Administration and Management, AB
Criminal Justice/Law Enforcement Administration, B
Criminal Justice/Police Science, A
Fashion Merchandising, AB
Health Information/Medical Records
    Technology/Technician, A
Health/Health Care Administration/Management, AB
Marketing/Marketing Management, AB

BETH HATALMUD RABBINICAL COL-LEGE

Talmudic Studies, B

BINGHAMTON UNIVER-SITY, STATE UNIVERSITY OF NEW YORK

Accounting, BM
Actuarial Science, B
African-American/Black Studies, B
Analytical Chemistry, D
Anthropology, BMD
Applied Economics, B
Applied Physics, MD
Arabic Language and Literature, B
Art History, Criticism and Conservation, BMD
Art/Art Studies, General, B
Asian Studies/Civilization, BMO
Asian-American Studies, BMO
Biochemistry, B
Biological and Biomedical Sciences, MD
Biology/Biological Sciences, B
Biomedical Engineering, MD
Biomedical/Medical Engineering, B
Biopsychology, D
Business Administration and Management, B
Business Administration, Management and Opera-
    tions, MD
Cartography, B
Cell/Cellular and Molecular Biology, B
Chemistry, BMD
Cinematography and Film/Video Production, B
Classics and Classical Languages, Litera-
    tures, and Linguistics, B
Clinical Psychology, D
Cognitive Sciences, D
Comparative Literature, BMD
Computer Engineering, B
Computer Science, BMD
Computer and Information Sciences, B
Cultural Studies, MD
Directing and Theatrical Production, B
Drama and Dramatics/Theatre Arts, B
Early Childhood Education and Teaching, M
East Asian Studies, B
Economics, BMD
Education, MDO
Educational Administration and Supervision, M
Educational Leadership and Administration, O
Electrical Engineering, MD
Electrical, Electronics and Communications Engi-
    neering, B

Engineering, B
Engineering and Applied Sciences, MD
English, MD
English Education, M
English Language and Literature, B
Entrepreneurship/Entrepreneurial Studies, B
Environmental Sciences, D
Environmental Studies, B
Finance, B
Finance and Banking, MD
Foreign Language Teacher Education, M
Foreign Languages, Literatures, and Linguistics, B
Foundations and Philosophy of Education, MDO
French Language and Literature, BM
Geography, BM
Geology/Earth Science, BMD
German Language and Literature, B
Health Services Administration, M
Hebrew Language and Literature, B
History, BMD
Human Development and Family Studies, B
Industrial Engineering, B
Industrial/Management Engineering, MD
Inorganic Chemistry, D
International Business/Trade/Commerce, B
International Relations and Affairs, B
Italian Language and Literature, BM
Jewish/Judaic Studies, B
Latin American Studies, B
Latin Language and Literature, B
Legal and Justice Studies, MD
Linguistics, B
Logistics and Materials Management, B
Management, D
Management Information Systems and Services, B
Marketing/Marketing Management, B
Materials Engineering, MD
Materials Sciences, MD
Mathematics, BMD
Mathematics Teacher Education, M
Mechanical Engineering, BMD
Medieval and Renaissance Studies, B
Multi-/Interdisciplinary Studies, B
Music, BM
Music Performance, B
Nursing, MDO
Organic Chemistry, D
Philosophy, BMD
Physical Chemistry, D
Physics, BMD
Political Science and Government, BMD
Pre-Law Studies, B
Pre-Medicine/Pre-Medical Studies, B
Pre-Veterinary Studies, B
Psychology, BD
Public Administration, M
Reading Teacher Education, M
Science Teacher Education/General Science
    Teacher Education, M
Secondary Education and Teaching, M
Social Sciences, B
Social Studies Teacher Education, M
Social Work, M
Sociology, BMD
South Asian Studies, B
Spanish Language and Literature, BM
Special Education and Teaching, M
Student Personnel Services, M
Systems Science and Theory, MD
Technical Theatre/Theatre Design and Technol-
    ogy, B
Theater, M
Translation and Interpretation, DO
Writing, M

BORICUA COLLEGE

Business Administration and Management, B
Elementary Education and Teaching, B
English as a Second Language, M
Human Services, BM
Latin American Studies, M

Liberal Arts and Sciences Studies and Humani-
    ties, AB

BOROUGH OF MANHATTAN COMMU-
NITY COLLEGE OF THE CITY UNIVER-
SITY OF NEW YORK

Accounting, A
Accounting Technology/Technician and Bookkeep-
    ing, A
Administrative Assistant and Secretarial Science, A
Animation, Interactive Technology, Video Graphics
    and Special Effects, A
Art History, Criticism and Conservation, A
BioTechnology, A
Business Administration and Management, A
Cartography, A
Community Organization and Advocacy, A
Computer Science, A
Computer Systems Networking and Telecommunica-
    tions, A
Computer and Information Sciences, A
Criminal Justice/Law Enforcement Administration, A
Criminal Justice/Police Science, A
Emergency Medical Technology/Technician (EMT
    Paramedic), A
Engineering, A
English Language and Literature, A
Foreign Languages and Literatures, A
Forensic Science and Technology, A
General Studies, A
Health Information/Medical Records
    Technology/Technician, A
History, A
Liberal Arts and Sciences Studies and Humani-
    ties, A
Mathematics, A
Medical Informatics, A
Physical Sciences, A
Public Health Education and Promotion, A
Radio and Television Broadcasting
    Technology/Technician, A
Respiratory Therapy Technician/Assistant, A
Small Business Administration/Management, A
Sociology, A
Teacher Assistant/Aide, A
Visual and Performing Arts, A
Web Page, Digital/Multimedia and Information Re-
    sources Design, A

BRAMSON ORT COLLEGE

Accounting, A
Accounting Technology/Technician and Bookkeep-
    ing, A
Administrative Assistant and Secretarial Science, A
Business Administration and Management, A
Computer Programming/Programmer, A
Electrical, Electronic and Communications Engineer-
    ing Technology/Technician, A
Medical/Clinical Assistant, A

BRONX COMMUNITY COLLEGE OF
THE CITY UNIVERSITY OF NEW YORK

Accounting, A
Administrative Assistant and Secretarial Science, A
African-American/Black Studies, A
Art/Art Studies, General, A
Biology/Biological Sciences, A
Business Administration and Management, A
Business Teacher Education, A
Chemistry, A
Child Development, A
Clinical/Medical Laboratory Technician, A
Computer Science, A
Data Processing and Data Processing
    Technology/Technician, A
Electrical, Electronic and Communications Engineer-
    ing Technology/Technician, A
History, A
Human Services, A
International Relations and Affairs, A
Legal Assistant/Paralegal, A
Liberal Arts and Sciences Studies and Humani-
    ties, A
Marketing/Marketing Management, A
Mathematics, A

Medical Administrative Assistant/Secretary, A
Music, A
Nuclear Medical Technology/Technologist, A
Ornamental Horticulture, A
Psychology, A

BROOKLYN COLLEGE OF THE CITY
UNIVERSITY OF NEW YORK

Accounting, BM
African Studies, B
American/United States Studies/Civilization, B
Anthropology, B
Art Education, M
Art History, Criticism and Conservation, BM
Art Teacher Education, B
Art/Art Studies, General, B
Arts Management, M
Audiology/Audiologist and Speech-Language
    Pathology/Pathologist, B
Bilingual and Multilingual Education, B
Biological and Biomedical Sciences, M
Biology Teacher Education, B
Biology/Biological Sciences, B
Broadcast Journalism, B
Business Administration, Management and Opera-
    tions, M
Caribbean Studies, B
Chemistry, BMD
Chemistry Teacher Education, B
Chinese Language and Literature, B
Cinematography and Film/Video Production, B
Classics and Classical Languages, Litera-
    tures, and Linguistics, B
Communication Disorders, MD
Communication Studies/Speech Communication
    and Rhetoric, B
Community Health and Preventive Medicine, M
Comparative Literature, B
Composition, M
Computational Mathematics, B
Computer Graphics, B
Computer Science, MO
Computer and Information Sciences, B
Counseling Psychology, MO
Counselor Education/School Counseling and Guid-
    ance Services, M
Early Childhood Education and Teaching, BM
Economics, BM
Education, BMO
Education/Teaching of Individuals with Speech or
    Language Impairments, B
Educational Leadership and Administration, M
Elementary Education and Teaching, BM
English, M
English Education, M
English Language and Literature, B
English/Language Arts Teacher Education, B
Environmental Education, M
Environmental Studies, B
Exercise Physiology, B
Exercise and Sports Science, M
Experimental Psychology, M
Film, Television, and Video Production, M
Film/Cinema Studies, B
Finance and Banking, M
Fine Arts and Art Studies, M
Fine/Studio Arts, B
Foods, Nutrition, and Wellness Studies, B
Foreign Language Teacher Education, M
French Language Teacher Education, B
French Language and Literature, BM
Geology/Earth Science, BMD
Geosciences, M
German Language and Literature, B
Health Informatics, M
Health Services Administration, M
Health Teacher Education, B
Hebrew Language and Literature, B
Hebrew Studies, M
Hispanic-American, Puerto Rican, and Mexican-
    American/Chicano Studies, B
History, BM
Industrial and Organizational Psychology, M
Information Science/Studies, BMO
International Affairs, M
International Business/Trade/Commerce, BM

Internet and Interactive Multimedia, M
Italian Language and Literature, B
Jewish/Judaic Studies, B
Journalism, B
Kinesiology and Movement Studies, M
Liberal Studies, M
Linguistics, B
Mathematics, BM
Mathematics Teacher Education, BM
Media Studies, M
Middle School Education, M
Multilingual and Multicultural Education, M
Music, BM
Music Performance, B
Music Teacher Education, BM
Music Theory and Composition, B
Musicology and Ethnomusicology, M
Nutritional Sciences, M
Organizational Behavior Studies, M
Painting, M
Performance, M
Philosophy, B
Photography, M
Physical Education Teaching and Coaching, BM
Physics, BM
Physics Teacher Education, B
Political Science and Government, BM
Portuguese Language and Literature, B
Printmaking, M
Psychology, BMD
Public Health, M
Public Policy Analysis, M
Radio and Television, B
Religion/Religious Studies, B
Russian Language and Literature, B
School Psychology, MO
Science Teacher Education/General Science
    Teacher Education, M
Sculpture, M
Secondary Education and Teaching, M
Social Psychology, M
Social Studies Teacher Education, BM
Sociology, BMD
Spanish Language Teacher Education, B
Spanish Language and Literature, BM
Special Education and Teaching, MO
Speech Teacher Education, B
Speech and Interpersonal Communication, MD
Speech and Rhetorical Studies, M
Speech-Language Pathology/Pathologist, B
Sport and Fitness Administration/Management, M
Thanatology, M
Theater, M
Urban Studies/Affairs, M
Women's Studies, B
Writing, M

BROOME COMMUNITY COLLEGE

Accounting Technology/Technician and Bookkeep-
    ing, A
Business Administration and Management, A
Child Care and Support Services Management, A
Civil Engineering Technology/Technician, A
Clinical/Medical Laboratory Technician, A
Communication Studies/Speech Communication
    and Rhetoric, A
Communications Systems Installation and Repair
    Technology, A
Computer Engineering Technology/Technician, A
Computer and Information Sciences, A
Corrections, A
Criminal Justice/Police Science, A
Data Processing and Data Processing
    Technology/Technician, A
Dental Hygiene/Hygienist, A
Electrical, Electronic and Communications Engineer-
    ing Technology/Technician, A
Emergency Medical Technology/Technician (EMT
    Paramedic), A
Engineering Science, A
Executive Assistant/Executive Secretary, A
Financial Planning and Services, A
Fire Science/Firefighting, A
General Merchandising, Sales, and Related Market-
    ing Operations, A

Health Information/Medical Records
    Technology/Technician, A
Hotel/Motel Administration/Management, A
Industrial Production Technologies/Technicians, A
Information Science/Studies, A
International Finance, A
Legal Assistant/Paralegal, A
Liberal Arts and Sciences Studies and Humani-
    ties, A
Mechanical Engineering/Mechanical
    Technology/Technician, A
Medical Radiologic Technology/Science - Radiation
    Therapist, A
Medical/Clinical Assistant, A
Mental and Social Health Services and Allied Pro-
    fessions, A
Physical Therapist Assistant, A
Quality Control Technology/Technician, A
Substance Abuse/Addiction Counseling, A

BRYANT & STRATTON COL-
LEGE–ALBANY CAMPUS

Accounting, A
Administrative Assistant and Secretarial Science, A
Business/Commerce, A
Computer and Information Systems Security, A
Criminal Justice/Law Enforcement Administration, A
Human Resources Management and Services, A
Information Technology, A
Legal Assistant/Paralegal, A
Medical Administrative Assistant/Secretary, A
Medical/Clinical Assistant, A
System, Networking, and LAN/WAN
    Management/Manager, A

BRYANT & STRATTON COL-
LEGE–AMHERST CAMPUS

Accounting, A
Administrative Assistant and Secretarial Science, A
Business Administration and Management, B
Business Administration, Management and Opera-
    tions, B
Business/Commerce, A
Commercial and Advertising Art, A
Computer and Information Sciences, A
Computer and Information Systems Security, A
Design and Visual Communications, A
Graphic Design, A
Human Resources Management and Services, A
Human Resources Management/Personnel Adminis-
    tration, A
Information Technology, A
Legal Assistant/Paralegal, A
Medical Administrative Assistant/Secretary, A
System, Networking, and LAN/WAN
    Management/Manager, A

BRYANT & STRATTON COLLEGE–BUF-
FALO CAMPUS

Accounting, A
Administrative Assistant and Secretarial Science, A
Business Administration and Management, B
Business Administration, Management and Opera-
    tions, A
Business/Commerce, A
Computer and Information Sciences, A
Computer and Information Systems Security, A
Criminal Justice/Law Enforcement Administration, A
Human Resources Management and Services, A
Human Resources Management/Personnel Adminis-
    tration, A
Information Technology, A
Medical Administrative Assistant/Secretary, A
Medical/Clinical Assistant, A
System, Networking, and LAN/WAN
    Management/Manager, A

BRYANT & STRATTON COL-
LEGE–GREECE CAMPUS

Accounting, A
Administrative Assistant and Secretarial Science, A
Business Administration, Management and Opera-
    tions, A
Business/Commerce, A
Computer and Information Sciences, A

Computer and Information Systems Security, A
Criminal Justice/Law Enforcement Administration, A
Human Resources Management and Services, A
Human Resources Management/Personnel Adminis-
    tration, A
Information Technology, A
Medical Administrative Assistant/Secretary, A
Medical/Clinical Assistant, A
System, Networking, and LAN/WAN
    Management/Manager, A

BRYANT & STRATTON COL-
LEGE–HENRIETTA CAMPUS

Accounting, A
Administrative Assistant and Secretarial Science, A
Business Administration and Management, A
Business Administration, Management and Opera-
    tions, A
Business/Commerce, A
Commercial and Advertising Art, A
Computer and Information Sciences, A
Computer and Information Systems Security, A
Criminal Justice/Law Enforcement Administration, A
Design and Visual Communications, A
Graphic Design, A
Human Resources Management and Services, A
Human Resources Management/Personnel Adminis-
    tration, A
Information Technology, A
Legal Assistant/Paralegal, A
Medical Administrative Assistant/Secretary, A
Medical/Clinical Assistant, A
System, Networking, and LAN/WAN
    Management/Manager, A

BRYANT & STRATTON COL-
LEGE–LIVERPOOL CAMPUS

Accounting, A
Administrative Assistant and Secretarial Science, A
Business Administration and Management, A
Computer and Information Systems Security, A
Graphic Design, A
Human Resources Management/Personnel Adminis-
    tration, A
Information Technology, A
Legal Assistant/Paralegal, A
Medical Administrative Assistant/Secretary, A
Medical/Clinical Assistant, A
System, Networking, and LAN/WAN
    Management/Manager, A
Web Page, Digital/Multimedia and Information Re-
    sources Design, A

BRYANT & STRATTON COL-
LEGE–ORCHARD PARK CAMPUS

Accounting, A
Administrative Assistant and Secretarial Science, A
Business Administration and Management, B
Business Administration, Management and Opera-
    tions, A
Business/Commerce, A
Computer and Information Sciences, A
Court Reporting/Court Reporter, A
Criminal Justice/Law Enforcement Administration, A
Human Resources Management and Services, A
Human Resources Management/Personnel Adminis-
    tration, A
Information Technology, A
Medical Administrative Assistant/Secretary, A
Medical/Clinical Assistant, A

BRYANT & STRATTON COL-
LEGE–SYRACUSE CAMPUS

Accounting, A
Administrative Assistant and Secretarial Science, A
Business/Commerce, A
Hotel/Motel Administration/Management, A
Human Resources Management and Services, A
Information Technology, A
Medical Administrative Assistant/Secretary, A
Medical/Clinical Assistant, A

Tourism and Travel Services Management, A

BUFFALO STATE COLLEGE, STATE UNIVERSITY OF NEW YORK

Adult and Continuing Education and Teaching, MO
Anthropology, B
Applied Economics, M
Art Education, M
Art History, Criticism and Conservation, B
Art Teacher Education, M
Art/Art Studies, General, B
Audiology/Audiologist and Speech-Language Pathology/Pathologist, B
Biological and Biomedical Sciences, M
Biology/Biological Sciences, B
Broadcast Journalism, B
Business Administration and Management, B
Business Education, M
Business Teacher Education, B
Chemistry, BM
City/Urban, Community and Regional Planning, B
Commercial and Advertising Art, B
Communication Disorders, M
Communication Studies/Speech Communication and Rhetoric, B
Criminal Justice/Law Enforcement Administration, B
Criminology, M
Design and Applied Arts, B
Design and Visual Communications, B
Dietetics/Dieticians, B
Drama and Dramatics/Theatre Arts, B
Drawing, B
Early Childhood Education and Teaching, M
Economics, BM
Education/Teaching of Individuals with Speech or Language Impairments, B
Educational Leadership and Administration, O
Educational Media/Instructional Technology, M
Electrical, Electronic and Communications Engineering Technology/Technician, B
Electromechanical Technology/Electromechanical Engineering Technology, B
Elementary Education and Teaching, BM
Engineering, B
Engineering Technology, B
English, M
English Education, M
English Language and Literature, B
English/Language Arts Teacher Education, B
Fashion Merchandising, B
Fashion/Apparel Design, B
Fine/Studio Arts, B
Foreign Language Teacher Education, B
Forensic Science and Technology, B
French Language and Literature, B
General Studies, B
Geography, B
Geology/Earth Science, B
Historic Preservation and Conservation, MO
History, BM
Hospitality Administration/Management, B
Hotel/Motel Administration/Management, B
Human Resources Management and Services, O
Humanities/Humanistic Studies, B
Industrial Education, M
Industrial Technology/Technician, B
Industrial/Management Engineering, M
Information Science/Studies, B
Interdisciplinary Studies, M
Journalism, B
Kindergarten/PreSchool Education and Teaching, B
Kinesiology and Exercise Science, B
Liberal Arts and Sciences Studies and Humanities, B
Mass Communication/Media Studies, B
Mathematics, B
Mathematics Teacher Education, BM
Mechanical Engineering/Mechanical Technology/Technician, B
Multi-/Interdisciplinary Studies, B
Multilingual and Multicultural Education, M
Music, B
Music Teacher Education, B
Painting, B
Philosophy, B

Photography, B
Physics, B
Political Science and Government, B
Pre-Dentistry Studies, B
Pre-Law Studies, B
Pre-Medicine/Pre-Medical Studies, B
Pre-Veterinary Studies, B
Printmaking, B
Psychology, B
Public Relations/Image Management, B
Radio and Television, B
Reading Teacher Education, M
Science Teacher Education/General Science Teacher Education, BM
Sculpture, B
Secondary Education and Teaching, B
Social Studies Teacher Education, BM
Social Work, B
Sociology, B
Spanish Language and Literature, B
Special Education and Teaching, BM
Special Products Marketing Operations, B
Student Personnel Services, M
Technology Teacher Education/Industrial Arts Teacher Education, B
Trade and Industrial Teacher Education, B
Urban Studies/Affairs, B
Vocational and Technical Education, M

CANISIUS COLLEGE

Accounting, BM
Accounting and Business/Management, B
Allied Health and Medical Assisting Services, MO
Ancient/Classical Greek Language and Literature, B
Animal Behavior and Ethology, B
Anthropology, BM
Art History, Criticism and Conservation, B
Athletic Training and Sports Medicine, B
Bible/Biblical Studies, B
Bilingual and Multilingual Education, B
Biochemistry, B
Bioinformatics, B
Biology Teacher Education, B
Biology/Biological Sciences, B
Business Administration and Management, B
Business Administration, Management and Operations, M
Business Education, M
Business Teacher Education, B
Business/Commerce, B
Business/Managerial Economics, B
Cell/Cellular and Molecular Biology, B
Chemistry, B
Chemistry Teacher Education, B
Christian Studies, B
Clinical Laboratory Science/Medical Technology/Technologist, B
Cognitive Sciences, B
Communication Disorders, M
Communication and Media Studies, B
Community Health Services/Liaison/Counseling, B
Community Health and Preventive Medicine, BM
Community Psychology, M
Computer Science, B
Corporate and Organizational Communication, M
Counselor Education/School Counseling and Guidance Services, M
Criminal Justice/Law Enforcement Administration, B
Digital Communication and Media/Multimedia, B
Early Childhood Education and Teaching, BM
Economics, B
Education, BMO
Education/Teaching of Individuals in Early Childhood Special Education Programs, B
Education/Teaching of Individuals with Hearing Impairments, Including Deafness, B
Education/Teaching of Individuals with Specific Learning Disabilities, B
Education/Teaching of the Gifted and Talented, BO
Educational Administration and Supervision, BM
Educational Leadership and Administration, BMO
Educational Media/Instructional Technology, O
Educational, Instructional, and Curriculum Supervision, B
Educational/Instructional Media Design, B
Elementary Education and Teaching, BM

English Language and Literature, B
English as a Second Language, M
English/Language Arts Teacher Education, B
Entrepreneurship/Entrepreneurial Studies, B
Environmental Sciences, B
Environmental Studies, B
European Studies/Civilization, B
Finance, B
Fine/Studio Arts, B
French Language Teacher Education, B
French Language and Literature, B
German Language Teacher Education, B
German Language and Literature, B
Gerontology, B
Health Informatics, M
Health Services/Allied Health/Health Sciences, B
History, B
Human Resources Management/Personnel Administration, B
International Business/Trade/Commerce, BM
International Relations and Affairs, B
Journalism, B
Kinesiology and Movement Studies, M
Latin American Studies, B
Latin Language and Literature, B
Liberal Arts and Sciences Studies and Humanities, B
Management Information Systems and Services, B
Management Sciences and Quantitative Methods, B
Marketing/Marketing Management, B
Mathematics Teacher Education, B
Mental Health Counseling/Counselor, B
Middle School Education, M
Montessori Teacher Education, B
Music Performance, B
Nutritional Sciences, BMO
Operations Research, B
Philosophy, B
Physical Education Teaching and Coaching, BM
Physics, B
Physics Teacher Education, B
Political Science and Government, B
Psychology, B
Reading Teacher Education, BMO
Religion/Religious Studies, B
Respiratory Care Therapy/Therapist, B
School Psychology, M
Science Teacher Education/General Science Teacher Education, B
Secondary Education and Teaching, BM
Social Sciences, B
Social Studies Teacher Education, B
Sociology, B
Spanish Language Teacher Education, B
Spanish Language and Literature, B
Special Education and Teaching, BM
Sport and Fitness Administration/Management, BM
Student Personnel Services, M
Taxation, B
Teacher Education, Multiple Levels, B
Telecommunications Technology/Technician, B
Urban Studies/Affairs, B
Women's Studies, B
Zoology/Animal Biology, BM

CAYUGA COUNTY COMMUNITY COLLEGE

Accounting Technology/Technician and Bookkeeping, A
Art/Art Studies, General, A
Business Administration and Management, A
Child Care and Support Services Management, A
Communication, Journalism and Related Programs, A
Communications Systems Installation and Repair Technology, A
Computer and Information Sciences, A
Computer and Information Sciences and Support Services, A
Corrections, A
Criminal Justice/Police Science, A
Drafting and Design Technology/Technician, A
Electrical, Electronic and Communications Engineering Technology/Technician, A
Fine/Studio Arts, A
General Studies, A

Geography, A
Graphic Design, A
Health Services/Allied Health/Health Sciences, A
Humanities/Humanistic Studies, A
Information Science/Studies, A
Liberal Arts and Sciences Studies and Humanities, A
Mathematics, A
Mechanical Engineering, A
Mechanical Engineering/Mechanical
   Technology/Technician, A
Music, A
Psychology, A
Radio, Television, and Digital Communication, A
Science Technologies/Technicians, A
Sport and Fitness Administration/Management, A
Teacher Education, Multiple Levels, A
Telecommunications Technology/Technician, A

CAZENOVIA COLLEGE

Accounting, B
Biology/Biological Sciences, B
Business Administration and Management, AB
Comparative Literature, B
Criminal Justice/Safety Studies, AB
Design and Visual Communications, B
Early Childhood Education and Teaching, B
Education/Teaching of Individuals in Early Childhood
   Special Education Programs, B
English Language and Literature, B
Environmental Studies, B
Equestrian/Equine Studies, B
Fashion/Apparel Design, B
Fine/Studio Arts, B
Human Services, AB
Interior Design, B
Liberal Arts and Sciences Studies and Humanities, AB
Photography, B
Psychology, B
Secondary Education and Teaching, B
Social Sciences, B
Sport and Fitness Administration/Management, B
Visual and Performing Arts, B

CENTRAL YESHIVA TOMCHEI TMIMIM-LUBAVITCH

Jewish/Judaic Studies, M
Rabbinical Studies, M
Theology and Religious Vocations, M

CITY COLLEGE OF THE CITY UNIVERSITY OF NEW YORK

African-American/Black Studies, B
Anthropology, B
Architecture, BM
Art History, Criticism and Conservation, BM
Art Teacher Education, B
Art/Art Studies, General, B
Asian Studies/Civilization, B
Atmospheric Sciences and Meteorology, MD
BioTechnology, B
Biochemistry, BMD
Biological and Biomedical Sciences, MD
Biology Teacher Education, B
Biology/Biological Sciences, B
Biomedical Engineering, MD
Biomedical Sciences, B
Biomedical/Medical Engineering, B
Business Administration and Management, B
Ceramic Arts and Ceramics, M
Chemical Engineering, BMD
Chemistry, BMD
Chemistry Teacher Education, B
Cinematography and Film/Video Production, B
Civil Engineering, BMD
Clinical Psychology, D
Comparative Literature, B
Computer Science, BMD
Corporate and Organizational Communication, M
Crafts, M
Drama and Dramatics/Theatre Arts, B
Early Childhood Education and Teaching, BM
Economics, BM
Education, BMO
Educational Administration and Supervision, MO

Electrical Engineering, MD
Electrical, Electronics and Communications Engineering, B
Elementary Education and Teaching, B
Engineering and Applied Sciences, MD
English, M
English Education, M
English Language and Literature, B
English as a Second Language, M
Environmental Engineering
   Technology/Environmental Technology, B
Environmental Sciences, D
Environmental Studies, B
Experimental Psychology, D
Fine Arts and Art Studies, M
French Language and Literature, B
Geography, B
Geology/Earth Science, B
Geosciences, MD
Graphic Design, BM
History, BM
Intermedia/Multimedia, B
International Affairs, M
International Relations and Affairs, B
International/Global Studies, B
Jazz/Jazz Studies, B
Jewelry/Metalsmithing, M
Jewish/Judaic Studies, B
Landscape Architecture, M
Latin American Studies, B
Linguistics, B
Marketing, M
Mass Communication/Media Studies, B
Mathematics, BM
Mathematics Teacher Education, BMO
Mechanical Engineering, BMD
Media Studies, M
Middle School Education, M
Multilingual and Multicultural Education, M
Museology/Museum Studies, M
Music, BM
Music Performance, B
Music Teacher Education, B
Music Theory and Composition, B
Painting, M
Philosophy, B
Physics, BMD
Physics Teacher Education, B
Political Science and Government, B
Pre-Dentistry Studies, B
Pre-Law Studies, B
Pre-Medicine/Pre-Medical Studies, B
Pre-Veterinary Studies, B
Printmaking, M
Psychology, BMD
Public Administration, M
Reading Teacher Education, M
Romance Languages, Literatures, and Linguistics, B
Science Teacher Education/General Science
   Teacher Education, BM
Sculpture, M
Secondary Education and Teaching, BMO
Social Studies Teacher Education, BO
Sociology, BM
Spanish Language and Literature, BM
Special Education and Teaching, MO
Sustainable Development, M
Urban Design, M
Women's Studies, B
Writing, M

CLARKSON UNIVERSITY

Accounting and Finance, B
Aerospace, Aeronautical and Astronautical Engineering, B
Applied Mathematics, B
BioTechnology, D
Biology/Biological Sciences, B
Business Administration and Management, B
Business Administration, Management and Operations, M
Chemical Engineering, BMD
Chemistry, BMD
Civil Engineering, BMD
Communication Studies/Speech Communication
   and Rhetoric, B

Computer Engineering, BD
Computer Science, BMD
Computer Software Engineering, B
Digital Communication and Media/Multimedia, B
Electrical Engineering, MD
Electrical, Electronics and Communications Engineering, B
Engineering, B
Engineering Management, M
Engineering and Applied Sciences, MD
Engineering/Industrial Management, B
Entrepreneurship/Entrepreneurial Studies, B
Environmental Engineering
   Technology/Environmental Technology, MD
Environmental Policy and Resource Management, M
Environmental Sciences, BMD
Environmental Toxicology, B
Environmental/Environmental Health Engineering, B
Health Services Research, M
History, B
Humanities/Humanistic Studies, B
Information Science/Studies, M
Interdisciplinary Studies, MD
Liberal Arts and Sciences Studies and Humanities, B
Logistics and Materials Management, B
Management Information Systems and Services, B
Materials Engineering, D
Materials Sciences, D
Mathematics, BMD
Mechanical Engineering, BMD
Molecular Biochemistry, B
Multi-/Interdisciplinary Studies, B
Physical Therapy/Therapist, D
Physician Assistant, M
Physics, BMD
Political Science and Government, B
Psychology, B
Social Sciences, B
Sociology, B
Sustainable Development, MD

CLINTON COMMUNITY COLLEGE

Accounting, A
Biological and Physical Sciences, A
Business Administration and Management, A
Community Organization and Advocacy, A
Computer/Information Technology Services Administration and Management, A
Consumer Merchandising/Retailing Management, A
Criminal Justice/Law Enforcement Administration, A
Criminal Justice/Police Science, A
Electrical, Electronic and Communications Engineering Technology/Technician, A
Energy Management and Systems
   Technology/Technician, A
Engineering Technologies/Technicians, A
Humanities/Humanistic Studies, A
Industrial Technology/Technician, A
Liberal Arts and Sciences Studies and Humanities, A
Physical Education Teaching and Coaching, A
Social Sciences, A

COLGATE UNIVERSITY

African Studies, B
African-American/Black Studies, B
American Indian/Native American Studies, B
Anthropology, B
Art History, Criticism and Conservation, B
Art/Art Studies, General, B
Asian Studies/Civilization, B
Astronomy, B
Astrophysics, B
Biochemistry, B
Biology/Biological Sciences, B
Chemistry, B
Chinese Language and Literature, B
Classics and Classical Languages, Literatures, and Linguistics, B
Computer and Information Sciences, B
Drama and Dramatics/Theatre Arts, B
East Asian Studies, B
Economics, B
Education, B

English Language and Literature, B
Environmental Biology, B
Environmental Studies, B
French Language and Literature, B
Geography, B
Geology/Earth Science, B
German Language and Literature, B
History, B
Humanities/Humanistic Studies, B
International Relations and Affairs, B
Islamic Studies, B
Japanese Language and Literature, B
Latin American Studies, B
Latin Language and Literature, B
Mathematics, B
Modern Greek Language and Literature, B
Molecular Biology, B
Music, B
Natural Sciences, B
Near and Middle Eastern Studies, B
Peace Studies and Conflict Resolution, B
Philosophy, B
Physical Sciences, B
Physics, B
Political Science and Government, B
Psychology, B
Religion/Religious Studies, B
Romance Languages, Literatures, and Linguistics, B
Russian Language and Literature, B
Russian Studies, B
Secondary Education and Teaching, M
Social Sciences, B
Sociology, B
Spanish Language and Literature, B
Women's Studies, B

THE COLLEGE AT BROCKPORT, STATE UNIVERSITY OF NEW YORK

Accounting, BM
African-American/Black Studies, B
American/United States Studies/Civilization, M
Anthropology, B
Art/Art Studies, General, B
Arts Management, O
Athletic Training and Sports Medicine, B
Atmospheric Sciences and Meteorology, B
Biochemistry, B
Biological and Biomedical Sciences, MO
Biology/Biological Sciences, B
Broadcast Journalism, B
Business Administration and Management, B
Chemistry, BO
Clinical Laboratory Science/Medical Technology/Technologist, B
Communication Studies/Speech Communication and Rhetoric, B
Communication and Media Studies, M
Computer and Information Sciences, B
Counseling Psychology, MO
Counselor Education/School Counseling and Guidance Services, MO
Criminal Justice/Safety Studies, B
Curriculum and Instruction, M
Dance, BM
Drama and Dramatics/Theatre Arts, B
Early Childhood Education and Teaching, M
Education, MO
Educational Administration and Supervision, O
English, MO
English Education, M
English Language and Literature, B
Environmental Sciences, BM
Finance, B
Fine Arts and Art Studies, M
Forensic Science and Technology, M
French Language and Literature, B
Geology/Earth Science, B
Gerontology, O
Health Education, M
Health Services Administration, M
Health Services/Allied Health/Health Sciences, B
History, BM
Hydrology and Water Resources Science, B
Information Science/Studies, B
International Business/Trade/Commerce, B

International Relations and Affairs, B
Kinesiology and Exercise Science, B
Liberal Arts and Sciences Studies and Humanities, B
Liberal Studies, M
Marketing/Marketing Management, B
Mathematics, BM
Mathematics Teacher Education, M
Middle School Education, M
Multilingual and Multicultural Education, MO
Non-Profit/Public/Organizational Management, MO
Parks, Recreation and Leisure Facilities Management, B
Philosophy, B
Physical Education Teaching and Coaching, BMO
Physics, B
Political Science and Government, B
Psychology, BM
Public Administration, MO
Reading Teacher Education, M
Science Teacher Education/General Science Teacher Education, MO
Social Studies Teacher Education, M
Social Work, BMO
Sociology, B
Spanish Language and Literature, B
Sport and Fitness Administration/Management, BM
Women's Studies, B
Writing, MO

COLLEGE OF MOUNT SAINT VINCENT

Biochemistry, B
Biology/Biological Sciences, B
Business/Managerial Economics, B
Chemistry, B
Economics, B
Education, BMO
Educational Media/Instructional Technology, O
Elementary Education and Teaching, B
English Language and Literature, B
French Language and Literature, B
Gerontological Nursing, M
History, B
Liberal Arts and Sciences Studies and Humanities, B
Mass Communication/Media Studies, B
Mathematics, B
Middle School Education, O
Modern Languages, B
Multilingual and Multicultural Education, MO
Nursing, MO
Nursing - Adult, MO
Nursing - Advanced Practice, MO
Nursing Administration, M
Nursing Education, O
Philosophy, B
Pre-Dentistry Studies, B
Pre-Law Studies, B
Pre-Medicine/Pre-Medical Studies, B
Psychology, B
Religion/Religious Studies, B
Social Sciences, B
Sociology, B
Spanish Language and Literature, B
Urban Education and Leadership, M
Urban Studies/Affairs, B

THE COLLEGE OF NEW ROCHELLE

Acute Care/Critical Care Nursing, MO
Art Education, M
Art History, Criticism and Conservation, B
Art Teacher Education, B
Art Therapy/Therapist, BM
Biology/Biological Sciences, B
Broadcast Journalism, B
Business Administration and Management, B
Business/Commerce, B
Chemistry, B
Classics and Classical Languages, Literatures, and Linguistics, B
Communication Studies/Speech Communication and Rhetoric, B
Communication and Media Studies, MO
Counseling Psychology, MO
Early Childhood Education and Teaching, M
Economics, B

Education, BMO
Education/Teaching of the Gifted and Talented, O
Educational Leadership and Administration, MO
Elementary Education and Teaching, BM
English Language and Literature, B
English as a Second Language, MO
Environmental Studies, B
Fine/Studio Arts, B
French Language and Literature, B
History, B
Human Resources Development, MO
International/Global Studies, B
Liberal Arts and Sciences Studies and Humanities, B
Marriage and Family Therapy/Counseling, M
Mass Communication/Media Studies, B
Mathematics, B
Multi-/Interdisciplinary Studies, B
Multilingual and Multicultural Education, MO
Nursing, MO
Nursing - Advanced Practice, MO
Nursing Administration, M
Nursing Education, O
Philosophy, B
Political Science and Government, B
Pre-Law Studies, B
Pre-Medicine/Pre-Medical Studies, B
Psychology, B
Public Administration, M
Reading Teacher Education, M
Religion/Religious Studies, B
School Psychology, M
Social Work, B
Sociology, B
Spanish Language and Literature, B
Special Education and Teaching, BM
Thanatology, O
Women's Studies, B

THE COLLEGE OF SAINT ROSE

Accounting, BM
American History (United States), B
Art Education, MO
Audiology/Audiologist and Speech-Language Pathology/Pathologist, B
Biochemistry, B
Biology Teacher Education, B
Biology/Biological Sciences, B
Business Administration and Management, B
Business Administration, Management and Operations, M
Cell/Cellular Biology and Histology, B
Chemistry, B
Clinical Laboratory Science/Medical Technology/Technologist, B
Commercial and Advertising Art, B
Communication Disorders, M
Communication Studies/Speech Communication and Rhetoric, B
Communication and Media Studies, B
Computer Science, BM
Counseling Psychology, O
Counselor Education/School Counseling and Guidance Services, MO
Criminal Justice/Law Enforcement Administration, B
Curriculum and Instruction, M
Early Childhood Education and Teaching, BM
Education, MO
Educational Administration and Supervision, MO
Educational Leadership and Administration, M
Educational Media/Instructional Technology, MO
Educational Psychology, MO
Elementary Education and Teaching, B
English, M
English Language and Literature, B
English/Language Arts Teacher Education, B
Finance, B
Financial Planning and Services, B
Fine Arts and Art Studies, B
Forensic Science and Technology, B
General Studies, B
Higher Education/Higher Education Administration, M
History, BM
Human Resources Management/Personnel Administration, B

Information Science/Studies, M
Information Technology, B
Kindergarten/PreSchool Education and Teaching, B
Liberal Arts and Sciences Studies and Humanities, B
Marketing/Marketing Management, B
Mass Communication/Media Studies, M
Mathematics, B
Mathematics Teacher Education, B
Music, BM
Music Teacher Education, BMO
Non-Profit/Public/Organizational Management, O
Political Science and Government, BM
Pre-Law Studies, B
Psychology, B
Public Health (MPH, DPH), B
Reading Teacher Education, M
School Psychology, MO
Secondary Education and Teaching, BM
Social Studies Teacher Education, B
Social Work, B
Special Education and Teaching, BM
Student Personnel Services, M
Web Page, Digital/Multimedia and Information Resources Design, B

COLLEGE OF STATEN ISLAND OF THE CITY UNIVERSITY OF NEW YORK

Accounting, BM
African-American/Black Studies, B
American/United States Studies/Civilization, B
Biochemistry, B
Biological and Biomedical Sciences, M
Biology Teacher Education, B
Biology/Biological Sciences, B
Business Administration, Management and Operations, M
Business/Commerce, A
Chemistry, B
Chemistry Teacher Education, B
Clinical Laboratory Science/Medical Technology/Technologist, B
Clinical Psychology, M
Communication Studies/Speech Communication and Rhetoric, M
Computer Programming/Programmer, A
Computer Science, BM
Computer and Information Sciences and Support Services, B
Counseling Psychology, M
Drama and Dramatics/Theatre Arts, B
Economics, B
Education, MO
Educational Leadership and Administration, O
Electrical, Electronic and Communications Engineering Technology/Technician, A
Elementary Education and Teaching, BM
Engineering, AB
English, M
English Language and Literature, B
English as a Second Language, MO
English/Language Arts Teacher Education, B
Environmental Sciences, M
Film, Television, and Video Theory and Criticism, M
Film/Cinema Studies, B
Fine/Studio Arts, B
Foreign Language Teacher Education, B
Geography, B
Gerontological Nursing, MO
History, BM
History Teacher Education, B
International/Global Studies, B
Italian Language and Literature, B
Liberal Arts and Sciences Studies and Humanities, A
Liberal Studies, M
Mathematics, B
Mathematics Teacher Education, B
Media Studies, M
Music, B
Neuroscience, M
Nursing, MDO
Nursing - Adult, MO
Nursing - Advanced Practice, D
Philosophy, B
Physical Sciences, A

Physical Therapy/Therapist, D
Physics, B
Physics Teacher Education, B
Political Science and Government, B
Psychology, B
Secondary Education and Teaching, M
Social Sciences, B
Social Work, BM
Spanish Language Teacher Education, B
Spanish Language and Literature, B
Special Education and Teaching, MO

THE COLLEGE OF WESTCHESTER

Accounting, AB
Business Administration and Management, AB
Computer Software and Media Applications, A
Health Information/Medical Records Administration/Administrator, A
Health/Health Care Administration/Management, B
Medical/Clinical Assistant, A
System Administration/Administrator, A
Web Page, Digital/Multimedia and Information Resources Design, A

COLUMBIA-GREENE COMMUNITY COLLEGE

Accounting Technology/Technician and Bookkeeping, A
Administrative Assistant and Secretarial Science, A
Art/Art Studies, General, A
Automobile/Automotive Mechanics Technology/Technician, A
Business Administration and Management, A
Business/Commerce, A
Computer and Information Sciences, A
Criminal Justice/Law Enforcement Administration, A
Environmental Studies, A
General Studies, A
Health and Physical Education, A
Human Services, A
Humanities/Humanistic Studies, A
Information Technology, A
Liberal Arts and Sciences Studies and Humanities, A
Medical/Clinical Assistant, A

COLUMBIA UNIVERSITY

Accounting, MD
Actuarial Science, M
Acute Care/Critical Care Nursing, MO
African Studies, DO
African-American Studies, M
African-American/Black Studies, B
Allopathic Medicine, MD
American/United States Studies/Civilization, BM
Anatomy, MD
Ancient Studies/Civilization, B
Ancient/Classical Greek Language and Literature, B
Anthropology, BMD
Applied Mathematics, BMD
Applied Physics, MD
Archeology, BMD
Architecture, BMD
Architecture and Related Services, B
Archives/Archival Administration, M
Art History, Criticism and Conservation, BMD
Asian Studies/Civilization, O
Asian-American Studies, B
Astronomy, BD
Astrophysics, B
Atmospheric Sciences and Meteorology, M
Atomic/Molecular Physics, B
BioTechnology, M
Biochemistry, BMD
Bioethics/Medical Ethics, M
Biological and Biomedical Sciences, MDO
Biology/Biological Sciences, B
Biomedical Engineering, MD
Biomedical/Medical Engineering, B
Biophysics, BMD
Biopsychology, B
Biostatistics, MD
Business Administration, Management and Operations, MD
Cell Biology and Anatomy, MD
Chemical Engineering, BMD

Chemical Physics, D
Chemistry, BD
Civil Engineering, BMD
Classical, Ancient Mediterranean and Near Eastern Studies and Archaeology, B
Classics and Classical Languages, Literatures, and Linguistics, BMD
Communication Theory, MD
Communication and Media Studies, M
Community Health and Preventive Medicine, MD
Comparative Literature, BMD
Computer Engineering, BM
Computer Science, BMD
Conflict Resolution and Mediation/Peace Studies, M
Conservation Biology, M
Construction Engineering and Management, M
Construction Management, M
Corporate and Organizational Communication, M
Dance, B
Database Systems, M
Dentistry, D
Developmental Biology and Embryology, MD
Drama and Dramatics/Theatre Arts, B
East Asian Languages, Literatures, and Linguistics, B
East Asian Studies, BMDO
East European and Russian Studies, MO
Ecology, MD
Economics, BMD
Electrical Engineering, MD
Electrical, Electronics and Communications Engineering, B
Engineering Mechanics, B
Engineering Physics, B
Engineering and Applied Sciences, MD
Engineering/Industrial Management, B
English, MD
English Language and Literature, B
Entrepreneurship/Entrepreneurial Studies, M
Environmental Biology, B
Environmental Design/Architecture, M
Environmental Engineering Technology/Environmental Technology, MD
Environmental Policy, M
Environmental Sciences, MD
Environmental Studies, B
Environmental and Occupational Health, MD
Environmental/Environmental Health Engineering, B
Epidemiology, MD
Ethics, M
Evolutionary Biology, MD
Film, Television, and Video Production, M
Film/Cinema Studies, B
Finance and Banking, MD
Financial Engineering, M
Fine Arts and Art Studies, M
Foreign Language Teacher Education, M
Foundations and Philosophy of Education, M
French Language and Literature, BMD
French Studies, B
Genetics, MD
Geochemistry, B
Geology/Earth Science, B
Geosciences, D
German Language and Literature, BMD
German Studies, B
Gerontological Nursing, MO
Health Services Administration, M
Hispanic Studies, M
Hispanic-American, Puerto Rican, and Mexican-American/Chicano Studies, B
Historic Preservation and Conservation, MO
History, BMD
Human Resources Management and Services, M
Industrial Engineering, B
Industrial/Management Engineering, MD
Information Science/Studies, M
International Affairs, M
International Business/Trade/Commerce, M
Italian Language and Literature, BMD
Italian Studies, B
Japanese Studies, M
Jewish/Judaic Studies, M
Journalism, MD
Kinesiology and Movement Studies, D
Landscape Architecture, M

Latin American Studies, BMDO
Law and Legal Studies, MD
Legal and Justice Studies, M
Linguistics, B
Management, MD
Management of Technology, M
Marketing, MD
Materials Engineering, MD
Materials Sciences, MD
Maternal and Child Health, MD
Mathematics, BMD
Mechanical Engineering, BMD
Mechanics, MD
Medical Informatics, MD
Medical Physics, M
Medieval and Renaissance Studies, BM
Microbiology, MD
Modern Greek Language and Literature, B
Molecular Biology, D
Museology/Museum Studies, M
Music, BD
Near and Middle Eastern Studies, BMDO
Neurobiology and Neurophysiology, D
Non-Profit/Public/Organizational Management, M
Nurse Anesthetist, MO
Nurse Midwife/Nursing Midwifery, M
Nursing, MDO
Nursing - Adult, MO
Nursing - Advanced Practice, MO
Nutritional Sciences, MD
Occupational Therapy/Therapist, MD
Operations Research, BMD
Oral and Dental Sciences, MDO
Orthodontics, MO
Painting, M
Pathobiology, MD
Pathology/Experimental Pathology, MD
Pediatric Nurse/Nursing, MO
Periodontics, MO
Pharmaceutical Administration, M
Pharmacology, MD
Philosophy, BMD
Photography, M
Physical Therapy/Therapist, D
Physics, BMD
Physiology, MD
Political Science and Government, BMD
Printmaking, M
Psychiatric/Mental Health Nurse/Nursing, MO
Psychology, BD
Public Administration, M
Public Health, MD
Public Policy Analysis, M
Quantitative Analysis, M
Real Estate, M
Religion/Religious Studies, BMD
Romance Languages, Literatures, and Linguistics, MD
Russian Language and Literature, BM
Russian Studies, B
Science Teacher Education/General Science Teacher Education, M
Sculpture, M
Slavic Languages, Literatures, and Linguistics, BMD
Social Sciences, M
Social Work, MD
Sociology, BMD
South and Southeast Asian Studies, MO
Spanish Language and Literature, BD
Sport and Fitness Administration/Management, M
Statistics, BMD
Structural Biology, D
Sustainability Management, M
Sustainable Development, M
Teacher Education, Multiple Levels, B
Theater, MD
Toxicology, MD
Translation and Interpretation, M
Urban Planning, MD
Urban Studies/Affairs, B
Visual and Performing Arts, B
Western European Studies, MO
Women's Studies, B

Writing, M

COLUMBIA UNIVERSITY, SCHOOL OF GENERAL STUDIES

African Studies, B
African-American/Black Studies, B
American/United States Studies/Civilization, B
Ancient Studies/Civilization, B
Anthropology, B
Applied Mathematics, B
Archeology, B
Architectural History and Criticism, B
Architecture, B
Art History, Criticism and Conservation, B
Astronomy, B
Astrophysics, B
Biochemistry, B
Biology/Biological Sciences, B
Biophysics, B
Caribbean Studies, B
Chemical Physics, B
Chemistry, B
Classics and Classical Languages, Literatures, and Linguistics, B
Comparative Literature, B
Computer Science, B
Computer and Information Sciences, B
Dance, B
Design and Applied Arts, B
Drama and Dramatics/Theatre Arts, B
East Asian Languages, Literatures, and Linguistics, B
East Asian Studies, B
Economics, B
English Language and Literature, B
Environmental Biology, B
Environmental Sciences, B
Ethnic, Cultural Minority, and Gender Studies, B
Evolutionary Biology, B
Film/Cinema Studies, B
Finance and Financial Management Services, B
Fine/Studio Arts, B
French Language and Literature, B
French Studies, B
Geology/Earth Science, B
German Language and Literature, B
Germanic Languages, Literatures, and Linguistics, B
Hispanic-American, Puerto Rican, and Mexican-American/Chicano Studies, B
History, B
Information Science/Studies, B
Italian Language and Literature, B
Italian Studies, B
Latin American Studies, B
Mathematics, B
Mathematics and Statistics, B
Middle/Near Eastern and Semitic Languages, Literatures, and Linguistics, B
Music, B
Near and Middle Eastern Studies, B
Philosophy, B
Physics, B
Political Science and Government, B
Psychology, B
Regional Studies (U.S., Canadian, Foreign), B
Religion/Religious Studies, B
Russian Language and Literature, B
Russian Studies, B
Slavic Languages, Literatures, and Linguistics, B
Slavic Studies, B
Sociology, B
South Asian Studies, B
Statistics, B
Urban Studies/Affairs, B
Visual and Performing Arts, B
Women's Studies, B

CONCORDIA COLLEGE–NEW YORK

Accounting, B
Administrative Assistant and Secretarial Science, A
Adult and Continuing Education Administration, AB
Art/Art Studies, General, B
Behavioral Sciences, B
Biology/Biological Sciences, B
Biomedical Sciences, B
Business Administration and Management, AB

Business, Management, Marketing, and Related Support Services, B
Digital Communication and Media/Multimedia, B
Early Childhood Education and Teaching, B
Ecology, B
Education, B
Elementary Education and Teaching, B
English Language and Literature, B
Health Professions and Related Clinical Sciences, B
Health and Medical Administrative Services, B
History, B
International Business/Trade/Commerce, B
International Relations and Affairs, B
International/Global Studies, B
Junior High/Intermediate/Middle School Education and Teaching, B
Liberal Arts and Sciences Studies and Humanities, AB
Mathematical Statistics and Probability, B
Mathematics, B
Music, B
Music History, Literature, and Theory, B
Music Performance, B
Organizational Management, M
Philosophy, B
Pre-Law Studies, B
Pre-Theology/Pre-Ministerial Studies, B
Pre-Veterinary Studies, B
Psychology, B
Religion/Religious Studies, AB
Religious Education, B
Religious/Sacred Music, B
Science Teacher Education/General Science Teacher Education, B
Social Sciences, B
Social Work, B
Sociology, B
Special Education and Teaching, M
Sport and Fitness Administration/Management, B
Teacher Education and Professional Development, Specific Levels and Methods, B
Theology and Religious Vocations, B

COOPER UNION FOR THE ADVANCEMENT OF SCIENCE AND ART

Architecture, BM
Chemical Engineering, BM
Civil Engineering, BM
Electrical Engineering, M
Electrical, Electronics and Communications Engineering, B
Engineering, B
Engineering and Applied Sciences, M
Fine/Studio Arts, B
Mechanical Engineering, BM

CORNELL UNIVERSITY

Accounting, D
Adult and Continuing Education and Teaching, MD
Aerospace, Aeronautical and Astronautical Engineering, MD
African Studies, MD
African-American Studies, MD
African-American/Black Studies, B
Agricultural Business and Management, B
Agricultural Economics, BM
Agricultural Education, MD
Agricultural Engineering, MD
Agricultural/Biological Engineering and Bioengineering, B
Agriculture, B
Agronomy and Soil Sciences, MD
American/United States Studies/Civilization, BMD
Analytical Chemistry, D
Anatomy, D
Animal Behavior and Ethology, D
Animal Sciences, BMD
Anthropology, BD
Applied Economics, MD
Applied Mathematics, MD
Applied Physics, MD
Applied Statistics, M
Archeology, BMD
Architectural History and Criticism, BMD
Architecture, BMD
Art History, Criticism and Conservation, BD

Artificial Intelligence and Robotics, MD
Asian Languages, MD
Asian Studies/Civilization, BMD
Astronomy, BD
Astrophysics, D
Atmospheric Sciences and Meteorology, BMD
BioTechnology, MD
Biochemical Engineering, MD
Biochemistry, MD
Bioengineering, MD
Biological and Biomedical Sciences, MD
Biology/Biological Sciences, B
Biomedical Engineering, MD
Biometry/Biometrics, BMD
Biophysics, D
Biopsychology, D
Business Administration, Management and Operations, MD
Cell Biology and Anatomy, D
Chemical Engineering, BMD
Chemical Physics, D
Chemistry, BD
Child and Family Studies, MD
City/Urban, Community and Regional Planning, B
Civil Engineering, BMD
Classics and Classical Languages, Literatures, and Linguistics, BD
Clothing and Textiles, MD
Cognitive Sciences, D
Communication and Media Studies, MD
Comparative Literature, BD
Composition, D
Computational Biology, D
Computational Sciences, MD
Computer Art and Design, M
Computer Engineering, MD
Computer Science, BMD
Computer and Information Sciences, B
Conflict Resolution and Mediation/Peace Studies, MD
Conservation Biology, MD
Consumer Economics, D
Corporate and Organizational Communication, MD
Cultural Anthropology, D
Cultural Studies, D
Curriculum and Instruction, MD
Demography and Population Studies, M
Developmental Biology and Embryology, MD
Developmental Psychology, MD
Drama and Dramatics/Theatre Arts, B
East Asian Studies, MD
East European and Russian Studies, MD
Ecology, MD
Economic Development, MD
Economics, BMD
Education, MD
Educational Policy, MD
Electrical Engineering, MD
Electrical, Electronics and Communications Engineering, B
Energy and Power Engineering, MD
Engineering, B
Engineering Management, MD
Engineering Physics, BMD
Engineering and Applied Sciences, MD
English, MD
English Language and Literature, B
Entomology, BMD
Environmental Design/Architecture, BM
Environmental Engineering Technology/Environmental Technology, MD
Environmental Policy, MD
Environmental Policy and Resource Management, MD
Environmental Sciences, MD
Environmental Studies, MD
Environmental/Environmental Health Engineering, B
Epidemiology, MD
Ergonomics and Human Factors, M
Ethnic and Cultural Studies, MD
Evolutionary Biology, D
Experimental Psychology, D
Facilities Planning and Management, M
Fiber, Textile and Weaving Arts, B
Film/Cinema Studies, B
Finance and Banking, D

Fine Arts and Art Studies, M
Fine/Studio Arts, B
Fish, Game and Wildlife Management, MD
Food Engineering, MD
Food Science, B
Food Science and Technology, MD
Food Services Management, MD
Foreign Language Teacher Education, MD
Forestry, MD
French Language and Literature, BD
French Studies, B
Gay/Lesbian Studies, B
Gender Studies, MD
General Studies, B
Genetics, D
Genomic Sciences, D
Geochemistry, MD
Geological and Earth Sciences/Geosciences, B
Geology/Earth Science, MD
Geophysics and Seismology, MD
Geosciences, MD
Geotechnical Engineering, MD
German Language and Literature, BMD
German Studies, B
Health Communication, MD
Health Services Administration, MD
Hispanic and Latin American Languages, D
Historic Preservation and Conservation, M
History, BMD
History of Science and Technology, MD
Horticultural Science, MD
Hospitality Administration/Management, MD
Hotel/Motel Administration/Management, B
Human Development, MD
Human Development and Family Studies, B
Human Resources Management and Services, MD
Human-Computer Interaction, MD
Hydrology and Water Resources Science, MD
Immunology, MD
Industrial and Labor Relations, MD
Industrial/Management Engineering, MD
Infectious Diseases, MD
Information Science/Studies, D
Information Technology, B
Inorganic Chemistry, D
Interior Design, M
International Affairs, D
International Agriculture, B
International Public Health/International Health, B
Italian Language and Literature, BD
Jewish/Judaic Studies, MD
Labor and Industrial Relations, B
Landscape Architecture, BM
Latin American Studies, MD
Law and Legal Studies, MD
Liberal Arts and Sciences Studies and Humanities, B
Limnology, D
Linguistics, BMD
Manufacturing Engineering, D
Marine Geology, MD
Marine Sciences, MD
Marketing, D
Materials Engineering, BMD
Materials Sciences, MD
Mathematics, BD
Mathematics Teacher Education, M
Mechanical Engineering, BMD
Mechanics, MD
Media Studies, MD
Medieval and Renaissance Studies, MD
Microbiology, D
Mineralogy, MD
Molecular Biology, MD
Molecular Medicine, MD
Music, BMD
Music Theory and Composition, M
Musicology and Ethnomusicology, D
NanoTechnology, MD
Natural Resources and Conservation, BMD
Near and Middle Eastern Studies, BMD
Neurobiology and Neurophysiology, D
Nutritional Sciences, BMD
Oceanography, Chemical and Physical, D
Operations Research, BMD
Organic Chemistry, D

Organizational Behavior Studies, MD
Paleontology, MD
Performance, D
Pharmacology, MD
Philosophy, BD
Photography, MD
Physical Chemistry, D
Physics, BMD
Physiology, MD
Planetary Astronomy and Science, D
Plant Biology, MD
Plant Molecular Biology, MD
Plant Pathology/Phytopathology, MD
Plant Physiology, MD
Plant Sciences, BMD
Political Science and Government, BD
Polymer/Plastics Engineering, MD
Population Studies, MD
Psychology, BD
Public Affairs, M
Public Policy Analysis, BMD
Quantitative Analysis, MD
Real Estate, M
Religion/Religious Studies, BMD
Reproductive Biology, MD
Romance Languages, Literatures, and Linguistics, MD
Rural Sociology, MD
Russian Language and Literature, B
Scandinavian Languages, Literatures, and Linguistics, MD
Science, Technology and Society, B
Secondary Education and Teaching, M
Slavic Languages, Literatures, and Linguistics, MD
Social Psychology, MD
Social Work, D
Sociology, BMD
South and Southeast Asian Studies, MD
Spanish Language and Literature, BD
Statistics, BMD
Structural Biology, MD
Structural Engineering, MD
Sustainable Development, MD
Systems Engineering, M
Textile Design, MD
Textile Sciences and Engineering, MD
Theater, D
Theoretical Chemistry, D
Theoretical Physics, MD
Toxicology, MD
Transportation and Highway Engineering, MD
Urban Design, M
Urban and Regional Planning, MD
Veterinary Medicine, D
Water Resources, MD
Water Resources Engineering, MD
Western European Studies, MD
Women's Studies, D
Writing, M
Zoology/Animal Biology, D

CORNING COMMUNITY COLLEGE

Accounting, A
Art/Art Studies, General, A
Autobody/Collision and Repair Technology/Technician, A
Automobile/Automotive Mechanics Technology/Technician, A
Business Administration and Management, A
CAD/CADD Drafting and/or Design Technology/Technician, A
Chemical Technology/Technician, A
Computer Science, A
Computer Technology/Computer Systems Technology, A
Computer and Information Sciences, A
Computer and Information Sciences and Support Services, A
Computer/Information Technology Services Administration and Management, A
Corrections and Criminal Justice, A
Criminal Justice/Police Science, A
Customer Service Management, A
Drafting/Design Engineering Technologies/Technicians, A
Early Childhood Education and Teaching, A

Education, A
Electrical and Electronic Engineering
Technologies/Technicians, A
Electrical, Electronics and Communications Engineering, A
Energy Management and Systems
Technology/Technician, A
Engineering Science, A
Engineering Technology, A
Environmental Sciences, A
Fine Arts and Art Studies, A
Fine/Studio Arts, A
General Office Occupations and Clerical Services, A
Graphic Design, A
Health Professions and Related Clinical Sciences, A
Health and Physical Education, A
Health and Physical Education/Fitness, A
Hospitality Administration/Management, A
Human Services, A
Humanities/Humanistic Studies, A
Information Technology, A
Liberal Arts and Sciences Studies and Humanities, A
Machine Tool Technology/Machinist, A
Manufacturing Technology/Technician, A
Mathematics, A
Mechanic and Repair Technologies/Technicians, A
Mechanical Drafting and Mechanical Drafting
CAD/CADD, A
Mechanical Engineering Related
Technologies/Technicians, A
Mechanical Engineering/Mechanical
Technology/Technician, A
Mechanics and Repairers, A
Office Management and Supervision, A
Parks, Recreation, Leisure and Fitness Studies, A
Social Sciences, A
Substance Abuse/Addiction Counseling, A
System Administration/Administrator, A
Teacher Education and Professional Development, Specific Levels and Methods, A
Vehicle Maintenance and Repair Technologies, A
Web Page, Digital/Multimedia and Information Resources Design, A

THE CULINARY INSTITUTE OF AMERICA

Baking and Pastry Arts/Baker/Pastry Chef, A
Culinary Arts/Chef Training, A
Multi-/Interdisciplinary Studies, B
Restaurant/Food Services Management, B

DAEMEN COLLEGE

Accounting, BM
Art Teacher Education, B
Art/Art Studies, General, B
Arts Management, M
Biochemistry, B
Biology Teacher Education, B
Biology/Biological Sciences, B
Business Administration and Management, B
Community Health and Preventive Medicine, M
Drama and Dramatics/Theatre Arts, B
Early Childhood Education and Teaching, BM
Education, M
Elementary Education and Teaching, B
English Language and Literature, B
English/Language Arts Teacher Education, B
Epidemiology, M
Fine/Studio Arts, B
French Language Teacher Education, B
French Language and Literature, B
Graphic Design, B
Health Education, M
Health Services Administration, M
History, B
International Business/Trade/Commerce, M
Legal Assistant/Paralegal, B
Management, M
Management Information Systems and Services, M
Marketing, M
Mathematics, B
Mathematics Teacher Education, B
Medical/Surgical Nursing, O
Middle School Education, M
Natural Sciences, B

Non-Profit/Public/Organizational Management, M
Nursing, MDO
Nursing - Adult, MO
Nursing Administration, MO
Nursing Education, MO
Physical Therapy/Therapist, DO
Physician Assistant, BM
Political Science and Government, B
Psychology, B
Public Health, M
Religion/Religious Studies, B
Social Studies Teacher Education, B
Social Work, BM
Spanish Language Teacher Education, B
Spanish Language and Literature, B
Special Education and Teaching, BM

DAVIS COLLEGE

Bible/Biblical Studies, AB
Divinity/Ministry (BD, MDiv.), B
Early Childhood Education and Teaching, A
International/Global Studies, B
Pastoral Counseling and Specialized Ministries, B
Pastoral Studies/Counseling, B
Teaching English as a Second or Foreign
Language/ESL Language Instructor, B
Youth Ministry, B

DEVRY COLLEGE OF NEW YORK

Biomedical Technology/Technician, B
Business Administration and Management, B
Business Administration, Management and Operations, BM
Computer Engineering Technology/Technician, B
Computer Systems Analysis/Analyst, B
Computer Systems Networking and Telecommunications, AB
Electrical, Electronic and Communications Engineering Technology/Technician, AB

DOMINICAN COLLEGE

Accounting, BM
Allied Health and Medical Assisting Services, MD
Athletic Training and Sports Medicine, B
Biology Teacher Education, B
Biology/Biological Sciences, B
Business Administration and Management, B
Business Administration, Management and Operations, M
Computer and Information Sciences, B
Criminal Justice/Safety Studies, B
Economics, B
Education, B
Education/Teaching of Individuals with Multiple Disabilities, B
Elementary Education and Teaching, BM
English Language and Literature, B
English/Language Arts Teacher Education, B
Finance, B
Health Services Administration, M
Health/Health Care Administration/Management, B
History, B
History Teacher Education, B
Human Resources Management/Personnel Administration, B
Humanities/Humanistic Studies, B
International Business/Trade/Commerce, B
Liberal Arts and Sciences Studies and Humanities, A
Management Information Systems and Services, B
Marketing/Marketing Management, B
Mathematics, B
Mathematics Teacher Education, B
Nursing - Advanced Practice, MD
Occupational Therapy/Therapist, BM
Physical Therapy/Therapist, MD
Pre-Law Studies, B
Psychology, B
Secondary Education and Teaching, B
Social Science Teacher Education, B
Social Sciences, B
Social Work, B
Spanish Language and Literature, B

Special Education and Teaching, BM

DUTCHESS COMMUNITY COLLEGE

Accounting, A
Accounting Technology/Technician and Bookkeeping, A
Airline/Commercial/Professional Pilot and Flight
Crew, A
Architectural Engineering Technology/Technician, A
Art/Art Studies, General, A
Aviation/Airway Management and Operations, A
Business Administration and Management, A
Child Care and Support Services Management, A
Clinical/Medical Laboratory Technician, A
Commercial and Advertising Art, A
Communication Studies/Speech Communication
and Rhetoric, A
Communications Systems Installation and Repair
Technology, A
Community Health Services/Liaison/Counseling, A
Computer Science, A
Computer/Information Technology Services Administration and Management, A
Construction Trades, A
Criminal Justice/Police Science, A
Electrical, Electronic and Communications Engineering Technology/Technician, A
Emergency Medical Technology/Technician (EMT
Paramedic), A
Engineering, A
Fire Services Administration, A
General Studies, A
Human Services, A
Humanities/Humanistic Studies, A
Information Science/Studies, A
Legal Assistant/Paralegal, A
Liberal Arts and Sciences Studies and Humanities, A
Physical Education Teaching and Coaching, A
Visual and Performing Arts, A

D'YOUVILLE COLLEGE

Accounting, B
Biology/Biological Sciences, B
Business Administration and Management, B
Business Administration, Management and Operations, M
Chemistry, B
Chiropractic, D
Dietetics/Dieticians, B
Education, MDO
Educational Leadership and Administration, D
Elementary Education and Teaching, BMO
English Language and Literature, B
Health Services Administration, BMDO
History, B
International Business/Trade/Commerce, BM
Mathematics, B
Multi-/Interdisciplinary Studies, B
Nursing, MDO
Nursing - Advanced Practice, MO
Nutritional Sciences, M
Occupational Therapy/Therapist, BM
Pharmacy, D
Philosophy, B
Physical Therapy/Therapist, BDO
Physician Assistant, BM
Psychology, B
Secondary Education and Teaching, BMO
Sociology, B
Special Education and Teaching, M

ELMIRA BUSINESS INSTITUTE

Accounting, A
Administrative Assistant and Secretarial Science, A
Medical Insurance Coding Specialist/Coder, A
Medical/Clinical Assistant, A

ELMIRA COLLEGE

Accounting, B
Accounting and Finance, B
American/United States Studies/Civilization, B
Art Teacher Education, B
Art/Art Studies, General, B
Audiology/Audiologist and Speech-Language
Pathology/Pathologist, B

Biological and Physical Sciences, B
Biology Teacher Education, B
Biology/Biological Sciences, B
Business Administration and Management, AB
Chemistry, B
Chemistry Teacher Education, B
Classics and Classical Languages, Literatures, and Linguistics, B
Clinical Laboratory Science/Medical Technology/Technologist, B
Community Organization and Advocacy, AB
Criminal Justice/Law Enforcement Administration, B
Drama and Dramatics/Theatre Arts, B
Economics, B
Education, B
Education/Teaching of Individuals in Early Childhood Special Education Programs, B
Education/Teaching of Individuals with Speech or Language Impairments, B
Elementary Education and Teaching, B
English Language and Literature, B
English/Language Arts Teacher Education, B
Fine Arts and Art Studies, B
Foreign Language Teacher Education, B
Foreign Languages and Literatures, B
French Language Teacher Education, B
Health Professions and Related Clinical Sciences, B
History, B
International Relations and Affairs, B
Liberal Arts and Sciences Studies and Humanities, AB
Mathematics, B
Mathematics Teacher Education, B
Music, B
Philosophy and Religious Studies, B
Political Science and Government, B
Pre-Dentistry Studies, B
Pre-Law Studies, B
Pre-Medicine/Pre-Medical Studies, B
Pre-Veterinary Studies, B
Psychology, B
Secondary Education and Teaching, B
Social Sciences, B
Social Studies Teacher Education, B
Spanish Language Teacher Education, B

ERIE COMMUNITY COLLEGE

Building/Property Maintenance and Management, A
Business Administration and Management, A
Child Care and Support Services Management, A
Criminal Justice/Police Science, A
Culinary Arts/Chef Training, A
General Studies, A
Health and Physical Education, A
Humanities/Humanistic Studies, A
Legal Assistant/Paralegal, A
Liberal Arts and Sciences Studies and Humanities, A
Medical Radiologic Technology/Science - Radiation Therapist, A
Substance Abuse/Addiction Counseling, A

ERIE COMMUNITY COLLEGE, NORTH CAMPUS

Biology Technician/BioTechnology Laboratory Technician, A
Building/Construction Site Management/Manager, A
Business Administration and Management, A
Civil Engineering Technology/Technician, A
Clinical/Medical Laboratory Technician, A
Computer and Information Sciences, A
Criminal Justice/Law Enforcement Administration, A
Criminal Justice/Police Science, A
Culinary Arts/Chef Training, A
Dental Hygiene/Hygienist, A
Dietician Assistant, A
Electrical, Electronic and Communications Engineering Technology/Technician, A
Engineering, A
Environmental Engineering Technology/Environmental Technology, A
Environmental Sciences, A
General Studies, A
Health Information/Medical Records Technology/Technician, A
Health and Physical Education, A

Humanities/Humanistic Studies, A
Industrial Technology/Technician, A
Liberal Arts and Sciences Studies and Humanities, A
Mechanical Engineering/Mechanical Technology/Technician, A
Medical Administrative Assistant/Secretary, A
Occupational Therapist Assistant, A
Office Management and Supervision, A
Opticianry/Ophthalmic Dispensing Optician, A
Respiratory Care Therapy/Therapist, A
Restaurant/Food Services Management, A

ERIE COMMUNITY COLLEGE, SOUTH CAMPUS

Architectural Engineering Technology/Technician, A
Autobody/Collision and Repair Technology/Technician, A
Automobile/Automotive Mechanics Technology/Technician, A
Business Administration and Management, A
CAD/CADD Drafting and/or Design Technology/Technician, A
Communication Studies/Speech Communication and Rhetoric, A
Communications Systems Installation and Repair Technology, A
Computer Technology/Computer Systems Technology, A
Criminal Justice/Police Science, A
Dental Laboratory Technology/Technician, A
Emergency Medical Technology/Technician (EMT Paramedic), A
Fire Services Administration, A
General Studies, A
Graphic and Printing Equipment Operator Production, A
Health and Physical Education, A
Humanities/Humanistic Studies, A
Information Technology, A
Liberal Arts and Sciences Studies and Humanities, A
Office Management and Supervision, A
Telecommunications Technology/Technician, A

EUGENE LANG COLLEGE OF LIBERAL ARTS

Architecture and Related Services, B
Art/Art Studies, General, B
Biological and Physical Sciences, B
Design and Applied Arts, B
Design and Visual Communications, B
Digital Communication and Media/Multimedia, B
Drama and Dramatics/Theatre Arts, B
Economics, B
Environmental Studies, B
Fashion/Apparel Design, B
Film/Cinema Studies, B
Fine/Studio Arts, B
General Studies, B
Graphic Design, B
History, B
Illustration, B
Industrial Design, B
Interior Design, B
International/Global Studies, B
Jazz/Jazz Studies, B
Liberal Arts and Sciences Studies and Humanities, B
Mass Communication/Media Studies, B
Music History, Literature, and Theory, B
Philosophy, B
Photography, B
Political Science and Government, B
Psychology, B
Social and Philosophical Foundations of Education, B
Sociology, B
Urban Studies/Affairs, B

EUGENIO MARÍA DE HOSTOS COMMUNITY COLLEGE OF THE CITY UNIVERSITY OF NEW YORK

Accounting Technology/Technician and Bookkeeping, A

Administrative Assistant and Secretarial Science, A
Business Administration and Management, A
Community Health Services/Liaison/Counseling, A
Data Processing and Data Processing Technology/Technician, A
Dental Hygiene/Hygienist, A
Electrical and Electronic Engineering Technologies/Technicians, A
Gerontology, A
Legal Assistant/Paralegal, A
Liberal Arts and Sciences Studies and Humanities, A
Mathematics, A
Medical Radiologic Technology/Science - Radiation Therapist, A
Public Administration, A
Teacher Assistant/Aide, A

EXCELSIOR COLLEGE

Accounting, B
Avionics Maintenance Technology/Technician, A
Biology/Biological Sciences, B
Business Administration and Management, AB
Business Administration, Management and Operations, MO
Communication Studies/Speech Communication and Rhetoric, B
Computer and Information Sciences, AB
Criminal Justice/Law Enforcement Administration, B
Criminal Justice/Safety Studies, B
Electrical and Electronic Engineering Technologies/Technicians, B
Electromechanical Technology/Electromechanical Engineering Technology, AB
Electromechanical and Instrumentation and Maintenance Technologies/Technicians, AB
Emergency Management, M
Engineering Technologies/Technicians, AB
Finance, B
Foreign Languages and Literatures, B
Foreign Languages, Literatures, and Linguistics, B
Health Education, M
Health Professions and Related Clinical Sciences, B
Health Services Administration, M
Homeland Security, M
Information Science/Studies, B
Insurance, B
International Business/Trade/Commerce, B
Internet and Interactive Multimedia, M
Liberal Arts and Sciences Studies and Humanities, AB
Liberal Studies, M
Management Information Systems and Services, B
Management of Technology, M
Manufacturing Technology/Technician, A
Marketing/Marketing Management, B
Mathematics, B
Mechanical Engineering Related Technologies/Technicians, B
Medical Informatics, MO
Nuclear/Nuclear Power Technology/Technician, A
Nursing, M
Nursing Education, M
Nursing Informatics, M
Operations Management and Supervision, B
Political Science and Government, B
Psychology, B
Public Administration, M
Public Health, M
Securities Services Administration/Management, MO
Sociology, B

FARMINGDALE STATE COLLEGE

Airline/Commercial/Professional Pilot and Flight Crew, B
Applied Economics, B
Applied Horticulture/Horticultural Operations, B
Applied Mathematics, B
Architectural Engineering Technology/Technician, B
Automotive Engineering Technology/Technician, A
Aviation/Airway Management and Operations, B
Biology/Biological Sciences, B
Business Administration and Management, AB
Clinical Laboratory Science/Medical Technology/Technologist, B
Clinical/Medical Laboratory Technician, A

Communication, Journalism and Related Programs, B
Computer Engineering Technology/Technician, B
Computer Programming/Programmer, B
Computer Software Technology/Technician, B
Construction Engineering Technology/Technician, B
Criminal Justice/Police Science, A
Dental Hygiene/Hygienist, AB
Design and Visual Communications, B
Electrical, Electronic and Communications Engineering Technology/Technician, B
Forensic Science and Technology, B
Industrial Technology/Technician, B
International Business/Trade/Commerce, B
Liberal Arts and Sciences Studies and Humanities, A
Manufacturing Technology/Technician, B
Mechanical Engineering/Mechanical Technology/Technician, AB
Ornamental Horticulture, A
Science, Technology and Society, B
Security and Loss Prevention Services, B
Sport and Fitness Administration/Management, B
Telecommunications Technology/Technician, B

FASHION INSTITUTE OF TECHNOLOGY

Advertising, AB
Animation, Interactive Technology, Video Graphics and Special Effects, B
Apparel and Textile Manufacture, AB
Applied Arts and Design, M
Art History, Criticism and Conservation, M
Arts Management, M
Cinematography and Film/Video Production, B
Clothing and Textiles, M
Commercial Photography, AB
Commercial and Advertising Art, AB
Design and Applied Arts, B
Entrepreneurial and Small Business Operations, B
Fashion Merchandising, AB
Fashion Modeling, A
Fashion/Apparel Design, AB
Film/Cinema Studies, AB
Fine/Studio Arts, AB
Graphic Design, B
Illustration, ABM
Industrial Design, B
Interior Design, ABM
International Marketing, B
Management, M
Marketing, M
Marketing Research, B
Metal and Jewelry Arts, A
Museology/Museum Studies, M
Special Products Marketing Operations, B
Specialized Merchandising, Sales, and Marketing Operations, B
Sustainable Development, M

FINGER LAKES COMMUNITY COLLEGE

Accounting, A
Administrative Assistant and Secretarial Science, A
Animation, Interactive Technology, Video Graphics and Special Effects, A
Architectural Engineering Technology/Technician, A
Biological and Physical Sciences, A
Biology Technician/BioTechnology Laboratory Technician, A
Biology/Biological Sciences, A
Business Administration and Management, A
Chemistry, A
Commercial and Advertising Art, A
Computer Science, A
Computer and Information Sciences, A
Criminal Justice/Law Enforcement Administration, A
Criminal Justice/Police Science, A
Culinary Arts/Chef Training, A
Data Processing and Data Processing Technology/Technician, A
Digital Communication and Media/Multimedia, A
Drafting and Design Technology/Technician, A
Drama and Dramatics/Theatre Arts, A
E-Commerce/Electronic Commerce, A
Early Childhood Education and Teaching, A
Emergency Medical Technology/Technician (EMT Paramedic), A

Engineering Science, A
Environmental Studies, A
Fine/Studio Arts, A
Fishing and Fisheries Sciences and Management, A
Hotel/Motel Administration/Management, A
Human Services, A
Humanities/Humanistic Studies, A
Instrumentation Technology/Technician, A
Kindergarten/PreSchool Education and Teaching, A
Legal Assistant/Paralegal, A
Liberal Arts and Sciences Studies and Humanities, A
Marketing/Marketing Management, A
Mass Communication/Media Studies, A
Mathematics, A
Mechanical Engineering/Mechanical Technology/Technician, A
Music, A
Natural Resources Management/Development and Policy, A
Natural Resources and Conservation, A
Ornamental Horticulture, A
Physical Education Teaching and Coaching, A
Physics, A
Political Science and Government, A
Psychology, A
Recording Arts Technology/Technician, A
Resort Management, A
Social Sciences, A
Sociology, A
Substance Abuse/Addiction Counseling, A
Tourism and Travel Services Management, A

FIORELLO H. LAGUARDIA COMMUNITY COLLEGE OF THE CITY UNIVERSITY OF NEW YORK

Accounting Technology/Technician and Bookkeeping, A
Administrative Assistant and Secretarial Science, A
Adult Development and Aging, A
Biology/Biological Sciences, A
Business Administration and Management, A
Civil Engineering, A
Commercial Photography, A
Communication Studies/Speech Communication and Rhetoric, A
Computer Installation and Repair Technology/Technician, A
Computer Programming/Programmer, A
Computer Science, A
Computer Systems Networking and Telecommunications, A
Computer and Information Sciences and Support Services, A
Criminal Justice/Safety Studies, A
Data Entry/Microcomputer Applications, A
Dietetic Technician (DTR), A
Drama and Dramatics/Theatre Arts, A
Electrical, Electronics and Communications Engineering, A
Emergency Medical Technology/Technician (EMT Paramedic), A
English Language and Literature, A
Environmental Sciences, A
Fine/Studio Arts, A
Funeral Service and Mortuary Science, A
Industrial Design, A
Legal Assistant/Paralegal, A
Liberal Arts and Sciences Studies and Humanities, A
Mechanical Engineering, A
Medical Radiologic Technology/Science - Radiation Therapist, A
Occupational Therapist Assistant, A
Philosophy, A
Physical Therapist Assistant, A
Psychiatric/Mental Health Services Technician, A
Psychology, A
Recording Arts Technology/Technician, A
Restaurant/Food Services Management, A
Spanish Language and Literature, A
Teacher Assistant/Aide, A
Tourism and Travel Services Management, A
Veterinary/Animal Health Technology/Technician and Veterinary Assistant, A

Visual and Performing Arts, A

FIVE TOWNS COLLEGE

Acting, B
Broadcast Journalism, B
Business Administration and Management, AB
Business, Management, Marketing, and Related Support Services, AB
Cinematography and Film/Video Production, B
Composition, D
Drama and Dramatics/Theatre Arts, B
Early Childhood Education and Teaching, M
Education, B
Elementary Education and Teaching, B
Jazz/Jazz Studies, AB
Journalism, B
Liberal Arts and Sciences Studies and Humanities, A
Mass Communication/Media Studies, B
Music, ABMD
Music History, Literature, and Theory, D
Music Performance, AB
Music Teacher Education, BMD
Performance, D
Recording Arts Technology/Technician, B

FORDHAM UNIVERSITY

Accounting, BM
Accounting and Computer Science, B
Adult and Continuing Education and Teaching, M
African Studies, B
African-American/Black Studies, B
American/United States Studies/Civilization, B
Anthropology, B
Applied Psychology, MD
Art History, Criticism and Conservation, B
Biological and Biomedical Sciences, MDO
Biological and Physical Sciences, B
Biology/Biological Sciences, B
Business Administration and Management, B
Business Administration, Management and Operations, M
Business/Managerial Economics, B
Chemistry, B
Classics and Classical Languages, Literatures, and Linguistics, BMD
Clinical Psychology, D
Comparative Literature, B
Computer Science, BMO
Computer and Information Sciences, B
Conservation Biology, O
Corporate and Organizational Communication, M
Counseling Psychology, D
Counselor Education/School Counseling and Guidance Services, MO
Curriculum and Instruction, MD
Dance, B
Developmental Psychology, D
Drama and Dramatics/Theatre Arts, B
Early Childhood Education and Teaching, M
Economic Development, MO
Economics, BMDO
Education, BMDO
Educational Administration and Supervision, MDO
Educational Psychology, MDO
Elementary Education and Teaching, BM
Emergency Management, M
Engineering Physics, B
English, MD
English Language and Literature, B
English as a Second Language, M
Environmental Sciences, B
Ethics, MO
Finance, B
Finance and Banking, M
French Language and Literature, B
French Studies, B
German Language and Literature, B
German Studies, B
History, BMD
Human Resources Management and Services, M
Information Science/Studies, B
Intellectual Property Law, M
International Affairs, MO
International Business/Trade/Commerce, B
International Development, MO

International Economics, MO
International Relations and Affairs, B
Investment Management, M
Italian Language and Literature, B
Italian Studies, B
Latin American Studies, B
Latin Language and Literature, B
Law and Legal Studies, MD
Management Information Systems and Services, BM
Marketing, M
Marketing/Marketing Management, B
Mass Communication/Media Studies, B
Mathematics, B
Media Studies, M
Medieval and Renaissance Studies, BMO
Modern Languages, B
Multilingual and Multicultural Education, M
Music, B
Natural Sciences, B
Near and Middle Eastern Studies, B
Non-Profit/Public/Organizational Management, M
Pastoral Studies/Counseling, MDO
Philosophy, BMD
Physics, B
Political Science and Government, BM
Pre-Dentistry Studies, B
Pre-Law Studies, B
Pre-Medicine/Pre-Medical Studies, B
Pre-Veterinary Studies, B
Psychology, BMD .
Reading Teacher Education, MO
Religion/Religious Studies, BMDO
Religious Education, MDO
School Psychology, DO
Secondary Education and Teaching, BM
Social Work, BMD
Sociology, B
Spanish Language and Literature, B
Spanish and Iberian Studies, B
Special Education and Teaching, MO
System Management, M
Taxation, M
Theater, M
Theology and Religious Vocations, MD
Theology/Theological Studies, B
Urban Studies/Affairs, BM
Women's Studies, B

FULTON-MONTGOMERY COMMUNITY COLLEGE

Accounting, A
Administrative Assistant and Secretarial Science, A
Art/Art Studies, General, A
Automobile/Automotive Mechanics Technology/Technician, A
Behavioral Sciences, A
Biological and Physical Sciences, A
Biology/Biological Sciences, A
Business Administration and Management, A
Carpentry/Carpenter, A
Commercial and Advertising Art, A
Computer Engineering Technology/Technician, A
Computer Science, A
Computer Typography and Composition Equipment Operator, A
Construction Engineering Technology/Technician, A
Criminal Justice/Law Enforcement Administration, A
Data Processing and Data Processing Technology/Technician, A
Drama and Dramatics/Theatre Arts, A
Electrical, Electronic and Communications Engineering Technology/Technician, A
Elementary Education and Teaching, A
Engineering Science, A
English Language and Literature, A
Environmental Studies, A
Finance, A
Fine/Studio Arts, A
Graphic and Printing Equipment Operator Production, A
Health Teacher Education, A
History, A
Human Services, A
Humanities/Humanistic Studies, A
Information Science/Studies, A

Kindergarten/PreSchool Education and Teaching, A
Legal Administrative Assistant/Secretary, A
Liberal Arts and Sciences Studies and Humanities, A
Mass Communication/Media Studies, A
Mathematics, A
Medical Administrative Assistant/Secretary, A
Natural Resources and Conservation, A
Physical Education Teaching and Coaching, A
Physical Sciences, A
Psychology, A
Social Sciences, A
Teacher Assistant/Aide, A

GENESEE COMMUNITY COLLEGE

Accounting, A
Administrative Assistant and Secretarial Science, A
BioTechnology, A
Biology Technician/BioTechnology Laboratory Technician, A
Biology/Biological Sciences, A
Business Administration and Management, A
Business Administration, Management and Operations, A
Business Operations Support and Secretarial Services, A
Business, Management, Marketing, and Related Support Services, A
Chemistry, A
Civil Drafting and Civil Engineering CAD/CADD, A
Clinical/Medical Laboratory Technician, A
Computer Graphics, A
Computer Installation and Repair Technology/Technician, A
Computer Programming, A
Computer Science, A
Computer Software and Media Applications, A
Computer Systems Networking and Telecommunications, A
Computer and Information Sciences, A
Corrections and Criminal Justice, A
Criminal Justice/Law Enforcement Administration, A
Criminal Justice/Police Science, A
Criminal Justice/Safety Studies, A
Criminology, A
Drafting and Design Technology/Technician, A
Drafting/Design Engineering Technologies/Technicians, A
Drama and Dramatics/Theatre Arts, A
Dramatic/Theatre Arts and Stagecraft, A
E-Commerce/Electronic Commerce, A
Education, A
Elementary Education and Teaching, A
Engineering, A
Engineering Science, A
Entrepreneurship/Entrepreneurial Studies, A
Fashion Merchandising, A
Fashion/Apparel Design, A
Fine/Studio Arts, A
Food Technology and Processing, A
Foreign Languages, Literatures, and Linguistics, A
General Studies, A
Gerontology, A
Graphic Design, A
Health Professions and Related Clinical Sciences, A
Health and Physical Education, A
Health and Physical Education/Fitness, A
Hospitality Administration/Management, A
Hotel/Motel Administration/Management, A
Human Services, A
Humanities/Humanistic Studies, A
Information Science/Studies, A
Kindergarten/PreSchool Education and Teaching, A
Legal Assistant/Paralegal, A
Liberal Arts and Sciences Studies and Humanities, A
Marketing/Marketing Management, A
Mass Communication/Media Studies, A
Mathematics, A
Medical Administrative Assistant/Secretary, A
Parks, Recreation, Leisure and Fitness Studies, A
Physical Education Teaching and Coaching, A
Physical Therapist Assistant, A
Physical Therapy/Therapist, A
Psychology, A
Radio and Television, A

Radio and Television Broadcasting Technology/Technician, A
Radio, Television, and Digital Communication, A
Respiratory Care Therapy/Therapist, A
Social Sciences, A
Social Work, A
Substance Abuse/Addiction Counseling, A
System Administration/Administrator, A
Teacher Assistant/Aide, A
Teacher Education, Multiple Levels, A
Technical Theatre/Theatre Design and Technology, A
Tourism Promotion Operations, A
Tourism and Travel Services Management, A
Veterinary/Animal Health Technology/Technician and Veterinary Assistant, A
Web Page, Digital/Multimedia and Information Resources Design, A

GLOBE INSTITUTE OF TECHNOLOGY

Accounting, B
Banking and Financial Support Services, A
Business Administration and Management, AB
Computer Programming/Programmer, B
Computer and Information Sciences, AB
Finance, B
Health/Health Care Administration/Management, B
Hospitality Administration/Management, B
Management Information Systems and Services, A
Office Management and Supervision, B
Sport and Fitness Administration/Management, B

HAMILTON COLLEGE

African-American/Black Studies, B
American/United States Studies/Civilization, B
Anthropology, B
Archeology, B
Art History, Criticism and Conservation, B
Asian Studies/Civilization, B
Biochemistry, B
Biology/Biological Sciences, B
Chemical Physics, B
Chemistry, B
Chinese Language and Literature, B
Classics and Classical Languages, Literatures, and Linguistics, B
Communication and Media Studies, B
Comparative Literature, B
Computer and Information Sciences, B
Dance, B
Drama and Dramatics/Theatre Arts, B
Economics, B
English Language and Literature, B
Environmental Studies, B
Fine/Studio Arts, B
Foreign Languages and Literatures, B
French Language and Literature, B
Geological and Earth Sciences/Geosciences, B
Geology/Earth Science, B
German Studies, B
History, B
International Relations and Affairs, B
Mathematics, B
Music, B
Philosophy, B
Physics, B
Political Science and Government, B
Psychology, B
Public Policy Analysis, B
Religion/Religious Studies, B
Russian Studies, B
Sociology, B
Women's Studies, B

HARTWICK COLLEGE

Accounting, B
Anthropology, B
Art History, Criticism and Conservation, B
Art/Art Studies, General, B
Biochemistry, B
Biology/Biological Sciences, B
Business Administration and Management, B
Chemistry, B
Clinical Laboratory Science/Medical Technology/Technologist, B
Computer Science, B

Computer and Information Sciences, B
Drama and Dramatics/Theatre Arts, B
Economics, B
English Language and Literature, B
Environmental Sciences, B
French Language and Literature, B
Geology/Earth Science, B
German Language and Literature, B
History, B
Mathematics, B
Music, B
Music Teacher Education, B
Philosophy, B
Physics, B
Political Science and Government, B
Pre-Law Studies, B
Pre-Medicine/Pre-Medical Studies, B
Pre-Veterinary Studies, B
Psychology, B
Religion/Religious Studies, B
Sociology, B
Spanish Language and Literature, B

HERKIMER COUNTY COMMUNITY COLLEGE

Accounting Technology/Technician and Bookkeeping, A
Art/Art Studies, General, A
Broadcast Journalism, A
Business Administration and Management, A
Child Care and Support Services Management, A
Community Organization and Advocacy, A
Computer and Information Sciences, A
Computer and Information Sciences and Support Services, A
Corrections, A
Criminal Justice/Law Enforcement Administration, A
Emergency Medical Technology/Technician (EMT Paramedic), A
Entrepreneurship/Entrepreneurial Studies, A
Fashion Merchandising, A
Forensic Science and Technology, A
General Merchandising, Sales, and Related Marketing Operations, A
General Studies, A
Health Professions and Related Clinical Sciences, A
Health and Physical Education/Fitness, A
Human Resources Management/Personnel Administration, A
Humanities/Humanistic Studies, A
International Business/Trade/Commerce, A
Legal Administrative Assistant/Secretary, A
Legal Assistant/Paralegal, A
Liberal Arts and Sciences Studies and Humanities, A
Parks, Recreation and Leisure Facilities Management, A
Photographic and Film/Video Technology/Technician and Assistant, A
Physical Therapy/Therapist, A
Tourism and Travel Services Marketing Operations, A
Visual and Performing Arts, A

HILBERT COLLEGE

Accounting, B
Accounting Technology/Technician and Bookkeeping, A
Banking and Financial Support Services, A
Business Administration and Management, AB
Computer and Information Sciences and Support Services, B
Computer and Information Systems Security, B
Criminal Justice/Police Science, AB
Criminal Justice/Safety Studies, AB
Criminology, M
Digital Communication and Media/Multimedia, B
English Language and Literature, B
Forensic Science and Technology, B
Health Services Administration, M
Human Services, AB
International Business/Trade/Commerce, B
Legal Assistant/Paralegal, AB
Liberal Arts and Sciences Studies and Humanities, A
Political Science and Government, B

Psychology, B
Public Administration, M
Rehabilitation and Therapeutic Professions, B
Small Business Administration/Management, B
Social Sciences, B
Sport and Fitness Administration/Management, B

HOBART AND WILLIAM SMITH COLLEGES

African Studies, B
African-American/Black Studies, B
American/United States Studies/Civilization, B
Ancient/Classical Greek Language and Literature, B
Anthropology, B
Architecture, B
Art History, Criticism and Conservation, B
Art/Art Studies, General, B
Asian Studies/Civilization, B
Biochemistry, B
Biology/Biological Sciences, B
Chemistry, B
Chinese Language and Literature, B
Classics and Classical Languages, Literatures, and Linguistics, B
Comparative Literature, B
Computer Science, B
Dance, B
Economics, B
English Language and Literature, B
Environmental Studies, B
European Studies/Civilization, B
Fine/Studio Arts, B
French Language and Literature, B
Geology/Earth Science, B
History, B
International Relations and Affairs, B
Japanese Language and Literature, B
Latin American Studies, B
Latin Language and Literature, B
Mass Communication/Media Studies, B
Mathematics, B
Music, B
Philosophy, B
Physics, B
Political Science and Government, B
Pre-Dentistry Studies, B
Pre-Law Studies, B
Pre-Medicine/Pre-Medical Studies, B
Pre-Veterinary Studies, B
Psychology, B
Public Policy Analysis, B
Religion/Religious Studies, B
Russian Studies, B
Sociology, B
Spanish Language and Literature, B
Urban Studies/Affairs, B
Women's Studies, B

HOFSTRA UNIVERSITY

Accounting, BMO
Acting, B
Advertising and Public Relations, M
African Studies, B
Allied Health Diagnostic, Intervention, and Treatment Professions, B
Allopathic Medicine, D
American/United States Studies/Civilization, B
Anthropology, B
Applied Behavior Analysis, O
Area Studies, B
Art Education, MD
Art History, Criticism and Conservation, B
Art Teacher Education, B
Art Therapy/Therapist, M
Athletic Training and Sports Medicine, B
Audiology/Audiologist and Speech-Language Pathology/Pathologist, B
Biochemistry, B
Biological and Biomedical Sciences, M
Biology Teacher Education, B
Biology/Biological Sciences, B
Biomedical/Medical Engineering, B
Business Administration and Management, B
Business Administration, Management and Operations, BM
Business Education, M

Business Teacher Education, B
Business, Management, Marketing, and Related Support Services, B
Business/Commerce, B
Business/Managerial Economics, B
Caribbean Studies, B
Ceramic Arts and Ceramics, B
Chemistry, B
Chemistry Teacher Education, B
Chinese Language and Literature, B
Civil Engineering, B
Classics and Classical Languages, Literatures, and Linguistics, B
Clinical Psychology, D
Communication Disorders, MD
Communication Studies/Speech Communication and Rhetoric, B
Communication and Media Studies, M
Community Health and Preventive Medicine, BM
Community Psychology, D
Comparative Literature, B
Computer Engineering, B
Computer Science, B
Computer and Information Sciences and Support Services, B
Computer and Information Systems Security, M
Counseling Psychology, MO
Counselor Education/School Counseling and Guidance Services, MO
Criminology, B
Dance, B
Design and Applied Arts, B
Directing and Theatrical Production, B
Drama and Dance Teacher Education, B
Drama and Dramatics/Theatre Arts, B
Early Childhood Education and Teaching, BMDO
East Asian Studies, B
Ecology, Evolution, Systematics and Population Biology, B
Econometrics and Quantitative Economics, B
Economics, B
Education, MDO
Education/Teaching of the Gifted and Talented, O
Educational Media/Instructional Technology, O
Electrical, Electronics and Communications Engineering, B
Elementary Education and Teaching, BM
Engineering Science, B
Engineering and Applied Sciences, M
English, M
English Education, MD
English Language and Literature, B
English as a Second Language, M
English/Language Arts Teacher Education, B
Entertainment Management, M
Entrepreneurship/Entrepreneurial Studies, B
Environmental Studies, B
Film, Television, and Video Production, M
Finance, B
Finance and Banking, MO
Finance and Financial Management Services, B
Fine Arts and Art Studies, M
Fine/Studio Arts, B
Foreign Language Teacher Education, BM
Forensic Science and Technology, B
French Language Teacher Education, B
French Language and Literature, BM
Geography, B
Geology/Earth Science, BM
German Language Teacher Education, B
German Language and Literature, B
Health Law, M
Health Services Administration, M
Health Services/Allied Health/Health Sciences, B
Health Teacher Education, B
Health/Medical Preparatory Programs, B
Hebrew Language and Literature, B
History, B
Human Development, D
Human Resources Management and Services, MO
Humanities/Humanistic Studies, D
Industrial Engineering, B
Industrial and Organizational Psychology, MD
International Business/Trade/Commerce, BMO
International/Global Studies, B
Internet Engineering, M

Investment Management, MO
Italian Language and Literature, B
Japanese Language and Literature, B
Japanese Studies, B
Jazz/Jazz Studies, B
Jewish/Judaic Studies, B
Journalism, BM
Labor Studies, B
Latin American Studies, B
Latin Language and Literature, B
Law and Legal Studies, MD
Legal and Justice Studies, M
Liberal Arts and Sciences Studies and Humanities, B
Linguistics, BMD
Logistics and Materials Management, B
Management, MO
Management Information Systems and Services, BMO
Management Strategy and Policy, M
Manufacturing Engineering, B
Marketing, MO
Marketing Research, M
Marketing/Marketing Management, B
Marriage and Family Therapy/Counseling, M
Mass Communication/Media Studies, B
Mathematics, B
Mathematics Teacher Education, BMD
Mathematics and Computer Science, B
Mathematics and Statistics, B
Mechanical Engineering, B
Medical Physics, M
Metal and Jewelry Arts, B
Molecular Medicine, D
Multilingual and Multicultural Education, MD
Music, B
Music History, Literature, and Theory, B
Music Performance, B
Music Teacher Education, B
Music Theory and Composition, B
Natural Sciences, B
Painting, B
Philosophy, B
Photography, B
Physical Education Teaching and Coaching, BD
Physician Assistant, M
Physics, B
Physics Teacher Education, B
Political Science and Government, B
Pre-Dentistry Studies, B
Pre-Law Studies, B
Pre-Medicine/Pre-Medical Studies, B
Pre-Veterinary Studies, B
Psychology, BMD
Public Health, M
Public Relations/Image Management, B
Quality Management, M
Quantitative Analysis, M
Radio and Television, B
Radio, Television, and Digital Communication, B
Rehabilitation Counseling, MO
Religion/Religious Studies, B
Rhetoric, M
Russian Language and Literature, B
School Psychology, D
Science Teacher Education/General Science Teacher Education, BMD
Secondary Education and Teaching, BMO
Social Studies Teacher Education, BMD
Sociology, B
Spanish Language Teacher Education, B
Spanish Language and Literature, B
Special Education and Teaching, MDO
Sport and Fitness Administration/Management, M
Sustainable Development, M
Taxation, MO
Teacher Education, Multiple Levels, B
Urban Design, M
Women's Studies, B

Writing, M

HOLY TRINITY ORTHODOX SEMINARY

Theology/Theological Studies, B

HOUGHTON COLLEGE

Accounting, B
Art Teacher Education, B
Art/Art Studies, General, B
Bible/Biblical Studies, AB
Biochemistry, B
Biological and Physical Sciences, B
Biology/Biological Sciences, B
Business Administration and Management, B
Chemistry, B
Clinical Laboratory Science/Medical Technology/Technologist, B
Communication Studies/Speech Communication and Rhetoric, B
Communication and Media Studies, B
Comparative Literature, B
Composition, M
Computer Science, B
Design and Visual Communications, B
Development Economics and International Development, B
Elementary Education and Teaching, B
English Language and Literature, B
Environmental Biology, B
Equestrian/Equine Studies, B
Health Teacher Education, B
Health and Physical Education, B
History, B
Human Resources Development, B
Human Resources Management/Personnel Administration, B
Humanities/Humanistic Studies, B
Liberal Arts and Sciences Studies and Humanities, AB
Mathematics, B
Music, BM
Music Performance, B
Music Teacher Education, B
Music Theory and Composition, B
Natural Sciences, B
Parks, Recreation, Leisure and Fitness Studies, B
Pastoral Studies/Counseling, B
Performance, M
Philosophy, B
Physical Education Teaching and Coaching, B
Physics, B
Piano and Organ, B
Political Science and Government, B
Pre-Dentistry Studies, B
Pre-Law Studies, B
Pre-Medicine/Pre-Medical Studies, B
Pre-Nursing Studies, B
Pre-Pharmacy Studies, B
Pre-Veterinary Studies, B
Psychology, B
Regional Studies (U.S., Canadian, Foreign), B
Religion/Religious Studies, B
Religious Education, B
Secondary Education and Teaching, B
Sociology, B
Spanish Language and Literature, B
Special Education and Teaching, B
Teaching English as a Second or Foreign Language/ESL Language Instructor, B
Theology/Theological Studies, B
Violin, Viola, Guitar and Other Stringed Instruments, B
Voice and Opera, B

HUDSON VALLEY COMMUNITY COLLEGE

Accounting and Business/Management, A
Architectural Technology/Technician, A
Automobile/Automotive Mechanics Technology/Technician, A
BioTechnology, A
Biology/Biological Sciences, A
Business Administration and Management, A
CAD/CADD Drafting and/or Design Technology/Technician, A
Cardiovascular Technology/Technologist, A

Chemical Technology/Technician, A
Civil Engineering Technology/Technician, A
Computer and Information Sciences, A
Construction Trades, A
Criminal Justice/Law Enforcement Administration, A
Criminalistics and Criminal Science, A
Dental Hygiene/Hygienist, A
Drama and Dramatics/Theatre Arts, A
Early Childhood Education and Teaching, A
Education, A
Electrical, Electronics and Communications Engineering, A
Emergency Medical Technology/Technician (EMT Paramedic), A
Engineering Science, A
Environmental Sciences, A
Fine/Studio Arts, A
Forensic Science and Technology, A
Funeral Service and Mortuary Science, A
Health Information/Medical Records Technology/Technician, A
Heating, Air Conditioning, Ventilation and Refrigeration Maintenance Technology/Technician, A
Human Services, A
Information Technology, A
Liberal Arts and Sciences Studies and Humanities, A
Manufacturing Technology/Technician, A
Marketing/Marketing Management, A
Mass Communication/Media Studies, A
Mechanical Engineering Related Technologies/Technicians, A
Physical Education Teaching and Coaching, A
Physical Sciences, A
Public Administration, A
Radiologic Technology/Science - Radiographer, A
Respiratory Care Therapy/Therapist, A
Substance Abuse/Addiction Counseling, A
System Administration/Administrator, A
Telecommunications Technology/Technician, A
Web Page, Digital/Multimedia and Information Resources Design, A

HUNTER COLLEGE OF THE CITY UNIVERSITY OF NEW YORK

Accounting, BM
African-American/Black Studies, B
Ancient/Classical Greek Language and Literature, B
Anthropology, BM
Applied Mathematics, M
Applied Social Research, M
Archeology, B
Art History, Criticism and Conservation, BM
Art/Art Studies, General, B
Audiology/Audiologist and Speech-Language Pathology/Pathologist, B
BioTechnology, B
Biochemistry, MD
Biological and Biomedical Sciences, MD
Biology Teacher Education, B
Biology/Biological Sciences, B
Biostatistics, M
Chemistry, BMD
Chinese Language and Literature, B
Chinese Studies, M
Cinematography and Film/Video Production, B
Classics and Classical Languages, Literatures, and Linguistics, BM
Clinical/Medical Laboratory Science and Allied Professions, B
Communication Disorders, M
Community Health Nursing, M
Community Health and Preventive Medicine, M
Comparative Literature, B
Computer Science, B
Counselor Education/School Counseling and Guidance Services, M
Dance, B
Drama and Dramatics/Theatre Arts, B
Early Childhood Education and Teaching, M
Economics, BMD
Education, MO
Education/Teaching of Individuals with Multiple Disabilities, M
Educational Administration and Supervision, O
Elementary Education and Teaching, BM

English, M
English Education, M
English Language and Literature, B
English as a Second Language, M
Environmental Sciences, B
Environmental and Occupational Health, M
Epidemiology, M
Film/Cinema Studies, B
Fine Arts and Art Studies, M
Fine/Studio Arts, B
Foods, Nutrition, and Wellness Studies, B
Foreign Language Teacher Education, M
French Language and Literature, BM
Geography, BMO
Geosciences, M
German Language Teacher Education, B
German Language and Literature, B
Gerontological Nursing, M
Health Services Administration, M
Health Teacher Education, B
Hebrew Language and Literature, B
Hispanic-American, Puerto Rican, and Mexican-
American/Chicano Studies, B
History, BM
Humanities/Humanistic Studies, B
Italian Language and Literature, BM
Jewish/Judaic Studies, B
Kindergarten/PreSchool Education and Teaching, B
Latin American Studies, B
Latin Language and Literature, B
Mass Communication/Media Studies, B
Mathematics, BM
Mathematics Teacher Education, BM
Media Studies, M
Multilingual and Multicultural Education, M
Music, BM
Music Teacher Education, M
Nursing, MO
Nursing - Adult, M
Nutritional Sciences, M
Philosophy, B
Physical Education Teaching and Coaching, B
Physics, BMD
Political Science and Government, B
Psychiatric/Mental Health Nurse/Nursing, MO
Psychology, BM
Public Health, M
Public Health (MPH, DPH), B
Rehabilitation Counseling, M
Religion/Religious Studies, B
Romance Languages, Literatures, and Linguis-
tics, BM
Russian Language and Literature, B
Science Teacher Education/General Science
Teacher Education, BM
Secondary Education and Teaching, BM
Social Studies Teacher Education, M
Social Work, MD
Sociology, BM
Spanish Language and Literature, BM
Special Education and Teaching, M
Statistics, BM
Theater, M
Urban Planning, M
Urban Studies/Affairs, BM
Women's Studies, B
Writing, M

IONA COLLEGE

Accounting, BMO
Advertising, B
Advertising and Public Relations, O
Applied Mathematics, B
Audiology/Audiologist and Speech-Language
Pathology/Pathologist, B
Biochemistry, B
Biology Teacher Education, B
Biology/Biological Sciences, B
Business Administration and Management, B
Business Administration, Management and Opera-
tions, MO
Chemistry, B
Communication Disorders, M
Communication Studies/Speech Communication
and Rhetoric, B
Computer Science, BM

Computer Systems Networking and Telecommunica-
tions, B
Computer and Information Systems Security, M
Counseling Psychology, M
Criminal Justice/Law Enforcement Administration, B
Criminology, MO
Early Childhood Education and Teaching, BM
Economics, B
Education, M
Educational Leadership and Administration, M
Elementary Education and Teaching, B
English, M
English Education, M
English Language and Literature, B
English/Language Arts Teacher Education, B
Environmental Biology, B
Experimental Psychology, M
Finance, B
Finance and Banking, MO
Foreign Language Teacher Education, BM
Forensic Science and Technology, O
French Language Teacher Education, B
French Language and Literature, B
Health Services Administration, MO
Health/Health Care Administration/Management, B
History, BM
Human Resources Management and Services, O
Industrial and Organizational Psychology, M
International Business/Trade/Commerce, BMO
International Relations and Affairs, B
Italian Language and Literature, B
Journalism, B
Liberal Arts and Sciences Studies and Humani-
ties, B
Management Information Systems and Services, B
Management of Technology, MO
Marketing, MO
Marketing/Marketing Management, B
Marriage and Family Therapy/Counseling, M
Mass Communication/Media Studies, BMO
Mathematics, B
Mathematics Teacher Education, BM
Mental Health Counseling/Counselor, B
Non-Profit/Public/Organizational Management, O
Philosophy, B
Physics, B
Political Science and Government, B
Psychology, BMO
Public Relations/Image Management, B
Radio and Television, B
Recreation and Park Management, O
Religion/Religious Studies, B
School Psychology, M
Science Teacher Education/General Science
Teacher Education, M
Secondary Education and Teaching, B
Social Studies Teacher Education, BM
Social Work, B
Sociology, B
Spanish Language Teacher Education, B
Spanish Language and Literature, BM
Special Education and Teaching, M
Sport and Fitness Administration/Management, O
Web Page, Digital/Multimedia and Information Re-
sources Design, B

ISLAND DRAFTING AND TECHNICAL INSTITUTE

Architectural Drafting and Architectural
CAD/CADD, A
Computer Systems Networking and Telecommunica-
tions, A
Computer Technology/Computer Systems Technol-
ogy, A
Computer and Information Sciences and Support
Services, A
Computer and Information Systems Security, A
Electrical, Electronic and Communications Engineer-
ing Technology/Technician, A
Mechanical Drafting and Mechanical Drafting
CAD/CADD, A
System Administration/Administrator, A

ITHACA COLLEGE

Accounting, BM
Acting, B

Allied Health and Medical Assisting Services, MD
Anthropology, B
Applied Economics, B
Architecture, B
Art History, Criticism and Conservation, B
Art Teacher Education, B
Art/Art Studies, General, B
Athletic Training and Sports Medicine, B
Audiology/Audiologist and Speech-Language
Pathology/Pathologist, B
Biochemistry, B
Biology Teacher Education, B
Biology/Biological Sciences, B
Broadcast Journalism, B
Business Administration and Management, B
Business/Commerce, B
Business/Managerial Economics, B
Chemistry, B
Chemistry Teacher Education, B
Cinematography and Film/Video Production, B
Communication Disorders, M
Communication and Media Studies, M
Composition, M
Computer Science, B
Computer and Information Sciences, B
Drama and Dramatics/Theatre Arts, B
Economics, B
Education/Teaching of Individuals with Speech or
Language Impairments, B
Elementary Education and Teaching, M
English Education, M
English Language and Literature, B
English/Language Arts Teacher Education, B
Environmental Studies, B
Exercise and Sports Science, M
Film/Cinema Studies, B
Finance, B
Fine/Studio Arts, B
Foods, Nutrition, and Wellness Studies, B
Foreign Language Teacher Education, M
French Language Teacher Education, B
French Language and Literature, B
German Language Teacher Education, B
German Language and Literature, B
German Studies, B
Gerontology, B
Health Education, M
Health Teacher Education, B
Health and Physical Education, B
Health and Physical Education/Fitness, B
Health/Health Care Administration/Management, B
Health/Medical Preparatory Programs, B
History, B
History Teacher Education, B
Hospital and Health Care Facilities
Administration/Management, B
International Business/Trade/Commerce, B
Internet and Interactive Multimedia, M
Italian Language and Literature, B
Jazz/Jazz Studies, B
Journalism, B
Junior High/Intermediate/Middle School Education
and Teaching, B
Kinesiology and Exercise Science, B
Labor and Industrial Relations, B
Liberal Arts and Sciences Studies and Humani-
ties, B
Management, M
Marketing Research, B
Marketing/Marketing Management, B
Mass Communication/Media Studies, B
Mathematics, B
Mathematics Teacher Education, BM
Mathematics and Computer Science, B
Multi-/Interdisciplinary Studies, B
Music, BM
Music Performance, B
Music Teacher Education, BM
Music Theory and Composition, B
Occupational Therapy/Therapist, BM
Parks, Recreation, Leisure and Fitness Studies, B
Performance, M
Philosophy, B
Photography, B
Physical Education Teaching and Coaching, BM
Physical Therapy/Therapist, BD

Physics, B
Physics Teacher Education, B
Piano and Organ, B
Political Science and Government, B
Pre-Law Studies, B
Pre-Medicine/Pre-Medical Studies, B
Psychology, B
Public Health Education and Promotion, B
Public Relations/Image Management, B
Radio and Television, B
Recording Arts Technology/Technician, B
Rehabilitation and Therapeutic Professions, B
Science Teacher Education/General Science
   Teacher Education, BM
Secondary Education and Teaching, BM
Social Sciences, B
Social Studies Teacher Education, BM
Sociology, B
Spanish Language Teacher Education, B
Spanish Language and Literature, B
Sport and Fitness Administration/Management, B
Teacher Education, Multiple Levels, B
Technical Theatre/Theatre Design and Technol-
   ogy, B
Therapeutic Recreation/Recreational Therapy, B
Visual and Performing Arts, B
Voice and Opera, B

JAMESTOWN BUSINESS COLLEGE

Administrative Assistant and Secretarial Science, A
Business Administration and Management, AB
Medical/Clinical Assistant, A
Office Management and Supervision, A

JAMESTOWN COMMUNITY COLLEGE

Accounting Technology/Technician and Bookkeep-
   ing, A
Administrative Assistant and Secretarial Science, A
Airline/Commercial/Professional Pilot and Flight
   Crew, A
Biology Technician/BioTechnology Laboratory Tech-
   nician, A
Business Administration and Management, A
Communication Studies/Speech Communication
   and Rhetoric, A
Computer and Information Sciences, A
Criminal Justice/Law Enforcement Administration, A
Criminal Justice/Police Science, A
Engineering, A
Environmental Sciences, A
Fine/Studio Arts, A
General Studies, A
Health Information/Medical Records
   Technology/Technician, A
Health and Physical Education, A
Human Services, A
Humanities/Humanistic Studies, A
Information Science/Studies, A
Information Technology, A
International/Global Studies, A
Liberal Arts and Sciences Studies and Humani-
   ties, A
Mechanical Engineering/Mechanical
   Technology/Technician, A
Music, A
Occupational Therapist Assistant, A
Teacher Assistant/Aide, A
Welding Technology/Welder, A

JEFFERSON COMMUNITY COLLEGE

Accounting, A
Accounting Technology/Technician and Bookkeep-
   ing, A
Administrative Assistant and Secretarial Science, A
Animal/Livestock Husbandry and Production, A
Business Administration and Management, A
Child Care and Support Services Management, A
Child Development, A
Community Organization and Advocacy, A
Computer Science, A
Computer Technology/Computer Systems Technol-
   ogy, A
Computer and Information Sciences, A
Computer and Information Sciences and Support
   Services, A

Computer/Information Technology Services Adminis-
   tration and Management, A
Criminal Justice/Law Enforcement Administration, A
Early Childhood Education and Teaching, A
Emergency Medical Technology/Technician (EMT
   Paramedic), A
Engineering, A
Engineering Science, A
Fire Protection and Safety Technology/Technician, A
Fire Services Administration, A
General Office Occupations and Clerical Services, A
Hospitality Administration/Management, A
Human Services, A
Humanities/Humanistic Studies, A
Information Science/Studies, A
Legal Assistant/Paralegal, A
Liberal Arts and Sciences Studies and Humani-
   ties, A
Mathematics, A
Mechanical Engineering Related
   Technologies/Technicians, A
Medical Administrative Assistant/Secretary, A
Office Management and Supervision, A
Sport and Fitness Administration/Management, A
Teacher Assistant/Aide, A
Tourism Promotion Operations, A

THE JEWISH THEOLOGICAL SEMI-NARY

Ancient Near Eastern and Biblical Languages, Lit-
   eratures, and Linguistics, B
Bible/Biblical Studies, B
Comparative Literature, B
Hebrew Language and Literature, B
History, B
Jewish/Judaic Studies, BMD
Music, A
Philosophy, B
Religion/Religious Studies, BMD
Religious Education, BMD
Sacred Music, M
Talmudic Studies, B
Theology and Religious Vocations, MDO
Women's Studies, BM

JOHN JAY COLLEGE OF CRIMINAL JUSTICE OF THE CITY UNIVERSITY OF NEW YORK

Computer and Information Sciences, B
Computer and Information Sciences and Support
   Services, B
Corrections, B
Corrections Administration, A
Corrections and Criminal Justice, B
Criminal Justice/Law Enforcement Administration, B
Criminal Justice/Police Science, A
Criminology, BMD
Economics, B
English Language and Literature, B
Ethnic, Cultural Minority, and Gender Studies, B
Fire Science/Firefighting, B
Fire Services Administration, B
Forensic Psychology, MD
Forensic Science and Technology, BMD
History, B
Humanities/Humanistic Studies, B
Latin American Studies, B
Law and Legal Studies, B
Legal and Justice Studies, D
Organizational Behavior Studies, D
Philosophy, B
Political Science and Government, B
Public Administration, BM
Public Policy Analysis, D
Securities Services Administration/Management, BM
Security and Loss Prevention Services, A
Social Sciences, B
Sociology, B
Spanish Language and Literature, B

THE JUILLIARD SCHOOL

Dance, B
Drama and Dramatics/Theatre Arts, B
Music, BMDO

Music Performance, B

KEHILATH YAKOV RABBINICAL SEMI-NARY

Talmudic Studies, B

KEUKA COLLEGE

Accounting, B
Biochemistry, B
Biology Teacher Education, B
Biology/Biological Sciences, B
Biomedical Sciences, B
Business Administration and Management, B
Clinical Laboratory Science/Medical
   Technology/Technologist, B
Communication Studies/Speech Communication
   and Rhetoric, B
Criminal Justice/Law Enforcement Administration, B
Criminology, M
Early Childhood Education and Teaching, M
Education/Teaching of Individuals in Early Childhood
   Special Education Programs, B
Elementary Education and Teaching, B
English Language and Literature, B
English/Language Arts Teacher Education, B
Environmental Sciences, B
History, B
Hotel/Motel Administration/Management, B
Liberal Arts and Sciences Studies and Humani-
   ties, B
Management, M
Marketing/Marketing Management, B
Mathematics, B
Mathematics Teacher Education, B
Nursing, M
Occupational Therapy/Therapist, BM
Pre-Dentistry Studies, B
Pre-Law Studies, B
Pre-Medicine/Pre-Medical Studies, B
Pre-Veterinary Studies, B
Psychology, B
Secondary Education and Teaching, B
Social Sciences, B
Social Studies Teacher Education, B
Social Work, B
Sociology, B
Special Education and Teaching, B

THE KING'S COLLEGE

Business Administration and Management, B
Finance, B
Humanities/Humanistic Studies, B
Religion/Religious Studies, B

KINGSBOROUGH COMMUNITY COL-LEGE OF THE CITY UNIVERSITY OF NEW YORK

Accounting, A
Administrative Assistant and Secretarial Science, A
Art/Art Studies, General, A
Biology/Biological Sciences, A
Broadcast Journalism, A
Business Administration and Management, A
Chemistry, A
Commercial and Advertising Art, A
Community Health Services/Liaison/Counseling, A
Computer Science, A
Computer and Information Sciences, A
Cooking and Related Culinary Arts, A
Criminal Justice/Law Enforcement Administration, A
Data Processing and Data Processing
   Technology/Technician, A
Design and Applied Arts, A
Drama and Dramatics/Theatre Arts, A
Early Childhood Education and Teaching, A
Education, A
Elementary Education and Teaching, A
Engineering Science, A
Fashion Merchandising, A
Health and Physical Education/Fitness, A
Human Services, A
Journalism, A
Labor and Industrial Relations, A
Liberal Arts and Sciences Studies and Humani-
   ties, A

Marine Maintenance/Fitter and Ship Repair
  Technology/Technician, A
Marketing/Marketing Management, A
Mathematics, A
Mental Health Counseling/Counselor, A
Music, A
Parks, Recreation, Leisure and Fitness Studies, A
Physical Therapist Assistant, A
Physical Therapy/Therapist, A
Physics, A
Psychiatric/Mental Health Services Technician, A
Sport and Fitness Administration/Management, A
Teacher Assistant/Aide, A
Tourism and Travel Services Management, A

LE MOYNE COLLEGE

Accounting, B
Biochemistry, B
Biological and Physical Sciences, B
Biology Teacher Education, B
Biology/Biological Sciences, B
Business Administration, Management and Opera-
  tions, BM
Chemistry, B
Chemistry Teacher Education, B
Computer Programming/Programmer, B
Computer and Information Sciences, B
Criminology, B
Drama and Dramatics/Theatre Arts, B
Early Childhood Education and Teaching, M
Ecology, B
Economics, B
Education, MO
Educational Leadership and Administration, MO
Elementary Education and Teaching, BM
English Education, M
English Language and Literature, B
English as a Second Language, M
English/Language Arts Teacher Education, B
Environmental Studies, B
Finance, B
Foreign Language Teacher Education, M
French Language Teacher Education, B
French Language and Literature, B
Gerontological Nursing, MO
Health/Medical Preparatory Programs, B
History, B
Human Resources Management/Personnel Adminis-
  tration, B
International/Global Studies, B
Management Information Systems and Services, B
Marketing/Marketing Management, B
Mathematics, B
Mathematics Teacher Education, B
Middle School Education, M
Nursing, MO
Nursing Administration, MO
Nursing Education, MO
Nursing Informatics, MO
Operations Management and Supervision, B
Philosophy, B
Physician Assistant, M
Physics, B
Physics Teacher Education, B
Political Science and Government, B
Pre-Dentistry Studies, B
Pre-Law Studies, B
Pre-Medicine/Pre-Medical Studies, B
Pre-Pharmacy Studies, B
Pre-Veterinary Studies, B
Psychology, B
Reading Teacher Education, M
Religion/Religious Studies, B
Science Teacher Education/General Science
  Teacher Education, B
Secondary Education and Teaching, BM
Social Studies Teacher Education, BM
Sociology, B
Spanish Language Teacher Education, B
Spanish Language and Literature, B
Special Education and Teaching, BM
Teaching English as a Second or Foreign
  Language/ESL Language Instructor, B

Urban Studies/Affairs, M

LEHMAN COLLEGE OF THE CITY UNIVERSITY OF NEW YORK

Accounting, BM
African-American/Black Studies, B
American/United States Studies/Civilization, B
Anthropology, B
Art History, Criticism and Conservation, B
Art Teacher Education, B
Art/Art Studies, General, B
Audiology/Audiologist and Speech-Language
  Pathology/Pathologist, B
Biochemistry, B
Biological and Biomedical Sciences, M
Biology/Biological Sciences, B
Business Administration and Management, B
Business Education, M
Business Teacher Education, B
Chemistry, B
Classics and Classical Languages, Litera-
  tures, and Linguistics, B
Communication Disorders, M
Communication, Journalism and Related Pro-
  grams, B
Computer Science, BM
Computer and Information Sciences, B
Counselor Education/School Counseling and Guid-
  ance Services, M
Dance, B
Dietetics/Dieticians, B
Drama and Dramatics/Theatre Arts, B
Early Childhood Education and Teaching, M
Economics, B
Education, M
Elementary Education and Teaching, M
English, M
English Education, M
English Language and Literature, B
English as a Second Language, M
Fine Arts and Art Studies, M
Foods, Nutrition, and Wellness Studies, B
French Language and Literature, B
Geography, B
Geology/Earth Science, B
Gerontological Nursing, M
Health Education, M
Health Promotion, M
Health Teacher Education, B
Health/Health Care Administration/Management, B
Hebrew Language and Literature, B
History, BM
Italian Language and Literature, B
Jewish/Judaic Studies, B
Latin American Studies, B
Latin Language and Literature, B
Linguistics, B
Mass Communication/Media Studies, B
Maternal/Child Health and Neonatal
  Nurse/Nursing, M
Mathematics, BM
Mathematics Teacher Education, M
Modern Greek Language and Literature, B
Multilingual and Multicultural Education, M
Music, B
Music Teacher Education, M
Nursing, M
Nursing - Adult, M
Nutritional Sciences, M
Pediatric Nurse/Nursing, M
Philosophy, B
Physics, B
Plant Sciences, D
Political Science and Government, B
Psychology, B
Reading Teacher Education, M
Recreation and Park Management, M
Russian Language and Literature, B
Science Teacher Education/General Science
  Teacher Education, M
Social Studies Teacher Education, M
Social Work, B
Sociology, B
Spanish Language and Literature, BM
Special Education and Teaching, M

Speech-Language Pathology/Pathologist, B

LIM COLLEGE

Business Administration, Management and Opera-
  tions, M
Business/Commerce, B
Clothing and Textiles, B
Design and Visual Communications, B
Entrepreneurship/Entrepreneurial Studies, M
Fashion Merchandising, AB
International Business/Trade/Commerce, B
Marketing, M
Marketing/Marketing Management, B
Textile Design, M

LONG ISLAND BUSINESS INSTITUTE

Accounting, A
Business Administration and Management, A
Business, Management, Marketing, and Related
  Support Services, A
Court Reporting/Court Reporter, A
Hospitality Administration/Management, A
Medical Office Management/Administration, A

LONG ISLAND UNIVERSITY–LIU BROOKLYN

Accounting, BM
Applied Behavior Analysis, O
Art Teacher Education, B
Athletic Training and Sports Medicine, BM
Audiology/Audiologist and Speech-Language
  Pathology/Pathologist, B
Biochemistry, B
Biological and Physical Sciences, B
Biology Teacher Education, B
Biology/Biological Sciences, B
Business Administration and Management, AB
Chemistry, B
Chemistry Teacher Education, B
Clinical Laboratory Science/Medical
  Technology/Technologist, B
Clinical Psychology, D
Commercial and Advertising Art, B
Communication Studies/Speech Communication
  and Rhetoric, B
Computer Science, M
Computer and Information Sciences, B
Counseling Psychology, MO
Counselor Education/School Counseling and Guid-
  ance Services, O
Dance, B
Diagnostic Medical Sonography/Sonographer and
  Ultrasound Technician, B
Early Childhood Education and Teaching, MO
Economics, B
Education, MO
Educational Leadership and Administration, O
Elementary Education and Teaching, B
English Language and Literature, B
English as a Second Language, M
English/Language Arts Teacher Education, B
Entrepreneurship/Entrepreneurial Studies, M
Exercise and Sports Science, M
Finance, B
Finance and Banking, M
Fine/Studio Arts, B
Foreign Languages and Literatures, B
Health Professions and Related Clinical Sciences, B
Health Services Administration, M
History, B
Human Resources Management and Services, M
Humanities/Humanistic Studies, AB
International Business/Trade/Commerce, M
Journalism, B
Kinesiology and Exercise Science, B
Liberal Arts and Sciences Studies and Humani-
  ties, AB
Management, M
Management Information Systems and Services, M
Marketing, B
Marriage and Family Therapy/Counseling, O
Mathematics, B
Mathematics Teacher Education, B
Multi-/Interdisciplinary Studies, B
Multilingual and Multicultural Education, O
Music Performance, B

Music Teacher Education, B
Nursing, MO
Occupational Therapy/Therapist, B
Operations Research, B
Pharmaceutical Sciences, MD
Pharmacy, BMD
Philosophy, B
Physical Education Teaching and Coaching, B
Physical Therapy/Therapist, D
Physician Assistant, B
Political Science and Government, B
Psychology, B
Public Administration, M
Public Health (MPH, DPH), B
Respiratory Care Therapy/Therapist, B
Sales, Distribution and Marketing Operations, B
Social Sciences, AB
Social Studies Teacher Education, B
Social Work, B
Sociology, B
Spanish Language Teacher Education, B
Spanish Language and Literature, B
Sport and Fitness Administration/Management, B
Taxation, M
Urban Education and Leadership, MO
Visual and Performing Arts, B

LONG ISLAND UNIVERSITY–LIU POST

Accounting, B
Allied Health and Medical Assisting Services, MO
American/United States Studies/Civilization, B
Applied Mathematics, B
Art Education, M
Art History, Criticism and Conservation, B
Art Teacher Education, B
Art Therapy/Therapist, BM
Audiology/Audiologist and Speech-Language
   Pathology/Pathologist, B
Biology Teacher Education, B
Biology/Biological Sciences, B
Biomedical Technology/Technician, B
Business Administration and Management, B
Cell/Cellular Biology and Histology, B
Chemistry, B
Chemistry Teacher Education, B
Cinematography and Film/Video Production, B
Clinical Laboratory Science/Medical
   Technology/Technologist, B
Clinical Nutrition/Nutritionist, B
Clinical Psychology, O
Commercial and Advertising Art, B
Communication Disorders, M
Composition, M
Computer Science, B
Computer and Information Sciences and Support
   Services, B
Counseling Psychology, O
Criminal Justice/Law Enforcement Administration, B
Dance, B
Drama and Dramatics/Theatre Arts, B
Early Childhood Education and Teaching, BM
Economics, B
Education, MDO
Educational Leadership and Administration, O
Educational Media/Instructional Technology, M
Elementary Education and Teaching, B
English Language and Literature, B
English/Language Arts Teacher Education, B
Fine Arts and Art Studies, BM
Foreign Language Teacher Education, B
Foreign Languages and Literatures, B
Forensic Science and Technology, B
French Language Teacher Education, B
French Language and Literature, B
Game Design and Development, M
Geography, B
Geology/Earth Science, B
Health Information/Medical Records
   Administration/Administrator, B
Health Professions and Related Clinical Sciences, B
Health Teacher Education, B
Health/Health Care Administration/Management, B
History, B
History Teacher Education, B
Humanities/Humanistic Studies, B
Information Science/Studies, BM

Information Technology, B
International/Global Studies, B
Internet and Interactive Multimedia, M
Italian Language and Literature, B
Journalism, B
Kindergarten/PreSchool Education and Teaching, B
Liberal Arts and Sciences Studies and Humani-
   ties, AB
Library Science, O
Management, MO
Management Information Systems and Services, M
Mathematics, B
Mathematics Teacher Education, B
Medical Radiologic Technology/Science - Radiation
   Therapist, B
Middle School Education, M
Music History, Literature, and Theory, M
Music Performance, B
Music Teacher Education, BM
Music Theory and Composition, M
Performance, M
Philosophy, B
Photography, B
Physical Education Teaching and Coaching, B
Physics, B
Political Science and Government, B
Psychology, B
Public Administration, BM
Public Relations/Image Management, B
Radio and Television Broadcasting
   Technology/Technician, B
Reading Teacher Education, M
Secondary Education and Teaching, O
Social Sciences, B
Social Studies Teacher Education, B
Social Work, B
Sociology, B
Spanish Language Teacher Education, B
Spanish Language and Literature, B
Special Education and Teaching, MO
Theater, M
Voice and Opera, B

MACHZIKEI HADATH RABBINICAL COLLEGE

Talmudic Studies, B
Theology and Religious Vocations, O

MANHATTAN COLLEGE

Accounting, B
BioTechnology, B
Biochemistry, B
Biology/Biological Sciences, B
Chemical Engineering, BM
Chemistry, B
Civil Engineering, BM
Classics and Classical Languages, Litera-
   tures, and Linguistics, B
Computer Engineering, BM
Computer Science, B
Counselor Education/School Counseling and Guid-
   ance Services, MO
Early Childhood Education and Teaching, M
Economics, B
Education, BMO
Educational Leadership and Administration, MO
Electrical Engineering, M
Electrical, Electronics and Communications Engi-
   neering, B
Elementary Education and Teaching, B
Engineering, B
Engineering and Applied Sciences, M
English Language and Literature, B
Environmental Engineering
   Technology/Environmental Technology, M
Environmental/Environmental Health Engineering, B
Finance, B
French Language and Literature, B
History, B
International Relations and Affairs, B
Junior High/Intermediate/Middle School Education
   and Teaching, B
Liberal Arts and Sciences Studies and Humani-
   ties, B
Management Science, B
Marketing/Marketing Management, B

Mathematics, B
Mechanical Engineering, BM
Multi-/Interdisciplinary Studies, B
Multilingual and Multicultural Education, O
Nuclear Medical Technology/Technologist, B
Nuclear and Industrial Radiologic
   Technologies/Technicians, B
Organizational Behavior Studies, B
Organizational Management, M
Peace Studies and Conflict Resolution, B
Philosophy, B
Physical Education Teaching and Coaching, B
Physics, B
Political Science and Government, B
Psychology, B
Radiologic Technology/Science - Radiographer, B
Religion/Religious Studies, B
Sociology, B
Spanish Language and Literature, B
Special Education and Teaching, BMO
Student Personnel Services, O
Teacher Education, Multiple Levels, B
Urban Studies/Affairs, B

MANHATTAN SCHOOL OF MUSIC

Composition, MD
Jazz/Jazz Studies, B
Music, BMDO
Performance, MD
Piano and Organ, B
Violin, Viola, Guitar and Other Stringed Instru-
   ments, B
Voice and Opera, B

MANHATTANVILLE COLLEGE

Accounting, BM
American/United States Studies/Civilization, B
Art Education, M
Art History, Criticism and Conservation, B
Art Teacher Education, B
Asian Studies/Civilization, B
Biochemistry, B
Biology Teacher Education, B
Biology/Biological Sciences, B
Business Administration and Management, B
Chemistry, B
Chemistry Teacher Education, B
Communication Studies/Speech Communication
   and Rhetoric, B
Communication, Journalism and Related Pro-
   grams, B
Computer Science, B
Corporate and Organizational Communication, M
Dance, B
Digital Communication and Media/Multimedia, B
Early Childhood Education and Teaching, M
Economics, B
Education, BMDO
Educational Leadership and Administration, MDO
Elementary Education and Teaching, BM
English Education, M
English Language and Literature, B
English as a Second Language, MO
English/Language Arts Teacher Education, B
Environmental Studies, B
Exercise and Sports Science, M
Finance, B
Finance and Banking, M
Fine Arts and Art Studies, B
Fine/Studio Arts, B
Foreign Language Teacher Education, M
French Language Teacher Education, B
French Language and Literature, B
History, B
Human Resources Management and Services, M
International Business/Trade/Commerce, M
International/Global Studies, B
Investment Management, M
Liberal Arts and Sciences Studies and Humani-
   ties, B
Management Strategy and Policy, M
Marketing, M
Marketing/Marketing Management, B
Mathematics, B
Mathematics Teacher Education, BM
Middle School Education, M

Music, B
Music Teacher Education, BM
Organizational Management, M
Philosophy, B
Political Science and Government, B
Psychology, B
Reading Teacher Education, M
Religion/Religious Studies, B
Science Teacher Education/General Science
  Teacher Education, M
Secondary Education and Teaching, BM
Social Sciences, B
Social Studies Teacher Education, BM
Sociology, B
Spanish Language Teacher Education, B
Spanish Language and Literature, B
Special Education and Teaching, M
Sport and Fitness Administration/Management, M
Urban Education and Leadership, M
Visual and Performing Arts, B
Writing, M

MARIA COLLEGE

Accounting, A
Business Administration and Management, A
Computer/Information Technology Services Adminis-
  tration and Management, A
Kindergarten/PreSchool Education and Teaching, A
Law and Legal Studies, A
Legal Assistant/Paralegal, A
Liberal Arts and Sciences Studies and Humani-
  ties, A
Occupational Therapist Assistant, A
Psychology, B
Science Technologies/Technicians, A

MARIST COLLEGE

Accounting, B
American/United States Studies/Civilization, B
Applied Mathematics, B
Art History, Criticism and Conservation, B
Art/Art Studies, General, B
Athletic Training and Sports Medicine, B
Biochemistry, B
Biology Teacher Education, B
Biology/Biological Sciences, B
Biomedical Sciences, B
Business Administration and Management, B
Business Administration, Management and Opera-
  tions, MO
Chemistry, B
Chemistry Teacher Education, B
Clinical Laboratory Science/Medical
  Technology/Technologist, B
Communication and Media Studies, M
Computer Science, BMO
Computer and Information Sciences, B
Corporate and Organizational Communication, M
Counseling Psychology, M
Criminal Justice/Law Enforcement Administration, B
Economics, B
Education, M
English Language and Literature, B
English/Language Arts Teacher Education, B
Fashion/Apparel Design, B
Fine/Studio Arts, B
French Language Teacher Education, B
French Language and Literature, B
History, B
Interior Design, B
Intermedia/Multimedia, B
Italian Language and Literature, B
Liberal Arts and Sciences Studies and Humani-
  ties, B
Management, O
Management Information Systems and Ser-
  vices, MO
Management of Technology, M
Marketing, M
Mathematics, B
Mathematics Teacher Education, B
Museology/Museum Studies, M
Natural Resources Management/Development and
  Policy, M
Philosophy, B
Political Science and Government, B

Psychology, BMO
Public Administration, M
Radio and Television, B
Religion/Religious Studies, B
School Psychology, MO
Social Studies Teacher Education, B
Social Work, B
Software Engineering, M
Spanish Language Teacher Education, B
Spanish Language and Literature, B

MARYMOUNT MANHATTAN COLLEGE

Acting, B
Art History, Criticism and Conservation, B
Art/Art Studies, General, B
Audiology/Audiologist and Speech-Language
  Pathology/Pathologist, B
Ballet, B
Biology/Biological Sciences, B
Biomedical Sciences, B
Business Administration and Management, B
Business/Commerce, B
Business/Managerial Economics, B
Commercial and Advertising Art, B
Communication Studies/Speech Communication
  and Rhetoric, B
Communication and Media Studies, B
Dance, B
Directing and Theatrical Production, B
Drama and Dramatics/Theatre Arts, B
English Language and Literature, B
Entrepreneurship/Entrepreneurial Studies, B
Environmental Studies, B
Fashion Merchandising, B
Film/Cinema Studies, B
Finance, B
Fine/Studio Arts, B
Graphic Design, B
History, B
Human Resources Management/Personnel Adminis-
  tration, B
Humanities/Humanistic Studies, B
International Business/Trade/Commerce, B
International Relations and Affairs, B
International/Global Studies, B
Investments and Securities, B
Journalism, B
Liberal Arts and Sciences Studies and Humani-
  ties, B
Marketing/Marketing Management, B
Photography, B
Playwriting and Screenwriting, B
Political Science and Government, B
Psychology, B
Social Sciences, A
Sociology, B
Speech-Language Pathology/Pathologist, B
Technical Theatre/Theatre Design and Technol-
  ogy, B
Theatre Literature, History and Criticism, B

MEDAILLE COLLEGE

Accounting, B
Biology/Biological Sciences, B
Business Administration and Management, AB
Business Administration, Management and Opera-
  tions, M
Clinical Psychology, D
Counseling Psychology, MD
Criminal Justice/Law Enforcement Administration, B
Criminal Justice/Safety Studies, B
Curriculum and Instruction, M
Education, M
Elementary Education and Teaching, BM
English Language and Literature, B
English/Language Arts Teacher Education, B
General Studies, AB
Health Information/Medical Records
  Administration/Administrator, B
Information Science/Studies, B
Junior High/Intermediate/Middle School Education
  and Teaching, B
Liberal Arts and Sciences Studies and Humani-
  ties, AB
Marriage and Family Therapy/Counseling, M
Mass Communication/Media Studies, B

Mathematics, B
Mathematics Teacher Education, B
Organizational Management, M
Psychology, BMD
Reading Teacher Education, M
Secondary Education and Teaching, BM
Social Science Teacher Education, B
Special Education and Teaching, BM
Sport and Fitness Administration/Management, B
Veterinary/Animal Health Technology/Technician and
  Veterinary Assistant, AB

MEDGAR EVERS COLLEGE OF THE CITY UNIVERSITY OF NEW YORK

Accounting, B
Biology/Biological Sciences, B
Business Administration and Management, A
Business/Commerce, B
Computer Programming/Programmer, A
Ecology, B
Elementary Education and Teaching, B
Information Science/Studies, B
Liberal Arts and Sciences Studies and Humani-
  ties, A
Psychology, B
Religion/Religious Studies, B
Social Work, B
Special Education and Teaching, B

MERCY COLLEGE

Accounting, BM
Accounting and Business/Management, B
Allied Health and Medical Assisting Services, MD
Audiology/Audiologist and Speech-Language
  Pathology/Pathologist, B
Biology/Biological Sciences, B
Business Administration and Management, B
Business Administration, Management and Opera-
  tions, M
Clinical Laboratory Science/Medical
  Technology/Technologist, B
Commercial and Advertising Art, B
Communication Disorders, M
Computer Science, B
Computer and Information Sciences, B
Computer and Information Systems Security, BM
Counseling Psychology, MO
Counselor Education/School Counseling and Guid-
  ance Services, O
Criminal Justice/Law Enforcement Administration, B
Early Childhood Education and Teaching, M
Education, MO
Educational Leadership and Administration, MO
Elementary Education and Teaching, M
English, M
English Language and Literature, B
English as a Second Language, MO
Entrepreneurship/Entrepreneurial Studies, B
Health Services Administration, M
Health Services/Allied Health/Health Sciences, B
History, B
Human Resources Management and Services, M
Information Science/Studies, B
International Relations and Affairs, B
Kinesiology and Exercise Science, B
Law and Legal Studies, B
Legal Assistant/Paralegal, B
Liberal Arts and Sciences Studies and Humani-
  ties, AB
Marketing/Marketing Management, B
Marriage and Family Therapy/Counseling, MO
Mass Communication/Media Studies, B
Mathematics, B
Non-Profit/Public/Organizational Management, B
Nursing, M
Nursing Administration, M
Nursing Education, M
Occupational Therapist Assistant, A
Occupational Therapy/Therapist, M
Organizational Management, M
Physical Therapy/Therapist, D
Physician Assistant, M
Political Science and Government, B
Pre-Veterinary Studies, B
Psychology, BM
Reading Teacher Education, MO

School Psychology, M
Secondary Education and Teaching, M
Social Sciences, B
Social Work, B
Sociology, B
Spanish Language and Literature, B

MESIVTA OF EASTERN PARKWAY–YESHIVA ZICHRON MEILECH

Jewish/Judaic Studies, B

MESIVTA TORAH VODAATH RABBINI-CAL SEMINARY

Talmudic Studies, B

MESIVTHA TIFERETH JERUSALEM OF AMERICA

Talmudic Studies, B

METROPOLITAN COLLEGE OF NEW YORK

Business Administration, Management and Operations, M
Business/Commerce, AB
Community Organization and Advocacy, AB
Elementary Education and Teaching, M
Emergency Management, M
Finance and Banking, M
Health Information/Medical Records Administration/Administrator, B
Health Services Administration, M
Hospital and Health Care Facilities Administration/Management, B
Media Studies, M
Public Administration, BM
Public Administration and Social Service Professions, A
Public Affairs, M
Special Education and Teaching, M
Urban Studies/Affairs, B

MILDRED ELLEY SCHOOL

Business Administration and Management, A
Computer Technology/Computer Systems Technology, A
Executive Assistant/Executive Secretary, A
Legal Assistant/Paralegal, A
Medical/Clinical Assistant, A

MILDRED ELLEY–NEW YORK CITY

Business Administration and Management, A
Legal Assistant/Paralegal, A
Medical/Clinical Assistant, A

MIRRER YESHIVA

Talmudic Studies, B

MOHAWK VALLEY COMMUNITY COLLEGE

Accounting Technology/Technician and Bookkeeping, A
Administrative Assistant and Secretarial Science, A
Advertising, A
Airframe Mechanics and Aircraft Maintenance Technology/Technician, A
Art/Art Studies, General, A
Banking and Financial Support Services, A
Business Administration and Management, A
CAD/CADD Drafting and/or Design Technology/Technician, A
Chemical Technology/Technician, A
Civil Engineering Technology/Technician, A
Commercial Photography, A
Commercial and Advertising Art, A
Communications Systems Installation and Repair Technology, A
Computer Programming/Programmer, A
Computer and Information Sciences, A
Computer and Information Sciences and Support Services, A
Computer and Information Systems Security, A
Criminal Justice/Law Enforcement Administration, A
Dietetic Technician (DTR), A

Electrical, Electronic and Communications Engineering Technology/Technician, A
Electrical/Electronics Maintenance and Repair Technology, A
Emergency Care Attendant (EMT Ambulance), A
Engineering, A
Fire Services Administration, A
General Studies, A
Heating, Air Conditioning, Ventilation and Refrigeration Maintenance Technology/Technician, A
Hotel/Motel Administration/Management, A
Human Services, A
Humanities/Humanistic Studies, A
Liberal Arts and Sciences Studies and Humanities, A
Mechanical Engineering Related Technologies/Technicians, A
Mechanical Engineering/Mechanical Technology/Technician, A
Medical Radiologic Technology/Science - Radiation Therapist, A
Medical/Clinical Assistant, A
Operations Management and Supervision, A
Parks, Recreation and Leisure Facilities Management, A
Respiratory Care Therapy/Therapist, A
Restaurant, Culinary, and Catering Management/Manager, A
Sign Language Interpretation and Translation, A
Substance Abuse/Addiction Counseling, A
Survey Technology/Surveying, A
Web Page, Digital/Multimedia and Information Resources Design, A
Welding Technology/Welder, A

MOLLOY COLLEGE

Accounting, B
Art Teacher Education, B
Biology/Biological Sciences, B
Business Administration and Management, B
Business Administration, Management and Operations, M
Cardiovascular Technology/Technologist, A
Communication Disorders, M
Communication Studies/Speech Communication and Rhetoric, B
Communication and Media Studies, B
Computer and Information Sciences, B
Criminal Justice/Safety Studies, B
Criminology, M
Drama and Dramatics/Theatre Arts, B
Ecology, B
Education, MO
Elementary Education and Teaching, B
English Language and Literature, B
Finance, B
Fine/Studio Arts, B
General Studies, B
Gerontological Nursing, MO
Health Informatics, M
Health Professions and Related Clinical Sciences, B
History, B
Information Science/Studies, B
Liberal Arts and Sciences Studies and Humanities, AB
Marketing/Marketing Management, B
Mathematics, B
Music, B
Music Teacher Education, B
Music Therapy/Therapist, BM
Nuclear Medical Technology/Technologist, AB
Nursing, MDO
Nursing - Adult, MO
Nursing - Advanced Practice, MO
Nursing Administration, M
Nursing Education, M
Pediatric Nurse/Nursing, M
Philosophy, B
Political Science and Government, B
Psychiatric/Mental Health Nurse/Nursing, M
Psychology, B
Religion/Religious Studies, B
Respiratory Care Therapy/Therapist, A
Secondary Education and Teaching, B
Social Work, B
Sociology, B

Speech-Language Pathology/Pathologist, B
Teacher Education, Multiple Levels, B

MONROE COLLEGE

Accounting, AB
Baking and Pastry Arts/Baker/Pastry Chef, A
Business Administration and Management, AB
Business Administration, Management and Operations, M
Computer Science, AB
Criminal Justice/Law Enforcement Administration, AB
Criminal Justice/Police Science, AB
Criminology, M
Culinary Arts/Chef Training, A
Health Services Administration, B
Hospitality Administration/Management, ABM
Information Science/Studies, AB
Information Technology, AB
Medical Administrative Assistant/Secretary, A
Medical/Clinical Assistant, A
Public Health, M
Public Health (MPH, DPH), B

MONROE COMMUNITY COLLEGE

Accounting, A
Administrative Assistant and Secretarial Science, A
Art/Art Studies, General, A
Automobile/Automotive Mechanics Technology/Technician, A
Behavioral Sciences, A
Biological and Physical Sciences, A
Biology Technician/BioTechnology Laboratory Technician, A
Biology/Biological Sciences, A
Business Administration and Management, A
Chemical Engineering, A
Chemistry, A
Civil Engineering Technology/Technician, A
Commercial and Advertising Art, A
Computer Engineering, A
Computer Engineering Technology/Technician, A
Computer Science, A
Computer and Information Sciences, A
Computer and Information Sciences and Support Services, A
Construction Engineering Technology/Technician, A
Consumer Merchandising/Retailing Management, A
Corrections, A
Criminal Justice/Law Enforcement Administration, A
Criminal Justice/Police Science, A
Data Processing and Data Processing Technology/Technician, A
Dental Hygiene/Hygienist, A
Electrical, Electronic and Communications Engineering Technology/Technician, A
Engineering Science, A
Environmental Studies, A
Family and Consumer Sciences/Human Sciences, A
Fashion Merchandising, A
Fashion/Apparel Design, A
Fire Science/Firefighting, A
Food Technology and Processing, A
Forestry, A
Graphic and Printing Equipment Operator Production, A
Health Information/Medical Records Administration/Administrator, A
Heating, Air Conditioning, Ventilation and Refrigeration Maintenance Technology/Technician, A
History, A
Hotel/Motel Administration/Management, A
Human Services, A
Industrial Radiologic Technology/Technician, A
Industrial Technology/Technician, A
Information Science/Studies, A
Information Technology, A
Instrumentation Technology/Technician, A
Interior Design, A
International Business/Trade/Commerce, A
Landscape Architecture, A
Laser and Optical Technology/Technician, A
Legal Administrative Assistant/Secretary, A
Liberal Arts and Sciences Studies and Humanities, A
Marketing/Marketing Management, A

Mass Communication/Media Studies, A
Mathematics, A
Mechanical Engineering/Mechanical
  Technology/Technician, A
Music, A
Parks, Recreation, Leisure and Fitness Studies, A
Physical Education Teaching and Coaching, A
Physics, A
Political Science and Government, A
Pre-Pharmacy Studies, A
Quality Control Technology/Technician, A
Social Sciences, A
Special Products Marketing Operations, A
Telecommunications Technology/Technician, A
Tourism and Travel Services Management, A

MORRISVILLE STATE COLLEGE

Accounting, A
Accounting Technology/Technician and Bookkeep-
  ing, A
Administrative Assistant and Secretarial Science, A
Agribusiness, B
Agricultural Business and Management, A
Agricultural Mechanics and Equipment/Machine
  Technology, A
Agricultural/Biological Engineering and Bioengineer-
  ing, A
Agriculture, A
Animal Sciences, B
Applied Horticulture/Horticultural Business Ser-
  vices, AB
Aquaculture, A
Architectural Drafting and Architectural
  CAD/CADD, A
Architectural Engineering Technology/Technician, A
Architecture, A
Autobody/Collision and Repair
  Technology/Technician, A
Automobile/Automotive Mechanics
  Technology/Technician, AB
Broadcast Journalism, B
Business Administration and Management, AB
Business Administration, Management and Opera-
  tions, B
Business, Management, Marketing, and Related
  Support Services, B
CAD/CADD Drafting and/or Design
  Technology/Technician, A
Child Care and Support Services Management, A
Community Organization and Advocacy, A
Computer Engineering Technology/Technician, A
Computer Programming/Programmer, AB
Computer Science, A
Computer Software and Media Applications, B
Computer Systems Networking and Telecommunica-
  tions, A
Computer Technology/Computer Systems Technol-
  ogy, A
Computer and Information Sciences, AB
Computer and Information Sciences and Support
  Services, B
Construction Trades, A
Corrections and Criminal Justice, AB
Criminal Justice/Law Enforcement Administration, A
Criminal Justice/Safety Studies, A
Culinary Arts and Related Services, A
Dairy Husbandry and Production, AB
Dairy Science, B
Diesel Mechanics Technology/Technician, A
Dietetic Technician (DTR), A
Drafting and Design Technology/Technician, A
Drafting/Design Engineering
  Technologies/Technicians, A
Early Childhood Education and Teaching, A
Education, A
Electrical, Electronic and Communications Engineer-
  ing Technology/Technician, A
Elementary Education and Teaching, A
Engineering, A
Engineering Technologies/Technicians, A
Entrepreneurship/Entrepreneurial Studies, B
Equestrian/Equine Studies, A
Foods, Nutrition, and Wellness Studies, AB
Foodservice Systems
  Administration/Management, A
General Office Occupations and Clerical Services, A

General Studies, A
Health Professions and Related Clinical Sci-
  ences, AB
Horse Husbandry/Equine Science and Manage-
  ment, B
Horticultural Science, AB
Hospitality Administration/Management, AB
Human Services, A
Information Science/Studies, A
Information Technology, B
Journalism, A
Kinesiology and Exercise Science, B
Landscape Architecture, A
Liberal Arts and Sciences Studies and Humani-
  ties, A
Management Information Systems and Services, B
Massage Therapy/Therapeutic Massage, A
Mechanical Engineering/Mechanical
  Technology/Technician, A
Medical Administrative Assistant/Secretary, A
Multi-/Interdisciplinary Studies, B
Natural Resources Management/Development and
  Policy, AB
Natural Resources and Conservation, AB
Office Management and Supervision, AB
Ornamental Horticulture, B
Physical Sciences, B
Psychology, A
Public Relations, Advertising, and Applied Commu-
  nication, B
Resort Management, B
Restaurant, Culinary, and Catering
  Management/Manager, A
Restaurant/Food Services Management, AB
Science, Technology and Society, B
Sport and Fitness Administration/Management, A
System, Networking, and LAN/WAN
  Management/Manager, A
Tourism and Travel Services Management, A
Tourism and Travel Services Marketing Opera-
  tions, A
Web Page, Digital/Multimedia and Information Re-
  sources Design, B
Web/Multimedia Management and Webmaster, B
Wood Science and Wood Products/Pulp and Paper
  Technology, A

MOUNT SAINT MARY COLLEGE

Accounting, B
Biology/Biological Sciences, B
Business Administration and Management, B
Business Administration, Management and Opera-
  tions, M
Chemistry, B
Early Childhood Education and Teaching, BM
Education, MO
Elementary Education and Teaching, M
English Language and Literature, B
Finance and Banking, M
History, B
Human Services, B
Information Technology, B
Mass Communication/Media Studies, B
Mathematics, B
Middle School Education, M
Natural Sciences, B
Nursing, MO
Nursing - Adult, MO
Nursing - Advanced Practice, O
Nursing Administration, M
Nursing Education, M
Physical Therapy/Therapist, B
Political Science and Government, B
Psychology, B
Public Relations/Image Management, B
Reading Teacher Education, MO
Secondary Education and Teaching, BM
Social Sciences, B
Social Work, B
Sociology, B
Spanish Language and Literature, B
Special Education and Teaching, M

Teacher Education, Multiple Levels, B

NASSAU COMMUNITY COLLEGE

Accounting, A
Accounting Technology/Technician and Bookkeep-
  ing, A
Administrative Assistant and Secretarial Science, A
African-American/Black Studies, A
Art/Art Studies, General, A
Business Administration and Management, A
Civil Engineering Technology/Technician, A
Clinical/Medical Laboratory Technician, A
Commercial and Advertising Art, A
Communication Studies/Speech Communication
  and Rhetoric, A
Computer Graphics, A
Computer Science, A
Computer Systems Networking and Telecommunica-
  tions, A
Computer and Information Sciences, A
Criminal Justice/Law Enforcement Administration, A
Criminal Justice/Safety Studies, A
Dance, A
Data Processing and Data Processing
  Technology/Technician, A
Design and Visual Communications, A
Drama and Dramatics/Theatre Arts, A
Engineering, A
Entrepreneurship/Entrepreneurial Studies, A
Fashion Merchandising, A
Fashion/Apparel Design, A
Funeral Service and Mortuary Science, A
General Studies, A
Hotel/Motel Administration/Management, A
Instrumentation Technology/Technician, A
Insurance, A
Interior Design, A
Kindergarten/PreSchool Education and Teaching, A
Legal Administrative Assistant/Secretary, A
Legal Assistant/Paralegal, A
Liberal Arts and Sciences Studies and Humani-
  ties, A
Management Information Systems and Services, A
Marketing/Marketing Management, A
Mass Communication/Media Studies, A
Mathematics, A
Medical Administrative Assistant/Secretary, A
Medical Radiologic Technology/Science - Radiation
  Therapist, A
Music Performance, A
Photography, A
Physical Therapist Assistant, A
Real Estate, A
Rehabilitation and Therapeutic Professions, A
Respiratory Care Therapy/Therapist, A
Retailing and Retail Operations, A
Surgical Technology/Technologist, A
Technical Theatre/Theatre Design and Technol-
  ogy, A
Transportation and Materials Moving, A
Visual and Performing Arts, A

NAZARETH COLLEGE OF ROCHESTER

Accounting, B
Acting, B
American/United States Studies/Civilization, B
Anthropology, B
Art Education, M
Art History, Criticism and Conservation, B
Art Teacher Education, B
Art Therapy/Therapist, BM
Art/Art Studies, General, B
Asian Studies/Civilization, B
Audiology/Audiologist and Speech-Language
  Pathology/Pathologist, B
Biochemistry, B
Biology Teacher Education, B
Biology/Biological Sciences, B
Business Administration and Management, B
Business Education, M
Business Teacher Education, B
Chemistry, B
Chemistry Teacher Education, B
Chinese Language and Literature, B
Clinical Laboratory Science/Medical
  Technology/Technologist, B

Communication Disorders, M
Communication Studies/Speech Communication
 and Rhetoric, B
Community Organization and Advocacy, B
Dance, B
Design and Visual Communications, B
Drama and Dramatics/Theatre Arts, B
Early Childhood Education and Teaching, M
Economics, B
Education, BM
Educational Media/Instructional Technology, M
Elementary Education and Teaching, BM
English Language and Literature, B
English as a Second Language, M
English/Language Arts Teacher Education, B
Environmental Sciences, B
Finance, B
Fine/Studio Arts, B
Foreign Language Teacher Education, B
French Language and Literature, B
German Language and Literature, B
Gerontological Nursing, M
History, B
History Teacher Education, B
Human Resources Management and Services, M
Human Resources Management/Personnel Adminis-
 tration, B
International Business/Trade/Commerce, B
International Relations and Affairs, B
Italian Language and Literature, B
Law and Legal Studies, B
Liberal Studies, M
Management, M
Marketing/Marketing Management, B
Mathematics, B
Mathematics Teacher Education, B
Middle School Education, M
Modern Languages, B
Music, B
Music History, Literature, and Theory, B
Music Performance, B
Music Teacher Education, BM
Music Therapy/Therapist, BM
Nursing, M
Occupational Therapy/Therapist, B
Peace Studies and Conflict Resolution, B
Philosophy, B
Physical Therapy/Therapist, BMD
Political Science and Government, B
Pre-Dentistry Studies, B
Pre-Law Studies, B
Pre-Medicine/Pre-Medical Studies, B
Pre-Veterinary Studies, B
Psychology, B
Reading Teacher Education, M
Religion/Religious Studies, B
Secondary Education and Teaching, B
Social Sciences, B
Social Studies Teacher Education, B
Social Work, BM
Sociology, B
Spanish Language and Literature, B
Special Education and Teaching, B
Speech-Language Pathology/Pathologist, B
Technical Theatre/Theatre Design and Technol-
 ogy, B
Toxicology, B
Women's Studies, B

THE NEW SCHOOL COLLEGE OF PER-FORMING ARTS

Conducting, B
Drama and Dramatics/Theatre Arts, B
Jazz/Jazz Studies, B
Music Performance, B
Music Theory and Composition, B
Piano and Organ, B
Violin, Viola, Guitar and Other Stringed Instru-
 ments, B
Voice and Opera, B

THE NEW SCHOOL FOR PUBLIC ENGAGEMENT

Environmental Studies, B
Foods, Nutrition, and Wellness Studies, B
International/Global Studies, B

Liberal Arts and Sciences Studies and Humani-
 ties, B
Mass Communication/Media Studies, B
Psychology, B
Urban Studies/Affairs, B

NEW YORK CAREER INSTITUTE

Court Reporting/Court Reporter, A
Legal Assistant/Paralegal, A
Medical Office Assistant/Specialist, A

NEW YORK CITY COLLEGE OF TECHNOLOGY OF THE CITY UNIVERSITY OF NEW YORK

Accounting Technology/Technician and Bookkeep-
 ing, A
Applied Mathematics, B
Architectural Drafting and Architectural
 CAD/CADD, A
Architectural Technology/Technician, B
Bioinformatics, B
Chemical Technology/Technician, A
Civil Engineering Technology/Technician, A
Commercial and Advertising Art, AB
Computer Engineering Technology/Technician, B
Computer Science, A
Computer and Information Sciences, A
Construction Engineering Technology/Technician, A
Dental Hygiene/Hygienist, A
Dental Laboratory Technology/Technician, A
Design and Visual Communications, B
Electrical, Electronic and Communications Engineer-
 ing Technology/Technician, AB
Electromechanical Technology/Electromechanical
 Engineering Technology, A
Environmental Engineering
 Technology/Environmental Technology, A
Facilities Planning and Management, B
Fashion Merchandising, A
Hospital and Health Care Facilities
 Administration/Management, B
Hospitality Administration/Management, AB
Human Services, AB
Information Science/Studies, B
Legal Assistant/Paralegal, AB
Liberal Arts and Sciences Studies and Humani-
 ties, A
Marketing/Marketing Management, A
Mathematics Teacher Education, B
Mechanical Drafting and Mechanical Drafting
 CAD/CADD, A
Mechanical Engineering/Mechanical
 Technology/Technician, AB
Medical Radiologic Technology/Science - Radiation
 Therapist, AB
Opticianry/Ophthalmic Dispensing Optician, A
Physical Sciences, A
Technical Theatre/Theatre Design and Technol-
 ogy, B
Technology Teacher Education/Industrial Arts
 Teacher Education, B
Telecommunications Technology/Technician, AB
Web Page, Digital/Multimedia and Information Re-
 sources Design, B

NEW YORK COLLEGE OF HEALTH PROFESSIONS

Acupuncture and Oriental Medicine, M
Health Services/Allied Health/Health Sciences, AB
Massage Therapy/Therapeutic Massage, AB

NEW YORK INSTITUTE OF TECHNOLOGY

Accounting, BM
Advertising, B
Architectural Technology/Technician, AB
Architecture, BM
BioTechnology, B
Biological and Biomedical Sciences, B
Biology/Biological Sciences, B
Business Administration and Management, AB
Business Administration, Management and Opera-
 tions, M
Chemistry, B
Commercial and Advertising Art, B

Communication and Media Studies, M
Computer Art and Design, M
Computer Engineering, M
Computer Science, M
Computer and Information Sciences, B
Computer and Information Systems Security, M
Corrections and Criminal Justice, B
Counselor Education/School Counseling and Guid-
 ance Services, M
Criminal Justice/Law Enforcement Administration, B
Design and Applied Arts, B
Digital Communication and Media/Multimedia, B
Distance Education Development, O
Early Childhood Education and Teaching, M
Education, MO
Educational Leadership and Administration, O
Educational Media/Instructional Technology, MO
Electrical Engineering, M
Electrical, Electronics and Communications Engi-
 neering, B
Energy Management and Policy, MO
Energy and Power Engineering, O
Engineering Technologies/Technicians, B
Engineering Technology, B
Engineering and Applied Sciences, MO
Engineering/Industrial Management, B
English Language and Literature, B
Entrepreneurial and Small Business Operations, B
Environmental Engineering
 Technology/Environmental Technology, M
Environmental Policy and Resource Manage-
 ment, O
Finance, B
Finance and Banking, M
Fine Arts and Art Studies, M
Graphic Design, M
Health Professions and Related Clinical Sciences, B
Human Resources Management and Services, MO
Human Resources Management/Personnel Adminis-
 tration, B
Industrial and Labor Relations, MO
Information Technology, B
Interior Design, B
International Business/Trade/Commerce, B
Marketing, M
Marketing/Marketing Management, B
Mathematics Teacher Education, MO
Mechanical Engineering, B
Middle School Education, MO
Multi-/Interdisciplinary Studies, B
Nutritional Sciences, MO
Occupational Therapy/Therapist, M
Osteopathic Medicine, MD
Physical Therapy/Therapist, D
Physician Assistant, M
Political Science and Government, B
Psychology, B
Radio and Television Broadcasting
 Technology/Technician, B
Science Teacher Education/General Science
 Teacher Education, MO
Secondary Education and Teaching, MO
Sociology, B
Substance Abuse/Addiction Counseling, O
Urban Design, M
Urban Studies/Affairs, B

NEW YORK SCHOOL OF INTERIOR DESIGN

Interior Design, ABM
Lighting Design, M
Sustainable Development, M

NEW YORK UNIVERSITY

Accounting, BMD
Actuarial Science, B
Acute Care/Critical Care Nursing, MDO
Advertising and Public Relations, M
African Studies, MD
African-American/Black Studies, B
Allopathic Medicine, MD
American/United States Studies/Civilization, MD
Anthropology, BMD
Applied Economics, O
Applied Physics, MD
Applied Psychology, MDO

Applied Social Research, M
Applied Statistics, M
Archeology, BMD
Architectural History and Criticism, M
Archives/Archival Administration, MO
Area Studies, B
Art Education, M
Art History, Criticism and Conservation, BMD
Art Therapy/Therapist, M
Arts Management, M
Audiology/Audiologist and Speech-Language
 Pathology/Pathologist, B
BioTechnology, M
Biochemistry, B
Bioethics/Medical Ethics, M
Bioinformatics, MD
Biological and Biomedical Sciences, MD
Biology/Biological Sciences, B
Biomedical Engineering, MD
Biomedical/Medical Engineering, B
Business Administration, Management and Opera-
 tions, O
Business Education, MO
Business, Management, Marketing, and Related
 Support Services, B
Business/Commerce, AB
Business/Managerial Economics, B
Cancer Biology/Oncology, D
Cell Biology and Anatomy, D
Chemical Engineering, BMD
Chemistry, BMD
Chemistry Teacher Education, B
Chinese Studies, M
Cinematography and Film/Video Production, B
Civil Engineering, BMD
Classics and Classical Languages, Litera-
 tures, and Linguistics, BMDO
Clinical Research, M
Cognitive Sciences, D
Communication Disorders, MD
Communication Studies/Speech Communication
 and Rhetoric, B
Communication and Media Studies, BMD
Community Health and Preventive Medicine, MD
Community Organization and Advocacy, B
Community Psychology, D
Comparative Literature, BMD
Composition, MDO
Computational Biology, D
Computer Art and Design, M
Computer Engineering, BMO
Computer Science, MD
Computer and Information Sciences, B
Computer and Information Sciences and Support
 Services, A
Computer and Information Systems Security, O
Conflict Resolution and Mediation/Peace Stud-
 ies, MO
Construction Engineering, B
Construction Management, MO
Corporate and Organizational Communication, M
Counseling Psychology, MD
Counselor Education/School Counseling and Guid-
 ance Services, MDO
Cultural Studies, MDO
Dance, BMDO
Database Systems, M
Dental Hygiene/Hygienist, AB
Dental and Oral Surgery, O
Dentistry, D
Design and Applied Arts, M
Developmental Biology and Embryology, D
Developmental Psychology, MD
Digital Communication and Media/Multimedia, B
Drama Therapy, M
Drama and Dramatics/Theatre Arts, B
Early Childhood Education and Teaching, BM
East Asian Studies, BMD
Ecology, B
Economics, BMDO
Education, MDO
Educational Administration and Supervision, D
Educational Leadership and Administration, MDO
Educational Media/Instructional Technology, MDO
Educational Policy, M
Educational Psychology, MD

Electrical Engineering, MD
Electrical, Electronics and Communications Engi-
 neering, B
Electronic Commerce, O
Elementary Education and Teaching, BM
Energy Management and Policy, O
Engineering, B
Engineering Physics, B
Engineering and Applied Sciences, MDO
English, MD
English Education, MDO
English Language and Literature, B
English as a Second Language, MD
Entrepreneurship/Entrepreneurial Studies, MO
Environmental Education, M
Environmental Engineering
 Technology/Environmental Technology, M
Environmental Policy, M
Environmental Sciences, M
Environmental Studies, B
Environmental and Occupational Health, MD
Epidemiology, D
Ergonomics and Human Factors, D
Ethnic, Cultural Minority, and Gender Studies, B
Ethnomusicology, MD
European Studies/Civilization, B
Film, Television, and Video Production, M
Film/Cinema Studies, B
Finance, B
Finance and Banking, MDO
Financial Engineering, MO
Fine Arts and Art Studies, BMDO
Fine/Studio Arts, B
Food Engineering, D
Food Science and Technology, M
Food Services Management, MD
Foods, Nutrition, and Wellness Studies, B
Foreign Language Teacher Education, BM
Foreign Languages and Literatures, B
Foreign Languages, Literatures, and Linguistics, B
Foundations and Philosophy of Education, MD
French Language Teacher Education, B
French Language and Literature, BMDO
Game Design and Development, M
Genetics, M
Genomic Sciences, D
German Language and Literature, BMD
Gerontological Nursing, DO
Gerontology, D
Graphic Design, M
Health Professions and Related Clinical Sciences, A
Health Promotion, M
Health Services Administration, MDO
Hebrew Language and Literature, B
Higher Education/Higher Education Administra-
 tion, MD
History, BMDO
Hospitality Administration/Management, MO
Hotel/Motel Administration/Management, B
Human Development, MDO
Human Resources Development, MO
Human Resources Management and Services, MO
Humanities/Humanistic Studies, BMO
Immunology, D
Industrial and Organizational Psychology, M
Industrial/Management Engineering, M
Interdisciplinary Studies, M
International Affairs, MO
International Business/Trade/Commerce, BM
International Development, M
International Public Health/International Health, M
International Relations and Affairs, B
International and Comparative Education, MDO
International/Global Studies, B
Internet and Interactive Multimedia, MO
Investment Management, M
Italian Language and Literature, BMD
Japanese Studies, M
Jewish/Judaic Studies, MD
Journalism, BMO
Kinesiology and Movement Studies, M
Labor and Industrial Relations, B
Latin American Studies, BM
Latin Language and Literature, B
Law and Legal Studies, MDO
Legal and Justice Studies, MD

Liberal Arts and Sciences Studies and Humani-
 ties, AB
Linguistics, BMD
Management, M
Management Information Systems and Ser-
 vices, MDO
Management Strategy and Policy, MD
Management of Technology, MDO
Manufacturing Engineering, M
Marketing, M
Marketing/Marketing Management, B
Mathematical and Computational Finance, M
Mathematics, BMD
Mathematics Teacher Education, BM
Mathematics and Statistics, B
Mechanical Engineering, BMD
Media Studies, MD
Medical Imaging, D
Medieval and Renaissance Studies, B
Microbiology, D
Middle School Education, M
Molecular Biology, D
Molecular Biophysics, D
Molecular Genetics, D
Molecular Pharmacology, D
Molecular Toxicology, D
Multilingual and Multicultural Education, MDO
Museology/Museum Studies, MO
Music, BMDO
Music Performance, B
Music Teacher Education, BMDO
Music Theory and Composition, MDO
Music Therapy/Therapist, M
National Security, M
Near and Middle Eastern Studies, BMD
Neurobiology and Neurophysiology, D
Neuroscience, D
Non-Profit/Public/Organizational Management, MO
Nurse Midwife/Nursing Midwifery, MDO
Nursing, MD
Nursing - Adult, MDO
Nursing - Advanced Practice, MDO
Nursing Education, MO
Nursing Informatics, MO
Nutritional Sciences, BMD
Occupational Therapy/Therapist, MD
Operations Research, B
Oral Biology, M
Oral and Dental Sciences, MO
Organizational Behavior Studies, MDO
Organizational Management, MD
Orthodontics, O
Parks, Recreation and Leisure Facilities Manage-
 ment, B
Pathobiology, D
Pediatric Nurse/Nursing, MDO
Pedodontics, O
Performance, MDO
Periodontics, O
Philosophy, BMD
Photography, B
Physical Therapy/Therapist, MDO
Physics, BMD
Physiology, D
Piano and Organ, B
Plant Biology, D
Political Science and Government, BMD
Population Studies, D
Portuguese Language and Literature, MD
Project Management, M
Psychiatric/Mental Health Nurse/Nursing, MDO
Psychoanalysis and Psychotherapy, O
Psychology, BMDO
Public Administration, BMDO
Public Administration and Social Service Profes-
 sions, B
Public Health, MD
Public Health (MPH, DPH), B
Public History, O
Public Policy Analysis, M
Publishing, M
Radio and Television Broadcasting
 Technology/Technician, B
Reading Teacher Education, M
Real Estate, BMO
Rehabilitation Sciences, D

Religion/Religious Studies, BMO
Romance Languages, Literatures, and Linguistics, M
Russian Language and Literature, BM
Sales, Distribution and Marketing Operations, B
Science Teacher Education/General Science
    Teacher Education, BM
Secondary Education and Teaching, M
Slavic Languages, Literatures, and Linguistics, M
Social Psychology, D
Social Sciences, BM
Social Studies Teacher Education, BMO
Social Work, BMD
Sociology, BMD
Software Engineering, O
Spanish Language Teacher Education, B
Spanish Language and Literature, BMD
Spanish and Iberian Studies, B
Special Education and Teaching, BM
Speech and Rhetorical Studies, MD
Sport and Fitness Administration/Management, MO
Statistics, MD
Structural Biology, D
Student Personnel Services, M
Sustainable Development, M
System Management, M
Systems Engineering, M
Taxation, MO
Telecommunications Management, O
Theater, MD
Toxicology, MD
Translation and Interpretation, M
Transportation and Highway Engineering, MD
Transportation/Transportation Management, M
Travel and Tourism, MO
Urban Planning, M
Urban Studies/Affairs, BM
Urban and Regional Planning, M
Visual and Performing Arts, B
Western European Studies, M
Writing, M

NIAGARA COUNTY COMMUNITY COLLEGE

Accounting, A
Administrative Assistant and Secretarial Science, A
Animal Sciences, A
Baking and Pastry Arts/Baker/Pastry Chef, A
Biological and Physical Sciences, A
Business Administration and Management, A
Business, Management, Marketing, and Related
    Support Services, A
Chemical Technology/Technician, A
Computer Science, A
Consumer Merchandising/Retailing Management, A
Criminal Justice/Law Enforcement Administration, A
Culinary Arts/Chef Training, A
Design and Applied Arts, A
Drafting and Design Technology/Technician, A
Drafting/Design Engineering
    Technologies/Technicians, A
Drama and Dramatics/Theatre Arts, A
Elementary Education and Teaching, A
Fine/Studio Arts, A
General Studies, A
Hospitality Administration/Management, A
Human Services, A
Humanities/Humanistic Studies, A
Information Science/Studies, A
Liberal Arts and Sciences Studies and Humanities, A
Mass Communication/Media Studies, A
Massage Therapy/Therapeutic Massage, A
Mathematics, A
Medical Radiologic Technology/Science - Radiation
    Therapist, A
Medical/Clinical Assistant, A
Music, A
Natural Resources and Conservation, A
Occupational Health and Industrial Hygiene, A
Parks, Recreation, Leisure and Fitness Studies, A
Physical Education Teaching and Coaching, A
Physical Therapist Assistant, A
Social Sciences, A
Sport and Fitness Administration/Management, A
Surgical Technology/Technologist, A

Tourism and Travel Services Management, A
Web Page, Digital/Multimedia and Information Resources Design, A

NIAGARA UNIVERSITY

Accounting, BM
Actuarial Science, B
Biochemistry, B
Biology Teacher Education, B
Biology Technician/BioTechnology Laboratory Technician, B
Biology/Biological Sciences, B
Business Administration and Management, AB
Business Administration, Management and Operations, M
Business Teacher Education, B
Business/Commerce, B
Business/Managerial Economics, B
Chemistry, B
Chemistry Teacher Education, B
Computer Science, B
Counselor Education/School Counseling and Guidance Services, MO
Criminal Justice/Law Enforcement Administration, B
Criminology, BM
Drama and Dramatics/Theatre Arts, B
Early Childhood Education and Teaching, MO
Economics, B
Education, BMDO
Educational Administration and Supervision, M
Educational Leadership and Administration, MDO
Educational Policy, D
Elementary Education and Teaching, BMO
English Language and Literature, B
English as a Second Language, MO
Finance and Banking, M
Foundations and Philosophy of Education, M
French Language Teacher Education, B
French Language and Literature, B
Health Services Administration, M
History, B
Hospitality Administration/Management, B
Hotel/Motel Administration/Management, B
Human Resources Management and Services, BM
Human Resources Management/Personnel Administration, B
Information Science/Studies, B
Interdisciplinary Studies, M
International Business/Trade/Commerce, BM
International Relations and Affairs, B
Liberal Arts and Sciences Studies and Humanities, AB
Logistics and Materials Management, B
Management Strategy and Policy, M
Marketing, BM
Marketing/Marketing Management, B
Mass Communication/Media Studies, B
Mathematics, B
Mathematics Teacher Education, BM
Middle School Education, MO
Philosophy, B
Political Science and Government, B
Pre-Dentistry Studies, B
Pre-Law Studies, B
Pre-Medicine/Pre-Medical Studies, B
Pre-Veterinary Studies, B
Psychology, B
Reading Teacher Education, M
Religion/Religious Studies, B
Restaurant/Food Services Management, B
School Psychology, MO
Science Teacher Education/General Science
    Teacher Education, BM
Secondary Education and Teaching, BMO
Social Sciences, B
Social Studies Teacher Education, B
Social Work, B
Sociology, B
Spanish Language Teacher Education, B
Spanish Language and Literature, B
Special Education and Teaching, BMO
Sport and Fitness Administration/Management, B
Teaching English as a Second or Foreign
    Language/ESL Language Instructor, B
Tourism and Travel Services Management, B
Transportation and Materials Moving, B

Vocational and Technical Education, M

NORTH COUNTRY COMMUNITY COLLEGE

Biological and Physical Sciences, A
Business Administration and Management, A
Computer Graphics, A
Consumer Merchandising/Retailing Management, A
Criminal Justice/Safety Studies, A
General Office Occupations and Clerical Services, A
Kinesiology and Exercise Science, A
Liberal Arts and Sciences Studies and Humanities, A
Mathematics, A
Medical Radiologic Technology/Science - Radiation
    Therapist, A
Mental Health Counseling/Counselor, A
Parks, Recreation and Leisure Facilities Management, A

NYACK COLLEGE

Accounting, B
Bible/Biblical Studies, AB
Biology/Biological Sciences, B
Business Administration and Management, AB
Business Administration, Management and Operations, M
Computer Science, B
Counseling Psychology, M
Counselor Education/School Counseling and Guidance Services, M
Criminal Justice/Safety Studies, B
Early Childhood Education and Teaching, B
Elementary Education and Teaching, BM
English Language and Literature, B
English as a Second Language, M
English/Language Arts Teacher Education, B
History, B
Intercultural/Multicultural and Diversity Studies, AB
Liberal Arts and Sciences Studies and Humanities, A
Marriage and Family Therapy/Counseling, M
Mathematics, B
Mathematics Teacher Education, B
Missions/Missionary Studies and Missiology, MD
Music, AB
Music Performance, B
Music Teacher Education, B
Music Theory and Composition, B
Organizational Behavior Studies, B
Organizational Management, M
Pastoral Studies/Counseling, MD
Philosophy, B
Piano and Organ, B
Pre-Theology/Pre-Ministerial Studies, B
Psychology, B
Religion/Religious Studies, BM
Religious/Sacred Music, B
Social Studies Teacher Education, B
Social Work, B
Sociology, B
Special Education and Teaching, M
Teacher Education, Multiple Levels, B
Teaching English as a Second or Foreign
    Language/ESL Language Instructor, B
Theology and Religious Vocations, MD
Voice and Opera, B
Youth Ministry, B

OHR HAMEIR THEOLOGICAL SEMINARY

Theology/Theological Studies, B

OHR SOMAYACH/JOSEPH TANENBAUM EDUCATIONAL CENTER

Rabbinical Studies, B

ONONDAGA COMMUNITY COLLEGE

Accounting, A
Accounting Technology/Technician and Bookkeeping, A
Architectural Engineering Technology/Technician, A
Architectural Technology/Technician, A
Art/Art Studies, General, A

Automobile/Automotive Mechanics Technology/Technician, A
Business Administration and Management, A
Business/Commerce, A
Communication Studies/Speech Communication and Rhetoric, A
Computer Engineering Technology/Technician, A
Computer Science, A
Computer Systems Networking and Telecommunications, A
Construction Engineering Technology/Technician, A
Criminal Justice/Law Enforcement Administration, A
Criminal Justice/Police Science, A
Design and Applied Arts, A
Electrical and Electronic Engineering Technologies/Technicians, A
Electrical, Electronic and Communications Engineering Technology/Technician, A
Engineering Science, A
Environmental Engineering Technology/Environmental Technology, A
Fire Protection and Safety Technology/Technician, A
General Studies, A
Health Information/Medical Records Technology/Technician, A
Health Professions and Related Clinical Sciences, A
Hospitality Administration/Management, A
Humanities/Humanistic Studies, A
Interior Design, A
Liberal Arts and Sciences Studies and Humanities, A
Mechanical Engineering/Mechanical Technology/Technician, A
Music, A
Parks, Recreation, Leisure and Fitness Studies, A
Physical Therapist Assistant, A
Public Administration and Social Service Professions, A
Radio and Television, A
Security and Protective Services, A
Teacher Education, Multiple Levels, A

ORANGE COUNTY COMMUNITY COLLEGE

Accounting Technology/Technician and Bookkeeping, A
Administrative Assistant and Secretarial Science, A
Architectural Engineering, A
Business Administration and Management, A
Child Care and Support Services Management, A
Clinical/Medical Laboratory Technician, A
Community Organization and Advocacy, A
Computer and Information Sciences, A
Criminal Justice/Law Enforcement Administration, A
Criminal Justice/Police Science, A
Dental Hygiene/Hygienist, A
Engineering, A
General Merchandising, Sales, and Related Marketing Operations, A
Graphic and Printing Equipment Operator Production, A
Humanities/Humanistic Studies, A
Information Science/Studies, A
Liberal Arts and Sciences Studies and Humanities, A
Management Information Systems and Services, A
Medical Office Management/Administration, A
Medical Radiologic Technology/Science - Radiation Therapist, A
Music Performance, A
Occupational Therapist Assistant, A
Physical Therapist Assistant, A
Rehabilitation and Therapeutic Professions, A

PACE UNIVERSITY

Accounting, BM
Acting, B
Advertising, B
American/United States Studies/Civilization, B
Art History, Criticism and Conservation, B
Asian Studies/Civilization, B
Biochemistry, B
Biology Teacher Education, B
Biology/Biological Sciences, B
Business Administration and Management, B

Business Administration, Management and Operations, MDO
Business/Commerce, B
Business/Managerial Economics, B
Chemical Engineering, B
Chemistry, B
Chemistry Teacher Education, B
Clinical Psychology, MD
Communication Disorders, B
Communication and Media Studies, B
Computer Science, BMDO
Computer Software and Media Applications, A
Computer Systems Networking and Telecommunications, A
Computer and Information Sciences, B
Computer and Information Sciences and Support Services, A
Computer and Information Systems Security, O
Counseling Psychology, MD
Criminal Justice/Law Enforcement Administration, B
Dance, B
Directing and Theatrical Production, B
Early Childhood Education and Teaching, M
Economics, B
Education, MO
Education/Teaching of Individuals with Speech or Language Impairments, B
Educational Administration and Supervision, O
Educational Leadership and Administration, M
Educational Media/Instructional Technology, MO
Elementary Education and Teaching, BM
English Language and Literature, B
English/Language Arts Teacher Education, B
Entrepreneurship/Entrepreneurial Studies, BM
Environmental Law, MD
Environmental Policy and Resource Management, M
Environmental Sciences, BM
Environmental Studies, B
Film/Cinema Studies, B
Finance, B
Finance and Banking, M
Fine/Studio Arts, B
Foreign Languages and Literatures, B
Forensic Science and Technology, BM
General Studies, A
Health Services Administration, M
Health Services/Allied Health/Health Sciences, B
History, B
Homeland Security, M
Hotel/Motel Administration/Management, B
Human Resources Management and Services, M
Human Resources Management/Personnel Administration, B
Information Science/Studies, BMDO
International Business/Trade/Commerce, BM
Internet and Interactive Multimedia, M
Investment Management, M
Latin American Studies, B
Law and Legal Studies, MD
Legal and Justice Studies, M
Liberal Arts and Sciences Studies and Humanities, B
Management Information Systems and Services, M
Management Sciences and Quantitative Methods, B
Management Strategy and Policy, M
Marketing, M
Marketing Research, M
Marketing/Marketing Management, B
Mass Communication/Media Studies, B
Mathematics, B
Mathematics Teacher Education, B
Media Studies, M
Multi-/Interdisciplinary Studies, B
Non-Profit/Public/Organizational Management, M
Nursing, MDO
Nursing - Advanced Practice, M
Nursing Administration, O
Nursing Education, MO
Peace Studies and Conflict Resolution, B
Physician Assistant, M
Political Science and Government, B
Psychology, BM
Public Administration, M
Publishing, MO
Reading Teacher Education, MO

School Psychology, MD
Science Teacher Education/General Science Teacher Education, M
Social Sciences, B
Social Studies Teacher Education, B
Software Engineering, MO
Spanish Language Teacher Education, B
Spanish Language and Literature, B
Special Education and Teaching, BM
Substance Abuse/Addiction Counseling, MD
Sustainable Development, M
Taxation, M
Telecommunications, MO
Telecommunications Technology/Technician, AB
Theater, M
Women's Studies, B

PACE UNIVERSITY, PLEASANTVILLE CAMPUS

Accounting, B
Advertising, B
American/United States Studies/Civilization, B
Biochemistry, B
Biology Teacher Education, B
Biology/Biological Sciences, B
Business/Commerce, B
Business/Managerial Economics, B
Chemistry, B
Chemistry Teacher Education, B
Cinematography and Film/Video Production, B
Communication Studies/Speech Communication and Rhetoric, B
Communication and Media Studies, B
Computer Science, B
Computer Software and Media Applications, AB
Computer Systems Networking and Telecommunications, A
Computer and Information Sciences, B
Computer and Information Sciences and Support Services, A
Criminal Justice/Law Enforcement Administration, B
Data Processing and Data Processing Technology/Technician, A
Economics, B
Elementary Education and Teaching, B
English Language and Literature, B
English/Language Arts Teacher Education, B
Entrepreneurship/Entrepreneurial Studies, B
Environmental Sciences, B
Environmental Studies, B
Film/Cinema Studies, B
Finance, B
Foreign Language Teacher Education, B
General Studies, A
Health Services/Allied Health/Health Sciences, B
History, B
Human Resources Management/Personnel Administration, B
International Business/Trade/Commerce, B
International Marketing, B
International/Global Studies, B
Journalism, B
Liberal Arts and Sciences Studies and Humanities, B
Marketing/Marketing Management, B
Mathematics, B
Mathematics Teacher Education, B
Physics, B
Political Science and Government, B
Psychology, B
Social Sciences, B
Social Studies Teacher Education, B
Spanish Language and Literature, B
Special Education and Teaching, B
Telecommunications Technology/Technician, B

PARSONS SCHOOL OF DESIGN

Architecture and Related Services, B
Art/Art Studies, General, B
City/Urban, Community and Regional Planning, B
Design and Applied Arts, B
Design and Visual Communications, B
Fashion Merchandising, A
Fashion/Apparel Design, AB
Fine/Studio Arts, B
Graphic Design, A

Illustration, B
Industrial Design, B
Interior Design, AB
Liberal Arts and Sciences Studies and Humanities, B
Photography, B
Urban Studies/Affairs, B

PAUL SMITH'S COLLEGE

Business Administration and Management, B
Culinary Arts/Chef Training, AB
Ecology, B
Environmental Studies, AB
Forestry, B
Forestry Technology/Technician, A
Hospitality Administration/Management, AB
Hotel/Motel Administration/Management, AB
Liberal Arts and Sciences Studies and Humanities, AB
Natural Resources Management/Development and Policy, B
Parks, Recreation and Leisure Facilities Management, B
Survey Technology/Surveying, A

PHILLIPS BETH ISRAEL SCHOOL OF NURSING

Health Professions and Related Clinical Sciences, A

PLAZA COLLEGE

Accounting Technology/Technician and Bookkeeping, A
Administrative Assistant and Secretarial Science, A
Allied Health and Medical Assisting Services, A
Business Administration and Management, A
Business Administration, Management and Operations, B
Health Information/Medical Records Technology/Technician, A
Health/Health Care Administration/Management, B

PRATT INSTITUTE

Applied Arts and Design, MO
Architecture, BM
Archives/Archival Administration, O
Art Education, MO
Art History, Criticism and Conservation, BM
Art Teacher Education, B
Art Therapy/Therapist, M
Art/Art Studies, General, B
Arts Management, M
Building/Construction Finishing, Management, and Inspection, AB
Ceramic Arts and Ceramics, B
Cinematography and Film/Video Production, B
Commercial and Advertising Art, AB
Computer Graphics, B
Dance Therapy/Therapist, M
Design and Applied Arts, B
Drawing, AB
Facilities Planning and Management, M
Fashion/Apparel Design, B
Film/Video and Photographic Arts, B
Fine Arts and Art Studies, BM
Fine/Studio Arts, AB
Graphic Design, ABM
Historic Preservation and Conservation, M
Illustration, AB
Industrial Design, BM
Information Science/Studies, MO
Interior Design, BM
Internet and Interactive Multimedia, M
Library Science, MO
Media Studies, M
Metal and Jewelry Arts, B
Painting, ABM
Performance, M
Photography, BM
Printmaking, BM
Sculpture, BM
Sustainable Development, M
Urban Design, M
Urban and Regional Planning, M

Writing, M

PURCHASE COLLEGE, STATE UNIVERSITY OF NEW YORK

Anthropology, B
Art History, Criticism and Conservation, BM
Art/Art Studies, General, B
Biochemistry, B
Biology/Biological Sciences, B
Chemistry, B
Cinematography and Film/Video Production, B
Commercial and Advertising Art, B
Communication Studies/Speech Communication and Rhetoric, B
Comparative Literature, B
Composition, M
Dance, B
Drama and Dramatics/Theatre Arts, B
Economics, B
Environmental Studies, B
Film/Cinema Studies, B
Fine Arts and Art Studies, BM
Foreign Languages, Literatures, and Linguistics, B
French Language and Literature, B
History, B
Humanities/Humanistic Studies, B
Intermedia/Multimedia, B
Journalism, B
Liberal Arts and Sciences Studies and Humanities, B
Mathematics, B
Mathematics and Statistics, B
Modern Languages, B
Music, M
Philosophy, B
Photography, B
Physics, B
Playwriting and Screenwriting, B
Political Science and Government, B
Printmaking, B
Psychology, B
Social Sciences, B
Sociology, B
Spanish Language and Literature, B
Technical Theatre/Theatre Design and Technology, B
Theater, M
Urban Studies/Affairs, B
Visual and Performing Arts, B
Women's Studies, B

QUEENS COLLEGE OF THE CITY UNIVERSITY OF NEW YORK

Accounting, BM
Actuarial Science, B
African-American/Black Studies, B
American/United States Studies/Civilization, B
Anthropology, B
Area Studies, B
Art Education, M
Art History, Criticism and Conservation, BM
Art Teacher Education, B
Biochemistry, M
Biological and Biomedical Sciences, M
Biology Teacher Education, B
Biology/Biological Sciences, B
Chemistry, BM
Chemistry Teacher Education, B
Chinese Language and Literature, B
Classics and Classical Languages, Literatures, and Linguistics, B
Clinical Psychology, M
Communication Disorders, BM
Comparative Literature, B
Computer Science, BM
Counselor Education/School Counseling and Guidance Services, M
Dietetics/Dieticians, B
Drama and Dramatics/Theatre Arts, B
Early Childhood Education and Teaching, M
East Asian Studies, B
Economics, B
Education, MO
Educational Administration and Supervision, O
Elementary Education and Teaching, BMO
English, M

English Education, MO
English Language and Literature, B
English as a Second Language, M
English/Language Arts Teacher Education, B
Environmental Sciences, BM
Environmental Studies, B
Exercise and Sports Science, M
Family and Consumer Sciences/Home Economics Teacher Education, B
Family and Consumer Sciences/Human Sciences, BM
Film/Cinema Studies, B
Finance, B
Fine Arts and Art Studies, M
Fine/Studio Arts, B
Foreign Language Teacher Education, BMO
French Language Teacher Education, B
French Language and Literature, BM
Geology/Earth Science, BM
German Language and Literature, B
Graphic Design, B
Hebrew Language and Literature, B
Hispanic and Latin American Languages, M
History, BM
Home Economics Education, M
Information Science/Studies, MO
International Business/Trade/Commerce, B
Italian Language and Literature, BM
Jewish/Judaic Studies, B
Kinesiology and Exercise Science, B
Labor Studies, B
Latin American Studies, B
Latin Language and Literature, B
Liberal Studies, M
Library Science, MO
Linguistics, BM
Mass Communication/Media Studies, B
Mathematics, BM
Mathematics Teacher Education, BMO
Multi-/Interdisciplinary Studies, B
Multilingual and Multicultural Education, M
Music, M
Music Performance, B
Music Teacher Education, BMO
Near and Middle Eastern Studies, B
Philosophy, B
Physical Education Teaching and Coaching, B
Physics, BMD
Physics Teacher Education, B
Political Science and Government, B
Psychology, BM
Reading Teacher Education, M
Religion/Religious Studies, B
Romance Languages, Literatures, and Linguistics, M
Russian Language and Literature, B
School Psychology, MO
Science Teacher Education/General Science Teacher Education, MO
Secondary Education and Teaching, MO
Social Sciences, M
Social Studies Teacher Education, BMO
Sociology, BM
Spanish Language Teacher Education, B
Spanish Language and Literature, BM
Special Education and Teaching, M
Teaching English as a Second or Foreign Language/ESL Language Instructor, B
Urban Studies/Affairs, BM
Women's Studies, B
Writing, M

QUEENSBOROUGH COMMUNITY COLLEGE OF THE CITY UNIVERSITY OF NEW YORK

Accounting, A
Accounting Technology/Technician and Bookkeeping, A
Administrative Assistant and Secretarial Science, A
BioTechnology, A
Business Administration and Management, A
Business, Management, Marketing, and Related Support Services, A
Chemistry, A
Clinical/Medical Laboratory Technician, A

Communication, Journalism and Related Programs, A
Computer Engineering Technology/Technician, A
Computer Installation and Repair Technology/Technician, A
Criminal Justice/Law Enforcement Administration, A
Data Processing and Data Processing Technology/Technician, A
Electrical, Electronic and Communications Engineering Technology/Technician, A
Engineering, A
Engineering Science, A
Environmental Design/Architecture, A
Environmental Engineering Technology/Environmental Technology, A
Environmental Health, A
Fine/Studio Arts, A
Forensic Science and Technology, A
General Studies, A
Health Professions and Related Clinical Sciences, A
Health Services/Allied Health/Health Sciences, A
Information Science/Studies, A
Information Technology, A
Laser and Optical Technology/Technician, A
Liberal Arts and Sciences Studies and Humanities, A
Massage Therapy/Therapeutic Massage, A
Mechanical Drafting and Mechanical Drafting CAD/CADD, A
Mechanical Engineering/Mechanical Technology/Technician, A
Medical Office Management/Administration, A
Medical/Clinical Assistant, A
Museology/Museum Studies, A
Musical Instrument Fabrication and Repair, A
Physical Sciences, A
Recording Arts Technology/Technician, A
Telecommunications Technology/Technician, A
Visual and Performing Arts, A

RABBINICAL ACADEMY MESIVTA RABBI CHAIM BERLIN

Ancient Near Eastern and Biblical Languages, Literatures, and Linguistics, B
Bible/Biblical Studies, B
Rabbinical Studies, B
Theology and Religious Vocations, O
Theology/Theological Studies, B

RABBINICAL COLLEGE BETH SHRAGA

Talmudic Studies, B

RABBINICAL COLLEGE BOBOVER YESHIVA B'NEI ZION

Religious Education, B
Talmudic Studies, B

RABBINICAL COLLEGE CH'SAN SOFER

Talmudic Studies, B

RABBINICAL COLLEGE OF LONG ISLAND

Talmudic Studies, B

RABBINICAL COLLEGE OF OHR SHIMON YISROEL

Theology/Theological Studies, B

RABBINICAL SEMINARY OF AMERICA

Theology/Theological Studies, B

RENSSELAER POLYTECHNIC INSTITUTE

Acoustics, MD
Aerospace, Aeronautical and Astronautical Engineering, BMD
Applied Mathematics, M
Architecture, BMD
Astronomy, M
Biochemistry, MD
Biochemistry, Biophysics and Molecular Biology, B
Bioengineering, MD
Bioinformatics, B

Biological and Biomedical Sciences, MD
Biology/Biological Sciences, B
Biomedical Engineering, MD
Biomedical/Medical Engineering, B
Biophysics, MD
Building Science, MD
Business Administration and Management, B
Business Administration, Management and Operations, MD
Chemical Engineering, BMD
Chemistry, BMD
Civil Engineering, BMD
Cognitive Sciences, BD
Communication Studies/Speech Communication and Rhetoric, B
Computer Art and Design, MD
Computer Engineering, MD
Computer Science, BMD
Computer Technology/Computer Systems Technology, B
Design and Visual Communications, B
Digital Communication and Media/Multimedia, B
Economics, B
Electrical Engineering, MD
Electrical, Electronics and Communications Engineering, B
Engineering, B
Engineering Management, MD
Engineering Physics, BMD
Engineering Science, B
Engineering and Applied Sciences, MD
Entrepreneurship/Entrepreneurial Studies, M
Environmental Engineering Technology/Environmental Technology, MD
Environmental Sciences, B
Environmental/Environmental Health Engineering, B
Financial Engineering, M
Fine Arts and Art Studies, MD
Geology/Earth Science, BMD
History of Science and Technology, MD
Human-Computer Interaction, M
Hydrology and Water Resources Science, B
Industrial Engineering, B
Industrial/Management Engineering, MD
Information Science/Studies, M
Information Technology, B
Interdisciplinary Studies, MD
Lighting Design, MD
Management Information Systems and Services, M
Management of Technology, MD
Materials Engineering, BMD
Materials Sciences, MD
Mathematics, BMD
Mechanical Engineering, BMD
Nuclear Engineering, BMD
Philosophy, B
Physics, BMD
Pre-Law Studies, B
Pre-Medicine/Pre-Medical Studies, B
Psychology, B
Rhetoric, MD
Science, Technology and Society, B
Speech and Interpersonal Communication, MD
Supply Chain Management, M
Systems Engineering, MD
Technical Communication, M
Technology and Public Policy, MD
Transportation and Highway Engineering, MD
Visual and Performing Arts, B

ROBERTS WESLEYAN COLLEGE

Accounting, B
Art/Art Studies, General, B
Bible/Biblical Studies, B
Biochemistry, B
Biological and Biomedical Sciences, A
Biological and Physical Sciences, B
Biology Teacher Education, B
Biology/Biological Sciences, B
Business Administration and Management, B
Business Administration, Management and Operations, M
Chemistry, B
Chemistry Teacher Education, B
Child and Family Studies, M

Communication Studies/Speech Communication and Rhetoric, B
Computer and Information Sciences and Support Services, B
Criminal Justice/Law Enforcement Administration, B
Design and Applied Arts, B
Divinity/Ministry (BD, MDiv.), B
Early Childhood Education and Teaching, BM
Education, M
Education/Teaching of Individuals in Early Childhood Special Education Programs, B
English Language and Literature, B
English/Language Arts Teacher Education, B
Environmental Biology, B
Forensic Science and Technology, B
General Studies, B
Health Informatics, M
Health Services Administration, M
Health/Health Care Administration/Management, B
History, B
Human Resources Management/Personnel Administration, B
Human Services, M
Humanities/Humanistic Studies, B
Liberal Arts and Sciences Studies and Humanities, B
Management Strategy and Policy, M
Marketing, M
Marketing/Marketing Management, B
Mathematics, B
Mathematics Teacher Education, B
Middle School Education, M
Music, B
Music Teacher Education, B
Natural Sciences, A
Nursing, M
Nursing Administration, M
Nursing Education, M
Philosophy and Religious Studies, B
Physical Education Teaching and Coaching, B
Physical Sciences, A
Physics, B
Physics Teacher Education, B
Piano and Organ, B
Pre-Dentistry Studies, B
Pre-Law Studies, B
Pre-Medicine/Pre-Medical Studies, B
Pre-Pharmacy Studies, B
Pre-Veterinary Studies, B
Psychology, B
Reading Teacher Education, M
Religion/Religious Studies, B
Secondary Education and Teaching, M
Security and Protective Services, B
Social Studies Teacher Education, B
Social Work, BM
Spanish Language Teacher Education, B
Spanish Language and Literature, B
Special Education and Teaching, BM
Voice and Opera, B

ROCHESTER INSTITUTE OF TECHNOLOGY

Accounting, BM
Advertising, B
Aerospace, Aeronautical and Astronautical Engineering, B
American Sign Language (ASL), B
Animation, Interactive Technology, Video Graphics and Special Effects, B
Applied Mathematics, M
Applied Statistics, MO
Architecture, M
Art Education, M
Astrophysics, MD
BioTechnology, B
Biochemistry, B
Bioinformatics, BM
Biological and Biomedical Sciences, BM
Biology/Biological Sciences, B
Biomedical Sciences, B
Biomedical/Medical Engineering, B
Business Administration and Management, B
Business Administration, Management and Operations, M
Business/Commerce, B

Ceramic Arts and Ceramics, BM
Chemical Engineering, B
Chemistry, BM
Cinematography and Film/Video Production, B
Civil Engineering Technology/Technician, B
Clinical Laboratory Science/Medical
  Technology/Technologist, B
Commercial Photography, B
Commercial and Advertising Art, B
Communication Studies/Speech Communication
  and Rhetoric, B
Communication and Media Studies, BMO
Computational Mathematics, B
Computer Art and Design, M
Computer Engineering, BM
Computer Engineering Technology/Technician, B
Computer Graphics, B
Computer Science, BMD
Computer Software Engineering, B
Computer Systems Analysis/Analyst, B
Computer Systems Networking and Telecommunica-
  tions, B
Computer and Information Sciences, B
Computer and Information Systems Security, BMO
Crafts, M
Crafts/Craft Design, Folk Art and Artisanry, B
Criminal Justice/Law Enforcement Administration, B
Criminal Justice/Safety Studies, B
Criminology, M
Data Modeling/Warehousing and Database Adminis-
  tration, B
Database Systems, O
Design and Visual Communications, B
Diagnostic Medical Sonography/Sonographer and
  Ultrasound Technician, B
Digital Communication and Media/Multimedia, B
Economics, B
Electrical Engineering, M
Electrical and Electronic Engineering
  Technologies/Technicians, AB
Electrical, Electronics and Communications Engi-
  neering, B
Electromechanical Technology/Electromechanical
  Engineering Technology, B
Engineering, B
Engineering Management, M
Engineering Science, A
Engineering and Applied Sciences, MDO
Engineering-Related Technologies, B
Entrepreneurship/Entrepreneurial Studies, M
Environmental Sciences, BM
Environmental and Occupational Health, M
Experimental Psychology, M
Film, Television, and Video Production, M
Finance, B
Finance and Banking, M
Fine Arts and Art Studies, MO
Fine/Studio Arts, B
Food Services Management, M
Foodservice Systems
  Administration/Management, B
Game Design and Development, M
Graphic Communications, B
Graphic Design, BM
Health Services Administration, MO
Hospitality Administration/Management, BM
Hospitality and Recreation Marketing Operations, B
Hotel/Motel Administration/Management, B
Human Nutrition, B
Human Resources Development, M
Human-Computer Interaction, M
Illustration, B
Industrial Design, BM
Industrial Engineering, B
Industrial and Manufacturing Management, M
Industrial/Management Engineering, M
Information Science/Studies, MD
Information Technology, B
Interdisciplinary Studies, M
Interior Design, B
Intermedia/Multimedia, B
International Business/Trade/Commerce, BM
International Relations and Affairs, B
Internet and Interactive Multimedia, O
Jewelry/Metalsmithing, M
Journalism, B

Liberal Arts and Sciences Studies and Humani-
  ties, B
Management Information Systems and Ser-
  vices, BO
Manufacturing Engineering, M
Manufacturing Technology/Technician, B
Marketing/Marketing Management, B
Materials Engineering, M
Materials Sciences, M
Mathematical and Computational Finance, M
Mathematics, BM
Mathematics and Computer Science, B
Mechanical Engineering, BM
Media Studies, M
Medical Illustration and Informatics, M
Medical Illustration/Medical Illustrator, B
Medical Informatics, M
Metal and Jewelry Arts, B
Natural Resources Management/Development and
  Policy, B
Occupational Safety and Health
  Technology/Technician, B
Occupational Therapy/Therapist, M
Optics/Optical Sciences, MD
Organizational Management, O
Painting, B
Philosophy, B
Photographic and Film/Video Technology/Technician
  and Assistant, B
Photography, M
Photojournalism, B
Physical Sciences, B
Physician Assistant, B
Political Science and Government, B
Pre-Dentistry Studies, B
Pre-Law Studies, B
Pre-Medicine/Pre-Medical Studies, B
Pre-Veterinary Studies, B
Prepress/Desktop Publishing and Digital Imaging
  Design, B
Printing Management, B
Printmaking, O
Project Management, O
Psychology, BMO
Public Policy Analysis, BM
Public Relations, Advertising, and Applied Commu-
  nication, B
Public Relations/Image Management, B
Publishing, B
Resort Management, B
Restaurant/Food Services Management, B
Safety Engineering, M
School Psychology, MO
Sculpture, B
Secondary Education and Teaching, M
Sign Language Interpretation and Translation, B
Software Engineering, M
Special Education and Teaching, M
Special Products Marketing Operations, B
Statistics, BO
Sustainability Management, MD
Sustainable Development, MD
System Administration/Administrator, B
System, Networking, and LAN/WAN
  Management/Manager, B
Systems Engineering, BMD
Technology and Public Policy, M
Telecommunications Technology/Technician, B
Tourism and Travel Services Marketing Opera-
  tions, B
Travel and Tourism, M
Web Page, Digital/Multimedia and Information Re-
  sources Design, B
Web/Multimedia Management and Webmaster, B
Woodworking, B

ROCKLAND COMMUNITY COLLEGE

Accounting, A
Administrative Assistant and Secretarial Science, A
Advertising, A
Art/Art Studies, General, A
Automobile/Automotive Mechanics
  Technology/Technician, A
Biological and Physical Sciences, A
Business Administration and Management, A
Commercial and Advertising Art, A

Computer Graphics, A
Computer Programming, A
Computer Programming, Specific Applications, A
Computer Programming/Programmer, A
Computer Systems Networking and Telecommunica-
  tions, A
Computer and Information Sciences, A
Computer/Information Technology Services Adminis-
  tration and Management, A
Criminal Justice/Law Enforcement Administration, A
Culinary Arts/Chef Training, A
Data Processing and Data Processing
  Technology/Technician, A
Design and Applied Arts, A
Dietetics/Dieticians, A
Drafting and Design Technology/Technician, A
Drama and Dramatics/Theatre Arts, A
Electrical, Electronic and Communications Engineer-
  ing Technology/Technician, A
Emergency Medical Technology/Technician (EMT
  Paramedic), A
Finance, A
Fine/Studio Arts, A
Fire Science/Firefighting, A
Health Information/Medical Records
  Administration/Administrator, A
Hospitality Administration/Management, A
Human Services, A
Liberal Arts and Sciences Studies and Humani-
  ties, A
Marketing/Marketing Management, A
Mass Communication/Media Studies, A
Mathematics, A
Occupational Therapy/Therapist, A
Photography, A
Respiratory Care Therapy/Therapist, A
System Administration/Administrator, A
Tourism and Travel Services Management, A

THE SAGE COLLEGES

Accounting, B
Biochemistry, B
Biological and Biomedical Sciences, B
Biology/Biological Sciences, B
Business Administration and Management, B
Chemistry, B
Criminal Justice/Law Enforcement Administration, B
Drama and Dramatics/Theatre Arts, B
Elementary Education and Teaching, B
English Language and Literature, B
Environmental Studies, B
Fine/Studio Arts, B
Forensic Science and Technology, B
Graphic Design, B
Health Professions and Related Clinical Sciences, B
Health Services/Allied Health/Health Sciences, B
History, B
Humanities/Humanistic Studies, B
Information Science/Studies, B
Interior Design, B
International Relations and Affairs, B
Liberal Arts and Sciences Studies and Humani-
  ties, B
Mathematics, B
Nutritional Sciences, B
Physical Education Teaching and Coaching, B
Political Science and Government, B
Psychology, B
Public Policy Analysis, B
Social Sciences, B
Sociology, B
Visual and Performing Arts, B

ST. BONAVENTURE UNIVERSITY

Accounting, B
Art History, Criticism and Conservation, B
Biochemistry, B
Bioinformatics, B
Biology/Biological Sciences, B
Biophysics, B
Business Administration and Management, B
Business Administration, Management and Opera-
  tions, M
Chemistry, B
Child Development, B

Classics and Classical Languages, Literatures, and Linguistics, B
Community Psychology, M
Computer Science, B
Computer and Information Sciences, B
Corporate and Organizational Communication, M
Counseling Psychology, M
Counselor Education/School Counseling and Guidance Services, MO
Digital Communication and Media/Multimedia, B
Drama and Dramatics/Theatre Arts, B
Early Childhood Education and Teaching, M
Education, MO
Education/Teaching of the Gifted and Talented, MO
Educational Leadership and Administration, MO
Elementary Education and Teaching, B
English, M
English Language and Literature, B
Environmental Sciences, B
Finance, B
French Language and Literature, B
Gerontology, B
History, B
International/Global Studies, B
Journalism, B
Management Information Systems and Services, B
Marketing, M
Marketing/Marketing Management, B
Mathematics, B
Middle School Education, M
Modern Languages, B
Music History, Literature, and Theory, B
Philosophy, B
Physical Education Teaching and Coaching, B
Physics, B
Political Science and Government, B
Psychology, B
Reading Teacher Education, M
Rehabilitation Counseling, M
Religion/Religious Studies, M
Secondary Education and Teaching, M
Sociology, B
Spanish Language and Literature, B
Special Education and Teaching, BMO
Sport and Fitness Administration/Management, B
Theology/Theological Studies, B
Visual and Performing Arts, B
Women's Studies, B

ST. FRANCIS COLLEGE

Accounting, BM
Accounting and Business/Management, B
Area Studies, B
Biology Teacher Education, B
Biology/Biological Sciences, B
Biomedical Sciences, B
Business Administration and Management, AB
Chemistry, B
Chemistry Teacher Education, B
Clinical Laboratory Science/Medical Technology/Technologist, B
Communication Studies/Speech Communication and Rhetoric, B
Computer/Information Technology Services Administration and Management, B
Criminal Justice/Safety Studies, AB
Economics, B
Education/Teaching of Individuals with Vision Impairments, Including Blindness, B
English Language and Literature, B
English/Language Arts Teacher Education, B
Ethnic, Cultural Minority, and Gender Studies, B
Health Professions and Related Clinical Sciences, B
History, B
Liberal Arts and Sciences Studies and Humanities, AB
Mathematics, B
Mathematics Teacher Education, B
Medical Radiologic Technology/Science - Radiation Therapist, B
Organizational Communication, B
Philosophy, B
Physical Education Teaching and Coaching, B
Physician Assistant, B
Political Science and Government, B
Psychology, B

Radio and Television, B
Religion/Religious Studies, B
Social Studies Teacher Education, B
Sociology, B
Spanish Language and Literature, B

ST. JOHN FISHER COLLEGE

Accounting, B
American/United States Studies/Civilization, B
Anthropology, B
Biology Teacher Education, B
Biology/Biological Sciences, B
Business Administration and Management, B
Business Administration, Management and Operations, M
Chemistry, B
Chemistry Teacher Education, B
Computer and Information Sciences, B
Counseling Psychology, M
Criminology, B
Digital Communication and Media/Multimedia, B
Economics, B
Education, MDO
Educational Leadership and Administration, MD
Elementary Education and Teaching, BMO
English Education, M
English Language and Literature, B
English/Language Arts Teacher Education, B
Finance, B
Foreign Language Teacher Education, M
French Language Teacher Education, B
French Language and Literature, B
History, B
History Teacher Education, B
International Relations and Affairs, B
Law and Legal Studies, B
Liberal Arts and Sciences Studies and Humanities, B
Mathematics, B
Mathematics Teacher Education, B
Middle School Education, M
Nursing, MDO
Nursing - Advanced Practice, O
Nursing Education, O
Pharmacy, D
Philosophy, B
Physics, B
Physics Teacher Education, B
Political Science and Government, B
Psychology, B
Reading Teacher Education, M
Religion/Religious Studies, B
Social Studies Teacher Education, BM
Sociology, B
Spanish Language Teacher Education, B
Spanish Language and Literature, B
Special Education and Teaching, BMO
Sport and Fitness Administration/Management, B
Statistics, B

ST. JOHN'S UNIVERSITY

Accounting, BM
Actuarial Science, BM
Advertising, B
Anthropology, B
Asian Studies/Civilization, BMO
Audiology/Audiologist and Speech-Language Pathology/Pathologist, B
BioTechnology, M
Biological and Biomedical Sciences, MD
Biology Teacher Education, B
Biology/Biological Sciences, B
Business Administration and Management, AB
Business Administration, Management and Operations, M
Chemistry, BM
Clinical Laboratory Science/Medical Technology/Technologist, B
Clinical Psychology, MDO
Communication Disorders, MD
Communication Studies/Speech Communication and Rhetoric, B
Computer and Information Sciences, B
Computer and Information Systems Security, AB
Counseling Psychology, MO

Counselor Education/School Counseling and Guidance Services, MO
Criminal Justice/Law Enforcement Administration, AB
Criminology, M
Database Systems, M
Drama and Dramatics/Theatre Arts, B
Early Childhood Education and Teaching, M
East Asian Studies, MO
Economics, B
Education, MDO
Education/Teaching of the Gifted and Talented, O
Educational Administration and Supervision, DO
Educational Leadership and Administration, MDO
Elementary Education and Teaching, BM
English, MD
English Language and Literature, B
English as a Second Language, MO
English/Language Arts Teacher Education, B
Environmental Studies, B
Experimental Psychology, M
Finance, B
Finance and Banking, M
Fine Arts and Art Studies, B
French Language and Literature, B
Funeral Service and Mortuary Science, B
Graphic Design, B
Health Information/Medical Records Technology/Technician, B
Health Professions and Related Clinical Sciences, B
History, BMD
Hospitality Administration/Management, B
Illustration, B
Information Science/Studies, MO
Insurance, BM
International Affairs, MO
International Business/Trade/Commerce, M
Investment Management, M
Italian Language and Literature, B
Journalism, B
Law and Legal Studies, ABMD
Legal Professions and Studies, B
Legal and Justice Studies, M
Liberal Arts and Sciences Studies and Humanities, AB
Liberal Studies, M
Library Science, MO
Management Information Systems and Services, BM
Management Strategy and Policy, M
Marketing, M
Marketing/Marketing Management, B
Mathematics, B
Mathematics Teacher Education, B
Middle School Education, O
Multilingual and Multicultural Education, MO
Museology/Museum Studies, M
Pharmaceutical Administration, M
Pharmaceutical Sciences, MD
Pharmacy, B
Philosophy, B
Photographic and Film/Video Technology/Technician and Assistant, AB
Photography, B
Photojournalism, B
Physical Sciences, B
Physician Assistant, B
Physics, B
Physics Teacher Education, B
Political Science and Government, BMO
Psychology, BMD
Public Administration, BO
Public Health, M
Public History, M
Public Relations, Advertising, and Applied Communication, B
Quantitative Analysis, M
Radiologic Technology/Science - Radiographer, B
Reading Teacher Education, MDO
School Psychology, MD
Secondary Education and Teaching, MO
Securities Services Administration/Management, B
Social Sciences, B
Social Studies Teacher Education, B
Sociology, BM
Spanish Language Teacher Education, B

Spanish Language and Literature, BM
Special Education and Teaching, BMO
Sport and Fitness Administration/Management, BM
Taxation, M
Telecommunications Technology/Technician, B
Theology and Religious Vocations, M
Theology/Theological Studies, B
Toxicology, BM

ST. JOSEPH'S COLLEGE, LONG IS-
LAND CAMPUS

Accounting, BM
Biology Teacher Education, B
Biology/Biological Sciences, B
Business Administration and Management, B
Business Administration, Management and Opera-
    tions, M
Chemistry, B
Chemistry Teacher Education, B
Clinical Laboratory Science/Medical
    Technology/Technologist, B
Computer/Information Technology Services Adminis-
    tration and Management, B
Criminal Justice/Law Enforcement Administration, B
Early Childhood Education and Teaching, M
Education, B
Elementary Education and Teaching, B
English Language and Literature, B
English/Language Arts Teacher Education, B
Health Professions and Related Clinical Sciences, B
Health Services Administration, M
History, B
Hospital and Health Care Facilities
    Administration/Management, B
Hospitality Administration/Management, B
Human Development and Family Studies, B
Human Resources Management and Services, M
Human Services, B
Information Science/Studies, B
Journalism, B
Liberal Arts and Sciences Studies and Humani-
    ties, B
Management, MO
Marketing/Marketing Management, B
Mathematics, B
Mathematics Teacher Education, B
Mathematics and Statistics, B
Nursing, M
Organizational Management, M
Parks, Recreation and Leisure Facilities Manage-
    ment, B
Political Science and Government, B
Psychology, B
Reading Teacher Education, M
Social Sciences, B
Social Studies Teacher Education, B
Sociology, B
Spanish Language Teacher Education, B
Spanish Language and Literature, B
Special Education and Teaching, BM

ST. JOSEPH'S COLLEGE, NEW YORK

Accounting, BM
Biology Teacher Education, B
Biology/Biological Sciences, B
Business Administration and Management, B
Business Administration, Management and Opera-
    tions, M
Chemistry, B
Chemistry Teacher Education, B
Clinical Laboratory Science/Medical
    Technology/Technologist, B
Computer/Information Technology Services Adminis-
    tration and Management, B
Criminal Justice/Law Enforcement Administration, B
Early Childhood Education and Teaching, M
Education, BM
Elementary Education and Teaching, B
English Language and Literature, B
English/Language Arts Teacher Education, B
Health Professions and Related Clinical Sciences, B
Health Services Administration, M
History, B
Hospital and Health Care Facilities
    Administration/Management, B
Hospitality Administration/Management, B

Human Development and Family Studies, B
Human Services, BM
Information Science/Studies, B
Journalism, B
Liberal Arts and Sciences Studies and Humani-
    ties, B
Management, M
Marketing/Marketing Management, B
Mathematics, B
Mathematics Teacher Education, B
Mathematics and Statistics, B
Nursing, M
Parks, Recreation and Leisure Facilities Manage-
    ment, B
Political Science and Government, B
Psychology, B
Reading Teacher Education, M
Social Sciences, B
Social Studies Teacher Education, B
Sociology, B
Spanish Language Teacher Education, B
Spanish Language and Literature, B
Special Education and Teaching, BM
Writing, M

ST. LAWRENCE UNIVERSITY

Anthropology, B
Art History, Criticism and Conservation, B
Art/Art Studies, General, B
Biochemistry, B
Biology/Biological Sciences, B
Biophysics, B
Business/Commerce, B
Chemistry, B
Communication Studies/Speech Communication
    and Rhetoric, B
Computer and Information Sciences, B
Conservation Biology, B
Counselor Education/School Counseling and Guid-
    ance Services, MO
Economics, B
Education, MO
Educational Administration and Supervision, MO
English Language and Literature, B
Environmental Studies, B
Foreign Languages, Literatures, and Linguistics, B
French Language and Literature, B
General Studies, B
Geology/Earth Science, B
Geophysics and Seismology, B
History, B
Human Development, MO
Humanities/Humanistic Studies, B
International/Global Studies, B
Liberal Arts and Sciences Studies and Humani-
    ties, B
Mathematics, B
Multi-/Interdisciplinary Studies, B
Music, B
Philosophy, B
Physics, B
Political Science and Government, B
Psychology, B
Religion/Religious Studies, B
Social Sciences, B
Sociology, B
Spanish Language and Literature, B
Statistics, B

ST. THOMAS AQUINAS COLLEGE

Accounting, B
Applied Mathematics, B
Art Therapy/Therapist, B
Art/Art Studies, General, B
Biology/Biological Sciences, B
Business Administration and Management, AB
Business Administration, Management and Opera-
    tions, M
Clinical Laboratory Science/Medical
    Technology/Technologist, B
Clinical/Medical Laboratory Technician, B
Commercial and Advertising Art, B
Computer and Information Sciences, B
Criminal Justice/Law Enforcement Administration, B
Education, BMO
Educational Leadership and Administration, M

Elementary Education and Teaching, BM
Engineering Science, B
English Language and Literature, B
Finance, B
Finance and Banking, M
Fine/Studio Arts, B
Forensic Science and Technology, B
Graphic Design, B
History, B
Humanities/Humanistic Studies, B
Information Science/Studies, B
Journalism, B
Kindergarten/PreSchool Education and Teaching, B
Liberal Arts and Sciences Studies and Humani-
    ties, A
Management, M
Marketing, B
Marketing/Marketing Management, B
Mass Communication/Media Studies, B
Mathematics, B
Middle School Education, M
Modern Languages, B
Natural Sciences, B
Parks, Recreation, Leisure and Fitness Studies, B
Philosophy, B
Pre-Medicine/Pre-Medical Studies, B
Psychology, B
Reading Teacher Education, MO
Religion/Religious Studies, B
Romance Languages, Literatures, and Linguistics, B
Secondary Education and Teaching, BM
Social Sciences, B
Spanish Language and Literature, B
Special Education and Teaching, BMO
Sport and Fitness Administration/Management, B
Therapeutic Recreation/Recreational Therapy, B

SARAH LAWRENCE COLLEGE

Anthropology, B
Art History, Criticism and Conservation, B
Asian Studies/Civilization, B
Biology/Biological Sciences, B
Chemistry, B
Child Development, BM
Chinese Language and Literature, B
Dance, BM
Drama and Dramatics/Theatre Arts, B
Drawing, B
Economics, B
Education, M
Engineering, B
Environmental Studies, B
Ethnic and Cultural Studies, B
Ethnic, Cultural Minority, and Gender Studies, B
Film/Cinema Studies, B
Fine/Studio Arts, B
French Language and Literature, B
Gay/Lesbian Studies, B
Genetic Counseling/Counselor, M
Geography, B
German Language and Literature, B
History, BM
Human Genetics, M
International/Global Studies, B
Italian Language and Literature, B
Japanese Language and Literature, B
Kinesiology and Movement Studies, M
Latin American Studies, B
Latin Language and Literature, B
Liberal Arts and Sciences Studies and Humani-
    ties, B
Mathematics, B
Modern Languages, B
Music, B
Music History, Literature, and Theory, B
Painting, B
Philosophy, B
Photography, B
Physics, B
Political Science and Government, B
Pre-Law Studies, B
Pre-Medicine/Pre-Medical Studies, B
Printmaking, B
Psychology, B
Public Health, M
Public Policy Analysis, B

Religion/Religious Studies, B
Robotics Technology/Technician, B
Russian Language and Literature, B
Science, Technology and Society, B
Sculpture, B
Social Sciences, B
Sociology, B
Spanish Language and Literature, B
Theater, M
Women's Studies, BM
Writing, M

SCHENECTADY COUNTY COMMUNITY COLLEGE

Accounting Technology/Technician and Bookkeeping, A
Avionics Maintenance Technology/Technician, A
Business Administration and Management, A
Business, Management, Marketing, and Related Support Services, A
Community Organization and Advocacy, A
Computer Programming/Programmer, A
Computer/Information Technology Services Administration and Management, A
Criminal Justice/Law Enforcement Administration, A
Data Processing and Data Processing Technology/Technician, A
Education, A
Electrical, Electronic and Communications Engineering Technology/Technician, A
Fire Science/Firefighting, A
Hotel/Motel Administration/Management, A
Liberal Arts and Sciences Studies and Humanities, A
Public Administration and Social Service Professions, A
Restaurant/Food Services Management, A
Science Technologies/Technicians, A
Teacher Assistant/Aide, A
Transportation and Materials Moving, A
Visual and Performing Arts, A

SCHOOL OF VISUAL ARTS

Art Education, M
Art History, Criticism and Conservation, M
Art Therapy/Therapist, M
Cinematography and Film/Video Production, B
Commercial Photography, B
Commercial and Advertising Art, B
Computer Art and Design, M
Cultural Studies, M
Design and Applied Arts, BM
Drawing, B
Film, Television, and Video Production, M
Film/Cinema Studies, B
Film/Video and Photographic Arts, B
Fine Arts and Art Studies, M
Fine/Studio Arts, B
Graphic Design, BM
Illustration, BM
Interior Design, B
Internet and Interactive Multimedia, M
Painting, B
Photography, BM
Printmaking, M
Sculpture, B
Writing, M

SH'OR YOSHUV RABBINICAL COLLEGE

Hebrew Language and Literature, B
Jewish/Judaic Studies, B
Rabbinical Studies, B

SIENA COLLEGE

Accounting, B
Actuarial Science, B
American/United States Studies/Civilization, B
Biochemistry, B
Biology/Biological Sciences, B
Chemistry, B
Classics and Classical Languages, Literatures, and Linguistics, B
Computational Mathematics, B
Computer and Information Sciences, B

Economics, B
English Language and Literature, B
Environmental Sciences, B
Environmental Studies, B
Finance, B
Fine/Studio Arts, B
French Language and Literature, B
History, B
Management Science, B
Marketing/Marketing Management, B
Mathematics, B
Philosophy, B
Physics, B
Political Science and Government, B
Psychology, B
Religion/Religious Studies, B
Social Work, B
Sociology, B
Spanish Language and Literature, B

SKIDMORE COLLEGE

American/United States Studies/Civilization, B
Anthropology, B
Art History, Criticism and Conservation, B
Art/Art Studies, General, B
Asian Studies/Civilization, B
Biology/Biological Sciences, B
Business, Management, Marketing, and Related Support Services, B
Business/Commerce, B
Chemistry, B
Classics and Classical Languages, Literatures, and Linguistics, B
Computer and Information Sciences, B
Dance, B
Drama and Dramatics/Theatre Arts, B
Economics, B
Education, B
Elementary Education and Teaching, B
English Language and Literature, B
Environmental Sciences, B
Environmental Studies, B
Ethnic, Cultural Minority, and Gender Studies, B
Exercise Physiology, B
Fine Arts and Art Studies, B
French Language and Literature, B
French Studies, B
Geology/Earth Science, B
German Language and Literature, B
History, B
International Relations and Affairs, B
Liberal Arts and Sciences Studies and Humanities, B
Mathematics, B
Music History, Literature, and Theory, B
Philosophy, B
Physics, B
Political Science and Government, B
Psychology, B
Religion/Religious Studies, B
Social Sciences, B
Social Work, B
Sociology, B
Spanish Language and Literature, B

STATE UNIVERSITY OF NEW YORK COLLEGE OF AGRICULTURE AND TECHNOLOGY AT COBLESKILL

Accounting Technology/Technician and Bookkeeping, A
Agribusiness, A
Agricultural Business and Management, AB
Agriculture, A
Agronomy and Crop Science, AB
Animal Sciences, A
Banking and Financial Support Services, B
BioTechnology, B
Biology Technician/BioTechnology Laboratory Technician, A
Biology/Biological Sciences, A
Business Administration and Management, A
Business, Management, Marketing, and Related Support Services, B
Chemical Technology/Technician, A
Child Care and Support Services Management, AB

Clinical/Medical Laboratory Science and Allied Professions, A
Commercial and Advertising Art, A
Communication Studies/Speech Communication and Rhetoric, A
Computer Software and Media Applications, B
Computer and Information Sciences, A
Computer and Information Sciences and Support Services, B
Culinary Arts/Chef Training, A
Diesel Mechanics Technology/Technician, A
Emergency Medical Technology/Technician (EMT Paramedic), A
Engineering Technologies/Technicians, A
Environmental Studies, AB
Fishing and Fisheries Sciences and Management, A
Graphic Design, A
Health Services/Allied Health/Health Sciences, A
Hotel/Motel Administration/Management, A
Humanities/Humanistic Studies, A
Information Science/Studies, A
Information Technology, B
Kindergarten/PreSchool Education and Teaching, B
Landscaping and Groundskeeping, B
Liberal Arts and Sciences Studies and Humanities, A
Mathematics, A
Mechanical Engineering/Mechanical Technology/Technician, A
Natural Resources Conservation and Research, B
Ornamental Horticulture, A
Plant Sciences, AB
Poultry Science, A
Psychology, B
Radio, Television, and Digital Communication, B
Restaurant, Culinary, and Catering Management/Manager, B
Science Technologies/Technicians, A
Social Work, A
Teacher Assistant/Aide, A
Tourism and Travel Services Marketing Operations, A
Wildlife and Wildlands Science and Management, AB

STATE UNIVERSITY OF NEW YORK COLLEGE AT CORTLAND

African-American/Black Studies, B
Anthropology, B
Art History, Criticism and Conservation, B
Athletic Training and Sports Medicine, B
Audiology/Audiologist and Speech-Language Pathology/Pathologist, B
Biology Teacher Education, B
Biology/Biological Sciences, B
Chemistry, B
Chemistry Teacher Education, B
Communication Studies/Speech Communication and Rhetoric, B
Community Health and Preventive Medicine, M
Criminology, B
Early Childhood Education and Teaching, M
Economics, B
Education, MO
Education/Teaching of Individuals with Speech or Language Impairments, B
Educational Leadership and Administration, O
Elementary Education and Teaching, B
English, M
English Education, M
English Language and Literature, B
English as a Second Language, M
Environmental Biology, B
Environmental Education, M
Environmental Sciences, B
Environmental Studies, B
Exercise and Sports Science, M
Fine/Studio Arts, B
French Language Teacher Education, B
French Language and Literature, B
Geochemistry, B
Geography, B
Geology/Earth Science, B
German Language and Literature, B
Health Education, M
Health Professions and Related Clinical Sciences, B

Health Teacher Education, B
History, BM
Human Services, B
International Relations and Affairs, B
International/Global Studies, B
Junior High/Intermediate/Middle School Education
  and Teaching, B
Kindergarten/PreSchool Education and Teaching, B
Kinesiology and Exercise Science, B
Leisure Studies, M
Mathematics, B
Mathematics Teacher Education, BM
Parks, Recreation and Leisure Facilities Manage-
  ment, B
Parks, Recreation, Leisure and Fitness Studies, B
Philosophy, B
Physical Education Teaching and Coaching, BM
Physics, B
Physics Teacher Education, B
Political Science and Government, B
Pre-Dentistry Studies, B
Pre-Law Studies, B
Pre-Medicine/Pre-Medical Studies, B
Psychology, B
Reading Teacher Education, BM
Recreation and Park Management, M
Science Teacher Education/General Science
  Teacher Education, BM
Secondary Education and Teaching, BM
Social Studies Teacher Education, BM
Social Work, B
Sociology, B
Spanish Language Teacher Education, B
Spanish Language and Literature, B
Special Education and Teaching, M
Sport and Fitness Administration/Management, M
Therapeutic Recreation, M
Therapeutic Recreation/Recreational Therapy, B

STATE UNIVERSITY OF NEW YORK COLLEGE OF ENVIRONMENTAL SCIENCE AND FORESTRY

Animal Sciences, B
Aquatic Biology/Limnology, B
BioTechnology, B
Biochemistry, BMD
Biological and Biomedical Sciences, B
Biology/Biological Sciences, B
Biomedical/Medical Engineering, B
Botany/Plant Biology, B
Chemical Engineering, B
Chemistry, BMD
City/Urban, Community and Regional Planning, B
Conservation Biology, BMD
Construction Management, BMD
Ecology, BMD
Economics, M
Engineering, B
Entomology, MD
Environmental Biology, BMD
Environmental Design/Architecture, B
Environmental Engineering
  Technology/Environmental Technology, MD
Environmental Health, B
Environmental Policy, MD
Environmental Policy and Resource Manage-
  ment, M
Environmental Sciences, BMD
Environmental Studies, BM
Environmental/Environmental Health Engineering, B
Fish, Game and Wildlife Management, MD
Fishing and Fisheries Sciences and Management, B
Forest Management/Forest Resources Manage-
  ment, B
Forest Sciences and Biology, B
Forestry, BMD
Forestry Technology/Technician, A
Geographic Information Systems, MD
Hydrology and Water Resources Science, B
Land Use Planning and
  Management/Development, B
Landscape Architecture, BM
Materials Sciences, MD
Natural Resources Management/Development and
  Policy, BMD
Natural Resources and Conservation, ABMD

Organic Chemistry, MD
Paper and Pulp Engineering, MDO
Parks, Recreation, Leisure and Fitness Studies, B
Physical Therapy/Therapist, B
Plant Pathology/Phytopathology, MD
Plant Sciences, BMD
Polymer Chemistry, B
Pre-Dentistry Studies, B
Pre-Law Studies, B
Pre-Medicine/Pre-Medical Studies, B
Pre-Veterinary Studies, B
Resource Management, MD
Survey Technology/Surveying, A
Sustainability Management, M
Sustainable Development, MD
Urban Design, M
Urban and Regional Planning, M
Water Resources, M
Water Resources Engineering, BMD
Wildlife Biology, B
Wildlife and Wildlands Science and Management, B
Wood Science and Wood Products/Pulp and Paper
  Technology, B
Zoology/Animal Biology, B

STATE UNIVERSITY OF NEW YORK COLLEGE AT GENESEO

Accounting, BM
African-American/Black Studies, B
American/United States Studies/Civilization, B
Anthropology, B
Art History, Criticism and Conservation, B
Biochemistry, B
Biology/Biological Sciences, B
Biophysics, B
Business Administration and Management, B
Business Administration, Management and Opera-
  tions, M
Chemistry, B
Comparative Literature, B
Drama and Dramatics/Theatre Arts, B
Early Childhood Education and Teaching, BM
Economics, B
Education, BM
Education/Teaching of Individuals in Early Childhood
  Special Education Programs, B
Elementary Education and Teaching, B
English Language and Literature, B
French Language and Literature, B
Geochemistry, B
Geography, B
Geology/Earth Science, B
Geophysics and Seismology, B
History, B
International Relations and Affairs, B
Mathematics, B
Multilingual and Multicultural Education, M
Music, B
Natural Sciences, B
Philosophy, B
Physics, B
Political Science and Government, B
Pre-Dentistry Studies, B
Pre-Law Studies, B
Pre-Medicine/Pre-Medical Studies, B
Pre-Nursing Studies, B
Pre-Veterinary Studies, B
Psychology, B
Reading Teacher Education, M
Secondary Education and Teaching, M
Sociology, B
Spanish Language and Literature, B
Special Education and Teaching, B
Visual and Performing Arts, B

STATE UNIVERSITY OF NEW YORK COLLEGE AT OLD WESTBURY

Accounting, BM
American/United States Studies/Civilization, B
Art/Art Studies, General, B
Bilingual and Multilingual Education, B
Biochemistry, B
Biology Teacher Education, B
Biology/Biological Sciences, B
Business Administration and Management, B

Business Administration, Management and Opera-
  tions, M
Chemistry, B
Chemistry Teacher Education, B
Communication Studies/Speech Communication
  and Rhetoric, B
Comparative Literature, B
Computer Science, B
Computer and Information Sciences, B
Counseling Psychology, M
Criminology, B
Early Childhood Education and Teaching, B
Elementary Education and Teaching, B
English Education, M
Finance, B
Foreign Language Teacher Education, BM
Foreign Languages and Literatures, B
History, B
Humanities/Humanistic Studies, B
Information Science/Studies, B
Junior High/Intermediate/Middle School Education
  and Teaching, B
Labor and Industrial Relations, B
Management Information Systems and Services, B
Marketing/Marketing Management, B
Mathematics, B
Mathematics Teacher Education, BM
Middle School Education, M
Philosophy, B
Psychology, B
Public Health (MPH, DPH), B
Religion/Religious Studies, B
Science Teacher Education/General Science
  Teacher Education, BM
Secondary Education and Teaching, B
Social Sciences, B
Social Studies Teacher Education, BM
Sociology, B
Spanish Language Teacher Education, B
Spanish Language and Literature, B
Special Education and Teaching, B
Taxation, M
Visual and Performing Arts, B

STATE UNIVERSITY OF NEW YORK COLLEGE AT ONEONTA

Accounting, B
Anthropology, B
Art History, Criticism and Conservation, B
Art/Art Studies, General, B
Atmospheric Sciences and Meteorology, B
Biochemistry, B
Biological and Biomedical Sciences, M
Biology Teacher Education, B
Biology Technician/BioTechnology Laboratory Tech-
  nician, B
Biology/Biological Sciences, B
Business/Managerial Economics, B
Cartography, B
Chemistry, B
Chemistry Teacher Education, B
Child Development, B
Computer Graphics, B
Computer Science, B
Consumer Services and Advocacy, B
Counselor Education/School Counseling and Guid-
  ance Services, MO
Criminal Justice/Safety Studies, B
Dietetics/Dieticians, B
Drama and Dramatics/Theatre Arts, B
Economics, B
Education, BMO
Educational Media/Instructional Technology, M
Educational Psychology, MO
Elementary Education and Teaching, BM
Engineering Science, B
English Language and Literature, B
English/Language Arts Teacher Education, B
Environmental Studies, B
Family and Consumer Sciences/Home Economics
  Teacher Education, B
Family and Consumer Sciences/Human Sciences, B
Fashion Merchandising, B
Fine/Studio Arts, B
Foodservice Systems
  Administration/Management, B

French Language Teacher Education, B
French Language and Literature, B
Geography, B
Geology/Earth Science, B
Geosciences, M
Gerontology, B
Hispanic-American, Puerto Rican, and Mexican-
American/Chicano Studies, B
History, B
Hydrology and Water Resources Science, B
International Relations and Affairs, B
Junior High/Intermediate/Middle School Education
and Teaching, B
Kindergarten/PreSchool Education and Teaching, B
Liberal Arts and Sciences Studies and Humani-
ties, B
Mass Communication/Media Studies, B
Mathematics, B
Mathematics Teacher Education, B
Middle School Education, M
Museology/Museum Studies, M
Music, B
Nutritional Sciences, M
Philosophy, B
Physics, B
Physics Teacher Education, B
Political Science and Government, B
Pre-Dentistry Studies, B
Pre-Law Studies, B
Pre-Medicine/Pre-Medical Studies, B
Pre-Veterinary Studies, B
Psychology, B
Reading Teacher Education, BM
Science Teacher Education/General Science
Teacher Education, B
Secondary Education and Teaching, BM
Social Science Teacher Education, B
Sociology, B
Spanish Language Teacher Education, B
Spanish Language and Literature, B
Special Education and Teaching, M
Statistics, B

STATE UNIVERSITY OF NEW YORK COLLEGE AT POTSDAM

Anthropology, B
Archeology, B
Art History, Criticism and Conservation, B
Biochemistry, B
Biology Teacher Education, B
Biology/Biological Sciences, B
Business Administration and Management, B
Business/Managerial Economics, B
Chemistry, B
Chemistry Teacher Education, B
Communication Studies/Speech Communication
and Rhetoric, B
Communication and Media Studies, M
Community Health and Preventive Medicine, M
Computer Science, B
Criminal Justice/Safety Studies, B
Curriculum and Instruction, M
Dance, B
Drama and Dance Teacher Education, B
Drama and Dramatics/Theatre Arts, B
Early Childhood Education and Teaching, BM
Economics, B
Educational Media/Instructional Technology, M
Elementary Education and Teaching, BM
English, M
English Education, M
English Language and Literature, B
English/Language Arts Teacher Education, B
Environmental Studies, B
Exercise Physiology, B
Fine/Studio Arts, B
French Language Teacher Education, B
French Language and Literature, B
Geology/Earth Science, B
History, B
International/Global Studies, B
Labor and Industrial Relations, B
Mathematics, BM
Mathematics Teacher Education, BM
Middle School Education, M
Music, BM

Music Performance, B
Music Teacher Education, BM
Music Theory and Composition, B
Natural Sciences, B
Organizational Management, M
Performance, M
Philosophy, B
Physics, B
Physics Teacher Education, B
Psychology, B
Reading Teacher Education, M
Science Teacher Education/General Science
Teacher Education, M
Secondary Education and Teaching, M
Social Studies Teacher Education, BM
Sociology, B
Spanish Language Teacher Education, B
Spanish Language and Literature, B
Special Education and Teaching, M
Women's Studies, B

STATE UNIVERSITY OF NEW YORK COLLEGE OF TECHNOLOGY AT AL-FRED

Accounting Technology/Technician and Bookkeep-
ing, A
Agribusiness, A
Agriculture, A
Animation, Interactive Technology, Video Graphics
and Special Effects, AB
Architectural Engineering Technology/Technician, AB
Architecture, B
Autobody/Collision and Repair
Technology/Technician, A
Automobile/Automotive Mechanics
Technology/Technician, A
Biology/Biological Sciences, A
Business Administration and Management, AB
Business, Management, Marketing, and Related
Support Services, B
Computer Engineering Technology/Technician, AB
Computer Programming, Specific Applications, B
Computer and Information Sciences, A
Computer and Information Systems Security, B
Construction Engineering Technology/Technician, A
Construction Management, AB
Construction Trades, A
Court Reporting/Court Reporter, A
Criminology, A
Culinary Arts/Chef Training, A
Diesel Mechanics Technology/Technician, A
Drafting and Design Technology/Technician, A
Electrical and Power Transmission
Installation/Installer, A
Electrical, Electronic and Communications Engineer-
ing Technology/Technician, AB
Engineering, A
Environmental Engineering
Technology/Environmental Technology, A
Environmental Sciences, A
Financial Planning and Services, B
Forensic Science and Technology, B
General Studies, AB
Graphic Design, A
Health Information/Medical Records
Technology/Technician, A
Heating, Air Conditioning, Ventilation and Refrigera-
tion Maintenance Technology/Technician, A
Heavy/Industrial Equipment Maintenance Technolo-
gies, A
Human Resources Management/Personnel Adminis-
tration, B
Human Services, A
Humanities/Humanistic Studies, A
Information Science/Studies, A
Interior Design, A
Intermedia/Multimedia, B
Liberal Arts and Sciences Studies and Humani-
ties, A
Machine Shop Technology/Assistant, A
Mason/Masonry, A
Mechanical Engineering/Mechanical
Technology/Technician, A
Radiologic Technology/Science - Radiographer, A
Sales, Distribution and Marketing Operations, A
Sport and Fitness Administration/Management, A

Survey Technology/Surveying, AB
System, Networking, and LAN/WAN
Management/Manager, B
Vehicle Maintenance and Repair Technologies, A
Veterinary/Animal Health Technology/Technician and
Veterinary Assistant, A
Web/Multimedia Management and Webmaster, B
Welding Technology/Welder, A

STATE UNIVERSITY OF NEW YORK COLLEGE OF TECHNOLOGY AT CANTON

Accounting Technology/Technician and Bookkeep-
ing, A
Automobile/Automotive Mechanics
Technology/Technician, A
Building/Construction Site Management/Manager, A
Business Administration and Management, AB
Business, Management, Marketing, and Related
Support Services, B
Child Care and Support Services Management, A
Civil Engineering Technology/Technician, AB
Corrections and Criminal Justice, B
Criminal Justice/Law Enforcement Administration, B
Criminal Justice/Police Science, A
Dental Hygiene/Hygienist, AB
Electrical, Electronic and Communications Engineer-
ing Technology/Technician, AB
Engineering, A
Engineering Technologies/Technicians, A
Engineering/Industrial Management, B
Finance, B
General Studies, A
Graphic Design, B
Health and Medical Administrative Services, B
Health/Health Care Administration/Management, B
Heating, Air Conditioning and Refrigeration
Technology/Technician, A
Information Science/Studies, A
Information Technology, B
Legal Assistant/Paralegal, B
Mechanical Engineering Related
Technologies/Technicians, B
Mechanical Engineering/Mechanical
Technology/Technician, A
Natural Resources and Conservation, B
Physical Therapist Assistant, A
Pre-Veterinary Studies, B
Public Health Education and Promotion, B
Veterinary/Animal Health Technology/Technician and
Veterinary Assistant, AB

STATE UNIVERSITY OF NEW YORK COLLEGE OF TECHNOLOGY AT DELHI

Accounting Technology/Technician and Bookkeep-
ing, A
Applied Horticulture/Horticultural Operations, A
Architectural Engineering Technology/Technician, A
Architecture and Related Services, B
Auditing, B
Automobile/Automotive Mechanics
Technology/Technician, A
Business Administration and Management, A
Business, Management, Marketing, and Related
Support Services, B
CAD/CADD Drafting and/or Design
Technology/Technician, A
Construction Engineering Technology/Technician, A
Construction Management, B
Criminal Justice/Safety Studies, B
Culinary Arts/Chef Training, A
Curriculum and Instruction, A
Electrical and Power Transmission
Installation/Installer, A
Electrical, Electronic and Communications Engineer-
ing Technology/Technician, A
Electromechanical Technology/Electromechanical
Engineering Technology, A
General Merchandising, Sales, and Related Market-
ing Operations, A
General Studies, A
Health and Physical Education, A
Heating, Air Conditioning, Ventilation and Refrigera-
tion Maintenance Technology/Technician, A
Hospitality Administration/Management, B
Humanities/Humanistic Studies, A

Information Science/Studies, A
Landscaping and Groundskeeping, A
Liberal Arts and Sciences Studies and Humanities, A
Natural Resources Management/Development and Policy, A
Nursing Education, M
Pipefitting/Pipefitter and Sprinkler Fitter, A
Resort Management, A
Restaurant, Culinary, and Catering Management/Manager, AB
Sport and Fitness Administration/Management, A
Tourism and Travel Services Marketing Operations, A
Veterinary/Animal Health Technology/Technician and Veterinary Assistant, AB
Welding Technology/Welder, A

STATE UNIVERSITY OF NEW YORK DOWNSTATE MEDICAL CENTER

Allopathic Medicine, MD
Biological and Biomedical Sciences, MD
Biomedical Engineering, MD
Cell Biology and Anatomy, D
Community Health and Preventive Medicine, M
Diagnostic Medical Sonography/Sonographer and Ultrasound Technician, B
Medical/Surgical Nursing, MO
Molecular Biology, D
Neuroscience, D
Nurse Anesthetist, M
Nurse Midwife/Nursing Midwifery, MO
Nursing, MO
Nursing - Advanced Practice, MO
Occupational Therapy/Therapist, B
Physical Therapy/Therapist, B
Physician Assistant, B
Public Health, M

STATE UNIVERSITY OF NEW YORK EMPIRE STATE COLLEGE

Adult and Continuing Education and Teaching, M
Art/Art Studies, General, AB
Business Administration, Management and Operations, M
Business/Commerce, AB
Community Organization and Advocacy, AB
Economic Development, M
Education, ABM
Educational Media/Instructional Technology, M
English Language and Literature, AB
History, AB
Industrial and Labor Relations, M
International Business/Trade/Commerce, M
Labor and Industrial Relations, AB
Liberal Studies, M
Management, M
Multi-/Interdisciplinary Studies, AB
Nursing Education, M
Physical Sciences, AB
Psychology, AB
Public Administration and Social Service Professions, B
Public Policy Analysis, M
Social Sciences, AB

STATE UNIVERSITY OF NEW YORK AT FREDONIA

Accounting, B
American/United States Studies/Civilization, B
Art History, Criticism and Conservation, B
Art/Art Studies, General, B
Audiology/Audiologist and Speech-Language Pathology/Pathologist, B
Biochemistry, B
Biological and Biomedical Sciences, M
Biological and Physical Sciences, B
Biology Technician/BioTechnology Laboratory Technician, B
Biology/Biological Sciences, B
Biomedical Sciences, B
Business Administration and Management, B
Chemistry, B
Clinical Laboratory Science/Medical Technology/Technologist, B

Commercial and Advertising Art, B
Communication Disorders, BM
Computer Graphics, B
Computer Science, B
Criminal Justice/Law Enforcement Administration, B
Dance, B
Design and Applied Arts, B
Drama and Dramatics/Theatre Arts, B
Drawing, B
Early Childhood Education and Teaching, M
Economics, B
Education, BM
Elementary Education and Teaching, B
English Language and Literature, B
English as a Second Language, M
Environmental Studies, B
Film/Cinema Studies, B
Finance, B
Fine/Studio Arts, B
French Language and Literature, B
Geochemistry, B
Geology/Earth Science, B
Geophysics and Seismology, B
History, B
Information Science/Studies, B
Interdisciplinary Studies, M
Intermedia/Multimedia, B
Kindergarten/PreSchool Education and Teaching, B
Labor and Industrial Relations, B
Law and Legal Studies, B
Liberal Arts and Sciences Studies and Humanities, B
Marketing/Marketing Management, B
Mass Communication/Media Studies, B
Mathematics, B
Middle School Education, M
Music, B
Music History, Literature, and Theory, B
Music Teacher Education, BM
Music Therapy/Therapist, B
Philosophy, B
Physics, B
Piano and Organ, B
Political Science and Government, B
Pre-Law Studies, B
Pre-Medicine/Pre-Medical Studies, B
Pre-Veterinary Studies, B
Psychology, B
Radio and Television, B
Reading Teacher Education, M
Recording Arts Technology/Technician, B
Science Teacher Education/General Science Teacher Education, B
Secondary Education and Teaching, BM
Social Work, B
Sociology, B
Spanish Language and Literature, B
Violin, Viola, Guitar and Other Stringed Instruments, B
Voice and Opera, B
Women's Studies, B

STATE UNIVERSITY OF NEW YORK MARITIME COLLEGE

Atmospheric Sciences and Meteorology, B
Business, Management, Marketing, and Related Support Services, B
Electrical, Electronics and Communications Engineering, B
Engineering Technologies/Technicians, A
General Studies, B
Industrial Engineering, B
Liberal Arts and Sciences Studies and Humanities, B
Marine Science/Merchant Marine Officer, B
Mechanical Engineering, B
Naval Architecture and Marine Engineering, B
Transportation/Transportation Management, M

STATE UNIVERSITY OF NEW YORK AT NEW PALTZ

Accounting, BM
Accounting and Related Services, B
African-American/Black Studies, B
Anthropology, B
Art Education, M

Art History, Criticism and Conservation, B
Art Teacher Education, B
Asian Studies/Civilization, B
Astronomy, B
Biochemistry, B
Biology Teacher Education, B
Biology/Biological Sciences, B
Business Administration and Management, B
Business Administration, Management and Operations, BM
Business Operations Support and Secretarial Services, B
Business/Commerce, B
Ceramic Arts and Ceramics, BM
Chemistry, BM
Chemistry Teacher Education, B
Communication Disorders, BM
Communication Studies/Speech Communication and Rhetoric, B
Computer Engineering, B
Computer Science, M
Computer and Information Sciences, B
Counseling Psychology, MO
Counselor Education/School Counseling and Guidance Services, M
Digital Communication and Media/Multimedia, B
Drama and Dramatics/Theatre Arts, B
Early Childhood Education and Teaching, M
Economics, B
Education, BMO
Educational Administration and Supervision, MO
Educational Leadership and Administration, M
Electrical Engineering, M
Electrical, Electronics and Communications Engineering, B
Elementary Education and Teaching, BM
English, M
English Education, M
English Language and Literature, B
English as a Second Language, MO
English/Language Arts Teacher Education, B
Finance, B
Finance and Financial Management Services, B
Fine Arts and Art Studies, M
French Language and Literature, BM
General Studies, B
Geochemistry, B
Geography, B
Geology/Earth Science, B
Geosciences, M
Graphic Design, B
History, B
International Business/Trade/Commerce, B
International Relations and Affairs, B
Jewelry/Metalsmithing, M
Journalism, B
Latin American Studies, B
Liberal Arts and Sciences Studies and Humanities, B
Marketing, B
Marketing/Marketing Management, B
Mathematics, B
Mathematics Teacher Education, BM
Mechanical Engineering, B
Metal and Jewelry Arts, B
Multilingual and Multicultural Education, MO
Music, BM
Music Therapy/Therapist, M
Painting, BM
Philosophy, B
Photography, B
Physics, B
Physics Teacher Education, B
Political Science and Government, B
Printmaking, BM
Psychology, BMO
Reading Teacher Education, M
Science Teacher Education/General Science Teacher Education, BM
Sculpture, BM
Secondary Education and Teaching, MO
Social Studies Teacher Education, BM
Sociology, B
Spanish Language Teacher Education, B
Spanish Language and Literature, BM
Special Education and Teaching, M

Visual and Performing Arts, B
Women's Studies, B

STATE UNIVERSITY OF NEW YORK AT OSWEGO

Accounting, B
Accounting and Related Services, B
Agricultural Education, M
Agricultural Teacher Education, B
American/United States Studies/Civilization, B
Anthropology, B
Applied Mathematics, B
Art Education, M
Art/Art Studies, General, B
Atmospheric Sciences and Meteorology, B
Biochemistry, B
Biology/Biological Sciences, B
Broadcast Journalism, B
Business Administration and Management, B
Business Education, M
Chemistry, BM
Child and Family Studies, M
Cognitive Sciences, B
Commercial and Advertising Art, B
Computer Science, B
Computer Software Engineering, B
Consumer Economics, M
Counseling Psychology, M
Criminal Justice/Law Enforcement Administration, B
Curriculum and Instruction, M
Drama and Dramatics/Theatre Arts, B
Early Childhood Education and Teaching, M
Econometrics and Quantitative Economics, B
Economics, B
Education, BMO
Educational Administration and Supervision, O
Educational Leadership and Administration, O
Electrical, Electronics and Communications Engineering, B
Elementary Education and Teaching, BM
Engineering, B
English, M
English Language and Literature, B
Finance, B
Fine Arts and Art Studies, M
French Language and Literature, B
Geochemistry, B
Geology/Earth Science, B
German Language and Literature, B
Health Teacher Education, B
History, BM
Human Development and Family Studies, B
Human Resources Management/Personnel Administration, B
Human-Computer Interaction, M
Industrial Education, M
Information Science/Studies, B
International Economics, B
International Relations and Affairs, B
Journalism, B
Linguistics, B
Management Science, B
Marketing/Marketing Management, B
Mass Communication/Media Studies, B
Mathematics, B
Middle School Education, M
Music, B
Philosophy, B
Philosophy and Religious Studies, B
Physics, B
Political Science and Government, B
Pre-Dentistry Studies, B
Pre-Law Studies, B
Pre-Medicine/Pre-Medical Studies, B
Pre-Veterinary Studies, B
Psychology, B
Public Relations/Image Management, B
Reading Teacher Education, M
Sales and Marketing Operations/Marketing and Distribution Teacher Education, B
Science Teacher Education/General Science Teacher Education, B
Secondary Education and Teaching, BM
Sociology, B
Spanish Language and Literature, B
Special Education and Teaching, M

Sport and Fitness Administration/Management, B
Technology Teacher Education/Industrial Arts Teacher Education, B
Trade and Industrial Teacher Education, B
Vocational and Technical Education, M
Women's Studies, B
Zoology/Animal Biology, B

STATE UNIVERSITY OF NEW YORK AT PLATTSBURGH

Accounting, B
Anthropology, B
Area Studies, B
Art/Art Studies, General, B
Audiology/Audiologist and Speech-Language Pathology/Pathologist, B
Biochemistry, B
Biology Teacher Education, B
Biology/Biological Sciences, B
Business Administration and Management, B
Business, Management, Marketing, and Related Support Services, B
Business/Commerce, B
Business/Managerial Economics, B
Chemistry, B
Chemistry Teacher Education, B
Clinical Laboratory Science/Medical Technology/Technologist, B
Clinical Psychology, MO
Communication Disorders, M
Communication Studies/Speech Communication and Rhetoric, B
Computer and Information Sciences, B
Counseling Psychology, MO
Counselor Education/School Counseling and Guidance Services, MO
Criminal Justice/Safety Studies, B
Curriculum and Instruction, M
CytoTechnology/Cytotechnologist, B
Drama and Dramatics/Theatre Arts, B
Early Childhood Education and Teaching, O
Ecology, B
Economics, B
Education, B
Education/Teaching of Individuals with Specific Learning Disabilities, B
Educational Leadership and Administration, O
Elementary Education and Teaching, BMO
English Education, M
English Language and Literature, B
English/Language Arts Teacher Education, B
Entrepreneurial and Small Business Operations, B
Environmental Studies, B
Finance, B
Foods, Nutrition, and Wellness Studies, B
Foreign Language Teacher Education, M
French Language Teacher Education, B
French Language and Literature, B
Geography, B
Geology/Earth Science, B
History, B
Hotel/Motel Administration/Management, B
Human Development and Family Studies, B
International Business/Trade/Commerce, B
Journalism, B
Latin American Studies, B
Liberal Arts and Sciences Studies and Humanities, B
Management Information Systems and Services, B
Marketing/Marketing Management, B
Mathematics, B
Mathematics Teacher Education, M
Medical Informatics, B
Music, B
Natural Resources and Conservation, B
Philosophy, B
Physics, B
Political Science and Government, B
Psychology, BMO
Reading Teacher Education, M
School Psychology, MO
Science Teacher Education/General Science Teacher Education, M
Secondary Education and Teaching, M
Social Studies Teacher Education, M
Social Work, B

Sociology, B
Spanish Language and Literature, B
Special Education and Teaching, BM
Student Personnel Services, M
Women's Studies, B

STATE UNIVERSITY OF NEW YORK POLYTECHNIC INSTITUTE

Accounting, BM
Applied Mathematics, B
Biology/Biological Sciences, B
Business Administration and Management, B
Business Administration, Management and Operations, M
Civil Engineering, B
Civil Engineering Technology/Technician, B
Communication, Journalism and Related Programs, B
Computer Engineering Technology/Technician, B
Computer Science, M
Computer and Information Systems Security, BM
Electrical, Electronic and Communications Engineering Technology/Technician, B
Electrical, Electronics and Communications Engineering, B
Engineering, B
Finance and Banking, M
General Studies, B
Health Information/Medical Records Administration/Administrator, B
Human Resources Management and Services, M
Information Science/Studies, BM
Management of Technology, M
Marketing, M
Mechanical Engineering, B
Mechanical Engineering/Mechanical Technology/Technician, B
NanoTechnology, MD
Nursing - Advanced Practice, MO
Nursing Administration, M
Nursing Education, MO
Psychology, B
Social Sciences, B
Sociology, B
Telecommunications, M

STATE UNIVERSITY OF NEW YORK UPSTATE MEDICAL UNIVERSITY

Allopathic Medicine, D
Anatomy, MD
Biochemistry, MD
Biological and Biomedical Sciences, MD
Cell Biology and Anatomy, MD
Clinical Laboratory Science/Medical Technology/Technologist, B
Immunology, MD
Medical Radiologic Technology/Science - Radiation Therapist, B
Medical Technology, M
Microbiology, MD
Molecular Biology, MD
Neuroscience, D
Nursing, MO
Nursing - Advanced Practice, O
Perfusion Technology/Perfusionist, B
Pharmacology, D
Physical Therapy/Therapist, D
Physiology, MD
Radiologic Technology/Science - Radiographer, B
Respiratory Care Therapy/Therapist, B

STONY BROOK UNIVERSITY, STATE UNIVERSITY OF NEW YORK

African Studies, MO
African-American/Black Studies, B
Allopathic Medicine, D
American/United States Studies/Civilization, B
Anatomy, D
Anthropology, BMD
Applied Mathematics, BMDO
Art History, Criticism and Conservation, BMD
Art/Art Studies, General, B
Asian Studies/Civilization, B
Astronomy, BD

Athletic Training and Sports Medicine, B
Atmospheric Sciences and Meteorology, BMD
Biochemistry, BMD
Bioinformatics, MD
Biological and Biomedical Sciences, MDO
Biological and Physical Sciences, B
Biology/Biological Sciences, B
Biomedical Engineering, MDO
Biomedical/Medical Engineering, B
Biophysics, D
Business Administration and Management, B
Business Administration, Management and Operations, MO
Cell Biology and Anatomy, MD
Chemistry, BMD
Civil Engineering, B
Clinical Laboratory Science/Medical Technology/Technologist, B
Clinical Psychology, D
Cognitive Sciences, D
Community Health and Preventive Medicine, MD
Comparative Literature, BMDO
Computer Education, M
Computer Engineering, BMD
Computer Science, MDO
Computer and Information Sciences, B
Cultural Studies, DO
Dentistry, DO
Developmental Biology and Embryology, D
Drama and Dramatics/Theatre Arts, B
Ecology, BMD
Economics, BMD
Educational Administration and Supervision, MO
Educational Leadership and Administration, O
Educational Media/Instructional Technology, MO
Electrical Engineering, MD
Electrical, Electronics and Communications Engineering, B
Engineering, B
Engineering and Applied Sciences, MDO
English, MDO
English Education, M
English Language and Literature, B
English as a Second Language, M
Environmental Design/Architecture, B
Environmental Policy and Resource Management, MO
Environmental Studies, B
European Studies/Civilization, B
Evolutionary Biology, BMD
Experimental Psychology, D
Finance and Banking, MO
Fine Arts and Art Studies, M
Foreign Language Teacher Education, M
French Language and Literature, BM
Genetics, D
Geographic Information Systems, O
Geology/Earth Science, B
Geosciences, MD
German Language and Literature, B
Health Communication, O
Health Psychology, D
Health Services Administration, MDO
Health Services/Allied Health/Health Sciences, B
Higher Education/Higher Education Administration, MO
Hispanic and Latin American Languages, MD
History, BMD
Human Resources Management and Services, MO
Immunology, D
Information Science/Studies, B
Italian Language and Literature, BM
Journalism, BMO
Liberal Studies, M
Linguistics, BMD
Management Information Systems and Services, MO
Management of Technology, M
Marine Affairs, M
Marine Biology and Biological Oceanography, B
Marine Sciences, MD
Marketing, M
Materials Engineering, MD
Materials Sciences, MD
Maternal/Child Health and Neonatal Nurse/Nursing, MDO

Maternity Nursing, MDO
Mathematics, BMD
Mathematics Teacher Education, M
Mechanical Engineering, BMD
Medical Physics, MD
Microbiology, D
Molecular Biology, MD
Molecular Genetics, D
Molecular Physiology, D
Multi-/Interdisciplinary Studies, B
Music, M
Music History, Literature, and Theory, MD
Music Theory and Composition, MD
Neuroscience, MD
Nurse Midwife/Nursing Midwifery, MDO
Nursing, MDO
Nursing - Adult, MDO
Nursing - Advanced Practice, MDO
Nursing Education, MO
Nutritional Sciences, MO
Occupational Therapy/Therapist, M
Oral Biology, MD
Oral Pathology, MD
Oral and Dental Sciences, O
Orthodontics, O
Pathology/Experimental Pathology, D
Pediatric Nurse/Nursing, MDO
Performance, MD
Periodontics, O
Pharmacology, BD
Philosophy, BMDO
Physical Education Teaching and Coaching, O
Physical Sciences, B
Physical Therapy/Therapist, D
Physician Assistant, M
Physics, BMD
Physiology, D
Political Science and Government, BMD
Psychiatric/Mental Health Nurse/Nursing, MDO
Psychology, BMD
Public Health, MO
Public Policy Analysis, M
Religion/Religious Studies, B
Respiratory Care Therapy/Therapist, B
Romance Languages, Literatures, and Linguistics, M
Science Teacher Education/General Science Teacher Education, MD
Social Psychology, D
Social Studies Teacher Education, M
Social Work, BMD
Sociology, BMD
Software Engineering, O
Spanish Language and Literature, B
Statistics, MDO
Structural Biology, D
Substance Abuse/Addiction Counseling, M
Systems Engineering, M
Technology and Public Policy, D
Theater, M
Women's Health Nursing, MDO
Women's Studies, BO
Writing, MO

SUFFOLK COUNTY COMMUNITY COLLEGE

Accounting, A
Art/Art Studies, General, A
Automobile/Automotive Mechanics Technology/Technician, A
Biological and Physical Sciences, A
Biology/Biological Sciences, A
Business Administration and Management, A
Chemistry, A
Child Development, A
Civil Engineering Technology/Technician, A
Communications Systems Installation and Repair Technology, A
Computer Programming/Programmer, A
Computer Science, A
Computer and Information Sciences and Support Services, A
Construction Engineering Technology/Technician, A
Consumer Merchandising/Retailing Management, A
Criminal Justice/Law Enforcement Administration, A
Criminal Justice/Police Science, A

Culinary Arts/Chef Training, A
Data Processing and Data Processing Technology/Technician, A
Dietetics/Dieticians, A
Drafting and Design Technology/Technician, A
Drama and Dramatics/Theatre Arts, A
Electrical, Electronic and Communications Engineering Technology/Technician, A
Engineering, A
Engineering Science, A
English Language and Literature, A
Human Services, A
Humanities/Humanistic Studies, A
Information Science/Studies, A
Information Technology, A
Interior Design, A
Journalism, A
Kindergarten/PreSchool Education and Teaching, A
Legal Assistant/Paralegal, A
Liberal Arts and Sciences Studies and Humanities, A
Marketing/Marketing Management, A
Mathematics, A
Music, A
Photographic and Film/Video Technology/Technician and Assistant, A
Physical Therapy/Therapist, A
Sign Language Interpretation and Translation, A
Social Sciences, A
Substance Abuse/Addiction Counseling, A
Women's Studies, A

SULLIVAN COUNTY COMMUNITY COLLEGE

Accounting, A
Administrative Assistant and Secretarial Science, A
Baking and Pastry Arts/Baker/Pastry Chef, A
Business Administration and Management, A
Commercial and Advertising Art, A
Computer Graphics, A
Computer Programming, Specific Applications, A
Construction Engineering Technology/Technician, A
Consumer Merchandising/Retailing Management, A
Criminal Justice/Police Science, A
Culinary Arts/Chef Training, A
Data Entry/Microcomputer Applications, A
Electrical, Electronic and Communications Engineering Technology/Technician, A
Elementary Education and Teaching, A
Environmental Studies, A
Fire Protection and Safety Technology/Technician, A
Forensic Science and Technology, A
Hospitality Administration/Management, A
Human Services, A
Information Science/Studies, A
Kindergarten/PreSchool Education and Teaching, A
Legal Assistant/Paralegal, A
Liberal Arts and Sciences Studies and Humanities, A
Marketing/Marketing Management, A
Mathematics, A
Medical/Clinical Assistant, A
Parks, Recreation, Leisure and Fitness Studies, A
Photography, A
Psychology, A
Radio and Television, A
Radio, Television, and Digital Communication, A
Respiratory Care Therapy/Therapist, A
Science Technologies/Technicians, A
Sport and Fitness Administration/Management, A
Tourism and Travel Services Management, A

SWEDISH INSTITUTE, COLLEGE OF HEALTH SCIENCES

Acupuncture and Oriental Medicine, M
Massage Therapy/Therapeutic Massage, A
Medical/Clinical Assistant, A
Surgical Technology/Technologist, A

SYRACUSE UNIVERSITY

Accounting, BMD
Acting, B
Advertising, B
Advertising and Public Relations, M
Aerospace, Aeronautical and Astronautical Engineering, BMD

African Studies, M
African-American/Black Studies, BM
Anthropology, BMD
Applied Arts and Design, M
Applied Mathematics, B
Applied Statistics, M
Architectural History and Criticism, B
Architecture, BM
Art Education, M
Art History, Criticism and Conservation, BM
Art Teacher Education, B
Arts Journalism, M
Arts Management, MO
BioTechnology, B
Biochemistry, BD
Bioengineering, MD
Biological and Biomedical Sciences, MD
Biology Teacher Education, B
Biology/Biological Sciences, B
Biomedical/Medical Engineering, B
Biophysics, BD
Broadcast Journalism, BM
Business Administration and Management, B
Business Administration, Management and Operations, MD
Ceramic Arts and Ceramics, BM
Chemical Engineering, BMD
Chemistry, BMD
Chemistry Teacher Education, B
Child and Family Studies, MD
Cinematography and Film/Video Production, B
Civil Engineering, BMD
Classical, Ancient Mediterranean and Near Eastern Studies and Archaeology, B
Classics and Classical Languages, Literatures, and Linguistics, B
Clinical Psychology, MD
Commercial and Advertising Art, B
Communication Disorders, BMD
Communication Studies/Speech Communication and Rhetoric, B
Communication Theory, M
Communication and Media Studies, MD
Community Health and Preventive Medicine, M
Comparative Literature, B
Composition, M
Computer Art and Design, M
Computer Engineering, BMDO
Computer Science, M
Computer and Information Sciences, B
Computer and Information Sciences and Support Services, B
Computer and Information Systems Security, MO
Conflict Resolution and Mediation/Peace Studies, O
Consumer Merchandising/Retailing Management, B
Counselor Education/School Counseling and Guidance Services, MD
Curriculum and Instruction, MDO
Design and Applied Arts, B
Design and Visual Communications, B
Disability Studies, O
Drama and Dramatics/Theatre Arts, B
Dramatic/Theatre Arts and Stagecraft, B
Early Childhood Education and Teaching, M
Economics, BMD
Education, BMDO
Education/Teaching of Individuals in Early Childhood Special Education Programs, B
Education/Teaching of Individuals with Multiple Disabilities, M
Educational Leadership and Administration, MDO
Educational Measurement and Evaluation, MDO
Educational Media/Instructional Technology, MO
Educational Policy, O
Electrical Engineering, MDO
Electrical, Electronics and Communications Engineering, B
Energy and Power Engineering, M
Engineering Management, M
Engineering and Applied Sciences, MDO
English, MD
English Education, M
English Language and Literature, B
English as a Second Language, MO
English/Language Arts Teacher Education, B
Entertainment Management, M

Entrepreneurship/Entrepreneurial Studies, BM
Environmental Engineering Technology/Environmental Technology, M
Environmental/Environmental Health Engineering, B
Ethics, B
Exercise and Sports Science, M
Experimental Psychology, D
Family and Consumer Sciences/Home Economics Teacher Education, B
Fashion/Apparel Design, B
Fiber, Textile and Weaving Arts, B
Film, Television, and Video Production, M
Film, Television, and Video Theory and Criticism, M
Finance, B
Finance and Banking, MD
Fine/Studio Arts, B
Foods, Nutrition, and Wellness Studies, B
Foreign Languages and Literatures, B
Forensic Science and Technology, BM
Foundations and Philosophy of Education, MDO
French Language and Literature, BM
Geography, BMD
Geology/Earth Science, BMD
German Language and Literature, B
Health Law, O
Health Services Administration, O
Health and Physical Education, B
Higher Education/Higher Education Administration, MD
Historic Preservation and Conservation, O
History, BMD
Hospitality Administration/Management, B
Human Development and Family Studies, B
Human Nutrition, B
Human Resources Development, D
Human Services, B
Illustration, BM
Industrial Design, B
Industrial and Manufacturing Management, D
Information Science/Studies, BMD
Interior Architecture, B
International Affairs, M
International Public Health/International Health, O
International Relations and Affairs, B
Italian Language and Literature, B
Jewelry/Metalsmithing, M
Jewish/Judaic Studies, B
Journalism, BM
Kinesiology and Exercise Science, B
Knowledge Management, B
Latin American Studies, B
Law and Legal Studies, D
Legal Professions and Studies, B
Liberal Arts and Sciences Studies and Humanities, AB
Library Science, M
Linguistics, BM
Logistics and Materials Management, B
Management Information Systems and Services, MDO
Management Strategy and Policy, D
Marketing, MD
Marketing/Marketing Management, B
Marriage and Family Therapy/Counseling, M
Mass Communication/Media Studies, MD
Maternal and Child Health, M
Mathematics, BMD
Mathematics Teacher Education, BMD
Mechanical Engineering, BMD
Mechanical Engineering/Mechanical Technology/Technician, A
Media Studies, M
Metal and Jewelry Arts, B
Multi-/Interdisciplinary Studies, B
Museology/Museum Studies, M
Music, B
Music History, Literature, and Theory, B
Music Performance, B
Music Teacher Education, BM
Music Theory and Composition, B
Near and Middle Eastern Studies, B
Nutritional Sciences, BM
Organizational Behavior Studies, D
Organizational Management, O
Painting, BM
Performance, M

Philosophy, BMD
Philosophy and Religious Studies, B
Photography, BM
Photojournalism, B
Physical Education Teaching and Coaching, B
Physics, BMD
Physics Teacher Education, B
Piano and Organ, B
Political Science and Government, BMDO
Pre-Dentistry Studies, B
Pre-Law Studies, B
Pre-Medicine/Pre-Medical Studies, B
Pre-Veterinary Studies, B
Printmaking, BM
Psychology, B
Public Administration, BMDO
Public Health, MO
Public Health (MPH, DPH), B
Public Relations/Image Management, B
Quantitative Analysis, D
Radio and Television, B
Reading Teacher Education, M
Real Estate, B
Religion/Religious Studies, BMD
Rhetoric, MD
Russian Language and Literature, B
Russian Studies, B
Sales, Distribution and Marketing Operations, B
School Psychology, MDO
Science Teacher Education/General Science Teacher Education, MD
Sculpture, BM
Secondary Education and Teaching, M
Social Psychology, D
Social Sciences, MD
Social Studies Teacher Education, BM
Social Work, BM
Sociology, BD
Spanish Language Teacher Education, B
Spanish Language and Literature, BM
Special Education and Teaching, MD
Sport and Fitness Administration/Management, BM
Structural Biology, D
Student Personnel Services, M
Substance Abuse/Addiction Counseling, O
Supply Chain Management, MD
Systems Engineering, O
Systems Science and Theory, B
Technical Theatre/Theatre Design and Technology, B
Telecommunications, M
Telecommunications Management, MO
Travel and Tourism, M
Urban and Regional Planning, O
Violin, Viola, Guitar and Other Stringed Instruments, B
Voice and Opera, B
Women's Studies, B
Writing, MD

TALMUDICAL INSTITUTE OF UPSTATE NEW YORK

Talmudic Studies, B

TALMUDICAL SEMINARY OHOLEI TORAH

Rabbinical Studies, B

TCI–COLLEGE OF TECHNOLOGY

Accounting Technology/Technician and Bookkeeping, A
Automobile/Automotive Mechanics Technology/Technician, A
Building/Property Maintenance and Management, A
Business Administration and Management, A
Computer Software Technology/Technician, A
Computer Systems Networking and Telecommunications, A
Digital Communication and Media/Multimedia, A
Health Information/Medical Records Technology/Technician, A
Heating, Air Conditioning and Refrigeration Technology/Technician, A
Human Services, A
Legal Assistant/Paralegal, A
Optometric Technician/Assistant, A

Securities Services Administration/Management, A

TOMPKINS CORTLAND COMMUNITY COLLEGE

Accounting Technology/Technician and Bookkeeping, A
Administrative Assistant and Secretarial Science, A
Biology Technician/BioTechnology Laboratory Technician, A
Business Administration and Management, A
Child Care and Support Services Management, A
Commercial and Advertising Art, A
Communication Studies/Speech Communication and Rhetoric, A
Computer and Information Sciences, A
Construction Engineering Technology/Technician, A
Criminal Justice/Law Enforcement Administration, A
Criminal Justice/Police Science, A
Culinary Arts/Chef Training, A
Digital Communication and Media/Multimedia, A
Engineering, A
Entrepreneurship/Entrepreneurial Studies, A
Environmental Studies, A
Human Services, A
Humanities/Humanistic Studies, A
Information Science/Studies, A
International Business/Trade/Commerce, A
International/Global Studies, A
Legal Assistant/Paralegal, A
Liberal Arts and Sciences Studies and Humanities, A
Parks, Recreation and Leisure Facilities Management, A
Parks, Recreation, Leisure and Fitness Studies, A
Photographic and Film/Video Technology/Technician and Assistant, A
Radio and Television Broadcasting Technology/Technician, A
Special Products Marketing Operations, A
Sport and Fitness Administration/Management, A
Substance Abuse/Addiction Counseling, A

TORAH TEMIMAH TALMUDICAL SEMINARY

Talmudic Studies, B

TOURO COLLEGE

Accounting, B
American History (United States), B
Audiology/Audiologist and Speech-Language Pathology/Pathologist, B
Banking and Financial Support Services, A
Biology/Biological Sciences, B
Business Administration and Management, AB
Communication Disorders, M
Community Organization and Advocacy, AB
Comparative Literature, B
Computer Science, B
Counseling Psychology, M
Counselor Education/School Counseling and Guidance Services, M
Economics, B
Education, M
Educational Leadership and Administration, M
Educational Media/Instructional Technology, M
English Language and Literature, B
English as a Second Language, M
Finance, B
Health Professions and Related Clinical Sciences, B
History, B
Humanities/Humanistic Studies, B
Industrial and Organizational Psychology, M
Information Science/Studies, AB
Internet and Interactive Multimedia, M
Jewish/Judaic Studies, M
Law and Legal Studies, MD
Legal and Justice Studies, M
Liberal Arts and Sciences Studies and Humanities, AB
Management Information Systems and Services, M
Mathematics, B
Mathematics Teacher Education, M
Occupational Therapy/Therapist, AM
Physical Therapy/Therapist, AD
Physician Assistant, BM
Political Science and Government, B

Psychology, BM
Reading Teacher Education, M
School Psychology, M
Science Teacher Education/General Science Teacher Education, M
Social Sciences, B
Social Work, M
Sociology, B
Special Education and Teaching, BM

TROCAIRE COLLEGE

Business Administration and Management, A
Computer Systems Networking and Telecommunications, A
Diagnostic Medical Sonography/Sonographer and Ultrasound Technician, B
Dietetic Technician (DTR), A
General Studies, A
Health Information/Medical Records Technology/Technician, A
Hospitality Administration/Management, A
Human Resources Management/Personnel Administration, A
Liberal Arts and Sciences Studies and Humanities, A
Massage Therapy/Therapeutic Massage, A
Medical Informatics, B
Medical/Clinical Assistant, A
Radiologic Technology/Science - Radiographer, B
Surgical Technology/Technologist, A

ULSTER COUNTY COMMUNITY COLLEGE

Accounting Technology/Technician and Bookkeeping, A
Biology Teacher Education, A
Business Administration and Management, A
Chemistry Teacher Education, A
Commercial and Advertising Art, A
Communication Studies/Speech Communication and Rhetoric, A
Community Organization and Advocacy, A
Computer and Information Sciences, A
Computer and Information Sciences and Support Services, A
Criminal Justice/Law Enforcement Administration, A
Drafting/Design Engineering Technologies/Technicians, A
Drama and Dramatics/Theatre Arts, A
Engineering, A
Kindergarten/PreSchool Education and Teaching, A
Liberal Arts and Sciences Studies and Humanities, A
Management Information Systems and Services, A
Mathematics Teacher Education, A
Natural Resources and Conservation, A
Parks, Recreation and Leisure Facilities Management, A
Public Administration and Social Service Professions, A
Science Teacher Education/General Science Teacher Education, A
Social Studies Teacher Education, A
Spanish Language Teacher Education, A
Veterinary/Animal Health Technology/Technician and Veterinary Assistant, A
Visual and Performing Arts, A

UNION COLLEGE

African Studies, B
American/United States Studies/Civilization, B
Anthropology, B
Asian Studies/Civilization, B
Astronomy, B
Biochemistry, B
Biological and Biomedical Sciences, B
Biological and Physical Sciences, B
Biology/Biological Sciences, B
Biomedical/Medical Engineering, B
Business/Managerial Economics, B
Chemistry, B
Chinese Language and Literature, B
Classics and Classical Languages, Literatures, and Linguistics, B
Computer and Information Sciences, B
Economics, B

Electrical, Electronics and Communications Engineering, B
English Language and Literature, B
Fine/Studio Arts, B
Foreign Languages and Literatures, B
French Language and Literature, B
Geological and Earth Sciences/Geosciences, B
Geology/Earth Science, B
German Language and Literature, B
History, B
Humanities/Humanistic Studies, B
Liberal Arts and Sciences Studies and Humanities, B
Mathematics, B
Mechanical Engineering, B
Philosophy, B
Physical Sciences, B
Physics, B
Political Science and Government, B
Psychology, B
Religion/Religious Studies, B
Social Sciences, B
Sociology, B
Spanish Language and Literature, B

UNITED STATES MERCHANT MARINE ACADEMY

Engineering-Related Technologies, B
Engineering/Industrial Management, B
Logistics and Materials Management, B
Marine Engineering, M
Marine Science/Merchant Marine Officer, B
Marine Transportation, B
Naval Architecture and Marine Engineering, B
Transportation and Materials Moving, B

UNITED STATES MILITARY ACADEMY

African Studies, B
American Government and Politics (United States), B
American History (United States), B
Arabic Language and Literature, B
Biology/Biological Sciences, B
Business Administration and Management, B
Chemical Engineering, B
Chemistry, B
Chinese Language and Literature, B
Civil Engineering, B
Civil Engineering Technology/Technician, B
Cognitive Sciences, B
Computer and Information Sciences, B
Computer and Information Sciences and Support Services, B
East Asian Studies, B
Economics, B
Electrical, Electronics and Communications Engineering, B
Engineering/Industrial Management, B
English Language and Literature, B
Environmental Engineering Technology/Environmental Technology, B
Environmental Sciences, B
Environmental Studies, B
Environmental/Environmental Health Engineering, B
European Studies/Civilization, B
Foreign Languages, Literatures, and Linguistics, B
French Language and Literature, B
Geography, B
German Language and Literature, B
History, B
Humanities/Humanistic Studies, B
Information Technology, B
International Relations and Affairs, B
Kinesiology and Exercise Science, B
Latin American Studies, B
Law and Legal Studies, B
Mathematics, B
Mechanical Engineering, B
Mechanical Engineering/Mechanical Technology/Technician, B
Near and Middle Eastern Studies, B
Nuclear Engineering, B
Nuclear Engineering Technology/Technician, B
Operations Research, B
Organizational Behavior Studies, B
Philosophy, B

Physical Sciences, B
Physics, B
Political Science and Government, B
Portuguese Language and Literature, B
Russian Language and Literature, B
Russian Studies, B
Sociology, B
Spanish Language and Literature, B
Systems Engineering, B
Systems Science and Theory, B

UNITED TALMUDICAL SEMINARY

Talmudic Studies, B

UNIVERSITY AT ALBANY, STATE UNIVERSITY OF NEW YORK

Accounting, BM
Actuarial Science, B
African Studies, M
African-American Studies, M
African-American/Black Studies, B
Anthropology, BMD
Art History, Criticism and Conservation, B
Art/Art Studies, General, B
Asian Studies/Civilization, B
Atmospheric Sciences and Meteorology, BMD
Biochemistry, B
Biological and Biomedical Sciences, MD
Biology/Biological Sciences, B
Biostatistics, MD
Business Administration and Management, B
Business Administration, Management and Operations, M
Cell Biology and Anatomy, MD
Chemistry, BMD
Chinese Studies, B
Clinical Psychology, D
Cognitive Sciences, D
Communication Studies/Speech Communication and Rhetoric, B
Communication and Media Studies, MD
Computer Science, BMD
Computer and Information Sciences, B
Conservation Biology, M
Counseling Psychology, MDO
Criminal Justice/Law Enforcement Administration, B
Criminology, MD
Curriculum and Instruction, MDO
Demography, O
Developmental Biology and Embryology, D
Drama and Dramatics/Theatre Arts, B
East Asian Studies, B
Ecology, D
Economics, BMD
Education, MDO
Educational Administration and Supervision, MDO
Educational Measurement and Evaluation, O
Educational Media/Instructional Technology, M
Educational Psychology, MDO
English, MD
English Language and Literature, B
Environmental Policy and Resource Management, M
Environmental Sciences, BM
Environmental and Occupational Health, MD
Epidemiology, MD
Evolutionary Biology, D
Finance and Banking, M
Fine Arts and Art Studies, M
Forensic Science and Technology, M
Geography, BM
Health Services Administration, MD
Hispanic-American, Puerto Rican, and Mexican-American/Chicano Studies, B
History, BMDO
Homeland Security, M
Human Resources Management and Services, M
Immunology, MD
Industrial and Organizational Psychology, MD
Information Science/Studies, BMDO
International/Global Studies, B
Japanese Studies, B
Journalism, B
Latin American Studies, BMDO
Liberal Arts and Sciences Studies and Humanities, B

Liberal Studies, M
Library Science, O
Linguistics, B
Management Information Systems and Services, M
Management of Technology, M
Mass Communication/Media Studies, B
Materials Engineering, B
Mathematics, BMD
Mathematics and Computer Science, B
Medieval and Renaissance Studies, B
Molecular Biology, BD
Multi-/Interdisciplinary Studies, B
Music, B
Neurobiology and Neurophysiology, D
Neuroscience, MD
Non-Profit/Public/Organizational Management, MO
Organizational Behavior Studies, MD
Philosophy, BMD
Physics, BMD
Political Science and Government, BMD
Psychology, BMD
Public Administration, MDO
Public Health, MD
Public Health (MPH, DPH), B
Public History, O
Public Policy Analysis, BMDO
Reading Teacher Education, MDO
Religion/Religious Studies, B
School Psychology, DO
Social Psychology, D
Social Work, BMD
Sociology, BMDO
Spanish Language and Literature, BMD
Special Education and Teaching, MD
Structural Biology, MD
Taxation, M
Toxicology, MD
Urban Studies/Affairs, BO
Urban and Regional Planning, M
Women's Studies, BM

UNIVERSITY AT BUFFALO, THE STATE UNIVERSITY OF NEW YORK

Accounting, BM
Aerospace, Aeronautical and Astronautical Engineering, BMD
African-American/Black Studies, B
Allied Health and Medical Assisting Services, MDO
Allopathic Medicine, D
American/United States Studies/Civilization, BMDO
Anatomy, MD
Anthropology, BMD
Applied Mathematics, B
Architecture, BM
Art History, Criticism and Conservation, BM
Art/Art Studies, General, B
Arts Management, M
Asian Studies/Civilization, B
Audiology/Audiologist and Speech-Language Pathology/Pathologist, B
BioTechnology, BM
Biochemistry, BMD
Bioengineering, MD
Bioinformatics, BMD
Biological and Biomedical Sciences, MD
Biology/Biological Sciences, B
Biomedical Engineering, MD
Biomedical Sciences, D
Biomedical/Medical Engineering, B
Biophysics, BMD
Biostatistics, MD
Business Administration and Management, B
Business Administration, Management and Operations, MD
Canadian Studies, MO
Cancer Biology/Oncology, M
Cell Biology and Anatomy, D
Chemical Engineering, BMD
Chemistry, BMD
Civil Engineering, BMD
Classics and Classical Languages, Literatures, and Linguistics, BMDO
Clinical Laboratory Science/Medical Technology/Technologist, B
Clinical Laboratory Sciences, M
Communication Disorders, MD

Communication Studies/Speech Communication and Rhetoric, B
Communication and Media Studies, MD
Community Health and Preventive Medicine, MD
Comparative Literature, MD
Composition, MD
Computational Sciences, O
Computer Engineering, B
Computer Science, BMDO
Counseling Psychology, MO
Counselor Education/School Counseling and Guidance Services, MDO
Cultural Studies, M
Curriculum and Instruction, D
Dance, B
Dentistry, D
Drama and Dramatics/Theatre Arts, B
Early Childhood Education and Teaching, M
Ecology, MDO
Economics, BMDO
Education, MDO
Education/Teaching of the Gifted and Talented, O
Educational Administration and Supervision, MDO
Educational Leadership and Administration, O
Educational Media/Instructional Technology, MO
Educational Psychology, MDO
Electrical Engineering, MD
Electrical, Electronics and Communications Engineering, B
Electronic Commerce, O
Elementary Education and Teaching, MD
Engineering, B
Engineering Physics, B
Engineering and Applied Sciences, MDO
English, MD
English Education, M
English Language and Literature, B
English as a Second Language, MD
Environmental Design/Architecture, B
Environmental Engineering Technology/Environmental Technology, MD
Environmental Sciences, M
Environmental/Environmental Health Engineering, B
Epidemiology, MD
Ethnic, Cultural Minority, and Gender Studies, B
Evolutionary Biology, MDO
Exercise Physiology, B
Exercise and Sports Science, MDO
Film, Television, and Video Theory and Criticism, M
Film/Cinema Studies, B
Finance and Banking, M
Fine Arts and Art Studies, MD
Fine/Studio Arts, B
Foreign Language Teacher Education, MDO
Foundations and Philosophy of Education, D
French Language and Literature, BMDO
Gender Studies, MD
Genetics, MD
Genomic Sciences, MD
Geographic Information Systems, M
Geography, BMDO
Geological and Earth Sciences/Geosciences, B
Geology/Earth Science, BMD
Geosciences, M
German Language and Literature, BMO
Gerontological Nursing, D
Health Informatics, O
Health Services Administration, M
Higher Education/Higher Education Administration, D
Historic Preservation and Conservation, MO
History, BMD
Human Resources Management and Services, O
Humanities/Humanistic Studies, B
Immunology, MD
Industrial Engineering, B
Industrial/Management Engineering, MD
Information Science/Studies, BMO
International Business/Trade/Commerce, BM
Italian Language and Literature, B
Jewish/Judaic Studies, B
Latin American Studies, M
Law and Legal Studies, MD
Library Science, MO
Linguistics, BMD
Logistics and Materials Management, M

Management, D
Management Information Systems and Services, MO
Mathematics, BMD
Mathematics Teacher Education, MO
Mechanical Engineering, BMD
Media Studies, MDO
Medical Informatics, O
Medicinal and Pharmaceutical Chemistry, MD
Microbiology, MD
Modeling and Simulation, M
Molecular Biology, D
Molecular Pharmacology, D
Multi-/Interdisciplinary Studies, B
Multilingual and Multicultural Education, M
Music, BMDO
Music History, Literature, and Theory, M
Music Performance, B
Music Teacher Education, MO
Music Theory and Composition, MD
Musicology and Ethnomusicology, D
Neuroscience, MD
Nuclear Medical Technology/Technologist, B
Nurse Anesthetist, D
Nursing, MDO
Nursing - Adult, D
Nursing - Advanced Practice, D
Nursing Administration, M
Nutritional Sciences, MDO
Occupational Therapy/Therapist, BM
Oral Biology, D
Oral and Dental Sciences, M
Orthodontics, MO
Pathology/Experimental Pathology, MD
Performance, MO
Pharmaceutical Sciences, MD
Pharmacology, MD
Pharmacology and Toxicology, B
Pharmacy, D
Philosophy, BMD
Physical Therapy/Therapist, D
Physics, BMD
Physiology, MD
Political Science and Government, BMD
Psychiatric/Mental Health Nurse/Nursing, D
Psychology, BMD
Public Health, M
Quantitative Analysis, M
Reading Teacher Education, MO
Real Estate, M
Rehabilitation Counseling, MO
Rehabilitation Sciences, MDO
Romance Languages, Literatures, and Linguistics, MD
Science Teacher Education/General Science Teacher Education, MO
Social Sciences, B
Social Studies Teacher Education, MO
Social Work, MD
Sociology, BMD
Spanish Language and Literature, BMDO
Special Education and Teaching, D
Statistics, B
Structural Biology, MD
Structural Engineering, BMD
Theater, MD
Theoretical and Mathematical Physics, B
Toxicology, MD
Urban Design, MDO
Urban and Regional Planning, MDO

UNIVERSITY OF ROCHESTER

Accounting, M
African-American/Black Studies, B
Allopathic Medicine, D
American Sign Language (ASL), B
American/United States Studies/Civilization, BMD
Anatomy, D
Anthropology, B
Applied Mathematics, B
Archives/Archival Administration, M
Art History, Criticism and Conservation, BMD
Astronomy, D
Biochemistry, D
Bioethics/Medical Ethics, B
Biological and Biomedical Sciences, MD

Biology/Biological Sciences, B
Biomedical Engineering, MD
Biomedical/Medical Engineering, B
Biophysics, D
Biostatistics, M
Business Administration, Management and Operations, MD
Business/Commerce, B
Business/Managerial Economics, B
Chemical Engineering, BMD
Chemistry, BMD
Classics and Classical Languages, Literatures, and Linguistics, B
Clinical Psychology, D
Clinical Research, M
Cognitive Sciences, D
Community Psychology, M
Comparative Literature, B
Composition, MD
Computational Biology, D
Computer Engineering, MD
Computer Science, BMD
Counselor Education/School Counseling and Guidance Services, MD
Curriculum and Instruction, MD
Developmental Psychology, D
Digital Communication and Media/Multimedia, B
East Asian Studies, B
Economics, BMD
Education, MD
Educational Administration and Supervision, D
Educational Leadership and Administration, M
Educational Policy, MD
Electrical Engineering, MD
Electrical, Electronics and Communications Engineering, B
Electronic Commerce, M
Energy Management and Policy, M
Energy and Power Engineering, M
Engineering, B
Engineering Science, B
Engineering Technology, B
Engineering and Applied Sciences, MD
English, MD
English Language and Literature, B
Entrepreneurship/Entrepreneurial Studies, M
Environmental Sciences, B
Environmental Studies, BM
Epidemiology, BD
Ethnomusicology, M
Film/Cinema Studies, B
Finance and Banking, M
Fine Arts and Art Studies, MD
Fine/Studio Arts, B
Foundations and Philosophy of Education, D
French Language and Literature, B
Genetics, D
Genomic Sciences, D
Geological/Geophysical Engineering, B
Geology/Earth Science, BMD
Geosciences, MD
German Language and Literature, B
Health Services Administration, M
Health Services Research, D
Higher Education/Higher Education Administration, MD
Historic Preservation and Conservation, M
History, BMD
Human Development, MD
Immunology, MD
Industrial and Manufacturing Management, M
International Affairs, MD
International Business/Trade/Commerce, M
International Relations and Affairs, B
Japanese Language and Literature, B
Jazz/Jazz Studies, B
Liberal Arts and Sciences Studies and Humanities, B
Linguistics, BM
Management, M
Management Information Systems and Services, M
Management Strategy and Policy, M
Marketing, M
Marriage and Family Therapy/Counseling, M
Materials Sciences, MD

Maternal/Child Health and Neonatal Nurse/Nursing, M
Mathematics, BMD
Mathematics and Statistics, B
Mechanical Engineering, BMD
Microbiology, MD
Molecular Biology, D
Multi-/Interdisciplinary Studies, B
Music, BMD
Music Performance, B
Music Teacher Education, BMD
Music Theory and Composition, BMD
Musicology and Ethnomusicology, D
Neurobiology and Neurophysiology, D
Neuroscience, D
Nursing, MD
Nursing - Advanced Practice, M
Nursing Administration, M
Optics/Optical Sciences, BMD
Oral and Dental Sciences, M
Pathology/Experimental Pathology, D
Pediatric Nurse/Nursing, M
Performance, MD
Pharmacology, MD
Philosophy, BMD
Photography, M
Physics, BMD
Physiology, MD
Political Science and Government, BD
Psychiatric/Mental Health Nurse/Nursing, M
Psychology, BD
Public Health, M
Public Health (MPH, DPH), B
Public Policy Analysis, M
Religion/Religious Studies, B
Russian Language and Literature, B
Russian Studies, B
Social Psychology, D
Social Sciences, B
Spanish Language and Literature, B
Statistics, BMD
Structural Biology, D
Student Personnel Services, M
Toxicology, D
Translation and Interpretation, MO
Western European Studies, MD
Women's Studies, B

U.T.A. MESIVTA OF KIRYAS JOEL

Talmudic Studies, B

UTICA COLLEGE

Accounting, BM
Biology Teacher Education, B
Biology/Biological Sciences, B
Business Administration and Management, B
Business Teacher Education, B
Business, Management, Marketing, and Related Support Services, B
Business/Managerial Economics, B
Chemistry, B
Chemistry Teacher Education, B
Communication Studies/Speech Communication and Rhetoric, B
Computer Teacher Education, B
Computer and Information Sciences, B
Computer and Information Systems Security, M
Construction Trades, B
Criminal Justice/Law Enforcement Administration, B
Criminology, M
Economics, B
Education, MO
Elementary Education and Teaching, B
English Language and Literature, B
English/Language Arts Teacher Education, B
Foreign Languages and Literatures, B
Forensic Science and Technology, M
Geological and Earth Sciences/Geosciences, B
Gerontology, O
Health Services Administration, M
Health/Medical Preparatory Programs, B
History, B
History Teacher Education, B
International Business/Trade/Commerce, B
International Relations and Affairs, B
Journalism, B

Liberal Arts and Sciences Studies and Humanities, B
Liberal Studies, M
Mathematics, B
Mathematics Teacher Education, B
Occupational Therapy/Therapist, M
Philosophy, B
Physical Therapy/Therapist, D
Physics, B
Physics Teacher Education, B
Political Science and Government, B
Pre-Dentistry Studies, B
Pre-Law Studies, B
Pre-Medicine/Pre-Medical Studies, B
Pre-Veterinary Studies, B
Psychology, B
Public Relations/Image Management, B
Secondary Education and Teaching, B
Social Science Teacher Education, B
Social Sciences, B
Social Studies Teacher Education, B
Sociology, B
Therapeutic Recreation/Recreational Therapy, B

UTICA SCHOOL OF COMMERCE

Administrative Assistant and Secretarial Science, A
Architectural Engineering, A
Business Administration and Management, A

VASSAR COLLEGE

African Studies, B
American/United States Studies/Civilization, B
Anthropology, B
Art History, Criticism and Conservation, B
Asian Studies/Civilization, B
Astronomy, B
Biochemistry, B
Biology/Biological Sciences, B
Chemistry, B
Chinese Language and Literature, B
Classics and Classical Languages, Literatures, and Linguistics, B
Computer and Information Sciences, B
Drama and Dramatics/Theatre Arts, B
Economics, B
Education, B
English Language and Literature, B
Environmental Sciences, B
Environmental Studies, B
Film/Cinema Studies, B
Fine/Studio Arts, B
French Language and Literature, B
Geography, B
Geology/Earth Science, B
German Language and Literature, B
History, B
International Relations and Affairs, B
Italian Language and Literature, B
Japanese Language and Literature, B
Jewish/Judaic Studies, B
Latin American Studies, B
Liberal Arts and Sciences Studies and Humanities, B
Mass Communication/Media Studies, B
Mathematics, B
Medieval and Renaissance Studies, B
Multi-/Interdisciplinary Studies, B
Music, B
Philosophy, B
Physics, B
Political Science and Government, B
Psychology, B
Religion/Religious Studies, B
Russian Language and Literature, B
Science, Technology and Society, B
Sociology, B
Spanish Language and Literature, B
Urban Studies/Affairs, B
Visual and Performing Arts, B
Women's Studies, B

VAUGHN COLLEGE OF AERONAUTICS AND TECHNOLOGY

Aeronautical/Aerospace Engineering Technology/Technician, A

Aeronautics/Aviation/Aerospace Science and Technology, AB
Airframe Mechanics and Aircraft Maintenance Technology/Technician, B
Aviation/Airway Management and Operations, ABM
Avionics Maintenance Technology/Technician, AB
Digital Communication and Media/Multimedia, A
Electrical and Electronic Engineering Technologies/Technicians, AB
Electrical, Electronic and Communications Engineering Technology/Technician, B
Engineering, B
Management Science, B
Mechanical Engineering Related Technologies/Technicians, B

VILLA MARIA COLLEGE

Animation, Interactive Technology, Video Graphics and Special Effects, B
Art/Art Studies, General, B
Business Administration and Management, AB
Fashion/Apparel Design, B
Fine/Studio Arts, A
Graphic Design, AB
Health Professions and Related Clinical Sciences, A
Interior Design, AB
Liberal Arts and Sciences Studies and Humanities, AB
Music, B
Photographic and Film/Video Technology/Technician and Assistant, B
Photography, AB
Physical Therapist Assistant, A

WAGNER COLLEGE

Accounting, BM
Anthropology, B
Art/Art Studies, General, B
Biology/Biological Sciences, B
Biopsychology, B
Business Administration and Management, B
Business Administration, Management and Operations, M
Chemistry, B
Computer Science, B
Computer and Information Sciences, B
Drama and Dramatics/Theatre Arts, B
Early Childhood Education and Teaching, M
Economics, B
Education, BMO
Educational Leadership and Administration, MO
Elementary Education and Teaching, BM
English Education, M
English Language and Literature, B
Finance, B
Finance and Banking, M
Foreign Language Teacher Education, M
French Studies, B
Health Services Administration, M
History, B
International Business/Trade/Commerce, M
International Relations and Affairs, B
Kindergarten/PreSchool Education and Teaching, B
Marketing, M
Mathematics, B
Mathematics Teacher Education, M
Medical Microbiology and Bacteriology, B
Microbiology, M
Middle School Education, M
Music, B
Philosophy, B
Physician Assistant, B
Physics, B
Political Science and Government, B
Pre-Dentistry Studies, B
Pre-Law Studies, B
Pre-Medicine/Pre-Medical Studies, B
Psychology, B
Public Administration, B
Public Policy Analysis, B
Reading Teacher Education, M
Science Teacher Education/General Science Teacher Education, M
Secondary Education and Teaching, BM
Social Studies Teacher Education, M
Sociology, B

Spanish Language and Literature, B
Special Education and Teaching, M

WEBB INSTITUTE

Naval Architecture and Marine Engineering, B

WELLS COLLEGE

Anthropology, B
Art History, Criticism and Conservation, B
Art/Art Studies, General, B
Biochemistry, B
Biology/Biological Sciences, B
Business Administration and Management, B
Chemistry, B
Computer Science, B
Dance, B
Drama and Dramatics/Theatre Arts, B
Early Childhood Education and Teaching, B
Economics, B
Education, B
Elementary Education and Teaching, B
Engineering, B
English Language and Literature, B
Environmental Studies, B
Film/Cinema Studies, B
Fine/Studio Arts, B
History, B
International Relations and Affairs, B
Mathematics, B
Molecular Biology, B
Philosophy, B
Physics, B
Political Science and Government, B
Pre-Dentistry Studies, B
Pre-Law Studies, B
Pre-Medicine/Pre-Medical Studies, B
Pre-Veterinary Studies, B
Psychology, B
Secondary Education and Teaching, B
Sociology, B
Spanish Language and Literature, B
Women's Studies, B

WESTCHESTER COMMUNITY COLLEGE

Accounting, A
Administrative Assistant and Secretarial Science, A
Apparel and Textile Manufacture, A
Business Administration and Management, A
Child Development, A
Civil Engineering Technology/Technician, A
Clinical Laboratory Science/Medical Technology/Technologist, A
Clinical/Medical Laboratory Technician, A
Community Organization and Advocacy, A
Computer Science, A
Computer Systems Networking and Telecommunications, A
Computer and Information Sciences, A
Computer and Information Sciences and Support Services, A
Computer and Information Systems Security, A
Consumer Merchandising/Retailing Management, A
Corrections, A
Culinary Arts/Chef Training, A
Dance, A
Data Processing and Data Processing Technology/Technician, A
Design and Applied Arts, A
Dietetics/Dieticians, A
Electrical, Electronic and Communications Engineering Technology/Technician, A
Emergency Medical Technology/Technician (EMT Paramedic), A
Energy Management and Systems Technology/Technician, A
Engineering Science, A
Engineering Technology, A
Environmental Control Technologies/Technicians, A
Environmental Sciences, A
Environmental Studies, A
Film/Video and Photographic Arts, A
Finance, A
Fine/Studio Arts, A
Food Technology and Processing, A
Humanities/Humanistic Studies, A

Information Science/Studies, A
International Business/Trade/Commerce, A
Journalism, A
Legal Assistant/Paralegal, A
Liberal Arts and Sciences Studies and Humanities, A
Marketing/Marketing Management, A
Mass Communication/Media Studies, A
Mechanical Engineering/Mechanical
  Technology/Technician, A
Public Administration, A
Respiratory Care Therapy/Therapist, A
Social Sciences, A
Substance Abuse/Addiction Counseling, A
Teacher Education, Multiple Levels, A
Veterinary/Animal Health Technology/Technician and
  Veterinary Assistant, A

WOOD TOBE–COBURN SCHOOL

Accounting Technology/Technician and Bookkeeping, A
Administrative Assistant and Secretarial Science, A
Computer Programming/Programmer, A
Computer Systems Networking and Telecommunications, A
Fashion/Apparel Design, A
Graphic Design, A
Hotel/Motel Administration/Management, A
Medical/Clinical Assistant, A
Retailing and Retail Operations, A

YESHIVA DERECH CHAIM

Religion/Religious Studies, D
Talmudic Studies, B

YESHIVA D'MONSEY RABBINICAL COLLEGE

Talmudic Studies, B

YESHIVA GEDOLAH IMREI YOSEF D'SPINKA

Religious Education, B

YESHIVA KARLIN STOLIN RABBINICAL INSTITUTE

Talmudic Studies, B
Theology and Religious Vocations, O

YESHIVA AND KOLEL BAIS MEDRASH ELYON

Talmudic Studies, B

YESHIVA AND KOLLEL HARBOTZAS TORAH

Theology/Theological Studies, B

YESHIVA OF NITRA RABBINICAL COLLEGE

Theology/Theological Studies, B

YESHIVA SHAAR HATORAH TALMUDIC RESEARCH INSTITUTE

Talmudic Studies, B

YESHIVA SHAAREI TORAH OF ROCKLAND

Talmudic Studies, B

YESHIVA OF THE TELSHE ALUMNI

Talmudic Studies, B

YESHIVA UNIVERSITY

Accounting, BM
Audiology/Audiologist and Speech-Language
  Pathology/Pathologist, B
Biochemistry, B
Biology/Biological Sciences, B
Business Administration and Management, B
Chemistry, B
Classics and Classical Languages, Literatures, and Linguistics, B
Clinical Psychology, D
Communication Disorders, M

Computer Science, B
Computer and Information Sciences, B
Conflict Resolution and Mediation/Peace Studies, M
Counseling Psychology, M
Early Childhood Education and Teaching, B
Economics, BM
Educational Administration and Supervision, MDO
Elementary Education and Teaching, B
English Language and Literature, B
Finance, B
Health Psychology, D
Hebrew Language and Literature, AB
History, B
Intellectual Property Law, M
International Business/Trade/Commerce, B
Jewish/Judaic Studies, BMD
Law and Legal Studies, MD
Management Information Systems and Services, B
Marketing, B
Marketing/Marketing Management, B
Mathematics, BMD
Molecular Biology, B
Multi-/Interdisciplinary Studies, B
Philosophy, B
Physical Sciences, B
Physics, B
Political Science and Government, B
Psychology, BMD
Religious Education, MDO
School Psychology, D
Social Work, MD
Sociology, B

YESHIVAS NOVOMINSK

Talmudic Studies, B

YESHIVAT MIKDASH MELECH

Talmudic Studies, B

YESHIVATH VIZNITZ

Theology/Theological Studies, B

YESHIVATH ZICHRON MOSHE

Talmudic Studies, B
Theology and Religious Vocations, O

YORK COLLEGE OF THE CITY UNIVERSITY OF NEW YORK

Accounting, B
Adult Development and Aging, B
African-American/Black Studies, B
Anthropology, B
Art History, Criticism and Conservation, B
Art/Art Studies, General, B
Bilingual and Multilingual Education, B
BioTechnology, B
Biology Technician/BioTechnology Laboratory Technician, B
Biology/Biological Sciences, B
Business Administration and Management, B
Chemistry, B
Clinical Laboratory Science/Medical
  Technology/Technologist, B
Clinical/Medical Laboratory Technician, B
Communications Technology/Technician, B
Computer Science, B
Drama and Dramatics/Theatre Arts, B
Economics, B
Elementary Education and Teaching, B
English Language and Literature, B
Environmental Health, B
French Language and Literature, B
Geology/Earth Science, B
Gerontology, B
Health Teacher Education, B
History, B
Information Science/Studies, B
Italian Language and Literature, B
Liberal Arts and Sciences Studies and Humanities, B
Management Information Systems and Services, B
Marketing/Marketing Management, B
Mathematics, B
Music, B
Occupational Therapy/Therapist, B

Philosophy, B
Physical Education Teaching and Coaching, B
Physician Assistant, B
Physics, B
Political Science and Government, B
Psychology, B
Secondary Education and Teaching, B
Social Work, B
Sociology, B
Spanish Language and Literature, B

North Carolina

ALAMANCE COMMUNITY COLLEGE

Accounting Technology/Technician and Bookkeeping, A
Animal Sciences, A
Applied Horticulture/Horticultural Operations, A
Automobile/Automotive Mechanics
  Technology/Technician, A
Banking and Financial Support Services, A
BioTechnology, A
Business Administration and Management, A
Carpentry/Carpenter, A
Clinical/Medical Laboratory Technician, A
Commercial and Advertising Art, A
Criminal Justice/Safety Studies, A
Culinary Arts/Chef Training, A
Electrical, Electronic and Communications Engineering Technology/Technician, A
Executive Assistant/Executive Secretary, A
General Office Occupations and Clerical Services, A
Heating, Air Conditioning and Refrigeration
  Technology/Technician, A
Information Science/Studies, A
Kindergarten/PreSchool Education and Teaching, A
Legal Administrative Assistant/Secretary, A
Liberal Arts and Sciences Studies and Humanities, A
Machine Tool Technology/Machinist, A
Mechanical Engineering/Mechanical
  Technology/Technician, A
Medical Administrative Assistant/Secretary, A
Medical/Clinical Assistant, A
Retailing and Retail Operations, A
Teacher Assistant/Aide, A
Welding Technology/Welder, A

APEX SCHOOL OF THEOLOGY

Religious Education, A
Theology and Religious Vocations, MD
Theology/Theological Studies, B

APPALACHIAN STATE UNIVERSITY

Accounting, BM
Actuarial Science, B
Advertising, B
American/United States Studies/Civilization, M
Anthropology, B
Apparel and Textiles, B
Art Teacher Education, B
Art/Art Studies, General, B
Athletic Training and Sports Medicine, B
Biological and Biomedical Sciences, M
Biology/Biological Sciences, B
Business Administration and Management, B
Business Administration, Management and Operations, M
Cell Biology and Anatomy, M
Chemistry, B
Child Development, BM
City/Urban, Community and Regional Planning, B
Clinical Psychology, M
Commercial Photography, B
Communication Disorders, BM
Communication Studies/Speech Communication
  and Rhetoric, B
Computer Science, BM
Construction Management, B
Counseling Psychology, M
Counselor Education/School Counseling and Guidance Services, M
Criminal Justice/Safety Studies, B
Criminology, M
Cultural Studies, M

Curriculum and Instruction, M
Dance, B
Dietetics/Dieticians, B
Drama and Dramatics/Theatre Arts, B
Economics, B
Education/Teaching of Individuals with Specific Learning Disabilities, B
Educational Administration and Supervision, MO
Educational Leadership and Administration, D
Educational Media/Instructional Technology, M
Elementary Education and Teaching, BM
Energy and Power Engineering, M
Engineering Physics, M
English, M
English Education, M
English Language and Literature, B
English/Language Arts Teacher Education, B
Environmental Policy, M
Environmental Sciences, B
Environmental Studies, B
Exercise and Sports Science, M
Experimental Psychology, M
Family and Consumer Sciences/Human Sciences, M
Finance, B
Fine/Studio Arts, B
Food Science and Technology, B
Foreign Language Teacher Education, M
Geographic Information Systems, M
Geography, BM
Geology/Earth Science, B
Gerontology, MO
Graphic Design, B
Health Psychology, M
Health/Health Care Administration/Management, B
Higher Education/Higher Education Administration, MO
History, BM
History Teacher Education, B
Hospitality Administration/Management, B
Industrial Design, B
Industrial and Organizational Psychology, M
Insurance, B
Interior Design, B
International Affairs, M
International Business/Trade/Commerce, B
International/Global Studies, B
Journalism, B
Junior High/Intermediate/Middle School Education and Teaching, B
Kinesiology and Exercise Science, B
Liberal Arts and Sciences Studies and Humanities, B
Library Science, M
Linguistic, Comparative, and Related Language Studies and Services, B
Management, M
Management Information Systems and Services, B
Marketing/Marketing Management, B
Marriage and Family Therapy/Counseling, M
Mathematics, BM
Mathematics Teacher Education, M
Middle School Education, M
Molecular Biology, M
Music, M
Music Performance, B
Music Teacher Education, BM
Music Therapy/Therapist, BM
Nutritional Sciences, M
Parks, Recreation and Leisure Facilities Management, B
Performance, M
Philosophy, B
Physical Education Teaching and Coaching, B
Physics, B
Political Science and Government, BM
Psychology, BM
Public Administration, M
Public Health Education and Promotion, B
Public Relations/Image Management, B
Radio and Television, B
Reading Teacher Education, M
Rehabilitation Sciences, M
Religion/Religious Studies, B
Romance Languages, Literatures, and Linguistics, M

School Psychology, M
Science Teacher Education/General Science Teacher Education, M
Social Studies Teacher Education, M
Social Work, BM
Sociology, BMO
Special Education and Teaching, M
Student Personnel Services, M
Sustainable Development, M
Taxation, M
Teacher Education and Professional Development, Specific Levels and Methods, B
Teacher Education and Professional Development, Specific Subject Areas, B
Vocational and Technical Education, M
Women's Studies, B

THE ART INSTITUTE OF CHARLOTTE, A CAMPUS OF SOUTH UNIVERSITY

Apparel and Accessories Marketing Operations, AB
Cinematography and Film/Video Production, AB
Computer Graphics, B
Culinary Arts/Chef Training, A
Fashion/Apparel Design, A
Graphic Design, A
Interior Design, AB
Photography, AB
Restaurant, Culinary, and Catering Management/Manager, AB
Web Page, Digital/Multimedia and Information Resources Design, B

THE ART INSTITUTE OF RALEIGH-DURHAM, A CAMPUS OF SOUTH UNIVERSITY

Apparel and Accessories Marketing Operations, AB
Cinematography and Film/Video Production, B
Commercial Photography, B
Culinary Arts/Chef Training, A
Graphic Design, A
Interior Design, B
Restaurant, Culinary, and Catering Management/Manager, B
Web Page, Digital/Multimedia and Information Resources Design, B

ASHEVILLE-BUNCOMBE TECHNICAL COMMUNITY COLLEGE

Accounting, A
Automobile/Automotive Mechanics Technology/Technician, A
Baking and Pastry Arts/Baker/Pastry Chef, A
Biology Technician/BioTechnology Laboratory Technician, A
Building/Property Maintenance and Management, A
Business Administration and Management, A
CAD/CADD Drafting and/or Design Technology/Technician, A
Civil Engineering Technology/Technician, A
Clinical/Medical Laboratory Technician, A
Clinical/Medical Social Work, A
Computer Engineering Technology/Technician, A
Computer Software and Media Applications, A
Computer Systems Networking and Telecommunications, A
Computer and Information Systems Security, A
Criminal Justice/Safety Studies, A
Culinary Arts/Chef Training, A
Dental Hygiene/Hygienist, A
Diagnostic Medical Sonography/Sonographer and Ultrasound Technician, A
Diesel Mechanics Technology/Technician, A
Drafting/Design Engineering Technologies/Technicians, A
Early Childhood Education and Teaching, A
Electrical, Electronic and Communications Engineering Technology/Technician, A
Electrician, A
Electromechanical and Instrumentation and Maintenance Technologies/Technicians, A
Elementary Education and Teaching, A
Emergency Medical Technology/Technician (EMT Paramedic), A
Fire Protection and Safety Technology/Technician, A

General Studies, A
Heating, Air Conditioning, Ventilation and Refrigeration Maintenance Technology/Technician, A
Hotel/Motel Administration/Management, A
Human Resources Management/Personnel Administration, A
Information Science/Studies, A
Information Technology, A
Liberal Arts and Sciences Studies and Humanities, A
Machine Shop Technology/Assistant, A
Marketing/Marketing Management, A
Mechanical Engineering Related Technologies/Technicians, A
Office Management and Supervision, A
Radiologic Technology/Science - Radiographer, A
Surgical Technology/Technologist, A
Survey Technology/Surveying, A
Veterinary/Animal Health Technology/Technician and Veterinary Assistant, A
Welding Technology/Welder, A

BARTON COLLEGE

Accounting, B
Art Teacher Education, B
Biology/Biological Sciences, B
Business Administration and Management, B
Chemistry, B
Criminal Justice/Law Enforcement Administration, B
Design and Visual Communications, B
Drama and Dramatics/Theatre Arts, B
Early Childhood Education and Teaching, B
Education/Teaching of Individuals with Hearing Impairments, Including Deafness, B
Elementary Education and Teaching, BM
English Language and Literature, B
Fine/Studio Arts, B
Gerontology, B
History, B
Human Resources Management/Personnel Administration, B
Junior High/Intermediate/Middle School Education and Teaching, B
Liberal Arts and Sciences Studies and Humanities, B
Mass Communication/Media Studies, B
Mathematics, B
Philosophy and Religious Studies, B
Physical Education Teaching and Coaching, B
Political Science and Government, B
Psychology, B
Public Health Education and Promotion, B
Social Studies Teacher Education, B
Social Work, B
Spanish Language and Literature, B
Special Education and Teaching, B
Sport and Fitness Administration/Management, B

BEAUFORT COUNTY COMMUNITY COLLEGE

Accounting, A
Administrative Assistant and Secretarial Science, A
Automobile/Automotive Mechanics Technology/Technician, A
Business Administration and Management, A
Clinical/Medical Laboratory Technician, A
Computer Programming/Programmer, A
Criminal Justice/Law Enforcement Administration, A
Criminal Justice/Police Science, A
Drafting and Design Technology/Technician, A
Electrical, Electronic and Communications Engineering Technology/Technician, A
Heavy Equipment Maintenance Technology/Technician, A
Information Science/Studies, A
Kindergarten/PreSchool Education and Teaching, A
Liberal Arts and Sciences Studies and Humanities, A
Mechanical Engineering/Mechanical Technology/Technician, A
Medical Office Management/Administration, A

Welding Technology/Welder, A

BELMONT ABBEY COLLEGE

Accounting, B
American Government and Politics (United
  States), B
Biology/Biological Sciences, B
Business Administration and Management, B
Criminal Justice/Safety Studies, B
Education, B
Elementary Education and Teaching, B
English Language and Literature, B
History, B
Liberal Arts and Sciences Studies and Humani-
  ties, B
Mathematics, B
Parks, Recreation and Leisure Facilities Manage-
  ment, B
Psychology, B
Religious Education, B
Sport and Fitness Administration/Management, B
Theology/Theological Studies, B

BENNETT COLLEGE

Biology/Biological Sciences, B
Business Administration and Management, B
Chemistry, B
Computer Science, B
Computer and Information Sciences, B
Elementary Education and Teaching, B
English Language and Literature, B
English/Language Arts Teacher Education, B
Journalism, B
Mathematics, B
Mathematics Teacher Education, B
Multi-/Interdisciplinary Studies, B
Music, B
Political Science and Government, B
Psychology, B
Social Work, B
Special Education and Teaching, B
Visual and Performing Arts, B

BLADEN COMMUNITY COLLEGE

Administrative Assistant and Secretarial Science, A
BioTechnology, A
Business Administration and Management, A
Child Care Provider/Assistant, A
Computer Programming, Specific Applications, A
Computer Programming/Programmer, A
Cosmetology/Cosmetologist, A
Criminal Justice/Police Science, A
Electrical, Electronic and Communications Engineer-
  ing Technology/Technician, A
General Studies, A
Industrial Technology/Technician, A
Information Technology, A
Liberal Arts and Sciences Studies and Humani-
  ties, A
Welding Technology/Welder, A

BLUE RIDGE COMMUNITY COLLEGE

Agricultural Business Technology, A
Applied Horticulture/Horticultural Operations, A
Automobile/Automotive Mechanics
  Technology/Technician, A
Business Administration and Management, A
Child Care and Support Services Management, A
Computer Programming, A
Computer Programming/Programmer, A
Computer Systems Analysis/Analyst, A
Computer and Information Sciences and Support
  Services, A
Cosmetology/Cosmetologist, A
Early Childhood Education and Teaching, A
Education/Teaching of Individuals in Early Childhood
  Special Education Programs, A
Electrical, Electronic and Communications Engineer-
  ing Technology/Technician, A
Electromechanical Technology/Electromechanical
  Engineering Technology, A
Environmental Sciences, A
Executive Assistant/Executive Secretary, A
General Studies, A
Heavy/Industrial Equipment Maintenance Technolo-
  gies, A

Humanities/Humanistic Studies, A
Information Science/Studies, A
Information Technology, A
Liberal Arts and Sciences Studies and Humani-
  ties, A
Machine Tool Technology/Machinist, A
Marketing/Marketing Management, A
Mechanical Engineering Related
  Technologies/Technicians, A
Mechanical Engineering/Mechanical
  Technology/Technician, A
Retailing and Retail Operations, A
Sign Language Interpretation and Translation, A
Surgical Technology/Technologist, A
System, Networking, and LAN/WAN
  Management/Manager, A
Teacher Assistant/Aide, A
Tourism Promotion Operations, A
Tourism and Travel Services Management, A
Water Quality and Wastewater Treatment Manage-
  ment and Recycling Technology/Technician, A
Welding Technology/Welder, A

BREVARD COLLEGE

Biological and Physical Sciences, B
Biology/Biological Sciences, B
Business Administration and Management, B
Criminal Justice/Law Enforcement Administration, B
Drama and Dramatics/Theatre Arts, B
English Language and Literature, B
Environmental Sciences, B
Environmental Studies, B
Fine/Studio Arts, B
Health Services/Allied Health/Health Sciences, B
Health and Physical Education, B
History, B
Kinesiology and Exercise Science, B
Mathematics, B
Multi-/Interdisciplinary Studies, B
Music, B
Music Performance, B
Music Teacher Education, B
Parks, Recreation, Leisure and Fitness Studies, B
Psychology, B
Religion/Religious Studies, B

BRIGHTWOOD COLLEGE, CHAR-LOTTE CAMPUS

Computer Systems Networking and Telecommunications, A
Criminal Justice/Law Enforcement Administration, A

BRUNSWICK COMMUNITY COLLEGE

Accounting Technology/Technician and Bookkeep-
  ing, A
Applied Horticulture/Horticultural Operations, A
Aquaculture, A
BioTechnology, A
Business Administration and Management, A
Computer Programming/Programmer, A
Computer Systems Analysis/Analyst, A
Cosmetology/Cosmetologist, A
Early Childhood Education and Teaching, A
Executive Assistant/Executive Secretary, A
General Studies, A
Health Information/Medical Records
  Administration/Administrator, A
Information Science/Studies, A
Liberal Arts and Sciences Studies and Humani-
  ties, A
Special Education and Teaching, A
Teacher Assistant/Aide, A
Turf and Turfgrass Management, A

CABARRUS COLLEGE OF HEALTH SCIENCES

General Studies, A
Health/Medical Physics, B
Medical/Clinical Assistant, A
Multi-/Interdisciplinary Studies, B
Occupational Therapist Assistant, A
Pharmacy Technician/Assistant, A

Surgical Technology/Technologist, A

CALDWELL COMMUNITY COLLEGE AND TECHNICAL INSTITUTE

Accounting, A
Automobile/Automotive Mechanics
  Technology/Technician, A
BioTechnology, A
Biological and Physical Sciences, A
Biomedical Technology/Technician, A
Business Administration and Management, A
Computer Programming/Programmer, A
Construction Management, A
Cosmetology/Cosmetologist, A
Culinary Arts/Chef Training, A
Diagnostic Medical Sonography/Sonographer and
  Ultrasound Technician, A
E-Commerce/Electronic Commerce, A
Early Childhood Education and Teaching, A
Education, A
Electrical, Electronics and Communications Engi-
  neering, A
Emergency Medical Technology/Technician (EMT
  Paramedic), A
Fine/Studio Arts, A
General Office Occupations and Clerical Services, A
Information Technology, A
Landscape Architecture, A
Legal Assistant/Paralegal, A
Liberal Arts and Sciences Studies and Humani-
  ties, A
Mechanical Engineering/Mechanical
  Technology/Technician, A
Medical Office Management/Administration, A
Nuclear Medical Technology/Technologist, A
Physical Therapist Assistant, A
Radiologic Technology/Science - Radiographer, A

CAMPBELL UNIVERSITY

Accounting, B
Accounting and Business/Management, B
Accounting and Finance, B
Acting, B
Advertising, B
Army JROTC/ROTC, B
Art/Art Studies, General, B
Athletic Training and Sports Medicine, B
Biochemistry, B
Biology Teacher Education, B
Biology/Biological Sciences, B
Broadcast Journalism, B
Business Administration and Management, B
Business Administration, Management and Opera-
  tions, M
Business/Commerce, B
Chemistry, B
Commercial and Advertising Art, B
Communication Studies/Speech Communication
  and Rhetoric, B
Communication and Media Studies, B
Computer and Information Sciences, B
Counselor Education/School Counseling and Guid-
  ance Services, M
Criminal Justice/Law Enforcement Administration, B
Directing and Theatrical Production, B
Divinity/Ministry (BD, MDiv.), B
Drama and Dramatics/Theatre Arts, B
Economics, B
Education, BM
Educational Administration and Supervision, M
Educational Leadership and Administration, B
Elementary Education and Teaching, BM
Elementary and Middle School
  Administration/Principalship, B
Engineering, A
English Language and Literature, B
Family and Consumer Sciences/Home Economics
  Teacher Education, B
Family and Consumer Sciences/Human Sciences, B
Fine/Studio Arts, B
Foreign Languages and Literatures, B
French Language and Literature, B
General Studies, B
Graphic Design, B
Health and Physical Education, B
Health and Physical Education/Fitness, B

History, B
History Teacher Education, B
Information Technology, B
Interdisciplinary Studies, M
International Business/Trade/Commerce, B
International Relations and Affairs, B
Journalism, B
Junior High/Intermediate/Middle School Education and Teaching, B
Kinesiology and Exercise Science, B
Law and Legal Studies, D
Liberal Arts and Sciences Studies and Humanities, A
Marketing/Marketing Management, B
Mass Communication/Media Studies, B
Mathematics, B
Mathematics Teacher Education, B
Middle School Education, M
Music, B
Music Pedagogy, B
Music Performance, B
Music Teacher Education, B
Music Theory and Composition, B
Pastoral Studies/Counseling, M
Pharmaceutical Sciences, M
Pharmacy, MD
Pharmacy, Pharmaceutical Sciences, and Administration, B
Physical Education Teaching and Coaching, BM
Physical Therapy/Therapist, M
Physician Assistant, M
Piano and Organ, B
Political Science and Government, B
Pre-Dentistry Studies, B
Pre-Law Studies, B
Pre-Medicine/Pre-Medical Studies, B
Pre-Pharmacy Studies, B
Pre-Veterinary Studies, B
Psychology, B
Public Administration, B
Public Relations, Advertising, and Applied Communication, B
Radio, Television, and Digital Communication, B
Religion/Religious Studies, B
Science Teacher Education/General Science Teacher Education, B
Secondary Education and Teaching, BM
Social Sciences, B
Social Studies Teacher Education, B
Social Work, B
Spanish Language Teacher Education, B
Spanish Language and Literature, B
Sport and Fitness Administration/Management, B
Teacher Education, Multiple Levels, B
Teaching French as a Second or Foreign Language, B
Theology and Religious Vocations, MD

CAPE FEAR COMMUNITY COLLEGE

Accounting Technology/Technician and Bookkeeping, A
Architectural Engineering Technology/Technician, A
Automobile/Automotive Mechanics Technology/Technician, A
Baking and Pastry Arts/Baker/Pastry Chef, A
Building/Property Maintenance and Management, A
Business Administration and Management, A
Chemical Technology/Technician, A
Cinematography and Film/Video Production, A
Computer Systems Networking and Telecommunications, A
Computer Technology/Computer Systems Technology, A
Cosmetology/Cosmetologist, A
Criminal Justice/Police Science, A
Culinary Arts/Chef Training, A
Dental Hygiene/Hygienist, A
Diagnostic Medical Sonography/Sonographer and Ultrasound Technician, A
Early Childhood Education and Teaching, A
Electrical, Electronic and Communications Engineering Technology/Technician, A
Electrical/Electronics Equipment Installation and Repair, A
Electromechanical and Instrumentation and Maintenance Technologies/Technicians, A

Emergency Medical Technology/Technician (EMT Paramedic), A
Executive Assistant/Executive Secretary, A
Fire Protection and Safety Technology/Technician, A
Hotel/Motel Administration/Management, A
Instrumentation Technology/Technician, A
Interior Design, A
Landscaping and Groundskeeping, A
Language Interpretation and Translation, A
Liberal Arts and Sciences Studies and Humanities, A
Machine Shop Technology/Assistant, A
Marine Maintenance/Fitter and Ship Repair Technology/Technician, A
Mechanical Engineering/Mechanical Technology/Technician, A
Medical Office Management/Administration, A
Medical Radiologic Technology/Science - Radiation Therapist, A
Nuclear/Nuclear Power Technology/Technician, A
Occupational Therapist Assistant, A
Oceanography, Chemical and Physical, A
Surgical Technology/Technologist, A

CAROLINA CHRISTIAN COLLEGE

Bible/Biblical Studies, AB
Pastoral Studies/Counseling, M
Religious Education, M

CAROLINA COLLEGE OF BIBLICAL STUDIES

Bible/Biblical Studies, AB

CAROLINAS COLLEGE OF HEALTH SCIENCES

Medical Radiologic Technology/Science - Radiation Therapist, A
Radiologic Technology/Science - Radiographer, A

CARTERET COMMUNITY COLLEGE

Administrative Assistant and Secretarial Science, A
Business Administration and Management, A
Computer Engineering Technology/Technician, A
Computer Software and Media Applications, A
Computer Systems Networking and Telecommunications, A
Criminal Justice/Law Enforcement Administration, A
Industrial Radiologic Technology/Technician, A
Information Technology, A
Interior Design, A
Legal Administrative Assistant/Secretary, A
Legal Assistant/Paralegal, A
Liberal Arts and Sciences Studies and Humanities, A
Medical/Clinical Assistant, A
Photography, A
Respiratory Care Therapy/Therapist, A
Teacher Assistant/Aide, A

CATAWBA COLLEGE

Accounting, B
Athletic Training and Sports Medicine, B
Biology/Biological Sciences, B
Business Administration and Management, B
Chemistry, B
Clinical Laboratory Science/Medical Technology/Technologist, B
Communication Studies/Speech Communication and Rhetoric, B
Computer and Information Sciences, B
Criminal Justice/Law Enforcement Administration, B
Drama and Dance Teacher Education, B
Drama and Dramatics/Theatre Arts, B
Dramatic/Theatre Arts and Stagecraft, B
Economics, B
Elementary Education and Teaching, BM
English Language and Literature, B
Environmental Sciences, B
Environmental Studies, B
Health and Physical Education, B
History, B
Junior High/Intermediate/Middle School Education and Teaching, B
Kindergarten/PreSchool Education and Teaching, B
Kinesiology and Exercise Science, B

Management Information Systems and Services, B
Marketing/Marketing Management, B
Mathematics, B
Multi-/Interdisciplinary Studies, B
Music, B
Music Performance, B
Music Teacher Education, B
Parks, Recreation, Leisure and Fitness Studies, B
Physical Education Teaching and Coaching, B
Political Science and Government, B
Pre-Law Studies, B
Pre-Medicine/Pre-Medical Studies, B
Psychology, B
Public Administration, B
Religion/Religious Studies, B
Science Teacher Education/General Science Teacher Education, B
Sociology, B
Spanish Language and Literature, B
Special Education and Teaching, B
Sport and Fitness Administration/Management, B
Therapeutic Recreation/Recreational Therapy, B

CATAWBA VALLEY COMMUNITY COLLEGE

Accounting Technology/Technician and Bookkeeping, A
Applied Horticulture/Horticultural Operations, A
Architectural Engineering Technology/Technician, A
Automobile/Automotive Mechanics Technology/Technician, A
Business Administration and Management, A
Commercial and Advertising Art, A
Computer Engineering Technologies/Technicians, A
Computer Engineering Technology/Technician, A
Computer Programming/Programmer, A
Computer Systems Networking and Telecommunications, A
Criminal Justice/Safety Studies, A
Dental Hygiene/Hygienist, A
Early Childhood Education and Teaching, A
Electrical, Electronic and Communications Engineering Technology/Technician, A
Electromechanical and Instrumentation and Maintenance Technologies/Technicians, A
Electroneurodiagnostic/Electroencephalographic Technology/Technologist, A
Emergency Medical Technology/Technician (EMT Paramedic), A
Entrepreneurship/Entrepreneurial Studies, A
Fire Protection and Safety Technology/Technician, A
General Studies, A
Health Information/Medical Records Technology/Technician, A
Health and Physical Education/Fitness, A
Heating, Air Conditioning, Ventilation and Refrigeration Maintenance Technology/Technician, A
Industrial Mechanics and Maintenance Technology, A
Information Science/Studies, A
Information Technology, A
Liberal Arts and Sciences Studies and Humanities, A
Machine Shop Technology/Assistant, A
Mechanical Engineering/Mechanical Technology/Technician, A
Medical Office Management/Administration, A
Medical Radiologic Technology/Science - Radiation Therapist, A
Office Management and Supervision, A
Photographic and Film/Video Technology/Technician and Assistant, A
Radiologic Technology/Science - Radiographer, A
Respiratory Care Therapy/Therapist, A
Turf and Turfgrass Management, A
Welding Technology/Welder, A

CENTRAL CAROLINA COMMUNITY COLLEGE

Accounting, A
Administrative Assistant and Secretarial Science, A
Automobile/Automotive Mechanics Technology/Technician, A
Business Administration and Management, A
Computer Programming, Specific Applications, A
Computer Programming/Programmer, A

Computer Systems Networking and Telecommunications, A
Computer/Information Technology Services Administration and Management, A
Criminal Justice/Law Enforcement Administration, A
Drafting and Design Technology/Technician, A
Electrical, Electronic and Communications Engineering Technology/Technician, A
Information Science/Studies, A
Information Technology, A
Instrumentation Technology/Technician, A
Kindergarten/PreSchool Education and Teaching, A
Laser and Optical Technology/Technician, A
Legal Administrative Assistant/Secretary, A
Legal Assistant/Paralegal, A
Liberal Arts and Sciences Studies and Humanities, A
Marketing/Marketing Management, A
Medical Administrative Assistant/Secretary, A
Medical/Clinical Assistant, A
Operations Management and Supervision, A
Quality Control Technology/Technician, A
Radio and Television, A
Social Work, A
Telecommunications Technology/Technician, A
Veterinary/Animal Health Technology/Technician and Veterinary Assistant, A

CENTRAL PIEDMONT COMMUNITY COLLEGE

Accounting, A
Administrative Assistant and Secretarial Science, A
Advertising, A
Architectural Engineering Technology/Technician, A
Art/Art Studies, General, A
Automobile/Automotive Mechanics Technology/Technician, A
Biology/Biological Sciences, A
Business Administration and Management, A
Business Machine Repairer, A
Child Development, A
Civil Engineering Technology/Technician, A
Clinical Laboratory Science/Medical Technology/Technologist, A
Clinical/Medical Laboratory Technician, A
Commercial and Advertising Art, A
Computer Engineering Technology/Technician, A
Computer Programming, Specific Applications, A
Computer Programming/Programmer, A
Computer Science, A
Consumer Merchandising/Retailing Management, A
Criminal Justice/Law Enforcement Administration, A
Criminal Justice/Police Science, A
Culinary Arts/Chef Training, A
Dance, A
Data Processing and Data Processing Technology/Technician, A
Dental Hygiene/Hygienist, A
Design and Applied Arts, A
Drafting and Design Technology/Technician, A
Electrical, Electronic and Communications Engineering Technology/Technician, A
Electromechanical Technology/Electromechanical Engineering Technology, A
Engineering Technology, A
Environmental Engineering Technology/Environmental Technology, A
Fashion Merchandising, A
Finance, A
Fire Science/Firefighting, A
Food Science, A
Food Technology and Processing, A
Graphic and Printing Equipment Operator Production, A
Health Information/Medical Records Administration/Administrator, A
Health/Health Care Administration/Management, A
Horticultural Science, A
Hospitality Administration/Management, A
Hotel/Motel Administration/Management, A
Human Services, A
Industrial Technology/Technician, A
Insurance, A
Interior Design, A
Kindergarten/PreSchool Education and Teaching, A
Legal Administrative Assistant/Secretary, A

Legal Assistant/Paralegal, A
Liberal Arts and Sciences Studies and Humanities, A
Machine Tool Technology/Machinist, A
Marketing/Marketing Management, A
Mechanical Engineering/Mechanical Technology/Technician, A
Medical Administrative Assistant/Secretary, A
Medical/Clinical Assistant, A
Music, A
Physical Therapy/Therapist, A
Real Estate, A
Respiratory Care Therapy/Therapist, A
Sign Language Interpretation and Translation, A
Social Work, A
Special Products Marketing Operations, A
Survey Technology/Surveying, A
Tourism and Travel Services Management, A
Transportation and Materials Moving, A
Welding Technology/Welder, A

CHARLOTTE CHRISTIAN COLLEGE AND THEOLOGICAL SEMINARY

Bible/Biblical Studies, AB
Cultural Studies, M
Missions/Missionary Studies and Missiology, ABM
Pastoral Studies/Counseling, M
Religion/Religious Studies, M
Sacred Music, M
Theology and Religious Vocations, M

CHOWAN UNIVERSITY

Accounting, B
American/United States Studies/Civilization, B
Art Therapy/Therapist, B
Biology/Biological Sciences, B
Business Administration and Management, B
Comparative Literature, B
Computer Systems Networking and Telecommunications, B
Computer and Information Sciences, B
Criminal Justice/Safety Studies, B
Drama and Dramatics/Theatre Arts, B
Economics, B
Education, BM
Elementary Education and Teaching, B
English Language and Literature, B
Environmental Biology, B
Fine/Studio Arts, B
Geography, B
Graphic Communications, B
Graphic Design, B
Graphic and Printing Equipment Operator Production, AB
Health Services/Allied Health/Health Sciences, B
History, B
Humanities/Humanistic Studies, B
Information Science/Studies, B
Kinesiology and Exercise Science, B
Marketing/Marketing Management, B
Mathematics, B
Music, B
Music Teacher Education, B
Philosophy, B
Physical Education Teaching and Coaching, B
Physical Sciences, B
Political Science and Government, B
Pre-Law Studies, B
Pre-Medicine/Pre-Medical Studies, B
Prepress/Desktop Publishing and Digital Imaging Design, B
Psychology, B
Religion/Religious Studies, B
Small Business Administration/Management, B
Social Science Teacher Education, B
Sociology, B
Sport and Fitness Administration/Management, B
Substance Abuse/Addiction Counseling, B
Visual and Performing Arts, B

CLEVELAND COMMUNITY COLLEGE

Accounting, A
Banking and Financial Support Services, A
BioTechnology, A
Business Administration and Management, A
Criminal Justice/Safety Studies, A

Early Childhood Education and Teaching, A
Electrical, Electronic and Communications Engineering Technology/Technician, A
Electrician, A
Elementary Education and Teaching, A
Emergency Medical Technology/Technician (EMT Paramedic), A
Entrepreneurship/Entrepreneurial Studies, A
Fire Protection and Safety Technology/Technician, A
General Studies, A
Information Technology, A
Language Interpretation and Translation, A
Legal Administrative Assistant/Secretary, A
Liberal Arts and Sciences Studies and Humanities, A
Marketing/Marketing Management, A
Mechanical Drafting and Mechanical Drafting CAD/CADD, A
Medical Office Management/Administration, A
Medical/Clinical Assistant, A
Office Management and Supervision, A
Operations Management and Supervision, A
Radio and Television Broadcasting Technology/Technician, A
Radiologic Technology/Science - Radiographer, A

COASTAL CAROLINA COMMUNITY COLLEGE

Accounting, A
Architectural Engineering Technology/Technician, A
Business Administration and Management, A
Child Care Provider/Assistant, A
Clinical/Medical Laboratory Technician, A
Computer Programming, Specific Applications, A
Computer Systems Analysis/Analyst, A
Computer Systems Networking and Telecommunications, A
Computer/Information Technology Services Administration and Management, A
Criminal Justice/Law Enforcement Administration, A
Dental Hygiene/Hygienist, A
Emergency Medical Technology/Technician (EMT Paramedic), A
Executive Assistant/Executive Secretary, A
Fire Science/Firefighting, A
Legal Assistant/Paralegal, A
Liberal Arts and Sciences Studies and Humanities, A
Medical Administrative Assistant/Secretary, A
Surgical Technology/Technologist, A

COLLEGE OF THE ALBEMARLE

Administrative Assistant and Secretarial Science, A
Architectural Engineering Technology/Technician, A
Art/Art Studies, General, A
BioTechnology, A
Business Administration and Management, A
Computer Engineering Technology/Technician, A
Computer Programming, Specific Applications, A
Computer Programming/Programmer, A
Construction Trades, A
Crafts/Craft Design, Folk Art and Artisanry, A
Criminal Justice/Law Enforcement Administration, A
Culinary Arts/Chef Training, A
Data Entry/Microcomputer Applications, A
Drafting/Design Engineering Technologies/Technicians, A
Drama and Dramatics/Theatre Arts, A
Education, A
Information Science/Studies, A
Information Technology, A
Liberal Arts and Sciences Studies and Humanities, A
Marine Maintenance/Fitter and Ship Repair Technology/Technician, A
Medical Administrative Assistant/Secretary, A
Metal and Jewelry Arts, A
Music, A
Teacher Assistant/Aide, A

CRAVEN COMMUNITY COLLEGE

Accounting, A
Airframe Mechanics and Aircraft Maintenance Technology/Technician, A
Automobile/Automotive Mechanics Technology/Technician, A

Banking and Financial Support Services, A
Business Administration and Management, A
Computer Programming, Specific Applications, A
Computer Systems Networking and Telecommunications, A
Computer and Information Systems Security, A
Criminal Justice/Law Enforcement Administration, A
Criminal Justice/Safety Studies, A
Early Childhood Education and Teaching, A
Electrical, Electronic and Communications Engineering Technology/Technician, A
Electromechanical Technology/Electromechanical Engineering Technology, A
Elementary Education and Teaching, A
Entrepreneurship/Entrepreneurial Studies, AB
General Studies, A
Health Information/Medical Records Technology/Technician, A
Heating, Air Conditioning, Ventilation and Refrigeration Maintenance Technology/Technician, A
Information Technology, A
Legal Administrative Assistant/Secretary, A
Liberal Arts and Sciences Studies and Humanities, A
Machine Shop Technology/Assistant, A
Mechanical Engineering/Mechanical Technology/Technician, A
Medical Administrative Assistant/Secretary, A
Medical Office Management/Administration, A
Medical/Clinical Assistant, A
Office Management and Supervision, A
Physical Therapist Assistant, A
Special Education and Teaching, A
System, Networking, and LAN/WAN Management/Manager, A
Tool and Die Technology/Technician, A
Welding Technology/Welder, A

DAVIDSON COLLEGE

African Studies, B
Anthropology, B
Art/Art Studies, General, B
Biology/Biological Sciences, B
Chemistry, B
Chinese Language and Literature, B
Classics and Classical Languages, Literatures, and Linguistics, B
Drama and Dramatics/Theatre Arts, B
East Asian Studies, B
Economics, B
English Language and Literature, B
Environmental Studies, B
Ethnic, Cultural Minority, and Gender Studies, B
French Language and Literature, B
German Language and Literature, B
History, B
Latin American Studies, B
Mathematics, B
Multi-/Interdisciplinary Studies, B
Music, B
Philosophy, B
Physics, B
Political Science and Government, B
Psychology, B
Religion/Religious Studies, B
Sociology, B
Spanish Language and Literature, B

DAVIDSON COUNTY COMMUNITY COLLEGE

Accounting, A
Administrative Assistant and Secretarial Science, A
Business Administration and Management, A
Clinical/Medical Laboratory Technician, A
Computer Engineering Technology/Technician, A
Computer Programming/Programmer, A
Criminal Justice/Law Enforcement Administration, A
Criminal Justice/Police Science, A
Data Processing and Data Processing Technology/Technician, A
Electrical, Electronic and Communications Engineering Technology/Technician, A
Emergency Medical Technology/Technician (EMT Paramedic), A
Engineering Technology, A
Fire Science/Firefighting, A

Health Information/Medical Records Administration/Administrator, A
Legal Assistant/Paralegal, A
Liberal Arts and Sciences Studies and Humanities, A
Medical/Clinical Assistant, A
Plastics Engineering Technology/Technician, A

DEVRY UNIVERSITY

Business Administration and Management, B
Business Administration, Management and Operations, BM
Business/Commerce, B
Computer Systems Analysis/Analyst, B
Computer Systems Networking and Telecommunications, AB
Electrical, Electronic and Communications Engineering Technology/Technician, A
Health Information/Medical Records Technology/Technician, A

DUKE UNIVERSITY

Accounting, D
Acute Care/Critical Care Nursing, MO
African-American/Black Studies, B
Allopathic Medicine, D
Anatomy, BD
Ancient/Classical Greek Language and Literature, B
Anthropology, B
Art History, Criticism and Conservation, BMD
Art/Art Studies, General, B
Asian Studies/Civilization, B
Biochemistry, D
Bioethics/Medical Ethics, M
Bioinformatics, DO
Biological Anthropology, D
Biological and Biomedical Sciences, D
Biology/Biological Sciences, B
Biomedical Engineering, MD
Biomedical/Medical Engineering, B
Biopsychology, D
Biostatistics, M
Business Administration, Management and Operations, MDO
Canadian Studies, B
Cancer Biology/Oncology, D
Cell Biology and Anatomy, DO
Chemistry, BD
Civil Engineering, BMD
Classics and Classical Languages, Literatures, and Linguistics, BD
Clinical Laboratory Sciences, M
Clinical Psychology, D
Clinical Research, M
Cognitive Sciences, D
Comparative Literature, BD
Composition, D
Computational Biology, DO
Computer Engineering, MD
Computer Science, BMD
Cultural Anthropology, D
Design and Visual Communications, B
Developmental Biology and Embryology, O
Developmental Psychology, D
Drama and Dramatics/Theatre Arts, B
East Asian Studies, MO
Ecology, DO
Economics, BMD
Education, M
Electrical Engineering, MD
Electrical, Electronics and Communications Engineering, B
Energy Management and Policy, M
Engineering Management, M
Engineering and Applied Sciences, M
English, D
English Language and Literature, B
Entrepreneurship/Entrepreneurial Studies, M
Environmental Engineering Technology/Environmental Technology, MD
Environmental Policy, D
Environmental Policy and Resource Management, M
Environmental Sciences, MD
Environmental Studies, B
Environmental and Occupational Health, O

Ethics, M
Experimental Psychology, D
Finance and Banking, MDO
Fine Arts and Art Studies, MD
Forestry, M
French Language and Literature, BD
Genetics, D
Genomic Sciences, D
Geology/Earth Science, BMD
German Language and Literature, BD
Gerontological Nursing, MO
Health Psychology, D
Health Services Administration, O
History, BMD
Human Development, D
Humanities/Humanistic Studies, M
Immunology, D
Industrial and Manufacturing Management, MD
International Business/Trade/Commerce, MO
International Development, M
International Public Health/International Health, M
International Relations and Affairs, B
Italian Language and Literature, BD
Latin American Studies, D
Latin Language and Literature, B
Law and Legal Studies, MD
Liberal Studies, M
Linguistics, B
Management, M
Management Strategy and Policy, MD
Marine Sciences, D
Marketing, MD
Materials Engineering, M
Materials Sciences, MD
Maternal/Child Health and Neonatal Nurse/Nursing, MO
Mathematics, BD
Mechanical Engineering, BMD
Media Studies, M
Medical Physics, MD
Medieval and Renaissance Studies, B
Microbiology, D
Molecular Biology, DO
Molecular Biophysics, O
Molecular Genetics, D
Music, BD
Musicology and Ethnomusicology, D
Natural Resources and Conservation, MD
Neurobiology and Neurophysiology, D
Neuroscience, DO
Nurse Anesthetist, D
Nursing, D
Nursing - Adult, MO
Nursing - Advanced Practice, MO
Nursing Administration, M
Nursing Education, M
Nursing Informatics, MO
Optics/Optical Sciences, M
Organizational Management, MD
Paleontology, D
Pathology/Experimental Pathology, MD
Pediatric Nurse/Nursing, MO
Performance, D
Pharmacology, D
Philosophy, BD
Photonics, M
Physical Therapy/Therapist, D
Physician Assistant, M
Physics, BD
Political Science and Government, BMD
Psychology, BD
Public Policy Analysis, BMD
Quantitative Analysis, MD
Religion/Religious Studies, BMD
Russian Language and Literature, BD
Slavic Languages, Literatures, and Linguistics, BMO
Sociology, BMD
Spanish Language and Literature, BD
Statistics, MD
Structural Biology, O
Theology and Religious Vocations, MD
Toxicology, O
Women's Health Nursing, MO

Women's Studies, B

DURHAM TECHNICAL COMMUNITY COLLEGE

Accounting, A
Allied Health Diagnostic, Intervention, and Treatment Professions, A
Architectural Engineering Technology/Technician, A
Automobile/Automotive Mechanics Technology/Technician, A
Business Administration and Management, A
Computer Programming/Programmer, A
Computer Systems Networking and Telecommunications, A
Dental Laboratory Technology/Technician, A
Early Childhood Education and Teaching, A
Electrical, Electronic and Communications Engineering Technology/Technician, A
Electrician, A
Elementary Education and Teaching, A
Information Science/Studies, A
Information Technology, A
Legal Assistant/Paralegal, A
Liberal Arts and Sciences Studies and Humanities, A
Machine Shop Technology/Assistant, A
Medical Office Management/Administration, A
Occupational Safety and Health Technology/Technician, A
Occupational Therapy/Therapist, A
Office Management and Supervision, A
Operations Management and Supervision, A
Opticianry/Ophthalmic Dispensing Optician, A
Respiratory Care Therapy/Therapist, A
System, Networking, and LAN/WAN Management/Manager, A
Teacher Assistant/Aide, A

EAST CAROLINA UNIVERSITY

Accounting, M
Accounting and Business/Management, B
Adult and Continuing Education and Teaching, M
African-American/Black Studies, B
Allied Health and Medical Assisting Services, MDO
Allopathic Medicine, D
American/United States Studies/Civilization, M
Anatomy, D
Anthropology, BM
Apparel and Textiles, B
Applied Economics, M
Applied Physics, M
Art Education, M
Art History, Criticism and Conservation, B
Art Teacher Education, B
Athletic Training and Sports Medicine, B
Atmospheric Sciences and Meteorology, B
Audiology/Audiologist and Speech-Language Pathology/Pathologist, B
BioTechnology, M
Biochemistry, BMD
Biological and Biomedical Sciences, M
Biology/Biological Sciences, B
Biomedical Engineering, M
Biophysics, D
Business Administration and Management, B
Business Administration, Management and Operations, M
Business Education, M
Business Teacher Education, B
Business/Office Automation/Technology/Data Entry, B
Cell Biology and Anatomy, D
Ceramic Arts and Ceramics, M
Chemistry, BM
Child Development, BMD
Child and Family Studies, MD
City/Urban, Community and Regional Planning, B
Clinical Laboratory Science/Medical Technology/Technologist, B
Clinical Psychology, D
Communication Disorders, MD
Communication Studies/Speech Communication and Rhetoric, B
Community College Education, MO
Community Health and Preventive Medicine, O
Comparative Literature, MO

Composition, M
Computer Engineering, MDO
Computer Science, BMO
Computer and Information Systems Security, M
Construction Management, M
Counselor Education/School Counseling and Guidance Services, M
Crafts, M
Criminal Justice/Safety Studies, B
Criminology, MO
Curriculum and Instruction, MO
Dance, B
Dentistry, D
Dietetics/Dieticians, B
Drafting and Design Technology/Technician, B
Drama and Dance Teacher Education, B
Drama and Dramatics/Theatre Arts, B
Early Childhood Education and Teaching, M
Economic Development, O
Economics, B
Education, MDO
Educational Administration and Supervision, MO
Educational Leadership and Administration, MDO
Educational Media/Instructional Technology, MO
Elementary Education and Teaching, BMO
Engineering, B
Engineering Technologies/Technicians, B
English, MDO
English Education, MO
English Language and Literature, B
English as a Second Language, MO
English/Language Arts Teacher Education, B
Environmental Health, B
Environmental and Occupational Health, MD
Exercise Physiology, B
Exercise and Sports Science, MD
Family and Community Services, B
Family and Consumer Sciences/Home Economics Teacher Education, B
Family and Consumer Sciences/Human Sciences, M
Finance, B
Fine Arts and Art Studies, M
Fine/Studio Arts, B
Foreign Language Teacher Education, M
Foreign Languages and Literatures, B
General Studies, B
Geographic Information Systems, O
Geography, BMO
Geology/Earth Science, BMO
Gerontology, O
Graphic Design, M
Health Communication, M
Health Education, M
Health Informatics, M
Health Information/Medical Records Administration/Administrator, B
Health Physics/Radiological Health, M
Health Promotion, M
Health Psychology, D
Health Teacher Education, B
Health and Physical Education/Fitness, B
Health/Health Care Administration/Management, B
History, BM
Hospitality Administration/Management, BM
Hydrogeology, O
Illustration, M
Immunology, MD
Industrial Technology/Technician, B
Industrial and Manufacturing Management, MO
Industrial and Organizational Psychology, M
Information Science/Studies, B
Information Technology, B
Interior Design, B
International Affairs, M
Jewelry/Metalsmithing, M
Junior High/Intermediate/Middle School Education and Teaching, B
Kindergarten/PreSchool Education and Teaching, B
Kinesiology and Movement Studies, MDO
Leisure Studies, MO
Liberal Arts and Sciences Studies and Humanities, B
Library Science, M
Linguistics, M
Logistics and Materials Management, M

Management, O
Management Information Systems and Services, BO
Management of Technology, D
Manufacturing Technology/Technician, B
Marketing/Marketing Management, B
Marriage and Family Therapy/Counseling, MD
Maternal and Child Health, D
Mathematics, BMO
Mathematics Teacher Education, BMO
Medical Physics, M
Microbiology, MD
Middle School Education, M
Military and Defense Studies, M
Molecular Biology, MD
Music, BMO
Music Teacher Education, BMO
Music Theory and Composition, M
Music Therapy/Therapist, M
Nursing, MDO
Nutritional Sciences, M
Occupational Therapy/Therapist, MO
Painting, M
Parks, Recreation, Leisure and Fitness Studies, B
Pathology/Experimental Pathology, D
Performance, MO
Pharmacology, D
Philosophy, B
Photography, M
Physical Education Teaching and Coaching, BMDO
Physical Therapy/Therapist, D
Physician Assistant, M
Physics, BMD
Physiology, D
Political Science and Government, BMO
Printmaking, M
Psychology, B
Public Administration, MO
Public Health, M
Public Health Education and Promotion, B
Public History, M
Quality Management, M
Reading Teacher Education, M
Recreation and Park Management, MO
Rehabilitation Counseling, MDO
Rehabilitation Sciences, MDO
Rhetoric, MD
Rural Planning and Studies, M
Sacred Music, M
Science Teacher Education/General Science Teacher Education, BMO
Sculpture, M
Securities Services Administration/Management, O
Social Studies Teacher Education, BM
Social Work, BMO
Sociology, BM
Software Engineering, M
Special Education and Teaching, BMO
Sport and Fitness Administration/Management, MO
Statistics, MO
Substance Abuse/Addiction Counseling, MDO
Technical Communication, M
Telecommunications Management, M
Textile Design, M
Therapeutic Recreation/Recreational Therapy, B
Travel and Tourism, M
Urban and Regional Planning, M
Vocational Rehabilitation Counseling/Counselor, B
Vocational and Technical Education, M
Western European Studies, M
Writing, MD

ECPI UNIVERSITY (CHARLOTTE)

Computer Systems Networking and Telecommunications, A
Criminal Justice/Safety Studies, A
Diagnostic Medical Sonography/Sonographer and Ultrasound Technician, A
Electrical, Electronics and Communications Engineering, A
Medical Administrative Assistant/Secretary, A
Medical Office Assistant/Specialist, A

ECPI UNIVERSITY (GREENSBORO)

Computer Engineering Technology/Technician, A
Computer and Information Systems Security, A

Health and Medical Administrative Services, A
Medical/Clinical Assistant, A
Web Page, Digital/Multimedia and Information Resources Design, A

ECPI UNIVERSITY (RALEIGH)

Computer Engineering Technology/Technician, A
Computer Science, A
Computer Technology/Computer Systems Technology, A
Computer and Information Sciences, A
Criminal Justice/Law Enforcement Administration, A
Management Information Systems and Services, A
Medical/Clinical Assistant, A

EDGECOMBE COMMUNITY COLLEGE

Accounting Technology/Technician and Bookkeeping, A
Business Administration and Management, A
Child Care and Support Services Management, A
Computer Systems Analysis/Analyst, A
Computer Systems Networking and Telecommunications, A
Criminal Justice/Law Enforcement Administration, A
Health Information/Medical Records Administration/Administrator, A
History and Philosophy of Science and Technology, A
Industrial Production Technologies/Technicians, A
Liberal Arts and Sciences Studies and Humanities, A
Mechanical Engineering/Mechanical Technology/Technician, A
Medical Radiologic Technology/Science - Radiation Therapist, A
Medical/Clinical Assistant, A
Psychiatric/Mental Health Services Technician, A
Respiratory Care Therapy/Therapist, A

ELIZABETH CITY STATE UNIVERSITY

Accounting, B
Aeronautics/Aviation/Aerospace Science and Technology, B
Applied Mathematics, M
Art Teacher Education, B
Biological and Biomedical Sciences, M
Biology Teacher Education, B
Biology/Biological Sciences, B
Business Administration and Management, B
Chemistry, B
Chemistry Teacher Education, B
Communication Studies/Speech Communication and Rhetoric, B
Community College Education, M
Computer Science, B
Criminal Justice/Safety Studies, B
Education, M
Educational Administration and Supervision, M
Elementary Education and Teaching, BM
Engineering Technologies/Technicians, B
English Language and Literature, B
English/Language Arts Teacher Education, B
Fine/Studio Arts, B
Geographic Information Systems, M
Geology/Earth Science, B
Graphic Design, B
History, B
History Teacher Education, B
Industrial Technology/Technician, B
Junior High/Intermediate/Middle School Education and Teaching, B
Kindergarten/PreSchool Education and Teaching, B
Mathematics, BM
Mathematics Teacher Education, BM
Music, B
Oceanography, Chemical and Physical, B
Physical Education Teaching and Coaching, B
Physics, B
Political Science and Government, B
Psychology, B
Science Teacher Education/General Science Teacher Education, M
Social Work, B
Sociology, B

Special Education and Teaching, B

ELON UNIVERSITY

Accounting, B
Acting, B
Anthropology, B
Applied Mathematics, B
Art History, Criticism and Conservation, B
Art/Art Studies, General, B
Biochemistry, B
Biology/Biological Sciences, B
Biomedical/Medical Engineering, B
Biophysics, B
Broadcast Journalism, B
Business Administration and Management, B
Business Administration, Management and Operations, M
Business/Corporate Communications, B
Chemical Engineering, B
Chemistry, B
Communication Studies/Speech Communication and Rhetoric, B
Communication and Media Studies, B
Computer Engineering, B
Computer Science, B
Computer and Information Sciences, B
Dance, B
Drama and Dramatics/Theatre Arts, B
Early Childhood Education and Teaching, B
Economics, B
Education, BM
Education/Teaching of the Gifted and Talented, M
Elementary Education and Teaching, BM
Engineering, B
Engineering Physics, B
English Language and Literature, B
Entrepreneurship/Entrepreneurial Studies, B
Environmental Sciences, B
Environmental Studies, B
Environmental/Environmental Health Engineering, B
Finance, B
Foreign Languages and Literatures, B
French Language and Literature, B
Health Teacher Education, B
History, B
Human Services, B
Information Science/Studies, B
International Business/Trade/Commerce, B
International Economics, B
International Relations and Affairs, B
Internet and Interactive Multimedia, M
Journalism, B
Junior High/Intermediate/Middle School Education and Teaching, B
Kinesiology and Exercise Science, B
Law and Legal Studies, D
Liberal Arts and Sciences Studies and Humanities, B
Management Science, B
Marketing/Marketing Management, B
Mathematics, B
Music, B
Music Performance, B
Music Teacher Education, B
Parks, Recreation, Leisure and Fitness Studies, B
Philosophy, B
Physical Education Teaching and Coaching, B
Physical Therapy/Therapist, D
Physician Assistant, M
Physics, B
Political Science and Government, B
Psychology, B
Public Administration, B
Public Health (MPH, DPH), B
Public Policy Analysis, B
Radio and Television, B
Recording Arts Technology/Technician, B
Religion/Religious Studies, B
Science Teacher Education/General Science Teacher Education, B
Secondary Education and Teaching, B
Sociology, B
Spanish Language and Literature, B
Special Education and Teaching, BM
Sport and Fitness Administration/Management, B
Statistics, B

Technical Theatre/Theatre Design and Technology, B

FAYETTEVILLE STATE UNIVERSITY

Accounting, B
Art Teacher Education, B
Art/Art Studies, General, B
BioTechnology, B
Biological and Biomedical Sciences, M
Biology Teacher Education, B
Biology/Biological Sciences, B
Business Administration and Management, B
Business Administration, Management and Operations, M
Business Teacher Education, B
Chemistry, B
Communication Studies/Speech Communication and Rhetoric, B
Computer Science, B
Criminal Justice/Law Enforcement Administration, B
Criminology, M
Dramatic/Theatre Arts and Stagecraft, B
Early Childhood Education and Teaching, B
Educational Administration and Supervision, M
Elementary Education and Teaching, BM
English, M
English Language and Literature, B
English/Language Arts Teacher Education, B
Finance, B
Fire Services Administration, B
Forensic Science and Technology, B
Geography, B
Health Teacher Education, B
Health/Health Care Administration/Management, B
History, BM
Junior High/Intermediate/Middle School Education and Teaching, B
Management Information Systems and Services, B
Marketing/Marketing Management, B
Mathematics, BM
Mathematics Teacher Education, B
Middle School Education, M
Music, B
Music Teacher Education, B
Physical Education Teaching and Coaching, B
Political Science and Government, BM
Psychology, BM
Sales and Marketing Operations/Marketing and Distribution Teacher Education, B
Secondary Education and Teaching, M
Social Science Teacher Education, B
Social Studies Teacher Education, M
Social Work, BM
Sociology, BM
Spanish Language Teacher Education, B
Spanish Language and Literature, B
Visual and Performing Arts, B

FAYETTEVILLE TECHNICAL COMMUNITY COLLEGE

Accounting, A
Applied Horticulture/Horticultural Operations, A
Architectural Engineering Technology/Technician, A
Autobody/Collision and Repair Technology/Technician, A
Automobile/Automotive Mechanics Technology/Technician, A
Banking and Financial Support Services, A
Building/Construction Finishing, Management, and Inspection, A
Business Administration and Management, A
Civil Engineering Technology/Technician, A
Commercial and Advertising Art, A
Computer Programming/Programmer, A
Computer Systems Networking and Telecommunications, A
Computer and Information Systems Security, A
Cosmetology/Cosmetologist, A
Criminal Justice/Safety Studies, A
Culinary Arts/Chef Training, A
Dental Hygiene/Hygienist, A
Early Childhood Education and Teaching, A
Electrical, Electronic and Communications Engineering Technology/Technician, A
Electrician, A
Elementary Education and Teaching, A

Emergency Medical Technology/Technician (EMT Paramedic), A
Fire Protection and Safety Technology/Technician, A
Forensic Science and Technology, A
Funeral Service and Mortuary Science, A
General Studies, A
Gunsmithing/Gunsmith, A
Health and Physical Education/Fitness, A
Heating, Air Conditioning, Ventilation and Refrigeration Maintenance Technology/Technician, A
Human Resources Management/Personnel Administration, A
Information Science/Studies, A
Information Technology, A
Legal Assistant/Paralegal, A
Liberal Arts and Sciences Studies and Humanities, A
Logistics and Materials Management, A
Machine Shop Technology/Assistant, A
Marketing/Marketing Management, A
Medical Office Management/Administration, A
Office Management and Supervision, A
Operations Management and Supervision, A
Pharmacy Technician/Assistant, A
Physical Therapist Assistant, A
Public Administration, A
Radiologic Technology/Science - Radiographer, A
Respiratory Care Therapy/Therapist, A
Surgical Technology/Technologist, A
Survey Technology/Surveying, A

FORSYTH TECHNICAL COMMUNITY COLLEGE

Accounting, A
Allied Health Diagnostic, Intervention, and Treatment Professions, A
Animation, Interactive Technology, Video Graphics and Special Effects, A
Applied Horticulture/Horticultural Business Services, A
Architectural Engineering Technology/Technician, A
Automobile/Automotive Mechanics Technology/Technician, A
Biology Technician/BioTechnology Laboratory Technician, A
Biophysics, A
Business Administration and Management, A
Cardiovascular Sciences, A
Cardiovascular Technology/Technologist, A
Clinical/Medical Laboratory Technician, A
Communication Disorders, A
Computer Engineering Technology/Technician, A
Computer Hardware Technology/Technician, A
Computer Programming/Programmer, A
Computer Systems Networking and Telecommunications, A
Computer and Information Sciences, A
Criminal Justice/Safety Studies, A
Diagnostic Medical Sonography/Sonographer and Ultrasound Technician, A
E-Commerce/Electronic Commerce, A
Early Childhood Education and Teaching, A
Electrical, Electronic and Communications Engineering Technology/Technician, A
Emergency Medical Technology/Technician (EMT Paramedic), A
Fire Protection and Safety Technology/Technician, A
Forensic Science and Technology, A
General Studies, A
Graphic Design, A
Health Information/Medical Records Administration/Administrator, A
Health Professions and Related Clinical Sciences, A
Human Services, A
Industrial Technology/Technician, A
Information Science/Studies, A
Information Technology, A
Interior Design, A
International Business/Trade/Commerce, A
Legal Assistant/Paralegal, A
Liberal Arts and Sciences Studies and Humanities, A
Logistics and Materials Management, A
Machine Shop Technology/Assistant, A
Massage Therapy/Therapeutic Massage, A

Mechanical Engineering/Mechanical Technology/Technician, A
Medical Office Management/Administration, A
Medical Radiologic Technology/Science - Radiation Therapist, A
Medical/Clinical Assistant, A
Nuclear Medical Technology/Technologist, A
Office Management and Supervision, A
Radiologic Technology/Science - Radiographer, A

GARDNER-WEBB UNIVERSITY

Accounting, B
American Sign Language (ASL), B
Art/Art Studies, General, B
Athletic Training and Sports Medicine, B
Bible/Biblical Studies, B
Biology/Biological Sciences, B
Business Administration and Management, B
Business Administration, Management and Operations, M
Chemistry, B
Communication and Media Studies, B
Computer Science, B
Computer and Information Sciences, B
Counseling Psychology, M
Cultural Studies, M
Curriculum and Instruction, D
Drama and Dramatics/Theatre Arts, B
Economics, B
Education, BMDO
Educational Administration and Supervision, MO
Educational Leadership and Administration, D
Elementary Education and Teaching, BM
English, M
English Education, M
English Language and Literature, B
English/Language Arts Teacher Education, B
Environmental Sciences, B
Exercise and Sports Science, M
Finance, B
Fine/Studio Arts, B
Foreign Language Teacher Education, B
French Language Teacher Education, B
French Language and Literature, B
Health Teacher Education, B
Health and Physical Education, B
Health/Health Care Administration/Management, B
History, B
History Teacher Education, B
International Business/Trade/Commerce, B
Journalism, B
Junior High/Intermediate/Middle School Education and Teaching, B
Management Information Systems and Services, B
Marketing/Marketing Management, B
Mass Communication/Media Studies, B
Mathematics, B
Mathematics Teacher Education, B
Middle School Education, M
Missions/Missionary Studies and Missiology, BMD
Music, B
Music Performance, B
Music Teacher Education, B
Music Theory and Composition, B
Nursing, MD
Organizational Management, D
Pastoral Studies/Counseling, BMD
Physical Education Teaching and Coaching, BM
Physician Assistant, M
Political Science and Government, B
Pre-Dentistry Studies, B
Pre-Law Studies, B
Pre-Medicine/Pre-Medical Studies, B
Pre-Pharmacy Studies, B
Pre-Veterinary Studies, B
Psychology, BM
Radio and Television Broadcasting Technology/Technician, B
Religion/Religious Studies, B
Religious Education, BM
Religious/Sacred Music, B
School Psychology, M
Secondary Education and Teaching, B
Social Science Teacher Education, B
Social Sciences, B
Sociology, B

Spanish Language Teacher Education, B
Spanish Language and Literature, B
Sport and Fitness Administration/Management, B
Teacher Education and Professional Development, Specific Subject Areas, B
Teacher Education, Multiple Levels, B
Teaching English as a Second or Foreign Language/ESL Language Instructor, B
Theology and Religious Vocations, MD

GASTON COLLEGE

Accounting, A
Architectural Engineering Technology/Technician, A
Automobile/Automotive Mechanics Technology/Technician, A
BioTechnology, A
Biology Technician/BioTechnology Laboratory Technician, A
Biomedical Technology/Technician, A
Biomedical/Medical Engineering, A
Business Administration and Management, A
Civil Engineering Technology/Technician, A
Computer Engineering, A
Computer Engineering Technology/Technician, A
Computer Programming/Programmer, A
Computer Systems Networking and Telecommunications, A
Computer and Information Systems Security, A
Criminal Justice/Police Science, A
Dietetics/Dieticians, A
Early Childhood Education and Teaching, A
Electrical, Electronic and Communications Engineering Technology/Technician, A
Emergency Medical Technology/Technician (EMT Paramedic), A
Engineering/Industrial Management, A
Fire Protection and Safety Technology/Technician, A
Forensic Science and Technology, A
General Studies, A
Human Resources Management and Services, A
Industrial Electronics Technology/Technician, A
Information Science/Studies, A
Information Technology, A
Legal Administrative Assistant/Secretary, A
Legal Assistant/Paralegal, A
Liberal Arts and Sciences Studies and Humanities, A
Logistics and Materials Management, A
Machine Shop Technology/Assistant, A
Massage Therapy/Therapeutic Massage, A
Mechanical Engineering, A
Mechanical Engineering/Mechanical Technology/Technician, A
Medical Administrative Assistant/Secretary, A
Medical Office Management/Administration, A
Medical/Clinical Assistant, A
Office Management and Supervision, A
Radio and Television Broadcasting Technology/Technician, A
System, Networking, and LAN/WAN Management/Manager, A
Veterinary/Animal Health Technology/Technician and Veterinary Assistant, A

GRACE COLLEGE OF DIVINITY

Divinity/Ministry (BD, MDiv.), B

GREENSBORO COLLEGE

Accounting, B
Acting, B
Art Teacher Education, B
Art/Art Studies, General, B
Athletic Training and Sports Medicine, B
Biology Teacher Education, B
Biology/Biological Sciences, B
Business Administration and Management, B
Business/Managerial Economics, B
Chemistry, B
Clinical Laboratory Science/Medical Technology/Technologist, B
Communication Studies/Speech Communication and Rhetoric, B
Criminal Justice/Safety Studies, B
Drama and Dance Teacher Education, B
Drama and Dramatics/Theatre Arts, B
Early Childhood Education and Teaching, B

Ecology, B
Education, BM
Education/Teaching of Individuals with Emotional Disturbances, B
Education/Teaching of Individuals with Mental Retardation, B
Education/Teaching of Individuals with Specific Learning Disabilities, B
Elementary Education and Teaching, BM
English Language and Literature, B
English as a Second Language, M
English/Language Arts Teacher Education, B
Foreign Language Teacher Education, B
French Language and Literature, B
Health Services/Allied Health/Health Sciences, B
Health and Physical Education, B
Health and Physical Education/Fitness, B
History, B
Junior High/Intermediate/Middle School Education and Teaching, B
Kindergarten/PreSchool Education and Teaching, B
Kinesiology and Exercise Science, B
Mathematics, B
Mathematics Teacher Education, B
Music, B
Music Performance, B
Music Teacher Education, B
Physical Education Teaching and Coaching, B
Political Science and Government, B
Psychology, B
Religion/Religious Studies, B
Science Teacher Education/General Science Teacher Education, B
Secondary Education and Teaching, B
Social Studies Teacher Education, B
Sociology, B
Spanish Language Teacher Education, B
Spanish Language and Literature, B
Special Education and Teaching, BM
Sport and Fitness Administration/Management, B
Technical Theatre/Theatre Design and Technology, B

GUILFORD COLLEGE

Accounting, B
African-American/Black Studies, B
Art/Art Studies, General, B
Biological and Biomedical Sciences, B
Biology/Biological Sciences, B
Business Administration and Management, B
Chemistry, B
Computer and Information Sciences, B
Criminal Justice/Safety Studies, B
Drama and Dramatics/Theatre Arts, B
Economics, B
Education, B
Elementary Education and Teaching, B
English Language and Literature, B
Environmental Studies, B
French Language and Literature, B
Geology/Earth Science, B
German Language and Literature, B
Health/Medical Preparatory Programs, B
History, B
Kinesiology and Exercise Science, B
Mathematics, B
Multi-/Interdisciplinary Studies, B
Music, B
Peace Studies and Conflict Resolution, B
Philosophy, B
Physics, B
Political Science and Government, B
Psychology, B
Religion/Religious Studies, B
Secondary Education and Teaching, B
Sociology, B
Spanish Language and Literature, B
Sport and Fitness Administration/Management, B
Women's Studies, B

GUILFORD TECHNICAL COMMUNITY COLLEGE

Accounting Technology/Technician and Bookkeeping, A
Agricultural Power Machinery Operation, A
Airline/Commercial/Professional Pilot and Flight Crew, A
Architectural Engineering Technology/Technician, A
Automobile/Automotive Mechanics Technology/Technician, A
Avionics Maintenance Technology/Technician, A
Biology Technician/BioTechnology Laboratory Technician, A
Building/Property Maintenance and Management, A
Business Administration and Management, A
Chemical Technology/Technician, A
Civil Engineering Technology/Technician, A
Commercial and Advertising Art, A
Computer Programming/Programmer, A
Computer Systems Analysis/Analyst, A
Computer Systems Networking and Telecommunications, A
Cosmetology/Cosmetologist, A
Criminal Justice/Safety Studies, A
Culinary Arts/Chef Training, A
Dental Hygiene/Hygienist, A
Early Childhood Education and Teaching, A
Education, A
Electrical, Electronic and Communications Engineering Technology/Technician, A
Electrician, A
Electromechanical Technology/Electromechanical Engineering Technology, A
Emergency Medical Technology/Technician (EMT Paramedic), A
Fire Protection and Safety Technology/Technician, A
General Studies, A
Heating, Air Conditioning, Ventilation and Refrigeration Maintenance Technology/Technician, A
Hotel/Motel Administration/Management, A
Human Resources Management/Personnel Administration, A
Industrial Production Technologies/Technicians, A
Information Science/Studies, A
Information Technology, A
Legal Assistant/Paralegal, A
Liberal Arts and Sciences Studies and Humanities, A
Logistics and Materials Management, A
Machine Shop Technology/Assistant, A
Mechanical Engineering/Mechanical Technology/Technician, A
Medical Office Management/Administration, A
Medical/Clinical Assistant, A
Office Management and Supervision, A
Pharmacy Technician/Assistant, A
Physical Therapist Assistant, A
Psychiatric/Mental Health Services Technician, A
Recording Arts Technology/Technician, A
Substance Abuse/Addiction Counseling, A
Surgical Technology/Technologist, A
Survey Technology/Surveying, A
System, Networking, and LAN/WAN Management/Manager, A
Telecommunications Technology/Technician, A
Turf and Turfgrass Management, A
Vehicle Maintenance and Repair Technologies, A

HALIFAX COMMUNITY COLLEGE

Business Administration and Management, A
Clinical/Medical Laboratory Technician, A
Commercial and Advertising Art, A
Criminal Justice/Safety Studies, A
Dental Hygiene/Hygienist, A
Early Childhood Education and Teaching, A
Electromechanical and Instrumentation and Maintenance Technologies/Technicians, A
Information Technology, A
Legal Assistant/Paralegal, A
Liberal Arts and Sciences Studies and Humanities, A
Medical Administrative Assistant/Secretary, A
Medical Office Management/Administration, A
Mental and Social Health Services and Allied Professions, A
Office Management and Supervision, A

Welding Technology/Welder, A

HARRISON COLLEGE

Baking and Pastry Arts/Baker/Pastry Chef, A
Cooking and Related Culinary Arts, A

HAYWOOD COMMUNITY COLLEGE

Accounting Technology/Technician and Bookkeeping, A
Applied Horticulture/Horticultural Operations, A
Automobile/Automotive Mechanics Technology/Technician, A
Building/Construction Finishing, Management, and Inspection, A
Business Administration and Management, A
Child Care and Support Services Management, A
Civil Engineering, A
Computer Systems Analysis/Analyst, A
Computer Systems Networking and Telecommunications, A
Cosmetology/Cosmetologist, A
Criminal Justice/Law Enforcement Administration, A
Electrical, Electronic and Communications Engineering Technology/Technician, A
Electrician, A
Electromechanical Technology/Electromechanical Engineering Technology, A
Engineering Technologies/Technicians, A
Executive Assistant/Executive Secretary, A
Forest Management/Forest Resources Management, A
Forestry Technology/Technician, A
Liberal Arts and Sciences Studies and Humanities, A
Machine Shop Technology/Assistant, A
Management Information Systems and Services, A
Manufacturing Engineering, A
Mechanical Engineering/Mechanical Technology/Technician, A
Medical/Clinical Assistant, A
Precision Production, A
Teacher Assistant/Aide, A
Telecommunications Technology/Technician, A
Watchmaking and Jewelrymaking, A
Welding Technology/Welder, A
Wildlife and Wildlands Science and Management, A
Wood Science and Wood Products/Pulp and Paper Technology, A
Woodworking, A

HERITAGE BIBLE COLLEGE

Christian Studies, A
Religious Education, AB

HIGH POINT UNIVERSITY

Accounting, B
Actuarial Science, B
Biochemistry, B
Biology/Biological Sciences, B
Business Administration and Management, B
Business Administration, Management and Operations, M
Business/Managerial Economics, B
Chemistry, B
Computer Science, B
Corporate and Organizational Communication, M
Criminal Justice/Safety Studies, B
Drama and Dramatics/Theatre Arts, B
Econometrics and Quantitative Economics, B
Education, M
Educational Leadership and Administration, M
Elementary Education and Teaching, BM
English Language and Literature, B
Entrepreneurship/Entrepreneurial Studies, B
Finance, B
Fine/Studio Arts, B
French Language and Literature, B
Graphic Design, B
History, BM
Interior Design, B
International Business/Trade/Commerce, B
International Relations and Affairs, B
Junior High/Intermediate/Middle School Education and Teaching, B
Kinesiology and Exercise Science, B
Marketing/Marketing Management, B

Mathematics, B
Mathematics Teacher Education, M
Multi-/Interdisciplinary Studies, B
Music, B
Non-Profit/Public/Organizational Management, BM
Organizational Behavior Studies, B
Philosophy, B
Physical Education Teaching and Coaching, B
Physics, B
Political Science and Government, B
Psychology, B
Religion/Religious Studies, B
Secondary Education and Teaching, BM
Selling Skills and Sales Operations, B
Sociology, B
Spanish Language and Literature, B
Special Education and Teaching, BM
Specialized Merchandising, Sales, and Marketing
  Operations, B

ISOTHERMAL COMMUNITY COLLEGE

Administrative Assistant and Secretarial Science, A
Automobile/Automotive Mechanics
  Technology/Technician, A
Biological and Physical Sciences, A
Broadcast Journalism, A
Business Administration and Management, A
Business Teacher Education, A
Commercial and Advertising Art, A
Computer Programming/Programmer, A
Computer Science, A
Cosmetology/Cosmetologist, A
Criminal Justice/Law Enforcement Administration, A
Criminal Justice/Police Science, A
Drafting and Design Technology/Technician, A
Drafting/Design Engineering
  Technologies/Technicians, A
Education, A
Electrical, Electronic and Communications Engineer-
  ing Technology/Technician, A
Elementary Education and Teaching, A
Insurance, A
Kindergarten/PreSchool Education and Teaching, A
Liberal Arts and Sciences Studies and Humani-
  ties, A
Machine Tool Technology/Machinist, A
Marketing/Marketing Management, A
Mechanical Engineering/Mechanical
  Technology/Technician, A
Music, A
Pharmacy, A
Plastics Engineering Technology/Technician, A
Radio and Television, A
Real Estate, A
Teacher Assistant/Aide, A
Trade and Industrial Teacher Education, A
Welding Technology/Welder, A

JAMES SPRUNT COMMUNITY COL-LEGE

Accounting, A
Agribusiness, A
Animal Sciences, A
Business Administration and Management, A
Child Development, A
Commercial and Advertising Art, A
Criminal Justice/Safety Studies, A
Early Childhood Education and Teaching, A
Elementary Education and Teaching, A
General Studies, A
Information Technology, A
Institutional Food Workers, A
Liberal Arts and Sciences Studies and Humani-
  ties, A
Medical/Clinical Assistant, A

JOHN WESLEY UNIVERSITY

Bible/Biblical Studies, A
Business Administration and Management, B
Business Administration, Management and Opera-
  tions, M
Divinity/Ministry (BD, MDiv.), B
Elementary Education and Teaching, B
Pastoral Studies/Counseling, B
Psychology, B

Theology/Theological Studies, B

JOHNSON C. SMITH UNIVERSITY

Biological and Physical Sciences, B
Biology/Biological Sciences, B
Business Administration and Management, B
Chemistry, B
Community Health Services/Liaison/Counseling, B
Computer Engineering, B
Computer and Information Sciences, B
Criminology, B
Economics, B
English Language and Literature, B
French Language and Literature, B
History, B
Information Technology, B
Liberal Arts and Sciences Studies and Humani-
  ties, B
Mass Communication/Media Studies, B
Mathematics, B
Music, B
Political Science and Government, B
Psychology, B
Social Sciences, B
Social Work, B
Spanish Language and Literature, B
Sport and Fitness Administration/Management, B
Visual and Performing Arts, B

JOHNSON & WALES UNIVERSITY

Accounting, B
Baking and Pastry Arts/Baker/Pastry Chef, AB
Business Administration and Management, B
Culinary Arts/Chef Training, AB
Fashion Merchandising, B
Food Service, Waiter/Waitress, and Dining Room
  Management/Manager, B
Hotel/Motel Administration/Management, B
Management Science, B
Marketing/Marketing Management, B
Parks, Recreation and Leisure Facilities Manage-
  ment, B
Restaurant, Culinary, and Catering
  Management/Manager, B
Restaurant/Food Services Management, B
Sport and Fitness Administration/Management, B

JOHNSTON COMMUNITY COLLEGE

Accounting, A
Administrative Assistant and Secretarial Science, A
Business Administration and Management, A
Criminal Justice/Police Science, A
Diesel Mechanics Technology/Technician, A
Early Childhood Education and Teaching, A
Heating, Air Conditioning, Ventilation and Refrigera-
  tion Maintenance Technology/Technician, A
Legal Assistant/Paralegal, A
Liberal Arts and Sciences Studies and Humani-
  ties, A
Medical Office Management/Administration, A
Medical/Clinical Assistant, A
Office Management and Supervision, A

KING'S COLLEGE

Accounting Technology/Technician and Bookkeep-
  ing, A
Administrative Assistant and Secretarial Science, A
Computer Programming/Programmer, A
Computer Systems Networking and Telecommunica-
  tions, A
Graphic Design, A
Hotel/Motel Administration/Management, A
Legal Administrative Assistant/Secretary, A
Legal Assistant/Paralegal, A
Medical/Clinical Assistant, A

LEES-MCRAE COLLEGE

Athletic Training and Sports Medicine, B
Biology/Biological Sciences, B
Business Administration and Management, B
Communication and Media Studies, B
Criminal Justice/Law Enforcement Administration, B
Criminology, B
Design and Visual Communications, B
Drama and Dance Teacher Education, B

Drama and Dramatics/Theatre Arts, B
Early Childhood Education and Teaching, B
Elementary Education and Teaching, B
English Language and Literature, B
History, B
Human Services, B
Kindergarten/PreSchool Education and Teaching, B
Physical Education Teaching and Coaching, B
Psychology, B
Religion/Religious Studies, B
Sport and Fitness Administration/Management, B
Visual and Performing Arts, B
Wildlife Biology, B

LENOIR COMMUNITY COLLEGE

Accounting, A
Aeronautical/Aerospace Engineering
  Technology/Technician, A
Airline/Commercial/Professional Pilot and Flight
  Crew, A
Applied Horticulture/Horticultural Operations, A
Autobody/Collision and Repair
  Technology/Technician, A
Automobile/Automotive Mechanics
  Technology/Technician, A
Computer Engineering Technology/Technician, A
Computer Systems Networking and Telecommunica-
  tions, A
Cosmetology/Cosmetologist, A
Criminal Justice/Safety Studies, A
Culinary Arts/Chef Training, A
Elementary Education and Teaching, A
Emergency Medical Technology/Technician (EMT
  Paramedic), A
Energy Management and Systems
  Technology/Technician, A
Graphic Design, A
Gunsmithing/Gunsmith, A
Industrial Electronics Technology/Technician, A
Information Technology, A
Liberal Arts and Sciences Studies and Humani-
  ties, A
Logistics and Materials Management, A
Machine Shop Technology/Assistant, A
Marketing/Marketing Management, A
Massage Therapy/Therapeutic Massage, A
Medical Office Management/Administration, A
Medical/Clinical Assistant, A
Mental and Social Health Services and Allied Pro-
  fessions, A
Office Management and Supervision, A
Operations Management and Supervision, A
Public Administration, A
Radiologic Technology/Science - Radiographer, A
Trade and Industrial Teacher Education, A
Welding Technology/Welder, A

LENOIR-RHYNE UNIVERSITY

Accounting, BM
American Government and Politics (United
  States), B
American/United States Studies/Civilization, B
Athletic Training and Sports Medicine, M
Biology/Biological Sciences, B
Business Administration and Management, B
Business Administration, Management and Opera-
  tions, M
Chemistry, B
Clinical Psychology, M
Community College Education, M
Computer and Information Sciences, B
Counseling Psychology, M
Counselor Education/School Counseling and Guid-
  ance Services, M
Criminal Justice/Safety Studies, B
Distance Education Development, M
Drama and Dramatics/Theatre Arts, B
Economics, B
Education, B
Educational Leadership and Administration, M
Educational Media/Instructional Technology, M
Elementary Education and Teaching, B
Engineering Technology, B
English Language and Literature, B
Entrepreneurship/Entrepreneurial Studies, BM
Environmental Studies, B

Finance, B
Forestry, B
German Language and Literature, B
Graphic Design, B
Health/Medical Preparatory Programs, B
History, B
Human Services, BM
Information Science/Studies, B
International Business/Trade/Commerce, BM
International Finance, B
International Relations and Affairs, B
Junior High/Intermediate/Middle School Education
   and Teaching, B
Kinesiology and Exercise Science, B
Liberal Arts and Sciences Studies and Humani-
   ties, B
Management Information Systems and Services, M
Management Science, B
Management Strategy and Policy, M
Marketing/Marketing Management, B
Mathematics, B
Music, B
Music Performance, B
Music Teacher Education, B
Non-Profit/Public/Organizational Management, B
Nursing, M
Nursing Administration, M
Nursing Education, M
Occupational Therapy/Therapist, M
Organizational Management, M
Philosophy, B
Physician Assistant, M
Physics, B
Political Science and Government, B
Pre-Medicine/Pre-Medical Studies, B
Psychology, B
Public Health, M
Religion/Religious Studies, B
Religious/Sacred Music, B
School Psychology, M
Sociology, B
Spanish Language and Literature, B
Sport and Fitness Administration/Management, B
Substance Abuse/Addiction Counseling, M
Sustainable Development, M
Theology and Religious Vocations, MD
Writing, M

LIVING ARTS COLLEGE

Animation, Interactive Technology, Video Graphics
   and Special Effects, B
Cinematography and Film/Video Production, B
Interior Design, B
Photography, B
Recording Arts Technology/Technician, B
Web Page, Digital/Multimedia and Information Re-
   sources Design, B

LIVINGSTONE COLLEGE

Accounting, B
Biology/Biological Sciences, B
Business Administration and Management, B
Chemistry, B
Computer Science, B
Education, B
Elementary Education and Teaching, B
English Language and Literature, B
History, B
Human Services, B
Information Science/Studies, B
Kindergarten/PreSchool Education and Teaching, B
Mathematics, B
Music, B
Music Teacher Education, B
Physical Education Teaching and Coaching, B
Political Science and Government, B
Psychology, B
Social Sciences, B
Social Work, B
Sociology, B
Sport and Fitness Administration/Management, B

LOUISBURG COLLEGE

Athletic Training and Sports Medicine, A
Biological and Physical Sciences, A
Biology Teacher Education, A

Biology/Biological Sciences, A
Business Administration and Management, A
Business Teacher Education, A
Business/Commerce, A
Chemistry, A
Chemistry Teacher Education, A
Clinical Laboratory Science/Medical
   Technology/Technologist, A
Computer Science, A
Dance, A
Economics, A
Elementary Education and Teaching, A
English Language and Literature, A
English/Language Arts Teacher Education, A
Health and Physical Education, A
History, A
Information Science/Studies, A
Liberal Arts and Sciences Studies and Humani-
   ties, A
Management Science, A
Mathematics, A
Mathematics Teacher Education, A
Occupational Therapy/Therapist, A
Physical Therapy/Therapist, A
Physics, A
Political Science and Government, A
Pre-Law Studies, A
Pre-Medicine/Pre-Medical Studies, A
Pre-Pharmacy Studies, A
Pre-Veterinary Studies, A
Psychology, A
Sales and Marketing Operations/Marketing and Dis-
   tribution Teacher Education, A
Social Science Teacher Education, A
Social Work, A
Sociology, A
Special Education and Teaching, A
Sport and Fitness Administration/Management, A
Teacher Education, Multiple Levels, A

MARS HILL UNIVERSITY

Accounting, B
Adult and Continuing Education and Teaching, B
Art History, Criticism and Conservation, B
Art Teacher Education, B
Art/Art Studies, General, B
Athletic Training and Sports Medicine, B
Behavioral Sciences, B
Biological and Physical Sciences, B
Biology/Biological Sciences, B
Business Administration and Management, B
Business/Managerial Economics, B
Chemistry, B
Computer Science, B
Computer and Information Sciences, B
Criminal Justice/Law Enforcement Administration, B
Drama and Dramatics/Theatre Arts, B
Economics, B
Education, B
Elementary Education and Teaching, BM
English Language and Literature, B
Entrepreneurship/Entrepreneurial Studies, B
Fashion Merchandising, B
Finance, B
Fine/Studio Arts, B
Graphic Design, B
History, B
Junior High/Intermediate/Middle School Education
   and Teaching, B
Kinesiology and Exercise Science, B
Liberal Arts and Sciences Studies and Humani-
   ties, B
Marketing/Marketing Management, B
Mathematics, B
Music, B
Music Performance, B
Music Teacher Education, B
Parks, Recreation, Leisure and Fitness Studies, B
Physical Education Teaching and Coaching, B
Political Science and Government, B
Pre-Law Studies, B
Pre-Medicine/Pre-Medical Studies, B
Pre-Nursing Studies, B
Pre-Veterinary Studies, B
Psychology, B
Religion/Religious Studies, B

Science Teacher Education/General Science
   Teacher Education, B
Secondary Education and Teaching, B
Social Sciences, B
Social Work, B
Sociology, B
Spanish Language and Literature, B
Special Education and Teaching, B
Sport and Fitness Administration/Management, B
Zoology/Animal Biology, B

MARTIN COMMUNITY COLLEGE

Accounting, A
Administrative Assistant and Secretarial Science, A
Automobile/Automotive Mechanics
   Technology/Technician, A
Business Administration and Management, A
Cosmetology/Cosmetologist, A
Dietician Assistant, A
Electrical and Power Transmission Installers, A
Electromechanical Technology/Electromechanical
   Engineering Technology, A
Equestrian/Equine Studies, A
General Studies, A
Heating, Air Conditioning and Refrigeration
   Technology/Technician, A
Heating, Air Conditioning, Ventilation and Refrigera-
   tion Maintenance Technology/Technician, A
Information Science/Studies, A
Liberal Arts and Sciences Studies and Humani-
   ties, A
Management Information Systems and Services, A
Medical Administrative Assistant/Secretary, A
Medical/Clinical Assistant, A
Physical Therapist Assistant, A

MAYLAND COMMUNITY COLLEGE

Accounting Technology/Technician and Bookkeep-
   ing, A
Applied Horticulture/Horticultural Operations, A
Business Administration and Management, A
Child Care and Support Services Management, A
Computer Engineering Technology/Technician, A
Cosmetology/Cosmetologist, A
Criminal Justice/Safety Studies, A
Electrical, Electronic and Communications Engineer-
   ing Technology/Technician, A
Electromechanical Technology/Electromechanical
   Engineering Technology, A
Executive Assistant/Executive Secretary, A
General Studies, A
Industrial Electronics Technology/Technician, A
Liberal Arts and Sciences Studies and Humani-
   ties, A
Management Information Systems and Services, A
Medical Administrative Assistant/Secretary, A
Medical/Clinical Assistant, A

MCDOWELL TECHNICAL COMMUNITY
COLLEGE

Accounting, A
Automobile/Automotive Mechanics
   Technology/Technician, A
Business Administration and Management, A
Commercial and Advertising Art, A
Cosmetology/Cosmetologist, A
Early Childhood Education and Teaching, A
Electrician, A
Electromechanical and Instrumentation and Mainte-
   nance Technologies/Technicians, A
Elementary Education and Teaching, A
General Studies, A
Health Information/Medical Records
   Technology/Technician, A
Information Technology, A
Liberal Arts and Sciences Studies and Humani-
   ties, A
Machine Shop Technology/Assistant, A
Marketing/Marketing Management, A
Office Management and Supervision, A
Operations Management and Supervision, A
Photographic and Film/Video Technology/Technician
   and Assistant, A

Special Education and Teaching, A

MEREDITH COLLEGE

Accounting, B
Art Teacher Education, B
Biology/Biological Sciences, B
Business Administration and Management, B
Business Administration, Management and Operations, M
Chemistry, B
Child Development, B
Communication Studies/Speech Communication and Rhetoric, B
Computer Science, B
Dance, B
Dietetics/Dieticians, B
Drama and Dance Teacher Education, B
Drama and Dramatics/Theatre Arts, B
Dramatic/Theatre Arts and Stagecraft, B
Economics, B
Education, B
English Language and Literature, B
Environmental Studies, B
Family and Consumer Sciences/Human Sciences, B
Fashion Merchandising, B
Fashion/Apparel Design, B
Fine/Studio Arts, B
Graphic Design, B
Health/Medical Preparatory Programs, B
History, B
Interior Design, B
International Relations and Affairs, B
International/Global Studies, B
Kinesiology and Exercise Science, B
Mass Communication/Media Studies, B
Mathematics, B
Multi-/Interdisciplinary Studies, B
Music, B
Music Teacher Education, B
Nutritional Sciences, MO
Physical Education Teaching and Coaching, B
Political Science and Government, B
Psychology, B
Religion/Religious Studies, B
Social Work, B
Sociology, B
Spanish Language and Literature, B

METHODIST UNIVERSITY

Accounting, AB
Army JROTC/ROTC, A
Art Teacher Education, B
Art/Art Studies, General, AB
Athletic Training and Sports Medicine, B
Behavioral Sciences, AB
Bible/Biblical Studies, B
Biological and Physical Sciences, B
Biology/Biological Sciences, AB
Business Administration and Management, AB
Business Administration, Management and Operations, M
Chemistry, AB
Computer Science, AB
Criminal Justice/Law Enforcement Administration, AB
Criminology, M
Drama and Dramatics/Theatre Arts, AB
Economics, AB
Education, B
Elementary Education and Teaching, B
English Language and Literature, AB
Finance, AB
French Language and Literature, AB
German Language and Literature, A
Health/Health Care Administration/Management, AB
History, AB
Hospitality and Recreation Marketing Operations, B
International Relations and Affairs, B
Kindergarten/PreSchool Education and Teaching, B
Law and Legal Studies, B
Liberal Arts and Sciences Studies and Humanities, AB
Marketing Research, B
Mass Communication/Media Studies, AB
Mathematics, AB
Music, AB

Music Teacher Education, B
Parks, Recreation and Leisure Facilities Management, B
Philosophy, A
Physical Education Teaching and Coaching, AB
Physician Assistant, BM
Political Science and Government, AB
Pre-Dentistry Studies, B
Pre-Law Studies, B
Pre-Medicine/Pre-Medical Studies, B
Pre-Veterinary Studies, B
Psychology, AB
Religion/Religious Studies, B
Religious Education, A
Science Teacher Education/General Science Teacher Education, B
Secondary Education and Teaching, B
Social Work, AB
Sociology, AB
Spanish Language and Literature, AB
Special Education and Teaching, B
Sport and Fitness Administration/Management, B
Teacher Education, Multiple Levels, B

MID-ATLANTIC CHRISTIAN UNIVERSITY

Bible/Biblical Studies, AB
Business Administration and Management, B
Elementary Education and Teaching, B
Family Systems, B
Linguistics, B
Missions/Missionary Studies and Missiology, B
Pre-Theology/Pre-Ministerial Studies, B
Youth Ministry, B

MILLER-MOTTE COLLEGE (CARY)

Accounting, A
Allied Health and Medical Assisting Services, B
Business Administration and Management, AB
Cosmetology/Cosmetologist, A
Criminal Justice/Law Enforcement Administration, A
Data Entry/Microcomputer Applications, A
Data Processing and Data Processing Technology/Technician, A
Dental Assisting/Assistant, A
Health Information/Medical Records Technology/Technician, A
International Business/Trade/Commerce, A
Legal Assistant/Paralegal, A
Management Science, A
Massage Therapy/Therapeutic Massage, A
Medical/Clinical Assistant, A
Office Management and Supervision, A
Pharmacy Technician/Assistant, A
Surgical Technology/Technologist, A
System, Networking, and LAN/WAN Management/Manager, A

MILLER-MOTTE COLLEGE (WILMINGTON)

Accounting, A
Accounting and Business/Management, A
Allied Health and Medical Assisting Services, A
Business Administration and Management, A
Data Entry/Microcomputer Applications, A
Massage Therapy/Therapeutic Massage, A
Medical Office Assistant/Specialist, A
Surgical Technology/Technologist, A

MITCHELL COMMUNITY COLLEGE

Accounting, A
Agribusiness, A
Business Administration and Management, A
Child Care and Support Services Management, A
Computer Programming, Specific Applications, A
Computer Programming/Programmer, A
Computer Systems Analysis/Analyst, A
Criminal Justice/Law Enforcement Administration, A
Early Childhood Education and Teaching, A
Education/Teaching of Individuals in Early Childhood Special Education Programs, A
Electrical, Electronic and Communications Engineering Technology/Technician, A
Electrician, A

Electromechanical and Instrumentation and Maintenance Technologies/Technicians, A
Elementary Education and Teaching, A
Engineering/Industrial Management, A
Executive Assistant/Executive Secretary, A
General Studies, A
Health Professions and Related Clinical Sciences, A
Information Science/Studies, A
Information Technology, A
Kindergarten/PreSchool Education and Teaching, A
Liberal Arts and Sciences Studies and Humanities, A
Machine Shop Technology/Assistant, A
Manufacturing Engineering, A
Manufacturing Technology/Technician, A
Mechanical Drafting and Mechanical Drafting CAD/CADD, A
Mechanical Engineering/Mechanical Technology/Technician, A
Medical/Clinical Assistant, A
Office Management and Supervision, A
Operations Management and Supervision, A
Teacher Assistant/Aide, A

MONTGOMERY COMMUNITY COLLEGE

Business Administration and Management, A
Criminal Justice/Safety Studies, A
Early Childhood Education and Teaching, A
Electrician, A
Electromechanical and Instrumentation and Maintenance Technologies/Technicians, A
Forestry Technology/Technician, A
Gunsmithing/Gunsmith, A
Heating, Air Conditioning, Ventilation and Refrigeration Maintenance Technology/Technician, A
Information Technology, A
Liberal Arts and Sciences Studies and Humanities, A
Medical/Clinical Assistant, A
Mental and Social Health Services and Allied Professions, A
Office Management and Supervision, A

MONTREAT COLLEGE

American/United States Studies/Civilization, B
Bible/Biblical Studies, B
Biology/Biological Sciences, B
Business Administration and Management, AB
Business Administration, Management and Operations, M
Clinical Psychology, M
Communication and Media Studies, B
Computer and Information Sciences, B
Counseling Psychology, M
Education, A
Elementary Education and Teaching, B
English Language and Literature, B
Environmental Education, M
Environmental Studies, B
History, B
Human Services, B
Liberal Arts and Sciences Studies and Humanities, A
Management, M
Music Performance, B
Parks, Recreation, Leisure and Fitness Studies, B
Social Sciences, B

NASH COMMUNITY COLLEGE

Accounting, A
Architectural Engineering Technology/Technician, A
Business Administration and Management, A
Computer Engineering Technology/Technician, A
Criminal Justice/Safety Studies, A
Design and Visual Communications, A
E-Commerce/Electronic Commerce, A
Early Childhood Education and Teaching, A
Electrical, Electronic and Communications Engineering Technology/Technician, A
Electrician, A
Elementary Education and Teaching, A
Fire Protection, A
General Studies, A
Hotel/Motel Administration/Management, A
Industrial Technology/Technician, A
Information Technology, A

Legal Administrative Assistant/Secretary, A
Liberal Arts and Sciences Studies and Humanities, A
Lineworker, A
Machine Shop Technology/Assistant, A
Medical Office Management/Administration, A
Physical Therapy/Therapist, A
Restaurant, Culinary, and Catering Management/Manager, A
Special Education and Teaching, A
System, Networking, and LAN/WAN Management/Manager, A
Web/Multimedia Management and Webmaster, A
Welding Technology/Welder, A

NORTH CAROLINA AGRICULTURAL AND TECHNICAL STATE UNIVERSITY

Accounting, BM
Administrative Assistant and Secretarial Science, B
Adult and Continuing Education and Teaching, M
African-American Studies, M
Agribusiness, B
Agricultural Business and Management, B
Agricultural Economics, BM
Agricultural Education, M
Agricultural Mechanization, B
Agricultural Sciences, M
Agricultural Teacher Education, B
Agricultural/Biological Engineering and Bioengineering, B
Agriculture, B
Agronomy and Soil Sciences, M
Animal Sciences, BM
Apparel and Textiles, B
Applied Economics, M
Applied Mathematics, BM
Architectural Engineering, B
Art Teacher Education, B
Art/Art Studies, General, B
Atmospheric Sciences and Meteorology, B
Bioengineering, M
Biological and Biomedical Sciences, M
Biology Teacher Education, B
Biology/Biological Sciences, B
Biomedical/Medical Engineering, B
Broadcast Journalism, B
Business Administration and Management, B
Business Administration, Management and Operations, M
Business Education, M
Business Teacher Education, B
Chemical Engineering, BM
Chemistry, BMD
Chemistry Teacher Education, B
Child Development, BM
Child and Family Studies, M
Civil Engineering, BM
Communication Studies/Speech Communication and Rhetoric, B
Computational Sciences, M
Computer Art and Design, M
Computer Engineering, BMD
Computer Science, BM
Construction Management, M
Consumer Economics, M
Counselor Education/School Counseling and Guidance Services, M
Criminal Justice/Safety Studies, B
Drama and Dramatics/Theatre Arts, B
Early Childhood Education and Teaching, M
Economics, B
Education, BM
Educational Administration and Supervision, M
Educational Media/Instructional Technology, M
Electrical Engineering, MD
Electrical and Electronic Engineering Technologies/Technicians, B
Electrical, Electronic and Communications Engineering Technology/Technician, B
Electrical, Electronics and Communications Engineering, B
Elementary Education and Teaching, BM
Energy and Power Engineering, MD
Engineering, B
Engineering Physics, B
Engineering Technologies/Technicians, B

Engineering and Applied Sciences, MD
English, M
English Education, M
English Language and Literature, B
English/Language Arts Teacher Education, B
Environmental Sciences, M
Environmental and Occupational Health, M
Family and Consumer Sciences/Home Economics Teacher Education, B
Family and Consumer Sciences/Human Sciences, B
Finance, B
Food Science, B
Foods, Nutrition, and Wellness Studies, B
French Language Teacher Education, B
French Language and Literature, B
Graphic Design, BM
Health Education, M
History, B
History Teacher Education, B
Human Resources Management and Services, M
Industrial Engineering, B
Industrial Technology/Technician, B
Industrial/Management Engineering, MD
Journalism, B
Kindergarten/PreSchool Education and Teaching, B
Landscape Architecture, B
Liberal Arts and Sciences Studies and Humanities, B
Management Information Systems and Services, M
Management of Technology, M
Manufacturing Technology/Technician, B
Marketing/Marketing Management, B
Mass Communication/Media Studies, B
Mathematics, BM
Mathematics Teacher Education, B
Mechanical Engineering, BMD
Music, B
Music Teacher Education, B
Nutritional Sciences, M
Occupational Health and Industrial Hygiene, B
Optical Technologies, MD
Parks, Recreation and Leisure Facilities Management, B
Physical Education Teaching and Coaching, M
Physics, BM
Physics Teacher Education, B
Plant Sciences, M
Political Science and Government, B
Psychology, B
Public Relations/Image Management, B
Radio and Television, B
Reading Teacher Education, M
Romance Languages, Literatures, and Linguistics, B
Science Teacher Education/General Science Teacher Education, BM
Secondary Education and Teaching, BM
Social Sciences, B
Social Work, BM
Sociology, B
Spanish Language Teacher Education, B
Special Education and Teaching, B
Sport and Fitness Administration/Management, B
Supply Chain Management, M
Surveying Engineering, B
Systems Engineering, MD
Technology Teacher Education/Industrial Arts Teacher Education, B
Trade and Industrial Teacher Education, B
Transportation/Transportation Management, B
Vocational and Technical Education, M

NORTH CAROLINA CENTRAL UNIVERSITY

Accounting, B
Applied Mathematics, M
Art/Art Studies, General, B
Athletic Training and Sports Medicine, B
Biological and Biomedical Sciences, M
Biology/Biological Sciences, B
Biomedical Sciences, B
Business Administration and Management, B
Business Administration, Management and Operations, M
Chemistry, BM
Communication Disorders, M
Community Psychology, M

Counselor Education/School Counseling and Guidance Services, M
Criminal Justice/Safety Studies, B
Criminology, M
Curriculum and Instruction, M
Drama and Dramatics/Theatre Arts, B
Education, M
Educational Administration and Supervision, M
Educational Media/Instructional Technology, M
Elementary Education and Teaching, BM
English, M
English Language and Literature, B
Family and Consumer Sciences/Human Sciences, BM
Geosciences, M
Health Teacher Education, B
Health and Physical Education, B
History, BM
Hospitality Administration/Management, B
Information Science/Studies, M
Jazz/Jazz Studies, B
Junior High/Intermediate/Middle School Education and Teaching, B
Kindergarten/PreSchool Education and Teaching, B
Law and Legal Studies, D
Library Science, M
Mass Communication/Media Studies, B
Mathematics, BM
Mathematics Teacher Education, M
Middle School Education, M
Music, BM
Parks, Recreation and Leisure Facilities Management, B
Physical Education Teaching and Coaching, M
Physics, BM
Political Science and Government, B
Psychology, BM
Public Administration, M
Public Health Education and Promotion, B
Recreation and Park Management, M
Social Work, B
Sociology, M
Spanish Language and Literature, B
Special Education and Teaching, M
Sport and Fitness Administration/Management, M
Therapeutic Recreation, M

NORTH CAROLINA STATE UNIVERSITY

Accounting, BM
Adult and Continuing Education and Teaching, MD
Aerospace, Aeronautical and Astronautical Engineering, BMD
African-American/Black Studies, B
Agribusiness, B
Agricultural Business and Management, A
Agricultural Economics, M
Agricultural Education, MO
Agricultural Engineering, MDO
Agricultural Mechanization, B
Agricultural Sciences, MDO
Agricultural Teacher Education, B
Agricultural and Extension Education Services, B
Agricultural/Biological Engineering and Bioengineering, B
Agriculture, AB
Agronomy and Crop Science, B
Agronomy and Soil Sciences, MD
Animal Sciences, BMD
Animal/Livestock Husbandry and Production, A
Anthropology, BM
Applied Arts and Design, M
Applied Mathematics, BMD
Architecture, BM
Art History, Criticism and Conservation, B
Atmospheric Sciences and Meteorology, BMD
BioTechnology, M
Biochemistry, BD
Bioengineering, MDO
Bioinformatics, MD
Biological and Biomedical Sciences, MDO
Biology/Biological Sciences, B
Biomathematics and Bioinformatics, MD
Biomedical Engineering, MD
Biomedical/Medical Engineering, B
Botany/Plant Biology, BMD
Business Administration and Management, B

Business Administration, Management and Operations, M
Business Education, M
Business/Managerial Economics, B
Cell Biology and Anatomy, MD
Chemical Engineering, BMD
Chemistry, BMD
Civil Engineering, BMD
Clothing and Textiles, D
Communication Studies/Speech Communication and Rhetoric, B
Communication and Media Studies, M
Community College Education, MD
Community Psychology, M
Computer Art and Design, D
Computer Engineering, BMD
Computer Science, BMD
Construction Engineering, B
Counselor Education/School Counseling and Guidance Services, MD
Criminology, B
Crop Production, A
Cultural Anthropology, M
Curriculum and Instruction, MD
Design and Applied Arts, D
Design and Visual Communications, B
Developmental Education, MDO
Developmental Psychology, D
Economics, MD
Education, BMDO
Educational Administration and Supervision, MD
Educational Measurement and Evaluation, D
Educational Media/Instructional Technology, MD
Electrical Engineering, MD
Electrical, Electronics and Communications Engineering, B
Elementary Education and Teaching, BM
Engineering, B
Engineering and Applied Sciences, MD
English, M
English Education, M
English Language and Literature, B
Entomology, MD
Entrepreneurship/Entrepreneurial Studies, M
Environmental Design/Architecture, B
Environmental Engineering Technology/Environmental Technology, B
Environmental Sciences, B
Environmental/Environmental Health Engineering, B
Epidemiology, MD
Ergonomics and Human Factors, D
Experimental Psychology, D
Financial Engineering, M
Fish, Game and Wildlife Management, MD
Food Science, B
Food Science and Technology, MD
Foreign Languages and Literatures, B
Forest Management/Forest Resources Management, B
Forestry, MD
French Language and Literature, BM
Genetics, BMD
Genomic Sciences, MD
Geographic Information Systems, M
Geology/Earth Science, B
Geosciences, MD
German Studies, B
Graphic Design, BM
Higher Education/Higher Education Administration, MD
History, BM
Horticultural Science, BMDO
Human Resources Development, M
Immunology, MD
Industrial Design, BM
Industrial Engineering, B
Industrial and Organizational Psychology, D
Industrial/Management Engineering, MD
Infectious Diseases, MD
International Affairs, M
International/Global Studies, B
Junior High/Intermediate/Middle School Education and Teaching, B
Landscape Architecture, BM
Landscaping and Groundskeeping, A

Liberal Arts and Sciences Studies and Humanities, B
Liberal Studies, M
Management of Technology, D
Manufacturing Engineering, M
Marine Sciences, M
Materials Engineering, BMD
Materials Sciences, MD
Mathematical and Computational Finance, M
Mathematics, BMD
Mathematics Teacher Education, BMD
Mechanical Engineering, BMD
Meteorology, MD
Microbiology, BMD
Middle School Education, M
Molecular Toxicology, MD
Natural Resources Management/Development and Policy, BM
Natural Resources and Conservation, BM
Non-Profit/Public/Organizational Management, O
Nuclear Engineering, BMD
Nutritional Sciences, BMD
Oceanography, Chemical and Physical, BMD
Operations Research, MD
Paper and Pulp Engineering, MD
Parks, Recreation and Leisure Facilities Management, B
Pathology/Experimental Pathology, MD
Pharmacology, MD
Philosophy, B
Physics, BMD
Physiology, MD
Plant Biology, MD
Plant Pathology/Phytopathology, MD
Political Science and Government, B
Polymer/Plastics Engineering, D
Poultry Science, BMD
Psychology, BD
Public Administration, MD
Public History, M
Recreation and Park Management, MD
Religion/Religious Studies, B
Rhetoric, D
Sales and Marketing Operations/Marketing and Distribution Teacher Education, B
School Psychology, D
Science Teacher Education/General Science Teacher Education, BMD
Science Technologies/Technicians, B
Science, Technology and Society, B
Secondary Education and Teaching, B
Social Studies Teacher Education, M
Social Work, BM
Sociology, BMD
Soil Sciences, B
Spanish Language and Literature, BM
Special Education and Teaching, M
Sport and Fitness Administration/Management, BM
Statistics, BMD
Supply Chain Management, M
Technical Communication, M
Technology Teacher Education/Industrial Arts Teacher Education, B
Textile Sciences and Engineering, BMD
Toxicology, MD
Travel and Tourism, MD
Turf and Turfgrass Management, AB
Veterinary Medicine, MD
Veterinary Sciences, MD
Women's Studies, B
Wood Science and Wood Products/Pulp and Paper Technology, B
Writing, M
Zoology/Animal Biology, BMD

NORTH CAROLINA WESLEYAN COLLEGE

Accounting, B
Biological and Physical Sciences, B
Biology/Biological Sciences, B
Biomedical Sciences, B
Business Administration and Management, B
Chemistry, B
Computer and Information Sciences, B
Criminal Justice/Law Enforcement Administration, B
Drama and Dramatics/Theatre Arts, B

Education, B
Elementary Education and Teaching, B
English Language and Literature, B
Environmental Studies, B
History, B
Junior High/Intermediate/Middle School Education and Teaching, B
Kinesiology and Exercise Science, B
Liberal Arts and Sciences Studies and Humanities, B
Marketing/Marketing Management, B
Mathematics, B
Political Science and Government, B
Pre-Medicine/Pre-Medical Studies, B
Psychology, B
Religion/Religious Studies, B
Sociology, B
Special Education and Teaching, B

PAMLICO COMMUNITY COLLEGE

Accounting, A
Administrative Assistant and Secretarial Science, A
Automobile/Automotive Mechanics Technology/Technician, A
Business Administration and Management, A
Clinical/Medical Laboratory Technician, A
Computer Engineering Technology/Technician, A
Electrical, Electronic and Communications Engineering Technology/Technician, A
Environmental Studies, A
Liberal Arts and Sciences Studies and Humanities, A
Medical/Clinical Assistant, A

PFEIFFER UNIVERSITY

Accounting, B
Athletic Training and Sports Medicine, B
Biology/Biological Sciences, B
Business Administration and Management, B
Business Administration, Management and Operations, M
Business/Managerial Economics, B
Chemistry, B
Communication Studies/Speech Communication and Rhetoric, B
Criminal Justice/Law Enforcement Administration, B
Economics, B
Education, B
Elementary Education and Teaching, BM
Engineering, B
English Language and Literature, B
Environmental Sciences, B
Environmental Studies, B
Exercise Physiology, B
Finance, B
Health Services Administration, M
History, B
Human Services, B
International Business/Trade/Commerce, B
Journalism, B
Management Information Systems and Services, B
Marketing/Marketing Management, B
Mathematics, B
Mathematics and Computer Science, B
Music, B
Music Teacher Education, B
Organizational Communication, B
Organizational Management, M
Physical Education Teaching and Coaching, B
Political Science and Government, B
Pre-Law Studies, B
Pre-Medicine/Pre-Medical Studies, B
Psychology, B
Public Relations/Image Management, B
Religion/Religious Studies, B
Religious Education, BM
Religious/Sacred Music, B
Science Teacher Education/General Science Teacher Education, B
Social Sciences, B
Social Studies Teacher Education, B
Sociology, B
Special Education and Teaching, B
Sport and Fitness Administration/Management, B
Theology and Religious Vocations, M

Youth Ministry, B

PIEDMONT COMMUNITY COLLEGE

Accounting, A
Business Administration and Management, A
Child Care and Support Services Management, A
Cinematography and Film/Video Production, A
Criminal Justice/Safety Studies, A
Early Childhood Education and Teaching, A
Electrical and Power Transmission
  Installation/Installer, A
Electrician, A
Electromechanical and Instrumentation and Mainte-
  nance Technologies/Technicians, A
General Studies, A
Graphic Communications, A
Health Professions and Related Clinical Sciences, A
Historic Preservation and Conservation, A
Industrial Technology/Technician, A
Information Technology, A
Liberal Arts and Sciences Studies and Humani-
  ties, A
Medical Administrative Assistant/Secretary, A
Medical Office Management/Administration, A
Medical/Clinical Assistant, A
Mental and Social Health Services and Allied Pro-
  fessions, A
Office Management and Supervision, A

PIEDMONT INTERNATIONAL UNIVER-SITY

Bible/Biblical Studies, AB
Curriculum and Instruction, M
Elementary Education and Teaching, B
English/Language Arts Teacher Education, B
Jewish/Judaic Studies, B
Kindergarten/PreSchool Education and Teach-
  ing, AB
Marriage and Family Therapy/Counseling, B
Missions/Missionary Studies and Missiology, AB
Music Teacher Education, B
Pastoral Studies/Counseling, M
Physical Education Teaching and Coaching, B
Religious Education, AB
Religious/Sacred Music, B
Theology and Religious Vocations, MD
Theology/Theological Studies, AB
Youth Ministry, AB

PITT COMMUNITY COLLEGE

Accounting, A
Allied Health Diagnostic, Intervention, and Treat-
  ment Professions, A
Architectural Engineering Technology/Technician, A
Automobile/Automotive Mechanics
  Technology/Technician, A
Biology Technician/BioTechnology Laboratory Tech-
  nician, A
Building/Construction Finishing, Manage-
  ment, and Inspection, A
Business Administration and Management, A
Commercial and Advertising Art, A
Computer Programming, Specific Applications, A
Computer Systems Networking and Telecommunica-
  tions, A
Computer and Information Systems Security, A
Construction Trades, A
Corrections and Criminal Justice, A
Criminal Justice/Police Science, A
Criminal Justice/Safety Studies, A
Diagnostic Medical Sonography/Sonographer and
  Ultrasound Technician, A
E-Commerce/Electronic Commerce, A
Early Childhood Education and Teaching, A
Electrical, Electronic and Communications Engineer-
  ing Technology/Technician, A
Electrical/Electronics Maintenance and Repair Tech-
  nology, A
Electrician, A
Electromechanical and Instrumentation and Mainte-
  nance Technologies/Technicians, A
Elementary Education and Teaching, A
General Studies, A
Health Information/Medical Records
  Technology/Technician, A
Health Professions and Related Clinical Sciences, A

Health Services/Allied Health/Health Sciences, A
Heating, Air Conditioning, Ventilation and Refrigera-
  tion Maintenance Technology/Technician, A
Human Resources Management and Services, A
Information Science/Studies, A
Information Technology, A
International Business/Trade/Commerce, A
Legal Administrative Assistant/Secretary, A
Legal Assistant/Paralegal, A
Liberal Arts and Sciences Studies and Humani-
  ties, A
Logistics and Materials Management, A
Machine Shop Technology/Assistant, A
Manufacturing Technology/Technician, A
Marketing/Marketing Management, A
Massage Therapy/Therapeutic Massage, A
Mechanical Engineering/Mechanical
  Technology/Technician, A
Medical Office Management/Administration, A
Medical Radiologic Technology/Science - Radiation
  Therapist, A
Medical/Clinical Assistant, A
Nuclear Medical Technology/Technologist, A
Occupational Therapist Assistant, A
Office Management and Supervision, A
Operations Management and Supervision, A
Radiologic Technology/Science - Radiographer, A
Respiratory Care Therapy/Therapist, A
Substance Abuse/Addiction Counseling, A
System, Networking, and LAN/WAN
  Management/Manager, A
Welding Technology/Welder, A

QUEENS UNIVERSITY OF CHARLOTTE

Accounting, B
Art History, Criticism and Conservation, B
Biochemistry, B
Biology/Biological Sciences, B
Business Administration and Management, B
Business Administration, Management and Opera-
  tions, M
Chemistry, B
Communication and Media Studies, M
Drama and Dramatics/Theatre Arts, B
Education, M
Educational Leadership and Administration, M
Elementary Education and Teaching, BM
English Language and Literature, B
Environmental Sciences, B
Environmental Studies, B
Finance, B
Fine/Studio Arts, B
French Language and Literature, B
Graphic Design, B
Health Professions and Related Clinical Sciences, B
Health Services/Allied Health/Health Sciences, B
History, B
Human Services, B
Interior Design, BM
International Relations and Affairs, B
Journalism, B
Kinesiology and Exercise Science, B
Mathematics, B
Music, B
Music Therapy/Therapist, B
Nursing, M
Nursing Administration, M
Nursing Education, M
Organizational Management, M
Philosophy, B
Political Science and Government, B
Psychology, B
Public Health Education and Promotion, B
Reading Teacher Education, M
Religion/Religious Studies, B
Romance Languages, Literatures, and Linguistics, B
Sociology, B
Spanish Language and Literature, B
Sport and Fitness Administration/Management, B
Writing, M

RANDOLPH COMMUNITY COLLEGE

Accounting, A
Autobody/Collision and Repair
  Technology/Technician, A

Automobile/Automotive Mechanics
  Technology/Technician, A
Business Administration and Management, A
Commercial Photography, A
Commercial and Advertising Art, A
Computer Systems Networking and Telecommunica-
  tions, A
Cosmetology/Cosmetologist, A
Criminal Justice/Safety Studies, A
Early Childhood Education and Teaching, A
Electrician, A
Electromechanical Technology/Electromechanical
  Engineering Technology, A
Funeral Service and Mortuary Science, A
Human Services, A
Information Technology, A
Interior Design, A
Liberal Arts and Sciences Studies and Humani-
  ties, A
Logistics and Materials Management, A
Machine Shop Technology/Assistant, A
Medical Office Management/Administration, A
Medical/Clinical Assistant, A
Photographic and Film/Video Technology/Technician
  and Assistant, A
Photojournalism, A
Physical Therapist Assistant, A
Radiologic Technology/Science - Radiographer, A

RICHMOND COMMUNITY COLLEGE

Accounting, A
Business Administration and Management, A
Computer Engineering Technology/Technician, A
Criminal Justice/Safety Studies, A
Early Childhood Education and Teaching, A
Electrical and Power Transmission
  Installation/Installer, A
Electrical, Electronic and Communications Engineer-
  ing Technology/Technician, A
Electromechanical Technology/Electromechanical
  Engineering Technology, A
Electromechanical and Instrumentation and Mainte-
  nance Technologies/Technicians, A
Elementary Education and Teaching, A
Entrepreneurship/Entrepreneurial Studies, A
Health Information/Medical Records
  Technology/Technician, A
Health Professions and Related Clinical Sciences, A
Heating, Air Conditioning, Ventilation and Refrigera-
  tion Maintenance Technology/Technician, A
Information Technology, A
Liberal Arts and Sciences Studies and Humani-
  ties, A
Mechanical Engineering/Mechanical
  Technology/Technician, A
Medical Office Computer Specialist/Assistant, A
Medical Office Management/Administration, A
Medical/Clinical Assistant, A
Mental and Social Health Services and Allied Pro-
  fessions, A
Office Management and Supervision, A

ROANOKE-CHOWAN COMMUNITY COLLEGE

Architectural Engineering Technology/Technician, A
Business Administration and Management, A
Child Care and Support Services Management, A
Computer Systems Analysis/Analyst, A
Criminal Justice/Police Science, A
Criminal Justice/Safety Studies, A
Early Childhood Education and Teaching, A
Electromechanical and Instrumentation and Mainte-
  nance Technologies/Technicians, A
Elementary Education and Teaching, A
Environmental Sciences, A
Executive Assistant/Executive Secretary, A
General Studies, A
Health Professions and Related Clinical Sciences, A
Information Science/Studies, A
Information Technology, A
Liberal Arts and Sciences Studies and Humani-
  ties, A
Medical Office Management/Administration, A
Mental and Social Health Services and Allied Pro-
  fessions, A
Office Management and Supervision, A

Psychiatric/Mental Health Services Technician, A
Special Education and Teaching, A

ROBESON COMMUNITY COLLEGE

Administrative Assistant and Secretarial Science, A
Business Administration and Management, A
Computer Systems Networking and Telecommunications, A
Computer and Information Sciences, A
Computer and Information Sciences and Support Services, A
Criminal Justice/Law Enforcement Administration, A
Early Childhood Education and Teaching, A
Electrical, Electronic and Communications Engineering Technology/Technician, A
Food Technology and Processing, A
Industrial Technology/Technician, A
Respiratory Care Therapy/Therapist, A

ROCKINGHAM COMMUNITY COLLEGE

Accounting, A
Agricultural and Food Products Processing, A
Banking and Financial Support Services, A
Biology Technician/BioTechnology Laboratory Technician, A
Business Administration and Management, A
Corrections and Criminal Justice, A
Criminal Justice/Police Science, A
Early Childhood Education and Teaching, A
Electrical, Electronic and Communications Engineering Technology/Technician, A
Electrician, A
General Studies, A
Health/Health Care Administration/Management, A
Information Technology, A
Liberal Arts and Sciences Studies and Humanities, A
Logistics and Materials Management, A
Machine Shop Technology/Assistant, A
Medical Office Management/Administration, A
Office Management and Supervision, A
Respiratory Care Therapy/Therapist, A

ROWAN-CABARRUS COMMUNITY COLLEGE

Accounting, A
Automobile/Automotive Mechanics Technology/Technician, A
Building/Property Maintenance and Management, A
Business Administration and Management, A
Business Administration, Management and Operations, A
Computer Programming/Programmer, A
Computer and Information Systems Security, A
Cosmetology/Cosmetologist, A
Criminal Justice/Law Enforcement Administration, A
Early Childhood Education and Teaching, A
Electrical, Electronic and Communications Engineering Technology/Technician, A
Electrician, A
Elementary Education and Teaching, A
General Studies, A
Industrial Technology/Technician, A
Information Science/Studies, A
Information Technology, A
Liberal Arts and Sciences Studies and Humanities, A
Marketing/Marketing Management, A
Medical Office Management/Administration, A
Office Management and Supervision, A
Radiologic Technology/Science - Radiographer, A
System, Networking, and LAN/WAN Management/Manager, A

ST. ANDREWS UNIVERSITY

Art/Art Studies, General, B
Biology/Biological Sciences, B
Business Administration and Management, B
Elementary Education and Teaching, B
English Language and Literature, B
Forensic Science and Technology, B
Humanities/Humanistic Studies, B
Parks, Recreation, Leisure and Fitness Studies, B
Physical Education Teaching and Coaching, B
Pre-Medicine/Pre-Medical Studies, B

Pre-Veterinary Studies, B
Psychology, B
Social Sciences, B
Therapeutic Recreation/Recreational Therapy, B

SAINT AUGUSTINE'S UNIVERSITY

Accounting, B
Behavioral Sciences, B
Biology/Biological Sciences, B
Business Administration and Management, B
Chemistry, B
Computer Science, B
Computer and Information Sciences, B
Criminal Justice/Law Enforcement Administration, B
Dramatic/Theatre Arts and Stagecraft, B
Engineering, B
English Language and Literature, B
Film/Cinema Studies, B
Forensic Science and Technology, B
Health Professions and Related Clinical Sciences, B
History, B
Journalism, B
Kinesiology and Exercise Science, B
Mathematics, B
Music, B
Political Science and Government, B
Psychology, B
Sociology, B
Teacher Education, Multiple Levels, B
Visual and Performing Arts, B

SALEM COLLEGE

Accounting, B
Art Education, M
Art History, Criticism and Conservation, B
Biology/Biological Sciences, B
Business Administration and Management, B
Chemistry, B
Counselor Education/School Counseling and Guidance Services, M
Economics, B
Education, BM
Elementary Education and Teaching, M
English Language and Literature, B
English as a Second Language, M
Fine/Studio Arts, B
French Language and Literature, B
History, B
Interior Design, B
International Business/Trade/Commerce, B
International Relations and Affairs, B
Kinesiology and Exercise Science, B
Mass Communication/Media Studies, B
Mathematics, B
Middle School Education, M
Music, B
Music Performance, B
Non-Profit/Public/Organizational Management, B
Philosophy, B
Physician Assistant, B
Psychology, B
Reading Teacher Education, M
Religion/Religious Studies, B
Secondary Education and Teaching, M
Sociology, B
Spanish Language and Literature, B
Special Education and Teaching, M
Women's Studies, B

SAMPSON COMMUNITY COLLEGE

Accounting, A
Administrative Assistant and Secretarial Science, A
Business Administration and Management, A
Computer Programming/Programmer, A
Computer and Information Sciences, A
Criminal Justice/Law Enforcement Administration, A
Horticultural Science, A
Industrial Technology/Technician, A
Information Technology, A
Liberal Arts and Sciences Studies and Humanities, A
Poultry Science, A
System Administration/Administrator, A

Word Processing, A

SANDHILLS COMMUNITY COLLEGE

Accounting, A
Administrative Assistant and Secretarial Science, A
Architectural Engineering Technology/Technician, A
Art Teacher Education, A
Art/Art Studies, General, A
Automobile/Automotive Mechanics Technology/Technician, A
Biological and Physical Sciences, A
Business Administration and Management, A
Business, Management, Marketing, and Related Support Services, A
Child Development, A
Civil Engineering Technology/Technician, A
Clinical/Medical Laboratory Technician, A
Computer Engineering, A
Computer Engineering Technology/Technician, A
Computer Programming, Specific Applications, A
Computer Programming/Programmer, A
Computer/Information Technology Services Administration and Management, A
Cosmetology/Cosmetologist, A
Criminal Justice/Law Enforcement Administration, A
Criminal Justice/Police Science, A
Culinary Arts/Chef Training, A
Fine/Studio Arts, A
Gerontology, A
Hotel/Motel Administration/Management, A
Human Services, A
Information Science/Studies, A
Kindergarten/PreSchool Education and Teaching, A
Landscaping and Groundskeeping, A
Liberal Arts and Sciences Studies and Humanities, A
Mathematics, A
Medical Administrative Assistant/Secretary, A
Mental Health Counseling/Counselor, A
Music, A
Music Teacher Education, A
Radiologic Technology/Science - Radiographer, A
Respiratory Care Therapy/Therapist, A
Science Teacher Education/General Science Teacher Education, A
Substance Abuse/Addiction Counseling, A
Surgical Technology/Technologist, A
Survey Technology/Surveying, A
Turf and Turfgrass Management, A
Web/Multimedia Management and Webmaster, A

SHAW UNIVERSITY

Accounting, B
Athletic Training and Sports Medicine, B
Biology/Biological Sciences, B
Business Administration and Management, B
Chemistry, B
Communication Disorders, B
Computer Science, B
Computer and Information Sciences, B
Criminal Justice/Safety Studies, B
Curriculum and Instruction, M
Early Childhood Education and Teaching, M
Education, B
Elementary Education and Teaching, B
English Language and Literature, B
English/Language Arts Teacher Education, B
International Relations and Affairs, B
Kindergarten/PreSchool Education and Teaching, B
Kinesiology and Exercise Science, B
Kinesiotherapy/Kinesiotherapist, B
Liberal Arts and Sciences Studies and Humanities, B
Mass Communication/Media Studies, B
Mathematics, B
Music, B
Parks, Recreation, Leisure and Fitness Studies, B
Philosophy and Religious Studies, B
Political Science and Government, B
Psychology, B
Public Administration, B
Social Work, B
Sociology, B
Theology and Religious Vocations, M

Therapeutic Recreation/Recreational Therapy, B

SOUTH COLLEGE–ASHEVILLE

Accounting, A
Administrative Assistant and Secretarial Science, A
Business Administration and Management, A
Computer and Information Sciences, A
Criminal Justice/Law Enforcement Administration, A
Industrial Radiologic Technology/Technician, A
Law and Legal Studies, B
Legal Assistant/Paralegal, A
Medical/Clinical Assistant, A
Physical Therapist Assistant, A

SOUTH PIEDMONT COMMUNITY COLLEGE

Accounting, A
Allied Health Diagnostic, Intervention, and Treatment Professions, A
Automobile/Automotive Mechanics Technology/Technician, A
BioTechnology, A
Business Administration and Management, A
Commercial and Advertising Art, A
Criminal Justice/Safety Studies, A
Diagnostic Medical Sonography/Sonographer and Ultrasound Technician, A
Early Childhood Education and Teaching, A
Electrician, A
Electromechanical Technology/Electromechanical Engineering Technology, A
Electromechanical and Instrumentation and Maintenance Technologies/Technicians, A
Elementary Education and Teaching, A
Entrepreneurship/Entrepreneurial Studies, A
Fire Protection and Safety Technology/Technician, A
General Studies, A
Heating, Air Conditioning, Ventilation and Refrigeration Maintenance Technology/Technician, A
Information Science/Studies, A
Information Technology, A
Legal Assistant/Paralegal, A
Liberal Arts and Sciences Studies and Humanities, A
Massage Therapy/Therapeutic Massage, A
Mechanical Engineering/Mechanical Technology/Technician, A
Medical Office Management/Administration, A
Medical/Clinical Assistant, A
Mental and Social Health Services and Allied Professions, A

SOUTH UNIVERSITY

Business Administration and Management, B
Business Administration, Management and Operations, M
Counseling Psychology, M
Criminal Justice/Law Enforcement Administration, AB
Information Science/Studies, AB
Physical Therapist Assistant, A
Psychology, B

SOUTHEASTERN BAPTIST THEOLOGICAL SEMINARY

Ethics, BD
Missions/Missionary Studies and Missiology, D
Philosophy, D
Psychology, M
Religious Education, M
Sacred Music, M
Theology and Religious Vocations, MD
Women's Studies, M

SOUTHEASTERN COMMUNITY COLLEGE

Administrative Assistant and Secretarial Science, A
Art/Art Studies, General, A
BioTechnology, A
Biological and Physical Sciences, A
Business Administration and Management, A
Clinical/Medical Laboratory Technician, A
Computer Engineering Technology/Technician, A
Cosmetology/Cosmetologist, A
Criminal Justice/Law Enforcement Administration, A

Electrical, Electronic and Communications Engineering Technology/Technician, A
Environmental Studies, A
Forestry Technology/Technician, A
Industrial Technology/Technician, A
Kindergarten/PreSchool Education and Teaching, A
Liberal Arts and Sciences Studies and Humanities, A
Music, A
Parks, Recreation and Leisure Facilities Management, A
Parks, Recreation, Leisure and Fitness Studies, A
Teacher Assistant/Aide, A
Welding Technology/Welder, A

SOUTHWESTERN COMMUNITY COLLEGE

Accounting, A
Administrative Assistant and Secretarial Science, A
Automobile/Automotive Mechanics Technology/Technician, A
Business Administration and Management, A
Child Development, A
Clinical/Medical Laboratory Technician, A
Commercial and Advertising Art, A
Computer Engineering Technology/Technician, A
Cosmetology/Cosmetologist, A
Criminal Justice/Police Science, A
Culinary Arts/Chef Training, A
Electrical, Electronic and Communications Engineering Technology/Technician, A
Emergency Medical Technology/Technician (EMT Paramedic), A
Environmental Studies, A
Health Information/Medical Records Administration/Administrator, A
Health Information/Medical Records Technology/Technician, A
Information Science/Studies, A
Legal Assistant/Paralegal, A
Liberal Arts and Sciences Studies and Humanities, A
Marketing/Marketing Management, A
Massage Therapy/Therapeutic Massage, A
Medical Radiologic Technology/Science - Radiation Therapist, A
Mental Health Counseling/Counselor, A
Parks, Recreation, Leisure and Fitness Studies, A
Physical Therapist Assistant, A
Physical Therapy/Therapist, A
Respiratory Care Therapy/Therapist, A
Substance Abuse/Addiction Counseling, A
System, Networking, and LAN/WAN Management/Manager, A
Trade and Industrial Teacher Education, A

STANLY COMMUNITY COLLEGE

Accounting Technology/Technician and Bookkeeping, A
Autobody/Collision and Repair Technology/Technician, A
Biomedical Technology/Technician, A
Business Administration and Management, A
Child Care and Support Services Management, A
Computer Hardware Engineering, A
Computer Programming, A
Computer Programming, Specific Applications, A
Computer Systems Networking and Telecommunications, A
Computer Technology/Computer Systems Technology, A
Computer and Information Sciences and Support Services, A
Computer/Information Technology Services Administration and Management, A
Cosmetology/Cosmetologist, A
Criminal Justice/Police Science, A
Electrical, Electronic and Communications Engineering Technology/Technician, A
Executive Assistant/Executive Secretary, A
Human Services, A
Industrial Technology/Technician, A
Information Science/Studies, A
Legal Administrative Assistant/Secretary, A
Mechanical Drafting and Mechanical Drafting CAD/CADD, A

Medical Administrative Assistant/Secretary, A
Medical/Clinical Assistant, A
Occupational Therapist Assistant, A
Physical Therapist Assistant, A
Respiratory Care Therapy/Therapist, A
System Administration/Administrator, A
Web Page, Digital/Multimedia and Information Resources Design, A
Web/Multimedia Management and Webmaster, A
Word Processing, A

STRAYER UNIVERSITY–GREENSBORO CAMPUS

Accounting, B
Business Administration and Management, B
Criminal Justice/Law Enforcement Administration, B
Economics, B
International Business/Trade/Commerce, B
Management Information Systems and Services, B

STRAYER UNIVERSITY–HUNTERSVILLE CAMPUS

Accounting, B
Business Administration and Management, B
Criminal Justice/Law Enforcement Administration, B
Economics, B
International Business/Trade/Commerce, B
Management Information Systems and Services, B

STRAYER UNIVERSITY–NORTH CHARLOTTE CAMPUS

Accounting, B
Business Administration and Management, B
Criminal Justice/Law Enforcement Administration, B
Economics, B
International Business/Trade/Commerce, B
Management Information Systems and Services, B

STRAYER UNIVERSITY–NORTH RALEIGH CAMPUS

Accounting, B
Business Administration and Management, B
Criminal Justice/Law Enforcement Administration, B
Economics, B
International Business/Trade/Commerce, B
Management Information Systems and Services, B

STRAYER UNIVERSITY–RTP CAMPUS

Accounting, B
Business Administration and Management, B
Criminal Justice/Law Enforcement Administration, B
Economics, B
International Business/Trade/Commerce, B
Management Information Systems and Services, B

STRAYER UNIVERSITY–SOUTH CHARLOTTE CAMPUS

Accounting, B
Business Administration and Management, B
Criminal Justice/Law Enforcement Administration, B
Economics, B
International Business/Trade/Commerce, B
Management Information Systems and Services, B

STRAYER UNIVERSITY–SOUTH RALEIGH CAMPUS

Accounting, B
Business Administration and Management, B
Criminal Justice/Law Enforcement Administration, B
Economics, B
International Business/Trade/Commerce, B
Management Information Systems and Services, B

SURRY COMMUNITY COLLEGE

Accounting, A
Administrative Assistant and Secretarial Science, A
Advertising, A
Agricultural Business and Management, A
Automobile/Automotive Mechanics Technology/Technician, A
Business Administration and Management, A
Child Care Provider/Assistant, A
Commercial and Advertising Art, A
Computer Engineering, A

Computer Engineering Technology/Technician, A
Computer Programming, A
Computer Programming/Programmer, A
Computer Systems Networking and Telecommunications, A
Construction Engineering Technology/Technician, A
Cosmetology/Cosmetologist, A
Criminal Justice/Law Enforcement Administration, A
Drafting and Design Technology/Technician, A
Electrical, Electronic and Communications Engineering Technology/Technician, A
Heating, Air Conditioning, Ventilation and Refrigeration Maintenance Technology/Technician, A
Horticultural Science, A
Information Science/Studies, A
Information Technology, A
Legal Assistant/Paralegal, A
Liberal Arts and Sciences Studies and Humanities, A
Machine Tool Technology/Machinist, A
Medical Administrative Assistant/Secretary, A
Poultry Science, A

TRI-COUNTY COMMUNITY COLLEGE

Accounting, A
Automobile/Automotive Mechanics Technology/Technician, A
Business Administration and Management, A
Early Childhood Education and Teaching, A
Electrical, Electronic and Communications Engineering Technology/Technician, A
Engine Machinist, A
Information Technology, A
Liberal Arts and Sciences Studies and Humanities, A
Medical/Clinical Assistant, A
Welding Technology/Welder, A

UNIVERSITY OF MOUNT OLIVE

Art/Art Studies, General, B
Biology/Biological Sciences, B
Business Administration and Management, B
Chemistry, B
Criminal Justice/Law Enforcement Administration, B
Early Childhood Education and Teaching, B
Education, A
English Language and Literature, B
Environmental Studies, B
Forensic Science and Technology, B
Health Professions and Related Clinical Sciences, B
History, B
Human Services, B
Information Science/Studies, B
Junior High/Intermediate/Middle School Education and Teaching, B
Liberal Arts and Sciences Studies and Humanities, A
Management Information Systems and Services, B
Mathematics, B
Music, B
Parks, Recreation, Leisure and Fitness Studies, B
Psychology, B
Religion/Religious Studies, B
Secondary Education and Teaching, B
Visual and Performing Arts, B

UNIVERSITY OF NORTH CAROLINA AT ASHEVILLE

Accounting, B
Art/Art Studies, General, B
Atmospheric Sciences and Meteorology, B
Biology/Biological Sciences, B
Business Administration and Management, B
Chemistry, B
Classics and Classical Languages, Literatures, and Linguistics, B
Computer Science, B
Drama and Dramatics/Theatre Arts, B
Economics, B
Engineering, B
English Language and Literature, B
Environmental Studies, B
Fine/Studio Arts, B
French Language and Literature, B
German Language and Literature, B
History, B

Liberal Arts and Sciences Studies and Humanities, B
Liberal Studies, M
Mass Communication/Media Studies, B
Mathematics, B
Music, B
Operations Management and Supervision, B
Philosophy, B
Physics, B
Political Science and Government, B
Psychology, B
Religion/Religious Studies, B
Sociology, B
Spanish Language and Literature, B
Web Page, Digital/Multimedia and Information Resources Design, B
Women's Studies, B

THE UNIVERSITY OF NORTH CAROLINA AT CHAPEL HILL

Accounting, MD
African-American/Black Studies, B
Allied Health and Medical Assisting Services, MD
Allopathic Medicine, D
American/United States Studies/Civilization, B
Anthropology, BMD
Archeology, BMD
Art History, Criticism and Conservation, BMD
Asian Studies/Civilization, B
Astronomy, MD
Astrophysics, MD
Athletic Training and Sports Medicine, M
Atmospheric Sciences and Meteorology, MD
Biochemistry, MD
Bioinformatics, D
Biological and Biomedical Sciences, MD
Biology/Biological Sciences, B
Biomedical Engineering, MD
Biophysics, MD
Biopsychology, D
Biostatistics, BMD
Botany/Plant Biology, MD
Business Administration and Management, B
Business Administration, Management and Operations, MD
Cell Biology and Anatomy, MD
Chemistry, BMD
Classics and Classical Languages, Literatures, and Linguistics, BMD
Clinical Laboratory Science/Medical Technology/Technologist, B
Clinical Psychology, D
Cognitive Sciences, D
Communication Disorders, MD
Communication Studies/Speech Communication and Rhetoric, B
Communication and Media Studies, D
Comparative Literature, B
Computational Biology, D
Computer Science, BMD
Counselor Education/School Counseling and Guidance Services, M
Curriculum and Instruction, MD
Dental Hygiene/Hygienist, BM
Dental and Oral Surgery, M
Dentistry, D
Developmental Biology and Embryology, MD
Developmental Psychology, D
Drama and Dramatics/Theatre Arts, B
Early Childhood Education and Teaching, BMD
East European and Russian Studies, M
Ecology, MD
Economics, BMD
Education, MD
Educational Administration and Supervision, MD
Educational Leadership and Administration, D
Educational Measurement and Evaluation, MD
Educational Psychology, MD
Elementary Education and Teaching, B
English, MD
English Education, M
English Language and Literature, B
English as a Second Language, M
Environmental Engineering Technology/Environmental Technology, MD

Environmental Health, B
Environmental Policy and Resource Management, MD
Environmental Sciences, BMD
Environmental Studies, B
Environmental and Occupational Health, MD
Epidemiology, MD
European Studies/Civilization, B
Evolutionary Biology, MD
Exercise and Sports Science, M
Finance and Banking, D
Fine Arts and Art Studies, M
Fine/Studio Arts, B
Folklore, M
Foods, Nutrition, and Wellness Studies, B
Foreign Language Teacher Education, M
Foreign Languages and Literatures, B
French Language and Literature, MD
Genetics, MD
Geography, BMD
Geology/Earth Science, BMD
German Language and Literature, MD
Gerontological Nursing, M
Health Promotion, M
Health Psychology, MD
Health Services Administration, MD
Health and Physical Education, B
Health/Health Care Administration/Management, B
History, BMD
Human Resources Management/Personnel Administration, B
Immunology, MD
Industrial Hygiene, MD
Information Science/Studies, BMDO
International/Global Studies, B
Italian Language and Literature, MD
Journalism, B
Junior High/Intermediate/Middle School Education and Teaching, B
Kinesiology and Movement Studies, MD
Latin American Studies, BO
Law and Legal Studies, D
Liberal Arts and Sciences Studies and Humanities, B
Library Science, MDO
Linguistics, BMD
Management Information Systems and Services, D
Management Strategy and Policy, D
Marine Sciences, MD
Marketing, D
Mass Communication/Media Studies, BMD
Materials Sciences, MD
Maternal and Child Health, MD
Mathematics, BMD
Mathematics Teacher Education, M
Medical Radiologic Technology/Science - Radiation Therapist, B
Microbiology, MD
Molecular Biology, MD
Molecular Physiology, D
Music, BMD
Music Performance, B
Music Teacher Education, M
Neurobiology and Neurophysiology, D
Neuroscience, D
Nursing, MDO
Nursing - Adult, M
Nursing - Advanced Practice, M
Nursing Administration, MO
Nursing Education, M
Nursing Informatics, MO
Nutritional Sciences, MD
Occupational Health Nursing, M
Occupational Therapy/Therapist, MD
Operations Research, MD
Oral Biology, D
Oral and Dental Sciences, MD
Organizational Behavior Studies, D
Orthodontics, M
Pathology/Experimental Pathology, D
Peace Studies and Conflict Resolution, B
Pediatric Nurse/Nursing, M
Pedodontics, M
Periodontics, M
Pharmaceutical Sciences, MD
Pharmacology, D

Pharmacy, Pharmaceutical Sciences, and Adminis-
tration, B
Philosophy, BMD
Physical Education Teaching and Coaching, M
Physical Sciences, B
Physical Therapy/Therapist, MD
Physics, BMD
Political Science and Government, BMD
Portuguese Language and Literature, MD
Psychiatric/Mental Health Nurse/Nursing, MO
Psychology, BD
Public Administration, M
Public Health, MD
Public Policy Analysis, BD
Reading Teacher Education, MD
Rehabilitation Counseling, M
Religion/Religious Studies, BMD
Romance Languages, Literatures, and Linguis-
tics, BMD
Russian Language and Literature, MD
School Psychology, MD
Science Teacher Education/General Science
Teacher Education, M
Secondary Education and Teaching, M
Slavic Languages, Literatures, and Linguistics, MD
Social Psychology, D
Social Studies Teacher Education, M
Social Work, MD
Sociology, BMD
Spanish Language and Literature, MD
Sport and Fitness Administration/Management, M
Statistics, MD
Telecommunications, M
Theater, M
Toxicology, MD
Urban and Regional Planning, MD
Women's Studies, B

THE UNIVERSITY OF NORTH CARO-LINA AT CHARLOTTE

Accounting, BM
Advertising and Public Relations, M
African Studies, O
African-American/Black Studies, B
Allied Health Diagnostic, Intervention, and Treat-
ment Professions, B
Anthropology, BM
Applied Mathematics, MD
Applied Physics, MD
Applied Statistics, M
Architecture, BM
Art Education, M
Art History, Criticism and Conservation, B
Art/Art Studies, General, B
Arts Management, M
Athletic Training and Sports Medicine, B
Bioinformatics, MDO
Biological and Biomedical Sciences, MD
Biology/Biological Sciences, B
Business Administration and Management, B
Business Administration, Management and Opera-
tions, MDO
Business/Managerial Economics, B
Chemistry, BMD
Child Development, MDO
Civil Engineering, BMD
Civil Engineering Technology/Technician, B
Clinical Laboratory Science/Medical
Technology/Technologist, B
Clinical Psychology, M
Cognitive Sciences, O
Communication Studies/Speech Communication
and Rhetoric, B
Communication and Media Studies, MO
Community Health and Preventive Medicine, MO
Community Psychology, M
Computer Engineering, BMD
Computer Science, BMO
Computer and Information Systems Security, O
Construction Management, M
Corporate and Organizational Communication, M
Counselor Education/School Counseling and Guid-
ance Services, MDO
Criminal Justice/Safety Studies, B
Criminology, M
Curriculum and Instruction, MD

Dance, BM
Database Systems, O
Drama and Dance Teacher Education, B
Drama and Dramatics/Theatre Arts, B
Economics, BM
Education/Teaching of the Gifted and Talented, MO
Educational Administration and Supervision, MO
Educational Leadership and Administration, MDO
Educational Media/Instructional Technology, M
Electrical Engineering, MD
Electrical, Electronic and Communications Engineer-
ing Technology/Technician, B
Electrical, Electronics and Communications Engi-
neering, B
Elementary Education and Teaching, BM
Emergency Management, MO
Energy and Power Engineering, MO
Engineering Management, MDO
Engineering Technologies/Technicians, B
Engineering and Applied Sciences, MDO
English, MO
English Education, M
English Language and Literature, B
English as a Second Language, M
Environmental Engineering
Technology/Environmental Technology, D
Ethics, MO
Ethnic and Cultural Studies, M
Exercise and Sports Science, O
Facilities Planning and Management, M
Finance, B
Finance and Banking, MO
Fine/Studio Arts, B
Fire Protection Engineering, M
Fire Services Administration, B
Foreign Language Teacher Education, M
French Language and Literature, B
Game Design and Development, O
Gender Studies, M
Geographic Information Systems, M
Geography, BMD
Geology/Earth Science, B
Geosciences, M
German Language and Literature, B
Gerontology, MO
Health Communication, M
Health Informatics, MO
Health Psychology, D
Health Services Administration, MDO
Health Services Research, D
Health and Physical Education, B
History, BM
Industrial and Manufacturing Management, O
Industrial and Organizational Psychology, MD
Information Science/Studies, MDO
Interdisciplinary Studies, MDO
International Business/Trade/Commerce, B
International/Global Studies, B
Japanese Language and Literature, B
Junior High/Intermediate/Middle School Education
and Teaching, B
Kindergarten/PreSchool Education and Teaching, B
Kinesiology and Movement Studies, MO
Latin American Studies, BM
Liberal Studies, M
Logistics and Materials Management, O
Management, MDO
Management Information Systems and Ser-
vices, BO
Marketing/Marketing Management, B
Mathematical and Computational Finance, M
Mathematics, BMD
Mathematics Teacher Education, M
Mathematics and Statistics, M
Mechanical Engineering, BMD
Mechanical Engineering/Mechanical
Technology/Technician, B
Media Studies, M
Meteorology, B
Middle School Education, MD
Music, BO
Music Performance, B
Music Teacher Education, M
Non-Profit/Public/Organizational Management, MO
Nurse Anesthetist, MO
Nursing, MDO

Nursing - Advanced Practice, MO
Nursing Administration, M
Nursing Education, MO
Operations Management and Supervision, B
Optics/Optical Sciences, MD
Philosophy, BMO
Physics, B
Political Science and Government, BM
Psychology, BMDO
Public Administration, MO
Public Health, M
Public Health (MPH, DPH), B
Public Health Education and Promotion, B
Public Policy Analysis, DO
Reading Teacher Education, M
Real Estate, MO
Religion/Religious Studies, BM
Respiratory Care Therapy/Therapist, B
Rhetoric, M
Secondary Education and Teaching, MD
Social Psychology, M
Social Sciences, M
Social Studies Teacher Education, M
Social Work, BM
Sociology, BM
Spanish Language and Literature, BMO
Special Education and Teaching, BMDO
Statistics, MO
Substance Abuse/Addiction Counseling, O
Supply Chain Management, O
Systems Engineering, BMDO
Technical Communication, O
Theater, M
Translation and Interpretation, O
Urban Design, M
Urban and Regional Planning, O
Women's Studies, O

THE UNIVERSITY OF NORTH CARO-LINA AT GREENSBORO

Accounting, BMO
Adult and Continuing Education and Teaching, O
African-American/Black Studies, B
Anthropology, B
Apparel and Textiles, B
Applied Economics, M
Architecture, MO
Art Teacher Education, B
Art/Art Studies, General, B
Athletic Training and Sports Medicine, M
Audiology/Audiologist and Speech-Language
Pathology/Pathologist, B
Biochemistry, BM
Biological and Biomedical Sciences, M
Biology Teacher Education, B
Biology/Biological Sciences, B
Business Administration and Management, B
Business Administration, Management and Opera-
tions, MO
Business/Managerial Economics, B
Chemistry, BM
Child and Family Studies, MD
Classics and Classical Languages, Litera-
tures, and Linguistics, BM
Clinical Psychology, MD
Cognitive Sciences, MD
Communication Disorders, MD
Communication Studies/Speech Communication
and Rhetoric, B
Communication and Media Studies, M
Community Health and Preventive Medicine, MD
Composition, M
Computer Science, BM
Computer Systems Networking and Telecommunica-
tions, B
Conflict Resolution and Mediation/Peace Stud-
ies, MO
Counseling Psychology, MD
Counselor Education/School Counseling and Guid-
ance Services, MDO
Criminology, M
Curriculum and Instruction, MD
Dance, BM
Developmental Psychology, MD
Drama and Dance Teacher Education, B
Drama and Dramatics/Theatre Arts, B

Early Childhood Education and Teaching, BM
Economic Development, O
Economics, BD
Education, MDO
Education/Teaching of Individuals with Hearing Impairments, Including Deafness, B
Educational Administration and Supervision, M
Educational Leadership and Administration, MDO
Educational Measurement and Evaluation, D
Educational Media/Instructional Technology, M
Elementary Education and Teaching, BMD
English, MDO
English Education, M
English Language and Literature, B
English as a Second Language, MO
English/Language Arts Teacher Education, B
Entrepreneurship/Entrepreneurial Studies, B
Film, Television, and Video Production, M
Finance, B
Finance and Banking, O
Fine Arts and Art Studies, M
Fine/Studio Arts, B
Foodservice Systems Administration/Management, B
Foreign Language Teacher Education, M
French Language Teacher Education, B
French Language and Literature, BM
Gender Studies, MO
Genetic Counseling/Counselor, M
Geographic Information Systems, O
Geography, BMDO
German Language and Literature, B
Gerontological Nursing, MO
Gerontology, MO
Higher Education/Higher Education Administration, MDO
Hispanic Studies, O
Hispanic and Latin American Languages, O
Historic Preservation and Conservation, O
History, BMDO
Hospitality Administration/Management, B
Human Development, MD
Human Development and Family Studies, B
Information Science/Studies, M
Interior Design, BMO
International Business/Trade/Commerce, B
Jazz/Jazz Studies, B
Junior High/Intermediate/Middle School Education and Teaching, B
Kinesiology and Exercise Science, B
Kinesiology and Movement Studies, MD
Liberal Arts and Sciences Studies and Humanities, B
Liberal Studies, M
Library Science, M
Management Information Systems and Services, MDO
Marketing, MD
Marriage and Family Therapy/Counseling, O
Mass Communication/Media Studies, B
Mathematics, BMD
Mathematics Teacher Education, BM
Media Studies, M
Middle School Education, M
Multilingual and Multicultural Education, D
Museology/Museum Studies, O
Music, BMD
Music Performance, B
Music Teacher Education, BMD
Music Theory and Composition, BM
Non-Profit/Public/Organizational Management, O
Nurse Anesthetist, MO
Nursing, MDO
Nursing - Adult, MO
Nursing Administration, M
Nursing Education, M
Nutritional Sciences, BMD
Parks, Recreation, Leisure and Fitness Studies, B
Peace Studies and Conflict Resolution, B
Performance, MD
Philosophy, B
Physical Education Teaching and Coaching, B
Physics, B
Political Science and Government, BMO
Psychology, BMD
Public Affairs, M

Public Health Education and Promotion, B
Reading Teacher Education, M
Recreation and Park Management, M
Religion/Religious Studies, B
Rhetoric, D
School Psychology, O
Science Teacher Education/General Science Teacher Education, M
Secondary Education and Teaching, B
Social Psychology, MD
Social Science Teacher Education, B
Social Studies Teacher Education, BM
Social Work, BM
Sociology, BM
Spanish Language Teacher Education, B
Spanish Language and Literature, BMO
Special Education and Teaching, BMDO
Supply Chain Management, O
Technical and Business Writing, O
Textile Design, MD
Theater, M
Therapeutic Recreation, M
Women's Studies, BMO
Writing, M

THE UNIVERSITY OF NORTH CAROLINA AT PEMBROKE

Accounting, B
American Indian/Native American Studies, B
Art Education, M
Art Teacher Education, B
Athletic Training and Sports Medicine, B
BioTechnology, B
Biology/Biological Sciences, B
Business Administration and Management, B
Business Administration, Management and Operations, M
Chemistry, B
College Student Counseling and Personnel Services, B
Computer Science, B
Counseling Psychology, M
Counselor Education/School Counseling and Guidance Services, BM
Criminal Justice/Safety Studies, B
Drama and Dramatics/Theatre Arts, B
Education, M
Educational Administration and Supervision, M
Elementary Education and Teaching, BM
English Education, M
English Language and Literature, B
English/Language Arts Teacher Education, B
Entrepreneurship/Entrepreneurial Studies, B
Environmental Sciences, B
Fine/Studio Arts, B
Health and Physical Education, B
History, B
Information Technology, B
Junior High/Intermediate/Middle School Education and Teaching, M
Kindergarten/PreSchool Education and Teaching, B
Kinesiology and Movement Studies, M
Mass Communication/Media Studies, B
Mathematics, B
Mathematics Teacher Education, BM
Middle School Education, M
Multi-/Interdisciplinary Studies, B
Music, BM
Music Performance, B
Music Teacher Education, BM
Nursing, M
Nursing Administration, M
Nursing Education, M
Philosophy and Religious Studies, B
Physical Education Teaching and Coaching, BM
Physics, B
Political Science and Government, B
Psychology, B
Public Administration, BM
Reading Teacher Education, BM
Science Teacher Education/General Science Teacher Education, BM
Secondary School Administration/Principalship, B
Social Studies Teacher Education, BM
Social Work, BM
Sociology, B

Spanish Language and Literature, B
Special Education and Teaching, B

UNIVERSITY OF NORTH CAROLINA SCHOOL OF THE ARTS

Arts Management, M
Cinematography and Film/Video Production, B
Composition, M
Dance, B
Drama and Dramatics/Theatre Arts, B
Film, Television, and Video Production, M
Film/Cinema Studies, B
Music, M
Music Performance, B
Performance, M
Technical Theatre/Theatre Design and Technology, B
Theater, M

THE UNIVERSITY OF NORTH CAROLINA WILMINGTON

Accounting, M
Anthropology, B
Art History, Criticism and Conservation, B
Athletic Training and Sports Medicine, B
Biological and Biomedical Sciences, MD
Biology Teacher Education, B
Biology/Biological Sciences, B
Business Administration and Management, B
Business Administration, Management and Operations, M
Chemistry, BM
Chemistry Teacher Education, B
Cinematography and Film/Video Production, B
Clinical Research, M
Communication Studies/Speech Communication and Rhetoric, B
Computer Science, BM
Conflict Resolution and Mediation/Peace Studies, MO
Criminology, BM
Drama and Dramatics/Theatre Arts, B
Early Childhood Education and Teaching, M
Economics, B
Education, MD
Education/Teaching of Individuals with Multiple Disabilities, B
Educational Administration and Supervision, D
Educational Leadership and Administration, MD
Educational Media/Instructional Technology, M
Elementary Education and Teaching, BM
English, M
English Language and Literature, B
English as a Second Language, M
English/Language Arts Teacher Education, B
Environmental Sciences, B
Environmental Studies, BM
Fine/Studio Arts, B
French Language Teacher Education, B
French Language and Literature, B
Geography, B
Geology/Earth Science, B
Geosciences, M
German Language and Literature, B
Gerontology, MO
Health Professions and Related Clinical Sciences, B
Health and Physical Education, B
Hispanic Studies, MO
History, BM
Information Technology, B
International/Global Studies, B
Junior High/Intermediate/Middle School Education and Teaching, B
Kindergarten/PreSchool Education and Teaching, B
Kinesiology and Exercise Science, B
Liberal Studies, M
Management Information Systems and Services, M
Marine Biology and Biological Oceanography, BMD
Marine Sciences, MD
Mathematics, BMO
Mathematics Teacher Education, B
Middle School Education, M
Music, B
Music Performance, B
Music Teacher Education, B
Nursing, MO

Nursing - Advanced Practice, MO
Oceanography, Chemical and Physical, B
Parks, Recreation and Leisure Facilities Management, B
Philosophy and Religious Studies, B
Physical Education Teaching and Coaching, B
Physics, B
Political Science and Government, B
Psychology, BM
Public Administration, MO
Public Health Education and Promotion, B
Reading Teacher Education, M
Social Work, BM
Sociology, BM
Spanish Language Teacher Education, B
Spanish Language and Literature, BM
Special Education and Teaching, BM
Statistics, BMO
Teacher Education and Professional Development, Specific Subject Areas, B
Therapeutic Recreation/Recreational Therapy, B
Writing, M

UNIVERSITY OF PHOENIX–CHARLOTTE CAMPUS

Accounting, M
Business Administration and Management, AB
Business Administration, Management and Operations, M
E-Commerce/Electronic Commerce, AB
Gerontology, M
Health Education, M
Health Informatics, M
Health Services Administration, M
Information Technology, AB
International Business/Trade/Commerce, M
Management Information Systems and Services, M
Management Science, B
Management of Technology, M
Marketing/Marketing Management, AB
Nursing, M
Nursing Education, M
Nursing Informatics, M

VANCE-GRANVILLE COMMUNITY COLLEGE

Accounting, A
Administrative Assistant and Secretarial Science, A
Automobile/Automotive Mechanics Technology/Technician, A
Business Administration and Management, A
Carpentry/Carpenter, A
Child Development, A
Computer Engineering Technology/Technician, A
Construction Engineering Technology/Technician, A
Corrections, A
Cosmetology/Cosmetologist, A
Criminal Justice/Law Enforcement Administration, A
Criminal Justice/Police Science, A
Data Processing and Data Processing Technology/Technician, A
Education, A
Electrical, Electronic and Communications Engineering Technology/Technician, A
Elementary Education and Teaching, A
Heating, Air Conditioning, Ventilation and Refrigeration Maintenance Technology/Technician, A
Human Services, A
Industrial Radiologic Technology/Technician, A
Industrial Technology/Technician, A
Kindergarten/PreSchool Education and Teaching, A
Legal Administrative Assistant/Secretary, A
Liberal Arts and Sciences Studies and Humanities, A
Medical Administrative Assistant/Secretary, A
Medical/Clinical Assistant, A
Parks, Recreation, Leisure and Fitness Studies, A
Teacher Assistant/Aide, A
Welding Technology/Welder, A

WAKE FOREST UNIVERSITY

Accounting, BM
Allopathic Medicine, D
Analytical Chemistry, MD
Anatomy, D
Ancient/Classical Greek Language and Literature, B

Anthropology, B
Art History, Criticism and Conservation, B
Biochemistry, D
Biological and Biomedical Sciences, MD
Biology/Biological Sciences, B
Biomedical Engineering, MD
Business Administration, Management and Operations, M
Business/Commerce, B
Cancer Biology/Oncology, D
Chemistry, BMD
Chinese Language and Literature, B
Classics and Classical Languages, Literatures, and Linguistics, B
Clinical Laboratory Science/Medical Technology/Technologist, B
Communication Studies/Speech Communication and Rhetoric, B
Communication and Media Studies, M
Computer Science, M
Computer and Information Sciences, B
Counselor Education/School Counseling and Guidance Services, M
Drama and Dramatics/Theatre Arts, B
Econometrics and Quantitative Economics, B
Economics, B
Education, M
Engineering, B
English, M
English Language and Literature, B
Exercise and Sports Science, M
Finance, B
Finance and Banking, M
Fine/Studio Arts, B
French Language and Literature, B
Genomic Sciences, D
German Language and Literature, B
Health Services Research, M
History, B
Human Genetics, D
Immunology, D
Industrial and Manufacturing Management, M
Inorganic Chemistry, MD
Japanese Language and Literature, B
Kinesiology and Exercise Science, B
Latin Language and Literature, B
Law and Legal Studies, MD
Liberal Studies, M
Management Information Systems and Services, B
Management Science, B
Marketing, M
Mathematics, BM
Microbiology, D
Molecular Biology, D
Molecular Genetics, D
Molecular Medicine, MD
Music, B
Neurobiology and Neurophysiology, D
Neuroscience, D
Organic Chemistry, MD
Pathobiology, MD
Pharmacology, D
Philosophy, B
Physical Chemistry, MD
Physics, BMD
Physiology, D
Political Science and Government, B
Psychology, BM
Religion/Religious Studies, BM
Russian Language and Literature, B
Secondary Education and Teaching, M
Sociology, B
Spanish Language and Literature, B
Speech and Interpersonal Communication, M
Taxation, M
Teacher Education, Multiple Levels, B

WAKE TECHNICAL COMMUNITY COLLEGE

Accounting, A
Animation, Interactive Technology, Video Graphics and Special Effects, A
Automobile/Automotive Mechanics Technology/Technician, A
Business Administration and Management, A
Civil Engineering Technology/Technician, A

Clinical/Medical Laboratory Technician, A
Commercial and Advertising Art, A
Computer Engineering Technology/Technician, A
Computer Programming/Programmer, A
Computer Systems Networking and Telecommunications, A
Computer and Information Sciences, A
Computer and Information Sciences and Support Services, A
Criminal Justice/Safety Studies, A
Culinary Arts/Chef Training, A
Data Modeling/Warehousing and Database Administration, A
Dental Hygiene/Hygienist, A
Diesel Mechanics Technology/Technician, A
E-Commerce/Electronic Commerce, A
Early Childhood Education and Teaching, A
Electrical, Electronic and Communications Engineering Technology/Technician, A
Electrical/Electronics Maintenance and Repair Technology, A
Electrician, A
Electromechanical and Instrumentation and Maintenance Technologies/Technicians, A
Emergency Medical Technology/Technician (EMT Paramedic), A
Environmental Sciences, A
General Studies, A
Health Professions and Related Clinical Sciences, A
Health Services/Allied Health/Health Sciences, A
Heating, Air Conditioning, Ventilation and Refrigeration Maintenance Technology/Technician, A
Hotel/Motel Administration/Management, A
Human Resources Management/Personnel Administration, A
Industrial Electronics Technology/Technician, A
Industrial Technology/Technician, A
Information Science/Studies, A
Information Technology, A
Landscape Architecture, A
Legal Administrative Assistant/Secretary, A
Liberal Arts and Sciences Studies and Humanities, A
Machine Shop Technology/Assistant, A
Management Information Systems and Services, A
Manufacturing Technology/Technician, A
Mechanical Drafting and Mechanical Drafting CAD/CADD, A
Mechanical Engineering/Mechanical Technology/Technician, A
Medical Office Management/Administration, A
Medical/Clinical Assistant, A
Office Management and Supervision, A
Plastics Engineering Technology/Technician, A
Radiologic Technology/Science - Radiographer, A
Robotics Technology/Technician, A
Substance Abuse/Addiction Counseling, A
Survey Technology/Surveying, A
Telecommunications Technology/Technician, A
Tool and Die Technology/Technician, A

WARREN WILSON COLLEGE

Art/Art Studies, General, B
Biology/Biological Sciences, B
Chemistry, B
English Language and Literature, B
Environmental Studies, B
General Studies, B
History, B
International/Global Studies, B
Mathematics, B
Philosophy, B
Psychology, B
Religion/Religious Studies, B
Social Sciences, B
Social Work, B
Sociology, B
Spanish Language and Literature, B
Women's Studies, B
Writing, M

WAYNE COMMUNITY COLLEGE

Accounting, A
Agribusiness, A
Airframe Mechanics and Aircraft Maintenance Technology/Technician, A

Animal/Livestock Husbandry and Production, A
Autobody/Collision and Repair
 Technology/Technician, A
Automobile/Automotive Mechanics
 Technology/Technician, A
Biology Technician/BioTechnology Laboratory Tech-
 nician, A
Business Administration and Management, A
Criminal Justice/Police Science, A
Criminal Justice/Safety Studies, A
Dental Hygiene/Hygienist, A
Early Childhood Education and Teaching, A
Electrical, Electronic and Communications Engineer-
 ing Technology/Technician, A
Electromechanical and Instrumentation and Mainte-
 nance Technologies/Technicians, A
Elementary Education and Teaching, A
Energy Management and Systems
 Technology/Technician, A
Forensic Science and Technology, A
Forestry Technology/Technician, A
Information Technology, A
Liberal Arts and Sciences Studies and Humani-
 ties, A
Machine Shop Technology/Assistant, A
Mechanical Engineering/Mechanical
 Technology/Technician, A
Medical Office Management/Administration, A
Medical/Clinical Assistant, A
Mental and Social Health Services and Allied Pro-
 fessions, A
Office Management and Supervision, A
Operations Management and Supervision, A
Turf and Turfgrass Management, A

WESTERN CAROLINA UNIVERSITY

Accounting, BM
Anthropology, B
Art Teacher Education, B
Art/Art Studies, General, B
Athletic Training and Sports Medicine, B
Biological and Biomedical Sciences, M
Biology/Biological Sciences, B
Business Administration and Management, B
Business Administration, Management and Opera-
 tions, M
Chemistry, BM
Communication Disorders, BM
Communication Studies/Speech Communication
 and Rhetoric, B
Community College Education, M
Community Psychology, M
Computer Science, BM
Construction Engineering Technology/Technician, B
Construction Management, BM
Counselor Education/School Counseling and Guid-
 ance Services, M
Criminal Justice/Safety Studies, B
Design and Applied Arts, M
Dietetics/Dieticians, B
Drama and Dramatics/Theatre Arts, B
Education, MDO
Educational Administration and Supervision, M
Educational Leadership and Administration, MDO
Electrical, Electronic and Communications Engineer-
 ing Technology/Technician, B
Electrical, Electronics and Communications Engi-
 neering, B
Elementary Education and Teaching, B
Emergency Medical Technology/Technician (EMT
 Paramedic), B
Engineering Technology, B
English, M
English Language and Literature, B
English as a Second Language, M
English/Language Arts Teacher Education, B
Entrepreneurship/Entrepreneurial Studies, BM
Environmental Health, B
Environmental Sciences, B
Finance, B
Fine Arts and Art Studies, M
Fine/Studio Arts, B
French Language and Literature, B
Geography, B
Geology/Earth Science, B
German Language and Literature, B

Health Information/Medical Records
 Administration/Administrator, B
Health Services Administration, M
Health/Health Care Administration/Management, B
Higher Education/Higher Education Administra-
 tion, M
History, BM
Hospitality Administration/Management, B
Human Resources Development, M
Industrial/Management Engineering, M
Interior Design, B
International/Global Studies, B
Junior High/Intermediate/Middle School Education
 and Teaching, B
Kindergarten/PreSchool Education and Teaching, B
Liberal Arts and Sciences Studies and Humani-
 ties, B
Management Information Systems and Services, B
Manufacturing Technology/Technician, B
Marketing, B
Marketing/Marketing Management, B
Mathematics, BM
Mathematics Teacher Education, B
Music, BM
Music Performance, B
Music Teacher Education, B
Natural Resources Management/Development and
 Policy, B
Nursing, MO
Nursing Education, O
Parks, Recreation and Leisure Facilities Manage-
 ment, B
Philosophy, B
Physical Education Teaching and Coaching, BM
Physical Therapy/Therapist, MD
Political Science and Government, B
Project Management, M
Psychology, BM
Public Affairs, M
Radio, Television, and Digital Communication, B
School Psychology, M
Science Teacher Education/General Science
 Teacher Education, B
Social Studies Teacher Education, B
Social Work, BM
Sociology, B
Spanish Language Teacher Education, B
Spanish Language and Literature, B
Special Education and Teaching, B
Sport and Fitness Administration/Management, B
Therapeutic Recreation/Recreational Therapy, B

WESTERN PIEDMONT COMMUNITY COLLEGE

Accounting, A
Accounting Technology/Technician and Bookkeep-
 ing, A
Animation, Interactive Technology, Video Graphics
 and Special Effects, A
Applied Horticulture/Horticultural Operations, A
Building/Construction Finishing, Manage-
 ment, and Inspection, A
Business Administration and Management, A
Child Care and Support Services Management, A
Cinematography and Film/Video Production, A
Civil Engineering Technology/Technician, A
Clinical/Medical Laboratory Technician, A
Computer Engineering Technology/Technician, A
Crafts/Craft Design, Folk Art and Artisanry, A
Criminal Justice/Law Enforcement Administration, A
Criminal Justice/Police Science, A
Early Childhood Education and Teaching, A
Electrical, Electronic and Communications Engineer-
 ing Technology/Technician, A
Engineering Technologies/Technicians, A
Environmental Sciences, A
Executive Assistant/Executive Secretary, A
Information Technology, A
Legal Assistant/Paralegal, A
Liberal Arts and Sciences Studies and Humani-
 ties, A
Machine Shop Technology/Assistant, A
Mechanical Engineering/Mechanical
 Technology/Technician, A
Medical Administrative Assistant/Secretary, A
Medical Office Management/Administration, A

Medical/Clinical Assistant, A
Mental and Social Health Services and Allied Pro-
 fessions, A
Office Management and Supervision, A
Precision Production, A
Psychiatric/Mental Health Services Technician, A
Sign Language Interpretation and Translation, A
Substance Abuse/Addiction Counseling, A
Survey Technology/Surveying, A
Therapeutic Recreation/Recreational Therapy, A
Welding Technology/Welder, A

WILKES COMMUNITY COLLEGE

Accounting Technology/Technician and Bookkeep-
 ing, A
Applied Horticulture/Horticultural Operations, A
Architectural Engineering Technology/Technician, A
Automobile/Automotive Mechanics
 Technology/Technician, A
Building/Construction Finishing, Manage-
 ment, and Inspection, A
Business Administration and Management, A
Child Care and Support Services Management, A
Computer Programming, Specific Applications, A
Computer Systems Analysis/Analyst, A
Computer Systems Networking and Telecommunica-
 tions, A
Criminal Justice/Police Science, A
Diesel Mechanics Technology/Technician, A
Electrical, Electronic and Communications Engineer-
 ing Technology/Technician, A
Electromechanical Technology/Electromechanical
 Engineering Technology, A
Executive Assistant/Executive Secretary, A
Hotel/Motel Administration/Management, A
Institutional Food Workers, A
Liberal Arts and Sciences Studies and Humani-
 ties, A
Medical/Clinical Assistant, A
Psychiatric/Mental Health Services Technician, A
Radio and Television Broadcasting
 Technology/Technician, A
Speech-Language Pathology/Pathologist, A

WILLIAM PEACE UNIVERSITY

Anthropology, B
Biology/Biological Sciences, B
Business Administration and Management, B
Communication Studies/Speech Communication
 and Rhetoric, B
Criminal Justice/Law Enforcement Administration, B
Drama and Dramatics/Theatre Arts, B
Education, B
English Language and Literature, B
Environmental Studies, B
International/Global Studies, B
Liberal Arts and Sciences Studies and Humani-
 ties, B
Political Science and Government, B
Pre-Law Studies, B
Psychology, B

WILSON COMMUNITY COLLEGE

Accounting, A
Automobile/Automotive Mechanics
 Technology/Technician, A
Biology Technician/BioTechnology Laboratory Tech-
 nician, A
Business Administration and Management, A
Computer Systems Networking and Telecommunica-
 tions, A
Computer and Information Systems Security, A
Criminal Justice/Safety Studies, A
Culinary Arts/Chef Training, A
Early Childhood Education and Teaching, A
Electrician, A
Elementary Education and Teaching, A
Executive Assistant/Executive Secretary, A
Fire Protection and Safety Technology/Technician, A
General Studies, A
Heating, Air Conditioning, Ventilation and Refrigera-
 tion Maintenance Technology/Technician, A
Information Technology, A
Legal Assistant/Paralegal, A
Liberal Arts and Sciences Studies and Humani-
 ties, A

Mechanical Engineering/Mechanical
Technology/Technician, A
Medical Office Management/Administration, A
Office Management and Supervision, A
Sign Language Interpretation and Translation, A
Surgical Technology/Technologist, A

WINGATE UNIVERSITY

Accounting, B
Athletic Training and Sports Medicine, B
Biology Teacher Education, B
Biology/Biological Sciences, B
Business Administration and Management, B
Business Administration, Management and Opera-
tions, M
Chemistry, B
Communication Studies/Speech Communication
and Rhetoric, B
Community College Education, D
Criminal Justice/Law Enforcement Administration, B
Education, MD
Educational Leadership and Administration, MD
Elementary Education and Teaching, BM
English Language and Literature, B
English/Language Arts Teacher Education, B
Environmental Biology, B
Finance, B
Health Education, M
Health and Physical Education, B
History, B
History Teacher Education, B
Human Services, B
Junior High/Intermediate/Middle School Education
and Teaching, B
Kinesiology and Exercise Science, B
Liberal Arts and Sciences Studies and Humani-
ties, A
Marketing/Marketing Management, B
Mathematics, B
Mathematics Teacher Education, B
Music, B
Music Teacher Education, B
Parks, Recreation, Leisure and Fitness Studies, B
Pharmacy, D
Physical Education Teaching and Coaching, BM
Political Science and Government, B
Pre-Law Studies, B
Pre-Medicine/Pre-Medical Studies, B
Pre-Pharmacy Studies, B
Pre-Veterinary Studies, B
Psychology, B
Reading Teacher Education, B
Religion/Religious Studies, B
Sociology, B
Sport and Fitness Administration/Management, BM

WINSTON-SALEM STATE UNIVERSITY

Accounting, B
African-American/Black Studies, B
Art Teacher Education, B
Art/Art Studies, General, B
BioTechnology, B
Biology/Biological Sciences, B
Business Administration and Management, B
Business Administration, Management and Opera-
tions, M
Chemistry, B
Clinical Laboratory Science/Medical
Technology/Technologist, B
Computer Science, BM
Criminal Justice/Safety Studies, B
Economics, B
Education, BM
Education/Teaching of Individuals with Specific
Learning Disabilities, B
Elementary Education and Teaching, B
English Language and Literature, B
English/Language Arts Teacher Education, B
General Studies, B
Gerontology, B
Health Services Administration, M
Health/Health Care Administration/Management, B
History, B
Information Science/Studies, B
Information Technology, B

Junior High/Intermediate/Middle School Education
and Teaching, B
Kindergarten/PreSchool Education and Teaching, B
Kinesiology and Exercise Science, B
Management Information Systems and Ser-
vices, BM
Mass Communication/Media Studies, B
Mathematics, B
Mathematics Teacher Education, B
Middle School Education, M
Molecular Biology, B
Music, B
Music Teacher Education, B
Nursing, MD
Nursing - Advanced Practice, M
Nursing Education, M
Occupational Therapy/Therapist, BM
Parks, Recreation and Leisure Facilities Manage-
ment, B
Physical Education Teaching and Coaching, B
Physical Therapy/Therapist, D
Political Science and Government, B
Psychology, B
Rehabilitation Counseling, M
Social Sciences, B
Social Studies Teacher Education, B
Sociology, B
Spanish Language Teacher Education, B
Spanish Language and Literature, B
Special Education and Teaching, BM
Sport and Fitness Administration/Management, B
Therapeutic Recreation/Recreational Therapy, B
Vocational Rehabilitation Counseling/Counselor, B

North Dakota

BISMARCK STATE COLLEGE

Administrative Assistant and Secretarial Science, A
Agricultural Business and Management, A
Autobody/Collision and Repair
Technology/Technician, A
Automobile/Automotive Mechanics
Technology/Technician, A
Building/Home/Construction Inspection/Inspector, A
Business/Commerce, A
Business/Office Automation/Technology/Data En-
try, A
Carpentry/Carpenter, A
Clinical/Medical Laboratory Technician, A
Commercial and Advertising Art, A
Computer Systems Networking and Telecommunica-
tions, A
Criminal Justice/Safety Studies, A
Electrical, Electronic and Communications Engineer-
ing Technology/Technician, A
Emergency Medical Technology/Technician (EMT
Paramedic), A
Engineering Technology, A
Environmental Control Technologies/Technicians, A
Farm/Farm and Ranch Management, A
Heating, Air Conditioning, Ventilation and Refrigera-
tion Maintenance Technology/Technician, A
Human Services, A
Industrial Mechanics and Maintenance Technol-
ogy, A
Industrial Production Technologies/Technicians, A
Industrial Technology/Technician, A
Instrumentation Technology/Technician, A
Legal Administrative Assistant/Secretary, A
Liberal Arts and Sciences Studies and Humani-
ties, A
Lineworker, A
Medical Administrative Assistant/Secretary, A
Multi-/Interdisciplinary Studies, A
Nuclear Engineering Technology/Technician, A
Operations Management and Supervision, B
Petroleum Technology/Technician, A
Public Relations/Image Management, A
Recording Arts Technology/Technician, A
Surgical Technology/Technologist, A
Survey Technology/Surveying, A
Web Page, Digital/Multimedia and Information Re-
sources Design, A

Welding Technology/Welder, A

CANKDESKA CIKANA COMMUNITY COLLEGE

Accounting, A
Administrative Assistant and Secretarial Science, A
Automotive Engineering Technology/Technician, A
Business Administration and Management, A
Computer and Information Sciences, A
Early Childhood Education and Teaching, A
Liberal Arts and Sciences Studies and Humani-
ties, A
Natural Resources Management/Development and
Policy, A
Pre-Nursing Studies, A
Public Administration, A

DAKOTA COLLEGE AT BOTTINEAU

Accounting, A
Accounting Technology/Technician and Bookkeep-
ing, A
Accounting and Related Services, A
Administrative Assistant and Secretarial Science, A
Adult Development and Aging, A
Advertising, A
Agriculture, A
Applied Horticulture/Horticultural Business Ser-
vices, A
Applied Horticulture/Horticultural Operations, A
Biology/Biological Sciences, A
Business Administration and Management, A
Business/Office Automation/Technology/Data En-
try, A
Chemistry, A
Child Care Provider/Assistant, A
Child Care and Support Services Management, A
Computer Software and Media Applications, A
Computer Technology/Computer Systems Technol-
ogy, A
Computer and Information Sciences, A
Computer and Information Sciences and Support
Services, A
Crop Production, A
Education, A
Entrepreneurial and Small Business Operations, A
Environmental Engineering
Technology/Environmental Technology, A
Executive Assistant/Executive Secretary, A
Fishing and Fisheries Sciences and Management, A
Floriculture/Floristry Operations and Management, A
General Office Occupations and Clerical Services, A
General Studies, A
Greenhouse Operations and Management, A
Health Services/Allied Health/Health Sciences, A
Health and Physical Education, A
History, A
Horticultural Science, A
Hospitality and Recreation Marketing Operations, A
Humanities/Humanistic Studies, A
Information Science/Studies, A
Information Technology, A
Land Use Planning and
Management/Development, A
Landscaping and Groundskeeping, A
Liberal Arts and Sciences Studies and Humani-
ties, A
Marketing, A
Marketing/Marketing Management, A
Mathematics, A
Medical Administrative Assistant/Secretary, A
Medical Insurance Coding Specialist/Coder, A
Medical Office Assistant/Specialist, A
Medical/Clinical Assistant, A
Natural Resources and Conservation, A
Office Management and Supervision, A
Ornamental Horticulture, A
Parks, Recreation and Leisure Facilities Manage-
ment, A
Parks, Recreation, Leisure and Fitness Studies, A
Photography, A
Physical Sciences, A
Pre-Medicine/Pre-Medical Studies, A
Pre-Nursing Studies, A
Pre-Veterinary Studies, A
Psychology, A
Receptionist, A

Science Technologies/Technicians, A
Small Business Administration/Management, A
Social Sciences, A
System Administration/Administrator, A
Teacher Assistant/Aide, A
Urban Forestry, A
Wildlife and Wildlands Science and Management, A
Zoology/Animal Biology, A

DICKINSON STATE UNIVERSITY

Accounting, B
Administrative Assistant and Secretarial Science, A
Agricultural Business and Management, AB
Art Teacher Education, B
Art/Art Studies, General, B
Biology/Biological Sciences, B
Business Administration and Management, B
Business Teacher Education, B
Chemistry, B
Computer Science, B
Drama and Dramatics/Theatre Arts, B
Education, B
Elementary Education and Teaching, B
English Language and Literature, B
Environmental Studies, AB
Finance, B
Geography, B
Geology/Earth Science, B
History, B
International Business/Trade/Commerce, B
Liberal Arts and Sciences Studies and Humanities, AB
Marketing/Marketing Management, B
Mathematics, B
Medical Administrative Assistant/Secretary, A
Music, B
Music Teacher Education, B
Physical Education Teaching and Coaching, B
Political Science and Government, B
Pre-Dentistry Studies, B
Pre-Law Studies, B
Pre-Medicine/Pre-Medical Studies, B
Pre-Veterinary Studies, B
Psychology, B
Science Teacher Education/General Science Teacher Education, B
Secondary Education and Teaching, B
Social Sciences, B
Social Work, B
Spanish Language and Literature, B
Speech Teacher Education, B
Teacher Education, Multiple Levels, B

LAKE REGION STATE COLLEGE

Administrative Assistant and Secretarial Science, A
Agricultural Business and Management, A
Automobile/Automotive Mechanics Technology/Technician, A
Business Administration and Management, A
Child Care Provider/Assistant, A
Computer Installation and Repair Technology/Technician, A
Criminal Justice/Police Science, A
Electrical and Electronic Engineering Technologies/Technicians, A
General Merchandising, Sales, and Related Marketing Operations, A
Language Interpretation and Translation, A
Liberal Arts and Sciences Studies and Humanities, A
Management Information Systems and Services, A
Speech-Language Pathology/Pathologist, A

MAYVILLE STATE UNIVERSITY

Biology Teacher Education, B
Biology/Biological Sciences, B
Business Administration and Management, B
Business Administration, Management and Operations, B
Business/Commerce, A
Chemistry, B
Chemistry Teacher Education, B
Child Care Provider/Assistant, A
Clinical Laboratory Science/Medical Technology/Technologist, B

Communication Studies/Speech Communication and Rhetoric, B
Computer and Information Sciences, B
Computer and Information Sciences and Support Services, B
Early Childhood Education and Teaching, B
Education, B
Elementary Education and Teaching, B
English Language and Literature, B
English/Language Arts Teacher Education, B
General Studies, B
Geography Teacher Education, B
Health Teacher Education, B
Health and Physical Education, B
Health and Physical Education/Fitness, B
History Teacher Education, B
Mathematics, B
Mathematics Teacher Education, B
Physical Education Teaching and Coaching, B
Pre-Dentistry Studies, B
Pre-Law Studies, B
Pre-Medicine/Pre-Medical Studies, B
Pre-Pharmacy Studies, B
Pre-Veterinary Studies, B
Psychology, B
Social Science Teacher Education, B
Social Sciences, B
Special Education and Teaching, B

MINOT STATE UNIVERSITY

Accounting, B
Art Teacher Education, B
Art/Art Studies, General, B
Athletic Training and Sports Medicine, B
Biology Teacher Education, B
Biology/Biological Sciences, B
Business Administration and Management, B
Business Teacher Education, B
Chemistry, B
Chemistry Teacher Education, B
Clinical Laboratory Science/Medical Technology/Technologist, B
Communication Disorders, BM
Communication, Journalism and Related Programs, B
Communications Technologies/Technicians and Support Services, B
Computer Science, B
Computer and Information Sciences, B
Criminal Justice/Safety Studies, B
Education/Teaching of Individuals with Hearing Impairments, Including Deafness, B
Education/Teaching of Individuals with Mental Retardation, B
Education/Teaching of Individuals with Speech or Language Impairments, B
Elementary Education and Teaching, BM
English Language and Literature, B
English/Language Arts Teacher Education, B
Finance, B
Finance and Financial Management Services, B
General Studies, B
Geology/Earth Science, B
German Language Teacher Education, B
German Language and Literature, B
History, B
History Teacher Education, B
International Business/Trade/Commerce, B
Management, M
Management Information Systems and Services, BM
Marketing/Marketing Management, B
Mathematics, B
Mathematics Teacher Education, BM
Medical Radiologic Technology/Science - Radiation Therapist, B
Middle School Education, M
Music, B
Music Teacher Education, B
Physical Education Teaching and Coaching, B
Physical Sciences, B
Physics, B
Physics Teacher Education, B
Psychology, B
Radio and Television, B
School Psychology, O

Science Teacher Education/General Science Teacher Education, BM
Social Science Teacher Education, B
Social Sciences, B
Social Work, B
Sociology, B
Spanish Language Teacher Education, B
Spanish Language and Literature, B
Special Education and Teaching, ABM
Sport and Fitness Administration/Management, B
Substance Abuse/Addiction Counseling, B
Teacher Education and Professional Development, Specific Subject Areas, B

NORTH DAKOTA STATE COLLEGE OF SCIENCE

Agricultural Business and Management, A
Agricultural Mechanics and Equipment/Machine Technology, A
Architectural Engineering Technology/Technician, A
Autobody/Collision and Repair Technology/Technician, A
Automobile/Automotive Mechanics Technology/Technician, A
Biology Technician/BioTechnology Laboratory Technician, A
Business Administration and Management, A
Civil Engineering Technology/Technician, A
Computer Programming/Programmer, A
Computer Systems Networking and Telecommunications, A
Computer and Information Sciences, A
Computer and Information Systems Security, A
Construction Engineering Technology/Technician, A
Culinary Arts/Chef Training, A
Data Entry/Microcomputer Applications, A
Dental Assisting/Assistant, A
Dental Hygiene/Hygienist, A
Diesel Mechanics Technology/Technician, A
E-Commerce/Electronic Commerce, A
Electrical and Electronic Engineering Technologies/Technicians, A
Emergency Medical Technology/Technician (EMT Paramedic), A
Energy Management and Systems Technology/Technician, A
Health Information/Medical Records Technology/Technician, A
Heating, Air Conditioning and Refrigeration Technology/Technician, A
Heating, Air Conditioning, Ventilation and Refrigeration Maintenance Technology/Technician, A
Liberal Arts and Sciences Studies and Humanities, A
Machine Tool Technology/Machinist, A
Manufacturing Technology/Technician, A
Medical Insurance Coding Specialist/Coder, A
Multi-/Interdisciplinary Studies, A
Occupational Therapist Assistant, A
Pharmacy Technician/Assistant, A
Psychiatric/Mental Health Services Technician, A
Small Engine Mechanics and Repair Technology/Technician, A
Vehicle Maintenance and Repair Technologies, A
Web Page, Digital/Multimedia and Information Resources Design, A
Welding Technology/Welder, A

NORTH DAKOTA STATE UNIVERSITY

Accounting, B
Accounting and Related Services, B
Adult and Continuing Education and Teaching, D
Agribusiness, B
Agricultural Communication/Journalism, B
Agricultural Economics, BM
Agricultural Education, M
Agricultural Engineering, MD
Agricultural Mechanization, B
Agricultural Sciences, MD
Agricultural Teacher Education, B
Agricultural/Biological Engineering and Bioengineering, B
Agriculture, B
Agronomy and Soil Sciences, MD
Animal Sciences, BMD
Anthropology, BM

Apparel and Textiles, B
Applied Horticulture/Horticultural Business Services, B
Applied Mathematics, MD
Applied Statistics, MO
Architecture, M
Art/Art Studies, General, B
Athletic Training and Sports Medicine, M
BioTechnology, B
Biochemistry, MD
Biochemistry, Biophysics and Molecular Biology, B
Bioinformatics, MD
Biological and Biomedical Sciences, MD
Biology Teacher Education, B
Biology/Biological Sciences, B
Biosystems Engineering, MD
Botany/Plant Biology, BMD
Business Administration and Management, B
Business Administration, Management and Operations, BM
Business/Corporate Communications, B
Cell Biology and Anatomy, D
Chemistry, BMD
Chemistry Teacher Education, B
Child Development, MDO
Child and Family Studies, MDO
Civil Engineering, BMD
Clinical Laboratory Science/Medical Technology/Technologist, B
Clinical Psychology, M
Clothing and Textiles, MO
Cognitive Sciences, D
Communication and Media Studies, MD
Computer Engineering, BMD
Computer Science, BMDO
Construction Engineering, B
Construction Management, BM
Consumer Economics, MO
Counselor Education/School Counseling and Guidance Services, MD
Criminal Justice/Safety Studies, B
Criminology, MD
Crop Production, B
Curriculum and Instruction, M
Developmental Psychology, D
Dietetics/Dieticians, B
Drama and Dramatics/Theatre Arts, B
Ecology, MD
Economics, B
Education, MDO
Educational Administration and Supervision, MDO
Electrical Engineering, MD
Electrical, Electronics and Communications Engineering, B
Electronic Commerce, O
Engineering and Applied Sciences, MD
English, MD
English Language and Literature, B
English/Language Arts Teacher Education, B
Entomology, MD
Environmental Design/Architecture, B
Environmental Engineering Technology/Environmental Technology, MD
Environmental Sciences, MD
Epidemiology, M
Equestrian/Equine Studies, B
Exercise and Sports Science, M
Family and Consumer Sciences/Home Economics Teacher Education, B
Family and Consumer Sciences/Human Sciences, M
Finance, B
Food Science, B
Food Science and Technology, BMDO
French Language Teacher Education, B
French Language and Literature, B
Genomic Sciences, MD
Geology/Earth Science, B
Gerontology, MDO
Health Communication, B
Health Psychology, D
Health Teacher Education, B
Higher Education/Higher Education Administration, O
History, BMD
History Teacher Education, B

Hospitality Administration/Management, B
Human Development, MD
Human Development and Family Studies, B
Industrial Engineering, B
Industrial/Management Engineering, MD
Interior Design, B
International Public Health/International Health, M
International/Global Studies, B
Kinesiology and Exercise Science, B
Landscape Architecture, B
Logistics and Materials Management, MD
Management Information Systems and Services, B
Manufacturing Engineering, BMD
Marketing/Marketing Management, B
Marriage and Family Therapy/Counseling, M
Mass Communication/Media Studies, M
Materials Sciences, MD
Mathematics, BMD
Mathematics Teacher Education, BMD
Mechanical Engineering, BMD
Microbiology, BMD
Molecular Biology, D
Molecular Pathogenesis, D
Music, BMD
Music Teacher Education, BM
NanoTechnology, MD
Natural Resources Management/Development and Policy, BMD
Nursing, M
Nutritional Sciences, M
Operations Research, M
Pathology/Experimental Pathology, D
Pharmaceutical Sciences, MD
Pharmacy, Pharmaceutical Sciences, and Administration, B
Philosophy, B
Physical Education Teaching and Coaching, B
Physics, BMD
Physics Teacher Education, B
Plant Pathology/Phytopathology, MD
Plant Sciences, MD
Political Science and Government, B
Polymer/Plastics Engineering, MD
Psychology, BMD
Public Health, MD
Public Relations/Image Management, B
Public/Applied History and Archival Administration, B
Radio, Television, and Digital Communication, B
Radiologic Technology/Science - Radiographer, B
Range Science and Management, B
Respiratory Care Therapy/Therapist, B
Rhetoric, D
Science Teacher Education/General Science Teacher Education, BMD
Security and Protective Services, B
Social Psychology, D
Social Sciences, BM
Social Studies Teacher Education, BM
Sociology, BM
Software Engineering, MDO
Soil Science and Agronomy, B
Spanish Language Teacher Education, B
Spanish Language and Literature, B
Speech and Interpersonal Communication, M
Sport and Fitness Administration/Management, B
Statistics, BMDO
Transportation/Transportation Management, MD
Turf and Turfgrass Management, B
Urban Studies/Affairs, M
Urban and Regional Planning, M
Veterinary Sciences, MD
Veterinary/Animal Health Technology/Technician and Veterinary Assistant, B
Vocational and Technical Education, D
Women's Studies, B
Writing, D
Zoology/Animal Biology, BMD

NUETA HIDATSA SAHNISH COLLEGE

Business Administration and Management, A
Business/Office Automation/Technology/Data Entry, A
Computer and Information Sciences, A
Environmental Sciences, A
Human Services, A

Liberal Arts and Sciences Studies and Humanities, A
Science Technologies/Technicians, A

RASMUSSEN COLLEGE FARGO

Accounting, B
Business Administration and Management, B
Computer Programming/Programmer, A
Computer Science, B
Computer Software Engineering, A
Computer and Information Systems Security, B
Corrections and Criminal Justice, B
Early Childhood Education and Teaching, A
Graphic Communications, B
Health Information/Medical Records Administration/Administrator, B
Health/Health Care Administration/Management, B
Human Resources Management/Personnel Administration, A
Human Services, A
Legal Assistant/Paralegal, A
Management Information Systems and Services, A
Marketing/Marketing Management, A
Medical Administrative Assistant/Secretary, A
Web Page, Digital/Multimedia and Information Resources Design, A

SITTING BULL COLLEGE

Administrative Assistant and Secretarial Science, A
Agribusiness, A
American Indian/Native American Studies, A
Business Administration and Management, A
Carpentry/Carpenter, A
Child Care and Support Services Management, A
Education, A
Environmental Sciences, M
Environmental Studies, A
Farm/Farm and Ranch Management, A
General Office Occupations and Clerical Services, A
Human Services, A
Liberal Arts and Sciences Studies and Humanities, A
Marketing/Marketing Management, A
Social Work, A
Teacher Assistant/Aide, A

TRINITY BIBLE COLLEGE

Bible/Biblical Studies, AB
Business Administration and Management, AB
Divinity/Ministry (BD, MDiv.), B
General Studies, B
Intercultural/Multicultural and Diversity Studies, B
Liberal Arts and Sciences Studies and Humanities, A
Management Science, B
Physical Education Teaching and Coaching, B
Youth Ministry, B

TURTLE MOUNTAIN COMMUNITY COLLEGE

Accounting Technology/Technician and Bookkeeping, A
Administrative Assistant and Secretarial Science, A
Art/Art Studies, General, A
Biological and Physical Sciences, A
Biology/Biological Sciences, A
Business Administration and Management, A
Carpentry/Carpenter, A
Clinical Laboratory Science/Medical Technology/Technologist, A
Clinical/Medical Laboratory Technician, A
Computer Science, A
Elementary Education and Teaching, A
Emergency Medical Technology/Technician (EMT Paramedic), A
English Language and Literature, A
Environmental Studies, A
Health Information/Medical Records Administration/Administrator, A
History, A
Human Services, A
Journalism, A
Kindergarten/PreSchool Education and Teaching, A
Liberal Arts and Sciences Studies and Humanities, A

Marketing/Marketing Management, A
Mathematics, A
Pharmacy, A
Physical Therapy/Therapist, A
Social Sciences, A
Social Work, A
Trade and Industrial Teacher Education, A
Veterinary/Animal Health Technology/Technician and
　Veterinary Assistant, A

UNITED TRIBES TECHNICAL COLLEGE

Administrative Assistant and Secretarial Science, A
Animation, Interactive Technology, Video Graphics
　and Special Effects, A
Art/Art Studies, General, A
Automobile/Automotive Mechanics
　Technology/Technician, A
Business Administration and Management, A
Business/Office Automation/Technology/Data En-
　try, A
Child Care Provider/Assistant, A
Community Health and Preventive Medicine, A
Computer Systems Analysis/Analyst, A
Construction Trades, A
Criminal Justice/Law Enforcement Administration, A
Early Childhood Education and Teaching, A
Education, A
Entrepreneurship/Entrepreneurial Studies, A
Environmental Sciences, A
Fine Arts and Art Studies, A
Foods, Nutrition, and Wellness Studies, A
General Office Occupations and Clerical Services, A
Health Information/Medical Records
　Technology/Technician, A
Hospitality Administration/Management, A
Medical Administrative Assistant/Secretary, A

UNIVERSITY OF JAMESTOWN

Accounting, B
Applied Mathematics, B
Art/Art Studies, General, B
Biochemistry, B
Biology Teacher Education, B
Biology/Biological Sciences, B
Business Administration and Management, B
Chemistry, B
Chemistry Teacher Education, B
Clinical Laboratory Science/Medical
　Technology/Technologist, B
Communication Studies/Speech Communication
　and Rhetoric, B
Computer Science, B
Criminal Justice/Safety Studies, B
Curriculum and Instruction, M
Drama and Dramatics/Theatre Arts, B
Education, M
Elementary Education and Teaching, B
English Language and Literature, B
English/Language Arts Teacher Education, B
Financial Planning and Services, B
Fine/Studio Arts, B
French Language and Literature, B
German Language and Literature, B
History, B
History Teacher Education, B
Information Technology, B
International Business/Trade/Commerce, B
Kinesiology and Exercise Science, B
Management Information Systems and Services, B
Marketing/Marketing Management, B
Mass Communication/Media Studies, B
Mathematics, B
Mathematics Teacher Education, B
Mechanical Engineering, B
Music, B
Music Performance, B
Music Teacher Education, B
Physical Education Teaching and Coaching, B
Physical Therapy/Therapist, D
Political Science and Government, B
Psychology, B
Radiologic Technology/Science - Radiographer, B
Religion/Religious Studies, B
Spanish Language and Literature, B

Sport and Fitness Administration/Management, B

UNIVERSITY OF MARY

Accounting, B
Athletic Training and Sports Medicine, B
Bioethics/Medical Ethics, M
Biology Teacher Education, B
Biology/Biological Sciences, B
Business Administration and Management, B
Business Administration, Management and Opera-
　tions, BM
Business Teacher Education, B
Business/Corporate Communications, B
Cardiovascular Sciences, M
Clinical Laboratory Science/Medical
　Technology/Technologist, B
Clinical Psychology, M
Computer and Information Sciences, B
Corrections Administration, B
Counseling Psychology, M
Criminal Justice/Safety Studies, B
Curriculum and Instruction, M
Early Childhood Education and Teaching, B
Education, MD
Education/Teaching of Individuals with Mental Retar-
　dation, B
Educational Administration and Supervision, M
Elementary Education and Teaching, B
Energy Management and Policy, M
Engineering, B
English Language and Literature, B
English/Language Arts Teacher Education, B
Exercise and Sports Science, M
Finance, B
General Studies, B
Health Services Administration, M
Health Unit Manager/Ward Supervisor, B
Health and Physical Education, B
History Teacher Education, B
Human Resources Management and Services, M
Information Resources Management/CIO Training, B
Information Science/Studies, B
Kinesiology and Exercise Science, B
Kinesiology and Movement Studies, M
Management Information Systems and Services, B
Management Science, B
Marketing/Marketing Management, B
Mass Communication/Media Studies, B
Mathematics, B
Mathematics Teacher Education, B
Music Performance, B
Music Teacher Education, B
Nursing, MD
Nursing - Advanced Practice, D
Nursing Administration, M
Nursing Education, M
Occupational Therapy/Therapist, M
Physical Education Teaching and Coaching, BM
Physical Therapy/Therapist, D
Project Management, M
Psychology, B
Radiologic Technology/Science - Radiographer, B
Reading Teacher Education, M
Religion/Religious Studies, B
Religious/Sacred Music, B
Respiratory Care Therapy/Therapist, B
School Psychology, M
Social Science Teacher Education, B
Social Sciences, B
Social Work, B
Special Education and Teaching, M
Sport and Fitness Administration/Management, BM
Student Personnel Services, M
Substance Abuse/Addiction Counseling, BM
Theology/Theological Studies, B

UNIVERSITY OF NORTH DAKOTA

Accounting, BM
Accounting and Finance, B
Air Traffic Controller, B
Air Transportation, B
Airline/Commercial/Professional Pilot and Flight
　Crew, B
Allopathic Medicine, D
American Indian/Native American Studies, B
Anatomy, MD

Anthropology, B
Applied Economics, M
Art/Art Studies, General, B
Athletic Training and Sports Medicine, B
Atmospheric Sciences and Meteorology, BMD
Aviation, M
Aviation/Airway Management and Operations, B
Biochemistry, MD
Biological and Biomedical Sciences, BMD
Biology/Biological Sciences, B
Botany/Plant Biology, MD
Business Administration and Management, B
Business Administration, Management and Opera-
　tions, M
Business/Managerial Economics, B
Cell Biology and Anatomy, MD
Chemical Engineering, BM
Chemistry, BMD
Chinese Studies, B
Civil Engineering, BM
Classics and Classical Languages, Litera-
　tures, and Linguistics, B
Clinical Laboratory Science/Medical
　Technology/Technologist, B
Clinical Laboratory Sciences, M
Clinical Nutrition/Nutritionist, B
Clinical Psychology, D
Communication Disorders, BMD
Communication and Media Studies, MD
Community Health Nursing, M
Computer Science, MD
Computer Systems Analysis/Analyst, B
Computer and Information Sciences, B
Counseling Psychology, M
Criminal Justice/Safety Studies, B
Criminology, D
CytoTechnology/Cytotechnologist, B
Dietetics/Dieticians, B
Drama and Dramatics/Theatre Arts, B
Early Childhood Education and Teaching, BM
Ecology, MD
Economics, B
Education, MDO
Educational Leadership and Administration, MDO
Educational Measurement and Evaluation, D
Educational Media/Instructional Technology, M
Electrical Engineering, M
Electrical, Electronics and Communications Engi-
　neering, B
Elementary Education and Teaching, BMD
Engineering and Applied Sciences, D
English, MD
English Language and Literature, B
Entomology, MD
Entrepreneurship/Entrepreneurial Studies, B
Environmental Biology, MD
Environmental Engineering
　Technology/Environmental Technology, M
Environmental Studies, B
Environmental/Environmental Health Engineering, B
Experimental Psychology, D
Finance, B
Fine Arts and Art Studies, M
Fish, Game and Wildlife Management, MD
Flight Instructor, B
Forensic Psychology, M
Forensic Science and Technology, B
French Language and Literature, B
General Studies, B
Genetics, MD
Geography, BM
Geological Engineering, M
Geological/Geophysical Engineering, B
Geology/Earth Science, BMD
Geosciences, MD
German Language and Literature, B
Gerontological Nursing, M
Graphic Communications, B
Graphic Design, B
History, BMD
Human Resources Management/Personnel Adminis-
　tration, B
Immunology, MD
Industrial Technology/Technician, B
International/Global Studies, B
Investments and Securities, B

Junior High/Intermediate/Middle School Education and Teaching, B
Kinesiology and Exercise Science, B
Kinesiology and Movement Studies, M
Law and Legal Studies, D
Linguistics, M
Management of Technology, M
Marketing/Marketing Management, B
Mathematics, BM
Mechanical Engineering, BM
Microbiology, MD
Mineral/Mining Engineering, M
Molecular Biology, BMD
Multi-/Interdisciplinary Studies, B
Music, BMD
Music Performance, B
Music Teacher Education, BMD
Music Therapy/Therapist, B
Norwegian Language and Literature, B
Nurse Anesthetist, M
Nursing, MD
Nursing - Advanced Practice, M
Nursing Education, M
Occupational Therapy/Therapist, M
Operations Management and Supervision, B
Parks, Recreation and Leisure Facilities Management, B
Petroleum Engineering, B
Pharmacology, MD
Philosophy, B
Physical Sciences, B
Physical Therapy/Therapist, MD
Physician Assistant, M
Physics, BMD
Physiology, MD
Planetary Astronomy and Science, M
Political Science and Government, B
Psychiatric/Mental Health Nurse/Nursing, M
Psychology, BMD
Public Administration, M
Public Health, M
Reading Teacher Education, M
Religion/Religious Studies, B
Science Teacher Education/General Science Teacher Education, B
Secondary Education and Teaching, BD
Social Science Teacher Education, B
Social Sciences, B
Social Work, BM
Sociology, BM
Spanish Language and Literature, B
Special Education and Teaching, MD
Structural Engineering, M
Theater, M
Zoology/Animal Biology, MD

VALLEY CITY STATE UNIVERSITY

Art Teacher Education, B
Art/Art Studies, General, B
Athletic Training and Sports Medicine, B
Biology Teacher Education, B
Biology/Biological Sciences, B
Business Administration and Management, B
Business Teacher Education, B
Chemistry, B
Chemistry Teacher Education, B
Computer and Information Sciences, B
Computer and Information Sciences and Support Services, B
Education, BM
Educational Media/Instructional Technology, M
Elementary Education and Teaching, BM
English Education, M
English Language and Literature, B
English as a Second Language, M
English/Language Arts Teacher Education, B
Health Teacher Education, B
Health and Physical Education, B
Health/Medical Preparatory Programs, B
History, B
History Teacher Education, B
Human Resources Management/Personnel Administration, B
Library Science, M
Management Information Systems and Services, B
Mass Communication/Media Studies, B

Mathematics, B
Mathematics Teacher Education, B
Music, B
Music Teacher Education, B
Office Management and Supervision, B
Physical Education Teaching and Coaching, B
Pre-Dentistry Studies, B
Pre-Law Studies, B
Pre-Medicine/Pre-Medical Studies, B
Pre-Pharmacy Studies, B
Pre-Veterinary Studies, B
Psychology, B
Science Teacher Education/General Science Teacher Education, B
Secondary Education and Teaching, B
Social Science Teacher Education, B
Social Sciences, B
Spanish Language Teacher Education, B
Spanish Language and Literature, B
Technical Teacher Education, B
Technology Teacher Education/Industrial Arts Teacher Education, B
Vocational and Technical Education, M
Wildlife and Wildlands Science and Management, B

WILLISTON STATE COLLEGE

Accounting Technology/Technician and Bookkeeping, A
Agriculture, A
Business Administration, Management and Operations, A
Diesel Mechanics Technology/Technician, A
Health Information/Medical Records Technology/Technician, A
Liberal Arts and Sciences Studies and Humanities, A
Massage Therapy/Therapeutic Massage, A
Multi-/Interdisciplinary Studies, A
Petroleum Technology/Technician, A
Psychiatric/Mental Health Services Technician, A
Speech-Language Pathology/Pathologist, A
System, Networking, and LAN/WAN Management/Manager, A
Welding Technology/Welder, A

Ohio

ALLEGHENY WESLEYAN COLLEGE

Missions/Missionary Studies and Missiology, B
Religious Education, B

AMERICAN NATIONAL UNIVERSITY (CINCINNATI)

Accounting, A
Administrative Assistant and Secretarial Science, A
Business, Management, Marketing, and Related Support Services, A
Computer Programming, Specific Applications, A
Medical/Clinical Assistant, A
Pharmacy Technician/Assistant, A
Surgical Technology/Technologist, A
Systems Engineering, A
Web Page, Digital/Multimedia and Information Resources Design, A

AMERICAN NATIONAL UNIVERSITY (KETTERING)

Accounting, A
Administrative Assistant and Secretarial Science, A
Business Administration and Management, A
Computer Technology/Computer Systems Technology, A
Health Information/Medical Records Technology/Technician, A
Information Technology, A
Legal Assistant/Paralegal, A
Medical/Clinical Assistant, A
Pharmacy Technician/Assistant, A
Surgical Technology/Technologist, A

Web Page, Digital/Multimedia and Information Resources Design, A

AMERICAN NATIONAL UNIVERSITY (YOUNGSTOWN)

Accounting and Business/Management, A
Business Administration and Management, A
Health Information/Medical Records Administration/Administrator, A
Medical/Clinical Assistant, A
Pharmacy Technician/Assistant, A
Surgical Technology/Technologist, A

ANTIOCH COLLEGE

Anthropology, B
Biomedical Sciences, B
Environmental Sciences, B
Fine/Studio Arts, B
History, B
Liberal Arts and Sciences Studies and Humanities, B
Philosophy, B
Psychology, B
Visual and Performing Arts, B

ANTIOCH UNIVERSITY MIDWEST

Business Administration and Management, B
Comparative Literature, M
Conflict Resolution and Mediation/Peace Studies, M
Counseling Psychology, M
Early Childhood Education and Teaching, B
Education, M
Fine Arts and Art Studies, M
General Studies, B
Human Development and Family Studies, B
Human Resources Management/Personnel Administration, B
Human Services, B
Humanities/Humanistic Studies, B
Liberal Arts and Sciences Studies and Humanities, B
Liberal Studies, M
Management, M
Management Strategy and Policy, M
Mathematics, B
Psychology, M
Writing, M

ANTONELLI COLLEGE

Accounting and Business/Management, A
Commercial and Advertising Art, A
Computer Systems Networking and Telecommunications, A
Computer and Information Sciences, A
Graphic Design, A
Interior Design, A
Photography, A
Web/Multimedia Management and Webmaster, A

ART ACADEMY OF CINCINNATI

Art Education, M
Art History, Criticism and Conservation, B
Design and Visual Communications, B
Drawing, B
Graphic Design, A
Illustration, B
Intermedia/Multimedia, B
Painting, B
Photography, B
Prepress/Desktop Publishing and Digital Imaging Design, B
Printmaking, B
Sculpture, B

THE ART INSTITUTE OF CINCINNATI

Computer Graphics, AB

ASHLAND UNIVERSITY

Accounting, B
Acting, B
Actuarial Science, B
American/United States Studies/Civilization, B
Art Teacher Education, B
Athletic Training and Sports Medicine, B
BioTechnology, B

Biology Teacher Education, B
Biology/Biological Sciences, B
Business Administration and Management, B
Business Administration, Management and Operations, M
Chemistry, B
Chemistry Teacher Education, B
Commercial and Advertising Art, B
Communication Studies/Speech Communication and Rhetoric, B
Communication and Media Studies, B
Computer Science, B
Curriculum and Instruction, M
Dietetics/Dieticians, B
Digital Communication and Media/Multimedia, B
Drama and Dramatics/Theatre Arts, B
Economics, M
Education, BMD
Education/Teaching of the Gifted and Talented, M
Educational Administration and Supervision, M
Educational Leadership and Administration, MD
Educational Media/Instructional Technology, M
Elementary Education and Teaching, B
English Language and Literature, B
Entrepreneurship/Entrepreneurial Studies, B
Environmental Sciences, B
Exercise and Sports Science, M
Fashion Merchandising, B
Finance, B
Fine/Studio Arts, B
Foreign Language Teacher Education, B
Foundations and Philosophy of Education, M
French Language Teacher Education, B
French Language and Literature, B
Geology/Earth Science, B
Health Communication, B
History, BM
Hospitality Administration/Management, B
Hotel/Motel Administration/Management, B
Information Science/Studies, B
Jazz/Jazz Studies, B
Journalism, B
Junior High/Intermediate/Middle School Education and Teaching, B
Kindergarten/PreSchool Education and Teaching, B
Liberal Arts and Sciences Studies and Humanities, B
Marketing Research, B
Marketing/Marketing Management, B
Mass Communication/Media Studies, B
Mathematics, B
Music, B
Music Teacher Education, B
Philosophy, B
Physical Education Teaching and Coaching, M
Physics, B
Piano and Organ, B
Political Science and Government, BM
Pre-Dentistry Studies, B
Pre-Law Studies, B
Pre-Medicine/Pre-Medical Studies, B
Pre-Pharmacy Studies, B
Pre-Theology/Pre-Ministerial Studies, B
Pre-Veterinary Studies, B
Psychology, B
Radio and Television, B
Radio, Television, and Digital Communication, B
Reading Teacher Education, M
Religion/Religious Studies, B
Religious Education, B
Science Teacher Education/General Science Teacher Education, B
Secondary Education and Teaching, B
Social Sciences, B
Social Work, B
Sociology, B
Spanish Language Teacher Education, B
Spanish Language and Literature, B
Special Education and Teaching, BM
Sport and Fitness Administration/Management, M
Student Personnel Services, M
Technical Theatre/Theatre Design and Technology, B
Toxicology, B

Writing, M

AULTMAN COLLEGE OF NURSING AND HEALTH SCIENCES

Health Services/Allied Health/Health Sciences, A
Radiologic Technology/Science - Radiographer, A

BALDWIN WALLACE UNIVERSITY

Accounting, BM
Acting, B
Art/Art Studies, General, B
Athletic Training and Sports Medicine, B
Biological and Physical Sciences, B
Biology/Biological Sciences, B
Business Administration and Management, B
Business Administration, Management and Operations, M
Chemistry, B
Communication Disorders, BM
Communication Studies/Speech Communication and Rhetoric, B
Computer Science, B
Computer Software Engineering, B
Computer Systems Analysis/Analyst, B
Computer Systems Networking and Telecommunications, B
Criminal Justice/Safety Studies, B
Digital Communication and Media/Multimedia, B
Directing and Theatrical Production, B
Early Childhood Education and Teaching, B
Econometrics and Quantitative Economics, B
Economics, B
Education, M
Education/Teaching of Individuals with Specific Learning Disabilities, B
Educational Administration and Supervision, M
Educational Leadership and Administration, M
Educational Media/Instructional Technology, M
English Language and Literature, B
Entrepreneurship/Entrepreneurial Studies, BM
Exercise Physiology, B
Film/Cinema Studies, B
Finance, B
Fine/Studio Arts, B
French Language and Literature, B
German Language and Literature, B
Graphic Design, B
Health Professions and Related Clinical Sciences, B
Health Services Administration, M
Health and Physical Education, B
Health/Health Care Administration/Management, B
History, B
Human Resources Management and Services, M
Human Resources Management/Personnel Administration, B
International Business/Trade/Commerce, BM
International/Global Studies, B
Junior High/Intermediate/Middle School Education and Teaching, B
Management, M
Marketing/Marketing Management, B
Mass Communication/Media Studies, B
Mathematics, B
Multi-/Interdisciplinary Studies, B
Music, B
Music History, Literature, and Theory, B
Music Performance, B
Music Teacher Education, B
Music Theory and Composition, B
Music Therapy/Therapist, B
Natural Resource Economics, B
Philosophy, B
Physician Assistant, M
Physics, B
Piano and Organ, B
Political Science and Government, B
Pre-Dentistry Studies, B
Pre-Medicine/Pre-Medical Studies, B
Pre-Pharmacy Studies, B
Pre-Veterinary Studies, B
Psychology, B
Public Administration, B
Public Health (MPH, DPH), B
Public Relations/Image Management, B
Public/Applied History and Archival Administration, B
Reading Teacher Education, M

Religion/Religious Studies, B
Sociology, B
Spanish Language and Literature, B
Special Education and Teaching, M
Sport and Fitness Administration/Management, B
Sustainability Management, M
Technical Theatre/Theatre Design and Technology, B
Visual and Performing Arts, B
Voice and Opera, B

BELMONT COLLEGE

Accounting, A
Administrative Assistant and Secretarial Science, A
Architectural Engineering Technology/Technician, A
Business Administration and Management, A
Business/Commerce, A
Child Development, A
Computer Engineering Technology/Technician, A
Computer Graphics, A
Computer Systems Networking and Telecommunications, A
Corrections, A
Electrical and Electronic Engineering Technologies/Technicians, A
Electromechanical Technology/Electromechanical Engineering Technology, A
Engineering Technology, A
Entrepreneurship/Entrepreneurial Studies, A
Fire Protection and Safety Technology/Technician, A
General Studies, A
Health Professions and Related Clinical Sciences, A
Heating, Air Conditioning, Ventilation and Refrigeration Maintenance Technology/Technician, A
Information Science/Studies, A
Medical Office Management/Administration, A
Medical Transcription/Transcriptionist, A
Medical/Clinical Assistant, A
Mental and Social Health Services and Allied Professions, A
Real Estate, A
System, Networking, and LAN/WAN Management/Manager, A
Web Page, Digital/Multimedia and Information Resources Design, A
Welding Technology/Welder, A

BLUFFTON UNIVERSITY

Accounting, B
Art/Art Studies, General, B
Bible/Biblical Studies, B
Biology/Biological Sciences, B
Broadcast Journalism, B
Business Administration and Management, B
Business Administration, Management and Operations, M
Chemistry, B
Communication Studies/Speech Communication and Rhetoric, B
Criminal Justice/Safety Studies, B
Curriculum and Instruction, M
Economics, B
Education, M
Elementary Education and Teaching, B
English Language and Literature, B
Foods, Nutrition, and Wellness Studies, B
Graphic Design, B
Health and Physical Education, B
Health/Health Care Administration/Management, B
History, B
Information Technology, B
Junior High/Intermediate/Middle School Education and Teaching, B
Kindergarten/PreSchool Education and Teaching, B
Marketing/Marketing Management, B
Mathematics, B
Multi-/Interdisciplinary Studies, B
Music, B
Music Teacher Education, B
Organizational Behavior Studies, B
Organizational Management, M
Physics, B
Pre-Medicine/Pre-Medical Studies, B
Psychology, B
Public Health (MPH, DPH), B
Social Sciences, B

Social Work, B
Spanish Language and Literature, B
Special Education and Teaching, B
Sport and Fitness Administration/Management, B
Visual and Performing Arts, B
Youth Ministry, B

BOWLING GREEN STATE UNIVERSITY

Accounting, BM
Accounting Technology/Technician and Bookkeeping, B
Actuarial Science, B
Adult Development and Aging, B
Advertising, B
Aeronautical/Aerospace Engineering Technology/Technician, B
Aeronautics/Aviation/Aerospace Science and Technology, B
African Studies, B
African-American/Black Studies, B
American/United States Studies/Civilization, BMD
Apparel and Textiles, B
Applied Economics, B
Applied Statistics, M
Art Education, M
Art History, Criticism and Conservation, BM
Art Teacher Education, B
Art/Art Studies, General, B
Asian Studies/Civilization, B
Athletic Training and Sports Medicine, B
Audiology/Audiologist and Speech-Language Pathology/Pathologist, B
Biochemistry, B
Biological and Biomedical Sciences, MD
Biology Teacher Education, B
Biology/Biological Sciences, B
Broadcast Journalism, B
Business Administration and Management, B
Business Administration, Management and Operations, BM
Business Education, M
Business Teacher Education, B
Business, Management, Marketing, and Related Support Services, B
Business/Commerce, B
Business/Managerial Economics, B
Ceramic Arts and Ceramics, B
Chemistry, BMD
Chemistry Teacher Education, B
Child Development, B
Child and Family Studies, M
Classics and Classical Languages, Literatures, and Linguistics, B
Clinical Laboratory Science/Medical Technology/Technologist, B
Clinical Psychology, MD
College Student Counseling and Personnel Services, B
Commercial and Advertising Art, B
Communication Disorders, BMD
Communication Studies/Speech Communication and Rhetoric, B
Communication and Media Studies, MD
Communication, Journalism and Related Programs, B
Communications Technologies/Technicians and Support Services, B
Community Health and Preventive Medicine, B
Composition, MD
Computer Art and Design, M
Computer Engineering, B
Computer Engineering Technology/Technician, B
Computer Programming/Programmer, B
Computer Science, M
Computer Software Engineering, B
Computer Systems Networking and Telecommunications, B
Computer Teacher Education, B
Computer Technology/Computer Systems Technology, B
Computer and Information Sciences, B
Construction Engineering, B
Construction Engineering Technology/Technician, B
Construction Management, M
Corrections, B
Counseling Psychology, M

Counselor Education/School Counseling and Guidance Services, BM
Crafts/Craft Design, Folk Art and Artisanry, B
Criminal Justice/Law Enforcement Administration, B
Criminal Justice/Police Science, B
Criminal Justice/Safety Studies, B
Criminology, M
Curriculum and Instruction, M
Demography and Population Studies, M
Design and Applied Arts, M
Design and Visual Communications, B
Developmental Psychology, MD
Diagnostic Medical Sonography/Sonographer and Ultrasound Technician, B
Dietetics/Dieticians, B
Drama and Dance Teacher Education, B
Drama and Dramatics/Theatre Arts, B
Drawing, B
Early Childhood Education and Teaching, M
Economics, BM
Education, B
Education/Teaching of Individuals in Early Childhood Special Education Programs, B
Education/Teaching of Individuals with Hearing Impairments, Including Deafness, B
Education/Teaching of Individuals with Mental Retardation, B
Education/Teaching of Individuals with Multiple Disabilities, B
Education/Teaching of Individuals with Specific Learning Disabilities, B
Education/Teaching of the Gifted and Talented, M
Educational Administration and Supervision, MDO
Educational Leadership and Administration, D
Educational Media/Instructional Technology, M
Educational/Instructional Media Design, B
Electrical, Electronic and Communications Engineering Technology/Technician, B
Electromechanical Technology/Electromechanical Engineering Technology, B
Elementary Education and Teaching, B
Emergency Medical Technology/Technician (EMT Paramedic), B
Engineering Technologies/Technicians, B
Engineering/Industrial Management, B
English, MD
English Language and Literature, B
English/Language Arts Teacher Education, B
Environmental Design/Architecture, B
Environmental Engineering Technology/Environmental Technology, B
Environmental Health, B
Environmental Studies, B
Ethnic, Cultural Minority, and Gender Studies, B
Ethnomusicology, M
European Studies/Civilization, B
Executive Assistant/Executive Secretary, B
Experimental Psychology, MD
Family Systems, B
Family and Community Services, B
Family and Consumer Economics and Related Services, B
Family and Consumer Sciences/Home Economics Teacher Education, B
Family and Consumer Sciences/Human Sciences, BM
Fashion Merchandising, B
Fashion/Apparel Design, B
Fiber, Textile and Weaving Arts, B
Film, Television, and Video Production, MD
Film/Cinema Studies, B
Finance, B
Fine Arts and Art Studies, BM
Fine/Studio Arts, B
Fire Services Administration, B
Foods, Nutrition, and Wellness Studies, B
Foreign Language Teacher Education, BM
French Language and Literature, BM
Geochemistry, B
Geography, B
Geology/Earth Science, BM
Geophysics and Seismology, BM
German Language and Literature, BM
Gerontology, B
Graphic Design, M

Health Information/Medical Records Administration/Administrator, B
Health Information/Medical Records Technology/Technician, B
Health Professions and Related Clinical Sciences, B
Health Teacher Education, B
Health and Physical Education/Fitness, B
Health/Health Care Administration/Management, B
Higher Education/Higher Education Administration, D
Hispanic-American, Puerto Rican, and Mexican-American/Chicano Studies, B
History, BMD
History Teacher Education, B
Hospitality Administration/Management, B
Human Development, M
Human Development and Family Studies, B
Human Resources Management/Personnel Administration, B
Humanities/Humanistic Studies, B
Industrial Production Technologies/Technicians, B
Industrial Technology/Technician, B
Industrial and Organizational Psychology, MD
Information Science/Studies, B
Instrumentation Technology/Technician, B
Insurance, B
Interdisciplinary Studies, MD
Interior Architecture, B
International Business/Trade/Commerce, B
International Relations and Affairs, B
International and Comparative Education, M
International/Global Studies, B
Jazz/Jazz Studies, B
Journalism, B
Junior High/Intermediate/Middle School Education and Teaching, B
Kindergarten/PreSchool Education and Teaching, B
Kinesiology and Movement Studies, M
Labor and Industrial Relations, B
Latin American Studies, B
Latin Language and Literature, B
Leisure Studies, M
Liberal Arts and Sciences Studies and Humanities, B
Logistics and Materials Management, B
Management Information Systems and Services, B
Manufacturing Engineering, M
Manufacturing Technology/Technician, B
Marketing, B
Marketing Research, B
Marketing/Marketing Management, B
Mathematics, BMD
Mathematics Teacher Education, BM
Mechanical Engineering/Mechanical Technology/Technician, B
Medical Microbiology and Bacteriology, B
Medical Radiologic Technology/Science - Radiation Therapist, B
Metal and Jewelry Arts, B
Microbiology, B
Multi-/Interdisciplinary Studies, B
Music, BMD
Music History, Literature, and Theory, BM
Music Performance, B
Music Teacher Education, BM
Music Theory and Composition, BM
Musicology and Ethnomusicology, B
Natural Resources Management/Development and Policy, B
Natural Resources and Conservation, B
Nutritional Sciences, BM
Office Management and Supervision, B
Operations Management and Supervision, B
Operations Research, BM
Organizational Behavior Studies, B
Organizational Management, M
Painting, B
Paleontology, B
Parasitology, B
Parks, Recreation, Leisure and Fitness Studies, B
Performance, M
Philosophy, BMD
Photography, B
Physical Education Teaching and Coaching, B
Physical Sciences, B
Physical Therapy/Therapist, B

Physics, BM
Physics Teacher Education, B
Piano and Organ, B
Political Science and Government, B
Pre-Dentistry Studies, B
Pre-Law Studies, B
Pre-Medicine/Pre-Medical Studies, B
Printmaking, B
Psychology, BMD
Public Administration, BM
Public Health, M
Public Relations/Image Management, B
Quality Control Technology/Technician, B
Radio and Television, B
Reading Teacher Education, MO
Real Estate, B
Recreation and Park Management, M
Rehabilitation Counseling, M
Religious/Sacred Music, B
Respiratory Care Therapy/Therapist, B
Restaurant, Culinary, and Catering
  Management/Manager, B
Retailing and Retail Operations, B
Rhetoric, D
Russian Language and Literature, B
Russian Studies, B
Sales and Marketing Operations/Marketing and Dis-
  tribution Teacher Education, B
Sales, Distribution and Marketing Operations, B
School Psychology, MO
Science Teacher Education/General Science
  Teacher Education, BM
Science Technologies/Technicians, B
Sculpture, B
Social Psychology, M
Social Science Teacher Education, B
Social Sciences, B
Social Studies Teacher Education, B
Social Work, B
Sociology, BMD
Software Engineering, M
Spanish Language and Literature, BM
Special Education and Teaching, BM
Speech Teacher Education, B
Speech and Interpersonal Communication, MD
Sport and Fitness Administration/Management, BM
Statistics, BMD
Student Personnel Services, M
Teacher Education and Professional Develop-
  ment, Specific Subject Areas, B
Teacher Education, Multiple Levels, B
Technical Communication, M
Technical Teacher Education, B
Technology Teacher Education/Industrial Arts
  Teacher Education, B
Theater, MD
Tourism Promotion Operations, B
Tourism and Travel Services Management, B
Trade and Industrial Teacher Education, B
Vocational Rehabilitation Counseling/Counselor, B
Vocational and Technical Education, M
Voice and Opera, B
Women's Studies, B
Writing, MD

**BOWLING GREEN STATE
UNIVERSITY–FIRELANDS COLLEGE**

Allied Health and Medical Assisting Services, AB
Business Administration and Management, AB
Communications Technologies/Technicians and Sup-
  port Services, A
Computer Engineering Technology/Technician, A
Computer Systems Networking and Telecommunica-
  tions, A
Computer and Information Sciences and Support
  Services, A
Criminal Justice/Safety Studies, AB
Design and Visual Communications, B
Diagnostic Medical Sonography/Sonographer and
  Ultrasound Technician, A
Education, AB
Electrical, Electronic and Communications Engineer-
  ing Technology/Technician, A
Electromechanical Technology/Electromechanical
  Engineering Technology, A

Health Information/Medical Records
  Administration/Administrator, A
Health Professions and Related Clinical Sciences, A
Human Services, A
Industrial Technology/Technician, A
Liberal Arts and Sciences Studies and Humani-
  ties, AB
Management Information Systems and Services, A
Manufacturing Technology/Technician, A
Mechanical Engineering/Mechanical
  Technology/Technician, A
Medical Radiologic Technology/Science - Radiation
  Therapist, A
Respiratory Care Therapy/Therapist, AB
Social Work, AB

BRADFORD SCHOOL

Cooking and Related Culinary Arts, A
Graphic Design, A
Medical/Clinical Assistant, A
Physical Therapist Assistant, A
Veterinary/Animal Health Technology/Technician and
  Veterinary Assistant, A

**BRIGHTWOOD COLLEGE, DAY-
TON CAMPUS**

Computer Systems Networking and Telecommunications, A
Photographic and Film/Video Technology/Technician
  and Assistant, A

BROWN MACKIE COLLEGE–AKRON

Business Administration and Management, B
Business/Commerce, A
Medical Office Management/Administration, A
Occupational Therapist Assistant, A
Veterinary/Animal Health Technology/Technician and
  Veterinary Assistant, A

**BROWN MACKIE COLLEGE–NORTH
CANTON**

Business Administration and Management, B
Computer and Information Sciences and Support
  Services, A
Health/Health Care Administration/Management, B
Legal Assistant/Paralegal, A
Surgical Technology/Technologist, A
Veterinary/Animal Health Technology/Technician and
  Veterinary Assistant, A

**BRYANT & STRATTON COL-
LEGE–CLEVELAND CAMPUS**

Administrative Assistant and Secretarial Science, A
Business Administration and Management, B
Business/Commerce, A
Computer and Information Systems Security, A
Criminal Justice/Law Enforcement Administration, A
Electrical, Electronic and Communications Engineer-
  ing Technology/Technician, AB
Human Resources Management and Services, A
Information Technology, A
Legal Administrative Assistant/Secretary, A
Legal Assistant/Paralegal, A
System, Networking, and LAN/WAN
  Management/Manager, A

**BRYANT & STRATTON COL-
LEGE–EASTLAKE CAMPUS**

Accounting, A
Administrative Assistant and Secretarial Science, A
Business Administration and Management, AB
Computer and Information Systems Security, A
Data Processing and Data Processing
  Technology/Technician, A
Electrical and Electronic Engineering
  Technologies/Technicians, B
Electrical, Electronic and Communications Engineer-
  ing Technology/Technician, A
Human Resources Management/Personnel Adminis-
  tration, A
Information Technology, A
Legal Assistant/Paralegal, A
Medical Administrative Assistant/Secretary, A
Medical/Clinical Assistant, A

System, Networking, and LAN/WAN
  Management/Manager, A

**BRYANT & STRATTON COL-
LEGE–PARMA CAMPUS**

Accounting, A
Administrative Assistant and Secretarial Science, A
Business Administration and Management, B
Business/Commerce, A
Computer and Information Systems Security, A
Criminal Justice/Law Enforcement Administration, A
Human Resources Management and Services, A
Information Technology, A
Legal Administrative Assistant/Secretary, A
Medical Administrative Assistant/Secretary, A
Medical/Clinical Assistant, A
System, Networking, and LAN/WAN
  Management/Manager, A

CAPITAL UNIVERSITY

Accounting, B
Art Teacher Education, B
Art Therapy/Therapist, B
Art/Art Studies, General, B
Athletic Training and Sports Medicine, B
Biochemistry, B
Biology/Biological Sciences, B
Business Administration and Management, B
Business Administration, Management and Opera-
  tions, BM
Business/Managerial Economics, B
Chemistry, B
Communication Studies/Speech Communication
  and Rhetoric, B
Computer Engineering, B
Computer Science, B
Criminology, B
Drama and Dramatics/Theatre Arts, B
Early Childhood Education and Teaching, B
Economics, B
English Language and Literature, B
English/Language Arts Teacher Education, B
Environmental Sciences, B
French Language and Literature, B
Health Teacher Education, B
Health and Physical Education, B
History, B
International Relations and Affairs, B
Jazz/Jazz Studies, B
Junior High/Intermediate/Middle School Education
  and Teaching, B
Kinesiology and Exercise Science, B
Law and Legal Studies, MD
Legal and Justice Studies, M
Marketing/Marketing Management, B
Mathematics, B
Mathematics Teacher Education, B
Multi-/Interdisciplinary Studies, B
Music, BM
Music Performance, B
Music Teacher Education, BM
Music Theory and Composition, B
Nursing, M
Nursing Administration, M
Organizational Communication, B
Philosophy, B
Physical Education Teaching and Coaching, B
Piano and Organ, B
Political Science and Government, B
Psychology, B
Public Administration, B
Public Relations/Image Management, B
Religion/Religious Studies, B
Science Teacher Education/General Science
  Teacher Education, B
Social Studies Teacher Education, B
Social Work, B
Sociology, B
Spanish Language and Literature, B
Special Education and Teaching, B
Speech Teacher Education, B
Taxation, M

Voice and Opera, B

CASE WESTERN RESERVE UNIVERSITY

Accounting, BMD
Acute Care/Critical Care Nursing, M
Aerospace, Aeronautical and Astronautical Engineering, BMD
Allopathic Medicine, D
American/United States Studies/Civilization, B
Anatomy, M
Anesthesiologist Assistant, M
Anthropology, BMD
Applied Mathematics, BMD
Architecture and Related Services, B
Art Education, M
Art History, Criticism and Conservation, BMD
Art Teacher Education, B
Asian Studies/Civilization, B
Astronomy, BMD
Biochemistry, BMD
Bioethics/Medical Ethics, M
Biological and Biomedical Sciences, MD
Biology/Biological Sciences, B
Biomedical Engineering, MD
Biomedical/Medical Engineering, B
Biophysics, MD
Biostatistics, MD
Business Administration and Management, B
Business Administration, Management and Operations, M
Cancer Biology/Oncology, D
Cell Biology and Anatomy, MD
Chemical Engineering, BMD
Chemistry, BMD
Civil Engineering, BMD
Classics and Classical Languages, Literatures, and Linguistics, B
Clinical Psychology, D
Clinical Research, M
Cognitive Sciences, BM
Communication Disorders, BMD
Comparative Literature, BM
Computer Engineering, BMD
Computer Science, BMD
Dance, BM
Dental and Oral Surgery, O
Dentistry, D
Dietetics/Dieticians, B
Drama and Dramatics/Theatre Arts, B
Economics, B
Electrical Engineering, MD
Electrical, Electronics and Communications Engineering, B
Engineering, B
Engineering Management, M
Engineering Physics, B
Engineering and Applied Sciences, MD
English, MD
English Language and Literature, B
Environmental Studies, B
Epidemiology, MD
Evolutionary Biology, B
Experimental Psychology, D
Finance, B
Finance and Banking, M
French Language and Literature, BM
French Studies, B
Genetic Counseling/Counselor, M
Genetics, D
Genomic Sciences, D
Geology/Earth Science, BMD
Geosciences, MD
German Language and Literature, B
German Studies, B
Gerontological Nursing, M
Gerontology, B
Health Services Administration, M
Health Services Research, MD
History, BMD
History and Philosophy of Science and Technology, B
Human Genetics, D
Human Nutrition, B
Immunology, MD
Industrial and Manufacturing Management, MD

Information Science/Studies, MD
Intellectual Property Law, M
International Relations and Affairs, B
International/Global Studies, B
Japanese Studies, B
Law and Legal Studies, MD
Legal and Justice Studies, M
Linguistics, M
Logistics and Materials Management, M
Management, D
Marketing/Marketing Management, B
Materials Engineering, BMD
Materials Sciences, MD
Maternal/Child Health and Neonatal Nurse/Nursing, M
Mathematics, BMD
Mechanical Engineering, BMD
Microbiology, D
Molecular Biology, D
Molecular Medicine, D
Molecular Physiology, M
Museology/Museum Studies, M
Music, B
Music History, Literature, and Theory, MD
Music Teacher Education, BMD
Musicology and Ethnomusicology, D
Natural Sciences, B
Neuroscience, D
Non-Profit/Public/Organizational Management, MO
Nurse Anesthetist, M
Nurse Midwife/Nursing Midwifery, M
Nursing, MD
Nursing - Advanced Practice, M
Nursing Education, M
Nutritional Sciences, BMD
Oncology Nursing, M
Operations Research, MD
Oral and Dental Sciences, MO
Organizational Behavior Studies, MD
Orthodontics, MO
Pathology/Experimental Pathology, MD
Pediatric Nurse/Nursing, M
Pedodontics, MO
Performance, MD
Periodontics, MO
Pharmacology, D
Philosophy, B
Physician Assistant, M
Physics, BMD
Physiology, MD
Political Science and Government, BMD
Polymer/Plastics Engineering, BMD
Psychiatric/Mental Health Nurse/Nursing, M
Psychology, BMD
Public Health, M
Religion/Religious Studies, B
Social Work, MD
Sociology, BMD
Spanish Language and Literature, B
Statistics, BMD
Supply Chain Management, MD
Sustainability Management, D
Systems Engineering, BD
Theater, M
Virology, D
Women's Health Nursing, M
Women's Studies, B

CEDARVILLE UNIVERSITY

Accounting, B
Allied Health and Medical Assisting Services, B
Athletic Training and Sports Medicine, B
Bible/Biblical Studies, B
Biology Teacher Education, B
Biology/Biological Sciences, B
Business Administration and Management, B
Business Administration, Management and Operations, M
Cell/Cellular and Molecular Biology, B
Chemistry, B
Chemistry Teacher Education, B
Computer Engineering, B
Computer Science, B
Corrections and Criminal Justice, B
Curriculum and Instruction, M
Design and Visual Communications, B

Digital Communication and Media/Multimedia, B
Drama and Dramatics/Theatre Arts, B
Early Childhood Education and Teaching, B
Economics, B
Education, MD
Educational Leadership and Administration, M
Electrical, Electronics and Communications Engineering, B
English Language and Literature, B
English/Language Arts Teacher Education, B
Environmental Sciences, B
Finance, B
Fine/Studio Arts, B
Forensic Science and Technology, B
Geological and Earth Sciences/Geosciences, B
Geology/Earth Science, B
Graphic Design, B
History, B
Industrial Design, B
Information Technology, B
International Business/Trade/Commerce, B
International Public Health/International Health, M
International/Global Studies, B
Journalism, B
Junior High/Intermediate/Middle School Education and Teaching, B
Kinesiology and Exercise Science, B
Liberal Arts and Sciences Studies and Humanities, B
Linguistics, B
Marketing/Marketing Management, B
Mathematics, B
Mathematics Teacher Education, B
Mechanical Engineering, B
Missions/Missionary Studies and Missiology, B
Music, B
Music Performance, B
Music Teacher Education, B
Music Theory and Composition, B
Nursing - Advanced Practice, M
Pharmacy, D
Physical Education Teaching and Coaching, B
Physics, B
Physics Teacher Education, B
Piano and Organ, B
Political Science and Government, B
Pre-Law Studies, B
Pre-Nursing Studies, B
Psychology, B
Public Administration, B
Religious Education, B
Science Teacher Education/General Science Teacher Education, B
Social Studies Teacher Education, B
Social Work, B
Spanish Language Teacher Education, B
Spanish Language and Literature, B
Special Education and Teaching, B
Sport and Fitness Administration/Management, B
Theology and Religious Vocations, B
Web Page, Digital/Multimedia and Information Resources Design, B
Youth Ministry, B

CENTRAL OHIO TECHNICAL COLLEGE

Accounting, A
Advertising, A
Architectural Drafting and Architectural CAD/CADD, A
Business Administration and Management, A
CAD/CADD Drafting and/or Design Technology/Technician, A
Civil Drafting and Civil Engineering CAD/CADD, A
Civil Engineering Technology/Technician, A
Computer Graphics, A
Computer Programming/Programmer, A
Criminal Justice/Law Enforcement Administration, A
Criminal Justice/Police Science, A
Culinary Arts/Chef Training, A
Diagnostic Medical Sonography/Sonographer and Ultrasound Technician, A
Early Childhood Education and Teaching, A
Electrical, Electronic and Communications Engineering Technology/Technician, A
Emergency Medical Technology/Technician (EMT Paramedic), A

Fire Science/Firefighting, A
Forensic Science and Technology, A
Human Services, A
Liberal Arts and Sciences Studies and Humanities, A
Manufacturing Technology/Technician, A
Mechanical Engineering/Mechanical Technology/Technician, A
Radiologic Technology/Science - Radiographer, A
Surgical Technology/Technologist, A
Web Page, Digital/Multimedia and Information Resources Design, A

CENTRAL STATE UNIVERSITY

Accounting, B
Art Teacher Education, B
Art/Art Studies, General, B
Biology/Biological Sciences, B
Broadcast Journalism, B
Business/Commerce, B
Chemistry, B
Computer Science, B
Computer and Information Sciences, B
Criminal Justice/Safety Studies, B
Early Childhood Education and Teaching, B
Economics, B
Education, B
English Language and Literature, B
Environmental/Environmental Health Engineering, B
Geography, B
Geology/Earth Science, B
History, B
Industrial Technology/Technician, B
Jazz/Jazz Studies, B
Journalism, B
Junior High/Intermediate/Middle School Education and Teaching, B
Manufacturing Engineering, B
Mathematics, B
Music Performance, B
Music Teacher Education, B
Parks, Recreation, Leisure and Fitness Studies, B
Political Science and Government, B
Psychology, B
Secondary Education and Teaching, B
Social Work, B
Sociology, B
Special Education and Teaching, B
Teacher Education, Multiple Levels, B
Water Resources Engineering, B

CHATFIELD COLLEGE

Liberal Arts and Sciences Studies and Humanities, A

CINCINNATI CHRISTIAN UNIVERSITY

Bible/Biblical Studies, AB
Divinity/Ministry (BD, MDiv.), AB
Education, AB
Journalism, B
Kindergarten/PreSchool Education and Teaching, B
Pastoral Studies/Counseling, M
Piano and Organ, B
Psychology, AB
Religion/Religious Studies, M
Religious Education, AB
Religious/Sacred Music, AB
Sign Language Interpretation and Translation, A
Theology and Religious Vocations, M
Voice and Opera, B

CINCINNATI COLLEGE OF MORTUARY SCIENCE

Funeral Service and Mortuary Science, AB

CINCINNATI STATE TECHNICAL AND COMMUNITY COLLEGE

Accounting, A
Administrative Assistant and Secretarial Science, A
Aeronautical/Aerospace Engineering Technology/Technician, A
Allied Health and Medical Assisting Services, A
Applied Horticulture/Horticultural Business Services, A
Architectural Engineering Technology/Technician, A

Audiovisual Communications Technologies/Technicians, A
Automobile/Automotive Mechanics Technology/Technician, A
Automotive Engineering Technology/Technician, A
Baking and Pastry Arts/Baker/Pastry Chef, A
Biology/Biological Sciences, A
Biomedical Technology/Technician, A
Business Administration and Management, A
Business Administration, Management and Operations, A
Chemical Technology/Technician, A
Civil Engineering Technology/Technician, A
Clinical/Medical Laboratory Technician, A
Commercial and Advertising Art, A
Computer Engineering Technology/Technician, A
Computer Programming, Specific Applications, A
Computer Systems Analysis/Analyst, A
Computer and Information Sciences, A
Culinary Arts/Chef Training, A
Diagnostic Medical Sonography/Sonographer and Ultrasound Technician, A
Dietetics/Dieticians, A
Early Childhood Education and Teaching, A
Electrical, Electronic and Communications Engineering Technology/Technician, A
Electromechanical Technology/Electromechanical Engineering Technology, A
Emergency Medical Technology/Technician (EMT Paramedic), A
Energy Management and Systems Technology/Technician, A
Engineering Technologies/Technicians, A
Entrepreneurship/Entrepreneurial Studies, A
Environmental Control Technologies/Technicians, A
Environmental Engineering Technology/Environmental Technology, A
Executive Assistant/Executive Secretary, A
Financial Planning and Services, A
Fire Science/Firefighting, A
General Studies, A
Health Information/Medical Records Technology/Technician, A
Hospitality Administration/Management, A
Industrial Technology/Technician, A
Landscaping and Groundskeeping, A
Liberal Arts and Sciences Studies and Humanities, A
Marketing/Marketing Management, A
Mechanical Engineering/Mechanical Technology/Technician, A
Medical Office Assistant/Specialist, A
Multi-/Interdisciplinary Studies, A
Nuclear Medical Technology/Technologist, A
Occupational Safety and Health Technology/Technician, A
Occupational Therapist Assistant, A
Parks, Recreation, Leisure and Fitness Studies, A
Plastics Engineering Technology/Technician, A
Prepress/Desktop Publishing and Digital Imaging Design, A
Real Estate, A
Restaurant, Culinary, and Catering Management/Manager, A
Sign Language Interpretation and Translation, A
Surgical Technology/Technologist, A
System Administration/Administrator, A
Turf and Turfgrass Management, A

CLARK STATE COMMUNITY COLLEGE

Accounting, A
Administrative Assistant and Secretarial Science, A
Agricultural Business and Management, A
Agricultural Mechanization, A
Agriculture, A
Applied Horticulture/Horticultural Operations, A
Business Administration and Management, A
Business Operations Support and Secretarial Services, A
Business, Management, Marketing, and Related Support Services, A
Cartography, A
Civil Engineering Technology/Technician, A
Clinical/Medical Laboratory Technician, A
Commercial and Advertising Art, A
Computer Programming, A

Computer Programming/Programmer, A
Computer Systems Networking and Telecommunications, A
Computer and Information Sciences and Support Services, A
Computer and Information Systems Security, A
Corrections, A
Court Reporting/Court Reporter, A
Criminal Justice/Law Enforcement Administration, A
Criminal Justice/Police Science, A
Diesel Mechanics Technology/Technician, A
Drafting and Design Technology/Technician, A
Drama and Dramatics/Theatre Arts, A
Early Childhood Education and Teaching, A
Electrical, Electronic and Communications Engineering Technology/Technician, A
Emergency Medical Technology/Technician (EMT Paramedic), A
Engineering, A
Engineering Technologies/Technicians, A
Health Services/Allied Health/Health Sciences, A
Heating, Air Conditioning and Refrigeration Technology/Technician, A
Horticultural Science, A
Human Resources Management/Personnel Administration, A
Human Services, A
Industrial Technology/Technician, A
Information Science/Studies, A
Information Technology, A
Insurance, A
Kindergarten/PreSchool Education and Teaching, A
Kinesiology and Exercise Science, A
Landscaping and Groundskeeping, A
Legal Assistant/Paralegal, A
Liberal Arts and Sciences Studies and Humanities, A
Library Assistant/Technician, A
Logistics and Materials Management, A
Marketing/Marketing Management, A
Mechanical Engineering/Mechanical Technology/Technician, A
Medical Administrative Assistant/Secretary, A
Medical/Clinical Assistant, A
Physical Therapist Assistant, A
Physical Therapy/Therapist, A
Social Work, A

CLEVELAND INSTITUTE OF ART

Animation, Interactive Technology, Video Graphics and Special Effects, B
Ceramic Arts and Ceramics, B
Drawing, B
Fine Arts and Art Studies, B
Graphic Design, B
Illustration, B
Industrial Design, B
Interior Design, B
Medical Illustration/Medical Illustrator, B
Metal and Jewelry Arts, B
Painting, B
Photography, B
Printmaking, B
Sculpture, B

CLEVELAND INSTITUTE OF MUSIC

Music, B
Music Performance, B
Music Theory and Composition, B
Performance, MDO

CLEVELAND STATE UNIVERSITY

Accounting, BM
Adult and Continuing Education and Teaching, MDO
African-American/Black Studies, B
Allied Health and Medical Assisting Services, M
Analytical Chemistry, M
Anthropology, B
Applied Statistics, M
Art Education, M
Art History, Criticism and Conservation, M
Art/Art Studies, General, B
Audiology/Audiologist and Hearing Sciences, B
Bioethics/Medical Ethics, MO
Biological and Biomedical Sciences, MD

Biology Technician/BioTechnology Laboratory Technician, B
Biology/Biological Sciences, B
Biomedical Engineering, D
Biomedical Technology/Technician, B
Business Administration and Management, B
Business Administration, Management and Operations, MD
Business/Managerial Economics, B
Chemical Engineering, BMD
Chemistry, BMD
Cinematography and Film/Video Production, B
Civil Engineering, BMD
Communication Disorders, M
Communication Studies/Speech Communication and Rhetoric, B
Communication Theory, M
Communication and Media Studies, MDO
Community Health Nursing, M
Community Psychology, M
Composition, M
Computer Engineering, B
Computer Science, M
Computer and Information Sciences, B
Condensed Matter Physics, M
Counseling Psychology, MDO
Counselor Education/School Counseling and Guidance Services, MD
Criminology, B
Digital Communication and Media/Multimedia, B
Drama and Dramatics/Theatre Arts, B
Early Childhood Education and Teaching, BM
Economic Development, MO
Economics, BMO
Education, MDO
Education/Teaching of Individuals with Multiple Disabilities, M
Educational Administration and Supervision, MDO
Educational Media/Instructional Technology, D
Educational Policy, D
Electrical Engineering, MD
Electrical, Electronic and Communications Engineering Technology/Technician, B
Electrical, Electronics and Communications Engineering, B
Engineering and Applied Sciences, MD
English, M
English Language and Literature, B
English as a Second Language, M
Environmental Engineering Technology/Environmental Technology, MD
Environmental Policy, M
Environmental Policy and Resource Management, M
Environmental Sciences, BMD
Environmental Studies, BMO
Exercise and Sports Science, M
Film/Video and Photographic Arts, B
Finance, B
Finance and Banking, MDO
Foreign Language Teacher Education, M
Forensic Nursing, M
French Language and Literature, BM
Geographic Information Systems, MO
Health Communication, O
Health Education, M
Health Law, O
Health Professions and Related Clinical Sciences, B
Health Services Administration, M
Health and Physical Education, B
Health/Medical Preparatory Programs, B
Higher Education/Higher Education Administration, D
Historic Preservation and Conservation, M
History, BM
Human Resources Management and Services, M
Industrial and Labor Relations, MD
Industrial and Manufacturing Management, D
Industrial/Management Engineering, MD
Information Science/Studies, M
Inorganic Chemistry, M
International Affairs, M
International Business/Trade/Commerce, BDO
International Economics, M
International Relations and Affairs, B
Journalism, B

Junior High/Intermediate/Middle School Education and Teaching, B
Labor and Industrial Relations, B
Latin American Studies, M
Law and Legal Studies, MDO
Liberal Arts and Sciences Studies and Humanities, B
Linguistics, BM
Management Information Systems and Services, BMD
Marketing, MDO
Marketing/Marketing Management, B
Mathematics, BM
Mathematics Teacher Education, M
Mechanical Engineering, BMD
Mechanical Engineering Related Technologies/Technicians, B
Medical Imaging, M
Medical Physics, M
Medicinal and Pharmaceutical Chemistry, M
Medieval and Renaissance Studies, B
Middle School Education, M
Molecular Medicine, D
Multi-/Interdisciplinary Studies, B
Museology/Museum Studies, M
Music, BM
Music Teacher Education, M
Non-Profit/Public/Organizational Management, BMO
Nursing, MD
Nursing Education, MD
Occupational Therapy/Therapist, M
Operations Management and Supervision, B
Optical Technologies, M
Optics/Optical Sciences, M
Organic Chemistry, M
Organizational Communication, B
Organizational Management, M
Performance, M
Philosophy, BMO
Physical Chemistry, M
Physical Education Teaching and Coaching, M
Physical Therapy/Therapist, D
Physician Assistant, BM
Physics, BM
Political Science and Government, B
Pre-Nursing Studies, B
Psychology, BMDO
Public Administration, BMDO
Public Affairs, D
Public Health, M
Public Policy Analysis, M
Public Relations/Image Management, B
Real Estate, MO
Religion/Religious Studies, B
Science Teacher Education/General Science Teacher Education, M
Social Sciences, B
Social Studies Teacher Education, B
Social Work, BM
Sociology, BM
Software Engineering, M
Spanish Language and Literature, BM
Special Education and Teaching, BM
Speech-Language Pathology/Pathologist, B
Sport Psychology, M
Sport and Fitness Administration/Management, BM
Substance Abuse/Addiction Counseling, O
Sustainable Development, M
Taxation, M
Urban Education and Leadership, D
Urban Planning, MO
Urban Studies/Affairs, BMDO
Urban and Regional Planning, M
Women's Studies, B
Writing, M

THE COLLEGE OF WOOSTER

African-American/Black Studies, B
Anthropology, B
Archeology, B
Art History, Criticism and Conservation, B
Biochemistry, B
Biology/Biological Sciences, B
Business/Managerial Economics, B
Chemistry, B

Classics and Classical Languages, Literatures, and Linguistics, B
Communication Studies/Speech Communication and Rhetoric, B
Comparative Literature, B
Computer Science, B
Drama and Dramatics/Theatre Arts, B
Economics, B
English Language and Literature, B
Fine/Studio Arts, B
French Language and Literature, B
Geology/Earth Science, B
German Language and Literature, B
German Studies, B
History, B
International Relations and Affairs, B
Mass Communication/Media Studies, B
Mathematics, B
Molecular Biology, B
Multi-/Interdisciplinary Studies, B
Music, B
Music History, Literature, and Theory, B
Music Performance, B
Music Teacher Education, B
Music Theory and Composition, B
Music Therapy/Therapist, B
Philosophy, B
Physics, B
Political Science and Government, B
Psychology, B
Religion/Religious Studies, B
Russian Studies, B
Sociology, B
Spanish Language and Literature, B
Urban Studies/Affairs, B
Women's Studies, B

COLUMBUS COLLEGE OF ART & DESIGN

Animation, Interactive Technology, Video Graphics and Special Effects, B
Art History, Criticism and Conservation, B
Cinematography and Film/Video Production, B
Commercial and Advertising Art, B
Fashion/Apparel Design, B
Film/Video and Photographic Arts, B
Fine Arts and Art Studies, BM
Illustration, B
Industrial Design, B
Interior Design, B
Photography, B

COLUMBUS CULINARY INSTITUTE AT BRADFORD SCHOOL

Cooking and Related Culinary Arts, A

COLUMBUS STATE COMMUNITY COLLEGE

Accounting Technology/Technician and Bookkeeping, A
Administrative Assistant and Secretarial Science, A
Adult Development and Aging, A
Aeronautical/Aerospace Engineering Technology/Technician, A
Architectural Engineering Technology/Technician, A
Automotive Engineering Technology/Technician, A
Business Administration and Management, A
Business, Management, Marketing, and Related Support Services, A
Clinical Laboratory Science/Medical Technology/Technologist, A
Clinical/Medical Laboratory Assistant, A
Communications Technologies/Technicians and Support Services, A
Computer Engineering Technology/Technician, A
Computer Programming, Specific Applications, A
Computer Programming/Programmer, A
Computer and Information Sciences, A
Construction Engineering Technology/Technician, A
Criminal Justice/Police Science, A
Culinary Arts/Chef Training, A
Dental Hygiene/Hygienist, A
Dental Laboratory Technology/Technician, A
Electrical and Electronic Engineering Technologies/Technicians, A

Electrical, Electronic and Communications Engineering Technology/Technician, A
Electromechanical Technology/Electromechanical Engineering Technology, A
Emergency Medical Technology/Technician (EMT Paramedic), A
Engineering Technologies/Technicians, A
Entrepreneurship/Entrepreneurial Studies, A
Environmental Control Technologies/Technicians, A
Finance and Financial Management Services, A
Fire Science/Firefighting, A
Graphic and Printing Equipment Operator Production, A
Health Information/Medical Records Administration/Administrator, A
Health Information/Medical Records Technology/Technician, A
Health and Physical Education/Fitness, A
Heating, Air Conditioning, Ventilation and Refrigeration Maintenance Technology/Technician, A
Hospitality Administration/Management, A
Human Development and Family Studies, A
Human Resources Management and Services, A
Human Resources Management/Personnel Administration, A
Legal Assistant/Paralegal, A
Liberal Arts and Sciences Studies and Humanities, A
Logistics and Materials Management, A
Marketing, A
Marketing/Marketing Management, A
Mechanical Engineering/Mechanical Technology/Technician, A
Medical Radiologic Technology/Science - Radiation Therapist, A
Medical/Clinical Assistant, A
Mental and Social Health Services and Allied Professions, A
Multi-/Interdisciplinary Studies, A
Nuclear Medical Technology/Technologist, A
Parks, Recreation, Leisure and Fitness Studies, A
Purchasing, Procurement/Acquisitions and Contracts Management, A
Quality Control Technology/Technician, A
Real Estate, A
Rehabilitation and Therapeutic Professions, A
Respiratory Care Therapy/Therapist, A
Sign Language Interpretation and Translation, A
Sport and Fitness Administration/Management, A
Surgical Technology/Technologist, A
Tourism and Travel Services Management, A
Veterinary/Animal Health Technology/Technician and Veterinary Assistant, A

CUYAHOGA COMMUNITY COLLEGE

Accounting, A
Administrative Assistant and Secretarial Science, A
Automobile/Automotive Mechanics Technology/Technician, A
Avionics Maintenance Technology/Technician, A
Business Administration and Management, A
Clinical Laboratory Science/Medical Technology/Technologist, A
Commercial and Advertising Art, A
Computer Engineering Technology/Technician, A
Computer Typography and Composition Equipment Operator, A
Court Reporting/Court Reporter, A
Criminal Justice/Police Science, A
Engineering Technology, A
Finance, A
Fire Science/Firefighting, A
Industrial Radiologic Technology/Technician, A
Kindergarten/PreSchool Education and Teaching, A
Legal Assistant/Paralegal, A
Liberal Arts and Sciences Studies and Humanities, A
Marketing/Marketing Management, A
Merchandising and Buying Operations, A
Opticianry/Ophthalmic Dispensing Optician, A
Photography, A
Physician Assistant, A
Quality Control and Safety Technologies/Technicians, A
Real Estate, A
Respiratory Care Therapy/Therapist, A

Restaurant, Culinary, and Catering Management/Manager, A
Sales, Distribution and Marketing Operations, A
Selling Skills and Sales Operations, A
Surgical Technology/Technologist, A
Veterinary/Animal Health Technology/Technician and Veterinary Assistant, A

DAVIS COLLEGE

Accounting and Related Services, A
Administrative Assistant and Secretarial Science, A
Business Administration and Management, A
Business Operations Support and Secretarial Services, A
Computer Systems Networking and Telecommunications, A
Early Childhood Education and Teaching, A
Graphic Design, A
Interior Design, A
Marketing/Marketing Management, A
Medical Administrative Assistant/Secretary, A
Medical Insurance Coding Specialist/Coder, A
Medical/Clinical Assistant, A

DAYMAR COLLEGE

Administrative Assistant and Secretarial Science, A
Allied Health and Medical Assisting Services, A
Business Administration and Management, A
Criminal Justice/Law Enforcement Administration, A
Medical Administrative Assistant/Secretary, A

DEFIANCE COLLEGE

Accounting, B
Adult and Continuing Education and Teaching, M
Athletic Training and Sports Medicine, B
Biology/Biological Sciences, B
Business Administration and Management, AB
Business Administration, Management and Operations, M
Criminal Justice/Safety Studies, AB
Criminology, M
Ecology, B
Education, BM
Elementary Education and Teaching, B
English Language and Literature, B
Forensic Science and Technology, B
Graphic Design, AB
Health Services Administration, M
Health Teacher Education, B
History, B
Kinesiology and Exercise Science, B
Liberal Arts and Sciences Studies and Humanities, B
Management Strategy and Policy, M
Mass Communication/Media Studies, B
Mathematics, B
Natural Sciences, B
Physical Education Teaching and Coaching, B
Physical Sciences, B
Pre-Dentistry Studies, B
Pre-Law Studies, B
Pre-Medicine/Pre-Medical Studies, B
Pre-Veterinary Studies, B
Psychology, B
Religion/Religious Studies, B
Religious Education, B
Science Teacher Education/General Science Teacher Education, B
Secondary Education and Teaching, BM
Social Sciences, B
Social Work, B
Special Education and Teaching, M
Sport and Fitness Administration/Management, BM

DENISON UNIVERSITY

African-American/Black Studies, B
Anthropology, B
Art History, Criticism and Conservation, B
Art/Art Studies, General, B
Biochemistry, B
Biology/Biological Sciences, B
Chemistry, B
Classics and Classical Languages, Literatures, and Linguistics, B
Computer Science, B
Dance, B

Drama and Dramatics/Theatre Arts, B
East Asian Studies, B
Economics, B
English Language and Literature, B
Environmental Studies, B
Film/Cinema Studies, B
Fine/Studio Arts, B
French Language and Literature, B
Geology/Earth Science, B
German Language and Literature, B
History, B
International Business/Trade/Commerce, B
International Relations and Affairs, B
Latin American Studies, B
Mass Communication/Media Studies, B
Mathematics, B
Music, B
Philosophy, B
Physical Education Teaching and Coaching, B
Physics, B
Political Science and Government, B
Psychology, B
Religion/Religious Studies, B
Sociology, B
Spanish Language and Literature, B
Women's Studies, B

DEVRY UNIVERSITY (COLUMBUS)

Biomedical Technology/Technician, B
Business Administration and Management, B
Business Administration, Management and Operations, BM
Business/Commerce, B
Computer Engineering Technology/Technician, B
Computer Systems Analysis/Analyst, B
Computer Systems Networking and Telecommunications, AB
Electrical, Electronic and Communications Engineering Technology/Technician, AB
Health Information/Medical Records Technology/Technician, A
Web Page, Digital/Multimedia and Information Resources Design, AB

DEVRY UNIVERSITY (SEVEN HILLS)

Business Administration and Management, B
Business Administration, Management and Operations, BMO
Business/Commerce, B
Computer Systems Analysis/Analyst, B
Computer Systems Networking and Telecommunications, AB
Health Information/Medical Records Technology/Technician, A
Web Page, Digital/Multimedia and Information Resources Design, AB

EASTERN GATEWAY COMMUNITY COLLEGE

Accounting, A
Administrative Assistant and Secretarial Science, A
Business Administration and Management, A
Child Care and Support Services Management, A
Computer Engineering, A
Corrections, A
Criminal Justice/Police Science, A
Data Processing and Data Processing Technology/Technician, A
Dental Assisting/Assistant, A
Drafting and Design Technology/Technician, A
Electrical, Electronic and Communications Engineering Technology/Technician, A
Emergency Medical Technology/Technician (EMT Paramedic), A
Industrial Radiologic Technology/Technician, A
Industrial Technology/Technician, A
Legal Administrative Assistant/Secretary, A
Mechanical Engineering/Mechanical Technology/Technician, A
Medical Administrative Assistant/Secretary, A
Medical/Clinical Assistant, A
Real Estate, A

Respiratory Care Therapy/Therapist, A

EDISON COMMUNITY COLLEGE

Accounting, A
Art/Art Studies, General, A
Biology/Biological Sciences, A
Business Administration and Management, A
Child Development, A
Clinical/Medical Laboratory Technician, A
Communication Studies/Speech Communication
    and Rhetoric, A
Computer Programming/Programmer, A
Computer Systems Networking and Telecommunica-
    tions, A
Computer and Information Sciences, A
Computer and Information Systems Security, A
Criminal Justice/Police Science, A
Drama and Dramatics/Theatre Arts, A
Economics, A
Education, A
Electrical, Electronic and Communications Engineer-
    ing Technology/Technician, A
Electromechanical Technology/Electromechanical
    Engineering Technology, A
English Language and Literature, A
Executive Assistant/Executive Secretary, A
Geology/Earth Science, A
Health/Medical Preparatory Programs, A
History, A
Human Resources Management/Personnel Adminis-
    tration, A
Industrial Technology/Technician, A
Legal Assistant/Paralegal, A
Liberal Arts and Sciences Studies and Humani-
    ties, A
Manufacturing Technology/Technician, A
Marketing/Marketing Management, A
Mathematics, A
Mechanical Drafting and Mechanical Drafting
    CAD/CADD, A
Medical Administrative Assistant/Secretary, A
Medical/Clinical Assistant, A
Medium/Heavy Vehicle and Truck
    Technology/Technician, A
Philosophy and Religious Studies, A
Physical Therapist Assistant, A
Pre-Nursing Studies, A
Psychology, A
Social Work, A

ETI TECHNICAL COLLEGE OF NILES

Computer Programming, Specific Applications, A
Computer Software and Media Applications, A
Computer/Information Technology Services Adminis-
    tration and Management, A
Data Entry/Microcomputer Applications, A
Electrical and Electronic Engineering
    Technologies/Technicians, A
Electrical, Electronic and Communications Engineer-
    ing Technology/Technician, A
Legal Assistant/Paralegal, A
Medical/Clinical Assistant, A
Word Processing, A

FORTIS COLLEGE (CENTERVILLE)

Computer Engineering Technology/Technician, A
Computer Programming/Programmer, A
Computer Science, A
Electrical, Electronic and Communications Engineer-
    ing Technology/Technician, A
Legal Assistant/Paralegal, A
Medical/Clinical Assistant, A

FORTIS COLLEGE (CUYAHOGA FALLS)

Business Administration, Management and Opera-
    tions, A
Computer Technology/Computer Systems Technol-
    ogy, A
Computer and Information Sciences and Support
    Services, A
Corrections and Criminal Justice, A
Dental Assisting/Assistant, A
Medical Office Management/Administration, A

Medical/Clinical Assistant, A

FORTIS COLLEGE (RAVENNA)

Accounting, A
Business Administration and Management, A
Criminal Justice/Law Enforcement Administration, A
Executive Assistant/Executive Secretary, A
Heating, Air Conditioning, Ventilation and Refrigera-
    tion Maintenance Technology/Technician, A
Legal Administrative Assistant/Secretary, A
Marketing/Marketing Management, A
Medical Administrative Assistant/Secretary, A
Medical/Clinical Assistant, A

FRANCISCAN UNIVERSITY OF
STEUBENVILLE

Accounting, AB
Anthropology, B
Biology/Biological Sciences, B
Business Administration and Management, AB
Business Administration, Management and Opera-
    tions, M
Chemistry, B
Child Development, A
Classics and Classical Languages, Litera-
    tures, and Linguistics, B
Clinical Psychology, M
Communication Studies/Speech Communication
    and Rhetoric, B
Computer Science, B
Computer and Information Sciences, B
Counseling Psychology, M
Curriculum and Instruction, M
Drama and Dramatics/Theatre Arts, B
Economics, B
Education, M
Educational Administration and Supervision, M
Elementary Education and Teaching, B
English Language and Literature, B
French Language and Literature, B
General Studies, A
German Language and Literature, B
History, B
Humanities/Humanistic Studies, B
Mathematics, B
Nursing, M
Philosophy, BM
Political Science and Government, B
Psychology, B
Religious Education, B
Religious/Sacred Music, B
Social Work, B
Sociology, B
Spanish Language and Literature, B
Theology and Religious Vocations, M
Theology/Theological Studies, AB

FRANKLIN UNIVERSITY

Accounting, ABM
Accounting and Related Services, AB
Business Administration and Management, AB
Business Administration, Management and Opera-
    tions, BM
Computer Science, ABM
Computer and Information Systems Security, B
Corporate and Organizational Communication, M
Criminal Justice/Law Enforcement Administration, B
Digital Communication and Media/Multimedia, B
Economics, B
Educational Media/Instructional Technology, M
Entrepreneurship/Entrepreneurial Studies, B
Finance, AB
Financial Planning and Services, B
Health Information/Medical Records
    Technology/Technician, B
Health/Health Care Administration/Management, B
Human Resources Management/Personnel Adminis-
    tration, B
Information Technology, AB
Insurance, B
Management Information Systems and Services, B
Marketing, BM
Marketing/Marketing Management, B
Multi-/Interdisciplinary Studies, B
Operations Management and Supervision, B
Organizational Communication, AB

Public Administration, B
Public Relations/Image Management, AB
Security and Protective Services, B
Social Sciences, B
Web Page, Digital/Multimedia and Information Re-
    sources Design, B

GALLIPOLIS CAREER COLLEGE

Accounting, A
Administrative Assistant and Secretarial Science, A
Business Administration and Management, A
Business/Commerce, A
Computer Science, A
Computer Software and Media Applications, A
Computer and Information Sciences and Support
    Services, A
Data Entry/Microcomputer Applications, A
Medical Administrative Assistant/Secretary, A

GOD'S BIBLE SCHOOL AND COLLEGE

Bible/Biblical Studies, A
Business/Commerce, A
Elementary Education and Teaching, AB
Family and Community Services, B
General Studies, A
Missions/Missionary Studies and Missiology, AB
Music Teacher Education, B
Religious/Sacred Music, A
Secondary Education and Teaching, B
Theological and Ministerial Studies, B

HARRISON COLLEGE

Accounting, AB
Administrative Assistant and Secretarial Science, A
Banking and Financial Support Services, A
Business Administration and Management, AB
Criminal Justice/Law Enforcement Administration, A
Finance, A
Health/Health Care Administration/Management, B
Human Resources Management/Personnel Adminis-
    tration, AB
Manufacturing Technology/Technician, A
Marketing/Marketing Management, A
Medical Insurance Specialist/Medical Biller, A
Medical/Clinical Assistant, A

HEIDELBERG UNIVERSITY

Accounting, B
Athletic Training and Sports Medicine, B
Biology/Biological Sciences, B
Business Administration and Management, B
Business Administration, Management and Opera-
    tions, M
Chemistry, B
Community Psychology, M
Computer Science, B
Counseling Psychology, M
Criminal Justice/Police Science, B
Drama and Dramatics/Theatre Arts, B
Economics, B
Education, BM
Elementary Education and Teaching, B
English Language and Literature, B
Environmental Biology, B
Environmental Sciences, B
Environmental Studies, B
German Language and Literature, B
Health Services/Allied Health/Health Sciences, B
Health Teacher Education, B
Health/Health Care Administration/Management, B
History, B
Hydrology and Water Resources Science, B
Information Science/Studies, B
International Relations and Affairs, B
Mass Communication/Media Studies, B
Mathematics, B
Music, B
Music Teacher Education, BM
Philosophy, B
Physical Education Teaching and Coaching, B
Piano and Organ, B
Political Science and Government, B
Pre-Dentistry Studies, B
Pre-Law Studies, B
Pre-Medicine/Pre-Medical Studies, B
Pre-Veterinary Studies, B

Psychology, B
Public Administration, B
Public Relations/Image Management, B
Religion/Religious Studies, B
School Psychology, M
Science Teacher Education/General Science
  Teacher Education, B
Secondary Education and Teaching, B
Spanish Language and Literature, B
Special Education and Teaching, B
Violin, Viola, Guitar and Other Stringed Instru-
  ments, B
Voice and Opera, B

HIRAM COLLEGE

Accounting and Finance, B
Art History, Criticism and Conservation, B
Art/Art Studies, General, B
Biochemistry, B
Biological and Biomedical Sciences, B
Biology/Biological Sciences, B
Biomedical Sciences, B
Business Administration and Management, B
Chemistry, B
Communication Studies/Speech Communication
  and Rhetoric, B
Computer Science, B
Computer and Information Sciences, B
Drama and Dramatics/Theatre Arts, B
Economics, B
Education, B
English Language and Literature, B
Environmental Studies, B
Fine/Studio Arts, B
French Language and Literature, B
History, B
Interdisciplinary Studies, M
Mathematics, B
Music, B
Philosophy, B
Physics, B
Political Science and Government, B
Psychology, B
Religion/Religious Studies, B
Sociology, B
Spanish Language and Literature, B

HOCKING COLLEGE

Accounting, A
Business Administration and Management, A
Ceramic Sciences and Engineering, A
Child Development, A
Computer Engineering Technology/Technician, A
Computer Programming/Programmer, A
Computer Science, A
Corrections, A
Criminal Justice/Law Enforcement Administration, A
Criminal Justice/Police Science, A
Culinary Arts/Chef Training, A
Dietetics/Dieticians, A
Drafting and Design Technology/Technician, A
Ecology, A
Electrical, Electronic and Communications Engineer-
  ing Technology/Technician, A
Emergency Medical Technology/Technician (EMT
  Paramedic), A
Equestrian/Equine Studies, A
Fire Science/Firefighting, A
Fishing and Fisheries Sciences and Management, A
Food Science, A
Forestry, A
Forestry Technology/Technician, A
Health Information/Medical Records
  Administration/Administrator, A
Hospitality Administration/Management, A
Hotel/Motel Administration/Management, A
Industrial Technology/Technician, A
Land Use Planning and
  Management/Development, A
Marketing/Marketing Management, A
Medical Administrative Assistant/Secretary, A
Medical/Clinical Assistant, A
Natural Resources Management/Development and
  Policy, A
Natural Resources and Conservation, A
Ophthalmic Laboratory Technology/Technician, A

Physical Therapist Assistant, A
Tourism and Travel Services Management, A
Wildlife and Wildlands Science and Management, A

HONDROS COLLEGE

Real Estate, A
Selling Skills and Sales Operations, A

INTERNATIONAL COLLEGE OF BROADCASTING

Audiovisual Communications
  Technologies/Technicians, A
Radio and Television Broadcasting
  Technology/Technician, A

JAMES A. RHODES STATE COLLEGE

Accounting Technology/Technician and Bookkeep-
  ing, A
Administrative Assistant and Secretarial Science, A
Business, Management, Marketing, and Related
  Support Services, A
Child Development, A
Civil Engineering Technology/Technician, A
Computer Programming/Programmer, A
Computer Technology/Computer Systems Technol-
  ogy, A
Corrections, A
Criminal Justice/Police Science, A
Dental Hygiene/Hygienist, A
Drafting/Design Engineering
  Technologies/Technicians, A
Electrical, Electronic and Communications Engineer-
  ing Technology/Technician, A
Emergency Medical Technology/Technician (EMT
  Paramedic), A
Environmental Control Technologies/Technicians, A
Finance, A
Industrial Technology/Technician, A
Legal Assistant/Paralegal, A
Marketing/Marketing Management, A
Mechanical Engineering/Mechanical
  Technology/Technician, A
Medical Radiologic Technology/Science - Radiation
  Therapist, A
Medical/Clinical Assistant, A
Multi-/Interdisciplinary Studies, A
Occupational Therapist Assistant, A
Physical Therapy/Therapist, A
Quality Control Technology/Technician, A
Respiratory Care Therapy/Therapist, A
Robotics Technology/Technician, A
Social Work, A

JOHN CARROLL UNIVERSITY

Accounting, BM
Art History, Criticism and Conservation, B
Asian Studies/Civilization, B
Biological and Biomedical Sciences, M
Biological and Physical Sciences, B
Biology/Biological Sciences, B
Business Administration and Management, B
Business Administration, Management and Opera-
  tions, M
Chemistry, B
Classics and Classical Languages, Litera-
  tures, and Linguistics, B
Comparative Literature, B
Computer Science, B
Corporate and Organizational Communication, M
Counseling Psychology, MO
Counselor Education/School Counseling and Guid-
  ance Services, MO
Early Childhood Education and Teaching, M
East Asian Studies, B
Economics, B
Education, BM
Educational Administration and Supervision, M
Educational Psychology, M
Elementary Education and Teaching, B
Engineering Physics, B
English, M
English Language and Literature, B
Environmental Studies, B
Finance, B
French Language and Literature, B

German Language and Literature, B
Gerontology, B
History, BM
Human Resources Management/Personnel Adminis-
  tration, B
Humanities/Humanistic Studies, BM
International Business/Trade/Commerce, B
International Economics, B
International Relations and Affairs, B
Kindergarten/PreSchool Education and Teaching, B
Latin Language and Literature, B
Marketing/Marketing Management, B
Mass Communication/Media Studies, B
Mathematics, BM
Middle School Education, M
Modern Greek Language and Literature, B
Non-Profit/Public/Organizational Management, M
Peace Studies and Conflict Resolution, B
Philosophy, B
Physical Education Teaching and Coaching, B
Physics, B
Political Science and Government, B
Pre-Dentistry Studies, B
Pre-Law Studies, B
Pre-Medicine/Pre-Medical Studies, B
Pre-Veterinary Studies, B
Psychology, B
Public Administration, B
Religion/Religious Studies, BM
Religious Education, B
Science Teacher Education/General Science
  Teacher Education, M
Secondary Education and Teaching, BM
Sociology, B
Spanish Language and Literature, B
Special Education and Teaching, B
Teacher Education, Multiple Levels, B

KENT STATE UNIVERSITY

Accounting, BMD
Advertising, B
Advertising and Public Relations, M
Aeronautics/Aviation/Aerospace Science and Tech-
  nology, B
Aerospace, Aeronautical and Astronautical Engi-
  neering, B
African-American/Black Studies, B
Anthropology, BM
Applied Mathematics, BMD
Architecture, BM
Art Education, M
Art History, Criticism and Conservation, BM
Art Teacher Education, B
Athletic Training and Sports Medicine, BM
Audiology/Audiologist and Speech-Language
  Pathology/Pathologist, B
BioTechnology, B
Biological Anthropology, D
Biological and Biomedical Sciences, BMD
Biology/Biological Sciences, B
Botany/Plant Biology, B
Business Administration and Management, B
Business Administration, Management and Opera-
  tions, M
Business/Managerial Economics, B
Cell Biology and Anatomy, D
Chemical Physics, MD
Chemistry, BMD
Chemistry Teacher Education, B
Child and Family Studies, M
Clinical Laboratory Science/Medical
  Technology/Technologist, B
Clinical Nutrition/Nutritionist, B
Clinical Psychology, MD
Commercial and Advertising Art, B
Communication Disorders, MD
Communication Studies/Speech Communication
  and Rhetoric, B
Communication Theory, MD
Communication and Media Studies, MD
Composition, MO
Computer Education, M
Computer Science, MD
Computer Systems Analysis/Analyst, B
Computer and Information Sciences, B
Computer and Information Systems Security, MO

Construction Management, B
Counseling Psychology, M
Counselor Education/School Counseling and Guidance Services, MDO
Crafts, M
Crafts/Craft Design, Folk Art and Artisanry, B
Criminal Justice/Safety Studies, B
Curriculum and Instruction, MDO
Dance, B
Digital Communication and Media/Multimedia, B
Drama and Dramatics/Theatre Arts, B
Early Childhood Education and Teaching, BM
Ecology, MD
Economics, M
Education, BMDO
Education/Teaching of the Gifted and Talented, M
Educational Leadership and Administration, MDO
Educational Measurement and Evaluation, MD
Educational Media/Instructional Technology, MD
Educational Psychology, M
Engineering Technology, B
Engineering and Applied Sciences, M
English, MDO
English Education, M
English Language and Literature, B
English as a Second Language, MO
Entrepreneurship/Entrepreneurial Studies, B
Environmental Design/Architecture, M
Ethnomusicology, M
Exercise and Sports Science, MD
Experimental Psychology, MD
Fashion Merchandising, B
Fashion/Apparel Design, B
Finance, B
Finance and Banking, D
Fine Arts and Art Studies, M
Fine/Studio Arts, B
Foundations and Philosophy of Education, MD
French Language and Literature, B
General Studies, B
Genetics, D
Geography, BMD
Geology/Earth Science, BMD
German Language and Literature, B
Gerontological Nursing, MD
Graphic Design, M
Health Education, MD
Health Promotion, MD
Health Teacher Education, B
Health/Medical Preparatory Programs, B
Higher Education/Higher Education Administration, MDO
History, BMD
Hospitality Administration/Management, BM
Human Development, MD
Human Development and Family Studies, B
Human Services, MDO
Humanities/Humanistic Studies, B
Illustration, B
Industrial Engineering, B
Information Science/Studies, MO
Interior Design, B
International Relations and Affairs, B
Japanese Studies, M
Journalism, BM
Junior High/Intermediate/Middle School Education and Teaching, B
Kinesiology and Exercise Science, B
Language Interpretation and Translation, B
Legal Assistant/Paralegal, B
Liberal Studies, M
Library Science, MO
Marketing, D
Marketing/Marketing Management, B
Mass Communication/Media Studies, M
Mathematics, BMD
Mathematics Teacher Education, B
Middle School Education, M
Molecular Biology, D
Music, BMDO
Music Teacher Education, BMD
Music Theory and Composition, MD
Natural Resources and Conservation, B
Neuroscience, D
Nursing, MDO
Nursing - Adult, M

Nursing - Advanced Practice, MD
Nursing Administration, M
Nursing Education, MO
Nutritional Sciences, M
Parks, Recreation and Leisure Facilities Management, B
Peace Studies and Conflict Resolution, B
Pediatric Nurse/Nursing, MO
Performance, MO
Pharmacology, M
Philosophy, BM
Photojournalism, B
Physical Education Teaching and Coaching, B
Physics, BMD
Physiology, MD
Podiatric Medicine, D
Political Science and Government, BMD
Psychiatric/Mental Health Nurse/Nursing, M
Psychology, BMD
Public Administration, M
Public Health (MPH, DPH), B
Public Relations/Image Management, B
Radio and Television, B
Reading Teacher Education, M
Recreation and Park Management, M
Rehabilitation Counseling, M
Rhetoric, D
Russian Language and Literature, BM
Russian Studies, B
School Psychology, MDO
Science Teacher Education/General Science Teacher Education, B
Secondary Education and Teaching, M
Sign Language Interpretation and Translation, B
Social Studies Teacher Education, B
Sociology, BMD
Spanish Language and Literature, B
Special Education and Teaching, BMDO
Sport and Fitness Administration/Management, BM
Student Personnel Services, M
System Management, D
Teaching English as a Second or Foreign Language/ESL Language Instructor, B
Theater, M
Translation and Interpretation, MD
Travel and Tourism, M
Urban Design, M
Visual and Performing Arts, B
Vocational and Technical Education, M
Women's Health Nursing, MO
Writing, M
Zoology/Animal Biology, B

KENT STATE UNIVERSITY AT ASHTABULA

Accounting Technology/Technician and Bookkeeping, A
Administrative Assistant and Secretarial Science, A
Aerospace, Aeronautical and Astronautical Engineering, A
Business Administration and Management, B
Business/Commerce, A
Communication Studies/Speech Communication and Rhetoric, B
Computer Programming, Specific Applications, A
Criminal Justice/Safety Studies, AB
English Language and Literature, B
General Studies, B
Health and Medical Administrative Services, A
Health/Medical Preparatory Programs, B
Hospitality Administration/Management, B
Liberal Arts and Sciences Studies and Humanities, AB
Medical Radiologic Technology/Science - Radiation Therapist, A
Occupational Therapist Assistant, A
Physical Therapist Assistant, A
Psychology, B
Respiratory Care Therapy/Therapist, AB
Sociology, B

KENT STATE UNIVERSITY AT EAST LIVERPOOL

Accounting Technology/Technician and Bookkeeping, A
Business/Commerce, A

Communication Studies/Speech Communication and Rhetoric, B
Computer Programming, Specific Applications, A
Criminal Justice/Safety Studies, AB
English Language and Literature, B
General Studies, B
Legal Assistant/Paralegal, A
Liberal Arts and Sciences Studies and Humanities, AB
Occupational Therapist Assistant, A
Physical Therapist Assistant, A
Psychology, B

KENT STATE UNIVERSITY AT GEAUGA

Accounting Technology/Technician and Bookkeeping, A
Business Administration and Management, B
Business/Commerce, A
Computer Programming, Specific Applications, A
English Language and Literature, B
General Studies, B
Junior High/Intermediate/Middle School Education and Teaching, B
Liberal Arts and Sciences Studies and Humanities, AB
Psychology, B

KENT STATE UNIVERSITY AT SALEM

Accounting Technology/Technician and Bookkeeping, A
Administrative Assistant and Secretarial Science, A
Applied Horticulture/Horticultural Operations, AB
Biological and Biomedical Sciences, B
Business Administration and Management, B
Business/Commerce, A
Communication Studies/Speech Communication and Rhetoric, B
Computer Programming, Specific Applications, A
Criminal Justice/Safety Studies, AB
Early Childhood Education and Teaching, B
Education, B
English Language and Literature, B
General Studies, B
Health and Medical Administrative Services, A
Human Development and Family Studies, B
Insurance, B
Liberal Arts and Sciences Studies and Humanities, AB
Medical Radiologic Technology/Science - Radiation Therapist, AB
Psychology, B

KENT STATE UNIVERSITY AT STARK

Biology/Biological Sciences, B
Business Administration and Management, B
Business Administration, Management and Operations, M
Communication Studies/Speech Communication and Rhetoric, B
Criminal Justice/Safety Studies, AB
Curriculum and Instruction, M
Education, M
English Language and Literature, B
General Studies, B
History, B
Human Development and Family Studies, B
Junior High/Intermediate/Middle School Education and Teaching, B
Liberal Arts and Sciences Studies and Humanities, AB
Marketing/Marketing Management, B
Mathematics, B
Music, B
Psychology, B
Sociology, B
Visual and Performing Arts, B

KENT STATE UNIVERSITY AT TRUMBULL

Accounting Technology/Technician and Bookkeeping, A
Administrative Assistant and Secretarial Science, A
Business Administration and Management, B
Business/Commerce, A

Communication Studies/Speech Communication
and Rhetoric, B
Computer Programming, Specific Applications, A
Criminal Justice/Safety Studies, AB
Electrical and Electronic Engineering
Technologies/Technicians, A
Emergency Medical Technology/Technician (EMT
Paramedic), A
English Language and Literature, B
Environmental Engineering
Technology/Environmental Technology, A
General Studies, B
Health/Health Care Administration/Management, A
Industrial Production Technologies/Technicians, A
Industrial Technology/Technician, A
Legal Assistant/Paralegal, A
Liberal Arts and Sciences Studies and Humani-
ties, AB
Mechanical Engineering/Mechanical
Technology/Technician, A
Psychology, B
Public Health (MPH, DPH), B
Urban Forestry, A

KENT STATE UNIVERSITY AT TUSCARAWAS

Accounting Technology/Technician and Bookkeep-
ing, A
Administrative Assistant and Secretarial Science, A
Agribusiness, B
Business Administration and Management, B
Business/Commerce, A
CAD/CADD Drafting and/or Design
Technology/Technician, A
Communication Studies/Speech Communication
and Rhetoric, B
Computer Programming, Specific Applications, A
Criminal Justice/Safety Studies, AB
Early Childhood Education and Teaching, B
Education, A
Electrical and Electronic Engineering
Technologies/Technicians, A
Engineering Technology, B
English Language and Literature, B
General Studies, B
Industrial Technology/Technician, A
Liberal Arts and Sciences Studies and Humani-
ties, AB
Mechanical Engineering/Mechanical
Technology/Technician, A
Psychology, B
Veterinary/Animal Health Technology/Technician and
Veterinary Assistant, A

KENYON COLLEGE

American/United States Studies/Civilization, B
Ancient/Classical Greek Language and Literature, B
Anthropology, B
Art History, Criticism and Conservation, B
Asian Studies/Civilization, B
Biochemistry, B
Biology/Biological Sciences, B
Chemistry, B
Classics and Classical Languages, Litera-
tures, and Linguistics, B
Dance, B
Drama and Dramatics/Theatre Arts, B
Economics, B
English Language and Literature, B
Film/Cinema Studies, B
Fine Arts and Art Studies, B
Fine/Studio Arts, B
Foreign Languages and Literatures, B
French Language and Literature, B
German Language and Literature, B
History, B
International/Global Studies, B
Latin Language and Literature, B
Mathematics, B
Molecular Biology, B
Multi-/Interdisciplinary Studies, B
Music, B
Philosophy, B
Physics, B
Political Science and Government, B
Psychology, B

Religion/Religious Studies, B
Sociology, B
Spanish Language and Literature, B
Women's Studies, B

KETTERING COLLEGE

General Studies, A
Health Professions and Related Clinical Sciences, B
Nuclear Medical Technology/Technologist, A
Physician Assistant, ABM
Pre-Medicine/Pre-Medical Studies, B
Radiologic Technology/Science - Radiographer, AB
Respiratory Care Therapy/Therapist, AB

LAKE ERIE COLLEGE

Accounting, B
Biology/Biological Sciences, B
Business Administration and Management, B
Business Administration, Management and Opera-
tions, M
Chemistry, B
Communication, Journalism and Related Pro-
grams, B
Criminal Justice/Law Enforcement Administration, B
Early Childhood Education and Teaching, B
Education, M
English Language and Literature, B
Entrepreneurship/Entrepreneurial Studies, B
Equestrian/Equine Studies, B
Farm/Farm and Ranch Management, B
Finance, B
Fine Arts and Art Studies, B
Foreign Languages and Literatures, B
French Language and Literature, B
Health Services Administration, M
History, B
Human Resources Management/Personnel Adminis-
tration, B
International Business/Trade/Commerce, B
Italian Language and Literature, B
Legal Assistant/Paralegal, B
Management, M
Marketing/Marketing Management, B
Mathematics, B
Multi-/Interdisciplinary Studies, B
Political Science and Government, B
Psychology, B
Secondary Education and Teaching, B
Social Sciences, B
Spanish Language and Literature, B
Special Education and Teaching, B
Sport and Fitness Administration/Management, B

LAKELAND COMMUNITY COLLEGE

Accounting, A
Administrative Assistant and Secretarial Science, A
BioTechnology, A
Business Administration and Management, A
Child Care Provider/Assistant, A
Civil Engineering Technology/Technician, A
Clinical/Medical Laboratory Technician, A
Commercial and Advertising Art, A
Computer Engineering Technology/Technician, A
Computer Programming, Specific Applications, A
Computer Systems Analysis/Analyst, A
Computer Systems Networking and Telecommunica-
tions, A
Computer Technology/Computer Systems Technol-
ogy, A
Corrections, A
Criminal Justice/Police Science, A
Dental Hygiene/Hygienist, A
Electrical, Electronic and Communications Engineer-
ing Technology/Technician, A
Energy Management and Systems
Technology/Technician, A
Fire Protection and Safety Technology/Technician, A
Health Professions and Related Clinical Sciences, A
Hospitality Administration/Management, A
Instrumentation Technology/Technician, A
Legal Assistant/Paralegal, A
Liberal Arts and Sciences Studies and Humani-
ties, A
Management Information Systems and Services, A
Marketing/Marketing Management, A

Mechanical Engineering/Mechanical
Technology/Technician, A
Medical Radiologic Technology/Science - Radiation
Therapist, A
Nuclear Medical Technology/Technologist, A
Ophthalmic Technician/Technologist, A
Quality Control Technology/Technician, A
Respiratory Care Therapy/Therapist, A
Restaurant, Culinary, and Catering
Management/Manager, A
Security and Protective Services, A
Sign Language Interpretation and Translation, A
Social Work, A
Surgical Technology/Technologist, A
Tourism and Travel Services Management, A

LORAIN COUNTY COMMUNITY COL-LEGE

Accounting, A
Administrative Assistant and Secretarial Science, A
Art/Art Studies, General, A
Artificial Intelligence and Robotics, A
Athletic Training and Sports Medicine, A
Biological and Physical Sciences, A
Biology/Biological Sciences, A
Business Administration and Management, A
Chemistry, A
Civil Engineering Technology/Technician, A
Clinical/Medical Laboratory Technician, A
Computer Engineering Technology/Technician, A
Computer Programming, A
Computer Programming, Specific Applications, A
Computer Programming, Vendor/Product Certifica-
tion, A
Computer Programming/Programmer, A
Computer Science, A
Computer Systems Networking and Telecommunica-
tions, A
Computer Technology/Computer Systems Technol-
ogy, A
Computer and Information Sciences, A
Consumer Merchandising/Retailing Management, A
Corrections, A
Cosmetology and Related Personal Grooming
Arts, A
Cosmetology/Cosmetologist, A
Criminal Justice/Police Science, A
Data Entry/Microcomputer Applications, A
Diagnostic Medical Sonography/Sonographer and
Ultrasound Technician, A
Drafting and Design Technology/Technician, A
Drafting/Design Engineering
Technologies/Technicians, A
Drama and Dramatics/Theatre Arts, A
Education, A
Electrical, Electronic and Communications Engineer-
ing Technology/Technician, A
Elementary Education and Teaching, A
Engineering, A
Engineering Technology, A
Finance, A
Fire Science/Firefighting, A
History, A
Human Services, A
Industrial Radiologic Technology/Technician, A
Industrial Technology/Technician, A
Information Science/Studies, A
Information Technology, A
Journalism, A
Kindergarten/PreSchool Education and Teaching, A
Liberal Arts and Sciences Studies and Humani-
ties, A
Machine Tool Technology/Machinist, A
Marketing/Marketing Management, A
Mass Communication/Media Studies, A
Mathematics, A
Music, A
Nuclear Medical Technology/Technologist, A
Pharmacy, A
Physical Education Teaching and Coaching, A
Physical Therapist Assistant, A
Physics, A
Plastics Engineering Technology/Technician, A
Political Science and Government, A
Psychology, A
Quality Control Technology/Technician, A

Real Estate, A
Social Sciences, A
Social Work, A
Sociology, A
Sport and Fitness Administration/Management, A
Surgical Technology/Technologist, A
Tourism and Travel Services Management, A
Urban Studies/Affairs, A
Word Processing, A

LOURDES UNIVERSITY

Accounting, B
Accounting and Finance, B
Art History, Criticism and Conservation, B
Art/Art Studies, General, AB
Biology/Biological Sciences, AB
Business Administration and Management, B
Business Administration, Management and Operations, M
Business/Commerce, AB
Criminal Justice/Safety Studies, AB
Curriculum and Instruction, M
Early Childhood Education and Teaching, B
Educational Leadership and Administration, M
English Language and Literature, AB
Environmental Sciences, B
Health/Health Care Administration/Management, B
History, AB
Human Resources Management/Personnel Administration, B
Junior High/Intermediate/Middle School Education and Teaching, B
Liberal Arts and Sciences Studies and Humanities, A
Management Science, B
Marketing, B
Multi-/Interdisciplinary Studies, B
Natural Sciences, B
Nurse Anesthetist, M
Nursing Administration, M
Nursing Education, M
Organizational Management, M
Psychology, B
Public Health, B
Reading Teacher Education, M
Religion/Religious Studies, AB
Secondary Education and Teaching, B
Social Work, B
Sociology, AB
Theology and Religious Vocations, M

MALONE UNIVERSITY

Accounting, B
Bible/Biblical Studies, B
Biochemistry, B
Biology/Biological Sciences, B
Business Administration and Management, B
Business Administration, Management and Operations, BM
Chemistry, B
Clinical Laboratory Science/Medical Technology/Technologist, B
Communication, Journalism and Related Programs, B
Computer Science, B
Counselor Education/School Counseling and Guidance Services, M
Crafts/Craft Design, Folk Art and Artisanry, B
Curriculum and Instruction, M
Early Childhood Education and Teaching, B
Education, M
Education/Teaching of Individuals with Specific Learning Disabilities, B
Educational Leadership and Administration, M
English Language and Literature, B
English/Language Arts Teacher Education, B
Finance, B
Graphic Design, B
Health/Health Care Administration/Management, B
History, B
International/Global Studies, B
Junior High/Intermediate/Middle School Education and Teaching, B
Kinesiology and Exercise Science, B
Liberal Arts and Sciences Studies and Humanities, B

Marketing/Marketing Management, B
Mathematics, B
Music, B
Music Teacher Education, B
Natural Resource Economics, B
Nursing, M
Nursing - Advanced Practice, M
Organizational Management, M
Pastoral Counseling and Specialized Ministries, B
Philosophy, B
Political Science and Government, B
Psychology, B
Public Health Education and Promotion, B
Recording Arts Technology/Technician, B
Religious Education, B
Religious/Sacred Music, B
Science Teacher Education/General Science Teacher Education, B
Social Studies Teacher Education, B
Social Work, B
Special Education and Teaching, M
Sport and Fitness Administration/Management, B
Theology and Religious Vocations, M
Youth Ministry, B
Zoology/Animal Biology, B

MARIETTA COLLEGE

Accounting, B
Art/Art Studies, General, B
Asian Studies/Civilization, B
Athletic Training and Sports Medicine, B
Biochemistry, B
Biology/Biological Sciences, B
Business Administration and Management, AB
Business/Corporate Communications, B
Chemistry, B
Commercial and Advertising Art, B
Communication Studies/Speech Communication and Rhetoric, B
Computer Science, B
Drama and Dramatics/Theatre Arts, B
Economics, B
Education, B
Elementary Education and Teaching, B
English Language and Literature, B
Environmental Sciences, B
Environmental Studies, B
Finance, B
Fine/Studio Arts, B
Geology/Earth Science, B
Graphic Design, B
History, B
Information Science/Studies, B
International Business/Trade/Commerce, B
Journalism, B
Liberal Arts and Sciences Studies and Humanities, AB
Marketing/Marketing Management, B
Mathematics, B
Music, B
Music Teacher Education, B
Natural Resources Management/Development and Policy, B
Petroleum Engineering, B
Philosophy, B
Physician Assistant, M
Physics, B
Political Science and Government, B
Psychology, BM
Public Relations, Advertising, and Applied Communication, B
Radio and Television, B
Secondary Education and Teaching, B
Spanish Language and Literature, B
Sport and Fitness Administration/Management, B

MARION TECHNICAL COLLEGE

Accounting, A
Administrative Assistant and Secretarial Science, A
Business Administration and Management, A
Clinical/Medical Laboratory Technician, A
Computer Programming, Vendor/Product Certification, A
Computer Software and Media Applications, A
Computer Systems Networking and Telecommunications, A

Drafting and Design Technology/Technician, A
Electrical, Electronic and Communications Engineering Technology/Technician, A
Engineering Technology, A
Human Services, A
Information Technology, A
Marketing/Marketing Management, A
Mechanical Engineering/Mechanical Technology/Technician, A
Medical Administrative Assistant/Secretary, A
Physical Therapist Assistant, A
Radiologic Technology/Science - Radiographer, A
Social Work, A

MERCY COLLEGE OF OHIO

Biology/Biological Sciences, B
Cardiovascular Technology/Technologist, A
General Studies, A
Health Information/Medical Records Technology/Technician, A
Health Services/Allied Health/Health Sciences, B
Health/Health Care Administration/Management, B
Medical Radiologic Technology/Science - Radiation Therapist, A

MIAMI-JACOBS CAREER COLLEGE (DAYTON)

Business Administration and Management, A
Criminal Justice/Law Enforcement Administration, A
Massage Therapy/Therapeutic Massage, A
Medical Administrative Assistant/Secretary, A
Medical/Clinical Assistant, A
Surgical Technology/Technologist, A

MIAMI-JACOBS CAREER COLLEGE (INDEPENDENCE)

Allied Health and Medical Assisting Services, A
Court Reporting/Court Reporter, A
Criminal Justice/Law Enforcement Administration, A
Health Information/Medical Records Administration/Administrator, A
Legal Administrative Assistant/Secretary, A
Legal Assistant/Paralegal, A
Security and Loss Prevention Services, A

MIAMI UNIVERSITY

Accounting, BM
Accounting Technology/Technician and Bookkeeping, A
Administrative Assistant and Secretarial Science, A
African-American/Black Studies, B
American/United States Studies/Civilization, B
Anthropology, B
Architecture, BM
Art Education, M
Art History, Criticism and Conservation, B
Art Teacher Education, B
Art/Art Studies, General, B
Athletic Training and Sports Medicine, B
Audiology/Audiologist and Speech-Language Pathology/Pathologist, B
Biochemistry, BMD
Biological and Biomedical Sciences, MD
Biology Teacher Education, B
Biology/Biological Sciences, B
Biomedical/Medical Engineering, B
Biophysics, B
Botany/Plant Biology, B
Business Administration and Management, B
Business Administration, Management and Operations, M
Business/Commerce, A
Business/Managerial Economics, B
Chemical Engineering, BM
Chemistry, BMD
Chemistry Teacher Education, B
Child and Family Studies, M
City/Urban, Community and Regional Planning, B
Classics and Classical Languages, Literatures, and Linguistics, B
Clinical Laboratory Science/Medical Technology/Technologist, B
Commercial and Advertising Art, B
Communication Disorders, M
Community Organization and Advocacy, B

Computational Sciences, M
Computer Engineering, B
Computer Software Engineering, B
Computer and Information Sciences, B
Criminal Justice/Law Enforcement Administration, AB
Data Processing and Data Processing Technology/Technician, A
Demography and Population Studies, M
Dietetics/Dieticians, B
Digital Communication and Media/Multimedia, B
Drama and Dramatics/Theatre Arts, B
Early Childhood Education and Teaching, B
East Asian Studies, B
Economics, BM
Education, MDO
Educational Psychology, MO
Electrical, Electronics and Communications Engineering, B
Engineering, B
Engineering Physics, B
Engineering Technology, AB
Engineering and Applied Sciences, M
Engineering/Industrial Management, B
English, MD
English Language and Literature, B
English/Language Arts Teacher Education, B
Environmental Sciences, BM
Exercise and Sports Science, M
Finance, B
Fine Arts and Art Studies, M
Foreign Language Teacher Education, B
Forensic Science and Technology, B
French Language Teacher Education, B
French Language and Literature, BM
General Studies, A
Geography, BM
Geology/Earth Science, BMD
German Language Teacher Education, B
German Language and Literature, B
Gerontology, BMD
Health and Physical Education, B
History, BM
Human Development and Family Studies, B
Information Technology, B
Interior Architecture, B
International Relations and Affairs, B
Italian Studies, B
Journalism, B
Junior High/Intermediate/Middle School Education and Teaching, B
Kindergarten/PreSchool Education and Teaching, A
Kinesiology and Exercise Science, B
Latin American Studies, B
Latin Teacher Education, B
Liberal Arts and Sciences Studies and Humanities, B
Linguistics, B
Management Information Systems and Services, B
Management Science, B
Management Sciences and Quantitative Methods, B
Manufacturing Engineering, B
Marketing/Marketing Management, AB
Mass Communication/Media Studies, B
Mathematics, BM
Mathematics Teacher Education, BM
Mechanical Engineering, B
Mechanical Engineering/Mechanical Technology/Technician, A
Microbiology, BMD
Multi-/Interdisciplinary Studies, A
Music, B
Music Performance, B
Music Teacher Education, BM
Natural Resources Conservation and Research, B
Office Management and Supervision, A
Operations Management and Supervision, B
Performance, M
Philosophy, BM
Physics, BM
Political Science and Government, BM
Pre-Medicine/Pre-Medical Studies, B
Psychology, BMD
Public Administration, B
Public Relations/Image Management, B
Religion/Religious Studies, B

Science Teacher Education/General Science Teacher Education, B
Social Studies Teacher Education, B
Social Work, B
Sociology, B
Spanish Language Teacher Education, B
Spanish Language and Literature, B
Special Education and Teaching, B
Sport and Fitness Administration/Management, B
Statistics, BM
Systems Science and Theory, M
Theater, M
Women's Studies, B
Zoology/Animal Biology, B

MIAMI UNIVERSITY HAMILTON

Accounting, B
American/United States Studies/Civilization, B
Anthropology, B
Architectural History and Criticism, B
Architecture, B
Art Teacher Education, B
Art/Art Studies, General, B
Athletic Training and Sports Medicine, B
Audiology/Audiologist and Speech-Language Pathology/Pathologist, B
Biochemistry, B
Botany/Plant Biology, B
Business Administration and Management, A
Business Administration, Management and Operations, B
Business/Commerce, B
Business/Managerial Economics, B
Chemistry, B
Chemistry Teacher Education, B
City/Urban, Community and Regional Planning, B
Classics and Classical Languages, Literatures, and Linguistics, B
Clinical Laboratory Science/Medical Technology/Technologist, B
Communication Studies/Speech Communication and Rhetoric, B
Computer Engineering, B
Computer Science, B
Computer Systems Analysis/Analyst, B
Computer Technology/Computer Systems Technology, A
Computer and Information Sciences, B
Dietetics/Dieticians, B
Early Childhood Education and Teaching, B
Econometrics and Quantitative Economics, B
Economics, B
Electrical and Electronic Engineering Technologies/Technicians, A
Electromechanical Technology/Electromechanical Engineering Technology, B
Engineering Physics, B
Engineering Technology, B
Engineering/Industrial Management, B
English Language and Literature, B
English/Language Arts Teacher Education, B
Environmental Sciences, B
Environmental Studies, B
Ethnic, Cultural Minority, and Gender Studies, B
Exercise Physiology, B
Finance, B
French Language Teacher Education, B
French Language and Literature, B
General Studies, A
Geography, B
Geology/Earth Science, B
German Language Teacher Education, B
German Language and Literature, B
Gerontology, B
Graphic Design, B
Health Teacher Education, B
History, B
Human Resources Management and Services, B
Interior Design, B
International/Global Studies, B
Journalism, B
Latin Language and Literature, B
Latin Teacher Education, B
Linguistics, B
Management Information Systems and Services, A
Marketing, B

Marketing/Marketing Management, A
Mass Communication/Media Studies, B
Mathematics, B
Mathematics Teacher Education, B
Mathematics and Statistics, B
Mechanical Engineering/Mechanical Technology/Technician, AB
Microbiology, B
Multi-/Interdisciplinary Studies, B
Music, B
Music Teacher Education, B
Office Management and Supervision, B
Philosophy, B
Physical Education Teaching and Coaching, B
Physics, B
Physics Teacher Education, B
Political Science and Government, B
Psychology, B
Public Administration, B
Purchasing, Procurement/Acquisitions and Contracts Management, A
Real Estate, A
Russian Language and Literature, B
Science Teacher Education/General Science Teacher Education, B
Social Studies Teacher Education, B
Social Work, B
Sociology, B
Spanish Language Teacher Education, B
Spanish Language and Literature, B
Special Education and Teaching, B
Speech-Language Pathology/Pathologist, B
Statistics, B
Teacher Education, Multiple Levels, B
Work and Family Studies, B
Zoology/Animal Biology, B

MIAMI UNIVERSITY MIDDLETOWN

Accounting, A
Administrative Assistant and Secretarial Science, A
Anthropology, A
Art/Art Studies, General, A
Biological and Physical Sciences, A
Botany/Plant Biology, A
Business Administration and Management, A
Business/Commerce, A
Business/Managerial Economics, A
Chemical Engineering, A
Chemistry, A
Communication Studies/Speech Communication and Rhetoric, A
Computer Engineering Technology/Technician, A
Computer Science, A
Computer and Information Sciences, A
Economics, A
Education, A
Electrical, Electronic and Communications Engineering Technology/Technician, A
Electromechanical Technology/Electromechanical Engineering Technology, A
Elementary Education and Teaching, A
Engineering, A
English Language and Literature, A
Geography, A
History, A
Industrial Technology/Technician, A
Information Science/Studies, A
Kindergarten/PreSchool Education and Teaching, A
Legal Administrative Assistant/Secretary, A
Liberal Arts and Sciences Studies and Humanities, A
Management Information Systems and Services, A
Marketing/Marketing Management, A
Mass Communication/Media Studies, A
Mathematics, A
Mechanical Engineering/Mechanical Technology/Technician, A
Medical Administrative Assistant/Secretary, A
Office Management and Supervision, A
Philosophy, A
Physics, A
Political Science and Government, A
Psychology, A
Real Estate, A
Social Sciences, A
Social Work, A

Sociology, A
Spanish Language and Literature, A
Systems Science and Theory, A
Zoology/Animal Biology, A

MOUNT CARMEL COLLEGE OF NURSING

Acute Care/Critical Care Nursing, M
Gerontological Nursing, M
Nursing, M
Nursing - Adult, M
Nursing - Advanced Practice, M
Nursing Administration, M
Nursing Education, M

MOUNT ST. JOSEPH UNIVERSITY

Accounting, AB
Art Teacher Education, B
Art/Art Studies, General, AB
Athletic Training and Sports Medicine, B
Biochemistry, B
Biology/Biological Sciences, B
Business Administration and Management, AB
Business Administration, Management and Operations, M
Chemistry, B
Communication Studies/Speech Communication and Rhetoric, AB
Criminology, B
Design and Visual Communications, B
Early Childhood Education and Teaching, BM
Education, BMO
Educational Leadership and Administration, M
English Language and Literature, B
General Studies, AB
Graphic Design, AB
Health Promotion, O
Health Services Administration, D
History, B
Interior Architecture, B
Junior High/Intermediate/Middle School Education and Teaching, M
Legal Assistant/Paralegal, AB
Mathematics, B
Medical Informatics, B
Middle School Education, M
Multilingual and Multicultural Education, M
Music, B
Nursing, MD
Nursing Administration, M
Nursing Education, M
Organizational Behavior Studies, B
Organizational Management, M
Pastoral Studies/Counseling, O
Physical Therapy/Therapist, D
Psychology, B
Reading Teacher Education, MO
Religion/Religious Studies, BM
Secondary Education and Teaching, M
Social Work, B
Sociology, B
Special Education and Teaching, BO
Sport and Fitness Administration/Management, B
Theology and Religious Vocations, MO

MOUNT VERNON NAZARENE UNIVERSITY

Accounting, B
Administrative Assistant and Secretarial Science, B
Art Teacher Education, B
Art/Art Studies, General, B
Bible/Biblical Studies, B
Biology Teacher Education, B
Biology/Biological Sciences, B
Broadcast Journalism, B
Business Administration and Management, B
Business Teacher Education, B
Business/Commerce, AB
Business/Office Automation/Technology/Data Entry, B
Chemistry, B
Chemistry Teacher Education, B
Clinical Laboratory Science/Medical Technology/Technologist, B
Communication Disorders, B

Communication Studies/Speech Communication and Rhetoric, B
Computer Science, B
Computer Systems Networking and Telecommunications, B
Criminal Justice/Law Enforcement Administration, B
Criminal Justice/Safety Studies, B
Drama and Dramatics/Theatre Arts, B
Early Childhood Education and Teaching, B
Education, BM
Electrical, Electronics and Communications Engineering, B
English Language and Literature, B
English/Language Arts Teacher Education, B
Finance, B
General Studies, A
Graphic Design, B
Health and Physical Education/Fitness, B
History, B
History Teacher Education, B
International Business/Trade/Commerce, B
Journalism, B
Junior High/Intermediate/Middle School Education and Teaching, B
Kinesiology and Exercise Science, B
Management, M
Management Information Systems and Services, B
Marketing/Marketing Management, B
Mathematics, B
Mathematics Teacher Education, B
Mechanical Engineering, B
Missions/Missionary Studies and Missiology, B
Music, AB
Music Performance, B
Music Teacher Education, B
Pastoral Studies/Counseling, B
Philosophy, B
Physical Sciences, B
Physics Teacher Education, B
Political Science and Government, B
Pre-Dentistry Studies, B
Pre-Law Studies, B
Pre-Medicine/Pre-Medical Studies, B
Pre-Pharmacy Studies, B
Pre-Veterinary Studies, B
Psychology, B
Public Relations/Image Management, B
Religion/Religious Studies, AB
Religious Education, B
Religious/Sacred Music, AB
Science Teacher Education/General Science Teacher Education, B
Social Studies Teacher Education, B
Social Work, B
Spanish Language Teacher Education, B
Spanish Language and Literature, B
Special Education and Teaching, B
Sport and Fitness Administration/Management, AB
Theology and Religious Vocations, M
Theology/Theological Studies, B
Youth Ministry, B

MUSKINGUM UNIVERSITY

Accounting, B
American/United States Studies/Civilization, B
Anthropology, B
Art Teacher Education, B
Art/Art Studies, General, B
Biology/Biological Sciences, B
Business Administration and Management, B
Chemistry, B
Clinical Laboratory Science/Medical Technology/Technologist, B
Computer Science, B
Criminal Justice/Law Enforcement Administration, B
Design and Visual Communications, B
Digital Communication and Media/Multimedia, B
Drama and Dramatics/Theatre Arts, B
Early Childhood Education and Teaching, B
Economics, B
Education, BM
Engineering Science, B
English Language and Literature, B
Environmental Sciences, B
Environmental Studies, B
French Language Teacher Education, B

French Language and Literature, B
Geology/Earth Science, B
German Language Teacher Education, B
German Language and Literature, B
Health Teacher Education, B
History, B
Humanities/Humanistic Studies, B
International Business/Trade/Commerce, B
International Relations and Affairs, B
Journalism, B
Junior High/Intermediate/Middle School Education and Teaching, B
Mathematics, B
Molecular Biology, B
Music, B
Music Teacher Education, B
Natural Resources and Conservation, B
Philosophy, B
Physical Education Teaching and Coaching, B
Physical Therapy/Therapist, B
Physics, B
Political Science and Government, B
Pre-Dentistry Studies, B
Pre-Law Studies, B
Pre-Medicine/Pre-Medical Studies, B
Pre-Pharmacy Studies, B
Pre-Veterinary Studies, B
Psychology, B
Public Policy Analysis, B
Religion/Religious Studies, B
Sociology, B
Spanish Language Teacher Education, B
Spanish Language and Literature, B
Special Education and Teaching, B

NORTH CENTRAL STATE COLLEGE

Accounting, A
Administrative Assistant and Secretarial Science, A
Business Administration and Management, A
Business/Commerce, A
Child Development, A
Communication, Journalism and Related Programs, A
Communications Technologies/Technicians and Support Services, A
Computer Science, A
Computer/Information Technology Services Administration and Management, A
Criminal Justice/Law Enforcement Administration, A
Drafting and Design Technology/Technician, A
Electrical, Electronic and Communications Engineering Technology/Technician, A
Electromechanical Technology/Electromechanical Engineering Technology, A
Heating, Air Conditioning, Ventilation and Refrigeration Maintenance Technology/Technician, A
Legal Assistant/Paralegal, A
Mechanical Drafting and Mechanical Drafting CAD/CADD, A
Mechanical Engineering/Mechanical Technology/Technician, A
Medical Radiologic Technology/Science - Radiation Therapist, A
Multi-/Interdisciplinary Studies, A
Physical Therapist Assistant, A
Psychiatric/Mental Health Services Technician, A
Rehabilitation and Therapeutic Professions, A
Respiratory Care Therapy/Therapist, A
Teacher Assistant/Aide, A
Therapeutic Recreation/Recreational Therapy, A
Tool and Die Technology/Technician, A
Web Page, Digital/Multimedia and Information Resources Design, A

NORTHWEST STATE COMMUNITY COLLEGE

Accounting, A
Accounting and Related Services, A
Administrative Assistant and Secretarial Science, A
Banking and Financial Support Services, A
Business Administration and Management, A
Business/Commerce, A
CAD/CADD Drafting and/or Design Technology/Technician, A
Child Care and Support Services Management, A
Computer Engineering, A

Computer Engineering Technology/Technician, A
Computer Programming/Programmer, A
Computer and Information Systems Security, A
Construction Engineering Technology/Technician, A
Corrections and Criminal Justice, A
Criminal Justice/Police Science, A
Criminal Justice/Safety Studies, A
Data Entry/Microcomputer Applications, A
Design and Visual Communications, A
Electrical, Electronic and Communications Engineering Technology/Technician, A
Energy Management and Systems Technology/Technician, A
Engineering, A
Engineering Technologies/Technicians, A
Engineering/Industrial Management, A
Entrepreneurship/Entrepreneurial Studies, A
History, A
Human Development and Family Studies, A
Human Resources Management/Personnel Administration, A
Industrial Electronics Technology/Technician, A
Industrial Mechanics and Maintenance Technology, A
Industrial Production Technologies/Technicians, A
International Business/Trade/Commerce, A
Kindergarten/PreSchool Education and Teaching, A
Legal Administrative Assistant/Secretary, A
Legal Assistant/Paralegal, A
Liberal Arts and Sciences Studies and Humanities, A
Logistics and Materials Management, A
Machine Tool Technology/Machinist, A
Marketing/Marketing Management, A
Mechanical Engineering, A
Mechanical Engineering/Mechanical Technology/Technician, A
Medical Administrative Assistant/Secretary, A
Medical/Clinical Assistant, A
Non-Profit/Public/Organizational Management, A
Office Management and Supervision, A
Plastics Engineering Technology/Technician, A
Precision Metal Working, A
Social Work, A
System Administration/Administrator, A
Teacher Assistant/Aide, A
Web Page, Digital/Multimedia and Information Resources Design, A

NOTRE DAME COLLEGE

Accounting, B
Art Teacher Education, B
Art/Art Studies, General, B
Biochemistry, B
Biology/Biological Sciences, B
Business Administration and Management, AB
Chemistry, B
Communication Studies/Speech Communication and Rhetoric, B
Computer Science, M
Early Childhood Education and Teaching, B
Education/Teaching of Individuals with Specific Learning Disabilities, B
Elementary Education and Teaching, B
English Language and Literature, B
Environmental Sciences, B
Fine/Studio Arts, B
Graphic Communications, B
History, B
Homeland Security, MO
Human Resources Management/Personnel Administration, B
Information Science/Studies, B
Junior High/Intermediate/Middle School Education and Teaching, B
Kindergarten/PreSchool Education and Teaching, B
Marketing/Marketing Management, B
Mathematics, B
Multi-/Interdisciplinary Studies, B
Pastoral Studies/Counseling, AB
Political Science and Government, B
Pre-Law Studies, B
Pre-Medicine/Pre-Medical Studies, B
Psychology, B
Public Administration, B

Public Relations, Advertising, and Applied Communication, B
Reading Teacher Education, M
Spanish Language Teacher Education, B
Special Education and Teaching, M
Sport and Fitness Administration/Management, B
Theology/Theological Studies, B

OBERLIN COLLEGE

African-American/Black Studies, B
Anthropology, B
Archeology, B
Art History, Criticism and Conservation, B
Art/Art Studies, General, B
Biochemistry, B
Biology/Biological Sciences, B
Chemistry, B
Classics and Classical Languages, Literatures, and Linguistics, B
Comparative Literature, B
Computer Science, B
Dance, B
Drama and Dramatics/Theatre Arts, B
East Asian Studies, B
Ecology, B
Economics, B
English Language and Literature, B
Environmental Studies, B
Fine/Studio Arts, B
French Language and Literature, B
Geology/Earth Science, B
German Language and Literature, B
History, B
Jazz/Jazz Studies, B
Jewish/Judaic Studies, B
Latin American Studies, B
Latin Language and Literature, B
Law and Legal Studies, B
Mathematics, B
Modern Greek Language and Literature, B
Music, BMO
Music History, Literature, and Theory, B
Music Teacher Education, BM
Music Theory and Composition, B
Near and Middle Eastern Studies, B
Performance, MO
Philosophy, B
Physics, B
Piano and Organ, B
Political Science and Government, B
Psychology, B
Religion/Religious Studies, B
Romance Languages, Literatures, and Linguistics, B
Russian Language and Literature, B
Russian Studies, B
Sociology, B
Spanish Language and Literature, B
Violin, Viola, Guitar and Other Stringed Instruments, B
Voice and Opera, B
Women's Studies, B

OHIO BUSINESS COLLEGE (SANDUSKY)

Accounting, A
Administrative Assistant and Secretarial Science, A
Business Administration and Management, A
Hospitality and Recreation Marketing Operations, A
Human Resources Management/Personnel Administration, A
Legal Administrative Assistant/Secretary, A
Medical Administrative Assistant/Secretary, A

OHIO BUSINESS COLLEGE (SHEFFIELD VILLAGE)

Accounting, A
Administrative Assistant and Secretarial Science, A
Banking and Financial Support Services, A
Business Administration and Management, A
Computer Programming/Programmer, A
Computer Software and Media Applications, A
Computer Technology/Computer Systems Technology, A
Data Entry/Microcomputer Applications, A
Human Resources Management/Personnel Administration, A

Legal Administrative Assistant/Secretary, A
Medical Administrative Assistant/Secretary, A
Web Page, Digital/Multimedia and Information Resources Design, A

OHIO CHRISTIAN UNIVERSITY

Accounting and Finance, AB
Business Administration and Management, AB
Criminal Justice/Safety Studies, B
Divinity/Ministry (BD, MDiv.), AB
Early Childhood Education and Teaching, B
Education, AB
English Language and Literature, B
History, B
Human Services, A
Junior High/Intermediate/Middle School Education and Teaching, B
Missions/Missionary Studies and Missiology, AB
Music Teacher Education, B
Political Science and Government, B
Psychology, B
Religious/Sacred Music, AB
Substance Abuse/Addiction Counseling, B
Youth Ministry, B

OHIO COLLEGE OF MASSOTHERAPY

Massage Therapy/Therapeutic Massage, A

OHIO DOMINICAN UNIVERSITY

Accounting, BM
Art Teacher Education, B
Art/Art Studies, General, B
Biology Teacher Education, B
Biology/Biological Sciences, B
Biopsychology, B
Business Administration and Management, AB
Business Administration, Management and Operations, M
Chemistry, AB
Chemistry Teacher Education, B
Communication Studies/Speech Communication and Rhetoric, B
Computer Science, B
Computer Software Engineering, B
Criminalistics and Criminal Science, B
Curriculum and Instruction, M
Design and Visual Communications, B
Early Childhood Education and Teaching, B
Economics, B
Education, BM
Educational Leadership and Administration, M
English, M
English Language and Literature, B
English as a Second Language, M
English/Language Arts Teacher Education, B
Finance, B
Finance and Banking, M
General Studies, AB
Gerontology, A
Health Services Administration, M
Health Services/Allied Health/Health Sciences, A
History, B
Information Science/Studies, B
Insurance, B
Junior High/Intermediate/Middle School Education and Teaching, B
Kindergarten/PreSchool Education and Teaching, B
Kinesiology and Exercise Science, B
Liberal Arts and Sciences Studies and Humanities, B
Mathematics, B
Mathematics Teacher Education, B
Peace Studies and Conflict Resolution, B
Philosophy, B
Physician Assistant, M
Political Science and Government, B
Psychology, B
Public Administration, M
Social Science Teacher Education, B
Social Work, B
Sociology, B
Special Education and Teaching, B
Sport and Fitness Administration/Management, BM
Teacher Education, Multiple Levels, B
Theology and Religious Vocations, M
Theology/Theological Studies, AB

Youth Ministry, B

OHIO NORTHERN UNIVERSITY

Accounting, B
Actuarial Science, B
Applied Mathematics, B
Art Teacher Education, B
Art/Art Studies, General, B
Athletic Training and Sports Medicine, B
Biochemistry, B
Biology Teacher Education, B
Biology/Biological Sciences, B
Business Administration and Management, B
Business Administration, Management and Opera-
    tions, B
Business/Commerce, B
Ceramic Arts and Ceramics, B
Chemistry, B
Chemistry Teacher Education, B
Civil Engineering, B
Clinical Laboratory Science/Medical
    Technology/Technologist, B
Commercial and Advertising Art, B
Communication Studies/Speech Communication
    and Rhetoric, B
Communication and Media Studies, B
Communication, Journalism and Related Pro-
    grams, B
Computer Engineering, B
Computer Science, B
Construction Management, B
Criminal Justice/Law Enforcement Administration, B
Criminal Justice/Police Science, B
Criminal Justice/Safety Studies, B
Design and Visual Communications, B
Drama and Dramatics/Theatre Arts, B
Early Childhood Education and Teaching, B
Education, B
Electrical, Electronics and Communications Engi-
    neering, B
Engineering, B
English/Language Arts Teacher Education, B
Entrepreneurship/Entrepreneurial Studies, B
Environmental Biology, B
Environmental Studies, B
Exercise Physiology, B
Fine/Studio Arts, B
Foreign Language Teacher Education, B
Forest Sciences and Biology, B
French Language Teacher Education, B
French Language and Literature, B
General Studies, B
German Language Teacher Education, B
Germanic Languages, Literatures, and Linguistics, B
Graphic Design, B
History, B
History Teacher Education, B
Insurance, B
International Business/Trade/Commerce, B
International Relations and Affairs, B
Journalism, B
Junior High/Intermediate/Middle School Education
    and Teaching, B
Kindergarten/PreSchool Education and Teaching, B
Kinesiology and Exercise Science, B
Law and Legal Studies, MD
Management Information Systems and Services, B
Management Science, B
Manufacturing Technology/Technician, B
Marketing, B
Marketing Research, B
Marketing/Marketing Management, B
Mathematics, B
Mathematics Teacher Education, B
Mechanical Engineering, B
Molecular Biology, B
Music, B
Music Performance, B
Music Teacher Education, B
Music Theory and Composition, B
Organizational Communication, B
Painting, B
Pharmacy, D
Pharmacy, Pharmaceutical Sciences, and Adminis-
    tration, B
Philosophy, B

Physics, B
Physics Teacher Education, B
Political Science and Government, B
Pre-Dentistry Studies, B
Pre-Law Studies, B
Pre-Medicine/Pre-Medical Studies, B
Pre-Theology/Pre-Ministerial Studies, B
Pre-Veterinary Studies, B
Printmaking, B
Psychology, B
Public Relations, Advertising, and Applied Commu-
    nication, B
Radio and Television, B
Religion/Religious Studies, B
Religious Education, B
Science Teacher Education/General Science
    Teacher Education, B
Sculpture, B
Social Studies Teacher Education, B
Sociology, B
Spanish Language Teacher Education, B
Spanish Language and Literature, B
Sport and Fitness Administration/Management, B
Statistics, B
Teacher Education, Multiple Levels, B
Technical Theatre/Theatre Design and Technol-
    ogy, B
Technology Teacher Education/Industrial Arts
    Teacher Education, B
Visual and Performing Arts, B
Youth Ministry, B

THE OHIO STATE UNIVERSITY

Accounting, BMD
Actuarial Science, B
Aeronautics/Aviation/Aerospace Science and Tech-
    nology, B
Aerospace, Aeronautical and Astronautical Engi-
    neering, BMD
African Studies, BMD
African-American Studies, MD
African-American/Black Studies, B
Agricultural Business and Management, B
Agricultural Communication/Journalism, B
Agricultural Economics, BMD
Agricultural Education, MD
Agricultural Engineering, MD
Agricultural Sciences, MD
Agricultural Teacher Education, B
Agricultural and Extension Education Services, B
Agricultural and Food Products Processing, B
Agricultural/Biological Engineering and Bioengineer-
    ing, B
Agriculture, Agriculture Operations and Related Sci-
    ences, B
Agronomy and Crop Science, B
Agronomy and Soil Sciences, MD
Allied Health and Medical Assisting Services, BM
Allopathic Medicine, D
Anatomy, MD
Animal Sciences, BMD
Anthropology, BMD
Apparel and Textiles, B
Arabic Language and Literature, B
Architecture, BMD
Art Education, MD
Art History, Criticism and Conservation, BMD
Art Teacher Education, B
Art/Art Studies, General, B
Arts Management, M
Asian Languages, MD
Astronomy, BMD
Athletic Training and Sports Medicine, B
Atmospheric Sciences and Meteorology, BMD
Audiology/Audiologist and Hearing Sciences, B
Audiology/Audiologist and Speech-Language
    Pathology/Pathologist, B
Aviation/Airway Management and Operations, B
Biochemistry, BMD
Bioengineering, MD
Biological and Biomedical Sciences, MD
Biology/Biological Sciences, B
Biomedical Engineering, MD
Biomedical Sciences, M
Biomedical/Medical Engineering, B
Biophysics, MD

Biostatistics, D
Botany/Plant Biology, B
Business Administration and Management, B
Business Administration, Management and Opera-
    tions, MD
Business Family and Consumer Sciences/Human
    Sciences, B
Business/Commerce, B
Business/Managerial Economics, B
Cartography, B
Cell Biology and Anatomy, MD
Chemical Engineering, BMD
Chemical Physics, MD
Chemistry, BMD
Child and Family Studies, D
Chinese Language and Literature, B
Chinese Studies, MD
City/Urban, Community and Regional Planning, B
Civil Engineering, BMD
Classics and Classical Languages, Litera-
    tures, and Linguistics, BMD
Clinical Laboratory Science/Medical
    Technology/Technologist, B
Clinical Psychology, D
Cognitive Sciences, M
Communication Disorders, MD
Communication Studies/Speech Communication
    and Rhetoric, B
Communication and Media Studies, MD
Communication, Journalism and Related Pro-
    grams, B
Comparative Literature, B
Computational Sciences, M
Computer Art and Design, M
Computer Engineering, BMD
Computer Science, BMD
Computer and Information Sciences, B
Construction Engineering Technology/Technician, B
Construction Management, B
Criminology, B
Dance, BMD
Dental Hygiene/Hygienist, BM
Dental and Oral Surgery, M
Dentistry, MD
Design and Visual Communications, B
Developmental Biology and Embryology, MD
Developmental Psychology, D
Dietetics/Dieticians, B
Drama and Dramatics/Theatre Arts, B
East Asian Studies, M
East European and Russian Studies, MD
Ecology, MD
Ecology, Evolution, Systematics and Population Bi-
    ology, B
Economics, BMD
Education, MDO
Educational Leadership and Administration, MDO
Educational Policy, MDO
Electrical Engineering, MD
Electrical, Electronics and Communications Engi-
    neering, B
Elementary Education and Teaching, B
Elementary and Middle School
    Administration/Principalship, B
Engineering, B
Engineering Physics, B
Engineering and Applied Sciences, MD
English, MD
English Language and Literature, B
Entomology, BMD
Environmental Policy and Resource Manage-
    ment, MD
Environmental Sciences, BMD
Environmental Studies, B
Environmental/Environmental Health Engineering, B
Ethnic, Cultural Minority, and Gender Studies, B
Evolutionary Biology, MD
Family Resource Management Studies, B
Family and Consumer Sciences/Home Economics
    Teacher Education, B
Family and Consumer Sciences/Human Sci-
    ences, MD
Film/Cinema Studies, B
Finance, B
Finance and Banking, M
Fine Arts and Art Studies, BM

Fine/Studio Arts, B
Fish, Game and Wildlife Management, MD
Fishing and Fisheries Sciences and Management, B
Food Engineering, MD
Food Science, B
Food Science and Technology, MD
Foods, Nutrition, and Wellness Studies, B
Foodservice Systems
  Administration/Management, B
Forestry, BMD
French Language and Literature, BMD
Gender Studies, MD
General Studies, AB
Genetics, MD
Geodetic Sciences, MD
Geography, BMD
Geology/Earth Science, BMD
Geosciences, MD
German Language and Literature, BMD
Health Information/Medical Records
  Administration/Administrator, B
Health Professions and Related Clinical Sciences, B
Health Services Administration, MD
Health and Physical Education, B
Hebrew Language and Literature, B
History, BMD
Horticultural Science, MD
Hospitality Administration/Management, B
Hotel/Motel Administration/Management, B
Human Development, D
Human Development and Family Studies, B
Human Nutrition, B
Human Resources Development, B
Human Resources Management and Services, MD
Human Resources Management/Personnel Adminis-
  tration, B
Humanities/Humanistic Studies, B
Industrial Design, BM
Industrial Engineering, B
Industrial and Labor Relations, D
Industrial/Management Engineering, MD
Information Science/Studies, B
Insurance, B
Interdisciplinary Studies, MD
Interior Design, BM
International Business/Trade/Commerce, B
International Relations and Affairs, B
International/Global Studies, B
Internet and Interactive Multimedia, M
Islamic Studies, B
Italian Language and Literature, BMD
Japanese Language and Literature, B
Japanese Studies, MD
Jazz/Jazz Studies, B
Jewish/Judaic Studies, B
Journalism, B
Junior High/Intermediate/Middle School Education
  and Teaching, B
Kinesiology and Exercise Science, B
Kinesiology and Movement Studies, MD
Korean Language and Literature, B
Landscape Architecture, BMD
Latin American Studies, M
Law and Legal Studies, MD
Linguistics, BMD
Livestock Management, B
Logistics and Materials Management, BM
Management Information Systems and Ser-
  vices, BMD
Marketing, MD
Marketing/Marketing Management, B
Materials Engineering, BMD
Materials Sciences, MD
Mathematics, BMD
Mathematics Teacher Education, M
Mechanical Engineering, BMD
Medical Radiologic Technology/Science - Radiation
  Therapist, B
Medieval and Renaissance Studies, B
Metallurgical Engineering, MD
Microbiology, BMD
Modern Greek Language and Literature, B
Molecular Biology, MD
Molecular Genetics, BMD
Multi-/Interdisciplinary Studies, B
Music, BMD

Music History, Literature, and Theory, B
Music Performance, B
Music Teacher Education, B
Music Theory and Composition, B
Natural Resources Management/Development and
  Policy, B
Natural Resources and Conservation, BMD
Near and Middle Eastern Languages, MD
Neuroscience, D
Nuclear Engineering, MD
Nursing, MD
Nutritional Sciences, BMD
Occupational Therapy/Therapist, M
Operations Management and Supervision, B
Operations Research, M
Optics/Optical Sciences, BMD
Optometry, MD
Oral Biology, MD
Oral Pathology, M
Oral and Dental Sciences, M
Ornamental Horticulture, B
Orthodontics, M
Parks, Recreation, Leisure and Fitness Studies, B
Pathobiology, M
Pathology/Experimental Pathology, M
Performance, M
Periodontics, M
Pharmaceutical Administration, MD
Pharmaceutics and Drug Design, B
Pharmacology, MD
Pharmacy, BMD
Philosophy, BMD
Physical Education Teaching and Coaching, BMD
Physical Therapy/Therapist, D
Physics, BMD
Piano and Organ, B
Plant Pathology/Phytopathology, BMD
Plant Sciences, BD
Political Science and Government, BD
Portuguese Language and Literature, BMD
Pre-Dentistry Studies, B
Psychology, BD
Public Administration, BM
Public Affairs, MD
Public Health, MD
Public Health (MPH, DPH), B
Public Policy Analysis, D
Radiologic Technology/Science - Radiographer, B
Real Estate, B
Rehabilitation Sciences, D
Religion/Religious Studies, B
Respiratory Care Therapy/Therapist, B
Restaurant/Food Services Management, B
Rural Sociology, MD
Russian Language and Literature, B
Slavic Languages, Literatures, and Linguistics, MD
Social Psychology, D
Social Sciences, MD
Social Work, BMD
Sociology, BD
Spanish Language and Literature, BMD
Special Education and Teaching, BD
Sport and Fitness Administration/Management, B
Statistics, MD
Survey Technology/Surveying, B
Systems Engineering, MD
Technical Teacher Education, B
Technology Teacher Education/Industrial Arts
  Teacher Education, B
Theater, B
Turf and Turfgrass Management, B
Urban and Regional Planning, MD
Veterinary Sciences, MD
Voice and Opera, B
Welding Technology/Welder, B
Wildlife and Wildlands Science and Management, B
Women's Studies, BMD
Zoology/Animal Biology, B

THE OHIO STATE UNIVERSITY AGRI-CULTURAL TECHNICAL INSTITUTE

Agribusiness, A
Agricultural Business Technology, A
Agricultural Business and Management, A
Agricultural Communication/Journalism, A
Agricultural Economics, A

Agricultural Mechanization, A
Agricultural Power Machinery Operation, A
Agricultural Teacher Education, A
Agronomy and Crop Science, A
Animal Sciences, A
Animal/Livestock Husbandry and Production, A
Biology Technician/BioTechnology Laboratory Tech-
  nician, A
Building/Construction Site Management/Manager, A
Construction Engineering Technology/Technician, A
Construction Management, A
Crop Production, A
Dairy Husbandry and Production, A
Dairy Science, A
Environmental Sciences, A
Equestrian/Equine Studies, A
Floriculture/Floristry Operations and Management, A
Greenhouse Operations and Management, A
Heavy Equipment Maintenance
  Technology/Technician, A
Horse Husbandry/Equine Science and Manage-
  ment, A
Horticultural Science, A
Hydraulics and Fluid Power Technology, A
Industrial Technology/Technician, A
Landscaping and Groundskeeping, A
Livestock Management, A
Natural Resources Management/Development and
  Policy, A
Plant Nursery Operations and Management, A
Soil Science and Agronomy, A
Turf and Turfgrass Management, A

THE OHIO STATE UNIVERSITY AT LIMA

Allied Health and Medical Assisting Services, B
Biology/Biological Sciences, B
Business Administration and Management, B
Business/Commerce, B
Business/Managerial Economics, B
Dental Hygiene/Hygienist, B
Drama and Dramatics/Theatre Arts, B
Elementary Education and Teaching, B
Elementary and Middle School
  Administration/Principalship, B
English Language and Literature, B
English/Language Arts Teacher Education, B
Family Resource Management Studies, B
Family and Consumer Sciences/Home Economics
  Teacher Education, B
General Studies, A
Health Information/Medical Records
  Administration/Administrator, B
History, B
Junior High/Intermediate/Middle School Education
  and Teaching, B
Psychology, B
Social Work, M

THE OHIO STATE UNIVERSITY AT MARION

Business Administration and Management, B
Business/Commerce, B
Business/Managerial Economics, B
Criminology, B
Education, M
Elementary Education and Teaching, B
Elementary and Middle School
  Administration/Principalship, B
English Language and Literature, B
English/Language Arts Teacher Education, B
General Studies, A
History, B
Junior High/Intermediate/Middle School Education
  and Teaching, B
Liberal Arts and Sciences Studies and Humani-
  ties, A
Psychology, B
Sociology, B

THE OHIO STATE UNIVERSITY–MANSFIELD CAMPUS

Business Administration and Management, B
Business/Commerce, B
Business/Managerial Economics, B
Criminology, B
Education, M

Elementary Education and Teaching, B
Elementary and Middle School
  Administration/Principalship, B
English Language and Literature, B
English/Language Arts Teacher Education, B
General Studies, A
History, B
Junior High/Intermediate/Middle School Education
  and Teaching, B
Liberal Arts and Sciences Studies and Humani-
  ties, A
Psychology, B
Social Work, M
Sociology, B

THE OHIO STATE UNIVERSITY–NEWARK CAMPUS

Business Administration and Management, B
Business/Commerce, B
Business/Managerial Economics, B
Early Childhood Education and Teaching, M
Education, M
Elementary Education and Teaching, B
Elementary and Middle School
  Administration/Principalship, B
English Language and Literature, B
English/Language Arts Teacher Education, B
General Studies, A
History, B
Junior High/Intermediate/Middle School Education
  and Teaching, B
Liberal Arts and Sciences Studies and Humani-
  ties, A
Middle School Education, M
Political Science and Government, B
Psychology, B
Social Work, M
Sociology, B

OHIO TECHNICAL COLLEGE

Autobody/Collision and Repair
  Technology/Technician, A
Automobile/Automotive Mechanics
  Technology/Technician, A
Diesel Mechanics Technology/Technician, A
Mechanic and Repair Technologies/Technicians, A
Welding Technology/Welder, A

OHIO UNIVERSITY

Accounting, B
Acting, B
Actuarial Science, B
Acute Care/Critical Care Nursing, M
Aeronautics/Aviation/Aerospace Science and Tech-
  nology, AB
African Studies, BM
African-American/Black Studies, B
Anthropology, B
Apparel and Textiles, B
Applied Economics, M
Applied Mathematics, B
Art History, Criticism and Conservation, BM
Art/Art Studies, General, B
Asian Studies/Civilization, BM
Astronomy, MD
Astrophysics, B
Athletic Training and Sports Medicine, BM
Atmospheric Sciences and Meteorology, B
Audiology/Audiologist and Speech-Language
  Pathology/Pathologist, B
Aviation/Airway Management and Operations, B
Biochemistry, MD
Biological and Biomedical Sciences, MD
Biology/Biological Sciences, B
Biomedical Engineering, M
Botany/Plant Biology, B
Broadcast Journalism, B
Business Administration and Management, B
Business Administration, Management and Opera-
  tions, M
Business/Managerial Economics, B
Cell Biology and Anatomy, MD
Cell/Cellular and Molecular Biology, B
Ceramic Arts and Ceramics, BM
Chemical Engineering, BMD
Chemistry, B

Child Development, AM
Child and Family Studies, M
Cinematography and Film/Video Production, B
Civil Engineering, BMD
Classics and Classical Languages, Litera-
  tures, and Linguistics, B
Clinical Psychology, MD
Clothing and Textiles, M
Communication Disorders, MD
Communication Studies/Speech Communication
  and Rhetoric, B
Communication and Media Studies, MD
Community Health Services/Liaison/Counseling, B
Comparative and Interdisciplinary Arts, D
Composition, M
Computer Education, M
Computer Science, BMD
Computer Systems Networking and Telecommunica-
  tions, B
Computer and Information Sciences, B
Construction Engineering and Management, M
Consumer Economics, M
Corporate and Organizational Communication, M
Counselor Education/School Counseling and Guid-
  ance Services, MD
Criminology, B
Curriculum and Instruction, MD
Customer Service Management, B
Dance, B
Dietetics/Dieticians, B
Digital Communication and Media/Multimedia, B
Drama and Dramatics/Theatre Arts, B
Early Childhood Education and Teaching, B
Ecology, BMD
Economics, BM
Education, MD
Educational Administration and Supervision, MD
Educational Measurement and Evaluation, MD
Educational Media/Instructional Technology, D
Electrical Engineering, MD
Electrical, Electronics and Communications Engi-
  neering, B
Engineering and Applied Sciences, MD
English, MD
English Language and Literature, B
Environmental Biology, MD
Environmental Engineering
  Technology/Environmental Technology, M
Environmental Health, B
Environmental Studies, BM
European Studies/Civilization, B
Evolutionary Biology, MD
Exercise and Sports Science, MD
Experimental Psychology, MD
Family Resource Management Studies, B
Family and Consumer Sciences/Home Economics
  Teacher Education, B
Family and Consumer Sciences/Human Sci-
  ences, M
Film, Television, and Video Production, M
Film, Television, and Video Theory and Criticism, M
Finance, B
Finance and Banking, M
Fine Arts and Art Studies, M
Fine/Studio Arts, B
Foods, Nutrition, and Wellness Studies, B
Foodservice Systems
  Administration/Management, B
French Language Teacher Education, B
French Language and Literature, BM
Geochemistry, M
Geography, BM
Geology/Earth Science, BM
Geophysics and Seismology, M
Geotechnical Engineering, M
German Language Teacher Education, B
German Language and Literature, B
Graphic Design, BM
Health Communication, D
Health Services Administration, M
Health and Physical Education, B
Health/Health Care Administration/Management, B
Higher Education/Higher Education Administra-
  tion, MD
History, BMD
Housing and Human Environments, B

Human Development and Family Studies, B
Human Resources Management/Personnel Adminis-
  tration, B
Humanities/Humanistic Studies, A
Hydrogeology, M
Industrial Engineering, B
Industrial Technology/Technician, B
Industrial and Organizational Psychology, MD
Industrial/Management Engineering, MD
International Affairs, M
International Business/Trade/Commerce, B
International Development, M
International Relations and Affairs, B
Journalism, BMD
Kinesiology and Exercise Science, B
Latin American Studies, BM
Liberal Arts and Sciences Studies and Humani-
  ties, AB
Linguistics, BM
Management Information Systems and Services, B
Marketing/Marketing Management, B
Mathematics, BMD
Mathematics Teacher Education, D
Mathematics and Statistics, B
Mechanical Engineering, BMD
Mechanics, M
Media Studies, MD
Microbiology, BMD
Middle School Education, M
Molecular Biology, MD
Multilingual and Multicultural Education, M
Music, MO
Music History, Literature, and Theory, BM
Music Performance, B
Music Teacher Education, M
Music Theory and Composition, BM
Music Therapy/Therapist, M
Neuroscience, MD
Nursing, M
Nursing - Advanced Practice, M
Nursing Administration, M
Nursing Education, M
Nutritional Sciences, M
Occupational Health and Industrial Hygiene, B
Osteopathic Medicine, D
Painting, M
Parks, Recreation, Leisure and Fitness Studies, B
Performance, MO
Philosophy, BM
Photography, BM
Photojournalism, B
Physical Education Teaching and Coaching, BM
Physical Therapy/Therapist, D
Physics, BMD
Physiology, MD
Piano and Organ, B
Plant Biology, MD
Playwriting and Screenwriting, B
Political Science and Government, BM
Printmaking, BM
Psychology, BMD
Public Administration, M
Public Health, M
Public Health (MPH, DPH), B
Radio and Television, B
Reading Teacher Education, M
Recreation and Park Management, M
Rehabilitation Counseling, M
Religion/Religious Studies, B
Rhetoric, D
Russian Language and Literature, B
Science Teacher Education/General Science
  Teacher Education, M
Sculpture, M
Secondary Education and Teaching, BM
Social Sciences, M°
Social Studies Teacher Education, D
Social Work, BM
Sociology, BM
South and Southeast Asian Studies, M
Spanish Language Teacher Education, B
Spanish Language and Literature, BM
Special Education and Teaching, BM
Speech and Interpersonal Communication, MD
Sport and Fitness Administration/Management, M
Structural Engineering, M

Student Personnel Services, M
Systems Engineering, M
Telecommunications, M
Theater, M
Transportation and Highway Engineering, M
Urban Studies/Affairs, B
Voice and Opera, B
Water Resources Engineering, M
Wildlife Biology, B
Women's Studies, B
Zoology/Animal Biology, B

OHIO UNIVERSITY–CHILLICOTHE

Administrative Assistant and Secretarial Science, A
Business Administration and Management, A
Child Development, A
Communication Disorders, A
Criminal Justice/Police Science, A
Criminology, B
Early Childhood Education and Teaching, B
Environmental Engineering
   Technology/Environmental Technology, A
Hazardous Materials Management and Waste
   Technology/Technician, A
Health Professions and Related Clinical Sciences, A
History, B
Human Resources Management/Personnel Adminis-
   tration, B
Humanities/Humanistic Studies, A
Information Technology, B
Liberal Arts and Sciences Studies and Humani-
   ties, AB
Management Information Systems and Services, A
Medical/Clinical Assistant, A
Multi-/Interdisciplinary Studies, A
Secondary Education and Teaching, AB

OHIO UNIVERSITY–EASTERN

Business Administration and Management, B
Community Health and Preventive Medicine, B
Criminal Justice/Law Enforcement Administration, B
Early Childhood Education and Teaching, B
Exercise Physiology, B
Health Communication, B
Health/Health Care Administration/Management, B
Junior High/Intermediate/Middle School Education
   and Teaching, B
Liberal Arts and Sciences Studies and Humani-
   ties, AB
Organizational Communication, B

OHIO UNIVERSITY–LANCASTER

Accounting Technology/Technician and Bookkeep-
   ing, A
Biological and Physical Sciences, A
Business Administration and Management, AB
Child Development, A
Computer Science, A
Criminal Justice/Law Enforcement Administration, B
Criminal Justice/Police Science, A
Early Childhood Education and Teaching, B
Education, B
Industrial Technology/Technician, A
Junior High/Intermediate/Middle School Education
   and Teaching, B
Medical Administrative Assistant/Secretary, A
Organizational Communication, B

OHIO UNIVERSITY–SOUTHERN CAM-PUS

Accounting Technology/Technician and Bookkeep-
   ing, A
Biological and Physical Sciences, A
Criminal Justice/Law Enforcement Administra-
   tion, AB
Early Childhood Education and Teaching, AB
Equestrian/Equine Studies, A
General Office Occupations and Clerical Services, A
Health Professions and Related Clinical Sciences, A
Health Services/Allied Health/Health Sciences, A
Humanities/Humanistic Studies, A
Kindergarten/PreSchool Education and Teaching, A
Liberal Arts and Sciences Studies and Humani-
   ties, A
Management Information Systems and Services, A

Multi-/Interdisciplinary Studies, B
Radio and Television Broadcasting
   Technology/Technician, A
Tourism and Travel Services Marketing Opera-
   tions, A

OHIO UNIVERSITY–ZANESVILLE

Biological and Physical Sciences, A
Broadcast Journalism, A
Criminal Justice/Law Enforcement Administration, B
Elementary Education and Teaching, B
Public Relations/Image Management, B
Radio and Television, A
Social Sciences, A

OHIO VALLEY COLLEGE OF TECHNOL-OGY

Business Administration and Management, A
Dental Assisting/Assistant, A
Medical Office Management/Administration, A
Medical/Clinical Assistant, A

OHIO WESLEYAN UNIVERSITY

Accounting, B
African-American/Black Studies, B
Ancient Studies/Civilization, B
Animal Genetics, B
Art History, Criticism and Conservation, B
Art Teacher Education, B
Astronomy, B
Astrophysics, B
Biology Teacher Education, B
Biology/Biological Sciences, B
Botany/Plant Biology, B
Broadcast Journalism, B
Business Administration and Management, B
Business Teacher Education, B
Business/Commerce, B
Business/Managerial Economics, B
Chemistry, B
Chemistry Teacher Education, B
Classics and Classical Languages, Litera-
   tures, and Linguistics, B
Comparative Literature, B
Computer Science, B
Drama and Dance Teacher Education, B
Drama and Dramatics/Theatre Arts, B
Early Childhood Education and Teaching, B
East Asian Studies, B
Economics, B
Education, B
Elementary Education and Teaching, B
Engineering, B
Engineering Science, B
English Language and Literature, B
Environmental Studies, B
Fine/Studio Arts, B
Foreign Language Teacher Education, B
French Language Teacher Education, B
French Language and Literature, B
General Studies, B
Genetics, B
Geography, B
Geology/Earth Science, B
German Language Teacher Education, B
German Language and Literature, B
Health Teacher Education, B
History, B
History Teacher Education, B
Humanities/Humanistic Studies, B
International Business/Trade/Commerce, B
International Relations and Affairs, B
Journalism, B
Junior High/Intermediate/Middle School Education
   and Teaching, B
Kindergarten/PreSchool Education and Teaching, B
Latin American Studies, B
Latin Teacher Education, B
Mathematics, B
Mathematics Teacher Education, B
Medical Microbiology and Bacteriology, B
Medieval and Renaissance Studies, B
Multi-/Interdisciplinary Studies, B
Music, B
Music Performance, B
Music Teacher Education, B

Philosophy, B
Physics, B
Physics Teacher Education, B
Political Science and Government, B
Pre-Dentistry Studies, B
Pre-Law Studies, B
Pre-Medicine/Pre-Medical Studies, B
Pre-Theology/Pre-Ministerial Studies, B
Pre-Veterinary Studies, B
Psychology, B
Psychology Teacher Education, B
Public Administration, B
Religion/Religious Studies, B
Secondary Education and Teaching, B
Small Business Administration/Management, B
Social Studies Teacher Education, B
Sociology, B
Spanish Language Teacher Education, B
Spanish Language and Literature, B
Statistics, B
Teacher Education, Multiple Levels, B
Urban Studies/Affairs, B
Women's Studies, B
Zoology/Animal Biology, B

OTTERBEIN UNIVERSITY

Accounting, B
Art Teacher Education, B
Art/Art Studies, General, B
Athletic Training and Sports Medicine, B
Audiology/Audiologist and Speech-Language
   Pathology/Pathologist, B
Biochemistry, B
Biology/Biological Sciences, B
Business Administration and Management, B
Business Administration, Management and Opera-
   tions, M
Business/Managerial Economics, B
Chemistry, B
Comparative Literature, B
Computer Science, B
Drama and Dramatics/Theatre Arts, B
Economics, B
Education, BM
Elementary Education and Teaching, B
English Language and Literature, B
Environmental Biology, B
Environmental Sciences, B
Equestrian/Equine Studies, B
Finance, B
French Language and Literature, B
Health Teacher Education, B
History, B
International Business/Trade/Commerce, B
International Relations and Affairs, B
Journalism, B
Junior High/Intermediate/Middle School Education
   and Teaching, B
Marketing/Marketing Management, B
Mathematics, B
Molecular Biology, B
Multi-/Interdisciplinary Studies, B
Music, B
Music History, Literature, and Theory, B
Music Performance, B
Music Teacher Education, B
Nurse Anesthetist, MO
Nursing, MDO
Nursing - Advanced Practice, MO
Nursing Administration, M
Nursing Education, O
Philosophy, B
Physical Education Teaching and Coaching, B
Physical Sciences, B
Physics, B
Piano and Organ, B
Political Science and Government, B
Pre-Dentistry Studies, B
Pre-Law Studies, B
Pre-Medicine/Pre-Medical Studies, B
Pre-Veterinary Studies, B
Psychology, B
Public Relations/Image Management, B
Radio and Television, B
Religion/Religious Studies, B

Science Teacher Education/General Science
Teacher Education, B
Secondary Education and Teaching, B
Sociology, B
Spanish Language and Literature, B
Sport and Fitness Administration/Management, B
Violin, Viola, Guitar and Other Stringed Instru-
ments, B
Voice and Opera, B

OWENS COMMUNITY COLLEGE

Accounting Technology/Technician and Bookkeep-
ing, A
Agricultural Mechanization, A
Architectural Drafting and Architectural
CAD/CADD, A
Architectural Engineering Technology/Technician, A
Automotive Engineering Technology/Technician, A
Biomedical Technology/Technician, A
Business/Commerce, A
Commercial Photography, A
Commercial and Advertising Art, A
Computer Engineering Technology/Technician, A
Computer Programming, Specific Applications, A
Computer and Information Systems Security, A
Construction Engineering Technology/Technician, A
Criminal Justice/Law Enforcement Administration, A
Criminal Justice/Police Science, A
Dental Hygiene/Hygienist, A
Diagnostic Medical Sonography/Sonographer and
Ultrasound Technician, A
Dietetics/Dieticians, A
Early Childhood Education and Teaching, A
Electrical, Electronic and Communications Engineer-
ing Technology/Technician, A
Executive Assistant/Executive Secretary, A
General Studies, A
Health Information/Medical Records
Technology/Technician, A
Industrial Technology/Technician, A
Information Technology, A
Landscaping and Groundskeeping, A
Logistics and Materials Management, A
Manufacturing Technology/Technician, A
Massage Therapy/Therapeutic Massage, A
Medical Administrative Assistant/Secretary, A
Medical Radiologic Technology/Science - Radiation
Therapist, A
Medical/Health Management and Clinical
Assistant/Specialist, A
Nuclear Medical Technology/Technologist, A
Occupational Therapist Assistant, A
Office Management and Supervision, A
Physical Therapist Assistant, A
Restaurant/Food Services Management, A
Sales, Distribution and Marketing Operations, A
Security and Protective Services, A
Surgical Technology/Technologist, A
Welding Technology/Welder, A

PONTIFICAL COLLEGE JOSEPHINUM

Classics and Classical Languages, Litera-
tures, and Linguistics, B
English Language and Literature, B
History, B
Humanities/Humanistic Studies, B
Latin American Studies, B
Philosophy, B
Theology and Religious Vocations, M

PROFESSIONAL SKILLS INSTITUTE

Health Information/Medical Records
Technology/Technician, A
Medical Office Assistant/Specialist, A
Physical Therapist Assistant, A

RABBINICAL COLLEGE OF TELSHE

Theology/Theological Studies, B

REMINGTON COLLEGE–CLEVELAND
CAMPUS

Business Administration and Management, A
Computer Systems Networking and Telecommunications, A

Criminal Justice/Law Enforcement Administration, A

ROSEDALE BIBLE COLLEGE

Bible/Biblical Studies, A

SCHOOL OF ADVERTISING ART

Commercial and Advertising Art, A

SHAWNEE STATE UNIVERSITY

Accounting, AB
Art Teacher Education, B
Art/Art Studies, General, B
Athletic Training and Sports Medicine, AB
Biology/Biological Sciences, AB
Business Administration and Management, AB
CAD/CADD Drafting and/or Design
Technology/Technician, A
Chemistry, B
Clinical Laboratory Science/Medical
Technology/Technologist, A
Computer Engineering Technology/Technician, B
Curriculum and Instruction, M
Dental Hygiene/Hygienist, A
Design and Applied Arts, B
Early Childhood Education and Teaching, B
Education, BM
Electromechanical Technology/Electromechanical
Engineering Technology, A
Emergency Medical Technology/Technician (EMT
Paramedic), A
Engineering Technologies/Technicians, B
English Language and Literature, B
Environmental Engineering
Technology/Environmental Technology, B
Fine/Studio Arts, B
General Studies, AB
Geology/Earth Science, B
Health and Physical Education, B
History, B
International Relations and Affairs, B
Kindergarten/PreSchool Education and Teaching, A
Legal Administrative Assistant/Secretary, A
Legal Assistant/Paralegal, A
Management Information Systems and Services, AB
Mathematics, AB
Mathematics Teacher Education, B
Medical Radiologic Technology/Science - Radiation
Therapist, A
Occupational Therapy/Therapist, ABM
Office Management and Supervision, A
Philosophy and Religious Studies, B
Physical Therapist Assistant, A
Plastics Engineering Technology/Technician, AB
Psychology, B
Respiratory Care Therapy/Therapist, A
Science Teacher Education/General Science
Teacher Education, B
Social Science Teacher Education, B
Social Sciences, AB
Sociology, B
Special Education and Teaching, B
Sport and Fitness Administration/Management, B
Teacher Education, Multiple Levels, B

SINCLAIR COMMUNITY COLLEGE

Accounting, A
Administrative Assistant and Secretarial Science, A
African Studies, A
Architectural Engineering Technology/Technician, A
Art/Art Studies, General, A
Artificial Intelligence and Robotics, A
Automobile/Automotive Mechanics
Technology/Technician, A
Aviation/Airway Management and Operations, A
BioTechnology, A
Business Administration and Management, A
Child Development, A
Civil Engineering Technology/Technician, A
Commercial and Advertising Art, A
Computer Engineering, A
Computer Graphics, A
Computer Hardware Engineering, A
Computer Programming, A
Computer Programming, Specific Applications, A
Computer Programming, Vendor/Product Certifica-
tion, A

Computer Software Engineering, A
Computer Systems Networking and Telecommunica-
tions, A
Computer and Information Sciences, A
Computer/Information Technology Services Adminis-
tration and Management, A
Consumer Merchandising/Retailing Management, A
Corrections, A
Criminal Justice/Law Enforcement Administration, A
Criminal Justice/Police Science, A
Culinary Arts/Chef Training, A
Dance, A
Data Entry/Microcomputer Applications, A
Dental Hygiene/Hygienist, A
Design and Applied Arts, A
Dietetics/Dieticians, A
Drafting and Design Technology/Technician, A
Drama and Dramatics/Theatre Arts, A
Education, A
Electrical, Electronic and Communications Engineer-
ing Technology/Technician, A
Electromechanical Technology/Electromechanical
Engineering Technology, A
Emergency Medical Technology/Technician (EMT
Paramedic), A
Engineering, A
Finance, A
Fine/Studio Arts, A
Fire Science/Firefighting, A
Foods, Nutrition, and Wellness Studies, A
Gerontology, A
Graphic and Printing Equipment Operator Produc-
tion, A
Health Information/Medical Records
Administration/Administrator, A
Hotel/Motel Administration/Management, A
Human Services, A
Industrial Radiologic Technology/Technician, A
Industrial Technology/Technician, A
Information Science/Studies, A
Information Technology, A
Interior Design, A
Kindergarten/PreSchool Education and Teaching, A
Labor and Industrial Relations, A
Legal Administrative Assistant/Secretary, A
Legal Assistant/Paralegal, A
Liberal Arts and Sciences Studies and Humani-
ties, A
Logistics and Materials Management, A
Machine Tool Technology/Machinist, A
Marketing/Marketing Management, A
Mass Communication/Media Studies, A
Mechanical Engineering/Mechanical
Technology/Technician, A
Medical Administrative Assistant/Secretary, A
Medical/Clinical Assistant, A
Mental Health Counseling/Counselor, A
Music, A
Occupational Therapy/Therapist, A
Physical Education Teaching and Coaching, A
Physical Therapy/Therapist, A
Plastics Engineering Technology/Technician, A
Public Administration, A
Quality Control Technology/Technician, A
Radiologic Technology/Science - Radiographer, A
Real Estate, A
Respiratory Care Therapy/Therapist, A
Sign Language Interpretation and Translation, A
Special Products Marketing Operations, A
Surgical Technology/Technologist, A
Survey Technology/Surveying, A
System Administration/Administrator, A
Tourism and Travel Services Management, A
Transportation and Materials Moving, A
Web/Multimedia Management and Webmaster, A
Word Processing, A

SOUTH UNIVERSITY

Business Administration and Management, B
Business Administration, Management and Opera-
tions, M
Clinical Psychology, M
Counseling Psychology, M
Criminal Justice/Law Enforcement Administration, B
Health/Health Care Administration/Management, B
Health/Medical Preparatory Programs, B

Information Science/Studies, B
Legal Assistant/Paralegal, AB
Physical Therapist Assistant, A
Psychology, B

SOUTHERN STATE COMMUNITY COLLEGE

Accounting Technology/Technician and Bookkeeping, A
Administrative Assistant and Secretarial Science, A
Agricultural Production Operations, A
Agriculture, A
Business Administration and Management, A
Business/Commerce, A
CAD/CADD Drafting and/or Design Technology/Technician, A
Computer Programming, Specific Applications, A
Computer Programming/Programmer, A
Computer Systems Analysis/Analyst, A
Computer Technology/Computer Systems Technology, A
Corrections, A
Criminal Justice/Law Enforcement Administration, A
Criminal Justice/Police Science, A
Drafting and Design Technology/Technician, A
Early Childhood Education and Teaching, A
Electrical, Electronic and Communications Engineering Technology/Technician, A
Electromechanical Technology/Electromechanical Engineering Technology, A
Emergency Medical Technology/Technician (EMT Paramedic), A
Entrepreneurship/Entrepreneurial Studies, A
Executive Assistant/Executive Secretary, A
Human Services, A
Kindergarten/PreSchool Education and Teaching, A
Liberal Arts and Sciences Studies and Humanities, A
Medical/Clinical Assistant, A
Respiratory Care Therapy/Therapist, A
Substance Abuse/Addiction Counseling, A
Teacher Assistant/Aide, A

STARK STATE COLLEGE

Accounting, A
Administrative Assistant and Secretarial Science, A
Architectural Engineering Technology/Technician, A
Automobile/Automotive Mechanics Technology/Technician, A
Biomedical Technology/Technician, A
Business Administration and Management, A
Child Development, A
Civil Engineering Technology/Technician, A
Clinical/Medical Laboratory Technician, A
Computer Engineering, A
Computer Hardware Engineering, A
Computer Programming, A
Computer Programming, Specific Applications, A
Computer Programming, Vendor/Product Certification, A
Computer Programming/Programmer, A
Computer Software Engineering, A
Computer Software and Media Applications, A
Computer Systems Networking and Telecommunications, A
Computer and Information Sciences, A
Computer and Information Sciences and Support Services, A
Computer/Information Technology Services Administration and Management, A
Consumer Merchandising/Retailing Management, A
Court Reporting/Court Reporter, A
Data Entry/Microcomputer Applications, A
Dental Hygiene/Hygienist, A
Drafting and Design Technology/Technician, A
Environmental Studies, A
Finance, A
Fire Science/Firefighting, A
Food Technology and Processing, A
Health Information/Medical Records Administration/Administrator, A
Human Services, A
Industrial Technology/Technician, A
Information Technology, A
International Business/Trade/Commerce, A
Legal Administrative Assistant/Secretary, A

Marketing/Marketing Management, A
Mechanical Engineering/Mechanical Technology/Technician, A
Medical/Clinical Assistant, A
Occupational Therapy/Therapist, A
Operations Management and Supervision, A
Physical Therapy/Therapist, A
Respiratory Care Therapy/Therapist, A
Survey Technology/Surveying, A
Web Page, Digital/Multimedia and Information Resources Design, A
Web/Multimedia Management and Webmaster, A
Word Processing, A

STAUTZENBERGER COLLEGE (BRECKSVILLE)

Accounting, A
Banking and Financial Support Services, A
Business Administration and Management, A
Legal Assistant/Paralegal, A
Medical/Clinical Assistant, A
Office Management and Supervision, A
Veterinary/Animal Health Technology/Technician and Veterinary Assistant, A

STAUTZENBERGER COLLEGE (MAUMEE)

Accounting, A
Business, Management, Marketing, and Related Support Services, A
Business/Office Automation/Technology/Data Entry, A
Computer Systems Networking and Telecommunications, A
Legal Assistant/Paralegal, A
Massage Therapy/Therapeutic Massage, A
Medical Administrative Assistant/Secretary, A
Medical/Clinical Assistant, A
Veterinary/Animal Health Technology/Technician and Veterinary Assistant, A
Web Page, Digital/Multimedia and Information Resources Design, A

TERRA STATE COMMUNITY COLLEGE

Accounting, A
Agricultural Business and Management, A
Animation, Interactive Technology, Video Graphics and Special Effects, A
Architectural Engineering Technology/Technician, A
Art History, Criticism and Conservation, A
Automotive Engineering Technology/Technician, A
Banking and Financial Support Services, A
Biological and Physical Sciences, A
Biology/Biological Sciences, A
Business Administration and Management, A
Business/Commerce, A
Chemistry, A
Commercial and Advertising Art, A
Computer Programming/Programmer, A
Computer Systems Networking and Telecommunications, A
Computer and Information Sciences, A
Criminal Justice/Police Science, A
Data Processing and Data Processing Technology/Technician, A
Economics, A
Education, A
Electrical and Electronic Engineering Technologies/Technicians, A
Electrical, Electronic and Communications Engineering Technology/Technician, A
Engineering, A
English Language and Literature, A
Executive Assistant/Executive Secretary, A
Fine/Studio Arts, A
General Studies, A
Health Information/Medical Records Administration/Administrator, A
Health Information/Medical Records Technology/Technician, A
Health Professions and Related Clinical Sciences, A
Health/Health Care Administration/Management, A
Heating, Air Conditioning and Refrigeration Technology/Technician, A
History, A
Hospitality Administration/Management, A

Humanities/Humanistic Studies, A
Kindergarten/PreSchool Education and Teaching, A
Language Interpretation and Translation, A
Liberal Arts and Sciences Studies and Humanities, A
Manufacturing Technology/Technician, A
Marketing/Marketing Management, A
Mathematics, A
Mechanical Engineering Related Technologies/Technicians, A
Mechanical Engineering/Mechanical Technology/Technician, A
Medical Administrative Assistant/Secretary, A
Medical Insurance Coding Specialist/Coder, A
Medical Office Assistant/Specialist, A
Medical/Clinical Assistant, A
Medical/Health Management and Clinical Assistant/Specialist, A
Music, A
Music Performance, A
Nuclear/Nuclear Power Technology/Technician, A
Operations Management and Supervision, A
Physics, A
Plastics Engineering Technology/Technician, A
Prepress/Desktop Publishing and Digital Imaging Design, A
Psychology, A
Real Estate, A
Robotics Technology/Technician, A
Sheet Metal Technology/Sheetworking, A
Social Sciences, A
Social Work, A
Teaching Assistants/Aides, A
Web Page, Digital/Multimedia and Information Resources Design, A
Welding Technology/Welder, A

TIFFIN UNIVERSITY

Accounting, AB
Art/Art Studies, General, B
Athletic Training and Sports Medicine, B
Business Administration and Management, AB
Business Administration, Management and Operations, M
Communication Studies/Speech Communication and Rhetoric, B
Communication and Media Studies, M
Computer Science, B
Computer Systems Analysis/Analyst, B
Computer Systems Networking and Telecommunications, B
Computer and Information Sciences, B
Corrections, B
Criminal Justice/Law Enforcement Administration, AB
Criminalistics and Criminal Science, B
Criminology, M
Digital Communication and Media/Multimedia, B
Education, BM
Educational Administration and Supervision, M
Educational Media/Instructional Technology, M
English, M
English Language and Literature, B
English/Language Arts Teacher Education, B
Film, Television, and Video Theory and Criticism, M
Finance, B
Finance and Banking, M
Fine Arts and Art Studies, M
Forensic Psychology, M
Forensic Science and Technology, B
General Studies, AB
Health Services Administration, M
Health/Health Care Administration/Management, B
Higher Education/Higher Education Administration, M
History, B
History Teacher Education, B
Homeland Security, M
Horse Husbandry/Equine Science and Management, B
Hospital and Health Care Facilities Administration/Management, B
Hospitality Administration/Management, B
Human Resources Management and Services, M
Human Resources Management/Personnel Administration, B

Humanities/Humanistic Studies, M
Information Technology, AB
International Business/Trade/Commerce, BM
International Relations and Affairs, B
Journalism, B
Legal Assistant/Paralegal, B
Logistics and Materials Management, B
Management, M
Management Information Systems and Services, B
Marketing, M
Marketing/Marketing Management, B
Music, B
Non-Profit/Public/Organizational Management, B
Psychology, BM
Public Relations/Image Management, B
Science Teacher Education/General Science
 Teacher Education, B
Security and Protective Services, B
Sport and Fitness Administration/Management, BM
Substance Abuse/Addiction Counseling, B
Writing, M

TRI-STATE BIBLE COLLEGE

Bible/Biblical Studies, AB
Divinity/Ministry (BD, MDiv.), B
Religious Education, B
Theology and Religious Vocations, M

TRUMBULL BUSINESS COLLEGE

Accounting, A
Administrative Assistant and Secretarial Science, A
Business Administration and Management, A
Data Processing and Data Processing
 Technology/Technician, A
Legal Administrative Assistant/Secretary, A
Management Information Systems and Services, A
Medical Administrative Assistant/Secretary, A

UNION INSTITUTE & UNIVERSITY

Business Administration and Management, B
Child Development, B
Clinical Psychology, D
Criminal Justice/Law Enforcement Administration, B
Cultural Studies, M
Education, D
Educational Leadership and Administration, D
Elementary Education and Teaching, B
Ethics, D
Health Promotion, M
Higher Education/Higher Education Administra-
 tion, D
History, M
Humanities/Humanistic Studies, D
Interdisciplinary Studies, MD
Maternal and Child Health, B
Organizational Management, M
Psychology, BMD
Public Policy Analysis, MD
Secondary Education and Teaching, B
Social Work, B
Special Education and Teaching, B
Writing, M

THE UNIVERSITY OF AKRON

Accounting, BM
Accounting Technology/Technician and Bookkeep-
 ing, A
Administrative Assistant and Secretarial Science, A
American Government and Politics (United
 States), B
Animal Physiology, B
Anthropology, B
Apparel and Textiles, B
Applied Economics, B
Applied Mathematics, BM
Art History, Criticism and Conservation, B
Art Teacher Education, B
Arts Management, M
Athletic Training and Sports Medicine, AB
Biochemistry, B
Biological and Biomedical Sciences, MD
Biology/Biological Sciences, B
Biomedical Engineering, MD
Biomedical/Medical Engineering, B
Botany/Plant Biology, B
Business Administration and Management, AB

Business/Commerce, B
Business/Office Automation/Technology/Data En-
 try, A
Cartography, AB
Ceramic Arts and Ceramics, B
Chemical Engineering, BMD
Chemistry, BMD
Child Development, BM
Child and Family Studies, M
City/Urban, Community and Regional Planning, B
Civil Engineering, BMD
Classics and Classical Languages, Litera-
 tures, and Linguistics, B
Clinical Laboratory Science/Medical
 Technology/Technologist, B
Clinical Psychology, M
Clothing and Textiles, M
Communication Disorders, BMD
Communication Studies/Speech Communication
 and Rhetoric, B
Communication and Media Studies, M
Community Organization and Advocacy, A
Composition, M
Computer Engineering, BMD
Computer Programming, B
Computer Programming/Programmer, B
Computer Science, BM
Computer Systems Analysis/Analyst, A
Computer Systems Networking and Telecommunica-
 tions, AB
Construction Engineering Technology/Technician, AB
Counseling Psychology, MD
Counselor Education/School Counseling and Guid-
 ance Services, MD
Criminal Justice/Police Science, A
Criminal Justice/Safety Studies, B
Criminology, B
Culinary Arts/Chef Training, A
Dance, B
Dietetics/Dieticians, B
Drafting and Design Technology/Technician, A
Drama and Dance Teacher Education, B
Drama and Dramatics/Theatre Arts, B
E-Commerce/Electronic Commerce, B
Early Childhood Education and Teaching, B
Ecology, B
Economics, BM
Education, AM
Education/Teaching of Individuals in Early Childhood
 Special Education Programs, B
Education/Teaching of Individuals with Multiple Dis-
 abilities, B
Educational Administration and Supervision, M
Electrical Engineering, MD
Electrical, Electronic and Communications Engineer-
 ing Technology/Technician, AB
Electrical, Electronics and Communications Engi-
 neering, B
Electronic Commerce, M
Elementary Education and Teaching, M
Emergency Medical Technology/Technician (EMT
 Paramedic), A
Engineering, B
Engineering and Applied Sciences, MD
English, M
English Language and Literature, B
English/Language Arts Teacher Education, B
Exercise and Sports Science, M
Family Systems, B
Family and Consumer Sciences/Home Economics
 Teacher Education, B
Fashion Merchandising, A
Finance and Banking, M
Financial Planning and Services, B
Fine Arts and Art Studies, B
Fine/Studio Arts, B
Fire Protection, B
Fire Protection and Safety Technology/Technician, A
Foods, Nutrition, and Wellness Studies, B
French Language Teacher Education, B
French Language and Literature, B
Geography, B
Geological Engineering, M
Geology/Earth Science, BM
Geophysics and Seismology, BM
Geosciences, M

Gerontology, D
Graphic Design, B
Health Services Administration, M
Health Teacher Education, B
Higher Education/Higher Education Administra-
 tion, M
History, BMD
History Teacher Education, B
Hospitality Administration/Management, A
Hotel/Motel Administration/Management, A
Housing and Human Environments, B
Human Resources Management and Services, M
Human Resources Management/Personnel Adminis-
 tration, B
Humanities/Humanistic Studies, B
Industrial and Organizational Psychology, MD
International Business/Trade/Commerce, BM
Jazz/Jazz Studies, B
Journalism, B
Junior High/Intermediate/Middle School Education
 and Teaching, B
Law and Legal Studies, MD
Legal Assistant/Paralegal, A
Liberal Arts and Sciences Studies and Humani-
 ties, AB
Management, M
Management Information Systems and Ser-
 vices, BM
Management of Technology, M
Manufacturing Technology/Technician, AB
Marketing, M
Marketing/Marketing Management, AB
Marriage and Family Therapy/Counseling, M
Mathematics, BM
Mathematics Teacher Education, B
Mathematics and Computer Science, B
Mechanical Engineering, BMD
Mechanical Engineering/Mechanical
 Technology/Technician, AB
Medical Office Management/Administration, A
Medical Radiologic Technology/Science - Radiation
 Therapist, A
Medical/Clinical Assistant, A
Merchandising and Buying Operations, A
Metal and Jewelry Arts, B
Microbiology, B
Multi-/Interdisciplinary Studies, AB
Music, BM
Music History, Literature, and Theory, BM
Music Performance, B
Music Teacher Education, BM
Music Theory and Composition, BM
Nursing, MD
Nutritional Sciences, M
Office Management and Supervision, A
Operations Management and Supervision, B
Organizational Communication, B
Performance, M
Philosophy, B
Photography, B
Physical Education Teaching and Coaching, BM
Physical Therapy/Therapist, B
Physics, BM
Piano and Organ, B
Political Science and Government, BM
Polymer Chemistry, B
Polymer/Plastics Engineering, BMD
Pre-Medicine/Pre-Medical Studies, B
Psychology, BMD
Public Administration, M
Public Administration and Social Service Profes-
 sions, A
Public Health, M
Public Relations/Image Management, B
Radio and Television, B
Radio, Television, and Digital Communication, B
Reading Teacher Education, M
Real Estate, B
Respiratory Care Therapy/Therapist, B
Restaurant/Food Services Management, A
Sales, Distribution and Marketing Operations, B
School Psychology, MD
Science Teacher Education/General Science
 Teacher Education, B
Sculpture, B
Selling Skills and Sales Operations, A

Small Business Administration/Management, A
Social Sciences, B
Social Studies Teacher Education, B
Social Work, ABM
Sociology, BMD
Spanish Language Teacher Education, B
Spanish Language and Literature, BM
Special Education and Teaching, BM
Sport and Fitness Administration/Management, B
Statistics, B
Supply Chain Management, M
Surgical Technology/Technologist, A
Survey Technology/Surveying, AB
Taxation, M
Technical Teacher Education, B
Theater, M
Violin, Viola, Guitar and Other Stringed Instruments, B
Voice and Opera, B
Writing, M
Zoology/Animal Biology, B

THE UNIVERSITY OF AKRON WAYNE COLLEGE

Administrative Assistant and Secretarial Science, A
Business Administration and Management, A
General Studies, A
Liberal Arts and Sciences Studies and Humanities, A
Medical Office Management/Administration, A
Office Management and Supervision, B
Social Work, AB
Teacher Assistant/Aide, A

UNIVERSITY OF CINCINNATI

Accounting, BMD
Acute Care/Critical Care Nursing, M
Adult and Continuing Education and Teaching, O
Aerospace, Aeronautical and Astronautical Engineering, BMD
African-American/Black Studies, B
Allopathic Medicine, D
Analytical Chemistry, MD
Anthropology, M
Applied Arts and Design, M
Applied Economics, M
Applied Mathematics, MD
Arabic Language and Literature, B
Archeology, B
Architectural Engineering, B
Architecture, BM
Art Education, M
Art History, Criticism and Conservation, BM
Arts Management, MD
Asian Studies/Civilization, B
Astrophysics, B
Athletic Training and Sports Medicine, B
Biochemistry, BMD
Bioinformatics, DO
Biological and Biomedical Sciences, BMDO
Biology/Biological Sciences, B
Biomedical Engineering, MD
Biomedical/Medical Engineering, B
Biophysics, D
Biostatistics, MD
Business Administration, Management and Operations, M
Cancer Biology/Oncology, D
Cartography, B
Cell Biology and Anatomy, D
Chemical Engineering, BMD
Chemistry, BMD
City/Urban, Community and Regional Planning, B
Civil Engineering, BMD
Classics and Classical Languages, Literatures, and Linguistics, BMD
Clinical Laboratory Science/Medical Technology/Technologist, B
Clinical Psychology, D
Commercial and Advertising Art, B
Communication Disorders, BMDO
Communication Studies/Speech Communication and Rhetoric, B
Communication and Media Studies, M
Community Health Nursing, M
Composition, MD

Computer Engineering, BMD
Computer Engineering Technology/Technician, B
Computer Science, MD
Computer and Information Sciences, B
Computer and Information Systems Security, B
Counselor Education/School Counseling and Guidance Services, MDO
Criminal Justice/Safety Studies, B
Criminology, MD
Curriculum and Instruction, MD
Dance, B
Design and Visual Communications, B
Developmental Biology and Embryology, D
Dietetics/Dieticians, B
Drama and Dramatics/Theatre Arts, B
Early Childhood Education and Teaching, AM
Economics, BD
Education, MDO
Educational Leadership and Administration, MDO
Electrical Engineering, MD
Electrical, Electronic and Communications Engineering Technology/Technician, B
Electrical, Electronics and Communications Engineering, B
Elementary Education and Teaching, M
Engineering, B
Engineering and Applied Sciences, MD
English, MD
English Language and Literature, B
English as a Second Language, DO
Environmental Engineering Technology/Environmental Technology, MD
Environmental Sciences, MD
Environmental Studies, B
Environmental and Occupational Health, MD
Environmental/Environmental Health Engineering, B
Epidemiology, MD
Ergonomics and Human Factors, MD
Experimental Psychology, D
Fashion/Apparel Design, B
Finance, B
Finance and Banking, MD
Fine Arts and Art Studies, M
Fine/Studio Arts, B
Fire Science/Firefighting, A
Fire Services Administration, B
Foundations and Philosophy of Education, MD
French Language and Literature, BMD
Genetic Counseling/Counselor, M
Genomic Sciences, MD
Geography, BMD
Geology/Earth Science, BMD
German Language and Literature, BMD
Graphic Design, M
Health Education, MD
Health Information/Medical Records Administration/Administrator, B
Health Physics/Radiological Health, M
Health Professions and Related Clinical Sciences, B
Health Teacher Education, B
Hebrew Language and Literature, B
History, BMD
Horticultural Science, B
Immunology, MD
Industrial Design, BM
Industrial Hygiene, MD
Industrial and Labor Relations, M
Industrial and Manufacturing Management, D
Industrial/Management Engineering, D
Information Science/Studies, B
Information Technology, B
Inorganic Chemistry, MD
Insurance, B
Interdisciplinary Studies, D
Interior Design, BM
International Business/Trade/Commerce, B
International Relations and Affairs, B
Journalism, B
Junior High/Intermediate/Middle School Education and Teaching, B
Law and Legal Studies, D
Liberal Arts and Sciences Studies and Humanities, B
Management, D
Management Information Systems and Services, MD

Marketing, MD
Marketing/Marketing Management, B
Materials Engineering, MD
Materials Sciences, MD
Maternity Nursing, M
Mathematics, BMD
Mathematics Teacher Education, M
Mechanical Engineering, BMD
Mechanics, MD
Medical Imaging, D
Medical Physics, M
Microbiology, MD
Molecular Biology, MD
Molecular Genetics, MD
Molecular Medicine, D
Molecular Toxicology, MD
Multi-/Interdisciplinary Studies, B
Music, BMDO
Music History, Literature, and Theory, BMD
Music Performance, B
Music Teacher Education, BM
Music Theory and Composition, BMD
Musicology and Ethnomusicology, D
Neuroscience, D
Nuclear Engineering, D
Nuclear Medical Technology/Technologist, B
Nurse Anesthetist, M
Nurse Midwife/Nursing Midwifery, M
Nursing, MD
Nursing - Adult, M
Nursing Administration, M
Nutritional Sciences, BM
Occupational Health Nursing, M
Operations Management and Supervision, B
Organic Chemistry, MD
Organizational Behavior Studies, B
Organizational Management, M
Pathobiology, D
Pathology/Experimental Pathology, D
Pediatric Nurse/Nursing, M
Performance, MDO
Pharmaceutical Sciences, MD
Pharmacology, D
Pharmacy, BD
Philosophy, BMD
Physical Chemistry, MD
Physics, BMD
Physiology, D
Piano and Organ, B
Political Science and Government, BMD
Psychiatric/Mental Health Nurse/Nursing, M
Psychology, BD
Quantitative Analysis, MD
Radio and Television, B
Reading Teacher Education, MDO
Real Estate, B
Rehabilitation Sciences, D
Respiratory Care Therapy/Therapist, B
Romance Languages, Literatures, and Linguistics, MD
School Psychology, DO
Science Teacher Education/General Science Teacher Education, M
Secondary Education and Teaching, BMD
Sign Language Interpretation and Translation, B
Social Studies Teacher Education, M
Social Work, BM
Sociology, BMD
Spanish Language and Literature, BMD
Special Education and Teaching, BMDO
Sport and Fitness Administration/Management, B
Statistics, BD
Substance Abuse/Addiction Counseling, B
Taxation, M
Technical Theatre/Theatre Design and Technology, B
Textile Design, M
Theater, MD
Urban Studies/Affairs, B
Urban and Regional Planning, M
Visual and Performing Arts, B
Voice and Opera, B
Women's Health Nursing, M

Women's Studies, BMO

UNIVERSITY OF CINCINNATI BLUE ASH COLLEGE

Accounting Technology/Technician and Bookkeeping, A
Business Administration and Management, A
Business Administration, Management and Operations, A
Business/Commerce, A
Chemical Technology/Technician, A
Commercial and Advertising Art, A
Communication Studies/Speech Communication and Rhetoric, A
Computer Technology/Computer Systems Technology, A
Criminal Justice/Safety Studies, A
Dental Hygiene/Hygienist, A
Education, A
Emergency Medical Technology/Technician (EMT Paramedic), A
Executive Assistant/Executive Secretary, A
General Studies, A
Health/Medical Preparatory Programs, A
Kindergarten/PreSchool Education and Teaching, A
Liberal Arts and Sciences Studies and Humanities, A
Library Science, A
Medical Administrative Assistant/Secretary, A
Medical Radiologic Technology/Science - Radiation Therapist, A
Medical Transcription/Transcriptionist, A
Medical/Clinical Assistant, A
Nuclear Medical Technology/Technologist, A
Personal and Culinary Services, A
Photographic and Film/Video Technology/Technician and Assistant, A
Pre-Law Studies, A
Pre-Pharmacy Studies, A
Psychology, A
Public Health Education and Promotion, A
Real Estate, A
Retailing and Retail Operations, A
Science Technologies/Technicians, A
Secondary Education and Teaching, A
Social Work, A
Veterinary/Animal Health Technology/Technician and Veterinary Assistant, A

UNIVERSITY OF CINCINNATI CLERMONT COLLEGE

Accounting, A
Aeronautics/Aviation/Aerospace Science and Technology, A
Audiology/Audiologist and Speech-Language Pathology/Pathologist, A
Biology/Biological Sciences, A
Business Administration and Management, A
Business/Commerce, A
Chemistry, A
Computer Technology/Computer Systems Technology, A
Computer Typography and Composition Equipment Operator, A
Criminal Justice/Safety Studies, A
Data Processing and Data Processing Technology/Technician, A
Elementary Education and Teaching, A
Emergency Medical Technology/Technician (EMT Paramedic), A
Environmental Studies, A
General Studies, A
Health Information/Medical Records Technology/Technician, A
Health Professions and Related Clinical Sciences, A
Information Science/Studies, A
Junior High/Intermediate/Middle School Education and Teaching, A
Kindergarten/PreSchool Education and Teaching, A
Legal Assistant/Paralegal, A
Liberal Arts and Sciences Studies and Humanities, A
Manufacturing Technology/Technician, A
Multi-/Interdisciplinary Studies, A
Organizational Behavior Studies, A
Physical Therapist Assistant, A

Pre-Law Studies, A
Pre-Pharmacy Studies, A
Psychology, A
Respiratory Care Therapy/Therapist, A
Science Technologies/Technicians, A
Secondary Education and Teaching, A
Social Sciences, A
Social Work, A
Special Education and Teaching, A
Sport and Fitness Administration/Management, A
Surgical Technology/Technologist, A

UNIVERSITY OF DAYTON

Accounting, BM
Aerospace, Aeronautical and Astronautical Engineering, MD
American/United States Studies/Civilization, B
Applied Mathematics, M
Art History, Criticism and Conservation, B
Biochemistry, B
Bioengineering, M
Biological and Biomedical Sciences, MD
Biology/Biological Sciences, B
Business Administration, Management and Operations, M
Business/Managerial Economics, B
Chemical Engineering, BM
Chemistry, BM
Civil Engineering, BM
Clinical Psychology, M
Communication Studies/Speech Communication and Rhetoric, B
Communication and Media Studies, M
Computer Engineering, BMD
Computer Science, BM
Computer and Information Sciences, B
Computer and Information Systems Security, M
Counseling Psychology, M
Counselor Education/School Counseling and Guidance Services, MO
Criminal Justice/Law Enforcement Administration, B
Design and Visual Communications, B
Development Economics and International Development, B
Dietetics/Dieticians, B
Drama and Dramatics/Theatre Arts, B
Early Childhood Education and Teaching, BM
Econometrics and Quantitative Economics, B
Economics, B
Educational Administration and Supervision, M
Educational Leadership and Administration, MDO
Educational Media/Instructional Technology, M
Electrical Engineering, MD
Electrical, Electronic and Communications Engineering Technology/Technician, B
Electrical, Electronics and Communications Engineering, B
Engineering Management, M
English, M
English Language and Literature, B
Entrepreneurship/Entrepreneurial Studies, B
Environmental Biology, B
Environmental Engineering Technology/Environmental Technology, M
Environmental Policy and Resource Management, M
Exercise Physiology, B
Exercise and Sports Science, M
Finance, B
Finance and Banking, M
Fine/Studio Arts, B
Foreign Language Teacher Education, B
Foreign Languages and Literatures, B
French Language and Literature, B
Geology/Earth Science, B
Geotechnical Engineering, M
German Language and Literature, B
History, B
Human Development, M
Human Nutrition, B
Industrial Technology/Technician, B
International Business/Trade/Commerce, B
International/Global Studies, B
Junior High/Intermediate/Middle School Education and Teaching, B
Kinesiology and Exercise Science, B

Law and Legal Studies, MD
Management Information Systems and Services, B
Marketing, M
Marketing/Marketing Management, B
Materials Engineering, MD
Mathematical and Computational Finance, M
Mathematics, B
Mathematics Teacher Education, M
Mechanical Engineering, BMD
Mechanical Engineering/Mechanical Technology/Technician, B
Mechanics, M
Medicinal and Pharmaceutical Chemistry, B
Middle School Education, M
Music, B
Music Performance, B
Music Teacher Education, BM
Music Theory and Composition, B
Music Therapy/Therapist, B
Operations Management and Supervision, B
Optical Technologies, MD
Pastoral Studies/Counseling, M
Philosophy, B
Photography, B
Physical Education Teaching and Coaching, M
Physical Sciences, B
Physical Therapy/Therapist, D
Physician Assistant, M
Physics, B
Political Science and Government, B
Pre-Dentistry Studies, B
Pre-Medicine/Pre-Medical Studies, B
Psychology, B
Public Administration, M
Radio and Television, B
Reading Teacher Education, M
Religion/Religious Studies, B
Religious Education, B
School Psychology, MO
Science Teacher Education/General Science Teacher Education, B
Secondary Education and Teaching, BM
Sociology, B
Spanish Language and Literature, B
Special Education and Teaching, BM
Sport and Fitness Administration/Management, B
Structural Engineering, M
Student Personnel Services, M
Theology and Religious Vocations, MD
Transportation and Highway Engineering, M
Water Resources Engineering, M
Women's Studies, B

THE UNIVERSITY OF FINDLAY

Accounting, AB
Animal Sciences, B
Art Teacher Education, B
Art/Art Studies, General, B
Athletic Training and Sports Medicine, BM
Bilingual and Multilingual Education, B
Biological and Physical Sciences, B
Biology/Biological Sciences, B
Broadcast Journalism, B
Business Administration and Management, AB
Business Administration, Management and Operations, M
Business Teacher Education, B
Business/Corporate Communications, B
Chemistry, B
Clinical Laboratory Science/Medical Technology/Technologist, B
Commercial and Advertising Art, B
Communication Studies/Speech Communication and Rhetoric, B
Computer Science, AB
Computer Systems Networking and Telecommunications, B
Computer and Information Sciences, AB
Criminal Justice/Law Enforcement Administration, B
Diagnostic Medical Sonography/Sonographer and Ultrasound Technician, AB
Drama and Dramatics/Theatre Arts, B
Early Childhood Education and Teaching, M
Economics, B
Education, BM
Educational Administration and Supervision, M

Educational Media/Instructional Technology, M
Elementary Education and Teaching, B
English Language and Literature, B
English as a Second Language, M
Environmental Policy and Resource Manage-
ment, M
Environmental Studies, B
Equestrian/Equine Studies, AB
Farm/Farm and Ranch Management, B
Finance, AB
Forensic Science and Technology, B
Hazardous Materials Management and Waste
Technology/Technician, B
Health Informatics, M
Health Services Administration, M
Health and Physical Education, B
Health/Health Care Administration/Management, B
Health/Medical Preparatory Programs, B
History, B
Hospitality Administration/Management, M
Hotel/Motel Administration/Management, B
Human Resources Management/Personnel Adminis-
tration, AB
International Business/Trade/Commerce, B
Japanese Language and Literature, B
Journalism, B
Logistics and Materials Management, B
Marketing/Marketing Management, B
Mathematics, B
Medical Radiologic Technology/Science - Radiation
Therapist, B
Multilingual and Multicultural Education, BM
Nuclear Medical Technology/Technologist, AB
Occupational Therapy/Therapist, BM
Organizational Management, M
Pharmacy, D
Philosophy, B
Physical Education Teaching and Coaching, B
Physical Therapy/Therapist, BD
Physician Assistant, M
Political Science and Government, B
Pre-Law Studies, B
Pre-Medicine/Pre-Medical Studies, B
Pre-Veterinary Studies, B
Psychology, B
Public Administration, M
Public Relations/Image Management, B
Reading Teacher Education, M
Religion/Religious Studies, B
Rhetoric, M
Sales, Distribution and Marketing Operations, AB
Science Teacher Education/General Science
Teacher Education, BM
Secondary Education and Teaching, B
Social Work, B
Sociology, B
Spanish Language and Literature, B
Special Education and Teaching, B
Sport and Fitness Administration/Management, B
Teaching English as a Second or Foreign
Language/ESL Language Instructor, B
Writing, M

UNIVERSITY OF MOUNT UNION

Accounting, B
American/United States Studies/Civilization, B
Asian Studies/Civilization, B
Athletic Training and Sports Medicine, B
Biochemistry, B
Biology/Biological Sciences, B
Business Administration and Management, B
Chemistry, B
Civil Engineering, B
Clinical Laboratory Science/Medical
Technology/Technologist, B
Computer Programming/Programmer, B
Computer and Information Sciences and Support
Services, B
Criminal Justice/Safety Studies, B
Criminology, B
Drama and Dramatics/Theatre Arts, B
Early Childhood Education and Teaching, B
Economics, B
Education/Teaching of Individuals in Early Childhood
Special Education Programs, B
Educational Leadership and Administration, M

English Language and Literature, B
Environmental Biology, B
Environmental Sciences, B
Finance, B
Financial Planning and Services, B
Fine/Studio Arts, B
French Language and Literature, B
Geology/Earth Science, B
German Language and Literature, B
Health Teacher Education, B
Health/Health Care Administration/Management, B
History, B
Human Resources Management and Services, B
International Business/Trade/Commerce, B
International Relations and Affairs, B
Japanese Language and Literature, B
Junior High/Intermediate/Middle School Education
and Teaching, B
Kinesiology and Exercise Science, B
Marketing/Marketing Management, B
Mathematics, B
Mechanical Engineering, B
Music, B
Music Performance, B
Music Teacher Education, B
Organizational Communication, B
Philosophy, B
Physical Education Teaching and Coaching, B
Physician Assistant, M
Physics, B
Political Science and Government, B
Psychology, B
Public Health Education and Promotion, B
Religion/Religious Studies, B
Sociology, B
Spanish Language and Literature, B
Special Education and Teaching, B
Sport and Fitness Administration/Management, B
Visual and Performing Arts, B
Web Page, Digital/Multimedia and Information Re-
sources Design, B

UNIVERSITY OF NORTHWESTERN OHIO

Accounting, AB
Administrative Assistant and Secretarial Science, A
Agricultural Business and Management, A
Automobile/Automotive Mechanics
Technology/Technician, A
Business Administration and Management, AB
Computer Programming/Programmer, A
Diesel Mechanics Technology/Technician, A
Health/Health Care Administration/Management, B
Heating, Air Conditioning, Ventilation and Refrigera-
tion Maintenance Technology/Technician, A
Legal Administrative Assistant/Secretary, A
Legal Assistant/Paralegal, A
Marketing/Marketing Management, AB
Medical Administrative Assistant/Secretary, A
Medical/Clinical Assistant, A
Pharmacy Technician/Assistant, A
Tourism and Travel Services Management, A

UNIVERSITY OF RIO GRANDE

Accounting, AB
Accounting Technology/Technician and Bookkeep-
ing, A
Administrative Assistant and Secretarial Science, A
American/United States Studies/Civilization, B
Art Education, M
Art Teacher Education, B
Art/Art Studies, General, AB
Biology Teacher Education, B
Biology/Biological Sciences, AB
Business Administration and Management, AB
Business Teacher Education, B
Business/Corporate Communications, B
Business/Office Automation/Technology/Data En-
try, A
Chemistry, AB
Clinical Laboratory Science/Medical
Technology/Technologist, B
Clinical/Medical Laboratory Technician, A
Communication Studies/Speech Communication
and Rhetoric, AB
Computer Science, AB

Drafting and Design Technology/Technician, AB
Ecology, B
Economics, B
Education, BM
Education/Teaching of Individuals with Mental Retar-
dation, B
Education/Teaching of Individuals with Specific
Learning Disabilities, B
Educational Leadership and Administration, M
Elementary Education and Teaching, B
Energy Management and Systems
Technology/Technician, A
English Language and Literature, B
English/Language Arts Teacher Education, B
Entrepreneurship/Entrepreneurial Studies, M
General Studies, A
Graphic Design, B
Health Teacher Education, B
Health and Physical Education, B
History, AB
History Teacher Education, B
Humanities/Humanistic Studies, B
Industrial Technology/Technician, AB
Information Technology, B
International Business/Trade/Commerce, B
Kindergarten/PreSchool Education and Teaching, A
Legal Administrative Assistant/Secretary, A
Marketing/Marketing Management, B
Mass Communication/Media Studies, AB
Mathematics, AB
Mathematics Teacher Education, B
Mechanical Engineering/Mechanical
Technology/Technician, AB
Medical Administrative Assistant/Secretary, A
Music, AB
Music Teacher Education, B
Physical Education Teaching and Coaching, ABM
Physical Sciences, B
Physics Teacher Education, B
Political Science and Government, B
Pre-Dentistry Studies, B
Pre-Law Studies, B
Pre-Medicine/Pre-Medical Studies, B
Pre-Theology/Pre-Ministerial Studies, B
Pre-Veterinary Studies, B
Psychology, A
Public Relations/Image Management, B
Radiologic Technology/Science - Radiographer, A
Robotics Technology/Technician, AB
Science Teacher Education/General Science
Teacher Education, B
Secondary Education and Teaching, B
Social Science Teacher Education, B
Social Sciences, B
Social Work, AB
Sociology, AB
Special Education and Teaching, M
Speech Teacher Education, B
Teacher Education, Multiple Levels, B
Technical Theatre/Theatre Design and Technol-
ogy, A
Visual and Performing Arts, B

THE UNIVERSITY OF TOLEDO

Accounting, BM
Accounting Technology/Technician and Bookkeep-
ing, A
African-American/Black Studies, B
American/United States Studies/Civilization, B
Analytical Chemistry, MD
Anthropology, B
Applied Mathematics, MD
Art Education, M
Art History, Criticism and Conservation, B
Asian Studies/Civilization, B
Astronomy, B
Astrophysics, D
Athletic Training and Sports Medicine, B
Biochemistry, BMD
Bioengineering, MD
Bioinformatics, MO
Biological and Biomedical Sciences, MD
Biology/Biological Sciences, B
Biomedical Engineering, D
Biomedical/Medical Engineering, B
Biostatistics, O

Business Administration and Management, B
Business Education, M
Business/Commerce, B
Cancer Biology/Oncology, MD
Cardiovascular Sciences, MD
Chemical Engineering, BMD
Chemistry, BMD
Civil Engineering, BMD
Clinical Laboratory Science/Medical
   Technology/Technologist, B
Clinical Psychology, MD
Communication Disorders, M
Communication Studies/Speech Communication
   and Rhetoric, B
Communication and Media Studies, O
Community Health Nursing, MO
Computer Engineering, B
Computer Programming/Programmer, A
Computer Science, MD
Computer and Information Sciences, A
Construction Engineering Technology/Technician, B
Counselor Education/School Counseling and Guid-
   ance Services, MD
Criminal Justice/Safety Studies, B
Criminology, MO
Curriculum and Instruction, MDO
Drama and Dramatics/Theatre Arts, B
E-Commerce/Electronic Commerce, B
Early Childhood Education and Teaching, MO
Ecology, MD
Economics, BM
Education, MDO
Education/Teaching of the Gifted and Talented, D
Educational Administration and Supervision, MDO
Educational Measurement and Evaluation, MD
Educational Media/Instructional Technology, MDO
Educational Psychology, MD
Electrical Engineering, MD
Electrical, Electronics and Communications Engi-
   neering, B
Electromechanical Technology/Electromechanical
   Engineering Technology, B
Elementary Education and Teaching, D
Emergency Management, O
Engineering Technology, A
Engineering and Applied Sciences, M
English, MO
English Education, M
English Language and Literature, B
English as a Second Language, M
Entrepreneurship/Entrepreneurial Studies, B
Environmental Sciences, BMD
Environmental Studies, B
Environmental and Occupational Health, MO
Epidemiology, MO
Exercise Physiology, B
Exercise and Sports Science, MD
Experimental Psychology, MD
Film/Cinema Studies, B
Finance, B
Finance and Banking, M
Foreign Language Teacher Education, M
Foundations and Philosophy of Education, MD
French Language and Literature, BM
Gender Studies, O
General Studies, AB
Genomic Sciences, M
Geographic Information Systems, O
Geography, BMDO
Geology/Earth Science, BMD
German Language and Literature, BM
Gerontology, O
Health Education, MDO
Health Information/Medical Records
   Administration/Administrator, B
Health Promotion, MD
Health Services Administration, MO
Higher Education/Higher Education Administra-
   tion, MDO
History, BMD
Hospital and Health Care Facilities
   Administration/Management, B
Human Resources Management/Personnel Adminis-
   tration, B
Humanities/Humanistic Studies, B
Immunology, MD

Industrial Hygiene, M
Industrial/Management Engineering, MD
Information Science/Studies, B
Information Technology, B
Inorganic Chemistry, MD
Intermedia/Multimedia, B
International Business/Trade/Commerce, BM
International Public Health/International Health, O
International Relations and Affairs, B
Kindergarten/PreSchool Education and Teaching, B
Kinesiology and Exercise Science, B
Law and Legal Studies, MD
Legal Assistant/Paralegal, AB
Leisure Studies, M
Liberal Arts and Sciences Studies and Humani-
   ties, B
Liberal Studies, M
Linguistics, B
Logistics and Materials Management, B
Management, M
Marketing, M
Marketing/Marketing Management, B
Materials Sciences, MD
Mathematics, BMD
Mathematics Teacher Education, M
Mechanical Engineering, BMD
Mechanical Engineering/Mechanical
   Technology/Technician, B
Medical Physics, MD
Medicinal and Pharmaceutical Chemistry, MD
Middle School Education, M
Music, BMO
Music Teacher Education, MO
Near and Middle Eastern Studies, B
Neuroscience, MD
Non-Profit/Public/Organizational Management, O
Nursing, MDO
Nursing - Advanced Practice, MO
Nursing Administration, M
Nursing Education, MO
Nutritional Sciences, M
Occupational Therapy/Therapist, D
Operations Management and Supervision, B
Oral Biology, M
Organic Chemistry, MD
Pathology/Experimental Pathology, MO
Pediatric Nurse/Nursing, MO
Performance, M
Pharmaceutical Administration, M
Pharmaceutical Sciences, M
Pharmaceutics and Drug Design, B
Pharmacology, MD
Pharmacy, B
Philosophy, BM
Physical Chemistry, MD
Physical Education Teaching and Coaching, M
Physical Therapy/Therapist, MD
Physician Assistant, M
Physics, BMD
Political Science and Government, BM
Psychology, BMD
Public Administration, MO
Public Health, MO
Public Health Education and Promotion, B
Recreation and Park Management, MD
Religion/Religious Studies, B
Respiratory Care Therapy/Therapist, B
School Psychology, MO
Science Teacher Education/General Science
   Teacher Education, M
Secondary Education and Teaching, BMD
Social Studies Teacher Education, M
Social Work, BMO
Sociology, BM
Spanish Language and Literature, BM
Special Education and Teaching, BMD
Speech-Language Pathology/Pathologist, B
Statistics, MD
Therapeutic Recreation/Recreational Therapy, B
Trade and Industrial Teacher Education, B
Transportation and Highway Engineering, A
Urban Studies/Affairs, B
Urban and Regional Planning, MDO
Vocational and Technical Education, MO
Women's Studies, BO

Writing, O

URBANA UNIVERSITY

Accounting, AB
Adult and Continuing Education and Teaching, B
Athletic Training and Sports Medicine, B
Biology/Biological Sciences, B
Business Administration and Management, AB
Business Administration, Management and Opera-
   tions, M
Business/Managerial Economics, AB
Chemistry, B
Criminal Justice/Law Enforcement Administra-
   tion, AB
Criminology, M
Education, BM
Elementary Education and Teaching, B
English Language and Literature, B
Health Teacher Education, B
History, B
Human Resources Management/Personnel Adminis-
   tration, AB
Junior High/Intermediate/Middle School Education
   and Teaching, B
Liberal Arts and Sciences Studies and Humani-
   ties, AB
Marketing/Marketing Management, AB
Mass Communication/Media Studies, B
Nursing, M
Philosophy, B
Pre-Dentistry Studies, B
Pre-Law Studies, B
Pre-Medicine/Pre-Medical Studies, B
Pre-Veterinary Studies, B
Psychology, B
Religion/Religious Studies, B
Secondary Education and Teaching, B
Sociology, B

URSULINE COLLEGE

Accounting, B
Art Education, M
Art History, Criticism and Conservation, B
Art Teacher Education, B
Art Therapy/Therapist, BM
BioTechnology, B
Biological and Biomedical Sciences, B
Biology Technician/BioTechnology Laboratory Tech-
   nician, B
Biology/Biological Sciences, B
Business Administration and Management, B
Business Administration, Management and Opera-
   tions, M
Christian Studies, B
Design and Visual Communications, B
Early Childhood Education and Teaching, BM
Education, M
Educational Administration and Supervision, M
English Language and Literature, B
English/Language Arts Teacher Education, B
Fashion Merchandising, B
Fashion/Apparel Design, B
Health Information/Medical Records
   Administration/Administrator, B
Health/Health Care Administration/Management, B
Historic Preservation and Conservation, BM
History, B
Human Resources Management/Personnel Adminis-
   tration, B
Humanities/Humanistic Studies, B
Junior High/Intermediate/Middle School Education
   and Teaching, B
Legal Assistant/Paralegal, B
Liberal Studies, M
Management Information Systems and Services, B
Marketing/Marketing Management, B
Mathematics, B
Mathematics Teacher Education, BM
Medical/Surgical Nursing, M
Middle School Education, M
Nursing, MD
Nursing Administration, M
Nursing Education, M
Philosophy, B
Political Science and Government, B
Psychology, B

Public Relations/Image Management, B
Reading Teacher Education, M
Religion/Religious Studies, B
Science Teacher Education/General Science
  Teacher Education, BM
Social Studies Teacher Education, BM
Social Work, B
Sociology, B
Special Education and Teaching, BM
Theology and Religious Vocations, M

VATTEROTT COLLEGE

Building/Construction Finishing, Manage-
  ment, and Inspection, A
Electrician, A
Heating, Air Conditioning and Refrigeration
  Technology/Technician, A
Information Technology, A
System Administration/Administrator, A

VET TECH INSTITUTE AT BRADFORD SCHOOL

Veterinary/Animal Health Technology/Technician and
  Veterinary Assistant, A

VIRGINIA MARTI COLLEGE OF ART AND DESIGN

Commercial and Advertising Art, A
Digital Communication and Media/Multimedia, A
Fashion Merchandising, A
Fashion/Apparel Design, A
Interior Design, A

WALSH UNIVERSITY

Accounting, AB
Art/Art Studies, General, B
Behavioral Sciences, B
Biological and Physical Sciences, B
Biology/Biological Sciences, B
Biomathematics and Bioinformatics, B
Business Administration and Management, AB
Business Administration, Management and Opera-
  tions, M
Business/Corporate Communications, B
Chemistry, B
Clinical Laboratory Science/Medical
  Technology/Technologist, B
Communication and Media Studies, B
Computer Graphics, B
Computer Programming/Programmer, B
Computer Science, AB
Counseling Psychology, M
Counselor Education/School Counseling and Guid-
  ance Services, M
Criminology, B
Early Childhood Education and Teaching, B
Education, BM
Education/Teaching of Individuals with Mental Retar-
  dation, B
Education/Teaching of Individuals with Multiple Dis-
  abilities, B
English Language and Literature, B
Environmental Sciences, B
Finance, B
French Language and Literature, B
Graphic Design, B
Health Services Administration, O
Health and Physical Education, B
Higher Education/Higher Education Administra-
  tion, M
History, B
Human Services, A
International Relations and Affairs, B
Junior High/Intermediate/Middle School Education
  and Teaching, B
Kindergarten/PreSchool Education and Teaching, B
Kinesiology and Exercise Science, B
Liberal Arts and Sciences Studies and Humani-
  ties, AB
Marketing, M
Marketing/Marketing Management, AB
Mathematics, B
Mathematics Teacher Education, B
Modern Languages, B
Museology/Museum Studies, B

Music, B
Nursing, MD
Nursing Administration, M
Nursing Education, M
Pastoral Studies/Counseling, BM
Philosophy, B
Physical Education Teaching and Coaching, B
Physical Therapy/Therapist, D
Political Science and Government, B
Pre-Dentistry Studies, B
Pre-Medicine/Pre-Medical Studies, B
Pre-Pharmacy Studies, B
Pre-Veterinary Studies, B
Psychology, B
Religious Education, M
Science Teacher Education/General Science
  Teacher Education, B
Secondary Education and Teaching, B
Sociology, B
Spanish Language and Literature, B
Special Education and Teaching, B
Student Personnel Services, M
System Administration/Administrator, B
Theology and Religious Vocations, M
Theology/Theological Studies, B
Web Page, Digital/Multimedia and Information Re-
  sources Design, B

WASHINGTON STATE COMMUNITY COLLEGE

Accounting, A
Administrative Assistant and Secretarial Science, A
Automobile/Automotive Mechanics
  Technology/Technician, A
Biological and Physical Sciences, A
Biology/Biological Sciences, A
Business Administration and Management, A
Chemical Engineering, A
Clinical/Medical Laboratory Technician, A
Computer Engineering Technology/Technician, A
Data Processing and Data Processing
  Technology/Technician, A
Drafting and Design Technology/Technician, A
Education, A
Electrical, Electronic and Communications Engineer-
  ing Technology/Technician, A
Engineering, A
Heating, Air Conditioning, Ventilation and Refrigera-
  tion Maintenance Technology/Technician, A
Industrial Technology/Technician, A
Kindergarten/PreSchool Education and Teaching, A
Liberal Arts and Sciences Studies and Humani-
  ties, A
Marketing/Marketing Management, A
Mathematics, A
Mechanical Engineering/Mechanical
  Technology/Technician, A
Medical Administrative Assistant/Secretary, A
Physical Sciences, A
Radio and Television, A
Social Work, A

WILBERFORCE UNIVERSITY

Accounting, B
Biology/Biological Sciences, B
Business Administration and Management, B
Computer Engineering, B
Computer Science, B
Electrical, Electronics and Communications Engi-
  neering, B
Health/Health Care Administration/Management, B
Information Science/Studies, B
Marketing/Marketing Management, B
Mass Communication/Media Studies, B
Music, B
Political Science and Government, B
Psychology, B
Rehabilitation Counseling, M
Rehabilitation and Therapeutic Professions, B
Social Work, B
Sociology, B

WILMINGTON COLLEGE

Accounting, B
Agricultural Business and Management, B
Agricultural Teacher Education, B

Agriculture, B
Art Teacher Education, B
Athletic Training and Sports Medicine, B
Biological and Physical Sciences, B
Biology/Biological Sciences, B
Business Administration and Management, B
Business Teacher Education, B
Business/Managerial Economics, B
Chemistry, B
Computer Science, B
Criminal Justice/Law Enforcement Administration, B
Drama and Dramatics/Theatre Arts, B
Economics, B
Education, BM
Elementary Education and Teaching, B
English Language and Literature, B
Health Teacher Education, B
History, B
Liberal Arts and Sciences Studies and Humani-
  ties, B
Marketing/Marketing Management, B
Mass Communication/Media Studies, B
Mathematics, B
Modern Languages, B
Music Teacher Education, B
Philosophy, B
Physical Education Teaching and Coaching, B
Political Science and Government, B
Pre-Dentistry Studies, B
Pre-Law Studies, B
Pre-Medicine/Pre-Medical Studies, B
Pre-Veterinary Studies, B
Psychology, B
Reading Teacher Education, M
Religion/Religious Studies, B
Science Teacher Education/General Science
  Teacher Education, B
Secondary Education and Teaching, B
Social Sciences, B
Social Work, B
Spanish Language and Literature, B
Special Education and Teaching, M
Sport and Fitness Administration/Management, B

WITTENBERG UNIVERSITY

Accounting, B
American/United States Studies/Civilization, B
Art/Art Studies, General, B
Biochemistry, Biophysics and Molecular Biology, B
Biology/Biological Sciences, B
Business Administration and Management, B
Central/Middle and Eastern European Studies, B
Chemistry, B
Communication Studies/Speech Communication
  and Rhetoric, B
Computer Science, B
Criminology, B
Dance, B
Drama and Dramatics/Theatre Arts, B
East Asian Studies, B
Economics, B
Education, BM
English Language and Literature, B
Entrepreneurship/Entrepreneurial Studies, B
Environmental Sciences, B
Finance, B
French Language and Literature, B
Geology/Earth Science, B
German Language and Literature, B
History, B
International Relations and Affairs, B
Liberal Arts and Sciences Studies and Humani-
  ties, B
Marketing/Marketing Management, B
Mathematics, B
Music, B
Philosophy, B
Physics, B
Political Science and Government, B
Psychology, B
Religion/Religious Studies, B
Sociology, B
Spanish Language and Literature, B
Sport and Fitness Administration/Management, B

Visual and Performing Arts, B

WRIGHT STATE UNIVERSITY

Accounting, BM
Acting, B
Acute Care/Critical Care Nursing, M
Adult and Continuing Education and Teaching, O
African-American/Black Studies, B
Agricultural Business Technology, AB
Allopathic Medicine, D
Anatomy, M
Anthropology, B
Applied Behavior Analysis, M
Applied Economics, M
Applied Mathematics, M
Applied Statistics, M
Area Studies, B
Art History, Criticism and Conservation, B
Art/Art Studies, General, B
Athletic Training and Sports Medicine, B
Biochemistry, M
Biological and Biomedical Sciences, MD
Biology/Biological Sciences, AB
Biomedical Engineering, M
Biomedical Technology/Technician, B
Biomedical/Medical Engineering, B
Biophysics, M
Business Administration and Management, AB
Business Administration, Management and Operations, M
Business Education, M
Business Teacher Education, AB
Business/Commerce, AB
Business/Managerial Economics, B
Cartography, B
Chemistry, ABM
Classics and Classical Languages, Literatures, and Linguistics, B
Clinical Laboratory Science/Medical Technology/Technologist, B
Clinical Psychology, D
Communication Studies/Speech Communication and Rhetoric, AB
Community Health Nursing, M
Community Organization and Advocacy, B
Computer Education, M
Computer Engineering, BMD
Computer Science, MD
Computer Teacher Education, B
Computer and Information Sciences, B
Computer and Information Systems Security, B
Counselor Education/School Counseling and Guidance Services, BM
Criminal Justice/Law Enforcement Administration, A
Criminology, BM
Curriculum and Instruction, BMO
Dance, B
Drafting and Design Technology/Technician, A
Drama and Dramatics/Theatre Arts, B
Early Childhood Education and Teaching, BM
Economics, BM
Education, BMO
Education/Teaching of Individuals with Autism, B
Education/Teaching of Individuals with Multiple Disabilities, B
Education/Teaching of Individuals with Specific Learning Disabilities, B
Education/Teaching of the Gifted and Talented, BM
Educational Administration and Supervision, MO
Educational Leadership and Administration, BMO
Educational, Instructional, and Curriculum Supervision, B
Electrical Engineering, M
Electrical, Electronics and Communications Engineering, B
Elementary Education and Teaching, BM
Engineering, B
Engineering Physics, B
Engineering Science, B
Engineering Technology, A
Engineering and Applied Sciences, MD
English, M
English Language and Literature, B
English as a Second Language, M
Environmental Health, B
Environmental Sciences, MD

Ergonomics and Human Factors, MD
Film/Cinema Studies, B
Finance, B
Finance and Banking, M
Financial Planning and Services, B
Foreign Languages and Literatures, B
French Language and Literature, B
Geography, AB
Geology/Earth Science, ABM
Geophysics and Seismology, M
German Language and Literature, B
Gerontology, B
Graphic Design, AB
Health Education, M
Health Promotion, M
Health Services Administration, M
Health and Physical Education, B
Health/Health Care Administration/Management, B
Higher Education/Higher Education Administration, MO
History, ABM
Human Resources Management/Personnel Administration, B
Human Services, B
Humanities/Humanistic Studies, M
Immunology, M
Industrial and Organizational Psychology, MD
Information Science/Studies, B
Interdisciplinary Studies, M
International Business/Trade/Commerce, BM
International Relations and Affairs, B
International and Comparative Education, M
Junior High/Intermediate/Middle School Education and Teaching, AB
Kindergarten/PreSchool Education and Teaching, B
Latin Language and Literature, B
Liberal Arts and Sciences Studies and Humanities, B
Library Science, M
Logistics and Materials Management, BM
Management Information Systems and Services, ABM
Manufacturing Engineering, B
Manufacturing Technology/Technician, A
Marketing, M
Marketing/Marketing Management, AB
Mass Communication/Media Studies, B
Materials Engineering, BM
Materials Sciences, M
Mathematics, BM
Mathematics Teacher Education, M
Mechanical Engineering, BM
Medical Physics, M
Microbiology, M
Middle School Education, M
Modern Greek Language and Literature, B
Modern Languages, B
Molecular Biology, M
Museology/Museum Studies, B
Music, B
Music History, Literature, and Theory, B
Music Performance, B
Music Teacher Education, ABM
Non-Profit/Public/Organizational Management, B
Nursing, M
Nursing - Adult, M
Nursing - Advanced Practice, M
Nursing Administration, M
Pediatric Nurse/Nursing, M
Performance, M
Pharmacology, M
Philosophy, B
Physical Education Teaching and Coaching, BM
Physical Sciences, B
Physics, BM
Physiology, M
Political Science and Government, B
Pre-Medicine/Pre-Medical Studies, B
Pre-Nursing Studies, B
Project Management, M
Psychology, ABMD
Public Administration, M
Public Health, M
Public/Applied History and Archival Administration, B
Reading Teacher Education, B
Recreation and Park Management, M

Rehabilitation Counseling, M
Religion/Religious Studies, B
Restaurant/Food Services Management, B
Rhetoric, M
Sales and Marketing Operations/Marketing and Distribution Teacher Education, AB
School Nursing, M
Science Teacher Education/General Science Teacher Education, ABM
Secondary Education and Teaching, BM
Sign Language Interpretation and Translation, B
Social Sciences, B
Social Work, AB
Sociology, AB
Spanish Language and Literature, B
Special Education and Teaching, BM
Statistics, M
Supply Chain Management, M
Teacher Education and Professional Development, Specific Levels and Methods, M
Teacher Education and Professional Development, Specific Subject Areas, B
Teacher Education, Multiple Levels, B
Teaching English as a Second or Foreign Language/ESL Language Instructor, B
Technical Teacher Education, B
Technical Theatre/Theatre Design and Technology, B
Toxicology, M
Transportation/Transportation Management, B
Urban Studies/Affairs, BM
Vocational Rehabilitation Counseling/Counselor, B
Vocational and Technical Education, M
Women's Studies, B
Writing, M

WRIGHT STATE UNIVERSITY–LAKE CAMPUS

Accounting, A
Administrative Assistant and Secretarial Science, A
Agribusiness, AB
Biology/Biological Sciences, A
Business Administration and Management, A
Business/Commerce, B
Chemistry, A
Communication Studies/Speech Communication and Rhetoric, A
Criminology, B
Early Childhood Education and Teaching, B
Elementary Education and Teaching, B
Engineering, B
Engineering Technology, A
English Language and Literature, B
Foodservice Systems Administration/Management, AB
Geology/Earth Science, A
Graphic Communications, AB
Graphic Design, A
History, A
Junior High/Intermediate/Middle School Education and Teaching, B
Liberal Arts and Sciences Studies and Humanities, AB
Mass Communication/Media Studies, A
Mechanical Engineering, B
Mechanical Engineering/Mechanical Technology/Technician, B
Physical Sciences, B
Psychology, AB
Social Work, A
Sociology, A

XAVIER UNIVERSITY

Accounting, BM
Actuarial Science, B
Advertising, B
Art/Art Studies, General, B
Athletic Training and Sports Medicine, BM
Biochemistry, Biophysics and Molecular Biology, B
Biological and Physical Sciences, B
Biology Teacher Education, B
Biology/Biological Sciences, B
Business Administration and Management, AB
Business Administration, Management and Operations, M

Business, Management, Marketing, and Related Support Services, B
Business/Managerial Economics, B
Chemical Engineering, B
Chemistry, B
Chemistry Teacher Education, B
Classics and Classical Languages, Literatures, and Linguistics, B
Clinical Laboratory Science/Medical Technology/Technologist, B
Clinical Psychology, MD
Computer Science, B
Corrections, A
Counseling Psychology, M
Counselor Education/School Counseling and Guidance Services, M
Criminal Justice/Safety Studies, AB
Criminology, M
Drama and Dance Teacher Education, B
Drama and Dramatics/Theatre Arts, B
Early Childhood Education and Teaching, ABM
Economics, B
Education, BMD
Educational Administration and Supervision, M
Elementary Education and Teaching, BM
Engineering Physics, B
English, M
English Language and Literature, AB
Entrepreneurship/Entrepreneurial Studies, B
Ethics, M
Ethnic, Cultural Minority, and Gender Studies, B
Finance, B
Finance and Banking, M
Fine/Studio Arts, B
French Language and Literature, AB
German Language and Literature, AB
Graphic Design, B
Health Services Administration, M
History, AB
Human Resources Development, M
Human Resources Management/Personnel Administration, B
Industrial and Organizational Psychology, M
International Business/Trade/Commerce, BM
International Relations and Affairs, B
Junior High/Intermediate/Middle School Education and Teaching, B
Liberal Arts and Sciences Studies and Humanities, AB
Management Information Systems and Services, B
Management Strategy and Policy, M
Marketing, M
Marketing/Marketing Management, B
Mathematics, B
Montessori Teacher Education, B
Multi-/Interdisciplinary Studies, B
Multilingual and Multicultural Education, M
Music, B
Music Teacher Education, B
Natural Resources Management/Development and Policy, B
Natural Sciences, B
Nursing, MDO
Occupational Therapy/Therapist, BM
Pastoral Studies/Counseling, M
Philosophy, B
Physical Sciences, B
Physics, B
Physics Teacher Education, B
Political Science and Government, AB
Psychology, ABMD
Public Relations/Image Management, AB
Radio and Television, AB
Radiologic Technology/Science - Radiographer, A
Reading Teacher Education, M
Religion/Religious Studies, AB
Religious Education, M
Science Teacher Education/General Science Teacher Education, B
Secondary Education and Teaching, M
Social Work, B
Sociology, AB
Spanish Language and Literature, AB
Special Education and Teaching, BM
Sport and Fitness Administration/Management, BM
Sustainable Development, M

Teacher Education and Professional Development, Specific Levels and Methods, B
Theology and Religious Vocations, M

YOUNGSTOWN STATE UNIVERSITY

Accounting, ABM
Advertising, B
African-American/Black Studies, B
American/United States Studies/Civilization, B
Analytical Chemistry, M
Anatomy, M
Anthropology, B
Applied Behavior Analysis, M
Applied Mathematics, M
Art History, Criticism and Conservation, B
Art Teacher Education, B
Art/Art Studies, General, B
Astronomy, B
Athletic Training and Sports Medicine, B
Banking and Financial Support Services, B
Biochemistry, BM
Biological and Biomedical Sciences, M
Biology Teacher Education, B
Biology/Biological Sciences, B
Business Administration and Management, AB
Business Administration, Management and Operations, MO
Business/Commerce, AB
Business/Managerial Economics, B
Chemical Engineering, B
Chemistry, BM
Child Care and Support Services Management, A
Child Development, AB
Civil Engineering, BM
Civil Engineering Technology/Technician, AB
Clinical Laboratory Science/Medical Technology/Technologist, B
Clinical/Medical Laboratory Science and Allied Professions, B
Clinical/Medical Laboratory Technician, A
Communication Studies/Speech Communication and Rhetoric, B
Community Health Services/Liaison/Counseling, B
Composition, M
Computer Engineering, M
Computer Programming/Programmer, AB
Computer Science, BM
Computer and Information Sciences, AB
Corrections, AB
Counseling Psychology, M
Counselor Education/School Counseling and Guidance Services, M
Criminal Justice/Law Enforcement Administration, AB
Criminal Justice/Police Science, A
Criminal Justice/Safety Studies, AB
Criminology, M
Curriculum and Instruction, M
Dance, B
Data Processing and Data Processing Technology/Technician, A
Dental Hygiene/Hygienist, B
Dietetic Technician (DTR), A
Dietetics/Dieticians, B
Dietician Assistant, A
Drafting and Design Technology/Technician, A
Drama and Dramatics/Theatre Arts, B
Early Childhood Education and Teaching, BM
Econometrics and Quantitative Economics, B
Economics, BM
Education, BMD
Education/Teaching of the Gifted and Talented, M
Educational Administration and Supervision, MD
Educational Leadership and Administration, D
Educational Media/Instructional Technology, M
Electrical Engineering, M
Electrical and Electronic Engineering Technologies/Technicians, A
Electrical, Electronic and Communications Engineering Technology/Technician, AB
Electrical, Electronics and Communications Engineering, B
Elementary Education and Teaching, B
Emergency Medical Technology/Technician (EMT Paramedic), A
Engineering, B

Engineering Technology, AB
Engineering and Applied Sciences, M
English, M
English Language and Literature, B
English/Language Arts Teacher Education, B
Environmental Biology, M
Environmental Engineering Technology/Environmental Technology, M
Environmental Sciences, B
Environmental Studies, MO
Family and Community Services, B
Family and Consumer Sciences/Home Economics Teacher Education, B
Family and Consumer Sciences/Human Sciences, B
Fashion Merchandising, B
Finance, AB
Finance and Banking, M
Financial Planning and Services, B
Fine/Studio Arts, B
Foods, Nutrition, and Wellness Studies, AB
Foreign Language Teacher Education, B
Foreign Languages and Literatures, B
Forensic Science and Technology, B
French Language Teacher Education, B
General Studies, B
Geography, B
Geology/Earth Science, B
Gerontology, BM
Graphic Design, B
Health Professions and Related Clinical Sciences, B
Health Services Administration, M
Health Services/Allied Health/Health Sciences, B
Health Teacher Education, B
Health and Physical Education, B
History, BM
Hospital and Health Care Facilities Administration/Management, M
Hospitality Administration/Management, AB
Human Development and Family Studies, B
Human Resources Management/Personnel Administration, B
Human Services, M
Industrial Engineering, B
Industrial/Management Engineering, M
Information Science/Studies, M
Information Technology, AB
Inorganic Chemistry, M
International Economics, B
Italian Language and Literature, B
Jazz/Jazz Studies, B
Journalism, B
Junior High/Intermediate/Middle School Education and Teaching, B
Kinesiology and Exercise Science, B
Labor and Industrial Relations, A
Legal Administrative Assistant/Secretary, A
Liberal Arts and Sciences Studies and Humanities, A
Management Information Systems and Services, B
Marketing, M
Marketing/Marketing Management, AB
Mathematics, BM
Mathematics Teacher Education, BM
Mechanical Engineering, BM
Mechanical Engineering/Mechanical Technology/Technician, AB
Medical/Clinical Assistant, A
Microbiology, M
Middle School Education, M
Molecular Biology, M
Music, BM
Music History, Literature, and Theory, BM
Music Performance, B
Music Teacher Education, BM
Music Theory and Composition, BM
Nursing, M
Operations Management and Supervision, B
Organic Chemistry, M
Painting, B
Performance, M
Philosophy, B
Photography, B
Physical Chemistry, M
Physical Education Teaching and Coaching, B
Physical Sciences, B
Physical Therapy/Therapist, D

Physics, B
Physiology, M
Piano and Organ, B
Political Science and Government, B
Pre-Dentistry Studies, B
Pre-Law Studies, B
Pre-Medicine/Pre-Medical Studies, B
Pre-Pharmacy Studies, B
Pre-Veterinary Studies, B
Printmaking, B
Psychology, BM
Public Health (MPH, DPH), B
Radio and Television, B
Reading Teacher Education, M
Religion/Religious Studies, B
Respiratory Care Therapy/Therapist, B
School Psychology, M
Science Teacher Education/General Science
  Teacher Education, BM
Secondary Education and Teaching, BM
Social Science Teacher Education, B
Social Studies Teacher Education, B
Social Work, AB
Sociology, B
Spanish Language Teacher Education, B
Spanish Language and Literature, B
Special Education and Teaching, BM
Statistics, M
Violin, Viola, Guitar and Other Stringed Instru-
  ments, B
Visual and Performing Arts, B
Voice and Opera, B

ZANE STATE COLLEGE

Accounting, A
Administrative Assistant and Secretarial Science, A
Business Administration and Management, A
Child Care Provider/Assistant, A
Clinical/Medical Laboratory Assistant, A
Computer Programming, Specific Applications, A
Criminal Justice/Law Enforcement Administration, A
Culinary Arts/Chef Training, A
Data Entry/Microcomputer Applications, A
Drafting and Design Technology/Technician, A
Electrical, Electronic and Communications Engineer-
  ing Technology/Technician, A
Environmental Studies, A
Human Resources Management/Personnel Adminis-
  tration, A
Industrial Radiologic Technology/Technician, A
Industrial Technology/Technician, A
Legal Assistant/Paralegal, A
Marketing/Marketing Management, A
Medical/Clinical Assistant, A
Mental Health Counseling/Counselor, A
Natural Resources Management/Development and
  Policy, A
Occupational Therapy/Therapist, A
Parks, Recreation and Leisure Facilities Manage-
  ment, A
Parks, Recreation, Leisure and Fitness Studies, A
Physical Therapist Assistant, A
Social Work, A
Tourism and Travel Services Management, A
Web Page, Digital/Multimedia and Information Re-
  sources Design, A

Oklahoma

BACONE COLLEGE

Accounting, AB
American Indian/Native American Studies, A
Art/Art Studies, General, A
Business Administration and Management, AB
Cardiopulmonary Technology/Technologist, A
Child Development, A
Criminal Justice/Law Enforcement Administration, A
Diagnostic Medical Sonography/Sonographer and
  Ultrasound Technician, A
Drama and Dramatics/Theatre Arts, A
E-Commerce/Electronic Commerce, B
Early Childhood Education and Teaching, B
Education, AB
Elementary Education and Teaching, B
Finance, B

General Studies, A
Health Information/Medical Records
  Technology/Technician, A
Information Science/Studies, B
International Business/Trade/Commerce, B
Journalism, A
Marketing/Marketing Management, B
Medical Radiologic Technology/Science - Radiation
  Therapist, A
Natural Resources Management/Development and
  Policy, A
Physical Education Teaching and Coaching, B
Sociology, A
Theological and Ministerial Studies, A

CAMERON UNIVERSITY

Accounting, B
Agriculture, B
Allied Health Diagnostic, Intervention, and Treat-
  ment Professions, A
Art/Art Studies, General, B
Biology/Biological Sciences, B
Broadcast Journalism, B
Business Administration and Management, AB
Business Administration, Management and Opera-
  tions, M
Chemistry, B
Child Development, B
Clinical Laboratory Science/Medical
  Technology/Technologist, B
Communication and Media Studies, B
Computer Science, B
Corrections and Criminal Justice, AB
Early Childhood Education and Teaching, B
Education, M
Educational Leadership and Administration, M
Educational/Instructional Media Design, AB
Elementary Education and Teaching, B
Engineering, A
Engineering Technologies/Technicians, B
English Language and Literature, B
English/Language Arts Teacher Education, B
Entrepreneurship/Entrepreneurial Studies, M
Foreign Languages and Literatures, B
General Studies, AB
Health Services/Allied Health/Health Sciences, A
Health and Physical Education, B
History, B
Information Technology, AB
Mathematics, B
Mathematics Teacher Education, B
Multi-/Interdisciplinary Studies, B
Music, B
Music Teacher Education, B
Physics, B
Political Science and Government, B
Psychology, BM
Social Studies Teacher Education, B
Sociology, B
Visual and Performing Arts, B

CARL ALBERT STATE COLLEGE

Biology/Biological Sciences, A
Business Administration and Management, A
Business/Commerce, A
Child Development, A
Computer and Information Sciences, A
Elementary Education and Teaching, A
Engineering, A
Engineering Technologies/Technicians, A
English Language and Literature, A
Foods, Nutrition, and Wellness Studies, A
Health Professions and Related Clinical Sciences, A
Health Services/Allied Health/Health Sciences, A
Hotel/Motel Administration/Management, A
Management Information Systems and Services, A
Mathematics, A
Physical Education Teaching and Coaching, A
Physical Sciences, A
Physical Therapist Assistant, A
Pre-Law Studies, A
Secondary Education and Teaching, A
Social Sciences, A

Telecommunications Technology/Technician, A

CLARY SAGE COLLEGE

Cosmetology/Cosmetologist, A
Fashion/Apparel Design, A
Interior Design, A
Massage Therapy/Therapeutic Massage, A

COMMUNITY CARE COLLEGE

Accounting Technology/Technician and Bookkeep-
  ing, A
Business Administration, Management and Opera-
  tions, A
Dental Assisting/Assistant, A
Early Childhood Education and Teaching, A
Health and Physical Education, A
Health/Health Care Administration/Management, A
Legal Assistant/Paralegal, A
Medical Insurance Coding Specialist/Coder, A
Medical/Clinical Assistant, A
Pharmacy Technician/Assistant, A
Surgical Technology/Technologist, A
Veterinary/Animal Health Technology/Technician and
  Veterinary Assistant, A

CONNORS STATE COLLEGE

Agriculture, A
Applied Horticulture/Horticultural Operations, A
Art/Art Studies, General, A
Biology/Biological Sciences, A
Business Administration and Management, A
Child Care Provider/Assistant, A
Criminal Justice/Police Science, A
Education, A
Equestrian/Equine Studies, A
Family and Community Services, A
Health/Medical Preparatory Programs, A
History, A
Information Science/Studies, A
Mathematics, A
Physics, A
Pre-Law Studies, A
Psychology, A
Social Work, A
Sociology, A

DEVRY UNIVERSITY

Business Administration and Management, B
Business Administration, Management and Opera-
  tions, B
Computer Systems Analysis/Analyst, B
Computer Systems Networking and Telecommunica-
  tions, AB
Criminal Justice/Law Enforcement Administration, B
Web Page, Digital/Multimedia and Information Re-
  sources Design, AB

EAST CENTRAL UNIVERSITY

Accounting, B
Accounting and Finance, B
Administrative Assistant and Secretarial Science, B
American Indian/Native American Studies, B
Applied Mathematics, B
Art Teacher Education, B
Art/Art Studies, General, B
Athletic Training and Sports Medicine, B
Biology Teacher Education, B
Biology/Biological Sciences, B
Business Administration and Management, B
Business Teacher Education, B
Business/Commerce, B
Cartography, B
Chemistry, B
Chemistry Teacher Education, B
Child Care Provider/Assistant, B
Clinical Laboratory Science/Medical
  Technology/Technologist, B
Communication Studies/Speech Communication
  and Rhetoric, B
Computer and Information Sciences, B
Counselor Education/School Counseling and Guid-
  ance Services, BM
Criminal Justice/Law Enforcement Administration, B
Criminal Justice/Police Science, B
Criminology, M

Drafting and Design Technology/Technician, B
Drama and Dance Teacher Education, B
Drama and Dramatics/Theatre Arts, B
Early Childhood Education and Teaching, B
Education, M
Elementary Education and Teaching, B
Engineering, B
Engineering Technologies/Technicians, B
English Language and Literature, B
English/Language Arts Teacher Education, B
Entrepreneurship/Entrepreneurial Studies, B
Environmental Health, B
Environmental/Environmental Health Engineering, B
Family and Consumer Sciences/Home Economics
    Teacher Education, B
Family and Consumer Sciences/Human Sciences, B
Fashion Merchandising, B
Finance, B
General Office Occupations and Clerical Services, B
General Studies, B
Geography, B
Graphic Design, B
Health Information/Medical Records
    Administration/Administrator, B
Health Information/Medical Records
    Technology/Technician, B
Health and Physical Education, B
Health/Health Care Administration/Management, B
History, B
History Teacher Education, B
Human Resources Management and Services, M
Human Resources Management/Personnel Adminis-
    tration, B
Human Services, M
International Business/Trade/Commerce, B
Journalism, B
Kinesiology and Exercise Science, B
Legal Assistant/Paralegal, B
Management Information Systems and Services, B
Marketing/Marketing Management, B
Mass Communication/Media Studies, B
Mathematics, B
Mathematics Teacher Education, B
Multi-/Interdisciplinary Studies, B
Music, B
Music Performance, B
Music Teacher Education, B
Nuclear Medical Technology/Technologist, B
Office Management and Supervision, B
Parks, Recreation, Leisure and Fitness Studies, B
Physical Education Teaching and Coaching, B
Physics, B
Physics Teacher Education, B
Piano and Organ, B
Political Science and Government, B
Psychology, BM
Reading Teacher Education, B
Rehabilitation Counseling, M
Religious/Sacred Music, B
School Librarian/School Library Media Specialist, B
Science Teacher Education/General Science
    Teacher Education, B
Social Studies Teacher Education, B
Social Work, B
Sociology, B
Spanish Language Teacher Education, B
Special Education and Teaching, B
Speech Teacher Education, B
Teacher Assistant/Aide, B
Vocational Rehabilitation Counseling/Counselor, B
Voice and Opera, B

EASTERN OKLAHOMA STATE COL-LEGE

Accounting Technology/Technician and Bookkeep-
    ing, A
Administrative Assistant and Secretarial Science, A
Agricultural Teacher Education, A
Agronomy and Crop Science, A
Animal Sciences, A
Art/Art Studies, General, A
Automotive Engineering Technology/Technician, A
Biology/Biological Sciences, A
Business Administration and Management, A
Business Teacher Education, A
Child Development, A

Computer and Information Sciences and Support
    Services, A
Computer/Information Technology Services Adminis-
    tration and Management, A
Electrical and Electronic Engineering
    Technologies/Technicians, A
Elementary Education and Teaching, A
Engineering, A
Farm/Farm and Ranch Management, A
Forestry, A
Health Professions and Related Clinical Sciences, A
Horticultural Science, A
Industrial Technology/Technician, A
Journalism, A
Management Science, A
Mathematics, A
Meat Cutting/Meat Cutter, A
Music, A
Natural Resources Management/Development and
    Policy, A
Parks, Recreation and Leisure Facilities Manage-
    ment, A
Physical Education Teaching and Coaching, A
Physical Sciences, A
Pre-Medicine/Pre-Medical Studies, A
Psychology, A
Secondary Education and Teaching, A
Security and Loss Prevention Services, A
Social Sciences, A
Teaching English as a Second or Foreign
    Language/ESL Language Instructor, A
Technology Teacher Education/Industrial Arts
    Teacher Education, A
Wildlife and Wildlands Science and Management, A

FAMILY OF FAITH COLLEGE

Divinity/Ministry (BD, MDiv.), B
Education, B

HERITAGE COLLEGE

Aesthetician/Esthetician and Skin Care Specialist, A
Allied Health and Medical Assisting Services, A
Health and Physical Education, A
Massage Therapy/Therapeutic Massage, A
Surgical Technology/Technologist, A

HILLSDALE FREE WILL BAPTIST COL-LEGE

Business/Commerce, AB
Communication Studies/Speech Communication
    and Rhetoric, B
Elementary Education and Teaching, AB
English Language and Literature, A
General Studies, A
Humanities/Humanistic Studies, B
Kinesiology and Exercise Science, B
Liberal Arts and Sciences Studies and Humani-
    ties, B
Missions/Missionary Studies and Missiology, AB
Multi-/Interdisciplinary Studies, B
Music, A
Music Performance, B
Pastoral Studies/Counseling, BM
Physical Education Teaching and Coaching, A
Physical Sciences, A
Piano and Organ, B
Psychology, AB
Religious Education, AB
Religious/Sacred Music, AB
Secondary Education and Teaching, A
Social Sciences, A
Theology/Theological Studies, B
Youth Ministry, B

LANGSTON UNIVERSITY

Accounting, B
Animal Sciences, B
Biology/Biological Sciences, B
Broadcast Journalism, B
Business Administration and Management, B
Chemistry, B
Computer Science, B
Corrections, AB
Drafting and Design Technology/Technician, A
Economics, B

Education, BM
Electrical, Electronic and Communications Engineer-
    ing Technology/Technician, A
Elementary Education and Teaching, BM
English Language and Literature, B
English as a Second Language, M
Family and Consumer Sciences/Home Economics
    Teacher Education, B
Health/Health Care Administration/Management, B
Hospital and Health Care Facilities
    Administration/Management, B
Journalism, B
Liberal Arts and Sciences Studies and Humani-
    ties, B
Mass Communication/Media Studies, B
Mathematics, B
Multilingual and Multicultural Education, M
Music, B
Music Teacher Education, B
Physical Education Teaching and Coaching, B
Physical Therapy/Therapist, BD
Psychology, B
Public Health (MPH, DPH), B
Rehabilitation Counseling, M
Secondary Education and Teaching, B
Sociology, B
Special Education and Teaching, B
Teaching English as a Second or Foreign
    Language/ESL Language Instructor, B
Urban Education and Leadership, M

MID-AMERICA CHRISTIAN UNIVERSITY

Behavioral Sciences, B
Business Administration and Management, B
Business Administration, Management and Opera-
    tions, M
Counseling Psychology, M
Criminal Justice/Law Enforcement Administration, B
Divinity/Ministry (BD, MDiv.), B
Elementary Education and Teaching, B
English Language and Literature, B
History, B
Liberal Arts and Sciences Studies and Humani-
    ties, A
Management Information Systems and Services, B
Management Science, B
Marketing/Marketing Management, B
Marriage and Family Therapy/Counseling, M
Mathematics, B
Music, B
Music Teacher Education, B
Organizational Management, M
Pastoral Counseling and Specialized Ministries, B
Pastoral Studies/Counseling, M
Public Administration, M
Religious/Sacred Music, B
Secondary Education and Teaching, B
Social Sciences, B

MURRAY STATE COLLEGE

Agricultural Teacher Education, A
Agriculture, A
Biological and Biomedical Sciences, A
Biology/Biological Sciences, A
Chemistry, A
Child Care Provider/Assistant, A
Child Development, A
Computer and Information Sciences, A
Corrections and Criminal Justice, A
Elementary Education and Teaching, A
Fine Arts and Art Studies, A
General Studies, A
Gunsmithing/Gunsmith, A
History, A
Humanities/Humanistic Studies, A
Industrial Production Technologies/Technicians, A
Information Science/Studies, A
Management Science, A
Mathematics, A
Natural Resources and Conservation, A
Occupational Therapist Assistant, A
Physical Education Teaching and Coaching, A
Physical Therapist Assistant, A
Psychology, A

Veterinary/Animal Health Technology/Technician and
   Veterinary Assistant, A

NORTHEASTERN OKLAHOMA AGRI-CULTURAL AND MECHANICAL COLLEGE

Administrative Assistant and Secretarial Science, A
Agriculture, A
American Indian/Native American Studies, A
Architectural Drafting and Architectural
   CAD/CADD, A
Art/Art Studies, General, A
Business Administration and Management, A
Clinical/Medical Laboratory Technician, A
Computer and Information Sciences, A
Criminal Justice/Police Science, A
Drama and Dramatics/Theatre Arts, A
Elementary Education and Teaching, A
Engineering, A
English/Language Arts Teacher Education, A
Farm/Farm and Ranch Management, A
Forestry, A
General Studies, A
Kindergarten/PreSchool Education and Teaching, A
Marketing/Marketing Management, A
Mass Communication/Media Studies, A
Music, A
Physical Education Teaching and Coaching, A
Physical Therapist Assistant, A
Pre-Medicine/Pre-Medical Studies, A
Pre-Nursing Studies, A
Pre-Veterinary Studies, A
Psychology, A
Social Sciences, A

NORTHEASTERN STATE UNIVERSITY

Accounting, BM
American Indian/Native American Studies, B
American/United States Studies/Civilization, M
Area Studies, B
Art Teacher Education, B
Art/Art Studies, General, B
Audiology/Audiologist and Speech-Language
   Pathology/Pathologist, B
Biology/Biological Sciences, B
Business Administration and Management, B
Business Administration, Management and Operations, M
Chemistry, B
Clinical Laboratory Science/Medical
   Technology/Technologist, B
Communication Disorders, M
Communication Studies/Speech Communication
   and Rhetoric, B
Communication and Media Studies, M
Computer Science, B
Counseling Psychology, M
Counselor Education/School Counseling and Guidance Services, M
Criminal Justice/Law Enforcement Administration, B
Criminology, M
Drama and Dramatics/Theatre Arts, B
Early Childhood Education and Teaching, BM
Education, M
Education/Teaching of Individuals with Specific
   Learning Disabilities, B
Educational Administration and Supervision, M
Educational Leadership and Administration, M
Educational Media/Instructional Technology, M
Elementary Education and Teaching, B
Engineering Technologies/Technicians, B
English, M
English Language and Literature, B
English/Language Arts Teacher Education, B
Entrepreneurship/Entrepreneurial Studies, B
Environmental Policy and Resource Management, M
Environmental and Occupational Health, M
Family and Consumer Sciences/Human Sciences, B
Finance, B
Finance and Banking, M
Foundations and Philosophy of Education, M
General Studies, B
Geography, B
Health Education, M
Health Professions and Related Clinical Sciences, B

Health Services Administration, B
History, B
Indian/Native American Education, B
Industrial Safety Technology/Technician, B
International Business/Trade/Commerce, B
Kinesiology and Exercise Science, B
Kinesiology and Movement Studies, M
Logistics and Materials Management, B
Management Information Systems and Services, B
Marketing/Marketing Management, B
Mass Communication/Media Studies, B
Mathematics, B
Mathematics Teacher Education, BM
Music, B
Music Teacher Education, B
Natural Resources and Conservation, M
Nursing Education, M
Occupational Therapy/Therapist, M
Operations Management and Supervision, B
Optometry, D
Physical Education Teaching and Coaching, B
Political Science and Government, B
Psychology, BM
Reading Teacher Education, M
Science Teacher Education/General Science
   Teacher Education, BM
Social Studies Teacher Education, B
Social Work, B
Sociology, B
Spanish Language Teacher Education, B
Spanish Language and Literature, B
Substance Abuse/Addiction Counseling, M
Tourism and Travel Services Management, B

NORTHERN OKLAHOMA COLLEGE

Accounting, A
Administrative Assistant and Secretarial Science, A
Agricultural Business and Management, A
Biological and Physical Sciences, A
Broadcast Journalism, A
Business Administration and Management, A
Commercial and Advertising Art, A
Computer Science, A
Construction Engineering Technology/Technician, A
Criminal Justice/Law Enforcement Administration, A
Drafting and Design Technology/Technician, A
Elementary Education and Teaching, A
Engineering, A
Graphic and Printing Equipment Operator Production, A
Information Science/Studies, A
Liberal Arts and Sciences Studies and Humanities, A

NORTHWESTERN OKLAHOMA STATE UNIVERSITY

Accounting, B
Adult and Continuing Education and Teaching, M
Agricultural and Extension Education Services, B
Agriculture, B
American/United States Studies/Civilization, M
Biology/Biological Sciences, B
Business Administration and Management, B
Chemistry, B
Computer Science, B
Computer Systems Networking and Telecommunications, B
Counseling Psychology, M
Counselor Education/School Counseling and Guidance Services, M
Criminal Justice/Police Science, B
Curriculum and Instruction, M
Early Childhood Education and Teaching, B
Education, M
Educational Leadership and Administration, M
Elementary Education and Teaching, BM
English Language and Literature, B
English/Language Arts Teacher Education, B
General Studies, B
Health Teacher Education, B
History, B
Information Science/Studies, B
Kindergarten/PreSchool Education and Teaching, B
Mass Communication/Media Studies, B
Mathematics, B
Mathematics Teacher Education, B

Multi-/Interdisciplinary Studies, B
Music, B
Music Teacher Education, B
Physical Education Teaching and Coaching, B
Political Science and Government, B
Pre-Dentistry Studies, B
Pre-Law Studies, B
Pre-Medicine/Pre-Medical Studies, B
Psychology, B
Reading Teacher Education, M
Science Teacher Education/General Science
   Teacher Education, B
Secondary Education and Teaching, BM
Security and Protective Services, B
Social Sciences, B
Social Work, B
Sociology, B
Spanish Language and Literature, B
Special Education and Teaching, B

OKLAHOMA BAPTIST UNIVERSITY

Accounting, B
Ancient Near Eastern and Biblical Languages, Literatures, and Linguistics, B
Anthropology, B
Art/Art Studies, General, B
Athletic Training and Sports Medicine, B
Bible/Biblical Studies, B
Biochemistry, B
Biology/Biological Sciences, B
Business Administration, Management and Operations, M
Chemistry, B
Christian Studies, AB
Communication Studies/Speech Communication
   and Rhetoric, B
Computer Science, B
Computer and Information Sciences, B
Divinity/Ministry (BD, MDiv.), B
Drama and Dramatics/Theatre Arts, B
Early Childhood Education and Teaching, B
Education, B
Elementary Education and Teaching, B
Energy Management and Policy, M
English/Language Arts Teacher Education, B
Family and Community Services, B
Finance, B
Fine/Studio Arts, B
Graphic Design, B
Health and Physical Education, B
History, B
Humanities/Humanistic Studies, B
Information Science/Studies, B
International Business/Trade/Commerce, B
International Marketing, B
International Relations and Affairs, B
Journalism, B
Kindergarten/PreSchool Education and Teaching, B
Kinesiology and Exercise Science, B
Management Information Systems and Services, B
Management Science, B
Marketing/Marketing Management, B
Marriage and Family Therapy/Counseling, BM
Mass Communication/Media Studies, B
Mathematics, B
Mathematics Teacher Education, B
Music, B
Music Performance, B
Music Teacher Education, B
Music Theory and Composition, B
Natural Sciences, B
Nursing, M
Nursing Education, M
Parks, Recreation, Leisure and Fitness Studies, B
Philosophy, B
Physical Education Teaching and Coaching, B
Physics, B
Physiology, B
Political Science and Government, B
Psychology, B
Religion/Religious Studies, B
Religious/Sacred Music, B
Science Teacher Education/General Science
   Teacher Education, B
Social Sciences, B
Social Studies Teacher Education, B

Sociology, B
Spanish Language Teacher Education, B
Spanish Language and Literature, B
Special Education and Teaching, B
Sport and Fitness Administration/Management, B
Voice and Opera, B

OKLAHOMA CHRISTIAN UNIVERSITY

Accounting, BM
Advertising, B
American Government and Politics (United
    States), B
Art/Art Studies, General, B
Bible/Biblical Studies, B
Biochemistry, B
Biology/Biological Sciences, B
Broadcast Journalism, B
Business Administration and Management, B
Business Administration, Management and Opera-
    tions, M
Business/Commerce, B
Chemistry, B
Child Development, B
Clinical Laboratory Science/Medical
    Technology/Technologist, B
Commercial and Advertising Art, B
Communication, Journalism and Related Pro-
    grams, B
Computer Engineering, B
Computer Science, B
Drama and Dramatics/Theatre Arts, B
Early Childhood Education and Teaching, B
Electrical, Electronics and Communications Engi-
    neering, B
Electronic Commerce, M
Elementary Education and Teaching, B
Engineering, B
Engineering and Applied Sciences, M
English Language and Literature, B
English/Language Arts Teacher Education, B
Family and Community Services, B
Finance, B
Finance and Banking, M
Health Services Administration, M
History, B
Human Resources Management and Services, M
Information Science/Studies, B
Interior Design, B
International Business/Trade/Commerce, M
Journalism, B
Kindergarten/PreSchool Education and Teaching, B
Liberal Arts and Sciences Studies and Humani-
    ties, B
Marketing, M
Marketing/Marketing Management, B
Mass Communication/Media Studies, B
Mathematics, B
Mathematics Teacher Education, B
Mechanical Engineering, B
Missions/Missionary Studies and Missiology, B
Music, B
Music Teacher Education, B
Organizational Management, M
Pastoral Studies/Counseling, M
Physical Education Teaching and Coaching, B
Pre-Law Studies, B
Project Management, M
Psychology, B
Public Relations/Image Management, B
Radio and Television, B
Religion/Religious Studies, B
Religious Education, B
Science Teacher Education/General Science
    Teacher Education, B
Secondary Education and Teaching, B
Social Studies Teacher Education, B
Spanish Language and Literature, B
Sport and Fitness Administration/Management, B
Teaching English as a Second or Foreign
    Language/ESL Language Instructor, B
Theology and Religious Vocations, M

Voice and Opera, B

OKLAHOMA CITY COMMUNITY COLLEGE

Administrative Assistant and Secretarial Science, A
American Government and Politics (United
    States), A
Animation, Interactive Technology, Video Graphics
    and Special Effects, A
Architectural Drafting and Architectural
    CAD/CADD, A
Art/Art Studies, General, A
Automobile/Automotive Mechanics
    Technology/Technician, A
Automotive Engineering Technology/Technician, A
Banking and Financial Support Services, A
BioTechnology, A
Biology/Biological Sciences, A
Broadcast Journalism, A
Business Administration and Management, A
Business/Commerce, A
Cartography, A
Chemistry, A
Child Development, A
Cinematography and Film/Video Production, A
Commercial and Advertising Art, A
Computer Engineering Technology/Technician, A
Computer Science, A
Computer Systems Analysis/Analyst, A
Computer Systems Networking and Telecommunica-
    tions, A
Design and Applied Arts, A
Design and Visual Communications, A
Diesel Mechanics Technology/Technician, A
Digital Communication and Media/Multimedia, A
Drafting and Design Technology/Technician, A
Drama and Dramatics/Theatre Arts, A
Elementary Education and Teaching, A
Emergency Medical Technology/Technician (EMT
    Paramedic), A
Engineering Technologies/Technicians, A
Fine/Studio Arts, A
Foreign Languages and Literatures, A
General Studies, A
Graphic Communications, A
Health Information/Medical Records
    Administration/Administrator, A
History, A
Humanities/Humanistic Studies, A
Legal Administrative Assistant/Secretary, A
Liberal Arts and Sciences Studies and Humani-
    ties, A
Mass Communication/Media Studies, A
Mathematics, A
Medical/Clinical Assistant, A
Multi-/Interdisciplinary Studies, A
Music, A
Philosophy, A
Photographic and Film/Video Technology/Technician
    and Assistant, A
Physics, A
Political Science and Government, A
Psychology, A
Respiratory Care Therapy/Therapist, A
Sociology, A
Surgical Technology/Technologist, A
System, Networking, and LAN/WAN
    Management/Manager, A

OKLAHOMA CITY UNIVERSITY

Accounting, BM
Acting, B
Applied Behavior Analysis, M
Art/Art Studies, General, B
Biochemistry, B
Biological and Biomedical Sciences, B
Biology/Biological Sciences, B
Biomedical Sciences, B
Broadcast Journalism, B
Business Administration and Management, B
Business Administration, Management and Opera-
    tions, M
Cell/Cellular and Molecular Biology, B
Cinematography and Film/Video Production, B
Communication and Media Studies, B
Composition, M

Computer Science, M
Computer Software Engineering, B
Computer and Information Sciences, B
Criminal Justice/Law Enforcement Administration, B
Criminal Justice/Police Science, B
Criminology, M
Dance, BM
Drama and Dramatics/Theatre Arts, B
Early Childhood Education and Teaching, BM
Economics, B
Education, BM
Elementary Education and Teaching, B
Energy Management and Policy, M
English Language and Literature, B
English as a Second Language, M
English/Language Arts Teacher Education, B
Environmental Studies, B
Film/Video and Photographic Arts, B
Finance, B
Fine Arts and Art Studies, B
Fine/Studio Arts, B
French Language and Literature, B
History, B
Law and Legal Studies, MD
Legal and Justice Studies, M
Liberal Arts and Sciences Studies and Humani-
    ties, B
Liberal Studies, M
Marketing/Marketing Management, B
Mass Communication/Media Studies, B
Mathematics, B
Music, BM
Music Performance, B
Music Theory and Composition, B
Nursing, MD
Performance, M
Philosophy, B
Photography, B
Physical Education Teaching and Coaching, B
Physics, B
Piano and Organ, B
Political Science and Government, B
Pre-Law Studies, B
Pre-Medicine/Pre-Medical Studies, B
Pre-Nursing Studies, B
Psychology, B
Public Relations, Advertising, and Applied Commu-
    nication, B
Religion/Religious Studies, BM
Religious/Sacred Music, B
Secondary Education and Teaching, B
Sociology, BM
Spanish Language and Literature, B
Special Education and Teaching, B
Speech Teacher Education, B
Teaching English as a Second or Foreign
    Language/ESL Language Instructor, B
Technical Theatre/Theatre Design and Technol-
    ogy, B
Theater, M
Violin, Viola, Guitar and Other Stringed Instru-
    ments, B
Visual and Performing Arts, B
Voice and Opera, B

OKLAHOMA PANHANDLE STATE UNIVERSITY

Accounting, B
Agricultural Business and Management, B
Agricultural Teacher Education, B
Agriculture, A
Agronomy and Crop Science, B
Animal Sciences, B
Art/Art Studies, General, B
Biological and Physical Sciences, B
Biology/Biological Sciences, B
Business Administration and Management, AB
Business Teacher Education, B
Chemistry, B
Clinical Laboratory Science/Medical
    Technology/Technologist, B
Computer and Information Sciences, B
Criminal Justice/Police Science, A
Elementary Education and Teaching, B
English Language and Literature, B
General Studies, A

Health and Physical Education, B
History, B
Horse Husbandry/Equine Science and Management, B
Industrial Technology/Technician, AB
Liberal Arts and Sciences Studies and Humanities, B
Mathematics, B
Music, B
Psychology, B
Social Sciences, B

OKLAHOMA STATE UNIVERSITY

Accounting, BMD
Aeronautics/Aviation/Aerospace Science and Technology, B
Aerospace, Aeronautical and Astronautical Engineering, B
Agricultural Business and Management, B
Agricultural Communication/Journalism, B
Agricultural Economics, BMD
Agricultural Education, MD
Agricultural Engineering, MD
Agricultural Public Services, B
Agricultural Sciences, MD
Agricultural Teacher Education, B
Agricultural/Biological Engineering and Bioengineering, B
Agronomy and Soil Sciences, MD
American/United States Studies/Civilization, B
Animal Sciences, BMD
Applied Behavior Analysis, D
Applied Mathematics, MD
Applied Psychology, MDO
Architectural Engineering, B
Architecture, B
Art/Art Studies, General, B
Athletic Training and Sports Medicine, B
Biochemistry, BMD
Bioengineering, MD
Biological and Biomedical Sciences, MD
Biology/Biological Sciences, B
Botany/Plant Biology, BMD
Business Administration and Management, B
Business/Managerial Economics, B
Chemical Engineering, BMD
Chemistry, BMD
Child and Family Studies, MD
Civil Engineering, BMD
Clinical Psychology, D
Clothing and Textiles, MD
Communication Disorders, M
Computer Engineering, BMD
Computer Science, MD
Computer and Information Sciences, B
Construction Engineering Technology/Technician, B
Consumer Economics, M
Curriculum and Instruction, MD
Design and Applied Arts, MD
Drama and Dramatics/Theatre Arts, B
Ecology, B
Economics, BMD
Education, MDO
Educational Leadership and Administration, MD
Educational Psychology, MDO
Electrical Engineering, MD
Electrical, Electronic and Communications Engineering Technology/Technician, B
Electrical, Electronics and Communications Engineering, B
Elementary Education and Teaching, B
Emergency Management, MD
Engineering and Applied Sciences, MD
English, MD
English Language and Literature, B
Entomology, BMD
Entrepreneurship/Entrepreneurial Studies, BMD
Environmental Engineering Technology/Environmental Technology, MD
Environmental Sciences, BMD
Family and Consumer Sciences/Human Sciences, MD
Finance, B
Finance and Banking, MD
Fire Protection Engineering, MD
Fire Protection and Safety Technology/Technician, B

Food Science, B
Food Science and Technology, MD
Foods, Nutrition, and Wellness Studies, B
Forestry, MD
French Language and Literature, B
General Studies, B
Geography, BMD
Geology/Earth Science, BMD
German Language and Literature, B
Health Education, MDO
Health Psychology, MDO
Higher Education/Higher Education Administration, D
History, BMD
Home Economics, MD
Horticultural Science, BMD
Hospitality Administration/Management, BMD
Housing and Human Environments, B
Human Development, D
Human Development and Family Studies, B
Industrial Engineering, B
Industrial/Management Engineering, MD
Information Science/Studies, D
Information Technology, B
International Affairs, M
International Business/Trade/Commerce, B
Journalism, B
Landscape Architecture, BMD
Landscaping and Groundskeeping, B
Liberal Arts and Sciences Studies and Humanities, B
Management, MD
Management Information Systems and Services, MD
Marketing, MD
Marketing/Marketing Management, B
Marriage and Family Therapy/Counseling, M
Mass Communication/Media Studies, M
Mathematics, BMD
Mathematics Teacher Education, MD
Mechanical Engineering, BMD
Mechanical Engineering/Mechanical Technology/Technician, B
Microbiology, BMD
Molecular Biology, MD
Molecular Genetics, MD
Music, BM
Music Teacher Education, BM
Natural Resources and Conservation, MD
Non-Profit/Public/Organizational Management, O
Nutritional Sciences, MD
Parks, Recreation, Leisure and Fitness Studies, B
Performance, M
Philosophy, BM
Photonics, MD
Physical Education Teaching and Coaching, B
Physics, BMD
Physiology, B
Plant Pathology/Phytopathology, MD
Plant Sciences, MD
Political Science and Government, BMD
Psychology, BMD
Public Health Education and Promotion, B
Public Relations, Advertising, and Applied Communication, B
Russian Language and Literature, B
Secondary Education and Teaching, B
Sociology, BMD
Soil Science and Agronomy, B
Spanish Language and Literature, B
Speech-Language Pathology/Pathologist, B
Statistics, BMD
Sustainability Management, O
Technical Teacher Education, B
Telecommunications Management, M
Theater, M
Veterinary Medicine, D
Veterinary Sciences, MD
Writing, M
Zoology/Animal Biology, B

OKLAHOMA STATE UNIVERSITY INSTITUTE OF TECHNOLOGY

Autobody/Collision and Repair Technology/Technician, A
Automotive Engineering Technology/Technician, A

Business/Commerce, A
Civil Engineering Technology/Technician, B
Computer and Information Systems Security, B
Construction Engineering Technology/Technician, A
Culinary Arts and Related Services, A
Diesel Mechanics Technology/Technician, A
Engineering Technology, A
General Office Occupations and Clerical Services, A
Graphic Design, A
Health Services/Allied Health/Health Sciences, A
Heating, Air Conditioning, Ventilation and Refrigeration Maintenance Technology/Technician, A
Information Technology, A
Instrumentation Technology/Technician, B
Intermedia/Multimedia, A
Mechanic and Repair Technologies/Technicians, A
Mechanical Engineering/Mechanical Technology/Technician, A
Multi-/Interdisciplinary Studies, A
Orthotist/Prosthetist, A
Petroleum Technology/Technician, A
Photography, A
Teacher Education, Multiple Levels, A

OKLAHOMA STATE UNIVERSITY, OKLAHOMA CITY

Accounting, A
American Sign Language (ASL), A
Architectural Drafting and Architectural CAD/CADD, A
Architectural Engineering Technology/Technician, A
Art/Art Studies, General, A
Building/Home/Construction Inspection/Inspector, A
Business Administration and Management, A
Civil Engineering Technology/Technician, A
Construction Engineering Technology/Technician, A
Construction Management, A
Construction Trades, A
Criminal Justice/Police Science, A
Drafting and Design Technology/Technician, A
Early Childhood Education and Teaching, A
Economics, A
Electrical and Power Transmission Installation/Installer, A
Electrical, Electronic and Communications Engineering Technology/Technician, A
Electrocardiograph Technology/Technician, A
Emergency Medical Technology/Technician (EMT Paramedic), A
Engineering Technology, A
Fire Protection and Safety Technology/Technician, A
Fire Science/Firefighting, A
General Studies, A
Health/Health Care Administration/Management, A
History, A
Horticultural Science, A
Human Services, A
Humanities/Humanistic Studies, A
Illustration, A
Information Science/Studies, A
Information Technology, A
Language Interpretation and Translation, A
Occupational Safety and Health Technology/Technician, A
Physics, A
Pre-Nursing Studies, A
Psychology, A
Public Administration and Social Service Professions, A
Radiologic Technology/Science - Radiographer, A
Sign Language Interpretation and Translation, A
Substance Abuse/Addiction Counseling, A
Survey Technology/Surveying, A
Turf and Turfgrass Management, A
Veterinary/Animal Health Technology/Technician and Veterinary Assistant, A
Web Page, Digital/Multimedia and Information Resources Design, A

OKLAHOMA TECHNICAL COLLEGE

Automobile/Automotive Mechanics Technology/Technician, A
Diesel Mechanics Technology/Technician, A
Heating, Air Conditioning and Refrigeration Technology/Technician, A

Welding Technology/Welder, A

OKLAHOMA WESLEYAN UNIVERSITY

Bible/Biblical Studies, B
Biological and Physical Sciences, A
Biology/Biological Sciences, AB
Business Administration and Management, AB
Business, Management, Marketing, and Related
  Support Services, AB
Business/Commerce, B
Business/Managerial Economics, B
Chemistry, AB
Christian Studies, AB
Criminology, B
Early Childhood Education and Teaching, AB
Elementary Education and Teaching, B
English Language and Literature, B
English/Language Arts Teacher Education, B
General Studies, AB
History, AB
Human Resources Management/Personnel Adminis-
  tration, B
Kinesiology and Exercise Science, B
Management Strategy and Policy, M
Marketing, B
Mathematics, AB
Mathematics Teacher Education, B
Missions/Missionary Studies and Missiology, B
Music, B
Music Teacher Education, B
Nursing Administration, M
Nursing Education, M
Pastoral Counseling and Specialized Ministries, B
Physical Education Teaching and Coaching, B
Physical Sciences, AB
Pre-Law Studies, B
Psychology, B
Religion/Religious Studies, B
Religious/Sacred Music, B
Science Teacher Education/General Science
  Teacher Education, B
Social Sciences, B
Social Studies Teacher Education, B
Theological and Ministerial Studies, B
Theology and Religious Vocations, BM
Theology/Theological Studies, B

ORAL ROBERTS UNIVERSITY

Accounting, BM
Acting, B
Art Teacher Education, B
Art/Art Studies, General, B
Bible/Biblical Studies, B
Biochemistry, B
Biology/Biological Sciences, B
Biomedical/Medical Engineering, B
Business Administration and Management, B
Business Administration, Management and Opera-
  tions, M
Business Teacher Education, B
Chemistry, B
Clinical Laboratory Science/Medical
  Technology/Technologist, B
Commercial and Advertising Art, B
Communication Studies/Speech Communication
  and Rhetoric, B
Computer Engineering, B
Computer Science, B
Computer and Information Sciences, B
Curriculum and Instruction, M
Dance, B
Design and Visual Communications, B
Drama and Dramatics/Theatre Arts, B
Early Childhood Education and Teaching, B
Education, MD
Educational Administration and Supervision, MD
Electrical, Electronics and Communications Engi-
  neering, B
Elementary Education and Teaching, B
Engineering, B
Engineering Physics, B
English Language and Literature, B
English/Language Arts Teacher Education, B
Entrepreneurship/Entrepreneurial Studies, M
Environmental/Environmental Health Engineering, B
Finance, B

Finance and Banking, M
Fine/Studio Arts, B
Foreign Language Teacher Education, B
French Language and Literature, B
Graphic Design, B
Health Teacher Education, B
Health and Physical Education, B
Higher Education/Higher Education Administra-
  tion, D
History, B
International Business/Trade/Commerce, BM
International Marketing, B
International Relations and Affairs, B
Kinesiology and Exercise Science, B
Liberal Arts and Sciences Studies and Humani-
  ties, B
Management, M
Management Information Systems and Services, B
Management Science, B
Marketing, M
Marketing/Marketing Management, B
Marriage and Family Therapy/Counseling, M
Mathematics, B
Mathematics Teacher Education, B
Mechanical Engineering, B
Missions/Missionary Studies and Missiology, BMD
Music, B
Music Performance, B
Music Teacher Education, B
Music Theory and Composition, B
Near and Middle Eastern Languages, M
Non-Profit/Public/Organizational Management, M
Organizational Behavior Studies, B
Parks, Recreation and Leisure Facilities Manage-
  ment, B
Pastoral Studies/Counseling, BM
Physical Education Teaching and Coaching, B
Physics, B
Piano and Organ, B
Political Science and Government, B
Pre-Theology/Pre-Ministerial Studies, B
Psychology, B
Religious Education, BM
Religious/Sacred Music, B
Science Teacher Education/General Science
  Teacher Education, B
Social Studies Teacher Education, B
Social Work, B
Spanish Language Teacher Education, B
Spanish Language and Literature, B
Special Education and Teaching, B
Technical Theatre/Theatre Design and Technol-
  ogy, B
Theology and Religious Vocations, MD
Theology/Theological Studies, B
Voice and Opera, B

REDLANDS COMMUNITY COLLEGE

Administrative Assistant and Secretarial Science, A
Agricultural Business and Management, A
Agricultural Teacher Education, A
Agriculture, A
Animal Sciences, A
Art/Art Studies, General, A
Biological and Physical Sciences, A
Biology/Biological Sciences, A
Business Administration and Management, A
Child Development, A
Commercial and Advertising Art, A
Computer Programming/Programmer, A
Computer Science, A
Construction Engineering Technology/Technician, A
Corrections, A
Criminal Justice/Law Enforcement Administration, A
Criminal Justice/Police Science, A
Drafting and Design Technology/Technician, A
Education, A
Electrical, Electronic and Communications Engineer-
  ing Technology/Technician, A
Elementary Education and Teaching, A
Emergency Medical Technology/Technician (EMT
  Paramedic), A
English Language and Literature, A
Equestrian/Equine Studies, A
Kindergarten/PreSchool Education and Teaching, A

Liberal Arts and Sciences Studies and Humani-
  ties, A
Mathematics, A
Physical Education Teaching and Coaching, A
Physical Sciences, A
Psychology, A
Social Sciences, A

ROGERS STATE UNIVERSITY

Accounting, A
Biology/Biological Sciences, AB
Business Administration and Management, AB
Computer Graphics, B
Computer and Information Sciences, A
Criminal Justice/Law Enforcement Administration, B
Criminal Justice/Police Science, A
Elementary Education and Teaching, A
Emergency Medical Technology/Technician (EMT
  Paramedic), A
Engineering Technologies/Technicians, AB
History, AB
Liberal Arts and Sciences Studies and Humani-
  ties, AB
Management Information Systems and Services, B
Multi-/Interdisciplinary Studies, B
Non-Profit/Public/Organizational Management, B
Physics, A
Public Administration, B
Radio, Television, and Digital Communication, B
Secondary Education and Teaching, A
Social Sciences, AB
Sport and Fitness Administration/Management, B
Visual and Performing Arts, B

ROSE STATE COLLEGE

Accounting, A
Administrative Assistant and Secretarial Science, A
Art/Art Studies, General, A
Avionics Maintenance Technology/Technician, A
Biology/Biological Sciences, A
Broadcast Journalism, A
Business Administration and Management, A
Business/Commerce, A
Chemistry, A
Clinical/Medical Laboratory Technician, A
Court Reporting/Court Reporter, A
Criminal Justice/Law Enforcement Administration, A
Dental Assisting/Assistant, A
Dental Hygiene/Hygienist, A
Drafting and Design Technology/Technician, A
Drama and Dramatics/Theatre Arts, A
Electrical, Electronic and Communications Engineer-
  ing Technology/Technician, A
Elementary Education and Teaching, A
English Language and Literature, A
Environmental Engineering
  Technology/Environmental Technology, A
Family and Consumer Sciences/Human Sciences, A
History, A
Industrial Radiologic Technology/Technician, A
Information Science/Studies, A
Journalism, A
Kindergarten/PreSchool Education and Teaching, A
Kinesiology and Exercise Science, A
Legal Administrative Assistant/Secretary, A
Liberal Arts and Sciences Studies and Humani-
  ties, A
Library Science, A
Management Information Systems and Services, A
Mathematics, A
Medical Radiologic Technology/Science - Radiation
  Therapist, A
Modern Languages, A
Music, A
Parks, Recreation and Leisure Facilities Manage-
  ment, A
Physical Education Teaching and Coaching, A
Physical Therapy/Therapist, A
Physics, A
Political Science and Government, A
Pre-Pharmacy Studies, A
Psychology, A
Respiratory Care Therapy/Therapist, A

Sociology, A

ST. GREGORY'S UNIVERSITY

Accounting, B
Biological and Physical Sciences, B
Biology Teacher Education, B
Biology/Biological Sciences, B
Biomedical Sciences, B
Business Administration and Management, AB
Communication Studies/Speech Communication
and Rhetoric, B
Criminal Justice/Police Science, B
Dance, B
Drama and Dramatics/Theatre Arts, B
Early Childhood Education and Teaching, A
Elementary Education and Teaching, B
English Language and Literature, B
English/Language Arts Teacher Education, B
Finance, B
Health and Physical Education, B
History, B
Kinesiology and Exercise Science, B
Liberal Arts and Sciences Studies and Humanities, AB
Management Information Systems and Services, B
Management Science, B
Marketing/Marketing Management, B
Mathematics, B
Mathematics Teacher Education, B
Pastoral Studies/Counseling, B
Philosophy, B
Political Science and Government, B
Psychology, B
Social Sciences, AB
Social Studies Teacher Education, B
Theology/Theological Studies, B
Visual and Performing Arts, B

SEMINOLE STATE COLLEGE

Accounting, A
Art/Art Studies, General, A
Behavioral Sciences, A
Biological and Biomedical Sciences, A
Biology/Biological Sciences, A
Business Administration and Management, A
Business/Commerce, A
Child Development, A
Clinical/Medical Laboratory Technician, A
Computer Science, A
Criminal Justice/Law Enforcement Administration, A
Criminal Justice/Police Science, A
Elementary Education and Teaching, A
Engineering, A
English Language and Literature, A
Fine Arts and Art Studies, A
General Studies, A
Humanities/Humanistic Studies, A
Liberal Arts and Sciences Studies and Humanities, A
Management Information Systems and Services, A
Mathematics, A
Physical Education Teaching and Coaching, A
Physical Sciences, A
Psychology, A
Social Sciences, A

SOUTHEASTERN OKLAHOMA STATE UNIVERSITY

Accounting, B
Airframe Mechanics and Aircraft Maintenance
Technology/Technician, B
Airline/Commercial/Professional Pilot and Flight
Crew, B
Art Teacher Education, B
Art/Art Studies, General, B
Aviation, M
Aviation/Airway Management and Operations, M
BioTechnology, BM
Biology/Biological Sciences, B
Business Administration and Management, B
Business Administration, Management and Operations, M
Chemistry, B
Child Care Provider/Assistant, B
Clinical Psychology, M

Communication Studies/Speech Communication
and Rhetoric, B
Communication, Journalism and Related Programs, B
Computer and Information Sciences, B
Counseling Psychology, M
Counselor Education/School Counseling and Guidance Services, M
Criminal Justice/Safety Studies, B
Drama and Dramatics/Theatre Arts, B
Education, M
Educational Administration and Supervision, M
Elementary Education and Teaching, B
English Language and Literature, B
English/Language Arts Teacher Education, B
Environmental and Occupational Health, M
Finance, B
General Studies, B
History, B
Information Science/Studies, B
Kindergarten/PreSchool Education and Teaching, B
Management Information Systems and Services, M
Management Science, B
Marketing/Marketing Management, B
Mathematics, B
Mathematics Teacher Education, BM
Multi-/Interdisciplinary Studies, B
Music, B
Music Performance, B
Music Teacher Education, B
Natural Resources and Conservation, B
Occupational Safety and Health
Technology/Technician, B
Parks, Recreation, Leisure and Fitness Studies, B
Physical Education Teaching and Coaching, B
Political Science and Government, B
Psychology, B
Reading Teacher Education, M
Science Teacher Education/General Science
Teacher Education, B
Social Studies Teacher Education, B
Sociology, B
Spanish Language Teacher Education, B
Spanish Language and Literature, B
Special Education and Teaching, B

SOUTHERN NAZARENE UNIVERSITY

Accounting, B
Aeronautics/Aviation/Aerospace Science and Technology, B
American Government and Politics (United
States), B
American/United States Studies/Civilization, B
Athletic Training and Sports Medicine, B
Biochemistry, B
Biology/Biological Sciences, B
Biophysics, B
Business Administration and Management, B
Business Administration, Management and Operations, BM
Business/Commerce, A
Chemistry, B
Computer and Information Sciences, B
Counseling Psychology, M
Early Childhood Education and Teaching, B
Education, B
Elementary Education and Teaching, B
English Language and Literature, B
English/Language Arts Teacher Education, B
Environmental Biology, B
Finance, B
General Studies, A
Graphic Communications, B
Health Services Administration, M
Health and Physical Education/Fitness, B
Health/Medical Preparatory Programs, B
History, B
Information Science/Studies, B
International Relations and Affairs, B
Journalism, B
Kinesiology and Exercise Science, B
Language Interpretation and Translation, B
Management, B
Marketing/Marketing Management, B
Marriage and Family Therapy/Counseling, M
Mathematics, B

Mathematics Teacher Education, B
Missions/Missionary Studies and Missiology, B
Music, B
Music Performance, B
Music Teacher Education, B
Nursing, M
Nursing Administration, M
Nursing Education, M
Parks, Recreation, Leisure and Fitness Studies, A
Philosophy, B
Physical Education Teaching and Coaching, B
Physical Sciences, B
Physics, B
Psychology, BM
Religious Education, B
Religious/Sacred Music, B
Science Teacher Education/General Science
Teacher Education, B
Social Studies Teacher Education, B
Sociology, B
Spanish Language and Literature, B
Speech Teacher Education, B
Sport and Fitness Administration/Management, BM
System, Networking, and LAN/WAN
Management/Manager, B
Theology and Religious Vocations, B
Theology/Theological Studies, B
Youth Ministry, B

SOUTHWESTERN CHRISTIAN UNIVERSITY

Bible/Biblical Studies, B
Business Administration and Management, B
Education, B
English Language and Literature, B
English/Language Arts Teacher Education, B
Finance, B
General Studies, A
Health and Physical Education, B
History Teacher Education, B
Human Development and Family Studies, B
Human Services, B
International Marketing, B
Kinesiology and Exercise Science, B
Liberal Arts and Sciences Studies and Humanities, B
Marketing/Marketing Management, B
Missions/Missionary Studies and Missiology, BM
Music, B
Music Performance, B
Non-Profit/Public/Organizational Management, B
Pastoral Studies/Counseling, BM
Physical Education Teaching and Coaching, B
Religion/Religious Studies, B
Religious Education, B
Religious/Sacred Music, B
Social Sciences, B
Sport and Fitness Administration/Management, B
Theology/Theological Studies, B
Youth Ministry, B
Youth Services/Administration, B

SOUTHWESTERN OKLAHOMA STATE UNIVERSITY

Allied Health and Medical Assisting Services, M
American Indian/Native American Studies, A
Art Education, M
Art Teacher Education, B
Athletic Training and Sports Medicine, B
Biology/Biological Sciences, B
Business Administration and Management, AB
Business Administration, Management and Operations, M
Chemistry, B
Clinical Laboratory Science/Medical
Technology/Technologist, B
Clinical/Medical Laboratory Technician, A
Computer Science, A
Computer and Information Sciences, B
Counselor Education/School Counseling and Guidance Services, M
Criminal Justice/Safety Studies, AB
Early Childhood Education and Teaching, BM
Education, M
Educational Administration and Supervision, M
Educational Measurement and Evaluation, M

Elementary Education and Teaching, BM
Engineering Physics, B
Engineering Technology, B
English Education, M
English Language and Literature, B
English/Language Arts Teacher Education, B
Fire Science/Firefighting, A
General Studies, A
Graphic Design, B
Health Information/Medical Records Administration/Administrator, B
Health Professions and Related Clinical Sciences, B
Health/Health Care Administration/Management, B
History, B
History Teacher Education, B
Kinesiology and Exercise Science, B
Kinesiology and Movement Studies, M
Manufacturing Technology/Technician, B
Mathematics, B
Mathematics Teacher Education, BM
Medical Radiologic Technology/Science - Radiation Therapist, A
Microbiology, M
Multi-/Interdisciplinary Studies, B
Music, BM
Music Teacher Education, BM
Occupational Therapist Assistant, A
Parks, Recreation and Leisure Facilities Management, B
Parks, Recreation, Leisure and Fitness Studies, B
Performance, M
Pharmacy, D
Physical Education Teaching and Coaching, B
Physical Therapist Assistant, A
Political Science and Government, B
Psychology, B
Recreation and Park Management, M
School Psychology, M
Science Teacher Education/General Science Teacher Education, BM
Secondary Education and Teaching, M
Social Studies Teacher Education, M
Spanish Language and Literature, B
Special Education and Teaching, BM

SOUTHWESTERN OKLAHOMA STATE UNIVERSITY AT SAYRE

Business Administration and Management, A
Clinical/Medical Laboratory Technician, A
Computer Science, A
Corrections, A
Criminal Justice/Safety Studies, A
General Studies, A
Medical Radiologic Technology/Science - Radiation Therapist, A

SPARTAN COLLEGE OF AERONAUTICS AND TECHNOLOGY

Aeronautical/Aerospace Engineering Technology/Technician, AB
Airline/Commercial/Professional Pilot and Flight Crew, AB
Instrumentation Technology/Technician, AB
Quality Control Technology/Technician, AB
Telecommunications Technology/Technician, AB

TULSA COMMUNITY COLLEGE

Accounting Technology/Technician and Bookkeeping, A
Aeronautical/Aerospace Engineering Technology/Technician, A
Air Traffic Controller, A
Applied Horticulture/Horticultural Operations, A
BioTechnology, A
Business Administration and Management, A
Business, Management, Marketing, and Related Support Services, A
Business/Commerce, A
Child Development, A
Clinical/Medical Laboratory Technician, A
Computer Installation and Repair Technology/Technician, A
Computer Science, A
Computer and Information Sciences, A
Computer and Information Sciences and Support Services, A

Criminal Justice/Police Science, A
Dental Hygiene/Hygienist, A
Diagnostic Medical Sonography/Sonographer and Ultrasound Technician, A
Digital Communication and Media/Multimedia, A
Drama and Dramatics/Theatre Arts, A
Education, A
Electrical, Electronic and Communications Engineering Technology/Technician, A
Engineering-Related Technologies, A
Environmental Sciences, A
Fine/Studio Arts, A
Fire Services Administration, A
Foreign Languages, Literatures, and Linguistics, A
General Studies, A
Graphic and Printing Equipment Operator Production, A
Health Information/Medical Records Technology/Technician, A
Health/Medical Preparatory Programs, A
Human Resources Management/Personnel Administration, A
Interior Design, A
International Business/Trade/Commerce, A
Legal Assistant/Paralegal, A
Marketing/Marketing Management, A
Mathematics, A
Medical Radiologic Technology/Science - Radiation Therapist, A
Multi-/Interdisciplinary Studies, A
Music, A
Nutritional Sciences, A
Occupational Therapy/Therapist, A
Physical Sciences, A
Physical Therapist Assistant, A
Pre-Nursing Studies, A
Pre-Pharmacy Studies, A
Respiratory Care Therapy/Therapist, A
Sign Language Interpretation and Translation, A
Social Sciences, A
Social Work, A
Sport and Fitness Administration/Management, A
Surgical Technology/Technologist, A
Veterinary/Animal Health Technology/Technician and Veterinary Assistant, A

TULSA WELDING SCHOOL

Welding Technology/Welder, A

UNIVERSITY OF CENTRAL OKLAHOMA

Accounting, BM
Actuarial Science, B
Adult Development and Aging, B
Adult and Continuing Education and Teaching, BM
Advertising, B
Apparel and Accessories Marketing Operations, B
Apparel and Textiles, B
Applied Economics, B
Applied Mathematics, BM
Art History, Criticism and Conservation, B
Art Teacher Education, B
Art/Art Studies, General, B
Athletic Training and Sports Medicine, M
Audiology/Audiologist and Speech-Language Pathology/Pathologist, B
Biological and Biomedical Sciences, M
Biology Teacher Education, B
Biology/Biological Sciences, B
Biomedical Engineering, M
Biomedical Sciences, B
Biomedical/Medical Engineering, B
Broadcast Journalism, B
Business Administration and Management, B
Business Teacher Education, B
Business/Commerce, B
Business/Managerial Economics, B
Chemistry, B
Chemistry Teacher Education, B
Child Development, B
Child and Family Studies, M
Clinical Laboratory Science/Medical Technology/Technologist, B
Commercial and Advertising Art, B
Communication Disorders, B
Communication Studies/Speech Communication and Rhetoric, B

Communications Technologies/Technicians and Support Services, B
Computer Science, BM
Computer and Information Sciences, B
Consumer Merchandising/Retailing Management, B
Corrections, B
Counseling Psychology, M
Counselor Education/School Counseling and Guidance Services, BM
Criminal Justice/Law Enforcement Administration, B
Criminal Justice/Safety Studies, B
Criminology, M
Dance, B
Design and Applied Arts, M
Dietetics/Dieticians, B
Drama and Dance Teacher Education, B
Drama and Dramatics/Theatre Arts, B
Early Childhood Education and Teaching, BM
Economics, B
Education, M
Educational Leadership and Administration, BM
Educational Media/Instructional Technology, M
Educational/Instructional Media Design, B
Electrical Engineering, M
Electrical, Electronics and Communications Engineering, B
Elementary Education and Teaching, BM
Engineering Physics, BM
Engineering and Applied Sciences, M
English, M
English Language and Literature, B
English as a Second Language, M
English/Language Arts Teacher Education, B
Exercise and Sports Science, M
Experimental Psychology, M
Family and Consumer Sciences/Home Economics Teacher Education, B
Family and Consumer Sciences/Human Sciences, B
Fashion Merchandising, B
Finance, B
Fine/Studio Arts, B
Foods, Nutrition, and Wellness Studies, B
Forensic Psychology, M
Forensic Science and Technology, BM
French Language Teacher Education, B
French Language and Literature, B
Funeral Service and Mortuary Science, B
General Studies, B
Geography, B
German Language Teacher Education, B
German Language and Literature, B
Gerontology, M
Graphic Design, B
Health Occupations Teacher Education, B
Health Promotion, M
Health and Physical Education/Fitness, B
Higher Education/Higher Education Administration, M
History, BM
History Teacher Education, B
Home Economics, M
Hotel/Motel Administration/Management, B
Human Development, M
Human Nutrition, B
Human Resources Management/Personnel Administration, B
Humanities/Humanistic Studies, B
Information Technology, B
Insurance, B
Interdisciplinary Studies, M
Interior Design, B
International Affairs, M
International Business/Trade/Commerce, B
Journalism, B
Juvenile Corrections, B
Kindergarten/PreSchool Education and Teaching, B
Kinesiology and Exercise Science, B
Law and Legal Studies, B
Liberal Arts and Sciences Studies and Humanities, B
Library Science, M
Management Information Systems and Services, B
Marketing/Marketing Management, B
Marriage and Family Therapy/Counseling, M
Mathematics, BM

Mathematics Teacher Education, B
Mechanical Engineering, BM
Museology/Museum Studies, M
Music, BM
Music Performance, AB
Music Teacher Education, B
Nursing, M
Nutritional Sciences, M
Occupational Health and Industrial Hygiene, B
Occupational Safety and Health Technology/Technician, B
Operations Management and Supervision, B
Parks, Recreation, Leisure and Fitness Studies, B
Performance, M
Philosophy, B
Photography, B
Photojournalism, B
Physical Education Teaching and Coaching, B
Physics, B
Physics Teacher Education, B
Piano and Organ, B
Political Science and Government, BM
Pre-Pharmacy Studies, B
Psychology, BM
Public Administration, BM
Public Health Education and Promotion, B
Public Relations/Image Management, B
Quality Control and Safety Technologies/Technicians, B
Radio and Television, B
Reading Teacher Education, BM
Real Estate, B
Retailing and Retail Operations, B
Sales, Distribution and Marketing Operations, B
School Psychology, M
Science Teacher Education/General Science Teacher Education, B
Secondary Education and Teaching, BM
Selling Skills and Sales Operations, B
Social Studies Teacher Education, B
Sociology, BM
Spanish Language Teacher Education, B
Spanish Language and Literature, B
Special Education and Teaching, BM
Speech-Language Pathology/Pathologist, B
Statistics, BM
Student Personnel Services, M
Substance Abuse/Addiction Counseling, M
Teacher Education and Professional Development, Specific Subject Areas, B
Technical Theatre/Theatre Design and Technology, B
Trade and Industrial Teacher Education, B
Violin, Viola, Guitar and Other Stringed Instruments, B
Voice and Opera, B
Writing, M

UNIVERSITY OF OKLAHOMA

Accounting, BM
Adult and Continuing Education and Teaching, MD
Advertising, B
Aeronautics/Aviation/Aerospace Science and Technology, B
Aerospace, Aeronautical and Astronautical Engineering, BMD
African-American/Black Studies, B
American Indian/Native American Studies, BMD
Anthropology, BMD
Applied Economics, M
Arabic Language and Literature, B
Archeology, D
Architectural Engineering, B
Architecture, BM
Archives/Archival Administration, M
Area Studies, B
Art History, Criticism and Conservation, BMD
Astronomy, B
Astrophysics, B
Biochemistry, BMD
Bioengineering, MD
Bioinformatics, MD
Biological and Biomedical Sciences, MD
Botany/Plant Biology, BMD
Broadcast Journalism, B
Business Administration and Management, B

Business Administration, Management and Operations, MD
Business/Managerial Economics, B
Cartography, B
Ceramic Arts and Ceramics, M
Chemical Engineering, BMD
Chemistry, BMD
Chinese Language and Literature, B
Civil Engineering, BMD
Classics and Classical Languages, Literatures, and Linguistics, B
Communication Studies/Speech Communication and Rhetoric, B
Communication and Media Studies, MD
Composition, MD
Computer Engineering, BMD
Computer Science, BMD
Construction Management, BM
Corporate and Organizational Communication, M
Counseling Psychology, MD
Criminal Justice/Law Enforcement Administration, B
Curriculum and Instruction, MDO
Dance, BM
Design and Visual Communications, B
Drama and Dramatics/Theatre Arts, B
Early Childhood Education and Teaching, B
Ecology, D
Economics, BMD
Education, MDO
Educational Administration and Supervision, MD
Educational Leadership and Administration, MDO
Educational Media/Instructional Technology, M
Educational Psychology, MD
Electrical Engineering, MD
Electrical, Electronics and Communications Engineering, B
Elementary Education and Teaching, B
Engineering, B
Engineering Physics, BMD
Engineering and Applied Sciences, MD
English, MD
English Language and Literature, B
English/Language Arts Teacher Education, B
Environmental Design/Architecture, B
Environmental Engineering Technology/Environmental Technology, MD
Environmental Sciences, BMD
Environmental Studies, B
Environmental/Environmental Health Engineering, B
Evolutionary Biology, D
Exercise and Sports Science, MD
Film, Television, and Video Production, M
Film/Cinema Studies, B
Finance, B
Fine Arts and Art Studies, M
Fine/Studio Arts, B
Foreign Language Teacher Education, B
French Language and Literature, BMD
Gender Studies, O
Geography, BMD
Geological Engineering, MD
Geology/Earth Science, BMD
Geophysics and Seismology, BMD
German Language and Literature, M
Germanic Languages, Literatures, and Linguistics, B
Health Promotion, M
Health Services Administration, M
Higher Education/Higher Education Administration, MDO
History, BMD
History and Philosophy of Science and Technology, B
History of Science and Technology, MD
Hospital and Health Care Facilities Administration/Management, B
Human Resources Management and Services, BM
Human Services, MO
Humanities/Humanistic Studies, B
Industrial Engineering, B
Industrial and Organizational Psychology, MD
Industrial/Management Engineering, MD
Information Science/Studies, BM
Interdisciplinary Studies, MD
Interior Design, BM
International Affairs, MO
International/Global Studies, B

Italian Language and Literature, B
Japanese Language and Literature, B
Jewish/Judaic Studies, B
Journalism, BMD
Kinesiology and Exercise Science, B
Landscape Architecture, M
Law and Legal Studies, MD
Liberal Arts and Sciences Studies and Humanities, B
Liberal Studies, MO
Library Science, M
Lighting Design, M
Linguistics, B
Management Information Systems and Services, BMO
Marketing/Marketing Management, B
Mass Communication/Media Studies, MD
Mathematics, BMD
Mathematics Teacher Education, BD
Mechanical Engineering, BMD
Meteorology, BMD
Microbiology, BMD
Museology/Museum Studies, M
Music, BMD
Music Pedagogy, B
Music Teacher Education, BD
Music Theory and Composition, M
Musicology and Ethnomusicology, M
Neurobiology and Neurophysiology, D
Non-Profit/Public/Organizational Management, M
Organizational Behavior Studies, BM
Painting, M
Performance, MD
Petroleum Engineering, BMD
Philosophy, BMD
Photography, M
Physics, BMD
Political Science and Government, BMD
Printmaking, M
Project Management, M
Psychology, BMD
Public Administration, BM
Public Policy Analysis, M
Religion/Religious Studies, B
Russian Language and Literature, B
Science Teacher Education/General Science Teacher Education, B
Sculpture, M
Social Studies Teacher Education, B
Social Work, BM
Sociology, BMD
Spanish Language and Literature, BMD
Special Education and Teaching, BMD
Substance Abuse/Addiction Counseling, M
Sustainable Development, MD
Telecommunications, M
Theater, M
Urban Studies/Affairs, M
Urban and Regional Planning, M
Women's Studies, BO
Writing, M
Zoology/Animal Biology, B

UNIVERSITY OF OKLAHOMA HEALTH SCIENCES CENTER

Allied Health and Medical Assisting Services, MDO
Allopathic Medicine, D
Biochemistry, MD
Biological and Biomedical Sciences, MD
Biopsychology, MD
Biostatistics, MD
Cell Biology and Anatomy, MD
Communication Disorders, BMDO
Dental Hygiene/Hygienist, B
Dentistry, DO
Diagnostic Medical Sonography/Sonographer and Ultrasound Technician, B
Dietetics/Dieticians, B
Environmental and Occupational Health, MD
Epidemiology, MD
Genetic Counseling/Counselor, M
Health Education, D
Health Physics/Radiological Health, MD
Health Promotion, M
Health Services Administration, MD
Health Services/Allied Health/Health Sciences, B

Homeland Security, M
Immunology, MD
Medical Physics, MD
Medical Radiologic Technology/Science - Radiation
 Therapist, B
Microbiology, MD
Molecular Biology, MD
Neuroscience, MD
Nuclear Medical Technology/Technologist, B
Nursing, M
Nutritional Sciences, BM
Occupational Therapy/Therapist, M
Orthodontics, M
Pathology/Experimental Pathology, D
Periodontics, M
Pharmaceutical Sciences, MD
Pharmacy, BD
Physical Therapy/Therapist, M
Physician Assistant, M
Physiology, MD
Public Health, MD
Radiation Biology/Radiobiology, MD
Radiologic Technology/Science - Radiographer, B
Reading Teacher Education, O
Rehabilitation Sciences, M
Special Education and Teaching, M
Speech-Language Pathology/Pathologist, B

UNIVERSITY OF SCIENCE AND ARTS OF OKLAHOMA

American Indian/Native American Studies, B
Art/Art Studies, General, B
Biology/Biological Sciences, B
Business/Commerce, B
Chemistry, B
Clinical/Medical Laboratory Technician, B
Communication Studies/Speech Communication
 and Rhetoric, B
Drama and Dramatics/Theatre Arts, B
Early Childhood Education and Teaching, B
Economics, B
Education/Teaching of Individuals with Hearing Im-
 pairments, Including Deafness, B
Elementary Education and Teaching, B
English Language and Literature, B
Fine/Studio Arts, B
Health and Physical Education, B
History, B
Mathematics, B
Music, B
Natural Sciences, B
Physics, B
Political Science and Government, B
Psychology, B
Sociology, B
Speech-Language Pathology/Pathologist, B

THE UNIVERSITY OF TULSA

Accounting, BM
American Indian/Native American Studies, M
Anthropology, BMD
Applied Mathematics, B
Art History, Criticism and Conservation, B
Athletic Training and Sports Medicine, B
Audiology/Audiologist and Speech-Language
 Pathology/Pathologist, B
Biochemistry, BM
Biological and Biomedical Sciences, MD
Biology/Biological Sciences, B
Business Administration and Management, B
Business Administration, Management and Opera-
 tions, M
Business/Commerce, B
Chemical Engineering, BMD
Chemistry, BMD
Chinese Studies, B
Clinical Psychology, MD
Communication Disorders, M
Communication Studies/Speech Communication
 and Rhetoric, B
Computer Engineering, BD
Computer Science, BMD
Drama and Dramatics/Theatre Arts, B
Early Childhood Education and Teaching, B
Economics, B
Education, BM

Education/Teaching of Individuals with Hearing Im-
 pairments, Including Deafness, B
Electrical Engineering, MD
Electrical, Electronics and Communications Engi-
 neering, D
Elementary Education and Teaching, BM
Energy Management and Policy, M
Engineering Physics, BM
Engineering and Applied Sciences, MD
English, MD
English Education, M
English Language and Literature, B
Environmental Law, O
Environmental Studies, B
Film/Cinema Studies, B
Finance, B
Finance and Banking, M
Financial Engineering, M
Fine Arts and Art Studies, M
Fine/Studio Arts, B
French Language and Literature, B
Geology/Earth Science, B
Geophysics and Seismology, B
Geosciences, MD
German Language and Literature, B
Health Law, O
History, BM
Industrial and Organizational Psychology, MD
Information Science/Studies, B
Information Technology, B
International Business/Trade/Commerce, BM
Investment Management, M
Kinesiology and Exercise Science, B
Law and Legal Studies, MDO
Legal Professions and Studies, B
Liberal Arts and Sciences Studies and Humani-
 ties, A
Management Information Systems and Ser-
 vices, BM
Marketing/Marketing Management, B
Mathematics, BMD
Mathematics Teacher Education, BM
Mechanical Engineering, BMD
Museology/Museum Studies, M
Music, B
Music Performance, B
Music Teacher Education, B
Music Theory and Composition, B
Organizational Behavior Studies, B
Petroleum Engineering, BMD
Philosophy, B
Physics, BMD
Piano and Organ, B
Political Science and Government, B
Psychology, BMD
Religion/Religious Studies, B
Russian Studies, B
Science Teacher Education/General Science
 Teacher Education, M
Secondary Education and Teaching, M
Sociology, B
Spanish Language and Literature, B
Sport and Fitness Administration/Management, B
Taxation, M
Voice and Opera, B
Women's Studies, B

VATTEROTT COLLEGE (TULSA)

Computer Programming/Programmer, A
Computer Technology/Computer Systems Technol-
 ogy, A
Criminal Justice/Safety Studies, A
Electrical, Electronic and Communications Engineer-
 ing Technology/Technician, A
Heating, Air Conditioning and Refrigeration
 Technology/Technician, A
Medical Administrative Assistant/Secretary, A

VATTEROTT COLLEGE (WARR ACRES)

Computer Programming/Programmer, A
Criminal Justice/Safety Studies, A
Electrical and Electronic Engineering
 Technologies/Technicians, A
Heating, Air Conditioning and Refrigeration
 Technology/Technician, A
Information Technology, A

Legal Assistant/Paralegal, A
Medical Office Assistant/Specialist, A

WESTERN OKLAHOMA STATE COL- LEGE

Accounting Technology/Technician and Bookkeep-
 ing, A
Aviation/Airway Management and Operations, A
Child Development, A
Computer/Information Technology Services Adminis-
 tration and Management, A
Criminal Justice/Police Science, A
Fire Protection, A
Liberal Arts and Sciences Studies and Humani-
 ties, A
Mechanics and Repairers, A
Medical Radiologic Technology/Science - Radiation
 Therapist, A

Oregon

AMERICAN COLLEGE OF HEALTHCARE SCIENCES

Allied Health and Medical Assisting Services, MO
Alternative and Complementary Medicine and Medi-
 cal Systems, A
Nutritional Sciences, O

THE ART INSTITUTE OF PORTLAND

Advertising, B
Animation, Interactive Technology, Video Graphics
 and Special Effects, B
Apparel and Accessories Marketing Operations, B
Cinematography and Film/Video Production, B
Commercial Photography, B
Computer Graphics, B
Culinary Arts/Chef Training, A
Graphic Design, AB
Industrial Design, B
Interior Design, B
Restaurant, Culinary, and Catering
 Management/Manager, B
Web Page, Digital/Multimedia and Information Re-
 sources Design, B

BIRTHINGWAY COLLEGE OF MID- WIFERY

Direct Entry Midwifery (LM, CPM), B

BLUE MOUNTAIN COMMUNITY COL- LEGE

Accounting, A
Administrative Assistant and Secretarial Science, A
Adult Literacy Tutor/Instructor, A
Agricultural Business and Management, A
Agricultural Production Operations, A
Child Care and Support Services Management, A
Civil Engineering Technology/Technician, A
Drafting and Design Technology/Technician, A
Electrical, Electronic and Communications Engineer-
 ing Technology/Technician, A
General Studies, A
Hospitality Administration/Management, A
Industrial Technology/Technician, A
Liberal Arts and Sciences Studies and Humani-
 ties, A
Marketing/Marketing Management, A
Medical Administrative Assistant/Secretary, A
Retailing and Retail Operations, A
Small Business Administration/Management, A
Social Work, A

CENTRAL OREGON COMMUNITY COL- LEGE

Accounting, A
Airline/Commercial/Professional Pilot and Flight
 Crew, A
Art/Art Studies, General, A
Automobile/Automotive Mechanics
 Technology/Technician, A
Biological and Physical Sciences, A
Biology/Biological Sciences, A
Business Administration and Management, A

CAD/CADD Drafting and/or Design Technology/Technician, A
Child Care and Support Services Management, A
Communication Studies/Speech Communication and Rhetoric, A
Computer Science, A
Computer Systems Networking and Telecommunications, A
Computer and Information Sciences, A
Cooking and Related Culinary Arts, A
Customer Service Management, A
Dental Assisting/Assistant, A
Dietetics/Dieticians, A
Drafting and Design Technology/Technician, A
Early Childhood Education and Teaching, A
Education, A
Electrical, Electronic and Communications Engineering Technology/Technician, A
Emergency Medical Technology/Technician (EMT Paramedic), A
Engineering, A
Entrepreneurship/Entrepreneurial Studies, A
Fire Science/Firefighting, A
Fishing and Fisheries Sciences and Management, A
Foreign Languages and Literatures, A
Forestry, A
Forestry Technology/Technician, A
Health Information/Medical Records Technology/Technician, A
Health and Physical Education, A
Hotel/Motel Administration/Management, A
Humanities/Humanistic Studies, A
Industrial Technology/Technician, A
Kinesiology and Exercise Science, A
Liberal Arts and Sciences Studies and Humanities, A
Management Information Systems and Services, A
Manufacturing Technology/Technician, A
Marketing/Marketing Management, A
Massage Therapy/Therapeutic Massage, A
Mathematics, A
Medical/Clinical Assistant, A
Natural Resources and Conservation, A
Physical Sciences, A
Physical Therapy/Therapist, A
Polymer/Plastics Engineering, A
Pre-Law Studies, A
Pre-Medicine/Pre-Medical Studies, A
Pre-Pharmacy Studies, A
Radiologic Technology/Science - Radiographer, A
Retailing and Retail Operations, A
Social Sciences, A
Sport and Fitness Administration/Management, A
Substance Abuse/Addiction Counseling, A

CHEMEKETA COMMUNITY COLLEGE

Accounting, A
Accounting Technology/Technician and Bookkeeping, A
Administrative Assistant and Secretarial Science, A
Agricultural Business and Management, A
Applied Horticulture/Horticultural Operations, A
Automobile/Automotive Mechanics Technology/Technician, A
Building/Home/Construction Inspection/Inspector, A
Business Administration and Management, A
CAD/CADD Drafting and/or Design Technology/Technician, A
Child Care and Support Services Management, A
Civil Engineering Technology/Technician, A
Computer Engineering Technology/Technician, A
Computer Programming, Specific Applications, A
Computer Technology/Computer Systems Technology, A
Construction Trades, A
Criminal Justice/Safety Studies, A
Crop Production, A
Design and Visual Communications, A
Education/Teaching of Individuals with Speech or Language Impairments, A
Electrical, Electronic and Communications Engineering Technology/Technician, A
Electrical, Electronics and Communications Engineering, A
Electromechanical and Instrumentation and Maintenance Technologies/Technicians, A

Emergency Medical Technology/Technician (EMT Paramedic), A
Executive Assistant/Executive Secretary, A
Fire Protection and Safety Technology/Technician, A
Fire Science/Firefighting, A
General Studies, A
Graphic Design, A
Graphic and Printing Equipment Operator Production, A
Hospitality Administration/Management, A
Hotel/Motel Administration/Management, A
Industrial Mechanics and Maintenance Technology, A
Juvenile Corrections, A
Liberal Arts and Sciences Studies and Humanities, A
Machine Shop Technology/Assistant, A
Mechanical Drafting and Mechanical Drafting CAD/CADD, A
Medical Administrative Assistant/Secretary, A
Medical Office Management/Administration, A
Medical Transcription/Transcriptionist, A
Office Management and Supervision, A
Pharmacy Technician/Assistant, A
Social Work, A
Substance Abuse/Addiction Counseling, A
Technical Teacher Education, A
Tourism and Travel Services Management, A
Welding Technology/Welder, A

CLACKAMAS COMMUNITY COLLEGE

Accounting, A
Administrative Assistant and Secretarial Science, A
Applied Horticulture/Horticultural Operations, A
Architectural Drafting and Architectural CAD/CADD, A
Autobody/Collision and Repair Technology/Technician, A
Automobile/Automotive Mechanics Technology/Technician, A
CAD/CADD Drafting and/or Design Technology/Technician, A
Child Care and Support Services Management, A
Community Organization and Advocacy, A
Computer Programming, Specific Applications, A
Computer Systems Networking and Telecommunications, A
Computer Technology/Computer Systems Technology, A
Construction Trades, A
Corrections, A
Criminal Justice/Police Science, A
Digital Communication and Media/Multimedia, A
Drafting and Design Technology/Technician, A
Electrical and Power Transmission Installation/Installer, A
Electrical, Electronic and Communications Engineering Technology/Technician, A
Emergency Medical Technology/Technician (EMT Paramedic), A
Fire Science/Firefighting, A
General Studies, A
Industrial Engineering, A
Industrial Technology/Technician, A
Landscaping and Groundskeeping, A
Liberal Arts and Sciences Studies and Humanities, A
Machine Tool Technology/Machinist, A
Manufacturing Technology/Technician, A
Marketing/Marketing Management, A
Office Management and Supervision, A
Operations Management and Supervision, A
Ornamental Horticulture, A
Retailing and Retail Operations, A
Social Work, A
Survey Technology/Surveying, A
Water Quality and Wastewater Treatment Management and Recycling Technology/Technician, A
Web/Multimedia Management and Webmaster, A
Welding Technology/Welder, A

CLATSOP COMMUNITY COLLEGE

Accounting, A
Business Administration and Management, A
Fire Science/Firefighting, A

Liberal Arts and Sciences Studies and Humanities, A

COLUMBIA GORGE COMMUNITY COLLEGE

Accounting, A
Administrative Assistant and Secretarial Science, A
Business Administration and Management, A
Child Care and Support Services Management, A
Electrical, Electronic and Communications Engineering Technology/Technician, A
General Studies, A
Liberal Arts and Sciences Studies and Humanities, A
Management Information Systems and Services, A

CONCORDIA UNIVERSITY

Biological and Physical Sciences, B
Biology/Biological Sciences, B
Business Administration and Management, AB
Business Administration, Management and Operations, M
Chemistry, B
Curriculum and Instruction, M
Drama and Dramatics/Theatre Arts, B
Early Childhood Education and Teaching, M
Education, BMD
Educational Administration and Supervision, M
Educational Leadership and Administration, MD
Educational Media/Instructional Technology, M
Elementary Education and Teaching, BM
English Language and Literature, B
English as a Second Language, M
English/Language Arts Teacher Education, B
Environmental Education, M
Health/Health Care Administration/Management, B
Humanities/Humanistic Studies, B
Kindergarten/PreSchool Education and Teaching, B
Liberal Arts and Sciences Studies and Humanities, AB
Marketing/Marketing Management, B
Mathematics Teacher Education, BM
Music, B
Natural Sciences, B
Physical Education Teaching and Coaching, B
Pre-Medicine/Pre-Medical Studies, B
Pre-Theology/Pre-Ministerial Studies, B
Psychology, B
Reading Teacher Education, M
Religion/Religious Studies, B
Religious Education, B
Science Teacher Education/General Science Teacher Education, BM
Secondary Education and Teaching, BM
Social Sciences, B
Social Studies Teacher Education, B
Social Work, B
Special Education and Teaching, M
Sport and Fitness Administration/Management, B
Theology/Theological Studies, B
Vocational and Technical Education, M

CORBAN UNIVERSITY

Accounting, B
Bible/Biblical Studies, AB
Biology Teacher Education, B
Business Administration and Management, AB
Business Administration, Management and Operations, M
Business Teacher Education, B
Business, Management, Marketing, and Related Support Services, B
Communication Studies/Speech Communication and Rhetoric, B
Corrections and Criminal Justice, B
Divinity/Ministry (BD, MDiv.), B
Education, ABM
Elementary Education and Teaching, B
English Language and Literature, B
English/Language Arts Teacher Education, B
Finance, B
Health Professions and Related Clinical Sciences, B
Health Services/Allied Health/Health Sciences, B
Health/Health Care Administration/Management, B
History, B
Humanities/Humanistic Studies, B

Journalism, B
Kinesiology and Exercise Science, B
Liberal Arts and Sciences Studies and Humanities, B
Management Information Systems and Services, B
Mathematics, B
Mathematics Teacher Education, B
Missions/Missionary Studies and Missiology, B
Music, B
Music Performance, B
Music Teacher Education, B
Non-Profit/Public/Organizational Management, M
Pastoral Studies/Counseling, BMDO
Physical Education Teaching and Coaching, B
Pre-Law Studies, B
Pre-Theology/Pre-Ministerial Studies, B
Psychology, B
Religion/Religious Studies, AB
Religious Education, B
Religious/Sacred Music, B
Secondary Education and Teaching, B
Social Science Teacher Education, B
Social Sciences, B
Social Studies Teacher Education, B
Sport and Fitness Administration/Management, B
Theology and Religious Vocations, MDO
Youth Ministry, B

EASTERN OREGON UNIVERSITY

Art/Art Studies, General, B
Biology/Biological Sciences, B
Business Administration, Management and Operations, ABM
Chemistry, B
Communication Studies/Speech Communication and Rhetoric, B
Computer and Information Sciences, B
Drama and Dramatics/Theatre Arts, B
Early Childhood Education and Teaching, B
Economics, B
Education, ABM
Elementary Education and Teaching, M
English Language and Literature, B
Fire Services Administration, B
Health and Medical Administrative Services, B
Health and Physical Education, B
History, B
Liberal Arts and Sciences Studies and Humanities, B
Mathematics, B
Music, B
Psychology, B
Secondary Education and Teaching, M
Social Sciences, B

GEORGE FOX UNIVERSITY

Accounting, B
American/United States Studies/Civilization, B
Art/Art Studies, General, B
Athletic Training and Sports Medicine, B
Behavioral Sciences, B
Bible/Biblical Studies, B
Biochemistry, B
Biology/Biological Sciences, B
Business Administration and Management, B
Business Administration, Management and Operations, MD
Chemistry, B
Cinematography and Film/Video Production, B
Civil Engineering, B
Clinical Psychology, MD
Cognitive Sciences, B
Communication Studies/Speech Communication and Rhetoric, B
Computer Engineering, B
Computer and Information Sciences, B
Counseling Psychology, M
Counselor Education/School Counseling and Guidance Services, MO
Curriculum and Instruction, M
Drama and Dramatics/Theatre Arts, B
Economics, B
Education, MDO
Educational Administration and Supervision, O
Educational Leadership and Administration, MDO
Educational Media/Instructional Technology, MO

Electrical, Electronics and Communications Engineering, B
Elementary Education and Teaching, B
Engineering, B
English Language and Literature, B
English as a Second Language, MO
Entrepreneurship/Entrepreneurial Studies, B
Finance, B
Finance and Banking, M
Health and Physical Education, B
Higher Education/Higher Education Administration, M
History, B
Human Resources Management and Services, M
Information Science/Studies, B
International Business/Trade/Commerce, B
International/Global Studies, B
Journalism, B
Management, MD
Management Information Systems and Services, B
Marketing, D
Marketing/Marketing Management, B
Marriage and Family Therapy/Counseling, MO
Mathematics, B
Mechanical Engineering, B
Multilingual and Multicultural Education, M
Music, B
Music Teacher Education, B
Organizational Communication, B
Organizational Management, M
Pastoral Studies/Counseling, BMD
Philosophy, B
Physical Therapy/Therapist, D
Political Science and Government, B
Psychology, B
Reading Teacher Education, M
Religious Education, M
School Psychology, O
Secondary Education and Teaching, M
Social Work, BM
Sociology, B
Spanish Language and Literature, B
Special Education and Teaching, M
Theology and Religious Vocations, MDO

GUTENBERG COLLEGE

Liberal Arts and Sciences Studies and Humanities, B

KLAMATH COMMUNITY COLLEGE

Accounting, A
Administrative Assistant and Secretarial Science, A
Agriculture, A
Automobile/Automotive Mechanics Technology/Technician, A
Business Administration and Management, A
Construction Management, A
Corrections, A
Diesel Mechanics Technology/Technician, A
Education, A
Environmental Studies, A
General Studies, A
Health Services/Allied Health/Health Sciences, A
Liberal Arts and Sciences Studies and Humanities, A
Science Technologies/Technicians, A

LANE COMMUNITY COLLEGE

Accounting Technology/Technician and Bookkeeping, A
Administrative Assistant and Secretarial Science, A
Airframe Mechanics and Aircraft Maintenance Technology/Technician, A
Airline/Commercial/Professional Pilot and Flight Crew, A
Animation, Interactive Technology, Video Graphics and Special Effects, A
Autobody/Collision and Repair Technology/Technician, A
Automobile/Automotive Mechanics Technology/Technician, A
Business/Commerce, A
Child Care Provider/Assistant, A
Commercial and Advertising Art, A
Community Organization and Advocacy, A
Computer Programming/Programmer, A

Computer Systems Networking and Telecommunications, A
Construction Engineering Technology/Technician, A
Criminal Justice/Law Enforcement Administration, A
Dental Hygiene/Hygienist, A
Diesel Mechanics Technology/Technician, A
Drafting and Design Technology/Technician, A
E-Commerce/Electronic Commerce, A
Electrical, Electronic and Communications Engineering Technology/Technician, A
Emergency Medical Technology/Technician (EMT Paramedic), A
Energy Management and Systems Technology/Technician, A
General Studies, A
Hotel/Motel Administration/Management, A
Legal Administrative Assistant/Secretary, A
Liberal Arts and Sciences Studies and Humanities, A
Management Information Systems and Services, A
Manufacturing Technology/Technician, A
Mechanical Drafting and Mechanical Drafting CAD/CADD, A
Office Management and Supervision, A
Respiratory Care Therapy/Therapist, A
Restaurant, Culinary, and Catering Management/Manager, A
Sport and Fitness Administration/Management, A
Welding Technology/Welder, A

LEWIS & CLARK COLLEGE

Art History, Criticism and Conservation, B
Art/Art Studies, General, B
Biochemistry, B
Biology/Biological Sciences, B
Chemistry, B
Classics and Classical Languages, Literatures, and Linguistics, B
Communication Disorders, M
Communication Studies/Speech Communication and Rhetoric, B
Computer Science, B
Counseling Psychology, M
Cultural Studies, M
Curriculum and Instruction, M
Drama and Dramatics/Theatre Arts, B
Early Childhood Education and Teaching, M
East Asian Studies, B
Economics, B
Educational Leadership and Administration, DO
Elementary Education and Teaching, M
English Language and Literature, B
Environmental Law, M
Environmental Studies, B
Ethnic and Cultural Studies, B
Fine/Studio Arts, B
Foreign Languages and Literatures, B
French Studies, B
German Studies, B
Hispanic-American, Puerto Rican, and Mexican-American/Chicano Studies, B
History, B
International Relations and Affairs, B
Law and Legal Studies, MD
Marriage and Family Therapy/Counseling, M
Mathematics, B
Mathematics and Computer Science, B
Middle School Education, M
Music, B
Music Theory and Composition, B
Philosophy, B
Physics, B
Political Science and Government, B
Psychology, BM
Religion/Religious Studies, B
School Psychology, MO
Secondary Education and Teaching, M
Special Education and Teaching, M
Substance Abuse/Addiction Counseling, M

LINFIELD COLLEGE

Accounting, B
Anthropology, B
Art/Art Studies, General, B
Athletic Training and Sports Medicine, B
Biochemistry, Biophysics and Molecular Biology, B

Biology/Biological Sciences, B
Business Administration and Management, B
Chemistry, B
Communication Studies/Speech Communication
    and Rhetoric, B
Computer Science, B
Design and Visual Communications, B
Drama and Dramatics/Theatre Arts, B
Economics, B
Elementary Education and Teaching, B
Engineering Physics, B
Environmental Sciences, B
Environmental Studies, B
Finance, B
Fine/Studio Arts, B
French Language and Literature, B
French Studies, B
German Language and Literature, B
German Studies, B
Health Teacher Education, B
Health and Physical Education, B
History, B
International Business/Trade/Commerce, B
International Relations and Affairs, B
Japanese Language and Literature, B
Japanese Studies, B
Kinesiology and Exercise Science, B
Management Information Systems and Services, B
Marketing/Marketing Management, B
Mass Communication/Media Studies, B
Mathematics, B
Music, B
Philosophy, B
Physical Education Teaching and Coaching, B
Physics, B
Political Science and Government, B
Psychology, B
Religion/Religious Studies, B
Sociology, B
Spanish Language and Literature, B

LINN-BENTON COMMUNITY COLLEGE

Accounting Technology/Technician and Bookkeep-
    ing, A
Administrative Assistant and Secretarial Science, A
Agricultural Business and Management, A
Agriculture, A
Animal Sciences, A
Art/Art Studies, General, A
Automobile/Automotive Mechanics
    Technology/Technician, A
Biological and Physical Sciences, A
Biology/Biological Sciences, A
Business Administration and Management, A
Chemistry, A
Commercial and Advertising Art, A
Computer and Information Sciences, A
Criminal Justice/Safety Studies, A
Culinary Arts and Related Services, A
Culinary Arts/Chef Training, A
Diesel Mechanics Technology/Technician, A
Drafting and Design Technology/Technician, A
Drama and Dramatics/Theatre Arts, A
Economics, A
Elementary Education and Teaching, A
Engineering, A
English Language and Literature, A
Family and Consumer Sciences/Human Sciences, A
Foreign Languages and Literatures, A
Horse Husbandry/Equine Science and Manage-
    ment, A
Legal Administrative Assistant/Secretary, A
Liberal Arts and Sciences Studies and Humani-
    ties, A
Machine Tool Technology/Machinist, A
Mathematics, A
Medical Administrative Assistant/Secretary, A
Medical/Clinical Assistant, A
Metallurgical Technology/Technician, A
Physical Education Teaching and Coaching, A
Physics, A
Restaurant, Culinary, and Catering
    Management/Manager, A
System Administration/Administrator, A
Teacher Assistant/Aide, A

Water Quality and Wastewater Treatment Manage-
    ment and Recycling Technology/Technician, A
Welding Technology/Welder, A

MARYLHURST UNIVERSITY

Art Therapy/Therapist, MO
Art/Art Studies, General, B
Business Administration and Management, B
Business Administration, Management and Opera-
    tions, M
Counseling Psychology, O
Education, M
Elementary Education and Teaching, M
English Language and Literature, B
Environmental Sciences, B
Finance and Banking, M
Fine/Studio Arts, B
Food Services Management, M
Health Services Administration, M
Humanities/Humanistic Studies, B
Interdisciplinary Studies, M
Interior Design, B
Management, M
Marketing, M
Mass Communication/Media Studies, B
Multi-/Interdisciplinary Studies, B
Music, B
Music Performance, B
Music Theory and Composition, B
Music Therapy/Therapist, B
Non-Profit/Public/Organizational Management, M
Organizational Behavior Studies, M
Organizational Communication, B
Psychology, B
Real Estate, BM
Social Sciences, B
Theology and Religious Vocations, M

MOUNT ANGEL SEMINARY

Philosophy, B
Theology and Religious Vocations, M

MT. HOOD COMMUNITY COLLEGE

Accounting, A
Administrative Assistant and Secretarial Science, A
Architectural Engineering Technology/Technician, A
Automobile/Automotive Mechanics
    Technology/Technician, A
Avionics Maintenance Technology/Technician, A
Broadcast Journalism, A
Business Administration and Management, A
Business Teacher Education, A
Civil Engineering Technology/Technician, A
Commercial and Advertising Art, A
Computer Engineering Technology/Technician, A
Cosmetology/Cosmetologist, A
Dental Hygiene/Hygienist, A
Electrical, Electronic and Communications Engineer-
    ing Technology/Technician, A
Environmental Health, A
Fire Science/Firefighting, A
Fishing and Fisheries Sciences and Management, A
Food Science, A
Forestry Technology/Technician, A
Funeral Service and Mortuary Science, A
Horticultural Science, A
Hospitality Administration/Management, A
Industrial Technology/Technician, A
Journalism, A
Kindergarten/PreSchool Education and Teaching, A
Legal Administrative Assistant/Secretary, A
Liberal Arts and Sciences Studies and Humani-
    ties, A
Marketing/Marketing Management, A
Mechanical Engineering/Mechanical
    Technology/Technician, A
Medical Administrative Assistant/Secretary, A
Medical/Clinical Assistant, A
Mental Health Counseling/Counselor, A
Occupational Therapy/Therapist, A
Ornamental Horticulture, A
Physical Therapy/Therapist, A
Radio and Television, A
Respiratory Care Therapy/Therapist, A
Surgical Technology/Technologist, A

Tourism and Travel Services Management, A

MULTNOMAH UNIVERSITY

Ancient/Classical Greek Language and Literature, B
Bible/Biblical Studies, B
Business, Management, Marketing, and Related
    Support Services, B
Business/Commerce, B
Counselor Education/School Counseling and Guid-
    ance Services, M
Education, M
Elementary Education and Teaching, B
English Language and Literature, B
English as a Second Language, M
Hebrew Language and Literature, B
History, B
Missions/Missionary Studies and Missiology, B
Pastoral Counseling and Specialized Ministries, B
Pastoral Studies/Counseling, B
Psychology, B
Religious Education, B
Religious/Sacred Music, B
Teaching English as a Second or Foreign
    Language/ESL Language Instructor, B
Theology and Religious Vocations, MD
Theology/Theological Studies, B
Youth Ministry, B

NEW HOPE CHRISTIAN COLLEGE

Bible/Biblical Studies, B
Divinity/Ministry (BD, MDiv.), B
Missions/Missionary Studies and Missiology, B
Pastoral Studies/Counseling, B
Religious Education, B
Religious/Sacred Music, B
Youth Ministry, B

NORTHWEST CHRISTIAN UNIVERSITY

Accounting, B
Bible/Biblical Studies, B
Biology/Biological Sciences, B
Business Administration and Management, B
Business Administration, Management and Opera-
    tions, M
Communication Studies/Speech Communication
    and Rhetoric, B
Counseling Psychology, M
Counselor Education/School Counseling and Guid-
    ance Services, M
Criminal Justice/Law Enforcement Administration, B
Curriculum and Instruction, M
Early Childhood Education and Teaching, B
Education, M
Educational Media/Instructional Technology, M
Elementary Education and Teaching, B
English Language and Literature, B
Exercise Physiology, B
General Studies, A
History, B
Junior High/Intermediate/Middle School Education
    and Teaching, B
Marketing/Marketing Management, B
Mathematics, B
Missions/Missionary Studies and Missiology, B
Multi-/Interdisciplinary Studies, B
Pastoral Studies/Counseling, B
Psychology, B
Religious/Sacred Music, B
Secondary Education and Teaching, B
Youth Ministry, B

OREGON COAST COMMUNITY COL-
LEGE

Criminal Justice/Safety Studies, A
General Studies, A
Liberal Arts and Sciences Studies and Humani-
    ties, A
Marine Biology and Biological Oceanography, A

OREGON COLLEGE OF ART & CRAFT

Crafts, M
Crafts/Craft Design, Folk Art and Artisanry, B

Fine Arts and Art Studies, B

OREGON HEALTH & SCIENCE UNIVERSITY

Allopathic Medicine, D
Biochemistry, MD
Biological and Biomedical Sciences, MDO
Biomedical Engineering, D
Biopsychology, D
Biostatistics, MO
Cancer Biology/Oncology, D
Cell Biology and Anatomy, D
Clinical Research, MO
Community Health Nursing, MO
Computational Biology, MD
Computer Engineering, MD
Computer Science, MD
Dental and Oral Surgery, O
Dentistry, DO
Developmental Biology and Embryology, D
Electrical Engineering, MD
Environmental Engineering
   Technology/Environmental Technology, MD
Environmental Sciences, MD
Epidemiology, MO
Genetics, D
Gerontological Nursing, MDO
Gerontology, MO
Health Informatics, O
Health Services Administration, MO
Immunology, D
Medical Informatics, MDO
Medical Radiologic Technology/Science - Radiation
   Therapist, B
Microbiology, D
Molecular Biology, MD
Neuroscience, D
Nurse Anesthetist, M
Nurse Midwife/Nursing Midwifery, MDO
Nursing, MDO
Nursing - Advanced Practice, MDO
Nursing Education, MO
Nutritional Sciences, MO
Oral and Dental Sciences, MO
Orthodontics, MO
Pediatric Nurse/Nursing, MDO
Pedodontics, O
Periodontics, MO
Pharmacology, D
Physician Assistant, M
Physiology, D
Psychiatric/Mental Health Nurse/Nursing, MO

OREGON INSTITUTE OF TECHNOLOGY

Accounting, B
Business Administration and Management, B
Civil Engineering, B
Communication Studies/Speech Communication
   and Rhetoric, B
Computer Engineering Technology/Technician, AB
Computer Programming/Programmer, AB
Computer and Information Sciences, B
Dental Hygiene/Hygienist, B
Electrical, Electronic and Communications Engineer-
   ing Technology/Technician, AB
Environmental Studies, B
Industrial Radiologic Technology/Technician, B
Laser and Optical Technology/Technician, B
Liberal Arts and Sciences Studies and Humani-
   ties, A
Management Information Systems and Services, B
Manufacturing Engineering, M
Mechanical Engineering/Mechanical
   Technology/Technician, B
Pre-Medicine/Pre-Medical Studies, B
Radiologic Technology/Science - Radiographer, B
Survey Technology/Surveying, B

OREGON STATE UNIVERSITY

Accounting, BM
Adult and Continuing Education and Teaching, M
Agricultural Business and Management, B
Agricultural Economics, B
Agricultural Education, M
Agricultural/Biological Engineering and Bioengineer-
   ing, B

Agriculture, B
Agronomy and Crop Science, B
Agronomy and Soil Sciences, MD
Allied Health and Medical Assisting Services, MD
American/United States Studies/Civilization, B
Analytical Chemistry, MD
Animal Sciences, BMD
Anthropology, BMD
Apparel and Textiles, B
Art/Art Studies, General, B
Artificial Intelligence and Robotics, MD
Atmospheric Sciences and Meteorology, MD
BioTechnology, BM
Biochemistry, MD
Biochemistry, Biophysics and Molecular Biology, B
Bioengineering, MD
Biology/Biological Sciences, B
Biomedical/Medical Engineering, B
Biophysics, MD
Biostatistics, M
Botany/Plant Biology, BM
Business Administration and Management, B
Business Administration, Management and Opera-
   tions, MD
Cell Biology and Anatomy, D
Chemical Engineering, BMD
Chemistry, BMD
Child and Family Studies, MD
Civil Engineering, BMD
Clothing and Textiles, MD
Communication Studies/Speech Communication
   and Rhetoric, B
Computer Engineering, MD
Computer Science, BMD
Construction Engineering, B
Consumer Merchandising/Retailing Management, B
Counselor Education/School Counseling and Guid-
   ance Services, MD
Design and Visual Communications, B
Digital Communication and Media/Multimedia, B
Economics, BMD
Education, BMD
Educational Leadership and Administration, M
Electrical Engineering, MD
Electrical, Electronics and Communications Engi-
   neering, B
Elementary Education and Teaching, M
Engineering, B
Engineering Physics, B
Engineering and Applied Sciences, MD
English, M
English Language and Literature, B
Environmental Engineering
   Technology/Environmental Technology, MD
Environmental Sciences, BMD
Environmental and Occupational Health, MD
Environmental/Environmental Health Engineering, B
Epidemiology, M
Ethics, M
Ethnic and Cultural Studies, B
Exercise and Sports Science, MD
Finance, B
Finance and Banking, M
Fish, Game and Wildlife Management, MD
Fishing and Fisheries Sciences and Management, B
Food Science, B
Food Science and Technology, MD
Forest Engineering, B
Forestry, MD
French Language and Literature, B
Gender Studies, M
Geography, MD
Geological and Earth Sciences/Geosciences, B
Geology/Earth Science, MD
Geophysics and Seismology, MD
German Language and Literature, B
Health Physics/Radiological Health, MD
Health Promotion, MD
Health Services Administration, MD
Health/Medical Physics, B
Health/Medical Preparatory Programs, B
Hispanic Studies, M
History, B
History of Science and Technology, MD
Horticultural Science, BMD
Hospitality Administration/Management, B

Human Development, MD
Human Development and Family Studies, B
Industrial Engineering, B
Industrial/Management Engineering, MD
Inorganic Chemistry, MD
Interdisciplinary Studies, M
Interior Design, B
International Public Health/International Health, M
International/Global Studies, B
Investment Management, M
Kinesiology and Exercise Science, B
Kinesiology and Movement Studies, MD
Liberal Arts and Sciences Studies and Humani-
   ties, B
Management Information Systems and Services, B
Manufacturing Engineering, B
Marine Affairs, M
Marine Sciences, M
Marketing, M
Marketing/Marketing Management, B
Materials Sciences, MD
Mathematics, BMD
Mathematics Teacher Education, MD
Mechanical Engineering, BMD
Medical Physics, MD
Microbiology, BMD
Molecular Biology, D
Music, B
Music Teacher Education, M
Natural Resources Management/Development and
   Policy, B
Natural Resources and Conservation, M
Nuclear Engineering, BMD
Nutritional Sciences, MD
Oceanography, Chemical and Physical, MD
Operations Management and Supervision, B
Organic Chemistry, MD
Parks, Recreation, Leisure and Fitness Studies, B
Pharmaceutical Sciences, MD
Pharmacy, D
Philosophy, B
Physical Chemistry, MD
Physics, BMD
Political Science and Government, B
Psychology, B
Public Health, MD
Public Health (MPH, DPH), B
Public Policy Analysis, MD
Range Science and Management, BMD
Religion/Religious Studies, B
Science Teacher Education/General Science
   Teacher Education, MD
Social Sciences, B
Sociology, B
Spanish Language and Literature, B
Sport Psychology, D
Statistics, MD
Student Personnel Services, M
Supply Chain Management, M
Sustainability Management, MD
Toxicology, MD
Veterinary Medicine, D
Veterinary Sciences, MD
Visual and Performing Arts, B
Water Resources, MD
Water Resources Engineering, MD
Wildlife and Wildlands Science and Management, B
Women's Studies, BM
Wood Science and Wood Products/Pulp and Paper
   Technology, B
Writing, M
Zoology/Animal Biology, BMD

OREGON STATE UNIVERSITY–CASCADES

Art/Art Studies, General, B
Biological and Physical Sciences, B
Business Administration and Management, B
Community Psychology, M
Education, M
Human Development and Family Studies, B
Liberal Arts and Sciences Studies and Humani-
   ties, B
Mathematics, B
Natural Resources Management/Development and
   Policy, B

Parks, Recreation, Leisure and Fitness Studies, B
Psychology, B
School Psychology, M
Social Sciences, B
Tourism and Travel Services Management, B
Visual and Performing Arts, B

PACIFIC NORTHWEST COLLEGE OF ART

Applied Arts and Design, M
Cultural Studies, M
Design and Visual Communications, B
Fine Arts and Art Studies, M
Fine/Studio Arts, B
Graphic Design, B
Illustration, B
Intermedia/Multimedia, B
Painting, B
Photography, B
Printmaking, B
Sculpture, B

PACIFIC UNIVERSITY

Accounting, B
Art Teacher Education, B
Art/Art Studies, General, B
Athletic Training and Sports Medicine, BM
Biology/Biological Sciences, B
Broadcast Journalism, B
Business Administration and Management, B
Business Administration, Management and Operations, M
Chemistry, B
Chinese Language and Literature, B
Clinical Psychology, MD
Communication Disorders, MD
Comparative Literature, B
Computer Science, B
Drama and Dramatics/Theatre Arts, B
Early Childhood Education and Teaching, M
Economics, B
Education, BM
Education/Teaching of the Gifted and Talented, M
Elementary Education and Teaching, BM
English Language and Literature, B
English as a Second Language, M
Environmental Studies, B
Finance, B
Finance and Banking, M
French Language and Literature, B
German Language and Literature, B
Health Professions and Related Clinical Sciences, B
Health Services Administration, M
History, B
Humanities/Humanistic Studies, B
International Relations and Affairs, B
Japanese Language and Literature, B
Journalism, B
Kindergarten/PreSchool Education and Teaching, B
Kinesiology and Exercise Science, B
Liberal Arts and Sciences Studies and Humanities, B
Marketing/Marketing Management, B
Mass Communication/Media Studies, B
Mathematics, B
Middle School Education, M
Modern Languages, B
Music, B
Music Performance, B
Music Teacher Education, B
Occupational Therapy/Therapist, D
Optometry, MD
Pharmacy, D
Philosophy, B
Physical Therapy/Therapist, MD
Physician Assistant, M
Physics, B
Political Science and Government, B
Pre-Dentistry Studies, B
Pre-Medicine/Pre-Medical Studies, B
Pre-Veterinary Studies, B
Psychology, BMD
Radio and Television, B
Science Teacher Education/General Science Teacher Education, M
Secondary Education and Teaching, BM

Social Work, BM
Sociology, B
Spanish Language and Literature, B
Special Education and Teaching, M
Telecommunications Technology/Technician, B
Vision Science/Physiological Optics, MD
Writing, M

PIONEER PACIFIC COLLEGE

Accounting, A
Business Administration and Management, AB
Criminal Justice/Police Science, AB
Health/Health Care Administration/Management, AB
Information Science/Studies, A
Information Technology, A
Legal Assistant/Paralegal, AB
Medical/Clinical Assistant, A

PIONEER PACIFIC COLLEGE–EUGENE/SPRINGFIELD BRANCH

Accounting, A
Business Administration and Management, A
Computer Systems Networking and Telecommunications, A
Criminal Justice/Law Enforcement Administration, A
Health/Health Care Administration/Management, A
Marketing/Marketing Management, A
Medical/Clinical Assistant, A

PORTLAND COMMUNITY COLLEGE

Accounting, A
Administrative Assistant and Secretarial Science, A
Agricultural Power Machinery Operation, A
Airframe Mechanics and Aircraft Maintenance Technology/Technician, A
Airline/Commercial/Professional Pilot and Flight Crew, A
Architectural Drafting and Architectural CAD/CADD, A
Autobody/Collision and Repair Technology/Technician, A
Automobile/Automotive Mechanics Technology/Technician, A
Biology Technician/BioTechnology Laboratory Technician, A
Building/Home/Construction Inspection/Inspector, A
Business Administration and Management, A
Child Care and Support Services Management, A
Civil Engineering Technology/Technician, A
Clinical/Medical Laboratory Technician, A
Commercial and Advertising Art, A
Computer Programming/Programmer, A
Computer Technology/Computer Systems Technology, A
Construction Engineering Technology/Technician, A
Construction Trades, A
Criminal Justice/Safety Studies, A
Dental Hygiene/Hygienist, A
Dental Laboratory Technology/Technician, A
Diesel Mechanics Technology/Technician, A
Electrical, Electronic and Communications Engineering Technology/Technician, A
Emergency Medical Technology/Technician (EMT Paramedic), A
Fire Protection and Safety Technology/Technician, A
General Studies, A
Gerontology, A
Health Information/Medical Records Administration/Administrator, A
Health and Physical Education/Fitness, A
Heating, Air Conditioning, Ventilation and Refrigeration Maintenance Technology/Technician, A
Interior Design, A
Landscaping and Groundskeeping, A
Legal Assistant/Paralegal, A
Liberal Arts and Sciences Studies and Humanities, A
Machine Tool Technology/Machinist, A
Management Information Systems and Services, A
Mechanical Engineering/Mechanical Technology/Technician, A
Medical Radiologic Technology/Science - Radiation Therapist, A
Multi-/Interdisciplinary Studies, A
Office Management and Supervision, A

Optometric Technician/Assistant, A
Security and Protective Services, A
Special Education and Teaching, A
Substance Abuse/Addiction Counseling, A
Teacher Assistant/Aide, A
Veterinary/Animal Health Technology/Technician and Veterinary Assistant, A
Welding Technology/Welder, A

PORTLAND STATE UNIVERSITY

Accounting, B
Advertising, B
African Studies, B
African-American/Black Studies, B
American Indian/Native American Studies, B
Anthropology, BMD
Applied Economics, M
Applied Social Research, D
Arabic Language and Literature, B
Architecture, BM
Art History, Criticism and Conservation, B
Art/Art Studies, General, B
Artificial Intelligence and Robotics, O
Biochemistry, B
Bioinformatics, B
Biological and Biomedical Sciences, MD
Biological and Physical Sciences, B
Biology/Biological Sciences, B
Business Administration and Management, B
Business Administration, Management and Operations, MD
Central/Middle and Eastern European Studies, B
Chemistry, BMD
Child Development, B
Chinese Language and Literature, B
City/Urban, Community and Regional Planning, B
Civil Engineering, BMD
Commercial and Advertising Art, B
Communication Disorders, BM
Community Health and Preventive Medicine, B
Computer Engineering, BMD
Computer Science, BMD
Computer and Information Sciences, B
Conflict Resolution and Mediation/Peace Studies, M
Criminal Justice/Law Enforcement Administration, B
Criminology, MD
Curriculum and Instruction, MD
Design and Applied Arts, B
Drama and Dramatics/Theatre Arts, B
Drawing, B
Early Childhood Education and Teaching, M
East Asian Studies, B
Economics, BMD
Education, MD
Educational Administration and Supervision, MD
Educational Leadership and Administration, MD
Educational Media/Instructional Technology, M
Electrical Engineering, MD
Electrical, Electronics and Communications Engineering, B
Elementary Education and Teaching, M
Engineering Management, MD
Engineering and Applied Sciences, MDO
English, M
English Language and Literature, B
English as a Second Language, M
Environmental Engineering Technology/Environmental Technology, MD
Environmental Policy and Resource Management, M
Environmental Sciences, MD
Environmental Studies, BM
European Studies/Civilization, B
Film/Video and Photographic Arts, B
Finance, B
Finance and Banking, M
Fine Arts and Art Studies, M
Foreign Language Teacher Education, M
French Language and Literature, BM
Geography, BMD
Geology/Earth Science, BMD
German Language and Literature, BM
Gerontology, O
Graphic Design, B
Health Education, M
Health Promotion, M

Health Services Administration, MD
Health Teacher Education, B
History, BM
Human Resources Management/Personnel Adminis-
tration, B
Humanities/Humanistic Studies, B
Industrial and Manufacturing Management, M
Information Science/Studies, B
International Business/Trade/Commerce, M
International Relations and Affairs, B
Japanese Language and Literature, B
Japanese Studies, M
Latin American Studies, B
Liberal Arts and Sciences Studies and Humani-
ties, B
Linguistics, B
Logistics and Materials Management, B
Management Science, B
Management of Technology, MD
Manufacturing Engineering, M
Marketing/Marketing Management, B
Mathematics, BMD
Mathematics Teacher Education, D
Mechanical Engineering, BMD
Modeling and Simulation, O
Music, BM
Music Performance, B
Music Teacher Education, M
Near and Middle Eastern Studies, B
Painting, M
Performance, M
Philosophy, B
Physics, BMD
Political Science and Government, BMD
Printmaking, M
Psychology, BMD
Public Administration, M
Public Affairs, D
Public Health, MDO
Public Health (MPH, DPH), B
Public Policy Analysis, D
Reading Teacher Education, M
Real Estate, BM
Religion/Religious Studies, B
Russian Language and Literature, B
Science Teacher Education/General Science
Teacher Education, M
Sculpture, BM
Secondary Education and Teaching, M
Social Sciences, B
Social Studies Teacher Education, M
Social Work, BMD
Sociology, BMD
Software Engineering, M
Spanish Language and Literature, BM
Speech and Interpersonal Communication, MO
Statistics, M
Supply Chain Management, M
Systems Science and Theory, MDO
Theater, M
Urban Studies/Affairs, BMD
Urban and Regional Planning, M
Women's Studies, B

REED COLLEGE

American/United States Studies/Civilization, B
Anthropology, B
Art/Art Studies, General, B
Biochemistry, B
Biology/Biological Sciences, B
Chemistry, B
Chinese Language and Literature, B
Classics and Classical Languages, Litera-
tures, and Linguistics, B
Comparative Literature, B
Computer Science, B
Dance, B
Drama and Dramatics/Theatre Arts, B
Economics, B
English Language and Literature, B
Environmental Studies, B
Fine/Studio Arts, B
French Language and Literature, B
German Language and Literature, B
History, B
International Relations and Affairs, B

Liberal Studies, M
Linguistics, B
Mathematics, B
Music, B
Philosophy, B
Physics, B
Political Science and Government, B
Psychology, B
Religion/Religious Studies, B
Russian Language and Literature, B
Sociology, B
Spanish Language and Literature, B
Statistics, B

ROGUE COMMUNITY COLLEGE

Accounting Technology/Technician and Bookkeep-
ing, A
Automobile/Automotive Mechanics
Technology/Technician, A
Business Administration and Management, A
Business/Commerce, A
Child Care and Support Services Management, A
Computer Science, A
Computer Software Technology/Technician, A
Computer and Information Sciences, A
Construction Engineering Technology/Technician, A
Construction Trades, A
Criminal Justice/Police Science, A
Diesel Mechanics Technology/Technician, A
Electrical and Power Transmission
Installation/Installer, A
Electrical, Electronic and Communications Engineer-
ing Technology/Technician, A
Emergency Medical Technology/Technician (EMT
Paramedic), A
Family and Community Services, A
Fire Protection and Safety Technology/Technician, A
General Studies, A
Liberal Arts and Sciences Studies and Humani-
ties, A
Manufacturing Technology/Technician, A
Marketing/Marketing Management, A
Mechanics and Repairers, A
Medical Office Computer Specialist/Assistant, A
Social Work, A
Visual and Performing Arts, A
Welding Technology/Welder, A

SOUTHERN OREGON UNIVERSITY

Accounting, BO
Anthropology, B
Applied Mathematics, M
Art/Art Studies, General, B
Biochemistry, B
Biology/Biological Sciences, B
Business Administration and Management, B
Business Administration, Management and Opera-
tions, MO
Business Statistics, B
Chemistry, B
Communication Studies/Speech Communication
and Rhetoric, B
Computer Science, BM
Counseling Psychology, M
Criminology, B
Digital Communication and Media/Multimedia, B
Drama and Dramatics/Theatre Arts, B
Early Childhood Education and Teaching, M
Economics, B
Education, M
Educational Administration and Supervision, M
Elementary Education and Teaching, M
English Language and Literature, B
Environmental Education, M
Environmental Studies, B
Foreign Language Teacher Education, M
French Language and Literature, BM
Geology/Earth Science, B
Health Teacher Education, B
History, B
Hotel/Motel Administration/Management, B
Interdisciplinary Studies, M
International Business/Trade/Commerce, M
International Relations and Affairs, B
Liberal Arts and Sciences Studies and Humani-
ties, B

Marketing/Marketing Management, B
Mathematics, B
Mathematics and Computer Science, B
Music, B
Performance, M
Physical Education Teaching and Coaching, B
Political Science and Government, B
Pre-Law Studies, B
Pre-Medicine/Pre-Medical Studies, B
Psychology, BM
Reading Teacher Education, M
Secondary Education and Teaching, M
Social Sciences, B
Sociology, B
Spanish Language and Literature, BM
Special Education and Teaching, M
Theater, M

SOUTHWESTERN OREGON COMMU-
NITY COLLEGE

Accounting, A
Business Administration and Management, A
Child Care Provider/Assistant, A
Criminal Justice/Police Science, A
Criminal Justice/Safety Studies, A
Fire Science/Firefighting, A
Liberal Arts and Sciences Studies and Humani-
ties, A
Machine Tool Technology/Machinist, A
Medical/Clinical Assistant, A
Restaurant, Culinary, and Catering
Management/Manager, A
Welding Technology/Welder, A

SUMNER COLLEGE

Court Reporting/Court Reporter, A
Legal Assistant/Paralegal, A

TILLAMOOK BAY COMMUNITY COL-
LEGE

Accounting, A
Accounting Technology/Technician and Bookkeep-
ing, A
Administrative Assistant and Secretarial Science, A
Business/Office Automation/Technology/Data En-
try, A
Criminal Justice/Law Enforcement Administration, A
Early Childhood Education and Teaching, A
Emergency Medical Technology/Technician (EMT
Paramedic), A
General Studies, A
Liberal Arts and Sciences Studies and Humani-
ties, A
Management Science, A
Marketing, A
Office Management and Supervision, A
Substance Abuse/Addiction Counseling, A

TREASURE VALLEY COMMUNITY COL-
LEGE

Agricultural Business and Management, A
Agricultural Economics, A
Agriculture, A
Agronomy and Crop Science, A
Airline/Commercial/Professional Pilot and Flight
Crew, A
Animal Sciences, A
Business/Commerce, A
Carpentry/Carpenter, A
Computer and Information Sciences, A
Criminal Justice/Police Science, A
Drafting and Design Technology/Technician, A
Elementary Education and Teaching, A
Farm/Farm and Ranch Management, A
Fire Protection and Safety Technology/Technician, A
Fire Science/Firefighting, A
Horse Husbandry/Equine Science and Manage-
ment, A
Horticultural Science, A
Legal Administrative Assistant/Secretary, A
Management Information Systems and Services, A
Medical Administrative Assistant/Secretary, A
Medical Transcription/Transcriptionist, A
Natural Resources and Conservation, A
Office Management and Supervision, A

Range Science and Management, A
Soil Science and Agronomy, A
Solar Energy Technology/Technician, A
Substance Abuse/Addiction Counseling, A
Welding Technology/Welder, A
Wildlife and Wildlands Science and Management, A

UMPQUA COMMUNITY COLLEGE

Accounting, A
Administrative Assistant and Secretarial Science, A
Agriculture, A
Anthropology, A
Art History, Criticism and Conservation, A
Art Teacher Education, A
Art/Art Studies, General, A
Automobile/Automotive Mechanics
   Technology/Technician, A
Behavioral Sciences, A
Biological and Physical Sciences, A
Biology/Biological Sciences, A
Business Administration and Management, A
Chemistry, A
Child Development, A
Civil Engineering Technology/Technician, A
Computer Engineering Technology/Technician, A
Computer Science, A
Cosmetology/Cosmetologist, A
Criminal Justice/Law Enforcement Administration, A
Drama and Dramatics/Theatre Arts, A
Economics, A
Education, A
Electrical, Electronic and Communications Engineer-
   ing Technology/Technician, A
Elementary Education and Teaching, A
Emergency Medical Technology/Technician (EMT
   Paramedic), A
Engineering, A
English Language and Literature, A
Fire Science/Firefighting, A
Forestry, A
Health Teacher Education, A
History, A
Human Resources Management/Personnel Adminis-
   tration, A
Humanities/Humanistic Studies, A
Journalism, A
Kindergarten/PreSchool Education and Teaching, A
Legal Administrative Assistant/Secretary, A
Liberal Arts and Sciences Studies and Humani-
   ties, A
Marketing/Marketing Management, A
Mathematics, A
Medical Administrative Assistant/Secretary, A
Music, A
Music Teacher Education, A
Natural Sciences, A
Physical Education Teaching and Coaching, A
Physical Sciences, A
Political Science and Government, A
Prepress/Desktop Publishing and Digital Imaging
   Design, A
Psychology, A
Social Sciences, A
Social Work, A
Sociology, A

UNIVERSITY OF OREGON

Accounting, BMD
Advertising, B
Anthropology, BMD
Architecture, BM
Art History, Criticism and Conservation, BMD
Art/Art Studies, General, B
Arts Management, M
Asian Languages, MD
Asian Studies/Civilization, BM
Biochemistry, BMD
Biological and Biomedical Sciences, MD
Biological and Physical Sciences, B
Biology/Biological Sciences, B
Biopsychology, MD
Business Administration, Management and Opera-
   tions, M
Business/Commerce, B
Ceramic Arts and Ceramics, B
Chemistry, BMD

Chinese Language and Literature, B
Chinese Studies, MD
Classics and Classical Languages, Litera-
   tures, and Linguistics, BM
Clinical Psychology, D
Cognitive Sciences, MD
Communication Disorders, B
Communication and Media Studies, MD
Comparative Literature, BMD
Computer Science, MD
Computer and Information Sciences, B
Dance, BM
Design and Applied Arts, B
Developmental Psychology, MD
Drama and Dramatics/Theatre Arts, B
Ecology, MD
Economics, BMD
Education, BMD
English, MD
English Language and Literature, B
Environmental Sciences, B
Environmental Studies, BMD
Ethnic and Cultural Studies, B
Evolutionary Biology, MD
Fiber, Textile and Weaving Arts, B
Film/Cinema Studies, B
Finance and Banking, D
Fine Arts and Art Studies, M
Fine/Studio Arts, B
Folklore, M
French Language and Literature, BM
Genetics, D
Geography, BMD
Geology/Earth Science, BMD
German Language and Literature, BMD
Historic Preservation and Conservation, M
History, BMD
Human Services, B
Humanities/Humanistic Studies, B
Information Science/Studies, MD
Interdisciplinary Studies, M
Interior Architecture, B
Interior Design, M
International Affairs, M
International/Global Studies, B
Italian Language and Literature, BM
Japanese Language and Literature, B
Japanese Studies, MD
Jazz/Jazz Studies, B
Jewish/Judaic Studies, B
Journalism, BMD
Landscape Architecture, BM
Latin American Studies, B
Law and Legal Studies, MD
Linguistics, BMD
Management, D
Management Information Systems and Services, M
Marine Biology and Biological Oceanography, BMD
Marketing, D
Mass Communication/Media Studies, B
Mathematics, BMD
Mathematics and Computer Science, B
Media Studies, MD
Medieval and Renaissance Studies, B
Metal and Jewelry Arts, B
Molecular Biology, D
Music, BMD
Music Performance, B
Music Teacher Education, BMD
Music Theory and Composition, B
Neuroscience, D
Painting, B
Philosophy, BMD
Photography, B
Physics, BMD
Physiology, BMD
Political Science and Government, BMD
Printmaking, B
Psychology, BMD
Public Administration, B
Public Policy Analysis, M
Public Relations/Image Management, B
Quantitative Analysis, M
Religion/Religious Studies, B
Romance Languages, Literatures, and Linguis-
   tics, BMD

Russian Language and Literature, M
Russian Studies, B
Sculpture, B
Social Psychology, MD
Social Sciences, B
Sociology, BMD
Spanish Language and Literature, BM
Sport and Fitness Administration/Management, M
Theater, MD
Urban and Regional Planning, M
Women's Studies, B
Writing, M

UNIVERSITY OF PORTLAND

Accounting, B
Biology/Biological Sciences, B
Biomedical Engineering, M
Business Administration and Management, B
Business Administration, Management and Opera-
   tions, M
Chemistry, B
Civil Engineering, BM
Communication and Media Studies, M
Computer Engineering, B
Computer Science, BM
Corporate and Organizational Communication, M
Drama and Dramatics/Theatre Arts, B
Economics, B
Education, BMD
Educational Administration and Supervision, M
Educational Leadership and Administration, M
Electrical Engineering, M
Electrical, Electronics and Communications Engi-
   neering, B
Elementary Education and Teaching, B
Engineering, B
Engineering Science, B
Engineering and Applied Sciences, M
English Language and Literature, B
English as a Second Language, M
Entrepreneurship/Entrepreneurial Studies, M
Environmental Studies, B
Finance, B
Finance and Banking, M
Health Services Administration, M
History, B
Industrial and Manufacturing Management, M
International Business/Trade/Commerce, B
Management of Technology, M
Marketing, M
Marketing/Marketing Management, B
Mass Communication/Media Studies, B
Mathematics, B
Mechanical Engineering, BM
Music, B
Non-Profit/Public/Organizational Management, M
Nursing, MD
Nursing - Advanced Practice, D
Nursing Education, M
Organizational Management, D
Pastoral Studies/Counseling, M
Philosophy, B
Physics, B
Political Science and Government, B
Pre-Dentistry Studies, B
Pre-Law Studies, B
Pre-Medicine/Pre-Medical Studies, B
Psychology, B
Reading Teacher Education, M
Secondary Education and Teaching, B
Social Work, B
Sociology, B
Spanish Language and Literature, B
Special Education and Teaching, M
Sustainability Management, M
Theater, M
Theology/Theological Studies, B

WARNER PACIFIC COLLEGE

American/United States Studies/Civilization, B
Biological and Physical Sciences, B
Biology/Biological Sciences, B
Business Administration and Management, B
Early Childhood Education and Teaching, B
Education, M
Elementary Education and Teaching, B

English Language and Literature, B
History, B
Human Development and Family Studies, B
Junior High/Intermediate/Middle School Education
   and Teaching, B
Kinesiology and Exercise Science, B
Liberal Arts and Sciences Studies and Humani-
   ties, B
Management, M
Music, B
Music Teacher Education, B
Non-Profit/Public/Organizational Management, M
Organizational Management, M
Pastoral Studies/Counseling, B
Physical Education Teaching and Coaching, B
Physical Sciences, B
Pre-Law Studies, B
Pre-Medicine/Pre-Medical Studies, B
Pre-Veterinary Studies, B
Psychology, B
Religion/Religious Studies, B
Science Teacher Education/General Science
   Teacher Education, B
Secondary Education and Teaching, B
Social Sciences, B
Social Studies Teacher Education, B
Social Work, B
Theology/Theological Studies, B
Urban Studies/Affairs, B

WESTERN OREGON UNIVERSITY

Anthropology, B
Art/Art Studies, General, B
Biology/Biological Sciences, B
Business/Commerce, B
Chemistry, B
Computer Science, B
Corrections, B
Criminal Justice/Law Enforcement Administration, B
Criminal Justice/Police Science, B
Criminology, M
Dance, B
Drama and Dramatics/Theatre Arts, B
Early Childhood Education and Teaching, M
Economics, B
Education, M
Educational Media/Instructional Technology, M
Educational/Instructional Media Design, B
English Language and Literature, B
Fire Services Administration, B
Geography, B
German Language and Literature, B
Health Education, M
History, B
Humanities/Humanistic Studies, B
Intercultural/Multicultural and Diversity Studies, B
International Relations and Affairs, B
Kinesiology and Exercise Science, B
Mathematics, B
Mathematics Teacher Education, M
Multilingual and Multicultural Education, M
Music, BM
Natural Sciences, B
Philosophy, B
Political Science and Government, B
Psychology, B
Public Administration, B
Rehabilitation Counseling, M
Science Teacher Education/General Science
   Teacher Education, M
Secondary Education and Teaching, BM
Sign Language Interpretation and Translation, B
Social Sciences, B
Social Studies Teacher Education, M
Sociology, B
Spanish Language and Literature, B
Special Education and Teaching, M

WILLAMETTE UNIVERSITY

African Studies, B
American/United States Studies/Civilization, B
Anthropology, B
Applied Mathematics, B
Art History, Criticism and Conservation, B
Art/Art Studies, General, B
Asian Studies/Civilization, B

Biology/Biological Sciences, B
Business Administration, Management and Opera-
   tions, M
Chemistry, B
Chinese Studies, B
Classics and Classical Languages, Litera-
   tures, and Linguistics, B
Communication Studies/Speech Communication
   and Rhetoric, B
Comparative Literature, B
Computer Science, B
Computer and Information Sciences, B
Conflict Resolution and Mediation/Peace Studies, M
Drama and Dramatics/Theatre Arts, B
East Asian Studies, B
Economics, B
English Language and Literature, B
Environmental Health, B
Environmental Sciences, B
Ethnic and Cultural Studies, B
Fine/Studio Arts, B
French Language and Literature, B
German Language and Literature, B
History, B
Humanities/Humanistic Studies, B
International/Global Studies, B
Japanese Studies, B
Kinesiology and Exercise Science, B
Latin American Studies, B
Law and Legal Studies, MD
Liberal Arts and Sciences Studies and Humani-
   ties, B
Mathematics, B
Music, B
Music Pedagogy, B
Music Performance, B
Music Theory and Composition, B
Music Therapy/Therapist, B
Peace Studies and Conflict Resolution, B
Philosophy, B
Physics, B
Piano and Organ, B
Political Science and Government, B
Psychology, B
Public Administration, B
Religion/Religious Studies, B
Russian Language and Literature, B
Science Technologies/Technicians, B
Sociology, B
Spanish Language and Literature, B
Violin, Viola, Guitar and Other Stringed Instru-
   ments, B
Voice and Opera, B
Western European Studies, B
Women's Studies, B

Pennsylvania

ALBRIGHT COLLEGE

Accounting, B
American/United States Studies/Civilization, B
Art Teacher Education, B
Art/Art Studies, General, B
Biochemistry, B
Biology/Biological Sciences, B
Business Administration and Management, B
Chemistry, B
Communication Studies/Speech Communication
   and Rhetoric, B
Computer Science, B
Criminology, B
Design and Visual Communications, B
Drama and Dramatics/Theatre Arts, B
Early Childhood Education and Teaching, M
Economics, B
Education, M
Elementary Education and Teaching, M
English Language and Literature, B
English as a Second Language, M
Environmental Sciences, B
Finance, B
Forestry, B
French Language and Literature, B
History, B
Information Science/Studies, B
International Business/Trade/Commerce, B

Latin American Studies, B
Marketing/Marketing Management, B
Mathematics, B
Multi-/Interdisciplinary Studies, B
Music, B
Philosophy, B
Physics, B
Political Science and Government, B
Pre-Law Studies, B
Psychology, B
Religion/Religious Studies, B
Secondary Education and Teaching, B
Sociology, B
Spanish Language and Literature, B
Special Education and Teaching, M
Urban Studies/Affairs, B
Women's Studies, B

ALLEGHENY COLLEGE

Applied Economics, B
Art History, Criticism and Conservation, B
Art/Art Studies, General, B
Biochemistry, B
Biological and Physical Sciences, B
Biology/Biological Sciences, B
Business/Managerial Economics, B
Chemistry, B
Communication Studies/Speech Communication
   and Rhetoric, B
Community Organization and Advocacy, B
Computer Science, B
Computer Software Engineering, B
Drama and Dramatics/Theatre Arts, B
Economics, B
English Language and Literature, B
Environmental Sciences, B
Environmental Studies, B
Fine Arts and Art Studies, B
Fine/Studio Arts, B
French Language and Literature, B
Geological and Earth Sciences/Geosciences, B
Geology/Earth Science, B
German Language and Literature, B
Health/Medical Preparatory Programs, B
History, B
International Public Health/International Health, B
International Relations and Affairs, B
Mass Communication/Media Studies, B
Mathematics, B
Multi-/Interdisciplinary Studies, B
Music, B
Music Performance, B
Philosophy, B
Physics, B
Political Science and Government, B
Pre-Dentistry Studies, B
Pre-Law Studies, B
Pre-Medicine/Pre-Medical Studies, B
Pre-Nursing Studies, B
Pre-Pharmacy Studies, B
Pre-Veterinary Studies, B
Psychology, B
Religion/Religious Studies, B
Spanish Language and Literature, B

ALVERNIA UNIVERSITY

Accounting, B
Athletic Training and Sports Medicine, B
Biochemistry, B
Biological and Biomedical Sciences, B
Biological and Physical Sciences, B
Biology Teacher Education, B
Biology/Biological Sciences, B
Business Administration and Management, B
Business Administration, Management and Opera-
   tions, M
Business/Commerce, AB
Chemistry, B
Chemistry Teacher Education, B
Community Psychology, M
Criminal Justice/Law Enforcement Administration, B
Drama and Dramatics/Theatre Arts, B
Early Childhood Education and Teaching, B
Education, M
English Language and Literature, B
English/Language Arts Teacher Education, B

Forensic Science and Technology, B
Health Professions and Related Clinical Sciences, B
Health Services/Allied Health/Health Sciences, B
History, B
Human Resources Management/Personnel Adminis-
tration, B
Junior High/Intermediate/Middle School Education
and Teaching, B
Liberal Arts and Sciences Studies and Humani-
ties, B
Liberal Studies, M
Marketing/Marketing Management, B
Mathematics, B
Mathematics Teacher Education, B
Occupational Therapy/Therapist, M
Organizational Management, D
Philosophy, B
Political Science and Government, B
Psychology, B
Radiologic Technology/Science - Radiographer, A
Religion/Religious Studies, B
Social Studies Teacher Education, B
Social Work, B
Sport and Fitness Administration/Management, B
Substance Abuse/Addiction Counseling, B
Urban Education and Leadership, M

ANTONELLI INSTITUTE

Graphic Design, A
Photography, A

ARCADIA UNIVERSITY

Accounting, B
Acting, B
Actuarial Science, B
Advertising and Public Relations, M
Art Education, M
Art History, Criticism and Conservation, B
Art Teacher Education, B
Art Therapy/Therapist, B
Art/Art Studies, General, B
Biology/Biological Sciences, B
Business Administration and Management, B
Business Administration, Management and Opera-
tions, M
Business/Managerial Economics, B
Ceramic Arts and Ceramics, B
Chemistry, B
Commercial and Advertising Art, B
Communication Studies/Speech Communication
and Rhetoric, B
Community Health and Preventive Medicine, M
Community Psychology, M
Comparative Literature, B
Computer Education, O
Computer Programming/Programmer, B
Computer Science, B
Computer and Information Sciences, B
Conflict Resolution and Mediation/Peace Studies, M
Criminal Justice/Law Enforcement Administration, B
Criminology, B
Curriculum and Instruction, MO
Drama and Dramatics/Theatre Arts, B
Drawing, B
Early Childhood Education and Teaching, BMO
Education, BMDO
Educational Leadership and Administration, MDO
Educational Media/Instructional Technology, M
Elementary Education and Teaching, BMO
English, M
English Education, MO
English Language and Literature, B
Environmental Biology, B
Environmental Education, MO
Finance, B
Fine/Studio Arts, B
Forensic Science and Technology, M
French Language and Literature, B
Genetic Counseling/Counselor, M
Health Education, M
Health/Health Care Administration/Management, B
History, B
Human Resources Management/Personnel Adminis-
tration, B
Human Services, B
Humanities/Humanistic Studies, M

Illustration, B
Interior Design, B
International Affairs, M
International Business/Trade/Commerce, B
International/Global Studies, B
Italian Studies, B
Kindergarten/PreSchool Education and Teaching, B
Liberal Arts and Sciences Studies and Humani-
ties, B
Management Information Systems and Services, B
Marketing/Marketing Management, M
Mass Communication/Media Studies, B
Mathematics, B
Mathematics Teacher Education, MO
Medical Illustration/Medical Illustrator, B
Metal and Jewelry Arts, B
Multi-/Interdisciplinary Studies, B
Music Teacher Education, M
Natural Sciences, B
Painting, B
Philosophy, B
Photography, B
Physical Therapy/Therapist, D
Physician Assistant, M
Physics, B
Political Science and Government, B
Pre-Dentistry Studies, B
Pre-Law Studies, B
Pre-Medicine/Pre-Medical Studies, B
Pre-Veterinary Studies, B
Psychology, BM
Public Health, M
Reading Teacher Education, MO
School Psychology, M
Science Teacher Education/General Science
Teacher Education, BMO
Secondary Education and Teaching, BMO
Small Business Administration/Management, B
Social Studies Teacher Education, M
Sociology, B
Spanish Language and Literature, B
Special Education and Teaching, MDO
Theater, M

THE ART INSTITUTE OF PHILADEL-
PHIA

Advertising, B
Animation, Interactive Technology, Video Graphics
and Special Effects, B
Apparel and Textile Marketing Management, AB
Cinematography and Film/Video Production, AB
Commercial Photography, AB
Computer Graphics, B
Culinary Arts/Chef Training, A
Digital Communication and Media/Multimedia, B
Fashion Merchandising, A
Fashion/Apparel Design, AB
Graphic Design, AB
Industrial Design, B
Interior Design, AB
Recording Arts Technology/Technician, B
Restaurant, Culinary, and Catering
Management/Manager, B
Web Page, Digital/Multimedia and Information Re-
sources Design, AB

THE ART INSTITUTE OF PITTSBURGH

Animation, Interactive Technology, Video Graphics
and Special Effects, B
Apparel and Accessories Marketing Operations, B
Baking and Pastry Arts/Baker/Pastry Chef, A
Cinematography and Film/Video Production, AB
Commercial Photography, AB
Computer Graphics, B
Culinary Arts/Chef Training, A
Fashion/Apparel Design, B
Graphic Design, AB
Hotel/Motel Administration/Management, B
Industrial Design, AB
Interior Design, B
Restaurant, Culinary, and Catering
Management/Manager, B

Web Page, Digital/Multimedia and Information Resources Design, AB

BERKS TECHNICAL INSTITUTE

Computer Graphics, A
Computer Programming, A
Computer Programming/Programmer, A
Computer and Information Sciences, A
Drafting and Design Technology/Technician, A
Information Technology, A
Medical/Clinical Assistant, A
System Administration/Administrator, A

BIDWELL TRAINING CENTER

Chemical Technology/Technician, A

BLOOMSBURG UNIVERSITY OF PENN-
SYLVANIA

Accounting, BM
Anthropology, B
Art History, Criticism and Conservation, B
Athletic Training and Sports Medicine, M
Audiology/Audiologist and Speech-Language
Pathology/Pathologist, A
Biological and Biomedical Sciences, M
Biology/Biological Sciences, B
Business Administration and Management, B
Business Administration, Management and Opera-
tions, M
Business Education, M
Business/Commerce, B
Chemistry, B
Communication Disorders, MD
Community Health and Preventive Medicine, M
Computer Science, B
Computer/Information Technology Services Adminis-
tration and Management, B
Counselor Education/School Counseling and Guid-
ance Services, M
Criminal Justice/Safety Studies, B
Curriculum and Instruction, MO
Drama and Dramatics/Theatre Arts, B
Early Childhood Education and Teaching, BM
Economics, B
Education, MO
Educational Media/Instructional Technology, MO
Electrical, Electronics and Communications Engi-
neering, B
Elementary Education and Teaching, M
English Education, M
English Language and Literature, B
Exercise and Sports Science, M
Fine/Studio Arts, B
Foreign Languages and Literatures, B
Geology/Earth Science, B
Health and Physical Education/Fitness, B
Health/Medical Physics, B
Health/Medical Preparatory Programs, B
History, B
Junior High/Intermediate/Middle School Education
and Teaching, B
Logistics and Materials Management, B
Mass Communication/Media Studies, B
Mathematics, B
Mathematics Teacher Education, M
Medical Radiologic Technology/Science - Radiation
Therapist, B
Middle School Education, M
Music, B
Nurse Anesthetist, M
Nursing, M
Nursing - Adult, M
Nursing - Advanced Practice, M
Nursing Administration, M
Organizational Communication, B
Philosophy, B
Physics, B
Political Science and Government, B
Psychology, B
Reading Teacher Education, M
Science Teacher Education/General Science
Teacher Education, M
Secondary Education and Teaching, M
Sign Language Interpretation and Translation, B
Social Sciences, B
Social Studies Teacher Education, M

Social Work, B
Sociology, B
Special Education and Teaching, BMO
Student Personnel Services, M

BRADFORD SCHOOL

Accounting Technology/Technician and Bookkeeping, A
Administrative Assistant and Secretarial Science, A
Computer Programming/Programmer, A
Computer Systems Networking and Telecommunications, A
Dental Assisting/Assistant, A
Graphic Design, A
Hotel/Motel Administration/Management, A
Legal Administrative Assistant/Secretary, A
Legal Assistant/Paralegal, A
Medical/Clinical Assistant, A
Retailing and Retail Operations, A

BRIGHTWOOD CAREER INSTITUTE, BROOMALL CAMPUS

Medical/Clinical Assistant, A

BRIGHTWOOD CAREER INSTITUTE, HARRISBURG CAMPUS

Business Administration and Management, A
Computer Systems Networking and Telecommunications, A
Criminal Justice/Law Enforcement Administration, A
Medical/Clinical Assistant, A

BRIGHTWOOD CAREER INSTITUTE, PHILADELPHIA CAMPUS

Criminal Justice/Law Enforcement Administration, A

BRIGHTWOOD CAREER INSTITUTE, PHILADELPHIA MILLS CAMPUS

Computer Engineering Technology/Technician, A
Criminal Justice/Law Enforcement Administration, A
Respiratory Care Therapy/Therapist, A

BRIGHTWOOD CAREER INSTITUTE, PITTSBURGH CAMPUS

Accounting and Business/Management, A
Business Administration and Management, A
Computer Systems Networking and Telecommunications, A
Criminal Justice/Law Enforcement Administration, A
Medical/Clinical Assistant, A
Occupational Therapy/Therapist, A

BRYN ATHYN COLLEGE OF THE NEW CHURCH

Biological and Physical Sciences, B
Biology/Biological Sciences, B
Business/Commerce, B
Elementary Education and Teaching, B
English Language and Literature, B
History, B
Liberal Arts and Sciences Studies and Humanities, A
Multi-/Interdisciplinary Studies, B
Psychology, B
Religion/Religious Studies, BM
Theology and Religious Vocations, M

BRYN MAWR COLLEGE

Ancient/Classical Greek Language and Literature, B
Anthropology, B
Archeology, BMD
Art History, Criticism and Conservation, BMD
Astronomy, B
Biochemistry, Biophysics and Molecular Biology, B
Biology/Biological Sciences, B
Chemistry, BMD
Classics and Classical Languages, Literatures, and Linguistics, BMD
Comparative Literature, B
Computer Science, B
East Asian Studies, B
Economics, B
English Language and Literature, B
Fine/Studio Arts, B

French Language and Literature, B
Geology/Earth Science, B
German Language and Literature, B
History, B
International/Global Studies, B
Italian Language and Literature, B
Latin Language and Literature, B
Linguistics, B
Mathematics, BMD
Multi-/Interdisciplinary Studies, B
Music, B
Philosophy, B
Physics, BMD
Political Science and Government, B
Psychology, B
Religion/Religious Studies, B
Romance Languages, Literatures, and Linguistics, B
Russian Language and Literature, B
Social Work, MD
Sociology, B
Spanish Language and Literature, B
Urban Studies/Affairs, B

BUCKNELL UNIVERSITY

Accounting and Finance, B
Animal Behavior and Ethology, BM
Anthropology, B
Applied Mathematics, B
Art History, Criticism and Conservation, B
Art/Art Studies, General, B
Biochemistry, B
Biological and Biomedical Sciences, M
Biology/Biological Sciences, B
Biomedical/Medical Engineering, B
Biopsychology, B
Business Administration and Management, B
Business/Commerce, B
Cell/Cellular and Molecular Biology, B
Chemical Engineering, BM
Chemistry, BM
Civil Engineering, BM
Classics and Classical Languages, Literatures, and Linguistics, B
Computer Engineering, B
Computer and Information Sciences, B
Drama and Dramatics/Theatre Arts, B
Early Childhood Education and Teaching, B
East Asian Studies, B
Econometrics and Quantitative Economics, B
Economics, B
Education, BM
Educational Statistics and Research Methods, B
Electrical Engineering, M
Electrical, Electronics and Communications Engineering, B
Elementary Education and Teaching, B
Engineering and Applied Sciences, M
English, M
English Language and Literature, B
Environmental Sciences, B
Environmental Studies, B
Environmental/Environmental Health Engineering, B
Fine/Studio Arts, B
French Language and Literature, B
Geography, B
Geology/Earth Science, B
German Language and Literature, B
History, B
Humanities/Humanistic Studies, B
International Business/Trade/Commerce, B
International Relations and Affairs, B
Kindergarten/PreSchool Education and Teaching, B
Latin American Studies, B
Linguistics, B
Marketing/Marketing Management, B
Mathematics, BM
Mechanical Engineering, BM
Multi-/Interdisciplinary Studies, B
Music, B
Music History, Literature, and Theory, B
Music Performance, B
Music Teacher Education, B
Music Theory and Composition, B
Philosophy, B
Physics, B
Political Science and Government, B

Psychology, BM
Religion/Religious Studies, B
Russian Language and Literature, B
Secondary Education and Teaching, B
Sociology, B
Spanish Language and Literature, B
Student Personnel Services, M
Visual and Performing Arts, B
Voice and Opera, B
Women's Studies, B

BUCKS COUNTY COMMUNITY COLLEGE

Accounting Technology/Technician and Bookkeeping, A
Art History, Criticism and Conservation, A
Baking and Pastry Arts/Baker/Pastry Chef, A
Biology Teacher Education, A
Biology Technician/BioTechnology Laboratory Technician, A
Building/Home/Construction Inspection/Inspector, A
Business Administration and Management, A
Business, Management, Marketing, and Related Support Services, A
Cabinetmaking and Millwork/Millwright, A
Chemical Technology/Technician, A
Child Care Provider/Assistant, A
Cinematography and Film/Video Production, A
Commercial Photography, A
Commercial and Advertising Art, A
Communication Studies/Speech Communication and Rhetoric, A
Computer Systems Networking and Telecommunications, A
Computer and Information Sciences, A
Criminal Justice/Safety Studies, A
Culinary Arts/Chef Training, A
Early Childhood Education and Teaching, A
Engineering Technology, A
English Language and Literature, A
Environmental Sciences, A
Foodservice Systems Administration/Management, A
Health Professions and Related Clinical Sciences, A
History, A
History Teacher Education, A
Human Development and Family Studies, A
Humanities/Humanistic Studies, A
Industrial Technology/Technician, A
Information Science/Studies, A
Journalism, A
Kinesiology and Exercise Science, A
Legal Professions and Studies, A
Liberal Arts and Sciences Studies and Humanities, A
Mathematics, A
Mathematics Teacher Education, A
Medical Insurance Coding Specialist/Coder, A
Medical/Clinical Assistant, A
Multi-/Interdisciplinary Studies, A
Music, A
Physical Education Teaching and Coaching, A
Psychology, A
Retailing and Retail Operations, A
Small Business Administration/Management, A
Sport and Fitness Administration/Management, A
System Administration/Administrator, A
Tourism and Travel Services Management, A
Visual and Performing Arts, A
Web Page, Digital/Multimedia and Information Resources Design, A

BUTLER COUNTY COMMUNITY COLLEGE

Administrative Assistant and Secretarial Science, A
Architectural Drafting and Architectural CAD/CADD, A
Biology/Biological Sciences, A
Business Administration and Management, A
Business, Management, Marketing, and Related Support Services, A
Business/Commerce, A
CAD/CADD Drafting and/or Design Technology/Technician, A
Civil Engineering Technology/Technician, A
Computer Programming, Specific Applications, A

Computer Technology/Computer Systems Technology, A
Computer and Information Sciences, A
Computer and Information Systems Security, A
Cooking and Related Culinary Arts, A
Corrections, A
Cosmetology/Cosmetologist, A
Criminal Justice/Law Enforcement Administration, A
Criminal Justice/Police Science, A
Digital Communication and Media/Multimedia, A
Education, A
Electrical, Electronic and Communications Engineering Technology/Technician, A
Elementary Education and Teaching, A
Engineering, A
English Language and Literature, A
Fine Arts and Art Studies, A
Fire Science/Firefighting, A
Food Technology and Processing, A
Foodservice Systems Administration/Management, A
General Office Occupations and Clerical Services, A
General Studies, A
Health and Medical Administrative Services, A
Health/Health Care Administration/Management, A
Heating, Air Conditioning, Ventilation and Refrigeration Maintenance Technology/Technician, A
Hospitality Administration/Management, A
Human Resources Management/Personnel Administration, A
Instrumentation Technology/Technician, A
Kindergarten/PreSchool Education and Teaching, A
Legal Administrative Assistant/Secretary, A
Machine Shop Technology/Assistant, A
Machine Tool Technology/Machinist, A
Manufacturing Technology/Technician, A
Massage Therapy/Therapeutic Massage, A
Mathematics, A
Mechanical Drafting and Mechanical Drafting CAD/CADD, A
Medical Insurance Coding Specialist/Coder, A
Medical Office Assistant/Specialist, A
Organizational Communication, A
Parks, Recreation and Leisure Facilities Management, A
Photography, A
Physical Sciences, A
Physical Therapist Assistant, A
Precision Production Trades, A
Psychology, A
Radiologic Technology/Science - Radiographer, A
Robotics Technology/Technician, A
Security and Protective Services, A
Selling Skills and Sales Operations, A
Social Work, A
Sport and Fitness Administration/Management, A
System Administration/Administrator, A
Web Page, Digital/Multimedia and Information Resources Design, A

CABRINI UNIVERSITY

Accounting, BM
African-American/Black Studies, B
American/United States Studies/Civilization, B
Biology Teacher Education, B
Biology/Biological Sciences, B
Business Administration and Management, B
Chemistry, B
Chemistry Teacher Education, B
Communication Studies/Speech Communication and Rhetoric, B
Computer and Information Sciences and Support Services, B
Criminology, B
Education, BM
Elementary Education and Teaching, B
English Language and Literature, B
English/Language Arts Teacher Education, B
Finance, B
French Language and Literature, B
Graphic Design, B
History, B
Human Resources Management/Personnel Administration, B
Information Technology, B
Italian Language and Literature, B

Kindergarten/PreSchool Education and Teaching, B
Kinesiology and Exercise Science, B
Liberal Arts and Sciences Studies and Humanities, B
Marketing/Marketing Management, B
Mathematics, B
Mathematics Teacher Education, B
Organizational Management, M
Philosophy, B
Political Science and Government, B
Psychology, B
Religion/Religious Studies, B
Social Studies Teacher Education, B
Social Work, B
Sociology, B
Spanish Language and Literature, B
Special Education and Teaching, B
Women's Studies, B

CAIRN UNIVERSITY

Bible/Biblical Studies, B
Business Administration and Management, B
Business Administration, Management and Operations, MO
Education, M
Educational Administration and Supervision, M
Elementary Education and Teaching, B
English Language and Literature, B
English/Language Arts Teacher Education, B
Kindergarten/PreSchool Education and Teaching, B
Liberal Arts and Sciences Studies and Humanities, B
Mathematics Teacher Education, B
Music, B
Music History, Literature, and Theory, B
Organizational Management, MO
Pastoral Studies/Counseling, M
Physical Education Teaching and Coaching, B
Psychology, B
Public/Applied History and Archival Administration, B
Religion/Religious Studies, BM
Social Studies Teacher Education, B
Social Work, B
Teacher Education and Professional Development, Specific Levels and Methods, B
Teacher Education and Professional Development, Specific Subject Areas, B
Theology and Religious Vocations, M
Youth Ministry, B

CALIFORNIA UNIVERSITY OF PENNSYLVANIA

Accounting, AB
Anthropology, B
Arabic Language and Literature, B
Art/Art Studies, General, B
Athletic Training and Sports Medicine, BM
Biology/Biological Sciences, B
Business Administration and Management, AB
Business Administration, Management and Operations, M
Chemistry, B
Commercial and Advertising Art, AB
Communication Disorders, BM
Communication Studies/Speech Communication and Rhetoric, B
Computer Engineering Technology/Technician, AB
Computer and Information Sciences, AB
Corrections, AB
Counselor Education/School Counseling and Guidance Services, M
Criminology, M
Drafting and Design Technology/Technician, A
Drama and Dramatics/Theatre Arts, B
Early Childhood Education and Teaching, B
Education, M
Educational Administration and Supervision, M
Electrical, Electronic and Communications Engineering Technology/Technician, AB
Elementary Education and Teaching, BM
Engineering Technology, B
English Language and Literature, B
Environmental Sciences, B
Exercise and Sports Science, M
French Language and Literature, B
Geography, B

Geology/Earth Science, B
Gerontology, B
Graphic Design, AB
History, B
Industrial Production Technologies/Technicians, AB
Junior High/Intermediate/Middle School Education and Teaching, M
Kindergarten/PreSchool Education and Teaching, AB
Legal Professions and Studies, B
Legal and Justice Studies, M
Liberal Arts and Sciences Studies and Humanities, AB
Mathematics, B
Occupational Therapist Assistant, A
Parks, Recreation and Leisure Facilities Management, B
Philosophy, B
Physical Sciences, B
Physical Therapist Assistant, A
Physics, B
Political Science and Government, B
Psychology, B
Reading Teacher Education, M
Rehabilitation Sciences, M
Robotics Technology/Technician, A
School Psychology, M
Secondary Education and Teaching, M
Social Sciences, BM
Social Work, BM
Spanish Language and Literature, B
Special Education and Teaching, BM
Sport Psychology, M
Sport and Fitness Administration/Management, BM
Vocational and Technical Education, M

CAMBRIA-ROWE BUSINESS COLLEGE (INDIANA)

Accounting, A
Administrative Assistant and Secretarial Science, A
Business Administration and Management, A
Health Services/Allied Health/Health Sciences, A
Legal Administrative Assistant/Secretary, A
Medical Office Assistant/Specialist, A

CAMBRIA-ROWE BUSINESS COLLEGE (JOHNSTOWN)

Accounting, A
Administrative Assistant and Secretarial Science, A
Business Administration and Management, A
Computer Technology/Computer Systems Technology, A
Health Services/Allied Health/Health Sciences, A
Legal Administrative Assistant/Secretary, A
Management Information Systems and Services, A
Management Science, A
Medical Administrative Assistant/Secretary, A

CAREER TRAINING ACADEMY (LOWER BURRELL)

Massage Therapy/Therapeutic Massage, A
Medical Insurance Coding Specialist/Coder, A
Medical/Clinical Assistant, A

CAREER TRAINING ACADEMY (MONROEVILLE)

Massage Therapy/Therapeutic Massage, A
Medical Insurance Coding Specialist/Coder, A
Medical/Clinical Assistant, A

CAREER TRAINING ACADEMY (PITTSBURGH)

Massage Therapy/Therapeutic Massage, A
Medical Insurance Coding Specialist/Coder, A
Medical/Clinical Assistant, A

CARLOW UNIVERSITY

Accounting, B
Art Education, M
Art Teacher Education, B
Art Therapy/Therapist, B
Auditing, B
Biology/Biological Sciences, B
Business Administration and Management, B

Business Administration, Management and Operations, M
Chemistry, B
Communication, Journalism and Related Programs, B
Computer and Information Systems Security, M
Counseling Psychology, MDO
Counselor Education/School Counseling and Guidance Services, MO
Criminology, B
Early Childhood Education and Teaching, BM
Education, M
Educational Leadership and Administration, M
Educational Media/Instructional Technology, M
English Language and Literature, B
Fine/Studio Arts, B
Forensic Science and Technology, M
Health Services Administration, M
Health/Health Care Administration/Management, B
History, B
Human Resources Management and Services, B
Junior High/Intermediate/Middle School Education and Teaching, B
Liberal Arts and Sciences Studies and Humanities, B
Mathematics, B
Nursing, D
Nursing - Advanced Practice, MO
Nursing Administration, M
Nursing Education, M
Organizational Management, MDO
Perfusion Technology/Perfusionist, B
Philosophy, B
Political Science and Government, B
Project Management, M
Psychology, B
Secondary Education and Teaching, M
Social Work, B
Sociology, B
Special Education and Teaching, M
Substance Abuse/Addiction Counseling, MO
Theology/Theological Studies, B
Writing, M

CARNEGIE MELLON UNIVERSITY

Accounting, D
Actuarial Science, B
African Studies, D
African-American Studies, D
Applied Physics, D
Architectural Engineering, MD
Architecture, BMD
Art/Art Studies, General, B
Artificial Intelligence and Robotics, MD
Arts Management, M
Astrophysics, B
Atmospheric Sciences and Meteorology, D
Behavioral Sciences, B
BioTechnology, M
Biochemistry, D
Bioengineering, MD
Biological and Biomedical Sciences, MD
Biology/Biological Sciences, B
Biomedical Engineering, MD
Biometry/Biometrics, B
Biophysics, D
Biopsychology, BD
Building Science, MD
Business Administration and Management, B
Business Administration, Management and Operations, B
Cell Biology and Anatomy, D
Chemical Engineering, BMD
Chemistry, BD
Chinese Language and Literature, B
Civil Engineering, BMD
Cognitive Sciences, BD
Communication and Media Studies, M
Comparative Literature, MD
Composition, M
Computational Biology, MD
Computational Mathematics, B
Computer Art and Design, M
Computer Engineering, MD
Computer Science, BMD
Computer and Information Sciences, B

Computer and Information Systems Security, M
Construction Management, MD
Corporate and Organizational Communication, M
Cultural Studies, D
Design and Applied Arts, MD
Design and Visual Communications, B
Developmental Biology and Embryology, D
Developmental Psychology, D
Drama and Dramatics/Theatre Arts, B
Econometrics and Quantitative Economics, B
Economics, BD
Electrical Engineering, MD
Electrical, Electronics and Communications Engineering, B
Energy and Power Engineering, MD
Engineering, B
English, MD
English Language and Literature, B
Entertainment Management, M
Entrepreneurship/Entrepreneurial Studies, BD
Environmental Engineering Technology/Environmental Technology, MD
Environmental Sciences, D
Film, Television, and Video Production, M
Finance, B
Finance and Banking, D
Fine Arts and Art Studies, M
French Language and Literature, B
Gender Studies, D
Genetics, D
German Language and Literature, B
Health Services Administration, M
History, BD
History of Science and Technology, D
Human-Computer Interaction, MD
Industrial Design, B
Industrial and Labor Relations, D
Industrial and Manufacturing Management, MD
Information Science/Studies, MD
Information Technology, M
International Business/Trade/Commerce, B
International Relations and Affairs, B
International/Global Studies, B
Japanese Language and Literature, B
Liberal Arts and Sciences Studies and Humanities, B
Linguistics, BMD
Logic, B
Management, M
Management Information Systems and Services, MD
Marketing, D
Marketing/Marketing Management, B
Materials Engineering, MD
Materials Sciences, MD
Mathematical Statistics and Probability, B
Mathematical and Computational Finance, MD
Mathematics, BMD
Mathematics and Statistics, B
Mechanical Engineering, BMD
Mechanics, MD
Media Studies, M
Modeling and Simulation, M
Molecular Biology, D
Molecular Biophysics, D
Music, BM
Music Performance, B
Music Teacher Education, M
Music Theory and Composition, B
NanoTechnology, D
Neurobiology and Neurophysiology, D
Neuroscience, D
Operations Management and Supervision, B
Operations Research, BD
Organizational Behavior Studies, D
Performance, M
Philosophy, BMD
Physics, BMD
Polymer/Plastics Engineering, M
Psychology, BD
Public Administration, M
Public Policy Analysis, BMD
Publishing, M
Rhetoric, MD
Russian Language and Literature, B
Russian Studies, B

Securities Services Administration/Management, M
Social Psychology, D
Social Sciences, D
Software Engineering, MD
Spanish Language and Literature, B
Statistics, BMD
Structural Biology, D
Sustainable Development, M
Systems Engineering, M
Systems Science and Theory, B
Technical and Business Writing, M
Technology and Public Policy, D
Telecommunications Management, M
Theater, M
Theoretical Chemistry, D
Theoretical and Mathematical Physics, B
Urban Design, M
Violin, Viola, Guitar and Other Stringed Instruments, B
Voice and Opera, B
Water Resources Engineering, M
Women's Studies, D
Writing, M

CEDAR CREST COLLEGE

Accounting, B
Art Therapy/Therapist, BM
Art/Art Studies, General, B
Biochemistry, B
Biology/Biological Sciences, B
Business Administration and Management, B
Chemistry, B
Communication Studies/Speech Communication and Rhetoric, B
Computer and Information Sciences, B
Conservation Biology, B
Criminology, B
Dance, B
Digital Communication and Media/Multimedia, B
Drama and Dramatics/Theatre Arts, B
Early Childhood Education and Teaching, B
Education, BM
Elementary Education and Teaching, B
English Language and Literature, B
Environmental Biology, B
Foods, Nutrition, and Wellness Studies, B
Forensic Science and Technology, BM
Genetics, B
History, B
Human Nutrition, B
International/Global Studies, B
Mass Communication/Media Studies, B
Mathematics, B
Nuclear Medical Technology/Technologist, B
Nursing, M
Nursing Administration, M
Nursing Education, M
Nutritional Sciences, O
Political Science and Government, B
Pre-Dentistry Studies, B
Pre-Law Studies, B
Pre-Medicine/Pre-Medical Studies, B
Pre-Veterinary Studies, B
Psychology, B
Secondary Education and Teaching, B
Social Work, B
Writing, M

CENTRAL PENN COLLEGE

Accounting, AB
Business Administration and Management, AB
Computer Science, A
Criminal Justice/Safety Studies, AB
Entrepreneurship/Entrepreneurial Studies, A
Information Technology, B
Legal Assistant/Paralegal, A
Legal Professions and Studies, B
Management Information Systems and Services, M
Marketing/Marketing Management, A
Mass Communication/Media Studies, B
Medical/Clinical Assistant, A
Organizational Management, M

Securities Services Administration/Management, B

CHATHAM UNIVERSITY

Accounting, BM
Art Education, M
Art History, Criticism and Conservation, B
Biochemistry, B
Biological and Biomedical Sciences, M
Biology/Biological Sciences, B
Business Administration and Management, B
Business Administration, Management and Operations, M
Business/Managerial Economics, B
Chemistry, B
Communication Studies/Speech Communication and Rhetoric, B
Computer Art and Design, M
Counseling Psychology, MD
Criminology, B
Developmental Psychology, M
Early Childhood Education and Teaching, BM
Education, M
Elementary Education and Teaching, BM
English Education, M
English Language and Literature, B
Environmental Biology, M
Environmental Education, M
Environmental Sciences, B
Environmental Studies, B
Ethnic, Cultural Minority, and Gender Studies, B
Film, Television, and Video Production, M
Film/Video and Photographic Arts, B
Fine/Studio Arts, B
Graphic Design, B
Health Psychology, M
History, B
Industrial and Organizational Psychology, M
Interior Architecture, B
Interior Design, M
International Business/Trade/Commerce, B
International Relations and Affairs, B
International/Global Studies, B
Journalism, B
Kinesiology and Exercise Science, B
Landscape Architecture, M
Liberal Arts and Sciences Studies and Humanities, B
Marketing/Marketing Management, B
Marriage and Family Therapy/Counseling, M
Mathematics, B
Mathematics Teacher Education, M
Music, B
Nursing, MD
Nursing Administration, M
Nursing Education, M
Occupational Therapy/Therapist, MD
Photography, B
Physical Therapy/Therapist, D
Physician Assistant, M
Physics, B
Political Science and Government, B
Psychology, B
Public Policy Analysis, B
Public Relations/Image Management, B
Science Teacher Education/General Science Teacher Education, M
Secondary Education and Teaching, M
Social Studies Teacher Education, M
Social Work, B
Special Education and Teaching, M
Sport Psychology, M
Sustainability Management, M
Women's Studies, BM
Writing, M

CHESTNUT HILL COLLEGE

Accounting, B
Accounting and Business/Management, B
Biochemistry, B
Biology/Biological Sciences, B
Business Administration and Management, B
Business/Corporate Communications, B
Chemistry, B
Child Care and Support Services Management, B
Clinical Psychology, MDO

Communication, Journalism and Related Programs, B
Communications Technologies/Technicians and Support Services, B
Computer and Information Sciences, B
Computer/Information Technology Services Administration and Management, B
Counseling Psychology, MO
Criminal Justice/Law Enforcement Administration, B
Distance Education Development, M
Early Childhood Education and Teaching, BMO
Education, MO
Educational Leadership and Administration, MO
Educational Media/Instructional Technology, MO
Elementary Education and Teaching, BMO
English Language and Literature, B
Environmental Sciences, B
Fine/Studio Arts, B
Forensic Science and Technology, B
French Language and Literature, B
Health/Health Care Administration/Management, B
History, B
Human Resources Management/Personnel Administration, B
Human Services, BMO
Information Resources Management/CIO Training, B
International Business/Trade/Commerce, B
International/Global Studies, B
Liberal Arts and Sciences Studies and Humanities, AB
Marketing/Marketing Management, B
Marriage and Family Therapy/Counseling, MDO
Mass Communication/Media Studies, B
Mathematics, B
Mathematics and Computer Science, B
Middle School Education, MO
Molecular Biology, B
Multi-/Interdisciplinary Studies, B
Music, B
Music Teacher Education, B
Political Science and Government, B
Psychology, BMDO
Reading Teacher Education, MO
Secondary Education and Teaching, MO
Sociology, B
Spanish Language and Literature, B
Special Education and Teaching, MO
Substance Abuse/Addiction Counseling, MO

CHEYNEY UNIVERSITY OF PENNSYLVANIA

Accounting, B
Aquaculture, B
Art/Art Studies, General, B
Biological and Physical Sciences, B
Biology/Biological Sciences, B
Business Administration and Management, B
Chemistry, B
Computer and Information Sciences, B
Criminal Justice/Law Enforcement Administration, B
Drama and Dramatics/Theatre Arts, B
Early Childhood Education and Teaching, B
Ecology, B
Education, MO
Educational Administration and Supervision, O
Educational Leadership and Administration, MO
Elementary Education and Teaching, M
English Language and Literature, B
Environmental Sciences, B
Fashion Merchandising, B
Finance, B
Fine/Studio Arts, B
Health Services/Allied Health/Health Sciences, B
Hospitality Administration/Management, B
Liberal Arts and Sciences Studies and Humanities, B
Management Science, B
Marine Biology and Biological Oceanography, B
Marketing/Marketing Management, B
Mathematics, B
Music, B
Parks, Recreation and Leisure Facilities Management, B
Political Science and Government, B
Psychology, B
Public Administration, M

Social Sciences, B
Sociology, B
Special Education and Teaching, BM
Urban Education and Leadership, M
Visual and Performing Arts, B

CLARION UNIVERSITY OF PENNSYLVANIA

Administrative Assistant and Secretarial Science, A
Advertising and Public Relations, O
Allied Health and Medical Assisting Services, A
Anthropology, A
Applied Mathematics, A
Art/Art Studies, General, B
Biological and Physical Sciences, B
Biology/Biological Sciences, B
Business Administration and Management, AB
Business Administration, Management and Operations, M
Business/Managerial Economics, B
Chemistry, B
Clinical/Medical Laboratory Technician, B
Communication Disorders, M
Communication and Media Studies, M
Computer and Information Sciences, B
Criminal Justice/Law Enforcement Administration, AB
Curriculum and Instruction, M
Database Systems, M
Drama and Dramatics/Theatre Arts, B
Early Childhood Education and Teaching, ABM
Economics, B
Education, M
Education/Teaching of Individuals in Early Childhood Special Education Programs, B
Elementary Education and Teaching, B
English Language and Literature, B
Environmental Sciences, B
Finance, B
Foreign Languages and Literatures, B
French Language and Literature, B
Geology/Earth Science, B
History, B
Industrial Production Technologies/Technicians, A
Industrial Technology/Technician, B
Information Science/Studies, B
International Business/Trade/Commerce, B
Junior High/Intermediate/Middle School Education and Teaching, M
Labor and Industrial Relations, B
Legal Administrative Assistant/Secretary, A
Liberal Arts and Sciences Studies and Humanities, AB
Library Science, BMO
Marketing/Marketing Management, B
Mathematics, B
Mathematics Teacher Education, M
Medical Radiologic Technology/Science - Radiation Therapist, B
Mental and Social Health Services and Allied Professions, AB
Molecular Biology, B
Music Teacher Education, B
Nursing, MD
Nursing - Advanced Practice, MO
Nursing Education, MO
Philosophy, B
Physics, B
Political Science and Government, B
Psychology, B
Reading Teacher Education, M
Real Estate, B
Rehabilitation Sciences, M
Respiratory Care Therapy/Therapist, A
Science Teacher Education/General Science Teacher Education, M
Social Sciences, B
Sociology, B
Spanish Language and Literature, B
Special Education and Teaching, BM
Speech-Language Pathology/Pathologist, B

Vocational and Technical Education, M

COMMONWEALTH TECHNICAL INSTITUTE

Architectural Drafting and Architectural CAD/CADD, A
Computer Technology/Computer Systems Technology, A
Culinary Arts/Chef Training, A
Dental Laboratory Technology/Technician, A
Mechanical Drafting and Mechanical Drafting CAD/CADD, A
Medical Office Assistant/Specialist, A

COMMUNITY COLLEGE OF ALLEGHENY COUNTY

Accounting Technology/Technician and Bookkeeping, A
Administrative Assistant and Secretarial Science, A
Airline/Commercial/Professional Pilot and Flight Crew, A
Applied Horticulture/Horticultural Operations, A
Architectural Drafting and Architectural CAD/CADD, A
Art/Art Studies, General, A
Athletic Training and Sports Medicine, A
Automotive Engineering Technology/Technician, A
Aviation/Airway Management and Operations, A
Banking and Financial Support Services, A
Biology/Biological Sciences, A
Building/Property Maintenance and Management, A
Business Administration and Management, A
Business Machine Repairer, A
Business/Office Automation/Technology/Data Entry, A
Carpentry/Carpenter, A
Chemical Technology/Technician, A
Chemistry, A
Child Care Provider/Assistant, A
Child Development, A
Civil Drafting and Civil Engineering CAD/CADD, A
Civil Engineering Technology/Technician, A
Clinical/Medical Laboratory Technician, A
Commercial and Advertising Art, A
Communications Technologies/Technicians and Support Services, A
Community Health Services/Liaison/Counseling, A
Computer Engineering Technology/Technician, A
Computer Systems Networking and Telecommunications, A
Computer Technology/Computer Systems Technology, A
Construction Engineering Technology/Technician, A
Construction Trades, A
Corrections, A
Cosmetology and Related Personal Grooming Arts, A
Court Reporting/Court Reporter, A
Criminal Justice/Police Science, A
Culinary Arts/Chef Training, A
Diagnostic Medical Sonography/Sonographer and Ultrasound Technician, A
Dietician Assistant, A
Drafting and Design Technology/Technician, A
Drafting/Design Engineering Technologies/Technicians, A
Drama and Dramatics/Theatre Arts, A
Electrical, Electronic and Communications Engineering Technology/Technician, A
Electroneurodiagnostic/Electroencephalographic Technology/Technologist, A
Energy Management and Systems Technology/Technician, A
Engineering Technologies/Technicians, A
English Language and Literature, A
Entrepreneurship/Entrepreneurial Studies, A
Environmental Engineering Technology/Environmental Technology, A
Fire Protection and Safety Technology/Technician, A
Foodservice Systems Administration/Management, A
Foreign Languages and Literatures, A
General Studies, A
Greenhouse Operations and Management, A
Health Information/Medical Records Technology/Technician, A

Health Professions and Related Clinical Sciences, A
Health Unit Coordinator/Ward Clerk, A
Health and Physical Education, A
Heating, Air Conditioning, Ventilation and Refrigeration Maintenance Technology/Technician, A
Hotel/Motel Administration/Management, A
Housing and Human Environments, A
Human Development and Family Studies, A
Human Resources Management/Personnel Administration, A
Humanities/Humanistic Studies, A
Industrial Technology/Technician, A
Insurance, A
Journalism, A
Landscaping and Groundskeeping, A
Legal Administrative Assistant/Secretary, A
Legal Assistant/Paralegal, A
Liberal Arts and Sciences Studies and Humanities, A
Machine Shop Technology/Assistant, A
Management Information Systems and Services, A
Marketing/Marketing Management, A
Mathematics, A
Mechanical Drafting and Mechanical Drafting CAD/CADD, A
Medical Administrative Assistant/Secretary, A
Medical Radiologic Technology/Science - Radiation Therapist, A
Medical/Clinical Assistant, A
Music, A
Nuclear Medical Technology/Technologist, A
Occupational Therapist Assistant, A
Office Management and Supervision, A
Ornamental Horticulture, A
Pharmacy Technician/Assistant, A
Physical Therapist Assistant, A
Physics, A
Plant Nursery Operations and Management, A
Psychiatric/Mental Health Services Technician, A
Psychology, A
Quality Control Technology/Technician, A
Real Estate, A
Respiratory Care Therapy/Therapist, A
Restaurant, Culinary, and Catering Management/Manager, A
Retailing and Retail Operations, A
Robotics Technology/Technician, A
Science Technologies/Technicians, A
Sheet Metal Technology/Sheetworking, A
Sign Language Interpretation and Translation, A
Social Sciences, A
Social Work, A
Sociology, A
Solar Energy Technology/Technician, A
Substance Abuse/Addiction Counseling, A
Surgical Technology/Technologist, A
Teacher Education and Professional Development, Specific Levels and Methods, A
Teacher Education and Professional Development, Specific Subject Areas, A
Therapeutic Recreation/Recreational Therapy, A
Tourism Promotion Operations, A
Turf and Turfgrass Management, A
Visual and Performing Arts, A
Welding Technology/Welder, A

COMMUNITY COLLEGE OF BEAVER COUNTY

Accounting Technology/Technician and Bookkeeping, A
Administrative Assistant and Secretarial Science, A
Adult Development and Aging, A
Aeronautical/Aerospace Engineering Technology/Technician, A
Air Traffic Controller, A
Airline/Commercial/Professional Pilot and Flight Crew, A
Architectural Drafting and Architectural CAD/CADD, A
Autobody/Collision and Repair Technology/Technician, A
Automobile/Automotive Mechanics Technology/Technician, A
Aviation/Airway Management and Operations, A
Banking and Financial Support Services, A
Biological and Physical Sciences, A

Business Administration and Management, A
Business/Commerce, A
Carpentry/Carpenter, A
Chemical Technology/Technician, A
Chemistry, A
Clinical/Medical Laboratory Assistant, A
Communication Studies/Speech Communication and Rhetoric, A
Communication, Journalism and Related Programs, A
Communications Technologies/Technicians and Support Services, A
Computer Systems Networking and Telecommunications, A
Computer and Information Sciences, A
Computer and Information Systems Security, A
Cosmetology/Cosmetologist, A
Criminal Justice/Police Science, A
Culinary Arts/Chef Training, A
Diesel Mechanics Technology/Technician, A
Digital Communication and Media/Multimedia, A
Education, A
Electrical, Electronic and Communications Engineering Technology/Technician, A
Electrician, A
Engineering Technology, A
Entrepreneurship/Entrepreneurial Studies, A
Environmental Engineering Technology/Environmental Technology, A
Executive Assistant/Executive Secretary, A
Finance, A
Fine/Studio Arts, A
General Studies, A
Health and Medical Administrative Services, A
Health and Physical Education, A
Heating, Air Conditioning, Ventilation and Refrigeration Maintenance Technology/Technician, A
Human Resources Management/Personnel Administration, A
Humanities/Humanistic Studies, A
Industrial Production Technologies/Technicians, A
Journalism, A
Liberal Arts and Sciences Studies and Humanities, A
Machine Tool Technology/Machinist, A
Marketing/Marketing Management, A
Mason/Masonry, A
Materials Engineering, A
Mathematics, A
Mechanical Engineering Related Technologies/Technicians, A
Medical Administrative Assistant/Secretary, A
Medical Radiologic Technology/Science - Radiation Therapist, A
Music, A
Physics, A
Plumbing Technology/Plumber, A
Psychology, A
Public Relations, Advertising, and Applied Communication, A
Security and Loss Prevention Services, A
Small Business Administration/Management, A
Social Sciences, A
Sociology, A
System, Networking, and LAN/WAN Management/Manager, A
Teacher Assistant/Aide, A
Teacher Education, Multiple Levels, A
Tourism and Travel Services Marketing Operations, A
Web/Multimedia Management and Webmaster, A
Welding Technology/Welder, A

COMMUNITY COLLEGE OF PHILADELPHIA

Accounting, A
Architectural Engineering Technology/Technician, A
Art/Art Studies, General, A
Automobile/Automotive Mechanics Technology/Technician, A
Business Administration and Management, A
Chemical Technology/Technician, A
Clinical/Medical Laboratory Technician, A
Computer Science, A
Construction Engineering Technology/Technician, A
Criminal Justice/Law Enforcement Administration, A

Culinary Arts/Chef Training, A
Dental Hygiene/Hygienist, A
Drafting and Design Technology/Technician, A
Education, A
Engineering, A
Engineering Technology, A
Facilities Planning and Management, A
Finance, A
Fire Science/Firefighting, A
Forensic Science and Technology, A
Health Information/Medical Records
  Administration/Administrator, A
Health Professions and Related Clinical Sciences, A
Hotel/Motel Administration/Management, A
Human Services, A
Kindergarten/PreSchool Education and Teaching, A
Liberal Arts and Sciences Studies and Humani-
  ties, A
Medical Radiologic Technology/Science - Radiation
  Therapist, A
Music, A
Photography, A
Psychology, A
Recording Arts Technology/Technician, A
Respiratory Care Therapy/Therapist, A
Sign Language Interpretation and Translation, A

CONSOLIDATED SCHOOL OF BUSI-NESS (LANCASTER)

Accounting, A
Business Administration and Management, A
Health/Health Care Administration/Management, A
Legal Administrative Assistant/Secretary, A
Medical Administrative Assistant/Secretary, A
Office Management and Supervision, A

CONSOLIDATED SCHOOL OF BUSI-NESS (YORK)

Accounting, A
Business Administration and Management, A
Health/Health Care Administration/Management, A
Legal Administrative Assistant/Secretary, A
Medical Administrative Assistant/Secretary, A
Office Management and Supervision, A
Tourism and Travel Services Management, A

CURTIS INSTITUTE OF MUSIC

Music, BM
Music Performance, B
Music Theory and Composition, B

DEAN INSTITUTE OF TECHNOLOGY

Electrician, A
Heating, Air Conditioning and Refrigeration
  Technology/Technician, A

DELAWARE COUNTY COMMUNITY COLLEGE

Accounting Technology/Technician and Bookkeep-
  ing, A
Animation, Interactive Technology, Video Graphics
  and Special Effects, A
Anthropology, A
Architectural Engineering Technology/Technician, A
Automobile/Automotive Mechanics
  Technology/Technician, A
Biological and Physical Sciences, A
Biomedical Technology/Technician, A
Building/Property Maintenance and Management, A
Business Administration and Management, A
CAD/CADD Drafting and/or Design
  Technology/Technician, A
Commercial and Advertising Art, A
Communication Studies/Speech Communication
  and Rhetoric, A
Communication, Journalism and Related Pro-
  grams, A
Computer Programming, Specific Applications, A
Computer Systems Networking and Telecommunica-
  tions, A
Computer Technology/Computer Systems Technol-
  ogy, A
Computer and Information Sciences, A
Construction Management, A
Criminal Justice/Police Science, A

Data Entry/Microcomputer Applications, A
E-Commerce/Electronic Commerce, A
Early Childhood Education and Teaching, A
Electrical and Power Transmission
  Installation/Installer, A
Electrical, Electronic and Communications Engineer-
  ing Technology/Technician, A
Emergency Medical Technology/Technician (EMT
  Paramedic), A
Engineering, A
Entrepreneurship/Entrepreneurial Studies, A
Fine/Studio Arts, A
Fire Protection and Safety Technology/Technician, A
General Studies, A
Health Services/Allied Health/Health Sciences, A
Health Unit Manager/Ward Supervisor, A
Heating, Air Conditioning and Refrigeration
  Technology/Technician, A
Heating, Air Conditioning, Ventilation and Refrigera-
  tion Maintenance Technology/Technician, A
Hotel/Motel Administration/Management, A
Human Services, A
Industrial Mechanics and Maintenance Technol-
  ogy, A
Journalism, A
Legal Assistant/Paralegal, A
Liberal Arts and Sciences Studies and Humani-
  ties, A
Machine Tool Technology/Machinist, A
Management Information Systems and Services, A
Mechanical Engineering/Mechanical
  Technology/Technician, A
Medical/Clinical Assistant, A
Office Management and Supervision, A
Psychology, A
Respiratory Care Therapy/Therapist, A
Retailing and Retail Operations, A
Robotics Technology/Technician, A
Science Technologies/Technicians, A
Sociology, A
Surgical Technology/Technologist, A
Teacher Education, Multiple Levels, A
Telecommunications Technology/Technician, A
Web Page, Digital/Multimedia and Information Re-
  sources Design, A
Web/Multimedia Management and Webmaster, A

DELAWARE VALLEY UNIVERSITY

Accounting, BM
Agribusiness, BM
Agronomy and Crop Science, B
Animal Sciences, B
Applied Horticulture/Horticultural Business Ser-
  vices, B
Biology/Biological Sciences, B
Business Administration and Management, B
Business Administration, Management and Opera-
  tions, M
Business/Commerce, A
Chemistry, B
Community Psychology, M
Counseling Psychology, M
Criminal Justice/Law Enforcement Administration, B
Crop Production, B
Curriculum and Instruction, M
Dairy Science, B
Developmental Psychology, M
Educational Administration and Supervision, M
Educational Leadership and Administration, M
Educational Media/Instructional Technology, M
English Language and Literature, B
Entrepreneurship/Entrepreneurial Studies, M
Environmental Design/Architecture, B
Equestrian/Equine Studies, B
Finance and Banking, M
Food Science, B
Horse Husbandry/Equine Science and Manage-
  ment, AB
Horticultural Science, B
Human Resources Management and Services, M
International Business/Trade/Commerce, M
Marketing/Marketing Management, B
Ornamental Horticulture, B
Secondary Education and Teaching, B
Supply Chain Management, M
Turf and Turfgrass Management, B

Wildlife and Wildlands Science and Management, B
Zoology/Animal Biology, B

DESALES UNIVERSITY

Accounting, BM
Biochemistry, B
Biology/Biological Sciences, B
Business Administration, Management and Opera-
  tions, M
Chemistry, B
Communication and Media Studies, B
Computer Science, B
Computer/Information Technology Services Adminis-
  tration and Management, B
Criminal Justice/Safety Studies, B
Criminology, M
Dance, B
Drama and Dramatics/Theatre Arts, B
Early Childhood Education and Teaching, BM
Economics, B
Education, M
Educational Media/Instructional Technology, M
Elementary Education and Teaching, B
English Language and Literature, B
English as a Second Language, M
Film/Cinema Studies, B
Finance, B
Finance and Banking, M
Fine Arts and Art Studies, B
Forensic Science and Technology, M
Health Services Administration, M
History, B
Human Resources Management and Services, M
Human Resources Management/Personnel Adminis-
  tration, B
Information Science/Studies, M
Information Technology, B
Interdisciplinary Studies, M
International Business/Trade/Commerce, B
Kinesiology and Exercise Science, B
Law and Legal Studies, B
Liberal Arts and Sciences Studies and Humani-
  ties, B
Logistics and Materials Management, B
Management, M
Management Information Systems and Ser-
  vices, BM
Marketing, M
Marketing/Marketing Management, B
Marriage and Family Therapy/Counseling, B
Mathematics, B
Nurse Midwife/Nursing Midwifery, M
Nursing, MDO
Nursing - Advanced Practice, MO
Nursing Administration, D
Nursing Education, M
Philosophy, B
Physical Education Teaching and Coaching, B
Physical Therapy/Therapist, D
Physician Assistant, BM
Political Science and Government, B
Pre-Law Studies, B
Project Management, M
Psychology, B
Secondary Education and Teaching, BM
Spanish Language and Literature, B
Special Education and Teaching, M
Sport and Fitness Administration/Management, B
Theology/Theological Studies, B

DEVRY UNIVERSITY (FORT WASHING-TON)

Biomedical Technology/Technician, B
Business Administration and Management, B
Business Administration, Management and Opera-
  tions, BM
Business/Commerce, B
Computer Engineering Technology/Technician, B
Computer Software Engineering, B
Computer Systems Analysis/Analyst, B
Computer Systems Networking and Telecommunica-
  tions, AB
Electrical, Electronic and Communications Engineer-
  ing Technology/Technician, AB
Health Information/Medical Records
  Technology/Technician, A

Web Page, Digital/Multimedia and Information Resources Design, AB

DEVRY UNIVERSITY (KING OF PRUSSIA)

Business Administration and Management, B
Business Administration, Management and Operations, BMO
Business/Commerce, B
Computer Systems Analysis/Analyst, B
Computer Systems Networking and Telecommunications, AB
Web Page, Digital/Multimedia and Information Resources Design, AB

DEVRY UNIVERSITY (PHILADELPHIA)

Business Administration and Management, B
Business Administration, Management and Operations, B
Business/Commerce, B
Computer Systems Analysis/Analyst, B
Computer Systems Networking and Telecommunications, AB
Electrical, Electronic and Communications Engineering Technology/Technician, A
Web Page, Digital/Multimedia and Information Resources Design, AB

DICKINSON COLLEGE

African Studies, B
American/United States Studies/Civilization, B
Anthropology, B
Archeology, B
Biochemistry, B
Biology/Biological Sciences, B
Chemistry, B
Classics and Classical Languages, Literatures, and Linguistics, B
Computer and Information Sciences, B
Dance, B
Drama and Dramatics/Theatre Arts, B
East Asian Studies, B
Economics, B
English Language and Literature, B
Environmental Sciences, B
Environmental Studies, B
Fine/Studio Arts, B
French Language and Literature, B
Geology/Earth Science, B
German Language and Literature, B
History, B
International Business/Trade/Commerce, B
International Relations and Affairs, B
Italian Studies, B
Jewish/Judaic Studies, B
Latin American Studies, B
Law and Legal Studies, B
Mathematics, B
Medieval and Renaissance Studies, B
Music, B
Near and Middle Eastern Studies, B
Philosophy, B
Physics, B
Political Science and Government, B
Psychology, B
Public Policy Analysis, B
Religion/Religious Studies, B
Russian Language and Literature, B
Social and Philosophical Foundations of Education, B
Sociology, B
Spanish Language and Literature, B
Women's Studies, B

DOUGLAS EDUCATION CENTER

Art/Art Studies, General, A
Business Administration and Management, A
Cosmetology/Cosmetologist, A
Design and Visual Communications, A
Film/Cinema Studies, A
Graphic Design, A
Illustration, A
Medical Office Management/Administration, A

Medical/Clinical Assistant, A

DREXEL UNIVERSITY

Accounting, BMD
Acute Care/Critical Care Nursing, M
Allied Health and Medical Assisting Services, MDO
Allopathic Medicine, D
Anthropology, B
Applied Arts and Design, M
Applied Behavior Analysis, M
Architectural Engineering, BMD
Architecture, B
Archives/Archival Administration, M
Art Therapy/Therapist, MO
Arts Management, M
Biochemical Engineering, M
Biochemistry, MD
Biological and Biomedical Sciences, MDO
Biological and Physical Sciences, B
Biology/Biological Sciences, B
Biomedical Engineering, MD
Biomedical/Medical Engineering, B
Biopsychology, MD
Biostatistics, MO
Business Administration, Management and Operations, MDO
Business/Commerce, B
Cell Biology and Anatomy, MD
Chemical Engineering, BMD
Chemistry, BMD
Cinematography and Film/Video Production, B
Civil Engineering, BMD
Clinical Psychology, MD
Communication and Media Studies, M
Communication, Journalism and Related Programs, B
Computer Art and Design, M
Computer Engineering, BM
Computer Science, BMD
Computer Software Engineering, B
Computer and Information Systems Security, B
Construction Management, BM
Corporate and Organizational Communication, M
Criminal Justice/Law Enforcement Administration, B
Criminology, B
Culinary Arts/Chef Training, B
Curriculum and Instruction, M
Customer Service Management, B
Dance, B
Dance Therapy/Therapist, MO
Design and Applied Arts, B
Economics, BMD
Education, MD
Educational Administration and Supervision, D
Educational Leadership and Administration, D
Educational Media/Instructional Technology, MD
Electrical Engineering, M
Electrical, Electronics and Communications Engineering, B
Elementary Education and Teaching, B
Emergency Management, M
Emergency Medical Services, M
Engineering, B
Engineering Management, MO
Engineering Technology, B
Engineering and Applied Sciences, MDO
English Language and Literature, B
Entrepreneurship/Entrepreneurial Studies, BM
Environmental Engineering Technology/Environmental Technology, MD
Environmental Policy, M
Environmental Sciences, BMD
Environmental Studies, B
Environmental/Environmental Health Engineering, B
Epidemiology, DO
Fashion/Apparel Design, B
Film, Television, and Video Production, M
Finance, B
Finance and Banking, MD
Food Science and Technology, M
Forensic Psychology, D
General Studies, B
Genetics, MD
Geology/Earth Science, B
Geotechnical Engineering, MD
Graphic Design, B

Health Informatics, M
Health Psychology, D
Health/Health Care Administration/Management, B
Health/Medical Preparatory Programs, B
Higher Education/Higher Education Administration, M
History, B
History of Science and Technology, M
Homeland Security, M
Hospitality Administration/Management, M
Hotel/Motel Administration/Management, B
Human Resources Development, M
Humanities/Humanistic Studies, B
Hydraulics and Fluid Power Technology, MD
Hydrology and Water Resources Science, MD
Immunology, MD
Industrial Design, B
Information Science/Studies, BMD
Interior Design, BM
International Business/Trade/Commerce, B
International and Comparative Education, M
International/Global Studies, B
Journalism, M
Legal Professions and Studies, B
Liberal Arts and Sciences Studies and Humanities, B
Library Science, MDO
Management, M
Management Information Systems and Services, B
Management Strategy and Policy, D
Marketing, MD
Marketing/Marketing Management, B
Marriage and Family Therapy/Counseling, MD
Mass Communication/Media Studies, M
Materials Engineering, BMD
Mathematics, BMD
Mechanical Engineering, BMD
Mechanics, MD
Medical Radiologic Technology/Science - Radiation Therapist, A
Microbiology, MD
Molecular Biology, MD
Molecular Medicine, M
Music Therapy/Therapist, MO
National Security, M
Neuroscience, MD
Nurse Anesthetist, M
Nursing, MD
Nursing - Advanced Practice, M
Nursing Administration, M
Nursing Education, M
Nutritional Sciences, BM
Operations Management and Supervision, B
Organizational Behavior Studies, D
Pathobiology, MD
Pediatric Nurse/Nursing, M
Pharmaceutical Sciences, M
Pharmacology, MD
Philosophy, B
Photography, B
Physical Therapy/Therapist, MDO
Physician Assistant, M
Physics, BMD
Playwriting and Screenwriting, B
Political Science and Government, B
Project Management, M
Psychiatric/Mental Health Nurse/Nursing, M
Psychology, BMD
Public Health, MDO
Public Health (MPH, DPH), B
Publishing, M
Quantitative Analysis, MD
Real Estate, BM
Secondary Education and Teaching, B
Sociology, B
Software Engineering, M
Special Education and Teaching, M
Sport and Fitness Administration/Management, BM
Structural Engineering, M
Substance Abuse/Addiction Counseling, B
Technical Communication, M
Technical and Business Writing, M
Telecommunications, M
Textile Design, M
Veterinary Sciences, M
Visual and Performing Arts, B

Web Page, Digital/Multimedia and Information Resources Design, B
Women's Health Nursing, M

DUBOIS BUSINESS COLLEGE (DUBOIS)

Accounting, A
Business Administration and Management, A
Computer/Information Technology Services Administration and Management, A
Executive Assistant/Executive Secretary, A
Legal Administrative Assistant/Secretary, A
Medical Administrative Assistant/Secretary, A
Web/Multimedia Management and Webmaster, A

DUQUESNE UNIVERSITY

Accounting, BM
Allied Health and Medical Assisting Services, MD
Ancient/Classical Greek Language and Literature, B
Art History, Criticism and Conservation, B
Athletic Training and Sports Medicine, B
Behavioral Sciences, B
BioTechnology, M
Biochemistry, B
Bioethics/Medical Ethics, MDO
Biological and Biomedical Sciences, MD
Biology/Biological Sciences, B
Biomedical/Medical Engineering, B
Business Administration, Management and Operations, M
Business, Management, Marketing, and Related Support Services, B
Business/Corporate Communications, B
Business/Managerial Economics, B
Chemistry, BMD
Classics and Classical Languages, Literatures, and Linguistics, BM
Clinical Psychology, MDO
Communication Disorders, M
Communication Studies/Speech Communication and Rhetoric, B
Communication and Media Studies, MD
Community Health and Preventive Medicine, M
Computer Science, B
Computer Software and Media Applications, B
Conflict Resolution and Mediation/Peace Studies, O
Counseling Psychology, MO
Counselor Education/School Counseling and Guidance Services, MDO
Curriculum and Instruction, O
Drama and Dramatics/Theatre Arts, B
Early Childhood Education and Teaching, BM
Economics, B
Education, BMDO
Educational Administration and Supervision, MO
Educational Leadership and Administration, D
Educational Measurement and Evaluation, M
Educational Media/Instructional Technology, MDO
Elementary Education and Teaching, M
English, MD
English Education, M
English Language and Literature, B
English as a Second Language, M
English/Language Arts Teacher Education, B
Entrepreneurship/Entrepreneurial Studies, B
Environmental Policy and Resource Management, MO
Environmental Sciences, BMO
Finance, B
Finance and Banking, M
Foreign Language Teacher Education, M
Foreign Languages and Literatures, B
Forensic Nursing, MO
Forensic Science and Technology, M
Foundations and Philosophy of Education, M
Health Information/Medical Records Administration/Administrator, B
Health Services Administration, M
Health/Medical Preparatory Programs, B
History, BM
International Business/Trade/Commerce, B
International Relations and Affairs, B
Internet and Interactive Multimedia, MO
Journalism, B
Junior High/Intermediate/Middle School Education and Teaching, B

Latin Language and Literature, B
Latin Teacher Education, B
Law and Legal Studies, MD
Liberal Arts and Sciences Studies and Humanities, B
Logistics and Materials Management, B
Management, M
Management Information Systems and Services, BM
Management Science, B
Marketing, BM
Marketing/Marketing Management, B
Marriage and Family Therapy/Counseling, M
Mathematics, BM
Mathematics Teacher Education, BM
Medicinal and Pharmaceutical Chemistry, MD
Middle School Education, M
Music, BMO
Music Performance, B
Music Teacher Education, BM
Music Therapy/Therapist, B
Non-Profit/Public/Organizational Management, B
Nursing, MDO
Nursing - Advanced Practice, MO
Nursing Education, M
Occupational Therapy/Therapist, BMD
Organizational Management, M
Pharmaceutical Administration, M
Pharmaceutical Sciences, MD
Pharmacology, MD
Pharmacy, D
Pharmacy, Pharmaceutical Sciences, and Administration, B
Philosophy, BMD
Physical Therapy/Therapist, BD
Physician Assistant, BM
Physics, B
Political Science and Government, B
Psychology, BD
Public Administration, MO
Public History, M
Public Policy Analysis, MO
Public Relations, Advertising, and Applied Communication, B
Reading Teacher Education, M
Rehabilitation Sciences, MD
Rhetoric, MD
School Psychology, MDO
Science Teacher Education/General Science Teacher Education, M
Secondary Education and Teaching, M
Social Studies Teacher Education, BM
Sociology, B
Spanish Language Teacher Education, B
Spanish Language and Literature, B
Special Education and Teaching, M
Speech-Language Pathology/Pathologist, B
Sustainability Management, M
Theology and Religious Vocations, MD
Theology/Theological Studies, B
Web Page, Digital/Multimedia and Information Resources Design, B
Women's Studies, B

EAST STROUDSBURG UNIVERSITY OF PENNSYLVANIA

Athletic Training and Sports Medicine, BM
BioTechnology, B
Biochemistry, B
Biological and Biomedical Sciences, M
Biological and Physical Sciences, B
Biology/Biological Sciences, B
Business Administration and Management, B
Chemistry, B
Clinical Laboratory Science/Medical Technology/Technologist, B
Communication Disorders, M
Communication Studies/Speech Communication and Rhetoric, B
Communications Technology/Technician, AB
Computer Science, M
Computer and Information Sciences, B
Computer and Information Systems Security, B
Drama and Dramatics/Theatre Arts, B
Early Childhood Education and Teaching, B
Economics, B

Education, M
Educational Media/Instructional Technology, M
Elementary Education and Teaching, M
English Language and Literature, B
Environmental Biology, M
Exercise and Sports Science, M
Geology/Earth Science, B
Health Education, M
Health Teacher Education, B
History, BM
Hospitality Administration/Management, B
Kinesiology and Exercise Science, B
Marine Biology and Biological Oceanography, B
Mathematics, B
Parks, Recreation and Leisure Facilities Management, B
Philosophy, B
Physical Education Teaching and Coaching, BM
Physics, B
Political Science and Government, BM
Psychology, B
Reading Teacher Education, M
Rehabilitation Sciences, M
Rehabilitation and Therapeutic Professions, B
Science Teacher Education/General Science Teacher Education, M
Secondary Education and Teaching, M
Social Studies Teacher Education, M
Sociology, B
Spanish Language and Literature, B
Special Education and Teaching, M
Sport and Fitness Administration/Management, M
Visual and Performing Arts, B

EASTERN UNIVERSITY

Accounting and Finance, B
Allied Health and Medical Assisting Services, A
Applied Behavior Analysis, M
Athletic Training and Sports Medicine, B
Bible/Biblical Studies, B
Biochemistry, B
Biological and Biomedical Sciences, B
Biology/Biological Sciences, B
Business Administration, Management and Operations, M
Business, Management, Marketing, and Related Support Services, B
Chemistry, B
Communication Studies/Speech Communication and Rhetoric, B
Communication and Media Studies, O
Counseling Psychology, MO
Counselor Education/School Counseling and Guidance Services, MO
Criminology, B
Cultural Anthropology, M
Dance, B
Early Childhood Education and Teaching, BO
Economic Development, M
Education, MO
Educational Administration and Supervision, O
Elementary Education and Teaching, O
English Education, O
English Language and Literature, B
English as a Second Language, MO
Entrepreneurship/Entrepreneurial Studies, B
Environmental Sciences, B
Environmental Studies, B
Foreign Language Teacher Education, O
French Language and Literature, O
Health Education, MO
Health Services Administration, M
History, B
International Business/Trade/Commerce, B
International Development, M
Junior High/Intermediate/Middle School Education and Teaching, B
Kinesiology and Exercise Science, B
Liberal Arts and Sciences Studies and Humanities, A
Management, M
Marketing, B
Marriage and Family Therapy/Counseling, D
Mathematics, B
Mathematics Teacher Education, O
Middle School Education, O

Missions/Missionary Studies and Missiology, BD
Multilingual and Multicultural Education, M
Music, B
Non-Profit/Public/Organizational Management, M
Organizational Management, MD
Pastoral Studies/Counseling, M
Philosophy, B
Physical Education Teaching and Coaching, O
Political Science and Government, B
Psychology, B
Public Policy Analysis, M
Reading Teacher Education, MO
School Nursing, O
School Psychology, MO
Science Teacher Education/General Science
 Teacher Education, O
Secondary Education and Teaching, O
Social Studies Teacher Education, O
Social Work, B
Sociology, B
Spanish Language and Literature, BO
Special Education and Teaching, MO
Theology and Religious Vocations, MD
Theology/Theological Studies, B
Urban Studies/Affairs, M
Urban and Regional Planning, M
Youth Ministry, B

EDINBORO UNIVERSITY OF PENNSYLVANIA

Anthropology, BM
Art Education, M
Art Therapy/Therapist, M
Art/Art Studies, General, B
Biological and Biomedical Sciences, M
Biological and Physical Sciences, B
Biology/Biological Sciences, B
Business Administration and Management, AB
Ceramic Arts and Ceramics, M
Chemistry, B
Clinical Laboratory Science/Medical
 Technology/Technologist, B
Clinical Psychology, M
Communication Disorders, M
Communication and Media Studies, M
Computer and Information Sciences, AB
Counseling Psychology, M
Counselor Education/School Counseling and Guidance Services, MO
Criminal Justice/Safety Studies, AB
Early Childhood Education and Teaching, BMO
Economics, B
Educational Leadership and Administration, M
Educational Psychology, M
Elementary Education and Teaching, A
Engineering Technology, A
English Language and Literature, B
Environmental Sciences, B
Fine Arts and Art Studies, M
Fine/Studio Arts, B
Geography, B
Geology/Earth Science, B
Health and Physical Education/Fitness, B
History, BM
Jewelry/Metalsmithing, M
Journalism, B
Junior High/Intermediate/Middle School Education
 and Teaching, B
Manufacturing Technology/Technician, A
Mass Communication/Media Studies, B
Mathematics, B
Middle School Education, M
Music, B
Nuclear Medical Technology/Technologist, B
Nursing, MD
Nursing - Advanced Practice, M
Nursing Education, M
Operations Management and Supervision, B
Painting, M
Physics, B
Political Science and Government, B
Pre-Pharmacy Studies, A
Printmaking, M
Psychology, B
Reading Teacher Education, MO
Rehabilitation Counseling, M

School Psychology, MO
Sculpture, M
Secondary Education and Teaching, M
Social Sciences, BM
Social Work, ABM
Sociology, B
Special Education and Teaching, ABMO
Speech-Language Pathology/Pathologist, B

ELIZABETHTOWN COLLEGE

Accounting, B
Applied Mathematics, B
BioTechnology, B
Biochemistry, B
Biology/Biological Sciences, B
Business Administration and Management, B
Chemistry, B
Computer Engineering, B
Computer and Information Sciences, B
Drama and Dramatics/Theatre Arts, B
Early Childhood Education and Teaching, B
Economics, B
Engineering, B
English Language and Literature, B
Environmental Biology, B
Fine/Studio Arts, B
Forest Management/Forest Resources Management, B
French Language and Literature, B
German Language and Literature, B
History, B
Industrial Engineering, B
Information Science/Studies, B
International Business/Trade/Commerce, B
Japanese Language and Literature, B
Junior High/Intermediate/Middle School Education
 and Teaching, B
Mass Communication/Media Studies, B
Mathematics, B
Music, B
Music Therapy/Therapist, B
Occupational Therapy/Therapist, BM
Philosophy, B
Physics, B
Political Science and Government, B
Psychology, B
Science Teacher Education/General Science
 Teacher Education, B
Social Sciences, B
Social Work, B
Sociology, B
Spanish Language and Literature, B

ELIZABETHTOWN COLLEGE SCHOOL OF CONTINUING AND PROFESSIONAL STUDIES

Accounting, AB
Business Administration and Management, AB
Communication and Media Studies, B
Criminal Justice/Police Science, AB
Criminology, AB
Health/Health Care Administration/Management, AB
Human Resources Management and Services, B
Human Services, AB
Information Science/Studies, AB
Management Information Systems and Services, B
Marketing/Marketing Management, B
Mass Communication/Media Studies, AB
Public Administration, B
Religion/Religious Studies, B
Social Work, A

ERIE INSTITUTE OF TECHNOLOGY

Computer and Information Sciences and Support
 Services, A
Electrical, Electronic and Communications Engineering Technology/Technician, A

FORTIS INSTITUTE (ERIE)

Accounting, A
Administrative Assistant and Secretarial Science, A
Computer Programming, A
Computer Science, A
Computer and Information Sciences, A

Computer and Information Sciences and Support
 Services, A
Cosmetology/Cosmetologist, A
Legal Assistant/Paralegal, A
Marketing/Marketing Management, A
Medical Transcription/Transcriptionist, A

FORTIS INSTITUTE (FORTY FORT)

Allied Health and Medical Assisting Services, A

FRANKLIN & MARSHALL COLLEGE

African Studies, B
American/United States Studies/Civilization, B
Ancient/Classical Greek Language and Literature, B
Animal Behavior and Ethology, B
Anthropology, B
Art History, Criticism and Conservation, B
Astronomy, B
Astrophysics, B
Biochemistry, B
Biology/Biological Sciences, B
Business Administration and Management, B
Chemistry, B
Classics and Classical Languages, Literatures, and Linguistics, B
Computer and Information Sciences, B
Dance, B
Drama and Dramatics/Theatre Arts, B
Economics, B
English Language and Literature, B
Environmental Sciences, B
Environmental Studies, B
Fine/Studio Arts, B
French Language and Literature, B
Geology/Earth Science, B
German Language and Literature, B
German Studies, B
History, B
Latin Language and Literature, B
Mathematics, B
Multi-/Interdisciplinary Studies, B
Music, B
Philosophy, B
Physics, B
Political Science and Government, B
Psychology, B
Public Health, B
Religion/Religious Studies, B
Sociology, B
Spanish Language and Literature, B

GANNON UNIVERSITY

Accounting, B
Advertising, B
Aquatic Biology/Limnology, B
Area Studies, B
Athletic Training and Sports Medicine, M
Biochemistry, B
Bioinformatics, B
Biology/Biological Sciences, B
Biomedical/Medical Engineering, B
Business Administration and Management, B
Business Administration, Management and Operations, M
Business/Commerce, A
Chemistry, B
Clinical Laboratory Science/Medical
 Technology/Technologist, B
Clinical Psychology, M
Computer Programming/Programmer, B
Computer Science, M
Computer and Information Sciences, B
Counseling Psychology, M
Criminal Justice/Safety Studies, AB
Curriculum and Instruction, MO
Drama and Dramatics/Theatre Arts, B
Early Childhood Education and Teaching, AB
Education, MO
Educational Administration and Supervision, O
Educational Leadership and Administration, DO
Electrical Engineering, M
Electrical, Electronics and Communications Engineering, B
Engineering Management, M
English, M
English as a Second Language, O

Entrepreneurship/Entrepreneurial Studies, B
Environmental Engineering
   Technology/Environmental Technology, M
Environmental Sciences, BM
Environmental and Occupational Health, M
Environmental/Environmental Health Engineering, B
Exercise and Sports Science, M
Finance, B
Finance and Banking, M
Foreign Languages and Literatures, B
Forensic Science and Technology, B
Funeral Service and Mortuary Science, B
Health Professions and Related Clinical Sciences, B
Health/Health Care Administration/Management, B
Health/Medical Preparatory Programs, B
History, B
Human Resources Management and Services, M
Industrial Engineering, B
Information Science/Studies, M
Insurance, B
International Business/Trade/Commerce, B
International/Global Studies, B
Internet and Interactive Multimedia, M
Journalism, B
Junior High/Intermediate/Middle School Education
   and Teaching, B
Kinesiology and Exercise Science, B
Legal Assistant/Paralegal, AB
Liberal Arts and Sciences Studies and Humani-
   ties, AB
Logistics and Materials Management, B
Management Information Systems and Services, B
Marketing, M
Marketing/Marketing Management, B
Mathematics, B
Mechanical Engineering, BM
Multi-/Interdisciplinary Studies, B
Nurse Anesthetist, MO
Nursing, D
Nursing - Advanced Practice, MO
Nursing Administration, M
Occupational Therapy/Therapist, BM
Organizational Management, DO
Pastoral Studies/Counseling, MO
Philosophy, B
Physical Therapy/Therapist, D
Physician Assistant, BM
Political Science and Government, B
Psychology, B
Public Administration, M
Public Health (MPH, DPH), B
Radio and Television Broadcasting
   Technology/Technician, B
Radiologic Technology/Science - Radiographer, A
Reading Teacher Education, MO
Respiratory Care Therapy/Therapist, AB
Social Studies Teacher Education, B
Social Work, B
Software Engineering, M
Special Education and Teaching, O
Sport and Fitness Administration/Management, B
Teacher Education, Multiple Levels, B
Theology and Religious Vocations, O
Theology/Theological Studies, B
Visual and Performing Arts, B

GENEVA COLLEGE

Accounting, B
Applied Mathematics, B
Bible/Biblical Studies, B
Biochemistry, B
Biology/Biological Sciences, B
Biopsychology, B
Business Administration and Management, AB
Business Administration, Management and Opera-
   tions, M
Cardiovascular Sciences, M
Chemistry, B
Clinical Psychology, M
Computer and Information Sciences, B
Counseling Psychology, M
Counselor Education/School Counseling and Guid-
   ance Services, M
Criminology, B
Education, M
Educational Administration and Supervision, M

Educational Leadership and Administration, M
Elementary Education and Teaching, B
Engineering, AB
English Language and Literature, B
Environmental Sciences, B
Finance and Banking, M
Higher Education/Higher Education Administra-
   tion, M
History, B
Human Services, B
Marketing, M
Marriage and Family Therapy/Counseling, M
Mathematics Teacher Education, B
Missions/Missionary Studies and Missiology, B
Music, B
Music Teacher Education, B
Organizational Management, M
Philosophy, B
Physics, B
Political Science and Government, B
Pre-Theology/Pre-Ministerial Studies, B
Psychology, BM
Reading Teacher Education, M
Sociology, B
Special Education and Teaching, BM
Speech-Language Pathology/Pathologist, B
Sport and Fitness Administration/Management, B
Teacher Education, Multiple Levels, B
Youth Ministry, B

GETTYSBURG COLLEGE

African-American/Black Studies, B
American History (United States), B
American/United States Studies/Civilization, B
Ancient/Classical Greek Language and Literature, B
Anthropology, B
Area Studies, B
Art History, Criticism and Conservation, B
Art/Art Studies, General, B
Asian History, B
Biochemistry, B
Biological and Physical Sciences, B
Biology/Biological Sciences, B
Broadcast Journalism, B
Business Administration and Management, B
Business Administration, Management and Opera-
   tions, B
Chemistry, B
Chinese Studies, B
Classics and Classical Languages, Litera-
   tures, and Linguistics, B
Comparative Literature, B
Computer Science, B
Drama and Dramatics/Theatre Arts, B
East Asian Studies, B
Economics, B
Education, B
Elementary Education and Teaching, B
Engineering, B
English Language and Literature, B
Environmental Sciences, B
Environmental Studies, B
European History, B
European Studies/Civilization, B
Fine/Studio Arts, B
French Language and Literature, B
German Language and Literature, B
Health Professions and Related Clinical Sciences, B
Hispanic-American, Puerto Rican, and Mexican-
   American/Chicano Studies, B
History, B
International Business/Trade/Commerce, B
International Economics, B
International Relations and Affairs, B
Italian Language and Literature, B
Japanese Language and Literature, B
Japanese Studies, B
Jewish/Judaic Studies, B
Journalism, B
Junior High/Intermediate/Middle School Education
   and Teaching, B
Latin American Studies, B
Latin Language and Literature, B
Liberal Arts and Sciences Studies and Humani-
   ties, B
Marine Biology and Biological Oceanography, B

Mathematics, B
Modern Languages, B
Molecular Biology, B
Music, B
Music Teacher Education, B
Non-Profit/Public/Organizational Management, B
Peace Studies and Conflict Resolution, B
Philosophy, B
Physical Education Teaching and Coaching, B
Physics, B
Political Science and Government, B
Pre-Dentistry Studies, B
Pre-Law Studies, B
Pre-Medicine/Pre-Medical Studies, B
Pre-Nursing Studies, B
Pre-Pharmacy Studies, B
Pre-Veterinary Studies, B
Psychology, B
Religion/Religious Studies, B
Romance Languages, Literatures, and Linguistics, B
Science Teacher Education/General Science
   Teacher Education, B
Secondary Education and Teaching, B
Social Sciences, B
Sociology, B
South Asian Studies, B
Spanish Language and Literature, B
Visual and Performing Arts, B
Women's Studies, B

GROVE CITY COLLEGE

Accounting, B
Accounting and Computer Science, B
Biochemistry, B
Biology Teacher Education, B
Biology/Biological Sciences, B
Business Administration and Management, B
Business/Managerial Economics, B
Chemistry, B
Chemistry Teacher Education, B
Communication Studies/Speech Communication
   and Rhetoric, B
Computer Science, B
Early Childhood Education and Teaching, B
Economics, B
Electrical, Electronics and Communications Engi-
   neering, B
Engineering/Industrial Management, B
English/Language Arts Teacher Education, B
Entrepreneurship/Entrepreneurial Studies, B
Finance, B
French Language Teacher Education, B
French Language and Literature, B
History, B
International Business/Trade/Commerce, B
Junior High/Intermediate/Middle School Education
   and Teaching, B
Kinesiology and Exercise Science, B
Marketing/Marketing Management, B
Mathematics, B
Mathematics Teacher Education, B
Mechanical Engineering, B
Music, B
Music Performance, B
Music Teacher Education, B
Philosophy, B
Physics, B
Physics Teacher Education, B
Political Science and Government, B
Psychology, B
Religion/Religious Studies, B
Social Studies Teacher Education, B
Sociology, B
Spanish Language Teacher Education, B
Spanish Language and Literature, B
Special Education and Teaching, B

GWYNEDD MERCY UNIVERSITY

Accounting, B
Allied Health Diagnostic, Intervention, and Treat-
   ment Professions, AB
Biological and Biomedical Sciences, A
Biology/Biological Sciences, B
Business Administration and Management, B
Business Teacher Education, B

Clinical Laboratory Science/Medical Technology/Technologist, B
Communication Studies/Speech Communication and Rhetoric, B
Computer and Information Sciences, B
Counselor Education/School Counseling and Guidance Services, M
Criminal Justice/Police Science, B
Education, M
Educational Administration and Supervision, M
Elementary Education and Teaching, B
English Language and Literature, B
Gerontological Nursing, M
Gerontology, B
Health Professions and Related Clinical Sciences, B
Health Services Administration, M
Health Services/Allied Health/Health Sciences, B
History, B
History Teacher Education, B
Human Services, B
Liberal Arts and Sciences Studies and Humanities, A
Management, M
Management Strategy and Policy, M
Mathematics, B
Mathematics Teacher Education, B
Medical Radiologic Technology/Science - Radiation Therapist, B
Nursing, MD
Nursing - Adult, M
Nursing - Advanced Practice, M
Nursing Education, M
Oncology Nursing, M
Pediatric Nurse/Nursing, M
Philosophy, B
Psychology, B
Radiologic Technology/Science - Radiographer, B
Respiratory Care Therapy/Therapist, AB
Secondary Education and Teaching, B
Sociology, B
Special Education and Teaching, BM

HARCUM COLLEGE

Allied Health Diagnostic, Intervention, and Treatment Professions, A
Animal Sciences, A
Business Administration and Management, A
Child Care Provider/Assistant, A
Clinical/Medical Laboratory Technician, A
Consumer Merchandising/Retailing Management, A
Criminal Justice/Law Enforcement Administration, A
Dental Assisting/Assistant, A
Dental Hygiene/Hygienist, A
Electroneurodiagnostic/Electroencephalographic Technology/Technologist, A
Entrepreneurship/Entrepreneurial Studies, A
Fashion Merchandising, A
Fashion/Apparel Design, A
General Studies, A
Health Professions and Related Clinical Sciences, A
Histologic Technology/Histotechnologist, A
Human Services, A
Interior Design, A
International Business/Trade/Commerce, A
Law and Legal Studies, A
Medical Radiologic Technology/Science - Radiation Therapist, A
Occupational Therapist Assistant, A
Physical Therapist Assistant, A
Pre-Nursing Studies, A
Sport and Fitness Administration/Management, A
Veterinary/Animal Health Technology/Technician and Veterinary Assistant, A

HARRISBURG AREA COMMUNITY COLLEGE

Accounting Technology/Technician and Bookkeeping, A
Administrative Assistant and Secretarial Science, A
Adult Development and Aging, A
Architectural Engineering Technology/Technician, A
Architecture, A
Automobile/Automotive Mechanics Technology/Technician, A
Banking and Financial Support Services, A
Biology/Biological Sciences, A

Business Administration and Management, A
Business/Commerce, A
Cardiovascular Technology/Technologist, A
Cartography, A
Chemistry, A
Civil Engineering Technology/Technician, A
Clinical/Medical Laboratory Technician, A
Communication, Journalism and Related Programs, A
Computer Science, A
Computer Systems Networking and Telecommunications, A
Computer and Information Sciences, A
Computer and Information Systems Security, A
Construction Engineering Technology/Technician, A
Construction Trades, A
Criminal Justice/Law Enforcement Administration, A
Criminal Justice/Police Science, A
Culinary Arts/Chef Training, A
Dental Hygiene/Hygienist, A
Design and Visual Communications, A
Diagnostic Medical Sonography/Sonographer and Ultrasound Technician, A
Dietetics/Dieticians, A
Drama and Dramatics/Theatre Arts, A
Early Childhood Education and Teaching, A
Electrical, Electronic and Communications Engineering Technology/Technician, A
Electrician, A
Emergency Medical Technology/Technician (EMT Paramedic), A
Engineering, A
Engineering Technologies/Technicians, A
Environmental Sciences, A
Environmental Studies, A
Fire Science/Firefighting, A
General Studies, A
Graphic Design, A
Health Professions and Related Clinical Sciences, A
Health Services Administration, A
Health/Health Care Administration/Management, A
Heating, Air Conditioning, Ventilation and Refrigeration Maintenance Technology/Technician, A
Human Services, A
International Relations and Affairs, A
Legal Assistant/Paralegal, A
Mathematics, A
Mechanical Engineering/Mechanical Technology/Technician, A
Medical Informatics, A
Medical/Clinical Assistant, A
Nuclear Medical Technology/Technologist, A
Philosophy, A
Photography, A
Physical Sciences, A
Psychology, A
Radiologic Technology/Science - Radiographer, A
Real Estate, A
Respiratory Care Therapy/Therapist, A
Sales, Distribution and Marketing Operations, A
Secondary Education and Teaching, A
Social Sciences, A
Social Work, A
Structural Engineering, A
Surgical Technology/Technologist, A
Visual and Performing Arts, A
Web Page, Digital/Multimedia and Information Resources Design, A

HARRISBURG UNIVERSITY OF SCIENCE AND TECHNOLOGY

Biology/Biological Sciences, B
Computer and Information Sciences, B
Construction Management, M
E-Commerce/Electronic Commerce, B
Educational Media/Instructional Technology, M
Entrepreneurship/Entrepreneurial Studies, M
Geography, B
Health Services Administration, M
Management Information Systems and Services, M
Management of Technology, M
Project Management, M
Public Administration, M

Systems Engineering, M

HAVERFORD COLLEGE

African Studies, B
Anthropology, B
Archeology, B
Art History, Criticism and Conservation, B
Art/Art Studies, General, B
Astronomy, B
Astrophysics, B
Biochemistry, B
Biology/Biological Sciences, B
Biophysics, B
Chemistry, B
Classics and Classical Languages, Literatures, and Linguistics, B
Comparative Literature, B
Computer Science, B
East Asian Studies, B
Economics, B
Education, B
English Language and Literature, B
French Language and Literature, B
Geology/Earth Science, B
German Language and Literature, B
History, B
Italian Language and Literature, B
Latin American Studies, B
Latin Language and Literature, B
Mathematics, B
Music, B
Peace Studies and Conflict Resolution, B
Philosophy, B
Physics, B
Political Science and Government, B
Psychology, B
Religion/Religious Studies, B
Romance Languages, Literatures, and Linguistics, B
Russian Language and Literature, B
Sociology, B
Spanish Language and Literature, B
Urban Studies/Affairs, B

HOLY FAMILY UNIVERSITY

Accounting, B
Accounting and Finance, B
Art Teacher Education, B
Biochemistry, B
Biology Teacher Education, B
Biology/Biological Sciences, B
Business Administration and Management, B
Business Administration, Management and Operations, M
Chemistry Teacher Education, B
Clinical Laboratory Science/Medical Technology/Technologist, B
Community Health Nursing, M
Counseling Psychology, M
Criminal Justice/Safety Studies, B
Criminology, M
Early Childhood Education and Teaching, BM
Education, MD
Educational Leadership and Administration, MD
Elementary Education and Teaching, BM
English Language and Literature, B
English as a Second Language, M
English/Language Arts Teacher Education, B
Finance, B
Finance and Banking, M
Fine/Studio Arts, B
Fire Services Administration, B
French Language Teacher Education, B
General Studies, B
Graphic Design, B
Health Services Administration, M
History, B
History Teacher Education, B
Human Resources Management and Services, M
Human Resources Management/Personnel Administration, B
Humanities/Humanistic Studies, B
International Business/Trade/Commerce, B
Management Information Systems and Services, BM
Marketing/Marketing Management, B
Mass Communication/Media Studies, B

Mathematics, B
Mathematics Teacher Education, B
Middle School Education, M
Nursing, M
Nursing Administration, M
Nursing Education, M
Political Science and Government, B
Psychology, B
Radiologic Technology/Science - Radiographer, AB
Reading Teacher Education, M
Religion/Religious Studies, B
Secondary Education and Teaching, M
Social Science Teacher Education, B
Social Studies Teacher Education, B
Sociology, B
Spanish Language Teacher Education, B
Special Education and Teaching, BM
Sport and Fitness Administration/Management, B

HUSSIAN COLLEGE, SCHOOL OF ART

Advertising, A
Commercial and Advertising Art, A

IMMACULATA UNIVERSITY

Accounting, AB
Allied Health Diagnostic, Intervention, and Treatment Professions, B
Athletic Training and Sports Medicine, B
Biology/Biological Sciences, AB
Biopsychology, B
Business Administration and Management, AB
Business Teacher Education, B
Chemistry, AB
Clinical Psychology, MD
Communication, Journalism and Related Programs, AB
Counseling Psychology, M
Criminal Justice/Safety Studies, B
Dietetics/Dieticians, B
Educational Administration and Supervision, O
Educational Leadership and Administration, MDO
Educational Psychology, MO
Elementary Education and Teaching, B
English Language and Literature, AB
English as a Second Language, M
Family and Consumer Sciences/Home Economics Teacher Education, B
Fashion Merchandising, AB
Finance, B
Finance and Financial Management Services, B
Forensic Psychology, O
French Language and Literature, B
Health Promotion, M
Health/Health Care Administration/Management, B
Health/Medical Preparatory Programs, AB
History, AB
Human Resources Management and Services, B
Information Science/Studies, AB
International Relations and Affairs, B
Kinesiology and Exercise Science, B
Liberal Arts and Sciences Studies and Humanities, B
Management Information Systems and Services, B
Marketing/Marketing Management, B
Mathematics, B
Mathematics and Computer Science, B
Multi-/Interdisciplinary Studies, B
Multilingual and Multicultural Education, M
Music, B
Music Performance, B
Music Teacher Education, B
Music Therapy/Therapist, BM
Neuroscience, O
Nursing, M
Nursing Administration, M
Nursing Education, M
Nutritional Sciences, M
Organizational Management, M
Political Science and Government, AB
Pre-Medicine/Pre-Medical Studies, B
Psychoanalysis and Psychotherapy, O
Psychology, BMDO
School Psychology, M
Secondary Education and Teaching, O
Social Work, B
Sociology, B

Spanish Language and Literature, AB
Special Education and Teaching, O
Teacher Education and Professional Development, Specific Levels and Methods, B
Theology/Theological Studies, AB

INDIANA UNIVERSITY OF PENNSYLVANIA

Accounting, B
Adult and Continuing Education and Teaching, M
Anthropology, B
Applied Mathematics, M
Archeology, M
Art/Art Studies, General, B
Asian Studies/Civilization, B
Athletic Training and Sports Medicine, B
Audiology/Audiologist and Speech-Language Pathology/Pathologist, B
Biochemistry, B
Biological and Biomedical Sciences, M
Biological and Physical Sciences, B
Biology/Biological Sciences, B
Business Administration and Management, B
Business Administration, Management and Operations, M
Business Education, M
Business/Commerce, B
Chemistry, BM
City/Urban, Community and Regional Planning, B
Clinical Laboratory Science/Medical Technology/Technologist, B
Clinical Psychology, MD
Communication Disorders, M
Communication Studies/Speech Communication and Rhetoric, B
Communication and Media Studies, MD
Community Psychology, M
Computer and Information Sciences, B
Counselor Education/School Counseling and Guidance Services, M
Criminology, BMD
Curriculum and Instruction, D
Drama and Dramatics/Theatre Arts, B
Early Childhood Education and Teaching, B
Economics, B
Education, MDO
Education/Teaching of Individuals in Early Childhood Special Education Programs, B
Educational Administration and Supervision, DO
Educational Media/Instructional Technology, MD
Educational Psychology, MO
Emergency Management, M
English, MD
English Education, MD
English Language and Literature, B
English as a Second Language, MD
Environmental Policy and Resource Management, M
Environmental and Occupational Health, MD
Exercise and Sports Science, M
Family and Consumer Sciences/Human Sciences, B
Fashion Merchandising, B
Finance, B
Fine Arts and Art Studies, M
Fine/Studio Arts, B
Foods, Nutrition, and Wellness Studies, B
Foreign Language Teacher Education, M
Foreign Languages, Literatures, and Linguistics, B
Geographic Information Systems, MO
Geography, BM
Geology/Earth Science, B
Health Education, M
Health Services Administration, M
Health and Physical Education, B
Higher Education/Higher Education Administration, M
Hispanic and Latin American Languages, M
History, BM
Hospitality Administration/Management, B
Human Development and Family Studies, B
Human Resources Development, M
Human Resources Management/Personnel Administration, B
Industrial and Labor Relations, M
Interior Design, B
Intermedia/Multimedia, B

International Business/Trade/Commerce, B
International Relations and Affairs, B
Journalism, B
Junior High/Intermediate/Middle School Education and Teaching, B
Liberal Arts and Sciences Studies and Humanities, AB
Management Information Systems and Services, B
Marketing/Marketing Management, B
Mathematics, BM
Mathematics Teacher Education, M
Media Studies, D
Music, BM
Music Performance, B
Music Teacher Education, M
NanoTechnology, M
Non-Profit/Public/Organizational Management, D
Nuclear Medical Technology/Technologist, B
Nursing, MD
Nursing Administration, M
Nursing Education, M
Nutritional Sciences, M
Occupational Safety and Health Technology/Technician, M
Optics/Optical Sciences, A
Performance, M
Philosophy, B
Physical Education Teaching and Coaching, M
Physics, BM
Political Science and Government, B
Psychology, BMD
Public Affairs, M
Public History, M
Reading Teacher Education, MO
Religion/Religious Studies, B
Respiratory Care Therapy/Therapist, B
School Psychology, DO
Social Sciences, B
Sociology, BM
Spanish Language and Literature, B
Special Education and Teaching, M
Sport and Fitness Administration/Management, M
Student Personnel Services, M
Trade and Industrial Teacher Education, B
Urban and Regional Planning, M
Visual and Performing Arts, B
Vocational and Technical Education, M

JNA INSTITUTE OF CULINARY ARTS

Restaurant, Culinary, and Catering Management/Manager, A

JOHNSON COLLEGE

Architectural Drafting and Architectural CAD/CADD, A
Automobile/Automotive Mechanics Technology/Technician, A
Biomedical Technology/Technician, A
Building/Home/Construction Inspection/Inspector, A
Cabinetmaking and Millwork/Millwright, A
Carpentry/Carpenter, A
Diesel Mechanics Technology/Technician, A
Electrical, Electronic and Communications Engineering Technology/Technician, A
Electrician, A
Heating, Air Conditioning, Ventilation and Refrigeration Maintenance Technology/Technician, A
Industrial Electronics Technology/Technician, A
Industrial Mechanics and Maintenance Technology, A
Information Technology, A
Machine Shop Technology/Assistant, A
Machine Tool Technology/Machinist, A
Medical Radiologic Technology/Science - Radiation Therapist, A
Precision Production Trades, A
Sales, Distribution and Marketing Operations, A
Veterinary/Animal Health Technology/Technician and Veterinary Assistant, A

JUNIATA COLLEGE

Accounting, BM
Anthropology, B
Art History, Criticism and Conservation, B
Art/Art Studies, General, B
Biochemistry, B

Biology Teacher Education, B
Biology/Biological Sciences, B
Business/Commerce, B
Chemistry, B
Chemistry Teacher Education, B
Communication Studies/Speech Communication and Rhetoric, B
Computer and Information Sciences, B
Digital Communication and Media/Multimedia, B
Economics, B
Education, B
Education/Teaching of Individuals in Early Childhood Special Education Programs, B
Engineering Physics, B
English Language and Literature, B
English/Language Arts Teacher Education, B
Entrepreneurship/Entrepreneurial Studies, B
Environmental Sciences, B
Environmental Studies, B
Finance, B
Fine/Studio Arts, B
Foreign Languages and Literatures, B
French Language Teacher Education, B
French Language and Literature, B
German Language and Literature, B
Health Communication, B
History, B
Human Resources Management/Personnel Administration, B
Humanities/Humanistic Studies, B
Information Technology, B
International Business/Trade/Commerce, B
International Relations and Affairs, B
International/Global Studies, B
Liberal Arts and Sciences Studies and Humanities, B
Marketing/Marketing Management, B
Mathematics, B
Mathematics Teacher Education, B
Multi-/Interdisciplinary Studies, B
Museology/Museum Studies, B
Natural Resource Economics, B
Natural Sciences, B
Peace Studies and Conflict Resolution, B
Philosophy, B
Philosophy and Religious Studies, B
Physical Sciences, B
Physics, B
Physics Teacher Education, B
Political Science and Government, B
Psychology, B
Religion/Religious Studies, B
Russian Language and Literature, B
Science Teacher Education/General Science Teacher Education, B
Social Studies Teacher Education, B
Social Work, B
Sociology, B
Spanish Language and Literature, B
Web Page, Digital/Multimedia and Information Resources Design, B
Wildlife and Wildlands Science and Management, B

KEYSTONE COLLEGE

Accounting, AB
Art Teacher Education, B
Biology/Biological Sciences, B
Business Administration and Management, AB
Communication and Media Studies, A
Criminal Justice/Law Enforcement Administration, AB
Criminal Justice/Police Science, B
Diagnostic Medical Sonography/Sonographer and Ultrasound Technician, A
Early Childhood Education and Teaching, AB
Education/Teaching of Individuals in Early Childhood Special Education Programs, B
English/Language Arts Teacher Education, B
Environmental Biology, B
Fine/Studio Arts, AB
Forensic Science and Technology, B
Geology/Earth Science, B
Health Services/Allied Health/Health Sciences, A
Hospitality Administration/Management, B
Human Development and Family Studies, B
Information Technology, AB

Liberal Arts and Sciences Studies and Humanities, A
Mathematics Teacher Education, B
Medical Radiologic Technology/Science - Radiation Therapist, A
Natural Resources Management/Development and Policy, B
Occupational Therapy/Therapist, A
Physical Therapy/Therapist, B
Pre-Law Studies, B
Pre-Medicine/Pre-Medical Studies, B
Pre-Nursing Studies, A
Pre-Pharmacy Studies, A
Psychology, B
Public Health (MPH, DPH), B
Radio, Television, and Digital Communication, AB
Radiologic Technology/Science - Radiographer, A
Social Sciences, B
Social Studies Teacher Education, B
Sport and Fitness Administration/Management, B
Wildlife Biology, B

KEYSTONE TECHNICAL INSTITUTE

Child Care Provider/Assistant, A
Culinary Arts/Chef Training, A
Dental Assisting/Assistant, A
Legal Assistant/Paralegal, A
Massage Therapy/Therapeutic Massage, A
Medical Office Management/Administration, A
Medical/Clinical Assistant, A

KING'S COLLEGE

Accounting, B
Athletic Training and Sports Medicine, B
Biological and Physical Sciences, B
Biology/Biological Sciences, B
Business Administration and Management, B
Chemistry, B
Clinical Laboratory Science/Medical Technology/Technologist, B
Communication and Media Studies, B
Computer Science, B
Computer and Information Sciences, B
Criminal Justice/Safety Studies, B
Drama and Dramatics/Theatre Arts, B
Early Childhood Education and Teaching, B
Economics, B
Education, M
Elementary Education and Teaching, B
English Language and Literature, B
Environmental Sciences, B
Environmental Studies, B
Finance, B
French Language and Literature, B
Health Professions and Related Clinical Sciences, B
Health Services Administration, M
History, B
Human Resources Management/Personnel Administration, B
International Business/Trade/Commerce, B
Kinesiology and Exercise Science, B
Marketing/Marketing Management, B
Mathematics, B
Philosophy, B
Physician Assistant, M
Physics, B
Political Science and Government, B
Pre-Dentistry Studies, B
Pre-Law Studies, B
Pre-Medicine/Pre-Medical Studies, B
Pre-Pharmacy Studies, B
Pre-Veterinary Studies, B
Psychology, B
Sociology, B
Spanish Language and Literature, B
Theology/Theological Studies, B

KUTZTOWN UNIVERSITY OF PENNSYLVANIA

Anthropology, B
Art Education, M
Art Teacher Education, B
Biochemistry, B
Biological and Physical Sciences, B
Biology/Biological Sciences, B
Business Administration and Management, B

Business Administration, Management and Operations, M
Chemistry, B
Commercial and Advertising Art, B
Computer Science, M
Computer and Information Sciences, B
Counseling Psychology, M
Counselor Education/School Counseling and Guidance Services, M
Crafts/Craft Design, Folk Art and Artisanry, B
Criminal Justice/Safety Studies, B
Curriculum and Instruction, M
Digital Communication and Media/Multimedia, B
Early Childhood Education and Teaching, B
Education, M
Education/Teaching of Individuals with Vision Impairments, Including Blindness, B
Educational Administration and Supervision, M
Educational Media/Instructional Technology, M
Elementary Education and Teaching, BM
English, M
English Education, M
English Language and Literature, B
Environmental Sciences, B
Fine/Studio Arts, B
General Studies, B
Geography, B
Geology/Earth Science, B
German Studies, B
History, B
Internet and Interactive Multimedia, M
Junior High/Intermediate/Middle School Education and Teaching, B
Liberal Arts and Sciences Studies and Humanities, B
Library Science, BM
Marriage and Family Therapy/Counseling, M
Mathematics, B
Mathematics Teacher Education, M
Media Studies, M
Music, B
Music Teacher Education, B
Oceanography, Chemical and Physical, B
Parks, Recreation, Leisure and Fitness Studies, B
Philosophy, B
Physics, B
Political Science and Government, B
Psychology, B
Public Administration, BM
Reading Teacher Education, M
Science Teacher Education/General Science Teacher Education, M
Secondary Education and Teaching, BM
Social Sciences, B
Social Studies Teacher Education, M
Social Work, BM
Sociology, B
Spanish Language and Literature, B
Special Education and Teaching, B

LA ROCHE COLLEGE

Accounting, BM
Biochemistry, B
Biology/Biological Sciences, B
Business Administration, Management and Operations, B
Chemistry, B
Communication and Media Studies, B
Computer Science, B
Computer and Information Sciences, B
Corrections and Criminal Justice, B
Criminal Justice/Safety Studies, B
Dance, B
Design and Visual Communications, B
Elementary Education and Teaching, B
English Language and Literature, B
English/Language Arts Teacher Education, B
Family and Community Services, B
Film/Video and Photographic Arts, B
Finance, B
General Studies, B
History, B
Human Resources Management and Services, MO
Information Technology, B
Interior Architecture, B
International Business/Trade/Commerce, B

International Relations and Affairs, B
Liberal Arts and Sciences Studies and Humanities, B
Management Science, B
Marketing/Marketing Management, B
Mathematics, B
Medical Radiologic Technology/Science - Radiation Therapist, AB
Nurse Anesthetist, M
Nursing, M
Nursing Administration, M
Nursing Education, M
Political Science and Government, B
Psychology, B
Religion/Religious Studies, B
Sociology, B

LA SALLE UNIVERSITY

Accounting, BMO
Advertising and Public Relations, M
Air Force JROTC/ROTC, B
American Government and Politics (United States), B
American/United States Studies/Civilization, BMO
Applied Mathematics, B
Army JROTC/ROTC, B
Art History, Criticism and Conservation, B
Biochemistry, B
Biology/Biological Sciences, B
Business Administration and Management, B
Business Administration, Management and Operations, MO
Business/Commerce, B
Chemistry, B
Clinical Nutrition/Nutritionist, B
Clinical Psychology, MD
Communication Disorders, BM
Communication and Media Studies, MO
Community Health Nursing, MO
Comparative Literature, O
Computer Programming/Programmer, B
Computer Science, BMO
Computer and Information Sciences, B
Corporate and Organizational Communication, MO
Counseling Psychology, M
Criminal Justice/Safety Studies, B
Cultural Studies, M
Developmental Psychology, D
Early Childhood Education and Teaching, BM
East European and Russian Studies, MO
Economics, B
Education, MO
Educational Leadership and Administration, M
Educational Media/Instructional Technology, MO
English, MO
English Education, M
English Language and Literature, B
English as a Second Language, MO
Environmental Sciences, B
Environmental Studies, B
Finance, B
Finance and Banking, MO
Fine Arts and Art Studies, O
Forensic Science and Technology, MO
French Language and Literature, B
General Studies, AB
Geology/Earth Science, B
German Language and Literature, B
Gerontological Nursing, MO
Gerontology, O
Health Psychology, D
Hispanic Studies, MO
History, BMO
Human Resources Development, MO
Human Resources Management and Services, MO
Human Resources Management/Personnel Administration, B
Information Technology, B
International Business/Trade/Commerce, BO
International Economics, B
International Relations and Affairs, B
Italian Language and Literature, B
Junior High/Intermediate/Middle School Education and Teaching, B
Latin American Studies, MO
Management Information Systems and Services, B

Management Science, B
Management of Technology, MO
Marketing, MO
Marketing/Marketing Management, B
Marriage and Family Therapy/Counseling, M
Mathematics, B
Media Studies, O
Middle School Education, M
Multilingual and Multicultural Education, M
National Security, O
Non-Profit/Public/Organizational Management, M
Nurse Anesthetist, MO
Nursing, MDO
Nursing - Adult, MO
Nursing - Advanced Practice, MDO
Nursing Administration, MO
Nursing Education, O
Nutritional Sciences, B
Pastoral Studies/Counseling, MDO
Philosophy, B
Political Science and Government, B
Pre-Medicine/Pre-Medical Studies, B
Pre-Nursing Studies, B
Prepress/Desktop Publishing and Digital Imaging Design, B
Psychology, BMD
Public Administration, B
Public Health, M
Public Health (MPH, DPH), B
Public History, M
Public Relations/Image Management, B
Quantitative Analysis, MO
Radio and Television Broadcasting Technology/Technician, B
Reading Teacher Education, MO
Religion/Religious Studies, BMDO
Religious Education, O
Russian Language and Literature, B
School Nursing, O
Secondary Education and Teaching, BM
Social Sciences, B
Social Studies Teacher Education, MO
Social Work, B
Sociology, B
Spanish Language and Literature, B
Special Education and Teaching, MO
Theology and Religious Vocations, MDO
Translation and Interpretation, MO
Western European Studies, O

LACKAWANNA COLLEGE

Accounting, A
Accounting Technology/Technician and Bookkeeping, A
Administrative Assistant and Secretarial Science, A
Banking and Financial Support Services, A
BioTechnology, A
Biology/Biological Sciences, A
Business Administration and Management, A
Business Administration, Management and Operations, A
Business/Commerce, A
Cardiopulmonary Technology/Technologist, A
Communication Studies/Speech Communication and Rhetoric, A
Communications Technology/Technician, A
Computer and Information Sciences, A
Criminal Justice/Safety Studies, A
Diagnostic Medical Sonography/Sonographer and Ultrasound Technician, A
Early Childhood Education and Teaching, A
Education, A
Emergency Medical Technology/Technician (EMT Paramedic), A
Environmental Studies, A
General Studies, A
Human Services, A
Humanities/Humanistic Studies, A
Industrial Electronics Technology/Technician, A
Industrial Technology/Technician, A
Legal Assistant/Paralegal, A
Liberal Arts and Sciences Studies and Humanities, A
Management Information Systems and Services, A
Mass Communication/Media Studies, A
Medical Administrative Assistant/Secretary, A

Mental Health Counseling/Counselor, A
Petroleum Technology/Technician, A
Surgical Technology/Technologist, A

LAFAYETTE COLLEGE

American/United States Studies/Civilization, B
Anthropology, B
Art History, Criticism and Conservation, B
Art/Art Studies, General, B
Biochemistry, B
Biology/Biological Sciences, B
Chemical Engineering, B
Chemistry, B
Civil Engineering, B
Computer Science, B
Drama and Dramatics/Theatre Arts, B
Economics, B
Electrical, Electronics and Communications Engineering, B
Engineering, B
English Language and Literature, B
Environmental/Environmental Health Engineering, B
Film/Cinema Studies, B
Fine/Studio Arts, B
French Language and Literature, B
Geology/Earth Science, B
German Language and Literature, B
History, B
International Relations and Affairs, B
Mathematics, B
Mechanical Engineering, B
Music, B
Philosophy, B
Physics, B
Political Science and Government, B
Psychology, B
Religion/Religious Studies, B
Russian Studies, B
Sociology, B
Spanish Language and Literature, B
Women's Studies, B

LANCASTER BIBLE COLLEGE

Administrative Assistant and Secretarial Science, A
Bible/Biblical Studies, AB
Computer and Information Sciences, B
Counseling Psychology, M
Counselor Education/School Counseling and Guidance Services, BM
Early Childhood Education and Teaching, AB
Education, B
Elementary Education and Teaching, BM
Marriage and Family Therapy/Counseling, M
Missions/Missionary Studies and Missiology, B
Music Teacher Education, B
Pastoral Counseling and Specialized Ministries, B
Pastoral Studies/Counseling, BMO
Physical Education Teaching and Coaching, B
Religious Education, B
Religious/Sacred Music, B
Secondary Education and Teaching, M
Social Work, B
Special Education and Teaching, M
Theology and Religious Vocations, MDO
Youth Ministry, B

LANSDALE SCHOOL OF BUSINESS

Accounting and Business/Management, A
Business/Office Automation/Technology/Data Entry, A
Computer Graphics, A
Computer Software and Media Applications, A
Computer Systems Networking and Telecommunications, A
Legal Assistant/Paralegal, A
Marketing/Marketing Management, A
Medical/Clinical Assistant, A
Web Page, Digital/Multimedia and Information Resources Design, A
Web/Multimedia Management and Webmaster, A

LAUREL BUSINESS INSTITUTE

Accounting, A
Administrative Assistant and Secretarial Science, A
Banking and Financial Support Services, A
Business Administration and Management, A

Business/Office Automation/Technology/Data Entry, A
Child Development, A
Computer Software and Media Applications, A
Computer Systems Networking and Telecommunications, A
Computer and Information Sciences, A
Computer and Information Sciences and Support Services, A
Computer and Information Systems Security, A
Computer/Information Technology Services Administration and Management, A
Consumer Merchandising/Retailing Management, A
Data Entry/Microcomputer Applications, A
Executive Assistant/Executive Secretary, A
General Office Occupations and Clerical Services, A
Home Health Aide/Home Attendant, A
Information Technology, A
Insurance, A
Legal Administrative Assistant/Secretary, A
Medical Administrative Assistant/Secretary, A
Medical Transcription/Transcriptionist, A
Medical/Clinical Assistant, A
System Administration/Administrator, A
Web Page, Digital/Multimedia and Information Resources Design, A
Word Processing, A

LAUREL TECHNICAL INSTITUTE

Administrative Assistant and Secretarial Science, A
Business Administration and Management, A
Business/Office Automation/Technology/Data Entry, A
Computer Programming/Programmer, A
Executive Assistant/Executive Secretary, A
Health Information/Medical Records Administration/Administrator, A
Legal Administrative Assistant/Secretary, A
Medical Administrative Assistant/Secretary, A
Medical/Clinical Assistant, A

LEBANON VALLEY COLLEGE

Accounting, B
Actuarial Science, B
Art History, Criticism and Conservation, B
Art/Art Studies, General, B
Athletic Training and Sports Medicine, M
Biochemistry, Biophysics and Molecular Biology, B
Biology/Biological Sciences, B
Business Administration and Management, B
Business Administration, Management and Operations, M
Chemistry, B
Clinical Laboratory Science/Medical Technology/Technologist, B
Computer Science, B
Criminology, B
Digital Communication and Media/Multimedia, B
Early Childhood Education and Teaching, B
Economics, B
English Language and Literature, B
French Language and Literature, B
German Language and Literature, B
Health Services Administration, M
Health Services/Allied Health/Health Sciences, B
Health/Health Care Administration/Management, B
History, B
International/Global Studies, B
Kinesiology and Exercise Science, B
Mathematics, B
Multi-/Interdisciplinary Studies, B
Music Performance, B
Music Teacher Education, BM
Philosophy, B
Physical Therapy/Therapist, D
Physics, B
Political Science and Government, B
Psychology, B
Religion/Religious Studies, B
Science Teacher Education/General Science Teacher Education, M
Sociology, B
Spanish Language and Literature, B

Special Education and Teaching, B

LEHIGH CARBON COMMUNITY COLLEGE

Accounting Technology/Technician and Bookkeeping, A
Aeronautics/Aviation/Aerospace Science and Technology, A
Airline/Commercial/Professional Pilot and Flight Crew, A
Animation, Interactive Technology, Video Graphics and Special Effects, A
Art/Art Studies, General, A
BioTechnology, A
Biology/Biological Sciences, A
Building/Construction Site Management/Manager, A
Business Administration and Management, A
Business/Commerce, A
Cartography, A
Chemical Technology/Technician, A
Chemistry, A
Communication Studies/Speech Communication and Rhetoric, A
Computer Programming, Specific Applications, A
Computer Programming/Programmer, A
Computer Systems Networking and Telecommunications, A
Computer and Information Sciences, A
Computer and Information Systems Security, A
Construction Trades, A
Criminal Justice/Law Enforcement Administration, A
Criminal Justice/Safety Studies, A
Drafting and Design Technology/Technician, A
Early Childhood Education and Teaching, A
Education, A
Electrical, Electronic and Communications Engineering Technology/Technician, A
Engineering, A
Environmental Sciences, A
Fashion/Apparel Design, A
General Studies, A
Graphic Design, A
Health Information/Medical Records Technology/Technician, A
Health Services/Allied Health/Health Sciences, A
Heating, Air Conditioning, Ventilation and Refrigeration Maintenance Technology/Technician, A
Human Resources Management/Personnel Administration, A
Human Services, A
Industrial Electronics Technology/Technician, A
Interior Design, A
Kinesiology and Exercise Science, A
Legal Assistant/Paralegal, A
Liberal Arts and Sciences Studies and Humanities, A
Manufacturing Technology/Technician, A
Mathematics, A
Mechanical Engineering/Mechanical Technology/Technician, A
Medical/Clinical Assistant, A
Occupational Therapist Assistant, A
Physical Sciences, A
Physical Therapist Assistant, A
Psychology, A
Public Administration, A
Radio and Television Broadcasting Technology/Technician, A
Recording Arts Technology/Technician, A
Resort Management, A
Social Work, A
Special Education and Teaching, A
Sport and Fitness Administration/Management, A
Teacher Assistant/Aide, A
Veterinary/Animal Health Technology/Technician and Veterinary Assistant, A
Web Page, Digital/Multimedia and Information Resources Design, A

LEHIGH UNIVERSITY

Accounting, BM
African Studies, B
American/United States Studies/Civilization, MDO
Ancient Studies/Civilization, B
Anthropology, B
Applied Mathematics, B

Architecture, B
Art History, Criticism and Conservation, B
Art/Art Studies, General, B
Asian Studies/Civilization, B
Astronomy, B
Astrophysics, B
Biochemistry, BD
Bioengineering, MD
Biological and Biomedical Sciences, MD
Biology/Biological Sciences, B
Biomedical/Medical Engineering, B
Business Administration, Management and Operations, M
Business, Management, Marketing, and Related Support Services, B
Business/Managerial Economics, B
Cell Biology and Anatomy, D
Chemical Engineering, BMD
Chemistry, BMD
Chinese Language and Literature, B
Civil Engineering, BMD
Classics and Classical Languages, Literatures, and Linguistics, B
Cognitive Sciences, B
Computational Sciences, M
Computer Engineering, BMD
Computer Science, BMD
Computer and Information Sciences and Support Services, B
Counseling Psychology, MDO
Counselor Education/School Counseling and Guidance Services, M
Design and Visual Communications, B
Drama and Dramatics/Theatre Arts, B
Economics, MD
Education, MDO
Educational Leadership and Administration, MDO
Educational Media/Instructional Technology, MDO
Electrical Engineering, MD
Electrical, Electronics and Communications Engineering, B
Energy and Power Engineering, M
Engineering, B
Engineering Management, M
Engineering Mechanics, B
Engineering Physics, B
Engineering and Applied Sciences, MD
English, MD
English Language and Literature, B
English as a Second Language, O
Entrepreneurship/Entrepreneurial Studies, M
Environmental Engineering Technology/Environmental Technology, MD
Environmental Law, O
Environmental Policy, O
Environmental Policy and Resource Management, MO
Environmental Sciences, MD
Environmental Studies, B
Environmental/Environmental Health Engineering, B
Finance, B
Finance and Banking, M
French Language and Literature, B
Geological and Earth Sciences/Geosciences, B
Geology/Earth Science, MD
Geosciences, MD
German Language and Literature, B
Health Services Administration, M
History, BMD
Human Services, M
Industrial Engineering, B
Industrial/Management Engineering, MD
Information Science/Studies, M
Information Technology, B
Interdisciplinary Studies, MD
International Development, O
International Relations and Affairs, B
International and Comparative Education, MDO
International/Global Studies, B
Journalism, B
Logistics and Materials Management, B
Management Science, B
Manufacturing Engineering, M
Marketing/Marketing Management, B
Materials Engineering, BMD
Materials Sciences, MD

Mathematics, BMD
Mechanical Engineering, BMD
Mechanics, MD
Molecular Biology, BMD
Multi-/Interdisciplinary Studies, B
Music, B
Music History, Literature, and Theory, B
Philosophy, B
Photonics, M
Physics, BMD
Political Science and Government, BM
Polymer/Plastics Engineering, MD
Pre-Dentistry Studies, B
Pre-Medicine/Pre-Medical Studies, B
Project Management, M
Psychology, BMD
Public History, M
Quantitative Analysis, M
Religion/Religious Studies, B
School Psychology, DO
Science, Technology and Society, B
Sociology, BM
Spanish Language and Literature, B
Special Education and Teaching, MD
Statistics, B
Systems Engineering, MD
Women's Studies, B

LINCOLN TECHNICAL INSTITUTE (AL-LENTOWN)

Computer Systems Networking and Telecommunications, A
Drafting and Design Technology/Technician, A
Electrical/Electronics Equipment Installation and Repair, A
Medical Administrative Assistant/Secretary, A

LINCOLN TECHNICAL INSTITUTE (PHILADELPHIA)

Automobile/Automotive Mechanics Technology/Technician, A
Diesel Mechanics Technology/Technician, A

LINCOLN UNIVERSITY

Accounting, B
Anthropology, B
Biochemistry, Biophysics and Molecular Biology, B
Biology Teacher Education, B
Biology/Biological Sciences, B
Broadcast Journalism, B
Business Administration and Management, B
Business Administration, Management and Operations, M
Chemistry, B
Communication Studies/Speech Communication and Rhetoric, B
Computer and Information Sciences, B
Criminal Justice/Safety Studies, B
Early Childhood Education and Teaching, M
Educational Leadership and Administration, M
English Language and Literature, B
English/Language Arts Teacher Education, B
Environmental Sciences, B
Environmental Studies, B
Finance, B
Finance and Banking, M
Fine/Studio Arts, B
Foreign Language Teacher Education, B
French Language Teacher Education, B
French Language and Literature, B
Health Services/Allied Health/Health Sciences, B
Health and Physical Education, B
Health and Physical Education/Fitness, B
History, B
Human Resources Management and Services, M
Human Services, BM
Information Technology, B
Journalism, B
Kindergarten/PreSchool Education and Teaching, B
Mathematics, B
Mathematics Teacher Education, B
Music, B
Music Teacher Education, B
Philosophy, B
Physical Sciences, B
Physics, B

Political Science and Government, B
Public Administration, B
Reading Teacher Education, M
Religion/Religious Studies, B
Secondary Education and Teaching, B
Sociology, B
Spanish Language and Literature, B
Therapeutic Recreation/Recreational Therapy, B

LOCK HAVEN UNIVERSITY OF PENN-SYLVANIA

Accounting, B
Art/Art Studies, General, B
Athletic Training and Sports Medicine, B
Biology/Biological Sciences, B
Business Administration and Management, AB
Chemistry, B
Clinical Psychology, M
Computer and Information Sciences, B
Counseling Psychology, M
Criminal Justice/Law Enforcement Administration, AB
Drama and Dramatics/Theatre Arts, B
Early Childhood Education and Teaching, B
Education, M
Education/Teaching of Individuals in Early Childhood Special Education Programs, B
Educational Leadership and Administration, M
Elementary Education and Teaching, M
English Language and Literature, B
Fine/Studio Arts, B
Foreign Languages and Literatures, B
Geology/Earth Science, B
Health Professions and Related Clinical Sciences, AB
Health and Physical Education/Fitness, B
Health/Medical Preparatory Programs, B
History, B
International Relations and Affairs, B
Junior High/Intermediate/Middle School Education and Teaching, B
Liberal Arts and Sciences Studies and Humanities, B
Mass Communication/Media Studies, B
Mathematics, B
Music, B
Parks, Recreation and Leisure Facilities Management, B
Philosophy, B
Physician Assistant, M
Physics, B
Political Science and Government, B
Psychology, B
Rehabilitation and Therapeutic Professions, B
Secondary Education and Teaching, B
Social Sciences, B
Social Work, B
Sociology, B
Spanish Language and Literature, B
Sport Psychology, M
Sport and Fitness Administration/Management, BM

LUZERNE COUNTY COMMUNITY COL-LEGE

Accounting, A
Administrative Assistant and Secretarial Science, A
Airline/Commercial/Professional Pilot and Flight Crew, A
Architectural Engineering, A
Architectural Engineering Technology/Technician, A
Automobile/Automotive Mechanics Technology/Technician, A
Aviation/Airway Management and Operations, A
Baking and Pastry Arts/Baker/Pastry Chef, A
Banking and Financial Support Services, A
Biological and Physical Sciences, A
Building/Property Maintenance and Management, A
Business Administration and Management, A
Child Care Provider/Assistant, A
Commercial Photography, A
Commercial and Advertising Art, A
Computer Graphics, A
Computer Programming, A
Computer Science, A
Computer Systems Networking and Telecommunications, A

Computer Technology/Computer Systems Technology, A
Computer and Information Sciences, A
Court Reporting/Court Reporter, A
Criminal Justice/Law Enforcement Administration, A
Culinary Arts/Chef Training, A
Data Entry/Microcomputer Applications, A
Data Processing and Data Processing Technology/Technician, A
Dental Assisting/Assistant, A
Dental Hygiene/Hygienist, A
Drafting and Design Technology/Technician, A
Drafting/Design Engineering Technologies/Technicians, A
Drawing, A
Early Childhood Education and Teaching, A
Education, A
Electrical, Electronic and Communications Engineering Technology/Technician, A
Electrician, A
Emergency Medical Technology/Technician (EMT Paramedic), A
Engineering Technology, A
Executive Assistant/Executive Secretary, A
Fire Science/Firefighting, A
Food Technology and Processing, A
Funeral Service and Mortuary Science, A
General Studies, A
Graphic Design, A
Graphic and Printing Equipment Operator Production, A
Health and Physical Education, A
Health/Health Care Administration/Management, A
Heating, Air Conditioning, Ventilation and Refrigeration Maintenance Technology/Technician, A
Horticultural Science, A
Hospitality and Recreation Marketing Operations, A
Hotel/Motel Administration/Management, A
Human Services, A
Humanities/Humanistic Studies, A
Industrial Design, A
International Business/Trade/Commerce, A
Journalism, A
Legal Assistant/Paralegal, A
Liberal Arts and Sciences Studies and Humanities, A
Mathematics, A
Medical Administrative Assistant/Secretary, A
Painting, A
Photography, A
Physical Education Teaching and Coaching, A
Plumbing Technology/Plumber, A
Pre-Pharmacy Studies, A
Radio and Television Broadcasting Technology/Technician, A
Real Estate, A
Respiratory Care Therapy/Therapist, A
Social Sciences, A
Surgical Technology/Technologist, A
Tourism and Travel Services Management, A
Tourism and Travel Services Marketing Operations, A

LYCOMING COLLEGE

Accounting, B
American/United States Studies/Civilization, B
Applied Mathematics, B
Area Studies, B
Art History, Criticism and Conservation, B
Art/Art Studies, General, B
Astronomy, B
Astrophysics, B
Biology/Biological Sciences, B
Business Administration and Management, B
Business/Corporate Communications, B
Chemistry, B
Classical, Ancient Mediterranean and Near Eastern Studies and Archaeology, B
Commercial and Advertising Art, B
Communication and Media Studies, B
Comparative Literature, B
Criminology, B
Digital Communication and Media/Multimedia, B
Drama and Dramatics/Theatre Arts, B
Economics, B
English Language and Literature, B

Finance, B
Fine/Studio Arts, B
Foreign Languages and Literatures, B
French Language and Literature, B
German Language and Literature, B
History, B
International Finance, B
Mathematics, B
Mathematics and Statistics, B
Multi-/Interdisciplinary Studies, B
Music, B
Philosophy, B
Physics, B
Political Science and Government, B
Psychology, B
Religion/Religious Studies, B
Sociology, B
Spanish Language and Literature, B

MANOR COLLEGE

Accounting, A
Business Administration and Management, A
Business, Management, Marketing, and Related Support Services, A
Communication and Media Studies, A
Computer Programming, Specific Applications, A
Criminal Justice/Law Enforcement Administration, A
Dental Assisting/Assistant, A
Dental Hygiene/Hygienist, A
Elementary Education and Teaching, A
Health Professions and Related Clinical Sciences, A
Legal Assistant/Paralegal, A
Liberal Arts and Sciences Studies and Humanities, A
Marketing/Marketing Management, A
Psychology, A
Sport and Fitness Administration/Management, A
Teacher Education and Professional Development, Specific Levels and Methods, A
Veterinary/Animal Health Technology/Technician and Veterinary Assistant, A

MANSFIELD UNIVERSITY OF PENNSYLVANIA

Accounting, B
Art Education, M
Art History, Criticism and Conservation, B
Biochemistry, B
Biological and Physical Sciences, B
Biology/Biological Sciences, B
Business Administration and Management, B
Cell/Cellular Biology and Histology, B
Chemistry, B
Clinical Laboratory Science/Medical Technology/Technologist, B
Communication Studies/Speech Communication and Rhetoric, B
Community Health and Preventive Medicine, B
Computer Science, B
Computer and Information Sciences, B
Criminal Justice/Law Enforcement Administration, AB
Design and Applied Arts, B
Dietetics/Dieticians, B
Education, BM
Elementary Education and Teaching, BM
English Language and Literature, B
Environmental Studies, B
Fishing and Fisheries Sciences and Management, B
Graphic Design, B
History, B
Human Resources Management/Personnel Administration, B
Industrial Safety Technology/Technician, B
Information Science/Studies, ABM
International Business/Trade/Commerce, B
Kindergarten/PreSchool Education and Teaching, B
Liberal Arts and Sciences Studies and Humanities, AB
Library Science, M
Marketing/Marketing Management, B
Mass Communication/Media Studies, B
Mathematics, B
Music, BM
Music Performance, B
Music Teacher Education, B

Nursing, M
Organizational Management, M
Performance, M
Petroleum Technology/Technician, A
Philosophy, B
Political Science and Government, B
Pre-Law Studies, B
Psychology, BM
Public Relations/Image Management, B
Radiologic Technology/Science - Radiographer, A
Respiratory Care Therapy/Therapist, A
Secondary Education and Teaching, BM
Social Science Teacher Education, B
Social Sciences, B
Social Studies Teacher Education, B
Social Work, B
Special Education and Teaching, BM

MARYWOOD UNIVERSITY

Accounting, B
Architecture, BM
Art Education, M
Art Teacher Education, B
Art Therapy/Therapist, BMO
Athletic Training and Sports Medicine, B
Audiology/Audiologist and Speech-Language Pathology/Pathologist, B
Aviation/Airway Management and Operations, B
BioTechnology, BM
Biology Teacher Education, B
Biology/Biological Sciences, B
Broadcast Journalism, B
Business Administration and Management, B
Business Administration, Management and Operations, M
Ceramic Arts and Ceramics, B
Clinical Laboratory Science/Medical Technology/Technologist, B
Clinical Psychology, MD
Communication Disorders, M
Communication and Media Studies, M
Computer Science, B
Computer and Information Systems Security, BM
Computer/Information Technology Services Administration and Management, B
Counseling Psychology, M
Counselor Education/School Counseling and Guidance Services, M
Criminal Justice/Law Enforcement Administration, B
Criminology, M
Dietetics/Dieticians, B
Digital Communication and Media/Multimedia, B
Drama and Dramatics/Theatre Arts, B
Early Childhood Education and Teaching, BM
Education, M
Educational Administration and Supervision, MD
Educational Leadership and Administration, MD
Elementary Education and Teaching, BM
English Language and Literature, B
English/Language Arts Teacher Education, B
Environmental Design/Architecture, B
Environmental Sciences, B
Exercise and Sports Science, M
Finance and Banking, M
Financial Planning and Services, B
Fine Arts and Art Studies, M
General Studies, B
Gerontology, M
Graphic Design, BM
Health Education, D
Health Professions and Related Clinical Sciences, B
Health Services Administration, M
Health Services/Allied Health/Health Sciences, B
Health and Physical Education, B
Health/Health Care Administration/Management, B
Higher Education/Higher Education Administration, MD
History, B
Hospitality Administration/Management, B
Human Development, D
Illustration, BM
Interdisciplinary Studies, D
Interior Design, BM
International Business/Trade/Commerce, B
Investment Management, M
Management, M

Management Information Systems and Services, M
Marketing/Marketing Management, B
Mathematics, B
Mathematics Teacher Education, B
Music Performance, B
Music Teacher Education, BM
Music Therapy/Therapist, B
Nutritional Sciences, MO
Painting, BM
Philosophy, B
Photography, BM
Physical Education Teaching and Coaching, B
Physician Assistant, M
Printmaking, M
Psychology, BM
Public Administration, M
Public Relations, Advertising, and Applied Communication, B
Reading Teacher Education, M
Religion/Religious Studies, B
Science Teacher Education/General Science Teacher Education, B
Sculpture, BM
Secondary Education and Teaching, M
Social Science Teacher Education, B
Social Sciences, B
Social Work, BMD
Sociology, B
Spanish Language Teacher Education, B
Spanish Language and Literature, B
Special Education and Teaching, BM
Teacher Education and Professional Development, Specific Subject Areas, B

MCCANN SCHOOL OF BUSINESS & TECHNOLOGY (HAZLETON)

Accounting, A
Marketing/Marketing Management, A

MCCANN SCHOOL OF BUSINESS & TECHNOLOGY (LEWISBURG)

Accounting, A
Computer Science, A
Criminal Justice/Law Enforcement Administration, A
Early Childhood Education and Teaching, A
Legal Administrative Assistant/Secretary, A
Legal Assistant/Paralegal, A
Marketing/Marketing Management, A
Medical Office Management/Administration, A
Medical/Clinical Assistant, A
Office Management and Supervision, A
Surgical Technology/Technologist, A
System, Networking, and LAN/WAN Management/Manager, A

MCCANN SCHOOL OF BUSINESS & TECHNOLOGY (POTTSVILLE)

Accounting, A
Business Administration and Management, A
Computer Science, A
Computer and Information Sciences, A
Cosmetology/Cosmetologist, A
Criminal Justice/Safety Studies, A
Early Childhood Education and Teaching, A
Legal Assistant/Paralegal, A
Massage Therapy/Therapeutic Massage, A
Medical Administrative Assistant/Secretary, A
Medical/Clinical Assistant, A
Surgical Technology/Technologist, A

MERCYHURST NORTH EAST

Accounting, A
Athletic Training and Sports Medicine, A
Biological and Physical Sciences, A
Business/Commerce, A
Communication Studies/Speech Communication and Rhetoric, A
Computer Systems Analysis/Analyst, A
Criminal Justice/Law Enforcement Administration, A
Culinary Arts/Chef Training, A
Early Childhood Education and Teaching, A
Education, A
Hospitality Administration/Management, A
Liberal Arts and Sciences Studies and Humanities, A

Medical Office Management/Administration, A
Medical/Clinical Assistant, A
Occupational Therapist Assistant, A
Physical Therapist Assistant, A
Radio and Television Broadcasting
Technology/Technician, A
Respiratory Care Therapy/Therapist, A
Sport and Fitness Administration/Management, A

MERCYHURST UNIVERSITY

Accounting, BM
Anthropology, BM
Applied Behavior Analysis, M
Archeology, BM
Art Teacher Education, B
Art Therapy/Therapist, B
Art/Art Studies, General, B
Biochemistry, B
Biological Anthropology, M
Biology Teacher Education, B
Biology/Biological Sciences, B
Business Administration and Management, B
Business Teacher Education, B
Business, Management, Marketing, and Related
Support Services, B
Business/Managerial Economics, B
Chemistry, B
Chemistry Teacher Education, B
Communication Studies/Speech Communication
and Rhetoric, B
Computer Science, B
Computer and Information Sciences, B
Computer and Information Systems Security, M
Corrections, B
Criminal Justice/Safety Studies, B
Criminology, MO
Dance, B
Education, B
Educational Administration and Supervision, M
Elementary Education and Teaching, B
English Language and Literature, B
English/Language Arts Teacher Education, B
Entrepreneurship/Entrepreneurial Studies, M
Exercise Physiology, B
Fashion Merchandising, B
Finance, B
Fine/Studio Arts, B
Foreign Language Teacher Education, B
Foreign Languages and Literatures, B
Forensic Science and Technology, BM
Geology/Earth Science, B
Graphic Design, B
Health Services/Allied Health/Health Sciences, B
Health/Medical Preparatory Programs, B
Higher Education/Higher Education Administra-
tion, M
History, B
Hospitality Administration/Management, B
Human Resources Management and Services, M
Human Resources Management/Personnel Adminis-
tration, B
Information Science/Studies, B
Interior Design, B
International/Global Studies, B
Junior High/Intermediate/Middle School Education
and Teaching, B
Management Strategy and Policy, M
Marketing Research, B
Marketing/Marketing Management, B
Mathematics, B
Mathematics Teacher Education, B
Multi-/Interdisciplinary Studies, B
Music, B
Music Performance, B
Music Teacher Education, B
Music Therapy/Therapist, B
Organizational Management, MO
Paleontology, B
Petroleum Technology/Technician, B
Philosophy, B
Physician Assistant, M
Political Science and Government, B
Pre-Dentistry Studies, B
Pre-Veterinary Studies, B
Psychology, B
Public Health (MPH, DPH), B

Religion/Religious Studies, B
Science Teacher Education/General Science
Teacher Education, B
Secondary Education and Teaching, BM
Securities Services Administration/Management, MO
Social Science Teacher Education, B
Social Sciences, B
Social Work, B
Sociology, B
Special Education and Teaching, BM
Sport and Fitness Administration/Management, M
Web Page, Digital/Multimedia and Information Re-
sources Design, B

MESSIAH COLLEGE

Accounting, B
Art History, Criticism and Conservation, B
Art Teacher Education, B
Athletic Training and Sports Medicine, B
Bible/Biblical Studies, B
Biochemistry, B
Biology Teacher Education, B
Biology/Biological Sciences, B
Biopsychology, B
Business Administration and Management, B
Business Administration, Management and Opera-
tions, MO
Business, Management, Marketing, and Related
Support Services, B
Chemistry, B
Chemistry Teacher Education, B
Child Care and Support Services Management, B
Chinese Language and Literature, B
Cinematography and Film/Video Production, B
Clinical Nutrition/Nutritionist, B
Clinical Psychology, M
Communication Studies/Speech Communication
and Rhetoric, B
Communications Technology/Technician, B
Computer Science, B
Counseling Psychology, MO
Counselor Education/School Counseling and Guid-
ance Services, M
Criminal Justice/Safety Studies, B
Curriculum and Instruction, M
Dance, B
Development Economics and International Develop-
ment, B
Digital Communication and Media/Multimedia, B
Drama and Dramatics/Theatre Arts, B
Early Childhood Education and Teaching, B
Economics, B
Elementary Education and Teaching, B
Engineering, B
English Language and Literature, B
English as a Second Language, M
English/Language Arts Teacher Education, B
Environmental Sciences, B
Ethnic and Cultural Studies, B
Family and Community Services, B
Family and Consumer Sciences/Home Economics
Teacher Education, B
Fine/Studio Arts, B
Foreign Language Teacher Education, B
French Language Teacher Education, B
French Language and Literature, B
German Language Teacher Education, B
German Language and Literature, B
Health Services/Allied Health/Health Sciences, B
Higher Education/Higher Education Administra-
tion, M
History, B
Humanities/Humanistic Studies, B
International Business/Trade/Commerce, B
Journalism, B
Junior High/Intermediate/Middle School Education
and Teaching, B
Management Strategy and Policy, M
Marketing/Marketing Management, B
Marriage and Family Therapy/Counseling, M
Mathematics, B
Mathematics Teacher Education, B
Molecular Biology, B
Multi-/Interdisciplinary Studies, B
Music, B
Music Performance, B

Music Teacher Education, B
Nursing Education, M
Organizational Management, MO
Parks, Recreation, Leisure and Fitness Studies, B
Peace Studies and Conflict Resolution, B
Performance, M
Philosophy, B
Physical Education Teaching and Coaching, B
Physics, B
Physics Teacher Education, B
Political Science and Government, B
Psychology, B
Religious Education, B
Restaurant/Food Services Management, B
Social Studies Teacher Education, B
Social Work, B
Sociology, B
Spanish Language Teacher Education, B
Spanish Language and Literature, B
Special Education and Teaching, M
Sport and Fitness Administration/Management, BM
Student Personnel Services, M

METROPOLITAN CAREER CENTER COMPUTER TECHNOLOGY INSTITUTE

Computer Technology/Computer Systems Technology, A

MILLERSVILLE UNIVERSITY OF PENN-SYLVANIA

Allied Health Diagnostic, Intervention, and Treat-
ment Professions, B
Anthropology, B
Area Studies, B
Art Education, M
Art/Art Studies, General, B
Atmospheric Sciences and Meteorology, BM
Biology/Biological Sciences, B
Business Administration and Management, B
Chemistry, B
Clinical Psychology, M
Communication Studies/Speech Communication
and Rhetoric, B
Computer and Information Sciences, B
Design and Visual Communications, B
Early Childhood Education and Teaching, BM
Economics, B
Education, M
Education/Teaching of the Gifted and Talented, M
Educational Leadership and Administration, M
Elementary Education and Teaching, M
Emergency Management, M
English, M
English Language and Literature, B
English as a Second Language, M
Environmental Policy and Resource Manage-
ment, M
Fine Arts and Art Studies, M
Foundations and Philosophy of Education, M
French Language and Literature, BM
Geographic Information Systems, M
Geography, B
Geology/Earth Science, B
German Language and Literature, BM
History, BM
Industrial Production Technologies/Technicians, B
Industrial Technology/Technician, AB
Junior High/Intermediate/Middle School Education
and Teaching, B
Mathematics, B
Mathematics Teacher Education, M
Meteorology, M
Music, B
Nursing, M
Nursing - Advanced Practice, M
Nursing Education, M
Occupational Safety and Health
Technology/Technician, B
Oceanography, Chemical and Physical, B
Philosophy, B
Physical Education Teaching and Coaching, M
Physics, B
Political Science and Government, B
Psychology, BM
Reading Teacher Education, M
School Psychology, M

Social Sciences, B
Social Work, BM
Sociology, B
Spanish Language and Literature, BM
Special Education and Teaching, BM
Sport and Fitness Administration/Management, M
Vocational and Technical Education, M

MISERICORDIA UNIVERSITY

Accounting, BM
Allied Health and Medical Assisting Services, MD
American Government and Politics (United States), B
Biochemistry, B
Biology Teacher Education, B
Biology/Biological Sciences, B
Business Administration and Management, B
Business Administration, Management and Operations, M
Chemistry, B
Chemistry Teacher Education, B
Clinical Laboratory Science/Medical Technology/Technologist, B
Communication Disorders, M
Computer and Information Sciences, B
Curriculum and Instruction, M
Diagnostic Medical Sonography/Sonographer and Ultrasound Technician, B
Early Childhood Education and Teaching, B
Education, M
Educational Media/Instructional Technology, M
Elementary Education and Teaching, B
English Language and Literature, B
English/Language Arts Teacher Education, B
General Studies, B
Health Services Administration, M
Health Services/Allied Health/Health Sciences, B
Health/Health Care Administration/Management, B
History, B
Human Resources Management and Services, M
Junior High/Intermediate/Middle School Education and Teaching, B
Management, M
Management Information Systems and Services, BM
Mathematics, B
Mathematics Teacher Education, B
Medical Radiologic Technology/Science - Radiation Therapist, B
Nursing, MD
Occupational Therapy/Therapist, MD
Organizational Management, M
Philosophy, B
Physical Therapy/Therapist, D
Psychology, B
Reading Teacher Education, M
Social Sciences, B
Social Studies Teacher Education, B
Social Work, B
Special Education and Teaching, M
Sport and Fitness Administration/Management, BM

MONTGOMERY COUNTY COMMUNITY COLLEGE

Accounting, A
Accounting Technology/Technician and Bookkeeping, A
Administrative Assistant and Secretarial Science, A
Art/Art Studies, General, A
Baking and Pastry Arts/Baker/Pastry Chef, A
BioTechnology, A
Biology/Biological Sciences, A
Business Administration and Management, A
Business/Commerce, A
Business/Corporate Communications, A
Child Care and Support Services Management, A
Clinical/Medical Laboratory Technician, A
Commercial and Advertising Art, A
Communication Studies/Speech Communication and Rhetoric, A
Communications Technologies/Technicians and Support Services, A
Computer Programming/Programmer, A
Computer Systems Networking and Telecommunications, A
Computer and Information Sciences, A

Criminal Justice/Police Science, A
Culinary Arts/Chef Training, A
Dental Hygiene/Hygienist, A
Electrical, Electronic and Communications Engineering Technology/Technician, A
Electromechanical Technology/Electromechanical Engineering Technology, A
Elementary Education and Teaching, A
Engineering Science, A
Engineering Technologies/Technicians, A
Environmental Sciences, A
Fire Protection and Safety Technology/Technician, A
Health and Physical Education, A
Hospitality and Recreation Marketing Operations, A
Humanities/Humanistic Studies, A
Information Science/Studies, A
Liberal Arts and Sciences Studies and Humanities, A
Management Information Systems and Services, A
Mathematics, A
Mechanical Engineering/Mechanical Technology/Technician, A
Medical Radiologic Technology/Science - Radiation Therapist, A
Medical/Clinical Assistant, A
Physical Education Teaching and Coaching, A
Physical Sciences, A
Psychiatric/Mental Health Services Technician, A
Psychology, A
Radio, Television, and Digital Communication, A
Radiologic Technology/Science - Radiographer, A
Real Estate, A
Recording Arts Technology/Technician, A
Sales, Distribution and Marketing Operations, A
Secondary Education and Teaching, A
Social Sciences, A
Surgical Technology/Technologist, A
System Administration/Administrator, A
Teacher Assistant/Aide, A
Tourism and Travel Services Marketing Operations, A
Web/Multimedia Management and Webmaster, A

MOORE COLLEGE OF ART & DESIGN

Art Education, M
Art History, Criticism and Conservation, B
Art Teacher Education, B
Arts Management, M
Communication and Media Studies, M
Fashion/Apparel Design, B
Fine Arts and Art Studies, M
Fine/Studio Arts, B
Graphic Design, B
Illustration, B
Interior Design, BM
Museology/Museum Studies, B
Photography, B

MORAVIAN COLLEGE

Accounting, BM
Allied Health and Medical Assisting Services, M
Art/Art Studies, General, B
Biochemistry, B
Biology/Biological Sciences, B
Business Administration and Management, B
Business Administration, Management and Operations, M
Chemistry, B
Community Health and Preventive Medicine, B
Computer Science, B
Curriculum and Instruction, M
Economics, B
Education, M
English Language and Literature, B
Environmental Sciences, B
Environmental Studies, B
French Language and Literature, B
French Studies, B
Geology/Earth Science, B
German Language and Literature, B
German Studies, B
Health Services Administration, M
History, B
Human Resources Development, M
Human Resources Management and Services, M
International Business/Trade/Commerce, B

Mathematics, B
Music, B
Non-Profit/Public/Organizational Management, B
Nursing, M
Nursing Administration, M
Nursing Education, M
Philosophy, B
Physics, B
Political Science and Government, B
Psychology, B
Religion/Religious Studies, B
Sociology, B
Spanish Language and Literature, B
Supply Chain Management, M

MOUNT ALOYSIUS COLLEGE

Accounting, ABM
Applied Behavior Analysis, M
Biological and Biomedical Sciences, B
Biology/Biological Sciences, B
Business Administration and Management, AB
Business Administration, Management and Operations, M
Clinical/Medical Laboratory Technician, A
Community Psychology, M
Corrections, A
Criminal Justice/Law Enforcement Administration, B
Early Childhood Education and Teaching, AB
English Language and Literature, B
General Studies, A
Health Services Administration, M
Information Technology, B
Junior High/Intermediate/Middle School Education and Teaching, B
Legal Assistant/Paralegal, A
Liberal Arts and Sciences Studies and Humanities, AB
Management Information Systems and Services, A
Medical Radiologic Technology/Science - Radiation Therapist, AB
Medical/Clinical Assistant, A
Non-Profit/Public/Organizational Management, M
Physical Therapist Assistant, A
Project Management, M
Psychology, BM
Secondary Education and Teaching, B
Sign Language Interpretation and Translation, AB
Social Sciences, A
Surgical Technology/Technologist, A

MUHLENBERG COLLEGE

Accounting, AB
American/United States Studies/Civilization, B
Anthropology, B
Art History, Criticism and Conservation, B
Art/Art Studies, General, B
Biochemistry, B
Biology/Biological Sciences, B
Business Administration and Management, AB
Chemistry, B
Dance, B
Drama and Dramatics/Theatre Arts, B
Economics, B
English Language and Literature, B
Environmental Sciences, B
Film/Cinema Studies, B
Fine/Studio Arts, B
French Language and Literature, B
History, B
International Relations and Affairs, B
Jewish/Judaic Studies, B
Mathematics, B
Music, B
Natural Sciences, B
Philosophy, B
Physical Sciences, B
Physics, B
Political Science and Government, B
Psychology, AB
Religion/Religious Studies, B
Russian Studies, B
Social Sciences, B
Sociology, B

Spanish Language and Literature, B

NEUMANN UNIVERSITY

Accounting, B
Athletic Training and Sports Medicine, B
Biology/Biological Sciences, B
Business Administration and Management, B
Communication and Media Studies, B
Computer and Information Sciences, B
Criminal Justice/Safety Studies, B
Education, M
Educational Leadership and Administration, D
Elementary Education and Teaching, B
English Language and Literature, B
International Business/Trade/Commerce, B
Liberal Arts and Sciences Studies and Humanities, AB
Management Strategy and Policy, M
Marketing/Marketing Management, B
Nursing, M
Organizational Behavior Studies, B
Pastoral Studies/Counseling, MO
Physical Therapy/Therapist, D
Political Science and Government, B
Psychology, B
Security and Protective Services, B
Social Work, B
Sport and Fitness Administration/Management, BM
Visual and Performing Arts, B

NEW CASTLE SCHOOL OF TRADES

Automotive Engineering Technology/Technician, A
Construction Engineering Technology/Technician, A
Diesel Mechanics Technology/Technician, A
Electrical, Electronic and Communications Engineering Technology/Technician, A
Heating, Air Conditioning and Refrigeration Technology/Technician, A
Industrial Mechanics and Maintenance Technology, A
Machine Tool Technology/Machinist, A

NORTHAMPTON COMMUNITY COLLEGE

Accounting Technology/Technician and Bookkeeping, A
Acting, A
Administrative Assistant and Secretarial Science, A
Architectural Engineering Technology/Technician, A
Athletic Training and Sports Medicine, A
Automobile/Automotive Mechanics Technology/Technician, A
BioTechnology, A
Biology/Biological Sciences, A
Business Administration and Management, A
Business/Commerce, A
CAD/CADD Drafting and/or Design Technology/Technician, A
Chemistry, A
Communication Studies/Speech Communication and Rhetoric, A
Computer Installation and Repair Technology/Technician, A
Computer Programming/Programmer, A
Computer Science, A
Computer Systems Networking and Telecommunications, A
Computer and Information Systems Security, A
Construction Management, A
Criminal Justice/Safety Studies, A
Culinary Arts/Chef Training, A
Dental Hygiene/Hygienist, A
Diagnostic Medical Sonography/Sonographer and Ultrasound Technician, A
Early Childhood Education and Teaching, A
Electrical, Electronic and Communications Engineering Technology/Technician, A
Electrician, A
Electromechanical Technology/Electromechanical Engineering Technology, A
Engineering, A
Environmental Sciences, A
Fine/Studio Arts, A
Fire Science/Firefighting, A
Fire Services Administration, A
Funeral Service and Mortuary Science, A

General Studies, A
Graphic Design, A
Heating, Air Conditioning, Ventilation and Refrigeration Maintenance Technology/Technician, A
Hotel/Motel Administration/Management, A
Industrial Electronics Technology/Technician, A
Interior Design, A
International/Global Studies, A
Journalism, A
Junior High/Intermediate/Middle School Education and Teaching, A
Legal Assistant/Paralegal, A
Liberal Arts and Sciences Studies and Humanities, A
Marketing/Marketing Management, A
Mathematics, A
Medical Administrative Assistant/Secretary, A
Physics, A
Public Health Education and Promotion, A
Quality Control Technology/Technician, A
Radio and Television Broadcasting Technology/Technician, A
Radiologic Technology/Science - Radiographer, A
Restaurant/Food Services Management, A
Secondary Education and Teaching, A
Social Work, A
Sport and Fitness Administration/Management, A
Teacher Assistant/Aide, A
Veterinary/Animal Health Technology/Technician and Veterinary Assistant, A
Web Page, Digital/Multimedia and Information Resources Design, A

PEIRCE COLLEGE

Accounting, B
Business Administration and Management, AB
Criminal Justice/Law Enforcement Administration, A
General Studies, A
Health Information/Medical Records Administration/Administrator, B
Health Information/Medical Records Technology/Technician, A
Health/Health Care Administration/Management, B
Human Resources Management/Personnel Administration, B
Information Technology, AB
Legal Assistant/Paralegal, AB
Organizational Management, M

PENN COMMERCIAL BUSINESS AND TECHNICAL SCHOOL

Administrative Assistant and Secretarial Science, A
Business Administration and Management, A
Computer Systems Networking and Telecommunications, A
Computer Technology/Computer Systems Technology, A
Drafting and Design Technology/Technician, A
Heating, Air Conditioning and Refrigeration Technology/Technician, A
Information Technology, A
Legal Administrative Assistant/Secretary, A
Medical Administrative Assistant/Secretary, A
Medical Office Assistant/Specialist, A

PENN STATE ABINGTON

Accounting, B
Acting, B
Actuarial Science, B
Adult and Continuing Education Administration, B
Advertising, B
Aerospace, Aeronautical and Astronautical Engineering, B
African-American/Black Studies, B
Agribusiness, B
Agricultural Business and Management, A
Agricultural Mechanization, B
Agricultural and Extension Education Services, B
Agricultural/Biological Engineering and Bioengineering, B
Agriculture, B
Agronomy and Crop Science, B
American/United States Studies/Civilization, B
Animal Sciences, B
Anthropology, B
Applied Economics, B

Archeology, B
Architectural Engineering, B
Art History, Criticism and Conservation, B
Art Teacher Education, B
Art/Art Studies, General, B
Astronomy, B
Atmospheric Sciences and Meteorology, B
Biochemistry, B
Biological and Biomedical Sciences, B
Biological and Physical Sciences, B
Biology Technician/BioTechnology Laboratory Technician, B
Biology/Biological Sciences, B
Biomedical/Medical Engineering, B
Business/Commerce, AB
Business/Corporate Communications, B
Business/Managerial Economics, B
Chemical Engineering, B
Chemistry, B
Civil Engineering, B
Classics and Classical Languages, Literatures, and Linguistics, B
Communication Disorders, B
Communication Studies/Speech Communication and Rhetoric, B
Communication, Journalism and Related Programs, B
Comparative Literature, B
Computer Engineering, B
Computer and Information Sciences, B
Criminal Justice/Law Enforcement Administration, B
Criminal Justice/Safety Studies, B
East Asian Studies, B
Economics, B
Electrical, Electronics and Communications Engineering, B
Elementary Education and Teaching, B
Engineering Science, B
English Language and Literature, B
Environmental/Environmental Health Engineering, B
Film/Cinema Studies, B
Finance, B
Food Science, B
Foreign Language Teacher Education, B
Forest Sciences and Biology, B
Forestry Technology/Technician, B
French Language and Literature, B
Geography, B
Geological and Earth Sciences/Geosciences, B
Geology/Earth Science, B
German Language and Literature, B
Graphic Design, B
Health/Health Care Administration/Management, B
History, B
Horticultural Science, B
Hospitality Administration/Management, B
Human Development and Family Studies, AB
Human Nutrition, B
Industrial Engineering, B
Information Science/Studies, AB
International Relations and Affairs, B
Italian Language and Literature, B
Japanese Language and Literature, B
Jewish/Judaic Studies, B
Journalism, B
Kinesiology and Exercise Science, B
Labor and Industrial Relations, B
Landscaping and Groundskeeping, B
Latin American Studies, B
Liberal Arts and Sciences Studies and Humanities, AB
Management Information Systems and Services, B
Marketing/Marketing Management, B
Mathematics, B
Mechanical Engineering, B
Medical Microbiology and Bacteriology, B
Medieval and Renaissance Studies, B
Mining and Mineral Engineering, B
Natural Resources and Conservation, B
Nuclear Engineering, B
Organizational Behavior Studies, B
Parks, Recreation and Leisure Facilities Management, B
Petroleum Engineering, B
Philosophy, B
Physics, B

Political Science and Government, B
Pre-Medicine/Pre-Medical Studies, B
Psychology, B
Rehabilitation and Therapeutic Professions, B
Religion/Religious Studies, B
Russian Language and Literature, B
Secondary Education and Teaching, B
Sociology, B
Soil Science and Agronomy, B
Spanish Language and Literature, B
Special Education and Teaching, B
Statistics, B
Technical Theatre/Theatre Design and Technology, B
Turf and Turfgrass Management, B
Visual and Performing Arts, B
Women's Studies, B

PENN STATE ALTOONA

Accounting, B
Acting, B
Actuarial Science, B
Adult and Continuing Education Administration, B
Advertising, B
Aerospace, Aeronautical and Astronautical Engineering, B
African-American/Black Studies, B
Agribusiness, B
Agricultural Business and Management, A
Agricultural Mechanization, B
Agricultural and Extension Education Services, B
Agriculture, B
Agronomy and Crop Science, B
Animal Sciences, B
Anthropology, B
Archeology, B
Architectural Engineering, B
Art History, Criticism and Conservation, B
Art Teacher Education, B
Art/Art Studies, General, B
Astronomy, B
Atmospheric Sciences and Meteorology, B
Biochemistry, B
Biological and Biomedical Sciences, B
Biological and Physical Sciences, AB
Biology Technician/BioTechnology Laboratory Technician, B
Biomedical Technology/Technician, A
Biomedical/Medical Engineering, B
Business/Commerce, AB
Business/Managerial Economics, B
Chemical Engineering, B
Chemistry, B
Civil Engineering, B
Classics and Classical Languages, Literatures, and Linguistics, B
Communication Disorders, B
Communication Studies/Speech Communication and Rhetoric, B
Communication, Journalism and Related Programs, B
Comparative Literature, B
Computer Engineering, B
Computer and Information Sciences, B
Criminal Justice/Law Enforcement Administration, B
Criminal Justice/Safety Studies, AB
Design and Applied Arts, B
Development Economics and International Development, B
East Asian Studies, B
Economics, B
Educational Assessment, Evaluation, and Research, B
Electrical, Electronic and Communications Engineering Technology/Technician, A
Electrical, Electronics and Communications Engineering, B
Elementary Education and Teaching, B
Engineering, B
Engineering Science, B
English Language and Literature, B
Environmental Studies, B
Environmental/Environmental Health Engineering, B
Film/Cinema Studies, B
Finance, B

Food Science, B
Foreign Language Teacher Education, B
Forensic Science and Technology, B
Forest Sciences and Biology, B
Forestry Technology/Technician, B
French Language and Literature, B
Geography, B
Geological and Earth Sciences/Geosciences, B
Geology/Earth Science, B
German Language and Literature, B
Graphic Design, B
Health/Health Care Administration/Management, B
History, B
Horticultural Science, B
Hospitality Administration/Management, B
Human Development and Family Studies, AB
Human Nutrition, B
Industrial Engineering, B
Information Science/Studies, AB
International Relations and Affairs, B
Italian Language and Literature, B
Japanese Language and Literature, B
Jewish/Judaic Studies, B
Journalism, B
Kinesiology and Exercise Science, B
Labor and Industrial Relations, B
Landscaping and Groundskeeping, B
Latin American Studies, B
Liberal Arts and Sciences Studies and Humanities, AB
Management Information Systems and Services, B
Marketing/Marketing Management, B
Mathematics, B
Mechanical Engineering, B
Mechanical Engineering/Mechanical Technology/Technician, A
Medical Microbiology and Bacteriology, B
Medieval and Renaissance Studies, B
Metallurgical Technology/Technician, A
Mining and Mineral Engineering, B
Music, B
Natural Resources and Conservation, B
Nuclear Engineering, B
Organizational Behavior Studies, B
Parks, Recreation and Leisure Facilities Management, B
Petroleum Engineering, B
Philosophy, B
Physics, B
Political Science and Government, B
Pre-Medicine/Pre-Medical Studies, B
Psychology, B
Rehabilitation and Therapeutic Professions, B
Religion/Religious Studies, B
Russian Language and Literature, B
Secondary Education and Teaching, B
Security and Protective Services, B
Sociology, B
Soil Science and Agronomy, B
Spanish Language and Literature, B
Special Education and Teaching, B
Statistics, B
Technical Theatre/Theatre Design and Technology, B
Turf and Turfgrass Management, B
Visual and Performing Arts, B
Women's Studies, B

PENN STATE BEAVER

Accounting, B
Acting, B
Actuarial Science, B
Adult and Continuing Education Administration, B
Advertising, B
Aerospace, Aeronautical and Astronautical Engineering, B
African-American/Black Studies, B
Agribusiness, B
Agricultural Business and Management, A
Agricultural Mechanization, B
Agricultural and Extension Education Services, B
Agricultural/Biological Engineering and Bioengineering, B
Agriculture, B
Agronomy and Crop Science, B
Animal Sciences, B

Anthropology, B
Applied Economics, B
Archeology, B
Architectural Engineering, B
Art History, Criticism and Conservation, B
Art Teacher Education, B
Art/Art Studies, General, B
Astronomy, B
Atmospheric Sciences and Meteorology, B
Biochemistry, B
Biological and Biomedical Sciences, B
Biological and Physical Sciences, AB
Biology Technician/BioTechnology Laboratory Technician, B
Biology/Biological Sciences, B
Biomedical/Medical Engineering, B
Business Administration and Management, B
Business/Commerce, A
Business/Managerial Economics, B
Chemical Engineering, B
Chemistry, B
Civil Engineering, B
Classics and Classical Languages, Literatures, and Linguistics, B
Communication Disorders, B
Communication Studies/Speech Communication and Rhetoric, B
Communication, Journalism and Related Programs, B
Comparative Literature, B
Computer Engineering, B
Computer and Information Sciences, B
Criminal Justice/Law Enforcement Administration, B
East Asian Studies, B
Economics, B
Electrical, Electronics and Communications Engineering, B
Elementary Education and Teaching, B
Engineering Science, B
English Language and Literature, B
Environmental/Environmental Health Engineering, B
Film/Cinema Studies, B
Finance, B
Food Science, B
Foreign Language Teacher Education, B
Forest Sciences and Biology, B
Forestry Technology/Technician, B
French Language and Literature, B
Geography, B
Geological and Earth Sciences/Geosciences, B
Geology/Earth Science, B
German Language and Literature, B
Graphic Design, B
Health/Health Care Administration/Management, B
History, B
Horticultural Science, B
Hospitality Administration/Management, AB
Human Development and Family Studies, B
Human Nutrition, B
Industrial Engineering, B
Information Science/Studies, B
International Relations and Affairs, B
Italian Language and Literature, B
Japanese Language and Literature, B
Jewish/Judaic Studies, B
Journalism, B
Kinesiology and Exercise Science, B
Labor and Industrial Relations, B
Landscaping and Groundskeeping, B
Latin American Studies, B
Liberal Arts and Sciences Studies and Humanities, AB
Logistics and Materials Management, B
Management Information Systems and Services, B
Marketing/Marketing Management, B
Mathematics, B
Mechanical Engineering, B
Medical Microbiology and Bacteriology, B
Medieval and Renaissance Studies, B
Mining and Mineral Engineering, B
Music, B
Natural Resources and Conservation, B
Nuclear Engineering, B
Organizational Behavior Studies, B
Parks, Recreation and Leisure Facilities Management, B

Petroleum Engineering, B
Philosophy, B
Physics, B
Political Science and Government, B
Pre-Medicine/Pre-Medical Studies, B
Psychology, B
Rehabilitation and Therapeutic Professions, B
Religion/Religious Studies, B
Russian Language and Literature, B
Secondary Education and Teaching, B
Sociology, B
Soil Science and Agronomy, B
Spanish Language and Literature, B
Special Education and Teaching, B
Statistics, B
Technical Theatre/Theatre Design and Technology, B
Toxicology, B
Turf and Turfgrass Management, B
Visual and Performing Arts, B
Women's Studies, B

PENN STATE BERKS

Accounting, B
Acting, B
Actuarial Science, B
Adult and Continuing Education Administration, B
Advertising, B
Aerospace, Aeronautical and Astronautical Engineering, B
African-American/Black Studies, B
Agribusiness, B
Agricultural Business and Management, A
Agricultural Mechanization, B
Agricultural and Extension Education Services, B
Agriculture, B
Agronomy and Crop Science, B
American/United States Studies/Civilization, B
Animal Sciences, B
Anthropology, B
Archeology, B
Architectural Engineering, B
Art History, Criticism and Conservation, B
Art Teacher Education, B
Art/Art Studies, General, B
Astronomy, B
Atmospheric Sciences and Meteorology, B
Biochemistry, B
Biological and Biomedical Sciences, B
Biological and Physical Sciences, B
Biology Technician/BioTechnology Laboratory Technician, B
Biology/Biological Sciences, B
Biomedical Technology/Technician, A
Biomedical/Medical Engineering, B
Business/Commerce, AB
Business/Managerial Economics, B
Chemical Engineering, B
Chemistry, B
Civil Engineering, B
Classics and Classical Languages, Literatures, and Linguistics, B
Communication Disorders, B
Communication Studies/Speech Communication and Rhetoric, B
Communication, Journalism and Related Programs, B
Comparative Literature, B
Computer Engineering, B
Computer and Information Sciences, B
Criminal Justice/Law Enforcement Administration, B
Design and Applied Arts, B
Development Economics and International Development, B
East Asian Studies, B
Economics, B
Educational Assessment, Evaluation, and Research, B
Electrical and Electronic Engineering Technologies/Technicians, B
Electrical, Electronic and Communications Engineering Technology/Technician, A
Electrical, Electronics and Communications Engineering, B
Elementary Education and Teaching, B
Engineering, B

Engineering Science, B
English Language and Literature, B
Environmental/Environmental Health Engineering, B
Film/Cinema Studies, B
Finance, B
Food Science, B
Foreign Language Teacher Education, B
Foreign Languages and Literatures, B
Forensic Science and Technology, B
Forest Sciences and Biology, B
Forestry Technology/Technician, B
French Language and Literature, B
Geography, B
Geological and Earth Sciences/Geosciences, B
Geology/Earth Science, B
German Language and Literature, B
Graphic Design, B
Health/Health Care Administration/Management, B
History, B
Horticultural Science, B
Hospitality Administration/Management, AB
Human Development and Family Studies, AB
Human Nutrition, B
Industrial Engineering, B
Information Science/Studies, AB
International Relations and Affairs, B
Italian Language and Literature, B
Japanese Language and Literature, B
Jewish/Judaic Studies, B
Journalism, B
Kinesiology and Exercise Science, B
Labor and Industrial Relations, B
Landscaping and Groundskeeping, B
Latin American Studies, B
Liberal Arts and Sciences Studies and Humanities, AB
Management Information Systems and Services, B
Marketing/Marketing Management, B
Mathematics, B
Mechanical Engineering, B
Mechanical Engineering/Mechanical Technology/Technician, A
Medical Microbiology and Bacteriology, B
Medieval and Renaissance Studies, B
Metallurgical Technology/Technician, A
Mining and Mineral Engineering, B
Music, B
Natural Resources and Conservation, B
Nuclear Engineering, B
Occupational Therapist Assistant, A
Organizational Behavior Studies, B
Parks, Recreation and Leisure Facilities Management, B
Pathology/Experimental Pathology, B
Petroleum Engineering, B
Philosophy, B
Physics, B
Political Science and Government, B
Pre-Medicine/Pre-Medical Studies, B
Psychology, B
Rehabilitation and Therapeutic Professions, B
Religion/Religious Studies, B
Russian Language and Literature, B
Secondary Education and Teaching, B
Security and Protective Services, B
Sociology, B
Soil Science and Agronomy, B
Spanish Language and Literature, B
Special Education and Teaching, B
Statistics, B
Technical Theatre/Theatre Design and Technology, B
Toxicology, B
Turf and Turfgrass Management, B
Visual and Performing Arts, B
Women's Studies, B

PENN STATE BRANDYWINE

Accounting, B
Acting, B
Actuarial Science, B
Adult and Continuing Education Administration, B
Advertising, B
Aerospace, Aeronautical and Astronautical Engineering, B
African-American/Black Studies, B

Agribusiness, B
Agricultural Business and Management, A
Agricultural Mechanization, B
Agricultural and Extension Education Services, B
Agricultural/Biological Engineering and Bioengineering, B
Agriculture, B
Agronomy and Crop Science, B
American/United States Studies/Civilization, B
Animal Sciences, B
Anthropology, B
Applied Economics, B
Archeology, B
Architectural Engineering, B
Art History, Criticism and Conservation, B
Art Teacher Education, B
Art/Art Studies, General, B
Astronomy, B
Atmospheric Sciences and Meteorology, B
Biochemistry, B
Biological and Biomedical Sciences, B
Biological and Physical Sciences, B
Biology Technician/BioTechnology Laboratory Technician, B
Biology/Biological Sciences, B
Biomedical/Medical Engineering, B
Business Administration and Management, B
Business/Commerce, A
Business/Managerial Economics, B
Chemical Engineering, B
Chemistry, B
Civil Engineering, B
Classics and Classical Languages, Literatures, and Linguistics, B
Communication Disorders, B
Communication Studies/Speech Communication and Rhetoric, B
Communication, Journalism and Related Programs, A
Comparative Literature, B
Computer Engineering, B
Computer and Information Sciences, B
Criminal Justice/Law Enforcement Administration, B
East Asian Studies, B
Economics, B
Electrical, Electronic and Communications Engineering Technology/Technician, A
Electrical, Electronics and Communications Engineering, B
Elementary Education and Teaching, B
Engineering Science, B
English Language and Literature, B
Environmental/Environmental Health Engineering, B
Film/Cinema Studies, B
Finance, B
Food Science, B
Foreign Language Teacher Education, B
Forest Sciences and Biology, B
Forestry Technology/Technician, B
French Language and Literature, B
Geography, B
Geological and Earth Sciences/Geosciences, B
Geology/Earth Science, B
German Language and Literature, B
Graphic Design, B
Health/Health Care Administration/Management, B
History, B
Horticultural Science, B
Hospitality Administration/Management, B
Human Development and Family Studies, AB
Human Nutrition, B
Industrial Engineering, B
Information Science/Studies, B
International Relations and Affairs, B
Italian Language and Literature, B
Japanese Language and Literature, B
Jewish/Judaic Studies, B
Journalism, B
Kinesiology and Exercise Science, B
Labor and Industrial Relations, B
Landscape Architecture, B
Landscaping and Groundskeeping, B
Latin American Studies, B
Liberal Arts and Sciences Studies and Humanities, AB
Logistics and Materials Management, B

Management Information Systems and Services, B
Marketing/Marketing Management, B
Mathematics, B
Mechanical Engineering, B
Medical Microbiology and Bacteriology, B
Medieval and Renaissance Studies, B
Mining and Mineral Engineering, B
Music, B
Natural Resources and Conservation, B
Nuclear Engineering, B
Organizational Behavior Studies, B
Parks, Recreation and Leisure Facilities Management, B
Petroleum Engineering, B
Philosophy, B
Physics, B
Political Science and Government, B
Pre-Medicine/Pre-Medical Studies, B
Psychology, B
Rehabilitation and Therapeutic Professions, B
Religion/Religious Studies, B
Russian Language and Literature, B
Secondary Education and Teaching, B
Sociology, B
Soil Science and Agronomy, B
Spanish Language and Literature, B
Special Education and Teaching, B
Statistics, B
Technical Theatre/Theatre Design and Technology, B
Turf and Turfgrass Management, B
Visual and Performing Arts, B
Women's Studies, B

PENN STATE DUBOIS

Accounting, B
Acting, B
Actuarial Science, B
Adult and Continuing Education Administration, B
Advertising, B
Aerospace, Aeronautical and Astronautical Engineering, B
African-American/Black Studies, B
Agribusiness, B
Agricultural Business and Management, A
Agricultural Mechanization, B
Agricultural and Extension Education Services, B
Agricultural/Biological Engineering and Bioengineering, B
Agriculture, B
Agronomy and Crop Science, B
Animal Sciences, B
Anthropology, B
Applied Economics, B
Archeology, B
Architectural Engineering, B
Art History, Criticism and Conservation, B
Art Teacher Education, B
Art/Art Studies, General, B
Astronomy, B
Atmospheric Sciences and Meteorology, B
Biochemistry, B
Biological and Biomedical Sciences, B
Biological and Physical Sciences, AB
Biology Technician/BioTechnology Laboratory Technician, B
Biology/Biological Sciences, B
Biomedical Technology/Technician, A
Biomedical/Medical Engineering, B
Business Administration and Management, B
Business/Commerce, A
Business/Managerial Economics, B
Chemical Engineering, B
Chemistry, B
Civil Engineering, B
Classics and Classical Languages, Literatures, and Linguistics, B
Clinical/Medical Laboratory Technician, B
Communication Disorders, B
Communication Studies/Speech Communication and Rhetoric, B
Communication, Journalism and Related Programs, B
Comparative Literature, B
Computer Engineering, B
Computer and Information Sciences, B

Criminal Justice/Law Enforcement Administration, B
East Asian Studies, B
Economics, B
Electrical, Electronic and Communications Engineering Technology/Technician, A
Electrical, Electronics and Communications Engineering, B
Elementary Education and Teaching, B
Engineering Science, B
English Language and Literature, B
Environmental/Environmental Health Engineering, B
Film/Cinema Studies, B
Finance, B
Food Science, B
Foreign Language Teacher Education, B
Forest Sciences and Biology, B
Forestry Technology/Technician, B
French Language and Literature, B
Geography, B
Geological and Earth Sciences/Geosciences, B
Geology/Earth Science, B
German Language and Literature, B
Graphic Design, B
Health/Health Care Administration/Management, B
History, B
Horticultural Science, B
Hospitality Administration/Management, B
Human Development and Family Studies, AB
Human Nutrition, B
Industrial Engineering, B
Information Science/Studies, AB
International Business/Trade/Commerce, B
International Relations and Affairs, B
Italian Language and Literature, B
Japanese Language and Literature, B
Jewish/Judaic Studies, B
Journalism, B
Kinesiology and Exercise Science, B
Labor and Industrial Relations, B
Landscaping and Groundskeeping, B
Latin American Studies, B
Liberal Arts and Sciences Studies and Humanities, AB
Management Information Systems and Services, B
Marketing/Marketing Management, B
Mathematics, B
Mechanical Engineering, B
Mechanical Engineering/Mechanical Technology/Technician, A
Medical Microbiology and Bacteriology, B
Medieval and Renaissance Studies, B
Metallurgical Technology/Technician, A
Mining and Mineral Engineering, B
Music, B
Natural Resources and Conservation, B
Nuclear Engineering, B
Occupational Therapist Assistant, A
Organizational Behavior Studies, B
Parks, Recreation and Leisure Facilities Management, B
Petroleum Engineering, B
Philosophy, B
Physical Therapist Assistant, A
Physics, B
Political Science and Government, B
Pre-Medicine/Pre-Medical Studies, B
Psychology, B
Rehabilitation and Therapeutic Professions, B
Religion/Religious Studies, B
Russian Language and Literature, B
Secondary Education and Teaching, B
Sociology, B
Soil Science and Agronomy, B
Spanish Language and Literature, B
Special Education and Teaching, B
Statistics, B
Technical Theatre/Theatre Design and Technology, B
Telecommunications Technology/Technician, A
Toxicology, B
Turf and Turfgrass Management, B
Visual and Performing Arts, B
Wildlife and Wildlands Science and Management, A

Women's Studies, B

PENN STATE ERIE, THE BEHREND COLLEGE

Accounting, B
Acting, B
Actuarial Science, B
Adult and Continuing Education Administration, B
Advertising, B
Aerospace, Aeronautical and Astronautical Engineering, B
African-American/Black Studies, B
Agribusiness, B
Agricultural Business and Management, A
Agricultural Mechanization, B
Agricultural and Extension Education Services, B
Agricultural/Biological Engineering and Bioengineering, B
Agriculture, B
Agronomy and Crop Science, B
American/United States Studies/Civilization, B
Animal Sciences, B
Anthropology, B
Applied Economics, B
Archeology, B
Architectural Engineering, B
Art History, Criticism and Conservation, B
Art Teacher Education, B
Art/Art Studies, General, B
Astronomy, B
Atmospheric Sciences and Meteorology, B
Biochemistry, B
Biological and Biomedical Sciences, B
Biological and Physical Sciences, B
Biology Technician/BioTechnology Laboratory Technician, B
Biology/Biological Sciences, B
Biomedical Technology/Technician, A
Biomedical/Medical Engineering, B
Business Administration and Management, B
Business Administration, Management and Operations, M
Business/Commerce, A
Business/Managerial Economics, B
Chemical Engineering, B
Chemistry, B
Civil Engineering, B
Classics and Classical Languages, Literatures, and Linguistics, B
Communication Disorders, B
Communication Studies/Speech Communication and Rhetoric, B
Communication and Media Studies, B
Communication, Journalism and Related Programs, B
Comparative Literature, B
Computer Engineering, B
Computer Science, B
Computer Software Engineering, B
Computer and Information Sciences, B
Criminal Justice/Law Enforcement Administration, B
Criminal Justice/Safety Studies, B
East Asian Studies, B
Economics, B
Electrical, Electronic and Communications Engineering Technology/Technician, AB
Electrical, Electronics and Communications Engineering, B
Elementary Education and Teaching, B
Engineering Science, B
Engineering and Applied Sciences, M
English Language and Literature, B
Environmental/Environmental Health Engineering, B
Film/Cinema Studies, B
Finance, B
Food Science, B
Foreign Language Teacher Education, B
Forest Sciences and Biology, B
Forestry Technology/Technician, B
French Language and Literature, B
Geography, B
Geological and Earth Sciences/Geosciences, B
Geology/Earth Science, B
German Language and Literature, B
Graphic Design, B
Health/Health Care Administration/Management, B

History, B
Horticultural Science, B
Hospitality Administration/Management, B
Human Development and Family Studies, AB
Human Nutrition, B
Industrial Engineering, B
Industrial and Manufacturing Management, M
Information Science/Studies, AB
International Business/Trade/Commerce, B
International Relations and Affairs, B
Italian Language and Literature, B
Japanese Language and Literature, B
Jewish/Judaic Studies, B
Journalism, B
Kinesiology and Exercise Science, B
Labor and Industrial Relations, B
Landscaping and Groundskeeping, B
Latin American Studies, B
Liberal Arts and Sciences Studies and Humanities, AB
Management Information Systems and Services, B
Marketing/Marketing Management, B
Mathematics, B
Mechanical Engineering, B
Mechanical Engineering/Mechanical Technology/Technician, AB
Medical Microbiology and Bacteriology, B
Medieval and Renaissance Studies, B
Metallurgical Technology/Technician, A
Mining and Mineral Engineering, B
Multi-/Interdisciplinary Studies, B
Natural Resources and Conservation, B
Nuclear Engineering, B
Organizational Behavior Studies, B
Parks, Recreation and Leisure Facilities Management, B
Petroleum Engineering, B
Philosophy, B
Physical Sciences, B
Physics, B
Plastics Engineering Technology/Technician, A
Political Science and Government, B
Polymer/Plastics Engineering, B
Pre-Medicine/Pre-Medical Studies, B
Project Management, M
Psychology, B
Quality Management, M
Rehabilitation and Therapeutic Professions, B
Religion/Religious Studies, B
Russian Language and Literature, B
Secondary Education and Teaching, B
Sociology, B
Soil Science and Agronomy, B
Spanish Language and Literature, B
Special Education and Teaching, B
Statistics, B
Technical Theatre/Theatre Design and Technology, B
Turf and Turfgrass Management, B
Visual and Performing Arts, B
Women's Studies, B

PENN STATE FAYETTE, THE EBERLY CAMPUS

Accounting, B
Acting, B
Actuarial Science, B
Adult and Continuing Education Administration, B
Advertising, B
Aerospace, Aeronautical and Astronautical Engineering, B
African-American/Black Studies, B
Agribusiness, B
Agricultural Business and Management, A
Agricultural Mechanization, B
Agricultural and Extension Education Services, B
Agricultural/Biological Engineering and Bioengineering, B
Agriculture, B
Agronomy and Crop Science, B
Animal Sciences, B
Anthropology, B
Applied Economics, B
Archeology, B
Architectural Engineering, B
Architectural Engineering Technology/Technician, A

Art History, Criticism and Conservation, B
Art Teacher Education, B
Art/Art Studies, General, B
Astronomy, B
Atmospheric Sciences and Meteorology, B
Biochemistry, B
Biological and Biomedical Sciences, B
Biological and Physical Sciences, AB
Biology Technician/BioTechnology Laboratory Technician, B
Biology/Biological Sciences, B
Biomedical Technology/Technician, A
Biomedical/Medical Engineering, B
Business Administration and Management, B
Business/Commerce, A
Business/Managerial Economics, B
Chemical Engineering, B
Chemistry, B
Civil Engineering, B
Classics and Classical Languages, Literatures, and Linguistics, B
Communication Disorders, B
Communication Studies/Speech Communication and Rhetoric, B
Communication, Journalism and Related Programs, B
Comparative Literature, B
Computer Engineering, B
Computer and Information Sciences, B
Criminal Justice/Law Enforcement Administration, B
Criminal Justice/Safety Studies, B
East Asian Studies, B
Economics, B
Electrical, Electronic and Communications Engineering Technology/Technician, A
Electrical, Electronics and Communications Engineering, B
Elementary Education and Teaching, B
Engineering Science, B
English Language and Literature, B
Environmental/Environmental Health Engineering, B
Film/Cinema Studies, B
Finance, B
Food Science, B
Foreign Language Teacher Education, B
Forest Sciences and Biology, B
Forestry Technology/Technician, B
French Language and Literature, B
Geography, B
Geological and Earth Sciences/Geosciences, B
Geology/Earth Science, B
German Language and Literature, B
Graphic Design, B
Health/Health Care Administration/Management, B
History, B
Horticultural Science, B
Hospitality Administration/Management, B
Human Development and Family Studies, AB
Human Nutrition, B
Industrial Engineering, B
Information Science/Studies, B
International Relations and Affairs, B
Italian Language and Literature, B
Japanese Language and Literature, B
Jewish/Judaic Studies, B
Journalism, B
Kinesiology and Exercise Science, B
Labor and Industrial Relations, B
Landscaping and Groundskeeping, B
Latin American Studies, B
Liberal Arts and Sciences Studies and Humanities, AB
Logistics and Materials Management, B
Management Information Systems and Services, B
Manufacturing Engineering, A
Marketing/Marketing Management, B
Mathematics, B
Mechanical Engineering, B
Medical Microbiology and Bacteriology, B
Medieval and Renaissance Studies, B
Metallurgical Technology/Technician, A
Mining and Mineral Engineering, B
Natural Resources and Conservation, B
Nuclear Engineering, B
Organizational Behavior Studies, B

Parks, Recreation and Leisure Facilities Management, B
Petroleum Engineering, B
Philosophy, B
Physics, B
Political Science and Government, B
Pre-Medicine/Pre-Medical Studies, B
Psychology, B
Rehabilitation and Therapeutic Professions, B
Religion/Religious Studies, B
Russian Language and Literature, B
Secondary Education and Teaching, B
Sociology, B
Soil Science and Agronomy, B
Spanish Language and Literature, B
Special Education and Teaching, B
Statistics, B
Technical Theatre/Theatre Design and Technology, B
Telecommunications Technology/Technician, A
Toxicology, B
Turf and Turfgrass Management, B
Visual and Performing Arts, B
Women's Studies, B

PENN STATE GREATER ALLEGHENY

Accounting, B
Acting, B
Actuarial Science, B
Adult and Continuing Education Administration, B
Advertising, B
Aerospace, Aeronautical and Astronautical Engineering, B
African-American/Black Studies, B
Agribusiness, B
Agricultural Business and Management, A
Agricultural Mechanization, B
Agricultural and Extension Education Services, B
Agricultural/Biological Engineering and Bioengineering, B
Agriculture, B
Agronomy and Crop Science, B
Animal Sciences, B
Anthropology, B
Applied Economics, B
Archeology, B
Architectural Engineering, B
Art History, Criticism and Conservation, B
Art Teacher Education, B
Art/Art Studies, General, B
Astronomy, B
Atmospheric Sciences and Meteorology, B
Biochemistry, B
Biological and Biomedical Sciences, B
Biological and Physical Sciences, AB
Biology Technician/BioTechnology Laboratory Technician, B
Biology/Biological Sciences, B
Biomedical/Medical Engineering, B
Business Administration and Management, B
Business/Commerce, A
Business/Managerial Economics, B
Chemical Engineering, B
Chemistry, B
Civil Engineering, B
Classics and Classical Languages, Literatures, and Linguistics, B
Communication Disorders, B
Communication Studies/Speech Communication and Rhetoric, B
Communication, Journalism and Related Programs, B
Comparative Literature, B
Computer Engineering, B
Computer and Information Sciences, B
Criminal Justice/Law Enforcement Administration, B
East Asian Studies, B
Economics, B
Electrical, Electronics and Communications Engineering, B
Elementary Education and Teaching, B
Engineering Science, B
English Language and Literature, B
Environmental/Environmental Health Engineering, B
Film/Cinema Studies, B
Finance, B

Food Science, B
Foreign Language Teacher Education, B
Forest Sciences and Biology, B
Forestry Technology/Technician, B
French Language and Literature, B
Geography, B
Geological and Earth Sciences/Geosciences, B
Geology/Earth Science, B
German Language and Literature, B
Graphic Design, B
Health/Health Care Administration/Management, B
History, B
Horticultural Science, B
Hospitality Administration/Management, B
Human Development and Family Studies, B
Human Nutrition, B
Industrial Engineering, B
Information Science/Studies, B
International Relations and Affairs, B
Italian Language and Literature, B
Japanese Language and Literature, B
Jewish/Judaic Studies, B
Journalism, B
Kinesiology and Exercise Science, B
Labor and Industrial Relations, B
Landscaping and Groundskeeping, B
Latin American Studies, B
Liberal Arts and Sciences Studies and Humanities, AB
Logistics and Materials Management, B
Management Information Systems and Services, B
Manufacturing Engineering, A
Marketing/Marketing Management, B
Mathematics, B
Mechanical Engineering, B
Medical Microbiology and Bacteriology, B
Medieval and Renaissance Studies, B
Mining and Mineral Engineering, B
Music, B
Natural Resources and Conservation, B
Nuclear Engineering, B
Organizational Behavior Studies, B
Parks, Recreation and Leisure Facilities Management, B
Petroleum Engineering, B
Philosophy, B
Physics, B
Political Science and Government, B
Pre-Medicine/Pre-Medical Studies, B
Psychology, B
Rehabilitation and Therapeutic Professions, B
Religion/Religious Studies, B
Russian Language and Literature, B
Secondary Education and Teaching, B
Sociology, B
Soil Science and Agronomy, B
Spanish Language and Literature, B
Special Education and Teaching, B
Statistics, B
Technical Theatre/Theatre Design and Technology, B
Toxicology, B
Turf and Turfgrass Management, B
Visual and Performing Arts, B
Women's Studies, B

PENN STATE HARRISBURG

American/United States Studies/Civilization, BMD
Applied Behavior Analysis, M
Applied Mathematics, B
Applied Psychology, M
Business Administration and Management, B
Business Administration, Management and Operations, M
Business/Commerce, A
Civil Engineering, B
Clinical Psychology, M
Communication Studies/Speech Communication and Rhetoric, B
Communication and Media Studies, M
Community Psychology, M
Computer Science, M
Computer and Information Sciences, B
Criminal Justice/Safety Studies, B
Criminology, M
Curriculum and Instruction, M

Developmental Education, M
Education, MDO
Electrical Engineering, M
Electrical, Electronics and Communications Engineering, B
Elementary Education and Teaching, B
Engineering Management, M
Engineering and Applied Sciences, MO
English Language and Literature, B
Environmental Engineering Technology/Environmental Technology, M
Environmental Sciences, MO
Environmental/Environmental Health Engineering, B
Finance, B
Finance and Banking, O
Folklore, O
Health Education, M
Health Services Administration, M
Historic Preservation and Conservation, O
Human Development and Family Studies, B
Human Resources Management and Services, O
Humanities/Humanistic Studies, BMDO
Information Science/Studies, B
International Business/Trade/Commerce, B
Liberal Arts and Sciences Studies and Humanities, A
Management Information Systems and Services, BM
Marketing/Marketing Management, B
Mechanical Engineering, B
Multi-/Interdisciplinary Studies, B
Museology/Museum Studies, O
Non-Profit/Public/Organizational Management, O
Organizational Behavior Studies, B
Psychology, BMDO
Public Administration, MDO
Public Affairs, MDO
Public Policy Analysis, BO
Reading Teacher Education, M
Social Studies Teacher Education, B
Sociology, B
Structural Engineering, BO
Writing, O

PENN STATE HAZLETON

Accounting, B
Acting, B
Actuarial Science, B
Adult and Continuing Education Administration, B
Advertising, B
Aerospace, Aeronautical and Astronautical Engineering, B
African-American/Black Studies, B
Agribusiness, B
Agricultural Business and Management, A
Agricultural Mechanization, B
Agricultural and Extension Education Services, B
Agricultural/Biological Engineering and Bioengineering, B
Agriculture, B
Agronomy and Crop Science, B
Animal Sciences, B
Anthropology, B
Applied Economics, B
Archeology, B
Architectural Engineering, B
Art History, Criticism and Conservation, B
Art Teacher Education, B
Art/Art Studies, General, B
Astronomy, B
Atmospheric Sciences and Meteorology, B
Biochemistry, B
Biological and Biomedical Sciences, B
Biological and Physical Sciences, B
Biology Technician/BioTechnology Laboratory Technician, B
Biology/Biological Sciences, B
Biomedical Technology/Technician, A
Biomedical/Medical Engineering, B
Business Administration and Management, B
Business/Commerce, A
Business/Managerial Economics, B
Chemical Engineering, B
Chemistry, B
Civil Engineering, B

Classics and Classical Languages, Literatures, and Linguistics, B
Clinical/Medical Laboratory Technician, A
Communication Disorders, B
Communication Studies/Speech Communication and Rhetoric, B
Communication, Journalism and Related Programs, B
Comparative Literature, B
Computer Engineering, B
Computer and Information Sciences, B
Criminal Justice/Law Enforcement Administration, B
East Asian Studies, B
Economics, B
Electrical, Electronic and Communications Engineering Technology/Technician, A
Electrical, Electronics and Communications Engineering, B
Elementary Education and Teaching, B
Engineering Science, B
English Language and Literature, B
Environmental/Environmental Health Engineering, B
Film/Cinema Studies, B
Finance, B
Food Science, B
Forest Sciences and Biology, B
Forestry Technology/Technician, B
French Language and Literature, B
Geography, B
Geological and Earth Sciences/Geosciences, B
Geology/Earth Science, B
German Language and Literature, B
Graphic Design, B
Health/Health Care Administration/Management, B
History, B
Horticultural Science, B
Hospitality Administration/Management, B
Human Development and Family Studies, B
Human Nutrition, B
Industrial Engineering, B
Information Science/Studies, A
International Relations and Affairs, B
Italian Language and Literature, B
Japanese Language and Literature, B
Jewish/Judaic Studies, B
Journalism, B
Kinesiology and Exercise Science, B
Labor and Industrial Relations, B
Landscaping and Groundskeeping, B
Latin American Studies, B
Liberal Arts and Sciences Studies and Humanities, A
Logistics and Materials Management, B
Management Information Systems and Services, B
Manufacturing Engineering, A
Marketing/Marketing Management, B
Mathematics, B
Mechanical Engineering, B
Mechanical Engineering/Mechanical Technology/Technician, A
Medical Microbiology and Bacteriology, B
Medieval and Renaissance Studies, B
Metallurgical Technology/Technician, A
Mining and Mineral Engineering, B
Music, B
Natural Resources and Conservation, B
Nuclear Engineering, B
Organizational Behavior Studies, B
Parks, Recreation and Leisure Facilities Management, B
Petroleum Engineering, B
Philosophy, B
Physical Therapist Assistant, A
Physics, B
Political Science and Government, B
Pre-Medicine/Pre-Medical Studies, B
Psychology, B
Rehabilitation and Therapeutic Professions, B
Religion/Religious Studies, B
Russian Language and Literature, B
Secondary Education and Teaching, B
Sociology, B
Soil Science and Agronomy, B
Spanish Language and Literature, B
Special Education and Teaching, B
Statistics, B

Technical Theatre/Theatre Design and Technology, B
Telecommunications Technology/Technician, A
Toxicology, B
Turf and Turfgrass Management, B
Visual and Performing Arts, B
Women's Studies, B

PENN STATE LEHIGH VALLEY

Accounting, B
Acting, B
Actuarial Science, B
Adult and Continuing Education Administration, B
Advertising, B
Aerospace, Aeronautical and Astronautical Engineering, B
African-American/Black Studies, B
Agribusiness, B
Agricultural Business and Management, A
Agricultural Mechanization, B
Agricultural and Extension Education Services, B
Agricultural/Biological Engineering and Bioengineering, B
Agriculture, B
American/United States Studies/Civilization, B
Animal Sciences, B
Anthropology, B
Applied Economics, B
Archeology, B
Architectural Engineering, B
Art History, Criticism and Conservation, B
Art Teacher Education, B
Art/Art Studies, General, B
Astronomy, B
Atmospheric Sciences and Meteorology, B
Biochemistry, B
Biological and Biomedical Sciences, B
Biological and Physical Sciences, B
Biology Technician/BioTechnology Laboratory Technician, B
Biology/Biological Sciences, B
Biomedical/Medical Engineering, B
Business/Commerce, AB
Business/Managerial Economics, B
Chemical Engineering, B
Chemistry, B
Civil Engineering, B
Classics and Classical Languages, Literatures, and Linguistics, B
Communication Disorders, B
Communication Studies/Speech Communication and Rhetoric, B
Communication, Journalism and Related Programs, B
Comparative Literature, B
Computer Engineering, B
Computer and Information Sciences, B
Criminal Justice/Law Enforcement Administration, B
East Asian Studies, B
Economics, B
Electrical, Electronics and Communications Engineering, B
Elementary Education and Teaching, B
Engineering Science, B
English Language and Literature, B
Environmental/Environmental Health Engineering, B
Film/Cinema Studies, B
Finance, B
Food Science, B
Foreign Languages and Literatures, B
Forest Sciences and Biology, B
Forestry Technology/Technician, B
French Language and Literature, B
Geography, B
Geological and Earth Sciences/Geosciences, B
Geology/Earth Science, B
German Language and Literature, B
Graphic Design, B
Health/Health Care Administration/Management, B
History, B
Horticultural Science, B
Hospitality Administration/Management, B
Human Development and Family Studies, B
Human Nutrition, B
Industrial Engineering, B
Information Science/Studies, AB

International Business/Trade/Commerce, B
International Relations and Affairs, B
Italian Language and Literature, B
Japanese Language and Literature, B
Jewish/Judaic Studies, B
Journalism, B
Kinesiology and Exercise Science, B
Labor and Industrial Relations, B
Landscape Architecture, B
Landscaping and Groundskeeping, B
Latin American Studies, B
Liberal Arts and Sciences Studies and Humanities, AB
Logistics and Materials Management, B
Management Information Systems and Services, B
Management Sciences and Quantitative Methods, B
Marketing/Marketing Management, B
Mathematics, B
Mechanical Engineering, B
Medical Microbiology and Bacteriology, B
Medieval and Renaissance Studies, B
Mining and Mineral Engineering, B
Natural Resources and Conservation, B
Nuclear Engineering, B
Organizational Behavior Studies, B
Parks, Recreation and Leisure Facilities Management, B
Petroleum Engineering, B
Philosophy, B
Physics, B
Political Science and Government, B
Pre-Medicine/Pre-Medical Studies, B
Psychology, B
Rehabilitation and Therapeutic Professions, B
Religion/Religious Studies, B
Russian Language and Literature, B
Secondary Education and Teaching, B
Sociology, B
Soil Science and Agronomy, B
Spanish Language and Literature, B
Special Education and Teaching, B
Statistics, B
Technical Theatre/Theatre Design and Technology, B
Turf and Turfgrass Management, B
Visual and Performing Arts, B
Women's Studies, B

PENN STATE MONT ALTO

Accounting, B
Acting, B
Actuarial Science, B
Adult and Continuing Education Administration, B
Advertising, B
Aerospace, Aeronautical and Astronautical Engineering, B
African-American/Black Studies, B
Agribusiness, B
Agricultural Business and Management, A
Agricultural Mechanization, B
Agricultural and Extension Education Services, B
Agricultural/Biological Engineering and Bioengineering, B
Agriculture, B
Agronomy and Crop Science, B
Animal Sciences, B
Anthropology, B
Applied Economics, B
Archeology, B
Architectural Engineering, B
Art History, Criticism and Conservation, B
Art Teacher Education, B
Art/Art Studies, General, B
Astronomy, B
Atmospheric Sciences and Meteorology, B
Biochemistry, B
Biological and Biomedical Sciences, B
Biological and Physical Sciences, B
Biology Technician/BioTechnology Laboratory Technician, B
Biology/Biological Sciences, B
Biomedical/Medical Engineering, B
Business Administration and Management, B
Business/Commerce, A
Business/Managerial Economics, B
Chemical Engineering, B

Chemistry, B
Civil Engineering, B
Classics and Classical Languages, Literatures, and Linguistics, B
Communication Disorders, B
Communication Studies/Speech Communication and Rhetoric, B
Communication, Journalism and Related Programs, B
Comparative Literature, B
Computer Engineering, B
Computer and Information Sciences, B
Criminal Justice/Law Enforcement Administration, B
East Asian Studies, B
Economics, B
Electrical, Electronics and Communications Engineering, B
Elementary Education and Teaching, B
Engineering Science, B
English Language and Literature, B
Environmental/Environmental Health Engineering, B
Film/Cinema Studies, B
Finance, B
Food Science, B
Foreign Language Teacher Education, B
Forest Sciences and Biology, B
Forestry Technology/Technician, AB
French Language and Literature, B
Geography, B
Geological and Earth Sciences/Geosciences, B
Geology/Earth Science, B
German Language and Literature, B
Graphic Design, B
Health/Health Care Administration/Management, B
History, B
Horticultural Science, B
Hospitality Administration/Management, B
Human Development and Family Studies, AB
Human Nutrition, B
Industrial Engineering, B
Information Science/Studies, B
International Relations and Affairs, B
Italian Language and Literature, B
Japanese Language and Literature, B
Jewish/Judaic Studies, B
Journalism, B
Kinesiology and Exercise Science, B
Labor and Industrial Relations, B
Landscaping and Groundskeeping, B
Latin American Studies, B
Liberal Arts and Sciences Studies and Humanities, AB
Management Information Systems and Services, B
Marketing/Marketing Management, B
Mathematics, B
Mechanical Engineering, B
Medical Microbiology and Bacteriology, B
Medieval and Renaissance Studies, B
Mining and Mineral Engineering, B
Music, B
Natural Resources and Conservation, B
Nuclear Engineering, B
Occupational Therapist Assistant, A
Occupational Therapy/Therapist, B
Organizational Behavior Studies, B
Parks, Recreation and Leisure Facilities Management, B
Petroleum Engineering, B
Philosophy, B
Physical Therapist Assistant, A
Physics, B
Political Science and Government, B
Pre-Medicine/Pre-Medical Studies, B
Psychology, B
Rehabilitation and Therapeutic Professions, B
Religion/Religious Studies, B
Russian Language and Literature, B
Secondary Education and Teaching, B
Sociology, B
Soil Science and Agronomy, B
Spanish Language and Literature, B
Special Education and Teaching, B
Statistics, B
Technical Theatre/Theatre Design and Technology, B
Toxicology, B

Turf and Turfgrass Management, B
Visual and Performing Arts, B
Women's Studies, B

PENN STATE NEW KENSINGTON

Accounting, B
Acting, B
Actuarial Science, B
Adult and Continuing Education Administration, B
Advertising, B
Aerospace, Aeronautical and Astronautical Engineering, B
African-American/Black Studies, B
Agribusiness, B
Agricultural Business and Management, AB
Agricultural Mechanization, B
Agricultural and Extension Education Services, B
Agricultural/Biological Engineering and Bioengineering, B
Agriculture, B
Agronomy and Crop Science, B
Animal Sciences, B
Anthropology, B
Applied Economics, B
Archeology, B
Architectural Engineering, B
Art History, Criticism and Conservation, B
Art Teacher Education, B
Art/Art Studies, General, B
Astronomy, B
Atmospheric Sciences and Meteorology, B
Biochemistry, B
Biological and Biomedical Sciences, B
Biological and Physical Sciences, AB
Biology Technician/BioTechnology Laboratory Technician, B
Biology/Biological Sciences, B
Biomedical Technology/Technician, A
Biomedical/Medical Engineering, B
Business Administration and Management, B
Business/Commerce, A
Business/Managerial Economics, B
Chemical Engineering, B
Chemistry, B
Civil Engineering, B
Classics and Classical Languages, Literatures, and Linguistics, B
Communication Disorders, B
Communication Studies/Speech Communication and Rhetoric, B
Communication, Journalism and Related Programs, B
Comparative Literature, B
Computer Engineering, B
Computer Engineering Technology/Technician, A
Computer and Information Sciences, B
Criminal Justice/Law Enforcement Administration, B
East Asian Studies, B
Economics, B
Electrical, Electronic and Communications Engineering Technology/Technician, A
Electrical, Electronics and Communications Engineering, B
Elementary Education and Teaching, B
Engineering Science, B
English Language and Literature, B
Environmental/Environmental Health Engineering, B
Film/Cinema Studies, B
Finance, B
Food Science, B
Forest Sciences and Biology, B
Forestry Technology/Technician, B
French Language and Literature, B
Geography, B
Geological and Earth Sciences/Geosciences, B
Geology/Earth Science, B
German Language and Literature, B
Graphic Design, B
Health/Health Care Administration/Management, B
History, B
Horticultural Science, B
Hospitality Administration/Management, B
Human Development and Family Studies, AB
Human Nutrition, B
Industrial Engineering, B
Information Science/Studies, AB

International Relations and Affairs, B
Italian Language and Literature, B
Japanese Language and Literature, B
Jewish/Judaic Studies, B
Journalism, B
Kinesiology and Exercise Science, B
Labor and Industrial Relations, B
Landscaping and Groundskeeping, B
Latin American Studies, B
Liberal Arts and Sciences Studies and Humanities, AB
Logistics and Materials Management, B
Management Information Systems and Services, B
Marketing/Marketing Management, B
Mathematics, B
Mechanical Engineering, B
Mechanical Engineering/Mechanical Technology/Technician, A
Medical Microbiology and Bacteriology, B
Medical Radiologic Technology/Science - Radiation Therapist, A
Medieval and Renaissance Studies, B
Metallurgical Technology/Technician, A
Mining and Mineral Engineering, B
Music, B
Natural Resources and Conservation, B
Nuclear Engineering, B
Organizational Behavior Studies, B
Parks, Recreation and Leisure Facilities Management, B
Petroleum Engineering, B
Philosophy, B
Physics, B
Political Science and Government, B
Pre-Medicine/Pre-Medical Studies, B
Psychology, B
Rehabilitation and Therapeutic Professions, B
Religion/Religious Studies, B
Russian Language and Literature, B
Secondary Education and Teaching, B
Sociology, B
Soil Science and Agronomy, B
Spanish Language and Literature, B
Special Education and Teaching, B
Statistics, B
Technical Theatre/Theatre Design and Technology, B
Telecommunications Technology/Technician, A
Toxicology, B
Turf and Turfgrass Management, B
Visual and Performing Arts, B
Women's Studies, B

PENN STATE SCHUYLKILL

Accounting, B
Acting, B
Actuarial Science, B
Adult and Continuing Education Administration, B
Advertising, B
Aerospace, Aeronautical and Astronautical Engineering, B
African-American/Black Studies, B
Agribusiness, B
Agricultural Business and Management, A
Agricultural Mechanization, B
Agricultural and Extension Education Services, B
Agricultural/Biological Engineering and Bioengineering, B
Agriculture, B
American/United States Studies/Civilization, B
Animal Sciences, B
Anthropology, B
Applied Economics, B
Archeology, B
Architectural Engineering, B
Art History, Criticism and Conservation, B
Art Teacher Education, B
Art/Art Studies, General, B
Astronomy, B
Atmospheric Sciences and Meteorology, B
Biochemistry, B
Biological and Biomedical Sciences, B
Biological and Physical Sciences, AB
Biology Technician/BioTechnology Laboratory Technician, A
Biology/Biological Sciences, B

Biomedical Technology/Technician, A
Biomedical/Medical Engineering, B
Business/Commerce, AB
Business/Managerial Economics, B
Chemical Engineering, B
Chemistry, B
Civil Engineering, B
Classics and Classical Languages, Literatures, and Linguistics, B
Clinical/Medical Laboratory Technician, A
Communication Disorders, B
Communication Studies/Speech Communication and Rhetoric, B
Communication, Journalism and Related Programs, B
Comparative Literature, B
Computer Engineering, B
Computer and Information Sciences, AB
Criminal Justice/Law Enforcement Administration, B
Criminal Justice/Safety Studies, B
East Asian Studies, B
Economics, B
Electrical, Electronic and Communications Engineering Technology/Technician, A
Electrical, Electronics and Communications Engineering, B
Elementary Education and Teaching, B
Engineering Science, B
English Language and Literature, B
Environmental/Environmental Health Engineering, B
Film/Cinema Studies, B
Finance, B
Food Science, B
Forest Sciences and Biology, B
Forestry Technology/Technician, B
French Language and Literature, B
Geography, B
Geological and Earth Sciences/Geosciences, B
Geology/Earth Science, B
German Language and Literature, B
Graphic Design, B
Health/Health Care Administration/Management, B
History, B
Horticultural Science, B
Hospitality Administration/Management, B
Human Development and Family Studies, AB
Human Nutrition, B
Industrial Engineering, B
Information Science/Studies, AB
International Business/Trade/Commerce, B
International Relations and Affairs, B
Italian Language and Literature, B
Japanese Language and Literature, B
Jewish/Judaic Studies, B
Journalism, B
Kinesiology and Exercise Science, B
Labor and Industrial Relations, B
Landscape Architecture, B
Landscaping and Groundskeeping, B
Latin American Studies, B
Liberal Arts and Sciences Studies and Humanities, AB
Logistics and Materials Management, B
Management Information Systems and Services, B
Management Sciences and Quantitative Methods, B
Marketing/Marketing Management, B
Mathematics, B
Mechanical Engineering, B
Medical Microbiology and Bacteriology, B
Medical Radiologic Technology/Science - Radiation Therapist, A
Medieval and Renaissance Studies, B
Metallurgical Technology/Technician, A
Mining and Mineral Engineering, B
Natural Resources and Conservation, B
Nuclear Engineering, B
Organizational Behavior Studies, B
Parks, Recreation and Leisure Facilities Management, B
Petroleum Engineering, B
Philosophy, B
Physics, B
Political Science and Government, B
Pre-Medicine/Pre-Medical Studies, B
Psychology, B
Rehabilitation and Therapeutic Professions, B

Religion/Religious Studies, B
Russian Language and Literature, B
Secondary Education and Teaching, B
Sociology, B
Soil Science and Agronomy, B
Spanish Language and Literature, B
Special Education and Teaching, B
Statistics, B
Technical Theatre/Theatre Design and Technology, B
Telecommunications Technology/Technician, A
Turf and Turfgrass Management, B
Visual and Performing Arts, B
Women's Studies, B

PENN STATE SHENANGO

Accounting, B
Acting, B
Actuarial Science, B
Adult and Continuing Education Administration, B
Advertising, B
Aerospace, Aeronautical and Astronautical Engineering, B
African-American/Black Studies, B
Agribusiness, B
Agricultural Business and Management, A
Agricultural Mechanization, B
Agricultural and Extension Education Services, B
Agricultural/Biological Engineering and Bioengineering, B
Agriculture, B
Agronomy and Crop Science, B
Animal Sciences, B
Anthropology, B
Applied Economics, B
Archeology, B
Architectural Engineering, B
Art History, Criticism and Conservation, B
Art Teacher Education, B
Art/Art Studies, General, B
Astronomy, B
Atmospheric Sciences and Meteorology, B
Biochemistry, B
Biological and Biomedical Sciences, B
Biological and Physical Sciences, AB
Biology Technician/BioTechnology Laboratory Technician, B
Biology/Biological Sciences, B
Biomedical Technology/Technician, A
Biomedical/Medical Engineering, B
Business Administration and Management, B
Business/Commerce, A
Business/Managerial Economics, B
Chemical Engineering, B
Chemistry, B
Civil Engineering, B
Classics and Classical Languages, Literatures, and Linguistics, B
Communication Disorders, B
Communication Studies/Speech Communication and Rhetoric, B
Communication, Journalism and Related Programs, B
Comparative Literature, B
Computer Engineering, B
Computer and Information Sciences, B
Criminal Justice/Law Enforcement Administration, B
East Asian Studies, B
Economics, B
Electrical, Electronic and Communications Engineering Technology/Technician, A
Electrical, Electronics and Communications Engineering, B
Elementary Education and Teaching, B
Engineering Science, B
English Language and Literature, B
Environmental/Environmental Health Engineering, B
Film/Cinema Studies, B
Finance, B
Food Science, B
Foreign Language Teacher Education, B
Forest Sciences and Biology, B
Forestry Technology/Technician, B
French Language and Literature, B
Geography, B
Geological and Earth Sciences/Geosciences, B

Geology/Earth Science, B
German Language and Literature, B
Graphic Design, B
Health/Health Care Administration/Management, B
History, B
Horticultural Science, B
Hospitality Administration/Management, B
Human Development and Family Studies, AB
Human Nutrition, B
Industrial Engineering, B
Information Science/Studies, B
International Relations and Affairs, B
Italian Language and Literature, B
Japanese Language and Literature, B
Jewish/Judaic Studies, B
Journalism, B
Kinesiology and Exercise Science, B
Labor and Industrial Relations, B
Landscaping and Groundskeeping, B
Latin American Studies, B
Liberal Arts and Sciences Studies and Humanities, AB
Logistics and Materials Management, B
Management Information Systems and Services, B
Marketing/Marketing Management, B
Mathematics, B
Mechanical Engineering, B
Mechanical Engineering/Mechanical Technology/Technician, A
Medical Microbiology and Bacteriology, B
Medieval and Renaissance Studies, B
Metallurgical Technology/Technician, A
Mining and Mineral Engineering, B
Music, B
Natural Resources and Conservation, B
Nuclear Engineering, B
Organizational Behavior Studies, B
Parks, Recreation and Leisure Facilities Management, B
Petroleum Engineering, B
Philosophy, B
Physical Therapist Assistant, A
Physics, B
Political Science and Government, B
Pre-Medicine/Pre-Medical Studies, B
Psychology, B
Rehabilitation and Therapeutic Professions, B
Religion/Religious Studies, B
Russian Language and Literature, B
Secondary Education and Teaching, B
Sociology, B
Soil Science and Agronomy, B
Spanish Language and Literature, B
Special Education and Teaching, B
Statistics, B
Technical Theatre/Theatre Design and Technology, B
Telecommunications Technology/Technician, A
Toxicology, B
Turf and Turfgrass Management, B
Visual and Performing Arts, B
Women's Studies, B

PENN STATE UNIVERSITY PARK

Accounting, BM
Acoustics, MD
Acting, B
Adult and Continuing Education Administration, B
Adult and Continuing Education and Teaching, DO
Advertising, B
Aerospace, Aeronautical and Astronautical Engineering, BMD
African-American/Black Studies, B
Agribusiness, B
Agricultural Economics, MDO
Agricultural Education, MDO
Agricultural Engineering, MD
Agricultural Sciences, MDO
Agricultural Teacher Education, B
Agricultural/Biological Engineering and Bioengineering, B
Agriculture, B
Agriculture, Agriculture Operations and Related Sciences, B
Agronomy and Soil Sciences, MD
Animal Sciences, BMD

Anthropology, BMD
Applied Statistics, MD
Archeology, B
Architectural Engineering, BMD
Architecture, BMD
Art Education, MDO
Art History, Criticism and Conservation, BMD
Art Teacher Education, B
Art/Art Studies, General, B
Asian Studies/Civilization, B
Astronomy, BMD
Astrophysics, MD
Athletic Training and Sports Medicine, B
Atmospheric Sciences and Meteorology, B
BioTechnology, M
Biochemistry, BMD
Bioengineering, MD
Biological and Biomedical Sciences, BMD
Biological and Physical Sciences, B
Biology Technician/BioTechnology Laboratory Technician, B
Biology/Biological Sciences, B
Biomedical/Medical Engineering, B
Biopsychology, MD
Business Administration, Management and Operations, MD
Business, Management, Marketing, and Related Support Services, B
Cell Biology and Anatomy, MD
Chemical Engineering, BMD
Chemistry, BMD
Child and Family Studies, MD
Chinese Language and Literature, B
Civil Engineering, BMD
Classics and Classical Languages, Literatures, and Linguistics, B
Communication Disorders, BMDO
Communication Studies/Speech Communication and Rhetoric, B
Communication and Media Studies, MD
Communication, Journalism and Related Programs, B
Comparative Literature, BMD
Composition, M
Computer Engineering, BMD
Computer Science, MD
Computer and Information Sciences, B
Counselor Education/School Counseling and Guidance Services, MDO
Criminal Justice/Law Enforcement Administration, B
Criminology, MD
Curriculum and Instruction, MDO
Design and Applied Arts, B
Early Childhood Education and Teaching, B
Ecology, MD
Economics, BMD
Education, MDO
Educational Assessment, Evaluation, and Research, B
Educational Leadership and Administration, MD
Educational Media/Instructional Technology, MDO
Educational Policy, MDO
Educational Psychology, MDO
Electrical Engineering, MD
Electrical, Electronics and Communications Engineering, B
Elementary Education and Teaching, B
Engineering, B
Engineering Design, M
Engineering Science, B
Engineering and Applied Sciences, MD
English, MD
English Language and Literature, B
English as a Second Language, M
Entomology, MD
Entrepreneurial and Small Business Operations, B
Environmental Engineering Technology/Environmental Technology, MD
Environmental Policy and Resource Management, M
Environmental Sciences, M
Environmental Studies, B
Environmental/Environmental Health Engineering, B
Film/Cinema Studies, B
Finance, B
Fine Arts and Art Studies, MDO

Fish, Game and Wildlife Management, MD
Food Science, B
Food Science and Technology, MD
Foreign Language Teacher Education, B
Forensic Science and Technology, B
Forest Sciences and Biology, B
Forestry, MD
French Language and Literature, BMD
Geography, BMD
Geological and Earth Sciences/Geosciences, B
Geology/Earth Science, B
Geosciences, MD
Geotechnical Engineering, MD
German Language and Literature, BMD
Graphic Design, B
Health Services Administration, MD
Health/Health Care Administration/Management, B
History, BMD
Homeland Security, M
Horticultural Science, MD
Hospitality Administration/Management, BMD
Human Development, MD
Human Development and Family Studies, B
Human Nutrition, B
Human Resources Development, MD
Human Resources Management and Services, M
Industrial Engineering, B
Industrial and Labor Relations, M
Industrial/Management Engineering, MD
Information Science/Studies, ABMD
International Affairs, M
International Relations and Affairs, B
Italian Language and Literature, B
Japanese Language and Literature, B
Jewish/Judaic Studies, B
Journalism, B
Kinesiology and Exercise Science, B
Kinesiology and Movement Studies, MDO
Labor and Industrial Relations, B
Landscape Architecture, BMD
Landscaping and Groundskeeping, B
Latin American Studies, B
Law and Legal Studies, MD
Leisure Studies, MD
Liberal Arts and Sciences Studies and Humanities, AB
Linguistics, MD
Management Information Systems and Services, BMD
Marketing/Marketing Management, B
Mass Communication/Media Studies, D
Materials Engineering, MD
Materials Sciences, MD
Mathematics, BMD
Mechanical Engineering, BMD
Mechanics, MD
Media Studies, M
Medical Microbiology and Bacteriology, B
Medieval and Renaissance Studies, B
Meteorology, MD
Microbiology, MD
Mineral/Mining Engineering, MD
Mining and Mineral Engineering, B
Molecular Biology, MD
Music, BMDO
Music Performance, B
Music Teacher Education, BMO
Music Theory and Composition, M
Natural Resources and Conservation, B
Nuclear Engineering, BMD
Nursing, MD
Nutritional Sciences, MD
Organizational Behavior Studies, B
Parks, Recreation and Leisure Facilities Management, B
Pathobiology, M
Performance, MD
Petroleum Engineering, B
Philosophy, BMD
Physics, BMD
Physiology, MD
Plant Biology, MD
Plant Pathology/Phytopathology, MD
Plant Sciences, BMD
Political Science and Government, BMD
Pre-Medicine/Pre-Medical Studies, B

Pre-Veterinary Studies, B
Psychology, BMD
Recreation and Park Management, MD
Rehabilitation and Therapeutic Professions, B
Rural Sociology, MDO
Russian Language and Literature, BM
School Psychology, MDO
Science, Technology and Society, B
Secondary Education and Teaching, B
Security and Protective Services, B
Sociology, BMD
Spanish Language and Literature, BMD
Special Education and Teaching, BMDO
Statistics, BMD
Supply Chain Management, M
Sustainable Development, M
Teacher Education and Professional Development, Specific Subject Areas, A
Technical Theatre/Theatre Design and Technology, B
Theater, M
Toxicology, B
Travel and Tourism, MD
Turf and Turfgrass Management, B
Visual and Performing Arts, B
Vocational and Technical Education, MDO
Women's Studies, B

PENN STATE WILKES-BARRE

Accounting, B
Acting, B
Actuarial Science, B
Adult and Continuing Education Administration, B
Advertising, B
Aerospace, Aeronautical and Astronautical Engineering, B
African-American/Black Studies, B
Agribusiness, B
Agricultural Business and Management, A
Agricultural Mechanization, B
Agricultural and Extension Education Services, B
Agricultural/Biological Engineering and Bioengineering, B
Agriculture, B
Agronomy and Crop Science, B
Animal Sciences, B
Anthropology, B
Applied Economics, B
Archeology, B
Architectural Engineering, B
Art History, Criticism and Conservation, B
Art Teacher Education, B
Art/Art Studies, General, B
Astronomy, B
Atmospheric Sciences and Meteorology, B
Biochemistry, B
Biological and Biomedical Sciences, B
Biological and Physical Sciences, B
Biology Technician/BioTechnology Laboratory Technician, B
Biology/Biological Sciences, B
Biomedical/Medical Engineering, B
Business Administration and Management, B
Business/Commerce, A
Business/Managerial Economics, B
Chemical Engineering, B
Chemistry, B
Civil Engineering, B
Classics and Classical Languages, Literatures, and Linguistics, B
Communication Disorders, B
Communication Studies/Speech Communication and Rhetoric, B
Communication, Journalism and Related Programs, B
Comparative Literature, B
Computer Engineering, B
Computer and Information Sciences, B
Criminal Justice/Law Enforcement Administration, B
Criminal Justice/Safety Studies, B
Economics, B
Electrical, Electronic and Communications Engineering Technology/Technician, A
Electrical, Electronics and Communications Engineering, B
Elementary Education and Teaching, B

Engineering Science, B
English Language and Literature, B
Environmental/Environmental Health Engineering, B
Film/Cinema Studies, B
Finance, B
Food Science, B
Forest Sciences and Biology, B
Forestry Technology/Technician, B
French Language and Literature, B
Geography, B
Geological and Earth Sciences/Geosciences, B
Geology/Earth Science, B
German Language and Literature, B
Graphic Design, B
Health/Health Care Administration/Management, B
History, B
Horticultural Science, B
Hospitality Administration/Management, B
Human Development and Family Studies, B
Human Nutrition, B
Industrial Engineering, B
Information Science/Studies, B
International Relations and Affairs, B
Italian Language and Literature, B
Japanese Language and Literature, B
Jewish/Judaic Studies, B
Journalism, B
Kinesiology and Exercise Science, B
Labor and Industrial Relations, B
Landscape Architecture, B
Landscaping and Groundskeeping, B
Latin American Studies, B
Liberal Arts and Sciences Studies and Humanities, AB
Management Information Systems and Services, B
Manufacturing Engineering, A
Marketing/Marketing Management, B
Mathematics, B
Mechanical Engineering, B
Medical Microbiology and Bacteriology, B
Medieval and Renaissance Studies, B
Metallurgical Technology/Technician, A
Mining and Mineral Engineering, B
Music, B
Natural Resources and Conservation, B
Nuclear Engineering, B
Organizational Behavior Studies, B
Parks, Recreation and Leisure Facilities Management, B
Petroleum Engineering, B
Philosophy, B
Physics, B
Political Science and Government, B
Pre-Medicine/Pre-Medical Studies, B
Psychology, B
Rehabilitation and Therapeutic Professions, B
Religion/Religious Studies, B
Russian Language and Literature, B
Secondary Education and Teaching, B
Sociology, B
Soil Science and Agronomy, B
Spanish Language and Literature, B
Special Education and Teaching, B
Statistics, B
Survey Technology/Surveying, AB
Technical Theatre/Theatre Design and Technology, B
Telecommunications Technology/Technician, A
Toxicology, B
Turf and Turfgrass Management, B
Visual and Performing Arts, B
Women's Studies, B

PENN STATE WORTHINGTON SCRANTON

Accounting, B
Acting, B
Actuarial Science, B
Adult and Continuing Education Administration, B
Advertising, B
Aerospace, Aeronautical and Astronautical Engineering, B
African-American/Black Studies, B
Agribusiness, B
Agricultural Business and Management, A
Agricultural Mechanization, B

Agricultural and Extension Education Services, B
Agricultural/Biological Engineering and Bioengineering, B
Agriculture, B
Agronomy and Crop Science, B
American/United States Studies/Civilization, B
Animal Sciences, B
Anthropology, B
Applied Economics, B
Archeology, B
Architectural Engineering, B
Architectural Engineering Technology/Technician, A
Art History, Criticism and Conservation, B
Art Teacher Education, B
Art/Art Studies, General, B
Astronomy, B
Atmospheric Sciences and Meteorology, B
Biochemistry, B
Biological and Biomedical Sciences, B
Biological and Physical Sciences, B
Biology Technician/BioTechnology Laboratory Technician, B
Biology/Biological Sciences, B
Biomedical/Medical Engineering, B
Business Administration and Management, B
Business/Commerce, A
Business/Managerial Economics, B
Chemical Engineering, B
Chemistry, B
Civil Engineering, B
Classics and Classical Languages, Literatures, and Linguistics, B
Communication Disorders, B
Communication Studies/Speech Communication and Rhetoric, B
Communication, Journalism and Related Programs, B
Comparative Literature, B
Computer Engineering, B
Computer and Information Sciences, B
Criminal Justice/Law Enforcement Administration, B
East Asian Studies, B
Economics, B
Electrical, Electronic and Communications Engineering Technology/Technician, A
Electrical, Electronics and Communications Engineering, B
Elementary Education and Teaching, B
Engineering Science, B
English Language and Literature, B
Environmental/Environmental Health Engineering, B
Film/Cinema Studies, B
Finance, B
Food Science, B
Foreign Language Teacher Education, B
Forest Sciences and Biology, B
Forestry Technology/Technician, B
French Language and Literature, B
Geography, B
Geological and Earth Sciences/Geosciences, B
Geology/Earth Science, B
German Language and Literature, B
Graphic Design, B
Health/Health Care Administration/Management, B
History, B
Horticultural Science, B
Hospitality Administration/Management, B
Human Development and Family Studies, AB
Human Nutrition, B
Industrial Engineering, B
Information Science/Studies, B
International Relations and Affairs, B
Italian Language and Literature, B
Japanese Language and Literature, B
Jewish/Judaic Studies, B
Journalism, B
Kinesiology and Exercise Science, B
Labor and Industrial Relations, B
Landscaping and Groundskeeping, B
Latin American Studies, B
Liberal Arts and Sciences Studies and Humanities, AB
Management Information Systems and Services, B
Marketing/Marketing Management, B
Mathematics, B
Mechanical Engineering, B

Medical Microbiology and Bacteriology, B
Medieval and Renaissance Studies, B
Mining and Mineral Engineering, B
Music, B
Natural Resources and Conservation, B
Nuclear Engineering, B
Organizational Behavior Studies, B
Parks, Recreation and Leisure Facilities Management, B
Petroleum Engineering, B
Philosophy, B
Physics, B
Political Science and Government, B
Pre-Medicine/Pre-Medical Studies, B
Psychology, B
Rehabilitation and Therapeutic Professions, B
Religion/Religious Studies, B
Russian Language and Literature, B
Secondary Education and Teaching, B
Sociology, B
Soil Science and Agronomy, B
Spanish Language and Literature, B
Special Education and Teaching, B
Statistics, B
Technical Theatre/Theatre Design and Technology, B
Turf and Turfgrass Management, B
Visual and Performing Arts, B
Women's Studies, B

PENN STATE YORK

Accounting, B
Acting, B
Actuarial Science, B
Adult and Continuing Education Administration, B
Advertising, B
Aerospace, Aeronautical and Astronautical Engineering, B
African-American/Black Studies, B
Agribusiness, B
Agricultural Business and Management, A
Agricultural Mechanization, B
Agricultural and Extension Education Services, B
Agricultural/Biological Engineering and Bioengineering, B
Agriculture, B
Agronomy and Crop Science, B
American/United States Studies/Civilization, B
Animal Sciences, B
Anthropology, B
Applied Economics, B
Archeology, B
Architectural Engineering, B
Art History, Criticism and Conservation, B
Art Teacher Education, B
Art/Art Studies, General, B
Astronomy, B
Atmospheric Sciences and Meteorology, B
Biochemistry, B
Biological and Biomedical Sciences, B
Biological and Physical Sciences, B
Biology Technician/BioTechnology Laboratory Technician, B
Biology/Biological Sciences, B
Biomedical Technology/Technician, A
Biomedical/Medical Engineering, B
Business Administration and Management, B
Business/Commerce, A
Business/Managerial Economics, B
Chemical Engineering, B
Chemistry, B
Civil Engineering, B
Classics and Classical Languages, Literatures, and Linguistics, B
Communication Disorders, B
Communication Studies/Speech Communication and Rhetoric, B
Communication, Journalism and Related Programs, B
Comparative Literature, B
Computer Engineering, B
Computer and Information Sciences, B
Criminal Justice/Law Enforcement Administration, B
East Asian Studies, B
Economics, B

Electrical, Electronic and Communications Engineering Technology/Technician, A
Electrical, Electronics and Communications Engineering, B
Elementary Education and Teaching, B
Engineering Science, B
English Language and Literature, B
Environmental/Environmental Health Engineering, B
Film/Cinema Studies, B
Finance, B
Food Science, B
Foreign Language Teacher Education, B
Forest Sciences and Biology, B
Forestry Technology/Technician, B
French Language and Literature, B
Geography, B
Geological and Earth Sciences/Geosciences, B
Geology/Earth Science, B
German Language and Literature, B
Graphic Design, B
Health/Health Care Administration/Management, B
History, B
Horticultural Science, B
Hospitality Administration/Management, B
Human Development and Family Studies, AB
Human Nutrition, B
Industrial Engineering, B
Industrial Technology/Technician, A
Information Science/Studies, B
International Relations and Affairs, B
Italian Language and Literature, B
Japanese Language and Literature, B
Jewish/Judaic Studies, B
Journalism, B
Kinesiology and Exercise Science, B
Labor and Industrial Relations, B
Landscaping and Groundskeeping, B
Latin American Studies, B
Liberal Arts and Sciences Studies and Humanities, AB
Logistics and Materials Management, B
Management Information Systems and Services, B
Manufacturing Engineering, A
Marketing/Marketing Management, B
Mathematics, B
Mechanical Engineering, B
Mechanical Engineering/Mechanical Technology/Technician, A
Medical Microbiology and Bacteriology, B
Medieval and Renaissance Studies, B
Metallurgical Technology/Technician, A
Mining and Mineral Engineering, B
Music, B
Natural Resources and Conservation, B
Nuclear Engineering, B
Organizational Behavior Studies, B
Parks, Recreation and Leisure Facilities Management, B
Petroleum Engineering, B
Philosophy, B
Physics, B
Political Science and Government, B
Pre-Medicine/Pre-Medical Studies, B
Psychology, B
Rehabilitation and Therapeutic Professions, B
Religion/Religious Studies, B
Russian Language and Literature, B
Secondary Education and Teaching, B
Sociology, B
Soil Science and Agronomy, B
Spanish Language and Literature, B
Special Education and Teaching, B
Statistics, B
Technical Theatre/Theatre Design and Technology, B
Telecommunications Technology/Technician, A
Toxicology, B
Turf and Turfgrass Management, B
Visual and Performing Arts, B
Women's Studies, B

PENNCO TECH

Autobody/Collision and Repair Technology/Technician, A

Vehicle Maintenance and Repair Technologies, A

PENNSYLVANIA ACADEMY OF THE FINE ARTS

Fine Arts and Art Studies, MO
Fine/Studio Arts, B
Painting, MO
Printmaking, MO
Sculpture, MO

PENNSYLVANIA COLLEGE OF ART & DESIGN

Animation, Interactive Technology, Video Graphics and Special Effects, B
Commercial and Advertising Art, B
Fine/Studio Arts, B
Graphic Design, B
Illustration, B
Photography, B

PENNSYLVANIA COLLEGE OF HEALTH SCIENCES

Cardiovascular Technology/Technologist, A
Diagnostic Medical Sonography/Sonographer and Ultrasound Technician, A
Electrocardiograph Technology/Technician, A
Health Education, M
Health Services Administration, M
Health Services/Allied Health/Health Sciences, B
Health/Health Care Administration/Management, B
Medical Radiologic Technology/Science - Radiation Therapist, A
Nuclear Medical Technology/Technologist, A
Nursing Administration, M
Nursing Education, M
Radiologic Technology/Science - Radiographer, A
Respiratory Care Therapy/Therapist, A
Surgical Technology/Technologist, A

PENNSYLVANIA COLLEGE OF TECHNOLOGY

Accounting, B
Accounting Technology/Technician and Bookkeeping, A
Aircraft Powerplant Technology/Technician, A
Allied Health Diagnostic, Intervention, and Treatment Professions, A
Applied Horticulture/Horticultural Operations, A
Architectural Technology/Technician, A
Autobody/Collision and Repair Technology/Technician, AB
Automobile/Automotive Mechanics Technology/Technician, A
Automotive Engineering Technology/Technician, B
Avionics Maintenance Technology/Technician, B
Baking and Pastry Arts/Baker/Pastry Chef, A
Building/Construction Site Management/Manager, B
Business Administration and Management, AB
Business Administration, Management and Operations, B
Child Care Provider/Assistant, A
Civil Engineering Technology/Technician, AB
Commercial and Advertising Art, AB
Computer Systems Networking and Telecommunications, B
Computer and Information Systems Security, B
Computer/Information Technology Services Administration and Management, A
Construction Engineering Technology/Technician, A
Culinary Arts/Chef Training, A
Data Modeling/Warehousing and Database Administration, B
Dental Hygiene/Hygienist, AB
Diesel Mechanics Technology/Technician, A
Drafting/Design Engineering Technologies/Technicians, A
Electrical and Electronic Engineering Technologies/Technicians, A
Electrical, Electronic and Communications Engineering Technology/Technician, A
Electrician, A
Electromechanical Technology/Electromechanical Engineering Technology, A
Emergency Medical Technology/Technician (EMT Paramedic), A

Engineering Technologies/Technicians, B
Fine Arts and Art Studies, A
Forestry Technology/Technician, A
Health Information/Medical Records Administration/Administrator, B
Health Information/Medical Records Technology/Technician, A
Health and Medical Administrative Services, B
Health and Physical Education/Fitness, A
Heating, Air Conditioning and Refrigeration Technology/Technician, A
Heavy Equipment Maintenance Technology/Technician, A
Industrial Design, B
Industrial Electronics Technology/Technician, A
Industrial Mechanics and Maintenance Technology, A
Industrial Production Technologies/Technicians, B
Landscaping and Groundskeeping, A
Legal Assistant/Paralegal, AB
Liberal Arts and Sciences Studies and Humanities, A
Machine Tool Technology/Machinist, A
Manufacturing Technology/Technician, AB
Mason/Masonry, A
Mechanic and Repair Technologies/Technicians, A
Mechanical Engineering Related Technologies/Technicians, B
Mechanical Engineering/Mechanical Technology/Technician, A
Medical Radiologic Technology/Science - Radiation Therapist, A
Mental and Social Health Services and Allied Professions, B
Multi-/Interdisciplinary Studies, A
Occupational Therapist Assistant, A
Physician Assistant, B
Plastics Engineering Technology/Technician, AB
Psychiatric/Mental Health Services Technician, A
Restaurant, Culinary, and Catering Management/Manager, B
Restaurant/Food Services Management, A
Robotics Technology/Technician, A
Solar Energy Technology/Technician, A
Sport and Fitness Administration/Management, B
Surgical Technology/Technologist, A
Survey Technology/Surveying, A
Vehicle and Vehicle Parts and Accessories Marketing Operations, A
Web Page, Digital/Multimedia and Information Resources Design, B
Welding Technology/Welder, A

PENNSYLVANIA HIGHLANDS COMMUNITY COLLEGE

Accounting, A
Airline/Commercial/Professional Pilot and Flight Crew, A
Architectural Drafting and Architectural CAD/CADD, A
Business/Commerce, A
Child Care and Support Services Management, A
Computer Science, A
Computer and Information Sciences, A
Corrections, A
Criminal Justice/Law Enforcement Administration, A
Early Childhood Education and Teaching, A
Education, A
Emergency Medical Technology/Technician (EMT Paramedic), A
Engineering Technologies/Technicians, A
Environmental Sciences, A
General Studies, A
Health Information/Medical Records Technology/Technician, A
Health Professions and Related Clinical Sciences, A
Histologic Technician, A
Human Services, A
Lineworker, A
Medical/Clinical Assistant, A
Operations Management and Supervision, A
Psychology, A
Radio, Television, and Digital Communication, A
Radiologic Technology/Science - Radiographer, A

Welding Technology/Welder, A

PENNSYLVANIA INSTITUTE OF HEALTH AND TECHNOLOGY

Medical Office Management/Administration, A
Medical/Clinical Assistant, A

PENNSYLVANIA INSTITUTE OF TECHNOLOGY

Allied Health and Medical Assisting Services, A
Biomedical Technology/Technician, A
Business Administration and Management, A
Electrical, Electronic and Communications Engineering Technology/Technician, A
Engineering Technology, A
General Studies, A
Health Information/Medical Records Technology/Technician, A
Health Services/Allied Health/Health Sciences, A
Health/Health Care Administration/Management, A
Medical Office Management/Administration, A
Pharmacy Technician/Assistant, A
Physical Therapist Assistant, A

PHILADELPHIA UNIVERSITY

Accounting, B
Apparel and Accessories Marketing Operations, B
Apparel and Textiles, B
Architecture, BM
Biochemistry, B
Biology/Biological Sciences, B
Biopsychology, B
Business Administration and Management, B
Business Administration, Management and Operations, M
Chemistry, B
Clothing and Textiles, M
Commercial and Advertising Art, B
Community Psychology, M
Computer Science, B
Computer and Information Sciences, B
Conservation Biology, B
Construction Management, M
E-Commerce/Electronic Commerce, B
Emergency Management, M
Environmental Biology, B
Fashion Merchandising, B
Fashion/Apparel Design, B
Fiber, Textile and Weaving Arts, B
Finance, B
Fine Arts and Art Studies, M
Geography, M
Graphic Design, B
Industrial Design, BM
Information Science/Studies, B
Interior Architecture, B
Interior Design, BM
International Business/Trade/Commerce, B
Internet and Interactive Multimedia, M
Landscape Architecture, B
Management Information Systems and Services, B
Management Strategy and Policy, M
Marketing, M
Marketing/Marketing Management, B
Modeling and Simulation, M
Nurse Midwife/Nursing Midwifery, MO
Occupational Therapy/Therapist, MD
Physician Assistant, BM
Pre-Medicine/Pre-Medical Studies, B
Psychology, B
Sustainable Development, M
Taxation, M
Textile Design, M
Textile Sciences and Engineering, BMD
Urban and Regional Planning, M

PITTSBURGH CAREER INSTITUTE

Anesthesiologist Assistant, A
Business, Management, Marketing, and Related Support Services, A
Diagnostic Medical Sonography/Sonographer and Ultrasound Technician, A
Legal Assistant/Paralegal, A

Medical Radiologic Technology/Science - Radiation Therapist, A

PITTSBURGH INSTITUTE OF AERO-NAUTICS

Aeronautical/Aerospace Engineering Technology/Technician, A
Airframe Mechanics and Aircraft Maintenance Technology/Technician, A
Avionics Maintenance Technology/Technician, A
Electrical, Electronic and Communications Engineering Technology/Technician, A

PITTSBURGH INSTITUTE OF MORTU-ARY SCIENCE, INCORPORATED

Funeral Service and Mortuary Science, A

PITTSBURGH TECHNICAL INSTITUTE

Business Administration and Management, A
Computer Graphics, A
Computer Programming/Programmer, A
Computer Technology/Computer Systems Technology, A
Drafting and Design Technology/Technician, A
Electrical, Electronic and Communications Engineering Technology/Technician, A
Electrical/Electronics Equipment Installation and Repair, A
Heating, Air Conditioning, Ventilation and Refrigeration Maintenance Technology/Technician, A
Hotel/Motel Administration/Management, A
Medical Office Assistant/Specialist, A
Medical/Health Management and Clinical Assistant/Specialist, A
Security and Protective Services, A
Surgical Technology/Technologist, A
System Administration/Administrator, A
Web Page, Digital/Multimedia and Information Resources Design, A
Welding Technology/Welder, A

POINT PARK UNIVERSITY

Accounting, AB
Animation, Interactive Technology, Video Graphics and Special Effects, B
Behavioral Sciences, B
BioTechnology, B
Biology Teacher Education, B
Biology/Biological Sciences, B
Broadcast Journalism, B
Business Administration and Management, AB
Business Administration, Management and Operations, M
Business, Management, Marketing, and Related Support Services, B
Cinematography and Film/Video Production, B
Civil Engineering Technology/Technician, AB
Clinical Psychology, M
Communication and Media Studies, M
Communication, Journalism and Related Programs, B
Computer/Information Technology Services Administration and Management, B
Criminal Justice/Safety Studies, B
Criminology, M
Curriculum and Instruction, M
Dance, B
Digital Communication and Media/Multimedia, B
Drama and Dance Teacher Education, B
Drama and Dramatics/Theatre Arts, B
Economics, B
Education, BM
Educational Administration and Supervision, M
Educational Leadership and Administration, M
Electrical and Electronic Engineering Technologies/Technicians, AB
Elementary Education and Teaching, B
Engineering Management, M
English Language and Literature, B
English/Language Arts Teacher Education, B
Environmental Studies, M
Forensic Science and Technology, B
Funeral Service and Mortuary Science, B
Health Professions and Related Clinical Sciences, B
Health/Medical Preparatory Programs, B

History, B
Human Resources Management/Personnel Administration, B
Information Technology, B
International/Global Studies, B
Journalism, BM
Law and Legal Studies, B
Liberal Arts and Sciences Studies and Humanities, B
Mass Communication/Media Studies, BM
Mathematics Teacher Education, B
Mechanical Engineering/Mechanical Technology/Technician, AB
Multi-/Interdisciplinary Studies, B
Organizational Management, M
Performance, M
Photography, B
Photojournalism, B
Playwriting and Screenwriting, B
Political Science and Government, B
Psychology, B
Public Administration, AB
Public Administration and Social Service Professions, A
Public Relations/Image Management, B
Radio and Television, B
Security and Protective Services, B
Special Education and Teaching, M
Teacher Education and Professional Development, Specific Subject Areas, B
Theater, M

READING AREA COMMUNITY COLLEGE

Accounting, A
Accounting and Business/Management, A
Administrative Assistant and Secretarial Science, A
Art/Art Studies, General, A
Business Administration and Management, A
Child Care and Support Services Management, A
Child Development, A
Clinical/Medical Laboratory Technician, A
Communication and Media Studies, A
Computer Technology/Computer Systems Technology, A
Computer and Information Sciences, A
Criminal Justice/Police Science, A
Elementary Education and Teaching, A
Engineering, A
General Studies, A
Health Information/Medical Records Technology/Technician, A
Health Services/Allied Health/Health Sciences, A
Industrial Mechanics and Maintenance Technology, A
Liberal Arts and Sciences Studies and Humanities, A
Machine Tool Technology/Machinist, A
Medical Administrative Assistant/Secretary, A
Mental and Social Health Services and Allied Professions, A
Occupational Therapist Assistant, A
Physical Sciences, A
Physical Therapist Assistant, A
Psychology, A
Respiratory Care Therapy/Therapist, A
Restaurant, Culinary, and Catering Management/Manager, A
Science Technologies/Technicians, A
Secondary Education and Teaching, A
Social Sciences, A
Social Work, A
Web Page, Digital/Multimedia and Information Resources Design, A

THE RESTAURANT SCHOOL AT WAL-NUT HILL COLLEGE

Baking and Pastry Arts/Baker/Pastry Chef, AB
Culinary Arts/Chef Training, AB
Hotel/Motel Administration/Management, AB
Restaurant/Food Services Management, AB

ROBERT MORRIS UNIVERSITY

Accounting, B
Actuarial Science, B
Applied Mathematics, B

Biology/Biological Sciences, B
Business Administration and Management, B
Business Administration, Management and Operations, M
Business Education, M
Business Teacher Education, B
Communication Studies/Speech Communication and Rhetoric, B
Computer Software Engineering, B
Computer and Information Systems Security, M
Computer/Information Technology Services Administration and Management, B
Corrections and Criminal Justice, B
Design and Visual Communications, B
Economics, B
Education, MDO
Educational Leadership and Administration, MD
Elementary Education and Teaching, B
Engineering, B
Engineering Management, M
Engineering and Applied Sciences, M
English Language and Literature, B
Environmental Studies, B
Finance, B
Health Services Administration, B
Hospitality Administration/Management, B
Human Resources Management and Services, M
Information Science/Studies, BMD
Internet and Interactive Multimedia, M
Management Information Systems and Services, BMD
Manufacturing Engineering, B
Marketing/Marketing Management, B
Mass Communication/Media Studies, B
Multi-/Interdisciplinary Studies, B
Nuclear Medical Technology/Technologist, B
Nursing, MD
Organizational Behavior Studies, B
Organizational Management, M
Project Management, M
Psychology, B
Social Sciences, B
Sport and Fitness Administration/Management, BM
Taxation, M

ROSEDALE TECHNICAL INSTITUTE

Automobile/Automotive Mechanics Technology/Technician, A
Diesel Mechanics Technology/Technician, A
Electrician, A

ROSEMONT COLLEGE

Accounting, B
Art History, Criticism and Conservation, B
Biochemistry, B
Biology/Biological Sciences, B
Business Administration and Management, B
Business Administration, Management and Operations, M
Chemistry, B
Communication Studies/Speech Communication and Rhetoric, B
Communication, Journalism and Related Programs, B
Counseling Psychology, M
Counselor Education/School Counseling and Guidance Services, M
Criminal Justice/Safety Studies, B
Economics, B
Education, BM
Elementary Education and Teaching, BM
English Language and Literature, B
Finance, B
Fine/Studio Arts, B
History, B
Human Services, M
International Business/Trade/Commerce, B
Liberal Arts and Sciences Studies and Humanities, B
Management, M
Marketing/Marketing Management, B
Mathematics, B
Philosophy, B
Political Science and Government, B
Psychology, B
Publishing, M

Religion/Religious Studies, B
Social Sciences, B
Sociology, B
Spanish Language and Literature, B
Writing, M

SAINT CHARLES BORROMEO SEMINARY, OVERBROOK

Philosophy, B
Religion/Religious Studies, M
Theology and Religious Vocations, M

SAINT FRANCIS UNIVERSITY

Accounting, AB
Accounting and Finance, B
American/United States Studies/Civilization, B
Anthropology, B
Biological and Biomedical Sciences, M
Biology Teacher Education, B
Biology/Biological Sciences, B
Business Administration and Management, AB
Business Administration, Management and Operations, M
Chemistry, B
Chemistry Teacher Education, B
Clinical Laboratory Science/Medical Technology/Technologist, B
Comparative Literature, B
Computer Programming/Programmer, AB
Computer Science, B
Criminal Justice/Law Enforcement Administration, B
Criminology, B
Economics, B
Education, ABM
Educational Leadership and Administration, M
Elementary Education and Teaching, B
Engineering, B
English Language and Literature, B
English/Language Arts Teacher Education, B
Environmental Sciences, B
Environmental Studies, B
Exercise Physiology, B
Finance, B
Fine Arts and Art Studies, A
Foreign Language Teacher Education, B
Forensic Science and Technology, B
Health Education, M
History, B
History Teacher Education, B
Human Resources Management and Services, M
Human Resources Management/Personnel Administration, B
International Business/Trade/Commerce, B
International Relations and Affairs, B
Journalism, B
Labor and Industrial Relations, B
Management Information Systems and Services, B
Marine Biology and Biological Oceanography, B
Marketing/Marketing Management, B
Mass Communication/Media Studies, B
Mathematics, B
Mathematics Teacher Education, B
Mathematics and Computer Science, B
Modern Languages, B
Occupational Therapy/Therapist, BM
Pastoral Studies/Counseling, B
Petroleum Engineering, B
Philosophy, B
Physical Therapy/Therapist, BD
Physician Assistant, BM
Political Science and Government, B
Pre-Dentistry Studies, B
Pre-Law Studies, B
Pre-Medicine/Pre-Medical Studies, B
Pre-Veterinary Studies, B
Psychology, B
Public Administration, B
Public Health (MPH, DPH), B
Public Relations/Image Management, B
Reading Teacher Education, M
Real Estate, A
Religion/Religious Studies, B
Science Teacher Education/General Science Teacher Education, B
Secondary Education and Teaching, B
Social Studies Teacher Education, B

Social Work, B
Sociology, B
Spanish Language and Literature, B
Special Education and Teaching, B

SAINT JOSEPH'S UNIVERSITY

Accounting, BMO
Actuarial Science, B
Adult and Continuing Education and Teaching, M
Ancient Studies/Civilization, B
Art Teacher Education, B
Art/Art Studies, General, B
Asian Studies/Civilization, B
Biochemistry, B
Biological and Biomedical Sciences, M
Biology Teacher Education, B
Biology/Biological Sciences, B
Business Administration and Management, AB
Business Administration, Management and Operations, MO
Chemistry, B
Chemistry Teacher Education, B
Communication Studies/Speech Communication and Rhetoric, B
Computer Science, MO
Computer and Information Sciences, B
Corrections, M
Criminology, BMO
Curriculum and Instruction, O
Economics, B
Education, MDO
Educational Administration and Supervision, O
Educational Leadership and Administration, MDO
Educational Media/Instructional Technology, MO
Elementary Education and Teaching, BMO
English Language and Literature, B
Environmental Studies, B
Environmental and Occupational Health, M
European Studies/Civilization, B
Film/Video and Photographic Arts, B
Finance, B
Finance and Banking, M
Financial Planning and Services, B
French Language Teacher Education, B
French Language and Literature, B
French Studies, B
German Language Teacher Education, B
German Language and Literature, B
Gerontology, M
Health Education, M
Health Professions and Related Clinical Sciences, B
Health Services Administration, M
Health Services/Allied Health/Health Sciences, B
History, B
History Teacher Education, B
Homeland Security, M
Hospital and Health Care Facilities Administration/Management, B
Hospitality and Recreation Marketing Operations, B
Human Resources Management and Services, M
Human Resources Management/Personnel Administration, B
Industrial and Organizational Psychology, M
Information Science/Studies, B
Information Technology, B
Insurance, B
International Business/Trade/Commerce, BM
International Relations and Affairs, B
Italian Language and Literature, B
Italian Studies, B
Knowledge Management, B
Latin Language and Literature, B
Law Enforcement, M
Law and Legal Studies, BM
Liberal Arts and Sciences Studies and Humanities, AB
Linguistics, B
Management Information Systems and Services, BM
Management Strategy and Policy, M
Marketing, MO
Marketing/Marketing Management, B
Mathematics, BMO
Middle School Education, O
Music, B
Nurse Anesthetist, M

Nursing Administration, M
Organizational Behavior Studies, B
Organizational Management, M
Philosophy, B
Physics, B
Physics Teacher Education, B
Political Science and Government, B
Psychology, BM
Reading Teacher Education, MO
Religion/Religious Studies, B
School Nursing, M
Secondary Education and Teaching, BMO
Small Business Administration/Management, B
Sociology, B
Spanish Language Teacher Education, B
Spanish Language and Literature, B
Special Education and Teaching, BMO
Special Products Marketing Operations, B
Specialized Merchandising, Sales, and Marketing Operations, B
Teaching English as a Second or Foreign Language/ESL Language Instructor, B
Visual and Performing Arts, B
Writing, M

SAINT VINCENT COLLEGE

Accounting, B
Anthropology, B
Art History, Criticism and Conservation, B
Art Teacher Education, B
Biochemistry, B
Bioinformatics, B
Biology/Biological Sciences, B
Business Administration and Management, B
Business Administration, Management and Operations, M
Business Teacher Education, B
Business/Commerce, B
Chemistry, B
Communication Studies/Speech Communication and Rhetoric, B
Computer and Information Sciences, B
Criminology, B
Curriculum and Instruction, M
Early Childhood Education and Teaching, B
Economics, B
Education, M
Educational Administration and Supervision, M
Educational Media/Instructional Technology, M
Engineering, B
English Language and Literature, B
Environmental Sciences, B
Environmental Studies, B
Finance, B
Fine/Studio Arts, B
French Language and Literature, B
Graphic Design, B
History, B
International Business/Trade/Commerce, B
Junior High/Intermediate/Middle School Education and Teaching, B
Liberal Arts and Sciences Studies and Humanities, B
Marketing/Marketing Management, B
Mathematics, B
Music, B
Music Performance, B
Natural Sciences, B
Nurse Anesthetist, MD
Occupational Therapy/Therapist, B
Pharmacy, B
Philosophy, B
Physical Sciences, B
Physical Therapy/Therapist, B
Physician Assistant, B
Physics, B
Physics Teacher Education, B
Political Science and Government, B
Psychology, B
Public Policy Analysis, B
Sociology, B
Spanish Language and Literature, B
Special Education and Teaching, M

Theology/Theological Studies, B

SETON HILL UNIVERSITY

Accounting, BM
Acting, B
Art History, Criticism and Conservation, B
Art Teacher Education, B
Art Therapy/Therapist, BM
Biochemistry, B
Biology Teacher Education, B
Biology/Biological Sciences, B
Business Administration and Management, B
Business Administration, Management and Operations, MO
Business, Management, Marketing, and Related Support Services, B
Ceramic Arts and Ceramics, B
Chemistry, B
Chemistry Teacher Education, B
Child Care and Support Services Management, B
Child Development, B
Clinical Laboratory Science/Medical Technology/Technologist, B
Commercial and Advertising Art, B
Communication Studies/Speech Communication and Rhetoric, B
Computer Science, B
Criminal Justice/Safety Studies, B
Dance, B
Dietetics/Dieticians, B
Drama and Dramatics/Theatre Arts, B
Dramatic/Theatre Arts and Stagecraft, B
Drawing, B
Economics, B
Elementary Education and Teaching, BMO
English Language and Literature, B
English/Language Arts Teacher Education, B
Entrepreneurship/Entrepreneurial Studies, BMO
Family and Consumer Sciences/Home Economics Teacher Education, B
Family and Consumer Sciences/Human Sciences, B
Fine Arts and Art Studies, B
Fine/Studio Arts, B
Foreign Language Teacher Education, B
Forensic Science and Technology, B
General Studies, B
History, B
Holocaust Studies, O
Hospitality Administration/Management, B
Human Resources Management/Personnel Administration, B
Human Services, B
International Business/Trade/Commerce, B
International Relations and Affairs, B
Journalism, B
Kinesiology and Exercise Science, B
Management, M
Management Information Systems and Services, B
Marketing/Marketing Management, B
Marriage and Family Therapy/Counseling, M
Mathematics, B
Mathematics Teacher Education, B
Metal and Jewelry Arts, B
Middle School Education, MO
Music, B
Music Performance, B
Music Teacher Education, B
Music Therapy/Therapist, B
Orthodontics, M
Painting, B
Physician Assistant, BM
Political Science and Government, B
Pre-Law Studies, B
Printmaking, B
Psychology, B
Religion/Religious Studies, B
Religious/Sacred Music, B
Sales, Distribution and Marketing Operations, B
Sculpture, B
Social Work, B
Sociology, B
Spanish Language and Literature, B
Special Education and Teaching, MO
Sport and Fitness Administration/Management, BM
Technical Theatre/Theatre Design and Technology, B

Visual and Performing Arts, B
Writing, MO

SHIPPENSBURG UNIVERSITY OF PENNSYLVANIA

Accounting, B
Art/Art Studies, General, B
Biological and Biomedical Sciences, M
Biology/Biological Sciences, B
Business Administration and Management, B
Business Administration, Management and Operations, MO
Chemistry, B
Communication and Media Studies, M
Computer Science, M
Computer Software Engineering, B
Computer Systems Analysis/Analyst, B
Computer and Information Sciences, B
Counselor Education/School Counseling and Guidance Services, MO
Criminal Justice/Safety Studies, B
Criminology, M
Curriculum and Instruction, M
Early Childhood Education and Teaching, BM
Economics, B
Education, MO
Education/Teaching of Individuals in Early Childhood Special Education Programs, B
Educational Administration and Supervision, M
Electrical, Electronics and Communications Engineering, B
Elementary Education and Teaching, M
English Language and Literature, B
Environmental Policy and Resource Management, M
Environmental Studies, BM
Finance, B
Foreign Language Teacher Education, M
French Language and Literature, B
Geography, BM
Geology/Earth Science, B
Health/Health Care Administration/Management, B
Higher Education/Higher Education Administration, M
History, BM
International/Global Studies, B
Journalism, B
Junior High/Intermediate/Middle School Education and Teaching, B
Kinesiology and Exercise Science, B
Liberal Arts and Sciences Studies and Humanities, B
Logistics and Materials Management, B
Management Information Systems and Services, M
Marketing/Marketing Management, B
Marriage and Family Therapy/Counseling, O
Mathematics, B
Mathematics Teacher Education, M
Middle School Education, M
Multi-/Interdisciplinary Studies, B
Organizational Management, M
Physics, B
Political Science and Government, B
Psychology, BM
Public Administration, BM
Public History, M
Reading Teacher Education, M
Science Teacher Education/General Science Teacher Education, M
Social Work, BM
Sociology, BM
Spanish Language and Literature, B
Special Education and Teaching, M
Student Personnel Services, M

SLIPPERY ROCK UNIVERSITY OF PENNSYLVANIA

Accounting, B
Acting, B
Actuarial Science, B
Administration of Special Education, B
Art Teacher Education, B
Art/Art Studies, General, B
Athletic Training and Sports Medicine, B
Biochemistry, B
Biology/Biological Sciences, B

Biomedical Sciences, B
Business Administration and Management, B
Business Administration, Management and Operations, M
Chemistry, B
Clinical Psychology, M
Communication Studies/Speech Communication and Rhetoric, B
Computer Science, B
Counseling Psychology, M
Counselor Education/School Counseling and Guidance Services, M
Criminology, BM
CytoTechnology/Cytotechnologist, B
Dance, B
Digital Communication and Media/Multimedia, B
Drama and Dramatics/Theatre Arts, B
Economics, B
Education, M
Educational Administration and Supervision, M
Educational Leadership and Administration, M
Elementary Education and Teaching, BM
English Education, M
English Language and Literature, B
Environmental Education, M
Environmental Policy and Resource Management, M
Finance, B
Fine/Studio Arts, B
French Language and Literature, B
Geography, B
Geology/Earth Science, B
Gerontology, M
Health Services Administration, B
Health and Physical Education, B
Higher Education/Higher Education Administration, M
History, BM
Information Science/Studies, B
Information Technology, B
Journalism, B
Kinesiology and Exercise Science, B
Management Science, B
Marketing/Marketing Management, B
Mathematics, B
Mathematics Teacher Education, M
Music, B
Music Performance, B
Music Therapy/Therapist, B
Occupational Safety and Health Technology/Technician, B
Parks, Recreation and Leisure Facilities Management, B
Philosophy, B
Physical Education Teaching and Coaching, BM
Physical Therapy/Therapist, D
Physics, B
Political Science and Government, B
Pre-Medicine/Pre-Medical Studies, B
Pre-Pharmacy Studies, B
Psychology, B
Public Health (MPH, DPH), B
Public Relations/Image Management, B
Reading Teacher Education, M
Recreation and Park Management, M
School Psychology, M
Science Teacher Education/General Science Teacher Education, M
Secondary Education and Teaching, BM
Social Studies Teacher Education, M
Social Work, B
Spanish Language and Literature, B
Special Education and Teaching, BM
Sport and Fitness Administration/Management, B
Statistics, B
Student Personnel Services, M
Substance Abuse/Addiction Counseling, M
Technical Theatre/Theatre Design and Technology, B
Therapeutic Recreation/Recreational Therapy, B

SOUTH HILLS SCHOOL OF BUSINESS & TECHNOLOGY (ALTOONA)

Accounting, A
Accounting Technology/Technician and Bookkeeping, A

Administrative Assistant and Secretarial Science, A
Computer Science, A
Computer and Information Sciences, A
Criminal Justice/Safety Studies, A
Engineering Technologies/Technicians, A
Health Information/Medical Records
 Technology/Technician, A
Legal Administrative Assistant/Secretary, A
Marketing/Marketing Management, A
Medical Administrative Assistant/Secretary, A

SOUTH HILLS SCHOOL OF BUSINESS & TECHNOLOGY (STATE COLLEGE)

Accounting, A
Administrative Assistant and Secretarial Science, A
Business Administration and Management, A
Computer Science, A
Criminal Justice/Law Enforcement Administration, A
Diagnostic Medical Sonography/Sonographer and
 Ultrasound Technician, A
Graphic Design, A
Health Information/Medical Records
 Technology/Technician, A
Industrial Technology/Technician, A
Medical Administrative Assistant/Secretary, A
Medical/Clinical Assistant, A

STRAYER UNIVERSITY–ALLENTOWN CAMPUS

Accounting, B
Business Administration and Management, B
Criminal Justice/Law Enforcement Administration, B
Economics, B
International Business/Trade/Commerce, B
Management Information Systems and Services, B

STRAYER UNIVERSITY–CENTER CITY CAMPUS

Accounting, B
Business Administration and Management, B
Criminal Justice/Law Enforcement Administration, B
Economics, B
International Business/Trade/Commerce, B
Management Information Systems and Services, B

STRAYER UNIVERSITY–DELAWARE COUNTY CAMPUS

Accounting, B
Business Administration and Management, B
Criminal Justice/Law Enforcement Administration, B
Economics, B
International Business/Trade/Commerce, B
Management Information Systems and Services, B

STRAYER UNIVERSITY–KING OF PRUSSIA CAMPUS

Accounting, B
Business Administration and Management, B
Criminal Justice/Law Enforcement Administration, B
Economics, B
International Business/Trade/Commerce, B
Management Information Systems and Services, B

STRAYER UNIVERSITY–LOWER BUCKS COUNTY CAMPUS

Accounting, B
Business Administration and Management, B
Criminal Justice/Law Enforcement Administration, B
Economics, B
International Business/Trade/Commerce, B
Management Information Systems and Services, B

STRAYER UNIVERSITY–WARRENDALE CAMPUS

Accounting, B
Business Administration and Management, B
Criminal Justice/Law Enforcement Administration, B
Economics, B
International Business/Trade/Commerce, B
Management Information Systems and Services, B

SUMMIT UNIVERSITY

Administrative Assistant and Secretarial Science, A
Bible/Biblical Studies, B

Business Administration and Management, B
Communication Studies/Speech Communication
 and Rhetoric, B
Communication and Media Studies, MD
Counselor Education/School Counseling and Guid-
 ance Services, M
Cultural Studies, M
Curriculum and Instruction, M
Divinity/Ministry (BD, MDiv.), B
Early Childhood Education and Teaching, A
Education, B
Educational Administration and Supervision, M
Elementary Education and Teaching, B
English, M
English as a Second Language, M
General Studies, A
Mathematics Teacher Education, B
Missions/Missionary Studies and Missiology, BMD
Music, B
Music Teacher Education, B
Organizational Management, M
Pastoral Studies/Counseling, BMD
Philosophy, M
Physical Education Teaching and Coaching, B
Piano and Organ, B
Pre-Theology/Pre-Ministerial Studies, B
Psychology, B
Reading Teacher Education, M
Religion/Religious Studies, M
Religious Education, BM
Religious/Sacred Music, B
Science Teacher Education/General Science
 Teacher Education, B
Secondary Education and Teaching, B
Social Studies Teacher Education, B
Speech Teacher Education, B
Teacher Education, Multiple Levels, B
Theological and Ministerial Studies, B
Theology and Religious Vocations, BMD
Youth Ministry, B

SUSQUEHANNA UNIVERSITY

Accounting, B
Anthropology, B
Art History, Criticism and Conservation, B
Art/Art Studies, General, B
Biochemistry, B
Biology/Biological Sciences, B
Business Administration and Management, B
Business, Management, Marketing, and Related
 Support Services, B
Chemical Physics, B
Chemistry, B
Cognitive Sciences, B
Communication Studies/Speech Communication
 and Rhetoric, B
Computer Science, B
Drama and Dramatics/Theatre Arts, B
Early Childhood Education and Teaching, B
Ecology, B
Economics, B
English Language and Literature, B
Environmental Studies, B
Finance, B
Fine/Studio Arts, B
French Language and Literature, B
Geology/Earth Science, B
German Language and Literature, B
Graphic Design, B
History, B
Information Science/Studies, B
International Business/Trade/Commerce, B
International/Global Studies, B
Italian Language and Literature, B
Kindergarten/PreSchool Education and Teaching, B
Marketing/Marketing Management, B
Mathematics, B
Music, B
Music Performance, B
Music Teacher Education, B
Music Theory and Composition, B
Philosophy, B
Physics, B
Political Science and Government, B
Pre-Dentistry Studies, B
Pre-Law Studies, B

Pre-Medicine/Pre-Medical Studies, B
Pre-Veterinary Studies, B
Psychology, B
Public Policy Analysis, B
Religion/Religious Studies, B
Secondary Education and Teaching, B
Sociology, B
Spanish Language and Literature, B

SWARTHMORE COLLEGE

African-American/Black Studies, B
Ancient/Classical Greek Language and Literature, B
Art History, Criticism and Conservation, B
Asian Studies/Civilization, B
Astronomy, B
Astrophysics, B
Biochemistry, B
Biological and Biomedical Sciences, B
Biology/Biological Sciences, B
Chemical Physics, B
Chemistry, B
Chinese Language and Literature, B
Classical, Ancient Mediterranean and Near Eastern
 Studies and Archaeology, B
Classics and Classical Languages, Litera-
 tures, and Linguistics, B
Comparative Literature, B
Computer and Information Sciences, B
Dance, B
Drama and Dramatics/Theatre Arts, B
Economics, B
Education, B
Engineering, B
English Language and Literature, B
Film/Video and Photographic Arts, B
Fine/Studio Arts, B
French Language and Literature, B
German Language and Literature, B
History, B
Islamic Studies, B
Japanese Language and Literature, B
Latin American Studies, B
Latin Language and Literature, B
Linguistics, B
Mathematics, B
Medieval and Renaissance Studies, B
Music, B
Near and Middle Eastern Studies, B
Peace Studies and Conflict Resolution, B
Philosophy, B
Physics, B
Political Science and Government, B
Psychology, B
Religion/Religious Studies, B
Russian Language and Literature, B
Spanish Language and Literature, B
Women's Studies, B

TALMUDICAL YESHIVA OF PHILADEL-PHIA

Rabbinical Studies, B
Theology/Theological Studies, B

TEMPLE UNIVERSITY

Accounting, BMD
Acting, B
Actuarial Science, BM
Advertising, B
African-American Studies, MD
African-American/Black Studies, B
Allied Health and Medical Assisting Services, MDO
Allopathic Medicine, D
American/United States Studies/Civilization, B
Anthropology, BD
Applied Mathematics, BM
Architecture, BM
Art Education, M
Art History, Criticism and Conservation, BMD
Art Teacher Education, B
Art/Art Studies, General, B
Arts Management, MD
Asian Studies/Civilization, B
Athletic Training and Sports Medicine, B
Audiology/Audiologist and Speech-Language
 Pathology/Pathologist, B
BioTechnology, M

Biochemistry, B
Bioengineering, MD
Biological and Biomedical Sciences, MD
Biology/Biological Sciences, B
Biomedical/Medical Engineering, B
Biophysics, B
Business Administration, Management and Operations, MD
Business Education, M
Business/Commerce, B
Ceramic Arts and Ceramics, BM
Chemistry, BMD
Cinematography and Film/Video Production, B
City/Urban, Community and Regional Planning, B
Civil Engineering, BMDO
Civil Engineering Technology/Technician, B
Classics and Classical Languages, Literatures, and Linguistics, B
Clinical Research, M
Communication Disorders, M
Communication and Media Studies, MD
Community Psychology, M
Composition, MD
Computational Sciences, M
Computer Science, MD
Computer and Information Sciences, B
Corporate and Organizational Communication, M
Counseling Psychology, MD
Crafts, M
Criminal Justice/Safety Studies, B
Criminology, MD
Dance, BMD
Dentistry, D
Economics, BMD
Education, MDO
Educational Administration and Supervision, M
Educational Leadership and Administration, MD
Educational Psychology, M
Electrical Engineering, MD
Electrical, Electronics and Communications Engineering, B
Elementary Education and Teaching, BMD
Engineering, B
Engineering Management, MO
Engineering Technology, B
Engineering and Applied Sciences, D
English, MD
English Education, M
English Language and Literature, B
English as a Second Language, M
English/Language Arts Teacher Education, B
Entrepreneurship/Entrepreneurial Studies, BMD
Environmental Engineering Technology/Environmental Technology, M
Environmental Sciences, B
Environmental Studies, B
Environmental and Occupational Health, M
Environmental/Environmental Health Engineering, B
Epidemiology, M
Fiber, Textile and Weaving Arts, B
Film, Television, and Video Production, M
Film/Cinema Studies, B
Finance, B
Finance and Banking, MD
Financial Engineering, M
Financial Planning and Services, B
Fine Arts and Art Studies, M
Foreign Language Teacher Education, B
French Language and Literature, B
General Studies, AB
Geography, BMD
Geology/Earth Science, BM
German Language and Literature, B
Gerontology, D
Graphic Design, BM
Health Education, M
Health Informatics, M
Health Services Administration, M
History, BMD
Horticultural Science, AB
Hospitality Administration/Management, BMD
Human Development and Family Studies, B
Human Resources Management and Services, M
Human Resources Management/Personnel Administration, B
Hydrology and Water Resources Science, O

Industrial Education, M
Industrial and Organizational Psychology, M
Information Science/Studies, MD
Information Technology, B
Insurance, BD
International Business/Trade/Commerce, BMD
International Relations and Affairs, B
International/Global Studies, B
Italian Language and Literature, B
Japanese Language and Literature, B
Jazz/Jazz Studies, B
Jewelry/Metalsmithing, M
Jewish/Judaic Studies, B
Journalism, BM
Junior High/Intermediate/Middle School Education and Teaching, B
Kinesiology and Exercise Science, B
Kinesiology and Movement Studies, MD
Landscape Architecture, BM
Latin American Studies, B
Law and Legal Studies, MD
Legal Professions and Studies, B
Legal and Justice Studies, D
Liberal Arts and Sciences Studies and Humanities, B
Linguistics, B
Logistics and Materials Management, B
Management, M
Management Information Systems and Services, BMD
Management Strategy and Policy, D
Marketing, B
Marketing/Marketing Management, B
Mass Communication/Media Studies, B
Mathematics, BMD
Mathematics Teacher Education, BM
Mathematics and Computer Science, B
Mechanical Engineering, BMD
Media Studies, M
Medicinal and Pharmaceutical Chemistry, MD
Metal and Jewelry Arts, B
Middle School Education, M
Multi-/Interdisciplinary Studies, B
Music, BMD
Music History, Literature, and Theory, BM
Music Pedagogy, B
Music Performance, M
Music Teacher Education, BMD
Music Theory and Composition, BMD
Music Therapy/Therapist, BMD
Musicology and Ethnomusicology, MD
Natural Sciences, B
Nursing, MD
Nursing - Adult, D
Nursing - Advanced Practice, D
Nursing Administration, M
Nursing Education, M
Occupational Therapy/Therapist, MD
Oral and Dental Sciences, MO
Organizational Communication, B
Orthodontics, O
Painting, BM
Performance, MD
Periodontics, O
Pharmaceutical Administration, M
Pharmaceutical Sciences, MD
Pharmaceutics and Drug Design, B
Philosophy, BMD
Photography, BM
Physical Education Teaching and Coaching, MD
Physical Therapy/Therapist, D
Physics, BMD
Podiatric Medicine, D
Political Science and Government, BMD
Printmaking, BM
Psychology, BD
Public Health, MD
Public Health Education and Promotion, B
Radio and Television, B
Real Estate, B
Rehabilitation Sciences, MD
Religion/Religious Studies, BMD
School Psychology, MDO
Science Teacher Education/General Science Teacher Education, BM
Sculpture, BM

Secondary Education and Teaching, BM
Social Studies Teacher Education, BM
Social Work, BMO
Sociology, BMD
Spanish Language and Literature, BMD
Special Education and Teaching, M
Sport and Fitness Administration/Management, BD
Statistics, MD
Sustainable Development, M
Taxation, M
Textile Design, M
Theater, M
Therapeutic Recreation, M
Therapeutic Recreation/Recreational Therapy, B
Trade and Industrial Teacher Education, B
Transportation/Transportation Management, M
Travel and Tourism, MD
Urban Design, MD
Urban Education and Leadership, M
Urban Studies/Affairs, MD
Urban and Regional Planning, M
Visual and Performing Arts, B
Vocational and Technical Education, M
Women's Studies, B
Writing, M

THADDEUS STEVENS COLLEGE OF TECHNOLOGY

Architectural Technology/Technician, A
Autobody/Collision and Repair Technology/Technician, A
Automotive Engineering Technology/Technician, A
CAD/CADD Drafting and/or Design Technology/Technician, A
Cabinetmaking and Millwork/Millwright, A
Carpentry/Carpenter, A
Computer and Information Sciences and Support Services, A
Electrical and Electronic Engineering Technologies/Technicians, A
Electrical, Electronic and Communications Engineering Technology/Technician, A
Engineering-Related Technologies, A
Executive Assistant/Executive Secretary, A
Graphic Communications, A
Heating, Air Conditioning, Ventilation and Refrigeration Maintenance Technology/Technician, A
Machine Shop Technology/Assistant, A
Mason/Masonry, A
Plumbing Technology/Plumber, A
Respiratory Care Therapy/Therapist, A
Sheet Metal Technology/Sheetworking, A
Water Quality and Wastewater Treatment Management and Recycling Technology/Technician, A
Welding Technology/Welder, A

THIEL COLLEGE

Accounting, AB
Actuarial Science, B
Art/Art Studies, General, B
Audiology/Audiologist and Speech-Language Pathology/Pathologist, B
Biology/Biological Sciences, B
Business Administration and Management, B
Chemical Engineering, B
Chemistry, B
Clinical Laboratory Science/Medical Technology/Technologist, B
Communication Studies/Speech Communication and Rhetoric, B
Computer Science, B
Criminal Justice/Safety Studies, B
CytoTechnology/Cytotechnologist, B
E-Commerce/Electronic Commerce, B
Elementary Education and Teaching, B
Engineering Physics, B
English Language and Literature, B
Environmental Studies, B
Funeral Service and Mortuary Science, B
History, B
Information Science/Studies, B
International Business/Trade/Commerce, B
Liberal Arts and Sciences Studies and Humanities, A
Management Information Systems and Services, AB
Mass Communication/Media Studies, B

Mathematics, B
Philosophy, B
Physics, B
Political Science and Government, B
Pre-Dentistry Studies, B
Pre-Law Studies, B
Pre-Medicine/Pre-Medical Studies, B
Pre-Veterinary Studies, B
Psychology, B
Religion/Religious Studies, B
Religious Education, B
Secondary Education and Teaching, B
Sociology, B
Theology and Religious Vocations, B
Web Page, Digital/Multimedia and Information Resources Design, B

THOMAS JEFFERSON UNIVERSITY

Allied Health Diagnostic, Intervention, and Treatment Professions, B
Allopathic Medicine, D
Applied Economics, O
BioTechnology, D
Biochemistry, D
Biological and Biomedical Sciences, MDO
Biomedical Engineering, D
Biophysics, D
Cancer Biology/Oncology, D
Cell Biology and Anatomy, MD
Clinical Laboratory Science/Medical Technology/Technologist, B
Clinical Laboratory Sciences, M
Clinical Research, O
CytoTechnology/Cytotechnologist, B
Developmental Biology and Embryology, MD
Diagnostic Medical Sonography/Sonographer and Ultrasound Technician, B
Genetics, D
Genomic Sciences, D
Health Education, DO
Health Physics/Radiological Health, M
Health Professions and Related Clinical Sciences, B
Health Services Administration, MDO
Health Services Research, MDO
Immunology, D
Infectious Diseases, O
Liberal Arts and Sciences Studies and Humanities, AB
Marriage and Family Therapy/Counseling, M
Microbiology, MD
Molecular Pharmacology, D
Molecular Physiology, D
Neuroscience, D
Nursing, MD
Occupational Therapy/Therapist, MD
Pharmacology, M
Pharmacy, D
Physical Therapy/Therapist, D
Physician Assistant, M
Public Health, MO
Structural Biology, D

TRIANGLE TECH, BETHLEHEM

Carpentry/Carpenter, A
Electrician, A

TRIANGLE TECH, DUBOIS

Carpentry/Carpenter, A
Drafting and Design Technology/Technician, A
Electrical, Electronic and Communications Engineering Technology/Technician, A
Welding Technology/Welder, A

TRIANGLE TECH, ERIE

Architectural Drafting and Architectural CAD/CADD, A
Carpentry/Carpenter, A
Electrician, A
Mechanical Drafting and Mechanical Drafting CAD/CADD, A

TRIANGLE TECH, GREENSBURG

Carpentry/Carpenter, A
Construction Trades, A
Drafting and Design Technology/Technician, A

Electrical/Electronics Equipment Installation and Repair, A
Electrical/Electronics Maintenance and Repair Technology, A
Heating, Air Conditioning and Refrigeration Technology/Technician, A
Heating, Air Conditioning, Ventilation and Refrigeration Maintenance Technology/Technician, A
Mechanical Drafting and Mechanical Drafting CAD/CADD, A

TRIANGLE TECH, PITTSBURGH

Architectural Drafting and Architectural CAD/CADD, A
Carpentry/Carpenter, A
Educational/Instructional Media Design, A
Electrician, A
Heating, Air Conditioning, Ventilation and Refrigeration Maintenance Technology/Technician, A
Mechanical Drafting and Mechanical Drafting CAD/CADD, A

TRIANGLE TECH, SUNBURY

Carpentry/Carpenter, A
Electrician, A
Welding Technology/Welder, A

THE UNIVERSITY OF THE ARTS

Acting, B
Animation, Interactive Technology, Video Graphics and Special Effects, B
Art Education, M
Commercial and Advertising Art, B
Crafts/Craft Design, Folk Art and Artisanry, B
Dance, B
Directing and Theatrical Production, B
Film/Cinema Studies, B
Fine Arts and Art Studies, BM
Fine/Studio Arts, B
Graphic Design, B
Illustration, B
Industrial Design, BM
Intermedia/Multimedia, B
Museology/Museum Studies, M
Museum Education, M
Music, M
Music Performance, B
Music Teacher Education, M
Music Theory and Composition, B
Painting, B
Photography, B
Playwriting and Screenwriting, B
Printmaking, BM
Sculpture, B
Technical Theatre/Theatre Design and Technology, B
Web Page, Digital/Multimedia and Information Resources Design, B

UNIVERSITY OF PENNSYLVANIA

Accounting, BMD
Actuarial Science, B
Acute Care/Critical Care Nursing, M
African Studies, BMD
African-American/Black Studies, B
Allopathic Medicine, D
American/United States Studies/Civilization, B
Anthropology, BMD
Applied Economics, D
Applied Mathematics, D
Applied Psychology, MD
Archeology, MD
Architecture, BMDO
Art History, Criticism and Conservation, BMD
BioTechnology, M
Biochemistry, BD
Bioengineering, MD
Bioethics/Medical Ethics, M
Bioinformatics, B
Biological and Biomedical Sciences, MD
Biology/Biological Sciences, B
Biomedical Sciences, B
Biomedical/Medical Engineering, B
Biophysics, B
Biostatistics, MD
Business Administration and Management, AB

Business Administration, Management and Operations, BMD
Cancer Biology/Oncology, D
Cell Biology and Anatomy, D
Chemical Engineering, BMD
Chemistry, BMD
Classics and Classical Languages, Literatures, and Linguistics, BMD
Clinical Laboratory Sciences, M
Cognitive Sciences, B
Communication Studies/Speech Communication and Rhetoric, B
Communication and Media Studies, D
Community Health Services/Liaison/Counseling, B
Comparative Literature, BMD
Computational Biology, D
Computational Sciences, D
Computer Art and Design, M
Computer Engineering, B
Computer Graphics, B
Computer Science, MD
Computer Systems Networking and Telecommunications, B
Counseling Psychology, M
Criminology, MD
Dentistry, D
Developmental Biology and Embryology, D
Drama and Dramatics/Theatre Arts, B
E-Commerce/Electronic Commerce, B
East Asian Languages, Literatures, and Linguistics, B
East Asian Studies, BMD
Economic Development, O
Economics, BMD
Education, MDO
Educational Leadership and Administration, MD
Educational Measurement and Evaluation, MD
Educational Media/Instructional Technology, M
Educational Policy, MD
Electrical Engineering, MD
Electrical, Electronics and Communications Engineering, B
Elementary Education and Teaching, BM
Engineering, B
Engineering and Applied Sciences, MDO
English, MD
English Education, MD
English Language and Literature, B
English as a Second Language, MD
Entrepreneurship/Entrepreneurial Studies, M
Environmental Design/Architecture, B
Environmental Sciences, MD
Environmental Studies, BM
Environmental/Environmental Health Engineering, B
Epidemiology, M
Ethics, MD
Film/Cinema Studies, B
Finance, B
Finance and Banking, MD
Fine Arts and Art Studies, MO
Fine/Studio Arts, B
Foundations and Philosophy of Education, MD
French Language and Literature, BMD
Genetics, D
Genomic Sciences, D
Geographic Information Systems, MO
Geology/Earth Science, B
Geosciences, MD
German Language and Literature, BMD
Graphic Design, O
Health Professions and Related Clinical Sciences, B
Health Services Administration, MD
Health Services Research, M
Health/Health Care Administration/Management, B
Higher Education/Higher Education Administration, MD
Historic Preservation and Conservation, MO
History, BMD
History and Philosophy of Science and Technology, B
History of Science and Technology, MD
Human Development, MD
Human Resources Management/Personnel Administration, B
Humanities/Humanistic Studies, B
Immunology, D

Information Science/Studies, MD
Insurance, BMD
International Affairs, M
International Business/Trade/Commerce, BM
International Public Health/International Health, M
International Relations and Affairs, B
International and Comparative Education, M
International/Global Studies, B
Internet and Interactive Multimedia, O
Italian Language and Literature, BMD
Jewish/Judaic Studies, B
Landscape Architecture, MO
Latin American Studies, B
Law and Legal Studies, MD
Legal Professions and Studies, B
Legal and Justice Studies, MD
Liberal Arts and Sciences Studies and Humanities, B
Liberal Studies, M
Linguistics, BMD
Logic, B
Management, MD
Management Information Systems and Services, BMD
Management Sciences and Quantitative Methods, B
Management of Technology, M
Marketing, MD
Marketing/Marketing Management, B
Materials Engineering, BMD
Materials Sciences, MD
Maternal/Child Health and Neonatal Nurse/Nursing, MO
Maternity Nursing, M
Mathematics, BMD
Mechanical Engineering, BMD
Mechanics, MD
Medical Physics, M
Microbiology, D
Molecular Biology, D
Molecular Biophysics, D
Multilingual and Multicultural Education, M
Music, BMD
Natural Sciences, B
Near and Middle Eastern Studies, MD
Neuroscience, D
Non-Profit/Public/Organizational Management, O
Nurse Anesthetist, M
Nurse Midwife/Nursing Midwifery, M
Nursing, MDO
Nursing - Adult, M
Nursing - Advanced Practice, MO
Nursing Administration, MD
Operations Management and Supervision, B
Organizational Management, M
Pediatric Nurse/Nursing, M
Pharmacology, D
Philosophy, BMD
Physics, BMD
Physiology, D
Political Science and Government, BMDO
Population Studies, MD
Psychiatric/Mental Health Nurse/Nursing, M
Psychology, BD
Public Administration, MO
Public Health, M
Public Policy Analysis, BMD
Reading Teacher Education, M
Real Estate, BMD
Religion/Religious Studies, BD
Romance Languages, Literatures, and Linguistics, BMD
Russian Language and Literature, B
Sales, Distribution and Marketing Operations, B
Science Teacher Education/General Science Teacher Education, MO
Secondary Education and Teaching, M
Semitic Languages, Literatures, and Linguistics, B
Social Sciences, B
Social Work, MD
Sociology, BMD
South Asian Studies, B
South and Southeast Asian Studies, MD
Spanish Language and Literature, BMD
Statistics, BMD
Systems Engineering, BMD
Transportation/Transportation Management, B

Urban Design, O
Urban Education and Leadership, M
Urban Studies/Affairs, B
Urban and Regional Planning, MDO
Veterinary Medicine, D
Virology, D
Visual and Performing Arts, B
Women's Health Nursing, M
Women's Studies, B
Writing, MD

UNIVERSITY OF PHOENIX–PHILADELPHIA CAMPUS

Accounting, B
Business Administration and Management, B
Business/Corporate Communications, B
Computer Software Engineering, B
Computer and Information Systems Security, B
Consumer Merchandising/Retailing Management, B
Criminal Justice/Law Enforcement Administration, B
E-Commerce/Electronic Commerce, B
Finance, B
Health Information/Medical Records Technology/Technician, B
Health Services Administration, B
Health/Health Care Administration/Management, B
Hospitality Administration/Management, B
Human Services, B
Information Technology, B
International Business/Trade/Commerce, B
Management Information Systems and Services, B
Management Science, B
Marketing/Marketing Management, B
Operations Management and Supervision, B
Organizational Behavior Studies, B
Psychology, B
Public Administration, B
Security and Protective Services, B

UNIVERSITY OF PITTSBURGH

Accounting, BMD
African Studies, O
African-American/Black Studies, B
Allopathic Medicine, D
Anthropology, BMD
Applied Behavior Analysis, M
Applied Mathematics, BM
Applied Psychology, MD
Applied Statistics, M
Architectural History and Criticism, MD
Area Studies, B
Art History, Criticism and Conservation, BMD
Artificial Intelligence and Robotics, MD
Asian Studies/Civilization, O
Astronomy, BD
Audiology/Audiologist and Speech-Language Pathology/Pathologist, B
Bioengineering, MD
Bioethics/Medical Ethics, M
Bioinformatics, BMDO
Biological and Biomedical Sciences, D
Biological and Physical Sciences, B
Biology/Biological Sciences, B
Biomedical/Medical Engineering, B
Biostatistics, MD
Business Administration, Management and Operations, MD
Business/Commerce, B
Cell Biology and Anatomy, D
Chemical Engineering, BMD
Chemistry, BMD
Chinese Language and Literature, B
Civil Engineering, BMD
Classics and Classical Languages, Literatures, and Linguistics, B
Clinical Laboratory Sciences, D
Clinical Research, MO
Communication Disorders, MD
Communication and Media Studies, MD
Community Health and Preventive Medicine, MDO
Composition, MD
Computational Biology, D
Computer Engineering, BMD
Computer Science, BMD
Computer and Information Sciences and Support Services, B

Computer and Information Systems Security, O
Corrections, B
Criminology, M
Cultural Studies, O
Dental Hygiene/Hygienist, B
Dental and Oral Surgery, O
Dentistry, MDO
Developmental Biology and Embryology, D
Developmental Psychology, MD
Dietetics/Dieticians, B
Disability Studies, O
Drama and Dramatics/Theatre Arts, B
Early Childhood Education and Teaching, M
East Asian Studies, M
East European and Russian Studies, O
Ecology, BD
Economics, BMD
Education, MD
Educational Leadership and Administration, MD
Educational Measurement and Evaluation, MD
Educational Policy, D
Electrical Engineering, MD
Electrical, Electronics and Communications Engineering, B
Elementary Education and Teaching, M
Energy Management and Policy, M
Engineering Physics, B
Engineering Science, B
Engineering and Applied Sciences, MD
English, MD
English Education, M
English as a Second Language, O
Environmental Engineering Technology/Environmental Technology, MD
Environmental Law, M
Environmental and Occupational Health, MDO
Epidemiology, MD
Ethnic, Cultural Minority, and Gender Studies, B
Ethnomusicology, D
Evolutionary Biology, D
Exercise and Sports Science, MD
Film, Television, and Video Theory and Criticism, MDO
Film/Cinema Studies, B
Finance, B
Finance and Banking, MD
Fine/Studio Arts, B
Foreign Language Teacher Education, M
Foundations and Philosophy of Education, MD
French Language and Literature, BMD
Genetic Counseling/Counselor, M
Geographic Information Systems, M
Geological and Earth Sciences/Geosciences, B
Geology/Earth Science, BMD
German Language and Literature, B
German Studies, B
Gerontological Nursing, D
Health Education, M
Health Information/Medical Records Administration/Administrator, B
Health Law, M
Health Professions and Related Clinical Sciences, B
Health Promotion, M
Health Services Administration, MDO
Higher Education/Higher Education Administration, MD
Hispanic and Latin American Languages, MD
History, BMD
History and Philosophy of Science and Technology, B
History of Science and Technology, MD
Human Genetics, MDO
Human Resources Management and Services, BMD
Humanities/Humanistic Studies, B
Immunology, D
Industrial Engineering, B
Industrial and Manufacturing Management, M
Industrial/Management Engineering, MD
Infectious Diseases, MD
Information Science/Studies, BMDO
Intellectual Property Law, M
Interdisciplinary Studies, D
International Affairs, MDO
International Business/Trade/Commerce, BO
International Development, M
International and Comparative Education, MD

Italian Language and Literature, BM
Japanese Language and Literature, B
Latin American Studies, O
Law and Legal Studies, BM
Legal and Justice Studies, M
Liberal Arts and Sciences Studies and Humanities, B
Library Science, MD
Linguistics, BMD
Logistics and Materials Management, B
Management Information Systems and Services, BMD
Management Strategy and Policy, MD
Marketing, M
Marketing/Marketing Management, B
Mass Communication/Media Studies, B
Materials Engineering, B
Materials Sciences, MD
Maternal/Child Health and Neonatal Nurse/Nursing, M
Mathematics, BMD
Mathematics Teacher Education, MD
Mathematics and Statistics, B
Mechanical Engineering, BMD
Medieval and Renaissance Studies, O
Microbiology, BMD
Military and Defense Studies, M
Modeling and Simulation, D
Molecular Biology, BD
Molecular Biophysics, D
Molecular Genetics, D
Molecular Pathology, D
Molecular Pharmacology, D
Molecular Physiology, D
Multi-/Interdisciplinary Studies, B
Music, BMD
Music Theory and Composition, MD
Musicology and Ethnomusicology, MD
Neuroscience, D
Non-Profit/Public/Organizational Management, M
Nurse Anesthetist, MD
Nursing, D
Nursing - Advanced Practice, MD
Nursing Administration, MD
Nutritional Sciences, M
Occupational Therapy/Therapist, M
Oral Biology, MD
Oral Pathology, O
Oral and Dental Sciences, MO
Organizational Behavior Studies, MD
Orthodontics, MO
Pathology/Experimental Pathology, D
Pediatric Nurse/Nursing, D
Periodontics, MO
Petroleum Engineering, MD
Pharmaceutical Sciences, MD
Pharmacy, D
Philosophy, BMD
Physical Education Teaching and Coaching, B
Physical Sciences, B
Physical Therapy/Therapist, D
Physician Assistant, M
Physics, BMD
Planetary Astronomy and Science, MD
Polish Language and Literature, B
Political Science and Government, BMD
Psychiatric/Mental Health Nurse/Nursing, D
Psychology, BMD
Public Administration, BMD
Public Health, MDO
Public Policy Analysis, MD
Reading Teacher Education, MD
Rehabilitation Sciences, MD
Religion/Religious Studies, B
Russian Language and Literature, B
Science Teacher Education/General Science Teacher Education, MD
Secondary Education and Teaching, MD
Slavic Languages, Literatures, and Linguistics, BMD
Social Sciences, B
Social Studies Teacher Education, M
Social Work, BMDO
Sociology, BMD
Spanish Language and Literature, BMD
Special Education and Teaching, MD
Statistics, BMD

Structural Biology, D
Systematic Biology/Biological Systematics, D
Telecommunications, MDO
Theater, MD
Urban Planning, M
Urban Studies/Affairs, B
Virology, D
Vision Science/Physiological Optics, MD
Western European Studies, O
Women's Studies, BO
Writing, M

UNIVERSITY OF PITTSBURGH AT BRADFORD

Accounting, B
Applied Mathematics, B
Athletic Training and Sports Medicine, B
Biology/Biological Sciences, B
Business Administration and Management, B
Chemistry, B
Computer Science, B
Criminal Justice/Law Enforcement Administration, B
Economics, B
Elementary Education and Teaching, B
Engineering Science, A
English Language and Literature, B
Entrepreneurship/Entrepreneurial Studies, B
Environmental Studies, B
History, B
Hospitality Administration/Management, B
Humanities/Humanistic Studies, B
Information Science/Studies, A
Liberal Arts and Sciences Studies and Humanities, AB
Petroleum Technology/Technician, A
Physical Education Teaching and Coaching, B
Physical Sciences, B
Political Science and Government, B
Psychology, B
Public Relations/Image Management, B
Radio and Television, B
Radiologic Technology/Science - Radiographer, B
Secondary Education and Teaching, B
Social Sciences, B
Sociology, B
Sport and Fitness Administration/Management, B

UNIVERSITY OF PITTSBURGH AT GREENSBURG

Accounting, B
American/United States Studies/Civilization, B
Anthropology, B
Applied Mathematics, B
Biology/Biological Sciences, B
Business Administration and Management, B
Chemistry, B
Comparative Literature, B
Computer and Information Sciences, B
Criminal Justice/Law Enforcement Administration, B
Criminal Justice/Police Science, B
Education, B
English Language and Literature, B
Humanities/Humanistic Studies, B
Journalism, B
Mass Communication/Media Studies, B
Natural Sciences, B
Political Science and Government, B
Pre-Law Studies, B
Psychology, B
Public Policy Analysis, B
Social Sciences, B
Spanish Language and Literature, B
Visual and Performing Arts, B

UNIVERSITY OF PITTSBURGH AT JOHNSTOWN

Accounting, B
Biology Teacher Education, B
Biology/Biological Sciences, B
Biopsychology, B
Business Administration and Management, B
Business/Managerial Economics, B
Chemistry, B
Chemistry Teacher Education, B
Civil Engineering Technology/Technician, B

Comparative Literature, B
Computer Science, B
Drama and Dramatics/Theatre Arts, B
Ecology, B
Economics, B
Education, B
Electrical, Electronic and Communications Engineering Technology/Technician, B
Elementary Education and Teaching, B
Emergency Medical Technology/Technician (EMT Paramedic), A
Engineering Technology, B
English Language and Literature, B
English/Language Arts Teacher Education, B
Environmental Biology, B
Environmental Studies, B
Finance, B
Geography, B
Geology/Earth Science, B
History, B
History Teacher Education, B
Humanities/Humanistic Studies, B
Journalism, B
Mass Communication/Media Studies, B
Mathematics, B
Mathematics Teacher Education, B
Mechanical Engineering/Mechanical Technology/Technician, B
Natural Sciences, B
Political Science and Government, B
Pre-Dentistry Studies, B
Pre-Law Studies, B
Pre-Medicine/Pre-Medical Studies, B
Pre-Veterinary Studies, B
Psychology, B
Respiratory Care Therapy/Therapist, A
Science Teacher Education/General Science Teacher Education, B
Secondary Education and Teaching, B
Social Sciences, B
Social Studies Teacher Education, B
Sociology, B
Surgical Technology/Technologist, A

UNIVERSITY OF PITTSBURGH AT TITUSVILLE

Accounting, A
Biology/Biological Sciences, A
Business/Commerce, A
Criminal Justice/Law Enforcement Administration, A
History, A
Human Services, A
Information Technology, A
Liberal Arts and Sciences Studies and Humanities, A
Management Information Systems and Services, A
Natural Sciences, A
Physical Therapist Assistant, A
Psychology, A

UNIVERSITY OF THE SCIENCES

BioTechnology, M
Biochemistry, BMD
Bioinformatics, M
Biology/Biological Sciences, B
Cell Biology and Anatomy, MD
Chemistry, BMD
Clinical Laboratory Science/Medical Technology/Technologist, B
Environmental Sciences, B
Health Law, O
Health Psychology, M
Health Services Administration, MD
Health Services/Allied Health/Health Sciences, B
Humanities/Humanistic Studies, B
Kinesiology and Exercise Science, B
Medicinal and Pharmaceutical Chemistry, BMD
Microbiology, B
Molecular Biology, D
Occupational Therapy/Therapist, BMD
Pharmaceutical Administration, M
Pharmaceutical Sciences, MD
Pharmacology, MD
Pharmacology and Toxicology, B
Pharmacy, BD

Pharmacy, Pharmaceutical Sciences, and Administration, B
Physical Therapy/Therapist, BD
Physician Assistant, BM
Physics, B
Psychology, B
Public Health, M
Technical and Business Writing, MO
Toxicology, MD

THE UNIVERSITY OF SCRANTON

Accounting, BM
Applied Mathematics, B
Biochemistry, BM
Biology/Biological Sciences, B
Biophysics, B
Broadcast Journalism, B
Business Administration and Management, AB
Business Administration, Management and Operations, M
Chemistry, BM
Classics and Classical Languages, Literatures, and Linguistics, B
Clinical Laboratory Science/Medical Technology/Technologist, B
Clinical Psychology, M
Communication Studies/Speech Communication and Rhetoric, B
Computer Engineering, AB
Computer Science, B
Counseling Psychology, M
Counselor Education/School Counseling and Guidance Services, M
Criminal Justice/Safety Studies, AB
Curriculum and Instruction, M
Digital Communication and Media/Multimedia, B
Drama and Dramatics/Theatre Arts, B
E-Commerce/Electronic Commerce, B
Early Childhood Education and Teaching, BM
Economics, B
Education, M
Educational Administration and Supervision, M
Electrical, Electronics and Communications Engineering, AB
Elementary Education and Teaching, B
Engineering/Industrial Management, B
English Language and Literature, B
Environmental Sciences, B
Finance, B
Finance and Banking, M
Foreign Languages and Literatures, B
Forensic Science and Technology, B
French Language and Literature, B
French Studies, B
German Language and Literature, B
German Studies, B
Health Services Administration, M
Health/Health Care Administration/Management, AB
Hispanic-American, Puerto Rican, and Mexican-American/Chicano Studies, B
History, B
Human Resources Development, M
Human Resources Management/Personnel Administration, AB
Human Services, AB
Information Science/Studies, AB
International Business/Trade/Commerce, BM
International Relations and Affairs, B
Italian Language and Literature, B
Italian Studies, B
Junior High/Intermediate/Middle School Education and Teaching, B
Kinesiology and Exercise Science, B
Liberal Arts and Sciences Studies and Humanities, B
Management, M
Management Information Systems and Services, M
Marketing, M
Marketing/Marketing Management, B
Mathematics, B
Molecular Biology, B
Molecular Pharmacology, B
Nurse Anesthetist, MO
Nursing, MO
Nursing - Adult, M
Nursing - Advanced Practice, MO

Occupational Therapy/Therapist, BM
Operations Management and Supervision, B
Philosophy, B
Physical Therapy/Therapist, BD
Physics, B
Political Science and Government, B
Psychology, B
Public Health Education and Promotion, B
Reading Teacher Education, M
Rehabilitation Counseling, M
Religion/Religious Studies, B
Secondary Education and Teaching, BM
Small Business Administration/Management, B
Sociology, AB
Software Engineering, M
Spanish Language and Literature, B
Theology and Religious Vocations, M
Women's Studies, B

UNIVERSITY OF VALLEY FORGE

Ancient Near Eastern and Biblical Languages, Literatures, and Linguistics, B
Bible/Biblical Studies, AB
Business Administration and Management, B
Criminal Justice/Safety Studies, B
Digital Communication and Media/Multimedia, B
Divinity/Ministry (BD, MDiv.), B
Early Childhood Education and Teaching, AB
English Language and Literature, B
Human Development and Family Studies, B
Human Resources Management/Personnel Administration, B
Human Services, A
Junior High/Intermediate/Middle School Education and Teaching, B
Missions/Missionary Studies and Missiology, B
Music, M
Music Performance, B
Music Teacher Education, B
Pastoral Studies/Counseling, B
Psychology, B
Religion/Religious Studies, M
Religious Education, B
Religious/Sacred Music, B
Secondary Education and Teaching, B
Social Work, B
Sport and Fitness Administration/Management, B
Theology and Religious Vocations, ABM
Theology/Theological Studies, B
Youth Ministry, AB

URSINUS COLLEGE

American/United States Studies/Civilization, B
Anthropology, B
Applied Economics, B
Art History, Criticism and Conservation, B
Art/Art Studies, General, B
Biochemistry, B
Biological and Physical Sciences, B
Biology/Biological Sciences, B
Business Administration and Management, B
Chemistry, B
Civil Engineering, B
Computer Science, B
Dance, B
Drama and Dramatics/Theatre Arts, B
East Asian Studies, B
Economics, B
Electrical, Electronics and Communications Engineering, B
English Language and Literature, B
Environmental Studies, B
Exercise Physiology, B
Fine Arts and Art Studies, B
French Language and Literature, B
General Studies, B
German Language and Literature, B
Health and Physical Education, B
History, B
International Relations and Affairs, B
Linguistics, B
Mass Communication/Media Studies, B
Mathematics, B
Mechanical Engineering, B
Medieval and Renaissance Studies, B
Multi-/Interdisciplinary Studies, B

Music History, Literature, and Theory, B
Peace Studies and Conflict Resolution, B
Philosophy, B
Philosophy and Religious Studies, B
Physics, B
Political Science and Government, B
Psychology, B
Religion/Religious Studies, B
Social Sciences, B
Sociology, B
Spanish Language and Literature, B

VALLEY FORGE MILITARY COLLEGE

Biological and Physical Sciences, A
Business Administration and Management, A
Criminal Justice/Law Enforcement Administration, A
Engineering, A
Liberal Arts and Sciences Studies and Humanities, A

VET TECH INSTITUTE

Veterinary/Animal Health Technology/Technician and Veterinary Assistant, A

VILLANOVA UNIVERSITY

Accounting, BM
American/United States Studies/Civilization, O
Applied Statistics, M
Art History, Criticism and Conservation, B
Artificial Intelligence and Robotics, O
Astronomy, B
Astrophysics, B
Biochemical Engineering, O
Biochemistry, B
Biological and Biomedical Sciences, M
Biology/Biological Sciences, B
Business Administration and Management, B
Business Administration, Management and Operations, M
Business/Managerial Economics, B
Chemical Engineering, BMO
Chemistry, BM
Civil Engineering, BM
Classics and Classical Languages, Literatures, and Linguistics, BM
Communication and Media Studies, M
Computer Engineering, BMO
Computer Science, BMO
Counselor Education/School Counseling and Guidance Services, M
Criminal Justice/Law Enforcement Administration, B
Database Systems, M
Economics, B
Education, M
Educational Leadership and Administration, M
Electrical Engineering, MO
Electrical, Electronics and Communications Engineering, B
Engineering and Applied Sciences, MDO
English, M
English Language and Literature, B
Environmental Engineering Technology/Environmental Technology, MO
Environmental Sciences, BM
Environmental Studies, B
Finance, B
Finance and Banking, M
French Language and Literature, B
Geography, B
Health Services Administration, MO
Hispanic Studies, M
History, BM
Human Resources Development, M
Humanities/Humanistic Studies, B
Intercultural/Multicultural and Diversity Studies, B
International Business/Trade/Commerce, BM
International/Global Studies, B
Islamic Studies, B
Italian Language and Literature, B
Latin American Studies, B
Law and Legal Studies, D
Liberal Arts and Sciences Studies and Humanities, B
Liberal Studies, MO
Management Information Systems and Services, BM

Management Strategy and Policy, M
Manufacturing Engineering, O
Marketing, M
Marketing/Marketing Management, B
Mass Communication/Media Studies, B
Mathematics, BM
Mechanical Engineering, BMO
Missions/Missionary Studies and Missiology, M
Multi-/Interdisciplinary Studies, B
Nurse Anesthetist, MO
Nursing, MDO
Nursing - Adult, MO
Nursing - Advanced Practice, MO
Nursing Administration, MO
Nursing Education, MO
Pediatric Nurse/Nursing, MO
Philosophy, BD
Physical Sciences, B
Physics, B
Political Science and Government, BM
Psychology, BM
Public Administration, M
Real Estate, BM
Religion/Religious Studies, B
Secondary Education and Teaching, BM
Sociology, B
Software Engineering, M
Spanish Language and Literature, B
Taxation, M
Theater, M
Theology and Religious Vocations, M
Water Resources Engineering, MO
Women's Studies, B

WASHINGTON & JEFFERSON COLLEGE

Accounting, B
Art Teacher Education, B
Art/Art Studies, General, B
Biochemistry, B
Biology/Biological Sciences, B
Biophysics, B
Business/Commerce, B
Cell/Cellular Biology and Anatomical Sciences, B
Chemistry, B
Communication and Media Studies, B
Economics, B
Education, B
English Language and Literature, B
Environmental Studies, B
French Language and Literature, B
German Language and Literature, B
History, B
Information Technology, B
International Business/Trade/Commerce, B
International/Global Studies, B
Mathematics, B
Multi-/Interdisciplinary Studies, B
Music, B
Philosophy, B
Physics, B
Political Science and Government, B
Psychology, B
Sociology, B
Spanish Language and Literature, B

WAYNESBURG UNIVERSITY

Accounting, B
Advertising, B
Art/Art Studies, General, B
Athletic Training and Sports Medicine, B
Bible/Biblical Studies, B
Biology Teacher Education, B
Biology/Biological Sciences, B
Business Administration and Management, B
Business Administration, Management and Operations, MD
Chemistry, B
Chemistry Teacher Education, B
Clinical Psychology, M
Commercial and Advertising Art, B
Communication Studies/Speech Communication and Rhetoric, B
Computer Science, B
Computer and Information Sciences, B
Counseling Psychology, M

Criminal Justice/Law Enforcement Administration, B
Curriculum and Instruction, M
Distance Education Development, M
Education, M
Educational Leadership and Administration, M
Educational Media/Instructional Technology, M
Elementary Education and Teaching, B
Energy Management and Policy, M
Engineering, B
English Language and Literature, B
English/Language Arts Teacher Education, B
Entrepreneurship/Entrepreneurial Studies, B
Environmental Studies, B
Finance, B
Finance and Banking, M
Forensic Science and Technology, B
Graphic Design, B
Health Services Administration, M
Health/Health Care Administration/Management, B
History, B
Human Resources Management and Services, M
Human Services, B
International Business/Trade/Commerce, B
Journalism, B
Kinesiology and Exercise Science, B
Marine Biology and Biological Oceanography, B
Marketing/Marketing Management, B
Mathematics, B
Mathematics Teacher Education, B
Multi-/Interdisciplinary Studies, B
Nursing, MD
Nursing Administration, M
Nursing Education, M
Nursing Informatics, M
Organizational Management, M
Pre-Dentistry Studies, B
Pre-Law Studies, B
Pre-Medicine/Pre-Medical Studies, B
Pre-Theology/Pre-Ministerial Studies, B
Pre-Veterinary Studies, B
Psychology, B
Public Administration, B
Radio and Television, B
Science Teacher Education/General Science Teacher Education, B
Secondary Education and Teaching, B
Social Sciences, B
Social Studies Teacher Education, B
Sociology, B
Special Education and Teaching, BM
Substance Abuse/Addiction Counseling, M
Visual and Performing Arts, B

WEST CHESTER UNIVERSITY OF PENNSYLVANIA

Accounting, B
Analytical Chemistry, B
Anthropology, B
Applied Mathematics, M
Applied Statistics, MO
Art/Art Studies, General, B
Astronomy, MO
Athletic Training and Sports Medicine, BM
Audiology/Audiologist and Speech-Language Pathology/Pathologist, B
Biochemistry, B
Biological and Biomedical Sciences, MO
Biology/Biological Sciences, B
Business Administration and Management, B
Business Administration, Management and Operations, MO
Business/Managerial Economics, B
Chemistry, BO
Clinical Psychology, MO
Communication Disorders, MO
Communication and Media Studies, M
Community Health and Preventive Medicine, M
Composition, M
Computer Science, MO
Computer and Information Sciences, B
Computer and Information Systems Security, O
Counselor Education/School Counseling and Guidance Services, MO
Criminal Justice/Safety Studies, B
Criminology, M
Dietetics/Dieticians, B

Drama and Dramatics/Theatre Arts, B
Early Childhood Education and Teaching, BMO
Education, MO
Educational Media/Instructional Technology, O
Elementary Education and Teaching, O
Emergency Management, O
English, MO
English Language and Literature, B
English as a Second Language, M
Entrepreneurship/Entrepreneurial Studies, O
Environmental and Occupational Health, M
Ethics, MO
Exercise and Sports Science, M
Finance, B
Fine/Studio Arts, B
Foreign Language Teacher Education, MO
Foreign Languages and Literatures, B
French Language and Literature, BMO
Geographic Information Systems, O
Geography, BMO
Geology/Earth Science, BMO
Geosciences, M
German Language and Literature, B
Gerontological Nursing, M
Health Education, M
Health Services Administration, MO
Health Services/Allied Health/Health Sciences, B
Health and Physical Education, B
Higher Education/Higher Education Administration, O
History, BMO
Holocaust Studies, MO
Human Resources Management and Services, MO
Industrial and Organizational Psychology, M
Junior High/Intermediate/Middle School Education and Teaching, M
Kinesiology and Movement Studies, MO
Latin Language and Literature, B
Liberal Arts and Sciences Studies and Humanities, B
Management Information Systems and Services, O
Mathematics, BMO
Mathematics Teacher Education, M
Music, BM
Music History, Literature, and Theory, M
Music Performance, B
Music Teacher Education, MO
Music Theory and Composition, M
Non-Profit/Public/Organizational Management, MO
Nursing, MDO
Nursing Education, M
Nutritional Sciences, M
Performance, MO
Pharmaceutics and Drug Design, B
Philosophy, BMO
Physical Education Teaching and Coaching, MO
Physics, B
Planetary Astronomy and Science, O
Political Science and Government, B
Pre-Medicine/Pre-Medical Studies, B
Psychology, BMO
Public Administration, MO
Public Affairs, MO
Public Health, MO
Public Health (MPH, DPH), B
Reading Teacher Education, MO
Russian Language and Literature, B
Sales, Distribution and Marketing Operations, B
School Nursing, O
Science Teacher Education/General Science Teacher Education, O
Secondary Education and Teaching, MO
Social Work, BM
Sociology, B
Spanish Language and Literature, BMO
Special Education and Teaching, BMO
Student Personnel Services, O
Sustainable Development, O
Urban and Regional Planning, MO
Women's Studies, B

WESTMINSTER COLLEGE

Accounting, B
Biochemistry, B
Biology/Biological Sciences, B
Business Administration and Management, B

Chemistry, B
Computer Science, B
Computer and Information Sciences, B
Counselor Education/School Counseling and Guidance Services, MO
Criminal Justice/Law Enforcement Administration, B
Design and Visual Communications, B
Digital Communication and Media/Multimedia, B
Drama and Dramatics/Theatre Arts, B
Econometrics and Quantitative Economics, B
Economics, B
Education, MO
Educational Administration and Supervision, MO
Electrical, Electronics and Communications Engineering, B
Elementary Education and Teaching, B
Engineering Physics, B
English Language and Literature, B
Environmental Sciences, B
Fine/Studio Arts, B
French Language and Literature, B
History, B
Human Development and Family Studies, B
Human Resources Management/Personnel Administration, B
Information Science/Studies, B
International Business/Trade/Commerce, B
International/Global Studies, B
Latin Language and Literature, B
Marketing/Marketing Management, B
Mathematics, B
Molecular Biology, B
Multi-/Interdisciplinary Studies, B
Music, B
Music Teacher Education, B
Philosophy, B
Physics, B
Political Science and Government, B
Pre-Dentistry Studies, B
Pre-Law Studies, B
Pre-Medicine/Pre-Medical Studies, B
Pre-Veterinary Studies, B
Psychology, B
Public Relations/Image Management, B
Reading Teacher Education, MO
Religion/Religious Studies, B
Religious Education, B
Religious/Sacred Music, B
Sociology, B
Spanish Language and Literature, B
Sport and Fitness Administration/Management, B

WESTMORELAND COUNTY COMMUNITY COLLEGE

Accounting Technology/Technician and Bookkeeping, A
Administrative Assistant and Secretarial Science, A
Applied Horticulture/Horticultural Operations, A
Architectural Drafting and Architectural CAD/CADD, A
Baking and Pastry Arts/Baker/Pastry Chef, A
Banking and Financial Support Services, A
Biology Technician/BioTechnology Laboratory Technician, A
Business Administration and Management, A
Business/Commerce, A
Chemical Technology/Technician, A
Child Care Provider/Assistant, A
Clinical Laboratory Science/Medical Technology/Technologist, A
Clinical/Medical Laboratory Assistant, A
Communications Systems Installation and Repair Technology, A
Computer Programming, Specific Applications, A
Computer Programming/Programmer, A
Computer Systems Networking and Telecommunications, A
Computer and Information Systems Security, A
Corrections, A
Criminal Justice/Police Science, A
Criminal Justice/Safety Studies, A
Culinary Arts/Chef Training, A
Data Entry/Microcomputer Applications, A
Data Processing and Data Processing Technology/Technician, A
Dental Assisting/Assistant, A

Dental Hygiene/Hygienist, A
Diagnostic Medical Sonography/Sonographer and Ultrasound Technician, A
Dietetic Technician (DTR), A
Early Childhood Education and Teaching, A
Electrical and Power Transmission Installation/Installer, A
Electrical, Electronic and Communications Engineering Technology/Technician, A
Electromechanical Technology/Electromechanical Engineering Technology, A
Executive Assistant/Executive Secretary, A
Family and Community Services, A
Fire Protection and Safety Technology/Technician, A
Floriculture/Floristry Operations and Management, A
Food Service, Waiter/Waitress, and Dining Room Management/Manager, A
Graphic Communications, A
Graphic Design, A
Health and Medical Administrative Services, A
Heating, Air Conditioning, Ventilation and Refrigeration Maintenance Technology/Technician, A
Hotel/Motel Administration/Management, A
Human Resources Management/Personnel Administration, A
Industrial Mechanics and Maintenance Technology, A
Industrial Technology/Technician, A
Legal Assistant/Paralegal, A
Liberal Arts and Sciences Studies and Humanities, A
Library Science, A
Logistics and Materials Management, A
Machine Shop Technology/Assistant, A
Machine Tool Technology/Machinist, A
Manufacturing Technology/Technician, A
Mechanical Drafting and Mechanical Drafting CAD/CADD, A
Mechanical Engineering/Mechanical Technology/Technician, A
Medical Office Assistant/Specialist, A
Medical/Clinical Assistant, A
Occupational Safety and Health Technology/Technician, A
Phlebotomy/Phlebotomist, A
Physical Science Technologies/Technicians, A
Radio and Television Broadcasting Technology/Technician, A
Radiologic Technology/Science - Radiographer, A
Real Estate, A
Restaurant, Culinary, and Catering Management/Manager, A
Sales, Distribution and Marketing Operations, A
Security and Protective Services, A
Tourism and Travel Services Management, A
Turf and Turfgrass Management, A
Web Page, Digital/Multimedia and Information Resources Design, A
Welding Technology/Welder, A
Well Drilling/Driller, A

WIDENER UNIVERSITY

Accounting, BM
Adult and Continuing Education and Teaching, M
Advertising, B
Allied Health and Medical Assisting Services, AB
Anthropology, B
Behavioral Sciences, B
Biochemistry, B
Biology Teacher Education, B
Biology/Biological Sciences, B
Biomedical Engineering, M
Biomedical/Medical Engineering, B
Business Administration and Management, B
Business Administration, Management and Operations, BM
Business/Managerial Economics, B
Chemical Engineering, BM
Chemistry, B
Chemistry Teacher Education, B
Civil Engineering, BM
Clinical Psychology, D
Computer Science, B
Computer and Information Sciences, B
Counselor Education/School Counseling and Guidance Services, M

Criminal Justice/Law Enforcement Administration, B
Criminology, M
Early Childhood Education and Teaching, BM
Economics, B
Education, MD
Educational Administration and Supervision, MD
Educational Leadership and Administration, MD
Educational Media/Instructional Technology, M
Educational Psychology, M
Educational/Instructional Media Design, B
Electrical Engineering, M
Electrical, Electronics and Communications Engineering, B
Elementary Education and Teaching, BM
Engineering, B
Engineering Management, M
Engineering and Applied Sciences, M
Engineering/Industrial Management, B
English Education, M
English Language and Literature, B
English/Language Arts Teacher Education, B
Environmental Studies, B
Financial Planning and Services, B
Fine Arts and Art Studies, B
Foreign Languages and Literatures, B
Foundations and Philosophy of Education, M
French Language Teacher Education, B
French Language and Literature, B
General Studies, AB
Health Education, MD
Health Law, MD
Health Services Administration, M
Health Services/Allied Health/Health Sciences, B
History, B
History Teacher Education, B
Hospitality Administration/Management, B
Hotel/Motel Administration/Management, B
Human Resources Management and Services, BM
Humanities/Humanistic Studies, B
Industrial Radiologic Technology/Technician, A
Information Science/Studies, B
International Business/Trade/Commerce, B
International Relations and Affairs, B
Kindergarten/PreSchool Education and Teaching, B
Law and Legal Studies, MD
Legal Assistant/Paralegal, A
Liberal Studies, M
Management Information Systems and Services, B
Marketing/Marketing Management, B
Mass Communication/Media Studies, B
Mathematics, B
Mathematics Teacher Education, BM
Mechanical Engineering, BM
Middle School Education, M
Modern Languages, B
Nursing, MDO
Operations Management and Supervision, B
Physical Therapy/Therapist, MD
Physics, B
Political Science and Government, B
Pre-Dentistry Studies, B
Pre-Medicine/Pre-Medical Studies, B
Pre-Veterinary Studies, B
Psychology, B
Psychology Teacher Education, B
Public Administration, M
Radiologic Technology/Science - Radiographer, AB
Reading Teacher Education, MD
Science Teacher Education/General Science Teacher Education, BM
Social Sciences, B
Social Studies Teacher Education, BM
Social Work, BMD
Sociology, B
Spanish Language Teacher Education, B
Spanish Language and Literature, B
Special Education and Teaching, BM
Sport and Fitness Administration/Management, B
Taxation, M

WILKES UNIVERSITY

Accounting, BM
Biochemistry, B
Bioengineering, M
Biology/Biological Sciences, B
Business Administration and Management, B

Business Administration, Management and Operations, M
Chemistry, B
Clinical Laboratory Science/Medical Technology/Technologist, B
Communication Studies/Speech Communication and Rhetoric, B
Computer and Information Sciences, B
Criminal Justice/Safety Studies, B
Curriculum and Instruction, M
Digital Communication and Media/Multimedia, B
Distance Education Development, M
Drama and Dramatics/Theatre Arts, B
Early Childhood Education and Teaching, M
Education, BMD
Educational Administration and Supervision, D
Educational Leadership and Administration, M
Educational Measurement and Evaluation, M
Educational Media/Instructional Technology, MD
Electrical Engineering, M
Electrical, Electronics and Communications Engineering, B
Elementary Education and Teaching, B
Engineering, B
Engineering Management, M
Engineering and Applied Sciences, M
Engineering/Industrial Management, B
English Education, M
English Language and Literature, B
English as a Second Language, M
Entrepreneurship/Entrepreneurial Studies, BM
Environmental/Environmental Health Engineering, B
Finance, B
Finance and Banking, M
Geology/Earth Science, B
Health Services Administration, M
Higher Education/Higher Education Administration, D
History, B
Human Resources Management and Services, M
Industrial and Manufacturing Management, M
Information Science/Studies, B
International Business/Trade/Commerce, M
International Relations and Affairs, B
International and Comparative Education, M
Junior High/Intermediate/Middle School Education and Teaching, B
Liberal Arts and Sciences Studies and Humanities, B
Marketing, M
Marketing/Marketing Management, B
Mathematics, BM
Mathematics Teacher Education, M
Mechanical Engineering, BM
Middle School Education, M
Multi-/Interdisciplinary Studies, B
Nursing, MD
Organizational Management, M
Pharmacy, D
Philosophy, B
Physics, B
Political Science and Government, B
Psychology, B
Reading Teacher Education, M
Science Teacher Education/General Science Teacher Education, M
Secondary Education and Teaching, M
Social Studies Teacher Education, M
Sociology, B
Spanish Language and Literature, B
Special Education and Teaching, M
Writing, M

WILLIAMSON COLLEGE OF THE TRADES

Carpentry/Carpenter, A
Construction Engineering Technology/Technician, A
Electrical, Electronic and Communications Engineering Technology/Technician, A
Energy Management and Systems Technology/Technician, A
Horticultural Science, A
Landscaping and Groundskeeping, A
Machine Tool Technology/Machinist, A

Turf and Turfgrass Management, A

WILSON COLLEGE

Accounting, AB
Art/Art Studies, General, B
Biochemistry, Biophysics and Molecular Biology, B
Biology/Biological Sciences, B
Business Administration and Management, AB
Chemistry, B
Education, M
Elementary Education and Teaching, ABM
English Language and Literature, B
Environmental Sciences, B
Equestrian/Equine Studies, B
International Relations and Affairs, B
Journalism, B
Liberal Arts and Sciences Studies and Humanities, A
Management Information Systems and Services, A
Mass Communication/Media Studies, B
Mathematics, B
Philosophy, B
Psychology, B
Religion/Religious Studies, B
Secondary Education and Teaching, M
Social Sciences, B
Sociology, B
Spanish Language and Literature, B
Veterinary/Animal Health Technology/Technician and Veterinary Assistant, B

WYOTECH BLAIRSVILLE

Autobody/Collision and Repair Technology/Technician, A
Automobile/Automotive Mechanics Technology/Technician, A
Diesel Mechanics Technology/Technician, A

YESHIVA BETH MOSHE

Jewish/Judaic Studies, B
Theology and Religious Vocations, O

YORK COLLEGE OF PENNSYLVANIA

Accounting, B
Behavioral Sciences, B
Biology Teacher Education, B
Biology/Biological Sciences, AB
Business Administration and Management, AB
Business Administration, Management and Operations, M
Chemistry, AB
Clinical Laboratory Science/Medical Technology/Technologist, B
Commercial and Advertising Art, B
Communication Studies/Speech Communication and Rhetoric, B
Computer Engineering, B
Computer Science, B
Criminal Justice/Law Enforcement Administration, AB
Drama and Dramatics/Theatre Arts, B
Early Childhood Education and Teaching, B
Economics, B
Education, M
Education/Teaching of Individuals in Early Childhood Special Education Programs, B
Educational Leadership and Administration, M
Electrical, Electronics and Communications Engineering, B
Engineering, B
English Language and Literature, B
English/Language Arts Teacher Education, B
Entrepreneurship/Entrepreneurial Studies, B
Finance, B
Finance and Banking, M
Fine/Studio Arts, AB
Forensic Science and Technology, B
General Studies, AB
Gerontological Nursing, M
Health Services Administration, M
History, B
Hospitality Administration/Management, B
International Relations and Affairs, B
Logistics and Materials Management, B
Management, B
Management Information Systems and Services, B

Marketing, M
Marketing/Marketing Management, B
Mass Communication/Media Studies, AB
Mathematics, B
Mathematics Teacher Education, B
Mechanical Engineering, B
Music, AB
Music Teacher Education, B
Nuclear Medical Technology/Technologist, B
Nurse Anesthetist, M
Nursing, MD
Nursing - Adult, M
Nursing Administration, M
Nursing Education, M
Parks, Recreation, Leisure and Fitness Studies, B
Philosophy, B
Physics, A
Political Science and Government, B
Psychology, B
Public Relations/Image Management, B
Radiologic Technology/Science - Radiographer, B
Reading Teacher Education, M
Recording Arts Technology/Technician, B
Respiratory Care Therapy/Therapist, AB
Science Teacher Education/General Science Teacher Education, B
Social Studies Teacher Education, B
Sociology, B
Spanish Language Teacher Education, B
Spanish Language and Literature, B
Sport and Fitness Administration/Management, B

YTI CAREER INSTITUTE–ALTOONA

Business Administration and Management, A
Criminal Justice/Police Science, A
Medical/Clinical Assistant, A
Respiratory Care Therapy/Therapist, A

YTI CAREER INSTITUTE–YORK

Business Administration and Management, A
CAD/CADD Drafting and/or Design Technology/Technician, A
Computer and Information Sciences and Support Services, A
Electrical, Electronic and Communications Engineering Technology/Technician, A
Medical/Clinical Assistant, A

Rhode Island

BROWN UNIVERSITY

African-American/Black Studies, B
Allopathic Medicine, D
American/United States Studies/Civilization, BMD
Anthropology, BMD
Applied Mathematics, BMD
Archeology, BD
Architectural History and Criticism, B
Art History, Criticism and Conservation, BD
Art/Art Studies, General, B
Asian Studies/Civilization, D
Behavioral Sciences, B
BioTechnology, D
Biochemical Engineering, MD
Biochemistry, BMD
Biological and Biomedical Sciences, MD
Biology/Biological Sciences, B
Biomedical Engineering, MD
Biomedical Sciences, B
Biomedical/Medical Engineering, B
Biophysics, B
Biostatistics, MD
Cell Biology and Anatomy, MD
Chemical Engineering, BMD
Chemistry, BD
Classics and Classical Languages, Literatures, and Linguistics, BMD
Cognitive Sciences, MD
Community Health and Preventive Medicine, MD
Comparative Literature, BD
Computer Engineering, BMD
Computer Science, BMD
Development Economics and International Development, B
Drama and Dramatics/Theatre Arts, B

East Asian Studies, BD
East European and Russian Studies, MD
Ecology, D
Economics, BD
Education, BM
Electrical Engineering, MD
Electrical, Electronics and Communications Engineering, B
Elementary Education and Teaching, M
Engineering, B
Engineering Physics, B
Engineering and Applied Sciences, MD
English, MD
English Education, M
English Language and Literature, B
English as a Second Language, M
Environmental Engineering Technology/Environmental Technology, B
Environmental Sciences, B
Environmental Studies, B
Epidemiology, MD
Ethnomusicology, D
Evolutionary Biology, D
Film/Cinema Studies, B
Fine/Studio Arts, B
French Language and Literature, BD
French Studies, B
Geochemistry, B
Geology/Earth Science, B
Geophysics and Seismology, B
Geosciences, D
German Language and Literature, BD
German Studies, B
Health Services Research, D
Hispanic Studies, D
Hispanic-American, Puerto Rican, and Mexican-American/Chicano Studies, B
History, BMD
History of Science and Technology, D
International Relations and Affairs, B
Italian Language and Literature, BD
Italian Studies, B
Jewish/Judaic Studies, B
Latin American Studies, BMD
Linguistics, BMD
Marine Biology and Biological Oceanography, B
Materials Engineering, B
Materials Sciences, MD
Mathematics, BD
Mathematics and Computer Science, B
Mechanical Engineering, BMD
Mechanics, MD
Medieval and Renaissance Studies, B
Molecular Biology, BMD
Molecular Pharmacology, MD
Multilingual and Multicultural Education, M
Music, BD
Musicology and Ethnomusicology, B
Near and Middle Eastern Studies, BD
Neuroscience, D
Organizational Behavior Studies, B
Pathobiology, MD
Philosophy, BD
Physics, BMD
Physiology, MD
Political Science and Government, BD
Psychology, BD
Public Health, M
Public Policy Analysis, M
Publishing, D
Religion/Religious Studies, BD
Russian Language and Literature, M
Russian Studies, B
Science Teacher Education/General Science Teacher Education, M
Secondary Education and Teaching, M
Slavic Languages, Literatures, and Linguistics, MD
Social Studies Teacher Education, M
Sociology, BMD
South Asian Studies, B
Spanish Language and Literature, B
Theater, MD
Urban Education and Leadership, M
Urban Studies/Affairs, B
Visual and Performing Arts, B
Western European Studies, MD

Women's Studies, B
Writing, M

BRYANT UNIVERSITY

Accounting, BM
Actuarial Science, B
American/United States Studies/Civilization, B
Applied Economics, B
Applied Mathematics, B
Biochemistry, B
Biology/Biological Sciences, B
Business Administration and Management, B
Business Administration, Management and Operations, M
Business Statistics, B
Business/Corporate Communications, B
Business/Managerial Economics, B
Cell/Cellular and Molecular Biology, B
Chinese Language and Literature, B
Communication Studies/Speech Communication and Rhetoric, B
Community Organization and Advocacy, B
Computer and Information Sciences, B
Conservation Biology, B
Data Modeling/Warehousing and Database Administration, B
Design and Visual Communications, B
Ecology, B
Economics, B
English Language and Literature, B
Entrepreneurship/Entrepreneurial Studies, B
Environmental Sciences, B
Environmental Studies, B
Finance, B
Finance and Banking, M
Financial Planning and Services, B
Forensic Science and Technology, B
French Language and Literature, B
Gay/Lesbian Studies, B
History, B
Human Resources Management/Personnel Administration, B
Information Technology, B
International Business/Trade/Commerce, BM
International Economics, B
International Relations and Affairs, B
International/Global Studies, B
Liberal Arts and Sciences Studies and Humanities, B
Logistics and Materials Management, B
Management Information Systems and Services, B
Management Science, B
Marketing/Marketing Management, B
Mass Communication/Media Studies, B
Natural Resources Management/Development and Policy, B
Non-Profit/Public/Organizational Management, B
Operations Research, B
Political Science and Government, B
Pre-Law Studies, B
Pre-Medicine/Pre-Medical Studies, B
Psychology, B
Public Policy Analysis, B
Sociology, B
Spanish Language and Literature, B
Statistics, B
Supply Chain Management, M
Taxation, M
Women's Studies, B

COMMUNITY COLLEGE OF RHODE ISLAND

Accounting, A
Administrative Assistant and Secretarial Science, A
Adult Development and Aging, A
Art/Art Studies, General, A
Banking and Financial Support Services, A
Biological and Physical Sciences, A
Business Administration and Management, A
Business/Commerce, A
Chemical Technology/Technician, A
Clinical/Medical Laboratory Technician, A
Computer Engineering Technology/Technician, A
Computer Programming, Specific Applications, A
Computer Systems Networking and Telecommunications, A

Computer and Information Sciences, A
Criminal Justice/Police Science, A
Dental Hygiene/Hygienist, A
Diagnostic Medical Sonography/Sonographer and Ultrasound Technician, A
Drama and Dramatics/Theatre Arts, A
Electromechanical Technology/Electromechanical Engineering Technology, A
Engineering, A
Fire Science/Firefighting, A
General Studies, A
Histologic Technician, A
Jazz/Jazz Studies, A
Kindergarten/PreSchool Education and Teaching, A
Legal Administrative Assistant/Secretary, A
Legal Assistant/Paralegal, A
Liberal Arts and Sciences Studies and Humanities, A
Marketing/Marketing Management, A
Massage Therapy/Therapeutic Massage, A
Medical Administrative Assistant/Secretary, A
Mental Health Counseling/Counselor, A
Music, A
Occupational Therapist Assistant, A
Opticiary/Ophthalmic Dispensing Optician, A
Physical Therapist Assistant, A
Radiologic Technology/Science - Radiographer, A
Respiratory Care Therapy/Therapist, A
Social Work, A
Special Education and Teaching, A
Substance Abuse/Addiction Counseling, A
Surveying Engineering, A
Web/Multimedia Management and Webmaster, A

JOHNSON & WALES UNIVERSITY

Accounting, B
Advertising, B
Baking and Pastry Arts/Baker/Pastry Chef, AB
Business Administration and Management, B
Business Administration, Management and Operations, M
Business Education, M
Computer Engineering, AB
Computer Programming/Programmer, A
Computer Systems Analysis/Analyst, AB
Criminal Justice/Law Enforcement Administration, B
Criminology, M
Culinary Arts and Related Services, AB
Culinary Arts/Chef Training, AB
Drafting and Design Technology/Technician, AB
Education, M
Educational Leadership and Administration, D
Electrical, Electronics and Communications Engineering, B
Elementary Education and Teaching, M
Entrepreneurship/Entrepreneurial Studies, B
Equestrian/Equine Studies, B
Farm/Farm and Ranch Management, B
Fashion Merchandising, B
Finance, B
Foodservice Systems Administration/Management, B
Horse Husbandry/Equine Science and Management, B
Hospitality Administration/Management, BM
Hotel/Motel Administration/Management, B
Information Science/Studies, B
International Business/Trade/Commerce, B
Investments and Securities, B
Marketing/Marketing Management, B
Nutritional Sciences, B
Parks, Recreation and Leisure Facilities Management, B
Physician Assistant, M
Public Finance, B
Public Relations/Image Management, B
Restaurant, Culinary, and Catering Management/Manager, B
Secondary Education and Teaching, M
Security and Loss Prevention Services, B
Special Education and Teaching, M
Sport and Fitness Administration/Management, B
Systems Engineering, B
Tourism and Travel Services Management, B
Tourism and Travel Services Marketing Operations, B

Web Page, Digital/Multimedia and Information Resources Design, B

MATER ECCLESIAE COLLEGE

Religion/Religious Studies, B

NEW ENGLAND INSTITUTE OF TECHNOLOGY

Animation, Interactive Technology, Video Graphics and Special Effects, AB
Architectural Engineering Technology/Technician, AB
Autobody/Collision and Repair Technology/Technician, A
Automobile/Automotive Mechanics Technology/Technician, AB
Business Administration and Management, AB
Carpentry/Carpenter, A
Cinematography and Film/Video Production, AB
Civil Engineering Technology/Technician, A
Clinical Laboratory Science/Medical Technology/Technologist, A
Clinical/Medical Laboratory Assistant, A
Computer Engineering, AB
Computer Programming/Programmer, AB
Computer Science, AB
Computer Technology/Computer Systems Technology, AB
Computer and Information Sciences, AB
Construction Management, M
Criminal Justice/Law Enforcement Administration, AB
Electrical, Electronics and Communications Engineering, AB
Electrical/Electronics Equipment Installation and Repair, A
Emergency Medical Technology/Technician (EMT Paramedic), A
Graphic Communications, AB
Health Information/Medical Records Technology/Technician, A
Health/Health Care Administration/Management, B
Heating, Air Conditioning, Ventilation and Refrigeration Maintenance Technology/Technician, A
Information Technology, AB
Interior Design, AB
Management Information Systems and Services, M
Manufacturing Technology/Technician, AB
Marine Maintenance/Fitter and Ship Repair Technology/Technician, A
Mechanical Engineering, AB
Medical/Clinical Assistant, A
Occupational Therapist Assistant, A
Occupational Therapy/Therapist, M
Physical Therapist Assistant, A
Pipefitting/Pipefitter and Sprinkler Fitter, A
Prepress/Desktop Publishing and Digital Imaging Design, AB
Radio and Television Broadcasting Technology/Technician, A
Recording Arts Technology/Technician, B
Surgical Technology/Technologist, A
Veterinary/Animal Health Technology/Technician and Veterinary Assistant, A
Web Page, Digital/Multimedia and Information Resources Design, AB

PROVIDENCE COLLEGE

Accounting, BM
American/United States Studies/Civilization, BM
Art History, Criticism and Conservation, B
Biochemistry, B
Biology Teacher Education, B
Biology/Biological Sciences, B
Business Administration and Management, AB
Business Administration, Management and Operations, M
Ceramic Arts and Ceramics, B
Chemistry, B
Chemistry Teacher Education, B
Community Organization and Advocacy, B
Computer Science, B
Counselor Education/School Counseling and Guidance Services, M
Divinity/Ministry (BD, MDiv.), AB
Drama and Dramatics/Theatre Arts, B
Drawing, B

Economics, B
Educational Administration and Supervision, M
Elementary Education and Teaching, M
Engineering Physics, B
English Language and Literature, B
English/Language Arts Teacher Education, B
Finance, B
Finance and Banking, M
Fine Arts and Art Studies, B
Fine/Studio Arts, B
Fire Science/Firefighting, B
Foreign Language Teacher Education, B
French Language Teacher Education, B
French Language and Literature, B
Health/Health Care Administration/Management, B
History, BM
History Teacher Education, B
Humanities/Humanistic Studies, B
International Business/Trade/Commerce, M
International/Global Studies, B
Italian Language and Literature, B
Liberal Arts and Sciences Studies and Humanities, AB
Marketing, M
Marketing/Marketing Management, B
Mathematics, B
Mathematics Teacher Education, BM
Multi-/Interdisciplinary Studies, B
Music, B
Music Teacher Education, B
Non-Profit/Public/Organizational Management, M
Painting, B
Philosophy, B
Photography, B
Physics Teacher Education, B
Political Science and Government, B
Psychology, B
Reading Teacher Education, M
Religion/Religious Studies, M
Sculpture, B
Secondary Education and Teaching, M
Social Sciences, B
Social Work, B
Sociology, B
Spanish Language Teacher Education, B
Spanish Language and Literature, B
Special Education and Teaching, BM
Systems Engineering, B
Theology and Religious Vocations, M
Theology/Theological Studies, B
Urban Education and Leadership, M
Vision Science/Physiological Optics, B
Women's Studies, B

RHODE ISLAND COLLEGE

Accounting, BMO
Acting, B
Adult Development and Aging, B
African-American/Black Studies, B
Anthropology, B
Art Education, M
Art History, Criticism and Conservation, B
Art Teacher Education, B
Arts Management, M
Biological and Biomedical Sciences, MO
Biology Teacher Education, B
Biology/Biological Sciences, B
Business Administration and Management, B
Ceramic Arts and Ceramics, B
Chemistry, B
Chemistry Teacher Education, B
Clinical/Medical Laboratory Technician, B
Communication Disorders, B
Communication Studies/Speech Communication and Rhetoric, B
Community Health Services/Liaison/Counseling, B
Computer and Information Sciences, B
Counseling Psychology, O
Counselor Education/School Counseling and Guidance Services, MO
Criminal Justice/Safety Studies, B
Dance, B
Dental Hygiene/Hygienist, B
Diagnostic Medical Sonography/Sonographer and Ultrasound Technician, B
Drama and Dramatics/Theatre Arts, B

Early Childhood Education and Teaching, BM
Economics, B
Education, D
Educational Leadership and Administration, MO
Elementary Education and Teaching, BM
English, MO
English Education, M
English Language and Literature, B
English as a Second Language, M
English/Language Arts Teacher Education, B
Film/Cinema Studies, B
Finance, B
Finance and Banking, O
Fine Arts and Art Studies, M
Foreign Language Teacher Education, BM
French Language Teacher Education, B
French Language and Literature, B
French Studies, B
Geography, B
Geography Teacher Education, B
Graphic Design, B
Health Education, MO
Health Psychology, O
Health Services/Allied Health/Health Sciences, B
Health Teacher Education, B
Health and Physical Education, B
Health/Health Care Administration/Management, B
History, BM
History Teacher Education, B
Human Resources Management/Personnel Administration, B
International Business/Trade/Commerce, B
Latin American Studies, B
Liberal Arts and Sciences Studies and Humanities, B
Management Information Systems and Services, B
Marketing/Marketing Management, B
Mass Communication/Media Studies, B
Mathematics, BMO
Mathematics Teacher Education, BM
Metal and Jewelry Arts, B
Music, B
Music Performance, B
Music Teacher Education, BM
Nuclear Medical Technology/Technologist, B
Nursing, M
Operations Management and Supervision, B
Painting, B
Parks, Recreation, Leisure and Fitness Studies, B
Philosophy, B
Photography, B
Physical Education Teaching and Coaching, BO
Physics, B
Physics Teacher Education, B
Political Science and Government, B
Portuguese Language and Literature, B
Pre-Dentistry Studies, B
Pre-Law Studies, B
Pre-Medicine/Pre-Medical Studies, B
Pre-Veterinary Studies, B
Printmaking, B
Psychology, BMO
Public Administration, BM
Public/Applied History and Archival Administration, B
Radiologic Technology/Science - Radiographer, B
Reading Teacher Education, M
Respiratory Therapy Technician/Assistant, B
School Psychology, O
Science Teacher Education/General Science Teacher Education, B
Sculpture, B
Secondary Education and Teaching, BM
Social Science Teacher Education, B
Social Studies Teacher Education, M
Social Work, BM
Sociology, B
Spanish Language Teacher Education, B
Spanish Language and Literature, B
Special Education and Teaching, BMO
Technical Theatre/Theatre Design and Technology, B
Technology Teacher Education/Industrial Arts Teacher Education, B
Women's Studies, B
Writing, MO

Youth Services/Administration, B

RHODE ISLAND SCHOOL OF DESIGN

Apparel and Textiles, B
Applied Arts and Design, M
Architecture, BM
Art Education, M
Ceramic Arts and Ceramics, BM
Computer Art and Design, M
Fiber, Textile and Weaving Arts, B
Film/Video and Photographic Arts, B
Fine Arts and Art Studies, B
Furniture Design and Manufacturing, B
Graphic Design, BM
Illustration, B
Industrial Design, BM
Interior Architecture, B
Interior Design, M
Jewelry/Metalsmithing, M
Landscape Architecture, M
Metal and Jewelry Arts, B
Painting, BM
Photography, BM
Printmaking, BM
Sculpture, BM
Textile Design, M

ROGER WILLIAMS UNIVERSITY

Accounting, B
American/United States Studies/Civilization, B
Applied Mathematics, B
Architectural History and Criticism, M
Architecture, BM
Art History, Criticism and Conservation, BM
Art/Art Studies, General, B
Biochemistry, B
Biology/Biological Sciences, B
Business Administration and Management, B
Chemistry, B
Civil Engineering, B
Clinical Psychology, M
Communication and Media Studies, B
Computer Engineering, B
Computer Science, B
Computer and Information Sciences, B
Computer and Information Systems Security, M
Construction Management, BM
Corrections and Criminal Justice, B
Criminal Justice/Law Enforcement Administration, AB
Criminology, M
Dance, B
Drama and Dramatics/Theatre Arts, B
Economics, B
Education, BM
Electrical, Electronics and Communications Engineering, B
Elementary Education and Teaching, B
Engineering, B
English Language and Literature, B
English/Language Arts Teacher Education, B
Environmental Sciences, B
Environmental/Environmental Health Engineering, B
Film/Cinema Studies, B
Finance, B
Financial Planning and Services, B
Fine/Studio Arts, B
Foreign Language Teacher Education, B
Foreign Languages and Literatures, B
Forensic Psychology, M
Forensic Science and Technology, B
Graphic Communications, B
Health Services Administration, M
Health/Health Care Administration/Management, B
Historic Preservation and Conservation, BM
History, B
History Teacher Education, B
Humanities/Humanistic Studies, B
Industrial Technology/Technician, B
International Business/Trade/Commerce, B
International Relations and Affairs, B
International/Global Studies, B
Law and Legal Studies, D
Legal Assistant/Paralegal, B
Legal Professions and Studies, B

Liberal Arts and Sciences Studies and Humanities, B
Management Information Systems and Services, B
Marine Biology and Biological Oceanography, B
Marketing/Marketing Management, B
Mathematics, B
Mathematics Teacher Education, B
Mechanical Engineering, B
Mental and Social Health Services and Allied Professions, B
Multi-/Interdisciplinary Studies, B
Musicology and Ethnomusicology, B
Operations Management and Supervision, B
Philosophy, B
Political Science and Government, B
Psychology, B
Public Administration, BM
Public Health (MPH, DPH), B
Secondary Education and Teaching, B
Social Sciences, B
Sociology, B

SALVE REGINA UNIVERSITY

Accounting, B
American/United States Studies/Civilization, B
Art History, Criticism and Conservation, B
Biology Teacher Education, B
Biology/Biological Sciences, B
Business Administration and Management, B
Business Administration, Management and Operations, M
Ceramic Arts and Ceramics, B
Chemistry, B
Clinical Laboratory Science/Medical Technology/Technologist, B
Communication and Media Studies, B
Communications Technologies/Technicians and Support Services, B
Computer and Information Systems Security, MO
Conflict Resolution and Mediation/Peace Studies, M
Counseling Psychology, MO
Criminal Justice/Law Enforcement Administration, AB
Drama and Dramatics/Theatre Arts, B
Early Childhood Education and Teaching, B
Economics, B
Elementary Education and Teaching, B
English Language and Literature, B
Entrepreneurship/Entrepreneurial Studies, M
Environmental Studies, B
Finance, B
Fine/Studio Arts, B
French Language Teacher Education, B
French Language and Literature, B
Graphic Design, B
Health Services Administration, MO
Health/Health Care Administration/Management, B
Historic Preservation and Conservation, B
History, B
History Teacher Education, B
Homeland Security, MO
Humanities/Humanistic Studies, MD
Information Resources Management/CIO Training, B
International Affairs, MO
International Economics, M
International/Global Studies, B
Law Enforcement, MO
Liberal Arts and Sciences Studies and Humanities, AB
Management, MO
Management Science, B
Management Strategy and Policy, MO
Marketing/Marketing Management, B
Mathematics, B
Mathematics Teacher Education, B
Music, B
Music Teacher Education, B
Non-Profit/Public/Organizational Management, O
Nursing, D
Painting, B
Philosophy, B
Photography, B
Political Science and Government, B
Psychology, B
Rehabilitation Counseling, MO
Religion/Religious Studies, BM

Secondary Education and Teaching, B
Social Work, B
Sociology, B
Spanish Language Teacher Education, B
Spanish Language and Literature, B
Special Education and Teaching, B
Substance Abuse/Addiction Counseling, O

UNIVERSITY OF RHODE ISLAND

Accounting, BM
Adult and Continuing Education and Teaching, M
African-American/Black Studies, B
Animal Sciences, BMD
Anthropology, B
Apparel and Accessories Marketing Operations, B
Apparel and Textiles, B
Applied Horticulture/Horticultural Business Services, B
Applied Mathematics, MD
Aquaculture, MD
Art History, Criticism and Conservation, B
BioTechnology, M
Biochemistry, MD
Biological and Biomedical Sciences, MD
Biology/Biological Sciences, B
Biomedical Engineering, MDO
Biomedical/Medical Engineering, B
Business Administration and Management, B
Business Administration, Management and Operations, MD
Business/Commerce, B
Cell Biology and Anatomy, MD
Cell/Cellular and Molecular Biology, B
Chemical Engineering, BMD
Chemistry, BMD
Child and Family Studies, M
Chinese Language and Literature, B
Cinematography and Film/Video Production, B
Civil Engineering, BMD
Classics and Classical Languages, Literatures, and Linguistics, B
Clinical Laboratory Science/Medical Technology/Technologist, B
Clinical Laboratory Sciences, M
Clinical Psychology, MD
Clothing and Textiles, M
Communication Disorders, BM
Communication Studies/Speech Communication and Rhetoric, B
Communication and Media Studies, M
Computer Engineering, BMDO
Computer Science, MDO
Computer and Information Sciences, B
Counseling Psychology, M
Dietetics/Dieticians, B
Drama and Dramatics/Theatre Arts, B
Econometrics and Quantitative Economics, B
Economics, BMD
Education, MD
Electrical Engineering, MDO
Electrical, Electronics and Communications Engineering, B
Elementary Education and Teaching, BM
Engineering and Applied Sciences, MDO
English, MD
English Language and Literature, B
Entrepreneurship/Entrepreneurial Studies, M
Environmental Engineering Technology/Environmental Technology, MD
Environmental Policy and Resource Management, MD
Environmental Sciences, D
Environmental Studies, B
Exercise and Sports Science, M
Finance, B
Finance and Banking, MD
Fine/Studio Arts, B
Fish, Game and Wildlife Management, MD
Fishing and Fisheries Sciences and Management, B
Food Science and Technology, M
Forensic Science and Technology, O
French Language and Literature, B
Geological and Earth Sciences/Geosciences, B
Geology/Earth Science, B
Geosciences, MD
German Language and Literature, B

Gerontological Nursing, M
Gerontology, M
Health Education, M
Health Services Administration, M
Health/Health Care Administration/Management, B
History, BM
Human Development and Family Studies, B
Human Resources Management and Services, M
Industrial Engineering, M
Industrial and Labor Relations, M
Information Science/Studies, M
International Affairs, M
International Business/Trade/Commerce, B
Italian Language and Literature, B
Journalism, B
Kinesiology and Exercise Science, B
Landscape Architecture, B
Liberal Arts and Sciences Studies and Humanities, B
Library Science, M
Logistics and Materials Management, B
Management, MD
Management Strategy and Policy, M
Marine Affairs, MD
Marine Biology and Biological Oceanography, B
Marine Sciences, MD
Marketing, MD
Marketing/Marketing Management, B
Mathematics, BMD
Mechanical Engineering, B
Medicinal and Pharmaceutical Chemistry, MD
Microbiology, BMD
Molecular Biology, MD
Molecular Genetics, MD
Music, BM
Music Teacher Education, M
Natural Resource Economics, B
Natural Resources Management/Development and Policy, BMD
Natural Resources and Conservation, MD
Nursing, MD
Nursing - Advanced Practice, M
Nursing Administration, M
Nursing Education, M
Nutritional Sciences, MD
Ocean Engineering, BMD
Oceanography, Chemical and Physical, MD
Performance, M
Pharmaceutical Sciences, MD
Pharmaceutics and Drug Design, B
Pharmacognosy, MD
Pharmacology, MD
Pharmacy, MD
Philosophy, B
Physical Education Teaching and Coaching, M
Physical Therapy/Therapist, D
Physics, BMD
Political Science and Government, BM
Psychiatric/Mental Health Nurse/Nursing, M
Psychology, BD
Public Administration, M
Public Policy Analysis, BM
Public Relations/Image Management, B
Reading Teacher Education, M
Recreation and Park Management, M
School Psychology, MD
Secondary Education and Teaching, BM
Social Sciences, B
Sociology, B
Spanish Language and Literature, BM
Special Education and Teaching, M
Sport Psychology, M
Statistics, MDO
Student Personnel Services, M
Supply Chain Management, M
Toxicology, MD
Wildlife and Wildlands Science and Management, B
Women's Studies, B

South Carolina

AIKEN TECHNICAL COLLEGE

Accounting, A
Administrative Assistant and Secretarial Science, A
Business Administration and Management, A
Child Care and Support Services Management, A

Computer Programming/Programmer, A
Computer Systems Networking and Telecommunications, A
Computer and Information Sciences and Support Services, A
Criminal Justice/Law Enforcement Administration, A
Criminal Justice/Safety Studies, A
Data Processing and Data Processing Technology/Technician, A
Early Childhood Education and Teaching, A
Electrical, Electronic and Communications Engineering Technology/Technician, A
Industrial Mechanics and Maintenance Technology, A
Liberal Arts and Sciences Studies and Humanities, A
Medical Radiologic Technology/Science - Radiation Therapist, A
Multi-/Interdisciplinary Studies, A
Quality Control Technology/Technician, A
Radiation Protection/Health Physics Technician, A
Sales, Distribution and Marketing Operations, A

ALLEN UNIVERSITY

Biology/Biological Sciences, B
Business Administration and Management, B
Chemistry, B
English Language and Literature, B
Mathematics, B
Music, B
Religion/Religious Studies, B
Social Sciences, B

ANDERSON UNIVERSITY

Art Teacher Education, B
Art/Art Studies, General, B
Biology/Biological Sciences, B
Business Administration and Management, B
Business Administration, Management and Operations, M
Business/Commerce, B
Christian Studies, B
Criminal Justice/Law Enforcement Administration, B
Criminology, M
Early Childhood Education and Teaching, B
Education, M
Elementary Education and Teaching, B
Engineering, B
English Language and Literature, B
English/Language Arts Teacher Education, B
History, B
History Teacher Education, B
Human Resources Management/Personnel Administration, B
Interior Design, B
Kinesiology and Exercise Science, B
Mathematics, B
Mathematics Teacher Education, B
Music, B
Music Performance, B
Music Teacher Education, B
Organizational Behavior Studies, B
Pastoral Studies/Counseling, B
Physical Education Teaching and Coaching, B
Psychology, B
Religion/Religious Studies, B
Religious/Sacred Music, B
Spanish Language and Literature, B
Special Education and Teaching, B
Teacher Education and Professional Development, Specific Levels and Methods, B

THE ART INSTITUTE OF CHARLESTON, A BRANCH OF THE ART INSTITUTE OF ATLANTA

Apparel and Accessories Marketing Operations, B
Baking and Pastry Arts/Baker/Pastry Chef, A
Cinematography and Film/Video Production, B
Commercial Photography, B
Culinary Arts/Chef Training, A
Fashion/Apparel Design, B
Interior Design, B
Restaurant, Culinary, and Catering Management/Manager, AB

Web Page, Digital/Multimedia and Information Resources Design, AB

BENEDICT COLLEGE

Accounting, B
Art Teacher Education, B
Art/Art Studies, General, B
Biology/Biological Sciences, B
Business Administration and Management, B
Chemistry, B
Child Development, B
Computer Engineering, B
Computer Science, B
Computer and Information Sciences, B
Criminal Justice/Law Enforcement Administration, B
Early Childhood Education and Teaching, B
Economics, B
Electrical, Electronics and Communications Engineering, B
Elementary Education and Teaching, B
English Language and Literature, B
Environmental Health, B
Finance, B
History, B
Human Development and Family Studies, B
Mass Communication/Media Studies, B
Mathematics, B
Music, B
Music Teacher Education, B
Parks, Recreation, Leisure and Fitness Studies, B
Physics, B
Political Science and Government, B
Psychology, B
Public Health (MPH, DPH), B
Social Work, B
Sociology, B

BOB JONES UNIVERSITY

Accounting, BM
Actuarial Science, B
Bible/Biblical Studies, B
Biology/Biological Sciences, B
Business Administration and Management, B
Business Administration, Management and Operations, M
Chemistry, B
Cinematography and Film/Video Production, B
Communication Disorders, B
Communication, Journalism and Related Programs, B
Computer Science, B
Counselor Education/School Counseling and Guidance Services, M
Criminal Justice/Safety Studies, B
Culinary Arts/Chef Training, A
Curriculum and Instruction, D
Drama and Dramatics/Theatre Arts, B
Early Childhood Education and Teaching, B
Educational Leadership and Administration, MDO
Elementary Education and Teaching, BM
Engineering, B
English, M
English Education, M
English Language and Literature, B
English/Language Arts Teacher Education, B
Fashion/Apparel Design, B
Film, Television, and Video Production, M
Fine Arts and Art Studies, M
Fine/Studio Arts, B
General Office Occupations and Clerical Services, A
Graphic Design, BM
Health and Physical Education, B
History, BM
Housing and Human Environments, B
Humanities/Humanistic Studies, B
Illustration, M
Information Technology, B
International Relations and Affairs, B
Journalism, M
Junior High/Intermediate/Middle School Education and Teaching, M
Mathematics, B
Mathematics Teacher Education, BM
Media Studies, M
Missions/Missionary Studies and Missiology, B
Molecular Biochemistry, B

Music, M
Music Pedagogy, B
Music Performance, B
Music Teacher Education, BM
Pastoral Studies/Counseling, MD
Performance, M
Physics, B
Piano and Organ, B
Pre-Medicine/Pre-Medical Studies, B
Religion/Religious Studies, M
Rhetoric, M
Sacred Music, M
Science Teacher Education/General Science
    Teacher Education, B
Secondary Education and Teaching, M
Social Studies Teacher Education, BM
Spanish Language Teacher Education, B
Spanish Language and Literature, M
Special Education and Teaching, M
Speech and Interpersonal Communication, M
Speech and Rhetorical Studies, M
Student Personnel Services, MO
Theater, M
Theological and Ministerial Studies, AB
Theology and Religious Vocations, MDO
Voice and Opera, B

CENTRAL CAROLINA TECHNICAL COLLEGE

Accounting, A
Administrative Assistant and Secretarial Science, A
Business Administration and Management, A
Child Care and Support Services Management, A
Criminal Justice/Safety Studies, A
Data Processing and Data Processing
    Technology/Technician, A
Environmental Control Technologies/Technicians, A
Human Services, A
Industrial Electronics Technology/Technician, A
Legal Assistant/Paralegal, A
Liberal Arts and Sciences Studies and Humani-
    ties, A
Natural Resources Management/Development and
    Policy, A
Sales, Distribution and Marketing Operations, A
Surgical Technology/Technologist, A

CHARLESTON SOUTHERN UNIVERSITY

Accounting, BM
American History (United States), B
Applied Mathematics, B
Biochemistry, B
Biological and Biomedical Sciences, B
Biological and Physical Sciences, B
Biology/Biological Sciences, B
Business Administration and Management, B
Business Administration, Management and Opera-
    tions, BM
Business/Managerial Economics, B
Chemistry, B
Computer Science, B
Criminal Justice/Safety Studies, B
Criminology, M
Dramatic/Theatre Arts and Stagecraft, B
Early Childhood Education and Teaching, B
Economics, B
Education, M
Educational Administration and Supervision, M
Elementary Education and Teaching, BM
Elementary and Middle School
    Administration/Principalship, B
English Language and Literature, B
English/Language Arts Teacher Education, B
European History, B
Finance, B
Finance and Banking, M
Health and Physical Education, B
History, B
History Teacher Education, B
Humanities/Humanistic Studies, B
Management, M
Management Information Systems and Ser-
    vices, BM
Marketing/Marketing Management, B
Mathematics, B

Mathematics Teacher Education, B
Music, B
Music Performance, B
Music Teacher Education, B
Music Therapy/Therapist, B
Physical Education Teaching and Coaching, B
Political Science and Government, B
Psychology, B
Religion/Religious Studies, B
Religious/Sacred Music, B
Science Teacher Education/General Science
    Teacher Education, B
Secondary Education and Teaching, B
Secondary School Administration/Principalship, B
Social Sciences, B
Social Studies Teacher Education, B
Sociology, B
Spanish Language Teacher Education, B
Spanish Language and Literature, B
Youth Ministry, B

THE CITADEL, THE MILITARY COLLEGE OF SOUTH CAROLINA

Biological and Biomedical Sciences, M
Biology/Biological Sciences, B
Business Administration and Management, B
Business Administration, Management and Opera-
    tions, M
Chemistry, B
Civil Engineering, BM
Computer Science, M
Computer and Information Sciences, B
Counselor Education/School Counseling and Guid-
    ance Services, M
Criminal Justice/Law Enforcement Administration, B
Education, MO
Educational Administration and Supervision, MO
Electrical, Electronics and Communications Engi-
    neering, B
Elementary Education and Teaching, M
Engineering Management, M
English, M
English Education, M
English Language and Literature, B
Foreign Languages and Literatures, B
Health Education, M
History, BM
Information Science/Studies, M
Kinesiology and Exercise Science, B
Mathematics, B
Mathematics Teacher Education, M
Mechanical Engineering, B
Physical Education Teaching and Coaching, BM
Physics, B
Political Science and Government, B
Project Management, M
Psychology, BMO
Reading Teacher Education, M
School Psychology, O
Science Teacher Education/General Science
    Teacher Education, M
Secondary Education and Teaching, BM
Social Sciences, M
Social Studies Teacher Education, M
Sport and Fitness Administration/Management, B
Student Personnel Services, M

CLAFLIN UNIVERSITY

African-American/Black Studies, B
American/United States Studies/Civilization, B
Art Teacher Education, B
Art/Art Studies, General, B
BioTechnology, BM
Biochemistry, B
Bioinformatics, B
Biology/Biological Sciences, B
Business Administration and Management, B
Business Administration, Management and Opera-
    tions, M
Business, Management, Marketing, and Related
    Support Services, B
Chemistry, B
Computer Engineering, B
Computer Science, B
Criminal Justice/Law Enforcement Administration, B
Early Childhood Education and Teaching, B

Elementary Education and Teaching, B
English Language and Literature, B
English/Language Arts Teacher Education, B
Environmental Sciences, B
Fine/Studio Arts, B
Health and Physical Education, B
History, B
Junior High/Intermediate/Middle School Education
    and Teaching, B
Management Information Systems and Services, B
Marketing/Marketing Management, B
Mass Communication/Media Studies, B
Mathematics, B
Mathematics Teacher Education, B
Music, B
Music Teacher Education, B
Organizational Behavior Studies, B
Philosophy and Religious Studies, B
Political Science and Government, B
Psychology, B
Sociology, B
Sport and Fitness Administration/Management, B

CLEMSON UNIVERSITY

Accounting, BM
African-American/Black Studies, B
Agricultural Business and Management, B
Agricultural Economics, B
Agricultural Education, M
Agricultural Sciences, MD
Agricultural Teacher Education, B
Agricultural/Biological Engineering and Bioengineer-
    ing, B
Animal Genetics, B
Animal Sciences, BMD
Anthropology, B
Applied Economics, MD
Applied Mathematics, MD
Applied Psychology, M
Aquaculture, BMD
Architecture, BM
Art/Art Studies, General, B
Astronomy, MD
Astrophysics, MD
Atmospheric Sciences and Meteorology, MD
Automotive Engineering Technology/Technician, MD
Biochemistry, BD
Bioengineering, MDO
Biological and Biomedical Sciences, MD
Biology/Biological Sciences, B
Biomedical/Medical Engineering, B
Biophysics, MD
Biosystems Engineering, MD
Business Administration and Management, B
Business Administration, Management and Opera-
    tions, M
Chemical Engineering, BMD
Chemistry, BMD
Civil Engineering, BMD
Communication and Media Studies, MD
Computational Sciences, MD
Computer Art and Design, M
Computer Engineering, BMD
Computer Science, MD
Computer and Information Sciences, B
Construction Management, BM
Counseling Psychology, M
Counselor Education/School Counseling and Guid-
    ance Services, M
Curriculum and Instruction, D
Early Childhood Education and Teaching, B
Ecology, MD
Economics, BMD
Education, MDO
Educational Administration and Supervision, MO
Educational Leadership and Administration, D
Electrical Engineering, MD
Electrical, Electronics and Communications Engi-
    neering, B
Elementary Education and Teaching, B
Engineering and Applied Sciences, MDO
English, M
English Language and Literature, B
Entomology, MD
Entrepreneurship/Entrepreneurial Studies, M
Environmental Design/Architecture, D

Environmental Engineering
  Technology/Environmental Technology, MD
Environmental Sciences, MD
Environmental Studies, MD
Environmental and Occupational Health, M
Environmental/Environmental Health Engineering, B
Ergonomics and Human Factors, D
Evolutionary Biology, MD
Finance, B
Fine Arts and Art Studies, M
Fish, Game and Wildlife Management, MD
Food Science, B
Food Science and Technology, MD
Foreign Languages and Literatures, B
Foreign Languages, Literatures, and Linguistics, B
Forest Management/Forest Resources Management, B
Forestry, MD
Genetics, D
Geology/Earth Science, B
Health Professions and Related Clinical Sciences, B
Health Services Research, MD
Higher Education/Higher Education Administration, D
Historic Preservation and Conservation, M
History, BM
Horticultural Science, B
Human Development, M
Human Development and Family Studies, B
Human Resources Development, M
Human Resources Management and Services, M
Human-Computer Interaction, D
Humanities/Humanistic Studies, D
Hydrogeology, M
Industrial Design, B
Industrial Engineering, B
Industrial and Organizational Psychology, D
Industrial/Management Engineering, MD
Information Science/Studies, B
Landscape Architecture, BM
Manufacturing Engineering, M
Marketing/Marketing Management, B
Materials Engineering, BMD
Materials Sciences, MD
Mathematics, BMD
Mathematics Teacher Education, BM
Mechanical Engineering, BMD
Microbiology, BMD
Middle School Education, M
Molecular Biology, D
Natural Resources and Conservation, B
Nursing, MD
Nutritional Sciences, M
Operations Research, MD
Parks, Recreation and Leisure Facilities Management, B
Philosophy, B
Physics, BMD
Plant Biology, MD
Plant Sciences, MD
Political Science and Government, B
Pre-Dentistry Studies, B
Pre-Medicine/Pre-Medical Studies, B
Pre-Pharmacy Studies, B
Pre-Veterinary Studies, B
Psychology, BD
Public Administration, M
Public Affairs, D
Public Policy Analysis, DO
Reading Teacher Education, M
Real Estate, M
Recreation and Park Management, MD
Rhetoric, D
Science Teacher Education/General Science
  Teacher Education, BM
Secondary Education and Teaching, BM
Social Sciences, D
Sociology, BM
Soil Sciences, B
Spanish Language and Literature, B
Special Education and Teaching, BM
Statistics, MD
Student Personnel Services, M
Travel and Tourism, MD
Turf and Turfgrass Management, B
Urban and Regional Planning, M

Veterinary Sciences, MD
Visual and Performing Arts, B
Women's Studies, B
Writing, M

CLINTON COLLEGE

Biological and Physical Sciences, A
Business/Commerce, A
Early Childhood Education and Teaching, A
Liberal Arts and Sciences Studies and Humanities, A
Religion/Religious Studies, A

COASTAL CAROLINA UNIVERSITY

Accounting, BM
Applied Mathematics, B
Biochemistry, B
Biology/Biological Sciences, B
Business Administration and Management, B
Business Administration, Management and Operations, MO
Business/Managerial Economics, B
Chemistry, B
Communication Studies/Speech Communication
  and Rhetoric, B
Computer Science, O
Computer and Information Sciences, B
Drama and Dramatics/Theatre Arts, B
Dramatic/Theatre Arts and Stagecraft, B
Early Childhood Education and Teaching, B
Economics, B
Education, MO
Educational Leadership and Administration, M
Elementary Education and Teaching, B
English Language and Literature, B
Finance, B
Fine/Studio Arts, B
Graphic Design, B
Health/Health Care Administration/Management, B
History, B
Humanities/Humanistic Studies, B
Information Science/Studies, B
Information Technology, B
Junior High/Intermediate/Middle School Education
  and Teaching, B
Kinesiology and Exercise Science, B
Liberal Arts and Sciences Studies and Humanities, B
Management Information Systems and Services, O
Marine Biology and Biological Oceanography, B
Marine Sciences, M
Marketing/Marketing Management, B
Military Studies, B
Music, B
Philosophy, B
Physical Education Teaching and Coaching, B
Physics, B
Political Science and Government, B
Psychology, B
Public Health Education and Promotion, B
Resort Management, B
Sociology, B
Spanish Language and Literature, B
Special Education and Teaching, B
Sport and Fitness Administration/Management, B
Writing, M

COKER COLLEGE

Acting, B
Art Teacher Education, B
Biology Teacher Education, B
Biology/Biological Sciences, B
Business Administration and Management, B
Chemistry, B
Chemistry Teacher Education, B
Clinical Laboratory Science/Medical
  Technology/Technologist, B
Communication Studies/Speech Communication
  and Rhetoric, B
Computer Science, B
Criminology, B
Dance, B
Drama and Dramatics/Theatre Arts, B
Early Childhood Education and Teaching, B
Education, B
Elementary Education and Teaching, B

English Language and Literature, B
English/Language Arts Teacher Education, B
Fine/Studio Arts, B
Graphic Design, B
Health and Physical Education/Fitness, B
History, B
History Teacher Education, B
Kinesiology and Exercise Science, B
Mathematics, B
Mathematics Teacher Education, B
Music, B
Music Teacher Education, B
Parks, Recreation, Leisure and Fitness Studies, B
Photography, B
Physical Education Teaching and Coaching, B
Piano and Organ, B
Political Science and Government, B
Psychology, B
Social Work, B
Sociology, B
Sport and Fitness Administration/Management, BM
Technical Theatre/Theatre Design and Technology, B
Voice and Opera, B

COLLEGE OF CHARLESTON

Accounting, BM
African-American/Black Studies, B
Anthropology, B
Archeology, B
Art History, Criticism and Conservation, B
Arts Management, MO
Astronomy and Astrophysics, B
Athletic Training and Sports Medicine, B
Biology/Biological Sciences, B
Business Administration and Management, B
Business Administration, Management and Operations, M
Chemistry, B
Classics and Classical Languages, Literatures, and Linguistics, B
Communication Studies/Speech Communication
  and Rhetoric, B
Communication and Media Studies, M
Computer Science, M
Computer Software and Media Applications, B
Computer and Information Sciences, B
Dance, B
Drama and Dramatics/Theatre Arts, B
Early Childhood Education and Teaching, BM
Economics, B
Education, MO
Elementary Education and Teaching, BM
English, M
English Language and Literature, B
English as a Second Language, O
Environmental Sciences, M
Exercise Physiology, B
Finance, B
Fine/Studio Arts, B
Foreign Language Teacher Education, M
French Language and Literature, B
Geology/Earth Science, B
German Language and Literature, B
Historic Preservation and Conservation, BM
History, BM
Hospitality Administration/Management, B
Information Science/Studies, B
International Business/Trade/Commerce, B
International/Global Studies, B
Jewish/Judaic Studies, B
Junior High/Intermediate/Middle School Education
  and Teaching, B
Management Information Systems and Services, M
Marine Biology and Biological Oceanography, BM
Marine Sciences, M
Marketing/Marketing Management, B
Mathematics, BMO
Mathematics Teacher Education, M
Multi-/Interdisciplinary Studies, B
Music, B
Music Teacher Education, M
Philosophy, B
Physical Education Teaching and Coaching, B
Physics, B
Political Science and Government, B

Psychology, B
Public Administration, M
Public Health Education and Promotion, B
Religion/Religious Studies, B
Science Teacher Education/General Science
Teacher Education, M
Secondary Education and Teaching, B
Sociology, B
Spanish Language and Literature, B
Special Education and Teaching, BM
Teacher Education, Multiple Levels, B
Urban Studies/Affairs, B
Urban and Regional Planning, O
Women's Studies, B

COLUMBIA COLLEGE

Accounting, B
Art/Art Studies, General, B
Behavioral Sciences, B
Biochemistry, B
Biology/Biological Sciences, B
Business Administration and Management, B
Chemistry, B
Communication Studies/Speech Communication
and Rhetoric, B
Computer and Information Sciences, B
Conflict Resolution and Mediation/Peace Stud-
ies, MO
Criminal Justice/Safety Studies, B
Dance, B
Drama and Dance Teacher Education, B
Early Childhood Education and Teaching, B
Education, M
Educational Administration and Supervision, M
Elementary Education and Teaching, BM
English Language and Literature, B
Fine/Studio Arts, B
Higher Education/Higher Education Administra-
tion, M
History, B
Human Development and Family Studies, B
Journalism, B
Junior High/Intermediate/Middle School Education
and Teaching, B
Liberal Arts and Sciences Studies and Humani-
ties, B
Mathematics, B
Music, B
Music Performance, B
Music Teacher Education, B
Organizational Behavior Studies, O
Piano and Organ, B
Political Science and Government, B
Psychology, B
Public Administration and Social Service Profes-
sions, B
Religion/Religious Studies, B
Religious Education, B
Social Work, B
Spanish Language and Literature, B
Special Education and Teaching, B
Speech-Language Pathology/Pathologist, B
Voice and Opera, B

COLUMBIA INTERNATIONAL UNIVER-
SITY

Ancient Near Eastern and Biblical Languages, Lit-
eratures, and Linguistics, B
Communication and Media Studies, B
Counselor Education/School Counseling and Guid-
ance Services, M
Cultural Studies, M
Curriculum and Instruction, MD
Digital Communication and Media/Multimedia, B
Early Childhood Education and Teaching, M
Education, MDO
Educational Administration and Supervision, M
Educational Leadership and Administration, D
Elementary Education and Teaching, M
English Language and Literature, B
English as a Second Language, MO
General Studies, B
Higher Education/Higher Education Administra-
tion, D
Humanities/Humanistic Studies, B
Intercultural/Multicultural and Diversity Studies, B

International/Global Studies, B
Liberal Arts and Sciences Studies and Humani-
ties, B
Mass Communication/Media Studies, B
Missions/Missionary Studies and Missiology, MDO
Multilingual and Multicultural Education, M
Near and Middle Eastern Studies, B
Non-Profit/Public/Organizational Management, B
Pastoral Studies/Counseling, MDO
Pre-Theology/Pre-Ministerial Studies, B
Psychology, B
Religious Education, BM
Religious/Sacred Music, B
Teacher Education, Multiple Levels, B
Theology and Religious Vocations, MDO
Youth Ministry, B

CONVERSE COLLEGE

Accounting, B
Art Education, M
Art History, Criticism and Conservation, B
Art Teacher Education, B
Art Therapy/Therapist, B
Art/Art Studies, General, B
Biochemistry, B
Biology/Biological Sciences, B
Business Administration and Management, B
Business/Managerial Economics, B
Chemistry, B
Design and Applied Arts, B
Drama and Dramatics/Theatre Arts, B
Economics, B
Education, BMO
Education/Teaching of Individuals with Hearing Im-
pairments, Including Deafness, B
Education/Teaching of the Gifted and Talented, M
Educational Administration and Supervision, O
Educational Leadership and Administration, MO
Elementary Education and Teaching, BM
English, M
English Education, M
English Language and Literature, B
Finance, B
Fine/Studio Arts, B
German Language and Literature, B
Health/Health Care Administration/Management, B
History, BM
Human Resources Management/Personnel Adminis-
tration, B
Interior Design, B
International Business/Trade/Commerce, B
Kindergarten/PreSchool Education and Teaching, B
Liberal Studies, M
Marketing/Marketing Management, B
Marriage and Family Therapy/Counseling, M
Mathematics, B
Mathematics Teacher Education, M
Medical Staff Services Technology/Technician, B
Middle School Education, M
Music, BM
Music History, Literature, and Theory, B
Music Performance, B
Music Teacher Education, BM
Music Therapy/Therapist, B
Musicology and Ethnomusicology, B
Performance, M
Philosophy, B
Piano and Organ, B
Political Science and Government, BM
Psychology, B
Reading Teacher Education, O
Religion/Religious Studies, B
Science Teacher Education/General Science
Teacher Education, M
Secondary Education and Teaching, BM
Social Studies Teacher Education, M
Sociology, B
Spanish Language and Literature, B
Special Education and Teaching, BM
Violin, Viola, Guitar and Other Stringed Instru-
ments, B
Voice and Opera, B

DENMARK TECHNICAL COLLEGE

Administrative Assistant and Secretarial Science, A
Business/Commerce, A

Child Care and Support Services Management, A
Criminal Justice/Safety Studies, A
Data Processing and Data Processing
Technology/Technician, A
Electromechanical Technology/Electromechanical
Engineering Technology, A
Human Services, A
Industrial Electronics Technology/Technician, A
Liberal Arts and Sciences Studies and Humani-
ties, A
Multi-/Interdisciplinary Studies, A

ECPI UNIVERSITY (COLUMBIA)

Computer and Information Systems Security, A
Electrical, Electronic and Communications Engineer-
ing Technology/Technician, A
Medical Administrative Assistant/Secretary, A
Medical/Clinical Assistant, A

ECPI UNIVERSITY (GREENVILLE)

Computer Engineering Technology/Technician, A
Computer and Information Systems Security, A
Criminal Justice/Law Enforcement Administration, A
Health and Medical Administrative Services, A
Medical/Clinical Assistant, A
Web Page, Digital/Multimedia and Information Re-
sources Design, A

ECPI UNIVERSITY (NORTH CHARLES-
TON)

Computer Engineering Technology/Technician, A
Computer and Information Systems Security, A
Health and Medical Administrative Services, A
Medical/Clinical Assistant, A

ERSKINE COLLEGE

American/United States Studies/Civilization, B
Art/Art Studies, General, B
Athletic Training and Sports Medicine, B
Biology/Biological Sciences, B
Business Administration and Management, B
Chemistry, B
Elementary Education and Teaching, B
English Language and Literature, B
French Language and Literature, B
History, B
Kindergarten/PreSchool Education and Teaching, B
Mathematics, B
Music, B
Philosophy, B
Physical Education Teaching and Coaching, B
Physics, B
Political Science and Government, B
Psychology, B
Religion/Religious Studies, B
Social Studies Teacher Education, B
Spanish Language and Literature, B
Special Education and Teaching, B
Sport and Fitness Administration/Management, B

FLORENCE-DARLINGTON TECHNICAL
COLLEGE

Accounting, A
Administrative Assistant and Secretarial Science, A
Automobile/Automotive Mechanics
Technology/Technician, A
Business Administration and Management, A
Civil Engineering Technology/Technician, A
Clinical/Medical Laboratory Technician, A
Computer and Information Sciences and Support
Services, A
Criminal Justice/Law Enforcement Administration, A
Criminal Justice/Safety Studies, A
Data Processing and Data Processing
Technology/Technician, A
Dental Hygiene/Hygienist, A
Electrical, Electronic and Communications Engineer-
ing Technology/Technician, A
Electromechanical Technology/Electromechanical
Engineering Technology, A
Entrepreneurship/Entrepreneurial Studies, A
Health Information/Medical Records
Administration/Administrator, A
Heating, Air Conditioning, Ventilation and Refrigera-
tion Maintenance Technology/Technician, A

Industrial Radiologic Technology/Technician, A
Legal Assistant/Paralegal, A
Liberal Arts and Sciences Studies and Humanities, A
Machine Tool Technology/Machinist, A
Mechanical Drafting and Mechanical Drafting CAD/CADD, A
Mechanics and Repairers, A
Medical Radiologic Technology/Science - Radiation Therapist, A
Multi-/Interdisciplinary Studies, A
Respiratory Care Therapy/Therapist, A
Sales, Distribution and Marketing Operations, A
Social Work, A

FORREST COLLEGE

Accounting, A
Business Administration and Management, A
Child Care and Support Services Management, A
Computer Installation and Repair Technology/Technician, A
Computer Technology/Computer Systems Technology, A
Legal Administrative Assistant/Secretary, A
Legal Assistant/Paralegal, A
Medical Office Management/Administration, A
Medical/Clinical Assistant, A
Office Management and Supervision, A

FRANCIS MARION UNIVERSITY

Accounting, B
Applied Psychology, M
Art Teacher Education, B
Art/Art Studies, General, B
Biology/Biological Sciences, B
Business Administration and Management, B
Business Administration, Management and Operations, M
Business/Managerial Economics, B
Chemistry, B
Clinical Psychology, M
Computer and Information Sciences, B
Counseling Psychology, M
Drama and Dramatics/Theatre Arts, B
Early Childhood Education and Teaching, BM
Economics, B
Education, M
Elementary Education and Teaching, BM
English Language and Literature, B
Finance, B
Foreign Languages and Literatures, B
Health Services Administration, M
History, B
Industrial Engineering, B
International Relations and Affairs, B
Junior High/Intermediate/Middle School Education and Teaching, B
Liberal Arts and Sciences Studies and Humanities, B
Management Information Systems and Services, B
Marketing/Marketing Management, B
Mass Communication/Media Studies, B
Mathematics, B
Music, B
Nursing, M
Nursing - Advanced Practice, M
Nursing Education, M
Pharmacy, Pharmaceutical Sciences, and Administration, B
Physics, B
Political Science and Government, B
Psychology, BMO
School Psychology, MO
Secondary Education and Teaching, M
Sociology, B
Special Education and Teaching, M

FURMAN UNIVERSITY

Accounting, B
Anthropology, B
Art History, Criticism and Conservation, B
Art/Art Studies, General, B
Asian Studies/Civilization, B
Biochemistry, B
Biology/Biological Sciences, B
Business Administration and Management, B

Chemistry, BM
Classics and Classical Languages, Literatures, and Linguistics, B
Communication Studies/Speech Communication and Rhetoric, B
Computer Science, B
Curriculum and Instruction, M
Drama and Dramatics/Theatre Arts, B
Early Childhood Education and Teaching, M
Economics, B
Education, BMO
Educational Administration and Supervision, M
Educational Leadership and Administration, O
Elementary Education and Teaching, B
English Language and Literature, B
English as a Second Language, M
Environmental Studies, B
Fine/Studio Arts, B
French Language and Literature, B
Geology/Earth Science, B
German Language and Literature, B
Health Professions and Related Clinical Sciences, B
History, B
Information Technology, B
Kindergarten/PreSchool Education and Teaching, B
Latin Language and Literature, B
Mathematics, B
Modern Greek Language and Literature, B
Music, B
Music Teacher Education, B
Philosophy, B
Physics, B
Piano and Organ, B
Political Science and Government, B
Pre-Dentistry Studies, B
Pre-Law Studies, B
Pre-Medicine/Pre-Medical Studies, B
Pre-Veterinary Studies, B
Psychology, B
Reading Teacher Education, M
Religion/Religious Studies, B
Religious/Sacred Music, B
Secondary Education and Teaching, B
Sociology, B
Spanish Language and Literature, B
Special Education and Teaching, BM
Urban Studies/Affairs, B
Voice and Opera, B

GREENVILLE TECHNICAL COLLEGE

Accounting, A
Administrative Assistant and Secretarial Science, A
Architectural Engineering Technology/Technician, A
Automobile/Automotive Mechanics Technology/Technician, A
Business Administration and Management, A
Child Care and Support Services Management, A
Clinical/Medical Laboratory Technician, A
Construction Engineering Technology/Technician, A
Criminal Justice/Safety Studies, A
Culinary Arts/Chef Training, A
Data Processing and Data Processing Technology/Technician, A
Dental Hygiene/Hygienist, A
Diagnostic Medical Sonography/Sonographer and Ultrasound Technician, A
Electrical, Electronic and Communications Engineering Technology/Technician, A
Electromechanical and Instrumentation and Maintenance Technologies/Technicians, A
Emergency Medical Technology/Technician (EMT Paramedic), A
Fire Science/Firefighting, A
Health Information/Medical Records Technology/Technician, A
Legal Assistant/Paralegal, A
Liberal Arts and Sciences Studies and Humanities, A
Machine Tool Technology/Machinist, A
Mechanic and Repair Technologies/Technicians, A
Mechanical Drafting and Mechanical Drafting CAD/CADD, A
Mechanical Engineering/Mechanical Technology/Technician, A
Medical Radiologic Technology/Science - Radiation Therapist, A

Multi-/Interdisciplinary Studies, A
Occupational Therapist Assistant, A
Physical Therapist Assistant, A
Purchasing, Procurement/Acquisitions and Contracts Management, A
Respiratory Care Therapy/Therapist, A
Sales, Distribution and Marketing Operations, A

HORRY-GEORGETOWN TECHNICAL COLLEGE

Administrative Assistant and Secretarial Science, A
Business Administration and Management, A
Criminal Justice/Safety Studies, A
Culinary Arts/Chef Training, A
Electrical, Electronic and Communications Engineering Technology/Technician, A
Forestry Technology/Technician, A
Legal Assistant/Paralegal, A
Machine Tool Technology/Machinist, A

LANDER UNIVERSITY

Art/Art Studies, General, B
Athletic Training and Sports Medicine, B
Biology/Biological Sciences, B
Business Administration and Management, B
Chemistry, B
Computer and Information Sciences, B
Early Childhood Education and Teaching, BM
Education, M
Elementary Education and Teaching, B
Emergency Management, M
English Language and Literature, B
Environmental Sciences, B
History, B
Kinesiology and Exercise Science, B
Liberal Arts and Sciences Studies and Humanities, B
Mathematics, B
Music, B
Nursing, M
Physical Education Teaching and Coaching, B
Political Science and Government, B
Psychology, B
Secondary Education and Teaching, B
Sociology, B
Spanish Language and Literature, B
Special Education and Teaching, B

LIMESTONE COLLEGE

Accounting, B
Athletic Training and Sports Medicine, B
Biology/Biological Sciences, B
Business Administration and Management, B
Business Administration, Management and Operations, BM
Business/Commerce, AB
Business/Managerial Economics, B
Cell/Cellular and Molecular Biology, B
Chemistry, B
Computer Programming/Programmer, AB
Computer Science, B
Computer Software and Media Applications, B
Computer and Information Sciences, AB
Computer and Information Sciences and Support Services, B
Computer and Information Systems Security, B
Computer/Information Technology Services Administration and Management, AB
Corrections and Criminal Justice, B
Criminal Justice/Law Enforcement Administration, B
Criminal Justice/Safety Studies, B
Data Modeling/Warehousing and Database Administration, AB
Digital Communication and Media/Multimedia, B
Drama and Dramatics/Theatre Arts, B
E-Commerce/Electronic Commerce, AB
Early Childhood Education and Teaching, B
Economics, B
Education, B
Elementary Education and Teaching, B
English Language and Literature, B
English/Language Arts Teacher Education, B
Fine/Studio Arts, B
Graphic Design, B
Health and Physical Education/Fitness, B
Health/Health Care Administration/Management, B

History, B
Human Resources Development, B
Human Resources Management/Personnel Adminis-
tration, B
Information Science/Studies, B
Information Technology, AB
Jazz/Jazz Studies, B
Liberal Arts and Sciences Studies and Humani-
ties, AB
Marketing/Marketing Management, B
Mathematics, B
Mathematics Teacher Education, B
Music, B
Music Performance, B
Music Teacher Education, B
Parks, Recreation, Leisure and Fitness Studies, B
Physical Education Teaching and Coaching, B
Pre-Dentistry Studies, B
Pre-Law Studies, B
Pre-Medicine/Pre-Medical Studies, B
Pre-Nursing Studies, B
Pre-Pharmacy Studies, B
Pre-Veterinary Studies, B
Psychology, B
Social Work, B
Sport and Fitness Administration/Management, B
Web Page, Digital/Multimedia and Information Re-
sources Design, AB
Web/Multimedia Management and Webmaster, B

MEDICAL UNIVERSITY OF SOUTH CAROLINA

Allied Health and Medical Assisting Services, MD
Allopathic Medicine, D
Biochemistry, MD
Biological and Biomedical Sciences, MD
Biostatistics, MD
Cancer Biology/Oncology, D
Cardiovascular Sciences, D
Cardiovascular Technology/Technologist, B
Cell Biology and Anatomy, D
Clinical Research, M
Dentistry, D
Developmental Biology and Embryology, D
Epidemiology, MD
Genetics, D
Gerontological Nursing, MD
Health Services Administration, MD
Immunology, MD
International Public Health/International Health, M
Marine Sciences, D
Maternal/Child Health and Neonatal
Nurse/Nursing, MD
Medical Imaging, D
Medicinal and Pharmaceutical Chemistry, D
Microbiology, MD
Molecular Biology, MD
Molecular Pharmacology, MD
Neuroscience, MD
Nurse Anesthetist, M
Nursing, D
Nursing - Adult, MD
Nursing - Advanced Practice, MD
Nursing Administration, M
Nursing Education, M
Occupational Therapy/Therapist, M
Pathobiology, D
Pathology/Experimental Pathology, MD
Pharmacy, D
Physical Therapy/Therapist, D
Physician Assistant, M
Rehabilitation Sciences, D
Toxicology, D

MIDLANDS TECHNICAL COLLEGE

Accounting, A
Administrative Assistant and Secretarial Science, A
Architectural Engineering Technology/Technician, A
Automobile/Automotive Mechanics
Technology/Technician, A
Business Administration and Management, A
Business/Commerce, A
Child Care Provider/Assistant, A
Child Care and Support Services Management, A
Civil Engineering Technology/Technician, A
Clinical/Medical Laboratory Technician, A

Commercial and Advertising Art, A
Computer Installation and Repair
Technology/Technician, A
Computer Systems Networking and Telecommunica-
tions, A
Computer and Information Sciences and Support
Services, A
Construction Engineering Technology/Technician, A
Court Reporting/Court Reporter, A
Criminal Justice/Safety Studies, A
Data Processing and Data Processing
Technology/Technician, A
Dental Assisting/Assistant, A
Dental Hygiene/Hygienist, A
Electrical, Electronic and Communications Engineer-
ing Technology/Technician, A
Engineering Technology, A
Gerontology, A
Health Information/Medical Records
Technology/Technician, A
Health Professions and Related Clinical Sciences, A
Heating, Air Conditioning, Ventilation and Refrigera-
tion Maintenance Technology/Technician, A
Human Services, A
Industrial Electronics Technology/Technician, A
Industrial Mechanics and Maintenance Technol-
ogy, A
Legal Assistant/Paralegal, A
Liberal Arts and Sciences Studies and Humani-
ties, A
Machine Tool Technology/Machinist, A
Mechanical Drafting and Mechanical Drafting
CAD/CADD, A
Mechanical Engineering/Mechanical
Technology/Technician, A
Medical Radiologic Technology/Science - Radiation
Therapist, A
Medical/Clinical Assistant, A
Multi-/Interdisciplinary Studies, A
Nuclear Medical Technology/Technologist, A
Occupational Therapist Assistant, A
Pharmacy Technician/Assistant, A
Physical Therapist Assistant, A
Precision Production, A
Precision Production Trades, A
Respiratory Care Therapy/Therapist, A
Sales, Distribution and Marketing Operations, A
Surgical Technology/Technologist, A
Youth Services/Administration, A

MILLER-MOTTE TECHNICAL COLLEGE (NORTH CHARLESTON)

Business, Management, Marketing, and Related
Support Services, A
Computer and Information Sciences, A
Criminal Justice/Law Enforcement Administration, A
Legal Assistant/Paralegal, A
Massage Therapy/Therapeutic Massage, A
Medical/Clinical Assistant, A
Surgical Technology/Technologist, A

MORRIS COLLEGE

Biology Teacher Education, B
Biology/Biological Sciences, B
Business Administration and Management, B
Business Administration, Management and Opera-
tions, B
Community Health Services/Liaison/Counseling, B
Criminal Justice/Law Enforcement Administration, B
Early Childhood Education and Teaching, B
Elementary Education and Teaching, B
English Language and Literature, B
English/Language Arts Teacher Education, B
History, B
Liberal Arts and Sciences Studies and Humani-
ties, B
Mass Communication/Media Studies, B
Mathematics, B
Mathematics Teacher Education, B
Parks, Recreation, Leisure and Fitness Studies, B
Political Science and Government, B
Religious Education, B
Social Studies Teacher Education, B
Sociology, B

Theology/Theological Studies, B

NEWBERRY COLLEGE

Accounting, B
Art/Art Studies, General, B
Biology/Biological Sciences, B
Business Administration and Management, B
Chemistry, B
Communication and Media Studies, B
Communication, Journalism and Related Pro-
grams, B
Drama and Dramatics/Theatre Arts, B
Early Childhood Education and Teaching, B
Elementary Education and Teaching, B
English Language and Literature, B
Graphic Design, B
History, B
International Relations and Affairs, B
Junior High/Intermediate/Middle School Education
and Teaching, B
Management Information Systems and Services, B
Marketing, B
Mathematics, B
Music, B
Music Performance, B
Music Teacher Education, B
Music Theory and Composition, B
Parks, Recreation, Leisure and Fitness Studies, B
Philosophy and Religious Studies, B
Political Science and Government, B
Psychology, B
Religion/Religious Studies, B
Sociology, B
Spanish Language and Literature, B

NORTH GREENVILLE UNIVERSITY

Accounting, B
Bible/Biblical Studies, B
Biology/Biological Sciences, B
Broadcast Journalism, B
Business Administration and Management, B
Drama and Dramatics/Theatre Arts, B
Early Childhood Education and Teaching, B
Education, M
Elementary Education and Teaching, B
English Language and Literature, B
English/Language Arts Teacher Education, B
Finance and Banking, M
Fine/Studio Arts, B
General Studies, B
Health and Physical Education/Fitness, B
History, B
Human Resources Management and Services, M
International Business/Trade/Commerce, B
Journalism, B
Liberal Arts and Sciences Studies and Humani-
ties, B
Marketing/Marketing Management, B
Mass Communication/Media Studies, B
Mathematics, B
Mathematics Teacher Education, B
Missions/Missionary Studies and Missiology, B
Music, B
Music Performance, B
Music Teacher Education, B
Parks, Recreation, Leisure and Fitness Studies, B
Pastoral Studies/Counseling, MD
Psychology, B
Religious/Sacred Music, B
Social Studies Teacher Education, B
Spanish Language Teacher Education, B
Spanish Language and Literature, B
Sport and Fitness Administration/Management, B
Youth Ministry, B

NORTHEASTERN TECHNICAL COL-LEGE

Accounting, A
Administrative Assistant and Secretarial Science, A
Business Administration and Management, A
Computer Programming/Programmer, A
Computer Science, A
Data Processing and Data Processing
Technology/Technician, A
Drafting/Design Engineering
Technologies/Technicians, A

Electrical, Electronic and Communications Engineering Technology/Technician, A
Liberal Arts and Sciences Studies and Humanities, A
Machine Tool Technology/Machinist, A
Marketing/Marketing Management, A

ORANGEBURG-CALHOUN TECHNICAL COLLEGE

Accounting, A
Administrative Assistant and Secretarial Science, A
Automobile/Automotive Mechanics Technology/Technician, A
Business/Commerce, A
Clinical/Medical Laboratory Technician, A
Computer Programming, A
Criminal Justice/Safety Studies, A
Electrical, Electronic and Communications Engineering Technology/Technician, A
Instrumentation Technology/Technician, A
Kindergarten/PreSchool Education and Teaching, A
Legal Assistant/Paralegal, A
Liberal Arts and Sciences Studies and Humanities, A
Machine Tool Technology/Machinist, A
Medical Radiologic Technology/Science - Radiation Therapist, A
Respiratory Care Therapy/Therapist, A

PIEDMONT TECHNICAL COLLEGE

Accounting, A
Administrative Assistant and Secretarial Science, A
Automobile/Automotive Mechanics Technology/Technician, A
Biological and Physical Sciences, A
Building/Construction Finishing, Management, and Inspection, A
Business Administration and Management, A
Business/Commerce, A
Carpentry/Carpenter, A
Child Development, A
Commercial and Advertising Art, A
Computer Programming/Programmer, A
Construction Engineering Technology/Technician, A
Criminal Justice/Law Enforcement Administration, A
Criminal Justice/Safety Studies, A
Data Processing and Data Processing Technology/Technician, A
Drafting and Design Technology/Technician, A
Electrical, Electronic and Communications Engineering Technology/Technician, A
Engineering, A
Engineering Technology, A
Funeral Service and Mortuary Science, A
Heating, Air Conditioning, Ventilation and Refrigeration Maintenance Technology/Technician, A
Human Services, A
Legal Administrative Assistant/Secretary, A
Liberal Arts and Sciences Studies and Humanities, A
Machine Tool Technology/Machinist, A
Marketing/Marketing Management, A
Mechanical Drafting and Mechanical Drafting CAD/CADD, A
Mechanical Engineering/Mechanical Technology/Technician, A
Medical Administrative Assistant/Secretary, A
Medical Radiologic Technology/Science - Radiation Therapist, A
Office Management and Supervision, A
Respiratory Care Therapy/Therapist, A
Social Work, A

PRESBYTERIAN COLLEGE

Art History, Criticism and Conservation, B
Art/Art Studies, General, B
Biochemistry, B
Biology/Biological Sciences, B
Business Administration and Management, B
Business/Managerial Economics, B
Chemistry, B
Drama and Dramatics/Theatre Arts, B
Early Childhood Education and Teaching, B
Elementary Education and Teaching, B
English Language and Literature, B
Fine/Studio Arts, B

Foreign Languages and Literatures, B
French Language and Literature, B
History, B
International/Global Studies, B
Junior High/Intermediate/Middle School Education and Teaching, B
Mathematics, B
Modern Languages, B
Music, B
Music Teacher Education, B
Pharmacy, B
Philosophy, B
Physics, B
Political Science and Government, B
Psychology, B
Religion/Religious Studies, B
Religious Education, B
Sociology, B
Spanish Language and Literature, B

SOUTH CAROLINA STATE UNIVERSITY

Accounting, B
Agribusiness, BM
Allied Health and Medical Assisting Services, M
Art Teacher Education, B
Audiology/Audiologist and Speech-Language Pathology/Pathologist, B
Biology/Biological Sciences, B
Business Administration and Management, B
Business Education, M
Business Teacher Education, B
Business/Managerial Economics, B
Chemistry, B
Child and Family Studies, M
Civil Engineering, M
Civil Engineering Technology/Technician, B
Communication Disorders, M
Computer and Information Sciences, B
Counselor Education/School Counseling and Guidance Services, M
Criminal Justice/Law Enforcement Administration, B
Drama and Dramatics/Theatre Arts, B
Early Childhood Education and Teaching, BM
Education, M
Educational Administration and Supervision, DO
Electrical, Electronic and Communications Engineering Technology/Technician, B
Elementary Education and Teaching, BM
English Education, M
English Language and Literature, B
Family and Consumer Sciences/Human Sciences, BM
Fine/Studio Arts, B
Foods, Nutrition, and Wellness Studies, B
Foreign Languages and Literatures, B
Health and Physical Education, B
History, B
Home Economics Education, M
Human Services, M
Industrial Education, M
Industrial Technology/Technician, B
Junior High/Intermediate/Middle School Education and Teaching, B
Marketing/Marketing Management, B
Mass Communication/Media Studies, B
Mathematics, B
Mathematics Teacher Education, M
Mechanical Engineering, M
Mechanical Engineering/Mechanical Technology/Technician, B
Music Teacher Education, B
Nuclear Engineering, B
Physical Education Teaching and Coaching, B
Physics, B
Political Science and Government, B
Psychology, B
Science Teacher Education/General Science Teacher Education, M
Secondary Education and Teaching, M
Social Sciences, B
Social Studies Teacher Education, M
Social Work, B
Sociology, B
Special Education and Teaching, BM
Survey Technology/Surveying, B

Technology Teacher Education/Industrial Arts Teacher Education, B

SOUTH UNIVERSITY

Business Administration and Management, B
Business Administration, Management and Operations, M
Counseling Psychology, M
Criminal Justice/Law Enforcement Administration, B
Criminology, M
Graphic Design, AB
Health Services Administration, M
Health/Health Care Administration/Management, B
Health/Medical Preparatory Programs, B
Information Science/Studies, M
Legal Assistant/Paralegal, AB
Medical/Clinical Assistant, A
Nursing, M
Organizational Management, M
Pharmacy, D
Psychology, B

SOUTHERN WESLEYAN UNIVERSITY

Accounting, B
Biology/Biological Sciences, B
Business Administration and Management, B
Business Administration, Management and Operations, M
Business/Commerce, AB
Chemistry, B
Clinical Laboratory Science/Medical Technology/Technologist, B
Communication Studies/Speech Communication and Rhetoric, B
Computer and Information Sciences, B
Criminalistics and Criminal Science, B
Criminology, B
Early Childhood Education and Teaching, B
Education, BM
Elementary Education and Teaching, B
English Language and Literature, B
English/Language Arts Teacher Education, B
Forensic Science and Technology, B
General Studies, A
Health and Physical Education, B
History, B
Human Services, B
Information Resources Management/CIO Training, B
Kindergarten/PreSchool Education and Teaching, B
Management, M
Mathematics, B
Mathematics Teacher Education, B
Music, B
Music Teacher Education, B
Parks, Recreation, Leisure and Fitness Studies, B
Pastoral Studies/Counseling, M
Physical Education Teaching and Coaching, B
Pre-Medicine/Pre-Medical Studies, B
Psychology, B
Religion/Religious Studies, B
Religious/Sacred Music, B
Science Teacher Education/General Science Teacher Education, B
Social Sciences, B
Special Education and Teaching, B

SPARTANBURG COMMUNITY COLLEGE

Accounting, A
Administrative Assistant and Secretarial Science, A
Applied Horticulture/Horticultural Operations, A
Automobile/Automotive Mechanics Technology/Technician, A
Business Administration and Management, A
Clinical/Medical Laboratory Technician, A
Data Processing and Data Processing Technology/Technician, A
Electrical, Electronic and Communications Engineering Technology/Technician, A
Heating, Air Conditioning, Ventilation and Refrigeration Maintenance Technology/Technician, A
Industrial Electronics Technology/Technician, A
Liberal Arts and Sciences Studies and Humanities, A
Machine Tool Technology/Machinist, A
Manufacturing Technology/Technician, A

Mechanical Engineering/Mechanical
Technology/Technician, A
Medical Radiologic Technology/Science - Radiation
Therapist, A
Multi-/Interdisciplinary Studies, A
Radiation Protection/Health Physics Technician, A
Respiratory Care Therapy/Therapist, A

SPARTANBURG METHODIST COLLEGE

Business/Commerce, A
Criminal Justice/Law Enforcement Administration, A
Liberal Arts and Sciences Studies and Humani-
ties, A
Religion/Religious Studies, A
Visual and Performing Arts, A

STRAYER UNIVERSITY–CHARLESTON CAMPUS

Accounting, B
Business Administration and Management, B
Criminal Justice/Law Enforcement Administration, B
Economics, B
International Business/Trade/Commerce, B
Management Information Systems and Services, B

STRAYER UNIVERSITY–COLUMBIA CAMPUS

Accounting, B
Business Administration and Management, B
Criminal Justice/Law Enforcement Administration, B
Economics, B
International Business/Trade/Commerce, B
Management Information Systems and Services, B

STRAYER UNIVERSITY–GREENVILLE CAMPUS

Accounting, B
Business Administration and Management, B
Criminal Justice/Law Enforcement Administration, B
Economics, B
International Business/Trade/Commerce, B
Management Information Systems and Services, B

TECHNICAL COLLEGE OF THE LOWCOUNTRY

Administrative Assistant and Secretarial Science, A
Business/Commerce, A
Child Care Provider/Assistant, A
Civil Engineering Technology/Technician, A
Construction Engineering Technology/Technician, A
Data Processing and Data Processing
Technology/Technician, A
Early Childhood Education and Teaching, A
Education, A
Emergency Medical Technology/Technician (EMT
Paramedic), A
Fire Services Administration, A
Hospitality Administration/Management, A
Industrial Electronics Technology/Technician, A
Legal Assistant/Paralegal, A
Liberal Arts and Sciences Studies and Humani-
ties, A
Medical Radiologic Technology/Science - Radiation
Therapist, A
Physical Therapist Assistant, A

TRI-COUNTY TECHNICAL COLLEGE

Accounting, A
Administrative Assistant and Secretarial Science, A
Business Administration and Management, A
Clinical/Medical Laboratory Technician, A
Criminal Justice/Safety Studies, A
Data Processing and Data Processing
Technology/Technician, A
Electrical, Electronic and Communications Engineer-
ing Technology/Technician, A
Engineering Technology, A
Heating, Air Conditioning, Ventilation and Refrigera-
tion Maintenance Technology/Technician, A
Industrial Electronics Technology/Technician, A
Industrial Production Technologies/Technicians, A
Liberal Arts and Sciences Studies and Humani-
ties, A
Machine Tool Technology/Machinist, A

Mechanical Drafting and Mechanical Drafting
CAD/CADD, A
Multi-/Interdisciplinary Studies, A
Radio and Television Broadcasting
Technology/Technician, A
Respiratory Therapy Technician/Assistant, A
Technical Teacher Education, A
Veterinary/Animal Health Technology/Technician and
Veterinary Assistant, A

TRIDENT TECHNICAL COLLEGE

Accounting, A
Administrative Assistant and Secretarial Science, A
Airframe Mechanics and Aircraft Maintenance
Technology/Technician, A
Automobile/Automotive Mechanics
Technology/Technician, A
Biological and Physical Sciences, A
Business Administration and Management, A
Child Care Provider/Assistant, A
Civil Engineering Technology/Technician, A
Clinical/Medical Laboratory Technician, A
Commercial and Advertising Art, A
Computer Engineering Technology/Technician, A
Computer Graphics, A
Computer Programming, Specific Applications, A
Computer Systems Networking and Telecommunica-
tions, A
Computer/Information Technology Services Adminis-
tration and Management, A
Criminal Justice/Law Enforcement Administration, A
Culinary Arts/Chef Training, A
Dental Hygiene/Hygienist, A
Electrical, Electronic and Communications Engineer-
ing Technology/Technician, A
Engineering Technology, A
Horticultural Science, A
Hotel/Motel Administration/Management, A
Human Services, A
Industrial Technology/Technician, A
Law and Legal Studies, A
Legal Assistant/Paralegal, A
Liberal Arts and Sciences Studies and Humani-
ties, A
Machine Tool Technology/Machinist, A
Marketing/Marketing Management, A
Mechanical Engineering/Mechanical
Technology/Technician, A
Medical Administrative Assistant/Secretary, A
Occupational Therapy/Therapist, A
Physical Therapy/Therapist, A
Respiratory Care Therapy/Therapist, A
Telecommunications Technology/Technician, A
Veterinary/Animal Health Technology/Technician and
Veterinary Assistant, A
Web Page, Digital/Multimedia and Information Re-
sources Design, A
Web/Multimedia Management and Webmaster, A

UNIVERSITY OF SOUTH CAROLINA

Accounting, BM
Acute Care/Critical Care Nursing, MO
Advertising, B
African-American/Black Studies, B
Allopathic Medicine, D
Anthropology, BMD
Applied Statistics, O
Aquatic Biology/Limnology, B
Archives/Archival Administration, M
Art Education, M
Art History, Criticism and Conservation, BM
Art Teacher Education, B
Astronomy, MD
Biochemistry, MD
Biological and Biomedical Sciences, MD
Biology/Biological Sciences, B
Biomedical/Medical Engineering, B
Biostatistics, MD
Broadcast Journalism, B
Business Administration and Management, B
Business Administration, Management and Opera-
tions, MD
Business Education, M
Business/Managerial Economics, B
Cell Biology and Anatomy, MD
Chemical Engineering, BMD

Chemistry, BMD
Civil Engineering, BMD
Classics and Classical Languages, Litera-
tures, and Linguistics, B
Clinical Psychology, MD
Communication Disorders, MD
Community Health Nursing, M
Community Psychology, MD
Comparative Literature, BMD
Composition, MD
Computer Engineering, BMD
Computer Science, MD
Computer and Information Sciences, B
Consumer Economics, M
Counselor Education/School Counseling and Guid-
ance Services, DO
Criminal Justice/Law Enforcement Administration, B
Criminology, MD
Curriculum and Instruction, D
Dance, B
Developmental Biology and Embryology, MD
Drama and Dramatics/Theatre Arts, B
Early Childhood Education and Teaching, MD
Ecology, MD
Economics, BMD
Education, MDO
Educational Administration and Supervision, MDO
Educational Measurement and Evaluation, MD
Educational Media/Instructional Technology, M
Educational Psychology, MD
Electrical Engineering, MD
Electrical, Electronics and Communications Engi-
neering, B
Elementary Education and Teaching, BMD
Engineering Science, B
Engineering and Applied Sciences, MD
English, MD
English Education, M
English Language and Literature, B
English as a Second Language, O
Entertainment Management, M
Environmental Policy and Resource Manage-
ment, M
Environmental Sciences, B
Environmental and Occupational Health, MD
Epidemiology, MD
European Studies/Civilization, B
Evolutionary Biology, MD
Exercise and Sports Science, MD
Experimental Psychology, MD
Finance, B
Fine Arts and Art Studies, M
Fine/Studio Arts, B
Foreign Language Teacher Education, MD
Foundations and Philosophy of Education, D
French Language and Literature, BM
Genetic Counseling/Counselor, M
Geography, BMD
Geology/Earth Science, BMD
Geophysics and Seismology, B
Geosciences, MD
German Language and Literature, BM
Gerontology, O
Hazardous Materials Management and Waste
Technology/Technician, MD
Health Education, MDO
Health Promotion, MDO
Health Services Administration, MD
Higher Education/Higher Education Administra-
tion, M
Historic Preservation and Conservation, M
History, BMDO
Hospitality Administration/Management, BM
Human Resources Management and Services, M
Industrial Hygiene, MD
Information Science/Studies, BMDO
Insurance, B
International Affairs, MD
International Business/Trade/Commerce, BM
International Relations and Affairs, B
Journalism, BMD
Junior High/Intermediate/Middle School Education
and Teaching, B
Kinesiology and Exercise Science, B
Latin American Studies, B
Law and Legal Studies, D

Liberal Arts and Sciences Studies and Humanities, B
Library Science, MDO
Linguistics, MDO
Management Science, B
Marine Biology and Biological Oceanography, B
Marine Science/Merchant Marine Officer, B
Marine Sciences, MD
Marketing/Marketing Management, B
Mathematics, BMD
Mathematics Teacher Education, M
Mechanical Engineering, BMD
Media Studies, M
Medical/Surgical Nursing, M
Molecular Biology, MD
Museology/Museum Studies, MO
Music, BMDO
Music History, Literature, and Theory, M
Music Teacher Education, BMD
Music Theory and Composition, M
Nuclear Engineering, MD
Nurse Anesthetist, M
Nursing, MDO
Nursing - Adult, M
Nursing - Advanced Practice, M
Nursing Administration, M
Oceanography, Chemical and Physical, B
Office Management and Supervision, B
Pediatric Nurse/Nursing, M
Performance, MDO
Pharmaceutical Sciences, MD
Pharmacy, D
Philosophy, BMD
Physical Education Teaching and Coaching, BMD
Physics, BMD
Political Science and Government, BMD
Psychiatric/Mental Health Nurse/Nursing, MO
Psychology, MD
Public Administration, M
Public Health, BM
Public History, MO
Public Relations/Image Management, B
Reading Teacher Education, MD
Real Estate, B
Rehabilitation Counseling, MO
Rehabilitation Sciences, O
Religion/Religious Studies, BM
Retailing and Retail Operations, B
Russian Language and Literature, B
School Psychology, D
Science Teacher Education/General Science Teacher Education, M
Secondary Education and Teaching, MD
Social Studies Teacher Education, M
Social Work, BMD
Sociology, BMD
Software Engineering, M
Spanish Language and Literature, BM
Special Education and Teaching, MD
Speech and Rhetorical Studies, M
Sport and Fitness Administration/Management, BM
Statistics, BMDO
Student Personnel Services, M
Theater, M
Tourism and Travel Services Management, B
Travel and Tourism, M
Women's Health Nursing, M
Women's Studies, BO
Writing, M

UNIVERSITY OF SOUTH CAROLINA AIKEN

Applied Mathematics, B
Applied Psychology, M
Biology/Biological Sciences, B
Biomedical Sciences, B
Business Administration and Management, B
Chemistry, B
Clinical Psychology, M
Communication Studies/Speech Communication and Rhetoric, B
Early Childhood Education and Teaching, B
Educational Media/Instructional Technology, M
Elementary Education and Teaching, B
English Language and Literature, B
Fine/Studio Arts, B

History, B
Industrial Engineering, B
Junior High/Intermediate/Middle School Education and Teaching, B
Kinesiology and Exercise Science, B
Liberal Arts and Sciences Studies and Humanities, B
Music Teacher Education, B
Political Science and Government, B
Psychology, B
Secondary Education and Teaching, B
Sociology, B
Special Education and Teaching, B

UNIVERSITY OF SOUTH CAROLINA BEAUFORT

Biology/Biological Sciences, B
Business Administration and Management, B
Communication Studies/Speech Communication and Rhetoric, B
Early Childhood Education and Teaching, B
Elementary Education and Teaching, B
English Language and Literature, B
Fine/Studio Arts, B
History, B
Hospitality Administration/Management, B
Liberal Arts and Sciences Studies and Humanities, AB
Mathematics, B
Psychology, B
Public Health Education and Promotion, B
Social Sciences, B
Sociology, B
Spanish Language and Literature, B

UNIVERSITY OF SOUTH CAROLINA LANCASTER

Business Administration and Management, A
Criminal Justice/Law Enforcement Administration, A
Liberal Arts and Sciences Studies and Humanities, A

UNIVERSITY OF SOUTH CAROLINA SALKEHATCHIE

Liberal Arts and Sciences Studies and Humanities, A

UNIVERSITY OF SOUTH CAROLINA SUMTER

Liberal Arts and Sciences Studies and Humanities, A

UNIVERSITY OF SOUTH CAROLINA UNION

Biological and Physical Sciences, A
Liberal Arts and Sciences Studies and Humanities, A

UNIVERSITY OF SOUTH CAROLINA UPSTATE

Art Teacher Education, B
Biology/Biological Sciences, B
Business Administration and Management, B
Chemistry, B
Communication Studies/Speech Communication and Rhetoric, B
Computer and Information Sciences, B
Criminal Justice/Law Enforcement Administration, B
Drama and Dramatics/Theatre Arts, B
Early Childhood Education and Teaching, BM
Education, M
Education/Teaching of Individuals with Specific Learning Disabilities, B
Elementary Education and Teaching, BM
Engineering Technology, B
English Language and Literature, B
Fine/Studio Arts, B
Health Informatics, M
History, B
Human Development and Family Studies, B
Information Science/Studies, BM
Junior High/Intermediate/Middle School Education and Teaching, B
Kindergarten/PreSchool Education and Teaching, B

Mathematics, B
Music, B
Non-Profit/Public/Organizational Management, B
Physical Education Teaching and Coaching, B
Political Science and Government, B
Psychology, B
Secondary Education and Teaching, B
Sociology, B
Spanish Language and Literature, B
Special Education and Teaching, M

VIRGINIA COLLEGE IN SPARTANBURG

Business Administration and Management, A
Computer Engineering Technology/Technician, A
Medical Office Management/Administration, A
Medical/Clinical Assistant, A
Office Management and Supervision, A

VOORHEES COLLEGE

Accounting, B
Biology/Biological Sciences, B
Business Administration and Management, B
Computer Science, B
Criminal Justice/Law Enforcement Administration, B
Mass Communication/Media Studies, B
Sociology, B

WILLIAMSBURG TECHNICAL COLLEGE

Administrative Assistant and Secretarial Science, A
Business/Commerce, A
Child Care and Support Services Management, A
Liberal Arts and Sciences Studies and Humanities, A

WINTHROP UNIVERSITY

Art Education, M
Art History, Criticism and Conservation, B
Art/Art Studies, General, B
Arts Management, M
Biological and Biomedical Sciences, M
Biology/Biological Sciences, B
Business Administration and Management, B
Business Administration, Management and Operations, M
Chemistry, B
Communication Disorders, B
Counselor Education/School Counseling and Guidance Services, M
Dance, B
Drama and Dramatics/Theatre Arts, B
E-Commerce/Electronic Commerce, B
Education, M
Educational Leadership and Administration, M
Elementary Education and Teaching, B
English, M
English Language and Literature, B
Environmental Sciences, B
Family and Consumer Sciences/Home Economics Teacher Education, B
Fine Arts and Art Studies, M
Foreign Languages and Literatures, B
History, BM
Liberal Studies, M
Mass Communication/Media Studies, B
Mathematics, B
Middle School Education, M
Music, BM
Music Teacher Education, BM
Nutritional Sciences, M
Performance, M
Philosophy and Religious Studies, B
Physical Education Teaching and Coaching, BM
Political Science and Government, B
Project Management, MO
Psychology, BMO
Reading Teacher Education, M
Secondary Education and Teaching, M
Social Work, BM
Sociology, B
Software Engineering, MO
Spanish Language and Literature, M
Special Education and Teaching, BM

Sport and Fitness Administration/Management, B

WOFFORD COLLEGE

Accounting, B
African-American/Black Studies, B
Art History, Criticism and Conservation, B
Biology/Biological Sciences, B
Business/Managerial Economics, B
Chemistry, B
Chinese Language and Literature, B
Computer Science, B
Drama and Dramatics/Theatre Arts, B
Economics, B
Education, B
English Language and Literature, B
Environmental Studies, B
Finance, B
Fine/Studio Arts, B
French Language and Literature, B
German Language and Literature, B
History, B
Humanities/Humanistic Studies, B
Intercultural/Multicultural and Diversity Studies, B
Latin American Studies, B
Mathematics, B
Multi-/Interdisciplinary Studies, B
Philosophy, B
Physics, B
Political Science and Government, B
Pre-Dentistry Studies, B
Pre-Law Studies, B
Pre-Medicine/Pre-Medical Studies, B
Pre-Veterinary Studies, B
Psychology, B
Religion/Religious Studies, B
Sociology, B
Spanish Language and Literature, B

YORK TECHNICAL COLLEGE

Accounting, A
Administrative Assistant and Secretarial Science, A
Automobile/Automotive Mechanics
 Technology/Technician, A
Building/Home/Construction Inspection/Inspector, A
Business Administration and Management, A
Business/Commerce, A
Carpentry/Carpenter, A
Child Care Provider/Assistant, A
Child Care and Support Services Management, A
Clinical/Medical Laboratory Technician, A
Commercial and Advertising Art, A
Computer Engineering Technology/Technician, A
Computer and Information Sciences and Support
 Services, A
Criminal Justice/Safety Studies, A
Data Processing and Data Processing
 Technology/Technician, A
Dental Assisting/Assistant, A
Dental Hygiene/Hygienist, A
Early Childhood Education and Teaching, A
Education/Teaching of Individuals in Early Childhood
 Special Education Programs, A
Electrical and Electronic Engineering
 Technologies/Technicians, A
Electrical, Electronic and Communications Engineer-
 ing Technology/Technician, A
Electrical/Electronics Equipment Installation and Re-
 pair, A
Environmental Sciences, A
Forestry Technology/Technician, A
General Office Occupations and Clerical Services, A
Heating, Air Conditioning, Ventilation and Refrigera-
 tion Maintenance Technology/Technician, A
Human Resources Management/Personnel Adminis-
 tration, A
Industrial Electronics Technology/Technician, A
Industrial Mechanics and Maintenance Technol-
 ogy, A
Legal Administrative Assistant/Secretary, A
Liberal Arts and Sciences Studies and Humani-
 ties, A
Machine Tool Technology/Machinist, A
Mechanical Drafting and Mechanical Drafting
 CAD/CADD, A
Mechanical Engineering/Mechanical
 Technology/Technician, A

Medical Administrative Assistant/Secretary, A
Medical Radiologic Technology/Science - Radiation
 Therapist, A
Medical/Clinical Assistant, A
Multi-/Interdisciplinary Studies, A
Physical Therapist Assistant, A
Plumbing Technology/Plumber, A
Radio and Television Broadcasting
 Technology/Technician, A
Radiologic Technology/Science - Radiographer, A
Surgical Technology/Technologist, A
Water Quality and Wastewater Treatment Manage-
 ment and Recycling Technology/Technician, A
Welding Technology/Welder, A

South Dakota

AUGUSTANA UNIVERSITY

Accounting, B
American Sign Language (ASL), B
American/United States Studies/Civilization, B
Anthropology, B
Art Teacher Education, B
Art/Art Studies, General, B
Athletic Training and Sports Medicine, B
Audiology/Audiologist and Speech-Language
 Pathology/Pathologist, B
Biochemistry, B
Biology/Biological Sciences, B
Business Administration and Management, B
Business/Corporate Communications, B
Chemical Physics, B
Chemistry, B
Classics and Classical Languages, Litera-
 tures, and Linguistics, B
Clinical Laboratory Science/Medical
 Technology/Technologist, B
Communication Studies/Speech Communication
 and Rhetoric, B
Computer Science, B
Drama and Dramatics/Theatre Arts, B
Economics, B
Education, M
Educational Media/Instructional Technology, M
Elementary Education and Teaching, B
Engineering Physics, B
English Language and Literature, B
Foreign Languages and Literatures, B
Foreign Languages, Literatures, and Linguistics, B
French Language and Literature, B
German Language and Literature, B
Health/Health Care Administration/Management, B
History, B
International Relations and Affairs, B
Journalism, B
Kinesiology and Exercise Science, B
Liberal Arts and Sciences Studies and Humani-
 ties, B
Management Information Systems and Services, B
Mathematics, B
Music, B
Music Teacher Education, B
Philosophy, B
Physical Education Teaching and Coaching, B
Physics, B
Political Science and Government, B
Pre-Dentistry Studies, B
Pre-Law Studies, B
Pre-Medicine/Pre-Medical Studies, B
Pre-Pharmacy Studies, B
Pre-Theology/Pre-Ministerial Studies, B
Pre-Veterinary Studies, B
Psychology, B
Reading Teacher Education, M
Religion/Religious Studies, B
Secondary Education and Teaching, B
Sign Language Interpretation and Translation, B
Social Studies Teacher Education, B
Sociology, B
Spanish Language and Literature, B
Special Education and Teaching, BM
Speech Teacher Education, B
Sport and Fitness Administration/Management, BM

Teacher Education, Multiple Levels, B

BLACK HILLS STATE UNIVERSITY

Accounting, B
Administrative Assistant and Secretarial Science, A
American Indian/Native American Studies, B
Art/Art Studies, General, B
Biology/Biological Sciences, B
Business Administration and Management, B
Business Administration, Management and Opera-
 tions, M
Business Teacher Education, B
Chemistry, B
Commercial and Advertising Art, B
Computer Programming/Programmer, A
Computer Science, A
Computer and Information Sciences, A
Curriculum and Instruction, M
Drafting and Design Technology/Technician, A
Elementary Education and Teaching, B
English Language and Literature, B
Environmental Studies, B
General Studies, A
Genomic Sciences, M
Health and Physical Education, B
Health/Health Care Administration/Management, B
History, B
Hospital and Health Care Facilities
 Administration/Management, B
Human Resources Management/Personnel Adminis-
 tration, B
Human Services, B
Industrial Technology/Technician, B
Junior High/Intermediate/Middle School Education
 and Teaching, B
Kindergarten/PreSchool Education and Teaching, B
Management Strategy and Policy, M
Marketing/Marketing Management, B
Mass Communication/Media Studies, AB
Mathematics, B
Mathematics Teacher Education, B
Music, B
Music Performance, B
Parks, Recreation, Leisure and Fitness Studies, B
Physical Sciences, B
Political Science and Government, B
Psychology, B
Sales, Distribution and Marketing Operations, B
Science Teacher Education/General Science
 Teacher Education, B
Secondary Education and Teaching, B
Social Sciences, B
Sociology, B
Spanish Language and Literature, B
Special Education and Teaching, B
Sport and Fitness Administration/Management, B
Tourism and Travel Services Management, AB
Voice and Opera, B

DAKOTA STATE UNIVERSITY

Accounting, B
Biological and Biomedical Sciences, B
Biology Teacher Education, B
Business Administration and Management, AB
Business Administration, Management and Opera-
 tions, M
Business Teacher Education, B
Computer Graphics, B
Computer Science, M
Computer Teacher Education, B
Computer and Information Sciences, B
Computer and Information Systems Security, B
Education, M
Educational Media/Instructional Technology, M
Elementary Education and Teaching, B
English Language and Literature, B
English/Language Arts Teacher Education, B
Finance, B
General Studies, A
Health Informatics, M
Health Information/Medical Records
 Administration/Administrator, B
Health Information/Medical Records
 Technology/Technician, A
Information Science/Studies, BMDO
Kinesiology and Exercise Science, B

Liberal Arts and Sciences Studies and Humanities, B
Management Information Systems and Services, MD
Marketing/Marketing Management, B
Mathematics Teacher Education, B
Physical Education Teaching and Coaching, B
Physical Sciences, B
Respiratory Care Therapy/Therapist, AB
Special Education and Teaching, B
System, Networking, and LAN/WAN Management/Manager, AB

DAKOTA WESLEYAN UNIVERSITY

Accounting, AB
Actuarial Science, B
Adult and Continuing Education and Teaching, B
Art Teacher Education, B
Athletic Training and Sports Medicine, B
Behavioral Sciences, B
Biochemistry, B
Biological and Physical Sciences, B
Biology Teacher Education, B
Biology/Biological Sciences, B
Business Administration and Management, AB
Business Teacher Education, B
Communication Studies/Speech Communication and Rhetoric, B
Computer Software and Media Applications, B
Computer and Information Sciences, B
Criminal Justice/Safety Studies, AB
Curriculum and Instruction, M
Drama and Dramatics/Theatre Arts, B
Education, BM
Educational Administration and Supervision, M
Elementary Education and Teaching, B
English Language and Literature, B
English/Language Arts Teacher Education, B
Ethnic, Cultural Minority, and Gender Studies, B
Fine/Studio Arts, B
History, B
History Teacher Education, B
Human Services, B
Junior High/Intermediate/Middle School Education and Teaching, B
Kinesiology and Exercise Science, B
Liberal Arts and Sciences Studies and Humanities, B
Mathematics, B
Mathematics Teacher Education, B
Music, B
Music Teacher Education, B
Philosophy, B
Physical Education Teaching and Coaching, B
Psychology, B
Public Administration and Social Service Professions, B
Public Policy Analysis, B
Secondary Education and Teaching, M
Special Education and Teaching, B
Sport and Fitness Administration/Management, B
Teacher Education, Multiple Levels, B
Web Page, Digital/Multimedia and Information Resources Design, B
Wildlife and Wildlands Science and Management, B

GLOBE UNIVERSITY–SIOUX FALLS

Accounting, AB
Business Administration and Management, AB
Computer Programming, Specific Applications, AB
Criminal Justice/Law Enforcement Administration, AB
Health/Health Care Administration/Management, B
Marketing/Marketing Management, A
Massage Therapy/Therapeutic Massage, A
Medical Administrative Assistant/Secretary, A
Medical/Clinical Assistant, A
Veterinary/Animal Health Technology/Technician and Veterinary Assistant, A

LAKE AREA TECHNICAL INSTITUTE

Agricultural Business and Management, A
Aircraft Powerplant Technology/Technician, A
Autobody/Collision and Repair Technology/Technician, A

Automobile/Automotive Mechanics Technology/Technician, A
Banking and Financial Support Services, A
Clinical/Medical Laboratory Technician, A
Computer Science, A
Construction Engineering Technology/Technician, A
Construction/Heavy Equipment/Earthmoving Equipment Operation, A
Criminal Justice/Police Science, A
Dental Assisting/Assistant, A
Diesel Mechanics Technology/Technician, A
Electrical, Electronic and Communications Engineering Technology/Technician, A
Emergency Medical Technology/Technician (EMT Paramedic), A
Engine Machinist, A
Environmental Sciences, A
Human Services, A
Machine Tool Technology/Machinist, A
Manufacturing Technology/Technician, A
Marketing/Marketing Management, A
Medical/Clinical Assistant, A
Occupational Therapist Assistant, A
Physical Therapist Assistant, A
Robotics Technology/Technician, A
Welding Technology/Welder, A

MITCHELL TECHNICAL INSTITUTE

Accounting and Business/Management, A
Agricultural Mechanics and Equipment/Machine Technology, A
Agricultural Production Operations, A
Building/Property Maintenance and Management, A
Business/Office Automation/Technology/Data Entry, A
Cartography, A
Clinical/Medical Laboratory Technician, A
Construction Trades, A
Culinary Arts/Chef Training, A
Electrician, A
Energy Management and Systems Technology/Technician, A
Heating, Air Conditioning, Ventilation and Refrigeration Maintenance Technology/Technician, A
Human Services, A
Lineworker, A
Medical Office Assistant/Specialist, A
Medical Radiologic Technology/Science - Radiation Therapist, A
Medical/Clinical Assistant, A
Radio, Television, and Digital Communication, A
Radiologic Technology/Science - Radiographer, A
Small Engine Mechanics and Repair Technology/Technician, A
System Administration/Administrator, A
Telecommunications Technology/Technician, A

MOUNT MARTY COLLEGE

Accounting, AB
Biology/Biological Sciences, B
Business Administration and Management, AB
Business Administration, Management and Operations, M
Chemistry, B
Chemistry Teacher Education, B
Clinical Laboratory Science/Medical Technology/Technologist, B
Computer Science, B
Criminal Justice/Safety Studies, B
Digital Communication and Media/Multimedia, B
Drama and Dramatics/Theatre Arts, B
Education, B
Elementary Education and Teaching, B
English Language and Literature, B
English/Language Arts Teacher Education, B
Forensic Science and Technology, B
General Studies, AB
History, B
History Teacher Education, B
Human Services, B
Information Technology, B
Liberal Arts and Sciences Studies and Humanities, AB
Mathematics, B
Mathematics Teacher Education, B

Medical Radiologic Technology/Science - Radiation Therapist, B
Music, B
Music Teacher Education, B
Nurse Anesthetist, M
Nursing, B
Parks, Recreation and Leisure Facilities Management, B
Pastoral Studies/Counseling, M
Psychology, B
Religion/Religious Studies, AB
Secondary Education and Teaching, B
Special Education and Teaching, B

NATIONAL AMERICAN UNIVERSITY (ELLSWORTH AFB)

Business Administration, Management and Operations, A
Computer and Information Sciences, A

NATIONAL AMERICAN UNIVERSITY (RAPID CITY)

Athletic Training and Sports Medicine, B
Business Administration, Management and Operations, M
Computer Engineering Technology/Technician, A
Finance, B
International Business/Trade/Commerce, B
Legal Assistant/Paralegal, A
Liberal Arts and Sciences Studies and Humanities, B
Marketing/Marketing Management, B
Operations Management and Supervision, B
Pre-Law Studies, B
System, Networking, and LAN/WAN Management/Manager, B
Veterinary/Animal Health Technology/Technician and Veterinary Assistant, A

NATIONAL AMERICAN UNIVERSITY (SIOUX FALLS)

Accounting, AB
Business Administration and Management, AB
Computer Programming, Vendor/Product Certification, B
Computer Programming/Programmer, AB
Customer Service Support/Call Center/Teleservice Operation, AB
Information Science/Studies, AB
Information Technology, AB
Legal Assistant/Paralegal, AB
Management Information Systems and Services, AB
Massage Therapy/Therapeutic Massage, A
Medical/Clinical Assistant, A
Web Page, Digital/Multimedia and Information Resources Design, B

NORTHERN STATE UNIVERSITY

Accounting, B
Art Teacher Education, B
Art/Art Studies, General, B
Biology/Biological Sciences, B
Business/Managerial Economics, B
Chemistry, B
Clinical Laboratory Science/Medical Technology/Technologist, B
Clinical Psychology, M
Clinical/Medical Laboratory Technician, B
Commercial and Advertising Art, A
Community Organization and Advocacy, B
Counseling Psychology, M
Counselor Education/School Counseling and Guidance Services, M
Criminal Justice/Police Science, B
Curriculum and Instruction, M
Data Processing and Data Processing Technology/Technician, A
Drama and Dramatics/Theatre Arts, B
Economics, B
Education, BM
Educational Administration and Supervision, M
Educational Leadership and Administration, M
Educational Media/Instructional Technology, M
Elementary Education and Teaching, B
English Language and Literature, B

Environmental Studies, B
Finance, B
Finance and Banking, M
French Language and Literature, B
German Language and Literature, B
Health Teacher Education, B
History, B
International Business/Trade/Commerce, B
Liberal Arts and Sciences Studies and Humanities, A
Management Information Systems and Services, B
Marketing/Marketing Management, B
Mathematics, B
Music, B
Music Teacher Education, BM
Physical Education Teaching and Coaching, B
Political Science and Government, B
Pre-Dentistry Studies, B
Pre-Law Studies, B
Pre-Medicine/Pre-Medical Studies, B
Psychology, B
Public Administration, B
Secondary Education and Teaching, B
Social Work, A
Sociology, B
Spanish Language and Literature, B
Special Education and Teaching, B
Sport and Fitness Administration/Management, BM
Voice and Opera, B

OGLALA LAKOTA COLLEGE

Accounting, A
Administrative Assistant and Secretarial Science, A
Agriculture, A
American Indian/Native American Studies, AB
Bilingual and Multilingual Education, B
Business Administration and Management, AB
Carpentry/Carpenter, A
Computer Science, A
Counselor Education/School Counseling and Guidance Services, AB
Criminal Justice/Law Enforcement Administration, AB
Educational Administration and Supervision, M
Electrical, Electronic and Communications Engineering Technology/Technician, A
Elementary Education and Teaching, AB
Family and Consumer Sciences/Human Sciences, A
History, B
Human Services, AB
Kindergarten/PreSchool Education and Teaching, AB
Legal Assistant/Paralegal, AB
Liberal Arts and Sciences Studies and Humanities, A
Management, M
Mass Communication/Media Studies, A
Natural Resources Management/Development and Policy, A
Social Work, AB
Special Education and Teaching, B

PRESENTATION COLLEGE

Athletic Training and Sports Medicine, B
Biology/Biological Sciences, AB
Business, Management, Marketing, and Related Support Services, AB
Chemistry, A
Communication Studies/Speech Communication and Rhetoric, A
English Language and Literature, A
General Studies, A
Medical Office Management/Administration, A
Medical/Clinical Assistant, A
Psychology, B
Radiologic Technology/Science - Radiographer, AB
Religion/Religious Studies, A
Secondary Education and Teaching, B
Social Work, B
Surgical Technology/Technologist, A

SINTE GLESKA UNIVERSITY

Accounting Technology/Technician and Bookkeeping, A
Administrative Assistant and Secretarial Science, A
American Indian/Native American Studies, AB

Art Teacher Education, B
Biological and Biomedical Sciences, A
Business Administration and Management, AB
Business Administration, Management and Operations, AB
Business/Commerce, A
Computer Science, B
Construction Trades, A
Criminal Justice/Law Enforcement Administration, A
Criminal Justice/Safety Studies, B
Data Processing and Data Processing Technology/Technician, A
Early Childhood Education and Teaching, AB
Education, AM
Electrical/Electronics Equipment Installation and Repair, A
Elementary Education and Teaching, BM
Fine Arts and Art Studies, AB
General Office Occupations and Clerical Services, A
General Studies, A
Junior High/Intermediate/Middle School Education and Teaching, B
Legal Administrative Assistant/Secretary, A
Liberal Arts and Sciences Studies and Humanities, AB
Medical Administrative Assistant/Secretary, A
Mental and Social Health Services and Allied Professions, AB
Natural Resources Management/Development and Policy, A
Plumbing Technology/Plumber, A
Secondary Education and Teaching, B
Special Education and Teaching, AB
Substance Abuse/Addiction Counseling, B

SISSETON-WAHPETON COLLEGE

Accounting, A
American Indian/Native American Studies, A
Business Administration and Management, A
Electrical, Electronic and Communications Engineering Technology/Technician, A
Hospitality Administration/Management, A
Information Science/Studies, A
Kindergarten/PreSchool Education and Teaching, A
Liberal Arts and Sciences Studies and Humanities, A
Natural Sciences, A
Nutritional Sciences, A
Substance Abuse/Addiction Counseling, A

SOUTH DAKOTA SCHOOL OF MINES AND TECHNOLOGY

Artificial Intelligence and Robotics, M
Atmospheric Sciences and Meteorology, MD
Bioengineering, D
Biomedical Engineering, MD
Chemical Engineering, BMD
Chemistry, B
Civil Engineering, BM
Computer Engineering, B
Computer Science, B
Construction Management, M
Electrical Engineering, M
Electrical, Electronics and Communications Engineering, B
Engineering Management, M
Engineering and Applied Sciences, MD
Environmental Sciences, D
Environmental/Environmental Health Engineering, B
General Studies, B
Geological Engineering, MD
Geological/Geophysical Engineering, B
Geology/Earth Science, BMD
Industrial Engineering, B
Management of Technology, M
Materials Engineering, MD
Materials Sciences, MD
Mathematics, B
Mechanical Engineering, BMD
Metallurgical Engineering, B
Mineral/Mining Engineering, M
Mining and Mineral Engineering, B
NanoTechnology, D
Paleontology, M

Physics, BMD

SOUTH DAKOTA STATE UNIVERSITY

Advertising, B
Aeronautics/Aviation/Aerospace Science and Technology, B
Agribusiness, B
Agricultural Communication/Journalism, B
Agricultural Economics, B
Agricultural Engineering, MD
Agricultural Mechanization, B
Agricultural Public Services, B
Agricultural Sciences, MD
Agricultural Teacher Education, B
Agricultural/Biological Engineering and Bioengineering, B
Agriculture, AB
Agronomy and Crop Science, B
Agronomy and Soil Sciences, D
American Indian/Native American Studies, B
Animal Sciences, BMD
Apparel and Textile Marketing Management, B
Applied Horticulture/Horticultural Operations, B
Architecture, B
Athletic Training and Sports Medicine, B
BioTechnology, B
Biochemistry, B
Biological and Biomedical Sciences, MD
Biology/Biological Sciences, B
Biosystems Engineering, MD
Cartography, B
Chemistry, BMD
Civil Engineering, BM
Clinical Laboratory Science/Medical Technology/Technologist, B
Clothing and Textiles, M
Communication Studies/Speech Communication and Rhetoric, B
Communication and Media Studies, M
Computational Sciences, D
Computer and Information Sciences, B
Construction Engineering Technology/Technician, B
Consumer Economics, BM
Counselor Education/School Counseling and Guidance Services, M
Curriculum and Instruction, M
Dairy Science, BMD
Dietetics/Dieticians, B
Drama and Dramatics/Theatre Arts, B
Early Childhood Education and Teaching, B
Economics, BM
Education, MD
Educational Administration and Supervision, M
Educational Leadership and Administration, M
Electrical Engineering, MD
Electrical, Electronic and Communications Engineering Technology/Technician, B
Electrical, Electronics and Communications Engineering, B
Engineering and Applied Sciences, MD
English, M
English Language and Literature, B
Entrepreneurship/Entrepreneurial Studies, B
Environmental Sciences, B
Family and Consumer Sciences/Home Economics Teacher Education, B
Family and Consumer Sciences/Human Sciences, M
Fine/Studio Arts, B
Fish, Game and Wildlife Management, MD
Flight Instructor, B
Food Science, B
Food Science and Technology, MD
French Language and Literature, B
General Studies, AB
Geography, BM
Geosciences, D
German Language and Literature, B
Graphic Design, B
Health Education, M
Health Teacher Education, B
Health and Physical Education, B
Health and Physical Education/Fitness, B
History, B
Hospitality Administration/Management, BMD
Human Development and Family Studies, B

Industrial/Management Engineering, M
Interior Design, BM
International/Global Studies, B
Journalism, BM
Landscape Architecture, B
Liberal Arts and Sciences Studies and Humanities, B
Mathematics, BMD
Mechanical Engineering, BMD
Microbiology, BMD
Music, B
Music Teacher Education, B
Natural Resources Management/Development and Policy, B
Nursing, MD
Nutritional Sciences, MD
Operations Management and Supervision, B
Parks, Recreation and Leisure Facilities Management, B
Pharmaceutical Sciences, MD
Pharmacy, BD
Physical Education Teaching and Coaching, M
Physics, BM
Plant Sciences, MD
Political Science and Government, B
Psychology, B
Range Science and Management, B
Recreation and Park Management, M
Sociology, BMD
Spanish Language and Literature, B
Statistics, MD
Veterinary Sciences, MD
Wildlife and Wildlands Science and Management, B

SOUTHEAST TECHNICAL INSTITUTE

Accounting, A
Animation, Interactive Technology, Video Graphics and Special Effects, A
Applied Horticulture/Horticultural Operations, A
Architectural Engineering Technology/Technician, A
Autobody/Collision and Repair Technology/Technician, A
Automobile/Automotive Mechanics Technology/Technician, A
Banking and Financial Support Services, A
Biomedical Technology/Technician, A
Building/Construction Finishing, Management, and Inspection, A
Business Administration and Management, A
Cardiovascular Technology/Technologist, A
Child Care Provider/Assistant, A
Child Care and Support Services Management, A
Civil Engineering Technology/Technician, A
Clinical/Medical Laboratory Science and Allied Professions, A
Clinical/Medical Laboratory Technician, A
Commercial and Advertising Art, A
Computer Installation and Repair Technology/Technician, A
Computer Programming, A
Computer Programming/Programmer, A
Computer Software Engineering, A
Computer Systems Networking and Telecommunications, A
Computer Technology/Computer Systems Technology, A
Computer and Information Sciences and Support Services, A
Computer and Information Systems Security, A
Computer/Information Technology Services Administration and Management, A
Construction Engineering Technology/Technician, A
Criminal Justice/Police Science, A
Diagnostic Medical Sonography/Sonographer and Ultrasound Technician, A
Diesel Mechanics Technology/Technician, A
Electrical, Electronic and Communications Engineering Technology/Technician, A
Electrical/Electronics Equipment Installation and Repair, A
Electrician, A
Electromechanical Technology/Electromechanical Engineering Technology, A
Electroneurodiagnostic/Electroencephalographic Technology/Technologist, A
Finance, A

General Merchandising, Sales, and Related Marketing Operations, A
General Office Occupations and Clerical Services, A
Health Unit Coordinator/Ward Clerk, A
Heating, Air Conditioning, Ventilation and Refrigeration Maintenance Technology/Technician, A
Horticultural Science, A
Industrial Technology/Technician, A
Marketing/Marketing Management, A
Mechanical Engineering/Mechanical Technology/Technician, A
Medical Insurance Coding Specialist/Coder, A
Nuclear Medical Technology/Technologist, A
Plumbing Technology/Plumber, A
Prepress/Desktop Publishing and Digital Imaging Design, A
Surgical Technology/Technologist, A
Survey Technology/Surveying, A
Turf and Turfgrass Management, A
Welding Technology/Welder, A

UNIVERSITY OF SIOUX FALLS

Accounting, B
Applied Mathematics, B
Art Teacher Education, B
Art/Art Studies, General, B
Biology/Biological Sciences, B
Business Administration and Management, B
Business Administration, Management and Operations, M
Chemistry, B
Clinical Laboratory Science/Medical Technology/Technologist, B
Commercial and Advertising Art, B
Communication Studies/Speech Communication and Rhetoric, B
Computer Science, B
Computer and Information Sciences, B
Education, BMO
Educational Administration and Supervision, O
Educational Leadership and Administration, MO
Educational Media/Instructional Technology, M
Elementary Education and Teaching, B
Emergency Medical Technology/Technician (EMT Paramedic), AB
English Language and Literature, B
Entrepreneurship/Entrepreneurial Studies, M
Health Services Administration, M
History, B
Junior High/Intermediate/Middle School Education and Teaching, B
Kinesiology and Exercise Science, B
Liberal Arts and Sciences Studies and Humanities, AB
Management, M
Marketing, M
Mass Communication/Media Studies, B
Mathematics, B
Medical Radiologic Technology/Science - Radiation Therapist, B
Music, B
Music Teacher Education, B
Philosophy, B
Political Science and Government, B
Pre-Dentistry Studies, B
Pre-Law Studies, B
Pre-Medicine/Pre-Medical Studies, B
Pre-Veterinary Studies, B
Psychology, B
Radio and Television, B
Reading Teacher Education, M
Science Teacher Education/General Science Teacher Education, B
Secondary Education and Teaching, B
Social Sciences, A
Social Work, B
Sociology, B
Youth Ministry, B

THE UNIVERSITY OF SOUTH DAKOTA

Accounting, BM
Allied Health and Medical Assisting Services, MDO
Allopathic Medicine, D
American Indian/Native American Studies, B
Anthropology, B
Art Teacher Education, B

Biological and Biomedical Sciences, MD
Biology Teacher Education, B
Business Administration, Management and Operations, M
Business/Commerce, B
Cardiovascular Sciences, MD
Cell Biology and Anatomy, MD
Chemistry, BMD
Clinical Psychology, MD
Communication Disorders, BMD
Communication and Media Studies, M
Computer Science, M
Computer and Information Sciences, B
Counselor Education/School Counseling and Guidance Services, BMDO
Criminal Justice/Law Enforcement Administration, B
Criminology, M
Curriculum and Instruction, BMDO
Dental Hygiene/Hygienist, B
Drama and Dance Teacher Education, B
Drama and Dramatics/Theatre Arts, B
Economics, B
Education, BMDO
Educational Administration and Supervision, MDO
Educational Media/Instructional Technology, M
Educational Psychology, MDO
Elementary Education and Teaching, BM
English, MD
English Language and Literature, B
English/Language Arts Teacher Education, B
Exercise and Sports Science, M
Finance, B
Fine Arts and Art Studies, M
Foreign Language Teacher Education, B
French Language Teacher Education, B
French Language and Literature, B
Geology/Earth Science, B
German Language Teacher Education, B
German Language and Literature, B
Graphic Design, M
Health Services Administration, M
Health Teacher Education, B
History, BM
History Teacher Education, B
Hospital and Health Care Facilities Administration/Management, B
Human Development, MDO
Human Resources Management and Services, M
Immunology, MD
Interdisciplinary Studies, M
International/Global Studies, B
Kinesiology and Movement Studies, M
Law and Legal Studies, D
Liberal Arts and Sciences Studies and Humanities, AB
Marketing/Marketing Management, B
Mathematics, BM
Mathematics Teacher Education, B
Microbiology, MD
Molecular Biology, MD
Multi-/Interdisciplinary Studies, B
Music, M
Music History, Literature, and Theory, M
Music Performance, M
Music Teacher Education, BM
Neuroscience, MD
Occupational Therapy/Therapist, M
Organizational Management, M
Painting, M
Parks, Recreation, Leisure and Fitness Studies, B
Performance, M
Pharmacology, MD
Philosophy, B
Physical Education Teaching and Coaching, B
Physical Therapy/Therapist, D
Physician Assistant, BM
Physics, BMD
Physics Teacher Education, B
Physiology, MD
Political Science and Government, BMD
Printmaking, M
Psychology, BMD
Public Administration, MD
Public Policy Analysis, M
School Psychology, DO

Science Teacher Education/General Science
  Teacher Education, B
Sculpture, M
Secondary Education and Teaching, BM
Social Science Teacher Education, B
Social Work, BM
Sociology, B
Spanish Language Teacher Education, B
Spanish Language and Literature, B
Special Education and Teaching, BM
Speech Teacher Education, B
Substance Abuse/Addiction Counseling, BMO
Theater, M
Visual and Performing Arts, B

WESTERN DAKOTA TECHNICAL INSTITUTE

Accounting, A
Business Administration and Management, A
Computer Systems Networking and Telecommunications, A
Criminal Justice/Police Science, A
Criminal Justice/Safety Studies, A
Drafting and Design Technology/Technician, A
Electrician, A
Emergency Medical Technology/Technician (EMT
  Paramedic), A
Environmental Control Technologies/Technicians, A
Fire Science/Firefighting, A
Heating, Air Conditioning, Ventilation and Refrigeration Maintenance Technology/Technician, A
Legal Assistant/Paralegal, A
Library Assistant/Technician, A
Machine Tool Technology/Machinist, A
Medical Transcription/Transcriptionist, A
Medical/Clinical Assistant, A
Pharmacy Technician/Assistant, A
Precision Metal Working, A
Surgical Technology/Technologist, A
Vehicle Maintenance and Repair Technologies, A

Tennessee

AMERICAN BAPTIST COLLEGE

Behavioral Sciences, B
General Studies, A
Human Services, B
Theology/Theological Studies, B

AQUINAS COLLEGE

Business Administration and Management, B
Education, M
Elementary Education and Teaching, B
English Language and Literature, B
English/Language Arts Teacher Education, B
Finance, B
History, B
History Teacher Education, B
Humanities/Humanistic Studies, AB
Marketing/Marketing Management, B
Nursing, M
Nursing Education, M
Philosophy, B
Psychology, B
Theology/Theological Studies, B

ARGOSY UNIVERSITY, NASHVILLE

Accounting, D
Business Administration and Management, AB
Business Administration, Management and Operations, MD
Counseling Psychology, M
Counselor Education/School Counseling and Guidance Services, D
Criminal Justice/Law Enforcement Administration, B
Education, MDO
Educational Administration and Supervision, D
Educational Leadership and Administration, MDO
Educational Media/Instructional Technology, MDO
Elementary Education and Teaching, D
Finance and Banking, M
Health Services Administration, M
Higher Education/Higher Education Administration, D
Information Technology, AB

International Business/Trade/Commerce, MD
Liberal Arts and Sciences Studies and Humanities, B
Management, MD
Management Information Systems and Services, MD
Marketing, MD
Psychology, ABMD
Public Health, M
Secondary Education and Teaching, D

THE ART INSTITUTE OF TENNESSEE–NASHVILLE, A BRANCH OF THE ART INSTITUTE OF ATLANTA

Advertising, B
Apparel and Accessories Marketing Operations, B
Baking and Pastry Arts/Baker/Pastry Chef, A
Cinematography and Film/Video Production, AB
Commercial Photography, B
Computer Graphics, B
Culinary Arts/Chef Training, A
Graphic Design, AB
Interior Design, B
Recording Arts Technology/Technician, B
Restaurant, Culinary, and Catering
  Management/Manager, B

AUSTIN PEAY STATE UNIVERSITY

Accounting, B
Agriculture, B
Art/Art Studies, General, B
Biological and Biomedical Sciences, M
Biology/Biological Sciences, B
Business Administration and Management, A
Business Administration, Management and Operations, M
Business/Commerce, B
Chemistry, B
Clinical Laboratory Science/Medical
  Technology/Technologist, B
Clinical Laboratory Sciences, M
Communication and Media Studies, M
Community Health and Preventive Medicine, M
Computer and Information Sciences, B
Counseling Psychology, M
Counselor Education/School Counseling and Guidance Services, M
Criminal Justice/Law Enforcement Administration, B
Curriculum and Instruction, M
Database Systems, M
Drama and Dramatics/Theatre Arts, B
Education, MO
Educational Administration and Supervision, O
Educational Leadership and Administration, M
Elementary Education and Teaching, MO
Engineering Technology, AB
Engineering and Applied Sciences, M
English, M
English Language and Literature, B
Exercise and Sports Science, M
Finance, B
Foreign Languages and Literatures, B
General Studies, AB
Geology/Earth Science, B
Health Education, M
Health and Physical Education, B
Health/Medical Preparatory Programs, B
History, B
Industrial and Organizational Psychology, M
Liberal Arts and Sciences Studies and Humanities, B
Management Strategy and Policy, M
Marketing/Marketing Management, B
Mass Communication/Media Studies, B
Mathematics, B
Military and Defense Studies, M
Music, BM
Music Teacher Education, M
Non-Profit/Public/Organizational Management, B
Nursing, M
Nursing Administration, M
Nursing Education, M
Nursing Informatics, M
Performance, M
Philosophy, B
Physics, B

Political Science and Government, B
Psychology, BM
Public Health, M
Radiation Biology/Radiobiology, M
Reading Teacher Education, M
Secondary Education and Teaching, MO
Social Work, BM
Sociology, B
Special Education and Teaching, BM
Teacher Education, Multiple Levels, B

BAPTIST COLLEGE OF HEALTH SCIENCES

Diagnostic Medical Sonography/Sonographer and
  Ultrasound Technician, B
Health/Health Care Administration/Management, B
Medical Radiologic Technology/Science - Radiation
  Therapist, B
Nuclear Medical Technology/Technologist, B
Radiologic Technology/Science - Radiographer, B
Respiratory Care Therapy/Therapist, B

BELHAVEN UNIVERSITY

Business Administration and Management, B
Health Services Administration, B
Liberal Arts and Sciences Studies and Humanities, A
Management Science, B
Social Work, B

BELMONT UNIVERSITY

Accounting, BM
Acting, B
Allied Health and Medical Assisting Services, MD
Ancient Near Eastern and Biblical Languages, Literatures, and Linguistics, B
Applied Mathematics, B
Art History, Criticism and Conservation, B
Art Teacher Education, B
Art/Art Studies, General, B
Asian Studies/Civilization, B
Bible/Biblical Studies, B
Biochemistry, B
Biochemistry, Biophysics and Molecular Biology, B
Biology/Biological Sciences, B
Broadcast Journalism, B
Business Administration and Management, B
Business Administration, Management and Operations, M
Business/Commerce, B
Business/Managerial Economics, B
Chemistry, B
Cinematography and Film/Video Production, B
Classics and Classical Languages, Literatures, and Linguistics, B
Clinical Laboratory Science/Medical
  Technology/Technologist, B
Communication Studies/Speech Communication
  and Rhetoric, B
Communication and Media Studies, B
Composition, B
Computer Programming/Programmer, B
Computer Science, B
Computer and Information Sciences, B
Curriculum and Instruction, M
Design and Visual Communications, B
Directing and Theatrical Production, B
Divinity/Ministry (BD, MDiv.), B
Drama and Dance Teacher Education, B
Drama and Dramatics/Theatre Arts, B
Early Childhood Education and Teaching, B
Education, BM
Elementary Education and Teaching, B
Engineering Physics, B
Engineering Science, B
English, M
English Language and Literature, B
Entrepreneurship/Entrepreneurial Studies, B
Environmental Sciences, B
European Studies/Civilization, B
Finance, B
Fine/Studio Arts, B
French Language and Literature, B
German Language and Literature, B
Health Services Administration, M
Health and Physical Education, B

Health/Medical Physics, B
History, B
Hospitality Administration/Management, B
Information Science/Studies, B
International Business/Trade/Commerce, B
International Economics, B
International Relations and Affairs, B
Journalism, B
Junior High/Intermediate/Middle School Education and Teaching, B
Kinesiology and Exercise Science, B
Law and Legal Studies, D
Liberal Arts and Sciences Studies and Humanities, B
Management Information Systems and Services, B
Management Science, B
Marketing/Marketing Management, B
Mass Communication/Media Studies, B
Mathematics, B
Medical Radiologic Technology/Science - Radiation Therapist, B
Multi-/Interdisciplinary Studies, B
Music, BM
Music Teacher Education, BM
Music Theory and Composition, B
Nursing, MD
Occupational Therapy/Therapist, MD
Performance, M
Pharmacy, D
Philosophy, B
Physical Education Teaching and Coaching, B
Physical Therapy/Therapist, D
Physics, B
Political Science and Government, B
Psychology, B
Public Relations, Advertising, and Applied Communication, B
Public Relations/Image Management, B
Recording Arts Technology/Technician, B
Religion/Religious Studies, B
Sacred Music, M
Secondary Education and Teaching, B
Social Work, B
Sociology, B
Spanish Language and Literature, B
Special Education and Teaching, M
Sport and Fitness Administration/Management, M
Systems Engineering, B
Technical Theatre/Theatre Design and Technology, B
Theology and Religious Vocations, B
Voice and Opera, B

BETHEL UNIVERSITY

Accounting and Business/Management, B
Biology/Biological Sciences, B
Business Administration and Management, B
Business Administration, Management and Operations, BM
Chemistry, B
Christian Studies, B
Conflict Resolution and Mediation/Peace Studies, M
Criminal Justice/Law Enforcement Administration, B
Drama and Dramatics/Theatre Arts, B
Educational Administration and Supervision, M
Elementary Education and Teaching, B
English Language and Literature, B
Health and Physical Education, B
History, B
Human Services, B
Management Information Systems and Services, B
Mathematics, B
Multi-/Interdisciplinary Studies, B
Music, B
Music Teacher Education, B
Physician Assistant, BM
Pre-Pharmacy Studies, B
Psychology, B
Religious/Sacred Music, B
Sociology, B

Special Education and Teaching, B

BRIGHTWOOD COLLEGE, NASHVILLE CAMPUS

Criminal Justice/Law Enforcement Administration, A
Legal Assistant/Paralegal, A

BRYAN COLLEGE

Bible/Biblical Studies, B
Biology Teacher Education, B
Biology/Biological Sciences, B
Business Administration and Management, AB
Business Administration, Management and Operations, M
Christian Studies, B
Communication Studies/Speech Communication and Rhetoric, B
Criminal Justice/Safety Studies, B
Drama and Dramatics/Theatre Arts, B
Elementary Education and Teaching, B
English Language and Literature, B
English/Language Arts Teacher Education, B
Health and Physical Education, B
History, B
History Teacher Education, B
Liberal Arts and Sciences Studies and Humanities, AB
Mathematics, B
Mathematics Teacher Education, B
Mathematics and Computer Science, B
Music, B
Music Teacher Education, B
Physical Education Teaching and Coaching, B
Political Science and Government, B
Psychology, B
Religious Education, B
Spanish Language Teacher Education, B
Spanish Language and Literature, B

CARSON-NEWMAN UNIVERSITY

Accounting, B
Ancient Near Eastern and Biblical Languages, Literatures, and Linguistics, B
Art Teacher Education, B
Art/Art Studies, General, B
Bible/Biblical Studies, B
Biochemistry, B
Biology/Biological Sciences, B
Business Administration and Management, B
Business Administration, Management and Operations, M
Business Teacher Education, B
Business/Managerial Economics, B
Chemistry, B
Child Development, B
Commercial and Advertising Art, B
Computer Science, B
Consumer Services and Advocacy, B
Counselor Education/School Counseling and Guidance Services, M
Curriculum and Instruction, M
Dietetics/Dieticians, B
Digital Communication and Media/Multimedia, B
Divinity/Ministry (BD, MDiv.), AB
Drama and Dramatics/Theatre Arts, B
Drawing, B
Early Childhood Education and Teaching, B
Education, BM
Educational Leadership and Administration, M
Elementary Education and Teaching, BM
English Language and Literature, B
English as a Second Language, M
Family and Consumer Economics and Related Services, B
Family and Consumer Sciences/Home Economics Teacher Education, B
Family and Consumer Sciences/Human Sciences, B
Fashion Merchandising, B
Fashion/Apparel Design, B
Film/Cinema Studies, B
Foods, Nutrition, and Wellness Studies, B
Graphic Design, B
History, B
Human Services, B
Information Science/Studies, B
Interior Design, B

Junior High/Intermediate/Middle School Education and Teaching, B
Kindergarten/PreSchool Education and Teaching, B
Kinesiology and Exercise Science, B
Liberal Arts and Sciences Studies and Humanities, AB
Linguistics, B
Management Information Systems and Services, B
Marketing/Marketing Management, B
Mass Communication/Media Studies, B
Mathematics, B
Missions/Missionary Studies and Missiology, B
Music, B
Music Performance, B
Music Teacher Education, B
Music Theory and Composition, B
Nursing, M
Nursing - Advanced Practice, M
Nursing Education, M
Painting, B
Pastoral Studies/Counseling, M
Philosophy, B
Photography, B
Physical Education Teaching and Coaching, B
Physics, B
Piano and Organ, B
Political Science and Government, B
Psychology, B
Religion/Religious Studies, B
Religious/Sacred Music, B
Secondary Education and Teaching, BM
Small Business Administration/Management, B
Sociology, B
Spanish Language and Literature, B
Special Education and Teaching, B
Theology and Religious Vocations, M
Voice and Opera, B
Youth Ministry, B

CHATTANOOGA COLLEGE—MEDICAL, DENTAL AND TECHNICAL CAREERS

Electrical, Electronic and Communications Engineering Technology/Technician, A

CHATTANOOGA STATE COMMUNITY COLLEGE

Accounting Technology/Technician and Bookkeeping, A
Business Administration and Management, A
Child Development, A
Commercial and Advertising Art, A
Community Organization and Advocacy, A
Dental Assisting/Assistant, A
Dental Hygiene/Hygienist, A
Education, A
Electrical, Electronic and Communications Engineering Technology/Technician, A
Engineering, A
Engineering Technology, A
Fire Science/Firefighting, A
Foods, Nutrition, and Wellness Studies, A
General Studies, A
Health Information/Medical Records Technology/Technician, A
Industrial Technology/Technician, A
Legal Assistant/Paralegal, A
Liberal Arts and Sciences Studies and Humanities, A
Management Information Systems and Services, A
Medical Radiologic Technology/Science - Radiation Therapist, A
Operations Management and Supervision, A
Physical Therapist Assistant, A
Respiratory Care Therapy/Therapist, A
Veterinary/Animal Health Technology/Technician and Veterinary Assistant, A
Web Page, Digital/Multimedia and Information Resources Design, A

CHRISTIAN BROTHERS UNIVERSITY

Accounting, BM
Biochemistry, B
Biology/Biological Sciences, B
Biomedical Sciences, B

Business Administration and Management, B
Business Administration, Management and Operations, MO
Business/Commerce, AB
Business/Corporate Communications, B
Chemical Engineering, B
Chemistry, B
Civil Engineering, B
Computer Engineering, B
Computer Science, B
Early Childhood Education and Teaching, B
Ecology, B
Education, BM
Educational Leadership and Administration, M
Electrical, Electronics and Communications Engineering, B
Engineering Physics, B
Engineering and Applied Sciences, M
Engineering/Industrial Management, B
English Language and Literature, B
Ethnic, Cultural Minority, and Gender Studies, B
Fine/Studio Arts, B
General Studies, A
History, B
International Business/Trade/Commerce, M
Liberal Arts and Sciences Studies and Humanities, B
Mathematics, B
Mathematics and Computer Science, B
Mechanical Engineering, B
Natural Sciences, B
Physician Assistant, M
Physics, B
Project Management, O
Psychology, B
Religion/Religious Studies, M
Special Education and Teaching, B

CLEVELAND STATE COMMUNITY COLLEGE

Administrative Assistant and Secretarial Science, A
Business Administration and Management, A
Child Development, A
Community Organization and Advocacy, A
Criminal Justice/Police Science, A
General Studies, A
Industrial Technology/Technician, A
Kindergarten/PreSchool Education and Teaching, A
Liberal Arts and Sciences Studies and Humanities, A
Public Administration and Social Service Professions, A
Science Technologies/Technicians, A

COLUMBIA STATE COMMUNITY COLLEGE

Applied Horticulture/Horticultural Operations, A
Child Development, A
Criminal Justice/Police Science, A
General Studies, A
Liberal Arts and Sciences Studies and Humanities, A
Management Information Systems and Services, A
Medical Radiologic Technology/Science - Radiation Therapist, A
Respiratory Care Therapy/Therapist, A
Science Technologies/Technicians, A
Veterinary/Animal Health Technology/Technician and Veterinary Assistant, A

CONCORDE CAREER COLLEGE

Dental Assisting/Assistant, A
Medical Office Management/Administration, A
Medical/Clinical Assistant, A
Pharmacy Technician/Assistant, A
Respiratory Care Therapy/Therapist, A
Surgical Technology/Technologist, A

CUMBERLAND UNIVERSITY

Accounting, B
American/United States Studies/Civilization, B
Athletic Training and Sports Medicine, B
Biology Teacher Education, B
Biology/Biological Sciences, AB

Business Administration, Management and Operations, M
Business/Commerce, AB
Criminal Justice/Law Enforcement Administration, B
Drama and Dramatics/Theatre Arts, B
Education, ABM
Elementary Education and Teaching, B
English Language and Literature, B
Fine/Studio Arts, B
Geography Teacher Education, B
Health/Medical Preparatory Programs, B
History, B
History Teacher Education, B
Liberal Arts and Sciences Studies and Humanities, AB
Mathematics, B
Mathematics Teacher Education, B
Music, B
Music Teacher Education, B
Parks, Recreation, Leisure and Fitness Studies, B
Physical Education Teaching and Coaching, B
Political Science and Government, B
Pre-Dentistry Studies, B
Pre-Law Studies, B
Pre-Medicine/Pre-Medical Studies, B
Pre-Pharmacy Studies, B
Pre-Veterinary Studies, B
Psychology, B
Psychology Teacher Education, B
Public Administration, M
Secondary Education and Teaching, B
Social Sciences, B
Sociology, B
Special Education and Teaching, B
Visual and Performing Arts, B

DAYMAR COLLEGE (CLARKSVILLE)

Accounting Technology/Technician and Bookkeeping, A
Business Administration and Management, AB
Business Administration, Management and Operations, A
Computer Systems Networking and Telecommunications, A
Computer and Information Sciences, A
E-Commerce/Electronic Commerce, A
Health Information/Medical Records Administration/Administrator, A
Legal Assistant/Paralegal, A
Medical/Clinical Assistant, A
Pharmacy Technician/Assistant, A

DAYMAR COLLEGE (MURFREESBORO)

Accounting, A
Business Administration and Management, B
Criminal Justice/Police Science, A
Medical Insurance Specialist/Medical Biller, A

DAYMAR COLLEGE (NASHVILLE)

Accounting, A
Business Administration and Management, A
Computer and Information Sciences and Support Services, A
Criminal Justice/Safety Studies, A
E-Commerce/Electronic Commerce, A
Health Information/Medical Records Administration/Administrator, A
Legal Assistant/Paralegal, A
Medical/Clinical Assistant, A
Pharmacy Technician/Assistant, A

DEVRY UNIVERSITY

Business Administration and Management, B
Business Administration, Management and Operations, BM
Business/Commerce, B
Computer Systems Analysis/Analyst, B
Computer Systems Networking and Telecommunications, AB
Criminal Justice/Law Enforcement Administration, B
Health/Health Care Administration/Management, B

Web Page, Digital/Multimedia and Information Resources Design, AB

DYERSBURG STATE COMMUNITY COLLEGE

Agriculture, A
Business Administration and Management, A
Child Development, A
Computer and Information Systems Security, A
Criminal Justice/Police Science, A
Criminal Justice/Safety Studies, A
Education, A
Emergency Medical Technology/Technician (EMT Paramedic), A
General Studies, A
Health Information/Medical Records Technology/Technician, A
Health Services/Allied Health/Health Sciences, A
Industrial Electronics Technology/Technician, A
Industrial Mechanics and Maintenance Technology, A
Information Science/Studies, A
Liberal Arts and Sciences Studies and Humanities, A
Medical Informatics, A
Music Performance, A
Web Page, Digital/Multimedia and Information Resources Design, A

EAST TENNESSEE STATE UNIVERSITY

Accounting, BM
Allied Health and Medical Assisting Services, MDO
Allopathic Medicine, D
Anatomy, D
Animation, Interactive Technology, Video Graphics and Special Effects, B
Anthropology, B
Art/Art Studies, General, B
Biochemistry, D
Biological and Biomedical Sciences, MD
Biology/Biological Sciences, B
Business Administration and Management, B
Business Administration, Management and Operations, MO
Business/Managerial Economics, B
Chemistry, BM
Child Development, B
Communication Disorders, MD
Communication and Media Studies, M
Computer Art and Design, MO
Computer Science, MO
Computer and Information Sciences, B
Corporate and Organizational Communication, M
Counselor Education/School Counseling and Guidance Services, M
Criminal Justice/Law Enforcement Administration, B
Criminology, MO
Curriculum and Instruction, MO
Dental Hygiene/Hygienist, B
Drama and Dramatics/Theatre Arts, B
Early Childhood Education and Teaching, MDO
Economic Development, O
Economics, B
Education, MDO
Educational Leadership and Administration, MDO
Educational Media/Instructional Technology, M
Elementary Education and Teaching, M
Engineering Technology, B
English, MO
English Language and Literature, B
Entrepreneurship/Entrepreneurial Studies, O
Environmental Health, B
Environmental and Occupational Health, MD
Exercise and Sports Science, MD
Family and Consumer Sciences/Human Sciences, B
Finance, B
Finance and Banking, M
Fine Arts and Art Studies, M
Foreign Languages and Literatures, B
General Studies, A
Geography, B
Geology/Earth Science, B
Geosciences, M
Health Professions and Related Clinical Sciences, B
Health Services Administration, O
Health and Physical Education, B

History, BMO
Human Development, M
Human Services, B
Information Science/Studies, MO
Interior Design, B
International Relations and Affairs, B
Kinesiology and Movement Studies, MO
Liberal Arts and Sciences Studies and Humani-
ties, B
Liberal Studies, MO
Library Science, O
Manufacturing Engineering, MO
Marketing, MO
Marketing/Marketing Management, B
Mass Communication/Media Studies, B
Mathematics, BMO
Microbiology, D
Middle School Education, M
Multi-/Interdisciplinary Studies, B
Music, B
Musicology and Ethnomusicology, B
Non-Profit/Public/Organizational Management, M
Nursing, MDO
Nursing - Advanced Practice, D
Nutritional Sciences, M
Paleontology, M
Pharmaceutical Sciences, D
Pharmacology, D
Pharmacy, D
Philosophy, B
Physical Therapy/Therapist, D
Physics, B
Physiology, D
Political Science and Government, BMO
Psychology, BD
Public Administration, MO
Public Health, MDO
Public Health (MPH, DPH), B
Reading Teacher Education, M
Secondary Education and Teaching, M
Social Work, BM
Sociology, BM
Special Education and Teaching, BM
Sport and Fitness Administration/Management, BM
Survey Technology/Surveying, B
Urban and Regional Planning, MO
Women's Studies, B

L'ECOLE CULINAIRE–MEMPHIS

Restaurant/Food Services Management, A

FISK UNIVERSITY

Art/Art Studies, General, B
Biological and Biomedical Sciences, M
Biology/Biological Sciences, B
Business Administration and Management, B
Chemistry, BM
Clinical Psychology, M
Computer Science, B
English Language and Literature, B
History, B
Mathematics, B
Music, B
Music Performance, B
Music Teacher Education, B
Physics, BM
Political Science and Government, B
Psychology, BM
Sociology, B
Spanish Language and Literature, B
Special Education and Teaching, B

FORTIS INSTITUTE (COOKEVILLE)

Clinical/Medical Laboratory Technician, A
Radiologic Technology/Science - Radiographer, A

FOUNTAINHEAD COLLEGE OF TECH-
NOLOGY

Communications Technology/Technician, A
Computer Engineering Technology/Technician, A
Computer Programming/Programmer, A
Computer and Information Systems Security, B
Electrical, Electronic and Communications Engineer-
ing Technology/Technician, A

Health Information/Medical Records
Technology/Technician, A
Information Technology, A
Medical Insurance Coding Specialist/Coder, A

FREED-HARDEMAN UNIVERSITY

Accounting, BM
Acting, B
Art/Art Studies, General, B
Bible/Biblical Studies, B
Biochemistry, B
Biology/Biological Sciences, B
Business Administration and Management, B
Business Administration, Management and Opera-
tions, M
Chemistry, B
Communication Studies/Speech Communication
and Rhetoric, B
Computer and Information Sciences, B
Counselor Education/School Counseling and Guid-
ance Services, M
Criminal Justice/Safety Studies, B
Curriculum and Instruction, M
Early Childhood Education and Teaching, B
Education, MO
Educational Administration and Supervision, M
Educational Leadership and Administration, O
Elementary Education and Teaching, B
English Language and Literature, B
Environmental Sciences, B
Ethics, M
Finance, B
Health and Physical Education, B
History, B
Human Development and Family Studies, B
Journalism, B
Junior High/Intermediate/Middle School Education
and Teaching, B
Kinesiology and Exercise Science, B
Management Strategy and Policy, M
Marketing/Marketing Management, B
Mass Communication/Media Studies, B
Mathematics, B
Missions/Missionary Studies and Missiology, B
Multi-/Interdisciplinary Studies, B
Music, B
Pastoral Studies/Counseling, M
Philosophy, B
Political Science and Government, B
Psychology, B
Public Relations/Image Management, B
Secondary Education and Teaching, B
Social Work, B
Spanish Language and Literature, B
Special Education and Teaching, BM
Technical Theatre/Theatre Design and Technol-
ogy, B
Theology and Religious Vocations, M
Youth Ministry, B

HIWASSEE COLLEGE

Accounting, A
Agriculture, A
Animal Sciences, A
Apparel and Textiles, A
Biology/Biological Sciences, A
Business Administration and Management, A
Chemistry, A
Clinical Laboratory Science/Medical
Technology/Technologist, A
Communication Studies/Speech Communication
and Rhetoric, A
Computer and Information Sciences, A
Criminal Justice/Law Enforcement Administration, A
Dental Hygiene/Hygienist, A
Drama and Dramatics/Theatre Arts, A
Economics, A
Elementary Education and Teaching, A
English Language and Literature, A
Family and Consumer Sciences/Human Sciences, A
Finance, A
Fishing and Fisheries Sciences and Management, A
Foods, Nutrition, and Wellness Studies, A
Forestry, A
Health Information/Medical Records
Technology/Technician, A

Health and Physical Education, A
History, A
Hospitality Administration/Management, A
Human Services, A
Kinesiology and Exercise Science, A
Liberal Arts and Sciences Studies and Humani-
ties, A
Marketing/Marketing Management, A
Music, A
Optometric Technician/Assistant, A
Physical Therapy/Therapist, A
Pre-Dentistry Studies, A
Pre-Law Studies, A
Pre-Medicine/Pre-Medical Studies, A
Pre-Nursing Studies, A
Pre-Pharmacy Studies, A
Pre-Theology/Pre-Ministerial Studies, A
Pre-Veterinary Studies, A
Psychology, A
Secondary Education and Teaching, A
Sociology, A
Wildlife and Wildlands Science and Management, A

HUNTINGTON COLLEGE OF HEALTH
SCIENCES

Foods, Nutrition, and Wellness Studies, A
Nutritional Sciences, BMD

JACKSON STATE COMMUNITY COL-
LEGE

Agriculture, A
Business Administration and Management, A
Clinical/Medical Laboratory Technician, A
Computer Science, A
Education, A
General Studies, A
Industrial Technology/Technician, A
Liberal Arts and Sciences Studies and Humani-
ties, A
Management Information Systems and Services, A
Medical Radiologic Technology/Science - Radiation
Therapist, A
Physical Therapist Assistant, A
Science Technologies/Technicians, A

JOHN A. GUPTON COLLEGE

Funeral Service and Mortuary Science, A

JOHNSON UNIVERSITY

Bible/Biblical Studies, B
Counselor Education/School Counseling and Guid-
ance Services, M
Cultural Studies, M
Education, M
Educational Media/Instructional Technology, M
Elementary Education and Teaching, B
Higher Education/Higher Education Administra-
tion, M
Junior High/Intermediate/Middle School Education
and Teaching, B
Marriage and Family Therapy/Counseling, M
Mass Communication/Media Studies, B
Religious/Sacred Music, B
Teacher Assistant/Aide, A
Theology and Religious Vocations, M

KING UNIVERSITY

Accounting, BM
Athletic Training and Sports Medicine, B
Bible/Biblical Studies, B
Biochemistry, B
Biological and Biomedical Sciences, B
Biological and Physical Sciences, B
Biology Teacher Education, B
Biology/Biological Sciences, B
Business Administration and Management, B
Business Administration, Management and Opera-
tions, M
Chemistry, B
Chemistry Teacher Education, B
Clinical Laboratory Science/Medical
Technology/Technologist, B
Computer Science, B
Criminal Justice/Safety Studies, B
Economics, B

English Language and Literature, B
English/Language Arts Teacher Education, B
Finance, B
Finance and Banking, M
Forensic Science and Technology, B
French Language Teacher Education, B
French Language and Literature, B
Health Professions and Related Clinical Sciences, B
Health Services Administration, M
Health/Health Care Administration/Management, B
History, B
History Teacher Education, B
Human Resources Management and Services, M
Information Science/Studies, B
Marketing, M
Marketing/Marketing Management, B
Mathematics, B
Mathematics Teacher Education, B
Medicinal and Pharmaceutical Chemistry, B
Music, B
Music Teacher Education, B
Philosophy, B
Photography, B
Physical Education Teaching and Coaching, B
Physics, B
Physics Teacher Education, B
Political Science and Government, B
Pre-Law Studies, B
Pre-Medicine/Pre-Medical Studies, B
Pre-Pharmacy Studies, B
Pre-Theology/Pre-Ministerial Studies, B
Pre-Veterinary Studies, B
Project Management, M
Psychology, B
Religion/Religious Studies, B
Social Work, B
Spanish Language Teacher Education, B
Spanish Language and Literature, B
Sport and Fitness Administration/Management, B
Visual and Performing Arts, B
Youth Ministry, B

LANE COLLEGE

Biology/Biological Sciences, B
Business Administration and Management, B
Chemistry, B
Communication and Media Studies, B
Computer and Information Sciences, B
Criminal Justice/Safety Studies, B
English Language and Literature, B
French Language and Literature, B
History, B
Mathematics, B
Multi-/Interdisciplinary Studies, B
Music, B
Physical Education Teaching and Coaching, B
Physics, B
Religion/Religious Studies, B
Sociology, B

LEE UNIVERSITY

Accounting, B
Advertising, B
Anthropology, B
Art Teacher Education, B
Athletic Training and Sports Medicine, B
Bible/Biblical Studies, B
Biochemistry, B
Biology Teacher Education, B
Biology/Biological Sciences, B
Business Administration and Management, B
Business Administration, Management and Operations, M
Business Teacher Education, B
Chemistry, B
Chemistry Teacher Education, B
Child Development, M
Christian Studies, B
Communication Studies/Speech Communication and Rhetoric, B
Counseling Psychology, M
Counselor Education/School Counseling and Guidance Services, M
Curriculum and Instruction, MO
Digital Communication and Media/Multimedia, B
Drama and Dance Teacher Education, B

Dramatic/Theatre Arts and Stagecraft, B
Early Childhood Education and Teaching, B
Education, BMO
Educational Leadership and Administration, MO
Elementary Education and Teaching, BM
English Language and Literature, B
English/Language Arts Teacher Education, B
Fine/Studio Arts, B
French Language Teacher Education, B
French Language and Literature, B
General Studies, B
Health Services/Allied Health/Health Sciences, B
Health Teacher Education, B
Health and Physical Education, B
Health/Health Care Administration/Management, B
Health/Medical Preparatory Programs, B
History, B
History Teacher Education, B
Humanities/Humanistic Studies, B
Journalism, B
Junior High/Intermediate/Middle School Education and Teaching, B
Kinesiology and Exercise Science, B
Management Information Systems and Services, B
Marriage and Family Therapy/Counseling, M
Mathematics, B
Mathematics Teacher Education, BM
Middle School Education, M
Missions/Missionary Studies and Missiology, B
Multi-/Interdisciplinary Studies, B
Music, B
Music Performance, B
Music Teacher Education, BM
Pastoral Counseling and Specialized Ministries, B
Pastoral Studies/Counseling, BM
Performance, M
Philosophy, B
Political Science and Government, B
Pre-Theology/Pre-Ministerial Studies, B
Psychology, B
Psychology Teacher Education, B
Public Relations/Image Management, B
Religion/Religious Studies, M
Religious Education, B
Religious/Sacred Music, B
Sacred Music, M
Secondary Education and Teaching, M
Social Studies Teacher Education, M
Sociology, B
Spanish Language Teacher Education, B
Spanish Language and Literature, B
Special Education and Teaching, BM
Speech Teacher Education, B
Student Personnel Services, M
Teaching English as a Second or Foreign Language/ESL Language Instructor, B
Theology and Religious Vocations, BM
Theology/Theological Studies, B
Youth Ministry, B

LEMOYNE-OWEN COLLEGE

Accounting, B
Art/Art Studies, General, B
Biology/Biological Sciences, B
Business Administration and Management, B
Chemistry, B
Communication Studies/Speech Communication and Rhetoric, B
Communication, Journalism and Related Programs, B
Computer Science, B
Criminal Justice/Law Enforcement Administration, B
Early Childhood Education and Teaching, B
English Language and Literature, B
English/Language Arts Teacher Education, B
History, B
Humanities/Humanistic Studies, B
Information Technology, B
Mathematics, B
Mathematics Teacher Education, B
Music, B
Political Science and Government, B
Science Teacher Education/General Science Teacher Education, B
Social Sciences, B
Social Studies Teacher Education, B

Social Work, B
Sociology, B
Special Education and Teaching, B

LINCOLN COLLEGE OF TECHNOLOGY

Autobody/Collision and Repair Technology/Technician, A
Automobile/Automotive Mechanics Technology/Technician, A
Diesel Mechanics Technology/Technician, A

LINCOLN MEMORIAL UNIVERSITY

Accounting, B
Art Teacher Education, B
Art/Art Studies, General, B
Athletic Training and Sports Medicine, B
Biology Teacher Education, B
Biology/Biological Sciences, B
Business Administration and Management, B
Business Administration, Management and Operations, BM
Business/Managerial Economics, B
Chemistry, B
Chemistry Teacher Education, B
Clinical Laboratory Science/Medical Technology/Technologist, B
Computer and Information Sciences, B
Counselor Education/School Counseling and Guidance Services, M
Criminal Justice/Law Enforcement Administration, B
Curriculum and Instruction, MDO
Economics, B
Education, BMDO
Educational Administration and Supervision, MDO
Educational Leadership and Administration, D
Elementary Education and Teaching, B
English Education, M
English Language and Literature, B
Environmental Studies, B
Finance, B
Health Teacher Education, B
Health and Physical Education, B
Higher Education/Higher Education Administration, D
History, B
History Teacher Education, B
Human Resources Development, D
Humanities/Humanistic Studies, B
Kindergarten/PreSchool Education and Teaching, B
Kinesiology and Exercise Science, B
Law and Legal Studies, D
Liberal Arts and Sciences Studies and Humanities, B
Marketing/Marketing Management, B
Mass Communication/Media Studies, B
Mathematics, B
Mathematics Teacher Education, B
Nurse Anesthetist, M
Nursing, M
Nursing - Advanced Practice, M
Osteopathic Medicine, D
Physical Education Teaching and Coaching, B
Pre-Law Studies, B
Pre-Medicine/Pre-Medical Studies, B
Pre-Veterinary Studies, B
Psychiatric/Mental Health Nurse/Nursing, M
Psychology, B
Science Teacher Education/General Science Teacher Education, B
Secondary Education and Teaching, B
Social Work, B
Veterinary/Animal Health Technology/Technician and Veterinary Assistant, A
Wildlife and Wildlands Science and Management, B

LIPSCOMB UNIVERSITY

Accounting, BMO
Acting, B
American/United States Studies/Civilization, B
Apparel and Textiles, B
Applied Behavior Analysis, MO
Applied Mathematics, B
Architecture and Related Services, B
Art Teacher Education, B
Art Therapy/Therapist, B
Bible/Biblical Studies, B

Biochemistry, B
Biology Teacher Education, B
Biology/Biological Sciences, B
Biophysics, B
Business Administration and Management, B
Business Administration, Management and Operations, MO
Business/Managerial Economics, B
Chemistry, B
Chemistry Teacher Education, B
Civil Engineering, B
Clinical Psychology, M
Commercial and Advertising Art, B
Computer Engineering, B
Computer Science, B
Computer and Information Systems Security, BM
Conflict Resolution and Mediation/Peace Studies, MO
Counseling Psychology, MO
Criminal Justice/Safety Studies, B
Database Systems, M
Dietetics/Dieticians, B
Directing and Theatrical Production, B
Drama and Dance Teacher Education, B
Drama and Dramatics/Theatre Arts, B
Education, BMDO
Educational Administration and Supervision, D
Educational Leadership and Administration, MO
Educational Media/Instructional Technology, MO
Elementary Education and Teaching, B
Engineering Management, M
English, M
English Education, O
English Language and Literature, B
English/Language Arts Teacher Education, B
Entrepreneurial and Small Business Operations, B
Entrepreneurship/Entrepreneurial Studies, B
Environmental Sciences, B
Exercise and Sports Science, M
Family Systems, B
Family and Consumer Sciences/Human Sciences, B
Fashion Merchandising, B
Film, Television, and Video Production, M
Finance and Banking, M
Fine/Studio Arts, B
Foodservice Systems Administration/Management, B
French Language Teacher Education, B
French Language and Literature, B
General Studies, AB
German Language and Literature, B
Health Informatics, M
Health Services Administration, M
Health/Medical Preparatory Programs, B
History, B
History Teacher Education, B
Human Resources Management and Services, M
Human Resources Management/Personnel Administration, B
Information Resources Management/CIO Training, B
Information Science/Studies, B
Information Technology, B
International Business/Trade/Commerce, B
Junior High/Intermediate/Middle School Education and Teaching, B
Kinesiology and Exercise Science, B
Law and Legal Studies, B
Management, M
Management of Technology, MO
Marketing/Marketing Management, B
Marriage and Family Therapy/Counseling, M
Mass Communication/Media Studies, B
Mathematics, B
Mathematics Teacher Education, BMO
Mechanical Engineering, B
Missions/Missionary Studies and Missiology, B
Molecular Biology, M
Music, B
Music Performance, B
Music Teacher Education, B
Music Theory and Composition, B
Non-Profit/Public/Organizational Management, M
Nutritional Sciences, M
Organizational Management, M
Pastoral Counseling and Specialized Ministries, B
Pastoral Studies/Counseling, MDO

Pharmacy, MD
Philosophy, B
Physical Education Teaching and Coaching, B
Physics, B
Physics Teacher Education, B
Piano and Organ, B
Political Science and Government, B
Pre-Dentistry Studies, B
Pre-Law Studies, B
Pre-Medicine/Pre-Medical Studies, B
Pre-Nursing Studies, B
Pre-Pharmacy Studies, B
Pre-Veterinary Studies, B
Psychology, BM
Public Administration, B
Public Relations, Advertising, and Applied Communication, B
Public Relations/Image Management, B
Reading Teacher Education, MO
Social Work, B
Spanish Language Teacher Education, B
Spanish Language and Literature, B
Special Education and Teaching, BM
Sport and Fitness Administration/Management, BM
Sustainability Management, M
Sustainable Development, MO
Technical Theatre/Theatre Design and Technology, B
Theology and Religious Vocations, MDO
Urban Studies/Affairs, B
Voice and Opera, B
Web Page, Digital/Multimedia and Information Resources Design, B
Youth Ministry, B

MARTIN METHODIST COLLEGE

Accounting, B
Behavioral Sciences, B
Biology/Biological Sciences, B
Business Administration and Management, B
Business Administration, Management and Operations, B
Business Teacher Education, B
Criminal Justice/Law Enforcement Administration, B
Elementary Education and Teaching, B
English Language and Literature, B
English/Language Arts Teacher Education, B
Health and Physical Education, B
History, B
History Teacher Education, B
Human Services, B
Liberal Arts and Sciences Studies and Humanities, A
Philosophy, B
Physical Education Teaching and Coaching, B
Political Science and Government, B
Psychology, B
Religious Education, B
Religious/Sacred Music, B
Science Teacher Education/General Science Teacher Education, B
Sport and Fitness Administration/Management, B
System Administration/Administrator, B
Theology/Theological Studies, B

MARYVILLE COLLEGE

Accounting and Finance, B
American Sign Language (ASL), B
Biochemistry, B
Biology Teacher Education, B
Biology/Biological Sciences, B
Business Administration and Management, B
Chemistry, B
Chemistry Teacher Education, B
Computer and Information Sciences, B
Criminology, B
Design and Visual Communications, B
Drama and Dance Teacher Education, B
Drama and Dramatics/Theatre Arts, B
Economics, B
Education, B
Engineering, B
English Language and Literature, B
English/Language Arts Teacher Education, B
Environmental Studies, B
Fine/Studio Arts, B

Health Professions and Related Clinical Sciences, B
Health Teacher Education, B
Health and Physical Education, B
History, B
History Teacher Education, B
Human Resources Management/Personnel Administration, B
International Business/Trade/Commerce, B
International Relations and Affairs, B
Kinesiology and Exercise Science, B
Marketing/Marketing Management, B
Mathematics, B
Mathematics Teacher Education, B
Multi-/Interdisciplinary Studies, B
Music, B
Music Performance, B
Music Teacher Education, B
Music Theory and Composition, B
Parks, Recreation, Leisure and Fitness Studies, B
Pharmacology, B
Philosophy, B
Physical Education Teaching and Coaching, B
Piano and Organ, B
Political Science and Government, B
Psychology, B
Religion/Religious Studies, B
Sign Language Interpretation and Translation, B
Social Studies Teacher Education, B
Sociology, B
Spanish Language Teacher Education, B
Spanish Language and Literature, B
Teaching English as a Second or Foreign Language/ESL Language Instructor, B
Voice and Opera, B

MEMPHIS COLLEGE OF ART

Applied Arts and Design, M
Art Education, M
Design and Visual Communications, B
Film/Cinema Studies, B
Fine Arts and Art Studies, M
Fine/Studio Arts, B
Painting, B
Photography, B

MID-AMERICA BAPTIST THEOLOGICAL SEMINARY

Theology and Religious Vocations, MD
Theology/Theological Studies, A

MIDDLE TENNESSEE STATE UNIVERSITY

Accounting, BM
Actuarial Science, M
Aeronautics/Aviation/Aerospace Science and Technology, B
Aerospace, Aeronautical and Astronautical Engineering, M
Agribusiness, B
Animal Sciences, B
Anthropology, B
Apparel and Textiles, B
Archives/Archival Administration, O
Art Teacher Education, B
Art/Art Studies, General, B
Athletic Training and Sports Medicine, B
Aviation/Airway Management and Operations, M
BioTechnology, M
Biological and Biomedical Sciences, M
Biological and Physical Sciences, B
Biology/Biological Sciences, B
Biostatistics, M
Business Administration and Management, B
Business Education, M
Business Teacher Education, B
Business/Managerial Economics, B
Chemistry, BM
Clinical Psychology, M
Computational Sciences, D
Computer Science, BM
Counseling Psychology, M
Counselor Education/School Counseling and Guidance Services, M
Criminal Justice/Law Enforcement Administration, B
Criminal Justice/Police Science, B
Criminology, M

Curriculum and Instruction, MO
Drama and Dramatics/Theatre Arts, B
Early Childhood Education and Teaching, M
Economics, BMD
Education, MDO
Educational Administration and Supervision, MO
Educational Media/Instructional Technology, O
Elementary Education and Teaching, MO
Engineering Management, M
Engineering Technology, B
Engineering/Industrial Management, B
English, MD
English Language and Literature, B
English as a Second Language, MO
Environmental Engineering
   Technology/Environmental Technology, B
Exercise and Sports Science, MD
Experimental Psychology, M
Family Resource Management Studies, B
Finance, B
Foods, Nutrition, and Wellness Studies, B
Foreign Language Teacher Education, M
Foreign Languages and Literatures, B
French Language and Literature, M
Gender Studies, O
Geology/Earth Science, B
Geosciences, O
German Language and Literature, M
Gerontology, O
Health Education, M
Health Teacher Education, B
Health and Physical Education, B
History, BM
Human Resources Management and Services, M
Industrial Education, M
Industrial Technology/Technician, B
Industrial and Organizational Psychology, M
Interior Design, B
International Affairs, M
International Relations and Affairs, B
Kindergarten/PreSchool Education and Teaching, B
Liberal Arts and Sciences Studies and Humani-
   ties, B
Management, M
Management Information Systems and Ser-
   vices, BM
Management Strategy and Policy, M
Marketing/Marketing Management, B
Mass Communication/Media Studies, BM
Mathematics, BM
Mathematics Teacher Education, MD
Medical Informatics, M
Middle School Education, M
Molecular Biology, D
Multi-/Interdisciplinary Studies, B
Music, BM
Nursing, MO
Nursing - Advanced Practice, MO
Nursing Administration, M
Nursing Education, M
Office Management and Supervision, B
Parks, Recreation and Leisure Facilities Manage-
   ment, B
Philosophy, B
Physical Education Teaching and Coaching, M
Physics, B
Plant Sciences, B
Political Science and Government, BM
Psychology, BMO
Public History, D
Public Relations/Image Management, B
Reading Teacher Education, MD
Recreation and Park Management, M
Sales and Marketing Operations/Marketing and Dis-
   tribution Teacher Education, B
Sales, Distribution and Marketing Operations, B
School Psychology, M
Science Teacher Education/General Science
   Teacher Education, MD
Secondary Education and Teaching, M
Social Work, BM
Sociology, BM
Spanish Language and Literature, M
Special Education and Teaching, M
Technology Teacher Education/Industrial Arts
   Teacher Education, B

Women's Studies, O

MILLER-MOTTE TECHNICAL COLLEGE (CHATTANOOGA)

Business Administration and Management, A
Computer Programming, Specific Applications, A
Criminal Justice/Law Enforcement Administration, A
Massage Therapy/Therapeutic Massage, A
Medical/Clinical Assistant, A
Surgical Technology/Technologist, A

MILLER-MOTTE TECHNICAL COLLEGE (CLARKSVILLE)

Accounting, A
Accounting Technology/Technician and Bookkeep-
   ing, A
Business, Management, Marketing, and Related
   Support Services, A
Computer Programming, Specific Applications, A
Computer and Information Sciences and Support
   Services, A
Corrections and Criminal Justice, A
Drafting and Design Technology/Technician, A
Executive Assistant/Executive Secretary, A
Legal Assistant/Paralegal, A
Massage Therapy/Therapeutic Massage, A
Medical/Clinical Assistant, A
Surgical Technology/Technologist, A

MILLIGAN COLLEGE

Accounting, B
Bible/Biblical Studies, B
Biology/Biological Sciences, B
Business Administration and Management, B
Business Administration, Management and Opera-
   tions, M
Chemistry, B
Child Development, B
Communication and Media Studies, B
Computer Science, B
Computer and Information Sciences, B
Early Childhood Education and Teaching, B
Economics, B
Education, BM
English Language and Literature, B
Fine/Studio Arts, B
Health Professions and Related Clinical Sciences, B
Health and Physical Education, B
History, B
Humanities/Humanistic Studies, B
Mathematics, B
Missions/Missionary Studies and Missiology, M
Music, B
Music Teacher Education, B
Occupational Therapy/Therapist, M
Pastoral Studies/Counseling, BMD
Political Science and Government, B
Psychology, B
Public Administration and Social Service Profes-
   sions, B
Religion/Religious Studies, MD
Religious Education, M
Social Work, B
Sociology, B
Theology and Religious Vocations, MD

MOTLOW STATE COMMUNITY COLLEGE

Business Administration and Management, A
Education, A
Education/Teaching of Individuals in Early Childhood
   Special Education Programs, A
Electromechanical Technology/Electromechanical
   Engineering Technology, A
General Studies, A
Liberal Arts and Sciences Studies and Humani-
   ties, A
Web Page, Digital/Multimedia and Information Re-
   sources Design, A

NASHVILLE STATE COMMUNITY COLLEGE

Accounting, A
Administrative Assistant and Secretarial Science, A
Architectural Engineering, A

Architectural Engineering Technology/Technician, A
Art/Art Studies, General, A
Automobile/Automotive Mechanics
   Technology/Technician, A
Biology/Biological Sciences, A
Business Administration and Management, A
Chemistry, A
Child Development, A
Civil Engineering, A
Civil Engineering Technology/Technician, A
Commercial and Advertising Art, A
Communication Studies/Speech Communication
   and Rhetoric, A
Computer Engineering Technology/Technician, A
Computer Science, A
Computer Systems Networking and Telecommunica-
   tions, A
Computer Technology/Computer Systems Technol-
   ogy, A
Computer and Information Sciences, A
Construction Engineering Technology/Technician, A
Criminal Justice/Police Science, A
Culinary Arts/Chef Training, A
Design and Visual Communications, A
Early Childhood Education and Teaching, A
Economics, A
Electrical, Electronic and Communications Engineer-
   ing Technology/Technician, A
Elementary Education and Teaching, A
English Language and Literature, A
Foreign Languages, Literatures, and Linguistics, A
Geography, A
Health Information/Medical Records
   Administration/Administrator, A
Health Professions and Related Clinical Sciences, A
Health/Health Care Administration/Management, A
History, A
Industrial Engineering, A
Industrial Production Technologies/Technicians, A
Industrial Technology/Technician, A
Information Science/Studies, A
Information Technology, A
Junior High/Intermediate/Middle School Education
   and Teaching, A
Kindergarten/PreSchool Education and Teaching, A
Kinesiology and Exercise Science, A
Legal Assistant/Paralegal, A
Mathematics, A
Mechanical Engineering, A
Medical Informatics, A
Music, A
Occupational Therapist Assistant, A
Occupational Therapy/Therapist, A
Philosophy, A
Photography, A
Physics, A
Political Science and Government, A
Pre-Law Studies, A
Pre-Medicine/Pre-Medical Studies, A
Pre-Nursing Studies, A
Psychology, A
Secondary Education and Teaching, A
Sign Language Interpretation and Translation, A
Social Work, A
Sociology, A
Special Education and Teaching, A

NATIONAL COLLEGE (BRISTOL)

Accounting, AB
Administrative Assistant and Secretarial Science, A
Business Administration and Management, AB
Computer and Information Sciences, A
Medical/Clinical Assistant, A

NATIONAL COLLEGE (KNOXVILLE)

Administrative Assistant and Secretarial Science, A
Business Administration and Management, A
Computer Programming, Specific Applications, A
Computer Technology/Computer Systems Technol-
   ogy, A

NATIONAL COLLEGE (NASHVILLE)

Accounting and Business/Management, A
Administrative Assistant and Secretarial Science, A
Business Administration and Management, A
Medical/Clinical Assistant, A

Systems Engineering, A

NORTH CENTRAL INSTITUTE

Avionics Maintenance Technology/Technician, A

NORTHEAST STATE COMMUNITY COLLEGE

Accounting, A
Administrative Assistant and Secretarial Science, A
Automobile/Automotive Mechanics
 Technology/Technician, A
Business Administration and Management, A
Cardiovascular Technology/Technologist, A
Chemistry, A
Computer Programming, A
Computer Programming/Programmer, A
Computer Systems Networking and Telecommunications, A
Data Processing and Data Processing
 Technology/Technician, A
Drafting and Design Technology/Technician, A
Electrical, Electronic and Communications Engineering Technology/Technician, A
Emergency Medical Technology/Technician (EMT
 Paramedic), A
Engineering Technology, A
General Studies, A
Industrial Technology/Technician, A
Information Technology, A
Instrumentation Technology/Technician, A
Kindergarten/PreSchool Education and Teaching, A
Liberal Arts and Sciences Studies and Humanities, A
Machine Tool Technology/Machinist, A
Medical/Clinical Assistant, A
Surgical Technology/Technologist, A
Welding Technology/Welder, A

NOSSI COLLEGE OF ART

Commercial Photography, A
Commercial and Advertising Art, A
Film/Video and Photographic Arts, B
Graphic Design, B
Illustration, B

O'MORE COLLEGE OF DESIGN

Commercial and Advertising Art, B
Fashion Merchandising, B
Fashion/Apparel Design, B
Graphic Design, B
Interior Design, B
Prepress/Desktop Publishing and Digital Imaging
 Design, B

PELLISSIPPI STATE COMMUNITY COLLEGE

Accounting Technology/Technician and Bookkeeping, A
Administrative Assistant and Secretarial Science, A
Business Administration and Management, A
Cartography, A
Child Development, A
Cinematography and Film/Video Production, A
Civil Engineering Technology/Technician, A
Commercial and Advertising Art, A
Communications Technology/Technician, A
Computer Systems Networking and Telecommunications, A
Computer and Information Sciences, A
Drafting and Design Technology/Technician, A
Education, A
Electrical, Electronic and Communications Engineering Technology/Technician, A
Engineering Technology, A
General Studies, A
Hotel/Motel Administration/Management, A
Information Science/Studies, A
Interior Design, A
Legal Assistant/Paralegal, A
Liberal Arts and Sciences Studies and Humanities, A
Mechanical Engineering/Mechanical
 Technology/Technician, A
Office Management and Supervision, A
Photography, A

Sales, Distribution and Marketing Operations, A
Science Technologies/Technicians, A
Securities Services Administration/Management, A
System, Networking, and LAN/WAN
 Management/Manager, A
Web Page, Digital/Multimedia and Information Resources Design, A

REMINGTON COLLEGE–MEMPHIS CAMPUS

Business Administration and Management, A
Computer Systems Networking and Telecommunications, A
Criminal Justice/Law Enforcement Administration, A
Electrical, Electronics and Communications Engineering, A
Operations Management and Supervision, B

REMINGTON COLLEGE–NASHVILLE CAMPUS

Criminal Justice/Law Enforcement Administration, A

RHODES COLLEGE

Accounting, M
African-American/Black Studies, B
Anthropology, B
Art/Art Studies, General, B
Biochemistry, Biophysics and Molecular Biology, B
Biology/Biological Sciences, B
Business Administration and Management, B
Chemistry, B
Classics and Classical Languages, Literatures, and Linguistics, B
Computer Science, B
Drama and Dramatics/Theatre Arts, B
Economics, B
Education, B
English Language and Literature, B
Environmental Sciences, B
French Language and Literature, B
German Language and Literature, B
History, B
International Business/Trade/Commerce, B
International Economics, B
International Relations and Affairs, B
Latin American Studies, B
Mathematics, B
Music, B
Philosophy, B
Physics, B
Political Science and Government, B
Psychology, B
Religion/Religious Studies, B
Russian Studies, B
Spanish Language and Literature, B
Urban Studies/Affairs, B

ROANE STATE COMMUNITY COLLEGE

Accounting, A
Administrative Assistant and Secretarial Science, A
Art Teacher Education, A
Art/Art Studies, General, A
Biology/Biological Sciences, A
Business Administration and Management, A
Business Teacher Education, A
Chemistry, A
Clinical/Medical Laboratory Technician, A
Computer Engineering Technology/Technician, A
Computer Science, A
Corrections, A
Criminal Justice/Law Enforcement Administration, A
Criminal Justice/Police Science, A
Dental Hygiene/Hygienist, A
Early Childhood Education and Teaching, A
Education, A
Elementary Education and Teaching, A
Emergency Medical Technology/Technician (EMT
 Paramedic), A
Engineering, A
Environmental Health, A
General Studies, A
Health Information/Medical Records
 Administration/Administrator, A
Industrial Radiologic Technology/Technician, A
Information Technology, A

Kindergarten/PreSchool Education and Teaching, A
Laser and Optical Technology/Technician, A
Legal Administrative Assistant/Secretary, A
Liberal Arts and Sciences Studies and Humanities, A
Mathematics, A
Medical Administrative Assistant/Secretary, A
Music Teacher Education, A
Occupational Therapy/Therapist, A
Pharmacy Technician/Assistant, A
Physical Education Teaching and Coaching, A
Physical Sciences, A
Physical Therapy/Therapist, A
Respiratory Care Therapy/Therapist, A
Social Sciences, A
Technology Teacher Education/Industrial Arts
 Teacher Education, A

SEWANEE: THE UNIVERSITY OF THE SOUTH

American/United States Studies/Civilization, B
Ancient/Classical Greek Language and Literature, B
Anthropology, B
Art History, Criticism and Conservation, B
Asian Studies/Civilization, B
Biochemistry, B
Biology/Biological Sciences, B
Chemistry, B
Classics and Classical Languages, Literatures, and Linguistics, B
Computer Science, B
Drama and Dramatics/Theatre Arts, B
Economics, B
English, M
English Language and Literature, B
Environmental Biology, B
Environmental Studies, B
Fine/Studio Arts, B
Forest Sciences and Biology, B
French Language and Literature, B
Geology/Earth Science, B
German Language and Literature, B
History, B
International/Global Studies, B
Latin Language and Literature, B
Mathematics, B
Medieval and Renaissance Studies, B
Multi-/Interdisciplinary Studies, B
Music, B
Natural Resources and Conservation, B
Philosophy, B
Physics, B
Political Science and Government, B
Psychology, B
Religion/Religious Studies, B
Russian Language and Literature, B
Spanish Language and Literature, B
Theology and Religious Vocations, MD
Women's Studies, B
Writing, M

SOUTH COLLEGE

Accounting, A
Administrative Assistant and Secretarial Science, A
Business Administration and Management, A
Computer Science, A
Elementary Education and Teaching, A
Hotel/Motel Administration/Management, A
Information Science/Studies, A
Legal Administrative Assistant/Secretary, A
Legal Assistant/Paralegal, A
Medical Administrative Assistant/Secretary, A
Medical/Clinical Assistant, A
Physical Therapist Assistant, A
Physician Assistant, M
Radiologic Technology/Science - Radiographer, A

SOUTHERN ADVENTIST UNIVERSITY

Accounting, ABM
Acute Care/Critical Care Nursing, M
Advertising, B
Archeology, B
Art Teacher Education, B
Art Therapy/Therapist, B
Art/Art Studies, General, B

Automobile/Automotive Mechanics Technology/Technician, A
Bible/Biblical Studies, AB
Biochemistry, B
Biology Teacher Education, B
Biology/Biological Sciences, B
Biophysics, B
Broadcast Journalism, B
Building/Property Maintenance and Management, A
Business Administration and Management, AB
Business Administration, Management and Operations, M
Chemistry, B
Chemistry Teacher Education, B
Cinematography and Film/Video Production, B
Clinical Laboratory Science/Medical Technology/Technologist, B
Commercial and Advertising Art, A
Communications Technologies/Technicians and Support Services, A
Communications Technology/Technician, B
Computer Science, B
Computer and Information Sciences and Support Services, B
Counseling Psychology, M
Counselor Education/School Counseling and Guidance Services, M
Culinary Arts/Chef Training, A
Dental Hygiene/Hygienist, A
Education, BM
Educational Leadership and Administration, M
Elementary Education and Teaching, B
Engineering, A
English Language and Literature, B
English/Language Arts Teacher Education, B
Ethnic, Cultural Minority, and Gender Studies, B
Family Systems, B
Finance, B
Finance and Banking, M
Foods, Nutrition, and Wellness Studies, A
Foreign Languages and Literatures, B
French Language Teacher Education, B
French Language and Literature, B
Graphic Design, B
Health Services Administration, M
Health/Health Care Administration/Management, B
History, B
History Teacher Education, B
Human Resources Management/Personnel Administration, B
International Business/Trade/Commerce, B
Journalism, B
Kinesiology and Exercise Science, B
Liberal Arts and Sciences Studies and Humanities, A
Management, M
Management Information Systems and Services, B
Management Science, B
Marketing, M
Marketing/Marketing Management, B
Mass Communication/Media Studies, A
Mathematics, B
Mathematics Teacher Education, B
Missions/Missionary Studies and Missiology, BM
Multi-/Interdisciplinary Studies, B
Music, B
Music Performance, B
Music Teacher Education, B
Music Theory and Composition, B
Non-Profit/Public/Organizational Management, BM
Nursing, M
Nursing - Adult, M
Nursing - Advanced Practice, M
Nursing Administration, M
Occupational Therapy/Therapist, A
Photography, B
Physical Education Teaching and Coaching, B
Physical Therapy/Therapist, A
Physics, B
Physics Teacher Education, B
Psychology, BM
Public Relations/Image Management, B
Reading Teacher Education, M
Recreation and Park Management, M
Religion/Religious Studies, ABM
Religious Education, BM

Sales, Distribution and Marketing Operations, AB
Social Work, BM
Spanish Language and Literature, B
Speech-Language Pathology/Pathologist, A
Sport and Fitness Administration/Management, B
Teaching English as a Second or Foreign Language/ESL Language Instructor, B
Theology and Religious Vocations, M
Theology/Theological Studies, B

SOUTHWEST TENNESSEE COMMUNITY COLLEGE

Accounting, A
Administrative Assistant and Secretarial Science, A
Applied Horticulture/Horticultural Business Services, A
Architectural Engineering Technology/Technician, A
Automobile/Automotive Mechanics Technology/Technician, A
Biomedical Technology/Technician, A
Business Administration and Management, A
Business/Commerce, A
Cartography, A
Clinical/Medical Laboratory Technician, A
Commercial and Advertising Art, A
Computer Engineering Technology/Technician, A
Court Reporting/Court Reporter, A
Criminal Justice/Safety Studies, A
Dietician Assistant, A
Electrical, Electronic and Communications Engineering Technology/Technician, A
Electrical/Electronics Equipment Installation and Repair, A
Fire Science/Firefighting, A
General Studies, A
Health Professions and Related Clinical Sciences, A
Heavy Equipment Maintenance Technology/Technician, A
Industrial Technology/Technician, A
Information Technology, A
Kindergarten/PreSchool Education and Teaching, A
Legal Assistant/Paralegal, A
Management Information Systems and Services, A
Mechanical Engineering/Mechanical Technology/Technician, A
Medical Radiologic Technology/Science - Radiation Therapist, A
Medical/Clinical Assistant, A
Physical Therapist Assistant, A

STRAYER UNIVERSITY–KNOXVILLE CAMPUS

Accounting, B
Business Administration and Management, B
Criminal Justice/Law Enforcement Administration, B
Economics, B
International Business/Trade/Commerce, B
Management Information Systems and Services, B

STRAYER UNIVERSITY–NASHVILLE CAMPUS

Accounting, B
Business Administration and Management, B
Criminal Justice/Law Enforcement Administration, B
Economics, B
International Business/Trade/Commerce, B
Management Information Systems and Services, B

STRAYER UNIVERSITY–SHELBY CAMPUS

Accounting, B
Business Administration and Management, B
Criminal Justice/Law Enforcement Administration, B
Economics, B
International Business/Trade/Commerce, B
Management Information Systems and Services, B

STRAYER UNIVERSITY–THOUSAND OAKS CAMPUS

Accounting, B
Business Administration and Management, B
Criminal Justice/Law Enforcement Administration, B
Economics, B
International Business/Trade/Commerce, B

Management Information Systems and Services, B

TENNESSEE STATE UNIVERSITY

Accounting, B
Administrative Assistant and Secretarial Science, AB
Adult and Continuing Education and Teaching, B
African Studies, B
Agricultural Education, M
Agricultural Sciences, MD
Agriculture, B
Agronomy and Soil Sciences, M
Allied Health and Medical Assisting Services, MD
Animal Sciences, B
Architectural Engineering, B
Art/Art Studies, General, B
Audiology/Audiologist and Speech-Language Pathology/Pathologist, B
BioTechnology, D
Biological and Biomedical Sciences, MD
Biology/Biological Sciences, B
Biomedical Engineering, M
Business Administration and Management, B
Business Administration, Management and Operations, M
Business Teacher Education, B
Business/Managerial Economics, B
Chemistry, BM
Civil Engineering, BM
Clinical Laboratory Science/Medical Technology/Technologist, B
Communication Disorders, M
Computer Engineering, MD
Computer Science, B
Consumer Services and Advocacy, B
Counseling Psychology, MD
Counselor Education/School Counseling and Guidance Services, M
Criminal Justice/Law Enforcement Administration, B
Criminology, M
Curriculum and Instruction, MD
Dental Hygiene/Hygienist, AB
Education, BMDO
Educational Administration and Supervision, MDO
Educational Leadership and Administration, B
Electrical Engineering, M
Electrical, Electronics and Communications Engineering, B
Elementary Education and Teaching, BM
Engineering, B
Engineering and Applied Sciences, MD
English Language and Literature, B
Environmental Engineering Technology/Environmental Technology, M
Exercise and Sports Science, M
Family and Consumer Economics and Related Services, B
Family and Consumer Sciences/Human Sciences, MD
Food Technology and Processing, B
French Language and Literature, B
Health Information/Medical Records Administration/Administrator, B
Health Teacher Education, B
Health/Health Care Administration/Management, B
History, B
Human Resources Management and Services, M
Humanities/Humanistic Studies, B
Industrial Engineering, B
Industrial Technology/Technician, B
Kindergarten/PreSchool Education and Teaching, AB
Liberal Arts and Sciences Studies and Humanities, B
Management Strategy and Policy, M
Manufacturing Engineering, M
Mass Communication/Media Studies, B
Mathematics, BM
Mechanical Engineering, BM
Music, B
Music Teacher Education, M
Nursing, M
Nursing - Advanced Practice, M
Occupational Therapy/Therapist, M
Parks, Recreation, Leisure and Fitness Studies, B
Physical Education Teaching and Coaching, BM
Physical Therapy/Therapist, BD

Physics, B
Plant Sciences, M
Political Science and Government, B
Psychology, BMD
Public Administration, BMD
Public Health, M
Reading Teacher Education, B
Respiratory Care Therapy/Therapist, B
School Psychology, MD
Social Work, BM
Sociology, B
Spanish Language and Literature, B
Special Education and Teaching, BM
Sport and Fitness Administration/Management, M
Systems Engineering, MD
Transportation and Materials Moving, B

TENNESSEE TECHNOLOGICAL UNIVERSITY

Accounting, BM
Agricultural Business and Management, B
Agricultural Teacher Education, B
Agricultural/Biological Engineering and Bioengineering, B
Agronomy and Crop Science, B
Animal Sciences, B
Apparel and Textiles, B
Applied Behavior Analysis, D
Art Teacher Education, B
Art/Art Studies, General, B
Biochemistry, B
Biological and Biomedical Sciences, MD
Biology/Biological Sciences, B
Business Administration and Management, B
Business Administration, Management and Operations, M
Chemical Engineering, BM
Chemistry, BMD
Child Development, B
Civil Engineering, BM
Computer Engineering, B
Computer Science, BM
Counseling Psychology, M
Curriculum and Instruction, MO
Dietetics/Dieticians, B
Early Childhood Education and Teaching, MO
Economics, B
Education, BMDO
Education/Teaching of the Gifted and Talented, D
Educational Leadership and Administration, MO
Educational Measurement and Evaluation, D
Educational Media/Instructional Technology, MO
Educational Psychology, MO
Electrical Engineering, M
Electrical, Electronics and Communications Engineering, B
Elementary Education and Teaching, BMO
Engineering and Applied Sciences, MD
English, M
English Language and Literature, B
Environmental Policy and Resource Management, M
Environmental Sciences, D
Family and Consumer Sciences/Home Economics Teacher Education, B
Family and Consumer Sciences/Human Sciences, B
Fashion Merchandising, B
Finance, B
Finance and Banking, M
Fish, Game and Wildlife Management, M
Foods, Nutrition, and Wellness Studies, B
French Language and Literature, B
Geology/Earth Science, B
German Language and Literature, B
Health Education, M
Health Promotion, M
Health Teacher Education, B
History, B
Horticultural Science, B
Human Resources Management and Services, M
Industrial Technology/Technician, B
Industrial and Manufacturing Management, M
Information Science/Studies, B
International Business/Trade/Commerce, BM
Internet and Interactive Multimedia, M
Journalism, B

Kindergarten/PreSchool Education and Teaching, B
Kinesiology and Movement Studies, M
Labor and Industrial Relations, B
Landscaping and Groundskeeping, B
Library Science, MO
Management Information Systems and Services, M
Management Strategy and Policy, M
Marketing/Marketing Management, B
Mathematics, BM
Mathematics Teacher Education, MO
Mechanical Engineering, BM
Middle School Education, M
Music, B
Music Teacher Education, BM
Nursing, M
Nursing - Advanced Practice, M
Nursing Administration, M
Nursing Education, M
Nursing Informatics, M
Operations Management and Supervision, B
Physical Education Teaching and Coaching, BM
Physics, B
Political Science and Government, B
Pre-Dentistry Studies, B
Pre-Law Studies, B
Pre-Medicine/Pre-Medical Studies, B
Pre-Veterinary Studies, B
Psychology, B
Reading Teacher Education, MDO
School Psychology, MO
Science Teacher Education/General Science Teacher Education, MO
Secondary Education and Teaching, BMO
Social Work, B
Sociology, B
Software Engineering, M
Spanish Language and Literature, B
Special Education and Teaching, BMO
Sport and Fitness Administration/Management, M
Turf and Turfgrass Management, B
Web Page, Digital/Multimedia and Information Resources Design, B
Wildlife and Wildlands Science and Management, B

TENNESSEE WESLEYAN COLLEGE

Accounting, B
Allied Health Diagnostic, Intervention, and Treatment Professions, B
American/United States Studies/Civilization, B
Behavioral Sciences, B
Biology/Biological Sciences, B
Business Administration and Management, B
Chemistry, B
Christian Studies, B
Computer and Information Sciences, B
Criminal Justice/Safety Studies, B
Curriculum and Instruction, M
Drama and Dramatics/Theatre Arts, B
Early Childhood Education and Teaching, B
Education, BM
Educational Leadership and Administration, M
Elementary Education and Teaching, B
English Language and Literature, B
Environmental Studies, B
Finance, B
French Language and Literature, B
Health Professions and Related Clinical Sciences, B
Health and Physical Education, B
History, B
Human Resources Management/Personnel Administration, B
Human Services, B
International/Global Studies, B
Kinesiology and Exercise Science, B
Marketing/Marketing Management, B
Mathematics, B
Multi-/Interdisciplinary Studies, B
Music, B
Ophthalmic and Optometric Support Services and Allied Professions, B
Pre-Nursing Studies, B
Pre-Theology/Pre-Ministerial Studies, B
Psychology, B
Religion/Religious Studies, B
Secondary Education and Teaching, B
Sociology, B

TREVECCA NAZARENE UNIVERSITY

Accounting, B
Applied Mathematics, B
Behavioral Sciences, B
Biological and Biomedical Sciences, B
Biology Teacher Education, B
Biology/Biological Sciences, B
Broadcast Journalism, B
Business Administration and Management, AB
Business Administration, Management and Operations, M
Business Teacher Education, B
Business, Management, Marketing, and Related Support Services, B
Chemistry, B
Chemistry Teacher Education, B
Communication Studies/Speech Communication and Rhetoric, AB
Communication, Journalism and Related Programs, B
Counselor Education/School Counseling and Guidance Services, MD
Criminal Justice/Law Enforcement Administration, AB
Curriculum and Instruction, M
Digital Communication and Media/Multimedia, B
Divinity/Ministry (BD, MDiv.), B
Drama and Dance Teacher Education, B
Drama and Dramatics/Theatre Arts, B
E-Commerce/Electronic Commerce, B
Early Childhood Education and Teaching, B
Education, MD
Educational Leadership and Administration, MD
Elementary Education and Teaching, BM
Engineering Physics, B
English Language and Literature, B
English/Language Arts Teacher Education, B
General Studies, A
Health Information/Medical Records Administration/Administrator, B
Health Services Administration, O
Health/Health Care Administration/Management, B
History, B
History Teacher Education, B
Information Science/Studies, M
Information Technology, AB
Intercultural/Multicultural and Diversity Studies, B
International Business/Trade/Commerce, B
Journalism, B
Library Science, M
Management Information Systems and Services, MO
Management of Technology, M
Marketing/Marketing Management, B
Mass Communication/Media Studies, B
Mathematics, AB
Mathematics Teacher Education, B
Multi-/Interdisciplinary Studies, B
Music, B
Music Performance, AB
Music Teacher Education, B
Music Theory and Composition, B
Non-Profit/Public/Organizational Management, B
Organizational Communication, B
Organizational Management, M
Pastoral Studies/Counseling, M
Physical Education Teaching and Coaching, B
Physician Assistant, M
Physics, B
Physics Teacher Education, B
Political Science and Government, B
Project Management, O
Psychology, B
Public Administration and Social Service Professions, B
Public Policy Analysis, B
Purchasing, Procurement/Acquisitions and Contracts Management, A
Religion/Religious Studies, BM
Religious/Sacred Music, AB
Secondary Education and Teaching, M

Social Work, B
Sociology, B
Special Education and Teaching, BM
Speech Teacher Education, B
Sport and Fitness Administration/Management, B
Theology and Religious Vocations, ABM
Web Page, Digital/Multimedia and Information Resources Design, B
Web/Multimedia Management and Webmaster, B
Youth Ministry, B

TUSCULUM COLLEGE

Adult and Continuing Education and Teaching, M
Athletic Training and Sports Medicine, B
Biology/Biological Sciences, B
Business Administration, Management and Operations, M
Chemistry, B
Criminal Justice/Law Enforcement Administration, B
Education, M
English Language and Literature, B
Environmental Studies, B
History, B
Kinesiology and Exercise Science, B
Mathematics, B
Multi-/Interdisciplinary Studies, B
Museology/Museum Studies, B
Natural Resources and Conservation, B
Psychology, B
Special Education and Teaching, B
Sport and Fitness Administration/Management, B
Visual and Performing Arts, B

UNION UNIVERSITY

Accounting, BM
Advertising, B
Ancient Near Eastern and Biblical Languages, Literatures, and Linguistics, B
Art Teacher Education, B
Art/Art Studies, General, B
Athletic Training and Sports Medicine, B
Bible/Biblical Studies, B
Biological and Physical Sciences, B
Biology/Biological Sciences, B
Broadcast Journalism, B
Business Administration and Management, B
Business Administration, Management and Operations, M
Business Teacher Education, B
Business/Managerial Economics, B
Chemistry, B
Clinical Laboratory Science/Medical Technology/Technologist, B
Computer Science, B
Cultural Studies, M
Drama and Dramatics/Theatre Arts, B
Economics, B
Education, BMDO
Educational Administration and Supervision, O
Educational Leadership and Administration, DO
Elementary Education and Teaching, B
English Language and Literature, B
Family and Community Services, B
Finance, B
Foreign Languages and Literatures, B
French Language and Literature, B
Higher Education/Higher Education Administration, D
History, B
Information Science/Studies, B
Journalism, B
Kindergarten/PreSchool Education and Teaching, B
Kinesiology and Exercise Science, B
Marketing/Marketing Management, B
Mass Communication/Media Studies, B
Mathematics, B
Music, B
Music Performance, B
Music Teacher Education, B
Nurse Anesthetist, D
Nursing, MDO
Nursing - Advanced Practice, D
Nursing Administration, D
Nursing Education, MO
Parks, Recreation and Leisure Facilities Management, B

Pastoral Studies/Counseling, D
Philosophy, B
Philosophy and Religious Studies, B
Physical Education Teaching and Coaching, B
Physics, B
Piano and Organ, B
Political Science and Government, B
Pre-Dentistry Studies, B
Pre-Law Studies, B
Pre-Medicine/Pre-Medical Studies, B
Pre-Pharmacy Studies, B
Psychology, B
Public Relations/Image Management, B
Radio and Television, B
Religion/Religious Studies, BMD
Religious/Sacred Music, B
Science Teacher Education/General Science Teacher Education, B
Secondary Education and Teaching, B
Social Work, BM
Sociology, B
Spanish Language and Literature, B
Special Education and Teaching, B
Sport and Fitness Administration/Management, B
Teaching English as a Second or Foreign Language/ESL Language Instructor, B
Theology and Religious Vocations, B
Theology/Theological Studies, B
Voice and Opera, B

UNIVERSITY OF MEMPHIS

Accounting, BMD
Adult and Continuing Education and Teaching, D
African-American Studies, DO
African-American/Black Studies, B
Analytical Chemistry, D
Anthropology, BM
Applied Mathematics, M
Applied Statistics, D
Archeology, M
Architecture, BM
Art History, Criticism and Conservation, BM
Art/Art Studies, General, B
Bioinformatics, B
Biological and Biomedical Sciences, MD
Biology/Biological Sciences, B
Biomedical Engineering, MD
Biomedical/Medical Engineering, B
Biostatistics, M
Business Administration and Management, B
Business Administration, Management and Operations, MD
Business/Managerial Economics, B
Ceramic Arts and Ceramics, M
Chemistry, BMD
Civil Engineering, BMD
Clinical Psychology, MD
Communication Disorders, MD
Communication Studies/Speech Communication and Rhetoric, B
Communication and Media Studies, MD
Comparative Literature, D
Computer Engineering, BMD
Computer Engineering Technology/Technician, B
Computer Science, BMD
Consumer Merchandising/Retailing Management, B
Counseling Psychology, D
Counselor Education/School Counseling and Guidance Services, MD
Criminal Justice/Law Enforcement Administration, B
Criminology, BM
Curriculum and Instruction, MD
Drama and Dramatics/Theatre Arts, B
Early Childhood Education and Teaching, MD
Economics, BMD
Education, MDO
Educational Administration and Supervision, MD
Educational Leadership and Administration, M
Educational Measurement and Evaluation, MD
Educational Media/Instructional Technology, MD
Educational Psychology, MD
Electrical Engineering, MD
Electrical, Electronic and Communications Engineering Technology/Technician, B
Electrical, Electronics and Communications Engineering, B

Elementary Education and Teaching, M
Energy and Power Engineering, M
Engineering Technology, B
Engineering and Applied Sciences, MD
English, MDO
English Language and Literature, B
English as a Second Language, MO
Environmental Design/Architecture, B
Environmental Engineering Technology/Environmental Technology, M
Environmental and Occupational Health, M
Epidemiology, M
Exercise and Sports Science, M
Experimental Psychology, MD
Family and Consumer Sciences/Human Sciences, M
Film, Television, and Video Production, M
Finance, B
Finance and Banking, D
Fine Arts and Art Studies, MO
Foreign Languages and Literatures, B
French Language and Literature, M
General Studies, B
Geographic Information Systems, O
Geography, BM
Geology/Earth Science, BMDO
Geophysics and Seismology, M
Graphic Design, M
Health Services Administration, M
Higher Education/Higher Education Administration, D
History, BMD
Hospitality Administration/Management, B
Hotel/Motel Administration/Management, B
Human Development and Family Studies, B
Industrial/Management Engineering, M
Inorganic Chemistry, M
Interdisciplinary Studies, M
Interior Design, M
International Business/Trade/Commerce, B
International Relations and Affairs, B
Journalism, BM
Kinesiology and Exercise Science, B
Law and Legal Studies, D
Liberal Arts and Sciences Studies and Humanities, B
Liberal Studies, M
Linguistics, MD
Logistics and Materials Management, B
Management, D
Management Information Systems and Services, B
Management Science, B
Manufacturing Technology/Technician, B
Marketing, MD
Marketing/Marketing Management, B
Mass Communication/Media Studies, B
Mathematics, BMD
Mechanical Engineering, BMD
Middle School Education, M
Multi-/Interdisciplinary Studies, B
Music, BMD
Music Teacher Education, MD
Musicology and Ethnomusicology, MD
Near and Middle Eastern Studies, MD
Nursing, MO
Nursing - Advanced Practice, M
Nursing Administration, M
Nursing Education, M
Painting, M
Philosophy, BMD
Photography, M
Physical Chemistry, M
Physical Education Teaching and Coaching, B
Physics, BM
Political Science and Government, BM
Printmaking, M
Psychology, BMDO
Public Administration, M
Public Health, M
Public Policy Analysis, M
Reading Teacher Education, MD
Real Estate, M
Rehabilitation Counseling, M
Sales, Distribution and Marketing Operations, B
School Psychology, MDO
Secondary Education and Teaching, M

Selling Skills and Sales Operations, B
Social Sciences, M
Social Work, B
Sociology, BM
Special Education and Teaching, BMD
Sport and Fitness Administration/Management, B
Statistics, M
Structural Engineering, M
Supply Chain Management, D
Teacher Education, Multiple Levels, B
Theater, M
Transportation and Highway Engineering, M
Urban and Regional Planning, M
Water Resources Engineering, M
Writing, MD

THE UNIVERSITY OF TENNESSEE

Accounting, BMD
Adult and Continuing Education and Teaching, M
Advertising, B
Advertising and Public Relations, MD
Aerospace, Aeronautical and Astronautical Engineering, BMD
Agricultural Business and Management, B
Agricultural Education, M
Agricultural Engineering, M
Agricultural Sciences, MD
Agricultural and Extension Education Services, B
Agricultural/Biological Engineering and Bioengineering, B
Analytical Chemistry, MD
Anatomy, D
Animal Behavior and Ethology, MD
Animal Sciences, BMD
Anthropology, BMD
Applied Mathematics, M
Applied Psychology, M
Archeology, MD
Architecture, BM
Art Education, M
Art History, Criticism and Conservation, B
Audiology/Audiologist and Speech-Language Pathology/Pathologist, B
Aviation, M
Biochemistry, MD
Bioethics/Medical Ethics, MD
Biological and Biomedical Sciences, MD
Biology/Biological Sciences, B
Biomedical Engineering, MD
Biomedical/Medical Engineering, B
Biosystems Engineering, M
Business Administration and Management, B
Business Administration, Management and Operations, MD
Business Statistics, B
Business/Managerial Economics, B
Ceramic Arts and Ceramics, M
Chemical Engineering, BMD
Chemical Physics, D
Chemistry, BMD
Child and Family Studies, MD
Civil Engineering, BMD
Classics and Classical Languages, Literatures, and Linguistics, B
Clinical Laboratory Science/Medical Technology/Technologist, B
Clinical Psychology, D
Clothing and Textiles, MD
Commercial and Advertising Art, B
Communication Disorders, MD
Communication Studies/Speech Communication and Rhetoric, B
Communication and Media Studies, MD
Community Health and Preventive Medicine, MD
Composition, M
Computer Engineering, BMD
Computer Science, BMD
Consumer Economics, BMD
Counseling Psychology, M
Counselor Education/School Counseling and Guidance Services, MDO
Criminology, MD
Cultural Anthropology, MD
Curriculum and Instruction, MDO
Drama and Dramatics/Theatre Arts, B
Early Childhood Education and Teaching, MD

Ecology, MD
Economics, BMD
Education, MDO
Educational Administration and Supervision, MDO
Educational Leadership and Administration, D
Educational Measurement and Evaluation, D
Educational Media/Instructional Technology, MDO
Educational Psychology, MD
Electrical Engineering, MD
Electrical, Electronics and Communications Engineering, B
Elementary Education and Teaching, MO
Energy and Power Engineering, D
Engineering Management, MD
Engineering and Applied Sciences, MD
English, MD
English Education, MO
English Language and Literature, B
English as a Second Language, MDO
Entomology, MD
Environmental Engineering Technology/Environmental Technology, M
Environmental Policy and Resource Management, MD
Evolutionary Biology, MD
Exercise and Sports Science, MD
Experimental Psychology, MD
Finance, B
Finance and Banking, MD
Fine Arts and Art Studies, M
Fine/Studio Arts, B
Fish, Game and Wildlife Management, M
Food Science, B
Food Science and Technology, MD
Foods, Nutrition, and Wellness Studies, B
Foreign Language Teacher Education, MO
Foreign Languages and Literatures, B
Forestry, BM
Foundations and Philosophy of Education, MD
French Language and Literature, BMD
Genetics, MD
Genomic Sciences, MD
Geography, BMD
Geology/Earth Science, BMD
German Language and Literature, BMD
Gerontology, M
Graphic Design, M
Health Education, M
Health Promotion, M
Health Services Administration, M
History, BMD
Home Economics, D
Hospitality Administration/Management, M
Hotel/Motel Administration/Management, B
Human Development and Family Studies, B
Human Resources Development, M
Human Resources Management/Personnel Administration, B
Industrial Engineering, B
Industrial and Manufacturing Management, M
Industrial and Organizational Psychology, D
Industrial/Management Engineering, MD
Information Science/Studies, MD
Inorganic Chemistry, MD
Interior Design, B
Italian Language and Literature, BD
Journalism, BMD
Kinesiology and Exercise Science, B
Kinesiology and Movement Studies, MD
Landscape Architecture, M
Law and Legal Studies, D
Leisure Studies, M
Linguistics, D
Logistics and Materials Management, BMD
Management, MD
Marketing, MD
Marketing/Marketing Management, B
Materials Engineering, BMD
Materials Sciences, MD
Mathematics, BMD
Mathematics Teacher Education, MO
Mechanical Engineering, BMD
Media Studies, MD
Microbiology, MD
Multi-/Interdisciplinary Studies, B
Multilingual and Multicultural Education, D

Music, BM
Music Teacher Education, M
Music Theory and Composition, M
Musicology and Ethnomusicology, M
Natural Resource Economics, B
Nuclear Engineering, BMD
Nursing, MD
Nutritional Sciences, M
Organic Chemistry, MD
Painting, M
Performance, M
Philosophy, BMD
Photography, M
Physical Chemistry, MD
Physics, BMD
Physiology, MD
Plant Pathology/Phytopathology, MD
Plant Physiology, MD
Plant Sciences, BM
Political Science and Government, BMD
Polymer/Plastics Engineering, MD
Portuguese Language and Literature, D
Printmaking, M
Psychology, BMD
Public Administration, BM
Public Health, M
Public Relations/Image Management, B
Reading Teacher Education, MDO
Recreation and Park Management, M
Rehabilitation Counseling, M
Reliability Engineering, M
Religion/Religious Studies, BM
Russian Language and Literature, BD
School Psychology, DO
Science Teacher Education/General Science Teacher Education, MO
Sculpture, M
Secondary Education and Teaching, M
Social Studies Teacher Education, MO
Social Work, BMD
Sociology, BMD
Soil Chemistry and Physics, B
Spanish Language and Literature, BMD
Special Education and Teaching, BMO
Speech and Interpersonal Communication, MD
Sport and Fitness Administration/Management, BM
Sports Medicine, MD
Statistics, BMD
Student Personnel Services, M
Theater, M
Theoretical Chemistry, D
Therapeutic Recreation, M
Transportation/Transportation Management, MD
Travel and Tourism, M
Veterinary Medicine, D
Wildlife and Wildlands Science and Management, B

THE UNIVERSITY OF TENNESSEE AT CHATTANOOGA

Accounting, M
Applied Mathematics, BM
Applied Statistics, M
Art Teacher Education, B
Art/Art Studies, General, B
Athletic Training and Sports Medicine, M
Biology/Biological Sciences, B
Business Administration and Management, B
Business Administration, Management and Operations, M
Chemical Engineering, BM
Chemistry, B
Civil Engineering, BM
Communication Studies/Speech Communication and Rhetoric, B
Community Psychology, M
Computational Sciences, MD
Computer Science, BMO
Counselor Education/School Counseling and Guidance Services, M
Criminal Justice/Law Enforcement Administration, B
Criminology, M
Drama and Dramatics/Theatre Arts, B
Early Childhood Education and Teaching, B
Economics, B
Education, MDO
Educational Administration and Supervision, MO

Educational Leadership and Administration, D
Educational Media/Instructional Technology, O
Electrical Engineering, M
Electrical, Electronics and Communications Engineering, B
Elementary Education and Teaching, M
Energy and Power Engineering, O
Engineering, B
Engineering Management, MO
Engineering/Industrial Management, B
English, M
English Language and Literature, B
English/Language Arts Teacher Education, B
Environmental Sciences, BM
Ethics, O
Experimental Psychology, M
Foreign Language Teacher Education, B
Foreign Languages and Literatures, B
Geology/Earth Science, B
History, B
Humanities/Humanistic Studies, B
Industrial and Organizational Psychology, M
Industrial/Management Engineering, M
Interior Design, B
Junior High/Intermediate/Middle School Education and Teaching, B
Kinesiology and Exercise Science, B
Legal Assistant/Paralegal, B
Logistics and Materials Management, O
Mass Communication/Media Studies, B
Mathematics, BM
Mathematics Teacher Education, BM
Mechanical Engineering, BM
Medical Informatics, O
Music, B
Music Teacher Education, BM
Non-Profit/Public/Organizational Management, MO
Nuclear Engineering, O
Nurse Anesthetist, MO
Nursing, MDO
Nursing - Advanced Practice, MO
Nursing Administration, M
Nursing Education, MO
Performance, M
Philosophy and Religious Studies, B
Physical Education Teaching and Coaching, M
Physical Therapy/Therapist, BD
Physics, B
Political Science and Government, B
Project Management, O
Psychology, BM
Public Administration, MO
Quality Management, O
Rhetoric, MO
School Psychology, O
Science Teacher Education/General Science Teacher Education, B
Secondary Education and Teaching, BM
Social Sciences, B
Social Studies Teacher Education, B
Social Work, B
Special Education and Teaching, BM
Supply Chain Management, O
Writing, MO

THE UNIVERSITY OF TENNESSEE AT MARTIN

Accounting, B
Agricultural Business and Management, B
Agricultural Sciences, M
Agricultural Teacher Education, B
Agriculture, B
Agronomy and Crop Science, B
Animal Sciences, B
Athletic Training and Sports Medicine, B
Biology Teacher Education, B
Biology/Biological Sciences, B
Business Administration and Management, B
Business Administration, Management and Operations, M
Business Teacher Education, B
Business/Managerial Economics, B
Cell/Cellular and Molecular Biology, B
Chemistry, B
Chemistry Teacher Education, B
Child Development, BM

Child and Family Studies, M
Community Psychology, M
Computer Science, B
Counselor Education/School Counseling and Guidance Services, M
Criminal Justice/Law Enforcement Administration, B
Curriculum and Instruction, M
Design and Visual Communications, B
Dietetics/Dieticians, B
Drama and Dramatics/Theatre Arts, B
Economics, B
Education, M
Educational Leadership and Administration, M
Elementary Education and Teaching, BM
Engineering, B
English Language and Literature, B
English/Language Arts Teacher Education, B
Environmental Biology, B
Environmental Studies, B
Family and Consumer Sciences/Home Economics Teacher Education, B
Family and Consumer Sciences/Human Sciences, BM
Fashion Merchandising, B
Finance, B
Fishing and Fisheries Sciences and Management, B
Food Science and Technology, M
French Language Teacher Education, B
French Language and Literature, B
General Studies, B
Geography, B
Geography Teacher Education, B
Geology/Earth Science, B
German Language Teacher Education, B
Graphic Design, B
Health Professions and Related Clinical Sciences, B
Health and Physical Education, B
History, B
History Teacher Education, B
Human Resources Management/Personnel Administration, B
Interdisciplinary Studies, M
Interior Design, B
International Business/Trade/Commerce, B
International Relations and Affairs, B
Kindergarten/PreSchool Education and Teaching, B
Management Information Systems and Services, B
Management Science, B
Marketing/Marketing Management, B
Mathematics, B
Mathematics Teacher Education, B
Music, B
Music Pedagogy, B
Music Performance, B
Music Teacher Education, B
Natural Resources Management/Development and Policy, B
Nutritional Sciences, M
Philosophy, B
Physical Education Teaching and Coaching, M
Piano and Organ, B
Political Science and Government, B
Pre-Dentistry Studies, B
Pre-Medicine/Pre-Medical Studies, B
Pre-Pharmacy Studies, B
Pre-Veterinary Studies, B
Psychology, B
Public Administration, B
Science Teacher Education/General Science Teacher Education, B
Secondary Education and Teaching, M
Social Work, B
Sociology, B
Soil Science and Agronomy, B
Spanish Language Teacher Education, B
Spanish Language and Literature, B
Special Education and Teaching, BM
Statistics, B
Teacher Education, Multiple Levels, B
Visual and Performing Arts, B
Voice and Opera, B
Wildlife and Wildlands Science and Management, B

VANDERBILT UNIVERSITY

Accounting, M
Acute Care/Critical Care Nursing, M

African-American/Black Studies, B
Allopathic Medicine, M
American/United States Studies/Civilization, B
Analytical Chemistry, MD
Ancient Studies/Civilization, B
Anthropology, BMD
Art History, Criticism and Conservation, B
Asian Studies/Civilization, B
Astronomy, M
Biochemistry, MD
Bioinformatics, MD
Biological and Biomedical Sciences, MD
Biology/Biological Sciences, B
Biomedical Engineering, MD
Biomedical/Medical Engineering, B
Biophysics, MD
Business Administration, Management and Operations, M
Cancer Biology/Oncology, MD
Cell Biology and Anatomy, MD
Chemical Engineering, BMD
Chemistry, BMD
Child Development, B
Child and Family Studies, M
Civil Engineering, BMD
Classics and Classical Languages, Literatures, and Linguistics, BM
Clinical Research, M
Cognitive Sciences, B
Communication Disorders, MD
Communication Studies/Speech Communication and Rhetoric, B
Computer Engineering, B
Computer Science, BMD
Counselor Education/School Counseling and Guidance Services, M
Developmental Biology and Embryology, MD
Drama and Dramatics/Theatre Arts, B
Early Childhood Education and Teaching, B
Economic Development, M
Economics, BMD
Education, BMD
Educational Administration and Supervision, MD
Educational Leadership and Administration, D
Educational Policy, D
Electrical Engineering, MD
Electrical, Electronics and Communications Engineering, B
Elementary Education and Teaching, BM
Engineering Science, B
Engineering and Applied Sciences, MD
English, MD
English Education, M
English Language and Literature, B
Environmental Engineering Technology/Environmental Technology, MD
Environmental Policy and Resource Management, MD
Environmental Sciences, M
European Studies/Civilization, B
Film/Cinema Studies, B
Finance and Banking, M
Fine/Studio Arts, B
Foreign Language Teacher Education, BM
French Language and Literature, BMD
Geology/Earth Science, BM
German Language and Literature, BMD
Gerontological Nursing, M
Health Physics/Radiological Health, M
Health Services Administration, M
Higher Education/Higher Education Administration, MD
Hispanic-American, Puerto Rican, and Mexican-American/Chicano Studies, B
History, BMD
Human Development, M
Human Genetics, D
Immunology, MD
Inorganic Chemistry, MD
International and Comparative Education, M
Jewish/Judaic Studies, B
Latin American Studies, BM
Law and Legal Studies, MD
Liberal Studies, M
Management Strategy and Policy, M
Marketing, M

Materials Sciences, MD
Maternal/Child Health and Neonatal
Nurse/Nursing, M
Mathematics, BMD
Mechanical Engineering, BMD
Medical Physics, M
Microbiology, MD
Molecular Biology, BMD
Molecular Physiology, MD
Multi-/Interdisciplinary Studies, B
Multilingual and Multicultural Education, M
Music, B
Music Teacher Education, B
Music Theory and Composition, B
Nurse Midwife/Nursing Midwifery, M
Nursing, MDO
Nursing - Adult, M
Nursing - Advanced Practice, M
Nursing Administration, M
Nursing Informatics, M
Organic Chemistry, MD
Organizational Management, M
Pathology/Experimental Pathology, D
Pediatric Nurse/Nursing, M
Pharmacology, D
Philosophy, BMD
Physical Chemistry, MD
Physics, BMD
Piano and Organ, B
Political Science and Government, BMD
Portuguese Language and Literature, MD
Psychiatric/Mental Health Nurse/Nursing, M
Psychology, BM
Public Health, M
Public Policy Analysis, B
Reading Teacher Education, M
Religion/Religious Studies, BMD
Romance Languages, Literatures, and Linguistics, B
Russian Language and Literature, M
Science Teacher Education/General Science
Teacher Education, M
Science, Technology and Society, B
Secondary Education and Teaching, BM
Social Sciences, B
Sociology, BMD
Spanish Language and Literature, BMD
Special Education and Teaching, BM
Theology and Religious Vocations, M
Theoretical Chemistry, M
Urban Education and Leadership, M
Urban and Regional Planning, M
Violin, Viola, Guitar and Other Stringed Instruments, B
Voice and Opera, B
Women's Health Nursing, M
Women's Studies, B
Writing, M

VATTEROTT COLLEGE (MEMPHIS)

CAD/CADD Drafting and/or Design
Technology/Technician, A
Computer Technology/Computer Systems Technology, A
Heating, Air Conditioning and Refrigeration
Technology/Technician, A
Medical/Clinical Assistant, A
System Administration/Administrator, A

VIRGINIA COLLEGE IN CHATTANOOGA

Business Administration and Management, A
CAD/CADD Drafting and/or Design
Technology/Technician, A
Criminal Justice/Law Enforcement Administration, A
Health/Health Care Administration/Management, A
Massage Therapy/Therapeutic Massage, A
Medical Office Management/Administration, A
Office Management and Supervision, A

VOLUNTEER STATE COMMUNITY COLLEGE

Business Administration and Management, A
Child Development, A
Clinical/Medical Laboratory Technician, A
Computer and Information Sciences, A
Criminal Justice/Police Science, A
Education, A

Fire Science/Firefighting, A
General Studies, A
Health Information/Medical Records
Technology/Technician, A
Health Professions and Related Clinical Sciences, A
Legal Assistant/Paralegal, A
Liberal Arts and Sciences Studies and Humanities, A
Medical Informatics, A
Medical Radiologic Technology/Science - Radiation
Therapist, A
Music Performance, A
Ophthalmic Technician/Technologist, A
Physical Therapist Assistant, A
Respiratory Care Therapy/Therapist, A
Veterinary/Animal Health Technology/Technician and
Veterinary Assistant, A

WALTERS STATE COMMUNITY COLLEGE

Business Administration and Management, A
Child Development, A
Computer and Information Sciences, A
Criminal Justice/Police Science, A
Criminal Justice/Safety Studies, A
Data Processing and Data Processing
Technology/Technician, A
Education, A
Energy Management and Systems
Technology/Technician, A
General Studies, A
Health Information/Medical Records
Technology/Technician, A
Industrial Technology/Technician, A
Liberal Arts and Sciences Studies and Humanities, A
Music Performance, A
Occupational Therapist Assistant, A
Ornamental Horticulture, A
Physical Therapist Assistant, A
Respiratory Care Therapy/Therapist, A
Surgical Technology/Technologist, A
Web Page, Digital/Multimedia and Information Resources Design, A

WATKINS COLLEGE OF ART, DESIGN, & FILM

Art/Art Studies, General, B
Design and Visual Communications, B
Film/Cinema Studies, B
Fine/Studio Arts, B
Interior Design, B
Photography, B

WELCH COLLEGE

Administrative Assistant and Secretarial Science, A
Adult and Continuing Education and Teaching, B
Athletic Training and Sports Medicine, B
Bible/Biblical Studies, AB
Biological and Physical Sciences, A
Biology Teacher Education, B
Biology/Biological Sciences, A
Business Administration and Management, AB
Business/Commerce, B
Curriculum and Instruction, B
Early Childhood Education and Teaching, B
Education, B
Educational Leadership and Administration, B
Elementary Education and Teaching, B
English Language and Literature, B
English/Language Arts Teacher Education, B
Health and Physical Education, B
History, B
History Teacher Education, B
Humanities/Humanistic Studies, B
Missions/Missionary Studies and Missiology, B
Music, B
Music Performance, B
Music Teacher Education, B
Pastoral Studies/Counseling, B
Physical Education Teaching and Coaching, B
Religious Education, B
Religious/Sacred Music, B

Secondary Education and Teaching, B

WILLIAMSON COLLEGE

Bible/Biblical Studies, B
Business Administration, Management and Operations, B
Liberal Arts and Sciences Studies and Humanities, A
Non-Profit/Public/Organizational Management, B
Pre-Theology/Pre-Ministerial Studies, B
Theological and Ministerial Studies, B
Theology and Religious Vocations, B

Texas

ABILENE CHRISTIAN UNIVERSITY

Accounting, BM
Agribusiness, B
Animal Sciences, B
Architecture and Related Services, A
Art Teacher Education, B
Bible/Biblical Studies, B
Biochemistry, B
Biology Teacher Education, B
Biology/Biological Sciences, B
Business Administration and Management, B
Chemistry, B
Clinical Psychology, M
Communication Disorders, M
Communication Studies/Speech Communication
and Rhetoric, B
Communication and Media Studies, M
Computer Science, B
Computer Teacher Education, B
Conflict Resolution and Mediation/Peace Studies, MO
Counseling Psychology, M
Criminal Justice/Law Enforcement Administration, B
Curriculum and Instruction, M
Dietetics/Dieticians, B
Digital Communication and Media/Multimedia, B
Drama and Dramatics/Theatre Arts, B
Education, MO
Educational Administration and Supervision, O
Educational Leadership and Administration, MO
Educational Measurement and Evaluation, O
Educational Media/Instructional Technology, MO
Elementary Education and Teaching, B
Engineering, B
English, M
English Language and Literature, B
English/Language Arts Teacher Education, B
Environmental Sciences, B
Finance, B
Fine/Studio Arts, B
Graphic Design, B
Health/Medical Preparatory Programs, B
Higher Education/Higher Education Administration, M
History, B
History Teacher Education, B
Human Development and Family Studies, B
Human Resources Development, M
Human Services, MO
Information Resources Management/CIO Training, B
Information Technology, B
Interior Design, B
International/Global Studies, B
Journalism, B
Liberal Arts and Sciences Studies and Humanities, B
Liberal Studies, M
Marketing/Marketing Management, B
Marriage and Family Therapy/Counseling, M
Mathematics, B
Mathematics Teacher Education, B
Missions/Missionary Studies and Missiology, M
Multi-/Interdisciplinary Studies, B
Music, B
Music Teacher Education, B
Nursing, MO
Nursing - Advanced Practice, M
Nursing Administration, M
Nursing Education, M
Nutritional Sciences, O

Occupational Therapy/Therapist, M
Pastoral Studies/Counseling, MD
Physics, B
Physics Teacher Education, B
Piano and Organ, B
Political Science and Government, B
Pre-Dentistry Studies, B
Pre-Law Studies, B
Pre-Medicine/Pre-Medical Studies, B
Pre-Veterinary Studies, B
Psychology, BM
Public Relations, Advertising, and Applied Commu-
nication, B
Religion/Religious Studies, M
Rhetoric, M
School Psychology, O
Science Teacher Education/General Science
Teacher Education, B
Secondary Education and Teaching, B
Social Studies Teacher Education, B
Social Work, BM
Sociology, B
Spanish Language Teacher Education, B
Spanish Language and Literature, B
Speech-Language Pathology/Pathologist, B
Sport and Fitness Administration/Management, B
Theology and Religious Vocations, BM
Voice and Opera, B
Writing, M

ALVIN COMMUNITY COLLEGE

Accounting, A
Administrative Assistant and Secretarial Science, A
Aeronautics/Aviation/Aerospace Science and Tech-
nology, A
Art/Art Studies, General, A
Automobile/Automotive Mechanics
Technology/Technician, A
Biology/Biological Sciences, A
Business Administration and Management, A
Business/Commerce, A
Chemical Technology/Technician, A
Child Development, A
Computer Engineering Technology/Technician, A
Computer Programming/Programmer, A
Corrections, A
Court Reporting/Court Reporter, A
Criminal Justice/Police Science, A
Criminal Justice/Safety Studies, A
Criminalistics and Criminal Science, A
Culinary Arts/Chef Training, A
Diagnostic Medical Sonography/Sonographer and
Ultrasound Technician, A
Drafting and Design Technology/Technician, A
Drama and Dramatics/Theatre Arts, A
Early Childhood Education and Teaching, A
Electrical, Electronic and Communications Engineer-
ing Technology/Technician, A
Electroneurodiagnostic/Electroencephalographic
Technology/Technologist, A
Emergency Medical Technology/Technician (EMT
Paramedic), A
Executive Assistant/Executive Secretary, A
General Office Occupations and Clerical Services, A
General Studies, A
Health Services/Allied Health/Health Sciences, A
Health and Physical Education, A
History, A
Junior High/Intermediate/Middle School Education
and Teaching, A
Law and Legal Studies, A
Legal Administrative Assistant/Secretary, A
Legal Assistant/Paralegal, A
Liberal Arts and Sciences Studies and Humani-
ties, A
Marketing/Marketing Management, A
Mathematics, A
Medical Administrative Assistant/Secretary, A
Mental Health Counseling/Counselor, A
Music, A
Pharmacy Technician/Assistant, A
Physical Education Teaching and Coaching, A
Physical Sciences, A
Prepress/Desktop Publishing and Digital Imaging
Design, A
Psychiatric/Mental Health Services Technician, A

Psychology, A
Radio and Television, A
Respiratory Care Therapy/Therapist, A
Secondary Education and Teaching, A
Sociology, A
Substance Abuse/Addiction Counseling, A
Voice and Opera, A

AMARILLO COLLEGE

Accounting, A
Administrative Assistant and Secretarial Science, A
Airframe Mechanics and Aircraft Maintenance
Technology/Technician, A
Architectural Engineering Technology/Technician, A
Art/Art Studies, General, A
Automobile/Automotive Mechanics
Technology/Technician, A
Behavioral Sciences, A
Bible/Biblical Studies, A
Biology/Biological Sciences, A
Broadcast Journalism, A
Business Administration and Management, A
Business Teacher Education, A
Chemical Technology/Technician, A
Chemistry, A
Child Development, A
Clinical Laboratory Science/Medical
Technology/Technologist, A
Commercial and Advertising Art, A
Computer Engineering Technology/Technician, A
Computer Programming/Programmer, A
Computer Science, A
Computer Systems Analysis/Analyst, A
Corrections, A
Criminal Justice/Law Enforcement Administration, A
Criminal Justice/Police Science, A
Dental Hygiene/Hygienist, A
Drafting and Design Technology/Technician, A
Drama and Dramatics/Theatre Arts, A
Electrical, Electronic and Communications Engineer-
ing Technology/Technician, A
Elementary Education and Teaching, A
Emergency Medical Technology/Technician (EMT
Paramedic), A
Engineering, A
English Language and Literature, A
Environmental Health, A
Fine/Studio Arts, A
Fire Science/Firefighting, A
Funeral Service and Mortuary Science, A
General Studies, A
Geology/Earth Science, A
Health Information/Medical Records
Administration/Administrator, A
Heating, Air Conditioning, Ventilation and Refrigera-
tion Maintenance Technology/Technician, A
Heavy Equipment Maintenance
Technology/Technician, A
History, A
Industrial Radiologic Technology/Technician, A
Information Science/Studies, A
Instrumentation Technology/Technician, A
Interior Design, A
Journalism, A
Laser and Optical Technology/Technician, A
Legal Administrative Assistant/Secretary, A
Liberal Arts and Sciences Studies and Humani-
ties, A
Machine Tool Technology/Machinist, A
Mass Communication/Media Studies, A
Mathematics, A
Medical Administrative Assistant/Secretary, A
Modern Languages, A
Music, A
Music Teacher Education, A
Natural Sciences, A
Nuclear Medical Technology/Technologist, A
Occupational Therapy/Therapist, A
Photography, A
Physical Education Teaching and Coaching, A
Physical Sciences, A
Physical Therapy/Therapist, A
Physics, A
Pre-Pharmacy Studies, A
Psychology, A
Public Relations/Image Management, A

Radio and Television, A
Radiologic Technology/Science - Radiographer, A
Real Estate, A
Religion/Religious Studies, A
Respiratory Care Therapy/Therapist, A
Social Sciences, A
Social Work, A
Substance Abuse/Addiction Counseling, A
Telecommunications Technology/Technician, A
Tourism and Travel Services Management, A
Visual and Performing Arts, A

AMBERTON UNIVERSITY

Accounting, B
Business Administration and Management, B
Business Administration, Management and Opera-
tions, M
Child and Family Studies, M
Computer and Information Sciences, B
Counseling Psychology, M
Counselor Education/School Counseling and Guid-
ance Services, B
Human Development and Family Studies, B
Human Resources Development, M
Human Resources Management and Services, M
Human Resources Management/Personnel Adminis-
tration, B
Interdisciplinary Studies, M
Management, M
Management Information Systems and Services, B
Management Strategy and Policy, M
Marketing/Marketing Management, B
Project Management, M

AMERICAN INTERCONTINENTAL UNI-
VERSITY HOUSTON

Business Administration and Management, AB
Business Administration, Management and Opera-
tions, M
Criminal Justice/Law Enforcement Administration, B
Design and Visual Communications, B
Management, M

ANGELINA COLLEGE

Accounting, A
Administrative Assistant and Secretarial Science, A
Art/Art Studies, General, A
Biological and Physical Sciences, A
Business Administration and Management, A
Business/Commerce, A
Child Development, A
Communication Studies/Speech Communication
and Rhetoric, A
Computer Systems Networking and Telecommunica-
tions, A
Computer and Information Sciences, A
Criminal Justice/Law Enforcement Administration, A
Data Processing and Data Processing
Technology/Technician, A
Design and Visual Communications, A
Drafting and Design Technology/Technician, A
Drama and Dramatics/Theatre Arts, A
Electrical, Electronic and Communications Engineer-
ing Technology/Technician, A
Electromechanical Technology/Electromechanical
Engineering Technology, A
Emergency Medical Technology/Technician (EMT
Paramedic), A
Engineering, A
Environmental Engineering
Technology/Environmental Technology, A
General Studies, A
Health Teacher Education, A
Human Services, A
Legal Assistant/Paralegal, A
Machine Tool Technology/Machinist, A
Mathematics, A
Multi-/Interdisciplinary Studies, A
Music, A
Physics, A
Pre-Law Studies, A
Pre-Medicine/Pre-Medical Studies, A
Pre-Pharmacy Studies, A
Pre-Veterinary Studies, A
Psychology, A
Respiratory Care Therapy/Therapist, A

Science, Technology and Society, A
Social Work, A
Substance Abuse/Addiction Counseling, A
Teacher Assistant/Aide, A
Welding Technology/Welder, A

ANGELO STATE UNIVERSITY

Accounting, BM
Agribusiness, B
Agricultural Sciences, M
Agricultural and Food Products Processing, B
Agriculture, B
Animal Sciences, BM
Applied Psychology, M
Biological and Biomedical Sciences, M
Biology/Biological Sciences, B
Business Administration and Management, B
Chemistry, B
Civil Engineering, B
Communication and Media Studies, M
Computer and Information Sciences, B
Counseling Psychology, M
Counselor Education/School Counseling and Guidance Services, M
Criminal Justice/Safety Studies, B
Curriculum and Instruction, M
Drama and Dramatics/Theatre Arts, B
Education, M
Educational Administration and Supervision, MO
English, M
English Language and Literature, B
Finance, B
Fine/Studio Arts, B
Geology/Earth Science, B
Higher Education/Higher Education Administration, M
History, B
Industrial and Organizational Psychology, M
International Business/Trade/Commerce, B
Journalism, BM
Kinesiology and Exercise Science, B
Management, M
Management Information Systems and Services, B
Marketing/Marketing Management, B
Mathematics, B
Medical/Surgical Nursing, M
Multi-/Interdisciplinary Studies, B
Music, B
National Security, M
Natural Resources Management/Development and Policy, B
Nursing - Adult, M
Nursing Education, M
Philosophy, B
Physical Therapy/Therapist, D
Physics, B
Political Science and Government, B
Psychology, BM
Social Work, B
Sociology, B
Spanish Language and Literature, B
Special Education and Teaching, M
Sport and Fitness Administration/Management, M

ARGOSY UNIVERSITY, DALLAS

Accounting, DO
Business Administration and Management, AB
Business Administration, Management and Operations, MDO
Clinical Laboratory Science/Medical Technology/Technologist, B
Clinical Psychology, MD
Clinical/Medical Laboratory Technician, A
Community Psychology, M
Counselor Education/School Counseling and Guidance Services, D
Criminal Justice/Law Enforcement Administration, B
Education, MD
Educational Administration and Supervision, M
Educational Leadership and Administration, MD
Finance and Banking, MO
Forensic Psychology, M
Health Services Administration, MO
Higher Education/Higher Education Administration, M
Histologic Technology/Histotechnologist, A

Industrial and Organizational Psychology, M
Information Technology, AB
International Business/Trade/Commerce, MDO
Liberal Arts and Sciences Studies and Humanities, B
Management, MD
Management Information Systems and Services, MDO
Marketing, MDO
Psychology, ABMD
Public Administration, MO
Public Health, M
School Psychology, M
Sustainability Management, MDO

ARLINGTON BAPTIST COLLEGE

Bible/Biblical Studies, B
Business, Management, Marketing, and Related Support Services, B
Curriculum and Instruction, M
Early Childhood Education and Teaching, B
Education, BM
Educational Leadership and Administration, M
Elementary Education and Teaching, B
English/Language Arts Teacher Education, B
Junior High/Intermediate/Middle School Education and Teaching, B
Music, B
Music Teacher Education, B
Religion/Religious Studies, B
Theology and Religious Vocations, BM

THE ART INSTITUTE OF AUSTIN, A BRANCH OF THE ART INSTITUTE OF HOUSTON

Advertising, B
Animation, Interactive Technology, Video Graphics and Special Effects, B
Apparel and Accessories Marketing Operations, B
Baking and Pastry Arts/Baker/Pastry Chef, A
CAD/CADD Drafting and/or Design Technology/Technician, B
Cinematography and Film/Video Production, B
Commercial Photography, B
Computer Graphics, B
Culinary Arts/Chef Training, A
Fashion/Apparel Design, B
Graphic Design, A
Interior Design, B
Recording Arts Technology/Technician, B
Restaurant, Culinary, and Catering Management/Manager, AB
Web Page, Digital/Multimedia and Information Resources Design, AB

THE ART INSTITUTE OF DALLAS, A CAMPUS OF SOUTH UNIVERSITY

Advertising, B
Animation, Interactive Technology, Video Graphics and Special Effects, B
Apparel and Accessories Marketing Operations, B
Baking and Pastry Arts/Baker/Pastry Chef, A
Cinematography and Film/Video Production, AB
Computer Graphics, B
Culinary Arts/Chef Training, A
Design and Applied Arts, M
Fashion/Apparel Design, AB
Graphic Design, A
Interior Design, B
Photography, AB
Recording Arts Technology/Technician, B
Restaurant, Culinary, and Catering Management/Manager, AB
Web Page, Digital/Multimedia and Information Resources Design, B

THE ART INSTITUTE OF HOUSTON

Advertising, B
Animation, Interactive Technology, Video Graphics and Special Effects, B
Apparel and Accessories Marketing Operations, B
Baking and Pastry Arts/Baker/Pastry Chef, A
CAD/CADD Drafting and/or Design Technology/Technician, B

Cinematography and Film/Video Production, B
Commercial Photography, B
Computer Graphics, B
Culinary Arts/Chef Training, A
Fashion/Apparel Design, B
Graphic Design, AB
Interior Design, B
Recording Arts Technology/Technician, B
Restaurant, Culinary, and Catering Management/Manager, AB
Web Page, Digital/Multimedia and Information Resources Design, AB

THE ART INSTITUTE OF SAN ANTONIO, A BRANCH OF THE ART INSTITUTE OF HOUSTON

Advertising, B
Animation, Interactive Technology, Video Graphics and Special Effects, B
Apparel and Accessories Marketing Operations, B
Baking and Pastry Arts/Baker/Pastry Chef, A
CAD/CADD Drafting and/or Design Technology/Technician, B
Cinematography and Film/Video Production, B
Commercial and Advertising Art, B
Computer Graphics, B
Culinary Arts/Chef Training, A
Fashion/Apparel Design, B
Graphic Design, A
Interior Design, B
Restaurant, Culinary, and Catering Management/Manager, AB
Web Page, Digital/Multimedia and Information Resources Design, AB

AUSTIN COLLEGE

American/United States Studies/Civilization, B
Anthropology, B
Art/Art Studies, General, B
Asian Studies/Civilization, B
Biochemistry, B
Biology/Biological Sciences, B
Business Administration and Management, B
Business Administration, Management and Operations, B
Business/Commerce, B
Chemistry, B
Classics and Classical Languages, Literatures, and Linguistics, B
Communication Studies/Speech Communication and Rhetoric, B
Communication and Media Studies, B
Computer Science, B
Computer and Information Sciences, B
Drama and Dance Teacher Education, B
East Asian Languages, Literatures, and Linguistics, B
East Asian Studies, B
Economics, B
Education, M
Elementary Education and Teaching, B
English Language and Literature, B
Environmental Studies, B
Finance, B
French Language Teacher Education, B
French Language and Literature, B
General Studies, B
German Language and Literature, B
History, B
International Business/Trade/Commerce, B
International Economics, B
International Relations and Affairs, B
Junior High/Intermediate/Middle School Education and Teaching, B
Latin Language and Literature, B
Mass Communication/Media Studies, B
Mathematics, B
Multi-/Interdisciplinary Studies, B
Music, B
Non-Profit/Public/Organizational Management, B
Philosophy, B
Physical Education Teaching and Coaching, B
Physics, B
Political Science and Government, B
Psychology, B
Religion/Religious Studies, B

Secondary Education and Teaching, B
Sociology, B
Spanish Language and Literature, B
Spanish and Iberian Studies, B
Speech Teacher Education, B
Visual and Performing Arts, B
Women's Studies, B

AUSTIN COMMUNITY COLLEGE DISTRICT

Accounting Technology/Technician and Bookkeeping, A
Administrative Assistant and Secretarial Science, A
Animation, Interactive Technology, Video Graphics and Special Effects, A
Anthropology, A
Arabic Language and Literature, A
Art/Art Studies, General, A
Automobile/Automotive Mechanics Technology/Technician, A
Biology Technician/BioTechnology Laboratory Technician, A
Biology/Biological Sciences, A
Business Administration and Management, A
Business/Commerce, A
Carpentry/Carpenter, A
Cartography, A
Chemistry, A
Child Development, A
Chinese Language and Literature, A
Clinical/Medical Laboratory Technician, A
Commercial Photography, A
Commercial and Advertising Art, A
Computer Programming/Programmer, A
Computer Systems Networking and Telecommunications, A
Computer and Information Sciences, A
Corrections, A
Criminal Justice/Police Science, A
Culinary Arts/Chef Training, A
Dance, A
Dental Hygiene/Hygienist, A
Diagnostic Medical Sonography/Sonographer and Ultrasound Technician, A
Drafting and Design Technology/Technician, A
Drama and Dramatics/Theatre Arts, A
Early Childhood Education and Teaching, A
Economics, A
Electrical, Electronic and Communications Engineering Technology/Technician, A
Emergency Medical Technology/Technician (EMT Paramedic), A
Engineering, A
Environmental Engineering Technology/Environmental Technology, A
Fire Protection and Safety Technology/Technician, A
French Language and Literature, A
General Studies, A
Geography, A
Geology/Earth Science, A
German Language and Literature, A
Health Information/Medical Records Technology/Technician, A
Health Teacher Education, A
Health and Physical Education, A
Heating, Air Conditioning and Refrigeration Technology/Technician, A
History, A
Hospitality Administration/Management, A
Human Services, A
International Business/Trade/Commerce, A
Japanese Language and Literature, A
Journalism, A
Junior High/Intermediate/Middle School Education and Teaching, A
Latin Language and Literature, A
Legal Assistant/Paralegal, A
Marketing/Marketing Management, A
Mathematics, A
Music, A
Occupational Therapist Assistant, A
Pharmacy Technician/Assistant, A
Philosophy, A
Physical Sciences, A
Physical Therapist Assistant, A
Physics, A

Political Science and Government, A
Pre-Dentistry Studies, A
Pre-Medicine/Pre-Medical Studies, A
Pre-Pharmacy Studies, A
Pre-Veterinary Studies, A
Psychology, A
Radio and Television, A
Radiologic Technology/Science - Radiographer, A
Real Estate, A
Russian Language and Literature, A
Secondary Education and Teaching, A
Sign Language Interpretation and Translation, A
Social Work, A
Sociology, A
Spanish Language and Literature, A
Substance Abuse/Addiction Counseling, A
Surgical Technology/Technologist, A
Survey Technology/Surveying, A
Therapeutic Recreation/Recreational Therapy, A
Tourism and Travel Services Management, A
Veterinary/Animal Health Technology/Technician and Veterinary Assistant, A
Watchmaking and Jewelrymaking, A
Welding Technology/Welder, A

AUSTIN GRADUATE SCHOOL OF THEOLOGY

Bible/Biblical Studies, B
Theology and Religious Vocations, M

BAPTIST MISSIONARY ASSOCIATION THEOLOGICAL SEMINARY

Theology and Religious Vocations, M
Theology/Theological Studies, AB

BAPTIST UNIVERSITY OF THE AMERICAS

Bible/Biblical Studies, B
Business Administration and Management, B
Humanities/Humanistic Studies, B
Intercultural/Multicultural and Diversity Studies, A
Music, B
Religion/Religious Studies, B
Spanish Language and Literature, B

BAYLOR UNIVERSITY

Accounting, BM
Acting, B
Airline/Commercial/Professional Pilot and Flight Crew, B
Allied Health and Medical Assisting Services, MD
American/United States Studies/Civilization, BMD
Ancient Near Eastern and Biblical Languages, Literatures, and Linguistics, B
Ancient/Classical Greek Language and Literature, B
Anthropology, B
Applied Behavior Analysis, M
Applied Mathematics, B
Arabic Language and Literature, B
Art History, Criticism and Conservation, B
Art Teacher Education, B
Art/Art Studies, General, B
Asian Studies/Civilization, B
Astronomy, B
Astrophysics, B
Athletic Training and Sports Medicine, B
Aviation/Airway Management and Operations, B
Biochemistry, B
Bioinformatics, B
Biological and Biomedical Sciences, MD
Biology Teacher Education, B
Biology/Biological Sciences, B
Biomedical Engineering, M
Business Administration and Management, B
Business Administration, Management and Operations, MD
Business Statistics, B
Business Teacher Education, B
Business, Management, Marketing, and Related Support Services, B
Business/Commerce, B
Business/Managerial Economics, B
Chemistry, BMD
Chemistry Teacher Education, B

Classics and Classical Languages, Literatures, and Linguistics, B
Clinical Laboratory Science/Medical Technology/Technologist, B
Clinical Psychology, D
Communication Disorders, BM
Communication Studies/Speech Communication and Rhetoric, B
Communication and Media Studies, M
Community Health and Preventive Medicine, M
Composition, M
Computer Engineering, MD
Computer Science, BM
Computer Teacher Education, B
Criminology, D
Cultural Studies, D
Curriculum and Instruction, MD
Digital Communication and Media/Multimedia, B
Drama and Dramatics/Theatre Arts, B
Early Childhood Education and Teaching, B
Ecology, D
Economics, BM
Education, BMDO
Education/Teaching of Individuals with Speech or Language Impairments, B
Educational Administration and Supervision, MO
Educational Measurement and Evaluation, D
Educational Psychology, MDO
Electrical Engineering, MD
Electrical, Electronics and Communications Engineering, B
Elementary Education and Teaching, B
Emergency Medical Services, D
Engineering, B
English, MD
English Language and Literature, B
English/Language Arts Teacher Education, B
Entrepreneurship/Entrepreneurial Studies, B
Environmental Biology, M
Environmental Health, B
Environmental Law, D
Environmental Sciences, BD
Environmental Studies, BM
Exercise Physiology, B
Exercise and Sports Science, M
Family and Consumer Sciences/Home Economics Teacher Education, B
Family and Consumer Sciences/Human Sciences, B
Fashion Merchandising, B
Fashion/Apparel Design, B
Finance, B
Financial Planning and Services, B
Fine/Studio Arts, B
Foreign Language Teacher Education, B
French Language and Literature, B
Geology/Earth Science, BMD
Geophysics and Seismology, BMD
Geosciences, D
German Language and Literature, B
Health Education, MD
Health Law, D
Health Occupations Teacher Education, B
Health Promotion, D
Health Services Administration, M
Health Teacher Education, B
Health and Physical Education, B
Health/Medical Preparatory Programs, B
History, BMD
Human Development and Family Studies, B
Human Nutrition, B
Human Resources Management/Personnel Administration, B
Humanities/Humanistic Studies, B
Information Technology, B
Insurance, B
Intellectual Property Law, D
Interdisciplinary Studies, D
Interior Design, B
International Affairs, M
International Business/Trade/Commerce, B
International Relations and Affairs, B
Journalism, BM
Kindergarten/PreSchool Education and Teaching, B
Kinesiology and Exercise Science, B
Kinesiology and Movement Studies, D
Latin American Studies, B

Latin Language and Literature, B
Law and Legal Studies, D
Limnology, M
Linguistics, B
Logistics and Materials Management, B
Management Information Systems and Services, BMD
Marketing/Marketing Management, B
Maternal/Child Health and Neonatal Nurse/Nursing, M
Mathematics, BMD
Mathematics Teacher Education, B
Mechanical Engineering, BM
Multi-/Interdisciplinary Studies, B
Museology/Museum Studies, M
Music, BMD
Music History, Literature, and Theory, BM
Music Pedagogy, B
Music Performance, B
Music Teacher Education, B
Music Theory and Composition, BM
Nurse Midwife/Nursing Midwifery, D
Nursing, MD
Nursing - Advanced Practice, M
Nutritional Sciences, M
Performance, M
Philosophy, BMD
Physical Education Teaching and Coaching, BMD
Physical Therapy/Therapist, D
Physics, BMD
Political Science and Government, BMD
Pre-Law Studies, B
Pre-Nursing Studies, B
Psychology, BMD
Public Administration, BM
Public Policy Analysis, M
Reading Teacher Education, B
Real Estate, BD
Religion/Religious Studies, BMD
Religious/Sacred Music, B
Russian Language and Literature, B
Sacred Music, MD
Sales, Distribution and Marketing Operations, B
School Psychology, O
Science Teacher Education/General Science Teacher Education, B
Secondary Education and Teaching, B
Slavic Studies, B
Social Science Teacher Education, B
Social Studies Teacher Education, B
Social Work, BMD
Sociology, BMD
Spanish Language Teacher Education, B
Spanish Language and Literature, BM
Special Education and Teaching, BD
Specialized Merchandising, Sales, and Marketing Operations, B
Sport and Fitness Administration/Management, M
Statistics, BMD
Teacher Education and Professional Development, Specific Subject Areas, B
Technical Theatre/Theatre Design and Technology, B
Theater, M
Theology and Religious Vocations, MD
Western European Studies, D

BLINN COLLEGE

Accounting, A
Administrative Assistant and Secretarial Science, A
Agriculture, A
Biology/Biological Sciences, A
Business Administration and Management, A
Chemistry, A
Child Development, A
Comparative Literature, A
Computer Science, A
Computer Systems Networking and Telecommunications, A
Criminal Justice/Law Enforcement Administration, A
Dental Hygiene/Hygienist, A
Drama and Dramatics/Theatre Arts, A
English Language and Literature, A
Fire Science/Firefighting, A
French Language and Literature, A
German Language and Literature, A

Health Information/Medical Records Technology/Technician, A
History, A
Industrial Radiologic Technology/Technician, A
Legal Administrative Assistant/Secretary, A
Mass Communication/Media Studies, A
Mathematics, A
Mental Health Counseling/Counselor, A
Music, A
Philosophy, A
Physical Education Teaching and Coaching, A
Physical Therapist Assistant, A
Physics, A
Psychology, A
Real Estate, A
Spanish Language and Literature, A

BRAZOSPORT COLLEGE

Administrative Assistant and Secretarial Science, A
Automobile/Automotive Mechanics Technology/Technician, A
Business Administration and Management, B
Chemical Technology/Technician, A
Child Development, A
Computer Hardware Technology/Technician, A
Computer Programming/Programmer, A
Construction Engineering Technology/Technician, A
Construction/Heavy Equipment/Earthmoving Equipment Operation, A
Criminal Justice/Police Science, A
Drafting and Design Technology/Technician, A
Electrician, A
Emergency Medical Technology/Technician (EMT Paramedic), A
Heating, Air Conditioning, Ventilation and Refrigeration Maintenance Technology/Technician, A
Instrumentation Technology/Technician, A
Liberal Arts and Sciences Studies and Humanities, A
Machine Tool Technology/Machinist, A
Occupational Safety and Health Technology/Technician, A
Pipefitting/Pipefitter and Sprinkler Fitter, A
Welding Technology/Welder, A

BRIGHTWOOD COLLEGE, ARLINGTON CAMPUS

Computer Systems Networking and Telecommunications, A
Criminal Justice/Law Enforcement Administration, A

BRIGHTWOOD COLLEGE, BEAUMONT CAMPUS

Computer Systems Networking and Telecommunications, A
Criminal Justice/Law Enforcement Administration, A

BRIGHTWOOD COLLEGE, BROWNSVILLE CAMPUS

Medical Office Management/Administration, A

BRIGHTWOOD COLLEGE, CORPUS CHRISTI CAMPUS

Criminal Justice/Law Enforcement Administration, A
Medical Office Management/Administration, A

BRIGHTWOOD COLLEGE, DALLAS CAMPUS

Criminal Justice/Law Enforcement Administration, A
Legal Assistant/Paralegal, A

BRIGHTWOOD COLLEGE, EL PASO CAMPUS

Computer Systems Networking and Telecommunications, A

Criminal Justice/Law Enforcement Administration, A

BRIGHTWOOD COLLEGE, FORT WORTH CAMPUS

Criminal Justice/Law Enforcement Administration, A

BRIGHTWOOD COLLEGE, FRIENDSWOOD CAMPUS

Criminal Justice/Safety Studies, A

BRIGHTWOOD COLLEGE, HOUSTON CAMPUS

Criminal Justice/Safety Studies, A

BRIGHTWOOD COLLEGE, LAREDO CAMPUS

Criminal Justice/Law Enforcement Administration, A

BRIGHTWOOD COLLEGE, MCALLEN CAMPUS

Criminal Justice/Police Science, A
Medical Office Management/Administration, A

BRIGHTWOOD COLLEGE, SAN ANTONIO INGRAM CAMPUS

Health Information/Medical Records Technology/Technician, A
Legal Assistant/Paralegal, A

BRIGHTWOOD COLLEGE, SAN ANTONIO SAN PEDRO CAMPUS

Criminal Justice/Law Enforcement Administration, A
Medical Office Management/Administration, A

BROOKHAVEN COLLEGE

Accounting, A
Automobile/Automotive Mechanics Technology/Technician, A
Business Administration and Management, A
Business/Commerce, A
Cartography, A
Child Development, A
Communication Studies/Speech Communication and Rhetoric, A
Computer Engineering Technology/Technician, A
Computer Programming/Programmer, A
Computer Technology/Computer Systems Technology, A
Criminal Justice/Law Enforcement Administration, A
Design and Visual Communications, A
E-Commerce/Electronic Commerce, A
Emergency Medical Technology/Technician (EMT Paramedic), A
Executive Assistant/Executive Secretary, A
General Studies, A
Graphic Design, A
Humanities/Humanistic Studies, A
Information Science/Studies, A
Liberal Arts and Sciences Studies and Humanities, A
Marketing/Marketing Management, A
Music, A
Office Management and Supervision, A
Radiologic Technology/Science - Radiographer, A
Secondary Education and Teaching, A
Teacher Education, Multiple Levels, A

CEDAR VALLEY COLLEGE

Accounting, A
Automobile/Automotive Mechanics Technology/Technician, A
Business Administration and Management, A
Business/Commerce, A
Computer Programming/Programmer, A
Computer Systems Networking and Telecommunications, A
Criminal Justice/Safety Studies, A
Data Processing and Data Processing Technology/Technician, A
Education, A
Executive Assistant/Executive Secretary, A
General Studies, A
Graphic Design, A

Heating, Air Conditioning, Ventilation and Refrigeration Maintenance Technology/Technician, A
Marketing/Marketing Management, A
Multi-/Interdisciplinary Studies, A
Music Performance, A
Music Theory and Composition, A
Radio and Television Broadcasting Technology/Technician, A
Real Estate, A
Veterinary/Animal Health Technology/Technician and Veterinary Assistant, A

CENTER FOR ADVANCED LEGAL STUDIES

Legal Assistant/Paralegal, A

CENTRAL TEXAS COLLEGE

Administrative Assistant and Secretarial Science, A
Agriculture, A
Aircraft Powerplant Technology/Technician, A
Airline/Commercial/Professional Pilot and Flight Crew, A
Autobody/Collision and Repair Technology/Technician, A
Automobile/Automotive Mechanics Technology/Technician, A
Biology/Biological Sciences, A
Building/Property Maintenance and Management, A
Business Administration and Management, A
Chemistry, A
Child Care Provider/Assistant, A
Clinical/Medical Laboratory Technician, A
Clinical/Medical Social Work, A
Commercial and Advertising Art, A
Computer Technology/Computer Systems Technology, A
Computer and Information Systems Security, A
Criminal Justice/Police Science, A
Diesel Mechanics Technology/Technician, A
Drafting and Design Technology/Technician, A
Drama and Dramatics/Theatre Arts, A
Early Childhood Education and Teaching, A
Emergency Medical Technology/Technician (EMT Paramedic), A
Engineering, A
Environmental Sciences, A
Farm/Farm and Ranch Management, A
Fine/Studio Arts, A
Fire Services Administration, A
Foreign Languages and Literatures, A
General Studies, A
Geology/Earth Science, A
Graphic and Printing Equipment Operator Production, A
Health and Physical Education, A
Heating, Air Conditioning, Ventilation and Refrigeration Maintenance Technology/Technician, A
Hospitality Administration/Management, A
Journalism, A
Legal Assistant/Paralegal, A
Liberal Arts and Sciences Studies and Humanities, A
Marketing/Marketing Management, A
Mathematics, A
Music, A
Public Administration, A
Radio and Television, A
Restaurant/Food Services Management, A
Social Sciences, A
System, Networking, and LAN/WAN Management/Manager, A
Telecommunications Technology/Technician, A
Welding Technology/Welder, A

CISCO COLLEGE

Accounting, A
Agricultural Business and Management, A
Agriculture, A
Automobile/Automotive Mechanics Technology/Technician, A
Biology/Biological Sciences, A
Business Administration and Management, A
Business Teacher Education, A
Chemistry, A
Child Development, A

Clinical Laboratory Science/Medical Technology/Technologist, A
Computer Programming/Programmer, A
Computer Science, A
Consumer Merchandising/Retailing Management, A
Cosmetology/Cosmetologist, A
Criminal Justice/Police Science, A
Dairy Science, A
Data Processing and Data Processing Technology/Technician, A
Education, A
Electrical, Electronic and Communications Engineering Technology/Technician, A
Finance, A
Fire Science/Firefighting, A
History, A
Human Services, A
Kindergarten/PreSchool Education and Teaching, A
Marketing/Marketing Management, A
Mathematics, A
Physical Education Teaching and Coaching, A
Psychology, A
Real Estate, A
Welding Technology/Welder, A

CLARENDON COLLEGE

Accounting, A
Agribusiness, A
Agricultural Economics, A
Agriculture, A
Architecture, A
Art/Art Studies, General, A
Behavioral Sciences, A
Biology/Biological Sciences, A
Business Administration and Management, A
Chemistry, A
Computer and Information Sciences, A
Drama and Dramatics/Theatre Arts, A
Economics, A
Education, A
Electromechanical Technology/Electromechanical Engineering Technology, A
Elementary Education and Teaching, A
Engineering, A
English Language and Literature, A
Environmental Sciences, A
Farm/Farm and Ranch Management, A
Finance, A
General Studies, A
Health Services/Allied Health/Health Sciences, A
History, A
Horse Husbandry/Equine Science and Management, A
Kinesiology and Exercise Science, A
Liberal Arts and Sciences Studies and Humanities, A
Marketing/Marketing Management, A
Mass Communication/Media Studies, A
Mathematics, A
Music, A
Physical Education Teaching and Coaching, A
Physical Therapy/Therapist, A
Pre-Dentistry Studies, A
Pre-Law Studies, A
Pre-Medicine/Pre-Medical Studies, A
Psychology, A
Secondary Education and Teaching, A
Social Sciences, A
Social Work, A
Sociology, A

COASTAL BEND COLLEGE

Accounting, A
Administrative Assistant and Secretarial Science, A
Automobile/Automotive Mechanics Technology/Technician, A
Business Administration and Management, A
Child Development, A
Computer Programming, A
Computer Programming, Specific Applications, A
Computer Science, A
Computer and Information Sciences, A
Cosmetology/Cosmetologist, A
Criminal Justice/Law Enforcement Administration, A
Criminal Justice/Police Science, A
Dental Hygiene/Hygienist, A

Drafting and Design Technology/Technician, A
Information Technology, A
Liberal Arts and Sciences Studies and Humanities, A
Petroleum Technology/Technician, A
Welding Technology/Welder, A

COLLEGE OF BIBLICAL STUDIES–HOUSTON

Bible/Biblical Studies, AB
Christian Studies, B
Pastoral Counseling and Specialized Ministries, B
Pastoral Studies/Counseling, B

THE COLLEGE OF HEALTH CARE PROFESSIONS (HOUSTON)

Dental Assisting/Assistant, A
Diagnostic Medical Sonography/Sonographer and Ultrasound Technician, A
Massage Therapy/Therapeutic Massage, A
Medical Radiologic Technology/Science - Radiation Therapist, A
Medical/Clinical Assistant, A
Surgical Technology/Technologist, A

COLLEGE OF THE MAINLAND

Business/Commerce, A
CAD/CADD Drafting and/or Design Technology/Technician, A
Chemical Technology/Technician, A
Child Development, A
Computer and Information Sciences, A
Cosmetology, Barber/Styling, and Nail Instructor, A
Criminal Justice/Safety Studies, A
Drama and Dramatics/Theatre Arts, A
Early Childhood Education and Teaching, A
Fine/Studio Arts, A
Fire Protection and Safety Technology/Technician, A
General Studies, A
Health Information/Medical Records Technology/Technician, A
Junior High/Intermediate/Middle School Education and Teaching, A
Mathematics, A
Music, A
Natural Sciences, A
Occupational Safety and Health Technology/Technician, A
Pharmacy Technician/Assistant, A
Secondary Education and Teaching, A
Web Page, Digital/Multimedia and Information Resources Design, A

COLLIN COUNTY COMMUNITY COLLEGE DISTRICT

Administrative Assistant and Secretarial Science, A
Baking and Pastry Arts/Baker/Pastry Chef, A
Biology Technician/BioTechnology Laboratory Technician, A
Business Administration and Management, A
Business/Commerce, A
Cartography, A
Child Care Provider/Assistant, A
Child Development, A
Commercial and Advertising Art, A
Communication Studies/Speech Communication and Rhetoric, A
Computer Science, A
Computer and Information Sciences, A
Computer and Information Systems Security, A
Criminal Justice/Police Science, A
Culinary Arts/Chef Training, A
Dental Hygiene/Hygienist, A
Drafting and Design Technology/Technician, A
Early Childhood Education and Teaching, A
Electrical, Electronic and Communications Engineering Technology/Technician, A
Electroneurodiagnostic/Electroencephalographic Technology/Technologist, A
Emergency Medical Technology/Technician (EMT Paramedic), A
Engineering, A
Engineering Technology, A
Fire Protection and Safety Technology/Technician, A
Fire Science/Firefighting, A

Graphic Design, A
Health Information/Medical Records
    Technology/Technician, A
Hospitality Administration/Management, A
Illustration, A
Interior Design, A
Junior High/Intermediate/Middle School Education
    and Teaching, A
Legal Assistant/Paralegal, A
Liberal Arts and Sciences Studies and Humani-
    ties, A
Medical Insurance Coding Specialist/Coder, A
Music, A
Real Estate, A
Respiratory Care Therapy/Therapist, A
Secondary Education and Teaching, A
Sign Language Interpretation and Translation, A
Surgical Technology/Technologist, A
System Administration/Administrator, A
System, Networking, and LAN/WAN
    Management/Manager, A
Telecommunications Technology/Technician, A
Web Page, Digital/Multimedia and Information Re-
    sources Design, A

COMMONWEALTH INSTITUTE OF FU-NERAL SERVICE

Funeral Service and Mortuary Science, A

CONCORDIA UNIVERSITY TEXAS

Biology/Biological Sciences, B
Business Administration and Management, B
Business/Commerce, B
Computer Science, B
Criminal Justice/Law Enforcement Administration, B
Education, M
Elementary Education and Teaching, B
English Language and Literature, B
Environmental Sciences, B
Environmental Studies, B
General Studies, A
Health and Physical Education, B
History, B
Human Resources Development, B
Human Resources Management/Personnel Adminis-
    tration, B
Junior High/Intermediate/Middle School Education
    and Teaching, B
Kinesiology and Exercise Science, B
Liberal Arts and Sciences Studies and Humani-
    ties, AB
Mass Communication/Media Studies, B
Mathematics, B
Religious Education, B
Religious/Sacred Music, B
Secondary Education and Teaching, B
Social Sciences, AB

CRISWELL COLLEGE

Bible/Biblical Studies, AB
Jewish/Judaic Studies, M
Pastoral Studies/Counseling, M
Religion/Religious Studies, AB
Theology and Religious Vocations, M

CULINARY INSTITUTE LENOTRE

Baking and Pastry Arts/Baker/Pastry Chef, A
Culinary Arts/Chef Training, A
Restaurant, Culinary, and Catering
    Management/Manager, A

DALLAS BAPTIST UNIVERSITY

Accounting, BM
Art/Art Studies, General, B
Bible/Biblical Studies, AB
Biology Teacher Education, B
Biology/Biological Sciences, AB
Business Administration and Management, AB
Business Administration, Management and Opera-
    tions, M
Cell Biology and Anatomy, B
Communication Studies/Speech Communication
    and Rhetoric, B
Computer Science, B
Computer Teacher Education, B

Computer and Information Sciences, B
Conflict Resolution and Mediation/Peace Studies, M
Corporate and Organizational Communication, M
Counseling Psychology, M
Counselor Education/School Counseling and Guid-
    ance Services, MO
Criminal Justice/Safety Studies, B
Criminology, M
Curriculum and Instruction, M
Digital Communication and Media/Multimedia, B
Distance Education Development, M
Early Childhood Education and Teaching, M
East Asian Studies, M
Education, M
Educational Leadership and Administration, BM
Elementary Education and Teaching, BM
Engineering Management, M
English Language and Literature, B
English as a Second Language, M
English/Language Arts Teacher Education, B
Entrepreneurship/Entrepreneurial Studies, BM
Environmental Sciences, B
Experimental Psychology, M
Finance, B
Finance and Banking, M
Health Services Administration, M
Health and Physical Education, B
Health/Health Care Administration/Management, B
Higher Education/Higher Education Administra-
    tion, M
History, B
History Teacher Education, B
Hospitality Administration/Management, B
Human Resources Management and Services, M
Interdisciplinary Studies, M
International Business/Trade/Commerce, M
Kinesiology and Movement Studies, M
Liberal Arts and Sciences Studies and Humani-
    ties, A
Liberal Studies, M
Management, M
Management Information Systems and Ser-
    vices, BM
Management of Technology, M
Marketing, M
Marketing/Marketing Management, B
Mathematics, B
Mathematics Teacher Education, B
Missions/Missionary Studies and Missiology, BM
Multi-/Interdisciplinary Studies, B
Multilingual and Multicultural Education, M
Music, B
Music Performance, B
Music Teacher Education, B
Music Theory and Composition, B
Natural Sciences, B
Non-Profit/Public/Organizational Management, M
Organizational Management, M
Pastoral Studies/Counseling, MD
Philosophy, B
Physical Education Teaching and Coaching, B
Piano and Organ, B
Political Science and Government, B
Project Management, M
Psychology, B
Radio, Television, and Digital Communication, B
Reading Teacher Education, M
Religion/Religious Studies, M
Religious Education, ABM
Religious/Sacred Music, AB
Sacred Music, M
Science Teacher Education/General Science
    Teacher Education, B
Secondary Education and Teaching, M
Sociology, B
Special Education and Teaching, M
Speech Teacher Education, B
Sport and Fitness Administration/Management, B
Theology and Religious Vocations, BM
Voice and Opera, B

DALLAS CHRISTIAN COLLEGE

Bible/Biblical Studies, B
Business Administration and Management, AB
Education, B
Multi-/Interdisciplinary Studies, B

Psychology, B

DALLAS INSTITUTE OF FUNERAL SER-VICE

Funeral Service and Mortuary Science, A

DEL MAR COLLEGE

Accounting, A
Accounting Technology/Technician and Bookkeep-
    ing, A
Administrative Assistant and Secretarial Science, A
Architectural Engineering Technology/Technician, A
Art Teacher Education, A
Art/Art Studies, General, A
Automobile/Automotive Mechanics
    Technology/Technician, A
Biology/Biological Sciences, A
Building/Property Maintenance and Management, A
Business Administration and Management, A
Business Machine Repairer, A
Business/Commerce, A
Chemical Technology/Technician, A
Chemistry, A
Child Development, A
Clinical Laboratory Science/Medical
    Technology/Technologist, A
Clinical/Medical Laboratory Technician, A
Community Organization and Advocacy, A
Computer Programming, A
Computer Programming, Specific Applications, A
Computer Programming, Vendor/Product Certifica-
    tion, A
Computer Programming/Programmer, A
Computer Science, A
Computer Systems Networking and Telecommunica-
    tions, A
Computer Typography and Composition Equipment
    Operator, A
Computer and Information Sciences, A
Computer and Information Sciences and Support
    Services, A
Consumer Merchandising/Retailing Management, A
Cosmetology/Cosmetologist, A
Court Reporting/Court Reporter, A
Criminal Justice/Law Enforcement Administration, A
Criminal Justice/Police Science, A
Culinary Arts/Chef Training, A
Data Entry/Microcomputer Applications, A
Dental Hygiene/Hygienist, A
Design and Applied Arts, A
Diagnostic Medical Sonography/Sonographer and
    Ultrasound Technician, A
Drafting and Design Technology/Technician, A
Drama and Dramatics/Theatre Arts, A
E-Commerce/Electronic Commerce, A
Education, A
Electrical, Electronic and Communications Engineer-
    ing Technology/Technician, A
Elementary Education and Teaching, A
Emergency Medical Technology/Technician (EMT
    Paramedic), A
English Language and Literature, A
Finance, A
Fine/Studio Arts, A
Fire Protection and Safety Technology/Technician, A
Fire Science/Firefighting, A
General Office Occupations and Clerical Services, A
Geography, A
Geology/Earth Science, A
Health Information/Medical Records
    Technology/Technician, A
Health Teacher Education, A
Heavy Equipment Maintenance
    Technology/Technician, A
History, A
Hotel/Motel Administration/Management, A
Industrial Radiologic Technology/Technician, A
Information Science/Studies, A
Information Technology, A
Journalism, A
Kindergarten/PreSchool Education and Teaching, A
Law and Legal Studies, A
Legal Administrative Assistant/Secretary, A
Liberal Arts and Sciences Studies and Humani-
    ties, A
Machine Tool Technology/Machinist, A

Management Information Systems and Services, A
Mathematics, A
Medical Administrative Assistant/Secretary, A
Medical Radiologic Technology/Science - Radiation Therapist, A
Mental Health Counseling/Counselor, A
Music, A
Music Teacher Education, A
Nuclear Medical Technology/Technologist, A
Occupational Safety and Health Technology/Technician, A
Occupational Therapist Assistant, A
Parks, Recreation, Leisure and Fitness Studies, A
Physical Education Teaching and Coaching, A
Physics, A
Political Science and Government, A
Psychology, A
Public Administration, A
Public Policy Analysis, A
Radio and Television, A
Real Estate, A
Respiratory Care Therapy/Therapist, A
Sign Language Interpretation and Translation, A
Social Work, A
Sociology, A
Special Products Marketing Operations, A
System Administration/Administrator, A
Trade and Industrial Teacher Education, A
Transportation/Transportation Management, A
Voice and Opera, A
Web Page, Digital/Multimedia and Information Resources Design, A
Web/Multimedia Management and Webmaster, A
Welding Technology/Welder, A
Word Processing, A

DEVRY UNIVERSITY (AUSTIN)

Business Administration and Management, B
Business Administration, Management and Operations, B
Business/Commerce, B
Computer Engineering Technology/Technician, B
Computer Software Engineering, B
Computer Systems Analysis/Analyst, B
Computer Systems Networking and Telecommunications, AB
Electrical, Electronic and Communications Engineering Technology/Technician, B
Web Page, Digital/Multimedia and Information Resources Design, AB

DEVRY UNIVERSITY (IRVING)

Biomedical Technology/Technician, B
Business Administration and Management, B
Business Administration, Management and Operations, BM
Business/Commerce, B
Computer Engineering Technology/Technician, B
Computer Software Engineering, B
Computer Systems Analysis/Analyst, B
Computer Systems Networking and Telecommunications, AB
Electrical, Electronic and Communications Engineering Technology/Technician, AB
Health Information/Medical Records Technology/Technician, A
Web Page, Digital/Multimedia and Information Resources Design, AB

DEVRY UNIVERSITY (SAN ANTONIO)

Business Administration and Management, B
Business Administration, Management and Operations, B
Business/Commerce, B
Computer Systems Analysis/Analyst, B
Computer Systems Networking and Telecommunications, AB
Web Page, Digital/Multimedia and Information Resources Design, AB

EAST TEXAS BAPTIST UNIVERSITY

Athletic Training and Sports Medicine, B
Bible/Biblical Studies, B
Biology Teacher Education, B
Biology/Biological Sciences, B
Business/Commerce, B

Chemistry, B
Counseling Psychology, M
Criminal Justice/Law Enforcement Administration, B
Curriculum and Instruction, M
Drama and Dance Teacher Education, B
Drama and Dramatics/Theatre Arts, B
Education, BM
Elementary Education and Teaching, B
English Language and Literature, B
English/Language Arts Teacher Education, B
Health and Physical Education, B
History, B
History Teacher Education, B
International/Global Studies, B
Kinesiology and Exercise Science, B
Mass Communication/Media Studies, B
Mathematics, B
Mathematics Teacher Education, B
Missions/Missionary Studies and Missiology, B
Multi-/Interdisciplinary Studies, B
Music, B
Music Teacher Education, B
Pastoral Studies/Counseling, BM
Physical Education Teaching and Coaching, BM
Piano and Organ, B
Political Science and Government, B
Psychology, B
Religion/Religious Studies, BM
Religious/Sacred Music, B
Social Studies Teacher Education, B
Sociology, B
Spanish Language Teacher Education, B
Spanish Language and Literature, B
Speech Teacher Education, B
Voice and Opera, B
Youth Ministry, B

EASTFIELD COLLEGE

Accounting, A
Autobody/Collision and Repair Technology/Technician, A
Automobile/Automotive Mechanics Technology/Technician, A
Business Administration and Management, A
Business/Commerce, A
Child Care and Support Services Management, A
Communication Studies/Speech Communication and Rhetoric, A
Computer Engineering Technology/Technician, A
Computer Hardware Engineering, A
Computer Programming, A
Computer Programming/Programmer, A
Computer Systems Networking and Telecommunications, A
Computer and Information Sciences, A
Computer/Information Technology Services Administration and Management, A
Criminal Justice/Safety Studies, A
Data Entry/Microcomputer Applications, A
Data Processing and Data Processing Technology/Technician, A
Drafting and Design Technology/Technician, A
E-Commerce/Electronic Commerce, A
Education, A
Electrical, Electronic and Communications Engineering Technology/Technician, A
Electrical/Electronics Drafting and Electrical/Electronics CAD/CADD, A
Executive Assistant/Executive Secretary, A
Graphic and Printing Equipment Operator Production, A
Heating, Air Conditioning, Ventilation and Refrigeration Maintenance Technology/Technician, A
Legal Administrative Assistant/Secretary, A
Liberal Arts and Sciences Studies and Humanities, A
Multi-/Interdisciplinary Studies, A
Music, A
Psychiatric/Mental Health Services Technician, A
Sign Language Interpretation and Translation, A
Social Work, A
Substance Abuse/Addiction Counseling, A
System Administration/Administrator, A

Word Processing, A

EL CENTRO COLLEGE

Accounting, A
Apparel and Accessories Marketing Operations, A
Baking and Pastry Arts/Baker/Pastry Chef, A
BioTechnology, A
Business Administration and Management, A
Business/Commerce, A
Business/Office Automation/Technology/Data Entry, A
Cardiovascular Technology/Technologist, A
Clinical/Medical Laboratory Technician, A
Computer Programming/Programmer, A
Computer Science, A
Computer and Information Systems Security, A
Computer/Information Technology Services Administration and Management, A
Culinary Arts/Chef Training, A
Data Processing and Data Processing Technology/Technician, A
Diagnostic Medical Sonography/Sonographer and Ultrasound Technician, A
Emergency Medical Technology/Technician (EMT Paramedic), A
Executive Assistant/Executive Secretary, A
Fashion/Apparel Design, A
General Office Occupations and Clerical Services, A
Health Information/Medical Records Administration/Administrator, A
Information Science/Studies, A
Interior Design, A
Legal Administrative Assistant/Secretary, A
Legal Assistant/Paralegal, A
Medical Radiologic Technology/Science - Radiation Therapist, A
Medical Transcription/Transcriptionist, A
Medical/Clinical Assistant, A
Peace Studies and Conflict Resolution, A
Radiologic Technology/Science - Radiographer, A
Respiratory Care Therapy/Therapist, A
Special Products Marketing Operations, A
Surgical Technology/Technologist, A
Teacher Assistant/Aide, A
Web Page, Digital/Multimedia and Information Resources Design, A

EL PASO COMMUNITY COLLEGE

Accounting, A
Administrative Assistant and Secretarial Science, A
Adult Development and Aging, A
Automobile/Automotive Mechanics Technology/Technician, A
Business Administration and Management, A
Business/Commerce, A
Business/Office Automation/Technology/Data Entry, A
Child Care and Support Services Management, A
Child Development, A
Cinematography and Film/Video Production, A
Clinical/Medical Laboratory Technician, A
Commercial and Advertising Art, A
Communication Studies/Speech Communication and Rhetoric, A
Computer Programming/Programmer, A
Computer and Information Sciences, A
Corrections, A
Corrections and Criminal Justice, A
Court Reporting/Court Reporter, A
Criminal Justice/Police Science, A
Criminal Justice/Safety Studies, A
Culinary Arts/Chef Training, A
Dental Assisting/Assistant, A
Dental Hygiene/Hygienist, A
Diagnostic Medical Sonography/Sonographer and Ultrasound Technician, A
Dietetics/Dieticians, A
Drafting and Design Technology/Technician, A
Electrical, Electronic and Communications Engineering Technology/Technician, A
Emergency Medical Technology/Technician (EMT Paramedic), A
Engineering, A
Environmental Engineering Technology/Environmental Technology, A
Fashion/Apparel Design, A

Fire Protection and Safety Technology/Technician, A
General Studies, A
Health Information/Medical Records
   Administration/Administrator, A
Heating, Air Conditioning, Ventilation and Refrigera-
   tion Maintenance Technology/Technician, A
Hotel/Motel Administration/Management, A
Institutional Food Workers, A
Interior Design, A
International Business/Trade/Commerce, A
Junior High/Intermediate/Middle School Education
   and Teaching, A
Kindergarten/PreSchool Education and Teaching, A
Legal Assistant/Paralegal, A
Liberal Arts and Sciences Studies and Humani-
   ties, A
Machine Tool Technology/Machinist, A
Medical Radiologic Technology/Science - Radiation
   Therapist, A
Medical/Clinical Assistant, A
Multi-/Interdisciplinary Studies, A
Music, A
Opticianry/Ophthalmic Dispensing Optician, A
Optometric Technician/Assistant, A
Pharmacy Technician/Assistant, A
Physical Therapist Assistant, A
Plastics Engineering Technology/Technician, A
Psychiatric/Mental Health Services Technician, A
Radiologic Technology/Science - Radiographer, A
Real Estate, A
Respiratory Care Therapy/Therapist, A
Security and Protective Services, A
Sign Language Interpretation and Translation, A
Social Work, A
Substance Abuse/Addiction Counseling, A
Surgical Technology/Technologist, A
System, Networking, and LAN/WAN
   Management/Manager, A
Tourism and Travel Services Management, A

EVEREST COLLEGE (ARLINGTON)

Business Administration and Management, A
Criminal Justice/Safety Studies, A
Medical/Clinical Assistant, A

FRANK PHILLIPS COLLEGE

Accounting, A
Agricultural Business and Management, A
Animal/Livestock Husbandry and Production, A
Biology/Biological Sciences, A
Business Administration and Management, A
Business/Commerce, A
Chemistry, A
Elementary Education and Teaching, A
English Language and Literature, A
Farm/Farm and Ranch Management, A
General Studies, A
History, A
Industrial Technology/Technician, A
Liberal Arts and Sciences Studies and Humani-
   ties, A
Mathematics, A
Physics, A
Psychology, A
Secondary Education and Teaching, A
Sociology, A
Visual and Performing Arts, A

GALVESTON COLLEGE

Administrative Assistant and Secretarial Science, A
Behavioral Sciences, A
Biological and Physical Sciences, A
Business Administration and Management, A
Computer Science, A
Criminal Justice/Safety Studies, A
Culinary Arts/Chef Training, A
Data Entry/Microcomputer Applications, A
Drama and Dramatics/Theatre Arts, A
Education, A
Electromechanical Technology/Electromechanical
   Engineering Technology, A
Emergency Medical Technology/Technician (EMT
   Paramedic), A
English Language and Literature, A
General Studies, A

Heating, Air Conditioning, Ventilation and Refrigera-
   tion Maintenance Technology/Technician, A
History, A
Humanities/Humanistic Studies, A
Information Technology, A
Liberal Arts and Sciences Studies and Humani-
   ties, A
Mathematics, A
Medical Administrative Assistant/Secretary, A
Medical Radiologic Technology/Science - Radiation
   Therapist, A
Music, A
Natural Sciences, A
Nuclear Medical Technology/Technologist, A
Physical Education Teaching and Coaching, A
Radiologic Technology/Science - Radiographer, A
Social Sciences, A
Social Work, A
Welding Technology/Welder, A
Word Processing, A

GRAYSON COLLEGE

Accounting, A
Art/Art Studies, General, A
Autobody/Collision and Repair
   Technology/Technician, A
Biology/Biological Sciences, A
Business Administration and Management, A
Business/Office Automation/Technology/Data En-
   try, A
Chemistry, A
Clinical/Medical Laboratory Technician, A
Computer Programming/Programmer, A
Computer Technology/Computer Systems Technol-
   ogy, A
Cooking and Related Culinary Arts, A
Criminal Justice/Safety Studies, A
Data Processing and Data Processing
   Technology/Technician, A
Dental Assisting/Assistant, A
Drafting and Design Technology/Technician, A
Drama and Dramatics/Theatre Arts, A
Early Childhood Education and Teaching, A
Electrical, Electronic and Communications Engineer-
   ing Technology/Technician, A
Electrician, A
Elementary Education and Teaching, A
Emergency Medical Technology/Technician (EMT
   Paramedic), A
Engineering, A
English Language and Literature, A
Food Science, A
Forensic Science and Technology, A
Geology/Earth Science, A
Heating, Air Conditioning, Ventilation and Refrigera-
   tion Maintenance Technology/Technician, A
Industrial Mechanics and Maintenance Technol-
   ogy, A
Junior High/Intermediate/Middle School Education
   and Teaching, A
Kindergarten/PreSchool Education and Teaching, A
Liberal Arts and Sciences Studies and Humani-
   ties, A
Machine Tool Technology/Machinist, A
Mathematics, A
Music, A
Physical Education Teaching and Coaching, A
Physics, A
Psychology, A
Radiologic Technology/Science - Radiographer, A
Secondary Education and Teaching, A
Sociology, A
Spanish Language and Literature, A
Substance Abuse/Addiction Counseling, A
Welding Technology/Welder, A

HALLMARK UNIVERSITY

Aircraft Powerplant Technology/Technician, A
Airframe Mechanics and Aircraft Maintenance
   Technology/Technician, A
Aviation/Airway Management and Operations, B
Avionics Maintenance Technology/Technician, A
Business Administration and Management, AB
Business Administration, Management and Opera-
   tions, BM

Business/Office Automation/Technology/Data En-
   try, A
Data Processing and Data Processing
   Technology/Technician, A
Electrical, Electronic and Communications Engineer-
   ing Technology/Technician, A
Information Technology, A
International Business/Trade/Commerce, M
Medical Administrative Assistant/Secretary, A
Medical/Clinical Assistant, A
System, Networking, and LAN/WAN
   Management/Manager, B

HARDIN-SIMMONS UNIVERSITY

Accounting, B
Art Teacher Education, B
Athletic Training and Sports Medicine, B
Audiology/Audiologist and Speech-Language
   Pathology/Pathologist, B
Bible/Biblical Studies, B
Biochemistry, Biophysics and Molecular Biology, B
Biology/Biological Sciences, B
Business Administration and Management, B
Business Administration, Management and Opera-
   tions, M
Business Teacher Education, B
Chemistry, B
Christian Studies, B
Communication Studies/Speech Communication
   and Rhetoric, B
Composition, M
Computer Programming/Programmer, B
Counseling Psychology, M
Counselor Education/School Counseling and Guid-
   ance Services, M
Criminal Justice/Safety Studies, B
Drama and Dance Teacher Education, B
Drama and Dramatics/Theatre Arts, B
Early Childhood Education and Teaching, B
Economics, B
Education, BMD
Education/Teaching of the Gifted and Talented, M
Educational Leadership and Administration, D
English, M
English Language and Literature, B
English/Language Arts Teacher Education, B
Environmental Policy and Resource Manage-
   ment, M
Environmental Sciences, B
Finance, B
Fine/Studio Arts, B
Geology/Earth Science, B
Graphic Design, B
History, BM
History Teacher Education, B
Human Services, B
Kinesiology and Exercise Science, B
Kinesiology and Movement Studies, M
Management Information Systems and Services, B
Management Science, B
Marketing/Marketing Management, B
Marriage and Family Therapy/Counseling, M
Maternal/Child Health and Neonatal
   Nurse/Nursing, M
Mathematics, BM
Mathematics Teacher Education, B
Music, BM
Music Performance, B
Music Teacher Education, BM
Music Theory and Composition, BM
Non-Profit/Public/Organizational Management, B
Nursing, M
Nursing - Advanced Practice, M
Pastoral Studies/Counseling, MD
Performance, M
Philosophy, B
Physical Education Teaching and Coaching, B
Physical Therapy/Therapist, D
Physics, B
Piano and Organ, B
Political Science and Government, B
Pre-Nursing Studies, B
Psychology, BM
Reading Teacher Education, M
Recreation and Park Management, M
Religion/Religious Studies, M

Religious/Sacred Music, B
Sacred Music, M
Science Teacher Education/General Science
 Teacher Education, BMD
Social Studies Teacher Education, B
Social Work, B
Sociology, B
Spanish Language Teacher Education, B
Spanish Language and Literature, B
Speech Teacher Education, B
Sport and Fitness Administration/Management, BM
Theological and Ministerial Studies, B
Theology and Religious Vocations, MD
Theology/Theological Studies, B
Violin, Viola, Guitar and Other Stringed Instru-
 ments, B
Voice and Opera, B

HILL COLLEGE

Accounting, A
Administrative Assistant and Secretarial Science, A
Agricultural Business and Management, A
Agriculture, A
Art/Art Studies, General, A
Autobody/Collision and Repair
 Technology/Technician, A
Automobile/Automotive Mechanics
 Technology/Technician, A
Behavioral Sciences, A
Biology/Biological Sciences, A
Business Administration and Management, A
Business/Commerce, A
Chemistry, A
Child Care Provider/Assistant, A
Commercial and Advertising Art, A
Communication Studies/Speech Communication
 and Rhetoric, A
Computer Programming/Programmer, A
Computer and Information Sciences, A
Corrections, A
Corrections and Criminal Justice, A
Cosmetology, Barber/Styling, and Nail Instructor, A
Cosmetology/Cosmetologist, A
Criminal Justice/Law Enforcement Administration, A
Drafting and Design Technology/Technician, A
Drama and Dramatics/Theatre Arts, A
Economics, A
Elementary Education and Teaching, A
Emergency Medical Technology/Technician (EMT
 Paramedic), A
Engineering, A
English Language and Literature, A
Family and Consumer Sciences/Human Sciences, A
Fire Science/Firefighting, A
Foreign Languages and Literatures, A
General Studies, A
Geology/Earth Science, A
Health and Physical Education, A
Heating, Air Conditioning, Ventilation and Refrigera-
 tion Maintenance Technology/Technician, A
History, A
Industrial Electronics Technology/Technician, A
Industrial Mechanics and Maintenance Technol-
 ogy, A
Mathematics, A
Music, A
Philosophy, A
Physical Therapy/Therapist, A
Physics, A
Political Science and Government, A
Pre-Dentistry Studies, A
Pre-Law Studies, A
Pre-Medicine/Pre-Medical Studies, A
Pre-Nursing Studies, A
Pre-Pharmacy Studies, A
Pre-Veterinary Studies, A
Psychology, A
Religion/Religious Studies, A
Secondary Education and Teaching, A
Security and Loss Prevention Services, A
Sociology, A
Special Education and Teaching, A
System, Networking, and LAN/WAN
 Management/Manager, A
Teacher Assistant/Aide, A

Welding Technology/Welder, A

HOUSTON BAPTIST UNIVERSITY

Accounting, BM
Ancient Near Eastern and Biblical Languages, Lit-
 eratures and Linguistics, B
Art Teacher Education, B
Art Therapy/Therapist, B
Athletic Training and Sports Medicine, B
Biochemistry, Biophysics and Molecular Biology, B
Bioethics/Medical Ethics, B
Biology Teacher Education, B
Biology/Biological Sciences, B
Business Administration and Management, B
Chemistry, B
Christian Studies, B
Classics and Classical Languages, Litera-
 tures, and Linguistics, B
Communication and Media Studies, B
Counseling Psychology, M
Counselor Education/School Counseling and Guid-
 ance Services, M
Curriculum and Instruction, M
Design and Applied Arts, B
Education, M
Educational Administration and Supervision, M
Educational Measurement and Evaluation, M
English Language and Literature, B
English as a Second Language, M
English/Language Arts Teacher Education, B
Film/Cinema Studies, B
Finance, B
Fine Arts and Art Studies, M
Fine/Studio Arts, B
History Teacher Education, B
Human Resources Management and Services, M
International Business/Trade/Commerce, BM
Journalism, B
Kinesiology and Exercise Science, B
Law and Legal Studies, B
Liberal Arts and Sciences Studies and Humani-
 ties, B
Liberal Studies, M
Management, M
Marketing/Marketing Management, B
Mathematics Teacher Education, B
Music, B
Music Teacher Education, B
Pastoral Studies/Counseling, M
Philosophy, BM
Physical Education Teaching and Coaching, B
Physics, B
Piano and Organ, B
Political Science and Government, B
Psychology, BM
Reading Teacher Education, M
Science Teacher Education/General Science
 Teacher Education, B
Social Studies Teacher Education, B
Spanish Language Teacher Education, B
Spanish Language and Literature, B
Special Education and Teaching, B
Speech Teacher Education, B
Theology and Religious Vocations, M
Voice and Opera, B

HOUSTON COMMUNITY COLLEGE

Accounting, A
Animation, Interactive Technology, Video Graphics
 and Special Effects, A
Anthropology, A
Applied Horticulture/Horticultural Operations, A
Automobile/Automotive Mechanics
 Technology/Technician, A
Banking and Financial Support Services, A
Biology Technician/BioTechnology Laboratory Tech-
 nician, A
Biology/Biological Sciences, A
Business Administration and Management, A
Business/Corporate Communications, A
Business/Office Automation/Technology/Data En-
 try, A
Cardiovascular Technology/Technologist, A
Chemical Technology/Technician, A
Chemistry, A
Child Development, A

Cinematography and Film/Video Production, A
Clinical/Medical Laboratory Science and Allied Pro-
 fessions, A
Clinical/Medical Laboratory Technician, A
Commercial Photography, A
Communication Studies/Speech Communication
 and Rhetoric, A
Computer Engineering Technology/Technician, A
Computer Programming, Specific Applications, A
Computer Programming/Programmer, A
Computer Science, A
Computer Systems Networking and Telecommunica-
 tions, A
Construction Engineering Technology/Technician, A
Cosmetology/Cosmetologist, A
Court Reporting/Court Reporter, A
Criminal Justice/Police Science, A
Culinary Arts/Chef Training, A
Drafting and Design Technology/Technician, A
Early Childhood Education and Teaching, A
Emergency Medical Technology/Technician (EMT
 Paramedic), A
Energy Management and Systems
 Technology/Technician, A
Engineering Science, A
English Language and Literature, A
Fashion Merchandising, A
Fashion/Apparel Design, A
Fine/Studio Arts, A
Fire Protection and Safety Technology/Technician, A
General Studies, A
Health Information/Medical Records
 Technology/Technician, A
Health Services/Allied Health/Health Sciences, A
Health and Physical Education, A
Histologic Technician, A
Hotel/Motel Administration/Management, A
Instrumentation Technology/Technician, A
Interior Design, A
International Business/Trade/Commerce, A
Legal Assistant/Paralegal, A
Logistics and Materials Management, A
Manufacturing Technology/Technician, A
Marketing/Marketing Management, A
Mathematics, A
Music Performance, A
Music Theory and Composition, A
Nuclear Medical Technology/Technologist, A
Occupational Safety and Health
 Technology/Technician, A
Occupational Therapist Assistant, A
Petroleum Technology/Technician, A
Physical Therapist Assistant, A
Physics, A
Prepress/Desktop Publishing and Digital Imaging
 Design, A
Psychiatric/Mental Health Services Technician, A
Public Administration, A
Radio and Television Broadcasting
 Technology/Technician, A
Radiologic Technology/Science - Radiographer, A
Real Estate, A
Respiratory Care Therapy/Therapist, A
Secondary Education and Teaching, A
Sign Language Interpretation and Translation, A
System Administration/Administrator, A
Teacher Education, Multiple Levels, A
Tourism and Travel Services Management, A
Turf and Turfgrass Management, A

HOWARD COLLEGE

Accounting, A
Administrative Assistant and Secretarial Science, A
Agriculture, A
Art/Art Studies, General, A
Automobile/Automotive Mechanics
 Technology/Technician, A
Behavioral Sciences, A
Biology/Biological Sciences, A
Business Administration and Management, A
Business/Commerce, A
Chemistry, A
Chemistry Teacher Education, A
Child Development, A
Communication Studies/Speech Communication
 and Rhetoric, A

Computer Programming/Programmer, A
Computer Science, A
Computer and Information Sciences, A
Cosmetology/Cosmetologist, A
Criminal Justice/Law Enforcement Administration, A
Criminal Justice/Police Science, A
Criminal Justice/Safety Studies, A
Dental Hygiene/Hygienist, A
Drafting and Design Technology/Technician, A
Drama and Dance Teacher Education, A
Drama and Dramatics/Theatre Arts, A
Education, A
Elementary Education and Teaching, A
English Language and Literature, A
Finance, A
Foreign Language Teacher Education, A
General Studies, A
Health Information/Medical Records Administration/Administrator, A
Health Information/Medical Records Technology/Technician, A
Health Occupations Teacher Education, A
Health and Physical Education, A
History, A
History Teacher Education, A
Industrial Production Technologies/Technicians, A
Junior High/Intermediate/Middle School Education and Teaching, A
Mathematics, A
Mathematics Teacher Education, A
Music, A
Music Teacher Education, A
Ornamental Horticulture, A
Physical Education Teaching and Coaching, A
Physics Teacher Education, A
Prepress/Desktop Publishing and Digital Imaging Design, A
Psychology, A
Radiologic Technology/Science - Radiographer, A
Reading Teacher Education, A
Respiratory Care Therapy/Therapist, A
Secondary Education and Teaching, A
Sign Language Interpretation and Translation, A
Social Science Teacher Education, A
Social Sciences, A
Social Studies Teacher Education, A
Sociology, A
Spanish Language and Literature, A
Special Education and Teaching, A
Speech Teacher Education, A
Substance Abuse/Addiction Counseling, A
Technical Teacher Education, A
Trade and Industrial Teacher Education, A
Web/Multimedia Management and Webmaster, A

HOWARD PAYNE UNIVERSITY

Accounting, B
American History (United States), B
Ancient Near Eastern and Biblical Languages, Literatures, and Linguistics, B
Art Teacher Education, B
Art/Art Studies, General, B
Athletic Training and Sports Medicine, B
Bible/Biblical Studies, AB
Biology Teacher Education, B
Biology/Biological Sciences, B
Business Administration and Management, B
Business Administration, Management and Operations, BM
Business Teacher Education, B
Business, Management, Marketing, and Related Support Services, B
Business/Commerce, B
Chemistry, B
Communication Studies/Speech Communication and Rhetoric, B
Computer Teacher Education, B
Computer and Information Sciences, B
Criminology, B
Digital Communication and Media/Multimedia, B
Drama and Dance Teacher Education, B
Drama and Dramatics/Theatre Arts, B
Educational Leadership and Administration, M
Elementary Education and Teaching, B
English Language and Literature, B
English/Language Arts Teacher Education, B

European History, B
Finance, B
Fine/Studio Arts, B
General Studies, B
Health Services/Allied Health/Health Sciences, A
Health and Physical Education, B
History, B
History Teacher Education, B
Human Development and Family Studies, B
International Relations and Affairs, B
Liberal Arts and Sciences Studies and Humanities, B
Management Information Systems and Services, B
Marketing/Marketing Management, B
Mathematics, B
Mathematics Teacher Education, B
Multi-/Interdisciplinary Studies, B
Music Performance, B
Music Teacher Education, B
Organizational Communication, B
Pastoral Studies/Counseling, M
Philosophy, B
Physical Education Teaching and Coaching, B
Piano and Organ, B
Political Science and Government, B
Pre-Law Studies, B
Psychology, B
Public Policy Analysis, B
Religious Education, B
Religious/Sacred Music, B
Social Sciences, B
Social Studies Teacher Education, B
Social Work, B
Sociology, B
Spanish Language Teacher Education, B
Spanish Language and Literature, B
Speech Teacher Education, B
Sport and Fitness Administration/Management, B
Theological and Ministerial Studies, B
Theology and Religious Vocations, M
Theology/Theological Studies, B
Voice and Opera, B
Youth Ministry, B

HUSTON-TILLOTSON UNIVERSITY

Accounting, B
Biology/Biological Sciences, B
Business Administration and Management, B
Chemistry, B
Computer Science, B
Computer and Information Sciences, B
Criminal Justice/Law Enforcement Administration, B
Criminal Justice/Safety Studies, B
Education, B
Elementary Education and Teaching, B
English Language and Literature, B
Environmental Studies, B
History, B
Kinesiology and Exercise Science, B
Liberal Arts and Sciences Studies and Humanities, A
Mass Communication/Media Studies, B
Mathematics, B
Music, B
Physical Education Teaching and Coaching, B
Political Science and Government, B
Psychology, B
Secondary Education and Teaching, B
Social Studies Teacher Education, B
Sociology, B
Teacher Education, Multiple Levels, B

JACKSONVILLE COLLEGE

Liberal Arts and Sciences Studies and Humanities, A

JARVIS CHRISTIAN COLLEGE

Biology/Biological Sciences, B
Business Administration and Management, AB
Chemistry, B
Criminal Justice/Safety Studies, AB
Elementary Education and Teaching, B
English Language and Literature, B
General Studies, A
Health and Physical Education, B
History, B

Kindergarten/PreSchool Education and Teaching, B
Mathematics, B
Music Teacher Education, B
Physical Education Teaching and Coaching, B
Religion/Religious Studies, AB
Secondary Education and Teaching, B
Social Work, B
Sociology, B

KD CONSERVATORY COLLEGE OF FILM AND DRAMATIC ARTS

Acting, A
Film/Cinema Studies, A

KILGORE COLLEGE

Accounting Technology/Technician and Bookkeeping, A
Aerospace, Aeronautical and Astronautical Engineering, A
Agriculture, A
Architecture, A
Art/Art Studies, General, A
Autobody/Collision and Repair Technology/Technician, A
Automobile/Automotive Mechanics Technology/Technician, A
Biological and Physical Sciences, A
Business Administration and Management, A
Business/Commerce, A
Chemical Engineering, A
Chemistry, A
Child Care Provider/Assistant, A
Child Care and Support Services Management, A
Civil Engineering, A
Commercial Photography, A
Commercial and Advertising Art, A
Computer Programming/Programmer, A
Computer Systems Networking and Telecommunications, A
Computer and Information Sciences, A
Criminal Justice/Law Enforcement Administration, A
Dance, A
Diesel Mechanics Technology/Technician, A
Drafting and Design Technology/Technician, A
Drama and Dramatics/Theatre Arts, A
Electrical, Electronic and Communications Engineering Technology/Technician, A
Elementary Education and Teaching, A
Emergency Medical Technology/Technician (EMT Paramedic), A
English Language and Literature, A
Executive Assistant/Executive Secretary, A
General Studies, A
Geology/Earth Science, A
Health Teacher Education, A
Heating, Air Conditioning, Ventilation and Refrigeration Maintenance Technology/Technician, A
Journalism, A
Legal Assistant/Paralegal, A
Mathematics, A
Mechanical Engineering, A
Medical Radiologic Technology/Science - Radiation Therapist, A
Metallurgical Technology/Technician, A
Music, A
Occupational Safety and Health Technology/Technician, A
Operations Management and Supervision, A
Petroleum Engineering, A
Physical Education Teaching and Coaching, A
Physical Therapist Assistant, A
Physical Therapy/Therapist, A
Physics, A
Pre-Dentistry Studies, A
Pre-Law Studies, A
Pre-Medicine/Pre-Medical Studies, A
Pre-Pharmacy Studies, A
Pre-Veterinary Studies, A
Psychology, A
Radiologic Technology/Science - Radiographer, A
Religion/Religious Studies, A
Social Sciences, A
Surgical Technology/Technologist, A

Welding Technology/Welder, A

THE KING'S UNIVERSITY

Pastoral Studies/Counseling, MO
Theology and Religious Vocations, MDO
Theology/Theological Studies, AB

LAMAR INSTITUTE OF TECHNOLOGY

Accounting Technology/Technician and Bookkeeping, A
Administrative Assistant and Secretarial Science, A
Business Administration, Management and Operations, A
Chemical Technology/Technician, A
Child Care Provider/Assistant, A
Child Care and Support Services Management, A
Computer Technology/Computer Systems Technology, A
Computer and Information Sciences, A
Dental Hygiene/Hygienist, A
Diagnostic Medical Sonography/Sonographer and Ultrasound Technician, A
Diesel Mechanics Technology/Technician, A
Drafting and Design Technology/Technician, A
Emergency Medical Technology/Technician (EMT Paramedic), A
Fire Protection and Safety Technology/Technician, A
Health Information/Medical Records Technology/Technician, A
Heating, Air Conditioning and Refrigeration Technology/Technician, A
Industrial Mechanics and Maintenance Technology, A
Institutional Food Workers, A
Instrumentation Technology/Technician, A
Machine Tool Technology/Machinist, A
Medical Radiologic Technology/Science - Radiation Therapist, A
Occupational Safety and Health Technology/Technician, A
Public Administration, A
Real Estate, A
Respiratory Care Therapy/Therapist, A
Welding Technology/Welder, A

LAMAR STATE COLLEGE–ORANGE

Accounting, A
Administrative Assistant and Secretarial Science, A
Architectural Engineering Technology/Technician, A
Business Administration and Management, A
Clinical/Medical Laboratory Technician, A
Comparative Literature, A
Computer Science, A
Data Processing and Data Processing Technology/Technician, A
Environmental Studies, A
Information Science/Studies, A
Liberal Arts and Sciences Studies and Humanities, A
Mass Communication/Media Studies, A
Mathematics, A
Real Estate, A
Social Sciences, A

LAMAR STATE COLLEGE–PORT ARTHUR

Accounting Technology/Technician and Bookkeeping, A
Administrative Assistant and Secretarial Science, A
Automobile/Automotive Mechanics Technology/Technician, A
Business Administration and Management, A
Business/Commerce, A
Computer Programming/Programmer, A
Computer Systems Networking and Telecommunications, A
Cosmetology/Cosmetologist, A
Criminal Justice/Safety Studies, A
Electrical, Electronic and Communications Engineering Technology/Technician, A
Family and Consumer Sciences/Human Sciences, A
General Studies, A
Health and Physical Education, A
Heating, Air Conditioning, Ventilation and Refrigeration Maintenance Technology/Technician, A

Law and Legal Studies, A
Legal Administrative Assistant/Secretary, A
Legal Assistant/Paralegal, A
Liberal Arts and Sciences Studies and Humanities, A
Medical Administrative Assistant/Secretary, A
Multi-/Interdisciplinary Studies, A
Music, A
Occupational Safety and Health Technology/Technician, A
Social Sciences, A
Substance Abuse/Addiction Counseling, A
Surgical Technology/Technologist, A

LAMAR UNIVERSITY

Accounting, BM
Advertising, B
American Sign Language (ASL), B
Apparel and Textiles, B
Biochemistry, B
Biological and Biomedical Sciences, M
Biology/Biological Sciences, B
Business Administration, Management and Operations, M
Business/Commerce, B
Business/Managerial Economics, B
Chemical Engineering, BD
Chemistry, BM
Civil Engineering, B
Clinical Psychology, M
Communication Disorders, BMD
Computer Science, M
Computer and Information Sciences, B
Construction Engineering, B
Counseling Psychology, M
Counselor Education/School Counseling and Guidance Services, M
Criminal Justice/Safety Studies, B
Criminology, M
Drama and Dramatics/Theatre Arts, B
Education, MDO
Educational Administration and Supervision, M
Educational Leadership and Administration, M
Educational Media/Instructional Technology, M
Electrical Engineering, MD
Electrical, Electronics and Communications Engineering, B
Engineering Management, M
Engineering and Applied Sciences, MD
English, M
English Language and Literature, B
Entrepreneurship/Entrepreneurial Studies, BM
Environmental Engineering Technology/Environmental Technology, M
Environmental Sciences, B
Environmental Studies, M
Family and Consumer Sciences/Human Sciences, M
Finance, B
Fine/Studio Arts, B
Foodservice Systems Administration/Management, B
Foreign Language Teacher Education, M
Foreign Languages and Literatures, B
General Studies, B
Geology/Earth Science, B
Graphic Design, B
Health Services Administration, M
History, BM
Human Development and Family Studies, B
Human Resources Management/Personnel Administration, B
Industrial Engineering, B
Industrial Technology/Technician, B
Industrial and Organizational Psychology, M
Industrial/Management Engineering, MD
Kinesiology and Exercise Science, B
Kinesiology and Movement Studies, M
Management Information Systems and Services, B
Marketing/Marketing Management, B
Mathematics, BM
Mechanical Engineering, BMD
Multi-/Interdisciplinary Studies, B
Music, BM
Nursing, M
Nursing Administration, M

Nursing Education, M
Operations Management and Supervision, B
Physics, B
Political Science and Government, BM
Psychology, BM
Public Administration, M
Retailing and Retail Operations, B
Social Work, B
Sociology, B
Special Education and Teaching, MD
Sport and Fitness Administration/Management, B

LAREDO COMMUNITY COLLEGE

Administrative Assistant and Secretarial Science, A
Child Development, A
Clinical/Medical Laboratory Technician, A
Computer Programming, A
Computer Programming/Programmer, A
Computer Software and Media Applications, A
Computer Systems Networking and Telecommunications, A
Construction Engineering Technology/Technician, A
Criminal Justice/Police Science, A
Data Entry/Microcomputer Applications, A
Data Processing and Data Processing Technology/Technician, A
Electrical, Electronic and Communications Engineering Technology/Technician, A
Emergency Medical Technology/Technician (EMT Paramedic), A
Fashion Merchandising, A
Fire Science/Firefighting, A
Hotel/Motel Administration/Management, A
Industrial Radiologic Technology/Technician, A
Information Science/Studies, A
Information Technology, A
International Business/Trade/Commerce, A
Liberal Arts and Sciences Studies and Humanities, A
Marketing/Marketing Management, A
Medical/Clinical Assistant, A
Physical Therapy/Therapist, A
Radiologic Technology/Science - Radiographer, A
Real Estate, A
Social Sciences, A

LEE COLLEGE

Accounting Technology/Technician and Bookkeeping, A
Administrative Assistant and Secretarial Science, A
American/United States Studies/Civilization, A
Art/Art Studies, General, A
Biology/Biological Sciences, A
Business Administration and Management, A
Chemistry, A
Communication Studies/Speech Communication and Rhetoric, A
Computer Programming/Programmer, A
Computer Systems Analysis/Analyst, A
Criminal Justice/Police Science, A
Data Processing and Data Processing Technology/Technician, A
Drafting and Design Technology/Technician, A
Drama and Dramatics/Theatre Arts, A
Economics, A
Education, A
Electrical, Electronic and Communications Engineering Technology/Technician, A
Emergency Medical Technology/Technician (EMT Paramedic), A
English Language and Literature, A
Environmental Studies, A
Executive Assistant/Executive Secretary, A
Fashion Merchandising, A
French Language and Literature, A
Geology/Earth Science, A
German Language and Literature, A
Health Information/Medical Records Technology/Technician, A
Heating, Air Conditioning, Ventilation and Refrigeration Maintenance Technology/Technician, A
History, A
Humanities/Humanistic Studies, A
Information Science/Studies, A
Instrumentation Technology/Technician, A
International Business/Trade/Commerce, A

Journalism, A
Kinesiology and Exercise Science, A
Legal Assistant/Paralegal, A
Liberal Arts and Sciences Studies and Humanities, A
Logistics and Materials Management, A
Machine Tool Technology/Machinist, A
Mathematics, A
Music, A
Natural Sciences, A
Office Management and Supervision, A
Operations Management and Supervision, A
Photography, A
Physical Education Teaching and Coaching, A
Physics, A
Political Science and Government, A
Prepress/Desktop Publishing and Digital Imaging Design, A
Psychology, A
Radio and Television, A
Sociology, A
Spanish Language and Literature, A
Substance Abuse/Addiction Counseling, A
Telecommunications Technology/Technician, A
Visual and Performing Arts, A
Welding Technology/Welder, A

LETOURNEAU UNIVERSITY

Accounting, B
Aeronautical/Aerospace Engineering Technology/Technician, B
Aeronautics/Aviation/Aerospace Science and Technology, B
Air Traffic Controller, AB
Airline/Commercial/Professional Pilot and Flight Crew, B
Aviation/Airway Management and Operations, B
Bible/Biblical Studies, B
Biology/Biological Sciences, B
Biomedical/Medical Engineering, B
Business Administration and Management, B
Business Administration, Management and Operations, M
Business Teacher Education, B
Chemistry, B
Civil Engineering, B
Computer Engineering, B
Computer Engineering Technology/Technician, B
Computer Science, B
Computer Software and Media Applications, B
Computer and Information Systems Security, B
Counseling Psychology, M
Criminology, AB
Curriculum and Instruction, M
Drafting and Design Technology/Technician, A
Education, M
Educational Administration and Supervision, M
Educational Leadership and Administration, M
Educational/Instructional Media Design, B
Electrical and Electronic Engineering Technologies/Technicians, B
Electrical, Electronic and Communications Engineering Technology/Technician, B
Electrical, Electronics and Communications Engineering, B
Elementary Education and Teaching, B
Engineering, B
Engineering Management, M
Engineering Physics, B
Engineering and Applied Sciences, M
English Language and Literature, B
English/Language Arts Teacher Education, B
Finance, B
Health Services Administration, M
Health Services/Allied Health/Health Sciences, B
Health/Health Care Administration/Management, AB
History, B
History Teacher Education, B
Human Resources Development, B
Human Resources Management/Personnel Administration, B
Human Services, B
Information Science/Studies, B
International Business/Trade/Commerce, B
International/Global Studies, B
Kinesiology and Exercise Science, B

Management Strategy and Policy, M
Marketing/Marketing Management, B
Marriage and Family Therapy/Counseling, M
Mass Communication/Media Studies, B
Mathematics, B
Mathematics Teacher Education, B
Mathematics and Computer Science, B
Mechanical Engineering, B
Mechanical Engineering Related Technologies/Technicians, B
Mechanical Engineering/Mechanical Technology/Technician, B
Metallurgical Engineering, B
Missions/Missionary Studies and Missiology, B
Multi-/Interdisciplinary Studies, B
Non-Profit/Public/Organizational Management, B
Operations Management and Supervision, B
Physical Education Teaching and Coaching, B
Physical and Theoretical Chemistry, B
Psychology, BM
Science Teacher Education/General Science Teacher Education, B
Secondary Education and Teaching, B
Social Studies Teacher Education, B
Sport and Fitness Administration/Management, B
Statistics, B
Theology and Religious Vocations, B
Transportation/Transportation Management, B
Youth Ministry, B

LONE STAR COLLEGE–CYFAIR

Accounting, A
Accounting and Computer Science, A
Animation, Interactive Technology, Video Graphics and Special Effects, A
Business Administration and Management, A
Cartography, A
Communication Studies/Speech Communication and Rhetoric, A
Computer Science, A
Computer and Information Sciences, A
Criminal Justice/Law Enforcement Administration, A
Dance, A
Design and Visual Communications, A
Diagnostic Medical Sonography/Sonographer and Ultrasound Technician, A
Economics, A
Education, A
Electrical, Electronic and Communications Engineering Technology/Technician, A
Emergency Medical Technology/Technician (EMT Paramedic), A
Fire Science/Firefighting, A
General Office Occupations and Clerical Services, A
Health Information/Medical Records Technology/Technician, A
Industrial Technology/Technician, A
Information Technology, A
Liberal Arts and Sciences Studies and Humanities, A
Logistics and Materials Management, A
Marketing/Marketing Management, A
Medical Radiologic Technology/Science - Radiation Therapist, A
Music, A
Radiation Protection/Health Physics Technician, A
Sign Language Interpretation and Translation, A
Welding Technology/Welder, A

LONE STAR COLLEGE–KINGWOOD

Administrative Assistant and Secretarial Science, A
Business Administration and Management, A
Computer Science, A
Computer and Information Sciences, A
Cosmetology/Cosmetologist, A
Criminal Justice/Law Enforcement Administration, A
Dental Hygiene/Hygienist, A
Design and Visual Communications, A
Education, A
Electroneurodiagnostic/Electroencephalographic Technology/Technologist, A
Fire Science/Firefighting, A
Interior Design, A
Marketing/Marketing Management, A
Music, A
Occupational Therapy/Therapist, A

Respiratory Care Therapy/Therapist, A

LONE STAR COLLEGE–MONTGOMERY

Accounting and Business/Management, A
Automobile/Automotive Mechanics Technology/Technician, A
Biology Technician/BioTechnology Laboratory Technician, A
Business Administration and Management, A
Computer Science, A
Criminal Justice/Law Enforcement Administration, A
Education, A
Emergency Medical Technology/Technician (EMT Paramedic), A
Fire Science/Firefighting, A
Human Services, A
Information Technology, A
Music, A
Physical Therapist Assistant, A

LONE STAR COLLEGE–NORTH HARRIS

Accounting, A
Automobile/Automotive Mechanics Technology/Technician, A
Business Administration and Management, A
Computer Science, A
Cosmetology/Cosmetologist, A
Criminal Justice/Law Enforcement Administration, A
Design and Visual Communications, A
Drafting and Design Technology/Technician, A
Education, A
Educational/Instructional Media Design, A
Electrical, Electronic and Communications Engineering Technology/Technician, A
Emergency Medical Technology/Technician (EMT Paramedic), A
Health Information/Medical Records Technology/Technician, A
Heating, Air Conditioning, Ventilation and Refrigeration Maintenance Technology/Technician, A
Industrial Technology/Technician, A
Legal Assistant/Paralegal, A
Mechanical Engineering, A
Music, A
Pharmacy Technician/Assistant, A
Sign Language Interpretation and Translation, A
Welding Technology/Welder, A

LONE STAR COLLEGE–TOMBALL

Accounting, A
Administrative Assistant and Secretarial Science, A
Animation, Interactive Technology, Video Graphics and Special Effects, A
Business Administration and Management, A
Computer Programming/Programmer, A
Computer Science, A
Criminal Justice/Law Enforcement Administration, A
Education, A
Electrical, Electronic and Communications Engineering Technology/Technician, A
Industrial Technology/Technician, A
Music, A
Surgical Technology/Technologist, A
System, Networking, and LAN/WAN Management/Manager, A
Veterinary/Animal Health Technology/Technician and Veterinary Assistant, A

LONE STAR COLLEGE–UNIVERSITY PARK

Accounting, A
Business Administration and Management, A
Communication Studies/Speech Communication and Rhetoric, A
Criminal Justice/Law Enforcement Administration, A

LUBBOCK CHRISTIAN UNIVERSITY

Accounting, B
Animal Sciences, B
Art Teacher Education, B
Athletic Training and Sports Medicine, B
Bible/Biblical Studies, B
Biochemistry, B
Biology/Biological Sciences, B

Business Administration and Management, B
Chemistry, B
Computer and Information Sciences, B
Criminal Justice/Law Enforcement Administration, B
Design and Visual Communications, B
Digital Communication and Media/Multimedia, B
Drama and Dance Teacher Education, B
Early Childhood Education and Teaching, B
Economics, B
Family Systems, B
Finance, B
Financial Planning and Services, B
Health and Physical Education, B
History, B
Humanities/Humanistic Studies, B
Information Resources Management/CIO Training, B
Journalism, B
Junior High/Intermediate/Middle School Education
    and Teaching, B
Marketing/Marketing Management, B
Mass Communication/Media Studies, B
Mathematics, B
Missions/Missionary Studies and Missiology, B
Music, B
Music Teacher Education, B
Natural Resources and Conservation, B
Organizational Communication, B
Physical Education Teaching and Coaching, B
Pre-Veterinary Studies, B
Psychology, B
Secondary Education and Teaching, B
Social Work, B
Spanish Language Teacher Education, B
Sport and Fitness Administration/Management, B
Theological and Ministerial Studies, B
Theology and Religious Vocations, M
Youth Ministry, B

MCLENNAN COMMUNITY COLLEGE

Accounting, A
Administrative Assistant and Secretarial Science, A
Art Teacher Education, A
Business Administration and Management, A
Clinical/Medical Laboratory Technician, A
Computer Engineering Technology/Technician, A
Criminal Justice/Law Enforcement Administration, A
Criminal Justice/Police Science, A
Finance, A
Health Information/Medical Records
    Administration/Administrator, A
Industrial Radiologic Technology/Technician, A
Information Science/Studies, A
Kindergarten/PreSchool Education and Teaching, A
Legal Administrative Assistant/Secretary, A
Legal Assistant/Paralegal, A
Liberal Arts and Sciences Studies and Humani-
    ties, A
Medical Administrative Assistant/Secretary, A
Mental Health Counseling/Counselor, A
Music, A
Physical Education Teaching and Coaching, A
Physical Therapy/Therapist, A
Real Estate, A
Respiratory Care Therapy/Therapist, A
Sign Language Interpretation and Translation, A

MCMURRY UNIVERSITY

Accounting, B
Art Teacher Education, B
Athletic Training and Sports Medicine, B
Biochemistry, B
Biology Teacher Education, B
Biology/Biological Sciences, B
Biomedical Sciences, B
Business Administration and Management, B
Business/Commerce, B
Chemistry, B
Chemistry Teacher Education, B
Christian Studies, B
Computer Teacher Education, B
Computer and Information Sciences, B
Conducting, B
Design and Applied Arts, B
Drama and Dramatics/Theatre Arts, B
Early Childhood Education and Teaching, B
Elementary Education and Teaching, B

English Language and Literature, B
English/Language Arts Teacher Education, B
Finance, B
Fine/Studio Arts, B
History, B
History Teacher Education, B
Information Technology, B
Junior High/Intermediate/Middle School Education
    and Teaching, B
Kinesiology and Exercise Science, B
Management Information Systems and Services, B
Marketing/Marketing Management, B
Mathematics, B
Mathematics Teacher Education, B
Multi-/Interdisciplinary Studies, B
Music, B
Nursing, M
Nursing - Advanced Practice, M
Nursing Education, M
Physical Education Teaching and Coaching, B
Physics, B
Political Science and Government, B
Pre-Nursing Studies, B
Psychology, B
Public/Applied History and Archival Administration, B
Secondary Education and Teaching, B
Sociology, B
Spanish Language Teacher Education, B
Spanish Language and Literature, B

MESSENGER COLLEGE

Bible/Biblical Studies, B
Business Administration and Management, B
Divinity/Ministry (BD, MDiv.), B
Education, B
General Studies, A
Missions/Missionary Studies and Missiology, B
Music, B
Pastoral Studies/Counseling, B
Religion/Religious Studies, B
Religious Education, B
Religious/Sacred Music, B
Theological and Ministerial Studies, B
Youth Ministry, B

MIDLAND COLLEGE

Automobile/Automotive Mechanics
    Technology/Technician, A
Business Administration and Management, B
Business/Commerce, A
Child Development, A
Cosmetology/Cosmetologist, A
Criminal Justice/Police Science, A
Diagnostic Medical Sonography/Sonographer and
    Ultrasound Technician, A
Diesel Mechanics Technology/Technician, A
Electromechanical Technology/Electromechanical
    Engineering Technology, A
Emergency Medical Technology/Technician (EMT
    Paramedic), A
Fire Science/Firefighting, A
General Office Occupations and Clerical Services, A
General Studies, A
Health Information/Medical Records
    Technology/Technician, A
Heating, Air Conditioning and Refrigeration
    Technology/Technician, A
Legal Assistant/Paralegal, A
Mechanical Drafting and Mechanical Drafting
    CAD/CADD, A
Respiratory Care Therapy/Therapist, A
Substance Abuse/Addiction Counseling, A
System, Networking, and LAN/WAN
    Management/Manager, A
Teacher Education, Multiple Levels, A
Welding Technology/Welder, A

MIDWESTERN STATE UNIVERSITY

Accounting, B
Art/Art Studies, General, B
Athletic Training and Sports Medicine, B
Bilingual and Multilingual Education, B
Biological and Biomedical Sciences, M
Biology/Biological Sciences, B
Business Administration, Management and Opera-
    tions, M

Business/Commerce, B
Business/Managerial Economics, B
Chemistry, B
Clinical Laboratory Science/Medical
    Technology/Technologist, B
Clinical Psychology, M
Community Health and Preventive Medicine, M
Computer Engineering, B
Computer Science, M
Computer and Information Sciences, B
Counseling Psychology, M
Counselor Education/School Counseling and Guid-
    ance Services, BM
Criminal Justice/Law Enforcement Administration, B
Criminology, MO
Curriculum and Instruction, BM
Dental Hygiene/Hygienist, B
Design and Applied Arts, B
Early Childhood Education and Teaching, B
Economics, B
Education, BM
Educational Administration and Supervision, M
Educational Leadership and Administration, B
Educational Media/Instructional Technology, M
Educational/Instructional Media Design, B
Engineering Technology, B
English, MD
English Language and Literature, B
English/Language Arts Teacher Education, B
Environmental Sciences, B
Exercise and Sports Science, M
Finance, B
Geology/Earth Science, B
Health Informatics, B
Health Occupations Teacher Education, B
Health Physics/Radiological Health, M
Health Services Administration, MO
Health and Physical Education/Fitness, B
History, BM
Human Resources Development, BM
Humanities/Humanistic Studies, B
Information Science/Studies, B
International Business/Trade/Commerce, B
International/Global Studies, B
Liberal Arts and Sciences Studies and Humani-
    ties, AB
Management Information Systems and Services, B
Manufacturing Technology/Technician, B
Marketing/Marketing Management, B
Mass Communication/Media Studies, B
Mathematics, B
Mathematics Teacher Education, B
Mechanical Engineering/Mechanical
    Technology/Technician, B
Music, B
Music Performance, B
Music Teacher Education, B
Nursing, M
Nursing - Advanced Practice, M
Nursing Education, M
Philosophy, MD
Physical Sciences, B
Physics, B
Political Science and Government, BM
Pre-Dentistry Studies, B
Pre-Law Studies, B
Pre-Medicine/Pre-Medical Studies, B
Pre-Pharmacy Studies, B
Pre-Veterinary Studies, B
Psychiatric/Mental Health Nurse/Nursing, M
Psychology, B
Public Administration, B
Reading Teacher Education, BM
Respiratory Care Therapy/Therapist, B
Science Teacher Education/General Science
    Teacher Education, B
Secondary Education and Teaching, B
Social Sciences, B
Social Studies Teacher Education, B
Social Work, B
Sociology, B
Spanish Language and Literature, B
Special Education and Teaching, BM

Sport and Fitness Administration/Management, BM

MOUNTAIN VIEW COLLEGE

Accounting, A
Business Administration and Management, A
Communication Studies/Speech Communication and Rhetoric, A
Computer Systems Networking and Telecommunications, A
Criminal Justice/Safety Studies, A
Drafting and Design Technology/Technician, A
Education, A
Electrical, Electronic and Communications Engineering Technology/Technician, A
Liberal Arts and Sciences Studies and Humanities, A
Music, A
Welding Technology/Welder, A

NAVARRO COLLEGE

Accounting, A
Administrative Assistant and Secretarial Science, A
Agricultural Mechanization, A
Art/Art Studies, General, A
Biological and Physical Sciences, A
Biology/Biological Sciences, A
Business Administration and Management, A
Chemistry, A
Clinical/Medical Laboratory Technician, A
Commercial and Advertising Art, A
Computer Graphics, A
Computer Programming/Programmer, A
Computer Science, A
Consumer Merchandising/Retailing Management, A
Corrections, A
Criminal Justice/Law Enforcement Administration, A
Criminal Justice/Police Science, A
Data Processing and Data Processing Technology/Technician, A
Drafting and Design Technology/Technician, A
Drama and Dramatics/Theatre Arts, A
Education, A
Elementary Education and Teaching, A
Engineering, A
English Language and Literature, A
Fire Science/Firefighting, A
Industrial Technology/Technician, A
Law and Legal Studies, A
Legal Administrative Assistant/Secretary, A
Legal Assistant/Paralegal, A
Marketing/Marketing Management, A
Mathematics, A
Music, A
Occupational Therapy/Therapist, A
Pharmacy, A
Physical Education Teaching and Coaching, A
Physical Sciences, A
Physics, A
Psychology, A
Social Sciences, A
Sociology, A
Voice and Opera, A

NORTH AMERICAN UNIVERSITY

Business Administration and Management, B
Computer and Information Sciences, B
Educational Leadership and Administration, M
Teacher Education, Multiple Levels, B

NORTH CENTRAL TEXAS COLLEGE

Administrative Assistant and Secretarial Science, A
Agricultural Mechanization, A
Animal/Livestock Husbandry and Production, A
Automobile/Automotive Mechanics Technology/Technician, A
Biological and Physical Sciences, A
Business Administration and Management, A
Business and Personal/Financial Services Marketing Operations, A
Computer Engineering Technology/Technician, A
Computer Graphics, A
Computer Programming, A
Computer Programming, Specific Applications, A
Computer Programming, Vendor/Product Certification, A
Computer Programming/Programmer, A

Computer Science, A
Computer and Information Sciences and Support Services, A
Computer/Information Technology Services Administration and Management, A
Criminal Justice/Law Enforcement Administration, A
Criminal Justice/Police Science, A
Data Processing and Data Processing Technology/Technician, A
Drafting and Design Technology/Technician, A
Electrical, Electronic and Communications Engineering Technology/Technician, A
Emergency Medical Technology/Technician (EMT Paramedic), A
Engineering Technology, A
Equestrian/Equine Studies, A
Farm/Farm and Ranch Management, A
Health Information/Medical Records Administration/Administrator, A
Industrial Mechanics and Maintenance Technology, A
Information Science/Studies, A
Legal Administrative Assistant/Secretary, A
Legal Assistant/Paralegal, A
Liberal Arts and Sciences Studies and Humanities, A
Machine Shop Technology/Assistant, A
Machine Tool Technology/Machinist, A
Merchandising and Buying Operations, A
Occupational Therapy/Therapist, A
Real Estate, A
Retailing and Retail Operations, A
Sales, Distribution and Marketing Operations, A
Welding Technology/Welder, A
Word Processing, A

NORTH LAKE COLLEGE

Accounting, A
Administrative Assistant and Secretarial Science, A
Business Administration and Management, A
Carpentry/Carpenter, A
Communications Technology/Technician, A
Computer Programming/Programmer, A
Construction Engineering Technology/Technician, A
Data Processing and Data Processing Technology/Technician, A
Electrical, Electronic and Communications Engineering Technology/Technician, A
Heating, Air Conditioning, Ventilation and Refrigeration Maintenance Technology/Technician, A
Information Science/Studies, A
Kinesiology and Exercise Science, A
Legal Administrative Assistant/Secretary, A
Liberal Arts and Sciences Studies and Humanities, A
Real Estate, A

NORTHEAST TEXAS COMMUNITY COLLEGE

Accounting, A
Accounting and Business/Management, A
Agricultural Business and Management, A
Art/Art Studies, General, A
Autobody/Collision and Repair Technology/Technician, A
Automobile/Automotive Mechanics Technology/Technician, A
Biology/Biological Sciences, A
Biomedical Sciences, A
Business Administration and Management, A
Chemistry, A
Civil Engineering, A
Clinical/Medical Laboratory Technician, A
Computer Systems Networking and Telecommunications, A
Computer and Information Sciences, A
Corrections, A
Cosmetology/Cosmetologist, A
Criminal Justice/Law Enforcement Administration, A
Criminal Justice/Police Science, A
Culinary Arts/Chef Training, A
Data Entry/Microcomputer Applications, A
Dental Hygiene/Hygienist, A
Drama and Dramatics/Theatre Arts, A
Electrical, Electronics and Communications Engineering, A

Computer Science, A

Emergency Medical Technology/Technician (EMT Paramedic), A
English Language and Literature, A
Environmental Sciences, A
Executive Assistant/Executive Secretary, A
Health and Physical Education, A
History, A
Industrial Engineering, A
Industrial Technology/Technician, A
Legal Administrative Assistant/Secretary, A
Liberal Arts and Sciences Studies and Humanities, A
Mathematics, A
Mechanical Engineering, A
Medical Administrative Assistant/Secretary, A
Medical/Clinical Assistant, A
Music, A
Physical Therapist Assistant, A
Physics, A
Political Science and Government, A
Psychology, A
Social Work, A
Sociology, A
Spanish Language and Literature, A
Teacher Education, Multiple Levels, A
Welding Technology/Welder, A

NORTHWEST VISTA COLLEGE

Accounting, A
Accounting Technology/Technician and Bookkeeping, A
Administrative Assistant and Secretarial Science, A
Biology Technician/BioTechnology Laboratory Technician, A
Business Administration, Management and Operations, A
Community Health and Preventive Medicine, A
Computer Programming/Programmer, A
Computer Science, A
Computer and Information Sciences, A
Computer and Information Sciences and Support Services, A
Computer and Information Systems Security, A
Computer/Information Technology Services Administration and Management, A
Criminal Justice/Safety Studies, A
International/Global Studies, A
Liberal Arts and Sciences Studies and Humanities, A
Recording Arts Technology/Technician, A
Water Quality and Wastewater Treatment Management and Recycling Technology/Technician, A
Web Page, Digital/Multimedia and Information Resources Design, A

NORTHWOOD UNIVERSITY, TEXAS CAMPUS

Accounting, B
Business Administration and Management, B
Marketing/Marketing Management, B

ODESSA COLLEGE

Accounting, A
Administrative Assistant and Secretarial Science, A
Agriculture, A
Art/Art Studies, General, A
Athletic Training and Sports Medicine, A
Automobile/Automotive Mechanics Technology/Technician, A
Biology/Biological Sciences, A
Business Administration and Management, A
Chemistry, A
Child Development, A
Clinical/Medical Laboratory Technician, A
Computer Science, A
Computer Systems Networking and Telecommunications, A
Computer and Information Sciences, A
Construction Engineering Technology/Technician, A
Cosmetology/Cosmetologist, A
Criminal Justice/Law Enforcement Administration, A
Criminal Justice/Police Science, A
Culinary Arts/Chef Training, A
Data Processing and Data Processing Technology/Technician, A
Design and Applied Arts, A

Drafting and Design Technology/Technician, A
Education, A
Electrical, Electronic and Communications Engineering Technology/Technician, A
Emergency Medical Technology/Technician (EMT Paramedic), A
English Language and Literature, A
Fire Science/Firefighting, A
Geology/Earth Science, A
Hazardous Materials Management and Waste Technology/Technician, A
Heating, Air Conditioning, Ventilation and Refrigeration Maintenance Technology/Technician, A
History, A
Human Services, A
Industrial Radiologic Technology/Technician, A
Information Science/Studies, A
Kindergarten/PreSchool Education and Teaching, A
Legal Administrative Assistant/Secretary, A
Liberal Arts and Sciences Studies and Humanities, A
Machine Tool Technology/Machinist, A
Mathematics, A
Modern Languages, A
Music, A
Photography, A
Physical Education Teaching and Coaching, A
Physical Therapy/Therapist, A
Physics, A
Political Science and Government, A
Psychology, A
Social Sciences, A
Sociology, A
Substance Abuse/Addiction Counseling, A
Teacher Assistant/Aide, A
Welding Technology/Welder, A

OUR LADY OF THE LAKE UNIVERSITY OF SAN ANTONIO

Accounting, BM
Art/Art Studies, General, B
Bilingual and Multilingual Education, B
Biology/Biological Sciences, B
Business Administration and Management, B
Business Administration, Management and Operations, M
Chemistry, B
Communication Disorders, BM
Communication and Media Studies, M
Communication, Journalism and Related Programs, B
Computer and Information Sciences, B
Computer and Information Systems Security, M
Counseling Psychology, MD
Counselor Education/School Counseling and Guidance Services, M
Criminal Justice/Safety Studies, B
Curriculum and Instruction, M
Drama and Dramatics/Theatre Arts, B
Early Childhood Education and Teaching, M
Economics, B
Education, MD
Educational Administration and Supervision, M
Educational Media/Instructional Technology, M
Elementary Education and Teaching, M
English, M
English Education, M
English Language and Literature, B
English as a Second Language, M
Finance, B
Finance and Banking, M
Health Services Administration, M
Health/Health Care Administration/Management, B
Hispanic-American, Puerto Rican, and Mexican-American/Chicano Studies, B
History, B
Human Development, M
Human Resources Management/Personnel Administration, B
Kinesiology and Exercise Science, B
Management, M
Management Information Systems and Services, M
Marketing, B
Marriage and Family Therapy/Counseling, M
Mathematics, B
Mathematics Teacher Education, M

Middle School Education, M
Multi-/Interdisciplinary Studies, B
Multilingual and Multicultural Education, M
Music, B
Non-Profit/Public/Organizational Management, M
Nursing, M
Nursing Administration, M
Nursing Education, M
Organizational Management, MD
Political Science and Government, B
Psychology, BMD
Reading Teacher Education, M
Religion/Religious Studies, B
School Psychology, M
Science Teacher Education/General Science Teacher Education, M
Secondary Education and Teaching, M
Social Sciences, B
Social Work, BM
Sociology, B
Spanish Language Teacher Education, B
Spanish Language and Literature, B
Special Education and Teaching, BM
Writing, M

PALO ALTO COLLEGE

Agriculture, A
Architectural Engineering Technology/Technician, A
Art/Art Studies, General, A
Aviation/Airway Management and Operations, A
Avionics Maintenance Technology/Technician, A
Biology/Biological Sciences, A
Business Administration and Management, A
Chemistry, A
Computer Engineering Technology/Technician, A
Computer Science, A
Computer and Information Sciences, A
Economics, A
Education, A
Engineering, A
English Language and Literature, A
Finance, A
Geology/Earth Science, A
Health Professions and Related Clinical Sciences, A
History, A
Horticultural Science, A
Information Science/Studies, A
Information Technology, A
Journalism, A
Law and Legal Studies, A
Liberal Arts and Sciences Studies and Humanities, A
Library Science, A
Mathematics, A
Modern Languages, A
Music, A
Philosophy, A
Physical Education Teaching and Coaching, A
Physics, A
Psychology, A
Sociology, A
Trade and Industrial Teacher Education, A

PANOLA COLLEGE

Administrative Assistant and Secretarial Science, A
Agriculture, A
Architecture, A
Art/Art Studies, General, A
Biology/Biological Sciences, A
Business Administration and Management, A
Business/Office Automation/Technology/Data Entry, A
Chemistry, A
Clinical/Medical Laboratory Technician, A
Communication Studies/Speech Communication and Rhetoric, A
Computer Science, A
Computer/Information Technology Services Administration and Management, A
Construction Engineering Technology/Technician, A
Criminology, A
Drama and Dramatics/Theatre Arts, A
Early Childhood Education and Teaching, A
Education, A
Electrician, A
English Language and Literature, A

Foreign Languages and Literatures, A
Forestry, A
General Studies, A
Geology/Earth Science, A
Health Information/Medical Records Technology/Technician, A
Health Professions and Related Clinical Sciences, A
History, A
Industrial Technology/Technician, A
Information Science/Studies, A
Information Technology, A
Journalism, A
Junior High/Intermediate/Middle School Education and Teaching, A
Liberal Arts and Sciences Studies and Humanities, A
Management Information Systems and Services, A
Mathematics, A
Medical/Clinical Assistant, A
Music, A
Occupational Therapist Assistant, A
Petroleum Technology/Technician, A
Physical Education Teaching and Coaching, A
Physics, A
Pre-Dentistry Studies, A
Pre-Law Studies, A
Pre-Pharmacy Studies, A
Pre-Veterinary Studies, A
Psychology, A
Sociology, A
Welding Technology/Welder, A

PARIS JUNIOR COLLEGE

Accounting, A
Agricultural Mechanization, A
Agriculture, A
Art/Art Studies, General, A
Biological and Physical Sciences, A
Biology/Biological Sciences, A
Business Administration and Management, A
Business Teacher Education, A
Business/Commerce, A
Business/Office Automation/Technology/Data Entry, A
Chemistry, A
Computer Engineering Technology/Technician, A
Computer Typography and Composition Equipment Operator, A
Computer and Information Sciences, A
Cosmetology/Cosmetologist, A
Criminal Justice/Safety Studies, A
Criminology, A
Drafting and Design Technology/Technician, A
Drama and Dramatics/Theatre Arts, A
Early Childhood Education and Teaching, A
Education, A
Electrical, Electronic and Communications Engineering Technology/Technician, A
Electromechanical Technology/Electromechanical Engineering Technology, A
Elementary Education and Teaching, A
Emergency Medical Technology/Technician (EMT Paramedic), A
Engineering, A
English Language and Literature, A
Foreign Languages and Literatures, A
General Studies, A
Health Information/Medical Records Technology/Technician, A
Health Services/Allied Health/Health Sciences, A
Health and Physical Education, A
Heating, Air Conditioning, Ventilation and Refrigeration Maintenance Technology/Technician, A
History, A
Information Science/Studies, A
Journalism, A
Liberal Arts and Sciences Studies and Humanities, A
Mathematics, A
Medical Insurance Coding Specialist/Coder, A
Metal and Jewelry Arts, A
Music, A
Physical Sciences, A
Physics, A
Political Science and Government, A
Pre-Law Studies, A

Pre-Medicine/Pre-Medical Studies, A
Pre-Nursing Studies, A
Pre-Pharmacy Studies, A
Psychology, A
Radiologic Technology/Science - Radiographer, A
Secondary Education and Teaching, A
Social Sciences, A
Social Work, A
Sociology, A
Surgical Technology/Technologist, A
System, Networking, and LAN/WAN
    Management/Manager, A
Teacher Education, Multiple Levels, A
Watchmaking and Jewelrymaking, A
Welding Technology/Welder, A

PAUL QUINN COLLEGE

Biology/Biological Sciences, B
Business Administration and Management, B
Criminal Justice/Law Enforcement Administration, B
Education, B
History, B
Mass Communication/Media Studies, B
Mathematics, B
Physical Education Teaching and Coaching, B
Religion/Religious Studies, B

PIMA MEDICAL INSTITUTE

Health/Health Care Administration/Management, A
Radiologic Technology/Science - Radiographer, A
Respiratory Therapy Technician/Assistant, A

PRAIRIE VIEW A&M UNIVERSITY

Accounting, BM
Agricultural Sciences, M
Agriculture, B
Architecture, BM
Biological and Biomedical Sciences, M
Biology/Biological Sciences, B
Business Administration and Management, B
Business Administration, Management and Opera-
    tions, M
Chemical Engineering, B
Chemistry, BM
Civil Engineering, B
Clinical Psychology, MD
Communication Studies/Speech Communication
    and Rhetoric, B
Computer Engineering, B
Computer Engineering Technology/Technician, B
Computer Science, BM
Construction Engineering Technology/Technician, B
Counselor Education/School Counseling and Guid-
    ance Services, MD
Criminal Justice/Safety Studies, B
Curriculum and Instruction, M
Drama and Dramatics/Theatre Arts, B
Education, MD
Educational Administration and Supervision, M
Educational Leadership and Administration, MD
Electrical Engineering, MD
Electrical, Electronic and Communications Engineer-
    ing Technology/Technician, B
Electrical, Electronics and Communications Engi-
    neering, B
Engineering and Applied Sciences, MD
English, M
English Language and Literature, B
Family and Consumer Sciences/Human Sci-
    ences, BM
Finance, B
Foods, Nutrition, and Wellness Studies, B
Forensic Psychology, MD
Graphic Design, B
Health Education, M
Health and Physical Education, B
History, B
Human Nutrition, B
Information Science/Studies, B
Juvenile Corrections, B
Legal and Justice Studies, MD
Management Information Systems and Ser-
    vices, BM
Marketing/Marketing Management, B
Mathematics, B
Mechanical Engineering, B

Multi-/Interdisciplinary Studies, B
Music, B
Nursing, M
Nursing - Advanced Practice, M
Nursing Administration, M
Nursing Education, M
Physical Education Teaching and Coaching, M
Physics, B
Political Science and Government, B
Psychology, B
Social Work, B
Sociology, BM
Spanish Language and Literature, B
Special Education and Teaching, M
Toxicology, M
Urban Design, M

RANGER COLLEGE

Administrative Assistant and Secretarial Science, A
Automobile/Automotive Mechanics
    Technology/Technician, A
Computer Engineering Technology/Technician, A
Liberal Arts and Sciences Studies and Humani-
    ties, A
Science Teacher Education/General Science
    Teacher Education, B
Welding Technology/Welder, A

REMINGTON COLLEGE–DALLAS CAM-
PUS

Business Administration and Management, A
Computer Systems Networking and Telecommunica-
    tions, A
Cooking and Related Culinary Arts, A
Criminal Justice/Law Enforcement Administration, A

REMINGTON COLLEGE–FORT WORTH
CAMPUS

Business Administration and Management, A
Computer Graphics, A
Computer Systems Networking and Telecommunica-
    tions, A
Criminal Justice/Law Enforcement Administration, A

REMINGTON COLLEGE–HOUSTON
SOUTHEAST CAMPUS

Business Administration and Management, A
Computer Systems Networking and Telecommunica-
    tions, A

REMINGTON COLLEGE–NORTH HOUS-
TON CAMPUS

Business Administration and Management, A
Criminal Justice/Law Enforcement Administration, A

RICE UNIVERSITY

African Studies, D
American/United States Studies/Civilization, D
Ancient/Classical Greek Language and Literature, B
Anthropology, BMD
Applied Mathematics, BMD
Applied Physics, MD
Archeology, MD
Architecture, BMD
Art History, Criticism and Conservation, BD
Art/Art Studies, General, B
Asian Studies/Civilization, B
Astronomy, BMD
Astrophysics, B
Biochemistry, BMD
Bioengineering, MD
Bioinformatics, D
Biology/Biological Sciences, B
Biomedical Engineering, MD
Biomedical/Medical Engineering, B
Biostatistics, D
Business Administration and Management, B
Business Administration, Management and Opera-
    tions, M
Cell Biology and Anatomy, MD
Chemical Engineering, BMD
Chemistry, BMD
Civil Engineering, BMD
Classics and Classical Languages, Litera-
    tures, and Linguistics, B

Cognitive Sciences, MD
Composition, MD
Computational Sciences, MD
Computer Engineering, BMD
Computer Science, MD
Computer and Information Sciences, B
Cultural Anthropology, MD
Ecology, BMD
Economics, BMD
Education, M
Electrical Engineering, MD
Electrical, Electronics and Communications Engi-
    neering, B
Engineering and Applied Sciences, MD
English, MD
English Language and Literature, B
Environmental Engineering
    Technology/Environmental Technology, MD
Environmental Policy and Resource Manage-
    ment, M
Environmental Sciences, MD
Environmental/Environmental Health Engineering, B
Evolutionary Biology, BMD
Fine/Studio Arts, B
French Language and Literature, B
Geology/Earth Science, B
Geophysics and Seismology, BM
Geosciences, MD
German Language and Literature, B
Health Services Administration, M
History, BMD
Industrial and Organizational Psychology, MD
Inorganic Chemistry, D
Jewish/Judaic Studies, D
Kinesiology and Exercise Science, B
Latin American Studies, B
Latin Language and Literature, B
Liberal Studies, M
Linguistics, BMD
Materials Engineering, B
Materials Sciences, MD
Mathematical and Computational Finance, D
Mathematics, BD
Mechanical Engineering, BMD
Multi-/Interdisciplinary Studies, B
Music, BMD
Music History, Literature, and Theory, B
Music Performance, B
Music Theory and Composition, BM
Musicology and Ethnomusicology, M
Near and Middle Eastern Studies, D
Organic Chemistry, D
Performance, MD
Philosophy, BMD
Physical Chemistry, D
Physical and Theoretical Chemistry, B
Physics, BMD
Political Science and Government, BD
Psychology, BMD
Public Policy Analysis, B
Religion/Religious Studies, BD
Science Teacher Education/General Science
    Teacher Education, M
Sociology, BD
Spanish Language and Literature, B
Sport and Fitness Administration/Management, B
Statistics, BMD
Urban Design, M
Visual and Performing Arts, B
Women's Studies, B

RICHLAND COLLEGE

Accounting, A
Administrative Assistant and Secretarial Science, A
Artificial Intelligence and Robotics, A
Business Administration and Management, A
Computer Programming/Programmer, A
Data Processing and Data Processing
    Technology/Technician, A
Drafting/Design Engineering
    Technologies/Technicians, A
Electrical, Electronic and Communications Engineer-
    ing Technology/Technician, A
Engineering, A
Horticultural Science, A
Industrial Technology/Technician, A

International Business/Trade/Commerce, A
Liberal Arts and Sciences Studies and Humanities, A
Mechanical Engineering/Mechanical Technology/Technician, A
Ornamental Horticulture, A
Real Estate, A

RIO GRANDE BIBLE INSTITUTE

Bible/Biblical Studies, B

ST. EDWARD'S UNIVERSITY

Accounting, BM
Accounting Technology/Technician and Bookkeeping, B
Acting, B
Art Teacher Education, B
Art/Art Studies, General, B
Biochemistry, B
Bioinformatics, B
Biology Teacher Education, B
Biology/Biological Sciences, B
Business Administration and Management, B
Business Administration, Management and Operations, MO
Chemistry, B
Chemistry Teacher Education, B
Christian Studies, B
Clinical Laboratory Science/Medical Technology/Technologist, B
Computer Art and Design, M
Computer Science, B
Computer and Information Sciences, B
Counseling Psychology, M
Criminal Justice/Safety Studies, B
Criminology, B
Digital Communication and Media/Multimedia, B
Drama and Dance Teacher Education, B
Drama and Dramatics/Theatre Arts, B
Economics, B
English Language and Literature, B
English/Language Arts Teacher Education, B
Entrepreneurship/Entrepreneurial Studies, B
Environmental Policy and Resource Management, M
Environmental Studies, B
Ethics, M
Finance, B
Finance and Banking, O
Forensic Science and Technology, B
French Language and Literature, B
Graphic Design, B
History, B
History Teacher Education, B
Humanities/Humanistic Studies, M
International Business/Trade/Commerce, B
International/Global Studies, B
Kinesiology and Exercise Science, B
Liberal Arts and Sciences Studies and Humanities, B
Liberal Studies, MO
Marketing/Marketing Management, B
Mathematics, B
Mathematics Teacher Education, B
Media Studies, M
Organizational Management, M
Philosophy, B
Photography, B
Physical Education Teaching and Coaching, B
Political Science and Government, B
Psychology, B
Social Sciences, M
Social Studies Teacher Education, B
Social Work, B
Sociology, B
Spanish Language Teacher Education, B
Spanish Language and Literature, B
Special Education and Teaching, B
Student Personnel Services, M
Sustainable Development, M
Theology/Theological Studies, B

ST. MARY'S UNIVERSITY

Accounting, BM
Art Teacher Education, B
Biochemistry, B

Biochemistry, Biophysics and Molecular Biology, B
Biology/Biological Sciences, B
Business Administration and Management, B
Business Administration, Management and Operations, M
Chemistry, B
Communication Studies/Speech Communication and Rhetoric, B
Communication and Media Studies, MO
Computer Engineering, BM
Computer Science, BMO
Computer Software Engineering, B
Computer and Information Sciences, B
Conflict Resolution and Mediation/Peace Studies, MO
Counseling Psychology, M
Counselor Education/School Counseling and Guidance Services, D
Criminal Justice/Law Enforcement Administration, B
Criminology, B
Economics, B
Education, MO
Educational Leadership and Administration, MO
Electrical Engineering, M
Electrical, Electronics and Communications Engineering, B
Engineering Management, M
Engineering Science, B
Engineering and Applied Sciences, M
Engineering/Industrial Management, B
English, M
English Language and Literature, B
Entrepreneurship/Entrepreneurial Studies, B
Environmental Sciences, B
Finance, B
Financial Planning and Services, B
Forensic Science and Technology, B
History, B
Homeland Security, M
Human Services, MD
Industrial Engineering, B
Industrial and Organizational Psychology, M
Industrial/Management Engineering, M
Information Science/Studies, BM
International Affairs, MO
International Business/Trade/Commerce, B
International Development, M
International Relations and Affairs, B
Kinesiology and Exercise Science, B
Law and Legal Studies, D
Marketing/Marketing Management, B
Marriage and Family Therapy/Counseling, MD
Mathematics, B
Mechanical Engineering, B
Music, B
Philosophy, B
Physics, B
Political Science and Government, BM
Psychology, B
Public Administration, MO
Public Policy Analysis, O
Sociology, B
Software Engineering, M
Spanish Language and Literature, B
Theology and Religious Vocations, MO
Theology/Theological Studies, B

ST. PHILIP'S COLLEGE

Accounting, A
Administrative Assistant and Secretarial Science, A
Aircraft Powerplant Technology/Technician, A
Airframe Mechanics and Aircraft Maintenance Technology/Technician, A
Art/Art Studies, General, A
Autobody/Collision and Repair Technology/Technician, A
Automobile/Automotive Mechanics Technology/Technician, A
Biology/Biological Sciences, A
Biomedical Technology/Technician, A
Building/Construction Finishing, Management, and Inspection, A
Business Administration and Management, A
CAD/CADD Drafting and/or Design Technology/Technician, A
Chemistry, A

Clinical/Medical Laboratory Technician, A
Computer Systems Networking and Telecommunications, A
Computer Technology/Computer Systems Technology, A
Computer and Information Systems Security, A
Construction Engineering Technology/Technician, A
Criminal Justice/Law Enforcement Administration, A
Culinary Arts/Chef Training, A
Data Entry/Microcomputer Applications, A
Diesel Mechanics Technology/Technician, A
Drama and Dramatics/Theatre Arts, A
Dramatic/Theatre Arts and Stagecraft, A
E-Commerce/Electronic Commerce, A
Early Childhood Education and Teaching, A
Economics, A
Education, A
Electrical/Electronics Equipment Installation and Repair, A
Electromechanical Technology/Electromechanical Engineering Technology, A
Energy Management and Systems Technology/Technician, A
English Language and Literature, A
Environmental Sciences, A
Geology/Earth Science, A
Health Information/Medical Records Technology/Technician, A
Heating, Air Conditioning, Ventilation and Refrigeration Maintenance Technology/Technician, A
History, A
Hotel/Motel Administration/Management, A
Kinesiology and Exercise Science, A
Legal Administrative Assistant/Secretary, A
Liberal Arts and Sciences Studies and Humanities, A
Mathematics, A
Medical Administrative Assistant/Secretary, A
Medical Radiologic Technology/Science - Radiation Therapist, A
Music, A
Natural Resources and Conservation, A
Occupational Safety and Health Technology/Technician, A
Occupational Therapist Assistant, A
Philosophy, A
Physical Therapist Assistant, A
Political Science and Government, A
Pre-Dentistry Studies, A
Pre-Law Studies, A
Pre-Medicine/Pre-Medical Studies, A
Pre-Nursing Studies, A
Pre-Pharmacy Studies, A
Psychology, A
Respiratory Care Therapy/Therapist, A
Restaurant/Food Services Management, A
Social Work, A
Sociology, A
Spanish Language and Literature, A
System, Networking, and LAN/WAN Management/Manager, A
Teacher Assistant/Aide, A
Telecommunications Technology/Technician, A
Welding Technology/Welder, A

SAM HOUSTON STATE UNIVERSITY

Accounting, BM
Advertising, B
Agribusiness, B
Agricultural Communication/Journalism, B
Agricultural Mechanization, B
Agricultural Sciences, M
Agricultural Teacher Education, B
Agriculture, B
Allied Health and Medical Assisting Services, M
Animal Sciences, B
Animation, Interactive Technology, Video Graphics and Special Effects, B
Art/Art Studies, General, B
Athletic Training and Sports Medicine, B
Banking and Financial Support Services, B
Biological and Biomedical Sciences, M
Biological and Physical Sciences, B
Biology/Biological Sciences, B
Biomedical Sciences, B
Business Administration and Management, B

Business Administration, Management and Operations, M
Business Teacher Education, B
Business/Commerce, B
Business/Managerial Economics, B
Chemistry, BM
Clinical Laboratory Science/Medical Technology/Technologist, B
Clinical Psychology, MD
Commercial and Advertising Art, B
Communication Studies/Speech Communication and Rhetoric, B
Communication and Media Studies, M
Computational Sciences, M
Computer Engineering Technology/Technician, B
Computer Science, MD
Computer Software Technology/Technician, B
Computer and Information Sciences, B
Computer and Information Systems Security, BM
Construction Engineering Technology/Technician, B
Corrections and Criminal Justice, B
Counselor Education/School Counseling and Guidance Services, B
Criminal Justice/Law Enforcement Administration, B
Criminal Justice/Police Science, B
Criminal Justice/Safety Studies, B
Criminology, MD
Curriculum and Instruction, BMD
Dance, BM
Developmental Education, D
Drafting and Design Technology/Technician, B
Drama and Dramatics/Theatre Arts, B
Education, MD
Educational Administration and Supervision, MD
Educational Leadership and Administration, BMD
Educational, Instructional, and Curriculum Supervision, B
Educational/Instructional Media Design, B
Electrical, Electronic and Communications Engineering Technology/Technician, B
English, M
English Language and Literature, B
Entrepreneurship/Entrepreneurial Studies, B
Environmental Sciences, B
Family and Consumer Sciences/Human Sciences, BM
Fashion Merchandising, B
Finance, B
Finance and Banking, M
Fine/Studio Arts, B
Foods, Nutrition, and Wellness Studies, B
Foodservice Systems Administration/Management, B
Forensic Science and Technology, BM
French Language and Literature, B
General Studies, B
Geographic Information Systems, MO
Geography, B
Geology/Earth Science, B
German Language and Literature, B
Graphic Communications, B
Health Services/Allied Health/Health Sciences, B
Health Teacher Education, B
Health and Physical Education, B
Health/Health Care Administration/Management, B
Higher Education/Higher Education Administration, M
History, BM
Homeland Security, M
Horticultural Science, B
Human Resources Management/Personnel Administration, B
Humanities/Humanistic Studies, BMDO
Industrial Technology/Technician, B
Information Science/Studies, M
Interior Architecture, B
International Business/Trade/Commerce, B
Internet and Interactive Multimedia, M
Journalism, B
Kinesiology and Exercise Science, B
Kinesiology and Movement Studies, M
Library Science, BM
Management Information Systems and Services, B
Manufacturing Technology/Technician, B
Marketing/Marketing Management, B
Mass Communication/Media Studies, B

Mathematics, BM
Multi-/Interdisciplinary Studies, B
Music, BM
Music Performance, B
Music Teacher Education, B
Music Theory and Composition, B
Music Therapy/Therapist, B
Nutritional Sciences, M
Operations Management and Supervision, B
Philosophy, B
Photography, B
Physical Education Teaching and Coaching, B
Physical Sciences, B
Physics, B
Political Science and Government, BM
Project Management, M
Psychology, BMDO
Public Administration, BM
Public Health (MPH, DPH), B
Publishing, M
Radio and Television, B
Reading Teacher Education, BMD
Sales, Distribution and Marketing Operations, B
School Psychology, O
Secondary Education and Teaching, B
Sociology, BM
Spanish Language and Literature, BM
Special Education and Teaching, BMD
Sport and Fitness Administration/Management, M
Statistics, M
Writing, M

SAN ANTONIO COLLEGE

Biological and Physical Sciences, A
Business Administration and Management, A
Business Machine Repairer, A
Child Care Provider/Assistant, A
Child Care and Support Services Management, A
Child Development, A
Civil Engineering Technology/Technician, A
Commercial and Advertising Art, A
Computer Engineering Technology/Technician, A
Computer Graphics, A
Computer Programming, A
Computer Programming, Specific Applications, A
Computer Programming, Vendor/Product Certification, A
Computer Programming/Programmer, A
Computer/Information Technology Services Administration and Management, A
Corrections, A
Court Reporting/Court Reporter, A
Criminal Justice/Law Enforcement Administration, A
Criminal Justice/Police Science, A
Data Entry/Microcomputer Applications, A
Data Processing and Data Processing Technology/Technician, A
Dental Hygiene/Hygienist, A
Drafting and Design Technology/Technician, A
Electrical, Electronic and Communications Engineering Technology/Technician, A
Engineering Technology, A
Fire Science/Firefighting, A
Funeral Service and Mortuary Science, A
Industrial Technology/Technician, A
Legal Administrative Assistant/Secretary, A
Liberal Arts and Sciences Studies and Humanities, A
Mechanical Engineering/Mechanical Technology/Technician, A
Medical/Clinical Assistant, A
Metal and Jewelry Arts, A
Psychology, A
Public Administration, A
Radio and Television, A
Real Estate, A
Speech Teacher Education, A
System Administration/Administrator, A
Web Page, Digital/Multimedia and Information Resources Design, A
Word Processing, A

SAN JACINTO COLLEGE DISTRICT

Accounting, A
Administrative Assistant and Secretarial Science, A
Agribusiness, A

Agriculture, A
Airline/Commercial/Professional Pilot and Flight Crew, A
Art/Art Studies, General, A
Autobody/Collision and Repair Technology/Technician, A
Automobile/Automotive Mechanics Technology/Technician, A
Aviation/Airway Management and Operations, A
Baking and Pastry Arts/Baker/Pastry Chef, A
Behavioral Sciences, A
Biology/Biological Sciences, A
Business Administration and Management, A
Business/Commerce, A
Chemical Technology/Technician, A
Chemistry, A
Child Development, A
Clinical/Medical Laboratory Technician, A
Commercial and Advertising Art, A
Computer and Information Sciences, A
Construction Engineering Technology/Technician, A
Cosmetology, Barber/Styling, and Nail Instructor, A
Cosmetology/Cosmetologist, A
Criminal Justice/Police Science, A
Culinary Arts/Chef Training, A
Dance, A
Diagnostic Medical Sonography/Sonographer and Ultrasound Technician, A
Diesel Mechanics Technology/Technician, A
Digital Communication and Media/Multimedia, A
Drafting and Design Technology/Technician, A
Drama and Dramatics/Theatre Arts, A
Electrical and Power Transmission Installation/Installer, A
Electrical, Electronic and Communications Engineering Technology/Technician, A
Emergency Medical Technology/Technician (EMT Paramedic), A
Engineering, A
English Language and Literature, A
Environmental Sciences, A
Fire Science/Firefighting, A
Foodservice Systems Administration/Management, A
Foreign Languages and Literatures, A
General Studies, A
Geology/Earth Science, A
Health Information/Medical Records Technology/Technician, A
Health and Physical Education, A
Heating, Air Conditioning, Ventilation and Refrigeration Maintenance Technology/Technician, A
Hispanic-American, Puerto Rican, and Mexican-American/Chicano Studies, A
History, A
Instrumentation Technology/Technician, A
Interior Design, A
International Business/Trade/Commerce, A
Journalism, A
Legal Assistant/Paralegal, A
Management Information Systems and Services, A
Marine Science/Merchant Marine Officer, A
Mathematics, A
Medical/Clinical Assistant, A
Music, A
Occupational Safety and Health Technology/Technician, A
Optometric Technician/Assistant, A
Pharmacy Technician/Assistant, A
Philosophy, A
Physical Sciences, A
Physical Therapist Assistant, A
Physics, A
Political Science and Government, A
Psychology, A
Radio and Television Broadcasting Technology/Technician, A
Radiologic Technology/Science - Radiographer, A
Real Estate, A
Respiratory Care Therapy/Therapist, A
Restaurant, Culinary, and Catering Management/Manager, A
Science Teacher Education/General Science Teacher Education, A
Secondary Education and Teaching, A
Social Sciences, A

Sociology, A
Surgical Technology/Technologist, A
Welding Technology/Welder, A

SCHREINER UNIVERSITY

Accounting, B
Biochemistry, B
Biology Teacher Education, B
Biology/Biological Sciences, B
Business Administration and Management, B
Business Administration, Management and Operations, M
Business/Commerce, B
Chemistry, B
Chemistry Teacher Education, B
Communication Studies/Speech Communication and Rhetoric, B
Design and Applied Arts, B
Drama and Dramatics/Theatre Arts, B
Early Childhood Education and Teaching, B
Education, BMO
Educational Administration and Supervision, MO
Elementary Education and Teaching, B
Engineering, B
English Language and Literature, B
English/Language Arts Teacher Education, B
Ethics, M
Finance, B
Graphic Design, B
History, B
History Teacher Education, B
Junior High/Intermediate/Middle School Education and Teaching, B
Kinesiology and Exercise Science, B
Liberal Arts and Sciences Studies and Humanities, AB
Management Information Systems and Services, B
Marketing/Marketing Management, B
Mathematics, B
Mathematics Teacher Education, B
Music, B
Music Teacher Education, B
Physical Education Teaching and Coaching, B
Political Science and Government, B
Psychology, B
Religion/Religious Studies, B
Sport and Fitness Administration/Management, B

SOUTH PLAINS COLLEGE

Accounting, A
Administrative Assistant and Secretarial Science, A
Advertising, A
Agricultural Economics, A
Agriculture, A
Agronomy and Crop Science, A
Art/Art Studies, General, A
Automobile/Automotive Mechanics Technology/Technician, A
Biological and Physical Sciences, A
Biology/Biological Sciences, A
Business Administration and Management, A
Carpentry/Carpenter, A
Chemistry, A
Child Development, A
Commercial and Advertising Art, A
Computer Engineering Technology/Technician, A
Computer Programming/Programmer, A
Computer Science, A
Consumer Merchandising/Retailing Management, A
Cosmetology/Cosmetologist, A
Criminal Justice/Law Enforcement Administration, A
Criminal Justice/Police Science, A
Data Processing and Data Processing Technology/Technician, A
Dietetics/Dieticians, A
Drafting and Design Technology/Technician, A
Education, A
Electrical, Electronic and Communications Engineering Technology/Technician, A
Engineering, A
Fashion Merchandising, A
Fire Science/Firefighting, A
Health Information/Medical Records Administration/Administrator, A
Health/Health Care Administration/Management, A

Heating, Air Conditioning, Ventilation and Refrigeration Maintenance Technology/Technician, A
Industrial Radiologic Technology/Technician, A
Journalism, A
Legal Administrative Assistant/Secretary, A
Liberal Arts and Sciences Studies and Humanities, A
Machine Tool Technology/Machinist, A
Marketing/Marketing Management, A
Mass Communication/Media Studies, A
Medical Administrative Assistant/Secretary, A
Mental Health Counseling/Counselor, A
Music, A
Petroleum Technology/Technician, A
Physical Education Teaching and Coaching, A
Physical Therapy/Therapist, A
Real Estate, A
Recording Arts Technology/Technician, A
Respiratory Care Therapy/Therapist, A
Social Work, A
Special Products Marketing Operations, A
Surgical Technology/Technologist, A
Telecommunications Technology/Technician, A
Welding Technology/Welder, A

SOUTH TEXAS COLLEGE

Accounting, A
Automobile/Automotive Mechanics Technology/Technician, A
Behavioral Sciences, A
Business Administration and Management, A
Clinical Laboratory Science/Medical Technology/Technologist, A
Computer Science, A
Computer Typography and Composition Equipment Operator, A
Education, A
Emergency Medical Technology/Technician (EMT Paramedic), A
Heating, Air Conditioning, Ventilation and Refrigeration Maintenance Technology/Technician, A
Heavy Equipment Maintenance Technology/Technician, A
Hospitality Administration/Management, A
Hotel/Motel Administration/Management, A
Human Services, A
Industrial Radiologic Technology/Technician, A
Industrial Technology/Technician, A
Information Science/Studies, A
Legal Administrative Assistant/Secretary, A
Legal Assistant/Paralegal, A
Liberal Arts and Sciences Studies and Humanities, A
Machine Tool Technology/Machinist, A
Occupational Therapy/Therapist, A
Plastics Engineering Technology/Technician, A

SOUTH UNIVERSITY

Business Administration and Management, B
Business Administration, Management and Operations, M
Counseling Psychology, M
Criminal Justice/Law Enforcement Administration, B
Health/Health Care Administration/Management, B
Information Science/Studies, B
Legal Assistant/Paralegal, B
Management Information Systems and Services, M
Physical Therapist Assistant, A
Psychology, B

SOUTHERN METHODIST UNIVERSITY

Accounting, BM
Advertising, B
Advertising and Public Relations, M
African-American/Black Studies, B
Anthropology, BMD
Applied Economics, M
Applied Mathematics, MD
Applied Science and Technology, M
Art History, Criticism and Conservation, BMD
Arts Management, M
Atmospheric Sciences and Meteorology, D
Biochemistry, B
Biological and Biomedical Sciences, MD
Biology/Biological Sciences, B
Business Administration and Management, B

Business Administration, Management and Operations, M
Cell Biology and Anatomy, MD
Ceramic Arts and Ceramics, M
Chemistry, BMD
Cinematography and Film/Video Production, B
Civil Engineering, BMD
Clinical Psychology, D
Communication and Media Studies, B
Composition, M
Computational Sciences, MD
Computer Engineering, BMD
Computer Science, BMD
Conflict Resolution and Mediation/Peace Studies, M
Counselor Education/School Counseling and Guidance Services, M
Dance, B
Database Systems, M
Design and Applied Arts, B
Drama and Dramatics/Theatre Arts, B
Econometrics and Quantitative Economics, B
Economics, BMD
Education, MD
Education/Teaching of the Gifted and Talented, M
Electrical Engineering, MD
Electrical, Electronics and Communications Engineering, B
Engineering Management, MD
Engineering and Applied Sciences, MD
English, MD
English Language and Literature, B
Entrepreneurship/Entrepreneurial Studies, M
Environmental Engineering Technology/Environmental Technology, MD
Environmental Sciences, BD
Environmental Studies, B
Environmental/Environmental Health Engineering, B
Ethics, D
Experimental Psychology, M
Finance, B
Finance and Banking, M
Financial Planning and Services, B
Fine Arts and Art Studies, M
Fine/Studio Arts, B
French Language and Literature, B
Geology/Earth Science, BMD
Geophysics and Seismology, BM
German Language and Literature, B
Health Professions and Related Clinical Sciences, B
Hispanic-American, Puerto Rican, and Mexican-American/Chicano Studies, B
History, BMD
Information Science/Studies, MD
Insurance, B
International/Global Studies, B
Italian Studies, B
Journalism, B
Latin American Studies, B
Law and Legal Studies, MD
Liberal Arts and Sciences Studies and Humanities, B
Liberal Studies, M
Management, M
Management Information Systems and Services, M
Management Strategy and Policy, M
Manufacturing Engineering, M
Marketing, M
Marketing/Marketing Management, B
Materials Engineering, MD
Materials Sciences, MD
Mathematics, BMD
Mechanical Engineering, BMD
Medieval and Renaissance Studies, BM
Molecular Biology, MD
Multi-/Interdisciplinary Studies, B
Multilingual and Multicultural Education, M
Music, BM
Music History, Literature, and Theory, M
Music Performance, B
Music Teacher Education, BM
Music Theory and Composition, BM
Music Therapy/Therapist, B
Operations Research, BMD
Painting, M
Performance, M
Philosophy, B

Photography, M
Physics, BMD
Physiology, M
Piano and Organ, B
Political Science and Government, B
Printmaking, M
Psychology, BD
Public Policy Analysis, B
Public Relations/Image Management, B
Reading Teacher Education, M
Real Estate, BM
Religion/Religious Studies, BMD
Sculpture, M
Sociology, B
Software Engineering, MD
Spanish Language and Literature, B
Special Education and Teaching, M
Sport and Fitness Administration/Management, BM
Statistics, BMD
Structural Engineering, D
Sustainable Development, M
Systems Engineering, MD
Systems Science and Theory, MD
Taxation, M
Telecommunications, M
Theater, M
Theology and Religious Vocations, MD
Voice and Opera, B
Water Resources Engineering, D

SOUTHWEST TEXAS JUNIOR COLLEGE

Agricultural Mechanization, A
Automobile/Automotive Mechanics
   Technology/Technician, A
Avionics Maintenance Technology/Technician, A
Biological and Physical Sciences, A
Business Administration and Management, A
Computer Engineering Technology/Technician, A
Cosmetology/Cosmetologist, A
Criminal Justice/Law Enforcement Administration, A
Data Processing and Data Processing
   Technology/Technician, A
Education, A
Engineering, A
Farm/Farm and Ranch Management, A
Liberal Arts and Sciences Studies and Humanities, A
Teacher Assistant/Aide, A

SOUTHWESTERN ADVENTIST UNIVERSITY

Accounting, BM
Biochemistry, B
Biology Teacher Education, B
Biology/Biological Sciences, B
Business Administration, Management and Operations, M
Business Teacher Education, B
Chemistry, B
Chemistry Teacher Education, B
Clinical Laboratory Science/Medical
   Technology/Technologist, B
Computer Science, B
Curriculum and Instruction, M
Education, M
Educational Leadership and Administration, M
Elementary Education and Teaching, B
English Language and Literature, B
English/Language Arts Teacher Education, B
Finance, B
Finance and Banking, M
Fire Science/Firefighting, A
General Studies, AB
Health and Physical Education, B
History, B
International Business/Trade/Commerce, B
International Relations and Affairs, B
Journalism, B
Kinesiology and Exercise Science, AB
Management, M
Marketing/Marketing Management, B
Mathematics, B
Multi-/Interdisciplinary Studies, B
Music, B
Music Performance, B

Physics Teacher Education, B
Psychology, B
Reading Teacher Education, M
Religion/Religious Studies, B
Social Sciences, B
Social Studies Teacher Education, B
Sport and Fitness Administration/Management, AB
Theology/Theological Studies, B

SOUTHWESTERN ASSEMBLIES OF GOD UNIVERSITY

Accounting, B
Bible/Biblical Studies, AB
Bilingual and Multilingual Education, B
Broadcast Journalism, B
Business Administration and Management, AB
Business/Commerce, A
Communication Studies/Speech Communication
   and Rhetoric, B
Counseling Psychology, M
Criminal Justice/Safety Studies, B
Curriculum and Instruction, M
Divinity/Ministry (BD, MDiv.), B
Drama and Dramatics/Theatre Arts, B
Early Childhood Education and Teaching, A
Education, ABM
Educational Administration and Supervision, M
Elementary Education and Teaching, B
English Language and Literature, AB
English/Language Arts Teacher Education, B
Foreign Languages and Literatures, A
General Studies, A
History, BM
Human Services, B
Management Science, B
Marketing/Marketing Management, B
Mass Communication/Media Studies, A
Missions/Missionary Studies and Missiology, M
Music, B
Music Performance, B
Music Teacher Education, B
Pastoral Studies/Counseling, BM
Psychology, A
Religion/Religious Studies, M
Religious Education, M
Religious/Sacred Music, B
Secondary Education and Teaching, BM
Social Sciences, A
Social Studies Teacher Education, B
Social Work, B
Sport and Fitness Administration/Management, B
Theology and Religious Vocations, M
Theology/Theological Studies, B
Youth Ministry, B

SOUTHWESTERN CHRISTIAN COLLEGE

Bible/Biblical Studies, B
Liberal Arts and Sciences Studies and Humanities, A

SOUTHWESTERN UNIVERSITY

Accounting, B
Ancient/Classical Greek Language and Literature, B
Animal Behavior and Ethology, B
Anthropology, B
Art History, Criticism and Conservation, B
Art/Art Studies, General, B
Biochemistry, B
Biology/Biological Sciences, B
Business/Commerce, B
Chemistry, B
Classics and Classical Languages, Literatures, and Linguistics, B
Communication Studies/Speech Communication
   and Rhetoric, B
Computational Mathematics, B
Computer and Information Sciences, B
Drama and Dramatics/Theatre Arts, B
Economics, B
Education, B
English Language and Literature, B
Environmental Studies, B
French Language and Literature, B
German Language and Literature, B
History, B

International Relations and Affairs, B
Kinesiology and Exercise Science, B
Latin American Studies, B
Latin Language and Literature, B
Mathematics, B
Music, B
Philosophy, B
Physical Sciences, B
Physics, B
Political Science and Government, B
Psychology, B
Religion/Religious Studies, B
Sociology, B
Spanish Language and Literature, B
Women's Studies, B

STEPHEN F. AUSTIN STATE UNIVERSITY

Accounting, BM
Agribusiness, B
Agricultural Education, M
Agricultural Mechanization, B
Agricultural Production Operations, B
Agriculture, B
Animal Sciences, B
Art History, Criticism and Conservation, B
Art/Art Studies, General, B
Athletic Training and Sports Medicine, M
Audiology/Audiologist and Hearing Sciences, B
BioTechnology, M
Biochemistry, B
Biological and Biomedical Sciences, M
Biology/Biological Sciences, B
Business Administration and Management, B
Business Administration, Management and Operations, M
Business/Commerce, B
Business/Corporate Communications, B
Business/Managerial Economics, B
Cartography, B
Chemistry, BM
Communication Disorders, BM
Communication and Media Studies, M
Computer Science, M
Computer and Information Sciences, B
Corrections, B
Counselor Education/School Counseling and Guidance Services, M
Criminal Justice/Police Science, B
Dance, B
Design and Applied Arts, M
Drama and Dramatics/Theatre Arts, B
Early Childhood Education and Teaching, M
Economics, B
Education, MD
Educational Leadership and Administration, MD
Elementary Education and Teaching, M
Engineering Physics, B
English, M
English Language and Literature, B
Environmental Sciences, BM
Fashion Merchandising, B
Finance, B
Fine Arts and Art Studies, M
Foods, Nutrition, and Wellness Studies, B
Foreign Languages and Literatures, B
Forest Management/Forest Resources Management, B
Forestry, BMD
Geography, B
Geology/Earth Science, BM
Health Services/Allied Health/Health Sciences, B
History, BM
Home Economics, M
Horticultural Science, B
Hospitality Administration/Management, B
Human Resources Management/Personnel Administration, B
Information Technology, B
Interdisciplinary Studies, M
Interior Architecture, B
International Business/Trade/Commerce, B
Kinesiology and Exercise Science, B
Kinesiology and Movement Studies, M
Legal Assistant/Paralegal, B

Liberal Arts and Sciences Studies and Humanities, B
Management, M
Marketing, M
Marketing/Marketing Management, B
Mass Communication/Media Studies, BM
Mathematics, BM
Mathematics Teacher Education, M
Multi-/Interdisciplinary Studies, B
Music, BM
Painting, M
Philosophy, B
Physics, BM
Political Science and Government, B
Poultry Science, B
Psychology, BM
Public Administration, BM
School Psychology, M
Sculpture, M
Secondary Education and Teaching, MD
Social Work, BM
Sociology, B
Special Education and Teaching, M
Special Products Marketing Operations, B
Statistics, M
Wildlife and Wildlands Science and Management, B

STRAYER UNIVERSITY–CEDAR HILL CAMPUS

Accounting, B
Business Administration and Management, B
Criminal Justice/Law Enforcement Administration, B
Economics, B
International Business/Trade/Commerce, B
Management Information Systems and Services, B

STRAYER UNIVERSITY–IRVING CAMPUS

Accounting, B
Business Administration and Management, B
Criminal Justice/Law Enforcement Administration, B
Economics, B
International Business/Trade/Commerce, B
Management Information Systems and Services, B

STRAYER UNIVERSITY–KATY CAMPUS

Accounting, B
Business Administration and Management, B
Criminal Justice/Law Enforcement Administration, B
Economics, B
International Business/Trade/Commerce, B
Management Information Systems and Services, B

STRAYER UNIVERSITY–NORTH AUSTIN CAMPUS

Accounting, B
Business Administration and Management, B
Criminal Justice/Law Enforcement Administration, B
Economics, B
International Business/Trade/Commerce, B
Management Information Systems and Services, B

STRAYER UNIVERSITY–NORTHWEST HOUSTON CAMPUS

Accounting, B
Business Administration and Management, B
Criminal Justice/Law Enforcement Administration, B
Economics, B
International Business/Trade/Commerce, B
Management Information Systems and Services, B

STRAYER UNIVERSITY–PLANO CAMPUS

Accounting, B
Business Administration and Management, B
Criminal Justice/Law Enforcement Administration, B
Economics, B
International Business/Trade/Commerce, B
Management Information Systems and Services, B

SUL ROSS STATE UNIVERSITY

Agricultural Business and Management, B
Animal Health, B
Animal Sciences, M

Art Education, M
Art History, Criticism and Conservation, M
Art/Art Studies, General, B
Biological and Biomedical Sciences, M
Biology/Biological Sciences, B
Business Administration and Management, B
Business Administration, Management and Operations, M
Ceramic Arts and Ceramics, M
Chemistry, B
Clinical Psychology, M
Counselor Education/School Counseling and Guidance Services, M
Criminal Justice/Law Enforcement Administration, B
Criminology, M
Drama and Dramatics/Theatre Arts, B
Education, MO
Educational Administration and Supervision, M
Educational Measurement and Evaluation, MO
Elementary Education and Teaching, M
English, M
English Language and Literature, B
Fine Arts and Art Studies, M
Fish, Game and Wildlife Management, M
Geology/Earth Science, BM
History, BM
Mass Communication/Media Studies, B
Mathematics, B
Multilingual and Multicultural Education, M
Music, B
Natural Resources Management/Development and Policy, M
Painting, M
Physical Education Teaching and Coaching, BM
Political Science and Government, BM
Psychology, BM
Range Science and Management, BM
Reading Teacher Education, MO
Sculpture, M
Secondary Education and Teaching, M
Social Sciences, B
Spanish Language and Literature, B
Wildlife and Wildlands Science and Management, B

TARLETON STATE UNIVERSITY

Accounting, B
Agribusiness, B
Agricultural Economics, B
Agricultural Education, M
Agricultural Mechanization, B
Agricultural Production Operations, B
Agricultural Sciences, M
Agricultural Teacher Education, B
Agricultural and Domestic Animals Services, B
Agricultural and Extension Education Services, B
Agricultural/Farm Supplies Retailing and Wholesaling, B
Agriculture, B
Agriculture, Agriculture Operations and Related Sciences, B
Agronomy and Crop Science, B
Airline/Commercial/Professional Pilot and Flight Crew, B
Animal Sciences, BM
Animal/Livestock Husbandry and Production, B
Art/Art Studies, General, B
Aviation/Airway Management and Operations, B
Biological and Biomedical Sciences, M
Biology/Biological Sciences, B
Biomedical Sciences, B
Business Administration and Management, B
Business Administration, Management and Operations, M
Business/Commerce, B
Business/Managerial Economics, B
Chemistry, B
Clinical Laboratory Science/Medical Technology/Technologist, B
Clinical/Medical Laboratory Technician, A
Communication Studies/Speech Communication and Rhetoric, B
Computer and Information Sciences, B
Counseling Psychology, MO
Counselor Education/School Counseling and Guidance Services, BM
Criminal Justice/Law Enforcement Administration, B

Criminal Justice/Safety Studies, B
Criminology, M
Curriculum and Instruction, BM
Drama and Dramatics/Theatre Arts, B
Economics, B
Education, BMDO
Educational Administration and Supervision, MDO
Educational Leadership and Administration, BDO
Elementary Education and Teaching, B
Engineering Management, M
Engineering Physics, B
Engineering Technology, B
English, M
English Language and Literature, B
Environmental Sciences, BM
Environmental Studies, B
Environmental/Environmental Health Engineering, B
Family and Consumer Sciences/Human Sciences, B
Farm/Farm and Ranch Management, B
Finance, B
Fine/Studio Arts, B
Geology/Earth Science, B
Health and Physical Education, B
Histologic Technician, A
Histologic Technology/Histotechnologist, A
History, BM
Horticultural Science, B
Human Nutrition, B
Human Resources Management and Services, M
Human Resources Management/Personnel Administration, B
Hydrology and Water Resources Science, B
Industrial Production Technologies/Technicians, B
Industrial Technology/Technician, B
Information Science/Studies, B
International Agriculture, B
International Business/Trade/Commerce, B
International/Global Studies, B
Junior High/Intermediate/Middle School Education and Teaching, B
Kinesiology and Exercise Science, B
Liberal Arts and Sciences Studies and Humanities, B
Livestock Management, B
Management Information Systems and Services, BM
Manufacturing Technology/Technician, B
Marketing/Marketing Management, B
Mathematics, BM
Medical Technology, M
Multi-/Interdisciplinary Studies, B
Music, B
Music Teacher Education, BM
Nursing, M
Office Management and Supervision, B
Ornamental Horticulture, B
Physical Education Teaching and Coaching, BM
Physical Therapy/Therapist, B
Physics, B
Political Science and Government, BM
Pre-Dentistry Studies, B
Pre-Medicine/Pre-Medical Studies, B
Pre-Pharmacy Studies, B
Pre-Veterinary Studies, B
Psychology, B
Quality Control Technology/Technician, B
Range Science and Management, B
School Psychology, M
Science Teacher Education/General Science Teacher Education, B
Secondary Education and Teaching, BO
Social Work, B
Sociology, B
Spanish Language and Literature, B
Special Education and Teaching, O
Teacher Education, Multiple Levels, B
Teaching English as a Second or Foreign Language/ESL Language Instructor, B
Wildlife and Wildlands Science and Management, B

TARRANT COUNTY COLLEGE DISTRICT

Accounting, A
Administrative Assistant and Secretarial Science, A
Architectural Engineering Technology/Technician, A

Automobile/Automotive Mechanics Technology/Technician, A
Avionics Maintenance Technology/Technician, A
Business Administration and Management, A
Clinical Laboratory Science/Medical Technology/Technologist, A
Clinical/Medical Laboratory Technician, A
Computer Programming/Programmer, A
Computer Science, A
Construction Engineering Technology/Technician, A
Consumer Merchandising/Retailing Management, A
Criminal Justice/Law Enforcement Administration, A
Dental Hygiene/Hygienist, A
Dietetics/Dieticians, A
Drafting and Design Technology/Technician, A
Educational/Instructional Media Design, A
Electrical, Electronic and Communications Engineering Technology/Technician, A
Electromechanical Technology/Electromechanical Engineering Technology, A
Emergency Medical Technology/Technician (EMT Paramedic), A
Fashion Merchandising, A
Fire Science/Firefighting, A
Food Technology and Processing, A
Graphic and Printing Equipment Operator Production, A
Health Information/Medical Records Administration/Administrator, A
Heating, Air Conditioning, Ventilation and Refrigeration Maintenance Technology/Technician, A
Horticultural Science, A
Industrial Radiologic Technology/Technician, A
Legal Assistant/Paralegal, A
Liberal Arts and Sciences Studies and Humanities, A
Machine Tool Technology/Machinist, A
Marketing/Marketing Management, A
Mechanical Engineering/Mechanical Technology/Technician, A
Mental Health Counseling/Counselor, A
Physical Therapy/Therapist, A
Quality Control Technology/Technician, A
Respiratory Care Therapy/Therapist, A
Sign Language Interpretation and Translation, A
Surgical Technology/Technologist, A
Welding Technology/Welder, A

TEMPLE COLLEGE

Administrative Assistant and Secretarial Science, A
Art/Art Studies, General, A
Biology Technician/BioTechnology Laboratory Technician, A
Business Administration and Management, A
Computer Programming/Programmer, A
Computer Science, A
Computer and Information Sciences, A
Criminal Justice/Law Enforcement Administration, A
Criminal Justice/Police Science, A
Data Processing and Data Processing Technology/Technician, A
Dental Hygiene/Hygienist, A
Diagnostic Medical Sonography/Sonographer and Ultrasound Technician, A
Drafting and Design Technology/Technician, A
Emergency Medical Technology/Technician (EMT Paramedic), A
Liberal Arts and Sciences Studies and Humanities, A
Respiratory Care Therapy/Therapist, A
System, Networking, and LAN/WAN Management/Manager, A
Web/Multimedia Management and Webmaster, A

TEXARKANA COLLEGE

Administrative Assistant and Secretarial Science, A
Agriculture, A
Art/Art Studies, General, A
Automobile/Automotive Mechanics Technology/Technician, A
Biology/Biological Sciences, A
Business Administration and Management, A
Business/Commerce, A
Chemistry, A
Child Care and Support Services Management, A
Child Development, A

Computer and Information Sciences, A
Cosmetology/Cosmetologist, A
Criminal Justice/Law Enforcement Administration, A
Criminal Justice/Safety Studies, A
Culinary Arts/Chef Training, A
Diesel Mechanics Technology/Technician, A
Drafting and Design Technology/Technician, A
Drama and Dramatics/Theatre Arts, A
Electrical, Electronic and Communications Engineering Technology/Technician, A
Emergency Medical Technology/Technician (EMT Paramedic), A
Engineering, A
Foreign Languages and Literatures, A
Health Aide, A
Heating, Air Conditioning, Ventilation and Refrigeration Maintenance Technology/Technician, A
History, A
Humanities/Humanistic Studies, A
Industrial Mechanics and Maintenance Technology, A
Journalism, A
Liberal Arts and Sciences Studies and Humanities, A
Marketing/Marketing Management, A
Mathematics, A
Music, A
Pharmacy Technician/Assistant, A
Physics, A
Political Science and Government, A
Real Estate, A
Social Sciences, A
Substance Abuse/Addiction Counseling, A
Welding Technology/Welder, A

TEXAS A&M INTERNATIONAL UNIVERSITY

Accounting, BM
Bilingual and Multilingual Education, B
Biological and Biomedical Sciences, M
Biology Teacher Education, B
Biology/Biological Sciences, B
Business Administration and Management, B
Business Administration, Management and Operations, MD
Business/Managerial Economics, B
Chemistry, B
Communication Disorders, B
Communication Studies/Speech Communication and Rhetoric, B
Counseling Psychology, M
Counselor Education/School Counseling and Guidance Services, M
Criminal Justice/Police Science, B
Criminology, M
Curriculum and Instruction, M
Education, M
Educational Administration and Supervision, M
English, MD
English Language and Literature, B
English/Language Arts Teacher Education, B
Finance, B
Finance and Banking, M
Fine/Studio Arts, B
Foreign Language Teacher Education, MD
Health and Physical Education, B
Hispanic Studies, D
History, BM
History Teacher Education, B
Information Science/Studies, B
International Business/Trade/Commerce, MD
Kindergarten/PreSchool Education and Teaching, B
Kinesiology and Exercise Science, B
Management Information Systems and Services, BMD
Marketing/Marketing Management, B
Mathematics, BM
Mathematics Teacher Education, B
Multi-/Interdisciplinary Studies, B
Music, B
Nursing, M
Nursing - Advanced Practice, M
Physical Education Teaching and Coaching, B
Physical Sciences, B
Political Science and Government, BM
Psychology, BM

Public Administration, M
Reading Teacher Education, B
Science Teacher Education/General Science Teacher Education, B
Social Sciences, BM
Social Studies Teacher Education, B
Sociology, B
Spanish Language Teacher Education, B
Spanish Language and Literature, B
Special Education and Teaching, BM
Systems Engineering, B
Translation and Interpretation, M

TEXAS A&M UNIVERSITY

Accounting, BMD
Aerospace, Aeronautical and Astronautical Engineering, BMD
Agribusiness, B
Agricultural Business and Management, B
Agricultural Communication/Journalism, B
Agricultural Economics, BMD
Agricultural Education, MD
Agricultural Engineering, MD
Agricultural Sciences, MD
Agricultural and Food Products Processing, B
Agricultural/Biological Engineering and Bioengineering, B
Agricultural/Farm Supplies Retailing and Wholesaling, B
Agriculture, B
Agronomy and Crop Science, B
Agronomy and Soil Sciences, MD
Allied Health and Medical Assisting Services, MD
Animal Sciences, BMD
Animal/Livestock Husbandry and Production, B
Anthropology, BMD
Applied Horticulture/Horticultural Operations, B
Applied Mathematics, B
Applied Physics, D
Architecture, BMDO
Athletic Training and Sports Medicine, M
Atmospheric Sciences and Meteorology, B
Biochemistry, BMD
Bioengineering, MD
Biological and Biomedical Sciences, MD
Biology/Biological Sciences, B
Biomedical Engineering, MD
Biomedical Sciences, B
Biomedical/Medical Engineering, B
Biopsychology, D
Business Administration and Management, B
Cartography, B
Cell/Cellular and Molecular Biology, B
Chemical Engineering, BMD
Chemistry, BMD
City/Urban, Community and Regional Planning, B
Civil Engineering, BMD
Classics and Classical Languages, Literatures, and Linguistics, B
Clinical Psychology, D
Cognitive Sciences, D
Communication and Media Studies, MD
Community Health Services/Liaison/Counseling, B
Community Health and Preventive Medicine, M
Computer Engineering, BMD
Computer Graphics, B
Computer Science, BMD
Construction Engineering Technology/Technician, B
Construction Management, M
Counseling Psychology, D
Cultural Studies, M
Curriculum and Instruction, MD
Dentistry, MDO
Developmental Psychology, D
Digital Communication and Media/Multimedia, B
Drama and Dramatics/Theatre Arts, B
Economics, BMD
Education, MD
Educational Administration and Supervision, MD
Educational Media/Instructional Technology, M
Educational Psychology, MD
Electrical Engineering, MD
Electrical, Electronic and Communications Engineering Technology/Technician, B
Electrical, Electronics and Communications Engineering, B

Engineering Technology, B
English, MD
English Language and Literature, B
Entomology, BMD
Environmental Biology, B
Environmental Sciences, B
Environmental Studies, B
Farm/Farm and Ranch Management, B
Finance, B
Finance and Banking, MD
Fine Arts and Art Studies, M
Fish, Game and Wildlife Management, MD
Fishing and Fisheries Sciences and Management, B
Food Science and Technology, MD
Foods, Nutrition, and Wellness Studies, B
Foreign Languages and Literatures, B
Forensic Science and Technology, B
Forestry, BMD
French Language and Literature, B
Geography, BMD
Geological and Earth Sciences/Geosciences, B
Geology/Earth Science, BMD
Geophysics and Seismology, BMD
German Language and Literature, B
Health Education, MD
Health Physics/Radiological Health, M
Health Promotion, M
Health Services Administration, M
Health Services Research, D
History, BMD
Homeland Security, O
Horticultural Science, MD
Human Resources Development, BMD
Industrial Engineering, B
Industrial and Organizational Psychology, D
Industrial/Management Engineering, MD
International Affairs, MO
International/Global Studies, B
Kinesiology and Exercise Science, B
Kinesiology and Movement Studies, MD
Landscape Architecture, BMD
Law and Legal Studies, D
Logistics and Materials Management, B
Management, MD
Management Information Systems and Services, BM
Manufacturing Engineering, M
Manufacturing Technology/Technician, B
Marine Biology and Biological Oceanography, B
Marine Science/Merchant Marine Officer, B
Marketing, MD
Marketing/Marketing Management, B
Materials Engineering, MD
Materials Sciences, MD
Mathematics, BMD
Mechanical Engineering, BMD
Meteorology, MD
Microbiology, BMD
Molecular Genetics, B
Multi-/Interdisciplinary Studies, B
Multilingual and Multicultural Education, M
Music, B
National Security, O
Natural Resources Management/Development and Policy, MD
Natural Resources and Conservation, BM
Naval Architecture and Marine Engineering, B
Neuroscience, D
Non-Profit/Public/Organizational Management, O
Nuclear Engineering, BMD
Nursing, M
Nursing - Advanced Practice, M
Nursing Education, M
Nutritional Sciences, MD
Ocean Engineering, BMD
Oceanography, Chemical and Physical, MD
Ornamental Horticulture, B
Parks, Recreation and Leisure Facilities Management, B
Parks, Recreation, Leisure and Fitness Studies, B
Performance, M
Petroleum Engineering, BMD
Pharmacy, D
Philosophy, BMD
Physics, BMD
Plant Pathology/Phytopathology, MD

Plant Sciences, MD
Political Science and Government, BMD
Poultry Science, BMD
Psychology, BMD
Public Administration, M
Public Affairs, MO
Public Health, MD
Public Health (MPH, DPH), B
Range Science and Management, BMD
Real Estate, M
Recreation and Park Management, MD
Russian Language and Literature, B
Sales, Distribution and Marketing Operations, B
School Psychology, D
Social Psychology, D
Sociology, BMD
Spanish Language and Literature, BMD
Special Education and Teaching, M
Sport and Fitness Administration/Management, BM
Statistics, MD
System, Networking, and LAN/WAN Management/Manager, B
Tourism and Travel Services Management, B
Transportation/Transportation Management, B
Turf and Turfgrass Management, B
Urban and Regional Planning, MD
Veterinary Medicine, MD
Veterinary Sciences, MD
Water, Wetlands, and Marine Resources Management, B
Wildlife and Wildlands Science and Management, B
Women's Studies, B
Zoology/Animal Biology, B

TEXAS A&M UNIVERSITY–CENTRAL TEXAS

Accounting, BM
Aeronautics/Aviation/Aerospace Science and Technology, B
Airline/Commercial/Professional Pilot and Flight Crew, B
Aviation/Airway Management and Operations, B
Business Administration and Management, B
Business Administration, Management and Operations, M
Clinical Psychology, M
Computer and Information Sciences, B
Counselor Education/School Counseling and Guidance Services, M
Criminal Justice/Safety Studies, B
Criminology, M
Curriculum and Instruction, M
Economics, B
Educational Administration and Supervision, M
Educational Psychology, M
English Language and Literature, B
Experimental Psychology, M
Finance, B
History, BM
Human Resources Management and Services, M
Human Resources Management/Personnel Administration, B
Information Science/Studies, B
International Business/Trade/Commerce, B
Liberal Arts and Sciences Studies and Humanities, B
Liberal Studies, M
Management, M
Management Information Systems and Services, BM
Marketing/Marketing Management, B
Marriage and Family Therapy/Counseling, M
Mathematics, BM
Multi-/Interdisciplinary Studies, B
Office Management and Supervision, B
Physics, B
Political Science and Government, BM
Psychology, B
School Psychology, O
Social Work, B
Sociology, B
Teacher Education, Multiple Levels, B

TEXAS A&M UNIVERSITY–COMMERCE

Accounting, BM
Agribusiness, B

Agricultural Sciences, M
Agriculture, B
Animal Sciences, B
Biology/Biological Sciences, B
Business Administration and Management, B
Business Administration, Management and Operations, M
Business/Commerce, B
Chemistry, B
Computer and Information Sciences, B
Construction Engineering, B
Criminal Justice/Safety Studies, B
Drama and Dramatics/Theatre Arts, B
Education, MDO
English Language and Literature, B
Environmental Sciences, B
Finance, B
Finance and Banking, M
Fine/Studio Arts, B
General Studies, B
History, B
Industrial Engineering, B
Industrial Technology/Technician, B
Information Science/Studies, B
Journalism, B
Kinesiology and Exercise Science, B
Legal Assistant/Paralegal, B
Liberal Arts and Sciences Studies and Humanities, B
Management Information Systems and Services, B
Marketing, M
Marketing/Marketing Management, B
Mathematics, B
Multi-/Interdisciplinary Studies, B
Music, B
Physics, B
Political Science and Government, B
Psychology, B
Radio and Television, B
Social Work, B
Sociology, B
Spanish Language and Literature, B
Sport and Fitness Administration/Management, B
Wildlife and Wildlands Science and Management, B

TEXAS A&M UNIVERSITY–CORPUS CHRISTI

Accounting, BM
Aquaculture, M
Art/Art Studies, General, B
Athletic Training and Sports Medicine, B
Biological and Biomedical Sciences, M
Biology/Biological Sciences, B
Biomedical Sciences, B
Business Administration and Management, B
Business Administration, Management and Operations, M
Chemistry, B
Communication and Media Studies, M
Computer Science, M
Counselor Education/School Counseling and Guidance Services, MD
Curriculum and Instruction, MD
Early Childhood Education and Teaching, M
Economics, B
Education, MD
Educational Administration and Supervision, M
Educational Leadership and Administration, D
Educational Media/Instructional Technology, M
Electrical, Electronic and Communications Engineering Technology/Technician, B
Elementary Education and Teaching, M
English, M
English Language and Literature, B
Environmental Sciences, BM
Finance, B
Fine Arts and Art Studies, M
Geology/Earth Science, B
Health Services Administration, M
History, BM
International Business/Trade/Commerce, M
Kinesiology and Exercise Science, B
Kinesiology and Movement Studies, M
Management Information Systems and Services, B
Marine Sciences, D
Marketing/Marketing Management, B

Mathematics, BM
Mechanical Engineering, B
Mechanical Engineering/Mechanical
  Technology/Technician, B
Music, B
Nursing, M
Nursing - Advanced Practice, M
Nursing Administration, M
Political Science and Government, B
Psychology, BM
Public Administration, M
Reading Teacher Education, M
Secondary Education and Teaching, M
Sociology, B
Spanish Language and Literature, B
Special Education and Teaching, M

TEXAS A&M UNIVERSITY–KINGSVILLE

Accounting, B
Adult and Continuing Education and Teaching, M
Agribusiness, B
Agricultural Economics, M
Agricultural Sciences, MD
Agriculture, B
Agronomy and Crop Science, B
Agronomy and Soil Sciences, M
Animal Sciences, BM
Apparel and Textiles, B
Architectural Engineering, B
Biological and Biomedical Sciences, M
Biology/Biological Sciences, B
Biomedical Sciences, B
Business Administration and Management, B
Business Administration, Management and Opera-
  tions, M
Business/Commerce, B
Chemical Engineering, BM
Chemistry, BM
Civil Engineering, BM
Communication Disorders, BM
Computer Science, M
Computer and Information Sciences, B
Counselor Education/School Counseling and Guid-
  ance Services, M
Criminal Justice/Safety Studies, B
Criminology, BM
Cultural Studies, M
Dietetics/Dieticians, B
Drama and Dramatics/Theatre Arts, B
Early Childhood Education and Teaching, M
Education, MDO
Educational Administration and Supervision, MD
Educational Media/Instructional Technology, M
Electrical Engineering, M
Electrical, Electronics and Communications Engi-
  neering, B
Energy and Power Engineering, D
Engineering and Applied Sciences, MD
English, M
English Language and Literature, B
English as a Second Language, MD
Environmental Engineering
  Technology/Environmental Technology, MD
Environmental/Environmental Health Engineering, B
Family and Consumer Sciences/Human Sciences, B
Finance, B
Fine/Studio Arts, B
Fish, Game and Wildlife Management, MD
Foreign Language Teacher Education, MD
Geology/Earth Science, B
Health Education, M
Health and Physical Education, B
Higher Education/Higher Education Administra-
  tion, D
Hispanic Studies, D
History, BM
Home Economics, M
Horticultural Science, D
Human Development and Family Studies, B
Human Services, B
Industrial Engineering, B
Industrial Technology/Technician, B
Industrial and Manufacturing Management, M
Industrial/Management Engineering, M
International Business/Trade/Commerce, B
Kinesiology and Exercise Science, B

Kinesiology and Movement Studies, M
Management Information Systems and Services, B
Marketing/Marketing Management, B
Mathematics, BM
Mechanical Engineering, BM
Multi-/Interdisciplinary Studies, B
Multilingual and Multicultural Education, MD
Music, B
Music Performance, B
Music Teacher Education, M
Petroleum Engineering, BM
Physics, B
Plant Sciences, M
Political Science and Government, BM
Psychology, BMD
Range Science and Management, M
Reading Teacher Education, M
Social Work, B
Sociology, BM
Spanish Language and Literature, BM
Special Education and Teaching, M
Statistics, M
Sustainable Development, D
Systems Engineering, D
Veterinary/Animal Health Technology/Technician and
  Veterinary Assistant, B
Wildlife and Wildlands Science and Management, B

TEXAS A&M UNIVERSITY–SAN ANTO-NIO

Accounting, BM
Biology/Biological Sciences, B
Business Administration and Management, B
Business Administration, Management and Opera-
  tions, M
Computer and Information Sciences, B
Computer and Information Systems Security, M
Counselor Education/School Counseling and Guid-
  ance Services, M
Criminology, B
Early Childhood Education and Teaching, M
Educational Administration and Supervision, M
Educational Measurement and Evaluation, M
English, M
English Language and Literature, B
Finance, B
Finance and Banking, M
Health Services Administration, M
History, B
Human Resources Management and Services, M
International Business/Trade/Commerce, M
Kinesiology and Movement Studies, M
Management Information Systems and Services, M
Management Science, B
Marketing/Marketing Management, B
Mathematics, B
Multilingual and Multicultural Education, M
Political Science and Government, B
Project Management, M
Reading Teacher Education, M
Social Sciences, B
Sociology, B
Special Education and Teaching, M
Supply Chain Management, M

TEXAS A&M UNIVERSITY–TEXARKANA

Accounting, BM
Adult and Continuing Education and Teaching, M
Biology/Biological Sciences, B
Business Administration and Management, B
Business Administration, Management and Opera-
  tions, M
Business/Commerce, B
Counseling Psychology, M
Criminal Justice/Safety Studies, B
Curriculum and Instruction, M
Education, M
Educational Administration and Supervision, M
Educational Media/Instructional Technology, M
English, M
English Language and Literature, B
Finance, B
General Studies, B
History, B
Human Resources Management/Personnel Adminis-
  tration, B

Interdisciplinary Studies, M
International Business/Trade/Commerce, B
Management Information Systems and Services, B
Marketing/Marketing Management, B
Mass Communication/Media Studies, B
Mathematics, B
Multi-/Interdisciplinary Studies, B
Political Science and Government, B
Psychology, BM
Special Education and Teaching, M

TEXAS CHRISTIAN UNIVERSITY

Accounting, BM
Acting, B
Actuarial Science, B
Advertising, B
Allied Health and Medical Assisting Services, MDO
American/United States Studies/Civilization, MD
Anthropology, B
Applied Mathematics, MD
Art History, Criticism and Conservation, BM
Art Teacher Education, B
Astronomy and Astrophysics, B
Astrophysics, D
Athletic Training and Sports Medicine, B
Ballet, B
Bilingual and Multilingual Education, B
Biochemistry, B
Biological and Biomedical Sciences, M
Biology/Biological Sciences, B
Biophysics, D
Business Administration, Management and Opera-
  tions, M
Ceramic Arts and Ceramics, B
Chemistry, BMD
Cognitive Sciences, M
Communication Disorders, M
Communication Studies/Speech Communication
  and Rhetoric, B
Composition, D
Computer Systems Analysis/Analyst, B
Computer and Information Sciences, B
Counselor Education/School Counseling and Guid-
  ance Services, M
Criminal Justice/Safety Studies, B
Criminology, M
Curriculum and Instruction, MO
Dance, BM
Design and Visual Communications, B
Developmental Psychology, M
Dietetics and Clinical Nutrition Services, B
Dietetics/Dieticians, B
Directing and Theatrical Production, B
Drama and Dramatics/Theatre Arts, B
Early Childhood Education and Teaching, B
Economics, B
Education, MDO
Education/Teaching of Individuals with Hearing Im-
  pairments, Including Deafness, B
Educational Leadership and Administration, MD
Elementary Education and Teaching, B
Energy Management and Policy, M
Engineering, B
English, MD
English Language and Literature, B
English/Language Arts Teacher Education, B
Entrepreneurship/Entrepreneurial Studies, B
Environmental Sciences, BM
Experimental Psychology, MD
Farm/Farm and Ranch Management, B
Fashion Merchandising, B
Finance, B
Finance and Banking, M
Fine Arts and Art Studies, M
Fine/Studio Arts, B
French Language and Literature, B
General Studies, B
Geography, B
Geological and Earth Sciences/Geosciences, B
Geology/Earth Science, BM
German Language and Literature, B
Gerontological Nursing, M
Graphic Design, B
Health and Physical Education, B
History, BMD
Information Technology, B

Interior Design, B
International Business/Trade/Commerce, B
International Economics, B
International Finance, B
International Marketing, B
International Relations and Affairs, B
Journalism, BM
Kinesiology and Movement Studies, M
Liberal Studies, M
Logistics and Materials Management, B
Marketing, M
Marketing/Marketing Management, B
Mass Communication/Media Studies, M
Mathematics, BMD
Mathematics Teacher Education, BM
Movement Therapy and Movement Education, B
Music, BMD
Music History, Literature, and Theory, D
Music Performance, B
Music Teacher Education, BMD
Music Theory and Composition, B
Neuroscience, M
Nurse Anesthetist, D
Nursing, MDO
Nursing - Adult, M
Nursing Administration, MDO
Nursing Education, M
Painting, BM
Pediatric Nurse/Nursing, M
Philosophy, B
Photography, BM
Physical Education Teaching and Coaching, B
Physics, BMD
Piano and Organ, B
Political Science and Government, B
Printmaking, B
Psychology, BMD
Public Relations/Image Management, B
Radio, Television, and Digital Communication, B
Reading Teacher Education, M
Real Estate, B
Religion/Religious Studies, B
Religious/Sacred Music, B
Rhetoric, D
Science Teacher Education/General Science
   Teacher Education, BM
Sculpture, BM
Secondary Education and Teaching, B
Social Psychology, M
Social Studies Teacher Education, B
Social Work, BM
Sociology, B
Spanish Language and Literature, B
Special Education and Teaching, BM
Speech and Interpersonal Communication, M
Speech-Language Pathology/Pathologist, B
Supply Chain Management, M
Taxation, M
Technical Theatre/Theatre Design and Technol-
   ogy, B
Violin, Viola, Guitar and Other Stringed Instru-
   ments, B
Voice and Opera, B

TEXAS COLLEGE

Art/Art Studies, General, B
Biology/Biological Sciences, B
Business Administration and Management, B
Computer Science, B
Criminal Justice/Safety Studies, B
Early Childhood Education and Teaching, A
Elementary Education and Teaching, B
English Language and Literature, B
General Studies, A
Health and Physical Education, B
History, B
Liberal Arts and Sciences Studies and Humani-
   ties, B
Mathematics, B
Music, B
Political Science and Government, B
Religion/Religious Studies, B
Social Work, B

Sociology, B

TEXAS LUTHERAN UNIVERSITY

Accounting, BM
Aeronautics/Aviation/Aerospace Science and Tech-
   nology, B
Art Teacher Education, B
Art/Art Studies, General, B
Athletic Training and Sports Medicine, B
Biology/Biological Sciences, B
Business Administration and Management, B
Chemistry, B
Communication Studies/Speech Communication
   and Rhetoric, B
Computer Science, B
Drama and Dramatics/Theatre Arts, B
Economics, B
Education, B
Elementary Education and Teaching, B
English Language and Literature, B
Finance, B
Health and Physical Education/Fitness, B
History, B
History Teacher Education, B
Information Science/Studies, B
Junior High/Intermediate/Middle School Education
   and Teaching, B
Kinesiology and Exercise Science, B
Mathematics, B
Mathematics Teacher Education, B
Music, B
Music Teacher Education, B
Philosophy, B
Physical Education Teaching and Coaching, B
Physics, B
Political Science and Government, B
Pre-Medicine/Pre-Medical Studies, B
Psychology, B
Social Studies Teacher Education, B
Sociology, B
Spanish Language and Literature, B
Sport and Fitness Administration/Management, B
Teacher Education, Multiple Levels, B
Theology/Theological Studies, B

TEXAS SOUTHERN UNIVERSITY

Accounting, B
Aeronautics/Aviation/Aerospace Science and Tech-
   nology, B
Aviation/Airway Management and Operations, B
Banking and Financial Support Services, B
Biological and Biomedical Sciences, M
Biology/Biological Sciences, B
Business Administration and Management, B
Business Administration, Management and Opera-
   tions, M
Chemistry, BM
Civil Engineering Technology/Technician, B
Clinical Laboratory Science/Medical
   Technology/Technologist, B
Communication Studies/Speech Communication
   and Rhetoric, B
Communication and Media Studies, M
Computer Engineering Technology/Technician, B
Computer Science, M
Computer and Information Sciences, B
Counselor Education/School Counseling and Guid-
   ance Services, MD
Criminal Justice/Law Enforcement Administration, B
Criminology, MD
Curriculum and Instruction, MD
Dietetics/Dieticians, B
Drafting and Design Technology/Technician, B
Drama and Dramatics/Theatre Arts, B
Economics, B
Education, MD
Educational Administration and Supervision, MD
Electrical, Electronic and Communications Engineer-
   ing Technology/Technician, B
English, M
English Language and Literature, B
Environmental Health, B
Environmental Policy, MD
Family and Consumer Sciences/Human Sci-
   ences, BM
Fine Arts and Art Studies, M

Fine/Studio Arts, B
General Studies, B
Health Education, M
Health Information/Medical Records
   Administration/Administrator, B
Health Services Administration, M
Health Services/Allied Health/Health Sciences, B
Health/Health Care Administration/Management, B
Higher Education/Higher Education Administra-
   tion, MD
History, BM
Human Services, M
Industrial Technology/Technician, B
Industrial/Management Engineering, M
Journalism, B
Kinesiology and Exercise Science, B
Law and Legal Studies, D
Management Information Systems and Ser-
   vices, BM
Marketing/Marketing Management, B
Mass Communication/Media Studies, B
Mathematics, BM
Multilingual and Multicultural Education, M
Music, BM
Operations Management and Supervision, B
Pharmaceutical Sciences, MD
Pharmacy, D
Physical Education Teaching and Coaching, M
Physics, B
Political Science and Government, B
Psychology, BM
Public Administration, BM
Radio and Television, B
Respiratory Care Therapy/Therapist, B
Secondary Education and Teaching, M
Social Work, B
Sociology, BM
Spanish Language and Literature, B
Sport and Fitness Administration/Management, B
Toxicology, MD
Transportation and Highway Engineering, M
Transportation/Transportation Management, M
Urban and Regional Planning, MD
Visual and Performing Arts, B

TEXAS SOUTHMOST COLLEGE

Accounting, A
Art/Art Studies, General, A
Business/Commerce, A
Cardiovascular Technology/Technologist, A
Child Care Provider/Assistant, A
Clinical/Medical Laboratory Technician, A
Computer and Information Sciences, A
Criminal Justice/Law Enforcement Administration, A
Diagnostic Medical Sonography/Sonographer and
   Ultrasound Technician, A
Drafting and Design Technology/Technician, A
Emergency Medical Technology/Technician (EMT
   Paramedic), A
General Office Occupations and Clerical Services, A
Industrial Technology/Technician, A
International Marketing, A
Legal Administrative Assistant/Secretary, A
Liberal Arts and Sciences Studies and Humani-
   ties, A
Medical Administrative Assistant/Secretary, A
Multi-/Interdisciplinary Studies, A
Music, A
Operations Research, A
Respiratory Care Therapy/Therapist, A
Social Work, A
Spanish Language and Literature, A

TEXAS STATE TECHNICAL COLLEGE

Air Traffic Controller, A
Aircraft Powerplant Technology/Technician, A
Airframe Mechanics and Aircraft Maintenance
   Technology/Technician, A
Airline/Commercial/Professional Pilot and Flight
   Crew, A
Autobody/Collision and Repair
   Technology/Technician, A
Automobile/Automotive Mechanics
   Technology/Technician, A
Avionics Maintenance Technology/Technician, A
Biomedical Technology/Technician, A

Chemical Technology/Technician, A
Computer Programming/Programmer, A
Computer Technology/Computer Systems Technology, A
Computer and Information Systems Security, A
Construction Trades, A
Culinary Arts/Chef Training, A
Diesel Mechanics Technology/Technician, A
Drafting and Design Technology/Technician, A
Educational/Instructional Media Design, A
Electrical, Electronic and Communications Engineering Technology/Technician, A
Electromechanical Technology/Electromechanical Engineering Technology, A
Environmental Engineering Technology/Environmental Technology, A
Graphic Design, A
Heating, Air Conditioning and Refrigeration Technology/Technician, A
Instrumentation Technology/Technician, A
Laser and Optical Technology/Technician, A
Manufacturing Technology/Technician, A
Mechanical Engineering/Mechanical Technology/Technician, A
Nuclear/Nuclear Power Technology/Technician, A
Occupational Safety and Health Technology/Technician, A
Robotics Technology/Technician, A
Solar Energy Technology/Technician, A
Survey Technology/Surveying, A
System Administration/Administrator, A
System, Networking, and LAN/WAN Management/Manager, A
Telecommunications Technology/Technician, A
Turf and Turfgrass Management, A
Web Page, Digital/Multimedia and Information Resources Design, A

TEXAS STATE UNIVERSITY

Accounting, BM
Adult and Continuing Education and Teaching, MD
Advertising, B
Agribusiness, B
Agricultural Education, M
Agriculture, B
Allied Health and Medical Assisting Services, MD
American/United States Studies/Civilization, B
Animal Sciences, B
Anthropology, BM
Applied Mathematics, BM
Aquatic Biology/Limnology, B
Art History, Criticism and Conservation, B
Art/Art Studies, General, B
Asian Studies/Civilization, B
Athletic Training and Sports Medicine, BM
Biochemistry, BM
Biological and Biomedical Sciences, M
Biological and Physical Sciences, B
Biology/Biological Sciences, B
Business Administration and Management, B
Business Administration, Management and Operations, M
Business/Managerial Economics, B
Cartography, B
Chemistry, BM
Child and Family Studies, M
City/Urban, Community and Regional Planning, B
Clinical Laboratory Science/Medical Technology/Technologist, B
Communication Disorders, BM
Communication and Media Studies, M
Community Psychology, M
Composition, M
Computer Art and Design, M
Computer Science, BM
Computer and Information Sciences, B
Conservation Biology, M
Construction Engineering Technology/Technician, B
Consumer Services and Advocacy, B
Corrections, B
Counselor Education/School Counseling and Guidance Services, M
Criminal Justice/Police Science, B
Criminal Justice/Safety Studies, B
Criminology, MD
Dance, B

Design and Visual Communications, B
Developmental Education, MD
Drama and Dramatics/Theatre Arts, B
Economics, B
Education, MDO
Educational Leadership and Administration, MD
Educational Media/Instructional Technology, M
Electrical, Electronics and Communications Engineering, B
Elementary Education and Teaching, M
Engineering Technology, B
Engineering and Applied Sciences, M
Engineering/Industrial Management, B
English, M
English Language and Literature, B
Environmental Policy and Resource Management, M
Environmental Sciences, B
Environmental Studies, M
Ethics, M
European Studies/Civilization, B
Exercise and Sports Science, M
Family and Consumer Sciences/Human Sciences, M
Fashion Merchandising, B
Finance, B
Finance and Banking, M
Fine/Studio Arts, B
Fish, Game and Wildlife Management, M
Foods, Nutrition, and Wellness Studies, B
French Language and Literature, B
General Studies, B
Geographic Information Systems, MD
Geography, BMD
German Language and Literature, B
Gerontology, M
Graphic Design, M
Health Education, M
Health Information/Medical Records Administration/Administrator, B
Health Services Administration, M
Health Services Research, M
Health/Health Care Administration/Management, B
Higher Education/Higher Education Administration, M
History, BM
Human Development and Family Studies, B
Human Resources Management and Services, M
Industrial Engineering, B
Industrial Technology/Technician, B
Industrial/Management Engineering, M
Interdisciplinary Studies, M
Interior Design, B
International Affairs, M
International Relations and Affairs, B
International/Global Studies, B
Jazz/Jazz Studies, B
Journalism, B
Kinesiology and Exercise Science, B
Legal and Justice Studies, M
Leisure Studies, M
Liberal Arts and Sciences Studies and Humanities, B
Management Information Systems and Services, M
Management of Technology, M
Manufacturing Engineering, BM
Manufacturing Technology/Technician, B
Marine Biology and Biological Oceanography, MD
Marketing/Marketing Management, B
Marriage and Family Therapy/Counseling, M
Mass Communication/Media Studies, BM
Materials Engineering, D
Materials Sciences, MD
Mathematics, BM
Mathematics Teacher Education, MD
Medical Radiologic Technology/Science - Radiation Therapist, B
Microbiology, B
Multi-/Interdisciplinary Studies, B
Multilingual and Multicultural Education, M
Music, BM
Music Performance, B
Music Teacher Education, M
Music Theory and Composition, M
Near and Middle Eastern Studies, B
Nursing - Advanced Practice, M

Nutritional Sciences, M
Parks, Recreation and Leisure Facilities Management, B
Performance, M
Philosophy, BM
Photography, B
Physical Education Teaching and Coaching, M
Physical Therapy/Therapist, D
Physics, BM
Political Science and Government, BM
Psychology, BM
Public Administration, BM
Public Health Education and Promotion, B
Public Relations/Image Management, B
Radio and Television, B
Reading Teacher Education, M
Recording Arts Technology/Technician, B
Recreation and Park Management, M
Respiratory Care Therapy/Therapist, B
Rhetoric, M
School Psychology, O
Science Teacher Education/General Science Teacher Education, M
Secondary Education and Teaching, M
Social Work, BM
Sociology, BM
Software Engineering, M
Spanish Language and Literature, BM
Special Education and Teaching, M
Sport and Fitness Administration/Management, B
Student Personnel Services, M
Sustainable Development, M
Technical Communication, M
Theater, M
Therapeutic Recreation, M
Urban Planning, M
Vocational and Technical Education, M
Water, Wetlands, and Marine Resources Management, B
Wildlife Biology, B
Writing, M

TEXAS TECH UNIVERSITY

Accounting, BMD
Advertising, B
Agribusiness, M
Agricultural Business and Management, B
Agricultural Communication/Journalism, B
Agricultural Economics, BMD
Agricultural Education, MD
Agricultural Sciences, MD
Agriculture, B
Agronomy and Crop Science, B
Agronomy and Soil Sciences, MD
Animal Sciences, BMD
Anthropology, BM
Applied Economics, MD
Applied Horticulture/Horticultural Operations, B
Applied Physics, M
Architecture, BMD
Art Education, M
Art History, Criticism and Conservation, M
Art/Art Studies, General, B
Atmospheric Sciences and Meteorology, M
BioTechnology, M
Biochemistry, B
Bioengineering, M
Biological and Biomedical Sciences, MD
Biological and Physical Sciences, B
Biology/Biological Sciences, B
Business Administration and Management, B
Business Administration, Management and Operations, BMD
Business/Commerce, B
Cell/Cellular and Molecular Biology, B
Chemical Engineering, BMD
Chemistry, BMD
Child Care and Support Services Management, B
Child Development, B
Child and Family Studies, MD
Civil Engineering, BMD
Classics and Classical Languages, Literatures, and Linguistics, BM
Clinical Psychology, D
Communication and Media Studies, M
Computer Engineering, B

Computer Science, MD
Computer and Information Sciences, B
Construction Engineering, B
Consumer Economics, MD
Counseling Psychology, MD
Counselor Education/School Counseling and Guidance Services, MD
Cultural Studies, M
Curriculum and Instruction, MD
Dance, B
Dietetics/Dieticians, B
Drama and Dramatics/Theatre Arts, B
Economics, BMD
Education, MD
Educational Leadership and Administration, MD
Educational Media/Instructional Technology, MD
Educational Psychology, MD
Electrical Engineering, B
Electrical, Electronics and Communications Engineering, B
Elementary Education and Teaching, M
Energy and Power Engineering, D
Engineering Management, M
Engineering and Applied Sciences, MD
English, MD
English Language and Literature, B
Environmental Design/Architecture, MD
Environmental Engineering Technology/Environmental Technology, MD
Environmental Policy and Resource Management, MD
Environmental Sciences, MD
Environmental/Environmental Health Engineering, B
Exercise and Sports Science, M
Experimental Psychology, MD
Family Resource Management Studies, B
Family and Community Services, B
Family and Consumer Sciences/Human Sciences, B
Fashion Merchandising, B
Fashion/Apparel Design, B
Finance, B
Finance and Banking, MD
Fine Arts and Art Studies, MD
Fish, Game and Wildlife Management, MD
Food Science, B
Food Science and Technology, MD
Foods, Nutrition, and Wellness Studies, B
Foreign Languages and Literatures, B
Forensic Science and Technology, M
French Language and Literature, B
General Studies, B
Geography, BM
Geology/Earth Science, B
Geosciences, MD
German Language and Literature, BM
Health Services Administration, M
Higher Education/Higher Education Administration, MD
Historic Preservation and Conservation, M
History, BMD
Home Economics, MD
Home Economics Education, MD
Horticultural Science, M
Hospitality Administration/Management, MD
Hotel/Motel Administration/Management, B
Human Development, MD
Human Development and Family Studies, B
Industrial Engineering, B
Industrial/Management Engineering, MD
Information Science/Studies, B
Interdisciplinary Studies, MD
Interior Architecture, B
Interior Design, D
International Business/Trade/Commerce, B
International Economics, B
International/Global Studies, B
Journalism, B
Kinesiology and Exercise Science, B
Landscape Architecture, BM
Latin American Studies, B
Law and Legal Studies, MD
Liberal Arts and Sciences Studies and Humanities, B
Linguistics, M
Management Information Systems and Services, MD

Marketing, D
Marketing/Marketing Management, B
Marriage and Family Therapy/Counseling, MD
Mass Communication/Media Studies, BMD
Mathematics, BMD
Mechanical Engineering, BMD
Microbiology, BM
Multi-/Interdisciplinary Studies, B
Multilingual and Multicultural Education, M
Museology/Museum Studies, M
Music, BMD
Music Teacher Education, M
Natural Resources Management/Development and Policy, MD
Natural Resources and Conservation, B
Nutritional Sciences, MD
Operations Research, D
Petroleum Engineering, BMD
Philosophy, BM
Physics, BMD
Plant Sciences, BMD
Political Science and Government, BMD
Psychology, BMD
Public Administration, M
Public Relations/Image Management, B
Radio and Television, B
Reading Teacher Education, M
Rhetoric, D
Romance Languages, Literatures, and Linguistics, M
Russian Studies, B
Science Teacher Education/General Science Teacher Education, M
Science, Technology and Society, B
Secondary Education and Teaching, M
Social Work, BM
Sociology, BM
Software Engineering, M
Spanish Language and Literature, BD
Special Education and Teaching, MD
Sport and Fitness Administration/Management, B
Statistics, MD
Sustainable Development, M
Systems Engineering, M
Taxation, M
Technical and Business Writing, MD
Theater, M
Toxicology, MD
Zoology/Animal Biology, BMD

TEXAS WESLEYAN UNIVERSITY

Accounting, B
Advertising, B
Athletic Training and Sports Medicine, B
Bilingual and Multilingual Education, B
Biochemistry, B
Biology Teacher Education, B
Biology/Biological Sciences, B
Business Administration and Management, B
Business Administration, Management and Operations, M
Chemistry, B
Christian Studies, B
Computer Science, B
Counseling Psychology, M
Counselor Education/School Counseling and Guidance Services, M
Criminal Justice/Safety Studies, B
Education, BMD
English Language and Literature, B
English/Language Arts Teacher Education, B
Finance, B
History, B
History Teacher Education, B
Journalism, B
Kinesiology and Exercise Science, B
Law and Legal Studies, D
Legal Assistant/Paralegal, B
Liberal Arts and Sciences Studies and Humanities, B
Management Science, B
Marketing/Marketing Management, B
Marriage and Family Therapy/Counseling, M
Mass Communication/Media Studies, B
Mathematics, B
Mathematics Teacher Education, B

Multi-/Interdisciplinary Studies, B
Music, B
Music Teacher Education, B
Nurse Anesthetist, MD
Political Science and Government, B
Pre-Dentistry Studies, B
Psychology, B
Radio and Television, B
Reading Teacher Education, B
Religion/Religious Studies, B
Sociology, B
Spanish Language Teacher Education, B
Spanish Language and Literature, B

TEXAS WOMAN'S UNIVERSITY

Accounting, B
Acute Care/Critical Care Nursing, M
Allied Health and Medical Assisting Services, MD
Art/Art Studies, General, B
Audiology/Audiologist and Speech-Language Pathology/Pathologist, B
Biochemistry, B
Biological and Biomedical Sciences, MD
Biology/Biological Sciences, B
Business Administration and Management, B
Business Administration, Management and Operations, M
Chemistry, BM
Child Development, BM
Child and Family Studies, MD
Clinical Laboratory Science/Medical Technology/Technologist, B
Communication Disorders, M
Computer and Information Sciences, B
Counseling Psychology, MD
Counselor Education/School Counseling and Guidance Services, M
Criminal Justice/Safety Studies, B
Curriculum and Instruction, M
Dance, BMD
Dental Hygiene/Hygienist, B
Drama and Dramatics/Theatre Arts, B
Early Childhood Education and Teaching, MD
Education, BMD
Educational Administration and Supervision, M
English, MD
English Language and Literature, B
Exercise and Sports Science, M
Family and Consumer Sciences/Human Sciences, B
Fashion Merchandising, B
Fashion/Apparel Design, B
Finance, B
Fine Arts and Art Studies, M
Food Science and Technology, MD
Foods, Nutrition, and Wellness Studies, B
General Studies, B
Health Education, MD
Health Services Administration, M
Health Services/Allied Health/Health Sciences, B
History, BM
Human Development and Family Studies, B
Human Resources Management/Personnel Administration, B
Kinesiology and Exercise Science, B
Kinesiology and Movement Studies, MD
Legal Assistant/Paralegal, B
Library Science, MD
Marketing/Marketing Management, B
Marriage and Family Therapy/Counseling, MD
Mathematics, BM
Mathematics Teacher Education, M
Molecular Biology, D
Multi-/Interdisciplinary Studies, B
Music, BM
Nursing, MD
Nursing - Adult, M
Nursing - Advanced Practice, M
Nursing Administration, M
Nursing Education, M
Nutritional Sciences, BMD
Occupational Therapy/Therapist, MD
Pediatric Nurse/Nursing, M
Physical Education Teaching and Coaching, MD
Physical Therapy/Therapist, D
Political Science and Government, BM
Psychology, BMDO

Reading Teacher Education, MD
Rhetoric, D
School Psychology, DO
Social Work, B
Sociology, BMD
Special Education and Teaching, MD
Sport and Fitness Administration/Management, MD
Theater, M
Women's Health Nursing, M
Women's Studies, MD

TRINITY UNIVERSITY

Accounting, BM
Acting, B
Anthropology, B
Art History, Criticism and Conservation, B
Art/Art Studies, General, B
Asian Studies/Civilization, B
Biochemistry, B
Biology/Biological Sciences, B
Business Administration and Management, B
Business Administration, Management and Operations, M
Chemistry, B
Chinese Language and Literature, B
Classics and Classical Languages, Literatures, and Linguistics, B
Communication Studies/Speech Communication and Rhetoric, B
Computer and Information Sciences, B
Drama and Dramatics/Theatre Arts, B
East Asian Studies, B
Economics, B
Education, M
Educational Leadership and Administration, M
Engineering Science, B
English Language and Literature, B
Environmental Studies, B
European Studies/Civilization, B
Finance, B
French Language and Literature, B
Geology/Earth Science, B
German Language and Literature, B
Health Services Administration, M
History, B
Humanities/Humanistic Studies, B
International Business/Trade/Commerce, B
International Economics, B
International Relations and Affairs, B
Latin American Studies, B
Latin Language and Literature, B
Management Science, B
Marketing/Marketing Management, B
Mathematics, B
Multi-/Interdisciplinary Studies, B
Music, B
Music Performance, B
Music Teacher Education, B
Music Theory and Composition, B
Near and Middle Eastern Studies, B
Philosophy, B
Physics, B
Political Science and Government, B
Pre-Dentistry Studies, B
Pre-Law Studies, B
Pre-Medicine/Pre-Medical Studies, B
Pre-Veterinary Studies, B
Psychology, B
Religion/Religious Studies, B
Russian Language and Literature, B
School Psychology, M
Sociology, B
Spanish Language and Literature, B
Technical Theatre/Theatre Design and Technology, B
Urban Studies/Affairs, B
Voice and Opera, B

TRINITY VALLEY COMMUNITY COLLEGE

Accounting, A
Agricultural Teacher Education, A
Animal Sciences, A
Art/Art Studies, General, A
Automobile/Automotive Mechanics Technology/Technician, A

Biology/Biological Sciences, A
Business Administration and Management, A
Business Teacher Education, A
Chemistry, A
Child Development, A
Commercial Photography, A
Computer Science, A
Corrections, A
Cosmetology/Cosmetologist, A
Criminal Justice/Law Enforcement Administration, A
Criminal Justice/Police Science, A
Dance, A
Data Processing and Data Processing Technology/Technician, A
Drafting and Design Technology/Technician, A
Drama and Dramatics/Theatre Arts, A
Education, A
Elementary Education and Teaching, A
Emergency Medical Technology/Technician (EMT Paramedic), A
English Language and Literature, A
Farm/Farm and Ranch Management, A
Fashion Merchandising, A
Finance, A
Geology/Earth Science, A
Heating, Air Conditioning, Ventilation and Refrigeration Maintenance Technology/Technician, A
History, A
Horticultural Science, A
Insurance, A
Journalism, A
Kindergarten/PreSchool Education and Teaching, A
Legal Administrative Assistant/Secretary, A
Liberal Arts and Sciences Studies and Humanities, A
Marketing/Marketing Management, A
Mathematics, A
Music, A
Physical Education Teaching and Coaching, A
Physical Sciences, A
Political Science and Government, A
Psychology, A
Range Science and Management, A
Real Estate, A
Religion/Religious Studies, A
Sociology, A
Spanish Language and Literature, A
Surgical Technology/Technologist, A
Welding Technology/Welder, A

TYLER JUNIOR COLLEGE

Accounting, A
Administrative Assistant and Secretarial Science, A
Art/Art Studies, General, A
Athletic Training and Sports Medicine, A
Automobile/Automotive Mechanics Technology/Technician, A
Behavioral Sciences, A
Biology/Biological Sciences, A
Business Administration and Management, A
CAD/CADD Drafting and/or Design Technology/Technician, A
Chemistry, A
Child Development, A
Clinical/Medical Laboratory Technician, A
Commercial Photography, A
Commercial and Advertising Art, A
Communication Studies/Speech Communication and Rhetoric, A
Computer Engineering Technology/Technician, A
Computer Graphics, A
Computer Programming, A
Computer Programming/Programmer, A
Computer Science, A
Computer Systems Networking and Telecommunications, A
Computer Technology/Computer Systems Technology, A
Computer and Information Sciences, A
Criminal Justice/Law Enforcement Administration, A
Criminal Justice/Police Science, A
Criminal Justice/Safety Studies, A
Criminalistics and Criminal Science, A
Dance, A
Data Entry/Microcomputer Applications, A
Dental Hygiene/Hygienist, A

Diagnostic Medical Sonography/Sonographer and Ultrasound Technician, A
Drafting and Design Technology/Technician, A
Drama and Dramatics/Theatre Arts, A
Economics, A
Electromechanical Technology/Electromechanical Engineering Technology, A
Emergency Medical Technology/Technician (EMT Paramedic), A
Engineering, A
Environmental Sciences, A
Family and Consumer Sciences/Human Sciences, A
Fire Science/Firefighting, A
Foreign Languages and Literatures, A
General Studies, A
Geology/Earth Science, A
Health Information/Medical Records Technology/Technician, A
Health and Physical Education, A
Health/Health Care Administration/Management, A
Heating, Air Conditioning, Ventilation and Refrigeration Maintenance Technology/Technician, A
History, A
Industrial Electronics Technology/Technician, A
Industrial Radiologic Technology/Technician, A
Information Technology, A
Junior High/Intermediate/Middle School Education and Teaching, A
Legal Administrative Assistant/Secretary, A
Legal Assistant/Paralegal, A
Liberal Arts and Sciences Studies and Humanities, A
Mathematics, A
Medical Administrative Assistant/Secretary, A
Modern Languages, A
Music, A
Natural Sciences, A
Occupational Therapist Assistant, A
Photography, A
Physical Education Teaching and Coaching, A
Physical Therapist Assistant, A
Physics, A
Political Science and Government, A
Pre-Nursing Studies, A
Psychology, A
Public Administration, A
Radio and Television, A
Radiologic Technology/Science - Radiographer, A
Respiratory Care Therapy/Therapist, A
Secondary Education and Teaching, A
Sign Language Interpretation and Translation, A
Social Sciences, A
Social Work, A
Sociology, A
Substance Abuse/Addiction Counseling, A
Surgical Technology/Technologist, A
Survey Technology/Surveying, A
System, Networking, and LAN/WAN Management/Manager, A
Teacher Education, Multiple Levels, A
Welding Technology/Welder, A

UNIVERSITY OF DALLAS

Accounting, M
American/United States Studies/Civilization, M
Art History, Criticism and Conservation, B
Art/Art Studies, General, B
Biochemistry, B
Biology/Biological Sciences, B
Business Administration and Management, B
Business Administration, Management and Operations, M
Ceramic Arts and Ceramics, B
Chemistry, B
Classics and Classical Languages, Literatures, and Linguistics, B
Comparative Literature, D
Drama and Dramatics/Theatre Arts, B
Economics, B
Education, B
Elementary Education and Teaching, B
English, M
English Language and Literature, B
Entertainment Management, M
Finance and Banking, M
Fine Arts and Art Studies, M

Fine/Studio Arts, B
French Language and Literature, B
German Language and Literature, B
Health Services Administration, M
History, B
Human Resources Management and Services, M
Humanities/Humanistic Studies, M
International Business/Trade/Commerce, M
Logistics and Materials Management, M
Management, M
Management Information Systems and Services, M
Management Strategy and Policy, M
Management of Technology, M
Marketing, M
Mathematics, B
Organizational Management, M
Painting, B
Pastoral Studies/Counseling, M
Philosophy, BMD
Physics, B
Political Science and Government, BMD
Pre-Dentistry Studies, B
Pre-Law Studies, B
Pre-Medicine/Pre-Medical Studies, B
Pre-Theology/Pre-Ministerial Studies, B
Printmaking, B
Project Management, M
Psychology, BM
Sculpture, B
Secondary Education and Teaching, B
Social Sciences, B
Spanish Language and Literature, B
Sport and Fitness Administration/Management, M
Supply Chain Management, M
Theology and Religious Vocations, M
Theology/Theological Studies, B

UNIVERSITY OF HOUSTON

Accounting, BMD
Advertising, B
Advertising and Public Relations, M
American Sign Language (ASL), B
Anthropology, BM
Applied Economics, M
Applied Mathematics, M
Architecture, BM
Art History, Criticism and Conservation, BM
Art/Art Studies, General, B
Atmospheric Sciences and Meteorology, D
BioTechnology, B
Biochemistry, BMD
Biological and Biomedical Sciences, MD
Biology/Biological Sciences, B
Biomedical Engineering, D
Biomedical/Medical Engineering, B
Business Administration and Management, B
Business Administration, Management and Operations, MD
Business Family and Consumer Sciences/Human Sciences, B
Business/Corporate Communications, B
Chemical Engineering, BMD
Chemistry, BMD
Chinese Language and Literature, B
Civil Engineering, BMD
Clinical Psychology, D
Communication Disorders, BM
Communication Studies/Speech Communication and Rhetoric, B
Communication and Media Studies, M
Comparative Literature, M
Composition, M
Computer Engineering, B
Computer Engineering Technology/Technician, B
Computer Graphics, B
Computer Science, MD
Computer Systems Analysis/Analyst, B
Computer and Information Sciences, B
Computer and Information Systems Security, M
Construction Engineering Technology/Technician, B
Construction Management, M
Counseling Psychology, MD
Cultural Studies, M
Curriculum and Instruction, MD
Dance, B
Developmental Psychology, D

Drama and Dramatics/Theatre Arts, B
Economics, BMD
Education, MD
Educational Administration and Supervision, MD
Educational Leadership and Administration, MD
Educational Psychology, MD
Electrical Engineering, MD
Electrical, Electronic and Communications Engineering Technology/Technician, B
Electrical, Electronics and Communications Engineering, B
Engineering and Applied Sciences, MD
English Language and Literature, B
Entrepreneurship/Entrepreneurial Studies, B
Environmental Design/Architecture, B
Environmental Law, M
Environmental Sciences, B
Ethnic, Cultural Minority, and Gender Studies, B
Exercise and Sports Science, M
Family and Consumer Sciences/Human Sciences, M
Finance, B
Finance and Banking, M
Fine Arts and Art Studies, M
Foreign Languages and Literatures, B
Foundations and Philosophy of Education, MD
French Language and Literature, B
Geology/Earth Science, BMD
Geophysics and Seismology, BMD
Graphic Design, B
Health Communication, BM
Health Education, MD
Health Law, M
Higher Education/Higher Education Administration, M
Hispanic Studies, MD
History, BMD
Hospitality Administration/Management, M
Hotel/Motel Administration/Management, B
Human Development and Family Studies, B
Human Nutrition, B
Human Resources Development, BM
Industrial Design, B
Industrial Engineering, B
Industrial and Organizational Psychology, D
Industrial/Management Engineering, MD
Information Science/Studies, BMD
Intellectual Property Law, M
Interior Architecture, B
Italian Language and Literature, B
Journalism, B
Kinesiology and Exercise Science, B
Kinesiology and Movement Studies, D
Law and Legal Studies, MD
Liberal Arts and Sciences Studies and Humanities, B
Linguistics, BM
Logistics and Materials Management, M
Management Information Systems and Services, B
Marketing, D
Marketing/Marketing Management, B
Mass Communication/Media Studies, BM
Mathematics, BMD
Mechanical Engineering, BMD
Mechanical Engineering/Mechanical Technology/Technician, B
Multi-/Interdisciplinary Studies, B
Music, BMD
Music Performance, B
Music Teacher Education, D
Music Theory and Composition, M
Nutritional Sciences, M
Operations Management and Supervision, B
Optometry, D
Painting, BM
Performance, D
Petroleum Engineering, BM
Pharmaceutical Administration, MD
Pharmaceutical Sciences, MD
Pharmacology, MD
Pharmacy, MD
Philosophy, BM
Photography, B
Physical Education Teaching and Coaching, MD
Physics, BMD
Planetary Astronomy and Science, M

Political Science and Government, BMD
Project Management, M
Psychology, BMD
Public Administration, M
Public Relations/Image Management, B
Radio and Television, B
Religion/Religious Studies, B
Sales, Distribution and Marketing Operations, B
Sculpture, B
Social Psychology, D
Social Work, MD
Sociology, BM
Spanish Language and Literature, BMD
Special Education and Teaching, M
Speech and Interpersonal Communication, M
Sport and Fitness Administration/Management, B
Supply Chain Management, M
Taxation, M
Telecommunications, M
Theater, M
Vision Science/Physiological Optics, MD
Writing, MD

UNIVERSITY OF HOUSTON–CLEAR LAKE

Accounting, BM
Anthropology, B
Behavioral Sciences, B
BioTechnology, M
Biological and Biomedical Sciences, M
Biology/Biological Sciences, B
Business Administration and Management, B
Business Administration, Management and Operations, BM
Business/Commerce, B
Chemistry, BM
Clinical Psychology, M
Computer Engineering, BM
Computer Science, BM
Computer and Information Sciences, B
Counselor Education/School Counseling and Guidance Services, M
Criminology, BM
Cultural Studies, M
Curriculum and Instruction, M
Early Childhood Education and Teaching, M
Education, MD
Educational Administration and Supervision, M
Educational Leadership and Administration, MD
Educational Media/Instructional Technology, M
English, M
English Language and Literature, B
Environmental Policy and Resource Management, M
Environmental Sciences, BM
Exercise and Sports Science, M
Finance, B
Finance and Banking, M
Fine/Studio Arts, B
Foundations and Philosophy of Education, M
Geography, B
Health Services Administration, M
Health/Health Care Administration/Management, B
History, BM
Human Resources Management and Services, M
Humanities/Humanistic Studies, BM
Information Science/Studies, M
Information Technology, M
Kinesiology and Exercise Science, B
Legal Assistant/Paralegal, B
Library Science, M
Management Information Systems and Services, M
Marketing/Marketing Management, B
Marriage and Family Therapy/Counseling, M
Mathematics, BM
Multi-/Interdisciplinary Studies, B
Multilingual and Multicultural Education, M
Physics, BM
Psychology, BM
Public Administration, B
Reading Teacher Education, M
School Psychology, M
Social Work, B
Sociology, BM
Software Engineering, M
Statistics, M

Systems Engineering, M
Women's Studies, B

UNIVERSITY OF HOUSTON–DOWNTOWN

Accounting, B
Applied Mathematics, B
BioTechnology, B
Biological and Physical Sciences, B
Biology/Biological Sciences, B
Business Administration and Management, B
Business Administration, Management and Operations, M
Business/Commerce, B
Chemistry, B
Civil Engineering Technology/Technician, B
Computer Engineering Technology/Technician, B
Computer and Information Sciences, B
Criminal Justice/Safety Studies, B
Criminology, M
Curriculum and Instruction, M
Elementary Education and Teaching, M
English, M
English Language and Literature, B
Finance, B
Geology/Earth Science, B
History, B
Humanities/Humanistic Studies, B
Industrial Safety Technology/Technician, B
Insurance, B
International Business/Trade/Commerce, B
Management Information Systems and Services, B
Marketing/Marketing Management, B
Mathematics, B
Middle School Education, M
Multi-/Interdisciplinary Studies, B
Non-Profit/Public/Organizational Management, M
Occupational Safety and Health Technology/Technician, B
Philosophy, B
Political Science and Government, B
Psychology, B
Purchasing, Procurement/Acquisitions and Contracts Management, B
Rhetoric, M
Secondary Education and Teaching, M
Securities Services Administration/Management, M
Social Sciences, B
Social Work, B
Sociology, B
Spanish Language and Literature, B
Technical Communication, M
Urban Education and Leadership, M
Visual and Performing Arts, B

UNIVERSITY OF HOUSTON–VICTORIA

Accounting, BM
Adult and Continuing Education and Teaching, M
Biological and Biomedical Sciences, M
Biology/Biological Sciences, B
Business Administration and Management, B
Business Administration, Management and Operations, M
Computer Science, BM
Counseling Psychology, M
Counselor Education/School Counseling and Guidance Services, M
Criminal Justice/Safety Studies, B
Curriculum and Instruction, M
Economic Development, M
Education, M
Educational Administration and Supervision, M
English Language and Literature, B
Entrepreneurship/Entrepreneurial Studies, M
Finance, B
Finance and Banking, M
Forensic Psychology, M
Forensic Science and Technology, M
Higher Education/Higher Education Administration, M
History, B
Humanities/Humanistic Studies, B
Interdisciplinary Studies, M
International Business/Trade/Commerce, M
Liberal Arts and Sciences Studies and Humanities, B

Management, M
Management Information Systems and Services, M
Marketing, M
Marketing/Marketing Management, B
Mathematics, B
Multi-/Interdisciplinary Studies, B
Nursing, M
Nursing - Advanced Practice, M
Nursing Administration, M
Nursing Education, M
Psychology, BM
Publishing, M
School Psychology, M
Special Education and Teaching, M
Writing, M

UNIVERSITY OF THE INCARNATE WORD

Accounting, BM
Adult and Continuing Education and Teaching, M
Animation, Interactive Technology, Video Graphics and Special Effects, B
Apparel and Textile Marketing Management, AB
Art History, Criticism and Conservation, B
Art/Art Studies, General, B
Athletic Training and Sports Medicine, B
Atmospheric Sciences and Meteorology, B
Banking and Financial Support Services, B
Biochemistry, B
Biological and Biomedical Sciences, M
Biology/Biological Sciences, B
Business Administration and Management, AB
Business Administration, Management and Operations, BMD
Business/Managerial Economics, B
Chemistry, AB
Child Development, B
Communication Studies/Speech Communication and Rhetoric, B
Communication and Media Studies, BM /
Community Health and Preventive Medicine, B
Computer Systems Networking and Telecommunications, B
Computer and Information Sciences, B
Criminal Justice/Law Enforcement Administration, B
Criminal Justice/Safety Studies, B
Digital Communication and Media/Multimedia, B
Distance Education Development, M
Drama and Dramatics/Theatre Arts, B
Education, MD
Educational Leadership and Administration, B
Educational Media/Instructional Technology, M
Educational Psychology, M
Elementary Education and Teaching, BM
Engineering/Industrial Management, B
English Language and Literature, B
Entrepreneurship/Entrepreneurial Studies, D
Environmental Sciences, B
Fashion/Apparel Design, B
Fine/Studio Arts, B
Graphic Design, B
Health Promotion, M
Health Services Administration, M
Health Services/Allied Health/Health Sciences, AB
Higher Education/Higher Education Administration, D
History, B
Human Resources Management/Personnel Administration, B
Industrial and Organizational Psychology, M
Intercultural/Multicultural and Diversity Studies, B
Interdisciplinary Studies, M
Interior Design, B
International Business/Trade/Commerce, BM
International Relations and Affairs, B
Journalism, B
Kinesiology and Exercise Science, B
Kinesiology and Movement Studies, M
Liberal Arts and Sciences Studies and Humanities, AB
Management Information Systems and Services, B
Marketing, M
Marketing/Marketing Management, B
Mass Communication/Media Studies, AB
Mathematics, BM
Mathematics Teacher Education, M

Meteorology, B
Music, B
Music Performance, B
Music Teacher Education, B
Music Therapy/Therapist, B
Nuclear Medical Technology/Technologist, B
Nursing, MD
Nursing Administration, M
Nutritional Sciences, BM
Optometry, D
Organizational Behavior Studies, B
Organizational Management, MD
Pharmacy, D
Philosophy, B
Physical Education Teaching and Coaching, B
Political Science and Government, B
Psychology, BM
Radio and Television, B
Religion/Religious Studies, BM
Sales, Distribution and Marketing Operations, B
Secondary Education and Teaching, M
Sociology, B
Spanish Language and Literature, B
Sport and Fitness Administration/Management, BM
Statistics, M
Vision Science/Physiological Optics, B

UNIVERSITY OF MARY HARDIN-BAYLOR

Accounting, BM
Art Teacher Education, B
Biochemistry, B
Biology Teacher Education, B
Biology/Biological Sciences, B
Business Administration and Management, B
Business Administration, Management and Operations, M
Business/Managerial Economics, B
Cell/Cellular Biology and Anatomical Sciences, B
Chemistry, B
Chemistry Teacher Education, B
Christian Studies, B
Clinical Laboratory Science/Medical Technology/Technologist, B
Clinical Psychology, M
Communication Studies/Speech Communication and Rhetoric, B
Computer Education, M
Computer Graphics, B
Computer Science, B
Computer and Information Sciences, B
Counseling Psychology, M
Counselor Education/School Counseling and Guidance Services, M
Criminal Justice/Law Enforcement Administration, B
Curriculum and Instruction, M
Design and Visual Communications, B
Education, MD
Educational Administration and Supervision, MD
Elementary Education and Teaching, BD
English Language and Literature, B
English/Language Arts Teacher Education, B
Exercise and Sports Science, M
Film/Cinema Studies, B
Finance, B
Fine/Studio Arts, B
Foreign Language Teacher Education, B
General Studies, B
Graphic Design, B
Higher Education/Higher Education Administration, D
History, B
History Teacher Education, B
Information Science/Studies, B
International Business/Trade/Commerce, BM
Kinesiology and Exercise Science, B
Management, M
Management Information Systems and Services, BM
Marketing/Marketing Management, B
Marriage and Family Therapy/Counseling, M
Mass Communication/Media Studies, B
Mathematics, B
Mathematics Teacher Education, B
Music, B
Music Performance, B

Music Teacher Education, B
Nursing, MO
Nursing - Advanced Practice, MO
Nursing Administration, M
Nursing Education, MDO
Pastoral Studies/Counseling, B
Physical Education Teaching and Coaching, B
Political Science and Government, B
Psychology, B
Religious/Sacred Music, B
Science Teacher Education/General Science
  Teacher Education, B
Secondary Education and Teaching, D
Social Work, B
Sociology, B
Spanish Language Teacher Education, B
Spanish Language and Literature, B
Speech Teacher Education, B
Sport and Fitness Administration/Management, BM

UNIVERSITY OF NORTH TEXAS

Accounting, BM
Advertising and Public Relations, O
Aeronautics/Aviation/Aerospace Science and Tech-
  nology, B
Anthropology, BM
Applied Behavior Analysis, O
Art Education, M
Art History, Criticism and Conservation, BM
Audiology/Audiologist and Speech-Language
  Pathology/Pathologist, B
Behavioral Sciences, B
Biochemistry, BM
Biological and Biomedical Sciences, M
Biology/Biological Sciences, B
Biomedical Engineering, M
Biomedical/Medical Engineering, B
Broadcast Journalism, B
Business Administration, Management and Opera-
  tions, D
Business/Commerce, B
Business/Managerial Economics, B
Chemistry, BM
Child Development, B
Child and Family Studies, M
Clinical Laboratory Science/Medical
  Technology/Technologist, B
Clinical Psychology, M
Commercial and Advertising Art, B
Communication Disorders, MD
Communication and Media Studies, M
Composition, D
Computer Engineering, M
Computer Science, M
Computer and Information Sciences, B
Construction Engineering Technology/Technician, B
Counseling Psychology, MD
Counselor Education/School Counseling and Guid-
  ance Services, M
Criminal Justice/Safety Studies, B
Criminology, M
Curriculum and Instruction, M
Dance, B
Design and Applied Arts, M
Design and Visual Communications, B
Drama and Dramatics/Theatre Arts, B
Early Childhood Education and Teaching, M
Ecology, B
Economics, BM
Education, BM
Education/Teaching of the Gifted and Talented, M
Educational Leadership and Administration, MD
Educational Measurement and Evaluation, M
Educational Psychology, MD
Electrical Engineering, M
Electrical, Electronic and Communications Engineer-
  ing Technology/Technician, B
Electrical, Electronics and Communications Engi-
  neering, B
Emergency Management, M
Energy and Power Engineering, MD
Engineering, B
Engineering Physics, B
Engineering and Applied Sciences, M
English, M
English Language and Literature, B

English as a Second Language, M
Entrepreneurship/Entrepreneurial Studies, B
Environmental Sciences, M
Ethnomusicology, M
Fashion Merchandising, B
Fashion/Apparel Design, B
Film, Television, and Video Production, M
Finance, B
Finance and Banking, M
Fine Arts and Art Studies, M
Fine/Studio Arts, B
French Language and Literature, BM
General Studies, B
Geography, BM
German Language and Literature, B
Gerontology, BM
Health Services Administration, M
Higher Education/Higher Education Administra-
  tion, MD
History, BM
Hospitality Administration/Management, BM
Human Development, M
Human Development and Family Studies, B
Human Resources Management and Services, M
Human Services, B
Industrial and Manufacturing Management, M
Information Science/Studies, BM
Information Technology, B
Insurance, B
Interdisciplinary Studies, M
Interior Architecture, B
Interior Design, M
International Affairs, M
International/Global Studies, B
Internet and Interactive Multimedia, O
Jazz/Jazz Studies, B
Journalism, BMO
Kinesiology and Exercise Science, B
Kinesiology and Movement Studies, M
Liberal Arts and Sciences Studies and Humani-
  ties, B
Linguistics, BM
Logistics and Materials Management, BMD
Management Information Systems and Ser-
  vices, BMD
Management Strategy and Policy, M
Marketing, M
Marketing/Marketing Management, B
Materials Engineering, B
Mathematics, BM
Mechanical Engineering, BMD
Mechanical Engineering/Mechanical
  Technology/Technician, B
Molecular Biology, M
Multi-/Interdisciplinary Studies, B
Museology/Museum Studies, O
Music, BMD
Music Performance, B
Music Teacher Education, MD
Music Theory and Composition, BM
Musicology and Ethnomusicology, M
Non-Profit/Public/Organizational Management, M
Operations Management and Supervision, B
Organizational Behavior Studies, B
Parks, Recreation and Leisure Facilities Manage-
  ment, B
Performance, MD
Philosophy, BM
Physics, B
Political Science and Government, BM
Psychology, BMO
Public Administration, M
Public Health Education and Promotion, B
Quantitative Analysis, M
Radio and Television, B
Real Estate, B
Rehabilitation Counseling, O
Religion/Religious Studies, B
Social Sciences, B
Social Work, B
Sociology, BM
Spanish Language and Literature, BM
Special Education and Teaching, M
Special Products Marketing Operations, B
Supply Chain Management, M
Textile Design, M

Travel and Tourism, M
Vocational and Technical Education, M
Writing, M

UNIVERSITY OF PHOENIX–DALLAS CAMPUS

Accounting, BM
Business Administration and Management, B
Business Administration, Management and Opera-
  tions, M
Business/Corporate Communications, B
Computer Software Engineering, B
Computer and Information Systems Security, B
Consumer Merchandising/Retailing Management, B
Criminal Justice/Law Enforcement Administration, B
Criminology, M
Curriculum and Instruction, M
E-Commerce/Electronic Commerce, B
Education, M
Electronic Commerce, M
Finance, B
Health Services Administration, B
Hospitality Administration/Management, B
Human Resources Management and Services, M
Human Services, B
Information Technology, B
International Business/Trade/Commerce, BM
Management, M
Management Information Systems and Ser-
  vices, BM
Management Science, B
Management of Technology, M
Marketing, M
Marketing/Marketing Management, B
Operations Management and Supervision, B
Organizational Behavior Studies, B
Psychology, B
Public Administration, BM
Security and Protective Services, B

UNIVERSITY OF PHOENIX–HOUSTON CAMPUS

Accounting, BM
Business Administration and Management, B
Business Administration, Management and Opera-
  tions, M
Business/Commerce, B
Business/Corporate Communications, B
Computer Software Engineering, B
Computer and Information Sciences, B
Computer and Information Systems Security, B
Consumer Merchandising/Retailing Management, B
Criminal Justice/Law Enforcement Administration, B
Curriculum and Instruction, M
E-Commerce/Electronic Commerce, B
Education, M
Electronic Commerce, M
Finance, B
General Studies, B
Graphic Communications, B
Health Services Administration, BM
Hospitality Administration/Management, B
Human Resources Management and Services, M
Human Services, B
Information Technology, B
International Business/Trade/Commerce, BM
Management Information Systems and Ser-
  vices, BM
Management Science, B
Management of Technology, M
Marketing, M
Marketing/Marketing Management, B
Nursing, M
Operations Management and Supervision, B
Organizational Behavior Studies, B
Psychology, B
Public Administration, BM
Security and Protective Services, B
Teacher Assistant/Aide, B

UNIVERSITY OF PHOENIX–SAN ANTO-NIO CAMPUS

Accounting, BM
Business Administration and Management, B

Business Administration, Management and Operations, M
Criminal Justice/Law Enforcement Administration, B
Criminology, M
Curriculum and Instruction, M
E-Commerce/Electronic Commerce, B
Electronic Commerce, M
Finance, B
Health Services Administration, BM
Human Resources Management and Services, M
Human Services, B
Information Technology, B
International Business/Trade/Commerce, BM
Management Information Systems and Services, BM
Management Science, B
Management of Technology, M
Marketing, M
Marketing/Marketing Management, B
Nursing, M
Public Administration, M

UNIVERSITY OF ST. THOMAS

Accounting, BM
Biochemistry, B
Bioinformatics, B
Biology/Biological Sciences, B
Business Administration and Management, B
Business Administration, Management and Operations, M
Chemistry, B
Communication Studies/Speech Communication and Rhetoric, B
Computer Science, B
Counselor Education/School Counseling and Guidance Services, M
Criminology, B
Curriculum and Instruction, M
Development Economics and International Development, B
Drama and Dramatics/Theatre Arts, B
Economics, B
Education, BM
Educational Leadership and Administration, M
Educational Measurement and Evaluation, M
Elementary Education and Teaching, BM
English Language and Literature, B
English as a Second Language, M
Environmental Sciences, B
Environmental Studies, B
Finance, B
Finance and Banking, M
Fine/Studio Arts, B
French Language and Literature, B
General Studies, B
History, B
International Business/Trade/Commerce, M
International Relations and Affairs, B
Liberal Arts and Sciences Studies and Humanities, B
Liberal Studies, M
Marketing/Marketing Management, B
Mathematics, B
Multilingual and Multicultural Education, BM
Music, B
Music Teacher Education, B
Pastoral Studies/Counseling, BM
Philosophy, BMD
Political Science and Government, B
Psychology, B
Reading Teacher Education, M
Religion/Religious Studies, M
Religious Education, M
Secondary Education and Teaching, BM
Spanish Language and Literature, B
Special Education and Teaching, M
Theology and Religious Vocations, BM
Theology/Theological Studies, B

THE UNIVERSITY OF TEXAS AT ARLINGTON

Accounting, BMD
Advertising, B
Aerospace, Aeronautical and Astronautical Engineering, BMD
Anthropology, BM

Applied Mathematics, M
Architecture, BM
Art History, Criticism and Conservation, B
Art/Art Studies, General, B
Athletic Training and Sports Medicine, B
Banking and Financial Support Services, B
Biochemistry, B
Bioengineering, MD
Biological and Biomedical Sciences, MD
Biology/Biological Sciences, B
Biomedical/Medical Engineering, B
Business Administration and Management, B
Business Administration, Management and Operations, MD
Business/Managerial Economics, B
Ceramic Arts and Ceramics, M
Chemistry, BMD
Child Development, B
Civil Engineering, BMD
Clinical Laboratory Science/Medical Technology/Technologist, B
Communication and Media Studies, M
Computer Engineering, BMD
Computer Science, BMD
Computer Software Engineering, B
Construction Management, M
Criminal Justice/Safety Studies, B
Criminology, M
Curriculum and Instruction, M
Digital Communication and Media/Multimedia, B
Drama and Dramatics/Theatre Arts, B
Economics, BM
Education, MD
Educational Leadership and Administration, MD
Educational Policy, MD
Electrical Engineering, MD
Electrical, Electronics and Communications Engineering, B
Engineering Management, M
Engineering and Applied Sciences, MD
English, MD
English Language and Literature, B
English as a Second Language, M
Environmental Sciences, BMD
Exercise and Sports Science, M
Experimental Psychology, D
Film, Television, and Video Production, M
Finance and Banking, MD
Fine Arts and Art Studies, M
Fine/Studio Arts, B
Foreign Languages and Literatures, B
French Language and Literature, BM
General Studies, B
Geological and Earth Sciences/Geosciences, B
Geology/Earth Science, BMD
German Language and Literature, B
Health Psychology, D
Health Services Administration, M
Higher Education/Higher Education Administration, M
History, BMD
Human Resources Management and Services, M
Industrial Engineering, B
Industrial and Manufacturing Management, M
Industrial and Organizational Psychology, M
Industrial/Management Engineering, MD
Information Science/Studies, B
Interdisciplinary Studies, M
Interior Architecture, B
International Business/Trade/Commerce, B
International/Global Studies, B
Journalism, B
Kinesiology and Exercise Science, B
Landscape Architecture, M
Language Interpretation and Translation, B
Linguistics, BMD
Logistics and Materials Management, M
Management, MD
Management Information Systems and Services, BMD
Marketing, MD
Marketing Research, M
Marketing/Marketing Management, B
Materials Engineering, MD
Materials Sciences, MD
Mathematics, BMD

Mathematics Teacher Education, M
Mechanical Engineering, BMD
Microbiology, B
Multi-/Interdisciplinary Studies, B
Multilingual and Multicultural Education, M
Music, BM
Music Performance, B
Music Teacher Education, M
Nursing, MD
Nursing - Advanced Practice, M
Nursing Administration, M
Nursing Education, M
Performance, M
Philosophy, B
Physics, BMD
Political Science and Government, BM
Psychology, BMD
Public Administration, M
Public Affairs, D
Public Relations/Image Management, B
Quantitative Analysis, MD
Radio and Television, B
Real Estate, BMD
Russian Language and Literature, B
Social Work, BMD
Sociology, BM
Software Engineering, MD
Spanish Language and Literature, BM
Sustainable Development, M
Systems Engineering, M
Taxation, M
Urban Planning, D
Urban Studies/Affairs, M
Urban and Regional Planning, M

THE UNIVERSITY OF TEXAS AT AUSTIN

Accounting, BMD
Acting, B
Actuarial Science, MD
Advertising, B
Advertising and Public Relations, MD
Aerospace, Aeronautical and Astronautical Engineering, BMD
African Studies, MD
African-American/Black Studies, B
American/United States Studies/Civilization, BMD
Analytical Chemistry, D
Ancient Studies/Civilization, B
Animal Behavior and Ethology, D
Anthropology, BMD
Apparel and Textiles, B
Applied Mathematics, MD
Applied Physics, MD
Arabic Language and Literature, B
Archeology, BMD
Architectural Engineering, BM
Architectural History and Criticism, MD
Architecture, BM
Art Education, M
Art History, Criticism and Conservation, BMD
Art/Art Studies, General, B
Asian Languages, MD
Asian Studies/Civilization, BMD
Astronomy, BMD
Athletic Training and Sports Medicine, B
Biochemistry, BD
Biological and Biomedical Sciences, MD
Biology/Biological Sciences, B
Biomedical Engineering, MD
Biomedical/Medical Engineering, B
Biopsychology, D
Business Administration and Management, B
Business Administration, Management and Operations, M
Business/Commerce, B
Cell Biology and Anatomy, D
Chemical Engineering, BMD
Chemistry, BD
Child Development, MD
Child and Family Studies, MD
Civil Engineering, BMD
Classics and Classical Languages, Literatures, and Linguistics, BMD
Clinical Laboratory Science/Medical Technology/Technologist, B

Clinical Laboratory Sciences, D
Clinical Psychology, D
Communication Disorders, BMD
Communication Studies/Speech Communication
and Rhetoric, B
Communication and Media Studies, MD
Community Health Nursing, M
Comparative Literature, MD
Composition, MD
Computational Sciences, MD
Computer Engineering, MD
Computer Science, MD
Computer and Information Sciences, B
Counseling Psychology, D
Counselor Education/School Counseling and Guid-
ance Services, M
Cultural Studies, MD
Curriculum and Instruction, MD
Czech Language and Literature, B
Dance, BM
Design and Applied Arts, M
Design and Visual Communications, B
Developmental Psychology, D
Drama and Dramatics/Theatre Arts, B
Early Childhood Education and Teaching, MD
East Asian Languages, Literatures, and Linguis-
tics, B
East European and Russian Studies, M
Ecology, D
Economics, BMD
Education, MD
Educational Administration and Supervision, MD
Educational Media/Instructional Technology, MD
Educational Psychology, MD
Electrical Engineering, MD
Electrical, Electronics and Communications Engi-
neering, B
Engineering and Applied Sciences, MD
English, MD
English Language and Literature, B
Entrepreneurship/Entrepreneurial Studies, M
Environmental Engineering
Technology/Environmental Technology, MD
Environmental Studies, M
Ethnic and Cultural Studies, B
Ethnomusicology, MD
European Studies/Civilization, B
Evolutionary Biology, D
Exercise and Sports Science, MD
Family and Consumer Sciences/Human Sci-
ences, BMD
Film, Television, and Video Production, M
Finance, B
Finance and Banking, MD
Fine Arts and Art Studies, M
Fine/Studio Arts, B
Folklore, MD
Foods, Nutrition, and Wellness Studies, B
French Language and Literature, BMD
Geography, BMD
Geological/Geophysical Engineering, B
Geology/Earth Science, BMD
Geophysics and Seismology, B
Geosciences, MD
Geotechnical Engineering, MD
German Language and Literature, BMD
Gerontological Nursing, M
Health Education, MD
Health and Physical Education, B
Hebrew Language and Literature, B
Hispanic Studies, M
Hispanic and Latin American Languages, MD
Historic Preservation and Conservation, M
History, BMD
Human Development, MD
Human Development and Family Studies, B
Humanities/Humanistic Studies, B
Hydrology and Water Resources Science, B
Industrial and Manufacturing Management, MD
Industrial/Management Engineering, MD
Information Science/Studies, MD
Inorganic Chemistry, D
Interior Design, BM
International/Global Studies, B
Iranian/Persian Languages, Literatures, and Linguis-
tics, B

Islamic Studies, B
Italian Language and Literature, BMD
Jazz/Jazz Studies, B
Jewish/Judaic Studies, B
Journalism, BMD
Kinesiology and Exercise Science, B
Kinesiology and Movement Studies, MD
Landscape Architecture, M
Latin American Studies, BM
Latin Language and Literature, B
Law and Legal Studies, MD
Liberal Arts and Sciences Studies and Humani-
ties, B
Linguistics, BMD
Logistics and Materials Management, B
Management, D
Management Information Systems and Ser-
vices, BMD
Marine Sciences, MD
Marketing, MD
Marketing/Marketing Management, B
Materials Engineering, MD
Materials Sciences, MD
Maternity Nursing, M
Mathematics, BMD
Mathematics and Computer Science, B
Mechanical Engineering, BMD
Mechanics, MD
Media Studies, MD
Medicinal and Pharmaceutical Chemistry, D
Microbiology, D
Mineral Economics, M
Mineral/Mining Engineering, M
Molecular Biology, D
Multi-/Interdisciplinary Studies, B
Multilingual and Multicultural Education, MD
Music, BMD
Music Performance, B
Music Teacher Education, MD
Music Theory and Composition, BMD
Musicology and Ethnomusicology, MD
Natural Resources Management/Development and
Policy, M
Near and Middle Eastern Languages, MD
Near and Middle Eastern Studies, BMD
Neurobiology and Neurophysiology, D
Neuroscience, D
Nursing, MD
Nursing - Adult, M
Nursing - Advanced Practice, M
Nursing Administration, M
Nursing Education, M
Nutritional Sciences, MD
Operations Research, MD
Organic Chemistry, D
Organizational Behavior Studies, M
Pediatric Nurse/Nursing, M
Performance, MD
Petroleum Engineering, BMD
Pharmaceutical Sciences, MD
Pharmacology, D
Pharmacy, D
Philosophy, BD
Physical Chemistry, D
Physical Education Teaching and Coaching, MD
Physics, BMD
Plant Biology, MD
Political Science and Government, BMD
Portuguese Language and Literature, BMD
Psychiatric/Mental Health Nurse/Nursing, M
Psychology, BD
Public Administration, M
Public Affairs, MD
Public Health (MPH, DPH), B
Public Health Education and Promotion, B
Public History, D
Public Policy Analysis, D
Public Relations/Image Management, B
Quantitative Analysis, M
Radio and Television, B
Reading Teacher Education, MD
Rehabilitation Counseling, MD
Religion/Religious Studies, B
Romance Languages, Literatures, and Linguistics, D
Russian Language and Literature, B
Russian Studies, B

Sacred Music, M
Scandinavian Languages, Literatures, and Linguis-
tics, B
School Psychology, MD
Semitic Languages, Literatures, and Linguistics, B
Slavic Languages, Literatures, and Linguistics, MD
Social Work, BMD
Sociology, BMD
Spanish Language and Literature, BMD
Special Education and Teaching, MD
Sport Psychology, M
Sport and Fitness Administration/Management, B
Statistics, MD
Supply Chain Management, MD
Sustainable Development, M
Technology and Public Policy, M
Textile Sciences and Engineering, M
Theater, MD
Toxicology, D
Turkish Language and Literature, B
Urban Design, M
Urban Studies/Affairs, B
Urban and Regional Planning, MD
Visual and Performing Arts, B
Water Resources Engineering, MD
Women's Studies, B
Writing, M

THE UNIVERSITY OF TEXAS AT DALLAS

Accounting, BMD
Actuarial Science, BM
American/United States Studies/Civilization, B
Applied Mathematics, BM
Audiology/Audiologist and Speech-Language
Pathology/Pathologist, B
BioTechnology, M
Biochemistry, B
Biological and Biomedical Sciences, MD
Biology/Biological Sciences, B
Biomedical Engineering, MD
Biomedical/Medical Engineering, B
Business Administration, Management and Opera-
tions, MD
Business/Commerce, B
Cartography, B
Cell Biology and Anatomy, MD
Chemistry, BMD
Child and Family Studies, M
Cognitive Sciences, BMD
Communication Disorders, MD
Communication and Media Studies, MD
Comparative Literature, BMD
Computer Engineering, BMD
Computer Science, MD
Computer Software Engineering, B
Computer and Information Sciences, B
Criminology, BMD
Digital Communication and Media/Multimedia, B
Economics, BMD
Electrical Engineering, MD
Electrical, Electronics and Communications Engi-
neering, B
Engineering and Applied Sciences, MD
English, MD
Entrepreneurship/Entrepreneurial Studies, M
Finance, B
Finance and Banking, MD
Geochemistry, MD
Geographic Information Systems, MD
Geography, MD
Geology/Earth Science, B
Geophysics and Seismology, MD
Geosciences, MD
Health Services Administration, M
Health Services/Allied Health/Health Sciences, B
Health/Health Care Administration/Management, B
History, BM
Humanities/Humanistic Studies, MD
Hydrogeology, MD
Information Technology, B
Interdisciplinary Studies, M
International Business/Trade/Commerce, BMD
Internet and Interactive Multimedia, MD
Investment Management, M
Latin American Studies, M

Law and Legal Studies, M
Logistics and Materials Management, B
Management Information Systems and Services, BMD
Management Science, B
Management Strategy and Policy, MD
Management of Technology, M
Marketing, MD
Marketing/Marketing Management, B
Materials Engineering, MD
Materials Sciences, MD
Mathematics, BMD
Mathematics Teacher Education, M
Mechanical Engineering, BMD
Molecular Biology, BMD
Neuroscience, MD
Paleontology, MD
Philosophy, MD
Physics, BMD
Political Science and Government, BMD
Project Management, M
Psychology, BMD
Public Administration, B
Public Affairs, MD
Public Policy Analysis, BM
Science Teacher Education/General Science Teacher Education, M
Sociology, BMD
Software Engineering, MD
Statistics, MD
Supply Chain Management, M
Systems Engineering, M
Telecommunications, MD
Visual and Performing Arts, B

THE UNIVERSITY OF TEXAS AT EL PASO

Accounting, BM
Allied Health and Medical Assisting Services, D
Anthropology, BO
Applied Mathematics, B
Applied Psychology, O
Art Education, M
Art Teacher Education, B
Audiology/Audiologist and Speech-Language Pathology/Pathologist, B
Bioinformatics, M
Biological and Biomedical Sciences, MD
Biology/Biological Sciences, B
Biomedical Engineering, D
Botany/Plant Biology, B
Broadcast Journalism, B
Business Administration and Management, B
Business Administration, Management and Operations, MDO
Ceramic Arts and Ceramics, B
Chemistry, BMD
Civil Engineering, BMDO
Clinical Laboratory Science/Medical Technology/Technologist, B
Clinical Psychology, M
Commercial and Advertising Art, B
Communication Disorders, M
Communication and Media Studies, M
Community Organization and Advocacy, B
Computational Sciences, MD
Computer Engineering, MD
Computer Science, BMD
Construction Management, MO
Counselor Education/School Counseling and Guidance Services, M
Criminal Justice/Law Enforcement Administration, B
Curriculum and Instruction, M
Drama and Dramatics/Theatre Arts, B
Drawing, B
Economics, BM
Education, MD
Educational Administration and Supervision, MD
Educational Leadership and Administration, MD
Educational Measurement and Evaluation, M
Educational Psychology, M
Electrical Engineering, MD
Electrical, Electronics and Communications Engineering, B
Engineering and Applied Sciences, MDO
English, MDO

English Education, M
English Language and Literature, B
English as a Second Language, O
Environmental Engineering Technology/Environmental Technology, MD
Environmental Sciences, MD
Experimental Psychology, M
Finance, B
Fine Arts and Art Studies, M
Fine/Studio Arts, B
French Language and Literature, B
Geography, B
Geology/Earth Science, BMD
Geophysics and Seismology, BM
German Language and Literature, B
Health Professions and Related Clinical Sciences, B
Health Services Administration, O
Health/Health Care Administration/Management, B
Hispanic-American, Puerto Rican, and Mexican-American/Chicano Studies, B
History, BMD
Industrial Engineering, B
Industrial/Management Engineering, MO
Information Science/Studies, BM
Interdisciplinary Studies, B
International Business/Trade/Commerce, D
Journalism, B
Kinesiology and Movement Studies, M
Latin American Studies, B
Liberal Studies, M
Linguistics, BMO
Manufacturing Engineering, M
Marketing/Marketing Management, B
Mass Communication/Media Studies, B
Materials Engineering, D
Materials Sciences, D
Mathematics, BM
Mathematics Teacher Education, M
Mechanical Engineering, BMD
Medical Microbiology and Bacteriology, B
Metallurgical Engineering, BMD
Multilingual and Multicultural Education, O
Music, BM
Music Teacher Education, M
Nursing, MDO
Nursing - Advanced Practice, M
Nursing Administration, M
Nursing Education, MO
Occupational Therapy/Therapist, M
Philosophy, BM
Physical Therapy/Therapist, D
Physics, BM
Political Science and Government, BM
Printmaking, B
Psychology, BMD
Reading Teacher Education, M
Real Estate, B
Rehabilitation Counseling, M
Rhetoric, MD
Science Teacher Education/General Science Teacher Education, M
Sculpture, B
Social Work, BM
Sociology, BMO
Software Engineering, M
Spanish Language and Literature, BM
Special Education and Teaching, M
Statistics, BM
Systems Engineering, MO
Writing, MO
Zoology/Animal Biology, B

THE UNIVERSITY OF TEXAS HEALTH SCIENCE CENTER AT HOUSTON

Allopathic Medicine, D
Biochemistry, MD
Biological and Biomedical Sciences, MD
Biomathematics and Bioinformatics, MD
Biostatistics, MD
Cancer Biology/Oncology, MD
Cell Biology and Anatomy, MD
Dental Hygiene/Hygienist, B
Dentistry, MD
Developmental Biology and Embryology, MD
Genetic Counseling/Counselor, M
Genetics, MD

Health Informatics, MDO
Human Genetics, MD
Immunology, MD
Medical Physics, MD
Microbiology, MD
Molecular Biology, MD
Molecular Genetics, MD
Molecular Pathology, MD
Neuroscience, MD
Nursing, MD
Public Health, MDO
Virology, MD

THE UNIVERSITY OF TEXAS HEALTH SCIENCE CENTER AT SAN ANTONIO

Acute Care/Critical Care Nursing, O
Allopathic Medicine, MD
Biochemistry, MD
Biological and Biomedical Sciences, D
Biomedical Engineering, MD
Cell Biology and Anatomy, MD
Clinical Laboratory Science/Medical Technology/Technologist, B
Clinical Laboratory Sciences, D
Clinical Research, M
Communication Disorders, M
Community Health Nursing, O
Cytogenetics/Genetics/Clinical Genetics Technology/Technologist, B
Dental Hygiene/Hygienist, B
Dental Laboratory Technology/Technician, B
Dentistry, MDO
Dietetics/Dieticians, B
Emergency Medical Technology/Technician (EMT Paramedic), B
Gerontological Nursing, O
Immunology, MD
Interdisciplinary Studies, D
Medical Physics, D
Microbiology, MD
Molecular Medicine, MD
Neuroscience, D
Nursing, MDO
Nursing - Advanced Practice, MDO
Nursing Administration, MD
Nursing Education, MO
Occupational Therapy/Therapist, M
Pediatric Nurse/Nursing, O
Pharmacology, D
Physical Therapy/Therapist, D
Physician Assistant, M
Psychiatric/Mental Health Nurse/Nursing, O
Respiratory Care Therapy/Therapist, B
Special Education and Teaching, M
Structural Biology, MD
Toxicology, M

THE UNIVERSITY OF TEXAS MEDICAL BRANCH

Allied Health and Medical Assisting Services, MD
Allopathic Medicine, D
Bacteriology, D
Biochemistry, D
Bioinformatics, D
Biological and Biomedical Sciences, MD
Biophysics, D
Cell Biology and Anatomy, D
Clinical Laboratory Science/Medical Technology/Technologist, B
Clinical Laboratory Sciences, MD
Community Health and Preventive Medicine, MD
Computational Biology, D
Genetics, D
Humanities/Humanistic Studies, MD
Immunology, MD
Infectious Diseases, D
Microbiology, MD
Molecular Biophysics, MD
Neuroscience, D
Nursing, MD
Occupational Therapy/Therapist, M
Pathology/Experimental Pathology, D
Pharmacology, MD
Physical Therapy/Therapist, MD
Physician Assistant, M
Physiology, MD

Public Health, M
Rehabilitation Sciences, D
Respiratory Care Therapy/Therapist, B
Structural Biology, D
Toxicology, D
Virology, D

THE UNIVERSITY OF TEXAS OF THE PERMIAN BASIN

Accounting, BM
Applied Psychology, M
Art/Art Studies, General, B
Athletic Training and Sports Medicine, B
Biological and Biomedical Sciences, M
Biology/Biological Sciences, B
Business Administration and Management, B
Business Administration, Management and Operations, M
Business/Managerial Economics, B
Chemistry, B
Clinical Psychology, M
Computer Science, M
Computer and Information Sciences, B
Counselor Education/School Counseling and Guidance Services, M
Criminal Justice/Safety Studies, B
Criminology, BM
Early Childhood Education and Teaching, M
Education, M
Educational Administration and Supervision, M
English, M
English Language and Literature, B
English as a Second Language, M
Experimental Psychology, M
Finance, B
Foundations and Philosophy of Education, M
Geology/Earth Science, BM
History, BM
Human Development and Family Studies, B
Humanities/Humanistic Studies, B
Industrial Technology/Technician, B
Information Science/Studies, B
Kinesiology and Exercise Science, B
Kinesiology and Movement Studies, M
Marketing/Marketing Management, B
Mathematics, B
Mechanical Engineering, B
Multi-/Interdisciplinary Studies, B
Music, B
Petroleum Engineering, B
Political Science and Government, BM
Psychology, BM
Reading Teacher Education, M
Social Work, B
Sociology, B
Spanish Language and Literature, BM
Special Education and Teaching, M

THE UNIVERSITY OF TEXAS RIO GRANDE VALLEY

Accounting, BM
Advertising and Public Relations, O
Allopathic Medicine, D
Anthropology, B
Applied Mathematics, M
Art/Art Studies, General, B
Biological and Biomedical Sciences, M
Biology/Biological Sciences, B
Biomedical Sciences, B
Business Administration, Management and Operations, MD
Chemistry, BM
Child Care and Support Services Management, B
Civil Engineering, B
Clinical Laboratory Science/Medical Technology/Technologist, B
Clinical Psychology, M
Communication Disorders, BM
Communication Studies/Speech Communication and Rhetoric, B
Communication and Media Studies, MO
Computer Engineering, B
Computer Science, BM
Computer and Information Sciences, B
Counselor Education/School Counseling and Guidance Services, M

Criminal Justice/Law Enforcement Administration, B
Criminal Justice/Safety Studies, B
Criminology, M
Dance, B
Dietetics/Dieticians, B
Drama and Dramatics/Theatre Arts, B
Early Childhood Education and Teaching, M
Economics, B
Education, MD
Education/Teaching of the Gifted and Talented, M
Educational Leadership and Administration, MD
Educational Measurement and Evaluation, M
Educational Psychology, M
Electrical Engineering, M
Electrical, Electronics and Communications Engineering, B
Elementary Education and Teaching, M
Engineering Management, M
Engineering Physics, B
Engineering Technology, B
English, M
English Language and Literature, B
English as a Second Language, M
Entrepreneurship/Entrepreneurial Studies, B
Environmental Sciences, B
Ethnomusicology, M
Experimental Psychology, M
Finance, B
Finance and Banking, D
Fine Arts and Art Studies, M
Fine/Studio Arts, B
French Language and Literature, B
General Studies, B
Health Services/Allied Health/Health Sciences, B
Hispanic-American, Puerto Rican, and Mexican-American/Chicano Studies, B
History, BM
Interdisciplinary Studies, M
International Business/Trade/Commerce, B
Kinesiology and Exercise Science, B
Kinesiology and Movement Studies, M
Language Interpretation and Translation, B
Law and Legal Studies, B
Logistics and Materials Management, B
Management Information Systems and Services, BM
Manufacturing Engineering, BM
Marine Biology and Biological Oceanography, B
Marketing, D
Marketing/Marketing Management, B
Mass Communication/Media Studies, B
Mathematics, BM
Mathematics Teacher Education, M
Mechanical Engineering, BM
Multi-/Interdisciplinary Studies, B
Multilingual and Multicultural Education, M
Music, BM
Music Performance, B
Music Teacher Education, M
Nursing, M
Nursing - Adult, M
Nursing - Advanced Practice, M
Occupational Therapy/Therapist, M
Performance, M
Philosophy, B
Physical Sciences, B
Physics, B
Political Science and Government, B
Psychology, BM
Public Administration, BM
Public Affairs, M
Public Policy Analysis, M
Reading Teacher Education, M
Rehabilitation Counseling, MD
Rhetoric, M
School Psychology, M
Science Teacher Education/General Science Teacher Education, M
Secondary Education and Teaching, M
Social Sciences, B
Social Work, B
Sociology, BM
Spanish Language and Literature, BM
Special Education and Teaching, M
Systems Engineering, M
Theater, MO

Writing, M

THE UNIVERSITY OF TEXAS AT SAN ANTONIO

Accounting, BMD
Actuarial Science, B
American/United States Studies/Civilization, B
Anthropology, BMD
Applied Behavior Analysis, O
Applied Mathematics, M
Applied Statistics, MD
Architecture, BM
Art History, Criticism and Conservation, BM
Art/Art Studies, General, B
Bilingual and Multilingual Education, B
BioTechnology, M
Biochemistry, B
Biological and Biomedical Sciences, MD
Biological and Physical Sciences, B
Biology/Biological Sciences, B
Biomedical Engineering, MD
Biomedical/Medical Engineering, B
Building/Construction Site Management/Manager, B
Business Administration and Management, B
Business Administration, Management and Operations, D
Business/Commerce, B
Business/Managerial Economics, B
Cell Biology and Anatomy, D
Chemistry, BMD
Civil Engineering, BMD
Classics and Classical Languages, Literatures, and Linguistics, B
Clinical Laboratory Science/Medical Technology/Technologist, B
Communication and Media Studies, M
Computer Engineering, BMD
Computer Science, MD
Computer and Information Sciences, B
Computer and Information Systems Security, BMDO
Counselor Education/School Counseling and Guidance Services, MD
Criminal Justice/Safety Studies, B
Criminology, M
Cultural Studies, D
Curriculum and Instruction, MD
Demography, D
Dietetics/Dieticians, B
Early Childhood Education and Teaching, M
Economics, M
Education, B
Educational Administration and Supervision, M
Educational Leadership and Administration, MD
Educational Media/Instructional Technology, MO
Electrical Engineering, MD
Electrical, Electronics and Communications Engineering, B
Elementary Education and Teaching, B
Engineering and Applied Sciences, MD
English, MD
English Language and Literature, B
English as a Second Language, MO
Entrepreneurship/Entrepreneurial Studies, B
Environmental Engineering Technology/Environmental Technology, MD
Environmental Sciences, BMD
Finance, B
Finance and Banking, MD
Fine Arts and Art Studies, M
Fine/Studio Arts, B
Foreign Languages and Literatures, B
French Language and Literature, B
General Studies, B
Geography, B
Geology/Earth Science, BM
Germanic Languages, Literatures, and Linguistics, B
Health Education, M
Higher Education/Higher Education Administration, M
Hispanic-American, Puerto Rican, and Mexican-American/Chicano Studies, B
History, BM
Human Resources Management/Personnel Administration, B
Humanities/Humanistic Studies, B
Information Science/Studies, MDO

Interdisciplinary Studies, MD
Interior Architecture, B
International Business/Trade/Commerce, B
International Relations and Affairs, B
Junior High/Intermediate/Middle School Education
   and Teaching, B
Kinesiology and Exercise Science, B
Kinesiology and Movement Studies, M
Management, MD
Management Information Systems and Services, B
Management Science, B
Management of Technology, M
Manufacturing Engineering, M
Marketing, MD
Marketing/Marketing Management, B
Materials Engineering, M
Mathematics, BM
Mathematics Teacher Education, M
Mechanical Engineering, BMD
Molecular Biology, D
Multi-/Interdisciplinary Studies, B
Multilingual and Multicultural Education, MD
Music, BM
Neurobiology and Neurophysiology, D
Organizational Management, D
Philosophy, BM
Physics, BMD
Political Science and Government, BM
Psychology, BMD
Public Administration, BM
Public Health (MPH, DPH), B
Reading Teacher Education, MD
Real Estate, B
School Psychology, MO
Social Sciences, B
Social Work, M
Sociology, BM
Spanish Language and Literature, BM
Special Education and Teaching, BM
Statistics, BMD
Teaching English as a Second or Foreign
   Language/ESL Language Instructor, B
Tourism and Travel Services Management, B
Translational Biology, D
Urban and Regional Planning, M
Women's Studies, B

THE UNIVERSITY OF TEXAS AT TYLER

Accounting, B
Art History, Criticism and Conservation, M
Art/Art Studies, General, B
Biological and Biomedical Sciences, M
Biology/Biological Sciences, B
Business Administration and Management, B
Business Administration, Management and Opera-
   tions, M
Chemistry, B
Civil Engineering, BM
Clinical Laboratory Science/Medical
   Technology/Technologist, B
Clinical Psychology, M
Communication and Media Studies, M
Computer Science, BM
Computer and Information Sciences, B
Construction Management, B
Counseling Psychology, M
Criminal Justice/Safety Studies, B
Criminology, M
Early Childhood Education and Teaching, M
Economics, B
Educational Leadership and Administration, M
Electrical Engineering, M
Electrical, Electronics and Communications Engi-
   neering, B
Engineering Technology, B
English, M
English Language and Literature, B
Environmental Engineering
   Technology/Environmental Technology, M
Environmental and Occupational Health, M
Finance, B
Fine Arts and Art Studies, M
Foreign Languages and Literatures, M
General Studies, B
Health Education, M
Health Professions and Related Clinical Sciences, B

Health Services Administration, M
Health and Physical Education, B
History, BM
Human Resources Development, BMD
Industrial Safety Technology/Technician, B
Industrial Technology/Technician, B
Industrial and Manufacturing Management, M
Interdisciplinary Studies, M
Kinesiology and Exercise Science, B
Kinesiology and Movement Studies, M
Liberal Arts and Sciences Studies and Humani-
   ties, B
Management, M
Marketing/Marketing Management, B
Marriage and Family Therapy/Counseling, M
Mass Communication/Media Studies, B
Mathematics, BM
Mechanical Engineering, BM
Multi-/Interdisciplinary Studies, B
Music, B
Nursing, MD
Nursing - Advanced Practice, M
Nursing Administration, M
Nursing Education, M
Political Science and Government, BM
Psychology, BM
Public Administration, M
Reading Teacher Education, M
Religion/Religious Studies, B
School Psychology, M
Social Sciences, BM
Sociology, M
Spanish Language and Literature, B
Special Education and Teaching, M
Structural Engineering, M
Transportation and Highway Engineering, M
Vocational and Technical Education, MD
Water Resources Engineering, M

VERNON COLLEGE

Accounting, A
Administrative Assistant and Secretarial Science, A
Automobile/Automotive Mechanics
   Technology/Technician, A
Business Administration and Management, A
Child Care and Support Services Management, A
Cosmetology/Cosmetologist, A
Criminal Justice/Law Enforcement Administration, A
Data Processing and Data Processing
   Technology/Technician, A
Drafting and Design Technology/Technician, A
Farm/Farm and Ranch Management, A
Health Information/Medical Records
   Technology/Technician, A
Law and Legal Studies, A
Liberal Arts and Sciences Studies and Humani-
   ties, A
Machine Tool Technology/Machinist, A

VET TECH INSTITUTE OF HOUSTON

Veterinary/Animal Health Technology/Technician and
   Veterinary Assistant, A

VICTORIA COLLEGE

Administrative Assistant and Secretarial Science, A
Business Administration and Management, A
Chemical Technology/Technician, A
Clinical/Medical Laboratory Technician, A
Computer Systems Networking and Telecommunica-
   tions, A
Criminal Justice/Police Science, A
Early Childhood Education and Teaching, A
Electrical, Electronic and Communications Engineer-
   ing Technology/Technician, A
Emergency Medical Technology/Technician (EMT
   Paramedic), A
Fire Science/Firefighting, A
General Studies, A
Physical Therapist Assistant, A
Respiratory Care Therapy/Therapist, A

VIRGINIA COLLEGE IN AUSTIN

Accounting, A
Business Administration and Management, A
Business Operations Support and Secretarial Ser-
   vices, A

Computer Systems Networking and Telecommunica-
   tions, A
Computer and Information Systems Security, A
Diagnostic Medical Sonography/Sonographer and
   Ultrasound Technician, A
Entrepreneurial and Small Business Operations, A
Hospitality Administration/Management, A
Legal Assistant/Paralegal, A
Medical Insurance Specialist/Medical Biller, A
Medical Office Assistant/Specialist, A
Office Management and Supervision, A
Pre-Law Studies, A
Resort Management, A
Surgical Technology/Technologist, A

VISTA COLLEGE

Business Administration and Management, A
Medical/Clinical Assistant, A

WADE COLLEGE

Fashion/Apparel Design, A
Graphic Design, A
Interior Design, A
Specialized Merchandising, Sales, and Marketing
   Operations, A

WAYLAND BAPTIST UNIVERSITY

Accounting, M
American Government and Politics (United
   States), B
Art/Art Studies, General, B
Biology/Biological Sciences, B
Business Administration and Management, AB
Business Administration, Management and Opera-
   tions, M
Business Teacher Education, B
Chemistry, B
Communication Studies/Speech Communication
   and Rhetoric, B
Computer Science, B
Counseling Psychology, M
Criminal Justice/Law Enforcement Administra-
   tion, AB
Criminology, M
Drama and Dramatics/Theatre Arts, B
Early Childhood Education and Teaching, AB
Education, M
Educational Administration and Supervision, M
Educational Leadership and Administration, M
Educational Measurement and Evaluation, M
Educational Media/Instructional Technology, M
Elementary Education and Teaching, BM
English Education, M
English Language and Literature, B
English as a Second Language, M
English/Language Arts Teacher Education, B
Environmental Sciences, B
Fine/Studio Arts, B
General Studies, A
Geology/Earth Science, B
Graphic Design, B
Health Services Administration, M
Health and Physical Education, B
Higher Education/Higher Education Administra-
   tion, M
History, BM
Homeland Security, M
Human Resources Management and Services, M
Human Services, AB
Interdisciplinary Studies, M
International Business/Trade/Commerce, M
Junior High/Intermediate/Middle School Education
   and Teaching, B
Liberal Arts and Sciences Studies and Humani-
   ties, AB
Management Information Systems and Services, M
Mass Communication/Media Studies, B
Mathematics, B
Missions/Missionary Studies and Missiology, B
Molecular Biology, B
Music, B
Music Performance, B
Music Teacher Education, B
Nursing, M
Organizational Management, M

Parks, Recreation and Leisure Facilities Management, B
Pastoral Studies/Counseling, M
Physical Education Teaching and Coaching, B
Pre-Law Studies, AB
Project Management, M
Psychology, B
Religion/Religious Studies, M
Religious Education, B
Religious/Sacred Music, B
Science Teacher Education/General Science Teacher Education, BM
Secondary Education and Teaching, M
Social Sciences, AB
Social Studies Teacher Education, BM
Sociology, B
Spanish Language and Literature, B
Special Education and Teaching, M
Sport and Fitness Administration/Management, B
Teacher Education, Multiple Levels, B
Technology Teacher Education/Industrial Arts Teacher Education, B
Theology and Religious Vocations, M
Trade and Industrial Teacher Education, B

WEATHERFORD COLLEGE

Administrative Assistant and Secretarial Science, A
Biological and Physical Sciences, A
Business Administration and Management, A
Computer Graphics, A
Computer Programming/Programmer, A
Corrections, A
Cosmetology/Cosmetologist, A
Criminal Justice/Law Enforcement Administration, A
Emergency Medical Technology/Technician (EMT Paramedic), A
Fire Science/Firefighting, A
Information Science/Studies, A
Liberal Arts and Sciences Studies and Humanities, A
Occupational Therapist Assistant, A
Pharmacy Technician/Assistant, A
Physical Therapist Assistant, A
Radiologic Technology/Science - Radiographer, A
Respiratory Care Therapy/Therapist, A

WEST TEXAS A&M UNIVERSITY

Accounting, BM
Advertising, B
Agribusiness, B
Agricultural Business and Management, B
Agricultural Communication/Journalism, B
Agricultural Economics, M
Agricultural Sciences, MD
Agriculture, B
Agronomy and Crop Science, B
Animal Sciences, BM
Art/Art Studies, General, B
Athletic Training and Sports Medicine, B
BioTechnology, B
Biological and Biomedical Sciences, M
Biology/Biological Sciences, B
Broadcast Journalism, B
Business Administration and Management, B
Business Administration, Management and Operations, M
Business/Commerce, B
Business/Managerial Economics, B
Chemistry, BM
Civil Engineering, B
Clinical Laboratory Science/Medical Technology/Technologist, B
Communication Disorders, BM
Communication Studies/Speech Communication and Rhetoric, B
Communication and Media Studies, M
Computer Science, B
Computer and Information Sciences, B
Counselor Education/School Counseling and Guidance Services, M
Criminal Justice/Law Enforcement Administration, B
Criminal Justice/Safety Studies, B
Criminology, M
Curriculum and Instruction, M
Dance, B
Drama and Dramatics/Theatre Arts, B

Economics, M
Education, M
Educational Administration and Supervision, M
Educational Measurement and Evaluation, M
Educational Media/Instructional Technology, M
Elementary Education and Teaching, B
Engineering Technology, B
Engineering and Applied Sciences, M
English, M
English Language and Literature, B
Environmental Sciences, BM
Equestrian/Equine Studies, B
Exercise and Sports Science, M
Finance, B
Finance and Banking, M
Fine Arts and Art Studies, M
Fine/Studio Arts, B
Fire Protection and Safety Technology/Technician, B
General Studies, B
Geography, B
Geology/Earth Science, B
Graphic Design, B
Health Services/Allied Health/Health Sciences, B
History, BM
Interdisciplinary Studies, M
Journalism, B
Kinesiology and Exercise Science, B
Management Information Systems and Services, B
Marketing/Marketing Management, B
Mass Communication/Media Studies, B
Mathematics, BM
Mechanical Engineering, B
Multi-/Interdisciplinary Studies, B
Music, BM
Music Performance, B
Music Theory and Composition, B
Music Therapy/Therapist, B
Nursing, M
Nursing - Advanced Practice, M
Performance, M
Physics, B
Plant Protection and Integrated Pest Management, B
Plant Sciences, M
Political Science and Government, B
Pre-Law Studies, B
Psychology, BM
Public Administration, B
Reading Teacher Education, M
Secondary Education and Teaching, B
Social Sciences, B
Social Work, BM
Sociology, B
Spanish Language and Literature, B
Special Education and Teaching, M
Sport and Fitness Administration/Management, M
Wildlife Biology, B

WESTERN TECHNICAL COLLEGE (EL PASO)

Computer and Information Sciences and Support Services, A
Electrical, Electronic and Communications Engineering Technology/Technician, A

WESTERN TECHNICAL COLLEGE (EL PASO)

Automobile/Automotive Mechanics Technology/Technician, A
Computer Engineering Technology/Technician, A
Heating, Air Conditioning, Ventilation and Refrigeration Maintenance Technology/Technician, A

WESTERN TEXAS COLLEGE

Accounting, A
Administrative Assistant and Secretarial Science, A
Agricultural Teacher Education, A
Agriculture, A
Applied Horticulture/Horticultural Operations, A
Art Teacher Education, A
Art/Art Studies, General, A
Automobile/Automotive Mechanics Technology/Technician, A
Biology/Biological Sciences, A
Business Administration and Management, A
Child Care Provider/Assistant, A

Computer Engineering Technology/Technician, A
Computer Science, A
Computer and Information Sciences, A
Corrections, A
Criminal Justice/Law Enforcement Administration, A
Criminal Justice/Police Science, A
Drama and Dramatics/Theatre Arts, A
Early Childhood Education and Teaching, A
Engineering, A
Health and Physical Education, A
Landscape Architecture, A
Liberal Arts and Sciences Studies and Humanities, A
Marketing/Marketing Management, A
Mass Communication/Media Studies, A
Mathematics, A
Parks, Recreation and Leisure Facilities Management, A
Petroleum Technology/Technician, A
Pre-Law Studies, A
Pre-Medicine/Pre-Medical Studies, A
Radio and Television, A
Secondary Education and Teaching, A
Social Sciences, A
Turf and Turfgrass Management, A
Welding Technology/Welder, A

WHARTON COUNTY JUNIOR COLLEGE

Administrative Assistant and Secretarial Science, A
Agriculture, A
Art/Art Studies, General, A
Automobile/Automotive Mechanics Technology/Technician, A
Behavioral Sciences, A
Biology/Biological Sciences, A
Business Administration and Management, A
Chemistry, A
Clinical/Medical Laboratory Technician, A
Computer Science, A
Criminal Justice/Law Enforcement Administration, A
Data Processing and Data Processing Technology/Technician, A
Dental Hygiene/Hygienist, A
Drafting and Design Technology/Technician, A
Drama and Dramatics/Theatre Arts, A
Electrical, Electronic and Communications Engineering Technology/Technician, A
English Language and Literature, A
Farm/Farm and Ranch Management, A
Health Information/Medical Records Administration/Administrator, A
Industrial Radiologic Technology/Technician, A
Mathematics, A
Music, A
Ornamental Horticulture, A
Physical Education Teaching and Coaching, A
Physical Therapy/Therapist, A
Spanish Language and Literature, A

WILEY COLLEGE

Administrative Assistant and Secretarial Science, AB
Biology/Biological Sciences, B
Business Administration and Management, B
Business Teacher Education, B
Chemistry, B
Computer Science, AB
Computer and Information Sciences, AB
Criminal Justice/Safety Studies, B
Elementary Education and Teaching, B
English Language and Literature, B
History, B
Hotel/Motel Administration/Management, B
Mass Communication/Media Studies, B
Mathematics, B
Music, B
Music Teacher Education, B
Philosophy, B
Physical Education Teaching and Coaching, B
Physical Sciences, B
Physics, B
Pre-Dentistry Studies, B
Pre-Law Studies, B
Pre-Medicine/Pre-Medical Studies, B
Religion/Religious Studies, B
Social Sciences, B
Social Work, B

Sociology, B
Special Education and Teaching, B

Utah

ARGOSY UNIVERSITY, SALT LAKE CITY

Accounting, D
Business Administration and Management, AB
Business Administration, Management and Operations, MD
Counseling Psychology, MD
Counselor Education/School Counseling and Guidance Services, D
Criminal Justice/Law Enforcement Administration, B
Education, MD
Educational Leadership and Administration, MD
Finance and Banking, M
Forensic Psychology, M
Health Services Administration, M
Health/Health Care Administration/Management, B
Information Technology, AB
International Business/Trade/Commerce, MD
Liberal Arts and Sciences Studies and Humanities, B
Management Information Systems and Services, MD
Marketing, M
Marriage and Family Therapy/Counseling, MD
Psychology, ABMD
Public Administration, M
Public Health, M
Sustainability Management, MD

BRIGHAM YOUNG UNIVERSITY

Accounting and Related Services, B
Acting, B
Actuarial Science, B
Advertising, B
Agribusiness, B
Agricultural Business and Management, B
Agricultural Economics, B
Agricultural Sciences, MD
Analytical Chemistry, MD
Ancient/Classical Greek Language and Literature, B
Animal Sciences, MD
Animation, Interactive Technology, Video Graphics and Special Effects, B
Anthropology, M
Applied Economics, B
Applied Statistics, M
Art Education, M
Astronomy, BMD
Athletic Training and Sports Medicine, BM
Ballet, B
BioTechnology, M
Biochemistry, MD
Biological and Biomedical Sciences, MD
Biomedical Sciences, B
Biophysics, B
Broadcast Journalism, B
Business Administration, Management and Operations, M
Business Family and Consumer Sciences/Human Sciences, B
Cartography, B
Ceramic Arts and Ceramics, B
Chemical Engineering, MD
Chemistry, MD
Child Care Provider/Assistant, B
Child Care and Support Services Management, B
Child Development, B
Child and Family Studies, MD
Cinematography and Film/Video Production, B
Civil Engineering, MD
Classics and Classical Languages, Literatures, and Linguistics, M
Clinical Laboratory Science/Medical Technology/Technologist, B
Clinical Psychology, D
Communication Disorders, M
Communication and Media Studies, M
Communication, Journalism and Related Programs, B
Comparative Literature, M

Comparative and Interdisciplinary Arts, M
Composition, M
Computer Engineering, MD
Computer Science, MD
Construction Management, M
Counseling Psychology, MDO
Crafts/Craft Design, Folk Art and Artisanry, B
Dance, B
Developmental Biology and Embryology, MD
Directing and Theatrical Production, B
Dramatic/Theatre Arts and Stagecraft, B
Drawing, B
Early Childhood Education and Teaching, B
Education, BMDO
Educational Leadership and Administration, MD
Educational Media/Instructional Technology, MD
Educational Psychology, MD
Electrical Engineering, MD
Engineering and Applied Sciences, MD
English, M
English as a Second Language, M
Entrepreneurship/Entrepreneurial Studies, B
Environmental Sciences, BM
Exercise and Sports Science, MD
Family Resource Management Studies, B
Family and Consumer Economics and Related Services, B
Family and Consumer Sciences/Human Sciences, B
Family and Consumer Sciences/Human Sciences Business Services, B
Film, Television, and Video Production, M
Film/Cinema Studies, B
Film/Video and Photographic Arts, B
Finance and Banking, M
Financial Planning and Services, B
Fine Arts and Art Studies, M
Fine/Studio Arts, B
Fish, Game and Wildlife Management, MD
Food Science and Technology, M
Food Technology and Processing, B
Foreign Language Teacher Education, M
Foundations and Philosophy of Education, MD
French Language and Literature, M
Geography, B
Geological and Earth Sciences/Geosciences, B
Geology/Earth Science, M
Graphic Design, B
Health Education, M
Health Promotion, MD
Hebrew Language and Literature, B
Hispanic and Latin American Languages, M
Home Furnishings and Equipment Installers, B
Human Development, MD
Human Development and Family Studies, B
Human Resources Management and Services, M
Human Resources Management/Personnel Administration, B
Humanities/Humanistic Studies, M
Illustration, B
Industrial Design, M
Information Science/Studies, M
Information Technology, B
International Finance, B
Jazz/Jazz Studies, B
Journalism, B
Kinesiology and Exercise Science, B
Korean Language and Literature, B
Language Interpretation and Translation, B
Latin Teacher Education, B
Law and Legal Studies, MD
Liberal Arts and Sciences Studies and Humanities, B
Linguistic, Comparative, and Related Language Studies and Services, B
Linguistics, B
Logistics and Materials Management, B
Manufacturing Engineering, B
Marriage and Family Therapy/Counseling, MD
Mass Communication/Media Studies, M
Mathematics, MD
Mathematics Teacher Education, M
Mechanical Engineering, MD
Microbiology, BMD
Molecular Biology, MD
Music, BM
Music History, Literature, and Theory, B

Music Pedagogy, B
Music Teacher Education, M
Musicology and Ethnomusicology, M
Neuroscience, MD
Non-Profit/Public/Organizational Management, M
Norwegian Language and Literature, B
Nursing, M
Nursing - Advanced Practice, M
Nutritional Sciences, M
Organizational Communication, B
Painting, B
Parks, Recreation, Leisure and Fitness Studies, B
Performance, M
Physical Education Teaching and Coaching, M
Physics, BMD
Physiology, BMD
Piano and Organ, B
Plant Sciences, MD
Playwriting and Screenwriting, B
Political Science and Government, M
Portuguese Language and Literature, M
Pre-Nursing Studies, B
Printmaking, B
Psychology, MD
Psychology Teacher Education, B
Public Administration, M
Public Policy Analysis, B
Public Relations, Advertising, and Applied Communication, B
Radio, Television, and Digital Communication, B
Reading Teacher Education, M
Religious Education, M
Rhetoric, M
School Psychology, O
Science Teacher Education/General Science Teacher Education, BM
Sculpture, B
Slavic Languages, Literatures, and Linguistics, D
Social Science Teacher Education, B
Social Work, M
Sociology, M
Soil Sciences, B
Spanish Language and Literature, M
Special Education and Teaching, BMDO
Speech Teacher Education, B
Statistics, M
Swedish Language and Literature, B
Teacher Education and Professional Development, Specific Levels and Methods, B
Teacher Education and Professional Development, Specific Subject Areas, B
Teaching English as a Second or Foreign Language/ESL Language Instructor, B
Technical Theatre/Theatre Design and Technology, B
Theater, M
Therapeutic Recreation/Recreational Therapy, B
Veterinary/Animal Health Technology/Technician and Veterinary Assistant, B
Violin, Viola, Guitar and Other Stringed Instruments, B
Visual and Performing Arts, B
Voice and Opera, B
Work and Family Studies, B
Writing, M

BROADVIEW ENTERTAINMENT ARTS UNIVERSITY

Animation, Interactive Technology, Video Graphics and Special Effects, A
Design and Visual Communications, B
Recording Arts Technology/Technician, A

BROADVIEW UNIVERSITY–LAYTON

Accounting, AB
Business Administration and Management, AB
Computer Programming, Specific Applications, AB
Computer Systems Networking and Telecommunications, A
Criminal Justice/Law Enforcement Administration, AB
Information Technology, B
Legal Assistant/Paralegal, AB
Marketing/Marketing Management, A
Massage Therapy/Therapeutic Massage, A
Medical Administrative Assistant/Secretary, A

Medical/Clinical Assistant, A
Veterinary/Animal Health Technology/Technician and
Veterinary Assistant, A

BROADVIEW UNIVERSITY–WEST JORDAN

Accounting, AB
Business Administration and Management, AB
Business Administration, Management and Operations, M
Computer Programming, Specific Applications, AB
Computer Systems Networking and Telecommunications, A
Criminal Justice/Law Enforcement Administration, AB
Health Services Administration, M
Health/Health Care Administration/Management, B
Information Technology, B
Legal Assistant/Paralegal, AB
Management Information Systems and Services, M
Marketing/Marketing Management, A
Massage Therapy/Therapeutic Massage, A
Medical Administrative Assistant/Secretary, A
Medical/Clinical Assistant, A
Veterinary/Animal Health Technology/Technician and
Veterinary Assistant, A

DIXIE STATE UNIVERSITY

Accounting, B
Automobile/Automotive Mechanics
Technology/Technician, A
Aviation/Airway Management and Operations, B
Biology Teacher Education, B
Biology/Biological Sciences, B
Business Administration and Management, AB
Business Administration, Management and Operations, AB
Business and Personal/Financial Services Marketing
Operations, AB
Clinical Laboratory Science/Medical
Technology/Technologist, AB
Communication Studies/Speech Communication
and Rhetoric, B
Computer Graphics, B
Computer Science, B
Computer and Information Sciences, B
Criminal Justice/Safety Studies, AB
Dance, A
Dental Hygiene/Hygienist, AB
Digital Communication and Media/Multimedia, B
Drama and Dramatics/Theatre Arts, B
Drawing, B
Early Childhood Education and Teaching, A
Elementary Education and Teaching, B
Emergency Medical Technology/Technician (EMT
Paramedic), A
Engineering, A
English Language and Literature, B
English/Language Arts Teacher Education, B
Finance, B
Forensic Science and Technology, B
General Studies, A
Graphic Design, B
Graphic and Printing Equipment Operator Production, A
History, B
Information Technology, B
Mass Communication/Media Studies, B
Mathematics, B
Mathematics Teacher Education, B
Multi-/Interdisciplinary Studies, B
Music, B
Music Teacher Education, B
Organizational Communication, B
Painting, B
Photography, B
Physical Therapist Assistant, A
Psychology, B
Radiologic Technology/Science - Radiographer, A
Respiratory Care Therapy/Therapist, A
Science Teacher Education/General Science
Teacher Education, B
Sculpture, B
Secondary Education and Teaching, B
Social Science Teacher Education, B
Sociology, B

Spanish Language and Literature, B
Technical Theatre/Theatre Design and Technology, B

INDEPENDENCE UNIVERSITY

Accounting, AB
Business Administration, Management and Operations, M
Business/Commerce, AB
Community Health Nursing, M
Community Health and Preventive Medicine, M
Early Childhood Education and Teaching, A
Finance, AB
Gerontological Nursing, M
Health Promotion, M
Health Services Administration, M
Health Services/Allied Health/Health Sciences, A
Health/Health Care Administration/Management, B
Management Science, B
Marketing/Marketing Management, B
Nursing, M
Nursing Administration, M
Public Health, M
Respiratory Care Therapy/Therapist, AB

LDS BUSINESS COLLEGE

Accounting, A
Accounting Technology/Technician and Bookkeeping, A
Accounting and Business/Management, A
Architecture and Related Services, A
Business Administration and Management, A
Business Administration, Management and Operations, A
Business, Management, Marketing, and Related
Support Services, A
Computer Programming, A
Computer Programming, Specific Applications, A
Computer Programming/Programmer, A
Computer Science, A
Computer Software Engineering, A
Computer and Information Sciences, A
Computer and Information Sciences and Support
Services, A
Computer and Information Systems Security, A
Computer/Information Technology Services Administration and Management, A
Cosmetology and Related Personal Grooming
Arts, A
Data Modeling/Warehousing and Database Administration, A
Design and Applied Arts, A
Engineering/Industrial Management, A
Entrepreneurial and Small Business Operations, A
Entrepreneurship/Entrepreneurial Studies, A
Food Service, Waiter/Waitress, and Dining Room
Management/Manager, A
Health Information/Medical Records
Administration/Administrator, A
Health Professions and Related Clinical Sciences, A
Information Technology, A
Interior Design, A
Legal Assistant/Paralegal, A
Liberal Arts and Sciences Studies and Humanities, A
Logistics and Materials Management, A
Marketing, A
Medical Insurance Coding Specialist/Coder, A
Medical/Clinical Assistant, A
Public Relations, Advertising, and Applied Communication, A
Restaurant, Culinary, and Catering
Management/Manager, A
Restaurant/Food Services Management, A
Salon/Beauty Salon Management/Manager, A
System, Networking, and LAN/WAN
Management/Manager, A
Vehicle Maintenance and Repair Technologies, A

Web Page, Digital/Multimedia and Information Resources Design, A

MIDWIVES COLLEGE OF UTAH

Direct Entry Midwifery (LM, CPM), B
Nurse Midwife/Nursing Midwifery, M

NEUMONT UNIVERSITY

Computer Programming, B
Computer Programming, Specific Applications, B
Computer Programming, Vendor/Product Certification, B
Computer Programming/Programmer, B
Computer Science, B
Computer Software and Media Applications, B
Computer and Information Sciences, B
Computer and Information Systems Security, B
Data Modeling/Warehousing and Database Administration, B
Information Technology, B
Management Information Systems and Services, B
Web Page, Digital/Multimedia and Information Resources Design, B
Web/Multimedia Management and Webmaster, B

PROVO COLLEGE

Accounting Technology/Technician and Bookkeeping, A
Business Administration, Management and Operations, A
Business Operations Support and Secretarial Services, A
Commercial and Advertising Art, A
Computer Programming, A
Computer and Information Sciences, A
Criminal Justice/Law Enforcement Administration, A
Dental Assisting/Assistant, A
Hospitality Administration/Management, A
Massage Therapy/Therapeutic Massage, A
Medical/Clinical Assistant, A
Physical Therapist Assistant, A

SALT LAKE COMMUNITY COLLEGE

Accounting Technology/Technician and Bookkeeping, A
Airline/Commercial/Professional Pilot and Flight
Crew, A
Architectural Engineering Technology/Technician, A
Autobody/Collision and Repair
Technology/Technician, A
Avionics Maintenance Technology/Technician, A
Biology Technician/BioTechnology Laboratory Technician, A
Biology/Biological Sciences, A
Building/Construction Finishing, Management, and Inspection, A
Business Administration and Management, A
Chemistry, A
Clinical/Medical Laboratory Technician, A
Communication Studies/Speech Communication
and Rhetoric, A
Computer Science, A
Computer and Information Sciences, A
Cosmetology/Cosmetologist, A
Criminal Justice/Law Enforcement Administration, A
Culinary Arts/Chef Training, A
Dental Hygiene/Hygienist, A
Design and Visual Communications, A
Diesel Mechanics Technology/Technician, A
Drafting and Design Technology/Technician, A
Economics, A
Electrical, Electronic and Communications Engineering Technology/Technician, A
Engineering, A
Engineering Technology, A
English Language and Literature, A
Entrepreneurship/Entrepreneurial Studies, A
Environmental Engineering
Technology/Environmental Technology, A
Finance, A
General Studies, A
Geology/Earth Science, A
Graphic Design, A
Health Professions and Related Clinical Sciences, A
Heating, Air Conditioning, Ventilation and Refrigeration Maintenance Technology/Technician, A

History, A
Human Development and Family Studies, A
Humanities/Humanistic Studies, A
Industrial Radiologic Technology/Technician, A
Information Science/Studies, A
Information Technology, A
Instrumentation Technology/Technician, A
International Relations and Affairs, A
International/Global Studies, A
Kinesiology and Exercise Science, A
Legal Assistant/Paralegal, A
Marketing/Marketing Management, A
Mass Communication/Media Studies, A
Medical Radiologic Technology/Science - Radiation
    Therapist, A
Medical/Clinical Assistant, A
Music, A
Occupational Therapist Assistant, A
Photographic and Film/Video Technology/Technician
    and Assistant, A
Physical Sciences, A
Physical Therapist Assistant, A
Physics, A
Political Science and Government, A
Psychology, A
Public Health, A
Quality Control Technology/Technician, A
Radio and Television Broadcasting
    Technology/Technician, A
Sign Language Interpretation and Translation, A
Social Work, A
Sociology, A
Sport and Fitness Administration/Management, A
Survey Technology/Surveying, A
Teacher Assistant/Aide, A
Telecommunications Technology/Technician, A
Welding Technology/Welder, A

SNOW COLLEGE

Accounting, A
Administrative Assistant and Secretarial Science, A
Agricultural Business and Management, A
Agriculture, A
Animal Sciences, A
Art/Art Studies, General, A
Automobile/Automotive Mechanics
    Technology/Technician, A
Biology/Biological Sciences, A
Botany/Plant Biology, A
Building/Construction Finishing, Manage-
    ment, and Inspection, A
Business Administration and Management, A
Business Teacher Education, A
Chemistry, A
Child Development, A
Computer Science, A
Construction Engineering Technology/Technician, A
Criminal Justice/Law Enforcement Administration, A
Dance, A
Drama and Dramatics/Theatre Arts, A
Economics, A
Education, A
Elementary Education and Teaching, A
Family and Community Services, A
Family and Consumer Sciences/Human Sciences, A
Farm/Farm and Ranch Management, A
Foods, Nutrition, and Wellness Studies, A
Forestry, A
French Language and Literature, A
Geography, A
Geology/Earth Science, A
History, A
Humanities/Humanistic Studies, A
Industrial Mechanics and Maintenance Technol-
    ogy, A
Information Science/Studies, A
Japanese Language and Literature, A
Kindergarten/PreSchool Education and Teaching, A
Liberal Arts and Sciences Studies and Humani-
    ties, A
Mass Communication/Media Studies, A
Mathematics, A
Music, AB
Music History, Literature, and Theory, A
Music Teacher Education, A
Natural Resources and Conservation, A

Philosophy, A
Physical Education Teaching and Coaching, A
Physical Sciences, A
Physics, A
Political Science and Government, A
Range Science and Management, A
Science Teacher Education/General Science
    Teacher Education, A
Sociology, A
Soil Science and Agronomy, A
Spanish Language and Literature, A
Zoology/Animal Biology, A

SOUTHERN UTAH UNIVERSITY

Accounting, BM
Agriculture, B
Airline/Commercial/Professional Pilot and Flight
    Crew, A
Animal/Livestock Husbandry and Production, A
Anthropology, B
Art History, Criticism and Conservation, B
Art Teacher Education, B
Art/Art Studies, General, B
Arts Management, M
Athletic Training and Sports Medicine, B
Biology Teacher Education, B
Biology/Biological Sciences, B
Building/Construction Site Management/Manager, B
Business Administration and Management, B
Business Administration, Management and Opera-
    tions, M
Business Teacher Education, B
Business/Commerce, A
CAD/CADD Drafting and/or Design
    Technology/Technician, A
Carpentry/Carpenter, A
Chemistry, B
Chemistry Teacher Education, B
Child Development, A
Communication Studies/Speech Communication
    and Rhetoric, B
Communication and Media Studies, M
Computer Science, B
Computer and Information Sciences, B
Construction Engineering Technology/Technician, A
Criminal Justice/Police Science, AB
Dance, B
Drama and Dance Teacher Education, B
Drama and Dramatics/Theatre Arts, B
Economics, B
Education, MO
Elementary Education and Teaching, B
Engineering Science, B
Engineering Technology, B
English Language and Literature, B
English/Language Arts Teacher Education, B
Exercise and Sports Science, M
Family and Consumer Sciences/Human Sciences, B
Finance, B
Fine/Studio Arts, B
French Language Teacher Education, B
French Language and Literature, B
General Studies, AB
Geology/Earth Science, B
Graphic Design, B
History, B
History Teacher Education, B
Horse Husbandry/Equine Science and Manage-
    ment, A
Hospitality Administration/Management, B
Human Nutrition, B
Information Technology, A
Kinesiology and Exercise Science, B
Legal Assistant/Paralegal, A
Marketing/Marketing Management, B
Mathematics, B
Mathematics Teacher Education, B
Multi-/Interdisciplinary Studies, B
Music, B
Music Teacher Education, B
Parks, Recreation, Leisure and Fitness Studies, B
Philosophy, B
Physical Education Teaching and Coaching, B
Physical Sciences, B
Political Science and Government, B
Psychology, B

Public Administration, M
Science Teacher Education/General Science
    Teacher Education, B
Social Science Teacher Education, B
Sociology, B
Spanish Language Teacher Education, B
Spanish Language and Literature, B
Technology Teacher Education/Industrial Arts
    Teacher Education, B

STEVENS-HENAGER COLLEGE (LO-
GAN)

Accounting, A
Business Administration and Management, A
Computer Programming/Programmer, A
Computer and Information Sciences, A
E-Commerce/Electronic Commerce, A
Health/Health Care Administration/Management, A
Respiratory Care Therapy/Therapist, A
System, Networking, and LAN/WAN
    Management/Manager, A

STEVENS-HENAGER COLLEGE
(OREM)

Accounting, A
Business Administration and Management, A
Computer Programming/Programmer, A
Computer and Information Sciences, A
E-Commerce/Electronic Commerce, A
Health/Health Care Administration/Management, A
Respiratory Care Therapy/Therapist, A
System, Networking, and LAN/WAN
    Management/Manager, A

STEVENS-HENAGER COLLEGE (SALT
LAKE CITY)

Accounting, A
Business Administration and Management, A
Computer Programming/Programmer, A
Computer and Information Sciences, A
E-Commerce/Electronic Commerce, A
Health/Health Care Administration/Management, A
Respiratory Care Therapy/Therapist, A
System, Networking, and LAN/WAN
    Management/Manager, A

STEVENS-HENAGER COLLEGE (WEST
HAVEN)

Accounting, B
Business Administration and Management, B
Business/Commerce, A
Computer Installation and Repair
    Technology/Technician, A
Computer Programming/Programmer, A
Computer Science, B
Graphic Design, A
Health/Health Care Administration/Management, B
Medical/Clinical Assistant, A
Surgical Technology/Technologist, A

UNIVERSITY OF PHOENIX–UTAH CAM-
PUS

Accounting, BM
Business Administration and Management, B
Business Administration, Management and Opera-
    tions, M
Business/Corporate Communications, B
Criminal Justice/Law Enforcement Administration, B
Curriculum and Instruction, M
Digital Communication and Media/Multimedia, B
Education, M
Educational Administration and Supervision, M
Elementary Education and Teaching, BM
Finance, B
Health Services Administration, B
Health/Health Care Administration/Management, B
Human Resources Management and Services, M
Human Services, B
Information Technology, B
International Business/Trade/Commerce, M
Management, M
Management Information Systems and Ser-
    vices, BM
Management Science, B
Management of Technology, M

Marketing, M
Marketing/Marketing Management, B
Nursing, M
Nursing Education, M
Psychology, B
Public Administration and Social Service Professions, B
School Psychology, M
Secondary Education and Teaching, M
Special Education and Teaching, M

UNIVERSITY OF UTAH

Accounting, BMD
Allopathic Medicine, D
American/United States Studies/Civilization, MD
Anatomy, D
Anthropology, BMD
Applied Mathematics, B
Arabic Language and Literature, BMD
Architecture, BM
Architecture and Related Services, B
Art Education, M
Art History, Criticism and Conservation, BM
Art/Art Studies, General, B
Asian Studies/Civilization, BM
Athletic Training and Sports Medicine, B
Atmospheric Sciences and Meteorology, BMD
Audiology/Audiologist and Speech-Language
    Pathology/Pathologist, B
Ballet, B
BioTechnology, M
Biochemistry, MD
Bioengineering, MD
Bioinformatics, MDO
Biological and Biomedical Sciences, MDO
Biology/Biological Sciences, B
Biomedical/Medical Engineering, B
Biostatistics, M
Business Administration and Management, B
Business Administration, Management and Operations, MDO
Business/Commerce, B
Cancer Biology/Oncology, MD
Cartography, B
Ceramic Arts and Ceramics, M
Chemical Engineering, BMD
Chemical Physics, D
Chemistry, BMD
Child and Family Studies, M
Chinese Language and Literature, B
Civil Engineering, BMD
Classics and Classical Languages, Literatures, and Linguistics, B
Clinical Laboratory Science/Medical
    Technology/Technologist, B
Clinical Psychology, MD
Communication Disorders, MD
Communication and Media Studies, MD
Comparative Literature, BMD
Composition, MD
Computational Sciences, M
Computer Engineering, B
Computer Science, BMD
Computer and Information Systems Security, MO
Consumer Economics, BM
Counseling Psychology, MD
Counselor Education/School Counseling and Guidance Services, M
Dance, BM
Dentistry, D
Drama and Dramatics/Theatre Arts, B
Early Childhood Education and Teaching, MD
Economics, BMD
Education, BMD
Educational Administration and Supervision, M
Educational Leadership and Administration, MD
Educational Media/Instructional Technology, M
Educational Psychology, MD
Electrical Engineering, M
Electrical, Electronics and Communications Engineering, B
Elementary Education and Teaching, BMD
Engineering, B
Engineering and Applied Sciences, MD
English, MD
English Language and Literature, B

Entrepreneurship/Entrepreneurial Studies, B
Environmental Engineering
    Technology/Environmental Technology, MD
Environmental Sciences, M
Environmental Studies, B
Ethnic, Cultural Minority, and Gender Studies, B
Exercise and Sports Science, MD
Film, Television, and Video Production, M
Film/Cinema Studies, B
Finance, B
Finance and Banking, MD
Fine Arts and Art Studies, M
Foreign Language Teacher Education, M
Foundations and Philosophy of Education, MD
French Language and Literature, BM
Game Design and Development, M
Geographic Information Systems, M
Geography, MD
Geological Engineering, MD
Geological and Earth Sciences/Geosciences, B
Geological/Geophysical Engineering, B
Geology/Earth Science, BMD
Geophysics and Seismology, BMD
German Language and Literature, B
Gerontological Nursing, MO
Gerontology, MO
Graphic Design, M
Health Education, MD
Health Promotion, MD
Health Services Administration, MD
Health Services Research, D
Health Services/Allied Health/Health Sciences, B
Health and Physical Education, B
Hebrew Language and Literature, BM
Higher Education/Higher Education Administration, D
History, BMD
Human Development, M
Human Development and Family Studies, B
Human Genetics, MD
Humanities/Humanistic Studies, BM
Industrial Design, B
Industrial and Manufacturing Management, MDO
Information Science/Studies, B
International Affairs, MD
International/Global Studies, B
Internet and Interactive Multimedia, M
Iranian/Persian Languages, Literatures, and Linguistics, B
Japanese Language and Literature, B
Kinesiology and Exercise Science, B
Latin American Studies, BM
Law and Legal Studies, MD
Leisure Studies, MD
Liberal Arts and Sciences Studies and Humanities, B
Linguistics, MD
Management Information Systems and Services, MDO
Management Strategy and Policy, MDO
Marketing, D
Marketing/Marketing Management, B
Materials Engineering, BMD
Materials Sciences, MD
Mathematics, BMD
Mechanical Engineering, BMD
Medical Physics, MD
Medical Technology, M
Medicinal and Pharmaceutical Chemistry, MD
Metallurgical Engineering, BMD
Mineral/Mining Engineering, MD
Mining and Mineral Engineering, B
Molecular Biology, D
Music, BMD
Music History, Literature, and Theory, M
Music Teacher Education, MD
Musicology and Ethnomusicology, M
Near and Middle Eastern Languages, MD
Near and Middle Eastern Studies, BMD
Neurobiology and Neurophysiology, D
Neuroscience, D
Nuclear Engineering, MD
Nursing, MD
Nutritional Sciences, M
Occupational Therapy/Therapist, MD
Operations Management and Supervision, B

Organizational Behavior Studies, D
Painting, M
Parks, Recreation, Leisure and Fitness Studies, B
Pathology/Experimental Pathology, D
Peace Studies and Conflict Resolution, B
Performance, MD
Petroleum Engineering, M
Pharmaceutical Administration, M
Pharmaceutical Sciences, MD
Pharmacology, D
Pharmacy, D
Philosophy, BMD
Photography, M
Physical Sciences, B
Physical Therapy/Therapist, D
Physician Assistant, M
Physics, BMD
Physiology, D
Political Science and Government, BMD
Printmaking, M
Psychology, BD
Public Administration, MD
Public Health, MD
Public Health Education and Promotion, B
Public Policy Analysis, M
Reading Teacher Education, MD
Real Estate, M
Recreation and Park Management, MD
Rehabilitation Sciences, D
Religion/Religious Studies, B
Rhetoric, MD
Russian Language and Literature, B
School Psychology, MD
Science Teacher Education/General Science
    Teacher Education, MD
Sculpture, M
Secondary Education and Teaching, MD
Social Science Teacher Education, B
Social Sciences, B
Social Work, BMD
Sociology, BMD
Software Engineering, MO
Spanish Language and Literature, BMD
Special Education and Teaching, BMD
Statistics, M
Student Personnel Services, M
Systems Engineering, MO
Toxicology, D
Turkish Language and Literature, B
Urban Planning, MD
Urban Studies/Affairs, B
Visual and Performing Arts, B
Women's Studies, B
Writing, MD

UTAH STATE UNIVERSITY

Accounting, BM
Aeronautical/Aerospace Engineering
    Technology/Technician, B
Aerospace, Aeronautical and Astronautical Engineering, BMD
Agricultural Business and Management, B
Agricultural Economics, B
Agricultural Education, M
Agricultural Engineering, MD
Agricultural Sciences, M
Agricultural Teacher Education, B
Agricultural/Biological Engineering and Bioengineering, B
Agriculture, B
Agronomy and Crop Science, B
Agronomy and Soil Sciences, MD
American/United States Studies/Civilization, BM
Animal Physiology, B
Animal Sciences, BMD
Anthropology, B
Applied Economics, M
Applied Mathematics, M
Area Studies, B
Art/Art Studies, General, B
Asian Studies/Civilization, B
Audiology/Audiologist and Speech-Language
    Pathology/Pathologist, B
Biochemistry, MD
Biological and Biomedical Sciences, BMD
Biology Teacher Education, B

Biology/Biological Sciences, B
Botany/Plant Biology, B
Business Administration and Management, B
Business Administration, Management and Operations, M
Business Education, MD
Business Teacher Education, B
Business/Commerce, B
Chemistry, BMD
Chemistry Teacher Education, B
Child and Family Studies, MD
Civil Engineering, BMDO
Clinical Laboratory Science/Medical Technology/Technologist, B
Clinical Psychology, D
Communication Disorders, MDO
Communication and Media Studies, M
Computer Engineering, B
Computer Engineering Technology/Technician, B
Computer Science, MD
Computer and Information Sciences, B
Computer and Information Sciences and Support Services, B
Consumer Economics, M
Counseling Psychology, D
Counselor Education/School Counseling and Guidance Services, M
Curriculum and Instruction, BD
Dairy Science, BM
Dance, B
Disability Studies, D
Drama and Dramatics/Theatre Arts, B
Ecology, BMD
Economics, BMD
Education, MDO
Educational Measurement and Evaluation, D
Educational Media/Instructional Technology, MDO
Electrical Engineering, MD
Electrical, Electronics and Communications Engineering, D
Elementary Education and Teaching, BM
Engineering and Applied Sciences, MDO
English, M
English Language and Literature, B
Entomology, B
Environmental Engineering Technology/Environmental Technology, MDO
Environmental Policy and Resource Management, MD
Environmental/Environmental Health Engineering, B
Family and Consumer Economics and Related Services, B
Family and Consumer Sciences/Home Economics Teacher Education, B
Family and Consumer Sciences/Human Sciences, M
Fashion Merchandising, B
Finance, B
Fine Arts and Art Studies, M
Fish, Game and Wildlife Management, MD
Folklore, M
Food Science and Technology, MD
Foods, Nutrition, and Related Services, B
Forestry, BMD
French Language and Literature, B
General Studies, A
Geography, BMD
Geology/Earth Science, BM
German Language and Literature, B
Health Education, M
Health Teacher Education, B
History, BM
Home Economics Education, M
Horticultural Science, B
Housing and Human Environments, B
Human Development, MD
Human Development and Family Studies, AB
Human Resources Management and Services, M
Human Resources Management/Personnel Administration, B
Industrial Education, M
Information Science/Studies, B
Interior Design, BM
International Agriculture, B
Journalism, B
Kindergarten/PreSchool Education and Teaching, B

Landscape Architecture, BM
Liberal Arts and Sciences Studies and Humanities, B
Management Information Systems and Services, MD
Marketing/Marketing Management, B
Marriage and Family Therapy/Counseling, M
Mathematics, BMD
Mathematics Teacher Education, B
Mechanical Engineering, BMD
Medical Microbiology and Bacteriology, B
Meteorology, MD
Multi-/Interdisciplinary Studies, B
Multilingual and Multicultural Education, M
Music, B
Music Teacher Education, B
Music Therapy/Therapist, B
Natural Resources and Conservation, BM
Nutritional Sciences, MD
Operations Management and Supervision, B
Parks, Recreation, Leisure and Fitness Studies, B
Philosophy, B
Physical Education Teaching and Coaching, BM
Physics, BMD
Physics Teacher Education, B
Plant Sciences, BMD
Political Science and Government, BM
Pre-Dentistry Studies, B
Pre-Law Studies, B
Pre-Medicine/Pre-Medical Studies, B
Pre-Veterinary Studies, B
Psychology, BMD
Public Health, B
Range Science and Management, BMD
Recreation and Park Management, MD
Rehabilitation Counseling, M
Sales and Marketing Operations/Marketing and Distribution Teacher Education, B
School Psychology, M
Science Teacher Education/General Science Teacher Education, B
Secondary Education and Teaching, BM
Social Studies Teacher Education, B
Social Work, B
Sociology, BMD
Soil Science and Agronomy, B
Spanish Language and Literature, B
Special Education and Teaching, BMDO
Statistics, BM
Teacher Education and Professional Development, Specific Subject Areas, B
Teacher Education, Multiple Levels, B
Technical Teacher Education, B
Technology Teacher Education/Industrial Arts Teacher Education, B
Theater, M
Tool and Die Technology/Technician, B
Toxicology, MD
Urban and Regional Planning, M
Veterinary Sciences, MD
Water Resources, MD
Water Resources Engineering, MD
Wildlife and Wildlands Science and Management, B
Writing, M
Zoology/Animal Biology, B

UTAH VALLEY UNIVERSITY

Accounting, ABM
Airline/Commercial/Professional Pilot and Flight Crew, AB
American Sign Language (ASL), B
Art Teacher Education, B
Autobody/Collision and Repair Technology/Technician, A
Automobile/Automotive Mechanics Technology/Technician, A
BioTechnology, B
Biology Teacher Education, B
Biology/Biological Sciences, AB
Botany/Plant Biology, B
Building/Home/Construction Inspection/Inspector, A
Building/Property Maintenance and Management, A
Business Administration and Management, B
Business Administration, Management and Operations, M
Business Teacher Education, B

Business/Office Automation/Technology/Data Entry, A
Cabinetmaking and Millwork/Millwright, A
Chemistry, AB
Chemistry Teacher Education, B
Communication Studies/Speech Communication and Rhetoric, A
Community Health and Preventive Medicine, A
Computer Hardware Engineering, B
Computer Science, AB
Computer Software Engineering, B
Computer Systems Networking and Telecommunications, B
Computer and Information Sciences, A
Construction Management, AB
Criminal Justice/Law Enforcement Administration, AB
Culinary Arts/Chef Training, A
Dance, AB
Dental Hygiene/Hygienist, AB
Design and Visual Communications, AB
Diesel Mechanics Technology/Technician, A
Drafting and Design Technology/Technician, A
Drama and Dance Teacher Education, B
Drama and Dramatics/Theatre Arts, AB
Early Childhood Education and Teaching, A
Economics, B
Education, M
Education/Teaching of Individuals with Hearing Impairments, Including Deafness, B
Educational Media/Instructional Technology, M
Elementary Education and Teaching, BM
English Language and Literature, AB
English as a Second Language, M
English/Language Arts Teacher Education, B
Environmental Sciences, B
Finance, B
Financial Planning and Services, B
Fire Science/Firefighting, AB
Forensic Science and Technology, B
General Studies, A
Geology/Earth Science, B
Health Teacher Education, B
Health and Physical Education, AB
History, AB
History Teacher Education, B
Hospitality Administration/Management, AB
Humanities/Humanistic Studies, A
Information Science/Studies, B
Legal Assistant/Paralegal, A
Marketing/Marketing Management, B
Mathematics, AB
Mathematics Teacher Education, BM
Mechanics and Repairers, A
Multi-/Interdisciplinary Studies, AB
Music, AB
Music Performance, B
Music Teacher Education, B
Nursing, AB
Operations Management and Supervision, B
Philosophy, AB
Physical Education Teaching and Coaching, B
Physical Sciences, A
Physics, AB
Political Science and Government, B
Psychology, AB
Robotics Technology/Technician, A
Science Teacher Education/General Science Teacher Education, B
Social Work, B
Spanish Language Teacher Education, B
Spanish Language and Literature, B
Survey Technology/Surveying, AB
Technical Theatre/Theatre Design and Technology, A
Web Page, Digital/Multimedia and Information Resources Design, AB

WEBER STATE UNIVERSITY

Accounting, BM
Administrative Assistant and Secretarial Science, AB
Allied Health Diagnostic, Intervention, and Treatment Professions, B
American Sign Language (ASL), A
Anthropology, B
Applied Mathematics, B

Archeology, A
Art Teacher Education, B
Art/Art Studies, General, B
Athletic Training and Sports Medicine, BM
Automobile/Automotive Mechanics
    Technology/Technician, AB
Automotive Engineering Technology/Technician, B
Biology Teacher Education, B
Biology Technician/BioTechnology Laboratory Technician, A
Botany/Plant Biology, B
Building/Construction Finishing, Management, and Inspection, AB
Business Administration and Management, B
Business Administration, Management and Operations, M
Business Teacher Education, B
Business/Managerial Economics, B
Cardiovascular Technology/Technologist, B
Chemical Technology/Technician, A
Chemistry, B
Chemistry Teacher Education, B
Child Development, AB
Clinical Laboratory Science/Medical
    Technology/Technologist, B
Clinical/Medical Laboratory Technician, AB
Commercial and Advertising Art, B
Communication Studies/Speech Communication
    and Rhetoric, B
Communication and Media Studies, M
Computer Engineering Technology/Technician, AB
Computer Science, AB
Computer Systems Networking and Telecommunications, AB
Computer and Information Sciences, B
Computer and Information Systems Security, B
Corrections, B
Corrections and Criminal Justice, B
Criminal Justice/Police Science, B
Criminal Justice/Safety Studies, AB
Curriculum and Instruction, M
Dance, B
Dental Hygiene/Hygienist, AB
Design and Visual Communications, B
Diagnostic Medical Sonography/Sonographer and
    Ultrasound Technician, B
Diesel Mechanics Technology/Technician, A
Drafting and Design Technology/Technician, AB
Drama and Dance Teacher Education, B
Drama and Dramatics/Theatre Arts, B
Early Childhood Education and Teaching, AB
Econometrics and Quantitative Economics, B
Economics, B
Education, AM
Electrical, Electronic and Communications Engineering Technology/Technician, AB
Electrical, Electronics and Communications Engineering, B
Electrician, A
Elementary Education and Teaching, B
Emergency Medical Technology/Technician (EMT
    Paramedic), A
Engineering, AB
English, M
English Language and Literature, B
English/Language Arts Teacher Education, B
Family Systems, B
Finance, B
Forensic Science and Technology, B
French Language Teacher Education, B
French Language and Literature, AB
General Studies, A
Geography, B
Geography Teacher Education, B
Geology/Earth Science, B
German Language Teacher Education, B
German Language and Literature, AB
Health Information/Medical Records
    Administration/Administrator, B
Health Information/Medical Records
    Technology/Technician, A
Health Physics/Radiological Health, M
Health Services Administration, M
Health Services/Allied Health/Health Sciences, AB
Health and Medical Administrative Services, B
Health and Physical Education, B

Health and Physical Education/Fitness, B
Health/Health Care Administration/Management, B
Health/Medical Preparatory Programs, B
History, B
History Teacher Education, B
Human Resources Management/Personnel Administration, B
Information Science/Studies, B
Interior Design, A
Intermedia/Multimedia, B
International Economics, B
Japanese Language and Literature, A
Journalism, B
Legal and Justice Studies, M
Liberal Arts and Sciences Studies and Humanities, B
Logistics and Materials Management, B
Management Information Systems and Services, AB
Manufacturing Technology/Technician, AB
Marketing/Marketing Management, B
Mathematics, B
Mathematics Teacher Education, B
Mechanical Engineering/Mechanical
    Technology/Technician, AB
Mechanics and Repairers, A
Medical Radiologic Technology/Science - Radiation
    Therapist, AB
Microbiology, AB
Music, B
Music Pedagogy, B
Music Performance, B
Music Teacher Education, B
Nuclear Medical Technology/Technologist, B
Nursing, M
Organizational Communication, B
Philosophy, B
Photography, B
Physical Education Teaching and Coaching, B
Physics, B
Physics Teacher Education, B
Piano and Organ, B
Plastics Engineering Technology/Technician, B
Political Communication, B
Political Science and Government, B
Pre-Dentistry Studies, B
Pre-Law Studies, B
Pre-Medicine/Pre-Medical Studies, B
Pre-Pharmacy Studies, B
Pre-Veterinary Studies, B
Psychology, B
Psychology Teacher Education, B
Public Health Education and Promotion, B
Public Relations, Advertising, and Applied Communication, B
Public Relations/Image Management, B
Quality Control Technology/Technician, A
Radio and Television, B
Radiologic Technology/Science - Radiographer, AB
Respiratory Care Therapy/Therapist, AB
Retailing and Retail Operations, A
Science Teacher Education/General Science
    Teacher Education, B
Selling Skills and Sales Operations, B
Social Science Teacher Education, B
Social Studies Teacher Education, B
Social Work, B
Sociology, B
Spanish Language Teacher Education, B
Spanish Language and Literature, AB
Special Education and Teaching, B
Taxation, M
Teacher Education and Professional Development, Specific Levels and Methods, B
Teacher Education and Professional Development, Specific Subject Areas, B
Voice and Opera, B
Welding Technology/Welder, AB
Zoology/Animal Biology, B

WESTERN GOVERNORS UNIVERSITY

Business Administration, Management and Operations, BM
Computer and Information Sciences and Support
    Services, B
Computer and Information Systems Security, M
Education, MO

Educational Leadership and Administration, M
Educational Measurement and Evaluation, M
Educational Media/Instructional Technology, M
Elementary Education and Teaching, MO
English Education, M
Health Services Administration, M
Higher Education/Higher Education Administration, M
Information Science/Studies, M
Management Information Systems and Services, M
Management Strategy and Policy, M
Mathematics Teacher Education, BM
Nursing Administration, M
Nursing Education, M
Science Teacher Education/General Science
    Teacher Education, BM
Social Science Teacher Education, B
Social Studies Teacher Education, MO
Special Education and Teaching, M
Teacher Education, Multiple Levels, B

WESTMINSTER COLLEGE

Accounting, BM
Airline/Commercial/Professional Pilot and Flight
    Crew, B
Art/Art Studies, General, B
Aviation/Airway Management and Operations, B
Biology/Biological Sciences, B
Business Administration, Management and Operations, MO
Business/Managerial Economics, B
Chemistry, B
Communication and Media Studies, M
Computer Science, B
Computer and Information Sciences, B
Counseling Psychology, M
Criminal Justice/Safety Studies, B
Drama and Dramatics/Theatre Arts, B
Education, M
Elementary Education and Teaching, B
English Language and Literature, B
Environmental Studies, B
Finance, B
Finance and Financial Management Services, B
Fine/Studio Arts, B
Health Services/Allied Health/Health Sciences, B
History, B
International Business/Trade/Commerce, B
Latin American Studies, B
Management Information Systems and Services, B
Management of Technology, M
Marketing/Marketing Management, B
Mathematics, B
Music, B
Nurse Anesthetist, M
Nursing, M
Nursing - Advanced Practice, M
Nursing Education, M
Philosophy, B
Physics, B
Political Science and Government, B
Psychology, B
Public Health, M
Public Health (MPH, DPH), B
Social Sciences, B
Sociology, B
Special Education and Teaching, B
Writing, M

Vermont

BENNINGTON COLLEGE

Acting, B
Allied Health and Medical Assisting Services, O
American/United States Studies/Civilization, B
Animation, Interactive Technology, Video Graphics
    and Special Effects, B
Anthropology, B
Architecture, B
Art History, Criticism and Conservation, B
Asian Studies/Civilization, B
Astronomy, B
Biological and Physical Sciences, B
Biology/Biological Sciences, B
Botany/Plant Biology, B

Cell/Cellular and Molecular Biology, B
Ceramic Arts and Ceramics, B
Chemistry, B
Child Development, B
Chinese Language and Literature, B
Cinematography and Film/Video Production, B
Communication and Media Studies, B
Computer Science, B
Computer and Information Sciences, B
Dance, BM
Design and Visual Communications, B
Digital Communication and Media/Multimedia, B
Directing and Theatrical Production, B
Drama and Dramatics/Theatre Arts, B
Drawing, B
Ecology, B
Education, BM
English, M
English Language and Literature, B
Environmental Biology, B
Environmental Design/Architecture, B
Environmental Sciences, B
Environmental Studies, B
European Studies/Civilization, B
Evolutionary Biology, B
Fashion/Apparel Design, B
Film/Cinema Studies, B
Fine/Studio Arts, B
Foreign Language Teacher Education, M
Foreign Languages and Literatures, B
French Language and Literature, BM
Gay/Lesbian Studies, B
History, B
Humanities/Humanistic Studies, B
Intermedia/Multimedia, B
International Relations and Affairs, B
International/Global Studies, B
Italian Language and Literature, B
Japanese Language and Literature, B
Jazz/Jazz Studies, B
Jewish/Judaic Studies, B
Latin American Studies, B
Liberal Arts and Sciences Studies and Humanities, B
Mathematics, B
Mathematics and Computer Science, B
Multi-/Interdisciplinary Studies, B
Music, BM
Music History, Literature, and Theory, B
Music Performance, B
Music Theory and Composition, B
Musicology and Ethnomusicology, B
Painting, B
Peace Studies and Conflict Resolution, B
Philosophy, B
Photography, B
Physical Sciences, B
Physics, B
Playwriting and Screenwriting, B
Political Science and Government, B
Pre-Law Studies, B
Pre-Medicine/Pre-Medical Studies, B
Printmaking, B
Psychology, B
Public Policy Analysis, B
Sculpture, B
Social Sciences, B
Sociology, B
Spanish Language and Literature, BM
Technical Theatre/Theatre Design and Technology, B
Theatre Literature, History and Criticism, B
Visual and Performing Arts, B
Voice and Opera, B
Women's Studies, B
Writing, M
Zoology/Animal Biology, B

CASTLETON UNIVERSITY

Accounting, B
Area Studies, B
Art History, Criticism and Conservation, B
Art Teacher Education, B
Art/Art Studies, General, B
Athletic Training and Sports Medicine, B

Biochemistry, Biophysics and Molecular Biology, B
Biological and Physical Sciences, B
Biology/Biological Sciences, B
Business Administration and Management, AB
Business/Commerce, A
Chemistry, B
Comparative Literature, B
Computer and Information Sciences, B
Criminal Justice/Law Enforcement Administration, AB
Criminology, B
Curriculum and Instruction, M
Drama and Dramatics/Theatre Arts, B
Ecology, B
Economics, B
Education, MO
Educational Leadership and Administration, MO
Elementary Education and Teaching, B
Environmental Sciences, B
Environmental Studies, B
Forensic Psychology, M
General Studies, A
Geography, B
Geology/Earth Science, B
Graphic Communications, B
Graphic Design, B
Health Professions and Related Clinical Sciences, B
Health and Physical Education, B
History, B
Journalism, B
Kinesiology and Exercise Science, B
Marketing/Marketing Management, B
Mass Communication/Media Studies, B
Mathematics, B
Mathematics Teacher Education, B
Music, B
Music Performance, B
Music Teacher Education, B
Natural Sciences, B
Philosophy, B
Photography, B
Physical Education Teaching and Coaching, B
Psychology, BM
Public Relations/Image Management, B
Radio and Television, B
Reading Teacher Education, MO
Science Teacher Education/General Science Teacher Education, B
Secondary Education and Teaching, B
Social Sciences, B
Social Studies Teacher Education, B
Social Work, B
Sociology, B
Spanish Language and Literature, B
Special Education and Teaching, BMO
Sport and Fitness Administration/Management, B
Technical Teacher Education, B
Women's Studies, B

CHAMPLAIN COLLEGE

Accounting, AB
Broadcast Journalism, B
Business Administration and Management, B
Business Administration, Management and Operations, M
Business/Commerce, AB
Communication Studies/Speech Communication and Rhetoric, B
Computer Graphics, B
Computer Programming/Programmer, AB
Computer Science, B
Computer Software and Media Applications, AB
Computer Systems Networking and Telecommunications, B
Computer and Information Sciences, B
Computer and Information Sciences and Support Services, B
Computer/Information Technology Services Administration and Management, B
Conflict Resolution and Mediation/Peace Studies, M
Criminal Justice/Safety Studies, B
Early Childhood Education and Teaching, BM
Elementary Education and Teaching, B
Environmental Studies, B
Film/Cinema Studies, B
Forensic Science and Technology, M

General Studies, B
Graphic Design, B
Health Services Administration, M
Hospital and Health Care Facilities Administration/Management, B
Hospitality Administration/Management, B
Intermedia/Multimedia, B
International Business/Trade/Commerce, B
Junior High/Intermediate/Middle School Education and Teaching, B
Law and Legal Studies, M
Legal Assistant/Paralegal, AB
Liberal Arts and Sciences Studies and Humanities, B
Management of Technology, M
Marketing/Marketing Management, B
Mass Communication/Media Studies, B
Media Studies, M
Medical Informatics, AB
Pre-Law Studies, B
Psychology, B
Public Relations/Image Management, B
Radiologic Technology/Science - Radiographer, A
Secondary Education and Teaching, B
Social Work, B
System Administration/Administrator, B
System, Networking, and LAN/WAN Management/Manager, B
Visual and Performing Arts, B
Web Page, Digital/Multimedia and Information Resources Design, AB

COLLEGE OF ST. JOSEPH

Accounting, AB
Behavioral Sciences, B
Business Administration and Management, AB
Business Administration, Management and Operations, M
Clinical Psychology, M
Community Psychology, M
Counseling Psychology, M
Counselor Education/School Counseling and Guidance Services, M
Criminal Justice/Law Enforcement Administration, AB
Education, M
Elementary Education and Teaching, BM
English Education, M
English Language and Literature, B
History, B
Human Services, AB
Liberal Arts and Sciences Studies and Humanities, AB
Psychology, BM
Radiologic Technology/Science - Radiographer, AB
Reading Teacher Education, M
School Psychology, M
Secondary Education and Teaching, BM
Social Studies Teacher Education, M
Special Education and Teaching, M
Substance Abuse/Addiction Counseling, BM

COMMUNITY COLLEGE OF VERMONT

Accounting, A
Administrative Assistant and Secretarial Science, A
Art/Art Studies, General, A
Business Administration and Management, A
CAD/CADD Drafting and/or Design Technology/Technician, A
Child Development, A
Community Organization and Advocacy, A
Computer Science, A
Computer Systems Networking and Telecommunications, A
Computer and Information Sciences, A
Criminal Justice/Law Enforcement Administration, A
Data Entry/Microcomputer Applications, A
Digital Communication and Media/Multimedia, A
Early Childhood Education and Teaching, A
Education, A
Environmental Sciences, A
Graphic Design, A
Hospitality Administration/Management, A
Human Services, A
Industrial Technology/Technician, A
Information Technology, A

Liberal Arts and Sciences Studies and Humanities, A
Medical/Clinical Assistant, A
Social Sciences, A
Teacher Assistant/Aide, A

GODDARD COLLEGE

Adult Development and Aging, B
Art Teacher Education, B
Art/Art Studies, General, B
Behavioral Sciences, B
Bilingual and Multilingual Education, B
Botany/Plant Biology, B
Business Administration, Management and Operations, M
Child Development, B
Community Organization and Advocacy, B
Comparative Literature, B
Comparative and Interdisciplinary Arts, M
Counseling Psychology, M
Education, BM
Elementary Education and Teaching, B
English/Language Arts Teacher Education, B
Environmental Studies, B
Ethnic and Cultural Studies, B
Foods, Nutrition, and Wellness Studies, B
Health Promotion, M
History, B
Humanities/Humanistic Studies, B
Intercultural/Multicultural and Diversity Studies, B
Interdisciplinary Studies, M
International/Global Studies, B
Junior High/Intermediate/Middle School Education and Teaching, B
Labor Studies, B
Liberal Arts and Sciences Studies and Humanities, B
Mental Health Counseling/Counselor, B
Multilingual and Multicultural Education, B
Nutritional Sciences, B
Peace Studies and Conflict Resolution, B
Photography, B
Political Science and Government, B
Psychology, B
Reading Teacher Education, B
Religion/Religious Studies, B
Social and Philosophical Foundations of Education, B
Sociology, B
Somatic Bodywork, B
Somatic Bodywork and Related Therapeutic Services, B
Sustainability Management, M
Teacher Education, Multiple Levels, B
Women's Studies, B
Writing, M

GREEN MOUNTAIN COLLEGE

Art Teacher Education, B
Art/Art Studies, General, B
Biology Teacher Education, B
Biology/Biological Sciences, B
Business Administration and Management, B
Business Administration, Management and Operations, M
Business/Managerial Economics, B
Elementary Education and Teaching, B
English Language and Literature, B
English/Language Arts Teacher Education, B
Environmental Design/Architecture, B
Environmental Studies, BM
Fine/Studio Arts, B
History, B
Liberal Arts and Sciences Studies and Humanities, B
Mass Communication/Media Studies, B
Natural Resources and Conservation, B
Parks, Recreation, Leisure and Fitness Studies, B
Philosophy, B
Psychology, B
Resort Management, B
Social Studies Teacher Education, B

JOHNSON STATE COLLEGE

Accounting, AB
Acting, B

Alternative and Complementary Medicine and Medical Systems, B
Anthropology, B
Applied Behavior Analysis, M
Art Teacher Education, B
Art/Art Studies, General, B
Athletic Training and Sports Medicine, B
Biology Teacher Education, B
Biology/Biological Sciences, B
Business Administration and Management, AB
Business/Commerce, B
Comparative Literature, B
Counselor Education/School Counseling and Guidance Services, M
Curriculum and Instruction, M
Dance, B
Drama and Dance Teacher Education, B
Drama and Dramatics/Theatre Arts, B
Education, BM
Elementary Education and Teaching, B
English Language and Literature, B
English/Language Arts Teacher Education, B
Environmental Studies, B
Fine Arts and Art Studies, M
Fine/Studio Arts, B
General Studies, A
Health Professions and Related Clinical Sciences, B
Health and Physical Education, B
History, B
History Teacher Education, B
Hospitality Administration/Management, B
Humanities/Humanistic Studies, B
Information Science/Studies, AB
Jazz/Jazz Studies, B
Journalism, B
Junior High/Intermediate/Middle School Education and Teaching, B
Kinesiology and Exercise Science, B
Liberal Arts and Sciences Studies and Humanities, AB
Management Information Systems and Services, AB
Marketing/Marketing Management, B
Mathematics, B
Mathematics Teacher Education, B
Music, B
Music Performance, B
Music Teacher Education, B
Natural Resources Management/Development and Policy, B
Painting, M
Parks, Recreation, Leisure and Fitness Studies, B
Photojournalism, B
Physical Education Teaching and Coaching, B
Political Science and Government, B
Pre-Medicine/Pre-Medical Studies, B
Printmaking, M
Psychology, B
Public Relations, Advertising, and Applied Communication, B
Reading Teacher Education, M
Sculpture, M
Secondary Education and Teaching, BM
Social Science Teacher Education, B
Social Studies Teacher Education, B
Sociology, B
Special Education and Teaching, M
Sport and Fitness Administration/Management, B
Substance Abuse/Addiction Counseling, M
Technical Theatre/Theatre Design and Technology, A
Tourism and Travel Services Management, B
Visual and Performing Arts, B

LANDMARK COLLEGE

Biology/Biological Sciences, A
Business Administration and Management, A
Business/Commerce, A
Computer Science, AB
Fine/Studio Arts, B
General Studies, A
Liberal Arts and Sciences Studies and Humanities, AB

LYNDON STATE COLLEGE

Accounting, B
Athletic Training and Sports Medicine, B

Atmospheric Sciences and Meteorology, B
Biological and Physical Sciences, B
Commercial and Advertising Art, B
Communication Studies/Speech Communication and Rhetoric, A
Computer Science, A
Counselor Education/School Counseling and Guidance Services, M
Curriculum and Instruction, M
Education, M
Elementary Education and Teaching, B
English Language and Literature, B
English/Language Arts Teacher Education, A
Health and Physical Education, B
Journalism, B
Mathematics, B
Mathematics Teacher Education, B
Parks, Recreation and Leisure Facilities Management, B
Parks, Recreation, Leisure and Fitness Studies, B
Physical Education Teaching and Coaching, B
Physical Sciences, B
Psychology, B
Radio and Television, B
Radio and Television Broadcasting Technology/Technician, A
Reading Teacher Education, BM
Science Teacher Education/General Science Teacher Education, BM
Social Science Teacher Education, B
Social Sciences, B
Special Education and Teaching, BM
Sport and Fitness Administration/Management, B

MARLBORO COLLEGE

Acting, B
African Studies, B
Algebra and Number Theory, B
American Government and Politics (United States), B
American/United States Studies/Civilization, B
Analysis and Functional Analysis, B
Ancient/Classical Greek Language and Literature, B
Anthropology, B
Applied Mathematics, B
Arabic Language and Literature, B
Area Studies, B
Art History, Criticism and Conservation, B
Art/Art Studies, General, B
Asian Studies/Civilization, B
Astronomy, B
Astrophysics, B
Behavioral Sciences, B
Bible/Biblical Studies, B
Biochemistry, B
Biochemistry, Biophysics and Molecular Biology, B
Biology/Biological Sciences, B
Botany/Plant Biology, B
Buddhist Studies, B
Business Administration, Management and Operations, M
Cell/Cellular Biology and Histology, B
Central/Middle and Eastern European Studies, B
Ceramic Arts and Ceramics, B
Chemistry, B
Chinese Language and Literature, B
Chinese Studies, B
Christian Studies, B
Classics and Classical Languages, Literatures, and Linguistics, B
Comparative Literature, B
Computer Education, MO
Computer Programming, B
Computer Programming/Programmer, B
Computer Science, B
Computer and Information Sciences, B
Dance, B
Development Economics and International Development, B
Directing and Theatrical Production, B
Drama and Dramatics/Theatre Arts, B
Dramatic/Theatre Arts and Stagecraft, B
Drawing, B
East Asian Studies, B
Ecology, B
Economics, B

Education, MO
Educational Media/Instructional Technology, MO
English Language and Literature, B
English as a Second Language, M
Environmental Biology, B
Environmental Studies, B
Ethics, B
Ethnic, Cultural Minority, and Gender Studies, B
European Studies/Civilization, B
Film/Cinema Studies, B
Film/Video and Photographic Arts, B
Fine Arts and Art Studies, B
Fine/Studio Arts, B
Foreign Languages, Literatures, and Linguistics, B
French Language and Literature, B
Gay/Lesbian Studies, B
Health Services Administration, M
History, B
Holocaust and Related Studies, B
Humanities/Humanistic Studies, B
Information Science/Studies, MO
Intermedia/Multimedia, B
International Economics, B
International Relations and Affairs, B
International/Global Studies, B
Internet and Interactive Multimedia, MO
Islamic Studies, B
Jewish/Judaic Studies, B
Language Interpretation and Translation, B
Latin American Studies, B
Latin Language and Literature, B
Legal and Justice Studies, M
Liberal Arts and Sciences Studies and Humanities, B
Linguistics, B
Logic, B
Mathematics, B
Mathematics and Computer Science, B
Mathematics and Statistics, B
Medieval and Renaissance Studies, B
Modern Languages, B
Molecular Biology, B
Music, B
Music History, Literature, and Theory, B
Music Performance, B
Music Theory and Composition, B
Musicology and Ethnomusicology, B
Natural Resources and Conservation, B
Natural Sciences, B
Near and Middle Eastern Studies, B
Non-Profit/Public/Organizational Management, M
Painting, B
Philosophy, B
Philosophy and Religious Studies, B
Photography, B
Physics, B
Political Science and Government, B
Pre-Law Studies, B
Pre-Medicine/Pre-Medical Studies, B
Pre-Veterinary Studies, B
Project Management, MO
Psychology, B
Religion/Religious Studies, B
Sculpture, B
Social Sciences, B
Sociology, B
Spanish Language and Literature, B
Statistics, B
Sustainability Management, M
Theatre Literature, History and Criticism, B
Visual and Performing Arts, B
Women's Studies, B

MIDDLEBURY COLLEGE

African Studies, B
American/United States Studies/Civilization, B
Arabic Language and Literature, BM
Architecture, B
Art History, Criticism and Conservation, B
Biochemistry, B
Biochemistry, Biophysics and Molecular Biology, B
Biology/Biological Sciences, B
Chemistry, B
Chinese Language and Literature, B
Chinese Studies, M

Classics and Classical Languages, Literatures, and Linguistics, B
Comparative Literature, B
Computer Science, B
Dance, B
Drama and Dramatics/Theatre Arts, B
East Asian Studies, B
Economics, B
English, M
English Language and Literature, B
Environmental Studies, B
European Studies/Civilization, B
Film/Cinema Studies, B
Fine/Studio Arts, B
French Language and Literature, BMD
Geography, B
Geology/Earth Science, B
German Language and Literature, BMD
History, B
International Relations and Affairs, B
Italian Language and Literature, BMD
Japanese Language and Literature, B
Latin American Studies, B
Liberal Arts and Sciences Studies and Humanities, B
Mathematics, B
Museology/Museum Studies, B
Music, B
Near and Middle Eastern Studies, B
Philosophy, B
Physics, B
Political Science and Government, B
Psychology, B
Religion/Religious Studies, B
Russian Language and Literature, BMD
Russian Studies, B
Sociology, B
South Asian Studies, B
Spanish Language and Literature, BMD
Women's Studies, B

NEW ENGLAND CULINARY INSTITUTE

Baking and Pastry Arts/Baker/Pastry Chef, A
Culinary Arts/Chef Training, AB
Restaurant, Culinary, and Catering Management/Manager, AB

NORWICH UNIVERSITY

Accounting, B
American/United States Studies/Civilization, M
Architecture, B
Athletic Training and Sports Medicine, B
Biology/Biological Sciences, B
Business Administration and Management, B
Business Administration, Management and Operations, M
Chemical Technology/Technician, B
Chemistry, B
Civil Engineering, BM
Communication Studies/Speech Communication and Rhetoric, B
Computer Engineering, B
Computer Science, B
Computer and Information Systems Security, M
Conflict Resolution and Mediation/Peace Studies, M
Construction Management, M
Criminal Justice/Law Enforcement Administration, B
Economics, B
Electrical, Electronics and Communications Engineering, B
English Language and Literature, B
Environmental Engineering Technology/Environmental Technology, M
Environmental Studies, B
Finance and Banking, M
Geology/Earth Science, B
Geotechnical Engineering, M
Health Professions and Related Clinical Sciences, B
History, BM
International Affairs, M
International Development, M
International Relations and Affairs, B
International Trade, M
Logistics and Materials Management, M
Management Information Systems and Services, M
Mathematics, B

Mechanical Engineering, B
Military and Defense Studies, M
Nursing, M
Nursing Administration, M
Nursing Education, M
Organizational Management, M
Peace Studies and Conflict Resolution, B
Physical Education Teaching and Coaching, B
Physics, B
Political Science and Government, B
Project Management, M
Psychology, B
Public Administration, M
Public Policy Analysis, M
Structural Engineering, M
Supply Chain Management, M
Water Resources Engineering, M

SAINT MICHAEL'S COLLEGE

Accounting, B
American/United States Studies/Civilization, B
Art Education, O
Art Teacher Education, B
Art/Art Studies, General, B
Biochemistry, B
Biology/Biological Sciences, B
Business Administration and Management, B
Chemistry, B
Classics and Classical Languages, Literatures, and Linguistics, B
Clinical Psychology, M
Computer Science, B
Curriculum and Instruction, MO
Drama and Dramatics/Theatre Arts, B
Economics, B
Education, BMO
Elementary Education and Teaching, B
English Language and Literature, B
English as a Second Language, MO
Environmental Studies, B
Ethnic, Cultural Minority, and Gender Studies, B
French Language and Literature, B
History, B
Information Science/Studies, B
International Relations and Affairs, B
Mass Communication/Media Studies, B
Mathematics, B
Modern Languages, B
Music, B
Philosophy, B
Physical Sciences, B
Physics, B
Political Science and Government, B
Pre-Dentistry Studies, B
Pre-Law Studies, B
Pre-Medicine/Pre-Medical Studies, B
Pre-Pharmacy Studies, B
Pre-Veterinary Studies, B
Psychology, B
Reading Teacher Education, M
Religion/Religious Studies, B
Secondary Education and Teaching, B
Sociology, B
Spanish Language and Literature, B
Special Education and Teaching, MO

SOUTHERN VERMONT COLLEGE

Business Administration and Management, B
Criminal Justice/Law Enforcement Administration, B
English Language and Literature, B
Entrepreneurship/Entrepreneurial Studies, B
Health/Health Care Administration/Management, B
History, B
Liberal Arts and Sciences Studies and Humanities, AB
Mass Communication/Media Studies, B
Medical Radiologic Technology/Science - Radiation Therapist, B
Political Science and Government, B
Psychology, B
Sport and Fitness Administration/Management, B

STERLING COLLEGE

Agriculture, B
Conservation Biology, B
Ecology, B

Education, B
Environmental Studies, B
Forestry, B
Natural Resources Management/Development and Policy, B
Natural Resources and Conservation, B
Parks, Recreation, Leisure and Fitness Studies, B
Plant Sciences, B
Wildlife and Wildlands Science and Management, B

UNIVERSITY OF VERMONT

Accounting, M
Agricultural Economics, M
Agricultural Sciences, MD
Agriculture, B
Agronomy and Crop Science, B
Agronomy and Soil Sciences, MD
Allied Health and Medical Assisting Services, MD
Allopathic Medicine, D
Ancient/Classical Greek Language and Literature, B
Animal Sciences, BMD
Anthropology, B
Applied Economics, M
Art History, Criticism and Conservation, B
Art Teacher Education, B
Asian Studies/Civilization, B
Athletic Training and Sports Medicine, B
Biochemistry, B
Biological and Biomedical Sciences, MD
Biology/Biological Sciences, B
Biomedical Engineering, D
Biomedical/Medical Engineering, B
Biostatistics, M
Botany/Plant Biology, B
Business Administration and Management, B
Business Administration, Management and Operations, M
Cell Biology and Anatomy, MD
Chemistry, BMD
Chinese Language and Literature, B
Civil Engineering, BMD
Classics and Classical Languages, Literatures, and Linguistics, BM
Clinical Laboratory Science/Medical Technology/Technologist, B
Clinical Laboratory Sciences, MD
Clinical Psychology, D
Communication Disorders, BM
Communication and Media Studies, M
Computer Science, BMD
Computer Systems Analysis/Analyst, B
Computer and Information Sciences, B
Counseling Psychology, M
Counselor Education/School Counseling and Guidance Services, M
Curriculum and Instruction, M
Dairy Husbandry and Production, B
Development Economics and International Development, B
Dietetics/Dieticians, B
Drama and Dramatics/Theatre Arts, B
Early Childhood Education and Teaching, B
Economics, B
Education, BMD
Education/Teaching of Individuals in Early Childhood Special Education Programs, B
Educational Administration and Supervision, M
Educational Leadership and Administration, MD
Electrical Engineering, MD
Electrical, Electronics and Communications Engineering, B
Elementary Education and Teaching, B
Engineering and Applied Sciences, MD
Engineering/Industrial Management, B
English, M
English Language and Literature, B
English/Language Arts Teacher Education, B
Entrepreneurship/Entrepreneurial Studies, B
Environmental Engineering Technology/Environmental Technology, MD
Environmental Sciences, B
Environmental Studies, B
Environmental/Environmental Health Engineering, B
European Studies/Civilization, B
Film/Cinema Studies, B
Fine/Studio Arts, B

Food Science and Technology, MD
Foreign Language Teacher Education, BM
Forestry, BM
French Language and Literature, BM
Geography, B
Geology/Earth Science, BM
German Language and Literature, M
Historic Preservation and Conservation, M
History, BM
Horticultural Science, BMD
Human Development and Family Studies, B
Industrial Engineering, B
Information Science/Studies, B
Interdisciplinary Studies, M
Italian Studies, B
Japanese Language and Literature, B
Junior High/Intermediate/Middle School Education and Teaching, B
Kindergarten/PreSchool Education and Teaching, B
Kinesiology and Exercise Science, B
Latin American Studies, B
Latin Language and Literature, B
Liberal Arts and Sciences Studies and Humanities, B
Materials Sciences, MD
Mathematics, BMD
Mathematics Teacher Education, BM
Mechanical Engineering, BMD
Medical Microbiology and Bacteriology, B
Medical Radiologic Technology/Science - Radiation Therapist, B
Microbiology, B
Molecular Biology, BMD
Molecular Genetics, B
Movement Therapy and Movement Education, B
Music, B
Music History, Literature, and Theory, B
Music Performance, B
Music Teacher Education, B
Natural Resources Management/Development and Policy, MD
Natural Resources and Conservation, BMD
Neuroscience, D
Nuclear Medical Technology/Technologist, B
Nursing, MD
Nutritional Sciences, BMD
Parks, Recreation and Leisure Facilities Management, B
Pathology/Experimental Pathology, M
Pharmacology, M
Philosophy, B
Physical Education Teaching and Coaching, B
Physical Therapy/Therapist, D
Physics, BM
Plant Biology, MD
Plant Sciences, BMD
Political Science and Government, B
Psychology, BD
Public Administration, M
Public Relations, Advertising, and Applied Communication, B
Religion/Religious Studies, B
Russian Language and Literature, B
Russian Studies, B
Science Teacher Education/General Science Teacher Education, BM
Secondary Education and Teaching, B
Social Studies Teacher Education, B
Social Work, BM
Sociology, B
Spanish Language and Literature, B
Special Education and Teaching, M
Statistics, BM
Wildlife Biology, B
Women's Studies, B
Zoology/Animal Biology, B

VERMONT TECHNICAL COLLEGE

Agribusiness, AB
Architectural Engineering Technology/Technician, AB
Automotive Engineering Technology/Technician, A
Business Administration and Management, AB
Civil Engineering Technology/Technician, A
Computer Engineering Technology/Technician, AB
Computer Software Engineering, AB
Construction Engineering Technology/Technician, A

Construction Management, AB
Dairy Science, A
Dental Hygiene/Hygienist, AB
Diesel Mechanics Technology/Technician, A
Electrical, Electronic and Communications Engineering Technology/Technician, AB
Electromechanical Technology/Electromechanical Engineering Technology, B
Energy Management and Systems Technology/Technician, B
Fire Science/Firefighting, A
Horse Husbandry/Equine Science and Management, B
Information Technology, AB
Landscaping and Groundskeeping, A
Mechanical Engineering/Mechanical Technology/Technician, A
Ornamental Horticulture, A
Respiratory Care Therapy/Therapist, A
Veterinary/Animal Health Technology/Technician and Veterinary Assistant, A

Virginia

ADVANCED TECHNOLOGY INSTITUTE

Automobile/Automotive Mechanics Technology/Technician, A
Diesel Mechanics Technology/Technician, A
Heating, Air Conditioning, Ventilation and Refrigeration Maintenance Technology/Technician, A

AMERICAN NATIONAL UNIVERSITY (CHARLOTTESVILLE)

Accounting, A
Administrative Assistant and Secretarial Science, A
Business/Commerce, A
Computer and Information Sciences, A
Medical/Clinical Assistant, A

AMERICAN NATIONAL UNIVERSITY (DANVILLE)

Accounting, A
Administrative Assistant and Secretarial Science, A
Business Administration and Management, AB
Computer and Information Sciences, A
Medical/Clinical Assistant, A
Surgical Technology/Technologist, A
Systems Engineering, A

AMERICAN NATIONAL UNIVERSITY (HARRISONBURG)

Accounting, AB
Administrative Assistant and Secretarial Science, A
Business Administration and Management, AB
Computer and Information Sciences, A
Data Modeling/Warehousing and Database Administration, B
Information Technology, B
Legal Assistant/Paralegal, A
Medical/Clinical Assistant, A
Surgical Technology/Technologist, A

AMERICAN NATIONAL UNIVERSITY (LYNCHBURG)

Accounting, A
Administrative Assistant and Secretarial Science, A
Business Administration and Management, AB
Computer and Information Sciences, A
Medical/Clinical Assistant, A

AMERICAN NATIONAL UNIVERSITY (MARTINSVILLE)

Accounting, A
Administrative Assistant and Secretarial Science, A
Business Administration and Management, A
Computer and Information Sciences, A
Medical/Clinical Assistant, A

AMERICAN NATIONAL UNIVERSITY (SALEM)

Accounting, AB
Administrative Assistant and Secretarial Science, A
Business Administration and Management, AB

Business Administration, Management and Operations, M
Computer Technology/Computer Systems Technology, A
Data Modeling/Warehousing and Database Administration, B
Emergency Medical Technology/Technician (EMT Paramedic), A
Health/Health Care Administration/Management, B
Information Technology, AB
Legal Assistant/Paralegal, A
Medical/Clinical Assistant, A
Tourism and Travel Services Marketing Operations, A
Web Page, Digital/Multimedia and Information Resources Design, A

ARGOSY UNIVERSITY, WASHINGTON DC

Accounting, D
Business Administration and Management, AB
Business Administration, Management and Operations, MDO
Clinical Psychology, MD
Community College Education, D
Community Psychology, M
Counseling Psychology, D
Counselor Education/School Counseling and Guidance Services, D
Criminal Justice/Law Enforcement Administration, B
Education, MDO
Educational Administration and Supervision, D
Educational Leadership and Administration, MDO
Elementary Education and Teaching, D
Finance and Banking, M
Forensic Psychology, MD
Health Psychology, D
Health Services Administration, M
Higher Education/Higher Education Administration, D
Information Technology, AB
International Business/Trade/Commerce, MDO
Liberal Arts and Sciences Studies and Humanities, B
Management, MD
Management Information Systems and Services, MD
Marketing, MDO
Marriage and Family Therapy/Counseling, D
Organizational Management, D
Psychology, ABMD
Public Administration, M
Public Health, M
Secondary Education and Teaching, D
Sustainability Management, MD

THE ART INSTITUTE OF VIRGINIA BEACH, A BRANCH OF THE ART INSTITUTE OF ATLANTA

Advertising, B
Apparel and Accessories Marketing Operations, B
Baking and Pastry Arts/Baker/Pastry Chef, A
Commercial Photography, B
Computer Graphics, B
Culinary Arts/Chef Training, A
Interior Design, B
Restaurant, Culinary, and Catering Management/Manager, B
Web Page, Digital/Multimedia and Information Resources Design, AB

THE ART INSTITUTE OF WASHINGTON, A BRANCH OF THE ART INSTITUTE OF ATLANTA

Advertising, B
Animation, Interactive Technology, Video Graphics and Special Effects, B
Apparel and Accessories Marketing Operations, B
Baking and Pastry Arts/Baker/Pastry Chef, A
Cinematography and Film/Video Production, AB
Commercial Photography, B
Computer Graphics, B
Culinary Arts/Chef Training, A
Interior Design, B
Photography, A

Recording Arts Technology/Technician, B
Restaurant, Culinary, and Catering Management/Manager, B
Web Page, Digital/Multimedia and Information Resources Design, AB

AVERETT UNIVERSITY

Accounting, BM
Aeronautics/Aviation/Aerospace Science and Technology, B
Applied Mathematics, B
Art Education, M
Art Teacher Education, B
Art/Art Studies, General, B
Athletic Training and Sports Medicine, B
Aviation/Airway Management and Operations, B
Biological and Physical Sciences, B
Biology Teacher Education, B
Business Administration and Management, B
Business Administration, Management and Operations, M
Corrections and Criminal Justice, B
Criminal Justice/Law Enforcement Administration, B
Curriculum and Instruction, M
Drama and Dramatics/Theatre Arts, B
Early Childhood Education and Teaching, M
Education, M
Educational Administration and Supervision, M
English Education, M
English Language and Literature, B
English/Language Arts Teacher Education, B
Environmental Sciences, B
Equestrian/Equine Studies, B
Foreign Languages, Literatures, and Linguistics, B
Health Teacher Education, B
Health and Physical Education, B
Health and Physical Education/Fitness, B
History, BM
Horse Husbandry/Equine Science and Management, B
Information Science/Studies, B
Journalism, B
Liberal Arts and Sciences Studies and Humanities, AB
Liberal Studies, M
Management Science, B
Marketing/Marketing Management, B
Mathematics, B
Mathematics Teacher Education, BM
Medical Radiologic Technology/Science - Radiation Therapist, B
Middle School Education, M
Music, B
Physical Education Teaching and Coaching, M
Political Science and Government, B
Pre-Medicine/Pre-Medical Studies, B
Pre-Nursing Studies, B
Psychology, B
Reading Teacher Education, M
Religion/Religious Studies, B
Science Teacher Education/General Science Teacher Education, M
Social Studies Teacher Education, BM
Sociology, B
Special Education and Teaching, M
Sport and Fitness Administration/Management, B
Teacher Education and Professional Development, Specific Subject Areas, B
Teacher Education, Multiple Levels, B
Theater, M
Theatre Literature, History and Criticism, B

BETHEL COLLEGE

Divinity/Ministry (BD, MDiv.), AB

BLUE RIDGE COMMUNITY COLLEGE

Accounting and Related Services, A
Airframe Mechanics and Aircraft Maintenance Technology/Technician, A
Biological and Physical Sciences, A
Business Administration, Management and Operations, A
Computer and Information Sciences, A
Criminal Justice/Law Enforcement Administration, A
Electrical, Electronic and Communications Engineering Technology/Technician, A

Industrial Technology/Technician, A
Liberal Arts and Sciences Studies and Humanities, A
Mechanical Engineering Related Technologies/Technicians, A
Mental and Social Health Services and Allied Professions, A
Psychiatric/Mental Health Services Technician, A
Veterinary/Animal Health Technology/Technician and Veterinary Assistant, A

BLUEFIELD COLLEGE

Accounting, B
Art/Art Studies, General, B
Bible/Biblical Studies, B
Biology Teacher Education, B
Biology/Biological Sciences, B
Business Administration and Management, B
Business Teacher Education, B
Chemistry, B
Chemistry Teacher Education, B
Christian Studies, B
Criminal Justice/Law Enforcement Administration, B
Divinity/Ministry (BD, MDiv.), B
Drama and Dramatics/Theatre Arts, B
Education, BM
Elementary Education and Teaching, B
English Language and Literature, B
English/Language Arts Teacher Education, B
Forensic Science and Technology, B
Health Teacher Education, B
History, B
History Teacher Education, B
Information Technology, B
Junior High/Intermediate/Middle School Education and Teaching, B
Kindergarten/PreSchool Education and Teaching, B
Kinesiology and Exercise Science, B
Liberal Arts and Sciences Studies and Humanities, B
Mass Communication/Media Studies, B
Mathematics, B
Mathematics Teacher Education, B
Music, B
Music Teacher Education, B
Physical Education Teaching and Coaching, B
Psychology, B
Religion/Religious Studies, B
Religious/Sacred Music, B
Science Teacher Education/General Science Teacher Education, B
Secondary Education and Teaching, B
Social Studies Teacher Education, B
Theology/Theological Studies, B

BRIDGEWATER COLLEGE

Athletic Training and Sports Medicine, B
Biochemistry, B
Biology/Biological Sciences, B
Business Administration and Management, B
Chemistry, B
Computer Science, B
Economics, B
English Language and Literature, B
Environmental Sciences, B
Family and Consumer Sciences/Human Sciences, B
Fine/Studio Arts, B
French Language and Literature, B
Health and Physical Education, B
History, B
Human Nutrition, B
International Relations and Affairs, B
Liberal Arts and Sciences Studies and Humanities, B
Management Information Systems and Services, B
Mass Communication/Media Studies, B
Mathematics, B
Music History, Literature, and Theory, B
Philosophy and Religious Studies, B
Physics, B
Political Science and Government, B
Psychology, B
Sociology, B

Spanish Language and Literature, B

BRYANT & STRATTON COL-LEGE–RICHMOND CAMPUS

Accounting, A
Administrative Assistant and Secretarial Science, A
Business Administration and Management, B
Business/Commerce, A
Computer and Information Systems Security, A
Criminal Justice/Law Enforcement Administration, A
Executive Assistant/Executive Secretary, B
Health Services Administration, B
Human Resources Management and Services, A
Legal Administrative Assistant/Secretary, A
Legal Assistant/Paralegal, A
Medical/Clinical Assistant, A
System, Networking, and LAN/WAN Management/Manager, A

BRYANT & STRATTON COL-LEGE–VIRGINIA BEACH CAMPUS

Accounting, A
Administrative Assistant and Secretarial Science, A
Business Administration and Management, B
Business Administration, Management and Operations, A
Computer and Information Sciences, A
Computer and Information Systems Security, A
Criminal Justice/Law Enforcement Administration, AB
Executive Assistant/Executive Secretary, B
Financial Planning and Services, B
Health Services Administration, B
Human Resources Management/Personnel Administration, A
Legal Assistant/Paralegal, A
Medical/Clinical Assistant, A
System, Networking, and LAN/WAN Management/Manager, A

CENTRAL VIRGINIA COMMUNITY COLLEGE

Accounting and Related Services, A
Business Administration and Management, A
Business Operations Support and Secretarial Services, A
Business/Commerce, A
Computer and Information Sciences, A
Criminal Justice/Law Enforcement Administration, A
Culinary Arts/Chef Training, A
Design and Visual Communications, A
Education, A
Emergency Medical Technology/Technician (EMT Paramedic), A
Engineering, A
Engineering Technology, A
Industrial Technology/Technician, A
Liberal Arts and Sciences Studies and Humanities, A
Management Science, A
Medical/Clinical Assistant, A
Radiologic Technology/Science - Radiographer, A
Respiratory Care Therapy/Therapist, A

CENTURA COLLEGE (CHESAPEAKE)

Business Administration and Management, A
Computer Systems Networking and Telecommunications, A
Legal Assistant/Paralegal, A
Massage Therapy/Therapeutic Massage, A
Medical/Clinical Assistant, A
Medical/Health Management and Clinical Assistant/Specialist, A

CENTURA COLLEGE (NEWPORT NEWS)

Business Administration and Management, A
Computer Systems Networking and Telecommunications, A
Massage Therapy/Therapeutic Massage, A

Medical/Clinical Assistant, A

CENTURA COLLEGE (NORFOLK)

Medical/Health Management and Clinical Assistant/Specialist, A

CENTURA COLLEGE (NORTH CHES-TERFIELD)

Computer Systems Networking and Telecommunications, A
Legal Assistant/Paralegal, A
Massage Therapy/Therapeutic Massage, A
Medical/Clinical Assistant, A

CENTURA COLLEGE (VIRGINIA BEACH)

Business Administration and Management, AB
Computer Systems Networking and Telecommunications, A
Criminal Justice/Safety Studies, A
Legal Assistant/Paralegal, A
Massage Therapy/Therapeutic Massage, A
Medical/Clinical Assistant, A

CHRISTENDOM COLLEGE

Classics and Classical Languages, Literatures, and Linguistics, B
Comparative Literature, B
History, B
Liberal Arts and Sciences Studies and Humanities, A
Mathematics, B
Philosophy, B
Political Science and Government, B
Theology and Religious Vocations, M
Theology/Theological Studies, B

CHRISTOPHER NEWPORT UNIVERSITY

Accounting, B
American/United States Studies/Civilization, B
Applied Mathematics, B
Applied Physics, M
Biochemistry, B
Biological and Biomedical Sciences, B
Biology/Biological Sciences, B
Business Administration and Management, B
Cell/Cellular and Molecular Biology, B
Chemistry, B
Classics and Classical Languages, Literatures, and Linguistics, B
Communication Studies/Speech Communication and Rhetoric, B
Computational Mathematics, B
Computer Engineering, B
Computer Science, BM
Drama and Dramatics/Theatre Arts, B
Economics, B
Education, M
Electrical, Electronics and Communications Engineering, B
English Language and Literature, B
Environmental Biology, B
Environmental Sciences, M
Environmental Studies, B
Finance, B
Fine/Studio Arts, B
French Language and Literature, B
German Language and Literature, B
History, B
Information Science/Studies, B
Information Technology, B
Marketing/Marketing Management, B
Mathematics, B
Multi-/Interdisciplinary Studies, B
Music Performance, B
Philosophy, B
Physics, BM
Political Science and Government, B
Psychology, B
Social Work, B
Sociology, B

Spanish Language and Literature, B

THE COLLEGE OF WILLIAM AND MARY

Accounting, BM
African-American/Black Studies, B
American/United States Studies/Civilization, BMD
Anthropology, BMD
Applied Mathematics, D
Applied Physics, D
Applied Science and Technology, MD
Art History, Criticism and Conservation, B
Art/Art Studies, General, B
Artificial Intelligence and Robotics, D
Biological and Biomedical Sciences, M
Biology/Biological Sciences, B
Business Administration and Management, B
Business Administration, Management and Operations, M
Chemistry, BM
Chinese Studies, B
Classics and Classical Languages, Literatures, and Linguistics, B
Computational Sciences, M
Computer Science, MD
Computer and Information Sciences, B
Counselor Education/School Counseling and Guidance Services, MD
Curriculum and Instruction, MD
Drama and Dramatics/Theatre Arts, B
Economics, B
Education, MDO
Educational Leadership and Administration, MD
Educational Media/Instructional Technology, D
Educational Policy, D
English Language and Literature, B
Environmental Studies, B
Experimental Psychology, M
Finance, B
French Language and Literature, B
Geographic Information Systems, D
Geology/Earth Science, B
German Language and Literature, B
Health and Physical Education, B
History, BMD
Interdisciplinary Studies, MD
International Relations and Affairs, B
Latin American Studies, B
Law and Legal Studies, MD
Linguistics, B
Marine Sciences, MD
Marketing/Marketing Management, B
Mathematics, B
Medical Physics, D
Medieval and Renaissance Studies, B
Modern Languages, B
Multi-/Interdisciplinary Studies, B
Music, B
NanoTechnology, D
Operations Research, M
Optics/Optical Sciences, D
Philosophy, B
Physics, BMD
Political Science and Government, B
Polymer/Plastics Engineering, D
Psychology, B
Public Policy Analysis, BM
Religion/Religious Studies, B
School Psychology, MO
Sociology, B
Women's Studies, B

CULINARY INSTITUTE OF VIRGINIA

Culinary Arts/Chef Training, A
Restaurant/Food Services Management, B

DABNEY S. LANCASTER COMMUNITY COLLEGE

Administrative Assistant and Secretarial Science, A
Biological and Physical Sciences, A
Business Administration and Management, A
Computer Programming/Programmer, A
Criminal Justice/Law Enforcement Administration, A
Data Processing and Data Processing Technology/Technician, A
Drafting and Design Technology/Technician, A

Drafting/Design Engineering Technologies/Technicians, A
Education, A
Electrical, Electronic and Communications Engineering Technology/Technician, A
Forestry Technology/Technician, A
Information Science/Studies, A
Legal Administrative Assistant/Secretary, A
Liberal Arts and Sciences Studies and Humanities, A
Medical Administrative Assistant/Secretary, A
Wood Science and Wood Products/Pulp and Paper Technology, A

DANVILLE COMMUNITY COLLEGE

Accounting and Related Services, A
Allied Health Diagnostic, Intervention, and Treatment Professions, A
Business Administration, Management and Operations, A
Business Operations Support and Secretarial Services, A
Child Care Provider/Assistant, A
Computer and Information Sciences, A
Criminal Justice/Law Enforcement Administration, A
Engineering, A
Engineering Technology, A
Industrial Technology/Technician, A
Liberal Arts and Sciences Studies and Humanities, A

DEVRY UNIVERSITY (ARLINGTON)

Accounting, B
Business Administration and Management, B
Business Administration, Management and Operations, BM
Business/Commerce, B
Computer Engineering Technology/Technician, B
Computer Software Engineering, B
Computer Systems Analysis/Analyst, B
Computer Systems Networking and Telecommunications, AB
Corrections and Criminal Justice, B
Electrical, Electronic and Communications Engineering Technology/Technician, B
Web Page, Digital/Multimedia and Information Resources Design, AB

DEVRY UNIVERSITY (CHESAPEAKE)

Business Administration and Management, B
Business Administration, Management and Operations, BM
Business/Commerce, B
Computer Systems Analysis/Analyst, B
Computer Systems Networking and Telecommunications, AB
Criminal Justice/Law Enforcement Administration, B
Electrical, Electronic and Communications Engineering Technology/Technician, A
Health/Health Care Administration/Management, B
Web Page, Digital/Multimedia and Information Resources Design, AB

DEVRY UNIVERSITY (MANASSAS)

Accounting, B
Business Administration and Management, B
Business Administration, Management and Operations, BMO
Business/Commerce, B
Computer Systems Analysis/Analyst, B
Computer Systems Networking and Telecommunications, A
Criminal Justice/Law Enforcement Administration, B
Web Page, Digital/Multimedia and Information Resources Design, AB

EASTERN MENNONITE UNIVERSITY

Accounting, B
Art/Art Studies, General, B
Bible/Biblical Studies, AB
Biochemistry, B
Biological and Biomedical Sciences, M
Biology/Biological Sciences, B
Business Administration and Management, B

Business Administration, Management and Operations, M
Chemistry, B
Clinical Laboratory Science/Medical Technology/Technologist, B
Communication and Media Studies, B
Computer Science, B
Conflict Resolution and Mediation/Peace Studies, MO
Counselor Education/School Counseling and Guidance Services, M
Digital Communication and Media/Multimedia, B
Drama and Dramatics/Theatre Arts, B
Economics, B
Education, M
English Language and Literature, B
Environmental Studies, B
General Studies, A
Health Services Administration, M
History, B
International Business/Trade/Commerce, B
Kinesiology and Exercise Science, B
Liberal Arts and Sciences Studies and Humanities, B
Mathematics, B
Multi-/Interdisciplinary Studies, B
Music, B
Non-Profit/Public/Organizational Management, M
Nursing, M
Nursing Administration, M
Organizational Behavior Studies, B
Organizational Management, M
Pastoral Studies/Counseling, MO
Peace Studies and Conflict Resolution, B
Philosophy and Religious Studies, B
Photography, B
Physical Education Teaching and Coaching, B
Pre-Theology/Pre-Ministerial Studies, A
Psychology, B
Religion/Religious Studies, M
School Nursing, M
Social Sciences, B
Social Work, B
Spanish Language and Literature, B
Sport and Fitness Administration/Management, B
Teacher Assistant/Aide, A
Theology and Religious Vocations, MO
Theology/Theological Studies, B

EASTERN SHORE COMMUNITY COLLEGE

Administrative Assistant and Secretarial Science, A
Biological and Physical Sciences, A
Business Administration and Management, A
Computer and Information Sciences and Support Services, A
Computer/Information Technology Services Administration and Management, A
Education, A
Electrical, Electronic and Communications Engineering Technology/Technician, A
Liberal Arts and Sciences Studies and Humanities, A

ECPI UNIVERSITY (GLEN ALLEN)

Computer Programming/Programmer, A
Computer Technology/Computer Systems Technology, A
Computer and Information Systems Security, A
Data Entry/Microcomputer Applications, A
Telecommunications Technology/Technician, A
Web Page, Digital/Multimedia and Information Resources Design, A

ECPI UNIVERSITY (MANASSAS)

Computer and Information Systems Security, A
Criminal Justice/Law Enforcement Administration, A
Electrical, Electronic and Communications Engineering Technology/Technician, A
Medical/Clinical Assistant, A
Surgical Technology/Technologist, A

Web Page, Digital/Multimedia and Information Resources Design, A

ECPI UNIVERSITY (NEWPORT NEWS)

Accounting, A
Communications Technology/Technician, A
Computer Engineering Technology/Technician, A
Computer Science, A
Computer Typography and Composition Equipment Operator, A
Computer and Information Sciences, A
Electrical, Electronic and Communications Engineering Technology/Technician, A
Electromechanical Technology/Electromechanical Engineering Technology, A
Engineering Technology, A
Health Information/Medical Records Administration/Administrator, A
Health/Health Care Administration/Management, A
Information Science/Studies, A
Massage Therapy/Therapeutic Massage, A
Mechanical Engineering/Mechanical Technology/Technician, A
Medical Administrative Assistant/Secretary, A
Telecommunications Technology/Technician, A
Trade and Industrial Teacher Education, A

ECPI UNIVERSITY (RICHMOND)

Accounting, A
Business Machine Repairer, A
Communications Technology/Technician, A
Computer Programming/Programmer, A
Computer Science, A
Computer Technology/Computer Systems Technology, A
Computer Typography and Composition Equipment Operator, A
Computer and Information Sciences, A
Computer and Information Systems Security, A
Data Entry/Microcomputer Applications, A
Data Processing and Data Processing Technology/Technician, A
Electrical, Electronic and Communications Engineering Technology/Technician, A
Electromechanical Technology/Electromechanical Engineering Technology, A
Engineering Technology, A
Health Information/Medical Records Administration/Administrator, A
Health/Health Care Administration/Management, A
Information Science/Studies, A
Massage Therapy/Therapeutic Massage, A
Mechanical Engineering/Mechanical Technology/Technician, A
Medical Administrative Assistant/Secretary, A
Telecommunications Technology/Technician, A
Trade and Industrial Teacher Education, A
Web Page, Digital/Multimedia and Information Resources Design, A

ECPI UNIVERSITY (VIRGINIA BEACH)

Accounting, AB
Biomedical Technology/Technician, A
Business Administration and Management, B
Business Administration, Management and Operations, B
Business/Office Automation/Technology/Data Entry, A
Computer Graphics, AB
Computer Programming/Programmer, AB
Computer and Information Sciences, AB
Computer and Information Systems Security, AB
Criminal Justice/Law Enforcement Administration, AB
Culinary Arts/Chef Training, A
Dental Assisting/Assistant, A
Electrical, Electronic and Communications Engineering Technology/Technician, AB
Engineering Technology, AB
Health/Health Care Administration/Management, AB
Hospital and Health Care Facilities Administration/Management, B
Information Resources Management/CIO Training, B
Massage Therapy/Therapeutic Massage, A
Mechanical Engineering/Mechanical Technology/Technician, A

Medical/Clinical Assistant, A
Physical Therapist Assistant, A
Radiologic Technology/Science - Radiographer, A
Restaurant/Food Services Management, B
Surgical Technology/Technologist, A
Telecommunications Technology/Technician, A
Web/Multimedia Management and Webmaster, AB

EMORY & HENRY COLLEGE

Accounting, B
Acting, B
American Government and Politics (United States), B
American/United States Studies/Civilization, M
Art Teacher Education, B
Athletic Training and Sports Medicine, B
Biology Teacher Education, B
Biology/Biological Sciences, B
Business Administration and Management, B
Business Teacher Education, B
Chemistry, B
Chemistry Teacher Education, B
Community Organization and Advocacy, B
Directing and Theatrical Production, B
Drama and Dramatics/Theatre Arts, B
Economics, B
Education, M
English Language and Literature, B
English/Language Arts Teacher Education, B
Environmental Sciences, B
Environmental Studies, B
Equestrian/Equine Studies, B
European Studies/Civilization, B
Fine/Studio Arts, B
French Language Teacher Education, B
French Language and Literature, B
French Studies, B
General Studies, B
Geography, B
Graphic Design, B
Health and Physical Education, B
Health/Medical Preparatory Programs, B
History, BM
History Teacher Education, B
International Business/Trade/Commerce, B
Law and Legal Studies, B
Liberal Arts and Sciences Studies and Humanities, B
Library Science, B
Mass Communication/Media Studies, B
Mathematics, B
Mathematics Teacher Education, B
Music Performance, B
Music Teacher Education, B
Near and Middle Eastern Studies, B
Organizational Management, M
Philosophy, B
Physical Education Teaching and Coaching, B
Physics, B
Physics Teacher Education, B
Political Science and Government, B
Pre-Law Studies, B
Pre-Pharmacy Studies, B
Pre-Veterinary Studies, B
Psychology, B
Public Administration and Social Service Professions, B
Public/Applied History and Archival Administration, B
Reading Teacher Education, M
Religion/Religious Studies, B
Sociology, B
Spanish Language and Literature, B
Spanish and Iberian Studies, B
Sport and Fitness Administration/Management, B
Teacher Education and Professional Development, Specific Levels and Methods, B
Teacher Education, Multiple Levels, B

FERRUM COLLEGE

Accounting, B
Agriculture, B
Applied Horticulture/Horticultural Operations, B
Art/Art Studies, General, B
Biology/Biological Sciences, B
Business Administration and Management, B
Chemistry, B

Criminal Justice/Safety Studies, B
Drama and Dramatics/Theatre Arts, B
Education, B
English Language and Literature, B
Environmental Studies, B
Health Services/Allied Health/Health Sciences, B
Health and Physical Education, B
History, B
Horticultural Science, B
Information Science/Studies, B
International Relations and Affairs, B
Liberal Arts and Sciences Studies and Humanities, B
Management Information Systems and Services, B
Mathematics, B
Parks, Recreation, Leisure and Fitness Studies, B
Philosophy, B
Political Science and Government, B
Psychology, B
Religion/Religious Studies, B
Social Sciences, B
Social Work, B
Spanish Language and Literature, B
Sport and Fitness Administration/Management, B
Visual and Performing Arts, B

GEORGE MASON UNIVERSITY

Accounting, BMO
Animation, Interactive Technology, Video Graphics and Special Effects, B
Anthropology, BM
Applied Physics, M
Applied Psychology, O
Art Education, M
Art History, Criticism and Conservation, BM
Arts Management, MO
Astronomy, B
Athletic Training and Sports Medicine, B
Atmospheric Sciences and Meteorology, BD
Biochemistry, MD
Bioengineering, D
Bioinformatics, M
Biological and Biomedical Sciences, MDO
Biology/Biological Sciences, B
Biomedical/Medical Engineering, B
Biostatistics, M
Business Administration and Management, B
Business Administration, Management and Operations, M
Chemistry, BMD
Cinematography and Film/Video Production, B
Civil Engineering, BMD
Clinical Laboratory Science/Medical Technology/Technologist, B
Cognitive Sciences, M
Communication and Media Studies, MDO
Community College Education, MD
Community Health and Preventive Medicine, BMO
Composition, MD
Computational Biology, M
Computational Sciences, MDO
Computer Engineering, BMDO
Computer Science, BMDO
Computer and Information Sciences, B
Computer and Information Systems Security, M
Conflict Resolution and Mediation/Peace Studies, MDO
Conservation Biology, M
Construction Engineering and Management, M
Counselor Education/School Counseling and Guidance Services, MDO
Criminal Justice/Police Science, B
Criminology, MDO
Cultural Studies, MD
Curriculum and Instruction, MD
Dance, B
Developmental Psychology, O
Drama and Dramatics/Theatre Arts, B
Early Childhood Education and Teaching, M
Ecology, M
Economics, BMDO
Education, MDO
Education/Teaching of the Gifted and Talented, M
Educational Administration and Supervision, M
Educational Leadership and Administration, MDO
Educational Media/Instructional Technology, M

Educational Psychology, MDO
Electrical Engineering, MDO
Electrical, Electronics and Communications Engineering, B
Elementary Education and Teaching, M
Emergency Management, O
Energy Management and Policy, M
Engineering Physics, M
Engineering and Applied Sciences, MDO
English, MDO
English Education, M
English Language and Literature, B
English as a Second Language, M
Environmental Engineering Technology/Environmental Technology, M
Environmental Policy, MD
Environmental Sciences, BMD
Epidemiology, M
Ethics, M
Exercise and Sports Science, M
Film, Television, and Video Theory and Criticism, M
Finance, B
Fine Arts and Art Studies, M
Folklore, M
Foreign Language Teacher Education, M
Foreign Languages and Literatures, M
Forensic Science and Technology, BMO
French Language and Literature, M
Gender Studies, M
General Studies, B
Geochemistry, M
Geographic Information Systems, MD
Geography, BMDO
Geology/Earth Science, B
Geosciences, MD
Graphic Design, M
Health Informatics, M
Health Professions and Related Clinical Sciences, B
Health Promotion, M
Health Services Administration, MD
Health Teacher Education, B
Higher Education/Higher Education Administration, MDO
History, BMD
Homeland Security, MDO
Human Development and Family Studies, B
Human Resources Management and Services, M
Industrial and Organizational Psychology, MD
Infectious Diseases, M
Information Science/Studies, MDO
Information Technology, B
Interdisciplinary Studies, M
International Affairs, M
International Business/Trade/Commerce, M
International Public Health/International Health, M
International Relations and Affairs, B
International and Comparative Education, M
Kinesiology and Exercise Science, B
Latin American Studies, B
Law and Legal Studies, MD
Liberal Arts and Sciences Studies and Humanities, B
Linguistics, D
Logistics and Materials Management, MO
Management Information Systems and Services, M
Management Sciences and Quantitative Methods, B
Management of Technology, M
Marketing/Marketing Management, B
Mathematics, BMDO
Mathematics Teacher Education, M
Mechanical Engineering, B
Media Studies, MD
Microbiology, M
Military and Defense Studies, M
Molecular Biology, M
Multilingual and Multicultural Education, M
Music, MD
Music Performance, B
Music Teacher Education, MD
National Security, MD
Near and Middle Eastern Studies, M
Neuroscience, MD
Non-Profit/Public/Organizational Management, O
Nursing, MDO
Nutritional Sciences, M
Operations Research, MDO

Organizational Management, M
Painting, M
Peace Studies and Conflict Resolution, B
Performance, MDO
Philosophy, BM
Photography, M
Physical Education Teaching and Coaching, BM
Physical Sciences, B
Physics, BMDO
Political Science and Government, BMD
Printmaking, M
Project Management, M
Psychology, BMDO
Public Administration, BMDO
Public Affairs, M
Public Health, MO
Public History, D
Public Policy Analysis, MD
Reading Teacher Education, M
Real Estate, M
Recreation and Park Management, M
Rehabilitation Sciences, DO
Religion/Religious Studies, BM
Rhetoric, D
Russian Studies, B
School Psychology, MO
Science Teacher Education/General Science
   Teacher Education, M
Sculpture, M
Secondary Education and Teaching, M
Social Sciences, DO
Social Studies Teacher Education, M
Social Work, BM
Sociology, BMD
Software Engineering, M
Special Education and Teaching, MDO
Sport and Fitness Administration/Management, M
Statistics, MDO
Structural Engineering, M
Sustainability Management, M
Systems Engineering, BMDO
Telecommunications, M
Tourism and Travel Services Management, B
Transportation and Highway Engineering, MD
Transportation/Transportation Management, MO
Visual and Performing Arts, B
Water Resources Engineering, M
Women's Studies, M
Writing, MD

GERMANNA COMMUNITY COLLEGE

Biological and Physical Sciences, A
Business Administration and Management, A
Criminal Justice/Police Science, A
Dental Hygiene/Hygienist, A
Education, A
General Studies, A
Information Technology, A
Liberal Arts and Sciences Studies and Humani-
   ties, A

HAMPDEN-SYDNEY COLLEGE

Ancient/Classical Greek Language and Literature, B
Applied Mathematics, B
Biology/Biological Sciences, B
Business/Managerial Economics, B
Chemistry, B
Classics and Classical Languages, Litera-
   tures, and Linguistics, B
Computer Science, B
Econometrics and Quantitative Economics, B
Economics, B
English Language and Literature, B
Fine Arts and Art Studies, B
Fine/Studio Arts, B
French Language and Literature, B
German Language and Literature, B
History, B
International Relations and Affairs, B
Latin Language and Literature, B
Mathematics, B
Mathematics and Computer Science, B
Philosophy, B
Physics, B
Political Science and Government, B
Psychology, B

Religion/Religious Studies, B
Spanish Language and Literature, B

HAMPTON UNIVERSITY

Accounting, B
Advertising, B
Air Traffic Controller, B
Allied Health and Medical Assisting Services, M
Applied Mathematics, M
Architecture, BM
Army JROTC/ROTC, B
Art Teacher Education, B
Art/Art Studies, General, B
Atmospheric Sciences and Meteorology, MD
Aviation/Airway Management and Operations, B
Biological and Biomedical Sciences, M
Biology/Biological Sciences, B
Broadcast Journalism, B
Business Administration and Management, AB
Business Administration, Management and Opera-
   tions, MD
Business Teacher Education, B
Chemical Engineering, B
Chemistry, BM
Child Development, B
Commercial and Advertising Art, B
Communication Disorders, BM
Community Health Nursing, M
Computational Sciences, M
Computer Science, BM
Computer and Information Systems Security, M
Counselor Education/School Counseling and Guid-
   ance Services, MDO
Criminal Justice/Law Enforcement Administration, B
Drama and Dramatics/Theatre Arts, B
Economics, B
Education, BMDO
Educational Administration and Supervision, D
Educational Leadership and Administration, M
Electrical, Electronic and Communications Engineer-
   ing Technology/Technician, B
Electrical, Electronics and Communications Engi-
   neering, B
Elementary Education and Teaching, BM
English Language and Literature, B
Environmental Biology, M
Environmental Studies, B
Family and Consumer Sciences/Home Economics
   Teacher Education, B
Fashion Merchandising, B
Fashion/Apparel Design, B
Finance, B
Fire Science/Firefighting, B
General Studies, AB
Gerontological Nursing, M
Health Teacher Education, B
History, B
Hotel/Motel Administration/Management, B
Information Science/Studies, B
Interior Design, B
Jazz/Jazz Studies, B
Journalism, B
Junior High/Intermediate/Middle School Education
   and Teaching, B
Kindergarten/PreSchool Education and Teaching, B
Legal Assistant/Paralegal, B
Marine Biology and Biological Oceanography, B
Marine Science/Merchant Marine Officer, B
Marketing/Marketing Management, B
Mass Communication/Media Studies, B
Mathematics, B
Medical Physics, MD
Modern Languages, B
Molecular Biology, B
Music, B
Music Teacher Education, BM
Navy/Marine Corps JROTC/ROTC, B
Nursing, MD
Nursing - Adult, M
Pastoral Studies/Counseling, M
Pediatric Nurse/Nursing, M
Pharmacy, D
Photography, B
Physical Education Teaching and Coaching, B
Physical Sciences, B
Physical Therapy/Therapist, BD

Physics, BMD
Planetary Astronomy and Science, MD
Political Science and Government, B
Pre-Dentistry Studies, B
Pre-Law Studies, B
Pre-Medicine/Pre-Medical Studies, B
Pre-Veterinary Studies, B
Psychiatric/Mental Health Nurse/Nursing, M
Psychology, BM
Public Relations/Image Management, B
Religion/Religious Studies, B
Sales, Distribution and Marketing Operations, B
Secondary Education and Teaching, BM
Social Sciences, B
Social Work, B
Sociology, B
Special Education and Teaching, B
Sport and Fitness Administration/Management, BM
Statistics, M
Student Personnel Services, M
Therapeutic Recreation/Recreational Therapy, B
Women's Health Nursing, M

HOLLINS UNIVERSITY

Art History, Criticism and Conservation, B
Art/Art Studies, General, B
Biology/Biological Sciences, B
Business/Commerce, B
Chemistry, B
Classics and Classical Languages, Litera-
   tures, and Linguistics, B
Dance, BM
Drama and Dramatics/Theatre Arts, B
Economics, B
Education, M
English, M
English Language and Literature, B
Environmental Studies, B
Film, Television, and Video Production, M
Film, Television, and Video Theory and Criticism, M
Film/Video and Photographic Arts, B
Fine Arts and Art Studies, M
French Language and Literature, B
History, B
Humanities/Humanistic Studies, M
Illustration, M
Interdisciplinary Studies, M
International Relations and Affairs, B
Liberal Studies, MO
Mass Communication/Media Studies, B
Mathematics, B
Music, B
Performance, M
Philosophy, B
Physics, B
Political Science and Government, B
Psychology, B
Religion/Religious Studies, B
Social Sciences, M
Sociology, B
Spanish Language and Literature, B
Theater, MO
Women's Studies, B
Writing, MO

J. SARGEANT REYNOLDS COMMU-
NITY COLLEGE

Accounting and Related Services, A
Applied Horticulture/Horticultural Operations, A
Automobile/Automotive Mechanics
   Technology/Technician, A
Baking and Pastry Arts/Baker/Pastry Chef, A
Biological and Physical Sciences, A
Building/Construction Site Management/Manager, A
Business Administration and Management, A
Child Care Provider/Assistant, A
Clinical/Medical Laboratory Technician, A
Computer Programming/Programmer, A
Computer Systems Networking and Telecommunica-
   tions, A
Computer and Information Sciences, A
Consumer Merchandising/Retailing Management, A
Cooking and Related Culinary Arts, A
Criminal Justice/Law Enforcement Administration, A
Dental Laboratory Technology/Technician, A

Emergency Medical Technology/Technician (EMT Paramedic), A
Engineering, A
Fire Science/Firefighting, A
Floriculture/Floristry Operations and Management, A
Hospitality Administration/Management, A
Hotel/Motel Administration/Management, A
Legal Assistant/Paralegal, A
Liberal Arts and Sciences Studies and Humanities, A
Mathematics, A
Mental and Social Health Services and Allied Professions, A
Opticianry/Ophthalmic Dispensing Optician, A
Pharmacy Technician/Assistant, A
Respiratory Care Therapy/Therapist, A
Restaurant/Food Services Management, A
Sign Language Interpretation and Translation, A
Small Business Administration/Management, A
Social Sciences, A
Substance Abuse/Addiction Counseling, A
Web Page, Digital/Multimedia and Information Resources Design, A

JAMES MADISON UNIVERSITY

Accounting, BM
Anthropology, B
Applied Behavior Analysis, M
Applied Science and Technology, M
Art Education, M
Art History, Criticism and Conservation, BM
Art/Art Studies, General, B
Athletic Training and Sports Medicine, B
BioTechnology, B
Biological and Biomedical Sciences, M
Biology/Biological Sciences, B
Biosystems Engineering, M
Business Administration and Management, B
Business Administration, Management and Operations, M
Business/Managerial Economics, B
Chemistry, B
Clinical Psychology, MDO
Communication Disorders, MD
Communication Studies/Speech Communication and Rhetoric, B
Communication and Media Studies, M
Community Health Services/Liaison/Counseling, B
Computer Science, M
Computer and Information Sciences, B
Counseling Psychology, MDO
Curriculum and Instruction, M
Drama and Dramatics/Theatre Arts, B
Early Childhood Education and Teaching, M
Economics, B
Education/Teaching of the Gifted and Talented, M
Educational Leadership and Administration, M
Educational Measurement and Evaluation, MD
Educational Media/Instructional Technology, M
Elementary Education and Teaching, M
Engineering, B
Engineering and Applied Sciences, M
English, M
English Language and Literature, B
English as a Second Language, M
Entrepreneurship/Entrepreneurial Studies, M
Exercise and Sports Science, M
Finance, B
Finance and Financial Management Services, B
Fine Arts and Art Studies, M
Foods, Nutrition, and Wellness Studies, B
Foreign Language Teacher Education, M
Foreign Languages and Literatures, B
Geography, B
Geology/Earth Science, B
Gerontological Nursing, M
Health Education, M
Health and Physical Education, B
Health/Health Care Administration/Management, B
Higher Education/Higher Education Administration, M
History, BM
Hospitality Administration/Management, B
Human Resources Management and Services, M
Information Science/Studies, B
International Business/Trade/Commerce, B

International Relations and Affairs, B
Jewelry/Metalsmithing, M
Kinesiology and Movement Studies, M
Liberal Arts and Sciences Studies and Humanities, B
Management Information Systems and Services, M
Management Strategy and Policy, D
Marketing/Marketing Management, B
Mathematics, B
Mathematics Teacher Education, M
Middle School Education, M
Multilingual and Multicultural Education, M
Music, D
Music Performance, B
Music Teacher Education, M
Non-Profit/Public/Organizational Management, MD
Nurse Midwife/Nursing Midwifery, M
Nursing, MD
Nursing - Advanced Practice, M
Nursing Administration, M
Nutritional Sciences, M
Occupational Therapy/Therapist, M
Organizational Management, D
Painting, M
Performance, MD
Philosophy and Religious Studies, B
Photography, M
Physical Education Teaching and Coaching, M
Physician Assistant, M
Physics, B
Political Science and Government, BM
Psychology, BM
Public Administration, BM
Reading Teacher Education, M
Rhetoric, M
School Psychology, MDO
Science, Technology and Society, B
Secondary Education and Teaching, M
Social Work, B
Sociology, B
Special Education and Teaching, M
Speech-Language Pathology/Pathologist, B
Systems Science and Theory, B
Technical and Business Writing, M
Vocational and Technical Education, M
Writing, M

JEFFERSON COLLEGE OF HEALTH SCIENCES

Biological and Physical Sciences, A
Biomedical Sciences, B
Emergency Medical Technology/Technician (EMT Paramedic), B
Fire Protection and Safety Technology/Technician, B
Health/Health Care Administration/Management, B
Kinesiology and Exercise Science, B
Nursing, M
Nursing Administration, M
Nursing Education, M
Occupational Therapist Assistant, A
Occupational Therapy/Therapist, M
Physical Therapist Assistant, A
Physician Assistant, M
Respiratory Care Therapy/Therapist, A

JOHN TYLER COMMUNITY COLLEGE

Accounting and Related Services, A
Architectural Technology/Technician, A
Business Administration and Management, A
Business Administration, Management and Operations, A
Child Care Provider/Assistant, A
Computer and Information Sciences, A
Criminal Justice/Law Enforcement Administration, A
Emergency Medical Technology/Technician (EMT Paramedic), A
Engineering, A
Funeral Service and Mortuary Science, A
General Studies, A
Humanities/Humanistic Studies, A
Industrial Technology/Technician, A
Information Technology, A
Mechanical Engineering Related Technologies/Technicians, A
Mental and Social Health Services and Allied Professions, A

Visual and Performing Arts, A

LIBERTY UNIVERSITY

Accounting, BMD
Advertising and Public Relations, M
Aeronautics/Aviation/Aerospace Science and Technology, AB
Airline Flight Attendant, A
American Sign Language (ASL), B
Apparel and Textiles, M
Athletic Training and Sports Medicine, B
Bible/Biblical Studies, B
Biochemistry, B
Biological and Biomedical Sciences, M
Biology/Biological Sciences, B
Biomedical Sciences, B
Business Administration and Management, B
Business Administration, Management and Operations, MDO
Carpentry/Carpenter, A
Cell/Cellular and Molecular Biology, B
Chemistry, B
Child and Family Studies, M
Christian Studies, B
Cinematography and Film/Video Production, B
Clinical Psychology, M
Communication Studies/Speech Communication and Rhetoric, B
Communication and Media Studies, M
Computer Engineering, B
Computer Software Engineering, B
Computer and Information Sciences, B
Computer and Information Systems Security, M
Construction Trades, A
Counseling Psychology, M
Counselor Education/School Counseling and Guidance Services, MD
Criminal Justice/Safety Studies, AB
Criminology, M
Curriculum and Instruction, DO
Digital Communication and Media/Multimedia, B
Distance Education Development, M
Drama and Dramatics/Theatre Arts, B
Early Childhood Education and Teaching, MO
Education, MDO
Education/Teaching of the Gifted and Talented, MO
Educational Administration and Supervision, M
Educational Leadership and Administration, MDO
Educational Media/Instructional Technology, M
Electrical, Electronics and Communications Engineering, B
Electrician, A
Elementary Education and Teaching, M
Emergency Management, M
Engineering and Applied Sciences, M
English, M
English Language and Literature, AB
Environmental Biology, B
Ethnomusicology, M
Exercise and Sports Science, M
Family and Consumer Sciences/Human Sciences, B
Fine Arts and Art Studies, M
Fine/Studio Arts, B
Forensic Science and Technology, B
General Studies, AB
Graphic Design, B
Health Promotion, M
Health Services Administration, MO
Health and Physical Education, B
History, BM
Human Development and Family Studies, B
Human Resources Management and Services, D
Human Services, BM
Industrial Engineering, B
Information Technology, B
International Affairs, M
International Business/Trade/Commerce, MD
International Public Health/International Health, M
International Relations and Affairs, B
Jazz/Jazz Studies, B
Journalism, B
Kinesiology and Exercise Science, B
Law and Legal Studies, D
Liberal Arts and Sciences Studies and Humanities, B
Management, MD

Management Information Systems and Services, BM
Management of Technology, M
Marketing, MD
Marriage and Family Therapy/Counseling, M
Mathematics, B
Mathematics Teacher Education, M
Mechanical Engineering, B
Middle School Education, MO
Military and Defense Studies, M
Missions/Missionary Studies and Missiology, BMD
Multi-/Interdisciplinary Studies, AB
Music, BMD
Music History, Literature, and Theory, B
Music Pedagogy, B
Music Performance, B
Music Teacher Education, M
Music Theory and Composition, B
Musicology and Ethnomusicology, B
Near and Middle Eastern Studies, M
Nursing, MD
Nursing - Advanced Practice, D
Nursing Administration, M
Nursing Education, M
Nutritional Sciences, M
Osteopathic Medicine, D
Pastoral Studies/Counseling, BMD
Philosophy, BM
Piano and Organ, B
Political Science and Government, ABM
Project Management, MD
Psychology, AB
Public Administration, M
Public Health Education and Promotion, B
Public Policy Analysis, M
Reading Teacher Education, M
Recreation and Park Management, M
Religion/Religious Studies, ABMD
Religious Education, M
Religious/Sacred Music, B
Sacred Music, MD
Secondary Education and Teaching, M
Social Sciences, B
Spanish Language and Literature, B
Special Education and Teaching, M
Sport and Fitness
  Administration/Management, BMO
Student Personnel Services, M
Substance Abuse/Addiction Counseling, M
Teaching English as a Second or Foreign
  Language/ESL Language Instructor, B
Theology and Religious Vocations, MDO
Travel and Tourism, M
Violin, Viola, Guitar and Other Stringed Instruments, B
Voice and Opera, B
Welding Technology/Welder, A
Wildlife Biology, B
Zoology/Animal Biology, B

LONGWOOD UNIVERSITY

Anthropology, B
Athletic Training and Sports Medicine, B
Audiology/Audiologist and Speech-Language
  Pathology/Pathologist, B
Biology/Biological Sciences, B
Business Administration and Management, B
Business Administration, Management and Operations, M
Chemistry, B
Communication Disorders, M
Communication Studies/Speech Communication
  and Rhetoric, B
Computer Science, B
Counselor Education/School Counseling and Guidance Services, M
Criminal Justice/Safety Studies, B
Criminology, M
Economics, B
Education, M
Educational Media/Instructional Technology, M
Elementary Education and Teaching, M
English Language and Literature, B
Environmental Sciences, B
Foreign Languages and Literatures, B
Health Education, M

History, B
Kinesiology and Exercise Science, B
Liberal Arts and Sciences Studies and Humanities, B
Mathematics, B
Mathematics Teacher Education, M
Middle School Education, M
Physical Education Teaching and Coaching, M
Physics, B
Political Science and Government, B
Psychology, B
Public Policy Analysis, M
Reading Teacher Education, M
Real Estate, M
Social Work, B
Sociology, B
Special Education and Teaching, M
Therapeutic Recreation/Recreational Therapy, B
Visual and Performing Arts, B

LORD FAIRFAX COMMUNITY COLLEGE

Accounting and Related Services, A
Agricultural Business and Management, A
Business Administration, Management and Operations, A
Business Operations Support and Secretarial Services, A
Computer and Information Sciences, A
Engineering Technology, A
Industrial Electronics Technology/Technician, A
Liberal Arts and Sciences Studies and Humanities, A

LYNCHBURG COLLEGE

Accounting, B
Art/Art Studies, General, B
Athletic Training and Sports Medicine, B
Biology/Biological Sciences, B
Biomedical Sciences, B
Business Administration and Management, B
Business Administration, Management and Operations, M
Chemistry, B
Clinical Psychology, M
Communication Studies/Speech Communication
  and Rhetoric, B
Computer Science, B
Counseling Psychology, M
Counselor Education/School Counseling and Guidance Services, M
Criminology, B
Curriculum and Instruction, M
Drama and Dramatics/Theatre Arts, B
Economics, B
Educational Leadership and Administration, MD
Elementary Education and Teaching, B
English, M
English Language and Literature, B
Environmental Sciences, B
Environmental Studies, B
Exercise Physiology, B
French Language and Literature, B
Health and Physical Education, B
History, BM
Human Resources Management/Personnel Administration, B
International Relations and Affairs, B
Marketing/Marketing Management, B
Mathematics, B
Music, BM
Music Teacher Education, B
Nursing, M
Nursing Administration, M
Philosophy, B
Physical Therapy/Therapist, D
Physics, B
Political Science and Government, B
Psychology, B
Public Health Education and Promotion, B
Reading Teacher Education, M
Religion/Religious Studies, B
School Psychology, M
Science Teacher Education/General Science
  Teacher Education, M
Sociology, B
Spanish Language and Literature, B

Special Education and Teaching, M
Sport and Fitness Administration/Management, B
Teacher Education and Professional Development, Specific Levels and Methods, B

MARY BALDWIN COLLEGE

American/United States Studies/Civilization, B
Anthropology, B
Applied Mathematics, B
Art/Art Studies, General, B
Biology/Biological Sciences, B
Business Administration and Management, B
Chemistry, B
Clinical Laboratory Science/Medical
  Technology/Technologist, B
Communication, Journalism and Related Programs, B
Criminology, B
Drama and Dramatics/Theatre Arts, B
Economics, B
Education, M
Elementary Education and Teaching, M
English, M
English Language and Literature, B
French Language and Literature, B
Health/Health Care Administration/Management, B
History, B
International Economics, B
International Relations and Affairs, B
Marketing, B
Mathematics, B
Middle School Education, M
Music, B
Philosophy, B
Philosophy and Religious Studies, B
Physics, B
Political Science and Government, B
Psychology, B
Religion/Religious Studies, B
Social Sciences, B
Social Work, B
Sociology, B
Spanish Language and Literature, B
Theater, M

MARYMOUNT UNIVERSITY

Allied Health and Medical Assisting Services, MDO
Biochemistry, B
Biology/Biological Sciences, B
Business Administration and Management, B
Business Administration, Management and Operations, MO
Cell/Cellular and Molecular Biology, B
Clinical Psychology, M
Computer and Information Systems Security, MO
Counseling Psychology, MO
Counselor Education/School Counseling and Guidance Services, MD
Criminal Justice/Law Enforcement Administration, B
Design and Visual Communications, B
Economics, B
Education, MD
Elementary Education and Teaching, BM
English, M
English Language and Literature, B
English as a Second Language, M
Fashion Merchandising, B
Fashion/Apparel Design, B
Fine/Studio Arts, B
Forensic Psychology, M
Health Education, M
Health Information/Medical Records
  Administration/Administrator, B
Health Promotion, M
Health Services Administration, M
History, B
Human Resources Management and Services, MO
Information Technology, B
Interior Design, BM
Liberal Arts and Sciences Studies and Humanities, B
Management, MO
Management Information Systems and Services, MO
Mathematics, B
Medical Informatics, O

Non-Profit/Public/Organizational Management, O
Nursing, MDO
Nursing - Advanced Practice, MO
Pastoral Studies/Counseling, M
Philosophy, B
Physical Therapy/Therapist, D
Political Science and Government, B
Project Management, O
Psychology, B
Public Health Education and Promotion, B
Religion/Religious Studies, M
Secondary Education and Teaching, M
Sociology, B
Special Education and Teaching, BM

MILLER-MOTTE TECHNICAL COLLEGE (LYNCHBURG)

Administrative Assistant and Secretarial Science, A
Business Administration, Management and Operations, A
Criminal Justice/Law Enforcement Administration, A
Massage Therapy/Therapeutic Massage, A
Medical Administrative Assistant/Secretary, A
Pharmacy Technician/Assistant, A
Phlebotomy/Phlebotomist, A
Surgical Technology/Technologist, A

MOUNTAIN EMPIRE COMMUNITY COLLEGE

Accounting and Related Services, A
Business Administration, Management and Operations, A
Business Operations Support and Secretarial Services, A
CAD/CADD Drafting and/or Design Technology/Technician, A
Corrections, A
Criminal Justice/Law Enforcement Administration, A
Electrical, Electronic and Communications Engineering Technology/Technician, A
Emergency Medical Technology/Technician (EMT Paramedic), A
Environmental Control Technologies/Technicians, A
Industrial Production Technologies/Technicians, A
Industrial Technology/Technician, A
Legal Assistant/Paralegal, A
Liberal Arts and Sciences Studies and Humanities, A
Natural Resources and Conservation, A
Respiratory Care Therapy/Therapist, A

NEW RIVER COMMUNITY COLLEGE

Accounting, A
Administrative Assistant and Secretarial Science, A
Architectural Engineering Technology/Technician, A
Automobile/Automotive Mechanics Technology/Technician, A
Biological and Physical Sciences, A
Business Administration and Management, A
Child Development, A
Community Organization and Advocacy, A
Computer Engineering Technology/Technician, A
Computer Graphics, A
Criminal Justice/Law Enforcement Administration, A
Criminal Justice/Police Science, A
Drafting and Design Technology/Technician, A
Education, A
Electrical, Electronic and Communications Engineering Technology/Technician, A
Engineering, A
Forensic Science and Technology, A
General Studies, A
Information Science/Studies, A
Instrumentation Technology/Technician, A
Legal Assistant/Paralegal, A
Liberal Arts and Sciences Studies and Humanities, A
Machine Tool Technology/Machinist, A
Marketing/Marketing Management, A
Medical Administrative Assistant/Secretary, A
Mental and Social Health Services and Allied Professions, A

Welding Technology/Welder, A

NORFOLK STATE UNIVERSITY

Accounting, B
Architectural Engineering Technology/Technician, A
Art/Art Studies, General, B
Biology/Biological Sciences, B
Business Teacher Education, B
Business/Commerce, B
Chemistry, B
Clinical Laboratory Science/Medical Technology/Technologist, B
Clinical Psychology, M
Communication and Media Studies, M
Communication, Journalism and Related Programs, B
Community Psychology, M
Composition, M
Computer Engineering, M
Computer Engineering Technology/Technician, B
Computer Science, M
Computer and Information Sciences, B
Construction Engineering Technology/Technician, B
Criminology, M
Early Childhood Education and Teaching, M
Education, M
Education/Teaching of Individuals with Multiple Disabilities, M
Educational Administration and Supervision, M
Educational Leadership and Administration, M
Electrical Engineering, M
Electrical, Electronic and Communications Engineering Technology/Technician, A
Electrical, Electronics and Communications Engineering, B
Engineering, B
English Language and Literature, B
Family and Consumer Sciences/Human Sciences, B
Fine Arts and Art Studies, M
Health/Health Care Administration/Management, B
History, B
Journalism, B
Kindergarten/PreSchool Education and Teaching, B
Kinesiology and Exercise Science, B
Materials Sciences, M
Mathematics, B
Media Studies, M
Multi-/Interdisciplinary Studies, B
Music, BM
Music Teacher Education, M
Music Theory and Composition, M
Optical Technologies, M
Performance, M
Physics, B
Political Science and Government, B
Psychology, BMD
Secondary Education and Teaching, M
Social Work, BMD
Sociology, B
Special Education and Teaching, M
Trade and Industrial Teacher Education, B
Urban Education and Leadership, M
Urban Studies/Affairs, M

NORTHERN VIRGINIA COMMUNITY COLLEGE

Administrative Assistant and Secretarial Science, A
Agricultural Business and Management, A
Architectural Engineering Technology/Technician, A
Biological and Physical Sciences, A
Business Administration and Management, A
Business/Commerce, A
Clinical/Medical Laboratory Technician, A
Computer and Information Sciences, A
Dental Hygiene/Hygienist, A
Electrical, Electronic and Communications Engineering Technology/Technician, A
Emergency Medical Technology/Technician (EMT Paramedic), A
Engineering, A
Engineering Technologies/Technicians, A
Environmental Control Technologies/Technicians, A
General Studies, A
Graphic and Printing Equipment Operator Production, A

Health Information/Medical Records Administration/Administrator, A
Industrial Technology/Technician, A
Information Technology, A
Interior Design, A
Liberal Arts and Sciences Studies and Humanities, A
Management Information Systems and Services, A
Medical Radiologic Technology/Science - Radiation Therapist, A
Mental and Social Health Services and Allied Professions, A
Parks, Recreation, Leisure and Fitness Studies, A
Physical Therapy/Therapist, A
Respiratory Care Therapy/Therapist, A
Security and Protective Services, A
Social Sciences, A
Special Education and Teaching, A
Transportation and Materials Moving, A
Vehicle Maintenance and Repair Technologies, A
Visual and Performing Arts, A

OLD DOMINION UNIVERSITY

Accounting, BM
Aerospace, Aeronautical and Astronautical Engineering, MD
African-American/Black Studies, B
Allied Health and Medical Assisting Services, MD
Analytical Chemistry, M
Applied Economics, M
Applied Psychology, D
Art History, Criticism and Conservation, B
Art/Art Studies, General, B
Asian Studies/Civilization, B
Audiology/Audiologist and Speech-Language Pathology/Pathologist, B
Biochemistry, BM
Biological and Biomedical Sciences, MD
Biology/Biological Sciences, B
Biomedical Engineering, D
Business Administration and Management, B
Business Administration, Management and Operations, MD
Business Education, D
Business/Managerial Economics, B
Chemistry, BMD
Civil Engineering, BMD
Clinical Laboratory Science/Medical Technology/Technologist, B
Clinical Psychology, D
Communication Disorders, M
Community College Education, MD
Community Health and Preventive Medicine, M
Computer Art and Design, M
Computer Engineering, BMD
Computer Science, MD
Computer and Information Sciences, B
Conflict Resolution and Mediation/Peace Studies, MD
Counseling Psychology, M
Counselor Education/School Counseling and Guidance Services, MDO
Criminology, BD
Cultural Studies, MD
Curriculum and Instruction, MD
Dental Hygiene/Hygienist, BM
Drama and Dramatics/Theatre Arts, B
Early Childhood Education and Teaching, MD
Ecology, D
Economics, BM
Education, MDO
Educational Leadership and Administration, MDO
Educational Media/Instructional Technology, MD
Electrical Engineering, MD
Electrical, Electronics and Communications Engineering, B
Elementary Education and Teaching, M
Engineering, B
Engineering Management, MD
Engineering Technologies/Technicians, B
Engineering and Applied Sciences, MD
English, MD
English Language and Literature, B
Environmental Engineering Technology/Environmental Technology, MD
Ergonomics and Human Factors, D

Exercise and Sports Science, M
Experimental Psychology, D
Finance, B
Finance and Banking, MD
Foreign Languages and Literatures, B
Geography, B
Geological and Earth Sciences/Geosciences, B
Health Professions and Related Clinical Sciences, B
Health Promotion, M
Health Services Administration, M
Health Services Research, D
Higher Education/Higher Education Administration, MDO
History, BM
Humanities/Humanistic Studies, M
Information Science/Studies, D
International Affairs, MD
International Business/Trade/Commerce, M
International Development, MD
International Relations and Affairs, B
Kinesiology and Movement Studies, D
Library Science, M
Linguistics, M
Management, D
Management Information Systems and Services, BM
Management of Technology, M
Marine Affairs, M
Marketing, D
Marketing/Marketing Management, B
Mathematics, BMD
Mechanical Engineering, BMD
Mental and Social Health Services and Allied Professions, B
Middle School Education, M
Modeling and Simulation, MD
Multi-/Interdisciplinary Studies, B
Music Performance, B
Music Teacher Education, M
Nuclear Medical Technology/Technologist, B
Nurse Anesthetist, M
Nurse Midwife/Nursing Midwifery, M
Nursing, MD
Nursing - Advanced Practice, MD
Nursing Administration, MD
Nursing Education, M
Oceanography, Chemical and Physical, MD
Organic Chemistry, M
Parks, Recreation and Leisure Facilities Management, B
Philosophy, B
Physical Chemistry, M
Physical Education Teaching and Coaching, BM
Physical Therapy/Therapist, D
Physics, BMD
Political Science and Government, B
Psychology, BMD
Public Administration, MD
Reading Teacher Education, MD
Secondary Education and Teaching, M
Sociology, BM
Special Education and Teaching, MD
Speech and Interpersonal Communication, M
Sport and Fitness Administration/Management, M
Systems Engineering, MD
Teacher Education and Professional Development, Specific Subject Areas, B
Urban Studies/Affairs, D
Vocational and Technical Education, MD
Women's Health Nursing, M
Women's Studies, B
Writing, M

PATRICK HENRY COLLEGE

Business/Managerial Economics, B
English Language and Literature, B
History, B
Journalism, B
Liberal Arts and Sciences Studies and Humanities, B
Political Science and Government, B

PATRICK HENRY COMMUNITY COLLEGE

Accounting, A
Administrative Assistant and Secretarial Science, A
Agricultural Business and Management, A
Automobile/Automotive Mechanics Technology/Technician, A
Biological and Physical Sciences, A
Business Administration and Management, A
Criminal Justice/Law Enforcement Administration, A
Emergency Medical Technology/Technician (EMT Paramedic), A
Engineering Technology, A
Industrial Electronics Technology/Technician, A
Industrial Technology/Technician, A
Information Technology, A
Legal Assistant/Paralegal, A
Liberal Arts and Sciences Studies and Humanities, A
Medical Office Assistant/Specialist, A
Teacher Assistant/Aide, A

PAUL D. CAMP COMMUNITY COLLEGE

Administrative Assistant and Secretarial Science, A
Business Administration and Management, A
Computer Technology/Computer Systems Technology, A
Criminal Justice/Law Enforcement Administration, A
Data Processing and Data Processing Technology/Technician, A
Early Childhood Education and Teaching, A
Education, A
Industrial Technology/Technician, A
Liberal Arts and Sciences Studies and Humanities, A

RADFORD UNIVERSITY

Accounting, B
Anthropology, B
Art/Art Studies, General, B
Athletic Training and Sports Medicine, B
Biology/Biological Sciences, B
Business Administration and Management, B
Business Administration, Management and Operations, M
Cartography, B
Chemistry, B
Clinical Psychology, M
Communication Disorders, BM
Communication Studies/Speech Communication and Rhetoric, B
Computer Science, B
Corporate and Organizational Communication, M
Counseling Psychology, MD
Counselor Education/School Counseling and Guidance Services, M
Criminal Justice/Safety Studies, B
Criminology, MO
Curriculum and Instruction, M
Dance, B
Design and Applied Arts, M
Design and Visual Communications, B
Drama and Dramatics/Theatre Arts, B
Early Childhood Education and Teaching, M
Economics, B
Education, MO
Educational Leadership and Administration, MO
Educational Media/Instructional Technology, M
English, M
English Language and Literature, B
Experimental Psychology, M
Finance, B
Fine Arts and Art Studies, M
Foods, Nutrition, and Wellness Studies, B
Foreign Languages and Literatures, B
Geology/Earth Science, B
History, B
Industrial and Organizational Psychology, M
Information Science/Studies, B
Journalism, B
Marketing/Marketing Management, B
Mathematics, B
Mathematics Teacher Education, M
Multi-/Interdisciplinary Studies, B
Music, BM
Music Teacher Education, M
Music Therapy/Therapist, M
Nursing, D
Occupational Therapy/Therapist, M
Parks, Recreation, Leisure and Fitness Studies, B

Philosophy and Religious Studies, B
Physical Education Teaching and Coaching, B
Physical Therapy/Therapist, D
Physics, B
Political Science and Government, B
Psychology, BM
Reading Teacher Education, M
School Psychology, O
Social Sciences, B
Social Work, BM
Sociology, B
Special Education and Teaching, MO

RANDOLPH COLLEGE

Ancient/Classical Greek Language and Literature, B
Art History, Criticism and Conservation, B
Art/Art Studies, General, B
Biology/Biological Sciences, B
Business/Commerce, B
Chemistry, B
Classics and Classical Languages, Literatures, and Linguistics, B
Communication Studies/Speech Communication and Rhetoric, B
Curriculum and Instruction, BM
Dance, B
Drama and Dramatics/Theatre Arts, B
Economics, B
Education, M
Engineering Physics, B
English Language and Literature, B
Environmental Sciences, B
Environmental Studies, B
Fine/Studio Arts, B
French Language and Literature, B
Health Professions and Related Clinical Sciences, B
Health and Physical Education, B
History, B
International/Global Studies, B
Latin Language and Literature, B
Liberal Arts and Sciences Studies and Humanities, B
Mathematics, B
Museology/Museum Studies, B
Music History, Literature, and Theory, B
Music Performance, B
Music Theory and Composition, B
Philosophy, B
Physics, B
Political Science and Government, B
Psychology, B
Religion/Religious Studies, B
Sociology, B
Spanish Language and Literature, B
Special Education and Teaching, M

RANDOLPH-MACON COLLEGE

Accounting, B
Ancient/Classical Greek Language and Literature, B
Art History, Criticism and Conservation, B
Asian Studies/Civilization, B
Biology/Biological Sciences, B
Business/Managerial Economics, B
Chemistry, B
Classical, Ancient Mediterranean and Near Eastern Studies and Archaeology, B
Classics and Classical Languages, Literatures, and Linguistics, B
Computer Science, B
Drama and Dramatics/Theatre Arts, B
Economics, B
Engineering Physics, B
English Language and Literature, B
Environmental Studies, B
Fine/Studio Arts, B
French Language and Literature, B
German Language and Literature, B
History, B
International/Global Studies, B
Latin Language and Literature, B
Mathematics, B
Music, B
Philosophy, B
Physics, B
Political Science and Government, B
Psychology, B

Religion/Religious Studies, B
Sociology, B
Spanish Language and Literature, B
Women's Studies, B

RAPPAHANNOCK COMMUNITY COLLEGE

Accounting, A
Administrative Assistant and Secretarial Science, A
Biological and Physical Sciences, A
Business Administration and Management, A
Business Administration, Management and Operations, A
Criminal Justice/Law Enforcement Administration, A
Criminal Justice/Police Science, A
Engineering Technology, A
Information Science/Studies, A
Liberal Arts and Sciences Studies and Humanities, A

REGENT UNIVERSITY

Accounting, B
Adult and Continuing Education and Teaching, MD
American/United States Studies/Civilization, M
Animation, Interactive Technology, Video Graphics and Special Effects, B
Biophysics, B
Business Administration and Management, AB
Business Administration, Management and Operations, M
Christian Studies, A
Cinematography and Film/Video Production, B
Clinical Psychology, MD
Communication and Media Studies, MD
Computer Science, B
Corporate and Organizational Communication, M
Counseling Psychology, MDO
Counselor Education/School Counseling and Guidance Services, MDO
Criminal Justice/Law Enforcement Administration, AB
Cultural Studies, M
Curriculum and Instruction, M
Distance Education Development, D
Divinity/Ministry (BD, MDiv.), B
Early Childhood Education and Teaching, B
Education, BMDO
Educational Leadership and Administration, MD
Educational Psychology, D
Elementary Education and Teaching, M
Emergency Management, M
English Language and Literature, B
English as a Second Language, M
Entrepreneurship/Entrepreneurial Studies, MDO
Film, Television, and Video Production, M
General Studies, A
Health/Health Care Administration/Management, B
Higher Education/Higher Education Administration, D
History, ABD
Homeland Security, M
Human Resources Development, D
Information Technology, AB
Interdisciplinary Studies, M
International Affairs, M
International/Global Studies, B
Journalism, M
Law and Legal Studies, MD
Legal Assistant/Paralegal, B
Legal and Justice Studies, M
Management Strategy and Policy, D
Marriage and Family Therapy/Counseling, M
Mathematics, B
Mathematics Teacher Education, M
Missions/Missionary Studies and Missiology, M
Non-Profit/Public/Organizational Management, M
Organizational Management, MDO
Pastoral Studies/Counseling, MD
Political Communication, B
Political Science and Government, M
Psychoanalysis and Psychotherapy, M
Psychology, AB
Public Administration, BM
Reading Teacher Education, M
Religion/Religious Studies, D
Religious Education, D

Special Education and Teaching, MDO
Student Personnel Services, M
Theater, M
Theology and Religious Vocations, MD
Writing, M

RICHARD BLAND COLLEGE OF THE COLLEGE OF WILLIAM AND MARY

Liberal Arts and Sciences Studies and Humanities, A

ROANOKE COLLEGE

Art History, Criticism and Conservation, B
Art/Art Studies, General, B
Athletic Training and Sports Medicine, B
Biochemistry, B
Biology/Biological Sciences, B
Business Administration and Management, B
Chemistry, B
Christian Studies, B
Computer Science, B
Computer and Information Sciences, B
Criminal Justice/Safety Studies, B
Drama and Dramatics/Theatre Arts, B
Economics, B
English Language and Literature, B
Environmental Studies, B
French Language and Literature, B
History, B
International Relations and Affairs, B
Kinesiology and Exercise Science, B
Mathematics, B
Music, B
Philosophy, B
Physical Education Teaching and Coaching, B
Physics, B
Political Science and Government, B
Psychology, B
Religion/Religious Studies, B
Sociology, B
Spanish Language and Literature, B
Sport and Fitness Administration/Management, B

SENTARA COLLEGE OF HEALTH SCIENCES

Cardiovascular Technology/Technologist, A
Surgical Technology/Technologist, A

SHENANDOAH UNIVERSITY

Acting, B
Allied Health and Medical Assisting Services, MDO
Applied Behavior Analysis, M
Athletic Training and Sports Medicine, MO
Biology/Biological Sciences, B
Business Administration and Management, B
Business Administration, Management and Operations, BMO
Chemistry, B
Communication Studies/Speech Communication and Rhetoric, B
Criminal Justice/Law Enforcement Administration, B
Dance, B
Education, MDO
English Language and Literature, B
Entrepreneurship/Entrepreneurial Studies, B
Environmental Studies, B
Exercise Physiology, B
General Studies, B
Health Informatics, O
History, B
Jazz/Jazz Studies, B
Liberal Arts and Sciences Studies and Humanities, B
Mathematics, B
Music, MDO
Music Teacher Education, BD
Music Theory and Composition, B
Music Therapy/Therapist, B
Nursing, MDO
Nursing - Advanced Practice, O
Nursing Education, O
Occupational Therapy/Therapist, M
Performance, MD
Pharmacy, D
Physical Therapy/Therapist, D

Physician Assistant, M
Piano and Organ, B
Political Science and Government, B
Psychology, B
Public Health, B
Religion/Religious Studies, B
Religious/Sacred Music, B
Respiratory Care Therapy/Therapist, B
Sacred Music, MO
Sociology, B
Spanish Language and Literature, B
Sport and Fitness Administration/Management, B
Sports Medicine, O
Technical Theatre/Theatre Design and Technology, B

SOUTH UNIVERSITY (GLEN ALLEN)

Business Administration and Management, B
Business Administration, Management and Operations, M
Counseling Psychology, M
Criminal Justice/Law Enforcement Administration, AB
Health/Health Care Administration/Management, B
Health/Medical Preparatory Programs, B
Information Science/Studies, B
Legal Assistant/Paralegal, AB
Nursing, M
Physical Therapist Assistant, A
Psychology, B

SOUTH UNIVERSITY (VIRGINIA BEACH)

Business Administration and Management, B
Business Administration, Management and Operations, M
Counseling Psychology, M
Criminal Justice/Law Enforcement Administration, B
Health/Health Care Administration/Management, B
Health/Medical Preparatory Programs, B
Information Science/Studies, B
Legal Assistant/Paralegal, AB
Management Information Systems and Services, M
Nursing, M
Nursing - Advanced Practice, M
Organizational Management, M
Physical Therapist Assistant, A
Psychology, B
Public Relations/Image Management, B

SOUTHERN VIRGINIA UNIVERSITY

Art/Art Studies, General, B
Biology/Biological Sciences, B
Business Administration and Management, B
Computer and Information Sciences, B
Drama and Dramatics/Theatre Arts, B
English Language and Literature, B
Family and Consumer Sciences/Human Sciences, B
History, B
Liberal Arts and Sciences Studies and Humanities, B
Music, B
Philosophy, B
Spanish Language and Literature, B
Web Page, Digital/Multimedia and Information Resources Design, B

SOUTHSIDE VIRGINIA COMMUNITY COLLEGE

Administrative Assistant and Secretarial Science, A
Biological and Physical Sciences, A
Business Administration and Management, A
Criminal Justice/Law Enforcement Administration, A
Education, A
Electrical, Electronic and Communications Engineering Technology/Technician, A
Emergency Care Attendant (EMT Ambulance), A
Fire Science/Firefighting, A
General Studies, A
Human Services, A
Information Science/Studies, A
Information Technology, A
Liberal Arts and Sciences Studies and Humanities, A

Respiratory Care Therapy/Therapist, A

SOUTHWEST VIRGINIA COMMUNITY COLLEGE

Accounting and Related Services, A
Business Administration, Management and Operations, A
Business Operations Support and Secretarial Services, A
Child Care Provider/Assistant, A
Computer and Information Sciences, A
Criminal Justice/Law Enforcement Administration, A
Electrical, Electronic and Communications Engineering Technology/Technician, A
Emergency Medical Technology/Technician (EMT Paramedic), A
Liberal Arts and Sciences Studies and Humanities, A
Mental and Social Health Services and Allied Professions, A
Radiologic Technology/Science - Radiographer, A

STRATFORD UNIVERSITY (ALEXANDRIA)

Baking and Pastry Arts/Baker/Pastry Chef, A
Business/Commerce, B
Culinary Arts/Chef Training, A
Health Information/Medical Records Administration/Administrator, B
Health/Health Care Administration/Management, B
Information Technology, B
Medical/Clinical Assistant, A
Restaurant/Food Services Management, B

STRATFORD UNIVERSITY (FALLS CHURCH)

Accounting, BM
Allied Health and Medical Assisting Services, A
Baking and Pastry Arts/Baker/Pastry Chef, A
Business Administration and Management, B
Business Administration, Management and Operations, M
Business/Commerce, A
Computer Programming, A
Computer Programming/Programmer, A
Computer Systems Networking and Telecommunications, A
Computer and Information Systems Security, AM
Culinary Arts/Chef Training, A
Entrepreneurship/Entrepreneurial Studies, M
Health Information/Medical Records Administration/Administrator, B
Health/Health Care Administration/Management, B
Hospitality Administration/Management, B
Hotel/Motel Administration/Management, A
Information Technology, B
Management Information Systems and Services, M
Medical Insurance Specialist/Medical Biller, A
Medical/Clinical Assistant, A
Pharmacy Technician/Assistant, A
Restaurant/Food Services Management, AB
Software Engineering, M
System, Networking, and LAN/WAN Management/Manager, A
Telecommunications, M

STRATFORD UNIVERSITY (GLEN ALLEN)

Accounting, B
Baking and Pastry Arts/Baker/Pastry Chef, A
Business Administration and Management, B
Business/Commerce, A
Computer and Information Systems Security, A
Culinary Arts/Chef Training, A
Health Information/Medical Records Administration/Administrator, B
Health/Health Care Administration/Management, B
Hospitality Administration/Management, B
Information Technology, B
Medical Insurance Specialist/Medical Biller, A
Medical/Clinical Assistant, A
Pharmacy Technician/Assistant, A
Phlebotomy/Phlebotomist, A

STRATFORD UNIVERSITY (NEWPORT NEWS)

Accounting, AB
Baking and Pastry Arts/Baker/Pastry Chef, A
Business Administration and Management, B
Business/Commerce, A
Culinary Arts/Chef Training, A
Health Information/Medical Records Administration/Administrator, B
Health/Health Care Administration/Management, B
Hospitality Administration/Management, B
Information Technology, B
Medical Insurance Specialist/Medical Biller, A
Medical/Clinical Assistant, A
Pharmacy Technician/Assistant, A
Phlebotomy/Phlebotomist, A
Restaurant/Food Services Management, AB

STRATFORD UNIVERSITY (VIRGINIA BEACH)

Baking and Pastry Arts/Baker/Pastry Chef, A
Business Administration and Management, B
Culinary Arts/Chef Training, A
Health Information/Medical Records Administration/Administrator, B
Health/Health Care Administration/Management, B
Information Technology, B
Medical/Clinical Assistant, A
Pharmacy Technician/Assistant, A
Restaurant/Food Services Management, B

STRATFORD UNIVERSITY (WOODBRIDGE)

Accounting, B
Baking and Pastry Arts/Baker/Pastry Chef, A
Business Administration and Management, B
Business/Commerce, A
Computer Software Engineering, B
Computer and Information Systems Security, A
Culinary Arts/Chef Training, A
Health Information/Medical Records Administration/Administrator, B
Health/Health Care Administration/Management, B
Hospitality Administration/Management, B
Hotel/Motel Administration/Management, A
Information Science/Studies, B
Information Technology, B
Medical Insurance Coding Specialist/Coder, A
Medical Insurance Specialist/Medical Biller, A
Medical/Clinical Assistant, A
Medical/Health Management and Clinical Assistant/Specialist, AB
Pharmacy Technician/Assistant, A
Phlebotomy/Phlebotomist, A
Restaurant/Food Services Management, AB
Web Page, Digital/Multimedia and Information Resources Design, A

STRAYER UNIVERSITY–ALEXANDRIA CAMPUS

Accounting, B
Business Administration and Management, B
Criminal Justice/Law Enforcement Administration, B
Economics, B
International Business/Trade/Commerce, B
Management Information Systems and Services, B

STRAYER UNIVERSITY–ARLINGTON CAMPUS

Accounting, B
Business Administration and Management, B
Criminal Justice/Law Enforcement Administration, B
Economics, B
International Business/Trade/Commerce, B
Management Information Systems and Services, B

STRAYER UNIVERSITY–CHESAPEAKE CAMPUS

Accounting, B
Business Administration and Management, B
Criminal Justice/Law Enforcement Administration, B
Economics, B

International Business/Trade/Commerce, B
Management Information Systems and Services, B

STRAYER UNIVERSITY–CHESTERFIELD CAMPUS

Accounting, B
Business Administration and Management, B
Criminal Justice/Law Enforcement Administration, B
Economics, B
International Business/Trade/Commerce, B
Management Information Systems and Services, B

STRAYER UNIVERSITY–FREDERICKSBURG CAMPUS

Accounting, B
Business Administration and Management, B
Criminal Justice/Law Enforcement Administration, B
Economics, B
International Business/Trade/Commerce, B
Management Information Systems and Services, B

STRAYER UNIVERSITY–HENRICO CAMPUS

Accounting, B
Business Administration and Management, B
Criminal Justice/Law Enforcement Administration, B
Economics, B
International Business/Trade/Commerce, B
Management Information Systems and Services, B

STRAYER UNIVERSITY–LOUDOUN CAMPUS

Accounting, B
Business Administration and Management, B
Criminal Justice/Law Enforcement Administration, B
Economics, B
International Business/Trade/Commerce, B
Management Information Systems and Services, B

STRAYER UNIVERSITY–MANASSAS CAMPUS

Accounting, B
Business Administration and Management, B
Criminal Justice/Law Enforcement Administration, B
Economics, B
International Business/Trade/Commerce, B
Management Information Systems and Services, B

STRAYER UNIVERSITY–NEWPORT NEWS CAMPUS

Accounting, B
Business Administration and Management, B
Criminal Justice/Law Enforcement Administration, B
Economics, B
International Business/Trade/Commerce, B
Management Information Systems and Services, B

STRAYER UNIVERSITY–VIRGINIA BEACH CAMPUS

Accounting, B
Business Administration and Management, B
Criminal Justice/Law Enforcement Administration, B
Economics, B
International Business/Trade/Commerce, B
Management Information Systems and Services, B

STRAYER UNIVERSITY–WOODBRIDGE CAMPUS

Accounting, B
Business Administration and Management, B
Criminal Justice/Law Enforcement Administration, B
Economics, B
International Business/Trade/Commerce, B
Management Information Systems and Services, B

SWEET BRIAR COLLEGE

Anthropology, B
Archeology, B
Art History, Criticism and Conservation, B
Biochemistry, Biophysics and Molecular Biology, B
Biology/Biological Sciences, B
Business/Commerce, B

Chemistry, B
Classics and Classical Languages, Literatures, and Linguistics, B
Dance, B
Drama and Dramatics/Theatre Arts, B
Economics, B
Education, M
Engineering Science, B
English Language and Literature, B
Environmental Sciences, B
Environmental Studies, B
Fine/Studio Arts, B
Foreign Languages and Literatures, B
French Language and Literature, B
History, B
International Relations and Affairs, B
Liberal Arts and Sciences Studies and Humanities, B
Mathematics, B
Music, B
Philosophy, B
Physics, B
Political Science and Government, B
Psychology, B
Religion/Religious Studies, B
Sociology, B
Spanish Language and Literature, B

THOMAS NELSON COMMUNITY COLLEGE

Accounting and Related Services, A
Automobile/Automotive Mechanics Technology/Technician, A
Biological and Physical Sciences, A
Business Administration and Management, A
Business Administration, Management and Operations, A
Business Operations Support and Secretarial Services, A
CAD/CADD Drafting and/or Design Technology/Technician, A
Child Care Provider/Assistant, A
Computer and Information Sciences, A
Criminal Justice/Law Enforcement Administration, A
Dental Hygiene/Hygienist, A
Design and Visual Communications, A
Emergency Medical Technology/Technician (EMT Paramedic), A
Engineering, A
Fire Science/Firefighting, A
General Studies, A
Industrial Electronics Technology/Technician, A
Industrial Technology/Technician, A
Information Technology, A
Legal Assistant/Paralegal, A
Liberal Arts and Sciences Studies and Humanities, A
Mechanical Engineering Related Technologies/Technicians, A
Mental and Social Health Services and Allied Professions, A
Photography, A
Public Administration, A
Social Sciences, A
Visual and Performing Arts, A

TIDEWATER COMMUNITY COLLEGE

Accounting, A
Administrative Assistant and Secretarial Science, A
Advertising, A
Automobile/Automotive Mechanics Technology/Technician, A
Biological and Physical Sciences, A
Business Administration and Management, A
Civil Engineering, A
Commercial and Advertising Art, A
Computer Programming/Programmer, A
Drafting and Design Technology/Technician, A
Education, A
Electrical, Electronic and Communications Engineering Technology/Technician, A
Engineering, A
Finance, A
Fine/Studio Arts, A
Graphic Design, A
Horticultural Science, A

Information Technology, A
Interior Design, A
Kindergarten/PreSchool Education and Teaching, A
Legal Assistant/Paralegal, A
Liberal Arts and Sciences Studies and Humanities, A
Marketing/Marketing Management, A
Music, A
Real Estate, A

UNIVERSITY OF MANAGEMENT AND TECHNOLOGY

Business Administration and Management, AB
Business Administration, Management and Operations, MDO
Computer Science, ABMO
Criminal Justice/Law Enforcement Administration, AB
Criminology, M
Engineering Management, M
Engineering/Industrial Management, AB
General Studies, AB
Health Services Administration, M
Health/Health Care Administration/Management, B
Homeland Security, M
Information Science/Studies, AB
Information Technology, AB
Management, MDO
Management Information Systems and Services, MO
Project Management, MO
Public Administration, MO
Software Engineering, M

UNIVERSITY OF MARY WASHINGTON

American/United States Studies/Civilization, B
Anthropology, B
Art History, Criticism and Conservation, B
Biology/Biological Sciences, B
Business Administration and Management, B
Business Administration, Management and Operations, M
Chemistry, B
Classics and Classical Languages, Literatures, and Linguistics, B
Computer and Information Sciences, B
Economics, B
Education, M
Elementary Education and Teaching, M
English Language and Literature, B
Fine Arts and Art Studies, B
Foreign Languages and Literatures, B
Geography, B
Historic Preservation and Conservation, B
History, B
International Relations and Affairs, B
Liberal Arts and Sciences Studies and Humanities, B
Mathematics, B
Multi-/Interdisciplinary Studies, B
Music, B
Philosophy and Religious Studies, B
Physical Sciences, B
Physics, B
Political Science and Government, B
Psychology, B
Sociology, B
Visual and Performing Arts, B

UNIVERSITY OF RICHMOND

Accounting, B
African Studies, B
American/United States Studies/Civilization, B
Ancient Studies/Civilization, B
Ancient/Classical Greek Language and Literature, B
Anthropology, B
Art History, Criticism and Conservation, B
Asian Studies/Civilization, B
Bioethics/Medical Ethics, B
Biology/Biological Sciences, B
Business Administration and Management, B
Business Administration, Management and Operations, M
Chemistry, B
Chinese Studies, B
Cognitive Sciences, B

Computer and Information Sciences, B
Criminal Justice/Safety Studies, B
Dance, B
Development Economics and International Development, B
Drama and Dramatics/Theatre Arts, B
Economics, B
English Language and Literature, B
Environmental Studies, B
European Studies/Civilization, B
Film/Cinema Studies, B
Fine/Studio Arts, B
French Language and Literature, B
Geography, B
German Studies, B
History, B
Humanities/Humanistic Studies, B
International Economics, B
International Relations and Affairs, B
Italian Studies, B
Journalism, B
Latin American Studies, B
Latin Language and Literature, B
Law and Legal Studies, D
Mathematics, B
Molecular Biochemistry, B
Multi-/Interdisciplinary Studies, B
Music, B
Near and Middle Eastern Studies, B
Organizational Behavior Studies, B
Philosophy, B
Physics, B
Political Science and Government, B
Psychology, B
Religion/Religious Studies, B
Russian Studies, B
Sociology, B
Spanish Language and Literature, B
Women's Studies, B

UNIVERSITY OF VALLEY FORGE VIRGINIA CAMPUS

Bible/Biblical Studies, B
Business Administration and Management, B
Divinity/Ministry (BD, MDiv.), B
Early Childhood Education and Teaching, B
Elementary Education and Teaching, B
General Studies, A
Pastoral Studies/Counseling, B
Psychology, B
Religious Education, B
Youth Ministry, B

UNIVERSITY OF VIRGINIA

Accounting, M
Acute Care/Critical Care Nursing, M
Aerospace, Aeronautical and Astronautical Engineering, BMD
African-American/Black Studies, B
Allopathic Medicine, MD
Anthropology, BMD
Architectural History and Criticism, BMD
Architecture, B
Area Studies, B
Art History, Criticism and Conservation, MD
Art/Art Studies, General, B
Astronomy, BMD
Audiology/Audiologist and Speech-Language Pathology/Pathologist, B
Biochemistry, D
Biological and Biomedical Sciences, MD
Biology/Biological Sciences, B
Biomedical Engineering, MD
Biomedical/Medical Engineering, B
Biophysics, MD
Business Administration, Management and Operations, MD
Business/Commerce, B
Cell Biology and Anatomy, D
Chemical Engineering, BMD
Chemistry, BMD
Child Development, B
City/Urban, Community and Regional Planning, B
Civil Engineering, BMD
Classics and Classical Languages, Literatures, and Linguistics, BMD

Clinical Psychology, D
Clinical Research, M
Communication Disorders, M
Community Health and Preventive Medicine, M
Comparative Literature, B
Computer Engineering, BMD
Computer Science, MD
Computer and Information Sciences, B
Construction Engineering and Management, D
Counselor Education/School Counseling and Guidance Services, MDO
Curriculum and Instruction, MDO
Database Systems, M
Drama and Dramatics/Theatre Arts, B
Early Childhood Education and Teaching, M
East Asian Studies, M
Economics, BMD
Education, MDO
Education/Teaching of the Gifted and Talented, M
Educational Administration and Supervision, MDO
Educational Measurement and Evaluation, MD
Educational Media/Instructional Technology, MDO
Educational Psychology, MDO
Electrical Engineering, MD
Electrical, Electronics and Communications Engineering, B
Elementary Education and Teaching, MD
Engineering, B
Engineering Physics, MD
Engineering and Applied Sciences, MD
English, MD
English Education, MD
English Language and Literature, B
Environmental Sciences, BMD
Finance and Banking, M
Foreign Language Teacher Education, M
French Language and Literature, BMD
German Language and Literature, BMD
Health Informatics, M
Health Services Administration, M
Health Services Research, M
Health/Health Care Administration/Management, B
Higher Education/Higher Education Administration, MDO
History, BMD
Interdisciplinary Studies, MD
International Affairs, MD
International Business/Trade/Commerce, M
International Relations and Affairs, B
Italian Language and Literature, BM
Kinesiology and Exercise Science, B
Kinesiology and Movement Studies, MD
Landscape Architecture, M
Law and Legal Studies, MD
Liberal Arts and Sciences Studies and Humanities, B
Linguistics, M
Management of Technology, M
Marketing, M
Materials Sciences, MD
Mathematics, BMD
Mathematics Teacher Education, MD
Mechanical Engineering, BMD
Microbiology, D
Molecular Genetics, D
Molecular Physiology, MD
Multi-/Interdisciplinary Studies, B
Music, BMD
Near and Middle Eastern Studies, M
Neuroscience, D
Nursing, MD
Nursing Administration, M
Pathology/Experimental Pathology, D
Pharmacology, D
Philosophy, BMD
Physical Education Teaching and Coaching, MD
Physics, BMD
Physiology, D
Political Science and Government, BMD
Psychiatric/Mental Health Nurse/Nursing, M
Psychology, BMD
Public Health, M
Public Policy Analysis, BM
Reading Teacher Education, D
Religion/Religious Studies, BMD

Romance Languages, Literatures, and Linguistics, MD
School Psychology, D
Science Teacher Education/General Science Teacher Education, MD
Slavic Languages, Literatures, and Linguistics, BMD
Social Studies Teacher Education, MD
Sociology, BMD
South and Southeast Asian Studies, M
Spanish Language and Literature, BMD
Special Education and Teaching, MDO
Statistics, MD
Student Personnel Services, M
Systems Engineering, BMD
Theater, M
Urban and Regional Planning, M
Writing, M

THE UNIVERSITY OF VIRGINIA'S COLLEGE AT WISE

Accounting, B
Art/Art Studies, General, B
Biology/Biological Sciences, B
Business Administration and Management, B
Chemistry, B
Clinical Laboratory Science/Medical Technology/Technologist, B
Communication Studies/Speech Communication and Rhetoric, B
Computer and Information Sciences, B
Criminal Justice/Safety Studies, B
Drama and Dramatics/Theatre Arts, B
Economics, B
Engineering, B
English Language and Literature, B
Environmental Studies, B
Foreign Languages and Literatures, B
French Language and Literature, B
History, B
Liberal Arts and Sciences Studies and Humanities, B
Mathematics, B
Political Science and Government, B
Psychology, B
Sociology, B
Spanish Language and Literature, B

VIRGINIA COLLEGE IN RICHMOND

Business Administration and Management, A
Medical Office Management/Administration, A
Medical/Clinical Assistant, A
Occupational Therapist Assistant, A
Office Management and Supervision, A
Surgical Technology/Technologist, A

VIRGINIA COMMONWEALTH UNIVERSITY

Accounting, BMD
Adult and Continuing Education and Teaching, M
Advertising and Public Relations, M
African-American/Black Studies, B
Allied Health and Medical Assisting Services, D
Allopathic Medicine, D
Analytical Chemistry, MD
Anatomy, MDO
Anthropology, B
Applied Arts and Design, M
Applied Mathematics, M
Applied Physics, M
Applied Social Research, O
Architectural History and Criticism, M
Area Studies, B
Art Education, M
Art History, Criticism and Conservation, BMD
Art Teacher Education, B
Athletic Training and Sports Medicine, M
Biochemistry, MDO
Bioengineering, MD
Bioinformatics, BMD
Biological and Biomedical Sciences, MDO
Biological and Physical Sciences, B
Biology/Biological Sciences, B
Biomedical Engineering, MD
Biomedical/Medical Engineering, B
Biopsychology, D
Biostatistics, MD

Business Administration, Management and Operations, MO
Business/Commerce, B
Business/Managerial Economics, B
Ceramic Arts and Ceramics, M
Chemical Engineering, BMD
Chemical Physics, D
Chemistry, BMD
Cinematography and Film/Video Production, B
Clinical Laboratory Science/Medical Technology/Technologist, B
Clinical Laboratory Sciences, MD
Clinical Psychology, D
Communication and Media Studies, D
Community Health and Preventive Medicine, MD
Computer Engineering, B
Computer Science, MD
Computer and Information Sciences, B
Counseling Psychology, MDO
Counselor Education/School Counseling and Guidance Services, M
Crafts/Craft Design, Folk Art and Artisanry, B
Criminal Justice/Law Enforcement Administration, B
Criminology, MO
Dance, B
Dental Hygiene/Hygienist, B
Dentistry, MD
Developmental Psychology, D
Drama and Dramatics/Theatre Arts, B
Early Childhood Education and Teaching, M
Economics, M
Education, MDO
Educational Leadership and Administration, D
Educational Measurement and Evaluation, D
Educational Media/Instructional Technology, M
Educational Policy, D
Educational Psychology, D
Electrical Engineering, MD
Electrical, Electronics and Communications Engineering, B
Elementary Education and Teaching, M
Emergency Management, MO
Engineering and Applied Sciences, MD
English, M
English Language and Literature, B
Environmental Studies, BM
Epidemiology, MD
Exercise and Sports Science, M
Fashion/Apparel Design, B
Finance and Banking, M
Finance and Financial Management Services, B
Fine Arts and Art Studies, MD
Foreign Languages and Literatures, B
Forensic Science and Technology, BM
Genetics, MD
Geographic Information Systems, O
Gerontology, MDO
Graphic Design, B
Health Education, M
Health Physics/Radiological Health, D
Health Psychology, D
Health Services Administration, MD
Health Services Research, D
Health Teacher Education, B
Historic Preservation and Conservation, O
History, BM
Homeland Security, MO
Human Genetics, MDO
Human Resources Development, M
Humanities/Humanistic Studies, MDO
Illustration, B
Immunology, MD
Industrial and Manufacturing Management, M
Information Science/Studies, B
Inorganic Chemistry, MD
Insurance, M
Interdisciplinary Studies, M
Interior Design, BM
Internet and Interactive Multimedia, M
Jewelry/Metalsmithing, M
Journalism, B
Management Information Systems and Services, MD
Management Strategy and Policy, M
Marketing, M
Marketing/Marketing Management, B

Mass Communication/Media Studies, BM
Mathematics, BM
Mechanical Engineering, BMD
Media Studies, D
Medical Physics, MD
Medicinal and Pharmaceutical Chemistry, M
Microbiology, MDO
Modeling and Simulation, D
Molecular Biology, MD
Multi-/Interdisciplinary Studies, B
Museology/Museum Studies, M
Music, M
Music Performance, B
Music Teacher Education, M
NanoTechnology, D
Neurobiology and Neurophysiology, MD
Neuroscience, MD
Non-Profit/Public/Organizational Management, O
Nuclear Engineering, MD
Nurse Anesthetist, MD
Nursing, MDO
Nursing - Adult, M
Nursing - Advanced Practice, MO
Nursing Administration, M
Nursing Education, M
Occupational Therapy/Therapist, MD
Operations Research, MD
Organic Chemistry, MD
Painting, BM
Pathology/Experimental Pathology, D
Pediatric Nurse/Nursing, M
Pharmaceutical Administration, M
Pharmaceutical Sciences, MD
Pharmacology, MDO
Pharmacy, D
Philosophy, B
Photography, BM
Physical Chemistry, MD
Physical Education Teaching and Coaching, MD
Physical Therapy/Therapist, D
Physics, BM
Physiology, MDO
Political Science and Government, BMDO
Printmaking, M
Psychiatric/Mental Health Nurse/Nursing, M
Psychology, BD
Public Administration, MO
Public Affairs, MDO
Public Health, M
Public Policy Analysis, D
Quantitative Analysis, M
Radiologic Technology/Science - Radiographer, B
Reading Teacher Education, MO
Real Estate, BMO
Recreation and Park Management, M
Rehabilitation Counseling, MO
Rehabilitation Sciences, D
Religion/Religious Studies, B
Rhetoric, M
Sculpture, BM
Secondary Education and Teaching, MO
Security and Protective Services, B
Social Psychology, D
Social Work, BMD
Sociology, BMO
Special Education and Teaching, MDO
Statistics, MD
Student Personnel Services, M
Systematic Biology/Biological Systematics, D
Theater, M
Toxicology, MDO
Urban Education and Leadership, D
Urban Studies/Affairs, B
Urban and Regional Planning, MO
Women's Health Nursing, M
Women's Studies, B
Writing, M

VIRGINIA HIGHLANDS COMMUNITY COLLEGE

Accounting, A
Administrative Assistant and Secretarial Science, A
Biological and Physical Sciences, A
Business Administration and Management, A
Criminal Justice/Police Science, A

Data Processing and Data Processing Technology/Technician, A
Drafting and Design Technology/Technician, A
Drama and Dramatics/Theatre Arts, A
Education, A
Electrical, Electronic and Communications Engineering Technology/Technician, A
Engineering Technology, A
Heating, Air Conditioning, Ventilation and Refrigeration Maintenance Technology/Technician, A
Human Services, A
Industrial Radiologic Technology/Technician, A
Information Science/Studies, A
Liberal Arts and Sciences Studies and Humanities, A
Machine Tool Technology/Machinist, A
Physical Therapy/Therapist, A

VIRGINIA INTERNATIONAL UNIVERSITY

Accounting, M
Advertising and Public Relations, M
Business Administration and Management, B
Business Administration, Management and Operations, MO
Computer Art and Design, M
Computer Science, BMO
Computer and Information Systems Security, M
Database Systems, M
Education, M
English as a Second Language, M
Entrepreneurship/Entrepreneurial Studies, M
Finance and Banking, M
Game Design and Development, M
Health Informatics, M
Health Services Administration, M
Hospitality Administration/Management, M
Human Resources Management and Services, M
International Affairs, M
International Business/Trade/Commerce, M
Linguistics, M
Logistics and Materials Management, M
Management, O
Management Information Systems and Services, M
Marketing, M
Project Management, M
Public Administration, M
Software Engineering, M

VIRGINIA MILITARY INSTITUTE

Biology/Biological Sciences, B
Chemistry, B
Civil Engineering, B
Computer Science, B
Economics, B
Electrical, Electronics and Communications Engineering, B
English Language and Literature, B
History, B
International Relations and Affairs, B
Mathematics, B
Mechanical Engineering, B
Modern Languages, B
Physics, B
Psychology, B

VIRGINIA POLYTECHNIC INSTITUTE AND STATE UNIVERSITY

Accounting, BM
Aerospace, Aeronautical and Astronautical Engineering, BMD
Agricultural Economics, BM
Agricultural Engineering, MD
Agricultural Sciences, MD
Agronomy and Crop Science, B
Agronomy and Soil Sciences, MD
Animal Sciences, BMD
Apparel and Textiles, B
Applied Economics, M
Architecture, BMD
Art/Art Studies, General, B
BioTechnology, M
Biochemistry, B
Bioengineering, MD
Bioinformatics, D
Biological and Biomedical Sciences, MD

Biology/Biological Sciences, B
Biomedical Engineering, MD
Building Science, D
Business Administration and Management, B
Business Administration, Management and Operations, MD
Business Family and Consumer Sciences/Human Sciences, B
Business/Managerial Economics, B
Chemical Engineering, BMD
Chemistry, BMD
Civil Engineering, BMD
Communication Studies/Speech Communication and Rhetoric, B
Communication and Media Studies, M
Computer Engineering, BMD
Computer Science, BMDO
Computer and Information Sciences, B
Computer and Information Systems Security, O
Construction Engineering and Management, M
Construction Management, BM
Counselor Education/School Counseling and Guidance Services, MDO
Curriculum and Instruction, MDO
Dairy Science, BM
Distance Education Development, MO
Drama and Dramatics/Theatre Arts, B
Economics, BMD
Education, M
Educational Leadership and Administration, MDO
Educational Measurement and Evaluation, D
Educational Media/Instructional Technology, M
Educational Policy, MDO
Electrical Engineering, MD
Electrical, Electronics and Communications Engineering, B
Engineering Management, M
Engineering Mechanics, B
Engineering and Applied Sciences, MD
English, M
English Language and Literature, B
Entomology, D
Environmental Design/Architecture, D
Environmental Engineering Technology/Environmental Technology, MO
Environmental Policy, O
Environmental Policy and Resource Management, D
Environmental Sciences, MD
Environmental Studies, B
Exercise and Sports Science, MD
Family and Consumer Sciences/Home Economics Teacher Education, B
Finance, B
Fish, Game and Wildlife Management, MD
Food Science, B
Foods, Nutrition, and Wellness Studies, B
Foreign Language Teacher Education, M
Forestry, BMD
French Language and Literature, B
Genetics, D
Geographic Information Systems, D
Geography, BM
Geology/Earth Science, B
Geosciences, MD
German Language and Literature, B
Higher Education/Higher Education Administration, M
History, BM
History of Science and Technology, MD
Horticultural Science, BMD
Hospitality Administration/Management, MD
Hotel/Motel Administration/Management, B
Human Development, MD
Human Development and Family Studies, B
Humanities/Humanistic Studies, MD
Industrial Design, B
Industrial Engineering, B
Industrial/Management Engineering, MD
Information Science/Studies, B
Interdisciplinary Studies, MD
Interior Design, B
International Affairs, MD
International Relations and Affairs, B
Internet and Interactive Multimedia, M
Landscape Architecture, BM
Liberal Studies, O

Management Information Systems and Services, MO
Management Science, B
Marketing/Marketing Management, B
Materials Engineering, BMD
Materials Sciences, MD
Mathematics, BMD
Mathematics Teacher Education, D
Mechanical Engineering, BMD
Mechanics, MD
Meteorology, B
Mineral/Mining Engineering, MD
Mining and Mineral Engineering, B
Music, B
National Security, O
Natural Resources and Conservation, MO
Non-Profit/Public/Organizational Management, O
Nuclear Engineering, MD
Nutritional Sciences, MD
Ocean Engineering, BM
Philosophy, BM
Physics, BMD
Plant Pathology/Phytopathology, D
Plant Physiology, D
Political Science and Government, BM
Poultry Science, BMD
Psychology, BMD
Public Administration, MDO
Public Affairs, MDO
Public Health, M
Public Policy Analysis, BM
Quantitative Analysis, O
Real Estate, B
Rhetoric, D
Russian Language and Literature, B
Secondary Education and Teaching, B
Social Studies Teacher Education, D
Sociology, BMD
Software Engineering, O
Spanish Language and Literature, B
Statistics, BMD
Student Personnel Services, M
Systems Engineering, MD
Theater, M
Transportation and Highway Engineering, O
Travel and Tourism, MD
Urban Studies/Affairs, MDO
Urban and Regional Planning, M
Veterinary Medicine, D
Veterinary Sciences, MD
Vocational and Technical Education, MDO
Water Quality and Wastewater Treatment Management and Recycling Technology/Technician, B
Writing, MD

VIRGINIA STATE UNIVERSITY

Accounting, B
Agriculture, B
Biological and Biomedical Sciences, M
Biology/Biological Sciences, B
Business Administration and Management, B
Business/Managerial Economics, B
Chemistry, B
Clinical Psychology, MD
Community Health and Preventive Medicine, D
Computer Engineering, B
Computer Science, BM
Counselor Education/School Counseling and Guidance Services, M
Criminal Justice/Safety Studies, B
Criminology, M
Economics, M
Education, MDO
Educational Administration and Supervision, MD
Electrical and Electronic Engineering Technologies/Technicians, B
English, M
English Language and Literature, B
Family and Consumer Economics and Related Services, B
Health Education, D
Health Psychology, D
History, B
Hospitality Administration/Management, B
Interdisciplinary Studies, M

Liberal Arts and Sciences Studies and Humanities, B
Management Information Systems and Services, B
Manufacturing Engineering, B
Marketing/Marketing Management, B
Mass Communication/Media Studies, B
Mathematics, BM
Mathematics Teacher Education, M
Mechanical Engineering/Mechanical Technology/Technician, B
Media Studies, M
Music, B
Physical Education Teaching and Coaching, B
Political Science and Government, B
Psychology, BMD
Public Relations, Advertising, and Applied Communication, B
Social Work, B
Sociology, B
Trade and Industrial Teacher Education, B
Visual and Performing Arts, B

VIRGINIA UNION UNIVERSITY

Accounting, B
Biology Teacher Education, B
Biology/Biological Sciences, B
Business Administration and Management, B
Business Teacher Education, B
Chemistry, B
Chemistry Teacher Education, B
Computer Systems Networking and Telecommunications, B
Computer and Information Sciences, B
Criminology, B
Drama Therapy, B
Drama and Dramatics/Theatre Arts, B
Elementary Education and Teaching, B
English Language and Literature, B
English/Language Arts Teacher Education, B
Entrepreneurship/Entrepreneurial Studies, B
Finance, B
Fine/Studio Arts, B
General Merchandising, Sales, and Related Marketing Operations, B
History, B
History Teacher Education, B
Journalism, B
Kindergarten/PreSchool Education and Teaching, B
Management Information Systems and Services, B
Marketing/Marketing Management, B
Mass Communication/Media Studies, B
Mathematics, B
Mathematics Teacher Education, B
Multi-/Interdisciplinary Studies, B
Music, B
Music Performance, B
Political Science and Government, B
Psychology, B
Social Work, B
Special Education and Teaching, B
Teacher Education, Multiple Levels, B
Theology and Religious Vocations, MD
Visual and Performing Arts, B

VIRGINIA UNIVERSITY OF LYNCHBURG

Business Administration and Management, B
Liberal Arts and Sciences Studies and Humanities, A
Religion/Religious Studies, BM
Sociology, B

VIRGINIA WESLEYAN COLLEGE

American/United States Studies/Civilization, B
Art Teacher Education, B
Art/Art Studies, General, B
Biology/Biological Sciences, B
Business Administration and Management, B
Chemistry, B
Classics and Classical Languages, Literatures, and Linguistics, B
Communication and Media Studies, B
Computer Science, B
Criminal Justice/Safety Studies, B
Criminology, B
Drama and Dramatics/Theatre Arts, B
Elementary Education and Teaching, B

English Language and Literature, B
Environmental Studies, B
Foreign Language Teacher Education, B
French Language and Literature, B
Geology/Earth Science, B
German Language and Literature, B
History, B
Human Services, B
Humanities/Humanistic Studies, B
International Relations and Affairs, B
Junior High/Intermediate/Middle School Education and Teaching, B
Latin Language and Literature, B
Mass Communication/Media Studies, B
Mathematics, B
Multi-/Interdisciplinary Studies, B
Music, B
Natural Sciences, B
Parks, Recreation, Leisure and Fitness Studies, B
Philosophy, B
Political Science and Government, B
Pre-Dentistry Studies, B
Pre-Medicine/Pre-Medical Studies, B
Pre-Veterinary Studies, B
Psychology, B
Religion/Religious Studies, B
Secondary Education and Teaching, B
Social Sciences, B
Social Studies Teacher Education, B
Social Work, B
Sociology, B
Spanish Language and Literature, B
Special Education and Teaching, B
Teacher Education, Multiple Levels, B
Visual and Performing Arts, B
Women's Studies, B

VIRGINIA WESTERN COMMUNITY COLLEGE

Accounting, A
Administrative Assistant and Secretarial Science, A
Art/Art Studies, General, A
Automobile/Automotive Mechanics Technology/Technician, A
Biological and Physical Sciences, A
Business Administration and Management, A
Child Development, A
Civil Engineering Technology/Technician, A
Commercial and Advertising Art, A
Computer Science, A
Criminal Justice/Law Enforcement Administration, A
Data Processing and Data Processing Technology/Technician, A
Dental Hygiene/Hygienist, A
Education, A
Electrical, Electronic and Communications Engineering Technology/Technician, A
Engineering, A
Industrial Radiologic Technology/Technician, A
Kindergarten/PreSchool Education and Teaching, A
Liberal Arts and Sciences Studies and Humanities, A
Mechanical Engineering/Mechanical Technology/Technician, A
Mental Health Counseling/Counselor, A
Radio and Television, A
Radiologic Technology/Science - Radiographer, A

WASHINGTON AND LEE UNIVERSITY

Accounting and Business/Management, B
Art History, Criticism and Conservation, B
Biochemistry, B
Biology/Biological Sciences, B
Business Administration and Management, B
Chemistry, B
Classics and Classical Languages, Literatures, and Linguistics, B
Computer Science, B
Drama and Dramatics/Theatre Arts, B
East Asian Languages, Literatures, and Linguistics, B
Economics, B
Engineering Physics, B
English Language and Literature, B
Environmental Studies, B
Fine/Studio Arts, B

French Language and Literature, B
Geology/Earth Science, B
German Language and Literature, B
History, B
Journalism, B
Law and Legal Studies, MD
Mathematics, B
Medieval and Renaissance Studies, B
Multi-/Interdisciplinary Studies, B
Music, B
Philosophy, B
Physics, B
Political Science and Government, B
Psychology, B
Religion/Religious Studies, B
Romance Languages, Literatures, and Linguistics, B
Russian Studies, B
Sociology, B
Spanish Language and Literature, B

WYTHEVILLE COMMUNITY COLLEGE

Accounting, A
Administrative Assistant and Secretarial Science, A
Biological and Physical Sciences, A
Business Administration and Management, A
Civil Engineering Technology/Technician, A
Clinical/Medical Laboratory Technician, A
Corrections, A
Criminal Justice/Law Enforcement Administration, A
Criminal Justice/Police Science, A
Dental Hygiene/Hygienist, A
Drafting and Design Technology/Technician, A
Education, A
Electrical, Electronic and Communications Engineering Technology/Technician, A
Information Science/Studies, A
Liberal Arts and Sciences Studies and Humanities, A
Machine Tool Technology/Machinist, A
Mass Communication/Media Studies, A
Mechanical Engineering/Mechanical Technology/Technician, A
Medical Administrative Assistant/Secretary, A
Physical Therapy/Therapist, A

Washington

ANTIOCH UNIVERSITY SEATTLE

Counselor Education/School Counseling and Guidance Services, M
Education, M
Environmental Policy and Resource Management, M
Liberal Arts and Sciences Studies and Humanities, B
Organizational Management, M
Psychology, MD

ARGOSY UNIVERSITY, SEATTLE

Accounting, D
Adult and Continuing Education and Teaching, M
Business Administration and Management, AB
Business Administration, Management and Operations, MD
Clinical Psychology, MDO
Community College Education, D
Counseling Psychology, MD
Criminal Justice/Law Enforcement Administration, B
Education, MD
Educational Administration and Supervision, D
Educational Leadership and Administration, MD
Educational Media/Instructional Technology, D
Elementary Education and Teaching, D
Finance and Banking, M
Health Services Administration, M
Higher Education/Higher Education Administration, MD
Information Technology, AB
International Business/Trade/Commerce, MD
Liberal Arts and Sciences Studies and Humanities, B
Management, MD
Management Information Systems and Services, MD
Marketing, MD

Organizational Management, D
Psychology, ABMDO
Public Administration, M
Public Health, M
Secondary Education and Teaching, D
Sustainability Management, MD

THE ART INSTITUTE OF SEATTLE

Advertising, B
Animation, Interactive Technology, Video Graphics and Special Effects, B
Apparel and Accessories Marketing Operations, AB
Baking and Pastry Arts/Baker/Pastry Chef, A
Cinematography and Film/Video Production, AB
Commercial Photography, AB
Computer Graphics, B
Culinary Arts/Chef Training, A
Fashion/Apparel Design, AB
Graphic Design, AB
Industrial Design, AB
Interior Design, AB
Recording Arts Technology/Technician, AB
Restaurant, Culinary, and Catering Management/Manager, B
Web Page, Digital/Multimedia and Information Resources Design, A

BASTYR UNIVERSITY

Acupuncture and Oriental Medicine, MDO
Biology/Biological Sciences, B
Counseling Psychology, M
Dietetics/Dieticians, B
Environmental Design/Architecture, O
Foods, Nutrition, and Wellness Studies, B
Health Professions and Related Clinical Sciences, B
Health Psychology, M
Herbalism/Herbalist, B
Kinesiology and Exercise Science, B
Landscape Architecture, O
Naturopathic Medicine/Naturopathy, D
Nurse Midwife/Nursing Midwifery, M
Nutritional Sciences, MO
Psychology, B

BATES TECHNICAL COLLEGE

Accounting Technology/Technician and Bookkeeping, A
Administrative Assistant and Secretarial Science, A
Architectural Engineering Technology/Technician, A
Biology Technician/BioTechnology Laboratory Technician, A
Building/Property Maintenance and Management, A
Carpentry/Carpenter, A
Child Care Provider/Assistant, A
Civil Engineering Technology/Technician, A
Communication Disorders Sciences and Services, A
Communications Systems Installation and Repair Technology, A
Computer Programming/Programmer, A
Computer Systems Networking and Telecommunications, A
Computer Technology/Computer Systems Technology, A
Court Reporting/Court Reporter, A
Culinary Arts/Chef Training, A
Dental Assisting/Assistant, A
Dental Laboratory Technology/Technician, A
Dental Services and Allied Professions, A
Diesel Mechanics Technology/Technician, A
Electrical, Electronic and Communications Engineering Technology/Technician, A
Electrician, A
Fire Science/Firefighting, A
Heating, Air Conditioning, Ventilation and Refrigeration Maintenance Technology/Technician, A
Industrial Electronics Technology/Technician, A
Legal Administrative Assistant/Secretary, A
Machine Tool Technology/Machinist, A
Mechanic and Repair Technologies/Technicians, A
Mechanical Engineering/Mechanical Technology/Technician, A
Occupational Safety and Health Technology/Technician, A
Radio and Television Broadcasting Technology/Technician, A
Retailing and Retail Operations, A

Small Engine Mechanics and Repair Technology/Technician, A
Survey Technology/Surveying, A

BELLEVUE COLLEGE

Accounting, A
Allied Health Diagnostic, Intervention, and Treatment Professions, A
Business Administration and Management, A
Business/Commerce, A
Computer Graphics, A
Computer Programming/Programmer, A
Computer Systems Networking and Telecommunications, A
Computer and Information Sciences and Support Services, A
Criminal Justice/Law Enforcement Administration, A
Data Modeling/Warehousing and Database Administration, A
Diagnostic Medical Sonography/Sonographer and Ultrasound Technician, A
E-Commerce/Electronic Commerce, A
Early Childhood Education and Teaching, A
Fire Science/Firefighting, A
Fire Services Administration, A
General Office Occupations and Clerical Services, A
Interior Design, A
Liberal Arts and Sciences Studies and Humanities, A
Marketing/Marketing Management, A
Medical Radiologic Technology/Science - Radiation Therapist, A
Office Management and Supervision, A
Photographic and Film/Video Technology/Technician and Assistant, A
Physical Sciences, A
Real Estate, A
Web Page, Digital/Multimedia and Information Resources Design, A

BELLINGHAM TECHNICAL COLLEGE

Accounting Technology/Technician and Bookkeeping, A
Autobody/Collision and Repair Technology/Technician, A
Automobile/Automotive Mechanics Technology/Technician, A
Building/Property Maintenance and Management, A
Civil Engineering Technology/Technician, A
Communications Systems Installation and Repair Technology, A
Computer Systems Networking and Telecommunications, A
Culinary Arts/Chef Training, A
Data Entry/Microcomputer Applications, A
Diesel Mechanics Technology/Technician, A
Electrician, A
Executive Assistant/Executive Secretary, A
Fishing and Fisheries Sciences and Management, A
Heating, Air Conditioning, Ventilation and Refrigeration Maintenance Technology/Technician, A
Heavy/Industrial Equipment Maintenance Technologies, A
Industrial Mechanics and Maintenance Technology, A
Instrumentation Technology/Technician, A
Legal Assistant/Paralegal, A
Machine Tool Technology/Machinist, A
Marketing/Marketing Management, A
Medical Radiologic Technology/Science - Radiation Therapist, A
Surgical Technology/Technologist, A
Survey Technology/Surveying, A
Welding Technology/Welder, A

BIG BEND COMMUNITY COLLEGE

Accounting Technology/Technician and Bookkeeping, A
Agricultural Production Operations, A
Airline/Commercial/Professional Pilot and Flight Crew, A
Automobile/Automotive Mechanics Technology/Technician, A
Avionics Maintenance Technology/Technician, A
Biomedical Technology/Technician, A
Computer Programming/Programmer, A

Computer Systems Networking and Telecommunications, A
Early Childhood Education and Teaching, A
Industrial Electronics Technology/Technician, A
Industrial Mechanics and Maintenance Technology, A
Liberal Arts and Sciences Studies and Humanities, A
Medical Office Management/Administration, A
Medical/Clinical Assistant, A
Office Management and Supervision, A
Welding Technology/Welder, A

CARRINGTON COLLEGE–SPOKANE

Medical Administrative Assistant/Secretary, A
Medical Office Management/Administration, A
Medical Radiologic Technology/Science - Radiation Therapist, A

CASCADIA COLLEGE

Liberal Arts and Sciences Studies and Humanities, A
Science Technologies/Technicians, A

CENTRAL WASHINGTON UNIVERSITY

Accounting, BM
Acting, B
Actuarial Science, B
Airline/Commercial/Professional Pilot and Flight Crew, B
Anthropology, B
Apparel and Textile Marketing Management, B
Art/Art Studies, General, B
Aviation/Airway Management and Operations, B
Behavioral Sciences, B
Biochemistry, B
Biological and Biomedical Sciences, BM
Biology Teacher Education, B
Biology/Biological Sciences, B
Biomedical Sciences, B
Broadcast Journalism, B
Business Administration and Management, B
Business Administration, Management and Operations, B
Business/Managerial Economics, B
Cartography, B
Cell/Cellular and Molecular Biology, B
Ceramic Arts and Ceramics, B
Chemistry, BM
Chemistry Teacher Education, B
Child and Family Studies, M
Cinematography and Film/Video Production, B
Computer Engineering Technology/Technician, B
Computer Science, B
Computer and Information Systems Security, B
Construction Management, B
Counseling Psychology, M
Counselor Education/School Counseling and Guidance Services, M
Criminal Justice/Safety Studies, B
Curriculum and Instruction, M
Data Modeling/Warehousing and Database Administration, B
Dietetics/Dieticians, B
Digital Communication and Media/Multimedia, B
Drama and Dance Teacher Education, B
Drawing, B
Early Childhood Education and Teaching, B
Ecology, B
Economics, B
Education, BM
Educational Administration and Supervision, M
Educational Leadership and Administration, M
Electrical, Electronic and Communications Engineering Technology/Technician, B
Elementary Education and Teaching, B
Emergency Medical Technology/Technician (EMT Paramedic), B
Engineering Physics, B
Engineering and Applied Sciences, M
English, M
English Language and Literature, B
English as a Second Language, M
English/Language Arts Teacher Education, B
Environmental Biology, B
Environmental Sciences, B

Environmental Studies, B
Exercise Physiology, B
Exercise and Sports Science, M
Experimental Psychology, M
Family Systems, B
Family and Consumer Sciences/Home Economics Teacher Education, B
Family and Consumer Sciences/Human Sciences, B
Film/Cinema Studies, B
Finance, B
Fine Arts and Art Studies, M
Fine/Studio Arts, B
Foundations and Philosophy of Education, M
French Language Teacher Education, B
French Language and Literature, B
Geography, B
Geological and Earth Sciences/Geosciences, B
Geology/Earth Science, BM
German Language and Literature, B
Graphic Design, B
Health Education, M
History, BM
History Teacher Education, B
Home Economics, M
Home Economics Education, M
Human Nutrition, B
Human Resources Management/Personnel Administration, B
Human Services, B
Industrial Production Technologies/Technicians, B
Industrial Safety Technology/Technician, B
Industrial Technology/Technician, B
Industrial/Management Engineering, M
Information Technology, B
Interdisciplinary Studies, M
Japanese Language and Literature, B
Jazz/Jazz Studies, B
Journalism, B
Kinesiology and Exercise Science, B
Logistics and Materials Management, B
Management Information Systems and Services, B
Manufacturing Technology/Technician, B
Marketing/Marketing Management, B
Mathematics, BM
Mathematics Teacher Education, B
Mechanical Engineering/Mechanical Technology/Technician, B
Metal and Jewelry Arts, B
Microbiology, B
Multi-/Interdisciplinary Studies, B
Museology/Museum Studies, B
Music, BM
Music Performance, B
Music Teacher Education, B
Music Theory and Composition, B
Natural Resources Management/Development and Policy, M
Nutritional Sciences, BM
Occupational Safety and Health Technology/Technician, B
Pacific Area/Pacific Rim Studies, B
Painting, B
Parks, Recreation and Leisure Facilities Management, B
Photography, B
Physical Education Teaching and Coaching, BM
Physics, B
Piano and Organ, B
Playwriting and Screenwriting, B
Political Science and Government, B
Pre-Nursing Studies, B
Psychology, BM
Public Health (MPH, DPH), B
Public Health Education and Promotion, B
Public Policy Analysis, B
Public Relations/Image Management, B
Reading Teacher Education, M
Religion/Religious Studies, B
Restaurant/Food Services Management, B
Retailing and Retail Operations, B
Russian Language and Literature, B
Sales and Marketing Operations/Marketing and Distribution Teacher Education, B
School Psychology, M
Science Teacher Education/General Science Teacher Education, B

Sculpture, B
Social Science Teacher Education, B
Social Sciences, B
Sociology, B
Spanish Language Teacher Education, B
Spanish Language and Literature, B
Special Education and Teaching, BM
Special Products Marketing Operations, B
Sport and Fitness Administration/Management, M
System, Networking, and LAN/WAN Management/Manager, B
Technical Teacher Education, B
Technical Theatre/Theatre Design and Technology, B
Theater, M
Tourism and Travel Services Management, B
Trade and Industrial Teacher Education, B
Violin, Viola, Guitar and Other Stringed Instruments, B
Vocational and Technical Education, M
Voice and Opera, B
Web Page, Digital/Multimedia and Information Resources Design, B

CENTRALIA COLLEGE

Accounting Technology/Technician and Bookkeeping, A
Business/Commerce, A
Civil Engineering Technology/Technician, A
Computer Programming/Programmer, A
Criminal Justice/Law Enforcement Administration, A
Criminal Justice/Police Science, A
Diesel Mechanics Technology/Technician, A
Legal Administrative Assistant/Secretary, A
Liberal Arts and Sciences Studies and Humanities, A
Marketing/Marketing Management, A
Mechanic and Repair Technologies/Technicians, A
Medical Administrative Assistant/Secretary, A
Office Management and Supervision, A
Physical Sciences, A
Welding Technology/Welder, A

CITY UNIVERSITY OF SEATTLE

Accounting, BO
Business Administration and Management, B
Business Administration, Management and Operations, MO
Computer Programming/Programmer, B
Computer Science, M
Computer and Information Sciences and Support Services, B
Computer and Information Systems Security, M
Counseling Psychology, M
Counselor Education/School Counseling and Guidance Services, M
Curriculum and Instruction, M
Early Childhood Education and Teaching, B
Education, MO
Educational Administration and Supervision, O
Educational Leadership and Administration, MD
Elementary Education and Teaching, BM
Finance and Banking, MO
General Studies, AB
Human Resources Management and Services, O
Human Services, B
International Business/Trade/Commerce, BM
Management, M
Management Information Systems and Services, M
Management of Technology, O
Marketing, MO
Mass Communication/Media Studies, B
Organizational Management, MO
Project Management, MO
Psychology, B
Reading Teacher Education, M
Special Education and Teaching, BM
Sustainability Management, O

CLARK COLLEGE

Accounting Technology/Technician and Bookkeeping, A
Applied Horticulture/Horticultural Operations, A
Automobile/Automotive Mechanics Technology/Technician, A
Baking and Pastry Arts/Baker/Pastry Chef, A

Business Administration and Management, A
Business/Office Automation/Technology/Data Entry, A
Computer Programming/Programmer, A
Computer Systems Networking and Telecommunications, A
Construction Engineering Technology/Technician, A
Culinary Arts/Chef Training, A
Data Entry/Microcomputer Applications, A
Dental Hygiene/Hygienist, A
Diesel Mechanics Technology/Technician, A
Early Childhood Education and Teaching, A
Electrical, Electronic and Communications Engineering Technology/Technician, A
Emergency Medical Technology/Technician (EMT Paramedic), A
Executive Assistant/Executive Secretary, A
Graphic Communications, A
Human Resources Management/Personnel Administration, A
Landscaping and Groundskeeping, A
Legal Administrative Assistant/Secretary, A
Legal Assistant/Paralegal, A
Liberal Arts and Sciences Studies and Humanities, A
Machine Tool Technology/Machinist, A
Manufacturing Technology/Technician, A
Medical Administrative Assistant/Secretary, A
Medical/Clinical Assistant, A
Radiologic Technology/Science - Radiographer, A
Retailing and Retail Operations, A
Selling Skills and Sales Operations, A
Sport and Fitness Administration/Management, A
Substance Abuse/Addiction Counseling, A
Survey Technology/Surveying, A
Telecommunications Technology/Technician, A
Web/Multimedia Management and Webmaster, A
Welding Technology/Welder, A

CLOVER PARK TECHNICAL COLLEGE

Accounting Technology/Technician and Bookkeeping, A
Aesthetician/Esthetician and Skin Care Specialist, A
Airline/Commercial/Professional Pilot and Flight Crew, A
Architectural Engineering Technology/Technician, A
Automobile/Automotive Mechanics Technology/Technician, A
Business Machine Repairer, A
Clinical/Medical Laboratory Assistant, A
Computer Programming/Programmer, A
Computer Systems Networking and Telecommunications, A
Computer and Information Systems Security, A
Culinary Arts/Chef Training, A
Dental Assisting/Assistant, A
Early Childhood Education and Teaching, A
Environmental Engineering Technology/Environmental Technology, A
Fire Protection, A
Graphic and Printing Equipment Operator Production, A
Heating, Air Conditioning, Ventilation and Refrigeration Maintenance Technology/Technician, A
Heavy Equipment Maintenance Technology/Technician, A
Interior Design, A
Landscaping and Groundskeeping, A
Legal Administrative Assistant/Secretary, A
Machine Tool Technology/Machinist, A
Marketing/Marketing Management, A
Massage Therapy/Therapeutic Massage, A
Mechanical Engineering/Mechanical Technology/Technician, A
Mental and Social Health Services and Allied Professions, A
Office Management and Supervision, A
Pharmacy Technician/Assistant, A
Prepress/Desktop Publishing and Digital Imaging Design, A
Quality Control and Safety Technologies/Technicians, A
Radio and Television Broadcasting Technology/Technician, A
Security and Protective Services, A
Surgical Technology/Technologist, A

Teacher Assistant/Aide, A
Telecommunications Technology/Technician, A
Turf and Turfgrass Management, A
Vehicle Maintenance and Repair Technologies, A
Web Page, Digital/Multimedia and Information Resources Design, A

COLUMBIA BASIN COLLEGE

Accounting Technology/Technician and Bookkeeping, A
Automobile/Automotive Mechanics Technology/Technician, A
Business, Management, Marketing, and Related Support Services, A
Business/Commerce, A
Computer Programming/Programmer, A
Computer Systems Networking and Telecommunications, A
Computer and Information Sciences and Support Services, A
Criminal Justice/Law Enforcement Administration, A
Data Processing and Data Processing Technology/Technician, A
Dental Hygiene/Hygienist, A
Early Childhood Education and Teaching, A
Engineering Technology, A
Fire Services Administration, A
Forensic Science and Technology, A
Legal Administrative Assistant/Secretary, A
Legal Assistant/Paralegal, A
Liberal Arts and Sciences Studies and Humanities, A
Machine Tool Technology/Machinist, A
Marketing/Marketing Management, A
Medical Insurance Coding Specialist/Coder, A
Medical/Clinical Assistant, A
Mental and Social Health Services and Allied Professions, A
Office Management and Supervision, A
Substance Abuse/Addiction Counseling, A
Surgical Technology/Technologist, A
Web Page, Digital/Multimedia and Information Resources Design, A
Web/Multimedia Management and Webmaster, A
Welding Technology/Welder, A

CORNISH COLLEGE OF THE ARTS

Acting, B
Art/Art Studies, General, B
Dance, B
Directing and Theatrical Production, B
Drama and Dramatics/Theatre Arts, B
Fine Arts and Art Studies, B
Fine/Studio Arts, B
Graphic Design, B
Illustration, B
Interior Design, B
Jazz/Jazz Studies, B
Music, B
Piano and Organ, B
Technical Theatre/Theatre Design and Technology, B
Violin, Viola, Guitar and Other Stringed Instruments, B
Voice and Opera, B

DIGIPEN INSTITUTE OF TECHNOLOGY

Animation, Interactive Technology, Video Graphics and Special Effects, B
Computer Art and Design, M
Computer Engineering, B
Computer Programming, Specific Applications, B
Computer Science, M
Computer Software Engineering, B
Music Theory and Composition, B

EASTERN WASHINGTON UNIVERSITY

Accounting, B
Adult and Continuing Education and Teaching, BM
Anthropology, B
Applied Psychology, M
Art History, Criticism and Conservation, B
Art Teacher Education, B
Athletic Training and Sports Medicine, B
Biological and Biomedical Sciences, M
Biology Teacher Education, B

Biology/Biological Sciences, B
Business Administration and Management, B
Business Administration, Management and Operations, M
Business Teacher Education, B
Business/Managerial Economics, B
Chemistry, B
Chemistry Teacher Education, B
Child Development, B
Cinematography and Film/Video Production, B
City/Urban, Community and Regional Planning, B
Clinical Psychology, M
Communication Disorders, M
Communication Studies/Speech Communication and Rhetoric, B
Communication and Media Studies, M
Community Health Services/Liaison/Counseling, B
Composition, M
Computer Education, M
Computer Science, M
Computer and Information Sciences, B
Counseling Psychology, M
Counselor Education/School Counseling and Guidance Services, M
Criminology, B
Curriculum and Instruction, BM
Dental Hygiene/Hygienist, BM
Drama and Dramatics/Theatre Arts, B
Early Childhood Education and Teaching, BM
Economics, B
Education, BM
Education/Teaching of Individuals in Early Childhood Special Education Programs, B
Educational Leadership and Administration, B
Educational/Instructional Media Design, B
Electrical, Electronics and Communications Engineering, B
Elementary Education and Teaching, M
Engineering Technologies/Technicians, B
English, M
English Language and Literature, B
English as a Second Language, M
English/Language Arts Teacher Education, B
Environmental Sciences, B
Exercise and Sports Science, M
Experimental Psychology, M
Film/Cinema Studies, B
Finance, B
Fine/Studio Arts, B
French Language Teacher Education, B
French Language and Literature, B
Geography, B
Geology/Earth Science, B
Graphic Communications, B
Graphic Design, B
Health Information/Medical Records Administration/Administrator, B
Health Teacher Education, B
Health and Physical Education, B
Health/Health Care Administration/Management, B
History, BM
Human Resources Management/Personnel Administration, B
Humanities/Humanistic Studies, B
Interdisciplinary Studies, M
International Relations and Affairs, B
Journalism, B
Kinesiology and Exercise Science, B
Management Information Systems and Services, B
Marketing/Marketing Management, B
Mathematics, BM
Mathematics Teacher Education, BM
Mechanical Engineering, B
Mechanical Engineering/Mechanical Technology/Technician, B
Multi-/Interdisciplinary Studies, B
Music, BM
Music Teacher Education, BM
Occupational Therapy/Therapist, BM
Parks, Recreation and Leisure Facilities Management, B
Parks, Recreation, Leisure and Fitness Studies, B
Performance, M
Philosophy, B
Physical Education Teaching and Coaching, M
Physical Therapy/Therapist, D

Physics, B
Physics Teacher Education, B
Political Science and Government, B
Psychology, BM
Public Administration, BM
Public Health Education and Promotion, B
Reading Teacher Education, BM
Recreation and Park Management, M
Rhetoric, M
School Psychology, M
Science Teacher Education/General Science
    Teacher Education, B
Secondary Education and Teaching, M
Social Science Teacher Education, B
Social Studies Teacher Education, B
Social Work, BM
Social and Philosophical Foundations of Educa-
    tion, B
Sociology, B
Spanish Language Teacher Education, B
Spanish Language and Literature, B
Special Education and Teaching, BM
Speech-Language Pathology/Pathologist, B
Sport and Fitness Administration/Management, M
Teacher Education, Multiple Levels, B
Teaching English as a Second or Foreign
    Language/ESL Language Instructor, B
Technical Communication, M
Therapeutic Recreation/Recreational Therapy, B
Urban and Regional Planning, M
Women's Studies, B
Writing, M

EDMONDS COMMUNITY COLLEGE

Accounting Technology/Technician and Bookkeep-
    ing, A
Administrative Assistant and Secretarial Science, A
Applied Horticulture/Horticultural Operations, A
Audiovisual Communications
    Technologies/Technicians, A
Building/Home/Construction Inspection/Inspector, A
Business Administration and Management, A
Clinical/Medical Laboratory Assistant, A
Computer Programming, Specific Applications, A
Computer Programming, Vendor/Product Certifica-
    tion, A
Computer Programming/Programmer, A
Computer Systems Networking and Telecommunica-
    tions, A
Computer Technology/Computer Systems Technol-
    ogy, A
Computer and Information Sciences and Support
    Services, A
Computer and Information Systems Security, A
Construction Engineering Technology/Technician, A
Culinary Arts/Chef Training, A
Data Entry/Microcomputer Applications, A
Data Modeling/Warehousing and Database Adminis-
    tration, A
Data Processing and Data Processing
    Technology/Technician, A
E-Commerce/Electronic Commerce, A
Early Childhood Education and Teaching, A
Electrical, Electronic and Communications Engineer-
    ing Technology/Technician, A
Electrocardiograph Technology/Technician, A
Entrepreneurship/Entrepreneurial Studies, A
Fashion Merchandising, A
Fire Services Administration, A
Health Aide, A
Health Information/Medical Records
    Technology/Technician, A
Health Professions and Related Clinical Sciences, A
Human Resources Management/Personnel Adminis-
    tration, A
International Business/Trade/Commerce, A
Landscaping and Groundskeeping, A
Legal Administrative Assistant/Secretary, A
Legal Assistant/Paralegal, A
Liberal Arts and Sciences Studies and Humani-
    ties, A
Marketing/Marketing Management, A
Medical Administrative Assistant/Secretary, A
Medical Reception/Receptionist, A
Mental and Social Health Services and Allied Pro-
    fessions, A

Office Management and Supervision, A
Pharmacy Technician/Assistant, A
Phlebotomy/Phlebotomist, A
Plant Nursery Operations and Management, A
Prepress/Desktop Publishing and Digital Imaging
    Design, A
Substance Abuse/Addiction Counseling, A
System Administration/Administrator, A
Tourism and Travel Services Marketing Opera-
    tions, A
Vocational Rehabilitation Counseling/Counselor, A
Web Page, Digital/Multimedia and Information Re-
    sources Design, A
Web/Multimedia Management and Webmaster, A

EVERETT COMMUNITY COLLEGE

Accounting, A
Administrative Assistant and Secretarial Science, A
Anthropology, A
Atmospheric Sciences and Meteorology, A
Avionics Maintenance Technology/Technician, A
Biology/Biological Sciences, A
Botany/Plant Biology, A
Business Administration and Management, A
Business/Commerce, A
CAD/CADD Drafting and/or Design
    Technology/Technician, A
Chemistry, A
Computer Science, A
Corrections, A
Cosmetology/Cosmetologist, A
Criminal Justice/Law Enforcement Administration, A
Criminal Justice/Police Science, A
Data Processing and Data Processing
    Technology/Technician, A
Drama and Dramatics/Theatre Arts, A
Early Childhood Education and Teaching, A
Education, A
Engineering, A
Engineering Technology, A
English Language and Literature, A
Entrepreneurship/Entrepreneurial Studies, A
Environmental Studies, A
Fire Science/Firefighting, A
Foreign Languages and Literatures, A
Geology/Earth Science, A
Graphic Design, A
History, A
Human Nutrition, A
Humanities/Humanistic Studies, A
Information Technology, A
International/Global Studies, A
Journalism, A
Liberal Arts and Sciences Studies and Humani-
    ties, A
Manufacturing Technology/Technician, A
Mathematics, A
Medical/Clinical Assistant, A
Music, A
Oceanography, Chemical and Physical, A
Philosophy, A
Photography, A
Physical Education Teaching and Coaching, A
Physics, A
Political Science and Government, A
Psychology, A
Sociology, A
Web Page, Digital/Multimedia and Information Re-
    sources Design, A
Welding Technology/Welder, A

THE EVERGREEN STATE COLLEGE

American Indian/Native American Studies, B
Art/Art Studies, General, B
Biochemistry, Biophysics and Molecular Biology, B
Biological and Physical Sciences, B
Biology/Biological Sciences, B
Business/Commerce, B
Cinematography and Film/Video Production, B
Classics and Classical Languages, Litera-
    tures, and Linguistics, B
Computer and Information Sciences, B
Digital Communication and Media/Multimedia, B
Drama and Dramatics/Theatre Arts, B
Ecology, B
Education, BM

English Language and Literature, B
Environmental Sciences, B
Environmental Studies, BM
Ethnic, Cultural Minority, and Gender Studies, B
Film/Cinema Studies, B
Fine/Studio Arts, B
Foreign Languages and Literatures, B
Health Services/Allied Health/Health Sciences, B
Humanities/Humanistic Studies, B
Intercultural/Multicultural and Diversity Studies, B
Intermedia/Multimedia, B
International/Global Studies, B
Liberal Arts and Sciences Studies and Humani-
    ties, B
Mass Communication/Media Studies, B
Multi-/Interdisciplinary Studies, B
Natural Resources and Conservation, B
Natural Sciences, B
Philosophy, B
Physical Sciences, B
Political Science and Government, B
Psychology, B
Public Administration, BM
Public Administration and Social Service Profes-
    sions, B
Religion/Religious Studies, B
Social Sciences, B
Sociology, B
Visual and Performing Arts, B
Zoology/Animal Biology, B

GONZAGA UNIVERSITY

Accounting, BM
Art/Art Studies, General, B
Asian Studies/Civilization, B
Biochemistry, B
Biology/Biological Sciences, B
Broadcast Journalism, B
Business Administration and Management, B
Business Administration, Management and Opera-
    tions, M
Business/Managerial Economics, B
Chemistry, B
Civil Engineering, B
Classics and Classical Languages, Litera-
    tures, and Linguistics, B
Communication Studies/Speech Communication
    and Rhetoric, B
Communication and Media Studies, M
Computer Engineering, B
Computer Science, B
Counseling Psychology, M
Criminal Justice/Safety Studies, B
Criminology, B
Drama and Dramatics/Theatre Arts, B
Economics, B
Education, M
Educational Administration and Supervision, M
Educational Leadership and Administration, D
Electrical, Electronics and Communications Engi-
    neering, B
Elementary Education and Teaching, B
Engineering, B
English Language and Literature, B
English as a Second Language, M
Environmental Sciences, B
Environmental Studies, B
Exercise Physiology, B
Finance, B
French Language and Literature, B
History, B
International Business/Trade/Commerce, B
International Relations and Affairs, B
Italian Language and Literature, B
Journalism, B
Kinesiology and Exercise Science, B
Law and Legal Studies, D
Liberal Arts and Sciences Studies and Humani-
    ties, B
Marketing/Marketing Management, B
Mass Communication/Media Studies, B
Mathematics, B
Mechanical Engineering, B
Music, B
Music Performance, B
Music Teacher Education, B

Nurse Anesthetist, M
Nursing, MD
Organizational Management, M
Philosophy, BM
Physical Education Teaching and Coaching, B
Physics, B
Political Science and Government, B
Psychology, B
Public Relations/Image Management, B
Radio and Television, B
Religion/Religious Studies, B
Secondary Education and Teaching, B
Sociology, B
Spanish Language and Literature, B
Special Education and Teaching, BM
Sport and Fitness Administration/Management, BM

GRAYS HARBOR COLLEGE

Accounting Technology/Technician and Bookkeeping, A
Automobile/Automotive Mechanics Technology/Technician, A
Business Administration and Management, A
Carpentry/Carpenter, A
Child Care and Support Services Management, A
Criminal Justice/Police Science, A
Diesel Mechanics Technology/Technician, A
General Studies, A
Human Services, A
Industrial Technology/Technician, A
Information Science/Studies, A
Liberal Arts and Sciences Studies and Humanities, A
Natural Resources and Conservation, A
Office Management and Supervision, A
Welding Technology/Welder, A

GREEN RIVER COLLEGE

Accounting Technology/Technician and Bookkeeping, A
Air Traffic Controller, A
Airline/Commercial/Professional Pilot and Flight Crew, A
Autobody/Collision and Repair Technology/Technician, A
Automobile/Automotive Mechanics Technology/Technician, A
Aviation/Airway Management and Operations, A
Business/Commerce, A
Carpentry/Carpenter, A
Computer Systems Networking and Telecommunications, A
Computer and Information Systems Security, A
Criminal Justice/Police Science, A
Data Entry/Microcomputer Applications, A
Drafting and Design Technology/Technician, A
Early Childhood Education and Teaching, A
Forensic Science and Technology, A
Forestry Technology/Technician, A
Geography, A
Legal Administrative Assistant/Secretary, A
Liberal Arts and Sciences Studies and Humanities, A
Machine Tool Technology/Machinist, A
Marketing/Marketing Management, A
Medical Administrative Assistant/Secretary, A
Occupational Therapist Assistant, A
Office Management and Supervision, A
Parks, Recreation, Leisure and Fitness Studies, A
Physical Sciences, A
Physical Therapist Assistant, A
Teacher Assistant/Aide, A
Welding Technology/Welder, A

HERITAGE UNIVERSITY

Accounting, B
Art Teacher Education, B
Biology/Biological Sciences, B
Biomedical Sciences, B
Business Administration and Management, AB
Clinical Laboratory Science/Medical Technology/Technologist, B
Computer Science, AB
Counselor Education/School Counseling and Guidance Services, M
Criminal Justice/Safety Studies, B

Early Childhood Education and Teaching, B
Education, BM
Educational Administration and Supervision, M
Elementary Education and Teaching, B
English, M
English Language and Literature, B
English as a Second Language, M
English/Language Arts Teacher Education, B
Environmental Sciences, B
Fine Arts and Art Studies, AB
Liberal Arts and Sciences Studies and Humanities, AB
Mathematics, B
Mathematics Teacher Education, B
Multi-/Interdisciplinary Studies, AB
Multilingual and Multicultural Education, M
Natural Resources and Conservation, A
Psychology, B
Reading Teacher Education, M
Science Teacher Education/General Science Teacher Education, BM
Science, Technology and Society, B
Social Sciences, A
Social Work, B
Special Education and Teaching, BM
Teacher Education, Multiple Levels, B

HIGHLINE COLLEGE

Accounting, A
Administrative Assistant and Secretarial Science, A
Art/Art Studies, General, A
Behavioral Sciences, A
Biological and Physical Sciences, A
Business Administration and Management, A
Clinical/Medical Laboratory Science and Allied Professions, A
Computer Engineering Technology/Technician, A
Computer Programming/Programmer, A
Computer Systems Networking and Telecommunications, A
Computer Typography and Composition Equipment Operator, A
Criminal Justice/Law Enforcement Administration, A
Criminal Justice/Police Science, A
Data Entry/Microcomputer Applications, A
Dental Hygiene/Hygienist, A
Drafting and Design Technology/Technician, A
Education, A
Engineering, A
Engineering Technology, A
English Language and Literature, A
Hotel/Motel Administration/Management, A
Human Services, A
Humanities/Humanistic Studies, A
Industrial Technology/Technician, A
Interior Design, A
International Business/Trade/Commerce, A
Journalism, A
Kindergarten/PreSchool Education and Teaching, A
Legal Administrative Assistant/Secretary, A
Legal Assistant/Paralegal, A
Library Science, A
Mathematics, A
Medical/Clinical Assistant, A
Music, A
Natural Sciences, A
Psychology, A
Respiratory Care Therapy/Therapist, A
Romance Languages, Literatures, and Linguistics, A
Social Sciences, A
Tourism and Travel Services Management, A
Transportation and Materials Moving, A
Web Page, Digital/Multimedia and Information Resources Design, A

LAKE WASHINGTON INSTITUTE OF TECHNOLOGY

Accounting Technology/Technician and Bookkeeping, A
Applied Horticulture/Horticultural Operations, A
Architectural Drafting and Architectural CAD/CADD, A
Automobile/Automotive Mechanics Technology/Technician, A
CAD/CADD Drafting and/or Design Technology/Technician, A

Computer Graphics, A
Diesel Mechanics Technology/Technician, A
Early Childhood Education and Teaching, A
Hotel/Motel Administration/Management, A
Industrial Mechanics and Maintenance Technology, A
Machine Tool Technology/Machinist, A
Medical/Clinical Assistant, A
Mental and Social Health Services and Allied Professions, A
Sport and Fitness Administration/Management, A

LOWER COLUMBIA COLLEGE

Accounting, A
Accounting Technology/Technician and Bookkeeping, A
Administrative Assistant and Secretarial Science, A
Automobile/Automotive Mechanics Technology/Technician, A
Business Administration and Management, A
Criminal Justice/Law Enforcement Administration, A
Data Entry/Microcomputer Applications, A
Diesel Mechanics Technology/Technician, A
Early Childhood Education and Teaching, A
Fire Science/Firefighting, A
Industrial Mechanics and Maintenance Technology, A
Instrumentation Technology/Technician, A
Legal Administrative Assistant/Secretary, A
Liberal Arts and Sciences Studies and Humanities, A
Machine Tool Technology/Machinist, A
Medical Administrative Assistant/Secretary, A
Medical/Clinical Assistant, A
Substance Abuse/Addiction Counseling, A
Welding Technology/Welder, A

NORTH SEATTLE COLLEGE

Accounting Technology/Technician and Bookkeeping, A
Administrative Assistant and Secretarial Science, A
Allied Health and Medical Assisting Services, A
Architectural Drafting and Architectural CAD/CADD, A
Art/Art Studies, General, A
Biomedical Technology/Technician, A
Business/Corporate Communications, A
Civil Drafting and Civil Engineering CAD/CADD, A
Communications Systems Installation and Repair Technology, A
Computer Systems Networking and Telecommunications, A
Computer and Information Systems Security, A
Early Childhood Education and Teaching, A
Electrical, Electronic and Communications Engineering Technology/Technician, A
Heating, Air Conditioning, Ventilation and Refrigeration Maintenance Technology/Technician, A
Liberal Arts and Sciences Studies and Humanities, A
Mechanical Drafting and Mechanical Drafting CAD/CADD, A
Medical/Clinical Assistant, A
Music, A
Pharmacy Technician/Assistant, A
Real Estate, A
Telecommunications Technology/Technician, A
Watchmaking and Jewelrymaking, A

NORTHWEST COLLEGE OF ART & DESIGN

Design and Visual Communications, B

NORTHWEST INDIAN COLLEGE

American Indian/Native American Studies, A
Computer Installation and Repair Technology/Technician, A
Early Childhood Education and Teaching, A
Environmental Sciences, AB
Information Technology, A
Liberal Arts and Sciences Studies and Humanities, A
Multi-/Interdisciplinary Studies, A
Physical Sciences, A

Substance Abuse/Addiction Counseling, A

NORTHWEST SCHOOL OF WOODEN BOATBUILDING

Marine Maintenance/Fitter and Ship Repair Technology/Technician, A

NORTHWEST UNIVERSITY

Accounting, B
Accounting and Finance, B
American Indian/Native American Studies, B
Ancient Near Eastern and Biblical Languages, Literatures, and Linguistics, B
Army JROTC/ROTC, B
Bible/Biblical Studies, B
Biology Teacher Education, B
Biology/Biological Sciences, B
Business Administration and Management, B
Business Administration, Management and Operations, BM
Comparative Literature, B
Counseling Psychology, MD
Criminal Justice/Law Enforcement Administration, B
Cultural Studies, M
Divinity/Ministry (BD, MDiv.), B
Drama and Dramatics/Theatre Arts, B
Education, BM
Elementary Education and Teaching, B
English Language and Literature, B
English/Language Arts Teacher Education, B
Environmental Sciences, B
Film/Cinema Studies, B
General Studies, AB
Health Occupations Teacher Education, B
Health Professions and Related Clinical Sciences, A
Health and Physical Education, B
History, B
Intercultural/Multicultural and Diversity Studies, B
International Business/Trade/Commerce, M
International/Global Studies, B
Law and Legal Studies, B
Liberal Arts and Sciences Studies and Humanities, A
Linguistic, Comparative, and Related Language Studies and Services, A
Marketing/Marketing Management, B
Mathematics, B
Mathematics Teacher Education, B
Missions/Missionary Studies and Missiology, BM
Multi-/Interdisciplinary Studies, B
Music, B
Music Teacher Education, B
Music Theory and Composition, B
Organizational Communication, B
Organizational Management, M
Pastoral Studies/Counseling, BM
Philosophy, B
Philosophy and Religious Studies, B
Political Science and Government, B
Project Management, M
Psychology, BMD
Recording Arts Technology/Technician, B
Religion/Religious Studies, AB
Religious Education, B
Religious/Sacred Music, B
Secondary Education and Teaching, B
Social Studies Teacher Education, B
Speech Teacher Education, B
Teaching English as a Second or Foreign Language/ESL Language Instructor, B
Theology and Religious Vocations, BM
Urban and Regional Planning, M
Youth Ministry, B

OLYMPIC COLLEGE

Accounting Technology/Technician and Bookkeeping, A
Administrative Assistant and Secretarial Science, A
Business Administration and Management, A
Chemical Engineering, A
Computer Systems Networking and Telecommunications, A
Cosmetology/Cosmetologist, A
Culinary Arts/Chef Training, A
Drafting and Design Technology/Technician, A
Early Childhood Education and Teaching, A

Electrical, Electronic and Communications Engineering Technology/Technician, A
Electrical, Electronics and Communications Engineering, A
Engineering Technology, A
Industrial Technology/Technician, A
Information Technology, B
Liberal Arts and Sciences Studies and Humanities, A
Marine Maintenance/Fitter and Ship Repair Technology/Technician, A
Mechanical Engineering, A
Medical/Clinical Assistant, A
Mental and Social Health Services and Allied Professions, A
Photographic and Film/Video Technology/Technician and Assistant, A
Physical Sciences, A
Physical Therapist Assistant, A
Substance Abuse/Addiction Counseling, A
Welding Technology/Welder, A

PACIFIC LUTHERAN UNIVERSITY

Anthropology, B
Art History, Criticism and Conservation, B
Biology/Biological Sciences, B
Business Administration and Management, B
Business Administration, Management and Operations, M
Chemistry, B
Chinese Studies, B
Classics and Classical Languages, Literatures, and Linguistics, B
Communication Studies/Speech Communication and Rhetoric, B
Computer Engineering, B
Computer Science, B
Curriculum and Instruction, M
Drama and Dramatics/Theatre Arts, B
Economics, B
Education, BM
Educational Administration and Supervision, M
Educational Leadership and Administration, M
Engineering, B
English Language and Literature, B
Environmental Studies, B
Finance and Banking, M
Fine/Studio Arts, B
French Language and Literature, B
Geology/Earth Science, B
German Language and Literature, B
History, B
International/Global Studies, B
Kinesiology and Exercise Science, B
Marriage and Family Therapy/Counseling, M
Mathematics, B
Multi-/Interdisciplinary Studies, B
Music, B
Music Teacher Education, B
Norwegian Language and Literature, B
Nursing, MD
Nursing - Advanced Practice, D
Nursing Administration, M
Philosophy, B
Physics, B
Political Science and Government, B
Pre-Law Studies, B
Pre-Medicine/Pre-Medical Studies, B
Psychology, B
Religion/Religious Studies, B
Scandinavian Studies, B
Social Work, B
Sociology, B
Theology/Theological Studies, B
Women's Studies, B
Writing, M

PENINSULA COLLEGE

Accounting, A
Automobile/Automotive Mechanics Technology/Technician, A
Biological and Physical Sciences, A
Business Administration and Management, A
Child Care and Support Services Management, A
Child Development, A
Civil Engineering Technology/Technician, A

Commercial Fishing, A
Computer Programming, Vendor/Product Certification, A
Criminal Justice/Law Enforcement Administration, A
Data Entry/Microcomputer Applications, A
Diesel Mechanics Technology/Technician, A
Electrical, Electronic and Communications Engineering Technology/Technician, A
Engineering Technology, A
Fishing and Fisheries Sciences and Management, A
Management Science, B
Office Management and Supervision, A
Substance Abuse/Addiction Counseling, A
Web Page, Digital/Multimedia and Information Resources Design, A

PIERCE COLLEGE AT FORT STEILACOOM

Accounting Technology/Technician and Bookkeeping, A
Administrative Assistant and Secretarial Science, A
Building/Property Maintenance and Management, A
Business Administration and Management, A
Business/Commerce, A
Computer Graphics, A
Computer Programming/Programmer, A
Computer Systems Networking and Telecommunications, A
Computer and Information Sciences and Support Services, A
Criminal Justice/Law Enforcement Administration, A
Data Modeling/Warehousing and Database Administration, A
Dental Hygiene/Hygienist, A
Early Childhood Education and Teaching, A
Fashion Merchandising, A
General Office Occupations and Clerical Services, A
Legal Assistant/Paralegal, A
Mathematics Teacher Education, A
Medical Administrative Assistant/Secretary, A
Physical Sciences, A
Psychiatric/Mental Health Services Technician, A
Substance Abuse/Addiction Counseling, A
Teacher Assistant/Aide, A
Veterinary/Animal Health Technology/Technician and Veterinary Assistant, A

PIERCE COLLEGE AT PUYALLUP

Accounting, A
Administrative Assistant and Secretarial Science, A
Business Administration and Management, A
Computer Programming/Programmer, A
Computer Typography and Composition Equipment Operator, A
Criminal Justice/Law Enforcement Administration, A
Dental Hygiene/Hygienist, A
Electrical, Electronic and Communications Engineering Technology/Technician, A
Fire Science/Firefighting, A
Industrial Technology/Technician, A
Information Science/Studies, A
Kindergarten/PreSchool Education and Teaching, A
Liberal Arts and Sciences Studies and Humanities, A
Marketing/Marketing Management, A
Mental Health Counseling/Counselor, A
Substance Abuse/Addiction Counseling, A
Veterinary/Animal Health Technology/Technician and Veterinary Assistant, A

PIMA MEDICAL INSTITUTE (RENTON)

Health/Health Care Administration/Management, A
Occupational Therapist Assistant, A
Respiratory Therapy Technician/Assistant, A
Veterinary/Animal Health Technology/Technician and Veterinary Assistant, A

PIMA MEDICAL INSTITUTE (SEATTLE)

Dental Hygiene/Hygienist, A
Health/Health Care Administration/Management, A
Physical Therapist Assistant, A
Radiologic Technology/Science - Radiographer, A

Veterinary/Animal Health Technology/Technician and Veterinary Assistant, A

RENTON TECHNICAL COLLEGE

Accounting and Business/Management, A
Anesthesiologist Assistant, A
Appliance Installation and Repair Technology/Technician, A
Autobody/Collision and Repair Technology/Technician, A
Automobile/Automotive Mechanics Technology/Technician, A
Building/Property Maintenance and Management, A
Business/Office Automation/Technology/Data Entry, A
Civil Drafting and Civil Engineering CAD/CADD, A
Computer Science, AB
Computer Systems Networking and Telecommunications, A
Construction Management, A
Culinary Arts/Chef Training, A
Dental Assisting/Assistant, A
Drafting and Design Technology/Technician, A
Early Childhood Education and Teaching, A
Heating, Air Conditioning, Ventilation and Refrigeration Maintenance Technology/Technician, A
Legal Administrative Assistant/Secretary, A
Machine Tool Technology/Machinist, A
Massage Therapy/Therapeutic Massage, A
Medical Administrative Assistant/Secretary, A
Medical Insurance Coding Specialist/Coder, A
Medical/Clinical Assistant, A
Musical Instrument Fabrication and Repair, A
Office Management and Supervision, A
Ophthalmic Technician/Technologist, A
Pharmacy Technician/Assistant, A
Surgical Technology/Technologist, A
Survey Technology/Surveying, A
Welding Technology/Welder, A

SAINT MARTIN'S UNIVERSITY

Accounting, B
Anthropology, B
Biology/Biological Sciences, B
Business Administration and Management, B
Business Administration, Management and Operations, M
Chemistry, B
Civil Engineering, BM
Community Organization and Advocacy, B
Community Psychology, M
Computer Science, B
Counseling Psychology, M
Counselor Education/School Counseling and Guidance Services, M
Criminal Justice/Safety Studies, B
Drama and Dramatics/Theatre Arts, B
Education, BM
Educational Administration and Supervision, M
Elementary Education and Teaching, B
Engineering Management, M
English Language and Literature, B
English as a Second Language, M
History, B
Mathematics, B
Mechanical Engineering, BM
Multi-/Interdisciplinary Studies, B
Music, B
Political Science and Government, B
Psychology, B
Reading Teacher Education, M
Religion/Religious Studies, B
Social Work, B
Special Education and Teaching, BM

SEATTLE CENTRAL COLLEGE

Accounting, A
Administrative Assistant and Secretarial Science, A
Biological and Physical Sciences, A
Biology Technician/BioTechnology Laboratory Technician, A
Carpentry/Carpenter, A
Cinematography and Film/Video Production, A
Commercial and Advertising Art, A
Computer Typography and Composition Equipment Operator, A

Cosmetology/Cosmetologist, A
Culinary Arts/Chef Training, A
Drafting and Design Technology/Technician, A
Fashion/Apparel Design, A
Graphic and Printing Equipment Operator Production, A
Hospitality Administration/Management, A
Hotel/Motel Administration/Management, A
Human Services, A
Kindergarten/PreSchool Education and Teaching, A
Liberal Arts and Sciences Studies and Humanities, A
Marine Maintenance/Fitter and Ship Repair Technology/Technician, A
Ophthalmic Laboratory Technology/Technician, A
Photography, A
Respiratory Care Therapy/Therapist, A
Sign Language Interpretation and Translation, A
Substance Abuse/Addiction Counseling, A

SEATTLE PACIFIC UNIVERSITY

Accounting, B
Apparel and Textiles, B
Art/Art Studies, General, B
Biochemistry, B
Biology/Biological Sciences, B
Business Administration and Management, B
Business Administration, Management and Operations, M
Business/Commerce, B
Cell/Cellular and Molecular Biology, B
Chemistry, B
Clinical Psychology, D
Communication Studies/Speech Communication and Rhetoric, B
Computer Systems Analysis/Analyst, B
Counselor Education/School Counseling and Guidance Services, MDO
Design and Visual Communications, B
Development Economics and International Development, B
Drama and Dramatics/Theatre Arts, B
Ecology, B
Economics, B
Education, B
Educational Administration and Supervision, O
Educational Leadership and Administration, MDO
Educational Media/Instructional Technology, M
Electrical, Electronics and Communications Engineering, B
Engineering, B
English Language and Literature, B
English as a Second Language, M
English/Language Arts Teacher Education, B
European Studies/Civilization, B
Family and Consumer Sciences/Human Sciences, B
Foods, Nutrition, and Wellness Studies, B
General Studies, B
Gerontological Nursing, M
Health/Medical Preparatory Programs, B
History, B
Human Development and Family Studies, B
Human Resources Management and Services, M
Industrial and Organizational Psychology, MD
Interior Design, B
Kinesiology and Exercise Science, B
Latin American Studies, B
Liberal Arts and Sciences Studies and Humanities, B
Linguistics, B
Management, M
Management Information Systems and Services, BM
Marriage and Family Therapy/Counseling, MO
Mathematics, B
Mathematics Teacher Education, M
Mathematics and Statistics, B
Music, B
Music Therapy/Therapist, B
Nursing, MO
Nursing - Adult, M
Nursing - Advanced Practice, MO
Nursing Administration, M
Nursing Education, M
Nursing Informatics, M
Philosophy, B

Physical Sciences, B
Physics, B
Physiology, B
Political Science and Government, B
Psychology, B
Reading Teacher Education, M
Religious Education, B
Russian Language and Literature, B
Science Teacher Education/General Science Teacher Education, M
Secondary Education and Teaching, M
Sociology, B
Special Education and Teaching, B
Sport and Fitness Administration/Management, B
Sustainability Management, M
Theology and Religious Vocations, MO
Theology/Theological Studies, B
Writing, M

SEATTLE UNIVERSITY

Accounting, BM
Adult and Continuing Education and Teaching, MO
Anthropology, B
Art History, Criticism and Conservation, B
Arts Management, M
Asian Studies/Civilization, B
Biochemistry, B
Biology Teacher Education, B
Biology/Biological Sciences, B
Business Administration and Management, B
Business Administration, Management and Operations, MO
Business/Commerce, B
Business/Managerial Economics, B
Cell/Cellular and Molecular Biology, B
Chemistry, B
Chemistry Teacher Education, B
Civil Engineering, B
Commercial and Advertising Art, B
Communication Studies/Speech Communication and Rhetoric, B
Community Health Nursing, M
Computer Science, BM
Conservation Biology, B
Counselor Education/School Counseling and Guidance Services, MO
Criminal Justice/Safety Studies, B
Criminalistics and Criminal Science, B
Criminology, MO
Diagnostic Medical Sonography/Sonographer and Ultrasound Technician, B
Drama and Dramatics/Theatre Arts, B
E-Commerce/Electronic Commerce, B
Economics, B
Education, MDO
Educational Administration and Supervision, MO
Educational Leadership and Administration, D
Electrical, Electronics and Communications Engineering, B
Engineering, B
Engineering and Applied Sciences, M
English Language and Literature, B
English as a Second Language, MO
Environmental Sciences, B
Environmental Studies, B
Environmental/Environmental Health Engineering, B
Film/Cinema Studies, B
Finance, B
Finance and Banking, MO
Fine Arts and Art Studies, B
Fine/Studio Arts, B
Forensic Science and Technology, O
French Language and Literature, B
Gerontological Nursing, M
Health/Medical Preparatory Programs, B
History, B
Humanities/Humanistic Studies, B
International Business/Trade/Commerce, B
International/Global Studies, B
Journalism, B
Kinesiology and Exercise Science, B
Law and Legal Studies, D
Liberal Arts and Sciences Studies and Humanities, B
Marketing/Marketing Management, B
Mathematics, B

Mathematics Teacher Education, B
Mechanical Engineering, B
Music, B
Nurse Midwife/Nursing Midwifery, M
Nursing, MD
Nursing - Adult, M
Nursing - Advanced Practice, M
Organizational Management, MO
Pastoral Studies/Counseling, M
Philosophy, B
Photography, B
Physical Sciences, B
Physics, B
Physics Teacher Education, B
Political Science and Government, B
Pre-Nursing Studies, B
Psychiatric/Mental Health Nurse/Nursing, M
Psychology, BM
Public Administration, BM
Reading Teacher Education, MO
Religion/Religious Studies, B
School Psychology, MO
Social Work, B
Sociology, B
Software Engineering, M
Spanish Language and Literature, B
Special Education and Teaching, MO
Sport and Fitness Administration/Management, M
Theology and Religious Vocations, MO
Transpersonal and Humanistic Psychology, M
Violin, Viola, Guitar and Other Stringed Instruments, B
Western European Studies, B
Women's Studies, B

SHORELINE COMMUNITY COLLEGE

Accounting, A
Automobile/Automotive Mechanics
    Technology/Technician, A
Biology Technician/BioTechnology Laboratory Technician, A
Business Administration and Management, A
Chemical Engineering, A
Child Development, A
Cinematography and Film/Video Production, A
Civil Engineering Technology/Technician, A
Clinical/Medical Laboratory Technician, A
Commercial and Advertising Art, A
Computer Graphics, A
Computer and Information Sciences, A
Consumer Merchandising/Retailing Management, A
Cosmetology/Cosmetologist, A
Dental Hygiene/Hygienist, A
Dietetics/Dieticians, A
Drafting and Design Technology/Technician, A
Education, A
Engineering Technology, A
Environmental Engineering
    Technology/Environmental Technology, A
Graphic and Printing Equipment Operator Production, A
Health Information/Medical Records
    Administration/Administrator, A
Human Development and Family Studies, A
Industrial Technology/Technician, A
International Business/Trade/Commerce, A
Kindergarten/PreSchool Education and Teaching, A
Liberal Arts and Sciences Studies and Humanities, A
Machine Tool Technology/Machinist, A
Marine Biology and Biological Oceanography, A
Marine Maintenance/Fitter and Ship Repair
    Technology/Technician, A
Marketing/Marketing Management, A
Mechanical Engineering/Mechanical
    Technology/Technician, A
Medical Administrative Assistant/Secretary, A
Music, A
Oceanography, Chemical and Physical, A
Photography, A
Purchasing, Procurement/Acquisitions and Contracts Management, A
Recording Arts Technology/Technician, A

Teacher Assistant/Aide, A

SKAGIT VALLEY COLLEGE

Accounting, A
Administrative Assistant and Secretarial Science, A
Agriculture, A
Anthropology, A
Applied Horticulture/Horticultural Operations, A
Art History, Criticism and Conservation, A
Art/Art Studies, General, A
Automobile/Automotive Mechanics
    Technology/Technician, A
Biological and Physical Sciences, A
Biology/Biological Sciences, A
Business Administration and Management, A
Chemistry, A
Child Development, A
Commercial and Advertising Art, A
Comparative Literature, A
Computer Engineering Technology/Technician, A
Computer Science, A
Computer Technology/Computer Systems Technology, A
Computer and Information Sciences, A
Criminal Justice/Police Science, A
Culinary Arts/Chef Training, A
Diesel Mechanics Technology/Technician, A
Economics, A
Electrical, Electronic and Communications Engineering Technology/Technician, A
English Language and Literature, A
Environmental Engineering
    Technology/Environmental Technology, A
Family and Community Services, A
Fire Science/Firefighting, A
Food Technology and Processing, A
Foreign Languages and Literatures, A
Geography, A
Geology/Earth Science, A
Heavy Equipment Maintenance
    Technology/Technician, A
History, A
Hotel/Motel Administration/Management, A
Human Services, A
Humanities/Humanistic Studies, A
Journalism, A
Kindergarten/PreSchool Education and Teaching, A
Legal Assistant/Paralegal, A
Liberal Arts and Sciences Studies and Humanities, A
Marine Maintenance/Fitter and Ship Repair
    Technology/Technician, A
Mathematics, A
Medical Administrative Assistant/Secretary, A
Medical/Clinical Assistant, A
Music, A
Natural Sciences, A
Office Management and Supervision, A
Parks, Recreation and Leisure Facilities Management, A
Parks, Recreation, Leisure and Fitness Studies, A
Philosophy, A
Physical Education Teaching and Coaching, A
Political Science and Government, A
Psychology, A
Social Sciences, A
Sociology, A
Spanish Language and Literature, A
Telecommunications Technology/Technician, A
Welding Technology/Welder, A

SOUTH PUGET SOUND COMMUNITY COLLEGE

Accounting, A
Administrative Assistant and Secretarial Science, A
Automobile/Automotive Mechanics
    Technology/Technician, A
Business Administration and Management, A
Computer Programming/Programmer, A
Computer and Information Sciences, A
Culinary Arts/Chef Training, A
Data Processing and Data Processing
    Technology/Technician, A
Dental Assisting/Assistant, A
Drafting and Design Technology/Technician, A
Fire Science/Firefighting, A

Food Technology and Processing, A
Horticultural Science, A
Information Science/Studies, A
Kindergarten/PreSchool Education and Teaching, A
Legal Administrative Assistant/Secretary, A
Legal Assistant/Paralegal, A
Liberal Arts and Sciences Studies and Humanities, A
Medical Administrative Assistant/Secretary, A
Medical/Clinical Assistant, A
Welding Technology/Welder, A

SOUTH SEATTLE COLLEGE

Accounting, A
Administrative Assistant and Secretarial Science, A
Airframe Mechanics and Aircraft Maintenance
    Technology/Technician, A
Artificial Intelligence and Robotics, A
Automobile/Automotive Mechanics
    Technology/Technician, A
Avionics Maintenance Technology/Technician, A
Biological and Physical Sciences, A
Business Administration and Management, A
Computer Engineering Technology/Technician, A
Computer Programming/Programmer, A
Cosmetology/Cosmetologist, A
Culinary Arts/Chef Training, A
Drafting and Design Technology/Technician, A
Engineering, A
Engineering Technology, A
Food Science, A
Food Technology and Processing, A
Heavy Equipment Maintenance
    Technology/Technician, A
Horticultural Science, A
Hospitality Administration/Management, A
Landscape Architecture, A
Landscaping and Groundskeeping, A
Liberal Arts and Sciences Studies and Humanities, A
Machine Tool Technology/Machinist, A
Quality Control Technology/Technician, A
Special Products Marketing Operations, A
Trade and Industrial Teacher Education, A
Welding Technology/Welder, A

SPOKANE COMMUNITY COLLEGE

Accounting Technology/Technician and Bookkeeping, A
Administrative Assistant and Secretarial Science, A
Agricultural Business and Management, A
Agronomy and Crop Science, A
Applied Horticulture/Horticultural Operations, A
Architectural Engineering Technology/Technician, A
Artificial Intelligence and Robotics, A
Automobile/Automotive Mechanics
    Technology/Technician, A
Avionics Maintenance Technology/Technician, A
Biomedical Technology/Technician, A
Business Administration and Management, A
Carpentry/Carpenter, A
Civil Engineering Technology/Technician, A
Computer Programming/Programmer, A
Computer Typography and Composition Equipment
    Operator, A
Construction Engineering Technology/Technician, A
Corrections, A
Cosmetology/Cosmetologist, A
Criminal Justice/Police Science, A
Culinary Arts/Chef Training, A
Data Processing and Data Processing
    Technology/Technician, A
Dental Hygiene/Hygienist, A
Dietetics/Dieticians, A
Drafting and Design Technology/Technician, A
Drafting/Design Engineering
    Technologies/Technicians, A
Electrical, Electronic and Communications Engineering Technology/Technician, A
Fire Science/Firefighting, A
Food Technology and Processing, A
Forestry, A
Health Information/Medical Records
    Administration/Administrator, A
Heating, Air Conditioning, Ventilation and Refrigeration Maintenance Technology/Technician, A

Heavy Equipment Maintenance
  Technology/Technician, A
Hotel/Motel Administration/Management, A
Hydrology and Water Resources Science, A
Industrial Technology/Technician, A
Landscaping and Groundskeeping, A
Legal Administrative Assistant/Secretary, A
Legal Assistant/Paralegal, A
Liberal Arts and Sciences Studies and Humani-
  ties, A
Machine Tool Technology/Machinist, A
Marketing/Marketing Management, A
Mechanical Engineering/Mechanical
  Technology/Technician, A
Medical Administrative Assistant/Secretary, A
Natural Resources Management/Development and
  Policy, A
Ophthalmic Laboratory Technology/Technician, A
Ornamental Horticulture, A
Parks, Recreation and Leisure Facilities Manage-
  ment, A
Respiratory Care Therapy/Therapist, A
Surgical Technology/Technologist, A
Welding Technology/Welder, A
Wildlife and Wildlands Science and Management, A

SPOKANE FALLS COMMUNITY COLLEGE

Accounting Technology/Technician and Bookkeep-
  ing, A
Administrative Assistant and Secretarial Science, A
Art/Art Studies, General, A
Business Administration and Management, A
Business and Personal/Financial Services Marketing
  Operations, A
Child Care and Support Services Management, A
Commercial Photography, A
Commercial and Advertising Art, A
Consumer Merchandising/Retailing Management, A
Fashion Merchandising, A
General Office Occupations and Clerical Services, A
Gerontology, A
Heavy Equipment Maintenance
  Technology/Technician, A
Information Science/Studies, A
Interior Design, A
International Business/Trade/Commerce, A
Liberal Arts and Sciences Studies and Humani-
  ties, A
Library Assistant/Technician, A
Marketing/Marketing Management, A
Mass Communication/Media Studies, A
Music, A
Orthotist/Prosthetist, A
Physical Therapist Assistant, A
Real Estate, A
Sign Language Interpretation and Translation, A
Social Work, A
Sport and Fitness Administration/Management, A
Substance Abuse/Addiction Counseling, A
Vocational Rehabilitation Counseling/Counselor, A
Welding Technology/Welder, A

TACOMA COMMUNITY COLLEGE

Accounting Technology/Technician and Bookkeep-
  ing, A
Business Administration and Management, A
Business/Commerce, A
Computer Programming/Programmer, A
Computer Systems Networking and Telecommunica-
  tions, A
Computer and Information Sciences and Support
  Services, A
Criminal Justice/Law Enforcement Administration, A
Diagnostic Medical Sonography/Sonographer and
  Ultrasound Technician, A
Electrical, Electronic and Communications Engineer-
  ing Technology/Technician, A
Emergency Medical Technology/Technician (EMT
  Paramedic), A
Health Information/Medical Records
  Technology/Technician, A
Legal Assistant/Paralegal, A
Liberal Arts and Sciences Studies and Humani-
  ties, A
Medical Administrative Assistant/Secretary, A

Medical Radiologic Technology/Science - Radiation
  Therapist, A
Mental and Social Health Services and Allied Pro-
  fessions, A
Office Management and Supervision, A
Pharmacy Technician/Assistant, A
Physical Sciences, A
Respiratory Care Therapy/Therapist, A
Teacher Assistant/Aide, A

UNIVERSITY OF PHOENIX–WESTERN WASHINGTON CAMPUS

Accounting, B
Business Administration and Management, B
Business Administration, Management and Opera-
  tions, M
Business/Corporate Communications, B
Computer Software Engineering, B
Computer and Information Systems Security, B
Consumer Merchandising/Retailing Management, B
Criminal Justice/Law Enforcement Administration, B
Criminology, M
Digital Communication and Media/Multimedia, B
E-Commerce/Electronic Commerce, B
Finance, B
Health Services Administration, B
Health/Health Care Administration/Management, B
Hospitality Administration/Management, B
Human Services, B
Information Technology, B
International Business/Trade/Commerce, B
Management Information Systems and Services, B
Management Science, B
Marketing/Marketing Management, B
Operations Management and Supervision, B
Organizational Behavior Studies, B
Psychology, B
Public Administration, B
Security and Protective Services, B

UNIVERSITY OF PUGET SOUND

Art/Art Studies, General, B
Asian Studies/Civilization, B
Biochemistry, B
Biological and Physical Sciences, B
Biology/Biological Sciences, B
Business Administration and Management, B
Chemistry, B
Chinese Language and Literature, B
Classics and Classical Languages, Litera-
  tures, and Linguistics, B
Communication Studies/Speech Communication
  and Rhetoric, B
Computer Science, B
Counseling Psychology, M
Counselor Education/School Counseling and Guid-
  ance Services, M
Drama and Dramatics/Theatre Arts, B
East Asian Languages, Literatures, and Linguis-
  tics, B
Economics, B
Education, M
Elementary Education and Teaching, M
English Language and Literature, B
Foreign Languages and Literatures, B
French Language and Literature, B
Geology/Earth Science, B
German Language and Literature, B
History, B
International Economics, B
Japanese Language and Literature, B
Kinesiology and Exercise Science, B
Management Information Systems and Services, B
Mathematics, B
Molecular Biology, B
Music, B
Music Performance, B
Music Teacher Education, B
Natural Sciences, B
Occupational Therapy/Therapist, MD
Philosophy, B
Physical Therapy/Therapist, D
Physics, B
Political Science and Government, B
Psychology, B
Religion/Religious Studies, B

Science, Technology and Society, B
Secondary Education and Teaching, M
Sociology, B
Spanish Language and Literature, B

UNIVERSITY OF WASHINGTON

Accounting, BMD
Acting, B
Aerospace, Aeronautical and Astronautical Engi-
  neering, BMD
Allopathic Medicine, D
American Indian/Native American Studies, B
Ancient Near Eastern and Biblical Languages, Lit-
  eratures, and Linguistics, B
Ancient/Classical Greek Language and Literature, B
Animal Behavior and Ethology, D
Anthropology, BMD
Applied Mathematics, BMD
Applied Physics, MD
Architecture, BMDO
Area Studies, B
Art History, Criticism and Conservation, BMD
Art/Art Studies, General, B
Asian Languages, MD
Asian Studies/Civilization, BM
Astronomy, BMD
Atmospheric Chemistry and Climatology, B
Atmospheric Sciences and Meteorology, BMD
Audiology/Audiologist and Speech-Language
  Pathology/Pathologist, B
Bacteriology, D
BioTechnology, D
Biochemistry, BD
Bioengineering, MD
Bioethics/Medical Ethics, M
Bioinformatics, MD
Biological and Biomedical Sciences, MD
Biology/Biological Sciences, B
Biomedical/Medical Engineering, B
Biophysics, D
Biostatistics, MD
Botany/Plant Biology, B
Business Administration and Management, B
Business Administration, Management and Opera-
  tions, MD
Business Education, MD
Canadian Studies, B
Cell Biology and Anatomy, D
Cell/Cellular and Molecular Biology, B
Ceramic Arts and Ceramics, B
Chemical Engineering, BMD
Chemistry, BMD
Chinese Language and Literature, B
Chinese Studies, BMD
City/Urban, Community and Regional Planning, B
Civil Engineering, BMD
Classics and Classical Languages, Litera-
  tures, and Linguistics, BMD
Clinical Laboratory Science/Medical
  Technology/Technologist, B
Clinical Laboratory Sciences, M
Clinical Psychology, D
Clinical Research, M
Cognitive Sciences, D
Communication Disorders, MD
Communication Studies/Speech Communication
  and Rhetoric, B
Communication and Media Studies, MD
Community Health and Preventive Medicine, M
Comparative Literature, BMD
Computational Mathematics, B
Computational Sciences, M
Computer Engineering, B
Computer Science, BMD
Construction Engineering and Management, MD
Construction Management, BM
Curriculum and Instruction, MD
Dance, BM
Danish Language and Literature, B
Dental Hygiene/Hygienist, B
Dental and Oral Surgery, MDO
Dentistry, D
Design and Applied Arts, M
Design and Visual Communications, B
Developmental Psychology, D
Directing and Theatrical Production, B

Drama and Dramatics/Theatre Arts, B
East Asian Studies, MD
East European and Russian Studies, M
Ecology, MD
Ecology, Evolution, Systematics and Population Biology, B
Economics, BD
Education, BMD
Educational Administration and Supervision, MD
Educational Leadership and Administration, MD
Educational Measurement and Evaluation, M
Educational Media/Instructional Technology, MD
Educational Policy, MD
Educational Psychology, MD
Electrical Engineering, MD
Electrical, Electronics and Communications Engineering, B
Emergency Medical Technology/Technician (EMT Paramedic), B
Engineering, B
Engineering and Applied Sciences, MD
English, MD
English Education, MD
English Language and Literature, B
English as a Second Language, M
Entrepreneurship/Entrepreneurial Studies, B
Environmental Engineering Technology/Environmental Technology, MD
Environmental Health, B
Environmental Policy and Resource Management, MD
Environmental Sciences, B
Environmental Studies, B
Environmental and Occupational Health, MD
Epidemiology, MD
Ethnic, Cultural Minority, and Gender Studies, B
Ethnomusicology, M
European Studies/Civilization, B
Finance, B
Fine Arts and Art Studies, BM
Finnish and Related Languages, Literatures, and Linguistics, B
Fish, Game and Wildlife Management, MD
Forestry, MD
Foundations and Philosophy of Education, MD
French Language and Literature, BMD
General Studies, B
Genetics, MD
Genomic Sciences, D
Geography, BMD
Geological and Earth Sciences/Geosciences, B
Geology/Earth Science, BMD
Geophysics and Seismology, BMD
Geotechnical Engineering, MD
German Language and Literature, MD
Germanic Languages, Literatures, and Linguistics, B
Health Informatics, MD
Health Information/Medical Records Administration/Administrator, B
Health Services Administration, M
Health Services Research, MD
Higher Education/Higher Education Administration, MD
Hispanic and Latin American Languages, M
Historic Preservation and Conservation, O
History, BMD
History and Philosophy of Science and Technology, B
Horticultural Science, MD
Human Development, M
Human Resources Management/Personnel Administration, B
Humanities/Humanistic Studies, B
Hydrology and Water Resources Science, MD
Immunology, D
Industrial Design, BM
Industrial Engineering, B
Industrial/Management Engineering, MD
Information Science/Studies, MD
Information Technology, B
Intellectual Property Law, M
International Affairs, D
International Business/Trade/Commerce, M
International Public Health/International Health, MD
International Trade, O
Islamic Studies, B

Italian Language and Literature, BMD
Japanese Language and Literature, B
Japanese Studies, BMD
Jazz/Jazz Studies, B
Jewish/Judaic Studies, B
Journalism, B
Korean Language and Literature, B
Korean Studies, B
Landscape Architecture, BM
Latin American Studies, B
Latin Language and Literature, B
Law and Legal Studies, BMD
Legal and Justice Studies, D
Library Science, MD
Lighting Design, O
Linguistics, BMD
Logistics and Materials Management, BO
Management Information Systems and Services, B
Management of Technology, M
Marine Affairs, MO
Marine Geology, MD
Marketing/Marketing Management, B
Materials Engineering, BMD
Materials Sciences, MD
Maternal and Child Health, M
Mathematics, BMD
Mathematics Teacher Education, BMD
Mechanical Engineering, BMD
Medical Informatics, MD
Medicinal and Pharmaceutical Chemistry, D
Microbiology, BD
Middle/Near Eastern and Semitic Languages, Literatures, and Linguistics, B
Molecular Biology, D
Molecular Medicine, D
Multilingual and Multicultural Education, MD
Museology/Museum Studies, M
Music, BMD
Music History, Literature, and Theory, BMD
Music Performance, B
Music Teacher Education, BMD
Music Theory and Composition, B
Musicology and Ethnomusicology, B
NanoTechnology, D
Natural Resources Management/Development and Policy, MD
Natural Resources and Conservation, MD
Natural Sciences, B
Near and Middle Eastern Studies, MD
Neurobiology and Neurophysiology, D
Norwegian Language and Literature, B
Nursing, MDO
Nutritional Sciences, MD
Occupational Therapy/Therapist, M
Oceanography, Chemical and Physical, BMD
Operations Research, B
Orthodontics, MO
Orthotist/Prosthetist, B
Painting, BM
Parasitology, D
Pathobiology, D
Pathology/Experimental Pathology, D
Performance, MD
Pharmaceutical Sciences, MD
Pharmacology, D
Pharmacy, MD
Philosophy, BMD
Photography, BM
Physical Anthropology, B
Physical Education Teaching and Coaching, M
Physical Therapy/Therapist, D
Physician Assistant, B
Physics, BMD
Physiology, BD
Piano and Organ, B
Political Communication, B
Political Science and Government, BMD
Portuguese Language and Literature, M
Psychology, BD
Public Administration, M
Public Affairs, MD
Public Health, M
Public Health (MPH, DPH), B
Public Policy Analysis, D
Reading Teacher Education, D
Rehabilitation Sciences, D

Religion/Religious Studies, BMD
Romance Languages, Literatures, and Linguistics, B
Russian Language and Literature, BMD
Scandinavian Languages, Literatures, and Linguistics, MD
Scandinavian Studies, B
School Psychology, M
Science Teacher Education/General Science Teacher Education, MD
Sculpture, B
Slavic Languages, Literatures, and Linguistics, BMD
Social Psychology, D
Social Sciences, BM
Social Studies Teacher Education, MD
Social Work, BMD
Sociology, BMD
South Asian Languages, Literatures, and Linguistics, B
South Asian Studies, B
South and Southeast Asian Studies, M
Southeast Asian Studies, B
Spanish Language and Literature, BM
Special Education and Teaching, MD
Statistics, BMD
Structural Biology, D
Structural Engineering, MD
Sustainable Development, MD
Swedish Language and Literature, B
Taxation, M
Technical Communication, MD
Theater, MD
Theatre Literature, History and Criticism, B
Toxicology, MD
Transportation and Highway Engineering, MD
Transportation/Transportation Management, O
Urban Design, MDO
Urban and Regional Planning, MD
Veterinary Sciences, M
Violin, Viola, Guitar and Other Stringed Instruments, B
Visual and Performing Arts, B
Voice and Opera, B
Water Resources Engineering, MD
Women's Studies, BD
Writing, M

UNIVERSITY OF WASHINGTON, BOTHELL

Accounting, B
American/United States Studies/Civilization, B
Biochemistry, B
Biology/Biological Sciences, B
Business Administration and Management, B
Business Administration, Management and Operations, M
Chemistry, B
Computer Engineering, BM
Computer Programming, Specific Applications, B
Computer Science, B
Computer Systems Analysis/Analyst, B
Computer and Information Sciences, B
Computer and Information Sciences and Support Services, B
Cultural Studies, M
Education, BM
Educational Leadership and Administration, M
Electrical, Electronics and Communications Engineering, B
Environmental Sciences, B
Environmental Studies, B
Ethics, B
General Studies, B
Health Services/Allied Health/Health Sciences, B
Humanities/Humanistic Studies, B
Information Science/Studies, B
International/Global Studies, B
Mass Communication/Media Studies, B
Mathematics, B
Mechanical Engineering, B
Middle School Education, M
Multi-/Interdisciplinary Studies, B
Nursing, M
Public Policy Analysis, M
Science, Technology and Society, B
Secondary Education and Teaching, M
Software Engineering, M

Visual and Performing Arts, B
Web Page, Digital/Multimedia and Information Resources Design, B
Writing, M

UNIVERSITY OF WASHINGTON, TACOMA

Accounting, BM
American History (United States), B
American/United States Studies/Civilization, B
Asian History, B
Business Administration and Management, B
Business Administration, Management and Operations, M
Community Health Nursing, M
Computer Engineering, M
Computer and Information Sciences, B
Criminal Justice/Police Science, B
Education, M
Educational Administration and Supervision, M
Elementary Education and Teaching, M
Environmental Sciences, B
Environmental Studies, B
Ethnic, Cultural Minority, and Gender Studies, B
European History, B
Finance, B
Finance and Banking, M
General Studies, B
Health Services Administration, B
History, B
Humanities/Humanistic Studies, B
Information Technology, B
Interdisciplinary Studies, M
International/Global Studies, B
Law and Legal Studies, B
Management Science, B
Marketing/Marketing Management, B
Mass Communication/Media Studies, B
Mathematics Teacher Education, M
Nursing, M
Nursing Administration, M
Nursing Education, M
Psychology, B
Science Teacher Education/General Science Teacher Education, M
Social Sciences, B
Social Work, BM
Software Engineering, M
Special Education and Teaching, M
Urban Studies/Affairs, B

WALLA WALLA COMMUNITY COLLEGE

Accounting Technology/Technician and Bookkeeping, A
Administrative Assistant and Secretarial Science, A
Agricultural Business and Management, A
Agricultural Mechanization, A
Agricultural Production Operations, A
Agricultural and Domestic Animals Services, A
Autobody/Collision and Repair Technology/Technician, A
Automobile/Automotive Mechanics Technology/Technician, A
Biology/Biological Sciences, A
Business Administration and Management, A
Computer Programming, Vendor/Product Certification, A
Computer Systems Networking and Telecommunications, A
Computer Technology/Computer Systems Technology, A
Cosmetology/Cosmetologist, A
Culinary Arts/Chef Training, A
Diesel Mechanics Technology/Technician, A
Early Childhood Education and Teaching, A
Electrician, A
Elementary Education and Teaching, A
Engineering Technology, A
Fire Science/Firefighting, A
Heating, Air Conditioning, Ventilation and Refrigeration Maintenance Technology/Technician, A
Legal Administrative Assistant/Secretary, A
Liberal Arts and Sciences Studies and Humanities, A
Mathematics Teacher Education, A
Medical Administrative Assistant/Secretary, A

Natural Resources Conservation and Research, A
Natural Resources and Conservation, A
Turf and Turfgrass Management, A
Web/Multimedia Management and Webmaster, A
Welding Technology/Welder, A

WALLA WALLA UNIVERSITY

Accounting, B
Accounting and Business/Management, B
Aeronautics/Aviation/Aerospace Science and Technology, AB
Agricultural/Biological Engineering and Bioengineering, B
Ancient Near Eastern and Biblical Languages, Literatures, and Linguistics, B
Art Teacher Education, B
Art/Art Studies, General, B
Automobile/Automotive Mechanics Technology/Technician, AB
Biochemistry, B
Biological and Biomedical Sciences, M
Biology/Biological Sciences, B
Biomedical/Medical Engineering, B
Biophysics, B
Business Administration and Management, AB
Business Teacher Education, B
Business and Personal/Financial Services Marketing Operations, B
Business, Management, Marketing, and Related Support Services, B
Chemistry, B
Cinematography and Film/Video Production, B
Civil Engineering, B
Clinical Laboratory Science/Medical Technology/Technologist, B
Commercial and Advertising Art, B
Computer Engineering, B
Computer Programming/Programmer, AB
Computer Science, B
Computer and Information Systems Security, B
Counseling Psychology, M
Curriculum and Instruction, M
Economics, B
Education, M
Educational Leadership and Administration, M
Electrical, Electronics and Communications Engineering, B
Elementary Education and Teaching, B
Engineering, B
Engineering Technology, B
English Language and Literature, B
Environmental Sciences, B
Environmental Studies, B
Finance, B
Fine/Studio Arts, B
French Language and Literature, B
Graphic Communications, AB
Graphic Design, B
Health Professions and Related Clinical Sciences, B
Health and Physical Education, B
History, B
Humanities/Humanistic Studies, B
Industrial Design, B
International Business/Trade/Commerce, B
Journalism, B
Kinesiology and Exercise Science, B
Management Information Systems and Services, B
Marketing/Marketing Management, B
Mass Communication/Media Studies, B
Mathematics, B
Mechanical Engineering, B
Modern Languages, B
Music, B
Music Performance, B
Music Teacher Education, B
Philosophy, B
Photojournalism, B
Physical Education Teaching and Coaching, B
Physics, B
Piano and Organ, B
Pre-Dentistry Studies, B
Pre-Law Studies, B
Pre-Medicine/Pre-Medical Studies, B
Pre-Veterinary Studies, B
Psychology, B
Public Health Education and Promotion, B

Public Relations/Image Management, B
Radio and Television, B
Reading Teacher Education, M
Religion/Religious Studies, B
Social Work, BM
Sociology, B
Spanish Language and Literature, B
Special Education and Teaching, M
Sport and Fitness Administration/Management, B
Teacher Education, Multiple Levels, B
Theology/Theological Studies, B
Web Page, Digital/Multimedia and Information Resources Design, B

WASHINGTON STATE UNIVERSITY

Accounting, BM
Advertising, B
Agricultural Business Technology, B
Agricultural Business and Management, B
Agricultural Communication/Journalism, B
Agricultural Economics, BMDO
Agricultural Engineering, MD
Agricultural Mechanization, B
Agricultural Teacher Education, B
Agricultural and Food Products Processing, B
Agriculture, B
Agronomy and Crop Science, B
Agronomy and Soil Sciences, MDO
American/United States Studies/Civilization, MD
Animal Sciences, BMD
Anthropology, BMD
Apparel and Textiles, B
Applied Mathematics, BMD
Archeology, BMD
Architecture, BM
Asian Studies/Civilization, B
Astronomy, B
Athletic Training and Sports Medicine, B
Audiology/Audiologist and Speech-Language Pathology/Pathologist, B
Bilingual and Multilingual Education, B
Biochemistry, BMD
Bioengineering, MD
Bioethics/Medical Ethics, O
Biological and Biomedical Sciences, MD
Biological and Physical Sciences, B
Biology Teacher Education, B
Biology/Biological Sciences, B
Biomedical Sciences, B
Biomedical/Medical Engineering, B
Biophysics, MD
Broadcast Journalism, B
Business Administration and Management, B
Business Administration, Management and Operations, MD
Business Education, M
Business/Commerce, B
Chemical Engineering, BMD
Chemistry, BMD
Chemistry Teacher Education, B
Chinese Studies, B
Civil Engineering, BMD
Clinical Psychology, D
Clothing and Textiles, M
Communication Disorders, M
Communication and Media Studies, MD
Community Health and Preventive Medicine, MD
Computer Engineering, BM
Computer Science, BMD
Computer and Information Sciences, B
Construction Management, B
Corporate and Organizational Communication, M
Counseling Psychology, D
Criminal Justice/Law Enforcement Administration, B
Criminology, MD
Crop Production, B
Cultural Anthropology, D
Cultural Studies, D
Curriculum and Instruction, M
Digital Communication and Media/Multimedia, B
Early Childhood Education and Teaching, B
Economics, BD
Education, BMD
Educational Leadership and Administration, MD
Educational Psychology, MD
Electrical Engineering, MD

Electrical, Electronics and Communications Engineering, B
Elementary Education and Teaching, BM
Energy and Power Engineering, M
Engineering Management, MO
Engineering and Applied Sciences, MDO
English, MD
English Language and Literature, B
English as a Second Language, M
English/Language Arts Teacher Education, B
Entomology, MD
Entrepreneurship/Entrepreneurial Studies, B
Environmental Engineering Technology/Environmental Technology, MD
Environmental Sciences, BMD
Epidemiology, MD
Ethnic, Cultural Minority, and Gender Studies, B
Exercise and Sports Science, M
Experimental Psychology, D
Family and Consumer Sciences/Home Economics Teacher Education, B
Family and Consumer Sciences/Human Sciences, B
Finance, B
Fine Arts and Art Studies, M
Fine/Studio Arts, B
Food Science, B
Food Science and Technology, MD
Foods, Nutrition, and Wellness Studies, B
Foreign Language Teacher Education, BM
Foreign Languages and Literatures, B
French Language Teacher Education, B
French Language and Literature, B
Genetics, B
Geology/Earth Science, BMD
Health Services Administration, M
Health Teacher Education, B
History, BMD
History Teacher Education, B
Horticultural Science, BMD
Hospitality Administration/Management, B
Human Development, D
Human Development and Family Studies, B
Human Nutrition, B
Humanities/Humanistic Studies, B
Immunology, MD
Interdisciplinary Studies, D
Interior Design, BM
International Business/Trade/Commerce, B
Journalism, B
Kindergarten/PreSchool Education and Teaching, B
Kinesiology and Exercise Science, B
Landscape Architecture, BM
Liberal Arts and Sciences Studies and Humanities, B
Linguistics, B
Management Information Systems and Services, B
Management of Technology, MO
Manufacturing Engineering, B
Marketing/Marketing Management, B
Mass Communication/Media Studies, B
Materials Engineering, BMD
Materials Sciences, MD
Mathematics, BMD
Mathematics Teacher Education, BMD
Mechanical Engineering, BMD
Microbiology, B
Molecular Genetics, B
Multi-/Interdisciplinary Studies, B
Music, BM
Music Performance, B
Music Teacher Education, B
Music Theory and Composition, B
Natural Resources and Conservation, BMD
Neuroscience, MD
Nursing, MDO
Nursing - Advanced Practice, MD
Nutritional Sciences, BM
Operations Management and Supervision, B
Organizational Communication, B
Pharmacy, MD
Philosophy, B
Physical Education Teaching and Coaching, B
Physical Sciences, B
Physics, BMD
Physics Teacher Education, B
Plant Pathology/Phytopathology, MD

Plant Protection and Integrated Pest Management, B
Plant Sciences, B
Political Science and Government, BMDO
Pre-Medicine/Pre-Medical Studies, B
Psychiatric/Mental Health Nurse/Nursing, MD
Psychology, BMD
Public Affairs, MDO
Public Policy Analysis, B
Public Relations, Advertising, and Applied Communication, B
Public Relations/Image Management, B
Radio, Television, and Digital Communication, B
Reading Teacher Education, BM
Real Estate, B
Religion/Religious Studies, B
Science Teacher Education/General Science Teacher Education, B
Secondary Education and Teaching, BM
Social Sciences, B
Social Studies Teacher Education, B
Sociology, BMD
Soil Science and Agronomy, B
Spanish Language Teacher Education, B
Spanish Language and Literature, B
Special Education and Teaching, BMD
Sport and Fitness Administration/Management, BM
Teacher Education, Multiple Levels, B
Teaching English as a Second or Foreign Language/ESL Language Instructor, B
Veterinary Medicine, D
Veterinary Sciences, MD
Vocational and Technical Education, D
Wildlife and Wildlands Science and Management, B
Women's Studies, B
Zoology/Animal Biology, B

WASHINGTON STATE UNIVERSITY–GLOBAL CAMPUS

Accounting, B
Criminal Justice/Police Science, B
Hospitality Administration/Management, B
Human Development and Family Studies, B
Humanities/Humanistic Studies, B
Management Information Systems and Services, B
Operations Management and Supervision, B
Psychology, B
Social Sciences, B

WASHINGTON STATE UNIVERSITY–SPOKANE

Audiology/Audiologist and Speech-Language Pathology/Pathologist, B
Exercise Physiology, B
Pharmacy, B

WASHINGTON STATE UNIVERSITY–TRI-CITIES

Biological and Physical Sciences, B
Business Administration and Management, B
Civil Engineering, B
Computer Science, B
Digital Communication and Media/Multimedia, B
Electrical, Electronics and Communications Engineering, B
Elementary Education and Teaching, B
English Language and Literature, B
Environmental Sciences, B
History, B
Hospitality Administration/Management, B
Mathematics, B
Mechanical Engineering, B
Plant Sciences, B
Psychology, B
Social Sciences, B

WASHINGTON STATE UNIVERSITY–VANCOUVER

Accounting, B
Anthropology, B
Biology/Biological Sciences, B
Business Administration and Management, B
Computer Science, B
Criminal Justice/Police Science, B
Digital Communication and Media/Multimedia, B

Education, B
Electrical, Electronics and Communications Engineering, B
Elementary Education and Teaching, B
English Language and Literature, B
Environmental Sciences, B
Finance, B
Fine Arts and Art Studies, B
Geology/Earth Science, B
History, B
Hospitality Administration/Management, B
Human Development and Family Studies, B
Human Resources Development, B
Humanities/Humanistic Studies, B
Management Information Systems and Services, B
Marketing/Marketing Management, B
Mechanical Engineering, B
Operations Management and Supervision, B
Political Science and Government, B
Psychology, B
Public Policy Analysis, B
Social Sciences, B
Sociology, B

WENATCHEE VALLEY COLLEGE

Accounting, A
Accounting Technology/Technician and Bookkeeping, A
Administrative Assistant and Secretarial Science, A
Agricultural Production Operations, A
Athletic Training and Sports Medicine, A
Automobile/Automotive Mechanics Technology/Technician, A
Biology/Biological Sciences, A
Business Administration and Management, A
Chemistry, A
Clinical/Medical Laboratory Assistant, A
Clinical/Medical Laboratory Technician, A
Computer Systems Networking and Telecommunications, A
Criminal Justice/Police Science, A
Design and Applied Arts, A
Early Childhood Education and Teaching, A
Economics, A
Education, A
Electrical/Electronics Equipment Installation and Repair, A
Heating, Air Conditioning, Ventilation and Refrigeration Maintenance Technology/Technician, A
History, A
Industrial Electronics Technology/Technician, A
Kindergarten/PreSchool Education and Teaching, A
Legal Administrative Assistant/Secretary, A
Liberal Arts and Sciences Studies and Humanities, A
Mathematics, A
Medical Administrative Assistant/Secretary, A
Medical/Clinical Assistant, A
Music, A
Music Teacher Education, A
Office Management and Supervision, A
Physical Sciences, A
Radiologic Technology/Science - Radiographer, A
Sociology, A
Substance Abuse/Addiction Counseling, A

WESTERN WASHINGTON UNIVERSITY

Adult and Continuing Education and Teaching, M
American/United States Studies/Civilization, B
Anthropology, BM
Applied Mathematics, B
Archeology, B
Art History, Criticism and Conservation, B
Art Teacher Education, B
Art/Art Studies, General, B
Audiology/Audiologist and Speech-Language Pathology/Pathologist, B
Automotive Engineering Technology/Technician, B
Biochemistry, B
Biological and Biomedical Sciences, M
Biological and Physical Sciences, B
Biology Teacher Education, B
Biology/Biological Sciences, B
Business Administration and Management, B
Business Administration, Management and Operations, M

Business/Commerce, B
Canadian Studies, B
Cell/Cellular Biology and Histology, B
Cell/Cellular and Molecular Biology, B
Ceramic Arts and Ceramics, B
Chemistry, BM
Chemistry Teacher Education, B
Communication Disorders, M
Communication Studies/Speech Communication
   and Rhetoric, B
Community Health Services/Liaison/Counseling, B
Computer Science, M
Computer Teacher Education, B
Computer and Information Sciences, B
Counseling Psychology, M
Counselor Education/School Counseling and Guid-
   ance Services, M
Dance, B
Design and Applied Arts, B
Design and Visual Communications, B
Drama and Dance Teacher Education, B
Drama and Dramatics/Theatre Arts, B
Drawing, B
Early Childhood Education and Teaching, B
East Asian Studies, B
Economics, B
Education, M
Education/Teaching of the Gifted and Talented, M
Educational Administration and Supervision, M
Electrical, Electronics and Communications Engi-
   neering, B
Elementary Education and Teaching, BM
English, M
English Language and Literature, B
English/Language Arts Teacher Education, B
Environmental Education, M
Environmental Sciences, BM
Environmental Studies, B
Exercise and Sports Science, M
Experimental Psychology, M
Fiber, Textile and Weaving Arts, B
Finance, B
Foreign Languages and Literatures, B
Foreign Languages, Literatures, and Linguistics, B
French Language Teacher Education, B
French Language and Literature, B
General Studies, B
Geography, BM
Geological and Earth Sciences/Geosciences, B
Geology/Earth Science, BM
Geophysics and Seismology, B
German Language Teacher Education, B
German Language and Literature, B
Health and Physical Education, B
Health/Medical Preparatory Programs, B
Higher Education/Higher Education Administra-
   tion, M
History, BM
History Teacher Education, B
Human Resources Management/Personnel Adminis-
   tration, B
Human Services, B
Humanities/Humanistic Studies, B
Industrial Design, B
Industrial Technology/Technician, B
Intermedia/Multimedia, B
International Business/Trade/Commerce, B
Japanese Language and Literature, B
Journalism, B
Liberal Arts and Sciences Studies and Humani-
   ties, B
Linguistics, B
Management Information Systems and Services, B
Manufacturing Engineering, B
Marine Biology and Biological Oceanography, B
Marine Sciences, M
Marketing/Marketing Management, B
Mathematics, BM
Mathematics Teacher Education, B
Mathematics and Computer Science, B
Multi-/Interdisciplinary Studies, B
Music, BM
Music History, Literature, and Theory, B
Music Performance, B
Music Teacher Education, B
Music Theory and Composition, B

Operations Management and Supervision, B
Optics/Optical Sciences, B
Painting, B
Parks, Recreation, Leisure and Fitness Studies, B
Philosophy, B
Photography, B
Physical Education Teaching and Coaching, BM
Physics, B
Political Science and Government, BM
Polymer/Plastics Engineering, B
Printmaking, B
Psychology, BM
Rehabilitation Counseling, M
Science Teacher Education/General Science
   Teacher Education, BM
Sculpture, B
Secondary Education and Teaching, M
Social Science Teacher Education, B
Social Studies Teacher Education, B
Sociology, B
Spanish Language Teacher Education, B
Spanish Language and Literature, B
Special Education and Teaching, B
Speech Teacher Education, B
Teacher Education and Professional Develop-
   ment, Specific Levels and Methods, B
Teacher Education and Professional Develop-
   ment, Specific Subject Areas, B
Technology Teacher Education/Industrial Arts
   Teacher Education, B
Visual and Performing Arts, B

WHATCOM COMMUNITY COLLEGE

Accounting, A
Administrative Assistant and Secretarial Science, A
Business Administration and Management, A
Commercial and Advertising Art, A
Computer Engineering Technology/Technician, A
Computer Science, A
Criminal Justice/Police Science, A
Kindergarten/PreSchool Education and Teaching, A
Legal Assistant/Paralegal, A
Liberal Arts and Sciences Studies and Humani-
   ties, A
Medical Administrative Assistant/Secretary, A
Medical/Clinical Assistant, A
Physical Therapist Assistant, A

WHITMAN COLLEGE

Ancient/Classical Greek Language and Literature, B
Anthropology, B
Art History, Criticism and Conservation, B
Art/Art Studies, General, B
Asian Studies/Civilization, B
Astronomy, B
Astronomy and Astrophysics, B
Astrophysics, B
Biochemistry, B
Biochemistry, Biophysics and Molecular Biology, B
Biological and Biomedical Sciences, B
Biology/Biological Sciences, B
Biophysics, B
Chemistry, B
Classics and Classical Languages, Litera-
   tures, and Linguistics, B
Communication Studies/Speech Communication
   and Rhetoric, B
Drama and Dramatics/Theatre Arts, B
Economics, B
English Language and Literature, B
Environmental Studies, B
Ethnic, Cultural Minority, and Gender Studies, B
Film/Cinema Studies, B
Fine/Studio Arts, B
Forest Management/Forest Resources Manage-
   ment, B
French Language and Literature, B
Geochemistry, B
Geological and Earth Sciences/Geosciences, B
Geology/Earth Science, B
Geophysics and Seismology, B
German Language and Literature, B
History, B
International/Global Studies, B
Jazz/Jazz Studies, B
Latin Language and Literature, B

Marine Biology and Biological Oceanography, B
Mathematics, B
Mathematics and Computer Science, B
Molecular Biology, B
Music, B
Music History, Literature, and Theory, B
Music Performance, B
Music Theory and Composition, B
Oceanography, Chemical and Physical, B
Philosophy, B
Physics, B
Political Science and Government, B
Psychology, B
Religion/Religious Studies, B
Social Sciences, B
Sociology, B
Spanish Language and Literature, B

WHITWORTH UNIVERSITY

Accounting, B
American/United States Studies/Civilization, B
Applied Mathematics, B
Art Teacher Education, B
Art/Art Studies, General, B
Athletic Training and Sports Medicine, B
Bioinformatics, B
Biology/Biological Sciences, B
Business Administration and Management, B
Business Administration, Management and Opera-
   tions, M
Chemistry, B
Christian Studies, B
Communication Studies/Speech Communication
   and Rhetoric, B
Computer Science, B
Counselor Education/School Counseling and Guid-
   ance Services, M
Drama and Dramatics/Theatre Arts, B
Economics, B
Education, BM
Education/Teaching of the Gifted and Talented, M
Educational Administration and Supervision, M
Elementary Education and Teaching, BM
Engineering Physics, B
English Language and Literature, B
Fine/Studio Arts, B
French Language and Literature, B
Health Services/Allied Health/Health Sciences, B
History, B
International Business/Trade/Commerce, B
International Relations and Affairs, B
Journalism, B
Kinesiology and Exercise Science, B
Marketing/Marketing Management, B
Mass Communication/Media Studies, B
Mathematics, B
Music, B
Music Teacher Education, B
Peace Studies and Conflict Resolution, B
Philosophy, B
Physical Education Teaching and Coaching, B
Physics, B
Piano and Organ, B
Political Science and Government, B
Pre-Dentistry Studies, B
Pre-Law Studies, B
Pre-Medicine/Pre-Medical Studies, B
Pre-Veterinary Studies, B
Psychology, B
Religion/Religious Studies, B
Secondary Education and Teaching, BM
Sociology, B
Spanish Language and Literature, B
Special Education and Teaching, BM
Theology and Religious Vocations, M
Theology/Theological Studies, B
Voice and Opera, B

YAKIMA VALLEY COMMUNITY COL-
LEGE

Accounting, A
Administrative Assistant and Secretarial Science, A
Agricultural Business and Management, A
Agricultural Mechanization, A
Agricultural Production Operations, A
Agriculture, A

Agronomy and Crop Science, A
Animal Sciences, A
Automobile/Automotive Mechanics
  Technology/Technician, A
Broadcast Journalism, A
Business Administration and Management, A
Child Development, A
Civil Engineering Technology/Technician, A
Computer Engineering Technology/Technician, A
Computer Graphics, A
Computer Science, A
Criminal Justice/Law Enforcement Administration, A
Criminal Justice/Police Science, A
Dental Hygiene/Hygienist, A
Electrical, Electronic and Communications Engineering Technology/Technician, A
Family and Consumer Economics and Related Services, A
Hotel/Motel Administration/Management, A
Industrial Radiologic Technology/Technician, A
Industrial Technology/Technician, A
Instrumentation Technology/Technician, A
Kindergarten/PreSchool Education and Teaching, A
Legal Administrative Assistant/Secretary, A
Liberal Arts and Sciences Studies and Humanities, A
Management Information Systems and Services, A
Marketing/Marketing Management, A
Medical Administrative Assistant/Secretary, A
Occupational Therapy/Therapist, A
Special Products Marketing Operations, A
Substance Abuse/Addiction Counseling, A
Tourism and Travel Services Management, A
Veterinary/Animal Health Technology/Technician and
  Veterinary Assistant, A

West Virginia

ALDERSON BROADDUS UNIVERSITY

Accounting, B
Applied Mathematics, B
Athletic Training and Sports Medicine, B
Biology/Biological Sciences, B
Business Administration and Management, B
Business/Commerce, A
Chemistry, B
Computer Science, B
Criminology, B
Education, A
Elementary Education and Teaching, B
Environmental Sciences, B
Fine/Studio Arts, B
General Studies, A
Graphic Design, B
Journalism, B
Kinesiology and Exercise Science, B
Law and Legal Studies, B
Marketing/Marketing Management, B
Mass Communication/Media Studies, B
Medical Radiologic Technology/Science - Radiation
  Therapist, B
Music, B
Music Performance, B
Music Teacher Education, B
Natural Resources Management/Development and
  Policy, B
Physical Education Teaching and Coaching, B
Physician Assistant, M
Political Science and Government, B
Pre-Theology/Pre-Ministerial Studies, B
Psychology, B
Public Relations/Image Management, B
Secondary Education and Teaching, B
Sport and Fitness Administration/Management, B

AMERICAN PUBLIC UNIVERSITY SYSTEM

Accounting, BM
Accounting Technology/Technician and Bookkeeping, A
Aeronautics/Aviation/Aerospace Science and Technology, B
Aerospace, Aeronautical and Astronautical Engineering, M
American/United States Studies/Civilization, M

Business Administration and Management, B
Business Administration, Management and Operations, M
Business/Commerce, A
Child Care Provider/Assistant, A
Classics and Classical Languages, Literatures, and Linguistics, M
Communication Studies/Speech Communication and Rhetoric, A
Computer Software and Media Applications, A
Computer and Information Systems Security, M
Conflict Resolution and Mediation/Peace Studies, M
Counselor Education/School Counseling and Guidance Services, M
Criminal Justice/Law Enforcement Administration, AB
Criminal Justice/Safety Studies, AB
Criminology, M
Curriculum and Instruction, M
Data Modeling/Warehousing and Database Administration, A
Data Processing and Data Processing
  Technology/Technician, A
Distance Education Development, M
Educational Leadership and Administration, M
Electrical, Electronics and Communications Engineering, B
Elementary Education and Teaching, M
Emergency Management, M
English Language and Literature, B
English as a Second Language, M
Entrepreneurship/Entrepreneurial Studies, BM
Environmental Policy, M
Environmental Policy and Resource Management, M
Environmental Sciences, B
Exercise and Sports Science, M
Finance and Banking, M
Fire Science/Firefighting, A
Fire Services Administration, AB
Fish, Game and Wildlife Management, M
Forensic Science and Technology, BM
General Studies, AB
Health Professions and Related Clinical Sciences, A
Health Services Administration, M
History, ABM
Homeland Security, M
Hospitality Administration/Management, B
Human Development and Family Studies, B
Human Resources Management and Services, AM
Humanities/Humanistic Studies, M
Information Technology, B
International Affairs, M
International Business/Trade/Commerce, M
International Relations and Affairs, B
Kinesiology and Exercise Science, B
Law and Legal Studies, B
Legal Assistant/Paralegal, A
Legal and Justice Studies, M
Logistics and Materials Management, BM
Management, M
Management Information Systems and Services, M
Management Strategy and Policy, M
Marine Affairs, M
Marketing, M
Marketing/Marketing Management, B
Military and Defense Studies, M
National Security, M
Natural Sciences, B
Non-Profit/Public/Organizational Management, M
Organizational Management, M
Philosophy, B
Planetary Astronomy and Science, M
Political Science and Government, BM
Project Management, M
Psychology, BM
Public Administration, M
Public Health, M
Public Health (MPH, DPH), AB
Public History, M
Public Policy Analysis, M
Reading Teacher Education, M
Real Estate, M
Religion/Religious Studies, B
Retailing and Retail Operations, AB
School Psychology, M

Secondary Education and Teaching, M
Securities Services Administration/Management, BM
Social Studies Teacher Education, M
Sociology, B
Software Engineering, M
Special Education and Teaching, M
Sport and Fitness Administration/Management, B
Transportation/Transportation Management, M
Web/Multimedia Management and Webmaster, AB
Western European Studies, M

APPALACHIAN BIBLE COLLEGE

Bible/Biblical Studies, AB
Pastoral Studies/Counseling, M
Theology/Theological Studies, AB

BETHANY COLLEGE

Accounting, B
Accounting and Computer Science, B
Acting, B
Actuarial Science, B
Art Teacher Education, B
Biochemistry, B
Biochemistry, Biophysics and Molecular Biology, B
Biology Teacher Education, B
Biology/Biological Sciences, B
Business Administration and Management, B
Chemistry, B
Chemistry Teacher Education, B
Communication Studies/Speech Communication
  and Rhetoric, B
Computer Science, B
Digital Communication and Media/Multimedia, B
Econometrics and Quantitative Economics, B
Economics, B
Education, M
Elementary Education and Teaching, B
English Language and Literature, B
English/Language Arts Teacher Education, B
Environmental Sciences, B
Equestrian/Equine Studies, B
Finance, B
Fine/Studio Arts, B
History, B
International Economics, B
International Relations and Affairs, B
Junior High/Intermediate/Middle School Education
  and Teaching, B
Marketing/Marketing Management, B
Mathematics, B
Mathematics Teacher Education, B
Mathematics and Computer Science, B
Music, B
Parks, Recreation and Leisure Facilities Management, B
Physical Education Teaching and Coaching, B
Physical Sciences, B
Political Science and Government, B
Pre-Dentistry Studies, B
Pre-Law Studies, B
Pre-Medicine/Pre-Medical Studies, B
Pre-Theology/Pre-Ministerial Studies, B
Pre-Veterinary Studies, B
Psychology, B
Religion/Religious Studies, B
Social Work, B
Spanish Language and Literature, B
Sport and Fitness Administration/Management, B
Technical Theatre/Theatre Design and Technology, B
Theoretical and Mathematical Physics, B

BLUE RIDGE COMMUNITY AND TECHNICAL COLLEGE

Accounting, A
Allied Health and Medical Assisting Services, A
Baking and Pastry Arts/Baker/Pastry Chef, A
Business Administration and Management, A
Business Administration, Management and Operations, A
Clinical/Medical Laboratory Technician, A
Computer and Information Systems Security, A
Criminal Justice/Safety Studies, A
Culinary Arts/Chef Training, A
Data Entry/Microcomputer Applications, A

Electrical and Electronic Engineering Technologies/Technicians, A
Emergency Medical Technology/Technician (EMT Paramedic), A
General Studies, A
Information Technology, A
Legal Assistant/Paralegal, A
Liberal Arts and Sciences Studies and Humanities, A
Medical/Clinical Assistant, A
Multi-/Interdisciplinary Studies, A
Operations Management and Supervision, A
Physical Therapist Assistant, A
Restaurant, Culinary, and Catering Management/Manager, A
Science Technologies/Technicians, A
System, Networking, and LAN/WAN Management/Manager, A

BLUEFIELD STATE COLLEGE

Accounting, B
Architectural Engineering Technology/Technician, AB
Biological and Physical Sciences, B
Business Administration and Management, B
Civil Engineering Technology/Technician, AB
Computer and Information Sciences, B
Criminal Justice/Safety Studies, B
Electrical, Electronic and Communications Engineering Technology/Technician, AB
Elementary Education and Teaching, B
General Studies, B
Health/Health Care Administration/Management, B
Humanities/Humanistic Studies, B
Mechanical Engineering/Mechanical Technology/Technician, AB
Medical Radiologic Technology/Science - Radiation Therapist, A
Mining Technology/Technician, B
Radiologic Technology/Science - Radiographer, B
Social Sciences, B

BRIDGEVALLEY COMMUNITY AND TECHNICAL COLLEGE (MONTGOMERY)

Administrative Assistant and Secretarial Science, A
Automotive Engineering Technology/Technician, A
Civil Engineering Technology/Technician, A
Computer Science, A
Computer Technology/Computer Systems Technology, A
Dental Hygiene/Hygienist, A
Electrical, Electronic and Communications Engineering Technology/Technician, A
Liberal Arts and Sciences Studies and Humanities, A
Management Information Systems and Services, A
Mechanical Engineering/Mechanical Technology/Technician, A
Medical Administrative Assistant/Secretary, A
Printing Press Operator, A
Respiratory Care Therapy/Therapist, A
Surgical Technology/Technologist, A

BRIDGEVALLEY COMMUNITY AND TECHNICAL COLLEGE (SOUTH CHARLESTON)

Accounting, A
Architectural Drafting and Architectural CAD/CADD, A
Banking and Financial Support Services, A
Behavioral Sciences, A
Business Administration, Management and Operations, A
CAD/CADD Drafting and/or Design Technology/Technician, A
Chemical Technology/Technician, A
Computer Science, A
Criminal Justice/Safety Studies, A
Electrical and Electronic Engineering Technologies/Technicians, A
Electrical/Electronics Maintenance and Repair Technology, A
General Office Occupations and Clerical Services, A
General Studies, A
Gerontology, A

Health Services/Allied Health/Health Sciences, A
Heating, Air Conditioning, Ventilation and Refrigeration Maintenance Technology/Technician, A
Legal Assistant/Paralegal, A
Marketing, A
Meteorology, A
Nuclear Medical Technology/Technologist, A

CONCORD UNIVERSITY

Accounting, B
Art Teacher Education, B
Athletic Training and Sports Medicine, B
Biology/Biological Sciences, B
Business Administration and Management, B
Business Teacher Education, B
Ceramic Arts and Ceramics, B
Chemistry, B
Clinical Laboratory Science/Medical Technology/Technologist, B
Computer Science, B
Education, BM
Educational Administration and Supervision, M
Educational Leadership and Administration, M
Elementary Education and Teaching, B
English Language and Literature, B
Environmental Sciences, B
Fine/Studio Arts, B
Geography, BM
Graphic Design, B
Health Promotion, M
Health Teacher Education, B
History, B
Hospitality Administration/Management, B
Hotel/Motel Administration/Management, B
Information Science/Studies, B
Kindergarten/PreSchool Education and Teaching, B
Mass Communication/Media Studies, B
Mathematics, B
Music Teacher Education, B
Parks, Recreation and Leisure Facilities Management, B
Physical Education Teaching and Coaching, B
Political Science and Government, B
Pre-Medicine/Pre-Medical Studies, B
Pre-Veterinary Studies, B
Psychology, B
Reading Teacher Education, M
Secondary Education and Teaching, B
Social Studies Teacher Education, M
Social Work, B
Sociology, B
Special Education and Teaching, BM
Special Products Marketing Operations, B
Tourism and Travel Services Management, B

DAVIS & ELKINS COLLEGE

Accounting, B
Accounting Technology/Technician and Bookkeeping, A
Art Teacher Education, B
Art/Art Studies, General, B
Biological and Biomedical Sciences, B
Business Administration and Management, AB
Business Teacher Education, B
Chemistry, B
Communication Studies/Speech Communication and Rhetoric, B
Computer Science, B
Criminology, AB
Drama and Dramatics/Theatre Arts, B
Economics, B
Elementary Education and Teaching, B
English Language and Literature, B
Environmental Control Technologies/Technicians, B
Forestry, B
History, B
Hospitality Administration/Management, AB
Information Science/Studies, B
International Business/Trade/Commerce, B
International Marketing, B
Kinesiology and Exercise Science, B
Management Information Systems and Services, AB
Marketing/Marketing Management, B
Mathematics, B
Mathematics Teacher Education, B
Music, B

Music Teacher Education, B
Parks, Recreation, Leisure and Fitness Studies, B
Physical Education Teaching and Coaching, B
Political Science and Government, B
Pre-Dentistry Studies, B
Pre-Law Studies, B
Pre-Medicine/Pre-Medical Studies, B
Pre-Veterinary Studies, B
Psychology, B
Religion/Religious Studies, B
Religious Education, B
Social Sciences, A
Sociology, B
Spanish Language and Literature, B
Sport and Fitness Administration/Management, B
Technical Theatre/Theatre Design and Technology, B

EASTERN WEST VIRGINIA COMMUNITY AND TECHNICAL COLLEGE

Accounting, A
Administrative Assistant and Secretarial Science, A
Business Administration and Management, A
Business Operations Support and Secretarial Services, A
Child Care Provider/Assistant, A
General Studies, A
Information Science/Studies, A
Liberal Arts and Sciences Studies and Humanities, A
Medical Administrative Assistant/Secretary, A
Multi-/Interdisciplinary Studies, A
Science Technologies/Technicians, A

FAIRMONT STATE UNIVERSITY

Accounting, B
Art Teacher Education, B
Aviation/Airway Management and Operations, B
Avionics Maintenance Technology/Technician, B
Biology/Biological Sciences, B
Business Administration and Management, B
Business Administration, Management and Operations, M
Business Teacher Education, B
Chemistry, B
Civil Engineering Technology/Technician, AB
Commercial and Advertising Art, B
Computer Science, B
Criminal Justice/Police Science, B
Criminology, M
Distance Education Development, M
Drama and Dramatics/Theatre Arts, B
Economics, B
Education, BM
Educational Media/Instructional Technology, M
Electrical, Electronic and Communications Engineering Technology/Technician, AB
Elementary Education and Teaching, B
Engineering Technology, AB
English Language and Literature, B
Exercise and Sports Science, M
Family and Consumer Economics and Related Services, B
Family and Consumer Sciences/Home Economics Teacher Education, B
Family and Consumer Sciences/Human Sciences, B
Finance, B
French Language and Literature, B
Graphic and Printing Equipment Operator Production, B
Health Professions and Related Clinical Sciences, B
Health Promotion, M
History, B
Human Services, B
Industrial Technology/Technician, B
Mathematics, B
Mechanical Engineering/Mechanical Technology/Technician, AB
Music Teacher Education, B
Occupational Safety and Health Technology/Technician, B
Physical Education Teaching and Coaching, B
Political Science and Government, B
Psychology, B
Reading Teacher Education, M

Science Teacher Education/General Science
Teacher Education, B
Secondary Education and Teaching, B
Sociology, B
Special Education and Teaching, BM

GLENVILLE STATE COLLEGE

Behavioral Sciences, B
Biology Teacher Education, B
Biology/Biological Sciences, B
Business Administration and Management, B
Business Teacher Education, B
Business/Commerce, AB
Chemistry, B
Chemistry Teacher Education, B
Computer Science, B
Criminal Justice/Law Enforcement Administration, A
Education, B
Elementary Education and Teaching, B
English Language and Literature, B
English/Language Arts Teacher Education, B
Forestry Technology/Technician, A
History, B
Information Science/Studies, B
Kindergarten/PreSchool Education and Teaching, B
Liberal Arts and Sciences Studies and Humani-
ties, A
Mathematics Teacher Education, B
Multi-/Interdisciplinary Studies, B
Music Performance, B
Music Teacher Education, B
Natural Resources Management/Development and
Policy, B
Physical Education Teaching and Coaching, B
Science Teacher Education/General Science
Teacher Education, B
Secondary Education and Teaching, B
Social Studies Teacher Education, B
Special Education and Teaching, B
Sport and Fitness Administration/Management, B
Survey Technology/Surveying, A

HUNTINGTON JUNIOR COLLEGE

Accounting, A
Administrative Assistant and Secretarial Science, A
Allied Health and Medical Assisting Services, A
Business Administration and Management, A
Computer Science, A
Court Reporting/Court Reporter, A
Dental Assisting/Assistant, A
Medical Insurance Specialist/Medical Biller, A

MARSHALL UNIVERSITY

Accounting, BM
Adult and Continuing Education Administration, B
Adult and Continuing Education and Teaching, M
Allopathic Medicine, D
Art/Art Studies, General, B
Athletic Training and Sports Medicine, BM
Biological and Biomedical Sciences, MD
Biology/Biological Sciences, B
Business Administration and Management, B
Business Administration, Management and Opera-
tions, M
Business/Managerial Economics, B
Chemistry, BM
Classics and Classical Languages, Litera-
tures, and Linguistics, MO
Clinical Laboratory Science/Medical
Technology/Technologist, B
Clinical Psychology, O
Clinical/Medical Laboratory Technician, A
Communication Disorders, M
Communication and Media Studies, M
Computer Science, M
Computer and Information Sciences, B
Computer and Information Systems Security, B
Counselor Education/School Counseling and Guid-
ance Services, BMO
Criminal Justice/Safety Studies, B
Criminology, M
CytoTechnology/Cytotechnologist, B
Dietetics/Dieticians, B
Early Childhood Education and Teaching, M
Economics, B
Education, MDO

Educational Leadership and Administration, MDO
Elementary Education and Teaching, BM
Engineering, B
Engineering Management, M
Engineering and Applied Sciences, M
English, MO
English Language and Literature, B
Environmental Engineering
Technology/Environmental Technology, M
Environmental Sciences, BM
Exercise and Sports Science, M
Family and Consumer Sciences/Human Sciences, B
Finance, B
Fine Arts and Art Studies, M
Foreign Languages and Literatures, B
Forensic Science and Technology, M
General Studies, B
Geography, BMO
Geology/Earth Science, B
Health Education, M
Health Informatics, M
Health Services Administration, M
History, BMO
Human Resources Management and Services, M
Humanities/Humanistic Studies, BMO
Information Science/Studies, M
International Business/Trade/Commerce, B
International Relations and Affairs, B
Journalism, BM
Kindergarten/PreSchool Education and Teaching, B
Kinesiology and Exercise Science, B
Liberal Arts and Sciences Studies and Humani-
ties, B
Management Information Systems and Services, B
Management of Technology, M
Marketing/Marketing Management, B
Mathematics, BM
Mechanical Engineering, BM
Music, M
Nurse Anesthetist, D
Nursing, M
Nutritional Sciences, M
Occupational Safety and Health
Technology/Technician, B
Parks, Recreation and Leisure Facilities Manage-
ment, B
Pharmacy, D
Physical Education Teaching and Coaching, B
Physical Therapy/Therapist, D
Physics, BM
Political Science and Government, BM
Psychology, BMDO
Public Administration, M
Public Health, M
Public Health (MPH, DPH), B
Radiologic Technology/Science - Radiographer, B
Reading Teacher Education, MO
Respiratory Care Therapy/Therapist, B
School Psychology, O
Secondary Education and Teaching, BM
Social Work, B
Sociology, BM
Spanish Language and Literature, M
Special Education and Teaching, M
Speech-Language Pathology/Pathologist, B
Sport and Fitness Administration/Management, M
Systems Science and Theory, B
Transportation and Highway Engineering, M
Vocational and Technical Education, M

MOUNTAIN STATE COLLEGE

Accounting and Business/Management, A
Administrative Assistant and Secretarial Science, A
Computer and Information Sciences, A
Legal Assistant/Paralegal, A
Medical Transcription/Transcriptionist, A
Medical/Clinical Assistant, A
Substance Abuse/Addiction Counseling, A

MOUNTWEST COMMUNITY & TECHNI-
CAL COLLEGE

Accounting Technology/Technician and Bookkeep-
ing, A
Administrative Assistant and Secretarial Science, A
Business/Commerce, A
Computer Engineering Technology/Technician, A

Computer and Information Sciences and Support
Services, A
Criminal Justice/Police Science, A
Culinary Arts/Chef Training, A
Data Processing and Data Processing
Technology/Technician, A
Dental Laboratory Technology/Technician, A
Early Childhood Education and Teaching, A
Electrical, Electronic and Communications Engineer-
ing Technology/Technician, A
Emergency Medical Technology/Technician (EMT
Paramedic), A
Finance, A
General Studies, A
Health Information/Medical Records
Technology/Technician, A
Hospitality Administration/Management, A
Information Technology, A
Interior Design, A
Legal Assistant/Paralegal, A
Liberal Arts and Sciences Studies and Humani-
ties, A
Library Assistant/Technician, A
Library Science, A
Manufacturing Technology/Technician, A
Massage Therapy/Therapeutic Massage, A
Medical Radiologic Technology/Science - Radiation
Therapist, A
Medical Transcription/Transcriptionist, A
Medical/Clinical Assistant, A
Multi-/Interdisciplinary Studies, A
Physical Therapist Assistant, A
Respiratory Care Therapy/Therapist, A
Science Technologies/Technicians, A

NEW RIVER COMMUNITY AND TECHNI-
CAL COLLEGE

Administrative Assistant and Secretarial Science, A
Aquaculture, A
Biological and Physical Sciences, A
Business/Commerce, A
Communications Technology/Technician, A
Computer and Information Sciences, A
Corrections, A
Criminal Justice/Police Science, A
Legal Assistant/Paralegal, A
Liberal Arts and Sciences Studies and Humani-
ties, A
Medical/Clinical Assistant, A
Science Technologies/Technicians, A

OHIO VALLEY UNIVERSITY

Accounting, B
Bible/Biblical Studies, B
Business Administration and Management, B
Business/Commerce, B
Curriculum and Instruction, M
Education, M
Elementary Education and Teaching, B
Health/Medical Preparatory Programs, A
History, B
Human Resources Management/Personnel Adminis-
tration, B
Liberal Arts and Sciences Studies and Humani-
ties, AB
Marketing/Marketing Management, B
Mathematics Teacher Education, B
Physical Education Teaching and Coaching, B
Psychology, B
Religion/Religious Studies, B
Science Technologies/Technicians, A
Secondary Education and Teaching, B

PIERPONT COMMUNITY & TECHNICAL
COLLEGE

Aeronautical/Aerospace Engineering
Technology/Technician, A
American Sign Language (ASL), A
Architectural Engineering Technology/Technician, A
Business/Commerce, A
Child Development, A
Civil Engineering Technology/Technician, A
Communications Technology/Technician, A
Drafting/Design Engineering
Technologies/Technicians, A

Electrical and Electronic Engineering Technologies/Technicians, A
Electrical, Electronic and Communications Engineering Technology/Technician, A
Emergency Medical Technology/Technician (EMT Paramedic), A
Finance, A
Food Service, Waiter/Waitress, and Dining Room Management/Manager, A
General Studies, A
Graphic Communications, A
Mechanical Engineering/Mechanical Technology/Technician, A
Physician Assistant, A

POTOMAC STATE COLLEGE OF WEST VIRGINIA UNIVERSITY

Administrative Assistant and Secretarial Science, A
Agricultural Business and Management, A
Agricultural and Extension Education Services, A
Agriculture, A
Agriculture, Agriculture Operations and Related Sciences, A
Agronomy and Crop Science, A
Animal Sciences, A
Biology/Biological Sciences, A
Business Administration and Management, AB
Business/Office Automation/Technology/Data Entry, A
Chemistry, A
Civil Engineering, A
Computer and Information Sciences, A
Criminal Justice/Safety Studies, AB
Criminology, A
Data Entry/Microcomputer Applications, A
Early Childhood Education and Teaching, A
Economics, A
Electrical, Electronics and Communications Engineering, A
Elementary Education and Teaching, A
English Language and Literature, A
Forensic Science and Technology, A
Forest Resources Production and Management, A
Geological and Earth Sciences/Geosciences, A
Geology/Earth Science, A
History, A
Horse Husbandry/Equine Science and Management, A
Horticultural Science, A
Hospitality Administration/Management, A
Journalism, A
Liberal Arts and Sciences Studies and Humanities, A
Mathematics, A
Mechanical Engineering, A
Medical/Clinical Assistant, A
Modern Languages, A
Parks, Recreation and Leisure Facilities Management, A
Physical Education Teaching and Coaching, A
Physics, A
Political Science and Government, A
Pre-Dentistry Studies, A
Pre-Law Studies, A
Pre-Medicine/Pre-Medical Studies, A
Pre-Nursing Studies, A
Pre-Pharmacy Studies, A
Pre-Veterinary Studies, A
Psychology, A
Secondary Education and Teaching, A
Social Work, A
Sociology, A
Wildlife and Wildlands Science and Management, A
Wood Science and Wood Products/Pulp and Paper Technology, A

SALEM INTERNATIONAL UNIVERSITY

Biology/Biological Sciences, B
Business Administration and Management, AB
Business Administration, Management and Operations, M
Computer and Information Sciences, AB
Computer and Information Systems Security, M
Criminal Justice/Law Enforcement Administration, AB
Curriculum and Instruction, M

Education, BM
Educational Leadership and Administration, M
International Business/Trade/Commerce, BM
Physical Education Teaching and Coaching, B
Secondary Education and Teaching, B
Sport and Fitness Administration/Management, B

SHEPHERD UNIVERSITY

Accounting, B
Art/Art Studies, General, B
Biology/Biological Sciences, B
Business Administration and Management, B
Chemistry, B
Communication Studies/Speech Communication and Rhetoric, B
Computer Engineering, B
Computer and Information Sciences, B
Curriculum and Instruction, M
Economics, B
Elementary Education and Teaching, B
English Language and Literature, B
Environmental Studies, B
Family and Consumer Sciences/Human Sciences, B
General Studies, B
History, B
Mathematics, B
Music, B
Parks, Recreation, Leisure and Fitness Studies, B
Political Science and Government, B
Psychology, B
Secondary Education and Teaching, B
Social Work, B
Sociology, B
Spanish Language and Literature, B

SOUTHERN WEST VIRGINIA COMMUNITY AND TECHNICAL COLLEGE

Accounting, A
Administrative Assistant and Secretarial Science, A
Automobile/Automotive Mechanics Technology/Technician, A
Business Administration and Management, A
Clinical/Medical Laboratory Technician, A
Communications Technology/Technician, A
Computer Programming, Specific Applications, A
Criminal Justice/Law Enforcement Administration, A
Drafting and Design Technology/Technician, A
Engineering Technology, A
Finance, A
Industrial Radiologic Technology/Technician, A
Information Science/Studies, A
Liberal Arts and Sciences Studies and Humanities, A
Welding Technology/Welder, A

STRAYER UNIVERSITY–TEAYS VALLEY CAMPUS

Accounting, B
Business Administration and Management, B
Criminal Justice/Law Enforcement Administration, B
Economics, B
International Business/Trade/Commerce, B
Management Information Systems and Services, B

UNIVERSITY OF CHARLESTON

Accounting, BM
Art/Art Studies, General, B
Athletic Training and Sports Medicine, B
Biochemistry, B
Biology Teacher Education, B
Biology/Biological Sciences, B
Business Administration and Management, B
Business Administration, Management and Operations, BM
Chemistry, B
Diagnostic Medical Sonography/Sonographer and Ultrasound Technician, B
Education, B
Elementary Education and Teaching, B
English Language and Literature, B
Finance, B
Forensic Science and Technology, M
General Studies, B
Health Professions and Related Clinical Sciences, B
Health Teacher Education, B

History, B
Interior Design, B
Legal and Justice Studies, M
Management Strategy and Policy, M
Marketing/Marketing Management, B
Mass Communication/Media Studies, B
Medical Radiologic Technology/Science - Radiation Therapist, A
Occupational Therapist Assistant, A
Organizational Management, D
Pharmacy, D
Physician Assistant, M
Political Science and Government, B
Pre-Pharmacy Studies, B
Psychology, B
Radiologic Technology/Science - Radiographer, B
Science Teacher Education/General Science Teacher Education, B
Social Studies Teacher Education, B
Sport and Fitness Administration/Management, B

VALLEY COLLEGE

Business Administration and Management, A

WEST LIBERTY UNIVERSITY

Accounting, B
Art Teacher Education, B
Banking and Financial Support Services, B
Biology/Biological Sciences, B
Business Administration and Management, B
Business/Managerial Economics, B
Chemistry, B
Clinical Laboratory Science/Medical Technology/Technologist, B
Commercial and Advertising Art, B
Criminal Justice/Law Enforcement Administration, B
Dental Hygiene/Hygienist, AB
Education, BM
Elementary Education and Teaching, B
English Language and Literature, B
Health Professions and Related Clinical Sciences, B
Health Teacher Education, B
History, B
Information Science/Studies, B
Kindergarten/PreSchool Education and Teaching, B
Kinesiology and Exercise Science, B
Law Enforcement, M
Marketing/Marketing Management, B
Mass Communication/Media Studies, B
Mathematics, B
Music Teacher Education, B
Organizational Management, M
Physical Education Teaching and Coaching, B
Political Science and Government, B
Pre-Dentistry Studies, B
Pre-Law Studies, B
Pre-Medicine/Pre-Medical Studies, B
Psychology, B
Secondary Education and Teaching, B
Social Sciences, B
Social Work, B
Sociology, B

WEST VIRGINIA BUSINESS COLLEGE (NUTTER FORT)

Accounting and Business/Management, A
Administrative Assistant and Secretarial Science, A
Executive Assistant/Executive Secretary, A
Legal Assistant/Paralegal, A
Medical Administrative Assistant/Secretary, A
Medical/Clinical Assistant, A

WEST VIRGINIA BUSINESS COLLEGE (WHEELING)

Accounting, A
Administrative Assistant and Secretarial Science, A
Business Administration and Management, A
Legal Assistant/Paralegal, A

WEST VIRGINIA JUNIOR COLLEGE–BRIDGEPORT

Dental Assisting/Assistant, A
Information Technology, A
Medical Office Management/Administration, A
Medical/Clinical Assistant, A

Pharmacy Technician/Assistant, A

WEST VIRGINIA JUNIOR COLLEGE–CHARLESTON

Computer Technology/Computer Systems Technology, A
Legal Administrative Assistant/Secretary, A
Medical Office Assistant/Specialist, A
Medical/Clinical Assistant, A
Web/Multimedia Management and Webmaster, A

WEST VIRGINIA JUNIOR COLLEGE–MORGANTOWN

Administrative Assistant and Secretarial Science, A
Business Administration and Management, A
Computer and Information Sciences and Support Services, A
Legal Administrative Assistant/Secretary, A
Legal Assistant/Paralegal, A
Medical Insurance Coding Specialist/Coder, A
Medical/Clinical Assistant, A

WEST VIRGINIA NORTHERN COMMUNITY COLLEGE

Administrative Assistant and Secretarial Science, A
Business/Commerce, A
Computer Programming/Programmer, A
Criminal Justice/Police Science, A
Culinary Arts/Chef Training, A
Executive Assistant/Executive Secretary, A
General Studies, A
Health Information/Medical Records Technology/Technician, A
Heating, Air Conditioning, Ventilation and Refrigeration Maintenance Technology/Technician, A
Hospitality Administration/Management, A
Information Technology, A
Legal Assistant/Paralegal, A
Liberal Arts and Sciences Studies and Humanities, A
Medical Radiologic Technology/Science - Radiation Therapist, A
Medical/Clinical Assistant, A
Multi-/Interdisciplinary Studies, A
Respiratory Care Therapy/Therapist, A
Science Technologies/Technicians, A
Social Work, A
Surgical Technology/Technologist, A

WEST VIRGINIA STATE UNIVERSITY

Art/Art Studies, General, B
BioTechnology, M
Biology/Biological Sciences, B
Business Administration and Management, B
Chemistry, B
Communication Studies/Speech Communication and Rhetoric, B
Computer Science, B
Criminal Justice/Safety Studies, B
Economics, B
Elementary Education and Teaching, B
English Language and Literature, B
General Studies, B
Health Professions and Related Clinical Sciences, B
Health and Physical Education, B
History, B
International/Global Studies, B
Law Enforcement, M
Mathematics, B
Media Studies, M
Parks, Recreation and Leisure Facilities Management, B
Political Science and Government, B
Psychology, B
Secondary Education and Teaching, B
Social Work, B
Sociology, B

WEST VIRGINIA UNIVERSITY

Accounting, BM
Aerospace, Aeronautical and Astronautical Engineering, BMD
African Studies, MD
African-American Studies, MD
Agricultural Economics, BM

Agricultural Education, MD
Agricultural Sciences, MD
Agricultural Teacher Education, B
Agronomy and Soil Sciences, MD
Allopathic Medicine, D
American/United States Studies/Civilization, MD
Analytical Chemistry, MD
Animal Sciences, BMD
Applied Mathematics, MD
Applied Physics, MD
Applied Social Research, M
Art Education, M
Art History, Criticism and Conservation, BM
Art/Art Studies, General, B
Athletic Training and Sports Medicine, M
Audiology/Audiologist and Speech-Language Pathology/Pathologist, B
Biochemistry, BMD
Biological and Biomedical Sciences, MD
Biology/Biological Sciences, B
Biomedical/Medical Engineering, B
Business Administration and Management, B
Business Administration, Management and Operations, M
Business/Commerce, B
Business/Managerial Economics, B
Cancer Biology/Oncology, MD
Cell Biology and Anatomy, MD
Ceramic Arts and Ceramics, M
Chemical Engineering, BMD
Chemical Physics, MD
Chemistry, BMD
Child Development, B
Child and Family Studies, M
Civil Engineering, BMD
Clinical Laboratory Science/Medical Technology/Technologist, B
Clinical Psychology, MD
Communication Disorders, MD
Communication Theory, M
Communication and Media Studies, MD
Communication, Journalism and Related Programs, B
Community Health and Preventive Medicine, M
Composition, MD
Computer Engineering, BD
Computer Science, BMD
Computer and Information Sciences, B
Condensed Matter Physics, MD
Corporate and Organizational Communication, MO
Counseling Psychology, D
Counselor Education/School Counseling and Guidance Services, M
Curriculum and Instruction, MD
Dental Hygiene/Hygienist, B
Dentistry, D
Design and Visual Communications, B
Developmental Biology and Embryology, MD
Developmental Psychology, D
Drama and Dramatics/Theatre Arts, B
Early Childhood Education and Teaching, M
East Asian Studies, MD
Economic Development, D
Economics, BMD
Education, MD
Education/Teaching of Individuals with Multiple Disabilities, M
Education/Teaching of the Gifted and Talented, M
Educational Administration and Supervision, MD
Educational Leadership and Administration, MD
Educational Media/Instructional Technology, MD
Educational Psychology, M
Electrical Engineering, MD
Electrical, Electronics and Communications Engineering, B
Elementary Education and Teaching, BM
Engineering and Applied Sciences, MDO
English, MDO
English Language and Literature, B
English as a Second Language, M
Entomology, M
Environmental Biology, MD
Environmental Education, MD
Environmental Engineering Technology/Environmental Technology, MD

Environmental Policy and Resource Management, MD
Environmental and Occupational Health, D
Evolutionary Biology, MD
Exercise Physiology, B
Exercise and Sports Science, MD
Finance, B
Fine Arts and Art Studies, M
Fish, Game and Wildlife Management, M
Food Science and Technology, MD
Foreign Languages and Literatures, B
Forensic Science and Technology, BMD
Forest Management/Forest Resources Management, B
Forestry, MD
French Language and Literature, M
Game Design and Development, O
General Studies, B
Genetics, MD
Genomic Sciences, MD
Geographic Information Systems, MD
Geography, BMD
Geology/Earth Science, BMD
Geophysics and Seismology, MD
Graphic Design, M
Health Education, D
Health Promotion, MD
Health and Physical Education, B
Higher Education/Higher Education Administration, M
History, BMD
History of Science and Technology, MD
Horticultural Science, M
Hospitality Administration/Management, B
Human Development, D
Human Genetics, MD
Human Services, M
Hydrogeology, MD
Immunology, MD
Industrial Engineering, B
Industrial Hygiene, M
Industrial and Labor Relations, M
Industrial/Management Engineering, MD
Inorganic Chemistry, MD
International Affairs, M
International Economics, D
Journalism, BMO
Land Use Planning and Management/Development, B
Landscape Architecture, B
Latin American Studies, M
Law and Legal Studies, D
Legal and Justice Studies, M
Liberal Arts and Sciences Studies and Humanities, B
Liberal Studies, M
Linguistics, M
Management Information Systems and Services, B
Marketing, MO
Marketing/Marketing Management, B
Mathematics, BMD
Mathematics Teacher Education, M
Mechanical Engineering, BMD
Medicinal and Pharmaceutical Chemistry, MD
Microbiology, MD
Mineral/Mining Engineering, MD
Mining and Mineral Engineering, B
Molecular Biology, MD
Multi-/Interdisciplinary Studies, B
Music, BMD
Music History, Literature, and Theory, M
Music Teacher Education, MD
Music Theory and Composition, M
Natural Resources Management/Development and Policy, D
Neurobiology and Neurophysiology, D
Neuroscience, D
Nursing, MDO
Nutritional Sciences, M
Occupational Therapy/Therapist, M
Oral and Dental Sciences, M
Organic Chemistry, MD
Orthodontics, M
Painting, M
Paleontology, MD

Parks, Recreation and Leisure Facilities Management, B
Performance, MD
Petroleum Engineering, BMD
Pharmaceutical Administration, MD
Pharmaceutical Sciences, MD
Pharmacology, MD
Pharmacy, MD
Philosophy, B
Physical Chemistry, MD
Physical Education Teaching and Coaching, BMD
Physical Therapy/Therapist, D
Physics, BMD
Physiology, MD
Plant Pathology/Phytopathology, M
Plant Sciences, BD
Plasma and High-Temperature Physics, MD
Political Science and Government, BMD
Printmaking, M
Psychology, BMD
Public Administration, M
Public Health, MD
Public Health (MPH, DPH), B
Public Policy Analysis, MD
Reading Teacher Education, M
Recreation and Park Management, M
Rehabilitation Counseling, M
Reproductive Biology, MD
Resource Management, D
Safety Engineering, M
Sculpture, M
Secondary Education and Teaching, M
Social Work, BM
Sociology, BM
Software Engineering, M
Spanish Language and Literature, M
Special Education and Teaching, MD
Sport Psychology, D
Sport and Fitness Administration/Management, MD
Statistics, M
Sustainable Development, D
Teratology, MD
Theater, M
Theatre Literature, History and Criticism, B
Theoretical Chemistry, MD
Theoretical Physics, MD
Toxicology, MD
Urban Planning, M
Urban and Regional Planning, MD
Wildlife and Wildlands Science and Management, B
Wood Science and Wood Products/Pulp and Paper Technology, B
Writing, M

WEST VIRGINIA UNIVERSITY INSTITUTE OF TECHNOLOGY

Accounting, B
Aerospace, Aeronautical and Astronautical Engineering, B
Biology/Biological Sciences, B
Business Administration and Management, B
Chemical Engineering, B
Chemistry, B
Civil Engineering, B
Community Organization and Advocacy, B
Computer Engineering, B
Computer Science, B
Computer Systems Analysis/Analyst, B
Computer and Information Sciences, B
Criminal Justice/Law Enforcement Administration, B
Electrical and Electronic Engineering Technologies/Technicians, B
Electrical, Electronics and Communications Engineering, B
Engineering Technology, B
Forensic Science and Technology, B
General Studies, B
Health/Health Care Administration/Management, B
History, B
Industrial Technology/Technician, B
Liberal Arts and Sciences Studies and Humanities, B
Mathematics, B
Mechanical Engineering, B
Multi-/Interdisciplinary Studies, B
Physical Education Teaching and Coaching, B

Political Science and Government, B
Psychology, B
Technical Teacher Education, B

WEST VIRGINIA UNIVERSITY AT PARKERSBURG

Accounting, A
Administrative Assistant and Secretarial Science, A
Automobile/Automotive Mechanics Technology/Technician, A
Business Administration and Management, AB
Chemical Engineering, A
Criminal Justice/Law Enforcement Administration, A
Data Processing and Data Processing Technology/Technician, A
Drafting and Design Technology/Technician, A
Education, A
Electrical, Electronic and Communications Engineering Technology/Technician, A
Electromechanical Technology/Electromechanical Engineering Technology, A
Elementary Education and Teaching, B
Environmental Engineering Technology/Environmental Technology, A
Finance, A
Liberal Arts and Sciences Studies and Humanities, A
Machine Tool Technology/Machinist, A
Marketing/Marketing Management, A
Mechanical Engineering/Mechanical Technology/Technician, A
Social Work, A
Welding Technology/Welder, A

WEST VIRGINIA WESLEYAN COLLEGE

Accounting, B
Art Teacher Education, B
Art Therapy/Therapist, B
Art/Art Studies, General, B
Athletic Training and Sports Medicine, BM
Biology/Biological Sciences, B
Business Administration and Management, B
Business Administration, Management and Operations, M
Business/Managerial Economics, B
Ceramic Arts and Ceramics, B
Chemistry, B
Communication Studies/Speech Communication and Rhetoric, B
Computer Science, B
Computer and Information Sciences, B
Criminal Justice/Law Enforcement Administration, B
Drama and Dramatics/Theatre Arts, B
Drawing, B
Economics, B
Education, BM
Education/Teaching of Individuals with Specific Learning Disabilities, B
Elementary Education and Teaching, B
English Language and Literature, B
English/Language Arts Teacher Education, B
Environmental Sciences, B
Fine/Studio Arts, B
Geophysics and Seismology, B
Health Teacher Education, B
Health and Physical Education, B
History, B
Information Science/Studies, B
International Relations and Affairs, B
Junior High/Intermediate/Middle School Education and Teaching, B
Kindergarten/PreSchool Education and Teaching, B
Kinesiology and Exercise Science, B
Marketing/Marketing Management, B
Mathematics, B
Mathematics Teacher Education, B
Music, B
Music Teacher Education, B
Nurse Midwife/Nursing Midwifery, M
Nursing, MO
Nursing - Advanced Practice, MO
Nursing Administration, MO
Nursing Education, MO
Painting, B
Philosophy, B
Philosophy and Religious Studies, B

Physical Education Teaching and Coaching, B
Physics, B
Political Science and Government, B
Pre-Dentistry Studies, B
Pre-Law Studies, B
Pre-Medicine/Pre-Medical Studies, B
Pre-Pharmacy Studies, B
Pre-Veterinary Studies, B
Psychiatric/Mental Health Nurse/Nursing, M
Psychology, B
Public Relations/Image Management, B
Religion/Religious Studies, B
Secondary Education and Teaching, B
Sociology, B
Special Education and Teaching, B
Sport and Fitness Administration/Management, B
Teacher Education, Multiple Levels, B
Writing, M

WHEELING JESUIT UNIVERSITY

Accounting, BM
Athletic Training and Sports Medicine, B
Biology/Biological Sciences, B
Business Administration and Management, B
Business Administration, Management and Operations, M
Chemistry, B
Computer and Information Sciences, B
Criminal Justice/Safety Studies, B
Education, B
Educational Leadership and Administration, M
Engineering Science, B
English Language and Literature, B
Environmental Sciences, B
French Language and Literature, B
General Studies, B
Health and Medical Administrative Services, B
History, B
Human Resources Management and Services, B
International Relations and Affairs, B
Liberal Arts and Sciences Studies and Humanities, B
Mathematics, B
Multi-/Interdisciplinary Studies, B
Nuclear Medical Technology/Technologist, B
Nursing, M
Organizational Communication, B
Organizational Management, M
Philosophy, B
Physical Therapy/Therapist, D
Physics, B
Psychology, B
Respiratory Care Therapy/Therapist, B
Romance Languages, Literatures, and Linguistics, B
Spanish Language and Literature, B

Wisconsin

ALVERNO COLLEGE

Adult and Continuing Education and Teaching, M
Art Teacher Education, B
Art Therapy/Therapist, B
Art/Art Studies, General, B
Biology/Biological Sciences, B
Business Administration and Management, B
Business Administration, Management and Operations, BM
Chemistry, B
Communication Studies/Speech Communication and Rhetoric, B
Communications Technologies/Technicians and Support Services, B
Community Organization and Advocacy, B
Community Psychology, M
Computer and Information Sciences, B
Design and Applied Arts, B
Education, BM
Educational Administration and Supervision, M
Educational Leadership and Administration, M
Educational Media/Instructional Technology, M
Elementary Education and Teaching, B
English Language and Literature, B
English/Language Arts Teacher Education, B
Environmental Sciences, B
General Studies, A

History, B
International Business/Trade/Commerce, B
International Relations and Affairs, B
Junior High/Intermediate/Middle School Education
   and Teaching, B
Liberal Arts and Sciences Studies and Humani-
   ties, AB
Mathematics, B
Molecular Biology, B
Multi-/Interdisciplinary Studies, B
Music, AB
Music Teacher Education, B
Music Therapy/Therapist, B
Nursing, M
Nursing - Advanced Practice, M
Philosophy, B
Political Science and Government, B
Psychiatric/Mental Health Nurse/Nursing, M
Psychology, B
Reading Teacher Education, M
Religion/Religious Studies, B
Science Teacher Education/General Science
   Teacher Education, BM
Social Sciences, B
Social Studies Teacher Education, B
Sociology, B
Special Education and Teaching, M
Teacher Assistant/Aide, A
Women's Studies, B

BELLIN COLLEGE

Nursing, M
Nursing - Advanced Practice, M
Nursing Education, M

BELOIT COLLEGE

Anthropology, B
Art History, Criticism and Conservation, B
Art Teacher Education, B
Biochemistry, B
Biology/Biological Sciences, B
Business/Managerial Economics, B
Cell/Cellular Biology and Histology, B
Chemistry, B
Chinese Language and Literature, B
Classics and Classical Languages, Litera-
   tures, and Linguistics, B
Comparative Literature, B
Computer Science, B
Dance, B
Drama and Dramatics/Theatre Arts, B
Ecology, B
Economics, B
Education, B
Elementary Education and Teaching, B
Engineering, B
English Language and Literature, B
Environmental Biology, B
Environmental Studies, B
Ethnic, Cultural Minority, and Gender Studies, B
Fine/Studio Arts, B
Forestry, B
French Language and Literature, B
Geology/Earth Science, B
German Language and Literature, B
History, B
International Relations and Affairs, B
Japanese Language and Literature, B
Mass Communication/Media Studies, B
Mathematics, B
Modern Languages, B
Molecular Biology, B
Museology/Museum Studies, B
Music Teacher Education, B
Philosophy, B
Physics, B
Political Science and Government, B
Psychology, B
Religion/Religious Studies, B
Romance Languages, Literatures, and Linguistics, B
Russian Language and Literature, B
Secondary Education and Teaching, B
Sociology, B

Spanish Language and Literature, B

BLACKHAWK TECHNICAL COLLEGE

Accounting, A
Administrative Assistant and Secretarial Science, A
Business Administration and Management, A
Clinical/Medical Laboratory Technician, A
Computer Systems Networking and Telecommunica-
   tions, A
Criminal Justice/Police Science, A
Culinary Arts/Chef Training, A
Diagnostic Medical Sonography/Sonographer and
   Ultrasound Technician, A
Early Childhood Education and Teaching, A
Electromechanical Technology/Electromechanical
   Engineering Technology, A
Fire Science/Firefighting, A
Human Resources Management/Personnel Adminis-
   tration, A
Legal Administrative Assistant/Secretary, A
Marketing/Marketing Management, A
Medical Administrative Assistant/Secretary, A
Physical Therapist Assistant, A
Web Page, Digital/Multimedia and Information Re-
   sources Design, A

BRYANT & STRATTON COL-
LEGE–MILWAUKEE CAMPUS

Accounting, A
Administrative Assistant and Secretarial Science, A
Business/Commerce, AB
Commercial and Advertising Art, A
Computer and Information Systems Security, A
Criminal Justice/Law Enforcement Administra-
   tion, AB
Design and Visual Communications, A
Financial Planning and Services, A
Human Resources Management and Services, A
Legal Assistant/Paralegal, A
Medical/Clinical Assistant, A
System, Networking, and LAN/WAN
   Management/Manager, A

BRYANT & STRATTON COL-
LEGE–WAUWATOSA CAMPUS

Accounting, A
Business Administration and Management, AB
Business/Commerce, A
Criminal Justice/Law Enforcement Administra-
   tion, AB
Graphic Design, A
Human Resources Management and Services, A
Legal Assistant/Paralegal, A
Medical Office Assistant/Specialist, A

CARDINAL STRITCH UNIVERSITY

Accounting, B
Applied Arts and Design, M
Art/Art Studies, General, B
Biology/Biological Sciences, B
Business Administration and Management, B
Business Administration, Management and Opera-
   tions, BM
Business/Commerce, B
Chemistry, B
Clinical Psychology, M
Communication Studies/Speech Communication
   and Rhetoric, B
Computer Education, M
Computer Science, B
Criminal Justice/Safety Studies, B
Drama and Dramatics/Theatre Arts, B
Early Childhood Education and Teaching, B
Education, MD
Educational Leadership and Administration, MD
Educational Media/Instructional Technology, M
Elementary Education and Teaching, B
English Language and Literature, B
English as a Second Language, M
General Studies, AM
Graphic Design, BM
History, BM
Human Resources Management/Personnel Adminis-
   tration, B
International Business/Trade/Commerce, B

Management Information Systems and Services, B
Mathematics, B
Music, M
Music Performance, B
Nursing, M
Pastoral Studies/Counseling, M
Photography, B
Political Science and Government, B
Psychology, BM
Reading Teacher Education, M
Religion/Religious Studies, BM
Respiratory Care Therapy/Therapist, B
Secondary Education and Teaching, B
Sociology, B
Spanish Language and Literature, B
Special Education and Teaching, M
Sport and Fitness Administration/Management, BM
Urban Education and Leadership, M
Visual and Performing Arts, B

CARROLL UNIVERSITY

Accounting, B
Actuarial Science, B
Animal Behavior and Ethology, B
Applied Mathematics, B
Art Teacher Education, B
Art/Art Studies, General, B
Athletic Training and Sports Medicine, B
Biochemistry, B
Biology Teacher Education, B
Biology/Biological Sciences, B
Business Administration and Management, B
Business Administration, Management and Opera-
   tions, M
Chemistry, B
Chemistry Teacher Education, B
Clinical Laboratory Science/Medical
   Technology/Technologist, B
Commercial and Advertising Art, B
Communication Studies/Speech Communication
   and Rhetoric, B
Computer Software Engineering, B
Computer and Information Sciences, B
Drama and Dramatics/Theatre Arts, B
Early Childhood Education and Teaching, B
Education, BM
Elementary Education and Teaching, B
Engineering Physics, B
English Language and Literature, B
English/Language Arts Teacher Education, B
Environmental Sciences, B
European Studies/Civilization, B
Finance, B
Fine/Studio Arts, B
Foreign Language Teacher Education, B
Graphic Communications, B
Health Teacher Education, B
Health and Physical Education, B
History, B
History Teacher Education, B
Human Resources Management/Personnel Adminis-
   tration, B
Information Science/Studies, B
International Relations and Affairs, B
International/Global Studies, B
Journalism, B
Junior High/Intermediate/Middle School Education
   and Teaching, B
Kinesiology and Exercise Science, B
Marketing/Marketing Management, B
Mathematics, B
Mathematics Teacher Education, B
Medical Radiologic Technology/Science - Radiation
   Therapist, B
Music, B
Music Teacher Education, B
Natural Resources and Conservation, B
Organizational Behavior Studies, B
Parks, Recreation and Leisure Facilities Manage-
   ment, B
Photography, B
Physical Education Teaching and Coaching, B
Physical Therapy/Therapist, MD
Physician Assistant, M
Physics, B
Political Science and Government, B

Pre-Dentistry Studies, B
Pre-Medicine/Pre-Medical Studies, B
Pre-Pharmacy Studies, B
Pre-Veterinary Studies, B
Printing Management, B
Psychology, B
Psychology Teacher Education, B
Public Health (MPH, DPH), B
Public Relations, Advertising, and Applied Communication, B
Public Relations/Image Management, B
Religion/Religious Studies, B
Science Teacher Education/General Science Teacher Education, B
Small Business Administration/Management, B
Social Science Teacher Education, B
Social Studies Teacher Education, B
Sociology, B
Software Engineering, M
Spanish Language Teacher Education, B
Spanish Language and Literature, B

CARTHAGE COLLEGE

Accounting, B
Art Education, M
Art History, Criticism and Conservation, B
Athletic Training and Sports Medicine, B
Biology/Biological Sciences, B
Business Administration and Management, B
Chemistry, B
Classics and Classical Languages, Literatures, and Linguistics, B
Communication Studies/Speech Communication and Rhetoric, B
Communication and Media Studies, B
Computer Science, B
Counselor Education/School Counseling and Guidance Services, M
Criminal Justice/Law Enforcement Administration, B
Drama and Dramatics/Theatre Arts, B
Economics, B
Education, MO
Education/Teaching of the Gifted and Talented, M
Educational Leadership and Administration, M
Elementary Education and Teaching, B
Engineering, B
English Education, M
English Language and Literature, B
Environmental Sciences, B
Environmental Studies, B
Fine/Studio Arts, B
French Language and Literature, B
Geography, B
German Language and Literature, B
Graphic Design, B
History, B
International Economics, B
Marketing/Marketing Management, B
Mathematics, B
Music, B
Music Teacher Education, B
Natural Sciences, B
Occupational Therapy/Therapist, B
Philosophy, B
Physical Education Teaching and Coaching, B
Physics, B
Political Science and Government, B
Pre-Dentistry Studies, B
Pre-Law Studies, B
Pre-Medicine/Pre-Medical Studies, B
Pre-Veterinary Studies, B
Psychology, B
Reading Teacher Education, MO
Religion/Religious Studies, B
Science Teacher Education/General Science Teacher Education, M
Secondary Education and Teaching, B
Social Sciences, B
Social Studies Teacher Education, M
Social Work, B
Sociology, B
Spanish Language and Literature, B
Special Education and Teaching, B

Sport and Fitness Administration/Management, B

CHIPPEWA VALLEY TECHNICAL COLLEGE

Accounting, A
Administrative Assistant and Secretarial Science, A
Agricultural Business and Management, A
Applied Horticulture/Horticultural Business Services, A
Business Administration and Management, A
Civil Engineering Technology/Technician, A
Clinical/Medical Laboratory Technician, A
Computer Programming/Programmer, A
Computer Systems Networking and Telecommunications, A
Criminal Justice/Police Science, A
Dental Hygiene/Hygienist, A
Diagnostic Medical Sonography/Sonographer and Ultrasound Technician, A
Early Childhood Education and Teaching, A
Electromechanical Technology/Electromechanical Engineering Technology, A
Emergency Medical Technology/Technician (EMT Paramedic), A
Health Information/Medical Records Technology/Technician, A
Heating, Air Conditioning and Refrigeration Technology/Technician, A
Human Resources Management/Personnel Administration, A
Industrial Mechanics and Maintenance Technology, A
Legal Assistant/Paralegal, A
Liberal Arts and Sciences Studies and Humanities, A
Manufacturing Technology/Technician, A
Marketing/Marketing Management, A
Medical Radiologic Technology/Science - Radiation Therapist, A
Multi-/Interdisciplinary Studies, A
Operations Management and Supervision, A
Physical Therapist Assistant, A
Respiratory Care Therapy/Therapist, A
Substance Abuse/Addiction Counseling, A

COLLEGE OF MENOMINEE NATION

Accounting, A
Administrative Assistant and Secretarial Science, A
Area Studies, A
Biology/Biological Sciences, A
Business Administration and Management, A
Computer and Information Sciences, A
Early Childhood Education and Teaching, A
Humanities/Humanistic Studies, A
Kindergarten/PreSchool Education and Teaching, A
Law and Legal Studies, A
Liberal Arts and Sciences Studies and Humanities, A
Mathematics, A
Natural Resources and Conservation, A
Pre-Nursing Studies, A
Social Work, A
Substance Abuse/Addiction Counseling, A

CONCORDIA UNIVERSITY WISCONSIN

Accounting, B
Actuarial Science, B
Ancient Near Eastern and Biblical Languages, Literatures, and Linguistics, B
Art Education, M
Art Teacher Education, B
Art/Art Studies, General, B
Athletic Training and Sports Medicine, B
Biology/Biological Sciences, B
Biomedical Sciences, B
Business Administration and Management, B
Business Administration, Management and Operations, M
Business Teacher Education, B
Child and Family Studies, M
Christian Studies, B
Commercial and Advertising Art, B
Computer Science, B
Corporate and Organizational Communication, M
Counseling Psychology, M

Counselor Education/School Counseling and Guidance Services, M
Criminal Justice/Law Enforcement Administration, B
Curriculum and Instruction, M
Digital Communication and Media/Multimedia, B
Early Childhood Education and Teaching, M
Economics, B
Education, BM
Educational Administration and Supervision, M
Elementary Education and Teaching, B
English Language and Literature, B
Environmental Education, M
Environmental Studies, B
Exercise Physiology, B
Finance and Banking, M
General Studies, B
German Language Teacher Education, B
German Language and Literature, B
Gerontological Nursing, M
Graphic Design, B
Health Services Administration, M
Health and Physical Education, B
Health and Physical Education/Fitness, B
Health/Health Care Administration/Management, B
Hebrew Language and Literature, B
History, B
History Teacher Education, B
Human Resources Management and Services, M
Human Services, MD
Humanities/Humanistic Studies, B
Industrial Radiologic Technology/Technician, B
Interior Design, B
International Business/Trade/Commerce, BM
Junior High/Intermediate/Middle School Education and Teaching, B
Kindergarten/PreSchool Education and Teaching, B
Legal Assistant/Paralegal, B
Liberal Arts and Sciences Studies and Humanities, B
Management, M
Management Information Systems and Services, M
Marketing, M
Marketing/Marketing Management, B
Mass Communication/Media Studies, B
Mathematics, B
Medical Office Assistant/Specialist, B
Medical Radiologic Technology/Science - Radiation Therapist, B
Missions/Missionary Studies and Missiology, B
Modern Greek Language and Literature, B
Music, B
Music Teacher Education, B
Music Therapy/Therapist, B
Nursing, M
Nursing - Advanced Practice, M
Nursing Education, M
Occupational Therapy/Therapist, BM
Pastoral Studies/Counseling, B
Photography, B
Physical Education Teaching and Coaching, B
Physical Therapy/Therapist, BMD
Political Science and Government, B
Pre-Dentistry Studies, A
Pre-Law Studies, B
Pre-Medicine/Pre-Medical Studies, A
Pre-Nursing Studies, A
Psychology, BM
Public Administration, M
Reading Teacher Education, M
Rehabilitation Sciences, M
Religion/Religious Studies, B
Religious/Sacred Music, B
Sacred Music, M
Science Teacher Education/General Science Teacher Education, B
Secondary Education and Teaching, B
Social Work, B
Spanish Language Teacher Education, B
Spanish Language and Literature, B
Special Education and Teaching, B
Sport and Fitness Administration/Management, B
Student Personnel Services, M
Teacher Education, Multiple Levels, B
Teaching English as a Second or Foreign Language/ESL Language Instructor, B
Theology/Theological Studies, B

Youth Ministry, B

EDGEWOOD COLLEGE

Accounting, BM
Adult and Continuing Education and Teaching, M
Art Teacher Education, B
Art Therapy/Therapist, B
Art/Art Studies, General, B
Biology Teacher Education, B
Biology/Biological Sciences, B
Biomedical Sciences, B
Business Administration and Management, B
Business Administration, Management and Operations, M
Business Teacher Education, B
Business/Commerce, B
Chemistry, B
Chemistry Teacher Education, B
Computer Teacher Education, B
Computer and Information Sciences, B
Criminal Justice/Safety Studies, B
CytoTechnology/Cytotechnologist, B
Drama and Dance Teacher Education, B
Drama and Dramatics/Theatre Arts, B
Early Childhood Education and Teaching, B
Economics, B
Education, BMDO
Education/Teaching of Individuals in Early Childhood
  Special Education Programs, B
Educational Administration and Supervision, MO
Educational Leadership and Administration, D
Elementary Education and Teaching, B
English Language and Literature, B
English as a Second Language, M
English/Language Arts Teacher Education, B
Environmental Sciences, B
Ethnic and Cultural Studies, B
Finance and Banking, M
French Language Teacher Education, B
French Language and Literature, B
Graphic Design, B
History, B
International Relations and Affairs, B
Management, M
Management Information Systems and Services, B
Marketing, M
Marriage and Family Therapy/Counseling, M
Mathematics, B
Mathematics Teacher Education, B
Multi-/Interdisciplinary Studies, B
Multilingual and Multicultural Education, M
Music, B
Music Teacher Education, B
Music Therapy/Therapist, B
Natural Sciences, B
Nursing, MD
Organizational Behavior Studies, B
Organizational Management, M
Physics, B
Political Science and Government, B
Psychology, B
Reading Teacher Education, M
Religion/Religious Studies, B
Religious Education, B
Science Teacher Education/General Science
  Teacher Education, B
Social Sciences, B
Sociology, B
Spanish Language Teacher Education, B
Spanish Language and Literature, B
Special Education and Teaching, MO
Sustainability Management, M

FOX VALLEY TECHNICAL COLLEGE

Accounting, A
Administrative Assistant and Secretarial Science, A
Agricultural Mechanization, A
Agricultural/Farm Supplies Retailing and Wholesaling, A
Airline/Commercial/Professional Pilot and Flight
  Crew, A
Autobody/Collision and Repair
  Technology/Technician, A
Automobile/Automotive Mechanics
  Technology/Technician, A
Avionics Maintenance Technology/Technician, A

Banking and Financial Support Services, A
Biology Technician/BioTechnology Laboratory Technician, A
Building/Construction Site Management/Manager, A
Business Administration and Management, A
Computer Programming/Programmer, A
Computer Systems Networking and Telecommunications, A
Court Reporting/Court Reporter, A
Criminal Justice/Police Science, A
Culinary Arts/Chef Training, A
Dental Hygiene/Hygienist, A
Diesel Mechanics Technology/Technician, A
Early Childhood Education and Teaching, A
Electrical and Electronic Engineering
  Technologies/Technicians, A
Electrical, Electronic and Communications Engineering Technology/Technician, A
Electromechanical Technology/Electromechanical
  Engineering Technology, A
Emergency Medical Technology/Technician (EMT
  Paramedic), A
Energy Management and Systems
  Technology/Technician, A
Fire Protection, A
Fire Science/Firefighting, A
Forensic Science and Technology, A
Graphic Communications, A
Health Information/Medical Records
  Technology/Technician, A
Hospitality Administration/Management, A
Human Resources Management/Personnel Administration, A
Industrial Safety Technology/Technician, A
Interior Design, A
Legal Assistant/Paralegal, A
Logistics and Materials Management, A
Manufacturing Technology/Technician, A
Marketing/Marketing Management, A
Mechanical Drafting and Mechanical Drafting
  CAD/CADD, A
Medical Office Management/Administration, A
Multi-/Interdisciplinary Studies, A
Natural Resources and Conservation, A
Occupational Therapist Assistant, A
Office Management and Supervision, A
Radio, Television, and Digital Communication, A
Substance Abuse/Addiction Counseling, A
Web/Multimedia Management and Webmaster, A
Welding Technology/Welder, A

GATEWAY TECHNICAL COLLEGE

Accounting, A
Administrative Assistant and Secretarial Science, A
Airline/Commercial/Professional Pilot and Flight
  Crew, A
Applied Horticulture/Horticultural Operations, A
Architectural Engineering Technology/Technician, A
Automobile/Automotive Mechanics
  Technology/Technician, A
Business Administration and Management, A
Computer Programming/Programmer, A
Computer Systems Networking and Telecommunications, A
Criminal Justice/Police Science, A
Culinary Arts/Chef Training, A
Diesel Mechanics Technology/Technician, A
Early Childhood Education and Teaching, A
Electrical, Electronic and Communications Engineering Technology/Technician, A
Electromechanical Technology/Electromechanical
  Engineering Technology, A
Emergency Medical Technology/Technician (EMT
  Paramedic), A
Graphic Design, A
Health Information/Medical Records
  Technology/Technician, A
Heating, Air Conditioning, Ventilation and Refrigeration Maintenance Technology/Technician, A
Hospitality Administration/Management, A
Industrial Mechanics and Maintenance Technology, A
Interior Design, A
Marketing/Marketing Management, A
Mechanical Drafting and Mechanical Drafting
  CAD/CADD, A

Physical Therapist Assistant, A
Psychiatric/Mental Health Services Technician, A
Surgical Technology/Technologist, A
Survey Technology/Surveying, A
Teacher Assistant/Aide, A
Transportation and Highway Engineering, A
Veterinary/Animal Health Technology/Technician and
  Veterinary Assistant, A
Water Resources Engineering, A
Web/Multimedia Management and Webmaster, A

GLOBE UNIVERSITY–APPLETON

Accounting, AB
Business Administration and Management, AB
Health/Health Care Administration/Management, B
Legal Assistant/Paralegal, AB
Massage Therapy/Therapeutic Massage, A
Medical Administrative Assistant/Secretary, A
Medical/Clinical Assistant, A
Veterinary/Animal Health Technology/Technician and
  Veterinary Assistant, A

GLOBE UNIVERSITY–EAU CLAIRE

Accounting, AB
Business Administration and Management, AB
Computer Programming, Specific Applications, AB
Computer Systems Networking and Telecommunications, A
Criminal Justice/Law Enforcement Administration, AB
Health/Health Care Administration/Management, B
Information Technology, B
Legal Assistant/Paralegal, AB
Marketing/Marketing Management, A
Massage Therapy/Therapeutic Massage, A
Medical Administrative Assistant/Secretary, A
Medical/Clinical Assistant, A
Veterinary/Animal Health Technology/Technician and
  Veterinary Assistant, A

GLOBE UNIVERSITY–GREEN BAY

Business Administration and Management, AB
Computer Programming, Specific Applications, AB
Computer Systems Networking and Telecommunications, A
Criminal Justice/Law Enforcement Administration, AB
Information Technology, B
Legal Assistant/Paralegal, AB
Marketing/Marketing Management, A
Massage Therapy/Therapeutic Massage, A
Medical Administrative Assistant/Secretary, A
Medical/Clinical Assistant, A
Veterinary/Animal Health Technology/Technician and
  Veterinary Assistant, A

GLOBE UNIVERSITY–LA CROSSE

Accounting, AB
Business Administration and Management, AB
Computer Programming, Specific Applications, AB
Computer Systems Networking and Telecommunications, A
Criminal Justice/Law Enforcement Administration, AB
Information Technology, B
Marketing/Marketing Management, A
Massage Therapy/Therapeutic Massage, A
Medical Administrative Assistant/Secretary, A
Medical/Clinical Assistant, A
Veterinary/Animal Health Technology/Technician and
  Veterinary Assistant, A

GLOBE UNIVERSITY–MADISON EAST

Accounting, AB
Business Administration and Management, AB
Computer Programming, Specific Applications, AB
Computer Systems Networking and Telecommunications, A
Criminal Justice/Law Enforcement Administration, AB
Health/Health Care Administration/Management, B
Information Technology, B
Legal Assistant/Paralegal, AB
Massage Therapy/Therapeutic Massage, A
Medical Administrative Assistant/Secretary, A

Medical/Clinical Assistant, A
Veterinary/Animal Health Technology/Technician and
Veterinary Assistant, AB

GLOBE UNIVERSITY–MADISON WEST

Accounting, AB
Business Administration and Management, AB
Computer Programming, Specific Applications, AB
Computer Systems Networking and Telecommunica-
tions, A
Criminal Justice/Law Enforcement Administra-
tion, AB
Information Technology, B
Legal Assistant/Paralegal, AB
Marketing/Marketing Management, A
Massage Therapy/Therapeutic Massage, A
Medical Administrative Assistant/Secretary, A
Medical/Clinical Assistant, A
Veterinary/Animal Health Technology/Technician and
Veterinary Assistant, A

GLOBE UNIVERSITY–WAUSAU

Accounting, AB
Business Administration and Management, AB
Computer Programming, Specific Applications, AB
Computer Systems Networking and Telecommunica-
tions, A
Criminal Justice/Law Enforcement Administra-
tion, AB
Health/Health Care Administration/Management, B
Information Technology, B
Legal Assistant/Paralegal, AB
Marketing/Marketing Management, A
Massage Therapy/Therapeutic Massage, A
Medical Administrative Assistant/Secretary, A
Medical/Clinical Assistant, A
Veterinary/Animal Health Technology/Technician and
Veterinary Assistant, A

HERZING UNIVERSITY ONLINE

Accounting, M
Business Administration, Management and Opera-
tions, M
Health Services Administration, M
Human Resources Management and Services, M
Management of Technology, M
Marketing, M
Nursing, M
Nursing Administration, M
Nursing Education, M
Project Management, M

LAC COURTE OREILLES OJIBWA COMMUNITY COLLEGE

Accounting, A
Administrative Assistant and Secretarial Science, A
Agriculture, A
American Indian/Native American Studies, A
Biological and Biomedical Sciences, A
Business Administration and Management, A
Carpentry/Carpenter, A
Computer Systems Analysis/Analyst, A
Early Childhood Education and Teaching, A
Hospitality and Recreation Marketing Operations, A
Liberal Arts and Sciences Studies and Humani-
ties, A
Medical Office Management/Administration, A
Medical Transcription/Transcriptionist, A
Medical/Clinical Assistant, A
Natural Resources Management/Development and
Policy, A
Sales, Distribution and Marketing Operations, A
Social Work, A
Solar Energy Technology/Technician, A
Substance Abuse/Addiction Counseling, A

LAKELAND COLLEGE

Accounting, BM
Art/Art Studies, General, B
Biochemistry, B
Biology/Biological Sciences, B
Business Administration and Management, B
Business Administration, Management and Opera-
tions, M
Chemistry, B

Computer Science, B
Counselor Education/School Counseling and Guid-
ance Services, M
Criminal Justice/Safety Studies, B
Education, M
Elementary Education and Teaching, B
English Language and Literature, B
Finance and Banking, M
German Language and Literature, B
Health Services Administration, M
History, B
International Business/Trade/Commerce, B
Junior High/Intermediate/Middle School Education
and Teaching, B
Kindergarten/PreSchool Education and Teaching, B
Kinesiology and Exercise Science, B
Marketing/Marketing Management, B
Mathematics, B
Music, B
Music Teacher Education, B
Non-Profit/Public/Organizational Management, B
Project Management, M
Psychology, B
Religion/Religious Studies, B
Resort Management, B
Science Teacher Education/General Science
Teacher Education, B
Secondary Education and Teaching, B
Sociology, B
Spanish Language and Literature, B
Theology and Religious Vocations, M

LAKESHORE TECHNICAL COLLEGE

Accounting, A
Administrative Assistant and Secretarial Science, A
Computer Programming, A
Computer Programming/Programmer, A
Computer Systems Analysis/Analyst, A
Computer and Information Sciences, A
Court Reporting/Court Reporter, A
Criminal Justice/Police Science, A
Dental Hygiene/Hygienist, A
Drafting/Design Engineering
Technologies/Technicians, A
Electrical, Electronic and Communications Engineer-
ing Technology/Technician, A
Electromechanical Technology/Electromechanical
Engineering Technology, A
Finance, A
Legal Assistant/Paralegal, A
Management Science, A
Marketing/Marketing Management, A
Medical Administrative Assistant/Secretary, A
Quality Control Technology/Technician, A
Radiologic Technology/Science - Radiographer, A

LAWRENCE UNIVERSITY

Ancient/Classical Greek Language and Literature, B
Anthropology, B
Archeology, B
Art History, Criticism and Conservation, B
Art Teacher Education, B
Biochemistry, B
Biology/Biological Sciences, B
Chemistry, B
Chinese Language and Literature, B
Classics and Classical Languages, Litera-
tures, and Linguistics, B
Cognitive Sciences, B
Computer Science, B
Drama and Dramatics/Theatre Arts, B
East Asian Studies, B
Ecology, B
Economics, B
English Language and Literature, B
Environmental Studies, B
Ethnic, Cultural Minority, and Gender Studies, B
Fine/Studio Arts, B
French Language and Literature, B
Geology/Earth Science, B
German Language and Literature, B
History, B
International Economics, B
International Relations and Affairs, B
Japanese Language and Literature, B
Latin Language and Literature, B

Linguistics, B
Mathematics, B
Mathematics and Computer Science, B
Music, B
Music Pedagogy, B
Music Performance, B
Music Teacher Education, B
Music Theory and Composition, B
Philosophy, B
Physics, B
Piano and Organ, B
Political Science and Government, B
Pre-Dentistry Studies, B
Pre-Law Studies, B
Pre-Medicine/Pre-Medical Studies, B
Pre-Veterinary Studies, B
Psychology, B
Religion/Religious Studies, B
Russian Language and Literature, B
Russian Studies, B
Secondary Education and Teaching, B
Slavic Studies, B
Spanish Language and Literature, B
Violin, Viola, Guitar and Other Stringed Instru-
ments, B
Voice and Opera, B

MADISON AREA TECHNICAL COLLEGE

Accounting, A
Administrative Assistant and Secretarial Science, A
Agricultural Mechanization, A
Architectural Engineering Technology/Technician, A
Automobile/Automotive Mechanics
Technology/Technician, A
Biology Technician/BioTechnology Laboratory Tech-
nician, A
Business Administration and Management, A
Business Teacher Education, A
Child Development, A
Civil Engineering Technology/Technician, A
Clinical/Medical Laboratory Technician, A
Commercial and Advertising Art, A
Communications Technology/Technician, A
Computer Engineering Technology/Technician, A
Computer Programming/Programmer, A
Computer Typography and Composition Equipment
Operator, A
Court Reporting/Court Reporter, A
Criminal Justice/Police Science, A
Culinary Arts/Chef Training, A
Data Processing and Data Processing
Technology/Technician, A
Dental Hygiene/Hygienist, A
Dietetics/Dieticians, A
Drafting/Design Engineering
Technologies/Technicians, A
Electrical, Electronic and Communications Engineer-
ing Technology/Technician, A
Emergency Medical Technology/Technician (EMT
Paramedic), A
Fashion Merchandising, A
Finance, A
Fire Science/Firefighting, A
Graphic and Printing Equipment Operator Produc-
tion, A
Hospitality Administration/Management, A
Human Services, A
Industrial Radiologic Technology/Technician, A
Insurance, A
Interior Design, A
Liberal Arts and Sciences Studies and Humani-
ties, A
Marketing/Marketing Management, A
Medical Administrative Assistant/Secretary, A
Occupational Therapy/Therapist, A
Parks, Recreation, Leisure and Fitness Studies, A
Photography, A
Real Estate, A
Respiratory Care Therapy/Therapist, A
Tourism and Travel Services Management, A
Veterinary/Animal Health Technology/Technician and
Veterinary Assistant, A

Welding Technology/Welder, A

MADISON MEDIA INSTITUTE

Animation, Interactive Technology, Video Graphics and Special Effects, A
Music, A
Recording Arts Technology/Technician, A
Web Page, Digital/Multimedia and Information Resources Design, A

MARANATHA BAPTIST UNIVERSITY

Accounting, B
Accounting and Business/Management, B
Bible/Biblical Studies, B
Biology Teacher Education, B
Biology/Biological Sciences, B
Business Administration and Management, B
Business Teacher Education, B
Cultural Studies, M
Early Childhood Education and Teaching, AB
Education, M
Elementary Education and Teaching, B
English Language and Literature, B
English/Language Arts Teacher Education, B
History Teacher Education, B
Humanities/Humanistic Studies, B
Marketing/Marketing Management, B
Mathematics Teacher Education, B
Missions/Missionary Studies and Missiology, B
Music Pedagogy, B
Music Performance, B
Music Teacher Education, B
Office Management and Supervision, AB
Pastoral Counseling and Specialized Ministries, B
Pastoral Studies/Counseling, BM
Physical Education Teaching and Coaching, B
Religion/Religious Studies, M
Religious/Sacred Music, B
Science Teacher Education/General Science Teacher Education, B
Social Studies Teacher Education, B
Sport and Fitness Administration/Management, B
Theology and Religious Vocations, M
Youth Ministry, B

MARIAN UNIVERSITY

Accounting, B
Biology/Biological Sciences, B
Business Administration and Management, B
Business Administration, Management and Operations, M
Chemistry, B
Communication Studies/Speech Communication and Rhetoric, B
Criminal Justice/Police Science, B
Criminology, M
CytoTechnology/Cytotechnologist, B
Diagnostic Medical Sonography/Sonographer and Ultrasound Technician, B
Early Childhood Education and Teaching, B
Education, MD
Educational Leadership and Administration, MD
Elementary Education and Teaching, B
English Language and Literature, B
English/Language Arts Teacher Education, B
Finance, B
Forensic Science and Technology, B
Graphic Design, B
Health/Health Care Administration/Management, B
History, B
Human Resources Management/Personnel Administration, B
Human Services, B
Information Technology, B
Junior High/Intermediate/Middle School Education and Teaching, B
Kinesiology and Exercise Science, B
Liberal Arts and Sciences Studies and Humanities, B
Marketing/Marketing Management, B
Mathematics, B
Multi-/Interdisciplinary Studies, B
Music, B
Nursing, M
Nursing - Adult, M
Nursing Education, M

Operations Management and Supervision, B
Organizational Communication, B
Organizational Management, M
Psychology, B
Quality Management, M
Radiologic Technology/Science - Radiographer, B
Science Teacher Education/General Science Teacher Education, B
Secondary Education and Teaching, B
Security and Protective Services, B
Social Studies Teacher Education, B
Social Work, B
Spanish Language Teacher Education, B
Spanish Language and Literature, B
Sport and Fitness Administration/Management, B
Theology/Theological Studies, B

MARQUETTE UNIVERSITY

Accounting, BM
Acute Care/Critical Care Nursing, DO
Advertising, B
Advertising and Public Relations, M
Analytical Chemistry, MD
Anthropology, B
Athletic Training and Sports Medicine, B
Biochemistry, Biophysics and Molecular Biology, B
Bioinformatics, M
Biological and Biomedical Sciences, MD
Biology Teacher Education, B
Biology/Biological Sciences, B
Biomedical Engineering, MD
Biomedical Sciences, B
Biomedical/Medical Engineering, B
Biophysics, B
Business Administration and Management, B
Business Administration, Management and Operations, BMO
Business/Managerial Economics, B
Cardiovascular Sciences, M
Cell Biology and Anatomy, MD
Chemical Physics, MD
Chemistry, BMD
Chemistry Teacher Education, B
Civil Engineering, BMDO
Classics and Classical Languages, Literatures, and Linguistics, B
Clinical Laboratory Science/Medical Technology/Technologist, B
Clinical Psychology, M
Communication Disorders, MO
Communication Disorders Sciences and Services, B
Communication and Media Studies, BMO
Communication, Journalism and Related Programs, B
Community Psychology, M
Computational Mathematics, B
Computational Sciences, MD
Computer Engineering, BMDO
Computer Science, M
Computer and Information Sciences, B
Conflict Resolution and Mediation/Peace Studies, M
Construction Engineering, B
Construction Engineering and Management, MDO
Construction Management, MDO
Counseling Psychology, MD
Counselor Education/School Counseling and Guidance Services, M
Criminology, BMO
Curriculum and Instruction, M
Dentistry, D
Developmental Biology and Embryology, MD
Digital Communication and Media/Multimedia, B
Drama and Dramatics/Theatre Arts, B
Ecology, MD
Economics, BM
Education, MDO
Educational Leadership and Administration, MDO
Educational Policy, MDO
Electrical Engineering, MDO
Electrical, Electronics and Communications Engineering, B
Elementary Education and Teaching, BO
Engineering Management, M
Engineering and Applied Sciences, MDO
English, MD
English Language and Literature, B

Entrepreneurship/Entrepreneurial Studies, BO
Environmental Engineering Technology/Environmental Technology, MDO
Environmental/Environmental Health Engineering, B
Ethics, D
Exercise Physiology, B
Finance, B
Finance and Banking, M
Foreign Language Teacher Education, M
Foundations and Philosophy of Education, M
French Language and Literature, B
Genetics, MD
German Language and Literature, B
Gerontological Nursing, D
Hazardous Materials Management and Waste Technology/Technician, O
Health Communication, M
Health Services Administration, M
History, BMD
Human Resources Development, M
Human Resources Management and Services, M
Human Resources Management/Personnel Administration, B
Industrial and Manufacturing Management, M
Information Technology, B
Inorganic Chemistry, MD
Interdisciplinary Studies, D
International Affairs, M
International Business/Trade/Commerce, M
Journalism, BM
Law and Legal Studies, D
Management Information Systems and Services, M
Management of Technology, M
Marketing, M
Marketing Research, M
Marketing/Marketing Management, B
Mass Communication/Media Studies, BM
Mathematics, BMD
Mathematics Teacher Education, BM
Mechanical Engineering, BMDO
Microbiology, MD
Molecular Biology, MD
Multi-/Interdisciplinary Studies, B
Neuroscience, D
Non-Profit/Public/Organizational Management, M
Nurse Midwife/Nursing Midwifery, MO
Nursing, MDO
Nursing - Adult, MDO
Nursing - Advanced Practice, O
Nursing Administration, D
Oral and Dental Sciences, MO
Organic Chemistry, MD
Orthodontics, MO
Peace Studies and Conflict Resolution, B
Pediatric Nurse/Nursing, MDO
Philosophy, BMD
Physical Chemistry, MD
Physical Therapy/Therapist, D
Physician Assistant, M
Physics, B
Physiology, BMD
Political Science and Government, BM
Psychology, BD
Public Administration, MO
Public Relations/Image Management, B
Radio, Television, and Digital Communication, B
Reading Teacher Education, MO
Real Estate, BM
Rehabilitation Sciences, MD
Secondary Education and Teaching, BO
Social Work, B
Sociology, B
Spanish Language and Literature, BM
Speech and Interpersonal Communication, M
Sport and Fitness Administration/Management, M
Structural Engineering, MD
Student Personnel Services, M
Supply Chain Management, M
Theological and Ministerial Studies, B
Theology and Religious Vocations, MD
Theology/Theological Studies, B
Transportation and Highway Engineering, MDO
Water Resources, O

Water Resources Engineering, O

MID-STATE TECHNICAL COLLEGE

Accounting, A
Administrative Assistant and Secretarial Science, A
Business Administration and Management, A
Civil Engineering Technology/Technician, A
Computer Engineering Technology/Technician, A
Computer Programming, A
Computer Programming, Specific Applications, A
Computer and Information Sciences, A
Corrections, A
Criminal Justice/Police Science, A
Data Entry/Microcomputer Applications, A
Drafting/Design Engineering
    Technologies/Technicians, A
Electrical, Electronic and Communications Engineer-
    ing Technology/Technician, A
Hotel/Motel Administration/Management, A
Industrial Technology/Technician, A
Information Science/Studies, A
Instrumentation Technology/Technician, A
Marketing/Marketing Management, A
Quality Control Technology/Technician, A
Respiratory Care Therapy/Therapist, A

MILWAUKEE AREA TECHNICAL COL-LEGE

Accounting, A
Administrative Assistant and Secretarial Science, A
Allied Health Diagnostic, Intervention, and Treat-
    ment Professions, A
Allied Health and Medical Assisting Services, A
Anesthesiologist Assistant, A
Apparel and Accessories Marketing Operations, A
Architectural Engineering Technology/Technician, A
Automobile/Automotive Mechanics
    Technology/Technician, A
Banking and Financial Support Services, A
Biomedical Technology/Technician, A
Business Administration and Management, A
Business Administration, Management and Opera-
    tions, A
Business, Management, Marketing, and Related
    Support Services, A
Cardiovascular Technology/Technologist, A
Chemical Technology/Technician, A
Civil Engineering Technology/Technician, A
Clinical/Medical Laboratory Technician, A
Commercial Photography, A
Commercial and Advertising Art, A
Computer Graphics, A
Computer Programming, Specific Applications, A
Computer Programming, Vendor/Product Certifica-
    tion, A
Computer Systems Analysis/Analyst, A
Computer Systems Networking and Telecommunica-
    tions, A
Computer Technology/Computer Systems Technol-
    ogy, A
Computer and Information Systems Security, A
Computer/Information Technology Services Adminis-
    tration and Management, A
Criminal Justice/Police Science, A
Culinary Arts/Chef Training, A
Dental Hygiene/Hygienist, A
Dietetic Technician (DTR), A
E-Commerce/Electronic Commerce, A
Early Childhood Education and Teaching, A
Education, A
Electrical, Electronic and Communications Engineer-
    ing Technology/Technician, A
Engineering, A
Engineering Technologies/Technicians, A
Fire Science/Firefighting, A
Funeral Service and Mortuary Science, A
Graphic Communications, A
Graphic Design, A
Health Professions and Related Clinical Sciences, A
Health and Medical Administrative Services, A
Heating, Air Conditioning and Refrigeration
    Technology/Technician, A
Hotel/Motel Administration/Management, A
Industrial Technology/Technician, A
Interior Design, A
Landscaping and Groundskeeping, A

Legal Administrative Assistant/Secretary, A
Legal Assistant/Paralegal, A
Liberal Arts and Sciences Studies and Humani-
    ties, A
Logistics and Materials Management, A
Machine Tool Technology/Machinist, A
Manufacturing Technology/Technician, A
Marketing/Marketing Management, A
Materials Engineering, A
Mechanical Drafting and Mechanical Drafting
    CAD/CADD, A
Mechanical Engineering/Mechanical
    Technology/Technician, A
Medical Administrative Assistant/Secretary, A
Medical Radiologic Technology/Science - Radiation
    Therapist, A
Mental and Social Health Services and Allied Pro-
    fessions, A
Music, A
Occupational Therapy/Therapist, A
Operations Management and Supervision, A
Opticianry/Ophthalmic Dispensing Optician, A
Physical Therapy/Therapist, A
Plastics Engineering Technology/Technician, A
Radio and Television Broadcasting
    Technology/Technician, A
Real Estate, A
Respiratory Care Therapy/Therapist, A
Restaurant, Culinary, and Catering
    Management/Manager, A
Sign Language Interpretation and Translation, A
Surgical Technology/Technologist, A
Tourism and Travel Services Marketing Opera-
    tions, A
Water Quality and Wastewater Treatment Manage-
    ment and Recycling Technology/Technician, A
Welding Technology/Welder, A

MILWAUKEE INSTITUTE OF ART AND DESIGN

Animation, Interactive Technology, Video Graphics
    and Special Effects, B
Design and Visual Communications, B
Drawing, B
Fine/Studio Arts, B
Graphic Design, B
Industrial Design, B
Interior Architecture, B
Painting, B
Photography, B
Printmaking, B
Sculpture, B

MILWAUKEE SCHOOL OF ENGINEER-ING

Actuarial Science, B
Architectural Engineering, BM
Biomedical/Medical Engineering, B
Business Administration and Management, B
Business Administration, Management and Opera-
    tions, M
Business Education, M
Business/Commerce, B
Cardiovascular Sciences, M
Civil Engineering, BM
Clinical Laboratory Sciences, M
Communication, Journalism and Related Pro-
    grams, B
Computer Engineering, B
Computer Software Engineering, B
Construction Management, BM
Electrical, Electronics and Communications Engi-
    neering, B
Engineering, B
Engineering Management, M
Engineering and Applied Sciences, M
Health Services Administration, M
Industrial Engineering, B
Industrial and Manufacturing Management, M
International Business/Trade/Commerce, B
International Trade, M
Management Information Systems and Services, B
Marketing, M
Mechanical Engineering, B
Medical Informatics, M
Nursing Administration, M

Operations Research, B
Perfusion Technology/Perfusionist, M

MORAINE PARK TECHNICAL COLLEGE

Accounting, A
Administrative Assistant and Secretarial Science, A
Automobile/Automotive Mechanics
    Technology/Technician, A
Business Administration and Management, A
Chiropractic, A
Clinical/Medical Laboratory Technician, A
Computer Programming, A
Computer Systems Networking and Telecommunica-
    tions, A
Corrections, A
Court Reporting/Court Reporter, A
Culinary Arts/Chef Training, A
Early Childhood Education and Teaching, A
Electrical and Electronic Engineering
    Technologies/Technicians, A
Electromechanical Technology/Electromechanical
    Engineering Technology, A
Emergency Medical Technology/Technician (EMT
    Paramedic), A
Graphic Design, A
Health Information/Medical Records
    Technology/Technician, A
Heating, Air Conditioning and Refrigeration
    Technology/Technician, A
Hotel/Motel Administration/Management, A
Human Resources Management/Personnel Adminis-
    tration, A
Legal Administrative Assistant/Secretary, A
Legal Assistant/Paralegal, A
Machine Tool Technology/Machinist, A
Marketing/Marketing Management, A
Mechanical Drafting and Mechanical Drafting
    CAD/CADD, A
Mechanical Engineering Related
    Technologies/Technicians, A
Medical Radiologic Technology/Science - Radiation
    Therapist, A
Multi-/Interdisciplinary Studies, A
Office Management and Supervision, A
Respiratory Care Therapy/Therapist, A
Structural Engineering, A
Substance Abuse/Addiction Counseling, A
Surgical Technology/Technologist, A
Teacher Assistant/Aide, A
Water Quality and Wastewater Treatment Manage-
    ment and Recycling Technology/Technician, A

MOUNT MARY UNIVERSITY

Accounting, B
Art Teacher Education, B
Art Therapy/Therapist, BMD
Art/Art Studies, General, B
Biology Teacher Education, B
Biology/Biological Sciences, B
Business Administration and Management, B
Business Administration, Management and Opera-
    tions, M
Business/Corporate Communications, B
Chemistry, B
Chemistry Teacher Education, B
Clinical Psychology, MO
Communication Studies/Speech Communication
    and Rhetoric, B
Counseling Psychology, MO
Counselor Education/School Counseling and Guid-
    ance Services, MO
Criminal Justice/Law Enforcement Administration, B
Dietetics/Dieticians, B
Education, BM
English, M
English Language and Literature, B
English/Language Arts Teacher Education, B
Fashion Merchandising, B
Fashion/Apparel Design, B
General Studies, B
Graphic Design, B
Health Education, M
History, B
History Teacher Education, B
Interior Design, B
International/Global Studies, B

Internet and Interactive Multimedia, M
Junior High/Intermediate/Middle School Education
and Teaching, B
Liberal Arts and Sciences Studies and Humanities, B
Marketing/Marketing Management, B
Mathematics, B
Mathematics Teacher Education, B
Multi-/Interdisciplinary Studies, B
Nursing Administration, M
Nutritional Sciences, M
Occupational Therapy/Therapist, BMD
Philosophy, B
Psychology, B
Radiologic Technology/Science - Radiographer, B
Science Teacher Education/General Science
Teacher Education, B
Social Sciences, B
Social Studies Teacher Education, B
Social Work, B
Spanish Language Teacher Education, B
Spanish Language and Literature, B
Teacher Education, Multiple Levels, B
Theology/Theological Studies, B
Writing, M

NICOLET AREA TECHNICAL COLLEGE

Accounting, A
Administrative Assistant and Secretarial Science, A
Automobile/Automotive Mechanics
Technology/Technician, A
Business Administration and Management, A
Child Development, A
Computer Science, A
Computer and Information Sciences, A
Criminal Justice/Police Science, A
Culinary Arts/Chef Training, A
Data Processing and Data Processing
Technology/Technician, A
Hotel/Motel Administration/Management, A
Kindergarten/PreSchool Education and Teaching, A
Liberal Arts and Sciences Studies and Humanities, A
Machine Tool Technology/Machinist, A
Marketing/Marketing Management, A
Medical Administrative Assistant/Secretary, A
Physical Therapist Assistant, A
Real Estate, A
Survey Technology/Surveying, A
Welding Technology/Welder, A

NORTHCENTRAL TECHNICAL COLLEGE

Accounting, A
Administrative Assistant and Secretarial Science, A
Agribusiness, A
Agronomy and Crop Science, A
Architectural Engineering Technology/Technician, A
Automobile/Automotive Mechanics
Technology/Technician, A
Business Administration and Management, A
Cinematography and Film/Video Production, A
Clinical/Medical Laboratory Technician, A
Computer Systems Analysis/Analyst, A
Computer Systems Networking and Telecommunications, A
Computer and Information Sciences and Support
Services, A
Criminal Justice/Police Science, A
Culinary Arts/Chef Training, A
Dental Hygiene/Hygienist, A
Diesel Mechanics Technology/Technician, A
Early Childhood Education and Teaching, A
Electromechanical Technology/Electromechanical
Engineering Technology, A
Emergency Medical Technology/Technician (EMT
Paramedic), A
Entrepreneurship/Entrepreneurial Studies, A
Furniture Design and Manufacturing, A
General Merchandising, Sales, and Related Marketing Operations, A
General Studies, A
Graphic Communications, A
Manufacturing Technology/Technician, A
Marketing/Marketing Management, A

Mechanical Drafting and Mechanical Drafting
CAD/CADD, A
Medical Insurance Specialist/Medical Biller, A
Medical Radiologic Technology/Science - Radiation
Therapist, A
Mental and Social Health Services and Allied Professions, A
Multi-/Interdisciplinary Studies, A
Operations Management and Supervision, A
Sign Language Interpretation and Translation, A
Substance Abuse/Addiction Counseling, A
Teacher Assistant/Aide, A

NORTHEAST WISCONSIN TECHNICAL COLLEGE

Accounting, A
Administrative Assistant and Secretarial Science, A
Architectural Engineering Technology/Technician, A
Autobody/Collision and Repair
Technology/Technician, A
Automobile/Automotive Mechanics
Technology/Technician, A
Business Administration and Management, A
Civil Engineering Technology/Technician, A
Clinical/Medical Laboratory Technician, A
Computer Systems Networking and Telecommunications, A
Computer and Information Sciences and Support
Services, A
Corrections, A
Credit Management, A
Criminal Justice/Police Science, A
Dental Hygiene/Hygienist, A
Diagnostic Medical Sonography/Sonographer and
Ultrasound Technician, A
Early Childhood Education and Teaching, A
Electrical, Electronic and Communications Engineering Technology/Technician, A
Electromechanical Technology/Electromechanical
Engineering Technology, A
Electromechanical and Instrumentation and Maintenance Technologies/Technicians, A
Finance, A
Health Information/Medical Records
Technology/Technician, A
Heating, Air Conditioning and Refrigeration
Technology/Technician, A
Heavy Equipment Maintenance
Technology/Technician, A
Hospitality Administration/Management, A
Landscaping and Groundskeeping, A
Legal Assistant/Paralegal, A
Logistics and Materials Management, A
Machine Shop Technology/Assistant, A
Marketing, A
Marketing/Marketing Management, A
Mechanical Drafting and Mechanical Drafting
CAD/CADD, A
Medical Insurance Specialist/Medical Biller, A
Medical Radiologic Technology/Science - Radiation
Therapist, A
Multi-/Interdisciplinary Studies, A
Operations Management and Supervision, A
Physical Therapist Assistant, A
Prepress/Desktop Publishing and Digital Imaging
Design, A
Quality Control Technology/Technician, A
Respiratory Care Therapy/Therapist, A
Retailing and Retail Operations, A
Teacher Assistant/Aide, A
Web/Multimedia Management and Webmaster, A

NORTHLAND COLLEGE

American Indian/Native American Studies, B
Biology/Biological Sciences, B
Business Administration and Management, B
Chemistry, B
Community Organization and Advocacy, B
Engineering, B
English Language and Literature, B
Entrepreneurship/Entrepreneurial Studies, B
Environmental Studies, B
Fine/Studio Arts, B
Forestry, B
Geology/Earth Science, B
Graphic Design, B

History, B
Humanities/Humanistic Studies, B
Hydrology and Water Resources Science, B
Mathematics, B
Meteorology, B
Natural Resources Conservation and Research, B
Natural Resources and Conservation, B
Psychology, B
Religion/Religious Studies, B
Science Teacher Education/General Science
Teacher Education, B
Secondary Education and Teaching, B
Social Studies Teacher Education, B
Sociology, B
Teacher Education, Multiple Levels, B
Women's Studies, B

RASMUSSEN COLLEGE APPLETON

Accounting, A
Accounting and Business/Management, B
Business Administration and Management, A
Computer Science, B
Computer Software Engineering, A
Computer and Information Systems Security, B
Corrections and Criminal Justice, A
Early Childhood Education and Teaching, A
Graphic Communications, B
Health Information/Medical Records
Administration/Administrator, B
Health Information/Medical Records
Technology/Technician, A
Health/Health Care Administration/Management, B
Human Resources Management/Personnel Administration, A
Human Services, A
Legal Assistant/Paralegal, A
Management Information Systems and Services, A
Marketing/Marketing Management, A
Medical Administrative Assistant/Secretary, A
Medical/Clinical Assistant, A
Pharmacy Technician/Assistant, A
Web Page, Digital/Multimedia and Information Resources Design, A

RASMUSSEN COLLEGE GREEN BAY

Accounting, A
Accounting and Business/Management, B
Business Administration and Management, A
Clinical/Medical Laboratory Technician, A
Computer Science, B
Computer Software Engineering, A
Computer and Information Systems Security, B
Corrections and Criminal Justice, A
Early Childhood Education and Teaching, A
Graphic Communications, B
Health Information/Medical Records
Administration/Administrator, B
Health Information/Medical Records
Technology/Technician, A
Health/Health Care Administration/Management, B
Human Resources Management/Personnel Administration, A
Human Services, A
Legal Assistant/Paralegal, A
Management Information Systems and Services, A
Marketing/Marketing Management, A
Medical Administrative Assistant/Secretary, A
Medical/Clinical Assistant, A
Pharmacy Technician/Assistant, A
Web Page, Digital/Multimedia and Information Resources Design, A

RASMUSSEN COLLEGE WAUSAU

Accounting, A
Accounting and Business/Management, B
Business Administration and Management, A
Computer Science, B
Computer Software Engineering, A
Computer and Information Systems Security, B
Corrections and Criminal Justice, A
Early Childhood Education and Teaching, A
Graphic Communications, B
Health Information/Medical Records
Administration/Administrator, B
Health Information/Medical Records
Technology/Technician, A

Health/Health Care Administration/Management, B
Human Resources Management/Personnel Adminis-
    tration, A
Human Services, A
Legal Assistant/Paralegal, A
Management Information Systems and Services, A
Marketing/Marketing Management, A
Medical Administrative Assistant/Secretary, A
Medical/Clinical Assistant, A
Pharmacy Technician/Assistant, A
Web Page, Digital/Multimedia and Information Re-
    sources Design, A

RIPON COLLEGE

Anthropology, B
Art/Art Studies, General, B
Biochemistry, B
Biology/Biological Sciences, B
Business Administration and Management, B
Chemistry, B
Communication Studies/Speech Communication
    and Rhetoric, B
Computer Science, B
Drama and Dramatics/Theatre Arts, B
Early Childhood Education and Teaching, B
Economics, B
Education, B
Elementary Education and Teaching, B
English Language and Literature, B
Environmental Studies, B
History, B
Latin American Studies, B
Mathematics, B
Music, B
Music Teacher Education, B
Philosophy, B
Physical Education Teaching and Coaching, B
Physical Sciences, B
Political Science and Government, B
Pre-Dentistry Studies, B
Pre-Law Studies, B
Pre-Medicine/Pre-Medical Studies, B
Pre-Veterinary Studies, B
Psychology, B
Religion/Religious Studies, B
Romance Languages, Literatures, and Linguistics, B
Secondary Education and Teaching, B
Sociology, B
Spanish Language and Literature, B

ST. NORBERT COLLEGE

Accounting, B
Art/Art Studies, General, B
Biological and Physical Sciences, B
Biology/Biological Sciences, B
Business Administration and Management, B
Chemistry, B
Commercial and Advertising Art, B
Communication Studies/Speech Communication
    and Rhetoric, B
Computer Science, B
Computer and Information Sciences, B
Drama and Dramatics/Theatre Arts, B
Economics, B
Elementary Education and Teaching, B
English Language and Literature, B
Environmental Sciences, B
French Language and Literature, B
Geology/Earth Science, B
German Language and Literature, B
Graphic Design, B
History, B
Humanities/Humanistic Studies, B
International Business/Trade/Commerce, B
International Relations and Affairs, B
International/Global Studies, B
Liberal Studies, M
Mass Communication/Media Studies, B
Mathematics, B
Music, B
Music Teacher Education, B
Philosophy, B
Physics, B
Political Science and Government, B
Psychology, B
Religion/Religious Studies, B

Sociology, B
Spanish Language and Literature, B
Theology and Religious Vocations, M

SILVER LAKE COLLEGE OF THE HOLY FAMILY

Accounting, B
Art Teacher Education, B
Art/Art Studies, General, B
Biology/Biological Sciences, B
Business Administration and Management, B
Computer Science, B
Early Childhood Education and Teaching, B
Education, M
Education/Teaching of Individuals in Early Childhood
    Special Education Programs, B
Education/Teaching of Individuals with Mental Retar-
    dation, B
Education/Teaching of Individuals with Specific
    Learning Disabilities, B
Educational Administration and Supervision, M
Educational Leadership and Administration, M
Elementary Education and Teaching, B
Engineering Technologies/Technicians, B
English Language and Literature, B
History, B
Human Resources Management/Personnel Adminis-
    tration, B
Information Science/Studies, B
Kindergarten/PreSchool Education and Teaching, B
Management, M
Mathematics, B
Music, B
Music Teacher Education, BM
Organizational Behavior Studies, M
Psychology, B
Public Administration, B
Special Education and Teaching, M
Theology/Theological Studies, B

SOUTHWEST WISCONSIN TECHNICAL COLLEGE

Accounting, A
Administrative Assistant and Secretarial Science, A
Agricultural/Farm Supplies Retailing and Wholesal-
    ing, A
Computer Graphics, A
Computer Programming/Programmer, A
Computer Systems Networking and Telecommunica-
    tions, A
Computer and Information Sciences and Support
    Services, A
Criminal Justice/Police Science, A
Direct Entry Midwifery (LM, CPM), A
Early Childhood Education and Teaching, A
Electromechanical Technology/Electromechanical
    Engineering Technology, A
Finance, A
Marketing/Marketing Management, A
Mechanical Drafting and Mechanical Drafting
    CAD/CADD, A
Mental and Social Health Services and Allied Pro-
    fessions, A
Multi-/Interdisciplinary Studies, A
Operations Management and Supervision, A
Parks, Recreation and Leisure Facilities Manage-
    ment, A
Restaurant, Culinary, and Catering
    Management/Manager, A

UNIVERSITY OF WISCONSIN–BARABOO/SAUK COUNTY

Liberal Arts and Sciences Studies and Humani-
    ties, A

UNIVERSITY OF WISCONSIN–BARRON COUNTY

Liberal Arts and Sciences Studies and Humani-
    ties, A

UNIVERSITY OF WISCONSIN–EAU CLAIRE

Accounting, B
American Indian/Native American Studies, B

Art/Art Studies, General, B
Athletic Training and Sports Medicine, B
Biology/Biological Sciences, B
Business Administration and Management, B
Business Administration, Management and Opera-
    tions, M
Chemistry, B
Communication Disorders, BM
Community Health and Preventive Medicine, B
Computer and Information Sciences, B
Criminal Justice/Safety Studies, B
Drama and Dramatics/Theatre Arts, B
Economics, B
Education, M
Elementary Education and Teaching, B
English, M
English Language and Literature, B
Finance, B
French Language and Literature, B
Geography, B
Geology/Earth Science, B
Germanic Languages, Literatures, and Linguistics, B
Gerontological Nursing, D
Health/Health Care Administration/Management, B
History, BM
Information Resources Management/CIO Training, B
International Business/Trade/Commerce, B
Journalism, B
Kinesiology and Exercise Science, B
Latin American Studies, B
Liberal Arts and Sciences Studies and Humani-
    ties, AB
Library Science, M
Marketing/Marketing Management, B
Mass Communication/Media Studies, B
Mathematics, B
Molecular Biology, B
Music, B
Nursing, MD
Nursing - Adult, MD
Nursing - Advanced Practice, MD
Nursing Administration, D
Nursing Education, M
Philosophy, B
Physics, B
Political Science and Government, B
Psychology, BMO
Reading Teacher Education, M
Religion/Religious Studies, B
School Psychology, MO
Science Teacher Education/General Science
    Teacher Education, B
Secondary Education and Teaching, M
Social Studies Teacher Education, B
Social Work, B
Sociology, B
Spanish Language and Literature, B
Special Education and Teaching, BM
Teacher Education and Professional Develop-
    ment, Specific Subject Areas, B
Women's Studies, B
Writing, M

UNIVERSITY OF WISCONSIN–FOND DU LAC

Liberal Arts and Sciences Studies and Humani-
    ties, A

UNIVERSITY OF WISCONSIN–FOX VAL-LEY

Liberal Arts and Sciences Studies and Humani-
    ties, A

UNIVERSITY OF WISCONSIN–GREEN BAY

Accounting, B
American Indian/Native American Studies, B
Art/Art Studies, General, B
Behavioral Sciences, B
Biology/Biological Sciences, B
Business Administration and Management, B
Chemistry, B
Communication, Journalism and Related Pro-
    grams, B
Computer Science, B

Design and Visual Communications, B
Drama and Dramatics/Theatre Arts, B
Economics, B
Education, BM
Electrical, Electronic and Communications Engineering Technology/Technician, B
English Language and Literature, B
Environmental Engineering Technology/Environmental Technology, B
Environmental Policy, M
Environmental Sciences, BM
Environmental Studies, B
French Language and Literature, B
Geology/Earth Science, B
Germanic Languages, Literatures, and Linguistics, B
Health Information/Medical Records Administration/Administrator, B
History, B
Humanities/Humanistic Studies, B
Information Science/Studies, B
Liberal Arts and Sciences Studies and Humanities, AB
Management, M
Management Information Systems and Services, B
Mathematics, B
Mechanical Engineering/Mechanical Technology/Technician, B
Multi-/Interdisciplinary Studies, B
Music, B
Music Teacher Education, B
Nursing Administration, M
Philosophy, B
Political Science and Government, B
Psychology, B
Public Administration, B
Social Sciences, B
Social Work, BM
Spanish Language and Literature, B
Sustainability Management, M
Urban Studies/Affairs, B
Visual and Performing Arts, B

UNIVERSITY OF WISCONSIN–LA CROSSE

Accounting, B
Archeology, B
Art Teacher Education, B
Art/Art Studies, General, B
Athletic Training and Sports Medicine, BM
Biochemistry, B
Biological and Biomedical Sciences, M
Biology/Biological Sciences, B
Business Administration and Management, B
Business Administration, Management and Operations, M
Cancer Biology/Oncology, M
Cell Biology and Anatomy, M
Chemistry, B
Clinical Laboratory Science/Medical Technology/Technologist, B
Clinical Microbiology, M
Communication Studies/Speech Communication and Rhetoric, B
Community Health and Preventive Medicine, BM
Computer and Information Sciences, B
Drama and Dramatics/Theatre Arts, B
Economics, B
Education, M
Elementary Education and Teaching, B
English Language and Literature, B
Exercise and Sports Science, M
Finance, B
French Language and Literature, B
Geography, B
German Language and Literature, B
Health Education, M
Health Teacher Education, B
Health and Physical Education, B
Higher Education/Higher Education Administration, M
History, B
Insurance, B
International Business/Trade/Commerce, B
Kinesiology and Exercise Science, M
Liberal Arts and Sciences Studies and Humanities, A

Management Information Systems and Services, B
Marine Sciences, M
Marketing/Marketing Management, B
Mathematics, B
Medical Microbiology and Bacteriology, B
Medical Radiologic Technology/Science - Radiation Therapist, B
Microbiology, BM
Molecular Biology, M
Music, B
Nuclear Medical Technology/Technologist, B
Nurse Anesthetist, M
Occupational Therapy/Therapist, M
Parks, Recreation and Leisure Facilities Management, B
Philosophy, B
Physical Education Teaching and Coaching, M
Physical Therapy/Therapist, D
Physician Assistant, M
Physics, B
Physiology, M
Political Science and Government, B
Psychology, BMO
Public Administration, B
Public Health Education and Promotion, B
Recreation and Park Management, M
Rehabilitation Sciences, M
School Psychology, MO
Science Teacher Education/General Science Teacher Education, B
Social Studies Teacher Education, B
Sociology, B
Software Engineering, M
Spanish Language and Literature, B
Student Personnel Services, M
Therapeutic Recreation, M
Therapeutic Recreation/Recreational Therapy, B
Women's Studies, B

UNIVERSITY OF WISCONSIN–MADISON

Accounting, BMD
Actuarial Science, B
African Languages, Literatures, and Linguistics, B
African Studies, MD
African-American Studies, M
African-American/Black Studies, B
Agricultural Business and Management, B
Agricultural Communication/Journalism, B
Agricultural Economics, BMD
Agricultural Engineering, MD
Agricultural Sciences, MD
Agricultural/Biological Engineering and Bioengineering, B
Agronomy and Crop Science, B
Agronomy and Soil Sciences, MD
Allopathic Medicine, D
American/United States Studies/Civilization, MD
Animal Sciences, BMD
Anthropology, BD
Apparel and Textiles, B
Applied Economics, MD
Applied Mathematics, B
Archeology, D
Art Education, M
Art History, Criticism and Conservation, BMD
Art Teacher Education, B
Art/Art Studies, General, B
Arts Management, M
Asian Languages, MD
Asian Studies/Civilization, BMD
Astronomy, D
Astrophysics, B
Athletic Training and Sports Medicine, B
Atmospheric Sciences and Meteorology, BMD
Audiology/Audiologist and Speech-Language Pathology/Pathologist, B
Bacteriology, M
Biochemistry, BMD
Biological and Biomedical Sciences, MD
Biology/Biological Sciences, B
Biomedical Engineering, MD
Biomedical/Medical Engineering, B
Biometry/Biometrics, M
Biophysics, D
Biopsychology, D
Botany/Plant Biology, BMD

Business Administration and Management, B
Business Administration, Management and Operations, M
Cancer Biology/Oncology, D
Cartography, B
Cell Biology and Anatomy, D
Chemical Engineering, BD
Chemistry, BMD
Child and Family Studies, MD
Chinese Language and Literature, B
Chinese Studies, MD
Civil Engineering, BMD
Classics and Classical Languages, Literatures, and Linguistics, BMD
Clinical Psychology, D
Cognitive Sciences, D
Communication Disorders, MD
Communication Studies/Speech Communication and Rhetoric, B
Communication and Media Studies, MD
Community Health and Preventive Medicine, MD
Comparative Literature, BMD
Composition, MD
Computer Engineering, B
Computer Science, MD
Computer and Information Sciences, B
Computer and Information Systems Security, M
Conservation Biology, BM
Consumer Economics, MD
Counseling Psychology, D
Counselor Education/School Counseling and Guidance Services, M
Cultural Anthropology, D
Curriculum and Instruction, MD
Dairy Science, BMD
Dance, B
Design and Applied Arts, MD
Developmental Psychology, D
Drama and Dramatics/Theatre Arts, B
East Asian Studies, MD
Ecology, M
Economics, BD
Education, MDO
Educational Administration and Supervision, O
Educational Leadership and Administration, MDO
Educational Policy, MD
Educational Psychology, MD
Electrical Engineering, MD
Electrical, Electronics and Communications Engineering, B
Elementary Education and Teaching, B
Engineering, B
Engineering Mechanics, B
Engineering Physics, BMD
Engineering and Applied Sciences, MD
English, MD
English Language and Literature, B
Entomology, BMD
Environmental Biology, MD
Environmental Engineering Technology/Environmental Technology, MD
Environmental Sciences, B
Environmental Studies, B
Epidemiology, MD
Ethnomusicology, MD
Family and Community Services, B
Family and Consumer Sciences/Human Sciences, MD
Film, Television, and Video Theory and Criticism, MD
Finance, B
Finance and Banking, MD
Financial Planning and Services, B
Fine Arts and Art Studies, M
Fish, Game and Wildlife Management, MD
Folklore, D
Food Science, B
Food Science and Technology, MD
Foreign Language Teacher Education, M
Forest Sciences and Biology, B
Forestry, MD
French Language and Literature, BMDO
Genetic Counseling/Counselor, MD
Genetics, BMD
Geographic Information Systems, MO
Geography, BMDO

Geological Engineering, MD
Geological/Geophysical Engineering, B
Geology/Earth Science, BMD
Geophysics and Seismology, MD
German Language and Literature, MD
Germanic Languages, Literatures, and Linguistics, B
Gerontological Nursing, D
Hebrew Language and Literature, MD
Hebrew Studies, MD
Higher Education/Higher Education Administration, M
History, BMD
History and Philosophy of Science and Technology, B
History of Science and Technology, MD
Horticultural Science, BMD
Human Development, MD
Human Development and Family Studies, B
Human Resources Management and Services, MD
Industrial Engineering, B
Industrial/Management Engineering, MD
Information Science/Studies, MD
Insurance, BMD
Interior Design, B
International Business/Trade/Commerce, B
International and Comparative Education, M
International/Global Studies, B
Investment Management, D
Italian Language and Literature, BMD
Japanese Language and Literature, B
Japanese Studies, MD
Jewish/Judaic Studies, B
Journalism, BMD
Kinesiology and Exercise Science, B
Kinesiology and Movement Studies, MD
Landscape Architecture, BM
Latin American Studies, MD
Latin Language and Literature, B
Law and Legal Studies, BMD
Library Science, MD
Limnology, MD
Linguistics, BMD
Management, M
Management Information Systems and Services, BD
Management Strategy and Policy, M
Management of Technology, M
Manufacturing Engineering, M
Marine Sciences, MD
Marketing, D
Marketing Research, M
Marketing/Marketing Management, B
Mass Communication/Media Studies, MD
Materials Engineering, BMD
Materials Sciences, MD
Mathematics, BD
Mathematics Teacher Education, M
Mechanical Engineering, BMD
Mechanics, MD
Media Studies, MD
Medical Microbiology and Bacteriology, D
Medical Physics, MD
Microbiology, BD
Molecular Biology, BD
Music, BMD
Music History, Literature, and Theory, MD
Music Performance, B
Music Teacher Education, BMD
Music Theory and Composition, MD
Musicology and Ethnomusicology, D
Natural Resources Management/Development and Policy, MD
Near and Middle Eastern Studies, MD
Neurobiology and Neurophysiology, D
Neuroscience, D
Nuclear Engineering, BMD
Nursing, D
Nursing - Adult, D
Nutritional Sciences, BMD
Occupational Therapy/Therapist, MD
Oceanography, Chemical and Physical, MD
Operations Management and Supervision, B
Pathology/Experimental Pathology, D
Pediatric Nurse/Nursing, D
Performance, MD
Pharmaceutical Administration, MD
Pharmaceutical Sciences, MD

Pharmacology, D
Pharmacology and Toxicology, B
Pharmacy, D
Philosophy, BMD
Physical Education Teaching and Coaching, B
Physics, BMD
Physiology, MD
Plant Pathology/Phytopathology, BMD
Plant Sciences, MD
Polish Language and Literature, B
Political Science and Government, BD
Polymer/Plastics Engineering, M
Portuguese Language and Literature, BMD
Poultry Science, B
Psychiatric/Mental Health Nurse/Nursing, D
Psychology, BD
Public Affairs, M
Real Estate, BMD
Rehabilitation Counseling, MD
Religion/Religious Studies, B
Retailing and Retail Operations, B
Rhetoric, MD
Rural Sociology, M
Russian Language and Literature, B
Scandinavian Languages, Literatures, and Linguistics, MD
Scandinavian Studies, B
Science Teacher Education/General Science Teacher Education, M
Slavic Languages, Literatures, and Linguistics, MD
Social Psychology, D
Social Work, BMD
Sociology, BMD
Soil Science and Agronomy, B
South and Southeast Asian Studies, MD
Spanish Language and Literature, BMD
Special Education and Teaching, BMD
Speech and Interpersonal Communication, MD
Statistics, BMD
Supply Chain Management, M
Sustainable Development, M
Systems Engineering, MD
Taxation, M
Theater, MD
Toxicology, MD
Urban and Regional Planning, MD
Veterinary Medicine, MD
Veterinary Sciences, MD
Vocational Rehabilitation Counseling/Counselor, B
Water Resources, M
Wildlife and Wildlands Science and Management, B
Women's Studies, BMD
Writing, M
Zoology/Animal Biology, BMD

UNIVERSITY OF WISCONSIN–MANITOWOC

Liberal Arts and Sciences Studies and Humanities, A

UNIVERSITY OF WISCONSIN–MARATHON COUNTY

Liberal Arts and Sciences Studies and Humanities, A

UNIVERSITY OF WISCONSIN–MARINETTE

Liberal Arts and Sciences Studies and Humanities, A

UNIVERSITY OF WISCONSIN–MARSHFIELD/WOOD COUNTY

Liberal Arts and Sciences Studies and Humanities, A

UNIVERSITY OF WISCONSIN–MILWAUKEE

Accounting, B
Actuarial Science, B
Adult and Continuing Education and Teaching, D
African Studies, D
African-American/Black Studies, B
Allied Health and Medical Assisting Services, MDO

Anthropology, BMDO
Applied Mathematics, B
Architecture, BMDO
Archives/Archival Administration, O
Art Education, M
Art History, Criticism and Conservation, BMO
Art Teacher Education, B
Art/Art Studies, General, B
Athletic Training and Sports Medicine, B
Audiology/Audiologist and Speech-Language Pathology/Pathologist, B
Biochemistry, BD
Biological and Biomedical Sciences, MD
Biology/Biological Sciences, B
Business Administration, Management and Operations, MDO
Business/Commerce, B
Chemistry, BMD
Civil Engineering, BM
Classics and Classical Languages, Literatures, and Linguistics, BM
Clinical Laboratory Science/Medical Technology/Technologist, B
Clinical Psychology, MD
Communication Disorders, MO
Communication Studies/Speech Communication and Rhetoric, B
Communication and Media Studies, MDO
Community Psychology, M
Comparative Literature, BMDO
Composition, M
Computer Engineering, BM
Computer Science, BM
Computer and Information Sciences, B
Conflict Resolution and Mediation/Peace Studies, O
Corrections, M
Counseling Psychology, D
Counselor Education/School Counseling and Guidance Services, MD
Criminal Justice/Safety Studies, B
Criminology, M
Curriculum and Instruction, MD
Dance, BM
Developmental Psychology, MD
Drama and Dramatics/Theatre Arts, B
Early Childhood Education and Teaching, M
Economics, BMD
Education, BMDO
Educational Administration and Supervision, MDO
Educational Measurement and Evaluation, MD
Educational Psychology, MD
Electrical Engineering, M
Electrical, Electronics and Communications Engineering, B
Elementary Education and Teaching, M
Engineering Management, M
Engineering and Applied Sciences, MDO
English, MDO
English Language and Literature, B
English as a Second Language, O
Environmental Sciences, B
Environmental and Occupational Health, D
Ergonomics and Human Factors, O
Film, Television, and Video Production, M
Film/Cinema Studies, B
Finance, B
Fine Arts and Art Studies, BM
Foundations and Philosophy of Education, MD
French Language and Literature, BMO
Geochemistry, D
Geographic Information Systems, O
Geography, BMD
Geology/Earth Science, BMD
German Language and Literature, M
Germanic Languages, Literatures, and Linguistics, B
Gerontology, O
Health Education, O
Health Informatics, MO
Health Promotion, M
Hebrew Studies, M
Higher Education/Higher Education Administration, O
Historic Preservation and Conservation, O
History, BMD
Hospital and Health Care Facilities Administration/Management, B

Human Resources Development, BMO
Industrial Engineering, B
Industrial and Labor Relations, MO
Industrial/Management Engineering, M
Information Science/Studies, BMDO
Interdisciplinary Studies, D
International Business/Trade/Commerce, O
International/Global Studies, B
Investment Management, O
Italian Language and Literature, BMO
Jewish/Judaic Studies, B
Kinesiology and Exercise Science, B
Kinesiology and Movement Studies, M
Law Enforcement, M
Liberal Arts and Sciences Studies and Humanities, B
Liberal Studies, M
Library Science, MDO
Linguistics, BMDO
Management Information Systems and Services, B
Manufacturing Engineering, BM
Marketing/Marketing Management, B
Marriage and Family Therapy/Counseling, O
Mass Communication/Media Studies, B
Materials Engineering, BM
Mathematics, BMD
Mechanical Engineering, BM
Mechanics, M
Media Studies, MO
Medical Informatics, D
Meteorology, B
Microbiology, B
Middle School Education, M
Multi-/Interdisciplinary Studies, B
Multilingual and Multicultural Education, D
Museology/Museum Studies, O
Music, BMO
Music History, Literature, and Theory, M
Music Teacher Education, BM
Non-Profit/Public/Organizational Management, MO
Nursing, MDO
Nursing - Advanced Practice, O
Nutritional Sciences, B
Occupational Therapy/Therapist, BMO
Operations Management and Supervision, B
Performance, MO
Philosophy, BM
Physical Therapy/Therapist, D
Physics, BMD
Political Science and Government, BMD
Pre-Medicine/Pre-Medical Studies, B
Psychology, BMD
Public Administration, M
Public Health, MDO
Reading Teacher Education, M
Real Estate, BO
Religion/Religious Studies, B
Rhetoric, DO
Russian Language and Literature, B
School Psychology, DO
Secondary Education and Teaching, M
Slavic Languages, Literatures, and Linguistics, M
Social Work, BMDO
Sociology, BM
Spanish Language and Literature, BMO
Special Education and Teaching, BMDO
Taxation, O
Technical Communication, O
Theater, M
Therapeutic Recreation, O
Therapeutic Recreation/Recreational Therapy, B
Translation and Interpretation, O
Urban Education and Leadership, BMD
Urban Planning, MO
Urban Studies/Affairs, MD
Water Resources, MD
Women's Studies, BM
Writing, DO

UNIVERSITY OF WISCONSIN–OSHKOSH

Accounting, B
Anthropology, B
Art Teacher Education, B
Art/Art Studies, General, B

Audiology/Audiologist and Speech-Language Pathology/Pathologist, B
Biological and Biomedical Sciences, M
Biology/Biological Sciences, B
Botany/Plant Biology, M
Broadcast Journalism, B
Business Administration and Management, B
Business Administration, Management and Operations, M
Chemistry, B
Clinical Laboratory Science/Medical Technology/Technologist, B
Computer Science, B
Counselor Education/School Counseling and Guidance Services, M
Criminal Justice/Law Enforcement Administration, B
Curriculum and Instruction, M
Drama and Dramatics/Theatre Arts, B
Early Childhood Education and Teaching, M
Economics, B
Education, BM
Educational Leadership and Administration, M
Elementary Education and Teaching, B
English, M
English Language and Literature, B
Experimental Psychology, M
Finance, B
Fine/Studio Arts, B
French Language and Literature, B
Geography, B
Geology/Earth Science, B
German Language and Literature, B
Health Services Administration, M
History, B
Human Services, B
Industrial and Organizational Psychology, M
International Business/Trade/Commerce, M
International Relations and Affairs, B
Journalism, B
Kindergarten/PreSchool Education and Teaching, B
Liberal Arts and Sciences Studies and Humanities, AB
Management Information Systems and Services, B
Marketing/Marketing Management, B
Mass Communication/Media Studies, B
Mathematics, B
Mathematics Teacher Education, M
Medical Microbiology and Bacteriology, B
Microbiology, M
Music, B
Music Teacher Education, B
Music Therapy/Therapist, B
Nursing, M
Nursing - Adult, M
Nursing - Advanced Practice, M
Philosophy, B
Physical Education Teaching and Coaching, B
Physics, B
Political Science and Government, B
Pre-Dentistry Studies, B
Pre-Law Studies, B
Pre-Medicine/Pre-Medical Studies, B
Pre-Veterinary Studies, B
Psychology, BM
Public Administration, M
Radio and Television, B
Reading Teacher Education, M
Religion/Religious Studies, B
Secondary Education and Teaching, B
Social Work, BM
Sociology, B
Spanish Language and Literature, B
Special Education and Teaching, BM
Teaching English as a Second or Foreign Language/ESL Language Instructor, B
Urban Studies/Affairs, B
Zoology/Animal Biology, M

UNIVERSITY OF WISCONSIN–PARKSIDE

Accounting, B
Art/Art Studies, General, B
Biological and Biomedical Sciences, B
Business Administration and Management, B
Business Administration, Management and Operations, M

Chemistry, B
Clinical Laboratory Science/Medical Technology/Technologist, A
Computer Science, BM
Criminal Justice/Law Enforcement Administration, B
Drama and Dramatics/Theatre Arts, B
Economics, AB
English Language and Literature, B
Geography, B
Geology/Earth Science, B
Health Professions and Related Clinical Sciences, B
History, B
Information Science/Studies, M
International Relations and Affairs, B
Kinesiology and Exercise Science, B
Liberal Arts and Sciences Studies and Humanities, AB
Marketing/Marketing Management, B
Mathematics, B
Molecular Biology, BM
Music, B
Philosophy, B
Physics, AB
Political Science and Government, B
Pre-Dentistry Studies, B
Pre-Medicine/Pre-Medical Studies, B
Pre-Pharmacy Studies, B
Pre-Veterinary Studies, B
Psychology, B
Social Sciences, A
Sociology, B
Spanish Language and Literature, B
Sport and Fitness Administration/Management, B

UNIVERSITY OF WISCONSIN–PLATTEVILLE

Accounting, B
Adult and Continuing Education and Teaching, M
Agribusiness, B
Agricultural Business and Management, B
Agricultural Teacher Education, B
Agronomy and Crop Science, B
Animal Sciences, B
Art/Art Studies, General, B
Biological and Physical Sciences, B
Biology/Biological Sciences, B
Business Administration and Management, B
Business/Commerce, B
Cartography, B
Chemistry, B
Civil Engineering, B
Communication Studies/Speech Communication and Rhetoric, B
Communications Technologies/Technicians and Support Services, B
Computer Science, BM
Computer Software Engineering, B
Computer and Information Sciences, B
Counselor Education/School Counseling and Guidance Services, M
Criminal Justice/Law Enforcement Administration, B
Criminal Justice/Safety Studies, B
Criminology, M
Economics, B
Education, BM
Electrical, Electronics and Communications Engineering, B
Elementary Education and Teaching, BM
Engineering, B
Engineering Physics, B
Engineering and Applied Sciences, M
English Education, B
English Language and Literature, B
Environmental/Environmental Health Engineering, B
Foreign Languages and Literatures, B
Forensic Science and Technology, B
Geography, B
German Language and Literature, B
History, B
Horticultural Science, B
Industrial Design, B
Industrial Engineering, B
Industrial Technology/Technician, B
International/Global Studies, B
Liberal Arts and Sciences Studies and Humanities, B

Manufacturing Technology/Technician, B
Mathematics, B
Mechanical Engineering, B
Middle School Education, M
Multi-/Interdisciplinary Studies, B
Music, B
Natural Resources and Conservation, B
Ornamental Horticulture, B
Philosophy, B
Physical Education Teaching and Coaching, B
Political Science and Government, B
Project Management, M
Psychology, B
Science Teacher Education/General Science
   Teacher Education, B
Secondary Education and Teaching, BM
Social Sciences, B
Spanish Language and Literature, B
Technology Teacher Education/Industrial Arts
   Teacher Education, B

UNIVERSITY OF WISCONSIN–RICHLAND

Biological and Physical Sciences, A
Liberal Arts and Sciences Studies and Humanities, A

UNIVERSITY OF WISCONSIN–RIVER FALLS

Accounting, B
Agribusiness, B
Agricultural Education, M
Agricultural Mechanization, B
Agricultural Sciences, M
Agricultural Teacher Education, B
Agriculture, B
Agronomy and Crop Science, B
Animal Sciences, B
Art Teacher Education, B
Art/Art Studies, General, B
BioTechnology, B
Biological and Physical Sciences, B
Biology/Biological Sciences, B
Business Administration and Management, B
Chemistry, B
Communication Disorders, BM
Communication Studies/Speech Communication
   and Rhetoric, B
Computer and Information Sciences, B
Counselor Education/School Counseling and Guid-
   ance Services, MO
Criminology, B
Dairy Science, B
Drama and Dramatics/Theatre Arts, B
Early Childhood Education and Teaching, B
Economics, B
Education, M
Elementary Education and Teaching, BM
English Language and Literature, B
English as a Second Language, M
Fine Arts and Art Studies, M
Food Science, B
Foreign Languages and Literatures, B
Geography, B
Geology/Earth Science, B
History, B
Horticultural Science, B
International/Global Studies, B
Journalism, B
Land Use Planning and
   Management/Development, B
Liberal Arts and Sciences Studies and Humani-
   ties, B
Management, M
Mathematics, B
Mathematics Teacher Education, M
Multi-/Interdisciplinary Studies, B
Music, B
Music Teacher Education, B
Natural Resources and Conservation, B
Physical Education Teaching and Coaching, B
Physics, B
Political Science and Government, B
Psychology, B
Reading Teacher Education, M
School Psychology, MO

Science Teacher Education/General Science
   Teacher Education, M
Social Sciences, B
Social Studies Teacher Education, M
Social Work, B
Sociology, B
Teaching English as a Second or Foreign
   Language/ESL Language Instructor, B

UNIVERSITY OF WISCONSIN–ROCK COUNTY

Liberal Arts and Sciences Studies and Humanities, A

UNIVERSITY OF WISCONSIN–SHEBOYGAN

Liberal Arts and Sciences Studies and Humanities, A

UNIVERSITY OF WISCONSIN–STEVENS POINT

Accounting, B
Advertising and Public Relations, M
Athletic Training and Sports Medicine, B
Audiology/Audiologist and Speech-Language
   Pathology/Pathologist, B
Biochemistry, B
Biological and Physical Sciences, B
Biology/Biological Sciences, B
Business Administration and Management, B
Business Administration, Management and Opera-
   tions, M
Chemical Engineering, B
Chemistry, B
Clinical Laboratory Science/Medical
   Technology/Technologist, B
Commercial and Advertising Art, B
Communication Disorders, BMD
Communication Studies/Speech Communication
   and Rhetoric, B
Communication and Media Studies, M
Computer and Information Sciences, B
Corporate and Organizational Communication, M
Counselor Education/School Counseling and Guid-
   ance Services, M
Dance, B
Design and Visual Communications, B
Dietetics/Dieticians, B
Drama and Dramatics/Theatre Arts, B
Early Childhood Education and Teaching, B
Economics, B
Education, BM
Educational Administration and Supervision, M
Elementary Education and Teaching, BM
English, M
English Language and Literature, B
Family and Consumer Economics and Related Ser-
   vices, B
Family and Consumer Sciences/Home Economics
   Teacher Education, B
Family and Consumer Sciences/Human Sci-
   ences, M
Fine/Studio Arts, B
Forestry, B
French Language and Literature, B
General Studies, B
Geography, B
Geology/Earth Science, B
German Language and Literature, B
Health Professions and Related Clinical Sciences, B
Health Promotion, M
Health and Physical Education, B
History, BM
Human Development, M
Hydrology and Water Resources Science, B
Information Technology, B
Interior Design, B
International Relations and Affairs, B
International/Global Studies, B
Kindergarten/PreSchool Education and Teaching, B
Liberal Arts and Sciences Studies and Humani-
   ties, A
Mathematics, B
Media Studies, M
Multi-/Interdisciplinary Studies, B

Music, B
Music Performance, B
Music Teacher Education, BM
Natural Resources Management/Development and
   Policy, B
Natural Resources and Conservation, BM
Natural Sciences, B
Nutritional Sciences, BM
Philosophy, B
Physical Education Teaching and Coaching, B
Physics, B
Political Science and Government, B
Polymer Chemistry, B
Psychology, B
Public Administration, B
Reading Teacher Education, M
Science Teacher Education/General Science
   Teacher Education, M
Secondary Education and Teaching, BM
Social Sciences, B
Sociology, B
Soil Science and Agronomy, B
Spanish Language and Literature, B
Special Education and Teaching, BM
Speech and Interpersonal Communication, M
Web Page, Digital/Multimedia and Information Re-
   sources Design, B
Wildlife and Wildlands Science and Management, B
Wood Science and Wood Products/Pulp and Paper
   Technology, B

UNIVERSITY OF WISCONSIN–STOUT

Apparel and Textiles, B
Applied Mathematics, BM
Applied Psychology, M
Art Teacher Education, B
Business Administration and Management, B
Business, Management, Marketing, and Related
   Support Services, B
Clinical Psychology, M
Computer Engineering, B
Computer Software and Media Applications, B
Computer Systems Networking and Telecommunica-
   tions, B
Computer and Information Sciences, B
Conservation Biology, M
Construction Management, BM
Counseling Psychology, M
Design and Applied Arts, B
Dietetics/Dieticians, B
Early Childhood Education and Teaching, B
Engineering Technology, B
Environmental Sciences, B
Family and Consumer Sciences/Home Economics
   Teacher Education, B
Fine Arts and Art Studies, M
Food Science and Technology, M
Foodservice Systems
   Administration/Management, B
Graphic Communications, B
Graphic Design, B
Hospitality Administration/Management, B
Human Resources Development, M
Industrial Design, B
Industrial Hygiene, M
Industrial/Management Engineering, M
Information Science/Studies, M
Interior Design, B
Logistics and Materials Management, B
Manufacturing Engineering, BM
Marriage and Family Therapy/Counseling, M
Nutritional Sciences, M
Operations Management and Supervision, B
Polymer/Plastics Engineering, B
Project Management, M
Psychology, B
Quality Management, M
Real Estate, B
Rehabilitation Counseling, M
Sales and Marketing Operations/Marketing and Dis-
   tribution Teacher Education, B
Sales, Distribution and Marketing Operations, B
School Psychology, MO
Science Teacher Education/General Science
   Teacher Education, B
Science Technologies/Technicians, B

Social Sciences, B
Special Education and Teaching, B
Supply Chain Management, M
Sustainability Management, M
Teacher Education and Professional Develop-
ment, Specific Subject Areas, B
Technical Communication, M
Technical Teacher Education, B
Technology Teacher Education/Industrial Arts
Teacher Education, B
Telecommunications Management, M
Vocational Rehabilitation Counseling/Counselor, B
Vocational and Technical Education, MDO

UNIVERSITY OF
WISCONSIN–SUPERIOR

Accounting, B
Art Education, M
Art History, Criticism and Conservation, BM
Art Teacher Education, B
Art Therapy/Therapist, BM
Biological and Physical Sciences, B
Biology Teacher Education, B
Biology/Biological Sciences, B
Botany/Plant Biology, B
Broadcast Journalism, B
Business Administration and Management, B
Business Teacher Education, B
Business/Managerial Economics, B
Cell/Cellular and Molecular Biology, B
Chemistry, B
Chemistry Teacher Education, B
Communication and Media Studies, BM
Community Psychology, M
Computer Science, B
Computer and Information Sciences, B
Counselor Education/School Counseling and Guid-
ance Services, M
Criminal Justice/Police Science, B
Criminal Justice/Safety Studies, B
Curriculum and Instruction, M
Drama and Dramatics/Theatre Arts, B
Economics, B
Education, BM
Educational Administration and Supervision, MO
Elementary Education and Teaching, B
English Language and Literature, B
English/Language Arts Teacher Education, B
Finance, B
Fine Arts and Art Studies, M
Fine/Studio Arts, B
General Studies, A
Health and Physical Education, B
Health and Physical Education/Fitness, B
History, B
History Teacher Education, B
Information Science/Studies, B
International Relations and Affairs, B
Journalism, B
Kinesiology and Exercise Science, B
Law and Legal Studies, B
Liberal Arts and Sciences Studies and Humani-
ties, A
Marketing/Marketing Management, B
Mass Communication/Media Studies, BM
Mathematics, B
Mathematics Teacher Education, B
Multi-/Interdisciplinary Studies, B
Music, B
Music Performance, B
Music Teacher Education, B
Peace Studies and Conflict Resolution, B
Physical Education Teaching and Coaching, B
Physical Sciences, B
Political Science and Government, B
Pre-Law Studies, B
Psychology, B
Radio and Television, B
Reading Teacher Education, M
Sales, Distribution and Marketing Operations, B
School Psychology, M
Science Teacher Education/General Science
Teacher Education, B
Social Science Teacher Education, B
Social Sciences, B
Social Studies Teacher Education, B

Social Work, B
Sociology, B
Special Education and Teaching, BM
Speech and Interpersonal Communication, M
Sustainability Management, M
Theater, M
Transportation/Transportation Management, B
Visual and Performing Arts, B

UNIVERSITY OF
WISCONSIN–WASHINGTON COUNTY

Liberal Arts and Sciences Studies and Humanities, A

UNIVERSITY OF
WISCONSIN–WAUKESHA

Liberal Arts and Sciences Studies and Humanities, AB

UNIVERSITY OF
WISCONSIN–WHITEWATER

Accounting, BM
Art Teacher Education, B
Art/Art Studies, General, B
Biology/Biological Sciences, B
Business Administration and Management, B
Business Administration, Management and Opera-
tions, M
Business Education, M
Business Teacher Education, B
Business, Management, Marketing, and Related
Support Services, B
Business/Commerce, B
Chemistry, B
Communication Disorders, BM
Communication Studies/Speech Communication
and Rhetoric, B
Communication and Media Studies, M
Community Psychology, M
Computer and Information Sciences, B
Corporate and Organizational Communication, M
Counselor Education/School Counseling and Guid-
ance Services, M
Criminology, B
Curriculum and Instruction, M
Drama and Dramatics/Theatre Arts, B
Driver and Safety Teacher Education, B
Early Childhood Education and Teaching, B
Economics, B
Education, M
Education/Teaching of the Gifted and Talented, M
Educational Administration and Supervision, M
Educational Leadership and Administration, M
Elementary Education and Teaching, B
English Language and Literature, B
Entrepreneurship/Entrepreneurial Studies, B
Environmental Engineering
Technology/Environmental Technology, B
Environmental Sciences, B
Environmental and Occupational Health, M
Exercise and Sports Science, M
Finance, B
Finance and Banking, M
French Language and Literature, B
Geography, B
German Language and Literature, B
Higher Education/Higher Education Administra-
tion, M
History, B
Human Resources Management and Services, M
Human Resources Management/Personnel Adminis-
tration, B
Information Technology, B
International Business/Trade/Commerce, BM
International/Global Studies, B
Japanese Studies, B
Journalism, B
Liberal Arts and Sciences Studies and Humani-
ties, AB
Library Science, M
Management, M
Management of Technology, M
Marketing, M
Marketing/Marketing Management, B
Mass Communication/Media Studies, M

Mathematics, B
Multi-/Interdisciplinary Studies, B
Multilingual and Multicultural Education, M
Music, B
Occupational Safety and Health
Technology/Technician, B
Operations Management and Supervision, B
Physical Education Teaching and Coaching, BM
Physics, B
Political Science and Government, B
Psychology, BMO
Public Administration, B
Reading Teacher Education, M
School Psychology, MO
Social Sciences, B
Social Work, B
Sociology, B
Spanish Language and Literature, B
Special Education and Teaching, BM
Supply Chain Management, M
Women's Studies, B

VITERBO UNIVERSITY

Accounting, B
Art Teacher Education, B
Art/Art Studies, General, B
Biochemistry, B
Biology Teacher Education, B
Biology/Biological Sciences, B
Biopsychology, B
Business Administration and Management, B
Business Administration, Management and Opera-
tions, BM
Business Teacher Education, B
Chemistry, B
Chemistry Teacher Education, B
Clinical/Medical Laboratory Technician, B
Counseling Psychology, M
Criminal Justice/Law Enforcement Administration, B
Criminal Justice/Safety Studies, B
Design and Visual Communications, B
Developmental Psychology, M
Dietetics/Dieticians, B
Drama and Dance Teacher Education, B
Drama and Dramatics/Theatre Arts, B
Education, BMO
Elementary Education and Teaching, B
English Language and Literature, B
English/Language Arts Teacher Education, B
Environmental Biology, B
Finance, B
Fine/Studio Arts, B
General Studies, A
Health Psychology, M
Health Services Administration, M
Health/Health Care Administration/Management, B
History, B
International Business/Trade/Commerce, M
Kinesiology and Exercise Science, B
Liberal Arts and Sciences Studies and Humani-
ties, B
Management Information Systems and Services, B
Marketing/Marketing Management, B
Mathematics, B
Mathematics Teacher Education, B
Multi-/Interdisciplinary Studies, B
Music, B
Music Pedagogy, B
Music Performance, B
Music Teacher Education, B
Nursing, MD
Organizational Communication, B
Organizational Management, M
Pastoral Studies/Counseling, M
Philosophy, B
Pre-Dentistry Studies, B
Pre-Law Studies, B
Pre-Medicine/Pre-Medical Studies, B
Pre-Pharmacy Studies, B
Pre-Veterinary Studies, B
Project Management, M
Psychology, B
Religion/Religious Studies, B
Science Teacher Education/General Science
Teacher Education, B
Social Sciences, B

Social Studies Teacher Education, B
Social Work, B
Sociology, B
Spanish Language Teacher Education, B
Spanish Language and Literature, B
Sport and Fitness Administration/Management, B
Substance Abuse/Addiction Counseling, BM
Technology Teacher Education/Industrial Arts
 Teacher Education, B
Theoretical and Mathematical Physics, B

WAUKESHA COUNTY TECHNICAL COLLEGE

Accounting, A
Administrative Assistant and Secretarial Science, A
Architectural Drafting and Architectural
 CAD/CADD, A
Automobile/Automotive Mechanics
 Technology/Technician, A
Baking and Pastry Arts/Baker/Pastry Chef, A
Biomedical Technology/Technician, A
Business Administration and Management, A
Business Administration, Management and Opera-
 tions, A
Clinical/Medical Laboratory Technician, A
Computer Programming/Programmer, A
Computer Systems Networking and Telecommunica-
 tions, A
Criminal Justice/Police Science, A
Dental Hygiene/Hygienist, A
Early Childhood Education and Teaching, A
Electrical, Electronic and Communications Engineer-
 ing Technology/Technician, A
Emergency Medical Technology/Technician (EMT
 Paramedic), A
Fire Science/Firefighting, A
Graphic Communications, A
Graphic Design, A
Health Information/Medical Records
 Technology/Technician, A
Human Resources Management/Personnel Adminis-
 tration, A
Interior Design, A
International Marketing, A
Marketing/Marketing Management, A
Mechanical Drafting and Mechanical Drafting
 CAD/CADD, A
Medical Radiologic Technology/Science - Radiation
 Therapist, A
Multi-/Interdisciplinary Studies, A
Office Management and Supervision, A
Physical Therapist Assistant, A
Psychiatric/Mental Health Services Technician, A
Real Estate, A
Restaurant, Culinary, and Catering
 Management/Manager, A
Surgical Technology/Technologist, A
Teacher Assistant/Aide, A

WESTERN TECHNICAL COLLEGE

Accounting, A
Administrative Assistant and Secretarial Science, A
Agricultural Mechanization, A
Architectural Engineering Technology/Technician, A
Automobile/Automotive Mechanics
 Technology/Technician, A
Business Administration and Management, A
Business Administration, Management and Opera-
 tions, A
Child Care Provider/Assistant, A
Child Development, A
Clinical/Medical Laboratory Technician, A
Commercial and Advertising Art, A
Communications Technologies/Technicians and Sup-
 port Services, A
Computer Programming/Programmer, A
Consumer Merchandising/Retailing Management, A
Criminal Justice/Police Science, A
Data Processing and Data Processing
 Technology/Technician, A
Dental Hygiene/Hygienist, A
Drafting/Design Engineering
 Technologies/Technicians, A
Electrical, Electronic and Communications Engineer-
 ing Technology/Technician, A

Electromechanical Technology/Electromechanical
 Engineering Technology, A
Electroneurodiagnostic/Electroencephalographic
 Technology/Technologist, A
Fashion Merchandising, A
Finance, A
Fire Protection and Safety Technology/Technician, A
Food Technology and Processing, A
Health Information/Medical Records
 Technology/Technician, A
Heating, Air Conditioning, Ventilation and Refrigera-
 tion Maintenance Technology/Technician, A
Hospital and Health Care Facilities
 Administration/Management, A
Human Resources Management/Personnel Adminis-
 tration, A
Interior Design, A
Legal Assistant/Paralegal, A
Marketing/Marketing Management, A
Mass Communication/Media Studies, A
Medical Administrative Assistant/Secretary, A
Occupational Therapy/Therapist, A
Office Management and Supervision, A
Physical Therapist Assistant, A
Precision Production, A
Public Health, A
Radiologic Technology/Science - Radiographer, A
Respiratory Care Therapy/Therapist, A
Retailing and Retail Operations, A
Sales, Distribution and Marketing Operations, A
Surgical Technology/Technologist, A
System Administration/Administrator, A

WISCONSIN INDIANHEAD TECHNICAL COLLEGE

Accounting, A
Administrative Assistant and Secretarial Science, A
Architectural Engineering Technology/Technician, A
Business Administration and Management, A
Computer Installation and Repair
 Technology/Technician, A
Computer Programming/Programmer, A
Computer Systems Networking and Telecommunica-
 tions, A
Corrections, A
Criminal Justice/Police Science, A
Early Childhood Education and Teaching, A
Emergency Medical Technology/Technician (EMT
 Paramedic), A
Finance, A
Gerontology, A
Health Information/Medical Records
 Technology/Technician, A
Human Resources Management/Personnel Adminis-
 tration, A
Marketing/Marketing Management, A
Materials Engineering, A
Medical Administrative Assistant/Secretary, A
Occupational Therapist Assistant, A
Office Management and Supervision, A
Psychiatric/Mental Health Services Technician, A
Web Page, Digital/Multimedia and Information Re-
 sources Design, A

WISCONSIN LUTHERAN COLLEGE

Anthropology, B
Art/Art Studies, General, B
Biochemistry, B
Biology/Biological Sciences, B
Business Administration and Management, B
Business Administration, Management and Opera-
 tions, B
Chemistry, B
Chinese Studies, B
Cinematography and Film/Video Production, B
Communication Studies/Speech Communication
 and Rhetoric, B
Communication, Journalism and Related Pro-
 grams, B
Computer Science, B
Curriculum and Instruction, M
Design and Applied Arts, B
Drama and Dramatics/Theatre Arts, B
Early Childhood Education and Teaching, B
Educational Leadership and Administration, M
Educational Media/Instructional Technology, M

Elementary Education and Teaching, B
English Language and Literature, B
English/Language Arts Teacher Education, B
Environmental Sciences, B
Environmental Studies, B
German Language and Literature, B
Germanic Languages, Literatures, and Linguistics, B
History, B
Human Services, B
Kinesiology and Exercise Science, B
Marine Biology and Biological Oceanography, B
Mathematics, B
Multi-/Interdisciplinary Studies, B
Music, B
Philosophy, B
Physics, B
Psychology, B
Religion/Religious Studies, B
Science Teacher Education/General Science
 Teacher Education, M
Secondary Education and Teaching, B
Social Sciences, B
Spanish Language and Literature, B
Special Education and Teaching, B

Wyoming
CASPER COLLEGE

Accounting, A
Accounting Technology/Technician and Bookkeep-
 ing, A
Acting, A
Administrative Assistant and Secretarial Science, A
Agricultural Business and Management, A
Agricultural Communication/Journalism, A
Agriculture, A
Airline/Commercial/Professional Pilot and Flight
 Crew, A
Animal Sciences, A
Anthropology, A
Art Teacher Education, A
Art/Art Studies, General, A
Athletic Training and Sports Medicine, A
Autobody/Collision and Repair
 Technology/Technician, A
Automobile/Automotive Mechanics
 Technology/Technician, A
Biology/Biological Sciences, A
Business Administration and Management, A
Business/Office Automation/Technology/Data En-
 try, A
Cartography, A
Chemistry, A
Clinical Laboratory Science/Medical
 Technology/Technologist, A
Communication Studies/Speech Communication
 and Rhetoric, A
Computer Programming/Programmer, A
Computer and Information Systems Security, A
Construction Management, A
Construction Trades, A
Criminal Justice/Law Enforcement Administration, A
Dance, A
Diesel Mechanics Technology/Technician, A
Drafting and Design Technology/Technician, A
Economics, A
Electrical, Electronic and Communications Engineer-
 ing Technology/Technician, A
Elementary Education and Teaching, A
Emergency Medical Technology/Technician (EMT
 Paramedic), A
Energy Management and Systems
 Technology/Technician, A
Engineering, A
English Language and Literature, A
Entrepreneurship/Entrepreneurial Studies, A
Environmental Sciences, A
Fine/Studio Arts, A
Fire Science/Firefighting, A
Foreign Languages and Literatures, A
Forensic Science and Technology, A
General Studies, A
Geology/Earth Science, A
Graphic Design, A
Health Services/Allied Health/Health Sciences, A
History, A

Hospitality Administration/Management, A
Industrial Mechanics and Maintenance Technology, A
International Relations and Affairs, A
Journalism, A
Kindergarten/PreSchool Education and Teaching, A
Legal Assistant/Paralegal, A
Liberal Arts and Sciences Studies and Humanities, A
Machine Tool Technology/Machinist, A
Manufacturing Technology/Technician, A
Marketing/Marketing Management, A
Mass Communication/Media Studies, A
Mathematics, A
Mining Technology/Technician, A
Museology/Museum Studies, A
Music, A
Music Performance, A
Music Teacher Education, A
Nutritional Sciences, A
Occupational Therapist Assistant, A
Pharmacy Technician/Assistant, A
Photography, A
Physical Education Teaching and Coaching, A
Physics, A
Political Science and Government, A
Pre-Dentistry Studies, A
Pre-Law Studies, A
Pre-Medicine/Pre-Medical Studies, A
Pre-Pharmacy Studies, A
Pre-Veterinary Studies, A
Psychology, A
Radiologic Technology/Science - Radiographer, A
Range Science and Management, A
Respiratory Care Therapy/Therapist, A
Retailing and Retail Operations, A
Robotics Technology/Technician, A
Social Studies Teacher Education, A
Social Work, A
Sociology, A
Statistics, A
Substance Abuse/Addiction Counseling, A
Technical Theatre/Theatre Design and Technology, A
Technology Teacher Education/Industrial Arts Teacher Education, A
Web Page, Digital/Multimedia and Information Resources Design, A
Web/Multimedia Management and Webmaster, A
Welding Technology/Welder, A
Wildlife and Wildlands Science and Management, A
Women's Studies, A

CENTRAL WYOMING COLLEGE

Accounting, A
Accounting Technology/Technician and Bookkeeping, A
Acting, A
Administrative Assistant and Secretarial Science, A
Agricultural Business and Management, A
American Indian/Native American Studies, A
Art/Art Studies, General, A
Athletic Training and Sports Medicine, A
Automobile/Automotive Mechanics Technology/Technician, A
Biology/Biological Sciences, A
Building/Property Maintenance and Management, A
Business Administration and Management, A
Business/Commerce, A
Carpentry/Carpenter, A
Commercial Photography, A
Computer Science, A
Computer Technology/Computer Systems Technology, A
Criminal Justice/Law Enforcement Administration, A
Culinary Arts/Chef Training, A
Customer Service Support/Call Center/Teleservice Operation, A
Drama and Dramatics/Theatre Arts, A
Early Childhood Education and Teaching, A
Elementary Education and Teaching, A
Engineering, A
English Language and Literature, A
Entrepreneurship/Entrepreneurial Studies, A
Environmental Sciences, A
Environmental/Environmental Health Engineering, A

Equestrian/Equine Studies, A
Fire Science/Firefighting, A
General Studies, A
Geology/Earth Science, A
Graphic Design, A
Hotel/Motel Administration/Management, A
International/Global Studies, A
Mathematics, A
Medical Office Assistant/Specialist, A
Music, A
Occupational Safety and Health Technology/Technician, A
Parks, Recreation and Leisure Facilities Management, A
Parks, Recreation, Leisure and Fitness Studies, A
Physical Sciences, A
Pre-Law Studies, A
Psychology, A
Radio and Television, A
Range Science and Management, A
Rehabilitation and Therapeutic Professions, A
Secondary Education and Teaching, A
Security and Protective Services, A
Social Sciences, A
Teacher Assistant/Aide, A
Technical Theatre/Theatre Design and Technology, A
Welding Technology/Welder, A

EASTERN WYOMING COLLEGE

Accounting, A
Administrative Assistant and Secretarial Science, A
Agribusiness, A
Agricultural Teacher Education, A
Art/Art Studies, General, A
Biology/Biological Sciences, A
Business Administration and Management, A
Business Teacher Education, A
Communication Studies/Speech Communication and Rhetoric, A
Computer Systems Networking and Telecommunications, A
Corrections Administration, A
Cosmetology/Cosmetologist, A
Criminal Justice/Law Enforcement Administration, A
Criminal Justice/Police Science, A
Criminal Justice/Safety Studies, A
Early Childhood Education and Teaching, A
Economics, A
Elementary Education and Teaching, A
English Language and Literature, A
Environmental Biology, A
Farm/Farm and Ranch Management, A
Foreign Languages and Literatures, A
General Studies, A
Health/Medical Preparatory Programs, A
Liberal Arts and Sciences Studies and Humanities, A
Mathematics, A
Mathematics Teacher Education, A
Music, A
Music Teacher Education, A
Office Management and Supervision, A
Physical Education Teaching and Coaching, A
Pre-Dentistry Studies, A
Pre-Medicine/Pre-Medical Studies, A
Pre-Pharmacy Studies, A
Pre-Veterinary Studies, A
Range Science and Management, A
Secondary Education and Teaching, A
Social Sciences, A
Statistics, A
Veterinary/Animal Health Technology/Technician and Veterinary Assistant, A
Welding Technology/Welder, A
Wildlife and Wildlands Science and Management, A

LARAMIE COUNTY COMMUNITY COLLEGE

Accounting, A
Agribusiness, A
Agricultural Business Technology, A
Agricultural Production Operations, A
Agriculture, A
Anthropology, A
Art/Art Studies, General, A

Autobody/Collision and Repair Technology/Technician, A
Automobile/Automotive Mechanics Technology/Technician, A
Biological and Physical Sciences, A
Biology/Biological Sciences, A
Business Administration and Management, A
Business/Commerce, A
Chemistry, A
Communication Studies/Speech Communication and Rhetoric, A
Computer Programming/Programmer, A
Computer Science, A
Corrections, A
Criminal Justice/Law Enforcement Administration, A
Dental Hygiene/Hygienist, A
Diagnostic Medical Sonography/Sonographer and Ultrasound Technician, A
Diesel Mechanics Technology/Technician, A
Digital Communication and Media/Multimedia, A
Drafting and Design Technology/Technician, A
Early Childhood Education and Teaching, A
Economics, A
Education, A
Emergency Medical Technology/Technician (EMT Paramedic), A
Energy Management and Systems Technology/Technician, A
Engineering, A
English Language and Literature, A
Entrepreneurship/Entrepreneurial Studies, A
Equestrian/Equine Studies, A
Fire Science/Firefighting, A
General Studies, A
Heating, Air Conditioning, Ventilation and Refrigeration Maintenance Technology/Technician, A
History, A
Human Services, A
Humanities/Humanistic Studies, A
Kinesiology and Exercise Science, A
Legal Assistant/Paralegal, A
Mass Communication/Media Studies, A
Mathematics, A
Mechanic and Repair Technologies/Technicians, A
Medical Insurance Coding Specialist/Coder, A
Music, A
Physical Education Teaching and Coaching, A
Physical Therapist Assistant, A
Political Science and Government, A
Pre-Law Studies, A
Pre-Pharmacy Studies, A
Psychology, A
Public Administration, A
Radiologic Technology/Science - Radiographer, A
Religion/Religious Studies, A
Security and Protective Services, A
Social Sciences, A
Sociology, A
Spanish Language and Literature, A
Surgical Technology/Technologist, A
Wildlife and Wildlands Science and Management, A

NORTHWEST COLLEGE

Accounting, A
Administrative Assistant and Secretarial Science, A
Aeronautics/Aviation/Aerospace Science and Technology, A
Agribusiness, A
Agricultural Communication/Journalism, A
Agricultural Production Operations, A
Agricultural Teacher Education, A
Allied Health and Medical Assisting Services, A
Animal Sciences, A
Anthropology, A
Archeology, A
Art/Art Studies, General, A
Athletic Training and Sports Medicine, A
Biology/Biological Sciences, A
Broadcast Journalism, A
Business Administration and Management, A
Business/Commerce, A
CAD/CADD Drafting and/or Design Technology/Technician, A
Chemistry, A
Cinematography and Film/Video Production, A
Commercial Photography, A

Commercial and Advertising Art, A
Communication Studies/Speech Communication and Rhetoric, A
Criminal Justice/Law Enforcement Administration, A
Crop Production, A
Elementary Education and Teaching, A
Engineering, A
English Language and Literature, A
Equestrian/Equine Studies, A
Farm/Farm and Ranch Management, A
General Studies, A
Graphic and Printing Equipment Operator Production, A
Health Services/Allied Health/Health Sciences, A
Health and Physical Education, A
Health/Medical Preparatory Programs, A
History, A
International Relations and Affairs, A
Journalism, A
Kindergarten/PreSchool Education and Teaching, A
Liberal Arts and Sciences Studies and Humanities, A
Mathematics, A
Music, A
Natural Resources Management/Development and Policy, A
Parks, Recreation, Leisure and Fitness Studies, A
Physics, A
Playwriting and Screenwriting, A
Political Science and Government, A
Pre-Pharmacy Studies, A
Prepress/Desktop Publishing and Digital Imaging Design, A
Psychology, A
Radio and Television, A
Radio and Television Broadcasting Technology/Technician, A
Range Science and Management, A
Secondary Education and Teaching, A
Social Sciences, A
Sociology, A
Spanish Language and Literature, A
Veterinary/Animal Health Technology/Technician and Veterinary Assistant, A
Visual and Performing Arts, A
Welding Technology/Welder, A

SHERIDAN COLLEGE

Agriculture, A
Agriculture, Agriculture Operations and Related Sciences, A
Animal Sciences, A
Art/Art Studies, General, A
Biological and Physical Sciences, A
Biology/Biological Sciences, A
Business/Commerce, A
CAD/CADD Drafting and/or Design Technology/Technician, A
Community Organization and Advocacy, A
Computer and Information Sciences, A
Computer and Information Systems Security, A
Criminal Justice/Safety Studies, A
Culinary Arts/Chef Training, A
Dental Hygiene/Hygienist, A
Diesel Mechanics Technology/Technician, A
Drama and Dramatics/Theatre Arts, A
Early Childhood Education and Teaching, A
Electrical and Electronic Engineering Technologies/Technicians, A
Elementary Education and Teaching, A
Engineering, A
English Language and Literature, A
Environmental Engineering Technology/Environmental Technology, A
General Studies, A
Health Services/Allied Health/Health Sciences, A
Health and Physical Education, A
History, A
Horticultural Science, A
Hospitality Administration/Management, A
Information Science/Studies, A
Machine Tool Technology/Machinist, A
Massage Therapy/Therapeutic Massage, A
Mathematics, A
Mining Technology/Technician, A
Music, A

Precision Production, A
Psychology, A
Range Science and Management, A
Secondary Education and Teaching, A
Survey Technology/Surveying, A
Welding Technology/Welder, A

UNIVERSITY OF WYOMING

Accounting, BM
African-American/Black Studies, B
Agribusiness, B
Agricultural Communication/Journalism, B
Agricultural Economics, M
Agricultural Sciences, MD
Agricultural Teacher Education, B
Agronomy and Soil Sciences, MD
American Indian/Native American Studies, B
American/United States Studies/Civilization, BM
Animal Sciences, BMD
Anthropology, BMD
Applied Economics, M
Architectural Engineering, B
Art History, Criticism and Conservation, B
Art/Art Studies, General, B
Astronomy and Astrophysics, B
Atmospheric Sciences and Meteorology, MD
Audiology/Audiologist and Speech-Language Pathology/Pathologist, B
BioTechnology, D
Biology/Biological Sciences, B
Botany/Plant Biology, BMD
Business Administration and Management, B
Business Administration, Management and Operations, BM
Business/Managerial Economics, B
Cell Biology and Anatomy, D
Chemical Engineering, BMD
Chemistry, BMD
Child Development, M
Civil Engineering, BMD
Clinical Laboratory Science/Medical Technology/Technologist, B
Communication Disorders, M
Communication Studies/Speech Communication and Rhetoric, B
Communication and Media Studies, M
Community Health and Preventive Medicine, M
Computational Biology, D
Computer Engineering, B
Computer Science, BMD
Consumer Economics, M
Counselor Education/School Counseling and Guidance Services, MD
Criminal Justice/Safety Studies, B
Curriculum and Instruction, MD
Dental Hygiene/Hygienist, B
Drama and Dramatics/Theatre Arts, B
Ecology, MD
Economics, MD
Educational Leadership and Administration, MDO
Educational Media/Instructional Technology, MD
Electrical Engineering, MD
Electrical, Electronics and Communications Engineering, B
Elementary Education and Teaching, B
Engineering and Applied Sciences, MD
English, M
English Language and Literature, B
Entomology, MD
Environmental Engineering Technology/Environmental Technology, M
Environmental Studies, B
Exercise and Sports Science, M
Family and Consumer Sciences/Human Sciences, B
Finance, B
Finance and Banking, M
Food Science and Technology, M
French Language and Literature, BM
Genetics, D
Geography, BM
Geological and Earth Sciences/Geosciences, B
Geology/Earth Science, BMD
Geophysics and Seismology, MD
German Language and Literature, BM
Health Education, M
Health Promotion, M

History, BM
Humanities/Humanistic Studies, B
International Affairs, M
International/Global Studies, B
Journalism, B
Kinesiology and Exercise Science, B
Kinesiology and Movement Studies, M
Law and Legal Studies, D
Management Science, B
Marketing/Marketing Management, B
Mathematics, BMD
Mathematics Teacher Education, M
Mechanical Engineering, BMD
Microbiology, BD
Molecular Biology, BMD
Multi-/Interdisciplinary Studies, B
Music, BM
Music Performance, B
Music Teacher Education, BM
Natural Resources and Conservation, MD
Nursing, M
Nutritional Sciences, M
Pathobiology, M
Performance, M
Petroleum Engineering, BMD
Pharmacy, D
Philosophy, BM
Physical Education Teaching and Coaching, BM
Physical Sciences, B
Physics, B
Physiology, BMD
Political Science and Government, BM
Psychology, BMD
Public Administration, M
Range Science and Management, BMD
Religion/Religious Studies, B
Reproductive Biology, MD
Rural Planning and Studies, M
Russian Language and Literature, B
Science Teacher Education/General Science Teacher Education, M
Secondary Education and Teaching, B
Social Sciences, B
Social Work, BM
Sociology, BM
Spanish Language and Literature, BM
Special Education and Teaching, BMDO
Statistics, BMD
Student Personnel Services, M
Systems Engineering, B
Systems Science and Theory, B
Technology Teacher Education/Industrial Arts Teacher Education, B
Trade and Industrial Teacher Education, B
Water Resources, MD
Wildlife Biology, B
Women's Studies, B
Writing, M
Zoology/Animal Biology, BMD

WESTERN WYOMING COMMUNITY COLLEGE

Accounting, A
Administrative Assistant and Secretarial Science, A
Anthropology, A
Archeology, A
Art/Art Studies, General, A
Automobile/Automotive Mechanics Technology/Technician, A
Biological and Physical Sciences, A
Biology/Biological Sciences, A
Business Administration and Management, A
Chemistry, A
Communication Studies/Speech Communication and Rhetoric, A
Computer Programming, Specific Applications, A
Computer Science, A
Computer and Information Sciences, A
Criminal Justice/Law Enforcement Administration, A
Criminology, A
Dance, A
Data Entry/Microcomputer Applications, A
Data Processing and Data Processing Technology/Technician, A
Diesel Mechanics Technology/Technician, A
Drama and Dramatics/Theatre Arts, A

Early Childhood Education and Teaching, A
Economics, A
Education, A
Electrical, Electronic and Communications Engineering Technology/Technician, A
Electrical/Electronics Equipment Installation and Repair, A
Electrician, A
Elementary Education and Teaching, A
Engineering Technology, A
English Language and Literature, A
Environmental Sciences, A
Forestry, A
General Studies, A
Geology/Earth Science, A
Health Services/Allied Health/Health Sciences, A
Health/Medical Preparatory Programs, A
Heavy Equipment Maintenance Technology/Technician, A
History, A
Human Services, A
Humanities/Humanistic Studies, A
Industrial Electronics Technology/Technician, A
Industrial Mechanics and Maintenance Technology, A
Information Science/Studies, A
Information Technology, A
Instrumentation Technology/Technician, A
International Relations and Affairs, A
Journalism, A
Kinesiology and Exercise Science, A
Legal Administrative Assistant/Secretary, A
Liberal Arts and Sciences Studies and Humanities, A
Marketing/Marketing Management, A
Mathematics, A
Mechanics and Repairers, A
Medical Administrative Assistant/Secretary, A
Medical Office Assistant/Specialist, A
Medical Office Computer Specialist/Assistant, A
Medical/Clinical Assistant, A
Mining Technology/Technician, A
Music, A
Photography, A
Political Science and Government, A
Pre-Dentistry Studies, A
Pre-Law Studies, A
Pre-Medicine/Pre-Medical Studies, A
Pre-Nursing Studies, A
Pre-Pharmacy Studies, A
Pre-Veterinary Studies, A
Psychology, A
Secondary Education and Teaching, A
Social Sciences, A
Social Work, A
Sociology, A
Spanish Language and Literature, A
Teacher Education, Multiple Levels, A
Technical Theatre/Theatre Design and Technology, A
Visual and Performing Arts, A
Web Page, Digital/Multimedia and Information Resources Design, A
Web/Multimedia Management and Webmaster, A
Welding Technology/Welder, A
Wildlife and Wildlands Science and Management, A
Word Processing, A

WYOTECH LARAMIE

Autobody/Collision and Repair Technology/Technician, A
Automobile/Automotive Mechanics Technology/Technician, A
Customer Service Management, A
Diesel Mechanics Technology/Technician, A

U.S. Territories-American Samoa

AMERICAN SAMOA COMMUNITY COLLEGE

Accounting, A
Agricultural Business and Management, A
Agriculture, A

Architectural Drafting and Architectural CAD/CADD, A
Art/Art Studies, General, A
Autobody/Collision and Repair Technology/Technician, A
Automobile/Automotive Mechanics Technology/Technician, A
Business Administration and Management, A
Civil Engineering, A
Construction Trades, A
Criminal Justice/Safety Studies, A
Education, A
Electrical, Electronic and Communications Engineering Technology/Technician, A
Family and Consumer Economics and Related Services, A
Forensic Science and Technology, A
General Office Occupations and Clerical Services, A
Health Services/Allied Health/Health Sciences, A
Human Services, A
Liberal Arts and Sciences Studies and Humanities, A
Marine Science/Merchant Marine Officer, A
Music, A
Natural Resources and Conservation, A
Political Science and Government, A
Pre-Law Studies, A
Welding Technology/Welder, A

U.S. Territories-Guam

GUAM COMMUNITY COLLEGE

Accounting, A
Architectural Drafting and Architectural CAD/CADD, A
Automobile/Automotive Mechanics Technology/Technician, A
Business/Office Automation/Technology/Data Entry, A
Computer Science, A
Computer Systems Networking and Telecommunications, A
Criminal Justice/Law Enforcement Administration, A
Culinary Arts and Related Services, A
Design and Visual Communications, A
Early Childhood Education and Teaching, A
Education, A
Hotel/Motel Administration/Management, A
Human Services, A
Liberal Arts and Sciences Studies and Humanities, A
Marketing/Marketing Management, A
Medical/Clinical Assistant, A
Office Management and Supervision, A
Restaurant, Culinary, and Catering Management/Manager, A
Sales, Distribution and Marketing Operations, A
Survey Technology/Surveying, A
Tourism and Travel Services Management, A

PACIFIC ISLANDS UNIVERSITY

Religion/Religious Studies, AB

UNIVERSITY OF GUAM

Accounting, B
Agriculture, B
Anthropology, B
Biological and Biomedical Sciences, M
Biology/Biological Sciences, B
Business Administration and Management, B
Business Administration, Management and Operations, M
Ceramic Arts and Ceramics, M
Chemistry, B
Communication, Journalism and Related Programs, B
Computer Science, B
Computer/Information Technology Services Administration and Management, B
Counselor Education/School Counseling and Guidance Services, M
Criminal Justice/Law Enforcement Administration, B
Early Childhood Education and Teaching, B
Education, M
Educational Administration and Supervision, M

Elementary Education and Teaching, B
English, M
English Language and Literature, B
English as a Second Language, M
Environmental Sciences, M
Family and Consumer Sciences/Home Economics Teacher Education, B
Fine Arts and Art Studies, BM
Graphic Design, M
Health and Physical Education, B
History, B
Marine Biology and Biological Oceanography, M
Mathematics, B
Pacific Area/Pacific Rim Studies, BM
Painting, M
Philosophy, B
Physical Education Teaching and Coaching, B
Political Science and Government, B
Psychology, B
Public Administration, BM
Reading Teacher Education, M
Secondary Education and Teaching, BM
Social Work, BM
Sociology, B
Special Education and Teaching, BM
Teaching English as a Second or Foreign Language/ESL Language Instructor, B

U.S. Territories-Northern Mariana Islands

NORTHERN MARIANAS COLLEGE

Accounting, A
Administrative Assistant and Secretarial Science, A
Agricultural Business and Management, A
Agricultural Mechanization, A
Agriculture, A
Business Administration and Management, A
Data Processing and Data Processing Technology/Technician, A
Education, A
Liberal Arts and Sciences Studies and Humanities, A
Marine Maintenance/Fitter and Ship Repair Technology/Technician, A
Marketing/Marketing Management, A
Public Administration, A

U.S. Territories-Puerto Rico

AMERICAN UNIVERSITY OF PUERTO RICO (BAYAMON)

Accounting, AB
Administrative Assistant and Secretarial Science, A
Art Education, M
Business Administration and Management, AB
Communication Studies/Speech Communication and Rhetoric, AB
Computer Science, A
Computer and Information Sciences, B
Criminal Justice/Safety Studies, AB
Criminology, M
Education, M
Elementary Education and Teaching, BM
General Merchandising, Sales, and Related Marketing Operations, A
General Office Occupations and Clerical Services, A
Human Resources Management/Personnel Administration, AB
Liberal Arts and Sciences Studies and Humanities, A
Office Management and Supervision, B
Physical Education Teaching and Coaching, BM
Sales, Distribution and Marketing Operations, B
Science Teacher Education/General Science Teacher Education, M
Special Education and Teaching, BM

ATLANTIC UNIVERSITY COLLEGE

Accounting, AB
Business Administration and Management, B
Computer Graphics, AB
Computer Programming/Programmer, A
Graphic Design, M

Information Science/Studies, B
Web Page, Digital/Multimedia and Information Resources Design, B

BAYAMÓN CENTRAL UNIVERSITY

Accounting, BM
Accounting and Related Services, A
Administrative Assistant and Secretarial Science, AB
Biology/Biological Sciences, B
Business Administration and Management, B
Business Administration, Management and Operations, M
Business/Commerce, AB
Chemistry, B
Computer Programming/Programmer, A
Computer Systems Networking and Telecommunications, B
Counselor Education/School Counseling and Guidance Services, M
Early Childhood Education and Teaching, BM
Education, MO
Educational Administration and Supervision, M
Educational/Instructional Media Design, AB
Elementary Education and Teaching, BM
English Language and Literature, B
English/Language Arts Teacher Education, B
Environmental Sciences, B
Finance, B
Finance and Banking, M
Human Resources Management/Personnel Administration, B
Industrial and Organizational Psychology, M
Journalism, B
Junior High/Intermediate/Middle School Education and Teaching, B
Kindergarten/PreSchool Education and Teaching, B
Management, M
Management Information Systems and Services, AB
Marketing, M
Marketing/Marketing Management, B
Marriage and Family Therapy/Counseling, O
Mathematics Teacher Education, B
Natural Sciences, B
Occupational Safety and Health Technology/Technician, B
Philosophy, B
Physical Education Teaching and Coaching, B
Psychology, B
Public Administration, B
Rehabilitation Counseling, M
Religion/Religious Studies, B
Science Teacher Education/General Science Teacher Education, B
Social Work, B
Spanish Language Teacher Education, B
Special Education and Teaching, BM
Teacher Education and Professional Development, Specific Levels and Methods, B
Teacher Education and Professional Development, Specific Subject Areas, B
Teaching English as a Second or Foreign Language/ESL Language Instructor, B

CARIBBEAN UNIVERSITY

Accounting, AB
Art History, Criticism and Conservation, M
Business Administration and Management, AB
Business/Commerce, B
Civil Engineering, B
Computer Programming/Programmer, AB
Computer Systems Analysis/Analyst, A
Criminal Justice/Police Science, AB
Criminology, M
Curriculum and Instruction, M
Drafting and Design Technology/Technician, A
Early Childhood Education and Teaching, M
Education, D
Educational Administration and Supervision, M
Educational Media/Instructional Technology, M
Electrical, Electronics and Communications Engineering, B
Elementary Education and Teaching, BM
English Education, M
Executive Assistant/Executive Secretary, B
Foreign Language Teacher Education, M
Gerontological Nursing, M

Health Professions and Related Clinical Sciences, AB
Human Resources Management and Services, M
Human Services, A
Industrial Engineering, B
Marketing/Marketing Management, B
Mathematics Teacher Education, M
Museology/Museum Studies, M
Pediatric Nurse/Nursing, M
Physical Education Teaching and Coaching, BM
Pre-Medicine/Pre-Medical Studies, B
Science Teacher Education/General Science Teacher Education, M
Secondary Education and Teaching, B
Social Studies Teacher Education, M
Social Work, B
Special Education and Teaching, BM

CARLOS ALBIZU UNIVERSITY

Clinical Psychology, MD
Communication Disorders, BM
Communication Studies/Speech Communication and Rhetoric, B
Industrial and Organizational Psychology, MD
Psychology, BMD

CENTRO DE ESTUDIOS MULTIDISCIPLINARIOS (RIO PIEDRAS)

Pharmacy Technician/Assistant, A
Respiratory Care Therapy/Therapist, A

COLEGIO UNIVERSITARIO DE SAN JUAN

Accounting, AB
Administrative Assistant and Secretarial Science, A
Criminal Justice/Law Enforcement Administration, B
Criminal Justice/Safety Studies, A
Electrical and Electronic Engineering Technologies/Technicians, A
Electrical/Electronics Equipment Installation and Repair, A
Electrical/Electronics Maintenance and Repair Technology, A
Information Science/Studies, AB
Laser and Optical Technology/Technician, A
Telecommunications Technology/Technician, A

COLUMBIA CENTRO UNIVERSITARIO (CAGUAS)

Administrative Assistant and Secretarial Science, A
Business Administration, Management and Operations, A
Business/Commerce, B
Computer Programming/Programmer, A
Graphic Design, A
Massage Therapy/Therapeutic Massage, A
Recording Arts Technology/Technician, A

COLUMBIA CENTRO UNIVERSITARIO (YAUCO)

Administrative Assistant and Secretarial Science, A
Business Administration and Management, AB
Management Information Systems and Services, A

CONSERVATORIO DE MUSICA DE PUERTO RICO

Jazz/Jazz Studies, B
Music, O
Music Performance, B
Music Teacher Education, BM
Performance, O
Piano and Organ, B
Violin, Viola, Guitar and Other Stringed Instruments, B
Voice and Opera, B

EDP UNIVERSITY OF PUERTO RICO

Accounting and Business/Management, B
Administrative Assistant and Secretarial Science, AB
BioTechnology, A
Business Administration and Management, AB
Computer Graphics, A
Computer Programming/Programmer, AB

Computer Systems Networking and Telecommunications, B
Corrections and Criminal Justice, A
Design and Visual Communications, B
Emergency Medical Technology/Technician (EMT Paramedic), A
Fashion/Apparel Design, AB
Interior Design, AB
Pharmacy, Pharmaceutical Sciences, and Administration, A
Physical Therapist Assistant, A
Prepress/Desktop Publishing and Digital Imaging Design, B

EDP UNIVERSITY OF PUERTO RICO–SAN SEBASTIAN

Accounting and Business/Management, B
Administrative Assistant and Secretarial Science, AB
Business Administration and Management, AB
Computer Programming, B
Computer Programming/Programmer, AB
Computer Systems Networking and Telecommunications, B
Corrections and Criminal Justice, A
Emergency Medical Technology/Technician (EMT Paramedic), A
Fashion/Apparel Design, A
Information Technology, A
Interior Design, A
Pharmacy, Pharmaceutical Sciences, and Administration, A
Physical Therapist Assistant, A

ESCUELA DE ARTES PLASTICAS Y DISEÑO DE PUERTO RICO

Art Teacher Education, B
Design and Visual Communications, B
Fashion/Apparel Design, B
Industrial Design, B
Painting, B
Printmaking, B
Sculpture, B

HUERTAS JUNIOR COLLEGE

Accounting, A
Administrative Assistant and Secretarial Science, A
Business Administration and Management, A
Computer and Information Sciences and Support Services, A
Dental Assisting/Assistant, A
Drafting and Design Technology/Technician, A
Electrical, Electronic and Communications Engineering Technology/Technician, A
Electrical, Electronics and Communications Engineering, A
Health Information/Medical Records Technology/Technician, A
Health and Physical Education/Fitness, A
Heating, Air Conditioning, Ventilation and Refrigeration Maintenance Technology/Technician, A
Legal Assistant/Paralegal, A
Manufacturing Technology/Technician, A
Pharmacy Technician/Assistant, A
Respiratory Care Therapy/Therapist, A
Tourism and Travel Services Marketing Operations, A

HUMACAO COMMUNITY COLLEGE

BioTechnology, A
Business/Commerce, AB
Chemical Technology/Technician, A
Computer Programming, Specific Applications, A
Dental Assisting/Assistant, A
Electrical, Electronics and Communications Engineering, A
Environmental Sciences, A
Executive Assistant/Executive Secretary, A
Health Information/Medical Records Administration/Administrator, A
Heating, Air Conditioning and Refrigeration Technology/Technician, A
Medical Administrative Assistant/Secretary, A
Microbiology, A

Pharmacy Technician/Assistant, A

ICPR JUNIOR COLLEGE–HATO REY CAMPUS

Accounting, A
Computer Technology/Computer Systems Technology, A
Computer and Information Sciences, A
Executive Assistant/Executive Secretary, A
General Office Occupations and Clerical Services, A
Hotel/Motel Administration/Management, A
Marketing/Marketing Management, A
Medical Administrative Assistant/Secretary, A
Tourism and Travel Services Management, A

INTER AMERICAN UNIVERSITY OF PUERTO RICO, AGUADILLA CAMPUS

Accounting, ABM
BioTechnology, B
Biology Teacher Education, B
Biology/Biological Sciences, B
Business Administration and Management, A
Computer Installation and Repair Technology/Technician, A
Computer Science, AB
Computer Systems Networking and Telecommunications, B
Corrections and Criminal Justice, A
Counseling Psychology, M
Criminal Justice/Safety Studies, AB
Criminology, M
Education/Teaching of Individuals in Early Childhood Special Education Programs, B
Educational Administration and Supervision, M
Electrical, Electronic and Communications Engineering Technology/Technician, AB
Elementary Education and Teaching, BM
Entrepreneurship/Entrepreneurial Studies, B
Finance and Banking, M
Foodservice Systems Administration/Management, A
Forensic Science and Technology, B
General Merchandising, Sales, and Related Marketing Operations, A
Hotel/Motel Administration/Management, B
Human Resources Management and Services, M
Human Resources Management/Personnel Administration, B
Kindergarten/PreSchool Education and Teaching, B
Management, M
Management Information Systems and Services, BM
Marketing, M
Marketing/Marketing Management, B
Medical Radiologic Technology/Science - Radiation Therapist, A
Microbiology, B
Office Management and Supervision, AB
Pharmacy Technician/Assistant, A
Physical Education Teaching and Coaching, B
Psychology, B
Radiologic Technology/Science - Radiographer, B
Sales, Distribution and Marketing Operations, A
Social Work, B
Spanish Language Teacher Education, B
Speech-Language Pathology/Pathologist, B
Teaching English as a Second or Foreign Language/ESL Language Instructor, B

INTER AMERICAN UNIVERSITY OF PUERTO RICO, ARECIBO CAMPUS

Accounting, ABM
Acute Care/Critical Care Nursing, M
BioTechnology, B
Biology Teacher Education, B
Biology/Biological Sciences, B
Business Administration and Management, AB
Business Administration, Management and Operations, M
Chemical Technology/Technician, B
Chemistry, B
Computer Science, A
Counselor Education/School Counseling and Guidance Services, M
Criminal Justice/Safety Studies, B

Curriculum and Instruction, M
Education, M
Educational Administration and Supervision, M
Elementary Education and Teaching, BM
English as a Second Language, M
Finance and Banking, M
Foreign Language Teacher Education, M
Human Resources Management and Services, M
Human Resources Management/Personnel Administration, B
Kindergarten/PreSchool Education and Teaching, B
Marketing/Marketing Management, B
Mathematics Teacher Education, BM
Nurse Anesthetist, M
Nursing, M
Office Management and Supervision, AB
Physical Education Teaching and Coaching, B
Science Teacher Education/General Science Teacher Education, M
Social Studies Teacher Education, M
Social Work, B
Spanish Language Teacher Education, B
Special Education and Teaching, B
Surgical Nursing, M
Teaching English as a Second or Foreign Language/ESL Language Instructor, B

INTER AMERICAN UNIVERSITY OF PUERTO RICO, BARRANQUITAS CAMPUS

Accounting, ABM
BioTechnology, AB
Biology Teacher Education, B
Biology/Biological Sciences, B
Business Administration and Management, AB
Business Administration, Management and Operations, M
Cardiopulmonary Technology/Technologist, A
Computer Science, A
Computer and Information Sciences, AB
Corrections Administration, A
Criminal Justice/Safety Studies, AB
Curriculum and Instruction, M
Education, M
Educational Administration and Supervision, M
Educational/Instructional Media Design, B
Elementary Education and Teaching, BM
English as a Second Language, M
Entrepreneurship/Entrepreneurial Studies, AB
Finance and Banking, M
Foreign Language Teacher Education, M
Health Teacher Education, B
Human Resources Management/Personnel Administration, B
Kindergarten/PreSchool Education and Teaching, B
Library Science, M
Management Information Systems and Services, B
Mathematics Teacher Education, M
Office Management and Supervision, AB
Radiologic Technology/Science - Radiographer, AB
Science Teacher Education/General Science Teacher Education, M
Social Studies Teacher Education, BM
Spanish Language Teacher Education, B
Special Education and Teaching, ABM
Teaching English as a Second or Foreign Language/ESL Language Instructor, B

INTER AMERICAN UNIVERSITY OF PUERTO RICO, BAYAMÓN CAMPUS

Accounting, AB
Air Transportation, B
Applied Mathematics, B
Auditing, B
Aviation/Airway Management and Operations, B
BioTechnology, BM
Bioinformatics, B
Biology/Biological Sciences, B
Business Administration and Management, A
Business/Managerial Economics, B
Chemistry, B
Communications Technology/Technician, B
Computer Engineering, B
Computer Engineering Technologies/Technicians, B
Computer Installation and Repair Technology/Technician, AB

Computer Science, AB
Computer Systems Networking and Telecommunications, B
Digital Communication and Media/Multimedia, B
Ecology, M
Electrical, Electronics and Communications Engineering, B
Entrepreneurship/Entrepreneurial Studies, B
Environmental Biology, B
Environmental Sciences, B
Finance, B
Forensic Science and Technology, B
Human Resources Management and Services, M
Human Resources Management/Personnel Administration, B
Industrial Engineering, B
Information Technology, B
Marketing/Marketing Management, B
Mathematics, B
Mechanical Engineering, B
Microbiology, B
Office Management and Supervision, A
Operations Management and Supervision, B

INTER AMERICAN UNIVERSITY OF PUERTO RICO, FAJARDO CAMPUS

Accounting, AB
Biology Teacher Education, B
Biology/Biological Sciences, B
Business Administration and Management, AB
Business Administration, Management and Operations, M
Computer Installation and Repair Technology/Technician, A
Computer Science, M
Computer and Information Sciences, AB
Corrections Administration, B
Corrections and Criminal Justice, A
Criminal Justice/Safety Studies, B
Educational Leadership and Administration, M
Elementary Education and Teaching, BM
Hotel/Motel Administration/Management, AB
Human Resources Management/Personnel Administration, B
Management Information Systems and Services, BM
Management Sciences and Quantitative Methods, B
Marketing, M
Marketing/Marketing Management, B
Office Management and Supervision, AB
Political Science and Government, A
Psychology, B
Religious Education, B
Social Studies Teacher Education, B
Social Work, B
Spanish Language Teacher Education, B
Special Education and Teaching, BM
Speech-Language Pathology/Pathologist, B
Teaching English as a Second or Foreign Language/ESL Language Instructor, B

INTER AMERICAN UNIVERSITY OF PUERTO RICO, GUAYAMA CAMPUS

Accounting, AB
BioTechnology, B
Biology/Biological Sciences, B
Business Administration and Management, AB
Business Administration, Management and Operations, M
Chemical Technology/Technician, AB
Computer Science, M
Computer and Information Sciences and Support Services, AB
Computer and Information Systems Security, M
Criminal Justice/Law Enforcement Administration, B
Criminal Justice/Police Science, A
Early Childhood Education and Teaching, M
Elementary Education and Teaching, BM
Human Resources Management/Personnel Administration, B
Kindergarten/PreSchool Education and Teaching, B
Marketing, M
Mechanic and Repair Technologies/Technicians, AB
Office Management and Supervision, AB
Pharmacy Technician/Assistant, A
Physical Education Teaching and Coaching, B

Respiratory Care Therapy/Therapist, A
Teaching English as a Second or Foreign
   Language/ESL Language Instructor, B

INTER AMERICAN UNIVERSITY OF PUERTO RICO, METROPOLITAN CAMPUS

Accounting, ABM
American/United States Studies/Civilization, D
Applied Mathematics, B
Athletic Training and Sports Medicine, M
Biology Teacher Education, B
Biology/Biological Sciences, B
Biomedical Sciences, B
Business Administration, Management and Operations, BM
Business Education, M
Business/Managerial Economics, B
Chemistry, B
Chemistry Teacher Education, B
Christian Studies, A
Clinical Laboratory Science/Medical
   Technology/Technologist, B
Clinical Laboratory Sciences, M
Computer Science, BM
Corrections and Criminal Justice, A
Counseling Psychology, MD
Counselor Education/School Counseling and Guidance Services, MD
Criminal Justice/Safety Studies, B
Criminalistics and Criminal Science, B
Criminology, M
Curriculum and Instruction, D
Design and Visual Communications, B
Education, MD
Educational Administration and Supervision, D
Educational Media/Instructional Technology, M
Elementary Education and Teaching, BM
English, M
English Language and Literature, B
English as a Second Language, M
Entrepreneurship/Entrepreneurial Studies, B
Environmental Policy and Resource Management, M
Exercise and Sports Science, M
Finance, B
Finance and Banking, M
Foreign Language Teacher Education, M
Health Education, M
Higher Education/Higher Education Administration, M
History, BMD
History Teacher Education, B
Human Resources Development, M
Human Resources Management and Services, M
Human Resources Management/Personnel Administration, B
Industrial and Labor Relations, M
Industrial and Manufacturing Management, M
Industrial and Organizational Psychology, MD
Insurance, A
International Business/Trade/Commerce, MD
Kindergarten/PreSchool Education and Teaching, B
Management Information Systems and Services, M
Marketing, M
Marketing/Marketing Management, B
Mathematics, B
Mathematics Teacher Education, BM
Medical Technology, M
Microbiology, BM
Molecular Biology, M
Music Performance, AB
Music Teacher Education, M
Office Management and Supervision, B
Operations Management and Supervision, B
Pastoral Studies/Counseling, D
Physical Education Teaching and Coaching, BM
Psychology, BMD
Real Estate, B
Religious Education, D
School Psychology, MD
Science Teacher Education/General Science
   Teacher Education, BM
Social Studies Teacher Education, BM
Social Work, BM
Sociology, B

Spanish Language Teacher Education, B
Spanish Language and Literature, BM
Special Education and Teaching, BM
Sport and Fitness Administration/Management, B
Teacher Education and Professional Development, Specific Levels and Methods, B
Teaching English as a Second or Foreign
   Language/ESL Language Instructor, B
Theology and Religious Vocations, D
Vocational and Technical Education, M
Women's Studies, M

INTER AMERICAN UNIVERSITY OF PUERTO RICO, PONCE CAMPUS

Accounting, ABM
BioTechnology, B
Biology Teacher Education, B
Biology/Biological Sciences, B
Biomedical Sciences, B
Business Administration and Management, AB
Computer Science, AB
Computer Systems Networking and Telecommunications, B
Computer and Information Sciences, A
Criminal Justice/Police Science, A
Criminal Justice/Safety Studies, B
Criminalistics and Criminal Science, B
Criminology, M
Education/Teaching of Individuals in Early Childhood
   Special Education Programs, B
Education/Teaching of Individuals with Autism, B
Elementary Education and Teaching, BM
English as a Second Language, M
Entrepreneurship/Entrepreneurial Studies, B
Environmental Sciences, B
Finance, B
Finance and Banking, M
Forensic Science and Technology, B
General Merchandising, Sales, and Related Marketing Operations, A
Health Professions and Related Clinical Sciences, B
Health Services Administration, B
Hotel/Motel Administration/Management, B
Human Resources Management and Services, M
Human Resources Management/Personnel Administration, B
Information Science/Studies, B
Kindergarten/PreSchool Education and Teaching, B
Management Information Systems and Services, AB
Marketing, M
Marketing/Marketing Management, B
Mathematics Teacher Education, B
Medical Radiologic Technology/Science - Radiation
   Therapist, A
Microbiology, B
Occupational Therapist Assistant, A
Office Management and Supervision, AB
Operations Management and Supervision, B
Optometric Technician/Assistant, A
Physical Therapist Assistant, A
Psychology, B
Public Health Education and Promotion, B
Public Relations/Image Management, B
Radiologic Technology/Science - Radiographer, B
Science Teacher Education/General Science
   Teacher Education, M
Social Studies Teacher Education, M
Sociology, B
Spanish Language and Literature, M
Special Education and Teaching, B
Speech-Language Pathology/Pathologist, B
Teaching English as a Second or Foreign
   Language/ESL Language Instructor, B

INTER AMERICAN UNIVERSITY OF PUERTO RICO, SAN GERMÁN CAMPUS

Accounting, ABM
Administrative Assistant and Secretarial Science, A
Anthropology, B
Applied Mathematics, BM
Architecture, B
Art Teacher Education, B
Art/Art Studies, General, B
Behavioral Sciences, B
Biology Teacher Education, B

Biology/Biological Sciences, B
Business Administration and Management, AB
Business Administration, Management and Operations, MD
Business Education, M
Business/Managerial Economics, B
Ceramic Arts and Ceramics, B
Chemistry, B
Chemistry Teacher Education, B
Clinical Laboratory Science/Medical
   Technology/Technologist, B
Comparative Literature, B
Computer Programming/Programmer, B
Computer Science, AB
Counseling Psychology, MD
Counselor Education/School Counseling and Guidance Services, MD
Criminal Justice/Police Science, B
Curriculum and Instruction, D
Design and Applied Arts, B
Drawing, B
Early Childhood Education and Teaching, B
Economics, B
Education, B
Electrical, Electronic and Communications Engineering Technology/Technician, AB
Elementary Education and Teaching, BM
Engineering, B
English Language and Literature, B
English as a Second Language, M
English/Language Arts Teacher Education, B
Entrepreneurship/Entrepreneurial Studies, B
Environmental Sciences, BM
Environmental Studies, B
Finance, B
Finance and Banking, M
Fine Arts and Art Studies, M
Graphic Design, AM
Health Education, M
Health Teacher Education, B
History, B
History Teacher Education, B
Human Resources Development, M
Human Resources Management and Services, MD
Human Resources Management/Personnel Administration, B
Industrial and Manufacturing Management, M
Information Science/Studies, B
International Business/Trade/Commerce, D
Kindergarten/PreSchool Education and Teaching, B
Kinesiology and Movement Studies, M
Library Science, M
Management, M
Management Information Systems and Services, M
Marketing, M
Marketing/Marketing Management, B
Mathematics, B
Mathematics Teacher Education, BM
Medical Radiologic Technology/Science - Radiation
   Therapist, A
Microbiology, B
Music, BM
Music Teacher Education, BM
Natural Sciences, B
Office Management and Supervision, AB
Painting, BM
Photography, BM
Physical Education Teaching and Coaching, BM
Political Science and Government, B
Printmaking, BM
Psychology, BMD
Radiologic Technology/Science - Radiographer, B
School Psychology, MD
Science Teacher Education/General Science
   Teacher Education, BM
Sculpture, BM
Secondary Education and Teaching, B
Selling Skills and Sales Operations, A
Social Studies Teacher Education, B
Sociology, B
Spanish Language Teacher Education, B
Special Education and Teaching, BM
Teacher Education and Professional Development, Specific Levels and Methods, B
Teaching English as a Second or Foreign
   Language/ESL Language Instructor, B

Visual and Performing Arts, B

NATIONAL UNIVERSITY COLLEGE (BAYAMÓN)

Accounting, AB
Banking and Financial Support Services, B
Business Teacher Education, B
Computer Teacher Education, B
Dental Assisting/Assistant, A
Entrepreneurial and Small Business Operations, A
Health Teacher Education, B
Industrial Electronics Technology/Technician, A
Information Technology, AB
Kindergarten/PreSchool Education and Teaching, B
Legal Administrative Assistant/Secretary, A
Management Information Systems and Services, B
Medical Administrative Assistant/Secretary, A
Pharmacy Technician/Assistant, A

POLYTECHNIC UNIVERSITY OF PUERTO RICO

Architecture, B
Business Administration and Management, B
Business Administration, Management and Operations, M
Business, Management, Marketing, and Related Support Services, B
Chemical Engineering, B
Civil Engineering, BM
Computer Engineering, BM
Computer Science, BM
Computer Software and Media Applications, A
Computer and Information Sciences, B
Electrical Engineering, B
Electrical, Electronics and Communications Engineering, B
Engineering, B
Engineering Management, M
Environmental Policy and Resource Management, M
Environmental/Environmental Health Engineering, B
Finance, B
Industrial Engineering, B
Industrial and Manufacturing Management, M
Interior Design, B
International Business/Trade/Commerce, M
Landscape Architecture, M
Logistics and Materials Management, A
Management Information Systems and Services, M
Management of Technology, M
Manufacturing Engineering, M
Marketing/Marketing Management, B
Mechanical Engineering, BM
Mechanical Engineering Related Technologies/Technicians, A
Secondary Education and Teaching, B
Survey Technology/Surveying, AB

PONTIFICAL CATHOLIC UNIVERSITY OF PUERTO RICO

Accounting, BMO
Administrative Assistant and Secretarial Science, B
Advertising, B
Art Teacher Education, B
Auditing, B
Biological and Biomedical Sciences, M
Biological and Physical Sciences, B
Biology Teacher Education, B
Biology/Biological Sciences, B
Business Administration and Management, AB
Business Administration, Management and Operations, BMDO
Business Education, MD
Business Operations Support and Secretarial Services, B
Business Teacher Education, B
Business/Commerce, B
Business/Corporate Communications, B
Business/Managerial Economics, B
Business/Office Automation/Technology/Data Entry, B
Cardiovascular Technology/Technologist, B
Chemistry, BM
Chemistry Teacher Education, B

Clinical Laboratory Science/Medical Technology/Technologist, B
Clinical Psychology, D
Computer Programming, Specific Applications, A
Computer and Information Sciences, A
Counselor Education/School Counseling and Guidance Services, M
Criminology, BM
Curriculum and Instruction, MD
Education, ABMD
Educational Administration and Supervision, D
Educational Leadership and Administration, D
Educational Psychology, M
Elementary Education and Teaching, B
English Language and Literature, B
English as a Second Language, M
English/Language Arts Teacher Education, B
Entrepreneurship/Entrepreneurial Studies, B
Environmental Sciences, BM
Family and Consumer Sciences/Home Economics Teacher Education, B
Family and Consumer Sciences/Human Sciences, B
Fashion/Apparel Design, A
Finance, B
Finance and Banking, M
Fine Arts and Art Studies, B
General Office Occupations and Clerical Services, A
Gerontology, B
Health Services/Allied Health/Health Sciences, B
Health Teacher Education, B
Health and Physical Education, B
Hispanic Studies, MO
History, BM
History Teacher Education, B
Human Resources Management and Services, MO
Human Resources Management/Personnel Administration, B
Human Services, MD
Industrial and Organizational Psychology, D
Information Technology, A
International Business/Trade/Commerce, BM
Law and Legal Studies, BD
Liberal Arts and Sciences Studies and Humanities, B
Logistics and Materials Management, O
Management Information Systems and Services, BMO
Marketing, M
Marketing/Marketing Management, B
Mass Communication/Media Studies, B
Mathematics, B
Mathematics Teacher Education, B
Medical Technology, O
Medical/Surgical Nursing, M
Music, B
Music Teacher Education, B
Nursing, M
Office Management and Supervision, B
Painting, M
Philosophy, B
Physical Education Teaching and Coaching, B
Physics, B
Political Science and Government, B
Pre-Law Studies, B
Pre-Medicine/Pre-Medical Studies, B
Psychiatric/Mental Health Nurse/Nursing, M
Psychology, BD
Public Administration, BM
Public Relations/Image Management, B
Radio and Television, B
Rehabilitation Counseling, M
Religious Education, M
Science Teacher Education/General Science Teacher Education, B
Small Business Administration/Management, B
Social Studies Teacher Education, B
Social Work, BM
Sociology, B
Spanish Language Teacher Education, B
Spanish Language and Literature, BO
Special Education and Teaching, B
Theology and Religious Vocations, M
Tourism and Travel Services Management, B

Transportation/Transportation Management, O

THEOLOGICAL UNIVERSITY OF THE CARIBBEAN

Bible/Biblical Studies, B
Pastoral Studies/Counseling, B
Pre-Theology/Pre-Ministerial Studies, A
Religious Education, B

UNIVERSIDAD ADVENTISTA DE LAS ANTILLAS

Accounting, B
Administrative Assistant and Secretarial Science, AB
Biology Teacher Education, B
Biology/Biological Sciences, B
Business Administration and Management, AB
Computer Science, AB
Curriculum and Instruction, M
Educational Administration and Supervision, M
Educational Leadership and Administration, M
Elementary Education and Teaching, B
History, B
History Teacher Education, B
Mathematics Teacher Education, B
Medical/Surgical Nursing, M
Psychology, B
Religious Education, B
Respiratory Care Therapy/Therapist, AB
Secondary Education and Teaching, B
Social Studies Teacher Education, B
Spanish Language and Literature, B
Theology/Theological Studies, B

UNIVERSIDAD CENTRAL DEL CARIBE

Allopathic Medicine, MD
Anatomy, M
Biochemistry, M
Biological and Biomedical Sciences, MD
Cell Biology and Anatomy, MD
Immunology, M
Medical Radiologic Technology/Science - Radiation Therapist, A
Microbiology, M
Molecular Biology, D
Pharmacology, M
Physiology, M
Radiologic Technology/Science - Radiographer, B
Substance Abuse/Addiction Counseling, M

UNIVERSIDAD DEL ESTE

Accounting, BM
Administrative Assistant and Secretarial Science, B
Adult and Continuing Education and Teaching, M
Agribusiness, M
Athletic Training and Sports Medicine, B
Avionics Maintenance Technology/Technician, A
BioTechnology, B
Biology/Biological Sciences, B
Business Administration and Management, B
Business/Office Automation/Technology/Data Entry, B
Computer Programming, Specific Applications, A
Computer Software Technology/Technician, A
Computer and Information Sciences and Support Services, A
Computer and Information Systems Security, M
Criminal Justice/Law Enforcement Administration, A
Criminal Justice/Police Science, A
Criminal Justice/Safety Studies, B
Criminology, M
Culinary Arts/Chef Training, A
Diagnostic Medical Sonography/Sonographer and Ultrasound Technician, AB
Digital Communication and Media/Multimedia, B
Early Childhood Education and Teaching, B
Electrical, Electronic and Communications Engineering Technology/Technician, A
Electronic Commerce, B
Elementary Education and Teaching, M
English as a Second Language, M
Executive Assistant/Executive Secretary, A
Foods, Nutrition, and Wellness Studies, B
Foreign Language Teacher Education, B
Health and Medical Administrative Services, B
Health/Health Care Administration/Management, B

Hotel/Motel Administration/Management, AB
Human Resources Management and Services, M
Human Resources Management/Personnel Administration, B
Insurance, B
Legal Administrative Assistant/Secretary, A
Legal Assistant/Paralegal, AB
Management, M
Management Information Systems and Services, BM
Management Strategy and Policy, M
Marketing/Marketing Management, B
Medical Administrative Assistant/Secretary, A
Medical Radiologic Technology/Science - Radiation Therapist, B
Medical/Clinical Assistant, A
Microbiology, B
Natural Sciences, A
Pharmacy Technician/Assistant, A
Physical Education Teaching and Coaching, B
Political Science and Government, B
Psychology, B
Public Policy Analysis, M
Radiologic Technology/Science - Radiographer, A
Restaurant, Culinary, and Catering Management/Manager, B
Social Work, BM
Special Education and Teaching, BM
System Administration/Administrator, B
Teaching English as a Second or Foreign Language/ESL Language Instructor, B

UNIVERSIDAD METROPOLITANA

Accounting, BM
Adult and Continuing Education and Teaching, M
Applied Mathematics, B
Banking and Financial Support Services, A
Biology/Biological Sciences, B
Business Administration and Management, B
Business Administration, Management and Operations, M
Business/Managerial Economics, B
Cardiovascular Technology/Technologist, B
Chemistry, B
Computer Installation and Repair Technology/Technician, A
Computer Science, AB
Counseling Psychology, M
Criminal Justice/Police Science, A
Criminal Justice/Safety Studies, AB
Curriculum and Instruction, M
Diagnostic Medical Sonography/Sonographer and Ultrasound Technician, A
Digital Communication and Media/Multimedia, B
Drafting and Design Technology/Technician, A
Early Childhood Education and Teaching, B
Education, M
Educational Administration and Supervision, M
Elementary Education and Teaching, BM
English/Language Arts Teacher Education, B
Environmental Health, B
Environmental Policy and Resource Management, M
Environmental Sciences, B
Environmental Studies, M
Finance and Banking, M
Health and Physical Education, AB
Health/Health Care Administration/Management, B
History Teacher Education, B
Human Resources Management and Services, M
International Business/Trade/Commerce, M
Kindergarten/PreSchool Education and Teaching, B
Leisure Studies, M
Management Information Systems and Services, BM
Marketing, M
Marketing/Marketing Management, AB
Molecular Biology, B
Natural Resources Management/Development and Policy, M
Nursing, MO
Nursing Administration, O
Office Management and Supervision, AB
Oncology Nursing, O
Physical Education Teaching and Coaching, BM
Psychology, B

Public Relations, Advertising, and Applied Communication, B
Recreation and Park Management, M
Respiratory Care Therapy/Therapist, AB
Sales, Distribution and Marketing Operations, AB
Secondary Education and Teaching, BM
Social Work, B
Spanish Language Teacher Education, B
Special Education and Teaching, BM
Speech-Language Pathology/Pathologist, B
Teacher Education, Multiple Levels, B

UNIVERSIDAD PENTECOSTAL MIZPA

Christian Studies, AB
Missions/Missionary Studies and Missiology, A
Pastoral Studies/Counseling, AB
Theology/Theological Studies, AB

UNIVERSIDAD DEL TURABO

Accounting, ABM
Architectural Drafting and Architectural CAD/CADD, A
Arts Management, M
Athletic Training and Sports Medicine, M
BioTechnology, AB
Biology Teacher Education, B
Biology/Biological Sciences, B
Business Administration and Management, AB
Chemistry, BM
Chemistry Teacher Education, B
Civil Engineering, B
Communication Disorders, M
Communication Studies/Speech Communication and Rhetoric, B
Community Health Services/Liaison/Counseling, B
Computer Engineering, B
Computer Engineering Technologies/Technicians, A
Computer and Information Sciences, AB
Conflict Resolution and Mediation/Peace Studies, M
Counseling Psychology, MDO
Counselor Education/School Counseling and Guidance Services, M
Criminal Justice/Police Science, AB
Criminology, BM
Curriculum and Instruction, MD
Dietetics and Clinical Nutrition Services, B
Early Childhood Education and Teaching, BM
Education, MDO
Educational Administration and Supervision, MO
Educational Leadership and Administration, D
Electrical, Electronic and Communications Engineering Technology/Technician, A
Electrical, Electronics and Communications Engineering, B
Electrician, A
Elementary Education and Teaching, B
Engineering/Industrial Management, B
English as a Second Language, M
English/Language Arts Teacher Education, B
Environmental Biology, D
Environmental Policy and Resource Management, M
Environmental Sciences, MD
Fashion/Apparel Design, A
Fine Arts and Art Studies, M
Forensic Science and Technology, M
Graphic Design, B
Health Promotion, M
Health and Physical Education, A
History Teacher Education, B
Human Resources Management and Services, M
Human Services, M
Humanities/Humanistic Studies, B
Industrial Design, B
Information Science/Studies, M
Interior Design, B
Landscape Architecture, B
Library Science, MO
Logistics and Materials Management, M
Management, MD
Management Information Systems and Services, B
Marketing, M
Marketing/Marketing Management, B
Mathematics Teacher Education, B
Mechanical Engineering, B

Mechanical Engineering/Mechanical Technology/Technician, A
Natural Sciences, B
Naturopathic Medicine/Naturopathy, D
Nursing - Adult, MO
Nursing - Advanced Practice, M
Office Management and Supervision, AB
Pharmacology, A
Pharmacy Technician/Assistant, A
Pharmacy, Pharmaceutical Sciences, and Administration, A
Physical Education Teaching and Coaching, BM
Project Management, M
Psychology, B
Public Administration, AB
Public Health (MPH, DPH), B
Quality Control Technology/Technician, A
Quality Management, M
Radio and Television Broadcasting Technology/Technician, A
Respiratory Care Therapy/Therapist, A
Science Teacher Education/General Science Teacher Education, B
Sign Language Interpretation and Translation, B
Social Sciences, AB
Social Work, B
Sociology, B
Special Education and Teaching, BM
Speech-Language Pathology/Pathologist, B
Sport and Fitness Administration/Management, B
System Management, D
Telecommunications, B
Trade and Industrial Teacher Education, B
Veterinary/Animal Health Technology/Technician and Veterinary Assistant, A
Web Page, Digital/Multimedia and Information Resources Design, A

UNIVERSITY OF PUERTO RICO IN AGUADILLA

Accounting, B
Biological and Biomedical Sciences, AB
Business/Commerce, B
Electrical, Electronic and Communications Engineering Technology/Technician, AB
Elementary Education and Teaching, B
English/Language Arts Teacher Education, B
Environmental Engineering Technology/Environmental Technology, B
Finance, B
General Office Occupations and Clerical Services, A
Human Resources Management/Personnel Administration, A
Liberal Arts and Sciences Studies and Humanities, A
Management Information Systems and Services, B
Marketing/Marketing Management, B
Office Management and Supervision, B
Quality Control Technology/Technician, B

UNIVERSITY OF PUERTO RICO IN ARECIBO

Accounting, B
Business Administration and Management, B
Business/Commerce, A
Computer Science, B
Elementary Education and Teaching, B
Executive Assistant/Executive Secretary, B
Finance, B
Industrial Production Technologies/Technicians, AB
Marketing/Marketing Management, B
Medical Microbiology and Bacteriology, B
Physical Education Teaching and Coaching, B
Radio and Television Broadcasting Technology/Technician, AB
Social Sciences, B
Veterinary/Animal Health Technology/Technician and Veterinary Assistant, A

UNIVERSITY OF PUERTO RICO IN BAYAMÓN

Accounting, B
Biological and Biomedical Sciences, B
Biology/Biological Sciences, B

Business Administration, Management and Operations, B
Civil Engineering Technology/Technician, A
Computer and Information Sciences, B
Education/Teaching of Individuals with Orthopedic and Other Physical Health Impairments, B
Electrical, Electronic and Communications Engineering Technology/Technician, B
Engineering Technologies/Technicians, A
Executive Assistant/Executive Secretary, B
Finance, B
Industrial Technology/Technician, A
Instrumentation Technology/Technician, A
Logistics and Materials Management, B
Marketing/Marketing Management, B
Teacher Education, Multiple Levels, B

UNIVERSITY OF PUERTO RICO IN CAROLINA

Administrative Assistant and Secretarial Science, AB
Advertising, AB
Automotive Engineering Technology/Technician, A
Business Administration and Management, B
Corrections and Criminal Justice, B
Criminal Justice/Law Enforcement Administration, B
Education, A
Finance, AB
Graphic and Printing Equipment Operator Production, AB
Health and Physical Education/Fitness, A
Hotel/Motel Administration/Management, AB
Instrumentation Technology/Technician, A
Interior Design, A
Liberal Arts and Sciences Studies and Humanities, A
Mechanical Engineering, A
Multi-/Interdisciplinary Studies, A
Social Sciences, A
Tourism and Travel Services Management, B

UNIVERSITY OF PUERTO RICO IN CAYEY

Accounting, B
Administrative Assistant and Secretarial Science, B
Biology/Biological Sciences, B
Business Administration, Management and Operations, B
Business/Commerce, B
Chemistry, B
Economics, B
English Language and Literature, B
English/Language Arts Teacher Education, B
General Office Occupations and Clerical Services, A
History, B
History Teacher Education, B
Humanities/Humanistic Studies, B
Mathematics, B
Mathematics Teacher Education, B
Natural Sciences, B
Physical Education Teaching and Coaching, B
Psychology, B
Science Teacher Education/General Science Teacher Education, B
Social Science Teacher Education, B
Social Sciences, B
Social Studies Teacher Education, B
Sociology, B
Spanish Language Teacher Education, B
Spanish Language and Literature, B
Special Education and Teaching, B

UNIVERSITY OF PUERTO RICO IN HUMACAO

Accounting, B
Administrative Assistant and Secretarial Science, B
Biology/Biological Sciences, B
Business Administration and Management, B
Chemical Technology/Technician, A
Chemistry, B
Communications Technology/Technician, A
Computational Mathematics, B
Electrical, Electronic and Communications Engineering Technology/Technician, A
Elementary Education and Teaching, B

Human Resources Management/Personnel Administration, B
International Business/Trade/Commerce, B
Marine Biology and Biological Oceanography, B
Microbiology, B
Occupational Therapist Assistant, A
Physical Therapist Assistant, A
Physics, B
Social Sciences, B
Social Work, B
Teaching English as a Second or Foreign Language/ESL Language Instructor, B
Wildlife and Wildlands Science and Management, B

UNIVERSITY OF PUERTO RICO, MAYAGÜEZ CAMPUS

Accounting, B
Administrative Assistant and Secretarial Science, B
Agribusiness, B
Agricultural Economics, BM
Agricultural Education, M
Agricultural Mechanization, B
Agricultural Sciences, M
Agricultural Teacher Education, B
Agricultural and Extension Education Services, B
Agriculture, B
Agronomy and Crop Science, B
Agronomy and Soil Sciences, M
Animal Sciences, BM
Applied Mathematics, M
Art History, Criticism and Conservation, B
Athletic Training and Sports Medicine, B
BioTechnology, B
Biological and Biomedical Sciences, M
Biology/Biological Sciences, B
Biomedical/Medical Engineering, B
Business Administration and Management, B
Business Administration, Management and Operations, M
Chemical Engineering, BMD
Chemistry, BMD
Civil Engineering, BMD
Comparative Literature, B
Computational Sciences, M
Computer Engineering, BMD
Computer Science, BD
Computer Systems Analysis/Analyst, B
Economics, B
Electrical Engineering, MD
Electrical, Electronics and Communications Engineering, B
Engineering and Applied Sciences, MD
English, M
English Education, M
English Language and Literature, B
Exercise and Sports Science, M
Finance, B
Finance and Banking, M
Fine/Studio Arts, B
Food Science and Technology, M
French Language and Literature, B
Geology/Earth Science, BM
Hispanic Studies, M
History, B
Horticultural Science, BM
Human Resources Management and Services, M
Human Resources Management/Personnel Administration, B
Industrial Engineering, B
Industrial and Manufacturing Management, M
Industrial/Management Engineering, M
Information Science/Studies, D
Kinesiology and Movement Studies, M
Marine Sciences, MD
Marketing/Marketing Management, B
Mathematics, BM
Mathematics Teacher Education, B
Mechanical Engineering, BM
Microbiology, B
Parks, Recreation and Leisure Facilities Management, B
Philosophy, B
Physical Education Teaching and Coaching, BM
Physical Sciences, B
Physics, BM

Plant Protection and Integrated Pest Management, B
Political Science and Government, B
Pre-Medicine/Pre-Medical Studies, B
Psychology, B
Social Sciences, B
Sociology, B
Soil Science and Agronomy, B
Spanish Language and Literature, B
Statistics, M
Survey Technology/Surveying, B

UNIVERSITY OF PUERTO RICO, MEDICAL SCIENCES CAMPUS

Acute Care/Critical Care Nursing, M
Allied Health and Medical Assisting Services, MDO
Allopathic Medicine, D
Anatomy, MD
Biochemistry, MD
Biological and Biomedical Sciences, MD
Biostatistics, M
Clinical Laboratory Science/Medical Technology/Technologist, B
Clinical Laboratory Sciences, M
Clinical Research, MO
Communication Disorders, MD
Community Health Nursing, M
Demography, M
Dental Assisting/Assistant, A
Dental and Oral Surgery, O
Dentistry, D
Environmental and Occupational Health, MD
Epidemiology, M
Gerontological Nursing, M
Gerontology, MO
Health Education, M
Health Informatics, M
Health Promotion, O
Health Services Administration, M
Health Services Research, M
Health Services/Allied Health/Health Sciences, B
Industrial Hygiene, M
Maternal and Child Health, M
Maternal/Child Health and Neonatal Nurse/Nursing, M
Maternity Nursing, M
Medical Technology, O
Microbiology, MD
Nuclear Medical Technology/Technologist, B
Nurse Midwife/Nursing Midwifery, MO
Nursing, M
Nursing - Adult, M
Nursing - Advanced Practice, M
Nutritional Sciences, MDO
Occupational Therapy/Therapist, M
Ophthalmic Technician/Technologist, A
Oral and Dental Sciences, O
Orthodontics, O
Pediatric Nurse/Nursing, M
Pedodontics, O
Pharmaceutical Sciences, M
Pharmacology, MD
Pharmacy, MD
Physical Therapy/Therapist, M
Physiology, MD
Psychiatric/Mental Health Nurse/Nursing, M
Public Health Education and Promotion, B
Radiologic Technology/Science - Radiographer, A
Special Education and Teaching, O
Toxicology, MD
Veterinary/Animal Health Technology/Technician and Veterinary Assistant, B

UNIVERSITY OF PUERTO RICO IN PONCE

Accounting, B
Administrative Assistant and Secretarial Science, A
Athletic Training and Sports Medicine, B
BioTechnology, B
Biological and Biomedical Sciences, B
Biology/Biological Sciences, A
Business Administration, Management and Operations, B
Business/Commerce, A
Civil Engineering Technology/Technician, A
Computer and Information Sciences, B

Data Processing and Data Processing
   Technology/Technician, A
Drafting and Design Technology/Technician, A
Elementary Education and Teaching, B
Executive Assistant/Executive Secretary, B
Finance, B
Industrial Technology/Technician, A
Marine Biology and Biological Oceanography, B
Marketing/Marketing Management, B
Mental and Social Health Services and Allied Pro-
   fessions, B
Physical Therapist Assistant, A
Psychology, B
Social Sciences, A

UNIVERSITY OF PUERTO RICO, RÍO PIEDRAS CAMPUS

Accounting, BM
American History (United States), B
Anthropology, B
Architecture, M
Art History, Criticism and Conservation, B
Art/Art Studies, General, B
Biological and Biomedical Sciences, MD
Biology/Biological Sciences, B
Business Administration, Management and Opera-
   tions, MD
Business Statistics, B
Business/Commerce, B
Business/Managerial Economics, B
Cell Biology and Anatomy, MD
Chemistry, BMD
Clinical Psychology, M
Communication Theory, M
Community Psychology, M
Comparative Literature, BM
Computer Science, B
Counselor Education/School Counseling and Guid-
   ance Services, MD
Curriculum and Instruction, MD
Digital Communication and Media/Multimedia, B
Drama and Dramatics/Theatre Arts, B
Drawing, B
Early Childhood Education and Teaching, M
Ecology, MD
Economic Development, M
Economics, BM
Education, MD
Educational Administration and Supervision, MD
Educational Measurement and Evaluation, M
Elementary Education and Teaching, B
English, MD
English Language and Literature, B
English as a Second Language, M
Environmental Design/Architecture, B
Environmental Policy and Resource Manage-
   ment, M
Environmental Sciences, BMD
European History, B
Evolutionary Biology, MD
Executive Assistant/Executive Secretary, B
Exercise and Sports Science, M
Family and Consumer Sciences/Human Sci-
   ences, BM
Finance, B
Finance and Banking, MD
Fine/Studio Arts, B
Foods, Nutrition, and Wellness Studies, B
Foreign Language Teacher Education, M
Foreign Languages and Literatures, B
French Language and Literature, B
Genetics, MD
Geography, B
Hispanic Studies, MD
History, MD
Human Resources Management and Services, M
Human Resources Management/Personnel Adminis-
   tration, B
Industrial and Manufacturing Management, M
Industrial and Organizational Psychology, M
Information Science/Studies, M
Intercultural/Multicultural and Diversity Studies, B
Intermedia/Multimedia, B
International Business/Trade/Commerce, MD
International Trade, MD
Journalism, BM

Labor and Industrial Relations, B
Law and Legal Studies, MD
Liberal Arts and Sciences Studies and Humani-
   ties, B
Library Science, MO
Linguistics, MD
Management Information Systems and Services, B
Marketing, M
Marketing/Marketing Management, B
Mass Communication/Media Studies, BM
Mathematics, BMD
Mathematics Teacher Education, M
Molecular Biology, MD
Music, B
Natural Sciences, B
Neuroscience, MD
Nutritional Sciences, M
Operations Management and Supervision, B
Painting, B
Philosophy, BM
Photography, B
Physics, BMD
Political Science and Government, B
Psychology, BMD
Public Administration, M
Public Policy Analysis, M
Public Relations/Image Management, B
Quantitative Analysis, M
Rehabilitation Counseling, M
Science Teacher Education/General Science
   Teacher Education, M
Sculpture, B
Secondary Education and Teaching, B
Social Psychology, M
Social Sciences, B
Social Studies Teacher Education, M
Social Work, BMD
Sociology, BM
Spanish Language and Literature, B
Special Education and Teaching, M
Translation and Interpretation, MO
Urban and Regional Planning, M
Visual and Performing Arts, B

UNIVERSITY OF PUERTO RICO IN UTUADO

Accounting, B
Agricultural Production Operations, A
Animal Sciences, A
Biological and Biomedical Sciences, B
Biology/Biological Sciences, B
Business Administration and Management, A
Chemistry, B
Computational Mathematics, B
Education, AB
Elementary Education and Teaching, B
English/Language Arts Teacher Education, B
Environmental Control Technologies/Technicians, B
Fine/Studio Arts, B
Food Science, A
French Language and Literature, B
History, B
History Teacher Education, B
Horticultural Science, A
Humanities/Humanistic Studies, B
Industrial Production Technologies/Technicians, B
Mathematics Teacher Education, B
Natural Sciences, AB
Office Management and Supervision, B
Physical Education Teaching and Coaching, B
Physics, B
Plant Protection and Integrated Pest Manage-
   ment, A
Political Science and Government, B
Psychology, B
Quality Control Technology/Technician, B
Radio and Television Broadcasting
   Technology/Technician, B
Science Teacher Education/General Science
   Teacher Education, B
Social Sciences, AB
Social Work, B
Sociology, B
Spanish Language Teacher Education, B
Spanish Language and Literature, B

Visual and Performing Arts, B

UNIVERSITY OF THE SACRED HEART

Accounting, BM
Administrative Assistant and Secretarial Science, B
Advertising, B
Advertising and Public Relations, MO
Bilingual and Multilingual Education, B
Biology/Biological Sciences, B
Broadcast Journalism, MO
Business Administration and Management, B
Business Administration, Management and Opera-
   tions, MO
Chemistry, B
Clinical Laboratory Science/Medical
   Technology/Technologist, B
Communication Studies/Speech Communication
   and Rhetoric, B
Communication and Media Studies, MO
Computer Science, B
Conflict Resolution and Mediation/Peace Studies, M
Criminal Justice/Safety Studies, B
Cultural Studies, M
Drama and Dramatics/Theatre Arts, B
Early Childhood Education and Teaching, M
Education, BMO
Educational Media/Instructional Technology, MO
Elementary Education and Teaching, B
English Education, M
Entrepreneurship/Entrepreneurial Studies, B
Environmental and Occupational Health, M
Film, Television, and Video Production, MO
Foreign Language Teacher Education, M
Human Resources Management and Services, M
Humanities/Humanistic Studies, B
Information Science/Studies, BO
Internet and Interactive Multimedia, MO
Journalism, B
Kinesiology and Exercise Science, B
Legal and Justice Studies, M
Management Information Systems and Services, M
Marketing, MO
Marketing/Marketing Management, B
Mass Communication/Media Studies, B
Mathematics Teacher Education, M
Non-Profit/Public/Organizational Management, M
Occupational Health Nursing, M
Office Management and Supervision, B
Psychology, B
Secondary Education and Teaching, B
Social Sciences, B
Social Work, B
Taxation, M
Telecommunications Technology/Technician, B
Tourism and Travel Services Management, B
Tourism and Travel Services Marketing Opera-
   tions, B
Visual and Performing Arts, B
Writing, MO

U.S. Territories-United States Virgin Islands

UNIVERSITY OF THE VIRGIN ISLANDS

Accounting, AB
Applied Mathematics, B
Biology/Biological Sciences, B
Business Administration and Management, AB
Business Administration, Management and Opera-
   tions, M
Chemistry, B
Communication Studies/Speech Communication
   and Rhetoric, B
Computer Science, AB
Criminal Justice/Police Science, AB
Early Childhood Education and Teaching, AB
Education, M
Elementary Education and Teaching, B
English Language and Literature, B
Environmental Sciences, M
Hospitality Administration/Management, B
Humanities/Humanistic Studies, B
Management Information Systems and Services, AB
Marine Biology and Biological Oceanography, B
Marine Sciences, M

Marketing/Marketing Management, B
Mathematics, B
Mathematics Teacher Education, M
Mining and Petroleum Technologies/Technicians, A
Music Teacher Education, B
Physics, A
Psychology, B
Public Administration, M
Social Sciences, B
Social Work, B

CANADIAN COLLEGES

Alberta

ALBERTA COLLEGE OF ART & DESIGN

Art/Art Studies, General, B
Ceramic Arts and Ceramics, B
Commercial and Advertising Art, B
Computer Graphics, B
Design and Visual Communications, B
Drawing, B
Fiber, Textile and Weaving Arts, B
Fine/Studio Arts, B
Graphic Design, B
Illustration, B
Intermedia/Multimedia, B
Metal and Jewelry Arts, B
Painting, B
Photography, B
Printmaking, B
Sculpture, B

AMBROSE UNIVERSITY

Behavioral Sciences, B
Biology/Biological Sciences, B
Business Administration and Management, B
Christian Studies, B
Cultural Studies, O
General Studies, B
History, B
Music, B
Pastoral Studies/Counseling, M
Religion/Religious Studies, O
Theology and Religious Vocations, MO
Theology/Theological Studies, B

ATHABASCA UNIVERSITY

Accounting, B
Adult and Continuing Education and Teaching, M
Allied Health and Medical Assisting Services, MO
Anthropology, B
Applied Psychology, MO
Art Therapy/Therapist, M
Biological and Physical Sciences, B
Business Administration and Management, B
Business Administration, Management and Operations, MO
Canadian Studies, B
Communication and Media Studies, B
Computer and Information Sciences, B
Counseling Psychology, M
Counselor Education/School Counseling and Guidance Services, M
Criminal Justice/Police Science, B
Cultural Studies, M
Design and Applied Arts, B
Distance Education Development, MO
Education, MO
English Language and Literature, B
French Language and Literature, B
General Studies, B
History, B
Human Resources Management/Personnel Administration, B
Information Science/Studies, BM
Interdisciplinary Studies, M
International Development, M
Labor and Industrial Relations, B
Liberal Arts and Sciences Studies and Humanities, B
Management, O
Management of Technology, M
Marketing/Marketing Management, B

Nursing, MO
Nursing Administration, M
Organizational Behavior Studies, B
Organizational Management, M
Political Science and Government, B
Project Management, MO
Psychology, B
Public Administration, B
Sociology, B
Women's Studies, B

CONCORDIA UNIVERSITY OF EDMONTON

Biology/Biological Sciences, B
Business Administration and Management, B
Canadian Studies, B
Chemistry, B
Computer and Information Systems Security, M
Education, B
Elementary Education and Teaching, B
English Language and Literature, B
Environmental Health, B
Environmental Sciences, B
Foreign Languages and Literatures, B
French Language and Literature, B
History, B
Human Resources Management and Services, B
Mathematics, B
Music, B
Philosophy, B
Political Science and Government, B
Pre-Theology/Pre-Ministerial Studies, B
Psychology, B
Public Health, B
Religion/Religious Studies, BM
Social Sciences, B
Sociology, B
Theology and Religious Vocations, BM
Visual and Performing Arts, B

THE KING'S UNIVERSITY

Biology/Biological Sciences, B
Business Administration and Management, B
Chemistry, B
Computer Science, B
Elementary Education and Teaching, B
English Language and Literature, B
Environmental Studies, B
History, B
Music, B
Philosophy, B
Psychology, B
Secondary Education and Teaching, B
Social Sciences, B
Sociology, B
Theology/Theological Studies, B

MOUNT ROYAL UNIVERSITY

Accounting, B
Anthropology, B
Business Administration and Management, B
Cell/Cellular and Molecular Biology, B
Child Development, B
Computer Science, B
Computer and Information Sciences, B
Criminal Justice/Law Enforcement Administration, B
Education, B
Engineering, B
English Language and Literature, B
Environmental Studies, B
Geology/Earth Science, B
Health and Physical Education, B
History, B
Human Resources Management/Personnel Administration, B
Information Science/Studies, B
Interior Design, B
Journalism, B
Management Science, B
Marketing/Marketing Management, B
Psychology, B
Public Policy Analysis, B
Public Relations/Image Management, B
Sociology, B
Spanish Language and Literature, B

Sport and Fitness Administration/Management, B

PRAIRIE BIBLE INSTITUTE

Aviation/Airway Management and Operations, A
Bible/Biblical Studies, AB
Divinity/Ministry (BD, MDiv), AB
Intercultural/Multicultural and Diversity Studies, B
Pastoral Counseling and Specialized Ministries, B
Pastoral Studies/Counseling, B
Religion/Religious Studies, A
Theological and Ministerial Studies, B
Theology and Religious Vocations, B
Theology/Theological Studies, B
Youth Ministry, AB

ROCKY MOUNTAIN COLLEGE

Behavioral Sciences, B
Bible/Biblical Studies, B
Divinity/Ministry (BD, MDiv.), B
Human Services, B
Intercultural/Multicultural and Diversity Studies, B
Pastoral Studies/Counseling, B
Theology/Theological Studies, B
Youth Ministry, B

SOUTHERN ALBERTA INSTITUTE OF TECHNOLOGY

Business Administration and Management, A
Business Administration, Management and Operations, A
Construction Management, B
Geography, A
Information Science/Studies, A
Petroleum Engineering, A

UNIVERSITY OF ALBERTA

Accounting, BD
Acting, B
Actuarial Science, B
Adult and Continuing Education and Teaching, BMD
Agricultural Business and Management, B
Agricultural Economics, BMD
Agricultural Sciences, MD
Agricultural Teacher Education, B
Agriculture, B
Agriculture, Agriculture Operations and Related Sciences, B
Agronomy and Soil Sciences, MD
American Indian/Native American Studies, B
Ancient Studies/Civilization, B
Animal Genetics, B
Animal Sciences, B
Anthropology, BMD
Apparel and Textiles, B
Applied Mathematics, BMD
Archeology, MD
Area Studies, B
Art History, Criticism and Conservation, BM
Art Teacher Education, B
Art/Art Studies, General, B
Astrophysics, BMD
Atmospheric Sciences and Meteorology, B
BioTechnology, BMD
Biochemistry, BMD
Bioinformatics, B
Biological and Biomedical Sciences, MD
Biology Teacher Education, B
Biology/Biological Sciences, B
Biomedical Engineering, MD
Biostatistics, M
Botany/Plant Biology, B
Business Administration, Management and Operations, BMD
Business Teacher Education, B
Business, Management, Marketing, and Related Support Services, B
Business/Commerce, B
Business/Managerial Economics, B
Canadian Studies, B
Cancer Biology/Oncology, MD
Cell Biology and Anatomy, MD
Cell/Cellular and Molecular Biology, B
Chemical Engineering, MD
Chemistry, BMD
Chemistry Teacher Education, B

Chinese Language and Literature, B
Chinese Studies, BM
City/Urban, Community and Regional Planning, B
Civil Engineering, MD
Classical, Ancient Mediterranean and Near Eastern
    Studies and Archaeology, B
Classics and Classical Languages, Litera-
    tures, and Linguistics, BMD
Clinical Laboratory Science/Medical
    Technology/Technologist, B
Clinical Laboratory Sciences, MD
Clinical/Medical Laboratory Science and Allied Pro-
    fessions, B
Clothing and Textiles, MD
Communication Disorders, MD
Communication and Media Studies, M
Community Health and Preventive Medicine, M
Comparative Literature, B
Composition, M
Computer Engineering, MD
Computer Programming, Specific Applications, B
Computer Science, BMD
Computer Software Engineering, B
Computer Teacher Education, B
Condensed Matter Physics, MD
Conservation Biology, BMD
Construction Engineering and Management, MD
Counseling Psychology, MD
Counselor Education/School Counseling and Guid-
    ance Services, M
Criminology, M
Crop Production, B
Demography and Population Studies, MD
Dental Hygiene/Hygienist, O
Dentistry, D
Design and Applied Arts, BM
Design and Visual Communications, B
Developmental Biology and Embryology, B
Drama and Dance Teacher Education, B
Drama and Dramatics/Theatre Arts, B
East Asian Languages, Literatures, and Linguis-
    tics, B
East Asian Studies, BM
East European and Russian Studies, MD
Ecology, MD
Economics, BMD
Education, B
Educational Administration and Supervision, MDO
Educational Leadership and Administration, MDO
Educational Media/Instructional Technology, M
Educational Policy, MDO
Educational Psychology, MD
Electrical Engineering, MD
Elementary Education and Teaching, BMD
Energy and Power Engineering, MD
Engineering, B
Engineering Management, M
English, MD
English Language and Literature, B
English as a Second Language, M
English/Language Arts Teacher Education, B
Entrepreneurship/Entrepreneurial Studies, B
Environmental Biology, BMD
Environmental Engineering
    Technology/Environmental Technology, MD
Environmental Policy and Resource Management, D
Environmental Sciences, BMD
Environmental Studies, B
Environmental and Occupational Health, M
Epidemiology, M
European Studies/Civilization, B
Evolutionary Biology, BMD
Exercise and Sports Science, MD
Family and Consumer Sciences/Home Economics
    Teacher Education, B
Family and Consumer Sciences/Human Sci-
    ences, BMD
Film/Cinema Studies, B
Finance, B
Finance and Banking, MD
Fine Arts and Art Studies, M
Folklore, MD
Food Science and Technology, B
Foods, Nutrition, and Related Services, B
Foreign Language Teacher Education, B
Foreign Languages, Literatures, and Linguistics, B

Forest Management/Forest Resources Manage-
    ment, B
Forest Sciences and Biology, B
Forestry, MD
French Language Teacher Education, B
French Language and Literature, BMD
French Studies, B
General Studies, B
Genetics, MD
Geography, B
Geological and Earth Sciences/Geosciences, B
Geology/Earth Science, B
Geophysics and Seismology, BMD
Geosciences, MD
Geotechnical Engineering, MD
German Language Teacher Education, B
German Language and Literature, BMD
German Studies, B
Germanic Languages, Literatures, and Linguistics, B
Health Physics/Radiological Health, MD
Health Promotion, MO
Health Services Administration, M
Health Services Research, M
Health Teacher Education, B
Health and Physical Education, B
Health and Physical Education/Fitness, B
Hispanic Studies, MD
Hispanic-American, Puerto Rican, and Mexican-
    American/Chicano Studies, B
History, BMD
Human Resources Management/Personnel Adminis-
    tration, B
Immunology, MD
Indian/Native American Education, B
Industrial and Labor Relations, D
Information Science/Studies, B
International Business/Trade/Commerce, BM
International Public Health/International Health, M
Italian Language and Literature, BM
Italian Studies, B
Japanese Language and Literature, B
Japanese Studies, BM
Latin American Studies, B
Latin Language and Literature, B
Law and Legal Studies, MD
Liberal Arts and Sciences Studies and Humani-
    ties, B
Library Science, M
Linguistic, Comparative, and Related Language
    Studies and Services, B
Linguistics, BMD
Management, D
Management Information Systems and Services, B
Management Science, B
Marketing, D
Marketing/Marketing Management, B
Materials Engineering, MD
Maternal/Child Health and Neonatal
    Nurse/Nursing, D
Mathematical Physics, MD
Mathematical Statistics and Probability, B
Mathematical and Computational Finance, MD
Mathematics, BMDO
Mathematics Teacher Education, B
Mathematics and Computer Science, B
Mathematics and Statistics, B
Mechanical Engineering, MD
Medical Microbiology and Bacteriology, MD
Medical Physics, MD
Microbiological Sciences and Immunology, B
Microbiology, BMD
Mineral/Mining Engineering, MD
Molecular Biology, MD
Molecular Genetics, D
Multi-/Interdisciplinary Studies, B
Multilingual and Multicultural Education, M
Music, BMD
Music Teacher Education, B
NanoTechnology, MD
Natural Resources and Conservation, BMD
Neuroscience, MD
Nursing, MD
Nutritional Sciences, B
Occupational Therapy/Therapist, MD
Operations Management and Supervision, B
Organizational Behavior Studies, B

Organizational Management, D
Orthodontics, MD
Painting, M
Paleontology, B
Pathology/Experimental Pathology, MD
Petroleum Engineering, MD
Pharmaceutical Sciences, MD
Pharmacology, BMD
Pharmacy, BMD
Pharmacy, Pharmaceutical Sciences, and Adminis-
    tration, B
Philosophy, BMD
Philosophy and Religious Studies, B
Physical Education Teaching and Coaching, BMD
Physical Sciences, B
Physical Therapy/Therapist, MD
Physics, BMD
Physics Teacher Education, B
Physiology, BMD
Piano and Organ, B
Plant Biology, MD
Political Science and Government, BMD
Pre-Veterinary Studies, B
Printmaking, BM
Psychology, BMD
Public Health, MD
Range Science and Management, B
Recreation and Park Management, MD
Rehabilitation Sciences, D
Religion/Religious Studies, B
Religious/Sacred Music, B
Retailing and Retail Operations, B
Romance Languages, Literatures, and Linguistics, B
Rural Sociology, MD
Russian Language and Literature, B
Scandinavian Languages, Literatures, and Linguis-
    tics, B
School Psychology, MD
Science Teacher Education/General Science
    Teacher Education, B
Science, Technology and Society, B
Sculpture, M
Secondary Education and Teaching, MD
Slavic Languages, Literatures, and Linguistics, BMD
Social Science Teacher Education, B
Social Sciences, B
Social Studies Teacher Education, B
Sociology, BMD
Soil Sciences, B
Spanish Language Teacher Education, B
Spanish Language and Literature, B
Special Education and Teaching, MD
Speech Teacher Education, B
Sport and Fitness Administration/Management, M
Statistics, MDO
Structural Engineering, MD
Systems Engineering, MD
Teaching French as a Second or Foreign Lan-
    guage, B
Technical Theatre/Theatre Design and Technol-
    ogy, B
Technology Teacher Education/Industrial Arts
    Teacher Education, B
Telecommunications, MD
Theater, M
Trade and Industrial Teacher Education, B
Ukraine Studies, B
Ukrainian Language and Literature, B
Vision Science/Physiological Optics, MD
Visual and Performing Arts, B
Voice and Opera, B
Water Resources Engineering, MD
Wildlife and Wildlands Science and Management, B
Women's Studies, B
Zoology/Animal Biology, B

UNIVERSITY OF CALGARY

Accounting, B
Actuarial Science, B
Adult and Continuing Education and Teaching, MD
Allopathic Medicine, D
American Indian/Native American Studies, B
Analytical Chemistry, MD
Anthropology, BMD
Applied Mathematics, B
Applied Psychology, MD

Archeology, BM
Architecture, M
Art History, Criticism and Conservation, B
Art Teacher Education, B
Art/Art Studies, General, B
Astronomy, MD
Astrophysics, B
BioTechnology, M
Biochemistry, BMD
Bioinformatics, B
Biological and Biomedical Sciences, MD
Biology/Biological Sciences, B
Biomedical Engineering, MD
Biomedical Sciences, B
Botany/Plant Biology, B
Business Administration and Management, B
Business Administration, Management and Operations, M
Canadian Studies, B
Cancer Biology/Oncology, MD
Cardiovascular Sciences, MD
Cell/Cellular Biology and Histology, B
Chemical Engineering, BMD
Chemistry, BMD
Civil Engineering, BMD
Classics and Classical Languages, Literatures, and Linguistics, BMD
Clinical Psychology, MD
Communication Studies/Speech Communication and Rhetoric, B
Communication and Media Studies, BMD
Community Health and Preventive Medicine, MD
Computer Engineering, BMD
Computer Science, BMD
Counseling Psychology, MD
Curriculum and Instruction, MD
Dance, B
Drama and Dance Teacher Education, B
Drama and Dramatics/Theatre Arts, B
East Asian Studies, B
Ecology, B
Economics, BMD
Education, B
Educational Leadership and Administration, MD
Educational Measurement and Evaluation, MD
Electrical Engineering, MD
Electrical, Electronics and Communications Engineering, B
Elementary Education and Teaching, B
Energy Management and Policy, MD
Energy and Power Engineering, MD
Engineering and Applied Sciences, MD
English, MD
English Language and Literature, B
Environmental Design/Architecture, MD
Environmental Engineering Technology/Environmental Technology, MD
Environmental Law, MO
Environmental Policy, MO
Environmental Policy and Resource Management, MD
Environmental Studies, B
Film/Cinema Studies, B
Finance, B
Fine Arts and Art Studies, M
French Language and Literature, BMD
Genetics, MD
Geography, BMD
Geological/Geophysical Engineering, B
Geology/Earth Science, BMD
Geophysics and Seismology, BMD
Geosciences, MD
Geotechnical Engineering, MD
German Language and Literature, BM
History, BMD
Humanities/Humanistic Studies, B
Hydrology and Water Resources Science, MD
Immunology, MD
Industrial Engineering, B
Infectious Diseases, MD
Inorganic Chemistry, MD
Insurance, B
International Relations and Affairs, B
Italian Studies, B
Kinesiology and Exercise Science, B
Kinesiology and Movement Studies, MD

Latin American Studies, B
Law and Legal Studies, BMDO
Legal and Justice Studies, MO
Linguistics, BMD
Management, MD
Management Information Systems and Services, B
Management Strategy and Policy, MD
Manufacturing Engineering, MD
Marketing/Marketing Management, B
Materials Sciences, MD
Mathematics, BMD
Mechanical Engineering, BMD
Mechanics, MD
Medieval and Renaissance Studies, B
Microbiology, MD
Military and Defense Studies, MD
Molecular Biology, BMD
Molecular Genetics, MD
Multilingual and Multicultural Education, MD
Music, BMD
Neuroscience, MD
Nursing, MDO
Organic Chemistry, MD
Parks, Recreation, Leisure and Fitness Studies, B
Pathology/Experimental Pathology, MD
Petroleum Engineering, MD
Philosophy, BMD
Physical Chemistry, MD
Physics, BMD
Physiology, MD
Political Science and Government, BMD
Project Management, MD
Psychology, BMD
Religion/Religious Studies, BMD
Russian Language and Literature, B
School Psychology, MD
Secondary Education and Teaching, B
Social Work, BMDO
Sociology, BMD
Software Engineering, M
Spanish Language and Literature, BMD
Statistics, BMD
Structural Engineering, MD
Sustainable Development, M
Theater, M
Theoretical Chemistry, MD
Tourism and Travel Services Management, B
Transportation and Highway Engineering, MD
Urban Studies/Affairs, B
Water Resources, MD
Women's Studies, B
Zoology/Animal Biology, B

UNIVERSITY OF LETHBRIDGE

Accounting, BM
Acting, B
Agricultural Sciences, M
Agriculture, B
American Indian/Native American Studies, BM
Animation, Interactive Technology, Video Graphics and Special Effects, B
Anthropology, BM
Archeology, BM
Art History, Criticism and Conservation, B
Art Teacher Education, B
Art/Art Studies, General, B
BioTechnology, B
Biochemistry, BM
Biological and Biomedical Sciences, M
Biology/Biological Sciences, B
Business Administration and Management, B
Business Teacher Education, B
Business/Managerial Economics, B
Canadian Studies, BM
Cartography, B
Chemistry, BM
Computational Sciences, D
Computer Science, BM
Counseling Psychology, M
Counselor Education/School Counseling and Guidance Services, M
Drama and Dance Teacher Education, B
Drama and Dramatics/Theatre Arts, B
Economics, BM
Education, BM
Educational Leadership and Administration, M

English, M
English Language and Literature, B
English/Language Arts Teacher Education, B
Environmental Sciences, BM
Exercise and Sports Science, M
Finance, B
Finance and Banking, M
Fine Arts and Art Studies, M
Fine/Studio Arts, B
Foreign Language Teacher Education, M
Foreign Languages, Literatures, and Linguistics, B
French Language Teacher Education, B
French Language and Literature, M
Gender Studies, M
General Studies, B
Geographic Information Systems, M
Geography, BM
German Language Teacher Education, B
German Language and Literature, BM
History, B
Human Resources Management and Services, M
Human Resources Management/Personnel Administration, B
Humanities/Humanistic Studies, B
Indian/Native American Education, B
International Business/Trade/Commerce, BM
Kinesiology and Exercise Science, B
Kinesiology and Movement Studies, M
Liberal Arts and Sciences Studies and Humanities, B
Management, M
Management Information Systems and Services, BM
Management Strategy and Policy, M
Marketing, M
Marketing/Marketing Management, B
Mathematics, BM
Mathematics Teacher Education, B
Media Studies, M
Molecular Biology, D
Multi-/Interdisciplinary Studies, B
Music, BM
Music Teacher Education, B
Neuroscience, MD
Nursing, M
Philosophy, BM
Physical Education Teaching and Coaching, B
Physics, BM
Political Science and Government, BM
Psychology, BM
Public Administration, B
Public Health (MPH, DPH), B
Religion/Religious Studies, BM
Romance Languages, Literatures, and Linguistics, B
Science Teacher Education/General Science Teacher Education, B
Social Sciences, B
Social Studies Teacher Education, B
Sociology, BM
Spanish Language and Literature, M
Special Education and Teaching, B
Substance Abuse/Addiction Counseling, BM
Teacher Education and Professional Development, Specific Subject Areas, B
Technical Theatre/Theatre Design and Technology, B
Theater, M
Urban Studies/Affairs, BM
Visual and Performing Arts, B
Women's Studies, BM

VANGUARD COLLEGE

Bible/Biblical Studies, B
Religious/Sacred Music, B

Theology/Theological Studies, B

British Columbia

THE ART INSTITUTE OF VANCOUVER

Graphic Design, B
Interior Design, B

BRITISH COLUMBIA INSTITUTE OF TECHNOLOGY

Accounting, AB
Accounting Technology/Technician and Bookkeeping, A
Administrative Assistant and Secretarial Science, A
Aeronautical/Aerospace Engineering Technology/Technician, A
Aircraft Powerplant Technology/Technician, A
Airframe Mechanics and Aircraft Maintenance Technology/Technician, A
Allied Health Diagnostic, Intervention, and Treatment Professions, A
Architectural Drafting and Architectural CAD/CADD, A
Architectural Engineering Technology/Technician, A
Autobody/Collision and Repair Technology/Technician, A
Automobile/Automotive Mechanics Technology/Technician, A
Avionics Maintenance Technology/Technician, A
BioTechnology, AB
Biology Technician/BioTechnology Laboratory Technician, A
Building/Construction Finishing, Management, and Inspection, A
Business Administration and Management, AB
Cabinetmaking and Millwork/Millwright, A
Cardiovascular Technology/Technologist, A
Carpentry/Carpenter, A
Chemical Technology/Technician, A
Civil Drafting and Civil Engineering CAD/CADD, A
Civil Engineering Technology/Technician, A
Clinical/Medical Laboratory Technician, A
Commercial and Advertising Art, A
Computer Science, AB
Computer Systems Analysis/Analyst, AB
Construction Engineering Technology/Technician, A
Construction Trades, A
Data Processing and Data Processing Technology/Technician, A
Diesel Mechanics Technology/Technician, A
Drafting and Design Technology/Technician, A
Electrical and Power Transmission Installation/Installer, A
Electrical, Electronic and Communications Engineering Technology/Technician, AB
Engineering, A
Entrepreneurship/Entrepreneurial Studies, A
Environmental Engineering Technology/Environmental Technology, B
Environmental Health, AB
Environmental/Environmental Health Engineering, A
Finance, A
Finance and Financial Management Services, A
Financial Planning and Services, A
Fire Protection and Safety Technology/Technician, A
Forensic Science and Technology, A
Forest Management/Forest Resources Management, A
Forestry Technology/Technician, A
Health Professions and Related Clinical Sciences, A
Health and Medical Administrative Services, A
Health/Health Care Administration/Management, AB
Heating, Air Conditioning, Ventilation and Refrigeration Maintenance Technology/Technician, A
Heavy Equipment Maintenance Technology/Technician, A
Human Resources Management/Personnel Administration, A
Industrial Mechanics and Maintenance Technology, A
Industrial Technology/Technician, A
Information Science/Studies, A
Interior Design, A
International Business/Trade/Commerce, A
Machine Tool Technology/Machinist, A

Management Science, A
Marketing/Marketing Management, A
Mechanical Drafting and Mechanical Drafting CAD/CADD, A
Mechanical Engineering/Mechanical Technology/Technician, AB
Medical Administrative Assistant/Secretary, A
Medical Radiologic Technology/Science - Radiation Therapist, AB
Mining Technology/Technician, A
Naval Architecture and Marine Engineering, A
Nuclear Medical Technology/Technologist, A
Occupational Health and Industrial Hygiene, A
Operations Management and Supervision, A
Petroleum Technology/Technician, A
Pipefitting/Pipefitter and Sprinkler Fitter, A
Plastics Engineering Technology/Technician, A
Precision Systems Maintenance and Repair Technologies, A
Radio and Television Broadcasting Technology/Technician, A
Real Estate, A
Robotics Technology/Technician, A
Science Technologies/Technicians, A
Sheet Metal Technology/Sheetworking, A
Small Engine Mechanics and Repair Technology/Technician, A
Survey Technology/Surveying, AB
Taxation, A
Tourism and Travel Services Management, A
Trade and Industrial Teacher Education, A
Transportation and Highway Engineering, A
Vehicle Maintenance and Repair Technologies, A
Welding Technology/Welder, A
Wildlife and Wildlands Science and Management, A

COLUMBIA BIBLE COLLEGE

Bible/Biblical Studies, B
Intercultural/Multicultural and Diversity Studies, B
Missions/Missionary Studies and Missiology, B
Pastoral Studies/Counseling, B
Pre-Theology/Pre-Ministerial Studies, B
Religion/Religious Studies, B

EMILY CARR UNIVERSITY OF ART + DESIGN

Animation, Interactive Technology, Video Graphics and Special Effects, B
Applied Arts and Design, M
Ceramic Arts and Ceramics, B
Cinematography and Film/Video Production, B
Computer Art and Design, M
Design and Visual Communications, B
Drawing, B
Fine Arts and Art Studies, M
Fine/Studio Arts, B
Illustration, B
Industrial Design, B
Painting, B
Photography, B
Printmaking, B
Sculpture, B
Web Page, Digital/Multimedia and Information Resources Design, B

OKANAGAN COLLEGE

Business Administration and Management, B
Computer and Information Sciences, B
Liberal Arts and Sciences Studies and Humanities, A

ROYAL ROADS UNIVERSITY

Advertising and Public Relations, O
Business Administration, Management and Operations, M
Conflict Resolution and Mediation/Peace Studies, MO
Criminal Justice/Safety Studies, B
Emergency Management, M
Entrepreneurship/Entrepreneurial Studies, B
Environmental Education, MO
Environmental Policy and Resource Management, MO
Environmental Sciences, B
Health Services Administration, O

Hospitality Administration/Management, MO
Hotel/Motel Administration/Management, B
Human Resources Management and Services, MO
Management, MO
Natural Resources Management/Development and Policy, B
Project Management, O
Public Relations, Advertising, and Applied Communication, B
Travel and Tourism, MO

SIMON FRASER UNIVERSITY

Actuarial Science, BMD
Anthropology, MD
Applied Mathematics, BMD
Archeology, BMD
Art Education, MD
Art/Art Studies, General, B
BioTechnology, M
Biochemistry, BMDO
Bioinformatics, O
Biological and Biomedical Sciences, MDO
Biological and Physical Sciences, B
Biology/Biological Sciences, B
Business Administration and Management, B
Business Administration, Management and Operations, MDO
Chemical Physics, B
Chemistry, BMD
Cognitive Sciences, B
Communication Studies/Speech Communication and Rhetoric, B
Communication and Media Studies, MD
Comparative and Interdisciplinary Arts, M
Computational Sciences, MD
Computer Science, BMD
Counselor Education/School Counseling and Guidance Services, M
Criminology, BMD
Cultural Studies, D
Curriculum and Instruction, MD
Dance, B
Drama and Dramatics/Theatre Arts, B
Economics, BMD
Education, BMDO
Educational Leadership and Administration, MD
Educational Media/Instructional Technology, MD
Educational Psychology, MD
Engineering Science, B
Engineering and Applied Sciences, MD
English, MD
English Education, M
English Language and Literature, B
English as a Second Language, M
Entomology, M
Environmental Policy and Resource Management, MDO
Environmental Sciences, B
Film/Cinema Studies, B
Finance and Banking, M
Fish, Game and Wildlife Management, O
Foundations and Philosophy of Education, MD
French Language and Literature, BM
Gender Studies, MD
General Studies, B
Geography, BMD
Geosciences, MD
Gerontology, MD
History, BMD
Humanities/Humanistic Studies, BM
International Affairs, M
International Public Health/International Health, O
Kinesiology and Exercise Science, B
Kinesiology and Movement Studies, MD
Latin American Studies, MO
Legal and Justice Studies, M
Liberal Arts and Sciences Studies and Humanities, B
Liberal Studies, M
Linguistics, BMD
Management Information Systems and Services, B
Management Science, B
Management of Technology, M
Mathematics, BMD
Mathematics Teacher Education, MD
Mechanical Engineering, MD

Molecular Biochemistry, B
Molecular Biology, BMDO
Music, B
Operations Research, MD
Philosophy, BMD
Physics, BMD
Political Science and Government, BMD
Psychology, BMD
Public Health, M
Public Policy Analysis, M
Publishing, M
Reading Teacher Education, D
Social Sciences, B
Sociology, BMD
Statistics, BMD
Systems Engineering, MD
Toxicology, M
Urban Studies/Affairs, MO
Visual and Performing Arts, B
Women's Studies, BMD

SUMMIT PACIFIC COLLEGE

Bible/Biblical Studies, B
Kindergarten/PreSchool Education and Teaching, B
Pastoral Studies/Counseling, B
Religious Education, B
Religious/Sacred Music, B
Theology/Theological Studies, B

THOMPSON RIVERS UNIVERSITY

Accounting, B
Applied Mathematics, B
Biochemistry, B
Biology/Biological Sciences, AB
Business Administration and Management, B
Business Administration, Management and Operations, M
Business/Commerce, B
Canadian Studies, AB
Chemistry, AB
Computer Science, AB
Computer Systems Analysis/Analyst, B
Computer Systems Networking and Telecommunications, B
Computer and Information Sciences, B
Computer/Information Technology Services Administration and Management, B
Construction Management, B
Criminal Justice/Law Enforcement Administration, B
Criminal Justice/Safety Studies, B
Criminology, B
Design and Visual Communications, B
Drama and Dramatics/Theatre Arts, B
Econometrics and Quantitative Economics, B
Economics, B
Education, BM
Electrical, Electronics and Communications Engineering, A
Elementary Education and Teaching, B
Engineering, A
English Language and Literature, B
Environmental Sciences, BM
Finance, B
Fine Arts and Art Studies, B
Fine/Studio Arts, B
General Studies, AB
Genetics, B
Geography, B
Geology/Earth Science, A
Health Services/Allied Health/Health Sciences, B
History, B
Human Resources Management/Personnel Administration, B
Information Science/Studies, B
Interior Design, B
Jazz/Jazz Studies, B
Journalism, B
Liberal Arts and Sciences Studies and Humanities, AB
Management Information Systems and Services, B
Mathematics, AB
Medical Radiologic Technology/Science - Radiation Therapist, B
Multi-/Interdisciplinary Studies, B
Music, AB
Music Performance, B

Music Therapy/Therapist, B
Non-Profit/Public/Organizational Management, B
Operations Management and Supervision, B
Philosophy, B
Physical Therapy/Therapist, B
Physics, AB
Political Science and Government, B
Psychology, B
Respiratory Care Therapy/Therapist, B
Social Work, BM
Sociology, B
Tourism and Travel Services Management, B
Youth Services/Administration, B
Zoology/Animal Biology, B

TRINITY WESTERN UNIVERSITY

Applied Mathematics, B
Art/Art Studies, General, B
Bible/Biblical Studies, B
BioTechnology, B
Biology/Biological Sciences, B
Business Administration and Management, B
Business Administration, Management and Operations, M
Chemistry, B
Christian Studies, B
Communication Studies/Speech Communication and Rhetoric, B
Computer Science, B
Counseling Psychology, M
Drama and Dramatics/Theatre Arts, B
Education, B
Educational Leadership and Administration, MO
Elementary Education and Teaching, B
English, M
English Language and Literature, B
English as a Second Language, M
Environmental Studies, B
European Studies/Civilization, B
General Studies, B
Geography, B
Health Services Administration, MO
History, BM
Humanities/Humanistic Studies, BM
Interdisciplinary Studies, M
International Business/Trade/Commerce, M
International Relations and Affairs, B
Kinesiology and Exercise Science, B
Linguistics, BM
Mathematics, B
Modern Languages, B
Music, B
Natural Sciences, B
Non-Profit/Public/Organizational Management, MO
Nursing, M
Organizational Management, MO
Pastoral Studies/Counseling, M
Philosophy, BM
Political Science and Government, B
Pre-Dentistry Studies, B
Pre-Medicine/Pre-Medical Studies, B
Pre-Pharmacy Studies, B
Pre-Veterinary Studies, B
Psychology, B
Religion/Religious Studies, B
Secondary Education and Teaching, B
Sociology, B
Sport and Fitness Administration/Management, B
Theology and Religious Vocations, MD

THE UNIVERSITY OF BRITISH COLUMBIA

Accounting, BD
Adult and Continuing Education and Teaching, M
Agricultural Economics, M
Agricultural Sciences, MD
Agricultural and Food Products Processing, B
Agriculture, B
Agronomy and Soil Sciences, MD
Allopathic Medicine, MD
Animal Genetics, B
Animal Sciences, BMD
Animal/Livestock Husbandry and Production, B
Anthropology, BMD
Applied Mathematics, BMD
Archeology, BM

Architecture, M
Archives/Archival Administration, MDO
Art Education, M
Art History, Criticism and Conservation, BMDO
Art Teacher Education, B
Asian Studies/Civilization, BMD
Astronomy, BMD
Atmospheric Sciences and Meteorology, BMD
BioTechnology, B
Biochemistry, BMD
Biochemistry, Biophysics and Molecular Biology, B
Biology/Biological Sciences, B
Biomedical/Medical Engineering, B
Biophysics, B
Biopsychology, MD
Botany/Plant Biology, MD
Business Administration and Management, B
Business Administration, Management and Operations, MD
Business Education, M
Business Teacher Education, B
Business/Commerce, B
Canadian Government and Politics, B
Canadian Studies, B
Cell Biology and Anatomy, MD
Cell/Cellular Biology and Histology, B
Central/Middle and Eastern European Studies, B
Chemical Engineering, BMD
Chemistry, BMD
Chinese Language and Literature, B
Civil Engineering, BMD
Classics and Classical Languages, Literatures, and Linguistics, BMD
Clinical Psychology, MD
Clinical/Medical Laboratory Technician, B
Cognitive Sciences, BMD
Communication Disorders, BMD
Computer Engineering, BMD
Computer Science, BMD
Counseling Psychology, MD
Curriculum and Instruction, MD
Dental Hygiene/Hygienist, B
Dentistry, D
Developmental Biology and Embryology, MD
Developmental Psychology, MD
Dietetics/Dieticians, B
Drama and Dramatics/Theatre Arts, B
Early Childhood Education and Teaching, M
East European and Russian Studies, MD
Economics, BMD
Education, BMDO
Educational Administration and Supervision, M
Educational Leadership and Administration, D
Educational Measurement and Evaluation, MD
Educational Policy, D
Electrical Engineering, MD
Electrical, Electronics and Communications Engineering, B
Elementary Education and Teaching, B
Engineering Physics, B
Engineering Technologies/Technicians, B
Engineering and Applied Sciences, MD
English, MD
English Language and Literature, B
English as a Second Language, MD
Environmental Biology, B
Environmental Engineering Technology/Environmental Technology, B
Environmental Studies, B
Environmental and Occupational Health, MD
Epidemiology, MD
European Studies/Civilization, B
Family and Consumer Sciences/Human Sciences, B
Film, Television, and Video Production, MO
Film, Television, and Video Theory and Criticism, MO
Film/Cinema Studies, B
Finance, B
Finance and Banking, D
Fine Arts and Art Studies, MDO
Fine/Studio Arts, B
Fishing and Fisheries Sciences and Management, B
Food Science, B
Food Science and Technology, BMD
Foods, Nutrition, and Related Services, B
Foods, Nutrition, and Wellness Studies, B

Forest Management/Forest Resources Manage-
ment, B
Forestry, BMD
Foundations and Philosophy of Education, D
French Language and Literature, BMD
Gender Studies, MD
Genetic Counseling/Counselor, M
Genetics, MD
Geography, BMD
Geological Engineering, MD
Geological/Geophysical Engineering, B
Geology/Earth Science, BMD
Geophysics and Seismology, BMD
German Language and Literature, BMD
Health Psychology, MD
Health Services Administration, M
Higher Education/Higher Education Administra-
tion, M
Hispanic Studies, MD
History, BMD
Home Economics Education, M
Horticultural Science, B
Human Development, M
Human Nutrition, B
Human Resources Management and Services, B
Immunology, MD
Industrial Education, M
Information Science/Studies, MDO
International Affairs, M
International Business/Trade/Commerce, B
International Relations and Affairs, B
Italian Language and Literature, B
Journalism, M
Kindergarten/PreSchool Education and Teaching, B
Kinesiology and Exercise Science, B
Kinesiology and Movement Studies, MD
Landscape Architecture, BM
Latin American Studies, B
Latin Language and Literature, B
Law and Legal Studies, MD
Liberal Arts and Sciences Studies and Humani-
ties, B
Library Science, MDO
Linguistics, BMD
Management, D
Management Information Systems and Services, BD
Management Strategy and Policy, D
Marine Biology and Biological Oceanography, B
Marine Sciences, MD
Marketing, D
Marketing/Marketing Management, B
Materials Engineering, BMD
Materials Sciences, MD
Mathematics, BMD
Mathematics Teacher Education, M
Mechanical Engineering, BMD
Mechanical Engineering/Mechanical
Technology/Technician, B
Medical Microbiology and Bacteriology, B
Metallurgical Engineering, BMD
Metallurgy, MD
Microbiology, MD
Mineral/Mining Engineering, MD
Mining and Mineral Engineering, B
Molecular Biology, MD
Museology/Museum Studies, M
Music, BMD
Music History, Literature, and Theory, B
Music Teacher Education, BM
Music Theory and Composition, B
Natural Resources Management/Development and
Policy, BMD
Natural Resources and Conservation, B
Neuroscience, MD
Nurse Anesthetist, MD
Nursing, MD
Nutritional Sciences, MD
Occupational Therapy/Therapist, M
Oceanography, Chemical and Physical, BMD
Operations Research, M
Oral and Dental Sciences, MDO
Organizational Behavior Studies, D
Parks, Recreation and Leisure Facilities Manage-
ment, B
Pathology/Experimental Pathology, MD
Periodontics, O

Pharmaceutical Sciences, MD
Pharmacology, BMD
Pharmacy, BMD
Philosophy, BMD
Physical Education Teaching and Coaching, M
Physics, BMD
Physiology, B
Piano and Organ, B
Plant Sciences, MD
Political Science and Government, BMD
Pre-Veterinary Studies, B
Psychology, BMD
Public Health, MD
Quantitative Analysis, MD
Reading Teacher Education, MD
Real Estate, B
Rehabilitation Sciences, MD
Religion/Religious Studies, BMD
Reproductive Biology, MD
Romance Languages, Literatures, and Linguistics, B
Russian Language and Literature, B
Russian Studies, B
School Psychology, MDO
Science Teacher Education/General Science
Teacher Education, BM
Secondary Education and Teaching, B
Slavic Languages, Literatures, and Linguistics, B
Social Psychology, MD
Social Sciences, B
Social Studies Teacher Education, M
Social Work, BMD
Sociology, BMD
Software Engineering, M
Soil Science and Agronomy, B
South Asian Languages, Literatures, and Linguis-
tics, B
South Asian Studies, B
Spanish Language and Literature, B
Special Education and Teaching, BMDO
Statistics, BMD
Teaching English as a Second or Foreign
Language/ESL Language Instructor, B
Theater, MD
Transportation and Materials Moving, B
Transportation/Transportation Management, D
Urban Studies/Affairs, B
Urban and Regional Planning, MD
Violin, Viola, Guitar and Other Stringed Instru-
ments, B
Visual and Performing Arts, B
Voice and Opera, B
Water Resources, M
Wildlife and Wildlands Science and Management, B
Women's Studies, B
Wood Science and Wood Products/Pulp and Paper
Technology, B
Writing, M
Zoology/Animal Biology, BMD

THE UNIVERSITY OF BRITISH COLUMBIA–OKANAGAN CAMPUS

Accounting, B
Anthropology, B
Art History, Criticism and Conservation, B
Biochemistry, B
Biology/Biological Sciences, B
Business Administration and Management, B
Chemistry, B
Civil Engineering, B
Computer Science, B
Drama and Dramatics/Theatre Arts, B
Ecology, Evolution, Systematics and Population Bi-
ology, B
Economics, B
Education, B
Electrical, Electronics and Communications Engi-
neering, B
English Language and Literature, B
Entrepreneurship/Entrepreneurial Studies, B
Environmental Studies, B
Finance, B
French Language and Literature, B
General Studies, B
Geography, B
Health Professions and Related Clinical Sciences, B
History, B

Human Resources Management/Personnel Adminis-
tration, B
Information Technology, B
International Relations and Affairs, B
Kinesiology and Exercise Science, B
Marketing/Marketing Management, B
Mathematics, B
Mathematics and Statistics, B
Mechanical Engineering, B
Microbiology, B
Molecular Biology, B
Philosophy, B
Physics, B
Political Science and Government, B
Psychology, B
Social Work, B
Sociology, B
Spanish Language and Literature, B
Statistics, B
Visual and Performing Arts, B
Zoology/Animal Biology, B

UNIVERSITY OF THE FRASER VALLEY

Adult and Continuing Education and Teaching, B
Agricultural Business and Management, B
Agricultural Production Operations, A
Animal/Livestock Husbandry and Production, A
Anthropology, B
Applied Horticulture/Horticultural Operations, A
Aviation/Airway Management and Operations, B
Biology/Biological Sciences, B
Business Administration and Management, AB
Chemistry, B
Child Care and Support Services Management, AB
Computer and Information Sciences, B
Criminal Justice/Safety Studies, AB
Criminology, M
Development Economics and International Develop-
ment, B
Drama and Dramatics/Theatre Arts, AB
Economics, B
English Language and Literature, B
Fine/Studio Arts, B
General Studies, AB
Geography, B
Graphic Design, A
History, B
Kinesiology and Exercise Science, B
Liberal Arts and Sciences Studies and Humani-
ties, A
Library Assistant/Technician, A
Management Science, B
Mathematics, B
Ornamental Horticulture, A
Philosophy, B
Physical Sciences, A
Physics, B
Political Science and Government, B
Psychology, B
Social Work, ABM
Sociology, B

UNIVERSITY OF NORTHERN BRITISH COLUMBIA

Accounting, B
Anthropology, B
Aquatic Biology/Limnology, B
Biochemistry, Biophysics and Molecular Biology, B
Biological and Physical Sciences, B
Biology/Biological Sciences, B
Botany/Plant Biology, B
Business Administration and Management, B
Business/Commerce, B
Canadian Studies, B
Chemistry, B
Community Health and Preventive Medicine, M
Computer Science, BM
Computer and Information Sciences, B
Disability Studies, M
Economics, B
Education, M
Elementary Education and Teaching, B
English Language and Literature, B
Environmental Sciences, B
Environmental Studies, BMD
Environmental/Environmental Health Engineering, B

Finance, B
Fishing and Fisheries Sciences and Management, B
Forest Sciences and Biology, B
Gender Studies, M
General Studies, B
Geography, B
History, BM
Interdisciplinary Studies, M
International Affairs, M
International Business/Trade/Commerce, B
International/Global Studies, B
Land Use Planning and
  Management/Development, B
Liberal Arts and Sciences Studies and Humanities, B
Marketing/Marketing Management, B
Mathematics, BM
Mathematics and Computer Science, B
Multi-/Interdisciplinary Studies, B
Natural Resources and Conservation, MD
Natural Sciences, B
Parks, Recreation and Leisure Facilities Management, B
Parks, Recreation, Leisure and Fitness Studies, B
Physics, B
Political Science and Government, BM
Psychology, BMD
Secondary Education and Teaching, B
Social Work, BM
Wildlife Biology, B
Wildlife and Wildlands Science and Management, B
Women's Studies, B
Youth Services/Administration, B

UNIVERSITY OF VICTORIA

Ancient/Classical Greek Language and Literature, B
Anthropology, BM
Art Education, MD
Art History, Criticism and Conservation, BMD
Art Teacher Education, B
Asian Studies/Civilization, BM
Astronomy, BMD
Astrophysics, MD
Atmospheric Sciences and Meteorology, B
Biochemistry, BMD
Biological and Biomedical Sciences, MD
Biology/Biological Sciences, B
Botany/Plant Biology, B
Business Administration, Management and Operations, M
Business/Commerce, B
Central/Middle and Eastern European Studies, B
Chemistry, BMD
Child Development, B
Child and Family Studies, MD
Chinese Language and Literature, B
Classics and Classical Languages, Literatures, and Linguistics, BMD
Clinical Psychology, MD
Community Psychology, M
Comparative Literature, B
Composition, M
Computer Art and Design, M
Computer Engineering, BMD
Computer Science, BMD
Computer Software Engineering, B
Condensed Matter Physics, MD
Conflict Resolution and Mediation/Peace Studies, M
Counseling Psychology, M
Counselor Education/School Counseling and Guidance Services, M
Curriculum and Instruction, MD
Developmental Psychology, MD
Drama and Dramatics/Theatre Arts, B
Early Childhood Education and Teaching, MD
Ecology, B
Economics, BMD
Education, BMD
Educational Leadership and Administration, MD
Educational Measurement and Evaluation, M
Educational Psychology, MD
Electrical Engineering, MD
Electrical, Electronics and Communications Engineering, B
Elementary Education and Teaching, B
Engineering and Applied Sciences, MD

English, MD
English Education, MD
English Language and Literature, B
Environmental Education, D
Environmental Studies, B
Experimental Psychology, MD
Film, Television, and Video Production, M
Fine Arts and Art Studies, M
Fine/Studio Arts, B
Foreign Language Teacher Education, M
Foundations and Philosophy of Education, MD
French Language and Literature, BM
French Studies, B
Geography, BMD
Geology/Earth Science, B
Geophysics and Seismology, B
Geosciences, MD
German Language and Literature, BM
German Studies, B
Health Informatics, M
Health and Physical Education/Fitness, B
Health/Health Care Administration/Management, B
Hispanic Studies, M
History, BMD
Hotel/Motel Administration/Management, B
Human Development, MD
International Business/Trade/Commerce, B
Italian Language and Literature, BM
Italian Studies, B
Japanese Language and Literature, B
Kindergarten/PreSchool Education and Teaching, B
Kinesiology and Exercise Science, B
Kinesiology and Movement Studies, M
Latin Language and Literature, B
Law and Legal Studies, MD
Leisure Studies, M
Liberal Arts and Sciences Studies and Humanities, B
Linguistics, BMD
Marine Biology and Biological Oceanography, B
Mathematics, BMD
Mathematics Teacher Education, MD
Mechanical Engineering, BMD
Medical Microbiology and Bacteriology, B
Medical Physics, MD
Medieval and Renaissance Studies, B
Microbiology, MD
Modern Languages, B
Music, BMD
Music History, Literature, and Theory, B
Music Teacher Education, BMD
Music Theory and Composition, B
Musicology and Ethnomusicology, MD
Nursing, MD
Nursing - Advanced Practice, M
Nursing Administration, M
Nursing Education, M
Oceanography, Chemical and Physical, BMD
Pacific Area/Pacific Rim Studies, BM
Painting, M
Performance, M
Philosophy, BM
Photography, M
Physical Education Teaching and Coaching, BM
Physics, BMD
Piano and Organ, B
Political Science and Government, BMD
Pre-Dentistry Studies, B
Pre-Law Studies, B
Pre-Medicine/Pre-Medical Studies, B
Pre-Veterinary Studies, B
Psychology, BMD
Public Administration, BMD
Reading Teacher Education, MD
Romance Languages, Literatures, and Linguistics, B
Russian Language and Literature, B
Russian Studies, B
Science Teacher Education/General Science Teacher Education, MD
Sculpture, M
Secondary Education and Teaching, B
Slavic Languages, Literatures, and Linguistics, B
Social Psychology, MD
Social Studies Teacher Education, MD
Social Work, BM
Sociology, BMD

Spanish Language and Literature, B
Special Education and Teaching, BM
Sport and Fitness Administration/Management, B
Statistics, BMD
Teaching English as a Second or Foreign Language/ESL Language Instructor, B
Theater, B
Theoretical Physics, MD
Vocational and Technical Education, D
Voice and Opera, B
Women's Studies, B
Writing, M
Zoology/Animal Biology, B

VANCOUVER ISLAND UNIVERSITY

American Indian/Native American Studies, B
Anthropology, B
Business Administration, Management and Operations, M
Criminology, B
English Language and Literature, B
Finance and Banking, M
Geography, B
Graphic Design, B
History, B
International Business/Trade/Commerce, M
International/Global Studies, B
Liberal Arts and Sciences Studies and Humanities, B
Marketing, M
Philosophy, B
Physical Education Teaching and Coaching, B
Psychology, B
Sociology, B
Women's Studies, B

Manitoba

BOOTH UNIVERSITY COLLEGE

English Language and Literature, B
General Studies, B
Psychology, B
Religion/Religious Studies, B
Social Work, B

BRANDON UNIVERSITY

American Indian/Native American Studies, B
Biology/Biological Sciences, B
Botany/Plant Biology, B
Business Administration and Management, B
Canadian Studies, B
Chemistry, B
Composition, M
Computer Science, B
Counselor Education/School Counseling and Guidance Services, BMO
Curriculum and Instruction, MO
Economics, B
Education, BMO
Educational Administration and Supervision, MO
Elementary Education and Teaching, B
English Language and Literature, B
French Language and Literature, B
General Studies, B
Geography, B
Geology/Earth Science, B
History, B
Junior High/Intermediate/Middle School Education and Teaching, B
Kindergarten/PreSchool Education and Teaching, B
Liberal Arts and Sciences Studies and Humanities, B
Mathematics, B
Mathematics and Computer Science, B
Mental Health Counseling/Counselor, B
Music, BM
Music History, Literature, and Theory, B
Music Performance, B
Music Teacher Education, BM
Music Theory and Composition, B
Performance, M
Philosophy, B
Physics, B
Political Science and Government, B
Pre-Dentistry Studies, B

Pre-Law Studies, B
Pre-Medicine/Pre-Medical Studies, B
Pre-Veterinary Studies, B
Psychology, B
Religion/Religious Studies, B
Rural Planning and Studies, MO
Sociology, B
Special Education and Teaching, MO
Voice and Opera, B
Zoology/Animal Biology, B

PROVIDENCE UNIVERSITY COLLEGE & THEOLOGICAL SEMINARY

Airline/Commercial/Professional Pilot and Flight
   Crew, B
Bible/Biblical Studies, B
Business Administration and Management, B
Communication and Media Studies, B
Counseling Psychology, M
Divinity/Ministry (BD, MDiv.), B
Drama and Dramatics/Theatre Arts, B
Education, B
English as a Second Language, MO
History, B
Humanities/Humanistic Studies, B
Liberal Arts and Sciences Studies and Humani-
   ties, B
Missions/Missionary Studies and Missiology, BMO
Music, B
Parks, Recreation, Leisure and Fitness Studies, B
Pastoral Studies/Counseling, BMO
Religion/Religious Studies, B
Religious Education, BMO
Social Sciences, B
Student Personnel Services, M
Teaching English as a Second or Foreign
   Language/ESL Language Instructor, B
Theology and Religious Vocations, MDO
Theology/Theological Studies, B
Youth Ministry, B

STEINBACH BIBLE COLLEGE

Christian Studies, B
Divinity/Ministry (BD, MDiv.), B

UNIVERSITÉ DE SAINT-BONIFACE

Art/Art Studies, General, B
Business Administration and Management, B
Canadian Studies, M
Education, M
Social Work, B
Teacher Education, Multiple Levels, B

UNIVERSITY OF MANITOBA

Accounting, B
Actuarial Science, B
Adult and Continuing Education and Teaching, M
Agricultural Economics, BMD
Agricultural Sciences, MD
Agricultural/Biological Engineering and Bioengineer-
   ing, B
Agriculture, B
Agronomy and Crop Science, B
Agronomy and Soil Sciences, MD
American Indian/Native American Studies, M
Anatomy, MD
Animal Genetics, B
Animal Sciences, BMD
Anthropology, BMD
Apparel and Textiles, B
Applied Mathematics, B
Architecture, BM
Archives/Archival Administration, M
Art History, Criticism and Conservation, B
Art/Art Studies, General, B
Astronomy, B
Biochemistry, MD
Biological and Biomedical Sciences, MDO
Biology/Biological Sciences, B
Biosystems Engineering, MD
Botany/Plant Biology, BMD
Business Administration and Management, B
Business Administration, Management and Opera-
   tions, MD
Business/Managerial Economics, B

Canadian Studies, BM
Cancer Biology/Oncology, M
Chemistry, BMD
Child Development, B
Child and Family Studies, M
Civil Engineering, BMD
Classics and Classical Languages, Litera-
   tures, and Linguistics, BM
Clinical Psychology, D
Clothing and Textiles, M
Community Health and Preventive Medicine, MDO
Computational Sciences, M
Computer Engineering, BMD
Computer Science, BMD
Counselor Education/School Counseling and Guid-
   ance Services, M
Curriculum and Instruction, M
Dental Hygiene/Hygienist, B
Dental and Oral Surgery, M
Dentistry, D
Disability Studies, M
Drama and Dramatics/Theatre Arts, B
Ecology, BMD
Economics, BMD
Education, BMD
Educational Administration and Supervision, M
Educational Psychology, M
Electrical Engineering, MD
Electrical, Electronics and Communications Engi-
   neering, B
Elementary Education and Teaching, B
Engineering Science, B
Engineering and Applied Sciences, MD
English, MD
English Education, M
English Language and Literature, B
English as a Second Language, M
Entomology, BMD
Environmental Design/Architecture, B
Environmental Sciences, MD
Environmental Studies, B
Family and Consumer Sciences/Human Sciences, B
Film/Cinema Studies, B
Finance, B
Food Science, B
Food Science and Technology, MD
Foods, Nutrition, and Wellness Studies, B
Foundations and Philosophy of Education, M
French Language and Literature, BMD
Geography, BMD
Geological/Geophysical Engineering, B
Geology/Earth Science, BMD
Geophysics and Seismology, MD
German Language and Literature, BM
Higher Education/Higher Education Administra-
   tion, M
History, BMD
Home Economics, M
Horticultural Science, MD
Human Genetics, MD
Immunology, MD
Industrial Engineering, B
Industrial/Management Engineering, MD
Interdisciplinary Studies, MD
Interior Design, BM
Jewish/Judaic Studies, M
Kindergarten/PreSchool Education and Teaching, B
Kinesiology and Movement Studies, M
Labor and Industrial Relations, B
Landscape Architecture, M
Latin Language and Literature, B
Law and Legal Studies, M
Linguistics, MD
Manufacturing Engineering, MD
Mathematics, BMD
Mechanical Engineering, BMD
Medical Microbiology and Bacteriology, BMD
Medieval and Renaissance Studies, B
Microbiology, MD
Modern Greek Language and Literature, B
Music, BM
Natural Resources Management/Development and
   Policy, MD
Northern Studies, M
Nursing, M
Nutritional Sciences, MD

Occupational Therapy/Therapist, BM
Oral Biology, MD
Orthodontics, M
Pathology/Experimental Pathology, M
Periodontics, M
Pharmaceutical Sciences, MD
Pharmacology, MD
Pharmacy, B
Philosophy, BM
Physical Education Teaching and Coaching, BM
Physical Therapy/Therapist, BM
Physics, BMD
Physiology, MD
Plant Physiology, MD
Plant Sciences, MD
Political Science and Government, BM
Pre-Dentistry Studies, B
Pre-Law Studies, B
Pre-Medicine/Pre-Medical Studies, B
Pre-Veterinary Studies, B
Psychology, BMD
Public Administration, BM
Recreation and Park Management, M
Rehabilitation Sciences, MD
Rehabilitation and Therapeutic Professions, B
Religion/Religious Studies, BMD
Russian Language and Literature, B
Russian Studies, B
School Psychology, M
Science Teacher Education/General Science
   Teacher Education, B
Secondary Education and Teaching, B
Slavic Languages, Literatures, and Linguistics, BM
Social Work, BMD
Sociology, BMD
South Asian Studies, B
Spanish Language and Literature, B
Special Education and Teaching, M
Statistics, BMD
Urban and Regional Planning, M
Women's Studies, B
Zoology/Animal Biology, BMD

THE UNIVERSITY OF WINNIPEG

Anthropology, B
Applied Mathematics, B
Art History, Criticism and Conservation, B
Biochemistry, B
Biology/Biological Sciences, B
Business Administration and Management, B
Canadian Studies, B
Chemistry, B
Classics and Classical Languages, Litera-
   tures, and Linguistics, B
Criminal Justice/Police Science, B
Data Processing and Data Processing
   Technology/Technician, B
Development Economics and International Develop-
   ment, B
Drama and Dramatics/Theatre Arts, B
Ecology, B
Economics, B
Education, B
Elementary Education and Teaching, B
English Language and Literature, B
Environmental Studies, B
French Language and Literature, B
French Studies, B
Geography, B
German Language and Literature, B
German Studies, B
History, BM
Information Science/Studies, B
Italian Studies, B
Journalism, B
Latin Language and Literature, B
Marriage and Family Therapy/Counseling, MO
Mathematics, B
Modern Greek Language and Literature, B
Molecular Biology, B
Music, B
Peace Studies and Conflict Resolution, B
Philosophy, B
Physics, B
Political Science and Government, B
Pre-Dentistry Studies, B

Pre-Law Studies, B
Pre-Medicine/Pre-Medical Studies, B
Pre-Nursing Studies, B
Pre-Pharmacy Studies, B
Pre-Veterinary Studies, B
Psychology, B
Public Administration, M
Religion/Religious Studies, BM
Secondary Education and Teaching, B
Sociology, B
Spanish and Iberian Studies, B
Statistics, B
Theology and Religious Vocations, MO
Theology/Theological Studies, B
Urban Studies/Affairs, B
Women's Studies, B

Maritime Provinces-New Brunswick

CRANDALL UNIVERSITY

Bible/Biblical Studies, B
Biology/Biological Sciences, B
Business Administration and Management, B
Education, B
English Language and Literature, B
History, B
Mass Communication/Media Studies, B
Psychology, B
Religion/Religious Studies, B
Sociology, B
Teacher Education, Multiple Levels, B

KINGSWOOD UNIVERSITY

Bible/Biblical Studies, B
Divinity/Ministry (BD, MDiv.), B
Elementary Education and Teaching, B
General Studies, B
Music, B
Pastoral Studies/Counseling, M
Religion/Religious Studies, B
Religious Education, B
Theology and Religious Vocations, M

MOUNT ALLISON UNIVERSITY

Accounting, B
American/United States Studies/Civilization, B
Ancient/Classical Greek Language and Literature, B
Anthropology, B
Applied Mathematics, B
Art History, Criticism and Conservation, B
Biochemistry, B
Biological and Biomedical Sciences, M
Biological and Physical Sciences, B
Biology/Biological Sciences, B
Biopsychology, B
Business Administration and Management, B
Business/Commerce, B
Business/Managerial Economics, B
Canadian Studies, B
Chemistry, BM
Classics and Classical Languages, Literatures, and Linguistics, B
Comparative Literature, B
Computer Science, B
Drama and Dramatics/Theatre Arts, B
Drawing, B
Economics, B
English Language and Literature, B
Environmental Studies, B
Fine/Studio Arts, B
French Language and Literature, B
Geography, B
Geology/Earth Science, B
German Language and Literature, B
History, B
Humanities/Humanistic Studies, B
International Business/Trade/Commerce, B
International Relations and Affairs, B
Latin Language and Literature, B
Liberal Arts and Sciences Studies and Humanities, B
Mathematics, B
Mathematics and Computer Science, B
Medieval and Renaissance Studies, B

Modern Languages, B
Music, B
Music History, Literature, and Theory, B
Music Performance, B
Natural Sciences, B
Philosophy, B
Photography, B
Physics, B
Piano and Organ, B
Political Science and Government, B
Pre-Dentistry Studies, B
Pre-Law Studies, B
Pre-Medicine/Pre-Medical Studies, B
Pre-Pharmacy Studies, B
Pre-Theology/Pre-Ministerial Studies, B
Pre-Veterinary Studies, B
Printmaking, B
Psychology, B
Religion/Religious Studies, B
Romance Languages, Literatures, and Linguistics, B
Sculpture, B
Sociology, B
Spanish Language and Literature, B
Violin, Viola, Guitar and Other Stringed Instruments, B
Voice and Opera, B

ST. THOMAS UNIVERSITY

Adult Development and Aging, B
American Indian/Native American Studies, B
Anthropology, B
Christian Studies, B
Criminology, B
Economics, B
Education, B
English Language and Literature, B
Environmental Studies, B
French Language and Literature, B
Gerontology, B
History, B
International Relations and Affairs, B
Journalism, B
Mathematics, B
Philosophy, B
Political Communication, B
Political Science and Government, B
Psychology, B
Religion/Religious Studies, B
Science, Technology and Society, B
Social Work, B
Sociology, B
Spanish Language and Literature, B
Women's Studies, B

UNIVERSITÉ DE MONCTON

Accounting, B
Adult and Continuing Education and Teaching, B
Astronomy, M
Biochemistry, BM
Biological and Biomedical Sciences, M
Biological and Physical Sciences, B
Biology/Biological Sciences, B
Business Administration and Management, B
Business Administration, Management and Operations, M
Chemistry, BM
Child Development, B
Civil Engineering, BM
Comparative Literature, B
Computer Science, BMO
Counselor Education/School Counseling and Guidance Services, M
Drama and Dramatics/Theatre Arts, B
Economics, BM
Education, BM
Educational Administration and Supervision, M
Educational Psychology, M
Electrical Engineering, M
Electrical, Electronics and Communications Engineering, B
Elementary Education and Teaching, B
Engineering, B
Engineering and Applied Sciences, M
English Language and Literature, B
Family and Consumer Economics and Related Services, B

Finance, B
Fine/Studio Arts, B
Food Science and Technology, M
Food Technology and Processing, B
Foods, Nutrition, and Wellness Studies, B
Forest Engineering, B
French Language and Literature, BMD
Geography, B
History, BM
Industrial Engineering, B
Industrial/Management Engineering, M
Kindergarten/PreSchool Education and Teaching, B
Language Interpretation and Translation, B
Law and Legal Studies, B
Liberal Arts and Sciences Studies and Humanities, B
Linguistics, B
Marketing/Marketing Management, B
Mass Communication/Media Studies, B
Mathematics, BM
Mechanical Engineering, BM
Modern Languages, B
Music, B
Music Teacher Education, B
Nutritional Sciences, M
Operations Management and Supervision, B
Parks, Recreation, Leisure and Fitness Studies, B
Philosophy, B
Physical Education Teaching and Coaching, B
Physics, BM
Political Science and Government, B
Psychology, B
Public Administration, M
Radiologic Technology/Science - Radiographer, B
Secondary Education and Teaching, B
Social Sciences, B
Social Work, BM
Sociology, B
Sport and Fitness Administration/Management, B

UNIVERSITY OF NEW BRUNSWICK FREDERICTON

Accounting, B
Adult and Continuing Education and Teaching, B
Animal Physiology, B
Anthropology, BM
Applied Economics, M
Applied Mathematics, B
Art Teacher Education, B
Biochemistry, B
Biological and Biomedical Sciences, MD
Biological and Physical Sciences, B
Biology/Biological Sciences, B
Biophysics, B
Botany/Plant Biology, B
Business Administration and Management, B
Business Administration, Management and Operations, M
Business Teacher Education, B
Business/Managerial Economics, B
Canadian Studies, B
Chemical Engineering, BMD
Chemistry, BMD
Civil Engineering, BMD
Classics and Classical Languages, Literatures, and Linguistics, BM
Comparative Literature, B
Computer Engineering, BMD
Computer Science, BMD
Conflict Resolution and Mediation/Peace Studies, M
Construction Engineering, B
Construction Engineering and Management, MD
Counselor Education/School Counseling and Guidance Services, B
Data Processing and Data Processing Technology/Technician, B
Drama and Dramatics/Theatre Arts, B
Ecology, B
Economics, BM
Education, BMD
Electrical Engineering, MD
Electrical, Electronics and Communications Engineering, B
Elementary Education and Teaching, B
Engineering, B
Engineering Management, M

Engineering and Applied Sciences, MDO
English, MD
English Language and Literature, B
Entomology, B
Entrepreneurship/Entrepreneurial Studies, M
Environmental Engineering
    Technology/Environmental Technology, MD
Environmental Policy and Resource Manage-
    ment, M
Environmental Studies, M
Exercise and Sports Science, M
Family and Consumer Sciences/Home Economics
    Teacher Education, B
Finance, B
Fire Science/Firefighting, B
Fishing and Fisheries Sciences and Management, B
Forest Engineering, B
Forestry, BMD
French Language and Literature, B
Geochemistry, B
Geodetic Sciences, MD
Geological/Geophysical Engineering, B
Geology/Earth Science, BMD
Geophysics and Seismology, B
Geotechnical Engineering, MD
German Language and Literature, B
Health Services Research, M
Health Teacher Education, B
History, BMD
Human Resources Management/Personnel Adminis-
    tration, B
Hydrology and Water Resources Science, MD
Information Science/Studies, B
Interdisciplinary Studies, MD
International Business/Trade/Commerce, B
International Development, M
International Relations and Affairs, B
Kindergarten/PreSchool Education and Teaching, B
Kinesiology and Exercise Science, B
Latin Language and Literature, B
Law and Legal Studies, B
Liberal Arts and Sciences Studies and Humani-
    ties, B
Linguistics, B
Marketing, M
Marketing/Marketing Management, B
Materials Sciences, MD
Mathematics, BMD
Mechanical Engineering, BMD
Mechanics, MD
Medical Microbiology and Bacteriology, B
Modern Greek Language and Literature, B
Modern Languages, B
Molecular Biology, B
Music Teacher Education, B
Nursing, M
Nursing Education, M
Operations Research, B
Parks, Recreation, Leisure and Fitness Studies, B
Philosophy, B
Physical Education Teaching and Coaching, BM
Physics, BMD
Political Science and Government, BM
Pre-Dentistry Studies, B
Pre-Law Studies, B
Pre-Medicine/Pre-Medical Studies, B
Pre-Veterinary Studies, B
Psychology, BMD
Public Administration, M
Public Policy Analysis, M
Recreation and Park Management, M
Romance Languages, Literatures, and Linguistics, B
Russian Language and Literature, B
Science Teacher Education/General Science
    Teacher Education, B
Secondary Education and Teaching, B
Sociology, BMD
Spanish Language and Literature, B
Special Education and Teaching, B
Sport and Fitness Administration/Management, M
Statistics, BMD
Structural Engineering, MD
Survey Technology/Surveying, B
Surveying Engineering, MD
Sustainable Development, M

Teaching English as a Second or Foreign
    Language/ESL Language Instructor, B
Transportation and Highway Engineering, MD
Urban and Regional Planning, M
Water Resources, MD
Wildlife Biology, B
Wildlife and Wildlands Science and Management, B
Zoology/Animal Biology, B

UNIVERSITY OF NEW BRUNSWICK SAINT JOHN

Accounting, B
Algebra and Number Theory, B
Biological and Biomedical Sciences, MD
Biology/Biological Sciences, B
Business Administration and Management, B
Business Administration, Management and Opera-
    tions, M
Chemistry, B
Classics and Classical Languages, Litera-
    tures, and Linguistics, B
Clinical Psychology, D
Communication Studies/Speech Communication
    and Rhetoric, B
Computer Science, B
Criminal Justice/Law Enforcement Administration, B
Development Economics and International Develop-
    ment, B
Economics, B
Education, B
Electronic Commerce, M
Engineering, B
English Language and Literature, B
Environmental Biology, B
Ethnic, Cultural Minority, and Gender Studies, B
Experimental Psychology, MD
French Language and Literature, B
Geology/Earth Science, B
German Language and Literature, B
Graphic Communications, B
Health Professions and Related Clinical Sciences, B
History, B
Hospitality Administration/Management, B
International Business/Trade/Commerce, M
International Relations and Affairs, B
Kinesiology and Exercise Science, B
Liberal Arts and Sciences Studies and Humani-
    ties, B
Linguistics, B
Mathematics, B
Natural Resources Management/Development and
    Policy, M
Philosophy, B
Physics, B
Political Science and Government, B
Psychology, BMD
Sociology, B
Spanish Language and Literature, B
Statistics, B
Teaching English as a Second or Foreign
    Language/ESL Language Instructor, B

Maritime Provinces-Nova Scotia

ACADIA UNIVERSITY

Applied Mathematics, M
Biological and Biomedical Sciences, M
Biology/Biological Sciences, B
Business Administration and Management, B
Canadian Studies, B
Chemistry, BM
Classics and Classical Languages, Litera-
    tures, and Linguistics, B
Clinical Psychology, M
Community Organization and Advocacy, B
Computer Science, BM
Counselor Education/School Counseling and Guid-
    ance Services, M
Curriculum and Instruction, M
Dietetics/Dieticians, B
Drama and Dramatics/Theatre Arts, B
Economics, B
Education, BMD
Educational Leadership and Administration, M

Educational Media/Instructional Technology, M
Elementary Education and Teaching, B
English, M
English Language and Literature, B
Environmental Studies, B
Food Science, B
Foods, Nutrition, and Wellness Studies, B
French Language and Literature, B
Geographic Information Systems, M
Geology/Earth Science, BM
History, B
Kinesiology and Exercise Science, B
Latin Language and Literature, B
Mathematics, B
Mathematics Teacher Education, M
Music, B
Music Teacher Education, B
Philosophy, BM
Physics, B
Piano and Organ, B
Political Science and Government, BM
Pre-Dentistry Studies, B
Pre-Law Studies, B
Pre-Medicine/Pre-Medical Studies, B
Pre-Veterinary Studies, B
Psychology, BM
Recreation and Park Management, M
Science Teacher Education/General Science
    Teacher Education, M
Secondary Education and Teaching, B
Social Studies Teacher Education, M
Sociology, BM
Special Education and Teaching, M
Statistics, M
Sustainable Development, M
Theology and Religious Vocations, MD
Violin, Viola, Guitar and Other Stringed Instru-
    ments, B
Voice and Opera, B

CAPE BRETON UNIVERSITY

Accounting, B
Anthropology, B
Biology/Biological Sciences, B
Business Administration, Management and Opera-
    tions, M
Chemistry, B
Communication Studies/Speech Communication
    and Rhetoric, B
Community Organization and Advocacy, B
Computer Systems Networking and Telecommunica-
    tions, B
Computer and Information Sciences, B
Economics, B
Education, B
Electrical/Electronics Equipment Installation and Re-
    pair, B
Engineering, B
English Language and Literature, B
Entrepreneurship/Entrepreneurial Studies, B
Environmental Studies, B
Finance, B
French Language and Literature, B
History, B
Hospitality Administration/Management, B
Hospitality and Recreation Marketing Operations, B
Human Nutrition, B
Human Resources Management/Personnel Adminis-
    tration, B
Information Science/Studies, B
Law and Legal Studies, B
Manufacturing Engineering, B
Marketing/Marketing Management, B
Mathematics, B
Petroleum Technology/Technician, B
Philosophy, B
Political Science and Government, B
Psychology, B
Public Health (MPH, DPH), B
Religion/Religious Studies, B
Sociology, B
Sport and Fitness Administration/Management, B
Tourism Promotion Operations, B

Tourism and Travel Services Management, B

DALHOUSIE UNIVERSITY

Accounting, B
Acting, B
Agricultural Engineering, MD
Agricultural Sciences, M
Agricultural and Food Products Processing, B
Agricultural/Biological Engineering and Bioengineering, B
Agriculture, B
Agronomy and Crop Science, B
Agronomy and Soil Sciences, M
Allopathic Medicine, MD
Anatomy, MD
Animal Health, B
Animal Nutrition, B
Animal Sciences, BM
Animal/Livestock Husbandry and Production, B
Anthropology, BMD
Applied Mathematics, MD
Aquaculture, BM
Architecture, BM
Atmospheric Sciences and Meteorology, B
Biochemistry, MD
Biochemistry, Biophysics and Molecular Biology, B
Bioengineering, MD
Bioinformatics, BM
Biological and Biomedical Sciences, MD
Biology/Biological Sciences, B
Biomedical Engineering, MD
Biomedical/Medical Engineering, B
Biophysics, MD
Botany/Plant Biology, BM
Business Administration and Management, B
Business Administration, Management and Operations, M
Business/Commerce, B
Canadian Studies, B
Chemical Engineering, BMD
Chemistry, BMD
City/Urban, Community and Regional Planning, B
Civil Engineering, MD
Classics and Classical Languages, Literatures, and Linguistics, BMD
Clinical Psychology, D
Communication Disorders, MD
Communication, Journalism and Related Programs, B
Community Health and Preventive Medicine, M
Comparative Literature, B
Computer Engineering, MD
Computer Science, BMD
Computer Software Engineering, B
Computer/Information Technology Services Administration and Management, B
Dental Hygiene/Hygienist, B
Development Economics and International Development, B
Diagnostic Medical Sonography/Sonographer and Ultrasound Technician, B
Drama and Dramatics/Theatre Arts, B
Dramatic/Theatre Arts and Stagecraft, B
Ecology, M
Economics, BMD
Electrical Engineering, MD
Electrical, Electronics and Communications Engineering, B
Electronic Commerce, M
Engineering, B
Engineering and Applied Sciences, MD
English, MD
English Language and Literature, B
Entrepreneurship/Entrepreneurial Studies, B
Environmental Biology, M
Environmental Design/Architecture, B
Environmental Engineering Technology/Environmental Technology, MD
Environmental Policy and Resource Management, M
Environmental Sciences, BM
Environmental Studies, BM
Environmental/Environmental Health Engineering, B
Epidemiology, M
European Studies/Civilization, B
Fashion/Apparel Design, B

Finance, B
Finance and Banking, M
Food Science, B
Food Science and Technology, MD
French Language and Literature, BMD
General Merchandising, Sales, and Related Marketing Operations, B
Geology/Earth Science, B
Geosciences, MD
German Language and Literature, BM
Health Education, M
Health Information/Medical Records Administration/Administrator, B
Health Professions and Related Clinical Sciences, B
Health Services Administration, MD
Health Services/Allied Health/Health Sciences, B
History, BMD
History and Philosophy of Science and Technology, B
Horticultural Science, M
Human-Computer Interaction, M
Immunology, MD
Industrial Engineering, B
Industrial/Management Engineering, MD
Information Science/Studies, M
Interdisciplinary Studies, D
International Agriculture, B
International Business/Trade/Commerce, B
International Development, M
International Relations and Affairs, B
Italian Studies, B
Kinesiology and Exercise Science, B
Kinesiology and Movement Studies, M
Law and Legal Studies, MD
Leisure Studies, M
Library Science, M
Management, M
Management Information Systems and Services, M
Management Science, B
Marine Affairs, M
Marine Biology and Biological Oceanography, B
Marketing/Marketing Management, B
Materials Engineering, MD
Mathematics, BMD
Mechanical Engineering, MD
Medical Informatics, M
Medical Microbiology and Bacteriology, B
Meteorology, B
Microbiological Sciences and Immunology, B
Microbiology, MD
Mineral/Mining Engineering, MD
Multi-/Interdisciplinary Studies, B
Music, B
Music History, Literature, and Theory, B
Music Performance, B
Music Theory and Composition, B
Musicology and Ethnomusicology, M
Natural Resources and Conservation, M
Neurobiology and Neurophysiology, MD
Neuroscience, MD
Non-Profit/Public/Organizational Management, B
Nuclear Medical Technology/Technologist, B
Nursing, MD
Occupational Therapy/Therapist, BM
Oceanography, Chemical and Physical, BMD
Parks, Recreation, Leisure and Fitness Studies, B
Pathology/Experimental Pathology, MD
Pharmacology, MD
Pharmacy, B
Pharmacy, Pharmaceutical Sciences, and Administration, B
Philosophy, BMD
Physical Therapy/Therapist, BM
Physics, BMD
Physiology, MD
Plant Nursery Operations and Management, A
Plant Pathology/Phytopathology, M
Plant Physiology, M
Plant Protection and Integrated Pest Management, A
Plant Sciences, B
Political Science and Government, BMD
Pre-Dentistry Studies, B
Pre-Law Studies, B
Pre-Medicine/Pre-Medical Studies, B
Pre-Pharmacy Studies, B

Pre-Veterinary Studies, B
Psychology, BMD
Public Administration, MO
Public Health Education and Promotion, B
Radiologic Technology/Science - Radiographer, B
Religion/Religious Studies, B
Respiratory Care Therapy/Therapist, B
Respiratory Therapy Technician/Assistant, B
Rural Planning and Studies, M
Russian Language and Literature, B
Russian Studies, B
Science, Technology and Society, B
Small Business Administration/Management, B
Social Work, BM
Sociology, BMD
Spanish Language and Literature, B
Statistics, BMD
Theatre Literature, History and Criticism, B
Therapeutic Recreation/Recreational Therapy, B
Urban and Regional Planning, M
Veterinary/Animal Health Technology/Technician and Veterinary Assistant, A
Water Resources, M
Women's Studies, B
Zoology/Animal Biology, B

MOUNT SAINT VINCENT UNIVERSITY

Accounting, B
Adult Development and Aging, B
Adult and Continuing Education and Teaching, M
Anthropology, B
Applied Mathematics, B
Art Teacher Education, B
Biological and Physical Sciences, B
Biology/Biological Sciences, B
Business Administration and Management, B
Chemistry, B
Child Development, B
Child and Family Studies, M
Comparative Literature, B
Computer Systems Analysis/Analyst, B
Computer and Information Sciences, B
Curriculum and Instruction, M
Dietetics/Dieticians, B
Economics, B
Education, BM
Educational Psychology, M
Elementary Education and Teaching, BM
English Language and Literature, B
English as a Second Language, M
Family and Consumer Economics and Related Services, B
Family and Consumer Sciences/Human Sciences, B
Fine/Studio Arts, B
Foods, Nutrition, and Wellness Studies, B
Foundations and Philosophy of Education, M
French Language and Literature, B
German Language and Literature, B
Gerontology, BM
History, B
Hospitality Administration/Management, B
Hotel/Motel Administration/Management, B
Humanities/Humanistic Studies, B
Information Science/Studies, B
Kindergarten/PreSchool Education and Teaching, B
Liberal Arts and Sciences Studies and Humanities, B
Linguistics, B
Management Information Systems and Services, B
Marketing Research, B
Marketing/Marketing Management, B
Mathematics, B
Mathematics and Computer Science, B
Middle School Education, M
Modern Languages, B
Nutritional Sciences, BM
Peace Studies and Conflict Resolution, B
Philosophy, B
Political Science and Government, B
Psychology, B
Public Relations/Image Management, B
Reading Teacher Education, BM
Religion/Religious Studies, B
School Psychology, M
Secondary Education and Teaching, B
Social Sciences, B

Sociology, B
Spanish Language and Literature, B
Special Education and Teaching, M
Special Products Marketing Operations, B
Statistics, B
Tourism and Travel Services Management, B
Tourism and Travel Services Marketing Operations, B
Women's Studies, BM

NSCAD UNIVERSITY

Art History, Criticism and Conservation, B
Art/Art Studies, General, B
Ceramic Arts and Ceramics, B
Commercial and Advertising Art, B
Crafts, M
Crafts/Craft Design, Folk Art and Artisanry, B
Design and Applied Arts, BM
Design and Visual Communications, B
Drawing, B
Fiber, Textile and Weaving Arts, B
Film/Cinema Studies, B
Fine Arts and Art Studies, M
Fine/Studio Arts, B
Graphic Design, B
Metal and Jewelry Arts, B
Painting, B
Photography, B
Printmaking, B
Sculpture, B

ST. FRANCIS XAVIER UNIVERSITY

Accounting, B
Adult and Continuing Education and Teaching, M
Anthropology, B
Biological and Biomedical Sciences, M
Biological and Physical Sciences, B
Biology/Biological Sciences, B
Business Administration and Management, B
Canadian Studies, B
Chemistry, BM
Classics and Classical Languages, Literatures, and Linguistics, B
Computer Science, M
Computer and Information Sciences, B
Cultural Studies, M
Curriculum and Instruction, M
Economics, B
Education, BM
Educational Administration and Supervision, M
Educational Leadership and Administration, M
Elementary Education and Teaching, B
English Language and Literature, B
Environmental Studies, B
Foods, Nutrition, and Wellness Studies, B
French Language and Literature, B
Geology/Earth Science, BM
Geosciences, M
History, B
Hydrology and Water Resources Science, B
Information Science/Studies, B
Jazz/Jazz Studies, B
Kinesiology and Exercise Science, B
Liberal Arts and Sciences Studies and Humanities, B
Management Information Systems and Services, B
Mathematics, B
Modern Languages, B
Music, B
Philosophy, B
Physical Education Teaching and Coaching, B
Physical Sciences, B
Physics, BM
Political Science and Government, B
Pre-Dentistry Studies, B
Pre-Law Studies, B
Pre-Medicine/Pre-Medical Studies, B
Pre-Veterinary Studies, B
Psychology, B
Religion/Religious Studies, B
Secondary Education and Teaching, B
Sociology, B

Women's Studies, B

SAINT MARY'S UNIVERSITY

Accounting, B
Anthropology, B
Applied Psychology, MD
Applied Science and Technology, M
Asian Studies/Civilization, B
Astronomy, BMD
Astrophysics, B
Biology/Biological Sciences, B
Business Administration and Management, B
Business Administration, Management and Operations, MD
Business/Managerial Economics, B
Canadian Studies, BMO
Chemistry, B
Classics and Classical Languages, Literatures, and Linguistics, B
Computer Science, B
Criminology, BM
Data Processing and Data Processing Technology/Technician, B
Economics, B
Engineering, B
English Language and Literature, B
Finance, B
French Language and Literature, B
Gender Studies, M
Geography, B
Geology/Earth Science, B
German Language and Literature, B
History, BM
Human Resources Management/Personnel Administration, B
Industrial and Organizational Psychology, M
International Development, MO
International Relations and Affairs, B
Marketing/Marketing Management, B
Mathematics, B
Modern Languages, B
Philosophy, BM
Physics, B
Political Science and Government, B
Psychology, BMD
Religion/Religious Studies, BM
Sociology, B
Theology and Religious Vocations, M
Women's Studies, BM

UNIVERSITÉ SAINTE-ANNE

Business Administration and Management, B
Canadian Studies, B
Education, BM
Elementary Education and Teaching, B
English Language and Literature, B
French Language Teacher Education, B
French Language and Literature, B
History, B
Secondary Education and Teaching, B

UNIVERSITY OF KING'S COLLEGE

Anthropology, B
Biochemistry, B
Biology/Biological Sciences, B
Chemistry, B
Classics and Classical Languages, Literatures, and Linguistics, B
Computer Science, B
Development Economics and International Development, B
Drama and Dramatics/Theatre Arts, B
Economics, B
English Language and Literature, B
European Studies/Civilization, B
French Language and Literature, B
Geology/Earth Science, B
German Language and Literature, B
History, B
Journalism, BM
Linguistics, B
Marine Biology and Biological Oceanography, B
Mathematics, B
Medical Microbiology and Bacteriology, B
Multi-/Interdisciplinary Studies, B
Music, B

Philosophy, B
Physics, B
Political Science and Government, B
Psychology, B
Religion/Religious Studies, B
Russian Language and Literature, B
Science, Technology and Society, B
Sociology, B
Spanish Language and Literature, B
Statistics, B
Women's Studies, B
Writing, M

Maritime Provinces-Prince Edward Island

UNIVERSITY OF PRINCE EDWARD ISLAND

Anatomy, MD
Anthropology, B
Bacteriology, MD
Biological and Biomedical Sciences, M
Biology/Biological Sciences, B
Business Administration and Management, B
Canadian Studies, B
Chemistry, BM
Computer Science, B
Economics, B
Education, BM
Educational Leadership and Administration, M
Elementary Education and Teaching, B
English Language and Literature, B
Epidemiology, MD
Family and Consumer Economics and Related Services, B
Foods, Nutrition, and Wellness Studies, B
French Language and Literature, B
Geography, M
German Language and Literature, B
History, B
Hospitality Administration/Management, B
Immunology, MD
Mathematics, B
Medical Radiologic Technology/Science - Radiation Therapist, B
Music, B
Music Teacher Education, B
Parasitology, MD
Pathology/Experimental Pathology, MD
Pharmacology, MD
Philosophy, B
Physics, B
Physiology, MD
Political Science and Government, B
Pre-Dentistry Studies, B
Pre-Medicine/Pre-Medical Studies, B
Pre-Veterinary Studies, B
Psychology, B
Religion/Religious Studies, B
Secondary Education and Teaching, B
Sociology, B
Spanish Language and Literature, B
Toxicology, MD
Veterinary Medicine, D
Veterinary Sciences, MD
Virology, MD

Newfoundland and Labrador

MEMORIAL UNIVERSITY OF NEWFOUNDLAND

Accounting, B
Acting, B
Adult and Continuing Education and Teaching, BMO
Anthropology, BMD
Applied Mathematics, B
Aquaculture, M
Archeology, BMD
Art History, Criticism and Conservation, B
Art/Art Studies, General, B
Athletic Training and Sports Medicine, B
Biochemistry, BMD
Biological and Biomedical Sciences, MDO
Biological and Physical Sciences, B

Biology/Biological Sciences, B
Biopsychology, MD
Business Administration and Management, B
Business Administration, Management and Operations, M
Canadian Studies, B
Cancer Biology/Oncology, MD
Cardiovascular Sciences, MD
Cartography, B
Cell/Cellular Biology and Histology, B
Chemical Engineering, B
Chemistry, BMD
Civil Engineering, BMD
Classics and Classical Languages, Literatures, and Linguistics, BM
Clinical Research, M
Community Health and Preventive Medicine, MDO
Comparative Literature, B
Computational Sciences, M
Computer Engineering, MD
Computer Programming/Programmer, B
Computer Science, BMD
Condensed Matter Physics, MD
Counselor Education/School Counseling and Guidance Services, B
Criminal Justice/Police Science, B
Criminology, B
Cultural Anthropology, MD
Curriculum and Instruction, M
Dietetics/Dieticians, B
Drama and Dramatics/Theatre Arts, B
Drawing, B
Ecology, B
Economics, BM
Education, BMDO
Educational Leadership and Administration, M
Educational Media/Instructional Technology, M
Educational Psychology, M
Electrical Engineering, MD
Electrical, Electronics and Communications Engineering, B
Elementary Education and Teaching, B
Engineering, B
Engineering and Applied Sciences, MD
English, MD
English Language and Literature, B
Entomology, B
Environmental Biology, B
Environmental Engineering Technology/Environmental Technology, M
Environmental Sciences, M
Environmental Studies, B
Epidemiology, MDO
Ethnic, Cultural Minority, and Gender Studies, B
Ethnomusicology, MD
Exercise and Sports Science, M
Experimental Psychology, MD
Finance, B
Fish, Game and Wildlife Management, MO
Folklore, MD
Food Science, B
Food Science and Technology, MD
Foods, Nutrition, and Wellness Studies, B
Forest Sciences and Biology, B
French Language and Literature, BM
Gender Studies, D
Geography, BMD
Geological/Geophysical Engineering, B
Geology/Earth Science, BMD
Geophysics and Seismology, BMD
Geosciences, MD
German Language and Literature, BM
History, BMD
Human Genetics, MD
Humanities/Humanistic Studies, BM
Immunology, MD
Industrial Engineering, B
Industrial and Labor Relations, M
Information Science/Studies, B
Junior High/Intermediate/Middle School Education and Teaching, B
Kinesiology and Exercise Science, B
Kinesiology and Movement Studies, M
Labor and Industrial Relations, B
Latin Language and Literature, B
Linguistics, BMD

Marine Affairs, MDO
Marine Biology and Biological Oceanography, BMD
Marine Science/Merchant Marine Officer, B
Marine Sciences, MO
Marketing/Marketing Management, B
Mathematics, BMD
Mechanical Engineering, BMD
Medical Microbiology and Bacteriology, B
Medieval and Renaissance Studies, B
Modern Greek Language and Literature, B
Music, BM
Music History, Literature, and Theory, B
Music Teacher Education, B
Music Theory and Composition, B
Naval Architecture and Marine Engineering, B
Neuroscience, MD
Nursing, MO
Ocean Engineering, BMD
Oceanography, Chemical and Physical, BMD
Organizational Behavior Studies, B
Painting, B
Parks, Recreation, Leisure and Fitness Studies, B
Performance, M
Pharmaceutical Sciences, MD
Pharmacy, B
Philosophy, BM
Photography, B
Physical Education Teaching and Coaching, BM
Physics, BMD
Piano and Organ, B
Political Science and Government, BM
Pre-Medicine/Pre-Medical Studies, B
Printmaking, B
Psychology, BMD
Religion/Religious Studies, BM
Russian Language and Literature, B
Science Teacher Education/General Science Teacher Education, B
Sculpture, B
Secondary Education and Teaching, B
Social Psychology, M
Social Sciences, B
Social Work, BM
Sociology, BMD
Spanish Language and Literature, B
Special Education and Teaching, B
Sport Psychology, M
Statistics, BMD
Technical Theatre/Theatre Design and Technology, B
Theatre Literature, History and Criticism, B
Trade and Industrial Teacher Education, B
Violin, Viola, Guitar and Other Stringed Instruments, B
Voice and Opera, B
Women's Studies, BM
Zoology/Animal Biology, B

Ontario

BROCK UNIVERSITY

Accounting, BM
Adult and Continuing Education and Teaching, B
Allied Health and Medical Assisting Services, MD
Ancient/Classical Greek Language and Literature, B
Applied Mathematics, B
Archeology, B
Art/Art Studies, General, B
BioTechnology, BMD
Biochemistry, B
Biological and Biomedical Sciences, MD
Biological and Physical Sciences, B
Biology/Biological Sciences, B
Biomedical Sciences, B
Business Administration and Management, B
Business Administration, Management and Operations, M
Business/Commerce, B
Business/Corporate Communications, B
Business/Managerial Economics, B
Canadian Studies, B
Chemistry, BMD
Child and Family Studies, M
Classics and Classical Languages, Literatures, and Linguistics, M
Communication Disorders, B

Communication Studies/Speech Communication and Rhetoric, B
Comparative Literature, BM
Computer Engineering Technology/Technician, B
Computer Programming/Programmer, B
Computer Science, BM
Computer Software Engineering, B
Cultural Studies, M
Disability Studies, MO
Drama and Dramatics/Theatre Arts, B
Economics, BM
Education, BMD
Elementary Education and Teaching, B
English, M
English Language and Literature, B
English as a Second Language, M
Film/Cinema Studies, B
Finance, B
Fine/Studio Arts, B
French Language and Literature, B
French Studies, B
Geography, BM
Geology/Earth Science, B
Geosciences, M
German Language and Literature, B
German Studies, B
Health Professions and Related Clinical Sciences, B
Health/Health Care Administration/Management, B
History, BM
Human Development, MD
Human Resources Management/Personnel Administration, B
Humanities/Humanistic Studies, B
Information Science/Studies, B
International Affairs, M
International Business/Trade/Commerce, B
International Economics, B
Italian Language and Literature, B
Italian Studies, B
Kinesiology and Exercise Science, B
Labor and Industrial Relations, B
Legal and Justice Studies, M
Liberal Arts and Sciences Studies and Humanities, B
Linguistics, B
Management, M
Marketing/Marketing Management, B
Mass Communication/Media Studies, B
Mathematics, BM
Mathematics Teacher Education, B
Movement Therapy and Movement Education, B
Music, B
Music Teacher Education, B
Neuroscience, MD
Parks, Recreation, Leisure and Fitness Studies, B
Philosophy, BM
Physical Education Teaching and Coaching, B
Physical Sciences, B
Physics, BM
Political Science and Government, BM
Psychology, BMD
Public Administration, B
Public Health (MPH, DPH), B
Public Policy Analysis, M
Sales, Distribution and Marketing Operations, B
Science Teacher Education/General Science Teacher Education, B
Secondary Education and Teaching, B
Social Psychology, MD
Social Sciences, B
Sociology, BM
Spanish Language and Literature, B
Sport and Fitness Administration/Management, B
Statistics, BM
Teaching English as a Second or Foreign Language/ESL Language Instructor, B
Tourism and Travel Services Management, B
Women's Studies, B

CARLETON UNIVERSITY

Accounting, B
Aerospace, Aeronautical and Astronautical Engineering, BMD
African Studies, B
Anthropology, BM
Applied Mathematics, B

Architecture, BM
Art History, Criticism and Conservation, BM
Asian Studies/Civilization, B
Biochemistry, B
Biological and Biomedical Sciences, MD
Biological and Physical Sciences, B
Biology Technician/BioTechnology Laboratory Technician, B
Biology/Biological Sciences, B
Biomedical Engineering, M
Botany/Plant Biology, B
Business Administration and Management, B
Business Administration, Management and Operations, MD
Canadian Studies, BMD
Central/Middle and Eastern European Studies, B
Chemistry, BMD
Child Development, B
City/Urban, Community and Regional Planning, B
Civil Engineering, BMD
Classics and Classical Languages, Literatures, and Linguistics, B
Cognitive Sciences, D
Communication and Media Studies, MD
Comparative Literature, BD
Computer Engineering, B
Computer Programming/Programmer, B
Computer Science, BMD
Computer Software and Media Applications, B
Conflict Resolution and Mediation/Peace Studies, O
Criminal Justice/Law Enforcement Administration, B
Criminal Justice/Police Science, B
Criminology, B
Drama and Dramatics/Theatre Arts, B
East Asian Studies, B
East European and Russian Studies, MO
Ecology, B
Economics, BMD
Electrical Engineering, MD
Electrical, Electronics and Communications Engineering, B
Engineering, B
Engineering and Applied Sciences, MD
English, MD
English Language and Literature, B
Environmental Engineering Technology/Environmental Technology, MD
Environmental Studies, B
Environmental/Environmental Health Engineering, B
Ethnomusicology, M
European Studies/Civilization, B
Film, Television, and Video Production, M
Film/Cinema Studies, B
Finance, B
French Language and Literature, BM
Geography, BMD
Geology/Earth Science, B
Geosciences, MD
German Language and Literature, B
History, BMD
Human Resources Management/Personnel Administration, B
Humanities/Humanistic Studies, B
Industrial Design, BM
Information Science/Studies, BM
International Affairs, MD
International Business/Trade/Commerce, B
International Relations and Affairs, B
Italian Language and Literature, B
Journalism, BMD
Labor and Industrial Relations, B
Latin American Studies, B
Latin Language and Literature, B
Legal and Justice Studies, M
Linguistics, BM
Management, D
Management Information Systems and Services, B
Management of Technology, M
Marketing/Marketing Management, B
Mass Communication/Media Studies, B
Materials Engineering, M
Mathematics, BMD
Mechanical Engineering, BMD
Medieval and Renaissance Studies, B
Modern Greek Language and Literature, B
Modern Languages, B

Music, B
Music History, Literature, and Theory, M
Near and Middle Eastern Studies, B
Neuroscience, M
Operations Research, B
Philosophy, BM
Physics, BMD
Political Science and Government, BMD
Pre-Law Studies, B
Psychology, BMD
Public Administration, BMD
Public Policy Analysis, D
Religion/Religious Studies, B
Russian Language and Literature, B
Russian Studies, B
Social Work, BM
Sociology, BMD
Spanish Language and Literature, B
Statistics, B
Systems Engineering, BM
Systems Science and Theory, M
Teaching English as a Second or Foreign Language/ESL Language Instructor, B
Urban Studies/Affairs, B
Western European Studies, O
Women's Studies, B

CENTENNIAL COLLEGE

Computer Software Engineering, B
Computer Systems Networking and Telecommunications, B

EMMANUEL BIBLE COLLEGE

Bible/Biblical Studies, B
Divinity/Ministry (BD, MDiv.), B
Missions/Missionary Studies and Missiology, B
Pastoral Studies/Counseling, B
Religious Education, B
Religious/Sacred Music, B
Theology/Theological Studies, B
Youth Ministry, B

HERITAGE COLLEGE AND SEMINARY

Bible/Biblical Studies, B
Religious Education, B
Religious/Sacred Music, B
Theology and Religious Vocations, MO
Theology/Theological Studies, B

LAKEHEAD UNIVERSITY

Accounting, B
Anthropology, B
Art/Art Studies, General, B
Athletic Training and Sports Medicine, B
Bioinformatics, B
Biological and Biomedical Sciences, M
Biological and Physical Sciences, B
Biology/Biological Sciences, B
Business Administration and Management, B
Chemical Engineering, B
Chemistry, BM
Civil Engineering, B
Civil Engineering Technology/Technician, B
Clinical Psychology, D
Computer Engineering, BM
Computer Science, BM
Criminology, B
Economics, BM
Education, BMD
Electrical Engineering, M
Electrical, Electronic and Communications Engineering Technology/Technician, B
Electrical, Electronics and Communications Engineering, B
Elementary Education and Teaching, B
Engineering, B
Engineering and Applied Sciences, M
English, M
English Language and Literature, B
Environmental Biology, B
Environmental Engineering Technology/Environmental Technology, M
Environmental Studies, B
Exercise and Sports Science, M
Experimental Psychology, M
Finance, B

Forest Management/Forest Resources Management, B
Forestry, BMD
French Language and Literature, B
General Studies, B
Geography, B
Geology/Earth Science, BM
Gerontology, BM
Health Services Research, M
History, BM
Human Resources Management/Personnel Administration, B
Hydrology and Water Resources Science, B
Information Science/Studies, B
Kinesiology and Exercise Science, B
Kinesiology and Movement Studies, M
Labor and Industrial Relations, B
Liberal Arts and Sciences Studies and Humanities, B
Management Information Systems and Services, B
Marketing/Marketing Management, B
Mathematics, BM
Mechanical Engineering, B
Mechanical Engineering/Mechanical Technology/Technician, B
Molecular Biology, B
Music, B
Natural Resources and Conservation, B
Natural Sciences, B
Parks, Recreation, Leisure and Fitness Studies, B
Philosophy, B
Physical Education Teaching and Coaching, B
Physics, BM
Plant Sciences, B
Political Science and Government, B
Pre-Law Studies, B
Psychology, BMD
Science Teacher Education/General Science Teacher Education, B
Secondary Education and Teaching, B
Social Work, BM
Sociology, BM
Women's Studies, BM

LAKEHEAD UNIVERSITY–ORILLIA

Business Administration, Management and Operations, M

LAURENTIAN UNIVERSITY

Adult and Continuing Education and Teaching, B
American Indian/Native American Studies, B
Analytical Chemistry, M
Applied Physics, M
Applied Psychology, M
Applied Social Research, M
Architecture, B
Astronomy, B
Behavioral Sciences, B
Biochemistry, BM
Biological and Biomedical Sciences, MD
Biophysics, B
Business Administration and Management, B
Business Administration, Management and Operations, M
Chemistry, BM
Classics and Classical Languages, Literatures, and Linguistics, B
Computer Science, B
Drama and Dramatics/Theatre Arts, B
Ecology, D
Economics, B
Education, B
Engineering and Applied Sciences, MD
English Language and Literature, B
Environmental Sciences, M
Ethnic, Cultural Minority, and Gender Studies, B
Experimental Psychology, M
Film/Cinema Studies, B
French Language and Literature, B
Geography, B
Geological/Geophysical Engineering, B
Geology/Earth Science, BMD
History, BM
Human Development, M
Humanities/Humanistic Studies, M
Italian Language and Literature, B

Kinesiology and Exercise Science, B
Language Interpretation and Translation, B
Law and Legal Studies, B
Liberal Arts and Sciences Studies and Humanities, B
Mathematics, B
Metallurgical Engineering, B
Mineral/Mining Engineering, MD
Mining and Mineral Engineering, B
Modern Languages, B
Music, B
Natural Resources Management/Development and Policy, D
Nursing, M
Organic Chemistry, M
Philosophy, B
Physical Chemistry, M
Physical Education Teaching and Coaching, B
Physics, B
Political Science and Government, B
Psychology, BM
Public Health, D
Public Health Education and Promotion, B
Religion/Religious Studies, B
Science Teacher Education/General Science Teacher Education, O
Social Work, BM
Sociology, BM
Spanish Language and Literature, B
Sport and Fitness Administration/Management, B
Technical and Business Writing, O
Theoretical Chemistry, M
Women's Studies, B

MASTER'S COLLEGE AND SEMINARY

Bible/Biblical Studies, B
Divinity/Ministry (BD, MDiv.), B
Religious Education, B
Theology and Religious Vocations, B
Theology/Theological Studies, B
Youth Ministry, B

MCMASTER UNIVERSITY

Analytical Chemistry, MD
Anthropology, BMD
Applied Mathematics, B
Applied Statistics, M
Art History, Criticism and Conservation, B
Art/Art Studies, General, B
Astrophysics, BD
Biochemistry, BMD
Biological and Biomedical Sciences, MD
Biological and Physical Sciences, B
Biology Technician/BioTechnology Laboratory Technician, B
Biology/Biological Sciences, B
Business Administration and Management, B
Business Administration, Management and Operations, MD
Cancer Biology/Oncology, MD
Cardiovascular Sciences, MD
Cell Biology and Anatomy, MD
Chemical Engineering, BMD
Chemical Physics, MD
Chemistry, BMD
Civil Engineering, BMD
Classics and Classical Languages, Literatures, and Linguistics, BMD
Communication, Journalism and Related Programs, B
Comparative Literature, B
Computer Engineering, B
Computer Science, BMD
Cultural Studies, MD
Drama and Dramatics/Theatre Arts, B
Economics, BMD
Electrical Engineering, MD
Electrical, Electronics and Communications Engineering, B
Engineering Physics, BMD
Engineering and Applied Sciences, MD
Engineering/Industrial Management, B
English, MD
English Language and Literature, B
Environmental Studies, B
French Language and Literature, BM

Genetics, MD
Geochemistry, D
Geography, BMD
Geology/Earth Science, BMD
Geosciences, MD
German Language and Literature, B
Gerontology, B
Health Physics/Radiological Health, M
Health Services Research, MD
Hispanic-American, Puerto Rican, and Mexican-American/Chicano Studies, B
History, BMD
Human Resources Management and Services, MD
Immunology, MD
Industrial Engineering, B
Industrial and Labor Relations, M
Inorganic Chemistry, MD
Intermedia/Multimedia, B
International Affairs, MD
Japanese Language and Literature, B
Kinesiology and Exercise Science, B
Kinesiology and Movement Studies, MD
Labor and Industrial Relations, B
Latin American Studies, B
Linguistics, B
Management Information Systems and Services, D
Materials Engineering, BMD
Materials Sciences, MD
Mathematics, BMD
Mechanical Engineering, BMD
Medical Physics, MD
Modern Languages, B
Molecular Biology, BMD
Music, B
Music History, Literature, and Theory, B
Music Teacher Education, B
Neuroscience, MD
Nuclear Engineering, D
Nursing, MD
Nutritional Sciences, MD
Occupational Therapy/Therapist, M
Organic Chemistry, MD
Pastoral Studies/Counseling, MO
Pharmacology, BMD
Philosophy, BMD
Physical Chemistry, MD
Physical Sciences, B
Physical Therapy/Therapist, M
Physics, BD
Physiology, MD
Political Science and Government, BMD
Psychology, BMD
Public Administration, M
Public Affairs, M
Public Policy Analysis, MD
Rehabilitation Sciences, MD
Religion/Religious Studies, BMD
Religious Education, B
Russian Language and Literature, B
Russian Studies, B
Social Work, BM
Sociology, BMD
Software Engineering, MD
Statistics, BM
Theology and Religious Vocations, MDO
Virology, MD
Women's Studies, B

NER ISRAEL YESHIVA COLLEGE OF TORONTO

Jewish/Judaic Studies, B
Theology/Theological Studies, B

NIPISSING UNIVERSITY

Biology/Biological Sciences, B
Business Administration and Management, B
Business and Personal/Financial Services Marketing Operations, B
Classics and Classical Languages, Literatures, and Linguistics, B
Computer Science, B
Economics, B
Education, BMO
English Language and Literature, B
Environmental Biology, B
Environmental Studies, B

Fine/Studio Arts, B
Geography, B
History, B
Liberal Arts and Sciences Studies and Humanities, B
Mathematics, B
Philosophy, B
Physical Education Teaching and Coaching, B
Psychology, B
Sociology, B
Women's Studies, B

QUEEN'S UNIVERSITY AT KINGSTON

Allopathic Medicine, D
Anatomy, MD
Art History, Criticism and Conservation, B
Biochemistry, BMD
Biological and Biomedical Sciences, MD
Biology/Biological Sciences, B
Business Administration, Management and Operations, M
Business/Commerce, B
Canadian Studies, BD
Cancer Biology/Oncology, MD
Cardiovascular Sciences, MD
Cartography, B
Cell Biology and Anatomy, MD
Chemical Engineering, BMD
Chemistry, BMD
Civil Engineering, BMD
Classics and Classical Languages, Literatures, and Linguistics, M
Clinical Psychology, MD
Cognitive Sciences, BMD
Communication and Media Studies, MD
Computer Engineering, BMD
Computer Science, BMD
Developmental Psychology, MD
Drama and Dramatics/Theatre Arts, B
Economics, B
Education, BMD
Electrical Engineering, MD
Electrical, Electronics and Communications Engineering, B
Elementary Education and Teaching, B
Engineering, B
Engineering Physics, B
Engineering and Applied Sciences, MD
English, MD
English Language and Literature, B
Entrepreneurship/Entrepreneurial Studies, M
Environmental Sciences, B
Epidemiology, MD
Exercise and Sports Science, MD
Film/Cinema Studies, B
Finance and Banking, M
French Language and Literature, BMD
Gender Studies, D
Geography, BMD
Geological/Geophysical Engineering, B
Geology/Earth Science, BMD
German Language and Literature, BMD
German Studies, B
Health Services Administration, M
Health and Physical Education, B
Hispanic Studies, M
History, B
Immunology, MD
Indian/Native American Education, B
Industrial and Labor Relations, M
Information Science/Studies, MD
International Affairs, D
Law and Legal Studies, MD
Legal and Justice Studies, MD
Linguistics, B
Marketing, M
Mathematics, BMD
Mechanical Engineering, BMD
Microbiology, MD
Mineral/Mining Engineering, MD
Mining and Mineral Engineering, B
Molecular Biology, MD
Molecular Medicine, MD
Music, B
Neurobiology and Neurophysiology, MD
Neuroscience, MD

Nursing, MDO
Nursing - Advanced Practice, O
Occupational Therapy/Therapist, BM
Pathology/Experimental Pathology, MD
Pediatric Nurse/Nursing, M
Pharmaceutical Sciences, MD
Pharmacology, MD
Philosophy, BMD
Physical Education Teaching and Coaching, B
Physical Therapy/Therapist, BM
Physics, BMD
Physiology, MD
Political Science and Government, BMD
Project Management, M
Psychology, BMD
Public Health, M
Public Policy Analysis, M
Rehabilitation Sciences, MD
Religion/Religious Studies, BM
Reproductive Biology, MD
Science Teacher Education/General Science
    Teacher Education, B
Social Psychology, MD
Sociology, BMD
Spanish Language and Literature, BM
Sport Psychology, M
Statistics, BMD
Teacher Education, Multiple Levels, B
Technical Teacher Education, B
Theology and Religious Vocations, MO
Theology/Theological Studies, B
Toxicology, MD
Urban and Regional Planning, M
Women's Health Nursing, M
Women's Studies, BMD

REDEEMER UNIVERSITY COLLEGE

Accounting, B
Art/Art Studies, General, B
Bible/Biblical Studies, B
Biology/Biological Sciences, B
Business Administration and Management, B
Chemistry, B
Computer Science, B
Drama and Dramatics/Theatre Arts, B
Education, B
Elementary Education and Teaching, B
English Language and Literature, B
Environmental Studies, B
French Language and Literature, B
Health and Physical Education, B
History, B
International Relations and Affairs, B
Kinesiology and Exercise Science, B
Marketing/Marketing Management, B
Mathematics, B
Mathematics and Computer Science, B
Music, B
Parks, Recreation, Leisure and Fitness Studies, B
Philosophy, B
Physical Education Teaching and Coaching, B
Political Science and Government, B
Psychology, B
Religion/Religious Studies, B
Social Work, B
Sociology, B
Teacher Education, Multiple Levels, B
Theology/Theological Studies, B
Youth Ministry, B

ROYAL MILITARY COLLEGE OF CANADA

Business Administration and Management, B
Business Administration, Management and Operations, M
Chemical Engineering, BMD
Chemistry, BMD
Civil Engineering, BMD
Computer Engineering, BMD
Computer Science, BM
Electrical Engineering, MD
Electrical, Electronics and Communications Engineering, B
Engineering and Applied Sciences, MD
English Language and Literature, B

Environmental Engineering
    Technology/Environmental Technology, MD
Environmental Sciences, MD
French Language and Literature, B
History, B
Materials Sciences, MD
Mathematics, M
Mechanical Engineering, BMD
Military and Defense Studies, MD
Nuclear Engineering, MD
Physics, BM
Psychology, B
Social Sciences, B
Software Engineering, MD

RYERSON UNIVERSITY

Acting, B
Aerospace, Aeronautical and Astronautical Engineering, B
Architecture, B
Arts Management, M
Biology/Biological Sciences, B
Biomedical/Medical Engineering, B
Business Administration and Management, B
Chemical Engineering, B
Chemistry, B
Child Care and Support Services Management, B
Cinematography and Film/Video Production, B
City/Urban, Community and Regional Planning, B
Civil Engineering, B
Computer Engineering, B
Computer Science, B
Criminal Justice/Safety Studies, B
Dance, B
Early Childhood Education and Teaching, B
Electrical, Electronics and Communications Engineering, B
Fashion/Apparel Design, B
Film/Video and Photographic Arts, B
Finance, B
General Studies, B
Geography, B
Graphic Communications, B
Health Information/Medical Records
    Administration/Administrator, B
Health Unit Manager/Ward Supervisor, B
Health/Medical Physics, B
Hospitality Administration/Management, B
Hotel/Motel Administration/Management, B
Human Nutrition, B
Humanities/Humanistic Studies, B
Industrial Engineering, B
Information Technology, B
Interior Design, B
International Economics, B
Journalism, B
Marketing/Marketing Management, B
Mechanical Engineering, B
Multi-/Interdisciplinary Studies, B
Occupational Health and Industrial Hygiene, B
Photography, B
Physics, B
Political Science and Government, B
Psychology, B
Public Administration, B
Public Health (MPH, DPH), B
Radio and Television, B
Retailing and Retail Operations, B
Sales, Distribution and Marketing Operations, B
Social Work, B
Sociology, B
Technical Theatre/Theatre Design and Technology, B
Urban Studies/Affairs, B

SAINT PAUL UNIVERSITY

Conflict Resolution and Mediation/Peace Studies, M
Counseling Psychology, M
Ethics, B
Marriage and Family Therapy/Counseling, BM
Missions/Missionary Studies and Missiology, BM
Pastoral Studies/Counseling, MDO
Philosophy, B
Religion/Religious Studies, B
Theology and Religious Vocations, MDO

Theology/Theological Studies, B

TRENT UNIVERSITY

American Indian/Native American Studies, BMD
Anthropology, BM
Applied Mathematics, B
Biochemistry, B
Biological and Biomedical Sciences, MD
Biological and Physical Sciences, B
Biology/Biological Sciences, B
Biomedical Sciences, B
Business Administration and Management, B
Canadian Studies, BMD
Chemistry, BM
Child Development, B
Classics and Classical Languages, Literatures, and Linguistics, B
Communication and Media Studies, B
Computer Science, BM
Cultural Studies, D
Economics, B
Education, B
Elementary Education and Teaching, B
English Language and Literature, B
Environmental Policy and Resource Management, MD
Environmental Studies, B
French Language and Literature, B
Geography, BMD
German Language and Literature, B
Hispanic-American, Puerto Rican, and Mexican-American/Chicano Studies, B
History, B
Humanities/Humanistic Studies, B
International Relations and Affairs, B
Journalism, B
Kinesiology and Exercise Science, B
Liberal Arts and Sciences Studies and Humanities, B
Materials Sciences, M
Mathematics, B
Modeling and Simulation, MD
Modern Languages, B
Natural Sciences, B
Philosophy, B
Physical Sciences, B
Physics, BM
Political Science and Government, B
Psychology, B
Secondary Education and Teaching, B
Social Sciences, B
Social Work, B
Sociology, B
Women's Studies, B

TYNDALE UNIVERSITY COLLEGE & SEMINARY

Bible/Biblical Studies, B
Business/Commerce, B
Divinity/Ministry (BD, MDiv.), B
English Language and Literature, B
History, B
Hospitality and Recreation Marketing Operations, B
Human Services, B
Liberal Arts and Sciences Studies and Humanities, B
Missions/Missionary Studies and Missiology, MO
Parks, Recreation, Leisure and Fitness Studies, B
Pastoral Studies/Counseling, BM
Philosophy, B
Psychology, B
Religious Education, B
Theology and Religious Vocations, MO

UNIVERSITY OF GUELPH

Accounting, B
Acute Care/Critical Care Nursing, O
Adult Development and Aging, B
Agribusiness, M
Agricultural Business and Management, AB
Agricultural Economics, BMD
Agricultural Sciences, MDO
Agriculture, A
Agronomy and Crop Science, B
Agronomy and Soil Sciences, MD
Anatomy, MD

Anesthesiologist Assistant, MD
Animal Sciences, BMD
Anthropology, BMD
Applied Mathematics, D
Applied Psychology, MD
Applied Statistics, D
Aquaculture, M
Art History, Criticism and Conservation, B
Atmospheric Sciences and Meteorology, MD
BioTechnology, MD
Biochemistry, BMD
Bioengineering, MD
Biological and Biomedical Sciences, MD
Biology/Biological Sciences, B
Biomedical Sciences, B
Biomedical/Medical Engineering, B
Biophysics, MD
Biopsychology, B
Botany/Plant Biology, MD
Business Administration, Management and Operations, MD
Business/Managerial Economics, B
Cardiovascular Sciences, DO
Cell Biology and Anatomy, MD
Chemical Physics, B
Chemistry, BMD
Child Development, B
Child and Family Studies, MD
Classics and Classical Languages, Literatures, and Linguistics, B
Clinical Psychology, MD
Cognitive Sciences, D
Comparative Literature, D
Computer Engineering, B
Computer Engineering Technologies/Technicians, B
Computer Science, BMD
Computer Software Engineering, B
Consumer Economics, M
Criminal Justice/Law Enforcement Administration, B
Criminology, M
Development Economics and International Development, B
Drama and Dramatics/Theatre Arts, B
Ecology, BMD
Ecology, Evolution, Systematics and Population Biology, B
Econometrics and Quantitative Economics, B
Economics, BMD
Emergency Medical Services, MD
Engineering and Applied Sciences, MD
English, M
English Language and Literature, B
Entomology, MD
Environmental Biology, BMD
Environmental Engineering Technology/Environmental Technology, BMD
Environmental Policy and Resource Management, MD
Environmental Sciences, BMD
Environmental Studies, B
Epidemiology, MD
European Studies/Civilization, B
Evolutionary Biology, MD
Finance, B
Fine Arts and Art Studies, M
Fine/Studio Arts, B
Food Science, B
Food Science and Technology, MD
Foods, Nutrition, and Related Services, AB
French Language and Literature, M
French Studies, B
Geography, BMD
Geological and Earth Sciences/Geosciences, B
Health/Medical Physics, B
History, BMD
Horse Husbandry/Equine Science and Management, AB
Horticultural Science, AMD
Hospitality Administration/Management, M
Hotel/Motel Administration/Management, B
Human Development, MD
Human Development and Family Studies, B
Human Nutrition, B
Human Resources Management/Personnel Administration, B
Immunology, MD

Industrial and Organizational Psychology, MD
Infectious Diseases, MD
International Development, MD
Kinesiology and Exercise Science, B
Landscape Architecture, M
Marine Biology and Biological Oceanography, B
Marketing/Marketing Management, B
Marriage and Family Therapy/Counseling, M
Mathematics, MD
Mechanical Engineering, B
Medical Imaging, MD
Medicinal and Pharmaceutical Chemistry, B
Medieval and Renaissance Studies, D
Microbiology, BMD
Molecular Biology, BMD
Molecular Genetics, BMD
Music, B
Natural Resource Economics, B
Natural Resources Management/Development and Policy, AB
Natural Resources and Conservation, MD
Neuroscience, MD
Nutritional Sciences, BMD
Organizational Management, M
Pathology/Experimental Pathology, MDO
Pharmacology, MD
Philosophy, BMD
Physical Sciences, B
Physics, BMD
Physiology, MD
Plant Pathology/Phytopathology, MD
Plant Sciences, B
Political Science and Government, BM
Population Studies, MD
Poultry Science, MD
Psychology, BMD
Public Administration, BM
Public Policy Analysis, M
Real Estate, B
Rural Planning and Studies, MD
Social Psychology, MD
Sociology, BMD
Spanish Language and Literature, B
Statistics, MD
Theater, M
Theoretical and Mathematical Physics, B
Tourism and Travel Services Management, B
Toxicology, BMD
Turf and Turfgrass Management, A
Veterinary Medicine, MD
Veterinary Sciences, MDO
Veterinary/Animal Health Technology/Technician and Veterinary Assistant, A
Vision Science/Physiological Optics, MD
Water Resources Engineering, BMD
Western European Studies, M
Wildlife Biology, B
Zoology/Animal Biology, BMD

UNIVERSITY OF OTTAWA

Accounting, B
Aerospace, Aeronautical and Astronautical Engineering, MD
Allopathic Medicine, MD
American Indian/Native American Studies, B
Anthropology, BM
Arabic Language and Literature, B
Art History, Criticism and Conservation, B
Biochemistry, BMD
Bioengineering, MD
Biological and Biomedical Sciences, BMD
Biology/Biological Sciences, B
Biomedical Engineering, M
Biomedical Sciences, B
Biomedical/Medical Engineering, B
Business Administration, Management and Operations, BM
Canadian Studies, BD
Cartography, B
Cell Biology and Anatomy, MD
Chemical Engineering, BMD
Chemistry, BMD
Civil Engineering, BMD
Classical, Ancient Mediterranean and Near Eastern Studies and Archaeology, B

Classics and Classical Languages, Literatures, and Linguistics, BMD
Communication Disorders, M
Communication Studies/Speech Communication and Rhetoric, B
Communication and Media Studies, M
Community Health and Preventive Medicine, MO
Computer Engineering, BMD
Computer Science, MD
Computer Software Engineering, B
Computer and Information Sciences, B
Criminology, BMD
Development Economics and International Development, B
Drama and Dramatics/Theatre Arts, B
E-Commerce/Electronic Commerce, B
Economics, BMD
Education, MDO
Electrical Engineering, MD
Electrical, Electronics and Communications Engineering, B
Electronic Commerce, MO
Engineering Management, MO
Engineering and Applied Sciences, MDO
English, MD
English Language and Literature, B
Entrepreneurship/Entrepreneurial Studies, B
Environmental Sciences, B
Environmental Studies, B
Epidemiology, M
Ethics, B
Finance, B
Finance and Banking, O
Fine/Studio Arts, B
Foods, Nutrition, and Wellness Studies, B
Foreign Languages and Literatures, B
French Language and Literature, BMD
Geography, BMD
Geology/Earth Science, B
Geophysics and Seismology, B
Geosciences, MD
German Language and Literature, B
Health Services Administration, M
Health Services Research, O
Health Services/Allied Health/Health Sciences, B
Health and Physical Education, B
History, BMD
Human Resources Management/Personnel Administration, B
Humanities/Humanistic Studies, B
Immunology, B
Information Science/Studies, O
Interdisciplinary Studies, DO
International Business/Trade/Commerce, B
International Development, M
International Relations and Affairs, B
International/Global Studies, B
Italian Language and Literature, B
Journalism, B
Kinesiology and Exercise Science, B
Kinesiology and Movement Studies, M
Language Interpretation and Translation, B
Latin Language and Literature, B
Law and Legal Studies, MD
Linguistics, BMD
Management Information Systems and Services, B
Marketing/Marketing Management, B
Mathematics, BMD
Mechanical Engineering, BMD
Medieval and Renaissance Studies, B
Microbiology, B
Modern Languages, B
Molecular Biology, MD
Music, BMO
Music Teacher Education, O
Nursing, MDO
Occupational Therapy/Therapist, B
Ophthalmic Laboratory Technology/Technician, B
Parks, Recreation, Leisure and Fitness Studies, B
Peace Studies and Conflict Resolution, B
Pharmacology, B
Philosophy, BMD
Physical Sciences, B
Physical Therapy/Therapist, B
Physics, BMD
Physiology, B

Political Science and Government, BMD
Project Management, O
Psychology, BD
Public Administration, BO
Public Health, D
Public Relations/Image Management, B
Rehabilitation Sciences, M
Religion/Religious Studies, BMD
Russian Language and Literature, B
Slavic Studies, B
Social Sciences, B
Social Work, BM
Sociology, BM
Spanish Language and Literature, BMD
Statistics, BMD
Systems Science and Theory, MO
Teacher Education and Professional Development, Specific Subject Areas, B
Teaching English or French as a Second or Foreign Language, B
Theater, M
Theoretical and Mathematical Physics, B
Translation and Interpretation, MD
Women's Studies, BM

UNIVERSITY OF TORONTO

Accounting, B
Actuarial Science, B
Aerospace, Aeronautical and Astronautical Engineering, BMD
African Studies, B
Allopathic Medicine, MD
American Indian/Native American Studies, B
American/United States Studies/Civilization, B
Ancient Near Eastern and Biblical Languages, Literatures, and Linguistics, B
Animal Behavior and Ethology, B
Animal Genetics, B
Animal Physiology, B
Anthropology, BMD
Applied Mathematics, B
Arabic Language and Literature, B
Archeology, B
Architecture, BM
Art History, Criticism and Conservation, MD
Asian Studies/Civilization, B
Astronomy, MD
Astrophysics, MD
BioTechnology, M
Biochemistry, BMD
Bioethics/Medical Ethics, M
Biology/Biological Sciences, B
Biomedical Engineering, MD
Biomedical/Medical Engineering, B
Biophysics, BMD
Biostatistics, MD
Botany/Plant Biology, B
Business Administration and Management, B
Business Administration, Management and Operations, MD
Canadian Studies, B
Cell Biology and Anatomy, MD
Central/Middle and Eastern European Studies, B
Chemical Engineering, BMD
Chemistry, MD
Civil Engineering, BMD
Classical, Ancient Mediterranean and Near Eastern Studies and Archaeology, B
Classics and Classical Languages, Literatures, and Linguistics, BMD
Communication Disorders, MD
Community Health and Preventive Medicine, MD
Comparative Literature, BMD
Computer Engineering, BMD
Computer Science, BMD
Computer Software Engineering, B
Computer Systems Networking and Telecommunications, B
Criminal Justice/Police Science, B
Criminology, BMD
Dental and Oral Surgery, M
Dentistry, D
Digital Communication and Media/Multimedia, B
E-Commerce/Electronic Commerce, B
East Asian Studies, BMD
East European and Russian Studies, M

Ecology, MD
Economics, BMD
Education, BMD
Electrical Engineering, MD
Electrical, Electronics and Communications Engineering, B
Engineering, B
Engineering Science, B
Engineering and Applied Sciences, MD
English, MD
English Language and Literature, B
Environmental Sciences, MD
Environmental Studies, B
Environmental and Occupational Health, M
Epidemiology, MD
Ethnomusicology, MD
European Studies/Civilization, B
Evolutionary Biology, MD
Film, Television, and Video Theory and Criticism, MD
Finance, B
Finance and Banking, M
Foods, Nutrition, and Wellness Studies, B
Forensic Science and Technology, B
Forest Management/Forest Resources Management, B
Forestry, BMD
French Language Teacher Education, B
French Language and Literature, BMD
Gender Studies, MD
Genetic Counseling/Counselor, M
Geography, BMD
Geological/Geophysical Engineering, B
Geology/Earth Science, MD
German Language and Literature, BMD
Health Informatics, M
Health Physics/Radiological Health, M
Health Promotion, M
Health Services Administration, MD
Health Teacher Education, B
Health and Physical Education, B
History, BMD
History and Philosophy of Science and Technology, B
History of Science and Technology, MD
Human Resources Management and Services, MD
Humanities/Humanistic Studies, B
Hydrology and Water Resources Science, B
Immunology, MD
Industrial Engineering, B
Industrial and Labor Relations, MD
Industrial/Management Engineering, MD
Information Science/Studies, MD
International Affairs, M
International Relations and Affairs, B
Italian Language and Literature, BMD
Kinesiology and Movement Studies, MD
Labor and Industrial Relations, B
Landscape Architecture, M
Latin American Studies, B
Latin Language and Literature, B
Law and Legal Studies, MD
Linguistics, BMD
Management of Technology, M
Manufacturing Engineering, BM
Mass Communication/Media Studies, B
Materials Engineering, BMD
Materials Sciences, MD
Mathematical and Computational Finance, M
Mathematics, MD
Mechanical Engineering, BMD
Medical Microbiology and Bacteriology, B
Medieval and Renaissance Studies, MD
Metallurgical Engineering, B
Microbiology, B
Mining and Mineral Engineering, B
Modern Greek Language and Literature, B
Modern Languages, B
Molecular Biology, B
Molecular Genetics, MD
Museology/Museum Studies, M
Music, MD
Music History, Literature, and Theory, B
Music Teacher Education, BMD
Near and Middle Eastern Studies, BMD
Nursing, MD

Nutritional Sciences, MD
Occupational Therapy/Therapist, M
Operations Research, B
Oral and Dental Sciences, MD
Orthodontics, M
Pathobiology, MD
Peace Studies and Conflict Resolution, B
Performance, MD
Periodontics, M
Petroleum Engineering, B
Pharmaceutical Sciences, MD
Pharmacology, MD
Pharmacy, D
Philosophy, MD
Physical Education Teaching and Coaching, MD
Physical Therapy/Therapist, M
Physics, MD
Physiology, MD
Political Science and Government, BMD
Portuguese Language and Literature, BMD
Psychology, MD
Public Administration, B
Public Health, MD
Public Relations/Image Management, B
Radiologic Technology/Science - Radiographer, B
Rehabilitation Sciences, MD
Religion/Religious Studies, MD
Romance Languages, Literatures, and Linguistics, B
Russian Language and Literature, B
Russian Studies, B
Science Teacher Education/General Science Teacher Education, B
Slavic Languages, Literatures, and Linguistics, BMD
Social Sciences, MD
Social Work, MD
Sociology, BMD
South Asian Studies, B
Spanish Language and Literature, BMD
Statistics, MD
Systematic Biology/Biological Systematics, MD
Teaching French as a Second or Foreign Language, B
Theater, MD
Toxicology, B
Transportation and Highway Engineering, B
Urban Design, MD
Urban and Regional Planning, MD
Visual and Performing Arts, B
Women's Studies, BMD
Wood Science and Wood Products/Pulp and Paper Technology, B
Writing, M
Zoology/Animal Biology, B

UNIVERSITY OF WATERLOO

Accounting, BMD
Accounting and Finance, B
Actuarial Science, BMD
Anthropology, BM
Applied Economics, B
Applied Mathematics, BMD
Architecture, BM
Art History, Criticism and Conservation, B
Atmospheric Sciences and Meteorology, B
Atomic/Molecular Physics, B
BioTechnology, B
Biochemistry, BMD
Biochemistry, Biophysics and Molecular Biology, B
Bioinformatics, B
Biological and Biomedical Sciences, MD
Biological and Physical Sciences, B
Biology Teacher Education, B
Biology/Biological Sciences, B
Biomedical/Medical Engineering, B
Biostatistics, MD
Business Administration and Management, B
Business Administration, Management and Operations, BM
Canadian Studies, B
Chemical Engineering, BMD
Chemical Physics, B
Chemistry, BMD
Chemistry Teacher Education, B
City/Urban, Community and Regional Planning, B
Civil Engineering, BMD

Classics and Classical Languages, Literatures, and Linguistics, B
Communication Studies/Speech Communication and Rhetoric, B
Computational Mathematics, B
Computer Engineering, BMD
Computer Science, BMD
Computer Software Engineering, B
Cultural Resource Management and Policy Analysis, B
Digital Communication and Media/Multimedia, B
Drama and Dramatics/Theatre Arts, B
Ecology, B
Economic Development, M
Economics, BMD
Education, B
Electrical Engineering, MD
Electrical, Electronics and Communications Engineering, B
Engineering, B
Engineering Management, MD
Engineering and Applied Sciences, MD
English, MD
English Language and Literature, B
Entrepreneurship/Entrepreneurial Studies, M
Environmental Engineering Technology/Environmental Technology, MD
Environmental Policy and Resource Management, M
Environmental Sciences, B
Environmental Studies, B
Environmental/Environmental Health Engineering, B
Film/Cinema Studies, B
Finance and Banking, M
Fine Arts and Art Studies, M
Fine/Studio Arts, B
French Language Teacher Education, B
French Language and Literature, BMD
French Studies, B
Geochemistry, B
Geography, BMD
Geological/Geophysical Engineering, B
Geology/Earth Science, B
Geophysics and Seismology, B
Geosciences, MD
German Language and Literature, BMD
Health Education, MD
Health Professions and Related Clinical Sciences, B
Health/Medical Preparatory Programs, B
History, BMD
Human Development and Family Studies, B
Human Resources Management/Personnel Administration, B
Information Science/Studies, MD
International Affairs, MD
International Business/Trade/Commerce, B
International Relations and Affairs, B
International/Global Studies, B
Kinesiology and Exercise Science, B
Kinesiology and Movement Studies, MD
Leisure Studies, MD
Liberal Arts and Sciences Studies and Humanities, B
Management of Technology, MD
Mathematics, BMD
Mathematics Teacher Education, B
Mathematics and Computer Science, B
Mechanical Engineering, BMD
Medical Informatics, B
Medieval and Renaissance Studies, B
Multi-/Interdisciplinary Studies, B
Music, B
Near and Middle Eastern Studies, M
Operations Research, BMD
Optometry, MD
Parks, Recreation and Leisure Facilities Management, B
Parks, Recreation, Leisure and Fitness Studies, B
Philosophy, BMD
Physics, BMD
Physics Teacher Education, B
Planetary Astronomy and Science, B
Political Science and Government, BMD
Psychology, BMD
Public Affairs, M
Public Health, M

Recreation and Park Management, MD
Rehabilitation and Therapeutic Professions, B
Religion/Religious Studies, BD
Respiratory Care Therapy/Therapist, B
Russian Language and Literature, BM
Russian Studies, B
Slavic Studies, B
Social Sciences, B
Social Work, B
Sociology, BMD
Software Engineering, M
Spanish Language and Literature, B
Statistics, BMD
Systems Engineering, BMD
Taxation, M
Technical and Business Writing, M
Therapeutic Recreation/Recreational Therapy, B
Travel and Tourism, M
Urban and Regional Planning, MD
Vision Science/Physiological Optics, MD
Women's Studies, B

THE UNIVERSITY OF WESTERN ONTARIO

Accounting, B
Accounting and Business/Management, B
Accounting and Finance, B
Actuarial Science, B
Allopathic Medicine, MD
American History (United States), B
American Indian/Native American Studies, B
American/United States Studies/Civilization, B
Analytical Chemistry, B
Anatomy, BMD
Ancient/Classical Greek Language and Literature, B
Animal Behavior and Ethology, B
Anthropology, BMD
Applied Mathematics, BMD
Art History, Criticism and Conservation, B
Art/Art Studies, General, B
Asian Studies/Civilization, B
Astronomy, BMD
Astrophysics, B
Aviation/Airway Management and Operations, B
Bible/Biblical Studies, B
Biochemical Engineering, MD
Biochemistry, BMD
Biochemistry, Biophysics and Molecular Biology, B
Bioinformatics, B
Biological and Biomedical Sciences, MD
Biology/Biological Sciences, B
Biophysics, BMD
Biostatistics, BMD
Business Administration and Management, B
Business Administration, Management and Operations, BMD
Business, Management, Marketing, and Related Support Services, B
Business/Commerce, B
Business/Corporate Communications, B
Business/Managerial Economics, B
Canadian Studies, B
Cartography, B
Cell Biology and Anatomy, BMD
Chemical Engineering, BMD
Chemistry, BMD
Child Development, B
Chinese Language and Literature, B
Chinese Studies, B
Civil Engineering, BMD
Classics and Classical Languages, Literatures, and Linguistics, BM
Communication Disorders, M
Communication and Media Studies, B
Community Health Services/Liaison/Counseling, B
Comparative Literature, BMD
Computer Engineering, BMD
Computer Programming/Programmer, B
Computer Science, BMD
Computer Software Engineering, B
Computer Software and Media Applications, B
Computer and Information Sciences, B
Conservation Biology, B
Counseling Psychology, M
Criminology, B
Curriculum and Instruction, BM

Dentistry, D
Dietetics/Dieticians, B
Digital Communication and Media/Multimedia, B
East Asian Languages, Literatures, and Linguistics, B
East Asian Studies, B
Ecology, B
Economics, BMD
Education, BM
Educational Administration and Supervision, B
Educational Policy, M
Educational Psychology, M
Educational/Instructional Media Design, B
Electrical Engineering, MD
Electrical, Electronics and Communications Engineering, B
Elementary Education and Teaching, B
Engineering, B
Engineering Physics, B
Engineering Science, B
Engineering and Applied Sciences, MD
English, MD
English Language and Literature, B
Entrepreneurship/Entrepreneurial Studies, BM
Environmental Engineering Technology/Environmental Technology, MD
Environmental Sciences, BMD
Environmental Studies, B
Environmental/Environmental Health Engineering, B
Epidemiology, BMD
Ethics, B
Ethnic, Cultural Minority, and Gender Studies, B
Family and Consumer Sciences/Human Sciences, B
Film/Cinema Studies, B
Finance, B
Finance and Banking, M
Fine/Studio Arts, B
Foods, Nutrition, and Wellness Studies, B
French Language and Literature, BMD
French Studies, B
Gay/Lesbian Studies, B
Genetics, B
Geography, BMD
Geology/Earth Science, BMD
Geophysics and Seismology, MD
Geosciences, MD
German Language and Literature, B
German Studies, B
Health Professions and Related Clinical Sciences, B
Health Services Administration, M
Health Services/Allied Health/Health Sciences, B
History, BMD
Human Resources Management/Personnel Administration, B
Immunology, MD
Information Science/Studies, BMD
Information Technology, B
Inorganic Chemistry, B
Interdisciplinary Studies, MD
International Business/Trade/Commerce, BM
International Relations and Affairs, B
Islamic Studies, B
Italian Language and Literature, B
Italian Studies, B
Japanese Language and Literature, B
Jewish/Judaic Studies, B
Journalism, M
Junior High/Intermediate/Middle School Education and Teaching, B
Kinesiology and Exercise Science, B
Kinesiology and Movement Studies, MD
Latin Language and Literature, B
Law and Legal Studies, MDO
Liberal Arts and Sciences Studies and Humanities, B
Library Science, MD
Linguistics, B
Management Information Systems and Services, B
Management Strategy and Policy, M
Marketing, M
Mass Communication/Media Studies, B
Materials Engineering, BMD
Mathematical Statistics and Probability, B
Mathematics, BMD
Mechanical Engineering, BMD
Media Studies, MD

Medical Informatics, B
Medieval and Renaissance Studies, B
Microbiology, MD
Music, BMD
Music History, Literature, and Theory, B
Music Performance, B
Music Theory and Composition, B
Natural Resources Management/Development and
 Policy, B
Near and Middle Eastern Studies, B
Neuroscience, MD
Non-Profit/Public/Organizational Management, B
Nursing, MD
Occupational Therapy/Therapist, M
Oral and Dental Sciences, M
Organic Chemistry, B
Organizational Behavior Studies, B
Pathology/Experimental Pathology, BMD
Peace Studies and Conflict Resolution, B
Pharmacology, B
Philosophy, BMD
Physical Anthropology, B
Physical Therapy/Therapist, MO
Physical and Theoretical Chemistry, B
Physics, BMD
Physiology, BMD
Piano and Organ, B
Planetary Astronomy and Science, B
Political Science and Government, BMD
Psychology, BMD
Public Administration, B
Radio and Television, B
Religion/Religious Studies, B
Secondary Education and Teaching, B
Social Sciences, B
Social Work, B
Sociology, BMD
Spanish Language and Literature, BMD
Spanish and Iberian Studies, B
Special Education and Teaching, M
Sport and Fitness Administration/Management, B
Statistics, BMD
Sustainable Development, M
Technical Theatre/Theatre Design and Technol-
 ogy, B
Theology/Theological Studies, B
Theoretical and Mathematical Physics, B
Toxicology, B
Urban Studies/Affairs, B
Violin, Viola, Guitar and Other Stringed Instru-
 ments, B
Voice and Opera, B
Women's Studies, B
Youth Services/Administration, B

UNIVERSITY OF WINDSOR

Accounting, B
Accounting and Finance, B
Acting, B
Applied Mathematics, B
Applied Psychology, MD
Art History, Criticism and Conservation, B
Art Teacher Education, B
Art/Art Studies, General, B
Artificial Intelligence and Robotics, B
BioTechnology, B
Biochemistry, BMD
Bioinformatics, B
Biological and Biomedical Sciences, MD
Biological and Physical Sciences, B
Biology Teacher Education, B
Biology/Biological Sciences, B
Biopsychology, MD
Business Administration and Management, B
Business Administration, Management and Opera-
 tions, M
Business/Commerce, B
Business/Managerial Economics, B
Chemistry, BMD
Chemistry Teacher Education, B
Civil Engineering, BMD
Classics and Classical Languages, Litera-
 tures, and Linguistics, B
Clinical Psychology, MD
Communication and Media Studies, M

Communications Technologies/Technicians and Sup-
 port Services, B
Computer Programming, Specific Applications, B
Computer Science, BMD
Computer and Information Sciences, B
Counselor Education/School Counseling and Guid-
 ance Services, B
Criminology, BM
Drama and Dance Teacher Education, B
Drama and Dramatics/Theatre Arts, B
Drawing, B
Economics, BM
Education, BMD
Electrical Engineering, MD
Electrical, Electronics and Communications Engi-
 neering, B
Elementary Education and Teaching, B
Engineering, B
Engineering Mechanics, B
Engineering and Applied Sciences, MD
English, M
English Language and Literature, B
English/Language Arts Teacher Education, B
Environmental Biology, B
Environmental Engineering
 Technology/Environmental Technology, MD
Environmental Sciences, BMD
Environmental Studies, B
Environmental/Environmental Health Engineering, B
Film/Cinema Studies, B
Finance, B
Fine Arts and Art Studies, M
Fine/Studio Arts, B
Foreign Language Teacher Education, B
Forensic Science and Technology, B
French Language Teacher Education, B
French Language and Literature, B
French Studies, B
Geography Teacher Education, B
Geology/Earth Science, B
Geosciences, MD
German Language Teacher Education, B
German Language and Literature, B
German Studies, B
Health Teacher Education, B
Health and Physical Education, B
History, BM
History Teacher Education, B
Human Resources Management/Personnel Adminis-
 tration, B
Industrial Engineering, B
Industrial/Management Engineering, MD
International Relations and Affairs, B
Italian Language and Literature, B
Italian Studies, B
Kindergarten/PreSchool Education and Teaching, B
Kinesiology and Exercise Science, B
Kinesiology and Movement Studies, M
Labor Studies, B
Latin Language and Literature, B
Law and Legal Studies, B
Legal and Justice Studies, B
Manufacturing Engineering, MD
Marketing/Marketing Management, B
Materials Engineering, BMD
Mathematics, BMD
Mathematics Teacher Education, B
Mathematics and Computer Science, B
Mechanical Engineering, BMD
Modern Languages, B
Music, B
Music History, Literature, and Theory, B
Music Performance, B
Music Teacher Education, B
Music Theory and Composition, B
Nursing, M
Painting, B
Philosophy, BM
Physical Education Teaching and Coaching, B
Physics, BMD
Physics Teacher Education, B
Political Science and Government, BM
Pre-Dentistry Studies, B
Pre-Law Studies, B
Pre-Medicine/Pre-Medical Studies, B
Pre-Pharmacy Studies, B

Printmaking, B
Psychology, BMD
Science Teacher Education/General Science
 Teacher Education, B
Science, Technology and Society, B
Sculpture, B
Secondary Education and Teaching, B
Social Psychology, MD
Social Sciences, B
Social Work, BM
Sociology, BMD
Spanish Language and Literature, B
Special Education and Teaching, B
Speech Teacher Education, B
Sport and Fitness Administration/Management, B
Statistics, MD
Teacher Education, Multiple Levels, B
Teaching French as a Second or Foreign Lan-
 guage, B
Visual and Performing Arts, B
Women's Studies, B
Writing, M

WILFRID LAURIER UNIVERSITY

Accounting, D
American/United States Studies/Civilization, BD
Anthropology, B
Archeology, B
BioTechnology, B
Biological and Biomedical Sciences, M
Biology/Biological Sciences, B
Business Administration and Management, B
Business Administration, Management and Opera-
 tions, M
Canadian Studies, BM
Chemistry, BM
Classics and Classical Languages, Litera-
 tures, and Linguistics, B
Cognitive Sciences, MD
Communication and Media Studies, M
Community Psychology, MD
Computer Science, B
Computer and Information Sciences, B
Conflict Resolution and Mediation/Peace Studies, D
Criminal Justice/Safety Studies, B
Criminology, M
Cultural Studies, M
Developmental Psychology, MD
Economics, BMD
Education, B
English, MD
English Language and Literature, B
Environmental Policy, M
Environmental Policy and Resource Manage-
 ment, MD
Environmental Sciences, MD
Environmental Studies, B
Film, Television, and Video Theory and Criti-
 cism, MD
Film/Cinema Studies, B
Finance and Banking, MD
French Language and Literature, B
Gender Studies, M
Geography, BMD
Health Professions and Related Clinical Sciences, B
Health Promotion, M
History, BMD
Human Resources Management and Services, MD
Intercultural/Multicultural and Diversity Studies, B
International Affairs, MD
International Economics, M
International/Global Studies, B
Journalism, B
Kinesiology and Exercise Science, B
Kinesiology and Movement Studies, M
Legal and Justice Studies, D
Management, MD
Management of Technology, M
Marketing, D
Mass Communication/Media Studies, B
Mathematics, BM
Media Studies, M
Medieval and Renaissance Studies, B
Music, B
Music Therapy/Therapist, BM
Neuroscience, MD

Organizational Behavior Studies, MD
Organizational Management, D
Pastoral Studies/Counseling, DO
Philosophy, BM
Physical Education Teaching and Coaching, BM
Physics, B
Political Science and Government, BMD
Psychology, BMD
Public Policy Analysis, M
Religion/Religious Studies, BMD
Social Psychology, MD
Social Sciences, M
Social Work, MD
Sociology, BM
Spanish Language and Literature, B
Supply Chain Management, MD
Theology and Religious Vocations, MDO
Women's Studies, B

YORK UNIVERSITY

Accounting, BM
Acting, B
Actuarial Science, B
Aeronautics/Aviation/Aerospace Science and Tech-
nology, B
Aerospace, Aeronautical and Astronautical Engi-
neering, B
African Studies, B
Anthropology, BMD
Applied Mathematics, BM
Art History, Criticism and Conservation, BMD
Art Teacher Education, B
Art/Art Studies, General, B
Astronomy, BMD
Atmospheric Sciences and Meteorology, B
Bilingual and Multilingual Education, B
BioTechnology, B
Biological and Biomedical Sciences, MD
Biological and Physical Sciences, B
Biology Teacher Education, B
Biology/Biological Sciences, B
Business Administration and Management, B
Business Administration, Management and Opera-
tions, MD
Business Statistics, B
Business/Commerce, B
Business/Managerial Economics, B
Canadian Studies, B
Chemistry, BMD
Chemistry Teacher Education, B
Cinematography and Film/Video Production, B
Classics and Classical Languages, Litera-
tures, and Linguistics, B
Commercial and Advertising Art, B
Communication Studies/Speech Communication
and Rhetoric, B
Communication and Media Studies, MD
Composition, M
Computer Engineering, B
Computer Hardware Engineering, B
Computer Science, BMD
Computer Software Engineering, B
Computer and Information Sciences, B
Dance, BMD
Design and Applied Arts, M
Design and Visual Communications, B
Development Economics and International Develop-
ment, B
Disability Studies, MD
Drama and Dance Teacher Education, B
Drama and Dramatics/Theatre Arts, B
East Asian Studies, B
Ecology, B
Economics, BMD
Education, BMD
Elementary Education and Teaching, B
Emergency Management, M
Engineering, B
English, MD
English Language and Literature, B
English/Language Arts Teacher Education, B
Entrepreneurship/Entrepreneurial Studies, B
Environmental Biology, B
Environmental Policy and Resource Manage-
ment, MD
Environmental Sciences, B

Environmental Studies, B
Ethnomusicology, M
European Studies/Civilization, B
Film, Television, and Video Production, MD
Film/Cinema Studies, B
Finance, B
Finance and Banking, M
Fine Arts and Art Studies, MD
Fine/Studio Arts, B
French Language and Literature, BMD
French Studies, B
Gender Studies, MD
Geography, BMD
Geology/Earth Science, B
Geosciences, MD
Geotechnical Engineering, B
German Language and Literature, B
German Studies, B
Gerontology, B
Health Professions and Related Clinical Sciences, B
Health Services/Allied Health/Health Sciences, B
Health and Physical Education, B
Hebrew Language and Literature, B
History, BMD
History Teacher Education, B
Hospital and Health Care Facilities
Administration/Management, B
Human Resources Management and Services, MD
Human Resources Management/Personnel Adminis-
tration, B
Humanities/Humanistic Studies, BMD
Information Technology, B
Interdisciplinary Studies, M
International Affairs, M
International Business/Trade/Commerce, BM
International Relations and Affairs, B
Italian Language and Literature, B
Italian Studies, B
Japanese Language and Literature, B
Jewish/Judaic Studies, B
Junior High/Intermediate/Middle School Education
and Teaching, B
Kindergarten/PreSchool Education and Teaching, B
Kinesiology and Movement Studies, MD
Labor and Industrial Relations, B
Language Interpretation and Translation, B
Latin American Studies, B
Latin Language and Literature, B
Law and Legal Studies, BMD
Liberal Arts and Sciences Studies and Humani-
ties, B
Linguistics, BMD
Management Information Systems and Services, B
Marketing/Marketing Management, B
Mass Communication/Media Studies, B
Mathematics, BMD
Mathematics Teacher Education, B
Mathematics and Computer Science, B
Modern Greek Language and Literature, B
Modern Languages, B
Molecular Biology, B
Music, BMD
Music History, Literature, and Theory, B
Music Performance, B
Music Teacher Education, B
Music Theory and Composition, B
Musicology and Ethnomusicology, BM
Natural Sciences, B
Nursing, M
Operations Research, B
Organizational Behavior Studies, B
Painting, B
Philosophy, BMD
Photography, B
Physical Education Teaching and Coaching, B
Physical Sciences, B
Physics, BMD
Physics Teacher Education, B
Piano and Organ, B
Planetary Astronomy and Science, MD
Playwriting and Screenwriting, B
Political Science and Government, BMD
Pre-Dentistry Studies, B
Pre-Law Studies, B
Pre-Medicine/Pre-Medical Studies, B
Pre-Pharmacy Studies, B

Pre-Veterinary Studies, B
Printmaking, B
Psychology, BMD
Public Administration, BM
Public Affairs, M
Public Health (MPH, DPH), B
Public Policy Analysis, BM
Rehabilitation and Therapeutic Professions, B
Religion/Religious Studies, B
Romance Languages, Literatures, and Linguistics, B
Russian Language and Literature, B
Russian Studies, B
Sales, Distribution and Marketing Operations, B
Science Teacher Education/General Science
Teacher Education, B
Science, Technology and Society, B
Sculpture, B
Secondary Education and Teaching, B
Sign Language Interpretation and Translation, B
Social Science Teacher Education, B
Social Sciences, B
Social Studies Teacher Education, B
Social Work, BMD
Sociology, BMD
Spanish Language and Literature, B
Spanish and Iberian Studies, B
Special Education and Teaching, B
Speech Teacher Education, B
Sport and Fitness Administration/Management, B
Statistics, BMD
Teacher Education, Multiple Levels, B
Teaching English as a Second or Foreign
Language/ESL Language Instructor, B
Theater, MD
Translation and Interpretation, M
Urban Studies/Affairs, B
Visual and Performing Arts, B
Voice and Opera, B
Women's Studies, BMD

Quebec

BISHOP'S UNIVERSITY

Accounting, B
Art Teacher Education, B
Art/Art Studies, General, B
Biochemistry, B
Biological and Physical Sciences, B
Biology Teacher Education, B
Biology/Biological Sciences, B
Business Administration and Management, B
Business/Managerial Economics, B
Canadian Studies, B
Chemistry, B
Chemistry Teacher Education, B
Classics and Classical Languages, Litera-
tures, and Linguistics, B
Comparative Literature, B
Computer Programming/Programmer, B
Computer Science, B
Computer Teacher Education, B
Computer and Information Sciences, B
Drama and Dance Teacher Education, B
Drama and Dramatics/Theatre Arts, B
Economics, B
Education, BMO
Elementary Education and Teaching, B
English Language and Literature, B
English as a Second Language, O
English/Language Arts Teacher Education, B
Environmental Studies, B
Film/Cinema Studies, B
Finance, B
Fine/Studio Arts, B
French Language Teacher Education, B
French Language and Literature, B
Geography, B
Geography Teacher Education, B
German Language and Literature, B
Gerontology, B
History, B
History Teacher Education, B
Human Resources Management/Personnel Adminis-
tration, B
Humanities/Humanistic Studies, B
International Business/Trade/Commerce, B

International Relations and Affairs, B
Italian Language and Literature, B
Liberal Arts and Sciences Studies and Humanities, B
Management Information Systems and Services, B
Marketing/Marketing Management, B
Mathematics, B
Mathematics Teacher Education, B
Modern Languages, B
Music, B
Music Teacher Education, B
Natural Sciences, B
Philosophy, B
Physics, B
Physics Teacher Education, B
Political Science and Government, B
Psychology, B
Religion/Religious Studies, B
Science Teacher Education/General Science Teacher Education, B
Secondary Education and Teaching, B
Social Sciences, B
Sociology, B
Spanish Language Teacher Education, B
Spanish Language and Literature, B
Teaching French as a Second or Foreign Language, B
Web Page, Digital/Multimedia and Information Resources Design, B
Women's Studies, B

CONCORDIA UNIVERSITY

Accounting, B
Actuarial Science, B
Adult and Continuing Education and Teaching, MO
Aerospace, Aeronautical and Astronautical Engineering, M
American Indian/Native American Studies, B
Ancient Studies/Civilization, B
Animation, Interactive Technology, Video Graphics and Special Effects, B
Anthropology, BM
Applied Economics, B
Art Education, MD
Art History, Criticism and Conservation, BMD
Art Teacher Education, B
Art Therapy/Therapist, M
BioTechnology, O
Biological and Biomedical Sciences, MDO
Biology/Biological Sciences, B
Business Administration and Management, B
Business Administration, Management and Operations, MDO
Cell/Cellular and Molecular Biology, B
Ceramic Arts and Ceramics, B
Chemistry, BMD
Child and Family Studies, M
Cinematography and Film/Video Production, B
City/Urban, Community and Regional Planning, B
Civil Engineering, BMDO
Classics and Classical Languages, Literatures, and Linguistics, B
Clinical Psychology, MDO
Communication and Media Studies, BMDO
Communication, Journalism and Related Programs, B
Computer Art and Design, O
Computer Engineering, BMD
Computer Graphics, B
Computer Science, BMDO
Computer Software Engineering, B
Computer Systems Analysis/Analyst, B
Computer Systems Networking and Telecommunications, B
Computer and Information Systems Security, M
Construction Engineering, B
Construction Engineering and Management, MDO
Cultural Anthropology, M
Dance, B
Design and Applied Arts, BO
Drama and Dramatics/Theatre Arts, B
Ecology, B
Economic Development, O
Economics, BMDO
Education, BMDO
Educational Media/Instructional Technology, MDO

Electrical Engineering, MD
Electrical, Electronics and Communications Engineering, B
Elementary Education and Teaching, B
Engineering and Applied Sciences, MDO
English, M
English Language and Literature, B
English as a Second Language, O
Environmental Engineering Technology/Environmental Technology, O
Environmental Sciences, B
Environmental Studies, MO
Exercise and Sports Science, M
Film, Television, and Video Production, M
Film, Television, and Video Theory and Criticism, M
Film/Cinema Studies, B
Finance, B
Finance and Banking, M
Fine Arts and Art Studies, M
Fine/Studio Arts, B
French Language and Literature, BMO
Game Design and Development, O
Genomic Sciences, O
Geography, BMO
History, BMD
Human Resources Management/Personnel Administration, B
Humanities/Humanistic Studies, BD
Industrial Engineering, B
Industrial/Management Engineering, MDO
Intercultural/Multicultural and Diversity Studies, B
Interdisciplinary Studies, MD
Intermedia/Multimedia, B
International Business/Trade/Commerce, B
Internet and Interactive Multimedia, O
Investment Management, M
Italian Language and Literature, B
Jazz/Jazz Studies, B
Jewish/Judaic Studies, BM
Journalism, BO
Kindergarten/PreSchool Education and Teaching, B
Kinesiology and Exercise Science, B
Language Interpretation and Translation, B
Linguistics, BM
Logistics and Materials Management, B
Management Information Systems and Services, B
Marketing, M
Marketing/Marketing Management, B
Mass Communication/Media Studies, B
Mathematical Statistics and Probability, B
Mathematics, BMD
Mathematics Teacher Education, M
Mechanical Engineering, BMDO
Media Studies, M
Music, BO
Music Performance, B
Music Theory and Composition, B
Operations Management and Supervision, B
Organic Chemistry, B
Organizational Management, M
Painting, BM
Parks, Recreation, Leisure and Fitness Studies, B
Performance, O
Philosophy, BM
Photography, B
Physical Therapy/Therapist, B
Physics, BMD
Playwriting and Screenwriting, B
Political Science and Government, BD
Printmaking, B
Psychology, BMD
Public Administration, BMD
Public Affairs, O
Public Policy Analysis, MD
Public/Applied History and Archival Administration, B
Religion/Religious Studies, BMD
Sculpture, BM
Social Sciences, B
Sociology, BM
Software Engineering, MDO
South Asian Studies, B
Spanish Language and Literature, B
Statistics, B
Systems Engineering, MO
Teaching English as a Second or Foreign Language/ESL Language Instructor, B

Technical Theatre/Theatre Design and Technology, B
Telecommunications Management, O
Theological and Ministerial Studies, B
Theology and Religious Vocations, M
Theology/Theological Studies, B
Therapeutic Recreation/Recreational Therapy, B
Translation and Interpretation, O
Urban Studies/Affairs, BM
Urban and Regional Planning, O
Visual and Performing Arts, B
Web Page, Digital/Multimedia and Information Resources Design, B
Women's Studies, B
Writing, M

ÉCOLE POLYTECHNIQUE DE MONTRÉAL

Aerospace, Aeronautical and Astronautical Engineering, MD
Applied Mathematics, MD
Biomedical Engineering, MDO
Chemical Engineering, MDO
Civil Engineering, MDO
Computer Engineering, MDO
Computer Science, MD
Electrical Engineering, MDO
Engineering Physics, MDO
Engineering and Applied Sciences, MDO
Environmental Engineering Technology/Environmental Technology, MD
Geotechnical Engineering, MD
Hydraulics and Fluid Power Technology, MD
Industrial/Management Engineering, MDO
Management of Technology, M
Mechanical Engineering, MDO
Mechanics, MD
Nuclear Engineering, MDO
Operations Research, MDO
Optical Technologies, MD
Structural Engineering, MD
Transportation and Highway Engineering, MD

HEC MONTREAL

Accounting, BMO
Applied Economics, BM
Arts Management, O
Business Administration and Management, B
Business Administration, Management and Operations, MD
Business Statistics, B
Business/Commerce, B
Business/Managerial Economics, B
Computer Systems Analysis/Analyst, B
Consumer Merchandising/Retailing Management, B
Corporate and Organizational Communication, O
Electronic Commerce, O
Entrepreneurship/Entrepreneurial Studies, B
Finance, B
Finance and Banking, MO
Financial Engineering, M
Human Resources Management and Services, M
Human Resources Management/Personnel Administration, B
Industrial and Manufacturing Management, M
Information Science/Studies, B
International Business/Trade/Commerce, BM
International Economics, B
International Finance, B
Logistics and Materials Management, BM
Management, O
Management Information Systems and Services, BM
Management Science, B
Management Sciences and Quantitative Methods, B
Management Strategy and Policy, M
Marketing, M
Marketing/Marketing Management, B
Operations Research, BM
Organizational Management, M
Sales, Distribution and Marketing Operations, B
Supply Chain Management, MO
Sustainable Development, O

Taxation, MO

MCGILL UNIVERSITY

Accounting, BO
Accounting and Finance, B
Aerospace, Aeronautical and Astronautical Engineering, M
Agricultural Economics, M
Agricultural Engineering, MD
Agricultural Sciences, MDO
Agronomy and Crop Science, B
Agronomy and Soil Sciences, MD
Allopathic Medicine, MD
Analytical Chemistry, B
Animal Behavior and Ethology, B
Animal Sciences, MD
Anthropology, BMD
Applied Horticulture/Horticultural Operations, B
Applied Mathematics, BM
Aquatic Biology/Limnology, B
Architecture, MDO
Art History, Criticism and Conservation, BMD
Asian History, B
Atmospheric Physics and Dynamics, B
Atmospheric Sciences and Meteorology, BMD
Auditing, B
Bilingual and Multilingual Education, B
BioTechnology, MO
Biochemistry, BMD
Bioengineering, MD
Bioethics/Medical Ethics, M
Bioinformatics, MD
Biological and Biomedical Sciences, MD
Biological and Physical Sciences, B
Biology/Biological Sciences, B
Biomedical Engineering, MD
Biomedical Sciences, B
Biostatistics, MDO
Botany/Plant Biology, B
Business Administration, Management and Operations, MDO
Business/Commerce, B
Business/Managerial Economics, B
Canadian History, B
Caribbean Studies, B
Cell Biology and Anatomy, BMD
Cell/Cellular Biology and Histology, B
Chemical Engineering, MD
Chemistry, BMD
Civil Engineering, BMD
Clinical Psychology, D
Cognitive Sciences, B
Communication Disorders, MD
Communication and Media Studies, MD
Community Health and Preventive Medicine, M
Composition, MD
Computational Sciences, M
Computer Engineering, BMD
Computer Science, MD
Computer Software Engineering, B
Counseling Psychology, MD
Curriculum and Instruction, M
Dental and Oral Surgery, MD
Dentistry, MDO
Development Economics and International Development, B
Developmental Psychology, MDO
Drama and Dramatics/Theatre Arts, B
E-Commerce/Electronic Commerce, B
East Asian Languages, Literatures, and Linguistics, B
East Asian Studies, MD
Ecology, B
Economics, BMD
Education, MDO
Educational Administration and Supervision, M
Educational Leadership and Administration, O
Educational Psychology, MDO
Electrical Engineering, MD
Elementary Education and Teaching, B
Engineering and Applied Sciences, MDO
English, MD
Entomology, MD
Entrepreneurship/Entrepreneurial Studies, BM
Environmental Biology, B

Environmental Engineering Technology/Environmental Technology, MD
Environmental Policy and Resource Management, M
Environmental Sciences, B
Environmental and Occupational Health, MD
Epidemiology, MDO
European History, B
Experimental Psychology, MD
Finance, B
Finance and Banking, M
Fish, Game and Wildlife Management, MD
Food Engineering, MD
Food Science and Technology, MD
Foreign Language Teacher Education, MD
Forensic Science and Technology, O
Forestry, MD
Foundations and Philosophy of Education, MD
French Language and Literature, MD
Genetic Counseling/Counselor, M
Genetics, B
Geography, BMD
Geography Teacher Education, B
Geology/Earth Science, B
Geophysics and Seismology, B
Geosciences, MD
Geotechnical Engineering, MD
German Language and Literature, MD
German Studies, B
Health Services Administration, M
Health Teacher Education, B
Health and Physical Education, B
Hispanic Studies, MD
Hispanic-American, Puerto Rican, and Mexican-American/Chicano Studies, B
History, BMD
History of Medicine, MD
Human Genetics, MD
Human Nutrition, B
Human Resources Management/Personnel Administration, B
Humanities/Humanistic Studies, B
Hydraulics and Fluid Power Technology, MD
Hydrology and Water Resources Science, B
Immunology, MD
Industrial and Manufacturing Management, M
Information Science/Studies, MDO
Inorganic Chemistry, B
Insurance, B
International Business/Trade/Commerce, BM
International Development, M
International Finance, B
Italian Language and Literature, MD
Italian Studies, B
Jazz/Jazz Studies, B
Jewish/Judaic Studies, BM
Kinesiology and Exercise Science, B
Kinesiology and Movement Studies, MDO
Labor and Industrial Relations, B
Language Interpretation and Translation, B
Law and Legal Studies, BMDO
Library Science, MDO
Linguistics, MD
Management, MO
Management Information Systems and Services, M
Management Science, B
Management Strategy and Policy, M
Marine Biology and Biological Oceanography, B
Marketing, M
Marketing/Marketing Management, B
Materials Engineering, BMD
Mathematical Statistics and Probability, B
Mathematics, BMD
Mathematics and Computer Science, B
Mechanical Engineering, BMD
Mechanics, MD
Medical Microbiology and Bacteriology, B
Medical Physics, MD
Metallurgical Engineering, B
Meteorology, MD
Microbiology, BMD
Mineral/Mining Engineering, MDO
Molecular Biology, B
Music, BMD
Music History, Literature, and Theory, B
Music Pedagogy, B

Music Performance, B
Music Teacher Education, MD
Music Theory and Composition, BMD
Musicology and Ethnomusicology, MD
Natural Resources and Conservation, MD
Natural Sciences, B
Near and Middle Eastern Studies, BMDO
Neuroscience, MD
Nursing, MDO
Nursing - Advanced Practice, O
Nutritional Sciences, BMDO
Oceanography, Chemical and Physical, MD
Operations Management and Supervision, B
Organic Chemistry, B
Organizational Behavior Studies, B
Parasitology, MDO
Pathology/Experimental Pathology, MD
Performance, MD
Pharmacology, MD
Philosophy, BMD
Physical Education Teaching and Coaching, MDO
Physics, BMD
Physiology, BMD
Piano and Organ, B
Planetary Astronomy and Science, BMD
Plant Sciences, MDO
Political Science and Government, BMD
Psychology, BMD
Regional Studies (U.S., Canadian, Foreign), B
Rehabilitation Sciences, MDO
Religion/Religious Studies, BMD
Religious Education, B
Religious/Sacred Music, B
Russian Language and Literature, MD
School Psychology, MDO
Social Work, BMDO
Sociology, BMDO
Spanish and Iberian Studies, B
Statistics, BMD
Structural Engineering, MD
Taxation, B
Teaching French as a Second or Foreign Language, B
Theology and Religious Vocations, MD
Theology/Theological Studies, B
Transportation/Transportation Management, BM
Urban Studies/Affairs, B
Urban and Regional Planning, MD
Violin, Viola, Guitar and Other Stringed Instruments, B
Voice and Opera, B
Water Resources Engineering, MD
Wildlife Biology, B
Zoology/Animal Biology, B

TÉLÉ-UNIVERSITÉ

Business Administration and Management, B
Computer Science, D
Distance Education Development, M
Education, B
Finance and Banking, M
Liberal Arts and Sciences Studies and Humanities, B
Mass Communication/Media Studies, B

UNIVERSITÉ LAVAL

Accounting, MO
Actuarial Science, B
Advertising and Public Relations, O
Aerospace, Aeronautical and Astronautical Engineering, M
Agricultural Economics, BM
Agricultural Engineering, M
Agricultural Sciences, MDO
Agronomy and Crop Science, B
Agronomy and Soil Sciences, MD
Allopathic Medicine, DO
Anatomy, B
Anesthesiologist Assistant, O
Animal Sciences, MD
Anthropology, ABMD
Archeology, BMD
Architecture, BM
Art History, Criticism and Conservation, ABMD
Art Teacher Education, B
Biochemistry, BMDO

Biological and Biomedical Sciences, MDO
Biology/Biological Sciences, B
Business Administration and Management, B
Business Administration, Management and Operations, MO
Cancer Biology/Oncology, O
Cardiovascular Sciences, O
Cell Biology and Anatomy, MD
Chemical Engineering, BMD
Chemistry, BMD
Civil Engineering, BMDO
Classics and Classical Languages, Literatures, and Linguistics, B
Clinical Psychology, D
Commercial and Advertising Art, B
Communication Disorders, M
Community Health and Preventive Medicine, MDO
Community Psychology, D
Comparative Literature, ABMD
Composition, M
Computer Engineering, B
Computer Science, BMD
Computer Software Engineering, B
Consumer Economics, O
Consumer Services and Advocacy, B
Counselor Education/School Counseling and Guidance Services, BMD
Curriculum and Instruction, MD
Dentistry, D
Drama and Dramatics/Theatre Arts, AB
Econometrics and Quantitative Economics, B
Economics, BMD
Education, MDO
Educational Administration and Supervision, MD
Educational Leadership and Administration, O
Educational Measurement and Evaluation, MD
Educational Media/Instructional Technology, MD
Educational Psychology, MD
Electrical Engineering, MD
Electrical, Electronics and Communications Engineering, B
Electronic Commerce, MO
Elementary Education and Teaching, B
Emergency Medical Services, O
Engineering, B
Engineering Physics, B
Engineering and Applied Sciences, MDO
English, MD
English Language and Literature, AB
Entrepreneurship/Entrepreneurial Studies, O
Environmental Engineering Technology/Environmental Technology, M
Environmental Policy, M
Environmental Sciences, M
Environmental Studies, BM
Environmental and Occupational Health, O
Environmental/Environmental Health Engineering, B
Epidemiology, MD
Ethics, O
Ethnic and Cultural Studies, MD
Ethnic, Cultural Minority, and Gender Studies, A
Facilities Planning and Management, M
Film, Television, and Video Theory and Criticism, MD
Finance and Banking, M
Fine Arts and Art Studies, M
Fine/Studio Arts, B
Food Science, B
Food Science and Technology, MD
Foods, Nutrition, and Wellness Studies, B
Forest Management/Forest Resources Management, B
Forestry, BMD
French Language Teacher Education, B
French Language and Literature, AB
Geodetic Sciences, MD
Geographic Information Systems, M
Geography, ABMD
Geography Teacher Education, B
Geological/Geophysical Engineering, B
Geology/Earth Science, BMD
Geosciences, MD
Gerontology, O
Graphic Design, M
Health Physics/Radiological Health, O
History, BMD

History Teacher Education, B
Immunology, MD
Industrial and Labor Relations, MD
Industrial/Management Engineering, O
Infectious Diseases, O
Insurance, A
International Affairs, MD
International Business/Trade/Commerce, M
Jazz/Jazz Studies, A
Journalism, O
Kindergarten/PreSchool Education and Teaching, B
Kinesiology and Exercise Science, B
Kinesiology and Movement Studies, MD
Labor and Industrial Relations, AB
Language Interpretation and Translation, B
Law and Legal Studies, BMDO
Legal and Justice Studies, O
Linguistics, BMD
Management, MDO
Management Information Systems and Services, M
Marketing, M
Mass Communication/Media Studies, BMD
Mathematics, BMD
Mathematics Teacher Education, B
Mathematics and Computer Science, B
Mechanical Engineering, BMD
Medical Microbiology and Bacteriology, B
Metallurgical Engineering, BMD
Microbiology, MD
Mineral/Mining Engineering, MD
Mining and Mineral Engineering, B
Modeling and Simulation, M
Modern Languages, B
Molecular Biology, MD
Multi-/Interdisciplinary Studies, B
Museology/Museum Studies, O
Music, BMD
Music Teacher Education, BMD
Musicology and Ethnomusicology, MD
Neurobiology and Neurophysiology, MD
Nursing, MDO
Nutritional Sciences, BMD
Occupational Therapy/Therapist, B
Oceanography, Chemical and Physical, D
Oral and Dental Sciences, MO
Organizational Management, M
Pathology/Experimental Pathology, O
Pharmaceutical Sciences, MDO
Pharmacy, B
Pharmacy, Pharmaceutical Sciences, and Administration, B
Philosophy, ABMD
Physical Education Teaching and Coaching, B
Physical Therapy/Therapist, B
Physics, BMD
Physiology, MD
Plant Biology, MD
Political Science and Government, ABMD
Pre-Dentistry Studies, B
Pre-Law Studies, B
Pre-Medicine/Pre-Medical Studies, B
Pre-Pharmacy Studies, B
Psychology, BD
Rabbinical Studies, AB
Religion/Religious Studies, MD
Rural Planning and Studies, O
Science Teacher Education/General Science Teacher Education, B
Secondary Education and Teaching, B
Social Work, BMD
Sociology, BMD
Software Engineering, O
Spanish Language and Literature, BMD
Statistics, BM
Survey Technology/Surveying, B
Teaching English as a Second or Foreign Language/ESL Language Instructor, B
Teaching French as a Second or Foreign Language, B
Technical Teacher Education, B
Theater, MD
Theology and Religious Vocations, MD
Theology/Theological Studies, AB
Translation and Interpretation, MO
Urban Forestry, B
Urban and Regional Planning, MD

Women's Studies, O
Wood Science and Wood Products/Pulp and Paper Technology, B

UNIVERSITÉ DE MONTRÉAL

Actuarial Science, B
Allopathic Medicine, D
Ancient Studies/Civilization, B
Anthropology, BMD
Applied Mathematics, B
Archeology, B
Architecture, B
Art History, Criticism and Conservation, BMD
Art/Art Studies, General, B
Asian Studies/Civilization, B
Audiology/Audiologist and Hearing Sciences, B
Audiology/Audiologist and Speech-Language Pathology/Pathologist, B
Bible/Biblical Studies, B
Biochemistry, BMDO
Biochemistry, Biophysics and Molecular Biology, B
Bioethics/Medical Ethics, MO
Bioinformatics, BMD
Biological and Biomedical Sciences, MD
Biology/Biological Sciences, B
Biomedical Engineering, MDO
Biomedical Sciences, B
Cell Biology and Anatomy, MD
Chemical Engineering, B
Chemistry, BMD
Cinematography and Film/Video Production, B
Classics and Classical Languages, Literatures, and Linguistics, BM
Cognitive Sciences, B
Communication Disorders, MO
Communication and Media Studies, MD
Community Health and Preventive Medicine, MDO
Comparative Literature, BMD
Composition, MD
Computer Science, BMD
Criminal Justice/Police Science, B
Criminology, BMD
Curriculum and Instruction, MDO
Demography and Population Studies, B
Dental Hygiene/Hygienist, O
Developmental Psychology, MD
East Asian Studies, B
Economics, BMDO
Education, BMDO
Educational Administration and Supervision, MDO
Educational Psychology, MDO
Electronic Commerce, M
Elementary Education and Teaching, B
Emergency Management, O
English, MD
English Language and Literature, B
Environmental Design/Architecture, MDO
Environmental Policy and Resource Management, O
Environmental and Occupational Health, M
Ergonomics and Human Factors, O
Film, Television, and Video Theory and Criticism, MD
Film/Cinema Studies, B
Foods, Nutrition, and Wellness Studies, B
Foreign Language Teacher Education, B
French Language Teacher Education, B
French Language and Literature, BMD
Genetic Counseling/Counselor, O
Genetics, O
Geography, BMDO
Geography Teacher Education, B
Geology/Earth Science, B
German Language and Literature, BMD
German Studies, B
Health Services Administration, MO
Hispanic and Latin American Languages, D
Hispanic-American, Puerto Rican, and Mexican-American/Chicano Studies, B
History, BMD
Human Nutrition, B
Human Services, D
Immunology, MD
Industrial Design, B
Industrial and Labor Relations, MDO
Information Science/Studies, MD

Interior Design, B
International Affairs, MO
International/Global Studies, B
Italian Studies, B
Jazz/Jazz Studies, B
Kindergarten/PreSchool Education and Teaching, B
Kinesiology and Exercise Science, B
Kinesiology and Movement Studies, MDO
Labor and Industrial Relations, B
Landscape Architecture, B
Language Interpretation and Translation, B
Law and Legal Studies, BMDO
Library Science, MD
Linguistics, BMDO
Mass Communication/Media Studies, B
Mathematical and Computational Finance, MO
Mathematics, BMDO
Mathematics Teacher Education, B
Medical Microbiology and Bacteriology, B
Medieval and Renaissance Studies, B
Microbiological Sciences and Immunology, B
Microbiology, BMD
Modern Languages, B
Molecular Biology, MD
Museology/Museum Studies, M
Music, BMDO
Music Performance, B
Music Theory and Composition, B
Musicology and Ethnomusicology, B
Neuroscience, MD
Nursing, MDO
Nutritional Sciences, BMDO
Occupational Therapy/Therapist, BO
Optometry, D
Oral Biology, M
Oral and Dental Sciences, MO
Orthodontics, M
Pathology/Experimental Pathology, MD
Pedodontics, M
Pharmaceutical Sciences, MDO
Pharmacology, MD
Pharmacy, B
Philosophy, BMD
Physical Education Teaching and Coaching, BMDO
Physical Therapy/Therapist, B
Physics, BMD
Physiology, MD
Playwriting and Screenwriting, B
Political Communication, B
Political Science and Government, BMD
Population Studies, MD
Pre-Dentistry Studies, B
Pre-Law Studies, B
Pre-Medicine/Pre-Medical Studies, B
Pre-Pharmacy Studies, B
Pre-Veterinary Studies, B
Psychology, BMD
Public Health, DO
Public Policy Analysis, O
Rehabilitation Sciences, O
Rehabilitation and Therapeutic Professions, B
Religion/Religious Studies, BMD
Secondary Education and Teaching, B
Social Sciences, B
Social Work, BMDO
Sociology, BMD
Spanish Language and Literature, M
Special Education and Teaching, B
Statistics, BMDO
Taxation, M
Theology and Religious Vocations, MDO
Theology/Theological Studies, B
Toxicology, O
Translation and Interpretation, MDO
Urban Planning, M
Urban Studies/Affairs, B
Urban and Regional Planning, O
Veterinary Medicine, D
Veterinary Sciences, MD
Virology, D
Vision Science/Physiological Optics, MO

Voice and Opera, B

UNIVERSITÉ DU QUÉBEC EN ABITIBI-TÉMISCAMINGUE

Accounting, B
Behavioral Sciences, B
Biological and Biomedical Sciences, M
Business Administration and Management, B
Business Administration, Management and Operations, M
Business Teacher Education, B
Education, BMDO
Electrical, Electronics and Communications Engineering, B
Electromechanical Technology/Electromechanical Engineering Technology, B
Elementary Education and Teaching, B
Engineering, B
Engineering Mechanics, B
Engineering and Applied Sciences, MO
Environmental Sciences, MD
Forestry, M
Kindergarten/PreSchool Education and Teaching, B
Mechanical Engineering, B
Mechanical Engineering/Mechanical Technology/Technician, B
Mineral/Mining Engineering, MO
Mining and Mineral Engineering, B
Natural Resources Management/Development and Policy, M
Project Management, MO
Psychology, B
Secondary Education and Teaching, B
Social Sciences, B
Social Work, BM
Special Education and Teaching, B

UNIVERSITÉ DU QUÉBEC À CHICOUTIMI

Accounting, B
Art Teacher Education, B
Art/Art Studies, General, B
Biology/Biological Sciences, B
Business Administration and Management, B
Business Administration, Management and Operations, M
Business Teacher Education, B
Canadian Studies, M
Chemistry, B
Comparative Literature, BM
Computer Engineering, B
Computer Science, B
Education, MD
Elementary Education and Teaching, B
Engineering, B
Engineering and Applied Sciences, MD
English Language and Literature, B
Environmental Policy and Resource Management, M
Ethics, O
Fine Arts and Art Studies, M
French Language and Literature, BO
Genetics, M
Geography, B
Geological/Geophysical Engineering, B
Geology/Earth Science, B
Geosciences, M
History, B
Information Science/Studies, B
Kindergarten/PreSchool Education and Teaching, B
Linguistics, BM
Management Information Systems and Services, B
Mathematics, B
Mineralogy, D
Modern Languages, B
Physical Education Teaching and Coaching, B
Physical Sciences, B
Physics, B
Political Science and Government, B
Project Management, M
Psychology, B
Religious Education, B
Science Teacher Education/General Science Teacher Education, B
Secondary Education and Teaching, B
Social Sciences, B

Social Work, B
Special Education and Teaching, B
Teaching English as a Second or Foreign Language/ESL Language Instructor, B
Theology and Religious Vocations, MD
Theology/Theological Studies, B
Trade and Industrial Teacher Education, B

UNIVERSITÉ DU QUÉBEC, ÉCOLE DE TECHNOLOGIE SUPÉRIEURE

Computer Software Engineering, B
Construction Engineering, B
Electrical, Electronics and Communications Engineering, B
Engineering, B
Engineering and Applied Sciences, MDO
Information Technology, B
Logistics and Materials Management, B
Mechanical Engineering, B

UNIVERSITÉ DU QUÉBEC À MONTRÉAL

Accounting, BMO
Actuarial Science, O
Art History, Criticism and Conservation, BMD
Art/Art Studies, General, B
Atmospheric Sciences and Meteorology, MDO
Biochemistry, B
Biological and Biomedical Sciences, MD
Biology/Biological Sciences, B
Business Administration and Management, B
Business Administration, Management and Operations, MDO
Chemistry, BMD
Commercial and Advertising Art, B
Communication and Media Studies, MD
Comparative Literature, BMD
Counselor Education/School Counseling and Guidance Services, B
Dance, BM
Drama and Dramatics/Theatre Arts, B
Economics, BMD
Education, BMDO
Elementary Education and Teaching, B
Environmental Design/Architecture, B
Environmental Education, O
Environmental Sciences, MDO
Environmental and Occupational Health, O
Ergonomics and Human Factors, O
Fashion/Apparel Design, B
Finance and Banking, O
Fine Arts and Art Studies, M
Geographic Information Systems, O
Geography, BM
Geology/Earth Science, BM
Geosciences, MDO
History, BMD
Hotel/Motel Administration/Management, B
Kindergarten/PreSchool Education and Teaching, B
Kinesiology and Movement Studies, M
Law and Legal Studies, BO
Linguistics, BMD
Management Information Systems and Services, BM
Mass Communication/Media Studies, B
Mathematics, BMD
Meteorology, DO
Mineralogy, D
Museology/Museum Studies, M
Music, B
Music History, Literature, and Theory, B
Music Teacher Education, B
Music Therapy/Therapist, B
Natural Resources and Conservation, O
Parks, Recreation, Leisure and Fitness Studies, B
Philosophy, BMD
Physical Education Teaching and Coaching, B
Physics, B
Political Science and Government, BMD
Project Management, MO
Psychology, BD
Public Administration, M
Religion/Religious Studies, BMD
Religious Education, B
Science Teacher Education/General Science Teacher Education, B

Science, Technology and Society, B
Secondary Education and Teaching, B
Social Work, BM
Sociology, BMD
Special Education and Teaching, B
Teaching English as a Second or Foreign
   Language/ESL Language Instructor, B
Trade and Industrial Teacher Education, B
Urban Studies/Affairs, BMD

UNIVERSITÉ DU QUÉBEC EN OUTAOUAIS

Accounting, BMO
Art/Art Studies, General, B
Business Administration and Management, B
Computer Engineering, B
Computer Science, BMDO
Design and Visual Communications, B
Education, BMDO
Educational Psychology, M
Elementary Education and Teaching, B
Finance and Banking, MO
Fine/Studio Arts, B
Foreign Language Teacher Education, O
Human Resources Management and Services, B
Industrial and Labor Relations, MDO
International Business/Trade/Commerce, B
Kindergarten/PreSchool Education and Teaching, B
Labor and Industrial Relations, B
Language Interpretation and Translation, B
Management Information Systems and Services, B
Nursing, MO
Project Management, MO
Psychology, B
Secondary Education and Teaching, B
Social Sciences, B
Social Work, BM
Sociology, B
Special Education and Teaching, B
Urban and Regional Planning, M

UNIVERSITÉ DU QUÉBEC À RIMOUSKI

Accounting, B
Biology/Biological Sciences, B
Business Administration and Management, B
Business Administration, Management and Opera-
   tions, M
Business Teacher Education, B
Chemistry, B
Comparative Literature, BMD
Computer Science, B
Education, MDO
Elementary Education and Teaching, B
Engineering, B
Engineering and Applied Sciences, M
Ethics, MO
Fish, Game and Wildlife Management, MDO
French Language and Literature, B
Geography, B
History, B
Kindergarten/PreSchool Education and Teaching, B
Management, MO
Marine Affairs, MO
Mathematics, B
Nursing, MO
Oceanography, Chemical and Physical, MD
Project Management, MO
Religion/Religious Studies, B
Religious Education, B
Science Teacher Education/General Science
   Teacher Education, B
Secondary Education and Teaching, B
Social Psychology, M
Sociology, B
Special Education and Teaching, B
Theology/Theological Studies, B
Trade and Industrial Teacher Education, B
Urban and Regional Planning, MDO

UNIVERSITÉ DU QUÉBEC À TROIS-RIVIÈRES

Accounting, BM
Adult and Continuing Education and Teaching, B
Art Teacher Education, B
Art/Art Studies, General, B
Artificial Intelligence and Robotics, B

Biochemistry, B
Biology/Biological Sciences, B
Biomedical Sciences, B
Biophysics, BMD
Business Administration and Management, B
Business Administration, Management and Opera-
   tions, MD
Business/Managerial Economics, B
Chemical Engineering, B
Chemistry, BM
Chiropractic, D
Communication and Media Studies, MO
Comparative Literature, M
Computer Engineering, B
Computer Programming/Programmer, B
Computer Science, BM
Computer Systems Analysis/Analyst, B
Economics, B
Education, BMD
Education/Teaching of Individuals with Mental Retar-
   dation, B
Educational Administration and Supervision, O
Educational Psychology, MD
Electrical Engineering, MD
Electrical, Electronics and Communications Engi-
   neering, B
Elementary Education and Teaching, B
Engineering Mechanics, B
Engineering/Industrial Management, B
English/Language Arts Teacher Education, B
Entrepreneurship/Entrepreneurial Studies, B
Environmental Sciences, MD
Finance and Banking, O
French Language and Literature, B
Geography, B
Health Professions and Related Clinical Sciences, B
Health and Physical Education, B
History, B
Human Resources Management/Personnel Adminis-
   tration, B
Industrial Engineering, B
Industrial and Labor Relations, O
Industrial/Management Engineering, MO
Information Science/Studies, B
Kindergarten/PreSchool Education and Teaching, B
Leisure Studies, MO
Mass Communication/Media Studies, B
Mathematics, BM
Mathematics Teacher Education, B
Mechanical Engineering, B
Nursing, MO
Operations Research, B
Parks, Recreation, Leisure and Fitness Studies, B
Philosophy, BMD
Physical Education Teaching and Coaching, M
Physics, BMD
Psychology, BDO
Secondary Education and Teaching, B
Theology/Theological Studies, B
Travel and Tourism, MO

UNIVERSITÉ DE SHERBROOKE

Accounting, BM
Allopathic Medicine, D
Athletic Training and Sports Medicine, B
Biochemistry, BMD
Biological and Biomedical Sciences, MDO
Biology/Biological Sciences, B
Biophysics, MD
Business Administration and Management, B
Business Administration, Management and Opera-
   tions, MD
Canadian Studies, MD
Cell Biology and Anatomy, MD
Chemical Engineering, BMD
Chemistry, BMDO
Civil Engineering, BMD
Clinical Laboratory Sciences, MD
Communication and Media Studies, B
Comparative Literature, MD
Computer Engineering, B
Computer Programming/Programmer, B
Computer Science, B
Computer and Information Sciences, B
Computer and Information Systems Security, M

Conflict Resolution and Mediation/Peace Stud-
   ies, M
Corporate and Organizational Communication, M
Counselor Education/School Counseling and Guid-
   ance Services, B
Ecology, B
Economic Development, D
Economics, M
Education, BMO
Educational Administration and Supervision, M
Electrical Engineering, MD
Electrical, Electronics and Communications Engi-
   neering, B
Electronic Commerce, M
Elementary Education and Teaching, BMO
Engineering Management, MO
Engineering and Applied Sciences, MDO
English Language and Literature, B
Environmental Engineering
   Technology/Environmental Technology, M
Environmental Sciences, MO
Environmental Studies, B
Ethics, O
Finance, B
Finance and Banking, M
French Language and Literature, BMD
Geography, MD
Gerontology, M
Health Law, MO
Higher Education/Higher Education Administra-
   tion, MO
History, BM
Immunology, MD
Information Science/Studies, BMD
Information Technology, B
International Business/Trade/Commerce, M
Kindergarten/PreSchool Education and Teaching, B
Kinesiology and Exercise Science, B
Kinesiology and Movement Studies, M
Law and Legal Studies, BMDO
Linguistics, M
Management, O
Management Information Systems and Ser-
   vices, MO
Marketing, M
Marketing/Marketing Management, B
Mathematics, BMD
Mechanical Engineering, BMD
Medical Microbiology and Bacteriology, B
Microbiology, MD
Organizational Behavior Studies, M
Pharmacology, MD
Philosophy, BMD
Physical Education Teaching and Coaching, BMO
Physics, BMD
Physiology, MD
Pre-Medicine/Pre-Medical Studies, B
Psychology, BM
Public Administration, M
Radiation Biology/Radiobiology, MD
Religion/Religious Studies, M
Secondary Education and Teaching, B
Social Work, BM
Special Education and Teaching, BMO
Taxation, M
Theater, M
Theology and Religious Vocations, MDO

Saskatchewan

BRIERCREST COLLEGE

Bible/Biblical Studies, AB
Business Administration and Management, B
Divinity/Ministry (BD, MDiv.), B
Humanities/Humanistic Studies, AB
International/Global Studies, AB
Missions/Missionary Studies and Missiology, B
Religion/Religious Studies, B
Religious/Sacred Music, AB
Social Sciences, A
Teaching English as a Second or Foreign
   Language/ESL Language Instructor, B
Theology/Theological Studies, B

Youth Ministry, B

ESTON COLLEGE

Bible/Biblical Studies, B

HORIZON COLLEGE & SEMINARY

Bible/Biblical Studies, B
Christian Studies, B
Missions/Missionary Studies and Missiology, B
Pastoral Counseling and Specialized Ministries, B
Pastoral Studies/Counseling, B
Religious/Sacred Music, B
Theological and Ministerial Studies, B
Theology and Religious Vocations, B
Theology/Theological Studies, B
Youth Ministry, B

UNIVERSITY OF REGINA

Accounting, B
Acting, B
Actuarial Science, B
Adult and Continuing Education and Teaching, BM
American Indian/Native American Languages, Literatures, and Linguistics, B
American Indian/Native American Studies, B
Analytical Chemistry, MD
Anthropology, BM
Applied Economics, M
Applied Psychology, MD
Art History, Criticism and Conservation, B
Art Teacher Education, B
Bilingual and Multilingual Education, B
Biochemistry, BMD
Biochemistry, Biophysics and Molecular Biology, B
Biological and Biomedical Sciences, MD
Biological and Physical Sciences, B
Biology Teacher Education, B
Biology/Biological Sciences, B
Biophysics, MD
Business Administration and Management, B
Business Administration, Management and Operations, MO
Business Teacher Education, B
Business/Commerce, B
Canadian Studies, MD
Cancer Biology/Oncology, MD
Cell/Cellular and Molecular Biology, B
Ceramic Arts and Ceramics, BM
Chemical Technology/Technician, B
Chemistry, BMD
Chemistry Teacher Education, B
Chinese Language and Literature, B
Cinematography and Film/Video Production, B
Classics and Classical Languages, Literatures, and Linguistics, B
Clinical Laboratory Science/Medical Technology/Technologist, B
Clinical Psychology, MD
Composition, M
Computer Engineering, MD
Computer Science, BMD
Computer Software Engineering, B
Criminal Justice/Law Enforcement Administration, B
Criminal Justice/Police Science, B
Criminal Justice/Safety Studies, B
Criminology, M
Curriculum and Instruction, M
Drama and Dance Teacher Education, B
Drama and Dramatics/Theatre Arts, B
Drawing, B
Early Childhood Education and Teaching, B
Ecology, Evolution, Systematics and Population Biology, B
Economics, BO
Education, BMDO
Educational Administration and Supervision, M
Educational Psychology, M
Electrical, Electronics and Communications Engineering, B
Elementary Education and Teaching, B
Engineering, B
Engineering Management, M
Engineering and Applied Sciences, MD
English, M
English Language and Literature, B
English/Language Arts Teacher Education, B

Entrepreneurship/Entrepreneurial Studies, B
Environmental Biology, B
Environmental Engineering Technology/Environmental Technology, MD
Environmental Health, B
Environmental Studies, B
Environmental/Environmental Health Engineering, B
Experimental Psychology, MD
Film, Television, and Video Production, M
Film/Cinema Studies, B
Finance, B
Fine Arts and Art Studies, BM
Fine/Studio Arts, B
French Language Teacher Education, B
French Language and Literature, BM
Geography, BMD
Geology/Earth Science, BMD
German Language and Literature, B
Gerontology, BM
Health Services Administration, MO
Health Teacher Education, B
Health and Physical Education, B
Health/Medical Preparatory Programs, B
History, BM
Human Resources Development, M
Human Resources Management and Services, MO
Human Resources Management/Personnel Administration, B
Humanities/Humanistic Studies, B
Indian/Native American Education, B
Industrial Engineering, B
Industrial/Management Engineering, MD
Inorganic Chemistry, MD
Intercultural/Multicultural and Diversity Studies, B
Interdisciplinary Studies, M
Intermedia/Multimedia, B
International Business/Trade/Commerce, BM
International/Global Studies, B
Japanese Language and Literature, B
Journalism, BM
Junior High/Intermediate/Middle School Education and Teaching, B
Kindergarten/PreSchool Education and Teaching, B
Kinesiology and Exercise Science, B
Kinesiology and Movement Studies, MD
Law Enforcement, M
Liberal Arts and Sciences Studies and Humanities, B
Linguistics, BM
Marketing/Marketing Management, B
Mathematics, BMD
Mathematics Teacher Education, B
Mathematics and Computer Science, B
Mathematics and Statistics, B
Medieval and Renaissance Studies, B
Music, BM
Music History, Literature, and Theory, B
Music Teacher Education, B
Music Theory and Composition, BM
Musicology and Ethnomusicology, M
Nursing, M
Organic Chemistry, MD
Organizational Management, O
Painting, BM
Performance, M
Petroleum Engineering, BMD
Philosophy, BM
Physical Education Teaching and Coaching, B
Physics, BMD
Physics Teacher Education, B
Political Science and Government, BM
Pre-Dentistry Studies, B
Pre-Law Studies, B
Pre-Medicine/Pre-Medical Studies, B
Pre-Pharmacy Studies, B
Pre-Veterinary Studies, B
Printmaking, B
Project Management, O
Psychology, BMD
Public Administration, MO
Public Policy Analysis, MDO
Regional Studies (U.S., Canadian, Foreign), B
Religion/Religious Studies, BM
Science Teacher Education/General Science Teacher Education, B
Sculpture, BM

Secondary Education and Teaching, B
Social Sciences, BM
Social Studies Teacher Education, B
Social Work, BMD
Sociology, BM
Software Engineering, M
Spanish Language and Literature, B
Sport and Fitness Administration/Management, B
Statistics, BMD
Systems Engineering, MD
Teacher Education and Professional Development, Specific Subject Areas, B
Technical Theatre/Theatre Design and Technology, B
Theoretical Chemistry, MD
Visual and Performing Arts, B
Women's Studies, BM
Writing, M

UNIVERSITY OF SASKATCHEWAN

Accounting, BM
Agribusiness, B
Agricultural Economics, BMDO
Agricultural Sciences, MDO
Agriculture, Agriculture Operations and Related Sciences, B
Agronomy and Crop Science, B
Agronomy and Soil Sciences, MDO
Allopathic Medicine, D
American Indian/Native American Studies, B
Anatomy, MD
Animal Sciences, BMD
Anthropology, BM
Archeology, BMD
Art History, Criticism and Conservation, B
BioTechnology, BM
Biochemistry, BMD
Bioengineering, MD
Bioinformatics, B
Biological and Biomedical Sciences, MD
Biology/Biological Sciences, B
Biomedical Engineering, MD
Biomedical Sciences, B
Business Administration and Management, B
Business Administration, Management and Operations, M
Business/Managerial Economics, B
Canadian Studies, MD
Cell Biology and Anatomy, BMD
Chemical Engineering, BMD
Chemistry, BMD
City/Urban, Community and Regional Planning, B
Civil Engineering, BMD
Community Health and Preventive Medicine, MD
Computer Engineering, B
Computer Science, BMD
Curriculum and Instruction, MDO
Dentistry, D
Digital Communication and Media/Multimedia, B
Drama and Dramatics/Theatre Arts, B
East European and Russian Studies, M
Ecology, B
Economics, BMO
Education, BMDO
Educational Administration and Supervision, MDO
Educational Psychology, MDO
Electrical Engineering, MDO
Electrical, Electronics and Communications Engineering, B
Engineering Physics, BMD
Engineering and Applied Sciences, MDO
English, MD
English Language and Literature, B
Environmental Biology, B
Environmental Sciences, BM
Environmental/Environmental Health Engineering, B
Epidemiology, MD
Family and Consumer Sciences/Home Economics Teacher Education, B
Finance, B
Finance and Banking, M
Fine Arts and Art Studies, M
Fine/Studio Arts, B
Food Science, B
Food Science and Technology, MD
Foreign Languages and Literatures, B

Foundations and Philosophy of Education, MDO
French Language and Literature, BM
Gender Studies, MD
Geography, BMD
Geological Engineering, MD
Geological/Geophysical Engineering, B
Geology/Earth Science, BMDO
Geophysics and Seismology, B
German Language and Literature, M
Health Services Administration, M
History, BMD
Horticultural Science, B
Human Resources Management/Personnel Administration, B
Immunology, MD
International Business/Trade/Commerce, M
International Trade, MD
International/Global Studies, B
Kinesiology and Exercise Science, B
Kinesiology and Movement Studies, MDO
Land Use Planning and Management/Development, B
Law and Legal Studies, MD
Linguistics, B
Marketing, M

Marketing/Marketing Management, B
Mathematics, BMD
Mechanical Engineering, BMD
Medical Microbiology and Bacteriology, B
Medieval and Renaissance Studies, B
Microbiology, MD
Music, BM
Music Teacher Education, B
Natural Resource Economics, B
Natural Resources Management/Development and Policy, B
Nursing, M
Nutritional Sciences, B
Operations Management and Supervision, B
Pathology/Experimental Pathology, MD
Pharmaceutical Sciences, MD
Pharmacology, BMD
Pharmacy, B
Philosophy, BM
Physical Education Teaching and Coaching, B
Physics, BMD
Physiology, BMD
Plant Sciences, MD
Political Science and Government, BM
Psychology, BMD

Public Administration, B
Public Affairs, MD
Public Policy Analysis, MD
Regional Studies (U.S., Canadian, Foreign), B
Religion/Religious Studies, BM
Reproductive Biology, MD
Russian Language and Literature, B
Secondary Education and Teaching, B
Sociology, BMD
Soil Science and Agronomy, B
Spanish Language and Literature, B
Special Education and Teaching, MDO
Statistics, BMD
Sustainability Management, M
Teacher Education, Multiple Levels, B
Technical Teacher Education, B
Theater, M
Toxicology, BMDO
Trade and Industrial Teacher Education, B
Ukrainian Language and Literature, B
Veterinary Medicine, MD
Veterinary Sciences, MD
Visual and Performing Arts, B
Women's Studies, BMD

ACCOUNTING

United States

Alabama

Alabama Agricultural and Mechanical University, B
Alabama State University, BM
Athens State University, B
Auburn University, BM
Auburn University at Montgomery, B
Chattahoochee Valley Community College, A
Faulkner University, B
George C. Wallace Community College, A
Huntingdon College, B
Jacksonville State University, B
Oakwood University, AB
Samford University, B
Spring Hill College, B
Strayer University - Birmingham Campus, B
Strayer University - Huntsville Campus, B
Talladega College, B
Troy University, BM
Tuskegee University, B
The University of Alabama, BMD
The University of Alabama at Birmingham, BM
The University of Alabama in Huntsville, BM
University of Mobile, B
University of Montevallo, B
University of North Alabama, BM
University of South Alabama, BM
The University of West Alabama, B
Virginia College in Birmingham, AB
Wallace State Community College, A

Alaska

Charter College, A
University of Alaska Anchorage, AB
University of Alaska Anchorage, Kodiak College, A
University of Alaska Anchorage, Matanuska-Susitna College, A
University of Alaska Fairbanks, B

Arizona

Argosy University, Phoenix, D
Arizona State University at the Tempe campus, BMD
Arizona State University at the West campus, B
Arizona Western College, A
Brookline College (Phoenix), A
Central Arizona College, A
Chandler-Gilbert Community College, A
DeVry University (Mesa), B
DeVry University (Phoenix), B
GateWay Community College, A
Grand Canyon University, BM
Mesa Community College, A
Mohave Community College, A
Northern Arizona University, B
Paradise Valley Community College, A
Penn Foster College, A
Phoenix College, A
Pima Community College, A
Scottsdale Community College, A

The University of Arizona, BMD
University of Phoenix - Online Campus, BMO
University of Phoenix - Phoenix Campus, BMO
University of Phoenix - Southern Arizona Campus, BM
Western International University, B
Yavapai College, A

Arkansas

Arkansas State University, BM
Arkansas Tech University, B
Central Baptist College, B
College of the Ouachitas, A
Harding University, B
Henderson State University, B
Hendrix College, BM
John Brown University, B
National Park College, A
NorthWest Arkansas Community College, A
Ouachita Baptist University, B
Southern Arkansas University - Magnolia, B
Strayer University - Little Rock Campus, B
University of Arkansas, BM
University of Arkansas at Little Rock, B
University of Arkansas at Monticello, B
University of Arkansas at Pine Bluff, B
University of Central Arkansas, BM
University of the Ozarks, B

California

Allan Hancock College, A
American River College, A
Argosy University, Inland Empire, D
Argosy University, Los Angeles, D
Argosy University, Orange County, DO
Argosy University, San Diego, D
Argosy University, San Francisco Bay Area, D
Ashford University, B
Azusa Pacific University, B
Bakersfield College, A
Berkeley City College, A
Biola University, B
Butte College, A
California Baptist University, BM
California College San Diego (San Diego), B
California Lutheran University, B
California State Polytechnic University, Pomona, M
California State University, Dominguez Hills, B
California State University, East Bay, B
California State University, Fresno, BM
California State University, Fullerton, BM
California State University, Long Beach, B
California State University, Los Angeles, M
California State University, Northridge, B
California State University, Sacramento, M
California State University, San Bernardino, BM
California State University, San Marcos, B
California State University, Stanislaus, B
Cambridge Junior College, A
Cerritos College, A
Chabot College, A
Chapman University, B
Claremont McKenna College, B
College of the Sequoias, A

Cuyamaca College, A
De Anza College, A
DeVry University (Alhambra), B
DeVry University (Anaheim), B
DeVry University (Bakersfield), AB
DeVry University (Fremont), A
DeVry University (Long Beach), B
DeVry University (Oakland), B
DeVry University (Oxnard), B
DeVry University (Palmdale), B
DeVry University (Pomona), B
DeVry University (Sherman Oaks), B
East Los Angeles College, A
El Camino College, A
Empire College, A
Folsom Lake College, A
Foothill College, A
Fresno Pacific University, B
Glendale Community College, A
Golden Gate University, BMO
Golden West College, A
Holy Names University, B
Humphreys College, AB
Imperial Valley College, A
Irvine Valley College, A
La Sierra University, BM
Lake Tahoe Community College, A
Laney College, A
Las Positas College, A
Lassen Community College District, A
Los Angeles City College, A
Los Angeles Harbor College, A
Los Angeles Mission College, A
Los Angeles Pierce College, A
Los Angeles Southwest College, A
Los Angeles Trade-Technical College, A
Los Angeles Valley College, A
Los Medanos College, A
Loyola Marymount University, BM
The Master's College and Seminary, B
Mendocino College, A
Menlo College, B
Merced College, A
Merritt College, A
Mission College, A
Modesto Junior College, A
Monterey Peninsula College, A
Moorpark College, A
Moreno Valley College, A
Mount Saint Mary's University, B
Mt. San Antonio College, A
Napa Valley College, A
National University, BM
Norco College, A
Ohlone College, A
Orange Coast College, A
Pacific States University, M
Pasadena City College, A
Pepperdine University, B
Point Loma Nazarene University, B
Reedley College, A
Riverside City College, A
Sacramento City College, A
Saddleback College, A

Saint Mary's College of California, B
San Bernardino Valley College, A
San Diego City College, A
San Diego Mesa College, A
San Diego Miramar College, A
San Diego State University, BM
San Francisco State University, BM
San Joaquin Delta College, A
San Jose City College, A
San Jose State University, BM
Santa Ana College, A
Santa Barbara City College, A
Santa Clara University, B
Santa Monica College, A
Santiago Canyon College, A
Scripps College, B
Shasta College, A
Sierra College, A
Simpson University, B
Skyline College, A
Solano Community College, A
Southern California Institute of Technology, B
Southwestern College, A
Taft College, A
University of California, Berkeley, DO
University of California, Davis, M
University of California, Irvine, M
University of California, Los Angeles, D
University of California, Riverside, M
University of La Verne, BM
University of Phoenix - Bay Area Campus, BM
University of Phoenix - Central Valley Campus, BM
University of Phoenix - Sacramento Valley Campus,
    BM
University of Phoenix - San Diego Campus, BM
University of Phoenix - Southern California Campus,
    BM
University of Redlands, B
University of San Diego, BM
University of San Francisco, B
University of Southern California, BM
Vanguard University of Southern California, B
Ventura College, A
West Hills Community College, A
West Los Angeles College, A
West Valley College, A
Woodbury University, B
Yuba College, A

Colorado

Adams State University, B
Argosy University, Denver, D
CollegeAmerica - Colorado Springs, B
CollegeAmerica - Denver, B
CollegeAmerica - Fort Collins, B
Colorado Christian University, B
Colorado Heights University, M
Colorado Mesa University, B
Colorado Mountain College (Glenwood Springs), A
Colorado Mountain College (Leadville), A
Colorado Mountain College (Steamboat Springs), A
Colorado Northwestern Community College, A
Colorado State University, BM
Colorado State University - Global Campus, M
Colorado State University - Pueblo, B
Colorado Technical University Colorado Springs,
    ABM
Colorado Technical University Denver South, ABM
Colorado Technical University Online, AB
Community College of Denver, A
DeVry University (Colorado Springs), AB
DeVry University (Westminster), B
Everest College (Colorado Springs), A
Everest College (Thornton), A
Fort Lewis College, B
Lamar Community College, A
Metropolitan State University of Denver, BM
National American University (Colorado Springs),
    AB
National American University (Denver), AB
Northeastern Junior College, A
Regis University, BM
University of Colorado Boulder, BMD
University of Colorado Denver, M
University of Denver, BM
University of Northern Colorado, M

University of Phoenix - Colorado Campus, BM
University of Phoenix - Colorado Springs Downtown
    Campus, BM
Western State Colorado University, B

Connecticut

Albertus Magnus College, BM
Central Connecticut State University, B
Eastern Connecticut State University, B
Fairfield University, BMO
Gateway Community College, A
Housatonic Community College, A
Manchester Community College, A
Middlesex Community College, A
Northwestern Connecticut Community College, A
Norwalk Community College, A
Post University, ABM
Quinebaug Valley Community College, A
Quinnipiac University, B
Sacred Heart University, BMO
Southern Connecticut State University, B
Three Rivers Community College, A
Tunxis Community College, A
University of Bridgeport, BM
University of Connecticut, BMD
University of Hartford, BMO
University of New Haven, BMO
University of Saint Joseph, B
Western Connecticut State University, BM
Yale University, D

Delaware

Delaware State University, B
Delaware Technical & Community College, Jack F.
    Owens Campus, A
Delaware Technical & Community College,
    Stanton/Wilmington Campus, A
Delaware Technical & Community College, Terry
    Campus, A
Goldey-Beacom College, AB
Strayer University - Christiana Campus, B
University of Delaware, BM
Wesley College, B
Wilmington University, BM

District of Columbia

American University, B
The Catholic University of America, BM
Gallaudet University, B
The George Washington University, BM
Georgetown University, B
Howard University, BM
Strayer University - Takoma Park Campus, B
Strayer University - Washington Campus, B
University of the District of Columbia, B
University of Phoenix - Washington D.C. Campus,
    BM
University of the Potomac, AB

Florida

Argosy University, Sarasota, DO
Argosy University, Tampa, D
Ave Maria University, B
Barry University, BM
Bethune-Cookman University, B
Broward College, A
Chipola College, A
City College (Fort Lauderdale), AB
City College (Miami), AB
College of Business and Technology - Cutler Bay
    Campus, A
College of Business and Technology - Flagler Cam-
    pus, A
College of Business and Technology - Main Cam-
    pus, A
Daytona State College, A
DeVry University (Jacksonville), AB
DeVry University (Miramar), B
DeVry University (Orlando), B
Everest University (Largo), ABM
Everest University (Orlando), ABM
Everest University (Tampa), ABM
Flagler College, B
Florida Agricultural and Mechanical University, BM
Florida Atlantic University, BMD
Florida Gulf Coast University, BM

Florida International University, BM
Florida Memorial University, B
Florida National University, B
Florida Southern College, B
Florida State University, BMD
Fortis College (Orange Park), A
Hobe Sound Bible College, A
Hodges University, M
Indian River State College, A
Jacksonville University, BM
Jose Maria Vargas University, A
Keiser University, ABM
Millennia Atlantic University, ABM
Nova Southeastern University, B
Palm Beach Atlantic University, B
Palm Beach State College, A
Pensacola State College, A
Polytechnic University of Puerto Rico, Miami Cam-
    pus, M
Polytechnic University of Puerto Rico, Orlando
    Campus, M
Rasmussen College Fort Myers, AB
Rasmussen College Land O' Lakes, AB
Rasmussen College New Port Richey, AB
Rasmussen College Ocala, AB
Rasmussen College Tampa/Brandon, AB
Saint Leo University, BM
St. Thomas University, BMO
Seminole State College of Florida, A
South Florida State College, A
Southeastern University, B
Southern Technical College (Fort Myers), AB
State College of Florida Manatee-Sarasota, A
Stetson University, BM
Strayer University - Baymeadows Campus, B
Strayer University - Brickell Campus, B
Strayer University - Coral Springs Campus, B
Strayer University - Doral Campus, B
Strayer University - Fort Lauderdale Campus, B
Strayer University - Maitland Campus, B
Strayer University - Miramar Campus, B
Strayer University - Orlando East Campus, B
Strayer University - Palm Beach Gardens Campus,
    B
Strayer University - Sand Lake Campus, B
Strayer University - Tampa East Campus, B
Strayer University - Tampa Westshore Campus, B
University of Central Florida, BM
University of Florida, BMD
University of Fort Lauderdale, B
University of Miami, BM
University of North Florida, BM
University of Phoenix - Central Florida Campus, B
University of Phoenix - North Florida Campus, BM
University of Phoenix - South Florida Campus, BM
University of South Florida, BMD
University of South Florida, St. Petersburg, B
University of South Florida Sarasota-Manatee, B
The University of Tampa, BM
University of West Florida, BM
Webber International University, ABM

Georgia

Abraham Baldwin Agricultural College, A
Albany State University, BM
Albany Technical College, A
Argosy University, Atlanta, D
Ashworth College, A
Athens Technical College, A
Atlanta Technical College, A
Augusta Technical College, A
Augusta University, B
Bainbridge State College, A
Berry College, B
Brenau University, BM
Brewton-Parker College, B
Central Georgia Technical College, A
Chattahoochee Technical College, A
Clark Atlanta University, BM
Clayton State University, BM
Columbus State University, B
Columbus Technical College, A
Dalton State College, B
Darton State College, A
DeVry University (Alpharetta), B
DeVry University (Decatur), B

DeVry University (Duluth), B
Emory University, D
Fort Valley State University, B
Georgia College & State University, BM
Georgia Northwestern Technical College, A
Georgia Piedmont Technical College, A
Georgia Southern University, BM
Georgia Southwestern State University, B
Georgia State University, BM
Gwinnett Technical College, A
Kennesaw State University, BM
LaGrange College, B
Lanier Technical College, A
Mercer University, BM
Oconee Fall Line Technical College, A
Ogeechee Technical College, A
Oglethorpe University, B
Point University, B
Reinhardt University, B
Savannah State University, B
Savannah Technical College, A
Shorter University, BM
South Georgia Technical College, A
Southeastern Technical College, A
Southern Crescent Technical College, A
Southern Regional Technical College, A
Strayer University - Augusta Campus, B
Strayer University - Chamblee Campus, B
Strayer University - Cobb County Campus, B
Strayer University - Columbus Campus, B
Strayer University - Douglasville Campus, B
Strayer University - Lithonia Campus, B
Strayer University - Morrow Campus, B
Strayer University - Roswell Campus, B
Strayer University - Savannah Campus, B
Thomas University, B
University of Georgia, BM
University of North Georgia, B
University of Phoenix - Atlanta Campus, BM
University of Phoenix - Augusta Campus, ABM
University of Phoenix - Columbus Georgia Campus, M
University of West Georgia, BM
Valdosta State University, B
Wesleyan College, B
West Georgia Technical College, A
Wiregrass Georgia Technical College, A

Hawaii

Argosy University, Hawai'i, D
Brigham Young University - Hawaii, B
Chaminade University of Honolulu, M
Hawaii Community College, A
Hawai'i Pacific University, ABM
Kapiolani Community College, A
Kauai Community College, A
Leeward Community College, A
University of Hawaii at Hilo, B
University of Hawaii at Manoa, BMD
University of Hawaii Maui College, A
University of Hawaii - West Oahu, B
University of Phoenix - Hawaii Campus, BM

Idaho

Boise State University, BM
Brigham Young University - Idaho, B
Broadview University - Boise, AB
The College of Idaho, B
College of Southern Idaho, A
Eastern Idaho Technical College, A
Idaho State University, B
Northwest Nazarene University, B
Stevens-Henager College (Boise), B
University of Idaho, BM

Illinois

American InterContinental University Online, M
Argosy University, Chicago, D
Argosy University, Schaumburg, DO
Augustana College, B
Aurora University, B
Benedictine University, BM
Black Hawk College, A
Blackburn College, B
Bradley University, BM
Carl Sandburg College, A

City Colleges of Chicago, Harold Washington College, A
City Colleges of Chicago, Harry S. Truman College, A
City Colleges of Chicago, Malcolm X College, A
City Colleges of Chicago, Olive-Harvey College, A
City Colleges of Chicago, Richard J. Daley College, A
City Colleges of Chicago, Wilbur Wright College, A
College of DuPage, A
Concordia University Chicago, B
DePaul University, BM
DeVry University (Downers Grove), M
Dominican University, BM
Eastern Illinois University, BM
Elgin Community College, A
Ellis University, ABM
Elmhurst College, BM
Eureka College, B
Governors State University, BM
Greenville College, B
Harper College, A
Highland Community College, A
Illinois Central College, A
Illinois College, B
Illinois Eastern Community Colleges, Olney Central College, A
Illinois State University, BM
Illinois Valley Community College, A
Illinois Wesleyan University, B
John A. Logan College, A
John Wood Community College, A
Joliet Junior College, A
Judson University, B
Kaskaskia College, A
Lewis and Clark Community College, A
Lewis University, BM
Lincoln Land Community College, A
Loyola University Chicago, BM
MacCormac College, A
MacMurray College, B
McHenry County College, A
McKendree University, B
Midstate College, B
Millikin University, B
Monmouth College, B
Morton College, A
North Central College, B
North Park University, B
Northeastern Illinois University, BM
Northern Illinois University, BM
Northwestern University, MD
Olivet Nazarene University, B
Quincy University, B
Rasmussen College Aurora, A
Rasmussen College Mokena/Tinley Park, A
Rasmussen College Rockford, B
Rasmussen College Romeoville/Joliet, A
Richland Community College, A
Robert Morris University Illinois, BM
Rock Valley College, A
Rockford Career College, A
Rockford University, B
Roosevelt University, BM
Saint Xavier University, B
Sauk Valley Community College, A
Shawnee Community College, A
Solex College, A
South Suburban College, A
Southeastern Illinois College, A
Southern Illinois University Carbondale, BMD
Southern Illinois University Edwardsville, BM
Southwestern Illinois College, A
Spoon River College, A
Trinity Christian College, B
Trinity International University, B
Triton College, A
University of Chicago, M
University of Illinois at Chicago, BM
University of Illinois at Springfield, BM
University of Illinois at Urbana - Champaign, BMD
University of St. Francis, BO
Waubonsee Community College, A
Western Illinois University, BM

Indiana

Anderson University, BM
Ball State University, BM
Bethel College, B
Butler University, BM
Calumet College of Saint Joseph, AB
Franklin College, B
Goshen College, B
Grace College, B
Harrison College, AB
Huntington University, B
Indiana State University, B
Indiana Tech, ABM
Indiana University - Purdue University Fort Wayne, B
Indiana University - Purdue University Indianapolis, M
Indiana University South Bend, M
Indiana Wesleyan University, ABMO
Ivy Tech Community College - Lafayette, A
Manchester University, B
Marian University, B
Martin University, B
Oakland City University, A
Purdue University, B
Purdue University Northwest (Hammond), BM
Saint Joseph's College, B
Saint Mary-of-the-Woods College, AB
Saint Mary's College, B
Taylor University, B
Trine University, AB
University of Evansville, B
University of Indianapolis, B
University of Notre Dame, BM
University of Saint Francis, B
University of Southern Indiana, B
Valparaiso University, B

Iowa

Briar Cliff University, B
Buena Vista University, B
Central College, B
Clarke University, B
Coe College, B
Des Moines Area Community College, A
Dordt College, B
Drake University, B
Ellsworth Community College, A
Graceland University, B
Grand View University, B
Hawkeye Community College, A
Iowa Central Community College, A
Iowa Lakes Community College, A
Iowa State University of Science and Technology, BM
Iowa Western Community College, A
Kaplan University, Cedar Rapids, AB
Kaplan University, Davenport Campus, A
Kaplan University, Des Moines, AB
Kaplan University, Mason City Campus, A
Kirkwood Community College, A
Loras College, B
Luther College, B
Maharishi University of Management, M
Marshalltown Community College, A
Mount Mercy University, B
Muscatine Community College, A
North Iowa Area Community College, A
Northeast Iowa Community College, A
Northwest Iowa Community College, A
Northwestern College, B
St. Ambrose University, BM
Scott Community College, A
Simpson College, B
Southeastern Community College, A
University of Dubuque, B
The University of Iowa, BMD
University of Northern Iowa, BM
Upper Iowa University, BM
Wartburg College, B
Western Iowa Tech Community College, A
William Penn University, B

Kansas

Allen Community College, A
Baker University, B
Barton County Community College, A
Benedictine College, B
Bethany College, B
Butler Community College, A
Central Christian College of Kansas, B
Cowley County Community College and Area Vocational - Technical School, A
Dodge City Community College, A
Emporia State University, B
Fort Hays State University, B
Friends University, BM
Grantham University, B
Independence Community College, A
Kansas City Kansas Community College, A
Kansas State University, BM
Kansas Wesleyan University, B
Labette Community College, A
McPherson College, B
MidAmerica Nazarene University, B
Neosho County Community College, A
Newman University, B
Ottawa University, B
Pittsburg State University, BM
Pratt Community College, A
Rasmussen College Kansas City/Overland Park, AB
Rasmussen College Topeka, AB
Seward County Community College and Area Technical School, A
Southwestern College, BM
Tabor College, M
The University of Kansas, BM
University of Saint Mary, B
Washburn University, BM
Wichita State University, BM

Kentucky

American National University (Danville), A
American National University (Florence), A
American National University (Lexington), AB
American National University (Louisville), AB
American National University (Pikeville), A
American National University (Richmond), A
Asbury University, B
Bellarmine University, B
Brescia University, B
Campbellsville University, B
Daymar College (Bowling Green), A
Eastern Kentucky University, B
Georgetown College, B
Kentucky Wesleyan College, B
Madisonville Community College, A
Midway University, B
Morehead State University, B
Murray State University, BM
Northern Kentucky University, BMO
Spalding University, B
Sullivan University, B
Thomas More College, AB
Transylvania University, B
Union College, B
University of the Cumberlands, BM
University of Kentucky, BM
University of Louisville, BM
West Kentucky Community and Technical College, A
Western Kentucky University, B

Louisiana

Delgado Community College, A
Delta School of Business and Technology, A
Dillard University, B
Fletcher Technical Community College, A
Grambling State University, B
Louisiana College, B
Louisiana State University and Agricultural & Mechanical College, BMD
Louisiana State University in Shreveport, B
Louisiana Tech University, BM
Loyola University New Orleans, B
McNeese State University, B
Northwestern State University of Louisiana, B
Southeastern Louisiana University, B

Southern University and Agricultural and Mechanical College, B
Southern University at Shreveport, A
Tulane University, BM
University of Holy Cross, B
University of Louisiana at Lafayette, B
University of Louisiana at Monroe, B
University of New Orleans, BM
Xavier University of Louisiana, B

Maine

Beal College, A
Central Maine Community College, A
Husson University, AB
Kaplan University, South Portland, A
Northern Maine Community College, A
Saint Joseph's College of Maine, BM
Thomas College, AB
University of Maine, BM
University of Maine at Augusta, B
University of Maine at Machias, B
University of Southern Maine, BM
York County Community College, A

Maryland

Bowie State University, B
Frederick Community College, A
Frostburg State University, B
Harford Community College, A
Hood College, BM
Howard Community College, A
Kaplan University, Hagerstown Campus, A
Loyola University Maryland, BMO
Morgan State University, B
Mount St. Mary's University, B
Prince George's Community College, A
Salisbury University, B
Stevenson University, B
Strayer University - Anne Arundel Campus, B
Strayer University - Owings Mills Campus, B
Strayer University - Prince George's Campus, B
Strayer University - Rockville Campus, B
Strayer University - White Marsh Campus, B
Towson University, BM
University of Baltimore, BMO
University of Maryland, College Park, B
University of Maryland Eastern Shore, B
University of Maryland University College, BMO

Massachusetts

American International College, BM
Assumption College, BM
Babson College, BM
Bay Path University, BM
Bay State College, A
Bentley University, BMD
Boston College, BM
Boston University, B
Bridgewater State University, BM
Bristol Community College, A
Bunker Hill Community College, A
Cape Cod Community College, A
Clark University, M
College of the Holy Cross, B
Eastern Nazarene College, B
Elms College, BM
Emmanuel College, B
Endicott College, B
Fisher College, B
Fitchburg State University, BM
Framingham State University, B
Gordon College, B
Harvard University, D
Lasell College, B
Massachusetts Bay Community College, A
Massachusetts College of Liberal Arts, B
Massasoit Community College, A
Merrimack College, B
New England College of Business and Finance, A
Newbury College, B
Nichols College, B
North Shore Community College, A
Northeastern University, BM
Northern Essex Community College, A
Quincy College, A
Roxbury Community College, A

Salem State University, B
Springfield Technical Community College, A
Stonehill College, B
Suffolk University, BMO
University of Massachusetts Amherst, BMD
University of Massachusetts Boston, B
University of Massachusetts Dartmouth, BO
University of Massachusetts Lowell, M
Western New England University, BM
Worcester State University, M

Michigan

Adrian College, BM
Albion College, B
Alma College, B
Alpena Community College, A
Andrews University, BM
Aquinas College, B
Baker College, AB
Bay de Noc Community College, A
Calvin College, B
Central Michigan University, BM
Cleary University, ABM
Cornerstone University, B
Davenport University, ABM
Eastern Michigan University, BM
Gogebic Community College, A
Grace Bible College, B
Grand Valley State University, BM
Hillsdale College, B
Hope College, B
Kellogg Community College, A
Kuyper College, B
Lake Michigan College, A
Lake Superior State University, B
Macomb Community College, A
Madonna University, B
Marygrove College, A
Michigan State University, BMD
Michigan Technological University, BM
Mid Michigan Community College, A
Monroe County Community College, A
Montcalm Community College, A
Muskegon Community College, A
Northern Michigan University, B
Northwood University, Michigan Campus, B
Oakland University, BMO
Rochester College, B
Saginaw Valley State University, B
Siena Heights University, AB
Spring Arbor University, B
University of Detroit Mercy, B
University of Michigan, M
University of Michigan - Dearborn, BM
University of Michigan - Flint, BM
University of Phoenix - Detroit Campus, B
Walsh College of Accountancy and Business Administration, BM
Wayne State University, BMO
West Shore Community College, A
Western Michigan University, BM

Minnesota

Academy College, A
Alexandria Technical and Community College, A
Anoka-Ramsey Community College, A
Anoka Technical College, A
Argosy University, Twin Cities, D
Augsburg College, B
Bemidji State University, B
Capella University, BMD
Central Lakes College, A
Century College, A
College of Saint Benedict, B
The College of St. Scholastica, B
Concordia College, B
Concordia University, St. Paul, B
Dakota County Technical College, A
Globe University - Minneapolis, AB
Globe University - Woodbury, AB
Gustavus Adolphus College, B
Hamline University, B
Hennepin Technical College, A
Inver Hills Community College, A
Itasca Community College, A
Lake Superior College, A

Metropolitan State University, B
Minneapolis Community and Technical College, A
Minnesota School of Business - Blaine, AB
Minnesota School of Business - Brooklyn Center, AB
Minnesota School of Business - Elk River, AB
Minnesota School of Business - Lakeville, AB
Minnesota School of Business - Plymouth, AB
Minnesota School of Business - Richfield, AB
Minnesota School of Business - Rochester, AB
Minnesota School of Business - St. Cloud, AB
Minnesota State College - Southeast Technical, A
Minnesota State Community and Technical College, A
Minnesota State Community and Technical College - Detroit Lakes, A
Minnesota State Community and Technical College - Moorhead, A
Minnesota State University Mankato, B
Minnesota State University Moorhead, B
Minnesota West Community and Technical College, A
National American University (Bloomington), A
National American University (Brooklyn Center), A
National American University (Roseville), B
North Hennepin Community College, A
Northland Community and Technical College, A
Northwest Technical College, A
Rasmussen College Blaine, A
Rasmussen College Bloomington, AB
Rasmussen College Brooklyn Park, AB
Rasmussen College Eagan, AB
Rasmussen College Lake Elmo/Woodbury, AB
Rasmussen College Mankato, AB
Rasmussen College Moorhead, AB
Rasmussen College St. Cloud, AB
Ridgewater College, A
Rochester Community and Technical College, A
St. Catherine University, B
St. Cloud State University, B
St. Cloud Technical & Community College, A
Saint John's University, B
Saint Mary's University of Minnesota, BM
Saint Paul College - A Community & Technical College, A
South Central College, A
Southwest Minnesota State University, AB
University of Minnesota, Crookston, B
University of Minnesota, Duluth, B
University of Minnesota, Twin Cities Campus, BMD
University of Northwestern - St. Paul, AB
University of St. Thomas, BM
Vermilion Community College, A
Walden University, BMDO
Winona State University, B

Mississippi

Alcorn State University, B
Belhaven University, B
Coahoma Community College, A
Copiah-Lincoln Community College, A
Delta State University, BM
East Mississippi Community College, A
Itawamba Community College, A
Jackson State University, BM
Jones County Junior College, A
Millsaps College, BM
Mississippi College, BMO
Mississippi Delta Community College, A
Mississippi Gulf Coast Community College, A
Mississippi State University, BMD
Mississippi University for Women, B
Mississippi Valley State University, B
Northeast Mississippi Community College, A
Northwest Mississippi Community College, A
Southwest Mississippi Community College, A
Strayer University - Jackson Campus, B
Tougaloo College, B
University of Mississippi, BMD
University of Southern Mississippi, BM

Missouri

American Business & Technology University, M
Avila University, BM
Central Methodist University, B
College of the Ozarks, B

Columbia College, B
Culver-Stockton College, B
DeVry University (Kansas City), B
Drury University, B
Everest College, A
Fontbonne University, M
Hannibal-LaGrange University, B
Harris-Stowe State University, B
Lincoln University, BM
Lindenwood University, BM
Maryville University of Saint Louis, BMO
Missouri Baptist University, B
Missouri Southern State University, B
Missouri State University, BM
Missouri State University - West Plains, A
Missouri Valley College, B
Missouri Western State University, B
North Central Missouri College, A
Northwest Missouri State University, B
Ozarks Technical Community College, A
Park University, B
Saint Louis University, BM
Southeast Missouri State University, BM
Southwest Baptist University, B
State Fair Community College, A
Three Rivers Community College, A
Truman State University, BM
University of Central Missouri, M
University of Missouri, BMDO
University of Missouri - Kansas City, BM
University of Missouri - St. Louis, BM
Washington University in St. Louis, BM
Webster University, BM
Westminster College, B
William Jewell College, B
William Woods University, B

Montana

Carroll College, B
Flathead Valley Community College, A
Fort Peck Community College, A
Helena College University of Montana, A
Montana State University, M
Montana State University Billings, B
Rocky Mountain College, B
University of Great Falls, B
University of Montana, BM

Nebraska

Bellevue University, B
Concordia University, Nebraska, B
Creighton University, B
Doane University, B
Grace University, B
Hastings College, B
Kaplan University, Lincoln, A
Kaplan University, Omaha, AB
Metropolitan Community College, A
Midland University, AB
Nebraska Wesleyan University, B
Northeast Community College, A
Peru State College, B
Union College, AB
University of Nebraska at Kearney, M
University of Nebraska - Lincoln, BMD
University of Nebraska at Omaha, BM
York College, B

Nevada

University of Nevada, Las Vegas, BMO
University of Nevada, Reno, BM
University of Phoenix - Las Vegas Campus, ABM
Western Nevada College, A

New Hampshire

Daniel Webster College, B
Franklin Pierce University, B
Great Bay Community College, A
Lakes Region Community College, A
Manchester Community College, A
Nashua Community College, A
New England College, BM
NHTI, Concord's Community College, A
Plymouth State University, B
River Valley Community College, A
Saint Anselm College, B

Southern New Hampshire University, ABMO
University of New Hampshire, M
White Mountains Community College, A

New Jersey

Atlantic Cape Community College, A
Bergen Community College, A
Berkeley College - Woodland Park Campus, B
Bloomfield College, BM
Brookdale Community College, A
Caldwell University, BM
Centenary College, BM
The College of New Jersey, B
Cumberland County College, A
Essex County College, A
Fairleigh Dickinson University, College at Florham, BM
Fairleigh Dickinson University, Metropolitan Campus, BMO
Felician University, B
Georgian Court University, B
Hudson County Community College, A
Kean University, BM
Mercer County Community College, A
Middlesex County College, A
Monmouth University, MO
Montclair State University, BMO
New Jersey City University, BM
Passaic County Community College, A
Ramapo College of New Jersey, B
Rider University, BM
Rowan College at Burlington County, A
Rutgers University - Camden, B
Rutgers University - New Brunswick, B
Rutgers University - Newark, BD
Saint Peter's University, BM
Seton Hall University, BMO
Strayer University - Cherry Hill Campus, B
Strayer University - Lawrenceville Campus, B
Strayer University - Piscataway Campus, B
Strayer University - Willingboro Campus, B
Sussex County Community College, A
Thomas Edison State University, B
University of Phoenix - Jersey City Campus, ABM
Warren County Community College, A
William Paterson University of New Jersey, B

New Mexico

Brookline College, A
Central New Mexico Community College, A
Eastern New Mexico University, B
Eastern New Mexico University - Roswell, A
Luna Community College, A
National American University (Albuquerque), AB
Navajo Technical University, A
New Mexico Highlands University, B
New Mexico Junior College, A
New Mexico Military Institute, A
New Mexico State University, BM
New Mexico State University - Carlsbad, A
Santa Fe Community College, A
University of New Mexico, M
University of New Mexico - Gallup, A
University of New Mexico - Los Alamos Branch, A
University of Phoenix - New Mexico Campus, BM
University of the Southwest, B
Western New Mexico University, B

New York

Adelphi University, BM
Adirondack Community College, A
Alfred University, BM
ASA College, A
Baruch College of the City University of New York, BMD
Berkeley College - New York City Campus, AB
Binghamton University, State University of New York, BM
Borough of Manhattan Community College of the City University of New York, A
Bramson ORT College, A
Bronx Community College of the City University of New York, A
Brooklyn College of the City University of New York, BM
Bryant & Stratton College - Albany Campus, A

Bryant & Stratton College - Amherst Campus, A
Bryant & Stratton College - Buffalo Campus, A
Bryant & Stratton College - Greece Campus, A
Bryant & Stratton College - Henrietta Campus, A
Bryant & Stratton College - Liverpool Campus, A
Bryant & Stratton College - Orchard Park Campus, A
Bryant & Stratton College - Syracuse Campus, A
Canisius College, BM
Cazenovia College, B
Clinton Community College, A
The College at Brockport, State University of New York, BM
The College of Saint Rose, BM
College of Staten Island of the City University of New York, BM
The College of Westchester, AB
Columbia University, MD
Concordia College - New York, B
Cornell University, D
Corning Community College, A
Daemen College, BM
Dominican College, BM
Dutchess Community College, A
D'Youville College, B
Elmira Business Institute, A
Elmira College, B
Excelsior College, B
Finger Lakes Community College, A
Fordham University, BM
Fulton-Montgomery Community College, A
Genesee Community College, A
Globe Institute of Technology, B
Hartwick College, B
Hilbert College, B
Hofstra University, BMO
Houghton College, B
Hunter College of the City University of New York, BM
Iona College, BMO
Ithaca College, BM
Jefferson Community College, A
Keuka College, B
Kingsborough Community College of the City University of New York, A
Le Moyne College, B
Lehman College of the City University of New York, BM
Long Island Business Institute, A
Long Island University - LIU Brooklyn, BM
Long Island University - LIU Post, B
Manhattan College, B
Manhattanville College, BM
Maria College, A
Marist College, B
Medaille College, B
Medgar Evers College of the City University of New York, B
Mercy College, BM
Molloy College, B
Monroe College, AB
Monroe Community College, A
Morrisville State College, A
Mount Saint Mary College, B
Nassau Community College, A
Nazareth College of Rochester, B
New York Institute of Technology, BM
New York University, BMD
Niagara County Community College, A
Niagara University, BM
Nyack College, B
Onondaga Community College, A
Pace University, BM
Pace University, Pleasantville Campus, B
Queens College of the City University of New York, BM
Queensborough Community College of the City University of New York, A
Roberts Wesleyan College, B
Rochester Institute of Technology, BM
Rockland Community College, A
The Sage Colleges, B
St. Bonaventure University, B
St. Francis College, BM
St. John Fisher College, B
St. John's University, BM

St. Joseph's College, Long Island Campus, BM
St. Joseph's College, New York, BM
St. Thomas Aquinas College, B
Siena College, B
State University of New York College at Geneseo, BM
State University of New York College at Old Westbury, BM
State University of New York College at Oneonta, B
State University of New York at Fredonia, B
State University of New York at New Paltz, BM
State University of New York at Oswego, B
State University of New York at Plattsburgh, B
State University of New York Polytechnic Institute, BM
Suffolk County Community College, A
Sullivan County Community College, A
Syracuse University, BMD
Touro College, B
University at Albany, State University of New York, BM
University at Buffalo, the State University of New York, BM
University of Rochester, M
Utica College, BM
Wagner College, BM
Westchester Community College, A
Yeshiva University, BM
York College of the City University of New York, B

North Carolina

Appalachian State University, BM
Asheville-Buncombe Technical Community College, A
Barton College, B
Beaufort County Community College, A
Belmont Abbey College, B
Caldwell Community College and Technical Institute, A
Campbell University, B
Catawba College, B
Central Carolina Community College, A
Central Piedmont Community College, A
Chowan University, B
Cleveland Community College, A
Coastal Carolina Community College, A
Craven Community College, A
Davidson County Community College, A
Duke University, D
Durham Technical Community College, A
East Carolina University, M
Elizabeth City State University, B
Elon University, B
Fayetteville State University, B
Fayetteville Technical Community College, A
Forsyth Technical Community College, A
Gardner-Webb University, B
Gaston College, A
Greensboro College, B
Guilford College, B
High Point University, B
James Sprunt Community College, A
Johnson & Wales University, B
Johnston Community College, A
Lenoir Community College, A
Lenoir-Rhyne University, BM
Livingstone College, B
Mars Hill University, B
Martin Community College, A
McDowell Technical Community College, A
Meredith College, B
Methodist University, AB
Miller-Motte College (Cary), A
Miller-Motte College (Wilmington), A
Mitchell Community College, A
Nash Community College, A
North Carolina Agricultural and Technical State University, BM
North Carolina Central University, B
North Carolina State University, BM
North Carolina Wesleyan College, B
Pamlico Community College, A
Pfeiffer University, B
Piedmont Community College, A
Pitt Community College, A
Queens University of Charlotte, B

Randolph Community College, A
Richmond Community College, A
Rockingham Community College, A
Rowan-Cabarrus Community College, A
Saint Augustine's University, B
Salem College, B
Sampson Community College, A
Sandhills Community College, A
Shaw University, B
South College - Asheville, A
South Piedmont Community College, A
Southwestern Community College, A
Strayer University - Greensboro Campus, B
Strayer University - Huntersville Campus, B
Strayer University - North Charlotte Campus, B
Strayer University - North Raleigh Campus, B
Strayer University - RTP Campus, B
Strayer University - South Charlotte Campus, B
Strayer University - South Raleigh Campus, B
Surry Community College, A
Tri-County Community College, A
University of North Carolina at Asheville, B
The University of North Carolina at Chapel Hill, MD
The University of North Carolina at Charlotte, BM
The University of North Carolina at Greensboro, BMO
The University of North Carolina at Pembroke, B
The University of North Carolina Wilmington, M
University of Phoenix - Charlotte Campus, M
Vance-Granville Community College, A
Wake Forest University, BM
Wake Technical Community College, A
Wayne Community College, A
Western Carolina University, BM
Western Piedmont Community College, A
Wilson Community College, A
Wingate University, B
Winston-Salem State University, B

North Dakota

Cankdeska Cikana Community College, A
Dakota College at Bottineau, A
Dickinson State University, B
Minot State University, B
North Dakota State University, B
Rasmussen College Fargo, B
University of Jamestown, B
University of Mary, B
University of North Dakota, BM

Ohio

American National University (Cincinnati), A
American National University (Kettering), A
Ashland University, B
Baldwin Wallace University, BM
Belmont College, A
Bluffton University, B
Bowling Green State University, BM
Bryant & Stratton College - Eastlake Campus, A
Bryant & Stratton College - Parma Campus, A
Capital University, B
Case Western Reserve University, BMD
Cedarville University, B
Central Ohio Technical College, A
Central State University, B
Cincinnati State Technical and Community College, A
Clark State Community College, A
Cleveland State University, BM
Cuyahoga Community College, A
Defiance College, B
Eastern Gateway Community College, A
Edison Community College, A
Fortis College (Ravenna), A
Franciscan University of Steubenville, AB
Franklin University, ABM
Gallipolis Career College, A
Harrison College, AB
Heidelberg University, B
Hocking College, A
John Carroll University, BM
Kent State University, BMD
Lake Erie College, B
Lakeland Community College, A
Lorain County Community College, A
Lourdes University, B

Malone University, B
Marietta College, B
Marion Technical College, A
Miami University, BM
Miami University Hamilton, B
Miami University Middletown, A
Mount St. Joseph University, AB
Mount Vernon Nazarene University, B
Muskingum University, B
North Central State College, A
Northwest State Community College, A
Notre Dame College, B
Ohio Business College (Sandusky), A
Ohio Business College (Sheffield Village), A
Ohio Dominican University, BM
Ohio Northern University, B
The Ohio State University, BMD
Ohio University, B
Ohio Wesleyan University, B
Otterbein University, B
Shawnee State University, AB
Sinclair Community College, A
Stark State College, A
Stautzenberger College (Brecksville), A
Stautzenberger College (Maumee), A
Terra State Community College, A
Tiffin University, AB
Trumbull Business College, A
The University of Akron, BM
University of Cincinnati, BMD
University of Cincinnati Clermont College, A
University of Dayton, BM
The University of Findlay, AB
University of Mount Union, B
University of Northwestern Ohio, AB
University of Rio Grande, AB
The University of Toledo, BM
Urbana University, AB
Ursuline College, B
Walsh University, AB
Washington State Community College, A
Wilberforce University, B
Wilmington College, B
Wittenberg University, B
Wright State University, BM
Wright State University - Lake Campus, A
Xavier University, BM
Youngstown State University, ABM
Zane State College, A

Oklahoma

Bacone College, AB
Cameron University, B
East Central University, B
Langston University, B
Northeastern State University, BM
Northern Oklahoma College, A
Northwestern Oklahoma State University, B
Oklahoma Baptist University, B
Oklahoma Christian University, BM
Oklahoma City University, BM
Oklahoma Panhandle State University, B
Oklahoma State University, BMD
Oklahoma State University, Oklahoma City, A
Oral Roberts University, BM
Rogers State University, A
Rose State College, A
St. Gregory's University, B
Seminole State College, A
Southeastern Oklahoma State University, B
Southern Nazarene University, B
University of Central Oklahoma, BM
University of Oklahoma, BM
The University of Tulsa, BM

Oregon

Blue Mountain Community College, A
Central Oregon Community College, A
Chemeketa Community College, A
Clackamas Community College, A
Clatsop Community College, A
Columbia Gorge Community College, A
Corban University, B
George Fox University, B
Klamath Community College, A
Linfield College, B

Mt. Hood Community College, A
Northwest Christian University, B
Oregon Institute of Technology, B
Oregon State University, BM
Pacific University, B
Pioneer Pacific College, A
Pioneer Pacific College - Eugene/Springfield
    Branch, A
Portland Community College, A
Portland State University, B
Southern Oregon University, BO
Southwestern Oregon Community College, A
Tillamook Bay Community College, A
Umpqua Community College, A
University of Oregon, BMD
University of Portland, B

Pennsylvania

Albright College, B
Alvernia University, B
Arcadia University, B
Bloomsburg University of Pennsylvania, BM
Cabrini University, BM
California University of Pennsylvania, AB
Cambria-Rowe Business College (Indiana), A
Cambria-Rowe Business College (Johnstown), A
Carlow University, B
Carnegie Mellon University, D
Cedar Crest College, B
Central Penn College, AB
Chatham University, BM
Chestnut Hill College, B
Cheyney University of Pennsylvania, B
Community College of Philadelphia, A
Consolidated School of Business (Lancaster), A
Consolidated School of Business (York), A
Delaware Valley University, BM
DeSales University, BM
Drexel University, BMD
DuBois Business College (DuBois), A
Duquesne University, BM
Elizabethtown College, B
Elizabethtown College School of Continuing and
    Professional Studies, AB
Fortis Institute (Erie), A
Gannon University, B
Geneva College, B
Grove City College, B
Gwynedd Mercy University, B
Holy Family University, B
Immaculata University, AB
Indiana University of Pennsylvania, B
Juniata College, BM
Keystone College, AB
King's College, B
La Roche College, BM
La Salle University, BMO
Lackawanna College, A
Laurel Business Institute, A
Lebanon Valley College, B
Lehigh University, BM
Lincoln University, B
Lock Haven University of Pennsylvania, B
Luzerne County Community College, A
Lycoming College, B
Manor College, A
Mansfield University of Pennsylvania, B
Marywood University, B
McCann School of Business & Technology
    (Hazleton), A
McCann School of Business & Technology
    (Lewisburg), A
McCann School of Business & Technology
    (Pottsville), A
Mercyhurst North East, A
Mercyhurst University, BM
Messiah College, B
Misericordia University, BM
Montgomery County Community College, A
Moravian College, BM
Mount Aloysius College, ABM
Muhlenberg College, AB
Neumann University, B
Peirce College, B
Penn State Abington, B
Penn State Altoona, B

Penn State Beaver, B
Penn State Berks, B
Penn State Brandywine, B
Penn State DuBois, B
Penn State Erie, The Behrend College, B
Penn State Fayette, The Eberly Campus, B
Penn State Greater Allegheny, B
Penn State Hazleton, B
Penn State Lehigh Valley, B
Penn State Mont Alto, B
Penn State New Kensington, B
Penn State Schuylkill, B
Penn State Shenango, B
Penn State University Park, BM
Penn State Wilkes-Barre, B
Penn State Worthington Scranton, B
Penn State York, B
Pennsylvania College of Technology, B
Pennsylvania Highlands Community College, A
Philadelphia University, B
Point Park University, AB
Reading Area Community College, A
Robert Morris University, B
Rosemont College, B
Saint Francis University, AB
Saint Joseph's University, BMO
Saint Vincent College, B
Seton Hill University, BM
Shippensburg University of Pennsylvania, B
Slippery Rock University of Pennsylvania, B
South Hills School of Business & Technology
    (Altoona), A
South Hills School of Business & Technology (State
    College), A
Strayer University - Allentown Campus, B
Strayer University - Center City Campus, B
Strayer University - Delaware County Campus, B
Strayer University - King of Prussia Campus, B
Strayer University - Lower Bucks County Campus,
    B
Strayer University - Warrendale Campus, B
Susquehanna University, B
Temple University, BMD
Thiel College, AB
University of Pennsylvania, BMD
University of Phoenix - Philadelphia Campus, B
University of Pittsburgh, BMD
University of Pittsburgh at Bradford, B
University of Pittsburgh at Greensburg, B
University of Pittsburgh at Johnstown, B
University of Pittsburgh at Titusville, A
The University of Scranton, BM
Villanova University, BM
Washington & Jefferson College, B
Waynesburg University, B
West Chester University of Pennsylvania, B
Westminster College, B
Widener University, BM
Wilkes University, BM
Wilson College, AB
York College of Pennsylvania, B

Rhode Island

Bryant University, BM
Community College of Rhode Island, A
Johnson & Wales University, B
Providence College, BM
Rhode Island College, BMO
Roger Williams University, B
Salve Regina University, B
University of Rhode Island, BM

South Carolina

Aiken Technical College, A
Benedict College, B
Bob Jones University, BM
Central Carolina Technical College, A
Charleston Southern University, BM
Clemson University, BM
Coastal Carolina University, BM
College of Charleston, BM
Columbia College, B
Converse College, B
Florence-Darlington Technical College, A
Forrest College, A
Francis Marion University, B

Furman University, B
Greenville Technical College, A
Limestone College, B
Midlands Technical College, A
Newberry College, B
North Greenville University, B
Northeastern Technical College, A
Orangeburg-Calhoun Technical College, A
Piedmont Technical College, A
South Carolina State University, B
Southern Wesleyan University, B
Spartanburg Community College, A
Strayer University - Charleston Campus, B
Strayer University - Columbia Campus, B
Strayer University - Greenville Campus, B
Tri-County Technical College, A
Trident Technical College, A
University of South Carolina, BM
Voorhees College, B
Wofford College, B
York Technical College, A

South Dakota

Augustana University, B
Black Hills State University, B
Dakota State University, B
Dakota Wesleyan University, AB
Globe University - Sioux Falls, AB
Mount Marty College, AB
National American University (Sioux Falls), AB
Northern State University, B
Oglala Lakota College, A
Sisseton-Wahpeton College, A
Southeast Technical Institute, A
University of Sioux Falls, B
The University of South Dakota, BM
Western Dakota Technical Institute, A

Tennessee

Argosy University, Nashville, D
Austin Peay State University, B
Belmont University, BM
Carson-Newman University, B
Christian Brothers University, BM
Cumberland University, B
Daymar College (Murfreesboro), A
Daymar College (Nashville), A
East Tennessee State University, BM
Freed-Hardeman University, BM
Hiwassee College, A
King University, BM
Lee University, B
LeMoyne-Owen College, B
Lincoln Memorial University, B
Lipscomb University, BMO
Martin Methodist College, B
Middle Tennessee State University, BM
Miller-Motte Technical College (Clarksville), A
Milligan College, B
Nashville State Community College, A
National College (Bristol), AB
Northeast State Community College, A
Rhodes College, M
Roane State Community College, A
South College, A
Southern Adventist University, ABM
Southwest Tennessee Community College, A
Strayer University - Knoxville Campus, B
Strayer University - Nashville Campus, B
Strayer University - Shelby Campus, B
Strayer University - Thousand Oaks Campus, B
Tennessee State University, B
Tennessee Technological University, BM
Tennessee Wesleyan College, B
Trevecca Nazarene University, B
Union University, BM
University of Memphis, BMD
The University of Tennessee, BMD
The University of Tennessee at Chattanooga, M
The University of Tennessee at Martin, B
Vanderbilt University, M

Texas

Abilene Christian University, BM
Alvin Community College, A
Amarillo College, A

Amberton University, B
Angelina College, A
Angelo State University, BM
Argosy University, Dallas, DO
Baylor University, BM
Blinn College, A
Brookhaven College, A
Cedar Valley College, A
Cisco College, A
Clarendon College, A
Coastal Bend College, A
Dallas Baptist University, BM
Del Mar College, A
Eastfield College, A
El Centro College, A
El Paso Community College, A
Frank Phillips College, A
Grayson College, A
Hardin-Simmons University, B
Hill College, A
Houston Baptist University, BM
Houston Community College, A
Howard College, A
Howard Payne University, B
Huston-Tillotson University, B
Lamar State College - Orange, A
Lamar University, BM
LeTourneau University, B
Lone Star College - CyFair, A
Lone Star College - North Harris, A
Lone Star College - Tomball, A
Lone Star College - University Park, A
Lubbock Christian University, B
McLennan Community College, A
McMurry University, B
Midwestern State University, B
Mountain View College, A
Navarro College, A
North Lake College, A
Northeast Texas Community College, A
Northwest Vista College, A
Northwood University, Texas Campus, B
Odessa College, A
Our Lady of the Lake University of San Antonio, BM
Paris Junior College, A
Prairie View A&M University, BM
Richland College, A
St. Edward's University, BM
St. Mary's University, BM
St. Philip's College, A
Sam Houston State University, BM
San Jacinto College District, A
Schreiner University, B
South Plains College, A
South Texas College, A
Southern Methodist University, BM
Southwestern Adventist University, BM
Southwestern Assemblies of God University, B
Southwestern University, B
Stephen F. Austin State University, BM
Strayer University - Cedar Hill Campus, B
Strayer University - Irving Campus, B
Strayer University - Katy Campus, B
Strayer University - North Austin Campus, B
Strayer University - Northwest Houston Campus, B
Strayer University - Plano Campus, B
Tarleton State University, B
Tarrant County College District, A
Texas A&M International University, BM
Texas A&M University, BMD
Texas A&M University - Central Texas, BM
Texas A&M University - Commerce, BM
Texas A&M University - Corpus Christi, BM
Texas A&M University - Kingsville, B
Texas A&M University - San Antonio, BM
Texas A&M University - Texarkana, BM
Texas Christian University, BM
Texas Lutheran University, BM
Texas Southern University, B
Texas Southmost College, A
Texas State University, BM
Texas Tech University, BMD
Texas Wesleyan University, B
Texas Woman's University, B
Trinity University, BM
Trinity Valley Community College, A

Tyler Junior College, A
University of Dallas, M
University of Houston, BMD
University of Houston - Clear Lake, BM
University of Houston - Downtown, B
University of Houston - Victoria, BM
University of the Incarnate Word, BM
University of Mary Hardin-Baylor, BM
University of North Texas, BM
University of Phoenix - Dallas Campus, BM
University of Phoenix - Houston Campus, BM
University of Phoenix - San Antonio Campus, BM
University of St. Thomas, BM
The University of Texas at Arlington, BMD
The University of Texas at Austin, BMD
The University of Texas at Dallas, BMD
The University of Texas at El Paso, BM
The University of Texas of the Permian Basin, BM
The University of Texas Rio Grande Valley, BM
The University of Texas at San Antonio, BMD
The University of Texas at Tyler, B
Vernon College, A
Virginia College in Austin, A
Wayland Baptist University, M
West Texas A&M University, BM
Western Texas College, A

Utah

Argosy University, Salt Lake City, D
Broadview University - Layton, AB
Broadview University - West Jordan, AB
Dixie State University, B
Independence University, AB
LDS Business College, A
Snow College, A
Southern Utah University, BM
Stevens-Henager College (Logan), A
Stevens-Henager College (Orem), A
Stevens-Henager College (Salt Lake City), A
Stevens-Henager College (West Haven), B
University of Phoenix - Utah Campus, BM
University of Utah, BMD
Utah State University, BM
Utah Valley University, ABM
Weber State University, BM
Westminster College, BM

Vermont

Castleton University, B
Champlain College, AB
College of St. Joseph, AB
Community College of Vermont, A
Johnson State College, AB
Lyndon State College, B
Norwich University, B
Saint Michael's College, B
University of Vermont, M

Virginia

American National University (Charlottesville), A
American National University (Danville), A
American National University (Harrisonburg), AB
American National University (Lynchburg), A
American National University (Martinsville), A
American National University (Salem), AB
Argosy University, Washington DC, D
Averett University, BM
Bluefield College, B
Bryant & Stratton College - Richmond Campus, A
Bryant & Stratton College - Virginia Beach Campus,
A
Christopher Newport University, B
The College of William and Mary, BM
DeVry University (Arlington), B
DeVry University (Manassas), B
Eastern Mennonite University, B
ECPI University (Newport News), A
ECPI University (Richmond), A
ECPI University (Virginia Beach), AB
Emory & Henry College, B
Ferrum College, B
George Mason University, BMO
Hampton University, B
James Madison University, BM
Liberty University, BMD
Lynchburg College, B

New River Community College, A
Norfolk State University, B
Old Dominion University, BM
Patrick Henry Community College, A
Radford University, B
Randolph-Macon College, B
Rappahannock Community College, A
Regent University, B
Stratford University (Falls Church), BM
Stratford University (Glen Allen), B
Stratford University (Newport News), AB
Stratford University (Woodbridge), B
Strayer University - Alexandria Campus, B
Strayer University - Arlington Campus, B
Strayer University - Chesapeake Campus, B
Strayer University - Chesterfield Campus, B
Strayer University - Fredericksburg Campus, B
Strayer University - Henrico Campus, B
Strayer University - Loudoun Campus, B
Strayer University - Manassas Campus, B
Strayer University - Newport News Campus, B
Strayer University - Virginia Beach Campus, B
Strayer University - Woodbridge Campus, B
Tidewater Community College, A
University of Richmond, B
University of Virginia, M
The University of Virginia's College at Wise, B
Virginia Commonwealth University, BMD
Virginia Highlands Community College, A
Virginia International University, M
Virginia Polytechnic Institute and State University,
    BM
Virginia State University, B
Virginia Union University, B
Virginia Western Community College, A
Wytheville Community College, A

Washington

Argosy University, Seattle, D
Bellevue College, A
Central Washington University, BM
City University of Seattle, BO
Eastern Washington University, B
Everett Community College, A
Gonzaga University, BM
Heritage University, B
Highline College, A
Lower Columbia College, A
Northwest University, B
Peninsula College, A
Pierce College at Puyallup, A
Saint Martin's University, B
Seattle Central College, A
Seattle Pacific University, B
Seattle University, BM
Shoreline Community College, A
Skagit Valley College, A
South Puget Sound Community College, A
South Seattle College, A
University of Phoenix - Western Washington Cam-
    pus, B
University of Washington, BMD
University of Washington, Bothell, B
University of Washington, Tacoma, BM
Walla Walla University, B
Washington State University, BM
Washington State University - Global Campus, B
Washington State University - Vancouver, B
Wenatchee Valley College, A
Whatcom Community College, A
Whitworth University, B
Yakima Valley Community College, A

West Virginia

Alderson Broaddus University, B
American Public University System, BM
Bethany College, B
Blue Ridge Community and Technical College, A
Bluefield State College, B
BridgeValley Community and Technical College
    (South Charleston), A
Concord University, B
Davis & Elkins College, B
Eastern West Virginia Community and Technical
    College, A
Fairmont State University, B

Huntington Junior College, A
Marshall University, BM
Ohio Valley University, B
Shepherd University, B
Southern West Virginia Community and Technical
    College, A
Strayer University - Teays Valley Campus, B
University of Charleston, BM
West Liberty University, B
West Virginia Business College (Wheeling), A
West Virginia University, BM
West Virginia University Institute of Technology, B
West Virginia University at Parkersburg, A
West Virginia Wesleyan College, B
Wheeling Jesuit University, BM

Wisconsin

Blackhawk Technical College, A
Bryant & Stratton College - Milwaukee Campus, A
Bryant & Stratton College - Wauwatosa Campus, A
Cardinal Stritch University, B
Carroll University, B
Carthage College, B
Chippewa Valley Technical College, A
College of Menominee Nation, A
Concordia University Wisconsin, B
Edgewood College, BM
Fox Valley Technical College, A
Gateway Technical College, A
Globe University - Appleton, AB
Globe University - Eau Claire, AB
Globe University - La Crosse, AB
Globe University - Madison East, AB
Globe University - Madison West, AB
Globe University - Wausau, AB
Herzing University Online, M
Lac Courte Oreilles Ojibwa Community College, A
Lakeland College, BM
Lakeshore Technical College, A
Madison Area Technical College, A
Maranatha Baptist University, B
Marian University, B
Marquette University, BM
Mid-State Technical College, A
Milwaukee Area Technical College, A
Moraine Park Technical College, A
Mount Mary University, B
Nicolet Area Technical College, A
Northcentral Technical College, A
Northeast Wisconsin Technical College, A
Rasmussen College Appleton, A
Rasmussen College Green Bay, A
Rasmussen College Wausau, A
St. Norbert College, B
Silver Lake College of the Holy Family, B
Southwest Wisconsin Technical College, A
University of Wisconsin - Eau Claire, B
University of Wisconsin - Green Bay, B
University of Wisconsin - La Crosse, B
University of Wisconsin - Madison, BMD
University of Wisconsin - Milwaukee, B
University of Wisconsin - Oshkosh, B
University of Wisconsin - Parkside, B
University of Wisconsin - Platteville, B
University of Wisconsin - River Falls, B
University of Wisconsin - Stevens Point, B
University of Wisconsin - Superior, B
University of Wisconsin - Whitewater, BM
Viterbo University, B
Waukesha County Technical College, A
Western Technical College, A
Wisconsin Indianhead Technical College, A

Wyoming

Casper College, A
Central Wyoming College, A
Eastern Wyoming College, A
Laramie County Community College, A
Northwest College, A
University of Wyoming, BM
Western Wyoming Community College, A

U.S. Territories: American Samoa

American Samoa Community College, A

U.S. Territories: Guam

Guam Community College, A
University of Guam, B

U.S. Territories: Northern Mariana Islands

Northern Marianas College, A

U.S. Territories: Puerto Rico

American University of Puerto Rico (Bayamon), AB
Atlantic University College, AB
Bayamón Central University, BM
Caribbean University, AB
Colegio Universitario de San Juan, AB
Huertas Junior College, A
ICPR Junior College - Hato Rey Campus, A
Inter American University of Puerto Rico, Aguadilla
    Campus, ABM
Inter American University of Puerto Rico, Arecibo
    Campus, ABM
Inter American University of Puerto Rico, Bar-
    ranquitas Campus, ABM
Inter American University of Puerto Rico, Bayamón
    Campus, AB
Inter American University of Puerto Rico, Fajardo
    Campus, AB
Inter American University of Puerto Rico, Guayama
    Campus, AB
Inter American University of Puerto Rico, Metropoli-
    tan Campus, ABM
Inter American University of Puerto Rico, Ponce
    Campus, ABM
Inter American University of Puerto Rico, San
    Germán Campus, ABM
National University College (Bayamón), AB
Pontifical Catholic University of Puerto Rico, BMO
Universidad Adventista de las Antillas, B
Universidad del Este, BM
Universidad Metropolitana, BM
Universidad del Turabo, ABM
University of Puerto Rico in Aguadilla, B
University of Puerto Rico in Arecibo, B
University of Puerto Rico in Bayamón, B
University of Puerto Rico in Cayey, B
University of Puerto Rico in Humacao, B
University of Puerto Rico, Mayagüez Campus, B
University of Puerto Rico in Ponce, B
University of Puerto Rico, Río Piedras Campus, BM
University of Puerto Rico in Utuado, B
University of the Sacred Heart, BM

U.S. Territories: United States Virgin Islands

University of the Virgin Islands, AB

Canada

Alberta

Athabasca University, B
Mount Royal University, B
University of Alberta, BD
University of Calgary, B
University of Lethbridge, BM

British Columbia

British Columbia Institute of Technology, AB
Thompson Rivers University, B
The University of British Columbia, BD
The University of British Columbia - Okanagan
    Campus, B
University of Northern British Columbia, B

Manitoba

University of Manitoba, B

Maritime Provinces: New Brunswick

Mount Allison University, B
Université de Moncton, B
University of New Brunswick Fredericton, B
University of New Brunswick Saint John, B

Maritime Provinces: Nova Scotia

Cape Breton University, B
Dalhousie University, B
Mount Saint Vincent University, B
St. Francis Xavier University, B
Saint Mary's University, B

Newfoundland and Labrador

Memorial University of Newfoundland, B

Ontario

Brock University, BM
Carleton University, B
Lakehead University, B
Redeemer University College, B
University of Guelph, B
University of Ottawa, B
University of Toronto, B
University of Waterloo, BMD
The University of Western Ontario, B
University of Windsor, B
Wilfrid Laurier University, D
York University, BM

Quebec

Bishop's University, B
Concordia University, B
HEC Montreal, BMO
McGill University, BO
Université Laval, MO
Université du Québec en Abitibi-Témiscamingue, B
Université du Québec à Chicoutimi, B
Université du Québec à Montréal, BMO
Université du Québec en Outaouais, BMO
Université du Québec à Rimouski, B
Université du Québec à Trois-Rivières, BM
Université de Sherbrooke, BM

Saskatchewan

University of Regina, B
University of Saskatchewan, BM

ACCOUNTING AND BUSINESS/ MANAGEMENT

United States

Alabama

Miles College, B

Arizona

Northcentral University, B

California

Berkeley City College, A
Cambridge Junior College, A
National University, B
Santa Clara University, B

Colorado

CollegeAmerica - Denver, A
IntelliTec College (Grand Junction), A
Western State Colorado University, B

Florida

City College (Gainesville), A
Rasmussen College Fort Myers, B
Rasmussen College Land O' Lakes, B
Rasmussen College New Port Richey, B
Rasmussen College Ocala, B
Rasmussen College Tampa/Brandon, B

Georgia

Carver College, B
Young Harris College, B

Hawaii

Chaminade University of Honolulu, B

Idaho

Stevens-Henager College (Boise), A

Illinois

Ellis University, B
University of Illinois at Urbana - Champaign, B

Iowa

Des Moines Area Community College, A

Kansas

Kansas City Kansas Community College, A
Kansas State University, A

Kentucky

Spalding University, B

Maine

Husson University, B

Massachusetts

Babson College, B
Eastern Nazarene College, B

Michigan

Hope College, B
Oakland Community College, A

Mississippi

Holmes Community College, A

Montana

Rocky Mountain College, B
University of Great Falls, B

Nevada

Sierra Nevada College, B

New York

Canisius College, B
Hudson Valley Community College, A
Mercy College, B
St. Francis College, B

North Carolina

Campbell University, B
East Carolina University, B
Miller-Motte College (Wilmington), A

Ohio

American National University (Youngstown), A
Antonelli College, A

Pennsylvania

Brightwood Career Institute, Pittsburgh Campus, A
Chestnut Hill College, B
Lansdale School of Business, A
Reading Area Community College, A

South Dakota

Mitchell Technical Institute, A

Tennessee

Bethel University, B
National College (Nashville), A

Texas

Lone Star College - Montgomery, A
Northeast Texas Community College, A

Utah

LDS Business College, A

Virginia

Washington and Lee University, B

Washington

Renton Technical College, A
Walla Walla University, B

West Virginia

Mountain State College, A
West Virginia Business College (Nutter Fort), A

Wisconsin

Maranatha Baptist University, B
Rasmussen College Appleton, B
Rasmussen College Green Bay, B
Rasmussen College Wausau, B

U.S. Territories: Puerto Rico

EDP University of Puerto Rico, B
EDP University of Puerto Rico - San Sebastian, B

Canada

Ontario

The University of Western Ontario, B

ACCOUNTING AND COMPUTER SCIENCE

United States

Arizona

GateWay Community College, A

Delaware

Goldey-Beacom College, B

Indiana

Saint Mary-of-the-Woods College, B

Michigan

Gogebic Community College, A

Missouri

State Fair Community College, A

New York

Fordham University, B

Pennsylvania

Grove City College, B

Texas

Lone Star College - CyFair, A

West Virginia

Bethany College, B

ACCOUNTING AND FINANCE

United States

Colorado

Colorado Technical University Online, B
Western State Colorado University, B

Idaho

Boise State University, B

Iowa

Drake University, B

Kansas

Central Christian College of Kansas, AB
Tabor College, B

Maine

University of Southern Maine, B

Massachusetts

Babson College, B
Bentley University, B
Bridgewater State University, B
Eastern Nazarene College, B
Massasoit Community College, A
Salem State University, B
Western New England University, B

Michigan

Ferris State University, B
Jackson College, A
Northern Michigan University, B

Minnesota

Bethel University, B

New Hampshire

Granite State College, B
Southern New Hampshire University, B

New York

Clarkson University, B
Elmira College, B

North Carolina

Campbell University, B

North Dakota

University of North Dakota, B

Ohio

Hiram College, B
Lourdes University, B
Ohio Christian University, AB

Oklahoma

East Central University, B

Pennsylvania

Bucknell University, B
Eastern University, B
Holy Family University, B
Saint Francis University, B

Tennessee

Maryville College, B

Washington

Northwest University, B

Canada

Ontario

University of Waterloo, B
The University of Western Ontario, B
University of Windsor, B

Quebec

McGill University, B

ACCOUNTING AND RELATED SERVICES

United States

California

Saint Mary's College of California, B

Colorado

Everest College (Thornton), A

Florida

Florida National University, A
Northwest Florida State College, A

Illinois

Northwestern College - Bridgeview Campus, A

Maryland

McDaniel College, B

Massachusetts

Bentley University, B
Eastern Nazarene College, B

Michigan

Eastern Michigan University, B
Henry Ford College, A
Lansing Community College, A
Northern Michigan University, B

Mississippi

Virginia College in Jackson, A

Missouri

Everest College, B
Maryville University of Saint Louis, B

Montana

Montana State University Billings, A
Rocky Mountain College, B

Nevada

Everest College, A

New Jersey

Raritan Valley Community College, A

New Mexico

Mesalands Community College, A

New York

State University of New York at New Paltz, B
State University of New York at Oswego, B

North Dakota

Dakota College at Bottineau, A
North Dakota State University, B

Ohio

Davis College, A
Franklin University, AB
Northwest State Community College, A

Utah

Brigham Young University, B

Virginia

Blue Ridge Community College, A
Central Virginia Community College, A
Danville Community College, A
J. Sargeant Reynolds Community College, A
John Tyler Community College, A
Lord Fairfax Community College, A
Mountain Empire Community College, A
Southwest Virginia Community College, A
Thomas Nelson Community College, A

U.S. Territories: Puerto Rico

Bayamón Central University, A

ACCOUNTING TECHNOLOGY/ TECHNICIAN AND BOOKKEEP- ING

United States

Alabama

Bishop State Community College, A
Gadsden State Community College, A
H. Councill Trenholm State Community College, A
Jefferson State Community College, A
Lawson State Community College, A
Virginia College in Huntsville, A

Alaska

Ilisagvik College, A
University of Alaska Anchorage, Kodiak College, A
University of Alaska Fairbanks, A

Arizona

Chandler-Gilbert Community College, A
Coconino Community College, A
GateWay Community College, A
Glendale Community College, A

Northland Pioneer College, A
Paradise Valley Community College, A

California

Antelope Valley College, A
Barstow Community College, A
Cabrillo College, A
Cañada College, A
Carrington College - Citrus Heights, A
Chaffey College, A
City College of San Francisco, A
College of Alameda, A
College of the Canyons, A
College of Marin, A
College of San Mateo, A
College of the Siskiyous, A
Cosumnes River College, A
Crafton Hills College, A
Cuyamaca College, A
Cypress College, A
DeVry University (Pomona), A
Evergreen Valley College, A
Feather River College, A
Fresno City College, A
Fullerton College, A
Gavilan College, A
Glendale Community College, A
Long Beach City College, A
MiraCosta College, A
Modesto Junior College, A
Orange Coast College, A
Palo Verde College, A
Palomar College, A
Pasadena City College, A

Colorado

Aims Community College, A
Arapahoe Community College, A
CollegeAmerica - Fort Collins, A
Community College of Aurora, A
Community College of Denver, A
DeVry University (Westminster), A
Front Range Community College, A
IBMC College (Fort Collins), A
Pikes Peak Community College, A
Pueblo Community College, A
Red Rocks Community College, A

Connecticut

Asnuntuck Community College, A
Capital Community College, A
Naugatuck Valley Community College, A
Three Rivers Community College, A

District of Columbia

University of the District of Columbia, A

Florida

Broward College, A
College of Central Florida, A
DeVry University (Miramar), A
DeVry University (Orlando), A
Florida National University, A
Florida SouthWestern State College, A
Fortis College (Winter Park), A
Gulf Coast State College, A
Hillsborough Community College, A
Miami Dade College, A
North Florida Community College, A
Northwest Florida State College, A
Pensacola State College, A
Polk State College, A
St. Johns River State College, A
South Florida State College, A
Tallahassee Community College, A
Valencia College, A

Georgia

DeVry University (Decatur), A
Interactive College of Technology (Chamblee), A

Idaho

Lewis-Clark State College, AB

Illinois

College of Lake County, A
Danville Area Community College, A
DeVry University Online, A
Fox College, A
Illinois Central College, A
Lake Land College, A
Midstate College, A
Northwestern College - Chicago Campus, A
Oakton Community College, A
Parkland College, A
St. Augustine College, A
South Suburban College, A
Taylor Business Institute, A

Indiana

International Business College (Fort Wayne), AB
International Business College (Indianapolis), A
Ivy Tech Community College - Bloomington, A
Ivy Tech Community College - Central Indiana, A
Ivy Tech Community College - Columbus, A
Ivy Tech Community College - East Central, A
Ivy Tech Community College - Kokomo, A
Ivy Tech Community College - Lafayette, A
Ivy Tech Community College - North Central, A
Ivy Tech Community College - Northeast, A
Ivy Tech Community College - Northwest, A
Ivy Tech Community College - Richmond, A
Ivy Tech Community College - Southeast, A
Ivy Tech Community College - Southern Indiana, A
Ivy Tech Community College - Southwest, A
Ivy Tech Community College - Wabash Valley, A
Vincennes University, A

Iowa

Des Moines Area Community College, A
Iowa Lakes Community College, A
North Iowa Area Community College, A
Southwestern Community College, A
Western Iowa Tech Community College, A

Kansas

Johnson County Community College, A
Manhattan Area Technical College, A

Kentucky

Jefferson Community and Technical College, A
Madisonville Community College, A
Sullivan University, A

Louisiana

Northwest Louisiana Technical College, A
South Central Louisiana Technical College, A
Southern University at Shreveport, A
Sowela Technical Community College, A

Maine

Kennebec Valley Community College, A

Maryland

Allegany College of Maryland, A
Anne Arundel Community College, A
Baltimore City Community College, A
Carroll Community College, A
Chesapeake College, A
College of Southern Maryland, A
Community College of Baltimore County, A
Hagerstown Community College, A
Montgomery College, A
Wor-Wic Community College, A

Massachusetts

Greenfield Community College, A
Holyoke Community College, A

Michigan

Bay de Noc Community College, A
Delta College, A
Ferris State University, AB
Kalamazoo Valley Community College, A
Kellogg Community College, A
Lansing Community College, A
Mott Community College, A
North Central Michigan College, A

Northwestern Michigan College, A
Oakland Community College, A
St. Clair County Community College, A
Schoolcraft College, A
Southwestern Michigan College, A
Washtenaw Community College, A
Wayne County Community College District, A

Minnesota

Anoka-Ramsey Community College, A
Duluth Business University, A
Minneapolis Business College, A
Minneapolis Community and Technical College, A
Minnesota State College - Southeast Technical, A
North Hennepin Community College, A
Northland Community and Technical College, A

Mississippi

Antonelli College (Hattiesburg), A
Antonelli College (Jackson), A
Hinds Community College, A

Missouri

East Central College, A
Hickey College, A
Jefferson College, A
Metro Business College (Rolla), A
Moberly Area Community College, A
St. Charles Community College, A

Montana

Great Falls College Montana State University, A
Montana State University Billings, A
Montana Tech of The University of Montana, A
University of Montana, A

Nevada

College of Southern Nevada, A
Great Basin College, A

New Jersey

Camden County College, A
Essex County College, A
Hudson County Community College, A
Raritan Valley Community College, A
Rowan College at Gloucester County, A
Rowan University, B
Union County College, A

New Mexico

San Juan College, A
Southwestern Indian Polytechnic Institute, A

New York

Adirondack Community College, A
Borough of Manhattan Community College of the
   City University of New York, A
Bramson ORT College, A
Broome Community College, A
Cayuga County Community College, A
Columbia-Greene Community College, A
Dutchess Community College, A
Eugenio María de Hostos Community College of the
   City University of New York, A
Fiorello H. LaGuardia Community College of the
   City University of New York, A
Herkimer County Community College, A
Hilbert College, A
Jamestown Community College, A
Jefferson Community College, A
Mohawk Valley Community College, A
Morrisville State College, A
Nassau Community College, A
New York City College of Technology of the City
   University of New York, A
Onondaga Community College, A
Orange County Community College, A
Plaza College, A
Queensborough Community College of the City Uni-
   versity of New York, A
Schenectady County Community College, A
State University of New York College of Agriculture
   and Technology at Cobleskill, A
State University of New York College of Technology
   at Alfred, A

State University of New York College of Technology
   at Canton, A
State University of New York College of Technology
   at Delhi, A
TCI - College of Technology, A
Tompkins Cortland Community College, A
Ulster County Community College, A
Wood Tobe - Coburn School, A

North Carolina

Alamance Community College, A
Brunswick Community College, A
Cape Fear Community College, A
Catawba Valley Community College, A
Edgecombe Community College, A
Guilford Technical Community College, A
Haywood Community College, A
King's College, A
Mayland Community College, A
Stanly Community College, A
Western Piedmont Community College, A
Wilkes Community College, A

North Dakota

Dakota College at Bottineau, A
Turtle Mountain Community College, A
Williston State College, A

Ohio

Bowling Green State University, B
Columbus State Community College, A
James A. Rhodes State College, A
Kent State University at Ashtabula, A
Kent State University at East Liverpool, A
Kent State University at Geauga, A
Kent State University at Salem, A
Kent State University at Trumbull, A
Kent State University at Tuscarawas, A
Miami University, A
Ohio University - Lancaster, A
Ohio University - Southern Campus, A
Owens Community College, A
Southern State Community College, A
The University of Akron, A
University of Cincinnati Blue Ash College, A
University of Rio Grande, A
The University of Toledo, A

Oklahoma

Community Care College, A
Eastern Oklahoma State College, A
Tulsa Community College, A
Western Oklahoma State College, A

Oregon

Chemeketa Community College, A
Lane Community College, A
Linn-Benton Community College, A
Rogue Community College, A
Tillamook Bay Community College, A

Pennsylvania

Bradford School, A
Bucks County Community College, A
Community College of Allegheny County, A
Community College of Beaver County, A
Delaware County Community College, A
Harrisburg Area Community College, A
Lackawanna College, A
Lehigh Carbon Community College, A
Montgomery County Community College, A
Northampton Community College, A
Pennsylvania College of Technology, A
South Hills School of Business & Technology
   (Altoona), A
Westmoreland County Community College, A

South Dakota

Sinte Gleska University, A

Tennessee

Chattanooga State Community College, A
Daymar College (Clarksville), A
Miller-Motte Technical College (Clarksville), A
Pellissippi State Community College, A

Texas

Austin Community College District, A
Del Mar College, A
Kilgore College, A
Lamar Institute of Technology, A
Lamar State College - Port Arthur, A
Lee College, A
Northwest Vista College, A
St. Edward's University, B

Utah

LDS Business College, A
Provo College, A
Salt Lake Community College, A

Washington

Bates Technical College, A
Bellingham Technical College, A
Big Bend Community College, A
Centralia College, A
Clark College, A
Clover Park Technical College, A
Columbia Basin College, A
Edmonds Community College, A
Grays Harbor College, A
Green River College, A
Lake Washington Institute of Technology, A
Lower Columbia College, A
North Seattle College, A
Olympic College, A
Pierce College at Fort Steilacoom, A
Spokane Community College, A
Spokane Falls Community College, A
Tacoma Community College, A
Walla Walla Community College, A
Wenatchee Valley College, A

West Virginia

American Public University System, A
Davis & Elkins College, A
Mountwest Community & Technical College, A

Wyoming

Casper College, A
Central Wyoming College, A

Canada

British Columbia

British Columbia Institute of Technology, A

ACOUSTICS

United States

Illinois

Columbia College Chicago, B

Massachusetts

University of Massachusetts Dartmouth, O

New York

Rensselaer Polytechnic Institute, MD

Pennsylvania

Penn State University Park, MD

ACTING

United States

California

Academy of Art University, AB
American Musical and Dramatic Academy, Los Angeles, B
California State University, Long Beach, B
Chapman University, B
New York Film Academy, A
Pacific Union College, B

Pepperdine University, B
Santa Barbara City College, A
University of Southern California, B

Connecticut

University of Connecticut, B
University of Hartford, B

Florida

Barry University, B
Florida Southern College, B
Florida State University, B
New World School of the Arts, B
University of Miami, B

Illinois

Bradley University, B
Columbia College Chicago, B
DePaul University, B
Illinois Wesleyan University, B
Roosevelt University, B

Indiana

Purdue University, B

Iowa

Drake University, B
University of Northern Iowa, B

Kansas

Central Christian College of Kansas, AB

Maryland

Stevenson University, B
Towson University, B
University of Maryland, Baltimore County, B

Massachusetts

Boston University, B
Emerson College, B
Greenfield Community College, A
Salem State University, B

Michigan

Central Michigan University, B
Michigan State University, B
Oakland University, B
Western Michigan University, B

Minnesota

Augsburg College, B

Missouri

College of the Ozarks, B
Lindenwood University, B
Webster University, B

Nebraska

Nebraska Wesleyan University, B

Nevada

University of Nevada, Las Vegas, B

New Hampshire

Keene State College, B

New Jersey

Bergen Community College, A
Kean University, B

New York

Five Towns College, B
Hofstra University, B
Ithaca College, B
Marymount Manhattan College, B
Nazareth College of Rochester, B
Pace University, B
Syracuse University, B

North Carolina

Campbell University, B
Elon University, B
Greensboro College, B

Ohio

Ashland University, B
Baldwin Wallace University, B
Ohio University, B
Wright State University, B

Oklahoma

Oklahoma City University, B
Oral Roberts University, B

Pennsylvania

Arcadia University, B
Northampton Community College, A
Penn State Abington, B
Penn State Altoona, B
Penn State Beaver, B
Penn State Berks, B
Penn State Brandywine, B
Penn State DuBois, B
Penn State Erie, The Behrend College, B
Penn State Fayette, The Eberly Campus, B
Penn State Greater Allegheny, B
Penn State Hazleton, B
Penn State Lehigh Valley, B
Penn State Mont Alto, B
Penn State New Kensington, B
Penn State Schuylkill, B
Penn State Shenango, B
Penn State University Park, B
Penn State Wilkes-Barre, B
Penn State Worthington Scranton, B
Penn State York, B
Seton Hill University, B
Slippery Rock University of Pennsylvania, B
Temple University, B
The University of the Arts, B

Rhode Island

Rhode Island College, B

South Carolina

Coker College, B

Tennessee

Belmont University, B
Freed-Hardeman University, B
Lipscomb University, B

Texas

Baylor University, B
KD Conservatory College of Film and Dramatic Arts, A
St. Edward's University, B
Texas Christian University, B
Trinity University, B
The University of Texas at Austin, B

Utah

Brigham Young University, B

Vermont

Bennington College, B
Johnson State College, B
Marlboro College, B

Virginia

Emory & Henry College, B
Shenandoah University, B

Washington

Central Washington University, B
Cornish College of the Arts, B
University of Washington, B

West Virginia

Bethany College, B

Wyoming

Casper College, A
Central Wyoming College, A

Canada

Alberta

University of Alberta, B
University of Lethbridge, B

Maritime Provinces: Nova Scotia

Dalhousie University, B

Newfoundland and Labrador

Memorial University of Newfoundland, B

Ontario

Ryerson University, B
University of Windsor, B
York University, B

Saskatchewan

University of Regina, B

ACTUARIAL SCIENCE

United States

Arizona

Arizona State University at the Tempe campus, B

California

California Baptist University, B
California State University, East Bay, M
University of California, Santa Barbara, B

Connecticut

Central Connecticut State University, M
University of Connecticut, BMD

Florida

Broward College, A
South Florida State College, A
University of Central Florida, MO

Georgia

Georgia State University, BM

Illinois

Aurora University, B
Bradley University, B
Elmhurst College, B
North Central College, B
Roosevelt University, BM
University of Illinois at Urbana - Champaign, BM

Indiana

Ball State University, BM
Butler University, B
Grace College, B
Indiana University Northwest, B
Indiana University South Bend, B
Purdue University, B
Valparaiso University, B

Iowa

Central College, B
Dordt College, B
Drake University, B
Mount Mercy University, B
Northwestern College, B
Simpson College, B
The University of Iowa, BMD

Kentucky

Bellarmine University, B

Maine

University of Maine at Farmington, B

Massachusetts

Assumption College, B
Bentley University, B
Boston University, M
Western New England University, B
Worcester Polytechnic Institute, B

Michigan

Central Michigan University, B
Eastern Michigan University, B
Michigan State University, B
Oakland University, B
Olivet College, B
Spring Arbor University, B
University of Michigan - Flint, B

Minnesota

Saint Mary's University of Minnesota, B
University of St. Thomas, B

Missouri

Maryville University of Saint Louis, BM

Nebraska

University of Nebraska - Lincoln, BM

New York

Baruch College of the City University of New York, B
Binghamton University, State University of New York, B
Columbia University, M
New York University, B
Niagara University, B
Queens College of the City University of New York, B
St. John's University, BM
Siena College, B
University at Albany, State University of New York, B

North Carolina

Appalachian State University, B
High Point University, B

Ohio

Ashland University, B
Bowling Green State University, B
Ohio Northern University, B
The Ohio State University, B
Ohio University, B
Xavier University, B

Oklahoma

University of Central Oklahoma, B

Pennsylvania

Arcadia University, B
Carnegie Mellon University, B
Lebanon Valley College, B
Penn State Abington, B
Penn State Altoona, B
Penn State Beaver, B
Penn State Berks, B
Penn State Brandywine, B
Penn State DuBois, B
Penn State Erie, The Behrend College, B
Penn State Fayette, The Eberly Campus, B
Penn State Greater Allegheny, B
Penn State Hazleton, B
Penn State Lehigh Valley, B
Penn State Mont Alto, B
Penn State New Kensington, B
Penn State Schuylkill, B
Penn State Shenango, B
Penn State Wilkes-Barre, B
Penn State Worthington Scranton, B
Penn State York, B
Robert Morris University, B
Saint Joseph's University, B
Slippery Rock University of Pennsylvania, B
Temple University, BM
Thiel College, B
University of Pennsylvania, B

Rhode Island

Bryant University, B

South Carolina

Bob Jones University, B

South Dakota

Dakota Wesleyan University, B

Tennessee

Middle Tennessee State University, M

Texas

Texas Christian University, B
The University of Texas at Austin, MD
The University of Texas at Dallas, BM
The University of Texas at San Antonio, B

Utah

Brigham Young University, B

Washington

Central Washington University, B

West Virginia

Bethany College, B

Wisconsin

Carroll University, B
Concordia University Wisconsin, B
Milwaukee School of Engineering, B
University of Wisconsin - Madison, B
University of Wisconsin - Milwaukee, B

Canada

Alberta

University of Alberta, B
University of Calgary, B

British Columbia

Simon Fraser University, BMD

Manitoba

University of Manitoba, B

Ontario

University of Toronto, B
University of Waterloo, BMD
The University of Western Ontario, B
York University, B

Quebec

Concordia University, B
Université Laval, B
Université de Montréal, B
Université du Québec à Montréal, O

Saskatchewan

University of Regina, B

ACUPUNCTURE AND ORIENTAL MEDICINE

United States

Connecticut

University of Bridgeport, M

New York

New York College of Health Professions, M
Swedish Institute, College of Health Sciences, M

Washington

Bastyr University, MDO

ACUTE CARE/CRITICAL CARE NURSING

United States

Alabama

The University of Alabama in Huntsville, M

Arizona

Grand Canyon University, MO

California

San Francisco State University, M

District of Columbia

Georgetown University, M

Florida

Barry University, M
University of Miami, M
University of South Florida, MD

Georgia

Armstrong State University, M

Illinois

Loyola University Chicago, MO
University of Illinois at Chicago, M

Indiana

Purdue University Northwest (Hammond), M

Iowa

Allen College, O

Massachusetts

Northeastern University, M

Michigan

University of Michigan, M
Wayne State University, M

Missouri

Goldfarb School of Nursing at Barnes-Jewish College, M
Maryville University of Saint Louis, M

New York

The College of New Rochelle, MO
Columbia University, MO
New York University, MDO

North Carolina

Duke University, MO

Ohio

Case Western Reserve University, M
Mount Carmel College of Nursing, M
Ohio University, M
University of Cincinnati, M
Wright State University, M

Pennsylvania

Drexel University, M
University of Pennsylvania, M

South Carolina

University of South Carolina, MO

Tennessee

Southern Adventist University, M
Vanderbilt University, M

Texas

Texas Woman's University, M
The University of Texas Health Science Center at San Antonio, O

Virginia

University of Virginia, M

Wisconsin

Marquette University, DO

U.S. Territories: Puerto Rico

Inter American University of Puerto Rico, Arecibo Campus, M
University of Puerto Rico, Medical Sciences Campus, M

Canada

Ontario

University of Guelph, O

ADMINISTRATION OF SPECIAL EDUCATION

United States

California

Foothill College, A

Pennsylvania

Slippery Rock University of Pennsylvania, B

ADMINISTRATIVE ASSISTANT AND SECRETARIAL SCIENCE

United States

Alabama

Bevill State Community College, A
Bishop State Community College, A
Central Alabama Community College, A
Chattahoochee Valley Community College, A
Enterprise State Community College, A
Gadsden State Community College, A
George C. Wallace Community College, A
George Corley Wallace State Community College, A
H. Councill Trenholm State Community College, A
James H. Faulkner State Community College, A
Jefferson Davis Community College, A
Jefferson State Community College, A
Lawson State Community College, A
Lurleen B. Wallace Community College, A
Northeast Alabama Community College, A
Northwest-Shoals Community College, A
Oakwood University, AB
Reid State Technical College, A
Shelton State Community College, A
Southern Union State Community College, A
Virginia College in Birmingham, A
Wallace State Community College, A

Alaska

University of Alaska Anchorage, Matanuska-Susitna College, A
University of Alaska, Prince William Sound College, A

Arizona

Central Arizona College, A
Cochise County Community College District, A
Diné College, A
GateWay Community College, A
Glendale Community College, A
Mesa Community College, A
Northland Pioneer College, A
Paradise Valley Community College, A
Phoenix College, A
Pima Community College, A
Scottsdale Community College, A
Yavapai College, A

Arkansas

Arkansas State University - Mountain Home, A
Arkansas Tech University, A
Black River Technical College, A
College of the Ouachitas, A

East Arkansas Community College, A
National Park College, A
Phillips Community College of the University of Arkansas, A
Pulaski Technical College, A
Rich Mountain Community College, A
Shorter College, A
South Arkansas Community College, A
Williams Baptist College, A

California

Allan Hancock College, A
American River College, A
Antelope Valley College, A
Bakersfield College, A
Butte College, A
Cabrillo College, A
Cañada College, A
Cerritos College, A
Cerro Coso Community College, A
Chabot College, A
Chaffey College, A
Citrus College, A
City College of San Francisco, A
College of Alameda, A
College of the Canyons, A
College of the Redwoods, A
College of San Mateo, A
College of the Sequoias, A
College of the Siskiyous, A
Columbia College, A
Contra Costa College, A
Cosumnes River College, A
Cuesta College, A
Cypress College, A
De Anza College, A
East Los Angeles College, A
El Camino College, A
Empire College, A
Evergreen Valley College, A
Feather River College, A
Fresno City College, A
Fullerton College, A
Gavilan College, A
Glendale Community College, A
Golden West College, A
Grossmont College, A
Hartnell College, A
Humphreys College, AB
Imperial Valley College, A
Irvine Valley College, A
Lake Tahoe Community College, A
Laney College, A
Las Positas College, A
Lassen Community College District, A
Long Beach City College, A
Los Angeles City College, A
Los Angeles Harbor College, A
Los Angeles Mission College, A
Los Angeles Southwest College, A
Los Angeles Valley College, A
Los Medanos College, A
Mendocino College, A
Merced College, A
Merritt College, A
MiraCosta College, A
Mission College, A
Modesto Junior College, A
Monterey Peninsula College, A
Mt. San Antonio College, A
Mt. San Jacinto College, A
Napa Valley College, A
Ohlone College, A
Oxnard College, A
Palo Verde College, A
Palomar College, A
Pasadena City College, A
Porterville College, A
Reedley College, A
Sacramento City College, A
Saddleback College, A
San Bernardino Valley College, A
San Diego City College, A
San Diego Mesa College, A
San Diego Miramar College, A
San Jose City College, A

Santa Ana College, A
Santa Barbara City College, A
Santa Monica College, A
Shasta College, A
Sierra College, A
Skyline College, A
Southwestern College, A
Taft College, A
Victor Valley College, A
West Hills Community College, A
West Los Angeles College, A
West Valley College, A
Yuba College, A

Colorado

Aims Community College, A
Community College of Denver, A
Everest College (Colorado Springs), A
Otero Junior College, A

Connecticut

Capital Community College, A
Housatonic Community College, A
Manchester Community College, A
Middlesex Community College, A
Northwestern Connecticut Community College, A
Norwalk Community College, A
Quinebaug Valley Community College, A
Tunxis Community College, A

District of Columbia

University of the District of Columbia, A

Florida

Daytona State College, A
Hobe Sound Bible College, A
Indian River State College, A
Lincoln College of Technology, A
Miami Dade College, A
Palm Beach State College, A
Pensacola State College, A
St. Johns River State College, A
Seminole State College of Florida, A
State College of Florida Manatee-Sarasota, A
Trinity Baptist College, A

Georgia

Athens Technical College, A
Augusta Technical College, A
Bainbridge State College, A
Central Georgia Technical College, A
Chattahoochee Technical College, A
Clayton State University, A
Coastal Pines Technical College, A
Columbus Technical College, A
Fort Valley State University, AB
Georgia Piedmont Technical College, A
Gwinnett Technical College, A
Interactive College of Technology (Chamblee), A
Lanier Technical College, A
North Georgia Technical College, A
Oconee Fall Line Technical College, A
Ogeechee Technical College, A
Savannah Technical College, A
South Georgia Technical College, A
Southeastern Technical College, A
Southern Crescent Technical College, A
Southern Regional Technical College, A
Valdosta State University, B
West Georgia Technical College, A
Wiregrass Georgia Technical College, A

Hawaii

Hawaii Community College, A
Kauai Community College, A
Leeward Community College, A
University of Hawaii Maui College, A

Idaho

College of Southern Idaho, A
College of Western Idaho, A
Eastern Idaho Technical College, A
Idaho State University, AB
Lewis-Clark State College, AB
North Idaho College, A

Illinois

Black Hawk College, A
Carl Sandburg College, A
City Colleges of Chicago, Malcolm X College, A
College of DuPage, A
College of Lake County, A
Elgin Community College, A
Fox College, A
Harper College, A
Heartland Community College, A
Highland Community College, A
Illinois Central College, A
John Wood Community College, A
Joliet Junior College, A
Kankakee Community College, A
Kishwaukee College, A
Lake Land College, A
Lewis and Clark Community College, A
Lincoln Land Community College, A
MacCormac College, A
McHenry County College, A
Midstate College, A
Moraine Valley Community College, A
Morton College, A
Northwestern College - Bridgeview Campus, A
Oakton Community College, A
Parkland College, A
Rend Lake College, A
Richland Community College, A
Rock Valley College, A
St. Augustine College, A
Sauk Valley Community College, A
Shawnee Community College, A
Southeastern Illinois College, A
Southwestern Illinois College, A
Spoon River College, A

Indiana

Ball State University, A
Harrison College, A
International Business College (Fort Wayne), AB
International Business College (Indianapolis), A
Ivy Tech Community College - Bloomington, A
Ivy Tech Community College - Columbus, A
Ivy Tech Community College - East Central, A
Ivy Tech Community College - Kokomo, A
Ivy Tech Community College - Southeast, A
Ivy Tech Community College - Southern Indiana, A
Ivy Tech Community College - Southwest, A
Vincennes University, A

Iowa

Clinton Community College, A
Dordt College, A
Ellsworth Community College, A
Faith Baptist Bible College and Theological Seminary, AB
Iowa Central Community College, A
Iowa Lakes Community College, A
Iowa Western Community College, A
Kirkwood Community College, A
Marshalltown Community College, A
Muscatine Community College, A
North Iowa Area Community College, A
Northeast Iowa Community College, A
Northwest Iowa Community College, A
Scott Community College, A
Southeastern Community College, A
Western Iowa Tech Community College, A

Kansas

Allen Community College, A
Barton County Community College, A
Butler Community College, A
Cloud County Community College, A
Coffeyville Community College, A
Colby Community College, A
Cowley County Community College and Area Vocational - Technical School, A
Dodge City Community College, A
Flint Hills Technical College, A
Fort Hays State University, A
Fort Scott Community College, A
Garden City Community College, A
Highland Community College, A

Hutchinson Community College, A
Independence Community College, A
Johnson County Community College, A
Kansas City Kansas Community College, A
Labette Community College, A
Manhattan Area Technical College, A
Neosho County Community College, A
North Central Kansas Technical College, A
Northwest Kansas Technical College, A
Pratt Community College, A
Seward County Community College and Area Technical School, A
Washburn University, A

Kentucky

American National University (Danville), A
American National University (Florence), A
American National University (Lexington), A
American National University (Louisville), A
American National University (Pikeville), A
American National University (Richmond), A
Campbellsville University, AB
Eastern Kentucky University, A
Hopkinsville Community College, A
Madisonville Community College, A
Southeast Kentucky Community and Technical College, A

Louisiana

Bossier Parish Community College, A
Delta School of Business and Technology, A
Louisiana Delta Community College, A
Louisiana State University at Eunice, A
McCann School of Business & Technology (Monroe), A
South Louisiana Community College, A
Sowela Technical Community College, A

Maine

Beal College, A
Central Maine Community College, A
Eastern Maine Community College, A
Kaplan University, South Portland, A
Northern Maine Community College, A

Maryland

Allegany College of Maryland, A
Baltimore City Community College, A
Carroll Community College, A
Cecil College, A
Community College of Baltimore County, A
Harford Community College, A
Kaplan University, Hagerstown Campus, A
Wor-Wic Community College, A

Massachusetts

Greenfield Community College, A
Holyoke Community College, A
Massasoit Community College, A
North Shore Community College, A
Northern Essex Community College, A
Roxbury Community College, A
Springfield Technical Community College, A

Michigan

Alpena Community College, A
Baker College, A
Bay Mills Community College, A
Bay de Noc Community College, A
Delta College, A
Jackson College, A
Kellogg Community College, A
Kirtland Community College, A
Kuyper College, A
Lake Michigan College, A
Lansing Community College, A
Macomb Community College, A
Mid Michigan Community College, A
Monroe County Community College, A
Montcalm Community College, A
Muskegon Community College, A
North Central Michigan College, A
Northern Michigan University, A
Washtenaw Community College, A

Minnesota

Anoka Technical College, A
Central Lakes College, A
Century College, A
Hennepin Technical College, A
Hibbing Community College, A
Mesabi Range College, A
Minneapolis Business College, A
Minneapolis Community and Technical College, A
Minnesota State College - Southeast Technical, A
Minnesota State Community and Technical College, A
Minnesota State Community and Technical College - Detroit Lakes, A
Minnesota State Community and Technical College - Moorhead, A
Minnesota West Community and Technical College, A
Northland Community and Technical College, A
Northwest Technical College, A
Pine Technical and Community College, A
Rainy River Community College, A
Ridgewater College, A
Riverland Community College, A
Rochester Community and Technical College, A
St. Cloud Technical & Community College, A
Saint Paul College - A Community & Technical College, A

Mississippi

Antonelli College (Hattiesburg), A
Coahoma Community College, A
East Central Community College, A
East Mississippi Community College, A
Hinds Community College, A
Itawamba Community College, A
Meridian Community College, A
Mississippi Delta Community College, A
Mississippi Gulf Coast Community College, A
Northeast Mississippi Community College, A
Pearl River Community College, A
Southeastern Baptist College, A
Southwest Mississippi Community College, A

Missouri

Crowder College, A
East Central College, A
Hickey College, A
Jefferson College, A
Mineral Area College, A
Moberly Area Community College, A
North Central Missouri College, A
Ozarks Technical Community College, A
Three Rivers Community College, A
Vatterott College (Kansas City), A
Vatterott College (Saint Joseph), A

Montana

Flathead Valley Community College, A
Montana State University Billings, A
Montana Tech of The University of Montana, A
Salish Kootenai College, A
Stone Child College, A
University of Montana, B

Nebraska

Central Community College - Columbus Campus, A
Central Community College - Grand Island Campus, A
Central Community College - Hastings Campus, A
Metropolitan Community College, A
Mid-Plains Community College, A
Midland University, B
Northeast Community College, A
Southeast Community College, Lincoln Campus, A

New Hampshire

Manchester Community College, A

New Jersey

Atlantic Cape Community College, A
Brookdale Community College, A
Camden County College, A
Cumberland County College, A
Essex County College, A

Mercer County Community College, A
Middlesex County College, A
Passaic County Community College, A
Raritan Valley Community College, A
Rowan College at Gloucester County, A
Salem Community College, A
Warren County Community College, A

New Mexico

Central New Mexico Community College, A
Clovis Community College, A
Doña Ana Community College, A
Eastern New Mexico University - Roswell, A
Luna Community College, A
Navajo Technical University, A
New Mexico Junior College, A
New Mexico State University - Alamogordo, A
New Mexico State University - Carlsbad, A
New Mexico State University - Grants, A
Santa Fe Community College, A
University of New Mexico - Gallup, A
University of New Mexico - Los Alamos Branch, A
University of New Mexico - Taos, A
University of New Mexico - Valencia Campus, A

New York

Borough of Manhattan Community College of the City University of New York, A
Bramson ORT College, A
Bronx Community College of the City University of New York, A
Bryant & Stratton College - Albany Campus, A
Bryant & Stratton College - Amherst Campus, A
Bryant & Stratton College - Buffalo Campus, A
Bryant & Stratton College - Greece Campus, A
Bryant & Stratton College - Henrietta Campus, A
Bryant & Stratton College - Liverpool Campus, A
Bryant & Stratton College - Orchard Park Campus, A
Bryant & Stratton College - Syracuse Campus, A
Columbia-Greene Community College, A
Concordia College - New York, A
Elmira Business Institute, A
Eugenio María de Hostos Community College of the City University of New York, A
Finger Lakes Community College, A
Fiorello H. LaGuardia Community College of the City University of New York, A
Fulton-Montgomery Community College, A
Genesee Community College, A
Jamestown Business College, A
Jamestown Community College, A
Jefferson Community College, A
Kingsborough Community College of the City University of New York, A
Mohawk Valley Community College, A
Monroe Community College, A
Morrisville State College, A
Nassau Community College, A
Niagara County Community College, A
Orange County Community College, A
Plaza College, A
Queensborough Community College of the City University of New York, A
Rockland Community College, A
Sullivan County Community College, A
Tompkins Cortland Community College, A
Utica School of Commerce, A
Westchester Community College, A
Wood Tobe - Coburn School, A

North Carolina

Beaufort County Community College, A
Bladen Community College, A
Carteret Community College, A
Central Carolina Community College, A
Central Piedmont Community College, A
College of The Albemarle, A
Davidson County Community College, A
Isothermal Community College, A
Johnston Community College, A
King's College, A
Martin Community College, A
North Carolina Agricultural and Technical State University, B
Pamlico Community College, A

Robeson Community College, A
Sampson Community College, A
Sandhills Community College, A
South College - Asheville, A
Southeastern Community College, A
Southwestern Community College, A
Surry Community College, A
Vance-Granville Community College, A

North Dakota

Bismarck State College, A
Cankdeska Cikana Community College, A
Dakota College at Bottineau, A
Dickinson State University, A
Lake Region State College, A
Sitting Bull College, A
Turtle Mountain Community College, A
United Tribes Technical College, A

Ohio

American National University (Cincinnati), A
American National University (Kettering), A
Belmont College, A
Bryant & Stratton College - Cleveland Campus, A
Bryant & Stratton College - Eastlake Campus, A
Bryant & Stratton College - Parma Campus, A
Cincinnati State Technical and Community College, A
Clark State Community College, A
Columbus State Community College, A
Cuyahoga Community College, A
Davis College, A
Daymar College, A
Eastern Gateway Community College, A
Gallipolis Career College, A
Harrison College, A
James A. Rhodes State College, A
Kent State University at Ashtabula, A
Kent State University at Salem, A
Kent State University at Trumbull, A
Kent State University at Tuscarawas, A
Lakeland Community College, A
Lorain County Community College, A
Marion Technical College, A
Miami University, A
Miami University Middletown, A
Mount Vernon Nazarene University, B
North Central State College, A
Northwest State Community College, A
Ohio Business College (Sandusky), A
Ohio Business College (Sheffield Village), A
Ohio University - Chillicothe, A
Sinclair Community College, A
Southern State Community College, A
Stark State College, A
Trumbull Business College, A
The University of Akron, A
The University of Akron Wayne College, A
University of Northwestern Ohio, A
University of Rio Grande, A
Washington State Community College, A
Wright State University - Lake Campus, A
Zane State College, A

Oklahoma

East Central University, B
Eastern Oklahoma State College, A
Northeastern Oklahoma Agricultural and Mechanical College, A
Northern Oklahoma College, A
Oklahoma City Community College, A
Redlands Community College, A
Rose State College, A

Oregon

Blue Mountain Community College, A
Chemeketa Community College, A
Clackamas Community College, A
Columbia Gorge Community College, A
Klamath Community College, A
Lane Community College, A
Linn-Benton Community College, A
Mt. Hood Community College, A
Portland Community College, A
Tillamook Bay Community College, A
Umpqua Community College, A

Pennsylvania

Bradford School, A
Butler County Community College, A
Cambria-Rowe Business College (Indiana), A
Cambria-Rowe Business College (Johnstown), A
Clarion University of Pennsylvania, A
Community College of Allegheny County, A
Community College of Beaver County, A
Fortis Institute (Erie), A
Harrisburg Area Community College, A
Lackawanna College, A
Lancaster Bible College, A
Laurel Business Institute, A
Laurel Technical Institute, A
Luzerne County Community College, A
Montgomery County Community College, A
Northampton Community College, A
Penn Commercial Business and Technical School, A
Reading Area Community College, A
South Hills School of Business & Technology
    (Altoona), A
South Hills School of Business & Technology (State
    College), A
Summit University, A
Westmoreland County Community College, A

Rhode Island

Community College of Rhode Island, A

South Carolina

Aiken Technical College, A
Central Carolina Technical College, A
Denmark Technical College, A
Florence-Darlington Technical College, A
Greenville Technical College, A
Horry-Georgetown Technical College, A
Midlands Technical College, A
Northeastern Technical College, A
Orangeburg-Calhoun Technical College, A
Piedmont Technical College, A
Spartanburg Community College, A
Technical College of the Lowcountry, A
Tri-County Technical College, A
Trident Technical College, A
Williamsburg Technical College, A
York Technical College, A

South Dakota

Black Hills State University, A
Oglala Lakota College, A
Sinte Gleska University, A

Tennessee

Cleveland State Community College, A
Nashville State Community College, A
National College (Bristol), A
National College (Knoxville), A
National College (Nashville), A
Northeast State Community College, A
Pellissippi State Community College, A
Roane State Community College, A
South College, A
Southwest Tennessee Community College, A
Tennessee State University, AB
Welch College, A

Texas

Alvin Community College, A
Amarillo College, A
Angelina College, A
Austin Community College District, A
Blinn College, A
Brazosport College, A
Central Texas College, A
Coastal Bend College, A
Collin County Community College District, A
Del Mar College, A
El Paso Community College, A
Galveston College, A
Hill College, A
Howard College, A
Lamar Institute of Technology, A
Lamar State College - Orange, A
Lamar State College - Port Arthur, A
Laredo Community College, A

Lee College, A
Lone Star College - Kingwood, A
Lone Star College - Tomball, A
McLennan Community College, A
Navarro College, A
North Central Texas College, A
North Lake College, A
Northwest Vista College, A
Odessa College, A
Panola College, A
Ranger College, A
Richland College, A
St. Philip's College, A
San Jacinto College District, A
South Plains College, A
Tarrant County College District, A
Temple College, A
Texarkana College, A
Tyler Junior College, A
Vernon College, A
Victoria College, A
Weatherford College, A
Western Texas College, A
Wharton County Junior College, A
Wiley College, AB

Utah

Snow College, A
Weber State University, AB

Vermont

Community College of Vermont, A

Virginia

American National University (Charlottesville), A
American National University (Danville), A
American National University (Harrisonburg), A
American National University (Lynchburg), A
American National University (Martinsville), A
American National University (Salem), A
Bryant & Stratton College - Richmond Campus, A
Bryant & Stratton College - Virginia Beach Campus,
    A
Dabney S. Lancaster Community College, A
Eastern Shore Community College, A
Miller-Motte Technical College (Lynchburg), A
New River Community College, A
Northern Virginia Community College, A
Patrick Henry Community College, A
Paul D. Camp Community College, A
Rappahannock Community College, A
Southside Virginia Community College, A
Tidewater Community College, A
Virginia Highlands Community College, A
Virginia Western Community College, A
Wytheville Community College, A

Washington

Bates Technical College, A
Edmonds Community College, A
Everett Community College, A
Highline College, A
Lower Columbia College, A
North Seattle College, A
Olympic College, A
Pierce College at Fort Steilacoom, A
Pierce College at Puyallup, A
Seattle Central College, A
Skagit Valley College, A
South Puget Sound Community College, A
South Seattle College, A
Spokane Community College, A
Spokane Falls Community College, A
Walla Walla Community College, A
Wenatchee Valley College, A
Whatcom Community College, A
Yakima Valley Community College, A

West Virginia

BridgeValley Community and Technical College
    (Montgomery), A
Eastern West Virginia Community and Technical
    College, A
Huntington Junior College, A
Mountain State College, A

Mountwest Community & Technical College, A
New River Community and Technical College, A
Potomac State College of West Virginia University,
    A
Southern West Virginia Community and Technical
    College, A
West Virginia Business College (Nutter Fort), A
West Virginia Business College (Wheeling), A
West Virginia Junior College - Morgantown, A
West Virginia Northern Community College, A
West Virginia University at Parkersburg, A

Wisconsin

Blackhawk Technical College, A
Bryant & Stratton College - Milwaukee Campus, A
Chippewa Valley Technical College, A
College of Menominee Nation, A
Fox Valley Technical College, A
Gateway Technical College, A
Lac Courte Oreilles Ojibwa Community College, A
Lakeshore Technical College, A
Madison Area Technical College, A
Mid-State Technical College, A
Milwaukee Area Technical College, A
Moraine Park Technical College, A
Nicolet Area Technical College, A
Northcentral Technical College, A
Northeast Wisconsin Technical College, A
Southwest Wisconsin Technical College, A
Waukesha County Technical College, A
Western Technical College, A
Wisconsin Indianhead Technical College, A

Wyoming

Casper College, A
Central Wyoming College, A
Eastern Wyoming College, A
Northwest College, A
Western Wyoming Community College, A

U.S. Territories: Northern Mariana Islands

Northern Marianas College, A

U.S. Territories: Puerto Rico

American University of Puerto Rico (Bayamon), A
Bayamón Central University, AB
Colegio Universitario de San Juan, A
Columbia Centro Universitario (Caguas), A
Columbia Centro Universitario (Yauco), A
EDP University of Puerto Rico, AB
EDP University of Puerto Rico - San Sebastian, AB
Huertas Junior College, A
Inter American University of Puerto Rico, San
    Germán Campus, A
Pontifical Catholic University of Puerto Rico, B
Universidad Adventista de las Antillas, AB
Universidad del Este, B
University of Puerto Rico in Carolina, AB
University of Puerto Rico in Cayey, B
University of Puerto Rico in Humacao, B
University of Puerto Rico, Mayagüez Campus, B
University of Puerto Rico in Ponce, A
University of the Sacred Heart, B

Canada

British Columbia

British Columbia Institute of Technology, A

ADULT AND CONTINUING EDUCATION ADMINISTRATION

United States

Arizona

University of Phoenix - Online Campus, AB

District of Columbia

University of the District of Columbia, B

New York

Concordia College - New York, AB

Pennsylvania

Penn State Abington, B
Penn State Altoona, B
Penn State Beaver, B
Penn State Berks, B
Penn State Brandywine, B
Penn State DuBois, B
Penn State Erie, The Behrend College, B
Penn State Fayette, The Eberly Campus, B
Penn State Greater Allegheny, B
Penn State Hazleton, B
Penn State Lehigh Valley, B
Penn State Mont Alto, B
Penn State New Kensington, B
Penn State Schuylkill, B
Penn State Shenango, B
Penn State University Park, B
Penn State Wilkes-Barre, B
Penn State Worthington Scranton, B
Penn State York, B

West Virginia

Marshall University, B

ADULT AND CONTINUING EDUCATION AND TEACHING

United States

Alabama

Auburn University, BMD
Troy University, M
The University of West Alabama, M

Arizona

Argosy University, Phoenix, M
Cochise County Community College District, A
South Mountain Community College, A
University of Phoenix - Online Campus, M
University of Phoenix - Phoenix Campus, M
University of Phoenix - Southern Arizona Campus, M

Arkansas

Arkansas Baptist College, B
University of Arkansas at Little Rock, M
University of Central Arkansas, O

California

California Baptist University, M
San Francisco State University, M
Trident University International, M
University of Phoenix - Bay Area Campus, M
University of Phoenix - Sacramento Valley Campus, M
University of Phoenix - Southern California Campus, M
University of San Francisco, B

Colorado

Colorado State University, M
Regis University, MO
University of Colorado Denver, M

Connecticut

University of Connecticut, MD

Delaware

Delaware State University, M

District of Columbia

The George Washington University, O
University of the District of Columbia, M
University of Phoenix - Washington D.C. Campus, M

Florida

Florida Agricultural and Mechanical University, M
Florida Atlantic University, MDO
Florida International University, MD
University of North Florida, M
University of South Florida, MDO

Georgia

Armstrong State University, MO
University of Georgia, MDO

Hawaii

Argosy University, Hawai'i, M

Illinois

Argosy University, Chicago, M
DePaul University, M
Eastern Illinois University, B
National Louis University, MDO
Northern Illinois University, MD

Indiana

Ball State University, MD

Kentucky

Morehead State University, MO
Western Kentucky University, M

Louisiana

Louisiana College, B
Louisiana State University and Agricultural & Mechanical College, B
Louisiana Tech University, M
Northwestern State University of Louisiana, M

Maine

Saint Joseph's College of Maine, M
University of Southern Maine, MO

Maryland

Coppin State University, M

Massachusetts

Lesley University, D
Merrimack College, M

Michigan

Adrian College, B
Grand Valley State University, M
Michigan State University, MD

Minnesota

Capella University, MD
University of Minnesota, Twin Cities Campus, MDO
Walden University, MDO

Mississippi

Mississippi College, B

Missouri

University of Missouri, MDO

Montana

Montana State University, MD

Nebraska

University of Nebraska - Lincoln, M

New Hampshire

Plymouth State University, D

New Jersey

Kean University, M

New York

Buffalo State College, State University of New York, MO
Cornell University, MD
Fordham University, M
State University of New York Empire State College, M

North Carolina

East Carolina University, M
Mars Hill University, B
North Carolina Agricultural and Technical State University, M
North Carolina State University, MD
The University of North Carolina at Greensboro, O

North Dakota

North Dakota State University, D

Ohio

Cleveland State University, MDO
Defiance College, M
University of Cincinnati, O
Urbana University, B
Wright State University, O

Oklahoma

Northwestern Oklahoma State University, M
University of Central Oklahoma, BM
University of Oklahoma, MD

Oregon

Oregon State University, M

Pennsylvania

Indiana University of Pennsylvania, M
Penn State University Park, DO
Saint Joseph's University, M
Widener University, M

Rhode Island

University of Rhode Island, M

South Dakota

Dakota Wesleyan University, B

Tennessee

Tennessee State University, B
Tusculum College, M
University of Memphis, D
The University of Tennessee, M
Welch College, B

Texas

Texas A&M University - Kingsville, M
Texas A&M University - Texarkana, M
Texas State University, MD
University of Houston - Victoria, M
University of the Incarnate Word, M

Virginia

Regent University, MD
Virginia Commonwealth University, M

Washington

Argosy University, Seattle, M
Eastern Washington University, BM
Seattle University, MO
Western Washington University, M

West Virginia

Marshall University, M

Wisconsin

Alverno College, M
Edgewood College, M
University of Wisconsin - Milwaukee, D
University of Wisconsin - Platteville, M

U.S. Territories: Puerto Rico

Universidad del Este, M
Universidad Metropolitana, M

Canada

Alberta

Athabasca University, M
University of Alberta, BMD
University of Calgary, MD

British Columbia

The University of British Columbia, M
University of the Fraser Valley, B

Manitoba

University of Manitoba, M

Maritime Provinces: New Brunswick

Université de Moncton, B
University of New Brunswick Fredericton, B

Maritime Provinces: Nova Scotia

Mount Saint Vincent University, M
St. Francis Xavier University, M

Newfoundland and Labrador

Memorial University of Newfoundland, BMO

Ontario

Brock University, B
Laurentian University, B

Quebec

Concordia University, MO
Université du Québec à Trois-Rivières, B

Saskatchewan

University of Regina, BM

ADULT DEVELOPMENT AND AGING

United States

California

American River College, A
Chabot College, A
Chaffey College, A
MiraCosta College, A
Mt. San Jacinto College, A

Georgia

Albany Technical College, A
Central Georgia Technical College, A

Michigan

Madonna University, AB

New York

Fiorello H. LaGuardia Community College of the
City University of New York, A
York College of the City University of New York, B

North Dakota

Dakota College at Bottineau, A

Ohio

Bowling Green State University, B
Columbus State Community College, A

Oklahoma

University of Central Oklahoma, B

Pennsylvania

Community College of Beaver County, A
Harrisburg Area Community College, A

Rhode Island

Community College of Rhode Island, A
Rhode Island College, B

Texas

El Paso Community College, A

Vermont

Goddard College, B

Canada

Maritime Provinces: New Brunswick

St. Thomas University, B

Maritime Provinces: Nova Scotia

Mount Saint Vincent University, B

Ontario

University of Guelph, B

ADULT LITERACY TUTOR/IN-
STRUCTOR

United States

Oregon

Blue Mountain Community College, A

ADVERTISING

United States

Alabama

The University of Alabama, B

Arizona

The Art Institute of Phoenix, B
The Art Institute of Tucson, B
Southwest University of Visual Arts, B

Arkansas

Harding University, B

California

Academy of Art University, AB
American River College, A
Art Center College of Design, B
The Art Institute of California - Hollywood, a campus
of Argosy University, B
The Art Institute of California - Inland Empire, a
campus of Argosy University, B
The Art Institute of California - Los Angeles, a cam-
pus of Argosy University, B
The Art Institute of California - Orange County, a
campus of Argosy University, B
The Art Institute of California - Sacramento, a cam-
pus of Argosy University, B
The Art Institute of California - San Diego, a cam-
pus of Argosy University, AB
The Art Institute of California - San Francisco, a
campus of Argosy University, B
California State University, East Bay, B
California State University, Fullerton, B
El Camino College, A
Los Angeles City College, A
Mt. San Antonio College, A
Palomar College, A
Pepperdine University, B
Sacramento City College, A
San Diego State University, B
San Jose State University, B
University of San Francisco, B
Yuba College, A

Colorado

Adams State University, B

Connecticut

Quinnipiac University, B

Florida

The Art Institute of Fort Lauderdale, B
Barry University, B
Broward College, A
College of Central Florida, A

Miami International University of Art & Design, B
Ringling College of Art and Design, B
South Florida State College, A
State College of Florida Manatee-Sarasota, A
University of Central Florida, B
University of Florida, B
University of Miami, B

Georgia

The Art Institute of Atlanta, B
University of Georgia, B
Wesleyan College, B

Hawaii

Hawai'i Pacific University, B

Idaho

University of Idaho, B

Illinois

Bradley University, B
Columbia College Chicago, B
The Illinois Institute of Art - Chicago, B
The Illinois Institute of Art - Schaumburg, B
Loyola University Chicago, B
North Park University, B
Parkland College, A
University of Illinois at Urbana - Champaign, B

Indiana

Ball State University, B
University of Southern Indiana, B

Iowa

Drake University, B
Iowa State University of Science and Technology, B

Kentucky

Murray State University, B
Western Kentucky University, B

Louisiana

Louisiana College, B

Maryland

Harford Community College, A

Massachusetts

Eastern Nazarene College, B
Emerson College, B
Salem State University, B
Suffolk University, B
Western New England University, B

Michigan

Central Michigan University, B
Ferris State University, B
Grand Valley State University, B
Michigan State University, B
Muskegon Community College, A
Spring Arbor University, B
Western Michigan University, B

Minnesota

Metropolitan State University, B
Minneapolis College of Art and Design, B
Minnesota State University Moorhead, B
St. Cloud State University, B
St. Cloud Technical & Community College, A
Winona State University, B

Mississippi

Mississippi Delta Community College, A
Mississippi Gulf Coast Community College, A
Southwest Mississippi Community College, A
University of Southern Mississippi, B

Missouri

Fontbonne University, B
Lindenwood University, B
Northwest Missouri State University, B
University of Missouri, B
Washington University in St. Louis, B
Webster University, B

Nebraska

Hastings College, B

Nevada

The Art Institute of Las Vegas, B

New Hampshire

Franklin Pierce University, B

New Jersey

Rider University, B
Rowan University, B

New York

Fashion Institute of Technology, AB
Iona College, B
Mohawk Valley Community College, A
New York Institute of Technology, B
Pace University, B
Pace University, Pleasantville Campus, B
Rochester Institute of Technology, B
Rockland Community College, A
St. John's University, B
Syracuse University, B

North Carolina

Appalachian State University, B
Campbell University, B
Central Piedmont Community College, A
Surry Community College, A

North Dakota

Dakota College at Bottineau, A

Ohio

Bowling Green State University, B
Central Ohio Technical College, A
Kent State University, B
Xavier University, B
Youngstown State University, B

Oklahoma

Oklahoma Christian University, B
University of Central Oklahoma, B
University of Oklahoma, B

Oregon

The Art Institute of Portland, B
Portland State University, B
University of Oregon, B

Pennsylvania

The Art Institute of Philadelphia, B
Gannon University, B
Hussian College, School of Art, A
Penn State Abington, B
Penn State Altoona, B
Penn State Beaver, B
Penn State Berks, B
Penn State Brandywine, B
Penn State DuBois, B
Penn State Erie, The Behrend College, B
Penn State Fayette, The Eberly Campus, B
Penn State Greater Allegheny, B
Penn State Hazleton, B
Penn State Lehigh Valley, B
Penn State Mont Alto, B
Penn State New Kensington, B
Penn State Schuylkill, B
Penn State Shenango, B
Penn State University Park, B
Penn State Wilkes-Barre, B
Penn State Worthington Scranton, B
Penn State York, B
Temple University, B
Waynesburg University, B
Widener University, B

Rhode Island

Johnson & Wales University, B

South Carolina

University of South Carolina, B

South Dakota

South Dakota State University, B

Tennessee

The Art Institute of Tennessee - Nashville, a branch
   of The Art Institute of Atlanta, B
Lee University, B
Southern Adventist University, B
Union University, B
The University of Tennessee, B

Texas

The Art Institute of Austin, a branch of The Art Insti-
   tute of Houston, B
The Art Institute of Dallas, a campus of South Uni-
   versity, B
The Art Institute of Houston, B
The Art Institute of San Antonio, a branch of The Art
   Institute of Houston, B
Lamar University, B
Sam Houston State University, B
South Plains College, A
Southern Methodist University, B
Texas Christian University, B
Texas State University, B
Texas Tech University, B
Texas Wesleyan University, B
University of Houston, B
The University of Texas at Arlington, B
The University of Texas at Austin, B
West Texas A&M University, B

Utah

Brigham Young University, B

Virginia

The Art Institute of Virginia Beach, a branch of The
   Art Institute of Atlanta, B
The Art Institute of Washington, a branch of The Art
   Institute of Atlanta, B
Hampton University, B
Tidewater Community College, A

Washington

The Art Institute of Seattle, B
Washington State University, B

Wisconsin

Marquette University, B

U.S. Territories: Puerto Rico

Pontifical Catholic University of Puerto Rico, B
University of Puerto Rico in Carolina, AB
University of the Sacred Heart, B

ADVERTISING AND PUBLIC RELATIONS

United States

Alabama

The University of Alabama, M

California

Academy of Art University, M
California Baptist University, M
California State University, Fullerton, M
Golden Gate University, MO
La Sierra University, M
San Diego State University, M
University of Southern California, M

Colorado

Colorado State University, MD
University of Denver, M

Connecticut

Central Connecticut State University, O
Quinnipiac University, M
Sacred Heart University, M

District of Columbia

Georgetown University, M

Florida

University of Florida, M
University of Miami, M

Georgia

Savannah College of Art and Design, M

Illinois

DePaul University, M
Southern Illinois University Edwardsville, M
University of Illinois at Urbana - Champaign, M

Indiana

Ball State University, M

Kansas

Kansas State University, M
University of Saint Mary, M

Kentucky

Northern Kentucky University, O

Maryland

University of Maryland, College Park, MD

Massachusetts

Boston University, M
Emerson College, M
Lasell College, MO
Suffolk University, M
Western New England University, M

Michigan

Michigan State University, MD
Wayne State University, M

Mississippi

Mississippi College, M

Missouri

Webster University, M
William Woods University, M

Montana

Montana State University Billings, M

Nebraska

University of Nebraska - Lincoln, MD

New Jersey

Monmouth University, O
Rowan University, M

New York

Hofstra University, M
Iona College, O
New York University, M
Syracuse University, M

North Carolina

The University of North Carolina at Charlotte, M

Ohio

Kent State University, M

Pennsylvania

Arcadia University, M
Clarion University of Pennsylvania, O
La Salle University, M

Tennessee

The University of Tennessee, MD

Texas

Southern Methodist University, M
University of Houston, M
University of North Texas, O
The University of Texas at Austin, MD
The University of Texas Rio Grande Valley, O

Virginia

Liberty University, M
Virginia Commonwealth University, M
Virginia International University, M

Wisconsin

Marquette University, M
University of Wisconsin - Stevens Point, M

U.S. Territories: Puerto Rico

University of the Sacred Heart, MO

Canada

British Columbia

Royal Roads University, O

Quebec

Université Laval, O

AERONAUTICAL/AEROSPACE ENGINEERING TECHNOLOGY/ TECHNICIAN

United States

Alabama

Calhoun Community College, A

Arizona

GateWay Community College, A

Delaware

Delaware Technical & Community College, Jack F. Owens Campus, A

District of Columbia

University of the District of Columbia, A

Florida

Broward College, A
Embry-Riddle Aeronautical University - Worldwide, B

Kansas

Wichita Area Technical College, A

New Jersey

Cumberland County College, A

New York

Vaughn College of Aeronautics and Technology, A

North Carolina

Lenoir Community College, A

Ohio

Bowling Green State University, B
Cincinnati State Technical and Community College, A
Columbus State Community College, A

Oklahoma

Spartan College of Aeronautics and Technology, AB
Tulsa Community College, A

Pennsylvania

Community College of Beaver County, A
Pittsburgh Institute of Aeronautics, A

Texas

LeTourneau University, B

Utah

Utah State University, B

West Virginia

Pierpont Community & Technical College, A

Canada

British Columbia

British Columbia Institute of Technology, A

AERONAUTICS/AVIATION/ AEROSPACE SCIENCE AND TECHNOLOGY

United States

Alabama

Community College of the Air Force, A

Alaska

University of Alaska Anchorage, AB

Arizona

Arizona State University at the Polytechnic campus, B
Embry-Riddle Aeronautical University - Prescott, B

Arkansas

Cossatot Community College of the University of Arkansas, A

California

Pacific Union College, AB
San Bernardino Valley College, A
San Diego Christian College, B
San Jose State University, B

Colorado

Metropolitan State University of Denver, B

Connecticut

Naugatuck Valley Community College, A

Delaware

Delaware State University, B

District of Columbia

University of the District of Columbia, A

Florida

Eastern Florida State College, A
Embry-Riddle Aeronautical University - Daytona, B
Embry-Riddle Aeronautical University - Worldwide, AB
Everglades University (Boca Raton), B
Everglades University (Maitland), B
Everglades University (Sarasota), B
Florida Institute of Technology, B
Miami Dade College, A
Polk State College, B

Illinois

Lewis University, B

Indiana

Indiana State University, B
Purdue University, AB

Kansas

Hesston College, A
Kansas State University, B

Kentucky

Jefferson Community and Technical College, A

Louisiana

Louisiana Tech University, B

Maryland

Cecil College, A
Community College of Baltimore County, A

Massachusetts

Bridgewater State University, B

Minnesota

Northland Community and Technical College, A
University of Minnesota, Crookston, B
Vermilion Community College, A

Mississippi

Delta State University, B
Hinds Community College, A

Missouri

Saint Louis University, B

Montana

Montana State University, A

Nebraska

University of Nebraska at Omaha, B

New York

Vaughn College of Aeronautics and Technology, AB

North Carolina

Elizabeth City State University, B

Ohio

Bowling Green State University, B
Kent State University, B
The Ohio State University, B
Ohio University, AB
University of Cincinnati Clermont College, A

Oklahoma

Oklahoma State University, B
Southern Nazarene University, B
University of Oklahoma, B

Pennsylvania

Lehigh Carbon Community College, A

South Dakota

South Dakota State University, B

Tennessee

Middle Tennessee State University, B

Texas

Alvin Community College, A
LeTourneau University, B
Texas A&M University - Central Texas, B
Texas Lutheran University, B
Texas Southern University, B
University of North Texas, B

Virginia

Averett University, B
Liberty University, AB

Washington

Walla Walla University, AB

West Virginia

American Public University System, B

Wyoming

Northwest College, A

Canada

Ontario

York University, B

AEROSPACE, AERONAUTICAL AND ASTRONAUTICAL ENGINEERING

United States

Alabama

Auburn University, BMD
Tuskegee University, B
The University of Alabama, BMD
The University of Alabama in Huntsville, BMD

Arizona

Arizona State University at the Tempe campus, BMD
Embry-Riddle Aeronautical University - Prescott, B
The University of Arizona, BMD

California

Allan Hancock College, A
California Institute of Technology, MDO
California Polytechnic State University, San Luis Obispo, BM
California State Polytechnic University, Pomona, BM
California State University, Long Beach, BM
San Diego State University, BMD
San Jose State University, BM
Stanford University, B
University of California, Davis, BMDO
University of California, Irvine, BMD
University of California, Los Angeles, BMD
University of California, San Diego, BMD
University of Southern California, BMDO

Colorado

United States Air Force Academy, B
University of Colorado Boulder, BMD
University of Colorado Colorado Springs, M

District of Columbia

The George Washington University, MDO

Florida

Embry-Riddle Aeronautical University - Daytona, BMD
Embry-Riddle Aeronautical University - Worldwide, AM
Florida Institute of Technology, BMD
South Florida State College, A
University of Central Florida, BM
University of Florida, BMD
University of Miami, BMD

Georgia

Georgia Institute of Technology, BMD

Illinois

Illinois Institute of Technology, BMD
University of Illinois at Urbana - Champaign, BMD

Indiana

Purdue University, BMD
University of Notre Dame, BMD

Iowa

Iowa State University of Science and Technology, BMD

Kansas

The University of Kansas, BMD
Wichita State University, BMD

Maryland

Capitol Technology University, B
Johns Hopkins University, MO
Prince George's Community College, A
United States Naval Academy, B
University of Maryland, College Park, BMD

Massachusetts

Eastern Nazarene College, B
Massachusetts Institute of Technology, BMDO

Worcester Polytechnic Institute, B

Michigan

University of Michigan, BMD
Western Michigan University, BMD

Minnesota

University of Minnesota, Twin Cities Campus, BMD

Mississippi

Mississippi State University, BMD

Missouri

Missouri University of Science and Technology, BMD
Saint Louis University, B
University of Central Missouri, M
University of Missouri, MD
Washington University in St. Louis, MD
Webster University, M

New Hampshire

Daniel Webster College, B

New Jersey

Princeton University, MD
Rutgers University - New Brunswick, MD
Stevens Institute of Technology, MO

New Mexico

New Mexico State University, BMD

New York

Clarkson University, B
Cornell University, MD
Rensselaer Polytechnic Institute, BMD
Rochester Institute of Technology, B
Syracuse University, BMD
University at Buffalo, the State University of New York, BMD

North Carolina

North Carolina State University, BMD

Ohio

Case Western Reserve University, BMD
Kent State University, B
Kent State University at Ashtabula, A
The Ohio State University, BMD
University of Cincinnati, BMD
University of Dayton, MD

Oklahoma

Oklahoma State University, B
University of Oklahoma, BMD

Pennsylvania

Penn State Abington, B
Penn State Altoona, B
Penn State Beaver, B
Penn State Berks, B
Penn State Brandywine, B
Penn State DuBois, B
Penn State Erie, The Behrend College, B
Penn State Fayette, The Eberly Campus, B
Penn State Greater Allegheny, B
Penn State Hazleton, B
Penn State Lehigh Valley, B
Penn State Mont Alto, B
Penn State New Kensington, B
Penn State Schuylkill, B
Penn State Shenango, B
Penn State University Park, BMD
Penn State Wilkes-Barre, B
Penn State Worthington Scranton, B
Penn State York, B

Tennessee

Middle Tennessee State University, M
The University of Tennessee, BMD

Texas

Kilgore College, A
Texas A&M University, BMD

The University of Texas at Arlington, BMD
The University of Texas at Austin, BMD

Utah

Utah State University, BMD

Virginia

Old Dominion University, MD
University of Virginia, BMD
Virginia Polytechnic Institute and State University, BMD

Washington

University of Washington, BMD

West Virginia

American Public University System, M
West Virginia University, BMD
West Virginia University Institute of Technology, B

Canada

Ontario

Carleton University, BMD
Ryerson University, B
University of Ottawa, MD
University of Toronto, BMD
York University, B

Quebec

Concordia University, M
École Polytechnique de Montréal, MD
McGill University, M
Université Laval, M

AESTHETICIAN/ESTHETICIAN AND SKIN CARE SPECIALIST

United States

Colorado

IBMC College (Fort Collins), A

Florida

Florida College of Natural Health (Maitland), A
Florida College of Natural Health (Miami), A
Florida College of Natural Health (Pompano Beach), A
Southeastern College - West Palm Beach, A

Illinois

Lincoln College - Normal, A

Minnesota

Saint Paul College - A Community & Technical College, A

Oklahoma

Heritage College, A

Washington

Clover Park Technical College, A

AFRICAN-AMERICAN/BLACK STUDIES

United States

Alabama

Talladega College, B
The University of Alabama, B
The University of Alabama at Birmingham, B

Arizona

Arizona State University at the Tempe campus, B
The University of Arizona, B

Arkansas

University of Central Arkansas, B

California

California State University, Dominguez Hills, B
California State University, East Bay, B
California State University, Fresno, B
California State University, Fullerton, B
California State University, Long Beach, B
California State University, Los Angeles, B
California State University, Northridge, B
Claremont McKenna College, B
El Camino College, A
Laney College, A
Los Angeles City College, A
Loyola Marymount University, B
Pitzer College, B
Pomona College, B
San Diego City College, A
San Diego Mesa College, A
San Diego State University, B
San Francisco State University, B
San Jose State University, B
Santa Ana College, A
Santa Barbara City College, A
Scripps College, B
Solano Community College, A
Sonoma State University, B
Stanford University, B
University of California, Berkeley, B
University of California, Davis, B
University of California, Irvine, B
University of California, Los Angeles, B
University of California, Riverside, B
University of California, Santa Barbara, B
University of Southern California, B
Yuba College, A

Colorado

Metropolitan State University of Denver, B
University of Northern Colorado, B

Connecticut

University of Connecticut, B
Wesleyan University, B
Yale University, B

Delaware

University of Delaware, B

District of Columbia

Howard University, B

Florida

Broward College, A
Florida Agricultural and Mechanical University, B
State College of Florida Manatee-Sarasota, A
University of Florida, B
University of Miami, B
University of South Florida, B

Georgia

Emory University, B
Georgia State University, B
Mercer University, B
Morehouse College, B
University of Georgia, B

Illinois

Chicago State University, B
DePaul University, B
Dominican University, B
Eastern Illinois University, B
Knox College, B
Loyola University Chicago, B
Northwestern University, B
Roosevelt University, B
Southern Illinois University Carbondale, B
University of Illinois at Chicago, B
Western Illinois University, B

Indiana

DePauw University, B
Earlham College, B

Indiana State University, B
Indiana University Bloomington, B
Indiana University Northwest, B
Indiana University - Purdue University Indianapolis, B
Purdue University, B
University of Notre Dame, B

Iowa

Coe College, B
Luther College, B
The University of Iowa, B

Kansas

The University of Kansas, B

Kentucky

Berea College, B
University of Louisville, B

Maine

Bates College, B
Colby College, B

Maryland

Johns Hopkins University, B
Morgan State University, B
University of Maryland, Baltimore County, B
University of Maryland, College Park, B

Massachusetts

Amherst College, B
Bard College at Simon's Rock, B
Brandeis University, B
Hampshire College, B
Harvard University, B
Mount Holyoke College, B
Northeastern University, B
Smith College, B
Tufts University, B
University of Massachusetts Amherst, B
University of Massachusetts Boston, B
Wellesley College, B
Wheaton College, B

Michigan

Eastern Michigan University, B
Lansing Community College, A
University of Michigan, B
University of Michigan - Flint, B
Wayne State University, B
Western Michigan University, B

Minnesota

University of Minnesota, Twin Cities Campus, B

Mississippi

Tougaloo College, B
University of Mississippi, B

Missouri

Saint Louis University, B
Washington University in St. Louis, B

Montana

University of Montana, B

Nebraska

University of Nebraska at Omaha, B

Nevada

University of Nevada, Las Vegas, B

New Hampshire

Dartmouth College, B

New Jersey

The College of New Jersey, B
Drew University, B
Ramapo College of New Jersey, B
Rutgers University - Camden, B
Rutgers University - Newark, B
Seton Hall University, B
William Paterson University of New Jersey, B

New Mexico

University of New Mexico, B

New York

Binghamton University, State University of New York, B
Bronx Community College of the City University of New York, A
City College of the City University of New York, B
Colgate University, B
The College at Brockport, State University of New York, B
College of Staten Island of the City University of New York, B
Columbia University, B
Columbia University, School of General Studies, B
Cornell University, B
Fordham University, B
Hamilton College, B
Hobart and William Smith Colleges, B
Hunter College of the City University of New York, B
Lehman College of the City University of New York, B
Nassau Community College, A
New York University, B
Queens College of the City University of New York, B
State University of New York College at Cortland, B
State University of New York College at Geneseo, B
State University of New York at New Paltz, B
Stony Brook University, State University of New York, B
Syracuse University, BM
University at Albany, State University of New York, B
University at Buffalo, the State University of New York, B
University of Rochester, B
York College of the City University of New York, B

North Carolina

Duke University, B
East Carolina University, B
Guilford College, B
North Carolina State University, B
The University of North Carolina at Chapel Hill, B
The University of North Carolina at Charlotte, B
The University of North Carolina at Greensboro, B
Winston-Salem State University, B

Ohio

Bowling Green State University, B
Cleveland State University, B
The College of Wooster, B
Denison University, B
Kent State University, B
Miami University, B
Oberlin College, B
The Ohio State University, B
Ohio University, B
Ohio Wesleyan University, B
University of Cincinnati, B
The University of Toledo, B
Wright State University, B
Youngstown State University, B

Oklahoma

University of Oklahoma, B

Oregon

Portland State University, B

Pennsylvania

Cabrini University, B
Gettysburg College, B
Penn State Abington, B
Penn State Altoona, B
Penn State Beaver, B
Penn State Berks, B
Penn State Brandywine, B
Penn State DuBois, B
Penn State Erie, The Behrend College, B
Penn State Fayette, The Eberly Campus, B
Penn State Greater Allegheny, B
Penn State Hazleton, B
Penn State Lehigh Valley, B

Penn State Mont Alto, B
Penn State New Kensington, B
Penn State Schuylkill, B
Penn State Shenango, B
Penn State University Park, B
Penn State Wilkes-Barre, B
Penn State Worthington Scranton, B
Penn State York, B
Swarthmore College, B
Temple University, B
University of Pennsylvania, B
University of Pittsburgh, B

Rhode Island

Brown University, B
Rhode Island College, B
University of Rhode Island, B

South Carolina

Claflin University, B
Clemson University, B
College of Charleston, B
University of South Carolina, B
Wofford College, B

Tennessee

Rhodes College, B
University of Memphis, B
Vanderbilt University, B

Texas

Southern Methodist University, B
The University of Texas at Austin, B

Virginia

The College of William and Mary, B
Old Dominion University, B
University of Virginia, B
Virginia Commonwealth University, B

Wisconsin

University of Wisconsin - Madison, B
University of Wisconsin - Milwaukee, B

Wyoming

University of Wyoming, B

AFRICAN-AMERICAN STUDIES

United States

California

University of California, Berkeley, D
University of California, Los Angeles, M
University of California, Santa Barbara, D

Connecticut

Yale University, D

Georgia

Clark Atlanta University, MD
Georgia State University, M

Illinois

Northwestern University, D

Indiana

Indiana University Bloomington, M

Kansas

The University of Kansas, MO

Kentucky

University of Louisville, M

Maryland

Morgan State University, M

Massachusetts

Boston University, M
Harvard University, D

University of Massachusetts Amherst, MD

Michigan

Eastern Michigan University, O
Michigan State University, MD

New Jersey

Rutgers University - New Brunswick, D

New York

Columbia University, M
Cornell University, MD
University at Albany, State University of New York, M

North Carolina

North Carolina Agricultural and Technical State University, M

Ohio

The Ohio State University, MD

Pennsylvania

Carnegie Mellon University, D
Temple University, MD

Tennessee

University of Memphis, DO

West Virginia

West Virginia University, MD

Wisconsin

University of Wisconsin - Madison, M

AFRICAN LANGUAGES, LITERATURES, AND LINGUISTICS

United States

California

University of California, Los Angeles, B

Wisconsin

University of Wisconsin - Madison, B

AFRICAN STUDIES

United States

Alabama

Miles College, B

Arizona

Arizona State University at the Tempe campus, O

California

California State University, Long Beach, M
Los Angeles Southwest College, A
Solano Community College, A
University of California, Los Angeles, M

Connecticut

Connecticut College, B
University of Connecticut, M
Yale University, BM

District of Columbia

Howard University, MD

Florida

Florida International University, M
University of Florida, O
University of South Florida, MO

Georgia

Agnes Scott College, B
Emory University, B
Fort Valley State University, B

Kennesaw State University, B

Illinois

Augustana College, B
Illinois Wesleyan University, B
North Park University, B
Northwestern University, BO
University of Chicago, B
University of Illinois at Urbana - Champaign, M

Indiana

Indiana University Bloomington, M

Iowa

The University of Iowa, B

Kansas

The University of Kansas, BMO

Kentucky

Kentucky State University, B
University of Louisville, M

Louisiana

Tulane University, B

Maine

Bowdoin College, B

Maryland

Morgan State University, B

Massachusetts

Hampshire College, B
Harvard University, D
Simmons College, B
Tufts University, B
Wellesley College, B

Michigan

Michigan State University, MD
Wayne State University, D

Minnesota

Carleton College, B

Missouri

Washington University in St. Louis, B

New Hampshire

Dartmouth College, B

New Jersey

Rowan University, B
Rutgers University - New Brunswick, BD

New York

Bard College, B
Barnard College, B
Brooklyn College of the City University of New York, B
Colgate University, B
Columbia University, DO
Columbia University, School of General Studies, B
Cornell University, MD
Fordham University, B
Hobart and William Smith Colleges, B
Hofstra University, B
New York University, MD
Stony Brook University, State University of New York, MO
Syracuse University, M
Union College, B
United States Military Academy, B
University at Albany, State University of New York, M
Vassar College, B

North Carolina

Davidson College, B
The University of North Carolina at Charlotte, O

Ohio

Bowling Green State University, B
The Ohio State University, BMD
Ohio University, BM
Sinclair Community College, A

Oregon

Portland State University, B
Willamette University, B

Pennsylvania

Carnegie Mellon University, D
Dickinson College, B
Franklin & Marshall College, B
Haverford College, B
Lehigh University, B
University of Pennsylvania, BMD
University of Pittsburgh, O

Tennessee

Tennessee State University, B

Texas

Rice University, D
The University of Texas at Austin, MD

Vermont

Marlboro College, B
Middlebury College, B

Virginia

University of Richmond, B

West Virginia

West Virginia University, MD

Wisconsin

University of Wisconsin - Madison, MD
University of Wisconsin - Milwaukee, D

Canada

Ontario

Carleton University, B
University of Toronto, B
York University, B

AGRIBUSINESS

United States

Alabama

Alabama Agricultural and Mechanical University, D

Arizona

Arizona State University at the Tempe campus, D
Yavapai College, A

Arkansas

Arkansas State University, B
Arkansas Tech University, B
Southern Arkansas University - Magnolia, A
University of Arkansas, B

California

Allan Hancock College, A
Butte College, A
California Polytechnic State University, San Luis Obispo, M
College of the Desert, A
College of the Redwoods, A
Cosumnes River College, A

Colorado

Adams State University, B
Colorado State University, B
Morgan Community College, B

Delaware

University of Delaware, B

Florida

College of Central Florida, A
Florida Agricultural and Mechanical University, B
South Florida State College, A

Georgia

Bainbridge State College, A
Ogeechee Technical College, A
University of Georgia, B

Idaho

University of Idaho, BM

Illinois

Illinois State University, M

Iowa

Iowa Lakes Community College, A
Iowa State University of Science and Technology, M
Northeast Iowa Community College, A
Southwestern Community College, A

Kansas

Colby Community College, A

Maryland

Harford Community College, A

Michigan

Andrews University, B

Minnesota

Minnesota West Community and Technical College, A
Ridgewater College, A
Southwest Minnesota State University, AB
University of Minnesota, Crookston, B

Mississippi

Copiah-Lincoln Community College, A
Hinds Community College, A
Mississippi State University, B

Missouri

Crowder College, A
Mineral Area College, A
Missouri State University, B
Northwest Missouri State University, B
Southeast Missouri State University, B
State Fair Community College, A
University of Central Missouri, B

Nebraska

Northeast Community College, A

New Jersey

Rowan College at Burlington County, A

New Mexico

Eastern New Mexico University, B
New Mexico State University, BM

New York

Morrisville State College, B
State University of New York College of Agriculture and Technology at Cobleskill, A
State University of New York College of Technology at Alfred, A

North Carolina

James Sprunt Community College, A
Mitchell Community College, A
North Carolina Agricultural and Technical State University, B
North Carolina State University, B
Wayne Community College, A

North Dakota

North Dakota State University, B
Sitting Bull College, A

Ohio

Kent State University at Tuscarawas, B
The Ohio State University Agricultural Technical Institute, A
Wright State University - Lake Campus, AB

Pennsylvania

Delaware Valley University, BM
Penn State Abington, B
Penn State Altoona, B
Penn State Beaver, B
Penn State Berks, B
Penn State Brandywine, B
Penn State DuBois, B
Penn State Erie, The Behrend College, B
Penn State Fayette, The Eberly Campus, B
Penn State Greater Allegheny, B
Penn State Hazleton, B
Penn State Lehigh Valley, B
Penn State Mont Alto, B
Penn State New Kensington, B
Penn State Schuylkill, B
Penn State Shenango, B
Penn State University Park, B
Penn State Wilkes-Barre, B
Penn State Worthington Scranton, B
Penn State York, B

South Carolina

South Carolina State University, BM

South Dakota

South Dakota State University, B

Tennessee

Middle Tennessee State University, B

Texas

Abilene Christian University, B
Angelo State University, B
Clarendon College, A
Sam Houston State University, B
San Jacinto College District, A
Stephen F. Austin State University, B
Tarleton State University, B
Texas A&M University, B
Texas A&M University - Commerce, B
Texas A&M University - Kingsville, B
Texas State University, B
Texas Tech University, M
West Texas A&M University, B

Utah

Brigham Young University, B

Vermont

Vermont Technical College, AB

Wisconsin

Northcentral Technical College, A
University of Wisconsin - Platteville, B
University of Wisconsin - River Falls, B

Wyoming

Eastern Wyoming College, A
Laramie County Community College, A
Northwest College, A
University of Wyoming, B

U.S. Territories: Puerto Rico

Universidad del Este, M
University of Puerto Rico, Mayagüez Campus, B

Canada

Ontario

University of Guelph, M

Saskatchewan

University of Saskatchewan, B

AGRICULTURAL/BIOLOGICAL ENGINEERING AND BIOENGINEERING

United States

Alabama

Auburn University, B

Arkansas

University of Arkansas, B

California

California Polytechnic State University, San Luis Obispo, B

Florida

Florida Agricultural and Mechanical University, B
South Florida State College, A

Georgia

Fort Valley State University, B
University of Georgia, B

Hawaii

University of Hawaii at Manoa, B

Illinois

University of Illinois at Urbana - Champaign, B

Indiana

Purdue University, B
Vincennes University, A

Iowa

Dordt College, B
Iowa State University of Science and Technology, B

Kansas

Kansas State University, B
Seward County Community College and Area Technical School, A

Kentucky

University of Kentucky, B

Maine

University of Maine, B

Maryland

University of Maryland, College Park, B

Michigan

Michigan State University, B

Minnesota

University of Minnesota, Twin Cities Campus, B

Missouri

Missouri University of Science and Technology, B

Nebraska

University of Nebraska - Lincoln, B

New Jersey

Rutgers University - New Brunswick, B

New York

Cornell University, B
Morrisville State College, A

North Carolina

North Carolina Agricultural and Technical State University, B
North Carolina State University, B

North Dakota

North Dakota State University, B

Ohio

The Ohio State University, B

Oklahoma

Oklahoma State University, B

Oregon

Oregon State University, B

Pennsylvania

Penn State Abington, B
Penn State Beaver, B
Penn State Brandywine, B
Penn State DuBois, B
Penn State Erie, The Behrend College, B
Penn State Fayette, The Eberly Campus, B
Penn State Greater Allegheny, B
Penn State Hazleton, B
Penn State Lehigh Valley, B
Penn State Mont Alto, B
Penn State New Kensington, B
Penn State Schuylkill, B
Penn State Shenango, B
Penn State University Park, B
Penn State Wilkes-Barre, B
Penn State Worthington Scranton, B
Penn State York, B

South Carolina

Clemson University, B

South Dakota

South Dakota State University, B

Tennessee

Tennessee Technological University, B
The University of Tennessee, B

Texas

Texas A&M University, B

Utah

Utah State University, B

Washington

Walla Walla University, B

Wisconsin

University of Wisconsin - Madison, B

Canada

Manitoba

University of Manitoba, B

Maritime Provinces: Nova Scotia

Dalhousie University, B

AGRICULTURAL BUSINESS AND MANAGEMENT

United States

Alabama

Alabama Southern Community College, A
Tuskegee University, B

Arizona

Arizona State University at the Polytechnic campus, B
Arizona Western College, A
Central Arizona College, A
Cochise County Community College District, A
Mesa Community College, A
The University of Arizona, B
Yavapai College, A

Arkansas

Cossatot Community College of the University of Arkansas, A

Southern Arkansas University - Magnolia, B

California

Bakersfield College, A
California Polytechnic State University, San Luis Obispo, B
California State Polytechnic University, Pomona, B
California State University, Chico, B
California State University, Fresno, B
College of the Sequoias, A
Hartnell College, A
Imperial Valley College, A
Lassen Community College District, A
Merced College, A
Modesto Junior College, A
Mt. San Antonio College, A
Porterville College, A
Reedley College, A
San Joaquin Delta College, A
Santa Rosa Junior College, A
Shasta College, A
University of California, Davis, B
West Hills Community College, A
Yuba College, A

Colorado

Colorado Mesa University, AB
Lamar Community College, A
Northeastern Junior College, A
Otero Junior College, A
Trinidad State Junior College, A

Delaware

Delaware State University, B
Delaware Technical & Community College, Jack F. Owens Campus, A
Delaware Technical & Community College, Stanton/Wilmington Campus, A
Delaware Technical & Community College, Terry Campus, A
University of Delaware, B

Florida

Florida Southern College, B
Indian River State College, A
Pensacola State College, A

Georgia

Abraham Baldwin Agricultural College, A
College of Coastal Georgia, A

Hawaii

University of Hawaii at Hilo, B

Idaho

Brigham Young University - Idaho, B
College of Southern Idaho, A
University of Idaho, B

Illinois

Black Hawk College, A
Danville Area Community College, A
Illinois Central College, A
Illinois Eastern Community Colleges, Wabash Valley College, A
John Wood Community College, A
Lake Land College, A
Parkland College, A
Richland Community College, A
Sauk Valley Community College, A
Shawnee Community College, A
Spoon River College, A
University of Illinois at Urbana - Champaign, B

Indiana

Purdue University, B
Vincennes University, A

Iowa

Ellsworth Community College, A
Iowa Lakes Community College, A
Iowa State University of Science and Technology, B
Iowa Western Community College, A
Kirkwood Community College, A

Southeastern Community College, A
Upper Iowa University, B

Kansas

Barton County Community College, A
Butler Community College, A
Cloud County Community College, A
Colby Community College, A
Dodge City Community College, A
Fort Hays State University, B
Kansas State University, B
Pratt Community College, A
Seward County Community College and Area Technical School, A
Tabor College, B

Louisiana

Louisiana State University and Agricultural & Mechanical College, B
Louisiana Tech University, B
University of Louisiana at Monroe, B

Maryland

University of Maryland Eastern Shore, B

Michigan

Lansing Community College, A
Michigan State University, B

Minnesota

South Central College, A
Southwest Minnesota State University, B
University of Minnesota, Twin Cities Campus, B
Vermilion Community College, A

Mississippi

Alcorn State University, B
Copiah-Lincoln Community College, A
Itawamba Community College, A
Mississippi Delta Community College, A
Mississippi Gulf Coast Community College, A
Northwest Mississippi Community College, A

Missouri

College of the Ozarks, B
Lincoln University, B
North Central Missouri College, A
Three Rivers Community College, A
University of Missouri, B

Montana

Dawson Community College, A
Miles Community College, A
Montana State University, B

Nebraska

Central Community College - Columbus Campus, A
Central Community College - Hastings Campus, A
Grace University, B
Hastings College, B
Nebraska College of Technical Agriculture, A
Southeast Community College, Beatrice Campus, A
University of Nebraska at Kearney, B
University of Nebraska - Lincoln, B

New Hampshire

University of New Hampshire, A

New Jersey

County College of Morris, A
Salem Community College, A

New Mexico

Mesalands Community College, A

New York

Cornell University, B
Morrisville State College, A
State University of New York College of Agriculture and Technology at Cobleskill, AB

North Carolina

North Carolina Agricultural and Technical State University, B

North Carolina State University, A
Surry Community College, A

North Dakota

Bismarck State College, A
Dickinson State University, AB
Lake Region State College, A
North Dakota State College of Science, A

Ohio

Clark State Community College, A
The Ohio State University, B
The Ohio State University Agricultural Technical Institute, A
Terra State Community College, A
University of Northwestern Ohio, A
Wilmington College, B

Oklahoma

Northern Oklahoma College, A
Oklahoma Panhandle State University, B
Oklahoma State University, B
Redlands Community College, A

Oregon

Blue Mountain Community College, A
Chemeketa Community College, A
Linn-Benton Community College, A
Oregon State University, B
Treasure Valley Community College, A

Pennsylvania

Penn State Abington, A
Penn State Altoona, A
Penn State Beaver, A
Penn State Berks, A
Penn State Brandywine, A
Penn State DuBois, A
Penn State Erie, The Behrend College, A
Penn State Fayette, The Eberly Campus, A
Penn State Greater Allegheny, A
Penn State Hazleton, A
Penn State Lehigh Valley, A
Penn State Mont Alto, A
Penn State New Kensington, AB
Penn State Schuylkill, A
Penn State Shenango, A
Penn State Wilkes-Barre, A
Penn State Worthington Scranton, A
Penn State York, A

South Carolina

Clemson University, B

South Dakota

Lake Area Technical Institute, A

Tennessee

Tennessee Technological University, B
The University of Tennessee, B
The University of Tennessee at Martin, B

Texas

Cisco College, A
Frank Phillips College, A
Hill College, A
Northeast Texas Community College, A
Sul Ross State University, B
Texas A&M University, B
Texas Tech University, B
West Texas A&M University, B

Utah

Brigham Young University, B
Snow College, A
Utah State University, B

Virginia

Lord Fairfax Community College, A
Northern Virginia Community College, A
Patrick Henry Community College, A

Washington

Spokane Community College, A
Walla Walla Community College, A
Washington State University, B
Yakima Valley Community College, A

West Virginia

Potomac State College of West Virginia University, A

Wisconsin

Chippewa Valley Technical College, A
University of Wisconsin - Madison, B
University of Wisconsin - Platteville, B

Wyoming

Casper College, A
Central Wyoming College, A

U.S. Territories: American Samoa

American Samoa Community College, A

U.S. Territories: Northern Mariana Islands

Northern Marianas College, A

Canada

Alberta

University of Alberta, B

British Columbia

University of the Fraser Valley, B

Ontario

University of Guelph, AB

AGRICULTURAL BUSINESS TECHNOLOGY

United States

Arizona

The University of Arizona, B

Colorado

Morgan Community College, B

Idaho

Brigham Young University - Idaho, B

Iowa

Iowa Lakes Community College, A

Minnesota

South Central College, A
University of Minnesota, Crookston, B

North Carolina

Blue Ridge Community College, A

Ohio

The Ohio State University Agricultural Technical Institute, A
Wright State University, AB

Washington

Washington State University, B

Wyoming

Laramie County Community College, A

AGRICULTURAL COMMUNICATION/JOURNALISM

United States

Alabama

Auburn University, B

California

California Polytechnic State University, San Luis Obispo, B
Santa Rosa Junior College, A

Georgia

University of Georgia, B

Idaho

University of Idaho, B

Illinois

University of Illinois at Urbana - Champaign, B

Indiana

Purdue University, B

Kansas

Kansas State University, B

Nebraska

University of Nebraska - Lincoln, B

North Dakota

North Dakota State University, B

Ohio

The Ohio State University, B
The Ohio State University Agricultural Technical Institute, A

Oklahoma

Oklahoma State University, B

South Dakota

South Dakota State University, B

Texas

Sam Houston State University, B
Texas A&M University, B
Texas Tech University, B
West Texas A&M University, B

Washington

Washington State University, B

Wisconsin

University of Wisconsin - Madison, B

Wyoming

Casper College, A
Northwest College, A
University of Wyoming, B

AGRICULTURAL AND DOMESTIC ANIMALS SERVICES

United States

Indiana

Saint Mary-of-the-Woods College, B

New Mexico

Mesalands Community College, A

Texas

Tarleton State University, B

Washington

Walla Walla Community College, A

AGRICULTURAL ECONOMICS

United States

Alabama

Alabama Agricultural and Mechanical University, B
Auburn University, BM
James H. Faulkner State Community College, A
Tuskegee University, M

Arizona

The University of Arizona, M

Arkansas

University of Arkansas, M
University of Arkansas at Pine Bluff, B

California

Lassen Community College District, A
University of California, Berkeley, D
University of California, Davis, MD
University of California, Santa Barbara, MD

Colorado

Colorado State University, BMD

Connecticut

University of Connecticut, BMD

Delaware

University of Delaware, M

Florida

South Florida State College, A
University of Florida, BMD

Georgia

Abraham Baldwin Agricultural College, A
Fort Valley State University, B
University of Georgia, BMD

Idaho

Brigham Young University - Idaho, B
University of Idaho, BM

Illinois

Joliet Junior College, A
Southern Illinois University Carbondale, BM
University of Illinois at Urbana - Champaign, BMD

Indiana

Purdue University, BMD

Iowa

Iowa Lakes Community College, A
Iowa State University of Science and Technology, MD
North Iowa Area Community College, A

Kansas

Dodge City Community College, A
Kansas State University, BMD
Pratt Community College, A

Kentucky

University of Kentucky, BMD

Louisiana

Louisiana State University and Agricultural & Mechanical College, MD
Southern University and Agricultural and Mechanical College, B

Maine

University of Maine, M

Maryland

University of Maryland, College Park, BMD

Massachusetts

University of Massachusetts Amherst, BMD

Michigan

Michigan State University, MD

Minnesota

Northland Community and Technical College, A
Vermilion Community College, A

Mississippi

Alcorn State University, BM
Copiah-Lincoln Community College, A
Mississippi Delta Community College, A
Mississippi State University, BM
Northwest Mississippi Community College, A

Missouri

Northwest Missouri State University, M
University of Missouri, BMDO

Nebraska

University of Nebraska - Lincoln, BMD

Nevada

University of Nevada, Reno, MD

New Jersey

Rutgers University - New Brunswick, M

New Mexico

New Mexico State University, MD

New York

Cornell University, BM

North Carolina

North Carolina Agricultural and Technical State University, BM
North Carolina State University, M

North Dakota

North Dakota State University, BM

Ohio

The Ohio State University, BMD
The Ohio State University Agricultural Technical Institute, A

Oklahoma

Oklahoma State University, BMD

Oregon

Oregon State University, B
Treasure Valley Community College, A

Pennsylvania

Penn State University Park, MDO

South Carolina

Clemson University, B

South Dakota

South Dakota State University, B

Texas

Clarendon College, A
South Plains College, A
Tarleton State University, B
Texas A&M University, BMD
Texas A&M University - Kingsville, M
Texas Tech University, BMD
West Texas A&M University, M

Utah

Brigham Young University, B
Utah State University, B

Vermont

University of Vermont, M

Virginia

Virginia Polytechnic Institute and State University, BM

Washington

Washington State University, BMDO

West Virginia

West Virginia University, BM

Wisconsin

University of Wisconsin - Madison, BMD

Wyoming

University of Wyoming, M

U.S. Territories: Puerto Rico

University of Puerto Rico, Mayagüez Campus, BM

Canada

Alberta

University of Alberta, BMD

British Columbia

The University of British Columbia, M

Manitoba

University of Manitoba, BMD

Ontario

University of Guelph, BMD

Quebec

McGill University, M
Université Laval, BM

Saskatchewan

University of Saskatchewan, BMDO

AGRICULTURAL EDUCATION

United States

Arizona

The University of Arizona, M

Arkansas

Arkansas State University, O
University of Arkansas, M

California

California Polytechnic State University, San Luis Obispo, M

Connecticut

University of Connecticut, MDO

Delaware

University of Delaware, M

Florida

University of Florida, MD

Georgia

University of Georgia, M

Idaho

University of Idaho, M

Illinois

University of Illinois at Urbana - Champaign, M

Indiana

Purdue University, MDO

Iowa

Iowa State University of Science and Technology, MD

Kansas

Kansas State University, M

Kentucky

Eastern Kentucky University, M
Murray State University, M

Louisiana

Louisiana State University and Agricultural & Mechanical College, MD

Minnesota

University of Minnesota, Twin Cities Campus, MD

Mississippi

Alcorn State University, M
Mississippi State University, MD

Missouri

Northwest Missouri State University, M
University of Missouri, MDO

Montana

Montana State University, M

Nebraska

University of Nebraska - Lincoln, M

New Mexico

New Mexico State University, M

New York

Cornell University, MD
State University of New York at Oswego, M

North Carolina

North Carolina Agricultural and Technical State University, M
North Carolina State University, MO

North Dakota

North Dakota State University, M

Ohio

The Ohio State University, MD

Oklahoma

Oklahoma State University, MD

Oregon

Oregon State University, M

Pennsylvania

Penn State University Park, MDO

South Carolina

Clemson University, M

Tennessee

Tennessee State University, M
The University of Tennessee, M

Texas

Stephen F. Austin State University, M
Tarleton State University, M
Texas A&M University, MD
Texas State University, M
Texas Tech University, MD

Utah

Utah State University, M

West Virginia

West Virginia University, MD

Wisconsin

University of Wisconsin - River Falls, M

U.S. Territories: Puerto Rico

University of Puerto Rico, Mayagüez Campus, M

AGRICULTURAL ENGINEERING

United States

Arizona

The University of Arizona, MD

Arkansas

University of Arkansas, MD

Florida

University of Florida, MDO

Georgia

University of Georgia, MD

Idaho

University of Idaho, MD

Illinois

University of Illinois at Urbana - Champaign, MD

Indiana

Purdue University, MD

Iowa

Iowa State University of Science and Technology, MD

Kansas

Kansas State University, MD

Kentucky

University of Kentucky, MD

Louisiana

Louisiana State University and Agricultural & Mechanical College, MD

Missouri

University of Missouri, MD

Nebraska

University of Nebraska - Lincoln, MD

New York

Cornell University, MD

North Carolina

North Carolina State University, MDO

North Dakota

North Dakota State University, MD

Ohio

The Ohio State University, MD

Oklahoma

Oklahoma State University, MD

Pennsylvania

Penn State University Park, MD

South Dakota

South Dakota State University, MD

Tennessee

The University of Tennessee, M

Texas

Texas A&M University, MD

Utah

Utah State University, MD

Virginia

Virginia Polytechnic Institute and State University, MD

Washington

Washington State University, MD

Wisconsin

University of Wisconsin - Madison, MD

Canada

Maritime Provinces: Nova Scotia

Dalhousie University, MD

Quebec

McGill University, MD
Université Laval, M

AGRICULTURAL AND EXTENSION EDUCATION SERVICES

United States

Arkansas

University of Arkansas, B

Illinois

University of Illinois at Urbana - Champaign, B

Louisiana

Louisiana State University and Agricultural & Mechanical College, B

New Mexico

New Mexico State University, B

North Carolina

North Carolina State University, B

Ohio

The Ohio State University, B

Oklahoma

Northwestern Oklahoma State University, B

Pennsylvania

Penn State Abington, B
Penn State Altoona, B
Penn State Beaver, B
Penn State Berks, B
Penn State Brandywine, B
Penn State DuBois, B
Penn State Erie, The Behrend College, B
Penn State Fayette, The Eberly Campus, B
Penn State Greater Allegheny, B
Penn State Hazleton, B
Penn State Lehigh Valley, B
Penn State Mont Alto, B
Penn State New Kensington, B
Penn State Schuylkill, B
Penn State Shenango, B
Penn State Wilkes-Barre, B
Penn State Worthington Scranton, B
Penn State York, B

Tennessee

The University of Tennessee, B

Texas

Tarleton State University, B

West Virginia

Potomac State College of West Virginia University, A

U.S. Territories: Puerto Rico

University of Puerto Rico, Mayagüez Campus, B

AGRICULTURAL/FARM SUPPLIES RETAILING AND WHOLESALING

United States

California

Modesto Junior College, A

Colorado

Morgan Community College, B

Illinois

Illinois Central College, A

Iowa

Des Moines Area Community College, A
Hawkeye Community College, A
Iowa Lakes Community College, A
Kirkwood Community College, A
Muscatine Community College, A
North Iowa Area Community College, A
Western Iowa Tech Community College, A

Kansas

Cloud County Community College, A

Minnesota

Minnesota West Community and Technical College, A

Mississippi

Copiah-Lincoln Community College, A

Texas

Tarleton State University, B
Texas A&M University, B

Wisconsin

Fox Valley Technical College, A
Southwest Wisconsin Technical College, A

AGRICULTURAL AND FOOD PRODUCTS PROCESSING

United States

Florida

University of Florida, B

Iowa

Morningside College, B
Northeast Iowa Community College, A

Kansas

Garden City Community College, A
Kansas State University, B

Minnesota

Minnesota State Community and Technical College, A
Minnesota West Community and Technical College, A

Nebraska

University of Nebraska - Lincoln, B

North Carolina

Rockingham Community College, A

Ohio

The Ohio State University, B

Texas

Angelo State University, B
Texas A&M University, B

Washington

Washington State University, B

Canada

British Columbia

The University of British Columbia, B

Maritime Provinces: Nova Scotia

Dalhousie University, B

AGRICULTURAL AND HORTICULTURAL PLANT BREEDING

United States

Delaware

Delaware State University, B

Michigan

Lake Michigan College, A
North Central Michigan College, A

AGRICULTURAL MECHANICS AND EQUIPMENT/MACHINE TECHNOLOGY

United States

Arizona

Central Arizona College, A

California

Butte College, A

Illinois

Black Hawk College, A
Illinois Central College, A
Rend Lake College, A
Spoon River College, A

Iowa

Iowa Lakes Community College, A

Kansas

Hutchinson Community College, A

Minnesota

Northland Community and Technical College, A

Montana

Montana State University - Northern, A

Nebraska

Northeast Community College, A

New York

Morrisville State College, A

North Dakota

North Dakota State College of Science, A

South Dakota

Mitchell Technical Institute, A

AGRICULTURAL MECHANIZATION

United States

Arizona

Mesa Community College, A

California

California Polytechnic State University, San Luis
  Obispo, B
College of the Sequoias, A
Imperial Valley College, A
Lassen Community College District, A
Modesto Junior College, A
Reedley College, A
San Joaquin Delta College, A
West Hills Community College, A
Yuba College, A

Georgia

Southern Regional Technical College, A

Hawaii

University of Hawaii Maui College, A

Idaho

University of Idaho, B

Illinois

Kishwaukee College, A
Lake Land College, A
Parkland College, A
Rend Lake College, A
Southeastern Illinois College, A
Spoon River College, A
University of Illinois at Urbana - Champaign, B

Indiana

Ivy Tech Community College - Wabash Valley, A
Purdue University, B

Iowa

Iowa Lakes Community College, A
Iowa State University of Science and Technology, B

Kansas

Dodge City Community College, A
Fort Scott Community College, A
Garden City Community College, A
Kansas State University, B
Pratt Community College, A

Minnesota

University of Minnesota, Crookston, B

Mississippi

Hinds Community College, A
Northwest Mississippi Community College, A

Missouri

Crowder College, A
Three Rivers Community College, A
University of Missouri, B

Montana

Montana State University, B
Montana State University - Northern, B

Nebraska

Northeast Community College, A
University of Nebraska - Lincoln, B

North Carolina

North Carolina Agricultural and Technical State University, B
North Carolina State University, B

North Dakota

North Dakota State University, B

Ohio

Clark State Community College, A
The Ohio State University Agricultural Technical Institute, A
Owens Community College, A

Pennsylvania

Penn State Abington, B
Penn State Altoona, B
Penn State Beaver, B

Penn State Berks, B
Penn State Brandywine, B
Penn State DuBois, B
Penn State Erie, The Behrend College, B
Penn State Fayette, The Eberly Campus, B
Penn State Greater Allegheny, B
Penn State Hazleton, B
Penn State Lehigh Valley, B
Penn State Mont Alto, B
Penn State New Kensington, B
Penn State Schuylkill, B
Penn State Shenango, B
Penn State Wilkes-Barre, B
Penn State Worthington Scranton, B
Penn State York, B

South Dakota

South Dakota State University, B

Texas

Navarro College, A
North Central Texas College, A
Paris Junior College, A
Sam Houston State University, B
Southwest Texas Junior College, A
Stephen F. Austin State University, B
Tarleton State University, B

Washington

Walla Walla Community College, A
Washington State University, B
Yakima Valley Community College, A

Wisconsin

Fox Valley Technical College, A
Madison Area Technical College, A
University of Wisconsin - River Falls, B
Western Technical College, A

U.S. Territories: Northern Mariana Islands

Northern Marianas College, A

U.S. Territories: Puerto Rico

University of Puerto Rico, Mayagüez Campus, B

AGRICULTURAL POWER MACHINERY OPERATION

United States

Iowa

Hawkeye Community College, A
Iowa Lakes Community College, A
Kirkwood Community College, A
Northeast Iowa Community College, A

Kansas

North Central Kansas Technical College, A

Minnesota

University of Minnesota, Crookston, B

North Carolina

Guilford Technical Community College, A

Ohio

The Ohio State University Agricultural Technical Institute, A

Oregon

Portland Community College, A

AGRICULTURAL PRODUCTION OPERATIONS

United States

Arkansas

University of Arkansas at Monticello, A

California

Modesto Junior College, A

Delaware

Delaware Technical & Community College, Jack F. Owens Campus, A

Hawaii

Hawaii Community College, A

Illinois

Black Hawk College, A
Illinois Central College, A
Illinois Eastern Community Colleges, Wabash Valley College, A
Joliet Junior College, A
Lake Land College, A
Lincoln Land Community College, A
Rend Lake College, A

Iowa

Iowa Lakes Community College, A
Kirkwood Community College, A
Muscatine Community College, A
North Iowa Area Community College, A
Northeast Iowa Community College, A

Kansas

Allen Community College, A
Garden City Community College, A

Kentucky

Eastern Kentucky University, B
Henderson Community College, A
Hopkinsville Community College, A
Owensboro Community and Technical College, A
Western Kentucky University, A

Michigan

Northwestern Michigan College, A
Southwestern Michigan College, A

Minnesota

Minnesota West Community and Technical College, A
Ridgewater College, A
South Central College, A

Montana

Miles Community College, A

Nebraska

Nebraska College of Technical Agriculture, A

New Mexico

Eastern New Mexico University, A

Ohio

Southern State Community College, A

Oregon

Blue Mountain Community College, A

South Dakota

Mitchell Technical Institute, A

Texas

Stephen F. Austin State University, B
Tarleton State University, B

Washington

Big Bend Community College, A
Walla Walla Community College, A

Wenatchee Valley College, A
Yakima Valley Community College, A

Wyoming

Laramie County Community College, A
Northwest College, A

U.S. Territories: Puerto Rico

University of Puerto Rico in Utuado, A

Canada

British Columbia

University of the Fraser Valley, A

AGRICULTURAL PUBLIC SERVICES

United States

Illinois

University of Illinois at Urbana - Champaign, B

Kentucky

University of Kentucky, B

Oklahoma

Oklahoma State University, B

South Dakota

South Dakota State University, B

AGRICULTURAL SCIENCES

United States

Alabama

Alabama Agricultural and Mechanical University, MD
Auburn University, MD

Arizona

The University of Arizona, MD

Arkansas

Arkansas State University, MO
Southern Arkansas University - Magnolia, M
University of Arkansas, MD

California

California Polytechnic State University, San Luis
   Obispo, M
California State Polytechnic University, Pomona, M
University of California, Davis, M

Colorado

Colorado State University, MD

Connecticut

University of Connecticut, MD

Delaware

University of Delaware, MD

Florida

University of Florida, MDO

Georgia

University of Georgia, MD

Hawaii

University of Hawaii at Manoa, MD

Illinois

Illinois State University, M
Southern Illinois University Carbondale, M
University of Illinois at Urbana - Champaign, M

Indiana

Purdue University, MD

Iowa

Iowa State University of Science and Technology,
   MD
The University of Iowa, MD

Kansas

Kansas State University, MDO

Kentucky

Morehead State University, M
Murray State University, M
University of Kentucky, MD
Western Kentucky University, M

Louisiana

Louisiana State University and Agricultural & Mechanical College, MD
McNeese State University, M
Southern University and Agricultural and Mechanical
   College, M

Maine

University of Maine, MDO

Maryland

University of Maryland, College Park, MD
University of Maryland Eastern Shore, MD

Michigan

Michigan State University, MD

Minnesota

University of Minnesota, Twin Cities Campus, MD

Mississippi

Alcorn State University, M
Mississippi State University, MD

Missouri

Missouri State University, M
Northwest Missouri State University, M
University of Missouri, MDO

Montana

Montana State University, MD

Nebraska

University of Nebraska - Lincoln, MD

Nevada

University of Nevada, Reno, MD

North Carolina

North Carolina Agricultural and Technical State University, M
North Carolina State University, MDO

North Dakota

North Dakota State University, MD

Ohio

The Ohio State University, MD

Oklahoma

Oklahoma State University, MD

Pennsylvania

Penn State University Park, MDO

South Carolina

Clemson University, MD

South Dakota

South Dakota State University, MD

Tennessee

Tennessee State University, MD
The University of Tennessee, MD
The University of Tennessee at Martin, M

Texas

Angelo State University, M
Prairie View A&M University, M
Sam Houston State University, M
Tarleton State University, M
Texas A&M University, MD
Texas A&M University - Commerce, M
Texas A&M University - Kingsville, MD
Texas Tech University, MD
West Texas A&M University, MD

Utah

Brigham Young University, MD
Utah State University, MD

Vermont

University of Vermont, MD

Virginia

Virginia Polytechnic Institute and State University,
   MD

West Virginia

West Virginia University, MD

Wisconsin

University of Wisconsin - Madison, MD
University of Wisconsin - River Falls, M

Wyoming

University of Wyoming, MD

U.S. Territories: Puerto Rico

University of Puerto Rico, Mayagüez Campus, M

Canada

Alberta

University of Alberta, MD
University of Lethbridge, M

British Columbia

The University of British Columbia, MD

Manitoba

University of Manitoba, MD

Maritime Provinces: Nova Scotia

Dalhousie University, M

Ontario

University of Guelph, MDO

Quebec

McGill University, MDO
Université Laval, MDO

Saskatchewan

University of Saskatchewan, MDO

AGRICULTURAL TEACHER EDUCATION

United States

Alabama

Auburn University, B

Arkansas

Arkansas Tech University, B
Southern Arkansas University - Magnolia, B
University of Arkansas, B
University of Arkansas at Pine Bluff, B

California

California Polytechnic State University, San Luis
   Obispo, B
California State Polytechnic University, Pomona, B
California State University, Fresno, B
College of the Sequoias, A

Victor Valley College, A

Colorado

Colorado State University, B
Northeastern Junior College, A

Connecticut

University of Connecticut, B

Delaware

Delaware State University, B
University of Delaware, B

Florida

South Florida State College, A
University of Florida, B

Georgia

University of Georgia, B

Idaho

University of Idaho, B

Illinois

Spoon River College, A
University of Illinois at Urbana - Champaign, B

Indiana

Purdue University, B

Iowa

Dordt College, B
Iowa Lakes Community College, A
Iowa State University of Science and Technology, B

Kansas

Colby Community College, A
Kansas State University, B
Pratt Community College, A

Louisiana

Louisiana State University and Agricultural & Mechanical College, B
Louisiana Tech University, B
Southern University and Agricultural and Mechanical College, B

Maryland

University of Maryland Eastern Shore, B

Minnesota

University of Minnesota, Twin Cities Campus, B
Vermilion Community College, A

Mississippi

Mississippi State University, B
Northeast Mississippi Community College, A

Missouri

College of the Ozarks, B
Missouri State University, B
Northwest Missouri State University, B
Southeast Missouri State University, B
University of Missouri, B

Montana

Montana State University, B

Nebraska

University of Nebraska - Lincoln, B

New Mexico

Eastern New Mexico University, B
New Mexico State University, B

New York

State University of New York at Oswego, B

North Carolina

North Carolina Agricultural and Technical State University, B
North Carolina State University, B

North Dakota

North Dakota State University, B

Ohio

The Ohio State University, B
The Ohio State University Agricultural Technical Institute, A
Wilmington College, B

Oklahoma

Eastern Oklahoma State College, A
Murray State College, A
Oklahoma Panhandle State University, B
Oklahoma State University, B
Redlands Community College, A

Pennsylvania

Penn State University Park, B

South Carolina

Clemson University, B

South Dakota

South Dakota State University, B

Tennessee

Tennessee Technological University, B
The University of Tennessee at Martin, B

Texas

Sam Houston State University, B
Tarleton State University, B
Trinity Valley Community College, A
Western Texas College, A

Utah

Utah State University, B

Washington

Washington State University, B

West Virginia

West Virginia University, B

Wisconsin

University of Wisconsin - Platteville, B
University of Wisconsin - River Falls, B

Wyoming

Eastern Wyoming College, A
Northwest College, A
University of Wyoming, B

U.S. Territories: Puerto Rico

University of Puerto Rico, Mayagüez Campus, B

Canada

Alberta

University of Alberta, B

AGRICULTURE

United States

Alabama

Alabama Southern Community College, A
Auburn University, B
Tuskegee University, B
Wallace State Community College, A

Arizona

Arizona Western College, A
Central Arizona College, A
Northland Pioneer College, A
Yavapai College, A

Arkansas

Arkansas State University - Beebe, A
Southern Arkansas University - Magnolia, B

University of Arkansas at Monticello, B
University of Arkansas at Pine Bluff, B

California

Bakersfield College, A
Butte College, A
California State University, Stanislaus, B
College of the Desert, A
College of the Redwoods, A
College of the Sequoias, A
Cosumnes River College, A
Feather River College, A
Hartnell College, A
Imperial Valley College, A
Lassen Community College District, A
Los Angeles Pierce College, A
Mendocino College, A
Merced College, A
Modesto Junior College, A
Mt. San Antonio College, A
Napa Valley College, A
Reedley College, A
San Joaquin Delta College, A
Sierra College, A
Ventura College, A
Woodland Community College, A
Yuba College, A

Colorado

Lamar Community College, A
Northeastern Junior College, A

Connecticut

University of Connecticut, B

Delaware

Delaware State University, B
University of Delaware, AB

Florida

Chipola College, A
College of Central Florida, A
Florida Agricultural and Mechanical University, B
Miami Dade College, A
Pensacola State College, A
South Florida State College, A

Georgia

Abraham Baldwin Agricultural College, AB
Andrew College, A
Bainbridge State College, A
Darton State College, A
Georgia Highlands College, A
University of Georgia, B

Hawaii

University of Hawaii at Hilo, B

Idaho

Brigham Young University - Idaho, B
College of Southern Idaho, A
College of Western Idaho, A
North Idaho College, A

Illinois

Illinois State University, B
Kankakee Community College, A
Kaskaskia College, A
Sauk Valley Community College, A
Shawnee Community College, A
Southern Illinois University Carbondale, B
Western Illinois University, B

Indiana

Ancilla College, A
Ivy Tech Community College - Columbus, A
Ivy Tech Community College - East Central, A
Ivy Tech Community College - Kokomo, A
Ivy Tech Community College - Lafayette, A
Ivy Tech Community College - Northeast, A
Ivy Tech Community College - Richmond, A
Ivy Tech Community College - Southwest, A
Ivy Tech Community College - Wabash Valley, A
Purdue University, B

Vincennes University, A

Iowa

Dordt College, B
Iowa Lakes Community College, A
Iowa State University of Science and Technology, B
Kirkwood Community College, A
Northwest Iowa Community College, A

Kansas

Barton County Community College, A
Coffeyville Community College, A
Cowley County Community College and Area Vocational - Technical School, A
Fort Hays State University, B
Highland Community College, A
Hutchinson Community College, A
Pratt Community College, A

Kentucky

Berea College, B
Kentucky State University, B
Morehead State University, B
Western Kentucky University, B

Louisiana

McNeese State University, B

Maryland

Harford Community College, A
University of Maryland, College Park, B
University of Maryland Eastern Shore, B

Massachusetts

Hampshire College, B

Michigan

Macomb Community College, A

Minnesota

Minnesota West Community and Technical College, A
Northland Community and Technical College, A
Ridgewater College, A

Mississippi

Alcorn State University, B
Copiah-Lincoln Community College, A
East Central Community College, A
Holmes Community College, A
Jones County Junior College, A
Mississippi State University, B
Northeast Mississippi Community College, A
Northwest Mississippi Community College, A

Missouri

Crowder College, A
Lincoln University, B
Missouri State University, B
Missouri State University - West Plains, A
Northwest Missouri State University, B
Truman State University, B
University of Missouri, B

Montana

Montana State University, B

Nebraska

Northeast Community College, A
University of Nebraska - Lincoln, B
Western Nebraska Community College, A

New Jersey

Rutgers University - New Brunswick, B

New Mexico

Eastern New Mexico University, B
New Mexico Junior College, A
New Mexico State University, B
University of New Mexico - Valencia Campus, A

New York

Cornell University, B
Morrisville State College, A

State University of New York College of Agriculture and Technology at Cobleskill, A
State University of New York College of Technology at Alfred, A

North Carolina

North Carolina Agricultural and Technical State University, B
North Carolina State University, AB

North Dakota

Dakota College at Bottineau, A
North Dakota State University, B
Williston State College, A

Ohio

Clark State Community College, A
Southern State Community College, A
Wilmington College, B

Oklahoma

Cameron University, B
Connors State College, A
Murray State College, A
Northeastern Oklahoma Agricultural and Mechanical College, A
Northwestern Oklahoma State University, B
Oklahoma Panhandle State University, A
Redlands Community College, A

Oregon

Klamath Community College, A
Linn-Benton Community College, A
Oregon State University, B
Treasure Valley Community College, A
Umpqua Community College, A

Pennsylvania

Penn State Abington, B
Penn State Altoona, B
Penn State Beaver, B
Penn State Berks, B
Penn State Brandywine, B
Penn State DuBois, B
Penn State Erie, The Behrend College, B
Penn State Fayette, The Eberly Campus, B
Penn State Greater Allegheny, B
Penn State Hazleton, B
Penn State Lehigh Valley, B
Penn State Mont Alto, B
Penn State New Kensington, B
Penn State Schuylkill, B
Penn State Shenango, B
Penn State University Park, B
Penn State Wilkes-Barre, B
Penn State Worthington Scranton, B
Penn State York, B

South Dakota

Oglala Lakota College, A
South Dakota State University, AB

Tennessee

Austin Peay State University, B
Dyersburg State Community College, A
Hiwassee College, A
Jackson State Community College, A
Tennessee State University, B
The University of Tennessee at Martin, B

Texas

Angelo State University, B
Blinn College, A
Central Texas College, A
Cisco College, A
Clarendon College, A
Hill College, A
Howard College, A
Kilgore College, A
Odessa College, A
Palo Alto College, A
Panola College, A
Paris Junior College, A
Prairie View A&M University, B
Sam Houston State University, B

San Jacinto College District, A
South Plains College, A
Stephen F. Austin State University, B
Tarleton State University, B
Texarkana College, A
Texas A&M University, B
Texas A&M University - Commerce, B
Texas A&M University - Kingsville, B
Texas State University, B
Texas Tech University, B
West Texas A&M University, B
Western Texas College, A
Wharton County Junior College, A

Utah

Snow College, A
Southern Utah University, B
Utah State University, B

Vermont

Sterling College, B
University of Vermont, B

Virginia

Ferrum College, B
Virginia State University, B

Washington

Skagit Valley College, A
Washington State University, B
Yakima Valley Community College, A

West Virginia

Potomac State College of West Virginia University, A

Wisconsin

Lac Courte Oreilles Ojibwa Community College, A
University of Wisconsin - River Falls, B

Wyoming

Casper College, A
Laramie County Community College, A
Sheridan College, A

U.S. Territories: American Samoa

American Samoa Community College, A

U.S. Territories: Guam

University of Guam, B

U.S. Territories: Northern Mariana Islands

Northern Marianas College, A

U.S. Territories: Puerto Rico

University of Puerto Rico, Mayagüez Campus, B

Canada

Alberta

University of Alberta, B
University of Lethbridge, B

British Columbia

The University of British Columbia, B

Manitoba

University of Manitoba, B

Maritime Provinces: Nova Scotia

Dalhousie University, B

Ontario

University of Guelph, A

AGRICULTURE, AGRICULTURE OPERATIONS AND RELATED SCIENCES

United States

Arizona
The University of Arizona, B

California
California State University, Stanislaus, B
Cuesta College, A
University of California, Davis, B

Kentucky
Murray State University, AB
University of Kentucky, B

Maine
College of the Atlantic, B

Nebraska
Northeast Community College, A
University of Nebraska - Lincoln, B

Nevada
University of Nevada, Reno, B

Ohio
The Ohio State University, B

Pennsylvania
Penn State University Park, B

Texas
Tarleton State University, B

West Virginia
Potomac State College of West Virginia University, A

Wyoming
Sheridan College, A

Canada

Alberta
University of Alberta, B

Saskatchewan
University of Saskatchewan, B

AGRONOMY AND CROP SCIENCE

United States

Alabama
Auburn University, B
Tuskegee University, B

Arizona
Mesa Community College, A

Arkansas
University of Arkansas, B

California
California Polytechnic State University, San Luis Obispo, B
California State University, Fresno, B
Lassen Community College District, A
Merced College, A
Modesto Junior College, A
West Hills Community College, A
Yuba College, A

Colorado
Colorado State University, B
Lamar Community College, A
Northeastern Junior College, A

Connecticut
University of Connecticut, B

Delaware
Delaware State University, B

Florida
Chipola College, A

Georgia
Fort Valley State University, B

Idaho
Brigham Young University - Idaho, B

Illinois
Shawnee Community College, A
University of Illinois at Urbana - Champaign, B

Indiana
Purdue University, B

Iowa
Iowa Lakes Community College, A
Iowa State University of Science and Technology, B
Southeastern Community College, A

Kansas
Colby Community College, A
Dodge City Community College, A
Fort Hays State University, B
Kansas State University, B

Kentucky
University of Kentucky, B

Minnesota
Minnesota West Community and Technical College, A
Northland Community and Technical College, A
Ridgewater College, A
University of Minnesota, Crookston, B
Vermilion Community College, A

Mississippi
Mississippi State University, B

Missouri
College of the Ozarks, B
Missouri State University, B
Northwest Missouri State University, B

Nebraska
Northeast Community College, A
University of Nebraska - Lincoln, B

New Mexico
New Mexico State University, B

New York
State University of New York College of Agriculture and Technology at Cobleskill, AB

North Carolina
North Carolina State University, B

Ohio
The Ohio State University, B
The Ohio State University Agricultural Technical Institute, A

Oklahoma
Eastern Oklahoma State College, A
Oklahoma Panhandle State University, B

Oregon
Oregon State University, B
Treasure Valley Community College, A

Pennsylvania
Delaware Valley University, B
Penn State Abington, B
Penn State Altoona, B
Penn State Beaver, B
Penn State Berks, B
Penn State Brandywine, B
Penn State DuBois, B
Penn State Erie, The Behrend College, B
Penn State Fayette, The Eberly Campus, B
Penn State Greater Allegheny, B
Penn State Hazleton, B
Penn State Mont Alto, B
Penn State New Kensington, B
Penn State Shenango, B
Penn State Wilkes-Barre, B
Penn State Worthington Scranton, B
Penn State York, B

South Dakota
South Dakota State University, B

Tennessee
Tennessee Technological University, B
The University of Tennessee at Martin, B

Texas
South Plains College, A
Tarleton State University, B
Texas A&M University, B
Texas A&M University - Kingsville, B
Texas Tech University, B
West Texas A&M University, B

Utah
Utah State University, B

Vermont
University of Vermont, B

Virginia
Virginia Polytechnic Institute and State University, B

Washington
Spokane Community College, A
Washington State University, B
Yakima Valley Community College, A

West Virginia
Potomac State College of West Virginia University, A

Wisconsin
Northcentral Technical College, A
University of Wisconsin - Madison, B
University of Wisconsin - Platteville, B
University of Wisconsin - River Falls, B

U.S. Territories: Puerto Rico
University of Puerto Rico, Mayagüez Campus, B

Canada

Manitoba
University of Manitoba, B

Maritime Provinces: Nova Scotia
Dalhousie University, B

Ontario
University of Guelph, B

Quebec
McGill University, B
Université Laval, B

Saskatchewan
University of Saskatchewan, B

AGRONOMY AND SOIL SCIENCES

United States

Alabama
Alabama Agricultural and Mechanical University, MD
Auburn University, MD
Tuskegee University, M

Arizona
The University of Arizona, MD

Arkansas
University of Arkansas, MD

California
University of California, Davis, MD
University of California, Riverside, MD

Colorado
Colorado State University, MD

Connecticut
University of Connecticut, MD

Delaware
University of Delaware, MD

Florida
University of Florida, MD

Georgia
University of Georgia, MD

Idaho
University of Idaho, MD

Illinois
Southern Illinois University Carbondale, M
University of Illinois at Urbana - Champaign, MD

Indiana
Purdue University, MD

Iowa
Iowa State University of Science and Technology, MD

Kansas
Kansas State University, MDO

Kentucky
University of Kentucky, MD

Michigan
Michigan State University, MD

Minnesota
University of Minnesota, Twin Cities Campus, MD

Mississippi
Alcorn State University, M
Mississippi State University, MD

Missouri
University of Missouri, MD

Nebraska
University of Nebraska - Lincoln, MD

New York
Cornell University, MD

North Carolina
North Carolina Agricultural and Technical State University, M
North Carolina State University, MD

North Dakota
North Dakota State University, MD

Ohio
The Ohio State University, MD

Oklahoma
Oklahoma State University, MD

Oregon
Oregon State University, MD

Pennsylvania
Penn State University Park, MD

South Dakota
South Dakota State University, D

Tennessee
Tennessee State University, M

Texas
Texas A&M University, MD
Texas A&M University - Kingsville, M
Texas Tech University, MD

Utah
Utah State University, MD

Vermont
University of Vermont, MD

Virginia
Virginia Polytechnic Institute and State University, MD

Washington
Washington State University, MDO

West Virginia
West Virginia University, MD

Wisconsin
University of Wisconsin - Madison, MD

Wyoming
University of Wyoming, MD

U.S. Territories: Puerto Rico
University of Puerto Rico, Mayagüez Campus, M

Canada

Alberta
University of Alberta, MD

British Columbia
The University of British Columbia, MD

Manitoba
University of Manitoba, MD

Maritime Provinces: Nova Scotia
Dalhousie University, M

Ontario
University of Guelph, MD

Quebec
McGill University, MD
Université Laval, MD

Saskatchewan
University of Saskatchewan, MDO

AIR FORCE JROTC/ROTC

United States

Iowa
The University of Iowa, B

Massachusetts
Elms College, B

Pennsylvania
La Salle University, B

AIR TRAFFIC CONTROLLER

United States

Alabama
Community College of the Air Force, A

Alaska
University of Alaska Anchorage, A

Arizona
Arizona State University at the Polytechnic campus, B
Embry-Riddle Aeronautical University - Prescott, B

California
Mt. San Antonio College, A

Florida
Broward College, A
Embry-Riddle Aeronautical University - Daytona, B
Florida Memorial University, B
Miami Dade College, A

Georgia
Middle Georgia State University, A

Illinois
Lewis University, AB

Kansas
Hesston College, A

Maryland
Cecil College, A
University of Maryland Eastern Shore, B

New Hampshire
Daniel Webster College, B

New Jersey
Thomas Edison State University, AB

North Dakota
University of North Dakota, B

Oklahoma
Tulsa Community College, A

Pennsylvania
Community College of Beaver County, A

Texas
LeTourneau University, AB
Texas State Technical College, A

Virginia
Hampton University, B

Washington
Green River College, A

AIR TRANSPORTATION

United States

Arizona

Cochise County Community College District, A

California

California Baptist University, B

Colorado

Aims Community College, A

Florida

Florida Institute of Technology, B

New Jersey

Thomas Edison State University, AB

North Dakota

University of North Dakota, B

U.S. Territories: Puerto Rico

Inter American University of Puerto Rico, Bayamón Campus, B

AIRCRAFT POWERPLANT TECHNOLOGY/TECHNICIAN

United States

Alabama

Enterprise State Community College, A

Alaska

University of Alaska Fairbanks, A

Arkansas

Black River Technical College, A
Pulaski Technical College, A
Southern Arkansas University Tech, A
University of Arkansas Community College at Batesville, A

California

Antelope Valley College, A
Chaffey College, A
City College of San Francisco, A
College of Alameda, A
Orange Coast College, A

Colorado

Colorado Northwestern Community College, A

Florida

Embry-Riddle Aeronautical University - Daytona, AB
Embry-Riddle Aeronautical University - Worldwide, AB

Georgia

Middle Georgia State University, A

Idaho

Idaho State University, AB

Indiana

Vincennes University, A

Kentucky

Somerset Community College, A

Louisiana

South Louisiana Community College, A
Sowela Technical Community College, A

Massachusetts

Middlesex Community College, A

Michigan

Lansing Community College, A
Wayne County Community College District, A

Missouri

State Technical College of Missouri, A

New Jersey

Thomas Edison State University, B

Pennsylvania

Pennsylvania College of Technology, A

South Dakota

Lake Area Technical Institute, A

Texas

Central Texas College, A
Hallmark University, A
St. Philip's College, A
Texas State Technical College, A

Canada

British Columbia

British Columbia Institute of Technology, A

AIRFRAME MECHANICS AND AIRCRAFT MAINTENANCE TECHNOLOGY/TECHNICIAN

United States

Alabama

Community College of the Air Force, A
Enterprise State Community College, A

Alaska

University of Alaska Anchorage, A

Arizona

Pima Community College, A

California

Antelope Valley College, A
Chaffey College, A
City College of San Francisco, A
College of Alameda, A
Gavilan College, A
Long Beach City College, A
Merced College, A
Mt. San Antonio College, A
Orange Coast College, A
Sacramento City College, A
San Diego Miramar College, A
San Joaquin Valley College - Fresno Aviation Campus, A
Solano Community College, A
Spartan College of Aeronautics and Technology, A
West Los Angeles College, A

Connecticut

Three Rivers Community College, A

Florida

Florida State College at Jacksonville, A
St. Petersburg College, A

Illinois

Lewis University, A
Lincoln Land Community College, A
Southwestern Illinois College, A

Indiana

Ivy Tech Community College - Wabash Valley, A

Kansas

Kansas State University, B
Wichita Area Technical College, A

Michigan

Lansing Community College, A
Northern Michigan University, A
Wayne County Community College District, A

Minnesota

Northland Community and Technical College, A

Mississippi

Hinds Community College, A

Missouri

State Technical College of Missouri, A

Montana

Helena College University of Montana, A

New Hampshire

Nashua Community College, A

New Jersey

Thomas Edison State University, AB

New Mexico

Central New Mexico Community College, A
Eastern New Mexico University - Roswell, A

New York

Mohawk Valley Community College, A
Vaughn College of Aeronautics and Technology, B

North Carolina

Craven Community College, A
Wayne Community College, A

Oklahoma

Southeastern Oklahoma State University, B

Oregon

Lane Community College, A
Portland Community College, A

Pennsylvania

Pittsburgh Institute of Aeronautics, A

South Carolina

Trident Technical College, A

Texas

Amarillo College, A
Hallmark University, A
St. Philip's College, A
Texas State Technical College, A

Virginia

Blue Ridge Community College, A

Washington

South Seattle College, A

Canada

British Columbia

British Columbia Institute of Technology, A

AIRLINE/COMMERCIAL/PRO-FESSIONAL PILOT AND FLIGHT CREW

United States

Alabama

Auburn University, B
Wallace State Community College, A

Alaska

University of Alaska Anchorage, A
University of Alaska Fairbanks, A

Arizona

Chandler-Gilbert Community College, A
Cochise County Community College District, A
Embry-Riddle Aeronautical University - Prescott, B

Arkansas

Henderson State University, B
Pulaski Technical College, A

California

California Baptist University, B
Cypress College, A
Glendale Community College, A
Long Beach City College, A
Mt. San Antonio College, A
Palomar College, A

Colorado

Aims Community College, A
Colorado Northwestern Community College, A
Morgan Community College, AB

Delaware

Delaware State University, B

Florida

Broward College, A
Embry-Riddle Aeronautical University - Daytona, B
Florida State College at Jacksonville, A
Indian River State College, A
Jacksonville University, B
Miami Dade College, A
Palm Beach State College, A
Polk State College, A
Santa Fe College, A

Georgia

Middle Georgia State University, A

Illinois

Kishwaukee College, A
Lewis University, A
Quincy University, B
Southern Illinois University Carbondale, A
Southwestern Illinois College, A
University of Illinois at Urbana - Champaign, B

Indiana

Indiana State University, B
Vincennes University, A

Iowa

Indian Hills Community College, A
Iowa Central Community College, A
Iowa Lakes Community College, A
Scott Community College, A
University of Dubuque, B

Kansas

Central Christian College of Kansas, A
Hesston College, A
Kansas State University, B

Kentucky

Eastern Kentucky University, B

Louisiana

University of Louisiana at Monroe, B

Massachusetts

Bridgewater State University, B
North Shore Community College, A

Michigan

Eastern Michigan University, B
Jackson College, A
Lansing Community College, A
Northwestern Michigan College, A
Western Michigan University, B

Minnesota

Academy College, A
Inver Hills Community College, A

Lake Superior College, A
University of Minnesota, Crookston, B
Vermilion Community College, A

Mississippi

Delta State University, B

Missouri

Saint Louis University, B

Montana

Rocky Mountain College, B

New Jersey

County College of Morris, A
Mercer County Community College, A

New Mexico

Eastern New Mexico University - Roswell, A

New York

Dutchess Community College, A
Farmingdale State College, B
Jamestown Community College, A

North Carolina

Guilford Technical Community College, A
Lenoir Community College, A

North Dakota

University of North Dakota, B

Oklahoma

Southeastern Oklahoma State University, B
Spartan College of Aeronautics and Technology, AB

Oregon

Central Oregon Community College, A
Lane Community College, A
Portland Community College, A
Treasure Valley Community College, A

Pennsylvania

Community College of Allegheny County, A
Community College of Beaver County, A
Lehigh Carbon Community College, A
Luzerne County Community College, A
Pennsylvania Highlands Community College, A

Texas

Baylor University, B
Central Texas College, A
LeTourneau University, B
San Jacinto College District, A
Tarleton State University, B
Texas A&M University - Central Texas, B
Texas State Technical College, A

Utah

Salt Lake Community College, A
Southern Utah University, A
Utah Valley University, AB
Westminster College, B

Washington

Big Bend Community College, A
Central Washington University, B
Clover Park Technical College, A
Green River College, A

Wisconsin

Fox Valley Technical College, A
Gateway Technical College, A

Wyoming

Casper College, A

Canada

Manitoba

Providence University College & Theological Seminary, B

AIRLINE FLIGHT ATTENDANT

United States

California

Cypress College, A
Glendale Community College, A
Orange Coast College, A

New Jersey

Mercer County Community College, A

Virginia

Liberty University, A

ALGEBRA AND NUMBER THEORY

United States

Vermont

Marlboro College, B

Canada

Maritime Provinces: New Brunswick

University of New Brunswick Saint John, B

ALLIED HEALTH DIAGNOSTIC, INTERVENTION, AND TREATMENT PROFESSIONS

United States

Alabama

Calhoun Community College, A

Arkansas

University of Arkansas for Medical Sciences, B

California

Point Loma Nazarene University, B

Connecticut

Sacred Heart University, B

Indiana

Ball State University, A

Michigan

Northern Michigan University, B

Minnesota

Minneapolis Community and Technical College, A

Missouri

Cox College, AB

Nebraska

University of Nebraska at Kearney, B

New Jersey

College of Saint Elizabeth, B
Fairleigh Dickinson University, College at Florham, B
Fairleigh Dickinson University, Metropolitan Campus, B
Georgian Court University, B
Rutgers University - New Brunswick, B
Rutgers University - Newark, B
Salem Community College, A
Thomas Edison State University, AB
Union County College, A

New York

Hofstra University, B

North Carolina

Durham Technical Community College, A
Forsyth Technical Community College, A
Pitt Community College, A
South Piedmont Community College, A
The University of North Carolina at Charlotte, B

Oklahoma

Cameron University, A

Pennsylvania

Gwynedd Mercy University, AB
Harcum College, A
Immaculata University, B
Millersville University of Pennsylvania, B
Pennsylvania College of Technology, A
Thomas Jefferson University, B

Tennessee

Tennessee Wesleyan College, B

Utah

Weber State University, B

Virginia

Danville Community College, A

Washington

Bellevue College, A

Wisconsin

Milwaukee Area Technical College, A

Canada

British Columbia

British Columbia Institute of Technology, A

ALLIED HEALTH AND MEDICAL ASSISTING SERVICES

United States

Alabama

Alabama State University, MD
The University of Alabama at Birmingham, MDO
University of South Alabama, MD

Arizona

Arizona College, A
Northern Arizona University, MDO

Arkansas

Harding University, MD

California

Carrington College - San Jose, A
Loma Linda University, MD
National University, A
Platt College (Alhambra), A
Platt College (Ontario), A
University of Antelope Valley, A

Colorado

CollegeAmerica - Colorado Springs, A
CollegeAmerica - Fort Collins, A
Everest College (Thornton), A
Heritage College, A
National American University (Colorado Springs), A
Regis University, MDO

Connecticut

Quinnipiac University, MD
University of Connecticut, BM

Florida

City College (Gainesville), A
Florida Agricultural and Mechanical University, MD
Florida Career College, A
Florida Gulf Coast University, MD

Florida National University, A
Jones College, AB
Nova Southeastern University, MD
University of Florida, MDO
University of North Florida, MDO

Georgia

Emory University, MD
Georgia Southern University, MDO
Georgia State University, M

Idaho

Idaho State University, MDO

Illinois

University of Illinois at Chicago, MDO

Indiana

Purdue University, D

Kansas

The University of Kansas, MDO
Wichita State University, MD

Kentucky

Eastern Kentucky University, M
Northern Kentucky University, M
University of Kentucky, MD

Maryland

Towson University, M

Massachusetts

Boston University, MD
Mount Wachusett Community College, A
Northeastern University, MDO
University of Massachusetts Lowell, MDO

Michigan

Andrews University, M
Ferris State University, M
Grand Valley State University, MD
Oakland University, MDO
University of Detroit Mercy, MO

Minnesota

Minnesota State University Mankato, MDO

Mississippi

Antonelli College (Hattiesburg), A
University of Mississippi Medical Center, M

Missouri

Everest College, A
Maryville University of Saint Louis, MD
National American University (Kansas City), A
St. Louis College of Health Careers (Saint Louis), A
Saint Louis University, MDO

Nebraska

Creighton University, MD
Nebraska Methodist College, A
University of Nebraska Medical Center, MDO

Nevada

Everest College, A
University of Nevada, Las Vegas, MDO
University of Phoenix - Las Vegas Campus, M

New Jersey

College of Saint Elizabeth, B
New Jersey City University, M
Ramapo College of New Jersey, B
Rutgers University - Newark, MDO
Seton Hall University, D
Thomas Edison State University, A

New Mexico

University of New Mexico, MDO

New York

Canisius College, MO
Dominican College, MD

Ithaca College, MD
Long Island University - LIU Post, MO
Mercy College, MD
Plaza College, A
University at Buffalo, the State University of New York, MDO

North Carolina

East Carolina University, MDO
Miller-Motte College (Cary), B
Miller-Motte College (Wilmington), A
The University of North Carolina at Chapel Hill, MD

Ohio

Bowling Green State University - Firelands College, AB
Cedarville University, B
Cincinnati State Technical and Community College, A
Cleveland State University, M
Daymar College, A
Miami-Jacobs Career College (Independence), A
The Ohio State University, BM
The Ohio State University at Lima, B

Oklahoma

Heritage College, A
Southwestern Oklahoma State University, M
University of Oklahoma Health Sciences Center, MDO

Oregon

American College of Healthcare Sciences, MO
Oregon State University, MD

Pennsylvania

Clarion University of Pennsylvania, A
Drexel University, MDO
Duquesne University, MD
Eastern University, A
Fortis Institute (Forty Fort), A
Misericordia University, MD
Moravian College, M
Pennsylvania Institute of Technology, A
Temple University, MDO
Widener University, AB

South Carolina

Medical University of South Carolina, MD
South Carolina State University, M

South Dakota

The University of South Dakota, MDO

Tennessee

Belmont University, MD
East Tennessee State University, MDO
Tennessee State University, MD

Texas

Baylor University, MD
Sam Houston State University, M
Texas A&M University, MD
Texas Christian University, MDO
Texas State University, MD
Texas Woman's University, MD
The University of Texas at El Paso, D
The University of Texas Medical Branch, MD

Vermont

Bennington College, O
University of Vermont, MD

Virginia

Hampton University, M
Marymount University, MDO
Old Dominion University, MD
Shenandoah University, MDO
Stratford University (Falls Church), A
Virginia Commonwealth University, D

Washington

North Seattle College, A

West Virginia

Blue Ridge Community and Technical College, A
Huntington Junior College, A

Wisconsin

Milwaukee Area Technical College, A
University of Wisconsin - Milwaukee, MDO

Wyoming

Northwest College, A

U.S. Territories: Puerto Rico

University of Puerto Rico, Medical Sciences Campus, MDO

Canada

Alberta

Athabasca University, MO

Ontario

Brock University, MD

ALLOPATHIC MEDICINE

United States

Alabama

The University of Alabama at Birmingham, D
University of South Alabama, D

Arizona

The University of Arizona, MD

Arkansas

University of Arkansas for Medical Sciences, D

California

Charles R. Drew University of Medicine and Science, D
Loma Linda University, MD
Stanford University, D
University of California, Davis, D
University of California, Irvine, D
University of California, Los Angeles, D
University of California, San Diego, D
University of Southern California, D

Colorado

University of Colorado Denver, D

Connecticut

Quinnipiac University, D
Yale University, D

District of Columbia

The George Washington University, D
Georgetown University, D
Howard University, D

Florida

Florida Atlantic University, D
Florida International University, MD
University of Central Florida, MD
University of Florida, D
University of Miami, D
University of South Florida, MD

Georgia

Augusta University, D
Emory University, D
Mercer University, MD

Hawaii

University of Hawaii at Manoa, D

Illinois

Loyola University Chicago, D
Rush University, D
University of Chicago, D

University of Illinois at Chicago, D

Indiana

Indiana University - Purdue University Indianapolis, MD

Iowa

The University of Iowa, D

Kansas

The University of Kansas, D

Kentucky

University of Kentucky, D
University of Louisville, D

Louisiana

Louisiana State University Health Sciences Center, MD
Tulane University, D

Maryland

Johns Hopkins University, D

Massachusetts

Boston University, D
Harvard University, D
Tufts University, D

Michigan

Michigan State University, D
University of Michigan, D
Wayne State University, D

Minnesota

University of Minnesota, Duluth, D
University of Minnesota, Twin Cities Campus, MD

Mississippi

University of Mississippi Medical Center, D

Missouri

Saint Louis University, D
University of Missouri, D
University of Missouri - Kansas City, MD
Washington University in St. Louis, D

Nebraska

Creighton University, D
University of Nebraska Medical Center, DO

New Hampshire

Dartmouth College, D

New Jersey

Rutgers University - New Brunswick, D
Rutgers University - Newark, D

New Mexico

University of New Mexico, D

New York

Columbia University, MD
Hofstra University, D
New York University, MD
State University of New York Downstate Medical Center, MD
State University of New York Upstate Medical University, D
Stony Brook University, State University of New York, D
University at Buffalo, the State University of New York, D
University of Rochester, D

North Carolina

Duke University, D
East Carolina University, D
The University of North Carolina at Chapel Hill, D
Wake Forest University, D

North Dakota

University of North Dakota, D

Ohio

Case Western Reserve University, D
The Ohio State University, D
University of Cincinnati, D
Wright State University, D

Oklahoma

University of Oklahoma Health Sciences Center, D

Oregon

Oregon Health & Science University, D

Pennsylvania

Drexel University, D
Temple University, D
Thomas Jefferson University, D
University of Pennsylvania, D
University of Pittsburgh, D

Rhode Island

Brown University, D

South Carolina

Medical University of South Carolina, D
University of South Carolina, D

South Dakota

The University of South Dakota, D

Tennessee

East Tennessee State University, D
Vanderbilt University, MD

Texas

The University of Texas Health Science Center at Houston, D
The University of Texas Health Science Center at San Antonio, MD
The University of Texas Medical Branch, D
The University of Texas Rio Grande Valley, D

Utah

University of Utah, D

Vermont

University of Vermont, D

Virginia

University of Virginia, MD
Virginia Commonwealth University, D

Washington

University of Washington, D

West Virginia

Marshall University, D
West Virginia University, D

Wisconsin

University of Wisconsin - Madison, D

U.S. Territories: Puerto Rico

Universidad Central del Caribe, MD
University of Puerto Rico, Medical Sciences Campus, D

Canada

Alberta

University of Calgary, D

British Columbia

The University of British Columbia, MD

Maritime Provinces: Nova Scotia

Dalhousie University, MD

Ontario

Queen's University at Kingston, D
University of Ottawa, MD
University of Toronto, MD

The University of Western Ontario, MD

Quebec

McGill University, MD
Université Laval, DO
Université de Montréal, D
Université de Sherbrooke, D

Saskatchewan

University of Saskatchewan, D

ALTERNATIVE AND COMPLEMENTARY MEDICAL SUPPORT SERVICES

United States

Arizona

Southwest Institute of Healing Arts, A

Massachusetts

Mount Wachusett Community College, A

ALTERNATIVE AND COMPLEMENTARY MEDICINE AND MEDICAL SYSTEMS

United States

Florida

Everglades University (Boca Raton), B
Everglades University (Maitland), B
Everglades University (Sarasota), B

Massachusetts

Quinsigamond Community College, A

Oregon

American College of Healthcare Sciences, A

Vermont

Johnson State College, B

ALTERNATIVE FUEL VEHICLE TECHNOLOGY/TECHNICIAN

United States

California

Cerritos College, A
Long Beach City College, A

AMERICAN GOVERNMENT AND POLITICS (UNITED STATES)

United States

Arizona

Arizona Christian University, B

California

American Jewish University, B
The Master's College and Seminary, B

District of Columbia

Gallaudet University, B

Florida

Ave Maria University, B
Southeastern University, B
State College of Florida Manatee-Sarasota, A

Maine

Thomas College, B

Massachusetts

Bridgewater State University, B
Emmanuel College, B
Fitchburg State University, B

Michigan

Western Michigan University, B

Mississippi

East Central Community College, A

Missouri

Drury University, B

Montana

University of Montana, B

New York

United States Military Academy, B

North Carolina

Belmont Abbey College, B
Lenoir-Rhyne University, B

Ohio

The University of Akron, B

Oklahoma

Oklahoma Christian University, B
Oklahoma City Community College, A
Southern Nazarene University, B

Pennsylvania

La Salle University, B
Misericordia University, B

Texas

Wayland Baptist University, B

Vermont

Marlboro College, B

Virginia

Emory & Henry College, B

AMERICAN HISTORY (UNITED STATES)

United States

Florida

Florida College, B

Iowa

Morningside College, B

Massachusetts

Salem State University, B

New Hampshire

Keene State College, B

New York

The College of Saint Rose, B
Touro College, B
United States Military Academy, B

Pennsylvania

Gettysburg College, B

South Carolina

Charleston Southern University, B

Texas

Howard Payne University, B

Washington

University of Washington, Tacoma, B

U.S. Territories: Puerto Rico

University of Puerto Rico, Río Piedras Campus, B

Canada

Ontario

The University of Western Ontario, B

AMERICAN INDIAN/NATIVE AMERICAN LANGUAGES, LITERATURES, AND LINGUISTICS

United States

Alaska

University of Alaska Fairbanks, AB

Idaho

Idaho State University, A

Michigan

Bay Mills Community College, A

Minnesota

Bemidji State University, B

Canada

Saskatchewan

University of Regina, B

AMERICAN INDIAN/NATIVE AMERICAN STUDIES

United States

Alaska

Ilisagvik College, A
University of Alaska Fairbanks, B

Arizona

Arizona State University at the Tempe campus, B
Arizona Western College, A
Diné College, A
Northern Arizona University, B
Pima Community College, A
The University of Arizona, BMD

California

California State University, East Bay, B
Humboldt State University, B
San Diego State University, B
San Francisco State University, B
Santa Barbara City College, A
Sonoma State University, B
Stanford University, B
University of California, Berkeley, B
University of California, Davis, BMD
University of California, Los Angeles, BM
University of California, Riverside, B

Colorado

Fort Lewis College, B

Hawaii

Hawaii Community College, A
Leeward Community College, A
University of Hawaii at Hilo, B
University of Hawaii at Manoa, B

Idaho

North Idaho College, A
University of Idaho, D

Kansas

Haskell Indian Nations University, B
The University of Kansas, MO

Massachusetts

Hampshire College, B

Michigan

Bay Mills Community College, A
Central Michigan University, M
Keweenaw Bay Ojibwa Community College, A
Saginaw Chippewa Tribal College, A

Minnesota

Augsburg College, B
Bemidji State University, B
Itasca Community College, A
University of Minnesota, Duluth, B
University of Minnesota, Morris, B
University of Minnesota, Twin Cities Campus, B

Missouri

Washington University in St. Louis, M

Montana

Aaniiih Nakoda College, A
Fort Peck Community College, A
Montana State University, M
Salish Kootenai College, A
University of Montana, B

Nebraska

Little Priest Tribal College, A
Nebraska Indian Community College, A
University of Nebraska at Omaha, B

New Hampshire

Dartmouth College, B

New Mexico

Institute of American Indian Arts, AB
Navajo Technical University, M
San Juan College, A
University of New Mexico, BM

New York

Colgate University, B

North Carolina

The University of North Carolina at Pembroke, B

North Dakota

Sitting Bull College, A
University of North Dakota, B

Oklahoma

Bacone College, A
East Central University, B
Northeastern Oklahoma Agricultural and Mechanical
    College, A
Northeastern State University, B
Southwestern Oklahoma State University, A
University of Oklahoma, BMD
University of Science and Arts of Oklahoma, B
The University of Tulsa, M

Oregon

Portland State University, B

South Dakota

Black Hills State University, B
Oglala Lakota College, AB
Sinte Gleska University, AB
Sisseton-Wahpeton College, A
South Dakota State University, B
The University of South Dakota, B

Washington

The Evergreen State College, B
Northwest Indian College, A
Northwest University, B
University of Washington, B

Wisconsin

Lac Courte Oreilles Ojibwa Community College, A
Northland College, B
University of Wisconsin - Eau Claire, B
University of Wisconsin - Green Bay, B

Wyoming

Central Wyoming College, A
University of Wyoming, B

Canada

Alberta

University of Alberta, B
University of Calgary, B
University of Lethbridge, BM

British Columbia

Vancouver Island University, B

Manitoba

Brandon University, B
University of Manitoba, M

Maritime Provinces: New Brunswick

St. Thomas University, B

Ontario

Laurentian University, B
Trent University, BMD
University of Ottawa, B
University of Toronto, B
The University of Western Ontario, B

Quebec

Concordia University, B

Saskatchewan

University of Regina, B
University of Saskatchewan, B

AMERICAN SIGN LANGUAGE

United States

Kentucky

Eastern Kentucky University, B

New Jersey

Union County College, A

AMERICAN SIGN LANGUAGE (ASL)

United States

Arizona

Pima Community College, A

California

American River College, A
Antelope Valley College, A
Berkeley City College, A
California State University, Sacramento, B
Grossmont College, A
Ohlone College, A
Santa Rosa Junior College, A
Sierra College, A

Idaho

College of Southern Idaho, A
Idaho State University, A

Indiana

Bethel College, A
Goshen College, B
Vincennes University, A

Maryland

Montgomery College, A

Massachusetts

Bristol Community College, A
Northeastern University, B

Michigan

Madonna University, AB

Minnesota

North Central University, AB
St. Catherine University, B

Missouri

William Woods University, B

New Jersey

Rowan College at Burlington County, A
Union County College, A

New York

Rochester Institute of Technology, B
University of Rochester, B

North Carolina

Gardner-Webb University, B

Oklahoma

Oklahoma State University, Oklahoma City, A

South Dakota

Augustana University, B

Tennessee

Maryville College, B

Texas

Lamar University, B
University of Houston, B

Utah

Utah Valley University, B
Weber State University, A

Virginia

Liberty University, B

West Virginia

Pierpont Community & Technical College, A

AMERICAN/UNITED STATES STUDIES/CIVILIZATION

United States

Alabama

The University of Alabama, BM

Arizona

Arizona State University at the West campus, B

Arkansas

Hendrix College, B
University of Arkansas, B

California

Cabrillo College, A
California State Polytechnic University, Pomona, B
California State University, Fullerton, BM
California State University, Long Beach, BM
California State University, San Bernardino, B
Claremont McKenna College, B
El Camino College, A
Foothill College, A
Los Angeles City College, A
Mills College, B
Mount Saint Mary's University, B
Occidental College, B
Pepperdine University, M

Pitzer College, B
Pomona College, B
Saddleback College, A
Saint Mary's College of California, B
San Francisco State University, B
Scripps College, B
Sonoma State University, B
Stanford University, B
University of California, Berkeley, B
University of California, Davis, B
University of California, Santa Cruz, B
University of San Francisco, B
University of Southern California, BD

Colorado

The Colorado College, M
University of Colorado Denver, M

Connecticut

Connecticut College, B
Fairfield University, BM
Trinity College, BM
University of Connecticut, B
Wesleyan University, B
Western Connecticut State University, B
Yale University, BD

Delaware

University of Delaware, M
Wesley College, B

District of Columbia

American University, BO
The George Washington University, BMD
Georgetown University, BM

Florida

Ave Maria University, B
Eckerd College, B
Florida State University, M
Miami Dade College, A
South Florida State College, A
State College of Florida Manatee-Sarasota, A
Stetson University, B
University of Miami, B
University of South Florida, BM

Georgia

Armstrong State University, M
College of Coastal Georgia, B
Emory University, B
Georgia College & State University, M
Kennesaw State University, M
Oglethorpe University, B
Wesleyan College, B

Hawaii

University of Hawaii at Manoa, BMDO

Illinois

DePaul University, B
Dominican University, B
Elmhurst College, B
Illinois Wesleyan University, B
Knox College, B
Lake Forest College, BM
Northwestern University, BM

Indiana

Indiana University Bloomington, B
Purdue University, BMD
University of Notre Dame, B
Valparaiso University, B

Iowa

Coe College, B
The University of Iowa, BMD

Kansas

Kansas State University, B
The University of Kansas, BMD

Kentucky

Georgetown College, B
Kentucky Wesleyan College, B
Lindsey Wilson College, B

Louisiana

Tulane University, B
University of Louisiana at Lafayette, D

Maine

Bates College, B
Colby College, B
University of Southern Maine, MO

Maryland

Goucher College, B
Towson University, B
University of Maryland, Baltimore County, B
University of Maryland, College Park, BMD
Washington College, B

Massachusetts

Amherst College, B
Boston University, BD
Brandeis University, B
Clark University, MD
Emmanuel College, B
Greenfield Community College, A
Hampshire College, B
Harvard University, D
Lesley University, B
Mount Ida College, B
Smith College, B
Springfield College, B
Stonehill College, B
Tufts University, B
University of Massachusetts Amherst, D
University of Massachusetts Boston, BM
University of Massachusetts Lowell, B
Wellesley College, B
Wheaton College, B
Wheelock College, B
Williams College, B

Michigan

Central Michigan University, O
Eastern Michigan University, M
Hillsdale College, B
Lansing Community College, A
Michigan State University, MD
University of Michigan, BMD
University of Michigan - Dearborn, B
University of Michigan - Flint, M
Wayne State University, D

Minnesota

Carleton College, B
St. Cloud State University, B
St. Olaf College, B
University of Minnesota, Twin Cities Campus, BD

Mississippi

Mississippi Delta Community College, A
Mississippi State University, MD
University of Southern Mississippi, B

Missouri

Columbia College, B
Saint Louis University, BMD
University of Missouri - Kansas City, B
University of Missouri - St. Louis, M
Washington University in St. Louis, B

Nebraska

Creighton University, B

New Hampshire

Franklin Pierce University, B
Keene State College, B

New Jersey

College of Saint Elizabeth, B
Monmouth University, M
Ramapo College of New Jersey, B

Rider University, B
Rowan University, B
Rutgers University - New Brunswick, B
Rutgers University - Newark, BMD
Saint Peter's University, B
Stockton University, MO

New Mexico

New Mexico Highlands University, M
University of New Mexico, BMD

New York

Bard College, B
Barnard College, B
Brooklyn College of the City University of New York, B
The College at Brockport, State University of New York, M
College of Staten Island of the City University of New York, B
Columbia University, BM
Columbia University, School of General Studies, B
Cornell University, BMD
Elmira College, B
Fordham University, B
Hamilton College, B
Hobart and William Smith Colleges, B
Hofstra University, B
Lehman College of the City University of New York, B
Long Island University - LIU Post, B
Manhattanville College, B
Marist College, B
Nazareth College of Rochester, B
New York University, MD
Pace University, B
Pace University, Pleasantville Campus, B
Queens College of the City University of New York, B
St. John Fisher College, B
Siena College, B
Skidmore College, B
State University of New York College at Geneseo, B
State University of New York College at Old Westbury, B
State University of New York at Fredonia, B
State University of New York at Oswego, B
Stony Brook University, State University of New York, B
Union College, B
University at Buffalo, the State University of New York, BMDO
University of Rochester, BMD
Vassar College, B

North Carolina

Appalachian State University, M
Chowan University, B
East Carolina University, M
Lenoir-Rhyne University, B
Montreat College, B
The University of North Carolina at Chapel Hill, B

Ohio

Ashland University, B
Bowling Green State University, BMD
Case Western Reserve University, B
Kenyon College, B
Miami University, B
Miami University Hamilton, B
Muskingum University, B
University of Dayton, B
University of Mount Union, B
University of Rio Grande, B
The University of Toledo, B
Wittenberg University, B
Youngstown State University, B

Oklahoma

Northeastern State University, M
Northwestern Oklahoma State University, M
Oklahoma State University, B
Southern Nazarene University, B

Oregon

George Fox University, B
Oregon State University, B
Reed College, B
Warner Pacific College, B
Willamette University, B

Pennsylvania

Albright College, B
Cabrini University, B
Dickinson College, B
Franklin & Marshall College, B
Gettysburg College, B
La Salle University, BMO
Lafayette College, B
Lehigh University, MDO
Lycoming College, B
Muhlenberg College, B
Penn State Abington, B
Penn State Berks, B
Penn State Brandywine, B
Penn State Erie, The Behrend College, B
Penn State Harrisburg, BMD
Penn State Lehigh Valley, B
Penn State Schuylkill, B
Penn State Worthington Scranton, B
Penn State York, B
Saint Francis University, B
Temple University, B
University of Pennsylvania, B
University of Pittsburgh at Greensburg, B
Ursinus College, B
Villanova University, O

Rhode Island

Brown University, BMD
Bryant University, B
Providence College, BM
Roger Williams University, B
Salve Regina University, B

South Carolina

Claflin University, B
Erskine College, B

South Dakota

Augustana University, B

Tennessee

Cumberland University, B
Lipscomb University, B
Sewanee: The University of the South, B
Tennessee Wesleyan College, B
Vanderbilt University, B

Texas

Austin College, B
Baylor University, BMD
Lee College, A
Rice University, D
Texas Christian University, MD
Texas State University, B
University of Dallas, M
The University of Texas at Austin, BMD
The University of Texas at Dallas, B
The University of Texas at San Antonio, B

Utah

University of Utah, MD
Utah State University, BM

Vermont

Bennington College, B
Marlboro College, B
Middlebury College, B
Norwich University, M
Saint Michael's College, B

Virginia

Christopher Newport University, B
The College of William and Mary, BMD
Emory & Henry College, M
Mary Baldwin College, B
Regent University, M

University of Mary Washington, B
University of Richmond, B
Virginia Wesleyan College, B

Washington

University of Washington, Bothell, B
University of Washington, Tacoma, B
Washington State University, MD
Western Washington University, B
Whitworth University, B

West Virginia

American Public University System, M
West Virginia University, MD

Wisconsin

University of Wisconsin - Madison, MD

Wyoming

University of Wyoming, BM

U.S. Territories: Puerto Rico

Inter American University of Puerto Rico, Metropolitan Campus, D

Canada

Maritime Provinces: New Brunswick

Mount Allison University, B

Ontario

University of Toronto, B
The University of Western Ontario, B
Wilfrid Laurier University, BD

ANALYSIS AND FUNCTIONAL ANALYSIS

United States

Vermont

Marlboro College, B

ANALYTICAL CHEMISTRY

United States

Alabama

Auburn University, MD

California

California State University, Los Angeles, M

District of Columbia

The George Washington University, MD
Georgetown University, D
Howard University, MD

Florida

Florida State University, MD

Georgia

Georgia State University, MD
University of Georgia, MD

Illinois

Governors State University, M
Illinois Institute of Technology, M
North Central College, B

Indiana

Indiana University Bloomington, D
Purdue University, MD

Iowa

Iowa State University of Science and Technology, D

Kansas

Kansas State University, M

Kentucky

University of Louisville, MD

Louisiana

Southern University and Agricultural and Mechanical College, M

Maryland

University of Maryland, College Park, MD

Massachusetts

Tufts University, MD
University of Massachusetts Lowell, D

Michigan

University of Michigan, D
Wayne State University, D

Missouri

University of Missouri, MD
University of Missouri - Kansas City, MD

Montana

University of Montana, MD

Nebraska

University of Nebraska - Lincoln, D

New Jersey

Rutgers University - Newark, MD
Seton Hall University, MD
Stevens Institute of Technology, DO

New Mexico

Eastern New Mexico University, M

New York

Binghamton University, State University of New York, D
Cornell University, D

North Carolina

Wake Forest University, MD

Ohio

Cleveland State University, M
University of Cincinnati, MD
The University of Toledo, MD
Youngstown State University, M

Oregon

Oregon State University, MD

Pennsylvania

West Chester University of Pennsylvania, B

Tennessee

University of Memphis, D
The University of Tennessee, MD
Vanderbilt University, MD

Texas

The University of Texas at Austin, D

Utah

Brigham Young University, MD

Virginia

Old Dominion University, M
Virginia Commonwealth University, MD

West Virginia

West Virginia University, MD

Wisconsin

Marquette University, MD

Canada

Alberta

University of Calgary, MD

Ontario

Laurentian University, M
McMaster University, MD
The University of Western Ontario, B

Quebec

McGill University, B

Saskatchewan

University of Regina, MD

ANATOMY

United States

Alabama

Auburn University, M

California

Loma Linda University, MD
University of California, Irvine, MD
University of California, Los Angeles, MD

Colorado

University of Colorado Denver, M

District of Columbia

Howard University, BMD

Florida

Barry University, M
University of South Florida, MD

Georgia

Augusta University, MD
University of Georgia, M

Illinois

Loyola University Chicago, MD
Rush University, MD
University of Chicago, D
University of Illinois at Chicago, M

Indiana

Indiana University - Purdue University Indianapolis,
  MD
Purdue University, MD

Iowa

Palmer College of Chiropractic, M
The University of Iowa, D

Kansas

The University of Kansas, MD

Kentucky

University of Kentucky, D
University of Louisville, MD

Louisiana

Louisiana State University Health Sciences Center,
  MD
Tulane University, B

Maryland

Johns Hopkins University, D

Massachusetts

Boston University, MD

Michigan

Andrews University, B
Wayne State University, MD

Minnesota

Minnesota State University Mankato, B

Mississippi

University of Mississippi Medical Center, MD

Missouri

Saint Louis University, MD
University of Missouri, M

Nebraska

Creighton University, M
University of Nebraska Medical Center, MD

New York

Columbia University, MD
Cornell University, D
State University of New York Upstate Medical Uni-
  versity, MD
Stony Brook University, State University of New
  York, D
University at Buffalo, the State University of New
  York, MD
University of Rochester, D

North Carolina

Duke University, BD
East Carolina University, D
Wake Forest University, D

North Dakota

University of North Dakota, MD

Ohio

Case Western Reserve University, M
The Ohio State University, MD
Wright State University, M
Youngstown State University, M

Tennessee

East Tennessee State University, D
The University of Tennessee, D

Utah

University of Utah, D

Virginia

Virginia Commonwealth University, MDO

U.S. Territories: Puerto Rico

Universidad Central del Caribe, M
University of Puerto Rico, Medical Sciences Campus, MD

Canada

Manitoba

University of Manitoba, MD

Maritime Provinces: Nova Scotia

Dalhousie University, MD

Maritime Provinces: Prince Edward Island

University of Prince Edward Island, MD

Ontario

Queen's University at Kingston, MD
University of Guelph, MD
The University of Western Ontario, BMD

Quebec

McGill University, BMD
Université Laval, O

Saskatchewan

University of Saskatchewan, MD

ANCIENT/CLASSICAL GREEK LANGUAGE AND LITERATURE

United States

Alabama

Samford University, B

California

California State University, Long Beach, B
Santa Clara University, B
Stanford University, B
University of California, Berkeley, B
University of California, Los Angeles, B

Connecticut

Yale University, B

Florida

University of Miami, B

Georgia

Emory University, B
University of Georgia, B

Illinois

Augustana College, B
Knox College, B
Loyola University Chicago, B
Monmouth College, B

Indiana

DePauw University, B
Indiana University Bloomington, B
University of Notre Dame, B
Wabash College, B

Iowa

The University of Iowa, B

Louisiana

Loyola University New Orleans, B

Massachusetts

Amherst College, B
Boston University, B
Mount Holyoke College, B
Smith College, B
Tufts University, B
Wellesley College, B

Michigan

Hillsdale College, B
Kalamazoo College, B
University of Michigan, B

Minnesota

Carleton College, B
St. Olaf College, B

Missouri

Washington University in St. Louis, B

New Hampshire

Dartmouth College, B
University of New Hampshire, B

New Jersey

Rutgers University - New Brunswick, B

New York

Bard College, B
Barnard College, B
Canisius College, B
Columbia University, B
Hobart and William Smith Colleges, B
Hunter College of the City University of New York, B

North Carolina

Duke University, B
Wake Forest University, B

Ohio
Kenyon College, B

Oregon
Multnomah University, B

Pennsylvania
Bryn Mawr College, B
Duquesne University, B
Franklin & Marshall College, B
Gettysburg College, B
Swarthmore College, B

Tennessee
Sewanee: The University of the South, B

Texas
Baylor University, B
Rice University, B
Southwestern University, B

Utah
Brigham Young University, B

Vermont
Marlboro College, B
University of Vermont, B

Virginia
Hampden-Sydney College, B
Randolph College, B
Randolph-Macon College, B
University of Richmond, B

Washington
University of Washington, B
Whitman College, B

Wisconsin
Lawrence University, B

Canada

British Columbia
University of Victoria, B

Maritime Provinces: New Brunswick
Mount Allison University, B

Ontario
Brock University, B
The University of Western Ontario, B

ANCIENT NEAR EASTERN AND BIBLICAL LANGUAGES, LITERATURES, AND LINGUISTICS

United States

California
Concordia University Irvine, B
The Master's College and Seminary, B

Georgia
Toccoa Falls College, B

Idaho
Northwest Nazarene University, B

Illinois
Concordia University Chicago, B
University of Chicago, B

Iowa
Luther College, B

Michigan
Concordia University Ann Arbor, B
Cornerstone University, B

Minnesota
North Central University, A

Missouri
Ozark Christian College, B

New York
The Jewish Theological Seminary, B
Rabbinical Academy Mesivta Rabbi Chaim Berlin, B

Oklahoma
Oklahoma Baptist University, B

Pennsylvania
University of Valley Forge, B

South Carolina
Columbia International University, B

Tennessee
Belmont University, B
Carson-Newman University, B
Union University, B

Texas
Baylor University, B
Houston Baptist University, B
Howard Payne University, B

Washington
Northwest University, B
University of Washington, B
Walla Walla University, B

Wisconsin
Concordia University Wisconsin, B

Canada

Ontario
University of Toronto, B

ANCIENT STUDIES/CIVILIZATION

United States

California
Loyola Marymount University, B
Santa Clara University, B

Connecticut
Wesleyan University, B

Florida
Eckerd College, B
University of Miami, B

Georgia
Emory University, B

Indiana
Purdue University, B

Iowa
The University of Iowa, B

Kansas
The University of Kansas, B

Maine
Bates College, B
Bowdoin College, B
Colby College, B

Maryland
University of Maryland, Baltimore County, B

Massachusetts
Boston University, B
Mount Holyoke College, B
Wheaton College, B

Michigan
University of Michigan, B

Minnesota
St. Olaf College, B

Missouri
Washington University in St. Louis, B

Nebraska
University of Nebraska - Lincoln, B

New York
Columbia University, B
Columbia University, School of General Studies, B

Ohio
Ohio Wesleyan University, B

Pennsylvania
Lehigh University, B
Saint Joseph's University, B

Tennessee
Vanderbilt University, B

Texas
The University of Texas at Austin, B

Virginia
University of Richmond, B

Canada

Alberta
University of Alberta, B

Quebec
Concordia University, B
Université de Montréal, B

ANESTHESIOLOGIST ASSISTANT

United States

Colorado
University of Colorado Denver, M

Connecticut
Quinnipiac University, M

Florida
Nova Southeastern University, M

Georgia
Emory University, M
South University, M

Missouri
University of Missouri - Kansas City, M

Ohio
Case Western Reserve University, M

Pennsylvania
Pittsburgh Career Institute, A

Washington
Renton Technical College, A

Wisconsin

Milwaukee Area Technical College, A

Canada

Ontario

University of Guelph, MD

Quebec

Université Laval, O

ANIMAL BEHAVIOR AND ETHOLOGY

United States

Arizona

Arizona State University at the Tempe campus, D

California

University of California, Davis, D

Colorado

University of Colorado Boulder, M
University of Colorado Denver, M

Georgia

Emory University, D

Illinois

Illinois State University, M

Indiana

Indiana University Bloomington, B

Maine

University of New England, B

Massachusetts

Hampshire College, B
University of Massachusetts Amherst, D

Minnesota

University of Minnesota, Twin Cities Campus, MD

Montana

University of Montana, D

New York

Canisius College, B
Cornell University, D

Pennsylvania

Bucknell University, BM
Franklin & Marshall College, B

Tennessee

The University of Tennessee, MD

Texas

Southwestern University, B
The University of Texas at Austin, D

Washington

University of Washington, D

Wisconsin

Carroll University, B

Canada

Ontario

University of Toronto, B
The University of Western Ontario, B

Quebec

McGill University, B

ANIMAL GENETICS

United States

Alabama

Jacksonville State University, B

Massachusetts

Worcester Polytechnic Institute, B

New Hampshire

Dartmouth College, B

New Jersey

Rutgers University - New Brunswick, B

Ohio

Ohio Wesleyan University, B

South Carolina

Clemson University, B

Canada

Alberta

University of Alberta, B

British Columbia

The University of British Columbia, B

Manitoba

University of Manitoba, B

Ontario

University of Toronto, B

ANIMAL HEALTH

United States

Georgia

University of Georgia, B

Idaho

Brigham Young University - Idaho, B

Montana

Miles Community College, A

Texas

Sul Ross State University, B

Canada

Maritime Provinces: Nova Scotia

Dalhousie University, B

ANIMAL/LIVESTOCK HUSBANDRY AND PRODUCTION

United States

California

Cuesta College, A
Sierra College, A

Connecticut

University of Connecticut, A

Illinois

Illinois Central College, A
University of Illinois at Urbana - Champaign, B

Iowa

Dordt College, B
Hawkeye Community College, A

Iowa Lakes Community College, A

Kansas

Pratt Community College, A

Minnesota

Ridgewater College, A

New Jersey

Rutgers University - New Brunswick, B

New York

Jefferson Community College, A

North Carolina

North Carolina State University, A
Wayne Community College, A

Ohio

The Ohio State University Agricultural Technical Institute, A

Texas

Frank Phillips College, A
North Central Texas College, A
Tarleton State University, B
Texas A&M University, B

Utah

Southern Utah University, A

Canada

British Columbia

The University of British Columbia, B
University of the Fraser Valley, A

Maritime Provinces: Nova Scotia

Dalhousie University, B

ANIMAL NUTRITION

Canada

Maritime Provinces: Nova Scotia

Dalhousie University, B

ANIMAL PHYSIOLOGY

United States

California

California State University, Fresno, B
Sonoma State University, B

Connecticut

University of Connecticut, B

Massachusetts

Massachusetts Bay Community College, A

Minnesota

Minnesota State University Mankato, B

New Jersey

Rutgers University - New Brunswick, B

Ohio

The University of Akron, B

Utah

Utah State University, B

Canada

Maritime Provinces: New Brunswick

University of New Brunswick Fredericton, B

Ontario

University of Toronto, B

ANIMAL SCIENCES

United States

Alabama

Alabama Agricultural and Mechanical University, B
Auburn University, BMD
Tuskegee University, BM

Arizona

The University of Arizona, BMD

Arkansas

Arkansas State University, B
Arkansas State University - Beebe, A
University of Arkansas, BMD

California

Bakersfield College, A
Bergin University of Canine Studies, M
California Polytechnic State University, San Luis
  Obispo, B
California State Polytechnic University, Pomona, B
California State University, Chico, B
California State University, Fresno, BM
College of the Sequoias, A
Los Angeles Pierce College, A
Merced College, A
Modesto Junior College, A
Moorpark College, A
Mt. San Antonio College, A
Reedley College, A
San Joaquin Delta College, A
Santa Rosa Junior College, A
Shasta College, A
University of California, Davis, BMD
West Hills Community College, A
Yuba College, A

Colorado

Colorado State University, BMD
Lamar Community College, A
Northeastern Junior College, A
University of Denver, B

Connecticut

University of Connecticut, ABMD

Delaware

Delaware State University, B
University of Delaware, BMD

Florida

College of Central Florida, A
Santa Fe College, A
South Florida State College, A
University of Florida, BMD

Georgia

Abraham Baldwin Agricultural College, A
Berry College, B
Fort Valley State University, BM
University of Georgia, BMD

Hawaii

University of Hawaii at Hilo, B
University of Hawaii at Manoa, BM

Idaho

Boise State University, M
Brigham Young University - Idaho, B
College of Southern Idaho, A
University of Idaho, BMD

Illinois

John Wood Community College, A
Kaskaskia College, A
Shawnee Community College, A

Southern Illinois University Carbondale, BM
University of Illinois at Urbana - Champaign, BMD

Indiana

Purdue University, BMD

Iowa

Dordt College, B
Iowa Lakes Community College, A
Iowa State University of Science and Technology,
  BMD

Kansas

Dodge City Community College, A
Fort Hays State University, B
Kansas State University, BMD
Pratt Community College, A

Kentucky

University of Kentucky, BMD

Louisiana

Louisiana State University and Agricultural & Me-
  chanical College, BMD
Louisiana Tech University, B
Southern University and Agricultural and Mechanical
  College, B

Maine

University of Maine, BM

Maryland

University of Maryland, College Park, BMD

Massachusetts

Becker College, AB
Tufts University, M
University of Massachusetts Amherst, BMD

Michigan

Michigan State University, BMD

Minnesota

Globe University - Woodbury, A
University of Minnesota, Crookston, B
University of Minnesota, Twin Cities Campus, BMD

Mississippi

Alcorn State University, M
Mississippi State University, BMD
Northwest Mississippi Community College, A

Missouri

College of the Ozarks, B
Missouri State University, B
Northwest Missouri State University, B
University of Missouri, BMD

Montana

Montana State University, BMD

Nebraska

Northeast Community College, A
University of Nebraska - Lincoln, BMD

Nevada

University of Nevada, Reno, M

New Hampshire

University of New Hampshire, ABMD

New Jersey

Rutgers University - New Brunswick, BMD

New Mexico

New Mexico State University, BMD

New York

Cornell University, BMD
Morrisville State College, B
Niagara County Community College, A
State University of New York College of Agriculture
  and Technology at Cobleskill, A

State University of New York College of Environmental Science and Forestry, B

North Carolina

Alamance Community College, A
James Sprunt Community College, A
North Carolina Agricultural and Technical State Uni-
  versity, BM
North Carolina State University, BMD

North Dakota

North Dakota State University, BMD

Ohio

The Ohio State University, BMD
The Ohio State University Agricultural Technical In-
  stitute, A
The University of Findlay, B

Oklahoma

Eastern Oklahoma State College, A
Langston University, B
Oklahoma Panhandle State University, B
Oklahoma State University, BMD
Redlands Community College, A

Oregon

Linn-Benton Community College, A
Oregon State University, BMD
Treasure Valley Community College, A

Pennsylvania

Delaware Valley University, B
Harcum College, A
Penn State Abington, B
Penn State Altoona, B
Penn State Beaver, B
Penn State Berks, B
Penn State Brandywine, B
Penn State DuBois, B
Penn State Erie, The Behrend College, B
Penn State Fayette, The Eberly Campus, B
Penn State Greater Allegheny, B
Penn State Hazleton, B
Penn State Lehigh Valley, B
Penn State Mont Alto, B
Penn State New Kensington, B
Penn State Schuylkill, B
Penn State Shenango, B
Penn State University Park, BMD
Penn State Wilkes-Barre, B
Penn State Worthington Scranton, B
Penn State York, B

Rhode Island

University of Rhode Island, BMD

South Carolina

Clemson University, BMD

South Dakota

South Dakota State University, BMD

Tennessee

Hiwassee College, A
Middle Tennessee State University, B
Tennessee State University, B
Tennessee Technological University, B
The University of Tennessee, BMD
The University of Tennessee at Martin, B

Texas

Abilene Christian University, B
Angelo State University, BM
Lubbock Christian University, B
Sam Houston State University, B
Stephen F. Austin State University, B
Sul Ross State University, M
Tarleton State University, BM
Texas A&M University, BMD
Texas A&M University - Commerce, B
Texas A&M University - Kingsville, BM
Texas State University, B
Texas Tech University, BMD

Trinity Valley Community College, A
West Texas A&M University, BM

Utah

Brigham Young University, MD
Snow College, A
Utah State University, BMD

Vermont

University of Vermont, BMD

Virginia

Virginia Polytechnic Institute and State University, BMD

Washington

Washington State University, BMD
Yakima Valley Community College, A

West Virginia

Potomac State College of West Virginia University, A
West Virginia University, BMD

Wisconsin

University of Wisconsin - Madison, BMD
University of Wisconsin - Platteville, B
University of Wisconsin - River Falls, B

Wyoming

Casper College, A
Northwest College, A
Sheridan College, A
University of Wyoming, BMD

U.S. Territories: Puerto Rico

University of Puerto Rico, Mayagüez Campus, BM
University of Puerto Rico in Utuado, A

Canada

Alberta

University of Alberta, B

British Columbia

The University of British Columbia, BMD

Manitoba

University of Manitoba, BMD

Maritime Provinces: Nova Scotia

Dalhousie University, BM

Ontario

University of Guelph, BMD

Quebec

McGill University, MD
Université Laval, MD

Saskatchewan

University of Saskatchewan, BMD

ANIMAL TRAINING

United States

Colorado

Lamar Community College, A

Massachusetts

Becker College, A

ANIMATION, INTERACTIVE TECHNOLOGY, VIDEO GRAPHICS AND SPECIAL EFFECTS

United States

Arizona

The Art Institute of Phoenix, B
The Art Institute of Tucson, B
Sessions College for Professional Design, A
Southwest University of Visual Arts, B

Arkansas

University of Arkansas - Fort Smith, B

California

Academy of Art University, AB
Antelope Valley College, A
Art Center College of Design, B
The Art Institute of California - Hollywood, a campus of Argosy University, B
The Art Institute of California - Los Angeles, a campus of Argosy University, B
The Art Institute of California - Orange County, a campus of Argosy University, B
The Art Institute of California - Sacramento, a campus of Argosy University, B
The Art Institute of California - San Francisco, a campus of Argosy University, B
California College of the Arts, B
Cañada College, A
Cerritos College, A
Cerro Coso Community College, A
Chaffey College, A
Cogswell Polytechnical College, B
College of the Canyons, A
College of Marin, A
College of the Redwoods, A
Ex'pression College for Digital Arts, B
Glendale Community College, A
Grossmont College, A
Hartnell College, A
Laguna College of Art & Design, B
Loyola Marymount University, B
Mt. Sierra College, B
NewSchool of Architecture and Design, B
Orange Coast College, A
Palomar College, A
Pasadena City College, A
Platt College San Diego, B
Santa Monica College, A
Southwestern College, A

Colorado

Aims Community College, A
The Art Institute of Colorado, B
Colorado Mesa University, A
Front Range Community College, A
Morgan Community College, AB
Pikes Peak Community College, A
Pueblo Community College, A
Red Rocks Community College, A
Rocky Mountain College of Art + Design, B

Delaware

Delaware College of Art and Design, A

Florida

The Art Institute of Fort Lauderdale, B
The Art Institute of Tampa, a branch of Miami International University of Art & Design, B
Digital Media Arts College, B
Florida State College at Jacksonville, B
Full Sail University, B
Gulf Coast State College, B
Miami International University of Art & Design, B
Ringling College of Art and Design, B
Southern Technical College (Tampa), A

Georgia

American InterContinental University Atlanta, B
The Art Institute of Atlanta, B
Savannah College of Art and Design, B

Illinois

American Academy of Art, B
Bradley University, B
City Colleges of Chicago, Harold Washington College, A
Columbia College Chicago, B
DePaul University, B
Elgin Community College, A
Elmhurst College, B
Illinois Central College, A
The Illinois Institute of Art - Schaumburg, B
Joliet Junior College, A
McHenry County College, A
North Central College, B
School of the Art Institute of Chicago, B
Tribeca Flashpoint College, A

Indiana

Huntington University, B

Iowa

University of Dubuque, B
Western Iowa Tech Community College, A

Kentucky

Sullivan College of Technology and Design, AB

Maine

College of the Atlantic, B
York County Community College, A

Maryland

Cecil College, A
Hagerstown Community College, A
Montgomery College, A

Massachusetts

Bay State College, AB
Becker College, B
Massachusetts College of Art and Design, B
Montserrat College of Art, B
Mount Ida College, B
Northeastern University, B
Springfield Technical Community College, A

Michigan

College for Creative Studies, B
Davenport University, B
Eastern Michigan University, B
Ferris State University, A
Kalamazoo Valley Community College, A
Kellogg Community College, A
Lansing Community College, A

Minnesota

Century College, A
Minneapolis College of Art and Design, B
Minneapolis Community and Technical College, A
Minnesota School of Business - Richfield, A
Saint Paul College - A Community & Technical College, A
University of Northwestern - St. Paul, B

Missouri

Kansas City Art Institute, B
Missouri Western State University, B
Webster University, B

Nevada

The Art Institute of Las Vegas, B
College of Southern Nevada, A
Nevada State College, B

New Hampshire

Lakes Region Community College, A
NHTI, Concord's Community College, A

New Jersey

Bergen Community College, A
Raritan Valley Community College, A
Rowan College at Burlington County, A
Union County College, A

New Mexico

New Mexico State University, B
New Mexico State University - Alamogordo, A

New York

Borough of Manhattan Community College of the
    City University of New York, A
Fashion Institute of Technology, B
Finger Lakes Community College, A
Rochester Institute of Technology, B
State University of New York College of Technology
    at Alfred, AB
Villa Maria College, B

North Carolina

Forsyth Technical Community College, A
Living Arts College, B
Wake Technical Community College, A
Western Piedmont Community College, A

North Dakota

United Tribes Technical College, A

Ohio

Cleveland Institute of Art, B
Columbus College of Art & Design, B
Terra State Community College, A

Oklahoma

Oklahoma City Community College, A

Oregon

The Art Institute of Portland, B
Lane Community College, A

Pennsylvania

The Art Institute of Philadelphia, B
The Art Institute of Pittsburgh, B
Delaware County Community College, A
Lehigh Carbon Community College, A
Pennsylvania College of Art & Design, B
Point Park University, B
The University of the Arts, B

Rhode Island

New England Institute of Technology, AB

South Dakota

Southeast Technical Institute, A

Tennessee

East Tennessee State University, B

Texas

The Art Institute of Austin, a branch of The Art Insti-
    tute of Houston, B
The Art Institute of Dallas, a campus of South Uni-
    versity, B
The Art Institute of Houston, B
The Art Institute of San Antonio, a branch of The Art
    Institute of Houston, B
Austin Community College District, A
Houston Community College, A
Lone Star College - CyFair, A
Lone Star College - Tomball, A
Sam Houston State University, B
University of the Incarnate Word, B

Utah

Brigham Young University, B
Broadview Entertainment Arts University, A

Vermont

Bennington College, B

Virginia

The Art Institute of Washington, a branch of The Art
    Institute of Atlanta, B
George Mason University, B
Regent University, B

Washington

The Art Institute of Seattle, B
DigiPen Institute of Technology, B

Wisconsin

Madison Media Institute, A
Milwaukee Institute of Art and Design, B

Canada

Alberta

University of Lethbridge, B

British Columbia

Emily Carr University of Art + Design, B

Quebec

Concordia University, B

ANTHROPOLOGY

United States

Alabama

Auburn University, B
Jacksonville State University, B
Troy University, B
The University of Alabama, BMD
The University of Alabama at Birmingham, BM
University of South Alabama, B

Alaska

University of Alaska Anchorage, BM
University of Alaska Fairbanks, BMD

Arizona

Arizona State University at the Tempe campus,
    BMDO
Coconino Community College, A
Eastern Arizona College, A
Northern Arizona University, BM
Pima Community College, A
The University of Arizona, BMD

Arkansas

Hendrix College, B
University of Arkansas, BMD
University of Arkansas at Little Rock, B

California

American River College, A
Antelope Valley College, A
Bakersfield College, A
Biola University, BM
Cabrillo College, A
California Baptist University, B
California State Polytechnic University, Pomona, B
California State University, Bakersfield, BM
California State University, Chico, BM
California State University, Dominguez Hills, B
California State University, East Bay, BM
California State University, Fresno, B
California State University, Fullerton, BM
California State University, Long Beach, BM
California State University, Los Angeles, BM
California State University, Northridge, BM
California State University, Sacramento, BM
California State University, San Bernardino, B
California State University, San Marcos, B
California State University, Stanislaus, B
Cañada College, A
Cerritos College, A
Chaffey College, A
College of Alameda, A
College of the Desert, A
College of the Siskiyous, A
Contra Costa College, A
Copper Mountain College, A
Crafton Hills College, A
Cypress College, A
East Los Angeles College, A

El Camino College, A
Feather River College, A
Foothill College, A
Fullerton College, A
Humboldt State University, BM
Imperial Valley College, A
Los Angeles Southwest College, A
Los Medanos College, A
Merritt College, A
Mills College, B
Monterey Peninsula College, A
Moorpark College, A
Ohlone College, A
Orange Coast College, A
Oxnard College, A
Pasadena City College, A
Pitzer College, B
Pomona College, B
Saddleback College, A
Saint Mary's College of California, B
San Bernardino Valley College, A
San Diego City College, A
San Diego Miramar College, A
San Diego State University, BM
San Francisco State University, BM
San Joaquin Delta College, A
San Jose State University, BM
Santa Ana College, A
Santa Barbara City College, A
Santa Clara University, B
Santa Monica College, A
Santa Rosa Junior College, A
Santiago Canyon College, A
Scripps College, B
Skyline College, A
Sonoma State University, BM
Southwestern College, A
Stanford University, BMD
University of California, Berkeley, BD
University of California, Davis, BMD
University of California, Irvine, BMD
University of California, Los Angeles, BMD
University of California, Merced, B
University of California, Riverside, BMD
University of California, San Diego, BD
University of California, Santa Barbara, BMD
University of California, Santa Cruz, BD
University of La Verne, B
University of Redlands, B
University of San Diego, B
University of Southern California, B
Vanguard University of Southern California, B
West Los Angeles College, A
Westmont College, B
Whittier College, B

Colorado

The Colorado College, B
Colorado State University, BM
Fort Lewis College, B
Metropolitan State University of Denver, B
Northeastern Junior College, A
University of Colorado Boulder, BMD
University of Colorado Colorado Springs, B
University of Colorado Denver, BM
University of Denver, BM
University of Northern Colorado, B
Western State Colorado University, B

Connecticut

Central Connecticut State University, B
Connecticut College, B
Southern Connecticut State University, B
Trinity College, B
University of Connecticut, BMD
Wesleyan University, B
Western Connecticut State University, B
Yale University, BMD

Delaware

University of Delaware, B

District of Columbia

American University, B
The Catholic University of America, BM
The George Washington University, BMD

Georgetown University, B
Howard University, B
University of the District of Columbia, B

Florida

Broward College, A
Eckerd College, B
Florida Atlantic University, BM
Florida Gulf Coast University, B
Indian River State College, A
Miami Dade College, A
New College of Florida, B
Rollins College, B
South Florida State College, A
University of Central Florida, BMO
University of Florida, BMD
University of Miami, B
University of North Florida, B
University of South Florida, BMDO
University of South Florida, St. Petersburg, B
University of West Florida, BM

Georgia

Agnes Scott College, B
Augusta University, B
Darton State College, A
Emory University, BD
Georgia Southern University, B
Georgia State University, BM
Kennesaw State University, B
University of Georgia, BMD
University of West Georgia, B

Hawaii

Brigham Young University - Hawaii, B
Hawai'i Pacific University, B
University of Hawaii at Hilo, B
University of Hawaii at Manoa, BMD
University of Hawaii - West Oahu, B

Idaho

Boise State University, BM
The College of Idaho, B
College of Southern Idaho, A
College of Western Idaho, A
Idaho State University, BM
North Idaho College, A
University of Idaho, BM

Illinois

Augustana College, B
DePaul University, B
Illinois State University, B
Illinois Wesleyan University, B
John A. Logan College, A
Knox College, B
Lake Forest College, B
Loyola University Chicago, B
Monmouth College, B
North Central College, B
Northeastern Illinois University, B
Northern Illinois University, BM
Northwestern University, BD
Rockford University, B
Roosevelt University, M
Southern Illinois University Carbondale, BMD
Southern Illinois University Edwardsville, B
Triton College, A
University of Chicago, BD
University of Illinois at Chicago, BMD
University of Illinois at Urbana - Champaign, BMD
Western Illinois University, B
Wheaton College, B

Indiana

Ball State University, BM
Butler University, B
DePauw University, B
Earlham College, B
Hanover College, B
Indiana State University, B
Indiana University Bloomington, BMD
Indiana University Northwest, B
Indiana University - Purdue University Fort Wayne, B

Indiana University - Purdue University Indianapolis, B
Indiana University South Bend, B
Purdue University, BMD
University of Indianapolis, BM
University of Notre Dame, B
University of Southern Indiana, B
Vincennes University, A

Iowa

Central College, B
Cornell College, B
Drake University, B
Grinnell College, B
Iowa State University of Science and Technology, BM
Luther College, B
The University of Iowa, BMD
University of Northern Iowa, B

Kansas

Barton County Community College, A
Kansas State University, B
The University of Kansas, BMD
Washburn University, B
Wichita State University, BM

Kentucky

Eastern Kentucky University, B
Northern Kentucky University, B
Transylvania University, B
University of Kentucky, BMD
University of Louisville, BM
Western Kentucky University, BM

Louisiana

Louisiana State University and Agricultural & Mechanical College, BMD
Tulane University, BMD
University of Louisiana at Lafayette, B
University of New Orleans, B

Maine

Bates College, B
Bowdoin College, B
Colby College, B
University of Maine, BD

Maryland

Harford Community College, A
Johns Hopkins University, BD
St. Mary's College of Maryland, B
University of Maryland, Baltimore County, B
University of Maryland, College Park, BM
Washington College, B

Massachusetts

Amherst College, B
Boston University, BMD
Brandeis University, BMD
Bridgewater State University, B
College of the Holy Cross, B
Hampshire College, B
Harvard University, BMD
Massachusetts Institute of Technology, B
Mount Holyoke College, B
Smith College, B
Tufts University, B
University of Massachusetts Amherst, BMD
University of Massachusetts Boston, B
Wellesley College, B
Wheaton College, B
Williams College, B

Michigan

Albion College, B
Alma College, B
Central Michigan University, B
Eastern Michigan University, B
Grand Valley State University, B
Lansing Community College, A
Michigan State University, BMD
Michigan Technological University, B
Muskegon Community College, A
Oakland University, B

University of Michigan, BD
University of Michigan - Dearborn, B
University of Michigan - Flint, B
Wayne State University, BMD
Western Michigan University, BM

Minnesota

Carleton College, B
Gustavus Adolphus College, B
Hamline University, B
Macalester College, B
Minnesota State University Mankato, BM
Minnesota State University Moorhead, B
St. Cloud State University, B
University of Minnesota, Duluth, BM
University of Minnesota, Morris, B
University of Minnesota, Twin Cities Campus, BMD

Mississippi

Mississippi State University, BM
University of Mississippi, BM
University of Southern Mississippi, BM

Missouri

Lindenwood University, B
Missouri State University, BM
Saint Louis University, B
University of Missouri, BMD
University of Missouri - St. Louis, B
Washington University in St. Louis, BD
Westminster College, B

Montana

Montana State University, B
University of Montana, BMD

Nebraska

Creighton University, BM
University of Nebraska - Lincoln, BM
Western Nebraska Community College, A

Nevada

College of Southern Nevada, A
Truckee Meadows Community College, A
University of Nevada, Las Vegas, BMD
University of Nevada, Reno, BMD

New Hampshire

Dartmouth College, B
Franklin Pierce University, B
University of New Hampshire, B

New Jersey

Drew University, B
Monmouth University, BM
Montclair State University, B
Princeton University, BD
Rutgers University - New Brunswick, BMD
Rutgers University - Newark, B
Seton Hall University, B
Thomas Edison State University, B
William Paterson University of New Jersey, B

New Mexico

Central New Mexico Community College, A
Eastern New Mexico University, BM
New Mexico Highlands University, M
New Mexico State University, BMO
University of New Mexico, BMD

New York

Adelphi University, B
Bard College, B
Barnard College, B
Binghamton University, State University of New York, BMD
Brooklyn College of the City University of New York, B
Buffalo State College, State University of New York, B
Canisius College, BM
City College of the City University of New York, B
Colgate University, B

The College at Brockport, State University of New York, B
Columbia University, BMD
Columbia University, School of General Studies, B
Cornell University, BD
Fordham University, B
Hamilton College, B
Hartwick College, B
Hobart and William Smith Colleges, B
Hofstra University, B
Hunter College of the City University of New York, BM
Ithaca College, B
Lehman College of the City University of New York, B
Nazareth College of Rochester, B
New York University, BMD
Purchase College, State University of New York, B
Queens College of the City University of New York, B
St. John Fisher College, B
St. John's University, B
St. Lawrence University, B
Sarah Lawrence College, B
Skidmore College, B
State University of New York College at Cortland, B
State University of New York College at Geneseo, B
State University of New York College at Oneonta, B
State University of New York College at Potsdam, B
State University of New York at New Paltz, B
State University of New York at Oswego, B
State University of New York at Plattsburgh, B
Stony Brook University, State University of New York, BMD
Syracuse University, BMD
Union College, B
University at Albany, State University of New York, BMD
University at Buffalo, the State University of New York, BMD
University of Rochester, B
Vassar College, B
Wagner College, B
Wells College, B
York College of the City University of New York, B

North Carolina

Appalachian State University, B
Davidson College, B
Duke University, B
East Carolina University, BM
Elon University, B
North Carolina State University, BM
The University of North Carolina at Chapel Hill, BMD
The University of North Carolina at Charlotte, BM
The University of North Carolina at Greensboro, B
The University of North Carolina Wilmington, B
Wake Forest University, B
Western Carolina University, B
William Peace University, B

North Dakota

North Dakota State University, BM
University of North Dakota, B

Ohio

Antioch College, B
Case Western Reserve University, BMD
Cleveland State University, B
The College of Wooster, B
Denison University, B
Franciscan University of Steubenville, B
Kent State University, BM
Kenyon College, B
Miami University, B
Miami University Hamilton, B
Miami University Middletown, A
Muskingum University, B
Oberlin College, B
The Ohio State University, BMD
Ohio University, B
The University of Akron, B
University of Cincinnati, M
The University of Toledo, B
Wright State University, B

Youngstown State University, B

Oklahoma

Oklahoma Baptist University, B
University of Oklahoma, BMD
The University of Tulsa, BMD

Oregon

Linfield College, B
Oregon State University, BMD
Portland State University, BMD
Reed College, B
Southern Oregon University, B
Umpqua Community College, A
University of Oregon, BMD
Western Oregon University, B
Willamette University, B

Pennsylvania

Bloomsburg University of Pennsylvania, B
Bryn Mawr College, B
Bucknell University, B
California University of Pennsylvania, B
Clarion University of Pennsylvania, B
Delaware County Community College, A
Dickinson College, B
Drexel University, B
Edinboro University of Pennsylvania, BM
Franklin & Marshall College, B
Gettysburg College, B
Haverford College, B
Indiana University of Pennsylvania, B
Juniata College, B
Kutztown University of Pennsylvania, B
Lafayette College, B
Lehigh University, B
Lincoln University, B
Mercyhurst University, BM
Millersville University of Pennsylvania, B
Muhlenberg College, B
Penn State Abington, B
Penn State Altoona, B
Penn State Beaver, B
Penn State Berks, B
Penn State Brandywine, B
Penn State DuBois, B
Penn State Erie, The Behrend College, B
Penn State Fayette, The Eberly Campus, B
Penn State Greater Allegheny, B
Penn State Hazleton, B
Penn State Lehigh Valley, B
Penn State Mont Alto, B
Penn State New Kensington, B
Penn State Schuylkill, B
Penn State Shenango, B
Penn State University Park, BMD
Penn State Wilkes-Barre, B
Penn State Worthington Scranton, B
Penn State York, B
Saint Francis University, B
Saint Vincent College, B
Susquehanna University, B
Temple University, BD
University of Pennsylvania, BMD
University of Pittsburgh, BMD
University of Pittsburgh at Greensburg, B
Ursinus College, B
West Chester University of Pennsylvania, B
Widener University, B

Rhode Island

Brown University, BMD
Rhode Island College, B
University of Rhode Island, B

South Carolina

Clemson University, B
College of Charleston, B
Furman University, B
University of South Carolina, BMD

South Dakota

Augustana University, B
The University of South Dakota, B

Tennessee

East Tennessee State University, B
Lee University, B
Middle Tennessee State University, B
Rhodes College, B
Sewanee: The University of the South, B
University of Memphis, BM
The University of Tennessee, BMD
Vanderbilt University, BMD

Texas

Austin College, B
Austin Community College District, A
Baylor University, B
Houston Community College, A
Rice University, BMD
Southern Methodist University, BMD
Southwestern University, B
Texas A&M University, BMD
Texas Christian University, B
Texas State University, BM
Texas Tech University, BM
Trinity University, B
University of Houston, BM
University of Houston - Clear Lake, B
University of North Texas, BM
The University of Texas at Arlington, BM
The University of Texas at Austin, BMD
The University of Texas at El Paso, BO
The University of Texas Rio Grande Valley, B
The University of Texas at San Antonio, BMD

Utah

Brigham Young University, M
Southern Utah University, B
University of Utah, BMD
Utah State University, B
Weber State University, B

Vermont

Bennington College, B
Johnson State College, B
Marlboro College, B
University of Vermont, B

Virginia

The College of William and Mary, BMD
George Mason University, BM
James Madison University, B
Longwood University, B
Mary Baldwin College, B
Radford University, B
Sweet Briar College, B
University of Mary Washington, B
University of Richmond, B
University of Virginia, BMD
Virginia Commonwealth University, B

Washington

Central Washington University, B
Eastern Washington University, B
Everett Community College, A
Pacific Lutheran University, B
Saint Martin's University, B
Seattle University, B
Skagit Valley College, A
University of Washington, BMD
Washington State University, BMD
Washington State University - Vancouver, B
Western Washington University, BM
Whitman College, B

Wisconsin

Beloit College, B
Lawrence University, B
Marquette University, B
Ripon College, B
University of Wisconsin - Madison, BD
University of Wisconsin - Milwaukee, BMDO
University of Wisconsin - Oshkosh, B
Wisconsin Lutheran College, B

Wyoming

Casper College, A
Laramie County Community College, A

Northwest College, A
University of Wyoming, BMD
Western Wyoming Community College, A

U.S. Territories: Guam

University of Guam, B

U.S. Territories: Puerto Rico

Inter American University of Puerto Rico, San Germán Campus, B
University of Puerto Rico, Río Piedras Campus, B

Canada

Alberta

Athabasca University, B
Mount Royal University, B
University of Alberta, BMD
University of Calgary, BMD
University of Lethbridge, BM

British Columbia

Simon Fraser University, MD
The University of British Columbia, BMD
The University of British Columbia - Okanagan Campus, B
University of the Fraser Valley, B
University of Northern British Columbia, B
University of Victoria, BM
Vancouver Island University, B

Manitoba

University of Manitoba, BMD
The University of Winnipeg, B

Maritime Provinces: New Brunswick

Mount Allison University, B
St. Thomas University, B
University of New Brunswick Fredericton, BM

Maritime Provinces: Nova Scotia

Cape Breton University, B
Dalhousie University, BMD
Mount Saint Vincent University, B
St. Francis Xavier University, B
Saint Mary's University, B
University of King's College, B

Maritime Provinces: Prince Edward Island

University of Prince Edward Island, B

Newfoundland and Labrador

Memorial University of Newfoundland, BMD

Ontario

Carleton University, BM
Lakehead University, B
McMaster University, BMD
Trent University, BM
University of Guelph, BMD
University of Ottawa, BM
University of Toronto, BMD
University of Waterloo, BM
The University of Western Ontario, BMD
Wilfrid Laurier University, B
York University, BMD

Quebec

Concordia University, BM
McGill University, BMD
Université Laval, ABMD
Université de Montréal, BMD

Saskatchewan

University of Regina, BM
University of Saskatchewan, BM

APPAREL AND ACCESSORIES MARKETING OPERATIONS

United States

Arizona

The Art Institute of Phoenix, B
The Art Institute of Tucson, B

California

The Art Institute of California - Hollywood, a campus of Argosy University, AB
The Art Institute of California - Inland Empire, a campus of Argosy University, AB
The Art Institute of California - Los Angeles, a campus of Argosy University, B
The Art Institute of California - Orange County, a campus of Argosy University, AB
The Art Institute of California - Sacramento, a campus of Argosy University, B
The Art Institute of California - San Diego, a campus of Argosy University, B
Woodbury University, B

Colorado

The Art Institute of Colorado, B

Florida

The Art Institute of Tampa, a branch of Miami International University of Art & Design, B

Georgia

The Art Institute of Atlanta, B

Illinois

The Illinois Institute of Art - Chicago, B
The Illinois Institute of Art - Schaumburg, B

Indiana

The Art Institute of Indianapolis, B

Iowa

Des Moines Area Community College, A
Kirkwood Community College, A
Marshalltown Community College, A

Michigan

The Art Institute of Michigan, B

Missouri

The Art Institute of St. Louis, B
Stephens College, B

Montana

University of Montana, A

Nevada

The Art Institute of Las Vegas, B

North Carolina

The Art Institute of Charlotte, a campus of South University, AB
The Art Institute of Raleigh-Durham, a campus of South University, AB

Oklahoma

University of Central Oklahoma, B

Oregon

The Art Institute of Portland, B

Pennsylvania

The Art Institute of Pittsburgh, B
Philadelphia University, B

Rhode Island

University of Rhode Island, B

South Carolina

The Art Institute of Charleston, a branch of The Art Institute of Atlanta, B

Tennessee

The Art Institute of Tennessee - Nashville, a branch of The Art Institute of Atlanta, B

Texas

The Art Institute of Austin, a branch of The Art Institute of Houston, B
The Art Institute of Dallas, a campus of South University, B
The Art Institute of Houston, B
The Art Institute of San Antonio, a branch of The Art Institute of Houston, B
El Centro College, A

Virginia

The Art Institute of Virginia Beach, a branch of The Art Institute of Atlanta, B
The Art Institute of Washington, a branch of The Art Institute of Atlanta, B

Washington

The Art Institute of Seattle, AB

Wisconsin

Milwaukee Area Technical College, A

APPAREL AND TEXTILE MANUFACTURE

United States

California

Academy of Art University, AB
Academy of Couture Art, AB
Cañada College, A
Cuesta College, A
FIDM/Fashion Institute of Design & Merchandising, Los Angeles Campus, B
Orange Coast College, A
Sierra College, A

Michigan

Michigan State University, B

New York

Fashion Institute of Technology, AB
Westchester Community College, A

APPAREL AND TEXTILE MARKETING MANAGEMENT

United States

Alabama

Auburn University, B
Community College of the Air Force, A

California

Academy of Art University, AB
American River College, A
Chaffey College, A
City College of San Francisco, A
FIDM/Fashion Institute of Design & Merchandising, Los Angeles Campus, A
FIDM/Fashion Institute of Design & Merchandising, Orange County Campus, A
FIDM/Fashion Institute of Design & Merchandising, San Francisco Campus, A
Fresno City College, A
Fullerton College, A
Long Beach City College, A
Orange Coast College, A
Palomar College, A
Santa Monica College, A
Sierra College, A

Colorado

Colorado State University, B

Georgia

Savannah College of Art and Design, B

Indiana

Indiana Tech, B

Michigan

Wayne State University, B

Nebraska

University of Nebraska - Lincoln, B

Pennsylvania

The Art Institute of Philadelphia, AB

South Dakota

South Dakota State University, B

Texas

University of the Incarnate Word, AB

Washington

Central Washington University, B

APPAREL AND TEXTILES

United States

Alabama

Auburn University, B
Central Alabama Community College, A
Jacksonville State University, B
The University of Alabama, B

Arizona

Northland Pioneer College, A

Arkansas

University of Arkansas, B

California

Antelope Valley College, A
California State Polytechnic University, Pomona, B
California State University, Long Beach, B
College of Alameda, A
Fullerton College, A
Los Angeles City College, A
Modesto Junior College, A
Monterey Peninsula College, A
Mt. San Antonio College, A
University of California, Davis, B

Delaware

Delaware State University, B
University of Delaware, B

Florida

Indian River State College, A
Palm Beach State College, A

Georgia

Georgia Southern University, B
Savannah College of Art and Design, B

Hawaii

University of Hawaii at Manoa, B

Idaho

University of Idaho, B

Illinois

Northern Illinois University, B
Southern Illinois University Carbondale, B

Indiana

Indiana State University, B
Indiana University Bloomington, B

Iowa

Iowa State University of Science and Technology, B
University of Northern Iowa, B

Kansas

Kansas State University, B

Kentucky

University of Kentucky, B
Western Kentucky University, B

Massachusetts

Framingham State University, B

Michigan

Michigan State University, B

Minnesota

University of Minnesota, Twin Cities Campus, B

Mississippi

University of Southern Mississippi, B

Missouri

Missouri State University, B
Stephens College, B
University of Central Missouri, B
University of Missouri, B

Nebraska

University of Nebraska - Lincoln, B

New Mexico

New Mexico State University, B

North Carolina

Appalachian State University, B
East Carolina University, B
North Carolina Agricultural and Technical State University, B
The University of North Carolina at Greensboro, B

North Dakota

North Dakota State University, B

Ohio

Bowling Green State University, B
The Ohio State University, B
Ohio University, B
The University of Akron, B

Oklahoma

University of Central Oklahoma, B

Oregon

Oregon State University, B

Pennsylvania

Philadelphia University, B

Rhode Island

Rhode Island School of Design, B
University of Rhode Island, B

Tennessee

Hiwassee College, A
Lipscomb University, B
Middle Tennessee State University, B
Tennessee Technological University, B

Texas

Lamar University, B
Texas A&M University - Kingsville, B
The University of Texas at Austin, B

Virginia

Liberty University, B
Virginia Polytechnic Institute and State University, B

Washington

Seattle Pacific University, B
Washington State University, B

Wisconsin

University of Wisconsin - Madison, B
University of Wisconsin - Stout, B

Canada

Alberta

University of Alberta, B

Manitoba

University of Manitoba, B

APPLIANCE INSTALLATION AND REPAIR TECHNOLOGY/TECHNICIAN

United States

Washington

Renton Technical College, A

APPLIED ARTS AND DESIGN

United States

California

Academy of Art University, M
California Institute of the Arts, MO
California State University, Los Angeles, M
San Diego State University, M
San Jose State University, M

Connecticut

Yale University, M

Florida

Florida Atlantic University, M

Georgia

Savannah College of Art and Design, MO

Illinois

Illinois Institute of Technology, MD
Southern Illinois University Carbondale, M
University of Illinois at Urbana - Champaign, MD

Louisiana

Louisiana Tech University, M

Maryland

Maryland Institute College of Art, M

Massachusetts

Massachusetts College of Art and Design, MO
Suffolk University, M

Michigan

Western Michigan University, M

Minnesota

Minneapolis College of Art and Design, M

New York

Alfred University, M
Fashion Institute of Technology, M
Pratt Institute, MO
Syracuse University, M

North Carolina

North Carolina State University, M

Ohio

University of Cincinnati, M

Oregon

Pacific Northwest College of Art, M

Pennsylvania

Drexel University, M

Rhode Island

Rhode Island School of Design, M

Tennessee

Memphis College of Art, M

Virginia

Virginia Commonwealth University, M

Wisconsin

Cardinal Stritch University, M

Canada

British Columbia

Emily Carr University of Art + Design, M

APPLIED BEHAVIOR ANALYSIS

United States

Alabama

Auburn University, M

Arizona

Arizona State University at the Tempe campus, M

California

California State University, Sacramento, M
California State University, Stanislaus, M
National University, MO

Connecticut

Fairfield University, O
University of Saint Joseph, MO

Florida

Florida Institute of Technology, MD
Florida International University, M
Florida State University, M
University of North Florida, M
University of South Florida, MD

Indiana

Ball State University, M

Kansas

The University of Kansas, MD

Kentucky

Spalding University, M

Louisiana

McNeese State University, M

Maine

University of Southern Maine, MO

Maryland

Johns Hopkins University, O

Massachusetts

Bay Path University, M
Endicott College, MD
Regis College, M
Simmons College, MDO
Western New England University, MD
Westfield State University, M

Michigan

Northern Michigan University, M

Minnesota

Capella University, M
St. Cloud State University, M

New Jersey

Caldwell University, MDO
Georgian Court University, M
Monmouth University, O
Rowan University, MO
Saint Peter's University, M

New York

Hofstra University, O
Long Island University - LIU Brooklyn, O

Ohio

Wright State University, M
Youngstown State University, M

Oklahoma

Oklahoma City University, M
Oklahoma State University, D

Pennsylvania

Drexel University, M
Eastern University, M
Mercyhurst University, M
Mount Aloysius College, M
Penn State Harrisburg, M
University of Pittsburgh, M

Tennessee

Lipscomb University, MO
Tennessee Technological University, D

Texas

Baylor University, M
University of North Texas, O
The University of Texas at San Antonio, O

Vermont

Johnson State College, M

Virginia

James Madison University, M
Shenandoah University, M

APPLIED ECONOMICS

United States

Alabama

Auburn University, D

Arizona

The University of Arizona, B

California

San Jose State University, M
University of California, Santa Cruz, M
University of San Francisco, B

Georgia

Georgia Southern University, MO
University of Georgia, MD

Idaho

University of Idaho, M

Illinois

DePaul University, M
Illinois Institute of Technology, B
Roosevelt University, M
University of Illinois at Urbana - Champaign, MD

Indiana

Wabash College, B

Iowa

University of Northern Iowa, B

Kentucky

Western Kentucky University, M

Maryland

Johns Hopkins University, M

Massachusetts

University of Massachusetts Boston, M

Michigan

University of Michigan, M
Western Michigan University, MD

Minnesota

Augsburg College, B
The College of St. Scholastica, B
St. Cloud State University, M
University of Minnesota, Twin Cities Campus, BMD

Mississippi

Mississippi State University, D

Nevada

University of Nevada, Reno, MD

New York

Binghamton University, State University of New York, B
Buffalo State College, State University of New York, M
Cornell University, MD
Farmingdale State College, B
Ithaca College, B
New York University, O

North Carolina

East Carolina University, M
North Carolina Agricultural and Technical State University, M
The University of North Carolina at Greensboro, M

North Dakota

University of North Dakota, M

Ohio

Bowling Green State University, B
Ohio University, M
The University of Akron, B
University of Cincinnati, M
Wright State University, M

Oklahoma

University of Central Oklahoma, B
University of Oklahoma, M

Oregon

Portland State University, M

Pennsylvania

Allegheny College, B
Penn State Abington, B
Penn State Beaver, B
Penn State Brandywine, B
Penn State DuBois, B
Penn State Erie, The Behrend College, B
Penn State Fayette, The Eberly Campus, B
Penn State Greater Allegheny, B
Penn State Hazleton, B
Penn State Lehigh Valley, B
Penn State Mont Alto, B
Penn State New Kensington, B
Penn State Schuylkill, B
Penn State Shenango, B
Penn State Wilkes-Barre, B
Penn State Worthington Scranton, B
Penn State York, B
Thomas Jefferson University, O
University of Pennsylvania, D
Ursinus College, B

Rhode Island

Bryant University, B

South Carolina

Clemson University, MD

Texas

Southern Methodist University, M
Texas Tech University, MD
University of Houston, M

Utah

Brigham Young University, B
Utah State University, M

Vermont

University of Vermont, M

Virginia

Old Dominion University, M
Virginia Polytechnic Institute and State University, M

Wisconsin

University of Wisconsin - Madison, MD

Wyoming

University of Wyoming, M

Canada

Maritime Provinces: New Brunswick

University of New Brunswick Fredericton, M

Ontario

University of Waterloo, B

Quebec

Concordia University, B
HEC Montreal, BM

Saskatchewan

University of Regina, M

APPLIED HISTORY

United States

California

Sonoma State University, M

APPLIED HORTICULTURE/ HORTICULTURAL BUSINESS SERVICES

United States

Iowa

Des Moines Area Community College, A
Kirkwood Community College, A

Massachusetts

University of Massachusetts Amherst, A

Mississippi

Hinds Community College, A

Nebraska

Northeast Community College, A

New York

Morrisville State College, AB

North Carolina

Forsyth Technical Community College, A

North Dakota

Dakota College at Bottineau, A
North Dakota State University, B

Ohio

Cincinnati State Technical and Community College, A

Pennsylvania

Delaware Valley University, B

Rhode Island

University of Rhode Island, B

Tennessee

Southwest Tennessee Community College, A

Wisconsin

Chippewa Valley Technical College, A

APPLIED HORTICULTURE/ HORTICULTURAL OPERATIONS

United States

California

Antelope Valley College, A
Cabrillo College, A
College of the Desert, A
Cuesta College, A
Fullerton College, A
Long Beach City College, A
Orange Coast College, A
Santa Barbara City College, A
Sierra College, A

Colorado

Colorado State University, B
Front Range Community College, A

Connecticut

University of Connecticut, A

Delaware

Delaware Technical & Community College, Jack F. Owens Campus, A

Georgia

University of Georgia, B

Idaho

College of Southern Idaho, A

Illinois

Black Hawk College, A
Illinois Central College, A
John Wood Community College, A
Kankakee Community College, A
Kaskaskia College, A
Kishwaukee College, A
McHenry County College, A
Rend Lake College, A
Southwestern Illinois College, A
University of Illinois at Urbana - Champaign, B

Indiana

Vincennes University, A

Kansas

Coffeyville Community College, A

Kentucky

Owensboro Community and Technical College, A

Maine

University of Maine, B

Maryland

Cecil College, A
Community College of Baltimore County, A
Montgomery College, A

Massachusetts

University of Massachusetts Amherst, AB

Michigan

Lake Michigan College, A

Minnesota

Central Lakes College, A

Missouri

Mineral Area College, A
State Fair Community College, A

Nebraska

Central Community College - Hastings Campus, A
Nebraska College of Technical Agriculture, A

New Hampshire

University of New Hampshire, A

New Jersey

Bergen Community College, A

New York

Farmingdale State College, B
State University of New York College of Technology at Delhi, A

North Carolina

Alamance Community College, A
Blue Ridge Community College, A
Brunswick Community College, A
Catawba Valley Community College, A
Fayetteville Technical Community College, A
Haywood Community College, A
Lenoir Community College, A
Mayland Community College, A
Western Piedmont Community College, A
Wilkes Community College, A

North Dakota

Dakota College at Bottineau, A

Ohio

Clark State Community College, A
Kent State University at Salem, AB

Oklahoma

Connors State College, A
Tulsa Community College, A

Oregon

Chemeketa Community College, A
Clackamas Community College, A

Pennsylvania

Community College of Allegheny County, A
Pennsylvania College of Technology, A
Westmoreland County Community College, A

South Carolina

Spartanburg Community College, A

South Dakota

South Dakota State University, B
Southeast Technical Institute, A

Tennessee

Columbia State Community College, A

Texas

Houston Community College, A
Texas A&M University, B
Texas Tech University, B
Western Texas College, A

Virginia

Ferrum College, B
J. Sargeant Reynolds Community College, A

Washington

Clark College, A
Edmonds Community College, A
Lake Washington Institute of Technology, A
Skagit Valley College, A
Spokane Community College, A

Wisconsin

Gateway Technical College, A

Canada

British Columbia

University of the Fraser Valley, A

Quebec

McGill University, B

APPLIED MATHEMATICS

United States

Alabama

Auburn University, BM
Oakwood University, B
The University of Alabama, D
The University of Alabama at Birmingham, D
The University of Alabama in Huntsville, D

Arizona

Arizona State University at the Tempe campus, BD
Arizona State University at the West campus, B
The University of Arizona, MD

Arkansas

University of Arkansas at Little Rock, MO
University of Central Arkansas, M

California

Biola University, B
California Institute of Technology, MD
California State Polytechnic University, Pomona, M
California State University, East Bay, BM
California State University, Fullerton, BM
California State University, Long Beach, BMD
California State University, Los Angeles, M
California State University, Northridge, M
Fresno Pacific University, B
Humboldt State University, B
Loyola Marymount University, B
The Master's College and Seminary, B
San Diego Miramar College, A
San Diego State University, BM
San Francisco State University, B
San Jose State University, BM
Santa Clara University, M
Sonoma State University, B
University of California, Berkeley, BD
University of California, Davis, BMD
University of California, Irvine, MD
University of California, Los Angeles, B
University of California, Merced, BMD
University of California, San Diego, BM
University of California, Santa Barbara, BM
University of California, Santa Cruz, MD
University of Southern California, MD

Colorado

Colorado School of Mines, MD
University of Colorado Boulder, BMD
University of Colorado Colorado Springs, M
University of Colorado Denver, MD

Connecticut

Quinnipiac University, B
University of Connecticut, BM
University of New Haven, B
Yale University, BMD

Delaware

Delaware State University, MD
University of Delaware, MD

District of Columbia

American University, B
The George Washington University, BM
Howard University, MD
University of the District of Columbia, B

Florida

Broward College, A
Florida Atlantic University, M
Florida Institute of Technology, B
Florida State University, MD
New College of Florida, B
South Florida State College, A
University of Miami, B
University of North Florida, B
University of South Florida, MD

Georgia

Emory University, B
Georgia Institute of Technology, B
Kennesaw State University, B
University of Georgia, M
University of West Georgia, M
Valdosta State University, B

Hawaii

Hawai'i Pacific University, B

Idaho

Boise State University, B
Brigham Young University - Idaho, B
The College of Idaho, B
University of Idaho, B

Illinois

Augustana College, B
DePaul University, BM
Illinois Institute of Technology, BMD
North Central College, B
Northeastern Illinois University, M
Northern Illinois University, B
Northwestern University, BMD
Southern Illinois University Edwardsville, M
University of Chicago, D
University of Illinois at Urbana - Champaign, M
Western Illinois University, O
Wheaton College, B

Indiana

Indiana University Bloomington, M
Indiana University - Purdue University Fort Wayne, M
Indiana University - Purdue University Indianapolis, MD
Indiana University South Bend, BM
Purdue University, B
Taylor University, B
University of Notre Dame, M

Iowa

Grand View University, B
Iowa State University of Science and Technology, MD
The University of Iowa, BD
University of Northern Iowa, BM
William Penn University, B

Kansas

Wichita State University, D

Kentucky

Berea College, B
Brescia University, B
University of Kentucky, M
University of Louisville, D

Louisiana

Tulane University, M

Maryland

Bowie State University, BM
Johns Hopkins University, BMDO
Loyola University Maryland, B
Stevenson University, B
Towson University, M
University of Maryland, Baltimore County, MD
University of Maryland, College Park, MD

Massachusetts

Endicott College, B
Fitchburg State University, B
Harvard University, BMD
Lasell College, B
Northeastern University, MD
Tufts University, B
University of Massachusetts Amherst, M
University of Massachusetts Lowell, BM
Wentworth Institute of Technology, B
Worcester Polytechnic Institute, BM

Michigan

Central Michigan University, B
Ferris State University, B
Hillsdale College, B
Kettering University, B
Michigan State University, MD
Muskegon Community College, A
Oakland University, MD
Saginaw Valley State University, B
Siena Heights University, B
University of Michigan - Dearborn, M
Wayne State University, MD
Western Michigan University, BM

Minnesota

Concordia University, St. Paul, B
Metropolitan State University, B
University of Minnesota, Duluth, M

Mississippi

Millsaps College, B

Missouri

Central Methodist University, A
Maryville University of Saint Louis, B
Missouri University of Science and Technology, BM
University of Central Missouri, M
University of Missouri, M
Washington University in St. Louis, B

Montana

Carroll College, B
University of Montana, B

New Hampshire

Keene State College, B
University of New Hampshire, B

New Jersey

Bloomfield College, B
Montclair State University, M
New Jersey Institute of Technology, BM
Princeton University, D
Rutgers University - Camden, M
Rutgers University - New Brunswick, MD
Rutgers University - Newark, B
Stevens Institute of Technology, M

New Mexico

New Mexico Institute of Mining and Technology, MD

New York

Clarkson University, B
Columbia University, BMD
Columbia University, School of General Studies, B
Cornell University, MD
Farmingdale State College, B
Hunter College of the City University of New York, M
Iona College, B
Long Island University - LIU Post, B
Marist College, B
New York City College of Technology of the City University of New York, B
Rensselaer Polytechnic Institute, M
Rochester Institute of Technology, M
St. Thomas Aquinas College, B
State University of New York at Oswego, B
State University of New York Polytechnic Institute, B
Stony Brook University, State University of New York, BMDO
Syracuse University, B

University at Buffalo, the State University of New York, B
University of Rochester, B

North Carolina

Elizabeth City State University, M
Elon University, B
North Carolina Agricultural and Technical State University, BM
North Carolina Central University, M
North Carolina State University, BMD
The University of North Carolina at Chapel Hill, B
The University of North Carolina at Charlotte, MD

North Dakota

North Dakota State University, MD
University of Jamestown, B

Ohio

Case Western Reserve University, BMD
Kent State University, BMD
Ohio Northern University, B
Ohio University, B
The University of Akron, BM
University of Cincinnati, MD
University of Dayton, M
The University of Toledo, MD
Wright State University, M
Youngstown State University, M

Oklahoma

East Central University, B
Oklahoma State University, MD
University of Central Oklahoma, BM
The University of Tulsa, B

Oregon

Southern Oregon University, M
Willamette University, B

Pennsylvania

Bucknell University, B
Clarion University of Pennsylvania, A
Elizabethtown College, B
Geneva College, B
Indiana University of Pennsylvania, M
La Salle University, B
Lehigh University, B
Lycoming College, B
Penn State Harrisburg, B
Robert Morris University, B
Temple University, BM
University of Pennsylvania, D
University of Pittsburgh, BM
University of Pittsburgh at Bradford, B
University of Pittsburgh at Greensburg, B
The University of Scranton, B
West Chester University of Pennsylvania, M

Rhode Island

Brown University, BMD
Bryant University, B
Roger Williams University, B
University of Rhode Island, MD

South Carolina

Charleston Southern University, B
Clemson University, MD
Coastal Carolina University, B
University of South Carolina Aiken, B

South Dakota

University of Sioux Falls, B

Tennessee

Belmont University, B
Lipscomb University, B
Trevecca Nazarene University, B
University of Memphis, M
The University of Tennessee, M
The University of Tennessee at Chattanooga, BM

Texas

Baylor University, B
Rice University, BMD
Southern Methodist University, MD
Texas A&M University, B
Texas Christian University, MD
Texas State University, BM
University of Houston, M
University of Houston - Downtown, B
The University of Texas at Arlington, M
The University of Texas at Austin, MD
The University of Texas at Dallas, MD
The University of Texas at El Paso, B
The University of Texas Rio Grande Valley, M
The University of Texas at San Antonio, M

Utah

University of Utah, B
Utah State University, M
Weber State University, B

Vermont

Marlboro College, B

Virginia

Averett University, B
Christopher Newport University, B
The College of William and Mary, D
Hampden-Sydney College, B
Hampton University, M
Mary Baldwin College, B
Virginia Commonwealth University, M

Washington

University of Washington, BMD
Washington State University, BMD
Western Washington University, B
Whitworth University, B

West Virginia

Alderson Broaddus University, B
West Virginia University, MD

Wisconsin

Carroll University, B
University of Wisconsin - Madison, B
University of Wisconsin - Milwaukee, B
University of Wisconsin - Stout, BM

U.S. Territories: Puerto Rico

Inter American University of Puerto Rico, Bayamón Campus, B
Inter American University of Puerto Rico, Metropolitan Campus, B
Inter American University of Puerto Rico, San Germán Campus, BM
Universidad Metropolitana, B
University of Puerto Rico, Mayagüez Campus, M

U.S. Territories: United States Virgin Islands

University of the Virgin Islands, B

Canada

Alberta

University of Alberta, BMD
University of Calgary, B

British Columbia

Simon Fraser University, BMD
Thompson Rivers University, B
Trinity Western University, B
The University of British Columbia, BMD

Manitoba

University of Manitoba, B
The University of Winnipeg, B

Maritime Provinces: New Brunswick

Mount Allison University, B
University of New Brunswick Fredericton, B

Maritime Provinces: Nova Scotia

Acadia University, M
Dalhousie University, MD
Mount Saint Vincent University, B

Newfoundland and Labrador

Memorial University of Newfoundland, B

Ontario

Brock University, B
Carleton University, B
McMaster University, B
Trent University, B
University of Guelph, D
University of Toronto, B
University of Waterloo, BMD
The University of Western Ontario, BMD
University of Windsor, B
York University, BM

Quebec

École Polytechnique de Montréal, MD
McGill University, BM
Université de Montréal, B

APPLIED PHYSICS

United States

Arizona

Northern Arizona University, M

Arkansas

University of Arkansas, M

California

California Institute of Technology, MD
Stanford University, MD
University of California, San Diego, MD

Colorado

Colorado School of Mines, MD
University of Denver, MD

Connecticut

Yale University, MD

Florida

University of South Florida, MD

Georgia

Georgia Southern University, M

Idaho

Idaho State University, D

Illinois

Illinois Institute of Technology, M
Northwestern University, D
Southern Illinois University Carbondale, MD

Iowa

Iowa State University of Science and Technology, MD

Kansas

Pittsburg State University, M

Louisiana

Louisiana Tech University, M

Maryland

Johns Hopkins University, MO
Towson University, M

Massachusetts

Harvard University, MD
University of Massachusetts Boston, M
University of Massachusetts Lowell, M

Michigan

University of Michigan, D

Mississippi

Mississippi State University, D

Missouri

University of Missouri - St. Louis, M

New Jersey

New Jersey Institute of Technology, MD
Rutgers University - Newark, MD

New York

Binghamton University, State University of New York, MD
Columbia University, MD
Cornell University, MD
New York University, MD

North Carolina

East Carolina University, M
The University of North Carolina at Charlotte, MD

Pennsylvania

Carnegie Mellon University, D

Texas

Rice University, MD
Texas A&M University, D
Texas Tech University, M
The University of Texas at Austin, MD

Virginia

Christopher Newport University, M
The College of William and Mary, D
George Mason University, M
Virginia Commonwealth University, M

Washington

University of Washington, MD

West Virginia

West Virginia University, MD

Canada

Ontario

Laurentian University, M

APPLIED PSYCHOLOGY

United States

Arizona

Arizona State University at the Tempe campus, M

Arkansas

University of Arkansas at Little Rock, M

California

California State University, Chico, M

Connecticut

Fairfield University, M
Sacred Heart University, M

District of Columbia

The Catholic University of America, D
The George Washington University, D

Florida

Lynn University, M
University of Central Florida, MD

Georgia

Clayton State University, M

Illinois

Loyola University Chicago, MD

Iowa

Loras College, M

Maryland

University of Baltimore, M
University of Maryland, Baltimore County, D

Massachusetts

Boston College, MD

Michigan

Central Michigan University, D

Minnesota

Walden University, M

New Jersey

Rider University, M
Rutgers University - New Brunswick, MD

New York

Fordham University, MD
New York University, MDO

Oklahoma

Oklahoma State University, MDO

Pennsylvania

Penn State Harrisburg, M
University of Pennsylvania, MD
University of Pittsburgh, MD

South Carolina

Clemson University, M
Francis Marion University, M
University of South Carolina Aiken, M

Tennessee

The University of Tennessee, M

Texas

Angelo State University, M
The University of Texas at El Paso, O
The University of Texas of the Permian Basin, M

Virginia

George Mason University, O
Old Dominion University, D

Washington

Eastern Washington University, M

Wisconsin

University of Wisconsin - Stout, M

Canada

Alberta

Athabasca University, MO
University of Calgary, MD

Maritime Provinces: Nova Scotia

Saint Mary's University, MD

Ontario

Laurentian University, M
University of Guelph, MD
University of Windsor, MD

Saskatchewan

University of Regina, MD

APPLIED SCIENCE AND TECHNOLOGY

United States

Arkansas

University of Arkansas at Little Rock, MD

California

University of California, Berkeley, D
University of California, Davis, MD

Colorado

Colorado State University - Pueblo, M
University of Colorado Denver, M

Louisiana

Louisiana State University and Agricultural & Mechanical College, M
Southeastern Louisiana University, M

Massachusetts

Harvard University, O

Mississippi

University of Mississippi, MD

Missouri

Missouri State University, M

New Jersey

Thomas Edison State University, O

Texas

Southern Methodist University, M

Virginia

The College of William and Mary, MD
James Madison University, M

Canada

Maritime Provinces: Nova Scotia

Saint Mary's University, M

APPLIED SOCIAL RESEARCH

United States

California

California State University, Dominguez Hills, O
Concordia University Irvine, M
University of California, Los Angeles, MD

New York

Hunter College of the City University of New York, M
New York University, M

Oregon

Portland State University, D

Virginia

Virginia Commonwealth University, O

West Virginia

West Virginia University, M

Canada

Ontario

Laurentian University, M

APPLIED STATISTICS

United States

Alabama

The University of Alabama, MD

Arizona

Northern Arizona University, O

Arkansas

University of Arkansas at Little Rock, O

California

California State University, East Bay, M
California State University, Long Beach, M
University of California, Riverside, D
University of California, Santa Barbara, M

Colorado

University of Colorado Denver, M
University of Northern Colorado, MD

District of Columbia

University of the District of Columbia, M

Florida

Florida State University, M
University of West Florida, M

Georgia

Kennesaw State University, M

Illinois

DePaul University, M
Loyola University Chicago, M
University of Chicago, M
University of Illinois at Urbana - Champaign, M

Indiana

Indiana University Bloomington, M
Indiana University - Purdue University Fort Wayne, O
Indiana University - Purdue University Indianapolis, M
University of Notre Dame, M

Louisiana

Louisiana State University and Agricultural & Mechanical College, M

Massachusetts

Worcester Polytechnic Institute, M

Michigan

Michigan State University, M
Oakland University, M
University of Michigan, M

Minnesota

St. Cloud State University, M

New Jersey

New Jersey Institute of Technology, M
Rutgers University - New Brunswick, M
Stevens Institute of Technology, O

New Mexico

New Mexico State University, M

New York

Cornell University, M
New York University, M
Rochester Institute of Technology, MO
Syracuse University, M

North Carolina

The University of North Carolina at Charlotte, M

North Dakota

North Dakota State University, MO

Ohio

Bowling Green State University, M
Cleveland State University, M
Wright State University, M

Pennsylvania

Penn State University Park, MD
University of Pittsburgh, M
Villanova University, M
West Chester University of Pennsylvania, MO

South Carolina

University of South Carolina, O

Tennessee

University of Memphis, D
The University of Tennessee at Chattanooga, M

Texas

The University of Texas at San Antonio, MD

Utah

Brigham Young University, M

Canada

Ontario

McMaster University, M
University of Guelph, D

AQUACULTURE

United States

Alabama

Auburn University, BMD

Arizona

Yavapai College, A

Arkansas

University of Arkansas at Pine Bluff, M

Colorado

Trinidad State Junior College, A

Florida

Hillsborough Community College, A
University of Florida, MD

Idaho

College of Southern Idaho, A

Indiana

Purdue University, MD

Kentucky

Kentucky State University, M

Maine

University of New England, B

New York

Morrisville State College, A

North Carolina

Brunswick Community College, A

Pennsylvania

Cheyney University of Pennsylvania, B

Rhode Island

University of Rhode Island, MD

South Carolina

Clemson University, BMD

Texas

Texas A&M University - Corpus Christi, M

West Virginia

New River Community and Technical College, A

Canada

Maritime Provinces: Nova Scotia

Dalhousie University, BM

Newfoundland and Labrador

Memorial University of Newfoundland, M

Ontario

University of Guelph, M

AQUATIC BIOLOGY/LIMNOLOGY

United States

Florida

Florida Institute of Technology, B
Stetson University, B

Michigan

Western Michigan University, B

New York

State University of New York College of Environmental Science and Forestry, B

Pennsylvania

Gannon University, B

South Carolina

University of South Carolina, B

Texas

Texas State University, B

Canada

British Columbia

University of Northern British Columbia, B

Quebec

McGill University, B

ARABIC LANGUAGE AND LITERATURE

United States

California

Grossmont College, A
National University, B
University of California, Los Angeles, B

District of Columbia

American University, B
The Catholic University of America, D
Georgetown University, BMO

Georgia

Emory University, B
University of Georgia, B

Illinois

DePaul University, BM

Indiana

University of Notre Dame, B

Kentucky

Western Kentucky University, B

Maryland

United States Naval Academy, B
University of Maryland, College Park, B

Massachusetts

Harvard University, MD
Tufts University, B

Michigan

Michigan State University, B
University of Michigan, MD
Wayne State University, M

Missouri

Washington University in St. Louis, B

New Hampshire

Dartmouth College, B

New York

Bard College, B
Binghamton University, State University of New York, B
United States Military Academy, B

Ohio

The Ohio State University, B
University of Cincinnati, B

Oklahoma

University of Oklahoma, B

Oregon

Portland State University, B

Pennsylvania

California University of Pennsylvania, B

Texas

Austin Community College District, A
Baylor University, B
The University of Texas at Austin, B

Utah

University of Utah, BMD

Vermont

Marlboro College, B
Middlebury College, BM

Canada

Ontario

University of Ottawa, B
University of Toronto, B

ARCHEOLOGY

United States

Arizona

Arizona State University at the Tempe campus, D
Northern Arizona University, M

California

Biola University, B
Cabrillo College, A
California State University, Northridge, M
Cañada College, A
Palomar College, A
Saint Mary's College of California, B
San Francisco State University, M
Stanford University, BD
University of California, Berkeley, MD
University of California, Los Angeles, MD
University of California, Santa Barbara, MD
University of Southern California, B

Colorado

University of Colorado Denver, M
University of Denver, M

Connecticut

Wesleyan University, B
Yale University, BMD

District of Columbia

The George Washington University, B

Florida

Florida State University, M
University of South Florida, MD
University of West Florida, M

Georgia

University of Georgia, M

Illinois

Illinois State University, M
Trinity International University, M
University of Chicago, D
Wheaton College, BM

Indiana

University of Evansville, B
University of Indianapolis, B

Iowa

Cornell College, B

Maine

Bowdoin College, B

Maryland

Johns Hopkins University, BD

Massachusetts

Boston University, BMD
Bridgewater State University, B
Harvard University, MD
Massachusetts Institute of Technology, D
Tufts University, BM
University of Massachusetts Boston, M

Michigan

Michigan Technological University, MD
University of Michigan, MD

Minnesota

St. Cloud State University, M
University of Minnesota, Twin Cities Campus, MD

Missouri

University of Missouri, BMD
Washington University in St. Louis, BMD

Nebraska

University of Nebraska - Lincoln, M

New Hampshire

Dartmouth College, B
Franklin Pierce University, B

New Jersey

Princeton University, D

New Mexico

University of New Mexico, MD

New York

Columbia University, BMD
Columbia University, School of General Studies, B
Cornell University, BMD
Hamilton College, B
Hunter College of the City University of New York, B
New York University, BMD
State University of New York College at Potsdam, B

North Carolina

The University of North Carolina at Chapel Hill, BMD

Ohio

The College of Wooster, B
Oberlin College, B
University of Cincinnati, B

Oklahoma

University of Oklahoma, D

Pennsylvania

Bryn Mawr College, BMD
Dickinson College, B
Haverford College, B
Indiana University of Pennsylvania, M
Mercyhurst University, BM
Penn State Abington, B
Penn State Altoona, B
Penn State Beaver, B
Penn State Berks, B
Penn State Brandywine, B
Penn State DuBois, B
Penn State Erie, The Behrend College, B
Penn State Fayette, The Eberly Campus, B
Penn State Greater Allegheny, B
Penn State Hazleton, B
Penn State Lehigh Valley, B
Penn State Mont Alto, B
Penn State New Kensington, B
Penn State Schuylkill, B
Penn State Shenango, B
Penn State University Park, B
Penn State Wilkes-Barre, B
Penn State Worthington Scranton, B
Penn State York, B
University of Pennsylvania, MD

Rhode Island

Brown University, BD

South Carolina

College of Charleston, B

Tennessee

Southern Adventist University, B
University of Memphis, M
The University of Tennessee, MD

Texas

Rice University, MD
The University of Texas at Austin, BMD

Utah

Weber State University, A

Virginia

Sweet Briar College, B

Washington

Washington State University, BMD
Western Washington University, B

Wisconsin

Lawrence University, B
University of Wisconsin - La Crosse, B
University of Wisconsin - Madison, D

Wyoming

Northwest College, A
Western Wyoming Community College, A

Canada

Alberta

University of Alberta, MD
University of Calgary, BM
University of Lethbridge, BM

British Columbia

Simon Fraser University, BMD
The University of British Columbia, BM

Newfoundland and Labrador

Memorial University of Newfoundland, BMD

Ontario

Brock University, B
University of Toronto, B
Wilfrid Laurier University, B

Quebec

Université Laval, BMD
Université de Montréal, B

Saskatchewan

University of Saskatchewan, BMD

ARCHITECTURAL DRAFTING AND ARCHITECTURAL CAD/ CADD

United States

Arizona

Coconino Community College, A
Glendale Community College, A
Phoenix College, A
Yavapai College, A

California

Chaffey College, A
College of the Canyons, A
College of the Redwoods, A
Cosumnes River College, A
Long Beach City College, A
Modesto Junior College, A
Palomar College, A
Sierra College, A

Colorado

IntelliTec College (Colorado Springs), A

Connecticut

Three Rivers Community College, A

Florida

Indian River State College, A
Lincoln College of Technology, A
Miami Dade College, A
North Florida Community College, A
St. Johns River State College, A

Hawaii

Hawaii Community College, A

Illinois

City Colleges of Chicago, Harold Washington Col-
lege, A
College of Lake County, A
Harper College, A
Kaskaskia College, A
Lincoln Land Community College, A
Oakton Community College, A
Rend Lake College, A
South Suburban College, A
Triton College, A

Indiana

Lincoln College of Technology, A
Vincennes University, A

Iowa

Clinton Community College, A
Des Moines Area Community College, A
Iowa Western Community College, A
Kirkwood Community College, A

Kansas

Hutchinson Community College, A

Kentucky

Bluegrass Community and Technical College, A
Sullivan College of Technology and Design, A

Maine

York County Community College, A

Maryland

Anne Arundel Community College, A
Carroll Community College, A
Community College of Baltimore County, A
Montgomery College, A

Massachusetts

Benjamin Franklin Institute of Technology, A

Michigan

Macomb Community College, A
Washtenaw Community College, A

Minnesota

Anoka Technical College, A
Dunwoody College of Technology, A
Globe University - Woodbury, A
Hennepin Technical College, A
Lake Superior College, A
Minnesota State Community and Technical College,
A
Northland Community and Technical College, A
St. Cloud Technical & Community College, A
South Central College, A

Nebraska

Northeast Community College, A

Nevada

College of Southern Nevada, A
Truckee Meadows Community College, A

New Mexico

Central New Mexico Community College, A
New Mexico State University - Carlsbad, A
Santa Fe Community College, A

New York

Island Drafting and Technical Institute, A
Morrisville State College, A
New York City College of Technology of the City
University of New York, A

Ohio

Central Ohio Technical College, A
Owens Community College, A

Oklahoma

Northeastern Oklahoma Agricultural and Mechanical
College, A
Oklahoma City Community College, A
Oklahoma State University, Oklahoma City, A

Oregon

Clackamas Community College, A
Portland Community College, A

Pennsylvania

Butler County Community College, A
Commonwealth Technical Institute, A
Community College of Allegheny County, A
Community College of Beaver County, A
Johnson College, A
Pennsylvania Highlands Community College, A
Triangle Tech, Erie, A
Triangle Tech, Pittsburgh, A
Westmoreland County Community College, A

Washington

Lake Washington Institute of Technology, A
North Seattle College, A

West Virginia

BridgeValley Community and Technical College
(South Charleston), A

Wisconsin

Waukesha County Technical College, A

U.S. Territories: American Samoa

American Samoa Community College, A

U.S. Territories: Guam

Guam Community College, A

U.S. Territories: Puerto Rico

Universidad del Turabo, A

Canada

British Columbia

British Columbia Institute of Technology, A

ARCHITECTURAL ENGINEER- ING

United States

Alabama

Auburn University, B
The University of Alabama, B

California

California Polytechnic State University, San Luis
Obispo, B
University of California, San Diego, M

Colorado

University of Colorado Boulder, BMD

Florida

University of Miami, BMD

Illinois

Illinois Institute of Technology, BMD

Kansas

Kansas State University, BM
The University of Kansas, BM

Louisiana

University of Louisiana at Lafayette, M

Massachusetts

Springfield Technical Community College, A
Tufts University, B
University of Massachusetts Amherst, MD
Worcester Polytechnic Institute, B

Michigan

Andrews University, B
Lawrence Technological University, BM
University of Detroit Mercy, BM

Missouri

Missouri University of Science and Technology, B

Nebraska

University of Nebraska - Lincoln, BMD

New Jersey

Rutgers University - New Brunswick, B

New York

Orange County Community College, A
Utica School of Commerce, A

North Carolina

North Carolina Agricultural and Technical State University, B

Ohio

University of Cincinnati, B

Oklahoma

Oklahoma State University, B
University of Oklahoma, B

Pennsylvania

Carnegie Mellon University, MD
Drexel University, BMD
Luzerne County Community College, A
Penn State Abington, B
Penn State Altoona, B
Penn State Beaver, B
Penn State Berks, B
Penn State Brandywine, B
Penn State DuBois, B
Penn State Erie, The Behrend College, B
Penn State Fayette, The Eberly Campus, B
Penn State Greater Allegheny, B
Penn State Hazleton, B
Penn State Lehigh Valley, B
Penn State Mont Alto, B
Penn State New Kensington, B
Penn State Schuylkill, B
Penn State Shenango, B
Penn State University Park, BMD
Penn State Wilkes-Barre, B
Penn State Worthington Scranton, B
Penn State York, B

Tennessee

Nashville State Community College, A
Tennessee State University, B

Texas

Texas A&M University - Kingsville, B
The University of Texas at Austin, BM

Wisconsin

Milwaukee School of Engineering, BM

Wyoming

University of Wyoming, B

ARCHITECTURAL ENGINEERING TECHNOLOGY/TECHNICIAN

United States

Alaska

University of Alaska Anchorage, A
University of Alaska Anchorage, Matanuska-Susitna College, A

Arizona

Coconino Community College, A

California

Allan Hancock College, A
Bakersfield College, A
Cerritos College, A
Chabot College, A
College of the Sequoias, A
East Los Angeles College, A
El Camino College, A
Golden West College, A
Laney College, A
Los Angeles City College, A
Los Angeles Harbor College, A
Los Angeles Pierce College, A
Los Angeles Trade-Technical College, A
Modesto Junior College, A
Mt. San Antonio College, A
Saddleback College, A
San Bernardino Valley College, A
San Diego Mesa College, A

Colorado

Arapahoe Community College, A
Front Range Community College, A
Pikes Peak Community College, A

Connecticut

Capital Community College, A
Norwalk Community College, A
Three Rivers Community College, A
University of Hartford, B

Delaware

Delaware State University, B
Delaware Technical & Community College, Jack F. Owens Campus, A
Delaware Technical & Community College, Stanton/Wilmington Campus, A
Delaware Technical & Community College, Terry Campus, A

District of Columbia

University of the District of Columbia, A

Florida

Daytona State College, A
Hillsborough Community College, A
Miami Dade College, A
Northwest Florida State College, A
Seminole State College of Florida, AB

Hawaii

Honolulu Community College, A

Idaho

Brigham Young University - Idaho, A

Illinois

City Colleges of Chicago, Richard J. Daley College, A
City Colleges of Chicago, Wilbur Wright College, A
Harper College, A
Lake Land College, A

Indiana

Indiana University - Purdue University Fort Wayne, A
Indiana University - Purdue University Indianapolis, B
Purdue University, B

Iowa

Western Iowa Tech Community College, A

Kansas

Independence Community College, A

Kentucky

Northern Kentucky University, B
Sullivan College of Technology and Design, A

Louisiana

Delgado Community College, A

Massachusetts

Benjamin Franklin Institute of Technology, A
Fitchburg State University, B
Massasoit Community College, A

Michigan

Baker College, A
Delta College, A
Ferris State University, AB
Lansing Community College, A
Monroe County Community College, A
Mott Community College, A
Oakland Community College, A

Minnesota

Northland Community and Technical College, A
Vermilion Community College, A

Mississippi

Hinds Community College, A
Holmes Community College, A
Mississippi Delta Community College, A
Northeast Mississippi Community College, A
University of Southern Mississippi, B

Missouri

Ranken Technical College, AB
Washington University in St. Louis, B

Nebraska

Metropolitan Community College, A
Southeast Community College, Milford Campus, A

New Hampshire

NHTI, Concord's Community College, A

New Jersey

Essex County College, A
Mercer County Community College, A

New Mexico

Doña Ana Community College, A

New York

Dutchess Community College, A
Erie Community College, South Campus, A
Farmingdale State College, B
Finger Lakes Community College, A
Morrisville State College, A
Onondaga Community College, A
State University of New York College of Technology at Alfred, AB
State University of New York College of Technology at Delhi, A

North Carolina

Cape Fear Community College, A
Catawba Valley Community College, A
Central Piedmont Community College, A
Coastal Carolina Community College, A
College of The Albemarle, A
Durham Technical Community College, A
Fayetteville Technical Community College, A
Forsyth Technical Community College, A
Gaston College, A
Guilford Technical Community College, A
Nash Community College, A
Pitt Community College, A
Roanoke-Chowan Community College, A
Sandhills Community College, A
Wilkes Community College, A

North Dakota

North Dakota State College of Science, A

Ohio

Belmont College, A
Cincinnati State Technical and Community College, A
Columbus State Community College, A
Owens Community College, A
Sinclair Community College, A
Stark State College, A
Terra State Community College, A

Oklahoma

Oklahoma State University, Oklahoma City, A

Oregon

Mt. Hood Community College, A

Pennsylvania

Community College of Philadelphia, A
Delaware County Community College, A
Harrisburg Area Community College, A
Luzerne County Community College, A
Northampton Community College, A
Penn State Fayette, The Eberly Campus, A
Penn State Worthington Scranton, A

Rhode Island

New England Institute of Technology, AB

South Carolina

Greenville Technical College, A
Midlands Technical College, A

South Dakota

Southeast Technical Institute, A

Tennessee

Nashville State Community College, A
Southwest Tennessee Community College, A

Texas

Amarillo College, A
Del Mar College, A
Lamar State College - Orange, A
Palo Alto College, A
Tarrant County College District, A

Utah

Salt Lake Community College, A

Vermont

Vermont Technical College, AB

Virginia

New River Community College, A
Norfolk State University, A
Northern Virginia Community College, A

Washington

Bates Technical College, A
Clover Park Technical College, A
Spokane Community College, A

West Virginia

Bluefield State College, AB
Pierpont Community & Technical College, A

Wisconsin

Gateway Technical College, A
Madison Area Technical College, A
Milwaukee Area Technical College, A
Northcentral Technical College, A
Northeast Wisconsin Technical College, A
Western Technical College, A
Wisconsin Indianhead Technical College, A

Canada

British Columbia

British Columbia Institute of Technology, A

ARCHITECTURAL HISTORY AND CRITICISM

United States

Arizona

Arizona State University at the Tempe campus, D

California

University of California, Berkeley, MD
University of San Diego, B

Colorado

University of Colorado Denver, D

Florida

University of Miami, B

Georgia

Savannah College of Art and Design, BM

Illinois

DePaul University, B

Kansas

The University of Kansas, B

Massachusetts

College of the Holy Cross, B
Harvard University, D
Massachusetts Institute of Technology, D

Michigan

Lawrence Technological University, B

New York

Columbia University, School of General Studies, B
Cornell University, BMD
New York University, M
Syracuse University, B

Ohio

Miami University Hamilton, B

Pennsylvania

University of Pittsburgh, MD

Rhode Island

Brown University, B
Roger Williams University, M

Texas

The University of Texas at Austin, MD

Virginia

University of Virginia, BMD
Virginia Commonwealth University, M

ARCHITECTURAL TECHNOLOGY/TECHNICIAN

United States

Arizona

Arizona Western College, A
Coconino Community College, A

California

Chabot College, A
City College of San Francisco, A
College of the Desert, A
College of Marin, A
College of San Mateo, A
Contra Costa College, A
Cosumnes River College, A
Cuesta College, A
Fresno City College, A
Fullerton College, A
Long Beach City College, A
MiraCosta College, A
Orange Coast College, A
Palomar College, A
Southwestern College, A

Florida

Florida SouthWestern State College, A
Florida State College at Jacksonville, A
Miami Dade College, A

Illinois

City Colleges of Chicago, Wilbur Wright College, A

Indiana

Indiana State University, B

Kentucky

Western Kentucky University, B

Maine

University of Maine at Augusta, B

Michigan

Grand Rapids Community College, A
Henry Ford College, A
Lansing Community College, A
Lawrence Technological University, B

Minnesota

Dunwoody College of Technology, A
Minnesota State Community and Technical College - Detroit Lakes, A

Missouri

Washington University in St. Louis, B

New York

Hudson Valley Community College, A
New York City College of Technology of the City University of New York, B
New York Institute of Technology, AB
Onondaga Community College, A

Pennsylvania

Pennsylvania College of Technology, A
Thaddeus Stevens College of Technology, A

Virginia

John Tyler Community College, A

ARCHITECTURE

United States

Alabama

Auburn University, BM
Tuskegee University, B

Arizona

Arizona State University at the Tempe campus, BMD
The University of Arizona, BM

Arkansas

University of Arkansas, B

California

Academy of Art University, BM
California Baptist University, BM
California College of the Arts, BM
California Polytechnic State University, San Luis Obispo, BM
California State Polytechnic University, Pomona, BM
NewSchool of Architecture and Design, BM
Pasadena City College, A
San Diego Mesa College, A
Southern California Institute of Architecture, BM
University of California, Berkeley, BMD
University of California, Los Angeles, BMD
University of San Francisco, B
University of Southern California, BMD
Woodbury University, BM

Colorado

University of Colorado Denver, BM

Connecticut

University of Hartford, M
Yale University, BMD

District of Columbia

The Catholic University of America, BM
Howard University, B
University of the District of Columbia, BM

Florida

Broward College, A
College of Central Florida, A
Florida Agricultural and Mechanical University, BM
Florida Atlantic University, B
Florida International University, MO
South Florida State College, A
University of Central Florida, B
University of Florida, BMD
University of Miami, BM
University of South Florida, M

Georgia

Georgia Institute of Technology, BMD
Kennesaw State University, BM
Savannah College of Art and Design, M

Hawaii

University of Hawaii at Manoa, BD

Idaho

University of Idaho, BM

Illinois

Illinois Institute of Technology, BMD
Judson University, BM
School of the Art Institute of Chicago, M
Southern Illinois University Carbondale, BM
University of Illinois at Chicago, BM
University of Illinois at Urbana - Champaign, BMD

Indiana

Ball State University, BM
University of Notre Dame, BM

Iowa

Cornell College, B
Iowa State University of Science and Technology, BM

Kansas

Allen Community College, A
Barton County Community College, A
Kansas State University, M
The University of Kansas, BMDO

Kentucky

University of Kentucky, BM

Louisiana

Louisiana State University and Agricultural & Mechanical College, BM
Louisiana Tech University, BMD
Southern University and Agricultural and Mechanical College, B
Tulane University, BM
University of Louisiana at Lafayette, B

Maine

University of Maine at Augusta, B

Maryland

Morgan State University, M
University of Maryland, College Park, BM

Massachusetts

Boston Architectural College, BM
Hampshire College, B
Harvard University, MD
Massachusetts College of Art and Design, BM
Massachusetts Institute of Technology, BMD
Northeastern University, BM
Smith College, B
University of Massachusetts Amherst, BM
Wellesley College, B
Wentworth Institute of Technology, BM

Michigan

Andrews University, BM
Grand Rapids Community College, A
Lawrence Technological University, BM
University of Detroit Mercy, B
University of Michigan, BMD

Minnesota

Dunwoody College of Technology, B
University of Minnesota, Twin Cities Campus, BM

Mississippi

Copiah-Lincoln Community College, A
Mississippi State University, B
Northeast Mississippi Community College, A

Missouri

Drury University, BM
University of Missouri, M
University of Missouri - Kansas City, B
Washington University in St. Louis, BM

Montana

Montana State University, M

Nebraska

University of Nebraska - Lincoln, BMD

Nevada

Truckee Meadows Community College, A
University of Nevada, Las Vegas, BMO

New Hampshire

Keene State College, B

New Jersey

Brookdale Community College, A
Kean University, B
New Jersey Institute of Technology, BMD
Princeton University, BMD

New Mexico

University of New Mexico, BMD

New York

Barnard College, B
City College of the City University of New York, BM
Columbia University, BMD
Columbia University, School of General Studies, B
Cooper Union for the Advancement of Science and Art, BM
Cornell University, BMD
Hobart and William Smith Colleges, B
Ithaca College, B
Morrisville State College, A
New York Institute of Technology, BM
Pratt Institute, BM
Rensselaer Polytechnic Institute, BMD
Rochester Institute of Technology, M
State University of New York College of Technology at Alfred, B
Syracuse University, BM
University at Buffalo, the State University of New York, BM

North Carolina

North Carolina State University, BM
The University of North Carolina at Charlotte, BM
The University of North Carolina at Greensboro, MO

North Dakota

North Dakota State University, M

Ohio

Kent State University, BM
Miami University, BM
Miami University Hamilton, B
The Ohio State University, BMD
University of Cincinnati, BM

Oklahoma

Oklahoma State University, B
University of Oklahoma, BM

Oregon

Portland State University, BM
University of Oregon, BM

Pennsylvania

Carnegie Mellon University, BMD
Drexel University, B
Harrisburg Area Community College, A
Lehigh University, B
Marywood University, BM
Penn State University Park, BMD
Philadelphia University, BM
Temple University, BM
University of Pennsylvania, BMDO

Rhode Island

Rhode Island School of Design, BM
Roger Williams University, BM

South Carolina

Clemson University, BM

South Dakota

South Dakota State University, B

Tennessee

University of Memphis, BM
The University of Tennessee, BM

Texas

Clarendon College, A
Kilgore College, A
Panola College, A
Prairie View A&M University, BM
Rice University, BMD
Texas A&M University, BMDO
Texas Tech University, BMD
University of Houston, BM
The University of Texas at Arlington, BM
The University of Texas at Austin, BM
The University of Texas at San Antonio, BM

Utah

University of Utah, BM

Vermont

Bennington College, B
Middlebury College, B
Norwich University, B

Virginia

Hampton University, BM
University of Virginia, B
Virginia Polytechnic Institute and State University, BMD

Washington

University of Washington, BMDO
Washington State University, BM

Wisconsin

University of Wisconsin - Milwaukee, BMDO

U.S. Territories: Puerto Rico

Inter American University of Puerto Rico, San Germán Campus, B
Polytechnic University of Puerto Rico, B
University of Puerto Rico, Río Piedras Campus, M

Canada

Alberta

University of Calgary, M

British Columbia

The University of British Columbia, M

Manitoba

University of Manitoba, BM

Maritime Provinces: Nova Scotia

Dalhousie University, BM

Ontario

Carleton University, BM
Laurentian University, B
Ryerson University, B
University of Toronto, BM
University of Waterloo, BM

Quebec

McGill University, MDO
Université Laval, BM
Université de Montréal, B

ARCHITECTURE AND RELATED SERVICES

United States

Arizona

The University of Arizona, B

Connecticut

Connecticut College, B

Illinois

School of the Art Institute of Chicago, B
University of Illinois at Chicago, B
University of Illinois at Urbana - Champaign, B

Kansas

Garden City Community College, A

Kentucky

Sullivan College of Technology and Design, A

Louisiana

University of Louisiana at Lafayette, B

Massachusetts

Mount Holyoke College, B

Michigan

Northern Michigan University, B

Missouri

Washington University in St. Louis, B

New Jersey

New Jersey Institute of Technology, B

New York

Columbia University, B
Eugene Lang College of Liberal Arts, B
Parsons School of Design, B
State University of New York College of Technology
    at Delhi, B

Ohio

Case Western Reserve University, B

Tennessee

Lipscomb University, B

Texas

Abilene Christian University, A

Utah

LDS Business College, A
University of Utah, B

ARCHIVES/ARCHIVAL ADMIN-ISTRATION

United States

California

University of California, Los Angeles, M
University of California, Riverside, M

Georgia

Clayton State University, M

Massachusetts

University of Massachusetts Boston, M

Michigan

University of Michigan, M
Wayne State University, O

New Jersey

Montclair State University, M

New York

Columbia University, M
New York University, MO
Pratt Institute, O
University of Rochester, M

Oklahoma

University of Oklahoma, M

Pennsylvania

Drexel University, M

South Carolina

University of South Carolina, M

Tennessee

Middle Tennessee State University, O

Wisconsin

University of Wisconsin - Milwaukee, O

Canada

British Columbia

The University of British Columbia, MDO

Manitoba

University of Manitoba, M

AREA STUDIES

United States

Alaska

University of Alaska Fairbanks, B

Arizona

Coconino Community College, A

California

Cabrillo College, A
Fullerton College, A
Stanford University, B
University of California, Santa Barbara, B

Illinois

Illinois Wesleyan University, B
Lake Forest College, B
Northwestern University, B
University of Illinois at Urbana - Champaign, B

Massachusetts

Bridgewater State University, B
Williams College, B

Michigan

Eastern Michigan University, B
University of Michigan - Dearborn, B

Minnesota

Augsburg College, B

Missouri

Washington University in St. Louis, B

Nevada

Nevada State College, B

New Jersey

Ramapo College of New Jersey, B

New York

Hofstra University, B
New York University, B
Queens College of the City University of New York,
    B
St. Francis College, B
State University of New York at Plattsburgh, B

Ohio

Wright State University, B

Oklahoma

Northeastern State University, B
University of Oklahoma, B

Pennsylvania

Gannon University, B
Gettysburg College, B
Lycoming College, B
Millersville University of Pennsylvania, B
University of Pittsburgh, B

Utah

Utah State University, B

Vermont

Castleton University, B
Marlboro College, B

Virginia

University of Virginia, B
Virginia Commonwealth University, B

Washington

University of Washington, B

Wisconsin

College of Menominee Nation, A

Canada

Alberta

University of Alberta, B

ARMY JROTC/ROTC

United States

Alabama

Jacksonville State University, B

California

Sacramento City College, A

Florida

Jacksonville University, B

Idaho

Brigham Young University - Idaho, A

Iowa

The University of Iowa, B

Minnesota

Minnesota State University Mankato, B

New Mexico

New Mexico Military Institute, A

North Carolina

Campbell University, B
Methodist University, A

Pennsylvania

La Salle University, B

Virginia

Hampton University, B

Washington

Northwest University, B

ART/ART STUDIES, GENERAL

United States

Alabama

Alabama Southern Community College, A
Alabama State University, B
Athens State University, B
Auburn University at Montgomery, B
Birmingham-Southern College, B
Jacksonville State University, B
Judson College, B
Samford University, B
Stillman College, B
Troy University, B
The University of Alabama at Birmingham, B
The University of Alabama in Huntsville, B
University of Mobile, B

University of Montevallo, B
University of North Alabama, B
University of South Alabama, B

Alaska

University of Alaska Anchorage, B
University of Alaska Fairbanks, B

Arizona

Arizona State University at the Tempe campus, B
Cochise County Community College District, A
Diné College, A
Eastern Arizona College, A
Mesa Community College, A
Mohave Community College, A
Phoenix College, A

Arkansas

Arkansas State University, B
Arkansas Tech University, B
Henderson State University, B
Hendrix College, B
Lyon College, B
National Park College, A
Southern Arkansas University - Magnolia, B
University of Arkansas, B
University of Arkansas - Fort Smith, B
University of Arkansas at Little Rock, B
University of Arkansas at Monticello, B
University of Arkansas at Pine Bluff, B
University of Central Arkansas, B
Williams Baptist College, B

California

Allan Hancock College, A
American River College, A
Antelope Valley College, A
Bakersfield College, A
Berkeley City College, A
Biola University, B
Butte College, A
Cabrillo College, A
California College of the Arts, B
California Lutheran University, B
California State Polytechnic University, Pomona, B
California State University, Bakersfield, B
California State University Channel Islands, B
California State University, Chico, B
California State University, Dominguez Hills, B
California State University, Fresno, B
California State University, Fullerton, B
California State University, Long Beach, B
California State University, Los Angeles, B
California State University, Monterey Bay, B
California State University, Northridge, B
California State University, Sacramento, B
California State University, San Bernardino, B
California State University, Stanislaus, B
Cañada College, A
Cerritos College, A
Cerro Coso Community College, A
Chabot College, A
Chaffey College, A
Chapman University, B
Citrus College, A
College of Alameda, A
College of the Canyons, A
College of the Desert, A
College of Marin, A
College of San Mateo, A
College of the Sequoias, A
College of the Siskiyous, A
Columbia College, A
Concordia University Irvine, B
Contra Costa College, A
Copper Mountain College, A
Cosumnes River College, A
Crafton Hills College, A
Cuesta College, A
Cypress College, A
De Anza College, A
Dominican University of California, B
East Los Angeles College, A
El Camino College, A
Evergreen Valley College, A
Folsom Lake College, A

Foothill College, A
Fresno City College, A
Fullerton College, A
Gavilan College, A
Glendale Community College, A
Golden West College, A
Grossmont College, A
Hartnell College, A
Humboldt State University, B
Imperial Valley College, A
Irvine Valley College, A
La Sierra University, B
Laguna College of Art & Design, B
Lake Tahoe Community College, A
Laney College, A
Lassen Community College District, A
Long Beach City College, A
Los Angeles City College, A
Los Angeles Pierce College, A
Los Angeles Valley College, A
Los Medanos College, A
Mendocino College, A
Merced College, A
MiraCosta College, A
Mission College, A
Modesto Junior College, A
Monterey Peninsula College, A
Moorpark College, A
Mount Saint Mary's University, B
Mt. San Jacinto College, A
Napa Valley College, A
National University, B
Notre Dame de Namur University, B
Occidental College, B
Ohlone College, A
Orange Coast College, A
Otis College of Art and Design, B
Oxnard College, A
Palomar College, A
Pasadena City College, A
Pepperdine University, B
Pitzer College, B
Pomona College, B
Porterville College, A
Reedley College, A
Sacramento City College, A
Saddleback College, A
Saint Katherine College, B
Saint Mary's College of California, B
San Bernardino Valley College, A
San Diego City College, A
San Diego Mesa College, A
San Diego Miramar College, A
San Diego State University, B
San Francisco State University, B
San Joaquin Delta College, A
San Jose City College, A
San Jose State University, B
Santa Ana College, A
Santa Monica College, A
Santa Rosa Junior College, A
Santiago Canyon College, A
Scripps College, B
Shasta College, A
Sierra College, A
Skyline College, A
Solano Community College, A
Sonoma State University, B
Southwestern College, A
Stanford University, B
Taft College, A
University of California, Berkeley, B
University of California, Los Angeles, B
University of California, Riverside, B
University of California, San Diego, B
University of California, Santa Cruz, B
University of La Verne, B
University of the Pacific, B
University of San Diego, B
University of San Francisco, B
University of Southern California, B
Victor Valley College, A
West Hills Community College, A
West Los Angeles College, A
West Valley College, A
Westmont College, B

Whittier College, B
William Jessup University, B
Yuba College, A

Colorado

Colorado Mesa University, B
Fort Lewis College, B
Metropolitan State University of Denver, B
Northeastern Junior College, A
Regis University, B
University of Denver, B
Western State Colorado University, B

Connecticut

Albertus Magnus College, B
Central Connecticut State University, B
Housatonic Community College, A
Naugatuck Valley Community College, A
Northwestern Connecticut Community College, A
Norwalk Community College, A
Quinebaug Valley Community College, A
Sacred Heart University, B
Trinity College, B
Tunxis Community College, A
Western Connecticut State University, B
Yale University, B

Delaware

Delaware State University, B
University of Delaware, B

District of Columbia

The Catholic University of America, B
The George Washington University, B
Howard University, B
University of the District of Columbia, B

Florida

Broward College, A
Chipola College, A
College of Central Florida, A
Eastern Florida State College, A
Florida Atlantic University, B
Florida Gulf Coast University, B
Florida International University, B
Jacksonville University, B
Miami Dade College, A
Palm Beach State College, A
Pensacola State College, A
Rollins College, B
St. Johns River State College, A
South Florida State College, A
State College of Florida Manatee-Sarasota, A
Stetson University, B
University of Central Florida, B
University of Miami, B
University of North Florida, B
University of South Florida, B
University of South Florida, St. Petersburg, B
The University of Tampa, B
University of West Florida, B

Georgia

Abraham Baldwin Agricultural College, A
Albany State University, B
Armstrong State University, B
Bainbridge State College, A
Berry College, B
Clark Atlanta University, B
College of Coastal Georgia, A
Darton State College, A
Georgia College & State University, B
Georgia Highlands College, A
Georgia Southern University, B
Georgia Southwestern State University, B
Gordon State College, A
Kennesaw State University, B
Mercer University, B
Middle Georgia State University, A
Morehouse College, B
Oglethorpe University, B
Piedmont College, B
Reinhardt University, B
Shorter University, B
Spelman College, B

University of Georgia, B
University of North Georgia, B
University of West Georgia, B
Valdosta State University, B
Young Harris College, B

Hawaii

Brigham Young University - Hawaii, B
University of Hawaii at Hilo, B
University of Hawaii at Manoa, B

Idaho

Brigham Young University - Idaho, B
The College of Idaho, B
College of Southern Idaho, A
Idaho State University, B
North Idaho College, A
Northwest Nazarene University, B
University of Idaho, B

Illinois

American Academy of Art, B
Augustana College, B
Aurora University, B
Black Hawk College, A
Blackburn College, B
Bradley University, B
Chicago State University, B
City Colleges of Chicago, Malcolm X College, A
City Colleges of Chicago, Wilbur Wright College, A
College of Lake County, A
Concordia University Chicago, B
DePaul University, B
Eastern Illinois University, B
Elmhurst College, B
Eureka College, B
Governors State University, B
Greenville College, B
Harper College, A
Illinois College, B
Illinois State University, B
Illinois Wesleyan University, B
John A. Logan College, A
Judson University, B
Kankakee Community College, A
Kishwaukee College, A
Knox College, B
Lake Forest College, B
Lewis and Clark Community College, A
Lewis University, B
MacMurray College, B
McKendree University, B
Monmouth College, B
Morton College, A
North Central College, B
North Park University, B
Northeastern Illinois University, B
Northern Illinois University, B
Northwestern University, B
Olivet Nazarene University, B
Parkland College, A
Rockford University, B
Saint Xavier University, B
Sauk Valley Community College, A
School of the Art Institute of Chicago, B
Southern Illinois University Carbondale, B
Southern Illinois University Edwardsville, B
Spoon River College, A
Triton College, A
Western Illinois University, B
Wheaton College, B

Indiana

Ball State University, B
Bethel College, B
Earlham College, B
Goshen College, B
Grace College, B
Hanover College, B
Holy Cross College, B
Huntington University, B
Indiana State University, B
Indiana University Bloomington, B
Indiana University East, B
Indiana University Kokomo, B

Indiana University - Purdue University Fort Wayne, B
Indiana University South Bend, B
Indiana University Southeast, B
Indiana Wesleyan University, AB
Manchester University, B
Oakland City University, AB
Saint Mary's College, B
Taylor University, B
University of Evansville, B
University of Indianapolis, B
University of Southern Indiana, B
Valparaiso University, B
Vincennes University, A
Wabash College, B

Iowa

Briar Cliff University, B
Buena Vista University, B
Central College, B
Coe College, B
Cornell College, B
Drake University, B
Graceland University, B
Grinnell College, B
Iowa State University of Science and Technology, B
Iowa Wesleyan University, B
Luther College, B
Mount Mercy University, B
Northwestern College, B
St. Ambrose University, B
Simpson College, B
The University of Iowa, B
University of Northern Iowa, B
Upper Iowa University, B
Wartburg College, B

Kansas

Allen Community College, A
Barton County Community College, A
Benedictine College, B
Butler Community College, A
Central Christian College of Kansas, AB
Cowley County Community College and Area Vocational - Technical School, A
Dodge City Community College, A
Emporia State University, B
Fort Hays State University, B
Friends University, B
Haskell Indian Nations University, A
Independence Community College, A
Kansas State University, B
Labette Community College, A
McPherson College, B
Newman University, B
Ottawa University, B
Pittsburg State University, B
Pratt Community College, A
Sterling College, B
University of Saint Mary, B
Washburn University, B

Kentucky

Berea College, B
Brescia University, B
Campbellsville University, B
Eastern Kentucky University, B
Kentucky Wesleyan College, B
Transylvania University, B
University of Pikeville, B

Louisiana

Centenary College of Louisiana, B
Dillard University, B
Louisiana College, B
Louisiana State University in Shreveport, B
Louisiana Tech University, B
McNeese State University, B
Nicholls State University, B
Southeastern Louisiana University, B
Tulane University, B
University of Louisiana at Lafayette, B
Xavier University of Louisiana, B

Maine

Bates College, B
Colby College, B
College of the Atlantic, B
University of Maine at Farmington, B
University of Maine at Machias, B
University of Maine at Presque Isle, B

Maryland

Bowie State University, B
Carroll Community College, A
Frederick Community College, A
Hood College, B
Howard Community College, A
Loyola University Maryland, B
Maryland Institute College of Art, B
McDaniel College, B
Montgomery College, A
Morgan State University, B
Mount St. Mary's University, B
Notre Dame of Maryland University, B
St. Mary's College of Maryland, B
Salisbury University, B
Towson University, B
Washington College, B

Massachusetts

Bard College at Simon's Rock, B
Bunker Hill Community College, A
Framingham State University, B
Gordon College, B
Greenfield Community College, A
Holyoke Community College, A
Lesley University, B
Massachusetts College of Liberal Arts, B
Middlesex Community College, A
Mount Wachusett Community College, A
Northeastern University, B
Salem State University, B
School of the Museum of Fine Arts, Boston, B
Simmons College, B
Smith College, B
Springfield College, B
University of Massachusetts Boston, B
Westfield State University, B
Williams College, B

Michigan

Adrian College, B
Albion College, B
Alma College, B
Andrews University, B
Aquinas College, B
Calvin College, B
Central Michigan University, B
Concordia University Ann Arbor, B
Eastern Michigan University, B
Finlandia University, B
Grand Rapids Community College, A
Henry Ford College, A
Hillsdale College, B
Kalamazoo College, B
Kirtland Community College, A
Lake Michigan College, A
Lansing Community College, A
Marygrove College, B
Michigan State University, B
Mid Michigan Community College, A
Monroe County Community College, A
Muskegon Community College, A
Northern Michigan University, AB
Northwestern Michigan College, A
Oakland Community College, A
Olivet College, B
Saginaw Valley State University, B
Siena Heights University, B
Spring Arbor University, B
University of Michigan, B
Wayne State University, B
Western Michigan University, B

Minnesota

Bemidji State University, B
Bethany Lutheran College, B
Bethel University, B

College of Saint Benedict, B
The College of St. Scholastica, B
Concordia College, B
Concordia University, St. Paul, B
Gustavus Adolphus College, B
Macalester College, B
Minnesota State Community and Technical College, A
Minnesota State University Mankato, B
Minnesota State University Moorhead, B
St. Catherine University, B
St. Cloud State University, B
Saint John's University, B
St. Olaf College, B
Southwest Minnesota State University, B
University of Minnesota, Duluth, B
University of Minnesota, Twin Cities Campus, B
Vermilion Community College, A
Winona State University, B

Mississippi

Belhaven University, B
East Mississippi Community College, A
Holmes Community College, A
Itawamba Community College, A
Mississippi Gulf Coast Community College, A
Mississippi Valley State University, B
Northwest Mississippi Community College, A
Tougaloo College, B
William Carey University, B

Missouri

Avila University, B
Columbia College, B
Crowder College, A
Culver-Stockton College, B
Evangel University, B
Fontbonne University, B
Hannibal-LaGrange University, AB
Lindenwood University, B
Missouri Southern State University, B
Missouri State University, B
Missouri Valley College, B
Southeast Missouri State University, B
Southwest Baptist University, B
Truman State University, B
University of Missouri, B
University of Missouri - Kansas City, B
Washington University in St. Louis, B
Webster University, B
William Jewell College, B
William Woods University, B

Montana

Fort Peck Community College, A
Montana State University, B
Montana State University Billings, B
Rocky Mountain College, B
University of Great Falls, B
University of Montana, B
The University of Montana Western, B

Nebraska

Bellevue University, B
Chadron State College, B
College of Saint Mary, B
Concordia University, Nebraska, B
Creighton University, B
Doane University, B
Hastings College, B
Midland University, B
Nebraska Wesleyan University, B
Northeast Community College, A
Peru State College, B
Union College, B
University of Nebraska at Kearney, B
University of Nebraska at Omaha, B
Wayne State College, B
Western Nebraska Community College, A

Nevada

College of Southern Nevada, A
Sierra Nevada College, B
University of Nevada, Las Vegas, B
University of Nevada, Reno, B

New Hampshire

Colby-Sawyer College, B
Franklin Pierce University, B
New England College, B
Plymouth State University, B
Saint Anselm College, B
University of New Hampshire, B

New Jersey

Caldwell University, B
The College of New Jersey, B
College of Saint Elizabeth, B
Essex County College, A
Felician University, AB
Georgian Court University, B
Kean University, B
Mercer County Community College, A
Monmouth University, B
New Jersey City University, B
New Jersey Institute of Technology, B
Rider University, B
Rowan College at Burlington County, A
Rowan University, B
Rutgers University - Camden, B
Rutgers University - New Brunswick, B
Rutgers University - Newark, B
Saint Peter's University, B
Thomas Edison State University, B
William Paterson University of New Jersey, B

New Mexico

Central New Mexico Community College, A
Eastern New Mexico University, AB
New Mexico Highlands University, B
New Mexico Junior College, A
New Mexico Military Institute, A
Santa Fe Community College, A
University of New Mexico, B
University of New Mexico - Gallup, A
University of New Mexico - Taos, A
Western New Mexico University, B

New York

Alfred University, B
Binghamton University, State University of New York, B
Bronx Community College of the City University of New York, A
Brooklyn College of the City University of New York, B
Buffalo State College, State University of New York, B
Cayuga County Community College, A
City College of the City University of New York, B
Colgate University, B
The College at Brockport, State University of New York, B
Columbia-Greene Community College, A
Concordia College - New York, B
Corning Community College, A
Daemen College, B
Dutchess Community College, A
Elmira College, B
Eugene Lang College of Liberal Arts, B
Fulton-Montgomery Community College, A
Hartwick College, B
Herkimer County Community College, A
Hobart and William Smith Colleges, B
Houghton College, B
Hunter College of the City University of New York, B
Ithaca College, B
Kingsborough Community College of the City University of New York, A
Lehman College of the City University of New York, B
Marist College, B
Marymount Manhattan College, B
Mohawk Valley Community College, A
Monroe Community College, A
Nassau Community College, A
Nazareth College of Rochester, B
Onondaga Community College, A
Parsons School of Design, B
Pratt Institute, B
Purchase College, State University of New York, B

Roberts Wesleyan College, B
Rockland Community College, A
St. Lawrence University, B
St. Thomas Aquinas College, B
Skidmore College, B
State University of New York College at Old Westbury, B
State University of New York College at Oneonta, B
State University of New York Empire State College, AB
State University of New York at Fredonia, B
State University of New York at Oswego, B
State University of New York at Plattsburgh, B
Stony Brook University, State University of New York, B
Suffolk County Community College, A
University at Albany, State University of New York, B
University at Buffalo, the State University of New York, B
Villa Maria College, B
Wagner College, B
Wells College, B
York College of the City University of New York, B

North Carolina

Appalachian State University, B
Campbell University, B
Central Piedmont Community College, A
College of The Albemarle, A
Davidson College, B
Duke University, B
Elon University, B
Fayetteville State University, B
Gardner-Webb University, B
Greensboro College, B
Guilford College, B
Mars Hill University, B
Methodist University, AB
North Carolina Agricultural and Technical State University, B
North Carolina Central University, B
St. Andrews University, B
Sandhills Community College, A
Southeastern Community College, A
University of Mount Olive, B
University of North Carolina at Asheville, B
The University of North Carolina at Charlotte, B
The University of North Carolina at Greensboro, B
Warren Wilson College, B
Western Carolina University, B
Winston-Salem State University, B

North Dakota

Dickinson State University, B
Minot State University, B
North Dakota State University, B
Turtle Mountain Community College, A
United Tribes Technical College, A
University of Jamestown, B
University of North Dakota, B
Valley City State University, B

Ohio

Baldwin Wallace University, B
Bluffton University, B
Bowling Green State University, B
Capital University, B
Central State University, B
Cleveland State University, B
Denison University, B
Edison Community College, A
Hiram College, B
Lorain County Community College, A
Lourdes University, AB
Marietta College, B
Miami University, B
Miami University Hamilton, B
Miami University Middletown, A
Mount St. Joseph University, AB
Mount Vernon Nazarene University, B
Muskingum University, B
Notre Dame College, B
Oberlin College, B
Ohio Dominican University, B
Ohio Northern University, B
The Ohio State University, B

Ohio University, B
Otterbein University, B
Shawnee State University, B
Sinclair Community College, A
Tiffin University, B
The University of Findlay, B
University of Rio Grande, AB
Walsh University, B
Wittenberg University, B
Wright State University, B
Xavier University, B
Youngstown State University, B

Oklahoma

Bacone College, A
Cameron University, B
Connors State College, A
East Central University, B
Eastern Oklahoma State College, A
Northeastern Oklahoma Agricultural and Mechanical
  College, A
Northeastern State University, B
Oklahoma Baptist University, B
Oklahoma Christian University, B
Oklahoma City Community College, A
Oklahoma City University, B
Oklahoma Panhandle State University, B
Oklahoma State University, B
Oklahoma State University, Oklahoma City, A
Oral Roberts University, B
Redlands Community College, A
Rose State College, A
Seminole State College, A
Southeastern Oklahoma State University, B
University of Central Oklahoma, B
University of Science and Arts of Oklahoma, B

Oregon

Central Oregon Community College, A
Eastern Oregon University, B
George Fox University, B
Lewis & Clark College, B
Linfield College, B
Linn-Benton Community College, A
Marylhurst University, B
Oregon State University, B
Oregon State University - Cascades, B
Pacific University, B
Portland State University, B
Reed College, B
Southern Oregon University, B
Umpqua Community College, A
University of Oregon, B
Western Oregon University, B
Willamette University, B

Pennsylvania

Albright College, B
Allegheny College, B
Arcadia University, B
Bucknell University, B
California University of Pennsylvania, B
Carnegie Mellon University, B
Cedar Crest College, B
Cheyney University of Pennsylvania, B
Clarion University of Pennsylvania, B
Community College of Allegheny County, A
Community College of Philadelphia, A
Douglas Education Center, A
Edinboro University of Pennsylvania, B
Gettysburg College, B
Haverford College, B
Indiana University of Pennsylvania, B
Juniata College, B
Lafayette College, B
Lebanon Valley College, B
Lehigh Carbon Community College, A
Lehigh University, B
Lock Haven University of Pennsylvania, B
Lycoming College, B
Mercyhurst University, B
Millersville University of Pennsylvania, B
Montgomery County Community College, A
Moravian College, B
Muhlenberg College, B
Penn State Abington, B

Penn State Altoona, B
Penn State Beaver, B
Penn State Berks, B
Penn State Brandywine, B
Penn State DuBois, B
Penn State Erie, The Behrend College, B
Penn State Fayette, The Eberly Campus, B
Penn State Greater Allegheny, B
Penn State Hazleton, B
Penn State Lehigh Valley, B
Penn State Mont Alto, B
Penn State New Kensington, B
Penn State Schuylkill, B
Penn State Shenango, B
Penn State University Park, B
Penn State Wilkes-Barre, B
Penn State Worthington Scranton, B
Penn State York, B
Reading Area Community College, A
Saint Joseph's University, B
Shippensburg University of Pennsylvania, B
Slippery Rock University of Pennsylvania, B
Susquehanna University, B
Temple University, B
Thiel College, B
Ursinus College, B
Washington & Jefferson College, B
Waynesburg University, B
West Chester University of Pennsylvania, B
Wilson College, B

Rhode Island

Brown University, B
Community College of Rhode Island, A
Roger Williams University, B

South Carolina

Anderson University, B
Benedict College, B
Claflin University, B
Clemson University, B
Columbia College, B
Converse College, B
Erskine College, B
Francis Marion University, B
Furman University, B
Lander University, B
Newberry College, B
Presbyterian College, B
Winthrop University, B

South Dakota

Augustana University, B
Black Hills State University, B
Northern State University, B
University of Sioux Falls, B

Tennessee

Austin Peay State University, B
Belmont University, B
Carson-Newman University, B
East Tennessee State University, B
Fisk University, B
Freed-Hardeman University, B
LeMoyne-Owen College, B
Lincoln Memorial University, B
Middle Tennessee State University, B
Nashville State Community College, A
Rhodes College, B
Roane State Community College, A
Southern Adventist University, B
Tennessee State University, B
Tennessee Technological University, B
Union University, B
University of Memphis, B
The University of Tennessee at Chattanooga, B
Watkins College of Art, Design, & Film, B

Texas

Alvin Community College, A
Amarillo College, A
Angelina College, A
Austin College, B
Austin Community College District, A
Baylor University, B

Clarendon College, A
Dallas Baptist University, B
Del Mar College, A
Grayson College, A
Hill College, A
Howard College, A
Howard Payne University, B
Kilgore College, A
Lee College, A
Midwestern State University, B
Navarro College, A
Northeast Texas Community College, A
Odessa College, A
Our Lady of the Lake University of San Antonio, B
Palo Alto College, A
Panola College, A
Paris Junior College, A
Rice University, B
St. Edward's University, B
St. Philip's College, A
Sam Houston State University, B
San Jacinto College District, A
South Plains College, A
Southwestern University, B
Stephen F. Austin State University, B
Sul Ross State University, B
Tarleton State University, B
Temple College, A
Texarkana College, A
Texas A&M University - Corpus Christi, B
Texas College, B
Texas Lutheran University, B
Texas Southmost College, A
Texas State University, B
Texas Tech University, B
Texas Woman's University, B
Trinity University, B
Trinity Valley Community College, A
Tyler Junior College, A
University of Dallas, B
University of Houston, B
University of the Incarnate Word, B
The University of Texas at Arlington, B
The University of Texas at Austin, B
The University of Texas of the Permian Basin, B
The University of Texas Rio Grande Valley, B
The University of Texas at San Antonio, B
The University of Texas at Tyler, B
Wayland Baptist University, B
West Texas A&M University, B
Western Texas College, A
Wharton County Junior College, A

Utah

Snow College, A
Southern Utah University, B
University of Utah, B
Utah State University, B
Weber State University, B
Westminster College, B

Vermont

Castleton University, B
Community College of Vermont, A
Goddard College, B
Green Mountain College, B
Johnson State College, B
Marlboro College, B
Saint Michael's College, B

Virginia

Averett University, B
Bluefield College, B
The College of William and Mary, B
Eastern Mennonite University, B
Ferrum College, B
Hampton University, B
Hollins University, B
James Madison University, B
Lynchburg College, B
Mary Baldwin College, B
Norfolk State University, B
Old Dominion University, B
Radford University, B
Randolph College, B
Roanoke College, B

Southern Virginia University, B
University of Virginia, B
The University of Virginia's College at Wise, B
Virginia Polytechnic Institute and State University, B
Virginia Wesleyan College, B
Virginia Western Community College, A

Washington

Central Washington University, B
Cornish College of the Arts, B
The Evergreen State College, B
Gonzaga University, B
Highline College, A
North Seattle College, A
Seattle Pacific University, B
Skagit Valley College, A
Spokane Falls Community College, A
University of Puget Sound, B
University of Washington, B
Walla Walla University, B
Western Washington University, B
Whitman College, B
Whitworth University, B

West Virginia

Davis & Elkins College, B
Marshall University, B
Shepherd University, B
University of Charleston, B
West Virginia State University, B
West Virginia University, B
West Virginia Wesleyan College, B

Wisconsin

Alverno College, B
Cardinal Stritch University, B
Carroll University, B
Concordia University Wisconsin, B
Edgewood College, B
Lakeland College, B
Mount Mary University, B
Ripon College, B
St. Norbert College, B
Silver Lake College of the Holy Family, B
University of Wisconsin - Eau Claire, B
University of Wisconsin - Green Bay, B
University of Wisconsin - La Crosse, B
University of Wisconsin - Madison, B
University of Wisconsin - Milwaukee, B
University of Wisconsin - Oshkosh, B
University of Wisconsin - Parkside, B
University of Wisconsin - Platteville, B
University of Wisconsin - River Falls, B
University of Wisconsin - Whitewater, B
Viterbo University, B
Wisconsin Lutheran College, B

Wyoming

Casper College, A
Central Wyoming College, A
Eastern Wyoming College, A
Laramie County Community College, A
Northwest College, A
Sheridan College, A
University of Wyoming, B
Western Wyoming Community College, A

U.S. Territories: American Samoa

American Samoa Community College, A

U.S. Territories: Puerto Rico

Inter American University of Puerto Rico, San
  Germán Campus, B
University of Puerto Rico, Río Piedras Campus, B

Canada

Alberta

Alberta College of Art & Design, B
University of Alberta, B
University of Calgary, B
University of Lethbridge, B

British Columbia

Simon Fraser University, B
Trinity Western University, B

Manitoba

Université de Saint-Boniface, B
University of Manitoba, B

Maritime Provinces: Nova Scotia

NSCAD University, B

Newfoundland and Labrador

Memorial University of Newfoundland, B

Ontario

Brock University, B
Lakehead University, B
McMaster University, B
Redeemer University College, B
The University of Western Ontario, B
University of Windsor, B
York University, B

Quebec

Bishop's University, B
Université de Montréal, B
Université du Québec à Chicoutimi, B
Université du Québec à Montréal, B
Université du Québec en Outaouais, B
Université du Québec à Trois-Rivières, B

ART EDUCATION

United States

Alabama

Alabama Agricultural and Mechanical University, M
Auburn University at Montgomery, M
Troy University, M
The University of Alabama at Birmingham, M

Arizona

Arizona State University at the Tempe campus, M
The University of Arizona, MD

Arkansas

Harding University, M
University of Arkansas at Little Rock, M

California

Academy of Art University, M
California State University, Long Beach, M
California State University, Los Angeles, M
California State University, Northridge, M
California State University, San Bernardino, M
Mills College, M

Colorado

The Colorado College, M
Colorado State University - Pueblo, M
Rocky Mountain College of Art + Design, M

Connecticut

Central Connecticut State University, MO
Southern Connecticut State University, M

Delaware

Delaware State University, M

District of Columbia

The George Washington University, M

Florida

Florida Atlantic University, M
Florida International University, M
Florida State University, MDO
University of Central Florida, M
University of Florida, M

Georgia

Columbus State University, M
Georgia State University, M
Kennesaw State University, M
Piedmont College, M
University of Georgia, MDO
University of North Georgia, M

Idaho

Boise State University, M
University of Idaho, M

Illinois

Eastern Illinois University, M
Lake Forest College, M
School of the Art Institute of Chicago, M
University of Illinois at Urbana - Champaign, MD
University of St. Francis, M

Indiana

Indiana University Bloomington, MD
Indiana University - Purdue University Indianapolis,
  M
Indiana University South Bend, M
Purdue University, D
University of Indianapolis, M

Iowa

The University of Iowa, M
University of Northern Iowa, M

Kansas

Pittsburg State University, M
The University of Kansas, M

Kentucky

Eastern Kentucky University, M
Morehead State University, M
Spalding University, M
University of Kentucky, M
University of Louisville, M
Western Kentucky University, M

Louisiana

University of Louisiana at Monroe, M

Maryland

Maryland Institute College of Art, M
Towson University, MO
University of Maryland, Baltimore County, M

Massachusetts

Anna Maria College, M
Boston University, M
Bridgewater State University, M
Fitchburg State University, MO
Harvard University, M
Lesley University, M
Massachusetts College of Art and Design, MO
Salem State University, M
School of the Museum of Fine Arts, Boston, M
Tufts University, M
University of Massachusetts Amherst, M
University of Massachusetts Dartmouth, M

Michigan

Eastern Michigan University, M
Wayne State University, MD
Western Michigan University, M

Minnesota

Minnesota State University Mankato, M
University of Minnesota, Twin Cities Campus, MD

Mississippi

Mississippi College, M
William Carey University, M

Missouri

Maryville University of Saint Louis, M
University of Missouri, MDO

Montana

University of Montana, M

Nebraska

University of Nebraska at Kearney, M

New Hampshire

New Hampshire Institute of Art, M
Plymouth State University, M

New Jersey

Kean University, M
Montclair State University, M
New Jersey City University, M

New Mexico

University of New Mexico, M

New York

Adelphi University, M
Brooklyn College of the City University of New York, M
Buffalo State College, State University of New York, M
The College of New Rochelle, M
The College of Saint Rose, MO
Hofstra University, MD
Long Island University - LIU Post, M
Manhattanville College, M
Nazareth College of Rochester, M
New York University, M
Pratt Institute, MO
Queens College of the City University of New York, M
Rochester Institute of Technology, M
School of Visual Arts, M
State University of New York at New Paltz, M
State University of New York at Oswego, M
Syracuse University, M

North Carolina

East Carolina University, M
Salem College, M
The University of North Carolina at Charlotte, M
The University of North Carolina at Pembroke, M

Ohio

Art Academy of Cincinnati, M
Bowling Green State University, M
Case Western Reserve University, M
Cleveland State University, M
Kent State University, M
Miami University, M
The Ohio State University, MD
University of Cincinnati, M
University of Rio Grande, M
The University of Toledo, M
Ursuline College, M

Oklahoma

Southwestern Oklahoma State University, M

Pennsylvania

Arcadia University, M
Carlow University, M
Chatham University, M
Edinboro University of Pennsylvania, M
Kutztown University of Pennsylvania, M
Mansfield University of Pennsylvania, M
Marywood University, M
Millersville University of Pennsylvania, M
Moore College of Art & Design, M
Penn State University Park, MDO
Temple University, M
The University of the Arts, M

Rhode Island

Rhode Island College, M
Rhode Island School of Design, M

South Carolina

Converse College, M
University of South Carolina, M
Winthrop University, M

Tennessee

Memphis College of Art, M
The University of Tennessee, M

Texas

Sul Ross State University, M
Texas Tech University, M
University of North Texas, M
The University of Texas at Austin, M
The University of Texas at El Paso, M

Utah

Brigham Young University, M
University of Utah, M

Vermont

Saint Michael's College, O

Virginia

Averett University, M
George Mason University, M
James Madison University, M
Virginia Commonwealth University, M

West Virginia

West Virginia University, M

Wisconsin

Carthage College, M
Concordia University Wisconsin, M
University of Wisconsin - Madison, M
University of Wisconsin - Milwaukee, M
University of Wisconsin - Superior, M

U.S. Territories: Puerto Rico

American University of Puerto Rico (Bayamon), M

Canada

British Columbia

Simon Fraser University, MD
The University of British Columbia, M
University of Victoria, MD

Quebec

Concordia University, MD

ART HISTORY, CRITICISM AND CONSERVATION

United States

Alabama

Birmingham-Southern College, B
The University of Alabama, BM
The University of Alabama at Birmingham, M

Arizona

Arizona State University at the Tempe campus, M
The University of Arizona, BMD

Arkansas

University of Arkansas at Little Rock, M

California

Academy of Art University, BM
California State Polytechnic University, Pomona, B
California State University, Chico, M
California State University, Dominguez Hills, B
California State University, East Bay, B
California State University, Fullerton, BM
California State University, Long Beach, BM
California State University, Los Angeles, M
California State University, Northridge, M
California State University, Stanislaus, B
Chapman University, B
De Anza College, A
Dominican University of California, BM
El Camino College, A
Foothill College, A

Humboldt State University, B
Loyola Marymount University, B
Mills College, B
Monterey Peninsula College, A
Pepperdine University, B
Pitzer College, B
Pomona College, B
Saint Mary's College of California, B
San Diego State University, BM
San Francisco Art Institute, BM
San Francisco State University, M
San Jose State University, BM
Santa Barbara City College, A
Santa Clara University, B
Santa Rosa Junior College, A
Scripps College, B
Skyline College, A
Sonoma State University, B
Stanford University, B
University of California, Berkeley, BD
University of California, Davis, BM
University of California, Irvine, B
University of California, Los Angeles, BMD
University of California, Riverside, BM
University of California, San Diego, BMD
University of California, Santa Barbara, BD
University of California, Santa Cruz, B
University of La Verne, B
University of the Pacific, B
University of Redlands, B
University of San Diego, B
University of San Francisco, B
University of Southern California, BMDO

Colorado

Adams State University, B
The Colorado College, B
Northeastern Junior College, A
Regis University, B
University of Colorado Boulder, BM
University of Denver, BM

Connecticut

Albertus Magnus College, B
Connecticut College, B
Fairfield University, B
Southern Connecticut State University, B
Trinity College, B
University of Connecticut, BM
University of Hartford, B
University of Saint Joseph, B
Wesleyan University, B
Yale University, BD

Delaware

University of Delaware, BMD

District of Columbia

American University, B
The Catholic University of America, B
Gallaudet University, B
The George Washington University, BM
Georgetown University, B
Howard University, M

Florida

Broward College, A
Flagler College, B
Florida International University, B
Florida Southern College, B
Florida State University, BMDO
Jacksonville University, B
New College of Florida, B
Palm Beach State College, A
Rollins College, B
South Florida State College, A
State College of Florida Manatee-Sarasota, A
Stetson University, B
University of Florida, BMD
University of Miami, BM
University of South Florida, BM
University of West Florida, B

Georgia

Agnes Scott College, B
Emory University, BD
Georgia State University, M
Kennesaw State University, B
Oglethorpe University, B
Savannah College of Art and Design, BM
University of Georgia, BM
Wesleyan College, B

Hawaii

University of Hawaii at Manoa, M

Idaho

Boise State University, B

Illinois

Augustana College, B
Bradley University, B
Columbia College Chicago, B
DePaul University, B
Dominican University, B
Illinois State University, M
Knox College, B
Lake Forest College, B
Loyola University Chicago, B
North Central College, B
Northern Illinois University, B
Northwestern University, BD
Principia College, B
Rockford University, B
School of the Art Institute of Chicago, BM
University of Chicago, BMD
University of Illinois at Chicago, BMD
University of Illinois at Urbana - Champaign, BMD

Indiana

DePauw University, B
Hanover College, B
Indiana University Bloomington, BMD
Indiana University - Purdue University Indianapolis, B
Marian University, B
Purdue University, B
University of Evansville, B
University of Notre Dame, BM
University of Saint Francis, B

Iowa

Clarke University, B
Coe College, B
Cornell College, B
Drake University, B
The University of Iowa, BMD
University of Northern Iowa, B

Kansas

Baker University, B
Fort Hays State University, B
The University of Kansas, BMD
Washburn University, B

Kentucky

Centre College, B
Thomas More College, AB
Transylvania University, B
University of Kentucky, BM
University of Louisville, BMD
Western Kentucky University, B

Louisiana

Louisiana State University and Agricultural & Mechanical College, M
Tulane University, BM
University of New Orleans, B

Maine

Bowdoin College, B
Colby College, B
University of Maine, B

Maryland

Goucher College, B
Johns Hopkins University, BMD
Loyola University Maryland, B
Maryland Institute College of Art, B
McDaniel College, B
Morgan State University, B
St. Mary's College of Maryland, B
Towson University, BM
University of Maryland, College Park, BMD

Massachusetts

Assumption College, B
Bard College at Simon's Rock, B
Boston College, B
Boston University, MDO
Brandeis University, B
Bridgewater State University, B
Clark University, B
College of the Holy Cross, B
Hampshire College, B
Harvard University, BD
Massachusetts College of Art and Design, B
Massachusetts Institute of Technology, D
Merrimack College, B
Mount Holyoke College, B
Salem State University, B
Smith College, B
Stonehill College, B
Tufts University, BM
University of Massachusetts Amherst, BM
University of Massachusetts Dartmouth, B
Wellesley College, B
Wheaton College, B
Williams College, BM

Michigan

Adrian College, B
Albion College, B
Aquinas College, B
Eastern Michigan University, B
Ferris State University, B
Grand Valley State University, B
Hope College, B
Kalamazoo College, B
Lansing Community College, A
Michigan State University, B
Muskegon Community College, A
Northern Michigan University, B
Oakland University, B
Siena Heights University, B
University of Michigan, BMD
University of Michigan - Dearborn, B
University of Michigan - Flint, B
Wayne State University, BM
Western Michigan University, B

Minnesota

Augsburg College, B
Carleton College, B
Gustavus Adolphus College, B
Hamline University, B
Minnesota State University Mankato, B
St. Catherine University, B
St. Cloud State University, B
St. Olaf College, B
University of Minnesota, Duluth, B
University of Minnesota, Morris, B
University of Minnesota, Twin Cities Campus, BMD
University of St. Thomas, BM
Vermilion Community College, A

Mississippi

Millsaps College, B
University of Mississippi, B

Missouri

Calvary Bible College and Theological Seminary, B
Drury University, B
Kansas City Art Institute, B
Lindenwood University, B
Missouri State University, B
Saint Louis University, B
Truman State University, B
University of Missouri, BMD
University of Missouri - Kansas City, BMD
University of Missouri - St. Louis, B
Washington University in St. Louis, BMD

Webster University, BM

Montana

Montana State University, M
University of Montana, BM

Nebraska

Hastings College, B
University of Nebraska - Lincoln, BM
University of Nebraska at Omaha, B

Nevada

University of Nevada, Las Vegas, B
University of Nevada, Reno, B

New Hampshire

Colby-Sawyer College, B
Dartmouth College, B
Plymouth State University, B

New Jersey

Drew University, B
Kean University, B
Mercer County Community College, A
Princeton University, B
Rutgers University - New Brunswick, BMDO
Saint Peter's University, B
Seton Hall University, B
William Paterson University of New Jersey, B

New Mexico

New Mexico State University, M
Santa Fe Community College, A
University of New Mexico, BMD

New York

Adelphi University, B
Bard College, B
Barnard College, B
Binghamton University, State University of New York, BMD
Borough of Manhattan Community College of the City University of New York, A
Brooklyn College of the City University of New York, BM
Buffalo State College, State University of New York, B
Canisius College, B
City College of the City University of New York, BM
Colgate University, B
The College of New Rochelle, B
Columbia University, BMD
Columbia University, School of General Studies, B
Cornell University, BD
Fashion Institute of Technology, M
Fordham University, B
Hamilton College, B
Hartwick College, B
Hobart and William Smith Colleges, B
Hofstra University, B
Hunter College of the City University of New York, BM
Ithaca College, B
Lehman College of the City University of New York, B
Long Island University - LIU Post, B
Manhattanville College, B
Marist College, B
Marymount Manhattan College, B
Nazareth College of Rochester, B
New York University, BMD
Pace University, B
Pratt Institute, BM
Purchase College, State University of New York, BM
Queens College of the City University of New York, BM
St. Bonaventure University, B
St. Lawrence University, B
Sarah Lawrence College, B
School of Visual Arts, M
Skidmore College, B
State University of New York College at Cortland, B
State University of New York College at Geneseo, B
State University of New York College at Oneonta, B
State University of New York College at Potsdam, B

State University of New York at Fredonia, B
State University of New York at New Paltz, B
Stony Brook University, State University of New York, BMD
Syracuse University, BM
University at Albany, State University of New York, B
University at Buffalo, the State University of New York, BM
University of Rochester, BMD
Vassar College, B
Wells College, B
York College of the City University of New York, B

North Carolina

Duke University, BMD
East Carolina University, B
Elon University, B
Mars Hill University, B
North Carolina State University, B
Queens University of Charlotte, B
Salem College, B
The University of North Carolina at Chapel Hill, BMD
The University of North Carolina at Charlotte, B
The University of North Carolina Wilmington, B
Wake Forest University, B

Ohio

Art Academy of Cincinnati, B
Bowling Green State University, BM
Case Western Reserve University, BMD
Cleveland State University, M
The College of Wooster, B
Columbus College of Art & Design, B
Denison University, B
Hiram College, B
John Carroll University, B
Kent State University, BM
Kenyon College, B
Lourdes University, B
Miami University, B
Oberlin College, B
The Ohio State University, BMD
Ohio University, BM
Ohio Wesleyan University, B
Terra State Community College, A
The University of Akron, B
University of Cincinnati, BM
University of Dayton, B
The University of Toledo, B
Ursuline College, B
Wright State University, B
Youngstown State University, B

Oklahoma

University of Central Oklahoma, B
University of Oklahoma, BMD
The University of Tulsa, B

Oregon

Lewis & Clark College, B
Portland State University, B
Umpqua Community College, A
University of Oregon, BMD
Willamette University, B

Pennsylvania

Allegheny College, B
Arcadia University, B
Bloomsburg University of Pennsylvania, B
Bryn Mawr College, BMD
Bucknell University, B
Bucks County Community College, A
Chatham University, B
Duquesne University, B
Franklin & Marshall College, B
Gettysburg College, B
Haverford College, B
Juniata College, B
La Salle University, B
Lafayette College, B
Lebanon Valley College, B
Lehigh University, B
Lycoming College, B
Mansfield University of Pennsylvania, B

Messiah College, B
Moore College of Art & Design, B
Muhlenberg College, B
Penn State Abington, B
Penn State Altoona, B
Penn State Beaver, B
Penn State Berks, B
Penn State Brandywine, B
Penn State DuBois, B
Penn State Erie, The Behrend College, B
Penn State Fayette, The Eberly Campus, B
Penn State Greater Allegheny, B
Penn State Hazleton, B
Penn State Lehigh Valley, B
Penn State Mont Alto, B
Penn State New Kensington, B
Penn State Schuylkill, B
Penn State Shenango, B
Penn State University Park, BMD
Penn State Wilkes-Barre, B
Penn State Worthington Scranton, B
Penn State York, B
Rosemont College, B
Saint Vincent College, B
Seton Hill University, B
Susquehanna University, B
Swarthmore College, B
Temple University, BMD
University of Pennsylvania, BMD
University of Pittsburgh, BMD
Ursinus College, B
Villanova University, B

Rhode Island

Brown University, BD
Providence College, B
Rhode Island College, B
Roger Williams University, BM
Salve Regina University, B
University of Rhode Island, B

South Carolina

College of Charleston, B
Converse College, B
Furman University, B
Presbyterian College, B
University of South Carolina, BM
Winthrop University, B
Wofford College, B

Tennessee

Belmont University, B
Sewanee: The University of the South, B
University of Memphis, BM
The University of Tennessee, B
Vanderbilt University, B

Texas

Baylor University, B
Rice University, BD
Southern Methodist University, BMD
Southwestern University, B
Stephen F. Austin State University, B
Sul Ross State University, M
Texas Christian University, BM
Texas State University, B
Texas Tech University, M
Trinity University, B
University of Dallas, B
University of Houston, BM
University of the Incarnate Word, B
University of North Texas, BM
The University of Texas at Arlington, B
The University of Texas at Austin, BMD
The University of Texas at San Antonio, BM
The University of Texas at Tyler, M

Utah

Southern Utah University, B
University of Utah, BM

Vermont

Bennington College, B
Castleton University, B
Marlboro College, B

Middlebury College, B
University of Vermont, B

Virginia

The College of William and Mary, B
George Mason University, BM
Hollins University, B
James Madison University, BM
Old Dominion University, B
Randolph College, B
Randolph-Macon College, B
Roanoke College, B
Sweet Briar College, B
University of Mary Washington, B
University of Richmond, B
University of Virginia, MD
Virginia Commonwealth University, BMD
Washington and Lee University, B

Washington

Eastern Washington University, B
Pacific Lutheran University, B
Seattle University, B
Skagit Valley College, A
University of Washington, BMD
Western Washington University, B
Whitman College, B

West Virginia

West Virginia University, BM

Wisconsin

Beloit College, B
Carthage College, B
Lawrence University, B
University of Wisconsin - Madison, BMD
University of Wisconsin - Milwaukee, BMO
University of Wisconsin - Superior, BM

Wyoming

University of Wyoming, B

U.S. Territories: Puerto Rico

Caribbean University, M
University of Puerto Rico, Mayagüez Campus, B
University of Puerto Rico, Río Piedras Campus, B

Canada

Alberta

University of Alberta, BM
University of Calgary, B
University of Lethbridge, B

British Columbia

The University of British Columbia, BMDO
The University of British Columbia - Okanagan Campus, B
University of Victoria, BMD

Manitoba

University of Manitoba, B
The University of Winnipeg, B

Maritime Provinces: New Brunswick

Mount Allison University, B

Maritime Provinces: Nova Scotia

NSCAD University, B

Newfoundland and Labrador

Memorial University of Newfoundland, B

Ontario

Carleton University, BM
McMaster University, B
Queen's University at Kingston, B
University of Guelph, B
University of Ottawa, B
University of Toronto, MD
University of Waterloo, B
The University of Western Ontario, B
University of Windsor, B

York University, BMD

Quebec

Concordia University, BMD
McGill University, BMD
Université Laval, ABMD
Université de Montréal, BMD
Université du Québec à Montréal, BMD

Saskatchewan

University of Regina, B
University of Saskatchewan, B

ART TEACHER EDUCATION

United States

Alabama

Birmingham-Southern College, B
Wallace State Community College, A

Arizona

Eastern Arizona College, A
The University of Arizona, B

Arkansas

Arkansas Tech University, B
Harding University, B
Henderson State University, B
Ouachita Baptist University, B
Southern Arkansas University - Magnolia, B
Williams Baptist College, B

California

Academy of Art University, B
Bakersfield College, A
California Lutheran University, B
California State University, Long Beach, B
Humboldt State University, B
Point Loma Nazarene University, B
Westmont College, B

Colorado

Adams State University, B
Colorado State University, B
Rocky Mountain College of Art + Design, B
University of Denver, B
Western State Colorado University, B

Connecticut

Central Connecticut State University, B
Southern Connecticut State University, B

Delaware

Delaware State University, B

District of Columbia

Gallaudet University, B
University of the District of Columbia, B

Florida

Broward College, A
Flagler College, B
Florida International University, B
Florida Southern College, B
Indian River State College, A
Jacksonville University, B
Nova Southeastern University, B
Palm Beach Atlantic University, B
Pensacola State College, A
South Florida State College, A
University of Central Florida, B
University of Florida, B
University of North Florida, B

Georgia

Armstrong State University, B
Berry College, B
Brenau University, B
Columbus State University, B
Darton State College, A
Georgia State University, B

Kennesaw State University, B
Piedmont College, B
University of North Georgia, B
Valdosta State University, B

Hawaii

Brigham Young University - Hawaii, B

Idaho

Boise State University, B
Brigham Young University - Idaho, B
Northwest Nazarene University, B
University of Idaho, B

Illinois

Augustana College, B
Blackburn College, B
Bradley University, B
City Colleges of Chicago, Harold Washington College, A
Concordia University Chicago, B
DePaul University, B
Elmhurst College, B
John A. Logan College, A
McKendree University, B
Millikin University, B
North Central College, B
Northern Illinois University, B
Parkland College, A
Saint Xavier University, B
School of the Art Institute of Chicago, B
Trinity Christian College, B
University of Illinois at Chicago, B
University of Illinois at Urbana - Champaign, B
University of St. Francis, B

Indiana

Goshen College, B
Grace College, B
Huntington University, B
Indiana State University, B
Indiana University Bloomington, B
Indiana University - Purdue University Fort Wayne, B
Indiana University - Purdue University Indianapolis, B
Indiana University South Bend, B
Indiana Wesleyan University, B
Manchester University, B
Purdue University, B
Saint Joseph's College, B
Saint Mary-of-the-Woods College, B
Saint Mary's College, B
Taylor University, B
University of Evansville, B
University of Indianapolis, B
University of Saint Francis, B
Valparaiso University, B
Vincennes University, A

Iowa

Buena Vista University, B
Clarke University, B
Coe College, B
Graceland University, B
Iowa Lakes Community College, A
Morningside College, B
Mount Mercy University, B
Northwestern College, B
St. Ambrose University, B
Simpson College, B
The University of Iowa, B
University of Northern Iowa, B
Upper Iowa University, B
Wartburg College, B

Kansas

Baker University, B
Benedictine College, B
Bethany College, B
Central Christian College of Kansas, AB
Fort Hays State University, B
Friends University, B
Kansas State University, B
Kansas Wesleyan University, B

Pratt Community College, A
The University of Kansas, B
Washburn University, B

Kentucky

Asbury University, B
Berea College, B
Brescia University, B
Campbellsville University, B
Kentucky Wesleyan College, B
Lindsey Wilson College, B
Thomas More College, B
Transylvania University, B
University of the Cumberlands, B
University of Kentucky, B

Louisiana

Louisiana College, B
Louisiana State University in Shreveport, B
Louisiana Tech University, B
Nicholls State University, B
Southern University and Agricultural and Mechanical College, B
Xavier University of Louisiana, B

Maine

University of Maine, B
University of Southern Maine, B

Maryland

Maryland Institute College of Art, B
Towson University, B
University of Maryland, College Park, B
University of Maryland Eastern Shore, B

Massachusetts

Anna Maria College, B
Boston University, B
Bridgewater State University, B
Framingham State University, B
Massachusetts College of Art and Design, B
Salem State University, B
University of Massachusetts Dartmouth, B

Michigan

Adrian College, B
Alma College, B
Andrews University, B
Calvin College, B
Central Michigan University, B
College for Creative Studies, B
Concordia University Ann Arbor, B
Eastern Michigan University, B
Ferris State University, B
Grand Valley State University, B
Hope College, B
Michigan State University, B
Muskegon Community College, A
Northern Michigan University, B
Olivet College, B
Saginaw Valley State University, B
Siena Heights University, B
Spring Arbor University, B
University of Michigan - Flint, B
Western Michigan University, B

Minnesota

Bemidji State University, B
Bethel University, B
Concordia College, B
Concordia University, St. Paul, B
Gustavus Adolphus College, B
Minnesota State University Mankato, B
Minnesota State University Moorhead, B
St. Catherine University, B
St. Cloud State University, B
Southwest Minnesota State University, B
University of Minnesota, Duluth, B
University of Northwestern - St. Paul, B
Vermilion Community College, A
Winona State University, B

Mississippi

Copiah-Lincoln Community College, A
Itawamba Community College, A

Jones County Junior College, A
Mississippi College, B
Mississippi Delta Community College, A
Mississippi Gulf Coast Community College, A
Mississippi University for Women, B
Northeast Mississippi Community College, A
William Carey University, B

Missouri

College of the Ozarks, B
Culver-Stockton College, B
Evangel University, B
Fontbonne University, B
Hannibal-LaGrange University, B
Lincoln University, B
Lindenwood University, B
Maryville University of Saint Louis, B
Missouri State University, B
Missouri Western State University, B
Northwest Missouri State University, B
Southeast Missouri State University, B
Southwest Baptist University, B
University of Central Missouri, B
University of Missouri, B
Washington University in St. Louis, B
William Woods University, B

Montana

Montana State University Billings, B
Rocky Mountain College, B
University of Great Falls, B
University of Montana, B
The University of Montana Western, B

Nebraska

Chadron State College, B
College of Saint Mary, B
Concordia University, Nebraska, B
Hastings College, B
Midland University, B
Peru State College, B
Union College, B
University of Nebraska at Omaha, B
Wayne State College, B
Western Nebraska Community College, A
York College, B

New Hampshire

Colby-Sawyer College, B
Franklin Pierce University, B
Plymouth State University, B

New Jersey

The College of New Jersey, B
New Jersey City University, B

New Mexico

New Mexico Junior College, A
University of New Mexico, B
Western New Mexico University, B

New York

Adelphi University, B
Alfred University, B
Brooklyn College of the City University of New York, B
Buffalo State College, State University of New York, B
City College of the City University of New York, B
The College of New Rochelle, B
Daemen College, B
Elmira College, B
Hofstra University, B
Houghton College, B
Ithaca College, B
Lehman College of the City University of New York, B
Long Island University - LIU Brooklyn, B
Long Island University - LIU Post, B
Manhattanville College, B
Molloy College, B
Nazareth College of Rochester, B
Pratt Institute, B
Queens College of the City University of New York, B

State University of New York at New Paltz, B
Syracuse University, B

North Carolina

Appalachian State University, B
Barton College, B
East Carolina University, B
Elizabeth City State University, B
Fayetteville State University, B
Greensboro College, B
Mars Hill University, B
Meredith College, B
Methodist University, B
North Carolina Agricultural and Technical State University, B
Sandhills Community College, A
The University of North Carolina at Greensboro, B
The University of North Carolina at Pembroke, B
Western Carolina University, B
Winston-Salem State University, B

North Dakota

Dickinson State University, B
Minot State University, B
Valley City State University, B

Ohio

Ashland University, B
Bowling Green State University, B
Capital University, B
Case Western Reserve University, B
Central State University, B
Kent State University, B
Miami University, B
Miami University Hamilton, B
Mount St. Joseph University, B
Mount Vernon Nazarene University, B
Muskingum University, B
Notre Dame College, B
Ohio Dominican University, B
Ohio Northern University, B
The Ohio State University, B
Ohio Wesleyan University, B
Otterbein University, B
Shawnee State University, B
The University of Akron, B
The University of Findlay, B
University of Rio Grande, B
Ursuline College, B
Wilmington College, B
Youngstown State University, B

Oklahoma

East Central University, B
Northeastern State University, B
Oral Roberts University, B
Southeastern Oklahoma State University, B
Southwestern Oklahoma State University, B
University of Central Oklahoma, B

Oregon

Pacific University, B
Umpqua Community College, A

Pennsylvania

Albright College, B
Arcadia University, B
Carlow University, B
Holy Family University, B
Keystone College, B
Kutztown University of Pennsylvania, B
Marywood University, B
Mercyhurst University, B
Messiah College, B
Moore College of Art & Design, B
Penn State Abington, B
Penn State Altoona, B
Penn State Beaver, B
Penn State Berks, B
Penn State Brandywine, B
Penn State DuBois, B
Penn State Erie, The Behrend College, B
Penn State Fayette, The Eberly Campus, B
Penn State Greater Allegheny, B
Penn State Hazleton, B

Penn State Lehigh Valley, B
Penn State Mont Alto, B
Penn State New Kensington, B
Penn State Schuylkill, B
Penn State Shenango, B
Penn State University Park, B
Penn State Wilkes-Barre, B
Penn State Worthington Scranton, B
Penn State York, B
Saint Joseph's University, B
Saint Vincent College, B
Seton Hill University, B
Slippery Rock University of Pennsylvania, B
Temple University, B
Washington & Jefferson College, B

Rhode Island

Rhode Island College, B

South Carolina

Anderson University, B
Benedict College, B
Claflin University, B
Coker College, B
Converse College, B
Francis Marion University, B
South Carolina State University, B
University of South Carolina, B
University of South Carolina Upstate, B

South Dakota

Augustana University, B
Dakota Wesleyan University, B
Northern State University, B
Sinte Gleska University, B
University of Sioux Falls, B
The University of South Dakota, B

Tennessee

Belmont University, B
Carson-Newman University, B
Lee University, B
Lincoln Memorial University, B
Lipscomb University, B
Middle Tennessee State University, B
Roane State Community College, A
Southern Adventist University, B
Tennessee Technological University, B
Union University, B
The University of Tennessee at Chattanooga, B

Texas

Abilene Christian University, B
Baylor University, B
Del Mar College, A
Hardin-Simmons University, B
Houston Baptist University, B
Howard Payne University, B
Lubbock Christian University, B
McLennan Community College, A
McMurry University, B
St. Edward's University, B
St. Mary's University, B
Texas Christian University, B
Texas Lutheran University, B
University of Mary Hardin-Baylor, B
The University of Texas at El Paso, B
Western Texas College, A

Utah

Southern Utah University, B
Utah Valley University, B
Weber State University, B

Vermont

Castleton University, B
Goddard College, B
Green Mountain College, B
Johnson State College, B
Saint Michael's College, B
University of Vermont, B

Virginia

Averett University, B
Emory & Henry College, B

Hampton University, B
Virginia Commonwealth University, B
Virginia Wesleyan College, B

Washington

Eastern Washington University, B
Heritage University, B
Walla Walla University, B
Western Washington University, B
Whitworth University, B

West Virginia

Bethany College, B
Concord University, B
Davis & Elkins College, B
Fairmont State University, B
West Liberty University, B
West Virginia Wesleyan College, B

Wisconsin

Alverno College, B
Beloit College, B
Carroll University, B
Concordia University Wisconsin, B
Edgewood College, B
Lawrence University, B
Mount Mary University, B
Silver Lake College of the Holy Family, B
University of Wisconsin - La Crosse, B
University of Wisconsin - Madison, B
University of Wisconsin - Milwaukee, B
University of Wisconsin - Oshkosh, B
University of Wisconsin - River Falls, B
University of Wisconsin - Stout, B
University of Wisconsin - Superior, B
University of Wisconsin - Whitewater, B
Viterbo University, B

Wyoming

Casper College, A

U.S. Territories: Puerto Rico

Escuela de Artes Plasticas y Diseño de Puerto
   Rico, B
Inter American University of Puerto Rico, San
   Germán Campus, B
Pontifical Catholic University of Puerto Rico, B

Canada
Alberta

University of Alberta, B
University of Calgary, B
University of Lethbridge, B

British Columbia

The University of British Columbia, B
University of Victoria, B

Maritime Provinces: New Brunswick

University of New Brunswick Fredericton, B

Maritime Provinces: Nova Scotia

Mount Saint Vincent University, B

Ontario

University of Windsor, B
York University, B

Quebec

Bishop's University, B
Concordia University, B
Université Laval, B
Université du Québec à Chicoutimi, B
Université du Québec à Trois-Rivières, B

Saskatchewan

University of Regina, B

ART THERAPY/THERAPIST

United States
Arizona

Prescott College, BM

Arkansas

Harding University, B

California

California Institute of Integral Studies, M
California State University, Los Angeles, M
Notre Dame de Namur University, MD

Colorado

Naropa University, BM

Connecticut

Albertus Magnus College, BM

District of Columbia

The George Washington University, MO
Howard University, B

Georgia

Georgia College & State University, M

Illinois

DePaul University, B
Millikin University, B
School of the Art Institute of Chicago, M
Southern Illinois University Edwardsville, M

Indiana

Indiana University - Purdue University Indianapolis,
   M
Indiana Wesleyan University, B
Saint Mary-of-the-Woods College, MO
University of Indianapolis, B
University of Saint Francis, B
Vincennes University, A

Kansas

Bethany College, B
Emporia State University, M
Ottawa University, M

Maryland

University of Maryland, College Park, M

Massachusetts

Anna Maria College, B
Emmanuel College, B
Lesley University, BMDO
Springfield College, BMO

Michigan

Marygrove College, B
Wayne State University, M

Nevada

Sierra Nevada College, B

New Jersey

Caldwell University, M

New York

The College of New Rochelle, BM
Hofstra University, M
Long Island University - LIU Post, BM
Nazareth College of Rochester, BM
New York University, M
Pratt Institute, M
St. Thomas Aquinas College, B
School of Visual Arts, M

North Carolina

Chowan University, B

Ohio

Capital University, B
Ursuline College, BM

Oregon

Marylhurst University, MO

Pennsylvania

Arcadia University, B
Carlow University, B
Cedar Crest College, BM
Drexel University, MO
Edinboro University of Pennsylvania, M
Marywood University, BMO
Mercyhurst University, B
Seton Hill University, BM

South Carolina

Converse College, B

Tennessee

Lipscomb University, B
Southern Adventist University, B

Texas

Houston Baptist University, B

West Virginia

West Virginia Wesleyan College, B

Wisconsin

Alverno College, B
Edgewood College, B
Mount Mary University, BMD
University of Wisconsin - Superior, BM

Canada
Alberta

Athabasca University, M

Quebec

Concordia University, M

ARTIFICIAL INTELLIGENCE AND ROBOTICS

United States
Arizona

University of Advancing Technology, B

California

California State University, Northridge, M
San Diego City College, A
University of California, Riverside, MD
University of California, San Diego, MD
University of Southern California, M

Georgia

Georgia Institute of Technology, D
University of Georgia, M

Illinois

Illinois Institute of Technology, M

Indiana

Indiana University Bloomington, D

Iowa

Southeastern Community College, A

Kentucky

Sullivan College of Technology and Design, AB

Maryland

Johns Hopkins University, M

Massachusetts

Worcester Polytechnic Institute, BMD

Michigan

Eastern Michigan University, O
University of Michigan, MD

Nebraska

University of Nebraska at Omaha, O

New York

Cornell University, MD

Ohio

Lorain County Community College, A
Sinclair Community College, A

Oregon

Oregon State University, MD
Portland State University, O

Pennsylvania

Carnegie Mellon University, MD
University of Pittsburgh, MD
Villanova University, O

South Dakota

South Dakota School of Mines and Technology, M

Texas

Richland College, A

Virginia

The College of William and Mary, D

Washington

South Seattle College, A
Spokane Community College, A

Canada

Ontario

University of Windsor, B

Quebec

Université du Québec à Trois-Rivières, B

ARTS JOURNALISM

United States

California

Academy of Art University, M

Illinois

School of the Art Institute of Chicago, M

New York

Syracuse University, M

ARTS MANAGEMENT

United States

Arizona

Arizona State University at the Tempe campus, M

California

University of Southern California, M

Colorado

Rocky Mountain College of Art + Design, M

Florida

Florida State University, M
St. Thomas University, M

Georgia

Savannah College of Art and Design, M

Illinois

Columbia College Chicago, M
Northwestern University, M
Robert Morris University Illinois, M
School of the Art Institute of Chicago, M

Indiana

Indiana University Bloomington, M
Valparaiso University, M

Kentucky

University of Kentucky, M

Louisiana

University of New Orleans, M

Maryland

Goucher College, M

Massachusetts

Boston University, MO

Michigan

Eastern Michigan University, M
University of Michigan - Flint, M

Minnesota

Saint Mary's University of Minnesota, M

New Jersey

Montclair State University, M
Rowan University, M

New York

Baruch College of the City University of New York, M
Brooklyn College of the City University of New York, M
The College at Brockport, State University of New York, O
Daemen College, M
Fashion Institute of Technology, M
New York University, M
Pratt Institute, M
Syracuse University, MO
University at Buffalo, the State University of New York, M

North Carolina

The University of North Carolina at Charlotte, M
University of North Carolina School of the Arts, M

Ohio

The Ohio State University, M
The University of Akron, M
University of Cincinnati, MD

Oregon

University of Oregon, M

Pennsylvania

Carnegie Mellon University, M
Drexel University, M
Moore College of Art & Design, M
Temple University, MD

Rhode Island

Rhode Island College, M

South Carolina

College of Charleston, MO
Winthrop University, M

Texas

Southern Methodist University, M

Utah

Southern Utah University, M

Virginia

George Mason University, MO

Washington

Seattle University, M

Wisconsin

University of Wisconsin - Madison, M

U.S. Territories: Puerto Rico

Universidad del Turabo, M

Canada

Ontario

Ryerson University, M

Quebec

HEC Montreal, O

ASIAN-AMERICAN STUDIES

United States

Arizona

Arizona State University at the Tempe campus, B

California

California State University, East Bay, B
California State University, Fullerton, B
California State University, Long Beach, BM
California State University, Los Angeles, B
California State University, Northridge, B
Pitzer College, B
Pomona College, B
San Francisco State University, BM
Scripps College, B
Stanford University, B
University of California, Berkeley, B
University of California, Davis, B
University of California, Irvine, B
University of California, Los Angeles, BM
University of California, Riverside, B
University of California, Santa Barbara, B
University of Southern California, B

Colorado

University of Denver, B

New York

Binghamton University, State University of New York, BMO
Columbia University, B

ASIAN HISTORY

United States

California

University of the West, B

Pennsylvania

Gettysburg College, B

Washington

University of Washington, Tacoma, B

Canada

Quebec

McGill University, B

ASIAN LANGUAGES

United States

California

Stanford University, MD
University of California, Berkeley, MD
University of California, Irvine, MD
University of California, Los Angeles, MD
University of California, Santa Barbara, MD
University of Southern California, MD

Colorado

Naropa University, M

Connecticut

Yale University, D

Hawaii

University of Hawaii at Manoa, MD

Illinois

University of Chicago, D
University of Illinois at Urbana - Champaign, MD

Indiana

Indiana University Bloomington, MD

Iowa

The University of Iowa, M

Kansas

The University of Kansas, M

Massachusetts

Harvard University, MD

Michigan

University of Michigan, D

Minnesota

University of Minnesota, Twin Cities Campus, D

Missouri

Washington University in St. Louis, MD

New Mexico

St. John's College, M

New York

Cornell University, MD

Ohio

The Ohio State University, MD

Oregon

University of Oregon, MD

Texas

The University of Texas at Austin, MD

Washington

University of Washington, MD

Wisconsin

University of Wisconsin - Madison, MD

ASIAN STUDIES/CIVILIZATION

United States

Alabama

Birmingham-Southern College, B

Arizona

Arizona State University at the Tempe campus, B

California

California Institute of Integral Studies, MD
California State University, Chico, B
California State University, Long Beach, BM
California State University, Los Angeles, B
California State University, Sacramento, B
Claremont McKenna College, B
East Los Angeles College, A
El Camino College, A
Laney College, A
Loyola Marymount University, B
Pepperdine University, B
Pitzer College, B
Pomona College, B
San Diego State University, BM
Scripps College, B
University of California, Berkeley, BMD
University of California, Los Angeles, MD
University of California, Riverside, B
University of California, Santa Barbara, B
University of Redlands, B
University of San Francisco, BM

Colorado

The Colorado College, B
University of Colorado Boulder, B
University of Northern Colorado, B

Delaware

University of Delaware, B

District of Columbia

The George Washington University, BM
Georgetown University, M

Florida

Florida International University, BM
Florida State University, M
Miami Dade College, A
State College of Florida Manatee-Sarasota, A

Hawaii

University of Hawaii at Manoa, B

Illinois

Augustana College, B
Illinois Wesleyan University, B
Knox College, B
Lake Forest College, B
Northwestern University, B

Indiana

Indiana University Bloomington, MD
Purdue University, B
Valparaiso University, M

Iowa

Coe College, B
Maharishi University of Management, MD
The University of Iowa, BM

Kentucky

Berea College, B
University of Louisville, BO
Western Kentucky University, B

Louisiana

Tulane University, B

Maine

Bowdoin College, B

Maryland

Johns Hopkins University, M
McDaniel College, B
St. Mary's College of Maryland, B
University of Maryland, Baltimore County, B
University of Maryland University College, B

Massachusetts

Amherst College, B
Bard College at Simon's Rock, B
Clark University, B
College of the Holy Cross, B
Elms College, B
Harvard University, MD
Mount Holyoke College, B
Northeastern University, B
Tufts University, B
University of Massachusetts Boston, B
Wheaton College, B
Williams College, B

Michigan

Calvin College, B
University of Michigan, BMD

Minnesota

Carleton College, B
Macalester College, B
St. Olaf College, B
University of Minnesota, Twin Cities Campus, D

Missouri

Washington University in St. Louis, BM

Montana

University of Montana, B

Nevada

University of Nevada, Las Vegas, B

New Hampshire

Dartmouth College, B

New Jersey

Kean University, B
Princeton University, D
Seton Hall University, BM
William Paterson University of New Jersey, B

New Mexico

St. John's College, M
University of New Mexico, B

New York

Bard College, B
Barnard College, B
Binghamton University, State University of New York, BMO
City College of the City University of New York, B
Colgate University, B
Columbia University, O
Cornell University, BMD
Hamilton College, B
Hobart and William Smith Colleges, B
Manhattanville College, B
Nazareth College of Rochester, B
Pace University, B
St. John's University, BMO
Sarah Lawrence College, B
Skidmore College, B
State University of New York at New Paltz, B
Stony Brook University, State University of New York, B
Union College, B
University at Albany, State University of New York, B
University at Buffalo, the State University of New York, B
Vassar College, B

North Carolina

Duke University, B
The University of North Carolina at Chapel Hill, B

Ohio

Bowling Green State University, B
Case Western Reserve University, B
John Carroll University, B
Kenyon College, B
Marietta College, B
Ohio University, BM
University of Cincinnati, B
University of Mount Union, B
The University of Toledo, B

Oregon

University of Oregon, BM
Willamette University, B

Pennsylvania

Indiana University of Pennsylvania, B
Lehigh University, B
Penn State University Park, B
Saint Joseph's University, B
Swarthmore College, B
Temple University, B
University of Pittsburgh, O

Rhode Island

Brown University, D

South Carolina

Furman University, B

Tennessee

Belmont University, B
Sewanee: The University of the South, B
Vanderbilt University, B

Texas

Austin College, B
Baylor University, B
Rice University, B
Texas State University, B
Trinity University, B
The University of Texas at Austin, BMD

Utah

University of Utah, BM
Utah State University, B

Vermont

Bennington College, B
Marlboro College, B
University of Vermont, B

Virginia

Old Dominion University, B
Randolph-Macon College, B
University of Richmond, B

Washington

Gonzaga University, B
Seattle University, B
University of Puget Sound, B
University of Washington, BM
Washington State University, B
Whitman College, B

Wisconsin

University of Wisconsin - Madison, BMD

Canada

British Columbia

The University of British Columbia, BMD
University of Victoria, BM

Maritime Provinces: Nova Scotia

Saint Mary's University, B

Ontario

Carleton University, B
University of Toronto, B
The University of Western Ontario, B

Quebec

Université de Montréal, B

ASTRONOMY

United States

Arizona

Embry-Riddle Aeronautical University - Prescott, B
Northern Arizona University, B
The University of Arizona, BMD

California

Cabrillo College, A
California Institute of Technology, D
El Camino College, A
Fullerton College, A
Palomar College, A
Pomona College, B
Saddleback College, A
San Bernardino Valley College, A
San Diego State University, BM
San Francisco State University, BM
Southwestern College, A
University of California, Los Angeles, MD
University of California, Santa Cruz, BD
University of Southern California, B

Colorado

University of Colorado Boulder, B
University of Denver, MD

Connecticut

Wesleyan University, BM
Yale University, BMD

Delaware

University of Delaware, MD

Florida

Broward College, A
South Florida State College, A
State College of Florida Manatee-Sarasota, A
University of Florida, BMD

Georgia

Georgia State University, D
Gordon State College, A
University of Georgia, B
Valdosta State University, B

Hawaii

University of Hawaii at Hilo, B
University of Hawaii at Manoa, BMD

Idaho

North Idaho College, A

Illinois

Northwestern University, BD
University of Chicago, D
University of Illinois at Urbana - Champaign, BMD

Indiana

Ball State University, B
Indiana University Bloomington, BMD
Valparaiso University, B

Iowa

Drake University, B
Iowa Lakes Community College, A
The University of Iowa, BM

Kansas

Benedictine College, B
The University of Kansas, BMD

Kentucky

University of Kentucky, MD

Louisiana

Louisiana State University and Agricultural & Mechanical College, MD

Maryland

Johns Hopkins University, D
University of Maryland, College Park, BMD

Massachusetts

Amherst College, B
Boston University, BMD
Hampshire College, B
Harvard University, D
Mount Holyoke College, B
Smith College, B
Tufts University, B
University of Massachusetts Amherst, BMD
Wellesley College, B
Williams College, B

Michigan

Central Michigan University, B
Michigan State University, MD
University of Michigan, BD
Wayne State University, B

Minnesota

Minnesota State University Mankato, BM

Missouri

University of Missouri, MD

Montana

University of Montana, B

Nebraska

University of Nebraska - Lincoln, MD

Nevada

University of Nevada, Las Vegas, MD

New Hampshire

Dartmouth College, BMD

New Jersey

Princeton University, D
Rutgers University - New Brunswick, MD

New Mexico

New Mexico State University, MD

New York

Barnard College, B
Colgate University, B
Columbia University, BD
Columbia University, School of General Studies, B
Cornell University, BD
Rensselaer Polytechnic Institute, M
State University of New York at New Paltz, B
Stony Brook University, State University of New York, BD
Union College, B
University of Rochester, D
Vassar College, B

North Carolina

The University of North Carolina at Chapel Hill, MD

Ohio

Case Western Reserve University, BMD
The Ohio State University, BMD
Ohio University, MD
Ohio Wesleyan University, B
The University of Toledo, B
Youngstown State University, B

Oklahoma

University of Oklahoma, B

Pennsylvania

Bryn Mawr College, B
Franklin & Marshall College, B
Haverford College, B
Lehigh University, B
Lycoming College, B
Penn State Abington, B
Penn State Altoona, B

Penn State Beaver, B
Penn State Berks, B
Penn State Brandywine, B
Penn State DuBois, B
Penn State Erie, The Behrend College, B
Penn State Fayette, The Eberly Campus, B
Penn State Greater Allegheny, B
Penn State Hazleton, B
Penn State Lehigh Valley, B
Penn State Mont Alto, B
Penn State New Kensington, B
Penn State Schuylkill, B
Penn State Shenango, B
Penn State University Park, BMD
Penn State Wilkes-Barre, B
Penn State Worthington Scranton, B
Penn State York, B
Swarthmore College, B
University of Pittsburgh, BD
Villanova University, B
West Chester University of Pennsylvania, MO

South Carolina

Clemson University, MD
University of South Carolina, MD

Tennessee

Vanderbilt University, M

Texas

Baylor University, B
Rice University, BMD
The University of Texas at Austin, BMD

Utah

Brigham Young University, BMD

Vermont

Bennington College, B
Marlboro College, B

Virginia

George Mason University, B
University of Virginia, BMD

Washington

University of Washington, BMD
Washington State University, B
Whitman College, B

Wisconsin

University of Wisconsin - Madison, D

Canada

Alberta

University of Calgary, MD

British Columbia

The University of British Columbia, BMD
University of Victoria, BMD

Manitoba

University of Manitoba, B

Maritime Provinces: New Brunswick

Université de Moncton, M

Maritime Provinces: Nova Scotia

Saint Mary's University, BMD

Ontario

Laurentian University, B
University of Toronto, MD
The University of Western Ontario, BMD
York University, BMD

ASTRONOMY AND ASTRO-PHYSICS

United States

Florida

Florida Institute of Technology, B

Georgia

Emory University, B

Indiana

Butler University, B

Massachusetts

Harvard University, B

South Carolina

College of Charleston, B

Texas

Texas Christian University, B

Washington

Whitman College, B

Wyoming

University of Wyoming, B

ASTROPHYSICS

United States

Alaska

University of Alaska Fairbanks, M

Arizona

Arizona State University at the Tempe campus, MD

California

California Institute of Technology, B
San Francisco State University, B
University of California, Berkeley, BD
University of California, Los Angeles, BMD
University of California, Santa Cruz, BD

Colorado

University of Colorado Boulder, MD

Connecticut

Yale University, BD

Georgia

Agnes Scott College, B

Hawaii

University of Hawaii at Manoa, B

Illinois

Illinois Institute of Technology, B
University of Chicago, D

Indiana

Indiana University Bloomington, D

Iowa

Iowa State University of Science and Technology, MD

Louisiana

Louisiana State University and Agricultural & Mechanical College, D

Massachusetts

Boston University, B
Harvard University, D
Tufts University, BMD
Wellesley College, B
Williams College, B

Michigan

Michigan State University, BM
University of Michigan, D

Minnesota

University of Minnesota, Twin Cities Campus, BMD

Missouri

University of Missouri - St. Louis, M

New Jersey

Princeton University, BD
Rutgers University - New Brunswick, B

New Mexico

New Mexico Institute of Mining and Technology, D
New Mexico State University, M
University of New Mexico, B

New York

Barnard College, B
Colgate University, B
Columbia University, B
Columbia University, School of General Studies, B
Cornell University, D
Rochester Institute of Technology, MD

North Carolina

The University of North Carolina at Chapel Hill, MD

Ohio

Ohio University, B
Ohio Wesleyan University, B
University of Cincinnati, B
The University of Toledo, D

Oklahoma

University of Oklahoma, B

Pennsylvania

Carnegie Mellon University, B
Franklin & Marshall College, B
Haverford College, B
Lehigh University, B
Lycoming College, B
Penn State University Park, MD
Swarthmore College, B
Villanova University, B

South Carolina

Clemson University, MD

Texas

Baylor University, B
Rice University, B
Texas Christian University, D

Vermont

Marlboro College, B

Washington

Whitman College, B

Wisconsin

University of Wisconsin - Madison, B

Canada

Alberta

University of Alberta, BMD
University of Calgary, B

British Columbia

University of Victoria, MD

Maritime Provinces: Nova Scotia

Saint Mary's University, B

Ontario

McMaster University, BD
University of Toronto, MD
The University of Western Ontario, B

ATHLETIC TRAINING AND SPORTS MEDICINE

United States

Alabama

Samford University, B
Troy University, B
The University of Alabama, B
University of Mobile, B
The University of West Alabama, B

Arizona

Grand Canyon University, B

Arkansas

Arkansas State University, B
Harding University, B
Henderson State University, B
Southern Arkansas University - Magnolia, B
University of Arkansas, M
University of Central Arkansas, B

California

Ashford University, B
Azusa Pacific University, B
California Baptist University, M
California State University, East Bay, B
California State University, Fullerton, B
California State University, Long Beach, B
California State University, Northridge, B
Chapman University, B
College of the Canyons, A
College of the Sequoias, A
Concordia University Irvine, B
Foothill College, A
Humboldt State University, M
Modesto Junior College, A
Point Loma Nazarene University, B
San Diego State University, B
Santa Barbara City College, A
University of La Verne, B
Vanguard University of Southern California, B

Colorado

Colorado Mesa University, B
Fort Lewis College, B
University of Northern Colorado, B

Connecticut

Central Connecticut State University, B
Quinnipiac University, B
Sacred Heart University, B
Southern Connecticut State University, B
University of Connecticut, B

Delaware

University of Delaware, B

Florida

Barry University, M
Florida Gulf Coast University, B
Florida International University, M
Florida Southern College, B
Florida State University, B
Palm Beach Atlantic University, B
University of Central Florida, B
University of Florida, BM
University of Miami, BM
University of North Florida, B
University of South Florida, M
The University of Tampa, B

Georgia

Andrew College, A
Georgia College & State University, B
Georgia Southern University, B
Piedmont College, B
University of Georgia, B
University of North Georgia, B
Valdosta State University, B

Idaho

North Idaho College, A
Northwest Nazarene University, B
University of Idaho, BMD

Illinois

Aurora University, B
Eastern Illinois University, B
Eureka College, B
Illinois State University, B
Lewis University, B
McKendree University, B
Millikin University, B
North Central College, B
North Park University, B
Northern Illinois University, B
Olivet Nazarene University, B
Sauk Valley Community College, A
Trinity International University, B
University of Illinois at Urbana - Champaign, B
Western Illinois University, B

Indiana

Anderson University, B
Ball State University, B
DePauw University, B
Franklin College, B
Huntington University, B
Indiana State University, BMD
Indiana University Bloomington, BM
Indiana Wesleyan University, B
Manchester University, B
Saint Joseph's College, B
University of Evansville, B
University of Indianapolis, B

Iowa

Buena Vista University, B
Central College, B
Clarke University, B
Coe College, B
Graceland University, B
Iowa Lakes Community College, A
Iowa State University of Science and Technology, B
Loras College, B
Luther College, B
Northwestern College, B
Simpson College, B
The University of Iowa, BM
University of Northern Iowa, BM
Upper Iowa University, B

Kansas

Allen Community College, A
Barton County Community College, A
Benedictine College, B
Bethany College, B
Bethel College, B
Central Christian College of Kansas, AB
Dodge City Community College, A
Emporia State University, B
Independence Community College, A
Kansas State University, B
MidAmerica Nazarene University, B
Neosho County Community College, A
Pratt Community College, A
Southwestern College, B
Sterling College, B
Tabor College, B
The University of Kansas, B
Washburn University, B
Wichita State University, B

Kentucky

Eastern Kentucky University, B
Georgetown College, B
Murray State University, B
Northern Kentucky University, B
Spalding University, M
Thomas More College, B
Union College, B
University of Kentucky, M

Louisiana

Louisiana College, B
Louisiana State University and Agricultural & Mechanical College, B
McNeese State University, B
Southeastern Louisiana University, B
University of Louisiana at Lafayette, B

Maine

University of Maine, B
University of Maine at Presque Isle, B
University of New England, B
University of Southern Maine, B

Maryland

Frostburg State University, B
Salisbury University, B
Towson University, B

Massachusetts

Boston University, BD
Bridgewater State University, B
Dean College, A
Endicott College, B
Lasell College, B
Massachusetts College of Liberal Arts, B
Merrimack College, B
Salem State University, B
Springfield College, BM
Westfield State University, B

Michigan

Adrian College, BM
Albion College, B
Aquinas College, B
Central Michigan University, B
Eastern Michigan University, B
Grand Valley State University, B
Hope College, B
Lake Superior State University, B
Michigan State University, B
Northern Michigan University, B
Olivet College, B
Saginaw Valley State University, B
University of Michigan, B
Western Michigan University, BM

Minnesota

Bethel University, B
The College of St. Scholastica, M
Gustavus Adolphus College, B
Minnesota State University Moorhead, B
Saint Paul College - A Community & Technical College, A
University of Minnesota, Duluth, B
Winona State University, B

Mississippi

Delta State University, B
Northeast Mississippi Community College, A
University of Southern Mississippi, B

Missouri

Central Methodist University, B
Culver-Stockton College, B
Lindenwood University, B
Missouri State University, BM
Missouri Valley College, B
Park University, B
Saint Louis University, M
Southeast Missouri State University, B
Southwest Baptist University, B
Truman State University, B
William Woods University, B

Montana

Montana State University Billings, M
Rocky Mountain College, B

Nebraska

Midland University, B
Nebraska Wesleyan University, B
University of Nebraska - Lincoln, B
University of Nebraska at Omaha, BM

Wayne State College, B

Nevada

University of Nevada, Las Vegas, B

New Hampshire

Colby-Sawyer College, B
Keene State College, B
Manchester Community College, A
Plymouth State University, BM

New Jersey

Kean University, B
Montclair State University, B
Rowan University, B
Seton Hall University, M
William Paterson University of New Jersey, B

New Mexico

New Mexico Junior College, A
New Mexico State University, B

New York

Alfred University, B
Canisius College, B
The College at Brockport, State University of New York, B
Dominican College, B
Hofstra University, B
Ithaca College, B
Long Island University - LIU Brooklyn, BM
Marist College, B
State University of New York College at Cortland, B
Stony Brook University, State University of New York, B

North Carolina

Appalachian State University, B
Campbell University, B
Catawba College, B
East Carolina University, B
Gardner-Webb University, B
Greensboro College, B
Lees-McRae College, B
Lenoir-Rhyne University, M
Louisburg College, A
Mars Hill University, B
Methodist University, B
North Carolina Central University, B
Pfeiffer University, B
Shaw University, B
The University of North Carolina at Chapel Hill, M
The University of North Carolina at Charlotte, B
The University of North Carolina at Greensboro, M
The University of North Carolina at Pembroke, B
The University of North Carolina Wilmington, B
Western Carolina University, B
Wingate University, B

North Dakota

Minot State University, B
North Dakota State University, M
University of Mary, B
University of North Dakota, B
Valley City State University, B

Ohio

Ashland University, B
Baldwin Wallace University, B
Bowling Green State University, B
Capital University, B
Cedarville University, B
Defiance College, B
Heidelberg University, B
Kent State University, BM
Lorain County Community College, A
Marietta College, B
Miami University, B
Miami University Hamilton, B
Mount St. Joseph University, B
Ohio Northern University, B
The Ohio State University, B
Ohio University, BM
Otterbein University, B
Shawnee State University, AB

Tiffin University, B
The University of Akron, AB
University of Cincinnati, B
The University of Findlay, BM
University of Mount Union, B
The University of Toledo, B
Urbana University, B
Wilmington College, B
Wright State University, B
Xavier University, BM
Youngstown State University, B

Oklahoma

East Central University, B
Oklahoma Baptist University, B
Oklahoma State University, B
Southern Nazarene University, B
Southwestern Oklahoma State University, B
University of Central Oklahoma, M
The University of Tulsa, B

Oregon

George Fox University, B
Linfield College, B
Pacific University, BM

Pennsylvania

Alvernia University, B
Bloomsburg University of Pennsylvania, M
California University of Pennsylvania, BM
Community College of Allegheny County, A
Duquesne University, B
East Stroudsburg University of Pennsylvania, BM
Eastern University, B
Gannon University, M
Immaculata University, B
Indiana University of Pennsylvania, B
King's College, B
Lebanon Valley College, M
Lock Haven University of Pennsylvania, B
Marywood University, B
Mercyhurst North East, A
Messiah College, B
Neumann University, B
Northampton Community College, A
Penn State University Park, B
Slippery Rock University of Pennsylvania, B
Temple University, B
University of Pittsburgh at Bradford, B
Waynesburg University, B
West Chester University of Pennsylvania, BM

South Carolina

College of Charleston, B
Erskine College, B
Lander University, B
Limestone College, B

South Dakota

Augustana University, B
Dakota Wesleyan University, B
National American University (Rapid City), B
Presentation College, B
South Dakota State University, B

Tennessee

Cumberland University, B
King University, B
Lee University, B
Lincoln Memorial University, B
Middle Tennessee State University, B
Tusculum College, B
Union University, B
The University of Tennessee at Chattanooga, M
The University of Tennessee at Martin, B
Welch College, B

Texas

Baylor University, B
East Texas Baptist University, B
Hardin-Simmons University, B
Houston Baptist University, B
Howard Payne University, B
Lubbock Christian University, B
McMurry University, B

Midwestern State University, B
Odessa College, A
Sam Houston State University, B
Stephen F. Austin State University, M
Texas A&M University, M
Texas A&M University - Corpus Christi, B
Texas Christian University, B
Texas Lutheran University, B
Texas State University, BM
Texas Wesleyan University, B
Tyler Junior College, A
University of the Incarnate Word, B
The University of Texas at Arlington, B
The University of Texas at Austin, M
The University of Texas of the Permian Basin, B
West Texas A&M University, B

Utah

Brigham Young University, BM
Southern Utah University, B
University of Utah, B
Weber State University, BM

Vermont

Castleton University, B
Johnson State College, B
Lyndon State College, B
Norwich University, B
University of Vermont, B

Virginia

Averett University, B
Bridgewater College, B
Emory & Henry College, B
George Mason University, B
James Madison University, B
Liberty University, B
Longwood University, B
Lynchburg College, B
Radford University, B
Roanoke College, B
Shenandoah University, MO
Virginia Commonwealth University, M

Washington

Eastern Washington University, B
Washington State University, B
Wenatchee Valley College, A
Whitworth University, B

West Virginia

Alderson Broaddus University, B
Concord University, B
Marshall University, BM
University of Charleston, B
West Virginia University, M
West Virginia Wesleyan College, BM
Wheeling Jesuit University, B

Wisconsin

Carroll University, B
Carthage College, B
Concordia University Wisconsin, B
Marquette University, B
University of Wisconsin - Eau Claire, B
University of Wisconsin - La Crosse, BM
University of Wisconsin - Madison, B
University of Wisconsin - Milwaukee, B
University of Wisconsin - Stevens Point, B

Wyoming

Casper College, A
Central Wyoming College, A
Northwest College, A

U.S. Territories: Puerto Rico

Inter American University of Puerto Rico, Metropolitan Campus, M
Universidad del Este, B
Universidad del Turabo, M
University of Puerto Rico, Mayagüez Campus, B

University of Puerto Rico in Ponce, B

Canada

Newfoundland and Labrador

Memorial University of Newfoundland, B

Ontario

Lakehead University, B

Quebec

Université de Sherbrooke, B

ATMOSPHERIC CHEMISTRY AND CLIMATOLOGY

United States

New Jersey

Rutgers University - New Brunswick, B

Washington

University of Washington, B

ATMOSPHERIC PHYSICS AND DYNAMICS

Canada

Quebec

McGill University, B

ATMOSPHERIC SCIENCES AND METEOROLOGY

United States

Alabama

Community College of the Air Force, A
The University of Alabama in Huntsville, MD

Alaska

University of Alaska Fairbanks, MD

Arizona

Embry-Riddle Aeronautical University - Prescott, B
Northern Arizona University, M
The University of Arizona, MD

California

Diablo Valley College, A
San Jose State University, B
University of California, Berkeley, B
University of California, Davis, BMD
University of California, Los Angeles, BMD

Colorado

Colorado State University, MD
United States Air Force Academy, B
University of Colorado Boulder, MD

Connecticut

Western Connecticut State University, B
Yale University, D

District of Columbia

Howard University, MD

Florida

Embry-Riddle Aeronautical University - Daytona, B
Florida State University, BD
Nova Southeastern University, O
South Florida State College, A
University of Miami, B
University of South Florida, M

Georgia

Georgia Institute of Technology, MD

Illinois

Northern Illinois University, B
University of Chicago, D
University of Illinois at Urbana - Champaign, BMD

Indiana

Purdue University, BMD
Valparaiso University, B

Iowa

Iowa State University of Science and Technology, B

Kansas

The University of Kansas, BM

Kentucky

University of Louisville, B

Louisiana

University of Louisiana at Monroe, B

Maryland

University of Maryland, Baltimore County, MD
University of Maryland, College Park, B

Massachusetts

Massachusetts Institute of Technology, MD
University of Massachusetts Lowell, MD

Michigan

Michigan Technological University, D
University of Michigan, BMD

Minnesota

St. Cloud State University, B

Mississippi

Jackson State University, B
Mississippi State University, D

Missouri

Saint Louis University, B
University of Missouri, BMD

Nebraska

University of Nebraska - Lincoln, B

Nevada

University of Nevada, Reno, BMD

New Hampshire

Plymouth State University, B

New Jersey

Princeton University, D
Rutgers University - New Brunswick, BMD

New Mexico

New Mexico Institute of Mining and Technology, D

New York

Bard College, MO
City College of the City University of New York, MD
The College at Brockport, State University of New York, B
Columbia University, M
Cornell University, BMD
State University of New York College at Oneonta, B
State University of New York Maritime College, B
State University of New York at Oswego, B
Stony Brook University, State University of New York, BMD
University at Albany, State University of New York, BMD

North Carolina

East Carolina University, B
North Carolina Agricultural and Technical State University, B

North Carolina State University, BMD
University of North Carolina at Asheville, B
The University of North Carolina at Chapel Hill, MD

North Dakota

University of North Dakota, BMD

Ohio

The Ohio State University, BMD
Ohio University, B

Oregon

Oregon State University, MD

Pennsylvania

Carnegie Mellon University, D
Millersville University of Pennsylvania, BM
Penn State Abington, B
Penn State Altoona, B
Penn State Beaver, B
Penn State Berks, B
Penn State Brandywine, B
Penn State DuBois, B
Penn State Erie, The Behrend College, B
Penn State Fayette, The Eberly Campus, B
Penn State Greater Allegheny, B
Penn State Hazleton, B
Penn State Lehigh Valley, B
Penn State Mont Alto, B
Penn State New Kensington, B
Penn State Schuylkill, B
Penn State Shenango, B
Penn State University Park, B
Penn State Wilkes-Barre, B
Penn State Worthington Scranton, B
Penn State York, B

South Carolina

Clemson University, MD

South Dakota

South Dakota School of Mines and Technology, MD

Texas

Southern Methodist University, D
Texas A&M University, B
Texas Tech University, M
University of Houston, D
University of the Incarnate Word, B

Utah

University of Utah, BMD

Vermont

Lyndon State College, B

Virginia

George Mason University, BD
Hampton University, MD

Washington

Everett Community College, A
University of Washington, BMD

Wisconsin

University of Wisconsin - Madison, BMD

Wyoming

University of Wyoming, MD

Canada

Alberta

University of Alberta, B

British Columbia

The University of British Columbia, BMD
University of Victoria, B

Maritime Provinces: Nova Scotia

Dalhousie University, B

Ontario

University of Guelph, MD
University of Waterloo, B
York University, B

Quebec

McGill University, BMD
Université du Québec à Montréal, MDO

ATOMIC/MOLECULAR PHYSICS

United States

California

San Diego State University, B

New York

Columbia University, B

Canada

Ontario

University of Waterloo, B

AUDIOLOGY/AUDIOLOGIST AND HEARING SCIENCES

United States

Alabama

University of Montevallo, B

California

Biola University, B
California State University, Long Beach, B

Illinois

Northwestern University, B
University of Illinois at Urbana - Champaign, B

Michigan

Western Michigan University, B

Ohio

Cleveland State University, B
The Ohio State University, B

Texas

Stephen F. Austin State University, B

Canada

Quebec

Université de Montréal, B

AUDIOLOGY/AUDIOLOGIST AND SPEECH-LANGUAGE PATHOLOGY/PATHOLOGIST

United States

Alabama

Auburn University, B
The University of Alabama, B

Arkansas

Arkansas State University, B
University of Arkansas, B
University of Arkansas at Little Rock, B
University of Central Arkansas, B

California

Biola University, B
California State University, East Bay, B
California State University, Fresno, B

California State University, Long Beach, B
California State University, Sacramento, B
Cerritos College, A
Grossmont College, A
Loma Linda University, AB
Orange Coast College, A
Pasadena City College, A
University of the Pacific, B
University of Redlands, B

Colorado

University of Northern Colorado, B

Connecticut

Southern Connecticut State University, B

District of Columbia

The George Washington University, B
University of the District of Columbia, B

Florida

Broward College, A
Miami Dade College, A
South Florida State College, A
University of Central Florida, B
University of Florida, B
University of South Florida, B

Idaho

The College of Idaho, B
Idaho State University, B

Illinois

Elmhurst College, B
Illinois State University, B
Northwestern University, B
Southern Illinois University Edwardsville, B
University of Illinois at Urbana - Champaign, B

Indiana

Ball State University, B
Indiana State University, B
Indiana University Bloomington, B
Indiana University - Purdue University Fort Wayne, B
Purdue University, B

Iowa

The University of Iowa, B

Kansas

Fort Hays State University, B

Kentucky

Brescia University, B
Eastern Kentucky University, B
Murray State University, B
University of Kentucky, B

Louisiana

Louisiana State University and Agricultural & Mechanical College, B
Louisiana Tech University, B
Nicholls State University, B
Southeastern Louisiana University, B
Southern University and Agricultural and Mechanical College, B
University of Louisiana at Lafayette, B
University of Louisiana at Monroe, B

Maryland

Towson University, B

Massachusetts

Boston University, B
Emerson College, B
Northeastern University, B

Michigan

Andrews University, B
Calvin College, B
Western Michigan University, B

Minnesota

Minnesota State University Mankato, B
Minnesota State University Moorhead, B
St. Cloud State University, B
University of Minnesota, Twin Cities Campus, B

Mississippi

Delta State University, B
University of Mississippi, B
University of Southern Mississippi, B

Missouri

Fontbonne University, B
Missouri State University, B

Montana

University of Montana, B

New Jersey

Stockton University, B

New Mexico

Eastern New Mexico University, B
University of New Mexico, B

New York

Adelphi University, B
Brooklyn College of the City University of New York, B
Buffalo State College, State University of New York, B
The College of Saint Rose, B
Elmira College, B
Hofstra University, B
Hunter College of the City University of New York, B
Iona College, B
Ithaca College, B
Lehman College of the City University of New York, B
Long Island University - LIU Brooklyn, B
Long Island University - LIU Post, B
Marymount Manhattan College, B
Mercy College, B
Nazareth College of Rochester, B
New York University, B
St. John's University, B
State University of New York College at Cortland, B
State University of New York at Fredonia, B
State University of New York at Plattsburgh, B
Touro College, B
University at Buffalo, the State University of New York, B
Yeshiva University, B

North Carolina

East Carolina University, B
The University of North Carolina at Greensboro, B

Ohio

Bowling Green State University, B
Kent State University, B
Miami University, B
Miami University Hamilton, B
The Ohio State University, B
Ohio University, B
Otterbein University, B
University of Cincinnati Clermont College, A

Oklahoma

Northeastern State University, B
University of Central Oklahoma, B
The University of Tulsa, B

Pennsylvania

Bloomsburg University of Pennsylvania, B
Indiana University of Pennsylvania, B
Marywood University, B
Temple University, B
Thiel College, B
University of Pittsburgh, B
West Chester University of Pennsylvania, B

South Carolina

South Carolina State University, B

South Dakota

Augustana University, B

Tennessee

Tennessee State University, B
The University of Tennessee, B

Texas

Hardin-Simmons University, B
Texas Woman's University, B
University of North Texas, B
The University of Texas at Dallas, B
The University of Texas at El Paso, B

Utah

University of Utah, B
Utah State University, B

Virginia

Longwood University, B
Old Dominion University, B
University of Virginia, B

Washington

University of Washington, B
Washington State University, B
Washington State University - Spokane, B
Western Washington University, B

West Virginia

West Virginia University, B

Wisconsin

University of Wisconsin - Madison, B
University of Wisconsin - Milwaukee, B
University of Wisconsin - Oshkosh, B
University of Wisconsin - Stevens Point, B

Wyoming

University of Wyoming, B

Canada

Quebec

Université de Montréal, B

AUDIOVISUAL COMMUNICATIONS TECHNOLOGIES/TECHNICIANS

United States

Florida

Full Sail University, B

Georgia

American InterContinental University Atlanta, B

Kentucky

Jefferson Community and Technical College, A

Louisiana

Bossier Parish Community College, A

Maine

Husson University, B

Missouri

College of the Ozarks, B
Webster University, B

Ohio

Cincinnati State Technical and Community College, A
International College of Broadcasting, A

Washington

Edmonds Community College, A

AUDITING

United States

Illinois

Bradley University, B
University of Illinois at Urbana - Champaign, B

Massachusetts

Babson College, B

New York

State University of New York College of Technology at Delhi, B

Pennsylvania

Carlow University, B

U.S. Territories: Puerto Rico

Inter American University of Puerto Rico, Bayamón Campus, B
Pontifical Catholic University of Puerto Rico, B

Canada

Quebec

McGill University, B

AUSTRALIAN/OCEANIC/PACIFIC LANGUAGES, LITERATURES, AND LINGUISTICS

United States

Hawaii

University of Hawaii - West Oahu, B

AUTOBODY/COLLISION AND REPAIR TECHNOLOGY/TECHNICIAN

United States

Alabama

George C. Wallace Community College, A
Southern Union State Community College, A

Arkansas

Arkansas State University - Newport, A
University of Arkansas Community College at Morrilton, A

California

Academy of Art University, A
American River College, A
Antelope Valley College, A
Cerritos College, A
Chaffey College, A
College of Alameda, A
College of Marin, A
Contra Costa College, A
Cuesta College, A
Cypress College, A
Fresno City College, A
Hartnell College, A
Long Beach City College, A
Modesto Junior College, A
Oxnard College, A
Palomar College, A
Riverside City College, A

Colorado

Aims Community College, A
Morgan Community College, AB
Pikes Peak Community College, A
Pueblo Community College, A
Red Rocks Community College, A

Florida

Florida State College at Jacksonville, A

Hawaii

Hawaii Community College, A
Kauai Community College, A

Idaho

College of Southern Idaho, A
College of Western Idaho, A
Idaho State University, AB
Lewis-Clark State College, AB

Illinois

Carl Sandburg College, A
Danville Area Community College, A
Highland Community College, A
Illinois Eastern Community Colleges, Olney Central College, A
John A. Logan College, A
Kaskaskia College, A
Kishwaukee College, A
Lincoln Land Community College, A
Parkland College, A
Southwestern Illinois College, A
Waubonsee Community College, A

Indiana

Vincennes University, A

Iowa

Des Moines Area Community College, A
Hawkeye Community College, A
Indian Hills Community College, A
Iowa Lakes Community College, A
Northwest Iowa Community College, A
Scott Community College, A
Southwestern Community College, A
Western Iowa Tech Community College, A

Kansas

Coffeyville Community College, A
Hutchinson Community College, A
Manhattan Area Technical College, A
Northwest Kansas Technical College, A
Wichita Area Technical College, A

Michigan

Lansing Community College, A
Wayne County Community College District, A

Minnesota

Dakota County Technical College, A
Dunwoody College of Technology, A
Hennepin Technical College, A
Minnesota State College - Southeast Technical, A
Minnesota State Community and Technical College, A
Minnesota State Community and Technical College - Detroit Lakes, A
Northland Community and Technical College, A
Ridgewater College, A
Riverland Community College, A
St. Cloud Technical & Community College, A
Saint Paul College - A Community & Technical College, A
South Central College, A

Mississippi

Coahoma Community College, A
East Central Community College, A
Holmes Community College, A

Missouri

Crowder College, A
Mineral Area College, A
Ozarks Technical Community College, A
Ranken Technical College, A
State Technical College of Missouri, A

Montana

Montana State University Billings, A

Nebraska

Central Community College - Hastings Campus, A
Mid-Plains Community College, A
Northeast Community College, A
Southeast Community College, Milford Campus, A

New Hampshire

Nashua Community College, A

New Mexico

Eastern New Mexico University - Roswell, A
Luna Community College, A
San Juan College, A

New York

Corning Community College, A
Erie Community College, South Campus, A
Morrisville State College, A
State University of New York College of Technology
　at Alfred, A

North Carolina

Fayetteville Technical Community College, A
Lenoir Community College, A
Randolph Community College, A
Stanly Community College, A
Wayne Community College, A

North Dakota

Bismarck State College, A
North Dakota State College of Science, A

Ohio

Ohio Technical College, A

Oklahoma

Oklahoma State University Institute of Technology, A

Oregon

Clackamas Community College, A
Lane Community College, A
Portland Community College, A

Pennsylvania

Community College of Beaver County, A
Pennco Tech, A
Pennsylvania College of Technology, AB
Thaddeus Stevens College of Technology, A
WyoTech Blairsville, A

Rhode Island

New England Institute of Technology, A

South Dakota

Lake Area Technical Institute, A
Southeast Technical Institute, A

Tennessee

Lincoln College of Technology, A

Texas

Central Texas College, A
Eastfield College, A
Grayson College, A
Hill College, A
Kilgore College, A
Northeast Texas Community College, A
St. Philip's College, A
San Jacinto College District, A
Texas State Technical College, A

Utah

Salt Lake Community College, A
Utah Valley University, A

Washington

Bellingham Technical College, A
Green River College, A
Renton Technical College, A
Walla Walla Community College, A

Wisconsin

Fox Valley Technical College, A
Northeast Wisconsin Technical College, A

Wyoming

Casper College, A
Laramie County Community College, A
WyoTech Laramie, A

U.S. Territories: American Samoa

American Samoa Community College, A

Canada

British Columbia

British Columbia Institute of Technology, A

AUTOMOBILE/AUTOMOTIVE MECHANICS TECHNOLOGY/ TECHNICIAN

United States

Alabama

Community College of the Air Force, A
George C. Wallace Community College, A
Southern Union State Community College, A
Wallace State Community College, A

Alaska

University of Alaska Anchorage, A

Arizona

Arizona Automotive Institute, A
Arizona Western College, A
Central Arizona College, A
Cochise County Community College District, A
Eastern Arizona College, A
GateWay Community College, A
Glendale Community College, A
Mesa Community College, A
Mohave Community College, A
Pima Community College, A
Universal Technical Institute, A
Yavapai College, A

Arkansas

Arkansas State University - Newport, A
College of the Ouachitas, A
Cossatot Community College of the University of
　Arkansas, A
Ozarka College, A
University of Arkansas Community College at Mor-
　rilton, A

California

Allan Hancock College, A
American River College, A
Antelope Valley College, A
Bakersfield College, A
Barstow Community College, A
Butte College, A
Cerritos College, A
Cerro Coso Community College, A
Chabot College, A
Chaffey College, A
Citrus College, A
City College of San Francisco, A
College of Alameda, A
College of the Canyons, A
College of the Desert, A
College of Marin, A
College of the Redwoods, A
College of the Sequoias, A
Columbia College, A
Contra Costa College, A
Copper Mountain College, A
Cosumnes River College, A
Cuesta College, A
Cuyamaca College, A
Cypress College, A

De Anza College, A
East Los Angeles College, A
El Camino College, A
Evergreen Valley College, A
Fresno City College, A
Fullerton College, A
Golden West College, A
Hartnell College, A
Imperial Valley College, A
Las Positas College, A
Lassen Community College District, A
Long Beach City College, A
Los Angeles Harbor College, A
Los Angeles Pierce College, A
Los Angeles Trade-Technical College, A
Los Medanos College, A
Mendocino College, A
Merced College, A
Modesto Junior College, A
Monterey Peninsula College, A
Mt. San Jacinto College, A
Oxnard College, A
Palomar College, A
Pasadena City College, A
Porterville College, A
Reedley College, A
Riverside City College, A
Saddleback College, A
San Bernardino Valley College, A
San Diego City College, A
San Diego Miramar College, A
San Joaquin Delta College, A
Santa Ana College, A
Santa Barbara City College, A
Santa Rosa Junior College, A
Shasta College, A
Sierra College, A
Skyline College, A
Solano Community College, A
Southwestern College, A
Taft College, A
Ventura College, A
Victor Valley College, A
West Hills Community College, A
Yuba College, A

Colorado

Aims Community College, A
Arapahoe Community College, A
Colorado Mesa University, A
Front Range Community College, A
IntelliTec College (Colorado Springs), A
Lincoln College of Technology, A
Morgan Community College, AB
Northeastern Junior College, A
Otero Junior College, A
Pikes Peak Community College, A
Pueblo Community College, A
Red Rocks Community College, A
Trinidad State Junior College, A

Connecticut

Gateway Community College, A
Naugatuck Valley Community College, A

Delaware

Delaware Technical & Community College, Jack F.
　Owens Campus, A
Delaware Technical & Community College,
　Stanton/Wilmington Campus, A

District of Columbia

University of the District of Columbia, A

Florida

Broward College, A
Daytona State College, A
Florida State College at Jacksonville, A
Indian River State College, A
Lincoln College of Technology, A
Seminole State College of Florida, A

Georgia

Chattahoochee Technical College, A
Columbus Technical College, A

Georgia Piedmont Technical College, A
Gwinnett Technical College, A
Ogeechee Technical College, A
Savannah Technical College, A
Southern Crescent Technical College, A
West Georgia Technical College, A

Hawaii

Hawaii Community College, A
Honolulu Community College, A
Kauai Community College, A
Leeward Community College, A
University of Hawaii Maui College, A

Idaho

Brigham Young University - Idaho, AB
College of Southern Idaho, A
College of Western Idaho, A
Eastern Idaho Technical College, A
Idaho State University, AB
Lewis-Clark State College, AB
North Idaho College, A

Illinois

Black Hawk College, A
Carl Sandburg College, A
City Colleges of Chicago, Harry S. Truman College, A
City Colleges of Chicago, Kennedy-King College, A
College of DuPage, A
College of Lake County, A
Danville Area Community College, A
Elgin Community College, A
Highland Community College, A
Illinois Central College, A
Illinois Eastern Community Colleges, Frontier Community College, A
Illinois Eastern Community Colleges, Olney Central College, A
Illinois Valley Community College, A
John A. Logan College, A
Joliet Junior College, A
Kankakee Community College, A
Kaskaskia College, A
Kishwaukee College, A
Lake Land College, A
Lewis and Clark Community College, A
Lincoln Land Community College, A
Moraine Valley Community College, A
Morton College, A
Oakton Community College, A
Parkland College, A
Prairie State College, A
Rend Lake College, A
Richland Community College, A
Rock Valley College, A
Shawnee Community College, A
Southeastern Illinois College, A
Triton College, A
Waubonsee Community College, A

Indiana

Ivy Tech Community College - Central Indiana, A
Ivy Tech Community College - Columbus, A
Ivy Tech Community College - East Central, A
Ivy Tech Community College - Kokomo, A
Ivy Tech Community College - Lafayette, A
Ivy Tech Community College - North Central, A
Ivy Tech Community College - Northeast, A
Ivy Tech Community College - Northwest, A
Ivy Tech Community College - Richmond, A
Ivy Tech Community College - Southern Indiana, A
Ivy Tech Community College - Southwest, A
Ivy Tech Community College - Wabash Valley, A
Lincoln College of Technology, A
Vincennes University, A

Iowa

Des Moines Area Community College, A
Hawkeye Community College, A
Indian Hills Community College, A
Iowa Central Community College, A
Iowa Lakes Community College, A
Iowa Western Community College, A
Kirkwood Community College, A

North Iowa Area Community College, A
Northeast Iowa Community College, A
Northwest Iowa Community College, A
Scott Community College, A
Southeastern Community College, A
Southwestern Community College, A
Western Iowa Tech Community College, A

Kansas

Barton County Community College, A
Butler Community College, A
Coffeyville Community College, A
Cowley County Community College and Area Vocational - Technical School, A
Dodge City Community College, A
Flint Hills Technical College, A
Garden City Community College, A
Hutchinson Community College, A
Johnson County Community College, A
Manhattan Area Technical College, A
McPherson College, B
North Central Kansas Technical College, A
Northwest Kansas Technical College, A
Pittsburg State University, A
Pratt Community College, A
Seward County Community College and Area Technical School, A
Wichita Area Technical College, A

Kentucky

Bluegrass Community and Technical College, A
Elizabethtown Community and Technical College, A
Jefferson Community and Technical College, A
Owensboro Community and Technical College, A
Southcentral Kentucky Community and Technical College, A

Louisiana

Delgado Community College, A
Fletcher Technical Community College, A
South Louisiana Community College, A

Maine

Central Maine Community College, A
Eastern Maine Community College, A
Northern Maine Community College, A
Southern Maine Community College, A
Washington County Community College, A

Maryland

Allegany College of Maryland, A
Community College of Baltimore County, A
Montgomery College, A

Massachusetts

Benjamin Franklin Institute of Technology, AB
Massachusetts Bay Community College, A
Mount Wachusett Community College, A
Quinsigamond Community College, A
Springfield Technical Community College, A

Michigan

Alpena Community College, A
Baker College, A
Bay de Noc Community College, A
Delta College, A
Ferris State University, A
Gogebic Community College, A
Grand Rapids Community College, A
Henry Ford College, A
Jackson College, A
Kalamazoo Valley Community College, A
Kirtland Community College, A
Lansing Community College, A
Macomb Community College, A
Mid Michigan Community College, A
Montcalm Community College, A
Mott Community College, A
Muskegon Community College, A
Northern Michigan University, A
Northwestern Michigan College, A
Oakland Community College, A
Southwestern Michigan College, A
Wayne County Community College District, A

Minnesota

Anoka Technical College, A
Dakota County Technical College, A
Dunwoody College of Technology, A
Hennepin Technical College, A
Lake Superior College, A
Minnesota West Community and Technical College, A
Northland Community and Technical College, A
Northwest Technical College, A
Pine Technical and Community College, A
Ridgewater College, A
St. Cloud Technical & Community College, A
Saint Paul College - A Community & Technical College, A
South Central College, A

Mississippi

East Central Community College, A
East Mississippi Community College, A
Holmes Community College, A
Mississippi Gulf Coast Community College, A
Southwest Mississippi Community College, A

Missouri

Crowder College, A
East Central College, A
Jefferson College, A
Metropolitan Community College - Kansas City, A
Mineral Area College, A
North Central Missouri College, A
Ozarks Technical Community College, A
Ranken Technical College, A
State Fair Community College, A
State Technical College of Missouri, A

Montana

Fort Peck Community College, A
Helena College University of Montana, A
Montana State University Billings, A
Montana State University - Northern, AB
Montana Tech of The University of Montana, A

Nebraska

Central Community College - Columbus Campus, A
Central Community College - Grand Island Campus, A
Central Community College - Hastings Campus, A
Metropolitan Community College, A
Mid-Plains Community College, A
Northeast Community College, A
Southeast Community College, Lincoln Campus, A
Southeast Community College, Milford Campus, A

Nevada

College of Southern Nevada, A
Truckee Meadows Community College, A
Western Nevada College, A

New Hampshire

Great Bay Community College, A
Lakes Region Community College, A
Manchester Community College, A
Nashua Community College, A
White Mountains Community College, A

New Jersey

Rowan College at Gloucester County, A
Union County College, A

New Mexico

Central New Mexico Community College, A
Clovis Community College, A
Doña Ana Community College, A
Eastern New Mexico University - Roswell, A
Mesalands Community College, A
New Mexico Junior College, A
New Mexico State University - Alamogordo, A
San Juan College, A
University of New Mexico - Gallup, A

New York

Columbia-Greene Community College, A
Corning Community College, A

Erie Community College, South Campus, A
Fulton-Montgomery Community College, A
Hudson Valley Community College, A
Monroe Community College, A
Morrisville State College, AB
Onondaga Community College, A
Rockland Community College, A
State University of New York College of Technology
   at Alfred, A
State University of New York College of Technology
   at Canton, A
State University of New York College of Technology
   at Delhi, A
Suffolk County Community College, A
TCI - College of Technology, A

North Carolina

Alamance Community College, A
Asheville-Buncombe Technical Community College,
   A
Beaufort County Community College, A
Blue Ridge Community College, A
Caldwell Community College and Technical Institute,
   A
Cape Fear Community College, A
Catawba Valley Community College, A
Central Carolina Community College, A
Central Piedmont Community College, A
Craven Community College, A
Durham Technical Community College, A
Fayetteville Technical Community College, A
Forsyth Technical Community College, A
Gaston College, A
Guilford Technical Community College, A
Haywood Community College, A
Isothermal Community College, A
Lenoir Community College, A
Martin Community College, A
McDowell Technical Community College, A
Pamlico Community College, A
Pitt Community College, A
Randolph Community College, A
Rowan-Cabarrus Community College, A
Sandhills Community College, A
South Piedmont Community College, A
Southwestern Community College, A
Surry Community College, A
Tri-County Community College, A
Vance-Granville Community College, A
Wake Technical Community College, A
Wayne Community College, A
Wilkes Community College, A
Wilson Community College, A

North Dakota

Bismarck State College, A
Lake Region State College, A
North Dakota State College of Science, A
United Tribes Technical College, A

Ohio

Cincinnati State Technical and Community College,
   A
Cuyahoga Community College, A
Ohio Technical College, A
Sinclair Community College, A
Stark State College, A
University of Northwestern Ohio, A
Washington State Community College, A

Oklahoma

Oklahoma City Community College, A
Oklahoma Technical College, A

Oregon

Central Oregon Community College, A
Chemeketa Community College, A
Clackamas Community College, A
Klamath Community College, A
Lane Community College, A
Linn-Benton Community College, A
Mt. Hood Community College, A
Portland Community College, A
Rogue Community College, A
Umpqua Community College, A

Pennsylvania

Community College of Beaver County, A
Community College of Philadelphia, A
Delaware County Community College, A
Harrisburg Area Community College, A
Johnson College, A
Lincoln Technical Institute (Philadelphia), A
Luzerne County Community College, A
Northampton Community College, A
Pennsylvania College of Technology, A
Rosedale Technical Institute, A
WyoTech Blairsville, A

Rhode Island

New England Institute of Technology, AB

South Carolina

Florence-Darlington Technical College, A
Greenville Technical College, A
Midlands Technical College, A
Orangeburg-Calhoun Technical College, A
Piedmont Technical College, A
Spartanburg Community College, A
Trident Technical College, A
York Technical College, A

South Dakota

Lake Area Technical Institute, A
Southeast Technical Institute, A

Tennessee

Lincoln College of Technology, A
Nashville State Community College, A
Northeast State Community College, A
Southern Adventist University, A
Southwest Tennessee Community College, A

Texas

Alvin Community College, A
Amarillo College, A
Austin Community College District, A
Brazosport College, A
Brookhaven College, A
Cedar Valley College, A
Central Texas College, A
Cisco College, A
Coastal Bend College, A
Del Mar College, A
Eastfield College, A
El Paso Community College, A
Hill College, A
Houston Community College, A
Howard College, A
Kilgore College, A
Lamar State College - Port Arthur, A
Lone Star College - Montgomery, A
Lone Star College - North Harris, A
Midland College, A
North Central Texas College, A
Northeast Texas Community College, A
Odessa College, A
Ranger College, A
St. Philip's College, A
San Jacinto College District, A
South Plains College, A
South Texas College, A
Southwest Texas Junior College, A
Tarrant County College District, A
Texarkana College, A
Texas State Technical College, A
Trinity Valley Community College, A
Tyler Junior College, A
Vernon College, A
Western Technical College (El Paso), A
Western Texas College, A
Wharton County Junior College, A

Utah

Dixie State University, A
Snow College, A
Utah Valley University, A
Weber State University, AB

Virginia

Advanced Technology Institute, A
J. Sargeant Reynolds Community College, A
New River Community College, A
Patrick Henry Community College, A
Thomas Nelson Community College, A
Tidewater Community College, A
Virginia Western Community College, A

Washington

Bellingham Technical College, A
Big Bend Community College, A
Clark College, A
Clover Park Technical College, A
Columbia Basin College, A
Grays Harbor College, A
Green River College, A
Lake Washington Institute of Technology, A
Lower Columbia College, A
Peninsula College, A
Renton Technical College, A
Shoreline Community College, A
Skagit Valley College, A
South Puget Sound Community College, A
South Seattle College, A
Spokane Community College, A
Walla Walla Community College, A
Walla Walla University, AB
Wenatchee Valley College, A
Yakima Valley Community College, A

West Virginia

Southern West Virginia Community and Technical
   College, A
West Virginia University at Parkersburg, A

Wisconsin

Fox Valley Technical College, A
Gateway Technical College, A
Madison Area Technical College, A
Milwaukee Area Technical College, A
Moraine Park Technical College, A
Nicolet Area Technical College, A
Northcentral Technical College, A
Northeast Wisconsin Technical College, A
Waukesha County Technical College, A
Western Technical College, A

Wyoming

Casper College, A
Central Wyoming College, A
Laramie County Community College, A
Western Wyoming Community College, A
WyoTech Laramie, A

U.S. Territories: American Samoa

American Samoa Community College, A

U.S. Territories: Guam

Guam Community College, A

Canada

British Columbia

British Columbia Institute of Technology, A

AUTOMOTIVE ENGINEERING TECHNOLOGY/TECHNICIAN

United States

Alabama

H. Councill Trenholm State Community College, A
J. F. Drake State Community and Technical College,
   A
Lawson State Community College, A

Arizona

Arizona Western College, A

California

Art Center College of Design, B
Palo Verde College, A

Colorado

Colorado State University - Pueblo, B
IntelliTec College (Grand Junction), A

Florida

Florida State College at Jacksonville, A
Santa Fe College, A

Illinois

Southern Illinois University Carbondale, B

Indiana

Indiana State University, B

Kansas

Pittsburg State University, B

Massachusetts

Benjamin Franklin Institute of Technology, AB
Springfield Technical Community College, A

Michigan

College for Creative Studies, M
Ferris State University, B
Lawrence Technological University, M
Macomb Community College, A
Michigan Technological University, O
University of Michigan, M
University of Michigan - Dearborn, MD
Wayne State University, MO

Minnesota

Minnesota State Community and Technical College,
    A
Minnesota State Community and Technical College -
    Detroit Lakes, A
Minnesota State Community and Technical College -
    Moorhead, A
Minnesota State University Mankato, BM

Montana

Miles Community College, A

New Jersey

Brookdale Community College, A
Camden County College, A
Mercer County Community College, A
Middlesex County College, A
Raritan Valley Community College, A
Rowan College at Burlington County, A
Sussex County Community College, A

New York

Farmingdale State College, A

North Dakota

Cankdeska Cikana Community College, A

Ohio

Cincinnati State Technical and Community College,
    A
Columbus State Community College, A
Owens Community College, A
Terra State Community College, A

Oklahoma

Eastern Oklahoma State College, A
Oklahoma City Community College, A
Oklahoma State University Institute of Technology, A

Pennsylvania

Community College of Allegheny County, A
New Castle School of Trades, A
Pennsylvania College of Technology, B
Thaddeus Stevens College of Technology, A

South Carolina

Clemson University, MD

Utah

Weber State University, B

Vermont

Vermont Technical College, A

Washington

Western Washington University, B

West Virginia

BridgeValley Community and Technical College
    (Montgomery), A

U.S. Territories: Puerto Rico

University of Puerto Rico in Carolina, A

AVIATION

United States

Florida

Everglades University (Boca Raton), M
Florida Institute of Technology, MD

Illinois

Lewis University, M

North Dakota

University of North Dakota, M

Oklahoma

Southeastern Oklahoma State University, M

Tennessee

The University of Tennessee, M

AVIATION/AIRWAY MANAGE-MENT AND OPERATIONS

United States

Alabama

Auburn University, B

Alaska

University of Alaska Anchorage, A

Arizona

Arizona State University at the Tempe campus, M
Embry-Riddle Aeronautical University - Prescott, B

California

California Baptist University, B
California State University, Los Angeles, B
Cypress College, A
Glendale Community College, A
Long Beach City College, A
Orange Coast College, A
Palomar College, A

Colorado

Metropolitan State University of Denver, B

Delaware

Delaware State University, B
Wilmington University, B

District of Columbia

University of the District of Columbia, A

Florida

Broward College, A
Embry-Riddle Aeronautical University - Daytona, MD
Embry-Riddle Aeronautical University - Worldwide,
    ABM
Florida Institute of Technology, BM
Florida Memorial University, B
Florida State College at Jacksonville, A

Jacksonville University, B
Lynn University, B
Miami Dade College, A
Polk State College, A
Santa Fe College, A

Georgia

Middle Georgia State University, B

Illinois

Lewis University, BM
Lincoln Land Community College, A
Quincy University, B
Southern Illinois University Carbondale, B
Southwestern Illinois College, A
University of Illinois at Urbana - Champaign, B

Indiana

Indiana State University, B
Purdue University, M

Iowa

Iowa Central Community College, A
Iowa Lakes Community College, A
University of Dubuque, B

Louisiana

Louisiana Tech University, B

Massachusetts

Bridgewater State University, B
Salem State University, B

Michigan

Eastern Michigan University, B
Western Michigan University, B

Minnesota

Academy College, A
Inver Hills Community College, A
Minnesota State University Mankato, B
Vermilion Community College, A

Mississippi

Delta State University, M
Hinds Community College, A

Montana

Rocky Mountain College, B

New Hampshire

Daniel Webster College, BM

New Jersey

Mercer County Community College, A

New Mexico

Eastern New Mexico University, B

New York

Dutchess Community College, A
Farmingdale State College, B
Vaughn College of Aeronautics and Technology,
    ABM

North Dakota

University of North Dakota, B

Ohio

The Ohio State University, B
Ohio University, B
Sinclair Community College, A

Oklahoma

Southeastern Oklahoma State University, M
Western Oklahoma State College, A

Pennsylvania

Community College of Allegheny County, A
Community College of Beaver County, A
Luzerne County Community College, A
Marywood University, B

Tennessee

Middle Tennessee State University, M

Texas

Baylor University, B
Hallmark University, B
LeTourneau University, B
Palo Alto College, A
San Jacinto College District, A
Tarleton State University, B
Texas A&M University - Central Texas, B
Texas Southern University, B

Utah

Dixie State University, B
Westminster College, B

Virginia

Averett University, B
Hampton University, B

Washington

Central Washington University, B
Green River College, A

West Virginia

Fairmont State University, B

U.S. Territories: Puerto Rico

Inter American University of Puerto Rico, Bayamón
Campus, B

Canada

Alberta

Prairie Bible Institute, A

British Columbia

University of the Fraser Valley, B

Ontario

The University of Western Ontario, B

AVIONICS MAINTENANCE TECHNOLOGY/TECHNICIAN

United States

Alabama

Community College of the Air Force, A
Enterprise State Community College, A
Wallace State Community College, A

Alaska

University of Alaska Anchorage, A

Arizona

Cochise County Community College District, A

California

City College of San Francisco, A
College of San Mateo, A
Mt. San Antonio College, A
Reedley College, A
Sacramento City College, A
San Diego Miramar College, A
Shasta College, A
Solano Community College, A
West Los Angeles College, A

Colorado

Redstone College - Denver, A

Connecticut

Gateway Community College, A
Housatonic Community College, A
Quinebaug Valley Community College, A

Georgia

Middle Georgia State University, A

Hawaii

Honolulu Community College, A

Illinois

Lewis University, B
Rock Valley College, A
Southern Illinois University Carbondale, B

Iowa

Indian Hills Community College, A
Iowa Western Community College, A

Kansas

Wichita Area Technical College, A

Louisiana

Southern University at Shreveport, A

Michigan

Lansing Community College, A
Western Michigan University, B

Minnesota

Northland Community and Technical College, A

New York

Excelsior College, A
Schenectady County Community College, A
Vaughn College of Aeronautics and Technology, AB

North Carolina

Guilford Technical Community College, A

Ohio

Cuyahoga Community College, A

Oklahoma

Rose State College, A

Oregon

Mt. Hood Community College, A

Pennsylvania

Pennsylvania College of Technology, B
Pittsburgh Institute of Aeronautics, A

Tennessee

North Central Institute, A

Texas

Hallmark University, A
Palo Alto College, A
Southwest Texas Junior College, A
Tarrant County College District, A
Texas State Technical College, A

Utah

Salt Lake Community College, A

Washington

Big Bend Community College, A
Everett Community College, A
South Seattle College, A
Spokane Community College, A

West Virginia

Fairmont State University, B

Wisconsin

Fox Valley Technical College, A

U.S. Territories: Puerto Rico

Universidad del Este, A

Canada

British Columbia

British Columbia Institute of Technology, A

AYURVEDIC MEDICINE/ AYURVEDA

United States

Iowa

Maharishi University of Management, B

BACTERIOLOGY

United States

Illinois

Illinois State University, M

Iowa

The University of Iowa, MD

Texas

The University of Texas Medical Branch, D

Washington

University of Washington, D

Wisconsin

University of Wisconsin - Madison, M

Canada

Maritime Provinces: Prince Edward Island

University of Prince Edward Island, MD

BAKING AND PASTRY ARTS/ BAKER/PASTRY CHEF

United States

Arizona

The Art Institute of Phoenix, A
The Art Institute of Tucson, A

California

The Art Institute of California - Hollywood, a campus of Argosy University, A
The Art Institute of California - Inland Empire, a campus of Argosy University, A
The Art Institute of California - Los Angeles, a campus of Argosy University, A
The Art Institute of California - Orange County, a campus of Argosy University, A
The Art Institute of California - Sacramento, a campus of Argosy University, A
The Art Institute of California - San Diego, a campus of Argosy University, A
The Art Institute of California - San Francisco, a campus of Argosy University, A

Colorado

The Art Institute of Colorado, A
Colorado Mesa University, A
Johnson & Wales University, B

Florida

The Art Institute of Fort Lauderdale, A
The Art Institute of Tampa, a branch of Miami International University of Art & Design, A
Johnson & Wales University, AB
Keiser University, A
Lincoln College of Technology, A
Lincoln Culinary Institute, A
Valencia College, A

Georgia

The Art Institute of Atlanta, A

Idaho

College of Western Idaho, A

Illinois

College of DuPage, A
Elgin Community College, A
Kendall College, A
Moraine Valley Community College, A

Indiana

The Art Institute of Indianapolis, A
Harrison College, A

Kentucky

Sullivan University, A

Maryland

Stratford University, A

Massachusetts

Newbury College, A

Michigan

Mott Community College, A

Nevada

The Art Institute of Las Vegas, A

New Hampshire

Southern New Hampshire University, A
White Mountains Community College, A

New Jersey

Hudson County Community College, A
Rowan College at Burlington County, A

New Mexico

Navajo Technical University, A

New York

The Culinary Institute of America, A
Monroe College, A
Niagara County Community College, A
Sullivan County Community College, A

North Carolina

Asheville-Buncombe Technical Community College,
A
Cape Fear Community College, A
Harrison College, A
Johnson & Wales University, AB

Ohio

Cincinnati State Technical and Community College,
A

Pennsylvania

The Art Institute of Pittsburgh, A
Bucks County Community College, A
Luzerne County Community College, A
Montgomery County Community College, A
Pennsylvania College of Technology, A
The Restaurant School at Walnut Hill College, AB
Westmoreland County Community College, A

Rhode Island

Johnson & Wales University, AB

South Carolina

The Art Institute of Charleston, a branch of The Art
Institute of Atlanta, A

Tennessee

The Art Institute of Tennessee - Nashville, a branch
of The Art Institute of Atlanta, A

Texas

The Art Institute of Austin, a branch of The Art Institute of Houston, A
The Art Institute of Dallas, a campus of South University, A
The Art Institute of Houston, A

The Art Institute of San Antonio, a branch of The Art
Institute of Houston, A
Collin County Community College District, A
Culinary Institute LeNotre, A
El Centro College, A
San Jacinto College District, A

Vermont

New England Culinary Institute, A

Virginia

The Art Institute of Virginia Beach, a branch of The
Art Institute of Atlanta, A
The Art Institute of Washington, a branch of The Art
Institute of Atlanta, A
J. Sargeant Reynolds Community College, A
Stratford University (Alexandria), A
Stratford University (Falls Church), A
Stratford University (Glen Allen), A
Stratford University (Newport News), A
Stratford University (Virginia Beach), A
Stratford University (Woodbridge), A

Washington

The Art Institute of Seattle, A
Clark College, A

West Virginia

Blue Ridge Community and Technical College, A

Wisconsin

Waukesha County Technical College, A

BALLET

United States

Indiana

Indiana University Bloomington, B

Kansas

Friends University, B

New York

Marymount Manhattan College, B

Texas

Texas Christian University, B

Utah

Brigham Young University, B
University of Utah, B

BANKING AND FINANCIAL SUPPORT SERVICES

United States

Arizona

Phoenix College, A

California

City College of San Francisco, A
Cosumnes River College, A
Hartnell College, A
Los Angeles Valley College, A
Modesto Junior College, A
Southwestern College, A

Colorado

Colorado Northwestern Community College, A

Connecticut

Asnuntuck Community College, A
Capital Community College, A
Three Rivers Community College, A

Delaware

Delaware State University, B

Florida

Indian River State College, A
Miami Dade College, A
St. Petersburg College, A
Seminole State College of Florida, A
South Florida State College, A
University of North Florida, B

Georgia

Central Georgia Technical College, A
Lanier Technical College, A
Ogeechee Technical College, A
Wiregrass Georgia Technical College, A

Hawaii

Hawai'i Pacific University, B

Illinois

Black Hawk College, A
Harper College, A
Illinois Central College, A
John A. Logan College, A
Oakton Community College, A
University of Illinois at Urbana - Champaign, B

Indiana

Harrison College, A

Iowa

Buena Vista University, B

Kansas

Allen Community College, A
Barton County Community College, A

Kentucky

Brescia University, AB
Madisonville Community College, A

Louisiana

Southern University at Shreveport, A

Maine

Eastern Maine Community College, A
Husson University, B

Massachusetts

Bristol Community College, A

Michigan

Lansing Community College, A
Northwood University, Michigan Campus, B

Mississippi

East Mississippi Community College, A
Hinds Community College, A

Nebraska

Northeast Community College, A
University of Nebraska - Lincoln, B
University of Nebraska at Omaha, B

Nevada

College of Southern Nevada, A

New Jersey

Saint Peter's University, B

New Mexico

Santa Fe Community College, A

New York

Globe Institute of Technology, A
Hilbert College, A
Mohawk Valley Community College, A
State University of New York College of Agriculture
and Technology at Cobleskill, B
Touro College, A

North Carolina

Alamance Community College, A
Cleveland Community College, A

Craven Community College, A
Fayetteville Technical Community College, A
Rockingham Community College, A

Ohio

Harrison College, A
Northwest State Community College, A
Ohio Business College (Sheffield Village), A
Stautzenberger College (Brecksville), A
Terra State Community College, A
Youngstown State University, B

Oklahoma

Oklahoma City Community College, A

Pennsylvania

Community College of Allegheny County, A
Community College of Beaver County, A
Harrisburg Area Community College, A
Lackawanna College, A
Laurel Business Institute, A
Luzerne County Community College, A
Westmoreland County Community College, A

Rhode Island

Community College of Rhode Island, A

South Dakota

Lake Area Technical Institute, A
Southeast Technical Institute, A

Texas

Houston Community College, A
Sam Houston State University, B
Texas Southern University, B
University of the Incarnate Word, B
The University of Texas at Arlington, B

West Virginia

BridgeValley Community and Technical College
    (South Charleston), A
West Liberty University, B

Wisconsin

Fox Valley Technical College, A
Milwaukee Area Technical College, A

U.S. Territories: Puerto Rico

National University College (Bayamón), B
Universidad Metropolitana, A

BARBERING/BARBER

United States

Illinois

Rend Lake College, A

Mississippi

Coahoma Community College, A

BEHAVIORAL SCIENCES

United States

Alabama

Athens State University, B
Miles College, B

Arizona

Glendale Community College, A
South Mountain Community College, A
Western International University, B

Arkansas

Shorter College, A

California

California Baptist University, B
California State University, Dominguez Hills, B
Citrus College, A
Concordia University Irvine, B
De Anza College, A
Glendale Community College, A
Imperial Valley College, A
Irvine Valley College, A
Los Angeles Southwest College, A
Los Medanos College, A
Modesto Junior College, A
Moorpark College, A
Napa Valley College, A
San Diego City College, A
San Jose State University, B
Santa Rosa Junior College, A
University of La Verne, B

Colorado

Colorado Mountain College (Glenwood Springs), A
Colorado Mountain College (Steamboat Springs), A
Metropolitan State University of Denver, B
United States Air Force Academy, B

Connecticut

Naugatuck Valley Community College, A
Northwestern Connecticut Community College, A

Delaware

Wilmington University, B

Florida

Miami Dade College, A
Nova Southeastern University, B

Georgia

Carver College, B

Hawaii

Chaminade University of Honolulu, B
Hawai'i Pacific University, B

Idaho

Lewis-Clark State College, A

Illinois

East-West University, B
Loyola University Chicago, A

Indiana

Ancilla College, A
Purdue University Northwest (Hammond), B
Purdue University Northwest (Westville), B
Vincennes University, A

Iowa

Iowa Lakes Community College, A

Kansas

Dodge City Community College, A
Labette Community College, A
Sterling College, B
Tabor College, B
The University of Kansas, B

Maine

University of Maine at Fort Kent, B
University of Maine at Machias, B

Maryland

Johns Hopkins University, B
Morgan State University, B

Massachusetts

Tufts University, B

Michigan

Andrews University, B
Northern Michigan University, B
Rochester College, B

Minnesota

Bemidji State University, B
Minnesota State University Mankato, B
St. Cloud State University, B

Mississippi

Mississippi Delta Community College, A

Missouri

Evangel University, B
Missouri Baptist University, B
University of Missouri, B

Nebraska

Concordia University, Nebraska, B
Midland University, B
University of Nebraska at Omaha, B

New Hampshire

Granite State College, A

New Jersey

Rider University, B

New Mexico

Santa Fe Community College, A
University of New Mexico - Taos, A

New York

Concordia College - New York, B
Fulton-Montgomery Community College, A
Monroe Community College, A

North Carolina

Mars Hill University, B
Methodist University, AB
Saint Augustine's University, B

Ohio

Walsh University, B

Oklahoma

Mid-America Christian University, B
Seminole State College, A

Oregon

George Fox University, B
Umpqua Community College, A

Pennsylvania

Carnegie Mellon University, B
Duquesne University, B
Point Park University, B
Widener University, B
York College of Pennsylvania, B

Rhode Island

Brown University, B

South Carolina

Columbia College, B

South Dakota

Dakota Wesleyan University, B

Tennessee

American Baptist College, B
Martin Methodist College, B
Tennessee Wesleyan College, B
Trevecca Nazarene University, B

Texas

Amarillo College, A
Clarendon College, A
Galveston College, A
Hill College, A
Howard College, A
San Jacinto College District, A
South Texas College, A
Tyler Junior College, A
University of Houston - Clear Lake, B
University of North Texas, B
Wharton County Junior College, A

Vermont

College of St. Joseph, B
Goddard College, B
Marlboro College, B

Washington

Central Washington University, B
Highline College, A

West Virginia

BridgeValley Community and Technical College
(South Charleston), A
Glenville State College, B

Wisconsin

University of Wisconsin - Green Bay, B

U.S. Territories: Puerto Rico

Inter American University of Puerto Rico, San
Germán Campus, B

Canada

Alberta

Ambrose University, B
Rocky Mountain College, B

Ontario

Laurentian University, B

Quebec

Université du Québec en Abitibi-Témiscamingue, B

BIBLE/BIBLICAL STUDIES

United States

Alabama

Amridge University, B
Faulkner University, B
Heritage Christian University, AB
Oakwood University, A
Selma University, AB
Southeastern Bible College, AB

Alaska

Alaska Bible College, AB

Arizona

Arizona Christian University, B
Grand Canyon University, B
International Baptist College and Seminary, AB

Arkansas

Central Baptist College, B
Crowley's Ridge College, A
Ecclesia College, AB
Harding University, B
John Brown University, B
Ouachita Baptist University, B

California

Azusa Pacific University, B
Bethesda University, B
Biola University, B
California Baptist University, B
Fresno Pacific University, B
Hope International University, B
Horizon University, A
Life Pacific College, AB
The Master's College and Seminary, B
Patten University, AB
Point Loma Nazarene University, B
San Diego Christian College, B
Shasta Bible College, AB
Simpson University, AB
Southern California Seminary, AB
SUM Bible College & Theological Seminary, AB
Vanguard University of Southern California, B

Colorado

Nazarene Bible College, B

Florida

The Baptist College of Florida, B
Belhaven University, A
Florida College, B
Hobe Sound Bible College, B
Johnson University Florida, AB
Palm Beach Atlantic University, B
Talmudic University, B
Trinity Baptist College, B
Trinity College of Florida, A
Warner University, B

Georgia

Beulah Heights University, AB
Carver College, AB
Covenant College, AB
Luther Rice College & Seminary, B
Point University, AB
Toccoa Falls College, B
Truett-McConnell College, B

Idaho

Boise Bible College, AB
Northwest Nazarene University, B

Illinois

Judson University, B
Lincoln Christian University, AB
Moody Bible Institute, B
North Park University, B
Trinity International University, B
Wheaton College, B

Indiana

Anderson University, B
Bethel College, AB
Crossroads Bible College, B
Goshen College, B
Grace College, AB
Huntington University, B
Indiana Wesleyan University, B
Taylor University, B

Iowa

Emmaus Bible College, AB
Faith Baptist Bible College and Theological Semi-
nary, AB
INSTE Bible College, B
Shiloh University, B

Kansas

Barclay College, AB
Central Christian College of Kansas, AB
Hesston College, A
Manhattan Christian College, AB
MidAmerica Nazarene University, B

Kentucky

Asbury University, B
Campbellsville University, AB
Clear Creek Baptist Bible College, AB
Kentucky Christian University, B
Kentucky Mountain Bible College, AB
The Southern Baptist Theological Seminary, B

Maryland

Maple Springs Baptist Bible College and Seminary,
AB

Massachusetts

Boston Baptist College, AB
Gordon College, B
Northpoint Bible College, B

Michigan

Andrews University, B
Calvin College, B
Cornerstone University, B
Grace Bible College, B
Great Lakes Christian College, B
Kuyper College, AB

Rochester College, B
Spring Arbor University, B

Minnesota

Bethel University, B
Crossroads College, B
North Central University, AB
University of Minnesota, Twin Cities Campus, B
University of Northwestern - St. Paul, B

Mississippi

Belhaven University, B
Blue Mountain College, B
Southeastern Baptist College, AB

Missouri

Calvary Bible College and Theological Seminary, AB
Central Christian College of the Bible, A
College of the Ozarks, B
Evangel University, B
Global University, B
Hannibal-LaGrange University, B
Midwest University, B
Ozark Christian College, B
Saint Louis Christian College, B
Southwest Baptist University, B

Nebraska

Grace University, AB
Union College, B
York College, B

New Jersey

Pillar College, AB

New York

Canisius College, B
Davis College, AB
Houghton College, AB
The Jewish Theological Seminary, B
Nyack College, AB
Rabbinical Academy Mesivta Rabbi Chaim Berlin, B
Roberts Wesleyan College, B

North Carolina

Carolina Christian College, AB
Carolina College of Biblical Studies, AB
Charlotte Christian College and Theological Semi-
nary, AB
Gardner-Webb University, B
John Wesley University, A
Methodist University, B
Mid-Atlantic Christian University, AB
Montreat College, B
Piedmont International University, AB

North Dakota

Trinity Bible College, AB

Ohio

Bluffton University, B
Cedarville University, B
Cincinnati Christian University, AB
God's Bible School and College, A
Malone University, B
Mount Vernon Nazarene University, B
Rosedale Bible College, A
Tri-State Bible College, AB

Oklahoma

Oklahoma Baptist University, B
Oklahoma Christian University, B
Oklahoma Wesleyan University, B
Oral Roberts University, B
Southwestern Christian University, B

Oregon

Corban University, AB
George Fox University, B
Multnomah University, B
New Hope Christian College, B
Northwest Christian University, B

Pennsylvania

Cairn University, B
Eastern University, B
Geneva College, B
Lancaster Bible College, AB
Messiah College, B
Summit University, B
University of Valley Forge, AB
Waynesburg University, B

South Carolina

Bob Jones University, B
North Greenville University, B

Tennessee

Belmont University, B
Bryan College, B
Carson-Newman University, B
Freed-Hardeman University, B
Johnson University, B
King University, B
Lee University, B
Lipscomb University, B
Milligan College, B
Southern Adventist University, AB
Union University, B
Welch College, AB
Williamson College, B

Texas

Abilene Christian University, B
Amarillo College, A
Arlington Baptist College, B
Austin Graduate School of Theology, B
Baptist University of the Americas, B
College of Biblical Studies - Houston, AB
Criswell College, AB
Dallas Baptist University, AB
Dallas Christian College, B
East Texas Baptist University, B
Hardin-Simmons University, B
Howard Payne University, AB
LeTourneau University, B
Lubbock Christian University, B
Messenger College, B
Rio Grande Bible Institute, B
Southwestern Assemblies of God University, AB
Southwestern Christian College, B

Vermont

Marlboro College, B

Virginia

Bluefield College, B
Eastern Mennonite University, AB
Liberty University, B
University of Valley Forge Virginia Campus, B

Washington

Northwest University, B

West Virginia

Appalachian Bible College, AB
Ohio Valley University, B

Wisconsin

Maranatha Baptist University, B

U.S. Territories: Puerto Rico

Theological University of the Caribbean, B

Canada

Alberta

Prairie Bible Institute, AB
Rocky Mountain College, B
Vanguard College, B

British Columbia

Columbia Bible College, B
Summit Pacific College, B
Trinity Western University, B

Manitoba

Providence University College & Theological Seminary, B

Maritime Provinces: New Brunswick

Crandall University, B
Kingswood University, B

Ontario

Emmanuel Bible College, B
Heritage College and Seminary, B
Master's College and Seminary, B
Redeemer University College, B
Tyndale University College & Seminary, B
The University of Western Ontario, B

Quebec

Université de Montréal, B

Saskatchewan

Briercrest College, AB
Eston College, B
Horizon College & Seminary, B

BILINGUAL AND MULTILINGUAL EDUCATION

United States

California

California State University, Stanislaus, B
University of San Francisco, B

Delaware

Delaware Technical & Community College, Terry Campus, A
University of Delaware, B

Idaho

Boise State University, B
College of Southern Idaho, A

Illinois

Aurora University, B
Chicago State University, B
Loyola University Chicago, B
Northeastern Illinois University, B
Western Illinois University, B

Massachusetts

Boston University, B

Michigan

Calvin College, B

Nevada

Nevada State College, B

New Mexico

University of the Southwest, B

New York

Brooklyn College of the City University of New York, B
Canisius College, B
State University of New York College at Old Westbury, B
York College of the City University of New York, B

Ohio

The University of Findlay, B

South Dakota

Oglala Lakota College, B

Texas

Midwestern State University, B
Our Lady of the Lake University of San Antonio, B
Southwestern Assemblies of God University, B
Texas A&M International University, B

Texas Christian University, B
Texas Wesleyan University, B
The University of Texas at San Antonio, B

Vermont

Goddard College, B

Washington

Washington State University, B

U.S. Territories: Puerto Rico

University of the Sacred Heart, B

Canada

Ontario

York University, B

Quebec

McGill University, B

Saskatchewan

University of Regina, B

BIOCHEMICAL ENGINEERING

United States

California

University of California, Irvine, MD

Georgia

University of Georgia, M

Iowa

The University of Iowa, MD

Maryland

University of Maryland, Baltimore County, MDO

New Hampshire

Dartmouth College, MD

New Jersey

Rutgers University - New Brunswick, MD

New York

Cornell University, MD

Pennsylvania

Drexel University, M
Villanova University, O

Rhode Island

Brown University, MD

Canada

Ontario

The University of Western Ontario, MD

BIOCHEMISTRY

United States

Alabama

Auburn University, BMD
Huntingdon College, B
Oakwood University, B
Samford University, B
Spring Hill College, B
The University of Alabama at Birmingham, D

Alaska

University of Alaska Fairbanks, MD

Arizona

Arizona State University at the Tempe campus, BMD
The University of Arizona, BD

Arkansas

Harding University, B
John Brown University, B
University of Arkansas for Medical Sciences, MD

California

Azusa Pacific University, B
Biola University, B
California Institute of Technology, MD
California Lutheran University, B
California Polytechnic State University, San Luis Obispo, BM
California State University, Chico, B
California State University, Dominguez Hills, B
California State University, East Bay, BM
California State University, Fullerton, B
California State University, Long Beach, BM
California State University, Los Angeles, BM
California State University, Northridge, BM
California State University, San Marcos, B
Chapman University, B
Claremont McKenna College, B
Humboldt State University, B
La Sierra University, B
Loma Linda University, MD
Loyola Marymount University, B
Mills College, B
Mount Saint Mary's University, B
Notre Dame de Namur University, B
Occidental College, B
Pacific Union College, B
Pasadena City College, A
Pitzer College, B
Point Loma Nazarene University, B
Saint Katherine College, B
Saint Mary's College of California, B
San Diego State University, MD
San Francisco State University, BM
San Jose State University, B
Santa Clara University, B
Scripps College, B
Sonoma State University, M
Stanford University, D
University of California, Berkeley, D
University of California, Davis, M
University of California, Irvine, MD
University of California, Los Angeles, BMD
University of California, Merced, MD
University of California, Riverside, BMD
University of California, San Diego, BMD
University of California, Santa Barbara, D
University of California, Santa Cruz, BMD
University of the Pacific, B
University of San Diego, B
University of Southern California, BM
Vanguard University of Southern California, B
Whittier College, B

Colorado

Adams State University, B
The Colorado College, B
Colorado State University, BMD
Colorado State University - Pueblo, M
Fort Lewis College, B
Regis University, B
United States Air Force Academy, B
University of Colorado Boulder, BMD
University of Colorado Colorado Springs, B
University of Colorado Denver, D
University of Denver, B
Western State Colorado University, B

Connecticut

Central Connecticut State University, BO
Connecticut College, B
Eastern Connecticut State University, B
Fairfield University, B
Quinnipiac University, B
Trinity College, B
University of Connecticut, MD

University of New Haven, B
University of Saint Joseph, BM
Wesleyan University, D
Yale University, D

Delaware

University of Delaware, BMD

District of Columbia

American University, B
The Catholic University of America, B
The George Washington University, MD
Georgetown University, BMD
Howard University, MD
Trinity Washington University, B

Florida

Ave Maria University, B
Broward College, A
Eckerd College, B
Florida Institute of Technology, BM
Florida State University, BMD
New College of Florida, B
Pensacola State College, A
Rollins College, B
South Florida State College, A
Stetson University, B
University of Florida, D
University of Miami, BD
The University of Tampa, B
University of West Florida, M

Georgia

Agnes Scott College, B
Armstrong State University, B
Augusta University, MD
Berry College, B
Emory University, D
Georgia Institute of Technology, B
Georgia State University, MD
Kennesaw State University, BM
LaGrange College, B
Mercer University, B
Spelman College, B
University of Georgia, MD

Hawaii

Brigham Young University - Hawaii, B
Chaminade University of Honolulu, B
University of Hawaii at Manoa, B

Idaho

Idaho State University, B
Northwest Nazarene University, B
University of Idaho, BD

Illinois

Augustana College, B
Bradley University, BM
Dominican University, B
Elmhurst College, B
Illinois Institute of Technology, BM
Illinois State University, BM
Judson University, B
Knox College, B
Lewis University, B
Loyola University Chicago, BMD
Monmouth College, B
North Central College, B
Northwestern University, BD
Rockford University, B
Roosevelt University, B
Rush University, MD
Southern Illinois University Carbondale, MD
Trinity Christian College, B
University of Chicago, D
University of Illinois at Chicago, BD
University of Illinois at Urbana - Champaign, BMD

Indiana

Anderson University, B
DePauw University, B
Earlham College, B
Hanover College, B
Indiana University Bloomington, BD

Indiana University East, B
Indiana University Kokomo, B
Indiana University - Purdue University Indianapolis, MD
Indiana University South Bend, B
Indiana Wesleyan University, B
Manchester University, B
Purdue University, BMD
Rose-Hulman Institute of Technology, B
Saint Joseph's College, AB
Taylor University, B
University of Evansville, B
University of Notre Dame, BMD
University of Southern Indiana, B
Valparaiso University, B
Vincennes University, A
Wabash College, B

Iowa

Central College, B
Clarke University, B
Coe College, B
Cornell College, B
Drake University, B
Grand View University, B
Grinnell College, B
Iowa State University of Science and Technology, B
Loras College, B
Mount Mercy University, B
Northwestern College, B
Simpson College, B
The University of Iowa, BMD
University of Northern Iowa, B
Wartburg College, B

Kansas

Benedictine College, B
Kansas State University, BMD
McPherson College, B
Newman University, B
Southwestern College, B
Tabor College, B
The University of Kansas, BMD
Washburn University, B

Kentucky

Asbury University, B
Georgetown College, B
Thomas More College, B
University of Kentucky, D
University of Louisville, MD
Western Kentucky University, B

Louisiana

Centenary College of Louisiana, B
Louisiana State University and Agricultural & Mechanical College, BMD
Loyola University New Orleans, B
Southern University and Agricultural and Mechanical College, M
Tulane University, BMD
Xavier University of Louisiana, B

Maine

Bates College, B
Bowdoin College, B
Colby College, B
University of Maine, B
University of New England, B

Maryland

Hood College, B
Johns Hopkins University, MD
Mount St. Mary's University, B
St. Mary's College of Maryland, B
Stevenson University, B
University of Maryland, Baltimore County, D
University of Maryland, College Park, BMD
Washington Adventist University, B

Massachusetts

American International College, B
Bay Path University, B
Boston College, BD
Boston University, MD

Brandeis University, BD
Bridgewater State University, B
Clark University, B
Curry College, B
Eastern Nazarene College, B
Emmanuel College, B
Harvard University, BD
Massachusetts Institute of Technology, D
Merrimack College, B
Mount Holyoke College, B
Northeastern University, B
Regis College, B
Salem State University, B
Smith College, B
Stonehill College, B
Tufts University, B
University of Massachusetts Amherst, MD
University of Massachusetts Boston, B
University of Massachusetts Dartmouth, MD
University of Massachusetts Lowell, D
Wellesley College, B
Wheaton College, B
Worcester Polytechnic Institute, BMD

Michigan

Adrian College, B
Albion College, B
Alma College, B
Andrews University, B
Calvin College, B
Central Michigan University, B
Eastern Michigan University, B
Ferris State University, B
Hillsdale College, B
Kettering University, B
Lake Superior State University, AB
Lawrence Technological University, B
Madonna University, B
Michigan State University, BMD
Michigan Technological University, D
Northern Michigan University, BM
Oakland University, B
Olivet College, B
Saginaw Valley State University, B
Spring Arbor University, B
University of Detroit Mercy, BM
University of Michigan, BMD
University of Michigan - Dearborn, B
University of Michigan - Flint, B
Wayne State University, MD
Western Michigan University, B

Minnesota

College of Saint Benedict, B
The College of St. Scholastica, B
Gustavus Adolphus College, B
Hamline University, B
Minnesota State University Mankato, B
St. Catherine University, B
Saint John's University, B
Saint Mary's University of Minnesota, B
University of Minnesota, Duluth, BMD
University of Minnesota, Twin Cities Campus, BD
University of Northwestern - St. Paul, B
University of St. Thomas, B
Winona State University, B

Mississippi

Millsaps College, B
Mississippi College, BM
Mississippi State University, BMD
University of Mississippi, B
University of Mississippi Medical Center, D
University of Southern Mississippi, MD

Missouri

Maryville University of Saint Louis, B
Missouri Baptist University, B
Missouri Southern State University, B
Missouri Western State University, B
Rockhurst University, B
Saint Louis University, BD
University of Missouri, BMD
University of Missouri - Kansas City, D
University of Missouri - St. Louis, BMD
Washington University in St. Louis, BD

Westminster College, B
William Jewell College, B

Montana

Montana State University, MD
University of Montana, BD

Nebraska

Doane University, B
University of Nebraska - Lincoln, BMD
University of Nebraska Medical Center, D

Nevada

University of Nevada, Las Vegas, BM
University of Nevada, Reno, BMD

New Hampshire

Dartmouth College, BD
Saint Anselm College, B
University of New Hampshire, BMD

New Jersey

College of Saint Elizabeth, B
Drew University, B
Fairleigh Dickinson University, College at Florham,
    B
Fairleigh Dickinson University, Metropolitan Cam-
    pus, B
Georgian Court University, B
Montclair State University, BM
New Jersey Institute of Technology, B
Ramapo College of New Jersey, B
Rider University, B
Rowan University, B
Rutgers University - New Brunswick, BMD
Rutgers University - Newark, MD
Saint Peter's University, B
Seton Hall University, BMD
Stevens Institute of Technology, BMDO
Stockton University, B

New Mexico

Eastern New Mexico University, BM
New Mexico State University, B
University of New Mexico, BMD

New York

Adelphi University, B
Barnard College, B
Binghamton University, State University of New
    York, B
Canisius College, B
City College of the City University of New York,
    BMD
Colgate University, B
The College at Brockport, State University of New
    York, B
College of Mount Saint Vincent, B
The College of Saint Rose, B
College of Staten Island of the City University of
    New York, B
Columbia University, BMD
Columbia University, School of General Studies, B
Cornell University, MD
Daemen College, B
Hamilton College, B
Hartwick College, B
Hobart and William Smith Colleges, B
Hofstra University, B
Houghton College, B
Hunter College of the City University of New York,
    MD
Iona College, B
Ithaca College, B
Keuka College, B
Le Moyne College, B
Lehman College of the City University of New York,
    B
Long Island University - LIU Brooklyn, B
Manhattan College, B
Manhattanville College, B
Marist College, B
Nazareth College of Rochester, B
New York University, B
Niagara University, B

Pace University, B
Pace University, Pleasantville Campus, B
Purchase College, State University of New York, B
Queens College of the City University of New York,
    M
Rensselaer Polytechnic Institute, MD
Roberts Wesleyan College, B
Rochester Institute of Technology, B
The Sage Colleges, B
St. Bonaventure University, B
St. Lawrence University, B
Siena College, B
State University of New York College of Environ-
    mental Science and Forestry, BMD
State University of New York College at Geneseo, B
State University of New York College at Old
    Westbury, B
State University of New York College at Oneonta, B
State University of New York College at Potsdam, B
State University of New York at Fredonia, B
State University of New York at New Paltz, B
State University of New York at Oswego, B
State University of New York at Plattsburgh, B
State University of New York Upstate Medical Uni-
    versity, MD
Stony Brook University, State University of New
    York, BMD
Syracuse University, BD
Union College, B
University at Albany, State University of New York, B
University at Buffalo, the State University of New
    York, BMD
University of Rochester, D
Vassar College, B
Wells College, B
Yeshiva University, B

North Carolina

Campbell University, B
Duke University, D
East Carolina University, BMD
Elon University, B
High Point University, B
North Carolina State University, BD
Queens University of Charlotte, B
The University of North Carolina at Chapel Hill, MD
The University of North Carolina at Greensboro, BM
Wake Forest University, D

North Dakota

North Dakota State University, MD
University of Jamestown, B
University of North Dakota, MD

Ohio

Bowling Green State University, B
Capital University, B
Case Western Reserve University, BMD
The College of Wooster, B
Denison University, B
Hiram College, B
Kenyon College, B
Malone University, B
Marietta College, B
Miami University, BMD
Miami University Hamilton, B
Mount St. Joseph University, B
Notre Dame College, B
Oberlin College, B
Ohio Northern University, B
The Ohio State University, BMD
Ohio University, MD
Otterbein University, B
The University of Akron, B
University of Cincinnati, BMD
University of Dayton, B
University of Mount Union, B
The University of Toledo, BMD
Wright State University, M
Youngstown State University, BM

Oklahoma

Oklahoma Baptist University, B
Oklahoma Christian University, B
Oklahoma City University, B
Oklahoma State University, BMD

Oral Roberts University, B
Southern Nazarene University, B
University of Oklahoma, BMD
University of Oklahoma Health Sciences Center, MD
The University of Tulsa, BM

Oregon

George Fox University, B
Lewis & Clark College, B
Oregon Health & Science University, MD
Oregon State University, MD
Portland State University, B
Reed College, B
Southern Oregon University, B
University of Oregon, BMD

Pennsylvania

Albright College, B
Allegheny College, B
Alvernia University, B
Bucknell University, B
Carnegie Mellon University, D
Cedar Crest College, B
Chatham University, B
Chestnut Hill College, B
DeSales University, B
Dickinson College, B
Drexel University, MD
Duquesne University, B
East Stroudsburg University of Pennsylvania, B
Eastern University, B
Elizabethtown College, B
Franklin & Marshall College, B
Gannon University, B
Geneva College, B
Gettysburg College, B
Grove City College, B
Haverford College, B
Holy Family University, B
Indiana University of Pennsylvania, B
Juniata College, B
Kutztown University of Pennsylvania, B
La Roche College, B
La Salle University, B
Lafayette College, B
Lehigh University, BD
Mansfield University of Pennsylvania, B
Mercyhurst University, B
Messiah College, B
Misericordia University, B
Moravian College, B
Muhlenberg College, B
Penn State Abington, B
Penn State Altoona, B
Penn State Beaver, B
Penn State Berks, B
Penn State Brandywine, B
Penn State DuBois, B
Penn State Erie, The Behrend College, B
Penn State Fayette, The Eberly Campus, B
Penn State Greater Allegheny, B
Penn State Hazleton, B
Penn State Lehigh Valley, B
Penn State Mont Alto, B
Penn State New Kensington, B
Penn State Schuylkill, B
Penn State Shenango, B
Penn State University Park, BMD
Penn State Wilkes-Barre, B
Penn State Worthington Scranton, B
Penn State York, B
Philadelphia University, B
Rosemont College, B
Saint Joseph's University, B
Saint Vincent College, B
Seton Hill University, B
Slippery Rock University of Pennsylvania, B
Susquehanna University, B
Swarthmore College, B
Temple University, B
Thomas Jefferson University, D
University of Pennsylvania, BD
University of the Sciences, BMD
The University of Scranton, BM
Ursinus College, B
Villanova University, B

Washington & Jefferson College, B
West Chester University of Pennsylvania, B
Westminster College, B
Widener University, B
Wilkes University, B

Rhode Island

Brown University, BMD
Bryant University, B
Providence College, B
Roger Williams University, B
University of Rhode Island, MD

South Carolina

Charleston Southern University, B
Claflin University, B
Clemson University, BD
Coastal Carolina University, B
Columbia College, B
Converse College, B
Furman University, B
Medical University of South Carolina, MD
Presbyterian College, B
University of South Carolina, MD

South Dakota

Augustana University, B
Dakota Wesleyan University, B
South Dakota State University, B

Tennessee

Belmont University, B
Carson-Newman University, B
Christian Brothers University, B
East Tennessee State University, D
Freed-Hardeman University, B
King University, B
Lee University, B
Lipscomb University, B
Maryville College, B
Sewanee: The University of the South, B
Southern Adventist University, B
Tennessee Technological University, B
The University of Tennessee, MD
Vanderbilt University, MD

Texas

Abilene Christian University, B
Austin College, B
Baylor University, B
Lamar University, B
Lubbock Christian University, B
McMurry University, B
Rice University, BMD
St. Edward's University, B
St. Mary's University, B
Schreiner University, B
Southern Methodist University, B
Southwestern Adventist University, B
Southwestern University, B
Stephen F. Austin State University, B
Texas A&M University, BMD
Texas Christian University, B
Texas State University, BM
Texas Tech University, B
Texas Wesleyan University, B
Texas Woman's University, B
Trinity University, B
University of Dallas, B
University of Houston, BMD
University of the Incarnate Word, B
University of Mary Hardin-Baylor, B
University of North Texas, BM
University of St. Thomas, B
The University of Texas at Arlington, B
The University of Texas at Austin, BD
The University of Texas at Dallas, B
The University of Texas Health Science Center at
  Houston, MD
The University of Texas Health Science Center at
  San Antonio, MD
The University of Texas Medical Branch, D
The University of Texas at San Antonio, B

Utah

Brigham Young University, MD
University of Utah, MD
Utah State University, MD

Vermont

Marlboro College, B
Middlebury College, B
Saint Michael's College, B
University of Vermont, B

Virginia

Bridgewater College, B
Christopher Newport University, B
Eastern Mennonite University, B
George Mason University, MD
Liberty University, B
Marymount University, B
Old Dominion University, BM
Roanoke College, B
University of Virginia, D
Virginia Commonwealth University, MDO
Virginia Polytechnic Institute and State University, B
Washington and Lee University, B

Washington

Central Washington University, B
Gonzaga University, B
Seattle Pacific University, B
Seattle University, B
University of Puget Sound, B
University of Washington, BD
University of Washington, Bothell, B
Walla Walla University, B
Washington State University, BMD
Western Washington University, B
Whitman College, B

West Virginia

Bethany College, B
University of Charleston, B
West Virginia University, BMD

Wisconsin

Beloit College, B
Carroll University, B
Lakeland College, B
Lawrence University, B
Ripon College, B
University of Wisconsin - La Crosse, B
University of Wisconsin - Madison, BMD
University of Wisconsin - Milwaukee, BD
University of Wisconsin - Stevens Point, B
Viterbo University, B
Wisconsin Lutheran College, B

U.S. Territories: Puerto Rico

Universidad Central del Caribe, M
University of Puerto Rico, Medical Sciences Campus, MD

Canada

Alberta

University of Alberta, BMD
University of Calgary, BMD
University of Lethbridge, BM

British Columbia

Simon Fraser University, BMDO
Thompson Rivers University, B
The University of British Columbia, BMD
The University of British Columbia - Okanagan
  Campus, B
University of Victoria, BMD

Manitoba

University of Manitoba, MD
The University of Winnipeg, B

Maritime Provinces: New Brunswick

Mount Allison University, B
Université de Moncton, BM

University of New Brunswick Fredericton, B

Maritime Provinces: Nova Scotia

Dalhousie University, MD
University of King's College, B

Newfoundland and Labrador

Memorial University of Newfoundland, BMD

Ontario

Brock University, B
Carleton University, B
Laurentian University, BM
McMaster University, BMD
Queen's University at Kingston, BMD
Trent University, B
University of Guelph, BMD
University of Ottawa, BMD
University of Toronto, BMD
University of Waterloo, BMD
The University of Western Ontario, BMD
University of Windsor, BMD

Quebec

Bishop's University, B
McGill University, BMD
Université Laval, BMDO
Université de Montréal, BMDO
Université du Québec à Montréal, B
Université du Québec à Trois-Rivières, B
Université de Sherbrooke, BMD

Saskatchewan

University of Regina, BMD
University of Saskatchewan, BMD

BIOCHEMISTRY, BIOPHYSICS AND MOLECULAR BIOLOGY

United States

Arkansas

Harding University, B
Hendrix College, B

California

California Baptist University, B
California State University, Long Beach, B
University of California, Irvine, B

Florida

Florida Southern College, B
University of Miami, B

Georgia

University of Georgia, B

Illinois

Benedictine University, B
Blackburn College, B

Indiana

Indiana University Kokomo, B
Purdue University, B

Kentucky

Bellarmine University, B
Centre College, B

Maryland

Goucher College, B
Towson University, B
University of Maryland, Baltimore County, B

Massachusetts

Amherst College, B
Boston University, B
Simmons College, B
University of Massachusetts Amherst, B

Michigan

Hope College, B
Michigan State University, B
Michigan Technological University, B

Minnesota

Minnesota State Community and Technical College, A
Minnesota State University Moorhead, B
University of Minnesota, Duluth, B

Missouri

Culver-Stockton College, B

Montana

Carroll College, B

Nebraska

Nebraska Wesleyan University, B

New Hampshire

University of New Hampshire, B

New York

Rensselaer Polytechnic Institute, B

North Dakota

North Dakota State University, B

Ohio

Wittenberg University, B
Xavier University, B

Oregon

Linfield College, B
Oregon State University, B

Pennsylvania

Bryn Mawr College, B
Lebanon Valley College, B
Lincoln University, B
Wilson College, B

Tennessee

Belmont University, B
Rhodes College, B

Texas

Hardin-Simmons University, B
Houston Baptist University, B
St. Mary's University, B

Vermont

Castleton University, B
Marlboro College, B
Middlebury College, B

Virginia

Sweet Briar College, B

Washington

The Evergreen State College, B
Whitman College, B

West Virginia

Bethany College, B

Wisconsin

Marquette University, B

Canada

British Columbia

The University of British Columbia, B
University of Northern British Columbia, B

Maritime Provinces: Nova Scotia

Dalhousie University, B

Ontario

University of Waterloo, B
The University of Western Ontario, B

Quebec

Université de Montréal, B

Saskatchewan

University of Regina, B

BIOENGINEERING

United States

Arkansas

University of Arkansas, M

California

California Institute of Technology, MD
Santa Clara University, M
Stanford University, MD
University of California, Berkeley, D
University of California, Davis, MD
University of California, Los Angeles, MD
University of California, Merced, MD
University of California, Riverside, MD
University of California, San Diego, MD
University of California, Santa Barbara, MD

Colorado

Colorado School of Mines, MD
University of Colorado Denver, MD
University of Denver, M

Florida

Florida Atlantic University, M
University of Florida, MDO

Georgia

Georgia Institute of Technology, MD
University of Georgia, MD

Hawaii

University of Hawaii at Manoa, M

Idaho

University of Idaho, MD

Illinois

Illinois Institute of Technology, M
Northwestern University, D
University of Chicago, D
University of Illinois at Chicago, MD
University of Illinois at Urbana - Champaign, MD

Indiana

University of Notre Dame, M

Kansas

Kansas State University, MD
The University of Kansas, MD

Kentucky

University of Louisville, M

Louisiana

Louisiana State University and Agricultural & Mechanical College, MD

Maryland

Johns Hopkins University, MD
University of Maryland, College Park, MD

Massachusetts

Massachusetts Institute of Technology, MD
Northeastern University, D
Tufts University, MDO

Mississippi

Mississippi State University, MD

Missouri

University of Missouri, MD

Nebraska

University of Nebraska - Lincoln, MD

New York

Alfred University, M
Cornell University, MD
Rensselaer Polytechnic Institute, MD
Syracuse University, MD
University at Buffalo, the State University of New York, MD

North Carolina

North Carolina Agricultural and Technical State University, M
North Carolina State University, MDO

Ohio

The Ohio State University, MD
University of Dayton, M
The University of Toledo, MD

Oklahoma

Oklahoma State University, MD
University of Oklahoma, MD

Oregon

Oregon State University, MD

Pennsylvania

Carnegie Mellon University, MD
Lehigh University, MD
Penn State University Park, MD
Temple University, MD
University of Pennsylvania, MD
University of Pittsburgh, MD
Wilkes University, M

South Carolina

Clemson University, MDO

South Dakota

South Dakota School of Mines and Technology, D

Texas

Rice University, MD
Texas A&M University, MD
Texas Tech University, M
The University of Texas at Arlington, MD

Utah

University of Utah, MD

Virginia

George Mason University, D
Virginia Commonwealth University, MD
Virginia Polytechnic Institute and State University, MD

Washington

University of Washington, MD
Washington State University, MD

Canada

Maritime Provinces: Nova Scotia

Dalhousie University, MD

Ontario

University of Guelph, MD
University of Ottawa, MD

Quebec

McGill University, MD

Saskatchewan

University of Saskatchewan, MD

BIOETHICS/MEDICAL ETHICS

United States

California

American Jewish University, B
Loma Linda University, MO
Loyola Marymount University, M

Florida

University of Miami, B
University of South Florida, O

Georgia

Emory University, M

Illinois

Loyola University Chicago, DO
Trinity International University, M

Indiana

Indiana University - Purdue University Indianapolis, O

Maryland

Johns Hopkins University, D

Massachusetts

Boston University, M

Missouri

Saint Louis University, DO

New Jersey

Drew University, MDO

New York

Columbia University, M
New York University, M
University of Rochester, B

North Carolina

Duke University, M

North Dakota

University of Mary, M

Ohio

Case Western Reserve University, M
Cleveland State University, MO

Pennsylvania

Duquesne University, MDO
University of Pennsylvania, M
University of Pittsburgh, M

Tennessee

The University of Tennessee, MD

Texas

Houston Baptist University, B

Virginia

University of Richmond, B

Washington

University of Washington, M
Washington State University, O

Canada

Ontario

University of Toronto, M

Quebec

McGill University, M
Université de Montréal, MO

BIOINFORMATICS

United States

Alabama

The University of Alabama at Birmingham, D

Arizona

Arizona State University at the Tempe campus, BMD
The University of Arizona, B

Arkansas

University of Arkansas at Little Rock, MD
University of Arkansas for Medical Sciences, MD

California

California State University Channel Islands, M
California State University, Dominguez Hills, M
California State University, San Bernardino, B
Coleman University, A
Pacific Union College, B
University of California, Irvine, B
University of California, Los Angeles, MD
University of California, Riverside, D
University of California, San Diego, D
University of California, Santa Cruz, BMD
University of Southern California, D

Colorado

University of Colorado Denver, D
University of Denver, B

Connecticut

Yale University, D

District of Columbia

The George Washington University, M
Georgetown University, M

Florida

Florida State University, M
Nova Southeastern University, MO
University of South Florida, MO

Georgia

Emory University, MD
Georgia Institute of Technology, MD
Georgia State University, MD
University of Georgia, MDO

Idaho

University of Idaho, MD

Illinois

Loyola University Chicago, B
Trinity Christian College, B
University of Illinois at Chicago, MD
University of Illinois at Urbana - Champaign, M

Indiana

Indiana University Bloomington, MD
Indiana University - Purdue University Indianapolis, MD

Iowa

Iowa State University of Science and Technology, BMD
The University of Iowa, MD
University of Northern Iowa, B

Maine

University of Maine, M

Maryland

Hood College, O
Johns Hopkins University, MO
Morgan State University, M
University of Maryland, Baltimore County, B
University of Maryland, College Park, D

Massachusetts

Boston University, MD
Brandeis University, M
Massachusetts Bay Community College, A
Massachusetts Institute of Technology, D
Northeastern University, M
Tufts University, M
Wheaton College, B
Worcester Polytechnic Institute, MD

Michigan

Davenport University, B
Grand Valley State University, M
Kettering University, B
Michigan Technological University, B
University of Michigan, MD
Wayne State University, D

Mississippi

Mississippi Valley State University, M

Missouri

University of Missouri, D
University of Missouri - Kansas City, M

Nebraska

University of Nebraska - Lincoln, MD
University of Nebraska Medical Center, MD
University of Nebraska at Omaha, BM

New Jersey

New Jersey Institute of Technology, BM
Ramapo College of New Jersey, B
Rowan University, BM
Rutgers University - Newark, MD
Stevens Institute of Technology, BDO

New Mexico

New Mexico State University, M

New York

Canisius College, B
New York City College of Technology of the City University of New York, B
New York University, MD
Rensselaer Polytechnic Institute, B
Rochester Institute of Technology, BM
St. Bonaventure University, B
Stony Brook University, State University of New York, MD
University at Buffalo, the State University of New York, BMD

North Carolina

Duke University, DO
North Carolina State University, MD
The University of North Carolina at Chapel Hill, D
The University of North Carolina at Charlotte, MDO

North Dakota

North Dakota State University, MD

Ohio

University of Cincinnati, DO
The University of Toledo, MO

Oklahoma

University of Oklahoma, MD

Oregon

Portland State University, B

Pennsylvania

Gannon University, B
Saint Vincent College, B
University of Pennsylvania, B
University of Pittsburgh, BMDO
University of the Sciences, M

South Carolina

Claflin University, B

Tennessee

University of Memphis, B
Vanderbilt University, MD

Texas

Baylor University, B
Rice University, D
St. Edward's University, B
University of St. Thomas, B
The University of Texas at El Paso, M
The University of Texas Medical Branch, D

Utah

University of Utah, MDO

Virginia

George Mason University, M
Virginia Commonwealth University, BMD
Virginia Polytechnic Institute and State University, D

Washington

University of Washington, MD
Whitworth University, B

Wisconsin

Marquette University, M

U.S. Territories: Puerto Rico

Inter American University of Puerto Rico, Bayamón Campus, B

Canada

Alberta

University of Alberta, B
University of Calgary, B

British Columbia

Simon Fraser University, O

Maritime Provinces: Nova Scotia

Dalhousie University, BM

Ontario

Lakehead University, B
University of Waterloo, B
The University of Western Ontario, B
University of Windsor, B

Quebec

McGill University, MD
Université de Montréal, BMD

Saskatchewan

University of Saskatchewan, B

BIOLOGICAL ANTHROPOLOGY

United States

North Carolina

Duke University, D

Ohio

Kent State University, D

Pennsylvania

Mercyhurst University, M

BIOLOGICAL AND BIOMEDICAL SCIENCES

United States

Alabama

Alabama Agricultural and Mechanical University, MD
Alabama State University, MD
Auburn University, MD

Jacksonville State University, M
Troy University, MO
Tuskegee University, MD
The University of Alabama, MD
The University of Alabama at Birmingham, MD
The University of Alabama in Huntsville, MD
University of South Alabama, MD

Alaska

University of Alaska Anchorage, M

Arizona

Arizona State University at the Tempe campus, MD
Northern Arizona University, MD
The University of Arizona, M

Arkansas

Arkansas State University, MO
University of Arkansas, MD
University of Arkansas at Little Rock, M
University of Arkansas for Medical Sciences, MDO
University of Central Arkansas, M

California

Biola University, B
California Institute of Technology, D
California Polytechnic State University, San Luis Obispo, M
California State Polytechnic University, Pomona, M
California State University, Bakersfield, M
California State University, Chico, M
California State University, Dominguez Hills, M
California State University, East Bay, M
California State University, Fresno, M
California State University, Fullerton, M
California State University, Long Beach, M
California State University, Los Angeles, M
California State University, Northridge, M
California State University, Sacramento, M
California State University, San Bernardino, M
California State University, San Marcos, M
Dominican University of California, M
Holy Names University, B
Humboldt State University, M
Loma Linda University, MD
Mills College, O
National University, M
Notre Dame de Namur University, O
Occidental College, M
Point Loma Nazarene University, M
Saint Mary's College of California, B
San Diego State University, MD
San Francisco State University, M
San Jose State University, BM
Sonoma State University, M
Stanford University, MD
University of California, Berkeley, D
University of California, Irvine, MD
University of California, Los Angeles, MD
University of California, Merced, MD
University of California, Riverside, MD
University of California, San Diego, D
University of the Pacific, M
University of San Francisco, M
University of Southern California, MDO

Colorado

Colorado State University, MD
Colorado State University - Pueblo, M
Regis University, M
University of Colorado Denver, MD
University of Denver, MD
University of Northern Colorado, M
Western State Colorado University, B

Connecticut

Central Connecticut State University, MO
Southern Connecticut State University, M
University of Hartford, M
University of Saint Joseph, M
Wesleyan University, D
Western Connecticut State University, M
Yale University, D

Delaware

Delaware State University, BM
University of Delaware, MD

District of Columbia

The Catholic University of America, MD
The George Washington University, MD
Georgetown University, MD
Howard University, MD

Florida

Barry University, M
Florida Atlantic University, MD
Florida Institute of Technology, MD
Florida International University, MD
Florida State University, MD
Nova Southeastern University, M
University of Central Florida, MD
University of Florida, MD
University of Miami, MD
University of North Florida, M
University of South Florida, MD
University of West Florida, M

Georgia

Clark Atlanta University, MD
Darton State College, A
Emory University, D
Georgia College & State University, M
Georgia Institute of Technology, MD
Georgia Southern University, M
Georgia State University, MD
Gordon State College, AB
Kennesaw State University, M
University of Georgia, D
University of West Georgia, M

Hawaii

University of Hawaii at Manoa, MD

Idaho

Boise State University, M
Idaho State University, MD
University of Idaho, MD

Illinois

Bradley University, M
Chicago State University, M
DePaul University, M
Eastern Illinois University, M
Illinois Institute of Technology, MD
Illinois State University, MD
Loyola University Chicago, MD
Northeastern Illinois University, M
Northern Illinois University, MD
Northwestern University, D
Southern Illinois University Carbondale, MD
Southern Illinois University Edwardsville, M
University of Chicago, D
University of Illinois at Chicago, MD
University of Illinois at Springfield, M
University of Illinois at Urbana - Champaign, BMD
Western Illinois University, MO

Indiana

Ball State University, MD
Indiana State University, MD
Indiana University Bloomington, BMD
Indiana University East, B
Indiana University - Purdue University Fort Wayne, M
Indiana University - Purdue University Indianapolis, MD
Purdue University, MD
Purdue University Northwest (Hammond), M
University of Indianapolis, M
University of Notre Dame, MD
Vincennes University, A

Iowa

Iowa State University of Science and Technology, MD
The University of Iowa, MD
University of Northern Iowa, M

Kansas

Emporia State University, M
Fort Hays State University, M
Kansas State University, MD
Pittsburg State University, M
The University of Kansas, MD
Wichita State University, M

Kentucky

Eastern Kentucky University, M
Morehead State University, M
Murray State University, MD
University of Kentucky, MD
University of Louisville, M
Western Kentucky University, M

Louisiana

Louisiana State University and Agricultural & Mechanical College, MD
Louisiana State University Health Sciences Center, MD
Louisiana State University in Shreveport, BM
Louisiana Tech University, MD
Our Lady of the Lake College, B
Southeastern Louisiana University, M
Southern University and Agricultural and Mechanical College, M
Tulane University, MD
University of Louisiana at Lafayette, MD
University of Louisiana at Monroe, M
University of New Orleans, MD

Maine

University of Maine, MD
University of New England, M
University of Southern Maine, M

Maryland

Frostburg State University, M
Goucher College, O
Hood College, MO
Johns Hopkins University, MD
Morgan State University, MD
Salisbury University, M
Towson University, M
University of Maryland, Baltimore County, MDO
University of Maryland, College Park, MD
University of Maryland University College, B

Massachusetts

Boston College, D
Boston University, BMD
Brandeis University, DO
Clark University, MD
Fitchburg State University, MO
Harvard University, DO
Massachusetts Bay Community College, A
Massachusetts Institute of Technology, MD
Northeastern University, MD
Regis College, M
Smith College, M
Tufts University, MD
University of Massachusetts Amherst, MD
University of Massachusetts Boston, MD
University of Massachusetts Dartmouth, M
University of Massachusetts Lowell, MD
Worcester Polytechnic Institute, MD

Michigan

Andrews University, M
Central Michigan University, BM
Eastern Michigan University, M
Grand Valley State University, BM
Michigan State University, MD
Michigan Technological University, MD
Northern Michigan University, M
Oakland University, MD
University of Michigan, BMD
University of Michigan - Flint, M
Wayne State University, MD
Western Michigan University, MD

Minnesota

Bemidji State University, M
Bethel University, B

Minnesota State University Mankato, M
St. Cloud State University, M
University of Minnesota, Duluth, MD
University of Minnesota, Twin Cities Campus, M

Mississippi

Alcorn State University, M
Delta State University, M
Jackson State University, MD
Mississippi College, M
Mississippi State University, MD
University of Mississippi, MD
University of Mississippi Medical Center, MD
University of Southern Mississippi, MD

Missouri

Logan University, B
Missouri State University, M
Missouri University of Science and Technology, M
Missouri Western State University, M
Northwest Missouri State University, M
Park University, B
Saint Louis University, MD
Southeast Missouri State University, M
Truman State University, M
University of Central Missouri, M
University of Missouri, MD
University of Missouri - Kansas City, M
University of Missouri - St. Louis, MDO
Washington University in St. Louis, BD

Montana

Montana State University, D
University of Montana, MD

Nebraska

Creighton University, MD
University of Nebraska at Kearney, M
University of Nebraska - Lincoln, MD
University of Nebraska Medical Center, MD
University of Nebraska at Omaha, MO

Nevada

Nevada State College, B
University of Nevada, Las Vegas, MD
University of Nevada, Reno, M

New Hampshire

Dartmouth College, D
Plymouth State University, M
University of New Hampshire, BMD

New Jersey

Drew University, M
Fairleigh Dickinson University, College at Florham, M
Fairleigh Dickinson University, Metropolitan Campus, M
Montclair State University, M
New Jersey Institute of Technology, MD
Rowan University, M
Rutgers University - Camden, M
Rutgers University - New Brunswick, MD
Rutgers University - Newark, BMDO
Seton Hall University, MD
William Paterson University of New Jersey, M

New Mexico

Eastern New Mexico University, M
New Mexico Institute of Mining and Technology, M
New Mexico State University, MD
University of New Mexico, MD

New York

Adelphi University, M
Binghamton University, State University of New York, MD
Brooklyn College of the City University of New York, M
Buffalo State College, State University of New York, M
City College of the City University of New York, MD
The College at Brockport, State University of New York, MO

College of Staten Island of the City University of
New York, M
Columbia University, MDO
Cornell University, MD
Fordham University, MDO
Hofstra University, M
Hunter College of the City University of New York,
MD
Lehman College of the City University of New York,
M
New York Institute of Technology, B
New York University, MD
Queens College of the City University of New York,
M
Rensselaer Polytechnic Institute, MD
Roberts Wesleyan College, A
Rochester Institute of Technology, BM
The Sage Colleges, B
St. John's University, MD
State University of New York College of Environ-
mental Science and Forestry, B
State University of New York College at Oneonta, M
State University of New York Downstate Medical
Center, MD
State University of New York at Fredonia, M
State University of New York Upstate Medical Uni-
versity, MD
Stony Brook University, State University of New
York, MDO
Syracuse University, MD
Union College, B
University at Albany, State University of New York,
MD
University at Buffalo, the State University of New
York, MD
University of Rochester, MD

North Carolina

Appalachian State University, M
Duke University, D
East Carolina University, M
Elizabeth City State University, M
Fayetteville State University, M
Guilford College, B
North Carolina Agricultural and Technical State Uni-
versity, M
North Carolina Central University, M
North Carolina State University, MDO
The University of North Carolina at Chapel Hill, MD
The University of North Carolina at Charlotte, MD
The University of North Carolina at Greensboro, M
The University of North Carolina Wilmington, MD
Wake Forest University, MD
Western Carolina University, M

North Dakota

North Dakota State University, MD
University of North Dakota, BMD

Ohio

Bowling Green State University, MD
Case Western Reserve University, MD
Cleveland State University, MD
Hiram College, B
John Carroll University, M
Kent State University, BMD
Kent State University at Salem, B
Miami University, M
The Ohio State University, MD
Ohio University, MD
The University of Akron, MD
University of Cincinnati, BMDO
University of Dayton, MD
The University of Toledo, MD
Ursuline College, B
Wright State University, MD
Youngstown State University, M

Oklahoma

Murray State College, A
Oklahoma City University, B
Oklahoma State University, MD
Seminole State College, A
University of Central Oklahoma, M
University of Oklahoma, MD
University of Oklahoma Health Sciences Center, MD

The University of Tulsa, MD

Oregon

Oregon Health & Science University, MDO
Portland State University, MD
University of Oregon, MD

Pennsylvania

Alvernia University, B
Bloomsburg University of Pennsylvania, M
Bucknell University, M
Carnegie Mellon University, MD
Chatham University, M
Drexel University, MDO
Duquesne University, MD
East Stroudsburg University of Pennsylvania, M
Eastern University, B
Edinboro University of Pennsylvania, M
Gwynedd Mercy University, A
Indiana University of Pennsylvania, M
Lehigh University, MD
Mount Aloysius College, B
Penn State Abington, B
Penn State Altoona, B
Penn State Beaver, B
Penn State Berks, B
Penn State Brandywine, B
Penn State DuBois, B
Penn State Erie, The Behrend College, B
Penn State Fayette, The Eberly Campus, B
Penn State Greater Allegheny, B
Penn State Hazleton, B
Penn State Lehigh Valley, B
Penn State Mont Alto, B
Penn State New Kensington, B
Penn State Schuylkill, B
Penn State Shenango, B
Penn State University Park, BMD
Penn State Wilkes-Barre, B
Penn State Worthington Scranton, B
Penn State York, B
Saint Francis University, M
Saint Joseph's University, M
Shippensburg University of Pennsylvania, M
Swarthmore College, B
Temple University, MD
Thomas Jefferson University, MDO
University of Pennsylvania, MD
University of Pittsburgh, D
Villanova University, M
West Chester University of Pennsylvania, MO

Rhode Island

Brown University, MD
Rhode Island College, MO
University of Rhode Island, MD

South Carolina

Charleston Southern University, B
The Citadel, The Military College of South Carolina,
M
Clemson University, MD
Medical University of South Carolina, MD
University of South Carolina, MD
Winthrop University, M

South Dakota

Dakota State University, B
Sinte Gleska University, A
South Dakota State University, MD
The University of South Dakota, MD

Tennessee

Austin Peay State University, M
East Tennessee State University, MD
Fisk University, M
King University, B
Middle Tennessee State University, M
Tennessee State University, MD
Tennessee Technological University, MD
Trevecca Nazarene University, B
University of Memphis, MD
The University of Tennessee, MD
Vanderbilt University, MD

Texas

Angelo State University, M
Baylor University, MD
Lamar University, M
Midwestern State University, M
Prairie View A&M University, M
Sam Houston State University, M
Southern Methodist University, M
Stephen F. Austin State University, M
Sul Ross State University, M
Tarleton State University, M
Texas A&M International University, M
Texas A&M University, MD
Texas A&M University - Corpus Christi, M
Texas A&M University - Kingsville, M
Texas Christian University, M
Texas Southern University, M
Texas State University, M
Texas Tech University, MD
Texas Woman's University, MD
University of Houston, MD
University of Houston - Clear Lake, M
University of Houston - Victoria, M
University of the Incarnate Word, M
University of North Texas, M
The University of Texas at Arlington, MD
The University of Texas at Austin, MD
The University of Texas at Dallas, MD
The University of Texas at El Paso, MD
The University of Texas Health Science Center at
Houston, MD
The University of Texas Health Science Center at
San Antonio, D
The University of Texas Medical Branch, MD
The University of Texas of the Permian Basin, M
The University of Texas Rio Grande Valley, M
The University of Texas at San Antonio, MD
The University of Texas at Tyler, M
West Texas A&M University, M

Utah

Brigham Young University, MD
University of Utah, MDO
Utah State University, BMD

Vermont

University of Vermont, MD

Virginia

Christopher Newport University, B
The College of William and Mary, M
Eastern Mennonite University, M
George Mason University, MDO
Hampton University, M
James Madison University, M
Liberty University, M
Old Dominion University, MD
University of Virginia, MD
Virginia Commonwealth University, MDO
Virginia Polytechnic Institute and State University,
MD
Virginia State University, M

Washington

Central Washington University, BM
Eastern Washington University, M
University of Washington, MD
Walla Walla University, M
Washington State University, MD
Western Washington University, M
Whitman College, B

West Virginia

Davis & Elkins College, B
Marshall University, MD
West Virginia University, MD

Wisconsin

Lac Courte Oreilles Ojibwa Community College, A
Marquette University, MD
University of Wisconsin - La Crosse, M
University of Wisconsin - Madison, MD
University of Wisconsin - Milwaukee, M
University of Wisconsin - Oshkosh, M
University of Wisconsin - Parkside, B

U.S. Territories: Guam

University of Guam, M

U.S. Territories: Puerto Rico

Pontifical Catholic University of Puerto Rico, M
Universidad Central del Caribe, MD
University of Puerto Rico in Aguadilla, AB
University of Puerto Rico in Bayamón, B
University of Puerto Rico, Mayagüez Campus, M
University of Puerto Rico, Medical Sciences Campus, MD
University of Puerto Rico in Ponce, B
University of Puerto Rico, Río Piedras Campus, MD
University of Puerto Rico in Utuado, B

Canada

Alberta

University of Alberta, MD
University of Calgary, MD
University of Lethbridge, M

British Columbia

Simon Fraser University, MDO
University of Victoria, MD

Manitoba

University of Manitoba, MDO

Maritime Provinces: New Brunswick

Mount Allison University, M
Université de Moncton, M
University of New Brunswick Fredericton, MD
University of New Brunswick Saint John, MD

Maritime Provinces: Nova Scotia

Acadia University, M
Dalhousie University, MD
St. Francis Xavier University, M

Maritime Provinces: Prince Edward Island

University of Prince Edward Island, M

Newfoundland and Labrador

Memorial University of Newfoundland, MDO

Ontario

Brock University, MD
Carleton University, MD
Lakehead University, M
Laurentian University, MD
McMaster University, MD
Queen's University at Kingston, MD
Trent University, MD
University of Guelph, MD
University of Ottawa, BMD
University of Waterloo, MD
The University of Western Ontario, MD
University of Windsor, MD
Wilfrid Laurier University, M
York University, MD

Quebec

Concordia University, MDO
McGill University, MD
Université Laval, MDO
Université de Montréal, MD
Université du Québec en Abitibi-Témiscamingue, M
Université du Québec à Montréal, MD
Université de Sherbrooke, MDO

Saskatchewan

University of Regina, MD
University of Saskatchewan, MD

BIOLOGICAL AND PHYSICAL SCIENCES

United States

Alabama

Marion Military Institute, A
Troy University, B
The University of Alabama at Birmingham, B
The University of West Alabama, B

Alaska

University of Alaska Anchorage, B
University of Alaska Fairbanks, B

Arizona

Northland Pioneer College, A

Arkansas

John Brown University, B
Philander Smith College, B
Shorter College, A
Southern Arkansas University - Magnolia, B
University of Arkansas at Monticello, B
University of Central Arkansas, B

California

American River College, A
Antelope Valley College, A
Barstow Community College, A
Cabrillo College, A
California State University, Fresno, B
Cañada College, A
Cerritos College, A
Cerro Coso Community College, A
Chaffey College, A
Citrus College, A
City College of San Francisco, A
College of the Canyons, A
College of the Desert, A
College of Marin, A
College of the Redwoods, A
College of San Mateo, A
College of the Sequoias, A
College of the Siskiyous, A
Columbia College, A
Cosumnes River College, A
Crafton Hills College, A
Cuesta College, A
Cuyamaca College, A
Cypress College, A
Evergreen Valley College, A
Fresno City College, A
Fullerton College, A
Gavilan College, A
Golden West College, A
Imperial Valley College, A
Irvine Valley College, A
Lake Tahoe Community College, A
Laney College, A
Lassen Community College District, A
Los Angeles City College, A
The Master's College and Seminary, B
Merced College, A
Merritt College, A
MiraCosta College, A
Mt. San Antonio College, A
Mt. San Jacinto College, A
Napa Valley College, A
National University, B
Palo Verde College, A
Palomar College, A
Pasadena City College, A
Porterville College, A
Sacramento City College, A
San Francisco State University, B
Santa Ana College, A
Santa Monica College, A
Sierra College, A
Skyline College, A
Solano Community College, A
Vanguard University of Southern California, B
Victor Valley College, A
Yuba College, A

Colorado

Colorado Christian University, B
Colorado Mountain College (Glenwood Springs), A
Colorado Mountain College (Steamboat Springs), A
Lamar Community College, A
Otero Junior College, A
Trinidad State Junior College, A
United States Air Force Academy, B
University of Denver, B

Connecticut

Middlesex Community College, A
Quinnipiac University, B
Wesleyan University, B

Florida

Chipola College, A
South Florida State College, A
University of South Florida, B
University of West Florida, B

Georgia

Abraham Baldwin Agricultural College, A
Andrew College, A
Covenant College, B
Emory University, B
University of Georgia, B
Young Harris College, B

Idaho

North Idaho College, A

Illinois

Black Hawk College, A
Carl Sandburg College, A
City Colleges of Chicago, Harold Washington College, A
City Colleges of Chicago, Harry S. Truman College, A
City Colleges of Chicago, Kennedy-King College, A
City Colleges of Chicago, Olive-Harvey College, A
City Colleges of Chicago, Wilbur Wright College, A
College of DuPage, A
College of Lake County, A
DePaul University, B
Dominican University, B
Elgin Community College, A
Eureka College, B
Heartland Community College, A
Highland Community College, A
Illinois Eastern Community Colleges, Frontier Community College, A
Illinois Eastern Community Colleges, Lincoln Trail College, A
Illinois Eastern Community Colleges, Olney Central College, A
Illinois Eastern Community Colleges, Wabash Valley College, A
Illinois Valley Community College, A
John A. Logan College, A
John Wood Community College, A
Joliet Junior College, A
Kaskaskia College, A
Kishwaukee College, A
Lake Land College, A
Lewis and Clark Community College, A
Lincoln Land Community College, A
McHenry County College, A
Moraine Valley Community College, A
Morton College, A
North Central College, B
Northwestern University, B
Oakton Community College, A
Parkland College, A
Prairie State College, A
Rend Lake College, A
Richland Community College, A
Rockford University, B
Saint Xavier University, B
Shawnee Community College, A
South Suburban College, A
Southwestern Illinois College, A
Spoon River College, A
Triton College, A
Waubonsee Community College, A

Indiana

Ancilla College, A
Calumet College of Saint Joseph, B
Grace College, B
Huntington University, B
Indiana University Kokomo, B
Indiana University - Purdue University Indianapolis, B
Purdue University, B
Trine University, A
University of Southern Indiana, B
Valparaiso University, A
Vincennes University, A

Iowa

Buena Vista University, B
Iowa Central Community College, A
Iowa Lakes Community College, A
Iowa Wesleyan University, B
Palmer College of Chiropractic, B
University of Dubuque, B
University of Northern Iowa, B
Upper Iowa University, B

Kansas

Central Christian College of Kansas, A
Dodge City Community College, A
Fort Hays State University, B
Neosho County Community College, A
Pratt Community College, A

Kentucky

Alice Lloyd College, B
Spalding University, B

Louisiana

Delgado Community College, A
Louisiana State University in Shreveport, B

Maine

College of the Atlantic, B

Maryland

Community College of Baltimore County, A
Howard Community College, A
Johns Hopkins University, B
St. Mary's College of Maryland, B
Wor-Wic Community College, A

Massachusetts

Eastern Nazarene College, B
University of Massachusetts Amherst, B

Michigan

Calvin College, B
Concordia University Ann Arbor, B
Eastern Michigan University, B
Ferris State University, A
Grand Valley State University, B
Marygrove College, B
Michigan State University, B
Mid Michigan Community College, A
Olivet College, B
Rochester College, B

Minnesota

Bemidji State University, B
College of Saint Benedict, B
Minnesota State University Mankato, B
Rainy River Community College, A
Saint John's University, B
Vermilion Community College, A

Mississippi

Copiah-Lincoln Community College, A
Delta State University, B
Itawamba Community College, A
Jones County Junior College, A
Mississippi Gulf Coast Community College, A
Mississippi State University, B
Northeast Mississippi Community College, A
Southwest Mississippi Community College, A
University of Southern Mississippi, B

Missouri

Maryville University of Saint Louis, B
Northwest Missouri State University, B
Washington University in St. Louis, B

Montana

Little Big Horn College, A

Nebraska

Midland University, B
Peru State College, B
York College, B

Nevada

College of Southern Nevada, A
Sierra Nevada College, B

New Hampshire

Keene State College, B
Saint Anselm College, B

New Jersey

Fairleigh Dickinson University, Metropolitan Campus, B
Hudson County Community College, A
Passaic County Community College, A
Ramapo College of New Jersey, B
Rowan College at Burlington County, A
Saint Peter's University, B
Sussex County Community College, A

New Mexico

New Mexico Junior College, A
New Mexico Military Institute, A
University of New Mexico - Los Alamos Branch, A
Western New Mexico University, B

New York

Adelphi University, B
Alfred University, B
Clinton Community College, A
Elmira College, B
Eugene Lang College of Liberal Arts, B
Finger Lakes Community College, A
Fordham University, B
Fulton-Montgomery Community College, A
Houghton College, B
Le Moyne College, B
Long Island University - LIU Brooklyn, B
Monroe Community College, A
Niagara County Community College, A
North Country Community College, A
Roberts Wesleyan College, B
Rockland Community College, A
State University of New York at Fredonia, B
Stony Brook University, State University of New York, B
Suffolk County Community College, A
Union College, B

North Carolina

Brevard College, B
Caldwell Community College and Technical Institute, A
Isothermal Community College, A
Johnson C. Smith University, B
Louisburg College, A
Mars Hill University, B
Methodist University, B
North Carolina Wesleyan College, B
Sandhills Community College, A
Southeastern Community College, A

North Dakota

Turtle Mountain Community College, A

Ohio

Baldwin Wallace University, B
John Carroll University, B
Lorain County Community College, A
Miami University Middletown, A
Ohio University - Lancaster, A
Ohio University - Southern Campus, A
Ohio University - Zanesville, A

Terra State Community College, A
The University of Findlay, B
Walsh University, B
Washington State Community College, A
Wilmington College, B
Xavier University, B

Oklahoma

Northern Oklahoma College, A
Oklahoma Panhandle State University, B
Oklahoma Wesleyan University, A
Redlands Community College, A
St. Gregory's University, B

Oregon

Central Oregon Community College, A
Concordia University, B
Linn-Benton Community College, A
Oregon State University - Cascades, B
Portland State University, B
Umpqua Community College, A
University of Oregon, B
Warner Pacific College, B

Pennsylvania

Allegheny College, B
Alvernia University, B
Bryn Athyn College of the New Church, B
Cheyney University of Pennsylvania, B
Clarion University of Pennsylvania, B
Community College of Beaver County, A
Delaware County Community College, A
Drexel University, B
East Stroudsburg University of Pennsylvania, B
Edinboro University of Pennsylvania, B
Gettysburg College, B
Indiana University of Pennsylvania, B
King's College, B
Kutztown University of Pennsylvania, B
Luzerne County Community College, A
Mansfield University of Pennsylvania, B
Mercyhurst North East, A
Penn State Abington, B
Penn State Altoona, AB
Penn State Beaver, AB
Penn State Berks, B
Penn State Brandywine, B
Penn State DuBois, AB
Penn State Erie, The Behrend College, B
Penn State Fayette, The Eberly Campus, AB
Penn State Greater Allegheny, AB
Penn State Hazleton, B
Penn State Lehigh Valley, B
Penn State Mont Alto, B
Penn State New Kensington, AB
Penn State Schuylkill, AB
Penn State Shenango, AB
Penn State University Park, B
Penn State Wilkes-Barre, B
Penn State Worthington Scranton, B
Penn State York, B
University of Pittsburgh, B
Ursinus College, B
Valley Forge Military College, A

Rhode Island

Community College of Rhode Island, A

South Carolina

Charleston Southern University, B
Clinton College, A
Piedmont Technical College, A
Trident Technical College, A
University of South Carolina Union, A

South Dakota

Dakota Wesleyan University, B

Tennessee

King University, B
Middle Tennessee State University, B
Union University, B
Welch College, B

Texas

Angelina College, A
Galveston College, A
Kilgore College, A
Navarro College, A
North Central Texas College, A
Paris Junior College, A
Sam Houston State University, B
San Antonio College, A
South Plains College, A
Southwest Texas Junior College, A
Texas State University, B
Texas Tech University, B
University of Houston - Downtown, B
The University of Texas at San Antonio, B
Weatherford College, A

Vermont

Bennington College, B
Castleton University, B
Lyndon State College, B

Virginia

Averett University, B
Blue Ridge Community College, A
Dabney S. Lancaster Community College, A
Eastern Shore Community College, A
Germanna Community College, A
J. Sargeant Reynolds Community College, A
Jefferson College of Health Sciences, A
New River Community College, A
Northern Virginia Community College, A
Patrick Henry Community College, A
Rappahannock Community College, A
Southside Virginia Community College, A
Thomas Nelson Community College, A
Tidewater Community College, A
Virginia Commonwealth University, B
Virginia Highlands Community College, A
Virginia Western Community College, A
Wytheville Community College, A

Washington

The Evergreen State College, B
Highline College, A
Peninsula College, A
Seattle Central College, A
Skagit Valley College, A
South Seattle College, A
University of Puget Sound, B
Washington State University, B
Washington State University - Tri-Cities, B
Western Washington University, B

West Virginia

Bluefield State College, B
New River Community and Technical College, A

Wisconsin

St. Norbert College, B
University of Wisconsin - Platteville, B
University of Wisconsin - Richland, A
University of Wisconsin - River Falls, B
University of Wisconsin - Stevens Point, B
University of Wisconsin - Superior, B

Wyoming

Laramie County Community College, A
Sheridan College, A
Western Wyoming Community College, A

U.S. Territories: Puerto Rico

Pontifical Catholic University of Puerto Rico, B

Canada

Alberta

Athabasca University, B

British Columbia

Simon Fraser University, B
University of Northern British Columbia, B

Maritime Provinces: New Brunswick

Mount Allison University, B
Université de Moncton, B
University of New Brunswick Fredericton, B

Maritime Provinces: Nova Scotia

Mount Saint Vincent University, B
St. Francis Xavier University, B

Newfoundland and Labrador

Memorial University of Newfoundland, B

Ontario

Brock University, B
Carleton University, B
Lakehead University, B
McMaster University, B
Trent University, B
University of Waterloo, B
University of Windsor, B
York University, B

Quebec

Bishop's University, B
McGill University, B

Saskatchewan

University of Regina, B

BIOLOGY/BIOLOGICAL SCIENCES

United States

Alabama

Alabama Agricultural and Mechanical University, B
Alabama Southern Community College, A
Alabama State University, B
Athens State University, B
Auburn University, B
Auburn University at Montgomery, B
Birmingham-Southern College, B
Faulkner University, B
Huntingdon College, B
Jacksonville State University, B
Judson College, B
Miles College, B
Oakwood University, B
Samford University, B
Selma University, B
Spring Hill College, B
Stillman College, B
Talladega College, B
Troy University, B
Tuskegee University, B
The University of Alabama, B
The University of Alabama at Birmingham, B
The University of Alabama in Huntsville, B
University of Mobile, B
University of Montevallo, B
University of North Alabama, B
University of South Alabama, B
The University of West Alabama, B

Alaska

University of Alaska Anchorage, B
University of Alaska Fairbanks, B
University of Alaska Southeast, B

Arizona

Arizona Christian University, B
Arizona State University at the Polytechnic campus, B
Arizona State University at the Tempe campus, B
Arizona State University at the West campus, B
Arizona Western College, A
Cochise County Community College District, A
Eastern Arizona College, A
Grand Canyon University, B
Mesa Community College, A
Northern Arizona University, B
The University of Arizona, B

Arkansas

Arkansas State University, B
Arkansas Tech University, B
Central Baptist College, B
Harding University, B
Henderson State University, B
Hendrix College, B
John Brown University, B
Lyon College, B
Ouachita Baptist University, B
Philander Smith College, B
Southern Arkansas University - Magnolia, B
University of Arkansas, B
University of Arkansas - Fort Smith, B
University of Arkansas at Little Rock, B
University of Arkansas at Monticello, B
University of Arkansas at Pine Bluff, B
University of Central Arkansas, B
University of the Ozarks, B
Williams Baptist College, B

California

Allan Hancock College, A
Ashford University, B
Azusa Pacific University, B
Bakersfield College, A
Biola University, B
Butte College, A
Cabrillo College, A
California Baptist University, B
California Institute of Technology, B
California Lutheran University, B
California Polytechnic State University, San Luis Obispo, B
California State Polytechnic University, Pomona, B
California State University, Bakersfield, B
California State University Channel Islands, B
California State University, Chico, B
California State University, Dominguez Hills, B
California State University, East Bay, B
California State University, Fresno, B
California State University, Fullerton, B
California State University, Long Beach, B
California State University, Los Angeles, B
California State University, Monterey Bay, B
California State University, Northridge, B
California State University, Sacramento, B
California State University, San Bernardino, B
California State University, San Marcos, B
California State University, Stanislaus, B
Cañada College, A
Cerritos College, A
Chabot College, A
Chaffey College, A
Chapman University, B
Citrus College, A
Claremont McKenna College, B
College of Alameda, A
College of the Desert, A
College of Marin, A
College of San Mateo, A
College of the Sequoias, A
College of the Siskiyous, A
Columbia College, A
Concordia University Irvine, B
Contra Costa College, A
Cuesta College, A
De Anza College, A
Dominican University of California, B
East Los Angeles College, A
El Camino College, A
Evergreen Valley College, A
Feather River College, A
Folsom Lake College, A
Foothill College, A
Fresno City College, A
Fresno Pacific University, B
Fullerton College, A
Gavilan College, A
Glendale Community College, A
Golden West College, A
Grossmont College, A
Hartnell College, A
Harvey Mudd College, B
Holy Names University, B
Humboldt State University, B

Irvine Valley College, A
La Sierra University, B
Lassen Community College District, A
Long Beach City College, A
Los Angeles City College, A
Los Angeles Harbor College, A
Los Angeles Mission College, A
Los Angeles Southwest College, A
Los Angeles Valley College, A
Los Medanos College, A
Loyola Marymount University, B
The Master's College and Seminary, B
Mendocino College, A
Mills College, B
Monterey Peninsula College, A
Moorpark College, A
Mount Saint Mary's University, B
National University, B
Notre Dame de Namur University, B
Occidental College, B
Ohlone College, A
Orange Coast College, A
Oxnard College, A
Pacific Union College, B
Palomar College, A
Pasadena City College, A
Pepperdine University, B
Pitzer College, B
Point Loma Nazarene University, B
Pomona College, B
Porterville College, A
Reedley College, A
Saddleback College, A
Saint Katherine College, B
Saint Mary's College of California, B
San Bernardino Valley College, A
San Diego Christian College, B
San Diego City College, A
San Diego Mesa College, A
San Diego Miramar College, A
San Diego State University, B
San Francisco State University, B
San Joaquin Delta College, A
San Jose City College, A
San Jose State University, B
Santa Ana College, A
Santa Barbara City College, A
Santa Clara University, B
Santa Rosa Junior College, A
Santiago Canyon College, A
Scripps College, B
Sierra College, A
Simpson University, B
Skyline College, A
Solano Community College, A
Sonoma State University, B
Southwestern College, A
Stanford University, B
Taft College, A
United States University, B
University of California, Berkeley, B
University of California, Davis, B
University of California, Irvine, B
University of California, Los Angeles, B
University of California, Merced, B
University of California, Riverside, B
University of California, San Diego, B
University of California, Santa Barbara, B
University of California, Santa Cruz, B
University of La Verne, B
University of the Pacific, B
University of Redlands, B
University of San Diego, B
University of San Francisco, B
University of Southern California, B
Vanguard University of Southern California, B
Ventura College, A
Victor Valley College, A
West Hills Community College, A
West Los Angeles College, A
West Valley College, A
Westmont College, B
Whittier College, B
William Jessup University, B
Yuba College, A

Colorado

Adams State University, B
Colorado Christian University, B
The Colorado College, B
Colorado Mesa University, B
Colorado Mountain College (Glenwood Springs), A
Colorado Mountain College (Steamboat Springs), A
Colorado State University, B
Colorado State University - Pueblo, B
Lamar Community College, A
Metropolitan State University of Denver, B
Northeastern Junior College, A
Otero Junior College, A
Regis University, B
Trinidad State Junior College, A
United States Air Force Academy, B
University of Colorado Colorado Springs, B
University of Colorado Denver, B
University of Denver, B
University of Northern Colorado, B
Western State Colorado University, B

Connecticut

Albertus Magnus College, B
Central Connecticut State University, B
Connecticut College, B
Eastern Connecticut State University, B
Fairfield University, B
Northwestern Connecticut Community College, A
Post University, B
Quinnipiac University, B
Sacred Heart University, B
Southern Connecticut State University, B
Trinity College, B
University of Bridgeport, B
University of Connecticut, B
University of Hartford, B
University of New Haven, B
University of Saint Joseph, B
Wesleyan University, B
Western Connecticut State University, B
Yale University, B

Delaware

Delaware State University, B
Delaware Technical & Community College, Jack F. Owens Campus, A
Delaware Technical & Community College, Stanton/Wilmington Campus, A
University of Delaware, B
Wesley College, B

District of Columbia

American University, B
The Catholic University of America, B
Gallaudet University, B
The George Washington University, B
Georgetown University, B
Howard University, B
Trinity Washington University, B
University of the District of Columbia, B

Florida

Ave Maria University, B
Barry University, B
Bethune-Cookman University, B
Broward College, A
College of Central Florida, A
Eckerd College, B
Edward Waters College, B
Florida Agricultural and Mechanical University, B
Florida Atlantic University, B
Florida Gulf Coast University, B
Florida Institute of Technology, B
Florida International University, B
Florida Memorial University, B
Florida Southern College, B
Indian River State College, A
Jacksonville University, B
Lynn University, B
Miami Dade College, AB
New College of Florida, B
Nova Southeastern University, B
Palm Beach Atlantic University, B
Palm Beach State College, A

Pensacola State College, A
Rollins College, B
Saint Leo University, B
St. Petersburg College, B
St. Thomas University, B
South Florida State College, A
Southeastern University, B
State College of Florida Manatee-Sarasota, A
Stetson University, B
University of Central Florida, B
University of Florida, B
University of Miami, B
University of North Florida, B
University of South Florida, B
University of South Florida, St. Petersburg, B
University of South Florida Sarasota-Manatee, B
The University of Tampa, B
University of West Florida, B
Warner University, B

Georgia

Abraham Baldwin Agricultural College, A
Agnes Scott College, B
Albany State University, B
Andrew College, A
Armstrong State University, B
Augusta University, B
Bainbridge State College, A
Berry College, B
Brenau University, B
Brewton-Parker College, AB
Clark Atlanta University, B
Clayton State University, B
College of Coastal Georgia, AB
Columbus State University, B
Covenant College, B
Dalton State College, AB
Darton State College, A
Emmanuel College, B
Emory University, B
Fort Valley State University, B
Georgia College & State University, B
Georgia Gwinnett College, B
Georgia Highlands College, A
Georgia Institute of Technology, B
Georgia Military College, A
Georgia Southern University, B
Georgia Southwestern State University, B
Georgia State University, B
Kennesaw State University, B
LaGrange College, B
Life University, B
Mercer University, B
Middle Georgia State University, B
Morehouse College, B
Oglethorpe University, B
Paine College, B
Piedmont College, B
Point University, B
Reinhardt University, B
Savannah State University, B
Shorter University, B
South Georgia State College, AB
Spelman College, B
Thomas University, B
Toccoa Falls College, B
Truett-McConnell College, B
University of Georgia, B
University of North Georgia, B
University of West Georgia, B
Valdosta State University, B
Wesleyan College, B
Young Harris College, B

Hawaii

Brigham Young University - Hawaii, B
Chaminade University of Honolulu, B
Hawai'i Pacific University, B
University of Hawaii at Hilo, B
University of Hawaii at Manoa, B

Idaho

Boise State University, B
Brigham Young University - Idaho, B
The College of Idaho, B
College of Southern Idaho, A

College of Western Idaho, A
Idaho State University, B
Lewis-Clark State College, B
North Idaho College, A
Northwest Nazarene University, B
University of Idaho, B

Illinois

Augustana College, B
Aurora University, B
Benedictine University, B
Blackburn College, B
Bradley University, B
Chicago State University, B
Concordia University Chicago, B
DePaul University, B
Dominican University, B
East-West University, A
Eastern Illinois University, B
Elmhurst College, B
Eureka College, B
Governors State University, B
Greenville College, B
Harper College, A
Illinois College, B
Illinois Institute of Technology, B
Illinois State University, B
Illinois Wesleyan University, B
John A. Logan College, A
Judson University, B
Kankakee Community College, A
Knox College, B
Lake Forest College, B
Lewis University, B
Loyola University Chicago, B
MacMurray College, B
McKendree University, B
Millikin University, B
Monmouth College, B
Moraine Valley Community College, A
National Louis University, B
North Central College, B
North Park University, B
Northeastern Illinois University, B
Northern Illinois University, B
Northwestern University, B
Olivet Nazarene University, B
Principia College, B
Quincy University, B
Rockford University, B
Roosevelt University, B
Saint Xavier University, B
Sauk Valley Community College, A
Southern Illinois University Carbondale, B
Southern Illinois University Edwardsville, B
Spoon River College, A
Trinity Christian College, B
Trinity International University, B
Triton College, A
University of Chicago, B
University of Illinois at Chicago, B
University of Illinois at Springfield, B
University of Illinois at Urbana - Champaign, B
University of St. Francis, B
Western Illinois University, B
Wheaton College, B

Indiana

Anderson University, B
Ball State University, B
Bethel College, B
Butler University, B
DePauw University, B
Earlham College, B
Franklin College, B
Goshen College, B
Grace College, B
Hanover College, B
Huntington University, B
Indiana State University, B
Indiana University Bloomington, B
Indiana University East, B
Indiana University Kokomo, B
Indiana University Northwest, B
Indiana University - Purdue University Fort Wayne, B

Indiana University - Purdue University Indianapolis, B
Indiana University South Bend, B
Indiana University Southeast, B
Indiana Wesleyan University, AB
Manchester University, B
Marian University, B
Martin University, B
Oakland City University, B
Purdue University, B
Purdue University Northwest (Hammond), B
Purdue University Northwest (Westville), B
Rose-Hulman Institute of Technology, B
Saint Joseph's College, B
Saint Mary-of-the-Woods College, B
Saint Mary's College, B
Taylor University, B
Trine University, B
University of Evansville, B
University of Indianapolis, B
University of Notre Dame, B
University of Saint Francis, B
University of Southern Indiana, B
Valparaiso University, B
Vincennes University, A
Wabash College, B

Iowa

Briar Cliff University, B
Buena Vista University, B
Central College, B
Clarke University, B
Coe College, B
Cornell College, B
Dordt College, B
Drake University, B
Graceland University, B
Grand View University, B
Grinnell College, B
Iowa Lakes Community College, A
Iowa State University of Science and Technology, B
Iowa Wesleyan University, B
Loras College, B
Luther College, B
Morningside College, B
Mount Mercy University, B
Northwestern College, B
St. Ambrose University, B
Simpson College, B
University of Dubuque, B
The University of Iowa, B
University of Northern Iowa, B
Upper Iowa University, B
Waldorf College, B
Wartburg College, B
William Penn University, B

Kansas

Allen Community College, A
Baker University, B
Barton County Community College, A
Benedictine College, B
Bethany College, B
Bethel College, B
Butler Community College, A
Cleveland University - Kansas City, AB
Cowley County Community College and Area Vocational - Technical School, A
Dodge City Community College, A
Emporia State University, B
Fort Hays State University, B
Friends University, B
Garden City Community College, A
Highland Community College, A
Hutchinson Community College, A
Independence Community College, A
Kansas State University, B
Kansas Wesleyan University, B
Labette Community College, A
McPherson College, B
MidAmerica Nazarene University, B
Newman University, B
Ottawa University, B
Pittsburg State University, B
Pratt Community College, A

Seward County Community College and Area Technical School, A
Southwestern College, B
Sterling College, B
Tabor College, B
The University of Kansas, B
University of Saint Mary, B
Washburn University, B
Wichita State University, B

Kentucky

Alice Lloyd College, B
Asbury University, B
Bellarmine University, B
Berea College, B
Brescia University, B
Campbellsville University, B
Centre College, B
Eastern Kentucky University, B
Georgetown College, B
Kentucky Christian University, B
Kentucky State University, B
Kentucky Wesleyan College, B
Lindsey Wilson College, B
Midway University, B
Morehead State University, B
Murray State University, B
Northern Kentucky University, B
Thomas More College, AB
Transylvania University, B
Union College, B
University of the Cumberlands, B
University of Kentucky, B
University of Louisville, B
University of Pikeville, B
Western Kentucky University, B

Louisiana

Centenary College of Louisiana, B
Dillard University, B
Grambling State University, B
Louisiana College, B
Louisiana State University and Agricultural & Mechanical College, B
Louisiana State University at Alexandria, B
Louisiana State University in Shreveport, B
Louisiana Tech University, B
Loyola University New Orleans, B
McNeese State University, B
Nicholls State University, B
Northwestern State University of Louisiana, B
Our Lady of the Lake College, B
Southeastern Louisiana University, B
Southern University and Agricultural and Mechanical College, B
Southern University at New Orleans, B
Southern University at Shreveport, A
Tulane University, B
University of Holy Cross, B
University of Louisiana at Lafayette, B
University of Louisiana at Monroe, B
University of New Orleans, B
Xavier University of Louisiana, B

Maine

Bates College, B
Bowdoin College, B
Central Maine Community College, A
Colby College, B
College of the Atlantic, B
Husson University, B
Saint Joseph's College of Maine, B
University of Maine, B
University of Maine at Augusta, B
University of Maine at Farmington, B
University of Maine at Fort Kent, B
University of Maine at Machias, B
University of Maine at Presque Isle, B
University of New England, B
University of Southern Maine, B

Maryland

Bowie State University, B
Cecil College, A
Coppin State University, B
Frederick Community College, A

Frostburg State University, B
Goucher College, B
Harford Community College, A
Hood College, B
Johns Hopkins University, B
Loyola University Maryland, B
McDaniel College, B
Morgan State University, B
Mount St. Mary's University, B
Notre Dame of Maryland University, B
St. Mary's College of Maryland, B
Salisbury University, B
Stevenson University, B
Towson University, B
University of Maryland, Baltimore County, B
University of Maryland, College Park, B
University of Maryland Eastern Shore, B
Washington Adventist University, B
Washington College, B

Massachusetts

American International College, B
Amherst College, B
Anna Maria College, B
Assumption College, B
Bard College at Simon's Rock, B
Bay Path University, B
Becker College, B
Boston College, B
Boston University, B
Brandeis University, B
Bridgewater State University, B
Bunker Hill Community College, A
Clark University, B
College of the Holy Cross, B
Curry College, B
Dean College, A
Eastern Nazarene College, B
Elms College, B
Emmanuel College, B
Fitchburg State University, B
Framingham State University, B
Gordon College, B
Hampshire College, B
Harvard University, B
Holyoke Community College, A
Massachusetts College of Liberal Arts, B
Massachusetts Institute of Technology, B
Merrimack College, B
Middlesex Community College, A
Mount Holyoke College, B
Mount Ida College, B
Northeastern University, B
Northern Essex Community College, A
Pine Manor College, AB
Regis College, B
Roxbury Community College, A
Salem State University, B
Simmons College, B
Smith College, B
Springfield College, B
Springfield Technical Community College, A
Stonehill College, B
Suffolk University, B
Tufts University, B
University of Massachusetts Amherst, B
University of Massachusetts Boston, B
University of Massachusetts Dartmouth, B
University of Massachusetts Lowell, B
Wellesley College, B
Western New England University, B
Westfield State University, B
Wheaton College, B
Williams College, B
Worcester Polytechnic Institute, B
Worcester State University, B

Michigan

Adrian College, B
Albion College, B
Alma College, B
Alpena Community College, A
Andrews University, B
Aquinas College, B
Calvin College, B
Central Michigan University, B

Concordia University Ann Arbor, B
Cornerstone University, B
Eastern Michigan University, B
Ferris State University, B
Grand Valley State University, B
Henry Ford College, A
Hillsdale College, B
Hope College, B
Kalamazoo College, B
Kettering University, B
Lake Michigan College, A
Lake Superior State University, B
Lansing Community College, A
Macomb Community College, A
Madonna University, B
Marygrove College, B
Michigan State University, B
Michigan Technological University, B
Mid Michigan Community College, A
Monroe County Community College, A
Mott Community College, A
Northern Michigan University, B
Northwestern Michigan College, A
Oakland University, B
Olivet College, B
Saginaw Valley State University, B
Siena Heights University, AB
Spring Arbor University, B
University of Detroit Mercy, B
University of Michigan, B
University of Michigan - Dearborn, B
University of Michigan - Flint, B
Wayne State University, B
Western Michigan University, B

Minnesota

Anoka-Ramsey Community College, A
Augsburg College, B
Bemidji State University, B
Bethany Lutheran College, B
Bethel University, B
Carleton College, B
College of Saint Benedict, B
The College of St. Scholastica, B
Concordia College, B
Concordia University, St. Paul, B
Crown College, B
Gustavus Adolphus College, B
Hamline University, B
Inver Hills Community College, A
Macalester College, B
Metropolitan State University, B
Minneapolis Community and Technical College, A
Minnesota State Community and Technical College, A
Minnesota State Community and Technical College - Moorhead, A
Minnesota State University Mankato, B
Minnesota State University Moorhead, B
North Hennepin Community College, A
Ridgewater College, A
St. Catherine University, B
St. Cloud State University, B
Saint John's University, B
Saint Mary's University of Minnesota, B
St. Olaf College, B
Southwest Minnesota State University, B
University of Minnesota, Crookston, B
University of Minnesota, Duluth, B
University of Minnesota, Morris, B
University of Minnesota, Twin Cities Campus, B
University of Northwestern - St. Paul, B
University of St. Thomas, B
Vermilion Community College, A
Winona State University, B

Mississippi

Alcorn State University, B
Belhaven University, B
Blue Mountain College, B
Coahoma Community College, A
Copiah-Lincoln Community College, A
Delta State University, B
East Mississippi Community College, A
Holmes Community College, A
Itawamba Community College, A

Jackson State University, B
Jones County Junior College, A
Millsaps College, B
Mississippi College, B
Mississippi Delta Community College, A
Mississippi State University, B
Mississippi University for Women, B
Mississippi Valley State University, B
Northeast Mississippi Community College, A
Rust College, B
Southwest Mississippi Community College, A
Tougaloo College, B
University of Mississippi, B
University of Southern Mississippi, B
William Carey University, B

Missouri

Avila University, B
Central Methodist University, B
Columbia College, B
Crowder College, A
Culver-Stockton College, B
Drury University, B
Evangel University, B
Fontbonne University, B
Hannibal-LaGrange University, B
Harris-Stowe State University, B
Lincoln University, B
Lindenwood University, B
Logan University, B
Maryville University of Saint Louis, B
Metropolitan Community College - Kansas City, A
Missouri Baptist University, B
Missouri Southern State University, B
Missouri State University, B
Missouri University of Science and Technology, B
Missouri Valley College, B
Missouri Western State University, B
Northwest Missouri State University, B
Park University, B
Rockhurst University, B
St. Charles Community College, A
Saint Louis University, B
Southeast Missouri State University, B
Southwest Baptist University, B
Stephens College, B
Truman State University, B
University of Central Missouri, B
University of Missouri, B
University of Missouri - Kansas City, B
University of Missouri - St. Louis, B
Washington University in St. Louis, B
Webster University, B
Westminster College, B
William Jewell College, B
William Woods University, B

Montana

Carroll College, B
Montana State University, B
Montana State University Billings, B
Montana State University - Northern, B
Montana Tech of The University of Montana, B
Rocky Mountain College, B
University of Great Falls, B
University of Montana, B
The University of Montana Western, B

Nebraska

Bellevue University, B
Chadron State College, B
College of Saint Mary, B
Concordia University, Nebraska, B
Creighton University, B
Doane University, B
Hastings College, B
Midland University, B
Nebraska Wesleyan University, B
Northeast Community College, A
Peru State College, B
Union College, B
University of Nebraska at Kearney, B
University of Nebraska - Lincoln, B
University of Nebraska at Omaha, B
Wayne State College, B
Western Nebraska Community College, A

York College, B

Nevada

College of Southern Nevada, A
Great Basin College, AB
Nevada State College, B
Truckee Meadows Community College, A
University of Nevada, Las Vegas, B
University of Nevada, Reno, B

New Hampshire

Colby-Sawyer College, B
Dartmouth College, B
Franklin Pierce University, B
Keene State College, B
New England College, B
Plymouth State University, B
Rivier University, B
Saint Anselm College, B
University of New Hampshire, B
University of New Hampshire at Manchester, AB

New Jersey

Bergen Community College, A
Bloomfield College, B
Caldwell University, B
Centenary College, B
The College of New Jersey, B
College of Saint Elizabeth, B
Drew University, B
Essex County College, A
Fairleigh Dickinson University, College at Florham, B
Fairleigh Dickinson University, Metropolitan Campus, B
Felician University, B
Georgian Court University, B
Kean University, B
Mercer County Community College, A
Monmouth University, B
Montclair State University, B
New Jersey City University, B
New Jersey Institute of Technology, B
Ramapo College of New Jersey, B
Rider University, B
Rowan College at Burlington County, A
Rowan College at Gloucester County, A
Rowan University, B
Rutgers University - Camden, B
Rutgers University - New Brunswick, B
Rutgers University - Newark, B
Saint Peter's University, B
Salem Community College, A
Seton Hall University, B
Stockton University, B
Thomas Edison State University, AB
Union County College, A
Warren County Community College, A
William Paterson University of New Jersey, B

New Mexico

Central New Mexico Community College, A
Eastern New Mexico University, B
New Mexico Highlands University, B
New Mexico Institute of Mining and Technology, B
New Mexico Junior College, A
New Mexico Military Institute, A
New Mexico State University, B
San Juan College, A
Santa Fe Community College, A
University of New Mexico, B
University of the Southwest, B
Western New Mexico University, B

New York

Adelphi University, B
Alfred University, B
Bard College, B
Barnard College, B
Binghamton University, State University of New York, B
Bronx Community College of the City University of New York, A
Brooklyn College of the City University of New York, B

Buffalo State College, State University of New York, B
Canisius College, B
Cazenovia College, B
City College of the City University of New York, B
Clarkson University, B
Colgate University, B
The College at Brockport, State University of New York, B
College of Mount Saint Vincent, B
The College of New Rochelle, B
The College of Saint Rose, B
College of Staten Island of the City University of New York, B
Columbia University, B
Columbia University, School of General Studies, B
Concordia College - New York, B
Cornell University, B
Daemen College, B
Dominican College, B
D'Youville College, B
Elmira College, B
Excelsior College, B
Farmingdale State College, B
Finger Lakes Community College, A
Fiorello H. LaGuardia Community College of the City University of New York, A
Fordham University, B
Fulton-Montgomery Community College, A
Genesee Community College, A
Hamilton College, B
Hartwick College, B
Hobart and William Smith Colleges, B
Hofstra University, B
Houghton College, B
Hudson Valley Community College, A
Hunter College of the City University of New York, B
Iona College, B
Ithaca College, B
Keuka College, B
Kingsborough Community College of the City University of New York, A
Le Moyne College, B
Lehman College of the City University of New York, B
Long Island University - LIU Brooklyn, B
Long Island University - LIU Post, B
Manhattan College, B
Manhattanville College, B
Marist College, B
Marymount Manhattan College, B
Medaille College, B
Medgar Evers College of the City University of New York, B
Mercy College, B
Molloy College, B
Monroe Community College, A
Mount Saint Mary College, B
Nazareth College of Rochester, B
New York Institute of Technology, B
New York University, B
Niagara University, B
Nyack College, B
Pace University, B
Pace University, Pleasantville Campus, B
Purchase College, State University of New York, B
Queens College of the City University of New York, B
Rensselaer Polytechnic Institute, B
Roberts Wesleyan College, B
Rochester Institute of Technology, B
The Sage Colleges, B
St. Bonaventure University, B
St. Francis College, B
St. John Fisher College, B
St. John's University, B
St. Joseph's College, Long Island Campus, B
St. Joseph's College, New York, B
St. Lawrence University, B
St. Thomas Aquinas College, B
Sarah Lawrence College, B
Siena College, B
Skidmore College, B
State University of New York College of Agriculture and Technology at Cobleskill, A
State University of New York College at Cortland, B

State University of New York College of Environmental Science and Forestry, B
State University of New York College at Geneseo, B
State University of New York College at Old Westbury, B
State University of New York College at Oneonta, B
State University of New York College at Potsdam, B
State University of New York College of Technology at Alfred, A
State University of New York at Fredonia, B
State University of New York at New Paltz, B
State University of New York at Oswego, B
State University of New York at Plattsburgh, B
State University of New York Polytechnic Institute, B
Stony Brook University, State University of New York, B
Suffolk County Community College, A
Syracuse University, B
Touro College, B
Union College, B
United States Military Academy, B
University at Albany, State University of New York, B
University at Buffalo, the State University of New York, B
University of Rochester, B
Utica College, B
Vassar College, B
Wagner College, B
Wells College, B
Yeshiva University, B
York College of the City University of New York, B

North Carolina

Appalachian State University, B
Barton College, B
Belmont Abbey College, B
Bennett College, B
Brevard College, B
Campbell University, B
Catawba College, B
Central Piedmont Community College, A
Chowan University, B
Davidson College, B
Duke University, B
East Carolina University, B
Elizabeth City State University, B
Elon University, B
Fayetteville State University, B
Gardner-Webb University, B
Greensboro College, B
Guilford College, B
High Point University, B
Johnson C. Smith University, B
Lees-McRae College, B
Lenoir-Rhyne University, B
Livingstone College, B
Louisburg College, A
Mars Hill University, B
Meredith College, B
Methodist University, AB
Montreat College, B
North Carolina Agricultural and Technical State University, B
North Carolina Central University, B
North Carolina State University, B
North Carolina Wesleyan College, B
Pfeiffer University, B
Queens University of Charlotte, B
St. Andrews University, B
Saint Augustine's University, B
Salem College, B
Shaw University, B
University of Mount Olive, B
University of North Carolina at Asheville, B
The University of North Carolina at Chapel Hill, B
The University of North Carolina at Charlotte, B
The University of North Carolina at Greensboro, B
The University of North Carolina at Pembroke, B
The University of North Carolina Wilmington, B
Wake Forest University, B
Warren Wilson College, B
Western Carolina University, B
William Peace University, B
Wingate University, B
Winston-Salem State University, B

North Dakota

Dakota College at Bottineau, A
Dickinson State University, B
Mayville State University, B
Minot State University, B
North Dakota State University, B
Turtle Mountain Community College, A
University of Jamestown, B
University of Mary, B
University of North Dakota, B
Valley City State University, B

Ohio

Ashland University, B
Baldwin Wallace University, B
Bluffton University, B
Bowling Green State University, B
Capital University, B
Case Western Reserve University, B
Cedarville University, B
Central State University, B
Cincinnati State Technical and Community College, A
Cleveland State University, B
The College of Wooster, B
Defiance College, B
Denison University, B
Edison Community College, A
Franciscan University of Steubenville, B
Heidelberg University, B
Hiram College, B
John Carroll University, B
Kent State University, B
Kent State University at Stark, B
Kenyon College, B
Lake Erie College, B
Lorain County Community College, A
Lourdes University, AB
Malone University, B
Marietta College, B
Mercy College of Ohio, B
Miami University, B
Mount St. Joseph University, B
Mount Vernon Nazarene University, B
Muskingum University, B
Notre Dame College, B
Oberlin College, B
Ohio Dominican University, B
Ohio Northern University, B
The Ohio State University, B
The Ohio State University at Lima, B
Ohio University, B
Ohio Wesleyan University, B
Otterbein University, B
Shawnee State University, AB
Terra State Community College, A
The University of Akron, B
University of Cincinnati, B
University of Cincinnati Clermont College, A
University of Dayton, B
The University of Findlay, B
University of Mount Union, B
University of Rio Grande, AB
The University of Toledo, B
Urbana University, B
Ursuline College, B
Walsh University, B
Washington State Community College, A
Wilberforce University, B
Wilmington College, B
Wittenberg University, B
Wright State University, AB
Wright State University - Lake Campus, A
Xavier University, B
Youngstown State University, B

Oklahoma

Cameron University, B
Carl Albert State College, A
Connors State College, A
East Central University, B
Eastern Oklahoma State College, A
Langston University, B
Murray State College, A
Northeastern State University, B

Northwestern Oklahoma State University, B
Oklahoma Baptist University, B
Oklahoma Christian University, B
Oklahoma City Community College, A
Oklahoma City University, B
Oklahoma Panhandle State University, B
Oklahoma State University, B
Oklahoma Wesleyan University, AB
Oral Roberts University, B
Redlands Community College, A
Rogers State University, AB
Rose State College, A
St. Gregory's University, B
Seminole State College, A
Southeastern Oklahoma State University, B
Southern Nazarene University, B
Southwestern Oklahoma State University, B
University of Central Oklahoma, B
University of Science and Arts of Oklahoma, B
The University of Tulsa, B

Oregon

Central Oregon Community College, A
Concordia University, B
Eastern Oregon University, B
George Fox University, B
Lewis & Clark College, B
Linfield College, B
Linn-Benton Community College, A
Northwest Christian University, B
Oregon State University, B
Pacific University, B
Portland State University, B
Reed College, B
Southern Oregon University, B
Umpqua Community College, A
University of Oregon, B
University of Portland, B
Warner Pacific College, B
Western Oregon University, B
Willamette University, B

Pennsylvania

Albright College, B
Allegheny College, B
Alvernia University, B
Arcadia University, B
Bloomsburg University of Pennsylvania, B
Bryn Athyn College of the New Church, B
Bryn Mawr College, B
Bucknell University, B
Butler County Community College, A
Cabrini University, B
California University of Pennsylvania, B
Carlow University, B
Carnegie Mellon University, B
Cedar Crest College, B
Chatham University, B
Chestnut Hill College, B
Cheyney University of Pennsylvania, B
Clarion University of Pennsylvania, B
Community College of Allegheny County, A
Delaware Valley University, B
DeSales University, B
Dickinson College, B
Drexel University, B
Duquesne University, B
East Stroudsburg University of Pennsylvania, B
Eastern University, B
Edinboro University of Pennsylvania, B
Elizabethtown College, B
Franklin & Marshall College, B
Gannon University, B
Geneva College, B
Gettysburg College, B
Grove City College, B
Gwynedd Mercy University, B
Harrisburg Area Community College, A
Harrisburg University of Science and Technology, B
Haverford College, B
Holy Family University, B
Immaculata University, AB
Indiana University of Pennsylvania, B
Juniata College, B
Keystone College, B
King's College, B

Kutztown University of Pennsylvania, B
La Roche College, B
La Salle University, B
Lackawanna College, A
Lafayette College, B
Lebanon Valley College, B
Lehigh Carbon Community College, A
Lehigh University, B
Lincoln University, B
Lock Haven University of Pennsylvania, B
Lycoming College, B
Mansfield University of Pennsylvania, B
Marywood University, B
Mercyhurst University, B
Messiah College, B
Millersville University of Pennsylvania, B
Misericordia University, B
Montgomery County Community College, A
Moravian College, B
Mount Aloysius College, B
Muhlenberg College, B
Neumann University, B
Northampton Community College, A
Penn State Abington, B
Penn State Altoona, B
Penn State Beaver, B
Penn State Berks, B
Penn State Brandywine, B
Penn State DuBois, B
Penn State Erie, The Behrend College, B
Penn State Fayette, The Eberly Campus, B
Penn State Greater Allegheny, B
Penn State Hazleton, B
Penn State Lehigh Valley, B
Penn State Mont Alto, B
Penn State New Kensington, B
Penn State Schuylkill, B
Penn State Shenango, B
Penn State University Park, B
Penn State Wilkes-Barre, B
Penn State Worthington Scranton, B
Penn State York, B
Philadelphia University, B
Point Park University, B
Robert Morris University, B
Rosemont College, B
Saint Francis University, B
Saint Joseph's University, B
Saint Vincent College, B
Seton Hill University, B
Shippensburg University of Pennsylvania, B
Slippery Rock University of Pennsylvania, B
Susquehanna University, B
Swarthmore College, B
Temple University, B
Thiel College, B
University of Pennsylvania, B
University of Pittsburgh, B
University of Pittsburgh at Bradford, B
University of Pittsburgh at Greensburg, B
University of Pittsburgh at Johnstown, B
University of Pittsburgh at Titusville, A
University of the Sciences, B
The University of Scranton, B
Ursinus College, B
Villanova University, B
Washington & Jefferson College, B
Waynesburg University, B
West Chester University of Pennsylvania, B
Westminster College, B
Widener University, B
Wilkes University, B
Wilson College, B
York College of Pennsylvania, AB

Rhode Island

Brown University, B
Bryant University, B
Providence College, B
Rhode Island College, B
Roger Williams University, B
Salve Regina University, B
University of Rhode Island, B

South Carolina

Allen University, B
Anderson University, B
Benedict College, B
Bob Jones University, B
Charleston Southern University, B
The Citadel, The Military College of South Carolina, B
Claflin University, B
Clemson University, B
Coastal Carolina University, B
Coker College, B
College of Charleston, B
Columbia College, B
Converse College, B
Erskine College, B
Francis Marion University, B
Furman University, B
Lander University, B
Limestone College, B
Morris College, B
Newberry College, B
North Greenville University, B
Presbyterian College, B
South Carolina State University, B
Southern Wesleyan University, B
University of South Carolina, B
University of South Carolina Aiken, B
University of South Carolina Beaufort, B
University of South Carolina Upstate, B
Voorhees College, B
Winthrop University, B
Wofford College, B

South Dakota

Augustana University, B
Black Hills State University, B
Dakota Wesleyan University, B
Mount Marty College, B
Northern State University, B
Presentation College, AB
South Dakota State University, B
University of Sioux Falls, B

Tennessee

Austin Peay State University, B
Belmont University, B
Bethel University, B
Bryan College, B
Carson-Newman University, B
Christian Brothers University, B
Cumberland University, AB
East Tennessee State University, B
Fisk University, B
Freed-Hardeman University, B
Hiwassee College, A
King University, B
Lane College, B
Lee University, B
LeMoyne-Owen College, B
Lincoln Memorial University, B
Lipscomb University, B
Martin Methodist College, B
Maryville College, B
Middle Tennessee State University, B
Milligan College, B
Nashville State Community College, A
Rhodes College, B
Roane State Community College, A
Sewanee: The University of the South, B
Southern Adventist University, B
Tennessee State University, B
Tennessee Technological University, B
Tennessee Wesleyan College, B
Trevecca Nazarene University, B
Tusculum College, B
Union University, B
University of Memphis, B
The University of Tennessee, B
The University of Tennessee at Chattanooga, B
The University of Tennessee at Martin, B
Vanderbilt University, B
Welch College, A

Texas

Abilene Christian University, B
Alvin Community College, A
Amarillo College, A
Angelo State University, B
Austin College, B
Austin Community College District, A
Baylor University, B
Blinn College, A
Central Texas College, A
Cisco College, A
Clarendon College, A
Concordia University Texas, B
Dallas Baptist University, AB
Del Mar College, A
East Texas Baptist University, B
Frank Phillips College, A
Grayson College, A
Hardin-Simmons University, B
Hill College, A
Houston Baptist University, B
Houston Community College, A
Howard College, A
Howard Payne University, B
Huston-Tillotson University, B
Jarvis Christian College, B
Lamar University, B
Lee College, A
LeTourneau University, B
Lubbock Christian University, B
McMurry University, B
Midwestern State University, B
Navarro College, A
Northeast Texas Community College, A
Odessa College, A
Our Lady of the Lake University of San Antonio, B
Palo Alto College, A
Panola College, A
Paris Junior College, A
Paul Quinn College, B
Prairie View A&M University, B
Rice University, B
St. Edward's University, B
St. Mary's University, B
St. Philip's College, A
Sam Houston State University, B
San Jacinto College District, A
Schreiner University, B
South Plains College, A
Southern Methodist University, B
Southwestern Adventist University, B
Southwestern University, B
Stephen F. Austin State University, B
Sul Ross State University, B
Tarleton State University, B
Texarkana College, A
Texas A&M International University, B
Texas A&M University, B
Texas A&M University - Commerce, B
Texas A&M University - Corpus Christi, B
Texas A&M University - Kingsville, B
Texas A&M University - San Antonio, B
Texas A&M University - Texarkana, B
Texas Christian University, B
Texas College, B
Texas Lutheran University, B
Texas Southern University, B
Texas State University, B
Texas Tech University, B
Texas Wesleyan University, B
Texas Woman's University, B
Trinity University, B
Trinity Valley Community College, A
Tyler Junior College, A
University of Dallas, B
University of Houston, B
University of Houston - Clear Lake, B
University of Houston - Downtown, B
University of Houston - Victoria, B
University of the Incarnate Word, B
University of Mary Hardin-Baylor, B
University of North Texas, B
University of St. Thomas, B
The University of Texas at Arlington, B
The University of Texas at Austin, B
The University of Texas at Dallas, B

The University of Texas at El Paso, B
The University of Texas of the Permian Basin, B
The University of Texas Rio Grande Valley, B
The University of Texas at San Antonio, B
The University of Texas at Tyler, B
Wayland Baptist University, B
West Texas A&M University, B
Western Texas College, A
Wharton County Junior College, A
Wiley College, B

Utah

Dixie State University, B
Salt Lake Community College, A
Snow College, A
Southern Utah University, B
University of Utah, B
Utah State University, B
Utah Valley University, AB
Westminster College, B

Vermont

Bennington College, B
Castleton University, B
Green Mountain College, B
Johnson State College, B
Landmark College, A
Marlboro College, B
Middlebury College, B
Norwich University, B
Saint Michael's College, B
University of Vermont, B

Virginia

Bluefield College, B
Bridgewater College, B
Christopher Newport University, B
The College of William and Mary, B
Eastern Mennonite University, B
Emory & Henry College, B
Ferrum College, B
George Mason University, B
Hampden-Sydney College, B
Hampton University, B
Hollins University, B
James Madison University, B
Liberty University, B
Longwood University, B
Lynchburg College, B
Mary Baldwin College, B
Marymount University, B
Norfolk State University, B
Old Dominion University, B
Radford University, B
Randolph College, B
Randolph-Macon College, B
Roanoke College, B
Shenandoah University, B
Southern Virginia University, B
Sweet Briar College, B
University of Mary Washington, B
University of Richmond, B
University of Virginia, B
The University of Virginia's College at Wise, B
Virginia Commonwealth University, B
Virginia Military Institute, B
Virginia Polytechnic Institute and State University, B
Virginia State University, B
Virginia Union University, B
Virginia Wesleyan College, B
Washington and Lee University, B

Washington

Bastyr University, B
Central Washington University, B
Eastern Washington University, B
Everett Community College, A
The Evergreen State College, B
Gonzaga University, B
Heritage University, B
Northwest University, B
Pacific Lutheran University, B
Saint Martin's University, B
Seattle Pacific University, B
Seattle University, B
Skagit Valley College, A

University of Puget Sound, B
University of Washington, B
University of Washington, Bothell, B
Walla Walla Community College, A
Walla Walla University, B
Washington State University, B
Washington State University - Vancouver, B
Wenatchee Valley College, A
Western Washington University, B
Whitman College, B
Whitworth University, B

West Virginia

Alderson Broaddus University, B
Bethany College, B
Concord University, B
Fairmont State University, B
Glenville State College, B
Marshall University, B
Potomac State College of West Virginia University,
  A
Salem International University, B
Shepherd University, B
University of Charleston, B
West Liberty University, B
West Virginia State University, B
West Virginia University, B
West Virginia University Institute of Technology, B
West Virginia Wesleyan College, B
Wheeling Jesuit University, B

Wisconsin

Alverno College, B
Beloit College, B
Cardinal Stritch University, B
Carroll University, B
Carthage College, B
College of Menominee Nation, A
Concordia University Wisconsin, B
Edgewood College, B
Lakeland College, B
Lawrence University, B
Maranatha Baptist University, B
Marian University, B
Marquette University, B
Mount Mary University, B
Northland College, B
Ripon College, B
St. Norbert College, B
Silver Lake College of the Holy Family, B
University of Wisconsin - Eau Claire, B
University of Wisconsin - Green Bay, B
University of Wisconsin - La Crosse, B
University of Wisconsin - Madison, B
University of Wisconsin - Milwaukee, B
University of Wisconsin - Oshkosh, B
University of Wisconsin - Platteville, B
University of Wisconsin - River Falls, B
University of Wisconsin - Stevens Point, B
University of Wisconsin - Superior, B
University of Wisconsin - Whitewater, B
Viterbo University, B
Wisconsin Lutheran College, B

Wyoming

Casper College, A
Central Wyoming College, A
Eastern Wyoming College, A
Laramie County Community College, A
Northwest College, A
Sheridan College, A
University of Wyoming, B
Western Wyoming Community College, A

U.S. Territories: Guam

University of Guam, B

U.S. Territories: Puerto Rico

Bayamón Central University, B
Inter American University of Puerto Rico, Aguadilla
  Campus, B
Inter American University of Puerto Rico, Arecibo
  Campus, B
Inter American University of Puerto Rico, Bar-
  ranquitas Campus, B

Inter American University of Puerto Rico, Bayamón
  Campus, B
Inter American University of Puerto Rico, Fajardo
  Campus, B
Inter American University of Puerto Rico, Guayama
  Campus, B
Inter American University of Puerto Rico, Metropoli-
  tan Campus, B
Inter American University of Puerto Rico, Ponce
  Campus, B
Inter American University of Puerto Rico, San
  Germán Campus, B
Pontifical Catholic University of Puerto Rico, B
Universidad Adventista de las Antillas, B
Universidad del Este, B
Universidad Metropolitana, B
Universidad del Turabo, B
University of Puerto Rico in Bayamón, B
University of Puerto Rico in Cayey, B
University of Puerto Rico in Humacao, B
University of Puerto Rico, Mayagüez Campus, B
University of Puerto Rico in Ponce, A
University of Puerto Rico, Río Piedras Campus, B
University of Puerto Rico in Utuado, B
University of the Sacred Heart, B

U.S. Territories: United States Virgin Islands

University of the Virgin Islands, B

Canada

Alberta

Ambrose University, B
Concordia University of Edmonton, B
The King's University, B
University of Alberta, B
University of Calgary, B
University of Lethbridge, B

British Columbia

Simon Fraser University, B
Thompson Rivers University, AB
Trinity Western University, B
The University of British Columbia, B
The University of British Columbia - Okanagan
  Campus, B
University of the Fraser Valley, B
University of Northern British Columbia, B
University of Victoria, B

Manitoba

Brandon University, B
University of Manitoba, B
The University of Winnipeg, B

Maritime Provinces: New Brunswick

Crandall University, B
Mount Allison University, B
Université de Moncton, B
University of New Brunswick Fredericton, B
University of New Brunswick Saint John, B

Maritime Provinces: Nova Scotia

Acadia University, B
Cape Breton University, B
Dalhousie University, B
Mount Saint Vincent University, B
St. Francis Xavier University, B
Saint Mary's University, B
University of King's College, B

Maritime Provinces: Prince Edward Island

University of Prince Edward Island, B

Newfoundland and Labrador

Memorial University of Newfoundland, B

Ontario

Brock University, B
Carleton University, B
Lakehead University, B
McMaster University, B

Nipissing University, B
Queen's University at Kingston, B
Redeemer University College, B
Ryerson University, B
Trent University, B
University of Guelph, B
University of Ottawa, B
University of Toronto, B
University of Waterloo, B
The University of Western Ontario, B
University of Windsor, B
Wilfrid Laurier University, B
York University, B

Quebec

Bishop's University, B
Concordia University, B
McGill University, B
Université Laval, B
Université de Montréal, B
Université du Québec à Chicoutimi, B
Université du Québec à Montréal, B
Université du Québec à Rimouski, B
Université du Québec à Trois-Rivières, B
Université de Sherbrooke, B

Saskatchewan

University of Regina, B
University of Saskatchewan, B

BIOLOGY TEACHER EDUCATION

United States

Alabama

Huntingdon College, B
Spring Hill College, B
Talladega College, B
University of Mobile, B

Arizona

Arizona Christian University, B
Grand Canyon University, B

Arkansas

Arkansas State University, B
Arkansas Tech University, B
Harding University, B
University of Arkansas - Fort Smith, B

California

Biola University, B
California State University, Long Beach, B
University of California, Irvine, B

Colorado

Adams State University, B
Colorado State University, B
Fort Lewis College, B
Western State Colorado University, B

Delaware

Delaware State University, B
University of Delaware, B

Florida

Bethune-Cookman University, B
Broward College, B
Daytona State College, B
Florida Institute of Technology, B
Florida Southern College, B
Florida SouthWestern State College, B
Indian River State College, B
Miami Dade College, B
Palm Beach Atlantic University, B
St. Petersburg College, B
Southeastern University, B
State College of Florida Manatee-Sarasota, A

Georgia

Brewton-Parker College, B
Gordon State College, B
Kennesaw State University, B
Middle Georgia State University, B
Paine College, B

Hawaii

Brigham Young University - Hawaii, B

Idaho

Boise State University, B
Brigham Young University - Idaho, B
Northwest Nazarene University, B

Illinois

Augustana College, B
Blackburn College, B
Bradley University, B
Concordia University Chicago, B
Elmhurst College, B
Greenville College, B
Illinois State University, B
McKendree University, B
Millikin University, B
Saint Xavier University, B
Trinity Christian College, B
University of Illinois at Chicago, B

Indiana

Ball State University, B
Franklin College, B
Goshen College, B
Grace College, B
Huntington University, B
Indiana University Bloomington, B
Indiana University Northwest, B
Indiana University - Purdue University Fort Wayne, B
Indiana University South Bend, B
Indiana University Southeast, B
Indiana Wesleyan University, B
Manchester University, B
Oakland City University, B
University of Evansville, B
University of Saint Francis, B
Valparaiso University, B

Iowa

Buena Vista University, B
Dordt College, B
Morningside College, B
Northwestern College, B
University of Dubuque, B
The University of Iowa, B

Kansas

Bethany College, B
Central Christian College of Kansas, A
Friends University, B
Kansas Wesleyan University, B
MidAmerica Nazarene University, B
Pittsburg State University, B
Tabor College, B
Washburn University, B

Kentucky

Campbellsville University, B
Eastern Kentucky University, B
Lindsey Wilson College, B

Louisiana

Louisiana State University in Shreveport, B
Louisiana Tech University, B
Southern University and Agricultural and Mechanical College, B
University of Louisiana at Monroe, B
Xavier University of Louisiana, B

Maine

Husson University, B
Saint Joseph's College of Maine, B
University of Maine, B
University of Maine at Farmington, B

University of Maine at Machias, B

Maryland

University of Maryland, Baltimore County, B

Massachusetts

Bay Path University, B
Bridgewater State University, B
Eastern Nazarene College, B
Fitchburg State University, B
Merrimack College, B

Michigan

Adrian College, B
Albion College, B
Alma College, B
Calvin College, B
Central Michigan University, B
Concordia University Ann Arbor, B
Cornerstone University, B
Eastern Michigan University, B
Ferris State University, B
Grand Valley State University, B
Hope College, B
Madonna University, B
Michigan State University, B
Northern Michigan University, B
Rochester College, B
Saginaw Valley State University, B
Spring Arbor University, B
Western Michigan University, B

Minnesota

Concordia College, B
Concordia University, St. Paul, B
Gustavus Adolphus College, B
Metropolitan State University, B
Minnesota State University Moorhead, B
St. Catherine University, B
Saint Mary's University of Minnesota, B
Southwest Minnesota State University, B
Winona State University, B

Mississippi

Blue Mountain College, B
Mississippi College, B
Rust College, B
William Carey University, B

Missouri

Central Methodist University, B
College of the Ozarks, B
Culver-Stockton College, B
Evangel University, B
Lincoln University, B
Lindenwood University, B
Missouri State University, B
Northwest Missouri State University, B
Southwest Baptist University, B
University of Missouri, B
Washington University in St. Louis, B
William Woods University, B

Montana

Carroll College, B
Montana State University Billings, B
Rocky Mountain College, B
University of Great Falls, B
The University of Montana Western, B

Nebraska

Chadron State College, B
College of Saint Mary, B
Concordia University, Nebraska, B
Hastings College, B
Peru State College, B
Union College, B
University of Nebraska - Lincoln, B
Wayne State College, B
York College, B

Nevada

Nevada State College, B

New Hampshire

Keene State College, B
Rivier University, B

New Jersey

The College of New Jersey, B

New York

Brooklyn College of the City University of New York, B
Canisius College, B
City College of the City University of New York, B
The College of Saint Rose, B
College of Staten Island of the City University of New York, B
Daemen College, B
Dominican College, B
Elmira College, B
Hofstra University, B
Hunter College of the City University of New York, B
Iona College, B
Ithaca College, B
Keuka College, B
Le Moyne College, B
Long Island University - LIU Brooklyn, B
Long Island University - LIU Post, B
Manhattanville College, B
Marist College, B
Nazareth College of Rochester, B
Niagara University, B
Pace University, B
Pace University, Pleasantville Campus, B
Queens College of the City University of New York, B
Roberts Wesleyan College, B
St. Francis College, B
St. John Fisher College, B
St. John's University, B
St. Joseph's College, Long Island Campus, B
St. Joseph's College, New York, B
State University of New York College at Cortland, B
State University of New York College at Old Westbury, B
State University of New York College at Oneonta, B
State University of New York College at Potsdam, B
State University of New York at New Paltz, B
State University of New York at Plattsburgh, B
Syracuse University, B
Ulster County Community College, A
Utica College, B

North Carolina

Campbell University, B
Elizabeth City State University, B
Fayetteville State University, B
Greensboro College, B
Louisburg College, A
North Carolina Agricultural and Technical State University, B
The University of North Carolina at Greensboro, B
The University of North Carolina Wilmington, B
Wingate University, B

North Dakota

Mayville State University, B
Minot State University, B
North Dakota State University, B
University of Jamestown, B
University of Mary, B
Valley City State University, B

Ohio

Ashland University, B
Bowling Green State University, B
Cedarville University, B
Miami University, B
Mount Vernon Nazarene University, B
Ohio Dominican University, B
Ohio Northern University, B
Ohio Wesleyan University, B
University of Rio Grande, B
Xavier University, B
Youngstown State University, B

Oklahoma

East Central University, B
St. Gregory's University, B
University of Central Oklahoma, B

Oregon

Corban University, B

Pennsylvania

Alvernia University, B
Bucks County Community College, A
Cabrini University, B
Grove City College, B
Holy Family University, B
Juniata College, B
Lincoln University, B
Marywood University, B
Mercyhurst University, B
Messiah College, B
Misericordia University, B
Point Park University, B
Saint Francis University, B
Saint Joseph's University, B
Seton Hill University, B
University of Pittsburgh at Johnstown, B
Waynesburg University, B
Widener University, B
York College of Pennsylvania, B

Rhode Island

Providence College, B
Rhode Island College, B
Salve Regina University, B

South Carolina

Coker College, B
Morris College, B

South Dakota

Dakota State University, B
Dakota Wesleyan University, B
The University of South Dakota, B

Tennessee

Bryan College, B
Cumberland University, B
King University, B
Lee University, B
Lincoln Memorial University, B
Lipscomb University, B
Maryville College, B
Southern Adventist University, B
Trevecca Nazarene University, B
The University of Tennessee at Martin, B
Welch College, B

Texas

Abilene Christian University, B
Baylor University, B
Dallas Baptist University, B
East Texas Baptist University, B
Houston Baptist University, B
Howard Payne University, B
McMurry University, B
St. Edward's University, B
Schreiner University, B
Southwestern Adventist University, B
Texas A&M International University, B
Texas Wesleyan University, B
University of Mary Hardin-Baylor, B

Utah

Dixie State University, B
Southern Utah University, B
Utah State University, B
Utah Valley University, B
Weber State University, B

Vermont

Green Mountain College, B
Johnson State College, B

Virginia

Averett University, B
Bluefield College, B
Emory & Henry College, B
Virginia Union University, B

Washington

Central Washington University, B
Eastern Washington University, B
Northwest University, B
Seattle University, B
Washington State University, B
Western Washington University, B

West Virginia

Bethany College, B
Glenville State College, B
University of Charleston, B

Wisconsin

Carroll University, B
Edgewood College, B
Maranatha Baptist University, B
Marquette University, B
Mount Mary University, B
University of Wisconsin - Superior, B
Viterbo University, B

U.S. Territories: Puerto Rico

Inter American University of Puerto Rico, Aguadilla Campus, B
Inter American University of Puerto Rico, Arecibo Campus, B
Inter American University of Puerto Rico, Barranquitas Campus, B
Inter American University of Puerto Rico, Fajardo Campus, B
Inter American University of Puerto Rico, Metropolitan Campus, B
Inter American University of Puerto Rico, Ponce Campus, B
Inter American University of Puerto Rico, San Germán Campus, B
Pontifical Catholic University of Puerto Rico, B
Universidad Adventista de las Antillas, B
Universidad del Turabo, B

Canada

Alberta

University of Alberta, B

Ontario

University of Waterloo, B
University of Windsor, B
York University, B

Quebec

Bishop's University, B

Saskatchewan

University of Regina, B

BIOLOGY TECHNICIAN/BIO-TECHNOLOGY LABORATORY TECHNICIAN

United States

California

American River College, A
Berkeley City College, A
Southwestern College, A

Connecticut

Middlesex Community College, A
University of New Haven, B

Delaware

Delaware State University, B
Delaware Technical & Community College, Jack F. Owens Campus, A
Delaware Technical & Community College, Stanton/Wilmington Campus, A

Florida

Florida SouthWestern State College, A
Florida State College at Jacksonville, A
Hillsborough Community College, A
Santa Fe College, A

Georgia

Athens Technical College, A

Illinois

Elgin Community College, A

Iowa

Indian Hills Community College, A

Kansas

Hutchinson Community College, A
Johnson County Community College, A
Manhattan Area Technical College, A
Washburn University, B

Maine

Kennebec Valley Community College, A

Maryland

Hagerstown Community College, A
Montgomery College, A

Massachusetts

Massachusetts Bay Community College, A
Middlesex Community College, A
North Shore Community College, A
Quincy College, A
Worcester Polytechnic Institute, B

Michigan

Muskegon Community College, A

Minnesota

Minnesota West Community and Technical College, A
St. Cloud State University, B

Missouri

East Central College, A

New Hampshire

Great Bay Community College, A

New Jersey

Camden County College, A
County College of Morris, A
Mercer County Community College, A
Middlesex County College, A

New York

Erie Community College, North Campus, A
Finger Lakes Community College, A
Genesee Community College, A
Jamestown Community College, A
Monroe Community College, A
Niagara University, B
State University of New York College of Agriculture and Technology at Cobleskill, A
State University of New York College at Oneonta, B
State University of New York at Fredonia, B
Tompkins Cortland Community College, A
York College of the City University of New York, B

North Carolina

Asheville-Buncombe Technical Community College, A
Forsyth Technical Community College, A
Gaston College, A
Guilford Technical Community College, A
Pitt Community College, A

Rockingham Community College, A
Wayne Community College, A
Wilson Community College, A

North Dakota

North Dakota State College of Science, A

Ohio

Cleveland State University, B
The Ohio State University Agricultural Technical Institute, A
Ursuline College, B

Oregon

Portland Community College, A

Pennsylvania

Bucks County Community College, A
Penn State Abington, B
Penn State Altoona, B
Penn State Beaver, B
Penn State Berks, B
Penn State Brandywine, B
Penn State DuBois, B
Penn State Erie, The Behrend College, B
Penn State Fayette, The Eberly Campus, B
Penn State Greater Allegheny, B
Penn State Hazleton, B
Penn State Lehigh Valley, B
Penn State Mont Alto, B
Penn State New Kensington, B
Penn State Schuylkill, B
Penn State Shenango, B
Penn State University Park, B
Penn State Wilkes-Barre, B
Penn State Worthington Scranton, B
Penn State York, B
Westmoreland County Community College, A

Texas

Austin Community College District, A
Collin County Community College District, A
Houston Community College, A
Lone Star College - Montgomery, A
Northwest Vista College, A
Temple College, A

Utah

Salt Lake Community College, A
Weber State University, A

Washington

Bates Technical College, A
Seattle Central College, A
Shoreline Community College, A

Wisconsin

Fox Valley Technical College, A
Madison Area Technical College, A

Canada

British Columbia

British Columbia Institute of Technology, A

Ontario

Carleton University, B
McMaster University, B

BIOMATHEMATICS AND BIOIN-FORMATICS

United States

California

Harvey Mudd College, B
University of California, Los Angeles, BMD

Florida

Florida Institute of Technology, B
Florida State University, B

Massachusetts

Worcester Polytechnic Institute, B

Missouri

Washington University in St. Louis, B

North Carolina

North Carolina State University, MD

Ohio

Walsh University, B

Texas

The University of Texas Health Science Center at Houston, MD

BIOMEDICAL ENGINEERING

United States

Alabama

The University of Alabama at Birmingham, MD

Arizona

Arizona State University at the Tempe campus, MD
The University of Arizona, MD

Arkansas

University of Arkansas, M

California

Stanford University, M
University of California, Davis, MD
University of California, Irvine, MD
University of California, Los Angeles, MD
University of Southern California, MD

Colorado

Colorado State University, MD

Connecticut

University of Bridgeport, M
University of Connecticut, MD
Yale University, MD

District of Columbia

The Catholic University of America, MD

Florida

Florida Agricultural and Mechanical University, MD
Florida Institute of Technology, MD
Florida International University, MD
Florida State University, MD
University of Florida, MDO
University of Miami, MD
University of South Florida, MDO

Georgia

Georgia Institute of Technology, MD
Mercer University, M

Illinois

Illinois Institute of Technology, MD
Northwestern University, MD
Southern Illinois University Carbondale, M

Indiana

Indiana University - Purdue University Indianapolis, MD
Purdue University, MD
Rose-Hulman Institute of Technology, M

Iowa

The University of Iowa, MD

Kentucky

University of Kentucky, MD

Louisiana

Louisiana Tech University, MD
Tulane University, MD

Maine

University of Maine, D

Maryland

Johns Hopkins University, MDO

Massachusetts

Boston University, MD
Harvard University, D
Massachusetts Institute of Technology, MD
Tufts University, MD
University of Massachusetts Boston, D
University of Massachusetts Dartmouth, MD
Worcester Polytechnic Institute, MDO

Michigan

Michigan Technological University, MD
University of Michigan, MD
Wayne State University, MDO

Minnesota

St. Cloud State University, M
University of Minnesota, Twin Cities Campus, MD

Missouri

Saint Louis University, MD
Washington University in St. Louis, MD

Nebraska

University of Nebraska - Lincoln, D

Nevada

University of Nevada, Las Vegas, M
University of Nevada, Reno, MD

New Hampshire

Dartmouth College, MD

New Jersey

New Jersey Institute of Technology, MD
Rutgers University - New Brunswick, MD
Rutgers University - Newark, DO
Stevens Institute of Technology, MO

New Mexico

University of New Mexico, MD

New York

Binghamton University, State University of New York, MD
City College of the City University of New York, MD
Columbia University, MD
Cornell University, MD
New York University, MD
Rensselaer Polytechnic Institute, MD
State University of New York Downstate Medical Center, MD
Stony Brook University, State University of New York, MDO
University at Buffalo, the State University of New York, MD
University of Rochester, MD

North Carolina

Duke University, MD
East Carolina University, M
North Carolina State University, MD
The University of North Carolina at Chapel Hill, MD
Wake Forest University, MD

Ohio

Case Western Reserve University, MD
Cleveland State University, D
The Ohio State University, MD
Ohio University, M
The University of Akron, MD
University of Cincinnati, MD
The University of Toledo, D
Wright State University, M

Oklahoma

University of Central Oklahoma, M

Oregon

Oregon Health & Science University, D
University of Portland, M

Pennsylvania

Carnegie Mellon University, MD
Drexel University, MD
Thomas Jefferson University, D
Widener University, M

Rhode Island

Brown University, MD
University of Rhode Island, MDO

South Dakota

South Dakota School of Mines and Technology, MD

Tennessee

Tennessee State University, M
University of Memphis, MD
The University of Tennessee, MD
Vanderbilt University, MD

Texas

Baylor University, M
Rice University, MD
Texas A&M University, MD
University of Houston, D
University of North Texas, M
The University of Texas at Austin, MD
The University of Texas at Dallas, MD
The University of Texas at El Paso, D
The University of Texas Health Science Center at San Antonio, MD
The University of Texas at San Antonio, MD

Vermont

University of Vermont, D

Virginia

Old Dominion University, D
University of Virginia, MD
Virginia Commonwealth University, MD
Virginia Polytechnic Institute and State University, MD

Wisconsin

Marquette University, MD
University of Wisconsin - Madison, MD

Canada

Alberta

University of Alberta, MD
University of Calgary, MD

Maritime Provinces: Nova Scotia

Dalhousie University, MD

Ontario

Carleton University, M
University of Ottawa, M
University of Toronto, MD

Quebec

École Polytechnique de Montréal, MDO
McGill University, MD
Université de Montréal, MDO

Saskatchewan

University of Saskatchewan, MD

BIOMEDICAL/MEDICAL ENGINEERING

United States

Alabama

Alabama State University, B
The University of Alabama at Birmingham, B

Arizona

Arizona State University at the Tempe campus, B
The University of Arizona, B

Arkansas

Harding University, B
University of Arkansas, B

California

California Baptist University, B
California Institute of Technology, B
California Polytechnic State University, San Luis Obispo, B
California State University, Long Beach, B
National University, B
Santa Clara University, B
Southern California Institute of Technology, B
Stanford University, B
University of California, Berkeley, B
University of California, Davis, B
University of California, Irvine, B
University of California, Merced, B
University of California, Riverside, B
University of California, San Diego, B
University of California, Santa Cruz, B
University of the Pacific, B
University of Southern California, B

Colorado

Colorado School of Mines, B
Colorado State University, B
University of Colorado Denver, B

Connecticut

Trinity College, B
University of Connecticut, B
Yale University, B

Delaware

Delaware State University, B
University of Delaware, B

District of Columbia

The Catholic University of America, B

Florida

Florida Gulf Coast University, B
Florida Institute of Technology, B
Florida International University, B
University of Florida, B
University of Miami, B

Georgia

Georgia Institute of Technology, B

Illinois

Illinois Institute of Technology, B
Loyola University Chicago, B
Northwestern University, B
University of Illinois at Chicago, B
University of Illinois at Urbana - Champaign, B

Indiana

Indiana Tech, B
Indiana University - Purdue University Indianapolis, B
Purdue University, B
Rose-Hulman Institute of Technology, B

Iowa

The University of Iowa, B

Kansas

Wichita State University, B

Kentucky

University of Louisville, B

Louisiana

Louisiana State University and Agricultural & Mechanical College, B
Louisiana Tech University, B
Tulane University, B

Maine

University of Maine, B

Maryland

Johns Hopkins University, B

Massachusetts

Benjamin Franklin Institute of Technology, A
Boston University, B
Bunker Hill Community College, A
Eastern Nazarene College, B
Endicott College, B
Harvard University, B
Massachusetts Institute of Technology, B
Quinsigamond Community College, A
Tufts University, B
University of Massachusetts Dartmouth, B
Wentworth Institute of Technology, B
Western New England University, B
Worcester Polytechnic Institute, B

Michigan

Central Michigan University, B
Lawrence Technological University, B
Michigan Technological University, B
University of Michigan, B
Wayne State University, B

Minnesota

University of Minnesota, Twin Cities Campus, B

Mississippi

Mississippi State University, B

Missouri

Saint Louis University, B
Washington University in St. Louis, B

New Hampshire

University of New Hampshire, B

New Jersey

The College of New Jersey, B
New Jersey Institute of Technology, B
Rowan University, B
Rutgers University - New Brunswick, B
Stevens Institute of Technology, B

New York

Alfred University, B
Binghamton University, State University of New York, B
City College of the City University of New York, B
Columbia University, B
Hofstra University, B
New York University, B
Rensselaer Polytechnic Institute, B
Rochester Institute of Technology, B
State University of New York College of Environmental Science and Forestry, B
Stony Brook University, State University of New York, B
Syracuse University, B
Union College, B
University at Buffalo, the State University of New York, B
University of Rochester, B

North Carolina

Duke University, B
Elon University, B

Gaston College, A
North Carolina Agricultural and Technical State University, B
North Carolina State University, B

Ohio

Case Western Reserve University, B
Miami University, B
The Ohio State University, B
The University of Akron, B
University of Cincinnati, B
The University of Toledo, B
Wright State University, B

Oklahoma

Oral Roberts University, B
University of Central Oklahoma, B

Oregon

Oregon State University, B

Pennsylvania

Bucknell University, B
Drexel University, B
Duquesne University, B
Gannon University, B
Lehigh University, B
Penn State Abington, B
Penn State Altoona, B
Penn State Beaver, B
Penn State Berks, B
Penn State Brandywine, B
Penn State DuBois, B
Penn State Erie, The Behrend College, B
Penn State Fayette, The Eberly Campus, B
Penn State Greater Allegheny, B
Penn State Hazleton, B
Penn State Lehigh Valley, B
Penn State Mont Alto, B
Penn State New Kensington, B
Penn State Schuylkill, B
Penn State Shenango, B
Penn State University Park, B
Penn State Wilkes-Barre, B
Penn State Worthington Scranton, B
Penn State York, B
Temple University, B
University of Pennsylvania, B
University of Pittsburgh, B
Widener University, B

Rhode Island

Brown University, B
University of Rhode Island, B

South Carolina

Clemson University, B
University of South Carolina, B

Tennessee

University of Memphis, B
The University of Tennessee, B
Vanderbilt University, B

Texas

LeTourneau University, B
Rice University, B
Texas A&M University, B
University of Houston, B
University of North Texas, B
The University of Texas at Arlington, B
The University of Texas at Austin, B
The University of Texas at Dallas, B
The University of Texas at San Antonio, B

Utah

University of Utah, B

Vermont

University of Vermont, B

Virginia

George Mason University, B
University of Virginia, B

Virginia Commonwealth University, B

Washington

University of Washington, B
Walla Walla University, B
Washington State University, B

West Virginia

West Virginia University, B

Wisconsin

Marquette University, B
Milwaukee School of Engineering, B
University of Wisconsin - Madison, B

U.S. Territories: Puerto Rico

University of Puerto Rico, Mayagüez Campus, B

Canada

British Columbia

The University of British Columbia, B

Maritime Provinces: Nova Scotia

Dalhousie University, B

Ontario

Ryerson University, B
University of Guelph, B
University of Ottawa, B
University of Toronto, B
University of Waterloo, B

BIOMEDICAL SCIENCES

United States

Alabama

Auburn University, B
Troy University, B
University of South Alabama, B

Arizona

Northern Arizona University, B

California

Charles R. Drew University of Medicine and Science, B
University of California, Riverside, B

Colorado

Colorado State University, B
University of Colorado Denver, B

Florida

Adventist University of Health Sciences, B
Florida Institute of Technology, B
Florida State College at Jacksonville, B
Keiser University, B
Saint Leo University, B
University of Central Florida, B
University of South Florida, B

Idaho

College of Western Idaho, A

Illinois

Bradley University, B
Lewis University, B

Indiana

Ivy Tech Community College - Wabash Valley, A

Kentucky

Morehead State University, B

Louisiana

Our Lady of the Lake College, B

Maine

University of New England, B

Massachusetts

Bridgewater State University, B
Fitchburg State University, B
Worcester Polytechnic Institute, B

Michigan

Central Michigan University, B
Madonna University, B
Oakland University, B
University of Michigan - Flint, B
Western Michigan University, B

Minnesota

Rochester Community and Technical College, A
St. Cloud State University, B
University of Minnesota, Duluth, B

Mississippi

Mississippi College, B

Missouri

College of the Ozarks, B
Maryville University of Saint Louis, B
St. Louis College of Pharmacy, B
Saint Louis University, B

Nebraska

Peru State College, B
Union College, B

New Hampshire

University of New Hampshire, B

New Jersey

Rowan University, B
Rutgers University - New Brunswick, B

New York

City College of the City University of New York, B
Concordia College - New York, B
Keuka College, B
Marist College, B
Marymount Manhattan College, B
Rochester Institute of Technology, B
St. Francis College, B
State University of New York at Fredonia, B
University at Buffalo, the State University of New York, B

North Carolina

North Carolina Central University, B
North Carolina Wesleyan College, B

Ohio

Antioch College, B
Hiram College, B
The Ohio State University, B

Oklahoma

Oklahoma City University, B
St. Gregory's University, B
University of Central Oklahoma, B

Pennsylvania

Slippery Rock University of Pennsylvania, B
University of Pennsylvania, B

Rhode Island

Brown University, B

South Carolina

University of South Carolina Aiken, B

Tennessee

Christian Brothers University, B

Texas

McMurry University, B
Northeast Texas Community College, A
Sam Houston State University, B

Tarleton State University, B
Texas A&M University, B
Texas A&M University - Corpus Christi, B
Texas A&M University - Kingsville, B
The University of Texas Rio Grande Valley, B

Utah

Brigham Young University, B

Virginia

Jefferson College of Health Sciences, B
Liberty University, B
Lynchburg College, B

Washington

Central Washington University, B
Heritage University, B
Washington State University, B

Wisconsin

Concordia University Wisconsin, B
Edgewood College, B
Marquette University, B

U.S. Territories: Puerto Rico

Inter American University of Puerto Rico, Metropolitan Campus, B
Inter American University of Puerto Rico, Ponce Campus, B

Canada
Alberta

University of Calgary, B

Ontario

Brock University, B
Trent University, B
University of Guelph, B
University of Ottawa, B

Quebec

McGill University, B
Université de Montréal, B
Université du Québec à Trois-Rivières, B

Saskatchewan

University of Saskatchewan, B

BIOMEDICAL TECHNOLOGY/ TECHNICIAN

United States
Alabama

Alabama Southern Community College, A
Community College of the Air Force, A

Arizona

DeVry University (Phoenix), B

Arkansas

North Arkansas College, A
University of Arkansas for Medical Sciences, A

California

California State University, East Bay, B
Cerritos College, A
City College of San Francisco, A
College of San Mateo, A
Contra Costa College, A
DeVry University (Fremont), B
Fullerton College, A
Los Angeles Valley College, A
MiraCosta College, A
Napa Valley College, A
Santa Barbara City College, A

Colorado

Aims Community College, A

Connecticut

Gateway Community College, A

Delaware

Delaware Technical & Community College, Terry Campus, A

Florida

Broward College, A
DeVry University (Miramar), B
DeVry University (Orlando), B
Florida State College at Jacksonville, A
Miami Dade College, A
Santa Fe College, A
South Florida State College, A

Georgia

Chattahoochee Technical College, A
DeVry University (Decatur), B

Illinois

DeVry University (Addison), B
DeVry University (Chicago), B
DeVry University (Tinley Park), B
Joliet Junior College, A
Parkland College, A

Indiana

Indiana University - Purdue University Indianapolis, AB

Iowa

Des Moines Area Community College, A
Southeastern Community College, A
Western Iowa Tech Community College, A

Kentucky

Madisonville Community College, A

Louisiana

Delgado Community College, A

Maryland

Howard Community College, A

Massachusetts

Benjamin Franklin Institute of Technology, A
Quinsigamond Community College, A

Michigan

Andrews University, B
Lawrence Technological University, B
Muskegon Community College, A
Schoolcraft College, A
Wayne County Community College District, A

Minnesota

Anoka-Ramsey Community College, A
Anoka Technical College, A
Dakota County Technical College, A
Minnesota State College - Southeast Technical, A
St. Cloud Technical & Community College, A
Saint Paul College - A Community & Technical College, A

Missouri

Jefferson College, A

New Jersey

DeVry University (North Brunswick), B
Rutgers University - Camden, B
Thomas Edison State University, AB

New Mexico

New Mexico State University - Alamogordo, A

New York

DeVry College of New York, B
Long Island University - LIU Post, B

North Carolina

Caldwell Community College and Technical Institute, A

Gaston College, A
Stanly Community College, A

Ohio

Cincinnati State Technical and Community College, A
Cleveland State University, B
DeVry University (Columbus), B
Owens Community College, A
Stark State College, A
Wright State University, B

Pennsylvania

Delaware County Community College, A
DeVry University (Fort Washington), B
Johnson College, A
Penn State Altoona, A
Penn State Berks, A
Penn State DuBois, A
Penn State Erie, The Behrend College, A
Penn State Fayette, The Eberly Campus, A
Penn State Hazleton, A
Penn State New Kensington, A
Penn State Schuylkill, A
Penn State Shenango, A
Penn State York, A
Pennsylvania Institute of Technology, A

South Dakota

Southeast Technical Institute, A

Tennessee

Southwest Tennessee Community College, A

Texas

DeVry University (Irving), B
St. Philip's College, A
Texas State Technical College, A

Virginia

ECPI University (Virginia Beach), A

Washington

Big Bend Community College, A
North Seattle College, A
Spokane Community College, A

Wisconsin

Milwaukee Area Technical College, A
Waukesha County Technical College, A

BIOMETRY/BIOMETRICS

United States
California

San Diego State University, M
Stanford University, B

Delaware

University of Delaware, B

New Jersey

Rutgers University - New Brunswick, B

New York

Cornell University, BMD

Pennsylvania

Carnegie Mellon University, B

Wisconsin

University of Wisconsin - Madison, M

BIOPHYSICS

United States

Arizona

Arizona State University at the Tempe campus, B

California

California Institute of Technology, D
Claremont McKenna College, B
La Sierra University, B
Pacific Union College, B
Scripps College, B
Stanford University, D
University of California, Berkeley, D
University of California, Davis, MD
University of California, Irvine, D
University of California, Los Angeles, B
University of California, San Diego, BD
University of California, Santa Barbara, D
University of San Diego, B
University of Southern California, BM

Colorado

University of Colorado Denver, MD

Connecticut

University of Connecticut, BMD
Yale University, D

District of Columbia

Howard University, D

Florida

University of Miami, D
University of South Florida, D

Georgia

Emory University, BD

Illinois

Illinois Institute of Technology, B
Illinois State University, M
Northwestern University, D
University of Chicago, D
University of Illinois at Chicago, MD
University of Illinois at Urbana - Champaign, BMD

Indiana

Purdue University, D
University of Southern Indiana, B

Iowa

Iowa State University of Science and Technology, BMD
The University of Iowa, MD

Kansas

The University of Kansas, MD

Kentucky

University of Louisville, MD

Maryland

Johns Hopkins University, BD
University of Maryland, College Park, D

Massachusetts

Boston University, MD
Brandeis University, BD
Harvard University, D
Northeastern University, B

Michigan

Andrews University, B
Oakland University, B
University of Michigan, BD

Minnesota

Augsburg College, B
University of Minnesota, Duluth, MD
University of Minnesota, Twin Cities Campus, MD

Mississippi

University of Mississippi Medical Center, D

Missouri

University of Missouri - Kansas City, D
Washington University in St. Louis, B

New Jersey

New Jersey Institute of Technology, B

New York

Columbia University, BMD
Columbia University, School of General Studies, B
Cornell University, D
Rensselaer Polytechnic Institute, MD
St. Bonaventure University, B
St. Lawrence University, B
State University of New York College at Geneseo, B
Stony Brook University, State University of New York, D
Syracuse University, BD
University at Buffalo, the State University of New York, BMD
University of Rochester, D

North Carolina

East Carolina University, D
Elon University, B
Forsyth Technical Community College, A
The University of North Carolina at Chapel Hill, MD

Ohio

Case Western Reserve University, MD
Miami University, B
The Ohio State University, MD
University of Cincinnati, D
Wright State University, M

Oklahoma

Southern Nazarene University, B

Oregon

Oregon State University, MD

Pennsylvania

Carnegie Mellon University, D
Haverford College, B
Temple University, B
Thomas Jefferson University, D
University of Pennsylvania, B
The University of Scranton, B
Washington & Jefferson College, B

Rhode Island

Brown University, B

South Carolina

Clemson University, MD

Tennessee

Lipscomb University, B
Southern Adventist University, B
Vanderbilt University, MD

Texas

Texas Christian University, D
The University of Texas Medical Branch, D

Utah

Brigham Young University, B

Virginia

Regent University, B
University of Virginia, MD

Washington

University of Washington, D
Walla Walla University, B
Washington State University, MD
Whitman College, B

Wisconsin

Marquette University, B
University of Wisconsin - Madison, D

Canada

British Columbia

The University of British Columbia, B

Maritime Provinces: New Brunswick

University of New Brunswick Fredericton, B

Maritime Provinces: Nova Scotia

Dalhousie University, MD

Ontario

Laurentian University, B
University of Guelph, MD
University of Toronto, BMD
The University of Western Ontario, BMD

Quebec

Université du Québec à Trois-Rivières, BMD
Université de Sherbrooke, MD

Saskatchewan

University of Regina, MD

BIOPSYCHOLOGY

United States

Alabama

Spring Hill College, B

California

Palo Alto University, D
University of California, Santa Barbara, B

Connecticut

Connecticut College, M
University of Connecticut, D

District of Columbia

Howard University, D

Georgia

Argosy University, Atlanta, D
Life University, B
Oglethorpe University, B

Illinois

Monmouth College, B
Northwestern University, D

Indiana

Indiana University - Purdue University Indianapolis, D

Iowa

Morningside College, B

Louisiana

Louisiana State University and Agricultural & Mechanical College, MD

Massachusetts

Boston University, M
Harvard University, D
Tufts University, B

Michigan

Grand Valley State University, B
University of Michigan, D
Wayne State University, D

Minnesota

Argosy University, Twin Cities, D
Augsburg College, B
University of Minnesota, Twin Cities Campus, D

Missouri

Washington University in St. Louis, B

Nebraska

Hastings College, B
Nebraska Wesleyan University, B
University of Nebraska - Lincoln, D

New Jersey

Rider University, B
Rutgers University - New Brunswick, D
Rutgers University - Newark, D

New York

Binghamton University, State University of New
 York, D
Columbia University, B
Cornell University, D
Wagner College, B

North Carolina

Duke University, D
The University of North Carolina at Chapel Hill, D

Ohio

Ohio Dominican University, B

Oklahoma

University of Oklahoma Health Sciences Center, MD

Oregon

Oregon Health & Science University, D
University of Oregon, MD

Pennsylvania

Bucknell University, B
Carnegie Mellon University, BD
Drexel University, MD
Geneva College, B
Immaculata University, B
Messiah College, B
Penn State University Park, MD
Philadelphia University, B
University of Pittsburgh at Johnstown, B

Texas

Texas A&M University, D
The University of Texas at Austin, D

Virginia

Virginia Commonwealth University, D

Wisconsin

University of Wisconsin - Madison, D
Viterbo University, B

Canada

British Columbia

The University of British Columbia, MD

Maritime Provinces: New Brunswick

Mount Allison University, B

Newfoundland and Labrador

Memorial University of Newfoundland, MD

Ontario

University of Guelph, B
University of Windsor, MD

BIOSTATISTICS

United States

Alabama

The University of Alabama at Birmingham, MD

Arizona

The University of Arizona, D

Arkansas

University of Arkansas for Medical Sciences, M

California

California State University, East Bay, M
Loma Linda University, MDO
National University, B
San Diego State University, M
Stanford University, D
University of California, Berkeley, MD
University of California, Davis, MD
University of California, Los Angeles, MD
University of Southern California, MD

Colorado

University of Colorado Denver, MD

Connecticut

Yale University, MD

District of Columbia

The George Washington University, MD
Georgetown University, MO

Florida

Florida International University, M
Florida State University, MD
University of Florida, MD
University of South Florida, MDO

Georgia

Augusta University, MD
Emory University, MD
Georgia Southern University, MD
Georgia State University, MD

Illinois

Northwestern University, D
University of Illinois at Chicago, MD

Indiana

Indiana University Bloomington, MD
Indiana University - Purdue University Indianapolis,
 MD

Iowa

Iowa State University of Science and Technology,
 MD
The University of Iowa, MDO

Kansas

The University of Kansas, MDO

Kentucky

University of Kentucky, D
University of Louisville, MD

Louisiana

Louisiana State University Health Sciences Center,
 MD
Tulane University, BMD

Maryland

Johns Hopkins University, MD
University of Maryland, Baltimore County, D
University of Maryland, College Park, MD

Massachusetts

Boston University, MD
Emmanuel College, B
Harvard University, MD
Simmons College, B
Tufts University, MD
University of Massachusetts Amherst, MD

Michigan

Grand Valley State University, M
University of Michigan, MD

Minnesota

University of Minnesota, Twin Cities Campus, MD

Mississippi

University of Southern Mississippi, M

Missouri

Saint Louis University, B
Washington University in St. Louis, MO

Nebraska

University of Nebraska Medical Center, D

New Hampshire

Dartmouth College, D

New Jersey

New Jersey Institute of Technology, M
Rutgers University - New Brunswick, MD

New York

Columbia University, MD
Hunter College of the City University of New York,
 M
University at Albany, State University of New York,
 MD
University at Buffalo, the State University of New
 York, MD
University of Rochester, M

North Carolina

Duke University, M
The University of North Carolina at Chapel Hill,
 BMD

Ohio

Case Western Reserve University, MD
The Ohio State University, D
University of Cincinnati, MD
The University of Toledo, O

Oklahoma

University of Oklahoma Health Sciences Center, MD

Oregon

Oregon Health & Science University, MO
Oregon State University, M

Pennsylvania

Drexel University, MO
University of Pennsylvania, MD
University of Pittsburgh, MD

Rhode Island

Brown University, MD

South Carolina

Medical University of South Carolina, MD
University of South Carolina, MD

Tennessee

Middle Tennessee State University, M
University of Memphis, M

Texas

Rice University, D
The University of Texas Health Science Center at
 Houston, MD

Utah

University of Utah, M

Vermont

University of Vermont, M

Virginia

George Mason University, M
Virginia Commonwealth University, MD

Washington

University of Washington, MD

U.S. Territories: Puerto Rico

University of Puerto Rico, Medical Sciences Campus, M

Canada

Alberta

University of Alberta, M

Ontario

University of Toronto, MD
University of Waterloo, MD
The University of Western Ontario, BMD

Quebec

McGill University, MDO

BIOSYSTEMS ENGINEERING

United States

Alabama

Auburn University, MD

Arizona

The University of Arizona, MD

Michigan

Michigan State University, MD

Minnesota

University of Minnesota, Twin Cities Campus, MD

North Dakota

North Dakota State University, MD

South Carolina

Clemson University, MD

South Dakota

South Dakota State University, MD

Tennessee

The University of Tennessee, MD

Virginia

James Madison University, M

Canada

Manitoba

University of Manitoba, MD

BIOTECHNOLOGY

United States

Alabama

The University of Alabama at Birmingham, M
The University of Alabama in Huntsville, D

Arizona

Arizona State University at the Tempe campus, M
GateWay Community College, A
Glendale Community College, A

Arkansas

Arkansas State University, M
Central Baptist College, B

California

California State Polytechnic University, Pomona, BM
California State University Channel Islands, M
California State University, Fullerton, M
California State University, San Marcos, B
Ohlone College, A
San Francisco State University, M

Santa Barbara City College, A
University of California, Davis, B
University of California, Irvine, M
University of California, San Diego, B
University of California, Santa Barbara, M
University of San Francisco, M

Colorado

Colorado State University, B

Delaware

Delaware State University, B
University of Delaware, M

District of Columbia

The George Washington University, M
Howard University, M

Florida

Florida Atlantic University, M
Florida Gulf Coast University, B
Florida Institute of Technology, M
Florida Southern College, B
Keiser University, AB
Miami Dade College, A
Santa Fe College, B
University of Central Florida, BM
University of South Florida, MO
University of West Florida, M

Georgia

Augusta Technical College, A
Kennesaw State University, B
University of Georgia, B

Hawaii

University of Hawaii at Manoa, B

Illinois

Illinois State University, M
Northwestern University, MD
Roosevelt University, BM
University of Illinois at Chicago, MD
University of Illinois at Urbana - Champaign, B

Indiana

Indiana University Bloomington, BM
Indiana University East, B
Indiana University - Purdue University Indianapolis, B
Ivy Tech Community College - Bloomington, A
Ivy Tech Community College - Central Indiana, A
Ivy Tech Community College - Lafayette, A
Ivy Tech Community College - North Central, A
Ivy Tech Community College - Southwest, A
Purdue University, D
Purdue University Northwest (Hammond), M
Vincennes University, A

Iowa

Ellsworth Community College, A
Grand View University, B
Kirkwood Community College, A
Northwest Iowa Community College, A
University of Northern Iowa, B

Kansas

The University of Kansas, M

Kentucky

University of Kentucky, B

Maine

Southern Maine Community College, A

Maryland

Cecil College, A
Hood College, M
Howard Community College, A
Johns Hopkins University, M
Mount St. Mary's University, M
Stevenson University, B
University of Maryland, Baltimore County, MO
University of Maryland University College, MO

Massachusetts

Assumption College, B
Bay Path University, B
Brandeis University, M
Bunker Hill Community College, A
Endicott College, B
Fitchburg State University, B
Harvard University, M
Holyoke Community College, A
Massachusetts College of Liberal Arts, B
Mount Wachusett Community College, A
Northeastern University, M
Quinsigamond Community College, A
Regis College, M
Springfield Technical Community College, A
Tufts University, BDO
University of Massachusetts Amherst, MD
University of Massachusetts Boston, MD
University of Massachusetts Dartmouth, MD
University of Massachusetts Lowell, M
Worcester Polytechnic Institute, MD
Worcester State University, BM

Michigan

Calvin College, B
Ferris State University, B
Lansing Community College, A
Oakland Community College, A
Wayne State University, D

Minnesota

University of Minnesota, Twin Cities Campus, M

Missouri

Missouri Baptist University, B
Missouri Western State University, B

Montana

Montana State University, B

Nebraska

University of Nebraska at Omaha, B

Nevada

University of Nevada, Reno, BM

New Hampshire

Dartmouth College, MD
Plymouth State University, B
University of New Hampshire at Manchester, B

New Jersey

Bergen Community College, A
Essex County College, A
Kean University, M
Middlesex County College, A
Raritan Valley Community College, A
Rowan College at Burlington County, A
Rutgers University - New Brunswick, B
William Paterson University of New Jersey, BM

New Mexico

Central New Mexico Community College, A
New Mexico State University, M
Northern New Mexico College, A

New York

Borough of Manhattan Community College of the City University of New York, A
City College of the City University of New York, B
Clarkson University, D
Columbia University, M
Cornell University, MD
Genesee Community College, A
Hudson Valley Community College, A
Hunter College of the City University of New York, B
Manhattan College, B
New York Institute of Technology, B
New York University, M
Queensborough Community College of the City University of New York, A
Rochester Institute of Technology, B
St. John's University, M

State University of New York College of Agriculture and Technology at Cobleskill, B
State University of New York College of Environmental Science and Forestry, B
Syracuse University, B
University at Buffalo, the State University of New York, BM
York College of the City University of New York, B

North Carolina

Alamance Community College, A
Bladen Community College, A
Brunswick Community College, A
Caldwell Community College and Technical Institute, A
Cleveland Community College, A
College of The Albemarle, A
East Carolina University, M
Fayetteville State University, B
Gaston College, A
North Carolina State University, M
South Piedmont Community College, A
Southeastern Community College, A
The University of North Carolina at Pembroke, B
Winston-Salem State University, B

North Dakota

North Dakota State University, B

Ohio

Ashland University, B
Kent State University, B
Lakeland Community College, A
Sinclair Community College, A
Ursuline College, B

Oklahoma

Oklahoma City Community College, A
Southeastern Oklahoma State University, BM
Tulsa Community College, A

Oregon

Oregon State University, BM

Pennsylvania

Carnegie Mellon University, M
Duquesne University, M
East Stroudsburg University of Pennsylvania, B
Elizabethtown College, B
Lackawanna College, A
Lehigh Carbon Community College, A
Marywood University, BM
Montgomery County Community College, A
Northampton Community College, A
Penn State University Park, M
Point Park University, B
Temple University, M
Thomas Jefferson University, D
University of Pennsylvania, M
University of the Sciences, M

Rhode Island

Brown University, D
University of Rhode Island, M

South Carolina

Claflin University, BM

South Dakota

South Dakota State University, B

Tennessee

Middle Tennessee State University, M
Tennessee State University, D

Texas

El Centro College, A
Stephen F. Austin State University, M
Texas Tech University, M
University of Houston, B
University of Houston - Clear Lake, M
University of Houston - Downtown, B
The University of Texas at Dallas, M
The University of Texas at San Antonio, M

West Texas A&M University, B

Utah

Brigham Young University, M
University of Utah, M
Utah Valley University, B

Virginia

James Madison University, B
Virginia Polytechnic Institute and State University, M

Washington

University of Washington, D

West Virginia

West Virginia State University, M

Wisconsin

University of Wisconsin - River Falls, B

Wyoming

University of Wyoming, D

U.S. Territories: Puerto Rico

EDP University of Puerto Rico, A
Humacao Community College, A
Inter American University of Puerto Rico, Aguadilla Campus, B
Inter American University of Puerto Rico, Arecibo Campus, B
Inter American University of Puerto Rico, Barranquitas Campus, AB
Inter American University of Puerto Rico, Bayamón Campus, BM
Inter American University of Puerto Rico, Guayama Campus, B
Inter American University of Puerto Rico, Ponce Campus, B
Universidad del Este, B
Universidad del Turabo, AB
University of Puerto Rico, Mayagüez Campus, B
University of Puerto Rico in Ponce, B

Canada

Alberta

University of Alberta, BMD
University of Calgary, M
University of Lethbridge, B

British Columbia

British Columbia Institute of Technology, AB
Simon Fraser University, M
Trinity Western University, B
The University of British Columbia, B

Ontario

Brock University, BMD
University of Guelph, MD
University of Toronto, M
University of Waterloo, B
University of Windsor, B
Wilfrid Laurier University, B
York University, B

Quebec

Concordia University, O
McGill University, MO

Saskatchewan

University of Saskatchewan, BM

BLOOD BANK TECHNOLOGY SPECIALIST

United States

Florida

City College (Gainesville), A

Minnesota

Rasmussen College St. Cloud, AB

BOILERMAKING/BOILER-MAKER

United States

Indiana

Ivy Tech Community College - Southwest, A

BOTANY/PLANT BIOLOGY

United States

Alabama

Auburn University, BM

California

California State University, Chico, M
California State University, Long Beach, B
El Camino College, A
Humboldt State University, B
Lassen Community College District, A
San Bernardino Valley College, A
San Francisco State University, B
Sonoma State University, B
University of California, Berkeley, B
University of California, Davis, B
University of California, Irvine, B
University of California, Riverside, BMD

Colorado

Colorado State University, BMD

Connecticut

Connecticut College, B
University of Connecticut, MD

Florida

Broward College, A
Palm Beach State College, A
Pensacola State College, A
South Florida State College, A
University of Florida, BMD

Georgia

Fort Valley State University, B
University of Georgia, B

Hawaii

University of Hawaii at Manoa, BMD

Idaho

North Idaho College, A

Illinois

Illinois State University, MD
Saint Xavier University, B
Southern Illinois University Carbondale, B
Spoon River College, A
University of Illinois at Urbana - Champaign, B

Indiana

Purdue University, BMD

Iowa

Iowa Lakes Community College, A
Iowa State University of Science and Technology, B

Kansas

Emporia State University, M
The University of Kansas, MD

Maine

College of the Atlantic, B
University of Maine, BM

Maryland

Frostburg State University, B

Michigan

Andrews University, B
Michigan State University, B

Minnesota

St. Cloud State University, B
University of Minnesota, Twin Cities Campus, B

Montana

University of Great Falls, B
University of Montana, B

Nebraska

University of Nebraska - Lincoln, B

New Jersey

Rutgers University - Newark, B

New Mexico

Eastern New Mexico University, M
Western New Mexico University, B

New York

State University of New York College of Environmental Science and Forestry, B

North Carolina

North Carolina State University, BMD
The University of North Carolina at Chapel Hill, MD

North Dakota

North Dakota State University, BMD
University of North Dakota, MD

Ohio

Kent State University, B
Miami University, B
Miami University Hamilton, B
Miami University Middletown, A
The Ohio State University, B
Ohio University, B
Ohio Wesleyan University, B
The University of Akron, B

Oklahoma

Oklahoma State University, BMD
University of Oklahoma, BMD

Oregon

Oregon State University, BM

Texas

The University of Texas at El Paso, B

Utah

Snow College, A
Utah State University, B
Utah Valley University, B
Weber State University, B

Vermont

Bennington College, B
Goddard College, B
Marlboro College, B
University of Vermont, B

Washington

Everett Community College, A
University of Washington, B

Wisconsin

University of Wisconsin - Madison, BMD
University of Wisconsin - Oshkosh, M
University of Wisconsin - Superior, B

Wyoming

University of Wyoming, BMD

Canada

Alberta

University of Alberta, B
University of Calgary, B

British Columbia

The University of British Columbia, MD
University of Northern British Columbia, B
University of Victoria, B

Manitoba

Brandon University, B
University of Manitoba, BMD

Maritime Provinces: New Brunswick

University of New Brunswick Fredericton, B

Maritime Provinces: Nova Scotia

Dalhousie University, BM

Ontario

Carleton University, B
University of Guelph, MD
University of Toronto, B

Quebec

McGill University, B

BROADCAST JOURNALISM

United States

Alabama

Auburn University, B

Arkansas

Harding University, B
John Brown University, B
University of the Ozarks, B

California

Bakersfield College, A
Biola University, B
California State University, East Bay, B
California State University, Long Beach, B
Cerritos College, A
Chapman University, B
Columbia College Hollywood, B
Cosumnes River College, A
Humboldt State University, B
Laney College, A
Long Beach City College, A
Los Angeles City College, A
Moorpark College, A
Ohlone College, A
Palomar College, A
Pasadena City College, A
Point Loma Nazarene University, B
San Joaquin Delta College, A
University of La Verne, B
University of Southern California, B

Colorado

Aims Community College, A

Connecticut

Middlesex Community College, A
Quinnipiac University, BM

Delaware

Delaware State University, B

District of Columbia

Howard University, B

Florida

Barry University, B
University of Miami, BM

Georgia

University of Georgia, B

Illinois

Northwestern University, M
University of Illinois at Urbana - Champaign, B

Indiana

Goshen College, B
Huntington University, B
Manchester University, B

Iowa

Drake University, B
Grand View University, B
Iowa Central Community College, A
Wartburg College, B
William Penn University, B

Kansas

Colby Community College, A
Dodge City Community College, A

Kentucky

Northern Kentucky University, B
Western Kentucky University, B

Louisiana

Louisiana College, B

Maryland

Bowie State University, B
University of Maryland, College Park, M
Washington Adventist University, B

Massachusetts

Emerson College, BM
Massachusetts College of Liberal Arts, B
Suffolk University, B

Michigan

Cornerstone University, B
Kuyper College, B
Washtenaw Community College, A

Minnesota

Bemidji State University, B
Minnesota State University Moorhead, B
St. Cloud State University, B

Mississippi

Rust College, B

Missouri

Evangel University, AB
Hannibal-LaGrange University, B
University of Missouri, B

Nebraska

Grace University, B
Hastings College, B
Midland University, B
University of Nebraska - Lincoln, B
University of Nebraska at Omaha, B

New Jersey

Ocean County College, A
Sussex County Community College, A

New York

Brooklyn College of the City University of New York,
B
Buffalo State College, State University of New York,
B
The College at Brockport, State University of New
York, B
The College of New Rochelle, B
Five Towns College, B
Herkimer County Community College, A

Ithaca College, B
Kingsborough Community College of the City University of New York, A
Morrisville State College, B
State University of New York at Oswego, B
Syracuse University, BM

North Carolina

Campbell University, B
Elon University, B
Isothermal Community College, A
North Carolina Agricultural and Technical State University, B

Ohio

Bluffton University, B
Bowling Green State University, B
Central State University, B
Mount Vernon Nazarene University, B
Ohio University, B
Ohio University - Zanesville, A
Ohio Wesleyan University, B
The University of Findlay, B

Oklahoma

Cameron University, B
Langston University, B
Northern Oklahoma College, A
Oklahoma Christian University, B
Oklahoma City Community College, A
Oklahoma City University, B
Rose State College, A
University of Central Oklahoma, B
University of Oklahoma, B

Oregon

Mt. Hood Community College, A
Pacific University, B

Pennsylvania

Gettysburg College, B
Lincoln University, B
Marywood University, B
Point Park University, B
The University of Scranton, B

South Carolina

North Greenville University, B
University of South Carolina, B

Tennessee

Belmont University, B
Southern Adventist University, B
Trevecca Nazarene University, B
Union University, B

Texas

Amarillo College, A
Southwestern Assemblies of God University, B
University of North Texas, B
The University of Texas at El Paso, B
West Texas A&M University, B

Utah

Brigham Young University, B

Vermont

Champlain College, B

Virginia

Hampton University, B

Washington

Central Washington University, B
Gonzaga University, B
Washington State University, B
Yakima Valley Community College, A

Wisconsin

University of Wisconsin - Oshkosh, B
University of Wisconsin - Superior, B

Wyoming

Northwest College, A

U.S. Territories: Puerto Rico

University of the Sacred Heart, MO

BUDDHIST STUDIES

United States

California

University of the West, B

Vermont

Marlboro College, B

BUILDING/CONSTRUCTION FINISHING, MANAGEMENT, AND INSPECTION

United States

Alabama

Lawson State Community College, A

Arizona

Mohave Community College, A

Arkansas

John Brown University, AB
Phillips Community College of the University of Arkansas, A

California

California State University, Long Beach, B
Laney College, A
Modesto Junior College, A
Mt. San Antonio College, A
Victor Valley College, A

Colorado

Pikes Peak Community College, A

District of Columbia

University of the District of Columbia, B

Florida

Palm Beach State College, A
Seminole State College of Florida, A

Georgia

Gwinnett Technical College, A

Idaho

College of Southern Idaho, A

Illinois

Heartland Community College, A
Oakton Community College, A
Parkland College, A

Indiana

Ivy Tech Community College - Northwest, A

Kansas

Manhattan Area Technical College, A

Louisiana

Delgado Community College, A

Maryland

Baltimore City Community College, A
College of Southern Maryland, A
Community College of Baltimore County, A
Frederick Community College, A
Montgomery College, A
University of Maryland Eastern Shore, B

Massachusetts

Springfield Technical Community College, A

Michigan

Baker College, A
Delta College, A

Minnesota

Inver Hills Community College, A
Minnesota State University Mankato, B
University of Minnesota, Twin Cities Campus, B

Missouri

Vatterott College (Sunset Hills), A

Montana

Fort Peck Community College, A

Nebraska

Central Community College - Hastings Campus, A
Mid-Plains Community College, A
Nebraska Indian Community College, A
Northeast Community College, A
Southeast Community College, Milford Campus, A

New Jersey

Cumberland County College, A

New Mexico

University of New Mexico - Valencia Campus, A

New York

Pratt Institute, AB

North Carolina

Fayetteville Technical Community College, A
Haywood Community College, A
Pitt Community College, A
Western Piedmont Community College, A
Wilkes Community College, A

Ohio

Vatterott College, A

South Carolina

Piedmont Technical College, A

South Dakota

Southeast Technical Institute, A

Texas

St. Philip's College, A

Utah

Salt Lake Community College, A
Snow College, A
Weber State University, AB

Canada

British Columbia

British Columbia Institute of Technology, A

BUILDING/CONSTRUCTION SITE MANAGEMENT/MANAGER

United States

California

Cabrillo College, A
City College of San Francisco, A
College of the Canyons, A
College of the Desert, A
Cosumnes River College, A
Fresno City College, A
Fullerton College, A
Hartnell College, A
NewSchool of Architecture and Design, B
Southwestern College, A

Colorado

Aims Community College, A
Arapahoe Community College, A

Indiana

Ivy Tech Community College - Kokomo, A

Maryland

Community College of Baltimore County, A

Massachusetts

Wentworth Institute of Technology, A

Michigan

Washtenaw Community College, A

Minnesota

Dunwoody College of Technology, A
Inver Hills Community College, A
Minnesota State Community and Technical College, A
Saint Paul College - A Community & Technical College, A

Missouri

Metropolitan Community College - Kansas City, A
State Fair Community College, A

Nevada

College of Southern Nevada, A

New York

Erie Community College, North Campus, A
State University of New York College of Technology at Canton, A

Ohio

The Ohio State University Agricultural Technical Institute, A

Pennsylvania

Lehigh Carbon Community College, A
Pennsylvania College of Technology, B

Texas

The University of Texas at San Antonio, B

Utah

Southern Utah University, B

Virginia

J. Sargeant Reynolds Community College, A

Wisconsin

Fox Valley Technical College, A

BUILDING/HOME/CONSTRUCTION INSPECTION/INSPECTOR

United States

Alabama

Tuskegee University, B

Arizona

Phoenix College, A

California

Cabrillo College, A
Chabot College, A
College of San Mateo, A
Cosumnes River College, A
Fresno City College, A
Fullerton College, A
Modesto Junior College, A
Palomar College, A
Pasadena City College, A
Southwestern College, A

Illinois

South Suburban College, A

Indiana

Vincennes University, A

Minnesota

Inver Hills Community College, A

North Dakota

Bismarck State College, A

Oklahoma

Oklahoma State University, Oklahoma City, A

Oregon

Chemeketa Community College, A
Portland Community College, A

Pennsylvania

Bucks County Community College, A
Johnson College, A

South Carolina

York Technical College, A

Utah

Utah Valley University, A

Washington

Edmonds Community College, A

BUILDING/PROPERTY MAINTENANCE AND MANAGEMENT

United States

Arizona

Northland Pioneer College, A
Pima Community College, A

Florida

Pensacola State College, A

Illinois

College of DuPage, A
Lincoln Land Community College, A

Indiana

Ivy Tech Community College - Bloomington, A
Ivy Tech Community College - Central Indiana, A
Ivy Tech Community College - Columbus, A
Ivy Tech Community College - East Central, A
Ivy Tech Community College - Kokomo, A
Ivy Tech Community College - Lafayette, A
Ivy Tech Community College - North Central, A
Ivy Tech Community College - Northeast, A
Ivy Tech Community College - Northwest, A
Ivy Tech Community College - Richmond, A
Ivy Tech Community College - Southern Indiana, A
Ivy Tech Community College - Southwest, A
Ivy Tech Community College - Wabash Valley, A

Kansas

Flint Hills Technical College, A
Manhattan Area Technical College, A

Louisiana

Delgado Community College, A

Michigan

Delta College, A
Henry Ford College, A
Wayne County Community College District, A

Minnesota

Century College, A
Rochester Community and Technical College, A

Montana

Miles Community College, A

New Mexico

New Mexico State University - Carlsbad, A

New York

Erie Community College, A
TCI - College of Technology, A

North Carolina

Asheville-Buncombe Technical Community College, A
Cape Fear Community College, A
Guilford Technical Community College, A
Rowan-Cabarrus Community College, A

Pennsylvania

Community College of Allegheny County, A
Delaware County Community College, A
Luzerne County Community College, A

South Dakota

Mitchell Technical Institute, A

Tennessee

Southern Adventist University, A

Texas

Central Texas College, A
Del Mar College, A

Utah

Utah Valley University, A

Washington

Bates Technical College, A
Bellingham Technical College, A
Pierce College at Fort Steilacoom, A
Renton Technical College, A

Wyoming

Central Wyoming College, A

BUILDING SCIENCE

United States

Alabama

Auburn University, M

Arizona

Arizona State University at the Tempe campus, M

California

University of California, Berkeley, D

Georgia

Georgia Institute of Technology, MD

New York

Rensselaer Polytechnic Institute, MD

Pennsylvania

Carnegie Mellon University, MD

Virginia

Virginia Polytechnic Institute and State University, D

BUSINESS ADMINISTRATION AND MANAGEMENT

United States

Alabama

Alabama Agricultural and Mechanical University, B
Alabama State University, B
Amridge University, B
Athens State University, B
Auburn University, B
Auburn University at Montgomery, B
Birmingham-Southern College, B
Calhoun Community College, A
Central Alabama Community College, A

Chattahoochee Valley Community College, A
Columbia Southern University, AB
Concordia College Alabama, B
Enterprise State Community College, A
Faulkner University, AB
George C. Wallace Community College, A
George Corley Wallace State Community College, A
Huntingdon College, B
J. F. Drake State Community and Technical College, A
Jacksonville State University, B
James H. Faulkner State Community College, A
Lawson State Community College, A
Miles College, B
Northeast Alabama Community College, A
Oakwood University, B
Samford University, B
Selma University, B
Snead State Community College, A
South University, B
Spring Hill College, B
Stillman College, B
Strayer University - Birmingham Campus, B
Strayer University - Huntsville Campus, B
Talladega College, B
Troy University, B
Tuskegee University, B
The University of Alabama, B
The University of Alabama at Birmingham, B
The University of Alabama in Huntsville, B
University of Mobile, B
University of Montevallo, B
University of North Alabama, B
University of South Alabama, B
The University of West Alabama, B
Virginia College in Birmingham, B
Virginia College in Huntsville, B
Wallace State Community College, A

Alaska

Alaska Career College, A
Alaska Pacific University, AB
Charter College, A
Ilisagvik College, A
University of Alaska Anchorage, AB
University of Alaska Anchorage, Kenai Peninsula College, A
University of Alaska Anchorage, Matanuska-Susitna College, A
University of Alaska Fairbanks, AB
University of Alaska Southeast, AB
University of Alaska Southeast, Ketchikan Campus, A
University of Alaska Southeast, Sitka Campus, AB

Arizona

Argosy University, Phoenix, AB
Arizona Christian University, B
Arizona State University at the Polytechnic campus, B
Arizona State University at the Tempe campus, B
Arizona State University at the West campus, B
Arizona Western College, A
Brookline College (Phoenix), AB
Brookline College (Tucson), A
Chandler-Gilbert Community College, A
Cochise County Community College District, A
Coconino Community College, A
CollegeAmerica - Flagstaff, A
DeVry University (Mesa), B
DeVry University (Phoenix), B
Diné College, A
Eastern Arizona College, A
GateWay Community College, A
Glendale Community College, A
Grand Canyon University, B
Mesa Community College, A
Mohave Community College, A
Northcentral University, B
Northern Arizona University, B
Northland Pioneer College, A
Paradise Valley Community College, A
Penn Foster College, AB
Phoenix College, A
Rio Salado College, A
Scottsdale Community College, A

South Mountain Community College, A
Tohono O'odham Community College, A
University of Phoenix - Online Campus, B
University of Phoenix - Phoenix Campus, B
University of Phoenix - Southern Arizona Campus, B
Western International University, AB
Yavapai College, A

Arkansas

Arkansas Baptist College, AB
Arkansas State University, B
Arkansas State University - Beebe, A
Arkansas Tech University, B
Central Baptist College, AB
College of the Ouachitas, A
Cossatot Community College of the University of Arkansas, A
East Arkansas Community College, A
Ecclesia College, B
Harding University, B
John Brown University, B
Lyon College, B
National Park College, A
NorthWest Arkansas Community College, A
Ouachita Baptist University, B
Philander Smith College, B
Shorter College, A
Southern Arkansas University - Magnolia, B
Southern Arkansas University Tech, A
Strayer University - Little Rock Campus, B
University of Arkansas, B
University of Arkansas - Fort Smith, AB
University of Arkansas at Little Rock, B
University of Arkansas at Monticello, B
University of Arkansas at Pine Bluff, B
University of Central Arkansas, B
University of the Ozarks, B
Williams Baptist College, AB

California

Allan Hancock College, A
Alliant International University - San Diego, B
Allied American University, AB
American River College, A
Antelope Valley College, A
Antioch University Los Angeles, B
Argosy University, Inland Empire, AB
Argosy University, Los Angeles, AB
Argosy University, Orange County, AB
Argosy University, San Diego, AB
Argosy University, San Francisco Bay Area, AB
Ashford University, B
Azusa Pacific University, B
Bakersfield College, A
Barstow Community College, A
Berkeley City College, A
Biola University, B
Brandman University, B
Butte College, A
California Coast University, AB
California College San Diego (San Diego), B
California Intercontinental University, B
California Lutheran University, B
California Maritime Academy, B
California Miramar University, AB
California National University for Advanced Studies, B
California Polytechnic State University, San Luis Obispo, B
California State Polytechnic University, Pomona, B
California State University, Bakersfield, B
California State University Channel Islands, B
California State University, Chico, B
California State University, Dominguez Hills, B
California State University, East Bay, B
California State University, Fresno, B
California State University, Fullerton, B
California State University, Long Beach, B
California State University, Los Angeles, B
California State University, Monterey Bay, B
California State University, Northridge, B
California State University, Sacramento, B
California State University, San Bernardino, B
California State University, San Marcos, B
California State University, Stanislaus, B

California University of Management and Sciences, B
Cañada College, A
Carrington College - Citrus Heights, A
Cerritos College, A
Cerro Coso Community College, A
Chaffey College, A
Chapman University, B
Citrus College, A
College of Alameda, A
College of the Canyons, A
College of the Desert, A
College of Marin, A
College of San Mateo, A
College of the Sequoias, A
College of the Siskiyous, A
Columbia College, A
Concordia University Irvine, B
Contra Costa College, A
Copper Mountain College, A
Cosumnes River College, A
Crafton Hills College, A
Cuesta College, A
Cuyamaca College, A
Cypress College, A
De Anza College, A
DeVry University (Alhambra), B
DeVry University (Anaheim), B
DeVry University (Bakersfield), B
DeVry University (Fremont), B
DeVry University (Long Beach), B
DeVry University (Oakland), B
DeVry University (Oxnard), B
DeVry University (Palmdale), B
DeVry University (Pomona), B
DeVry University (San Diego), B
DeVry University (Sherman Oaks), B
Dominican University of California, B
East Los Angeles College, A
El Camino College, A
Evergreen Valley College, A
Folsom Lake College, A
Foothill College, A
Fresno City College, A
Fullerton College, A
Gavilan College, A
Glendale Community College, A
Golden Gate University, B
Golden West College, A
Grossmont College, A
Hartnell College, A
Holy Names University, B
Hope International University, B
Humboldt State University, B
Humphreys College, AB
Imperial Valley College, A
Irvine Valley College, A
John F. Kennedy University, B
La Sierra University, B
Lake Tahoe Community College, A
Laney College, A
Las Positas College, A
Lassen Community College District, A
Lincoln University, B
Long Beach City College, A
Los Angeles City College, A
Los Angeles Harbor College, A
Los Angeles Mission College, A
Los Angeles Southwest College, A
Los Angeles Trade-Technical College, A
Los Medanos College, A
Marymount California University, B
The Master's College and Seminary, B
Mendocino College, A
Merced College, A
Merritt College, A
MiraCosta College, A
Mission College, A
Modesto Junior College, A
Monterey Peninsula College, A
Moorpark College, A
Mount Saint Mary's University, AB
Mt. San Antonio College, A
Mt. San Jacinto College, A
Mt. Sierra College, B
MTI College, A

Napa Valley College, A
National University, AB
Northwestern Polytechnic University, B
Notre Dame de Namur University, B
Ohlone College, A
Orange Coast College, A
Oxnard College, A
Pacific States University, B
Palo Verde College, A
Palomar College, A
Pasadena City College, A
Patten University, B
Pepperdine University, B
Point Loma Nazarene University, B
Porterville College, A
Riverside City College, A
Sacramento City College, A
Saddleback College, A
Saint Katherine College, B
Saint Mary's College of California, B
San Bernardino Valley College, A
San Diego Christian College, B
San Diego City College, A
San Diego Mesa College, A
San Diego Miramar College, A
San Diego State University, B
San Francisco State University, B
San Joaquin Delta College, A
San Joaquin Valley College (Bakersfield), A
San Joaquin Valley College - Online, A
San Jose City College, A
San Jose State University, B
Santa Ana College, A
Santa Barbara City College, A
Santa Monica College, A
Santa Rosa Junior College, A
Santiago Canyon College, A
Shasta College, A
Sierra College, A
Silicon Valley University, B
Simpson University, B
Skyline College, A
Solano Community College, A
Sonoma State University, B
Southern California Institute of Technology, A
Southwestern College, A
Taft College, A
Touro College Los Angeles, B
Trident University International, B
University of Antelope Valley, AB
University of California, Berkeley, B
University of California, Irvine, B
University of California, Merced, B
University of California, Riverside, B
University of La Verne, B
University of the Pacific, B
University of Phoenix - Bay Area Campus, B
University of Phoenix - Central Valley Campus, B
University of Phoenix - Sacramento Valley Campus, B
University of Phoenix - San Diego Campus, B
University of Phoenix - Southern California Campus, B
University of Redlands, B
University of San Diego, B
University of San Francisco, B
University of Southern California, B
University of the West, B
Vanguard University of Southern California, B
Ventura College, A
Victor Valley College, A
West Hills Community College, A
West Los Angeles College, A
West Valley College, A
Whittier College, B
William Jessup University, B
Woodbury University, B
Yuba College, A

Colorado

Adams State University, B
American Sentinel University, AB
Arapahoe Community College, A
Argosy University, Denver, AB
Aspen University, B
CollegeAmerica - Colorado Springs, AB

CollegeAmerica - Fort Collins, B
Colorado Christian University, B
Colorado Mountain College (Glenwood Springs), AB
Colorado Mountain College (Leadville), B
Colorado Mountain College (Steamboat Springs), AB
Colorado State University, B
Colorado Technical University Colorado Springs, AB
Colorado Technical University Denver South, AB
Colorado Technical University Online, AB
Community College of Denver, A
DeVry University (Colorado Springs), B
DeVry University (Westminster), B
Everest College (Colorado Springs), A
Everest College (Thornton), A
Fort Lewis College, B
Front Range Community College, A
IBMC College (Fort Collins), A
Johnson & Wales University, B
Lamar Community College, A
Metropolitan State University of Denver, B
Morgan Community College, AB
National American University (Colorado Springs), AB
National American University (Denver), AB
Northeastern Junior College, A
Otero Junior College, A
Pikes Peak Community College, A
Pueblo Community College, A
Red Rocks Community College, A
Regis University, B
Trinidad State Junior College, A
United States Air Force Academy, B
University of Colorado Boulder, B
University of Colorado Colorado Springs, B
University of Colorado Denver, B
University of Denver, B
University of Northern Colorado, B
University of Phoenix - Colorado Campus, B
University of Phoenix - Colorado Springs Downtown Campus, B
Western State Colorado University, B

Connecticut

Albertus Magnus College, AB
Charter Oak State College, B
Eastern Connecticut State University, B
Fairfield University, B
Gateway Community College, A
Goodwin College, AB
Housatonic Community College, A
Lincoln College of New England, A
Manchester Community College, A
Middlesex Community College, A
Mitchell College, B
Naugatuck Valley Community College, A
Northwestern Connecticut Community College, A
Norwalk Community College, A
Post University, AB
Quinebaug Valley Community College, A
Quinnipiac University, B
Sacred Heart University, B
Southern Connecticut State University, B
Tunxis Community College, A
University of Connecticut, B
University of Hartford, B
University of New Haven, AB
University of Saint Joseph, B
Western Connecticut State University, B

Delaware

Delaware State University, B
Delaware Technical & Community College, Stanton/Wilmington Campus, A
Delaware Technical & Community College, Terry Campus, A
Goldey-Beacom College, AB
Strayer University - Christiana Campus, B
Wesley College, AB
Wilmington University, B

District of Columbia

American University, B
The Catholic University of America, B
Gallaudet University, B
The George Washington University, B

Georgetown University, B
Howard University, B
Strayer University - Takoma Park Campus, B
Strayer University - Washington Campus, B
Trinity Washington University, B
University of the District of Columbia, B
University of Phoenix - Washington D.C. Campus, B
University of the Potomac, AB

Florida

Argosy University, Sarasota, AB
Argosy University, Tampa, AB
The Baptist College of Florida, B
Barry University, B
Beacon College, AB
Belhaven University, B
Bethune-Cookman University, B
Broward College, A
Carlos Albizu University, Miami Campus, B
Chipola College, AB
City College (Altamonte Springs), AB
City College (Fort Lauderdale), AB
City College (Gainesville), AB
City College (Miami), AB
College of Business and Technology - Cutler Bay Campus, A
College of Business and Technology - Flagler Campus, A
College of Business and Technology - Main Campus, AB
College of Business and Technology - Miami Gardens, AB
College of Central Florida, A
Daytona State College, AB
DeVry University (Jacksonville), B
DeVry University (Miramar), B
DeVry University (Orlando), B
Eastern Florida State College, A
Eckerd College, B
Edward Waters College, B
Embry-Riddle Aeronautical University - Worldwide, AB
Everest University (Orange Park), AB
Everest University (Orlando), AB
Everest University (Tampa), AB
Everglades University (Boca Raton), B
Everglades University (Maitland), B
Everglades University (Sarasota), B
Flagler College, B
Florida Agricultural and Mechanical University, B
Florida Atlantic University, B
Florida College, B
Florida Institute of Technology, B
Florida International University, B
Florida Keys Community College, A
Florida Memorial University, B
Florida National University, AB
Florida Southern College, B
Florida SouthWestern State College, A
Florida State College at Jacksonville, A
Florida State University, B
Florida Technical College (Orlando), A
Fortis College (Orange Park), A
Fortis College (Winter Park), A
Gulf Coast State College, A
Hillsborough Community College, A
Indian River State College, A
Jacksonville University, B
Johnson & Wales University, B
Jones College, AB
Jose Maria Vargas University, B
Keiser University, AB
Lake-Sumter State College, A
Lynn University, B
Meridian College, A
Miami Dade College, A
Millennia Atlantic University, AB
North Florida Community College, A
Northwest Florida State College, A
Nova Southeastern University, B
Palm Beach Atlantic University, B
Palm Beach State College, B
Pasco-Hernando State College, A
Pensacola State College, A
Polk State College, B

Polytechnic University of Puerto Rico, Miami Campus, B
Polytechnic University of Puerto Rico, Orlando Campus, B
Rasmussen College Fort Myers, AB
Rasmussen College Land O' Lakes, AB
Rasmussen College New Port Richey, AB
Rasmussen College Ocala, AB
Rasmussen College Tampa/Brandon, AB
St. Johns River State College, A
Saint Leo University, AB
St. Petersburg College, AB
St. Thomas University, B
Santa Fe College, A
Seminole State College of Florida, AB
South Florida State College, A
South University (Royal Palm Beach), B
South University (Tampa), B
Southeastern University, B
Southern Technical College (Fort Myers), B
State College of Florida Manatee-Sarasota, A
Stetson University, B
Strayer University - Baymeadows Campus, B
Strayer University - Brickell Campus, B
Strayer University - Coral Springs Campus, B
Strayer University - Doral Campus, B
Strayer University - Fort Lauderdale Campus, B
Strayer University - Maitland Campus, B
Strayer University - Miramar Campus, B
Strayer University - Orlando East Campus, B
Strayer University - Palm Beach Gardens Campus, B
Strayer University - Sand Lake Campus, B
Strayer University - Tampa East Campus, B
Strayer University - Tampa Westshore Campus, B
University of Central Florida, B
University of Florida, B
University of Fort Lauderdale, AB
University of Miami, B
University of North Florida, B
University of Phoenix - Central Florida Campus, B
University of Phoenix - North Florida Campus, B
University of Phoenix - South Florida Campus, B
University of South Florida, B
University of South Florida Sarasota-Manatee, B
The University of Tampa, B
University of West Florida, B
Valencia College, A
Warner University, B
Webber International University, AB

Georgia

Abraham Baldwin Agricultural College, A
Agnes Scott College, B
Albany State University, B
American InterContinental University Atlanta, AB
Andrew College, A
Argosy University, Atlanta, A
Ashworth College, AB
Augusta Technical College, A
Augusta University, B
Bainbridge State College, B
Beulah Heights University, AB
Brewton-Parker College, AB
Central Georgia Technical College, A
Chattahoochee Technical College, A
Clark Atlanta University, B
Clayton State University, B
College of Coastal Georgia, AB
Columbus State University, B
Dalton State College, AB
Darton State College, A
DeVry University (Alpharetta), B
DeVry University (Atlanta), B
DeVry University (Decatur), B
DeVry University (Duluth), B
Emory University, B
Fort Valley State University, B
Georgia College & State University, B
Georgia Highlands College, A
Georgia Institute of Technology, B
Georgia Military College, B
Georgia Southern University, B
Georgia Southwestern State University, B
Georgia State University, B
Gordon State College, A

Gwinnett Technical College, A
Kennesaw State University, B
LaGrange College, B
Life University, B
Morehouse College, B
Oglethorpe University, B
Paine College, B
Piedmont College, B
Point University, AB
Reinhardt University, B
Savannah State University, B
Shorter University, AB
South Georgia State College, A
South University, B
Southern Crescent Technical College, A
Strayer University - Augusta Campus, B
Strayer University - Chamblee Campus, B
Strayer University - Cobb County Campus, B
Strayer University - Columbus Campus, B
Strayer University - Douglasville Campus, B
Strayer University - Lithonia Campus, B
Strayer University - Morrow Campus, B
Strayer University - Roswell Campus, B
Strayer University - Savannah Campus, B
Thomas University, B
Toccoa Falls College, AB
Truett-McConnell College, B
University of Georgia, B
University of North Georgia, B
University of Phoenix - Atlanta Campus, B
University of Phoenix - Augusta Campus, B
University of Phoenix - Columbus Georgia Campus, AB
University of West Georgia, B
Valdosta State University, B
Virginia College in Macon, A
Wesleyan College, B
Young Harris College, B

Hawaii

Argosy University, Hawai'i, AB
Brigham Young University - Hawaii, B
Chaminade University of Honolulu, AB
Hawai'i Pacific University, AB
Leeward Community College, A
University of Hawaii at Hilo, B
University of Hawaii at Manoa, B
University of Hawaii Maui College, A
University of Hawaii - West Oahu, B
University of Phoenix - Hawaii Campus, B

Idaho

Boise State University, B
Brigham Young University - Idaho, B
Broadview University - Boise, AB
The College of Idaho, B
College of Southern Idaho, A
Idaho State University, B
Lewis-Clark State College, B
North Idaho College, A
Northwest Nazarene University, B
Stevens-Henager College (Boise), B
University of Idaho, B

Illinois

American InterContinental University Online, AB
Argosy University, Chicago, B
Argosy University, Schaumburg, B
Augustana College, B
Aurora University, B
Benedictine University, A
Bradley University, B
Chicago State University, B
City Colleges of Chicago, Harold Washington College, A
City Colleges of Chicago, Harry S. Truman College, A
City Colleges of Chicago, Kennedy-King College, A
City Colleges of Chicago, Olive-Harvey College, A
City Colleges of Chicago, Richard J. Daley College, A
City Colleges of Chicago, Wilbur Wright College, A
College of DuPage, A
College of Lake County, A
Concordia University Chicago, B
DePaul University, B

DeVry University (Addison), B
DeVry University (Chicago), B
DeVry University (Downers Grove), B
DeVry University (Elgin), B
DeVry University (Gurnee), B
DeVry University (Naperville), B
DeVry University (Tinley Park), B
DeVry University Online, B
Dominican University, B
East-West University, AB
Eastern Illinois University, B
Elgin Community College, A
Ellis University, AB
Elmhurst College, B
Eureka College, B
Governors State University, B
Greenville College, B
Harper College, A
Heartland Community College, A
Highland Community College, A
Illinois Central College, A
Illinois College, B
Illinois Eastern Community Colleges, Olney Central College, A
Illinois Eastern Community Colleges, Wabash Valley College, A
Illinois Institute of Technology, B
Illinois State University, B
Illinois Valley Community College, A
Illinois Wesleyan University, B
John A. Logan College, A
John Wood Community College, A
Judson University, B
Kankakee Community College, A
Kishwaukee College, A
Lake Land College, A
Lewis and Clark Community College, A
Lewis University, B
Lincoln College, A
Lincoln College - Normal, B
Loyola University Chicago, B
MacCormac College, A
MacMurray College, B
McHenry County College, A
McKendree University, AB
Midstate College, AB
Millikin University, B
Monmouth College, B
Moraine Valley Community College, A
Morton College, A
National Louis University, B
North Central College, B
North Park University, B
Northeastern Illinois University, B
Northern Illinois University, B
Northwestern College - Bridgeview Campus, A
Northwestern College - Chicago Campus, A
Olivet Nazarene University, B
Parkland College, A
Principia College, B
Quincy University, B
Rasmussen College Aurora, A
Rasmussen College Mokena/Tinley Park, A
Rasmussen College Rockford, A
Rasmussen College Romeoville/Joliet, A
Richland Community College, A
Robert Morris University Illinois, AB
Rock Valley College, A
Rockford Career College, A
Rockford University, B
St. Augustine College, A
Sauk Valley Community College, A
Shawnee Community College, A
Southeastern Illinois College, A
Southern Illinois University Carbondale, B
Southern Illinois University Edwardsville, B
Spoon River College, A
Trinity Christian College, B
Trinity International University, B
Triton College, A
University of Illinois at Chicago, B
University of Illinois at Springfield, B
University of Illinois at Urbana - Champaign, B
University of St. Francis, B
Waubonsee Community College, A
Western Illinois University, B

Indiana

Ancilla College, A
Anderson University, AB
Bethel College, AB
Calumet College of Saint Joseph, AB
DeVry University, B
Goshen College, B
Grace College, B
Harrison College, AB
Holy Cross College, B
Huntington University, B
Indiana State University, B
Indiana Tech, AB
Indiana University - Purdue University Fort Wayne, B
Indiana Wesleyan University, AB
International Business College (Fort Wayne), B
Ivy Tech Community College - Bloomington, A
Ivy Tech Community College - Central Indiana, A
Ivy Tech Community College - Columbus, A
Ivy Tech Community College - East Central, A
Ivy Tech Community College - Kokomo, A
Ivy Tech Community College - Lafayette, A
Ivy Tech Community College - North Central, A
Ivy Tech Community College - Northeast, A
Ivy Tech Community College - Northwest, A
Ivy Tech Community College - Richmond, A
Ivy Tech Community College - Southeast, A
Ivy Tech Community College - Southern Indiana, A
Ivy Tech Community College - Southwest, A
Ivy Tech Community College - Wabash Valley, A
Manchester University, B
Marian University, AB
Martin University, B
Oakland City University, AB
Purdue University, B
Purdue University Northwest (Hammond), B
Saint Mary-of-the-Woods College, B
Saint Mary's College, B
Taylor University, AB
Trine University, AB
University of Evansville, B
University of Saint Francis, B
University of Southern Indiana, B
Vincennes University, A

Iowa

Briar Cliff University, B
Brown Mackie College - Quad Cities, A
Buena Vista University, B
Central College, B
Clarke University, B
Clinton Community College, A
Coe College, B
Des Moines Area Community College, A
Dordt College, B
Drake University, B
Ellsworth Community College, A
Emmaus Bible College, B
Graceland University, B
Grand View University, B
Indian Hills Community College, A
Iowa Central Community College, A
Iowa Lakes Community College, A
Iowa State University of Science and Technology, B
Iowa Wesleyan University, B
Iowa Western Community College, A
Kaplan University, Cedar Rapids, AB
Kaplan University, Davenport Campus, AB
Kaplan University, Des Moines, AB
Kaplan University, Mason City Campus, AB
Kirkwood Community College, A
Loras College, B
Luther College, B
Maharishi University of Management, B
Marshalltown Community College, A
Morningside College, B
Mount Mercy University, B
Muscatine Community College, A
North Iowa Area Community College, A
Northeast Iowa Community College, A
Northwest Iowa Community College, A
Northwestern College, B
Scott Community College, A
Simpson College, B
Southeastern Community College, A

Southwestern Community College, A
University of Dubuque, B
The University of Iowa, B
University of Northern Iowa, B
Upper Iowa University, AB
Waldorf College, B
Wartburg College, B
Western Iowa Tech Community College, A

Kansas

Allen Community College, A
Barclay College, B
Barton County Community College, A
Benedictine College, B
Bethany College, B
Butler Community College, A
Cloud County Community College, A
Coffeyville Community College, A
Colby Community College, A
Cowley County Community College and Area Vocational - Technical School, A
Dodge City Community College, A
Emporia State University, B
Fort Hays State University, B
Friends University, B
Garden City Community College, A
Grantham University, AB
Haskell Indian Nations University, AB
Hesston College, A
Independence Community College, A
Johnson County Community College, A
Kansas City Kansas Community College, A
Kansas State University, B
Kansas Wesleyan University, AB
Labette Community College, A
McPherson College, B
MidAmerica Nazarene University, B
Neosho County Community College, A
Newman University, AB
Ottawa University, B
Pratt Community College, A
Rasmussen College Kansas City/Overland Park, AB
Rasmussen College Topeka, AB
Seward County Community College and Area Technical School, A
Southwestern College, B
Sterling College, B
Tabor College, B
The University of Kansas, B
University of Saint Mary, B
Washburn University, B
Wichita Area Technical College, A
Wichita State University, B

Kentucky

Alice Lloyd College, B
American National University (Danville), A
American National University (Florence), A
American National University (Lexington), AB
American National University (Louisville), AB
American National University (Pikeville), A
American National University (Richmond), A
Ashland Community and Technical College, A
Beckfield College, AB
Berea College, B
Big Sandy Community and Technical College, A
Bluegrass Community and Technical College, A
Campbellsville University, AB
Daymar College (Bellevue), A
Eastern Kentucky University, B
Elizabethtown Community and Technical College, A
Gateway Community and Technical College, A
Georgetown College, B
Hazard Community and Technical College, A
Henderson Community College, A
Hopkinsville Community College, A
Jefferson Community and Technical College, A
Kentucky Christian University, B
Kentucky Wesleyan College, B
Lindsey Wilson College, B
Madisonville Community College, A
Maysville Community and Technical College (Maysville), A
Maysville Community and Technical College (Morehead), A
Midway University, AB

Morehead State University, B
Murray State University, B
Northern Kentucky University, B
Owensboro Community and Technical College, A
Somerset Community College, A
Southeast Kentucky Community and Technical College, A
Sullivan University, AB
Thomas More College, AB
Union College, B
University of the Cumberlands, AB
University of Pikeville, AB
West Kentucky Community and Technical College, A
Western Kentucky University, AB

Louisiana

Centenary College of Louisiana, B
Delgado Community College, A
Delta School of Business and Technology, A
Dillard University, B
Grambling State University, B
Louisiana College, B
Louisiana State University and Agricultural & Mechanical College, B
Louisiana State University at Alexandria, B
Louisiana State University at Eunice, A
Louisiana State University in Shreveport, B
Louisiana Tech University, B
Loyola University New Orleans, B
McCann School of Business & Technology (Monroe), A
McNeese State University, B
Nicholls State University, B
Northwestern State University of Louisiana, B
Remington College - Baton Rouge Campus, A
Remington College - Lafayette Campus, A
Remington College - Shreveport, A
Southeastern Louisiana University, B
Southern University and Agricultural and Mechanical College, B
Southwest University, AB
Tulane University, AB
University of Holy Cross, B
University of Louisiana at Lafayette, B
University of Louisiana at Monroe, B
University of New Orleans, B
Virginia College in Baton Rouge, A
Xavier University of Louisiana, B

Maine

Beal College, A
Central Maine Community College, A
Eastern Maine Community College, A
Husson University, AB
Kaplan University, South Portland, A
Maine Maritime Academy, B
Northern Maine Community College, A
Saint Joseph's College of Maine, B
Southern Maine Community College, A
Thomas College, AB
University of Maine, B
University of Maine at Augusta, AB
University of Maine at Fort Kent, AB
University of Maine at Machias, B
University of Maine at Presque Isle, A
University of New England, B
University of Southern Maine, B
Washington County Community College, A
York County Community College, A

Maryland

Allegany College of Maryland, A
Anne Arundel Community College, A
Baltimore City Community College, A
Bowie State University, B
Capitol Technology University, B
Carroll Community College, A
Cecil College, A
Chesapeake College, A
College of Southern Maryland, A
Community College of Baltimore County, A
Frederick Community College, A
Frostburg State University, B
Garrett College, A
Goucher College, B
Hagerstown Community College, A

Harford Community College, A
Hood College, B
Howard Community College, A
Kaplan University, Hagerstown Campus, A
McDaniel College, B
Morgan State University, B
Notre Dame of Maryland University, B
Prince George's Community College, A
Salisbury University, B
Stevenson University, B
Strayer University - Anne Arundel Campus, B
Strayer University - Owings Mills Campus, B
Strayer University - Prince George's Campus, B
Strayer University - Rockville Campus, B
Strayer University - White Marsh Campus, B
Towson University, B
University of Baltimore, B
University of Maryland Eastern Shore, B
University of Maryland University College, B
Washington Adventist University, B
Washington College, B
Wor-Wic Community College, A

Massachusetts

American International College, B
Anna Maria College, B
Assumption College, B
Babson College, B
Bay Path University, AB
Bay State College, AB
Becker College, B
Bentley University, B
Berkshire Community College, A
Boston College, B
Boston University, B
Bridgewater State University, B
Bristol Community College, A
Bunker Hill Community College, A
Cape Cod Community College, A
Clark University, B
Curry College, B
Dean College, AB
Eastern Nazarene College, B
Elms College, B
Emmanuel College, B
Endicott College, B
Fisher College, AB
Fitchburg State University, B
Gordon College, B
Greenfield Community College, A
Hellenic College, B
Holyoke Community College, A
Hult International Business School, B
Lasell College, B
Lesley University, B
Massachusetts Bay Community College, A
Massachusetts College of Liberal Arts, B
Massasoit Community College, A
Merrimack College, B
Middlesex Community College, A
Mount Ida College, B
Mount Wachusett Community College, A
New England College of Business and Finance, A
Newbury College, AB
Nichols College, AB
North Shore Community College, A
Northeastern University, B
Northern Essex Community College, A
Pine Manor College, AB
Quincy College, A
Quinsigamond Community College, A
Roxbury Community College, A
Salem State University, B
Simmons College, B
Springfield College, B
Springfield Technical Community College, A
Stonehill College, B
Suffolk University, B
University of Massachusetts Amherst, B
University of Massachusetts Boston, B
University of Massachusetts Dartmouth, B
University of Massachusetts Lowell, B
Western New England University, B
Westfield State University, B
Worcester Polytechnic Institute, B
Worcester State University, B

Michigan

Adrian College, B
Albion College, B
Alma College, B
Alpena Community College, A
Aquinas College, B
Baker College, AB
Bay de Noc Community College, A
Calvin College, B
Central Michigan University, B
Cleary University, AB
Concordia University Ann Arbor, B
Cornerstone University, AB
Davenport University, AB
Delta College, A
Eastern Michigan University, B
Ferris State University, B
Finlandia University, B
Glen Oaks Community College, A
Gogebic Community College, A
Grace Bible College, AB
Grand Rapids Community College, A
Henry Ford College, A
Hope College, B
Jackson College, A
Kalamazoo Valley Community College, A
Kellogg Community College, A
Kettering University, B
Kirtland Community College, A
Kuyper College, B
Lake Michigan College, A
Lake Superior State University, AB
Lansing Community College, A
Lawrence Technological University, B
Macomb Community College, A
Madonna University, AB
Marygrove College, B
Michigan State University, B
Michigan Technological University, B
Mid Michigan Community College, A
Monroe County Community College, A
Montcalm Community College, A
Mott Community College, A
Muskegon Community College, A
North Central Michigan College, A
Northern Michigan University, B
Northwestern Michigan College, A
Northwood University, Michigan Campus, AB
Oakland Community College, A
Olivet College, B
Rochester College, B
Saginaw Valley State University, B
Schoolcraft College, A
Siena Heights University, AB
South University, B
Southwestern Michigan College, A
Spring Arbor University, B
University of Detroit Mercy, B
University of Michigan, B
University of Michigan - Dearborn, B
University of Michigan - Flint, B
University of Phoenix - Detroit Campus, B
Walsh College of Accountancy and Business Administration, B
Washtenaw Community College, A
Wayne County Community College District, A
Western Michigan University, B

Minnesota

Academy College, AB
Alexandria Technical and Community College, A
Anoka-Ramsey Community College, A
Argosy University, Twin Cities, AB
Augsburg College, B
Bemidji State University, B
Bethany Lutheran College, B
Bethel University, B
Capella University, B
Central Lakes College, A
Century College, A
College of Saint Benedict, B
The College of St. Scholastica, B
Concordia College, B
Concordia University, St. Paul, B
Crossroads College, B
Crown College, B

Dakota County Technical College, A
Duluth Business University, A
Dunwoody College of Technology, B
Globe University - Minneapolis, AB
Globe University - Woodbury, AB
Gustavus Adolphus College, B
Hamline University, B
Hennepin Technical College, A
Hibbing Community College, A
Inver Hills Community College, A
Itasca Community College, A
Lake Superior College, A
Metropolitan State University, B
Minneapolis Community and Technical College, A
Minnesota School of Business - Blaine, AB
Minnesota School of Business - Brooklyn Center, AB
Minnesota School of Business - Elk River, AB
Minnesota School of Business - Lakeville, AB
Minnesota School of Business - Plymouth, AB
Minnesota School of Business - Rochester, AB
Minnesota School of Business - St. Cloud, AB
Minnesota State College - Southeast Technical, A
Minnesota State Community and Technical College, A
Minnesota State Community and Technical College - Moorhead, A
Minnesota State University Mankato, B
Minnesota State University Moorhead, B
Minnesota West Community and Technical College, A
National American University (Bloomington), A
National American University (Brooklyn Center), A
National American University (Roseville), AB
North Central University, AB
North Hennepin Community College, A
Northland Community and Technical College, A
Northwest Technical College, A
Oak Hills Christian College, B
Rainy River Community College, A
Rasmussen College Blaine, A
Rasmussen College Bloomington, AB
Rasmussen College Brooklyn Park, AB
Rasmussen College Eagan, AB
Rasmussen College Lake Elmo/Woodbury, AB
Rasmussen College Mankato, AB
Rasmussen College Moorhead, AB
Rasmussen College St. Cloud, AB
Ridgewater College, A
Riverland Community College, A
Rochester Community and Technical College, A
St. Catherine University, B
St. Cloud State University, B
St. Cloud Technical & Community College, A
Saint John's University, B
Saint Paul College - A Community & Technical College, A
South Central College, A
Southwest Minnesota State University, AB
University of Minnesota, Crookston, B
University of Minnesota, Duluth, B
University of Minnesota, Morris, B
University of Northwestern - St. Paul, B
University of St. Thomas, B
Vermilion Community College, A
Walden University, B
Winona State University, B

Mississippi

Alcorn State University, B
Belhaven University, B
Blue Mountain College, B
Copiah-Lincoln Community College, A
Delta State University, B
East Central Community College, A
Itawamba Community College, A
Jackson State University, B
Jones County Junior College, A
Millsaps College, B
Mississippi College, B
Mississippi Gulf Coast Community College, A
Mississippi State University, B
Mississippi University for Women, B
Mississippi Valley State University, B
Northeast Mississippi Community College, A
Northwest Mississippi Community College, A

Pearl River Community College, A
Rust College, AB
Southeastern Baptist College, A
Southwest Mississippi Community College, A
Strayer University - Jackson Campus, B
Tougaloo College, B
University of Mississippi, B
University of Southern Mississippi, B
William Carey University, B

Missouri

Avila University, B
Calvary Bible College and Theological Seminary, B
Central Methodist University, B
City Vision University, AB
College of the Ozarks, B
Columbia College, B
Cottey College, B
Crowder College, A
Culver-Stockton College, B
DeVry University (Kansas City), B
Drury University, B
Evangel University, B
Everest College, AB
Fontbonne University, B
Hannibal-LaGrange University, B
Harris-Stowe State University, B
Hickey College, B
Jefferson College, A
Lincoln University, B
Lindenwood University, B
Maryville University of Saint Louis, B
Metro Business College (Jefferson City), A
Metropolitan Community College - Kansas City, A
Missouri Baptist University, AB
Missouri State University, B
Missouri State University - West Plains, A
Missouri University of Science and Technology, B
Missouri Western State University, B
National American University (Kansas City), AB
North Central Missouri College, A
Northwest Missouri State University, B
Ozarks Technical Community College, A
Park University, B
Ranken Technical College, B
Rockhurst University, B
Saint Louis University, B
Southeast Missouri State University, B
Southwest Baptist University, B
State Fair Community College, A
Stevens - The Institute of Business & Arts, AB
Three Rivers Community College, A
Truman State University, B
University of Central Missouri, B
University of Missouri, B
University of Missouri - Kansas City, B
University of Missouri - St. Louis, B
Washington University in St. Louis, B
Webster University, B
Westminster College, B
William Jewell College, B
William Woods University, B

Montana

Blackfeet Community College, A
Carroll College, AB
Chief Dull Knife College, A
Flathead Valley Community College, A
Fort Peck Community College, A
Little Big Horn College, A
Montana State University Billings, AB
Montana State University - Northern, B
Rocky Mountain College, B
Stone Child College, A
University of Great Falls, B
The University of Montana Western, AB

Nebraska

Central Community College - Columbus Campus, A
Central Community College - Grand Island Campus, A
Central Community College - Hastings Campus, A
Chadron State College, B
Clarkson College, B
College of Saint Mary, AB
Concordia University, Nebraska, B

Creighton University, B
Doane University, B
Grace University, B
Hastings College, B
Kaplan University, Lincoln, AB
Kaplan University, Omaha, AB
Metropolitan Community College, A
Mid-Plains Community College, A
Midland University, B
Nebraska Indian Community College, A
Nebraska Wesleyan University, B
Northeast Community College, A
Peru State College, B
Southeast Community College, Beatrice Campus, A
Southeast Community College, Lincoln Campus, A
Southeast Community College, Milford Campus, A
Union College, AB
University of Nebraska at Kearney, B
University of Nebraska - Lincoln, B
University of Nebraska at Omaha, B
Wayne State College, B
Western Nebraska Community College, A
York College, B

Nevada

Career College of Northern Nevada, A
College of Southern Nevada, A
DeVry University, B
Great Basin College, AB
Sierra Nevada College, B
University of Nevada, Las Vegas, B
University of Nevada, Reno, B
University of Phoenix - Las Vegas Campus, B
Western Nevada College, A

New Hampshire

Colby-Sawyer College, B
Daniel Webster College, B
Franklin Pierce University, B
Granite State College, B
Great Bay Community College, A
Keene State College, B
Manchester Community College, A
Nashua Community College, A
New England College, AB
NHTI, Concord's Community College, A
Plymouth State University, B
River Valley Community College, A
Rivier University, B
Southern New Hampshire University, AB
University of New Hampshire, B
University of New Hampshire at Manchester, AB
White Mountains Community College, A

New Jersey

Atlantic Cape Community College, A
Bergen Community College, A
Berkeley College - Woodland Park Campus, AB
Bloomfield College, B
Brookdale Community College, A
Caldwell University, B
Camden County College, A
Centenary College, B
The College of New Jersey, B
College of Saint Elizabeth, B
County College of Morris, A
Cumberland County College, A
DeVry University (North Brunswick), B
DeVry University (Paramus), B
Drew University, B
Essex County College, A
Fairleigh Dickinson University, College at Florham, B
Fairleigh Dickinson University, Metropolitan Campus, B
Felician University, AB
Georgian Court University, B
Hudson County Community College, A
Kean University, B
Mercer County Community College, A
Middlesex County College, A
Monmouth University, B
Montclair State University, B
New Jersey City University, B
New Jersey Institute of Technology, B
Ocean County College, A

Passaic County Community College, A
Ramapo College of New Jersey, B
Raritan Valley Community College, A
Rider University, B
Rowan College at Burlington County, A
Rowan College at Gloucester County, A
Rowan University, B
Rutgers University - Camden, B
Rutgers University - New Brunswick, B
Rutgers University - Newark, B
Saint Peter's University, AB
Seton Hall University, B
Stevens Institute of Technology, B
Stockton University, B
Strayer University - Cherry Hill Campus, B
Strayer University - Lawrenceville Campus, B
Strayer University - Piscataway Campus, B
Strayer University - Willingboro Campus, B
Sussex County Community College, A
Thomas Edison State University, AB
Union County College, A
Warren County Community College, A
William Paterson University of New Jersey, B

New Mexico

Brookline College, A
Central New Mexico Community College, A
Clovis Community College, A
Doña Ana Community College, A
Eastern New Mexico University, B
Eastern New Mexico University - Roswell, A
Luna Community College, A
Mesalands Community College, A
National American University (Albuquerque), AB
New Mexico Highlands University, B
New Mexico Institute of Mining and Technology, AB
New Mexico Junior College, A
New Mexico Military Institute, A
New Mexico State University, B
New Mexico State University - Grants, A
San Juan College, A
Santa Fe Community College, A
Santa Fe University of Art and Design, B
Southwestern Indian Polytechnic Institute, A
University of New Mexico, B
University of New Mexico - Gallup, A
University of New Mexico - Los Alamos Branch, A
University of New Mexico - Valencia Campus, A
University of Phoenix - New Mexico Campus, B
University of the Southwest, B
Western New Mexico University, B

New York

Adelphi University, B
Adirondack Community College, A
Alfred University, B
Baruch College of the City University of New York, B
Berkeley College - New York City Campus, AB
Berkeley College - White Plains Campus, AB
Binghamton University, State University of New York, B
Boricua College, B
Borough of Manhattan Community College of the City University of New York, A
Bramson ORT College, A
Bronx Community College of the City University of New York, A
Broome Community College, A
Bryant & Stratton College - Amherst Campus, B
Bryant & Stratton College - Buffalo Campus, B
Bryant & Stratton College - Henrietta Campus, A
Bryant & Stratton College - Liverpool Campus, A
Bryant & Stratton College - Orchard Park Campus, B
Buffalo State College, State University of New York, B
Canisius College, B
Cayuga County Community College, A
Cazenovia College, AB
City College of the City University of New York, B
Clarkson University, B
Clinton Community College, A
The College at Brockport, State University of New York, B
The College of New Rochelle, B

The College of Saint Rose, B
The College of Westchester, AB
Columbia-Greene Community College, A
Concordia College - New York, AB
Corning Community College, A
Daemen College, B
DeVry College of New York, B
Dominican College, B
Dutchess Community College, A
D'Youville College, B
Elmira College, AB
Erie Community College, A
Erie Community College, North Campus, A
Erie Community College, South Campus, A
Eugenio María de Hostos Community College of the
   City University of New York, A
Excelsior College, AB
Farmingdale State College, AB
Finger Lakes Community College, A
Fiorello H. LaGuardia Community College of the
   City University of New York, A
Five Towns College, AB
Fordham University, B
Fulton-Montgomery Community College, A
Genesee Community College, A
Globe Institute of Technology, AB
Hartwick College, B
Herkimer County Community College, A
Hilbert College, AB
Hofstra University, B
Houghton College, B
Hudson Valley Community College, A
Iona College, B
Ithaca College, B
Jamestown Business College, AB
Jamestown Community College, A
Jefferson Community College, A
Keuka College, B
The King's College, B
Kingsborough Community College of the City Uni-
   versity of New York, A
Lehman College of the City University of New York,
   B
Long Island Business Institute, A
Long Island University - LIU Brooklyn, AB
Long Island University - LIU Post, B
Manhattanville College, B
Maria College, A
Marist College, B
Marymount Manhattan College, B
Medaille College, AB
Medgar Evers College of the City University of New
   York, A
Mercy College, B
Mildred Elley - New York City, A
Mildred Elley School, A
Mohawk Valley Community College, A
Molloy College, B
Monroe College, AB
Monroe Community College, A
Morrisville State College, AB
Mount Saint Mary College, B
Nassau Community College, A
Nazareth College of Rochester, B
New York Institute of Technology, AB
Niagara County Community College, A
Niagara University, AB
North Country Community College, A
Nyack College, AB
Onondaga Community College, A
Orange County Community College, A
Pace University, B
Paul Smith's College, B
Plaza College, A
Queensborough Community College of the City Uni-
   versity of New York, A
Rensselaer Polytechnic Institute, B
Roberts Wesleyan College, B
Rochester Institute of Technology, B
Rockland Community College, A
The Sage Colleges, B
St. Bonaventure University, B
St. Francis College, AB
St. John Fisher College, B
St. John's University, AB
St. Joseph's College, Long Island Campus, B

St. Joseph's College, New York, B
St. Thomas Aquinas College, AB
Schenectady County Community College, A
State University of New York College of Agriculture
   and Technology at Cobleskill, A
State University of New York College at Geneseo, B
State University of New York College at Old
   Westbury, B
State University of New York College at Potsdam, B
State University of New York College of Technology
   at Alfred, AB
State University of New York College of Technology
   at Canton, AB
State University of New York College of Technology
   at Delhi, A
State University of New York at Fredonia, B
State University of New York at New Paltz, B
State University of New York at Oswego, B
State University of New York at Plattsburgh, B
State University of New York Polytechnic Institute, B
Stony Brook University, State University of New
   York, B
Suffolk County Community College, A
Sullivan County Community College, A
Syracuse University, B
TCI - College of Technology, A
Tompkins Cortland Community College, A
Touro College, AB
Trocaire College, A
Ulster County Community College, A
United States Military Academy, B
University at Albany, State University of New York, B
University at Buffalo, the State University of New
   York, B
Utica College, B
Utica School of Commerce, A
Villa Maria College, AB
Wagner College, B
Wells College, B
Westchester Community College, A
Yeshiva University, B
York College of the City University of New York, B

North Carolina

Alamance Community College, A
Appalachian State University, B
Asheville-Buncombe Technical Community College,
   A
Barton College, B
Beaufort County Community College, A
Belmont Abbey College, B
Bennett College, B
Bladen Community College, A
Blue Ridge Community College, A
Brevard College, B
Brunswick Community College, A
Caldwell Community College and Technical Institute,
   A
Campbell University, B
Cape Fear Community College, A
Carteret Community College, A
Catawba College, B
Catawba Valley Community College, A
Central Carolina Community College, A
Central Piedmont Community College, A
Chowan University, B
Cleveland Community College, A
Coastal Carolina Community College, A
College of The Albemarle, A
Craven Community College, A
Davidson County Community College, A
DeVry University, B
Durham Technical Community College, A
East Carolina University, B
Edgecombe Community College, A
Elizabeth City State University, B
Elon University, B
Fayetteville State University, B
Fayetteville Technical Community College, A
Forsyth Technical Community College, A
Gardner-Webb University, B
Gaston College, A
Greensboro College, B
Guilford College, B
Guilford Technical Community College, A
Halifax Community College, A

Haywood Community College, A
High Point University, B
Isothermal Community College, A
James Sprunt Community College, A
John Wesley University, B
Johnson C. Smith University, B
Johnson & Wales University, B
Johnston Community College, A
Lees-McRae College, B
Lenoir-Rhyne University, B
Livingstone College, B
Louisburg College, A
Mars Hill University, B
Martin Community College, A
Mayland Community College, A
McDowell Technical Community College, A
Meredith College, B
Methodist University, AB
Mid-Atlantic Christian University, B
Miller-Motte College (Cary), AB
Miller-Motte College (Wilmington), A
Mitchell Community College, A
Montgomery Community College, A
Montreat College, AB
Nash Community College, A
North Carolina Agricultural and Technical State Uni-
   versity, B
North Carolina Central University, B
North Carolina State University, B
North Carolina Wesleyan College, B
Pamlico Community College, A
Pfeiffer University, B
Piedmont Community College, A
Pitt Community College, A
Queens University of Charlotte, B
Randolph Community College, A
Richmond Community College, A
Roanoke-Chowan Community College, A
Robeson Community College, A
Rockingham Community College, A
Rowan-Cabarrus Community College, A
St. Andrews University, B
Saint Augustine's University, B
Salem College, B
Sampson Community College, A
Sandhills Community College, A
Shaw University, B
South College - Asheville, A
South Piedmont Community College, A
South University, B
Southeastern Community College, A
Southwestern Community College, A
Stanly Community College, A
Strayer University - Greensboro Campus, B
Strayer University - Huntersville Campus, B
Strayer University - North Charlotte Campus, B
Strayer University - North Raleigh Campus, B
Strayer University - RTP Campus, B
Strayer University - South Charlotte Campus, B
Strayer University - South Raleigh Campus, B
Surry Community College, A
Tri-County Community College, A
University of Mount Olive, B
University of North Carolina at Asheville, B
The University of North Carolina at Chapel Hill, B
The University of North Carolina at Charlotte, B
The University of North Carolina at Greensboro, B
The University of North Carolina at Pembroke, B
The University of North Carolina Wilmington, B
University of Phoenix - Charlotte Campus, AB
Vance-Granville Community College, A
Wake Technical Community College, A
Wayne Community College, A
Western Carolina University, B
Western Piedmont Community College, A
Wilkes Community College, A
William Peace University, B
Wilson Community College, A
Wingate University, B
Winston-Salem State University, B

North Dakota

Cankdeska Cikana Community College, A
Dakota College at Bottineau, A
Dickinson State University, B
Lake Region State College, A

Mayville State University, B
Minot State University, B
North Dakota State College of Science, A
North Dakota State University, B
Nueta Hidatsa Sahnish College, A
Rasmussen College Fargo, B
Sitting Bull College, A
Trinity Bible College, AB
Turtle Mountain Community College, A
United Tribes Technical College, A
University of Jamestown, B
University of Mary, B
University of North Dakota, B
Valley City State University, B

Ohio

American National University (Kettering), A
American National University (Youngstown), A
Antioch University Midwest, B
Ashland University, B
Baldwin Wallace University, B
Belmont College, A
Bluffton University, B
Bowling Green State University, B
Bowling Green State University - Firelands College, AB
Brown Mackie College - Akron, B
Brown Mackie College - North Canton, B
Bryant & Stratton College - Cleveland Campus, B
Bryant & Stratton College - Eastlake Campus, AB
Bryant & Stratton College - Parma Campus, B
Capital University, B
Case Western Reserve University, B
Cedarville University, B
Central Ohio Technical College, A
Cincinnati State Technical and Community College, A
Clark State Community College, A
Cleveland State University, B
Columbus State Community College, A
Cuyahoga Community College, A
Davis College, A
Daymar College, A
Defiance College, AB
DeVry University (Columbus), B
DeVry University (Seven Hills), B
Eastern Gateway Community College, A
Edison Community College, A
Fortis College (Ravenna), A
Franciscan University of Steubenville, AB
Franklin University, AB
Gallipolis Career College, A
Harrison College, AB
Heidelberg University, B
Hiram College, B
Hocking College, A
John Carroll University, B
Kent State University, B
Kent State University at Ashtabula, B
Kent State University at Geauga, B
Kent State University at Salem, B
Kent State University at Stark, B
Kent State University at Trumbull, B
Kent State University at Tuscarawas, B
Lake Erie College, B
Lakeland Community College, A
Lorain County Community College, A
Lourdes University, B
Malone University, B
Marietta College, AB
Marion Technical College, A
Miami-Jacobs Career College (Dayton), A
Miami University, B
Miami University Hamilton, A
Miami University Middletown, A
Mount St. Joseph University, AB
Mount Vernon Nazarene University, B
Muskingum University, B
North Central State College, A
Northwest State Community College, A
Notre Dame College, AB
Ohio Business College (Sandusky), A
Ohio Business College (Sheffield Village), A
Ohio Christian University, AB
Ohio Dominican University, AB
Ohio Northern University, B

The Ohio State University, B
The Ohio State University at Lima, B
The Ohio State University - Mansfield Campus, B
The Ohio State University at Marion, B
The Ohio State University - Newark Campus, B
Ohio University, B
Ohio University - Chillicothe, A
Ohio University - Eastern, B
Ohio University - Lancaster, AB
Ohio Valley College of Technology, A
Ohio Wesleyan University, B
Otterbein University, B
Remington College - Cleveland Campus, A
Shawnee State University, AB
Sinclair Community College, A
South University, B
Southern State Community College, A
Stark State College, A
Stautzenberger College (Brecksville), A
Terra State Community College, A
Tiffin University, AB
Trumbull Business College, A
Union Institute & University, B
The University of Akron, AB
The Univwrst of Akron Wayne College, A
University of Cincinnati Blue Ash College, A
University of Cincinnati Clermont College, A
The University of Findlay, AB
University of Mount Union, B
University of Northwestern Ohio, AB
University of Rio Grande, AB
The University of Toledo, B
Urbana University, AB
Ursuline College, B
Walsh University, AB
Washington State Community College, A
Wilberforce University, B
Wilmington College, B
Wittenberg University, B
Wright State University, AB
Wright State University - Lake Campus, A
Xavier University, AB
Youngstown State University, AB
Zane State College, A

Oklahoma

Bacone College, AB
Cameron University, AB
Carl Albert State College, A
Connors State College, A
DeVry University, B
East Central University, B
Eastern Oklahoma State College, A
Langston University, B
Mid-America Christian University, B
Northeastern Oklahoma Agricultural and Mechanical College, A
Northeastern State University, B
Northern Oklahoma College, A
Northwestern Oklahoma State University, B
Oklahoma Christian University, B
Oklahoma City Community College, A
Oklahoma City University, B
Oklahoma Panhandle State University, AB
Oklahoma State University, B
Oklahoma State University, Oklahoma City, A
Oklahoma Wesleyan University, AB
Oral Roberts University, B
Redlands Community College, A
Rogers State University, AB
Rose State College, A
St. Gregory's University, AB
Seminole State College, A
Southeastern Oklahoma State University, B
Southern Nazarene University, B
Southwestern Christian University, B
Southwestern Oklahoma State University, AB
Southwestern Oklahoma State University at Sayre, A
Tulsa Community College, A
University of Central Oklahoma, B
University of Oklahoma, B
The University of Tulsa, B

Oregon

Central Oregon Community College, A
Chemeketa Community College, A
Clatsop Community College, A
Columbia Gorge Community College, A
Concordia University, AB
Corban University, AB
George Fox University, B
Klamath Community College, A
Linfield College, B
Linn-Benton Community College, A
Marylhurst University, B
Mt. Hood Community College, A
Northwest Christian University, B
Oregon Institute of Technology, B
Oregon State University, B
Oregon State University - Cascades, B
Pacific University, B
Pioneer Pacific College, AB
Pioneer Pacific College - Eugene/Springfield Branch, A
Portland Community College, A
Portland State University, B
Rogue Community College, A
Southern Oregon University, B
Southwestern Oregon Community College, A
Umpqua Community College, A
University of Portland, B
Warner Pacific College, B

Pennsylvania

Albright College, B
Alvernia University, B
Arcadia University, B
Bloomsburg University of Pennsylvania, B
Brightwood Career Institute, Harrisburg Campus, A
Brightwood Career Institute, Pittsburgh Campus, A
Bucknell University, B
Bucks County Community College, A
Butler County Community College, A
Cabrini University, B
Cairn University, B
California University of Pennsylvania, AB
Cambria-Rowe Business College (Indiana), A
Cambria-Rowe Business College (Johnstown), A
Carlow University, B
Carnegie Mellon University, B
Cedar Crest College, B
Central Penn College, AB
Chatham University, B
Chestnut Hill College, B
Cheyney University of Pennsylvania, B
Clarion University of Pennsylvania, AB
Community College of Allegheny County, A
Community College of Beaver County, A
Community College of Philadelphia, A
Consolidated School of Business (Lancaster), A
Consolidated School of Business (York), A
Delaware County Community College, A
Delaware Valley University, A
DeVry University (Fort Washington), B
DeVry University (King of Prussia), B
DeVry University (Philadelphia), B
Douglas Education Center, A
DuBois Business College (DuBois), A
East Stroudsburg University of Pennsylvania, B
Edinboro University of Pennsylvania, AB
Elizabethtown College, B
Elizabethtown College School of Continuing and Professional Studies, AB
Franklin & Marshall College, B
Gannon University, B
Geneva College, AB
Gettysburg College, B
Grove City College, B
Gwynedd Mercy University, B
Harcum College, A
Harrisburg Area Community College, A
Holy Family University, B
Immaculata University, AB
Indiana University of Pennsylvania, B
Keystone College, AB
King's College, B
Kutztown University of Pennsylvania, B
La Salle University, B
Lackawanna College, A

Laurel Business Institute, A
Laurel Technical Institute, A
Lebanon Valley College, B
Lehigh Carbon Community College, A
Lincoln University, B
Lock Haven University of Pennsylvania, AB
Luzerne County Community College, A
Lycoming College, B
Manor College, A
Mansfield University of Pennsylvania, B
Marywood University, B
McCann School of Business & Technology
 (Pottsville), A
Mercyhurst University, B
Messiah College, B
Millersville University of Pennsylvania, B
Misericordia University, B
Montgomery County Community College, A
Moravian College, B
Mount Aloysius College, AB
Muhlenberg College, AB
Neumann University, B
Northampton Community College, A
Peirce College, AB
Penn Commercial Business and Technical School, A
Penn State Beaver, B
Penn State Brandywine, B
Penn State DuBois, B
Penn State Erie, The Behrend College, B
Penn State Fayette, The Eberly Campus, B
Penn State Greater Allegheny, B
Penn State Harrisburg, B
Penn State Hazleton, B
Penn State Mont Alto, B
Penn State New Kensington, B
Penn State Shenango, B
Penn State Wilkes-Barre, B
Penn State Worthington Scranton, B
Penn State York, B
Pennsylvania College of Technology, AB
Pennsylvania Institute of Technology, A
Philadelphia University, B
Pittsburgh Technical Institute, A
Point Park University, AB
Reading Area Community College, A
Robert Morris University, B
Rosemont College, B
Saint Francis University, AB
Saint Joseph's University, AB
Saint Vincent College, B
Seton Hill University, B
Shippensburg University of Pennsylvania, B
Slippery Rock University of Pennsylvania, B
South Hills School of Business & Technology (State
 College), A
Strayer University - Allentown Campus, B
Strayer University - Center City Campus, B
Strayer University - Delaware County Campus, B
Strayer University - King of Prussia Campus, B
Strayer University - Lower Bucks County Campus,
 B
Strayer University - Warrendale Campus, B
Summit University, B
Susquehanna University, B
Thiel College, B
University of Pennsylvania, AB
University of Phoenix - Philadelphia Campus, B
University of Pittsburgh at Bradford, B
University of Pittsburgh at Greensburg, B
University of Pittsburgh at Johnstown, B
The University of Scranton, AB
University of Valley Forge, B
Ursinus College, B
Valley Forge Military College, A
Villanova University, B
Waynesburg University, B
West Chester University of Pennsylvania, B
Westminster College, B
Westmoreland County Community College, A
Widener University, B
Wilkes University, B
Wilson College, AB
York College of Pennsylvania, AB
YTI Career Institute - Altoona, A
YTI Career Institute - York, A

Rhode Island

Bryant University, B
Community College of Rhode Island, A
Johnson & Wales University, B
New England Institute of Technology, AB
Providence College, AB
Rhode Island College, B
Roger Williams University, B
Salve Regina University, B
University of Rhode Island, B

South Carolina

Aiken Technical College, A
Allen University, B
Anderson University, B
Benedict College, B
Bob Jones University, B
Central Carolina Technical College, A
Charleston Southern University, B
The Citadel, The Military College of South Carolina,
 B
Claflin University, B
Clemson University, B
Coastal Carolina University, B
Coker College, B
College of Charleston, B
Columbia College, B
Converse College, B
Erskine College, B
Florence-Darlington Technical College, A
Forrest College, A
Francis Marion University, B
Furman University, B
Greenville Technical College, A
Horry-Georgetown Technical College, A
Lander University, B
Limestone College, B
Midlands Technical College, A
Morris College, B
Newberry College, B
North Greenville University, B
Northeastern Technical College, A
Piedmont Technical College, A
Presbyterian College, B
South Carolina State University, B
South University, B
Southern Wesleyan University, B
Spartanburg Community College, A
Strayer University - Charleston Campus, B
Strayer University - Columbia Campus, B
Strayer University - Greenville Campus, B
Tri-County Technical College, A
Trident Technical College, A
University of South Carolina, B
University of South Carolina Aiken, B
University of South Carolina Beaufort, B
University of South Carolina Lancaster, A
University of South Carolina Upstate, B
Virginia College in Spartanburg, A
Voorhees College, B
Winthrop University, B
York Technical College, A

South Dakota

Augustana University, B
Black Hills State University, B
Dakota State University, AB
Dakota Wesleyan University, AB
Globe University - Sioux Falls, AB
Mount Marty College, AB
National American University (Sioux Falls), AB
Oglala Lakota College, AB
Sinte Gleska University, AB
Sisseton-Wahpeton College, A
Southeast Technical Institute, A
University of Sioux Falls, A
Western Dakota Technical Institute, A

Tennessee

Aquinas College, B
Argosy University, Nashville, AB
Austin Peay State University, A
Belhaven University, B
Belmont University, B
Bethel University, B

Bryan College, AB
Carson-Newman University, B
Chattanooga State Community College, A
Christian Brothers University, B
Cleveland State Community College, A
Daymar College (Clarksville), AB
Daymar College (Murfreesboro), B
Daymar College (Nashville), A
DeVry University, B
Dyersburg State Community College, A
East Tennessee State University, B
Fisk University, B
Freed-Hardeman University, B
Hiwassee College, A
Jackson State Community College, A
King University, B
Lane College, B
Lee University, B
LeMoyne-Owen College, B
Lincoln Memorial University, B
Lipscomb University, B
Martin Methodist College, B
Maryville College, B
Middle Tennessee State University, B
Miller-Motte Technical College (Chattanooga), A
Milligan College, B
Motlow State Community College, A
Nashville State Community College, A
National College (Bristol), AB
National College (Knoxville), A
National College (Nashville), A
Northeast State Community College, A
Pellissippi State Community College, A
Remington College - Memphis Campus, A
Rhodes College, B
Roane State Community College, A
South College, B
Southern Adventist University, AB
Southwest Tennessee Community College, A
Strayer University - Knoxville Campus, B
Strayer University - Nashville Campus, B
Strayer University - Shelby Campus, B
Strayer University - Thousand Oaks Campus, B
Tennessee State University, B
Tennessee Technological University, B
Tennessee Wesleyan College, B
Trevecca Nazarene University, AB
Union University, B
University of Memphis, B
The University of Tennessee, B
The University of Tennessee at Chattanooga, B
The University of Tennessee at Martin, B
Virginia College in Chattanooga, A
Volunteer State Community College, A
Walters State Community College, A
Welch College, AB

Texas

Abilene Christian University, B
Alvin Community College, A
Amarillo College, A
Amberton University, B
American InterContinental University Houston, AB
Angelina College, A
Angelo State University, B
Argosy University, Dallas, AB
Austin College, B
Austin Community College District, A
Baptist University of the Americas, B
Baylor University, B
Blinn College, A
Brazosport College, B
Brookhaven College, A
Cedar Valley College, A
Central Texas College, A
Cisco College, A
Clarendon College, A
Coastal Bend College, A
Collin County Community College District, A
Concordia University Texas, B
Dallas Baptist University, AB
Dallas Christian College, AB
Del Mar College, A
DeVry University (Austin), B
DeVry University (Irving), B
DeVry University (San Antonio), B

Eastfield College, A
El Centro College, A
El Paso Community College, A
Everest College (Arlington), A
Frank Phillips College, A
Galveston College, A
Grayson College, A
Hallmark University, AB
Hardin-Simmons University, B
Hill College, A
Houston Baptist University, B
Houston Community College, A
Howard College, A
Howard Payne University, B
Huston-Tillotson University, B
Jarvis Christian College, AB
Kilgore College, A
Lamar State College - Orange, A
Lamar State College - Port Arthur, A
Lee College, A
LeTourneau University, B
Lone Star College - CyFair, A
Lone Star College - Kingwood, A
Lone Star College - Montgomery, A
Lone Star College - North Harris, A
Lone Star College - Tomball, A
Lone Star College - University Park, A
Lubbock Christian University, B
McLennan Community College, A
McMurry University, B
Messenger College, B
Midland College, B
Mountain View College, A
Navarro College, A
North American University, B
North Central Texas College, A
North Lake College, A
Northeast Texas Community College, A
Northwood University, Texas Campus, B
Odessa College, A
Our Lady of the Lake University of San Antonio, B
Palo Alto College, A
Panola College, A
Paris Junior College, A
Paul Quinn College, B
Prairie View A&M University, B
Remington College - Dallas Campus, A
Remington College - Fort Worth Campus, A
Remington College - Houston Southeast Campus, A
Remington College - North Houston Campus, A
Rice University, B
Richland College, A
St. Edward's University, B
St. Mary's University, B
St. Philip's College, A
Sam Houston State University, B
San Antonio College, A
San Jacinto College District, A
Schreiner University, B
South Plains College, A
South Texas College, A
South University, B
Southern Methodist University, B
Southwest Texas Junior College, A
Southwestern Assemblies of God University, AB
Stephen F. Austin State University, B
Strayer University - Cedar Hill Campus, B
Strayer University - Irving Campus, B
Strayer University - Katy Campus, B
Strayer University - North Austin Campus, B
Strayer University - Northwest Houston Campus, B
Strayer University - Plano Campus, B
Sul Ross State University, B
Tarleton State University, B
Tarrant County College District, A
Temple College, A
Texarkana College, A
Texas A&M International University, B
Texas A&M University, B
Texas A&M University - Central Texas, B
Texas A&M University - Commerce, B
Texas A&M University - Corpus Christi, B
Texas A&M University - Kingsville, B
Texas A&M University - San Antonio, B
Texas A&M University - Texarkana, B
Texas College, B

Texas Lutheran University, B
Texas Southern University, B
Texas State University, B
Texas Tech University, B
Texas Wesleyan University, B
Texas Woman's University, B
Trinity University, B
Trinity Valley Community College, A
Tyler Junior College, A
University of Dallas, B
University of Houston, B
University of Houston - Clear Lake, B
University of Houston - Downtown, B
University of Houston - Victoria, B
University of the Incarnate Word, AB
University of Mary Hardin-Baylor, B
University of Phoenix - Dallas Campus, B
University of Phoenix - Houston Campus, B
University of Phoenix - San Antonio Campus, B
University of St. Thomas, B
The University of Texas at Arlington, B
The University of Texas at Austin, B
The University of Texas at El Paso, B
The University of Texas of the Permian Basin, B
The University of Texas at San Antonio, B
The University of Texas at Tyler, B
Vernon College, A
Victoria College, A
Virginia College in Austin, A
Vista College, A
Wayland Baptist University, AB
Weatherford College, A
West Texas A&M University, B
Western Texas College, A
Wharton County Junior College, A
Wiley College, B

Utah

Argosy University, Salt Lake City, AB
Broadview University - Layton, AB
Broadview University - West Jordan, AB
Dixie State University, AB
LDS Business College, A
Salt Lake Community College, A
Snow College, A
Southern Utah University, B
Stevens-Henager College (Logan), A
Stevens-Henager College (Orem), A
Stevens-Henager College (Salt Lake City), A
Stevens-Henager College (West Haven), B
University of Phoenix - Utah Campus, B
University of Utah, B
Utah State University, B
Utah Valley University, AB
Weber State University, B

Vermont

Castleton University, AB
Champlain College, B
College of St. Joseph, AB
Community College of Vermont, A
Green Mountain College, B
Johnson State College, AB
Landmark College, A
Norwich University, B
Saint Michael's College, B
Southern Vermont College, B
University of Vermont, B
Vermont Technical College, AB

Virginia

American National University (Danville), AB
American National University (Harrisonburg), AB
American National University (Lynchburg), AB
American National University (Martinsville), A
American National University (Salem), AB
Argosy University, Washington DC, AB
Averett University, B
Bluefield College, B
Bridgewater College, B
Bryant & Stratton College - Richmond Campus, B
Bryant & Stratton College - Virginia Beach Campus, B
Central Virginia Community College, A
Centura College (Chesapeake), A
Centura College (Newport News), A

Centura College (Virginia Beach), AB
Christopher Newport University, B
The College of William and Mary, B
Dabney S. Lancaster Community College, A
DeVry University (Arlington), B
DeVry University (Chesapeake), B
DeVry University (Manassas), B
Eastern Mennonite University, B
Eastern Shore Community College, A
ECPI University (Virginia Beach), B
Emory & Henry College, B
Ferrum College, B
George Mason University, B
Germanna Community College, A
Hampton University, AB
J. Sargeant Reynolds Community College, A
James Madison University, B
John Tyler Community College, A
Liberty University, B
Longwood University, B
Lynchburg College, B
Mary Baldwin College, B
Marymount University, B
New River Community College, A
Northern Virginia Community College, A
Old Dominion University, B
Patrick Henry Community College, A
Paul D. Camp Community College, A
Radford University, B
Rappahannock Community College, A
Regent University, AB
Roanoke College, B
Shenandoah University, B
South University (Glen Allen), B
South University (Virginia Beach), B
Southern Virginia University, B
Southside Virginia Community College, A
Stratford University (Falls Church), B
Stratford University (Glen Allen), B
Stratford University (Newport News), B
Stratford University (Virginia Beach), B
Stratford University (Woodbridge), B
Strayer University - Alexandria Campus, B
Strayer University - Arlington Campus, B
Strayer University - Chesapeake Campus, B
Strayer University - Chesterfield Campus, B
Strayer University - Fredericksburg Campus, B
Strayer University - Henrico Campus, B
Strayer University - Loudoun Campus, B
Strayer University - Manassas Campus, B
Strayer University - Newport News Campus, B
Strayer University - Virginia Beach Campus, B
Strayer University - Woodbridge Campus, B
Thomas Nelson Community College, A
Tidewater Community College, A
University of Management and Technology, AB
University of Mary Washington, B
University of Richmond, B
University of Valley Forge Virginia Campus, B
The University of Virginia's College at Wise, B
Virginia College in Richmond, A
Virginia Highlands Community College, A
Virginia International University, B
Virginia Polytechnic Institute and State University, B
Virginia State University, B
Virginia Union University, B
Virginia University of Lynchburg, B
Virginia Wesleyan College, B
Virginia Western Community College, A
Washington and Lee University, B
Wytheville Community College, A

Washington

Argosy University, Seattle, AB
Bellevue College, A
Central Washington University, B
City University of Seattle, B
Clark College, A
Eastern Washington University, B
Edmonds Community College, A
Everett Community College, A
Gonzaga University, B
Grays Harbor College, A
Heritage University, AB
Highline College, A
Lower Columbia College, A

Northwest University, B
Olympic College, A
Pacific Lutheran University, B
Peninsula College, A
Pierce College at Fort Steilacoom, A
Pierce College at Puyallup, A
Saint Martin's University, B
Seattle Pacific University, B
Seattle University, B
Shoreline Community College, A
Skagit Valley College, A
South Puget Sound Community College, A
South Seattle College, A
Spokane Community College, A
Spokane Falls Community College, A
Tacoma Community College, A
University of Phoenix - Western Washington Campus, B
University of Puget Sound, B
University of Washington, B
University of Washington, Bothell, B
University of Washington, Tacoma, B
Walla Walla Community College, A
Walla Walla University, AB
Washington State University, B
Washington State University - Tri-Cities, B
Washington State University - Vancouver, B
Wenatchee Valley College, A
Western Washington University, B
Whatcom Community College, A
Whitworth University, B
Yakima Valley Community College, A

West Virginia

Alderson Broaddus University, B
American Public University System, B
Bethany College, B
Blue Ridge Community and Technical College, A
Bluefield State College, B
Concord University, B
Davis & Elkins College, AB
Eastern West Virginia Community and Technical College, A
Fairmont State University, B
Glenville State College, B
Huntington Junior College, A
Marshall University, B
Ohio Valley University, B
Potomac State College of West Virginia University, AB
Salem International University, AB
Shepherd University, B
Southern West Virginia Community and Technical College, A
Strayer University - Teays Valley Campus, B
University of Charleston, B
Valley College, A
West Liberty University, B
West Virginia Business College (Wheeling), A
West Virginia Junior College - Morgantown, A
West Virginia State University, B
West Virginia University, B
West Virginia University Institute of Technology, B
West Virginia University at Parkersburg, AB
West Virginia Wesleyan College, B
Wheeling Jesuit University, B

Wisconsin

Alverno College, B
Blackhawk Technical College, A
Bryant & Stratton College - Wauwatosa Campus, AB
Cardinal Stritch University, B
Carroll University, B
Carthage College, B
Chippewa Valley Technical College, A
College of Menominee Nation, A
Concordia University Wisconsin, B
Edgewood College, B
Fox Valley Technical College, A
Gateway Technical College, A
Globe University - Appleton, AB
Globe University - Eau Claire, AB
Globe University - Green Bay, AB
Globe University - La Crosse, AB
Globe University - Madison East, AB

Globe University - Madison West, AB
Globe University - Wausau, AB
Lac Courte Oreilles Ojibwa Community College, A
Lakeland College, B
Madison Area Technical College, A
Maranatha Baptist University, B
Marian University, B
Marquette University, B
Mid-State Technical College, A
Milwaukee Area Technical College, A
Milwaukee School of Engineering, B
Moraine Park Technical College, A
Mount Mary University, B
Nicolet Area Technical College, A
Northcentral Technical College, A
Northeast Wisconsin Technical College, A
Northland College, B
Rasmussen College Appleton, A
Rasmussen College Green Bay, A
Rasmussen College Wausau, A
Ripon College, B
St. Norbert College, B
Silver Lake College of the Holy Family, B
University of Wisconsin - Eau Claire, B
University of Wisconsin - Green Bay, B
University of Wisconsin - La Crosse, B
University of Wisconsin - Madison, B
University of Wisconsin - Oshkosh, B
University of Wisconsin - Parkside, B
University of Wisconsin - Platteville, B
University of Wisconsin - River Falls, B
University of Wisconsin - Stevens Point, B
University of Wisconsin - Stout, B
University of Wisconsin - Superior, B
University of Wisconsin - Whitewater, B
Viterbo University, B
Waukesha County Technical College, A
Western Technical College, A
Wisconsin Indianhead Technical College, A
Wisconsin Lutheran College, B

Wyoming

Casper College, A
Central Wyoming College, A
Eastern Wyoming College, A
Laramie County Community College, A
Northwest College, A
University of Wyoming, B
Western Wyoming Community College, A

U.S. Territories: American Samoa

American Samoa Community College, A

U.S. Territories: Guam

University of Guam, B

U.S. Territories: Northern Mariana Islands

Northern Marianas College, A

U.S. Territories: Puerto Rico

American University of Puerto Rico (Bayamon), AB
Atlantic University College, B
Bayamón Central University, B
Caribbean University, AB
Columbia Centro Universitario (Yauco), AB
EDP University of Puerto Rico, AB
EDP University of Puerto Rico - San Sebastian, AB
Huertas Junior College, A
Inter American University of Puerto Rico, Aguadilla Campus, A
Inter American University of Puerto Rico, Arecibo Campus, AB
Inter American University of Puerto Rico, Barranquitas Campus, AB
Inter American University of Puerto Rico, Bayamón Campus, A
Inter American University of Puerto Rico, Fajardo Campus, AB
Inter American University of Puerto Rico, Guayama Campus, AB
Inter American University of Puerto Rico, Ponce Campus, AB
Inter American University of Puerto Rico, San Germán Campus, AB

Polytechnic University of Puerto Rico, B
Pontifical Catholic University of Puerto Rico, AB
Universidad Adventista de las Antillas, AB
Universidad del Este, B
Universidad Metropolitana, B
Universidad del Turabo, AB
University of Puerto Rico in Arecibo, B
University of Puerto Rico in Carolina, B
University of Puerto Rico in Humacao, B
University of Puerto Rico, Mayagüez Campus, B
University of Puerto Rico in Utuado, A
University of the Sacred Heart, B

U.S. Territories: United States Virgin Islands

University of the Virgin Islands, AB

Canada

Alberta

Ambrose University, B
Athabasca University, B
Concordia University of Edmonton, B
The King's University, B
Mount Royal University, B
Southern Alberta Institute of Technology, A
University of Calgary, B
University of Lethbridge, B

British Columbia

British Columbia Institute of Technology, AB
Okanagan College, B
Simon Fraser University, B
Thompson Rivers University, B
Trinity Western University, B
The University of British Columbia, B
The University of British Columbia - Okanagan Campus, B
University of the Fraser Valley, AB
University of Northern British Columbia, B

Manitoba

Brandon University, B
Providence University College & Theological Seminary, B
Université de Saint-Boniface, B
University of Manitoba, B
The University of Winnipeg, B

Maritime Provinces: New Brunswick

Crandall University, B
Mount Allison University, B
Université de Moncton, B
University of New Brunswick Fredericton, B
University of New Brunswick Saint John, B

Maritime Provinces: Nova Scotia

Acadia University, B
Dalhousie University, B
Mount Saint Vincent University, B
St. Francis Xavier University, B
Saint Mary's University, B
Université Sainte-Anne, B

Maritime Provinces: Prince Edward Island

University of Prince Edward Island, B

Newfoundland and Labrador

Memorial University of Newfoundland, B

Ontario

Brock University, B
Carleton University, B
Lakehead University, B
Laurentian University, B
McMaster University, B
Nipissing University, B
Redeemer University College, B
Royal Military College of Canada, B
Ryerson University, B
Trent University, B
University of Toronto, B
University of Waterloo, B

The University of Western Ontario, B
University of Windsor, B
Wilfrid Laurier University, B
York University, B

Quebec

Bishop's University, B
Concordia University, B
HEC Montreal, B
Télé-université, B
Université Laval, B
Université du Québec en Abitibi-Témiscamingue, B
Université du Québec à Chicoutimi, B
Université du Québec à Montréal, B
Université du Québec en Outaouais, B
Université du Québec à Rimouski, B
Université du Québec à Trois-Rivières, B
Université de Sherbrooke, B

Saskatchewan

Briercrest College, B
University of Regina, B
University of Saskatchewan, B

BUSINESS ADMINISTRATION, MANAGEMENT AND OPERATIONS

United States

Alabama

Alabama Agricultural and Mechanical University, MD
Alabama State University, M
Auburn University, M
Auburn University at Montgomery, M
Columbia Southern University, MD
Faulkner University, M
Huntingdon College, B
Jacksonville State University, M
Samford University, M
South University, M
Spring Hill College, M
Troy University, M
The University of Alabama, M
The University of Alabama at Birmingham, BM
University of Mobile, M
University of Montevallo, M
University of North Alabama, M
University of South Alabama, MD
The University of West Alabama, M
Virginia College in Birmingham, M

Alaska

Alaska Pacific University, M
University of Alaska Anchorage, M
University of Alaska Fairbanks, M
University of Alaska Southeast, M

Arizona

Argosy University, Phoenix, MD
Arizona State University at the Tempe campus, MD
Chandler-Gilbert Community College, A
DeVry University (Mesa), BMO
DeVry University (Phoenix), BM
Embry-Riddle Aeronautical University - Prescott, B
GateWay Community College, A
Grand Canyon University, MD
Northcentral University, MDO
Northern Arizona University, M
Prescott College, B
South Mountain Community College, A
The University of Arizona, MD
University of Phoenix - Online Campus, MDO
University of Phoenix - Phoenix Campus, MO
University of Phoenix - Southern Arizona Campus, M
Western International University, M

Arkansas

Arkansas State University, M
Arkansas Tech University, M
Harding University, M
Henderson State University, M

John Brown University, BM
Southern Arkansas University - Magnolia, M
University of Arkansas, MD
University of Arkansas at Little Rock, MO
University of Central Arkansas, M

California

American Jewish University, M
Antioch University Santa Barbara, M
Argosy University, Inland Empire, MD
Argosy University, Los Angeles, MD
Argosy University, Orange County, MDO
Argosy University, San Diego, MD
Argosy University, San Francisco Bay Area, MD
Azusa Pacific University, M
Berkeley City College, A
Biola University, M
Brandman University, M
Bristol University, M
California Baptist University, M
California Coast University, M
California Intercontinental University, MD
California Lutheran University, MO
California Miramar University, M
California National University for Advanced Studies, M
California Polytechnic State University, San Luis Obispo, M
California State Polytechnic University, Pomona, M
California State University, Bakersfield, M
California State University Channel Islands, M
California State University, Chico, M
California State University, Dominguez Hills, M
California State University, East Bay, M
California State University, Fresno, M
California State University, Fullerton, M
California State University, Long Beach, M
California State University, Monterey Bay, M
California State University, Northridge, MO
California State University, Sacramento, M
California State University, San Bernardino, BM
California State University, San Marcos, M
California State University, Stanislaus, M
California University of Management and Sciences, MD
Chapman University, M
Concordia University Irvine, M
DeVry University (Alhambra), BM
DeVry University (Anaheim), BM
DeVry University (Bakersfield), B
DeVry University (Fremont), BM
DeVry University (Long Beach), BM
DeVry University (Oakland), BM
DeVry University (Oxnard), BMO
DeVry University (Palmdale), BMO
DeVry University (Pomona), M
DeVry University (San Diego), BMO
DeVry University (Sherman Oaks), B
Dominican University of California, BM
Fresno Pacific University, M
Golden Gate University, MDO
Golf Academy of America, A
Holy Names University, M
Humboldt State University, M
John F. Kennedy University, MO
La Sierra University, MO
Lincoln University, MD
Loyola Marymount University, M
Marymount California University, M
Mills College, M
Mount Saint Mary's University, M
National University, MO
New Charter University, M
Northwestern Polytechnic University, M
Notre Dame de Namur University, M
Pacific States University, MD
Pepperdine University, M
Point Loma Nazarene University, M
Saint Mary's College of California, M
San Diego State University, M
San Francisco State University, M
San Jose State University, BM
Santa Clara University, M
Santiago Canyon College, A
Silicon Valley University, M
Sonoma State University, M

Stanford University, MD
Trident University International, MD
University of Antelope Valley, M
University of California, Berkeley, MDO
University of California, Davis, M
University of California, Irvine, MD
University of California, Los Angeles, MD
University of California, Riverside, MD
University of California, San Diego, MD
University of La Verne, M
University of the Pacific, M
University of Phoenix - Bay Area Campus, MD
University of Phoenix - Central Valley Campus, M
University of Phoenix - Sacramento Valley Campus, M
University of Phoenix - San Diego Campus, M
University of Redlands, M
University of San Diego, M
University of San Francisco, M
University of Southern California, MD
University of the West, M
Woodbury University, BM

Colorado

Adams State University, B
American Sentinel University, M
Argosy University, Denver, MD
Aspen University, MO
Colorado Christian University, BM
Colorado Mesa University, BM
Colorado State University, M
Colorado State University - Global Campus, M
Colorado State University - Pueblo, M
Colorado Technical University Colorado Springs, MD
Colorado Technical University Denver South, M
DeVry University (Colorado Springs), BMO
DeVry University (Westminster), B
Red Rocks Community College, A
Regis University, M
University of Colorado Boulder, M
University of Colorado Colorado Springs, M
University of Colorado Denver, M
University of Denver, M
University of Phoenix - Colorado Campus, M
University of Phoenix - Colorado Springs Downtown Campus, M

Connecticut

Albertus Magnus College, M
Fairfield University, MO
Lincoln College of New England, B
Post University, M
Quinnipiac University, M
Sacred Heart University, MDO
Southern Connecticut State University, M
University of Bridgeport, M
University of Connecticut, MD
University of Hartford, M
University of New Haven, MO
Western Connecticut State University, M
Yale University, MD

Delaware

Delaware State University, BM
Goldey-Beacom College, M
University of Delaware, M
Wesley College, M
Wilmington University, MD

District of Columbia

The Catholic University of America, M
The George Washington University, MDO
Georgetown University, M
Howard University, M
Trinity Washington University, M
University of the District of Columbia, BM
University of Phoenix - Washington D.C. Campus, MD
University of the Potomac, M

Florida

Argosy University, Sarasota, MDO
Argosy University, Tampa, MD
Barry University, M
Carlos Albizu University, Miami Campus, BMD

College of Central Florida, AB
DeVry University (Jacksonville), BM
DeVry University (Miramar), BM
DeVry University (Orlando), BM
Embry-Riddle Aeronautical University - Daytona,
  BMD
Embry-Riddle Aeronautical University - Worldwide,
  ABM
Everest University (Largo), ABM
Everest University (Orlando), M
Everest University (Tampa), M
Everglades University (Boca Raton), M
Florida Agricultural and Mechanical University, M
Florida Atlantic University, M
Florida Gulf Coast University, M
Florida Institute of Technology, BMD
Florida International University, MD
Florida Memorial University, M
Florida National University, M
Florida Southern College, M
Florida SouthWestern State College, B
Florida State College at Jacksonville, B
Florida State University, MD
Fortis College (Orange Park), A
Full Sail University, M
Gulf Coast State College, B
Hodges University, BM
Jacksonville University, BM
Keiser University, MD
Lynn University, M
Marconi International University, MD
Miami Dade College, B
Millennia Atlantic University, M
Palm Beach Atlantic University, M
Pensacola State College, AB
Polk State College, B
Polytechnic University of Puerto Rico, Miami Campus, M
Polytechnic University of Puerto Rico, Orlando
  Campus, M
Rollins College, MD
Saint Leo University, BM
St. Petersburg College, B
St. Thomas University, BMO
Santa Fe College, B
Schiller International University, M
South Florida State College, B
South University (Royal Palm Beach), M
South University (Tampa), M
Southeastern University, M
Stetson University, M
University of Central Florida, MD
University of Florida, MD
University of Miami, BM
University of North Florida, M
University of Phoenix - North Florida Campus, M
University of Phoenix - South Florida Campus, M
University of South Florida, M
University of South Florida, St. Petersburg, M
University of South Florida Sarasota-Manatee, M
The University of Tampa, M
University of West Florida, M
Warner University, M
Webber International University, M

Georgia

Albany State University, BM
Argosy University, Atlanta, MD
Ashworth College, M
Augusta University, M
Berry College, M
Brenau University, BM
Clark Atlanta University, M
Clayton State University, BM
Columbus State University, MO
DeVry University (Alpharetta), BM
DeVry University (Decatur), BM
DeVry University (Duluth), BMO
Emory University, MD
Georgia Christian University, M
Georgia College & State University, M
Georgia Institute of Technology, M
Georgia Southern University, M
Georgia Southwestern State University, M
Georgia State University, MD
Kennesaw State University, MD

Mercer University, BM
Middle Georgia State University, B
Piedmont College, M
Reinhardt University, M
Savannah State University, M
Shorter University, M
South University, M
Thomas University, M
University of Georgia, MD
University of North Georgia, BM
University of Phoenix - Atlanta Campus, M
University of Phoenix - Augusta Campus, M
University of Phoenix - Columbus Georgia Campus,
  M
University of West Georgia, M
Valdosta State University, M
Wesleyan College, M

Hawaii

Argosy University, Hawai'i, MDO
Chaminade University of Honolulu, M
Hawai'i Pacific University, M
University of Hawaii at Manoa, M
University of Phoenix - Hawaii Campus, M

Idaho

Boise State University, M
Idaho State University, MO
Northwest Nazarene University, M
University of Idaho, MD

Illinois

American InterContinental University Online, M
Argosy University, Chicago, MD
Argosy University, Schaumburg, MDO
Aurora University, M
Benedictine University, BM
Blackburn College, B
Bradley University, M
Concordia University Chicago, M
DePaul University, BM
DeVry University (Addison), B
DeVry University (Chicago), BM
DeVry University (Downers Grove), B
DeVry University (Elgin), BMO
DeVry University (Gurnee), BMO
DeVry University (Naperville), BMO
DeVry University (Tinley Park), BM
DeVry University Online, BM
Dominican University, M
Eastern Illinois University, M
Ellis University, M
Elmhurst College, M
Governors State University, M
Illinois Institute of Technology, M
Illinois State University, M
Judson University, BM
Lewis University, M
Lincoln Christian University, B
Loyola University Chicago, M
McKendree University, M
Millikin University, BM
National Louis University, M
North Central College, M
North Park University, M
Northeastern Illinois University, M
Northern Illinois University, M
Northwestern University, MD
Olivet Nazarene University, BM
Quincy University, M
Robert Morris University Illinois, M
Rockford University, M
Roosevelt University, BM
St. Augustine College, A
Saint Xavier University, MO
Southern Illinois University Carbondale, MD
Southern Illinois University Edwardsville, M
University of Chicago, MDO
University of Illinois at Chicago, MD
University of Illinois at Springfield, BM
University of Illinois at Urbana - Champaign, MD
University of St. Francis, MO
Western Illinois University, MO

Indiana

Ancilla College, A
Anderson University, MD
Ball State University, MO
Bethel College, M
Butler University, M
Calumet College of Saint Joseph, B
DeVry University, BMO
Grace College, B
Holy Cross College, B
Indiana State University, M
Indiana Tech, M
Indiana University Bloomington, MD
Indiana University Kokomo, M
Indiana University Northwest, MO
Indiana University - Purdue University Fort Wayne,
  M
Indiana University - Purdue University Indianapolis,
  M
Indiana University South Bend, M
Indiana University Southeast, M
Indiana Wesleyan University, M
Oakland City University, M
Purdue University, M
Purdue University Northwest (Hammond), M
Taylor University, M
University of Indianapolis, MO
University of Notre Dame, M
University of Saint Francis, M
University of Southern Indiana, M
Valparaiso University, MO

Iowa

Clarke University, M
Drake University, M
Grand View University, M
Kaplan University, Davenport Campus, M
Maharishi University of Management, MD
Mount Mercy University, M
St. Ambrose University, MD
University of Dubuque, M
The University of Iowa, MD
University of Northern Iowa, M
Upper Iowa University, M

Kansas

Baker University, M
Benedictine College, M
Emporia State University, M
Fort Hays State University, M
Grantham University, M
Kansas State University, MO
Kansas Wesleyan University, BM
MidAmerica Nazarene University, M
National American University, A
Newman University, M
Ottawa University, M
Pittsburg State University, M
Southwestern College, M
Tabor College, M
The University of Kansas, MD
University of Saint Mary, M
Washburn University, M
Wichita State University, M

Kentucky

Bellarmine University, M
Brescia University, M
Campbellsville University, M
Daymar College (Bowling Green), A
Eastern Kentucky University, M
Kentucky State University, M
Midway University, M
Morehead State University, M
Murray State University, M
Northern Kentucky University, MO
Sullivan University, MD
Thomas More College, M
University of the Cumberlands, M
University of Kentucky, MD
University of Louisville, BM
University of Pikeville, M
Western Kentucky University, M

Louisiana

Centenary College of Louisiana, M
Louisiana State University and Agricultural & Mechanical College, MD
Louisiana State University in Shreveport, M
Louisiana Tech University, MD
Loyola University New Orleans, M
McNeese State University, M
Nicholls State University, M
Southeastern Louisiana University, M
Southern University and Agricultural and Mechanical College, M
Southwest University, M
Tulane University, MD
University of Louisiana at Lafayette, M
University of Louisiana at Monroe, M
University of New Orleans, M

Maine

Husson University, M
Saint Joseph's College of Maine, M
Thomas College, M
University of Maine, MO
University of Maine at Farmington, B
University of Southern Maine, BM

Maryland

Anne Arundel Community College, A
Bowie State University, M
Capitol Technology University, M
Frostburg State University, M
Hood College, M
Johns Hopkins University, M
Loyola University Maryland, M
Maryland Institute College of Art, M
Morgan State University, D
Mount St. Mary's University, M
Salisbury University, M
University of Baltimore, MO
University of Maryland, Baltimore County, B
University of Maryland, College Park, M
University of Maryland University College, BMO
Washington Adventist University, M

Massachusetts

American International College, M
Anna Maria College, BMO
Assumption College, MO
Babson College, BMO
Bay Path University, AB
Bentley University, MDO
Boston College, M
Boston University, M
Brandeis University, M
Bunker Hill Community College, A
Cambridge College, M
Cape Cod Community College, A
Clark University, M
Curry College, MO
Eastern Nazarene College, M
Elms College, M
Endicott College, M
Fitchburg State University, M
Framingham State University, M
Harvard University, MDO
Hult International Business School, M
Lasell College, MO
Massachusetts College of Liberal Arts, M
Massasoit Community College, A
Nichols College, M
Northeastern University, M
Salem State University, M
Simmons College, M
Springfield College, M
Suffolk University, MO
University of Massachusetts Boston, M
University of Massachusetts Dartmouth, MO
University of Massachusetts Lowell, MDO
Western New England University, M
Worcester Polytechnic Institute, MDO

Michigan

Central Michigan University, BMO
Cleary University, MO
Cornerstone University, BM

Davenport University, M
Eastern Michigan University, MO
Ferris State University, M
Grand Valley State University, M
Kettering University, B
Lawrence Technological University, MD
Madonna University, M
Michigan State University, MD
Michigan Technological University, M
Northern Michigan University, M
Northwood University, Michigan Campus, M
Oakland University, MO
Saginaw Valley State University, M
South University, M
University of Detroit Mercy, M
University of Michigan, MD
University of Michigan - Dearborn, BM
University of Michigan - Flint, MO
Walsh College of Accountancy and Business Administration, M
Wayne State University, MDO
Western Michigan University, M

Minnesota

Argosy University, Twin Cities, MD
Augsburg College, BM
Bethel University, M
Capella University, BMD
Concordia University, St. Paul, M
Crossroads College, B
Crown College, B
Globe University - Woodbury, M
Hamline University, M
Leech Lake Tribal College, A
Metropolitan State University, MDO
Minnesota State University Mankato, M
St. Catherine University, M
St. Cloud State University, M
Saint Mary's University of Minnesota, MD
Southwest Minnesota State University, M
University of Minnesota, Duluth, M
University of Minnesota, Twin Cities Campus, MD
University of Northwestern - St. Paul, M
University of St. Thomas, BM
Walden University, MO

Mississippi

Alcorn State University, M
Belhaven University, M
Delta State University, M
Jackson State University, MD
Millsaps College, M
Mississippi College, MO
Mississippi State University, MD
University of Mississippi, MD
University of Southern Mississippi, M
William Carey University, M

Missouri

American Business & Technology University, M
Avila University, M
Bryan University (Springfield), M
Columbia College, M
DeVry University (Kansas City), BM
Drury University, M
Fontbonne University, M
Lincoln University, M
Lindenwood University, M
Maryville University of Saint Louis, MO
Missouri Baptist University, BM
Missouri College, B
Missouri Southern State University, M
Missouri State University, BM
Missouri Western State University, M
Northwest Missouri State University, M
Park University, M
Saint Louis University, M
Southeast Missouri State University, M
Southwest Baptist University, M
Stephens College, M
University of Central Missouri, M
University of Missouri, MD
University of Missouri - Kansas City, MD
University of Missouri - St. Louis, MDO
Washington University in St. Louis, BMD
Webster University, M

Montana

University of Montana, M

Nebraska

Bellevue University, MD
Chadron State College, M
Creighton University, M
Doane University, M
University of Nebraska at Kearney, M
University of Nebraska - Lincoln, MD
University of Nebraska at Omaha, MO
Wayne State College, M

Nevada

DeVry University, BM
University of Nevada, Las Vegas, M
University of Nevada, Reno, M
University of Phoenix - Las Vegas Campus, M

New Hampshire

Daniel Webster College, M
Dartmouth College, M
Franklin Pierce University, M
Plymouth State University, M
Rivier University, M
Southern New Hampshire University, MO
University of New Hampshire, M

New Jersey

Caldwell University, M
Centenary College, M
College of Saint Elizabeth, M
DeVry University (North Brunswick), BM
DeVry University (Paramus), BM
Fairleigh Dickinson University, College at Florham, MO
Fairleigh Dickinson University, Metropolitan Campus, MO
Felician University, M
Georgian Court University, M
Kean University, M
Monmouth University, MO
Montclair State University, M
New Jersey City University, M
New Jersey Institute of Technology, M
Pillar College, B
Ramapo College of New Jersey, M
Rider University, BM
Rowan University, MO
Rutgers University - Camden, M
Rutgers University - Newark, M
Saint Peter's University, M
Seton Hall University, MO
Stevens Institute of Technology, M
Stockton University, M
University of Phoenix - Jersey City Campus, M
William Paterson University of New Jersey, M

New Mexico

Eastern New Mexico University, M
National American University (Albuquerque), A
New Mexico Highlands University, M
New Mexico State University, MD
University of New Mexico, M
University of New Mexico - Taos, A
University of Phoenix - New Mexico Campus, M
University of the Southwest, M
Western New Mexico University, M

New York

Adelphi University, M
Alfred University, M
Baruch College of the City University of New York, MDO
Binghamton University, State University of New York, MD
Brooklyn College of the City University of New York, M
Bryant & Stratton College - Amherst Campus, B
Bryant & Stratton College - Buffalo Campus, A
Bryant & Stratton College - Greece Campus, A
Bryant & Stratton College - Henrietta Campus, A
Bryant & Stratton College - Orchard Park Campus, A
Canisius College, M

Clarkson University, M
The College of Saint Rose, M
College of Staten Island of the City University of
New York, M
Columbia University, MD
Cornell University, MD
DeVry College of New York, BM
Dominican College, M
D'Youville College, M
Excelsior College, MO
Fordham University, M
Genesee Community College, A
Hofstra University, BM
Iona College, MO
Le Moyne College, BM
LIM College, M
Marist College, MO
Medaille College, M
Mercy College, M
Metropolitan College of New York, M
Molloy College, M
Monroe College, M
Morrisville State College, B
Mount Saint Mary College, M
New York Institute of Technology, M
New York University, O
Niagara University, M
Nyack College, M
Pace University, MDO
Plaza College, B
Rensselaer Polytechnic Institute, MD
Roberts Wesleyan College, M
Rochester Institute of Technology, M
St. Bonaventure University, M
St. John Fisher College, M
St. John's University, M
St. Joseph's College, Long Island Campus, M
St. Joseph's College, New York, M
St. Thomas Aquinas College, M
State University of New York College at Geneseo,
M
State University of New York College at Old
Westbury, M
State University of New York Empire State College,
M
State University of New York at New Paltz, BM
State University of New York Polytechnic Institute,
M
Stony Brook University, State University of New
York, MO
Syracuse University, MD
University at Albany, State University of New York,
M
University at Buffalo, the State University of New
York, MD
University of Rochester, MD
Wagner College, M

North Carolina

Appalachian State University, M
Campbell University, M
DeVry University, BM
Duke University, MDO
East Carolina University, M
Elon University, M
Fayetteville State University, M
Gardner-Webb University, M
High Point University, M
John Wesley University, M
Lenoir-Rhyne University, M
Meredith College, M
Methodist University, M
Montreat College, M
North Carolina Agricultural and Technical State Uni-
versity, M
North Carolina Central University, M
North Carolina State University, M
Pfeiffer University, M
Queens University of Charlotte, M
Rowan-Cabarrus Community College, A
South University, M
The University of North Carolina at Chapel Hill, MD
The University of North Carolina at Charlotte, MDO
The University of North Carolina at Greensboro, MO
The University of North Carolina at Pembroke, M
The University of North Carolina Wilmington, M

University of Phoenix - Charlotte Campus, M
Wake Forest University, M
Western Carolina University, M
Wingate University, M
Winston-Salem State University, M

North Dakota

Mayville State University, B
North Dakota State University, BM
University of Mary, BM
University of North Dakota, M
Williston State College, A

Ohio

Ashland University, M
Baldwin Wallace University, M
Bluffton University, M
Bowling Green State University, BM
Capital University, BM
Case Western Reserve University, M
Cedarville University, M
Cincinnati State Technical and Community College,
A
Cleveland State University, MD
Defiance College, M
DeVry University (Columbus), BM
DeVry University (Seven Hills), BMO
Fortis College (Cuyahoga Falls), A
Franciscan University of Steubenville, M
Franklin University, BM
Heidelberg University, M
John Carroll University, M
Kent State University, M
Kent State University at Stark, M
Lake Erie College, M
Lourdes University, M
Malone University, BM
Miami University, M
Miami University Hamilton, B
Mount St. Joseph University, M
Ohio Dominican University, M
Ohio Northern University, B
The Ohio State University, MD
Ohio University, M
Otterbein University, M
South University, M
Tiffin University, M
University of Cincinnati, M
University of Cincinnati Blue Ash College, A
University of Dayton, M
The University of Findlay, M
Urbana University, M
Ursuline College, M
Walsh University, M
Wright State University, M
Xavier University, M
Youngstown State University, MO

Oklahoma

Cameron University, M
Community Care College, A
DeVry University, B
Mid-America Christian University, M
Northeastern State University, M
Oklahoma Baptist University, M
Oklahoma Christian University, M
Oklahoma City University, M
Oral Roberts University, M
Southeastern Oklahoma State University, M
Southern Nazarene University, BM
Southwestern Oklahoma State University, M
University of Oklahoma, MD
The University of Tulsa, M

Oregon

Concordia University, M
Corban University, M
Eastern Oregon University, ABM
George Fox University, MD
Marylhurst University, M
Northwest Christian University, M
Oregon State University, MD
Pacific University, M
Portland State University, MD
Southern Oregon University, MO
University of Oregon, M

University of Portland, M
Willamette University, M

Pennsylvania

Alvernia University, M
Arcadia University, M
Bloomsburg University of Pennsylvania, M
Cairn University, MO
California University of Pennsylvania, M
Carlow University, M
Carnegie Mellon University, B
Chatham University, M
Clarion University of Pennsylvania, M
Delaware Valley University, M
DeSales University, M
DeVry University (Fort Washington), BM
DeVry University (King of Prussia), BMO
DeVry University (Philadelphia), B
Drexel University, MDO
Duquesne University, M
Eastern University, M
Gannon University, M
Geneva College, M
Gettysburg College, B
Holy Family University, M
Indiana University of Pennsylvania, M
Kutztown University of Pennsylvania, M
La Roche College, B
La Salle University, MO
Lackawanna College, A
Lebanon Valley College, A
Lehigh University, M
Lincoln University, M
Marywood University, M
Messiah College, MO
Misericordia University, M
Moravian College, M
Mount Aloysius College, M
Penn State Erie, The Behrend College, M
Penn State Harrisburg, M
Penn State University Park, MD
Pennsylvania College of Technology, B
Philadelphia University, M
Point Park University, M
Robert Morris University, M
Rosemont College, M
Saint Francis University, M
Saint Joseph's University, MO
Saint Vincent College, M
Seton Hill University, MO
Shippensburg University of Pennsylvania, MO
Slippery Rock University of Pennsylvania, M
Temple University, MD
University of Pennsylvania, BMD
University of Pittsburgh, MD
The University of Scranton, M
Villanova University, M
Waynesburg University, MD
West Chester University of Pennsylvania, MO
Widener University, BM
Wilkes University, M
York College of Pennsylvania, M

Rhode Island

Bryant University, M
Johnson & Wales University, M
Providence College, M
Salve Regina University, M
University of Rhode Island, MD

South Carolina

Anderson University, M
Bob Jones University, M
Charleston Southern University, BM
The Citadel, The Military College of South Carolina,
M
Claflin University, M
Clemson University, M
Coastal Carolina University, MO
College of Charleston, M
Francis Marion University, M
Limestone College, BM
Morris College, B
South University, M
Southern Wesleyan University, M
University of South Carolina, MD

Winthrop University, M

South Dakota

Black Hills State University, M
Dakota State University, M
Mount Marty College, M
National American University (Ellsworth AFB), A
National American University (Rapid City), M
Sinte Gleska University, AB
University of Sioux Falls, M
The University of South Dakota, M

Tennessee

Argosy University, Nashville, MD
Austin Peay State University, M
Belmont University, M
Bethel University, BM
Bryan College, M
Carson-Newman University, M
Christian Brothers University, MO
Cumberland University, M
Daymar College (Clarksville), A
DeVry University, BM
East Tennessee State University, MO
Freed-Hardeman University, M
King University, M
Lee University, M
Lincoln Memorial University, BM
Lipscomb University, MO
Martin Methodist College, B
Milligan College, M
Southern Adventist University, M
Tennessee State University, M
Tennessee Technological University, M
Trevecca Nazarene University, M
Tusculum College, M
Union University, M
University of Memphis, MD
The University of Tennessee, MD
The University of Tennessee at Chattanooga, M
The University of Tennessee at Martin, M
Vanderbilt University, M
Williamson College, B

Texas

Amberton University, M
American InterContinental University Houston, M
Argosy University, Dallas, MDO
Austin College, B
Baylor University, MD
Dallas Baptist University, M
DeVry University (Austin), B
DeVry University (Irving), BM
DeVry University (San Antonio), B
Hallmark University, BM
Hardin-Simmons University, M
Howard Payne University, BM
Lamar Institute of Technology, A
Lamar University, M
LeTourneau University, M
Midwestern State University, M
Northwest Vista College, A
Our Lady of the Lake University of San Antonio, M
Prairie View A&M University, M
Rice University, M
St. Edward's University, MO
St. Mary's University, M
Sam Houston State University, M
Schreiner University, M
South University, M
Southern Methodist University, M
Southwestern Adventist University, M
Stephen F. Austin State University, M
Sul Ross State University, M
Tarleton State University, M
Texas A&M International University, MD
Texas A&M University - Central Texas, M
Texas A&M University - Commerce, M
Texas A&M University - Corpus Christi, M
Texas A&M University - Kingsville, M
Texas A&M University - San Antonio, M
Texas A&M University - Texarkana, M
Texas Christian University, M
Texas Southern University, M
Texas State University, M
Texas Tech University, BMD

Texas Wesleyan University, M
Texas Woman's University, M
Trinity University, M
University of Dallas, M
University of Houston, MD
University of Houston - Clear Lake, BM
University of Houston - Downtown, M
University of Houston - Victoria, M
University of the Incarnate Word, BMD
University of Mary Hardin-Baylor, M
University of North Texas, D
University of Phoenix - Dallas Campus, M
University of Phoenix - Houston Campus, M
University of Phoenix - San Antonio Campus, M
University of St. Thomas, M
The University of Texas at Arlington, MD
The University of Texas at Austin, M
The University of Texas at Dallas, MD
The University of Texas at El Paso, MDO
The University of Texas of the Permian Basin, M
The University of Texas Rio Grande Valley, MD
The University of Texas at San Antonio, D
The University of Texas at Tyler, M
Wayland Baptist University, M
West Texas A&M University, M

Utah

Argosy University, Salt Lake City, MD
Brigham Young University, M
Broadview University - West Jordan, M
Dixie State University, AB
Independence University, M
LDS Business College, A
Provo College, A
Southern Utah University, M
University of Phoenix - Utah Campus, M
University of Utah, MDO
Utah State University, M
Utah Valley University, M
Weber State University, M
Western Governors University, BM
Westminster College, MO

Vermont

Champlain College, M
College of St. Joseph, M
Goddard College, M
Green Mountain College, M
Marlboro College, M
Norwich University, M
University of Vermont, M

Virginia

American National University (Salem), M
Argosy University, Washington DC, MDO
Averett University, M
Blue Ridge Community College, A
Bryant & Stratton College - Virginia Beach Campus, A
The College of William and Mary, M
Danville Community College, A
DeVry University (Arlington), BM
DeVry University (Chesapeake), BM
DeVry University (Manassas), BMO
Eastern Mennonite University, M
ECPI University (Virginia Beach), B
George Mason University, M
Hampton University, MD
James Madison University, M
John Tyler Community College, A
Liberty University, MDO
Longwood University, M
Lord Fairfax Community College, A
Lynchburg College, M
Marymount University, MO
Miller-Motte Technical College (Lynchburg), A
Mountain Empire Community College, A
Old Dominion University, MD
Radford University, M
Rappahannock Community College, A
Regent University, M
Shenandoah University, BMO
South University (Glen Allen), M
South University (Virginia Beach), M
Southwest Virginia Community College, A
Stratford University (Falls Church), M

Thomas Nelson Community College, A
University of Management and Technology, MDO
University of Mary Washington, M
University of Richmond, M
University of Virginia, MD
Virginia Commonwealth University, MO
Virginia International University, MO
Virginia Polytechnic Institute and State University, MD

Washington

Argosy University, Seattle, MD
Central Washington University, B
City University of Seattle, MO
Eastern Washington University, M
Gonzaga University, M
Northwest University, BM
Pacific Lutheran University, M
Saint Martin's University, M
Seattle Pacific University, M
Seattle University, MO
University of Phoenix - Western Washington Campus, M
University of Washington, MD
University of Washington, Bothell, M
University of Washington, Tacoma, M
Washington State University, MD
Western Washington University, M
Whitworth University, M

West Virginia

American Public University System, M
Blue Ridge Community and Technical College, A
BridgeValley Community and Technical College (South Charleston), A
Fairmont State University, M
Marshall University, M
Salem International University, M
University of Charleston, BM
West Virginia University, M
West Virginia Wesleyan College, M
Wheeling Jesuit University, M

Wisconsin

Alverno College, BM
Cardinal Stritch University, BM
Carroll University, M
Concordia University Wisconsin, M
Edgewood College, M
Herzing University Online, M
Lakeland College, M
Marian University, M
Marquette University, BMO
Milwaukee Area Technical College, A
Milwaukee School of Engineering, M
Mount Mary University, M
University of Wisconsin - Eau Claire, M
University of Wisconsin - La Crosse, M
University of Wisconsin - Madison, M
University of Wisconsin - Milwaukee, MDO
University of Wisconsin - Oshkosh, M
University of Wisconsin - Parkside, M
University of Wisconsin - Stevens Point, M
University of Wisconsin - Whitewater, M
Viterbo University, BM
Waukesha County Technical College, A
Western Technical College, A
Wisconsin Lutheran College, B

Wyoming

University of Wyoming, BM

U.S. Territories: Guam

University of Guam, M

U.S. Territories: Puerto Rico

Bayamón Central University, M
Columbia Centro Universitario (Caguas), A
Inter American University of Puerto Rico, Arecibo Campus, M
Inter American University of Puerto Rico, Barranquitas Campus, M
Inter American University of Puerto Rico, Fajardo Campus, M

Inter American University of Puerto Rico, Guayama Campus, M
Inter American University of Puerto Rico, Metropolitan Campus, BM
Inter American University of Puerto Rico, San Germán Campus, MD
Polytechnic University of Puerto Rico, M
Pontifical Catholic University of Puerto Rico, BMDO
Universidad Metropolitana, M
University of Puerto Rico in Bayamón, B
University of Puerto Rico in Cayey, B
University of Puerto Rico, Mayagüez Campus, M
University of Puerto Rico in Ponce, B
University of Puerto Rico, Río Piedras Campus, MD
University of the Sacred Heart, MO

U.S. Territories: United States Virgin Islands

University of the Virgin Islands, M

Canada

Alberta

Athabasca University, MO
Southern Alberta Institute of Technology, A
University of Alberta, BMD
University of Calgary, M

British Columbia

Royal Roads University, M
Simon Fraser University, MDO
Thompson Rivers University, M
Trinity Western University, M
The University of British Columbia, MD
University of Victoria, M
Vancouver Island University, M

Manitoba

University of Manitoba, MD

Maritime Provinces: New Brunswick

Université de Moncton, M
University of New Brunswick Fredericton, M
University of New Brunswick Saint John, M

Maritime Provinces: Nova Scotia

Cape Breton University, M
Dalhousie University, M
Saint Mary's University, MD

Newfoundland and Labrador

Memorial University of Newfoundland, M

Ontario

Brock University, M
Carleton University, MD
Lakehead University - Orillia, M
Laurentian University, M
McMaster University, MD
Queen's University at Kingston, M
Royal Military College of Canada, M
University of Guelph, MD
University of Ottawa, BM
University of Toronto, MD
University of Waterloo, BM
The University of Western Ontario, BMD
University of Windsor, M
Wilfrid Laurier University, M
York University, MD

Quebec

Concordia University, MDO
HEC Montreal, MD
McGill University, MDO
Université Laval, MO
Université du Québec en Abitibi-Témiscamingue, M
Université du Québec à Chicoutimi, M
Université du Québec à Montréal, MDO
Université du Québec à Rimouski, M
Université du Québec à Trois-Rivières, MD
Université de Sherbrooke, MD

Saskatchewan

University of Regina, MO
University of Saskatchewan, M

BUSINESS/COMMERCE

United States

Alabama

Alabama Agricultural and Mechanical University, B
Auburn University at Montgomery, B
Huntingdon College, B
Judson College, B
Northeast Alabama Community College, A
Shelton State Community College, A
Southern Union State Community College, A
University of South Alabama, B

Alaska

University of Alaska Anchorage, A

Arizona

Central Arizona College, A
Chandler-Gilbert Community College, A
Coconino Community College, A
DeVry University (Mesa), B
DeVry University (Phoenix), B
GateWay Community College, A
Glendale Community College, A
Northland Pioneer College, A
Paradise Valley Community College, A
Phoenix College, A
Pima Community College, A
South Mountain Community College, A
The University of Arizona, B
Western International University, B

Arkansas

Arkansas Northeastern College, A
Arkansas State University - Mountain Home, A
Arkansas State University - Newport, A
Cossatot Community College of the University of Arkansas, A
Henderson State University, B
North Arkansas College, A
South Arkansas Community College, A
Southeast Arkansas College, A
Southern Arkansas University - Magnolia, AB
University of Arkansas, B
University of Arkansas Community College at Batesville, A
University of Arkansas Community College at Hope, A
University of Arkansas Community College at Morrilton, A
University of Arkansas at Little Rock, B
University of Central Arkansas, B

California

American Jewish University, B
American River College, A
Antelope Valley College, A
Barstow Community College, A
Berkeley City College, A
Cabrillo College, A
California Baptist University, B
California State University, Dominguez Hills, B
Cerro Coso Community College, A
Chabot College, A
Citrus College, A
City College of San Francisco, A
College of the Desert, A
College of Marin, A
College of the Redwoods, A
College of San Mateo, A
Columbia College, A
Copper Mountain College, A
Cosumnes River College, A
Cuyamaca College, A
Cypress College, A
DeVry University (Alhambra), B
DeVry University (Bakersfield), B
DeVry University (Fremont), B

DeVry University (Long Beach), B
DeVry University (Oakland), B
DeVry University (Oxnard), B
DeVry University (Palmdale), B
DeVry University (Pomona), B
DeVry University (San Diego), B
DeVry University (Sherman Oaks), B
Feather River College, A
Gavilan College, A
Grossmont College, A
La Sierra University, B
Long Beach City College, A
Merritt College, A
New Charter University, AB
Norco College, A
Orange Coast College, A
Pacific Union College, AB
Palomar College, A
Reedley College, A
Saint Mary's College of California, B
San Joaquin Valley College (Visalia), A
San Jose City College, A
Sierra College, A
Trident University International, B
University of Phoenix - San Diego Campus, B
University of Redlands, B
University of San Francisco, B
Victor Valley College, A
Westmont College, B

Colorado

Adams State University, AB
Colorado Mesa University, B
Colorado Mountain College (Leadville), A
Colorado State University - Pueblo, B
DeVry University (Colorado Springs), B
DeVry University (Westminster), B
University of Denver, B

Connecticut

Goodwin College, A
Naugatuck Valley Community College, A
Three Rivers Community College, A
University of Bridgeport, AB
University of Connecticut, B

Delaware

Delaware Technical & Community College, Jack F. Owens Campus, A
Delaware Technical & Community College, Stanton/Wilmington Campus, A
Delaware Technical & Community College, Terry Campus, A
University of Delaware, B

District of Columbia

The Catholic University of America, B

Florida

Ave Maria University, B
College of Central Florida, AB
DeVry University (Jacksonville), B
DeVry University (Miramar), B
DeVry University (Orlando), B
Florida State University, B
Fortis College (Winter Park), A
Jacksonville University, B
Pensacola State College, A
Saint Leo University, B
St. Thomas University, B
South Florida State College, A
State College of Florida Manatee-Sarasota, A
Trinity College of Florida, B
University of Central Florida, B
University of South Florida, B
University of South Florida Sarasota-Manatee, B
University of West Florida, B
Warner University, B
Webber International University, B

Georgia

Argosy University, Atlanta, B
Brenau University, B
Clayton State University, B
Columbus State University, B

Covenant College, B
DeVry University (Alpharetta), B
DeVry University (Decatur), B
DeVry University (Duluth), B
Georgia Gwinnett College, B
Georgia Military College, B
Georgia Piedmont Technical College, A
Mercer University, B
Reinhardt University, B
Savannah State University, B
Thomas University, A
University of Georgia, B
University of Phoenix - Augusta Campus, A

Hawaii

Hawai'i Pacific University, B
University of Hawaii at Manoa, B

Idaho

Boise State University, B
Idaho State University, AB

Illinois

Aurora University, B
DeVry University (Addison), B
DeVry University (Chicago), B
DeVry University (Downers Grove), B
DeVry University (Elgin), B
DeVry University (Gurnee), B
DeVry University (Naperville), B
DeVry University (Tinley Park), B
DeVry University Online, B
Ellis University, B
Kaskaskia College, A
Kendall College, B
Lewis University, B
Lincoln Land Community College, A
Moraine Valley Community College, A
Northeastern Illinois University, B
Northern Illinois University, B
Olivet Nazarene University, A
Roosevelt University, B
Saint Xavier University, B
University of Illinois at Urbana - Champaign, B

Indiana

Ball State University, B
Bethel College, AB
DeVry University, B
Earlham College, B
Franklin College, B
Goshen College, B
Grace College, B
Indiana University Bloomington, B
Indiana University East, B
Indiana University Kokomo, B
Indiana University Northwest, B
Indiana University - Purdue University Fort Wayne,
    B
Indiana University - Purdue University Indianapolis,
    B
Indiana University South Bend, B
Indiana University Southeast, B
Manchester University, B
Purdue University Northwest (Hammond), B
Saint Joseph's College, B
Saint Mary-of-the-Woods College, A
Taylor University, B
University of Notre Dame, B
University of Saint Francis, B
University of Southern Indiana, AB
Vincennes University, A

Iowa

Drake University, B
Iowa Wesleyan University, B
Mount Mercy University, B
Waldorf College, B
William Penn University, B

Kansas

Allen Community College, A
Baker University, B
Bethel College, B
Central Christian College of Kansas, B

Highland Community College, A
Hutchinson Community College, A
Kansas State University, B
Pittsburg State University, B
Seward County Community College and Area Tech-
    nical School, A
Tabor College, B
The University of Kansas, B
Washburn University, B

Kentucky

Alice Lloyd College, B
Asbury University, B
Bellarmine University, B
Brescia University, AB
Brown Mackie College - Hopkinsville, A
Kentucky State University, B
Midway University, AB
Morehead State University, B
Murray State University, AB
Northern Kentucky University, B
Spalding University, AB
Sullivan University, B
Thomas More College, A
Transylvania University, B
University of Kentucky, B

Louisiana

Baton Rouge Community College, A
Bossier Parish Community College, A
Louisiana Delta Community College, A
Nunez Community College, A
South Louisiana Community College, A
Southern University at Shreveport, A
Tulane University, A

Maine

Husson University, B
Thomas College, A
University of Maine at Fort Kent, AB

Maryland

Anne Arundel Community College, A
Baltimore City Community College, A
Cecil College, A
Chesapeake College, A
College of Southern Maryland, A
Community College of Baltimore County, A
Garrett College, A
Hagerstown Community College, A
Johns Hopkins University, B
Loyola University Maryland, B
Montgomery College, A
Mount St. Mary's University, B
University of Baltimore, B
University of Maryland, College Park, B
Wor-Wic Community College, A

Massachusetts

Berkshire Community College, A
Brandeis University, B
Bristol Community College, A
Cambridge College, B
Eastern Nazarene College, AB
Framingham State University, B
Greenfield Community College, A
Massachusetts Bay Community College, A
Massachusetts Institute of Technology, B
Mount Wachusett Community College, A
Nichols College, B
Northeastern University, B
Northern Essex Community College, A
Quinsigamond Community College, A
Regis College, B
Springfield Technical Community College, A
University of Massachusetts Dartmouth, B
University of Massachusetts Lowell, A
Western New England University, B
Wheaton College, B

Michigan

Bay de Noc Community College, A
Davenport University, B
Eastern Michigan University, B
Ferris State University, A

Gogebic Community College, A
Grand Valley State University, B
Henry Ford College, A
Kalamazoo College, B
Lansing Community College, A
Macomb Community College, A
Marygrove College, AB
Mott Community College, A
Northern Michigan University, A
Oakland University, B
Saginaw Chippewa Tribal College, A
Saginaw Valley State University, B
St. Clair County Community College, A
Schoolcraft College, A
Walsh College of Accountancy and Business Admin-
    istration, B
Western Michigan University, B

Minnesota

Academy College, A
Anoka-Ramsey Community College, A
Crown College, A
Inver Hills Community College, A
Mesabi Range College, A
Minnesota West Community and Technical College,
    A

Mississippi

Coahoma Community College, A
Delta State University, B
East Mississippi Community College, A
Mississippi University for Women, B

Missouri

Avila University, B
Columbia College, AB
DeVry University (Kansas City), B
East Central College, A
Jefferson College, A
Maryville University of Saint Louis, B
Mineral Area College, A
Missouri Southern State University, B
Missouri State University, B
Missouri State University - West Plains, A
Southwest Baptist University, A
Vatterott College (Sunset Hills), A
Washington University in St. Louis, B

Montana

Aaniiih Nakoda College, A
Dawson Community College, A
Miles Community College, A
Montana State University, B
Montana State University Billings, AB
Montana Tech of The University of Montana, B
University of Montana, B

Nebraska

Bellevue University, B
Concordia University, Nebraska, B
Little Priest Tribal College, A
University of Nebraska at Omaha, B

Nevada

DeVry University, B
Great Basin College, A
Truckee Meadows Community College, A
University of Nevada, Reno, B
University of Phoenix - Las Vegas Campus, A
Western Nevada College, A

New Hampshire

Granite State College, A
Lakes Region Community College, A
Plymouth State University, B
Saint Anselm College, B
University of New Hampshire, A

New Jersey

Brookdale Community College, A
Ocean County College, A
Raritan Valley Community College, A
Union County College, A
University of Phoenix - Jersey City Campus, A

New Mexico

New Mexico State University, AB
New Mexico State University - Alamogordo, A
New Mexico State University - Carlsbad, A
New Mexico State University - Grants, A
Northern New Mexico College, A
Southwestern Indian Polytechnic Institute, A
University of the Southwest, B

New York

Bryant & Stratton College - Albany Campus, A
Bryant & Stratton College - Amherst Campus, A
Bryant & Stratton College - Buffalo Campus, A
Bryant & Stratton College - Greece Campus, A
Bryant & Stratton College - Henrietta Campus, A
Bryant & Stratton College - Orchard Park Campus, A
Bryant & Stratton College - Syracuse Campus, A
Canisius College, B
The College of New Rochelle, B
College of Staten Island of the City University of New York, A
Columbia-Greene Community College, A
Hofstra University, B
Ithaca College, B
LIM College, B
Marymount Manhattan College, B
Medgar Evers College of the City University of New York, B
Metropolitan College of New York, AB
New York University, AB
Niagara University, B
Onondaga Community College, A
Pace University, B
Pace University, Pleasantville Campus, B
Rochester Institute of Technology, B
St. Lawrence University, B
Skidmore College, B
State University of New York Empire State College, AB
State University of New York at New Paltz, B
State University of New York at Plattsburgh, B
University of Rochester, B

North Carolina

Campbell University, B
DeVry University, B
Louisburg College, A
Wake Forest University, B

North Dakota

Bismarck State College, A
Mayville State University, A

Ohio

Belmont College, A
Bowling Green State University, B
Brown Mackie College - Akron, A
Bryant & Stratton College - Cleveland Campus, A
Bryant & Stratton College - Parma Campus, A
Central State University, B
DeVry University (Columbus), B
DeVry University (Seven Hills), B
Gallipolis Career College, A
God's Bible School and College, A
Kent State University at Ashtabula, A
Kent State University at East Liverpool, A
Kent State University at Geauga, A
Kent State University at Salem, A
Kent State University at Trumbull, A
Kent State University at Tuscarawas, A
Lourdes University, AB
Miami University, A
Miami University Hamilton, B
Miami University Middletown, A
Mount Vernon Nazarene University, AB
North Central State College, A
Northwest State Community College, A
Ohio Northern University, B
The Ohio State University, B
The Ohio State University at Lima, B
The Ohio State University - Mansfield Campus, B
The Ohio State University at Marion, B
The Ohio State University - Newark Campus, B
Ohio Wesleyan University, B

Owens Community College, A
Southern State Community College, A
Terra State Community College, A
The University of Akron, B
University of Cincinnati Blue Ash College, A
University of Cincinnati Clermont College, A
The University of Toledo, B
Wright State University, AB
Wright State University - Lake Campus, B
Youngstown State University, AB

Oklahoma

Carl Albert State College, A
East Central University, B
Hillsdale Free Will Baptist College, AB
Oklahoma Christian University, B
Oklahoma City Community College, A
Oklahoma State University Institute of Technology, A
Oklahoma Wesleyan University, B
Rose State College, A
Seminole State College, A
Southern Nazarene University, A
Tulsa Community College, A
University of Central Oklahoma, B
University of Science and Arts of Oklahoma, B
The University of Tulsa, B

Oregon

Lane Community College, A
Multnomah University, B
Rogue Community College, A
Treasure Valley Community College, A
University of Oregon, B
Western Oregon University, B

Pennsylvania

Alvernia University, AB
Bloomsburg University of Pennsylvania, B
Bryn Athyn College of the New Church, B
Bucknell University, B
Butler County Community College, A
Community College of Beaver County, A
Delaware Valley University, A
DeVry University (Fort Washington), B
DeVry University (King of Prussia), B
DeVry University (Philadelphia), B
Drexel University, B
Gannon University, A
Harrisburg Area Community College, A
Indiana University of Pennsylvania, B
Juniata College, B
La Salle University, B
Lackawanna College, A
Lehigh Carbon Community College, A
Mercyhurst North East, A
Montgomery County Community College, A
Northampton Community College, A
Penn State Abington, AB
Penn State Altoona, AB
Penn State Beaver, A
Penn State Berks, AB
Penn State Brandywine, A
Penn State DuBois, A
Penn State Erie, The Behrend College, A
Penn State Fayette, The Eberly Campus, A
Penn State Greater Allegheny, A
Penn State Harrisburg, A
Penn State Hazleton, A
Penn State Lehigh Valley, AB
Penn State Mont Alto, A
Penn State New Kensington, A
Penn State Schuylkill, AB
Penn State Shenango, A
Penn State Wilkes-Barre, A
Penn State Worthington Scranton, A
Penn State York, B
Pennsylvania Highlands Community College, A
Saint Vincent College, B
Temple University, B
University of Pittsburgh, B
University of Pittsburgh at Titusville, A
Washington & Jefferson College, B
Westmoreland County Community College, A

Rhode Island

Community College of Rhode Island, A
University of Rhode Island, B

South Carolina

Anderson University, B
Clinton College, A
Denmark Technical College, A
Limestone College, AB
Midlands Technical College, A
Orangeburg-Calhoun Technical College, A
Piedmont Technical College, A
Southern Wesleyan University, AB
Spartanburg Methodist College, A
Technical College of the Lowcountry, A
Williamsburg Technical College, A
York Technical College, A

South Dakota

Sinte Gleska University, A
The University of South Dakota, B

Tennessee

Austin Peay State University, B
Belmont University, B
Christian Brothers University, AB
Cumberland University, AB
DeVry University, B
Southwest Tennessee Community College, A
Welch College, B

Texas

Alvin Community College, A
Angelina College, A
Austin College, B
Austin Community College District, A
Baylor University, B
Brookhaven College, A
Cedar Valley College, A
College of the Mainland, A
Collin County Community College District, A
Concordia University Texas, B
Del Mar College, A
DeVry University (Austin), B
DeVry University (Irving), B
DeVry University (San Antonio), B
East Texas Baptist University, B
Eastfield College, A
El Centro College, A
El Paso Community College, A
Frank Phillips College, A
Hill College, A
Howard College, A
Howard Payne University, B
Kilgore College, A
Lamar State College - Port Arthur, A
Lamar University, B
McMurry University, B
Midland College, A
Midwestern State University, B
Paris Junior College, A
Sam Houston State University, B
San Jacinto College District, A
Schreiner University, B
Southwestern Assemblies of God University, A
Southwestern University, B
Stephen F. Austin State University, B
Tarleton State University, B
Texarkana College, A
Texas A&M University - Commerce, B
Texas A&M University - Kingsville, B
Texas A&M University - Texarkana, B
Texas Southmost College, A
Texas Tech University, B
University of Houston - Clear Lake, B
University of Houston - Downtown, B
University of North Texas, B
University of Phoenix - Houston Campus, B
The University of Texas at Austin, B
The University of Texas at Dallas, B
The University of Texas at San Antonio, B
West Texas A&M University, B

Utah

Independence University, AB
Southern Utah University, A
Stevens-Henager College (West Haven), A
University of Utah, B
Utah State University, B

Vermont

Castleton University, A
Champlain College, AB
Johnson State College, B
Landmark College, A

Virginia

American National University (Charlottesville), A
Bryant & Stratton College - Richmond Campus, A
Central Virginia Community College, A
DeVry University (Arlington), B
DeVry University (Chesapeake), B
DeVry University (Manassas), B
Hollins University, B
Norfolk State University, B
Northern Virginia Community College, A
Randolph College, B
Stratford University (Alexandria), B
Stratford University (Falls Church), A
Stratford University (Glen Allen), A
Stratford University (Newport News), A
Stratford University (Woodbridge), A
Sweet Briar College, B
University of Virginia, B
Virginia Commonwealth University, B

Washington

Bellevue College, A
Centralia College, A
Columbia Basin College, A
Everett Community College, A
The Evergreen State College, B
Green River College, A
Pierce College at Fort Steilacoom, A
Seattle Pacific University, B
Seattle University, B
Tacoma Community College, A
Washington State University, B
Western Washington University, B

West Virginia

Alderson Broaddus University, A
American Public University System, A
Glenville State College, AB
Mountwest Community & Technical College, A
New River Community and Technical College, A
Ohio Valley University, B
Pierpont Community & Technical College, A
West Virginia Northern Community College, A
West Virginia University, B

Wisconsin

Bryant & Stratton College - Milwaukee Campus, AB
Bryant & Stratton College - Wauwatosa Campus, A
Cardinal Stritch University, B
Edgewood College, B
Milwaukee School of Engineering, B
University of Wisconsin - Milwaukee, B
University of Wisconsin - Platteville, B
University of Wisconsin - Whitewater, B

Wyoming

Central Wyoming College, A
Laramie County Community College, A
Northwest College, A
Sheridan College, A

U.S. Territories: Puerto Rico

Bayamón Central University, AB
Caribbean University, B
Columbia Centro Universitario (Caguas), B
Humacao Community College, AB
Pontifical Catholic University of Puerto Rico, B
University of Puerto Rico in Aguadilla, B
University of Puerto Rico in Arecibo, B
University of Puerto Rico in Cayey, B
University of Puerto Rico in Ponce, A

University of Puerto Rico, Río Piedras Campus, B

Canada

Alberta

University of Alberta, B

British Columbia

Thompson Rivers University, B
The University of British Columbia, B
University of Northern British Columbia, B
University of Victoria, B

Maritime Provinces: New Brunswick

Mount Allison University, B

Maritime Provinces: Nova Scotia

Dalhousie University, B

Ontario

Brock University, B
Queen's University at Kingston, B
Tyndale University College & Seminary, B
The University of Western Ontario, B
University of Windsor, B
York University, B

Quebec

HEC Montreal, B
McGill University, B

Saskatchewan

University of Regina, B

BUSINESS/CORPORATE COM-MUNICATIONS

United States

Arizona

University of Phoenix - Phoenix Campus, B
Western International University, B

California

Holy Names University, B
National University, B
Point Loma Nazarene University, B
University of Phoenix - Bay Area Campus, B
University of Phoenix - Sacramento Valley Campus, B
University of Phoenix - San Diego Campus, B

Colorado

University of Phoenix - Colorado Campus, B
University of Phoenix - Colorado Springs Downtown Campus, B

Florida

Saint Leo University, B

Georgia

University of Phoenix - Atlanta Campus, B
University of Phoenix - Augusta Campus, B
University of Phoenix - Columbus Georgia Campus, B

Hawaii

Hawai'i Pacific University, B
University of Phoenix - Hawaii Campus, B

Illinois

Concordia University Chicago, B
Roosevelt University, B
Trinity Christian College, B

Iowa

Morningside College, B

Kansas

Central Christian College of Kansas, A
Fort Hays State University, B
MidAmerica Nazarene University, B

Maine

University of New England, B

Maryland

Cecil College, A
Stevenson University, B

Massachusetts

Babson College, B
Bentley University, B
Nichols College, B

Michigan

Aquinas College, B
Calvin College, B
Cleary University, B
Rochester College, B

Minnesota

Walden University, B

Missouri

Rockhurst University, B
Westminster College, B

Nebraska

Concordia University, Nebraska, B

Nevada

University of Phoenix - Las Vegas Campus, B

New Jersey

University of Phoenix - Jersey City Campus, B

North Carolina

Elon University, B

North Dakota

North Dakota State University, B
University of Mary, B

Ohio

Marietta College, B
The University of Findlay, B
University of Rio Grande, B
Walsh University, B

Pennsylvania

Chestnut Hill College, B
Duquesne University, B
Lycoming College, B
Montgomery County Community College, A
Penn State Abington, B
University of Phoenix - Philadelphia Campus, B

Rhode Island

Bryant University, B

South Dakota

Augustana University, B

Tennessee

Christian Brothers University, B

Texas

Houston Community College, A
Stephen F. Austin State University, B
University of Houston, B
University of Phoenix - Dallas Campus, B
University of Phoenix - Houston Campus, B

Utah

University of Phoenix - Utah Campus, B

Washington

North Seattle College, A
University of Phoenix - Western Washington Campus, B

Wisconsin

Mount Mary University, B

U.S. Territories: Puerto Rico

Pontifical Catholic University of Puerto Rico, B

Canada

Ontario

Brock University, B
The University of Western Ontario, B

BUSINESS EDUCATION

United States

Alabama

Alabama Agricultural and Mechanical University, MO
Auburn University, MD

Arkansas

Arkansas State University, O

Colorado

Colorado Christian University, M

Delaware

University of Delaware, M

Florida

Florida Agricultural and Mechanical University, M

Georgia

University of Georgia, M

Illinois

University of St. Francis, MO

Indiana

Ball State University, M

Kansas

Emporia State University, M

Kentucky

Eastern Kentucky University, M
Morehead State University, M
Spalding University, M
University of the Cumberlands, M

Louisiana

Louisiana State University and Agricultural & Mechanical College, M

Maine

Thomas College, M

Minnesota

Capella University, D
University of Minnesota, Twin Cities Campus, MD

Mississippi

Mississippi College, M
Mississippi State University, M

Missouri

University of Missouri, MDO

Nebraska

Chadron State College, M
Wayne State College, M

New Hampshire

Southern New Hampshire University, M

New Jersey

Rider University, O

New York

Buffalo State College, State University of New York, M
Canisius College, M
Hofstra University, M
Lehman College of the City University of New York, M
Nazareth College of Rochester, M
New York University, MO
State University of New York at Oswego, M

North Carolina

East Carolina University, M
North Carolina Agricultural and Technical State University, M
North Carolina State University, M

Ohio

Bowling Green State University, M
The University of Toledo, M
Wright State University, M

Pennsylvania

Bloomsburg University of Pennsylvania, M
Indiana University of Pennsylvania, M
Robert Morris University, M
Temple University, M

Rhode Island

Johnson & Wales University, M

South Carolina

South Carolina State University, M
University of South Carolina, M

Tennessee

Middle Tennessee State University, M

Utah

Utah State University, MD

Virginia

Old Dominion University, D

Washington

University of Washington, MD
Washington State University, M

Wisconsin

Milwaukee School of Engineering, M
University of Wisconsin - Whitewater, M

U.S. Territories: Puerto Rico

Inter American University of Puerto Rico, Metropolitan Campus, M
Inter American University of Puerto Rico, San Germán Campus, M
Pontifical Catholic University of Puerto Rico, MD

Canada

British Columbia

The University of British Columbia, M

BUSINESS FAMILY AND CONSUMER SCIENCES/HUMAN SCIENCES

United States

California

Chaffey College, A
Long Beach City College, A

Ohio

The Ohio State University, B

Texas

University of Houston, B

Utah

Brigham Young University, B

Virginia

Virginia Polytechnic Institute and State University, B

BUSINESS MACHINE REPAIRER

United States

California

De Anza College, A
Irvine Valley College, A
Lassen Community College District, A
Moorpark College, A
Solano Community College, A

Iowa

Iowa Lakes Community College, A

Kansas

Neosho County Community College, A

Michigan

Muskegon Community College, A

Mississippi

Mississippi Delta Community College, A

Missouri

Ozarks Technical Community College, A

North Carolina

Central Piedmont Community College, A

Pennsylvania

Community College of Allegheny County, A

Texas

Del Mar College, A
San Antonio College, A

Virginia

ECPI University (Richmond), A

Washington

Clover Park Technical College, A

BUSINESS, MANAGEMENT, MARKETING, AND RELATED SUPPORT SERVICES

United States

Alabama

Athens State University, B
Troy University, B

Arizona

Arizona State University at the Polytechnic campus, B
Arizona State University at the Tempe campus, B
Arizona State University at the West campus, B
Chandler-Gilbert Community College, A
Eastern Arizona College, A

Arkansas

Central Baptist College, B

California

Berkeley City College, A
California College San Diego (San Diego), A
California State University, Dominguez Hills, B

FIDM/Fashion Institute of Design & Merchandising, Los Angeles Campus, B
FIDM/Fashion Institute of Design & Merchandising, San Francisco Campus, B
Southern California Institute of Technology, B

Colorado

Western State Colorado University, B

Connecticut

Capital Community College, A

District of Columbia

American University, B

Florida

Florida National University, A
Full Sail University, B
Northwest Florida State College, A
Southeastern College - West Palm Beach, A
Southeastern University, B

Georgia

Young Harris College, B

Idaho

College of Western Idaho, A

Illinois

Benedictine University, B
Loyola University Chicago, B

Indiana

Ball State University, A
Purdue University Northwest (Westville), AB

Kansas

Cloud County Community College, A
Seward County Community College and Area Technical School, A
Southwestern College, B

Louisiana

University of Louisiana at Lafayette, B

Massachusetts

Bentley University, B
Bridgewater State University, B
Bristol Community College, A
Eastern Nazarene College, B

Michigan

Glen Oaks Community College, A
Northwestern Michigan College, A

Minnesota

Hamline University, B
Saint Mary's University of Minnesota, B
University of Minnesota, Crookston, B

Mississippi

University of Southern Mississippi, B

Missouri

Missouri University of Science and Technology, B
Park University, B

Nebraska

Nebraska Wesleyan University, B
Peru State College, B

Nevada

Everest College, A
Sierra Nevada College, B
University of Phoenix - Las Vegas Campus, B

New Hampshire

Southern New Hampshire University, B

New Jersey

County College of Morris, A
New Jersey Institute of Technology, B

New Mexico

University of the Southwest, B

New York

Adelphi University, B
Concordia College - New York, B
Five Towns College, AB
Genesee Community College, A
Hofstra University, B
Long Island Business Institute, A
Morrisville State College, B
New York University, B
Niagara County Community College, A
Queensborough Community College of the City University of New York, A
Schenectady County Community College, A
Skidmore College, B
State University of New York College of Agriculture and Technology at Cobleskill, B
State University of New York College of Technology at Alfred, B
State University of New York College of Technology at Canton, B
State University of New York College of Technology at Delhi, B
State University of New York Maritime College, B
State University of New York at Plattsburgh, B
Utica College, B

North Carolina

Sandhills Community College, A

Ohio

American National University (Cincinnati), A
Bowling Green State University, B
Clark State Community College, A
Columbus State Community College, A
James A. Rhodes State College, A
Stautzenberger College (Maumee), A
Xavier University, B

Oklahoma

Oklahoma Wesleyan University, AB
Tulsa Community College, A

Oregon

Corban University, B
Multnomah University, B

Pennsylvania

Bucks County Community College, A
Butler County Community College, A
Duquesne University, B
Eastern University, B
Lehigh University, B
Manor College, A
Mercyhurst University, B
Messiah College, B
Penn State University Park, B
Pittsburgh Career Institute, A
Point Park University, B
Seton Hill University, B
Susquehanna University, B

South Carolina

Claflin University, B
Miller-Motte Technical College (North Charleston), A

South Dakota

Presentation College, AB

Tennessee

Miller-Motte Technical College (Clarksville), A
Trevecca Nazarene University, B

Texas

Arlington Baptist College, B
Baylor University, B
Howard Payne University, B

Utah

LDS Business College, A

Washington

Columbia Basin College, A
Walla Walla University, B

Wisconsin

Milwaukee Area Technical College, A
University of Wisconsin - Stout, B
University of Wisconsin - Whitewater, B

U.S. Territories: Puerto Rico

Polytechnic University of Puerto Rico, B

Canada

Alberta

University of Alberta, B

Ontario

The University of Western Ontario, B

BUSINESS/MANAGERIAL ECONOMICS

United States

Alabama

Alabama Agricultural and Mechanical University, B
Auburn University, B
Auburn University at Montgomery, B
Samford University, B
Spring Hill College, B
Troy University, B
The University of Alabama, B
The University of Alabama at Birmingham, B
The University of Alabama in Huntsville, B
University of North Alabama, B

Alaska

University of Alaska Anchorage, B

Arizona

Northern Arizona University, B
The University of Arizona, B

Arkansas

Arkansas State University, B
Arkansas Tech University, B
University of Arkansas, B

California

California Institute of Technology, B
California State University, East Bay, B
California State University, Fullerton, B
California State University, Long Beach, B
Chapman University, B
Los Medanos College, A
Mills College, B
Point Loma Nazarene University, B
Sonoma State University, B
University of California, Irvine, B
University of California, Los Angeles, B
University of California, Riverside, B
University of California, Santa Cruz, B
University of San Diego, B
University of San Francisco, B
Westmont College, B

Colorado

Colorado State University - Pueblo, B
Fort Lewis College, B
University of Denver, B
Western State Colorado University, B

Connecticut

Quinnipiac University, B
Southern Connecticut State University, B

Delaware

Delaware State University, B

District of Columbia

The George Washington University, B

Florida

Jacksonville University, B
South Florida State College, A
State College of Florida Manatee-Sarasota, A
Stetson University, B
University of Central Florida, B
University of Miami, B
University of North Florida, B
University of South Florida, St. Petersburg, B
University of West Florida, B

Georgia

Armstrong State University, B
Berry College, B
Clark Atlanta University, B
Georgia College & State University, B
Georgia Institute of Technology, B
Georgia Southern University, B
Georgia State University, B
Kennesaw State University, B
Oglethorpe University, B
Shorter University, B
University of Georgia, B
University of West Georgia, B
Valdosta State University, B

Hawaii

Hawai'i Pacific University, AB

Idaho

Boise State University, B
University of Idaho, B

Illinois

Benedictine University, B
Bradley University, B
DePaul University, B
Illinois College, B
Lake Forest College, B
Lewis University, B
Loyola University Chicago, B
Southern Illinois University Carbondale, B
Southern Illinois University Edwardsville, B
Western Illinois University, B
Wheaton College, B

Indiana

Anderson University, B
Ball State University, B
Huntington University, B
Indiana University - Purdue University Fort Wayne, B
Taylor University, B
University of Indianapolis, B

Iowa

Buena Vista University, B
The University of Iowa, B

Kansas

Bethany College, B
Central Christian College of Kansas, A
Fort Hays State University, B
Washburn University, B

Kentucky

Campbellsville University, AB
Georgetown College, B
Kentucky Wesleyan College, B
Morehead State University, B
Northern Kentucky University, B
University of Kentucky, B
University of Louisville, B
Western Kentucky University, B

Louisiana

Grambling State University, B
Louisiana State University and Agricultural & Mechanical College, B
Louisiana State University in Shreveport, B
Louisiana Tech University, B

Loyola University New Orleans, B
Southern University and Agricultural and Mechanical College, B
University of Louisiana at Lafayette, B

Maine

Husson University, B
University of Maine at Farmington, B

Maryland

Morgan State University, B
Salisbury University, B

Massachusetts

Bentley University, B
Boston College, B
Nichols College, B

Michigan

Andrews University, B
Eastern Michigan University, B
Grand Valley State University, B
Hope College, B
Lake Superior State University, B
Oakland University, B
Olivet College, B
Saginaw Valley State University, B
Western Michigan University, B

Minnesota

Gustavus Adolphus College, B
Vermilion Community College, A

Mississippi

Jackson State University, B
Mississippi State University, B
University of Mississippi, B
University of Southern Mississippi, B

Missouri

College of the Ozarks, B
Missouri Southern State University, B
Northwest Missouri State University, B
Park University, B
Saint Louis University, B
University of Missouri, B
Washington University in St. Louis, B

Montana

Montana State University Billings, B

Nebraska

University of Nebraska - Lincoln, B
University of Nebraska at Omaha, B

Nevada

College of Southern Nevada, A
University of Nevada, Reno, B

New Hampshire

Saint Anselm College, B

New Jersey

Rider University, B
Saint Peter's University, AB
Seton Hall University, B

New York

Bard College, B
Baruch College of the City University of New York, B
Canisius College, B
College of Mount Saint Vincent, B
Fordham University, B
Hofstra University, B
Ithaca College, B
Marymount Manhattan College, B
New York University, B
Niagara University, B
Pace University, B
Pace University, Pleasantville Campus, B
State University of New York College at Oneonta, B
State University of New York College at Potsdam, B
State University of New York at Plattsburgh, B

Union College, B
University of Rochester, B
Utica College, B

North Carolina

Greensboro College, B
High Point University, B
Mars Hill University, B
North Carolina State University, B
Pfeiffer University, B
The University of North Carolina at Charlotte, B
The University of North Carolina at Greensboro, B

North Dakota

University of North Dakota, B

Ohio

Bowling Green State University, B
Capital University, B
Cleveland State University, B
The College of Wooster, B
Kent State University, B
Miami University, B
Miami University Hamilton, B
Miami University Middletown, A
The Ohio State University, B
The Ohio State University at Lima, B
The Ohio State University - Mansfield Campus, B
The Ohio State University at Marion, B
The Ohio State University - Newark Campus, B
Ohio University, B
Ohio Wesleyan University, B
Otterbein University, B
University of Dayton, B
Urbana University, AB
Wilmington College, B
Wright State University, B
Xavier University, B
Youngstown State University, B

Oklahoma

Oklahoma State University, B
Oklahoma Wesleyan University, B
University of Central Oklahoma, B
University of Oklahoma, B

Pennsylvania

Allegheny College, B
Arcadia University, B
Chatham University, B
Clarion University of Pennsylvania, B
Duquesne University, B
Grove City College, B
Lehigh University, B
Mercyhurst University, B
Penn State Abington, B
Penn State Altoona, B
Penn State Beaver, B
Penn State Berks, B
Penn State Brandywine, B
Penn State DuBois, B
Penn State Erie, The Behrend College, B
Penn State Fayette, The Eberly Campus, B
Penn State Greater Allegheny, B
Penn State Hazleton, B
Penn State Lehigh Valley, B
Penn State Mont Alto, B
Penn State New Kensington, B
Penn State Schuylkill, B
Penn State Shenango, B
Penn State Wilkes-Barre, B
Penn State Worthington Scranton, B
Penn State York, B
University of Pittsburgh at Johnstown, B
Villanova University, B
West Chester University of Pennsylvania, B
Widener University, B

Rhode Island

Bryant University, B

South Carolina

Charleston Southern University, B
Coastal Carolina University, B
Converse College, B

Francis Marion University, B
Limestone College, B
Presbyterian College, B
South Carolina State University, B
University of South Carolina, B
Wofford College, B

South Dakota

Northern State University, B

Tennessee

Belmont University, B
Carson-Newman University, B
East Tennessee State University, B
Lincoln Memorial University, B
Lipscomb University, B
Middle Tennessee State University, B
Tennessee State University, B
Union University, B
University of Memphis, B
The University of Tennessee, B
The University of Tennessee at Martin, B

Texas

Baylor University, B
Lamar University, B
Midwestern State University, B
Sam Houston State University, B
Stephen F. Austin State University, B
Tarleton State University, B
Texas A&M International University, B
Texas State University, B
University of the Incarnate Word, B
University of Mary Hardin-Baylor, B
University of North Texas, B
The University of Texas at Arlington, B
The University of Texas of the Permian Basin, B
The University of Texas at San Antonio, B
West Texas A&M University, B

Utah

Weber State University, B
Westminster College, B

Vermont

Green Mountain College, B

Virginia

Hampden-Sydney College, B
James Madison University, B
Old Dominion University, B
Patrick Henry College, B
Randolph-Macon College, B
Virginia Commonwealth University, B
Virginia Polytechnic Institute and State University, B
Virginia State University, B

Washington

Central Washington University, B
Eastern Washington University, B
Gonzaga University, B
Seattle University, B

West Virginia

Marshall University, B
West Liberty University, B
West Virginia University, B
West Virginia Wesleyan College, B

Wisconsin

Beloit College, B
Marquette University, B
University of Wisconsin - Superior, B

Wyoming

University of Wyoming, B

U.S. Territories: Puerto Rico

Inter American University of Puerto Rico, Bayamón Campus, B
Inter American University of Puerto Rico, Metropolitan Campus, B
Inter American University of Puerto Rico, San Germán Campus, B

Pontifical Catholic University of Puerto Rico, B
Universidad Metropolitana, B
University of Puerto Rico, Río Piedras Campus, B

Canada

Alberta

University of Alberta, B
University of Lethbridge, B

Manitoba

University of Manitoba, B

Maritime Provinces: New Brunswick

Mount Allison University, B
University of New Brunswick Fredericton, B

Maritime Provinces: Nova Scotia

Saint Mary's University, B

Ontario

Brock University, B
University of Guelph, B
The University of Western Ontario, B
University of Windsor, B
York University, B

Quebec

Bishop's University, B
HEC Montreal, B
McGill University, B
Université du Québec à Trois-Rivières, B

Saskatchewan

University of Saskatchewan, B

BUSINESS/OFFICE AUTOMATION/TECHNOLOGY/DATA ENTRY

United States

Alaska

University of Alaska Anchorage, A

Arizona

GateWay Community College, A
Northland Pioneer College, A
Paradise Valley Community College, A

Arkansas

Ozarka College, A

California

Pasadena City College, A
Santiago Canyon College, A

Colorado

Aims Community College, A
Colorado Mesa University, A
Pueblo Community College, A
Trinidad State Junior College, A

Delaware

Delaware Technical & Community College, Jack F. Owens Campus, A
Delaware Technical & Community College, Stanton/Wilmington Campus, A
Delaware Technical & Community College, Terry Campus, A

District of Columbia

University of the District of Columbia, A

Florida

Fortis College (Orange Park), A
Miami Dade College, A

Illinois

Black Hawk College, A
College of Lake County, A
Danville Area Community College, A
Illinois Eastern Community Colleges, Frontier Community College, A
Illinois Eastern Community Colleges, Lincoln Trail College, A
Illinois Eastern Community Colleges, Olney Central College, A
Illinois Eastern Community Colleges, Wabash Valley College, A
Illinois Valley Community College, A
Kaskaskia College, A
Lincoln Land Community College, A
Parkland College, A
Shawnee Community College, A
Waubonsee Community College, A

Indiana

Ivy Tech Community College - Bloomington, A
Ivy Tech Community College - Central Indiana, A
Ivy Tech Community College - Columbus, A
Ivy Tech Community College - Lafayette, A
Ivy Tech Community College - North Central, A
Ivy Tech Community College - Northeast, A
Ivy Tech Community College - Northwest, A
Ivy Tech Community College - Richmond, A
Ivy Tech Community College - Southeast, A
Ivy Tech Community College - Southern Indiana, A
Ivy Tech Community College - Southwest, A

Iowa

Iowa Lakes Community College, A
Northeast Iowa Community College, A
Western Iowa Tech Community College, A

Kentucky

Daymar College (Owensboro), A
Maysville Community and Technical College (Morehead), A

Maryland

Garrett College, A

Massachusetts

Bay State College, AB
Berkshire Community College, A
Massasoit Community College, A

Michigan

Alpena Community College, A
Macomb Community College, A
Northern Michigan University, A
Northwestern Michigan College, A
Oakland Community College, A
Schoolcraft College, A

Minnesota

Lake Superior College, A
Minneapolis Community and Technical College, A
Minnesota State Community and Technical College, A

Mississippi

Antonelli College (Hattiesburg), A
Antonelli College (Jackson), A
East Central Community College, A
Holmes Community College, A

Missouri

Baptist Bible College, A
Crowder College, A
Metro Business College (Cape Girardeau), A
Metro Business College (Rolla), A

Montana

Fort Peck Community College, A
Montana State University Billings, A
Montana State University - Northern, A

New Hampshire

Lakes Region Community College, A

New Jersey

Bergen Community College, A

New York

ASA College, A

North Carolina

East Carolina University, B

North Dakota

Bismarck State College, A
Dakota College at Bottineau, A
Nueta Hidatsa Sahnish College, A
United Tribes Technical College, A

Ohio

Mount Vernon Nazarene University, B
Stautzenberger College (Maumee), A
The University of Akron, A
University of Rio Grande, A

Oregon

Tillamook Bay Community College, A

Pennsylvania

Community College of Allegheny County, A
Lansdale School of Business, A
Laurel Business Institute, A
Laurel Technical Institute, A

South Dakota

Mitchell Technical Institute, A

Texas

El Centro College, A
El Paso Community College, A
Grayson College, A
Hallmark University, A
Houston Community College, A
Panola College, A
Paris Junior College, A

Utah

Utah Valley University, A

Virginia

ECPI University (Virginia Beach), A

Washington

Clark College, A
Renton Technical College, A

West Virginia

Potomac State College of West Virginia University,
  A

Wyoming

Casper College, A

U.S. Territories: Guam

Guam Community College, A

U.S. Territories: Puerto Rico

Pontifical Catholic University of Puerto Rico, B
Universidad del Este, B

BUSINESS OPERATIONS SUPPORT AND SECRETARIAL SERVICES

United States

Arizona

Eastern Arizona College, A

Arkansas

Pulaski Technical College, A

Delaware

Delaware State University, B

Kansas

Seward County Community College and Area Technical School, A

Massachusetts

Bristol Community College, A
Bunker Hill Community College, A

Mississippi

Coahoma Community College, A

Nebraska

Northeast Community College, A

New Jersey

Thomas Edison State University, A

New York

Genesee Community College, A
State University of New York at New Paltz, B

Ohio

Clark State Community College, A
Davis College, A

Texas

Virginia College in Austin, A

Utah

Provo College, A

Virginia

Central Virginia Community College, A
Danville Community College, A
Lord Fairfax Community College, A
Mountain Empire Community College, A
Southwest Virginia Community College, A
Thomas Nelson Community College, A

West Virginia

Eastern West Virginia Community and Technical
  College, A

U.S. Territories: Puerto Rico

Pontifical Catholic University of Puerto Rico, B

BUSINESS AND PERSONAL/ FINANCIAL SERVICES MARKETING OPERATIONS

United States

Arizona

Northland Pioneer College, A

Florida

North Florida Community College, A

Illinois

Heartland Community College, A

Kansas

Hutchinson Community College, A

Massachusetts

Anna Maria College, B

Michigan

Northwestern Michigan College, A

Missouri

Lindenwood University, B

Texas

North Central Texas College, A

Utah

Dixie State University, AB

Washington

Spokane Falls Community College, A
Walla Walla University, B

Canada

Ontario

Nipissing University, B

BUSINESS STATISTICS

United States

Alabama

Alabama Agricultural and Mechanical University, B

Colorado

University of Denver, B

Louisiana

Loyola University New Orleans, B
Southwest University, B

Missouri

University of Central Missouri, B

Oregon

Southern Oregon University, B

Rhode Island

Bryant University, B

Tennessee

The University of Tennessee, B

Texas

Baylor University, B

U.S. Territories: Puerto Rico

University of Puerto Rico, Río Piedras Campus, B

Canada

Ontario

York University, B

Quebec

HEC Montreal, B

BUSINESS TEACHER EDUCATION

United States

Alabama

Auburn University, B
Oakwood University, B
Wallace State Community College, A

Arizona

Arizona Christian University, B
Eastern Arizona College, A

Arkansas

Arkansas State University, B
Arkansas Tech University, B
John Brown University, B
Shorter College, A
Southern Arkansas University - Magnolia, B
University of Arkansas at Pine Bluff, B
University of Central Arkansas, B

California

Ashford University, B
California State University, Dominguez Hills, B
Mt. San Antonio College, A
Porterville College, A

Rio Hondo College, A

Colorado

Adams State University, B

Delaware

Delaware State University, B

Florida

Bethune-Cookman University, B
St. Petersburg College, B
South Florida State College, A

Georgia

Bainbridge State College, A
Darton State College, A
Emmanuel College, B

Hawaii

Brigham Young University - Hawaii, B

Idaho

North Idaho College, A

Illinois

Illinois State University, B
John A. Logan College, A
McKendree University, B
Spoon River College, A
Trinity Christian College, B
University of Illinois at Urbana - Champaign, B

Indiana

Ball State University, B
Goshen College, B
Grace College, B
Indiana State University, B
Oakland City University, B
Saint Mary's College, B
University of Indianapolis, B
University of Saint Francis, B
University of Southern Indiana, B

Iowa

Buena Vista University, B
Dordt College, B
Iowa Central Community College, A
Iowa Lakes Community College, A
Northwestern College, B
University of Northern Iowa, B
Upper Iowa University, B

Kansas

Allen Community College, A
Bethany College, B
Central Christian College of Kansas, A
Fort Hays State University, B
Friends University, B
Pratt Community College, A
Tabor College, B

Kentucky

Campbellsville University, B
Eastern Kentucky University, B
Morehead State University, B
Northern Kentucky University, B
Thomas More College, B
Western Kentucky University, B

Louisiana

Louisiana College, B
Louisiana Tech University, B
Nicholls State University, B

Maine

University of Maine at Machias, B

Maryland

Morgan State University, B
Prince George's Community College, A
University of Maryland Eastern Shore, B

Massachusetts

Eastern Nazarene College, B
Northern Essex Community College, A

Michigan

Eastern Michigan University, B
Western Michigan University, B

Minnesota

Concordia College, B
Pine Technical and Community College, A
University of Minnesota, Twin Cities Campus, B
Winona State University, B

Mississippi

Coahoma Community College, A
Mississippi Gulf Coast Community College, A
Mississippi State University, B
Northeast Mississippi Community College, A
Rust College, B
Southwest Mississippi Community College, A
University of Southern Mississippi, B

Missouri

Avila University, B
Evangel University, B
Hannibal-LaGrange University, B
Lincoln University, B
Lindenwood University, B
Missouri Baptist University, B
Missouri State University, B
Northwest Missouri State University, B
University of Central Missouri, B
University of Missouri, B

Montana

Montana State University - Northern, B
University of Montana, B
The University of Montana Western, B

Nebraska

Chadron State College, B
College of Saint Mary, B
Concordia University, Nebraska, B
Doane University, B
Grace University, B
Hastings College, B
Midland University, B
Peru State College, B
Union College, B
University of Nebraska at Kearney, B
University of Nebraska - Lincoln, B
Wayne State College, B
York College, B

New Jersey

Essex County College, A
Rider University, B

New Mexico

New Mexico Junior College, A
Western New Mexico University, B

New York

Alfred University, B
Bronx Community College of the City University of
    New York, A
Buffalo State College, State University of New York,
    B
Canisius College, B
Hofstra University, B
Lehman College of the City University of New York,
    B
Nazareth College of Rochester, B
Niagara University, B
Utica College, B

North Carolina

East Carolina University, B
Fayetteville State University, B
Isothermal Community College, A
Louisburg College, A
North Carolina Agricultural and Technical State Uni-
    versity, B

North Dakota

Dickinson State University, B
Minot State University, B
University of Mary, B
Valley City State University, B

Ohio

Bowling Green State University, B
Mount Vernon Nazarene University, B
Ohio Wesleyan University, B
The University of Findlay, B
University of Rio Grande, B
Wilmington College, B
Wright State University, AB

Oklahoma

East Central University, B
Eastern Oklahoma State College, A
Oklahoma Panhandle State University, B
Oral Roberts University, B
University of Central Oklahoma, B

Oregon

Corban University, B
Mt. Hood Community College, A

Pennsylvania

Gwynedd Mercy University, B
Immaculata University, B
Mercyhurst University, B
Robert Morris University, B
Saint Vincent College, B

South Carolina

South Carolina State University, B

South Dakota

Black Hills State University, B
Dakota State University, B
Dakota Wesleyan University, B

Tennessee

Carson-Newman University, B
Lee University, B
Martin Methodist College, B
Middle Tennessee State University, B
Roane State Community College, A
Tennessee State University, B
Trevecca Nazarene University, B
Union University, B
The University of Tennessee at Martin, B

Texas

Amarillo College, A
Baylor University, B
Cisco College, A
Hardin-Simmons University, B
Howard Payne University, B
LeTourneau University, B
Paris Junior College, A
Sam Houston State University, B
Southwestern Adventist University, B
Trinity Valley Community College, A
Wayland Baptist University, B
Wiley College, B

Utah

Snow College, A
Southern Utah University, B
Utah State University, B
Utah Valley University, B
Weber State University, B

Virginia

Bluefield College, B
Emory & Henry College, B
Hampton University, B
Norfolk State University, B
Virginia Union University, B

Washington

Eastern Washington University, B
Walla Walla University, B

West Virginia

Concord University, B
Davis & Elkins College, B
Fairmont State University, B
Glenville State College, B

Wisconsin

Concordia University Wisconsin, B
Edgewood College, B
Madison Area Technical College, A
Maranatha Baptist University, B
University of Wisconsin - Superior, B
University of Wisconsin - Whitewater, B
Viterbo University, B

Wyoming

Eastern Wyoming College, A

U.S. Territories: Puerto Rico

National University College (Bayamón), B
Pontifical Catholic University of Puerto Rico, B

Canada

Alberta

University of Alberta, B
University of Lethbridge, B

British Columbia

The University of British Columbia, B

Maritime Provinces: New Brunswick

University of New Brunswick Fredericton, B

Quebec

Université du Québec en Abitibi-Témiscamingue, B
Université du Québec à Chicoutimi, B
Université du Québec à Rimouski, B

Saskatchewan

University of Regina, B

CABINETMAKING AND MILLWORK/MILLWRIGHT

United States

Alabama

George C. Wallace Community College, A

Arizona

GateWay Community College, A

California

Cerritos College, A
Long Beach City College, A
Palomar College, A
Sierra College, A

Georgia

Central Georgia Technical College, A

Idaho

College of Southern Idaho, A

Indiana

Ivy Tech Community College - Bloomington, A
Ivy Tech Community College - Central Indiana, A
Ivy Tech Community College - Columbus, A
Ivy Tech Community College - Lafayette, A
Ivy Tech Community College - North Central, A
Ivy Tech Community College - Northeast, A
Ivy Tech Community College - Northwest, A
Ivy Tech Community College - Richmond, A
Ivy Tech Community College - Southern Indiana, A
Ivy Tech Community College - Southwest, A
Ivy Tech Community College - Wabash Valley, A

Michigan

Macomb Community College, A

Pennsylvania

Bucks County Community College, A
Johnson College, A
Thaddeus Stevens College of Technology, A

Utah

Utah Valley University, A

Canada

British Columbia

British Columbia Institute of Technology, A

CAD/CADD DRAFTING AND/OR DESIGN TECHNOLOGY/TECHNICIAN

United States

Alabama

Virginia College in Mobile, A

Alaska

Charter College, A

Arizona

Arizona Western College, A
Glendale Community College, A
Pima Community College, A

Arkansas

University of Arkansas - Fort Smith, A

California

The Art Institute of California - Hollywood, a campus of Argosy University, B
The Art Institute of California - Inland Empire, a campus of Argosy University, B
The Art Institute of California - Los Angeles, a campus of Argosy University, B
The Art Institute of California - Orange County, a campus of Argosy University, B
The Art Institute of California - San Diego, a campus of Argosy University, B

Colorado

The Art Institute of Colorado, B
Front Range Community College, A
Pikes Peak Community College, A

Delaware

Delaware Technical & Community College, Stanton/Wilmington Campus, A

Florida

Florida Technical College (DeLand), A
Florida Technical College (Orlando), A
Gulf Coast State College, A
Keiser University, A
Miami Dade College, A
Southern Technical College (Tampa), A
Tallahassee Community College, A

Idaho

Idaho State University, AB

Illinois

Danville Area Community College, A
Elgin Community College, A
Heartland Community College, A
Illinois Valley Community College, A
John A. Logan College, A
John Wood Community College, A
Kishwaukee College, A
Lewis and Clark Community College, A
Morrison Institute of Technology, A
South Suburban College, A
Triton College, A
Waubonsee Community College, A

Iowa

Vatterott College, A

Kansas

Johnson County Community College, A
Kansas City Kansas Community College, A
Manhattan Area Technical College, A

Kentucky

Gateway Community and Technical College, A
Murray State University, B
Sullivan College of Technology and Design, A

Louisiana

Delta School of Business and Technology, A

Maine

Eastern Maine Community College, A

Michigan

Bay de Noc Community College, A
Eastern Michigan University, B
Ferris State University, AB
Henry Ford College, A
Kalamazoo Valley Community College, A
Kellogg Community College, A
Northern Michigan University, A
Washtenaw Community College, A
Wayne County Community College District, A

Minnesota

Century College, A
Dunwoody College of Technology, A
Hennepin Technical College, A
Lake Superior College, A
Minnesota State College - Southeast Technical, A
Northland Community and Technical College, A
Rochester Community and Technical College, A

Missouri

Jefferson College, A
Missouri Southern State University, A
State Fair Community College, A
Vatterott College (Kansas City), A
Vatterott College (Springfield), A
Vatterott College (Sunset Hills), A

Montana

Montana Tech of The University of Montana, A

Nevada

The Art Institute of Las Vegas, A
College of Southern Nevada, A

New Hampshire

Great Bay Community College, A

New Mexico

Navajo Technical University, A

New York

Corning Community College, A
Erie Community College, South Campus, A
Hudson Valley Community College, A
Mohawk Valley Community College, A
Morrisville State College, A
State University of New York College of Technology at Delhi, A

North Carolina

Asheville-Buncombe Technical Community College, A

Ohio

Central Ohio Technical College, A
Kent State University at Tuscarawas, A
Northwest State Community College, A
Shawnee State University, A
Southern State Community College, A

Oregon

Central Oregon Community College, A
Chemeketa Community College, A

Clackamas Community College, A

Pennsylvania

Butler County Community College, A
Delaware County Community College, A
Northampton Community College, A
Thaddeus Stevens College of Technology, A
YTI Career Institute - York, A

Tennessee

Vatterott College (Memphis), A
Virginia College in Chattanooga, A

Texas

The Art Institute of Austin, a branch of The Art Institute of Houston, B
The Art Institute of Houston, B
The Art Institute of San Antonio, a branch of The Art Institute of Houston, B
College of the Mainland, A
St. Philip's College, A
Tyler Junior College, A

Utah

Southern Utah University, A

Vermont

Community College of Vermont, A

Virginia

Mountain Empire Community College, A
Thomas Nelson Community College, A

Washington

Everett Community College, A
Lake Washington Institute of Technology, A

West Virginia

BridgeValley Community and Technical College (South Charleston), A

Wyoming

Northwest College, A
Sheridan College, A

CANADIAN GOVERNMENT AND POLITICS

Canada

British Columbia

The University of British Columbia, B

CANADIAN HISTORY

Canada

Quebec

McGill University, B

CANADIAN STUDIES

United States

Maine

University of Maine, M

New York

University at Buffalo, the State University of New York, MO

North Carolina

Duke University, B

Washington

University of Washington, B
Western Washington University, B

Canada

Alberta

Athabasca University, B
Concordia University of Edmonton, B
University of Alberta, B
University of Calgary, B
University of Lethbridge, BM

British Columbia

Thompson Rivers University, AB
The University of British Columbia, B
University of Northern British Columbia, B

Manitoba

Brandon University, B
Université de Saint-Boniface, M
University of Manitoba, BM
The University of Winnipeg, B

Maritime Provinces: New Brunswick

Mount Allison University, B
University of New Brunswick Fredericton, B

Maritime Provinces: Nova Scotia

Acadia University, B
Dalhousie University, B
St. Francis Xavier University, B
Saint Mary's University, BMO
Université Sainte-Anne, B

Maritime Provinces: Prince Edward Island

University of Prince Edward Island, B

Newfoundland and Labrador

Memorial University of Newfoundland, B

Ontario

Brock University, B
Carleton University, BMD
Queen's University at Kingston, BD
Trent University, BMD
University of Ottawa, BD
University of Toronto, B
University of Waterloo, B
The University of Western Ontario, B
Wilfrid Laurier University, BM
York University, B

Quebec

Bishop's University, B
Université du Québec à Chicoutimi, M
Université de Sherbrooke, MD

Saskatchewan

University of Regina, MD
University of Saskatchewan, MD

CANCER BIOLOGY/ONCOLOGY

United States

Alabama

The University of Alabama at Birmingham, D

Arizona

The University of Arizona, D

California

University of Southern California, D

Colorado

University of Colorado Denver, D

Connecticut

Yale University, D

Delaware

University of Delaware, MD

District of Columbia

University of the District of Columbia, M

Florida

University of Miami, D
University of South Florida, MD

Georgia

Emory University, D

Illinois

University of Chicago, D

Indiana

Purdue University, D

Michigan

University of Michigan, MD
Wayne State University, MD

Minnesota

University of Minnesota, Twin Cities Campus, D

Nebraska

University of Nebraska Medical Center, D

New Hampshire

Dartmouth College, D

New Jersey

Rutgers University - New Brunswick, MD
Rutgers University - Newark, D

New York

New York University, D
University at Buffalo, the State University of New York, M

North Carolina

Duke University, D
Wake Forest University, D

Ohio

Case Western Reserve University, D
University of Cincinnati, D
The University of Toledo, MD

Oregon

Oregon Health & Science University, D

Pennsylvania

Thomas Jefferson University, D
University of Pennsylvania, D

South Carolina

Medical University of South Carolina, D

Tennessee

Vanderbilt University, MD

Texas

The University of Texas Health Science Center at Houston, MD

Utah

University of Utah, MD

West Virginia

West Virginia University, MD

Wisconsin

University of Wisconsin - La Crosse, M
University of Wisconsin - Madison, D

Canada

Alberta

University of Alberta, MD
University of Calgary, MD

Manitoba

University of Manitoba, M

Newfoundland and Labrador

Memorial University of Newfoundland, MD

Ontario

McMaster University, MD
Queen's University at Kingston, MD

Quebec

Université Laval, O

Saskatchewan

University of Regina, MD

CARDIOPULMONARY TECH-NOLOGY/TECHNOLOGIST

United States

Louisiana

Fletcher Technical Community College, A

Oklahoma

Bacone College, A

Pennsylvania

Lackawanna College, A

U.S. Territories: Puerto Rico

Inter American University of Puerto Rico, Bar-ranquitas Campus, A

CARDIOVASCULAR SCIENCES

United States

Connecticut

Quinnipiac University, M

Florida

University of South Florida, O

Georgia

Augusta University, MD

Illinois

Loyola University Chicago, O

Maryland

Johns Hopkins University, MD

New Hampshire

Dartmouth College, D

North Carolina

Forsyth Technical Community College, A

North Dakota

University of Mary, M

Ohio

The University of Toledo, MD

Pennsylvania

Geneva College, M

South Carolina

Medical University of South Carolina, D

South Dakota

The University of South Dakota, MD

Wisconsin

Marquette University, M
Milwaukee School of Engineering, M

Canada

Alberta

University of Calgary, MD

Newfoundland and Labrador

Memorial University of Newfoundland, MD

Ontario

McMaster University, MD
Queen's University at Kingston, MD
University of Guelph, DO

Quebec

Université Laval, O

CARDIOVASCULAR TECHNOL-OGY/TECHNOLOGIST

United States

Alabama

Community College of the Air Force, A

Arkansas

Arkansas Tech University, A
Southeast Arkansas College, A

California

Grossmont College, A
Orange Coast College, A

Delaware

Delaware Technical & Community College, Stanton/Wilmington Campus, A

Florida

Florida SouthWestern State College, A
Florida State College at Jacksonville, A
Polk State College, A
Santa Fe College, A
Valencia College, A

Georgia

Augusta Technical College, A
Central Georgia Technical College, A
Darton State College, A

Illinois

Harper College, A

Kentucky

Daymar College (Bowling Green), A

Louisiana

Louisiana State University Health Sciences Center, B
Southern University at Shreveport, A

Maine

Southern Maine Community College, A

Maryland

Howard Community College, A

Massachusetts

Bunker Hill Community College, A

Michigan

Kirtland Community College, A

Minnesota

Rochester Community and Technical College, A
St. Cloud Technical & Community College, A

Nebraska

Nebraska Methodist College, A

Nevada

College of Southern Nevada, A

New York

Hudson Valley Community College, A
Molloy College, A

North Carolina

Forsyth Technical Community College, A

Ohio

Mercy College of Ohio, A

Pennsylvania

Harrisburg Area Community College, A
Pennsylvania College of Health Sciences, A

South Carolina

Medical University of South Carolina, B

South Dakota

Southeast Technical Institute, A

Tennessee

Northeast State Community College, A

Texas

El Centro College, A
Houston Community College, A
Texas Southmost College, A

Utah

Weber State University, B

Virginia

Sentara College of Health Sciences, A

Wisconsin

Milwaukee Area Technical College, A

U.S. Territories: Puerto Rico

Pontifical Catholic University of Puerto Rico, B
Universidad Metropolitana, B

Canada

British Columbia

British Columbia Institute of Technology, A

CARIBBEAN STUDIES

United States

Illinois

Northwestern University, B

New York

Brooklyn College of the City University of New York, B
Columbia University, School of General Studies, B
Hofstra University, B

Canada

Quebec

McGill University, B

CARPENTRY/CARPENTER

United States

Alabama

George C. Wallace Community College, A
Wallace State Community College, A

Alaska

University of Alaska Fairbanks, A
University of Alaska Southeast, A

Arizona

Arizona Western College, A
Coconino Community College, A
GateWay Community College, A
Northland Pioneer College, A

California

American River College, A
Bakersfield College, A
College of the Sequoias, A
Fresno City College, A
Fullerton College, A
Gavilan College, A
Laney College, A
Lassen Community College District, A
Long Beach City College, A
Los Angeles Trade-Technical College, A
Merced College, A
Palomar College, A
Porterville College, A
Saddleback College, A
San Diego City College, A
Santiago Canyon College, A

Florida

Indian River State College, A

Georgia

Central Georgia Technical College, A

Hawaii

Hawaii Community College, A
Honolulu Community College, A
Kauai Community College, A
University of Hawaii Maui College, A

Idaho

North Idaho College, A

Illinois

Black Hawk College, A
John A. Logan College, A
John Wood Community College, A
Kaskaskia College, A
Southwestern Illinois College, A

Indiana

Ivy Tech Community College - Central Indiana, A
Ivy Tech Community College - East Central, A
Ivy Tech Community College - Lafayette, A
Ivy Tech Community College - North Central, A
Ivy Tech Community College - Northwest, A
Ivy Tech Community College - Southern Indiana, A
Ivy Tech Community College - Southwest, A
Ivy Tech Community College - Wabash Valley, A

Iowa

Hawkeye Community College, A
Iowa Central Community College, A
Iowa Lakes Community College, A
North Iowa Area Community College, A
Southwestern Community College, A
Western Iowa Tech Community College, A

Kansas

Coffeyville Community College, A
Flint Hills Technical College, A
Hutchinson Community College, A
Manhattan Area Technical College, A
Neosho County Community College, A
Northwest Kansas Technical College, A

Kentucky

Bluegrass Community and Technical College, A

Louisiana

South Louisiana Community College, A

Maine

Northern Maine Community College, A

Michigan

Delta College, A
Lansing Community College, A
Oakland Community College, A
Southwestern Michigan College, A

Minnesota

Hennepin Technical College, A
Minnesota State College - Southeast Technical, A
Minnesota State Community and Technical College, A
Minnesota State Community and Technical College - Moorhead, A
Northland Community and Technical College, A
Ridgewater College, A
St. Cloud Technical & Community College, A
South Central College, A

Mississippi

Coahoma Community College, A
Southwest Mississippi Community College, A

Missouri

Mineral Area College, A
North Central Missouri College, A
Ranken Technical College, A

Montana

Flathead Valley Community College, A
Little Big Horn College, A
Montana State University Billings, A
Montana State University - Northern, A
Montana Tech of The University of Montana, A
Salish Kootenai College, A

Nebraska

Nebraska Indian Community College, A

Nevada

College of Southern Nevada, A

New Mexico

New Mexico Junior College, A
New Mexico State University - Carlsbad, A
San Juan College, A

New York

Fulton-Montgomery Community College, A

North Carolina

Alamance Community College, A
Vance-Granville Community College, A

North Dakota

Bismarck State College, A
Sitting Bull College, A
Turtle Mountain Community College, A

Oregon

Treasure Valley Community College, A

Pennsylvania

Community College of Allegheny County, A
Community College of Beaver County, A
Johnson College, A
Thaddeus Stevens College of Technology, A
Triangle Tech, Bethlehem, A
Triangle Tech, DuBois, A
Triangle Tech, Erie, A
Triangle Tech, Greensburg, A
Triangle Tech, Pittsburgh, A
Triangle Tech, Sunbury, A
Williamson College of the Trades, A

Rhode Island

New England Institute of Technology, A

South Carolina

Piedmont Technical College, A
York Technical College, A

South Dakota

Oglala Lakota College, A

Texas

Austin Community College District, A
North Lake College, A
South Plains College, A

Utah

Southern Utah University, A

Virginia

Liberty University, A

Washington

Bates Technical College, A
Grays Harbor College, A
Green River College, A
Seattle Central College, A
Spokane Community College, A

Wisconsin

Lac Courte Oreilles Ojibwa Community College, A

Wyoming

Central Wyoming College, A

Canada

British Columbia

British Columbia Institute of Technology, A

CARTOGRAPHY

United States

Alabama

Auburn University at Montgomery, B
University of North Alabama, B

Arizona

Arizona State University at the Tempe campus, B
The University of Arizona, B

California

Santiago Canyon College, A

Georgia

Kennesaw State University, B

Kentucky

Western Kentucky University, B

Massachusetts

Salem State University, B

Michigan

Central Michigan University, B
Michigan State University, B
Northern Michigan University, B

Minnesota

Fond du Lac Tribal and Community College, A
University of Minnesota, Duluth, B

Mississippi

Hinds Community College, A

Missouri

Northwest Missouri State University, B

New Jersey

Hudson County Community College, A
Rowan University, B

New Mexico

Central New Mexico Community College, A
Southwestern Indian Polytechnic Institute, A

New York

Binghamton University, State University of New York, B
Borough of Manhattan Community College of the City University of New York, A
State University of New York College at Oneonta, B

Ohio

Clark State Community College, A
The Ohio State University, B
The University of Akron, AB
University of Cincinnati, B
Wright State University, B

Oklahoma

East Central University, B
Oklahoma City Community College, A
University of Oklahoma, B

Pennsylvania

Harrisburg Area Community College, A
Lehigh Carbon Community College, A

South Dakota

Mitchell Technical Institute, A
South Dakota State University, B

Tennessee

Pellissippi State Community College, A
Southwest Tennessee Community College, A

Texas

Austin Community College District, A
Brookhaven College, A
Collin County Community College District, A
Lone Star College - CyFair, A
Stephen F. Austin State University, B
Texas A&M University, B
Texas State University, B
The University of Texas at Dallas, B

Utah

Brigham Young University, B
University of Utah, B

Virginia

Radford University, B

Washington

Central Washington University, B

Wisconsin

University of Wisconsin - Madison, B
University of Wisconsin - Platteville, B

Wyoming

Casper College, A

Canada

Alberta

University of Lethbridge, B

Newfoundland and Labrador

Memorial University of Newfoundland, B

Ontario

Queen's University at Kingston, B
University of Ottawa, B
The University of Western Ontario, B

CELL BIOLOGY AND ANATOMY

United States

Alabama

Auburn University, D
Huntingdon College, B
The University of Alabama at Birmingham, D

Arizona

Arizona State University at the Tempe campus, D
The University of Arizona, MD

Arkansas

University of Arkansas, MD

California

California Institute of Technology, D
California State University, Sacramento, M
San Diego State University, D
San Francisco State University, M
Sonoma State University, M
University of California, Berkeley, D
University of California, Davis, MD
University of California, Irvine, MD
University of California, Los Angeles, MD
University of California, Riverside, MD
University of California, Santa Barbara, MD
University of California, Santa Cruz, MD
University of Southern California, MD

Colorado

Colorado State University, MD
University of Colorado Boulder, MD
University of Colorado Denver, MD
University of Denver, M
Western State Colorado University, B

Connecticut

Quinnipiac University, M
University of Connecticut, MD
University of New Haven, MO
Yale University, D

Delaware

University of Delaware, MD

District of Columbia

The Catholic University of America, MD

Florida

Florida Institute of Technology, M
Florida State University, MD
University of Florida, MD
University of Miami, D
University of South Florida, MD

Georgia

Augusta University, MD
Emory University, D
Georgia State University, MD
University of Georgia, MD

Illinois

Illinois Institute of Technology, M
Illinois State University, M
Loyola University Chicago, MD
Northwestern University, D
Rush University, MD
University of Chicago, D
University of Illinois at Chicago, MD
University of Illinois at Urbana - Champaign, D

Indiana

Indiana State University, D
Indiana University Bloomington, D
Indiana University - Purdue University Indianapolis, MD
Purdue University, D
University of Notre Dame, MD

Iowa

Iowa State University of Science and Technology, MD
The University of Iowa, MD

Kansas

Emporia State University, M
The University of Kansas, MD

Louisiana

Louisiana State University Health Sciences Center, MD
Tulane University, MD

Maryland

Johns Hopkins University, D
University of Maryland, Baltimore County, D
University of Maryland, College Park, MD

Massachusetts

Boston University, MD
Brandeis University, MD
Harvard University, D
Massachusetts Institute of Technology, D
Tufts University, D
University of Massachusetts Amherst, MD

Michigan

Eastern Michigan University, M
Grand Valley State University, M
Michigan State University, MD
University of Michigan, MD
Wayne State University, D

Minnesota

University of Minnesota, Twin Cities Campus, MD

Missouri

Missouri State University, M
University of Missouri, MD
University of Missouri - Kansas City, MD
Washington University in St. Louis, D

Montana

University of Montana, D

Nebraska

University of Nebraska Medical Center, MD

Nevada

University of Nevada, Reno, MD

New Hampshire

Dartmouth College, D

New Jersey

Rutgers University - New Brunswick, MD
Rutgers University - Newark, D

New Mexico

Eastern New Mexico University, M
University of New Mexico, MD

New York

Albany College of Pharmacy and Health Sciences, M
Columbia University, MD
Cornell University, D
New York University, D
State University of New York Downstate Medical Center, D
State University of New York Upstate Medical University, MD
Stony Brook University, State University of New York, MD
University at Albany, State University of New York, MD
University at Buffalo, the State University of New York, D

North Carolina

Appalachian State University, M
Duke University, DO

East Carolina University, D
North Carolina State University, MD
The University of North Carolina at Chapel Hill, MD

North Dakota

North Dakota State University, D
University of North Dakota, MD

Ohio

Case Western Reserve University, MD
Kent State University, D
The Ohio State University, MD
Ohio University, MD
University of Cincinnati, D

Oklahoma

University of Oklahoma Health Sciences Center, MD

Oregon

Oregon Health & Science University, D
Oregon State University, D

Pennsylvania

Carnegie Mellon University, D
Drexel University, MD
Lehigh University, D
Penn State University Park, MD
Thomas Jefferson University, MD
University of Pennsylvania, D
University of Pittsburgh, D
University of the Sciences, MD

Rhode Island

Brown University, MD
University of Rhode Island, MD

South Carolina

Medical University of South Carolina, D
University of South Carolina, MD

South Dakota

The University of South Dakota, MD

Tennessee

Vanderbilt University, MD

Texas

Dallas Baptist University, B
Rice University, MD
Southern Methodist University, MD
The University of Texas at Austin, D
The University of Texas at Dallas, MD
The University of Texas Health Science Center at Houston, MD
The University of Texas Health Science Center at San Antonio, MD
The University of Texas Medical Branch, D
The University of Texas at San Antonio, D

Vermont

University of Vermont, MD

Virginia

University of Virginia, D

Washington

University of Washington, D

West Virginia

West Virginia University, MD

Wisconsin

Marquette University, MD
University of Wisconsin - La Crosse, M
University of Wisconsin - Madison, D

Wyoming

University of Wyoming, D

U.S. Territories: Puerto Rico

Universidad Central del Caribe, MD
University of Puerto Rico, Río Piedras Campus, MD

Canada

Alberta

University of Alberta, MD

British Columbia

The University of British Columbia, MD

Ontario

McMaster University, MD
Queen's University at Kingston, MD
University of Guelph, MD
University of Ottawa, MD
University of Toronto, MD
The University of Western Ontario, BMD

Quebec

McGill University, BMD
Université Laval, MD
Université de Montréal, MD
Université de Sherbrooke, MD

Saskatchewan

University of Saskatchewan, BMD

CELL/CELLULAR BIOLOGY AND ANATOMICAL SCIENCES

United States

California

National University, A

Connecticut

Yale University, B

Louisiana

Tulane University, B

New Jersey

Rutgers University - New Brunswick, B

Pennsylvania

Washington & Jefferson College, B

Texas

University of Mary Hardin-Baylor, B

CELL/CELLULAR BIOLOGY AND HISTOLOGY

United States

California

California State University, Dominguez Hills, B
California State University, Fresno, B
California State University, Long Beach, B
California State University, San Marcos, B
Humboldt State University, B
San Francisco State University, B
Sonoma State University, B
University of California, Davis, B
University of California, San Diego, B
University of California, Santa Cruz, B

Georgia

University of Georgia, B

Illinois

Northwestern University, B
University of Illinois at Urbana - Champaign, B

Louisiana

Tulane University, B

Maryland

Johns Hopkins University, B

Massachusetts

Worcester Polytechnic Institute, B

Minnesota

University of Minnesota, Duluth, B
University of Minnesota, Twin Cities Campus, B

Montana

Montana State University, B

New Jersey

Rutgers University - New Brunswick, B

New York

The College of Saint Rose, B
Long Island University - LIU Post, B

Pennsylvania

Mansfield University of Pennsylvania, B

Vermont

Marlboro College, B

Washington

Western Washington University, B

Wisconsin

Beloit College, B

Canada

Alberta

University of Calgary, B

British Columbia

The University of British Columbia, B

Newfoundland and Labrador

Memorial University of Newfoundland, B

Quebec

McGill University, B

CELL/CELLULAR AND MOLECULAR BIOLOGY

United States

Arizona

The University of Arizona, B

California

California State University Channel Islands, B
University of California, Berkeley, B
University of California, Irvine, B
University of California, Los Angeles, B

Colorado

Adams State University, B
The Colorado College, B
Fort Lewis College, B
University of Colorado Boulder, B

Connecticut

Connecticut College, B
University of Connecticut, B

Florida

Florida State University, B

Georgia

Augusta University, B

Hawaii

University of Hawaii at Manoa, B

Idaho

Northwest Nazarene University, B

Illinois

Bradley University, B
Illinois State University, B
University of Illinois at Urbana - Champaign, B

Indiana

Bethel College, B
Purdue University, B

Maryland

Johns Hopkins University, B

Massachusetts

Bridgewater State University, B
Harvard University, B
Salem State University, B

Michigan

Grand Valley State University, B
University of Michigan, B

Missouri

Missouri State University, B

New York

Binghamton University, State University of New York, B
Canisius College, B

Ohio

Cedarville University, B
Ohio University, B

Oklahoma

Oklahoma City University, B

Pennsylvania

Bucknell University, B

Rhode Island

Bryant University, B
University of Rhode Island, B

South Carolina

Limestone College, B

Tennessee

The University of Tennessee at Martin, B

Texas

Texas A&M University, B
Texas Tech University, B

Vermont

Bennington College, B

Virginia

Christopher Newport University, B
Liberty University, B
Marymount University, B

Washington

Central Washington University, B
Seattle Pacific University, B
Seattle University, B
University of Washington, B
Western Washington University, B

Wisconsin

University of Wisconsin - Superior, B

Canada

Alberta

Mount Royal University, B
University of Alberta, B

Quebec

Concordia University, B

Saskatchewan

University of Regina, B

CELTIC LANGUAGES, LITERATURES, AND LINGUISTICS

United States

California

University of California, Berkeley, B

Massachusetts

Harvard University, D

CENTRAL/MIDDLE AND EASTERN EUROPEAN STUDIES

United States

California

Pomona College, B
San Diego State University, B

Florida

State College of Florida Manatee-Sarasota, A

Maine

Bowdoin College, B

Massachusetts

Tufts University, B

Michigan

Wayne State University, B

Missouri

University of Missouri, B
Washington University in St. Louis, B

Ohio

Wittenberg University, B

Oregon

Portland State University, B

Vermont

Marlboro College, B

Canada

British Columbia

The University of British Columbia, B
University of Victoria, B

Ontario

Carleton University, B
University of Toronto, B

CERAMIC ARTS AND CERAMICS

United States

Alabama

The University of Alabama, M

Alaska

University of Alaska Fairbanks, M

Arizona

Arizona State University at the Tempe campus, M

California

Butte College, A
California College of the Arts, BM
California State University, East Bay, B
California State University, Fullerton, M
California State University, Long Beach, B
California State University, Los Angeles, M
Chabot College, A
Chaffey College, A
De Anza College, A
Glendale Community College, A
Grossmont College, A
Laney College, A
Lassen Community College District, A
Los Angeles City College, A
Mills College, M
Monterey Peninsula College, A
Palomar College, A
Ventura College, A

Colorado

Adams State University, B
University of Colorado Boulder, M
Western State Colorado University, B

Connecticut

University of Hartford, B

District of Columbia

The George Washington University, M
Howard University, BM

Florida

Florida Atlantic University, M
Palm Beach State College, A
University of Miami, BM

Georgia

Georgia State University, M

Idaho

Northwest Nazarene University, B

Illinois

Bradley University, BM
Illinois State University, M
School of the Art Institute of Chicago, BM
Southern Illinois University Carbondale, M

Indiana

Indiana State University, M
Indiana Wesleyan University, B
University of Notre Dame, M

Iowa

The University of Iowa, B

Kansas

Bethany College, B
The University of Kansas, BM
Wichita State University, M

Louisiana

Louisiana State University and Agricultural & Mechanical College, M

Maine

College of the Atlantic, B
Maine College of Art, B

Maryland

Hood College, MO
Maryland Institute College of Art, B

Massachusetts

Massachusetts College of Art and Design, B
School of the Museum of Fine Arts, Boston, B
University of Massachusetts Dartmouth, B

Michigan

Aquinas College, B
Finlandia University, B
Northern Michigan University, B

Oakland Community College, A
University of Michigan, B
Wayne State University, M

Minnesota

Minnesota State University Mankato, B

Mississippi

Mississippi College, B

Missouri

College of the Ozarks, B
Columbia College, B
Kansas City Art Institute, B
Washington University in St. Louis, B

New Hampshire

Franklin Pierce University, B
New Hampshire Institute of Art, B

New Jersey

Mercer County Community College, A
Rutgers University - New Brunswick, B

New Mexico

Santa Fe Community College, A

New York

Alfred University, BMD
City College of the City University of New York, M
Hofstra University, B
Pratt Institute, B
Rochester Institute of Technology, BM
State University of New York at New Paltz, BM
Syracuse University, BM

North Carolina

East Carolina University, M

Ohio

Bowling Green State University, B
Cleveland Institute of Art, B
Ohio Northern University, B
Ohio University, BM
The University of Akron, B

Oklahoma

University of Oklahoma, M

Oregon

University of Oregon, B

Pennsylvania

Arcadia University, B
Edinboro University of Pennsylvania, M
Marywood University, B
Seton Hill University, B
Temple University, BM

Rhode Island

Providence College, B
Rhode Island College, B
Rhode Island School of Design, BM
Salve Regina University, B

Tennessee

University of Memphis, M
The University of Tennessee, M

Texas

Southern Methodist University, M
Sul Ross State University, M
Texas Christian University, B
University of Dallas, B
The University of Texas at Arlington, M
The University of Texas at El Paso, B

Utah

Brigham Young University, B
University of Utah, M

Vermont

Bennington College, B
Marlboro College, B

Virginia

Virginia Commonwealth University, M

Washington

Central Washington University, B
University of Washington, B
Western Washington University, B

West Virginia

Concord University, B
West Virginia University, M
West Virginia Wesleyan College, B

U.S. Territories: Guam

University of Guam, M

U.S. Territories: Puerto Rico

Inter American University of Puerto Rico, San
Germán Campus, B

Canada
Alberta

Alberta College of Art & Design, B

British Columbia

Emily Carr University of Art + Design, B

Maritime Provinces: Nova Scotia

NSCAD University, B

Quebec

Concordia University, B

Saskatchewan

University of Regina, BM

CERAMIC SCIENCES AND ENGINEERING

United States
Illinois

University of Illinois at Urbana - Champaign, B

Missouri

Missouri University of Science and Technology, BMD

New Jersey

Rutgers University - New Brunswick, B

New York

Alfred University, BMD

Ohio

Hocking College, A

CHEMICAL ENGINEERING

United States
Alabama

Auburn University, BMD
Tuskegee University, B
The University of Alabama, BMD
The University of Alabama in Huntsville, BMD
University of South Alabama, BM

Arizona

Arizona State University at the Tempe campus, BMD
The University of Arizona, BMD

Arkansas

University of Arkansas, BMD

California

California Baptist University, B
California Institute of Technology, BMD
California State Polytechnic University, Pomona, B
California State University, Long Beach, BM
Los Angeles Trade-Technical College, A
Saddleback College, A
San Bernardino Valley College, A
San Jose State University, BM
Stanford University, BMD
University of California, Berkeley, BMD
University of California, Davis, BMD
University of California, Irvine, BMD
University of California, Los Angeles, BMD
University of California, Riverside, BMD
University of California, San Diego, BMD
University of California, Santa Barbara, BMD
University of Southern California, BMDO

Colorado

Colorado School of Mines, BMD
Colorado State University, BMD
University of Colorado Boulder, BMD

Connecticut

University of Connecticut, BMD
University of New Haven, B
Yale University, BMD

Delaware

University of Delaware, BMD

District of Columbia

Howard University, BM

Florida

Broward College, A
Florida Agricultural and Mechanical University, BMD
Florida Institute of Technology, BMD
Florida State University, MD
South Florida State College, A
University of Florida, BMDO
University of South Florida, BMDO

Georgia

Georgia Institute of Technology, BMD

Idaho

Brigham Young University - Idaho, A
University of Idaho, BMD

Illinois

Illinois Institute of Technology, BMD
Northwestern University, BMD
University of Illinois at Chicago, BMD
University of Illinois at Urbana - Champaign, BMD

Indiana

Purdue University, BMD
Rose-Hulman Institute of Technology, BM
Trine University, B
University of Notre Dame, BMD

Iowa

Iowa State University of Science and Technology, BMD
The University of Iowa, BMD

Kansas

Kansas State University, BMDO
The University of Kansas, BMD

Kentucky

University of Kentucky, BMD
University of Louisville, BMD

Louisiana

Louisiana State University and Agricultural & Mechanical College, BMD
Louisiana Tech University, BMD

McNeese State University, M
Tulane University, BD
University of Louisiana at Lafayette, BM

Maine

University of Maine, BMD

Maryland

Johns Hopkins University, BMD
University of Maryland, Baltimore County, BMD
University of Maryland, College Park, BMD

Massachusetts

Massachusetts Institute of Technology, BMD
Northeastern University, BMD
Tufts University, BMD
University of Massachusetts Amherst, BMD
University of Massachusetts Lowell, BMD
Worcester Polytechnic Institute, BMD

Michigan

Alpena Community College, A
Calvin College, B
Kettering University, B
Michigan State University, BMD
Michigan Technological University, BMD
Muskegon Community College, A
University of Michigan, BMDO
Wayne State University, BMD
Western Michigan University, BMD

Minnesota

Itasca Community College, A
University of Minnesota, Duluth, B
University of Minnesota, Twin Cities Campus, BMD

Mississippi

Mississippi Gulf Coast Community College, A
Mississippi State University, BMD
University of Mississippi, B

Missouri

Missouri University of Science and Technology, BMD
University of Missouri, BMD
Washington University in St. Louis, BMD

Montana

Montana State University, BMD

Nebraska

University of Nebraska - Lincoln, BMD

Nevada

University of Nevada, Reno, BMD

New Hampshire

University of New Hampshire, BMD

New Jersey

Fairleigh Dickinson University, College at Florham, MO
New Jersey Institute of Technology, BMD
Princeton University, BMD
Rowan College at Burlington County, A
Rowan University, BM
Rutgers University - New Brunswick, BMD
Stevens Institute of Technology, BMDO

New Mexico

New Mexico Institute of Mining and Technology, B
New Mexico State University, BMD
University of New Mexico, BMD

New York

City College of the City University of New York, BMD
Clarkson University, BMD
Columbia University, BMD
Cooper Union for the Advancement of Science and Art, BM
Cornell University, BMD
Manhattan College, BM
Monroe Community College, A

New York University, BMD
Pace University, B
Rensselaer Polytechnic Institute, BMD
Rochester Institute of Technology, B
State University of New York College of Environmental Science and Forestry, B
Syracuse University, BMD
United States Military Academy, B
University at Buffalo, the State University of New York, BMD
University of Rochester, BMD

North Carolina

Elon University, B
North Carolina Agricultural and Technical State University, BM
North Carolina State University, BMD

North Dakota

University of North Dakota, BM

Ohio

Case Western Reserve University, BMD
Cleveland State University, BMD
Miami University, BM
Miami University Middletown, A
The Ohio State University, BMD
Ohio University, BMD
The University of Akron, BMD
University of Cincinnati, BMD
University of Dayton, BM
The University of Toledo, BMD
Washington State Community College, A
Xavier University, B
Youngstown State University, B

Oklahoma

Oklahoma State University, BMD
University of Oklahoma, BMD
The University of Tulsa, BMD

Oregon

Oregon State University, BMD

Pennsylvania

Bucknell University, BM
Carnegie Mellon University, BMD
Drexel University, BMD
Lafayette College, B
Lehigh University, BMD
Penn State Abington, B
Penn State Altoona, B
Penn State Beaver, B
Penn State Berks, B
Penn State Brandywine, B
Penn State DuBois, B
Penn State Erie, The Behrend College, B
Penn State Fayette, The Eberly Campus, B
Penn State Greater Allegheny, B
Penn State Hazleton, B
Penn State Lehigh Valley, B
Penn State Mont Alto, B
Penn State New Kensington, B
Penn State Schuylkill, B
Penn State Shenango, B
Penn State University Park, BMD
Penn State Wilkes-Barre, B
Penn State Worthington Scranton, B
Penn State York, B
Thiel College, B
University of Pennsylvania, BMD
University of Pittsburgh, BMD
Villanova University, BMO
Widener University, BM

Rhode Island

Brown University, BMD
University of Rhode Island, BMD

South Carolina

Clemson University, BMD
University of South Carolina, BMD

South Dakota

South Dakota School of Mines and Technology, BMD

Tennessee

Christian Brothers University, B
Tennessee Technological University, BM
The University of Tennessee, BMD
The University of Tennessee at Chattanooga, BM
Vanderbilt University, BMD

Texas

Kilgore College, A
Lamar University, BD
Prairie View A&M University, B
Rice University, BMD
Texas A&M University, BMD
Texas A&M University - Kingsville, BM
Texas Tech University, BMD
University of Houston, BMD
The University of Texas at Austin, BMD

Utah

Brigham Young University, MD
University of Utah, BMD

Virginia

Hampton University, B
University of Virginia, BMD
Virginia Commonwealth University, BMD
Virginia Polytechnic Institute and State University, BMD

Washington

Olympic College, A
Shoreline Community College, A
University of Washington, BMD
Washington State University, BMD

West Virginia

West Virginia University, BMD
West Virginia University Institute of Technology, B
West Virginia University at Parkersburg, A

Wisconsin

University of Wisconsin - Madison, BD
University of Wisconsin - Stevens Point, B

Wyoming

University of Wyoming, BMD

U.S. Territories: Puerto Rico

Polytechnic University of Puerto Rico, B
University of Puerto Rico, Mayagüez Campus, BMD

Canada

Alberta

University of Alberta, MD
University of Calgary, BMD

British Columbia

The University of British Columbia, BMD

Maritime Provinces: New Brunswick

University of New Brunswick Fredericton, BMD

Maritime Provinces: Nova Scotia

Dalhousie University, BMD

Newfoundland and Labrador

Memorial University of Newfoundland, B

Ontario

Lakehead University, B
McMaster University, BMD
Queen's University at Kingston, BMD
Royal Military College of Canada, BMD
Ryerson University, B
University of Ottawa, BMD
University of Toronto, BMD
University of Waterloo, BMD

The University of Western Ontario, BMD

Quebec

École Polytechnique de Montréal, MDO
McGill University, MD
Université Laval, BMD
Université de Montréal, B
Université du Québec à Trois-Rivières, B
Université de Sherbrooke, BMD

Saskatchewan

University of Saskatchewan, BMD

CHEMICAL PHYSICS

United States

Arkansas

Hendrix College, B

Colorado

Adams State University, B
University of Colorado Boulder, D

Connecticut

Wesleyan University, D

Illinois

Lewis University, B
University of Illinois at Urbana - Champaign, D

Kentucky

Centre College, B
University of Louisville, D

Maine

Bowdoin College, B

Maryland

University of Maryland, College Park, MD

Massachusetts

Harvard University, BD
Tufts University, D

Michigan

Michigan State University, BD
Saginaw Valley State University, B

Minnesota

University of Minnesota, Twin Cities Campus, MD

Mississippi

Mississippi College, B

Nevada

University of Nevada, Reno, D

New York

Columbia University, D
Columbia University, School of General Studies, B
Cornell University, D
Hamilton College, B

Ohio

Kent State University, MD
The Ohio State University, MD

Pennsylvania

Susquehanna University, B
Swarthmore College, B

South Dakota

Augustana University, B

Tennessee

The University of Tennessee, D

Utah

University of Utah, D

Virginia

Virginia Commonwealth University, D

West Virginia

West Virginia University, MD

Wisconsin

Marquette University, MD

Canada

British Columbia

Simon Fraser University, B

Ontario

McMaster University, MD
University of Guelph, B
University of Waterloo, B

CHEMICAL TECHNOLOGY/ TECHNICIAN

United States

Alabama

Calhoun Community College, A

California

Cerro Coso Community College, A
Fullerton College, A
Southwestern College, A

Delaware

Delaware Technical & Community College, Stanton/Wilmington Campus, A

Florida

Eastern Florida State College, A
Pensacola State College, A
St. Johns River State College, A

Illinois

College of Lake County, A

Indiana

Ball State University, A
Indiana University - Purdue University Fort Wayne, A
Ivy Tech Community College - Lafayette, A
Ivy Tech Community College - Wabash Valley, A

Kentucky

Ashland Community and Technical College, A
Jefferson Community and Technical College, A

Michigan

Delta College, A
Kalamazoo Valley Community College, A
Lansing Community College, A
Lawrence Technological University, A

Minnesota

Saint Paul College - A Community & Technical College, A

Missouri

East Central College, A

New Jersey

County College of Morris, A
Essex County College, A
Raritan Valley Community College, A

New York

Corning Community College, A
Hudson Valley Community College, A
Mohawk Valley Community College, A
New York City College of Technology of the City University of New York, A
Niagara County Community College, A

State University of New York College of Agriculture and Technology at Cobleskill, A

North Carolina

Cape Fear Community College, A
Guilford Technical Community College, A

Ohio

Cincinnati State Technical and Community College, A
University of Cincinnati Blue Ash College, A

Pennsylvania

Bidwell Training Center, A
Bucks County Community College, A
Community College of Allegheny County, A
Community College of Beaver County, A
Community College of Philadelphia, A
Lehigh Carbon Community College, A
Westmoreland County Community College, A

Rhode Island

Community College of Rhode Island, A

Texas

Alvin Community College, A
Amarillo College, A
Brazosport College, A
College of the Mainland, A
Del Mar College, A
Houston Community College, A
Lamar Institute of Technology, A
San Jacinto College District, A
Texas State Technical College, A
Victoria College, A

Utah

Weber State University, A

Vermont

Norwich University, B

West Virginia

BridgeValley Community and Technical College (South Charleston), A

Wisconsin

Milwaukee Area Technical College, A

U.S. Territories: Puerto Rico

Humacao Community College, A
Inter American University of Puerto Rico, Arecibo Campus, B
Inter American University of Puerto Rico, Guayama Campus, AB
University of Puerto Rico in Humacao, A

Canada

British Columbia

British Columbia Institute of Technology, A

Saskatchewan

University of Regina, B

CHEMISTRY

United States

Alabama

Alabama Agricultural and Mechanical University, B
Alabama Southern Community College, A
Alabama State University, B
Athens State University, B
Auburn University, BMD
Auburn University at Montgomery, B
Birmingham-Southern College, B
Huntingdon College, B
Jacksonville State University, B
Judson College, B
Miles College, B

Oakwood University, B
Samford University, B
Spring Hill College, B
Talladega College, B
Troy University, B
Tuskegee University, BM
The University of Alabama, BMD
The University of Alabama at Birmingham, BMD
The University of Alabama in Huntsville, BMD
University of Montevallo, B
University of North Alabama, B
University of South Alabama, B
The University of West Alabama, B

Alaska

University of Alaska Anchorage, B
University of Alaska Fairbanks, BMD

Arizona

Arizona State University at the Tempe campus,
   BMD
Arizona Western College, A
Cochise County Community College District, A
Eastern Arizona College, A
Northern Arizona University, BM
The University of Arizona, BD

Arkansas

Arkansas State University, BMO
Arkansas Tech University, B
Harding University, B
Henderson State University, B
Hendrix College, B
John Brown University, B
Lyon College, B
Ouachita Baptist University, B
Philander Smith College, B
Southern Arkansas University - Magnolia, AB
University of Arkansas, BMD
University of Arkansas - Fort Smith, B
University of Arkansas at Little Rock, BM
University of Arkansas at Monticello, B
University of Arkansas at Pine Bluff, B
University of Central Arkansas, B
University of the Ozarks, B

California

Allan Hancock College, A
Azusa Pacific University, B
Bakersfield College, A
Biola University, B
Butte College, A
Cabrillo College, A
California Baptist University, B
California Institute of Technology, BMD
California Lutheran University, B
California Polytechnic State University, San Luis
   Obispo, BM
California State Polytechnic University, Pomona, BM
California State University, Bakersfield, B
California State University Channel Islands, B
California State University, Chico, B
California State University, Dominguez Hills, B
California State University, East Bay, BM
California State University, Fresno, BM
California State University, Fullerton, BM
California State University, Long Beach, BM
California State University, Los Angeles, BM
California State University, Northridge, BM
California State University, Sacramento, BM
California State University, San Bernardino, BM
California State University, San Marcos, B
California State University, Stanislaus, B
Cañada College, A
Cerritos College, A
Chabot College, A
Chaffey College, A
Chapman University, B
Claremont McKenna College, B
College of the Desert, A
College of Marin, A
College of San Mateo, A
College of the Sequoias, A
College of the Siskiyous, A
Concordia University Irvine, B
Contra Costa College, A

Cosumnes River College, A
Crafton Hills College, A
Cuesta College, A
Cuyamaca College, A
Dominican University of California, B
East Los Angeles College, A
El Camino College, A
Evergreen Valley College, A
Foothill College, A
Fresno Pacific University, B
Fullerton College, A
Grossmont College, A
Hartnell College, A
Harvey Mudd College, B
Humboldt State University, B
La Sierra University, B
Lassen Community College District, A
Los Angeles City College, A
Los Angeles Valley College, A
Los Medanos College, A
Loyola Marymount University, B
Mendocino College, A
Mills College, B
Monterey Peninsula College, A
Moorpark College, A
Mount Saint Mary's University, B
Occidental College, B
Orange Coast College, A
Pacific Union College, B
Palomar College, A
Pasadena City College, A
Pepperdine University, B
Pitzer College, B
Point Loma Nazarene University, B
Pomona College, B
Saddleback College, A
Saint Mary's College of California, B
San Bernardino Valley College, A
San Diego Mesa College, A
San Diego Miramar College, A
San Diego State University, BMD
San Francisco State University, BM
San Joaquin Delta College, A
San Jose City College, A
San Jose State University, BM
Santa Ana College, A
Santa Barbara City College, A
Santa Clara University, B
Santa Rosa Junior College, A
Santiago Canyon College, A
Scripps College, B
Sierra College, A
Skyline College, A
Solano Community College, A
Sonoma State University, B
Southwestern College, A
Stanford University, BD
University of California, Berkeley, BD
University of California, Davis, BMD
University of California, Irvine, BMD
University of California, Los Angeles, BMD
University of California, Merced, BMD
University of California, Riverside, BMD
University of California, San Diego, BMD
University of California, Santa Barbara, BMD
University of California, Santa Cruz, BMD
University of La Verne, B
University of the Pacific, B
University of Redlands, B
University of San Diego, B
University of San Francisco, BM
University of Southern California, BD
Vanguard University of Southern California, B
West Hills Community College, A
West Los Angeles College, A
West Valley College, A
Westmont College, B
Whittier College, B
Yuba College, A

Colorado

Adams State University, B
The Colorado College, B
Colorado Mesa University, B
Colorado School of Mines, BMD
Colorado State University, BMD

Colorado State University - Pueblo, BM
Fort Lewis College, B
Metropolitan State University of Denver, B
Northeastern Junior College, A
Regis University, B
Trinidad State Junior College, A
United States Air Force Academy, B
University of Colorado Boulder, BMD
University of Colorado Colorado Springs, B
University of Colorado Denver, BM
University of Denver, BMD
University of Northern Colorado, BMD
Western State Colorado University, B

Connecticut

Albertus Magnus College, B
Central Connecticut State University, BO
Connecticut College, B
Fairfield University, B
Quinnipiac University, B
Sacred Heart University, BM
Southern Connecticut State University, BM
Trinity College, B
University of Connecticut, BMD
University of Hartford, B
University of New Haven, B
University of Saint Joseph, BM
Wesleyan University, BD
Western Connecticut State University, B
Yale University, BD

Delaware

Delaware State University, BMD
University of Delaware, BMD

District of Columbia

American University, B
The Catholic University of America, B
Gallaudet University, B
The George Washington University, BMD
Georgetown University, BD
Howard University, BMD
Trinity Washington University, B
University of the District of Columbia, B

Florida

Barry University, B
Bethune-Cookman University, B
Broward College, A
College of Central Florida, A
Eckerd College, B
Edward Waters College, B
Florida Agricultural and Mechanical University, BM
Florida Atlantic University, BMD
Florida Gulf Coast University, B
Florida Institute of Technology, BMD
Florida International University, BMD
Florida Southern College, B
Florida State University, BMD
Indian River State College, A
Jacksonville University, B
Miami Dade College, A
New College of Florida, B
Nova Southeastern University, B
Palm Beach Atlantic University, B
Palm Beach State College, A
Pensacola State College, A
Rollins College, B
St. Thomas University, B
South Florida State College, A
State College of Florida Manatee-Sarasota, A
Stetson University, B
University of Central Florida, BMDO
University of Florida, BMD
University of Miami, BMD
University of North Florida, B
University of South Florida, BMD
The University of Tampa, B
University of West Florida, B

Georgia

Abraham Baldwin Agricultural College, A
Agnes Scott College, B
Albany State University, B
Armstrong State University, B

Augusta University, B
Bainbridge State College, A
Berry College, B
Clark Atlanta University, BMD
Clayton State University, B
College of Coastal Georgia, A
Columbus State University, B
Covenant College, B
Dalton State College, AB
Darton State College, A
Emory University, BD
Fort Valley State University, B
Georgia College & State University, B
Georgia Gwinnett College, B
Georgia Highlands College, A
Georgia Institute of Technology, BMD
Georgia Southern University, B
Georgia Southwestern State University, B
Georgia State University, BMD
Gordon State College, A
Kennesaw State University, BM
LaGrange College, B
Mercer University, B
Morehouse College, B
Oglethorpe University, B
Paine College, B
Piedmont College, B
Savannah State University, B
Shorter University, B
South Georgia State College, A
Spelman College, B
University of Georgia, BMD
University of North Georgia, B
University of West Georgia, B
Valdosta State University, B
Wesleyan College, B

Hawaii

Brigham Young University - Hawaii, B
University of Hawaii at Hilo, B
University of Hawaii at Manoa, BMD

Idaho

Boise State University, BMD
Brigham Young University - Idaho, B
The College of Idaho, B
College of Southern Idaho, A
Idaho State University, BM
Lewis-Clark State College, B
North Idaho College, A
Northwest Nazarene University, B
University of Idaho, BMD

Illinois

Augustana College, B
Benedictine University, B
Blackburn College, B
Bradley University, BM
Chicago State University, B
Concordia University Chicago, B
DePaul University, BM
Dominican University, B
Eastern Illinois University, BM
Elmhurst College, B
Eureka College, B
Governors State University, B
Greenville College, B
Harper College, A
Illinois College, B
Illinois Institute of Technology, BMD
Illinois State University, BM
Illinois Wesleyan University, B
John A. Logan College, A
Judson University, B
Kankakee Community College, A
Knox College, B
Lake Forest College, B
Lewis University, B
Loyola University Chicago, BMD
McKendree University, B
Millikin University, B
Monmouth College, B
North Central College, B
North Park University, B
Northeastern Illinois University, BM
Northern Illinois University, BMD

Northwestern University, BD
Olivet Nazarene University, B
Principia College, B
Quincy University, B
Rockford University, B
Roosevelt University, BM
Saint Xavier University, B
Sauk Valley Community College, A
Southern Illinois University Carbondale, BMD
Southern Illinois University Edwardsville, BM
Spoon River College, A
Trinity Christian College, B
Trinity International University, B
Triton College, A
University of Chicago, BD
University of Illinois at Chicago, BMD
University of Illinois at Springfield, B
University of Illinois at Urbana - Champaign, BMD
Western Illinois University, BM
Wheaton College, B

Indiana

Anderson University, B
Ball State University, BM
Bethel College, B
Butler University, B
DePauw University, B
Earlham College, B
Franklin College, B
Goshen College, B
Hanover College, B
Huntington University, B
Indiana State University, B
Indiana University Bloomington, BMD
Indiana University Kokomo, B
Indiana University Northwest, B
Indiana University - Purdue University Fort Wayne, B
Indiana University - Purdue University Indianapolis, BMD
Indiana University South Bend, B
Indiana University Southeast, B
Indiana Wesleyan University, AB
Manchester University, B
Marian University, B
Martin University, B
Purdue University, BMD
Purdue University Northwest (Hammond), B
Rose-Hulman Institute of Technology, B
Saint Joseph's College, B
Saint Mary's College, B
Taylor University, B
Trine University, B
University of Evansville, B
University of Notre Dame, BMD
University of Saint Francis, AB
University of Southern Indiana, B
Valparaiso University, B
Vincennes University, A
Wabash College, B

Iowa

Briar Cliff University, B
Buena Vista University, B
Central College, B
Clarke University, B
Coe College, B
Cornell College, B
Dordt College, B
Drake University, B
Graceland University, B
Grinnell College, B
Iowa Lakes Community College, A
Iowa State University of Science and Technology, BMD
Loras College, B
Luther College, B
Morningside College, B
Mount Mercy University, B
Northwestern College, B
St. Ambrose University, B
Simpson College, B
The University of Iowa, BD
University of Northern Iowa, B
Upper Iowa University, B
Wartburg College, B

Kansas

Allen Community College, A
Baker University, B
Barton County Community College, A
Benedictine College, B
Bethany College, B
Bethel College, B
Butler Community College, A
Cowley County Community College and Area Vocational - Technical School, A
Dodge City Community College, A
Emporia State University, B
Fort Hays State University, B
Friends University, B
Kansas State University, BMD
Kansas Wesleyan University, B
Labette Community College, A
McPherson College, B
MidAmerica Nazarene University, B
Newman University, B
Pittsburg State University, BM
Pratt Community College, A
Seward County Community College and Area Technical School, A
Southwestern College, B
Tabor College, B
The University of Kansas, BMD
University of Saint Mary, B
Washburn University, B
Wichita State University, BMD

Kentucky

Asbury University, B
Bellarmine University, B
Berea College, B
Brescia University, B
Campbellsville University, B
Centre College, B
Eastern Kentucky University, BM
Georgetown College, B
Kentucky State University, B
Kentucky Wesleyan College, B
Lindsey Wilson College, A
Morehead State University, B
Murray State University, BM
Northern Kentucky University, B
Thomas More College, AB
Transylvania University, B
Union College, B
University of the Cumberlands, B
University of Kentucky, BMD
University of Louisville, BMD
University of Pikeville, B
Western Kentucky University, BM

Louisiana

Centenary College of Louisiana, B
Dillard University, B
Grambling State University, B
Louisiana College, B
Louisiana State University and Agricultural & Mechanical College, BMD
Louisiana State University in Shreveport, B
Louisiana Tech University, BM
McNeese State University, BM
Nicholls State University, B
Southeastern Louisiana University, B
Southern University and Agricultural and Mechanical College, BM
Southern University at Shreveport, A
Tulane University, BMD
University of Louisiana at Lafayette, B
University of New Orleans, BMD
Xavier University of Louisiana, B

Maine

Bates College, B
Bowdoin College, B
Colby College, B
Husson University, B
Saint Joseph's College of Maine, B
University of Maine, BMD
University of New England, B
University of Southern Maine, B

Maryland

Cecil College, A
Coppin State University, B
Frederick Community College, A
Frostburg State University, B
Goucher College, B
Harford Community College, A
Hood College, B
Johns Hopkins University, BD
Loyola University Maryland, B
McDaniel College, B
Morgan State University, BM
Mount St. Mary's University, B
Notre Dame of Maryland University, B
St. Mary's College of Maryland, B
Salisbury University, B
Stevenson University, B
Towson University, B
United States Naval Academy, B
University of Maryland, Baltimore County, BMD
University of Maryland, College Park, BMD
University of Maryland Eastern Shore, BM
Washington Adventist University, B
Washington College, B

Massachusetts

American International College, B
Amherst College, B
Assumption College, B
Bard College at Simon's Rock, B
Boston College, BMD
Boston University, BMD
Brandeis University, BMD
Bridgewater State University, B
Bunker Hill Community College, A
Clark University, BMD
College of the Holy Cross, B
Eastern Nazarene College, B
Elms College, B
Emmanuel College, B
Fitchburg State University, B
Framingham State University, B
Gordon College, B
Hampshire College, B
Harvard University, BD
Holyoke Community College, A
Massachusetts College of Liberal Arts, B
Massachusetts Institute of Technology, BD
MCPHS University, BMD
Merrimack College, B
Mount Holyoke College, B
Northeastern University, BMD
Quinsigamond Community College, A
Salem State University, B
Simmons College, B
Smith College, BM
Springfield Technical Community College, A
Stonehill College, B
Tufts University, BMD
University of Massachusetts Amherst, BMD
University of Massachusetts Boston, BMD
University of Massachusetts Dartmouth, BMD
University of Massachusetts Lowell, BMD
Wellesley College, B
Western New England University, B
Westfield State University, B
Wheaton College, B
Williams College, B
Worcester Polytechnic Institute, BMD
Worcester State University, B

Michigan

Adrian College, B
Albion College, B
Alma College, B
Alpena Community College, A
Andrews University, B
Aquinas College, B
Calvin College, B
Central Michigan University, BM
Eastern Michigan University, BM
Ferris State University, B
Grand Rapids Community College, A
Grand Valley State University, B
Henry Ford College, A

Hillsdale College, B
Hope College, B
Kalamazoo College, B
Kettering University, B
Lake Michigan College, A
Lake Superior State University, AB
Lansing Community College, A
Lawrence Technological University, B
Macomb Community College, A
Madonna University, B
Marygrove College, B
Michigan State University, BMD
Michigan Technological University, BMD
Mid Michigan Community College, A
Northern Michigan University, B
Oakland University, BMD
Olivet College, B
Saginaw Valley State University, B
Siena Heights University, AB
Spring Arbor University, B
University of Detroit Mercy, BM
University of Michigan, BD
University of Michigan - Dearborn, B
University of Michigan - Flint, B
Wayne State University, BMD
Western Michigan University, BMD

Minnesota

Augsburg College, B
Bemidji State University, B
Bethany Lutheran College, B
Bethel University, B
Carleton College, B
College of Saint Benedict, B
The College of St. Scholastica, B
Concordia College, B
Concordia University, St. Paul, B
Gustavus Adolphus College, B
Hamline University, B
Macalester College, B
Minneapolis Community and Technical College, A
Minnesota State University Mankato, B
Minnesota State University Moorhead, B
North Hennepin Community College, A
Ridgewater College, A
St. Catherine University, B
St. Cloud State University, B
Saint John's University, B
Saint Mary's University of Minnesota, B
St. Olaf College, B
Southwest Minnesota State University, B
University of Minnesota, Duluth, BM
University of Minnesota, Morris, B
University of Minnesota, Twin Cities Campus, BMD
University of St. Thomas, B
Vermilion Community College, A
Winona State University, B

Mississippi

Alcorn State University, B
Belhaven University, B
Coahoma Community College, A
Copiah-Lincoln Community College, A
Delta State University, B
East Mississippi Community College, A
Itawamba Community College, A
Jackson State University, BMD
Jones County Junior College, A
Millsaps College, B
Mississippi College, BM
Mississippi State University, BMD
Mississippi University for Women, B
Mississippi Valley State University, B
Northeast Mississippi Community College, A
Rust College, B
Southwest Mississippi Community College, A
Tougaloo College, B
University of Mississippi, BMD
University of Southern Mississippi, BMD
William Carey University, B

Missouri

Central Methodist University, AB
College of the Ozarks, B
Columbia College, B
Drury University, B

Evangel University, B
Lincoln University, B
Lindenwood University, B
Maryville University of Saint Louis, B
Metropolitan Community College - Kansas City, A
Missouri Baptist University, B
Missouri Southern State University, B
Missouri State University, BM
Missouri University of Science and Technology, BMD
Missouri Western State University, BM
Northwest Missouri State University, B
Park University, B
Rockhurst University, B
St. Charles Community College, A
Saint Louis University, BMD
Southeast Missouri State University, BM
Southwest Baptist University, B
Truman State University, B
University of Central Missouri, B
University of Missouri, BMD
University of Missouri - Kansas City, BMD
University of Missouri - St. Louis, BMD
Washington University in St. Louis, BD
Westminster College, B
William Jewell College, B

Montana

Carroll College, B
Montana State University, BMD
Montana State University Billings, B
Montana Tech of The University of Montana, B
Rocky Mountain College, B
University of Great Falls, B
University of Montana, BMD

Nebraska

Chadron State College, B
College of Saint Mary, B
Concordia University, Nebraska, B
Creighton University, B
Doane University, B
Hastings College, B
Midland University, B
Nebraska Wesleyan University, B
Northeast Community College, A
Peru State College, B
Union College, B
University of Nebraska at Kearney, B
University of Nebraska - Lincoln, BMD
University of Nebraska at Omaha, B
Wayne State College, B
Western Nebraska Community College, A

Nevada

College of Southern Nevada, A
Truckee Meadows Community College, A
University of Nevada, Las Vegas, BMD
University of Nevada, Reno, BMD

New Hampshire

Dartmouth College, BD
Keene State College, B
Plymouth State University, B
Saint Anselm College, B
University of New Hampshire, BMD

New Jersey

Bergen Community College, A
Bloomfield College, B
The College of New Jersey, B
College of Saint Elizabeth, B
Drew University, BM
Essex County College, A
Fairleigh Dickinson University, College at Florham, BM
Fairleigh Dickinson University, Metropolitan Campus, BM
Georgian Court University, B
Kean University, B
Mercer County Community College, A
Monmouth University, B
Montclair State University, BM
New Jersey City University, B
New Jersey Institute of Technology, BMD

Princeton University, BMD
Ramapo College of New Jersey, B
Rider University, B
Rowan College at Burlington County, A
Rowan College at Gloucester County, A
Rowan University, B
Rutgers University - Camden, BM
Rutgers University - New Brunswick, BMD
Rutgers University - Newark, BMD
Saint Peter's University, B
Seton Hall University, BMD
Stevens Institute of Technology, BMDO
Stockton University, B
Union County College, A
William Paterson University of New Jersey, B

New Mexico

Central New Mexico Community College, A
Eastern New Mexico University, BM
New Mexico Highlands University, BM
New Mexico Institute of Mining and Technology, BMD
New Mexico Junior College, A
New Mexico Military Institute, A
New Mexico State University, BMD
San Juan College, A
University of New Mexico, BMD
Western New Mexico University, B

New York

Adelphi University, B
Albany College of Pharmacy and Health Sciences, B
Alfred University, B
Bard College, B
Barnard College, B
Binghamton University, State University of New York, BMD
Bronx Community College of the City University of New York, A
Brooklyn College of the City University of New York, BMD
Buffalo State College, State University of New York, BM
Canisius College, B
City College of the City University of New York, BMD
Clarkson University, BMD
Colgate University, B
The College at Brockport, State University of New York, BO
College of Mount Saint Vincent, B
The College of New Rochelle, B
The College of Saint Rose, B
College of Staten Island of the City University of New York, B
Columbia University, BD
Columbia University, School of General Studies, B
Cornell University, BD
D'Youville College, B
Elmira College, B
Finger Lakes Community College, A
Fordham University, B
Genesee Community College, A
Hamilton College, B
Hartwick College, B
Hobart and William Smith Colleges, B
Hofstra University, B
Houghton College, B
Hunter College of the City University of New York, BMD
Iona College, B
Ithaca College, B
Kingsborough Community College of the City University of New York, A
Le Moyne College, B
Lehman College of the City University of New York, B
Long Island University - LIU Brooklyn, B
Long Island University - LIU Post, B
Manhattan College, B
Manhattanville College, B
Marist College, B
Monroe Community College, A
Mount Saint Mary College, B
Nazareth College of Rochester, B

New York Institute of Technology, B
New York University, BMD
Niagara University, B
Pace University, B
Pace University, Pleasantville Campus, B
Purchase College, State University of New York, B
Queens College of the City University of New York, BM
Queensborough Community College of the City University of New York, A
Rensselaer Polytechnic Institute, BMD
Roberts Wesleyan College, B
Rochester Institute of Technology, BM
The Sage Colleges, B
St. Bonaventure University, B
St. Francis College, B
St. John Fisher College, B
St. John's University, BM
St. Joseph's College, Long Island Campus, B
St. Joseph's College, New York, B
St. Lawrence University, B
Sarah Lawrence College, B
Siena College, B
Skidmore College, B
State University of New York College at Cortland, B
State University of New York College of Environmental Science and Forestry, BMD
State University of New York College at Geneseo, B
State University of New York College at Old Westbury, B
State University of New York College at Oneonta, B
State University of New York College at Potsdam, B
State University of New York at Fredonia, B
State University of New York at New Paltz, BM
State University of New York at Oswego, BM
State University of New York at Plattsburgh, B
Stony Brook University, State University of New York, BMD
Suffolk County Community College, A
Syracuse University, BMD
Union College, B
United States Military Academy, B
University at Albany, State University of New York, BMD
University at Buffalo, the State University of New York, BMD
University of Rochester, BMD
Utica College, B
Vassar College, B
Wagner College, B
Wells College, B
Yeshiva University, B
York College of the City University of New York, B

North Carolina

Appalachian State University, B
Barton College, B
Bennett College, B
Campbell University, B
Catawba College, B
Davidson College, B
Duke University, BD
East Carolina University, BM
Elizabeth City State University, B
Elon University, B
Fayetteville State University, B
Gardner-Webb University, B
Greensboro College, B
Guilford College, B
High Point University, B
Johnson C. Smith University, B
Lenoir-Rhyne University, B
Livingstone College, B
Louisburg College, A
Mars Hill University, B
Meredith College, B
Methodist University, AB
North Carolina Agricultural and Technical State University, BMD
North Carolina Central University, BM
North Carolina State University, BMD
North Carolina Wesleyan College, B
Pfeiffer University, B
Queens University of Charlotte, B
Saint Augustine's University, B
Salem College, B

Shaw University, B
University of Mount Olive, B
University of North Carolina at Asheville, B
The University of North Carolina at Chapel Hill, BMD
The University of North Carolina at Charlotte, BMD
The University of North Carolina at Greensboro, BM
The University of North Carolina at Pembroke, B
The University of North Carolina Wilmington, BM
Wake Forest University, BMD
Warren Wilson College, B
Western Carolina University, BM
Wingate University, B
Winston-Salem State University, B

North Dakota

Dakota College at Bottineau, A
Dickinson State University, B
Mayville State University, B
Minot State University, B
North Dakota State University, BMD
University of Jamestown, B
University of North Dakota, BMD
Valley City State University, B

Ohio

Ashland University, B
Baldwin Wallace University, B
Bluffton University, B
Bowling Green State University, BMD
Capital University, B
Case Western Reserve University, BMD
Cedarville University, B
Central State University, B
Cleveland State University, BMD
The College of Wooster, B
Denison University, B
Franciscan University of Steubenville, B
Heidelberg University, B
Hiram College, B
John Carroll University, B
Kent State University, BMD
Kenyon College, B
Lake Erie College, B
Lorain County Community College, A
Malone University, B
Marietta College, B
Miami University, BMD
Miami University Hamilton, B
Miami University Middletown, A
Mount St. Joseph University, B
Mount Vernon Nazarene University, B
Muskingum University, B
Notre Dame College, B
Oberlin College, B
Ohio Dominican University, AB
Ohio Northern University, B
The Ohio State University, BMD
Ohio University, B
Ohio Wesleyan University, B
Otterbein University, B
Shawnee State University, B
Terra State Community College, A
The University of Akron, BMD
University of Cincinnati, BMD
University of Cincinnati Clermont College, A
University of Dayton, BM
The University of Findlay, B
University of Mount Union, B
University of Rio Grande, AB
The University of Toledo, BMD
Urbana University, B
Walsh University, B
Wilmington College, B
Wittenberg University, B
Wright State University, ABM
Wright State University - Lake Campus, A
Xavier University, B
Youngstown State University, BM

Oklahoma

Cameron University, B
East Central University, B
Langston University, B
Murray State College, A
Northeastern State University, B

Northwestern Oklahoma State University, B
Oklahoma Baptist University, B
Oklahoma Christian University, B
Oklahoma City Community College, A
Oklahoma Panhandle State University, B
Oklahoma State University, BMD
Oklahoma Wesleyan University, AB
Oral Roberts University, B
Rose State College, A
Southeastern Oklahoma State University, B
Southern Nazarene University, B
Southwestern Oklahoma State University, B
University of Central Oklahoma, B
University of Oklahoma, BMD
University of Science and Arts of Oklahoma, B
The University of Tulsa, BMD

Oregon

Concordia University, B
Eastern Oregon University, B
George Fox University, B
Lewis & Clark College, B
Linfield College, B
Linn-Benton Community College, A
Oregon State University, BMD
Pacific University, B
Portland State University, BMD
Reed College, B
Southern Oregon University, B
Umpqua Community College, A
University of Oregon, BMD
University of Portland, B
Western Oregon University, B
Willamette University, B

Pennsylvania

Albright College, B
Allegheny College, B
Alvernia University, B
Arcadia University, B
Bloomsburg University of Pennsylvania, B
Bryn Mawr College, BMD
Bucknell University, BM
Cabrini University, B
California University of Pennsylvania, B
Carlow University, B
Carnegie Mellon University, BD
Cedar Crest College, B
Chatham University, B
Chestnut Hill College, B
Cheyney University of Pennsylvania, B
Clarion University of Pennsylvania, B
Community College of Allegheny County, A
Community College of Beaver County, A
Delaware Valley University, B
DeSales University, B
Dickinson College, B
Drexel University, BMD
Duquesne University, BMD
East Stroudsburg University of Pennsylvania, B
Eastern University, B
Edinboro University of Pennsylvania, B
Elizabethtown College, B
Franklin & Marshall College, B
Gannon University, B
Geneva College, B
Gettysburg College, B
Grove City College, B
Harrisburg Area Community College, A
Haverford College, B
Immaculata University, AB
Indiana University of Pennsylvania, BM
Juniata College, B
King's College, B
Kutztown University of Pennsylvania, B
La Roche College, B
La Salle University, B
Lafayette College, B
Lebanon Valley College, B
Lehigh Carbon Community College, A
Lehigh University, BMD
Lincoln University, B
Lock Haven University of Pennsylvania, B
Lycoming College, B
Mansfield University of Pennsylvania, B
Mercyhurst University, B

Messiah College, B
Millersville University of Pennsylvania, B
Misericordia University, B
Moravian College, B
Muhlenberg College, B
Northampton Community College, A
Penn State Abington, B
Penn State Altoona, B
Penn State Beaver, B
Penn State Berks, B
Penn State Brandywine, B
Penn State DuBois, B
Penn State Erie, The Behrend College, B
Penn State Fayette, The Eberly Campus, B
Penn State Greater Allegheny, B
Penn State Hazleton, B
Penn State Lehigh Valley, B
Penn State Mont Alto, B
Penn State New Kensington, B
Penn State Schuylkill, B
Penn State Shenango, B
Penn State University Park, BMD
Penn State Wilkes-Barre, B
Penn State Worthington Scranton, B
Penn State York, B
Philadelphia University, B
Rosemont College, B
Saint Francis University, B
Saint Joseph's University, B
Saint Vincent College, B
Seton Hill University, B
Shippensburg University of Pennsylvania, B
Slippery Rock University of Pennsylvania, B
Susquehanna University, B
Swarthmore College, B
Temple University, BMD
Thiel College, B
University of Pennsylvania, BMD
University of Pittsburgh, BMD
University of Pittsburgh at Bradford, B
University of Pittsburgh at Greensburg, B
University of Pittsburgh at Johnstown, B
University of the Sciences, BMD
The University of Scranton, BM
Ursinus College, B
Villanova University, BM
Washington & Jefferson College, B
Waynesburg University, B
West Chester University of Pennsylvania, BO
Westminster College, B
Widener University, B
Wilkes University, B
Wilson College, B
York College of Pennsylvania, AB

Rhode Island

Brown University, BD
Providence College, B
Rhode Island College, B
Roger Williams University, B
Salve Regina University, B
University of Rhode Island, BMD

South Carolina

Allen University, B
Benedict College, B
Bob Jones University, B
Charleston Southern University, B
The Citadel, The Military College of South Carolina, B
Claflin University, B
Clemson University, BMD
Coastal Carolina University, B
Coker College, B
College of Charleston, B
Columbia College, B
Converse College, B
Erskine College, B
Francis Marion University, B
Furman University, BM
Lander University, B
Limestone College, B
Newberry College, B
Presbyterian College, B
South Carolina State University, B
Southern Wesleyan University, B

University of South Carolina, BMD
University of South Carolina Aiken, B
University of South Carolina Upstate, B
Winthrop University, B
Wofford College, B

South Dakota

Augustana University, B
Black Hills State University, B
Mount Marty College, B
Northern State University, B
Presentation College, A
South Dakota School of Mines and Technology, B
South Dakota State University, BMD
University of Sioux Falls, B
The University of South Dakota, BMD

Tennessee

Austin Peay State University, B
Belmont University, B
Bethel University, B
Carson-Newman University, B
Christian Brothers University, B
East Tennessee State University, BM
Fisk University, BM
Freed-Hardeman University, B
Hiwassee College, A
King University, B
Lane College, B
Lee University, B
LeMoyne-Owen College, B
Lincoln Memorial University, B
Lipscomb University, B
Maryville College, B
Middle Tennessee State University, BM
Milligan College, B
Nashville State Community College, A
Northeast State Community College, A
Rhodes College, B
Roane State Community College, A
Sewanee: The University of the South, B
Southern Adventist University, B
Tennessee State University, BM
Tennessee Technological University, BMD
Tennessee Wesleyan College, B
Trevecca Nazarene University, B
Tusculum College, B
Union University, B
University of Memphis, BMD
The University of Tennessee, BMD
The University of Tennessee at Chattanooga, B
The University of Tennessee at Martin, B
Vanderbilt University, BMD

Texas

Abilene Christian University, B
Amarillo College, A
Angelo State University, B
Austin College, B
Austin Community College District, A
Baylor University, BMD
Blinn College, A
Central Texas College, A
Cisco College, A
Clarendon College, A
Del Mar College, A
East Texas Baptist University, B
Frank Phillips College, A
Grayson College, A
Hardin-Simmons University, B
Hill College, A
Houston Baptist University, B
Houston Community College, A
Howard College, A
Howard Payne University, B
Huston-Tillotson University, B
Jarvis Christian College, B
Kilgore College, A
Lamar University, BM
Lee College, A
LeTourneau University, B
Lubbock Christian University, B
McMurry University, B
Midwestern State University, B
Navarro College, A
Northeast Texas Community College, A

Odessa College, A
Our Lady of the Lake University of San Antonio, B
Palo Alto College, A
Panola College, A
Paris Junior College, A
Prairie View A&M University, BM
Rice University, BMD
St. Edward's University, B
St. Mary's University, B
St. Philip's College, A
Sam Houston State University, BM
San Jacinto College District, A
Schreiner University, B
South Plains College, A
Southern Methodist University, BMD
Southwestern Adventist University, B
Southwestern University, B
Stephen F. Austin State University, BM
Sul Ross State University, B
Tarleton State University, B
Texarkana College, A
Texas A&M International University, B
Texas A&M University, BMD
Texas A&M University - Commerce, B
Texas A&M University - Corpus Christi, B
Texas A&M University - Kingsville, BM
Texas Christian University, BMD
Texas Lutheran University, B
Texas Southern University, BM
Texas State University, BM
Texas Tech University, BMD
Texas Wesleyan University, B
Texas Woman's University, BM
Trinity University, B
Trinity Valley Community College, A
Tyler Junior College, A
University of Dallas, B
University of Houston, BMD
University of Houston - Clear Lake, BM
University of Houston - Downtown, B
University of the Incarnate Word, AB
University of Mary Hardin-Baylor, B
University of North Texas, BM
University of St. Thomas, B
The University of Texas at Arlington, BMD
The University of Texas at Austin, BD
The University of Texas at Dallas, BMD
The University of Texas at El Paso, BMD
The University of Texas of the Permian Basin, B
The University of Texas Rio Grande Valley, BM
The University of Texas at San Antonio, BMD
The University of Texas at Tyler, B
Wayland Baptist University, B
West Texas A&M University, BM
Wharton County Junior College, A
Wiley College, B

Utah

Brigham Young University, MD
Salt Lake Community College, A
Snow College, A
Southern Utah University, B
University of Utah, BMD
Utah State University, BMD
Utah Valley University, AB
Weber State University, B
Westminster College, B

Vermont

Bennington College, B
Castleton University, B
Marlboro College, B
Middlebury College, B
Norwich University, B
Saint Michael's College, B
University of Vermont, BMD

Virginia

Bluefield College, B
Bridgewater College, B
Christopher Newport University, B
The College of William and Mary, BM
Eastern Mennonite University, B
Emory & Henry College, B
Ferrum College, B
George Mason University, BMD

Hampden-Sydney College, B
Hampton University, BM
Hollins University, B
James Madison University, B
Liberty University, B
Longwood University, B
Lynchburg College, B
Mary Baldwin College, B
Norfolk State University, B
Old Dominion University, BMD
Radford University, B
Randolph College, B
Randolph-Macon College, B
Roanoke College, B
Shenandoah University, B
Sweet Briar College, B
University of Mary Washington, B
University of Richmond, B
University of Virginia, BMD
The University of Virginia's College at Wise, B
Virginia Commonwealth University, BMD
Virginia Military Institute, B
Virginia Polytechnic Institute and State University,
   BMD
Virginia State University, B
Virginia Union University, B
Virginia Wesleyan College, B
Washington and Lee University, B

Washington

Central Washington University, BM
Eastern Washington University, B
Everett Community College, A
Gonzaga University, B
Pacific Lutheran University, B
Saint Martin's University, B
Seattle Pacific University, B
Seattle University, B
Skagit Valley College, A
University of Puget Sound, B
University of Washington, B
University of Washington, Bothell, B
Walla Walla University, B
Washington State University, BMD
Wenatchee Valley College, A
Western Washington University, BM
Whitman College, B
Whitworth University, B

West Virginia

Alderson Broaddus University, B
Bethany College, B
Concord University, B
Davis & Elkins College, B
Fairmont State University, B
Glenville State College, B
Marshall University, BM
Potomac State College of West Virginia University,
   A
Shepherd University, B
University of Charleston, B
West Liberty University, B
West Virginia State University, B
West Virginia University, BMD
West Virginia University Institute of Technology, B
West Virginia Wesleyan College, B
Wheeling Jesuit University, B

Wisconsin

Alverno College, B
Beloit College, B
Cardinal Stritch University, B
Carroll University, B
Carthage College, B
Edgewood College, B
Lakeland College, B
Lawrence University, B
Marian University, B
Marquette University, BMD
Mount Mary University, B
Northland College, B
Ripon College, B
St. Norbert College, B
University of Wisconsin - Eau Claire, B
University of Wisconsin - Green Bay, B
University of Wisconsin - La Crosse, B

University of Wisconsin - Madison, BMD
University of Wisconsin - Milwaukee, BMD
University of Wisconsin - Oshkosh, B
University of Wisconsin - Parkside, B
University of Wisconsin - Platteville, B
University of Wisconsin - River Falls, B
University of Wisconsin - Stevens Point, B
University of Wisconsin - Superior, B
University of Wisconsin - Whitewater, B
Viterbo University, B
Wisconsin Lutheran College, B

Wyoming

Casper College, A
Laramie County Community College, A
Northwest College, A
University of Wyoming, BMD
Western Wyoming Community College, A

U.S. Territories: Guam

University of Guam, B

U.S. Territories: Puerto Rico

Bayamón Central University, B
Inter American University of Puerto Rico, Arecibo
   Campus, B
Inter American University of Puerto Rico, Bayamón
   Campus, B
Inter American University of Puerto Rico, Metropoli-
   tan Campus, B
Inter American University of Puerto Rico, San
   Germán Campus, B
Pontifical Catholic University of Puerto Rico, BM
Universidad Metropolitana, B
Universidad del Turabo, BM
University of Puerto Rico in Cayey, B
University of Puerto Rico in Humacao, B
University of Puerto Rico, Mayagüez Campus, BMD
University of Puerto Rico, Río Piedras Campus,
   BMD
University of Puerto Rico in Utuado, B
University of the Sacred Heart, B

U.S. Territories: United States Virgin Islands

University of the Virgin Islands, B

Canada

Alberta

Concordia University of Edmonton, B
The King's University, B
University of Alberta, BMD
University of Calgary, BMD
University of Lethbridge, BM

British Columbia

Simon Fraser University, BMD
Thompson Rivers University, AB
Trinity Western University, B
The University of British Columbia, BMD
The University of British Columbia - Okanagan
   Campus, B
University of the Fraser Valley, B
University of Northern British Columbia, B
University of Victoria, BMD

Manitoba

Brandon University, B
University of Manitoba, BMD
The University of Winnipeg, B

Maritime Provinces: New Brunswick

Mount Allison University, BM
Université de Moncton, BM
University of New Brunswick Fredericton, BMD
University of New Brunswick Saint John, B

Maritime Provinces: Nova Scotia

Acadia University, BM
Cape Breton University, B
Dalhousie University, BMD
Mount Saint Vincent University, B
St. Francis Xavier University, BM

Saint Mary's University, B
University of King's College, B

Maritime Provinces: Prince Edward Island

University of Prince Edward Island, BM

Newfoundland and Labrador

Memorial University of Newfoundland, BMD

Ontario

Brock University, BMD
Carleton University, BMD
Lakehead University, BM
Laurentian University, BM
McMaster University, BMD
Queen's University at Kingston, BMD
Redeemer University College, B
Royal Military College of Canada, BMD
Ryerson University, B
Trent University, BM
University of Guelph, BMD
University of Ottawa, BMD
University of Toronto, MD
University of Waterloo, BMD
The University of Western Ontario, BMD
University of Windsor, BMD
Wilfrid Laurier University, BM
York University, BMD

Quebec

Bishop's University, B
Concordia University, BMD
McGill University, BMD
Université Laval, BMD
Université de Montréal, BMD
Université du Québec à Chicoutimi, B
Université du Québec à Montréal, BMD
Université du Québec à Rimouski, B
Université du Québec à Trois-Rivières, BM
Université de Sherbrooke, BMDO

Saskatchewan

University of Regina, BMD
University of Saskatchewan, BMD

CHEMISTRY TEACHER EDUCATION

United States

Alabama

Huntingdon College, B
Talladega College, B

Arizona

Grand Canyon University, B

Arkansas

Arkansas State University, B
University of Arkansas - Fort Smith, B

California

Pepperdine University, B
University of California, San Diego, B

Colorado

Adams State University, B
Colorado State University, B
Fort Lewis College, B
Western State Colorado University, B

Delaware

Delaware State University, B
University of Delaware, B

Florida

Bethune-Cookman University, B
Broward College, A
Florida Institute of Technology, B
Miami Dade College, A
State College of Florida Manatee-Sarasota, A

Hawaii

Brigham Young University - Hawaii, B

Idaho

Brigham Young University - Idaho, B
Northwest Nazarene University, B

Illinois

Augustana College, B
Bradley University, B
Concordia University Chicago, B
Elmhurst College, B
Greenville College, B
Millikin University, B
Trinity Christian College, B
University of Illinois at Chicago, B
University of Illinois at Urbana - Champaign, B

Indiana

Ball State University, B
Franklin College, B
Goshen College, B
Huntington University, B
Indiana University Bloomington, B
Indiana University Northwest, B
Indiana University - Purdue University Fort Wayne, B
Indiana University South Bend, B
Indiana Wesleyan University, B
Manchester University, B
University of Evansville, B
University of Saint Francis, B
Valparaiso University, B
Vincennes University, A

Iowa

Buena Vista University, B
Dordt College, B
Morningside College, B
The University of Iowa, B

Kansas

Bethany College, B
Central Christian College of Kansas, A
Kansas Wesleyan University, B
Pittsburg State University, B
Tabor College, B
Washburn University, B

Kentucky

Campbellsville University, B
Transylvania University, B

Louisiana

Louisiana State University in Shreveport, B
Louisiana Tech University, B
Southern University and Agricultural and Mechanical College, B
University of Louisiana at Monroe, B
Xavier University of Louisiana, B

Maine

Saint Joseph's College of Maine, B
University of Maine, B
University of Maine at Farmington, B

Maryland

Anne Arundel Community College, A
Carroll Community College, A
Community College of Baltimore County, A
Harford Community College, A
Montgomery College, A
University of Maryland, Baltimore County, B

Massachusetts

Boston University, B
Eastern Nazarene College, B
Merrimack College, B

Michigan

Adrian College, B
Albion College, B
Alma College, B
Calvin College, B

Central Michigan University, B
Eastern Michigan University, B
Ferris State University, B
Grand Valley State University, B
Hope College, B
Madonna University, B
Michigan State University, B
Northern Michigan University, B
Olivet College, B
Saginaw Valley State University, B
Spring Arbor University, B
University of Michigan - Dearborn, B
Western Michigan University, B

Minnesota

Concordia College, B
Concordia University, St. Paul, B
Gustavus Adolphus College, B
Minnesota State University Moorhead, B
St. Catherine University, B
St. Cloud State University, B
Saint Mary's University of Minnesota, B
Southwest Minnesota State University, B
University of St. Thomas, B
Winona State University, B

Mississippi

Mississippi College, B

Missouri

Central Methodist University, B
Evangel University, B
Lincoln University, B
Lindenwood University, B
Missouri State University, B
Northwest Missouri State University, B
Southwest Baptist University, B
University of Missouri, B
Washington University in St. Louis, B

Montana

Carroll College, B
Montana State University Billings, B
University of Great Falls, B

Nebraska

Chadron State College, B
College of Saint Mary, B
Concordia University, Nebraska, B
Hastings College, B
Nebraska Wesleyan University, B
Peru State College, B
Union College, B
University of Nebraska - Lincoln, B
Wayne State College, B

New Hampshire

Keene State College, B

New Jersey

The College of New Jersey, B

New York

Brooklyn College of the City University of New York, B
Canisius College, B
City College of the City University of New York, B
College of Staten Island of the City University of New York, B
Elmira College, B
Hofstra University, B
Ithaca College, B
Le Moyne College, B
Long Island University - LIU Brooklyn, B
Long Island University - LIU Post, B
Manhattanville College, B
Marist College, B
Nazareth College of Rochester, B
New York University, B
Niagara University, B
Pace University, B
Pace University, Pleasantville Campus, B
Queens College of the City University of New York, B
Roberts Wesleyan College, B

St. Francis College, B
St. John Fisher College, B
St. Joseph's College, Long Island Campus, B
St. Joseph's College, New York, B
State University of New York College at Cortland, B
State University of New York College at Old Westbury, B
State University of New York College at Oneonta, B
State University of New York College at Potsdam, B
State University of New York at New Paltz, B
State University of New York at Plattsburgh, B
Syracuse University, B
Ulster County Community College, A
Utica College, B

North Carolina

Elizabeth City State University, B
Louisburg College, A
North Carolina Agricultural and Technical State University, B
The University of North Carolina Wilmington, B

North Dakota

Mayville State University, B
Minot State University, B
North Dakota State University, B
University of Jamestown, B
Valley City State University, B

Ohio

Ashland University, B
Bowling Green State University, B
Cedarville University, B
Kent State University, B
Miami University, B
Miami University Hamilton, B
Mount Vernon Nazarene University, B
Ohio Dominican University, B
Ohio Northern University, B
Ohio Wesleyan University, B
Xavier University, B

Oklahoma

East Central University, B
University of Central Oklahoma, B

Pennsylvania

Alvernia University, B
Cabrini University, B
Grove City College, B
Holy Family University, B
Juniata College, B
Mercyhurst University, B
Messiah College, B
Misericordia University, B
Saint Francis University, B
Saint Joseph's University, B
Seton Hill University, B
University of Pittsburgh at Johnstown, B
Waynesburg University, B
Widener University, B

Rhode Island

Providence College, B
Rhode Island College, B

South Carolina

Coker College, B

South Dakota

Mount Marty College, B

Tennessee

King University, B
Lee University, B
Lincoln Memorial University, B
Lipscomb University, B
Maryville College, B
Southern Adventist University, B
Trevecca Nazarene University, B
The University of Tennessee at Martin, B

Texas

Baylor University, B
Howard College, A
McMurry University, B
St. Edward's University, B
Schreiner University, B
Southwestern Adventist University, B
University of Mary Hardin-Baylor, B

Utah

Southern Utah University, B
Utah State University, B
Utah Valley University, B
Weber State University, B

Virginia

Bluefield College, B
Emory & Henry College, B
Virginia Union University, B

Washington

Central Washington University, B
Eastern Washington University, B
Seattle University, B
Washington State University, B
Western Washington University, B

West Virginia

Bethany College, B
Glenville State College, B

Wisconsin

Carroll University, B
Edgewood College, B
Marquette University, B
Mount Mary University, B
University of Wisconsin - Superior, B
Viterbo University, B

U.S. Territories: Puerto Rico

Inter American University of Puerto Rico, Metropolitan Campus, B
Inter American University of Puerto Rico, San Germán Campus, B
Pontifical Catholic University of Puerto Rico, B
Universidad del Turabo, B

Canada

Alberta

University of Alberta, B

Ontario

University of Waterloo, B
University of Windsor, B
York University, B

Quebec

Bishop's University, B

Saskatchewan

University of Regina, B

CHILD CARE PROVIDER/ASSISTANT

United States

Alaska

University of Alaska Anchorage, A

Arizona

Northland Pioneer College, A

Arkansas

Southeast Arkansas College, A
Southern Arkansas University Tech, A

California

Antelope Valley College, A
Barstow Community College, A
Cabrillo College, A
Cañada College, A
Chaffey College, A
City College of San Francisco, A
College of the Canyons, A
College of Marin, A
College of the Redwoods, A
College of the Siskiyous, A
Columbia College, A
Contra Costa College, A
Cosumnes River College, A
Crafton Hills College, A
Cuesta College, A
Feather River College, A
Fresno City College, A
Fullerton College, A
Gavilan College, A
Hartnell College, A
Long Beach City College, A
MiraCosta College, A
Modesto Junior College, A
Orange Coast College, A
Palo Verde College, A
Palomar College, A
San Diego Mesa College, A

Colorado

Morgan Community College, AB

Florida

Florida SouthWestern State College, A
Florida State College at Jacksonville, A
Gulf Coast State College, A
Lake-Sumter State College, A
Miami Dade College, A
Northwest Florida State College, A
Pensacola State College, A
Santa Fe College, A

Illinois

Black Hawk College, A
Carl Sandburg College, A
City Colleges of Chicago, Harold Washington College, A
City Colleges of Chicago, Harry S. Truman College, A
City Colleges of Chicago, Kennedy-King College, A
City Colleges of Chicago, Malcolm X College, A
City Colleges of Chicago, Olive-Harvey College, A
College of DuPage, A
College of Lake County, A
Danville Area Community College, A
Harper College, A
Heartland Community College, A
Highland Community College, A
Illinois Central College, A
Illinois Valley Community College, A
John A. Logan College, A
John Wood Community College, A
Joliet Junior College, A
Kaskaskia College, A
Kishwaukee College, A
Lewis and Clark Community College, A
Lincoln Land Community College, A
McHenry County College, A
Moraine Valley Community College, A
Oakton Community College, A
Parkland College, A
Prairie State College, A
Rend Lake College, A
South Suburban College, A
Southwestern Illinois College, A
Triton College, A
Waubonsee Community College, A

Indiana

Vincennes University, A

Iowa

Des Moines Area Community College, A
Hawkeye Community College, A
Indian Hills Community College, A

Iowa Lakes Community College, A
Iowa Western Community College, A
Kirkwood Community College, A
Marshalltown Community College, A
Western Iowa Tech Community College, A

Kentucky

Ashland Community and Technical College, A
Bluegrass Community and Technical College, A
Eastern Kentucky University, A
Elizabethtown Community and Technical College, A
Hazard Community and Technical College, A
Henderson Community College, A
Hopkinsville Community College, A
Owensboro Community and Technical College, A
Somerset Community College, A

Louisiana

Bossier Parish Community College, A
Louisiana Delta Community College, A
Louisiana State University at Alexandria, A
Nunez Community College, A

Maryland

Montgomery College, A

Massachusetts

Massasoit Community College, A

Michigan

Delta College, A
Lansing Community College, A
Mid Michigan Community College, A
Montcalm Community College, A
Mott Community College, A
Washtenaw Community College, A

Minnesota

Dakota County Technical College, A
Northland Community and Technical College, A

Mississippi

East Central Community College, A
Hinds Community College, A
Meridian Community College, A
Northeast Mississippi Community College, A

Missouri

Metropolitan Community College - Kansas City, A
Mineral Area College, A
St. Charles Community College, A

Montana

Dawson Community College, A

Nebraska

Wayne State College, B

Nevada

College of Southern Nevada, A

New Jersey

Hudson County Community College, A
Raritan Valley Community College, A

New Mexico

Mesalands Community College, A
San Juan College, A

North Carolina

Bladen Community College, A
Coastal Carolina Community College, A
Surry Community College, A

North Dakota

Dakota College at Bottineau, A
Lake Region State College, A
Mayville State University, A
United Tribes Technical College, A

Ohio

Lakeland Community College, A
Zane State College, A

Oklahoma

Connors State College, A
East Central University, B
Murray State College, A
Southeastern Oklahoma State University, B

Oregon

Lane Community College, A
Southwestern Oregon Community College, A

Pennsylvania

Bucks County Community College, A
Community College of Allegheny County, A
Harcum College, A
Keystone Technical Institute, A
Luzerne County Community College, A
Pennsylvania College of Technology, A
Westmoreland County Community College, A

South Carolina

Midlands Technical College, A
Technical College of the Lowcountry, A
Trident Technical College, A
York Technical College, A

South Dakota

Southeast Technical Institute, A

Texas

Central Texas College, A
Collin County Community College District, A
Hill College, A
Kilgore College, A
Lamar Institute of Technology, A
San Antonio College, A
Texas Southmost College, A
Western Texas College, A

Utah

Brigham Young University, B

Virginia

Danville Community College, A
J. Sargeant Reynolds Community College, A
John Tyler Community College, A
Southwest Virginia Community College, A
Thomas Nelson Community College, A

Washington

Bates Technical College, A

West Virginia

American Public University System, A
Eastern West Virginia Community and Technical College, A

Wisconsin

Western Technical College, A

CHILD CARE AND SUPPORT SERVICES MANAGEMENT

United States

Alabama

Bevill State Community College, A
Bishop State Community College, A
Calhoun Community College, A
Enterprise State Community College, A
Gadsden State Community College, A
H. Councill Trenholm State Community College, A
Jefferson State Community College, A
Lawson State Community College, A
Lurleen B. Wallace Community College, A
Northeast Alabama Community College, A
Northwest-Shoals Community College, A
Reid State Technical College, A
Snead State Community College, A
Southern Union State Community College, A

Arizona

Northland Pioneer College, A
Phoenix College, A
South Mountain Community College, A

Arkansas

College of the Ouachitas, A
East Arkansas Community College, A
University of Arkansas Community College at Hope, A

California

College of the Desert, A
Cosumnes River College, A
Grossmont College, A
MiraCosta College, A
Modesto Junior College, A
Orange Coast College, A
Palomar College, A
Reedley College, A
Santa Barbara City College, A
Victor Valley College, A

Colorado

Aims Community College, A

Connecticut

Capital Community College, A
Goodwin College, A
Post University, A
Three Rivers Community College, A

Florida

Florida State College at Jacksonville, A
Hillsborough Community College, A
Pensacola State College, A
Polk State College, A

Georgia

Central Georgia Technical College, A

Idaho

College of Southern Idaho, A

Illinois

College of DuPage, A
Kishwaukee College, A
Lake Land College, A
National Louis University, B

Indiana

Ivy Tech Community College - Bloomington, A
Ivy Tech Community College - Central Indiana, A
Ivy Tech Community College - Columbus, A
Ivy Tech Community College - Lafayette, A
Ivy Tech Community College - North Central, A
Ivy Tech Community College - Northeast, A
Ivy Tech Community College - Northwest, A
Ivy Tech Community College - Richmond, A
Ivy Tech Community College - Southeast, A
Ivy Tech Community College - Southern Indiana, A
Ivy Tech Community College - Southwest, A
Purdue University Northwest (Hammond), B
Vincennes University, A

Iowa

Muscatine Community College, A
Scott Community College, A

Kansas

Barton County Community College, A
Cloud County Community College, A
Colby Community College, A
Cowley County Community College and Area Vocational - Technical School, A
Highland Community College, A
Hutchinson Community College, A
Independence Community College, A
Johnson County Community College, A
Kansas City Kansas Community College, A

Louisiana

Nicholls State University, A

Maine

Kaplan University, South Portland, A

Maryland

Anne Arundel Community College, A
Baltimore City Community College, A
Carroll Community College, A
Cecil College, A
Chesapeake College, A
College of Southern Maryland, A
Community College of Baltimore County, A
Hagerstown Community College, A
Wor-Wic Community College, A

Massachusetts

Bristol Community College, A
Holyoke Community College, A
Massasoit Community College, A
Mount Wachusett Community College, A

Michigan

Ferris State University, AB
Glen Oaks Community College, A
Grand Rapids Community College, A
Kellogg Community College, A
Macomb Community College, A
Montcalm Community College, A
Northwestern Michigan College, A
Oakland Community College, A
St. Clair County Community College, A
Siena Heights University, AB
Wayne County Community College District, A

Minnesota

Central Lakes College, A
Minneapolis Community and Technical College, A
Minnesota West Community and Technical College, A
Northwest Technical College, A
Rochester Community and Technical College, A
Saint Paul College - A Community & Technical College, A
South Central College, A

Mississippi

Coahoma Community College, A
Rust College, B

Missouri

East Central College, A
Jefferson College, A
Missouri State University - West Plains, A
Moberly Area Community College, A
St. Charles Community College, A
Southeast Missouri State University, A
State Fair Community College, A

Montana

Flathead Valley Community College, A

Nebraska

Central Community College - Columbus Campus, A
Central Community College - Grand Island Campus, A
Central Community College - Hastings Campus, A
Nebraska Indian Community College, A
Southeast Community College, Lincoln Campus, A

New Mexico

Eastern New Mexico University, A
Eastern New Mexico University - Roswell, A

New York

Broome Community College, A
Cayuga County Community College, A
Dutchess Community College, A
Erie Community College, A
Herkimer County Community College, A
Jefferson Community College, A
Morrisville State College, A
Orange County Community College, A
State University of New York College of Agriculture and Technology at Cobleskill, AB

State University of New York College of Technology at Canton, A
Tompkins Cortland Community College, A

North Carolina

Blue Ridge Community College, A
Edgecombe Community College, A
Haywood Community College, A
Mayland Community College, A
Mitchell Community College, A
Piedmont Community College, A
Roanoke-Chowan Community College, A
Stanly Community College, A
Western Piedmont Community College, A
Wilkes Community College, A

North Dakota

Dakota College at Bottineau, A
Sitting Bull College, A

Ohio

Eastern Gateway Community College, A
Northwest State Community College, A
Youngstown State University, A

Oregon

Blue Mountain Community College, A
Central Oregon Community College, A
Chemeketa Community College, A
Clackamas Community College, A
Columbia Gorge Community College, A
Portland Community College, A
Rogue Community College, A

Pennsylvania

Chestnut Hill College, B
Messiah College, B
Montgomery County Community College, A
Pennsylvania Highlands Community College, A
Reading Area Community College, A
Seton Hill University, B

South Carolina

Aiken Technical College, A
Central Carolina Technical College, A
Denmark Technical College, A
Forrest College, A
Greenville Technical College, A
Midlands Technical College, A
Williamsburg Technical College, A
York Technical College, A

South Dakota

Southeast Technical Institute, A

Texas

Eastfield College, A
El Paso Community College, A
Kilgore College, A
Lamar Institute of Technology, A
San Antonio College, A
Texarkana College, A
Texas Tech University, B
The University of Texas Rio Grande Valley, B
Vernon College, A

Utah

Brigham Young University, B

Washington

Grays Harbor College, A
Peninsula College, A
Spokane Falls Community College, A

Canada

British Columbia

University of the Fraser Valley, AB

Ontario

Ryerson University, B

CHILD DEVELOPMENT

United States

Alabama

Auburn University, B
Northwest-Shoals Community College, A
The University of West Alabama, O
Wallace State Community College, A

Alaska

University of Alaska Fairbanks, B

Arizona

Central Arizona College, A
Mesa Community College, A
Northland Pioneer College, A
South Mountain Community College, A
Tohono O'odham Community College, A

Arkansas

Arkansas Tech University, A
Harding University, B
Henderson State University, B
National Park College, A
Pulaski Technical College, A
University of Arkansas Community College at Morrilton, A

California

Alliant International University - San Diego, B
American River College, A
Bakersfield College, A
Butte College, A
California State University, East Bay, B
California State University, Fresno, B
California State University, Long Beach, B
California State University, Los Angeles, BM
California State University, Northridge, B
California State University, Sacramento, B
California State University, San Bernardino, M
Cerro Coso Community College, A
Chabot College, A
Citrus College, A
College of the Redwoods, A
Cuyamaca College, A
De Anza College, A
East Los Angeles College, A
Foothill College, A
Humboldt State University, B
Lassen Community College District, A
Los Angeles City College, A
Los Angeles Southwest College, A
Los Angeles Valley College, A
Mendocino College, A
Merritt College, A
Modesto Junior College, A
Monterey Peninsula College, A
Mount Saint Mary's University, B
Mt. San Antonio College, A
Mt. San Jacinto College, A
Napa Valley College, A
National University, B
Ohlone College, A
Oxnard College, A
Pacific Oaks College, B
Pasadena City College, A
Point Loma Nazarene University, B
Porterville College, A
Saddleback College, A
San Diego State University, M
San Jose City College, A
Santa Monica College, A
Santa Rosa Junior College, A
Sierra College, A
Southwestern College, A
University of California, Davis, M
University of La Verne, BM
Victor Valley College, A
West Hills Community College, A
Whittier College, BM
Yuba College, A

Colorado

Aims Community College, A
Community College of Aurora, A
Community College of Denver, A
Northeastern Junior College, A
Otero Junior College, A
Pikes Peak Community College, A

Connecticut

Albertus Magnus College, B
Goodwin College, AB
Housatonic Community College, A
Northwestern Connecticut Community College, A
Post University, B
Quinnipiac University, B
University of Saint Joseph, B

Delaware

Delaware State University, B

Florida

Daytona State College, A
Indian River State College, A
Miami Dade College, A
Polk State College, A
Seminole State College of Florida, A
State College of Florida Manatee-Sarasota, A
University of Florida, M

Georgia

Abraham Baldwin Agricultural College, A
Albany Technical College, A
Athens Technical College, A
Atlanta Technical College, A
Augusta Technical College, A
Central Georgia Technical College, A
Chattahoochee Technical College, A
Coastal Pines Technical College, A
Columbus Technical College, A
Georgia Northwestern Technical College, A
Lanier Technical College, A
Oconee Fall Line Technical College, A
Ogeechee Technical College, A
Point University, AB
Savannah Technical College, A
South Georgia Technical College, A
Southeastern Technical College, A
Southern Crescent Technical College, A
Southern Regional Technical College, A
West Georgia Technical College, A
Wiregrass Georgia Technical College, A

Hawaii

Chaminade University of Honolulu, M

Idaho

Brigham Young University - Idaho, B
Lewis-Clark State College, AB

Illinois

City Colleges of Chicago, Richard J. Daley College, A
College of DuPage, A
Ellis University, AB
Illinois Eastern Community Colleges, Wabash Valley College, A
Illinois Valley Community College, A
Olivet Nazarene University, B
Richland Community College, A
Rock Valley College, A
Shawnee Community College, A
Southeastern Illinois College, A
Spoon River College, A
University of Illinois at Urbana - Champaign, B

Indiana

Ivy Tech Community College - Central Indiana, A
Purdue University, MD
Purdue University Northwest (Hammond), M

Iowa

Iowa Lakes Community College, A
Southeastern Community College, A

Kansas

Allen Community College, A
Butler Community College, A
Cloud County Community College, A
Colby Community College, A
Cowley County Community College and Area Vocational - Technical School, A
Dodge City Community College, A
Kansas State University, BMO
Labette Community College, A
Pratt Community College, A
University of Saint Mary, B

Louisiana

Louisiana Tech University, B

Maine

Kennebec Valley Community College, A
Washington County Community College, A

Maryland

Frederick Community College, A
Howard Community College, A
University of Maryland Eastern Shore, B

Massachusetts

Lesley University, B
Mount Ida College, B
Mount Wachusett Community College, A
North Shore Community College, A
Springfield College, B
Tufts University, BMD
Wheelock College, B

Michigan

Bay de Noc Community College, A
Central Michigan University, B
Kuyper College, AB
Madonna University, AB
Michigan State University, BM
Mid Michigan Community College, A
Monroe County Community College, A
Muskegon Community College, A
Northern Michigan University, A
Schoolcraft College, A
Western Michigan University, B

Minnesota

Concordia University, St. Paul, B
Hennepin Technical College, A
Minneapolis Community and Technical College, A
Minnesota State University Mankato, B
North Central University, B
St. Cloud State University, B
University of Minnesota, Twin Cities Campus, MD

Mississippi

Alcorn State University, B
Copiah-Lincoln Community College, A
Holmes Community College, A
Jones County Junior College, A
Tougaloo College, AB

Missouri

College of the Ozarks, B
Evangel University, A
Hannibal-LaGrange University, B
Missouri Baptist University, B

Montana

Salish Kootenai College, A

Nebraska

Central Community College - Grand Island Campus, A
Central Community College - Hastings Campus, A
Metropolitan Community College, A
University of Nebraska - Lincoln, MD

Nevada

University of Nevada, Reno, B

New Hampshire

Manchester Community College, A
Nashua Community College, A
Southern New Hampshire University, M

New Jersey

Bergen Community College, A
Montclair State University, MO
Rutgers University - Camden, MD

New York

Bronx Community College of the City University of New York, A
Jefferson Community College, A
St. Bonaventure University, B
Sarah Lawrence College, BM
State University of New York College at Oneonta, B
Suffolk County Community College, A
Westchester Community College, A

North Carolina

Appalachian State University, BM
Central Piedmont Community College, A
East Carolina University, BMD
James Sprunt Community College, A
Meredith College, B
North Carolina Agricultural and Technical State University, BM
Sandhills Community College, A
Southwestern Community College, A
The University of North Carolina at Charlotte, MDO
Vance-Granville Community College, A

North Dakota

North Dakota State University, MDO

Ohio

Belmont College, A
Bowling Green State University, B
Edison Community College, A
Franciscan University of Steubenville, A
Hocking College, A
James A. Rhodes State College, A
North Central State College, A
Ohio University, AM
Ohio University - Chillicothe, A
Ohio University - Lancaster, A
Sinclair Community College, A
Stark State College, A
Union Institute & University, B
The University of Akron, BM
Youngstown State University, AB

Oklahoma

Bacone College, A
Cameron University, B
Carl Albert State College, A
Eastern Oklahoma State College, A
Murray State College, A
Oklahoma Christian University, B
Oklahoma City Community College, A
Redlands Community College, A
Seminole State College, A
Tulsa Community College, A
University of Central Oklahoma, B
Western Oklahoma State College, A

Oregon

Portland State University, B
Umpqua Community College, A

Pennsylvania

Community College of Allegheny County, A
Laurel Business Institute, A
Reading Area Community College, A
Seton Hill University, B

South Carolina

Benedict College, B
Piedmont Technical College, A

Tennessee

Carson-Newman University, B
Chattanooga State Community College, A

Cleveland State Community College, A
Columbia State Community College, A
Dyersburg State Community College, A
East Tennessee State University, B
Lee University, M
Milligan College, B
Nashville State Community College, A
Pellissippi State Community College, A
Tennessee Technological University, B
The University of Tennessee at Martin, BM
Vanderbilt University, B
Volunteer State Community College, A
Walters State Community College, A

Texas

Alvin Community College, A
Amarillo College, A
Angelina College, A
Austin Community College District, A
Blinn College, A
Brazosport College, A
Brookhaven College, A
Cisco College, A
Coastal Bend College, A
College of the Mainland, A
Collin County Community College District, A
Del Mar College, A
El Paso Community College, A
Houston Community College, A
Howard College, A
Laredo Community College, A
Midland College, A
Odessa College, A
San Antonio College, A
San Jacinto College District, A
South Plains College, A
Texarkana College, A
Texas Tech University, B
Texas Woman's University, BM
Trinity Valley Community College, A
Tyler Junior College, A
University of the Incarnate Word, B
University of North Texas, B
The University of Texas at Arlington, B
The University of Texas at Austin, MD

Utah

Brigham Young University, B
Snow College, A
Southern Utah University, A
Weber State University, AB

Vermont

Bennington College, B
Community College of Vermont, A
Goddard College, B

Virginia

Hampton University, B
New River Community College, A
University of Virginia, B
Virginia Western Community College, A

Washington

Eastern Washington University, B
Peninsula College, A
Shoreline Community College, A
Skagit Valley College, A
Yakima Valley Community College, A

West Virginia

Pierpont Community & Technical College, A
West Virginia University, B

Wisconsin

Madison Area Technical College, A
Nicolet Area Technical College, A
Western Technical College, A

Wyoming

University of Wyoming, M

Canada

Alberta

Mount Royal University, B

British Columbia

University of Victoria, B

Manitoba

University of Manitoba, B

Maritime Provinces: New Brunswick

Université de Moncton, B

Maritime Provinces: Nova Scotia

Mount Saint Vincent University, B

Ontario

Carleton University, B
Trent University, B
University of Guelph, B
The University of Western Ontario, B

CHILD AND FAMILY STUDIES

United States

Alabama

Alabama Agricultural and Mechanical University, M
Auburn University, MD
The University of Alabama, M
University of North Alabama, M

Arizona

Arizona State University at the Tempe campus, M
The University of Arizona, M

California

California State University, East Bay, M
California State University, Los Angeles, M
California State University, San Marcos, M
Loma Linda University, MDO
San Diego State University, M
San Jose State University, M
University of La Verne, M
University of Southern California, M

Colorado

Colorado State University, MD
University of Denver, M

Connecticut

Fairfield University, M
University of Connecticut, MDO

Delaware

University of Delaware, MD

Florida

Florida State University, MD
University of South Florida, MDO

Georgia

University of Georgia, MD

Illinois

Northern Illinois University, M
University of Illinois at Springfield, M

Indiana

Indiana University - Purdue University Indianapolis, M
Purdue University, MD
Purdue University Northwest (Hammond), M

Iowa

Iowa State University of Science and Technology, MD

Kansas

Kansas State University, MDO

Kentucky

Asbury University, M
University of Kentucky, MD

Maryland

Towson University, MO
University of Maryland, College Park, MD

Massachusetts

Assumption College, M
Brandeis University, MD
Tufts University, MD
University of Massachusetts Amherst, D
Wheelock College, M

Michigan

Central Michigan University, M
Michigan State University, MD
Spring Arbor University, M

Minnesota

Capella University, M
Concordia University, St. Paul, M
St. Cloud State University, M
University of Minnesota, Twin Cities Campus, MD
Walden University, MD

Mississippi

Mississippi State University, MD
University of Southern Mississippi, M

Missouri

Missouri State University, M
University of Missouri, MD
Washington University in St. Louis, M

Montana

University of Montana, M

Nebraska

University of Nebraska - Lincoln, MD

Nevada

University of Nevada, Reno, M

New Hampshire

University of New Hampshire, MO

New Jersey

Montclair State University, MDO

New Mexico

University of New Mexico, MD

New York

Cornell University, MD
Roberts Wesleyan College, M
State University of New York at Oswego, M
Syracuse University, MD

North Carolina

East Carolina University, MD
North Carolina Agricultural and Technical State University, M
The University of North Carolina at Greensboro, MD

North Dakota

North Dakota State University, MDO

Ohio

Bowling Green State University, M
Kent State University, M
Miami University, M
The Ohio State University, D
Ohio University, M

The University of Akron, M

Oklahoma

Oklahoma State University, MD
University of Central Oklahoma, M

Oregon

Oregon State University, MD

Pennsylvania

Penn State University Park, MD

Rhode Island

University of Rhode Island, M

South Carolina

South Carolina State University, M

Tennessee

The University of Tennessee, MD
The University of Tennessee at Martin, M
Vanderbilt University, M

Texas

Amberton University, M
Texas State University, M
Texas Tech University, MD
Texas Woman's University, MD
University of North Texas, M
The University of Texas at Austin, MD
The University of Texas at Dallas, M

Utah

Brigham Young University, MD
University of Utah, M
Utah State University, MD

Virginia

Liberty University, M

Washington

Central Washington University, M

West Virginia

West Virginia University, M

Wisconsin

Concordia University Wisconsin, M
University of Wisconsin - Madison, MD

Canada
British Columbia

University of Victoria, MD

Manitoba

University of Manitoba, M

Maritime Provinces: Nova Scotia

Mount Saint Vincent University, M

Ontario

Brock University, M
University of Guelph, MD

Quebec

Concordia University, M

CHINESE LANGUAGE AND LIT-ERATURE

United States
California

California State University, Long Beach, B
California State University, Los Angeles, B
City College of San Francisco, A
National University, B
Occidental College, B
Pomona College, B

San Francisco State University, B
San Jose State University, B
Scripps College, B
Stanford University, B
University of California, Berkeley, B
University of California, Davis, B
University of California, Los Angeles, B
University of California, San Diego, B
University of California, Santa Barbara, B
Whittier College, B

Colorado

University of Colorado Boulder, B

Connecticut

Trinity College, B
University of Connecticut, B
Yale University, B

District of Columbia

The George Washington University, B
Georgetown University, B

Florida

New College of Florida, B

Georgia

Emory University, B
University of Georgia, B
University of North Georgia, B

Hawaii

University of Hawaii at Manoa, B

Idaho

Brigham Young University - Idaho, A

Illinois

North Central College, B

Indiana

University of Notre Dame, B

Iowa

Grinnell College, B
The University of Iowa, B

Kentucky

University of Kentucky, B
Western Kentucky University, B

Maine

Bates College, B

Maryland

United States Naval Academy, B
University of Maryland, College Park, B

Massachusetts

Boston University, B
College of the Holy Cross, B
Tufts University, B
University of Massachusetts Amherst, B
Wellesley College, B
Williams College, B

Michigan

Calvin College, B
Michigan State University, B

Minnesota

Concordia College, B
Macalester College, B

Mississippi

University of Mississippi, B

Missouri

Washington University in St. Louis, B

Montana

University of Montana, B

New Hampshire

Dartmouth College, B

New Jersey

Rutgers University - New Brunswick, B

New York

Bard College, B
Brooklyn College of the City University of New York, B
Colgate University, B
Hamilton College, B
Hobart and William Smith Colleges, B
Hofstra University, B
Hunter College of the City University of New York, B
Nazareth College of Rochester, B
Queens College of the City University of New York, B
Sarah Lawrence College, B
Union College, B
United States Military Academy, B
Vassar College, B

North Carolina

Davidson College, B
Wake Forest University, B

Ohio

The Ohio State University, B

Oklahoma

University of Oklahoma, B

Oregon

Pacific University, B
Portland State University, B
Reed College, B
University of Oregon, B

Pennsylvania

Carnegie Mellon University, B
Lehigh University, B
Messiah College, B
Penn State University Park, B
Swarthmore College, B
University of Pittsburgh, B

Rhode Island

Bryant University, B
University of Rhode Island, B

South Carolina

Wofford College, B

Texas

Austin Community College District, A
Trinity University, B
University of Houston, B

Utah

University of Utah, B

Vermont

Bennington College, B
Marlboro College, B
Middlebury College, B
University of Vermont, B

Washington

University of Puget Sound, B
University of Washington, B

Wisconsin

Beloit College, B
Lawrence University, B
University of Wisconsin - Madison, B

Canada
Alberta

University of Alberta, B

British Columbia

The University of British Columbia, B
University of Victoria, B

Ontario

The University of Western Ontario, B

Saskatchewan

University of Regina, B

CHINESE STUDIES

United States

Arizona

Arizona State University at the Tempe campus, MD

California

San Francisco State University, M
Stanford University, MD
University of California, Berkeley, D
University of California, Irvine, BMD

Colorado

University of Colorado Boulder, MD

Delaware

University of Delaware, M

Hawaii

University of Hawaii at Manoa, MDO

Illinois

DePaul University, BM

Indiana

Indiana University Bloomington, MD

Iowa

The University of Iowa, M

Massachusetts

Harvard University, D
University of Massachusetts Amherst, M

Michigan

Oakland University, B

Minnesota

University of Minnesota, Duluth, B

Missouri

Washington University in St. Louis, MD

New Jersey

Drew University, B

New York

Hunter College of the City University of New York, M
New York University, M
University at Albany, State University of New York, B

North Dakota

University of North Dakota, B

Ohio

The Ohio State University, MD

Oklahoma

The University of Tulsa, B

Oregon

University of Oregon, MD
Willamette University, B

Pennsylvania

Gettysburg College, B

Vermont

Marlboro College, B
Middlebury College, M

Virginia

The College of William and Mary, B
University of Richmond, B

Washington

Pacific Lutheran University, B
University of Washington, BMD
Washington State University, B

Wisconsin

University of Wisconsin - Madison, MD
Wisconsin Lutheran College, B

Canada

Alberta

University of Alberta, BM

Ontario

The University of Western Ontario, B

CHIROPRACTIC

United States

Connecticut

University of Bridgeport, D

Georgia

Life University, D

Iowa

Palmer College of Chiropractic, AD

Kansas

Barton County Community College, A
Cleveland University - Kansas City, D

Missouri

Logan University, MD

New York

D'Youville College, D

Wisconsin

Moraine Park Technical College, A

Canada

Quebec

Université du Québec à Trois-Rivières, D

CHRISTIAN STUDIES

United States

Arizona

Grand Canyon University, B

Arkansas

Ouachita Baptist University, AB

California

California Baptist University, B
Epic Bible College, A
Simpson University, B

Georgia

Luther Rice College & Seminary, B
Mercer University, B
Toccoa Falls College, B
Truett-McConnell College, B

Indiana

Bethel College, B
Crossroads Bible College, B
Huntington University, A
Marian University, B

Iowa

Iowa Wesleyan University, B

Kansas

Bethany College, B
Southwestern College, B
Tabor College, B

Kentucky

The Southern Baptist Theological Seminary, B
University of the Cumberlands, B

Louisiana

Loyola University New Orleans, B

Massachusetts

College of the Holy Cross, B
Gordon College, B
Stonehill College, B

Michigan

Hillsdale College, B

Minnesota

The College of St. Scholastica, B
Crown College, AB
Saint Mary's University of Minnesota, B

Mississippi

Mississippi College, B

Missouri

Missouri Baptist University, B

New Jersey

Seton Hall University, B

New York

Canisius College, B

North Carolina

Heritage Bible College, A

Ohio

Ursuline College, B

Oklahoma

Oklahoma Baptist University, AB
Oklahoma Wesleyan University, AB

South Carolina

Anderson University, B

Tennessee

Bethel University, B
Bryan College, B
Lee University, B
Tennessee Wesleyan College, B

Texas

College of Biblical Studies - Houston, B
Hardin-Simmons University, B
Houston Baptist University, B
McMurry University, B
St. Edward's University, B
Texas Wesleyan University, B
University of Mary Hardin-Baylor, B

Vermont

Marlboro College, B

Virginia

Bluefield College, B
Liberty University, B
Regent University, A
Roanoke College, B

Washington

Whitworth University, B

Wisconsin

Concordia University Wisconsin, B

U.S. Territories: Puerto Rico

Inter American University of Puerto Rico, Metropolitan Campus, A
Universidad Pentecostal Mizpa, AB

Canada

Alberta

Ambrose University, B

British Columbia

Trinity Western University, B

Manitoba

Steinbach Bible College, B

Maritime Provinces: New Brunswick

St. Thomas University, B

Saskatchewan

Horizon College & Seminary, B

CINEMATOGRAPHY AND FILM/ VIDEO PRODUCTION

United States

Arizona

The Art Institute of Phoenix, B
The Art Institute of Tucson, B
Glendale Community College, A
Grand Canyon University, B
Pima Community College, A
University of Advancing Technology, AB

Arkansas

John Brown University, B
University of Central Arkansas, B

California

Academy of Art University, AB
Art Center College of Design, B
The Art Institute of California - Inland Empire, a campus of Argosy University, B
The Art Institute of California - Orange County, a campus of Argosy University, B
The Art Institute of California - Sacramento, a campus of Argosy University, B
The Art Institute of California - San Francisco, a campus of Argosy University, B
Biola University, B
Brooks Institute, B
California Institute of the Arts, B
California State University, Long Beach, B
California State University, Northridge, B
Cerritos College, A
Chapman University, B
City College of San Francisco, A
College of the Canyons, A
College of Marin, A
College of San Mateo, A
Columbia College Hollywood, B
FIDM/Fashion Institute of Design & Merchandising, Los Angeles Campus, AB
Gavilan College, A
John Paul the Great Catholic University, B
La Sierra University, B
Los Angeles Valley College, A
Loyola Marymount University, B
Mount Saint Mary's University, B
New York Film Academy, AB
Orange Coast College, A
Pacific Union College, AB
Pasadena City College, A
Saddleback College, A

San Francisco Art Institute, B
Stanford University, B
University of Southern California, B
Vanguard University of Southern California, B

Colorado

The Art Institute of Colorado, AB
Community College of Aurora, A
Red Rocks Community College, A

Connecticut

Quinnipiac University, B

Delaware

Wilmington University, B

District of Columbia

American University, B

Florida

The Art Institute of Fort Lauderdale, AB
The Art Institute of Tampa, a branch of Miami International University of Art & Design, B
Florida Keys Community College, A
Full Sail University, B
Hillsborough Community College, A
Lynn University, B
Miami Dade College, AB
Miami International University of Art & Design, B
Palm Beach Atlantic University, B
Ringling College of Art and Design, B
Santa Fe College, B
University of Central Florida, B
University of Miami, B
Valencia College, A

Georgia

The Art Institute of Atlanta, AB
Clayton State University, AB
Savannah College of Art and Design, B

Illinois

College of DuPage, A
Columbia College Chicago, B
DePaul University, B
The Illinois Institute of Art - Chicago, B
The Illinois Institute of Art - Schaumburg, B
School of the Art Institute of Chicago, B
Southern Illinois University Carbondale, B
Tribeca Flashpoint College, A
University of Illinois at Chicago, B

Indiana

Anderson University, B
Goshen College, B
Taylor University, B

Iowa

Maharishi University of Management, B
The University of Iowa, B
Western Iowa Tech Community College, A

Louisiana

Baton Rouge Community College, A
Loyola University New Orleans, B

Maryland

Stevenson University, B

Massachusetts

Emerson College, B
Fitchburg State University, B
Massachusetts College of Art and Design, B
School of the Museum of Fine Arts, Boston, B

Michigan

Cornerstone University, B
Lansing Community College, A
Mott Community College, A
Northern Michigan University, B
Wayne State University, B

Minnesota

Century College, A
Minneapolis College of Art and Design, B
Minneapolis Community and Technical College, A

Missouri

The Art Institute of St. Louis, B
Webster University, B

Montana

Montana State University, B
University of Montana, B

Nevada

The Art Institute of Las Vegas, B

New Hampshire

Keene State College, B

New Jersey

Camden County College, A
Fairleigh Dickinson University, College at Florham, B
Montclair State University, B
Raritan Valley Community College, A
Rutgers University - Newark, B

New Mexico

Eastern New Mexico University, B
Eastern New Mexico University - Roswell, A
Institute of American Indian Arts, AB
New Mexico Highlands University, B
New Mexico State University, B
Santa Fe Community College, A
Santa Fe University of Art and Design, B

New York

Binghamton University, State University of New York, B
Brooklyn College of the City University of New York, B
City College of the City University of New York, B
Fashion Institute of Technology, B
Five Towns College, B
Hunter College of the City University of New York, B
Ithaca College, B
Long Island University - LIU Post, B
New York University, B
Pace University, Pleasantville Campus, B
Pratt Institute, B
Purchase College, State University of New York, B
Rochester Institute of Technology, B
School of Visual Arts, B
Syracuse University, B

North Carolina

The Art Institute of Charlotte, a campus of South University, AB
The Art Institute of Raleigh-Durham, a campus of South University, B
Cape Fear Community College, A
Living Arts College, B
Piedmont Community College, A
University of North Carolina School of the Arts, B
The University of North Carolina Wilmington, B
Western Piedmont Community College, A

Ohio

Cleveland State University, B
Columbus College of Art & Design, B
Ohio University, B

Oklahoma

Oklahoma City Community College, A
Oklahoma City University, B

Oregon

The Art Institute of Portland, B
George Fox University, B

Pennsylvania

The Art Institute of Philadelphia, AB
The Art Institute of Pittsburgh, AB
Bucks County Community College, A

Drexel University, B
Messiah College, B
Point Park University, B
Temple University, B

Rhode Island

New England Institute of Technology, AB
University of Rhode Island, B

South Carolina

The Art Institute of Charleston, a branch of The Art
Institute of Atlanta, B
Bob Jones University, B

Tennessee

The Art Institute of Tennessee - Nashville, a branch
of The Art Institute of Atlanta, AB
Belmont University, B
Pellissippi State Community College, A
Southern Adventist University, B

Texas

The Art Institute of Austin, a branch of The Art Insti-
tute of Houston, B
The Art Institute of Dallas, a campus of South Uni-
versity, AB
The Art Institute of Houston, B
The Art Institute of San Antonio, a branch of The Art
Institute of Houston, B
El Paso Community College, A
Houston Community College, A
Southern Methodist University, B

Utah

Brigham Young University, B

Vermont

Bennington College, B

Virginia

The Art Institute of Washington, a branch of The Art
Institute of Atlanta, AB
George Mason University, B
Liberty University, B
Regent University, B
Virginia Commonwealth University, B

Washington

The Art Institute of Seattle, AB
Central Washington University, B
Eastern Washington University, B
The Evergreen State College, B
Seattle Central College, A
Shoreline Community College, A
Walla Walla University, B

Wisconsin

Northcentral Technical College, A
Wisconsin Lutheran College, B

Wyoming

Northwest College, A

Canada

British Columbia

Emily Carr University of Art + Design, B

Ontario

Ryerson University, B
York University, B

Quebec

Concordia University, B
Université de Montréal, B

Saskatchewan

University of Regina, B

CITY/URBAN, COMMUNITY AND REGIONAL PLANNING

United States

Alabama

Alabama Agricultural and Mechanical University, B

Arizona

Arizona State University at the Tempe campus, B
The University of Arizona, B

California

California Polytechnic State University, San Luis
Obispo, B
California State Polytechnic University, Pomona, B
Modesto Junior College, A
University of California, Davis, B
University of San Francisco, B

Florida

Broward College, A
Florida Atlantic University, B
South Florida State College, A

Illinois

University of Illinois at Urbana - Champaign, B

Indiana

Ball State University, B

Iowa

Iowa State University of Science and Technology, B

Maryland

Frostburg State University, B

Massachusetts

Bridgewater State University, B
Massachusetts Institute of Technology, B
Tufts University, B
Westfield State University, B

Michigan

Eastern Michigan University, B
Michigan State University, B
Western Michigan University, B

Minnesota

Minnesota State University Mankato, B
St. Cloud State University, B

Missouri

Missouri State University, B
University of Missouri - Kansas City, B

Montana

University of Montana, B

New Hampshire

Plymouth State University, B
University of New Hampshire, B

New Jersey

Rowan University, B

New York

Buffalo State College, State University of New York,
B
Cornell University, B
Parsons School of Design, B
State University of New York College of Environ-
mental Science and Forestry, B

North Carolina

Appalachian State University, B
East Carolina University, B

Ohio

Miami University, B
Miami University Hamilton, B

The Ohio State University, B
The University of Akron, B
University of Cincinnati, B

Oregon

Portland State University, B

Pennsylvania

Indiana University of Pennsylvania, B
Temple University, B

Texas

Texas A&M University, B
Texas State University, B

Virginia

University of Virginia, B

Washington

Eastern Washington University, B
University of Washington, B

Canada

Alberta

University of Alberta, B

Maritime Provinces: Nova Scotia

Dalhousie University, B

Ontario

Carleton University, B
Ryerson University, B
University of Waterloo, B

Quebec

Concordia University, B

Saskatchewan

University of Saskatchewan, B

CIVIL DRAFTING AND CIVIL ENGINEERING CAD/CADD

United States

California

College of the Redwoods, A

Delaware

Delaware Technical & Community College,
Stanton/Wilmington Campus, A

Iowa

Southwestern Community College, A

Kentucky

Sullivan College of Technology and Design, A

Maryland

Harford Community College, A

New York

Genesee Community College, A

Ohio

Central Ohio Technical College, A

Pennsylvania

Community College of Allegheny County, A

Washington

North Seattle College, A
Renton Technical College, A

Canada

British Columbia

British Columbia Institute of Technology, A

CIVIL ENGINEERING

United States

Alabama

Alabama Agricultural and Mechanical University, B
Auburn University, BMD
The University of Alabama, BMD
The University of Alabama at Birmingham, BMD
The University of Alabama in Huntsville, BMD
University of South Alabama, BM

Alaska

University of Alaska Anchorage, BMO
University of Alaska Fairbanks, BMDO

Arizona

Arizona State University at the Tempe campus,
  BMD
Northern Arizona University, BM
The University of Arizona, B

Arkansas

Arkansas State University, B
University of Arkansas, BMD

California

California Baptist University, B
California Institute of Technology, MDO
California Polytechnic State University, San Luis
  Obispo, BM
California State Polytechnic University, Pomona, BM
California State University, Chico, B
California State University, Fresno, BM
California State University, Fullerton, M
California State University, Long Beach, BM
California State University, Los Angeles, BM
California State University, Northridge, BM
California State University, Sacramento, BM
Loyola Marymount University, BM
San Diego State University, BM
San Francisco State University, B
San Jose State University, BM
Santa Clara University, BM
Stanford University, BMDO
University of California, Berkeley, BMD
University of California, Davis, BMDO
University of California, Irvine, BMD
University of California, Los Angeles, BMD
University of the Pacific, B
University of Southern California, BMD

Colorado

Colorado School of Mines, BMD
Colorado State University, BMD
United States Air Force Academy, B
University of Colorado Boulder, BMD
University of Colorado Denver, BMD

Connecticut

Central Connecticut State University, B
Quinnipiac University, B
United States Coast Guard Academy, B
University of Connecticut, BMD
University of Hartford, B
University of New Haven, B

Delaware

Delaware State University, B
University of Delaware, BMD

District of Columbia

The Catholic University of America, BMD
The George Washington University, BMDO
Howard University, BM
University of the District of Columbia, B

Florida

Broward College, A
Embry-Riddle Aeronautical University - Daytona, B
Florida Agricultural and Mechanical University, BMD
Florida Atlantic University, BM
Florida Gulf Coast University, B

Florida Institute of Technology, BMD
Florida International University, BMD
Florida State University, MD
Polytechnic University of Puerto Rico, Orlando
  Campus, B
South Florida State College, A
University of Central Florida, BMDO
University of Florida, BMD
University of Miami, BMD
University of North Florida, BM
University of South Florida, BMDO

Georgia

Georgia Institute of Technology, BMD
Georgia Southern University, B
Kennesaw State University, B
University of Georgia, B

Hawaii

University of Hawaii at Manoa, BMD

Idaho

Boise State University, BM
Idaho State University, BM
University of Idaho, BMD

Illinois

Bradley University, BM
Illinois Institute of Technology, BMD
Northwestern University, BMD
Southern Illinois University Carbondale, BM
Southern Illinois University Edwardsville, BM
University of Illinois at Chicago, BMD
University of Illinois at Urbana - Champaign, BMD

Indiana

Indiana University - Purdue University Fort Wayne,
  BM
Purdue University, BMD
Purdue University Northwest (Hammond), B
Rose-Hulman Institute of Technology, BM
Trine University, BM
University of Evansville, B
University of Notre Dame, BMD
Valparaiso University, B
Vincennes University, A

Iowa

Dordt College, B
Iowa State University of Science and Technology,
  BMD
The University of Iowa, BMD

Kansas

Kansas State University, BMD
The University of Kansas, BMD

Kentucky

University of Kentucky, BMD
University of Louisville, BMDO
Western Kentucky University, B

Louisiana

Louisiana State University and Agricultural & Me-
  chanical College, BMD
Louisiana Tech University, BMD
McNeese State University, M
Southern University and Agricultural and Mechanical
  College, B
University of Louisiana at Lafayette, BM
University of New Orleans, B

Maine

University of Maine, BMD

Maryland

Johns Hopkins University, BMD
Morgan State University, BMD
University of Maryland, College Park, BMD

Massachusetts

Bristol Community College, A
Massachusetts Institute of Technology, BMDO
Merrimack College, B

Northeastern University, BMD
Tufts University, BMD
University of Massachusetts Amherst, BMD
University of Massachusetts Dartmouth, BM
University of Massachusetts Lowell, BMDO
Wentworth Institute of Technology, B
Western New England University, B
Worcester Polytechnic Institute, BMDO

Michigan

Calvin College, B
Lawrence Technological University, BMD
Michigan State University, BMD
Michigan Technological University, BMD
University of Detroit Mercy, BMD
University of Michigan, BMDO
Wayne State University, BMD
Western Michigan University, BM

Minnesota

Itasca Community College, A
Minnesota State University Mankato, B
University of Minnesota, Duluth, B
University of Minnesota, Twin Cities Campus,
  BMDO

Mississippi

Jackson State University, B
Mississippi State University, BMD
University of Mississippi, B

Missouri

Missouri University of Science and Technology,
  BMD
Rockhurst University, B
St. Charles Community College, A
Saint Louis University, B
University of Missouri, BMD
University of Missouri - Kansas City, BM
University of Missouri - St. Louis, B
William Jewell College, B

Montana

Carroll College, B
Montana State University, BMD

Nebraska

University of Nebraska - Lincoln, BMD

Nevada

College of Southern Nevada, A
Truckee Meadows Community College, A
University of Nevada, Las Vegas, BMD
University of Nevada, Reno, BMD

New Hampshire

University of New Hampshire, BMD

New Jersey

The College of New Jersey, B
New Jersey Institute of Technology, B
Princeton University, BMD
Rowan University, BM
Rutgers University - New Brunswick, BMD
Stevens Institute of Technology, BMDO

New Mexico

New Mexico Institute of Mining and Technology, B
New Mexico State University, BMD
University of New Mexico, BMD

New York

City College of the City University of New York,
  BMD
Clarkson University, BMD
Columbia University, BMD
Cooper Union for the Advancement of Science and
  Art, BM
Cornell University, BMD
Fiorello H. LaGuardia Community College of the
  City University of New York, A
Hofstra University, B
Manhattan College, BM
New York University, BMD

Rensselaer Polytechnic Institute, BMD
State University of New York Polytechnic Institute, B
Stony Brook University, State University of New
   York, B
Syracuse University, BMD
United States Military Academy, B
University at Buffalo, the State University of New
   York, BMD

North Carolina

Duke University, BMD
Haywood Community College, A
North Carolina Agricultural and Technical State Uni-
   versity, BM
North Carolina State University, BMD
The University of North Carolina at Charlotte, BMD

North Dakota

North Dakota State University, BMD
University of North Dakota, BM

Ohio

Case Western Reserve University, BMD
Cleveland State University, BMD
Ohio Northern University, B
The Ohio State University, BMD
Ohio University, BMD
The University of Akron, BMD
University of Cincinnati, BMD
University of Dayton, BM
University of Mount Union, B
The University of Toledo, BMD
Youngstown State University, BM

Oklahoma

Oklahoma State University, BMD
University of Oklahoma, BMD

Oregon

George Fox University, B
Oregon Institute of Technology, B
Oregon State University, BMD
Portland State University, BMD
University of Portland, BM

Pennsylvania

Bucknell University, BM
Carnegie Mellon University, BMD
Drexel University, BMD
Lafayette College, B
Lehigh University, BMD
Penn State Abington, B
Penn State Altoona, B
Penn State Beaver, B
Penn State Berks, B
Penn State Brandywine, B
Penn State DuBois, B
Penn State Erie, The Behrend College, B
Penn State Fayette, The Eberly Campus, B
Penn State Greater Allegheny, B
Penn State Harrisburg, B
Penn State Hazleton, B
Penn State Lehigh Valley, B
Penn State Mont Alto, B
Penn State New Kensington, B
Penn State Schuylkill, B
Penn State Shenango, B
Penn State University Park, BMD
Penn State Wilkes-Barre, B
Penn State Worthington Scranton, B
Penn State York, B
Temple University, BMDO
University of Pittsburgh, BMD
Ursinus College, B
Villanova University, BM
Widener University, BM

Rhode Island

Roger Williams University, B
University of Rhode Island, BMD

South Carolina

The Citadel, The Military College of South Carolina,
   BM
Clemson University, BMD

South Carolina State University, M
University of South Carolina, BMD

South Dakota

South Dakota School of Mines and Technology, BM
South Dakota State University, BM

Tennessee

Christian Brothers University, B
Lipscomb University, B
Nashville State Community College, A
Tennessee State University, BM
Tennessee Technological University, BM
University of Memphis, BMD
The University of Tennessee, BMD
The University of Tennessee at Chattanooga, BM
Vanderbilt University, BMD

Texas

Angelo State University, B
Kilgore College, A
Lamar University, B
LeTourneau University, B
Northeast Texas Community College, A
Prairie View A&M University, B
Rice University, BMD
Southern Methodist University, BMD
Texas A&M University, BMD
Texas A&M University - Kingsville, BM
Texas Tech University, BMD
University of Houston, BMD
The University of Texas at Arlington, BMD
The University of Texas at Austin, BMD
The University of Texas at El Paso, BMDO
The University of Texas Rio Grande Valley, B
The University of Texas at San Antonio, BMD
The University of Texas at Tyler, BM
West Texas A&M University, B

Utah

Brigham Young University, MD
University of Utah, BMD
Utah State University, BMDO

Vermont

Norwich University, BM
University of Vermont, BMD

Virginia

George Mason University, BMD
Old Dominion University, BMD
Tidewater Community College, A
University of Virginia, BMD
Virginia Military Institute, B
Virginia Polytechnic Institute and State University,
   BMD

Washington

Gonzaga University, B
Saint Martin's University, BM
Seattle University, B
University of Washington, BMD
Walla Walla University, B
Washington State University, BMD
Washington State University - Tri-Cities, B

West Virginia

Potomac State College of West Virginia University,
   A
West Virginia University, BMD
West Virginia University Institute of Technology, B

Wisconsin

Marquette University, BMDO
Milwaukee School of Engineering, BM
University of Wisconsin - Madison, BMD
University of Wisconsin - Milwaukee, BM
University of Wisconsin - Platteville, B

Wyoming

University of Wyoming, BMD

U.S. Territories: American Samoa

American Samoa Community College, A

U.S. Territories: Puerto Rico

Caribbean University, B
Polytechnic University of Puerto Rico, BM
Universidad del Turabo, B
University of Puerto Rico, Mayagüez Campus, BMD

Canada

Alberta

University of Alberta, MD
University of Calgary, BMD

British Columbia

The University of British Columbia, BMD
The University of British Columbia - Okanagan
   Campus, B

Manitoba

University of Manitoba, BMD

Maritime Provinces: New Brunswick

Université de Moncton, BM
University of New Brunswick Fredericton, BMD

Maritime Provinces: Nova Scotia

Dalhousie University, MD

Newfoundland and Labrador

Memorial University of Newfoundland, BMD

Ontario

Carleton University, BMD
Lakehead University, B
McMaster University, BMD
Queen's University at Kingston, BMD
Royal Military College of Canada, BMD
Ryerson University, B
University of Ottawa, BMD
University of Toronto, BMD
University of Waterloo, BMD
The University of Western Ontario, BMD
University of Windsor, BMD

Quebec

Concordia University, BMDO
École Polytechnique de Montréal, MDO
McGill University, BMD
Université Laval, BMDO
Université de Sherbrooke, BMD

Saskatchewan

University of Saskatchewan, BMD

CIVIL ENGINEERING TECH-
NOLOGY/TECHNICIAN

United States

Alabama

Alabama Agricultural and Mechanical University, B
Bishop State Community College, A
Gadsden State Community College, A

Arizona

Arizona Western College, A
Central Arizona College, A
Eastern Arizona College, A
Phoenix College, A

California

Allan Hancock College, A
East Los Angeles College, A
Mt. San Antonio College, A
San Bernardino Valley College, A
San Joaquin Delta College, A
Santa Rosa Junior College, A
Shasta College, A

Colorado

Colorado State University - Pueblo, B
Metropolitan State University of Denver, B

Connecticut

Three Rivers Community College, A

Delaware

Delaware State University, B
Delaware Technical & Community College, Jack F.
   Owens Campus, A
Delaware Technical & Community College, Terry
   Campus, A

Florida

Florida SouthWestern State College, A
Gulf Coast State College, A
Indian River State College, A
Miami Dade College, A
Pensacola State College, A
Seminole State College of Florida, A
South Florida State College, A
State College of Florida Manatee-Sarasota, A
Valencia College, A

Georgia

Chattahoochee Technical College, A
Georgia Southern University, B
Kennesaw State University, B
Savannah State University, B

Idaho

Idaho State University, AB

Illinois

College of Lake County, A
Lake Land College, A

Indiana

Indiana State University, B
Indiana University - Purdue University Fort Wayne,
   A

Iowa

Des Moines Area Community College, A
Hawkeye Community College, A
Iowa Western Community College, A

Kansas

Johnson County Community College, A
Northwest Kansas Technical College, A

Kentucky

Bluegrass Community and Technical College, A
Murray State University, AB

Louisiana

Delgado Community College, A

Maine

Central Maine Community College, A
Eastern Maine Community College, A
University of Maine, B

Massachusetts

Northern Essex Community College, A
Springfield Technical Community College, A
University of Massachusetts Lowell, AB

Michigan

Ferris State University, A
Lansing Community College, A
Macomb Community College, A

Minnesota

Lake Superior College, A
Minnesota State Community and Technical College,
   A
Rochester Community and Technical College, A

Mississippi

Copiah-Lincoln Community College, A
Itawamba Community College, A

Mississippi Delta Community College, A
Northeast Mississippi Community College, A
Northwest Mississippi Community College, A

Missouri

Lincoln University, B
Mineral Area College, A
State Technical College of Missouri, A

Montana

Montana State University - Northern, AB
Montana Tech of The University of Montana, A

Nebraska

Metropolitan Community College, A
Southeast Community College, Milford Campus, A

New Hampshire

University of New Hampshire, A

New Jersey

Essex County College, A
Fairleigh Dickinson University, Metropolitan Cam-
   pus, B
Mercer County Community College, A
Middlesex County College, A
Rowan College at Gloucester County, A
Union County College, A

New Mexico

New Mexico Military Institute, A

New York

Broome Community College, A
Erie Community College, North Campus, A
Hudson Valley Community College, A
Mohawk Valley Community College, A
Monroe Community College, A
Nassau Community College, A
New York City College of Technology of the City
   University of New York, A
Rochester Institute of Technology, B
State University of New York College of Technology
   at Canton, AB
State University of New York Polytechnic Institute, B
Suffolk County Community College, A
United States Military Academy, B
Westchester Community College, A

North Carolina

Asheville-Buncombe Technical Community College,
   A
Central Piedmont Community College, A
Fayetteville Technical Community College, A
Gaston College, A
Guilford Technical Community College, A
Sandhills Community College, A
The University of North Carolina at Charlotte, B
Wake Technical Community College, A
Western Piedmont Community College, A

North Dakota

North Dakota State College of Science, A

Ohio

Central Ohio Technical College, A
Cincinnati State Technical and Community College,
   A
Clark State Community College, A
James A. Rhodes State College, A
Lakeland Community College, A
Lorain County Community College, A
Sinclair Community College, A
Stark State College, A
Youngstown State University, AB

Oklahoma

Oklahoma State University Institute of Technology, B
Oklahoma State University, Oklahoma City, A

Oregon

Blue Mountain Community College, A
Chemeketa Community College, A
Mt. Hood Community College, A

Portland Community College, A
Umpqua Community College, A

Pennsylvania

Butler County Community College, A
Community College of Allegheny County, A
Harrisburg Area Community College, A
Pennsylvania College of Technology, AB
Point Park University, AB
Temple University, B
University of Pittsburgh at Johnstown, B

Rhode Island

New England Institute of Technology, A

South Carolina

Florence-Darlington Technical College, A
Midlands Technical College, A
South Carolina State University, B
Technical College of the Lowcountry, A
Trident Technical College, A

South Dakota

Southeast Technical Institute, A

Tennessee

Nashville State Community College, A
Pellissippi State Community College, A

Texas

San Antonio College, A
Texas Southern University, B
University of Houston - Downtown, B

Vermont

Vermont Technical College, A

Virginia

Virginia Western Community College, A
Wytheville Community College, A

Washington

Bates Technical College, A
Bellingham Technical College, A
Centralia College, A
Peninsula College, A
Shoreline Community College, A
Spokane Community College, A
Yakima Valley Community College, A

West Virginia

Bluefield State College, AB
BridgeValley Community and Technical College
   (Montgomery), A
Fairmont State University, AB
Pierpont Community & Technical College, A

Wisconsin

Chippewa Valley Technical College, A
Madison Area Technical College, A
Mid-State Technical College, A
Milwaukee Area Technical College, A
Northeast Wisconsin Technical College, A

U.S. Territories: Puerto Rico

University of Puerto Rico in Bayamón, A
University of Puerto Rico in Ponce, A

Canada

British Columbia

British Columbia Institute of Technology, A

Ontario

Lakehead University, B

CLASSICAL, ANCIENT MEDITERRANEAN AND NEAR EASTERN STUDIES AND ARCHAEOLOGY

United States

California

University of California, Berkeley, B
University of California, Davis, B
University of California, Irvine, B
University of California, Los Angeles, B

Georgia

Emory University, B

Illinois

University of Illinois at Chicago, B

Indiana

Butler University, B
Hanover College, B

Maine

Bowdoin College, B

Massachusetts

Hampshire College, B

Michigan

Calvin College, B
Kalamazoo College, B
University of Michigan, B

New Hampshire

Saint Anselm College, B

New York

Bard College, B
Columbia University, B
Syracuse University, B

Pennsylvania

Lycoming College, B
Swarthmore College, B

Virginia

Randolph-Macon College, B

Canada

Alberta

University of Alberta, B

Ontario

University of Ottawa, B
University of Toronto, B

CLASSICS AND CLASSICAL LANGUAGES, LITERATURES, AND LINGUISTICS

United States

Alabama

Heritage Christian University, M
Samford University, B

Arizona

The University of Arizona, BM

Arkansas

Hendrix College, B
University of Arkansas, B

California

California State University, Long Beach, B
Claremont McKenna College, B
Foothill College, A
Pasadena City College, A
Pitzer College, B
Pomona College, B
San Diego State University, B
San Francisco State University, BM
Santa Clara University, B
Scripps College, B
Stanford University, BMD
University of California, Berkeley, BMD
University of California, Irvine, BMD
University of California, Los Angeles, BMD
University of California, Riverside, D
University of California, San Diego, B
University of California, Santa Barbara, BMD
University of California, Santa Cruz, B
University of the Pacific, B
University of Southern California, BMD

Colorado

The Colorado College, B
University of Colorado Boulder, BMD

Connecticut

Connecticut College, B
Trinity College, B
University of Connecticut, B
Wesleyan University, B
Yale University, BMD

District of Columbia

The Catholic University of America, BMDO
The George Washington University, B
Georgetown University, B
Howard University, B

Florida

Ave Maria University, B
Eckerd College, B
Florida State University, MD
New College of Florida, B
Rollins College, B
University of Florida, BMD
University of Miami, B
University of South Florida, B

Georgia

Agnes Scott College, B
Emory University, B
Mercer University, B
University of Georgia, BM

Hawaii

University of Hawaii at Manoa, B

Illinois

Augustana College, B
Illinois Wesleyan University, B
Knox College, B
Loyola University Chicago, B
Monmouth College, B
North Central College, B
Northwestern University, B
Rockford University, B
University of Chicago, BMD
University of Illinois at Chicago, B
University of Illinois at Urbana - Champaign, BMD
Wheaton College, B

Indiana

Ball State University, B
DePauw University, B
Earlham College, B
Hanover College, B
Indiana University Bloomington, BMD
University of Evansville, B
University of Notre Dame, B
Valparaiso University, B
Wabash College, B

Iowa

Coe College, B
Cornell College, B
Grinnell College, B
Luther College, B
The University of Iowa, BMD

Kansas

The University of Kansas, BM

Kentucky

Asbury University, BM
Centre College, B
Transylvania University, B
University of Kentucky, BM

Louisiana

Loyola University New Orleans, B
Tulane University, BM

Maine

Bowdoin College, B
Colby College, B
Saint Joseph's College of Maine, B

Maryland

Johns Hopkins University, BD
Loyola University Maryland, B
Notre Dame of Maryland University, B
University of Maryland, College Park, BM

Massachusetts

Amherst College, B
Assumption College, B
Boston College, BM
Boston University, BMD
Brandeis University, BMO
Clark University, B
College of the Holy Cross, B
Harvard University, BD
Hellenic College, B
Mount Holyoke College, B
Smith College, B
Tufts University, BM
University of Massachusetts Amherst, BM
University of Massachusetts Boston, BM
Wellesley College, B
Wheaton College, B
Williams College, B

Michigan

Grand Valley State University, B
Hillsdale College, B
Hope College, B
University of Michigan, BMDO
Wayne State University, BM

Minnesota

Carleton College, B
College of Saint Benedict, B
Concordia College, B
Gustavus Adolphus College, B
Macalester College, B
Saint John's University, B
St. Olaf College, B
University of Minnesota, Twin Cities Campus, BMD
University of St. Thomas, B

Mississippi

Millsaps College, B
University of Mississippi, B

Missouri

Saint Louis University, B
Truman State University, B
University of Missouri, BMD
Washington University in St. Louis, BM

Montana

Carroll College, B
University of Montana, B

Nebraska

Creighton University, B
University of Nebraska - Lincoln, BM

New Hampshire

Dartmouth College, B
Saint Anselm College, B

University of New Hampshire, B

New Jersey

Drew University, B
Montclair State University, B
Princeton University, BD
Rutgers University - New Brunswick, BMD
Rutgers University - Newark, B
Saint Peter's University, B
Seton Hall University, B

New Mexico

University of New Mexico, B

New York

Barnard College, B
Binghamton University, State University of New
    York, B
Brooklyn College of the City University of New York,
    B
Colgate University, B
The College of New Rochelle, B
Columbia University, BMD
Columbia University, School of General Studies, B
Cornell University, BD
Elmira College, B
Fordham University, BMD
Hamilton College, B
Hobart and William Smith Colleges, B
Hofstra University, B
Hunter College of the City University of New York,
    BM
Lehman College of the City University of New York,
    B
Manhattan College, B
New York University, BMDO
Queens College of the City University of New York,
    B
St. Bonaventure University, B
Siena College, B
Skidmore College, B
Syracuse University, B
Union College, B
University at Buffalo, the State University of New
    York, BMDO
University of Rochester, B
Vassar College, B
Yeshiva University, B

North Carolina

Davidson College, B
Duke University, BD
University of North Carolina at Asheville, B
The University of North Carolina at Chapel Hill,
    BMD
The University of North Carolina at Greensboro, BM
Wake Forest University, B

North Dakota

University of North Dakota, B

Ohio

Bowling Green State University, B
Case Western Reserve University, B
The College of Wooster, B
Denison University, B
Franciscan University of Steubenville, B
John Carroll University, B
Kenyon College, B
Miami University, B
Miami University Hamilton, B
Oberlin College, B
The Ohio State University, BMD
Ohio University, B
Ohio Wesleyan University, B
Pontifical College Josephinum, B
The University of Akron, B
University of Cincinnati, BMD
Wright State University, B
Xavier University, B

Oklahoma

University of Oklahoma, B

Oregon

Lewis & Clark College, B
Reed College, B
University of Oregon, BM
Willamette University, B

Pennsylvania

Bryn Mawr College, BMD
Bucknell University, B
Dickinson College, B
Duquesne University, BM
Franklin & Marshall College, B
Gettysburg College, B
Haverford College, B
Lehigh University, B
Penn State Abington, B
Penn State Altoona, B
Penn State Beaver, B
Penn State Berks, B
Penn State Brandywine, B
Penn State DuBois, B
Penn State Erie, The Behrend College, B
Penn State Fayette, The Eberly Campus, B
Penn State Greater Allegheny, B
Penn State Hazleton, B
Penn State Lehigh Valley, B
Penn State Mont Alto, B
Penn State New Kensington, B
Penn State Schuylkill, B
Penn State Shenango, B
Penn State University Park, B
Penn State Wilkes-Barre, B
Penn State Worthington Scranton, B
Penn State York, B
Swarthmore College, B
Temple University, B
University of Pennsylvania, BMD
University of Pittsburgh, B
The University of Scranton, B
Villanova University, BM

Rhode Island

Brown University, BMD
University of Rhode Island, B

South Carolina

College of Charleston, B
Furman University, B
University of South Carolina, B

South Dakota

Augustana University, B

Tennessee

Belmont University, B
Rhodes College, B
Sewanee: The University of the South, B
The University of Tennessee, B
Vanderbilt University, BM

Texas

Austin College, B
Baylor University, B
Houston Baptist University, B
Rice University, B
Southwestern University, B
Texas A&M University, B
Texas Tech University, BM
Trinity University, B
University of Dallas, B
The University of Texas at Austin, BMD
The University of Texas at San Antonio, B

Utah

Brigham Young University, M
University of Utah, B

Vermont

Marlboro College, B
Middlebury College, B
Saint Michael's College, B
University of Vermont, BM

Virginia

Christendom College, B
Christopher Newport University, B
The College of William and Mary, B
Hampden-Sydney College, B
Hollins University, B
Randolph College, B
Randolph-Macon College, B
Sweet Briar College, B
University of Mary Washington, B
University of Virginia, BMD
Virginia Wesleyan College, B
Washington and Lee University, B

Washington

The Evergreen State College, B
Gonzaga University, B
Pacific Lutheran University, B
University of Puget Sound, B
University of Washington, BMD
Whitman College, B

West Virginia

American Public University System, M
Marshall University, MO

Wisconsin

Beloit College, B
Carthage College, B
Lawrence University, B
Marquette University, B
University of Wisconsin - Madison, BMD
University of Wisconsin - Milwaukee, BM

Canada

Alberta

University of Alberta, BMD
University of Calgary, BMD

British Columbia

The University of British Columbia, BMD
University of Victoria, BMD

Manitoba

University of Manitoba, BM
The University of Winnipeg, B

Maritime Provinces: New Brunswick

Mount Allison University, B
University of New Brunswick Fredericton, BM
University of New Brunswick Saint John, B

Maritime Provinces: Nova Scotia

Acadia University, B
Dalhousie University, BMD
St. Francis Xavier University, B
Saint Mary's University, B
University of King's College, B

Newfoundland and Labrador

Memorial University of Newfoundland, BM

Ontario

Brock University, M
Carleton University, B
Laurentian University, B
McMaster University, BMD
Nipissing University, B
Queen's University at Kingston, M
Trent University, B
University of Guelph, B
University of Ottawa, BMD
University of Toronto, BMD
University of Waterloo, B
The University of Western Ontario, BM
University of Windsor, B
Wilfrid Laurier University, B
York University, B

Quebec

Bishop's University, B
Concordia University, B

Université Laval, B
Université de Montréal, BM

Saskatchewan

University of Regina, B

CLINICAL LABORATORY SCIENCE/MEDICAL TECHNOLOGY/TECHNOLOGIST

United States

Alabama

Auburn University, B
Auburn University at Montgomery, B
Oakwood University, B
Tuskegee University, B
The University of Alabama at Birmingham, B

Alaska

University of Alaska Anchorage, B

Arizona

DeVry University (Phoenix), B
GateWay Community College, A

Arkansas

Arkansas State University, AB
Arkansas Tech University, B
Henderson State University, B
National Park College, A
Southern Arkansas University - Magnolia, B
University of Arkansas for Medical Sciences, B
University of Central Arkansas, B

California

California State University, Dominguez Hills, B
Loma Linda University, AB
National University, B

Connecticut

University of Bridgeport, B
University of Connecticut, B
University of Hartford, B
Western Connecticut State University, B

Delaware

University of Delaware, B
Wesley College, B

District of Columbia

The Catholic University of America, B
The George Washington University, B
Howard University, B

Florida

Barry University, B
Bethune-Cookman University, B
Chipola College, A
College of Central Florida, A
Florida Gulf Coast University, B
Florida Memorial University, B
Jacksonville University, B
Saint Leo University, B
Santa Fe College, B
South Florida State College, A
University of Central Florida, B
University of South Florida, B
University of West Florida, B

Georgia

Andrew College, A
Armstrong State University, B
Athens Technical College, A
Augusta University, B
Dalton State College, A
Darton State College, A
Georgia Highlands College, A

Hawaii

University of Hawaii at Manoa, B

Idaho

College of Southern Idaho, A
Idaho State University, B
North Idaho College, A

Illinois

Benedictine University, B
Blackburn College, B
Bradley University, B
City Colleges of Chicago, Richard J. Daley College, A
DePaul University, B
Eastern Illinois University, B
Elmhurst College, B
Eureka College, B
Illinois College, B
Illinois State University, B
Northern Illinois University, B
Quincy University, B
Roosevelt University, B
Rush University, B
University of Illinois at Springfield, B
University of St. Francis, B
Western Illinois University, B

Indiana

Anderson University, B
Ball State University, B
Harrison College, A
Indiana State University, B
Indiana University - Purdue University Fort Wayne, B
Indiana University - Purdue University Indianapolis, B
Indiana University Southeast, B
Indiana Wesleyan University, B
Manchester University, B
Marian University, B
Purdue University, B
Purdue University Northwest (Hammond), B
Saint Joseph's College, B
Saint Mary-of-the-Woods College, B
University of Evansville, B
University of Indianapolis, B
University of Saint Francis, B

Iowa

Dordt College, B
Graceland University, B
Morningside College, B
Mount Mercy University, B
Northwestern College, B
The University of Iowa, B
Wartburg College, B

Kansas

Dodge City Community College, A
Fort Hays State University, B
Kansas State University, B
Pittsburg State University, B
The University of Kansas, B
Washburn University, B
Wichita State University, B

Kentucky

Bellarmine University, B
Brescia University, B
Campbellsville University, B
Eastern Kentucky University, B
Spencerian College, B
Thomas More College, B
University of Kentucky, B
Western Kentucky University, B

Louisiana

Louisiana College, B
Louisiana State University at Alexandria, B
Louisiana State University Health Sciences Center, B
Louisiana Tech University, B
McNeese State University, B
Our Lady of the Lake College, B
University of Louisiana at Monroe, B

Maine

University of Maine, B
University of New England, B

Maryland

Howard Community College, A
Morgan State University, B
Salisbury University, B
Stevenson University, B
University of Maryland Eastern Shore, B

Massachusetts

Salem State University, B
University of Massachusetts Dartmouth, B

Michigan

Andrews University, B
Eastern Michigan University, B
Ferris State University, B
Grand Valley State University, B
Lake Superior State University, AB
Michigan State University, B
Michigan Technological University, B
Monroe County Community College, A
Northern Michigan University, B
Oakland University, B
Saginaw Valley State University, B
University of Michigan - Flint, B
Wayne State University, B

Minnesota

Bemidji State University, B
Minnesota State University Mankato, B
Minnesota State University Moorhead, B
St. Catherine University, B
St. Cloud State University, B
Saint Mary's University of Minnesota, B
Winona State University, B

Mississippi

Blue Mountain College, B
Coahoma Community College, A
Mississippi State University, B
University of Mississippi, B
University of Mississippi Medical Center, B
University of Southern Mississippi, B

Missouri

Evangel University, B
Lincoln University, B
Maryville University of Saint Louis, B
Missouri Southern State University, B
Missouri State University, B
Missouri Western State University, B
Northwest Missouri State University, B
Rockhurst University, B
Saint Louis University, B
Southeast Missouri State University, B
Southwest Baptist University, B
University of Central Missouri, B

Montana

University of Montana, B

Nebraska

College of Saint Mary, B
Peru State College, B
Southeast Community College, Lincoln Campus, A
Union College, B
University of Nebraska Medical Center, B
Western Nebraska Community College, A

New Jersey

Caldwell University, B
College of Saint Elizabeth, B
Fairleigh Dickinson University, College at Florham, B
Fairleigh Dickinson University, Metropolitan Campus, B
Georgian Court University, B
Kean University, B
Monmouth University, B
Ramapo College of New Jersey, B
Rutgers University - Camden, B

Rutgers University - New Brunswick, B
Rutgers University - Newark, B
Thomas Edison State University, AB

New Mexico

Eastern New Mexico University, B
Western New Mexico University, B

New York

Albany College of Pharmacy and Health Sciences, B
Canisius College, B
The College at Brockport, State University of New York, B
The College of Saint Rose, B
College of Staten Island of the City University of New York, B
Elmira College, B
Farmingdale State College, B
Hartwick College, B
Houghton College, B
Keuka College, B
Long Island University - LIU Brooklyn, B
Long Island University - LIU Post, B
Marist College, B
Mercy College, B
Nazareth College of Rochester, B
Rochester Institute of Technology, B
St. Francis College, B
St. John's University, B
St. Joseph's College, Long Island Campus, B
St. Joseph's College, New York, B
St. Thomas Aquinas College, B
State University of New York at Fredonia, B
State University of New York at Plattsburgh, B
State University of New York Upstate Medical University, B
Stony Brook University, State University of New York, B
University at Buffalo, the State University of New York, B
Westchester Community College, A
York College of the City University of New York, B

North Carolina

Catawba College, B
Central Piedmont Community College, A
East Carolina University, B
Greensboro College, B
Louisburg College, A
The University of North Carolina at Chapel Hill, B
The University of North Carolina at Charlotte, B
Wake Forest University, B
Winston-Salem State University, B

North Dakota

Mayville State University, B
Minot State University, B
North Dakota State University, B
Turtle Mountain Community College, A
University of Jamestown, B
University of Mary, B
University of North Dakota, B

Ohio

Bowling Green State University, B
Columbus State Community College, A
Cuyahoga Community College, A
Kent State University, B
Malone University, B
Miami University, B
Miami University Hamilton, B
Mount Vernon Nazarene University, B
Muskingum University, B
Ohio Northern University, B
The Ohio State University, B
Shawnee State University, A
The University of Akron, B
University of Cincinnati, B
The University of Findlay, B
University of Mount Union, B
University of Rio Grande, B
The University of Toledo, B
Walsh University, B
Wright State University, B

Xavier University, B
Youngstown State University, B

Oklahoma

Cameron University, B
East Central University, B
Northeastern State University, B
Oklahoma Christian University, B
Oklahoma Panhandle State University, B
Oral Roberts University, B
Southwestern Oklahoma State University, B
University of Central Oklahoma, B

Pennsylvania

East Stroudsburg University of Pennsylvania, B
Edinboro University of Pennsylvania, B
Gannon University, B
Gwynedd Mercy University, B
Holy Family University, B
Indiana University of Pennsylvania, B
King's College, B
Lebanon Valley College, B
Mansfield University of Pennsylvania, B
Marywood University, B
Misericordia University, B
Saint Francis University, B
Seton Hill University, B
Thiel College, B
Thomas Jefferson University, B
University of the Sciences, B
The University of Scranton, B
Westmoreland County Community College, A
Wilkes University, B
York College of Pennsylvania, B

Rhode Island

New England Institute of Technology, A
Salve Regina University, B
University of Rhode Island, B

South Carolina

Coker College, B
Southern Wesleyan University, B

South Dakota

Augustana University, B
Mount Marty College, B
Northern State University, B
South Dakota State University, B
University of Sioux Falls, B

Tennessee

Austin Peay State University, B
Belmont University, B
Hiwassee College, A
King University, B
Lincoln Memorial University, B
Southern Adventist University, B
Tennessee State University, B
Union University, B
The University of Tennessee, B

Texas

Amarillo College, A
Argosy University, Dallas, B
Baylor University, B
Cisco College, A
Del Mar College, A
Midwestern State University, B
St. Edward's University, B
Sam Houston State University, B
South Texas College, A
Southwestern Adventist University, B
Tarleton State University, B
Tarrant County College District, A
Texas Southern University, B
Texas State University, B
Texas Woman's University, B
University of Mary Hardin-Baylor, B
University of North Texas, B
The University of Texas at Arlington, B
The University of Texas at Austin, B
The University of Texas at El Paso, B
The University of Texas Health Science Center at San Antonio, B

The University of Texas Medical Branch, B
The University of Texas Rio Grande Valley, B
The University of Texas at San Antonio, B
The University of Texas at Tyler, B
West Texas A&M University, B

Utah

Brigham Young University, B
Dixie State University, AB
University of Utah, B
Utah State University, B
Weber State University, B

Vermont

University of Vermont, B

Virginia

Eastern Mennonite University, B
George Mason University, B
Mary Baldwin College, B
Norfolk State University, B
Old Dominion University, B
The University of Virginia's College at Wise, B
Virginia Commonwealth University, B

Washington

Heritage University, B
University of Washington, B
Walla Walla University, B

West Virginia

Concord University, B
Marshall University, B
West Liberty University, B
West Virginia University, B

Wisconsin

Carroll University, B
Marquette University, B
University of Wisconsin - La Crosse, B
University of Wisconsin - Milwaukee, B
University of Wisconsin - Oshkosh, B
University of Wisconsin - Parkside, A
University of Wisconsin - Stevens Point, B

Wyoming

Casper College, A
University of Wyoming, B

U.S. Territories: Puerto Rico

Inter American University of Puerto Rico, Metropolitan Campus, B
Inter American University of Puerto Rico, San Germán Campus, B
Pontifical Catholic University of Puerto Rico, B
University of Puerto Rico, Medical Sciences Campus, B
University of the Sacred Heart, B

Canada

Alberta

University of Alberta, B

Saskatchewan

University of Regina, B

CLINICAL LABORATORY SCIENCES

United States

Alabama

The University of Alabama at Birmingham, M

California

Dominican University of California, M

Colorado

University of Colorado Denver, MD

Connecticut

Quinnipiac University, M

District of Columbia

The Catholic University of America, MD

Florida

University of Florida, MD

Illinois

Northwestern University, M
Rush University, M

Massachusetts

University of Massachusetts Dartmouth, M
University of Massachusetts Lowell, MO

Michigan

Michigan State University, M
Northern Michigan University, M

Nebraska

University of Nebraska Medical Center, M

New Jersey

Rutgers University - New Brunswick, M
Rutgers University - Newark, M

New Mexico

University of New Mexico, MO

New York

Albany College of Pharmacy and Health Sciences, M
University at Buffalo, the State University of New York, M

North Carolina

Duke University, M

North Dakota

University of North Dakota, M

Pennsylvania

Thomas Jefferson University, M
University of Pennsylvania, M
University of Pittsburgh, D

Rhode Island

University of Rhode Island, M

Tennessee

Austin Peay State University, M

Texas

The University of Texas at Austin, D
The University of Texas Health Science Center at San Antonio, D
The University of Texas Medical Branch, MD

Vermont

University of Vermont, MD

Virginia

Virginia Commonwealth University, MD

Washington

University of Washington, M

Wisconsin

Milwaukee School of Engineering, M

U.S. Territories: Puerto Rico

Inter American University of Puerto Rico, Metropolitan Campus, M

University of Puerto Rico, Medical Sciences Campus, M

Canada
Alberta

University of Alberta, MD

Quebec

Université de Sherbrooke, MD

CLINICAL/MEDICAL LABORATORY ASSISTANT

United States
Alaska

University of Alaska Fairbanks, A

Arizona

Pima Community College, A

California

National University, B

Colorado

IntelliTec College (Grand Junction), A

Delaware

Delaware Technical & Community College, Jack F. Owens Campus, A

Idaho

Brigham Young University - Idaho, A

Kentucky

Somerset Community College, A

Maine

University of Maine at Augusta, A
University of Maine at Presque Isle, A

Maryland

Allegany College of Maryland, A

Minnesota

Minnesota State Community and Technical College, A

Ohio

Columbus State Community College, A
Zane State College, A

Pennsylvania

Community College of Beaver County, A
Westmoreland County Community College, A

Rhode Island

New England Institute of Technology, A

Washington

Clover Park Technical College, A
Edmonds Community College, A
Wenatchee Valley College, A

CLINICAL/MEDICAL LABORATORY SCIENCE AND ALLIED PROFESSIONS

United States
Alabama

Auburn University, B

California

Grossmont College, A

Idaho

The College of Idaho, B

Illinois

Roosevelt University, B

Iowa

Allen College, B

Massachusetts

University of Massachusetts Lowell, B

Minnesota

University of Minnesota, Twin Cities Campus, B

Missouri

Saint Louis University, B

New Jersey

Bloomfield College, B
New Jersey Institute of Technology, B
Rutgers University - New Brunswick, B
Rutgers University - Newark, B

New York

Hunter College of the City University of New York, B
State University of New York College of Agriculture and Technology at Cobleskill, A

Ohio

Youngstown State University, A

South Dakota

Southeast Technical Institute, A

Texas

Houston Community College, A

Washington

Highline College, A

Canada
Alberta

University of Alberta, B

CLINICAL/MEDICAL LABORATORY TECHNICIAN

United States
Alabama

Auburn University, B
Auburn University at Montgomery, B
Calhoun Community College, A
Community College of the Air Force, A
Gadsden State Community College, A
George C. Wallace Community College, A
Jefferson State Community College, A
Wallace State Community College, A

Alaska

University of Alaska Anchorage, A

Arizona

Brookline College (Phoenix), AB
Brookline College (Tempe), A
Brookline College (Tucson), A
Carrington College - Phoenix West, A
Carrington College - Tucson, A
Phoenix College, A
Pima Community College, A

Arkansas

Arkansas State University - Beebe, A
National Park College, A
North Arkansas College, A
Shorter College, A
South Arkansas Community College, A

California

California State University, East Bay, B
College of the Canyons, A
Hartnell College, A
Orange Coast College, A
San Bernardino Valley College, A
San Diego Mesa College, A
Sonoma State University, B

Colorado

Arapahoe Community College, A
Colorado Mesa University, A
IBMC College (Colorado Springs), A

Connecticut

Housatonic Community College, A
Manchester Community College, A

Delaware

Delaware State University, B

District of Columbia

The George Washington University, A

Florida

Barry University, B
Eastern Florida State College, A
Florida State College at Jacksonville, A
Fortis Institute (Palm Springs), A
Indian River State College, A
Keiser University, A
Miami Dade College, A
St. Petersburg College, A

Georgia

Central Georgia Technical College, A
Coastal Pines Technical College, A
College of Coastal Georgia, A
Dalton State College, A
Georgia Piedmont Technical College, A

Hawaii

Kapiolani Community College, A

Illinois

City Colleges of Chicago, Malcolm X College, A
Elgin Community College, A
Illinois Central College, A
John A. Logan College, A
John Wood Community College, A
Kankakee Community College, A
Kaskaskia College, A
Oakton Community College, A
Rend Lake College, A
Shawnee Community College, A
Southeastern Illinois College, A
Southwestern Illinois College, A

Indiana

Indiana University - Purdue University Fort Wayne, B
Ivy Tech Community College - Lafayette, A
Ivy Tech Community College - North Central, A
Ivy Tech Community College - Southern Indiana, A
Ivy Tech Community College - Wabash Valley, A
University of Saint Francis, A

Iowa

Des Moines Area Community College, A
Hawkeye Community College, A
Iowa Central Community College, A
North Iowa Area Community College, A
Northeast Iowa Community College, A

Kansas

Barton County Community College, A
Hutchinson Community College, A
Manhattan Area Technical College, A
Seward County Community College and Area Technical School, A
Wichita Area Technical College, A

Kentucky

Eastern Kentucky University, A
Henderson Community College, A
Southeast Kentucky Community and Technical College, A
Spencerian College, A
Spencerian College - Lexington, A

Louisiana

Delgado Community College, A
Fortis College, A
Louisiana State University at Alexandria, A
Our Lady of the Lake College, AB
South Louisiana Community College, A
Southern University at Shreveport, A

Maine

University of Maine at Presque Isle, A

Maryland

Allegany College of Maryland, A
Anne Arundel Community College, A
College of Southern Maryland, A
Community College of Baltimore County, A
Morgan State University, B
University of Maryland Eastern Shore, B

Massachusetts

Bristol Community College, A
Bunker Hill Community College, A
Mount Wachusett Community College, A
Quincy College, A
Springfield Technical Community College, A

Michigan

Baker College, A
Ferris State University, A

Minnesota

Alexandria Technical and Community College, A
Argosy University, Twin Cities, AB
Hibbing Community College, A
Lake Superior College, A
Minnesota State Community and Technical College, A
Minnesota West Community and Technical College, A
North Hennepin Community College, A
Rasmussen College Lake Elmo/Woodbury, A
Rasmussen College Mankato, A
Rasmussen College Moorhead, A
Rasmussen College St. Cloud, A
Saint Paul College - A Community & Technical College, A
South Central College, A

Mississippi

Copiah-Lincoln Community College, A
Hinds Community College, A
Meridian Community College, A
Mississippi Delta Community College, A
Mississippi Gulf Coast Community College, A
Northeast Mississippi Community College, A

Missouri

Moberly Area Community College, A
Three Rivers Community College, A
University of Missouri - Kansas City, B

Montana

University of Montana, B

Nebraska

Central Community College - Hastings Campus, A
Mid-Plains Community College, A
Southeast Community College, Lincoln Campus, A

Nevada

College of Southern Nevada, A

New Hampshire

River Valley Community College, A

New Jersey

Camden County College, A
County College of Morris, A
Mercer County Community College, A
Middlesex County College, A

New Mexico

Central New Mexico Community College, A
New Mexico Junior College, A
San Juan College, A
University of New Mexico, B
University of New Mexico - Gallup, A

New York

Bronx Community College of the City University of New York, A
Broome Community College, A
Dutchess Community College, A
Erie Community College, North Campus, A
Farmingdale State College, A
Genesee Community College, A
Nassau Community College, A
Orange County Community College, A
Queensborough Community College of the City University of New York, A
St. Thomas Aquinas College, B
Westchester Community College, A
York College of the City University of New York, B

North Carolina

Alamance Community College, A
Asheville-Buncombe Technical Community College, A
Beaufort County Community College, A
Central Piedmont Community College, A
Coastal Carolina Community College, A
Davidson County Community College, A
Forsyth Technical Community College, A
Halifax Community College, A
Pamlico Community College, A
Sandhills Community College, A
Southeastern Community College, A
Southwestern Community College, A
Wake Technical Community College, A
Western Piedmont Community College, A

North Dakota

Bismarck State College, A
Turtle Mountain Community College, A

Ohio

Cincinnati State Technical and Community College, A
Clark State Community College, A
Edison Community College, A
Lakeland Community College, A
Lorain County Community College, A
Marion Technical College, A
Stark State College, A
University of Rio Grande, A
Washington State Community College, A
Youngstown State University, A

Oklahoma

Northeastern Oklahoma Agricultural and Mechanical College, A
Rose State College, A
Seminole State College, A
Southwestern Oklahoma State University, A
Southwestern Oklahoma State University at Sayre, A
Tulsa Community College, A
University of Science and Arts of Oklahoma, B

Oregon

Portland Community College, A

Pennsylvania

Clarion University of Pennsylvania, B
Community College of Allegheny County, A
Community College of Philadelphia, A
Harcum College, A
Harrisburg Area Community College, A
Montgomery County Community College, A

Mount Aloysius College, A
Penn State DuBois, B
Penn State Hazleton, B
Penn State Schuylkill, A
Reading Area Community College, A

Rhode Island

Community College of Rhode Island, A
Rhode Island College, B

South Carolina

Florence-Darlington Technical College, A
Greenville Technical College, A
Midlands Technical College, A
Orangeburg-Calhoun Technical College, A
Spartanburg Community College, A
Tri-County Technical College, A
Trident Technical College, A
York Technical College, A

South Dakota

Lake Area Technical Institute, A
Mitchell Technical Institute, A
Northern State University, B
Southeast Technical Institute, A

Tennessee

Fortis Institute (Cookeville), A
Jackson State Community College, A
Roane State Community College, A
Southwest Tennessee Community College, A
Volunteer State Community College, A

Texas

Argosy University, Dallas, A
Austin Community College District, A
Central Texas College, A
Del Mar College, A
El Centro College, A
El Paso Community College, A
Grayson College, A
Houston Community College, A
Lamar State College - Orange, A
Laredo Community College, A
McLennan Community College, A
Navarro College, A
Northeast Texas Community College, A
Odessa College, A
Panola College, A
St. Philip's College, A
San Jacinto College District, A
Tarleton State University, A
Tarrant County College District, A
Texas Southmost College, A
Tyler Junior College, A
Victoria College, A
Wharton County Junior College, A

Utah

Salt Lake Community College, A
Weber State University, AB

Virginia

J. Sargeant Reynolds Community College, A
Northern Virginia Community College, A
Wytheville Community College, A

Washington

Shoreline Community College, A
Wenatchee Valley College, A

West Virginia

Blue Ridge Community and Technical College, A
Marshall University, A
Southern West Virginia Community and Technical
   College, A

Wisconsin

Blackhawk Technical College, A
Chippewa Valley Technical College, A
Madison Area Technical College, A
Milwaukee Area Technical College, A
Moraine Park Technical College, A
Northcentral Technical College, A

Northeast Wisconsin Technical College, A
Rasmussen College Green Bay, A
Viterbo University, B
Waukesha County Technical College, A
Western Technical College, A

Canada

British Columbia

British Columbia Institute of Technology, A
The University of British Columbia, B

CLINICAL/MEDICAL SOCIAL WORK

United States

Arizona

Pima Community College, A

Montana

Dawson Community College, A

Nebraska

Central Community College - Grand Island Campus,
   A
Central Community College - Hastings Campus, A
Southeast Community College, Lincoln Campus, A

New Mexico

Eastern New Mexico University, B
New Mexico Highlands University, B

North Carolina

Asheville-Buncombe Technical Community College,
   A

Texas

Central Texas College, A

CLINICAL MICROBIOLOGY

United States

Idaho

Idaho State University, M

New Jersey

Rutgers University - New Brunswick, MD

Wisconsin

University of Wisconsin - La Crosse, M

CLINICAL NUTRITION/NUTRITIONIST

United States

Arizona

Central Arizona College, A

Georgia

Life University, B

Illinois

Southern Illinois University Edwardsville, B

New York

Long Island University - LIU Post, B

North Dakota

University of North Dakota, B

Ohio

Kent State University, B

Pennsylvania

La Salle University, B
Messiah College, B

CLINICAL PASTORAL COUNSELING/PATIENT COUNSELING

United States

Georgia

Luther Rice College & Seminary, B

New Jersey

Pillar College, B

CLINICAL PSYCHOLOGY

United States

Alabama

Alabama Agricultural and Mechanical University, M
Auburn University at Montgomery, M
Troy University, M
The University of Alabama, D
The University of Alabama at Birmingham, D
University of South Alabama, D

Alaska

University of Alaska Anchorage, MD
University of Alaska Fairbanks, D

Arizona

Argosy University, Phoenix, MD
Arizona State University at the Tempe campus, D
Northern Arizona University, M
University of Phoenix - Phoenix Campus, M

Arkansas

Arkansas State University, O
John Brown University, M

California

Antioch University Los Angeles, M
Antioch University Santa Barbara, MD
Argosy University, Inland Empire, M
Argosy University, Los Angeles, M
Argosy University, Orange County, MD
Argosy University, San Diego, M
Argosy University, San Francisco Bay Area, MD
Azusa Pacific University, MD
Biola University, D
California Institute of Integral Studies, D
California Lutheran University, MD
California State University, Dominguez Hills, M
California State University, Fullerton, M
California State University, Northridge, M
California State University, San Bernardino, M
National University, M
Notre Dame de Namur University, M
Palo Alto University, D
Pepperdine University, M
San Diego State University, MD
San Jose State University, M
Sonoma State University, M
University of California, San Diego, D
University of California, Santa Barbara, MDO
University of La Verne, D
University of Southern California, D
Vanguard University of Southern California, M

Colorado

Argosy University, Denver, MD
University of Colorado Denver, MD
University of Denver, MD

Connecticut

Connecticut College, M
Fairfield University, MO
University of Bridgeport, M
University of Connecticut, MD

University of Hartford, MD
University of Saint Joseph, M
Western Connecticut State University, M
Yale University, D

Delaware

University of Delaware, D
Wilmington University, M

District of Columbia

The Catholic University of America, D
Gallaudet University, D
The George Washington University, MD
Howard University, D
Trinity Washington University, M

Florida

Argosy University, Tampa, MD
Barry University, M
Carlos Albizu University, Miami Campus, D
Florida International University, MD
Florida State University, D
Hodges University, M
Nova Southeastern University, D
University of Central Florida, MD
University of Florida, MD
University of Miami, D
University of South Florida, D

Georgia

Argosy University, Atlanta, MDO
Clayton State University, M
Emory University, D
Georgia State University, D
Mercer University, M
University of North Georgia, M

Hawaii

Argosy University, Hawai'i, MDO
Hawai'i Pacific University, M
University of Hawaii at Manoa, D

Idaho

Idaho State University, D
Northwest Nazarene University, M

Illinois

Argosy University, Chicago, MD
Argosy University, Schaumburg, MD
Benedictine University, M
Bradley University, M
DePaul University, M
Eastern Illinois University, M
Illinois Institute of Technology, D
Illinois State University, M
Lewis University, M
Loyola University Chicago, MD
McKendree University, M
Northwestern University, D
Roosevelt University, M
Southern Illinois University Carbondale, D
Southern Illinois University Edwardsville, M
Western Illinois University, M
Wheaton College, MD

Indiana

Ball State University, M
Grace College, M
Indiana State University, MD
Indiana University - Purdue University Indianapolis,
  M
Purdue University, D
University of Indianapolis, MD
University of Saint Francis, O
Valparaiso University, M

Kansas

Emporia State University, M
The University of Kansas, MD
Washburn University, M
Wichita State University, D

Kentucky

Eastern Kentucky University, M
Morehead State University, M
Murray State University, M
Northern Kentucky University, M
Spalding University, MD
Union College, M
University of the Cumberlands, D
University of Louisville, D
Western Kentucky University, M

Louisiana

Louisiana State University and Agricultural & Me-
  chanical College, MD
Loyola University New Orleans, M
Nicholls State University, M
Northwestern State University of Louisiana, M
University of Louisiana at Monroe, M

Maine

Husson University, M

Maryland

Johns Hopkins University, MD
Loyola University Maryland, MDO
Towson University, M
University of Maryland, College Park, D

Massachusetts

American International College, M
Bay Path University, M
Clark University, D
Lesley University, M
Springfield College, D
Suffolk University, MDO
University of Massachusetts Amherst, MD
University of Massachusetts Boston, D

Michigan

Andrews University, M
Central Michigan University, D
Eastern Michigan University, M
Madonna University, M
Siena Heights University, M
University of Detroit Mercy, MD
University of Michigan, D
University of Michigan - Dearborn, M
Wayne State University, D
Western Michigan University, D

Minnesota

Argosy University, Twin Cities, MD
Capella University, MD
Minnesota State University Mankato, M
University of Minnesota, Twin Cities Campus, D
Walden University, MD

Mississippi

Jackson State University, D
Mississippi State University, M
University of Mississippi, D
University of Southern Mississippi, D

Missouri

Evangel University, M
Missouri State University, M
Saint Louis University, MD
University of Missouri - Kansas City, M
University of Missouri - St. Louis, MDO
Washington University in St. Louis, D

Montana

University of Montana, MD

Nebraska

University of Nebraska - Lincoln, D

Nevada

University of Nevada, Las Vegas, M
University of Nevada, Reno, MD

New Hampshire

Plymouth State University, MO
Rivier University, M

New Jersey

Fairleigh Dickinson University, College at Florham,
  M
Fairleigh Dickinson University, Metropolitan Cam-
  pus, MD
Georgian Court University, M
Kean University, MD
Montclair State University, M
Rowan University, MO
Rutgers University - New Brunswick, MD
William Paterson University of New Jersey, MD

New Mexico

New Mexico Highlands University, M
University of New Mexico, D

New York

Adelphi University, D
Binghamton University, State University of New
  York, D
City College of the City University of New York, D
College of Staten Island of the City University of
  New York, M
Fordham University, D
Hofstra University, D
Long Island University - LIU Brooklyn, D
Long Island University - LIU Post, O
Medaille College, D
Pace University, MD
Queens College of the City University of New York,
  M
St. John's University, MDO
State University of New York at Plattsburgh, MO
Stony Brook University, State University of New
  York, D
Syracuse University, MD
University at Albany, State University of New York,
  D
University of Rochester, D
Yeshiva University, D

North Carolina

Appalachian State University, M
Duke University, D
East Carolina University, D
Lenoir-Rhyne University, M
Montreat College, M
The University of North Carolina at Chapel Hill, D
The University of North Carolina at Charlotte, M
The University of North Carolina at Greensboro, MD

North Dakota

North Dakota State University, M
University of Mary, M
University of North Dakota, D

Ohio

Bowling Green State University, MD
Case Western Reserve University, D
Franciscan University of Steubenville, M
Kent State University, MD
The Ohio State University, D
Ohio University, MD
South University, M
Union Institute & University, D
The University of Akron, M
University of Cincinnati, D
University of Dayton, M
The University of Toledo, MD
Wright State University, D
Xavier University, MD

Oklahoma

Oklahoma State University, D
Southeastern Oklahoma State University, M
The University of Tulsa, MD

Oregon

George Fox University, MD
Pacific University, MD
University of Oregon, D

Pennsylvania

Chestnut Hill College, MDO
Drexel University, MD
Duquesne University, MDO
Edinboro University of Pennsylvania, M
Gannon University, M
Geneva College, M
Immaculata University, MD
Indiana University of Pennsylvania, MD
La Salle University, MD
Lock Haven University of Pennsylvania, M
Marywood University, MD
Messiah College, M
Millersville University of Pennsylvania, M
Penn State Harrisburg, M
Point Park University, M
Slippery Rock University of Pennsylvania, M
The University of Scranton, M
Waynesburg University, M
West Chester University of Pennsylvania, MO
Widener University, D

Rhode Island

Roger Williams University, M
University of Rhode Island, MD

South Carolina

Francis Marion University, M
University of South Carolina, MD
University of South Carolina Aiken, M

South Dakota

Northern State University, M
The University of South Dakota, MD

Tennessee

Fisk University, M
Lipscomb University, M
Middle Tennessee State University, M
University of Memphis, MD
The University of Tennessee, D

Texas

Abilene Christian University, M
Argosy University, Dallas, MD
Baylor University, D
Lamar University, M
Midwestern State University, M
Prairie View A&M University, MD
Sam Houston State University, MD
Southern Methodist University, D
Sul Ross State University, M
Texas A&M University, D
Texas A&M University - Central Texas, M
Texas Tech University, D
University of Houston, D
University of Houston - Clear Lake, M
University of Mary Hardin-Baylor, M
University of North Texas, M
The University of Texas at Austin, D
The University of Texas at El Paso, M
The University of Texas of the Permian Basin, M
The University of Texas Rio Grande Valley, M
The University of Texas at Tyler, M

Utah

Brigham Young University, D
University of Utah, MD
Utah State University, D

Vermont

College of St. Joseph, M
Saint Michael's College, M
University of Vermont, D

Virginia

Argosy University, Washington DC, MD
James Madison University, MDO
Liberty University, M
Lynchburg College, M
Marymount University, M
Norfolk State University, M
Old Dominion University, D
Radford University, M

Regent University, MD
University of Virginia, D
Virginia Commonwealth University, D
Virginia State University, MD

Washington

Argosy University, Seattle, MDO
Eastern Washington University, M
Seattle Pacific University, D
University of Washington, D
Washington State University, D

West Virginia

Marshall University, O
West Virginia University, MD

Wisconsin

Cardinal Stritch University, M
Marquette University, M
Mount Mary University, MO
University of Wisconsin - Madison, D
University of Wisconsin - Milwaukee, MD
University of Wisconsin - Stout, M

U.S. Territories: Puerto Rico

Carlos Albizu University, MD
Pontifical Catholic University of Puerto Rico, D
University of Puerto Rico, Río Piedras Campus, M

Canada

Alberta

University of Calgary, MD

British Columbia

The University of British Columbia, MD
University of Victoria, MD

Manitoba

University of Manitoba, D

Maritime Provinces: New Brunswick

University of New Brunswick Saint John, D

Maritime Provinces: Nova Scotia

Acadia University, M
Dalhousie University, D

Ontario

Lakehead University, D
Queen's University at Kingston, MD
University of Guelph, MD
University of Windsor, MD

Quebec

Concordia University, MDO
McGill University, D
Université Laval, D

Saskatchewan

University of Regina, MD

CLINICAL RESEARCH

United States

California

American University of Health Sciences, M
Stanford University, MD
Trident University International, MO
University of California, Berkeley, O
University of California, Davis, M
University of California, Los Angeles, M
University of California, San Diego, M
University of Southern California, O

Colorado

University of Colorado Denver, D

Florida

University of Florida, MD
University of South Florida, MDO

Georgia

Augusta University, MO
Emory University, M

Illinois

Loyola University Chicago, M
Northwestern University, MO

Iowa

Palmer College of Chiropractic, M
The University of Iowa, M

Kansas

The University of Kansas, M

Kentucky

University of Kentucky, M
University of Louisville, MO

Maryland

Johns Hopkins University, MD

Massachusetts

Boston University, M
Tufts University, MD

Michigan

Eastern Michigan University, MO
University of Michigan, M

Minnesota

University of Minnesota, Twin Cities Campus, M
Walden University, MO

Missouri

Washington University in St. Louis, M

New York

New York University, M
University of Rochester, M

North Carolina

Duke University, M
The University of North Carolina Wilmington, M

Ohio

Case Western Reserve University, M

Oregon

Oregon Health & Science University, MO

Pennsylvania

Temple University, M
Thomas Jefferson University, O
University of Pittsburgh, MO

South Carolina

Medical University of South Carolina, M

Tennessee

Vanderbilt University, M

Texas

The University of Texas Health Science Center at San Antonio, M

Virginia

University of Virginia, M

Washington

University of Washington, M

U.S. Territories: Puerto Rico

University of Puerto Rico, Medical Sciences Campus, MO

Canada

Newfoundland and Labrador

Memorial University of Newfoundland, M

CLOTHING AND TEXTILES

United States

Alabama

Alabama Agricultural and Mechanical University, M
Auburn University, MD
The University of Alabama, M

California

Academy of Art University, M
University of California, Davis, M

Delaware

University of Delaware, M

Georgia

Georgia State University, M
Savannah College of Art and Design, M
University of Georgia, MD

Iowa

Iowa State University of Science and Technology, MD

Kansas

Kansas State University, MD

Michigan

Central Michigan University, M
Eastern Michigan University, M

Minnesota

University of Minnesota, Twin Cities Campus, MD

Missouri

University of Missouri, MD

Nebraska

University of Nebraska - Lincoln, MD

New Jersey

Rutgers University - Newark, M

New York

Cornell University, MD
Fashion Institute of Technology, M
LIM College, M

North Carolina

North Carolina State University, D

North Dakota

North Dakota State University, MO

Ohio

Ohio University, M
The University of Akron, M

Oklahoma

Oklahoma State University, MD

Oregon

Oregon State University, MD

Pennsylvania

Philadelphia University, M

Rhode Island

University of Rhode Island, M

South Dakota

South Dakota State University, M

Tennessee

The University of Tennessee, MD

Washington

Washington State University, M

Canada

Alberta

University of Alberta, MD

Manitoba

University of Manitoba, M

COGNITIVE SCIENCES

United States

Arizona

Arizona State University at the Tempe campus, D
Grand Canyon University, D

California

California State University, Fresno, B
California State University, Stanislaus, B
Occidental College, B
Pomona College, B
University of California, Berkeley, B
University of California, Irvine, B
University of California, Los Angeles, B
University of California, Merced, BMD
University of California, San Diego, D
University of California, Santa Barbara, D
University of Southern California, BD

Colorado

University of Denver, D

Connecticut

University of Connecticut, MDO
Yale University, D

Delaware

University of Delaware, BMD

District of Columbia

The George Washington University, D

Florida

Florida State University, D
University of South Florida, D

Georgia

Emory University, D
Georgia State University, D
University of Georgia, B

Illinois

Northwestern University, D

Indiana

Ball State University, M
Indiana University Bloomington, BD
Purdue University, D
University of Evansville, B
University of Notre Dame, D

Iowa

Iowa State University of Science and Technology, D

Kansas

The University of Kansas, D

Louisiana

Louisiana State University and Agricultural & Mechanical College, MD
University of Louisiana at Lafayette, D

Maryland

Johns Hopkins University, BD
University of Maryland, Baltimore County, D
University of Maryland, College Park, D

Massachusetts

Brandeis University, D
Hampshire College, B
Harvard University, MD
Massachusetts Institute of Technology, BD
Tufts University, D
University of Massachusetts Amherst, MD
University of Massachusetts Boston, M

Michigan

Michigan Technological University, MD
University of Michigan, BD
Wayne State University, D

Minnesota

University of Minnesota, Twin Cities Campus, D

Mississippi

Millsaps College, B
Mississippi State University, D

Missouri

Washington University in St. Louis, D

Nebraska

University of Nebraska - Lincoln, MD

Nevada

University of Nevada, Reno, MD

New Hampshire

Dartmouth College, D

New Jersey

Rutgers University - New Brunswick, D
Rutgers University - Newark, D

New Mexico

New Mexico State University, D
University of New Mexico, D

New York

Binghamton University, State University of New York, D
Canisius College, B
Cornell University, D
New York University, D
Rensselaer Polytechnic Institute, BD
State University of New York at Oswego, B
Stony Brook University, State University of New York, D
United States Military Academy, B
University at Albany, State University of New York, D
University of Rochester, D

North Carolina

Duke University, D
The University of North Carolina at Chapel Hill, D
The University of North Carolina at Charlotte, O
The University of North Carolina at Greensboro, MD

North Dakota

North Dakota State University, D

Ohio

Case Western Reserve University, BM
The Ohio State University, D

Oregon

George Fox University, B
University of Oregon, MD

Pennsylvania

Carnegie Mellon University, BD
Lehigh University, B
Susquehanna University, B
University of Pennsylvania, B

Rhode Island

Brown University, MD

Tennessee

Vanderbilt University, B

Texas

Rice University, MD
Texas A&M University, D
Texas Christian University, M
The University of Texas at Dallas, BMD

Virginia

George Mason University, M
University of Richmond, B

Washington

University of Washington, D

Wisconsin

Lawrence University, B
University of Wisconsin - Madison, D

Canada

British Columbia

Simon Fraser University, B
The University of British Columbia, BMD

Ontario

Carleton University, D
Queen's University at Kingston, BMD
University of Guelph, D
Wilfrid Laurier University, MD

Quebec

McGill University, B
Université de Montréal, B

COLLEGE STUDENT COUNSELING AND PERSONNEL SERVICES

United States

North Carolina

The University of North Carolina at Pembroke, B

Ohio

Bowling Green State University, B

COMMERCIAL AND ADVERTISING ART

United States

Alabama

Community College of the Air Force, A
James H. Faulkner State Community College, A
Oakwood University, A

Arizona

Eastern Arizona College, A
Glendale Community College, A
Paradise Valley Community College, A
Phoenix College, A
University of Advancing Technology, AB
Yavapai College, A

Arkansas

Arkansas State University, B
National Park College, A
NorthWest Arkansas Community College, A
University of Arkansas Community College at Morrilton, A

California

Academy of Art University, AB
Allan Hancock College, A
Art Center College of Design, B
Biola University, B
California College of the Arts, B
California State University, East Bay, B
California State University, Fresno, B
California State University, Long Beach, B
Chabot College, A
Chaffey College, A
College of San Mateo, A
College of the Sequoias, A
Cuyamaca College, A
Cypress College, A
De Anza College, A
Glendale Community College, A
Golden West College, A
Laguna College of Art & Design, B
Laney College, A
Lassen Community College District, A
Los Angeles Trade-Technical College, A
Los Angeles Valley College, A
Los Medanos College, A
Mission College, A
Modesto Junior College, A
Monterey Peninsula College, A
Moorpark College, A
Mount Saint Mary's University, A
Mt. San Antonio College, A
Ohlone College, A
Orange Coast College, A
Otis College of Art and Design, B
Palomar College, A
Porterville College, A
Reedley College, A
Saddleback College, A
San Bernardino Valley College, A
San Diego City College, A
San Joaquin Delta College, A
Santa Ana College, A
Santa Barbara City College, A
Solano Community College, A
University of the Pacific, B
University of San Francisco, B
Ventura College, A
Woodbury University, B

Colorado

Colorado Mountain College (Glenwood Springs), A

Connecticut

Housatonic Community College, A
Manchester Community College, A
Middlesex Community College, A
Mitchell College, A
Northwestern Connecticut Community College, A
Norwalk Community College, A
Tunxis Community College, A
University of New Haven, B

Delaware

Delaware Technical & Community College, Terry Campus, A

Florida

Florida Keys Community College, A
Jacksonville University, B
Lake-Sumter State College, A
Miami Dade College, A
Northwest Florida State College, A
Palm Beach State College, A
Pensacola State College, A
Ringling College of Art and Design, B
St. Johns River State College, A
Santa Fe College, A
State College of Florida Manatee-Sarasota, A
Tallahassee Community College, A

Georgia

University of North Georgia, B

Hawaii

Honolulu Community College, A

Idaho

Boise State University, B
College of Southern Idaho, A
North Idaho College, A
Northwest Nazarene University, B

Illinois

American Academy of Art, B
College of DuPage, A
Columbia College Chicago, B
Concordia University Chicago, B
Dominican University, B
Lewis University, B
Millikin University, B
Robert Morris University Illinois, A

Indiana

Indiana University - Purdue University Fort Wayne, B
University of Indianapolis, B
Vincennes University, A

Iowa

Buena Vista University, B
Des Moines Area Community College, A
Dordt College, B
Drake University, B
Graceland University, B
Iowa Lakes Community College, A
Iowa State University of Science and Technology, B
Upper Iowa University, B
Wartburg College, B

Kansas

Labette Community College, A
Pratt Community College, A
Seward County Community College and Area Technical School, A

Kentucky

Northern Kentucky University, B

Louisiana

Delgado Community College, A
Louisiana College, B
Louisiana Tech University, B
Sowela Technical Community College, A

Maryland

Community College of Baltimore County, A
Hagerstown Community College, A
Montgomery College, A

Massachusetts

Cape Cod Community College, A
Clark University, B
Massachusetts College of Art and Design, B
Middlesex Community College, A
Northern Essex Community College, A
Salem State University, B
Springfield Technical Community College, A

Michigan

Baker College, A
College for Creative Studies, B
Henry Ford College, A
Macomb Community College, A
Muskegon Community College, A
Northwestern Michigan College, A
St. Clair County Community College, A
Washtenaw Community College, A

Minnesota

Academy College, A
Alexandria Technical and Community College, A
Bemidji State University, B
Central Lakes College, A
Dakota County Technical College, A
Duluth Business University, A
Minneapolis College of Art and Design, B
Minnesota State University Mankato, B
Minnesota State University Moorhead, B
South Central College, A
University of Minnesota, Duluth, B

Mississippi

Antonelli College (Jackson), A
Northwest Mississippi Community College, A

Missouri

East Central College, A
Fontbonne University, B
Metropolitan Community College - Kansas City, A
St. Charles Community College, A
Southwest Baptist University, B
University of Central Missouri, B
Washington University in St. Louis, B

Montana

Montana State University - Northern, AB

Nebraska

Central Community College - Columbus Campus, A
Central Community College - Hastings Campus, A
Metropolitan Community College, A
Mid-Plains Community College, A
Peru State College, B
Southeast Community College, Lincoln Campus, A

Nevada

Truckee Meadows Community College, A
Western Nevada College, A

New Hampshire

Franklin Pierce University, B
Keene State College, B
Manchester Community College, A

New Jersey

Centenary College, B
The College of New Jersey, B
Mercer County Community College, A
Rowan College at Burlington County, A
Rutgers University - New Brunswick, B
Seton Hall University, B
Sussex County Community College, A

New Mexico

Clovis Community College, A
New Mexico Junior College, A
San Juan College, A

New York

Bryant & Stratton College - Amherst Campus, A
Bryant & Stratton College - Henrietta Campus, A
Buffalo State College, State University of New York, B
The College of Saint Rose, B
Dutchess Community College, A
Fashion Institute of Technology, AB
Finger Lakes Community College, A
Fulton-Montgomery Community College, A
Kingsborough Community College of the City University of New York, A
Long Island University - LIU Brooklyn, B
Long Island University - LIU Post, B
Marymount Manhattan College, B
Mercy College, B
Mohawk Valley Community College, A
Monroe Community College, A
Nassau Community College, A
New York City College of Technology of the City University of New York, AB
New York Institute of Technology, B
Pratt Institute, AB
Purchase College, State University of New York, B
Rochester Institute of Technology, B
Rockland Community College, A
St. Thomas Aquinas College, B
School of Visual Arts, B
State University of New York College of Agriculture and Technology at Cobleskill, A
State University of New York at Fredonia, B
State University of New York at Oswego, B
Sullivan County Community College, A
Syracuse University, B
Tompkins Cortland Community College, A
Ulster County Community College, A

North Carolina

Alamance Community College, A
Campbell University, B
Catawba Valley Community College, A
Central Piedmont Community College, A
Fayetteville Technical Community College, A
Guilford Technical Community College, A
Halifax Community College, A
Isothermal Community College, A
James Sprunt Community College, A
McDowell Technical Community College, A
Pitt Community College, A
Randolph Community College, A
South Piedmont Community College, A
Southwestern Community College, A
Surry Community College, A
Wake Technical Community College, A

North Dakota

Bismarck State College, A

Ohio

Antonelli College, A
Ashland University, B
Bowling Green State University, B
Cincinnati State Technical and Community College, A
Clark State Community College, A
Columbus College of Art & Design, B
Cuyahoga Community College, A
Kent State University, B
Lakeland Community College, A
Marietta College, B
Miami University, B
Ohio Northern University, B
Owens Community College, A
School of Advertising Art, A
Sinclair Community College, A
Terra State Community College, A
University of Cincinnati, B
University of Cincinnati Blue Ash College, A
The University of Findlay, B
Virginia Marti College of Art and Design, A

Oklahoma

Northern Oklahoma College, A
Oklahoma Christian University, B
Oklahoma City Community College, A
Oral Roberts University, B
Redlands Community College, A
University of Central Oklahoma, B

Oregon

Lane Community College, A
Linn-Benton Community College, A
Mt. Hood Community College, A
Portland Community College, A
Portland State University, B

Pennsylvania

Arcadia University, B
Bucks County Community College, A
California University of Pennsylvania, AB
Community College of Allegheny County, A
Delaware County Community College, A
Hussian College, School of Art, A
Kutztown University of Pennsylvania, B
Luzerne County Community College, A
Lycoming College, B
Montgomery County Community College, A
Pennsylvania College of Art & Design, B
Pennsylvania College of Technology, AB
Philadelphia University, B
Seton Hill University, B
The University of the Arts, B
Waynesburg University, B
York College of Pennsylvania, B

South Carolina

Midlands Technical College, A
Piedmont Technical College, A
Trident Technical College, A
York Technical College, A

South Dakota

Black Hills State University, B
Northern State University, A
Southeast Technical Institute, A
University of Sioux Falls, B

Tennessee

Carson-Newman University, B
Chattanooga State Community College, A
Lipscomb University, B
Nashville State Community College, A
Nossi College of Art, A
O'More College of Design, B
Pellissippi State Community College, A
Southern Adventist University, A
Southwest Tennessee Community College, A
The University of Tennessee, B

Texas

Amarillo College, A
The Art Institute of San Antonio, a branch of The Art Institute of Houston, B
Austin Community College District, A
Central Texas College, A
Collin County Community College District, A
El Paso Community College, A
Hill College, A
Kilgore College, A
Navarro College, A
Sam Houston State University, B
San Antonio College, A
San Jacinto College District, A
South Plains College, A
Tyler Junior College, A
University of North Texas, B
The University of Texas at El Paso, B

Utah

Provo College, A
Weber State University, B

Vermont

Lyndon State College, B

Virginia

Hampton University, B
Tidewater Community College, A
Virginia Western Community College, A

Washington

Seattle Central College, A
Seattle University, B
Shoreline Community College, A
Skagit Valley College, A
Spokane Falls Community College, A
Walla Walla University, B
Whatcom Community College, A

West Virginia

Fairmont State University, B
West Liberty University, B

Wisconsin

Bryant & Stratton College - Milwaukee Campus, A
Carroll University, B
Concordia University Wisconsin, B
Madison Area Technical College, A
Milwaukee Area Technical College, A
St. Norbert College, B
University of Wisconsin - Stevens Point, B
Western Technical College, A

Wyoming

Northwest College, A

Canada

Alberta

Alberta College of Art & Design, B

British Columbia

British Columbia Institute of Technology, A

Maritime Provinces: Nova Scotia

NSCAD University, B

Ontario

York University, B

Quebec

Université Laval, B
Université du Québec à Montréal, B

COMMERCIAL FISHING

United States

Washington

Peninsula College, A

COMMERCIAL PHOTOGRAPHY

United States

Arizona

The Art Institute of Phoenix, B
The Art Institute of Tucson, B
Phoenix College, A

California

The Art Institute of California - Hollywood, a campus of Argosy University, AB
The Art Institute of California - Inland Empire, a campus of Argosy University, AB
The Art Institute of California - Los Angeles, a campus of Argosy University, AB
The Art Institute of California - Orange County, a campus of Argosy University, AB
The Art Institute of California - San Diego, a campus of Argosy University, B
The Art Institute of California - San Francisco, a campus of Argosy University, AB
Chabot College, A
Santa Monica College, A
Sierra College, A

Colorado

The Art Institute of Colorado, AB
Rocky Mountain College of Art + Design, B

Florida

The Art Institute of Tampa, a branch of Miami International University of Art & Design, B
Miami International University of Art & Design, B

Georgia

The Art Institute of Atlanta, AB

Illinois

The Illinois Institute of Art - Chicago, B
The Illinois Institute of Art - Schaumburg, B
McHenry County College, A
Prairie State College, A

Indiana

The Art Institute of Indianapolis, AB

Iowa

Hawkeye Community College, A
Western Iowa Tech Community College, A

Maryland

Cecil College, A
Montgomery College, A

Massachusetts

Springfield Technical Community College, A

Michigan

The Art Institute of Michigan, B

Minnesota

Century College, A
Minneapolis Community and Technical College, A
Ridgewater College, A

Missouri

The Art Institute of St. Louis, B

Nevada

The Art Institute of Las Vegas, AB

New Mexico

Santa Fe Community College, A

New York

Fashion Institute of Technology, AB
Fiorello H. LaGuardia Community College of the City University of New York, A
Mohawk Valley Community College, A
Rochester Institute of Technology, B
School of Visual Arts, B

North Carolina

Appalachian State University, B
The Art Institute of Raleigh-Durham, a campus of South University, B
Randolph Community College, A

Ohio

Owens Community College, A

Oregon

The Art Institute of Portland, B

Pennsylvania

The Art Institute of Philadelphia, AB
The Art Institute of Pittsburgh, AB
Bucks County Community College, A
Luzerne County Community College, A

South Carolina

The Art Institute of Charleston, a branch of The Art Institute of Atlanta, B

Tennessee

The Art Institute of Tennessee - Nashville, a branch of The Art Institute of Atlanta, B
Nossi College of Art, A

Texas

The Art Institute of Austin, a branch of The Art Institute of Houston, B
The Art Institute of Houston, B
Austin Community College District, A
Houston Community College, A
Kilgore College, A
Trinity Valley Community College, A
Tyler Junior College, A

Virginia

The Art Institute of Virginia Beach, a branch of The Art Institute of Atlanta, B
The Art Institute of Washington, a branch of The Art Institute of Atlanta, B

Washington

The Art Institute of Seattle, AB
Spokane Falls Community College, A

Wisconsin

Milwaukee Area Technical College, A

Wyoming

Central Wyoming College, A
Northwest College, A

COMMUNICATION DISORDERS

United States

Alabama

Alabama Agricultural and Mechanical University, M
Auburn University, BMD
Samford University, B
The University of Alabama, M
University of Montevallo, M
University of South Alabama, BMD

Arizona

Arizona State University at the Tempe campus, BMD
Northern Arizona University, M
The University of Arizona, BMD

Arkansas

Arkansas State University, M
Harding University, BM
University of Arkansas, M
University of Arkansas for Medical Sciences, MD
University of Central Arkansas, MD

California

Biola University, B
California Baptist University, B
California State University, Chico, BM
California State University, East Bay, M
California State University, Fresno, BM
California State University, Fullerton, BM
California State University, Long Beach, BM
California State University, Los Angeles, BM
California State University, Northridge, BM
California State University, Sacramento, M
California State University, San Marcos, M
Chapman University, MO
Loma Linda University, M
National University, M
San Diego State University, BMD
San Francisco State University, BM
San Jose State University, BM
University of California, San Diego, D
University of the Pacific, M
University of Redlands, BM
University of San Diego, M

Colorado

University of Colorado Boulder, BMD
University of Northern Colorado, MD

Connecticut

Sacred Heart University, M
Southern Connecticut State University, M
University of Connecticut, MD

District of Columbia

Gallaudet University, MDO
The George Washington University, M
Howard University, MD
University of the District of Columbia, M

Florida

Barry University, M
Florida Atlantic University, M
Florida International University, M
Florida State University, MD
Jacksonville University, B
Nova Southeastern University, MD
University of Central Florida, MDO
University of Florida, MD
University of North Florida, M
University of South Florida, MDO
University of South Florida Sarasota-Manatee, B

Georgia

Armstrong State University, M
Georgia State University, MD
University of Georgia, BMDO
University of West Georgia, M

Hawaii

University of Hawaii at Manoa, M

Idaho

Idaho State University, MDO

Illinois

Augustana College, B
Eastern Illinois University, BM
Elmhurst College, M
Governors State University, BM
Illinois State University, M
Northern Illinois University, BMD
Northwestern University, BMD
Rush University, MD
Saint Xavier University, M
Southern Illinois University Carbondale, BM
Southern Illinois University Edwardsville, M
University of Illinois at Urbana - Champaign, MD
Western Illinois University, BM

Indiana

Ball State University, MD
Butler University, B
Indiana State University, MDO
Indiana University Bloomington, MD
Indiana University - Purdue University Fort Wayne,
    M
Purdue University, MD
Saint Mary's College, B

Iowa

St. Ambrose University, M
The University of Iowa, MD
University of Northern Iowa, M

Kansas

Fort Hays State University, M
Kansas State University, BM
The University of Kansas, BMD
Wichita State University, BMD

Kentucky

Eastern Kentucky University, M
Murray State University, M
University of Kentucky, M
University of Louisville, MD
Western Kentucky University, BM

Louisiana

Louisiana State University and Agricultural & Me-
    chanical College, MD
Louisiana State University Health Sciences Center,
    MD
Louisiana Tech University, M
Southeastern Louisiana University, M
University of Louisiana at Lafayette, MD
University of Louisiana at Monroe, M
Xavier University of Louisiana, B

Maine

University of Maine, BM

Maryland

Loyola University Maryland, M
Towson University, MD
University of Maryland, College Park, BMD

Massachusetts

Boston University, MD
Bridgewater State University, B
Elms College, BMO
Emerson College, BM
Massachusetts Institute of Technology, D
Northeastern University, MD
Springfield College, B
University of Massachusetts Amherst, BMD
Worcester State University, BM

Michigan

Andrews University, M
Central Michigan University, BMD
Eastern Michigan University, M
Grand Valley State University, M

Michigan State University, MD
Wayne State University, BMD
Western Michigan University, MD

Minnesota

Minnesota State University Mankato, BM
Minnesota State University Moorhead, M
St. Cloud State University, BM
University of Minnesota, Duluth, BM
University of Minnesota, Twin Cities Campus, MD

Mississippi

Jackson State University, M
Mississippi University for Women, M
Northeast Mississippi Community College, A
University of Mississippi, BM
University of Southern Mississippi, MD

Missouri

Fontbonne University, BM
Maryville University of Saint Louis, B
Rockhurst University, M
Saint Louis University, BM
Southeast Missouri State University, BM
Truman State University, BM
University of Central Missouri, M
University of Missouri, MD
Washington University in St. Louis, MD
Webster University, M

Nebraska

University of Nebraska at Kearney, BM
University of Nebraska - Lincoln, MDO
University of Nebraska at Omaha, M

Nevada

University of Nevada, Reno, MD

New Hampshire

University of New Hampshire, M

New Jersey

Kean University, M
Monmouth University, M
Montclair State University, MD
Seton Hall University, M
Stockton University, M
William Paterson University of New Jersey, BM

New Mexico

Eastern New Mexico University, M
New Mexico State University, MDO
University of New Mexico, M

New York

Adelphi University, MD
Brooklyn College of the City University of New York,
    MD
Buffalo State College, State University of New York,
    M
Canisius College, M
The College of Saint Rose, M
Hofstra University, MD
Hunter College of the City University of New York,
    M
Iona College, M
Ithaca College, M
Lehman College of the City University of New York,
    M
Long Island University - LIU Post, M
Mercy College, M
Molloy College, M
Nazareth College of Rochester, M
New York University, MD
Pace University, B
Queens College of the City University of New York,
    BM
St. John's University, MD
State University of New York at Fredonia, BM
State University of New York at New Paltz, BM
State University of New York at Plattsburgh, M
Syracuse University, BMD
Touro College, M
University at Buffalo, the State University of New
    York, MD

Yeshiva University, M

North Carolina

Appalachian State University, BM
East Carolina University, MD
Forsyth Technical Community College, A
North Carolina Central University, M
Shaw University, B
The University of North Carolina at Chapel Hill, MD
The University of North Carolina at Greensboro, MD
Western Carolina University, BM

North Dakota

Minot State University, BM
University of North Dakota, BMD

Ohio

Baldwin Wallace University, BM
Bowling Green State University, BMD
Case Western Reserve University, BMD
Cleveland State University, M
Kent State University, MD
Miami University, M
Mount Vernon Nazarene University, B
The Ohio State University, MD
Ohio University, MD
Ohio University - Chillicothe, A
The University of Akron, BMD
University of Cincinnati, BMDO
The University of Toledo, M

Oklahoma

Northeastern State University, M
Oklahoma State University, M
University of Central Oklahoma, M
University of Oklahoma Health Sciences Center,
    BMDO
The University of Tulsa, M

Oregon

Lewis & Clark College, M
Pacific University, MD
Portland State University, BM
University of Oregon, B

Pennsylvania

Bloomsburg University of Pennsylvania, MD
California University of Pennsylvania, BM
Clarion University of Pennsylvania, M
Duquesne University, M
East Stroudsburg University of Pennsylvania, M
Edinboro University of Pennsylvania, M
Indiana University of Pennsylvania, M
La Salle University, BM
Marywood University, M
Misericordia University, M
Penn State Abington, B
Penn State Altoona, B
Penn State Beaver, B
Penn State Berks, B
Penn State Brandywine, B
Penn State DuBois, B
Penn State Erie, The Behrend College, B
Penn State Fayette, The Eberly Campus, B
Penn State Greater Allegheny, B
Penn State Hazleton, B
Penn State Lehigh Valley, B
Penn State Mont Alto, B
Penn State New Kensington, B
Penn State Schuylkill, B
Penn State Shenango, B
Penn State University Park, BMDO
Penn State Wilkes-Barre, B
Penn State Worthington Scranton, B
Penn State York, B
Temple University, M
University of Pittsburgh, MD
West Chester University of Pennsylvania, MO

Rhode Island

Rhode Island College, B
University of Rhode Island, BM

South Carolina

Bob Jones University, B
South Carolina State University, M
University of South Carolina, MD
Winthrop University, B

South Dakota

The University of South Dakota, BMD

Tennessee

East Tennessee State University, MD
Tennessee State University, M
University of Memphis, MD
The University of Tennessee, MD
Vanderbilt University, MD

Texas

Abilene Christian University, M
Baylor University, BM
Lamar University, BMD
Our Lady of the Lake University of San Antonio, BM
Stephen F. Austin State University, BM
Texas A&M International University, B
Texas A&M University - Kingsville, BM
Texas Christian University, M
Texas State University, BM
Texas Woman's University, M
University of Houston, BM
University of North Texas, M
The University of Texas at Austin, BMD
The University of Texas at Dallas, MD
The University of Texas at El Paso, M
The University of Texas Health Science Center at San Antonio, M
The University of Texas Rio Grande Valley, BM
West Texas A&M University, BM

Utah

Brigham Young University, M
University of Utah, MD
Utah State University, MDO

Vermont

University of Vermont, BM

Virginia

Hampton University, BM
James Madison University, MD
Longwood University, M
Old Dominion University, M
Radford University, BM
University of Virginia, M

Washington

Eastern Washington University, M
University of Washington, MD
Washington State University, M
Western Washington University, M

West Virginia

Marshall University, M
West Virginia University, MD

Wisconsin

Marquette University, MO
University of Wisconsin - Eau Claire, BM
University of Wisconsin - Madison, MD
University of Wisconsin - Milwaukee, MO
University of Wisconsin - River Falls, BM
University of Wisconsin - Stevens Point, BMD
University of Wisconsin - Whitewater, BM

Wyoming

University of Wyoming, M

U.S. Territories: Puerto Rico

Carlos Albizu University, BM
Universidad del Turabo, M

University of Puerto Rico, Medical Sciences Campus, MD

Canada
Alberta

University of Alberta, MD

British Columbia

The University of British Columbia, BMD

Maritime Provinces: Nova Scotia

Dalhousie University, MD

Ontario

Brock University, B
University of Ottawa, M
University of Toronto, MD
The University of Western Ontario, M

Quebec

McGill University, MD
Université Laval, M
Université de Montréal, MO

COMMUNICATION DISORDERS SCIENCES AND SERVICES

United States
Arkansas

Ouachita Baptist University, B

Minnesota

St. Cloud State University, B

Missouri

University of Missouri, B

New Hampshire

Granite State College, A
University of New Hampshire, B

New Jersey

Rowan College at Burlington County, A

Washington

Bates Technical College, A

Wisconsin

Marquette University, B

COMMUNICATION, JOURNALISM AND RELATED PROGRAMS

United States
Alabama

Auburn University, B
Gadsden State Community College, A

California

Ashford University, B
California Lutheran University, B
Dominican University of California, B
Folsom Lake College, A
National University, B
Notre Dame de Namur University, B
Saint Mary's College of California, B
San Jose City College, A

Connecticut

Quinnipiac University, B
Sacred Heart University, B

Florida

Florida Institute of Technology, B
University of Miami, B

Georgia

Berry College, B
Mercer University, B
Reinhardt University, B
Young Harris College, B

Hawaii

Brigham Young University - Hawaii, B

Illinois

Augustana College, B
Benedictine University, B
Quincy University, B
University of Illinois at Urbana - Champaign, B

Indiana

Ivy Tech Community College - Kokomo, A
Valparaiso University, A

Iowa

Clarke University, B
Iowa Lakes Community College, A
William Penn University, B

Kansas

Friends University, B
Sterling College, B

Kentucky

Morehead State University, B

Louisiana

Delgado Community College, A
Tulane University, A

Massachusetts

Eastern Nazarene College, B
Endicott College, B
Merrimack College, B
Newbury College, B
Springfield College, B

Michigan

Lake Superior State University, B
Madonna University, AB
Siena Heights University, B

Minnesota

University of Minnesota, Duluth, B
University of Minnesota, Twin Cities Campus, B

Missouri

Hannibal-LaGrange University, B
Washington University in St. Louis, B
Webster University, B

New Jersey

Seton Hall University, B

New Mexico

University of New Mexico - Taos, A

New York

Cayuga County Community College, A
Farmingdale State College, B
Lehman College of the City University of New York, B
Manhattanville College, B
Queensborough Community College of the City University of New York, A
State University of New York Polytechnic Institute, B

North Dakota

Minot State University, B

Ohio

Bowling Green State University, B
Lake Erie College, B
Malone University, B

North Central State College, A
Ohio Northern University, B
The Ohio State University, B

Oklahoma

Oklahoma Christian University, B
Southeastern Oklahoma State University, B

Pennsylvania

Carlow University, B
Chestnut Hill College, B
Community College of Beaver County, A
Delaware County Community College, A
Drexel University, B
Harrisburg Area Community College, A
Immaculata University, AB
Penn State Abington, B
Penn State Altoona, B
Penn State Beaver, B
Penn State Berks, B
Penn State Brandywine, B
Penn State DuBois, B
Penn State Erie, The Behrend College, B
Penn State Fayette, The Eberly Campus, B
Penn State Greater Allegheny, B
Penn State Hazleton, B
Penn State Lehigh Valley, B
Penn State Mont Alto, B
Penn State New Kensington, B
Penn State Schuylkill, B
Penn State Shenango, B
Penn State University Park, B
Penn State Wilkes-Barre, B
Penn State Worthington Scranton, B
Penn State York, B
Point Park University, B
Rosemont College, B

South Carolina

Bob Jones University, B
Newberry College, B

Tennessee

LeMoyne-Owen College, B
Trevecca Nazarene University, B

Texas

Our Lady of the Lake University of San Antonio, B

Utah

Brigham Young University, B

Virginia

Mary Baldwin College, B
Norfolk State University, B

West Virginia

West Virginia University, B

Wisconsin

Marquette University, B
Milwaukee School of Engineering, B
University of Wisconsin - Green Bay, B
Wisconsin Lutheran College, B

U.S. Territories: Guam

University of Guam, B

Canada

Maritime Provinces: Nova Scotia

Dalhousie University, B

Ontario

McMaster University, B

Quebec

Concordia University, B

COMMUNICATION AND MEDIA STUDIES

United States

Alabama

Auburn University, BMO
Miles College, B
Troy University, M
The University of Alabama, MD
The University of Alabama at Birmingham, M
University of Mobile, B
University of South Alabama, M
The University of West Alabama, B

Alaska

University of Alaska Fairbanks, M

Arizona

Arizona State University at the Tempe campus, MD
Northern Arizona University, M
The University of Arizona, MD

Arkansas

Arkansas State University, MO
University of Arkansas, M

California

Academy of Art University, B
Biola University, B
California Baptist University, M
California State University, Chico, M
California State University, East Bay, M
California State University, Fresno, M
California State University, Fullerton, M
California State University, Long Beach, M
California State University, Los Angeles, M
California State University, Northridge, M
California State University, Sacramento, M
California State University, San Bernardino, M
Pepperdine University, M
San Diego State University, M
San Jose State University, M
Stanford University, BMD
University of California, Davis, M
University of California, San Diego, D
University of California, Santa Barbara, D
University of California, Santa Cruz, O
University of the Pacific, M
University of Southern California, M

Colorado

University of Colorado Boulder, BMD
University of Colorado Colorado Springs, M
University of Colorado Denver, M

Connecticut

Central Connecticut State University, MO
Fairfield University, M
Mitchell College, B
Quinnipiac University, M
Sacred Heart University, M
University of Bridgeport, M
University of Connecticut, M
University of Hartford, M

Delaware

University of Delaware, M
Wesley College, B

District of Columbia

American University, MD
The George Washington University, M
Georgetown University, M
Howard University, MD
Trinity Washington University, M

Florida

Barry University, MO
Florida Atlantic University, MO
Florida Institute of Technology, M
Florida International University, M
Florida State University, BMD

Full Sail University, B
Lynn University, B
Rollins College, B
St. Thomas University, BMDO
University of Central Florida, MO
University of Florida, MD
University of Miami, BMD
University of South Florida, MD
University of West Florida, M

Georgia

Emory University, B
Georgia State University, MD
Kennesaw State University, BM
Middle Georgia State University, B
Reinhardt University, B
University of Georgia, MD
Young Harris College, B

Hawaii

Hawai'i Pacific University, M
University of Hawaii at Manoa, M

Idaho

Boise State University, M

Illinois

DePaul University, BM
DeVry University (Downers Grove), M
Governors State University, M
Greenville College, B
Illinois Institute of Technology, MD
Illinois State University, M
Judson University, B
Loyola University Chicago, B
Northeastern Illinois University, B
Northern Illinois University, M
Northwestern University, BMD
Quincy University, M
Roosevelt University, M
Southern Illinois University Carbondale, MD
Trinity International University, BM
University of Illinois at Chicago, MD
University of Illinois at Springfield, M
University of Illinois at Urbana - Champaign, MD
Western Illinois University, M

Indiana

Ball State University, M
Butler University, B
Indiana State University, M
Indiana University Bloomington, MD
Indiana University - Purdue University Fort Wayne, M
Indiana University - Purdue University Indianapolis, MD
Purdue University, MD
Purdue University Northwest (Hammond), M
Taylor University, B
University of Southern Indiana, M
Valparaiso University, MO

Iowa

Drake University, M
University of Dubuque, M
The University of Iowa, MD
University of Northern Iowa, M
Waldorf College, B

Kansas

Fort Hays State University, M
Kansas State University, M
Pittsburg State University, M
Southwestern College, B
The University of Kansas, MD
Wichita State University, M

Kentucky

Bellarmine University, M
Georgetown College, B
Morehead State University, BM
Northern Kentucky University, MO
University of Kentucky, MD
University of Louisville, M
Western Kentucky University, MO

Louisiana

Louisiana State University and Agricultural & Mechanical College, MD
Southeastern Louisiana University, M
University of Louisiana at Lafayette, M
University of Louisiana at Monroe, M

Maine

Unity College, B
University of Maine, MD

Maryland

College of Southern Maryland, A
Hood College, B
Johns Hopkins University, M
Notre Dame of Maryland University, M
Stevenson University, M
Towson University, M
University of Maryland, Baltimore County, M
University of Maryland, College Park, MD

Massachusetts

Boston University, MD
Brandeis University, M
Clark University, M
Curry College, B
Emerson College, M
Fitchburg State University, MO
Harvard University, O
Lasell College, BMO
Simmons College, M
Suffolk University, M
University of Massachusetts Amherst, MD
Western New England University, M
Wheelock College, B

Michigan

Albion College, B
Alma College, B
Andrews University, M
Central Michigan University, M
Eastern Michigan University, M
Grand Valley State University, M
Michigan State University, MD
Saginaw Valley State University, M
Spring Arbor University, BM
University of Michigan, D
Wayne State University, MDO
Western Michigan University, M

Minnesota

Bethel University, M
Crown College, B
Minnesota State University Mankato, MO
University of Minnesota, Twin Cities Campus, MD
Walden University, MO

Mississippi

Mississippi College, M

Missouri

Drury University, M
Lindenwood University, M
Missouri Baptist University, B
Missouri State University, M
Saint Louis University, M
University of Central Missouri, BM
University of Missouri, MDO
University of Missouri - St. Louis, M
Webster University, M

Montana

Montana State University Billings, M
University of Montana, M

Nebraska

University of Nebraska - Lincoln, MD
University of Nebraska at Omaha, MO
Wayne State College, M

Nevada

University of Nevada, Las Vegas, M

New Jersey

County College of Morris, A
Fairleigh Dickinson University, Metropolitan Campus, BM
Kean University, M
Monmouth University, MO
Montclair State University, B
New Jersey Institute of Technology, B
Raritan Valley Community College, A
Rutgers University - New Brunswick, D
Seton Hall University, M
Stevens Institute of Technology, MO
William Paterson University of New Jersey, M

New Mexico

Eastern New Mexico University, M
New Mexico State University, M
University of New Mexico, MD

New York

Adelphi University, B
Canisius College, B
The College at Brockport, State University of New York, M
The College of New Rochelle, MO
The College of Saint Rose, B
Columbia University, M
Cornell University, MD
Hamilton College, B
Hofstra University, M
Houghton College, B
Ithaca College, M
Marist College, M
Marymount Manhattan College, B
Molloy College, B
New York Institute of Technology, M
New York University, BMD
Pace University, B
Pace University, Pleasantville Campus, B
Rochester Institute of Technology, BMO
State University of New York College at Potsdam, M
Syracuse University, MD
University at Albany, State University of New York, MD
University at Buffalo, the State University of New York, MD

North Carolina

Campbell University, B
Elon University, B
Gardner-Webb University, B
Lees-McRae College, B
Montreat College, B
North Carolina State University, M
Queens University of Charlotte, M
The University of North Carolina at Chapel Hill, D
The University of North Carolina at Charlotte, MO
The University of North Carolina at Greensboro, M
Wake Forest University, M

North Dakota

North Dakota State University, MD
University of North Dakota, MD

Ohio

Ashland University, B
Bowling Green State University, MD
Cleveland State University, MDO
Kent State University, MD
Ohio Northern University, B
The Ohio State University, MD
Ohio University, MD
Tiffin University, M
The University of Akron, M
University of Cincinnati, M
University of Dayton, M
The University of Toledo, O
Walsh University, B

Oklahoma

Cameron University, B
Northeastern State University, M
Oklahoma City University, B
University of Oklahoma, MD

Oregon

University of Oregon, MD
University of Portland, M

Pennsylvania

Carnegie Mellon University, M
Clarion University of Pennsylvania, M
DeSales University, B
Drexel University, M
Duquesne University, MD
Eastern University, O
Edinboro University of Pennsylvania, M
Elizabethtown College School of Continuing and Professional Studies, B
Indiana University of Pennsylvania, MD
Keystone College, A
King's College, B
La Roche College, B
La Salle University, MO
Lycoming College, B
Manor College, A
Marywood University, M
Moore College of Art & Design, M
Neumann University, B
Penn State Erie, The Behrend College, B
Penn State Harrisburg, M
Penn State University Park, MD
Point Park University, M
Reading Area Community College, A
Shippensburg University of Pennsylvania, M
Summit University, MD
Temple University, MD
University of Pennsylvania, D
University of Pittsburgh, MD
Villanova University, M
Washington & Jefferson College, B
West Chester University of Pennsylvania, M

Rhode Island

Roger Williams University, B
Salve Regina University, B
University of Rhode Island, M

South Carolina

Clemson University, MD
College of Charleston, M
Columbia International University, B
Newberry College, B

South Dakota

South Dakota State University, M
The University of South Dakota, M

Tennessee

Austin Peay State University, M
Belmont University, B
East Tennessee State University, M
Lane College, B
Milligan College, B
University of Memphis, MD
The University of Tennessee, MD

Texas

Abilene Christian University, M
Angelo State University, M
Austin College, B
Baylor University, M
Houston Baptist University, B
Our Lady of the Lake University of San Antonio, M
St. Mary's University, MO
Sam Houston State University, M
Southern Methodist University, B
Stephen F. Austin State University, M
Texas A&M University, MD
Texas A&M University - Corpus Christi, M
Texas Southern University, M
Texas State University, M
Texas Tech University, M
University of Houston, M
University of the Incarnate Word, BM
University of North Texas, M
The University of Texas at Arlington, M
The University of Texas at Austin, MD
The University of Texas at Dallas, MD
The University of Texas at El Paso, M

The University of Texas Rio Grande Valley, MO
The University of Texas at San Antonio, M
The University of Texas at Tyler, M
West Texas A&M University, M

Utah

Brigham Young University, M
Southern Utah University, M
University of Utah, MD
Utah State University, M
Weber State University, M
Westminster College, M

Vermont

Bennington College, B
University of Vermont, M

Virginia

Eastern Mennonite University, B
George Mason University, MDO
James Madison University, M
Liberty University, M
Norfolk State University, M
Regent University, MD
Virginia Commonwealth University, D
Virginia Polytechnic Institute and State University, M
Virginia Wesleyan College, B

Washington

Eastern Washington University, M
Gonzaga University, M
University of Washington, MD
Washington State University, MD

West Virginia

Marshall University, M
West Virginia University, MD

Wisconsin

Carthage College, B
Marquette University, BMO
University of Wisconsin - Madison, MD
University of Wisconsin - Milwaukee, MDO
University of Wisconsin - Stevens Point, M
University of Wisconsin - Superior, BM
University of Wisconsin - Whitewater, M

Wyoming

University of Wyoming, M

U.S. Territories: Puerto Rico

University of the Sacred Heart, MO

Canada

Alberta

Athabasca University, B
University of Alberta, M
University of Calgary, BMD

British Columbia

Simon Fraser University, MD

Manitoba

Providence University College & Theological Seminary, B

Ontario

Carleton University, MD
Queen's University at Kingston, MD
Trent University, M
University of Ottawa, M
The University of Western Ontario, B
University of Windsor, M
Wilfrid Laurier University, M
York University, MD

Quebec

Concordia University, BMDO
McGill University, MD
Université de Montréal, MD
Université du Québec à Montréal, MD
Université du Québec à Trois-Rivières, MO

Université de Sherbrooke, B

COMMUNICATION STUDIES/ SPEECH COMMUNICATION AND RHETORIC

United States

Alabama

Alabama State University, B
Auburn University at Montgomery, B
Jacksonville State University, B
Samford University, B
Troy University, B
The University of Alabama, B
The University of Alabama at Birmingham, B
The University of Alabama in Huntsville, B
University of North Alabama, B
University of South Alabama, B

Alaska

University of Alaska Fairbanks, B
University of Alaska Southeast, B

Arizona

Arizona State University at the Downtown Phoenix campus, B
Arizona State University at the Polytechnic campus, B
Arizona State University at the Tempe campus, B
Arizona State University at the West campus, B
Cochise County Community College District, A
Northern Arizona University, B
The University of Arizona, B

Arkansas

Arkansas Tech University, B
Harding University, B
John Brown University, B
Ouachita Baptist University, B
University of Arkansas, B
University of Arkansas at Little Rock, B
University of Arkansas at Monticello, B

California

Antelope Valley College, A
Azusa Pacific University, B
Biola University, B
Cabrillo College, A
California Baptist University, B
California Polytechnic State University, San Luis Obispo, B
California State Polytechnic University, Pomona, B
California State University, Dominguez Hills, B
California State University, Fresno, B
California State University, Fullerton, B
California State University, Los Angeles, B
California State University, Sacramento, B
California State University, San Marcos, B
California State University, Stanislaus, B
Cañada College, A
Cerritos College, A
Chapman University, B
Citrus College, A
College of the Canyons, A
College of the Desert, A
College of Marin, A
College of the Siskiyous, A
Columbia College, A
Cosumnes River College, A
Crafton Hills College, A
Fresno City College, A
Fullerton College, A
Glendale Community College, A
Grossmont College, A
Hartnell College, A
La Sierra University, B
Loyola Marymount University, B
New Charter University, AB
Notre Dame de Namur University, B
Orange Coast College, A
Oxnard College, A
Palomar College, A

Pasadena City College, A
Pepperdine University, B
Point Loma Nazarene University, B
Saint Mary's College of California, B
San Diego Christian College, B
San Diego State University, B
San Francisco State University, B
Santa Ana College, A
Santa Barbara City College, A
Santa Clara University, B
Santiago Canyon College, A
Simpson University, B
Sonoma State University, B
University of California, Davis, B
University of La Verne, B
University of the Pacific, B
University of San Francisco, B
University of Southern California, B
Vanguard University of Southern California, B
Westmont College, B
Woodbury University, B
Yuba College, A

Colorado

Colorado State University, B
Regis University, B
University of Colorado Boulder, B
University of Colorado Denver, B
University of Denver, B
University of Northern Colorado, B

Connecticut

Albertus Magnus College, B
Capital Community College, A
Eastern Connecticut State University, B
Fairfield University, B
Lincoln College of New England, A
Manchester Community College, A
Norwalk Community College, A
Sacred Heart University, B
Southern Connecticut State University, B
University of Connecticut, B
University of Hartford, B
University of New Haven, B
Western Connecticut State University, B

Delaware

University of Delaware, B

District of Columbia

American University, B
The Catholic University of America, B
Gallaudet University, B
Trinity Washington University, B

Florida

Barry University, B
Bethune-Cookman University, B
Eckerd College, B
Embry-Riddle Aeronautical University - Daytona, B
Embry-Riddle Aeronautical University - Worldwide, B
Florida Atlantic University, B
Florida International University, B
Jacksonville University, B
Nova Southeastern University, B
Palm Beach Atlantic University, B
South Florida State College, A
University of Central Florida, B
University of Miami, B
University of South Florida, B
Warner University, B
Webber International University, B

Georgia

Augusta University, B
Brewton-Parker College, B
Clayton State University, B
Georgia Highlands College, A
Georgia Southern University, B
Georgia State University, B
Kennesaw State University, B
Mercer University, B
Oglethorpe University, B
Thomas University, B
University of Georgia, B

Valdosta State University, B
Wesleyan College, B

Hawaii

Brigham Young University - Hawaii, B
Chaminade University of Honolulu, B
Hawai'i Pacific University, B
University of Hawaii at Manoa, B

Idaho

Boise State University, B
College of Southern Idaho, A
Idaho State University, B
Lewis-Clark State College, B
Northwest Nazarene University, B

Illinois

Aurora University, B
Benedictine University, B
Blackburn College, B
Concordia University Chicago, B
DePaul University, B
Dominican University, B
Elmhurst College, B
Eureka College, B
Governors State University, B
Greenville College, B
Harper College, A
Illinois State University, B
Judson University, B
Lewis University, B
Loyola University Chicago, B
McKendree University, B
Millikin University, B
Monmouth College, B
Moody Bible Institute, B
North Central College, B
North Park University, B
Northern Illinois University, B
Northwestern University, B
Olivet Nazarene University, B
Roosevelt University, B
Saint Xavier University, B
Sauk Valley Community College, A
Southern Illinois University Edwardsville, B
Trinity Christian College, B
Triton College, A
University of Illinois at Chicago, B
University of Illinois at Urbana - Champaign, B
Western Illinois University, B
Wheaton College, B

Indiana

Ancilla College, A
Ball State University, B
Bethel College, B
Grace College, B
Huntington University, B
Indiana State University, B
Indiana Tech, B
Indiana University Bloomington, B
Indiana University East, B
Indiana University Kokomo, B
Indiana University Northwest, B
Indiana University - Purdue University Fort Wayne, B
Indiana University - Purdue University Indianapolis, B
Indiana University South Bend, B
Indiana University Southeast, B
Indiana Wesleyan University, AB
Manchester University, B
Marian University, B
Purdue University Northwest (Hammond), B
Purdue University Northwest (Westville), B
Saint Joseph's College, B
Saint Mary's College, B
Trine University, AB
University of Indianapolis, B
Valparaiso University, B

Iowa

Buena Vista University, B
Central College, B
Coe College, B

Kaplan University, Davenport Campus, B
Luther College, B
Mount Mercy University, B
The University of Iowa, B
University of Northern Iowa, B
Wartburg College, B

Kansas

Barton County Community College, A
Bethany College, B
Emporia State University, B
Garden City Community College, A
Highland Community College, A
Hutchinson Community College, A
Independence Community College, A
Kansas State University, B
Kansas Wesleyan University, B
McPherson College, B
Ottawa University, B
Pittsburg State University, B
Seward County Community College and Area Technical School, A
Southwestern College, B
Tabor College, B
The University of Kansas, B
Washburn University, B
Wichita State University, B

Kentucky

Bellarmine University, B
Eastern Kentucky University, B
Kentucky Wesleyan College, B
Northern Kentucky University, B
Spalding University, B
University of the Cumberlands, B
University of Kentucky, B
University of Louisville, B
University of Pikeville, B
Western Kentucky University, B

Louisiana

Louisiana State University and Agricultural & Mechanical College, B
Northwestern State University of Louisiana, B
Southeastern Louisiana University, B
Southern University and Agricultural and Mechanical College, B
Tulane University, A
University of Louisiana at Lafayette, B

Maine

University of Southern Maine, B

Maryland

Loyola University Maryland, B
McDaniel College, B
Montgomery College, A
Mount St. Mary's University, B
Notre Dame of Maryland University, B
Salisbury University, B
Towson University, B
University of Maryland, College Park, B
University of Maryland University College, B

Massachusetts

Bridgewater State University, B
Bristol Community College, A
Bunker Hill Community College, A
Cape Cod Community College, A
Emerson College, B
Emmanuel College, B
Fitchburg State University, B
Gordon College, B
Hampshire College, B
Northeastern University, B
Pine Manor College, B
Regis College, B
Salem State University, B
Simmons College, B
Stonehill College, B
Suffolk University, B
Western New England University, B
Westfield State University, B
Worcester State University, B

Michigan

Adrian College, B
Aquinas College, B
Calvin College, B
Central Michigan University, B
Cornerstone University, B
Eastern Michigan University, B
Ferris State University, B
Grand Valley State University, B
Great Lakes Christian College, B
Hillsdale College, B
Hope College, B
Kuyper College, B
Lansing Community College, A
Lawrence Technological University, B
Macomb Community College, A
Michigan State University, B
Northern Michigan University, B
Northwestern Michigan College, A
Rochester College, B
Saginaw Valley State University, B
Spring Arbor University, B
University of Detroit Mercy, B
University of Michigan, B
University of Michigan - Dearborn, B
Wayne State University, B
Western Michigan University, B

Minnesota

Augsburg College, B
Bethany Lutheran College, B
The College of St. Scholastica, B
Concordia College, B
Hamline University, B
Metropolitan State University, B
Minnesota State University Moorhead, B
Southwest Minnesota State University, B
University of Minnesota, Duluth, B
University of Northwestern - St. Paul, B

Mississippi

Belhaven University, B
Millsaps College, B
Mississippi College, B
Mississippi State University, B
Mississippi University for Women, B
University of Southern Mississippi, B
William Carey University, B

Missouri

Avila University, B
Central Methodist University, B
Columbia College, B
Culver-Stockton College, B
Fontbonne University, B
Hannibal-LaGrange University, B
Missouri Southern State University, B
Missouri State University, B
Missouri Western State University, B
Park University, B
Rockhurst University, B
Southeast Missouri State University, B
Southwest Baptist University, B
Truman State University, B
University of Missouri, B
Washington University in St. Louis, B
Webster University, B
William Jewell College, B
William Woods University, B

Montana

Rocky Mountain College, B
University of Montana, B

Nebraska

Chadron State College, B
Concordia University, Nebraska, B
Creighton University, B
Grace University, B
Hastings College, B
Nebraska Wesleyan University, B
University of Nebraska - Lincoln, B
University of Nebraska at Omaha, B
Wayne State College, B

Nevada

College of Southern Nevada, A
University of Nevada, Las Vegas, B
University of Nevada, Reno, B

New Hampshire

Keene State College, B
Plymouth State University, B
Saint Anselm College, B
University of New Hampshire, B

New Jersey

Caldwell University, B
Camden County College, A
College of Saint Elizabeth, B
Fairleigh Dickinson University, College at Florham, B
Felician University, B
Kean University, B
Monmouth University, B
Montclair State University, B
Ramapo College of New Jersey, B
Rider University, B
Rutgers University - New Brunswick, B
Saint Peter's University, B
Seton Hall University, B
Stockton University, B
Thomas Edison State University, AB
William Paterson University of New Jersey, B

New Mexico

Eastern New Mexico University, B
New Mexico Highlands University, B

New York

Adirondack Community College, A
Alfred University, B
Brooklyn College of the City University of New York, B
Broome Community College, A
Buffalo State College, State University of New York, B
Clarkson University, B
The College at Brockport, State University of New York, B
The College of New Rochelle, B
The College of Saint Rose, B
College of Staten Island of the City University of New York, B
Dutchess Community College, A
Erie Community College, South Campus, A
Excelsior College, B
Fiorello H. LaGuardia Community College of the City University of New York, A
Hofstra University, B
Houghton College, B
Iona College, B
Jamestown Community College, A
Keuka College, B
Long Island University - LIU Brooklyn, B
Manhattanville College, B
Marymount Manhattan College, B
Molloy College, B
Nassau Community College, A
Nazareth College of Rochester, B
New York University, B
Onondaga Community College, A
Pace University, Pleasantville Campus, B
Purchase College, State University of New York, B
Rensselaer Polytechnic Institute, B
Roberts Wesleyan College, B
Rochester Institute of Technology, B
St. Francis College, B
St. John's University, B
St. Lawrence University, B
State University of New York College of Agriculture and Technology at Cobleskill, A
State University of New York College at Cortland, B
State University of New York College at Old Westbury, B
State University of New York College at Potsdam, B
State University of New York at New Paltz, B
State University of New York at Plattsburgh, B
Syracuse University, B
Tompkins Cortland Community College, A

Ulster County Community College, A
University at Albany, State University of New York, B
University at Buffalo, the State University of New York, B
Utica College, B

North Carolina

Appalachian State University, B
Campbell University, B
Catawba College, B
East Carolina University, B
Elizabeth City State University, B
Elon University, B
Fayetteville State University, B
Greensboro College, B
Meredith College, B
North Carolina Agricultural and Technical State University, B
North Carolina State University, B
Pfeiffer University, B
The University of North Carolina at Chapel Hill, B
The University of North Carolina at Charlotte, B
The University of North Carolina at Greensboro, B
The University of North Carolina Wilmington, B
Wake Forest University, B
Western Carolina University, B
William Peace University, B
Wingate University, B

North Dakota

Mayville State University, B
University of Jamestown, B

Ohio

Ashland University, B
Baldwin Wallace University, B
Bluffton University, B
Bowling Green State University, B
Capital University, B
Cleveland State University, B
The College of Wooster, B
Edison Community College, A
Franciscan University of Steubenville, B
Hiram College, B
Kent State University, B
Kent State University at Ashtabula, B
Kent State University at East Liverpool, B
Kent State University at Salem, B
Kent State University at Stark, B
Kent State University at Trumbull, B
Kent State University at Tuscarawas, B
Marietta College, B
Miami University Hamilton, B
Miami University Middletown, A
Mount St. Joseph University, AB
Mount Vernon Nazarene University, B
Notre Dame College, B
Ohio Dominican University, B
Ohio Northern University, B
The Ohio State University, B
Ohio University, B
Tiffin University, B
The University of Akron, B
University of Cincinnati, B
University of Cincinnati Blue Ash College, A
University of Dayton, B
The University of Findlay, B
University of Rio Grande, AB
The University of Toledo, B
Wittenberg University, B
Wright State University, AB
Wright State University - Lake Campus, A
Youngstown State University, B

Oklahoma

East Central University, B
Hillsdale Free Will Baptist College, B
Northeastern State University, B
Oklahoma Baptist University, B
Oral Roberts University, B
St. Gregory's University, B
Southeastern Oklahoma State University, B
University of Central Oklahoma, B
University of Oklahoma, B
University of Science and Arts of Oklahoma, B
The University of Tulsa, B

Oregon

Central Oregon Community College, A
Corban University, B
Eastern Oregon University, B
George Fox University, B
Lewis & Clark College, B
Linfield College, B
Northwest Christian University, B
Oregon Institute of Technology, B
Oregon State University, B
Southern Oregon University, B
Willamette University, B

Pennsylvania

Albright College, B
Allegheny College, B
Arcadia University, B
Bucks County Community College, A
Cabrini University, B
California University of Pennsylvania, B
Cedar Crest College, B
Chatham University, B
Community College of Beaver County, A
Delaware County Community College, A
Duquesne University, B
East Stroudsburg University of Pennsylvania, B
Eastern University, B
Grove City College, B
Gwynedd Mercy University, B
Indiana University of Pennsylvania, B
Juniata College, B
Lackawanna College, A
Lehigh Carbon Community College, A
Lincoln University, B
Mansfield University of Pennsylvania, B
Mercyhurst North East, A
Mercyhurst University, B
Messiah College, B
Millersville University of Pennsylvania, B
Montgomery County Community College, A
Northampton Community College, A
Penn State Abington, B
Penn State Altoona, B
Penn State Beaver, B
Penn State Berks, B
Penn State Brandywine, B
Penn State DuBois, B
Penn State Erie, The Behrend College, B
Penn State Fayette, The Eberly Campus, B
Penn State Greater Allegheny, B
Penn State Harrisburg, B
Penn State Hazleton, B
Penn State Lehigh Valley, B
Penn State Mont Alto, B
Penn State New Kensington, B
Penn State Schuylkill, B
Penn State Shenango, B
Penn State University Park, B
Penn State Wilkes-Barre, B
Penn State Worthington Scranton, B
Penn State York, B
Robert Morris University, B
Rosemont College, B
Saint Joseph's University, B
Saint Vincent College, B
Seton Hill University, B
Slippery Rock University of Pennsylvania, B
Summit University, B
Susquehanna University, B
Thiel College, B
University of Pennsylvania, B
The University of Scranton, B
Waynesburg University, B
Wilkes University, B
York College of Pennsylvania, B

Rhode Island

Bryant University, B
Rhode Island College, B
University of Rhode Island, B

South Carolina

Coastal Carolina University, B
Coker College, B
College of Charleston, B

Columbia College, B
Furman University, B
Southern Wesleyan University, B
University of South Carolina Aiken, B
University of South Carolina Beaufort, B
University of South Carolina Upstate, B

South Dakota

Augustana University, B
Dakota Wesleyan University, B
Presentation College, A
South Dakota State University, B
University of Sioux Falls, B

Tennessee

Belmont University, B
Bryan College, B
Freed-Hardeman University, B
Hiwassee College, A
Lee University, B
LeMoyne-Owen College, B
Nashville State Community College, A
Trevecca Nazarene University, AB
University of Memphis, B
The University of Tennessee, B
The University of Tennessee at Chattanooga, B
Vanderbilt University, B

Texas

Abilene Christian University, B
Angelina College, A
Austin College, B
Baylor University, B
Brookhaven College, A
Collin County Community College District, A
Dallas Baptist University, B
Eastfield College, A
El Paso Community College, A
Hardin-Simmons University, B
Hill College, A
Houston Community College, A
Howard College, A
Howard Payne University, B
Lee College, A
Lone Star College - CyFair, A
Lone Star College - University Park, A
Mountain View College, A
Panola College, A
Prairie View A&M University, B
St. Mary's University, B
Sam Houston State University, B
Schreiner University, B
Southwestern Assemblies of God University, B
Southwestern University, B
Tarleton State University, B
Texas A&M International University, B
Texas Christian University, B
Texas Lutheran University, B
Texas Southern University, B
Trinity University, B
Tyler Junior College, A
University of Houston, B
University of the Incarnate Word, B
University of Mary Hardin-Baylor, B
University of St. Thomas, B
The University of Texas at Austin, B
The University of Texas Rio Grande Valley, B
Wayland Baptist University, B
West Texas A&M University, B

Utah

Dixie State University, B
Salt Lake Community College, A
Southern Utah University, B
Utah Valley University, A
Weber State University, B

Vermont

Champlain College, B
Lyndon State College, A
Norwich University, B

Virginia

Christopher Newport University, B
James Madison University, B

Liberty University, B
Longwood University, B
Lynchburg College, B
Radford University, B
Randolph College, B
Shenandoah University, B
The University of Virginia's College at Wise, B
Virginia Polytechnic Institute and State University, B

Washington

Eastern Washington University, B
Gonzaga University, B
Pacific Lutheran University, B
Seattle Pacific University, B
Seattle University, B
University of Puget Sound, B
University of Washington, B
Western Washington University, B
Whitman College, B
Whitworth University, B

West Virginia

American Public University System, A
Bethany College, B
Davis & Elkins College, B
Shepherd University, B
West Virginia State University, B
West Virginia Wesleyan College, B

Wisconsin

Alverno College, B
Cardinal Stritch University, B
Carroll University, B
Carthage College, B
Marian University, B
Mount Mary University, B
Ripon College, B
St. Norbert College, B
University of Wisconsin - La Crosse, B
University of Wisconsin - Madison, B
University of Wisconsin - Milwaukee, B
University of Wisconsin - Platteville, B
University of Wisconsin - River Falls, B
University of Wisconsin - Stevens Point, B
University of Wisconsin - Whitewater, B
Wisconsin Lutheran College, B

Wyoming

Casper College, A
Eastern Wyoming College, A
Laramie County Community College, A
Northwest College, A
University of Wyoming, B
Western Wyoming Community College, A

U.S. Territories: Puerto Rico

American University of Puerto Rico (Bayamon), AB
Carlos Albizu University, B
Universidad del Turabo, B
University of the Sacred Heart, B

U.S. Territories: United States Virgin Islands

University of the Virgin Islands, B

Canada

Alberta

University of Calgary, B

British Columbia

Simon Fraser University, B
Trinity Western University, B

Maritime Provinces: New Brunswick

University of New Brunswick Saint John, B

Maritime Provinces: Nova Scotia

Cape Breton University, B

Ontario

Brock University, B
University of Ottawa, B

University of Waterloo, B
York University, B

COMMUNICATION THEORY

United States

California

La Sierra University, M
Stanford University, D
University of Southern California, D

Colorado

University of Northern Colorado, M

Florida

Florida State University, D

New York

Columbia University, MD
Syracuse University, M

Ohio

Cleveland State University, M
Kent State University, MD

West Virginia

West Virginia University, M

U.S. Territories: Puerto Rico

University of Puerto Rico, Río Piedras Campus, M

COMMUNICATIONS SYSTEMS INSTALLATION AND REPAIR TECHNOLOGY

United States

California

Chabot College, A
Modesto Junior College, A
San Jose City College, A
Southwestern College, A

Illinois

College of DuPage, A

Iowa

Des Moines Area Community College, A

Kansas

North Central Kansas Technical College, A
Northwest Kansas Technical College, A

Missouri

Ranken Technical College, A

New York

Broome Community College, A
Cayuga County Community College, A
Dutchess Community College, A
Erie Community College, South Campus, A
Mohawk Valley Community College, A
Suffolk County Community College, A

Pennsylvania

Westmoreland County Community College, A

Washington

Bates Technical College, A
Bellingham Technical College, A
North Seattle College, A

COMMUNICATIONS TECH-NOLOGIES/TECHNICIANS AND SUPPORT SERVICES

United States

Illinois

Lewis University, B

Kansas

Coffeyville Community College, A
Seward County Community College and Area Technical School, A

Maryland

Anne Arundel Community College, A
Montgomery College, A

Massachusetts

Becker College, B
Framingham State University, B
Lesley University, B

New Jersey

Middlesex County College, A
Ocean County College, A

North Dakota

Minot State University, B

Ohio

Bowling Green State University, B
Bowling Green State University - Firelands College, A
Columbus State Community College, A
North Central State College, A

Oklahoma

University of Central Oklahoma, B

Pennsylvania

Chestnut Hill College, B
Community College of Allegheny County, A
Community College of Beaver County, A
Montgomery County Community College, A

Rhode Island

Salve Regina University, B

Tennessee

Southern Adventist University, A

Wisconsin

Alverno College, B
University of Wisconsin - Platteville, B
Western Technical College, A

Canada

Ontario

University of Windsor, B

COMMUNICATIONS TECHNOL-OGY/TECHNICIAN

United States

Alabama

Community College of the Air Force, A

California

Cuesta College, A
Lassen Community College District, A
Long Beach City College, A
Napa Valley College, A

Colorado

Aims Community College, A
Colorado Mesa University, A
Pueblo Community College, A

Connecticut

Northwestern Connecticut Community College, A

Florida

Daytona State College, A
Gulf Coast State College, A
Pensacola State College, A

Georgia

Athens Technical College, A

Illinois

College of DuPage, A

Indiana

Vincennes University, A

Kansas

Dodge City Community College, A
Hutchinson Community College, A

Kentucky

Jefferson Community and Technical College, A

Maryland

Allegany College of Maryland, A

Michigan

Eastern Michigan University, B
Lawrence Technological University, B
Mott Community College, A

Nebraska

Hastings College, B

New Jersey

Bergen Community College, A
Essex County College, A

New York

York College of the City University of New York, B

Pennsylvania

East Stroudsburg University of Pennsylvania, AB
Lackawanna College, A
Messiah College, B

Tennessee

Fountainhead College of Technology, A
Pellissippi State Community College, A
Southern Adventist University, B

Texas

North Lake College, A

Virginia

ECPI University (Newport News), A
ECPI University (Richmond), A

West Virginia

New River Community and Technical College, A
Pierpont Community & Technical College, A
Southern West Virginia Community and Technical College, A

Wisconsin

Madison Area Technical College, A

U.S. Territories: Puerto Rico

Inter American University of Puerto Rico, Bayamón Campus, B
University of Puerto Rico in Humacao, A

COMMUNITY COLLEGE EDU-CATION

United States

Arizona

Argosy University, Phoenix, D
Northern Arizona University, M

Arkansas

Arkansas State University, O
University of Arkansas at Little Rock, M

California

Argosy University, Inland Empire, D
Argosy University, Los Angeles, D
Argosy University, Orange County, D
Argosy University, San Diego, D
Argosy University, San Francisco Bay Area, D
California State University, Fullerton, D
California State University, Stanislaus, D

Colorado

Argosy University, Denver, D
Colorado State University, D

Florida

Argosy University, Tampa, D
Florida State University, M
University of Central Florida, M
University of South Florida, MD

Illinois

Argosy University, Chicago, D
Eastern Illinois University, M

Iowa

University of Northern Iowa, M

Kansas

Pittsburg State University, O

Maryland

Morgan State University, D

Michigan

Central Michigan University, M
Ferris State University, D

Minnesota

Walden University, D

Mississippi

Mississippi State University, MD

North Carolina

East Carolina University, MO
Elizabeth City State University, M
Lenoir-Rhyne University, M
North Carolina State University, MD
Western Carolina University, M
Wingate University, D

Virginia

Argosy University, Washington DC, D
George Mason University, MD
Old Dominion University, MD

Washington

Argosy University, Seattle, D

COMMUNITY HEALTH NURS-ING

United States

Alabama

University of South Alabama, M

California

Holy Names University, M
San Francisco State University, M

Connecticut

University of Hartford, M

Hawaii

University of Hawaii at Manoa, M

Illinois

Rush University, D
University of Illinois at Chicago, M

Iowa

Allen College, MO

Kansas

The University of Kansas, O

Louisiana

Louisiana State University Health Sciences Center, M

Maine

Husson University, MO

Massachusetts

University of Massachusetts Amherst, D
University of Massachusetts Dartmouth, MD
Worcester State University, M

Michigan

Wayne State University, MD

Minnesota

University of Minnesota, Twin Cities Campus, M

New Jersey

Kean University, M

New Mexico

New Mexico State University, D

New York

Hunter College of the City University of New York, M

North Dakota

University of North Dakota, M

Ohio

Cleveland State University, M
University of Cincinnati, M
The University of Toledo, MO
Wright State University, M

Oregon

Oregon Health & Science University, MO

Pennsylvania

Holy Family University, M
La Salle University, MO

South Carolina

University of South Carolina, M

Texas

The University of Texas at Austin, M
The University of Texas Health Science Center at San Antonio, D

Utah

Independence University, M

Virginia

Hampton University, M

Washington

Seattle University, M
University of Washington, Tacoma, M

U.S. Territories: Puerto Rico

University of Puerto Rico, Medical Sciences Campus, M

COMMUNITY HEALTH AND PREVENTIVE MEDICINE

United States

Alabama

The University of Alabama, M

Arizona

Arizona State University at the Tempe campus, O
Arizona Western College, A

Arkansas

University of Arkansas, MD

California

National University, AB
University of California, Los Angeles, MD
University of Phoenix - Central Valley Campus, M

Colorado

University of Colorado Denver, MD

Connecticut

Quinnipiac University, D

District of Columbia

The George Washington University, MD

Florida

Florida Gulf Coast University, B
University of Florida, B
University of Miami, D
University of North Florida, M
University of South Florida, MDO
University of West Florida, M

Georgia

Georgia College & State University, B
Georgia Southern University, MD

Hawaii

University of Phoenix - Hawaii Campus, M

Idaho

Idaho State University, O

Illinois

Governors State University, B
Southern Illinois University Carbondale, M
University of Illinois at Chicago, MD
University of Illinois at Springfield, O
University of Illinois at Urbana - Champaign, BMD

Indiana

Ball State University, B
Indiana University Bloomington, BM
Indiana University - Purdue University Indianapolis, M

Iowa

The University of Iowa, MD
University of Northern Iowa, M

Kentucky

Eastern Kentucky University, M
Murray State University, B
University of Louisville, M
Western Kentucky University, B

Louisiana

Louisiana State University Health Sciences Center, MD
Tulane University, MD

Maryland

Johns Hopkins University, D

Massachusetts

Massachusetts Bay Community College, A
Pine Manor College, B
Quinsigamond Community College, A
Tufts University, B
University of Massachusetts Amherst, MD

Minnesota

Anoka-Ramsey Community College, A
Minnesota State University Mankato, M
Minnesota State University Moorhead, B
University of Minnesota, Twin Cities Campus, M
Walden University, D

Missouri

Saint Louis University, M
University of Missouri, M

Montana

Carroll College, B
University of Montana, M

Nevada

University of Nevada, Las Vegas, MD

New Hampshire

Southern New Hampshire University, MO

New Jersey

New Jersey City University, M

New Mexico

University of New Mexico, M

New York

Adelphi University, MO
Brooklyn College of the City University of New York, M
Canisius College, BM
Columbia University, MD
Daemen College, M
Hofstra University, BM
Hunter College of the City University of New York, M
New York University, MD
State University of New York College at Cortland, M
State University of New York College at Potsdam, M
State University of New York Downstate Medical Center, M
Stony Brook University, State University of New York, MD
Syracuse University, M
University at Buffalo, the State University of New York, MD

North Carolina

East Carolina University, O
The University of North Carolina at Charlotte, MO
The University of North Carolina at Greensboro, MD

North Dakota

United Tribes Technical College, A

Ohio

Bowling Green State University, B
Ohio University - Eastern, B

Oregon

Portland State University, B

Pennsylvania

Arcadia University, M
Bloomsburg University of Pennsylvania, M
Duquesne University, M
Mansfield University of Pennsylvania, B
Moravian College, B
University of Pittsburgh, MDO
West Chester University of Pennsylvania, M

Rhode Island

Brown University, MD

Tennessee

Austin Peay State University, M
The University of Tennessee, MD

Texas

Baylor University, M
Midwestern State University, M
Northwest Vista College, A
Texas A&M University, M
University of the Incarnate Word, B
The University of Texas Medical Branch, MD

Utah

Independence University, M
Utah Valley University, A

Virginia

George Mason University, BMO
Old Dominion University, M
University of Virginia, M
Virginia Commonwealth University, MD
Virginia State University, D

Washington

University of Washington, M
Washington State University, MD

West Virginia

West Virginia University, M

Wisconsin

University of Wisconsin - Eau Claire, B
University of Wisconsin - La Crosse, BM
University of Wisconsin - Madison, MD

Wyoming

University of Wyoming, M

Canada

Alberta

University of Alberta, M
University of Calgary, MD

British Columbia

University of Northern British Columbia, M

Manitoba

University of Manitoba, MDO

Maritime Provinces: Nova Scotia

Dalhousie University, M

Newfoundland and Labrador

Memorial University of Newfoundland, MDO

Ontario

University of Ottawa, MO
University of Toronto, MD

Quebec

McGill University, M
Université Laval, MDO
Université de Montréal, MDO

Saskatchewan

University of Saskatchewan, MD

COMMUNITY HEALTH SER-
VICES/LIAISON/COUNSELING

United States

Arizona

The University of Arizona, B

Arkansas

University of Central Arkansas, B

California

Santa Rosa Junior College, A

Connecticut

Western Connecticut State University, B

Delaware

Delaware State University, B

Florida

Florida SouthWestern State College, A
Miami Dade College, A
State College of Florida Manatee-Sarasota, A
University of West Florida, B

Illinois

Illinois Central College, A
Northeastern Illinois University, B
Northern Illinois University, B
Waubonsee Community College, A

Indiana

Indiana State University, B
Indiana University - Purdue University Fort Wayne, B

Iowa

University of Northern Iowa, B

Kansas

The University of Kansas, B

Maine

University of Maine at Farmington, B

Massachusetts

Becker College, B
Greenfield Community College, A
University of Massachusetts Lowell, B
Worcester State University, B

Michigan

Central Michigan University, B
Cornerstone University, B
Mott Community College, A
Northern Michigan University, B
Oakland Community College, A

Montana

Carroll College, B

Nebraska

University of Nebraska at Omaha, B

New Jersey

William Paterson University of New Jersey, B

New Mexico

New Mexico State University, B

New York

Canisius College, B
Dutchess Community College, A
Eugenio María de Hostos Community College of the City University of New York, A
Kingsborough Community College of the City University of New York, A

North Carolina

Johnson C. Smith University, B

Ohio

Ohio University, B
Youngstown State University, B

Pennsylvania

Community College of Allegheny County, A
University of Pennsylvania, B

Rhode Island

Rhode Island College, B

South Carolina

Morris College, B

Texas

Texas A&M University, B

Virginia

James Madison University, B

Washington

Eastern Washington University, B
Western Washington University, B

U.S. Territories: Puerto Rico

Universidad del Turabo, B

Canada

Ontario

The University of Western Ontario, B

COMMUNITY ORGANIZATION
AND ADVOCACY

United States

Alaska

University of Alaska Fairbanks, AB

Arizona

Arizona State University at the Downtown Phoenix campus, B

Arkansas

Southern Arkansas University - Magnolia, B

California

College of the Sequoias, A
Humphreys College, B

Connecticut

University of Hartford, B

Georgia

Mercer University, B

Hawaii

Honolulu Community College, A

Illinois

DePaul University, B
Lewis University, B
Northwestern University, B

Indiana

Indiana Wesleyan University, B

Iowa

Iowa Central Community College, A
Kirkwood Community College, A

Kansas

University of Saint Mary, B

Maryland

University of Baltimore, B

Massachusetts

Berkshire Community College, A
University of Massachusetts Boston, B

Michigan

Central Michigan University, B
Kellogg Community College, A
Lansing Community College, A
Siena Heights University, B

Minnesota

Bemidji State University, B
Minneapolis Community and Technical College, A

Missouri

Rockhurst University, B

Montana

Montana State University - Northern, AB

Nebraska

Midland University, A

New Hampshire

Manchester Community College, A
University of New Hampshire, A

New Jersey

Mercer County Community College, A

New Mexico

New Mexico State University, B
University of New Mexico, B
University of New Mexico - Gallup, A

New York

Borough of Manhattan Community College of the
  City University of New York, A
Clinton Community College, A
Elmira College, AB
Herkimer County Community College, A
Jefferson Community College, A
Metropolitan College of New York, AB
Morrisville State College, A
Nazareth College of Rochester, B
New York University, B
Orange County Community College, A
Schenectady County Community College, A
State University of New York Empire State College,
  AB
Touro College, AB
Ulster County Community College, A
Westchester Community College, A

Ohio

Miami University, B
The University of Akron, A
Wright State University, B

Oregon

Clackamas Community College, A
Lane Community College, A

Pennsylvania

Allegheny College, B

Rhode Island

Bryant University, B
Providence College, B

South Dakota

Northern State University, B

Tennessee

Chattanooga State Community College, A
Cleveland State Community College, A

Texas

Del Mar College, A
The University of Texas at El Paso, B

Vermont

Community College of Vermont, A
Goddard College, B

Virginia

Emory & Henry College, B
New River Community College, A

Washington

Saint Martin's University, B

West Virginia

West Virginia University Institute of Technology, B

Wisconsin

Alverno College, B
Northland College, B

Wyoming

Sheridan College, A

Canada

Maritime Provinces: Nova Scotia

Acadia University, B
Cape Breton University, B

COMMUNITY PSYCHOLOGY

United States

Alabama

Troy University, O
University of Montevallo, M

Alaska

University of Alaska Anchorage, D
University of Alaska Fairbanks, MD

Arizona

University of Phoenix - Phoenix Campus, M

Arkansas

University of Central Arkansas, M

California

California Institute of Integral Studies, M
California State University, East Bay, M
California State University, Fullerton, M
Marymount California University, M

Connecticut

Central Connecticut State University, M
University of Bridgeport, M
University of New Haven, MO

Florida

Argosy University, Sarasota, M
Florida Agricultural and Mechanical University, M

Georgia

Argosy University, Atlanta, M
Georgia State University, D
Thomas University, M

Hawaii

University of Hawaii at Manoa, D

Illinois

Argosy University, Chicago, M
Loyola University Chicago, MO
Northeastern Illinois University, M
Western Illinois University, M

Indiana

Indiana Wesleyan University, M
Martin University, M

Kansas

Pittsburg State University, M
Wichita State University, D

Massachusetts

Lesley University, M

Michigan

Andrews University, M

Minnesota

St. Cloud State University, M
Walden University, M

Missouri

University of Missouri - Kansas City, D

Nebraska

Creighton University, M

New York

Canisius College, M
Hofstra University, D
New York University, D
St. Bonaventure University, M
University of Rochester, M

North Carolina

North Carolina Central University, M
North Carolina State University, M
The University of North Carolina at Charlotte, M
Western Carolina University, M

Ohio

Cleveland State University, M
Heidelberg University, M

Oregon

Oregon State University - Cascades, M

Pennsylvania

Alvernia University, M
Arcadia University, M
Delaware Valley University, M
Indiana University of Pennsylvania, M
Mount Aloysius College, M
Penn State Harrisburg, M
Philadelphia University, M
Temple University, M

South Carolina

University of South Carolina, MD

Tennessee

The University of Tennessee at Chattanooga, M
The University of Tennessee at Martin, M

Texas

Argosy University, Dallas, M
Texas State University, M

Vermont

College of St. Joseph, M

Virginia

Argosy University, Washington DC, M
Norfolk State University, M

Washington

Saint Martin's University, M

Wisconsin

Alverno College, M
Marquette University, M
University of Wisconsin - Milwaukee, M
University of Wisconsin - Superior, M
University of Wisconsin - Whitewater, M

U.S. Territories: Puerto Rico

University of Puerto Rico, Río Piedras Campus, M

Canada

British Columbia

University of Victoria, M

Ontario

Wilfrid Laurier University, MD

Quebec

Université Laval, D

COMPARATIVE AND INTERDIS-CIPLINARY ARTS

United States

California

John F. Kennedy University, M

Florida

Florida Atlantic University, D

Illinois

Bradley University, M
Columbia College Chicago, M

Ohio

Ohio University, D

Utah

Brigham Young University, M

Vermont

Goddard College, M

Canada

British Columbia

Simon Fraser University, M

COMPARATIVE LITERATURE

United States

Arizona

Arizona State University at the Tempe campus, M
Harrison Middleton University, BM

Arkansas

University of Arkansas, MD

California

California State University, Fullerton, B
California State University, Long Beach, B
California State University, Northridge, M
Foothill College, A
Irvine Valley College, A
Mills College, B
National University, B
Sacramento City College, A
Saddleback College, A
Saint Mary's College of California, B
San Diego State University, B
San Francisco State University, BM
San Joaquin Delta College, A
San Jose State University, M
Skyline College, A
Sonoma State University, B
Stanford University, BD
University of California, Berkeley, BD
University of California, Davis, BD
University of California, Irvine, BMD
University of California, Los Angeles, BMD
University of California, Merced, B
University of California, Riverside, MD
University of California, San Diego, B
University of California, Santa Barbara, BD
University of California, Santa Cruz, BMD
University of La Verne, B
University of Redlands, B
University of San Francisco, B
University of Southern California, BD

Colorado

The Colorado College, B
Otero Junior College, A
University of Colorado Boulder, MD

Connecticut

Quinnipiac University, B
Trinity College, B

University of Connecticut, MD
Yale University, BD

Delaware

University of Delaware, B

District of Columbia

Georgetown University, BM

Florida

Ave Maria University, B
Barry University, B
Eckerd College, B
Florida Atlantic University, M
Miami Dade College, A
New College of Florida, B
Palm Beach State College, A
University of South Florida, O
Warner University, B

Georgia

Andrew College, A
Emory University, BDO
University of Georgia, BMD

Hawaii

Hawai'i Pacific University, B

Illinois

Eureka College, B
North Park University, B
Northwestern University, BMD
Rockford University, B
Shimer College, B
University of Chicago, BMD
University of Illinois at Urbana - Champaign, BMD

Indiana

Earlham College, B
Indiana University Bloomington, BMD
Manchester University, B
Purdue University, BMD
University of Notre Dame, D

Iowa

Graceland University, B
Iowa Lakes Community College, A
The University of Iowa, B

Kansas

Pratt Community College, A

Kentucky

Western Kentucky University, M

Louisiana

Louisiana State University and Agricultural & Mechanical College, MD

Maine

College of the Atlantic, B

Maryland

Johns Hopkins University, D
University of Maryland, College Park, MD

Massachusetts

Boston University, B
Brandeis University, B
Clark University, B
College of the Holy Cross, B
Harvard University, BD
Smith College, B
Tufts University, B
University of Massachusetts Amherst, BMD
Wellesley College, B
Williams College, B

Michigan

Hillsdale College, B
Lake Superior State University, B
Rochester College, B
University of Michigan, BD
Wayne State University, M

Minnesota

Minnesota State University Mankato, B
North Central University, A
St. Catherine University, B
University of Minnesota, Twin Cities Campus, BD

Missouri

University of Missouri, M
Washington University in St. Louis, BD

Nebraska

Hastings College, B
University of Nebraska - Lincoln, MD

New Hampshire

Dartmouth College, BM
Franklin Pierce University, B
University of New Hampshire, M

New Jersey

Fairleigh Dickinson University, Metropolitan Campus, M
Princeton University, BD
Ramapo College of New Jersey, B
Rutgers University - New Brunswick, BMD

New Mexico

University of New Mexico, BMD

New York

Barnard College, B
Binghamton University, State University of New York, BMD
Brooklyn College of the City University of New York, B
Cazenovia College, B
City College of the City University of New York, B
Columbia University, BMD
Columbia University, School of General Studies, B
Cornell University, BD
Fordham University, B
Hamilton College, B
Hobart and William Smith Colleges, B
Hofstra University, B
Houghton College, B
Hunter College of the City University of New York, B
The Jewish Theological Seminary, B
New York University, BMD
Purchase College, State University of New York, B
Queens College of the City University of New York, B
State University of New York College at Geneseo, B
State University of New York College at Old Westbury, B
Stony Brook University, State University of New York, BMDO
Syracuse University, B
Touro College, B
University at Buffalo, the State University of New York, MD
University of Rochester, B

North Carolina

Chowan University, B
Duke University, BD
East Carolina University, MO
The University of North Carolina at Chapel Hill, B

Ohio

Antioch University Midwest, M
Case Western Reserve University, BM
The College of Wooster, B
John Carroll University, B
Oberlin College, B
The Ohio State University, B
Ohio Wesleyan University, B
Otterbein University, B

Oregon

Pacific University, B
Reed College, B
University of Oregon, BMD
Willamette University, B

Pennsylvania

Arcadia University, B
Bryn Mawr College, B
Carnegie Mellon University, MD
Gettysburg College, B
Haverford College, B
La Salle University, O
Lycoming College, B
Penn State Abington, B
Penn State Altoona, B
Penn State Beaver, B
Penn State Berks, B
Penn State Brandywine, B
Penn State DuBois, B
Penn State Erie, The Behrend College, B
Penn State Fayette, The Eberly Campus, B
Penn State Greater Allegheny, B
Penn State Hazleton, B
Penn State Lehigh Valley, B
Penn State Mont Alto, B
Penn State New Kensington, B
Penn State Schuylkill, B
Penn State Shenango, B
Penn State University Park, BMD
Penn State Wilkes-Barre, B
Penn State Worthington Scranton, B
Penn State York, B
Saint Francis University, B
Swarthmore College, B
University of Pennsylvania, BMD
University of Pittsburgh at Greensburg, B
University of Pittsburgh at Johnstown, B

Rhode Island

Brown University, BD

South Carolina

University of South Carolina, BMD

Tennessee

University of Memphis, D

Texas

Blinn College, A
Lamar State College - Orange, A
University of Dallas, D
University of Houston, M
The University of Texas at Austin, MD
The University of Texas at Dallas, BMD

Utah

Brigham Young University, M
University of Utah, BMD

Vermont

Castleton University, B
Goddard College, B
Johnson State College, B
Marlboro College, B
Middlebury College, B

Virginia

Christendom College, B
University of Virginia, B

Washington

Northwest University, B
Skagit Valley College, A
University of Washington, BMD

Wisconsin

Beloit College, B
University of Wisconsin - Madison, BMD
University of Wisconsin - Milwaukee, BMDO

U.S. Territories: Puerto Rico

Inter American University of Puerto Rico, San
    Germán Campus, B
University of Puerto Rico, Mayagüez Campus, B

University of Puerto Rico, Río Piedras Campus, BM

Canada

Alberta

University of Alberta, B

British Columbia

University of Victoria, B

Maritime Provinces: New Brunswick

Mount Allison University, B
Université de Moncton, B
University of New Brunswick Fredericton, B

Maritime Provinces: Nova Scotia

Dalhousie University, B
Mount Saint Vincent University, B

Newfoundland and Labrador

Memorial University of Newfoundland, B

Ontario

Brock University, BM
Carleton University, BD
McMaster University, B
University of Guelph, D
University of Toronto, BMD
The University of Western Ontario, BMD

Quebec

Bishop's University, B
Université Laval, ABMD
Université de Montréal, BMD
Université du Québec à Chicoutimi, BM
Université du Québec à Montréal, BMD
Université du Québec à Rimouski, BMD
Université du Québec à Trois-Rivières, M
Université de Sherbrooke, MD

COMPOSITION

United States

Alabama

The University of Alabama, MD
The University of Alabama at Birmingham, M

Arizona

Arizona State University at the Tempe campus, MD
Northern Arizona University, M
The University of Arizona, MD

California

California Institute of the Arts, MO
California State University, Fullerton, M
California State University, Long Beach, M
California State University, Los Angeles, M
California State University, Northridge, M
California State University, Sacramento, M
California State University, San Bernardino, M
Mills College, M
San Diego State University, M
San Francisco Conservatory of Music, M
San Francisco State University, M
Stanford University, D
University of California, Davis, MD
University of California, Riverside, D
University of California, Santa Barbara, MD
University of California, Santa Cruz, MD
University of Southern California, MD

Colorado

University of Colorado Boulder, MD
University of Northern Colorado, MD

Connecticut

University of Hartford, MDO
Wesleyan University, M

Delaware

University of Delaware, M

Florida

Florida Atlantic University, M
Florida State University, MD
Lynn University, M
University of Florida, MD
University of Miami, MD
University of South Florida, MD

Georgia

Georgia State University, M
Valdosta State University, M

Illinois

Columbia College Chicago, M
DePaul University, M
Northwestern University, D

Iowa

University of Northern Iowa, M

Kentucky

Eastern Kentucky University, M
Northern Kentucky University, O
University of Kentucky, MD
University of Louisville, M

Maine

University of Maine, M
University of Southern Maine, M

Maryland

Salisbury University, M
Towson University, M

Massachusetts

Berklee College of Music, M
Boston University, MD
Brandeis University, MD
Harvard University, MD
Tufts University, M
University of Massachusetts Amherst, MD

Michigan

Central Michigan University, M
Michigan State University, MD
University of Michigan, MD
Wayne State University, M
Western Michigan University, M

Missouri

University of Missouri - Kansas City, MD
Webster University, M

Nebraska

University of Nebraska - Lincoln, MD

New Hampshire

University of New Hampshire, M

New Jersey

Princeton University, D
Rider University, M

New Mexico

University of New Mexico, M

New York

Bard College, M
Brooklyn College of the City University of New York,
    M
Cornell University, D
Five Towns College, M
Houghton College, M
Ithaca College, M
Long Island University - LIU Post, M
Manhattan School of Music, MD
New York University, MDO
Purchase College, State University of New York, M
Syracuse University, M

University at Buffalo, the State University of New York, MD
University of Rochester, MD

North Carolina

Duke University, D
East Carolina University, M
The University of North Carolina at Greensboro, M
University of North Carolina School of the Arts, M

Ohio

Bowling Green State University, MD
Cleveland State University, M
Kent State University, MO
Ohio University, M
The University of Akron, M
University of Cincinnati, MD
Youngstown State University, M

Oklahoma

Oklahoma City University, M
University of Oklahoma, MD

Pennsylvania

Carnegie Mellon University, M
Penn State University Park, M
Temple University, MD
University of Pittsburgh, MD
West Chester University of Pennsylvania, M

South Carolina

University of South Carolina, MD

Tennessee

Belmont University, M
The University of Tennessee, M

Texas

Baylor University, M
Hardin-Simmons University, M
Rice University, MD
Southern Methodist University, M
Texas Christian University, D
Texas State University, M
University of Houston, M
University of North Texas, D
The University of Texas at Austin, MD

Utah

Brigham Young University, M
University of Utah, MD

Virginia

George Mason University, MD
Norfolk State University, M

Washington

Eastern Washington University, M

West Virginia

West Virginia University, MD

Wisconsin

University of Wisconsin - Madison, MD
University of Wisconsin - Milwaukee, M

Canada

Alberta

University of Alberta, M

British Columbia

University of Victoria, M

Manitoba

Brandon University, M

Ontario

York University, M

Quebec

McGill University, MD
Université Laval, M
Université de Montréal, MD

Saskatchewan

University of Regina, M

COMPUTATIONAL BIOLOGY

United States

California

University of California, Irvine, D
University of Southern California, MD

Colorado

University of Colorado Denver, MD

Connecticut

Yale University, D

Florida

Florida State University, D
University of South Florida, M

Idaho

University of Idaho, MD

Illinois

University of Illinois at Urbana - Champaign, MD

Iowa

Iowa State University of Science and Technology, MD
The University of Iowa, O

Kansas

The University of Kansas, D

Maryland

University of Maryland, College Park, D

Massachusetts

Massachusetts Institute of Technology, D
Worcester Polytechnic Institute, MD

Michigan

Wayne State University, D

Missouri

Washington University in St. Louis, D

New Jersey

New Jersey Institute of Technology, M
Princeton University, D
Rutgers University - Camden, MD
Rutgers University - New Brunswick, D
Rutgers University - Newark, M

New York

Cornell University, D
New York University, D
University of Rochester, D

North Carolina

Duke University, DO
The University of North Carolina at Chapel Hill, D

Oregon

Oregon Health & Science University, MD

Pennsylvania

Carnegie Mellon University, MD
University of Pennsylvania, D
University of Pittsburgh, D

Texas

The University of Texas Medical Branch, D

Virginia

George Mason University, M

Wyoming

University of Wyoming, D

COMPUTATIONAL MATHEMATICS

United States

Arizona

Arizona State University at the Tempe campus, B

California

California Institute of Technology, B
University of California, Davis, B
University of California, Los Angeles, B

Florida

Embry-Riddle Aeronautical University - Daytona, B

Illinois

McKendree University, B
University of Illinois at Urbana - Champaign, B

Indiana

Indiana University - Purdue University Fort Wayne, B

Kentucky

Asbury University, B

Louisiana

Loyola University New Orleans, B

Michigan

Michigan State University, B

Minnesota

College of Saint Benedict, B
Saint John's University, B

New Jersey

Stevens Institute of Technology, B

New York

Brooklyn College of the City University of New York, B
Rochester Institute of Technology, B
Siena College, B

Pennsylvania

Carnegie Mellon University, B

Texas

Southwestern University, B

Virginia

Christopher Newport University, B

Washington

University of Washington, B

Wisconsin

Marquette University, B

U.S. Territories: Puerto Rico

University of Puerto Rico in Humacao, B
University of Puerto Rico in Utuado, B

Canada

Ontario

University of Waterloo, B

COMPUTATIONAL SCIENCES

United States

Alabama

The University of Alabama at Birmingham, D

Alaska

University of Alaska Fairbanks, M

California

California Institute of Technology, MD
Chapman University, MD
San Diego State University, MD
Stanford University, MD
University of California, San Diego, MD
University of California, Santa Barbara, MD

Colorado

University of Colorado Denver, D

Florida

Florida State University, MD

Georgia

Emory University, D
Georgia Institute of Technology, MD

Illinois

Southern Illinois University Edwardsville, M
University of Chicago, M

Indiana

Purdue University, D
University of Notre Dame, MD
Valparaiso University, M

Iowa

The University of Iowa, D

Kansas

The University of Kansas, M

Kentucky

Western Kentucky University, M

Massachusetts

Massachusetts Institute of Technology, M
University of Massachusetts Dartmouth, D
University of Massachusetts Lowell, D

Michigan

Michigan Technological University, D
University of Michigan - Dearborn, M
Western Michigan University, M

Minnesota

University of Minnesota, Duluth, M
University of Minnesota, Twin Cities Campus, MD

Mississippi

University of Southern Mississippi, MD

New Jersey

Princeton University, D
Stockton University, M

New Mexico

University of New Mexico, O

New York

Cornell University, MD
University at Buffalo, the State University of New York, O

North Carolina

North Carolina Agricultural and Technical State University, M

Ohio

Miami University, M
The Ohio State University, M

Pennsylvania

Lehigh University, M
Temple University, M
University of Pennsylvania, D

South Carolina

Clemson University, MD

South Dakota

South Dakota State University, D

Tennessee

Middle Tennessee State University, D
The University of Tennessee at Chattanooga, MD

Texas

Rice University, MD
Sam Houston State University, M
Southern Methodist University, MD
The University of Texas at Austin, MD
The University of Texas at El Paso, MD

Utah

University of Utah, M

Virginia

The College of William and Mary, M
George Mason University, MDO
Hampton University, M

Washington

University of Washington, M

Wisconsin

Marquette University, MD

U.S. Territories: Puerto Rico

University of Puerto Rico, Mayagüez Campus, M

Canada

Alberta

University of Lethbridge, D

British Columbia

Simon Fraser University, MD

Manitoba

University of Manitoba, M

Newfoundland and Labrador

Memorial University of Newfoundland, M

Quebec

McGill University, M

COMPUTER ART AND DESIGN

United States

Alaska

University of Alaska Fairbanks, M

Arkansas

University of Central Arkansas, M

California

Academy of Art University, M
Art Center College of Design, M
The Art Institute of California - San Francisco, a campus of Argosy University, M
California College of the Arts, M
San Jose State University, M
Shepherd University, M
University of California, Santa Cruz, MD
University of Southern California, M

Colorado

University of Denver, M

Florida

Digital Media Arts College, M
Full Sail University, M
University of Central Florida, M
University of Florida, M
University of South Florida, St. Petersburg, M

Georgia

Georgia Institute of Technology, MD
Savannah College of Art and Design, MO

Illinois

DePaul University, M

Indiana

Indiana University Bloomington, M
Purdue University, MD

Kansas

The University of Kansas, M

Maryland

Goucher College, M
University of Maryland, Baltimore County, M

Massachusetts

University of Massachusetts Dartmouth, M

Michigan

Michigan State University, M

Minnesota

Minneapolis College of Art and Design, O

Missouri

University of Missouri, M

Montana

University of Montana, M

New Jersey

Stevens Institute of Technology, O

New Mexico

New Mexico Highlands University, M

New York

Alfred University, M
Cornell University, M
New York Institute of Technology, M
New York University, M
Rensselaer Polytechnic Institute, MD
Rochester Institute of Technology, M
School of Visual Arts, M
Syracuse University, M

North Carolina

North Carolina Agricultural and Technical State University, M
North Carolina State University, D

Ohio

Bowling Green State University, M
The Ohio State University, M

Pennsylvania

Carnegie Mellon University, M
Chatham University, M
Drexel University, M
University of Pennsylvania, M

Rhode Island

Rhode Island School of Design, M

South Carolina

Clemson University, M

Tennessee

East Tennessee State University, MO

Texas

St. Edward's University, M
Texas State University, M

Virginia

Old Dominion University, M
Virginia International University, M

Washington

DigiPen Institute of Technology, M

Canada

British Columbia

Emily Carr University of Art + Design, M
University of Victoria, M

Quebec

Concordia University, O

COMPUTER EDUCATION

United States

Alabama

Troy University, M

Arizona

University of Phoenix - Online Campus, M

California

California State University, Dominguez Hills, MO
University of Phoenix - Central Valley Campus, M
University of Phoenix - San Diego Campus, M

Connecticut

University of Bridgeport, O

District of Columbia

University of Phoenix - Washington D.C. Campus, M

Florida

Florida Institute of Technology, M
University of Phoenix - North Florida Campus, M
University of Phoenix - South Florida Campus, M

Illinois

Illinois Institute of Technology, M
University of Illinois at Chicago, D

Indiana

Indiana University - Purdue University Indianapolis, O

Maine

Thomas College, M

Massachusetts

Lesley University, MO

Michigan

University of Detroit Mercy, M

Mississippi

Mississippi College, M

Missouri

Fontbonne University, M

New York

Stony Brook University, State University of New York, M

Ohio

Kent State University, M
Ohio University, M
Wright State University, M

Pennsylvania

Arcadia University, O

Texas

University of Mary Hardin-Baylor, M

Vermont

Marlboro College, MO

Washington

Eastern Washington University, M

Wisconsin

Cardinal Stritch University, M

COMPUTER ENGINEERING

United States

Alabama

Auburn University, BMD
The University of Alabama, MD
The University of Alabama at Birmingham, D
The University of Alabama in Huntsville, BMD
University of South Alabama, B

Alaska

University of Alaska Fairbanks, B

Arizona

Arizona State University at the Tempe campus, BMD
Embry-Riddle Aeronautical University - Prescott, B
The University of Arizona, MD

Arkansas

Harding University, B
University of Arkansas, BMD

California

California Baptist University, B
California Institute of Technology, B
California Polytechnic State University, San Luis Obispo, B
California State Polytechnic University, Pomona, B
California State University, Chico, BM
California State University, Fresno, B
California State University, Fullerton, B
California State University, Long Beach, BM
California State University, Northridge, B
California State University, Sacramento, B
California State University, San Bernardino, B
Northwestern Polytechnic University, BM
Ohlone College, A
San Diego State University, B
San Francisco State University, B
San Jose State University, BM
Santa Barbara City College, A
Santa Clara University, BMDO
Silicon Valley University, BM
University of California, Davis, MD
University of California, Irvine, B
University of California, Los Angeles, B
University of California, Merced, B
University of California, Riverside, BM
University of California, San Diego, BMD
University of California, Santa Barbara, BMD
University of California, Santa Cruz, BMD
University of La Verne, B
University of the Pacific, B
University of Southern California, BMD

Colorado

Colorado State University, B
Colorado Technical University Colorado Springs, BM
Colorado Technical University Denver South, M
University of Colorado Boulder, BMD
University of Colorado Colorado Springs, B
University of Denver, BMD

Connecticut

Fairfield University, BM
Gateway Community College, A
Trinity College, B
University of Bridgeport, BMD
University of Connecticut, B
University of Hartford, B
University of New Haven, BM

Delaware

University of Delaware, BMD

District of Columbia

The George Washington University, BMDO
Howard University, B

Florida

Bethune-Cookman University, B
Broward College, A
Daytona State College, A
Embry-Riddle Aeronautical University - Daytona, BM
Florida Agricultural and Mechanical University, B
Florida Atlantic University, BMD
Florida Career College, A
Florida Institute of Technology, B
Florida International University, BM
Pensacola State College, A
Polytechnic University of Puerto Rico, Orlando Campus, B
Seminole State College of Florida, A
South Florida State College, A
University of Central Florida, BMD
University of Florida, BMD
University of Miami, BMD
University of South Florida, BMD
University of West Florida, B

Georgia

Columbus Technical College, A
Georgia Institute of Technology, BMD
Kennesaw State University, M
Mercer University, M
University of Georgia, B

Idaho

Boise State University, MD
Brigham Young University - Idaho, B
University of Idaho, BM

Illinois

Bradley University, B
Illinois Institute of Technology, BMD
Lewis University, B
Loyola University Chicago, B
Northwestern University, BMD
Southern Illinois University Carbondale, BMD
Southern Illinois University Edwardsville, B
University of Illinois at Chicago, B
University of Illinois at Urbana - Champaign, BMD

Indiana

Indiana State University, M
Indiana Tech, B
Indiana University - Purdue University Fort Wayne, BM
Indiana University - Purdue University Indianapolis, BMD
Purdue University, BMD
Purdue University Northwest (Hammond), BM
Rose-Hulman Institute of Technology, BM
Taylor University, B
Trine University, B
University of Evansville, B
University of Indianapolis, B
University of Notre Dame, BMD
Valparaiso University, B

Iowa

Dordt College, B
Iowa State University of Science and Technology, BMD
The University of Iowa, MD

Kansas

Kansas State University, BM
The University of Kansas, BM
Wichita State University, BM

Kentucky

Bellarmine University, B
University of Kentucky, B
University of Louisville, BMDO

Louisiana

Louisiana State University and Agricultural & Mechanical College, BMD
University of Louisiana at Lafayette, BMD
Xavier University of Louisiana, B

Maine

University of Maine, BMD

Maryland

Capitol Technology University, B
Carroll Community College, A
College of Southern Maryland, A
Community College of Baltimore County, A
Johns Hopkins University, BMDO
University of Maryland, Baltimore County, BMD
University of Maryland, College Park, BMD

Massachusetts

Boston University, BMD
Eastern Nazarene College, B
Massachusetts Institute of Technology, D
Northeastern University, BMD
Suffolk University, B
Tufts University, B
University of Massachusetts Amherst, BMD
University of Massachusetts Boston, B
University of Massachusetts Dartmouth, BMDO
University of Massachusetts Lowell, BM
Wentworth Institute of Technology, B
Western New England University, B
Worcester Polytechnic Institute, BMDO

Michigan

Central Michigan University, B
Grand Valley State University, M
Kettering University, B
Lake Superior State University, B
Lawrence Technological University, BM
Michigan State University, B
Michigan Technological University, BMDO
Oakland University, BM
University of Detroit Mercy, MD
University of Michigan, BMD
University of Michigan - Dearborn, M
Wayne State University, MD
Western Michigan University, BMD

Minnesota

Itasca Community College, A
Minnesota State University Mankato, B
St. Cloud State University, B
University of Minnesota, Duluth, M
University of Minnesota, Twin Cities Campus, BMD

Mississippi

Jackson State University, B
Mississippi State University, BMD

Missouri

Missouri University of Science and Technology, BMD
Saint Louis University, B
University of Missouri, B
University of Missouri - Kansas City, D
Washington University in St. Louis, BMD

Montana

Montana State University, BD

Nebraska

University of Nebraska - Lincoln, BMD

Nevada

University of Nevada, Las Vegas, BMD
University of Nevada, Reno, BMD

New Hampshire

Dartmouth College, MD
University of New Hampshire, B

New Jersey

The College of New Jersey, B
Fairleigh Dickinson University, Metropolitan Campus, M
New Jersey Institute of Technology, BMD
Princeton University, B
Rutgers University - New Brunswick, BMD
Stevens Institute of Technology, BMDO

New Mexico

New Mexico State University, MDO
University of New Mexico, BMD

New York

Binghamton University, State University of New York, B
Clarkson University, BD
Columbia University, BM
Cornell University, MD
Hofstra University, B
Manhattan College, BM
Monroe Community College, A
New York Institute of Technology, M
New York University, BMO
Rensselaer Polytechnic Institute, MD
Rochester Institute of Technology, BM
State University of New York at New Paltz, B
Stony Brook University, State University of New York, BMD
Syracuse University, BMDO
University at Buffalo, the State University of New York, B
University of Rochester, MD

North Carolina

Duke University, MD
East Carolina University, MDO
Elon University, B
Gaston College, A
Johnson C. Smith University, B
North Carolina Agricultural and Technical State University, BMD
North Carolina State University, BMD
Sandhills Community College, A
Surry Community College, A
The University of North Carolina at Charlotte, BMD

North Dakota

North Dakota State University, BMD

Ohio

Bowling Green State University, B
Capital University, B
Case Western Reserve University, BMD
Cedarville University, B
Cleveland State University, B
Eastern Gateway Community College, A
Miami University, B
Miami University Hamilton, B
Northwest State Community College, A
Ohio Northern University, B
The Ohio State University, BMD
Sinclair Community College, A
Stark State College, A
The University of Akron, BMD
University of Cincinnati, BMD
University of Dayton, BMD
The University of Toledo, B
Wilberforce University, B
Wright State University, BMD
Youngstown State University, M

Oklahoma

Oklahoma Christian University, B
Oklahoma State University, BMD
Oral Roberts University, B

University of Oklahoma, BMD
The University of Tulsa, BD

Oregon

George Fox University, B
Oregon Health & Science University, MD
Oregon State University, BMD
Portland State University, BMD
University of Portland, B

Pennsylvania

Bucknell University, B
Carnegie Mellon University, MD
Drexel University, BM
Elizabethtown College, B
Lehigh University, BMD
Penn State Abington, B
Penn State Altoona, B
Penn State Beaver, B
Penn State Berks, B
Penn State Brandywine, B
Penn State DuBois, B
Penn State Erie, The Behrend College, B
Penn State Fayette, The Eberly Campus, B
Penn State Greater Allegheny, B
Penn State Hazleton, B
Penn State Lehigh Valley, B
Penn State Mont Alto, B
Penn State New Kensington, B
Penn State Schuylkill, B
Penn State Shenango, B
Penn State University Park, BMD
Penn State Wilkes-Barre, B
Penn State Worthington Scranton, B
Penn State York, B
University of Pennsylvania, B
University of Pittsburgh, BMD
The University of Scranton, AB
Villanova University, BMO
York College of Pennsylvania, B

Rhode Island

Brown University, BMD
Johnson & Wales University, AB
New England Institute of Technology, AB
Roger Williams University, B
University of Rhode Island, BMDO

South Carolina

Benedict College, B
Claflin University, B
Clemson University, BMD
University of South Carolina, BMD

South Dakota

South Dakota School of Mines and Technology, B

Tennessee

Christian Brothers University, B
Lipscomb University, B
Tennessee State University, MD
Tennessee Technological University, B
University of Memphis, BMD
The University of Tennessee, BMD
Vanderbilt University, B

Texas

Baylor University, MD
LeTourneau University, B
Midwestern State University, B
Prairie View A&M University, B
Rice University, BMD
St. Mary's University, BM
Southern Methodist University, BMD
Texas A&M University, BMD
Texas Tech University, B
University of Houston, B
University of Houston - Clear Lake, BM
University of North Texas, M
The University of Texas at Arlington, BMD
The University of Texas at Austin, MD
The University of Texas at Dallas, BMD
The University of Texas at El Paso, MD
The University of Texas Rio Grande Valley, B
The University of Texas at San Antonio, BMD

Utah

Brigham Young University, MD
University of Utah, B
Utah State University, B

Vermont

Norwich University, B

Virginia

Christopher Newport University, B
George Mason University, BMDO
Liberty University, B
Norfolk State University, M
Old Dominion University, BMD
University of Virginia, BMD
Virginia Commonwealth University, B
Virginia Polytechnic Institute and State University, BMD
Virginia State University, B

Washington

DigiPen Institute of Technology, B
Gonzaga University, B
Pacific Lutheran University, B
University of Washington, B
University of Washington, Bothell, BM
University of Washington, Tacoma, M
Walla Walla University, B
Washington State University, BM

West Virginia

Shepherd University, B
West Virginia University, BD
West Virginia University Institute of Technology, B

Wisconsin

Marquette University, BMDO
Milwaukee School of Engineering, B
University of Wisconsin - Madison, B
University of Wisconsin - Milwaukee, BM
University of Wisconsin - Stout, B

Wyoming

University of Wyoming, B

U.S. Territories: Puerto Rico

Inter American University of Puerto Rico, Bayamón Campus, B
Polytechnic University of Puerto Rico, BM
Universidad del Turabo, B
University of Puerto Rico, Mayagüez Campus, BMD

Canada

Alberta

University of Alberta, MD
University of Calgary, BMD

British Columbia

The University of British Columbia, BMD
University of Victoria, BMD

Manitoba

University of Manitoba, BMD

Maritime Provinces: New Brunswick

University of New Brunswick Fredericton, BMD

Maritime Provinces: Nova Scotia

Dalhousie University, MD

Newfoundland and Labrador

Memorial University of Newfoundland, MD

Ontario

Carleton University, B
Lakehead University, BM
McMaster University, B
Queen's University at Kingston, BMD
Royal Military College of Canada, BMD
Ryerson University, B
University of Guelph, B

University of Ottawa, BMD
University of Toronto, BMD
University of Waterloo, BMD
The University of Western Ontario, BMD
York University, B

Quebec

Concordia University, BMD
École Polytechnique de Montréal, MDO
McGill University, BMD
Université Laval, B
Université du Québec à Chicoutimi, B
Université du Québec en Outaouais, B
Université du Québec à Trois-Rivières, B
Université de Sherbrooke, B

Saskatchewan

University of Regina, MD
University of Saskatchewan, B

COMPUTER ENGINEERING TECHNOLOGIES/TECHNICIANS

United States

Kentucky

Eastern Kentucky University, B

New Jersey

Thomas Edison State University, A

North Carolina

Catawba Valley Community College, A

U.S. Territories: Puerto Rico

Inter American University of Puerto Rico, Bayamón Campus, B
Universidad del Turabo, A

Canada

Ontario

University of Guelph, B

COMPUTER ENGINEERING TECHNOLOGY/TECHNICIAN

United States

Alaska

University of Alaska Anchorage, A

Arizona

Arizona State University at the Polytechnic campus, B
DeVry University (Phoenix), B

Arkansas

East Arkansas Community College, A
University of Arkansas at Little Rock, B

California

Allan Hancock College, A
California State University, Long Beach, B
College of the Sequoias, A
DeVry University (Fremont), B
DeVry University (Long Beach), B
DeVry University (Pomona), B
DeVry University (Sherman Oaks), B
East Los Angeles College, A
Glendale Community College, A
Irvine Valley College, A
Los Angeles City College, A
Los Angeles Harbor College, A
Los Angeles Pierce College, A
Los Angeles Trade-Technical College, A
Merced College, A
Mission College, A
Monterey Peninsula College, A

Mt. San Antonio College, A
San Bernardino Valley College, A
San Diego City College, A

Colorado

Colorado Mountain College (Glenwood Springs), A
Colorado Mountain College (Steamboat Springs), A
DeVry University (Westminster), B

Connecticut

Central Connecticut State University, B
Gateway Community College, A
Naugatuck Valley Community College, A
Northwestern Connecticut Community College, A
Three Rivers Community College, A
University of Hartford, AB

Delaware

Delaware Technical & Community College, Stanton/Wilmington Campus, A
Delaware Technical & Community College, Terry Campus, A

District of Columbia

University of the District of Columbia, A

Florida

DeVry University (Miramar), B
DeVry University (Orlando), B
Indian River State College, A
Miami Dade College, A
Polk State College, A
St. Johns River State College, A
St. Petersburg College, A
Seminole State College of Florida, A
South Florida State College, A
State College of Florida Manatee-Sarasota, A
Valencia College, A

Georgia

Abraham Baldwin Agricultural College, A
Dalton State College, A
DeVry University (Alpharetta), B
DeVry University (Decatur), B
Georgia Piedmont Technical College, A
Kennesaw State University, B
Savannah State University, B

Illinois

DeVry University (Addison), B
DeVry University (Chicago), B
DeVry University (Tinley Park), B
DeVry University Online, B
Heartland Community College, A
John A. Logan College, A
Rock Valley College, A

Indiana

Indiana State University, B
Indiana University - Purdue University Fort Wayne, B
Indiana University - Purdue University Indianapolis, B

Iowa

Des Moines Area Community College, A
Iowa Central Community College, A

Kansas

Grantham University, B
Kansas City Kansas Community College, A

Kentucky

Eastern Kentucky University, A
Southeast Kentucky Community and Technical College, A
Sullivan College of Technology and Design, A

Louisiana

Delgado Community College, A

Maine

Southern Maine Community College, A

Maryland

Allegany College of Maryland, A
Capitol Technology University, B
Prince George's Community College, A

Massachusetts

Benjamin Franklin Institute of Technology, A
Middlesex Community College, A
North Shore Community College, A
Northern Essex Community College, A
Quinsigamond Community College, A
Springfield Technical Community College, A

Michigan

Eastern Michigan University, B
Kellogg Community College, A
Lake Superior State University, B
Monroe County Community College, A
Northern Michigan University, A

Minnesota

Minnesota State Community and Technical College, A
Minnesota State University Mankato, B
Minnesota West Community and Technical College, A
Vermilion Community College, A

Mississippi

Mississippi Delta Community College, A
Mississippi Gulf Coast Community College, A
University of Southern Mississippi, B

Missouri

DeVry University (Kansas City), B
Missouri Western State University, B
North Central Missouri College, A
Ranken Technical College, A
Three Rivers Community College, A

Nevada

Nevada State College, B

New Hampshire

Nashua Community College, A
NHTI, Concord's Community College, A

New Jersey

Hudson County Community College, A

New Mexico

Doña Ana Community College, A
University of New Mexico - Los Alamos Branch, A

New York

Broome Community College, A
DeVry College of New York, B
Farmingdale State College, B
Fulton-Montgomery Community College, A
Monroe Community College, A
Morrisville State College, A
New York City College of Technology of the City University of New York, B
Onondaga Community College, A
Queensborough Community College of the City University of New York, A
Rochester Institute of Technology, B
State University of New York College of Technology at Alfred, AB
State University of New York Polytechnic Institute, B

North Carolina

Asheville-Buncombe Technical Community College, A
Carteret Community College, A
Catawba Valley Community College, A
Central Piedmont Community College, A
College of The Albemarle, A
Davidson County Community College, A
ECPI University (Greensboro), A
ECPI University (Raleigh), A
Forsyth Technical Community College, A
Gaston College, A
Lenoir Community College, A

Mayland Community College, A
Nash Community College, A
Pamlico Community College, A
Richmond Community College, A
Sandhills Community College, A
Southeastern Community College, A
Southwestern Community College, A
Surry Community College, A
Vance-Granville Community College, A
Wake Technical Community College, A
Western Piedmont Community College, A

Ohio

Belmont College, A
Bowling Green State University, B
Bowling Green State University - Firelands College, A
Cincinnati State Technical and Community College, A
Columbus State Community College, A
Cuyahoga Community College, A
DeVry University (Columbus), B
Fortis College (Centerville), A
Hocking College, A
Lakeland Community College, A
Lorain County Community College, A
Miami University Middletown, A
Northwest State Community College, A
Owens Community College, A
Shawnee State University, B
University of Cincinnati, B
Washington State Community College, A

Oklahoma

Oklahoma City Community College, A

Oregon

Chemeketa Community College, A
Mt. Hood Community College, A
Oregon Institute of Technology, AB
Umpqua Community College, A

Pennsylvania

Brightwood Career Institute, Philadelphia Mills Campus, A
California University of Pennsylvania, AB
Community College of Allegheny County, A
DeVry University (Fort Washington), B
Penn State New Kensington, A

Rhode Island

Community College of Rhode Island, A

South Carolina

ECPI University (Greenville), A
ECPI University (North Charleston), A
Trident Technical College, A
Virginia College in Spartanburg, A
York Technical College, A

South Dakota

National American University (Rapid City), A

Tennessee

Fountainhead College of Technology, A
Nashville State Community College, A
Roane State Community College, A
Southwest Tennessee Community College, A
University of Memphis, B

Texas

Alvin Community College, A
Amarillo College, A
Brookhaven College, A
DeVry University (Austin), B
DeVry University (Irving), B
Eastfield College, A
Houston Community College, A
LeTourneau University, B
McLennan Community College, A
North Central Texas College, A
Palo Alto College, A
Paris Junior College, A
Prairie View A&M University, B
Ranger College, A

Sam Houston State University, B
San Antonio College, A
South Plains College, A
Southwest Texas Junior College, A
Texas Southern University, B
Tyler Junior College, A
University of Houston, B
University of Houston - Downtown, B
Western Technical College (El Paso), A
Western Texas College, A

Utah

Utah State University, B
Weber State University, AB

Vermont

Vermont Technical College, AB

Virginia

DeVry University (Arlington), B
ECPI University (Newport News), A
New River Community College, A
Norfolk State University, B

Washington

Central Washington University, B
Highline College, A
Skagit Valley College, A
South Seattle College, A
Whatcom Community College, A
Yakima Valley Community College, A

West Virginia

Mountwest Community & Technical College, A

Wisconsin

Madison Area Technical College, A
Mid-State Technical College, A

Canada

Ontario

Brock University, B

COMPUTER GRAPHICS

United States

Alabama

Virginia College in Birmingham, AB
Virginia College in Huntsville, A

Arizona

Arizona Western College, A
The Art Institute of Tucson, B
Northland Pioneer College, A
Phoenix College, A
University of Advancing Technology, AB

Arkansas

John Brown University, B
National Park College, A

California

Antelope Valley College, A
The Art Institute of California - Hollywood, a campus of Argosy University, B
The Art Institute of California - Orange County, a campus of Argosy University, B
The Art Institute of California - Sacramento, a campus of Argosy University, B
The Art Institute of California - San Diego, a campus of Argosy University, B
The Art Institute of California - San Francisco, a campus of Argosy University, B
Berkeley City College, A
California State University, Chico, B
California State University, East Bay, B
Chaffey College, A
Citrus College, A
Coleman University, AB
College of the Desert, A

College of San Mateo, A
College of the Sequoias, A
De Anza College, A
Gavilan College, A
Long Beach City College, A
Los Angeles Film School, B
Modesto Junior College, A
Mt. San Antonio College, A
Orange Coast College, A
Palomar College, A
University of California, Santa Cruz, B

Colorado

The Art Institute of Colorado, B
CollegeAmerica - Fort Collins, A
Rocky Mountain College of Art + Design, B

Connecticut

Gateway Community College, A
Northwestern Connecticut Community College, A
Quinebaug Valley Community College, A

Delaware

Wilmington University, B

Florida

The Art Institute of Fort Lauderdale, B
The Art Institute of Tampa, a branch of Miami International University of Art & Design, B
College of Business and Technology - Main Campus, A
Daytona State College, A
Florida State College at Jacksonville, A
Full Sail University, B
Miami Dade College, A
Seminole State College of Florida, A
State College of Florida Manatee-Sarasota, A
Tallahassee Community College, A
University of Miami, B

Georgia

The Art Institute of Atlanta, B

Illinois

DePaul University, B
The Illinois Institute of Art - Chicago, B
The Illinois Institute of Art - Schaumburg, B
Lewis and Clark Community College, A
Moraine Valley Community College, A
Parkland College, A
Richland Community College, A
School of the Art Institute of Chicago, B
Shawnee Community College, A

Indiana

The Art Institute of Indianapolis, B
Indiana Tech, A
Indiana Wesleyan University, B
Purdue University, AB
Purdue University Northwest (Hammond), B

Iowa

Iowa Lakes Community College, A
University of Dubuque, B

Kansas

Cowley County Community College and Area Vocational - Technical School, A

Kentucky

Sullivan College of Technology and Design, AB

Maine

College of the Atlantic, B

Maryland

Bowie State University, B
Carroll Community College, A
Howard Community College, A

Massachusetts

Mount Wachusett Community College, A
North Shore Community College, A
Northern Essex Community College, A

Quinsigamond Community College, A
School of the Museum of Fine Arts, Boston, B
Springfield College, B

Michigan

The Art Institute of Michigan, B
Baker College, B
Kellogg Community College, A
Monroe County Community College, A
Schoolcraft College, A

Minnesota

Academy College, A
Mesabi Range College, A
Saint Paul College - A Community & Technical College, A

Mississippi

Mississippi Gulf Coast Community College, A

Missouri

Lindenwood University, B
Metropolitan Community College - Kansas City, A
Missouri State University - West Plains, A

Montana

University of Great Falls, B

Nevada

The Art Institute of Las Vegas, B
Great Basin College, AB

New Hampshire

Southern New Hampshire University, B

New Jersey

Hudson County Community College, A
Mercer County Community College, A
Rowan College at Burlington County, A
Rowan College at Gloucester County, A

New Mexico

New Mexico Junior College, A

New York

Brooklyn College of the City University of New York, B
Genesee Community College, A
Nassau Community College, A
North Country Community College, A
Pratt Institute, B
Rochester Institute of Technology, B
Rockland Community College, A
State University of New York College at Oneonta, B
State University of New York at Fredonia, B
Sullivan County Community College, A

North Carolina

The Art Institute of Charlotte, a campus of South University, B

Ohio

The Art Institute of Cincinnati, AB
Belmont College, A
Central Ohio Technical College, A
Sinclair Community College, A
Walsh University, B

Oklahoma

Rogers State University, B

Oregon

The Art Institute of Portland, B

Pennsylvania

The Art Institute of Philadelphia, B
The Art Institute of Pittsburgh, B
Berks Technical Institute, A
Lansdale School of Business, A
Luzerne County Community College, A
Pittsburgh Technical Institute, A
University of Pennsylvania, B

South Carolina

Trident Technical College, A

South Dakota

Dakota State University, B

Tennessee

The Art Institute of Tennessee - Nashville, a branch of The Art Institute of Atlanta, B

Texas

The Art Institute of Austin, a branch of The Art Institute of Houston, B
The Art Institute of Dallas, a campus of South University, B
The Art Institute of Houston, B
The Art Institute of San Antonio, a branch of The Art Institute of Houston, B
Navarro College, A
North Central Texas College, A
Remington College - Fort Worth Campus, A
San Antonio College, A
Texas A&M University, B
Tyler Junior College, A
University of Houston, B
University of Mary Hardin-Baylor, B
Weatherford College, A

Utah

Dixie State University, B

Vermont

Champlain College, B

Virginia

The Art Institute of Virginia Beach, a branch of The Art Institute of Atlanta, B
The Art Institute of Washington, a branch of The Art Institute of Atlanta, B
ECPI University (Virginia Beach), AB
New River Community College, A

Washington

The Art Institute of Seattle, B
Bellevue College, A
Lake Washington Institute of Technology, A
Pierce College at Fort Steilacoom, A
Shoreline Community College, A
Yakima Valley Community College, A

Wisconsin

Milwaukee Area Technical College, A
Southwest Wisconsin Technical College, A

U.S. Territories: Puerto Rico

Atlantic University College, AB
EDP University of Puerto Rico, A

Canada

Alberta

Alberta College of Art & Design, B

Quebec

Concordia University, B

COMPUTER HARDWARE ENGINEERING

United States

Alabama

Auburn University, B

Florida

Seminole State College of Florida, A

Kentucky

Sullivan College of Technology and Design, A

Maryland

United States Naval Academy, B

North Carolina

Stanly Community College, A

Ohio

Sinclair Community College, A
Stark State College, A

Texas

Eastfield College, A

Utah

Utah Valley University, B

Canada

Ontario

York University, B

COMPUTER HARDWARE TECHNOLOGY/TECHNICIAN

United States

Arizona

University of Advancing Technology, B

Kentucky

Sullivan College of Technology and Design, A

North Carolina

Forsyth Technical Community College, A

Texas

Brazosport College, A

COMPUTER AND INFORMATION SCIENCES

United States

Alabama

Alabama Agricultural and Mechanical University, B
Athens State University, B
Auburn University, B
Bevill State Community College, A
Bishop State Community College, A
Calhoun Community College, A
Chattahoochee Valley Community College, A
Enterprise State Community College, A
Gadsden State Community College, A
George C. Wallace Community College, A
H. Councill Trenholm State Community College, A
J. F. Drake State Community and Technical College, A
Jacksonville State University, B
James H. Faulkner State Community College, A
Jefferson State Community College, A
Lawson State Community College, A
Lurleen B. Wallace Community College, A
Miles College, B
Northeast Alabama Community College, A
Northwest-Shoals Community College, A
Reid State Technical College, A
Snead State Community College, A
Southern Union State Community College, A
Spring Hill College, B
Troy University, AB
The University of Alabama, B
The University of Alabama at Birmingham, B
The University of Alabama in Huntsville, B
University of Mobile, B
University of North Alabama, B
Virginia College in Huntsville, A

Alaska

University of Alaska Anchorage, A
University of Alaska Fairbanks, B
University of Alaska Southeast, Ketchikan Campus, A

Arizona

Arizona State University at the Tempe campus, B
Arizona Western College, A
Central Arizona College, A
Chandler-Gilbert Community College, A
GateWay Community College, A
Glendale Community College, A
Mohave Community College, A
Northland Pioneer College, A
Penn Foster College, A
Phoenix College, A
Rio Salado College, A
South Mountain Community College, A
The University of Arizona, B

Arkansas

Arkansas State University, B
Arkansas State University Mid-South, A
Arkansas Tech University, B
College of the Ouachitas, A
Henderson State University, B
North Arkansas College, A
Southern Arkansas University - Magnolia, B
University of Arkansas, B
University of Arkansas Community College at Hope, A
University of Arkansas Community College at Morrilton, A
University of Arkansas - Fort Smith, B
University of Central Arkansas, B
Williams Baptist College, B

California

Allied American University, AB
Ashford University, B
Berkeley City College, A
California Lutheran University, B
California State University, Dominguez Hills, B
California State University, Fresno, B
California State University, Los Angeles, B
California State University, Monterey Bay, B
Chabot College, A
Chapman University, B
Citrus College, A
Coleman University, AB
Empire College, A
Folsom Lake College, A
Glendale Community College, A
Los Angeles City College, A
Loyola Marymount University, B
The Master's College and Seminary, B
Mt. San Antonio College, A
Mt. Sierra College, B
National University, AB
Notre Dame de Namur University, B
Ohlone College, A
Reedley College, A
Saddleback College, A
San Diego Mesa College, A
Santa Ana College, A
Santiago Canyon College, A
Southwestern College, A
University of California, Irvine, B
University of California, Los Angeles, B
University of San Francisco, B
Ventura College, A
Victor Valley College, A
William Jessup University, B
Yuba College, A

Colorado

Arapahoe Community College, A
CollegeAmerica - Colorado Springs, AB
Colorado Christian University, B
The Colorado College, B
Colorado Mesa University, B
Colorado State University, B
Community College of Denver, A
Front Range Community College, A

Metropolitan State University of Denver, B
National American University (Colorado Springs), A
National American University (Denver), AB
Pueblo Community College, A
Regis University, B
University of Colorado Denver, B

Connecticut

Central Connecticut State University, B
Eastern Connecticut State University, B
Fairfield University, B
Gateway Community College, A
Quinebaug Valley Community College, A
Sacred Heart University, B
University of Hartford, B
University of New Haven, B
Yale University, B

Delaware

Delaware State University, B
Delaware Technical & Community College, Jack F. Owens Campus, A
Delaware Technical & Community College, Stanton/Wilmington Campus, A
Delaware Technical & Community College, Terry Campus, A
University of Delaware, B

District of Columbia

American University, B
The Catholic University of America, B
Gallaudet University, B
The George Washington University, B

Florida

Beacon College, AB
Broward College, A
Chipola College, A
College of Central Florida, A
Daytona State College, A
Everest University (Largo), AB
Everest University (Orlando), AB
Florida Agricultural and Mechanical University, B
Florida Atlantic University, B
Florida Gateway College, A
Florida Gulf Coast University, B
Florida International University, B
Jacksonville University, B
Jones College, AB
Lake-Sumter State College, A
Nova Southeastern University, B
Pensacola State College, A
Polytechnic University of Puerto Rico, Miami Campus, B
Rollins College, B
St. Johns River State College, A
Saint Leo University, B
St. Thomas University, B
Seminole State College of Florida, A
South Florida State College, A
State College of Florida Manatee-Sarasota, A
Stetson University, B
University of Central Florida, B
University of Florida, B
University of North Florida, B
University of South Florida, B
The University of Tampa, B
University of West Florida, B
Webber International University, AB

Georgia

Albany State University, B
Albany Technical College, A
Andrew College, A
Armstrong State University, B
Ashworth College, A
Augusta University, B
Brewton-Parker College, B
Clark Atlanta University, B
Columbus State University, B
Covenant College, B
Darton State College, A
DeVry University (Atlanta), B
Emmanuel College, B
Georgia Highlands College, A

Georgia Institute of Technology, B
Georgia Southern University, B
Georgia State University, B
Interactive College of Technology (Chamblee), A
Kennesaw State University, B
LaGrange College, B
Mercer University, B
Morehouse College, B
Shorter University, B
University of North Georgia, B
University of Phoenix - Columbus Georgia Campus, B
University of West Georgia, B
Valdosta State University, B

Hawaii

Hawai'i Pacific University, B
Leeward Community College, A
University of Hawaii at Manoa, B

Idaho

Idaho State University, B
Lewis-Clark State College, AB
North Idaho College, A

Illinois

Bradley University, B
City Colleges of Chicago, Wilbur Wright College, A
Concordia University Chicago, B
Eastern Illinois University, B
Eureka College, B
Greenville College, B
Harper College, A
Heartland Community College, A
Illinois Institute of Technology, B
John A. Logan College, A
Loyola University Chicago, B
MacCormac College, A
McKendree University, B
Midstate College, A
Moraine Valley Community College, A
Northwestern University, B
Parkland College, A
Principia College, B
Richland Community College, A
Rockford Career College, A
St. Augustine College, A
Saint Xavier University, B
Sauk Valley Community College, A
Southern Illinois University Edwardsville, B
Southwestern Illinois College, A
Trinity Christian College, B
Triton College, A
University of Illinois at Urbana - Champaign, B
Western Illinois University, B

Indiana

Ancilla College, A
Ball State University, B
Butler University, B
Calumet College of Saint Joseph, AB
Earlham College, B
Franklin College, B
Indiana State University, B
Indiana University - Purdue University Fort Wayne, B
Indiana Wesleyan University, AB
Ivy Tech Community College - Bloomington, A
Ivy Tech Community College - Central Indiana, A
Ivy Tech Community College - Columbus, A
Ivy Tech Community College - East Central, A
Ivy Tech Community College - Kokomo, A
Ivy Tech Community College - Lafayette, A
Ivy Tech Community College - North Central, A
Ivy Tech Community College - Northeast, A
Ivy Tech Community College - Northwest, A
Ivy Tech Community College - Richmond, A
Ivy Tech Community College - Southeast, A
Ivy Tech Community College - Southern Indiana, A
Ivy Tech Community College - Southwest, A
Ivy Tech Community College - Wabash Valley, A
Manchester University, A
Saint Joseph's College, B
Saint Mary-of-the-Woods College, B
Taylor University, B
University of Notre Dame, B

University of Southern Indiana, B
Vincennes University, A

Iowa

Clarke University, B
Emmaus Bible College, B
Iowa Lakes Community College, A
Kaplan University, Cedar Rapids, A
Scott Community College, A
Simpson College, B
University of Dubuque, B
Wartburg College, B
William Penn University, B

Kansas

Butler Community College, A
Coffeyville Community College, A
Colby Community College, A
Cowley County Community College and Area Vocational - Technical School, A
Emporia State University, B
Friends University, B
Highland Community College, A
Hutchinson Community College, A
Independence Community College, A
Kansas State University, B
Kansas Wesleyan University, B
National American University, A
Pittsburg State University, B
Seward County Community College and Area Technical School, A
Sterling College, B
The University of Kansas, B
University of Saint Mary, B
Washburn University, AB

Kentucky

American National University (Danville), A
American National University (Florence), A
American National University (Lexington), A
American National University (Louisville), A
American National University (Pikeville), A
American National University (Richmond), A
Ashland Community and Technical College, A
Bellarmine University, B
Berea College, B
Big Sandy Community and Technical College, A
Bluegrass Community and Technical College, A
Eastern Kentucky University, B
Elizabethtown Community and Technical College, A
Gateway Community and Technical College, A
Georgetown College, B
Hazard Community and Technical College, A
Henderson Community College, A
Hopkinsville Community College, A
Jefferson Community and Technical College, A
Kentucky State University, B
Kentucky Wesleyan College, B
Lindsey Wilson College, A
Maysville Community and Technical College (Maysville), A
Midway University, AB
Morehead State University, B
Northern Kentucky University, B
Owensboro Community and Technical College, A
Somerset Community College, A
Southcentral Kentucky Community and Technical College, A
Sullivan College of Technology and Design, A
Transylvania University, B
University of Kentucky, B
University of Pikeville, B
West Kentucky Community and Technical College, A
Western Kentucky University, B

Louisiana

Baton Rouge School of Computers, A
Loyola University New Orleans, B
Tulane University, AB
University of Holy Cross, B
University of Louisiana at Lafayette, B
Xavier University of Louisiana, B

Maine

Husson University, AB

Maryland

Anne Arundel Community College, A
Baltimore City Community College, A
Bowie State University, B
Capitol Technology University, B
College of Southern Maryland, A
Community College of Baltimore County, A
Hagerstown Community College, A
Harford Community College, A
Howard Community College, A
Johns Hopkins University, B
McDaniel College, B
Montgomery College, A
Mount St. Mary's University, B
St. Mary's College of Maryland, B
Salisbury University, B
Stevenson University, B
Towson University, B
United States Naval Academy, B
University of Baltimore, B
University of Maryland, College Park, B
University of Maryland University College, B
Wor-Wic Community College, A

Massachusetts

Anna Maria College, B
Assumption College, B
Becker College, B
Bentley University, B
Berkshire Community College, A
Boston College, B
Bristol Community College, A
Curry College, B
Elms College, B
Fisher College, B
Fitchburg State University, B
Framingham State University, B
Greenfield Community College, A
Massachusetts College of Liberal Arts, B
Massasoit Community College, A
Middlesex Community College, A
Mount Wachusett Community College, A
North Shore Community College, A
Northeastern University, B
Northern Essex Community College, A
Quinsigamond Community College, A
Salem State University, B
Simmons College, B
Springfield College, B
Suffolk University, B
Tufts University, B
University of Massachusetts Boston, B
University of Massachusetts Dartmouth, B
Worcester Polytechnic Institute, B
Worcester State University, B

Michigan

Alpena Community College, A
Andrews University, B
Aquinas College, B
Bay Mills Community College, A
Delta College, A
Eastern Michigan University, B
Gogebic Community College, A
Grace Bible College, B
Grand Rapids Community College, A
Grand Valley State University, B
Henry Ford College, A
Hope College, B
Kalamazoo College, B
Kuyper College, B
Lake Michigan College, A
Lansing Community College, A
Madonna University, A
Marygrove College, B
Michigan Jewish Institute, AB
Michigan State University, B
Monroe County Community College, A
Northern Michigan University, B
Northwood University, Michigan Campus, B
Oakland University, B
Olivet College, B
Saginaw Valley State University, B
Siena Heights University, B
University of Michigan, B

University of Michigan - Dearborn, B
Walsh College of Accountancy and Business Administration, B
Washtenaw Community College, A
Wayne State University, B
Western Michigan University, B

Minnesota

Academy College, A
Bethel University, B
The College of St. Scholastica, B
Herzing University, A
Macalester College, B
National American University (Bloomington), A
National American University (Brooklyn Center), A
St. Catherine University, B
Walden University, B

Mississippi

Alcorn State University, B
Coahoma Community College, A
East Central Community College, A
Holmes Community College, A
Itawamba Community College, A
Jackson State University, B
Mississippi College, B
Mississippi Gulf Coast Community College, A
Mississippi State University, B
Northeast Mississippi Community College, A
Northwest Mississippi Community College, A
University of Mississippi, B
University of Southern Mississippi, B

Missouri

Avila University, B
Columbia College, AB
Everest College, A
Hannibal-LaGrange University, B
Lincoln University, A
Lindenwood University, B
Metro Business College (Jefferson City), A
Metropolitan Community College - Kansas City, A
Missouri Southern State University, B
Missouri State University, B
Missouri State University - West Plains, A
Missouri Western State University, B
Moberly Area Community College, A
Northwest Missouri State University, B
Park University, B
Saint Louis University, B
Southeast Missouri State University, B
Southwest Baptist University, B
Three Rivers Community College, A
Truman State University, B
University of Central Missouri, B
University of Missouri, B
Washington University in St. Louis, B
Webster University, B

Montana

Aaniiih Nakoda College, A
Carroll College, B
Dawson Community College, A
Miles Community College, A
Montana State University Billings, A
Montana State University - Northern, AB
University of Great Falls, B
University of Montana, B

Nebraska

Bellevue University, B
Central Community College - Columbus Campus, A
Central Community College - Grand Island Campus, A
Concordia University, Nebraska, B
Doane University, B
Grace University, B
Hastings College, B
Kaplan University, Lincoln, A
Kaplan University, Omaha, A
Little Priest Tribal College, A
Mid-Plains Community College, A
Northeast Community College, A
Southeast Community College, Lincoln Campus, A
Union College, AB

University of Nebraska at Kearney, B
University of Nebraska - Lincoln, B
University of Nebraska at Omaha, B
Wayne State College, B
Western Nebraska Community College, A

Nevada

Career College of Northern Nevada, A
Great Basin College, A
Sierra Nevada College, B
University of Nevada, Reno, B
University of Phoenix - Las Vegas Campus, B
Western Nevada College, A

New Hampshire

Granite State College, B
Great Bay Community College, A
Keene State College, B
Lakes Region Community College, A
Nashua Community College, A
New England College, B
NHTI, Concord's Community College, A
Southern New Hampshire University, AB
University of New Hampshire, B
White Mountains Community College, A

New Jersey

Bloomfield College, B
Brookdale Community College, A
Caldwell University, B
Camden County College, A
The College of New Jersey, B
College of Saint Elizabeth, B
Cumberland County College, A
Essex County College, A
Fairleigh Dickinson University, College at Florham, B
Felician University, B
Hudson County Community College, A
Kean University, B
Middlesex County College, A
Monmouth University, B
Montclair State University, B
New Jersey City University, B
New Jersey Institute of Technology, B
Ocean County College, A
Ramapo College of New Jersey, B
Rider University, B
Rowan College at Gloucester County, A
Rutgers University - Camden, B
Rutgers University - Newark, B
Saint Peter's University, B
Seton Hall University, B
Sussex County Community College, A
William Paterson University of New Jersey, B

New Mexico

Central New Mexico Community College, A
Clovis Community College, A
Eastern New Mexico University, B
Eastern New Mexico University - Roswell, A
Mesalands Community College, A
National American University (Albuquerque), A
New Mexico Highlands University, B
New Mexico State University, B
Northern New Mexico College, A
Santa Fe Community College, A
University of New Mexico, B
University of New Mexico - Taos, A

New York

Adelphi University, B
Barnard College, B
Binghamton University, State University of New York, B
Borough of Manhattan Community College of the City University of New York, A
Brooklyn College of the City University of New York, B
Broome Community College, A
Bryant & Stratton College - Amherst Campus, A
Bryant & Stratton College - Buffalo Campus, A
Bryant & Stratton College - Greece Campus, A
Bryant & Stratton College - Henrietta Campus, A

Bryant & Stratton College - Orchard Park Campus, A
Cayuga County Community College, A
Colgate University, B
The College at Brockport, State University of New York, B
Columbia-Greene Community College, A
Columbia University, School of General Studies, B
Cornell University, B
Corning Community College, A
Dominican College, B
Erie Community College, North Campus, A
Excelsior College, AB
Finger Lakes Community College, A
Fordham University, B
Genesee Community College, A
Globe Institute of Technology, AB
Hamilton College, B
Hartwick College, B
Herkimer County Community College, A
Hudson Valley Community College, A
Ithaca College, B
Jamestown Community College, A
Jefferson Community College, A
John Jay College of Criminal Justice of the City University of New York, B
Kingsborough Community College of the City University of New York, A
Le Moyne College, B
Lehman College of the City University of New York, B
Long Island University - LIU Brooklyn, B
Marist College, B
Mercy College, B
Mohawk Valley Community College, A
Molloy College, B
Monroe Community College, A
Morrisville State College, AB
Nassau Community College, A
New York City College of Technology of the City University of New York, A
New York Institute of Technology, B
New York University, B
Orange County Community College, A
Pace University, B
Pace University, Pleasantville Campus, B
Rochester Institute of Technology, B
Rockland Community College, A
St. Bonaventure University, B
St. John Fisher College, B
St. John's University, B
St. Lawrence University, B
St. Thomas Aquinas College, B
Siena College, B
Skidmore College, B
State University of New York College of Agriculture and Technology at Cobleskill, A
State University of New York College at Old Westbury, B
State University of New York College of Technology at Alfred, A
State University of New York at New Paltz, B
State University of New York at Plattsburgh, B
Stony Brook University, State University of New York, B
Syracuse University, B
Tompkins Cortland Community College, A
Ulster County Community College, A
Union College, B
United States Military Academy, B
University at Albany, State University of New York, B
Utica College, B
Vassar College, B
Wagner College, B
Westchester Community College, A
Yeshiva University, B

North Carolina

Bennett College, B
Campbell University, B
Catawba College, B
Chowan University, B
ECPI University (Raleigh), A
Elon University, B
Forsyth Technical Community College, A
Gardner-Webb University, B

Guilford College, B
Johnson C. Smith University, B
Lenoir-Rhyne University, B
Mars Hill University, B
Montreat College, B
North Carolina Wesleyan College, B
Robeson Community College, A
Saint Augustine's University, B
Sampson Community College, A
Shaw University, B
South College - Asheville, A
Wake Forest University, B
Wake Technical Community College, A

North Dakota

Cankdeska Cikana Community College, A
Dakota College at Bottineau, A
Mayville State University, B
Minot State University, B
North Dakota State College of Science, A
Nueta Hidatsa Sahnish College, A
University of Mary, B
University of North Dakota, B
Valley City State University, B

Ohio

Antonelli College, A
Bowling Green State University, B
Central State University, B
Cincinnati State Technical and Community College, A
Cleveland State University, B
Columbus State Community College, A
Edison Community College, A
Franciscan University of Steubenville, B
Hiram College, B
Kent State University, B
Lorain County Community College, A
Miami University, B
Miami University Hamilton, B
Miami University Middletown, A
The Ohio State University, B
Ohio University, B
Sinclair Community College, A
Stark State College, A
Terra State Community College, A
Tiffin University, B
University of Cincinnati, B
University of Dayton, B
The University of Findlay, AB
The University of Toledo, A
Wright State University, B
Youngstown State University, AB

Oklahoma

Carl Albert State College, A
East Central University, B
Murray State College, A
Northeastern Oklahoma Agricultural and Mechanical College, A
Oklahoma Baptist University, B
Oklahoma City University, B
Oklahoma Panhandle State University, B
Oklahoma State University, B
Oral Roberts University, B
Rogers State University, A
Southeastern Oklahoma State University, B
Southern Nazarene University, B
Southwestern Oklahoma State University, B
Tulsa Community College, A
University of Central Oklahoma, B

Oregon

Central Oregon Community College, A
Eastern Oregon University, B
George Fox University, B
Linn-Benton Community College, A
Oregon Institute of Technology, B
Portland State University, B
Rogue Community College, A
Treasure Valley Community College, A
University of Oregon, B
Willamette University, B

Pennsylvania

Arcadia University, B
Berks Technical Institute, A
Bucknell University, B
Bucks County Community College, A
Butler County Community College, A
California University of Pennsylvania, AB
Carnegie Mellon University, B
Cedar Crest College, B
Chestnut Hill College, B
Cheyney University of Pennsylvania, B
Clarion University of Pennsylvania, B
Community College of Beaver County, A
Delaware County Community College, A
Dickinson College, B
East Stroudsburg University of Pennsylvania, B
Edinboro University of Pennsylvania, AB
Elizabethtown College, B
Fortis Institute (Erie), A
Franklin & Marshall College, B
Gannon University, B
Geneva College, B
Gwynedd Mercy University, B
Harrisburg Area Community College, A
Harrisburg University of Science and Technology, B
Indiana University of Pennsylvania, B
Juniata College, B
King's College, B
Kutztown University of Pennsylvania, B
La Roche College, B
La Salle University, B
Lackawanna College, A
Lancaster Bible College, B
Laurel Business Institute, A
Lehigh Carbon Community College, A
Lincoln University, B
Lock Haven University of Pennsylvania, B
Luzerne County Community College, A
Mansfield University of Pennsylvania, B
McCann School of Business & Technology (Pottsville), A
Mercyhurst University, B
Millersville University of Pennsylvania, B
Misericordia University, B
Montgomery County Community College, A
Neumann University, B
Penn State Abington, B
Penn State Altoona, B
Penn State Beaver, B
Penn State Berks, B
Penn State Brandywine, B
Penn State DuBois, B
Penn State Erie, The Behrend College, B
Penn State Fayette, The Eberly Campus, B
Penn State Greater Allegheny, B
Penn State Harrisburg, B
Penn State Hazleton, B
Penn State Lehigh Valley, B
Penn State Mont Alto, B
Penn State New Kensington, B
Penn State Schuylkill, AB
Penn State Shenango, B
Penn State University Park, B
Penn State Wilkes-Barre, B
Penn State Worthington Scranton, B
Penn State York, B
Pennsylvania Highlands Community College, A
Philadelphia University, B
Reading Area Community College, A
Saint Joseph's University, B
Saint Vincent College, B
Shippensburg University of Pennsylvania, B
South Hills School of Business & Technology (Altoona), A
Swarthmore College, B
Temple University, B
University of Pittsburgh at Greensburg, B
Waynesburg University, B
West Chester University of Pennsylvania, B
Westminster College, B
Widener University, B
Wilkes University, B

Rhode Island

Bryant University, B
Community College of Rhode Island, A

New England Institute of Technology, AB
Rhode Island College, B
Roger Williams University, B
University of Rhode Island, B

South Carolina

Benedict College, B
The Citadel, The Military College of South Carolina, B
Clemson University, B
Coastal Carolina University, B
College of Charleston, B
Columbia College, B
Francis Marion University, B
Lander University, B
Limestone College, AB
Miller-Motte Technical College (North Charleston), A
South Carolina State University, B
Southern Wesleyan University, B
University of South Carolina, B
University of South Carolina Upstate, B

South Dakota

Black Hills State University, A
Dakota State University, B
Dakota Wesleyan University, B
National American University (Ellsworth AFB), A
South Dakota State University, B
University of Sioux Falls, B
The University of South Dakota, B

Tennessee

Austin Peay State University, B
Belmont University, B
Daymar College (Clarksville), A
East Tennessee State University, B
Freed-Hardeman University, B
Hiwassee College, A
Lane College, B
Lincoln Memorial University, B
Maryville College, B
Milligan College, B
Nashville State Community College, A
National College (Bristol), A
Pellissippi State Community College, A
Tennessee Wesleyan College, B
Volunteer State Community College, A
Walters State Community College, A

Texas

Amberton University, B
Angelina College, A
Angelo State University, B
Austin College, B
Austin Community College District, A
Clarendon College, A
Coastal Bend College, A
College of the Mainland, A
Collin County Community College District, A
Dallas Baptist University, B
Del Mar College, A
Eastfield College, A
El Paso Community College, A
Hill College, A
Howard College, A
Howard Payne University, B
Huston-Tillotson University, B
Kilgore College, A
Lamar Institute of Technology, A
Lamar University, B
Lone Star College - CyFair, A
Lone Star College - Kingwood, A
Lubbock Christian University, B
McMurry University, B
Midwestern State University, B
North American University, B
Northeast Texas Community College, A
Northwest Vista College, A
Odessa College, A
Our Lady of the Lake University of San Antonio, B
Palo Alto College, A
Paris Junior College, A
Rice University, B
St. Edward's University, B
St. Mary's University, B
Sam Houston State University, B

San Jacinto College District, A
Southwestern University, B
Stephen F. Austin State University, B
Tarleton State University, B
Temple College, A
Texarkana College, A
Texas A&M University - Central Texas, B
Texas A&M University - Commerce, B
Texas A&M University - Kingsville, B
Texas A&M University - San Antonio, B
Texas Christian University, B
Texas Southern University, B
Texas Southmost College, A
Texas State University, B
Texas Tech University, B
Texas Woman's University, B
Trinity University, B
Tyler Junior College, A
University of Houston, B
University of Houston - Clear Lake, B
University of Houston - Downtown, B
University of the Incarnate Word, B
University of Mary Hardin-Baylor, B
University of North Texas, B
University of Phoenix - Houston Campus, B
The University of Texas at Austin, B
The University of Texas at Dallas, B
The University of Texas of the Permian Basin, B
The University of Texas Rio Grande Valley, B
The University of Texas at San Antonio, B
The University of Texas at Tyler, B
West Texas A&M University, B
Western Texas College, A
Wiley College, AB

Utah

Dixie State University, B
LDS Business College, A
Neumont University, B
Provo College, A
Salt Lake Community College, A
Southern Utah University, B
Stevens-Henager College (Logan), A
Stevens-Henager College (Orem), A
Stevens-Henager College (Salt Lake City), A
Utah State University, B
Utah Valley University, A
Weber State University, B
Westminster College, B

Vermont

Bennington College, B
Castleton University, B
Champlain College, B
Community College of Vermont, A
Marlboro College, B
University of Vermont, B

Virginia

American National University (Charlottesville), A
American National University (Danville), A
American National University (Harrisonburg), A
American National University (Lynchburg), A
American National University (Martinsville), A
Blue Ridge Community College, A
Bryant & Stratton College - Virginia Beach Campus, A
Central Virginia Community College, A
The College of William and Mary, B
Danville Community College, A
ECPI University (Newport News), A
ECPI University (Richmond), A
ECPI University (Virginia Beach), AB
George Mason University, B
J. Sargeant Reynolds Community College, A
James Madison University, B
John Tyler Community College, A
Liberty University, B
Lord Fairfax Community College, A
Norfolk State University, B
Northern Virginia Community College, A
Old Dominion University, B
Roanoke College, B
Southern Virginia University, B
Southwest Virginia Community College, A
Thomas Nelson Community College, A

University of Mary Washington, B
University of Richmond, B
University of Virginia, B
The University of Virginia's College at Wise, B
Virginia Commonwealth University, B
Virginia Polytechnic Institute and State University, B
Virginia Union University, B

Washington

Eastern Washington University, B
The Evergreen State College, B
Shoreline Community College, A
Skagit Valley College, A
South Puget Sound Community College, A
University of Washington, Bothell, B
University of Washington, Tacoma, B
Washington State University, B
Western Washington University, B

West Virginia

Bluefield State College, B
Marshall University, B
Mountain State College, A
New River Community and Technical College, A
Potomac State College of West Virginia University, A
Salem International University, AB
Shepherd University, B
West Virginia University, B
West Virginia University Institute of Technology, B
West Virginia Wesleyan College, B
Wheeling Jesuit University, B

Wisconsin

Alverno College, B
Carroll University, B
College of Menominee Nation, A
Edgewood College, B
Lakeshore Technical College, A
Marquette University, B
Mid-State Technical College, A
Nicolet Area Technical College, A
St. Norbert College, B
University of Wisconsin - Eau Claire, B
University of Wisconsin - La Crosse, B
University of Wisconsin - Madison, B
University of Wisconsin - Milwaukee, B
University of Wisconsin - Platteville, B
University of Wisconsin - River Falls, B
University of Wisconsin - Stevens Point, B
University of Wisconsin - Stout, B
University of Wisconsin - Superior, B
University of Wisconsin - Whitewater, B

Wyoming

Sheridan College, A
Western Wyoming Community College, A

U.S. Territories: Puerto Rico

American University of Puerto Rico (Bayamon), B
ICPR Junior College - Hato Rey Campus, A
Inter American University of Puerto Rico, Barranquitas Campus, AB
Inter American University of Puerto Rico, Fajardo Campus, AB
Inter American University of Puerto Rico, Ponce Campus, A
Polytechnic University of Puerto Rico, B
Pontifical Catholic University of Puerto Rico, A
Universidad del Turabo, AB
University of Puerto Rico in Bayamón, B
University of Puerto Rico in Ponce, B

Canada

Alberta

Athabasca University, B
Mount Royal University, B

British Columbia

Okanagan College, B
Thompson Rivers University, B
University of the Fraser Valley, B
University of Northern British Columbia, B

Maritime Provinces: Nova Scotia

Cape Breton University, B
Mount Saint Vincent University, B
St. Francis Xavier University, B

Ontario

University of Ottawa, B
The University of Western Ontario, B
University of Windsor, B
Wilfrid Laurier University, B
York University, B

Quebec

Bishop's University, B
Université de Sherbrooke, B

COMPUTER AND INFORMATION SCIENCES AND SUPPORT SERVICES

United States

Alabama

Amridge University, B

Arizona

Arizona State University at the West campus, B
Chandler-Gilbert Community College, A
Rio Salado College, A
South Mountain Community College, A

California

California State University, Los Angeles, B
Contra Costa College, A
Los Angeles City College, A
Mt. Sierra College, B
National University, B
San Joaquin Valley College (Visalia), A
Sierra College, A

Colorado

Colorado Mountain College (Glenwood Springs), A

Connecticut

Capital Community College, A

District of Columbia

University of the Potomac, AB

Florida

Everest University (Orlando), A
Palm Beach State College, A
Seminole State College of Florida, A
Southeastern College - West Palm Beach, A

Georgia

Darton State College, A
Interactive College of Technology (Chamblee), A

Idaho

North Idaho College, A

Illinois

Columbia College Chicago, B
DePaul University, B
Heartland Community College, A
Northwestern College - Bridgeview Campus, A
Parkland College, A

Indiana

Indiana Tech, B
Indiana University - Purdue University Indianapolis, B
Purdue University Northwest (Hammond), B
Purdue University Northwest (Westville), B
University of Notre Dame, B

Iowa

Des Moines Area Community College, A
Iowa Western Community College, A
Kirkwood Community College, A

University of Northern Iowa, B

Kansas

Pratt Community College, A
Southwestern College, B

Kentucky

Northern Kentucky University, B
Sullivan College of Technology and Design, A

Louisiana

McCann School of Business & Technology (Monroe), A

Maryland

Capitol Technology University, B
Chesapeake College, A

Massachusetts

Bunker Hill Community College, A
Greenfield Community College, A
Massachusetts Bay Community College, A
Massasoit Community College, A
Middlesex Community College, A

Michigan

Ferris State University, B
Jackson College, A
Oakland Community College, A
Wayne County Community College District, A

Minnesota

Academy College, A
Capella University, B
Inver Hills Community College, A
Riverland Community College, A

Missouri

Missouri University of Science and Technology, B
Park University, B
Three Rivers Community College, A
Washington University in St. Louis, B

Montana

Montana State University Billings, A
University of Great Falls, B

Nebraska

Northeast Community College, A

New Hampshire

Keene State College, B

New Jersey

Raritan Valley Community College, A
Union County College, A

New York

Cayuga County Community College, A
College of Staten Island of the City University of New York, B
Corning Community College, A
Fiorello H. LaGuardia Community College of the City University of New York, A
Herkimer County Community College, A
Hilbert College, B
Hofstra University, B
Island Drafting and Technical Institute, A
Jefferson Community College, A
John Jay College of Criminal Justice of the City University of New York, B
Long Island University - LIU Post, B
Mohawk Valley Community College, A
Monroe Community College, A
Morrisville State College, B
New York University, A
Pace University, A
Pace University, Pleasantville Campus, A
Roberts Wesleyan College, B
State University of New York College of Agriculture and Technology at Cobleskill, B
Suffolk County Community College, A
Syracuse University, B
Ulster County Community College, A

United States Military Academy, B
Westchester Community College, A

North Carolina

Blue Ridge Community College, A
Robeson Community College, A
Stanly Community College, A
Wake Technical Community College, A

North Dakota

Dakota College at Bottineau, A
Mayville State University, B
Valley City State University, B

Ohio

Bowling Green State University - Firelands College, A
Brown Mackie College - North Canton, A
Clark State Community College, A
Fortis College (Cuyahoga Falls), A
Gallipolis Career College, A
Stark State College, A
University of Mount Union, B

Oklahoma

Eastern Oklahoma State College, A
Tulsa Community College, A

Pennsylvania

Cabrini University, B
Erie Institute of Technology, A
Fortis Institute (Erie), A
Laurel Business Institute, A
Lehigh University, B
Thaddeus Stevens College of Technology, A
University of Pittsburgh, B
YTI Career Institute - York, A

South Carolina

Aiken Technical College, A
Florence-Darlington Technical College, A
Limestone College, B
Midlands Technical College, A
York Technical College, A

South Dakota

Southeast Technical Institute, A

Tennessee

Daymar College (Nashville), A
Miller-Motte Technical College (Clarksville), A
Southern Adventist University, B

Texas

Del Mar College, A
North Central Texas College, A
Northwest Vista College, A
Western Technical College (El Paso), A

Utah

LDS Business College, A
Utah State University, B
Western Governors University, B

Vermont

Champlain College, B

Virginia

Eastern Shore Community College, A

Washington

Bellevue College, A
City University of Seattle, B
Columbia Basin College, A
Edmonds Community College, A
Pierce College at Fort Steilacoom, A
Tacoma Community College, A
University of Washington, Bothell, B

West Virginia

Mountwest Community & Technical College, A
West Virginia Junior College - Morgantown, A

Wisconsin

Northcentral Technical College, A
Northeast Wisconsin Technical College, A
Southwest Wisconsin Technical College, A

U.S. Territories: Puerto Rico

Huertas Junior College, A
Inter American University of Puerto Rico, Guayama Campus, AB
Universidad del Este, A

COMPUTER AND INFORMATION SYSTEMS SECURITY

United States

Alabama

Auburn University at Montgomery, M
Columbia Southern University, B
Tuskegee University, M
The University of Alabama at Birmingham, M
The University of Alabama in Huntsville, MO
University of South Alabama, B
Virginia College in Birmingham, B

Alaska

Charter College, A

Arizona

Cochise County Community College District, A
Glendale Community College, A
South Mountain Community College, A
University of Advancing Technology, BM
University of Phoenix - Phoenix Campus, B

California

Berkeley City College, A
California State University, San Bernardino, M
California University of Management and Sciences, B
Los Angeles City College, A
Mt. Sierra College, B
National University, M
Ohlone College, A
Oxnard College, A
Santa Clara University, O
Stanbridge College, A
Trident University International, M
University of Phoenix - Bay Area Campus, B
University of Phoenix - Sacramento Valley Campus, B
University of Phoenix - Southern California Campus, B
University of Southern California, M

Colorado

American Sentinel University, B
Colorado Christian University, M
Colorado Technical University Colorado Springs, M
Colorado Technical University Denver South, M
Regis University, M
University of Colorado Colorado Springs, BM
University of Denver, M
University of Phoenix - Colorado Campus, B

Connecticut

Charter Oak State College, B
Fairfield University, O
Norwalk Community College, A
Sacred Heart University, MO
University of New Haven, MO

Delaware

Wilmington University, BM

District of Columbia

The George Washington University, M
University of the Potomac, AB

Florida

Embry-Riddle Aeronautical University - Daytona, M
Florida Institute of Technology, M

Florida State University, M
Keiser University, M
Nova Southeastern University, MD
Pensacola State College, A
Rasmussen College Fort Myers, B
Rasmussen College Land O' Lakes, B
Rasmussen College New Port Richey, B
Rasmussen College Ocala, B
Rasmussen College Tampa/Brandon, B
Saint Leo University, M
Seminole State College of Florida, A
University of Miami, B

Georgia

Armstrong State University, O
Chattahoochee Technical College, A
Columbus State University, O
Georgia Institute of Technology, M
Georgia Military College, A
Kennesaw State University, BO
Lanier Technical College, A
Southern Crescent Technical College, A
University of Phoenix - Atlanta Campus, B
University of Phoenix - Augusta Campus, B
Wiregrass Georgia Technical College, A

Hawaii

University of Phoenix - Hawaii Campus, B

Illinois

American InterContinental University Online, M
Benedictine University, M
City Colleges of Chicago, Wilbur Wright College, A
DePaul University, BM
Eastern Illinois University, O
Elgin Community College, A
Illinois Institute of Technology, M
Lewis University, BM
Loyola University Chicago, B
Moraine Valley Community College, A
Northwestern College - Bridgeview Campus, A
Northwestern University, M
Robert Morris University Illinois, M
Spoon River College, A
University of Illinois at Springfield, B
University of Illinois at Urbana - Champaign, B

Indiana

Indiana Tech, B
Indiana University Bloomington, MD
Purdue University, M
Valparaiso University, M

Iowa

Indian Hills Community College, A
Kaplan University, Davenport Campus, M
St. Ambrose University, B

Kansas

Cowley County Community College and Area Vocational - Technical School, A
Donnelly College, B
Rasmussen College Kansas City/Overland Park, B
Rasmussen College Topeka, B

Kentucky

Northern Kentucky University, O
Sullivan College of Technology and Design, AB
University of Louisville, O

Maine

University of Maine at Augusta, B
University of Maine at Fort Kent, A

Maryland

Anne Arundel Community College, A
Capitol Technology University, M
Chesapeake College, A
College of Southern Maryland, A
Community College of Baltimore County, A
Frostburg State University, B
Hagerstown Community College, A
Hood College, O
Johns Hopkins University, MO
Kaplan University, Hagerstown Campus, A

Loyola University Maryland, O
Montgomery College, A
Stevenson University, M
Towson University, O
University of Maryland, Baltimore County, MO
University of Maryland University College, BMO

Massachusetts

Bay Path University, BM
Boston University, M
Brandeis University, M
Bunker Hill Community College, A
Massachusetts Bay Community College, A
Northeastern University, D
Quinsigamond Community College, A
Springfield Technical Community College, A

Michigan

Central Michigan University, O
Davenport University, ABM
Delta College, A
Eastern Michigan University, O
Ferris State University, BM
Grand Rapids Community College, A
Oakland Community College, A
Washtenaw Community College, A

Minnesota

Academy College, A
Capella University, BMD
Century College, A
Metropolitan State University, BO
Minneapolis Community and Technical College, A
Minnesota State Community and Technical College, A
Minnesota State Community and Technical College - Detroit Lakes, A
Minnesota West Community and Technical College, A
Rasmussen College Blaine, B
Rasmussen College Bloomington, B
Rasmussen College Brooklyn Park, B
Rasmussen College Eagan, B
Rasmussen College Lake Elmo/Woodbury, B
Rasmussen College Mankato, B
Rasmussen College Moorhead, B
Rasmussen College St. Cloud, B
Riverland Community College, A
St. Cloud State University, M
University of Minnesota, Twin Cities Campus, M
University of St. Thomas, O
Walden University, M

Mississippi

Hinds Community College, A

Missouri

Lindenwood University, B
Missouri Western State University, M
Southeast Missouri State University, B

Montana

Miles Community College, A
University of Great Falls, B

Nebraska

University of Nebraska at Omaha, BMDO

Nevada

University of Phoenix - Las Vegas Campus, B

New Jersey

New Jersey City University, MD
New Jersey Institute of Technology, M
Stevens Institute of Technology, MO
University of Phoenix - Jersey City Campus, B

New Mexico

EC-Council University, M
University of New Mexico, M

New York

ASA College, A
Bryant & Stratton College - Albany Campus, A

Bryant & Stratton College - Amherst Campus, A
Bryant & Stratton College - Buffalo Campus, A
Bryant & Stratton College - Greece Campus, A
Bryant & Stratton College - Henrietta Campus, A
Bryant & Stratton College - Liverpool Campus, A
Hilbert College, B
Hofstra University, M
Iona College, M
Island Drafting and Technical Institute, A
Mercy College, BM
Mohawk Valley Community College, A
New York Institute of Technology, M
New York University, O
Pace University, O
Rochester Institute of Technology, BMO
St. John's University, AB
State University of New York College of Technology at Alfred, B
State University of New York Polytechnic Institute, BM
Syracuse University, MO
Utica College, M
Westchester Community College, A

North Carolina

Asheville-Buncombe Technical Community College, A
Craven Community College, A
East Carolina University, M
ECPI University (Greensboro), A
Fayetteville Technical Community College, A
Gaston College, A
Pitt Community College, A
Rowan-Cabarrus Community College, A
The University of North Carolina at Charlotte, O
Wilson Community College, A

North Dakota

North Dakota State College of Science, A
Rasmussen College Fargo, B

Ohio

Bryant & Stratton College - Cleveland Campus, A
Bryant & Stratton College - Eastlake Campus, A
Bryant & Stratton College - Parma Campus, A
Clark State Community College, A
Edison Community College, A
Franklin University, B
Kent State University, MO
Northwest State Community College, A
Owens Community College, A
University of Cincinnati, B
University of Dayton, M
Wright State University, B

Oklahoma

Oklahoma State University Institute of Technology, B

Pennsylvania

Butler County Community College, A
Carlow University, M
Carnegie Mellon University, M
Community College of Beaver County, A
Drexel University, B
East Stroudsburg University of Pennsylvania, B
Harrisburg Area Community College, A
Laurel Business Institute, A
Lehigh Carbon Community College, A
Marywood University, BM
Mercyhurst University, M
Northampton Community College, A
Pennsylvania College of Technology, B
Robert Morris University, M
University of Phoenix - Philadelphia Campus, B
University of Pittsburgh, O
West Chester University of Pennsylvania, O
Westmoreland County Community College, A

Rhode Island

Roger Williams University, M
Salve Regina University, MO

South Carolina

ECPI University (Columbia), A
ECPI University (Greenville), A

ECPI University (North Charleston), A
Limestone College, B

South Dakota

Dakota State University, B
Southeast Technical Institute, A

Tennessee

Dyersburg State Community College, A
Fountainhead College of Technology, B
Lipscomb University, BM

Texas

Central Texas College, A
Collin County Community College District, A
El Centro College, A
LeTourneau University, B
Northwest Vista College, A
Our Lady of the Lake University of San Antonio, M
St. Philip's College, A
Sam Houston State University, BM
Texas A&M University - San Antonio, M
Texas State Technical College, A
University of Houston, M
University of Phoenix - Dallas Campus, B
University of Phoenix - Houston Campus, B
The University of Texas at San Antonio, BMDO
Virginia College in Austin, A

Utah

LDS Business College, A
Neumont University, B
University of Utah, MO
Weber State University, B
Western Governors University, M

Vermont

Norwich University, M

Virginia

Bryant & Stratton College - Richmond Campus, A
Bryant & Stratton College - Virginia Beach Campus, A
ECPI University (Glen Allen), A
ECPI University (Manassas), A
ECPI University (Richmond), A
ECPI University (Virginia Beach), AB
George Mason University, M
Hampton University, M
Liberty University, M
Marymount University, MO
Stratford University (Falls Church), AM
Stratford University (Glen Allen), A
Stratford University (Woodbridge), A
Virginia International University, M
Virginia Polytechnic Institute and State University, O

Washington

Central Washington University, B
City University of Seattle, M
Clover Park Technical College, A
Edmonds Community College, A
Green River College, A
North Seattle College, A
University of Phoenix - Western Washington Campus, B
Walla Walla University, B

West Virginia

American Public University System, M
Blue Ridge Community and Technical College, A
Marshall University, B
Salem International University, M

Wisconsin

Bryant & Stratton College - Milwaukee Campus, A
Milwaukee Area Technical College, A
Rasmussen College Appleton, B
Rasmussen College Green Bay, B
Rasmussen College Wausau, B
University of Wisconsin - Madison, M

Wyoming

Casper College, A
Sheridan College, A

U.S. Territories: Puerto Rico

Inter American University of Puerto Rico, Guayama Campus, M
Universidad del Este, M

Canada

Alberta

Concordia University of Edmonton, M

Quebec

Concordia University, M
Université de Sherbrooke, M

COMPUTER/INFORMATION TECHNOLOGY SERVICES ADMINISTRATION AND MANAGEMENT

United States

Alaska

Charter College, B

California

Holy Names University, B
Los Angeles City College, A
Modesto Junior College, A
National University, B
Pasadena City College, A

Colorado

National American University (Denver), AB

Florida

Daytona State College, A
Florida State College at Jacksonville, B
Gulf Coast State College, B
Hodges University, B
Northwest Florida State College, A
St. Petersburg College, AB
Seminole State College of Florida, A

Illinois

Northwestern College - Bridgeview Campus, A
Parkland College, A
Southwestern Illinois College, A

Indiana

Vincennes University, A

Iowa

Clinton Community College, A
Dordt College, B
Hawkeye Community College, A
Iowa Lakes Community College, A
Iowa Western Community College, A
Kirkwood Community College, A
Muscatine Community College, A
Western Iowa Tech Community College, A

Kansas

Barton County Community College, A
Friends University, B
Hesston College, A

Kentucky

Southeast Kentucky Community and Technical College, A

Louisiana

Bossier Parish Community College, A

Maine

Thomas College, B

Maryland

Frostburg State University, B
Howard Community College, A
University of Maryland, Baltimore County, B

Massachusetts

Anna Maria College, B
Bunker Hill Community College, A
Massachusetts Bay Community College, A

Michigan

Alpena Community College, A
Oakland Community College, A

Minnesota

Concordia University, St. Paul, B
Mesabi Range College, A
National American University (Bloomington), A
National American University (Brooklyn Center), A

Missouri

Missouri State University, B
Washington University in St. Louis, B

Montana

Flathead Valley Community College, A
University of Great Falls, B

Nevada

Great Basin College, B

New Hampshire

Granite State College, B

New Jersey

Berkeley College - Woodland Park Campus, AB

New York

Berkeley College - New York City Campus, AB
Clinton Community College, A
Corning Community College, A
Dutchess Community College, A
Jefferson Community College, A
Maria College, A
Rockland Community College, A
St. Francis College, B
St. Joseph's College, Long Island Campus, B
St. Joseph's College, New York, B
Schenectady County Community College, A

North Carolina

Central Carolina Community College, A
Coastal Carolina Community College, A
Sandhills Community College, A
Stanly Community College, A

Ohio

ETI Technical College of Niles, A
North Central State College, A
Sinclair Community College, A
Stark State College, A

Oklahoma

Eastern Oklahoma State College, A
Western Oklahoma State College, A

Pennsylvania

Bloomsburg University of Pennsylvania, B
Chestnut Hill College, B
DeSales University, B
DuBois Business College (DuBois), A
Laurel Business Institute, A
Marywood University, B
Pennsylvania College of Technology, A
Point Park University, B
Robert Morris University, B

South Carolina

Limestone College, AB
Trident Technical College, A

South Dakota

Southeast Technical Institute, A

Texas

Eastfield College, A
El Centro College, A
North Central Texas College, A
Northwest Vista College, A
Panola College, A
San Antonio College, A

Utah

LDS Business College, A

Vermont

Champlain College, B

Virginia

Eastern Shore Community College, A

Wisconsin

Milwaukee Area Technical College, A

U.S. Territories: Guam

University of Guam, B

Canada

British Columbia

Thompson Rivers University, B

Maritime Provinces: Nova Scotia

Dalhousie University, B

COMPUTER INSTALLATION AND REPAIR TECHNOLOGY/ TECHNICIAN

United States

Alaska

University of Alaska Fairbanks, A

Arizona

Northland Pioneer College, A
Paradise Valley Community College, A
Penn Foster College, A

California

Chabot College, A
Los Angeles Valley College, A
Modesto Junior College, A
Orange Coast College, A
Sierra College, A
Southwestern College, A

Florida

Miami Dade College, A

Georgia

Dalton State College, A

Illinois

College of DuPage, A
College of Lake County, A
John A. Logan College, A

Kentucky

Sullivan College of Technology and Design, A

Louisiana

Delgado Community College, A

Maine

Washington County Community College, A

Michigan

Delta College, A
Montcalm Community College, A

Minnesota

Riverland Community College, A

Mississippi

Hinds Community College, A

New Mexico

Eastern New Mexico University - Roswell, A

New York

Fiorello H. LaGuardia Community College of the
 City University of New York, A
Genesee Community College, A
Queensborough Community College of the City University of New York, A

North Dakota

Lake Region State College, A

Oklahoma

Tulsa Community College, A

Pennsylvania

Northampton Community College, A

South Carolina

Forrest College, A
Midlands Technical College, A

South Dakota

Southeast Technical Institute, A

Utah

Stevens-Henager College (West Haven), A

Washington

Northwest Indian College, A

Wisconsin

Wisconsin Indianhead Technical College, A

U.S. Territories: Puerto Rico

Inter American University of Puerto Rico, Aguadilla
 Campus, A
Inter American University of Puerto Rico, Bayamón
 Campus, AB
Inter American University of Puerto Rico, Fajardo
 Campus, A
Universidad Metropolitana, A

COMPUTER PROGRAMMING

United States

Arizona

Rio Salado College, A

California

Los Angeles City College, A
San Diego Mesa College, A
Santa Ana College, A

Colorado

National American University (Denver), AB

Florida

Pasco-Hernando State College, A
Seminole State College of Florida, A
State College of Florida Manatee-Sarasota, A

Massachusetts

Cape Cod Community College, A
Curry College, B
Northern Essex Community College, A

Minnesota

Mesabi Range College, A

Mississippi

Mississippi Gulf Coast Community College, A
Southwest Mississippi Community College, A

New York

Genesee Community College, A
Rockland Community College, A

North Carolina

Blue Ridge Community College, A
Stanly Community College, A
Surry Community College, A

Ohio

Clark State Community College, A
Lorain County Community College, A
Sinclair Community College, A
Stark State College, A
The University of Akron, B

Pennsylvania

Berks Technical Institute, A
Fortis Institute (Erie), A
Luzerne County Community College, A

South Carolina

Orangeburg-Calhoun Technical College, A

South Dakota

Southeast Technical Institute, A

Tennessee

Northeast State Community College, A

Texas

Coastal Bend College, A
Del Mar College, A
Eastfield College, A
Laredo Community College, A
North Central Texas College, A
San Antonio College, A
Tyler Junior College, A

Utah

LDS Business College, A
Neumont University, B
Provo College, A

Vermont

Marlboro College, B

Virginia

Stratford University (Falls Church), A

Wisconsin

Lakeshore Technical College, A
Mid-State Technical College, A
Moraine Park Technical College, A

U.S. Territories: Puerto Rico

EDP University of Puerto Rico - San Sebastian, B

COMPUTER PROGRAMMING/ PROGRAMMER

United States

Alabama

Central Alabama Community College, A
Virginia College in Birmingham, A
Wallace State Community College, A

Arizona

Chandler-Gilbert Community College, A
Cochise County Community College District, A
University of Advancing Technology, AB
University of Phoenix - Online Campus, B

Arkansas

NorthWest Arkansas Community College, A
Shorter College, A
University of Arkansas at Little Rock, A

California

American River College, A
Antelope Valley College, A
California College San Diego (San Diego), A
Cerritos College, A
Chabot College, A
Cogswell Polytechnical College, B
College of the Redwoods, A
College of San Mateo, A
College of the Sequoias, A
Contra Costa College, A
Cosumnes River College, A
Cuesta College, A
Cypress College, A
De Anza College, A
East Los Angeles College, A
Feather River College, A
Gavilan College, A
Glendale Community College, A
Grossmont College, A
Hartnell College, A
Humphreys College, AB
Laney College, A
Long Beach City College, A
Los Angeles City College, A
Los Angeles Mission College, A
Los Angeles Pierce College, A
Los Angeles Trade-Technical College, A
Los Angeles Valley College, A
Merritt College, A
MiraCosta College, A
Mission College, A
Moreno Valley College, A
Norco College, A
Ohlone College, A
Orange Coast College, A
Palomar College, A
Riverside City College, A
Saddleback College, A
San Jose City College, A
Santa Monica College, A
Sierra College, A
Skyline College, A
Solano Community College, A
Southwestern College, A
West Los Angeles College, A

Colorado

CollegeAmerica - Fort Collins, A
Everest College (Colorado Springs), A
Lamar Community College, A
National American University (Denver), AB
Red Rocks Community College, A

Connecticut

Middlesex Community College, A
Northwestern Connecticut Community College, A

Florida

Broward College, A
Daytona State College, A
Eastern Florida State College, A
Everest University (Tampa), AB
Florida Career College, A
Florida Gateway College, A
Florida Keys Community College, A
Florida SouthWestern State College, A
Gulf Coast State College, A
Indian River State College, A
Miami Dade College, A
Palm Beach State College, A
Pensacola State College, A
Polk State College, A
St. Johns River State College, A
St. Petersburg College, A
Seminole State College of Florida, A
South Florida State College, A
Southern Technical College (Tampa), A
State College of Florida Manatee-Sarasota, A
Tallahassee Community College, A

Georgia

Athens Technical College, A
Atlanta Technical College, A
Augusta Technical College, A
Central Georgia Technical College, A
Chattahoochee Technical College, A
Georgia Northwestern Technical College, A
Georgia Piedmont Technical College, A
Gwinnett Technical College, A
Lanier Technical College, A
Southern Crescent Technical College, A
Wiregrass Georgia Technical College, A

Hawaii

Brigham Young University - Hawaii, B

Idaho

North Idaho College, A
Stevens-Henager College (Boise), A

Illinois

Carl Sandburg College, A
DePaul University, B
Harper College, A
Heartland Community College, A
Illinois Central College, A
Illinois Valley Community College, A
Joliet Junior College, A
Lewis and Clark Community College, A
Lincoln Land Community College, A
Oakton Community College, A
Parkland College, A
Southwestern Illinois College, A
University of Illinois at Urbana - Champaign, B
Waubonsee Community College, A

Indiana

International Business College (Fort Wayne), AB
International Business College (Indianapolis), A
Vincennes University, A

Iowa

Dordt College, B
Indian Hills Community College, A
Iowa Lakes Community College, A
Northwest Iowa Community College, A
Southeastern Community College, A

Kansas

Dodge City Community College, A
Flint Hills Technical College, A
Independence Community College, A
Johnson County Community College, A
Southwestern College, B

Kentucky

Daymar College (Owensboro), A

Louisiana

Louisiana State University at Eunice, A
Sowela Technical Community College, A

Maine

Husson University, B
Northern Maine Community College, A

Maryland

Capitol Technology University, B
College of Southern Maryland, A
Prince George's Community College, A

Massachusetts

Bristol Community College, A
Bunker Hill Community College, A
Cape Cod Community College, A
Massasoit Community College, A
Middlesex Community College, A
North Shore Community College, A
Northern Essex Community College, A
Tufts University, B

Michigan

Andrews University, B
Baker College, AB
Delta College, A
Grand Rapids Community College, A
Kalamazoo Valley Community College, A
Kellogg Community College, A
Macomb Community College, A
Mott Community College, A
North Central Michigan College, A
Oakland Community College, A
St. Clair County Community College, A
Schoolcraft College, A
Southwestern Michigan College, A
University of Michigan - Dearborn, B
Washtenaw Community College, A
Wayne County Community College District, A

Minnesota

Academy College, A
Dakota County Technical College, A
Hennepin Technical College, A
Inver Hills Community College, A
Minneapolis Business College, A
Minneapolis Community and Technical College, A
Minnesota School of Business - Richfield, A
Minnesota State College - Southeast Technical, A
Minnesota State Community and Technical College, A
Minnesota State Community and Technical College - Moorhead, A
Ridgewater College, A
St. Cloud Technical & Community College, A
Saint Paul College - A Community & Technical College, A
South Central College, A

Mississippi

Copiah-Lincoln Community College, A
East Central Community College, A
Hinds Community College, A
Holmes Community College, A
Northeast Mississippi Community College, A
Northwest Mississippi Community College, A

Missouri

American Business & Technology University, A
Metropolitan Community College - Kansas City, A
Mineral Area College, A
Missouri Southern State University, A
St. Charles Community College, A
Southeast Missouri State University, B
State Technical College of Missouri, A
Vatterott College (Kansas City), A
Vatterott College (Springfield), A

Montana

Helena College University of Montana, A
University of Great Falls, B

Nebraska

Bellevue University, B
Grace University, B
Metropolitan Community College, A
Midland University, AB
Northeast Community College, A

New Hampshire

Franklin Pierce University, B

New Jersey

Atlantic Cape Community College, A
Essex County College, A
Rowan College at Gloucester County, A

New Mexico

New Mexico Junior College, A
New Mexico Military Institute, A
New Mexico State University - Alamogordo, A
Santa Fe Community College, A
University of New Mexico - Los Alamos Branch, A

New York

Bramson ORT College, A
College of Staten Island of the City University of New York, A
Farmingdale State College, B
Fiorello H. LaGuardia Community College of the City University of New York, A
Globe Institute of Technology, B
Le Moyne College, B

Medgar Evers College of the City University of New York, A
Mohawk Valley Community College, A
Morrisville State College, AB
Rockland Community College, A
Schenectady County Community College, A
Suffolk County Community College, A
Wood Tobe - Coburn School, A

North Carolina

Beaufort County Community College, A
Bladen Community College, A
Blue Ridge Community College, A
Brunswick Community College, A
Caldwell Community College and Technical Institute, A
Catawba Valley Community College, A
Central Carolina Community College, A
Central Piedmont Community College, A
College of The Albemarle, A
Davidson County Community College, A
Durham Technical Community College, A
Fayetteville Technical Community College, A
Forsyth Technical Community College, A
Gaston College, A
Guilford Technical Community College, A
Isothermal Community College, A
King's College, A
Mitchell Community College, A
Rowan-Cabarrus Community College, A
Sampson Community College, A
Sandhills Community College, A
Surry Community College, A
Wake Technical Community College, A

North Dakota

North Dakota State College of Science, A
Rasmussen College Fargo, A

Ohio

Bowling Green State University, B
Central Ohio Technical College, A
Clark State Community College, A
Columbus State Community College, A
Edison Community College, A
Fortis College (Centerville), A
Hocking College, A
James A. Rhodes State College, A
Lorain County Community College, A
Northwest State Community College, A
Ohio Business College (Sheffield Village), A
Southern State Community College, A
Stark State College, A
Terra State Community College, A
The University of Akron, B
University of Mount Union, B
University of Northwestern Ohio, A
The University of Toledo, A
Walsh University, B
Youngstown State University, AB

Oklahoma

Redlands Community College, A
Vatterott College (Tulsa), A
Vatterott College (Warr Acres), A

Oregon

Lane Community College, A
Oregon Institute of Technology, AB
Portland Community College, A

Pennsylvania

Arcadia University, B
Berks Technical Institute, A
Bradford School, A
Gannon University, B
La Salle University, B
Laurel Technical Institute, A
Lehigh Carbon Community College, A
Montgomery County Community College, A
Northampton Community College, A
Pittsburgh Technical Institute, A
Saint Francis University, AB
Westmoreland County Community College, A

Rhode Island

Johnson & Wales University, A
New England Institute of Technology, AB

South Carolina

Aiken Technical College, A
Limestone College, AB
Northeastern Technical College, A
Piedmont Technical College, A

South Dakota

Black Hills State University, A
National American University (Sioux Falls), AB
Southeast Technical Institute, A

Tennessee

Belmont University, B
Fountainhead College of Technology, A
Northeast State Community College, A

Texas

Alvin Community College, A
Amarillo College, A
Austin Community College District, A
Brazosport College, A
Brookhaven College, A
Cedar Valley College, A
Cisco College, A
Del Mar College, A
Eastfield College, A
El Centro College, A
El Paso Community College, A
Grayson College, A
Hardin-Simmons University, B
Hill College, A
Houston Community College, A
Howard College, A
Kilgore College, A
Lamar State College - Port Arthur, A
Laredo Community College, A
Lee College, A
Lone Star College - Tomball, A
Navarro College, A
North Central Texas College, A
North Lake College, A
Northwest Vista College, A
Richland College, A
San Antonio College, A
South Plains College, A
Tarrant County College District, A
Temple College, A
Texas State Technical College, A
Tyler Junior College, A
Weatherford College, A

Utah

LDS Business College, A
Neumont University, B
Stevens-Henager College (Logan), A
Stevens-Henager College (Orem), A
Stevens-Henager College (Salt Lake City), A
Stevens-Henager College (West Haven), A

Vermont

Champlain College, AB
Marlboro College, B

Virginia

Dabney S. Lancaster Community College, A
ECPI University (Glen Allen), A
ECPI University (Richmond), A
ECPI University (Virginia Beach), AB
J. Sargeant Reynolds Community College, A
Stratford University (Falls Church), A
Tidewater Community College, A

Washington

Bates Technical College, A
Bellevue College, A
Big Bend Community College, A
Centralia College, A
City University of Seattle, B
Clark College, A
Clover Park Technical College, A

Columbia Basin College, A
Edmonds Community College, A
Highline College, A
Pierce College at Fort Steilacoom, A
Pierce College at Puyallup, A
South Puget Sound Community College, A
South Seattle College, A
Spokane Community College, A
Tacoma Community College, A
Walla Walla University, AB

West Virginia

West Virginia Northern Community College, A

Wisconsin

Chippewa Valley Technical College, A
Fox Valley Technical College, A
Gateway Technical College, A
Lakeshore Technical College, A
Madison Area Technical College, A
Southwest Wisconsin Technical College, A
Waukesha County Technical College, A
Western Technical College, A
Wisconsin Indianhead Technical College, A

Wyoming

Casper College, A
Laramie County Community College, A

U.S. Territories: Puerto Rico

Atlantic University College, A
Bayamón Central University, A
Caribbean University, AB
Columbia Centro Universitario (Caguas), A
EDP University of Puerto Rico, A
EDP University of Puerto Rico - San Sebastian, AB
Inter American University of Puerto Rico, San Germán Campus, B

Canada

Newfoundland and Labrador

Memorial University of Newfoundland, B

Ontario

Brock University, B
Carleton University, B
The University of Western Ontario, B

Quebec

Bishop's University, B
Université du Québec à Trois-Rivières, B
Université de Sherbrooke, B

COMPUTER PROGRAMMING, SPECIFIC APPLICATIONS

United States

Alaska

University of Alaska Anchorage, A
University of Alaska Anchorage, Kodiak College, A

Arizona

Mohave Community College, A

California

Academy of Art University, AB
Glendale Community College, A
Los Angeles City College, A
San Diego Mesa College, A
Victor Valley College, A

Colorado

National American University (Denver), AB

Connecticut

Yale University, B

Florida

Daytona State College, A
Full Sail University, B
Hillsborough Community College, A
Miami Dade College, A
Northwest Florida State College, A
Palm Beach State College, A
Pasco-Hernando State College, A
Pensacola State College, A
Seminole State College of Florida, A
Tallahassee Community College, A
Valencia College, A

Georgia

Kennesaw State University, B

Idaho

Broadview University - Boise, AB

Illinois

City Colleges of Chicago, Malcolm X College, A
College of DuPage, A
College of Lake County, A
Danville Area Community College, A
DePaul University, B
Harper College, A
Heartland Community College, A
Lake Land College, A
Lincoln Land Community College, A
Northwestern College - Bridgeview Campus, A
Parkland College, A
Richland Community College, A
Spoon River College, A

Indiana

Indiana University South Bend, A

Iowa

Des Moines Area Community College, A
Iowa Western Community College, A
Kirkwood Community College, A
Marshalltown Community College, A
Northeast Iowa Community College, A
Western Iowa Tech Community College, A

Kansas

Barton County Community College, A
Cowley County Community College and Area Vocational - Technical School, A
Johnson County Community College, A

Maryland

Baltimore City Community College, A

Massachusetts

Bunker Hill Community College, A
Holyoke Community College, A
North Shore Community College, A
Northern Essex Community College, A
Quinsigamond Community College, A
Springfield Technical Community College, A

Michigan

Bay de Noc Community College, A
Grand Rapids Community College, A
Henry Ford College, A
Kellogg Community College, A
Lansing Community College, A
Macomb Community College, A
Monroe County Community College, A
Mott Community College, A
Schoolcraft College, A

Minnesota

Globe University - Minneapolis, AB
Globe University - Woodbury, AB
Inver Hills Community College, A
Mesabi Range College, A
Minnesota School of Business - Blaine, AB
Minnesota School of Business - Brooklyn Center, AB
Minnesota School of Business - Elk River, AB
Minnesota School of Business - Lakeville, AB
Minnesota School of Business - Plymouth, AB

Minnesota School of Business - Richfield, AB
Minnesota School of Business - Rochester, AB
Minnesota School of Business - St. Cloud, AB
Riverland Community College, A

Mississippi

Northwest Mississippi Community College, A

Missouri

Missouri State University - West Plains, A
State Fair Community College, A

Nevada

Truckee Meadows Community College, A

New Hampshire

NHTI, Concord's Community College, A

New Jersey

Essex County College, A

New Mexico

National American University (Albuquerque), B

New York

Rockland Community College, A
State University of New York College of Technology at Alfred, B
Sullivan County Community College, A

North Carolina

Bladen Community College, A
Central Carolina Community College, A
Central Piedmont Community College, A
Coastal Carolina Community College, A
College of The Albemarle, A
Craven Community College, A
Mitchell Community College, A
Pitt Community College, A
Sandhills Community College, A
Stanly Community College, A
Wilkes Community College, A

Ohio

American National University (Cincinnati), A
Cincinnati State Technical and Community College, A
Columbus State Community College, A
ETI Technical College of Niles, A
Kent State University at Ashtabula, A
Kent State University at East Liverpool, A
Kent State University at Geauga, A
Kent State University at Salem, A
Kent State University at Trumbull, A
Kent State University at Tuscarawas, A
Lakeland Community College, A
Lorain County Community College, A
Owens Community College, A
Sinclair Community College, A
Southern State Community College, A
Stark State College, A
Zane State College, A

Oregon

Chemeketa Community College, A
Clackamas Community College, A

Pennsylvania

Butler County Community College, A
Delaware County Community College, A
Lehigh Carbon Community College, A
Manor College, A
Westmoreland County Community College, A

Rhode Island

Community College of Rhode Island, A

South Carolina

Trident Technical College, A

South Dakota

Globe University - Sioux Falls, AB

Tennessee

Miller-Motte Technical College (Chattanooga), A
Miller-Motte Technical College (Clarksville), A
National College (Knoxville), A

Texas

Coastal Bend College, A
Del Mar College, A
Houston Community College, A
North Central Texas College, A
San Antonio College, A

Utah

Broadview University - Layton, AB
Broadview University - West Jordan, AB
LDS Business College, A
Neumont University, B

Washington

DigiPen Institute of Technology, B
Edmonds Community College, A
University of Washington, Bothell, B

West Virginia

Southern West Virginia Community and Technical College, A

Wisconsin

Globe University - Eau Claire, AB
Globe University - Green Bay, AB
Globe University - La Crosse, AB
Globe University - Madison East, AB
Globe University - Madison West, AB
Globe University - Wausau, AB
Mid-State Technical College, A
Milwaukee Area Technical College, A

Wyoming

Western Wyoming Community College, A

U.S. Territories: Puerto Rico

Humacao Community College, A
Pontifical Catholic University of Puerto Rico, A
Universidad del Este, A

Canada

Alberta

University of Alberta, B

Ontario

University of Windsor, B

COMPUTER PROGRAMMING, VENDOR/PRODUCT CERTIFICATION

United States

Arizona

Chandler-Gilbert Community College, A
Paradise Valley Community College, A

Arkansas

Arkansas State University - Beebe, A

California

Los Angeles City College, A

Florida

Florida Technical College (Orlando), A
Gulf Coast State College, A
Miami Dade College, A
Pensacola State College, A
Seminole State College of Florida, A

Illinois

Heartland Community College, A
Parkland College, A

Kentucky

Sullivan College of Technology and Design, A

Minnesota

Inver Hills Community College, A
Riverland Community College, A

New Jersey

Raritan Valley Community College, A

New Mexico

Luna Community College, A

Ohio

Lorain County Community College, A
Marion Technical College, A
Sinclair Community College, A
Stark State College, A

South Dakota

National American University (Sioux Falls), B

Texas

Del Mar College, A
North Central Texas College, A
San Antonio College, A

Utah

Neumont University, B

Washington

Edmonds Community College, A
Peninsula College, A
Walla Walla Community College, A

Wisconsin

Milwaukee Area Technical College, A

COMPUTER SCIENCE

United States

Alabama

Alabama Agricultural and Mechanical University, M
Alabama Southern Community College, A
Alabama State University, B
Athens State University, B
Auburn University, MD
Auburn University at Montgomery, B
Central Alabama Community College, A
George C. Wallace Community College, A
George Corley Wallace State Community College, A
Jacksonville State University, M
Oakwood University, B
Samford University, B
Talladega College, B
Troy University, M
Tuskegee University, B
The University of Alabama, MD
The University of Alabama at Birmingham, MD
The University of Alabama in Huntsville, MDO
University of South Alabama, BMD
Wallace State Community College, A

Alaska

University of Alaska Anchorage, B
University of Alaska Fairbanks, BM

Arizona

Arizona State University at the Tempe campus, BMD
Central Arizona College, A
Cochise County Community College District, A
CollegeAmerica - Flagstaff, B
Diné College, A
Embry-Riddle Aeronautical University - Prescott, B
Mohave Community College, A
Northcentral University, B
Northern Arizona University, BM
Rio Salado College, A
University of Advancing Technology, BM

The University of Arizona, BMD

Arkansas

Arkansas State University, M
Harding University, B
Hendrix College, B
Ouachita Baptist University, B
Philander Smith College, B
Shorter College, A
Southern Arkansas University - Magnolia, M
Southern Arkansas University Tech, A
University of Arkansas, MD
University of Arkansas at Little Rock, BMD
University of Arkansas at Pine Bluff, B
University of Central Arkansas, M

California

Allan Hancock College, A
American River College, A
Aviation & Electronic Schools of America, A
Azusa Pacific University, B
Bakersfield College, A
Biola University, B
Butte College, A
Cabrillo College, A
California Baptist University, B
California College San Diego (San Diego), B
California Institute of Technology, MD
California Lutheran University, B
California National University for Advanced Studies, B
California Polytechnic State University, San Luis Obispo, BM
California State Polytechnic University, Pomona, BM
California State University, Bakersfield, B
California State University Channel Islands, BM
California State University, Chico, BM
California State University, Dominguez Hills, BM
California State University, East Bay, BM
California State University, Fresno, BM
California State University, Fullerton, BM
California State University, Long Beach, BM
California State University, Los Angeles, BM
California State University, Northridge, BM
California State University, Sacramento, BM
California State University, San Bernardino, BM
California State University, San Marcos, BM
California State University, Stanislaus, B
Cañada College, A
Cerritos College, A
Cerro Coso Community College, A
Chabot College, A
Chapman University, B
Citrus College, A
City College of San Francisco, A
College of the Canyons, A
College of the Desert, A
College of Marin, A
College of San Mateo, A
College of the Sequoias, A
College of the Siskiyous, A
Columbia College, A
Contra Costa College, A
Copper Mountain College, A
Cosumnes River College, A
Cuesta College, A
De Anza College, A
Foothill College, A
Fullerton College, A
Gavilan College, A
Glendale Community College, A
Harvey Mudd College, B
Humboldt State University, B
Humphreys College, AB
La Sierra University, B
Lake Tahoe Community College, A
Las Positas College, A
Lassen Community College District, A
Los Angeles Pierce College, A
Los Angeles Southwest College, A
Merced College, A
Mills College, BMO
MiraCosta College, A
Modesto Junior College, A
Monterey Peninsula College, A
Moorpark College, A

Mt. San Antonio College, A
Napa Valley College, A
National University, BM
Northwestern Polytechnic University, BM
Notre Dame de Namur University, M
Ohlone College, A
Orange Coast College, A
Pacific States University, BM
Pacific Union College, B
Pasadena City College, A
Pomona College, B
Porterville College, A
Sacramento City College, A
Saddleback College, A
San Bernardino Valley College, A
San Diego Mesa College, A
San Diego State University, BM
San Diego State University - Imperial Valley Campus, B
San Francisco State University, BM
San Joaquin Delta College, A
San Jose City College, A
San Jose State University, BM
Santa Ana College, A
Santa Barbara City College, A
Santa Clara University, MDO
Santa Monica College, A
Santa Rosa Junior College, A
Santiago Canyon College, A
Scripps College, B
Silicon Valley University, BM
Skyline College, A
Sonoma State University, B
Southern California Institute of Technology, AB
Southwestern College, A
Stanford University, BMD
Taft College, A
University of California, Berkeley, BMD
University of California, Davis, MD
University of California, Irvine, BMD
University of California, Los Angeles, MD
University of California, Merced, MD
University of California, Riverside, BMD
University of California, San Diego, BMD
University of California, Santa Barbara, BMD
University of California, Santa Cruz, BMD
University of La Verne, B
University of the Pacific, B
University of Redlands, B
University of San Diego, B
University of San Francisco, BM
University of Southern California, BMD
Victor Valley College, A
Westmont College, B
Yuba College, A

Colorado

Adams State University, B
American Sentinel University, ABM
CollegeAmerica - Fort Collins, B
Colorado School of Mines, BMD
Colorado State University, MD
Colorado Technical University Colorado Springs, ABMD
Colorado Technical University Denver South, ABM
Everest College (Thornton), A
Lamar Community College, A
Metropolitan State University of Denver, B
Regis University, BMO
United States Air Force Academy, B
University of Colorado Boulder, BMD
University of Colorado Colorado Springs, BM
University of Colorado Denver, MD
University of Denver, BMD
Western State Colorado University, B

Connecticut

Central Connecticut State University, M
Connecticut College, B
Northwestern Connecticut Community College, A
Quinnipiac University, B
Sacred Heart University, MO
Southern Connecticut State University, BM
Trinity College, B
University of Bridgeport, BMD
University of Connecticut, BMD

University of New Haven, ABMO
Wesleyan University, BMD
Western Connecticut State University, B
Yale University, MD

Delaware

Delaware State University, B
University of Delaware, BMD

District of Columbia

The Catholic University of America, BMD
The George Washington University, BMDO
Georgetown University, BMD
Howard University, BM
University of the District of Columbia, BM

Florida

Barry University, B
Bethune-Cookman University, B
Chipola College, A
Daytona State College, A
Eckerd College, B
Embry-Riddle Aeronautical University - Daytona, B
Everest University (Orlando), AB
Everest University (Tampa), A
Florida Atlantic University, MD
Florida Gulf Coast University, M
Florida Institute of Technology, BMD
Florida International University, MD
Florida Memorial University, B
Florida National University, A
Florida Southern College, B
Florida State University, MD
Florida Technical College (DeLand), A
Indian River State College, A
Lake-Sumter State College, A
Miami Dade College, A
Nova Southeastern University, BMD
Palm Beach Atlantic University, B
Palm Beach State College, A
Pensacola State College, A
Rasmussen College Fort Myers, B
Rasmussen College Land O' Lakes, B
Rasmussen College New Port Richey, B
Rasmussen College Ocala, B
Rasmussen College Tampa/Brandon, B
St. Thomas University, B
Stetson University, B
University of Central Florida, MD
University of Florida, MD
University of Miami, BMD
University of North Florida, M
University of South Florida, MD
University of West Florida, M

Georgia

Abraham Baldwin Agricultural College, A
Armstrong State University, M
Clark Atlanta University, BM
Clayton State University, B
College of Coastal Georgia, A
Columbus State University, MO
Dalton State College, A
Darton State College, A
Emory University, BMD
Fort Valley State University, B
Georgia College & State University, B
Georgia Institute of Technology, MD
Georgia Military College, A
Georgia Southern University, M
Georgia Southwestern State University, BMO
Georgia State University, BMD
Gordon State College, A
Gwinnett Technical College, A
Kennesaw State University, BM
Lanier Technical College, A
Mercer University, B
South Georgia State College, A
Spelman College, B
University of Georgia, BMD
University of West Georgia, M

Hawaii

Brigham Young University - Hawaii, B
Hawai'i Pacific University, AB

University of Hawaii at Hilo, B
University of Hawaii at Manoa, BD

Idaho

Boise State University, BM
Brigham Young University - Idaho, B
College of Southern Idaho, A
Lewis-Clark State College, B
North Idaho College, A
Northwest Nazarene University, B
Stevens-Henager College (Boise), B
University of Idaho, BMD

Illinois

Augustana College, B
Aurora University, B
Benedictine University, B
Blackburn College, B
Bradley University, BM
Chicago State University, BM
DePaul University, BMD
Dominican University, B
East-West University, B
Eastern Illinois University, MO
Eureka College, B
Governors State University, BM
Harper College, A
Heartland Community College, A
Illinois College, B
Illinois Institute of Technology, BMD
Illinois State University, B
Illinois Wesleyan University, B
Knox College, B
Lake Forest College, B
Lewis University, B
Loyola University Chicago, M
McKendree University, B
Monmouth College, B
Moraine Valley Community College, A
North Central College, BM
North Park University, B
Northeastern Illinois University, BM
Northern Illinois University, BM
Northwestern University, BMD
Olivet Nazarene University, B
Parkland College, A
Quincy University, B
Rock Valley College, A
Rockford University, B
Roosevelt University, BM
Saint Xavier University, BM
Southern Illinois University Carbondale, BMD
Southern Illinois University Edwardsville, BM
Trinity Christian College, B
Trinity International University, B
Triton College, A
University of Chicago, BMD
University of Illinois at Chicago, BMD
University of Illinois at Springfield, BM
University of Illinois at Urbana - Champaign, BMD
University of St. Francis, B
Western Illinois University, M
Wheaton College, B

Indiana

Anderson University, B
Ball State University, M
DePauw University, B
Franklin College, B
Goshen College, B
Hanover College, B
Huntington University, B
Indiana State University, M
Indiana Tech, B
Indiana University Bloomington, BMD
Indiana University Northwest, B
Indiana University - Purdue University Fort Wayne, M
Indiana University - Purdue University Indianapolis, BMDO
Indiana University South Bend, BM
Indiana University Southeast, B
Ivy Tech Community College - Bloomington, A
Ivy Tech Community College - Central Indiana, A
Ivy Tech Community College - Columbus, A
Ivy Tech Community College - East Central, A

Ivy Tech Community College - Kokomo, A
Ivy Tech Community College - Lafayette, A
Ivy Tech Community College - Northeast, A
Ivy Tech Community College - Richmond, A
Ivy Tech Community College - Southeast, A
Ivy Tech Community College - Southern Indiana, A
Ivy Tech Community College - Southwest, A
Ivy Tech Community College - Wabash Valley, A
Manchester University, B
Purdue University, BMD
Purdue University Northwest (Hammond), BM
Rose-Hulman Institute of Technology, B
Taylor University, B
Trine University, B
University of Evansville, B
University of Indianapolis, B
University of Notre Dame, MD
University of Southern Indiana, B
Valparaiso University, B
Vincennes University, A

Iowa

Buena Vista University, B
Central College, B
Coe College, B
Cornell College, B
Dordt College, B
Drake University, B
Graceland University, B
Grand View University, B
Grinnell College, B
Iowa Lakes Community College, A
Iowa State University of Science and Technology, MD
Loras College, B
Luther College, B
Maharishi University of Management, BM
Northwestern College, B
St. Ambrose University, B
Simpson College, B
University of Dubuque, B
The University of Iowa, BMD
University of Northern Iowa, B
Wartburg College, B
William Penn University, B

Kansas

Allen Community College, A
Baker University, B
Barton County Community College, A
Benedictine College, B
Butler Community College, A
Central Christian College of Kansas, A
Cowley County Community College and Area Vocational - Technical School, A
Dodge City Community College, A
Fort Hays State University, B
Garden City Community College, A
Grantham University, AB
Independence Community College, A
Kansas State University, MD
Labette Community College, A
Neosho County Community College, A
Rasmussen College Topeka, B
Southwestern College, B
The University of Kansas, MD
Wichita State University, MD

Kentucky

Centre College, B
Daymar College (Bowling Green), A
Eastern Kentucky University, B
Kentucky State University, M
Murray State University, B
Northern Kentucky University, MO
University of Kentucky, MD
University of Louisville, MDO
Western Kentucky University, M

Louisiana

Dillard University, B
Grambling State University, B
Louisiana State University and Agricultural & Mechanical College, BMD
Louisiana State University in Shreveport, BM
Louisiana Tech University, BMD

McNeese State University, BM
Northwest Louisiana Technical College, A
Southeastern Louisiana University, B
Southern University and Agricultural and Mechanical
   College, BM
Southern University at Shreveport, A
Tulane University, B
University of Louisiana at Lafayette, BMD
University of Louisiana at Monroe, B
University of New Orleans, BM
Xavier University of Louisiana, B

Maine

Bowdoin College, B
Colby College, B
Southern Maine Community College, A
Thomas College, B
University of Maine, BMDO
University of Maine at Farmington, B
University of Maine at Fort Kent, AB
University of Southern Maine, BMO
York County Community College, A

Maryland

Bowie State University, MD
Capitol Technology University, M
Chesapeake College, A
Coppin State University, B
Frederick Community College, A
Frostburg State University, BM
Goucher College, B
Harford Community College, A
Hood College, BMO
Howard Community College, A
Johns Hopkins University, MDO
Loyola University Maryland, BM
Morgan State University, B
Prince George's Community College, A
Towson University, BM
United States Naval Academy, B
University of Maryland, Baltimore County, BMD
University of Maryland, College Park, MD
University of Maryland Eastern Shore, BM
Washington College, B

Massachusetts

Amherst College, B
Bard College at Simon's Rock, B
Benjamin Franklin Institute of Technology, A
Boston College, B
Boston University, BMO
Brandeis University, BM
Bridgewater State University, BM
Bristol Community College, A
Bunker Hill Community College, A
Cape Cod Community College, A
Clark University, B
College of the Holy Cross, B
Endicott College, B
Fitchburg State University, BM
Gordon College, B
Hampshire College, B
Harvard University, BMD
Massachusetts Bay Community College, A
Massachusetts College of Liberal Arts, B
Massachusetts Institute of Technology, BMDO
Merrimack College, B
Mount Holyoke College, B
New England College of Business and Finance, A
Newbury College, B
North Shore Community College, A
Northeastern University, BMD
Northern Essex Community College, A
Quincy College, A
Quinsigamond Community College, A
Smith College, B
Springfield College, B
Springfield Technical Community College, A
Stonehill College, B
Suffolk University, B
Tufts University, BMDO
University of Massachusetts Amherst, BMD
University of Massachusetts Boston, MD
University of Massachusetts Dartmouth, MDO
University of Massachusetts Lowell, BMD
Wellesley College, B

Wentworth Institute of Technology, B
Western New England University, B
Westfield State University, B
Wheaton College, B
Williams College, B
Worcester Polytechnic Institute, BMDO

Michigan

Alma College, B
Andrews University, B
Baker College, AB
Calvin College, B
Central Michigan University, BM
Eastern Michigan University, BMO
Grand Valley State University, M
Kettering University, B
Lake Superior State University, AB
Lawrence Technological University, BM
Madonna University, AB
Michigan State University, MD
Michigan Technological University, BMD
Oakland University, M
Saginaw Valley State University, B
Spring Arbor University, B
University of Detroit Mercy, BM
University of Michigan, MD
University of Michigan - Flint, BM
Wayne State University, MDO
Western Michigan University, BMD

Minnesota

Academy College, B
Anoka-Ramsey Community College, A
Augsburg College, B
Bemidji State University, B
Carleton College, B
Century College, A
College of Saint Benedict, B
Concordia University, St. Paul, B
Dunwoody College of Technology, B
Gustavus Adolphus College, B
Inver Hills Community College, A
Metropolitan State University, BM
Minnesota State University Moorhead, B
Minnesota West Community and Technical College,
   A
Normandale Community College, A
North Hennepin Community College, A
Rasmussen College Blaine, B
Rasmussen College Bloomington, B
Rasmussen College Brooklyn Park, B
Rasmussen College Eagan, B
Rasmussen College Lake Elmo/Woodbury, B
Rasmussen College Mankato, B
Rasmussen College Moorhead, B
Rasmussen College St. Cloud, B
Ridgewater College, A
Rochester Community and Technical College, A
St. Cloud State University, BM
Saint John's University, B
Saint Mary's University of Minnesota, B
St. Olaf College, B
Saint Paul College - A Community & Technical Col-
   lege, A
Southwest Minnesota State University, B
University of Minnesota, Duluth, BM
University of Minnesota, Morris, B
University of Minnesota, Twin Cities Campus, BMD
Vermilion Community College, A
Winona State University, B

Mississippi

Alcorn State University, M
Belhaven University, B
Coahoma Community College, A
East Mississippi Community College, A
Holmes Community College, A
Itawamba Community College, A
Jackson State University, M
Millsaps College, B
Mississippi College, BM
Mississippi Gulf Coast Community College, A
Mississippi State University, MD
Mississippi Valley State University, B
Rust College, A
Southwest Mississippi Community College, A

Tougaloo College, B
University of Southern Mississippi, MD

Missouri

Calvary Bible College and Theological Seminary, B
Central Methodist University, AB
College of the Ozarks, B
Columbia College, B
Drury University, B
Evangel University, B
Everest College, B
Fontbonne University, B
Lindenwood University, B
Metropolitan Community College - Kansas City, A
Missouri State University, BM
Missouri University of Science and Technology,
   BMD
Missouri Valley College, B
Northwest Missouri State University, M
Park University, B
Saint Louis University, B
Southwest Baptist University, AB
University of Central Missouri, M
University of Missouri, BMD
University of Missouri - Kansas City, BMDO
University of Missouri - St. Louis, BMD
Washington University in St. Louis, BMD
Webster University, BM
Westminster College, B

Montana

Blackfeet Community College, A
Carroll College, AB
Little Big Horn College, A
Montana State University, BMD
Montana Tech of The University of Montana, B
Rocky Mountain College, B
Salish Kootenai College, A
Stone Child College, A
University of Great Falls, B
University of Montana, BM

Nebraska

Concordia University, Nebraska, B
Creighton University, AB
Doane University, B
Grace University, B
Hastings College, B
Midland University, B
Northeast Community College, A
Union College, B
University of Nebraska - Lincoln, MD
University of Nebraska at Omaha, BMO

Nevada

University of Nevada, Las Vegas, BMD
University of Nevada, Reno, BMD

New Hampshire

Daniel Webster College, B
Dartmouth College, BMD
Franklin Pierce University, B
Nashua Community College, A
Plymouth State University, B
River Valley Community College, A
Rivier University, M
Saint Anselm College, B
University of New Hampshire, MDO
University of New Hampshire at Manchester, B

New Jersey

Bloomfield College, B
College of Saint Elizabeth, B
County College of Morris, A
Drew University, B
Essex County College, A
Fairleigh Dickinson University, College at Florham,
   M
Fairleigh Dickinson University, Metropolitan Cam-
   pus, BM
Felician University, AB
Mercer County Community College, A
Monmouth University, MO
Montclair State University, MO
New Jersey Institute of Technology, BMD

Princeton University, MD
Rowan College at Burlington County, A
Rowan College at Gloucester County, A
Rowan University, BM
Rutgers University - Camden, M
Rutgers University - New Brunswick, MD
Stevens Institute of Technology, BMD
Thomas Edison State University, AB
Union County College, A
William Paterson University of New Jersey, B

New Mexico

Central New Mexico Community College, A
New Mexico Highlands University, M
New Mexico Institute of Mining and Technology,
   BMD
New Mexico Junior College, A
New Mexico Military Institute, A
New Mexico State University, MD
University of New Mexico, MD
University of New Mexico - Los Alamos Branch, A
University of New Mexico - Valencia Campus, A
Western New Mexico University, B

New York

Adirondack Community College, A
Bard College, B
Binghamton University, State University of New
   York, BMD
Borough of Manhattan Community College of the
   City University of New York, A
Bronx Community College of the City University of
   New York, A
Brooklyn College of the City University of New York,
   MO
Canisius College, B
City College of the City University of New York,
   BMD
Clarkson University, BMD
The College of Saint Rose, BM
College of Staten Island of the City University of
   New York, BM
Columbia University, BMD
Columbia University, School of General Studies, B
Cornell University, BMD
Corning Community College, A
Dutchess Community College, A
Finger Lakes Community College, A
Fiorello H. LaGuardia Community College of the
   City University of New York, A
Fordham University, BMO
Fulton-Montgomery Community College, A
Genesee Community College, A
Hartwick College, B
Hobart and William Smith Colleges, B
Hofstra University, B
Houghton College, B
Hunter College of the City University of New York, B
Iona College, BM
Ithaca College, B
Jefferson Community College, A
Kingsborough Community College of the City Uni-
   versity of New York, A
Lehman College of the City University of New York,
   BM
Long Island University - LIU Brooklyn, M
Long Island University - LIU Post, B
Manhattan College, B
Manhattanville College, B
Marist College, BMO
Mercy College, B
Monroe College, AB
Monroe Community College, A
Morrisville State College, A
Nassau Community College, A
New York City College of Technology of the City
   University of New York, A
New York Institute of Technology, M
New York University, MD
Niagara County Community College, A
Niagara University, B
Nyack College, B
Onondaga Community College, A
Pace University, BMDO
Pace University, Pleasantville Campus, B

Queens College of the City University of New York,
   BM
Rensselaer Polytechnic Institute, BMD
Rochester Institute of Technology, BMD
St. Bonaventure University, B
State University of New York College at Old
   Westbury, B
State University of New York College at Oneonta, B
State University of New York College at Potsdam, B
State University of New York at Fredonia, B
State University of New York at New Paltz, M
State University of New York at Oswego, B
State University of New York Polytechnic Institute,
   M
Stony Brook University, State University of New
   York, MDO
Suffolk County Community College, A
Syracuse University, M
Touro College, B
University at Albany, State University of New York,
   BMD
University at Buffalo, the State University of New
   York, BMDO
University of Rochester, BMD
Wagner College, B
Wells College, B
Westchester Community College, A
Yeshiva University, B
York College of the City University of New York, B

North Carolina

Appalachian State University, BM
Bennett College, B
Central Piedmont Community College, A
Duke University, BMD
East Carolina University, BMO
ECPI University (Raleigh), A
Elizabeth City State University, B
Elon University, B
Fayetteville State University, B
Gardner-Webb University, B
High Point University, B
Isothermal Community College, A
Livingstone College, B
Louisburg College, A
Mars Hill University, B
Meredith College, B
Methodist University, AB
North Carolina Agricultural and Technical Uni-
   versity, BM
North Carolina State University, BMD
Saint Augustine's University, B
Shaw University, B
University of North Carolina at Asheville, B
The University of North Carolina at Chapel Hill,
   BMD
The University of North Carolina at Charlotte, BMO
The University of North Carolina at Greensboro, BM
The University of North Carolina at Pembroke, B
The University of North Carolina Wilmington, BM
Wake Forest University, M
Western Carolina University, BM
Winston-Salem State University, BM

North Dakota

Dickinson State University, B
Minot State University, B
North Dakota State University, BMDO
Rasmussen College Fargo, B
Turtle Mountain Community College, A
University of Jamestown, B
University of North Dakota, MD

Ohio

Ashland University, B
Baldwin Wallace University, B
Bowling Green State University, M
Capital University, B
Case Western Reserve University, BMD
Cedarville University, B
Central State University, B
Cleveland State University, M
The College of Wooster, B
Denison University, B
Fortis College (Centerville), A
Franciscan University of Steubenville, B

Franklin University, ABM
Gallipolis Career College, A
Heidelberg University, B
Hiram College, B
Hocking College, A
John Carroll University, B
Kent State University, MD
Lorain County Community College, A
Malone University, B
Marietta College, B
Miami University Hamilton, B
Miami University Middletown, A
Mount Vernon Nazarene University, B
Muskingum University, B
North Central State College, A
Notre Dame College, M
Oberlin College, B
Ohio Dominican University, B
Ohio Northern University, B
The Ohio State University, BMD
Ohio University, BMD
Ohio University - Lancaster, A
Ohio Wesleyan University, B
Otterbein University, B
Tiffin University, B
The University of Akron, BM
University of Cincinnati, MD
University of Dayton, BM
The University of Findlay, AB
University of Rio Grande, AB
The University of Toledo, MD
Walsh University, AB
Wilberforce University, B
Wilmington College, B
Wittenberg University, B
Wright State University, MD
Xavier University, B
Youngstown State University, BM

Oklahoma

Cameron University, B
Langston University, B
Northeastern State University, B
Northern Oklahoma College, A
Northwestern Oklahoma State University, B
Oklahoma Baptist University, B
Oklahoma Christian University, B
Oklahoma City Community College, A
Oklahoma City University, M
Oklahoma State University, MD
Oral Roberts University, B
Redlands Community College, A
Seminole State College, A
Southwestern Oklahoma State University, A
Southwestern Oklahoma State University at Sayre,
   A
Tulsa Community College, A
University of Central Oklahoma, BM
University of Oklahoma, BMD
The University of Tulsa, BMD

Oregon

Central Oregon Community College, A
Lewis & Clark College, B
Linfield College, B
Oregon Health & Science University, MD
Oregon State University, BMD
Pacific University, B
Portland State University, BMD
Reed College, B
Rogue Community College, A
Southern Oregon University, BM
Umpqua Community College, A
University of Oregon, MD
University of Portland, BM
Western Oregon University, B
Willamette University, B

Pennsylvania

Albright College, B
Allegheny College, B
Arcadia University, B
Bloomsburg University of Pennsylvania, B
Bryn Mawr College, B
Carnegie Mellon University, BMD
Central Penn College, A

Community College of Philadelphia, A
DeSales University, B
Drexel University, BMD
Duquesne University, B
East Stroudsburg University of Pennsylvania, M
Fortis Institute (Erie), A
Gannon University, M
Gettysburg College, B
Grove City College, B
Harrisburg Area Community College, A
Haverford College, B
King's College, B
Kutztown University of Pennsylvania, M
La Roche College, B
La Salle University, BMO
Lafayette College, B
Lebanon Valley College, B
Lehigh University, BMD
Luzerne County Community College, A
Mansfield University of Pennsylvania, B
Marywood University, B
McCann School of Business & Technology
  (Lewisburg), A
McCann School of Business & Technology
  (Pottsville), A
Mercyhurst University, B
Messiah College, B
Moravian College, B
Northampton Community College, A
Penn State Erie, The Behrend College, B
Penn State Harrisburg, M
Penn State University Park, MD
Pennsylvania Highlands Community College, A
Philadelphia University, B
Saint Francis University, B
Saint Joseph's University, MO
Seton Hill University, B
Shippensburg University of Pennsylvania, M
Slippery Rock University of Pennsylvania, B
South Hills School of Business & Technology
  (Altoona), A
South Hills School of Business & Technology (State
  College), A
Susquehanna University, B
Temple University, MD
Thiel College, B
University of Pennsylvania, MD
University of Pittsburgh, BMD
University of Pittsburgh at Bradford, B
University of Pittsburgh at Johnstown, B
The University of Scranton, B
Ursinus College, B
Villanova University, BMO
Waynesburg University, B
West Chester University of Pennsylvania, MO
Westminster College, B
Widener University, B
York College of Pennsylvania, B

Rhode Island

Brown University, BMD
New England Institute of Technology, AB
Providence College, B
Roger Williams University, B
University of Rhode Island, MDO

South Carolina

Benedict College, B
Bob Jones University, B
Charleston Southern University, B
The Citadel, The Military College of South Carolina,
  M
Claflin University, B
Clemson University, MD
Coastal Carolina University, O
Coker College, B
College of Charleston, M
Furman University, B
Limestone College, B
Northeastern Technical College, A
University of South Carolina, MD
Voorhees College, B
Wofford College, B

South Dakota

Augustana University, B
Black Hills State University, A
Dakota State University, M
Lake Area Technical Institute, A
Mount Marty College, B
Oglala Lakota College, A
Sinte Gleska University, B
South Dakota School of Mines and Technology, B
University of Sioux Falls, B
The University of South Dakota, M

Tennessee

Belmont University, B
Carson-Newman University, B
Christian Brothers University, B
East Tennessee State University, MO
Fisk University, B
Jackson State Community College, A
King University, B
LeMoyne-Owen College, B
Lipscomb University, B
Middle Tennessee State University, BM
Milligan College, B
Nashville State Community College, A
Rhodes College, B
Roane State Community College, A
Sewanee: The University of the South, B
South College, A
Southern Adventist University, B
Tennessee State University, B
Tennessee Technological University, BM
Union University, B
University of Memphis, BMD
The University of Tennessee, BMD
The University of Tennessee at Chattanooga, BMO
The University of Tennessee at Martin, B
Vanderbilt University, BMD

Texas

Abilene Christian University, B
Amarillo College, A
Austin College, B
Baylor University, BM
Blinn College, A
Cisco College, A
Coastal Bend College, A
Collin County Community College District, A
Concordia University Texas, B
Dallas Baptist University, B
Del Mar College, A
El Centro College, A
Galveston College, A
Houston Community College, A
Howard College, A
Huston-Tillotson University, B
Lamar State College - Orange, A
Lamar University, M
LeTourneau University, B
Lone Star College - CyFair, A
Lone Star College - Kingwood, A
Lone Star College - Montgomery, A
Lone Star College - North Harris, A
Lone Star College - Tomball, A
Midwestern State University, M
Navarro College, A
North Central Texas College, A
Northwest Vista College, A
Odessa College, A
Palo Alto College, A
Panola College, A
Prairie View A&M University, BM
Rice University, MD
St. Edward's University, B
St. Mary's University, BMO
Sam Houston State University, MD
South Plains College, A
South Texas College, A
Southern Methodist University, BMD
Southwestern Adventist University, B
Stephen F. Austin State University, M
Tarrant County College District, A
Temple College, A
Texas A&M University, BMD
Texas A&M University - Corpus Christi, M

Texas A&M University - Kingsville, M
Texas College, B
Texas Lutheran University, B
Texas Southern University, M
Texas State University, BM
Texas Tech University, MD
Texas Wesleyan University, B
Trinity Valley Community College, A
Tyler Junior College, A
University of Houston, MD
University of Houston - Clear Lake, BM
University of Houston - Victoria, BM
University of Mary Hardin-Baylor, B
University of North Texas, M
University of St. Thomas, B
The University of Texas at Arlington, BMD
The University of Texas at Austin, MD
The University of Texas at Dallas, MD
The University of Texas at El Paso, BMD
The University of Texas of the Permian Basin, M
The University of Texas Rio Grande Valley, BM
The University of Texas at San Antonio, MD
The University of Texas at Tyler, BM
Wayland Baptist University, B
West Texas A&M University, B
Western Texas College, A
Wharton County Junior College, A
Wiley College, AB

Utah

Brigham Young University, MD
Dixie State University, B
LDS Business College, A
Neumont University, B
Salt Lake Community College, A
Snow College, A
Southern Utah University, B
Stevens-Henager College (West Haven), B
University of Utah, BMD
Utah State University, MD
Utah Valley University, AB
Weber State University, AB
Westminster College, B

Vermont

Bennington College, B
Champlain College, B
Community College of Vermont, A
Landmark College, AB
Lyndon State College, A
Marlboro College, B
Middlebury College, B
Norwich University, B
Saint Michael's College, B
University of Vermont, BMD

Virginia

Bridgewater College, B
Christopher Newport University, BM
The College of William and Mary, MD
Eastern Mennonite University, B
ECPI University (Newport News), A
ECPI University (Richmond), A
George Mason University, BMDO
Hampden-Sydney College, B
Hampton University, BM
James Madison University, M
Longwood University, B
Lynchburg College, B
Norfolk State University, M
Old Dominion University, MD
Radford University, B
Randolph-Macon College, B
Regent University, B
Roanoke College, B
University of Management and Technology, ABMO
University of Virginia, MD
Virginia Commonwealth University, MD
Virginia International University, BMO
Virginia Military Institute, B
Virginia Polytechnic Institute and State University,
  BMDO
Virginia State University, BM
Virginia Wesleyan College, B
Virginia Western Community College, A
Washington and Lee University, B

Washington

Central Washington University, B
City University of Seattle, M
DigiPen Institute of Technology, M
Eastern Washington University, M
Everett Community College, A
Gonzaga University, B
Heritage University, AB
Pacific Lutheran University, B
Renton Technical College, AB
Saint Martin's University, B
Seattle University, BM
Skagit Valley College, A
University of Puget Sound, B
University of Washington, BMD
University of Washington, Bothell, B
Walla Walla University, B
Washington State University, BMD
Washington State University - Tri-Cities, B
Washington State University - Vancouver, B
Western Washington University, M
Whatcom Community College, A
Whitworth University, B
Yakima Valley Community College, A

West Virginia

Alderson Broaddus University, B
Bethany College, B
BridgeValley Community and Technical College
  (Montgomery), A
BridgeValley Community and Technical College
  (South Charleston), A
Concord University, B
Davis & Elkins College, B
Fairmont State University, B
Glenville State College, B
Huntington Junior College, A
Marshall University, M
West Virginia State University, B
West Virginia University, BMD
West Virginia University Institute of Technology, B
West Virginia Wesleyan College, B

Wisconsin

Beloit College, B
Cardinal Stritch University, B
Carthage College, B
Concordia University Wisconsin, B
Lakeland College, B
Lawrence University, B
Marquette University, M
Nicolet Area Technical College, A
Rasmussen College Appleton, B
Rasmussen College Green Bay, B
Rasmussen College Wausau, B
Ripon College, B
St. Norbert College, B
Silver Lake College of the Holy Family, B
University of Wisconsin - Green Bay, B
University of Wisconsin - Madison, MD
University of Wisconsin - Milwaukee, BM
University of Wisconsin - Oshkosh, B
University of Wisconsin - Parkside, BM
University of Wisconsin - Platteville, BM
University of Wisconsin - Superior, B
Wisconsin Lutheran College, B

Wyoming

Central Wyoming College, A
Laramie County Community College, A
University of Wyoming, BMD
Western Wyoming Community College, A

U.S. Territories: Guam

Guam Community College, A
University of Guam, B

U.S. Territories: Puerto Rico

American University of Puerto Rico (Bayamon), A
Inter American University of Puerto Rico, Aguadilla
  Campus, AB
Inter American University of Puerto Rico, Arecibo
  Campus, A
Inter American University of Puerto Rico, Bar-
  ranquitas Campus, A

Inter American University of Puerto Rico, Bayamón
  Campus, AB
Inter American University of Puerto Rico, Fajardo
  Campus, M
Inter American University of Puerto Rico, Guayama
  Campus, M
Inter American University of Puerto Rico, Metropoli-
  tan Campus, BM
Inter American University of Puerto Rico, Ponce
  Campus, AB
Inter American University of Puerto Rico, San
  Germán Campus, AB
Polytechnic University of Puerto Rico, BM
Universidad Adventista de las Antillas, AB
Universidad Metropolitana, AB
University of Puerto Rico in Arecibo, B
University of Puerto Rico, Mayagüez Campus, BD
University of Puerto Rico, Río Piedras Campus, B
University of the Sacred Heart, B

U.S. Territories: United States Virgin Islands

University of the Virgin Islands, AB

Canada

Alberta

The King's University, B
Mount Royal University, B
University of Alberta, BMD
University of Calgary, BMD
University of Lethbridge, BM

British Columbia

British Columbia Institute of Technology, AB
Simon Fraser University, BMD
Thompson Rivers University, AB
Trinity Western University, B
The University of British Columbia, BMD
The University of British Columbia - Okanagan
  Campus, B
University of Northern British Columbia, BM
University of Victoria, BMD

Manitoba

Brandon University, B
University of Manitoba, BMD

Maritime Provinces: New Brunswick

Mount Allison University, B
Université de Moncton, BMO
University of New Brunswick Fredericton, BMD
University of New Brunswick Saint John, B

Maritime Provinces: Nova Scotia

Acadia University, BM
Dalhousie University, BMD
St. Francis Xavier University, M
Saint Mary's University, B
University of King's College, B

Maritime Provinces: Prince Edward Island

University of Prince Edward Island, B

Newfoundland and Labrador

Memorial University of Newfoundland, BMD

Ontario

Brock University, BM
Carleton University, BMD
Lakehead University, BM
Laurentian University, B
McMaster University, BMD
Nipissing University, B
Queen's University at Kingston, BMD
Redeemer University College, B
Royal Military College of Canada, BM
Ryerson University, B
Trent University, BM
University of Guelph, BMD
University of Ottawa, MD
University of Toronto, BMD
University of Waterloo, BMD

The University of Western Ontario, BMD
University of Windsor, BMD
Wilfrid Laurier University, B
York University, BMD

Quebec

Bishop's University, B
Concordia University, BMDO
École Polytechnique de Montréal, MD
McGill University, MD
Télé-université, D
Université Laval, BMD
Université de Montréal, BMD
Université du Québec à Chicoutimi, B
Université du Québec en Outaouais, BMDO
Université du Québec à Rimouski, B
Université du Québec à Trois-Rivières, BM
Université de Sherbrooke, B

Saskatchewan

University of Regina, BMD
University of Saskatchewan, BMD

COMPUTER SOFTWARE ENGINEERING

United States

Alabama

Auburn University, B

Arizona

Arizona State University at the Polytechnic campus,
  B
DeVry University (Phoenix), B
Embry-Riddle Aeronautical University - Prescott, B
University of Phoenix - Phoenix Campus, B

California

California Baptist University, B
DeVry University (Alhambra), B
DeVry University (Anaheim), B
DeVry University (Fremont), B
DeVry University (Long Beach), B
DeVry University (Palmdale), B
DeVry University (Pomona), B
DeVry University (San Diego), B
DeVry University (Sherman Oaks), B
National University, B
Point Loma Nazarene University, B
University of California, Irvine, B
University of Phoenix - Bay Area Campus, B
University of Phoenix - Sacramento Valley Campus,
  B

Colorado

DeVry University (Westminster), B
University of Northern Colorado, B
University of Phoenix - Colorado Campus, B
University of Phoenix - Colorado Springs Downtown
  Campus, B

Connecticut

Fairfield University, B
Quinnipiac University, B

Florida

DeVry University (Orlando), B
Embry-Riddle Aeronautical University - Daytona, B
Florida Institute of Technology, B
Keiser University, B
Nova Southeastern University, B
Rasmussen College Fort Myers, A
Rasmussen College Land O' Lakes, A
Rasmussen College New Port Richey, A
Rasmussen College Ocala, A
Rasmussen College Tampa/Brandon, A
Seminole State College of Florida, A
University of Miami, B

Georgia

DeVry University (Alpharetta), B
DeVry University (Decatur), B
Kennesaw State University, B
University of Phoenix - Atlanta Campus, B
University of Phoenix - Augusta Campus, B

Illinois

DeVry University (Addison), B
DeVry University (Tinley Park), B
DeVry University Online, B
University of Illinois at Urbana - Champaign, B

Indiana

Indiana Tech, B
Indiana Wesleyan University, B
Rose-Hulman Institute of Technology, B

Iowa

Iowa State University of Science and Technology, B
William Penn University, B

Kansas

Rasmussen College Kansas City/Overland Park, A
Rasmussen College Topeka, A
Wichita State University, B

Michigan

Michigan Technological University, B
University of Detroit Mercy, B

Minnesota

Rasmussen College Blaine, A
Rasmussen College Bloomington, A
Rasmussen College Brooklyn Park, A
Rasmussen College Eagan, A
Rasmussen College Lake Elmo/Woodbury, A
Rasmussen College Mankato, A
Rasmussen College Moorhead, A
Rasmussen College St. Cloud, A
University of Minnesota, Crookston, B

Montana

Montana Tech of The University of Montana, B

Nevada

University of Phoenix - Las Vegas Campus, B

New Jersey

Monmouth University, B
University of Phoenix - Jersey City Campus, B

New York

Clarkson University, B
Rochester Institute of Technology, B
State University of New York at Oswego, B

North Dakota

Rasmussen College Fargo, A

Ohio

Baldwin Wallace University, B
Bowling Green State University, B
Miami University, B
Ohio Dominican University, B
Sinclair Community College, A
Stark State College, A

Oklahoma

Oklahoma City University, B

Pennsylvania

Allegheny College, B
DeVry University (Fort Washington), B
Drexel University, B
Penn State Erie, The Behrend College, B
Robert Morris University, B
Shippensburg University of Pennsylvania, B
University of Phoenix - Philadelphia Campus, B

South Dakota

Southeast Technical Institute, A

Texas

DeVry University (Austin), B
DeVry University (Irving), B
St. Mary's University, B
University of Phoenix - Dallas Campus, B
University of Phoenix - Houston Campus, B
The University of Texas at Arlington, B
The University of Texas at Dallas, B

Utah

LDS Business College, A
Utah Valley University, B

Vermont

Vermont Technical College, AB

Virginia

DeVry University (Arlington), B
Liberty University, B
Stratford University (Woodbridge), B

Washington

DigiPen Institute of Technology, B
University of Phoenix - Western Washington Campus, B

Wisconsin

Carroll University, B
Milwaukee School of Engineering, B
Rasmussen College Appleton, A
Rasmussen College Green Bay, A
Rasmussen College Wausau, A
University of Wisconsin - Platteville, B

Canada

Alberta

University of Alberta, B

British Columbia

University of Victoria, B

Maritime Provinces: Nova Scotia

Dalhousie University, B

Ontario

Brock University, B
Centennial College, B
University of Guelph, B
University of Ottawa, B
University of Toronto, B
University of Waterloo, B
The University of Western Ontario, B
York University, B

Quebec

Concordia University, B
McGill University, B
Université Laval, B
Université du Québec, École de technologie supérieure, B

Saskatchewan

University of Regina, B

COMPUTER SOFTWARE AND MEDIA APPLICATIONS

United States

Arkansas

Southern Arkansas University Tech, A

California

Art Center College of Design, B
Berkeley City College, A
College of the Sequoias, A
Holy Names University, B
Los Angeles City College, A
Platt College San Diego, A

San Diego Mesa College, A

Colorado

University of Denver, B
University of Phoenix - Colorado Campus, B

Florida

Florida State University, B
Hobe Sound Bible College, A
Seminole State College of Florida, A
Southern Technical College (Fort Myers), A

Illinois

DePaul University, B
Loyola University Chicago, B
McKendree University, B
Northwestern College - Bridgeview Campus, A
Parkland College, A

Michigan

Kellogg Community College, A

Minnesota

Mesabi Range College, A
Riverland Community College, A

Montana

University of Great Falls, B

New Hampshire

Daniel Webster College, B

New York

The College of Westchester, A
Genesee Community College, A
Morrisville State College, B
Pace University, A
Pace University, Pleasantville Campus, AB
State University of New York College of Agriculture and Technology at Cobleskill, B

North Carolina

Asheville-Buncombe Technical Community College, A
Carteret Community College, A

North Dakota

Dakota College at Bottineau, A

Ohio

ETI Technical College of Niles, A
Gallipolis Career College, A
Marion Technical College, A
Ohio Business College (Sheffield Village), A
Stark State College, A

Pennsylvania

Duquesne University, B
Lansdale School of Business, A
Laurel Business Institute, A

South Carolina

College of Charleston, B
Limestone College, B

South Dakota

Dakota Wesleyan University, B

Texas

Laredo Community College, A
LeTourneau University, B

Utah

Neumont University, B

Vermont

Champlain College, AB

West Virginia

American Public University System, A

Wisconsin

University of Wisconsin - Stout, B

U.S. Territories: Puerto Rico

Polytechnic University of Puerto Rico, A

Canada

Ontario

Carleton University, B
The University of Western Ontario, B

COMPUTER SOFTWARE TECH-NOLOGY/TECHNICIAN

United States

Arizona

Coconino Community College, A
University of Advancing Technology, B

California

Cogswell Polytechnical College, B
Glendale Community College, A

Florida

Miami Dade College, A

Iowa

Iowa Lakes Community College, A

Kansas

Kansas City Kansas Community College, A

Minnesota

Globe University - Woodbury, A

Mississippi

Holmes Community College, A

Missouri

Vatterott College (Berkeley), B
Vatterott College (Sunset Hills), B

New York

Farmingdale State College, B
TCI - College of Technology, A

Oregon

Rogue Community College, A

Texas

Sam Houston State University, B

U.S. Territories: Puerto Rico

Universidad del Este, A

COMPUTER SYSTEMS ANALY-SIS/ANALYST

United States

Arizona

Arizona State University at the Polytechnic campus, B
Chandler-Gilbert Community College, A
DeVry University (Mesa), B
DeVry University (Phoenix), B
Glendale Community College, A
Northern Arizona University, B
Phoenix College, A
Pima Community College, A
Tohono O'odham Community College, A
University of Advancing Technology, AB

Arkansas

Arkansas Tech University, B
Rich Mountain Community College, A

California

California Polytechnic State University, San Luis Obispo, B
Cerritos College, A
DeVry University (Alhambra), B
DeVry University (Anaheim), B
DeVry University (Bakersfield), B
DeVry University (Fremont), B
DeVry University (Long Beach), B
DeVry University (Oakland), B
DeVry University (Oxnard), B
DeVry University (Palmdale), B
DeVry University (Pomona), B
DeVry University (San Diego), B
DeVry University (Sherman Oaks), B

Colorado

DeVry University (Colorado Springs), B
DeVry University (Westminster), B
University of Denver, B

Florida

Broward College, A
DeVry University (Jacksonville), B
DeVry University (Miramar), B
DeVry University (Orlando), B
Florida Keys Community College, A
Hillsborough Community College, A
Northwest Florida State College, A
Pensacola State College, A
Santa Fe College, A

Georgia

DeVry University (Alpharetta), B
DeVry University (Decatur), B
DeVry University (Duluth), B

Illinois

DeVry University (Addison), B
DeVry University (Chicago), B
DeVry University (Downers Grove), B
DeVry University (Elgin), B
DeVry University (Gurnee), B
DeVry University (Naperville), B
DeVry University (Tinley Park), B
DeVry University Online, B
University of Illinois at Springfield, B

Indiana

DeVry University, B
Taylor University, B

Iowa

St. Ambrose University, B

Kansas

Hutchinson Community College, A
Pittsburg State University, B

Louisiana

University of Louisiana at Lafayette, B

Maryland

Wor-Wic Community College, A

Massachusetts

Bristol Community College, A
Quinsigamond Community College, A

Michigan

Davenport University, AB
Kalamazoo Valley Community College, A
Oakland Community College, A
Saginaw Valley State University, B
Washtenaw Community College, A

Minnesota

University of Minnesota, Twin Cities Campus, B

Missouri

Crowder College, A
DeVry University (Kansas City), B

Montana

University of Great Falls, B

Nevada

DeVry University, B

New Jersey

DeVry University (North Brunswick), B
DeVry University (Paramus), B

New York

DeVry College of New York, B
Rochester Institute of Technology, B

North Carolina

Blue Ridge Community College, A
Brunswick Community College, A
Coastal Carolina Community College, A
DeVry University, B
Edgecombe Community College, A
Guilford Technical Community College, A
Haywood Community College, A
Mitchell Community College, A
Roanoke-Chowan Community College, A
Wilkes Community College, A

North Dakota

United Tribes Technical College, A
University of North Dakota, B

Ohio

Baldwin Wallace University, B
Cincinnati State Technical and Community College, A
DeVry University (Columbus), B
DeVry University (Seven Hills), B
Kent State University, B
Lakeland Community College, A
Miami University Hamilton, B
Southern State Community College, A
Tiffin University, B
The University of Akron, A

Oklahoma

DeVry University, B
Oklahoma City Community College, A

Pennsylvania

DeVry University (Fort Washington), B
DeVry University (King of Prussia), B
DeVry University (Philadelphia), B
Mercyhurst North East, A
Shippensburg University of Pennsylvania, B

Rhode Island

Johnson & Wales University, AB

Tennessee

DeVry University, B

Texas

Amarillo College, A
DeVry University (Austin), B
DeVry University (Irving), B
DeVry University (San Antonio), B
Lee College, A
Texas Christian University, B
University of Houston, B

Vermont

University of Vermont, B

Virginia

DeVry University (Arlington), B
DeVry University (Chesapeake), B
DeVry University (Manassas), B

Washington

Seattle Pacific University, B
University of Washington, Bothell, B

West Virginia

West Virginia University Institute of Technology, B

Wisconsin

Lac Courte Oreilles Ojibwa Community College, A
Lakeshore Technical College, A
Milwaukee Area Technical College, A
Northcentral Technical College, A

U.S. Territories: Puerto Rico

Caribbean University, A
University of Puerto Rico, Mayagüez Campus, B

Canada

British Columbia

British Columbia Institute of Technology, AB
Thompson Rivers University, B

Maritime Provinces: Nova Scotia

Mount Saint Vincent University, B

Quebec

Concordia University, B
HEC Montreal, B
Université du Québec à Trois-Rivières, B

COMPUTER SYSTEMS NET-WORKING AND TELECOMMU-NICATIONS

United States

Alabama

Remington College - Mobile Campus, A
Virginia College in Huntsville, AB

Alaska

Charter College, A
University of Alaska Anchorage, A

Arizona

Chandler-Gilbert Community College, A
Cochise County Community College District, A
CollegeAmerica - Flagstaff, A
DeVry University (Phoenix), AB
GateWay Community College, A
Glendale Community College, A
Northland Pioneer College, A
Paradise Valley Community College, A
Pima Community College, A
South Mountain Community College, A

Arkansas

Arkansas State University - Beebe, A
Phillips Community College of the University of Arkansas, A
Remington College - Little Rock Campus, A
Southeast Arkansas College, A

California

American River College, A
Antelope Valley College, A
Cabrillo College, A
California State University, East Bay, B
Cañada College, A
Cerritos College, A
Coleman University, AB
College of the Canyons, A
College of Marin, A
College of the Redwoods, A
College of San Mateo, A
Contra Costa College, A
Cosumnes River College, A
DeVry University (Alhambra), AB
DeVry University (Anaheim), AB
DeVry University (Bakersfield), AB
DeVry University (Fremont), AB
DeVry University (Long Beach), AB
DeVry University (Oakland), AB
DeVry University (Oxnard), AB
DeVry University (Palmdale), AB
DeVry University (Pomona), AB
DeVry University (San Diego), AB

DeVry University (Sherman Oaks), AB
Fresno City College, A
Gavilan College, A
Grossmont College, A
Long Beach City College, A
Los Angeles City College, A
Merritt College, A
MiraCosta College, A
Mt. Sierra College, B
Ohlone College, A
Oxnard College, A
Palomar College, A
San Jose City College, A
Sierra College, A
Southwestern College, A

Colorado

Arapahoe Community College, A
Colorado Mesa University, A
Colorado Mountain College (Glenwood Springs), A
DeVry University (Colorado Springs), AB
DeVry University (Westminster), AB
Everest College (Colorado Springs), A
Front Range Community College, A
IntelliTec College (Colorado Springs), A
National American University (Denver), AB
Red Rocks Community College, A
Western State Colorado University, B

Connecticut

Norwalk Community College, A
Quinebaug Valley Community College, A

Delaware

Delaware Technical & Community College, Stanton/Wilmington Campus, A
Delaware Technical & Community College, Terry Campus, A

Florida

College of Business and Technology - Flagler Campus, A
College of Business and Technology - Main Campus, A
College of Business and Technology - Miami Gardens, A
Daytona State College, A
DeVry University (Jacksonville), AB
DeVry University (Miramar), AB
DeVry University (Orlando), AB
Eastern Florida State College, A
Florida National University, A
Florida SouthWestern State College, A
Florida State College at Jacksonville, B
Florida Technical College (Orlando), A
Gulf Coast State College, A
Keiser University, B
Lincoln College of Technology, A
Miami Dade College, A
Pasco-Hernando State College, A
Seminole State College of Florida, A
Southeastern College - West Palm Beach, A
Southern Technical College (Fort Myers), A
Tallahassee Community College, A

Georgia

Athens Technical College, A
Augusta Technical College, A
Central Georgia Technical College, A
Chattahoochee Technical College, A
Clayton State University, A
Coastal Pines Technical College, A
Columbus Technical College, A
DeVry University (Alpharetta), AB
DeVry University (Decatur), AB
DeVry University (Duluth), AB
Georgia Piedmont Technical College, A
Gwinnett Technical College, A
Lanier Technical College, A
North Georgia Technical College, A
Oconee Fall Line Technical College, A
Ogeechee Technical College, A
Savannah Technical College, A
South Georgia Technical College, A
Southeastern Technical College, A

Southern Crescent Technical College, A
Southern Regional Technical College, A
West Georgia Technical College, A
Wiregrass Georgia Technical College, A

Hawaii

Remington College - Honolulu Campus, A

Idaho

Boise State University, B
Broadview University - Boise, A
College of Southern Idaho, A
Eastern Idaho Technical College, A
Idaho State University, AB
Stevens-Henager College (Boise), A

Illinois

Carl Sandburg College, A
City Colleges of Chicago, Harry S. Truman College, A
College of Lake County, A
Danville Area Community College, A
DePaul University, B
DeVry University (Addison), AB
DeVry University (Chicago), AB
DeVry University (Tinley Park), AB
DeVry University Online, AB
Heartland Community College, A
Illinois Central College, A
Illinois Eastern Community Colleges, Lincoln Trail College, A
Illinois State University, B
Illinois Valley Community College, A
Joliet Junior College, A
Lake Land College, A
Lewis and Clark Community College, A
Lincoln Land Community College, A
McHenry County College, A
Parkland College, A
Robert Morris University Illinois, A
Rock Valley College, A
Roosevelt University, B
Shawnee Community College, A
Triton College, A
Western Illinois University, B

Indiana

Brightwood College, Hammond Campus, A
Harrison College, A
Indiana Tech, AB
International Business College (Fort Wayne), A
International Business College (Indianapolis), A
Ivy Tech Community College - Bloomington, A
Ivy Tech Community College - East Central, A
Ivy Tech Community College - Kokomo, A
Ivy Tech Community College - Lafayette, A
Ivy Tech Community College - Southern Indiana, A
Ivy Tech Community College - Wabash Valley, A
Vincennes University, A

Iowa

Ellsworth Community College, A
Hawkeye Community College, A
Indian Hills Community College, A
Iowa Lakes Community College, A
Marshalltown Community College, A
North Iowa Area Community College, A
Northwest Iowa Community College, A
Southwestern Community College, A

Kansas

Allen Community College, A
Barton County Community College, A
Coffeyville Community College, A
Flint Hills Technical College, A
Garden City Community College, A
Grantham University, AB
Hutchinson Community College, A
Independence Community College, A
Johnson County Community College, A
Kansas City Kansas Community College, A
Kansas State University, B
Manhattan Area Technical College, A
Pratt Community College, A

Kentucky

Beckfield College, A
Daymar College (Bellevue), A
Daymar College (Owensboro), A
Sullivan College of Technology and Design, A

Louisiana

Baton Rouge School of Computers, A
Remington College - Baton Rouge Campus, A
Remington College - Lafayette Campus, A
South Louisiana Community College, A
Sowela Technical Community College, A

Maine

Northern Maine Community College, A

Maryland

Anne Arundel Community College, A
Brightwood College, Baltimore Campus, A
Brightwood College,-Beltsville Campus, A
Brightwood College, Towson Campus, A
Community College of Baltimore County, A
Howard Community College, A
Johns Hopkins University, B
Stevenson University, B

Massachusetts

Bunker Hill Community College, A
Cape Cod Community College, A
Northern Essex Community College, A
Wentworth Institute of Technology, B

Michigan

Alpena Community College, A
Baker College, A
Bay de Noc Community College, A
Davenport University, B
Delta College, A
Ferris State University, B
Grand Rapids Community College, A
Henry Ford College, A
Lansing Community College, A
Mott Community College, A
Northern Michigan University, B
St. Clair County Community College, A
Southwestern Michigan College, A
Washtenaw Community College, A

Minnesota

Academy College, A
Alexandria Technical and Community College, A
Anoka-Ramsey Community College, A
Central Lakes College, A
Century College, A
Dakota County Technical College, A
Dunwoody College of Technology, A
Globe University - Minneapolis, A
Globe University - Woodbury, A
Hennepin Technical College, A
Herzing University, A
Inver Hills Community College, A
Mesabi Range College, A
Minneapolis Business College, A
Minneapolis Community and Technical College, A
Minnesota School of Business - Blaine, A
Minnesota School of Business - Brooklyn Center, A
Minnesota School of Business - Elk River, A
Minnesota School of Business - Lakeville, A
Minnesota School of Business - Plymouth, A
Minnesota School of Business - Richfield, A
Minnesota School of Business - Rochester, A
Minnesota School of Business - St. Cloud, A
Minnesota State College - Southeast Technical, A
Minnesota State Community and Technical College, A
Minnesota West Community and Technical College, A
Northland Community and Technical College, A
Northwest Technical College, A
Ridgewater College, A
Riverland Community College, A
Saint Paul College - A Community & Technical College, A
South Central College, A
University of Minnesota, Duluth, B

University of Minnesota, Twin Cities Campus, B

Mississippi

Antonelli College (Jackson), A
East Central Community College, A
East Mississippi Community College, A
Hinds Community College, A
Holmes Community College, A
Mississippi Gulf Coast Community College, A
Southwest Mississippi Community College, A

Missouri

American Business & Technology University, A
Crowder College, A
DeVry University (Kansas City), AB
East Central College, A
Hickey College, A
Jefferson College, A
Lindenwood University, B
Ozarks Technical Community College, A
State Fair Community College, A
State Technical College of Missouri, A
Vatterott College (Saint Charles), A
Vatterott College (Saint Joseph), A

Montana

Blackfeet Community College, A
Fort Peck Community College, A
Great Falls College Montana State University, A
Montana Tech of The University of Montana, AB
University of Great Falls, B

Nevada

College of Southern Nevada, A
DeVry University, AB
Great Basin College, A
Truckee Meadows Community College, A

New Hampshire

Great Bay Community College, A
NHTI, Concord's Community College, A
River Valley Community College, A

New Jersey

Bloomfield College, B
Cumberland County College, A
DeVry University (North Brunswick), AB
DeVry University (Paramus), AB
Kean University, B
Mercer County Community College, A
Raritan Valley Community College, A
Rowan College at Gloucester County, A

New York

Adirondack Community College, A
Borough of Manhattan Community College of the City University of New York, A
DeVry College of New York, AB
Fiorello H. LaGuardia Community College of the City University of New York, A
Genesee Community College, A
Iona College, B
Island Drafting and Technical Institute, A
Morrisville State College, B
Nassau Community College, A
Onondaga Community College, A
Pace University, A
Pace University, Pleasantville Campus, A
Rochester Institute of Technology, B
Rockland Community College, A
TCI - College of Technology, A
Trocaire College, A
Westchester Community College, A
Wood Tobe - Coburn School, A

North Carolina

Asheville-Buncombe Technical Community College, A
Brightwood College, Charlotte Campus, A
Cape Fear Community College, A
Carteret Community College, A
Catawba Valley Community College, A
Central Carolina Community College, A
Chowan University, B
Coastal Carolina Community College, A

Craven Community College, A
DeVry University, AB
Durham Technical Community College, A
ECPI University (Charlotte), A
Edgecombe Community College, A
Fayetteville Technical Community College, A
Forsyth Technical Community College, A
Gaston College, A
Guilford Technical Community College, A
Haywood Community College, A
King's College, A
Lenoir Community College, A
Pitt Community College, A
Randolph Community College, A
Robeson Community College, A
Stanly Community College, A
Surry Community College, A
The University of North Carolina at Greensboro, B
Wake Technical Community College, A
Wilkes Community College, A
Wilson Community College, A

North Dakota

Bismarck State College, A
North Dakota State College of Science, A

Ohio

Antonelli College, A
Baldwin Wallace University, B
Belmont College, A
Bowling Green State University, B
Bowling Green State University - Firelands College, A
Brightwood College, Dayton Campus, A
Clark State Community College, A
Davis College, A
DeVry University (Columbus), AB
DeVry University (Seven Hills), AB
Edison Community College, A
Lakeland Community College, A
Lorain County Community College, A
Marion Technical College, A
Mount Vernon Nazarene University, B
Ohio University, B
Remington College - Cleveland Campus, A
Sinclair Community College, A
Stark State College, A
Stautzenberger College (Maumee), A
Terra State Community College, A
Tiffin University, B
The University of Akron, AB
The University of Findlay, B

Oklahoma

DeVry University, AB
Northwestern Oklahoma State University, B
Oklahoma City Community College, A

Oregon

Central Oregon Community College, A
Clackamas Community College, A
Lane Community College, A
Pioneer Pacific College - Eugene/Springfield Branch, A

Pennsylvania

Bradford School, A
Brightwood Career Institute, Harrisburg Campus, A
Brightwood Career Institute, Pittsburgh Campus, A
Bucks County Community College, A
Community College of Allegheny County, A
Community College of Beaver County, A
Delaware County Community College, A
DeVry University (Fort Washington), AB
DeVry University (King of Prussia), AB
DeVry University (Philadelphia), AB
Harrisburg Area Community College, A
Lansdale School of Business, A
Laurel Business Institute, A
Lehigh Carbon Community College, A
Lincoln Technical Institute (Allentown), A
Luzerne County Community College, A
Montgomery County Community College, A
Northampton Community College, A
Penn Commercial Business and Technical School, A

Pennsylvania College of Technology, B
University of Pennsylvania, B
Westmoreland County Community College, A

Rhode Island

Community College of Rhode Island, A

South Carolina

Aiken Technical College, A
Midlands Technical College, A
Trident Technical College, A

South Dakota

Southeast Technical Institute, A
Western Dakota Technical Institute, A

Tennessee

Daymar College (Clarksville), A
DeVry University, AB
Nashville State Community College, A
Northeast State Community College, A
Pellissippi State Community College, A
Remington College - Memphis Campus, A

Texas

Angelina College, A
Austin Community College District, A
Blinn College, A
Brightwood College, Arlington Campus, A
Brightwood College, Beaumont Campus, A
Brightwood College, El Paso Campus, A
Cedar Valley College, A
Del Mar College, A
DeVry University (Austin), AB
DeVry University (Irving), AB
DeVry University (San Antonio), AB
Eastfield College, A
Houston Community College, A
Kilgore College, A
Lamar State College - Port Arthur, A
Laredo Community College, A
Mountain View College, A
Northeast Texas Community College, A
Odessa College, A
Remington College - Dallas Campus, A
Remington College - Fort Worth Campus, A
Remington College - Houston Southeast Campus, A
St. Philip's College, A
Tyler Junior College, A
University of the Incarnate Word, B
Victoria College, A
Virginia College in Austin, A

Utah

Broadview University - Layton, A
Broadview University - West Jordan, A
Utah Valley University, B
Weber State University, AB

Vermont

Champlain College, B
Community College of Vermont, A

Virginia

Centura College (Chesapeake), A
Centura College (Newport News), A
Centura College (North Chesterfield), A
Centura College (Virginia Beach), A
DeVry University (Arlington), AB
DeVry University (Chesapeake), AB
DeVry University (Manassas), AB
J. Sargeant Reynolds Community College, A
Stratford University (Falls Church), A
Virginia Union University, B

Washington

Bates Technical College, A
Bellevue College, A
Bellingham Technical College, A
Big Bend Community College, A
Clark College, A
Clover Park Technical College, A
Columbia Basin College, A
Edmonds Community College, A
Green River College, A

Highline College, A
North Seattle College, A
Olympic College, A
Pierce College at Fort Steilacoom, A
Renton Technical College, A
Tacoma Community College, A
Walla Walla Community College, A
Wenatchee Valley College, A

Wisconsin

Blackhawk Technical College, A
Chippewa Valley Technical College, A
Fox Valley Technical College, A
Gateway Technical College, A
Globe University - Eau Claire, A
Globe University - Green Bay, A
Globe University - La Crosse, A
Globe University - Madison East, A
Globe University - Madison West, A
Globe University - Wausau, A
Milwaukee Area Technical College, A
Moraine Park Technical College, A
Northcentral Technical College, A
Northeast Wisconsin Technical College, A
Southwest Wisconsin Technical College, A
University of Wisconsin - Stout, B
Waukesha County Technical College, A
Wisconsin Indianhead Technical College, A

Wyoming

Eastern Wyoming College, A

U.S. Territories: Guam

Guam Community College, A

U.S. Territories: Puerto Rico

Bayamón Central University, B
EDP University of Puerto Rico, B
EDP University of Puerto Rico - San Sebastian, B
Inter American University of Puerto Rico, Aguadilla Campus, B
Inter American University of Puerto Rico, Bayamón Campus, B
Inter American University of Puerto Rico, Ponce Campus, B

Canada

British Columbia

Thompson Rivers University, B

Maritime Provinces: Nova Scotia

Cape Breton University, B

Ontario

Centennial College, B
University of Toronto, B

Quebec

Concordia University, B

COMPUTER TEACHER EDUCATION

United States

Colorado

Colorado State University, B

Florida

Full Sail University, B

Illinois

Concordia University Chicago, B

Iowa

Buena Vista University, B
Dordt College, B

Kansas

Central Christian College of Kansas, A

Louisiana

Southern University and Agricultural and Mechanical College, B

Michigan

Alma College, B
Eastern Michigan University, B
Michigan State University, B
Olivet College, B

Nebraska

University of Nebraska - Lincoln, B

New York

Utica College, B

Ohio

Bowling Green State University, B
Wright State University, B

South Dakota

Dakota State University, B

Texas

Abilene Christian University, B
Baylor University, B
Dallas Baptist University, B
Howard Payne University, B
McMurry University, B

Washington

Western Washington University, B

Wisconsin

Edgewood College, B

U.S. Territories: Puerto Rico

National University College (Bayamón), B

Canada

Alberta

University of Alberta, B

Quebec

Bishop's University, B

COMPUTER TECHNOLOGY/ COMPUTER SYSTEMS TECHNOLOGY

United States

Alabama

Enterprise State Community College, A

Alaska

University of Alaska Anchorage, A
University of Alaska Anchorage, Kodiak College, A

Arizona

Coconino Community College, A

Arkansas

Arkansas State University - Beebe, A
Arkansas State University - Newport, A
Pulaski Technical College, A
Southern Arkansas University Tech, A
University of Arkansas Community College at Morrilton, A

California

California College San Diego (San Diego), A
Pasadena City College, A
Point Loma Nazarene University, B

Colorado

CollegeAmerica - Denver, A
CollegeAmerica - Fort Collins, A

Colorado State University, B

Delaware

Delaware Technical & Community College, Jack F. Owens Campus, A
Delaware Technical & Community College, Terry Campus, A

Florida

Daytona State College, AB
Florida Atlantic University, B
Fortis Institute (Palm Springs), A
Hillsborough Community College, A
Lake-Sumter State College, A
Miami Dade College, A
Northwest Florida State College, A
Pasco-Hernando State College, A

Georgia

Coastal Pines Technical College, A
Dalton State College, A

Illinois

Rend Lake College, A

Indiana

Harrison College, A

Iowa

Vatterott College, AB

Kansas

Manhattan Area Technical College, A

Kentucky

Madisonville Community College, A
Sullivan College of Technology and Design, A

Louisiana

ITI Technical College, A

Maine

Eastern Maine Community College, A

Maryland

Capitol Technology University, A
Montgomery College, A

Massachusetts

Benjamin Franklin Institute of Technology, A

Michigan

Bay de Noc Community College, A
Kellogg Community College, A
Lansing Community College, A
Wayne State University, B

Minnesota

Anoka Technical College, A
Central Lakes College, A
Century College, A
Inver Hills Community College, A
Lake Superior College, A
Minnesota State College - Southeast Technical, A
Minnesota State Community and Technical College, A
Minnesota West Community and Technical College, A
Normandale Community College, A
Ridgewater College, A

Mississippi

Coahoma Community College, A

Missouri

Southeast Missouri State University, A

Montana

Aaniiih Nakoda College, A
Fort Peck Community College, A

New Mexico

Western New Mexico University, A

New York

Corning Community College, A
Erie Community College, South Campus, A
Island Drafting and Technical Institute, A
Jefferson Community College, A
Mildred Elley School, A
Morrisville State College, A
Rensselaer Polytechnic Institute, B

North Carolina

Cape Fear Community College, A
ECPI University (Raleigh), A
Stanly Community College, A

North Dakota

Dakota College at Bottineau, A

Ohio

American National University (Kettering), A
Bowling Green State University, B
Fortis College (Cuyahoga Falls), A
James A. Rhodes State College, A
Lakeland Community College, A
Lorain County Community College, A
Miami University Hamilton, A
Ohio Business College (Sheffield Village), A
Southern State Community College, A
University of Cincinnati Blue Ash College, A
University of Cincinnati Clermont College, A

Oklahoma

Vatterott College (Tulsa), A

Oregon

Chemeketa Community College, A
Clackamas Community College, A
Portland Community College, A

Pennsylvania

Butler County Community College, A
Cambria-Rowe Business College (Johnstown), A
Commonwealth Technical Institute, A
Community College of Allegheny County, A
Delaware County Community College, A
Luzerne County Community College, A
Metropolitan Career Center Computer Technology Institute, A
Penn Commercial Business and Technical School, A
Pittsburgh Technical Institute, A
Reading Area Community College, A

Rhode Island

New England Institute of Technology, AB

South Carolina

Forrest College, A

South Dakota

Southeast Technical Institute, A

Tennessee

Nashville State Community College, A
National College (Knoxville), A
Vatterott College (Memphis), A

Texas

Brookhaven College, A
Central Texas College, A
Grayson College, A
Lamar Institute of Technology, A
St. Philip's College, A
Texas State Technical College, A
Tyler Junior College, A

Virginia

American National University (Salem), A
ECPI University (Glen Allen), A
ECPI University (Richmond), A
Paul D. Camp Community College, A

Washington

Bates Technical College, A
Edmonds Community College, A

Skagit Valley College, A
Walla Walla Community College, A

West Virginia

BridgeValley Community and Technical College (Montgomery), A
West Virginia Junior College - Charleston, A

Wisconsin

Milwaukee Area Technical College, A

Wyoming

Central Wyoming College, A

U.S. Territories: Puerto Rico

ICPR Junior College - Hato Rey Campus, A

COMPUTER TYPOGRAPHY AND COMPOSITION EQUIPMENT OPERATOR

United States

Arizona

Paradise Valley Community College, A

California

College of the Sequoias, A
Laney College, A
Monterey Peninsula College, A
Ohlone College, A
Saddleback College, A

Colorado

Lamar Community College, A

Connecticut

Gateway Community College, A
Housatonic Community College, A

Florida

Indian River State College, A
St. Johns River State College, A

Illinois

College of DuPage, A
MacCormac College, A

Kansas

Pratt Community College, A

Maryland

Prince George's Community College, A

Massachusetts

Northern Essex Community College, A

Missouri

Metropolitan Community College - Kansas City, A

New Mexico

Doña Ana Community College, A
New Mexico Junior College, A
University of New Mexico - Valencia Campus, A

New York

Fulton-Montgomery Community College, A

Ohio

Cuyahoga Community College, A
University of Cincinnati Clermont College, A

Texas

Del Mar College, A
Paris Junior College, A
South Texas College, A

Virginia

ECPI University (Newport News), A
ECPI University (Richmond), A

Washington

Highline College, A
Pierce College at Puyallup, A
Seattle Central College, A
Spokane Community College, A

Wisconsin

Madison Area Technical College, A

CONCRETE FINISHING/CONCRETE FINISHER

United States

Illinois

Black Hawk College, A
Southwestern Illinois College, A

CONDENSED MATTER PHYSICS

United States

Iowa

Iowa State University of Science and Technology, MD

New Jersey

Rutgers University - New Brunswick, MD

Ohio

Cleveland State University, M

West Virginia

West Virginia University, MD

Canada

Alberta

University of Alberta, MD

British Columbia

University of Victoria, MD

Newfoundland and Labrador

Memorial University of Newfoundland, MD

CONDUCTING

United States

California

Chapman University, B

Nebraska

Union College, B

New York

The New School College of Performing Arts, B

Texas

McMurry University, B

CONFLICT RESOLUTION AND MEDIATION/PEACE STUDIES

United States

Arizona

University of Phoenix - Online Campus, O

Arkansas

University of Arkansas at Little Rock, O

California

California State University, Dominguez Hills, M
Fresno Pacific University, MO
Henley-Putnam University, M
Pepperdine University, M
Trident University International, M
University of San Diego, M

Colorado

Colorado Technical University Colorado Springs, M
Colorado Technical University Denver South, M
University of Denver, M

Connecticut

University of Bridgeport, M
University of New Haven, MO

District of Columbia

American University, MO
Georgetown University, M

Florida

Nova Southeastern University, MDO

Georgia

Kennesaw State University, MD

Hawaii

University of Hawaii at Manoa, O

Idaho

University of Idaho, D

Illinois

Dominican University, M

Indiana

University of Notre Dame, MD

Kansas

Kansas State University, O

Maryland

Salisbury University, M
University of Baltimore, M

Massachusetts

Brandeis University, M
Cambridge College, M
Hult International Business School, M
Lesley University, M
Tufts University, MD
University of Massachusetts Amherst, MD
University of Massachusetts Boston, MO
University of Massachusetts Lowell, MO

Michigan

Wayne State University, MO

Minnesota

Walden University, MD

Missouri

University of Missouri, MO

Nebraska

Creighton University, MO

New Hampshire

Southern New Hampshire University, M

New Jersey

Montclair State University, MO

New York

Columbia University, M
Cornell University, MD
New York University, MO
Syracuse University, O
Yeshiva University, M

North Carolina

The University of North Carolina at Greensboro, MO
The University of North Carolina Wilmington, MO

Ohio

Antioch University Midwest, M

Oregon

Portland State University, M
Willamette University, M

Pennsylvania

Arcadia University, M
Duquesne University, O

Rhode Island

Salve Regina University, M

South Carolina

Columbia College, MO

Tennessee

Bethel University, M
Lipscomb University, MO

Texas

Abilene Christian University, MO
Dallas Baptist University, M
St. Mary's University, MO
Southern Methodist University, M

Vermont

Champlain College, M
Norwich University, M

Virginia

Eastern Mennonite University, MO
George Mason University, MDO
Old Dominion University, MD

West Virginia

American Public University System, M

Wisconsin

Marquette University, M
University of Wisconsin - Milwaukee, O

U.S. Territories: Puerto Rico

Universidad del Turabo, M
University of the Sacred Heart, M

Canada

British Columbia

Royal Roads University, MO
University of Victoria, M

Maritime Provinces: New Brunswick

University of New Brunswick Fredericton, M

Ontario

Carleton University, O
Saint Paul University, M
Wilfrid Laurier University, D

Quebec

Université de Sherbrooke, MO

CONSERVATION BIOLOGY

United States

Arizona

Arizona State University at the Tempe campus, M
Prescott College, B

California

California State University, Sacramento, M
California State University, Stanislaus, M

Colorado

Colorado State University, MD

Florida

Florida Institute of Technology, BM
University of Central Florida, MDO

Hawaii

University of Hawaii at Hilo, M
University of Hawaii at Manoa, MD

Idaho

University of Idaho, B

Illinois

Illinois State University, M
University of Illinois at Urbana - Champaign, MD

Maine

University of Maine at Machias, B

Maryland

Frostburg State University, M
University of Maryland, College Park, M

Massachusetts

Boston University, B

Michigan

Central Michigan University, M
Lake Superior State University, B
University of Michigan, M

Minnesota

Central Lakes College, A
University of Minnesota, Twin Cities Campus, MD

Missouri

University of Missouri, O

Nevada

University of Nevada, Reno, D

New Hampshire

University of New Hampshire, M

New York

Columbia University, M
Cornell University, MD
Fordham University, O
St. Lawrence University, B
State University of New York College of Environmental Science and Forestry, BMD
University at Albany, State University of New York, M

Pennsylvania

Cedar Crest College, B
Philadelphia University, B

Rhode Island

Bryant University, B

Texas

Texas State University, M

Vermont

Sterling College, B

Virginia

George Mason University, M

Washington

Seattle University, B

Wisconsin

University of Wisconsin - Madison, BM
University of Wisconsin - Stout, M

Canada

Alberta

University of Alberta, BMD

Ontario

The University of Western Ontario, B

CONSTRUCTION ENGINEERING

United States

Alabama

The University of Alabama, B

Arizona

Arizona State University at the Tempe campus, B

Arkansas

John Brown University, B
University of Arkansas at Little Rock, B

California

California State University, Long Beach, B
National University, B

Georgia

Kennesaw State University, B

Illinois

Bradley University, B
University of Illinois at Urbana - Champaign, B

Indiana

Purdue University, B

Iowa

Iowa State University of Science and Technology, B

Louisiana

Bossier Parish Community College, A

Nebraska

University of Nebraska - Lincoln, B

New Hampshire

Daniel Webster College, B

New Mexico

University of New Mexico, B

New York

New York University, B

North Carolina

North Carolina State University, B

North Dakota

North Dakota State University, B

Ohio

Bowling Green State University, B

Oregon

Oregon State University, B

Texas

Lamar University, B
Texas A&M University - Commerce, B
Texas Tech University, B

Wisconsin

Marquette University, B

Canada

Maritime Provinces: New Brunswick

University of New Brunswick Fredericton, B

Quebec

Concordia University, B
Université du Québec, École de technologie supérieure, B

CONSTRUCTION ENGINEERING AND MANAGEMENT

United States

Alabama

Auburn University, MD
The University of Alabama, MD
The University of Alabama at Birmingham, M

Arizona

Arizona State University at the Tempe campus, M

California

Stanford University, M

Colorado

Colorado School of Mines, MD
University of Colorado Boulder, MD

Florida

University of Central Florida, O

Illinois

Bradley University, M
Illinois Institute of Technology, M

Iowa

Iowa State University of Science and Technology, MD

Kansas

Pittsburg State University, M

Massachusetts

Massachusetts Institute of Technology, D

Michigan

Lawrence Technological University, M
University of Michigan, M

Mississippi

University of Southern Mississippi, M

Missouri

Missouri University of Science and Technology, MD
University of Missouri - Kansas City, O

Montana

Montana State University, M

New Jersey

Stevens Institute of Technology, O

New York

Columbia University, M

Ohio

Ohio University, M

Virginia

George Mason University, M
University of Virginia, D
Virginia Polytechnic Institute and State University, M

Washington

University of Washington, MD

Wisconsin

Marquette University, MDO

Canada

Alberta

University of Alberta, MD

Maritime Provinces: New Brunswick

University of New Brunswick Fredericton, MD

Quebec

Concordia University, MDO

CONSTRUCTION ENGINEERING TECHNOLOGY/TECHNICIAN

United States

Alabama

Community College of the Air Force, A
Jefferson State Community College, A
Tuskegee University, B
Wallace State Community College, A

Arizona

Arizona Western College, A
Yavapai College, A

Arkansas

John Brown University, B
University of Arkansas at Little Rock, B

California

California Baptist University, B
California State Polytechnic University, Pomona, B
California State University, Chico, B
California State University, Fresno, B
California State University, Long Beach, B
California State University, Sacramento, B
College of the Sequoias, A
De Anza College, A
El Camino College, A
Lassen Community College District, A
Los Angeles Pierce College, A
Los Angeles Trade-Technical College, A
Merced College, A
Saddleback College, A
San Diego Mesa College, A
San Diego State University, B
San Joaquin Delta College, A
Shasta College, A
Ventura College, A
Victor Valley College, A

Colorado

Colorado Mesa University, B

Connecticut

Norwalk Community College, A

Florida

College of Central Florida, A
Florida Agricultural and Mechanical University, B
Florida Institute of Technology, B
Florida International University, B
Gulf Coast State College, A
Miami Dade College, A
Pensacola State College, A
Santa Fe College, A
Seminole State College of Florida, AB
South Florida State College, A
State College of Florida Manatee-Sarasota, A
Tallahassee Community College, A
University of Florida, B
University of North Florida, B

Valencia College, A

Georgia

Georgia Southern University, B

Hawaii

University of Hawaii Maui College, A

Illinois

Bradley University, B
College of Lake County, A
Illinois Central College, A
Joliet Junior College, A
Lincoln Land Community College, A
Morrison Institute of Technology, A
Richland Community College, A
Rock Valley College, A
South Suburban College, A
Southern Illinois University Edwardsville, B

Indiana

Indiana University - Purdue University Fort Wayne, B

Iowa

Iowa Lakes Community College, A
Southeastern Community College, A

Kansas

Dodge City Community College, A
Kansas State University, B
Neosho County Community College, A
Pittsburg State University, B

Kentucky

Western Kentucky University, B

Louisiana

Bossier Parish Community College, A
Louisiana Tech University, B

Maine

Eastern Maine Community College, A
Washington County Community College, A

Maryland

University of Maryland Eastern Shore, B

Massachusetts

Fitchburg State University, B

Michigan

Baker College, A
Central Michigan University, B
Delta College, A
Ferris State University, A
Gogebic Community College, A
Lawrence Technological University, A
Macomb Community College, A
Michigan State University, B
Northern Michigan University, B
Wayne State University, B

Minnesota

Bemidji State University, B

Mississippi

Itawamba Community College, A
Southwest Mississippi Community College, A

Missouri

Crowder College, A
Missouri Western State University, B
North Central Missouri College, A
Ozarks Technical Community College, A
Three Rivers Community College, A

Montana

Blackfeet Community College, A
Helena College University of Montana, A
Miles Community College, A
Montana State University, B

Nebraska

Central Community College - Hastings Campus, A
Metropolitan Community College, A
Mid-Plains Community College, A
University of Nebraska - Lincoln, B

Nevada

University of Nevada, Las Vegas, B

New Hampshire

Manchester Community College, A

New Jersey

Fairleigh Dickinson University, Metropolitan Campus, B
Raritan Valley Community College, A
Rowan College at Burlington County, A
Thomas Edison State University, B

New Mexico

New Mexico Junior College, A
Santa Fe Community College, A
University of New Mexico - Gallup, A
University of New Mexico - Valencia Campus, A

New York

Farmingdale State College, B
Fulton-Montgomery Community College, A
Monroe Community College, A
New York City College of Technology of the City University of New York, A
Onondaga Community College, A
State University of New York College of Technology at Alfred, A
State University of New York College of Technology at Delhi, A
Suffolk County Community College, A
Sullivan County Community College, A
Tompkins Cortland Community College, A

North Carolina

Surry Community College, A
Vance-Granville Community College, A
Western Carolina University, B

North Dakota

North Dakota State College of Science, A

Ohio

Bowling Green State University, B
Columbus State Community College, A
Northwest State Community College, A
The Ohio State University, B
The Ohio State University Agricultural Technical Institute, A
Owens Community College, A
The University of Akron, AB
The University of Toledo, B

Oklahoma

Northern Oklahoma College, A
Oklahoma State University, B
Oklahoma State University Institute of Technology, A
Oklahoma State University, Oklahoma City, A
Redlands Community College, A

Oregon

Lane Community College, A
Portland Community College, A
Rogue Community College, A

Pennsylvania

Community College of Allegheny County, A
Community College of Philadelphia, A
Harrisburg Area Community College, A
New Castle School of Trades, A
Pennsylvania College of Technology, A
Williamson College of the Trades, A

South Carolina

Greenville Technical College, A
Midlands Technical College, A
Piedmont Technical College, A
Technical College of the Lowcountry, A

South Dakota

Lake Area Technical Institute, A
South Dakota State University, B
Southeast Technical Institute, A

Tennessee

Nashville State Community College, A

Texas

Brazosport College, A
Houston Community College, A
Laredo Community College, A
North Lake College, A
Odessa College, A
Panola College, A
Prairie View A&M University, B
St. Philip's College, A
Sam Houston State University, B
San Jacinto College District, A
Tarrant County College District, A
Texas A&M University, B
Texas State University, B
University of Houston, B
University of North Texas, B

Utah

Snow College, A
Southern Utah University, A

Vermont

Vermont Technical College, A

Virginia

Norfolk State University, B

Washington

Clark College, A
Edmonds Community College, A
Spokane Community College, A

Canada

British Columbia

British Columbia Institute of Technology, A

CONSTRUCTION/HEAVY EQUIPMENT/EARTHMOVING EQUIPMENT OPERATION

United States

Alaska

University of Alaska Anchorage, A

Arizona

Central Arizona College, A
GateWay Community College, A

Colorado

Trinidad State Junior College, A

Indiana

Ivy Tech Community College - Southwest, A
Ivy Tech Community College - Wabash Valley, A

Michigan

Lansing Community College, A

South Dakota

Lake Area Technical Institute, A

Texas

Brazosport College, A

CONSTRUCTION MANAGEMENT

United States

Alabama

Alabama Agricultural and Mechanical University, M
Auburn University, M

Alaska

University of Alaska Anchorage, AB
University of Alaska Anchorage, Kodiak College, A
University of Alaska Fairbanks, AO

Arizona

Arizona State University at the Tempe campus, BMD
Arizona Western College, A
Coconino Community College, A
Northern Arizona University, B
Phoenix College, A

Arkansas

John Brown University, B
University of Arkansas at Little Rock, M

California

California Baptist University, M
California State University, East Bay, M
California State University, Fresno, B
California State University, Northridge, B
National University, B
NewSchool of Architecture and Design, BM
San Joaquin Valley College (Ontario), A
San Joaquin Valley College - Online, A
University of California, Berkeley, O
University of Southern California, M

Colorado

Colorado State University, BM
Redstone College - Denver, A
University of Denver, M

Connecticut

Central Connecticut State University, BMO
Three Rivers Community College, A

Delaware

Delaware Technical & Community College, Jack F. Owens Campus, A
Delaware Technical & Community College, Stanton/Wilmington Campus, A
Delaware Technical & Community College, Terry Campus, A

District of Columbia

University of the District of Columbia, A

Florida

Everglades University (Boca Raton), B
Everglades University (Maitland), B
Everglades University (Sarasota), B
Florida International University, M
Polytechnic University of Puerto Rico, Miami Campus, M
Polytechnic University of Puerto Rico, Orlando Campus, M
University of Florida, MD
University of North Florida, M

Georgia

Ashworth College, A
Kennesaw State University, BM

Idaho

Boise State University, B
Brigham Young University - Idaho, B

Illinois

Bradley University, B
Illinois Institute of Technology, M
Illinois State University, B

Kankakee Community College, A
Kaskaskia College, A
McHenry County College, A
Triton College, A
Waubonsee Community College, A
Western Illinois University, B

Indiana

Ball State University, B
Indiana State University, B
Purdue University, M

Iowa

Iowa Lakes Community College, A
University of Northern Iowa, B

Kansas

Pittsburg State University, B
The University of Kansas, M

Kentucky

Eastern Kentucky University, B
Northern Kentucky University, B

Louisiana

Louisiana State University and Agricultural & Mechanical College, BMD
University of Louisiana at Monroe, B

Massachusetts

Wentworth Institute of Technology, ABM
Worcester Polytechnic Institute, M

Michigan

Eastern Michigan University, BM
Ferris State University, B
Lansing Community College, A
Lawrence Technological University, B
Michigan State University, BMD
Michigan Technological University, B
Oakland Community College, A

Minnesota

Dunwoody College of Technology, AB
Minnesota State Community and Technical College - Moorhead, A
Minnesota State University Moorhead, B
North Hennepin Community College, A

Mississippi

Mississippi State University, B

Missouri

Missouri State University, BM

Nebraska

Hastings College, B

Nevada

University of Nevada, Las Vegas, B
Western Nevada College, B

New Jersey

Stevens Institute of Technology, MO

New Mexico

Central New Mexico Community College, A
University of New Mexico, M

New York

Columbia University, M
New York University, MO
State University of New York College of Environmental Science and Forestry, BMD
State University of New York College of Technology at Alfred, AB
State University of New York College of Technology at Delhi, B

North Carolina

Appalachian State University, B
Caldwell Community College and Technical Institute, A

East Carolina University, M
North Carolina Agricultural and Technical State University, M
The University of North Carolina at Charlotte, M
Western Carolina University, BM

North Dakota

North Dakota State University, BM

Ohio

Bowling Green State University, M
Kent State University, B
Ohio Northern University, B
The Ohio State University, B
The Ohio State University Agricultural Technical Institute, A

Oklahoma

Oklahoma State University, Oklahoma City, A
University of Oklahoma, BM

Oregon

Klamath Community College, A

Pennsylvania

Carnegie Mellon University, MD
Delaware County Community College, A
Drexel University, BM
Harrisburg University of Science and Technology, M
Northampton Community College, A
Philadelphia University, M

Rhode Island

New England Institute of Technology, M
Roger Williams University, BM

South Carolina

Clemson University, BM

South Dakota

South Dakota School of Mines and Technology, M

Texas

Texas A&M University, M
University of Houston, M
The University of Texas at Arlington, M
The University of Texas at El Paso, MO
The University of Texas at Tyler, B

Utah

Brigham Young University, M
Utah Valley University, AB

Vermont

Norwich University, M
Vermont Technical College, AB

Virginia

Virginia Polytechnic Institute and State University, BM

Washington

Central Washington University, B
Renton Technical College, A
University of Washington, BM
Washington State University, B

Wisconsin

Marquette University, MDO
Milwaukee School of Engineering, BM
University of Wisconsin - Stout, BM

Wyoming

Casper College, A

Canada

Alberta

Southern Alberta Institute of Technology, B

British Columbia

Thompson Rivers University, B

CONSTRUCTION TRADES

United States

Arizona

Coconino Community College, A

Arkansas

John Brown University, AB
Pulaski Technical College, A

California

Citrus College, A
College of the Redwoods, A
Cosumnes River College, A
Cuesta College, A
Fresno City College, A
Fullerton College, A
Lassen Community College District, A
National University, B
Orange Coast College, A
Palo Verde College, A
Palomar College, A
Pasadena City College, A
San Jose City College, A
Sierra College, A

Colorado

Colorado Mesa University, A
Lamar Community College, A
Red Rocks Community College, A
Trinidad State Junior College, A

Georgia

Ogeechee Technical College, A

Illinois

Illinois Eastern Community Colleges, Frontier Community College, A
Illinois Eastern Community Colleges, Lincoln Trail College, A
Southwestern Illinois College, A

Indiana

Ivy Tech Community College - East Central, A
Ivy Tech Community College - Kokomo, A
Ivy Tech Community College - Northeast, A
Ivy Tech Community College - Northwest, A
Ivy Tech Community College - Richmond, A
Vincennes University, A

Iowa

Ellsworth Community College, A
Indian Hills Community College, A
Iowa Lakes Community College, A
Iowa Western Community College, A
Kirkwood Community College, A
Marshalltown Community College, A
Northeast Iowa Community College, A
Northwest Iowa Community College, A

Kentucky

Owensboro Community and Technical College, A

Maine

Central Maine Community College, A
Northern Maine Community College, A
York County Community College, A

Michigan

Bay Mills Community College, A
Jackson College, A
Northern Michigan University, A

Missouri

Crowder College, A
East Central College, A

New Mexico

University of New Mexico - Taos, A

New York

Dutchess Community College, A
Hudson Valley Community College, A
Morrisville State College, A
State University of New York College of Technology at Alfred, A
Utica College, B

North Carolina

College of The Albemarle, A
Pitt Community College, A

North Dakota

United Tribes Technical College, A

Oklahoma

Oklahoma State University, Oklahoma City, A

Oregon

Chemeketa Community College, A
Clackamas Community College, A
Portland Community College, A
Rogue Community College, A

Pennsylvania

Community College of Allegheny County, A
Harrisburg Area Community College, A
Lehigh Carbon Community College, A
Triangle Tech, Greensburg, A

South Dakota

Mitchell Technical Institute, A
Sinte Gleska University, A

Texas

Texas State Technical College, A

Virginia

Liberty University, A

Wyoming

Casper College, A

U.S. Territories: American Samoa

American Samoa Community College, A

Canada

British Columbia

British Columbia Institute of Technology, A

CONSUMER ECONOMICS

United States

Alabama

The University of Alabama, M

California

California State University, Long Beach, M

Colorado

Colorado State University, M

Delaware

Delaware State University, B

Georgia

University of Georgia, BMD

Idaho

University of Idaho, M

Illinois

University of Illinois at Urbana - Champaign, BMD

Indiana

Purdue University, MD

Iowa

Iowa State University of Science and Technology, MD

Kansas

Kansas State University, D

Kentucky

University of Kentucky, B

Louisiana

Louisiana Tech University, B

Missouri

University of Missouri, MDO

Nebraska

University of Nebraska - Lincoln, MD

New York

Cornell University, D
State University of New York at Oswego, M

North Carolina

North Carolina Agricultural and Technical State University, M

North Dakota

North Dakota State University, MO

Ohio

Ohio University, M

Oklahoma

Oklahoma State University, M

South Carolina

University of South Carolina, M

South Dakota

South Dakota State University, BM

Tennessee

The University of Tennessee, BMD

Texas

Texas Tech University, MD

Utah

University of Utah, BM
Utah State University, M

Wisconsin

University of Wisconsin - Madison, MD

Wyoming

University of Wyoming, M

Canada

Ontario

University of Guelph, M

Quebec

Université Laval, O

CONSUMER MERCHANDISING/ RETAILING MANAGEMENT

United States

Arizona

University of Phoenix - Online Campus, AB
University of Phoenix - Phoenix Campus, B

California

Academy of Art University, AB
Glendale Community College, A
Golden West College, A

Los Angeles City College, A
Merced College, A
Saddleback College, A
San Francisco State University, B
University of Phoenix - Bay Area Campus, B
University of Phoenix - Sacramento Valley Campus, B
West Los Angeles College, A

Colorado

Colorado Mountain College (Steamboat Springs), A
University of Phoenix - Colorado Springs Downtown Campus, B

Connecticut

Gateway Community College, A

District of Columbia

University of Phoenix - Washington D.C. Campus, B

Florida

Indian River State College, A

Georgia

Savannah College of Art and Design, B
University of Phoenix - Atlanta Campus, B
University of Phoenix - Augusta Campus, B
University of Phoenix - Columbus Georgia Campus, AB

Hawaii

University of Phoenix - Hawaii Campus, B

Illinois

Bradley University, B
MacCormac College, A
Parkland College, A

Indiana

Purdue University, B

Iowa

Iowa Lakes Community College, A

Kentucky

Madisonville Community College, A

Massachusetts

Newbury College, B
Simmons College, B

Michigan

University of Phoenix - Detroit Campus, B

Missouri

Fontbonne University, B

Nevada

University of Phoenix - Las Vegas Campus, B

New Jersey

Passaic County Community College, A
University of Phoenix - Jersey City Campus, B

New Mexico

Doña Ana Community College, A

New York

Clinton Community College, A
Monroe Community College, A
Niagara County Community College, A
North Country Community College, A
Suffolk County Community College, A
Sullivan County Community College, A
Syracuse University, B
Westchester Community College, A

North Carolina

Central Piedmont Community College, A

Ohio

Lorain County Community College, A
Sinclair Community College, A

Stark State College, A

Oklahoma

University of Central Oklahoma, B

Oregon

Oregon State University, B

Pennsylvania

Harcum College, A
Laurel Business Institute, A
University of Phoenix - Philadelphia Campus, B

Tennessee

University of Memphis, B

Texas

Cisco College, A
Del Mar College, A
Navarro College, A
South Plains College, A
Tarrant County College District, A
University of Phoenix - Dallas Campus, B
University of Phoenix - Houston Campus, B

Virginia

J. Sargeant Reynolds Community College, A

Washington

Shoreline Community College, A
Spokane Falls Community College, A
University of Phoenix - Western Washington Campus, B

Wisconsin

Western Technical College, A

Canada

Quebec

HEC Montreal, B

CONSUMER SERVICES AND ADVOCACY

United States

Arizona

Rio Salado College, A

California

Ohlone College, A
Saddleback College, A
San Diego City College, A

Florida

Pensacola State College, A

New York

State University of New York College at Oneonta, B

Tennessee

Carson-Newman University, B
Tennessee State University, B

Texas

Texas State University, B

Canada

Quebec

Université Laval, B

COOKING AND RELATED CULINARY ARTS

United States

Alabama

Virginia College in Birmingham, A

California

Cabrillo College, A
Cerritos College, A
City College of San Francisco, A
Columbia College, A
Contra Costa College, A
Cuesta College, A
Cypress College, A
Feather River College, A
Grossmont College, A
Long Beach City College, A
Orange Coast College, A
Southwestern College, A

Colorado

Colorado Mesa University, A
Pikes Peak Community College, A
Pueblo Community College, A

Florida

Miami Dade College, A
Pensacola State College, A

Hawaii

Hawaii Community College, A
Kapiolani Community College, A
Leeward Community College, A

Indiana

Harrison College, A

Maine

Kennebec Valley Community College, A

Minnesota

Minnesota State Community and Technical College, A
South Central College, A

Missouri

Culinary Institute of St. Louis at Hickey College, A
Hickey College, A

Nevada

College of Southern Nevada, A
Truckee Meadows Community College, A

New York

Adirondack Community College, A
Kingsborough Community College of the City University of New York, A

North Carolina

Harrison College, A

Ohio

Bradford School, A
Columbus Culinary Institute at Bradford School, A

Oregon

Central Oregon Community College, A

Pennsylvania

Butler County Community College, A

Texas

Grayson College, A
Remington College - Dallas Campus, A

Virginia

J. Sargeant Reynolds Community College, A

CORPORATE AND ORGANIZATIONAL COMMUNICATION

United States

Alabama

Troy University, M

Alaska

University of Alaska Fairbanks, M

California

California State University, San Bernardino, M
Golden Gate University, MO
National University, M
University of Southern California, M

Colorado

University of Colorado Denver, M
University of Denver, M

Connecticut

Central Connecticut State University, M
Sacred Heart University, M
University of Connecticut, D

District of Columbia

Howard University, MD

Florida

Barry University, M
Florida State University, M
University of South Florida, MO

Georgia

Armstrong State University, MO

Illinois

Argosy University, Schaumburg, D
DePaul University, M
Illinois Institute of Technology, M
Loyola University Chicago, M
Northwestern University, M
Roosevelt University, M
Southern Illinois University Edwardsville, M

Iowa

Iowa State University of Science and Technology, MD

Kentucky

Murray State University, M
Spalding University, M
Western Kentucky University, O

Maryland

Bowie State University, MO
Towson University, M

Massachusetts

Assumption College, O
Boston University, M
Emerson College, M
Lasell College, MO
Northeastern University, M
Regis College, M
Suffolk University, M

Michigan

Eastern Michigan University, M

Minnesota

Concordia University, St. Paul, M
Minnesota State University Mankato, O
University of St. Thomas, M

Mississippi

Mississippi College, M

Missouri

University of Missouri, M
Webster University, M

Nebraska

Bellevue University, M
University of Nebraska - Lincoln, MD

New Jersey

Fairleigh Dickinson University, College at Florham, M
Monmouth University, MO
Rider University, M
Rowan University, O
Seton Hall University, M
Stevens Institute of Technology, O

New Mexico

New Mexico State University, MD

New York

Baruch College of the City University of New York, M
Canisius College, M
City College of the City University of New York, M
Columbia University, M
Cornell University, MD
Fordham University, M
Manhattanville College, M
Marist College, M
New York University, M
St. Bonaventure University, M

North Carolina

High Point University, M
The University of North Carolina at Charlotte, M

Ohio

Franklin University, M
John Carroll University, M
Ohio University, M

Oklahoma

University of Oklahoma, M

Oregon

University of Portland, M

Pennsylvania

Carnegie Mellon University, M
Drexel University, M
La Salle University, MO
Temple University, M

Tennessee

East Tennessee State University, M

Texas

Dallas Baptist University, M

Virginia

Radford University, M
Regent University, M

Washington

Washington State University, M

West Virginia

West Virginia University, MO

Wisconsin

Concordia University Wisconsin, M
University of Wisconsin - Stevens Point, M
University of Wisconsin - Whitewater, M

Canada

Quebec

HEC Montreal, O
Université de Sherbrooke, M

CORRECTIONS

United States

Alabama

Jacksonville State University, B
Troy University, M

Arizona

Central Arizona College, A
Coconino Community College, A
Northland Pioneer College, A

Arkansas

University of Arkansas at Pine Bluff, B

California

Bakersfield College, A
Cabrillo College, A
California State University, East Bay, B
California State University, Stanislaus, B
Chaffey College, A
College of the Redwoods, A
College of the Sequoias, A
Contra Costa College, A
De Anza College, A
Fresno City College, A
Gavilan College, A
Grossmont College, A
Hartnell College, A
Lassen Community College District, A
Los Angeles City College, A
Merritt College, A
Modesto Junior College, A
Moorpark College, A
Mt. San Antonio College, A
Napa Valley College, A
San Bernardino Valley College, A
San Diego Miramar College, A
San Joaquin Delta College, A
San Joaquin Valley College (Bakersfield), A
San Joaquin Valley College (Fresno), A
San Joaquin Valley College (Lancaster), A
San Joaquin Valley College (Ontario), A
San Joaquin Valley College (Visalia), A
Sierra College, A
Yuba College, A

Colorado

Adams State University, B
Colorado Mountain College (Leadville), A

Connecticut

Tunxis Community College, A

District of Columbia

University of the District of Columbia, A

Florida

Florida Gateway College, A
Indian River State College, A
Miami Dade College, A
Saint Leo University, M
Tallahassee Community College, A
University of Central Florida, O

Georgia

Albany State University, M
South University, M

Idaho

Lewis-Clark State College, B

Illinois

College of DuPage, A
Danville Area Community College, A
Ellis University, B
Heartland Community College, A
Illinois Central College, A
Illinois Eastern Community Colleges, Frontier Community College, A
Illinois Eastern Community Colleges, Lincoln Trail College, A

Illinois Valley Community College, A
Joliet Junior College, A
Lake Land College, A
Lincoln College - Normal, B
Sauk Valley Community College, A
Southeastern Illinois College, A

Iowa

Iowa Lakes Community College, A
Kaplan University, Davenport Campus, M
Kirkwood Community College, A

Kansas

Barton County Community College, A
Kansas City Kansas Community College, A
Washburn University, B

Kentucky

Eastern Kentucky University, BM

Louisiana

Tulane University, B

Maryland

Garrett College, A

Massachusetts

Mount Wachusett Community College, A

Michigan

Alpena Community College, A
Baker College, A
Bay de Noc Community College, A
Delta College, A
Grand Rapids Community College, A
Henry Ford College, A
Jackson College, A
Kellogg Community College, A
Lake Michigan College, A
Lake Superior State University, AB
Lansing Community College, A
Marygrove College, A
Mid Michigan Community College, A
Montcalm Community College, A
Mott Community College, A
Oakland Community College, A
Oakland University, B
St. Clair County Community College, A
Spring Arbor University, B
Wayne County Community College District, A
West Shore Community College, A

Minnesota

Fond du Lac Tribal and Community College, A
Minnesota State University Mankato, B
Riverland Community College, A
University of Minnesota, Crookston, B
Winona State University, B

Missouri

College of the Ozarks, B
Metropolitan Community College - Kansas City, A
Southeast Missouri State University, B

Montana

University of Great Falls, B

Nebraska

Northeast Community College, A

Nevada

College of Southern Nevada, A

New Jersey

Bergen Community College, A
Mercer County Community College, A
Raritan Valley Community College, A
Salem Community College, A

New Mexico

University of New Mexico, B
University of New Mexico - Gallup, A

New York

Broome Community College, A
Cayuga County Community College, A
Herkimer County Community College, A
John Jay College of Criminal Justice of the City University of New York, B
Monroe Community College, A
Westchester Community College, A

North Carolina

Vance-Granville Community College, A

Ohio

Belmont College, A
Bowling Green State University, B
Clark State Community College, A
Eastern Gateway Community College, A
Hocking College, A
James A. Rhodes State College, A
Lakeland Community College, A
Lorain County Community College, A
Sinclair Community College, A
Southern State Community College, A
Tiffin University, B
Xavier University, A
Youngstown State University, AB

Oklahoma

Langston University, AB
Redlands Community College, A
Southwestern Oklahoma State University at Sayre, A
University of Central Oklahoma, B

Oregon

Clackamas Community College, A
Klamath Community College, A
Western Oregon University, B

Pennsylvania

Butler County Community College, A
California University of Pennsylvania, AB
Community College of Allegheny County, A
Mercyhurst University, B
Mount Aloysius College, A
Pennsylvania Highlands Community College, A
Saint Joseph's University, M
University of Pittsburgh, B
Westmoreland County Community College, A

Tennessee

Roane State Community College, A

Texas

Alvin Community College, A
Amarillo College, A
Austin Community College District, A
El Paso Community College, A
Hill College, A
Navarro College, A
Northeast Texas Community College, A
San Antonio College, A
Stephen F. Austin State University, B
Texas State University, B
Trinity Valley Community College, A
Weatherford College, A
Western Texas College, A

Utah

Weber State University, B

Virginia

Mountain Empire Community College, A
Wytheville Community College, A

Washington

Everett Community College, A
Spokane Community College, A

West Virginia

New River Community and Technical College, A

Wisconsin

Mid-State Technical College, A
Moraine Park Technical College, A
Northeast Wisconsin Technical College, A
University of Wisconsin - Milwaukee, M
Wisconsin Indianhead Technical College, A

Wyoming

Laramie County Community College, A

CORRECTIONS ADMINISTRATION

United States

Montana

University of Great Falls, B

New York

John Jay College of Criminal Justice of the City University of New York, A

North Dakota

University of Mary, B

Wyoming

Eastern Wyoming College, A

U.S. Territories: Puerto Rico

Inter American University of Puerto Rico, Barranquitas Campus, B
Inter American University of Puerto Rico, Fajardo Campus, B

CORRECTIONS AND CRIMINAL JUSTICE

United States

Alabama

The University of Alabama at Birmingham, B
Virginia College in Huntsville, AB

Alaska

University of Alaska Fairbanks, B

Arizona

Central Arizona College, A
Coconino Community College, A
University of Phoenix - Online Campus, B
University of Phoenix - Southern Arizona Campus, B

California

Feather River College, A
Reedley College, A
University of Phoenix - Bay Area Campus, B
University of Phoenix - Central Valley Campus, B
University of Phoenix - Sacramento Valley Campus, B

Colorado

University of Phoenix - Colorado Springs Downtown Campus, B

Connecticut

University of Saint Joseph, B

Delaware

Delaware State University, B
Goldey-Beacom College, B

Florida

Bethune-Cookman University, B
Miami Dade College, A
Rasmussen College Fort Myers, AB
Rasmussen College Land O' Lakes, AB
Rasmussen College New Port Richey, AB

Rasmussen College Ocala, AB
Rasmussen College Tampa/Brandon, AB
University of Phoenix - Central Florida Campus, B

Georgia

Albany State University, B
Albany Technical College, A
Savannah State University, B

Illinois

Eureka College, B
Rasmussen College Aurora, A
Rasmussen College Mokena/Tinley Park, A
Rasmussen College Rockford, A
Rasmussen College Romeoville/Joliet, A

Indiana

Indiana Tech, B
Vincennes University, B

Iowa

Northwestern College, B

Kansas

Emporia State University, B
Kansas City Kansas Community College, A
Rasmussen College Kansas City/Overland Park, AB
Rasmussen College Topeka, AB
Seward County Community College and Area Technical School, A

Louisiana

McCann School of Business & Technology (Monroe), A

Maryland

Chesapeake College, A

Michigan

Adrian College, B
Bay Mills Community College, A
Northwestern Michigan College, A
University of Michigan - Flint, B

Minnesota

Rasmussen College Blaine, A
Rasmussen College Bloomington, AB
Rasmussen College Brooklyn Park, AB
Rasmussen College Eagan, AB
Rasmussen College Lake Elmo/Woodbury, AB
Rasmussen College Mankato, AB
Rasmussen College Moorhead, AB
Rasmussen College St. Cloud, AB
Saint Mary's University of Minnesota, B

Mississippi

Hinds Community College, A

Montana

University of Great Falls, B

Nebraska

Chadron State College, B
Concordia University, Nebraska, B
Hastings College, B
Nebraska Indian Community College, A

New Hampshire

Keene State College, B
Southern New Hampshire University, B

New Jersey

Sussex County Community College, A

New Mexico

University of New Mexico - Taos, A

New York

Corning Community College, A
Genesee Community College, A
John Jay College of Criminal Justice of the City University of New York, B
Morrisville State College, AB

New York Institute of Technology, B
State University of New York College of Technology at Canton, B

North Carolina

Pitt Community College, A
Rockingham Community College, A

North Dakota

Rasmussen College Fargo, B

Ohio

Cedarville University, B
Fortis College (Cuyahoga Falls), A
Northwest State Community College, A

Oklahoma

Cameron University, AB
Murray State College, A

Oregon

Corban University, B

Pennsylvania

La Roche College, B
Robert Morris University, B

Rhode Island

Roger Williams University, B

South Carolina

Limestone College, B

Tennessee

Miller-Motte Technical College (Clarksville), A

Texas

El Paso Community College, A
Hill College, A
Sam Houston State University, B

Utah

Weber State University, B

Virginia

Averett University, B
DeVry University (Arlington), B

Wisconsin

Rasmussen College Appleton, A
Rasmussen College Green Bay, A
Rasmussen College Wausau, A

U.S. Territories: Puerto Rico

EDP University of Puerto Rico, A
EDP University of Puerto Rico - San Sebastian, A
Inter American University of Puerto Rico, Aguadilla Campus, A
Inter American University of Puerto Rico, Fajardo Campus, A
Inter American University of Puerto Rico, Metropolitan Campus, A
University of Puerto Rico in Carolina, B

COSMETOLOGY, BARBER/ STYLING, AND NAIL INSTRUCTOR

United States

California

Pasadena City College, A

Colorado

IBMC College (Fort Collins), A

Texas

College of the Mainland, A
Hill College, A
San Jacinto College District, A

COSMETOLOGY/COSMETOLO-GIST

United States

Alabama

Southern Union State Community College, A
Virginia College in Huntsville, A
Wallace State Community College, A

Arizona

Eastern Arizona College, A
Northland Pioneer College, A

California

Allan Hancock College, A
Bakersfield College, A
Barstow Community College, A
Butte College, A
Cerritos College, A
Citrus College, A
College of San Mateo, A
College of the Sequoias, A
El Camino College, A
Fullerton College, A
Gavilan College, A
Golden West College, A
Laney College, A
Lassen Community College District, A
Los Angeles Trade-Technical College, A
Napa Valley College, A
Pasadena City College, A
Riverside City College, A
Sacramento City College, A
Saddleback College, A
San Diego City College, A
San Jose City College, A
Santa Ana College, A
Santa Barbara City College, A
Santa Monica College, A
Santiago Canyon College, A
Skyline College, A
Solano Community College, A
Yuba College, A

Colorado

Colorado Northwestern Community College, A
Lamar Community College, A
Northeastern Junior College, A
Pueblo Community College, A
Red Rocks Community College, A

Florida

Indian River State College, A

Hawaii

Honolulu Community College, A

Illinois

John A. Logan College, A
Kaskaskia College, A
Lincoln College - Normal, A
Rend Lake College, A
Shawnee Community College, A

Indiana

Vincennes University, A

Iowa

Northeast Iowa Community College, A
Southeastern Community College, A

Kansas

Cowley County Community College and Area Vocational - Technical School, A
Dodge City Community College, A
Fort Scott Community College, A
Garden City Community College, A
Independence Community College, A
Johnson County Community College, A
Northwest Kansas Technical College, A
Seward County Community College and Area Technical School, A

Michigan

Kirtland Community College, A
Montcalm Community College, A
Oakland Community College, A

Minnesota

Century College, A
Minnesota State College - Southeast Technical, A
Minnesota State Community and Technical College, A
Ridgewater College, A
Saint Paul College - A Community & Technical College, A

Mississippi

Coahoma Community College, A
Copiah-Lincoln Community College, A
Southwest Mississippi Community College, A
Virginia College in Jackson, A

New Mexico

Central New Mexico Community College, A
Clovis Community College, A
New Mexico Junior College, A
San Juan College, A
University of New Mexico - Gallup, A

North Carolina

Bladen Community College, A
Blue Ridge Community College, A
Brunswick Community College, A
Caldwell Community College and Technical Institute, A
Cape Fear Community College, A
Fayetteville Technical Community College, A
Guilford Technical Community College, A
Haywood Community College, A
Isothermal Community College, A
Lenoir Community College, A
Martin Community College, A
Mayland Community College, A
McDowell Technical Community College, A
Miller-Motte College (Cary), A
Randolph Community College, A
Rowan-Cabarrus Community College, A
Sandhills Community College, A
Southeastern Community College, A
Southwestern Community College, A
Stanly Community College, A
Surry Community College, A
Vance-Granville Community College, A

Ohio

Lorain County Community College, A

Oklahoma

Clary Sage College, A

Oregon

Mt. Hood Community College, A
Umpqua Community College, A

Pennsylvania

Butler County Community College, A
Community College of Beaver County, A
Douglas Education Center, A
Fortis Institute (Erie), A
McCann School of Business & Technology (Pottsville), A

Texas

Cisco College, A
Coastal Bend College, A
Del Mar College, A
Hill College, A
Houston Community College, A
Howard College, A
Lamar State College - Port Arthur, A
Lone Star College - Kingwood, A
Lone Star College - North Harris, A
Midland College, A
Northeast Texas Community College, A
Odessa College, A
Paris Junior College, A

San Jacinto College District, A
South Plains College, A
Southwest Texas Junior College, A
Texarkana College, A
Trinity Valley Community College, A
Vernon College, A
Weatherford College, A

Utah

Salt Lake Community College, A

Washington

Everett Community College, A
Olympic College, A
Seattle Central College, A
Shoreline Community College, A
South Seattle College, A
Spokane Community College, A
Walla Walla Community College, A

Wyoming

Eastern Wyoming College, A

COSMETOLOGY AND RELATED PERSONAL GROOMING ARTS

United States

Maryland

Allegany College of Maryland, A

Massachusetts

Bristol Community College, A

Ohio

Lorain County Community College, A

Pennsylvania

Community College of Allegheny County, A

Utah

LDS Business College, A

COUNSELING PSYCHOLOGY

United States

Alabama

Alabama Agricultural and Mechanical University, M
Amridge University, M
South University, M
University of South Alabama, D

Alaska

Alaska Pacific University, M

Arizona

Argosy University, Phoenix, M
Arizona State University at the Tempe campus, D
Grand Canyon University, M
Northern Arizona University, D
Prescott College, M
The University of Arizona, M
University of Phoenix - Phoenix Campus, M

Arkansas

Arkansas State University, O
Harding University, M
Henderson State University, M
John Brown University, M
University of Central Arkansas, M

California

Argosy University, Inland Empire, D
Argosy University, Los Angeles, MD
Argosy University, Orange County, MD
Argosy University, San Diego, MD
Argosy University, San Francisco Bay Area, MD
Brandman University, M

California Baptist University, M
California Institute of Integral Studies, M
California State University, Bakersfield, M
California State University, Sacramento, M
California State University, San Bernardino, M
California State University, Stanislaus, M
Dominican University of California, M
Holy Names University, M
Humboldt State University, M
John F. Kennedy University, M
Mount Saint Mary's University, M
National University, M
Palo Alto University, M
San Francisco State University, M
Santa Clara University, M
Simpson University, M
Sonoma State University, M
Southern California Seminary, M
University of California, Berkeley, O
University of California, Santa Barbara, MDO
University of San Diego, M
University of San Francisco, M

Colorado

Argosy University, Denver, MD
Colorado Christian University, M
Naropa University, M
Regis University, MO
University of Colorado Denver, M
University of Denver, D

Connecticut

Fairfield University, MO
University of Bridgeport, M
University of Connecticut, MDO
University of Saint Joseph, M

Delaware

Wilmington University, M

District of Columbia

Gallaudet University, M
Howard University, D
Trinity Washington University, M
University of the District of Columbia, M

Florida

Argosy University, Sarasota, MD
Argosy University, Tampa, M
Carlos Albizu University, Miami Campus, M
Florida Atlantic University, MO
Florida International University, M
Florida State University, D
Hodges University, M
Nova Southeastern University, M
Palm Beach Atlantic University, M
St. Thomas University, M
South University (Royal Palm Beach), M
Southeastern University, M
University of Florida, D
University of Miami, D
University of North Florida, M
University of South Florida, O
University of West Florida, M

Georgia

Columbus State University, M
Fort Valley State University, M
Georgia State University, MO
South University, M
University of North Georgia, M

Hawaii

Argosy University, Hawai'i, D
Chaminade University of Honolulu, M
University of Hawaii at Hilo, M

Idaho

Idaho State University, M

Illinois

Argosy University, Chicago, D
Argosy University, Schaumburg, M
Bradley University, M
Concordia University Chicago, M

DePaul University, M
Governors State University, M
Illinois State University, M
Lewis University, M
Loyola University Chicago, D
McKendree University, M
Southern Illinois University Carbondale, D
Trinity Christian College, M
Trinity International University, M
Wheaton College, M

Indiana

Ball State University, MD
Grace College, M
Indiana University Northwest, M
Indiana Wesleyan University, M
Purdue University Northwest (Hammond), M
University of Indianapolis, M
University of Notre Dame, D
University of Saint Francis, MO

Iowa

Iowa State University of Science and Technology, D
The University of Iowa, MD
University of Northern Iowa, M

Kansas

Emporia State University, M
MidAmerica Nazarene University, MO
Ottawa University, M
The University of Kansas, MD
University of Saint Mary, M

Kentucky

Lindsey Wilson College, MD
Morehead State University, M
Northern Kentucky University, M
Union College, M
University of the Cumberlands, M
University of Kentucky, MDO
Western Kentucky University, M

Louisiana

Louisiana State University in Shreveport, M
Louisiana Tech University, D
McNeese State University, M
University of Louisiana at Monroe, M

Maine

Husson University, M
University of Southern Maine, M

Maryland

Bowie State University, M
Frostburg State University, M
Johns Hopkins University, MO
Loyola University Maryland, MO
Towson University, O
University of Baltimore, M
University of Maryland, College Park, MD
Washington Adventist University, M

Massachusetts

American International College, M
Anna Maria College, M
Assumption College, MO
Bay Path University, M
Boston College, MD
Boston University, M
Cambridge College, MO
Eastern Nazarene College, M
Fitchburg State University, M
Lesley University, MO
Northeastern University, MDO
Salem State University, M
Springfield College, MDO
Suffolk University, MO
University of Massachusetts Boston, MD
Westfield State University, M

Michigan

Andrews University, MD
Central Michigan University, MO
Oakland University, MDO
Siena Heights University, M

South University, M
Spring Arbor University, M
Western Michigan University, MD

Minnesota

Bethel University, M
Capella University, M
Minnesota State University Mankato, M
Saint Mary's University of Minnesota, MDO
University of Minnesota, Twin Cities Campus, D
University of St. Thomas, MD
Walden University, MD

Mississippi

Mississippi College, M
University of Southern Mississippi, MD
William Carey University, M

Missouri

Avila University, M
Evangel University, M
Lindenwood University, M
Missouri State University, M
Southeast Missouri State University, M
Stephens College, M
University of Central Missouri, O
University of Missouri, MDO
University of Missouri - Kansas City, MDO
University of Missouri - St. Louis, M
Washington University in St. Louis, M
Webster University, M

Montana

Montana State University Billings, M
University of Great Falls, M
University of Montana, M

Nebraska

Grace University, M
University of Nebraska at Kearney, M
University of Nebraska - Lincoln, MD

Nevada

University of Nevada, Las Vegas, O
University of Phoenix - Las Vegas Campus, M

New Hampshire

New England College, M
Rivier University, M

New Jersey

Caldwell University, MO
Centenary College, M
College of Saint Elizabeth, MO
Fairleigh Dickinson University, College at Florham, M
Felician University, M
Georgian Court University, M
Kean University, M
Monmouth University, MO
New Jersey City University, M
Rutgers University - New Brunswick, M
Seton Hall University, MD
William Paterson University of New Jersey, M

New Mexico

New Mexico Highlands University, M
New Mexico State University, MDO
University of the Southwest, M

New York

Adelphi University, M
Alfred University, M
Baruch College of the City University of New York, M
Brooklyn College of the City University of New York, MO
The College at Brockport, State University of New York, MO
The College of New Rochelle, MO
The College of Saint Rose, O
College of Staten Island of the City University of New York, M
Fordham University, D

Hofstra University, MO
Iona College, M
Long Island University - LIU Brooklyn, MO
Long Island University - LIU Post, O
Marist College, M
Medaille College, MD
Mercy College, MO
New York University, MD
Nyack College, M
Pace University, MD
St. Bonaventure University, M
St. John Fisher College, M
St. John's University, MO
State University of New York College at Old Westbury, M
State University of New York at New Paltz, MO
State University of New York at Oswego, M
State University of New York at Plattsburgh, MO
Touro College, M
University at Albany, State University of New York, MDO
University at Buffalo, the State University of New York, MO
Yeshiva University, M

North Carolina

Appalachian State University, M
Gardner-Webb University, M
Lenoir-Rhyne University, M
Montreat College, M
South University, M
The University of North Carolina at Greensboro, MD
The University of North Carolina at Pembroke, M

North Dakota

University of Mary, M
University of North Dakota, M

Ohio

Antioch University Midwest, M
Bowling Green State University, M
Cleveland State University, MDO
Franciscan University of Steubenville, M
Heidelberg University, M
John Carroll University, MO
Kent State University, M
South University, M
The University of Akron, MD
University of Dayton, M
Walsh University, M
Xavier University, M
Youngstown State University, M

Oklahoma

Mid-America Christian University, M
Northeastern State University, M
Northwestern Oklahoma State University, M
Southeastern Oklahoma State University, M
Southern Nazarene University, M
University of Central Oklahoma, M
University of Oklahoma, MD

Oregon

George Fox University, M
Lewis & Clark College, M
Marylhurst University, O
Northwest Christian University, M
Southern Oregon University, M

Pennsylvania

Carlow University, MDO
Chatham University, MD
Chestnut Hill College, MO
Delaware Valley University, M
Duquesne University, MO
Eastern University, MO
Edinboro University of Pennsylvania, M
Gannon University, M
Geneva College, M
Holy Family University, M
Immaculata University, M
Kutztown University of Pennsylvania, M
La Salle University, M
Lancaster Bible College, M
Lehigh University, MDO

Lock Haven University of Pennsylvania, M
Marywood University, M
Messiah College, MO
Rosemont College, M
Slippery Rock University of Pennsylvania, M
Temple University, MD
University of Pennsylvania, M
The University of Scranton, M
Waynesburg University, M

Rhode Island

Rhode Island College, O
Salve Regina University, MO
University of Rhode Island, M

South Carolina

Clemson University, M
Francis Marion University, M
South University, M

South Dakota

Northern State University, M

Tennessee

Argosy University, Nashville, M
Austin Peay State University, M
Lee University, M
Lipscomb University, MO
Middle Tennessee State University, M
Southern Adventist University, M
Tennessee State University, MD
Tennessee Technological University, M
University of Memphis, D
The University of Tennessee, M

Texas

Abilene Christian University, M
Amberton University, M
Angelo State University, M
Dallas Baptist University, M
East Texas Baptist University, M
Hardin-Simmons University, M
Houston Baptist University, M
Lamar University, M
LeTourneau University, M
Midwestern State University, M
Our Lady of the Lake University of San Antonio, MD
St. Edward's University, M
St. Mary's University, M
South University, M
Southwestern Assemblies of God University, M
Tarleton State University, MO
Texas A&M International University, M
Texas A&M University, D
Texas A&M University - Texarkana, M
Texas Tech University, MD
Texas Wesleyan University, M
Texas Woman's University, MD
University of Houston, MD
University of Houston - Victoria, M
University of Mary Hardin-Baylor, M
University of North Texas, MD
The University of Texas at Austin, D
The University of Texas at Tyler, M
Wayland Baptist University, M

Utah

Argosy University, Salt Lake City, MD
Brigham Young University, MDO
University of Utah, MD
Utah State University, D
Westminster College, M

Vermont

College of St. Joseph, M
Goddard College, M
University of Vermont, M

Virginia

Argosy University, Washington DC, D
James Madison University, MDO
Liberty University, M
Lynchburg College, M
Marymount University, MO
Old Dominion University, M

Radford University, MD
Regent University, MDO
South University (Glen Allen), M
South University (Virginia Beach), M
Virginia Commonwealth University, MDO

Washington

Argosy University, Seattle, MD
Bastyr University, M
Central Washington University, M
City University of Seattle, M
Eastern Washington University, M
Gonzaga University, M
Northwest University, MD
Saint Martin's University, M
University of Puget Sound, M
Walla Walla University, M
Washington State University, D
Western Washington University, M

West Virginia

West Virginia University, D

Wisconsin

Concordia University Wisconsin, M
Marquette University, MD
Mount Mary University, MO
University of Wisconsin - Madison, D
University of Wisconsin - Milwaukee, D
University of Wisconsin - Stout, M
Viterbo University, M

U.S. Territories: Puerto Rico

Inter American University of Puerto Rico, Aguadilla Campus, M
Inter American University of Puerto Rico, Metropolitan Campus, MD
Inter American University of Puerto Rico, San Germán Campus, MD
Universidad Metropolitana, M
Universidad del Turabo, MDO

Canada

Alberta

Athabasca University, M
University of Alberta, MD
University of Calgary, MD
University of Lethbridge, M

British Columbia

Trinity Western University, M
The University of British Columbia, MD
University of Victoria, M

Manitoba

Providence University College & Theological Seminary, M

Ontario

Saint Paul University, M
The University of Western Ontario, M

Quebec

McGill University, MD

COUNSELOR EDUCATION/ SCHOOL COUNSELING AND GUIDANCE SERVICES

United States

Alabama

Alabama Agricultural and Mechanical University, MO
Alabama State University, MO
Amridge University, D
Auburn University at Montgomery, MO
Faulkner University, M
Jacksonville State University, M
Troy University, MO
The University of Alabama, MDO

The University of Alabama at Birmingham, M
University of Montevallo, M
University of North Alabama, M
The University of West Alabama, MO

Alaska

University of Alaska Anchorage, M
University of Alaska Fairbanks, MO

Arizona

Arizona State University at the Tempe campus, M
Northern Arizona University, M
Prescott College, M
The University of Arizona, M
University of Phoenix - Phoenix Campus, M
University of Phoenix - Southern Arizona Campus, M

Arkansas

Arkansas State University, MO
Arkansas Tech University, M
Harding University, MO
Henderson State University, MO
John Brown University, BMO
Southern Arkansas University - Magnolia, M
University of Arkansas, MDO
University of Arkansas at Little Rock, M
University of Central Arkansas, M

California

Azusa Pacific University, M
Brandman University, M
California Baptist University, M
California Lutheran University, M
California State University, Bakersfield, M
California State University, Dominguez Hills, M
California State University, East Bay, M
California State University, Fresno, M
California State University, Fullerton, M
California State University, Long Beach, M
California State University, Los Angeles, MD
California State University, Northridge, M
California State University, Sacramento, M
California State University, San Bernardino, M
California State University, Stanislaus, M
Chapman University, MO
Concordia University Irvine, M
East Los Angeles College, A
Fresno Pacific University, M
La Sierra University, MO
Loma Linda University, MDO
Loyola Marymount University, M
National University, M
Point Loma Nazarene University, M
Saint Mary's College of California, M
San Diego State University, M
San Francisco State University, O
San Jose State University, M
Santa Clara University, M
Sonoma State University, M
University of La Verne, MO
University of Phoenix - Southern California Campus, M
University of San Diego, M
University of San Francisco, M
University of Southern California, M

Colorado

Adams State University, M
Argosy University, Denver, D
Colorado State University, M
Naropa University, M
University of Colorado Colorado Springs, M
University of Colorado Denver, M
University of Northern Colorado, MD

Connecticut

Central Connecticut State University, MO
Fairfield University, MO
Southern Connecticut State University, MO
University of Connecticut, MO
University of Hartford, MO
University of Saint Joseph, M
Western Connecticut State University, M

Delaware

Wilmington University, M

District of Columbia

Gallaudet University, M
The George Washington University, MDO
Howard University, BM
Trinity Washington University, M

Florida

Argosy University, Sarasota, MDO
Argosy University, Tampa, MD
Barry University, MDO
Florida Agricultural and Mechanical University, M
Florida Atlantic University, MDO
Florida Gulf Coast University, BM
Florida International University, M
Nova Southeastern University, M
Palm Beach Atlantic University, M
Rollins College, M
St. Thomas University, MO
Southeastern University, M
Stetson University, M
University of Central Florida, MO
University of Florida, MDO
University of Miami, MO
University of North Florida, M
University of South Florida, MDO
University of West Florida, M

Georgia

Albany State University, M
Argosy University, Atlanta, D
Augusta University, MO
Clark Atlanta University, M
Columbus State University, MDO
Fort Valley State University, O
Georgia Southern University, MO
Georgia State University, MO
Mercer University, D
University of Georgia, MDO
University of West Georgia, MDO
Valdosta State University, MO

Idaho

Boise State University, MO
Idaho State University, MDO
Northwest Nazarene University, M
University of Idaho, M

Illinois

Argosy University, Chicago, D
Bradley University, BM
Chicago State University, M
Concordia University Chicago, MO
DePaul University, M
Eastern Illinois University, M
Lewis University, M
Loyola University Chicago, MO
National Louis University, M
Northeastern Illinois University, M
Northern Illinois University, MD
Quincy University, M
Roosevelt University, M
Saint Xavier University, M
University of Illinois at Urbana - Champaign, MDO
Western Illinois University, M

Indiana

Butler University, M
Indiana State University, M
Indiana University Bloomington, MDO
Indiana University - Purdue University Fort Wayne, M
Indiana University - Purdue University Indianapolis, M
Indiana University South Bend, M
Indiana University Southeast, M
Indiana Wesleyan University, M
Purdue University, MD
Purdue University Northwest (Hammond), M
University of Saint Francis, M
Valparaiso University, M

Iowa

Buena Vista University, BM
Iowa State University of Science and Technology, M
The University of Iowa, MD
University of Northern Iowa, M

Kansas

Emporia State University, M
Fort Hays State University, M
Kansas State University, MD
Ottawa University, M
Pittsburg State University, M
Pratt Community College, A
Wichita State University, M

Kentucky

Campbellsville University, M
Eastern Kentucky University, M
Lindsey Wilson College, D
Morehead State University, MO
Murray State University, MO
Northern Kentucky University, M
Spalding University, M
University of the Cumberlands, MD
University of Louisville, MD
Western Kentucky University, M

Louisiana

Grambling State University, M
Louisiana State University and Agricultural & Mechanical College, MO
Louisiana State University in Shreveport, M
Louisiana Tech University, M
McNeese State University, MO
Nicholls State University, M
Northwestern State University of Louisiana, MO
Southeastern Louisiana University, M
Southern University and Agricultural and Mechanical College, M
University of Holy Cross, M
University of Louisiana at Lafayette, M
University of Louisiana at Monroe, M
University of New Orleans, MDO
Xavier University of Louisiana, M

Maine

Husson University, M
University of Maine, MDO
University of Southern Maine, MO

Maryland

Bowie State University, M
Frostburg State University, M
Johns Hopkins University, MO
Loyola University Maryland, MO
McDaniel College, M
University of Maryland, College Park, MDO
University of Maryland Eastern Shore, M

Massachusetts

American International College, MO
Bridgewater State University, MO
Cambridge College, M
Fitchburg State University, M
Northeastern University, D
Salem State University, M
Springfield College, MO
Suffolk University, MO
University of Massachusetts Amherst, MO
University of Massachusetts Boston, M
Westfield State University, M

Michigan

Central Michigan University, M
Eastern Michigan University, MO
Michigan State University, MD
University of Detroit Mercy, M
Wayne State University, MDO
Western Michigan University, MD

Minnesota

Capella University, MD
Minnesota State University Mankato, MDO
Minnesota State University Moorhead, M

St. Cloud State University, BM
University of Minnesota, Twin Cities Campus, MDO
Walden University, MD
Winona State University, M

Mississippi

Alcorn State University, M
Delta State University, MDO
Jackson State University, M
Mississippi College, MO
Mississippi State University, MDO
University of Southern Mississippi, MDO

Missouri

Central Methodist University, M
Evangel University, M
Lincoln University, M
Missouri Baptist University, M
Missouri State University, M
Northwest Missouri State University, M
Saint Louis University, MDO
Southeast Missouri State University, MO
Stephens College, MO
University of Central Missouri, M
University of Missouri - Kansas City, O
University of Missouri - St. Louis, MD

Montana

Montana State University Billings, M
Montana State University - Northern, M
University of Montana, MDO

Nebraska

Bellevue University, M
Chadron State College, M
Creighton University, M
Doane University, M
University of Nebraska at Kearney, MO
University of Nebraska at Omaha, M
Wayne State College, M

Nevada

University of Nevada, Las Vegas, MDO
University of Nevada, Reno, MDO
University of Phoenix - Las Vegas Campus, M

New Hampshire

Keene State College, MO
Plymouth State University, M
Rivier University, M
University of New Hampshire, M

New Jersey

Caldwell University, MO
The College of New Jersey, M
Georgian Court University, O
Kean University, M
Montclair State University, MDO
New Jersey City University, M
Rider University, MO
Rowan University, M
Rutgers University - New Brunswick, M
Saint Peter's University, MO
Seton Hall University, M
William Paterson University of New Jersey, M

New Mexico

Eastern New Mexico University, M
New Mexico Highlands University, M
New Mexico State University, MDO
University of New Mexico, MD
University of Phoenix - New Mexico Campus, M
University of the Southwest, M

New York

Alfred University, MO
Brooklyn College of the City University of New York, M
Canisius College, M
The College at Brockport, State University of New York, MO
The College of Saint Rose, MO
Fordham University, MO
Hofstra University, MO

Hunter College of the City University of New York, M
Lehman College of the City University of New York, M
Long Island University - LIU Brooklyn, O
Manhattan College, MO
Mercy College, O
New York Institute of Technology, M
New York University, MDO
Niagara University, MO
Nyack College, M
Queens College of the City University of New York, M
St. Bonaventure University, MO
St. John's University, MO
St. Lawrence University, MO
State University of New York College at Oneonta, MO
State University of New York at New Paltz, M
State University of New York at Plattsburgh, MO
Syracuse University, MD
Touro College, M
University at Buffalo, the State University of New York, MDO
University of Rochester, MD

North Carolina

Appalachian State University, M
Campbell University, M
East Carolina University, M
Lenoir-Rhyne University, M
North Carolina Agricultural and Technical State University, M
North Carolina Central University, M
North Carolina State University, MD
Salem College, M
The University of North Carolina at Chapel Hill, M
The University of North Carolina at Charlotte, MDO
The University of North Carolina at Greensboro, MDO
The University of North Carolina at Pembroke, BM
Wake Forest University, M
Western Carolina University, M

North Dakota

North Dakota State University, MD

Ohio

Bowling Green State University, BM
Cleveland State University, MD
John Carroll University, MO
Kent State University, MDO
Malone University, M
Ohio University, MD
The University of Akron, MD
University of Cincinnati, MDO
University of Dayton, MO
The University of Toledo, MD
Walsh University, M
Wright State University, BM
Xavier University, M
Youngstown State University, M

Oklahoma

East Central University, BM
Northeastern State University, M
Northwestern Oklahoma State University, M
Southeastern Oklahoma State University, M
Southwestern Oklahoma State University, M
University of Central Oklahoma, BM

Oregon

George Fox University, MO
Multnomah University, M
Northwest Christian University, M
Oregon State University, MD

Pennsylvania

Bloomsburg University of Pennsylvania, M
California University of Pennsylvania, M
Carlow University, MO
Duquesne University, MDO
Eastern University, M
Edinboro University of Pennsylvania, MO
Geneva College, M

Gwynedd Mercy University, M
Indiana University of Pennsylvania, M
Kutztown University of Pennsylvania, M
Lancaster Bible College, BM
Lehigh University, M
Marywood University, M
Messiah College, M
Penn State University Park, MDO
Rosemont College, M
Shippensburg University of Pennsylvania, MO
Slippery Rock University of Pennsylvania, M
Summit University, M
The University of Scranton, M
Villanova University, M
West Chester University of Pennsylvania, MO
Westminster College, MO
Widener University, M

Rhode Island

Providence College, M
Rhode Island College, MO

South Carolina

Bob Jones University, M
The Citadel, The Military College of South Carolina, M
Clemson University, M
Columbia International University, M
South Carolina State University, M
University of South Carolina, DO
Winthrop University, M

South Dakota

Northern State University, M
Oglala Lakota College, AB
South Dakota State University, M
The University of South Dakota, BMDO

Tennessee

Argosy University, Nashville, D
Austin Peay State University, M
Carson-Newman University, M
East Tennessee State University, M
Freed-Hardeman University, M
Johnson University, M
Lee University, M
Lincoln Memorial University, M
Middle Tennessee State University, M
Southern Adventist University, M
Tennessee State University, M
Trevecca Nazarene University, MD
University of Memphis, MD
The University of Tennessee, MDO
The University of Tennessee at Chattanooga, M
The University of Tennessee at Martin, M
Vanderbilt University, M

Texas

Amberton University, B
Angelo State University, M
Argosy University, Dallas, D
Dallas Baptist University, MO
Hardin-Simmons University, M
Houston Baptist University, M
Lamar University, M
Midwestern State University, BM
Our Lady of the Lake University of San Antonio, M
Prairie View A&M University, MD
St. Mary's University, D
Sam Houston State University, B
Southern Methodist University, M
Stephen F. Austin State University, M
Sul Ross State University, M
Tarleton State University, BM
Texas A&M International University, M
Texas A&M University - Central Texas, M
Texas A&M University - Corpus Christi, MD
Texas A&M University - Kingsville, M
Texas A&M University - San Antonio, M
Texas Christian University, M
Texas Southern University, MD
Texas State University, M
Texas Tech University, MD
Texas Wesleyan University, M
Texas Woman's University, M

University of Houston - Clear Lake, M
University of Houston - Victoria, M
University of Mary Hardin-Baylor, M
University of North Texas, M
University of St. Thomas, M
The University of Texas at Austin, M
The University of Texas at El Paso, M
The University of Texas of the Permian Basin, M
The University of Texas Rio Grande Valley, M
The University of Texas at San Antonio, MD
West Texas A&M University, M

Utah

Argosy University, Salt Lake City, D
University of Utah, M
Utah State University, M

Vermont

College of St. Joseph, M
Johnson State College, M
Lyndon State College, M
University of Vermont, M

Virginia

Argosy University, Washington DC, D
The College of William and Mary, MD
Eastern Mennonite University, M
George Mason University, MDO
Hampton University, MDO
Liberty University, MD
Longwood University, M
Lynchburg College, M
Marymount University, MD
Old Dominion University, MDO
Radford University, M
Regent University, MDO
University of Virginia, MDO
Virginia Commonwealth University, M
Virginia Polytechnic Institute and State University, MDO
Virginia State University, M

Washington

Antioch University Seattle, M
Central Washington University, M
City University of Seattle, M
Eastern Washington University, M
Heritage University, M
Saint Martin's University, M
Seattle Pacific University, MDO
Seattle University, MO
University of Puget Sound, M
Western Washington University, M
Whitworth University, M

West Virginia

American Public University System, M
Marshall University, BMO
West Virginia University, M

Wisconsin

Carthage College, M
Concordia University Wisconsin, M
Lakeland College, M
Marquette University, M
Mount Mary University, MO
University of Wisconsin - Madison, M
University of Wisconsin - Milwaukee, MD
University of Wisconsin - Oshkosh, M
University of Wisconsin - Platteville, M
University of Wisconsin - River Falls, MO
University of Wisconsin - Stevens Point, M
University of Wisconsin - Superior, M
University of Wisconsin - Whitewater, M

Wyoming

University of Wyoming, MD

U.S. Territories: Guam

University of Guam, M

U.S. Territories: Puerto Rico

Bayamón Central University, M
Inter American University of Puerto Rico, Arecibo Campus, M

Inter American University of Puerto Rico, Metropolitan Campus, MD
Inter American University of Puerto Rico, San Germán Campus, MD
Pontifical Catholic University of Puerto Rico, M
Universidad del Turabo, M
University of Puerto Rico, Río Piedras Campus, MD

Canada

Alberta

Athabasca University, M
University of Alberta, M
University of Lethbridge, M

British Columbia

Simon Fraser University, M
University of Victoria, M

Manitoba

Brandon University, BMO
University of Manitoba, M

Maritime Provinces: New Brunswick

Université de Moncton, M
University of New Brunswick Fredericton, B

Maritime Provinces: Nova Scotia

Acadia University, M

Newfoundland and Labrador

Memorial University of Newfoundland, B

Ontario

University of Windsor, B

Quebec

Université Laval, BMD
Université du Québec à Montréal, B
Université de Sherbrooke, B

COURT REPORTING/COURT REPORTER

United States

Alabama

Gadsden State Community College, A

Arizona

GateWay Community College, A
Northland Pioneer College, A

California

Bryan College, A
Cerritos College, A
College of Marin, A
Cypress College, A
Humphreys College, A
Sage College, A
San Diego City College, A
West Valley College, A

Colorado

Colorado Technical University Online, B

Florida

Key College, A
Miami Dade College, A

Illinois

John A. Logan College, A
MacCormac College, A
Midstate College, A
South Suburban College, A

Indiana

College of Court Reporting, A

Kentucky

West Kentucky Community and Technical College, A

Michigan

Oakland Community College, A

Minnesota

Anoka Technical College, A

Mississippi

Hinds Community College, A
Mississippi Gulf Coast Community College, A
Northwest Mississippi Community College, A

Missouri

Court Reporting Institute of St. Louis, A

New York

Bryant & Stratton College - Orchard Park Campus, A
Long Island Business Institute, A
New York Career Institute, A
State University of New York College of Technology at Alfred, A

Ohio

Clark State Community College, A
Cuyahoga Community College, A
Miami-Jacobs Career College (Independence), A
Stark State College, A

Oklahoma

Rose State College, A

Oregon

Sumner College, A

Pennsylvania

Community College of Allegheny County, A
Luzerne County Community College, A

South Carolina

Midlands Technical College, A

Tennessee

Southwest Tennessee Community College, A

Texas

Alvin Community College, A
Del Mar College, A
El Paso Community College, A
Houston Community College, A
San Antonio College, A

Washington

Bates Technical College, A

West Virginia

Huntington Junior College, A

Wisconsin

Fox Valley Technical College, A
Lakeshore Technical College, A
Madison Area Technical College, A
Moraine Park Technical College, A

CRAFTS

United States

California

California College of the Arts, M
California State University, Fullerton, M
California State University, Los Angeles, M

Georgia

Savannah College of Art and Design, M

Illinois

Southern Illinois University Carbondale, M
University of Illinois at Urbana - Champaign, M

Indiana

Indiana University - Purdue University Indianapolis, M

New York

City College of the City University of New York, M
Rochester Institute of Technology, M

North Carolina

East Carolina University, M

Ohio

Kent State University, M

Oregon

Oregon College of Art & Craft, M

Pennsylvania

Temple University, M

Canada

Maritime Provinces: Nova Scotia

NSCAD University, M

CRAFTS/CRAFT DESIGN, FOLK ART AND ARTISANRY

United States

California

Southwestern College, A

Illinois

City Colleges of Chicago, Harold Washington College, A
University of Illinois at Urbana - Champaign, B

Indiana

Indiana University - Purdue University Fort Wayne, B

Kentucky

Hazard Community and Technical College, A

Maine

Maine College of Art, B

Massachusetts

Bridgewater State University, B
Montserrat College of Art, B

Michigan

College for Creative Studies, B

New Jersey

Bergen Community College, A

New Mexico

University of New Mexico - Taos, A

New York

Rochester Institute of Technology, B

North Carolina

College of The Albemarle, A
Western Piedmont Community College, A

Ohio

Bowling Green State University, B
Kent State University, B
Malone University, B

Oregon

Oregon College of Art & Craft, B

Pennsylvania

Kutztown University of Pennsylvania, B
The University of the Arts, B

Utah

Brigham Young University, B

Virginia

Virginia Commonwealth University, B

Canada

Maritime Provinces: Nova Scotia

NSCAD University, B

CREDIT MANAGEMENT

United States

Minnesota

St. Cloud Technical & Community College, A

Nevada

University of Phoenix - Las Vegas Campus, B

Wisconsin

Northeast Wisconsin Technical College, A

CRIMINAL JUSTICE/LAW ENFORCEMENT ADMINISTRATION

United States

Alabama

Alabama Southern Community College, A
Athens State University, B
Community College of the Air Force, A
Huntingdon College, B
Jacksonville State University, B
James H. Faulkner State Community College, A
Judson College, B
Miles College, B
Remington College - Mobile Campus, A
South University, B
Strayer University - Birmingham Campus, B
Strayer University - Huntsville Campus, B
University of North Alabama, B
University of South Alabama, B
Virginia College in Birmingham, AB
Wallace State Community College, A

Alaska

University of Alaska Southeast, Sitka Campus, A

Arizona

Argosy University, Phoenix, B
Arizona State University at the Downtown Phoenix campus, B
Arizona Western College, A
Brookline College (Phoenix), AB
Brookline College (Tempe), A
Brookline College (Tucson), A
Central Arizona College, A
Coconino Community College, A
DeVry University (Phoenix), B
Eastern Arizona College, A
Mesa Community College, A
Northcentral University, B
The Paralegal Institute at Brighton College, A
Penn Foster College, AB
Scottsdale Community College, A
University of Phoenix - Phoenix Campus, B
Western International University, B

Arkansas

Arkansas State University, A
Arkansas State University - Mountain Home, A
Arkansas State University - Newport, A
Black River Technical College, A

Cossatot Community College of the University of Arkansas, A
East Arkansas Community College, A
National Park College, A
North Arkansas College, A
NorthWest Arkansas Community College, A
Ozarka College, A
Remington College - Little Rock Campus, A
Southeast Arkansas College, A
Strayer University - Little Rock Campus, B
University of Arkansas Community College at Morrilton, A
University of Arkansas - Fort Smith, AB
University of Arkansas at Monticello, A
University of Arkansas at Pine Bluff, A

California

Alliant International University - San Diego, B
Allied American University, AB
Argosy University, Inland Empire, B
Argosy University, Los Angeles, B
Argosy University, Orange County, B
Argosy University, San Diego, B
Argosy University, San Francisco Bay Area, B
Bakersfield College, A
Brightwood College, Bakersfield Campus, A
Brightwood College, Chula Vista Campus, A
Brightwood College, Fresno Campus, A
Brightwood College, Modesto Campus, A
Brightwood College, Palm Springs Campus, A
Brightwood College, Riverside Campus, A
Brightwood College, Sacramento Campus, A
Brightwood College, San Diego Campus, A
Brightwood College, Vista Campus, A
California Baptist University, B
California Coast University, AB
California Lutheran University, B
California State University, Bakersfield, B
California State University, East Bay, B
California State University, Long Beach, B
California State University, Sacramento, B
Cerro Coso Community College, A
Citrus College, A
College of the Sequoias, A
De Anza College, A
DeVry University (Alhambra), B
DeVry University (Anaheim), B
DeVry University (Bakersfield), B
DeVry University (Fremont), B
DeVry University (Long Beach), B
DeVry University (Oakland), B
DeVry University (Oxnard), B
DeVry University (Palmdale), B
DeVry University (Pomona), B
DeVry University (San Diego), B
DeVry University (Sherman Oaks), B
East Los Angeles College, A
Folsom Lake College, A
Glendale Community College, A
Golden West College, A
Imperial Valley College, A
Irvine Valley College, A
Lake Tahoe Community College, A
Los Angeles City College, A
Los Angeles Southwest College, A
Marymount California University, B
Mendocino College, A
Modesto Junior College, A
Monterey Peninsula College, A
Moorpark College, A
Napa Valley College, A
National University, B
Ohlone College, A
Pasadena City College, A
Porterville College, A
Rio Hondo College, A
Sacramento City College, A
San Diego Christian College, B
San Diego Miramar College, A
San Diego State University - Imperial Valley Campus, B
San Francisco State University, B
San Joaquin Valley College (Hanford), A
San Joaquin Valley College (Hesperia), A
Santa Ana College, A
Santa Barbara City College, A

Santa Rosa Junior College, A
Shasta College, A
Skyline College, A
Solano Community College, A
Sonoma State University, B
Taft College, A
University of Phoenix - Bay Area Campus, B
University of Phoenix - Sacramento Valley Campus,
   B
University of Phoenix - San Diego Campus, B
University of Phoenix - Southern California Campus,
   B
Ventura College, A
West Hills Community College, A
West Los Angeles College, A
West Valley College, A
Yuba College, A

Colorado

Adams State University, B
Aims Community College, A
Arapahoe Community College, A
Argosy University, Denver, B
Aspen University, B
Colorado Mesa University, A
Colorado Mountain College (Glenwood Springs), A
Colorado Mountain College (Leadville), A
Colorado Technical University Colorado Springs, AB
Colorado Technical University Denver South, AB
Colorado Technical University Online, AB
Community College of Aurora, A
DeVry University (Westminster), B
Everest College (Colorado Springs), A
Johnson & Wales University, B
Pikes Peak Community College, A
Pueblo Community College, A
Trinidad State Junior College, A
University of Colorado Colorado Springs, B
University of Colorado Denver, B
University of Phoenix - Colorado Campus, B

Connecticut

Albertus Magnus College, B
Goodwin College, A
Housatonic Community College, A
Lincoln College of New England, AB
Manchester Community College, A
Northwestern Connecticut Community College, A
Norwalk Community College, A
Sacred Heart University, B
Tunxis Community College, A
University of New Haven, B

Delaware

Delaware State University, B
Delaware Technical & Community College, Jack F.
   Owens Campus, A
Delaware Technical & Community College,
   Stanton/Wilmington Campus, A
Delaware Technical & Community College, Terry
   Campus, A
Strayer University - Christiana Campus, B
Wilmington University, B

District of Columbia

The George Washington University, B
Strayer University - Takoma Park Campus, B
Strayer University - Washington Campus, B
Trinity Washington University, B

Florida

Argosy University, Sarasota, B
Argosy University, Tampa, B
Broward College, A
City College (Fort Lauderdale), A
City College (Miami), A
College of Central Florida, A
Daytona State College, A
DeVry University (Jacksonville), B
DeVry University (Miramar), B
DeVry University (Orlando), B
Eastern Florida State College, A
Edward Waters College, B
Everest University (Orange Park), AB
Everest University (Orlando), AB

Everest University (Tampa), AB
Florida Gateway College, A
Florida Keys Community College, A
Florida Memorial University, B
Florida National University, B
Florida SouthWestern State College, AB
Florida State College at Jacksonville, A
Florida Technical College (Orlando), A
Fortis College (Orange Park), A
Gulf Coast State College, A
Hillsborough Community College, A
Indian River State College, A
Johnson & Wales University, B
Keiser University, AB
Lake-Sumter State College, A
Lynn University, B
Miami Dade College, A
Northwest Florida State College, A
Palm Beach State College, A
Pasco-Hernando State College, A
Pensacola State College, A
Polk State College, AB
St. Johns River State College, A
St. Petersburg College, A
St. Thomas University, B
Santa Fe College, A
Seminole State College of Florida, A
South Florida State College, A
South University (Royal Palm Beach), B
South University (Tampa), A
Southeastern University, B
Southern Technical College (Fort Myers), A
Southern Technical College (Tampa), AB
Strayer University - Baymeadows Campus, B
Strayer University - Brickell Campus, B
Strayer University - Coral Springs Campus, B
Strayer University - Doral Campus, B
Strayer University - Fort Lauderdale Campus, B
Strayer University - Maitland Campus, B
Strayer University - Miramar Campus, B
Strayer University - Orlando East Campus, B
Strayer University - Palm Beach Gardens Campus,
   B
Strayer University - Sand Lake Campus, B
Strayer University - Tampa East Campus, B
Strayer University - Tampa Westshore Campus, B
Tallahassee Community College, A
University of Phoenix - Central Florida Campus, B
University of Phoenix - North Florida Campus, B
University of Phoenix - South Florida Campus, B
Valencia College, A
Webber International University, AB

Georgia

Abraham Baldwin Agricultural College, A
American InterContinental University Atlanta, AB
Argosy University, Atlanta, B
Ashworth College, AB
Athens Technical College, A
Bainbridge State College, A
College of Coastal Georgia, AB
Dalton State College, AB
Darton State College, A
DeVry University (Alpharetta), B
DeVry University (Decatur), B
DeVry University (Duluth), B
Emmanuel College, B
Fort Valley State University, AB
Georgia College & State University, B
Georgia Military College, A
Georgia Southwestern State University, B
Middle Georgia State University, A
Piedmont College, B
Reinhardt University, A
South Georgia State College, A
South University, B
Strayer University - Augusta Campus, B
Strayer University - Chamblee Campus, B
Strayer University - Cobb County Campus, B
Strayer University - Columbus Campus, B
Strayer University - Douglasville Campus, B
Strayer University - Lithonia Campus, B
Strayer University - Morrow Campus, B
Strayer University - Roswell Campus, B
Strayer University - Savannah Campus, B
Thomas University, AB

University of Georgia, B
University of Phoenix - Atlanta Campus, B
University of Phoenix - Augusta Campus, AB
University of Phoenix - Columbus Georgia Campus,
   AB

Hawaii

Hawaii Community College, A
Hawai'i Pacific University, AB
Remington College - Honolulu Campus, AB
University of Hawaii Maui College, A
University of Hawaii - West Oahu, B
University of Phoenix - Hawaii Campus, B

Idaho

Boise State University, AB
Broadview University - Boise, AB
College of Southern Idaho, A
North Idaho College, A
Northwest Nazarene University, B

Illinois

Argosy University, Chicago, B
Argosy University, Schaumburg, B
Blackburn College, B
Bradley University, B
College of DuPage, A
DeVry University (Addison), B
DeVry University (Chicago), B
DeVry University (Downers Grove), B
DeVry University (Elgin), B
DeVry University (Naperville), B
DeVry University (Tinley Park), B
DeVry University Online, B
Ellis University, B
Greenville College, B
Harper College, A
Illinois Valley Community College, A
Kankakee Community College, A
Kaskaskia College, A
Lewis and Clark Community College, A
Lincoln College, A
Lincoln College - Normal, B
MacMurray College, AB
Moraine Valley Community College, A
North Park University, B
Northwestern College - Bridgeview Campus, A
Northwestern College - Chicago Campus, A
Olivet Nazarene University, B
Rock Valley College, A
Sauk Valley Community College, A
Southwestern Illinois College, A
Spoon River College, A
Taylor Business Institute, A
Trinity Christian College, B
Triton College, A
University of St. Francis, B
Western Illinois University, B

Indiana

Anderson University, AB
Brightwood College, Indianapolis Campus, A
DeVry University, B
Harrison College, AB
Indiana Tech, B
Indiana University East, B
Trine University, AB

Iowa

Briar Cliff University, B
Des Moines Area Community College, A
Dordt College, B
Ellsworth Community College, A
Graceland University, B
Grand View University, B
Indian Hills Community College, A
Iowa Lakes Community College, A
Kaplan University, Cedar Rapids, AB
Kaplan University, Mason City Campus, A
Mount Mercy University, B
Simpson College, B
Southeastern Community College, A
University of Dubuque, B
Waldorf College, B

Kansas

Allen Community College, A
Central Christian College of Kansas, A
Colby Community College, A
Cowley County Community College and Area Vocational - Technical School, A
Dodge City Community College, A
Fort Scott Community College, A
Grantham University, AB
Kansas Wesleyan University, B
Labette Community College, A
MidAmerica Nazarene University, B
Neosho County Community College, A
Newman University, B
Sterling College, B
Washburn University, AB

Kentucky

Ashland Community and Technical College, A
Big Sandy Community and Technical College, A
Campbellsville University, AB
Eastern Kentucky University, B
Elizabethtown Community and Technical College, A
Gateway Community and Technical College, A
Hopkinsville Community College, A
Jefferson Community and Technical College, A
Lindsey Wilson College, B
Owensboro Community and Technical College, A
Somerset Community College, A
Union College, B
University of Louisville, B
West Kentucky Community and Technical College, A

Louisiana

Blue Cliff College - Shreveport, A
Remington College - Baton Rouge Campus, A
Remington College - Lafayette Campus, A
Remington College - Shreveport, A
Southern University at Shreveport, A
Southwest University, AB

Maine

Beal College, A
Central Maine Community College, A
Husson University, AB
Kaplan University, South Portland, A
Thomas College, B
University of Maine at Augusta, B
University of Maine at Fort Kent, A
University of Maine at Presque Isle, AB

Maryland

Anne Arundel Community College, A
Bowie State University, B
College of Southern Maryland, A
Coppin State University, B
Frederick Community College, A
Frostburg State University, B
Howard Community College, A
Kaplan University, Hagerstown Campus, A
Prince George's Community College, A
Stevenson University, B
University of Baltimore, B
University of Maryland Eastern Shore, B

Massachusetts

Anna Maria College, B
Bay Path University, B
Becker College, B
Bunker Hill Community College, A
Eastern Nazarene College, B
Elms College, B
Massachusetts Bay Community College, A
Merrimack College, B
Middlesex Community College, A
Mount Ida College, B
Mount Wachusett Community College, A
North Shore Community College, A
Northern Essex Community College, A
Quincy College, A
Roxbury Community College, A
Salem State University, B
Springfield College, B
University of Massachusetts Lowell, B

Michigan

Adrian College, B
Concordia University Ann Arbor, B
Ferris State University, B
Finlandia University, A
Gogebic Community College, A
Grand Rapids Community College, A
Grand Valley State University, B
Henry Ford College, A
Jackson College, A
Kellogg Community College, A
Kirtland Community College, A
Lake Michigan College, A
Lake Superior State University, AB
Macomb Community College, A
Michigan State University, B
Mid Michigan Community College, A
Montcalm Community College, A
Muskegon Community College, A
North Central Michigan College, A
Northern Michigan University, A
Oakland Community College, A
Oakland University, B
St. Clair County Community College, A
South University, B
University of Phoenix - Detroit Campus, B

Minnesota

Argosy University, Twin Cities, B
Bemidji State University, AB
Globe University - Minneapolis, AB
Globe University - Woodbury, AB
Gustavus Adolphus College, B
Minnesota School of Business - Blaine, AB
Minnesota School of Business - Brooklyn Center, AB
Minnesota School of Business - Elk River, AB
Minnesota School of Business - Lakeville, AB
Minnesota School of Business - Richfield, AB
Minnesota School of Business - Rochester, AB
Minnesota School of Business - St. Cloud, AB
Minnesota State Community and Technical College - Moorhead, A
St. Cloud State University, B
Southwest Minnesota State University, B
University of Minnesota, Crookston, B
Vermilion Community College, A
Walden University, B

Mississippi

Belhaven University, B
Holmes Community College, A
Mississippi College, B
Mississippi Delta Community College, A
Mississippi Gulf Coast Community College, A
Mississippi Valley State University, B
Strayer University - Jackson Campus, B
University of Mississippi, B
Virginia College in Biloxi, A

Missouri

American Business & Technology University, A
Calvary Bible College and Theological Seminary, B
Columbia College, AB
Culver-Stockton College, B
DeVry University (Kansas City), B
Evangel University, B
Hannibal-LaGrange University, AB
Harris-Stowe State University, B
Jefferson College, A
Lincoln University, AB
Metropolitan Community College - Kansas City, A
Missouri Southern State University, B
Missouri State University - West Plains, A
Missouri Valley College, B
North Central Missouri College, A
Rockhurst University, B
Southwest Baptist University, B
Three Rivers Community College, A
University of Central Missouri, B
University of Missouri - Kansas City, B

Montana

Flathead Valley Community College, A
University of Great Falls, B

Nebraska

Kaplan University, Lincoln, AB
Kaplan University, Omaha, AB
Midland University, B
Peru State College, B
Southeast Community College, Beatrice Campus, A
York College, B

Nevada

Brightwood College, Las Vegas Campus, A
DeVry University, B
Nevada State College, B
University of Phoenix - Las Vegas Campus, B
Western Nevada College, A

New Hampshire

Franklin Pierce University, B
Great Bay Community College, A
New England College, B
NHTI, Concord's Community College, A
River Valley Community College, A
Rivier University, B

New Jersey

Bergen Community College, A
Berkeley College - Woodland Park Campus, B
The College of New Jersey, B
Fairleigh Dickinson University, Metropolitan Campus, B
Felician University, B
Kean University, B
Passaic County Community College, A
Raritan Valley Community College, A
Rutgers University - New Brunswick, B
Thomas Edison State University, B
Union County College, A
University of Phoenix - Jersey City Campus, AB
Warren County Community College, A

New Mexico

Brookline College, AB
Central New Mexico Community College, A
New Mexico Military Institute, A
New Mexico State University - Carlsbad, A
University of New Mexico - Gallup, A
University of New Mexico - Valencia Campus, A
University of Phoenix - New Mexico Campus, B
University of the Southwest, B
Western New Mexico University, AB

New York

Alfred University, B
ASA College, A
Berkeley College - New York City Campus, B
Berkeley College - White Plains Campus, B
Borough of Manhattan Community College of the City University of New York, A
Bryant & Stratton College - Albany Campus, A
Bryant & Stratton College - Buffalo Campus, A
Bryant & Stratton College - Greece Campus, A
Bryant & Stratton College - Henrietta Campus, A
Bryant & Stratton College - Orchard Park Campus, A
Buffalo State College, State University of New York, B
Canisius College, B
Clinton Community College, A
The College of Saint Rose, B
Columbia-Greene Community College, A
Elmira College, B
Erie Community College, North Campus, A
Excelsior College, B
Finger Lakes Community College, A
Fulton-Montgomery Community College, A
Genesee Community College, A
Herkimer County Community College, A
Hudson Valley Community College, A
Iona College, B
Jamestown Community College, A
Jefferson Community College, A
John Jay College of Criminal Justice of the City University of New York, B
Keuka College, B
Kingsborough Community College of the City University of New York, A

Long Island University - LIU Post, B
Marist College, B
Medaille College, B
Mercy College, B
Mohawk Valley Community College, A
Monroe College, AB
Monroe Community College, A
Morrisville State College, A
Nassau Community College, A
New York Institute of Technology, B
Niagara County Community College, A
Niagara University, B
Onondaga Community College, A
Orange County Community College, A
Pace University, B
Pace University, Pleasantville Campus, B
Queensborough Community College of the City University of New York, A
Roberts Wesleyan College, B
Rochester Institute of Technology, B
Rockland Community College, A
The Sage Colleges, B
St. John's University, AB
St. Joseph's College, Long Island Campus, B
St. Joseph's College, New York, B
St. Thomas Aquinas College, B
Schenectady County Community College, A
State University of New York College of Technology at Canton, B
State University of New York at Fredonia, B
State University of New York at Oswego, B
Suffolk County Community College, A
Tompkins Cortland Community College, A
Ulster County Community College, A
University at Albany, State University of New York, B
Utica College, B

North Carolina

Barton College, B
Beaufort County Community College, A
Brevard College, B
Brightwood College, Charlotte Campus, A
Campbell University, B
Carteret Community College, A
Catawba College, B
Central Carolina Community College, A
Central Piedmont Community College, A
Coastal Carolina Community College, A
College of The Albemarle, A
Craven Community College, A
Davidson County Community College, A
ECPI University (Raleigh), A
Edgecombe Community College, A
Fayetteville State University, B
Haywood Community College, A
Isothermal Community College, A
Lees-McRae College, B
Mars Hill University, B
Methodist University, AB
Miller-Motte College (Cary), A
Mitchell Community College, A
North Carolina Wesleyan College, B
Pfeiffer University, B
Robeson Community College, A
Rowan-Cabarrus Community College, A
Saint Augustine's University, B
Sampson Community College, A
Sandhills Community College, A
South College - Asheville, A
South University, AB
Southeastern Community College, A
Strayer University - Greensboro Campus, B
Strayer University - Huntersville Campus, B
Strayer University - North Charlotte Campus, B
Strayer University - North Raleigh Campus, B
Strayer University - RTP Campus, B
Strayer University - South Charlotte Campus, B
Strayer University - South Raleigh Campus, B
Surry Community College, A
University of Mount Olive, B
Vance-Granville Community College, A
Western Piedmont Community College, A
William Peace University, B
Wingate University, B

North Dakota

United Tribes Technical College, A

Ohio

Bowling Green State University, B
Bryant & Stratton College - Cleveland Campus, A
Bryant & Stratton College - Parma Campus, A
Central Ohio Technical College, A
Clark State Community College, A
Daymar College, A
Fortis College (Ravenna), A
Franklin University, B
Harrison College, A
Hocking College, A
Lake Erie College, B
Miami-Jacobs Career College (Dayton), A
Miami-Jacobs Career College (Independence), A
Miami University, AB
Mount Vernon Nazarene University, B
Muskingum University, B
North Central State College, A
Ohio Northern University, B
Ohio University - Eastern, B
Ohio University - Lancaster, B
Ohio University - Southern Campus, AB
Ohio University - Zanesville, B
Owens Community College, A
Remington College - Cleveland Campus, A
Sinclair Community College, A
South University, B
Southern State Community College, A
Tiffin University, AB
Union Institute & University, B
University of Dayton, B
The University of Findlay, B
Urbana University, AB
Wilmington College, B
Wright State University, A
Youngstown State University, AB
Zane State College, A

Oklahoma

Bacone College, A
DeVry University, B
East Central University, B
Mid-America Christian University, B
Northeastern State University, B
Northern Oklahoma College, A
Oklahoma City University, B
Redlands Community College, A
Rogers State University, B
Rose State College, A
Seminole State College, A
University of Central Oklahoma, B
University of Oklahoma, B

Oregon

Lane Community College, A
Northwest Christian University, B
Pioneer Pacific College - Eugene/Springfield Branch, A
Portland State University, B
Tillamook Bay Community College, A
Umpqua Community College, A
Western Oregon University, B

Pennsylvania

Alvernia University, B
Arcadia University, B
Brightwood Career Institute, Harrisburg Campus, A
Brightwood Career Institute, Philadelphia Campus, A
Brightwood Career Institute, Philadelphia Mills Campus, A
Brightwood Career Institute, Pittsburgh Campus, A
Butler County Community College, A
Chestnut Hill College, B
Cheyney University of Pennsylvania, B
Clarion University of Pennsylvania, AB
Community College of Philadelphia, A
Delaware Valley University, B
Drexel University, B
Harcum College, A
Harrisburg Area Community College, A
Keystone College, AB

Lehigh Carbon Community College, A
Lock Haven University of Pennsylvania, AB
Luzerne County Community College, A
Manor College, A
Mansfield University of Pennsylvania, AB
Marywood University, B
McCann School of Business & Technology (Lewisburg), A
Mercyhurst North East, A
Mount Aloysius College, B
Peirce College, A
Penn State Abington, B
Penn State Altoona, B
Penn State Beaver, B
Penn State Berks, B
Penn State Brandywine, B
Penn State DuBois, B
Penn State Erie, The Behrend College, B
Penn State Fayette, The Eberly Campus, B
Penn State Greater Allegheny, B
Penn State Hazleton, B
Penn State Lehigh Valley, B
Penn State Mont Alto, B
Penn State New Kensington, B
Penn State Schuylkill, B
Penn State Shenango, B
Penn State University Park, B
Penn State Wilkes-Barre, B
Penn State Worthington Scranton, B
Penn State York, B
Pennsylvania Highlands Community College, A
Saint Francis University, B
South Hills School of Business & Technology (State College), A
Strayer University - Allentown Campus, B
Strayer University - Center City Campus, B
Strayer University - Delaware County Campus, B
Strayer University - King of Prussia Campus, B
Strayer University - Lower Bucks County Campus, B
Strayer University - Warrendale Campus, B
University of Phoenix - Philadelphia Campus, B
University of Pittsburgh at Bradford, B
University of Pittsburgh at Greensburg, B
University of Pittsburgh at Titusville, A
Valley Forge Military College, A
Villanova University, B
Waynesburg University, B
Westminster College, B
Widener University, B
York College of Pennsylvania, AB

Rhode Island

Johnson & Wales University, B
New England Institute of Technology, AB
Roger Williams University, AB
Salve Regina University, AB

South Carolina

Aiken Technical College, A
Anderson University, B
Benedict College, B
The Citadel, The Military College of South Carolina, B
Claflin University, B
ECPI University (Greenville), A
Florence-Darlington Technical College, A
Limestone College, B
Miller-Motte Technical College (North Charleston), A
Morris College, B
Piedmont Technical College, A
South Carolina State University, B
South University, B
Spartanburg Methodist College, A
Strayer University - Charleston Campus, B
Strayer University - Columbia Campus, B
Strayer University - Greenville Campus, B
Trident Technical College, A
University of South Carolina, B
University of South Carolina Lancaster, A
University of South Carolina Upstate, B
Voorhees College, B

South Dakota

Globe University - Sioux Falls, AB
Oglala Lakota College, AB

Sinte Gleska University, A
The University of South Dakota, B

Tennessee

Argosy University, Nashville, B
Austin Peay State University, B
Bethel University, B
Brightwood College, Nashville Campus, A
Cumberland University, B
DeVry University, B
East Tennessee State University, B
Hiwassee College, A
LeMoyne-Owen College, B
Lincoln Memorial University, B
Martin Methodist College, B
Middle Tennessee State University, B
Miller-Motte Technical College (Chattanooga), A
Remington College - Memphis Campus, A
Remington College - Nashville Campus, A
Roane State Community College, A
Strayer University - Knoxville Campus, B
Strayer University - Nashville Campus, B
Strayer University - Shelby Campus, B
Strayer University - Thousand Oaks Campus, B
Tennessee State University, B
Trevecca Nazarene University, AB
Tusculum College, B
University of Memphis, B
The University of Tennessee at Chattanooga, B
The University of Tennessee at Martin, B
Virginia College in Chattanooga, A

Texas

Abilene Christian University, B
Amarillo College, A
American InterContinental University Houston, B
Angelina College, A
Argosy University, Dallas, B
Blinn College, A
Brightwood College, Arlington Campus, A
Brightwood College, Beaumont Campus, A
Brightwood College, Corpus Christi Campus, A
Brightwood College, Dallas Campus, A
Brightwood College, El Paso Campus, A
Brightwood College, Fort Worth Campus, A
Brightwood College, Laredo Campus, A
Brightwood College, San Antonio San Pedro Campus, A
Brookhaven College, A
Coastal Bend College, A
Concordia University Texas, B
Del Mar College, A
East Texas Baptist University, B
Hill College, A
Howard College, A
Huston-Tillotson University, B
Kilgore College, A
Lone Star College - CyFair, A
Lone Star College - Kingwood, A
Lone Star College - Montgomery, A
Lone Star College - North Harris, A
Lone Star College - Tomball, A
Lone Star College - University Park, A
Lubbock Christian University, B
McLennan Community College, A
Midwestern State University, B
Navarro College, A
North Central Texas College, A
Northeast Texas Community College, A
Odessa College, A
Paul Quinn College, B
Remington College - Dallas Campus, A
Remington College - Fort Worth Campus, A
Remington College - North Houston Campus, A
St. Mary's University, B
St. Philip's College, A
Sam Houston State University, B
San Antonio College, A
South Plains College, A
South University, B
Southwest Texas Junior College, A
Strayer University - Cedar Hill Campus, B
Strayer University - Irving Campus, B
Strayer University - Katy Campus, B
Strayer University - North Austin Campus, B
Strayer University - Northwest Houston Campus, B

Strayer University - Plano Campus, B
Sul Ross State University, B
Tarleton State University, B
Tarrant County College District, A
Temple College, A
Texarkana College, A
Texas Southern University, B
Texas Southmost College, A
Trinity Valley Community College, A
Tyler Junior College, A
University of the Incarnate Word, B
University of Mary Hardin-Baylor, B
University of Phoenix - Dallas Campus, B
University of Phoenix - Houston Campus, B
University of Phoenix - San Antonio Campus, B
The University of Texas at El Paso, B
The University of Texas Rio Grande Valley, B
Vernon College, A
Wayland Baptist University, AB
Weatherford College, A
West Texas A&M University, B
Western Texas College, A
Wharton County Junior College, A

Utah

Argosy University, Salt Lake City, B
Broadview University - Layton, AB
Broadview University - West Jordan, AB
Provo College, A
Salt Lake Community College, A
Snow College, A
University of Phoenix - Utah Campus, B
Utah Valley University, AB

Vermont

Castleton University, AB
College of St. Joseph, AB
Community College of Vermont, A
Norwich University, B
Southern Vermont College, B

Virginia

Argosy University, Washington DC, B
Averett University, B
Blue Ridge Community College, A
Bluefield College, B
Bryant & Stratton College - Richmond Campus, A
Bryant & Stratton College - Virginia Beach Campus, AB
Central Virginia Community College, A
Dabney S. Lancaster Community College, A
Danville Community College, A
DeVry University (Chesapeake), B
DeVry University (Manassas), B
ECPI University (Manassas), A
ECPI University (Virginia Beach), AB
Hampton University, B
J. Sargeant Reynolds Community College, A
John Tyler Community College, A
Marymount University, B
Miller-Motte Technical College (Lynchburg), A
Mountain Empire Community College, A
New River Community College, A
Patrick Henry Community College, A
Paul D. Camp Community College, A
Rappahannock Community College, A
Regent University, AB
Shenandoah University, B
South University (Glen Allen), AB
South University (Virginia Beach), B
Southside Virginia Community College, A
Southwest Virginia Community College, A
Strayer University - Alexandria Campus, B
Strayer University - Arlington Campus, B
Strayer University - Chesapeake Campus, B
Strayer University - Chesterfield Campus, B
Strayer University - Fredericksburg Campus, B
Strayer University - Henrico Campus, B
Strayer University - Loudoun Campus, B
Strayer University - Manassas Campus, B
Strayer University - Newport News Campus, B
Strayer University - Virginia Beach Campus, B
Strayer University - Woodbridge Campus, B
Thomas Nelson Community College, A
University of Management and Technology, AB
Virginia Commonwealth University, B

Virginia Western Community College, A
Wytheville Community College, A

Washington

Argosy University, Seattle, B
Bellevue College, A
Centralia College, A
Columbia Basin College, A
Everett Community College, A
Highline College, A
Lower Columbia College, A
Northwest University, B
Peninsula College, A
Pierce College at Fort Steilacoom, A
Pierce College at Puyallup, A
Tacoma Community College, A
University of Phoenix - Western Washington Campus, B
Washington State University, B
Yakima Valley Community College, A

West Virginia

American Public University System, AB
Glenville State College, A
Salem International University, AB
Southern West Virginia Community and Technical College, A
Strayer University - Teays Valley Campus, B
West Liberty University, B
West Virginia University Institute of Technology, B
West Virginia University at Parkersburg, A
West Virginia Wesleyan College, B

Wisconsin

Bryant & Stratton College - Milwaukee Campus, AB
Bryant & Stratton College - Wauwatosa Campus, AB
Carthage College, B
Concordia University Wisconsin, B
Globe University - Eau Claire, AB
Globe University - Green Bay, AB
Globe University - La Crosse, AB
Globe University - Madison East, AB
Globe University - Madison West, AB
Globe University - Wausau, AB
Mount Mary University, B
University of Wisconsin - Oshkosh, B
University of Wisconsin - Parkside, B
University of Wisconsin - Platteville, B
Viterbo University, B

Wyoming

Casper College, A
Central Wyoming College, A
Eastern Wyoming College, A
Laramie County Community College, A
Northwest College, A
Western Wyoming Community College, A

U.S. Territories: Guam

Guam Community College, A
University of Guam, B

U.S. Territories: Puerto Rico

Colegio Universitario de San Juan, B
Inter American University of Puerto Rico, Guayama Campus, B
Universidad del Este, A
University of Puerto Rico in Carolina, B

Canada

Alberta

Mount Royal University, B

British Columbia

Thompson Rivers University, B

Maritime Provinces: New Brunswick

University of New Brunswick Saint John, B

Ontario

Carleton University, B
University of Guelph, B

Saskatchewan

University of Regina, B

CRIMINAL JUSTICE/POLICE SCIENCE

United States

Alabama

Chattahoochee Valley Community College, A
Columbia Southern University, AB
Gadsden State Community College, A
George C. Wallace Community College, A
Jacksonville State University, B
Jefferson State Community College, A
Lawson State Community College, A
Northwest-Shoals Community College, A
Wallace State Community College, A

Arizona

Cochise County Community College District, A
Eastern Arizona College, A
Mohave Community College, A
Pima Community College, A
Yavapai College, A

Arkansas

Arkansas Northeastern College, A
Arkansas State University, A
Arkansas State University - Mountain Home, A
Black River Technical College, A
East Arkansas Community College, A
South Arkansas Community College, A
University of Arkansas at Little Rock, A
University of Arkansas at Pine Bluff, A

California

Allan Hancock College, A
Antelope Valley College, A
Bakersfield College, A
Barstow Community College, A
Butte College, A
Cabrillo College, A
California State University, East Bay, B
Carrington College - Pleasant Hill, A
Cerritos College, A
Chabot College, A
Chaffey College, A
Citrus College, A
City College of San Francisco, A
College of the Canyons, A
College of the Desert, A
College of Marin, A
College of the Redwoods, A
College of San Mateo, A
College of the Sequoias, A
College of the Siskiyous, A
Contra Costa College, A
Copper Mountain College, A
Crafton Hills College, A
Cuesta College, A
De Anza College, A
East Los Angeles College, A
El Camino College, A
Evergreen Valley College, A
Fresno City College, A
Fullerton College, A
Gavilan College, A
Golden West College, A
Grossmont College, A
Hartnell College, A
Lake Tahoe Community College, A
Las Positas College, A
Lassen Community College District, A
Long Beach City College, A
Los Angeles City College, A
Los Angeles Harbor College, A
Los Angeles Mission College, A
Los Angeles Southwest College, A
Los Angeles Valley College, A
Mendocino College, A
Merced College, A
Merritt College, A

MiraCosta College, A
Modesto Junior College, A
Monterey Peninsula College, A
Moorpark College, A
Mt. San Antonio College, A
Mt. San Jacinto College, A
Napa Valley College, A
Ohlone College, A
Palo Verde College, A
Porterville College, A
Reedley College, A
San Bernardino Valley College, A
San Diego Miramar College, A
San Joaquin Delta College, A
San Jose City College, A
Santa Ana College, A
Sierra College, A
Southwestern College, A
University of Antelope Valley, AB
Victor Valley College, A
West Los Angeles College, A
West Valley College, A
Yuba College, A

Colorado

Colorado Mesa University, B
Northeastern Junior College, A
Red Rocks Community College, A

Connecticut

Asnuntuck Community College, A
Capital Community College, A
Middlesex Community College, A
Naugatuck Valley Community College, A
Northwestern Connecticut Community College, A
Three Rivers Community College, A
University of Hartford, B
University of New Haven, A
Western Connecticut State University, B

Delaware

Delaware Technical & Community College, Jack F. Owens Campus, A
Delaware Technical & Community College, Stanton/Wilmington Campus, A
Delaware Technical & Community College, Terry Campus, A

District of Columbia

Howard University, B

Florida

Daytona State College, A
Florida State College at Jacksonville, A
Indian River State College, A
Miami Dade College, A
Northwest Florida State College, A
Palm Beach State College, A
Tallahassee Community College, A

Georgia

Abraham Baldwin Agricultural College, A
Armstrong State University, AB
Coastal Pines Technical College, A
Dalton State College, A
Georgia Highlands College, A

Hawaii

Honolulu Community College, A

Idaho

College of Western Idaho, A
Idaho State University, AB
North Idaho College, A

Illinois

Black Hawk College, A
Carl Sandburg College, A
City Colleges of Chicago, Richard J. Daley College, A
City Colleges of Chicago, Wilbur Wright College, A
College of DuPage, A
College of Lake County, A
Danville Area Community College, A
Elgin Community College, A

Illinois Central College, A
Illinois Valley Community College, A
John A. Logan College, A
John Wood Community College, A
Kankakee Community College, A
Kishwaukee College, A
Lake Land College, A
Lincoln Land Community College, A
MacMurray College, AB
McHenry County College, A
Moraine Valley Community College, A
Morton College, A
Oakton Community College, A
Prairie State College, A
Rend Lake College, A
Richland Community College, A
Sauk Valley Community College, A
Shawnee Community College, A
Southeastern Illinois College, A
Spoon River College, A
Waubonsee Community College, A

Indiana

Vincennes University, A

Iowa

Hawkeye Community College, A
Iowa Central Community College, A
Iowa Lakes Community College, A
Kaplan University, Des Moines, AB
Kirkwood Community College, A
Marshalltown Community College, A
North Iowa Area Community College, A
Scott Community College, A
Western Iowa Tech Community College, A

Kansas

Barton County Community College, A
Butler Community College, A
Cloud County Community College, A
Colby Community College, A
Cowley County Community College and Area Vocational - Technical School, A
Garden City Community College, A
Highland Community College, A
Hutchinson Community College, A
Johnson County Community College, A
Kansas City Kansas Community College, A
Labette Community College, A
Neosho County Community College, A
Wichita Area Technical College, A

Kentucky

Eastern Kentucky University, AB
Madisonville Community College, A
Southeast Kentucky Community and Technical College, A
Sullivan University, A

Louisiana

Delgado Community College, A
Fletcher Technical Community College, A
Louisiana College, B
Louisiana State University at Eunice, A
Southern University and Agricultural and Mechanical College, A

Maryland

Allegany College of Maryland, A
Anne Arundel Community College, A
Baltimore City Community College, A
Carroll Community College, A
Cecil College, A
Community College of Baltimore County, A
Hagerstown Community College, A
Harford Community College, A
Montgomery College, A
Wor-Wic Community College, A

Massachusetts

Bunker Hill Community College, A
Cape Cod Community College, A
Eastern Nazarene College, B
Greenfield Community College, A
Massasoit Community College, A

Newbury College, B
Quinsigamond Community College, A
Springfield Technical Community College, A

Michigan

Alpena Community College, A
Delta College, A
Ferris State University, AB
Grand Rapids Community College, A
Kalamazoo Valley Community College, A
Kellogg Community College, A
Kirtland Community College, A
Lake Superior State University, AB
Lansing Community College, A
Macomb Community College, A
Monroe County Community College, A
Mott Community College, A
North Central Michigan College, A
Oakland Community College, A
Schoolcraft College, A
Washtenaw Community College, A
Wayne County Community College District, A
West Shore Community College, A

Minnesota

Alexandria Technical and Community College, A
Bemidji State University, B
Central Lakes College, A
Century College, A
Fond du Lac Tribal and Community College, A
Hibbing Community College, A
Inver Hills Community College, A
Metropolitan State University, B
Minneapolis Community and Technical College, A
Minnesota State University Mankato, B
Minnesota West Community and Technical College, A
Normandale Community College, A
North Hennepin Community College, A
Northland Community and Technical College, A
Rasmussen College Blaine, A
Rasmussen College Bloomington, A
Rasmussen College Brooklyn Park, A
Rasmussen College Eagan, A
Rasmussen College Lake Elmo/Woodbury, A
Rasmussen College Mankato, A
Rasmussen College St. Cloud, A
Ridgewater College, A
Riverland Community College, A
Rochester Community and Technical College, A
Vermilion Community College, A

Mississippi

Copiah-Lincoln Community College, A
Itawamba Community College, A
Jones County Junior College, A
Mississippi Gulf Coast Community College, A
Northeast Mississippi Community College, A

Missouri

College of the Ozarks, B
Jefferson College, A
Metropolitan Community College - Kansas City, A
Mineral Area College, A
Missouri Southern State University, A
Missouri State University - West Plains, A
Missouri Western State University, A
Moberly Area Community College, A
St. Charles Community College, A
State Fair Community College, A
Three Rivers Community College, A

Montana

Dawson Community College, A
University of Great Falls, B

Nebraska

Metropolitan Community College, A
Northeast Community College, A

Nevada

College of Southern Nevada, A
Nevada State College, B
Truckee Meadows Community College, A

New Jersey

Atlantic Cape Community College, A
Berkeley College - Woodland Park Campus, A
Brookdale Community College, A
Camden County College, A
County College of Morris, A
Cumberland County College, A
Essex County College, A
Hudson County Community College, A
Mercer County Community College, A
Middlesex County College, A
Ocean County College, A
Raritan Valley Community College, A
Rowan College at Burlington County, A
Rowan College at Gloucester County, A
Rowan University, B
Salem Community College, A
Union County College, A

New Mexico

Clovis Community College, A
Eastern New Mexico University - Roswell, A
Mesalands Community College, A
New Mexico Junior College, A
New Mexico Military Institute, A
San Juan College, A
Santa Fe Community College, A
Western New Mexico University, AB

New York

Adirondack Community College, A
Berkeley College - New York City Campus, A
Berkeley College - White Plains Campus, A
Borough of Manhattan Community College of the City University of New York, A
Broome Community College, A
Cayuga County Community College, A
Clinton Community College, A
Corning Community College, A
Dutchess Community College, A
Erie Community College, A
Erie Community College, North Campus, A
Erie Community College, South Campus, A
Farmingdale State College, A
Finger Lakes Community College, A
Genesee Community College, A
Hilbert College, AB
Jamestown Community College, A
John Jay College of Criminal Justice of the City University of New York, A
Monroe College, AB
Monroe Community College, A
Onondaga Community College, A
Orange County Community College, A
State University of New York College of Technology at Canton, A
Suffolk County Community College, A
Sullivan County Community College, A
Tompkins Cortland Community College, A

North Carolina

Beaufort County Community College, A
Bladen Community College, A
Cape Fear Community College, A
Central Piedmont Community College, A
Davidson County Community College, A
Gaston College, A
Isothermal Community College, A
Johnston Community College, A
Pitt Community College, A
Roanoke-Chowan Community College, A
Rockingham Community College, A
Sandhills Community College, A
Southwestern Community College, A
Stanly Community College, A
Vance-Granville Community College, A
Wayne Community College, A
Western Piedmont Community College, A
Wilkes Community College, A

North Dakota

Lake Region State College, A

Ohio

Bowling Green State University, B
Central Ohio Technical College, A
Clark State Community College, A
Columbus State Community College, A
Cuyahoga Community College, A
Eastern Gateway Community College, A
Edison Community College, A
Heidelberg University, B
Hocking College, A
James A. Rhodes State College, A
Lakeland Community College, A
Lorain County Community College, A
Northwest State Community College, A
Ohio Northern University, B
Ohio University - Chillicothe, A
Ohio University - Lancaster, A
Owens Community College, A
Sinclair Community College, A
Southern State Community College, A
Terra State Community College, A
The University of Akron, A
Youngstown State University, A

Oklahoma

Connors State College, A
East Central University, B
Northeastern Oklahoma Agricultural and Mechanical College, A
Northwestern Oklahoma State University, B
Oklahoma City University, B
Oklahoma Panhandle State University, A
Oklahoma State University, Oklahoma City, A
Redlands Community College, A
Rogers State University, A
St. Gregory's University, B
Seminole State College, A
Tulsa Community College, A
Western Oklahoma State College, A

Oregon

Clackamas Community College, A
Pioneer Pacific College, AB
Rogue Community College, A
Southwestern Oregon Community College, A
Treasure Valley Community College, A
Western Oregon University, B

Pennsylvania

Butler County Community College, A
Community College of Allegheny County, A
Community College of Beaver County, A
Delaware County Community College, A
Elizabethtown College School of Continuing and Professional Studies, AB
Gwynedd Mercy University, B
Harrisburg Area Community College, A
Keystone College, B
Montgomery County Community College, A
Reading Area Community College, A
University of Pittsburgh at Greensburg, B
Westmoreland County Community College, A
YTI Career Institute - Altoona, A

Rhode Island

Community College of Rhode Island, A

South Dakota

Lake Area Technical Institute, A
Northern State University, B
Southeast Technical Institute, A
Western Dakota Technical Institute, A

Tennessee

Cleveland State Community College, A
Columbia State Community College, A
Daymar College (Murfreesboro), A
Dyersburg State Community College, A
Middle Tennessee State University, B
Nashville State Community College, A
Roane State Community College, A
Volunteer State Community College, A
Walters State Community College, A

Texas

Alvin Community College, A
Amarillo College, A
Austin Community College District, A
Brazosport College, A
Brightwood College, McAllen Campus, A
Central Texas College, A
Cisco College, A
Coastal Bend College, A
Collin County Community College District, A
Del Mar College, A
El Paso Community College, A
Houston Community College, A
Howard College, A
Laredo Community College, A
Lee College, A
McLennan Community College, A
Midland College, A
Navarro College, A
North Central Texas College, A
Northeast Texas Community College, A
Odessa College, A
Sam Houston State University, B
San Antonio College, A
San Jacinto College District, A
South Plains College, A
Stephen F. Austin State University, B
Temple College, A
Texas A&M International University, B
Texas State University, B
Trinity Valley Community College, A
Tyler Junior College, A
Victoria College, A
Western Texas College, A

Utah

Southern Utah University, AB
Weber State University, B

Virginia

George Mason University, B
Germanna Community College, A
New River Community College, A
Rappahannock Community College, A
Virginia Highlands Community College, A
Wytheville Community College, A

Washington

Centralia College, A
Everett Community College, A
Grays Harbor College, A
Green River College, A
Highline College, A
Skagit Valley College, A
Spokane Community College, A
University of Washington, Tacoma, B
Washington State University - Global Campus, B
Washington State University - Vancouver, B
Wenatchee Valley College, A
Whatcom Community College, A
Yakima Valley Community College, A

West Virginia

Fairmont State University, B
Mountwest Community & Technical College, A
New River Community and Technical College, A
West Virginia Northern Community College, A

Wisconsin

Blackhawk Technical College, A
Chippewa Valley Technical College, A
Fox Valley Technical College, A
Gateway Technical College, A
Lakeshore Technical College, A
Madison Area Technical College, A
Marian University, B
Mid-State Technical College, A
Milwaukee Area Technical College, A
Nicolet Area Technical College, A
Northcentral Technical College, A
Northeast Wisconsin Technical College, A
Southwest Wisconsin Technical College, A
University of Wisconsin - Superior, B
Waukesha County Technical College, A
Western Technical College, A

Wisconsin Indianhead Technical College, A

Wyoming

Eastern Wyoming College, A

U.S. Territories: Puerto Rico

Caribbean University, AB
Inter American University of Puerto Rico, Guayama Campus, A
Inter American University of Puerto Rico, Ponce Campus, A
Inter American University of Puerto Rico, San Germán Campus, B
Universidad del Este, A
Universidad Metropolitana, A
Universidad del Turabo, AB

U.S. Territories: United States Virgin Islands

University of the Virgin Islands, AB

Canada

Alberta

Athabasca University, B

Manitoba

The University of Winnipeg, B

Newfoundland and Labrador

Memorial University of Newfoundland, B

Ontario

Carleton University, B
University of Toronto, B

Quebec

Université de Montréal, B

Saskatchewan

University of Regina, B

CRIMINAL JUSTICE/SAFETY STUDIES

United States

Alabama

Alabama State University, B
Athens State University, B
Auburn University at Montgomery, B
Samford University, B
Troy University, B
The University of Alabama, B

Arizona

Chandler-Gilbert Community College, A
Glendale Community College, A
Grand Canyon University, B
Paradise Valley Community College, A
Phoenix College, A
Pima Community College, A

Arkansas

Arkansas Tech University, A
Cossatot Community College of the University of Arkansas, A
Harding University, B
Henderson State University, B
NorthWest Arkansas Community College, A
Southeast Arkansas College, A
Southern Arkansas University - Magnolia, B
University of Arkansas, B
University of Arkansas Community College at Batesville, A
University of Arkansas at Little Rock, B
University of Arkansas at Monticello, B

California

Antioch University Los Angeles, B
Ashford University, B

Brandman University, B
California State University, Chico, B
California State University, Dominguez Hills, B
California State University, Fresno, B
California State University, Fullerton, B
California State University, Los Angeles, B
California State University, San Bernardino, B
California State University, Stanislaus, B
Carrington College - Citrus Heights, A
Carrington College - San Jose, A
La Sierra University, B
National University, B
New Charter University, AB
San Diego State University, B
San Jose State University, B

Colorado

Colorado Mesa University, B
Everest College (Thornton), A
Lamar Community College, A
Metropolitan State University of Denver, B
University of Northern Colorado, B

Connecticut

Goodwin College, B
Mitchell College, B
Post University, AB
Quinnipiac University, B
Sacred Heart University, B
University of Bridgeport, B

District of Columbia

American University, B

Florida

Carlos Albizu University, Miami Campus, B
Everest University (Largo), AB
Everest University (Orlando), A
Florida Agricultural and Mechanical University, B
Florida Atlantic University, B
Florida Gulf Coast University, B
Florida International University, B
Florida National University, A
Florida Technical College (DeLand), A
Fortis College (Winter Park), A
Indian River State College, B
Keiser University, B
North Florida Community College, A
Nova Southeastern University, B
Saint Leo University, B
St. Thomas University, B
South Florida State College, A
State College of Florida Manatee-Sarasota, A
University of Central Florida, B
University of North Florida, B
University of West Florida, B
Virginia College in Pensacola, A

Georgia

Albany State University, B
Andrew College, A
Augusta Technical College, A
Augusta University, AB
Central Georgia Technical College, A
Chattahoochee Technical College, A
Clark Atlanta University, B
Clayton State University, B
Columbus State University, AB
Georgia Gwinnett College, B
Georgia Northwestern Technical College, A
Georgia Piedmont Technical College, A
Georgia Southern University, B
Georgia State University, B
Gordon State College, A
Kennesaw State University, B
Lanier Technical College, A
Mercer University, B
Middle Georgia State University, B
North Georgia Technical College, A
Point University, AB
Savannah Technical College, A
South Georgia Technical College, A
Southeastern Technical College, A
Southern Crescent Technical College, A
Southern Regional Technical College, A

```

Truett-McConnell College, B
University of North Georgia, B
Valdosta State University, B
West Georgia Technical College, A
Wiregrass Georgia Technical College, A

## Hawaii

Chaminade University of Honolulu, AB
University of Hawaii at Hilo, B

## Idaho

Idaho State University, A

## Illinois

American InterContinental University Online, B
Aurora University, B
Benedictine University, B
Chicago State University, B
City Colleges of Chicago, Harold Washington College, A
City Colleges of Chicago, Harry S. Truman College, A
City Colleges of Chicago, Kennedy-King College, A
Governors State University, B
Heartland Community College, A
Illinois State University, B
Joliet Junior College, A
Judson University, B
Kishwaukee College, A
Lewis University, B
Loyola University Chicago, B
Northeastern Illinois University, B
Parkland College, A
Quincy University, B
Roosevelt University, B
Saint Xavier University, B
South Suburban College, A
Southern Illinois University Edwardsville, B
University of Illinois at Chicago, B
University of Illinois at Springfield, B

## Indiana

Ancilla College, A
Ball State University, AB
Bethel College, AB
Calumet College of Saint Joseph, AB
Grace College, B
Harrison College, AB
Indiana Tech, A
Indiana University Bloomington, B
Indiana University Kokomo, B
Indiana University Northwest, B
Indiana University - Purdue University Indianapolis, B
Indiana University South Bend, B
Indiana University Southeast, B
Indiana Wesleyan University, AB
Ivy Tech Community College - Bloomington, A
Ivy Tech Community College - Central Indiana, A
Ivy Tech Community College - Columbus, A
Ivy Tech Community College - East Central, A
Ivy Tech Community College - Kokomo, A
Ivy Tech Community College - Lafayette, A
Ivy Tech Community College - North Central, A
Ivy Tech Community College - Northeast, A
Ivy Tech Community College - Northwest, A
Ivy Tech Community College - Richmond, A
Ivy Tech Community College - Southeast, A
Ivy Tech Community College - Southwest, A
Ivy Tech Community College - Wabash Valley, A
Manchester University, AB
Martin University, B
Oakland City University, AB
Saint Joseph's College, B
University of Evansville, B
University of Saint Francis, AB
University of Southern Indiana, B

## Iowa

Brown Mackie College - Quad Cities, A
Buena Vista University, B
Iowa Wesleyan University, B
Kaplan University, Davenport Campus, AB
Loras College, B
St. Ambrose University, B

William Penn University, B

## Kansas

Bethany College, B
Central Christian College of Kansas, A
Fort Hays State University, B
Friends University, B
Pittsburg State University, B
Southwestern College, B
Wichita State University, B

## Kentucky

Bellarmine University, B
Brown Mackie College - Hopkinsville, A
Daymar College (Bowling Green), A
Daymar College (Owensboro), A
Kentucky State University, B
Kentucky Wesleyan College, B
Murray State University, B
Northern Kentucky University, B
Sullivan University, B
Thomas More College, AB
University of the Cumberlands, AB
University of Pikeville, AB

## Louisiana

Bossier Parish Community College, A
Grambling State University, B
Louisiana State University at Alexandria, B
Louisiana State University at Eunice, A
Louisiana State University in Shreveport, B
McNeese State University, B
Northwestern State University of Louisiana, B
South Louisiana Community College, A
Southeastern Louisiana University, B
Southern University and Agricultural and Mechanical College, B
Southern University at New Orleans, B
Sowela Technical Community College, A
University of Louisiana at Lafayette, B
University of Louisiana at Monroe, B

## Maine

Central Maine Community College, A
Husson University, AB
Saint Joseph's College of Maine, B
University of Maine at Augusta, A
York County Community College, A

## Maryland

Brightwood College, Beltsville Campus, A
Brightwood College, Towson Campus, A
Frostburg State University, B
Hood College, B
University of Maryland University College, B

## Massachusetts

American International College, B
Bay State College, AB
Berkshire Community College, A
Bridgewater State University, B
Bristol Community College, A
Curry College, B
Dean College, A
Eastern Nazarene College, AB
Endicott College, B
Fisher College, AB
Fitchburg State University, B
Holyoke Community College, A
Lasell College, B
Nichols College, B
Northeastern University, B
Regis College, B
University of Massachusetts Boston, B
Western New England University, B
Westfield State University, B
Worcester State University, B

## Michigan

Bay de Noc Community College, A
Kellogg Community College, A
Lake Superior State University, AB
Madonna University, AB
Michigan State University, B
Monroe County Community College, A

Northern Michigan University, AB
Olivet College, B
Saginaw Valley State University, B
Siena Heights University, B
Southwestern Michigan College, A
University of Detroit Mercy, B
University of Michigan - Dearborn, B
Wayne State University, B
Western Michigan University, B

## Minnesota

Capella University, B
Central Lakes College, A
Century College, A
Concordia University, St. Paul, B
Hamline University, B
Inver Hills Community College, A
Metropolitan State University, B
Minneapolis Community and Technical College, A
Minnesota State College - Southeast Technical, A
Minnesota State Community and Technical College, A
Minnesota State University Moorhead, B
Normandale Community College, A
North Hennepin Community College, A
Rochester Community and Technical College, A
Southwest Minnesota State University, B
University of Northwestern - St. Paul, B
Vermilion Community College, A

## Mississippi

Alcorn State University, B
Blue Mountain College, B
Coahoma Community College, A
Delta State University, B
East Mississippi Community College, A
Jackson State University, B
University of Southern Mississippi, B
Virginia College in Jackson, A

## Missouri

Central Methodist University, B
Harris-Stowe State University, B
Lindenwood University, B
Missouri Baptist University, B
Missouri Western State University, B
Saint Louis University, B
Truman State University, B
Vatterott College (Saint Joseph), A
William Woods University, B

## Montana

Montana State University Billings, B
University of Great Falls, B

## Nebraska

Central Community College - Columbus Campus, A
Central Community College - Grand Island Campus, A
Central Community College - Hastings Campus, A
Southeast Community College, Lincoln Campus, A
University of Nebraska at Kearney, B
University of Nebraska at Omaha, B
Wayne State College, B
Western Nebraska Community College, A

## Nevada

Everest College, A
Great Basin College, A
Truckee Meadows Community College, A
University of Nevada, Las Vegas, B

## New Hampshire

Granite State College, B
Plymouth State University, B
Saint Anselm College, B
White Mountains Community College, A

## New Jersey

Bergen Community College, A
Caldwell University, B
Georgian Court University, B
Monmouth University, B
New Jersey City University, B
Rider University, B
```

Rowan University, B
Rutgers University - Camden, B
Rutgers University - Newark, B
Saint Peter's University, B
Seton Hall University, B
Thomas Edison State University, AB
William Paterson University of New Jersey, B

New Mexico

Eastern New Mexico University, B
Eastern New Mexico University - Roswell, A
Luna Community College, A
Mesalands Community College, A
New Mexico Highlands University, B
New Mexico State University, B
New Mexico State University - Alamogordo, A
New Mexico State University - Carlsbad, A
Northern New Mexico College, A
Santa Fe Community College, A
University of New Mexico - Taos, A

New York

Adelphi University, B
Cazenovia College, AB
The College at Brockport, State University of New
    York, B
Dominican College, B
Excelsior College, B
Fiorello H. LaGuardia Community College of the
    City University of New York, A
Genesee Community College, A
Hilbert College, AB
Medaille College, B
Molloy College, B
Morrisville State College, A
Nassau Community College, A
North Country Community College, A
Nyack College, B
Rochester Institute of Technology, B
St. Francis College, AB
State University of New York College at Oneonta, B
State University of New York College at Potsdam, B
State University of New York College of Technology
    at Delhi, B
State University of New York at Plattsburgh, B

North Carolina

Alamance Community College, A
Appalachian State University, B
Asheville-Buncombe Technical Community College,
    A
Belmont Abbey College, B
Catawba Valley Community College, A
Chowan University, B
Cleveland Community College, A
Craven Community College, A
East Carolina University, B
ECPI University (Charlotte), A
Elizabeth City State University, B
Fayetteville Technical Community College, A
Forsyth Technical Community College, A
Greensboro College, B
Guilford College, B
Guilford Technical Community College, A
Halifax Community College, A
High Point University, B
James Sprunt Community College, A
Lenoir Community College, A
Lenoir-Rhyne University, B
Mayland Community College, A
Montgomery Community College, A
Nash Community College, A
North Carolina Agricultural and Technical State Uni-
    versity, B
North Carolina Central University, B
Piedmont Community College, A
Pitt Community College, A
Randolph Community College, A
Richmond Community College, A
Roanoke-Chowan Community College, A
Shaw University, B
South Piedmont Community College, A
The University of North Carolina at Charlotte, B
The University of North Carolina at Pembroke, B
Wake Technical Community College, A
Wayne Community College, A

Western Carolina University, B
Wilson Community College, A
Winston-Salem State University, B

North Dakota

Bismarck State College, A
Minot State University, B
North Dakota State University, B
University of Jamestown, B
University of Mary, B
University of North Dakota, B

Ohio

Baldwin Wallace University, B
Bluffton University, B
Bowling Green State University, B
Bowling Green State University - Firelands College,
    AB
Central State University, B
Defiance College, AB
Kent State University, B
Kent State University at Ashtabula, AB
Kent State University at East Liverpool, AB
Kent State University at Salem, AB
Kent State University at Stark, AB
Kent State University at Trumbull, AB
Kent State University at Tuscarawas, AB
Lourdes University, AB
Mount Vernon Nazarene University, B
Northwest State Community College, A
Ohio Christian University, B
Ohio Northern University, B
The University of Akron, B
University of Cincinnati, B
University of Cincinnati Blue Ash College, A
University of Cincinnati Clermont College, A
University of Mount Union, B
The University of Toledo, B
Xavier University, AB
Youngstown State University, AB

Oklahoma

Southeastern Oklahoma State University, B
Southwestern Oklahoma State University, AB
Southwestern Oklahoma State University at Sayre,
    A
University of Central Oklahoma, B
Vatterott College (Tulsa), A
Vatterott College (Warr Acres), A

Oregon

Chemeketa Community College, A
Linn-Benton Community College, A
Oregon Coast Community College, A
Portland Community College, A
Southwestern Oregon Community College, A

Pennsylvania

Bloomsburg University of Pennsylvania, B
Bucks County Community College, A
Central Penn College, AB
DeSales University, B
Edinboro University of Pennsylvania, AB
Gannon University, AB
Holy Family University, B
Immaculata University, B
King's College, B
Kutztown University of Pennsylvania, B
La Roche College, B
La Salle University, B
Lackawanna College, A
Lehigh Carbon Community College, A
Lincoln University, B
McCann School of Business & Technology
    (Pottsville), A
Mercyhurst University, B
Messiah College, B
Neumann University, B
Northampton Community College, A
Penn State Abington, B
Penn State Altoona, AB
Penn State Erie, The Behrend College, B
Penn State Fayette, The Eberly Campus, B
Penn State Harrisburg, B
Penn State Schuylkill, B

Penn State Wilkes-Barre, B
Point Park University, B
Rosemont College, B
Seton Hill University, B
Shippensburg University of Pennsylvania, B
South Hills School of Business & Technology
    (Altoona), A
Temple University, B
Thiel College, B
The University of Scranton, AB
University of Valley Forge, B
West Chester University of Pennsylvania, B
Westmoreland County Community College, A
Wilkes University, B

Rhode Island

Rhode Island College, B

South Carolina

Aiken Technical College, A
Bob Jones University, B
Central Carolina Technical College, A
Charleston Southern University, B
Columbia College, B
Denmark Technical College, A
Florence-Darlington Technical College, A
Greenville Technical College, A
Horry-Georgetown Technical College, A
Limestone College, B
Midlands Technical College, A
Orangeburg-Calhoun Technical College, A
Piedmont Technical College, A
Tri-County Technical College, A
York Technical College, A

South Dakota

Dakota Wesleyan University, AB
Mount Marty College, B
Sinte Gleska University, B
Western Dakota Technical Institute, A

Tennessee

Bryan College, B
Daymar College (Nashville), A
Dyersburg State Community College, A
Freed-Hardeman University, B
King University, B
Lane College, B
Lipscomb University, B
Southwest Tennessee Community College, A
Tennessee Wesleyan College, B
Walters State Community College, A

Texas

Alvin Community College, A
Angelo State University, B
Brightwood College, Friendswood Campus, A
Brightwood College, Houston Campus, A
Cedar Valley College, A
College of the Mainland, A
Dallas Baptist University, B
Eastfield College, A
El Paso Community College, A
Everest College (Arlington), A
Galveston College, A
Grayson College, A
Hardin-Simmons University, B
Howard College, A
Huston-Tillotson University, B
Jarvis Christian College, AB
Lamar State College - Port Arthur, A
Lamar University, B
Mountain View College, A
Northwest Vista College, A
Our Lady of the Lake University of San Antonio, B
Paris Junior College, A
Prairie View A&M University, B
St. Edward's University, B
Sam Houston State University, B
Southwestern Assemblies of God University, B
Tarleton State University, B
Texarkana College, A
Texas A&M University - Central Texas, B
Texas A&M University - Commerce, B
Texas A&M University - Kingsville, B

Texas A&M University - Texarkana, B
Texas Christian University, B
Texas College, B
Texas State University, B
Texas Wesleyan University, B
Texas Woman's University, B
Tyler Junior College, A
University of Houston - Downtown, B
University of Houston - Victoria, B
University of the Incarnate Word, B
University of North Texas, B
The University of Texas at Arlington, B
The University of Texas of the Permian Basin, B
The University of Texas Rio Grande Valley, B
The University of Texas at San Antonio, B
The University of Texas at Tyler, B
West Texas A&M University, B
Wiley College, B

Utah

Dixie State University, AB
Weber State University, AB
Westminster College, B

Vermont

Champlain College, B

Virginia

Centura College (Virginia Beach), A
Ferrum College, B
Liberty University, AB
Longwood University, B
Radford University, B
Roanoke College, B
University of Richmond, B
The University of Virginia's College at Wise, B
Virginia State University, B
Virginia Wesleyan College, B

Washington

Central Washington University, B
Gonzaga University, B
Heritage University, B
Saint Martin's University, B
Seattle University, B

West Virginia

American Public University System, AB
Blue Ridge Community and Technical College, A
Bluefield State College, B
BridgeValley Community and Technical College
   (South Charleston), A
Marshall University, B
Potomac State College of West Virginia University,
   AB
West Virginia State University, B
Wheeling Jesuit University, B

Wisconsin

Cardinal Stritch University, B
Edgewood College, B
Lakeland College, B
University of Wisconsin - Eau Claire, B
University of Wisconsin - Milwaukee, B
University of Wisconsin - Platteville, B
University of Wisconsin - Superior, B
Viterbo University, B

Wyoming

Eastern Wyoming College, A
Sheridan College, A
University of Wyoming, B

U.S. Territories: American Samoa

American Samoa Community College, A

U.S. Territories: Puerto Rico

American University of Puerto Rico (Bayamon), AB
Colegio Universitario de San Juan, A
Inter American University of Puerto Rico, Aguadilla
   Campus, AB
Inter American University of Puerto Rico, Arecibo
   Campus, B
Inter American University of Puerto Rico, Bar-
   ranquitas Campus, AB

Inter American University of Puerto Rico, Fajardo
   Campus, B
Inter American University of Puerto Rico, Metropoli-
   tan Campus, B
Inter American University of Puerto Rico, Ponce
   Campus, B
Universidad del Este, B
Universidad Metropolitana, AB
University of the Sacred Heart, B

Canada

British Columbia

Royal Roads University, B
Thompson Rivers University, B
University of the Fraser Valley, AB

Ontario

Ryerson University, B
Wilfrid Laurier University, B

Saskatchewan

University of Regina, B

CRIMINALISTICS AND CRIMI-NAL SCIENCE

United States

Alabama

Alabama State University, B

Florida

Everest University (Orange Park), A
Florida Gulf Coast University, B
Keiser University, A
Saint Leo University, B

Indiana

Indiana Tech, B

Massachusetts

Bay Path University, B

Michigan

Oakland Community College, A

Minnesota

Central Lakes College, A

New York

Hudson Valley Community College, A

Ohio

Ohio Dominican University, B
Tiffin University, B

South Carolina

Southern Wesleyan University, B

Texas

Alvin Community College, A
Tyler Junior College, A

Washington

Seattle University, B

U.S. Territories: Puerto Rico

Inter American University of Puerto Rico, Metropoli-
   tan Campus, B
Inter American University of Puerto Rico, Ponce
   Campus, B

CRIMINOLOGY

United States

Alabama

Auburn University, B
Auburn University at Montgomery, MO
Columbia Southern University, M
Faulkner University, M
Jacksonville State University, M
South University, M
Spring Hill College, B
Troy University, M
The University of Alabama, M
The University of Alabama at Birmingham, M
University of North Alabama, M
Virginia College in Birmingham, M

Alaska

University of Alaska Fairbanks, M

Arizona

Arizona State University at the Tempe campus,
   MDO
Northern Arizona University, BM
University of Phoenix - Online Campus, M
University of Phoenix - Phoenix Campus, M

Arkansas

Arkansas State University, BM
University of Arkansas at Little Rock, MD

California

Biola University, B
California Coast University, M
California State University, Fresno, BM
California State University, Long Beach, M
California State University, Los Angeles, M
California State University, Sacramento, M
California State University, San Bernardino, M
California State University, San Marcos, B
California State University, Stanislaus, BM
Mount Saint Mary's University, B
National University, M
New Charter University, M
San Diego State University, M
San Francisco State University, M
San Jose State University, M
Trident University International, M
University of Antelope Valley, M
University of California, Irvine, BMD
University of La Verne, M
University of Phoenix - Bay Area Campus, M
University of Phoenix - Southern California Campus,
   M

Colorado

Adams State University, B
Colorado State University - Global Campus, M
Colorado Technical University Colorado Springs, M
Regis University, BM
University of Colorado Colorado Springs, M
University of Colorado Denver, M
University of Denver, B
University of Northern Colorado, M
Western State Colorado University, B

Connecticut

Albertus Magnus College, M
Central Connecticut State University, BM
Sacred Heart University, M
University of New Haven, MDO
Western Connecticut State University, M

Delaware

Delaware State University, B
University of Delaware, BMD
Wilmington University, M

District of Columbia

The George Washington University, M
University of Phoenix - Washington D.C. Campus,
   M

Florida

Barry University, B
College of Central Florida, A
Flagler College, B
Florida Agricultural and Mechanical University, M
Florida Atlantic University, M
Florida Gulf Coast University, M
Florida International University, M
Florida Southern College, B
Florida State University, BMD
Keiser University, M
Lynn University, M
Saint Leo University, M
St. Thomas University, MO
South University (Royal Palm Beach), M
South University (Tampa), M
University of Central Florida, MDO
University of Florida, BMD
University of Miami, B
University of North Florida, M
University of South Florida, BMDO
University of South Florida, St. Petersburg, B
University of South Florida Sarasota-Manatee, BM
The University of Tampa, B
University of West Florida, M
Webber International University, M

Georgia

Albany State University, M
Armstrong State University, MO
Ashworth College, M
Clark Atlanta University, M
Georgia College & State University, M
Georgia State University, MD
Kennesaw State University, M
South University, M
Thomas University, B
University of North Georgia, M
University of Phoenix - Augusta Campus, M
University of West Georgia, BM
Valdosta State University, M

Hawaii

Chaminade University of Honolulu, MO

Idaho

Boise State University, MO

Illinois

Aurora University, M
Chicago State University, M
Dominican University, B
Elmhurst College, B
Illinois State University, M
Lewis University, M
Loyola University Chicago, M
Southern Illinois University Carbondale, M
University of Illinois at Chicago, MD

Indiana

Ball State University, M
Butler University, B
Indiana State University, BM
Indiana University Bloomington, MD
Indiana University Northwest, M
Indiana University - Purdue University Indianapolis, M
Saint Mary-of-the-Woods College, B
Trine University, M
Valparaiso University, B

Iowa

Kaplan University, Davenport Campus, M
Mount Mercy University, M
St. Ambrose University, M
Simpson College, M
University of Northern Iowa, B
Upper Iowa University, BM
William Penn University, B

Kansas

Benedictine College, B
Tabor College, B
University of Saint Mary, B
Washburn University, M

Wichita State University, M

Kentucky

Eastern Kentucky University, M
Morehead State University, M
University of Louisville, MD
Western Kentucky University, BM

Louisiana

Grambling State University, M
Loyola University New Orleans, BM
McNeese State University, M
Southern University and Agricultural and Mechanical College, M
Southern University at New Orleans, M
Southwest University, M
University of Holy Cross, B
University of Louisiana at Monroe, M

Maine

Husson University, BM
University of Southern Maine, B

Maryland

Coppin State University, M
Mount St. Mary's University, B
Notre Dame of Maryland University, B
University of Baltimore, M
University of Maryland, College Park, BMD
University of Maryland Eastern Shore, M

Massachusetts

Anna Maria College, M
Assumption College, B
Boston University, M
Bridgewater State University, M
Curry College, M
Emmanuel College, B
Framingham State University, B
Lasell College, BM
Northeastern University, MD
Salem State University, M
Stonehill College, B
Suffolk University, M
University of Massachusetts Dartmouth, B
University of Massachusetts Lowell, MD
Westfield State University, M

Michigan

Adrian College, M
Eastern Michigan University, BM
Ferris State University, M
Grand Valley State University, M
Madonna University, M
Michigan State University, MD
Northern Michigan University, M
University of Detroit Mercy, M
University of Michigan - Flint, M
Wayne State University, M

Minnesota

Capella University, MD
Concordia University, St. Paul, M
Metropolitan State University, M
Northland Community and Technical College, A
St. Cloud State University, M
University of Minnesota, Duluth, BM
University of Minnesota, Twin Cities Campus, B
University of St. Thomas, B
Walden University, MDO

Mississippi

Delta State University, M
Jackson State University, M
Mississippi College, M
Mississippi State University, B
Mississippi Valley State University, M
University of Mississippi, M
University of Southern Mississippi, MD

Missouri

Avila University, B
Columbia College, M
Drury University, BM
Lincoln University, M

Lindenwood University, M
Maryville University of Saint Louis, B
Missouri Southern State University, M
Missouri State University, BMO
Southeast Missouri State University, M
University of Central Missouri, M
University of Missouri - Kansas City, BM
University of Missouri - St. Louis, BMD

Montana

University of Great Falls, M
University of Montana, M

Nebraska

Bellevue University, M
Midland University, B
University of Nebraska at Omaha, MD

Nevada

College of Southern Nevada, A
University of Nevada, Las Vegas, MD
University of Nevada, Reno, BM

New Hampshire

Rivier University, B
University of New Hampshire, B

New Jersey

Centenary College, B
College of Saint Elizabeth, M
Fairleigh Dickinson University, College at Florham, B
Fairleigh Dickinson University, Metropolitan Campus, M
Kean University, M
Monmouth University, MO
New Jersey City University, M
Rowan University, M
Rutgers University - Camden, M
Rutgers University - Newark, MD
Saint Peter's University, M
Stockton University, BM
University of Phoenix - Jersey City Campus, M

New Mexico

Central New Mexico Community College, A
New Mexico State University, M

New York

Buffalo State College, State University of New York, M
Genesee Community College, A
Hilbert College, M
Hofstra University, B
Iona College, MO
John Jay College of Criminal Justice of the City University of New York, BMD
Keuka College, M
Le Moyne College, B
Molloy College, M
Monroe College, M
Niagara University, BM
Rochester Institute of Technology, M
St. John Fisher College, B
St. John's University, M
State University of New York College at Cortland, B
State University of New York College at Old Westbury, B
State University of New York College of Technology at Alfred, A
University at Albany, State University of New York, MD
Utica College, M

North Carolina

Appalachian State University, M
East Carolina University, MO
Fayetteville State University, M
Johnson C. Smith University, B
Lees-McRae College, B
Methodist University, M
North Carolina Central University, M
North Carolina State University, B
The University of North Carolina at Charlotte, M
The University of North Carolina at Greensboro, M

The University of North Carolina Wilmington, BM

North Dakota

North Dakota State University, MD
University of North Dakota, D

Ohio

Bowling Green State University, M
Capital University, B
Cleveland State University, B
Defiance College, M
Mount St. Joseph University, B
The Ohio State University, B
The Ohio State University - Mansfield Campus, B
The Ohio State University at Marion, B
Ohio University, B
Ohio University - Chillicothe, B
Tiffin University, B
The University of Akron, B
University of Cincinnati, MD
University of Mount Union, B
The University of Toledo, MO
Urbana University, M
Walsh University, B
Wittenberg University, B
Wright State University, BM
Wright State University - Lake Campus, B
Xavier University, M
Youngstown State University, M

Oklahoma

East Central University, M
Northeastern State University, M
Oklahoma City University, M
Oklahoma Wesleyan University, B
University of Central Oklahoma, M

Oregon

Portland State University, MD
Southern Oregon University, B
Western Oregon University, M

Pennsylvania

Albright College, B
Arcadia University, B
Cabrini University, B
California University of Pennsylvania, M
Carlow University, B
Cedar Crest College, B
Chatham University, B
DeSales University, M
Drexel University, B
Eastern University, B
Elizabethtown College School of Continuing and
    Professional Studies, AB
Geneva College, B
Holy Family University, M
Indiana University of Pennsylvania, BMD
Lebanon Valley College, B
Lycoming College, B
Marywood University, M
Mercyhurst University, MO
Penn State Harrisburg, M
Penn State University Park, MD
Point Park University, M
Saint Francis University, B
Saint Joseph's University, BMO
Saint Vincent College, B
Shippensburg University of Pennsylvania, M
Slippery Rock University of Pennsylvania, BM
Temple University, MD
University of Pennsylvania, MD
University of Pittsburgh, M
West Chester University of Pennsylvania, M
Widener University, M

Rhode Island

Johnson & Wales University, M
Roger Williams University, M

South Carolina

Anderson University, M
Charleston Southern University, M
Coker College, B
South University, M

Southern Wesleyan University, B
University of South Carolina, MD

South Dakota

The University of South Dakota, M

Tennessee

East Tennessee State University, MO
Maryville College, B
Middle Tennessee State University, M
Tennessee State University, M
University of Memphis, BM
The University of Tennessee, MD
The University of Tennessee at Chattanooga, M

Texas

Baylor University, D
Dallas Baptist University, M
Howard Payne University, B
Lamar University, M
LeTourneau University, AB
Midwestern State University, MO
Panola College, A
Paris Junior College, A
St. Edward's University, B
St. Mary's University, B
Sam Houston State University, MD
Sul Ross State University, M
Tarleton State University, M
Texas A&M International University, M
Texas A&M University - Central Texas, M
Texas A&M University - Kingsville, BM
Texas A&M University - San Antonio, B
Texas Christian University, M
Texas Southern University, MD
Texas State University, MD
University of Houston - Clear Lake, BM
University of Houston - Downtown, M
University of North Texas, M
University of Phoenix - Dallas Campus, M
University of Phoenix - San Antonio Campus, M
University of St. Thomas, B
The University of Texas at Arlington, M
The University of Texas at Dallas, BMD
The University of Texas of the Permian Basin, BM
The University of Texas Rio Grande Valley, M
The University of Texas at San Antonio, M
The University of Texas at Tyler, M
Wayland Baptist University, M
West Texas A&M University, M

Vermont

Castleton University, B

Virginia

George Mason University, MDO
Liberty University, M
Longwood University, M
Lynchburg College, B
Mary Baldwin College, B
Norfolk State University, M
Old Dominion University, BD
Radford University, MO
University of Management and Technology, M
Virginia Commonwealth University, MO
Virginia State University, B
Virginia Union University, B
Virginia Wesleyan College, B

Washington

Eastern Washington University, B
Gonzaga University, B
Seattle University, MO
University of Phoenix - Western Washington Cam-
    pus, M
Washington State University, MD

West Virginia

Alderson Broaddus University, B
American Public University System, M
Davis & Elkins College, AB
Fairmont State University, M
Marshall University, M
Potomac State College of West Virginia University,
    A

Wisconsin

Marian University, M
Marquette University, BMO
University of Wisconsin - Milwaukee, M
University of Wisconsin - Platteville, M
University of Wisconsin - River Falls, B
University of Wisconsin - Whitewater, B

Wyoming

Western Wyoming Community College, A

U.S. Territories: Puerto Rico

American University of Puerto Rico (Bayamon), M
Caribbean University, M
Inter American University of Puerto Rico, Aguadilla
    Campus, M
Inter American University of Puerto Rico, Metropoli-
    tan Campus, M
Inter American University of Puerto Rico, Ponce
    Campus, M
Pontifical Catholic University of Puerto Rico, BM
Universidad del Este, M
Universidad del Turabo, BM

Canada

Alberta

University of Alberta, M

British Columbia

Simon Fraser University, BMD
Thompson Rivers University, B
University of the Fraser Valley, M
Vancouver Island University, B

Maritime Provinces: New Brunswick

St. Thomas University, B

Maritime Provinces: Nova Scotia

Saint Mary's University, BM

Newfoundland and Labrador

Memorial University of Newfoundland, B

Ontario

Carleton University, B
Lakehead University, B
University of Guelph, M
University of Ottawa, BMD
University of Toronto, BMD
The University of Western Ontario, B
University of Windsor, BM
Wilfrid Laurier University, M

Quebec

Université de Montréal, BMD

Saskatchewan

University of Regina, M

CROP PRODUCTION

United States

Arizona

Arizona Western College, A

California

College of the Desert, A
College of the Redwoods, A
San Joaquin Delta College, A

Illinois

Black Hawk College, A
Illinois Central College, A

Iowa

Iowa Lakes Community College, A
Northeast Iowa Community College, A

Kansas

Barton County Community College, A

Massachusetts

Greenfield Community College, A
University of Massachusetts Amherst, AB

Michigan

Northwestern Michigan College, A

Minnesota

Ridgewater College, A
University of Minnesota, Crookston, B

North Carolina

North Carolina State University, A

North Dakota

Dakota College at Bottineau, A
North Dakota State University, B

Ohio

The Ohio State University Agricultural Technical Institute, A

Oregon

Chemeketa Community College, A

Pennsylvania

Delaware Valley University, B

Washington

Washington State University, B

Wyoming

Northwest College, A

Canada

Alberta

University of Alberta, B

CULINARY ARTS/CHEF TRAINING

United States

Alabama

H. Councill Trenholm State Community College, A
J. F. Drake State Community and Technical College, A
Shelton State Community College, A

Alaska

University of Alaska Anchorage, A
University of Alaska Fairbanks, A

Arizona

Arizona Western College, A
The Art Institute of Phoenix, A
The Art Institute of Tucson, AB
Cochise County Community College District, A
Mohave Community College, A
Phoenix College, A
Scottsdale Community College, A

Arkansas

NorthWest Arkansas Community College, A
Ozarka College, A
Pulaski Technical College, A

California

American River College, A
The Art Institute of California - Hollywood, a campus of Argosy University, A
The Art Institute of California - Inland Empire, a campus of Argosy University, A
The Art Institute of California - Los Angeles, a campus of Argosy University, A
The Art Institute of California - Orange County, a campus of Argosy University, A
The Art Institute of California - Sacramento, a campus of Argosy University, A
The Art Institute of California - San Diego, a campus of Argosy University, A
The Art Institute of California - San Francisco, a campus of Argosy University, A
Bakersfield College, A
College of the Desert, A
College of the Sequoias, A
El Camino College, A
Laney College, A
Los Angeles Mission College, A
Los Angeles Trade-Technical College, A
Modesto Junior College, A
Orange Coast College, A
Oxnard College, A
Riverside City College, A
San Joaquin Delta College, A
Santa Rosa Junior College, A
Shasta College, A

Colorado

The Art Institute of Colorado, A
Johnson & Wales University, AB
Red Rocks Community College, A

Delaware

Delaware Technical & Community College, Stanton/Wilmington Campus, A
Delaware Technical & Community College, Terry Campus, A

Florida

The Art Institute of Fort Lauderdale, A
The Art Institute of Tampa, a branch of Miami International University of Art & Design, A
Daytona State College, A
Florida State College at Jacksonville, A
Indian River State College, A
Johnson & Wales University, AB
Keiser University, A
Lincoln College of Technology, A
Lincoln Culinary Institute, A
Miami Dade College, A
Valencia College, A

Georgia

Albany Technical College, A
The Art Institute of Atlanta, A
Atlanta Technical College, A
Augusta Technical College, A
Chattahoochee Technical College, A
North Georgia Technical College, A
Ogeechee Technical College, A
Savannah Technical College, A
South Georgia Technical College, A

Hawaii

Kauai Community College, A

Idaho

College of Southern Idaho, A
College of Western Idaho, A
North Idaho College, A

Illinois

City Colleges of Chicago, Kennedy-King College, A
College of DuPage, A
Elgin Community College, A
Illinois Central College, A
Illinois Eastern Community Colleges, Olney Central College, A
The Illinois Institute of Art - Chicago, A
Joliet Junior College, A
Kaskaskia College, A
Kendall College, AB
Lincoln Land Community College, A
Rend Lake College, A
Robert Morris University Illinois, A
St. Augustine College, A
Triton College, A

Indiana

The Art Institute of Indianapolis, A
Harrison College, A
Vincennes University, A

Iowa

Des Moines Area Community College, A
Indian Hills Community College, A
Kirkwood Community College, A
Scott Community College, A

Kansas

Johnson County Community College, A

Kentucky

Ashland Community and Technical College, A
Jefferson Community and Technical College, A
Southcentral Kentucky Community and Technical College, A
Sullivan University, A
West Kentucky Community and Technical College, A

Louisiana

Bossier Parish Community College, A
Nicholls State University, AB
Nunez Community College, A
South Louisiana Community College, A
Sowela Technical Community College, A

Maine

Eastern Maine Community College, A
Southern Maine Community College, A
York County Community College, A

Maryland

Allegany College of Maryland, A
Stratford University, A

Massachusetts

Bunker Hill Community College, A
Massasoit Community College, A
Newbury College, AB
North Shore Community College, A

Michigan

The Art Institute of Michigan, A
Baker College, A
Grand Rapids Community College, A
Henry Ford College, A
Macomb Community College, A
Monroe County Community College, A
Mott Community College, A
Northwestern Michigan College, A
Oakland Community College, A
Schoolcraft College, A

Minnesota

St. Cloud Technical & Community College, A
Saint Paul College - A Community & Technical College, A

Mississippi

Coahoma Community College, A

Missouri

The Art Institute of St. Louis, A
College of the Ozarks, B
East Central College, A
Jefferson College, A
Mineral Area College, A
Ozarks Technical Community College, A

Montana

Flathead Valley Community College, A
University of Montana, A

Nebraska

Metropolitan Community College, A
Northeast Community College, A

Nevada

The Art Institute of Las Vegas, A
College of Southern Nevada, A

New Hampshire

Lakes Region Community College, A
Southern New Hampshire University, AB
White Mountains Community College, A

New Jersey

Atlantic Cape Community College, A
Bergen Community College, A
Brookdale Community College, A
County College of Morris, A
Hudson County Community College, A
Mercer County Community College, A
Rowan College at Burlington County, A
Salem Community College, A

New Mexico

Central New Mexico Community College, A
Eastern New Mexico University, A
Luna Community College, A
Navajo Technical University, A
Santa Fe Community College, A

New York

The Culinary Institute of America, A
Erie Community College, A
Erie Community College, North Campus, A
Finger Lakes Community College, A
Monroe College, A
Niagara County Community College, A
Paul Smith's College, AB
Rockland Community College, A
State University of New York College of Agriculture
    and Technology at Cobleskill, A
State University of New York College of Technology
    at Alfred, A
State University of New York College of Technology
    at Delhi, A
Suffolk County Community College, A
Sullivan County Community College, A
Tompkins Cortland Community College, A
Westchester Community College, A

North Carolina

Alamance Community College, A
The Art Institute of Charlotte, a campus of South
    University, A
The Art Institute of Raleigh-Durham, a campus of
    South University, A
Asheville-Buncombe Technical Community College,
    A
Caldwell Community College and Technical Institute,
    A
Cape Fear Community College, A
Central Piedmont Community College, A
College of The Albemarle, A
Fayetteville Technical Community College, A
Guilford Technical Community College, A
Johnson & Wales University, AB
Lenoir Community College, A
Sandhills Community College, A
Southwestern Community College, A
Wake Technical Community College, A
Wilson Community College, A

North Dakota

North Dakota State College of Science, A

Ohio

Central Ohio Technical College, A
Cincinnati State Technical and Community College,
    A
Columbus State Community College, A
Hocking College, A
Sinclair Community College, A
The University of Akron, A
Zane State College, A

Oregon

The Art Institute of Portland, A
Linn-Benton Community College, A

Pennsylvania

The Art Institute of Philadelphia, A
The Art Institute of Pittsburgh, A

Bucks County Community College, A
Commonwealth Technical Institute, A
Community College of Allegheny County, A
Community College of Beaver County, A
Community College of Philadelphia, A
Drexel University, B
Harrisburg Area Community College, A
Keystone Technical Institute, A
Luzerne County Community College, A
Mercyhurst North East, A
Montgomery County Community College, A
Northampton Community College, A
Pennsylvania College of Technology, A
The Restaurant School at Walnut Hill College, AB
Westmoreland County Community College, A

Rhode Island

Johnson & Wales University, AB

South Carolina

The Art Institute of Charleston, a branch of The Art
    Institute of Atlanta, A
Bob Jones University, A
Greenville Technical College, A
Horry-Georgetown Technical College, A
Trident Technical College, A

South Dakota

Mitchell Technical Institute, A

Tennessee

The Art Institute of Tennessee - Nashville, a branch
    of The Art Institute of Atlanta, A
Nashville State Community College, A
Southern Adventist University, A

Texas

Alvin Community College, A
The Art Institute of Austin, a branch of The Art Insti-
    tute of Houston, A
The Art Institute of Dallas, a campus of South Uni-
    versity, A
The Art Institute of Houston, A
The Art Institute of San Antonio, a branch of The Art
    Institute of Houston, A
Austin Community College District, A
Collin County Community College District, A
Culinary Institute LeNotre, A
Del Mar College, A
El Centro College, A
El Paso Community College, A
Galveston College, A
Houston Community College, A
Northeast Texas Community College, A
Odessa College, A
St. Philip's College, A
San Jacinto College District, A
Texarkana College, A
Texas State Technical College, A

Utah

Salt Lake Community College, A
Utah Valley University, A

Vermont

New England Culinary Institute, AB

Virginia

The Art Institute of Virginia Beach, a branch of The
    Art Institute of Atlanta, A
The Art Institute of Washington, a branch of The Art
    Institute of Atlanta, A
Central Virginia Community College, A
Culinary Institute of Virginia, A
ECPI University (Virginia Beach), A
Stratford University (Alexandria), A
Stratford University (Falls Church), A
Stratford University (Glen Allen), A
Stratford University (Newport News), A
Stratford University (Virginia Beach), A
Stratford University (Woodbridge), A

Washington

The Art Institute of Seattle, A
Bates Technical College, A

Bellingham Technical College, A
Clark College, A
Clover Park Technical College, A
Edmonds Community College, A
Olympic College, A
Renton Technical College, A
Seattle Central College, A
Skagit Valley College, A
South Puget Sound Community College, A
South Seattle College, A
Spokane Community College, A
Walla Walla Community College, A

West Virginia

Blue Ridge Community and Technical College, A
Mountwest Community & Technical College, A
West Virginia Northern Community College, A

Wisconsin

Blackhawk Technical College, A
Fox Valley Technical College, A
Gateway Technical College, A
Madison Area Technical College, A
Milwaukee Area Technical College, A
Moraine Park Technical College, A
Nicolet Area Technical College, A
Northcentral Technical College, A

Wyoming

Central Wyoming College, A
Sheridan College, A

U.S. Territories: Puerto Rico

Universidad del Este, A

CULINARY ARTS AND RE-LATED SERVICES

United States

Alabama

University of North Alabama, B

California

Santa Barbara City College, A

Colorado

Johnson & Wales University, AB

Florida

Johnson & Wales University, AB

Indiana

Ancilla College, A

Iowa

Iowa Lakes Community College, A

Massachusetts

Bristol Community College, A
Newbury College, B

Mississippi

Mississippi University for Women, B

Nevada

University of Nevada, Las Vegas, B

New Hampshire

University of New Hampshire, A

New York

Morrisville State College, A

Oklahoma

Oklahoma State University Institute of Technology, A

Oregon

Linn-Benton Community College, A

Rhode Island

Johnson & Wales University, AB

U.S. Territories: Guam

Guam Community College, A

CULTURAL ANTHROPOLOGY

United States

Arizona

Northern Arizona University, M

California

California Institute of Integral Studies, MD
San Francisco State University, M
University of California, Santa Barbara, MD
University of California, Santa Cruz, D

Colorado

University of Denver, M

Florida

University of South Florida, MD

Michigan

University of Michigan, D

New York

Cornell University, D

North Carolina

Duke University, D
North Carolina State University, M

Pennsylvania

Eastern University, M

Tennessee

The University of Tennessee, MD

Texas

Rice University, MD

Washington

Washington State University, D

Wisconsin

University of Wisconsin - Madison, D

Canada

Newfoundland and Labrador

Memorial University of Newfoundland, MD

Quebec

Concordia University, M

CULTURAL RESOURCE MANAGEMENT AND POLICY ANALYSIS

United States

California

California State University, Dominguez Hills, B

Canada

Ontario

University of Waterloo, B

CULTURAL STUDIES

United States

Alaska

University of Alaska Fairbanks, M

Arizona

Arizona State University at the Tempe campus, MD

California

Biola University, MDO
Chapman University, D
Concordia University Irvine, M
San Francisco State University, M
Stanford University, D
University of California, Davis, MD
University of California, Irvine, D
University of California, Merced, MD
University of California, Riverside, D
University of California, Santa Barbara, MD
University of Southern California, D

Colorado

University of Denver, MO

Connecticut

Trinity College, M

District of Columbia

American University, O

Florida

Florida State University, M

Hawaii

University of Hawaii at Hilo, MD
University of Hawaii at Manoa, O

Illinois

Lincoln Christian University, M
North Central College, M
Southern Illinois University Carbondale, M
Wheaton College, MO

Kentucky

Northern Kentucky University, O

Maine

University of Southern Maine, O

Maryland

Goucher College, M

Massachusetts

Boston University, M
Regis College, M

Michigan

Central Michigan University, M
Eastern Michigan University, MO

Minnesota

University of Minnesota, Twin Cities Campus, D

Missouri

Baptist Bible College, M
University of Missouri - St. Louis, O

Montana

University of Montana, M

New Hampshire

Plymouth State University, M

New Mexico

University of New Mexico, MD

New York

Binghamton University, State University of New York, MD

Cornell University, D
New York University, MDO
School of Visual Arts, M
Stony Brook University, State University of New York, DO
University at Buffalo, the State University of New York, M

North Carolina

Appalachian State University, M
Charlotte Christian College and Theological Seminary, M
Gardner-Webb University, M

Ohio

Union Institute & University, M

Oregon

Lewis & Clark College, M
Pacific Northwest College of Art, M

Pennsylvania

Carnegie Mellon University, D
La Salle University, M
Summit University, M
University of Pittsburgh, O

South Carolina

Columbia International University, M

Tennessee

Johnson University, M
Union University, M

Texas

Baylor University, D
Texas A&M University, M
Texas A&M University - Kingsville, M
Texas Tech University, M
University of Houston, M
University of Houston - Clear Lake, M
The University of Texas at Austin, MD
The University of Texas at San Antonio, D

Virginia

George Mason University, MD
Old Dominion University, MD
Regent University, M

Washington

Northwest University, M
University of Washington, Bothell, M
Washington State University, D

Wisconsin

Maranatha Baptist University, M

U.S. Territories: Puerto Rico

University of the Sacred Heart, M

Canada

Alberta

Ambrose University, O
Athabasca University, M

British Columbia

Simon Fraser University, D

Maritime Provinces: Nova Scotia

St. Francis Xavier University, M

Ontario

Brock University, M
McMaster University, MD
Trent University, D
Wilfrid Laurier University, M

CURRICULUM AND INSTRUC-TION

United States

Alabama

Auburn University, MDO
The University of Alabama at Birmingham, O
The University of West Alabama, MO

Arizona

Arizona State University at the Tempe campus, M
Grand Canyon University, M
University of Phoenix - Online Campus, MD
University of Phoenix - Phoenix Campus, M
University of Phoenix - Southern Arizona Campus, M

Arkansas

Arkansas Tech University, M
Henderson State University, MO
John Brown University, M
Southern Arkansas University - Magnolia, M
University of Arkansas, D
University of Arkansas at Little Rock, M
University of Central Arkansas, O

California

Azusa Pacific University, M
Biola University, O
California Baptist University, M
California Coast University, M
California State Polytechnic University, Pomona, M
California State University, Bakersfield, M
California State University, Chico, M
California State University, Dominguez Hills, M
California State University, Fresno, M
California State University, Northridge, M
California State University, Sacramento, M
California State University, San Bernardino, M
California State University, Stanislaus, M
Chapman University, D
Concordia University Irvine, M
Fresno Pacific University, M
La Sierra University, MDO
Mills College, M
Notre Dame de Namur University, M
Saint Mary's College of California, M
San Diego State University, M
San Jose State University, M
Simpson University, M
Sonoma State University, M
Stanford University, M
University of California, Davis, D
University of California, San Diego, M
University of the Pacific, MD
University of Phoenix - Central Valley Campus, M
University of Phoenix - Sacramento Valley Campus, M
University of Phoenix - San Diego Campus, M
University of San Diego, M
University of San Francisco, MD

Colorado

Colorado Christian University, M
Regis University, M
University of Colorado Boulder, MD
University of Colorado Colorado Springs, M
University of Denver, MDO
University of Phoenix - Colorado Campus, M
University of Phoenix - Colorado Springs Downtown Campus, M

Connecticut

Albertus Magnus College, B
University of Saint Joseph, M
Western Connecticut State University, M

Delaware

Delaware State University, M
University of Delaware, M

District of Columbia

The George Washington University, MDO
Trinity Washington University, M
University of Phoenix - Washington D.C. Campus, MD

Florida

Barry University, DO
Florida Atlantic University, MDO
Florida Gulf Coast University, MDO
Florida International University, MDO
Florida State University, MDO
Stetson University, O
University of Florida, MDO
University of Phoenix - North Florida Campus, M
University of Phoenix - South Florida Campus, M
University of South Florida, D
University of South Florida Sarasota-Manatee, M
University of West Florida, MO

Georgia

Armstrong State University, M
Augusta University, M
Berry College, MO
Clark Atlanta University, M
Columbus State University, D
Georgia College & State University, O
Georgia Southern University, MD
Georgia State University, D
LaGrange College, MO
Mercer University, D
Piedmont College, O
Shorter University, M

Hawaii

University of Hawaii at Manoa, MD
University of Phoenix - Hawaii Campus, M

Idaho

Boise State University, MD
The College of Idaho, M
Idaho State University, M
Northwest Nazarene University, M
University of Idaho, MO

Illinois

American InterContinental University Online, M
Aurora University, MD
Benedictine University, M
Bradley University, MO
Concordia University Chicago, M
DePaul University, MD
Dominican University, M
Illinois State University, MD
Loyola University Chicago, MD
McKendree University, DO
National Louis University, MO
North Central College, M
Northern Illinois University, MD
Olivet Nazarene University, M
Quincy University, M
Saint Xavier University, M
Southern Illinois University Carbondale, MD
Southern Illinois University Edwardsville, M
University of Illinois at Chicago, MD
University of Illinois at Urbana - Champaign, MDO
University of St. Francis, M

Indiana

Ball State University, MO
Indiana State University, MD
Indiana University Bloomington, MDO
Indiana University - Purdue University Indianapolis, M
Purdue University, MDO
University of Indianapolis, M

Iowa

Buena Vista University, M
Iowa State University of Science and Technology, MD

Kansas

Emporia State University, M
Kansas State University, MD
Newman University, M
Ottawa University, M
Southwestern College, M
The University of Kansas, MD
Washburn University, M
Wichita State University, M

Kentucky

Brescia University, M
Campbellsville University, M
Eastern Kentucky University, M
Morehead State University, O
University of Kentucky, MD
University of Louisville, D

Louisiana

Grambling State University, MD
Louisiana State University in Shreveport, M
Louisiana Tech University, MD
McNeese State University, M
Nicholls State University, M
Northwestern State University of Louisiana, M
Southeastern Louisiana University, M
University of Holy Cross, M
University of Louisiana at Lafayette, M
University of Louisiana at Monroe, MD
University of New Orleans, MD
Xavier University of Louisiana, M

Maine

University of New England, MO

Maryland

Coppin State University, M
Frostburg State University, M
Hood College, M
Loyola University Maryland, MO
McDaniel College, M
Salisbury University, M
University of Maryland, College Park, MDO

Massachusetts

Boston College, MDO
Cambridge College, O
Fitchburg State University, M
Framingham State University, M
Harvard University, M
Lasell College, B
Lesley University, MO
Massachusetts College of Liberal Arts, M
Merrimack College, M
Northeastern University, D
University of Massachusetts Lowell, MO
Western New England University, M

Michigan

Andrews University, MDO
Calvin College, M
Central Michigan University, MD
Concordia University Ann Arbor, M
Eastern Michigan University, M
Ferris State University, M
Grand Valley State University, M
Michigan State University, MDO
Northern Michigan University, M
University of Detroit Mercy, M
University of Michigan - Dearborn, DO
Wayne State University, MDO

Minnesota

Capella University, MD
Concordia University, St. Paul, M
Martin Luther College, M
Minnesota State University Mankato, O
Minnesota State University Moorhead, M
St. Catherine University, M
St. Cloud State University, M
University of Minnesota, Twin Cities Campus, MDO
University of St. Thomas, M
Walden University, MDO

Mississippi

Mississippi College, M
Mississippi State University, MDO
Mississippi University for Women, M
University of Southern Mississippi, MDO

Missouri

Evangel University, MD
Park University, M
Saint Louis University, MD
Stephens College, M
University of Missouri, MDO
University of Missouri - Kansas City, MO
University of Missouri - St. Louis, M
William Woods University, MO

Montana

Montana State University, MD
Montana State University Billings, M
University of Montana, BMD

Nebraska

Doane University, M
Peru State College, M
University of Nebraska at Kearney, M
University of Nebraska - Lincoln, MDO
Wayne State College, M

Nevada

University of Nevada, Las Vegas, MDO
University of Nevada, Reno, D
University of Phoenix - Las Vegas Campus, M

New Hampshire

Franklin Pierce University, BM
Keene State College, M
Plymouth State University, M
Rivier University, M
Southern New Hampshire University, M

New Jersey

Caldwell University, M
Fairleigh Dickinson University, Metropolitan Campus, M
Kean University, M
Montclair State University, M
Rider University, MO

New Mexico

Eastern New Mexico University, M
New Mexico Highlands University, M
New Mexico State University, MDO
University of Phoenix - New Mexico Campus, M
University of the Southwest, M

New York

The College at Brockport, State University of New York, M
The College of Saint Rose, M
Cornell University, MD
Fordham University, MD
Medaille College, M
State University of New York College at Potsdam, M
State University of New York College of Technology at Delhi, A
State University of New York at Oswego, M
State University of New York at Plattsburgh, M
Syracuse University, MDO
University at Albany, State University of New York, MDO
University at Buffalo, the State University of New York, D
University of Rochester, MD

North Carolina

Appalachian State University, M
East Carolina University, MO
Gardner-Webb University, D
North Carolina Central University, M
North Carolina State University, MD
Piedmont International University, M
Shaw University, MO
The University of North Carolina at Chapel Hill, MD
The University of North Carolina at Charlotte, MD

The University of North Carolina at Greensboro, MD

North Dakota

North Dakota State University, M
University of Jamestown, M
University of Mary, M

Ohio

Ashland University, M
Bluffton University, M
Bowling Green State University, M
Cedarville University, M
Franciscan University of Steubenville, M
Kent State University, MDO
Kent State University at Stark, M
Lourdes University, M
Malone University, M
Ohio Dominican University, M
Ohio University, MD
Shawnee State University, M
University of Cincinnati, MD
The University of Toledo, MDO
Wright State University, BMO
Youngstown State University, M

Oklahoma

Northwestern Oklahoma State University, M
Oklahoma State University, MD
Oral Roberts University, M
University of Oklahoma, MDO

Oregon

Concordia University, M
George Fox University, M
Lewis & Clark College, M
Northwest Christian University, M
Portland State University, MD

Pennsylvania

Arcadia University, MO
Bloomsburg University of Pennsylvania, MO
Clarion University of Pennsylvania, M
Delaware Valley University, M
Drexel University, M
Duquesne University, O
Gannon University, MO
Indiana University of Pennsylvania, D
Kutztown University of Pennsylvania, M
Messiah College, M
Misericordia University, M
Moravian College, M
Penn State Harrisburg, M
Penn State University Park, MDO
Point Park University, M
Saint Joseph's University, O
Saint Vincent College, M
Shippensburg University of Pennsylvania, M
Summit University, M
The University of Scranton, M
Waynesburg University, M
Wilkes University, M

South Carolina

Bob Jones University, D
Clemson University, D
Columbia International University, MD
Furman University, M
University of South Carolina, D

South Dakota

Black Hills State University, M
Dakota Wesleyan University, M
Northern State University, M
South Dakota State University, M
The University of South Dakota, BMDO

Tennessee

Austin Peay State University, M
Belmont University, M
Carson-Newman University, M
East Tennessee State University, MO
Freed-Hardeman University, M
Lee University, MO
Lincoln Memorial University, MDO
Middle Tennessee State University, MO

Tennessee State University, MD
Tennessee Technological University, MO
Tennessee Wesleyan College, M
Trevecca Nazarene University, M
University of Memphis, MD
The University of Tennessee, MDO
The University of Tennessee at Martin, M
Welch College, B

Texas

Abilene Christian University, M
Angelo State University, M
Arlington Baptist College, M
Baylor University, MD
Dallas Baptist University, M
East Texas Baptist University, M
Houston Baptist University, M
LeTourneau University, M
Midwestern State University, BM
Our Lady of the Lake University of San Antonio, M
Prairie View A&M University, M
Sam Houston State University, BMD
Southwestern Adventist University, M
Southwestern Assemblies of God University, M
Tarleton State University, BM
Texas A&M International University, M
Texas A&M University, MD
Texas A&M University - Central Texas, M
Texas A&M University - Corpus Christi, MD
Texas A&M University - Texarkana, M
Texas Christian University, MO
Texas Southern University, MD
Texas Tech University, MD
Texas Woman's University, M
University of Houston, MD
University of Houston - Clear Lake, M
University of Houston - Downtown, M
University of Houston - Victoria, M
University of Mary Hardin-Baylor, M
University of North Texas, M
University of Phoenix - Dallas Campus, M
University of Phoenix - Houston Campus, M
University of Phoenix - San Antonio Campus, M
University of St. Thomas, M
The University of Texas at Arlington, M
The University of Texas at Austin, MD
The University of Texas at El Paso, M
The University of Texas at San Antonio, MD
West Texas A&M University, M

Utah

University of Phoenix - Utah Campus, M
Utah State University, BD
Weber State University, M

Vermont

Castleton University, M
Johnson State College, M
Lyndon State College, M
Saint Michael's College, MO
University of Vermont, M

Virginia

Averett University, M
The College of William and Mary, MD
George Mason University, MD
James Madison University, M
Liberty University, DO
Lynchburg College, M
Old Dominion University, MD
Radford University, M
Randolph College, BM
Regent University, M
University of Virginia, MDO
Virginia Polytechnic Institute and State University, MDO

Washington

Central Washington University, M
City University of Seattle, M
Eastern Washington University, BM
Pacific Lutheran University, M
University of Washington, MD
Walla Walla University, M
Washington State University, M

West Virginia

American Public University System, M
Ohio Valley University, M
Salem International University, M
Shepherd University, M
West Virginia University, MD

Wisconsin

Concordia University Wisconsin, M
Marquette University, M
University of Wisconsin - Madison, MD
University of Wisconsin - Milwaukee, MD
University of Wisconsin - Oshkosh, M
University of Wisconsin - Superior, M
University of Wisconsin - Whitewater, M
Wisconsin Lutheran College, M

Wyoming

University of Wyoming, MD

U.S. Territories: Puerto Rico

Caribbean University, M
Inter American University of Puerto Rico, Arecibo
  Campus, M
Inter American University of Puerto Rico, Bar-
  ranquitas Campus, M
Inter American University of Puerto Rico, Metropoli-
  tan Campus, D
Inter American University of Puerto Rico, San
  Germán Campus, D
Pontifical Catholic University of Puerto Rico, MD
Universidad Adventista de las Antillas, M
Universidad Metropolitana, M
Universidad del Turabo, MD
University of Puerto Rico, Río Piedras Campus, MD

Canada

Alberta

University of Calgary, MD

British Columbia

Simon Fraser University, MD
The University of British Columbia, MD
University of Victoria, MD

Manitoba

Brandon University, MO
University of Manitoba, M

Maritime Provinces: Nova Scotia

Acadia University, M
Mount Saint Vincent University, M
St. Francis Xavier University, M

Newfoundland and Labrador

Memorial University of Newfoundland, M

Ontario

The University of Western Ontario, BM

Quebec

McGill University, M
Université Laval, MD
Université de Montréal, MDO

Saskatchewan

University of Regina, M
University of Saskatchewan, MDO

CUSTOMER SERVICE MAN-AGEMENT

United States

Delaware

Delaware Technical & Community College,
  Stanton/Wilmington Campus, A

Minnesota

Northland Community and Technical College, A
Rochester Community and Technical College, A

Missouri

Southwest Baptist University, B

Nebraska

Bellevue University, B

New York

Corning Community College, A

Ohio

Ohio University, B

Oregon

Central Oregon Community College, A

Pennsylvania

Drexel University, B

Wyoming

WyoTech Laramie, A

CUSTOMER SERVICE SUP-PORT/CALL CENTER/TELESERVICE OPERATION

United States

California

Fresno City College, A
Long Beach City College, A

Delaware

Delaware Technical & Community College, Jack F.
  Owens Campus, A
Delaware Technical & Community College,
  Stanton/Wilmington Campus, A

Florida

Miami Dade College, A

Michigan

Lansing Community College, A

New Jersey

Union County College, A

South Dakota

National American University (Sioux Falls), AB

Wyoming

Central Wyoming College, A

CYTOGENETICS/GENETICS/CLINICAL GENETICS TECH-NOLOGY/TECHNOLOGIST

United States

Michigan

Northern Michigan University, B

Texas

The University of Texas Health Science Center at
  San Antonio, B

CYTOTECHNOLOGY/CYTOTECHNOLOGIST

United States

Arkansas

University of Arkansas for Medical Sciences, B

California

Ashford University, B
Loma Linda University, B

Connecticut

University of Connecticut, B

Florida

Barry University, B

Illinois

Elmhurst College, B
Illinois College, B

Indiana

Indiana University - Purdue University Indianapolis,
  B

Kansas

Barton County Community College, A

Massachusetts

University of Massachusetts Dartmouth, B

Michigan

Oakland University, B

Minnesota

Saint Mary's University of Minnesota, B
Winona State University, B

Mississippi

University of Mississippi, B
University of Mississippi Medical Center, B

Missouri

Saint Louis University, B

New York

State University of New York at Plattsburgh, B

North Dakota

University of North Dakota, B

Pennsylvania

Slippery Rock University of Pennsylvania, B
Thiel College, B
Thomas Jefferson University, B

West Virginia

Marshall University, B

Wisconsin

Edgewood College, B
Marian University, B

CZECH LANGUAGE AND LIT-ERATURE

United States

Texas

The University of Texas at Austin, B

DAIRY HUSBANDRY AND PRO-DUCTION

United States

California

Cuesta College, A

Iowa

Northeast Iowa Community College, A

Minnesota

Ridgewater College, A

Missouri

College of the Ozarks, B

New York

Morrisville State College, AB

Ohio

The Ohio State University Agricultural Technical Institute, A

Vermont

University of Vermont, B

DAIRY SCIENCE

United States

California

California Polytechnic State University, San Luis Obispo, B
College of the Sequoias, A
Modesto Junior College, A
Mt. San Antonio College, A

Georgia

University of Georgia, BM

Iowa

Iowa State University of Science and Technology, B

Mississippi

Mississippi State University, MD
Northwest Mississippi Community College, A

Nebraska

Northeast Community College, A

New Mexico

Eastern New Mexico University, B

New York

Morrisville State College, B

Ohio

The Ohio State University Agricultural Technical Institute, A

Pennsylvania

Delaware Valley University, B

South Dakota

South Dakota State University, BMD

Texas

Cisco College, A

Utah

Utah State University, BM

Vermont

Vermont Technical College, A

Virginia

Virginia Polytechnic Institute and State University, BM

Wisconsin

University of Wisconsin - Madison, BMD
University of Wisconsin - River Falls, B

DANCE

United States

Alabama

Alabama State University, B
Troy University, B
The University of Alabama, B

Arizona

Arizona State University at the Tempe campus, BM
Grand Canyon University, B
The University of Arizona, BM

Arkansas

University of Arkansas at Little Rock, B

California

Allan Hancock College, A
American Musical and Dramatic Academy, Los Angeles, B
Cabrillo College, A
California Institute of the Arts, BMO
California State University, East Bay, B
California State University, Fresno, B
California State University, Fullerton, BM
California State University, Long Beach, BM
California State University, Los Angeles, B
California State University, Sacramento, B
Cerritos College, A
Chaffey College, A
Chapman University, B
Citrus College, A
College of Marin, A
Cuesta College, A
Cypress College, A
Dominican University of California, B
Fresno City College, A
Fullerton College, A
Glendale Community College, A
Grossmont College, A
Laney College, A
Long Beach City College, A
Loyola Marymount University, B
Mills College, BM
MiraCosta College, A
Monterey Peninsula College, A
Mt. San Jacinto College, A
Orange Coast College, A
Palomar College, A
Pasadena City College, A
Pitzer College, B
Pomona College, B
Saint Mary's College of California, BM
San Diego State University, B
San Francisco State University, B
San Joaquin Delta College, A
San Jose State University, B
Santa Ana College, A
Santa Monica College, A
Santa Rosa Junior College, A
Scripps College, B
Southwestern College, A
University of California, Berkeley, B
University of California, Irvine, BM
University of California, Los Angeles, BMD
University of California, Riverside, MD
University of California, San Diego, BMD
University of California, Santa Barbara, B
University of Southern California, B

Colorado

The Colorado College, B
Colorado State University, B
University of Colorado Boulder, BMD

Connecticut

Connecticut College, B
Trinity College, B
University of Hartford, B
Wesleyan University, B

District of Columbia

The George Washington University, BMO

Florida

Broward College, A
Eastern Florida State College, A
Florida Southern College, B
Florida State University, BM
Jacksonville University, BM
Miami Dade College, A
New World School of the Arts, B
Nova Southeastern University, B

Palm Beach Atlantic University, B
St. Johns River State College, A
University of Florida, B
University of South Florida, B

Georgia

Agnes Scott College, B
Brenau University, B
Darton State College, A
Emory University, B
Kennesaw State University, B
University of Georgia, B
Valdosta State University, B

Hawaii

University of Hawaii at Manoa, BMD

Idaho

Brigham Young University - Idaho, B
University of Idaho, B

Illinois

Columbia College Chicago, B
Loyola University Chicago, B
Northern Illinois University, M
Northwestern University, B
Rockford University, B
University of Illinois at Urbana - Champaign, BM

Indiana

Anderson University, B
Ball State University, B
Butler University, B
Indiana University Bloomington, B
University of Saint Francis, AB

Iowa

The University of Iowa, BM

Kansas

Barton County Community College, A
The University of Kansas, B

Kentucky

Western Kentucky University, B

Louisiana

Tulane University, BM

Maine

Bates College, B

Maryland

Goucher College, B
Towson University, B
University of Maryland, Baltimore County, BM
University of Maryland, College Park, BM

Massachusetts

Amherst College, B
Bard College at Simon's Rock, B
Dean College, AB
Greenfield Community College, A
Hampshire College, B
Mount Holyoke College, B
Northern Essex Community College, A
Smith College, BM
Springfield College, B
University of Massachusetts Amherst, B

Michigan

Alma College, B
Eastern Michigan University, B
Grand Valley State University, B
Hope College, B
Marygrove College, B
Oakland University, B
University of Michigan, BM
University of Michigan - Flint, B
Wayne State University, B
Western Michigan University, B

Minnesota

Gustavus Adolphus College, B
St. Olaf College, B
University of Minnesota, Twin Cities Campus, B

Mississippi

Belhaven University, B
University of Southern Mississippi, B

Missouri

Lindenwood University, B
Stephens College, B
University of Missouri - Kansas City, B
Washington University in St. Louis, B
Webster University, B

Montana

University of Montana, B

Nebraska

University of Nebraska - Lincoln, B

Nevada

University of Nevada, Las Vegas, B

New Hampshire

Keene State College, B

New Jersey

Bergen Community College, A
Georgian Court University, B
Mercer County Community College, A
Montclair State University, B
Raritan Valley Community College, A
Rider University, B
Rutgers University - New Brunswick, B

New Mexico

New Mexico State University, BM
University of New Mexico, BM

New York

Adelphi University, B
Bard College, B
Barnard College, B
The College at Brockport, State University of New
    York, BM
Columbia University, B
Columbia University, School of General Studies, B
Fordham University, B
Hamilton College, B
Hobart and William Smith Colleges, B
Hofstra University, B
Hunter College of the City University of New York, B
The Juilliard School, B
Lehman College of the City University of New York,
    B
Long Island University - LIU Brooklyn, B
Long Island University - LIU Post, B
Manhattanville College, B
Marymount Manhattan College, B
Nassau Community College, A
Nazareth College of Rochester, B
New York University, BMDO
Pace University, B
Purchase College, State University of New York, B
Sarah Lawrence College, BM
Skidmore College, B
State University of New York College at Potsdam, B
State University of New York at Fredonia, B
University at Buffalo, the State University of New
    York, B
Wells College, B
Westchester Community College, A

North Carolina

Appalachian State University, B
Central Piedmont Community College, A
East Carolina University, B
Elon University, B
Louisburg College, A
Meredith College, B
The University of North Carolina at Charlotte, BM
The University of North Carolina at Greensboro, BM

University of North Carolina School of the Arts, B

Ohio

Case Western Reserve University, BM
Denison University, B
Kent State University, B
Kenyon College, B
Oberlin College, B
The Ohio State University, BMD
Ohio University, B
Sinclair Community College, A
The University of Akron, B
University of Cincinnati, B
Wittenberg University, B
Wright State University, B
Youngstown State University, B

Oklahoma

Oklahoma City University, BM
Oral Roberts University, B
St. Gregory's University, B
University of Central Oklahoma, B
University of Oklahoma, BM

Oregon

Reed College, B
University of Oregon, BM
Western Oregon University, B

Pennsylvania

Cedar Crest College, B
DeSales University, B
Dickinson College, B
Drexel University, B
Eastern University, B
Franklin & Marshall College, B
La Roche College, B
Mercyhurst University, B
Messiah College, B
Muhlenberg College, B
Point Park University, B
Seton Hill University, B
Slippery Rock University of Pennsylvania, B
Swarthmore College, B
Temple University, BMD
The University of the Arts, B
Ursinus College, B

Rhode Island

Rhode Island College, B
Roger Williams University, B

South Carolina

Coker College, B
College of Charleston, B
Columbia College, B
University of South Carolina, B
Winthrop University, B

Texas

Austin Community College District, A
Kilgore College, A
Lone Star College - CyFair, A
Sam Houston State University, BM
San Jacinto College District, A
Southern Methodist University, B
Stephen F. Austin State University, B
Texas Christian University, BM
Texas State University, B
Texas Tech University, B
Texas Woman's University, BMD
Trinity Valley Community College, A
Tyler Junior College, A
University of Houston, B
University of North Texas, B
The University of Texas at Austin, BM
The University of Texas Rio Grande Valley, B
West Texas A&M University, B

Utah

Brigham Young University, B
Dixie State University, A
Snow College, A
Southern Utah University, B
University of Utah, BM

Utah State University, B
Utah Valley University, AB
Weber State University, B

Vermont

Bennington College, BM
Johnson State College, B
Marlboro College, B
Middlebury College, B

Virginia

George Mason University, B
Hollins University, BM
Radford University, B
Randolph College, B
Shenandoah University, B
Sweet Briar College, B
University of Richmond, B
Virginia Commonwealth University, B

Washington

Cornish College of the Arts, B
University of Washington, BM
Western Washington University, B

Wisconsin

Beloit College, B
University of Wisconsin - Madison, B
University of Wisconsin - Milwaukee, BM
University of Wisconsin - Stevens Point, B

Wyoming

Casper College, A
Western Wyoming Community College, A

Canada
Alberta

University of Calgary, B

British Columbia

Simon Fraser University, B

Ontario

Ryerson University, B
York University, BMD

Quebec

Concordia University, B
Université du Québec à Montréal, BM

DANCE THERAPY/THERAPIST

United States
Colorado

Naropa University, M

Illinois

Columbia College Chicago, BMO

New York

Pratt Institute, M

Pennsylvania

Drexel University, MO

DANISH LANGUAGE AND LIT-ERATURE

United States
Washington

University of Washington, B

DATA ENTRY/MICROCOM-PUTER APPLICATIONS

United States

Arizona

Arizona Western College, A
Chandler-Gilbert Community College, A
Glendale Community College, A
Rio Salado College, A

California

American River College, A
Antelope Valley College, A
Berkeley City College, A
Butte College, A
Cerritos College, A
Chabot College, A
College of the Redwoods, A
Contra Costa College, A
Cypress College, A
Gavilan College, A
Grossmont College, A
Los Angeles City College, A
MiraCosta College, A
Modesto Junior College, A
Pasadena City College, A
San Diego Mesa College, A
Santa Ana College, A
Santa Monica College, A
Sierra College, A
Southwestern College, A

Colorado

Colorado Mountain College (Glenwood Springs), A
Colorado Mountain College (Steamboat Springs), A
National American University (Denver), AB

Connecticut

Gateway Community College, A
Quinebaug Valley Community College, A

Florida

City College (Gainesville), A
City College (Miami), A
Seminole State College of Florida, A

Illinois

College of DuPage, A
Elgin Community College, A
Heartland Community College, A
Illinois Central College, A
John A. Logan College, A
Parkland College, A
Richland Community College, A

Iowa

Iowa Lakes Community College, A

Kansas

Pratt Community College, A

Maryland

Montgomery College, A

Massachusetts

Bunker Hill Community College, A
North Shore Community College, A
Roxbury Community College, A

Michigan

Kellogg Community College, A
West Shore Community College, A

Minnesota

Riverland Community College, A

Mississippi

Mississippi Gulf Coast Community College, A

Missouri

Three Rivers Community College, A

Nebraska

Nebraska Indian Community College, A

New York

Fiorello H. LaGuardia Community College of the City University of New York, A
Sullivan County Community College, A

North Carolina

College of The Albemarle, A
Miller-Motte College (Cary), A
Miller-Motte College (Wilmington), A

North Dakota

North Dakota State College of Science, A

Ohio

ETI Technical College of Niles, A
Gallipolis Career College, A
Lorain County Community College, A
Northwest State Community College, A
Ohio Business College (Sheffield Village), A
Sinclair Community College, A
Stark State College, A
Zane State College, A

Pennsylvania

Delaware County Community College, A
Laurel Business Institute, A
Luzerne County Community College, A
Westmoreland County Community College, A

Texas

Del Mar College, A
Eastfield College, A
Galveston College, A
Laredo Community College, A
Northeast Texas Community College, A
St. Philip's College, A
San Antonio College, A
Tyler Junior College, A

Vermont

Community College of Vermont, A

Virginia

ECPI University (Glen Allen), A
ECPI University (Richmond), A

Washington

Bellingham Technical College, A
Clark College, A
Edmonds Community College, A
Green River College, A
Highline College, A
Lower Columbia College, A
Peninsula College, A

West Virginia

Blue Ridge Community and Technical College, A
Potomac State College of West Virginia University, A

Wisconsin

Mid-State Technical College, A

Wyoming

Western Wyoming Community College, A

DATA MODELING/WAREHOUS-ING AND DATABASE ADMINIS-TRATION

United States

Alabama

Virginia College in Birmingham, A

Arizona

Chandler-Gilbert Community College, A
Northland Pioneer College, A

California

American River College, A
College of Marin, A
College of the Sequoias, A
Cuesta College, A
Santa Monica College, A

Colorado

Red Rocks Community College, A

Florida

Broward College, A
Seminole State College of Florida, A

Illinois

Southwestern Illinois College, A

Indiana

Ivy Tech Community College - Bloomington, A
Ivy Tech Community College - Central Indiana, A
Ivy Tech Community College - Columbus, A
Ivy Tech Community College - East Central, A
Ivy Tech Community College - Kokomo, A
Ivy Tech Community College - Lafayette, A
Ivy Tech Community College - Northeast, A
Ivy Tech Community College - Richmond, A
Ivy Tech Community College - Southeast, A
Ivy Tech Community College - Southern Indiana, A
Ivy Tech Community College - Southwest, A
Ivy Tech Community College - Wabash Valley, A

Kentucky

American National University (Louisville), B

Massachusetts

Quinsigamond Community College, A

Michigan

Lansing Community College, A
University of Michigan, B
Wayne County Community College District, A

New Jersey

Rowan College at Gloucester County, A

New York

Rochester Institute of Technology, B

North Carolina

Wake Technical Community College, A

Pennsylvania

Pennsylvania College of Technology, B

Rhode Island

Bryant University, B

South Carolina

Limestone College, AB

Utah

LDS Business College, A
Neumont University, B

Virginia

American National University (Harrisonburg), B
American National University (Salem), B

Washington

Bellevue College, A
Central Washington University, B
Edmonds Community College, A
Pierce College at Fort Steilacoom, A

West Virginia

American Public University System, A

DATA PROCESSING AND DATA PROCESSING TECHNOLOGY/TECHNICIAN

United States

Arizona

Mesa Community College, A
University of Advancing Technology, AB

Arkansas

Arkansas State University, B
Central Baptist College, B
National Park College, A
NorthWest Arkansas Community College, A
University of Arkansas, B

California

Bakersfield College, A
California State University, San Marcos, B
Citrus College, A
East Los Angeles College, A
El Camino College, A
Humphreys College, AB
Irvine Valley College, A
Los Angeles City College, A
Los Angeles Harbor College, A
Los Angeles Pierce College, A
Los Angeles Southwest College, A
Mendocino College, A
Merced College, A
Mission College, A
Monterey Peninsula College, A
Moorpark College, A
Mt. San Antonio College, A
Napa Valley College, A
Sacramento City College, A
San Bernardino Valley College, A
San Diego City College, A
Skyline College, A
Taft College, A
West Los Angeles College, A
West Valley College, A

Colorado

American Sentinel University, B
Lamar Community College, A
Otero Junior College, A

Connecticut

Gateway Community College, A
Housatonic Community College, A
Tunxis Community College, A

Delaware

Delaware State University, B

Florida

Florida Memorial University, B
Palm Beach State College, A
Seminole State College of Florida, A

Georgia

Bainbridge State College, A

Illinois

City Colleges of Chicago, Kennedy-King College, A
City Colleges of Chicago, Wilbur Wright College, A
Illinois Valley Community College, A
Morton College, A

Indiana

Ancilla College, A

Iowa

Dordt College, A
Iowa Central Community College, A
Iowa Lakes Community College, A

Kansas

Allen Community College, A
Butler Community College, A

Dodge City Community College, A
Labette Community College, A
Seward County Community College and Area Technical School, A

Kentucky

Bluegrass Community and Technical College, A
Campbellsville University, A
Elizabethtown Community and Technical College, A
Midway University, B
Southeast Kentucky Community and Technical College, A

Louisiana

Delgado Community College, A

Maryland

Kaplan University, Hagerstown Campus, A

Massachusetts

Bristol Community College, A
Northern Essex Community College, A

Michigan

Alpena Community College, A
Baker College, A
Jackson College, A
Monroe County Community College, A
Montcalm Community College, A
Muskegon Community College, A
St. Clair County Community College, A
West Shore Community College, A

Minnesota

Academy College, A
Bemidji State University, B
Vermilion Community College, A

Mississippi

Copiah-Lincoln Community College, A
Itawamba Community College, A
Jones County Junior College, A
Northwest Mississippi Community College, A
University of Southern Mississippi, B

Missouri

North Central Missouri College, A

Montana

Montana State University Billings, A

Nevada

Career College of Northern Nevada, A
Great Basin College, A

New Hampshire

Nashua Community College, A

New Jersey

Atlantic Cape Community College, A
Warren County Community College, A

New Mexico

New Mexico Junior College, A
San Juan College, A

New York

Bronx Community College of the City University of New York, A
Broome Community College, A
Eugenio María de Hostos Community College of the City University of New York, A
Finger Lakes Community College, A
Fulton-Montgomery Community College, A
Kingsborough Community College of the City University of New York, A
Monroe Community College, A
Nassau Community College, A
Pace University, Pleasantville Campus, A
Queensborough Community College of the City University of New York, A
Rockland Community College, A
Schenectady County Community College, A
Suffolk County Community College, A

Westchester Community College, A

North Carolina

Central Piedmont Community College, A
Davidson County Community College, A
Miller-Motte College (Cary), A
Vance-Granville Community College, A

Ohio

Bryant & Stratton College - Eastlake Campus, A
Eastern Gateway Community College, A
Miami University, A
Terra State Community College, A
Trumbull Business College, A
University of Cincinnati Clermont College, A
Washington State Community College, A
Youngstown State University, A

Pennsylvania

Luzerne County Community College, A
Westmoreland County Community College, A

South Carolina

Aiken Technical College, A
Central Carolina Technical College, A
Denmark Technical College, A
Florence-Darlington Technical College, A
Greenville Technical College, A
Midlands Technical College, A
Northeastern Technical College, A
Piedmont Technical College, A
Spartanburg Community College, A
Technical College of the Lowcountry, A
Tri-County Technical College, A
York Technical College, A

South Dakota

Northern State University, A
Sinte Gleska University, A

Tennessee

Northeast State Community College, A
Walters State Community College, A

Texas

Angelina College, A
Cedar Valley College, A
Cisco College, A
Eastfield College, A
El Centro College, A
Grayson College, A
Hallmark University, A
Lamar State College - Orange, A
Laredo Community College, A
Lee College, A
Navarro College, A
North Central Texas College, A
North Lake College, A
Odessa College, A
Richland College, A
San Antonio College, A
South Plains College, A
Southwest Texas Junior College, A
Temple College, A
Trinity Valley Community College, A
Vernon College, A
Wharton County Junior College, A

Virginia

Dabney S. Lancaster Community College, A
ECPI University (Richmond), A
Paul D. Camp Community College, A
Virginia Highlands Community College, A
Virginia Western Community College, A

Washington

Columbia Basin College, A
Edmonds Community College, A
Everett Community College, A
South Puget Sound Community College, A
Spokane Community College, A

West Virginia

American Public University System, A
Mountwest Community & Technical College, A
West Virginia University at Parkersburg, A

Wisconsin

Madison Area Technical College, A
Nicolet Area Technical College, A
Western Technical College, A

Wyoming

Western Wyoming Community College, A

U.S. Territories: Northern Mariana Islands

Northern Marianas College, A

U.S. Territories: Puerto Rico

University of Puerto Rico in Ponce, A

Canada

British Columbia

British Columbia Institute of Technology, A

Manitoba

The University of Winnipeg, B

Maritime Provinces: New Brunswick

University of New Brunswick Fredericton, B

Maritime Provinces: Nova Scotia

Saint Mary's University, B

DATABASE SYSTEMS

United States

California

National University, M
University of San Francisco, M

Colorado

Colorado Technical University Colorado Springs, M
Colorado Technical University Denver South, M
Regis University, MO

Connecticut

Fairfield University, O
Sacred Heart University, O
University of New Haven, M

Florida

University of West Florida, M

Illinois

Elmhurst College, M
Illinois Institute of Technology, M
Lewis University, M
Northwestern University, M

Indiana

Indiana University Bloomington, MO
University of Notre Dame, M

Maryland

Towson University, O
University of Maryland University College, MO

Massachusetts

Boston University, M
Worcester Polytechnic Institute, MO

Michigan

Ferris State University, M
University of Michigan - Dearborn, M

Minnesota

Metropolitan State University, O
Minnesota State University Mankato, O
University of Minnesota, Twin Cities Campus, M

Missouri

Washington University in St. Louis, M

New Jersey

Montclair State University, O
Saint Peter's University, M
Stevens Institute of Technology, O

New York

Columbia University, M
New York University, M
Rochester Institute of Technology, O
St. John's University, M

North Carolina

The University of North Carolina at Charlotte, O

Pennsylvania

Clarion University of Pennsylvania, M
Villanova University, M

Tennessee

Austin Peay State University, M
Lipscomb University, M

Texas

Southern Methodist University, M

Virginia

University of Virginia, M
Virginia International University, M

DEMOGRAPHY

United States

California

University of California, Berkeley, MD

Maryland

Johns Hopkins University, M

New York

University at Albany, State University of New York, O

Texas

The University of Texas at San Antonio, D

U.S. Territories: Puerto Rico

University of Puerto Rico, Medical Sciences Campus, M

DEMOGRAPHY AND POPULATION STUDIES

United States

California

University of California, Irvine, M

Florida

Florida State University, M

Hawaii

University of Hawaii at Manoa, O

New Jersey

Princeton University, DO

New York

Cornell University, M

Ohio

Bowling Green State University, M
Miami University, M

Canada

Alberta

University of Alberta, MD

Quebec

Université de Montréal, B

DENTAL ASSISTING/ASSISTANT

United States

Alabama

Calhoun Community College, A
Community College of the Air Force, A
H. Councill Trenholm State Community College, A
James H. Faulkner State Community College, A
Wallace State Community College, A

Alaska

University of Alaska Anchorage, A
University of Alaska Fairbanks, A

Arizona

Mohave Community College, A
Phoenix College, A

California

Allan Hancock College, A
Carrington College - Citrus Heights, A
Carrington College - Pleasant Hill, A
Carrington College - Pomona, A
Carrington College - Sacramento, A
Carrington College - San Jose, A
Carrington College - San Leandro, A
Chaffey College, A
Citrus College, A
City College of San Francisco, A
College of Alameda, A
College of Marin, A
College of the Redwoods, A
College of San Mateo, A
Contra Costa College, A
Cypress College, A
Foothill College, A
Hartnell College, A
Modesto Junior College, A
Orange Coast College, A
Palomar College, A
Pasadena City College, A
Reedley College, A
Sacramento City College, A
San Diego Mesa College, A
San Jose City College, A

Colorado

IBMC College (Fort Collins), A
Pikes Peak Community College, A
Pueblo Community College, A

Connecticut

Lincoln College of New England, A

Delaware

Delaware State University, B

Florida

College of Central Florida, A
Eastern Florida State College, A
Northwest Florida State College, A
Tallahassee Community College, A

Georgia

Athens Technical College, A

Idaho

Carrington College - Boise, A
College of Southern Idaho, A
College of Western Idaho, A

Illinois

Kaskaskia College, A

Indiana

International Business College (Indianapolis), A
Ivy Tech Community College - Columbus, A
Ivy Tech Community College - East Central, A
Ivy Tech Community College - Kokomo, A
Ivy Tech Community College - Lafayette, A
University of Southern Indiana, A

Iowa

Kirkwood Community College, A
Marshalltown Community College, A
Scott Community College, A
Vatterott College, A
Western Iowa Tech Community College, A

Kansas

Flint Hills Technical College, A
Wichita Area Technical College, A

Maine

University of Maine at Augusta, A

Massachusetts

Massasoit Community College, A
Middlesex Community College, A
Northern Essex Community College, A

Michigan

Delta College, A
Lake Michigan College, A
Mott Community College, A
Northwestern Michigan College, A

Minnesota

Century College, A
Dakota County Technical College, A
Hennepin Technical College, A
Herzing University, A
Minneapolis Community and Technical College, A
Minnesota State Community and Technical College, A
Minnesota State Community and Technical College - Detroit Lakes, A
Minnesota State Community and Technical College - Moorhead, A
Minnesota West Community and Technical College, A
Northwest Technical College, A
Rochester Community and Technical College, A
St. Cloud Technical & Community College, A
South Central College, A

Mississippi

Hinds Community College, A
Northeast Mississippi Community College, A

Missouri

Concorde Career College, A

Nebraska

Central Community College - Hastings Campus, A
Mid-Plains Community College, A

Nevada

Truckee Meadows Community College, A

New Hampshire

NHTI, Concord's Community College, A

New Jersey

Camden County College, A
Raritan Valley Community College, A
Union County College, A

New Mexico

Luna Community College, A
Santa Fe Community College, A

North Carolina

Miller-Motte College (Cary), A

North Dakota

North Dakota State College of Science, A

Ohio

Eastern Gateway Community College, A
Fortis College (Cuyahoga Falls), A
Ohio Valley College of Technology, A

Oklahoma

Community Care College, A
Rose State College, A

Oregon

Central Oregon Community College, A

Pennsylvania

Bradford School, A
Harcum College, A
Keystone Technical Institute, A
Luzerne County Community College, A
Manor College, A
Westmoreland County Community College, A

South Carolina

Midlands Technical College, A
York Technical College, A

South Dakota

Lake Area Technical Institute, A

Tennessee

Chattanooga State Community College, A
Concorde Career College, A

Texas

The College of Health Care Professions (Houston), A
El Paso Community College, A
Grayson College, A

Utah

Provo College, A

Virginia

ECPI University (Virginia Beach), A

Washington

Bates Technical College, A
Clover Park Technical College, A
Renton Technical College, A
South Puget Sound Community College, A

West Virginia

Huntington Junior College, A
West Virginia Junior College - Bridgeport, A

U.S. Territories: Puerto Rico

Huertas Junior College, A
Humacao Community College, A
National University College (Bayamón), A
University of Puerto Rico, Medical Sciences Campus, A

DENTAL HYGIENE/HYGIENIST

United States

Alabama

Wallace State Community College, A

Alaska

University of Alaska Anchorage, A
University of Alaska Fairbanks, A

Arizona

Carrington College - Mesa, A
Mohave Community College, A
Northern Arizona University, B
Phoenix College, A
Pima Community College, A
Rio Salado College, A

Arkansas

University of Arkansas - Fort Smith, B
University of Arkansas for Medical Sciences, AB

California

Bakersfield College, A
Cabrillo College, A
Carrington College - Sacramento, A
Carrington College - San Jose, A
Cerritos College, A
Chabot College, A
College of San Mateo, A
Cypress College, A
Foothill College, A
Fresno City College, A
Loma Linda University, B
Los Angeles City College, A
Merced College, A
Monterey Peninsula College, A
Moreno Valley College, A
Oxnard College, A
Pasadena City College, A
Sacramento City College, A
San Bernardino Valley College, A
San Joaquin Valley College (Chula Vista), A
San Joaquin Valley College (Ontario), A
San Joaquin Valley College (Visalia), A
Santa Rosa Junior College, A
Shasta College, A
Southwestern College, A
Taft College, A
University of Southern California, B
West Coast University (Anaheim), B
West Coast University (Ontario), B
West Los Angeles College, A

Colorado

Colorado Northwestern Community College, A
Community College of Denver, A
Pueblo Community College, A

Connecticut

Goodwin College, A
Tunxis Community College, A
University of Bridgeport, ABM
University of New Haven, AB

Delaware

Delaware Technical & Community College, Stanton/Wilmington Campus, A

District of Columbia

Howard University, B

Florida

Broward College, A
Daytona State College, A
Eastern Florida State College, A
Florida National University, A
Florida SouthWestern State College, A
Florida State College at Jacksonville, A
Gulf Coast State College, A
Hillsborough Community College, A
Indian River State College, A
Miami Dade College, A
Palm Beach State College, A
Pasco-Hernando State College, A
Pensacola State College, A
St. Petersburg College, AB
Santa Fe College, A
South Florida State College, A
Tallahassee Community College, A
Valencia College, A

Georgia

Andrew College, A
Athens Technical College, A
Atlanta Technical College, A
Augusta University, B
Central Georgia Technical College, A
Clayton State University, B
College of Coastal Georgia, A
Columbus Technical College, A
Dalton State College, A
Darton State College, A
Georgia Highlands College, AB
Ogeechee Technical College, A
Southeastern Technical College, A

Hawaii

University of Hawaii at Manoa, B

Idaho

Carrington College - Boise, A
Idaho State University, BM

Illinois

Carl Sandburg College, A
City Colleges of Chicago, Kennedy-King College, A
College of DuPage, A
College of Lake County, A
Fox College, A
Harper College, A
Illinois Central College, A
John A. Logan College, A
Lake Land College, A
Lewis and Clark Community College, A
Lewis University, B
Parkland College, A
Prairie State College, A
Rock Valley College, A
Southern Illinois University Carbondale, B

Indiana

Ball State University, B
Indiana University Northwest, B
Indiana University - Purdue University Fort Wayne, A
Indiana University - Purdue University Indianapolis, A
Indiana University South Bend, AB
Ivy Tech Community College - East Central, A
Ivy Tech Community College - Kokomo, A
University of Southern Indiana, B

Iowa

Allen College, B
Des Moines Area Community College, A
Hawkeye Community College, A
Iowa Western Community College, A
Kirkwood Community College, A
Muscatine Community College, A
Scott Community College, A

Kansas

Barton County Community College, A
Colby Community College, A
Fort Scott Community College, A
Johnson County Community College, A
Wichita State University, B

Kentucky

Big Sandy Community and Technical College, A
Bluegrass Community and Technical College, A
Elizabethtown Community and Technical College, A
University of Louisville, B
Western Kentucky University, AB

Louisiana

Delgado Community College, A
Louisiana State University Health Sciences Center, B
Southern University at Shreveport, A
University of Louisiana at Monroe, B

Maine

University of Maine at Augusta, AB
University of New England, B

Maryland

Allegany College of Maryland, A
Baltimore City Community College, A
Community College of Baltimore County, A
Hagerstown Community College, A

Massachusetts

Boston University, M
Bristol Community College, A
Cape Cod Community College, A
MCPHS University, B
Middlesex Community College, A
Mount Ida College, AB
Mount Wachusett Community College, A
Quinsigamond Community College, A
Springfield Technical Community College, A

Michigan

Baker College, A
Delta College, A
Ferris State University, AB
Grand Rapids Community College, A
Kalamazoo Valley Community College, A
Kellogg Community College, A
Lansing Community College, A
Mott Community College, A
Oakland Community College, A
University of Detroit Mercy, B
University of Michigan, BM
Wayne County Community College District, A

Minnesota

Argosy University, Twin Cities, A
Century College, A
Herzing University, A
Lake Superior College, A
Metropolitan State University, B
Minnesota State Community and Technical College, A
Minnesota State Community and Technical College - Moorhead, A
Minnesota State University Mankato, B
Normandale Community College, A
Rochester Community and Technical College, A
St. Cloud Technical & Community College, A
University of Minnesota, Twin Cities Campus, B

Mississippi

Meridian Community College, A
Mississippi Delta Community College, A
Northeast Mississippi Community College, A
University of Mississippi, B
University of Mississippi Medical Center, B

Missouri

Missouri Southern State University, AM
State Fair Community College, A
University of Missouri - Kansas City, BM

Montana

Great Falls College Montana State University, A
Salish Kootenai College, A

Nebraska

Central Community College - Hastings Campus, A
University of Nebraska Medical Center, B

Nevada

College of Southern Nevada, AB
Truckee Meadows Community College, A

New Hampshire

NHTI, Concord's Community College, A

New Jersey

Bergen Community College, A
Brookdale Community College, A
Camden County College, A
Essex County College, A
Middlesex County College, A
Raritan Valley Community College, A
Rowan College at Burlington County, A
Rutgers University - New Brunswick, A
Thomas Edison State University, AB

Union County College, A

New Mexico

Eastern New Mexico University - Roswell, A
Pima Medical Institute (Albuquerque), A
San Juan College, A
University of New Mexico, BM

New York

Broome Community College, A
Erie Community College, North Campus, A
Eugenio María de Hostos Community College of the City University of New York, A
Farmingdale State College, AB
Hudson Valley Community College, A
Monroe Community College, A
New York City College of Technology of the City University of New York, A
New York University, AB
Orange County Community College, A
State University of New York College of Technology at Canton, AB

North Carolina

Asheville-Buncombe Technical Community College, A
Cape Fear Community College, A
Catawba Valley Community College, A
Central Piedmont Community College, A
Coastal Carolina Community College, A
Fayetteville Technical Community College, A
Guilford Technical Community College, A
Halifax Community College, A
The University of North Carolina at Chapel Hill, BM
Wake Technical Community College, A
Wayne Community College, A

North Dakota

North Dakota State College of Science, A

Ohio

Columbus State Community College, A
James A. Rhodes State College, A
Lakeland Community College, A
The Ohio State University, BM
The Ohio State University at Lima, B
Owens Community College, A
Shawnee State University, A
Sinclair Community College, A
Stark State College, A
University of Cincinnati Blue Ash College, A
Youngstown State University, B

Oklahoma

Rose State College, A
Tulsa Community College, A
University of Oklahoma Health Sciences Center, B

Oregon

Lane Community College, A
Mt. Hood Community College, A
Oregon Institute of Technology, B
Portland Community College, A

Pennsylvania

Community College of Philadelphia, A
Harcum College, A
Harrisburg Area Community College, A
Luzerne County Community College, A
Manor College, A
Montgomery County Community College, A
Northampton Community College, A
Pennsylvania College of Technology, AB
University of Pittsburgh, B
Westmoreland County Community College, A

Rhode Island

Community College of Rhode Island, A
Rhode Island College, B

South Carolina

Florence-Darlington Technical College, A
Greenville Technical College, A
Midlands Technical College, A

Trident Technical College, A
York Technical College, A

South Dakota

The University of South Dakota, B

Tennessee

Chattanooga State Community College, A
East Tennessee State University, B
Hiwassee College, A
Roane State Community College, A
Southern Adventist University, A
Tennessee State University, AB

Texas

Amarillo College, A
Austin Community College District, A
Blinn College, A
Coastal Bend College, A
Collin County Community College District, A
Del Mar College, A
El Paso Community College, A
Howard College, A
Lamar Institute of Technology, A
Lone Star College - Kingwood, A
Midwestern State University, B
Northeast Texas Community College, A
San Antonio College, A
Tarrant County College District, A
Temple College, A
Texas Woman's University, B
Tyler Junior College, A
The University of Texas Health Science Center at
   Houston, B
The University of Texas Health Science Center at
   San Antonio, B
Wharton County Junior College, A

Utah

Dixie State University, AB
Salt Lake Community College, A
Utah Valley University, AB
Weber State University, AB

Vermont

Vermont Technical College, AB

Virginia

Germanna Community College, A
Northern Virginia Community College, A
Old Dominion University, BM
Thomas Nelson Community College, A
Virginia Commonwealth University, B
Virginia Western Community College, A
Wytheville Community College, A

Washington

Clark College, A
Columbia Basin College, A
Eastern Washington University, BM
Highline College, A
Pierce College at Fort Steilacoom, A
Pierce College at Puyallup, A
Pima Medical Institute (Seattle), A
Shoreline Community College, A
Spokane Community College, A
University of Washington, B
Yakima Valley Community College, A

West Virginia

BridgeValley Community and Technical College
   (Montgomery), A
West Liberty University, AB
West Virginia University, B

Wisconsin

Chippewa Valley Technical College, A
Fox Valley Technical College, A
Lakeshore Technical College, A
Madison Area Technical College, A
Milwaukee Area Technical College, A
Northcentral Technical College, A
Northeast Wisconsin Technical College, A
Waukesha County Technical College, A
Western Technical College, A

Wyoming

Laramie County Community College, A
Sheridan College, A
University of Wyoming, B

Canada

Alberta

University of Alberta, O

British Columbia

The University of British Columbia, B

Manitoba

University of Manitoba, B

Maritime Provinces: Nova Scotia

Dalhousie University, B

Quebec

Université de Montréal, O

DENTAL LABORATORY TECH-NOLOGY/TECHNICIAN

United States

Alabama

Community College of the Air Force, A

Arizona

Pima Community College, A

California

Pasadena City College, A

Florida

Florida National University, A

Indiana

Indiana University - Purdue University Fort Wayne,
   A

Iowa

Kirkwood Community College, A

Kentucky

Bluegrass Community and Technical College, A

Louisiana

Delgado Community College, A
Louisiana State University Health Sciences Center,
   A

Massachusetts

Middlesex Community College, A

New York

Erie Community College, South Campus, A
New York City College of Technology of the City
   University of New York, A

North Carolina

Durham Technical Community College, A

Ohio

Columbus State Community College, A

Oregon

Portland Community College, A

Pennsylvania

Commonwealth Technical Institute, A

Texas

The University of Texas Health Science Center at
   San Antonio, B

Virginia

J. Sargeant Reynolds Community College, A

Washington

Bates Technical College, A

West Virginia

Mountwest Community & Technical College, A

DENTAL AND ORAL SURGERY

United States

California

Loma Linda University, MO

District of Columbia

Howard University, O

Iowa

The University of Iowa, MDO

Massachusetts

Boston University, MDO
Harvard University, O
Tufts University, O

Missouri

University of Missouri - Kansas City, O

New York

New York University, O

North Carolina

The University of North Carolina at Chapel Hill, M

Ohio

Case Western Reserve University, O
The Ohio State University, M

Oregon

Oregon Health & Science University, O

Pennsylvania

University of Pittsburgh, O

Washington

University of Washington, MDO

U.S. Territories: Puerto Rico

University of Puerto Rico, Medical Sciences Campus, O

Canada

Manitoba

University of Manitoba, M

Ontario

University of Toronto, M

Quebec

McGill University, MD

DENTAL SERVICES AND AL-LIED PROFESSIONS

United States

Delaware

Delaware State University, B

Georgia

Gordon State College, A
Valdosta State University, A

Indiana

Indiana University - Purdue University Indianapolis, B

Massachusetts

Quinsigamond Community College, A

Washington

Bates Technical College, A

DENTISTRY

United States

Alabama

The University of Alabama at Birmingham, D

California

Loma Linda University, MDO
University of California, Los Angeles, DO
University of the Pacific, MDO
University of Southern California, D

Colorado

University of Colorado Denver, MD

District of Columbia

Howard University, DO

Florida

Nova Southeastern University, MDO
University of Florida, DO

Georgia

Augusta University, D

Idaho

Idaho State University, O

Illinois

Southern Illinois University Edwardsville, D
University of Illinois at Chicago, D

Indiana

Indiana University - Purdue University Indianapolis, MDO

Iowa

The University of Iowa, MDO

Kentucky

University of Kentucky, D
University of Louisville, MD

Louisiana

Louisiana State University Health Sciences Center, D

Maine

University of New England, D

Massachusetts

Harvard University, DO
Tufts University, D

Michigan

University of Detroit Mercy, D
University of Michigan, D

Minnesota

University of Minnesota, Twin Cities Campus, D

Mississippi

University of Mississippi Medical Center, MD

Missouri

Saint Louis University, M
University of Missouri - Kansas City, MDO

Nebraska

Creighton University, D

Nevada

University of Nevada, Las Vegas, MD

New Jersey

Rutgers University - Newark, MDO

New York

Columbia University, D
New York University, D
Stony Brook University, State University of New York, DO
University at Buffalo, the State University of New York, D

North Carolina

East Carolina University, D
The University of North Carolina at Chapel Hill, D

Ohio

Case Western Reserve University, D
The Ohio State University, MD

Oklahoma

University of Oklahoma Health Sciences Center, DO

Oregon

Oregon Health & Science University, DO

Pennsylvania

Temple University, D
University of Pennsylvania, D
University of Pittsburgh, MDO

South Carolina

Medical University of South Carolina, D

Texas

Texas A&M University, MDO
The University of Texas Health Science Center at Houston, MD
The University of Texas Health Science Center at San Antonio, MDO

Utah

University of Utah, D

Virginia

Virginia Commonwealth University, MD

Washington

University of Washington, D

West Virginia

West Virginia University, D

Wisconsin

Marquette University, D

U.S. Territories: Puerto Rico

University of Puerto Rico, Medical Sciences Campus, D

Canada

Alberta

University of Alberta, D

British Columbia

The University of British Columbia, D

Manitoba

University of Manitoba, D

Ontario

University of Toronto, D
The University of Western Ontario, D

Quebec

McGill University, MDO
Université Laval, D

Saskatchewan

University of Saskatchewan, D

DESIGN AND APPLIED ARTS

United States

Arizona

Arizona State University at the Tempe campus, BMD

Arkansas

Harding University, B

California

Allan Hancock College, A
Antioch University Los Angeles, B
The Art Institute of California - Hollywood, a campus of Argosy University, B
Azusa Pacific University, B
California College of the Arts, BM
California State University, Fresno, M
California State University, Fullerton, M
California State University, Los Angeles, M
Laguna College of Art & Design, B
Lassen Community College District, A
Los Angeles City College, A
Merced College, A
Otis College of Art and Design, B
Porterville College, A
San Diego State University, M
Skyline College, A
Stanford University, M
University of California, Berkeley, MO
University of California, Los Angeles, BM

Connecticut

Tunxis Community College, A
University of Bridgeport, M

Delaware

University of Delaware, M

District of Columbia

Howard University, BM

Florida

Full Sail University, B
Miami International University of Art & Design, M
St. Johns River State College, A

Georgia

Reinhardt University, B

Illinois

School of the Art Institute of Chicago, BM
University of Illinois at Chicago, BM
Western Illinois University, M

Indiana

Butler University, B
Indiana University - Purdue University Indianapolis, M
Purdue University, M
Taylor University, B
University of Notre Dame, M
Vincennes University, A

Iowa

Iowa Lakes Community College, A

Kansas

Kansas State University, M
Pratt Community College, A
Seward County Community College and Area Technical School, A
The University of Kansas, M

Washburn University, A

Kentucky

Asbury University, B
University of Kentucky, M

Louisiana

Louisiana State University and Agricultural & Mechanical College, M

Maine

University of Maine at Presque Isle, A

Maryland

Howard Community College, A
Maryland Institute College of Art, BM
University of Baltimore, M

Massachusetts

Hampshire College, B
Massachusetts College of Art and Design, MO
Merrimack College, B
Northeastern University, M
Salem State University, B
School of the Museum of Fine Arts, Boston, B
University of Massachusetts Dartmouth, MO

Michigan

College for Creative Studies, M
Ferris State University, BM
Marygrove College, B
Muskegon Community College, A
University of Michigan, MD
Wayne State University, M

Minnesota

Augsburg College, B
Bemidji State University, B
Minnesota State University Mankato, B
St. Cloud State University, B
University of Minnesota, Twin Cities Campus, MDO

Mississippi

Jones County Junior College, A
Mississippi Delta Community College, A

Missouri

Washington University in St. Louis, B

Nebraska

Peru State College, B
University of Nebraska at Omaha, B

New Hampshire

Franklin Pierce University, B

New Jersey

Berkeley College - Woodland Park Campus, B
County College of Morris, A
Montclair State University, B
Raritan Valley Community College, A
Rutgers University - New Brunswick, M

New Mexico

University of New Mexico - Los Alamos Branch, A

New York

Buffalo State College, State University of New York, B
Columbia University, School of General Studies, B
Eugene Lang College of Liberal Arts, B
Fashion Institute of Technology, B
Hofstra University, B
Kingsborough Community College of the City University of New York, A
New York Institute of Technology, B
New York University, M
Niagara County Community College, A
Onondaga Community College, A
Parsons School of Design, B
Pratt Institute, B
Roberts Wesleyan College, B
Rockland Community College, A
School of Visual Arts, BM

State University of New York at Fredonia, B
Syracuse University, B
Westchester Community College, A

North Carolina

Central Piedmont Community College, A
North Carolina State University, D
Western Carolina University, M

Ohio

Bowling Green State University, M
Shawnee State University, B
Sinclair Community College, A

Oklahoma

Oklahoma City Community College, A
Oklahoma State University, MD
University of Central Oklahoma, M

Oregon

Portland State University, B
University of Oregon, B

Pennsylvania

Carnegie Mellon University, MD
Drexel University, B
Mansfield University of Pennsylvania, B
Penn State Altoona, B
Penn State Berks, B
Penn State University Park, B

South Carolina

Converse College, B

Texas

The Art Institute of Dallas, a campus of South University, M
Del Mar College, A
Houston Baptist University, B
McMurry University, B
Midwestern State University, B
Odessa College, A
Schreiner University, B
Southern Methodist University, B
Stephen F. Austin State University, M
University of North Texas, M
The University of Texas at Austin, M

Utah

LDS Business College, A

Virginia

Radford University, M

Washington

University of Washington, M
Wenatchee Valley College, A
Western Washington University, B

Wisconsin

Alverno College, B
University of Wisconsin - Madison, MD
University of Wisconsin - Stout, B
Wisconsin Lutheran College, B

U.S. Territories: Puerto Rico

Inter American University of Puerto Rico, San Germán Campus, B

Canada

Alberta

Athabasca University, B
University of Alberta, BM

Maritime Provinces: Nova Scotia

NSCAD University, BM

Ontario

York University, M

Quebec

Concordia University, BO

DESIGN AND VISUAL COMMUNICATIONS

United States

Alabama

Auburn University, B
Calhoun Community College, A
Chattahoochee Valley Community College, A
Virginia College in Huntsville, A

Arizona

Northern Arizona University, B
Pima Community College, A
University of Advancing Technology, AB

California

Bethesda University, B
Biola University, B
California College of the Arts, B
California Institute of the Arts, B
California State University, Chico, B
California State University, Monterey Bay, B
College of Marin, A
FIDM/Fashion Institute of Design & Merchandising, Los Angeles Campus, A
FIDM/Fashion Institute of Design & Merchandising, Orange County Campus, A
FIDM/Fashion Institute of Design & Merchandising, San Diego Campus, A
FIDM/Fashion Institute of Design & Merchandising, San Francisco Campus, A
Glendale Community College, A
Laguna College of Art & Design, B
Long Beach City College, A
Mt. San Jacinto College, A
Mt. Sierra College, B
Palomar College, A
Platt College (Alhambra), B
Platt College (Ontario), B
San Francisco State University, B
Shasta College, A
University of Redlands, B
University of San Francisco, B

Colorado

Platt College, AB

Connecticut

Central Connecticut State University, B
University of Hartford, B

Delaware

Wilmington University, B

District of Columbia

American University, B

Florida

Full Sail University, B
Jacksonville University, B
Keiser University, A
Miami International University of Art & Design, B

Georgia

American InterContinental University Atlanta, AB
Savannah College of Art and Design, B
Southeastern Technical College, A

Idaho

Boise State University, B

Illinois

American InterContinental University Online, B
Black Hawk College, A
College of DuPage, A
Elgin Community College, A
Heartland Community College, A
The Illinois Institute of Art - Schaumburg, B
Lewis University, B
Loyola University Chicago, B
Moraine Valley Community College, A
Parkland College, A

School of the Art Institute of Chicago, B
Southern Illinois University Carbondale, B
Triton College, A

Indiana

Anderson University, B
Bethel College, B
Holy Cross College, B
Ivy Tech Community College - Central Indiana, A
Ivy Tech Community College - Columbus, A
Ivy Tech Community College - Kokomo, A
Ivy Tech Community College - North Central, A
Ivy Tech Community College - Southern Indiana, A
Ivy Tech Community College - Southwest, A
Ivy Tech Community College - Wabash Valley, A
Purdue University, B
Saint Mary-of-the-Woods College, B
University of Evansville, B
University of Notre Dame, B
University of Saint Francis, AB

Iowa

Iowa State University of Science and Technology, B
Iowa Wesleyan University, B

Kansas

Hutchinson Community College, A
The University of Kansas, B

Kentucky

Bellarmine University, B

Louisiana

Loyola University New Orleans, B

Maryland

Cecil College, A
Stevenson University, B
University of Maryland, Baltimore County, B

Massachusetts

Bristol Community College, A
Bunker Hill Community College, A
Endicott College, B
University of Massachusetts Dartmouth, B

Michigan

Alma College, B
Lawrence Technological University, B
Madonna University, B
Saginaw Valley State University, B
Spring Arbor University, B
University of Michigan - Flint, B

Minnesota

Academy College, A
Concordia University, St. Paul, B
Minneapolis Community and Technical College, A

Missouri

College of the Ozarks, B
Drury University, B
Missouri State University, B
Washington University in St. Louis, B

Nevada

Nevada State College, B

New Hampshire

New Hampshire Institute of Art, B

New Jersey

Kean University, B

New Mexico

Eastern New Mexico University - Roswell, A
New Mexico Highlands University, B
Santa Fe Community College, A

New York

Adirondack Community College, A
Bryant & Stratton College - Amherst Campus, A
Bryant & Stratton College - Henrietta Campus, A

Buffalo State College, State University of New York, B
Cazenovia College, B
Eugene Lang College of Liberal Arts, B
Farmingdale State College, B
Houghton College, B
LIM College, B
Nassau Community College, A
Nazareth College of Rochester, B
New York City College of Technology of the City University of New York, B
Parsons School of Design, B
Rensselaer Polytechnic Institute, B
Rochester Institute of Technology, B
Syracuse University, B

North Carolina

Barton College, B
Duke University, B
Lees-McRae College, B
Nash Community College, A
North Carolina State University, B

Ohio

Art Academy of Cincinnati, B
Bowling Green State University, B
Bowling Green State University - Firelands College, B
Cedarville University, B
Mount St. Joseph University, B
Muskingum University, B
Northwest State Community College, A
Ohio Dominican University, B
Ohio Northern University, B
The Ohio State University, B
University of Cincinnati, B
University of Dayton, B
Ursuline College, B

Oklahoma

Oklahoma City Community College, A
Oral Roberts University, B
University of Oklahoma, B

Oregon

Chemeketa Community College, A
Linfield College, B
Oregon State University, B
Pacific Northwest College of Art, B

Pennsylvania

Albright College, B
Carnegie Mellon University, B
Douglas Education Center, A
Harrisburg Area Community College, A
La Roche College, B
Lehigh University, B
Millersville University of Pennsylvania, B
Robert Morris University, B
Westminster College, B

Rhode Island

Bryant University, B

Tennessee

Belmont University, B
Maryville College, B
Memphis College of Art, B
Nashville State Community College, A
The University of Tennessee at Martin, B
Watkins College of Art, Design, & Film, B

Texas

American InterContinental University Houston, B
Angelina College, A
Brookhaven College, A
Lone Star College - CyFair, A
Lone Star College - Kingwood, A
Lone Star College - North Harris, A
Lubbock Christian University, B
Texas Christian University, B
Texas State University, B
University of Mary Hardin-Baylor, B
University of North Texas, B
The University of Texas at Austin, B

Utah

Broadview Entertainment Arts University, B
Salt Lake Community College, A
Utah Valley University, AB
Weber State University, B

Vermont

Bennington College, B

Virginia

Central Virginia Community College, A
Marymount University, B
Radford University, B
Thomas Nelson Community College, A

Washington

Northwest College of Art & Design, B
Seattle Pacific University, B
University of Washington, B
Western Washington University, B

West Virginia

West Virginia University, B

Wisconsin

Bryant & Stratton College - Milwaukee Campus, A
Milwaukee Institute of Art and Design, B
University of Wisconsin - Green Bay, B
University of Wisconsin - Stevens Point, B
Viterbo University, B

U.S. Territories: Guam

Guam Community College, A

U.S. Territories: Puerto Rico

EDP University of Puerto Rico, B
Escuela de Artes Plasticas y Diseño de Puerto Rico, B
Inter American University of Puerto Rico, Metropolitan Campus, B

Canada

Alberta

Alberta College of Art & Design, B
University of Alberta, B

British Columbia

Emily Carr University of Art + Design, B
Thompson Rivers University, B

Maritime Provinces: Nova Scotia

NSCAD University, B

Ontario

York University, B

Quebec

Université du Québec en Outaouais, B

DEVELOPMENT ECONOMICS AND INTERNATIONAL DEVELOPMENT

United States

Arkansas

John Brown University, B

California

Point Loma Nazarene University, B
University of California, Los Angeles, B
University of San Francisco, B

Georgia

Georgia Southern University, B

Illinois

Illinois Institute of Technology, B

Indiana

Taylor University, B

Massachusetts

Clark University, B

Michigan

Calvin College, B

New York

Houghton College, B

Ohio

University of Dayton, B

Pennsylvania

Messiah College, B
Penn State Altoona, B
Penn State Berks, B

Rhode Island

Brown University, B

Texas

University of St. Thomas, B

Vermont

Marlboro College, B
University of Vermont, B

Virginia

University of Richmond, B

Washington

Seattle Pacific University, B

Canada

British Columbia

University of the Fraser Valley, B

Manitoba

The University of Winnipeg, B

Maritime Provinces: New Brunswick

University of New Brunswick Saint John, B

Maritime Provinces: Nova Scotia

Dalhousie University, B
University of King's College, B

Ontario

University of Guelph, B
University of Ottawa, B
York University, B

Quebec

McGill University, B

DEVELOPMENTAL BIOLOGY AND EMBRYOLOGY

United States

Alabama

The University of Alabama at Birmingham, D

California

California Institute of Technology, D
California State University, Sacramento, M
San Francisco State University, M
Stanford University, MD
University of California, Davis, MD
University of California, Irvine, MD
University of California, Los Angeles, MD
University of California, Riverside, MD
University of California, Santa Barbara, BMD
University of California, Santa Cruz, MD
University of Southern California, D

Colorado

University of Colorado Boulder, MD
University of Colorado Denver, MD

Connecticut

University of Connecticut, MD
Wesleyan University, D
Yale University, D

Delaware

University of Delaware, MD

Florida

University of Miami, D

Georgia

Emory University, D

Hawaii

University of Hawaii at Manoa, MD

Illinois

Illinois State University, M
Northwestern University, D
University of Chicago, D
University of Illinois at Urbana - Champaign, D

Indiana

Purdue University, D

Iowa

Iowa State University of Science and Technology, MD

Kansas

The University of Kansas, MD

Louisiana

Louisiana State University Health Sciences Center, MD

Maryland

Johns Hopkins University, D

Massachusetts

Massachusetts Institute of Technology, D
Tufts University, D
University of Massachusetts Amherst, D

Michigan

University of Michigan, MD

Minnesota

University of Minnesota, Twin Cities Campus, MD

Missouri

Washington University in St. Louis, D

Montana

University of Montana, D

New Jersey

Rutgers University - New Brunswick, MD
Rutgers University - Newark, O

New York

Columbia University, MD
Cornell University, MD
New York University, D
Stony Brook University, State University of New York, D
University at Albany, State University of New York, D

North Carolina

Duke University, O
The University of North Carolina at Chapel Hill, MD

Ohio

The Ohio State University, MD
University of Cincinnati, D

Oregon

Oregon Health & Science University, D

Pennsylvania

Carnegie Mellon University, D
Thomas Jefferson University, MD
University of Pennsylvania, D
University of Pittsburgh, D

South Carolina

Medical University of South Carolina, D
University of South Carolina, MD

Tennessee

Vanderbilt University, MD

Texas

The University of Texas Health Science Center at Houston, MD

Utah

Brigham Young University, MD

West Virginia

West Virginia University, MD

Wisconsin

Marquette University, MD

Canada

Alberta

University of Alberta, B

British Columbia

The University of British Columbia, MD

DEVELOPMENTAL EDUCATION

United States

Illinois

National Louis University, MO

Iowa

The University of Iowa, M

Louisiana

Grambling State University, MDO

Michigan

Eastern Michigan University, M
Ferris State University, M

Minnesota

Walden University, MO

New Jersey

Rutgers University - New Brunswick, M

North Carolina

North Carolina State University, MDO

Pennsylvania

Penn State Harrisburg, M

Texas

Sam Houston State University, D
Texas State University, MD

DEVELOPMENTAL PSYCHOLOGY

United States

Alabama

The University of Alabama at Birmingham, D

Arizona

Arizona State University at the Tempe campus, D

California

University of Southern California, D

Colorado

University of Denver, D

Connecticut

University of Connecticut, MD
Yale University, D

District of Columbia

Howard University, D

Florida

Florida International University, MD
Florida State University, D
University of Miami, D

Georgia

Clayton State University, M
Emory University, D
Georgia State University, D

Illinois

Illinois State University, M
Loyola University Chicago, MD
University of Illinois at Chicago, M

Indiana

Indiana University Bloomington, D
University of Notre Dame, D

Kansas

The University of Kansas, D

Louisiana

Louisiana State University and Agricultural & Mechanical College, MD

Maryland

University of Maryland, Baltimore County, D
University of Maryland, College Park, D

Massachusetts

Bay Path University, M
Boston College, MD
Brandeis University, D
Clark University, D
Harvard University, D
University of Massachusetts Amherst, MD

Michigan

Andrews University, MD
University of Michigan, D
Wayne State University, D

Minnesota

Capella University, M

Missouri

Washington University in St. Louis, D

Montana

University of Montana, D

Nebraska

University of Nebraska - Lincoln, MD

New Mexico

University of New Mexico, D

New York

Cornell University, MD
Fordham University, D
New York University, MD
University of Rochester, D

North Carolina

Duke University, D
North Carolina State University, D
The University of North Carolina at Chapel Hill, D
The University of North Carolina at Greensboro, MD

North Dakota

North Dakota State University, D

Ohio

Bowling Green State University, MD
The Ohio State University, D

Oregon

University of Oregon, MD

Pennsylvania

Carnegie Mellon University, D
Chatham University, M
Delaware Valley University, M
La Salle University, D
University of Pittsburgh, MD

Texas

Texas A&M University, D
Texas Christian University, M
University of Houston, D
The University of Texas at Austin, D

Virginia

George Mason University, O
Virginia Commonwealth University, D

Washington

University of Washington, D

West Virginia

West Virginia University, D

Wisconsin

University of Wisconsin - Madison, D
University of Wisconsin - Milwaukee, MD
Viterbo University, M

Canada

British Columbia

The University of British Columbia, MD
University of Victoria, MD

Ontario

Queen's University at Kingston, MD
Wilfrid Laurier University, MD

Quebec

McGill University, MDO
Université de Montréal, MD

DIAGNOSTIC MEDICAL SONOGRAPHY/ SONOGRAPHER AND ULTRASOUND TECHNICIAN

United States

Alabama

H. Councill Trenholm State Community College, A
Lurleen B. Wallace Community College, A
Virginia College in Birmingham, A

Arizona

GateWay Community College, A

Arkansas

University of Arkansas for Medical Sciences, AB

California

Charles R. Drew University of Medicine and Science, B

Cypress College, A
Foothill College, A
Lincoln University, A
Mt. San Jacinto College, A
Orange Coast College, A

Colorado

Red Rocks Community College, A

Delaware

Delaware Technical & Community College, Jack F. Owens Campus, A
Delaware Technical & Community College, Stanton/Wilmington Campus, A

District of Columbia

The George Washington University, B

Florida

Adventist University of Health Sciences, AB
Broward College, A
Cambridge Institute of Allied Health and Technology, A
Florida National University, A
Gulf Coast State College, A
Hillsborough Community College, A
Keiser University, A
Meridian College, A
Miami Dade College, A
Nova Southeastern University, B
Pensacola State College, A
Polk State College, A
Santa Fe College, A
Southern Technical College (Fort Myers), A
Tallahassee Community College, A
Valencia College, A

Georgia

Athens Technical College, A
Columbus Technical College, A
Darton State College, A

Illinois

Benedictine University, B
Harper College, A
John A. Logan College, A
Lewis University, B
Northwestern College - Chicago Campus, A
Roosevelt University, B
Rush University, B
Triton College, A

Iowa

Mercy College of Health Sciences, A

Kansas

Newman University, B
Washburn University, B

Kentucky

Jefferson Community and Technical College, A
West Kentucky Community and Technical College, A

Maine

Kennebec Valley Community College, A

Maryland

Howard Community College, A
Montgomery College, A

Massachusetts

Bunker Hill Community College, A
Middlesex Community College, A
Springfield Technical Community College, A

Michigan

Baker College, A
Delta College, A
Ferris State University, A
Jackson College, A
Lake Michigan College, A
Lansing Community College, A
Oakland Community College, A

Minnesota

Argosy University, Twin Cities, A
St. Catherine University, A
St. Cloud Technical & Community College, A

Mississippi

Hinds Community College, A

Missouri

University of Missouri, B

Nebraska

Nebraska Methodist College, A
University of Nebraska Medical Center, B

New Hampshire

NHTI, Concord's Community College, A

New Jersey

Bergen Community College, A
Rowan College at Gloucester County, A
Union County College, A

New Mexico

Central New Mexico Community College, A

New York

Long Island University - LIU Brooklyn, B
Rochester Institute of Technology, B
State University of New York Downstate Medical
   Center, B
Trocaire College, B

North Carolina

Asheville-Buncombe Technical Community College,
   A
Caldwell Community College and Technical Institute,
   A
Cape Fear Community College, A
ECPI University (Charlotte), A
Forsyth Technical Community College, A
Pitt Community College, A
South Piedmont Community College, A

Ohio

Bowling Green State University, B
Bowling Green State University - Firelands College,
   A
Central Ohio Technical College, A
Cincinnati State Technical and Community College,
   A
Lorain County Community College, A
Owens Community College, A
The University of Findlay, AB

Oklahoma

Bacone College, A
Tulsa Community College, A
University of Oklahoma Health Sciences Center, B

Pennsylvania

Community College of Allegheny County, A
Harrisburg Area Community College, A
Keystone College, A
Lackawanna College, A
Misericordia University, B
Northampton Community College, A
Pennsylvania College of Health Sciences, A
Pittsburgh Career Institute, A
South Hills School of Business & Technology (State
   College), A
Thomas Jefferson University, B
Westmoreland County Community College, A

Rhode Island

Community College of Rhode Island, A
Rhode Island College, B

South Carolina

Greenville Technical College, A

South Dakota

Southeast Technical Institute, A

Tennessee

Baptist College of Health Sciences, B

Texas

Alvin Community College, A
Austin Community College District, A
The College of Health Care Professions (Houston),
   A
Del Mar College, A
El Centro College, A
El Paso Community College, A
Lamar Institute of Technology, A
Lone Star College - CyFair, A
Midland College, A
San Jacinto College District, A
Temple College, A
Texas Southmost College, A
Tyler Junior College, A
Virginia College in Austin, A

Utah

Weber State University, B

Washington

Bellevue College, A
Seattle University, B
Tacoma Community College, A

West Virginia

University of Charleston, B

Wisconsin

Blackhawk Technical College, A
Chippewa Valley Technical College, A
Marian University, B
Northeast Wisconsin Technical College, A

Wyoming

Laramie County Community College, A

U.S. Territories: Puerto Rico

Universidad del Este, AB
Universidad Metropolitana, A

Canada

Maritime Provinces: Nova Scotia

Dalhousie University, B

DIESEL MECHANICS TECH-NOLOGY/TECHNICIAN

United States

Alabama

Shelton State Community College, A

Arizona

Arizona Automotive Institute, A
Central Arizona College, A
Eastern Arizona College, A
Universal Technical Institute, A

California

American River College, A
Barstow Community College, A
Citrus College, A
College of Alameda, A
College of the Redwoods, A
Hartnell College, A
Long Beach City College, A
Palomar College, A
Santa Ana College, A
Santa Rosa Junior College, A
Shasta College, A

Colorado

Lincoln College of Technology, A
Trinidad State Junior College, A

Hawaii

Hawaii Community College, A

Idaho

College of Southern Idaho, A
Eastern Idaho Technical College, A
Idaho State University, AB
Lewis-Clark State College, AB

Illinois

Carl Sandburg College, A
City Colleges of Chicago, Olive-Harvey College, A
Illinois Central College, A
Illinois Eastern Community Colleges, Wabash Valley
   College, A
Kishwaukee College, A

Indiana

Lincoln College of Technology, A
Vincennes University, A

Iowa

Des Moines Area Community College, A
Hawkeye Community College, A
Indian Hills Community College, A
Iowa Western Community College, A
Kirkwood Community College, A
Northwest Iowa Community College, A
Scott Community College, A

Kansas

North Central Kansas Technical College, A
Northwest Kansas Technical College, A
Seward County Community College and Area Tech-
   nical School, A

Kentucky

Elizabethtown Community and Technical College, A
Owensboro Community and Technical College, A

Louisiana

South Louisiana Community College, A

Massachusetts

Massasoit Community College, A

Minnesota

Alexandria Technical and Community College, A
Central Lakes College, A
Minnesota State Community and Technical College,
   A
Minnesota State Community and Technical College -
   Moorhead, A
Minnesota West Community and Technical College,
   A
Riverland Community College, A

Mississippi

Hinds Community College, A
Southwest Mississippi Community College, A

Missouri

Ozarks Technical Community College, A

Montana

Montana State University Billings, A
Montana State University - Northern, AB

Nebraska

Central Community College - Hastings Campus, A
Mid-Plains Community College, A
Northeast Community College, A
Southeast Community College, Milford Campus, A

Nevada

Great Basin College, A
Truckee Meadows Community College, A

New Hampshire

White Mountains Community College, A

New Jersey

Raritan Valley Community College, A

New Mexico

Mesalands Community College, A
San Juan College, A

New York

Morrisville State College, A
State University of New York College of Agriculture and Technology at Cobleskill, A
State University of New York College of Technology at Alfred, A

North Carolina

Asheville-Buncombe Technical Community College, A
Johnston Community College, A
Wake Technical Community College, A
Wilkes Community College, A

North Dakota

North Dakota State College of Science, A
Williston State College, A

Ohio

Clark State Community College, A
Ohio Technical College, A
University of Northwestern Ohio, A

Oklahoma

Oklahoma City Community College, A
Oklahoma State University Institute of Technology, A
Oklahoma Technical College, A

Oregon

Klamath Community College, A
Lane Community College, A
Linn-Benton Community College, A
Portland Community College, A
Rogue Community College, A

Pennsylvania

Community College of Beaver County, A
Johnson College, A
Lincoln Technical Institute (Philadelphia), A
New Castle School of Trades, A
Pennsylvania College of Technology, A
Rosedale Technical Institute, A
WyoTech Blairsville, A

South Dakota

Lake Area Technical Institute, A
Southeast Technical Institute, A

Tennessee

Lincoln College of Technology, A

Texas

Central Texas College, A
Kilgore College, A
Lamar Institute of Technology, A
Midland College, A
St. Philip's College, A
San Jacinto College District, A
Texarkana College, A
Texas State Technical College, A

Utah

Salt Lake Community College, A
Utah Valley University, A
Weber State University, A

Vermont

Vermont Technical College, A

Virginia

Advanced Technology Institute, A

Washington

Bates Technical College, A
Bellingham Technical College, A
Centralia College, A
Clark College, A
Grays Harbor College, A
Lake Washington Institute of Technology, A

Lower Columbia College, A
Peninsula College, A
Skagit Valley College, A
Walla Walla Community College, A

Wisconsin

Fox Valley Technical College, A
Gateway Technical College, A
Northcentral Technical College, A

Wyoming

Casper College, A
Laramie County Community College, A
Sheridan College, A
Western Wyoming Community College, A
WyoTech Laramie, A

Canada

British Columbia

British Columbia Institute of Technology, A

DIETETIC TECHNICIAN (DTR)

United States

Arizona

Chandler-Gilbert Community College, A

California

Chaffey College, A
College of the Desert, A
Cosumnes River College, A
Long Beach City College, A
Merritt College, A
Orange Coast College, A
Santa Rosa Junior College, A

Florida

Miami Dade College, A

Illinois

Harper College, A

Maine

Southern Maine Community College, A

Maryland

Baltimore City Community College, A

Minnesota

Normandale Community College, A
Northland Community and Technical College, A

New Jersey

Camden County College, A
Hudson County Community College, A

New York

Fiorello H. LaGuardia Community College of the City University of New York, A
Mohawk Valley Community College, A
Morrisville State College, A
Trocaire College, A

Ohio

Youngstown State University, A

Pennsylvania

Westmoreland County Community College, A

Wisconsin

Milwaukee Area Technical College, A

DIETETICS AND CLINICAL NUTRITION SERVICES

United States

Kansas

Cowley County Community College and Area Vocational - Technical School, A

Michigan

Madonna University, B
Western Michigan University, B

Minnesota

College of Saint Benedict, B
Saint John's University, B

New Jersey

College of Saint Elizabeth, B

Texas

Texas Christian University, B

U.S. Territories: Puerto Rico

Universidad del Turabo, B

DIETETICS/DIETICIANS

United States

Alabama

Community College of the Air Force, A
Jacksonville State University, B
Oakwood University, AB
Tuskegee University, B
The University of Alabama, B

Arizona

Central Arizona College, A

Arkansas

Arkansas State University, B
Black River Technical College, A
Harding University, B
Ouachita Baptist University, B

California

Allan Hancock College, A
Bakersfield College, A
California Polytechnic State University, San Luis Obispo, B
California State Polytechnic University, Pomona, B
California State University, Chico, B
California State University, Fresno, B
California State University, Long Beach, B
California State University, Los Angeles, B
California State University, San Bernardino, B
Glendale Community College, A
Los Angeles City College, A
Merced College, A
Point Loma Nazarene University, B
San Diego State University, B
San Francisco State University, B
San Jose State University, B

Colorado

University of Northern Colorado, B

Connecticut

Gateway Community College, A
University of Connecticut, B
University of New Haven, B

Delaware

Delaware State University, B
University of Delaware, B

Florida

Broward College, A
Florida International University, B

Keiser University, B
Miami Dade College, A
Pensacola State College, A
South Florida State College, A
State College of Florida Manatee-Sarasota, A
University of Florida, B

Georgia

Georgia State University, B
Life University, B
University of Georgia, B

Idaho

Idaho State University, B

Illinois

Bradley University, B
Dominican University, B
Harper College, A
Northern Illinois University, B
Olivet Nazarene University, B
University of Illinois at Chicago, B
University of Illinois at Urbana - Champaign, B
Western Illinois University, B

Indiana

Ball State University, B
Purdue University, B
Vincennes University, A

Iowa

Iowa State University of Science and Technology, B

Kansas

Kansas State University, B

Louisiana

Delgado Community College, A
Louisiana Tech University, B
Nicholls State University, B
University of Louisiana at Lafayette, B

Maryland

Morgan State University, B
University of Maryland Eastern Shore, B

Massachusetts

Labouré College, A
Simmons College, B

Michigan

Andrews University, B
Central Michigan University, B
Eastern Michigan University, B
Ferris State University, A
Michigan State University, B
Wayne State University, B

Minnesota

Minnesota State University Mankato, B
St. Catherine University, B

Mississippi

University of Mississippi, B
University of Southern Mississippi, B

Missouri

College of the Ozarks, B
Fontbonne University, B
Missouri State University, B
Northwest Missouri State University, B
Saint Louis University, B
University of Central Missouri, B
University of Missouri, B

Nebraska

Western Nebraska Community College, A

Nevada

Truckee Meadows Community College, A

New Hampshire

Keene State College, B

New Jersey

Camden County College, A
College of Saint Elizabeth, B
Rutgers University - New Brunswick, B

New Mexico

New Mexico State University, B

New York

Buffalo State College, State University of New York, B
D'Youville College, B
Lehman College of the City University of New York, B
Queens College of the City University of New York, B
Rockland Community College, A
State University of New York College at Oneonta, B
Suffolk County Community College, A
Westchester Community College, A

North Carolina

Appalachian State University, B
East Carolina University, B
Gaston College, A
Meredith College, B
Western Carolina University, B

North Dakota

North Dakota State University, B
University of North Dakota, B

Ohio

Ashland University, B
Bowling Green State University, B
Case Western Reserve University, B
Cincinnati State Technical and Community College, A
Hocking College, A
Miami University, B
Miami University Hamilton, B
The Ohio State University, B
Ohio University, B
Owens Community College, A
Sinclair Community College, A
The University of Akron, B
University of Cincinnati, B
University of Dayton, B
Youngstown State University, B

Oklahoma

University of Central Oklahoma, B
University of Oklahoma Health Sciences Center, B

Oregon

Central Oregon Community College, A

Pennsylvania

Harrisburg Area Community College, A
Immaculata University, B
Mansfield University of Pennsylvania, B
Marywood University, B
Seton Hill University, B
University of Pittsburgh, B
West Chester University of Pennsylvania, B

Rhode Island

University of Rhode Island, B

South Dakota

South Dakota State University, B

Tennessee

Carson-Newman University, B
Lipscomb University, B
Tennessee Technological University, B
The University of Tennessee at Martin, B

Texas

Abilene Christian University, B
El Paso Community College, A
South Plains College, A
Tarrant County College District, A
Texas A&M University - Kingsville, B

Texas Christian University, B
Texas Southern University, B
Texas Tech University, B
The University of Texas Health Science Center at San Antonio, B
The University of Texas Rio Grande Valley, B
The University of Texas at San Antonio, B

Vermont

University of Vermont, B

Washington

Bastyr University, B
Central Washington University, B
Shoreline Community College, A
Spokane Community College, A

West Virginia

Marshall University, B

Wisconsin

Madison Area Technical College, A
Mount Mary University, B
University of Wisconsin - Stevens Point, B
University of Wisconsin - Stout, B
Viterbo University, B

Canada

British Columbia

The University of British Columbia, B

Maritime Provinces: Nova Scotia

Acadia University, B
Mount Saint Vincent University, B

Newfoundland and Labrador

Memorial University of Newfoundland, B

Ontario

The University of Western Ontario, B

DIETICIAN ASSISTANT

United States

Arizona

Chandler-Gilbert Community College, A

Florida

Hillsborough Community College, A

Illinois

City Colleges of Chicago, Malcolm X College, A

Kansas

Barton County Community College, A

New Jersey

Middlesex County College, A

New York

Erie Community College, North Campus, A

North Carolina

Martin Community College, A

Ohio

Youngstown State University, A

Pennsylvania

Community College of Allegheny County, A

Tennessee

Southwest Tennessee Community College, A

DIGITAL COMMUNICATION AND MEDIA/MULTIMEDIA

United States

Alaska

University of Alaska Anchorage, Kenai Peninsula College, A

Arizona

Cochise County Community College District, A
Pima Community College, A
University of Advancing Technology, B
University of Phoenix - Phoenix Campus, B

Arkansas

Harding University, B
John Brown University, B

California

The Art Institute of California - Inland Empire, a campus of Argosy University, B
The Art Institute of California - Orange County, a campus of Argosy University, B
Butte College, A
California College of the Arts, B
California Lutheran University, B
California State University, Dominguez Hills, B
College of the Redwoods, A
Mt. San Jacinto College, A
National University, AB
Pasadena City College, A
Platt College San Diego, A
San Diego State University, B
San Jose City College, A
Santa Monica College, A
Santa Rosa Junior College, A
Sierra College, A
University of Phoenix - Bay Area Campus, B
University of Phoenix - Sacramento Valley Campus, B
University of Phoenix - Southern California Campus, B

Colorado

Aims Community College, A
Colorado Mountain College (Glenwood Springs), A
Red Rocks Community College, A
University of Denver, B
University of Phoenix - Colorado Campus, B

Connecticut

Naugatuck Valley Community College, A
University of Connecticut, B

Delaware

Delaware Technical & Community College, Terry Campus, A

Florida

Eastern Florida State College, A
Florida Atlantic University, B
Florida National University, A
Gulf Coast State College, A
University of Miami, B
University of Phoenix - Central Florida Campus, B
University of Phoenix - South Florida Campus, B
The University of Tampa, B

Georgia

Georgia Institute of Technology, B
Georgia Southern University, B
Savannah College of Art and Design, B
University of Georgia, B

Hawaii

Hawai'i Pacific University, B
University of Phoenix - Hawaii Campus, B

Idaho

University of Idaho, B

Illinois

Bradley University, B
Columbia College Chicago, B
Lewis University, B
Loyola University Chicago, B
School of the Art Institute of Chicago, B

Indiana

Butler University, B
Huntington University, B
Indiana University Bloomington, B
Indiana University Kokomo, B
Indiana University - Purdue University Indianapolis, AB
Indiana University South Bend, B
Saint Joseph's College, B
Taylor University, B
Valparaiso University, B

Iowa

Dordt College, B
Hawkeye Community College, A
Mount Mercy University, B
Simpson College, B
University of Northern Iowa, B

Kansas

Southwestern College, B

Kentucky

Sullivan College of Technology and Design, AB

Maine

Saint Joseph's College of Maine, B
Southern Maine Community College, A
University of Maine, B

Maryland

College of Southern Maryland, A
Notre Dame of Maryland University, B
Stevenson University, B
University of Baltimore, B

Massachusetts

Endicott College, B
Fitchburg State University, B
Wellesley College, B

Michigan

Calvin College, B
Cornerstone University, B
Northern Michigan University, B
Saginaw Valley State University, B
University of Detroit Mercy, B
University of Phoenix - Detroit Campus, B
Wayne County Community College District, A

Minnesota

Hibbing Community College, A
Minneapolis Community and Technical College, A
Minnesota State University Moorhead, B
Ridgewater College, A
Rochester Community and Technical College, A
St. Cloud Technical & Community College, A

Mississippi

Hinds Community College, A
University of Mississippi, B

Missouri

Lindenwood University, B
Webster University, B

New Hampshire

Granite State College, B
Keene State College, B

New Jersey

Georgian Court University, B
Raritan Valley Community College, A

New Mexico

New Mexico State University - Carlsbad, A
Western New Mexico University, A

New York

Canisius College, B
Clarkson University, B
Concordia College - New York, B
Eugene Lang College of Liberal Arts, B
Finger Lakes Community College, A
Hilbert College, B
Manhattanville College, B
New York Institute of Technology, B
New York University, B
Rensselaer Polytechnic Institute, B
Rochester Institute of Technology, B
St. Bonaventure University, B
St. John Fisher College, B
State University of New York at New Paltz, B
TCI - College of Technology, A
Tompkins Cortland Community College, A
University of Rochester, B
Vaughn College of Aeronautics and Technology, A

Ohio

Ashland University, B
Baldwin Wallace University, B
Cedarville University, B
Cleveland State University, B
Franklin University, B
Kent State University, B
Miami University, B
Muskingum University, B
Ohio University, B
Tiffin University, B
Virginia Marti College of Art and Design, A

Oklahoma

Oklahoma City Community College, A
Tulsa Community College, A

Oregon

Clackamas Community College, A
Oregon State University, B
Southern Oregon University, B

Pennsylvania

The Art Institute of Philadelphia, B
Butler County Community College, A
Cedar Crest College, B
Community College of Beaver County, A
Juniata College, B
Kutztown University of Pennsylvania, B
Lebanon Valley College, B
Lycoming College, B
Marywood University, B
Messiah College, B
Point Park University, B
Slippery Rock University of Pennsylvania, B
The University of Scranton, B
University of Valley Forge, B
Westminster College, B
Wilkes University, B

South Carolina

Columbia International University, B
Limestone College, B

South Dakota

Mount Marty College, B

Tennessee

Carson-Newman University, B
Lee University, B
Trevecca Nazarene University, B

Texas

Abilene Christian University, B
Baylor University, B
Dallas Baptist University, B
Howard Payne University, B
Lubbock Christian University, B
St. Edward's University, B
San Jacinto College District, A

Texas A&M University, B
University of the Incarnate Word, B
The University of Texas at Arlington, B
The University of Texas at Dallas, B

Utah

Dixie State University, B
University of Phoenix - Utah Campus, B

Vermont

Bennington College, B
Community College of Vermont, A

Virginia

Eastern Mennonite University, B
Liberty University, B

Washington

Central Washington University, B
The Evergreen State College, B
University of Phoenix - Western Washington Campus, B
Washington State University, B
Washington State University - Tri-Cities, B
Washington State University - Vancouver, B

West Virginia

Bethany College, B

Wisconsin

Concordia University Wisconsin, B
Marquette University, B

Wyoming

Laramie County Community College, A

U.S. Territories: Puerto Rico

Inter American University of Puerto Rico, Bayamón Campus, B
Universidad del Este, B
Universidad Metropolitana, B
University of Puerto Rico, Río Piedras Campus, B

Canada

Ontario

University of Toronto, B
University of Waterloo, B
The University of Western Ontario, B

Saskatchewan

University of Saskatchewan, B

DIRECT ENTRY MIDWIFERY (LM, CPM)

United States

Florida

The Florida School of Traditional Midwifery, A

New Mexico

National College of Midwifery, AB

Oregon

Birthingway College of Midwifery, B

Utah

Midwives College of Utah, B

Wisconsin

Southwest Wisconsin Technical College, A

DIRECTING AND THEATRICAL PRODUCTION

United States

California

California Institute of the Arts, B
California State University, Long Beach, B
Pepperdine University, B

Florida

University of Miami, B

Illinois

Bradley University, B
Columbia College Chicago, B
University of Chicago, B
University of Illinois at Urbana - Champaign, B

Indiana

Saint Joseph's College, B

Iowa

Drake University, B

Massachusetts

Boston University, B
Quinsigamond Community College, A

Minnesota

Augsburg College, B

Missouri

Webster University, B

Nebraska

Nebraska Wesleyan University, B

New Hampshire

Keene State College, B

New Jersey

Rider University, B

New York

Binghamton University, State University of New York, B
Hofstra University, B
Marymount Manhattan College, B
Pace University, B

North Carolina

Campbell University, B

Ohio

Baldwin Wallace University, B

Pennsylvania

The University of the Arts, B

Tennessee

Belmont University, B
Lipscomb University, B

Texas

Texas Christian University, B

Utah

Brigham Young University, B

Vermont

Bennington College, B
Marlboro College, B

Virginia

Emory & Henry College, B

Washington

Cornish College of the Arts, B
University of Washington, B

DISABILITY STUDIES

United States

California

California Baptist University, M
Chapman University, D

Hawaii

University of Hawaii at Manoa, O

Illinois

University of Illinois at Chicago, MD

Massachusetts

Brandeis University, D

New Jersey

Montclair State University, MO

New York

Syracuse University, O

Pennsylvania

University of Pittsburgh, O

Utah

Utah State University, D

Canada

British Columbia

University of Northern British Columbia, M

Manitoba

University of Manitoba, M

Ontario

Brock University, MO
York University, MD

DISTANCE EDUCATION DEVELOPMENT

United States

California

California Baptist University, M
National University, MO

Colorado

Colorado Christian University, M
University of Colorado Denver, M

Connecticut

Post University, M

District of Columbia

The George Washington University, O

Florida

Barry University, O
Florida State University, M
Keiser University, M
Nova Southeastern University, M
University of South Florida, O

Illinois

Western Illinois University, O

Maryland

University of Maryland, Baltimore County, O
University of Maryland University College, MO

Massachusetts

Brandeis University, M
Endicott College, M
Lesley University, O

Michigan

Saginaw Valley State University, M
Wayne State University, O

Minnesota

Capella University, MD
Walden University, MO

New Jersey

Thomas Edison State University, O

New Mexico

New Mexico State University, O

New York

New York Institute of Technology, O

North Carolina

Lenoir-Rhyne University, M

Pennsylvania

Chestnut Hill College, M
Waynesburg University, M
Wilkes University, M

Texas

Dallas Baptist University, M
University of the Incarnate Word, M

Virginia

Liberty University, M
Regent University, D
Virginia Polytechnic Institute and State University,
MO

West Virginia

American Public University System, M
Fairmont State University, M

Canada

Alberta

Athabasca University, MO

Quebec

Télé-université, M

DIVINITY/MINISTRY (BD, MDIV.)

United States

Arkansas

Ecclesia College, B
John Brown University, B
Williams Baptist College, B

California

Azusa Pacific University, B
Bethesda University, B
Biola University, B
Epic Bible College, AB
The Master's College and Seminary, B
Patten University, B
The Salvation Army College for Officer Training at
Crestmont, A
San Diego Christian College, B

Colorado

Nazarene Bible College, B

Florida

Johnson University Florida, AB
University of Fort Lauderdale, AB
Warner University, AB

Georgia

Luther Rice College & Seminary, B
Shorter University, B
Toccoa Falls College, B

Idaho

Northwest Nazarene University, B

Illinois

Christian Life College, AB
Judson University, B
Moody Bible Institute, B

Indiana

Bethel College, B
Huntington University, B
Indiana Wesleyan University, B

Iowa

Faith Baptist Bible College and Theological Seminary, B

Kansas

Barclay College, B
Central Christian College of Kansas, B
Kansas Wesleyan University, B

Kentucky

Campbellsville University, B
Clear Creek Baptist Bible College, AB
The Southern Baptist Theological Seminary, B

Louisiana

New Orleans Baptist Theological Seminary, AB

Massachusetts

Eastern Nazarene College, B

Michigan

Great Lakes Christian College, AB
Kuyper College, B

Minnesota

North Central University, AB
Oak Hills Christian College, B

Missouri

Baptist Bible College, B
Calvary Bible College and Theological Seminary, B
Global University, B

Nebraska

Grace University, B
Nebraska Christian College, AB

New York

Davis College, B
Roberts Wesleyan College, B

North Carolina

Campbell University, B
Grace College of Divinity, B
John Wesley University, B

North Dakota

Trinity Bible College, B

Ohio

Cincinnati Christian University, AB
Ohio Christian University, AB
Tri-State Bible College, B

Oklahoma

Family of Faith College, B
Mid-America Christian University, B
Oklahoma Baptist University, B

Oregon

Corban University, B
New Hope Christian College, B

Pennsylvania

Summit University, B
University of Valley Forge, B

Rhode Island

Providence College, AB

Tennessee

Belmont University, B
Carson-Newman University, AB
Trevecca Nazarene University, B

Texas

Messenger College, B
Southwestern Assemblies of God University, B

Virginia

Bethel College, AB
Bluefield College, B
Regent University, B
University of Valley Forge Virginia Campus, B

Washington

Northwest University, B

Canada

Alberta

Prairie Bible Institute, AB
Rocky Mountain College, B

Manitoba

Providence University College & Theological Seminary, B
Steinbach Bible College, B

Maritime Provinces: New Brunswick

Kingswood University, B

Ontario

Emmanuel Bible College, B
Master's College and Seminary, B
Tyndale University College & Seminary, B

Saskatchewan

Briercrest College, B

DOG/PET/ANIMAL GROOMING

United States

Massachusetts

Becker College, A

DRAFTING/DESIGN ENGINEERING TECHNOLOGIES/TECHNICIANS

United States

California

Cuyamaca College, A
De Anza College, A
Mt. San Antonio College, A
National University, B

Illinois

College of DuPage, A
Illinois Valley Community College, A
Rock Valley College, A

Kentucky

Sullivan College of Technology and Design, A

Maine

Kennebec Valley Community College, A

Michigan

Central Michigan University, B
Macomb Community College, A

Minnesota

Hennepin Technical College, A

New Hampshire

Manchester Community College, A

New Jersey

Thomas Edison State University, AB

New York

Corning Community College, A
Genesee Community College, A
Morrisville State College, A
Niagara County Community College, A
Ulster County Community College, A

North Carolina

Asheville-Buncombe Technical Community College, A
College of The Albemarle, A
Isothermal Community College, A

Ohio

James A. Rhodes State College, A
Lorain County Community College, A

Pennsylvania

Community College of Allegheny County, A
Luzerne County Community College, A
Pennsylvania College of Technology, A

South Carolina

Northeastern Technical College, A

Texas

Richland College, A

Virginia

Dabney S. Lancaster Community College, A

Washington

Spokane Community College, A

West Virginia

Pierpont Community & Technical College, A

Wisconsin

Lakeshore Technical College, A
Madison Area Technical College, A
Mid-State Technical College, A
Western Technical College, A

DRAFTING AND DESIGN TECHNOLOGY/TECHNICIAN

United States

Alabama

Bevill State Community College, A
Bishop State Community College, A
Calhoun Community College, A
Central Alabama Community College, A
Gadsden State Community College, A
George C. Wallace Community College, A
George Corley Wallace State Community College, A
H. Councill Trenholm State Community College, A
J. F. Drake State Community and Technical College, A
Jefferson Davis Community College, A
Lawson State Community College, A
Northeast Alabama Community College, A
Northwest-Shoals Community College, A
Shelton State Community College, A
Wallace State Community College, A

Alaska

University of Alaska Anchorage, A
University of Alaska Fairbanks, A

Arizona

Eastern Arizona College, A
Mesa Community College, A
Mohave Community College, A
Northland Pioneer College, A

Arkansas

Arkansas State University - Beebe, A
East Arkansas Community College, A
NorthWest Arkansas Community College, A
Pulaski Technical College, A
Southeast Arkansas College, A
University of Arkansas Community College at Morrilton, A

California

American River College, A
Antelope Valley College, A
Bakersfield College, A
Butte College, A
Cerritos College, A
Cerro Coso Community College, A
Citrus College, A
College of the Desert, A
College of San Mateo, A
College of the Sequoias, A
Contra Costa College, A
Cuyamaca College, A
Cypress College, A
East Los Angeles College, A
El Camino College, A
Evergreen Valley College, A
Fresno City College, A
Fullerton College, A
Gavilan College, A
Golden West College, A
Hartnell College, A
Las Positas College, A
Lassen Community College District, A
Los Angeles City College, A
Los Angeles Harbor College, A
Los Angeles Pierce College, A
Los Angeles Southwest College, A
Los Angeles Trade-Technical College, A
Los Medanos College, A
MiraCosta College, A
Mission College, A
Modesto Junior College, A
Mt. San Antonio College, A
Mt. San Jacinto College, A
Napa Valley College, A
Ohlone College, A
Palomar College, A
Pasadena City College, A
Porterville College, A
Sacramento City College, A
Saddleback College, A
San Bernardino Valley College, A
San Diego City College, A
Santa Ana College, A
Santa Barbara City College, A
Shasta College, A
Solano Community College, A
Southwestern College, A
Taft College, A
West Los Angeles College, A
West Valley College, A

Colorado

Community College of Denver, A
Red Rocks Community College, A

Delaware

Delaware Technical & Community College, Jack F. Owens Campus, A
Delaware Technical & Community College, Stanton/Wilmington Campus, A
Delaware Technical & Community College, Terry Campus, A

Florida

College of Central Florida, A
Daytona State College, A
Eastern Florida State College, A
Florida SouthWestern State College, A
Florida State College at Jacksonville, A
Indian River State College, A
Key College, A
Miami Dade College, A
Northwest Florida State College, A
Palm Beach State College, A

Pasco-Hernando State College, A
Pensacola State College, A
Seminole State College of Florida, A
State College of Florida Manatee-Sarasota, A
Tallahassee Community College, A
Valencia College, A

Georgia

Albany Technical College, A
Bainbridge State College, A
Central Georgia Technical College, A
Chattahoochee Technical College, A
Columbus Technical College, A
Dalton State College, A
Georgia Piedmont Technical College, A
Gwinnett Technical College, A
Lanier Technical College, A
South Georgia Technical College, A
Southern Crescent Technical College, A
Wiregrass Georgia Technical College, A

Hawaii

Honolulu Community College, A

Idaho

College of Southern Idaho, A
College of Western Idaho, A
Lewis-Clark State College, AB
North Idaho College, A

Illinois

College of DuPage, A
Heartland Community College, A
Illinois Valley Community College, A
Kankakee Community College, A
Lake Land College, A
Morrison Institute of Technology, A
Morton College, A
Rend Lake College, A
Richland Community College, A

Indiana

Ivy Tech Community College - Bloomington, A
Ivy Tech Community College - Central Indiana, A
Ivy Tech Community College - Columbus, A
Ivy Tech Community College - East Central, A
Ivy Tech Community College - Kokomo, A
Ivy Tech Community College - Lafayette, A
Ivy Tech Community College - Northeast, A
Ivy Tech Community College - Northwest, A
Ivy Tech Community College - Southeast, A
Ivy Tech Community College - Southern Indiana, A
Ivy Tech Community College - Southwest, A
Ivy Tech Community College - Wabash Valley, A
Trine University, B

Iowa

Iowa Central Community College, A
Scott Community College, A
Southeastern Community College, A

Kansas

Allen Community College, A
Butler Community College, A
Cowley County Community College and Area Vocational - Technical School, A
Garden City Community College, A
Hutchinson Community College, A
Independence Community College, A
Labette Community College, A
Manhattan Area Technical College, A
Seward County Community College and Area Technical School, A
Wichita Area Technical College, A

Kentucky

Big Sandy Community and Technical College, A
Sullivan College of Technology and Design, A

Louisiana

Bossier Parish Community College, A
Delgado Community College, A
Fletcher Technical Community College, A
ITI Technical College, A
Louisiana Delta Community College, A

South Louisiana Community College, A
Sowela Technical Community College, A

Maine

Northern Maine Community College, A
Southern Maine Community College, A
York County Community College, A

Maryland

Baltimore City Community College, A
Frederick Community College, A
Prince George's Community College, A

Massachusetts

Benjamin Franklin Institute of Technology, A

Michigan

Alpena Community College, A
Baker College, A
Gogebic Community College, A
Kellogg Community College, A
Lake Michigan College, A
Macomb Community College, A
Mid Michigan Community College, A
Monroe County Community College, A
Montcalm Community College, A
Mott Community College, A
Muskegon Community College, A
Northern Michigan University, B
Northwestern Michigan College, A
Oakland Community College, A
St. Clair County Community College, A
Schoolcraft College, A
Western Michigan University, B

Mississippi

Copiah-Lincoln Community College, A
East Central Community College, A
East Mississippi Community College, A
Hinds Community College, A
Holmes Community College, A
Itawamba Community College, A
Jones County Junior College, A
Meridian Community College, A
Mississippi Gulf Coast Community College, A
Northeast Mississippi Community College, A
Northwest Mississippi Community College, A
Pearl River Community College, A

Missouri

Crowder College, A
East Central College, A
Lincoln University, A
Metropolitan Community College - Kansas City, A
Mineral Area College, A
Moberly Area Community College, A
North Central Missouri College, A
St. Charles Community College, A
State Technical College of Missouri, A

Montana

Montana State University, A
Montana State University Billings, A
Montana State University - Northern, AB

Nebraska

Central Community College - Columbus Campus, A
Central Community College - Grand Island Campus, A
Central Community College - Hastings Campus, A
Metropolitan Community College, A
Southeast Community College, Lincoln Campus, A

Nevada

Truckee Meadows Community College, A

New Hampshire

Manchester Community College, A
Nashua Community College, A

New Jersey

Bergen Community College, A
Brookdale Community College, A
Camden County College, A

Rowan College at Burlington County, A
Rowan College at Gloucester County, A

New Mexico

Doña Ana Community College, A
Eastern New Mexico University - Roswell, A
Luna Community College, A
New Mexico Junior College, A
San Juan College, A
Santa Fe Community College, A

New York

Cayuga County Community College, A
Finger Lakes Community College, A
Genesee Community College, A
Morrisville State College, A
Niagara County Community College, A
Rockland Community College, A
State University of New York College of Technology
   at Alfred, A
Suffolk County Community College, A

North Carolina

Beaufort County Community College, A
Central Carolina Community College, A
Central Piedmont Community College, A
East Carolina University, B
Isothermal Community College, A
Surry Community College, A

Ohio

Clark State Community College, A
Eastern Gateway Community College, A
Hocking College, A
Lorain County Community College, A
Marion Technical College, A
North Central State College, A
Sinclair Community College, A
Southern State Community College, A
Stark State College, A
The University of Akron, A
University of Rio Grande, AB
Washington State Community College, A
Wright State University, A
Youngstown State University, A
Zane State College, A

Oklahoma

East Central University, B
Langston University, A
Northern Oklahoma College, A
Oklahoma City Community College, A
Oklahoma State University, Oklahoma City, A
Redlands Community College, A
Rose State College, A

Oregon

Blue Mountain Community College, A
Central Oregon Community College, A
Clackamas Community College, A
Lane Community College, A
Linn-Benton Community College, A
Treasure Valley Community College, A

Pennsylvania

Berks Technical Institute, A
California University of Pennsylvania, A
Community College of Allegheny County, A
Community College of Philadelphia, A
Lehigh Carbon Community College, A
Lincoln Technical Institute (Allentown), A
Luzerne County Community College, A
Penn Commercial Business and Technical School, A
Pittsburgh Technical Institute, A
Triangle Tech, DuBois, A
Triangle Tech, Greensburg, A

Rhode Island

Johnson & Wales University, AB

South Carolina

Piedmont Technical College, A

South Dakota

Black Hills State University, A
Western Dakota Technical Institute, A

Tennessee

Miller-Motte Technical College (Clarksville), A
Northeast State Community College, A
Pellissippi State Community College, A

Texas

Alvin Community College, A
Amarillo College, A
Angelina College, A
Austin Community College District, A
Brazosport College, A
Central Texas College, A
Coastal Bend College, A
Collin County Community College District, A
Del Mar College, A
Eastfield College, A
El Paso Community College, A
Grayson College, A
Hill College, A
Houston Community College, A
Howard College, A
Kilgore College, A
Lamar Institute of Technology, A
Lee College, A
LeTourneau University, A
Lone Star College - North Harris, A
Mountain View College, A
Navarro College, A
North Central Texas College, A
Odessa College, A
Paris Junior College, A
Sam Houston State University, B
San Antonio College, A
San Jacinto College District, A
South Plains College, A
Tarrant County College District, A
Temple College, A
Texarkana College, A
Texas Southern University, B
Texas Southmost College, A
Texas State Technical College, A
Trinity Valley Community College, A
Tyler Junior College, A
Vernon College, A
Wharton County Junior College, A

Utah

Salt Lake Community College, A
Utah Valley University, A
Weber State University, AB

Virginia

Dabney S. Lancaster Community College, A
New River Community College, A
Tidewater Community College, A
Virginia Highlands Community College, A
Wytheville Community College, A

Washington

Green River College, A
Highline College, A
Olympic College, A
Renton Technical College, A
Seattle Central College, A
Shoreline Community College, A
South Puget Sound Community College, A
South Seattle College, A
Spokane Community College, A

West Virginia

Southern West Virginia Community and Technical
   College, A
West Virginia University at Parkersburg, A

Wyoming

Casper College, A
Laramie County Community College, A

U.S. Territories: Puerto Rico

Caribbean University, A
Huertas Junior College, A
Universidad Metropolitana, A
University of Puerto Rico in Ponce, A

Canada

British Columbia

British Columbia Institute of Technology, A

DRAMA AND DANCE TEACHER EDUCATION

United States

California

Glendale Community College, A

Colorado

Adams State University, B

Florida

Jacksonville University, B

Georgia

Brenau University, B
Columbus State University, B
Darton State College, A
Piedmont College, B

Idaho

Boise State University, B

Illinois

Bradley University, B

Indiana

University of Evansville, B
Valparaiso University, B

Iowa

Dordt College, B
The University of Iowa, B

Kansas

Central Christian College of Kansas, A
Hutchinson Community College, A

Massachusetts

Boston University, B
Bridgewater State University, B
Emerson College, B

Michigan

Hope College, B

Minnesota

St. Catherine University, B

Mississippi

William Carey University, B

Missouri

College of the Ozarks, B
Missouri Baptist University, B
Washington University in St. Louis, B

Nebraska

Chadron State College, B
Hastings College, B
Wayne State College, B
Western Nebraska Community College, A

New Hampshire

Keene State College, B

New Jersey

Montclair State University, B

New York

Hofstra University, B
State University of New York College at Potsdam, B

North Carolina

Catawba College, B
East Carolina University, B
Greensboro College, B
Lees-McRae College, B
Meredith College, B
The University of North Carolina at Charlotte, B
The University of North Carolina at Greensboro, B

Ohio

Bowling Green State University, B
Ohio Wesleyan University, B
The University of Akron, B
Xavier University, B

Oklahoma

East Central University, B
University of Central Oklahoma, B

Pennsylvania

Point Park University, B

South Carolina

Columbia College, B

South Dakota

The University of South Dakota, B

Tennessee

Belmont University, B
Lee University, B
Lipscomb University, B
Maryville College, B
Trevecca Nazarene University, B

Texas

Austin College, B
East Texas Baptist University, B
Hardin-Simmons University, B
Howard College, A
Howard Payne University, B
Lubbock Christian University, B
St. Edward's University, B

Utah

Southern Utah University, B
Utah Valley University, B
Weber State University, B

Vermont

Johnson State College, B

Washington

Central Washington University, B
Western Washington University, B

Wisconsin

Edgewood College, B
Viterbo University, B

Canada

Alberta

University of Alberta, B
University of Calgary, B
University of Lethbridge, B

Ontario

University of Windsor, B
York University, B

Quebec

Bishop's University, B

Saskatchewan

University of Regina, B

DRAMA AND DRAMATICS/THEATRE ARTS

United States

Alabama

Alabama Southern Community College, A
Alabama State University, B
Auburn University, B
Birmingham-Southern College, B
Faulkner University, B
Jacksonville State University, B
Spring Hill College, B
The University of Alabama, B
The University of Alabama at Birmingham, B
University of Mobile, B
University of Montevallo, B
University of North Alabama, B
University of South Alabama, B

Alaska

University of Alaska Anchorage, B

Arizona

Arizona State University at the Tempe campus, B
Arizona Western College, A
Chandler-Gilbert Community College, A
Cochise County Community College District, A
Eastern Arizona College, A
Grand Canyon University, B
Northern Arizona University, B
Phoenix College, A
Scottsdale Community College, A
South Mountain Community College, A
The University of Arizona, B

Arkansas

Arkansas State University, B
Harding University, B
Henderson State University, B
Hendrix College, B
Lyon College, B
Ouachita Baptist University, B
Southern Arkansas University - Magnolia, B
University of Arkansas, B
University of Arkansas - Fort Smith, B
University of Arkansas at Little Rock, B
University of Central Arkansas, B
University of the Ozarks, B

California

American Academy of Dramatic Arts - Los Angeles, A
American Musical and Dramatic Academy, Los Angeles, B
American River College, A
Bakersfield College, A
Biola University, B
Cabrillo College, A
California Baptist University, B
California Lutheran University, B
California Polytechnic State University, San Luis Obispo, B
California State Polytechnic University, Pomona, B
California State University, Bakersfield, B
California State University, Dominguez Hills, B
California State University, East Bay, B
California State University, Fresno, B
California State University, Fullerton, B
California State University, Long Beach, B
California State University, Los Angeles, B
California State University, Northridge, B
California State University, Sacramento, B
California State University, San Bernardino, B
California State University, Stanislaus, B
Cañada College, A
Cerritos College, A
Cerro Coso Community College, A
Chaffey College, A
Chapman University, B
Citrus College, A
Claremont McKenna College, B
College of the Canyons, A
College of the Desert, A

College of Marin, A
College of the Sequoias, A
College of the Siskiyous, A
Concordia University Irvine, B
Cosumnes River College, A
Crafton Hills College, A
Cuesta College, A
Cypress College, A
De Anza College, A
East Los Angeles College, A
El Camino College, A
Foothill College, A
Fresno City College, A
Fullerton College, A
Gavilan College, A
Glendale Community College, A
Grossmont College, A
Hartnell College, A
Humboldt State University, B
Lake Tahoe Community College, A
Laney College, A
Long Beach City College, A
Los Angeles City College, A
Los Angeles Mission College, A
Los Angeles Pierce College, A
Los Angeles Southwest College, A
Los Angeles Valley College, A
Loyola Marymount University, B
Mendocino College, A
Merced College, A
Mills College, B
Modesto Junior College, A
Monterey Peninsula College, A
Moorpark College, A
Mt. San Jacinto College, A
Notre Dame de Namur University, B
Occidental College, B
Orange Coast College, A
Palomar College, A
Pasadena City College, A
Pitzer College, B
Pomona College, B
Sacramento City College, A
Saddleback College, A
Saint Mary's College of California, B
San Diego City College, A
San Diego State University, B
San Francisco State University, B
San Joaquin Delta College, A
San Jose City College, A
San Jose State University, B
Santa Ana College, A
Santa Barbara City College, A
Santa Clara University, B
Santa Monica College, A
Santa Rosa Junior College, A
Santiago Canyon College, A
Scripps College, B
Shasta College, A
Sonoma State University, B
Stanford University, B
University of California, Berkeley, B
University of California, Irvine, B
University of California, Los Angeles, B
University of California, Riverside, B
University of California, San Diego, B
University of California, Santa Barbara, B
University of California, Santa Cruz, B
University of La Verne, B
University of the Pacific, B
University of San Diego, B
University of Southern California, B
Vanguard University of Southern California, B
Ventura College, A
Victor Valley College, A
West Valley College, A
Westmont College, B
Whittier College, B
William Jessup University, B
Yuba College, A

Colorado

Adams State University, A
The Colorado College, B
Colorado Mesa University, B
Colorado Mountain College (Glenwood Springs), A

Colorado State University, B
Fort Lewis College, B
Metropolitan State University of Denver, B
Naropa University, B
Northeastern Junior College, A
Otero Junior College, A
Trinidad State Junior College, A
University of Colorado Boulder, B
University of Colorado Denver, B
University of Denver, B
University of Northern Colorado, B
Western State Colorado University, B

Connecticut

Albertus Magnus College, B
Connecticut College, B
Eastern Connecticut State University, B
Fairfield University, B
Manchester Community College, A
Quinnipiac University, B
Sacred Heart University, B
Southern Connecticut State University, B
Trinity College, B
University of Connecticut, B
University of New Haven, B
Wesleyan University, B
Western Connecticut State University, B
Yale University, B

District of Columbia

American University, B
The Catholic University of America, B
The George Washington University, B
Howard University, B
University of the District of Columbia, B

Florida

Barry University, B
Broward College, A
College of Central Florida, A
Eastern Florida State College, A
Eckerd College, B
Flagler College, B
Florida Agricultural and Mechanical University, B
Florida Atlantic University, B
Florida Gulf Coast University, B
Florida International University, B
Florida Southern College, B
Florida State University, B
Indian River State College, A
Jacksonville University, B
Lynn University, B
Miami Dade College, A
New World School of the Arts, B
Nova Southeastern University, B
Palm Beach Atlantic University, B
Palm Beach State College, A
Pensacola State College, A
Rollins College, B
St. Johns River State College, A
South Florida State College, A
Southeastern University, B
State College of Florida Manatee-Sarasota, A
Stetson University, B
University of Central Florida, B
University of Florida, B
University of Miami, B
University of South Florida, B
The University of Tampa, B
University of West Florida, B

Georgia

Agnes Scott College, B
Armstrong State University, B
Bainbridge State College, A
Clayton State University, B
Columbus State University, B
Covenant College, B
Darton State College, A
Emory University, B
Georgia College & State University, B
Georgia Southern University, B
Georgia Southwestern State University, B
Gordon State College, A
Kennesaw State University, B
LaGrange College, B

Mercer University, B
Morehouse College, B
Piedmont College, B
Savannah College of Art and Design, B
Shorter University, B
South Georgia State College, A
Spelman College, B
University of Georgia, B
University of West Georgia, B
Valdosta State University, B
Young Harris College, B

Hawaii

Brigham Young University - Hawaii, A
University of Hawaii at Manoa, B

Idaho

Boise State University, B
Brigham Young University - Idaho, B
The College of Idaho, B
College of Southern Idaho, A
Idaho State University, B
North Idaho College, A
University of Idaho, B

Illinois

Augustana College, B
Aurora University, B
Blackburn College, B
Bradley University, B
Columbia College Chicago, B
Concordia University Chicago, B
DePaul University, B
Dominican University, B
Eastern Illinois University, B
Elmhurst College, B
Eureka College, B
Governors State University, B
Greenville College, B
Illinois College, B
Illinois State University, B
Illinois Wesleyan University, B
John A. Logan College, A
Knox College, B
Lake Forest College, B
Lewis University, B
Loyola University Chicago, B
Millikin University, B
Monmouth College, B
North Central College, B
North Park University, B
Northern Illinois University, B
Northwestern University, B
Principia College, B
Rockford University, B
Roosevelt University, B
Sauk Valley Community College, A
Southern Illinois University Carbondale, B
Southern Illinois University Edwardsville, B
Spoon River College, A
University of Illinois at Chicago, B
University of Illinois at Urbana - Champaign, B
Western Illinois University, B

Indiana

Ball State University, B
Bethel College, B
Butler University, B
DePauw University, B
Earlham College, B
Franklin College, B
Goshen College, B
Grace College, B
Hanover College, B
Huntington University, B
Indiana State University, B
Indiana University Bloomington, B
Indiana University Northwest, B
Indiana University - Purdue University Fort Wayne, B
Indiana University South Bend, B
Manchester University, B
Purdue University, B
Saint Mary's College, B
University of Evansville, B
University of Indianapolis, B

University of Notre Dame, B
University of Southern Indiana, B
Valparaiso University, B
Vincennes University, A
Wabash College, B

Iowa

Briar Cliff University, B
Central College, B
Clarke University, B
Coe College, B
Cornell College, B
Dordt College, B
Drake University, B
Graceland University, B
Grand View University, B
Grinnell College, B
Iowa State University of Science and Technology, B
Luther College, B
Morningside College, B
Northwestern College, B
St. Ambrose University, B
Simpson College, B
The University of Iowa, B
University of Northern Iowa, B
Waldorf College, B
Wartburg College, B

Kansas

Allen Community College, A
Baker University, B
Barton County Community College, A
Benedictine College, B
Butler Community College, A
Cowley County Community College and Area Vocational - Technical School, A
Dodge City Community College, A
Emporia State University, B
Fort Hays State University, B
Friends University, B
Independence Community College, A
Kansas State University, B
Kansas Wesleyan University, B
McPherson College, B
MidAmerica Nazarene University, B
Ottawa University, B
Southwestern College, B
Sterling College, B
Tabor College, B
The University of Kansas, B
University of Saint Mary, B
Washburn University, B
Wichita State University, B

Kentucky

Asbury University, B
Bellarmine University, B
Berea College, B
Centre College, B
Georgetown College, B
Kentucky Wesleyan College, B
Morehead State University, B
Murray State University, B
Northern Kentucky University, B
Owensboro Community and Technical College, A
Thomas More College, AB
Transylvania University, B
University of the Cumberlands, B
University of Kentucky, B
University of Louisville, B
Western Kentucky University, B

Louisiana

Bossier Parish Community College, A
Centenary College of Louisiana, B
Dillard University, B
Louisiana College, B
Louisiana State University and Agricultural & Mechanical College, B
Loyola University New Orleans, B
Northwestern State University of Louisiana, B
Southern University and Agricultural and Mechanical College, B
Tulane University, B
University of New Orleans, B

Maine

Bates College, B
Colby College, B
University of Maine, B
University of Maine at Machias, B
University of Southern Maine, B

Maryland

Baltimore City Community College, A
Frostburg State University, B
Goucher College, B
Howard Community College, A
McDaniel College, B
Morgan State University, B
St. Mary's College of Maryland, B
Salisbury University, B
Stevenson University, B
Towson University, B
University of Maryland, Baltimore County, B
University of Maryland, College Park, B
Washington College, B

Massachusetts

American International College, B
Amherst College, B
Anna Maria College, B
Bard College at Simon's Rock, B
Boston College, B
Boston University, B
Brandeis University, B
Bridgewater State University, B
Bunker Hill Community College, A
Cape Cod Community College, A
Clark University, B
College of the Holy Cross, B
Dean College, AB
Eastern Nazarene College, B
Elms College, B
Emerson College, B
Fitchburg State University, B
Gordon College, B
Hampshire College, B
Massachusetts Institute of Technology, B
Massasoit Community College, A
Merrimack College, B
Mount Holyoke College, B
Northeastern University, B
Northern Essex Community College, A
Pine Manor College, A
Salem State University, B
Smith College, B
Suffolk University, B
Tufts University, B
University of Massachusetts Amherst, B
University of Massachusetts Boston, B
Wellesley College, B
Westfield State University, B
Williams College, B

Michigan

Adrian College, B
Albion College, B
Alma College, B
Aquinas College, B
Eastern Michigan University, B
Grand Valley State University, B
Henry Ford College, A
Hillsdale College, B
Hope College, B
Kalamazoo College, B
Kuyper College, B
Lake Michigan College, A
Lansing Community College, A
Michigan State University, B
Mid Michigan Community College, A
Northern Michigan University, B
Northwestern Michigan College, A
Oakland University, B
Olivet College, B
Saginaw Valley State University, B
Siena Heights University, B
Spring Arbor University, B
University of Detroit Mercy, B
University of Michigan, B
University of Michigan - Flint, B

Wayne State University, B

Minnesota

Anoka-Ramsey Community College, A
Augsburg College, B
Bemidji State University, B
Bethany Lutheran College, B
Bethel University, B
Carleton College, B
College of Saint Benedict, B
Concordia College, B
Concordia University, St. Paul, B
Gustavus Adolphus College, B
Hamline University, B
Macalester College, B
Metropolitan State University, B
Minneapolis Community and Technical College, A
Minnesota State University Mankato, B
Minnesota State University Moorhead, B
Normandale Community College, A
North Hennepin Community College, A
St. Catherine University, B
St. Cloud State University, B
Saint John's University, B
Saint Mary's University of Minnesota, B
St. Olaf College, B
Southwest Minnesota State University, B
University of Minnesota, Duluth, B
University of Minnesota, Morris, B
University of Minnesota, Twin Cities Campus, B
University of Northwestern - St. Paul, B
Vermilion Community College, A
Winona State University, B

Mississippi

Belhaven University, B
Mississippi Delta Community College, A
University of Mississippi, B
University of Southern Mississippi, B
William Carey University, B

Missouri

Avila University, B
Calvary Bible College and Theological Seminary, B
Central Methodist University, B
College of the Ozarks, B
Crowder College, A
Culver-Stockton College, B
Drury University, B
Fontbonne University, B
Hannibal-LaGrange University, B
Lindenwood University, B
Missouri Baptist University, B
Missouri Southern State University, B
Missouri State University, B
Missouri Valley College, B
Missouri Western State University, B
Northwest Missouri State University, B
Park University, B
St. Charles Community College, A
Saint Louis University, B
Southeast Missouri State University, B
Southwest Baptist University, B
Stephens College, B
Truman State University, B
University of Central Missouri, B
University of Missouri, B
University of Missouri - Kansas City, B
University of Missouri - St. Louis, B
Washington University in St. Louis, B
Webster University, B
William Jewell College, B
William Woods University, B

Montana

Carroll College, B
Montana State University Billings, B
Rocky Mountain College, B
University of Montana, B

Nebraska

Chadron State College, B
Concordia University, Nebraska, B
Creighton University, B
Hastings College, B

Midland University, B
Nebraska Wesleyan University, B
Northeast Community College, A
University of Nebraska at Kearney, B
University of Nebraska - Lincoln, B
University of Nebraska at Omaha, B
Wayne State College, B

Nevada

College of Southern Nevada, A
University of Nevada, Las Vegas, B
University of Nevada, Reno, B

New Hampshire

Dartmouth College, B
Franklin Pierce University, B
New England College, B
Plymouth State University, B
University of New Hampshire, B

New Jersey

Drew University, B
Fairleigh Dickinson University, College at Florham,
    B
Kean University, B
Mercer County Community College, A
Montclair State University, B
Ramapo College of New Jersey, B
Rowan College at Burlington County, A
Rowan University, B
Rutgers University - Camden, B
Rutgers University - New Brunswick, B
Rutgers University - Newark, B
Seton Hall University, B
Thomas Edison State University, B

New Mexico

Central New Mexico Community College, A
Eastern New Mexico University, B
New Mexico Junior College, A
New Mexico State University, B
Santa Fe University of Art and Design, B
University of New Mexico, B

New York

Adelphi University, B
Alfred University, B
American Academy of Dramatic Arts - New York, A
Bard College, B
Barnard College, B
Binghamton University, State University of New
    York, B
Buffalo State College, State University of New York,
    B
City College of the City University of New York, B
Colgate University, B
The College at Brockport, State University of New
    York, B
College of Staten Island of the City University of
    New York, B
Columbia University, B
Columbia University, School of General Studies, B
Cornell University, B
Daemen College, B
Elmira College, B
Eugene Lang College of Liberal Arts, B
Finger Lakes Community College, A
Fiorello H. LaGuardia Community College of the
    City University of New York, A
Five Towns College, B
Fordham University, B
Fulton-Montgomery Community College, A
Genesee Community College, A
Hamilton College, B
Hartwick College, B
Hofstra University, B
Hudson Valley Community College, A
Hunter College of the City University of New York, B
Ithaca College, B
The Juilliard School, B
Kingsborough Community College of the City Uni-
    versity of New York, A
Le Moyne College, B
Lehman College of the City University of New York,
    B

Long Island University - LIU Post, B
Marymount Manhattan College, B
Molloy College, B
Nassau Community College, A
Nazareth College of Rochester, B
The New School College of Performing Arts, B
New York University, B
Niagara County Community College, A
Niagara University, B
Purchase College, State University of New York, B
Queens College of the City University of New York,
    B
Rockland Community College, A
The Sage Colleges, B
St. Bonaventure University, B
St. John's University, B
Sarah Lawrence College, B
Skidmore College, B
State University of New York College at Geneseo, B
State University of New York College at Oneonta, B
State University of New York College at Potsdam, B
State University of New York at Fredonia, B
State University of New York at New Paltz, B
State University of New York at Oswego, B
State University of New York at Plattsburgh, B
Stony Brook University, State University of New
    York, B
Suffolk County Community College, A
Syracuse University, B
Ulster County Community College, A
University at Albany, State University of New York, B
University at Buffalo, the State University of New
    York, B
Vassar College, B
Wagner College, B
Wells College, B
York College of the City University of New York, B

North Carolina

Appalachian State University, B
Barton College, B
Brevard College, B
Campbell University, B
Catawba College, B
Chowan University, B
College of The Albemarle, A
Davidson College, B
Duke University, B
East Carolina University, B
Elon University, B
Gardner-Webb University, B
Greensboro College, B
Guilford College, B
High Point University, B
Lees-McRae College, B
Lenoir-Rhyne University, B
Mars Hill University, B
Meredith College, B
Methodist University, AB
North Carolina Agricultural and Technical State Uni-
    versity, B
North Carolina Central University, B
North Carolina Wesleyan College, B
Queens University of Charlotte, B
University of North Carolina at Asheville, B
The University of North Carolina at Chapel Hill, B
The University of North Carolina at Charlotte, B
The University of North Carolina at Greensboro, B
The University of North Carolina at Pembroke, B
University of North Carolina School of the Arts, B
The University of North Carolina Wilmington, B
Wake Forest University, B
Western Carolina University, B
William Peace University, B

North Dakota

Dickinson State University, B
North Dakota State University, B
University of Jamestown, B
University of North Dakota, B

Ohio

Ashland University, B
Bowling Green State University, B
Capital University, B
Case Western Reserve University, B

Cedarville University, B
Clark State Community College, A
Cleveland State University, B
The College of Wooster, B
Denison University, B
Edison Community College, A
Franciscan University of Steubenville, B
Heidelberg University, B
Hiram College, B
Kent State University, B
Kenyon College, B
Lorain County Community College, A
Marietta College, B
Miami University, B
Mount Vernon Nazarene University, B
Muskingum University, B
Oberlin College, B
Ohio Northern University, B
The Ohio State University, B
The Ohio State University at Lima, B
Ohio University, B
Ohio Wesleyan University, B
Otterbein University, B
Sinclair Community College, A
The University of Akron, B
University of Cincinnati, B
University of Dayton, B
The University of Findlay, B
University of Mount Union, B
The University of Toledo, B
Wilmington College, B
Wittenberg University, B
Wright State University, B
Xavier University, B
Youngstown State University, B

Oklahoma

Bacone College, A
East Central University, B
Northeastern Oklahoma Agricultural and Mechanical
    College, A
Northeastern State University, B
Oklahoma Baptist University, B
Oklahoma Christian University, B
Oklahoma City Community College, A
Oklahoma City University, B
Oklahoma State University, B
Oral Roberts University, B
Rose State College, A
St. Gregory's University, B
Southeastern Oklahoma State University, B
Tulsa Community College, A
University of Central Oklahoma, B
University of Oklahoma, B
University of Science and Arts of Oklahoma, B
The University of Tulsa, B

Oregon

Concordia University, B
Eastern Oregon University, B
George Fox University, B
Lewis & Clark College, B
Linfield College, B
Linn-Benton Community College, A
Pacific University, B
Portland State University, B
Reed College, B
Southern Oregon University, B
Umpqua Community College, A
University of Oregon, B
University of Portland, B
Western Oregon University, B
Willamette University, B

Pennsylvania

Albright College, B
Allegheny College, B
Alvernia University, B
Arcadia University, B
Bloomsburg University of Pennsylvania, B
Bucknell University, B
California University of Pennsylvania, B
Carnegie Mellon University, B
Cedar Crest College, B
Cheyney University of Pennsylvania, B
Clarion University of Pennsylvania, B

Community College of Allegheny County, A
DeSales University, B
Dickinson College, B
Duquesne University, B
East Stroudsburg University of Pennsylvania, B
Elizabethtown College, B
Franklin & Marshall College, B
Gannon University, B
Gettysburg College, B
Harrisburg Area Community College, A
Indiana University of Pennsylvania, B
King's College, B
Lafayette College, B
Lehigh University, B
Lock Haven University of Pennsylvania, B
Lycoming College, B
Marywood University, B
Messiah College, B
Muhlenberg College, B
Point Park University, B
Seton Hill University, B
Slippery Rock University of Pennsylvania, B
Susquehanna University, B
Swarthmore College, B
University of Pennsylvania, B
University of Pittsburgh, B
University of Pittsburgh at Johnstown, B
The University of Scranton, B
Ursinus College, B
West Chester University of Pennsylvania, B
Westminster College, B
Wilkes University, B
York College of Pennsylvania, B

Rhode Island

Brown University, B
Community College of Rhode Island, A
Providence College, B
Rhode Island College, B
Roger Williams University, B
Salve Regina University, B
University of Rhode Island, B

South Carolina

Bob Jones University, B
Coastal Carolina University, B
Coker College, B
College of Charleston, B
Converse College, B
Francis Marion University, B
Furman University, B
Limestone College, B
Newberry College, B
North Greenville University, B
Presbyterian College, B
South Carolina State University, B
University of South Carolina, B
University of South Carolina Upstate, B
Winthrop University, B
Wofford College, B

South Dakota

Augustana University, B
Dakota Wesleyan University, B
Mount Marty College, B
Northern State University, B
South Dakota State University, B
The University of South Dakota, B

Tennessee

Austin Peay State University, B
Belmont University, B
Bethel University, B
Bryan College, B
Carson-Newman University, B
Cumberland University, B
East Tennessee State University, B
Hiwassee College, A
Lipscomb University, B
Maryville College, B
Middle Tennessee State University, B
Rhodes College, B
Sewanee: The University of the South, B
Tennessee Wesleyan College, B
Trevecca Nazarene University, B
Union University, B

University of Memphis, B
The University of Tennessee, B
The University of Tennessee at Chattanooga, B
The University of Tennessee at Martin, B
Vanderbilt University, B

Texas

Abilene Christian University, B
Alvin Community College, A
Amarillo College, A
Angelina College, A
Angelo State University, B
Austin Community College District, A
Baylor University, B
Blinn College, A
Central Texas College, A
Clarendon College, A
College of the Mainland, A
Del Mar College, A
East Texas Baptist University, B
Galveston College, A
Grayson College, A
Hardin-Simmons University, B
Hill College, A
Howard College, A
Howard Payne University, B
Kilgore College, A
Lamar University, B
Lee College, A
McMurry University, B
Navarro College, A
Northeast Texas Community College, A
Our Lady of the Lake University of San Antonio, B
Panola College, A
Paris Junior College, A
Prairie View A&M University, B
St. Edward's University, B
St. Philip's College, A
Sam Houston State University, B
San Jacinto College District, A
Schreiner University, B
Southern Methodist University, B
Southwestern Assemblies of God University, B
Southwestern University, B
Stephen F. Austin State University, B
Sul Ross State University, B
Tarleton State University, B
Texarkana College, A
Texas A&M University, B
Texas A&M University - Commerce, B
Texas A&M University - Kingsville, B
Texas Christian University, B
Texas Lutheran University, B
Texas Southern University, B
Texas State University, B
Texas Tech University, B
Texas Woman's University, B
Trinity University, B
Trinity Valley Community College, A
Tyler Junior College, A
University of Dallas, B
University of Houston, B
University of the Incarnate Word, B
University of North Texas, B
University of St. Thomas, B
The University of Texas at Arlington, B
The University of Texas at Austin, B
The University of Texas at El Paso, B
The University of Texas Rio Grande Valley, B
Wayland Baptist University, B
West Texas A&M University, B
Western Texas College, A
Wharton County Junior College, A

Utah

Dixie State University, B
Snow College, A
Southern Utah University, B
University of Utah, B
Utah State University, B
Utah Valley University, AB
Weber State University, B
Westminster College, B

Vermont

Bennington College, B
Castleton University, B
Johnson State College, B
Marlboro College, B
Middlebury College, B
Saint Michael's College, B
University of Vermont, B

Virginia

Averett University, B
Bluefield College, B
Christopher Newport University, B
The College of William and Mary, B
Eastern Mennonite University, B
Emory & Henry College, B
Ferrum College, B
George Mason University, B
Hampton University, B
Hollins University, B
James Madison University, B
Liberty University, B
Lynchburg College, B
Mary Baldwin College, B
Old Dominion University, B
Radford University, B
Randolph College, B
Randolph-Macon College, B
Roanoke College, B
Southern Virginia University, B
Sweet Briar College, B
University of Richmond, B
University of Virginia, B
The University of Virginia's College at Wise, B
Virginia Commonwealth University, B
Virginia Highlands Community College, A
Virginia Polytechnic Institute and State University, B
Virginia Union University, B
Virginia Wesleyan College, B
Washington and Lee University, B

Washington

Cornish College of the Arts, B
Eastern Washington University, B
Everett Community College, A
The Evergreen State College, B
Gonzaga University, B
Northwest University, B
Pacific Lutheran University, B
Saint Martin's University, B
Seattle Pacific University, B
Seattle University, B
University of Puget Sound, B
University of Washington, B
Western Washington University, B
Whitman College, B
Whitworth University, B

West Virginia

Davis & Elkins College, B
Fairmont State University, B
West Virginia University, B
West Virginia Wesleyan College, B

Wisconsin

Beloit College, B
Cardinal Stritch University, B
Carroll University, B
Carthage College, B
Edgewood College, B
Lawrence University, B
Marquette University, B
Ripon College, B
St. Norbert College, B
University of Wisconsin - Eau Claire, B
University of Wisconsin - Green Bay, B
University of Wisconsin - La Crosse, B
University of Wisconsin - Madison, B
University of Wisconsin - Milwaukee, B
University of Wisconsin - Oshkosh, B
University of Wisconsin - Parkside, B
University of Wisconsin - River Falls, B
University of Wisconsin - Stevens Point, B
University of Wisconsin - Superior, B
University of Wisconsin - Whitewater, B

Viterbo University, B
Wisconsin Lutheran College, B

Wyoming

Central Wyoming College, A
Sheridan College, A
University of Wyoming, B
Western Wyoming Community College, A

U.S. Territories: Puerto Rico

University of Puerto Rico, Río Piedras Campus, B
University of the Sacred Heart, B

Canada
Alberta

University of Alberta, B
University of Calgary, B
University of Lethbridge, B

British Columbia

Simon Fraser University, B
Thompson Rivers University, B
Trinity Western University, B
The University of British Columbia, B
The University of British Columbia - Okanagan
 Campus, B
University of the Fraser Valley, AB
University of Victoria, B

Manitoba

Providence University College & Theological Semi-
 nary, B
University of Manitoba, B
The University of Winnipeg, B

Maritime Provinces: New Brunswick

Mount Allison University, B
Université de Moncton, B
University of New Brunswick Fredericton, B

Maritime Provinces: Nova Scotia

Acadia University, B
Dalhousie University, B
University of King's College, B

Newfoundland and Labrador

Memorial University of Newfoundland, B

Ontario

Brock University, B
Carleton University, B
Laurentian University, B
McMaster University, B
Queen's University at Kingston, B
Redeemer University College, B
University of Guelph, B
University of Ottawa, B
University of Waterloo, B
University of Windsor, B
York University, B

Quebec

Bishop's University, B
Concordia University, B
McGill University, B
Université Laval, AB
Université du Québec à Montréal, B

Saskatchewan

University of Regina, B
University of Saskatchewan, B

DRAMA THERAPY

United States

California

California Institute of Integral Studies, M

District of Columbia

Howard University, B

Illinois

Columbia College Chicago, MO

New York

New York University, M

Virginia

Virginia Union University, B

DRAMATIC/THEATRE ARTS AND STAGECRAFT

United States
Arizona

Grand Canyon University, B

California

Pepperdine University, B
University of Southern California, B

Colorado

Adams State University, B
University of Northern Colorado, B

Connecticut

University of Connecticut, B

Florida

University of Miami, B

Illinois

Columbia College Chicago, B
DePaul University, B
Southern Illinois University Carbondale, B

Indiana

Indiana University South Bend, B

Iowa

Drake University, B

Kansas

Benedictine College, B
Southwestern College, B

Kentucky

Western Kentucky University, B

Massachusetts

Bristol Community College, A
Wheaton College, B

Michigan

Oakland Community College, A
University of Michigan - Flint, B
Western Michigan University, B

Minnesota

St. Cloud State University, B
Southwest Minnesota State University, B

Missouri

Lindenwood University, B
Webster University, B

Nebraska

Nebraska Wesleyan University, B

New York

Genesee Community College, A
Syracuse University, B

North Carolina

Catawba College, B
Fayetteville State University, B
Meredith College, B

Saint Augustine's University, B

Pennsylvania

Seton Hill University, B

South Carolina

Charleston Southern University, B
Coastal Carolina University, B

Tennessee

Lee University, B

Texas

St. Philip's College, A

Utah

Brigham Young University, B

Vermont

Marlboro College, B

Canada
Maritime Provinces: Nova Scotia

Dalhousie University, B

DRAWING

United States
Alabama

Birmingham-Southern College, B

California

Biola University, B
California College of the Arts, B
California State University, East Bay, B
California State University, Long Beach, B
Chabot College, A
Chaffey College, A
College of San Mateo, A
Copper Mountain College, A
Cuesta College, A
Cuyamaca College, A
De Anza College, A
Evergreen Valley College, A
Grossmont College, A
Laguna College of Art & Design, B
Lassen Community College District, A
Long Beach City College, A
Los Angeles Valley College, A
Monterey Peninsula College, A
Otis College of Art and Design, B
Palomar College, A
Sonoma State University, B
University of San Francisco, B

Colorado

Adams State University, B
Colorado State University, B

Connecticut

University of Hartford, B
University of New Haven, B

Georgia

Albany State University, B
Columbus State University, B
Georgia State University, B

Illinois

American Academy of Art, B
Bradley University, B
Lewis University, B
School of the Art Institute of Chicago, B

Indiana

Grace College, B
Indiana University - Purdue University Fort Wayne,
 B

Iowa

Drake University, B
The University of Iowa, B

Kansas

Bethany College, B
Kansas Wesleyan University, B

Maine

College of the Atlantic, B

Maryland

Cecil College, A
Maryland Institute College of Art, B

Massachusetts

Montserrat College of Art, B
School of the Museum of Fine Arts, Boston, B

Michigan

Aquinas College, B
Ferris State University, B
Northern Michigan University, B
Oakland University, B
University of Michigan, B

Minnesota

Minneapolis College of Art and Design, B
Minnesota State University Mankato, B
Vermilion Community College, A

Missouri

Lindenwood University, B
Washington University in St. Louis, B

Montana

University of Montana, B

New Hampshire

New England College, B

New Jersey

Rutgers University - New Brunswick, B

New York

Buffalo State College, State University of New York,
    B
Pratt Institute, AB
Sarah Lawrence College, B
School of Visual Arts, B
State University of New York at Fredonia, B

Ohio

Art Academy of Cincinnati, B
Bowling Green State University, B
Cleveland Institute of Art, B

Oregon

Portland State University, B

Pennsylvania

Arcadia University, B
Luzerne County Community College, A
Seton Hill University, B

Rhode Island

Providence College, B

Tennessee

Carson-Newman University, B

Texas

The University of Texas at El Paso, B

Utah

Brigham Young University, B
Dixie State University, B

Vermont

Bennington College, B
Marlboro College, B

Washington

Central Washington University, B
Western Washington University, B

West Virginia

West Virginia Wesleyan College, B

Wisconsin

Milwaukee Institute of Art and Design, B

U.S. Territories: Puerto Rico

Inter American University of Puerto Rico, San
    Germán Campus, B
University of Puerto Rico, Río Piedras Campus, B

Canada

Alberta

Alberta College of Art & Design, B

British Columbia

Emily Carr University of Art + Design, B

Maritime Provinces: New Brunswick

Mount Allison University, B

Maritime Provinces: Nova Scotia

NSCAD University, B

Newfoundland and Labrador

Memorial University of Newfoundland, B

Ontario

University of Windsor, B

Saskatchewan

University of Regina, B

DRIVER AND SAFETY TEACHER EDUCATION

United States

Wisconsin

University of Wisconsin - Whitewater, B

DRYWALL INSTALLATION/ DRYWALLER

United States

California

American River College, A
Palomar College, A

DUTCH/FLEMISH LANGUAGE AND LITERATURE

United States

California

University of California, Berkeley, B

E-COMMERCE/ELECTRONIC COMMERCE

United States

Arizona

University of Phoenix - Phoenix Campus, B

California

Mt. Sierra College, B
San Jose City College, A
Southwestern College, A
University of La Verne, B
University of Phoenix - Bay Area Campus, B
University of Phoenix - Sacramento Valley Campus,
    B

Colorado

Colorado Mountain College (Steamboat Springs), A
Colorado Technical University Colorado Springs, AB
University of Phoenix - Colorado Campus, B

Connecticut

Three Rivers Community College, A

Delaware

Delaware State University, B
Delaware Technical & Community College, Jack F.
    Owens Campus, A
Delaware Technical & Community College, Terry
    Campus, A

District of Columbia

University of Phoenix - Washington D.C. Campus, B

Florida

Full Sail University, B
Pasco-Hernando State College, A
University of Phoenix - Central Florida Campus, B
University of Phoenix - North Florida Campus, B

Georgia

Ashworth College, B
Augusta Technical College, A
Central Georgia Technical College, A
University of Phoenix - Atlanta Campus, B
University of Phoenix - Augusta Campus, B
University of Phoenix - Columbus Georgia Campus,
    AB
Wiregrass Georgia Technical College, A

Hawaii

Kapiolani Community College, A
University of Phoenix - Hawaii Campus, B

Illinois

DePaul University, B
Lewis University, B
Rend Lake College, A

Kentucky

Daymar College (Bellevue), A
Daymar College (Bowling Green), A

Louisiana

Southern University and Agricultural and Mechanical
    College, B

Maryland

Towson University, B

Michigan

Kalamazoo Valley Community College, A
Lansing Community College, A
Wayne County Community College District, A
Western Michigan University, B

Minnesota

Century College, A

Missouri

Maryville University of Saint Louis, B
North Central Missouri College, A

Nevada

University of Phoenix - Las Vegas Campus, B

New Jersey

Bloomfield College, B
University of Phoenix - Jersey City Campus, B

New Mexico

Western New Mexico University, A

New York

Finger Lakes Community College, A
Genesee Community College, A

North Carolina

Caldwell Community College and Technical Institute, A
Forsyth Technical Community College, A
Nash Community College, A
Pitt Community College, A
University of Phoenix - Charlotte Campus, AB
Wake Technical Community College, A

North Dakota

North Dakota State College of Science, A

Ohio

The University of Akron, B
The University of Toledo, B

Oklahoma

Bacone College, B

Oregon

Lane Community College, A

Pennsylvania

Delaware County Community College, A
Harrisburg University of Science and Technology, B
Philadelphia University, B
Thiel College, B
University of Pennsylvania, B
University of Phoenix - Philadelphia Campus, B
The University of Scranton, B

South Carolina

Limestone College, AB
Winthrop University, B

Tennessee

Daymar College (Clarksville), A
Daymar College (Nashville), A
Trevecca Nazarene University, B

Texas

Brookhaven College, A
Del Mar College, A
Eastfield College, A
St. Philip's College, A
University of Phoenix - Dallas Campus, B
University of Phoenix - Houston Campus, B
University of Phoenix - San Antonio Campus, B

Utah

Stevens-Henager College (Logan), A
Stevens-Henager College (Orem), A
Stevens-Henager College (Salt Lake City), A

Washington

Bellevue College, A
Edmonds Community College, A
Seattle University, B
University of Phoenix - Western Washington Campus, B

Wisconsin

Milwaukee Area Technical College, A

Canada

Ontario

University of Ottawa, B
University of Toronto, B

Quebec

McGill University, B

EARLY CHILDHOOD EDUCATION AND TEACHING

United States

Alabama

Alabama Agricultural and Mechanical University, MDO
Alabama Southern Community College, A
Alabama State University, BMO
Auburn University, BMDO
Auburn University at Montgomery, MO
Concordia College Alabama, B
Jacksonville State University, M
Miles College, B
Samford University, M
Spring Hill College, BM
Troy University, MO
The University of Alabama, B
The University of Alabama at Birmingham, BMD
University of Mobile, B
University of South Alabama, BM
The University of West Alabama, MO

Alaska

University of Alaska Anchorage, M
University of Alaska Anchorage, Kenai Peninsula College, A
University of Alaska Fairbanks, A
University of Alaska Southeast, AM

Arizona

Arizona State University at the Tempe campus, B
Arizona Western College, A
Cochise County Community College District, A
Coconino Community College, A
Diné College, A
Eastern Arizona College, A
Glendale Community College, A
Northern Arizona University, BM
Northland Pioneer College, A
Paradise Valley Community College, A
Penn Foster College, A
Pima Community College, A
Prescott College, BM
South Mountain Community College, A
Tohono O'odham Community College, A
University of Phoenix - Online Campus, M
University of Phoenix - Phoenix Campus, M

Arkansas

Arkansas State University, BM
Arkansas State University - Mountain Home, A
Arkansas State University - Newport, A
Arkansas Tech University, B
Black River Technical College, A
Central Baptist College, B
Cossatot Community College of the University of Arkansas, A
Harding University, BM
Henderson State University, M
John Brown University, B
NorthWest Arkansas Community College, A
Ouachita Baptist University, B
Phillips Community College of the University of Arkansas, A
Southern Arkansas University - Magnolia, B
University of Arkansas, BM
University of Arkansas Community College at Batesville, A
University of Arkansas - Fort Smith, AB
University of Arkansas at Little Rock, B
University of Arkansas at Pine Bluff, M

California

Bethesda University, B
Biola University, M
Brandman University, B
California Baptist University, B
California State University, Chico, B
California State University, Dominguez Hills, B
California State University, East Bay, M
California State University, Fresno, M
California State University, Los Angeles, B

California State University, Northridge, M
California State University, San Bernardino, B
California State University, San Marcos, B
California State University, Stanislaus, B
Folsom Lake College, A
Glendale Community College, A
Loyola Marymount University, M
Mills College, M
Moreno Valley College, A
Mount Saint Mary's University, A
National University, ABMO
Norco College, A
Ohlone College, A
Pacific Oaks College, M
Pacific Union College, AB
Riverside City College, A
Saint Mary's College of California, M
San Diego State University, B
San Francisco State University, BMO
San Jose State University, B
Santa Rosa Junior College, A
Shasta Bible College, A
Sonoma State University, M
Trident University International, M
University of Phoenix - Bay Area Campus, M

Colorado

Adams State University, AB
Aspen University, B
Colorado Christian University, M
Colorado Mountain College (Leadville), A
Colorado Mountain College (Steamboat Springs), A
Colorado Northwestern Community College, A
Colorado State University, B
Fort Lewis College, B
Front Range Community College, A
Naropa University, B
Nazarene Bible College, A
Pueblo Community College, A
Red Rocks Community College, A
Trinidad State Junior College, A
University of Colorado Colorado Springs, B
University of Colorado Denver, MD
University of Northern Colorado, BM

Connecticut

Central Connecticut State University, M
Eastern Connecticut State University, M
Fairfield University, O
Mitchell College, B
Naugatuck Valley Community College, A
Norwalk Community College, A
Southern Connecticut State University, B
University of Bridgeport, MO
University of Hartford, BM

Delaware

Delaware State University, B
Delaware Technical & Community College, Jack F. Owens Campus, A
Delaware Technical & Community College, Stanton/Wilmington Campus, A
Delaware Technical & Community College, Terry Campus, A
University of Delaware, B
Wilmington University, AB

District of Columbia

The Catholic University of America, B
Gallaudet University, MO
The George Washington University, M
Trinity Washington University, M
University of the District of Columbia, BM
University of Phoenix - Washington D.C. Campus, M

Florida

Barry University, MDO
Broward College, A
College of Central Florida, AB
Eastern Florida State College, A
Florida Agricultural and Mechanical University, B
Florida Atlantic University, BM
Florida Gateway College, AB
Florida Gulf Coast University, B

Florida International University, BM
Florida SouthWestern State College, A
Florida State College at Jacksonville, B
Florida State University, BMDO
Gulf Coast State College, A
Jose Maria Vargas University, ABM
Lake-Sumter State College, A
Miami Dade College, AB
Nova Southeastern University, A
Pensacola State College, A
Rasmussen College Fort Myers, A
Rasmussen College Land O' Lakes, A
Rasmussen College New Port Richey, A
Rasmussen College Ocala, A
Rasmussen College Tampa/Brandon, A
St. Petersburg College, A
Santa Fe College, B
South Florida State College, A
Southern Technical College (Fort Myers), AB
Southern Technical College (Tampa), AB
State College of Florida Manatee-Sarasota, B
Tallahassee Community College, A
University of Central Florida, BD
University of Florida, M
University of Miami, MO
University of North Florida, B
University of Phoenix - North Florida Campus, M
University of Phoenix - South Florida Campus, M
University of South Florida, BMDO
University of West Florida, BM

Georgia

Albany State University, BM
Armstrong State University, BM
Ashworth College, AB
Augusta University, B
Berry College, BM
Brenau University, MO
Brewton-Parker College, B
Clark Atlanta University, B
Columbus State University, BMO
Georgia College & State University, BMO
Georgia Gwinnett College, B
Georgia Military College, A
Georgia Southern University, MO
Georgia Southwestern State University, MO
Georgia State University, MDO
Gordon State College, AB
Kennesaw State University, BM
LaGrange College, B
Mercer University, MO
Middle Georgia State University, B
Morehouse College, B
Piedmont College, BM
Point University, B
Reinhardt University, BM
Thomas University, B
University of Georgia, BMDO
University of North Georgia, BM
University of West Georgia, MO
Valdosta State University, BMO
Wesleyan College, BM
Young Harris College, B

Hawaii

Chaminade University of Honolulu, ABM
Hawaii Community College, A
University of Hawaii at Manoa, BM
University of Hawaii - West Oahu, B

Idaho

Boise State University, ABM
Brigham Young University - Idaho, B
College of Western Idaho, A
Idaho State University, B

Illinois

Aurora University, M
Bradley University, B
Chicago State University, BM
Columbia College Chicago, B
Concordia University Chicago, BMD
DePaul University, BMD
Dominican University, BM
Eastern Illinois University, M
Ellis University, M

Governors State University, BM
Harper College, A
Highland Community College, A
Illinois College, B
Illinois State University, B
Illinois Valley Community College, A
Judson University, B
Kankakee Community College, A
Kendall College, B
Lewis University, M
Lincoln Land Community College, A
Loyola University Chicago, B
Millikin University, B
Moraine Valley Community College, A
National Louis University, BMO
North Park University, B
Northeastern Illinois University, BM
Northern Illinois University, BM
Rasmussen College Aurora, A
Rasmussen College Mokena/Tinley Park, A
Rasmussen College Rockford, A
Rasmussen College Romeoville/Joliet, A
Rockford University, BM
Roosevelt University, BM
St. Augustine College, A
Saint Xavier University, M
Sauk Valley Community College, A
Southern Illinois University Carbondale, B
Southern Illinois University Edwardsville, B
Triton College, A
University of Illinois at Chicago, M
University of Illinois at Urbana - Champaign, B

Indiana

Ancilla College, A
Ball State University, B
Bethel College, AB
Butler University, B
Indiana University Bloomington, B
Indiana University Kokomo, B
Indiana University - Purdue University Indianapolis, MO
Ivy Tech Community College - Bloomington, A
Ivy Tech Community College - Central Indiana, A
Ivy Tech Community College - Columbus, A
Ivy Tech Community College - East Central, A
Ivy Tech Community College - Kokomo, A
Ivy Tech Community College - Lafayette, A
Ivy Tech Community College - North Central, A
Ivy Tech Community College - Northeast, A
Ivy Tech Community College - Northwest, A
Ivy Tech Community College - Richmond, A
Ivy Tech Community College - Southeast, A
Ivy Tech Community College - Southern Indiana, A
Ivy Tech Community College - Southwest, A
Ivy Tech Community College - Wabash Valley, A
Manchester University, A
Martin University, B
Oakland City University, AB
Purdue University, B
Purdue University Northwest (Westville), B
Taylor University, B
University of Southern Indiana, AB
Vincennes University, A

Iowa

Clarke University, M
Iowa Lakes Community College, A
Iowa State University of Science and Technology, B
Iowa Wesleyan University, B
North Iowa Area Community College, A
St. Ambrose University, B
University of Northern Iowa, M

Kansas

Barton County Community College, A
Emporia State University, M
Hesston College, A
Kansas City Kansas Community College, A
Kansas State University, M
Newman University, M
Ottawa University, M
Pittsburg State University, M
Rasmussen College Kansas City/Overland Park, A
Rasmussen College Topeka, A
Southwestern College, BM

The University of Kansas, B
Washburn University, A
Wichita State University, M

Kentucky

Gateway Community and Technical College, A
Jefferson Community and Technical College, A
Lindsey Wilson College, A
Morehead State University, B
Murray State University, BM
Spalding University, B
Sullivan University, A
University of Kentucky, BM
University of Louisville, M
Western Kentucky University, ABM

Louisiana

Louisiana State University and Agricultural & Mechanical, College, B
Louisiana Tech University, BM
McNeese State University, BMO
Nicholls State University, B
Northwestern State University of Louisiana, BM
Southeastern Louisiana University, B
Southern University and Agricultural and Mechanical College, B
Southern University at New Orleans, B
University of Louisiana at Lafayette, B
University of Louisiana at Monroe, M
Xavier University of Louisiana, B

Maine

Central Maine Community College, A
Eastern Maine Community College, A
Southern Maine Community College, A
Thomas College, B
University of Maine, O
University of Maine at Farmington, BM
York County Community College, A

Maryland

Anne Arundel Community College, A
Carroll Community College, A
Chesapeake College, A
College of Southern Maryland, A
Community College of Baltimore County, A
Coppin State University, B
Frederick Community College, A
Frostburg State University, B
Garrett College, A
Hagerstown Community College, A
Harford Community College, A
Hood College, BM
Johns Hopkins University, MO
Loyola University Maryland, MO
Montgomery College, A
Salisbury University, B
Stevenson University, B
Towson University, BMO
University of Maryland, Baltimore County, M
Washington Adventist University, A
Wor-Wic Community College, A

Massachusetts

American International College, MO
Anna Maria College, BM
Bay Path University, B
Becker College, AB
Boston University, B
Bridgewater State University, BM
Bunker Hill Community College, A
Cambridge College, M
Cape Cod Community College, A
Curry College, B
Dean College, A
Eastern Nazarene College, ABMO
Elms College, M
Endicott College, BM
Fisher College, A
Fitchburg State University, BM
Framingham State University, BM
Gordon College, BM
Greenfield Community College, A
Lasell College, B
Lesley University, M

Massachusetts Bay Community College, A
Merrimack College, BM
Mount Ida College, B
Pine Manor College, AB
Quincy College, A
Salem State University, BM
Springfield College, B
Springfield Technical Community College, A
Stonehill College, B
Tufts University, BM
University of Massachusetts Amherst, M
University of Massachusetts Boston, M
Urban College of Boston, A
Westfield State University, M
Wheelock College, BM
Worcester State University, BM

Michigan

Alma College, B
Bay Mills Community College, A
Calvin College, B
Central Michigan University, BM
Cornerstone University, A
Eastern Michigan University, BM
Gogebic Community College, A
Grace Bible College, B
Grand Valley State University, M
Great Lakes Christian College, A
Henry Ford College, A
Jackson College, A
Keweenaw Bay Ojibwa Community College, A
Lake Michigan College, A
Lake Superior State University, AB
Madonna University, B
Michigan State University, B
Mott Community College, A
North Central Michigan College, A
Oakland University, MDO
Rochester College, B
Saginaw Valley State University, M
Siena Heights University, M
Southwestern Michigan College, A
University of Michigan - Dearborn, BM
University of Michigan - Flint, M
Wayne State University, MDO
Western Michigan University, B

Minnesota

Alexandria Technical and Community College, A
Capella University, M
Concordia University, St. Paul, BM
Leech Lake Tribal College, A
Metropolitan State University, B
Minnesota State College - Southeast Technical, A
Minnesota State Community and Technical College - Detroit Lakes, A
Minnesota State University Mankato, MO
Minnesota State University Moorhead, B
Rasmussen College Blaine, A
Rasmussen College Bloomington, A
Rasmussen College Brooklyn Park, A
Rasmussen College Eagan, A
Rasmussen College Lake Elmo/Woodbury, A
Rasmussen College Mankato, A
Rasmussen College Moorhead, A
Rasmussen College St. Cloud, A
Ridgewater College, A
St. Catherine University, M
Southwest Minnesota State University, M
University of Minnesota, Crookston, B
University of Minnesota, Twin Cities Campus, MD
University of Northwestern - St. Paul, B
University of St. Thomas, M
Walden University, MDO

Mississippi

Coahoma Community College, A
Jackson State University, MDO
Mississippi State University, MD
Rust College, A
Southwest Mississippi Community College, A
Tougaloo College, A

Missouri

Baptist Bible College, AB
Central Methodist University, B

College of the Ozarks, B
Evangel University, B
Hannibal-LaGrange University, B
Harris-Stowe State University, B
Lincoln University, A
Lindenwood University, B
Maryville University of Saint Louis, M
Missouri Baptist University, B
Missouri Southern State University, M
Missouri State University, BM
Missouri Western State University, B
North Central Missouri College, A
Northwest Missouri State University, M
Park University, B
Southeast Missouri State University, B
Southwest Baptist University, B
Stephens College, B
University of Central Missouri, M
University of Missouri, BMDO
University of Missouri - Kansas City, B
University of Missouri - St. Louis, BM
Webster University, B

Montana

Aaniiih Nakoda College, A
Blackfeet Community College, A
Fort Peck Community College, A
University of Great Falls, A
The University of Montana Western, AB

Nebraska

Chadron State College, B
College of Saint Mary, AB
Concordia University, Nebraska, BM
Hastings College, B
Nebraska Indian Community College, A
Northeast Community College, A
Peru State College, B
Union College, B
University of Nebraska at Kearney, M
University of Nebraska - Lincoln, MD
Wayne State College, BM

Nevada

Great Basin College, A
University of Nevada, Las Vegas, B

New Hampshire

Colby-Sawyer College, B
Granite State College, AB
Great Bay Community College, A
Keene State College, B
Lakes Region Community College, A
Plymouth State University, B
River Valley Community College, A
Rivier University, BM
Southern New Hampshire University, B
University of New Hampshire, M
White Mountains Community College, A

New Jersey

Bergen Community College, A
Camden County College, A
The College of New Jersey, BM
Kean University, M
New Jersey City University, BM
Rowan University, B
Rutgers University - New Brunswick, MD
William Paterson University of New Jersey, B

New Mexico

Central New Mexico Community College, A
Clovis Community College, A
Eastern New Mexico University, BM
Navajo Technical University, A
New Mexico State University, B
New Mexico State University - Alamogordo, A
New Mexico State University - Carlsbad, A
New Mexico State University - Grants, A
Southwestern Indian Polytechnic Institute, A
University of New Mexico, BD
University of New Mexico - Los Alamos Branch, A
University of New Mexico - Taos, A
University of New Mexico - Valencia Campus, A
University of the Southwest, M

Western New Mexico University, AB

New York

Binghamton University, State University of New York, M
Brooklyn College of the City University of New York, BM
Buffalo State College, State University of New York, M
Canisius College, BM
Cazenovia College, B
City College of the City University of New York, BM
The College at Brockport, State University of New York, M
The College of New Rochelle, M
The College of Saint Rose, BM
Concordia College - New York, B
Corning Community College, A
Daemen College, BM
Davis College, A
Finger Lakes Community College, A
Five Towns College, M
Fordham University, M
Hofstra University, BMDO
Hudson Valley Community College, A
Hunter College of the City University of New York, M
Iona College, BM
Jefferson Community College, A
Keuka College, M
Kingsborough Community College of the City University of New York, A
Le Moyne College, M
Lehman College of the City University of New York, M
Long Island University - LIU Brooklyn, MO
Long Island University - LIU Post, BM
Manhattan College, M
Manhattanville College, M
Mercy College, M
Morrisville State College, A
Mount Saint Mary College, BM
Nazareth College of Rochester, M
New York Institute of Technology, M
New York University, BM
Niagara University, MO
Nyack College, B
Pace University, M
Queens College of the City University of New York, M
Roberts Wesleyan College, BM
St. Bonaventure University, M
St. John's University, M
St. Joseph's College, Long Island Campus, M
St. Joseph's College, New York, M
State University of New York College at Cortland, M
State University of New York College at Geneseo, BM
State University of New York College at Old Westbury, B
State University of New York College at Potsdam, BM
State University of New York at Fredonia, M
State University of New York at New Paltz, M
State University of New York at Oswego, M
State University of New York at Plattsburgh, O
Syracuse University, M
University at Buffalo, the State University of New York, M
Wagner College, M
Wells College, B
Yeshiva University, B

North Carolina

Asheville-Buncombe Technical Community College, A
Barton College, B
Blue Ridge Community College, A
Brunswick Community College, A
Caldwell Community College and Technical Institute, A
Cape Fear Community College, A
Catawba Valley Community College, A
Cleveland Community College, A
Craven Community College, A
Durham Technical Community College, A

East Carolina University, M
Elon University, B
Fayetteville State University, B
Fayetteville Technical Community College, A
Forsyth Technical Community College, A
Gaston College, A
Greensboro College, B
Guilford Technical Community College, A
Halifax Community College, A
James Sprunt Community College, A
Johnston Community College, A
Lees-McRae College, B
McDowell Technical Community College, A
Mitchell Community College, A
Montgomery Community College, A
Nash Community College, A
North Carolina Agricultural and Technical State University, M
Piedmont Community College, A
Pitt Community College, A
Randolph Community College, A
Richmond Community College, A
Roanoke-Chowan Community College, A
Robeson Community College, A
Rockingham Community College, A
Rowan-Cabarrus Community College, A
Shaw University, M
South Piedmont Community College, A
Tri-County Community College, A
University of Mount Olive, B
The University of North Carolina at Chapel Hill, BMD
The University of North Carolina at Greensboro, BM
The University of North Carolina Wilmington, M
Wake Technical Community College, A
Wayne Community College, A
Western Piedmont Community College, A
Wilson Community College, A

North Dakota

Cankdeska Cikana Community College, A
Mayville State University, B
Rasmussen College Fargo, A
United Tribes Technical College, A
University of Mary, B
University of North Dakota, BM

Ohio

Antioch University Midwest, B
Baldwin Wallace University, B
Bowling Green State University, M
Capital University, B
Cedarville University, B
Central Ohio Technical College, A
Central State University, B
Cincinnati State Technical and Community College, A
Clark State Community College, A
Cleveland State University, BM
Davis College, A
John Carroll University, M
Kent State University, BM
Kent State University at Salem, B
Kent State University at Tuscarawas, B
Lake Erie College, B
Lourdes University, B
Malone University, B
Miami University, B
Miami University Hamilton, B
Mount St. Joseph University, BM
Mount Vernon Nazarene University, B
Muskingum University, B
Notre Dame College, B
Ohio Christian University, B
Ohio Dominican University, B
Ohio Northern University, B
The Ohio State University - Newark Campus, M
Ohio University, B
Ohio University - Chillicothe, B
Ohio University - Eastern, B
Ohio University - Lancaster, B
Ohio University - Southern Campus, AB
Ohio Wesleyan University, B
Owens Community College, A
Shawnee State University, B
Southern State Community College, A

The University of Akron, B
University of Cincinnati, AM
University of Dayton, BM
The University of Findlay, M
University of Mount Union, B
The University of Toledo, MO
Ursuline College, BM
Walsh University, B
Wright State University, BM
Wright State University - Lake Campus, B
Xavier University, ABM
Youngstown State University, BM

Oklahoma

Bacone College, B
Cameron University, B
Community Care College, A
East Central University, B
Northeastern State University, BM
Northwestern Oklahoma State University, B
Oklahoma Baptist University, B
Oklahoma Christian University, B
Oklahoma City University, BM
Oklahoma State University, Oklahoma City, A
Oklahoma Wesleyan University, AB
Oral Roberts University, B
St. Gregory's University, A
Southern Nazarene University, B
Southwestern Oklahoma State University, BM
University of Central Oklahoma, BM
University of Oklahoma, B
University of Science and Arts of Oklahoma, B
The University of Tulsa, B

Oregon

Central Oregon Community College, A
Concordia University, M
Eastern Oregon University, B
Lewis & Clark College, M
Northwest Christian University, B
Pacific University, M
Portland State University, M
Southern Oregon University, M
Tillamook Bay Community College, A
Warner Pacific College, B
Western Oregon University, M

Pennsylvania

Albright College, M
Alvernia University, B
Arcadia University, BMO
Bloomsburg University of Pennsylvania, BM
Bucknell University, B
Bucks County Community College, A
California University of Pennsylvania, B
Carlow University, BM
Cedar Crest College, B
Chatham University, BM
Chestnut Hill College, BMO
Cheyney University of Pennsylvania, B
Clarion University of Pennsylvania, ABM
Delaware County Community College, A
DeSales University, BM
Duquesne University, BM
East Stroudsburg University of Pennsylvania, B
Eastern University, BO
Edinboro University of Pennsylvania, BMO
Elizabethtown College, B
Gannon University, AB
Grove City College, B
Harrisburg Area Community College, A
Holy Family University, BM
Indiana University of Pennsylvania, B
Keystone College, AB
King's College, B
Kutztown University of Pennsylvania, B
La Salle University, BM
Lackawanna College, A
Lancaster Bible College, AB
Lebanon Valley College, B
Lehigh Carbon Community College, A
Lincoln University, M
Lock Haven University of Pennsylvania, B
Luzerne County Community College, A
Marywood University, BM

McCann School of Business & Technology (Lewisburg), B
McCann School of Business & Technology (Pottsville), A
Mercyhurst North East, A
Messiah College, B
Millersville University of Pennsylvania, BM
Misericordia University, B
Mount Aloysius College, AB
Northampton Community College, A
Penn State University Park, B
Pennsylvania Highlands Community College, A
Saint Vincent College, B
Shippensburg University of Pennsylvania, BM
Summit University, A
Susquehanna University, B
University of Pittsburgh, M
The University of Scranton, BM
University of Valley Forge, AB
West Chester University of Pennsylvania, BMO
Westmoreland County Community College, A
Widener University, BM
Wilkes University, M
York College of Pennsylvania, B

Rhode Island

Rhode Island College, BM
Salve Regina University, B

South Carolina

Aiken Technical College, A
Anderson University, B
Benedict College, B
Bob Jones University, B
Charleston Southern University, B
Claflin University, B
Clemson University, B
Clinton College, A
Coastal Carolina University, B
Coker College, B
College of Charleston, BM
Columbia College, B
Columbia International University, M
Francis Marion University, BM
Furman University, M
Lander University, BM
Limestone College, B
Morris College, B
Newberry College, B
North Greenville University, B
Presbyterian College, B
South Carolina State University, BM
Southern Wesleyan University, B
Technical College of the Lowcountry, A
University of South Carolina, MD
University of South Carolina Aiken, B
University of South Carolina Beaufort, B
University of South Carolina Upstate, BM
York Technical College, A

South Dakota

Sinte Gleska University, AB
South Dakota State University, B

Tennessee

Belmont University, B
Carson-Newman University, B
Christian Brothers University, B
East Tennessee State University, MDO
Freed-Hardeman University, B
Lee University, B
LeMoyne-Owen College, B
Middle Tennessee State University, M
Milligan College, B
Nashville State Community College, A
Roane State Community College, A
Tennessee Technological University, MO
Tennessee Wesleyan College, B
Trevecca Nazarene University, B
University of Memphis, MD
The University of Tennessee, MD
The University of Tennessee at Chattanooga, B
Vanderbilt University, B
Welch College, B

Texas

Alvin Community College, A
Arlington Baptist College, B
Austin Community College District, A
Baylor University, B
Central Texas College, A
College of the Mainland, A
Collin County Community College District, A
Dallas Baptist University, M
Grayson College, A
Hardin-Simmons University, B
Houston Community College, A
Lubbock Christian University, B
McMurry University, B
Midwestern State University, B
Our Lady of the Lake University of San Antonio, M
Panola College, A
Paris Junior College, A
St. Philip's College, A
Schreiner University, B
Southwestern Assemblies of God University, A
Stephen F. Austin State University, M
Texas A&M University - Corpus Christi, M
Texas A&M University - Kingsville, M
Texas A&M University - San Antonio, M
Texas Christian University, B
Texas College, A
Texas Woman's University, MD
University of Houston - Clear Lake, M
University of North Texas, M
The University of Texas at Austin, MD
The University of Texas of the Permian Basin, M
The University of Texas Rio Grande Valley, M
The University of Texas at San Antonio, M
The University of Texas at Tyler, M
Victoria College, A
Wayland Baptist University, AB
Western Texas College, A

Utah

Brigham Young University, B
Dixie State University, A
Independence University, A
University of Utah, MD
Utah Valley University, A
Weber State University, AB

Vermont

Champlain College, BM
Community College of Vermont, A
University of Vermont, B

Virginia

Averett University, M
George Mason University, M
James Madison University, M
Liberty University, MO
Norfolk State University, M
Old Dominion University, MD
Paul D. Camp Community College, A
Radford University, M
Regent University, M
University of Valley Forge Virginia Campus, B
University of Virginia, M
Virginia Commonwealth University, M

Washington

Bellevue College, A
Big Bend Community College, A
Central Washington University, B
City University of Seattle, B
Clark College, A
Clover Park Technical College, A
Columbia Basin College, A
Eastern Washington University, BM
Edmonds Community College, A
Everett Community College, A
Green River College, A
Heritage University, A
Lake Washington Institute of Technology, A
Lower Columbia College, A
North Seattle College, A
Northwest Indian College, A
Olympic College, A
Pierce College at Fort Steilacoom, A

Renton Technical College, A
Walla Walla Community College, A
Washington State University, B
Wenatchee Valley College, A
Western Washington University, B

West Virginia

Marshall University, M
Mountwest Community & Technical College, A
Potomac State College of West Virginia University, A
West Virginia University, M

Wisconsin

Blackhawk Technical College, A
Cardinal Stritch University, B
Carroll University, B
Chippewa Valley Technical College, A
College of Menominee Nation, A
Concordia University Wisconsin, M
Edgewood College, B
Fox Valley Technical College, A
Gateway Technical College, A
Lac Courte Oreilles Ojibwa Community College, A
Maranatha Baptist University, AB
Marian University, B
Milwaukee Area Technical College, A
Moraine Park Technical College, A
Northcentral Technical College, A
Northeast Wisconsin Technical College, A
Rasmussen College Appleton, A
Rasmussen College Green Bay, A
Rasmussen College Wausau, A
Ripon College, B
Silver Lake College of the Holy Family, B
Southwest Wisconsin Technical College, A
University of Wisconsin - Milwaukee, M
University of Wisconsin - Oshkosh, M
University of Wisconsin - River Falls, B
University of Wisconsin - Stevens Point, B
University of Wisconsin - Stout, B
University of Wisconsin - Whitewater, B
Waukesha County Technical College, A
Wisconsin Indianhead Technical College, A
Wisconsin Lutheran College, B

Wyoming

Central Wyoming College, A
Eastern Wyoming College, A
Laramie County Community College, A
Sheridan College, A
Western Wyoming Community College, A

U.S. Territories: Guam

Guam Community College, A
University of Guam, B

U.S. Territories: Puerto Rico

Bayamón Central University, BM
Caribbean University, M
Inter American University of Puerto Rico, Guayama Campus, M
Inter American University of Puerto Rico, San Germán Campus, B
Universidad del Este, B
Universidad Metropolitana, B
Universidad del Turabo, BM
University of Puerto Rico, Río Piedras Campus, M
University of the Sacred Heart, M

U.S. Territories: United States Virgin Islands

University of the Virgin Islands, AB

Canada

British Columbia

The University of British Columbia, M
University of Victoria, MD

Ontario

Ryerson University, B

Saskatchewan

University of Regina, B

EAST ASIAN LANGUAGES, LITERATURES, AND LINGUISTICS

United States

Arizona

Arizona State University at the Tempe campus, B

California

University of Southern California, B

Florida

Eckerd College, B
University of Florida, B

Illinois

Northwestern University, B
University of Chicago, B
University of Illinois at Urbana - Champaign, B

Indiana

Indiana University Bloomington, B

Kansas

The University of Kansas, B

Massachusetts

Smith College, B

Minnesota

University of Minnesota, Twin Cities Campus, B

Missouri

Washington University in St. Louis, B

New Hampshire

Dartmouth College, B

New York

Columbia University, B
Columbia University, School of General Studies, B

Pennsylvania

University of Pennsylvania, B

Texas

Austin College, B
The University of Texas at Austin, B

Virginia

Washington and Lee University, B

Washington

University of Puget Sound, B

Canada

Alberta

University of Alberta, B

Ontario

The University of Western Ontario, B

Quebec

McGill University, B

EAST ASIAN STUDIES

United States

Arizona

The University of Arizona, BMD

California

Occidental College, B
Stanford University, BM
University of California, Berkeley, M
University of California, Davis, B
University of California, Irvine, B
University of California, Los Angeles, M
University of California, Santa Barbara, MD
University of Southern California, BMD

Colorado

University of Colorado Boulder, MD

Connecticut

Connecticut College, B
University of Bridgeport, BM
Wesleyan University, B
Yale University, BM

District of Columbia

The George Washington University, BM

Georgia

Emory University, B

Hawaii

University of Hawaii at Manoa, O

Illinois

DePaul University, B
North Central College, B
University of Chicago, D
University of Illinois at Urbana - Champaign, BMD

Indiana

DePauw University, B
Indiana University Bloomington, BMD
Valparaiso University, B

Kansas

The University of Kansas, M

Maine

Bates College, B
Colby College, B
University of Maine, M

Maryland

Johns Hopkins University, B

Massachusetts

Boston University, B
Brandeis University, B
Hampshire College, B
Harvard University, BM
Mount Holyoke College, B
Simmons College, B
Smith College, B
Tufts University, B
Wellesley College, B

Michigan

Grand Valley State University, B
Kalamazoo College, B
University of Michigan, M
Wayne State University, B

Minnesota

Hamline University, B
Minnesota State University Moorhead, B

Missouri

University of Missouri, B
Washington University in St. Louis, B

Montana

University of Montana, B

Nebraska

Creighton University, M

New Jersey

Princeton University, B
Rutgers University - New Brunswick, BMD

New York

Binghamton University, State University of New York, B
Colgate University, B
Columbia University, BMDO
Columbia University, School of General Studies, B
Cornell University, MD
Hofstra University, B
New York University, BMD
Queens College of the City University of New York, B
St. John's University, MO
United States Military Academy, B
University at Albany, State University of New York, B
University of Rochester, B

North Carolina

Davidson College, B
Duke University, MO

Ohio

Denison University, B
John Carroll University, B
Miami University, B
Oberlin College, B
The Ohio State University, M
Ohio Wesleyan University, B
Wittenberg University, B

Oregon

Lewis & Clark College, B
Portland State University, B
Willamette University, B

Pennsylvania

Bryn Mawr College, B
Bucknell University, B
Dickinson College, B
Gettysburg College, B
Haverford College, B
Penn State Abington, B
Penn State Altoona, B
Penn State Beaver, B
Penn State Berks, B
Penn State Brandywine, B
Penn State DuBois, B
Penn State Erie, The Behrend College, B
Penn State Fayette, The Eberly Campus, B
Penn State Greater Allegheny, B
Penn State Hazleton, B
Penn State Lehigh Valley, B
Penn State Mont Alto, B
Penn State New Kensington, B
Penn State Schuylkill, B
Penn State Shenango, B
Penn State Worthington Scranton, B
Penn State York, B
University of Pennsylvania, BMD
University of Pittsburgh, M
Ursinus College, B

Rhode Island

Brown University, BD

Texas

Austin College, B
Dallas Baptist University, M
Trinity University, B

Vermont

Marlboro College, B
Middlebury College, B

Virginia

University of Virginia, M

Washington

University of Washington, MD
Western Washington University, B

West Virginia

West Virginia University, MD

Wisconsin

Lawrence University, B
University of Wisconsin - Madison, MD

Canada

Alberta

University of Alberta, BM
University of Calgary, B

Ontario

Carleton University, B
University of Toronto, BMD
The University of Western Ontario, B
York University, B

Quebec

McGill University, MD
Université de Montréal, B

EAST EUROPEAN AND RUSSIAN STUDIES

United States

California

Stanford University, M

Connecticut

Yale University, MD

District of Columbia

The George Washington University, M
Georgetown University, M

Florida

Florida State University, M

Illinois

University of Illinois at Chicago, MD
University of Illinois at Urbana - Champaign, M

Indiana

Indiana University Bloomington, MO

Kansas

The University of Kansas, MO

Massachusetts

Boston College, M
Harvard University, M

Michigan

University of Michigan, MO

New York

Columbia University, MO
Cornell University, MD

North Carolina

The University of North Carolina at Chapel Hill, M

Ohio

The Ohio State University, MD

Pennsylvania

La Salle University, MO
University of Pittsburgh, O

Rhode Island

Brown University, MD

Texas

The University of Texas at Austin, M

Washington

University of Washington, M

Canada

Alberta

University of Alberta, MD

British Columbia

The University of British Columbia, MD

Ontario

Carleton University, MO
University of Toronto, M

Saskatchewan

University of Saskatchewan, M

ECOLOGY

United States

Alabama

Jacksonville State University, B

Arizona

Prescott College, B
The University of Arizona, MD

California

California Institute of Integral Studies, MD
California State University, Dominguez Hills, B
California State University, East Bay, B
California State University, Fresno, B
California State University, Long Beach, B
California State University, San Marcos, B
California State University, Stanislaus, M
San Diego State University, BMD
San Francisco State University, BM
San Jose State University, M
Sonoma State University, BM
Stanford University, D
University of California, Davis, MD
University of California, Irvine, MD
University of California, Los Angeles, BMD
University of California, Riverside, D
University of California, San Diego, B
University of California, Santa Barbara, BMD
University of California, Santa Cruz, BMD

Colorado

Colorado State University, BMD
Fort Lewis College, B
University of Colorado Boulder, MD
University of Colorado Denver, M
University of Denver, BD

Connecticut

Connecticut College, B
University of Connecticut, BMD
University of New Haven, M
Wesleyan University, D
Yale University, BD

Delaware

University of Delaware, BMD

Florida

Barry University, B
Broward College, A
Florida Institute of Technology, M
Florida State University, MD
Saint Leo University, B
University of Florida, MDO
University of South Florida, MD

Georgia

Augusta University, B
Emory University, D
University of Georgia, BMD

Hawaii

University of Hawaii at Manoa, MD

Idaho

Brigham Young University - Idaho, B

Illinois

Illinois State University, MD
Northwestern University, B
University of Chicago, D
University of Illinois at Urbana - Champaign, BMD
Western Illinois University, D

Indiana

Indiana State University, D
Indiana University Bloomington, MD
Manchester University, B
Purdue University, MD
University of Notre Dame, MD

Iowa

Iowa Lakes Community College, A
Iowa State University of Science and Technology, BMD
University of Northern Iowa, B

Kansas

The University of Kansas, MD

Kentucky

Eastern Kentucky University, M
Georgetown College, B

Louisiana

Tulane University, BMD

Maine

University of Maine, MD
University of Maine at Machias, B

Maryland

Frostburg State University, M
Salisbury University, B
University of Maryland, College Park, BMD
University of Maryland Eastern Shore, B
Washington College, B

Massachusetts

Clark University, B
Lesley University, M
Tufts University, B

Michigan

Eastern Michigan University, M
Michigan State University, D
Michigan Technological University, M
Northern Michigan University, B
University of Michigan, MD
University of Michigan - Flint, B

Minnesota

Bemidji State University, B
Minnesota State University Mankato, B
St. Cloud State University, B
University of Minnesota, Twin Cities Campus, BMD
Vermilion Community College, A

Missouri

College of the Ozarks, B
University of Missouri, MD
Washington University in St. Louis, BD

Montana

Montana State University, MD
University of Montana, MD

Nebraska

Western Nebraska Community College, A

Nevada

Sierra Nevada College, B
University of Nevada, Reno, D

New Hampshire

Dartmouth College, BD

New Jersey

Montclair State University, M
Princeton University, BD
Rutgers University - New Brunswick, BMD

New Mexico

Eastern New Mexico University, M
New Mexico State University, B

New York

Columbia University, MD
Concordia College - New York, B
Cornell University, MD
Le Moyne College, B
Medgar Evers College of the City University of New York, B
Molloy College, B
New York University, B
Paul Smith's College, B
State University of New York College of Environmental Science and Forestry, BMD
State University of New York at Plattsburgh, B
Stony Brook University, State University of New York, BMD
University at Albany, State University of New York, D
University at Buffalo, the State University of New York, MDO

North Carolina

Duke University, DO
Greensboro College, B
The University of North Carolina at Chapel Hill, MD

North Dakota

North Dakota State University, MD
University of North Dakota, MD

Ohio

Defiance College, B
Hocking College, A
Kent State University, MD
Oberlin College, B
The Ohio State University, MD
Ohio University, BMD
The University of Akron, B
University of Rio Grande, B
The University of Toledo, MD

Oklahoma

Oklahoma State University, B
University of Oklahoma, D

Oregon

University of Oregon, MD

Pennsylvania

Cheyney University of Pennsylvania, B
Penn State University Park, MD
Susquehanna University, B
University of Pittsburgh, BD
University of Pittsburgh at Johnstown, B

Rhode Island

Brown University, D
Bryant University, B

South Carolina

Clemson University, MD
University of South Carolina, MD

Tennessee

Christian Brothers University, B
The University of Tennessee, MD

Texas

Baylor University, D
Rice University, BMD
University of North Texas, B
The University of Texas at Austin, D

Utah

Utah State University, BMD

Vermont

Bennington College, B
Castleton University, B
Marlboro College, B
Sterling College, B

Virginia

George Mason University, M
Old Dominion University, D

Washington

Central Washington University, B
The Evergreen State College, B
Seattle Pacific University, B
University of Washington, MD

Wisconsin

Beloit College, B
Lawrence University, B
Marquette University, MD
University of Wisconsin - Madison, M

Wyoming

University of Wyoming, MD

U.S. Territories: Puerto Rico

Inter American University of Puerto Rico, Bayamón
  Campus, M
University of Puerto Rico, Río Piedras Campus, MD

Canada

Alberta

University of Alberta, MD
University of Calgary, B

British Columbia

University of Victoria, B

Manitoba

University of Manitoba, BMD
The University of Winnipeg, B

Maritime Provinces: New Brunswick

University of New Brunswick Fredericton, B

Maritime Provinces: Nova Scotia

Dalhousie University, M

Newfoundland and Labrador

Memorial University of Newfoundland, B

Ontario

Carleton University, B
Laurentian University, D
University of Guelph, BMD
University of Toronto, MD
University of Waterloo, B
The University of Western Ontario, B
York University, B

Quebec

Concordia University, B
McGill University, B
Université de Sherbrooke, B

Saskatchewan

University of Saskatchewan, B

ECOLOGY, EVOLUTION, SYSTEMATICS AND POPULATION BIOLOGY

United States

California

University of California, Davis, B

Colorado

University of Colorado Boulder, B

New York

Hofstra University, B

Ohio

The Ohio State University, B

Washington

University of Washington, B

Canada

British Columbia

The University of British Columbia - Okanagan
  Campus, B

Ontario

University of Guelph, B

Saskatchewan

University of Regina, B

ECONOMETRICS AND QUANTITATIVE ECONOMICS

United States

California

Scripps College, B
University of California, Irvine, B
University of California, Santa Barbara, B

Colorado

The Colorado College, B

Kentucky

Western Kentucky University, B

Maine

Bowdoin College, B

Maryland

United States Naval Academy, B

Minnesota

University of Minnesota, Twin Cities Campus, B

New York

Hofstra University, B
State University of New York at Oswego, B

North Carolina

High Point University, B
Wake Forest University, B

Ohio

Baldwin Wallace University, B
Miami University Hamilton, B
University of Dayton, B
Youngstown State University, B

Pennsylvania

Bucknell University, B
Carnegie Mellon University, B
Westminster College, B

Rhode Island

University of Rhode Island, B

Texas

Southern Methodist University, B

Utah

Weber State University, B

Virginia

Hampden-Sydney College, B

West Virginia

Bethany College, B

Canada

British Columbia

Thompson Rivers University, B

Ontario

University of Guelph, B

Quebec

Université Laval, B

ECONOMIC DEVELOPMENT

United States

Alabama

Troy University, M

Arkansas

University of Central Arkansas, MO

California

University of Southern California, MD

Colorado

University of Colorado Denver, M

Connecticut

Yale University, M

District of Columbia

The Catholic University of America, M
Georgetown University, D

Florida

Florida Atlantic University, O
University of Miami, MD

Georgia

Albany State University, M
Georgia Institute of Technology, M
Georgia State University, MDO

Illinois

Western Illinois University, O

Indiana

Indiana University Bloomington, M

Massachusetts

Northeastern University, M
University of Massachusetts Lowell, MO
Williams College, M

Michigan

Wayne State University, MO

Mississippi

University of Southern Mississippi, M

Missouri

Washington University in St. Louis, M

New Mexico

New Mexico State University, D

New York

Cornell University, MD
Fordham University, MO
State University of New York Empire State College, M

North Carolina

East Carolina University, O
The University of North Carolina at Greensboro, O

Ohio

Cleveland State University, MO

Pennsylvania

Eastern University, M
University of Pennsylvania, O

Tennessee

East Tennessee State University, O
Vanderbilt University, M

Texas

University of Houston - Victoria, M

West Virginia

West Virginia University, D

U.S. Territories: Puerto Rico

University of Puerto Rico, Río Piedras Campus, M

Canada

Ontario

University of Waterloo, M

Quebec

Concordia University, O
Université de Sherbrooke, D

ECONOMICS

United States

Alabama

Alabama Agricultural and Mechanical University, B
Auburn University, BM
Auburn University at Montgomery, B
Birmingham-Southern College, B
Jacksonville State University, B
Oakwood University, B
Strayer University - Birmingham Campus, B
Strayer University - Huntsville Campus, B
Talladega College, B
Troy University, B
Tuskegee University, B
The University of Alabama, MD

Alaska

University of Alaska Anchorage, B
University of Alaska Fairbanks, BM

Arizona

Arizona State University at the Tempe campus, BD
Cochise County Community College District, A
The University of Arizona, BMD

Arkansas

Arkansas State University, B
Harding University, B
Hendrix College, B
John Brown University, B
Lyon College, B
University of Arkansas, BMD
University of Central Arkansas, BMO
University of the Ozarks, B

California

Bakersfield College, A
Cabrillo College, A
California Institute of Technology, B
California Lutheran University, BM
California Polytechnic State University, San Luis Obispo, B
California State Polytechnic University, Pomona, BM
California State University, Bakersfield, B
California State University Channel Islands, B
California State University, Chico, B
California State University, East Bay, BM
California State University, Fresno, B
California State University, Fullerton, BM
California State University, Long Beach, BM
California State University, Los Angeles, BM
California State University, Northridge, B
California State University, Sacramento, B
California State University, San Bernardino, B
California State University, San Marcos, B
California State University, Stanislaus, B
California University of Management and Sciences, BM
Cañada College, A
Cerritos College, A
Chaffey College, A
Claremont McKenna College, B
College of the Desert, A
Concordia University Irvine, B
Contra Costa College, A
Copper Mountain College, A
Crafton Hills College, A
De Anza College, A
El Camino College, A
Foothill College, A
Fullerton College, A
Grossmont College, A
Humboldt State University, B
La Sierra University, B
Lincoln University, B
Los Angeles Southwest College, A
Los Angeles Valley College, A
Loyola Marymount University, B
Merritt College, A
Mills College, B
Monterey Peninsula College, A
Occidental College, B
Ohlone College, A
Orange Coast College, A
Oxnard College, A
Palomar College, A
Pepperdine University, BM
Pitzer College, B
Pomona College, B
Saddleback College, A
Saint Mary's College of California, B
San Bernardino Valley College, A
San Diego State University, BM
San Francisco State University, BM
San Joaquin Delta College, A
San Jose State University, BM
Santa Ana College, A
Santa Barbara City College, A
Santa Clara University, B
Santa Rosa Junior College, A
Santiago Canyon College, A
Scripps College, B
Skyline College, A
Sonoma State University, B
Southwestern College, A
Stanford University, BD
University of California, Berkeley, BD
University of California, Davis, BMD
University of California, Irvine, BMD
University of California, Los Angeles, BMD
University of California, Merced, B
University of California, Riverside, BMD
University of California, San Diego, BD
University of California, Santa Barbara, BMD
University of California, Santa Cruz, BD
University of La Verne, B
University of the Pacific, B
University of Redlands, B
University of San Diego, B
University of San Francisco, BM
University of Southern California, BMD

West Los Angeles College, A
West Valley College, A
Westmont College, B
Whittier College, B

Colorado

Adams State University, B
Colorado Christian University, B
The Colorado College, B
Colorado School of Mines, B
Colorado State University, BMD
Fort Lewis College, B
Metropolitan State University of Denver, B
Northeastern Junior College, A
Regis University, B
United States Air Force Academy, B
University of Colorado Boulder, BMD
University of Colorado Colorado Springs, B
University of Colorado Denver, BM
University of Denver, BM
University of Northern Colorado, B
Western State Colorado University, B

Connecticut

Central Connecticut State University, B
Connecticut College, B
Eastern Connecticut State University, B
Fairfield University, B
Quinnipiac University, B
Sacred Heart University, B
Southern Connecticut State University, B
Trinity College, B
University of Connecticut, BMD
University of Hartford, B
University of New Haven, B
Wesleyan University, B
Western Connecticut State University, B
Yale University, BMD

Delaware

Goldey-Beacom College, B
Strayer University - Christiana Campus, B
University of Delaware, BMD

District of Columbia

American University, BM
The Catholic University of America, BM
The George Washington University, BMD
Georgetown University, BD
Howard University, BMD
Strayer University - Takoma Park Campus, B
Strayer University - Washington Campus, B
Trinity Washington University, B
University of the District of Columbia, B

Florida

Ave Maria University, B
Barry University, B
Broward College, A
College of Central Florida, A
Eckerd College, B
Flagler College, B
Florida Agricultural and Mechanical University, B
Florida Atlantic University, BM
Florida Gulf Coast University, B
Florida International University, BMD
Florida Southern College, B
Florida State University, BMD
Indian River State College, A
Jacksonville University, B
Miami Dade College, A
New College of Florida, B
Palm Beach State College, A
Rollins College, B
Saint Leo University, B
St. Thomas University, B
South Florida State College, A
State College of Florida Manatee-Sarasota, A
Stetson University, B
Strayer University - Baymeadows Campus, B
Strayer University - Brickell Campus, B
Strayer University - Coral Springs Campus, B
Strayer University - Doral Campus, B
Strayer University - Fort Lauderdale Campus, B
Strayer University - Maitland Campus, B

Strayer University - Miramar Campus, B
Strayer University - Orlando East Campus, B
Strayer University - Palm Beach Gardens Campus, B
Strayer University - Sand Lake Campus, B
Strayer University - Tampa East Campus, B
Strayer University - Tampa Westshore Campus, B
University of Central Florida, B
University of Florida, BMD
University of Miami, BMD
University of North Florida, BM
University of South Florida, BMD
The University of Tampa, B
University of West Florida, B

Georgia

Agnes Scott College, B
Albany State University, M
Armstrong State University, B
Clark Atlanta University, M
Darton State College, A
Emory University, BD
Fort Valley State University, B
Georgia Highlands College, A
Georgia Institute of Technology, MD
Georgia Southern University, B
Georgia State University, BMD
Mercer University, B
Morehouse College, B
Oglethorpe University, B
Shorter University, B
Spelman College, B
Strayer University - Augusta Campus, B
Strayer University - Chamblee Campus, B
Strayer University - Cobb County Campus, B
Strayer University - Columbus Campus, B
Strayer University - Douglasville Campus, B
Strayer University - Lithonia Campus, B
Strayer University - Morrow Campus, B
Strayer University - Roswell Campus, B
Strayer University - Savannah Campus, B
University of Georgia, MD
University of West Georgia, B
Wesleyan College, B

Hawaii

Hawai'i Pacific University, BM
University of Hawaii at Hilo, B
University of Hawaii at Manoa, BMD
University of Hawaii - West Oahu, B

Idaho

Boise State University, B
Brigham Young University - Idaho, B
Idaho State University, B
University of Idaho, B

Illinois

Augustana College, B
Benedictine University, B
Bradley University, B
Chicago State University, B
DePaul University, BM
Dominican University, B
Eastern Illinois University, BM
Elmhurst College, B
Governors State University, B
Illinois College, B
Illinois State University, BM
Illinois Wesleyan University, B
John A. Logan College, A
Knox College, B
Lake Forest College, B
Loyola University Chicago, M
McKendree University, B
Monmouth College, B
North Central College, B
North Park University, B
Northeastern Illinois University, B
Northern Illinois University, BMD
Northwestern University, BD
Olivet Nazarene University, B
Principia College, B
Rockford University, B
Roosevelt University, BM
Sauk Valley Community College, A

Southern Illinois University Carbondale, BMD
Southern Illinois University Edwardsville, BM
Triton College, A
University of Chicago, BMD
University of Illinois at Chicago, BMD
University of Illinois at Springfield, B
University of Illinois at Urbana - Champaign, BMD
Western Illinois University, BMO
Wheaton College, B

Indiana

Butler University, B
DePauw University, B
Earlham College, B
Franklin College, B
Hanover College, B
Huntington University, B
Indiana State University, B
Indiana University Bloomington, BD
Indiana University Northwest, B
Indiana University - Purdue University Fort Wayne, B
Indiana University - Purdue University Indianapolis, BM
Indiana University South Bend, B
Indiana University Southeast, B
Indiana Wesleyan University, B
Manchester University, B
Marian University, B
Purdue University, BD
Purdue University Northwest (Hammond), B
Rose-Hulman Institute of Technology, B
Saint Joseph's College, B
Saint Mary's College, B
Taylor University, B
University of Evansville, B
University of Notre Dame, BMD
University of Southern Indiana, B
Valparaiso University, B
Vincennes University, A
Wabash College, B

Iowa

Central College, B
Coe College, B
Cornell College, B
Graceland University, B
Grinnell College, B
Iowa Lakes Community College, A
Iowa State University of Science and Technology, BMD
Loras College, B
Luther College, B
Northwestern College, B
St. Ambrose University, B
Simpson College, B
The University of Iowa, BD
University of Northern Iowa, B
Wartburg College, B

Kansas

Allen Community College, A
Baker University, B
Barton County Community College, A
Benedictine College, B
Central Christian College of Kansas, A
Emporia State University, B
Fort Hays State University, B
Kansas State University, BMD
Pittsburg State University, B
The University of Kansas, BMD
Washburn University, B
Wichita State University, BM

Kentucky

Bellarmine University, B
Berea College, B
Campbellsville University, B
Centre College, B
Eastern Kentucky University, B
Georgetown College, B
Murray State University, BM
Thomas More College, AB
Transylvania University, B
University of Kentucky, BMD
University of Louisville, B

Western Kentucky University, B

Louisiana

Centenary College of Louisiana, B
Dillard University, B
Louisiana College, B
Louisiana State University and Agricultural & Mechanical College, BMD
Louisiana Tech University, MD
Loyola University New Orleans, B
Tulane University, BMD
University of New Orleans, MD

Maine

Bates College, B
Bowdoin College, B
Colby College, B
College of the Atlantic, B
University of Maine, BM
University of Southern Maine, B

Maryland

Bowie State University, B
Frostburg State University, B
Goucher College, B
Hood College, B
Johns Hopkins University, BD
Loyola University Maryland, B
McDaniel College, B
Morgan State University, BM
Mount St. Mary's University, B
St. Mary's College of Maryland, B
Salisbury University, B
Strayer University - Anne Arundel Campus, B
Strayer University - Owings Mills Campus, B
Strayer University - Prince George's Campus, B
Strayer University - Rockville Campus, B
Strayer University - White Marsh Campus, B
Towson University, B
United States Naval Academy, B
University of Maryland, Baltimore County, BMD
University of Maryland, College Park, BMD
Washington College, B

Massachusetts

American International College, B
Amherst College, B
Assumption College, BM
Babson College, B
Boston College, BD
Boston University, BMD
Brandeis University, BMD
Bridgewater State University, B
Clark University, BD
College of the Holy Cross, B
Emmanuel College, B
Fitchburg State University, B
Framingham State University, B
Gordon College, B
Greenfield Community College, A
Hampshire College, B
Harvard University, BD
Massachusetts Institute of Technology, BMD
Merrimack College, B
Mount Holyoke College, B
Nichols College, B
Northeastern University, BMD
Salem State University, B
Simmons College, B
Smith College, B
Stonehill College, B
Suffolk University, BM
Tufts University, BM
University of Massachusetts Amherst, BMD
University of Massachusetts Boston, B
University of Massachusetts Dartmouth, B
University of Massachusetts Lowell, BMO
Wellesley College, B
Western New England University, B
Westfield State University, B
Wheaton College, B
Williams College, B
Worcester Polytechnic Institute, B
Worcester State University, B

Michigan

Adrian College, B
Albion College, B
Alma College, B
Andrews University, BM
Aquinas College, B
Calvin College, B
Central Michigan University, BM
Cornerstone University, B
Eastern Michigan University, BMO
Grand Valley State University, B
Hillsdale College, B
Hope College, B
Kalamazoo College, B
Lansing Community College, A
Michigan State University, BMD
Michigan Technological University, B
Muskegon Community College, A
Northern Michigan University, B
Oakland University, BO
Saginaw Valley State University, B
University of Detroit Mercy, B
University of Michigan, BMD
University of Michigan - Dearborn, B
University of Michigan - Flint, B
Wayne State University, BMD
Western Michigan University, BMD

Minnesota

Augsburg College, B
Bemidji State University, B
Bethel University, B
Carleton College, B
College of Saint Benedict, B
Gustavus Adolphus College, B
Hamline University, B
Macalester College, B
Metropolitan State University, B
Minnesota State University Mankato, B
Minnesota State University Moorhead, B
St. Catherine University, B
St. Cloud State University, BM
Saint John's University, B
St. Olaf College, B
University of Minnesota, Duluth, B
University of Minnesota, Morris, B
University of Minnesota, Twin Cities Campus, BD
University of St. Thomas, B
Vermilion Community College, A
Winona State University, B

Mississippi

Copiah-Lincoln Community College, A
Itawamba Community College, A
Jones County Junior College, A
Millsaps College, B
Mississippi Delta Community College, A
Mississippi State University, BMD
Tougaloo College, B
University of Mississippi, BMD
University of Southern Mississippi, M

Missouri

Central Methodist University, B
Drury University, B
Lindenwood University, B
Missouri State University, B
Missouri University of Science and Technology, B
Missouri Valley College, B
Missouri Western State University, B
Northwest Missouri State University, B
Park University, B
Rockhurst University, B
St. Charles Community College, A
Southeast Missouri State University, B
Truman State University, B
University of Central Missouri, B
University of Missouri, BMD
University of Missouri - Kansas City, BMD
University of Missouri - St. Louis, BM
Washington University in St. Louis, BD
Webster University, B
Westminster College, B
William Jewell College, B

Montana

Montana State University, B
University of Montana, BM

Nebraska

Creighton University, B
Doane University, B
Hastings College, B
Midland University, B
Nebraska Wesleyan University, B
Peru State College, M
University of Nebraska at Kearney, B
University of Nebraska - Lincoln, BMD
University of Nebraska at Omaha, BM
Western Nebraska Community College, A

Nevada

Nevada State College, B
University of Nevada, Las Vegas, BM
University of Nevada, Reno, M

New Hampshire

Dartmouth College, B
Keene State College, B
Saint Anselm College, B
Southern New Hampshire University, B
University of New Hampshire, BMD

New Jersey

Bergen Community College, A
Caldwell University, B
The College of New Jersey, B
College of Saint Elizabeth, B
Drew University, B
Fairleigh Dickinson University, College at Florham, B
Fairleigh Dickinson University, Metropolitan Campus, B
Kean University, B
Montclair State University, B
New Jersey City University, B
Princeton University, BD
Ramapo College of New Jersey, B
Rider University, B
Rowan University, B
Rutgers University - Camden, B
Rutgers University - New Brunswick, BMD
Rutgers University - Newark, BMD
Saint Peter's University, B
Seton Hall University, B
Stockton University, B
Thomas Edison State University, B
William Paterson University of New Jersey, B

New Mexico

New Mexico Military Institute, A
New Mexico State University, BMDO
University of New Mexico, BMD

New York

Adelphi University, B
Bard College, BM
Barnard College, B
Baruch College of the City University of New York, BM
Binghamton University, State University of New York, BMD
Brooklyn College of the City University of New York, BM
Buffalo State College, State University of New York, BM
Canisius College, B
City College of the City University of New York, BM
Colgate University, B
College of Mount Saint Vincent, B
The College of New Rochelle, B
College of Staten Island of the City University of New York, B
Columbia University, BMD
Columbia University, School of General Studies, B
Cornell University, BMD
Dominican College, B
Elmira College, B
Eugene Lang College of Liberal Arts, B
Fordham University, BMDO

Hamilton College, B
Hartwick College, B
Hobart and William Smith Colleges, B
Hofstra University, B
Hunter College of the City University of New York, BMD
Iona College, B
Ithaca College, B
John Jay College of Criminal Justice of the City University of New York, B
Le Moyne College, B
Lehman College of the City University of New York, B
Long Island University - LIU Brooklyn, B
Long Island University - LIU Post, B
Manhattan College, B
Manhattanville College, B
Marist College, B
Nazareth College of Rochester, B
New York University, BMDO
Niagara University, B
Pace University, B
Pace University, Pleasantville Campus, B
Purchase College, State University of New York, B
Queens College of the City University of New York, B
Rensselaer Polytechnic Institute, B
Rochester Institute of Technology, B
St. Francis College, B
St. John Fisher College, B
St. John's University, B
St. Lawrence University, B
Sarah Lawrence College, B
Siena College, B
Skidmore College, B
State University of New York College at Cortland, B
State University of New York College of Environmental Science and Forestry, M
State University of New York College at Geneseo, B
State University of New York College at Oneonta, B
State University of New York College at Potsdam, B
State University of New York at Fredonia, B
State University of New York at New Paltz, B
State University of New York at Oswego, B
State University of New York at Plattsburgh, B
Stony Brook University, State University of New York, BMD
Syracuse University, BMD
Touro College, B
Union College, B
United States Military Academy, B
University at Albany, State University of New York, BMD
University at Buffalo, the State University of New York, BMDO
University of Rochester, BMD
Utica College, B
Vassar College, B
Wagner College, B
Wells College, B
Yeshiva University, BM
York College of the City University of New York, B

North Carolina

Appalachian State University, B
Campbell University, B
Catawba College, B
Chowan University, B
Davidson College, B
Duke University, BMD
East Carolina University, B
Elon University, B
Gardner-Webb University, B
Guilford College, B
Johnson C. Smith University, B
Lenoir-Rhyne University, B
Louisburg College, A
Mars Hill University, B
Meredith College, B
Methodist University, AB
North Carolina Agricultural and Technical State University, B
North Carolina State University, MD
Pfeiffer University, B
Salem College, B
Strayer University - Greensboro Campus, B

Strayer University - Huntersville Campus, B
Strayer University - North Charlotte Campus, B
Strayer University - North Raleigh Campus, B
Strayer University - RTP Campus, B
Strayer University - South Charlotte Campus, B
Strayer University - South Raleigh Campus, B
University of North Carolina at Asheville, B
The University of North Carolina at Chapel Hill, BMD
The University of North Carolina at Charlotte, BM
The University of North Carolina at Greensboro, BD
The University of North Carolina Wilmington, B
Wake Forest University, B
Winston-Salem State University, B

North Dakota

North Dakota State University, B
University of North Dakota, B

Ohio

Ashland University, B
Baldwin Wallace University, B
Bluffton University, B
Bowling Green State University, BM
Capital University, B
Case Western Reserve University, B
Cedarville University, B
Central State University, B
Cleveland State University, BMO
The College of Wooster, B
Denison University, B
Edison Community College, A
Franciscan University of Steubenville, B
Franklin University, B
Heidelberg University, B
Hiram College, B
John Carroll University, B
Kent State University, M
Kenyon College, B
Marietta College, B
Miami University, BM
Miami University Hamilton, B
Miami University Middletown, A
Muskingum University, B
Oberlin College, B
Ohio Dominican University, B
The Ohio State University, BMD
Ohio University, BM
Ohio Wesleyan University, B
Otterbein University, B
Terra State Community College, A
The University of Akron, BM
University of Cincinnati, BD
University of Dayton, B
The University of Findlay, B
University of Mount Union, B
University of Rio Grande, B
The University of Toledo, BM
Wilmington College, B
Wittenberg University, B
Wright State University, BM
Xavier University, B
Youngstown State University, BM

Oklahoma

Langston University, B
Oklahoma City University, B
Oklahoma State University, BMD
Oklahoma State University, Oklahoma City, A
University of Central Oklahoma, B
University of Oklahoma, BMD
University of Science and Arts of Oklahoma, B
The University of Tulsa, B

Oregon

Eastern Oregon University, B
George Fox University, B
Lewis & Clark College, B
Linfield College, B
Linn-Benton Community College, A
Oregon State University, BMD
Pacific University, B
Portland State University, BMD
Reed College, B
Southern Oregon University, B
Umpqua Community College, A

University of Oregon, BMD
University of Portland, B
Western Oregon University, B
Willamette University, B

Pennsylvania

Albright College, B
Allegheny College, B
Bloomsburg University of Pennsylvania, B
Bryn Mawr College, B
Bucknell University, B
Carnegie Mellon University, BD
Clarion University of Pennsylvania, B
DeSales University, B
Dickinson College, B
Drexel University, BMD
Duquesne University, B
East Stroudsburg University of Pennsylvania, B
Edinboro University of Pennsylvania, B
Elizabethtown College, B
Franklin & Marshall College, B
Gettysburg College, B
Grove City College, B
Haverford College, B
Indiana University of Pennsylvania, B
Juniata College, B
King's College, B
La Salle University, B
Lafayette College, B
Lebanon Valley College, B
Lehigh University, MD
Lycoming College, B
Messiah College, B
Millersville University of Pennsylvania, B
Moravian College, B
Muhlenberg College, B
Penn State Abington, B
Penn State Altoona, B
Penn State Beaver, B
Penn State Berks, B
Penn State Brandywine, B
Penn State DuBois, B
Penn State Erie, The Behrend College, B
Penn State Fayette, The Eberly Campus, B
Penn State Greater Allegheny, B
Penn State Hazleton, B
Penn State Lehigh Valley, B
Penn State Mont Alto, B
Penn State New Kensington, B
Penn State Schuylkill, B
Penn State Shenango, B
Penn State University Park, BMD
Penn State Wilkes-Barre, B
Penn State Worthington Scranton, B
Penn State York, B
Point Park University, B
Robert Morris University, B
Rosemont College, B
Saint Francis University, B
Saint Joseph's University, B
Saint Vincent College, B
Seton Hill University, B
Shippensburg University of Pennsylvania, B
Slippery Rock University of Pennsylvania, B
Strayer University - Allentown Campus, B
Strayer University - Center City Campus, B
Strayer University - Delaware County Campus, B
Strayer University - King of Prussia Campus, B
Strayer University - Lower Bucks County Campus, B
Strayer University - Warrendale Campus, B
Susquehanna University, B
Swarthmore College, B
Temple University, BMD
University of Pennsylvania, BMD
University of Pittsburgh, BMD
University of Pittsburgh at Bradford, B
University of Pittsburgh at Johnstown, B
The University of Scranton, B
Ursinus College, B
Villanova University, B
Washington & Jefferson College, B
Westminster College, B
Widener University, B
York College of Pennsylvania, B

Rhode Island

Brown University, BD
Bryant University, B
Providence College, B
Rhode Island College, B
Roger Williams University, B
Salve Regina University, B
University of Rhode Island, BMD

South Carolina

Benedict College, B
Charleston Southern University, B
Clemson University, BMD
Coastal Carolina University, B
College of Charleston, B
Converse College, B
Francis Marion University, B
Furman University, B
Limestone College, B
Strayer University - Charleston Campus, B
Strayer University - Columbia Campus, B
Strayer University - Greenville Campus, B
University of South Carolina, BMD
Wofford College, B

South Dakota

Augustana University, B
Northern State University, B
South Dakota State University, BM
The University of South Dakota, B

Tennessee

East Tennessee State University, B
Hiwassee College, A
King University, B
Lincoln Memorial University, B
Maryville College, B
Middle Tennessee State University, BMD
Milligan College, B
Nashville State Community College, A
Rhodes College, B
Sewanee: The University of the South, B
Strayer University - Knoxville Campus, B
Strayer University - Nashville Campus, B
Strayer University - Shelby Campus, B
Strayer University - Thousand Oaks Campus, B
Tennessee Technological University, B
Union University, B
University of Memphis, BMD
The University of Tennessee, BMD
The University of Tennessee at Chattanooga, B
The University of Tennessee at Martin, B
Vanderbilt University, BMD

Texas

Austin College, B
Austin Community College District, A
Baylor University, BM
Clarendon College, A
Hardin-Simmons University, B
Hill College, A
Lee College, A
Lone Star College - CyFair, A
Lubbock Christian University, B
Midwestern State University, B
Our Lady of the Lake University of San Antonio, B
Palo Alto College, A
Rice University, BMD
St. Edward's University, B
St. Mary's University, B
St. Philip's College, A
Southern Methodist University, BMD
Southwestern University, B
Stephen F. Austin State University, B
Strayer University - Cedar Hill Campus, B
Strayer University - Irving Campus, B
Strayer University - Katy Campus, B
Strayer University - North Austin Campus, B
Strayer University - Northwest Houston Campus, B
Strayer University - Plano Campus, B
Tarleton State University, B
Texas A&M University, BMD
Texas A&M University - Central Texas, B
Texas A&M University - Corpus Christi, B
Texas Christian University, B

Texas Lutheran University, B
Texas Southern University, B
Texas State University, B
Texas Tech University, BMD
Trinity University, B
Tyler Junior College, A
University of Dallas, B
University of Houston, BMD
University of North Texas, BM
University of St. Thomas, B
The University of Texas at Arlington, BM
The University of Texas at Austin, BMD
The University of Texas at Dallas, BMD
The University of Texas at El Paso, BM
The University of Texas Rio Grande Valley, B
The University of Texas at San Antonio, M
The University of Texas at Tyler, B
West Texas A&M University, M

Utah

Salt Lake Community College, A
Snow College, A
Southern Utah University, B
University of Utah, BMD
Utah State University, BMD
Utah Valley University, B
Weber State University, B

Vermont

Castleton University, B
Marlboro College, B
Middlebury College, B
Norwich University, B
Saint Michael's College, B
University of Vermont, B

Virginia

Bridgewater College, B
Christopher Newport University, B
The College of William and Mary, B
Eastern Mennonite University, B
Emory & Henry College, B
George Mason University, BMDO
Hampden-Sydney College, B
Hampton University, B
Hollins University, B
James Madison University, B
Longwood University, B
Lynchburg College, B
Mary Baldwin College, B
Marymount University, B
Old Dominion University, BM
Radford University, B
Randolph College, B
Randolph-Macon College, B
Roanoke College, B
Strayer University - Alexandria Campus, B
Strayer University - Arlington Campus, B
Strayer University - Chesapeake Campus, B
Strayer University - Chesterfield Campus, B
Strayer University - Fredericksburg Campus, B
Strayer University - Henrico Campus, B
Strayer University - Loudoun Campus, B
Strayer University - Manassas Campus, B
Strayer University - Newport News Campus, B
Strayer University - Virginia Beach Campus, B
Strayer University - Woodbridge Campus, B
Sweet Briar College, B
University of Mary Washington, B
University of Richmond, B
University of Virginia, BMD
The University of Virginia's College at Wise, B
Virginia Commonwealth University, M
Virginia Military Institute, B
Virginia Polytechnic Institute and State University,
   BMD
Virginia State University, M
Washington and Lee University, B

Washington

Central Washington University, B
Eastern Washington University, B
Gonzaga University, B
Pacific Lutheran University, B
Seattle Pacific University, B
Seattle University, B

Skagit Valley College, A
University of Puget Sound, B
University of Washington, BD
Walla Walla University, B
Washington State University, BD
Wenatchee Valley College, A
Western Washington University, B
Whitman College, B
Whitworth University, B

West Virginia

Bethany College, B
Davis & Elkins College, B
Fairmont State University, B
Marshall University, B
Potomac State College of West Virginia University,
   A
Shepherd University, B
Strayer University - Teays Valley Campus, B
West Virginia State University, B
West Virginia University, BMD
West Virginia Wesleyan College, B

Wisconsin

Beloit College, B
Carthage College, B
Concordia University Wisconsin, B
Edgewood College, B
Lawrence University, B
Marquette University, BM
Ripon College, B
St. Norbert College, B
University of Wisconsin - Eau Claire, B
University of Wisconsin - Green Bay, B
University of Wisconsin - La Crosse, B
University of Wisconsin - Madison, BD
University of Wisconsin - Milwaukee, BMD
University of Wisconsin - Oshkosh, B
University of Wisconsin - Parkside, AB
University of Wisconsin - Platteville, B
University of Wisconsin - River Falls, B
University of Wisconsin - Stevens Point, B
University of Wisconsin - Superior, B
University of Wisconsin - Whitewater, B

Wyoming

Casper College, A
Eastern Wyoming College, A
Laramie County Community College, A
University of Wyoming, MD
Western Wyoming Community College, A

U.S. Territories: Puerto Rico

Inter American University of Puerto Rico, San
   Germán Campus, B
University of Puerto Rico in Cayey, B
University of Puerto Rico, Mayagüez Campus, B
University of Puerto Rico, Río Piedras Campus, BM

Canada

Alberta

University of Alberta, BMD
University of Calgary, BMD
University of Lethbridge, BM

British Columbia

Simon Fraser University, BMD
Thompson Rivers University, B
The University of British Columbia, BMD
The University of British Columbia - Okanagan
   Campus, B
University of the Fraser Valley, B
University of Northern British Columbia, B
University of Victoria, BMD

Manitoba

Brandon University, B
University of Manitoba, BMD
The University of Winnipeg, B

Maritime Provinces: New Brunswick

Mount Allison University, B
St. Thomas University, B

Université de Moncton, BM
University of New Brunswick Fredericton, BM
University of New Brunswick Saint John, B

Maritime Provinces: Nova Scotia

Acadia University, B
Cape Breton University, B
Dalhousie University, BMD
Mount Saint Vincent University, B
St. Francis Xavier University, B
Saint Mary's University, B
University of King's College, B

Maritime Provinces: Prince Edward Island

University of Prince Edward Island, B

Newfoundland and Labrador

Memorial University of Newfoundland, BM

Ontario

Brock University, BM
Carleton University, BMD
Lakehead University, BM
Laurentian University, B
McMaster University, BMD
Nipissing University, B
Queen's University at Kingston, B
Trent University, B
University of Guelph, BMD
University of Ottawa, BMD
University of Toronto, BMD
University of Waterloo, BMD
The University of Western Ontario, BMD
University of Windsor, BM
Wilfrid Laurier University, BMD
York University, BMD

Quebec

Bishop's University, B
Concordia University, BMDO
McGill University, BMD
Université Laval, BMD
Université de Montréal, BMDO
Université du Québec à Montréal, BMD
Université du Québec à Trois-Rivières, B
Université de Sherbrooke, M

Saskatchewan

University of Regina, BO
University of Saskatchewan, BMO

EDUCATION

United States

Alabama

Alabama Agricultural and Mechanical University, MO
Alabama State University, MDO
Auburn University, BMDO
Auburn University at Montgomery, MO
Birmingham-Southern College, B
Faulkner University, M
Jacksonville State University, BMO
Miles College, B
Samford University, MDO
Spring Hill College, M
Talladega College, B
Troy University, MO
The University of Alabama at Birmingham, MDO
University of Mobile, M
University of Montevallo, MO
University of North Alabama, MO
University of South Alabama, BMDO
The University of West Alabama, MO
Wallace State Community College, A

Alaska

Alaska Pacific University, M
University of Alaska Anchorage, BMO
University of Alaska Fairbanks, MO
University of Alaska Southeast, BM

Arizona

Argosy University, Phoenix, MDO
Arizona State University at the Polytechnic campus, B
Arizona State University at the Tempe campus, BMDO
Arizona State University at the West campus, B
Grand Canyon University, MD
Harrison Middleton University, BMD
International Baptist College and Seminary, M
Mohave Community College, A
Northcentral University, MDO
Northern Arizona University, MDO
Pima Community College, A
Prescott College, BMD
South Mountain Community College, A
The University of Arizona, MDO
University of Phoenix - Online Campus, MO
University of Phoenix - Phoenix Campus, M
University of Phoenix - Southern Arizona Campus, MO
Yavapai College, A

Arkansas

Arkansas State University, MDO
Arkansas Tech University, M
Central Baptist College, A
Harding University, MO
Henderson State University, MO
John Brown University, BM
National Park College, A
NorthWest Arkansas Community College, A
Shorter College, A
Southern Arkansas University - Magnolia, M
University of Arkansas, BMDO
University of Arkansas at Little Rock, BMDO
University of Arkansas at Monticello, BM
University of Arkansas at Pine Bluff, M
University of Central Arkansas, MO
Williams Baptist College, B

California

American Jewish University, M
Antioch University Los Angeles, M
Antioch University Santa Barbara, M
Argosy University, Inland Empire, MD
Argosy University, Los Angeles, M
Argosy University, Orange County, MD
Argosy University, San Diego, MD
Argosy University, San Francisco Bay Area, MD
Ashford University, B
Azusa Pacific University, MDO
Biola University, BMO
Brandman University, M
California Baptist University, M
California Coast University, MD
California Lutheran University, MD
California Polytechnic State University, San Luis Obispo, M
California State Polytechnic University, Pomona, B
California State University, Bakersfield, M
California State University Channel Islands, B
California State University, Dominguez Hills, MO
California State University, East Bay, M
California State University, Fresno, MD
California State University, Long Beach, MD
California State University, Los Angeles, MD
California State University, Monterey Bay, M
California State University, Northridge, MD
California State University, Sacramento, M
California State University, San Bernardino, MD
California State University, San Marcos, MD
California State University, Stanislaus, MDO
Cañada College, A
Chapman University, BMDO
Concordia University Irvine, M
DeVry University (Pomona), M
Dominican University of California, M
Folsom Lake College, A
Fresno Pacific University, MO
Holy Names University, MO
Hope International University, M
Humboldt State University, BM
John F. Kennedy University, M
La Sierra University, MDO

Las Positas College, A
Los Angeles Southwest College, A
Loyola Marymount University, MD
The Master's College and Seminary, B
Mills College, MD
Mount Saint Mary's University, BMO
National University, AMO
Notre Dame de Namur University, MO
Occidental College, M
Pacific Oaks College, M
Pacific Union College, M
Palomar College, A
Pepperdine University, M
Point Loma Nazarene University, M
Porterville College, A
Saint Mary's College of California, MD
San Diego Christian College, B
San Diego State University, MD
San Francisco State University, MDO
San Jose State University, MDO
Santa Clara University, MO
Shasta Bible College, B
Simpson University, M
Sonoma State University, MDO
Stanford University, MD
Trident University International, MD
University of California, Berkeley, MDO
University of California, Davis, MD
University of California, Irvine, BMD
University of California, Los Angeles, MD
University of California, Riverside, MDO
University of California, San Diego, MD
University of California, Santa Barbara, MDO
University of California, Santa Cruz, BMD
University of La Verne, MO
University of the Pacific, BMDO
University of Phoenix - Bay Area Campus, MDO
University of Phoenix - Central Valley Campus, M
University of Phoenix - Sacramento Valley Campus, MO
University of Phoenix - San Diego Campus, M
University of Phoenix - Southern California Campus, MO
University of Redlands, BMDO
University of San Diego, MDO
University of San Francisco, BMD
University of Southern California, MD
Vanguard University of Southern California, BM
West Los Angeles College, A
Westmont College, B
Whittier College, M
William Jessup University, BM
Yuba College, A

Colorado

Adams State University, M
Argosy University, Denver, MD
Colorado Christian University, ABM
The Colorado College, BM
Colorado Mesa University, M
Colorado State University, MD
Colorado State University - Global Campus, M
Colorado State University - Pueblo, M
Metropolitan State University of Denver, M
Naropa University, M
Nazarene Bible College, B
Regis University, BMO
Trinidad State Junior College, A
University of Colorado Boulder, MD
University of Colorado Colorado Springs, MD
University of Colorado Denver, BMDO
University of Denver, MDO
University of Northern Colorado, MDO
University of Phoenix - Colorado Campus, M
University of Phoenix - Colorado Springs Downtown Campus, MO
Western State Colorado University, M

Connecticut

Albertus Magnus College, BM
Central Connecticut State University, MDO
Eastern Connecticut State University, M
Fairfield University, MO
Post University, M
Quinnipiac University, BMO
Sacred Heart University, BMO

Southern Connecticut State University, MDO
Three Rivers Community College, A
Trinity College, B
University of Bridgeport, MDO
University of Connecticut, MDO
University of Hartford, MDO
University of New Haven, M
University of Saint Joseph, M
Western Connecticut State University, MD

Delaware

Delaware State University, BMD
University of Delaware, MDO
Wesley College, BM
Wilmington University, MD

District of Columbia

The Catholic University of America, BMDO
Gallaudet University, BM
The George Washington University, MDO
Howard University, BMDO
Trinity Washington University, BM
University of the District of Columbia, A
University of Phoenix - Washington D.C. Campus, MDO

Florida

Argosy University, Sarasota, MDO
Argosy University, Tampa, MDO
The Baptist College of Florida, B
Barry University, BMDO
Bethune-Cookman University, B
Chipola College, AB
DeVry University (Miramar), M
DeVry University (Orlando), M
Edward Waters College, B
Florida Agricultural and Mechanical University, MD
Florida Atlantic University, MDO
Florida Gulf Coast University, BMDO
Florida Institute of Technology, M
Florida International University, MDO
Florida Memorial University, M
Florida National University, A
Florida Southern College, M
Florida State University, MDO
Indian River State College, A
Jacksonville University, M
Keiser University, M
Lynn University, MD
Miami Dade College, AB
Nova Southeastern University, BMDO
Palm Beach Atlantic University, M
Palm Beach State College, A
Pensacola State College, A
Rollins College, M
Saint Leo University, M
St. Petersburg College, B
St. Thomas University, MDO
Southeastern University, M
Stetson University, BMO
University of Florida, MDO
University of Miami, BMDO
University of North Florida, MD
University of Phoenix - North Florida Campus, M
University of Phoenix - South Florida Campus, M
University of South Florida, MDO
University of South Florida, St. Petersburg, M
University of South Florida Sarasota-Manatee, M
The University of Tampa, M
University of West Florida, D
Warner University, M

Georgia

Abraham Baldwin Agricultural College, A
Albany State University, BMO
Andrew College, A
Argosy University, Atlanta, MDO
Armstrong State University, MO
Augusta University, MO
Bainbridge State College, A
Berry College, MO
Brenau University, BMO
Brewton-Parker College, B
Clark Atlanta University, BMDO
Clayton State University, M
Columbus State University, MDO

Covenant College, M
Dalton State College, A
Emory University, BMD
Georgia College & State University, MO
Georgia Highlands College, A
Georgia Southern University, BMDO
Georgia Southwestern State University, MO
Georgia State University, MDO
Kennesaw State University, MDO
LaGrange College, MO
Mercer University, BMDO
Piedmont College, BMO
Reinhardt University, BM
Thomas University, M
University of Georgia, MDO
University of North Georgia, MO
University of West Georgia, MDO
Wesleyan College, M
Young Harris College, B

Hawaii

Argosy University, Hawai'i, MD
Brigham Young University - Hawaii, B
Chaminade University of Honolulu, M
University of Hawaii at Hilo, M
University of Hawaii at Manoa, BMDO
University of Phoenix - Hawaii Campus, M

Idaho

Boise State University, MDO
The College of Idaho, M
College of Southern Idaho, A
Idaho State University, MDO
North Idaho College, A
Northwest Nazarene University, BMDO
University of Idaho, MDO

Illinois

American InterContinental University Online, M
Argosy University, Chicago, MDO
Aurora University, MD
Benedictine University, M
Blackburn College, B
Bradley University, BMDO
Chicago State University, MD
Concordia University Chicago, BM
DePaul University, BMD
DeVry University (Chicago), M
DeVry University (Downers Grove), M
Dominican University, M
Eastern Illinois University, MO
Ellis University, M
Elmhurst College, B
Eureka College, B
Governors State University, M
Greenville College, M
Illinois College, BM
Illinois State University, MD
Illinois Valley Community College, A
Illinois Wesleyan University, B
Kankakee Community College, A
Knox College, B
Lake Forest College, BM
Lewis University, MDO
Lincoln Christian University, A
Loyola University Chicago, MDO
McKendree University, MDO
National Louis University, MDO
North Central College, BM
North Park University, M
Northeastern Illinois University, M
Northern Illinois University, BMDO
Northwestern University, BMD
Olivet Nazarene University, M
Quincy University, BM
Rockford University, BM
Roosevelt University, MD
Saint Xavier University, M
Sauk Valley Community College, A
Southern Illinois University Carbondale, MD
Southern Illinois University Edwardsville, MDO
Spoon River College, A
Trinity Christian College, B
Trinity International University, BM
Triton College, A
University of Illinois at Chicago, MD

University of Illinois at Springfield, MO
University of Illinois at Urbana - Champaign, MDO
University of St. Francis, MDO
Western Illinois University, MDO
Wheaton College, M

Indiana

Anderson University, BM
Ball State University, MDO
Bethel College, BM
Butler University, M
Earlham College, M
Goshen College, B
Grace College, B
Huntington University, BM
Indiana State University, MDO
Indiana University Bloomington, MDO
Indiana University East, M
Indiana University Northwest, M
Indiana University - Purdue University Fort Wayne,
  BMO
Indiana University - Purdue University Indianapolis,
  MO
Indiana University South Bend, M
Indiana University Southeast, M
Indiana Wesleyan University, B
Ivy Tech Community College - Bloomington, A
Ivy Tech Community College - Central Indiana, A
Ivy Tech Community College - Columbus, A
Ivy Tech Community College - East Central, A
Ivy Tech Community College - Kokomo, A
Ivy Tech Community College - Lafayette, A
Ivy Tech Community College - Richmond, A
Ivy Tech Community College - Southeast, A
Ivy Tech Community College - Southern Indiana, A
Ivy Tech Community College - Southwest, A
Ivy Tech Community College - Wabash Valley, A
Manchester University, B
Marian University, BM
Oakland City University, MD
Purdue University, BMDO
Purdue University Northwest (Hammond), M
Purdue University Northwest (Westville), M
Saint Mary-of-the-Woods College, B
Taylor University, B
Trine University, B
University of Indianapolis, BM
University of Notre Dame, M
University of Saint Francis, BMO
University of Southern Indiana, M
Valparaiso University, M
Vincennes University, A

Iowa

Briar Cliff University, B
Buena Vista University, M
Clarke University, M
Coe College, B
Dordt College, BM
Drake University, MDO
Graceland University, BM
Grand View University, M
Iowa Central Community College, A
Iowa Lakes Community College, A
Iowa State University of Science and Technology, B
Iowa Wesleyan University, B
Kaplan University, Davenport Campus, M
Kirkwood Community College, A
Morningside College, M
Mount Mercy University, M
St. Ambrose University, BM
Simpson College, BM
The University of Iowa, MDO
University of Northern Iowa, MDO
Upper Iowa University, BM
Waldorf College, B
William Penn University, B

Kansas

Baker University, MD
Bethany College, B
Coffeyville Community College, A
Cowley County Community College and Area Voca-
  tional - Technical School, A
Dodge City Community College, A
Emporia State University, M

Fort Hays State University, MO
Garden City Community College, A
Highland Community College, A
Hutchinson Community College, A
Independence Community College, A
Kansas State University, MD
Labette Community College, A
McPherson College, M
MidAmerica Nazarene University, M
Newman University, BM
Ottawa University, M
Pittsburg State University, MO
Seward County Community College and Area Tech-
  nical School, A
Southwestern College, MD
Tabor College, B
The University of Kansas, MDO
University of Saint Mary, BM
Washburn University, BM
Wichita State University, MDO

Kentucky

Bellarmine University, MDO
Berea College, B
Campbellsville University, M
Eastern Kentucky University, M
Georgetown College, M
Jefferson Community and Technical College, A
Lindsey Wilson College, B
Midway University, BM
Morehead State University, MO
Murray State University, MDO
Northern Kentucky University, MDO
Spalding University, BMD
Thomas More College, BM
Union College, BM
University of the Cumberlands, MDO
University of Kentucky, MDO
University of Louisville, MDO

Louisiana

Baton Rouge Community College, A
Bossier Parish Community College, A
Centenary College of Louisiana, M
Grambling State University, MDO
Louisiana College, M
Louisiana Delta Community College, A
Louisiana State University and Agricultural & Me-
  chanical College, MDO
Louisiana State University in Shreveport, M
Louisiana Tech University, MD
McNeese State University, O
Nicholls State University, M
Northwestern State University of Louisiana, MO
Nunez Community College, A
River Parishes Community College, A
South Louisiana Community College, A
Southeastern Louisiana University, MD
Southern University and Agricultural and Mechanical
  College, MD
University of Holy Cross, BM
University of Louisiana at Lafayette, MD
University of New Orleans, MD
Xavier University of Louisiana, BM

Maine

Colby College, B
College of the Atlantic, B
Saint Joseph's College of Maine, BM
University of Maine, MDO
University of Maine at Farmington, M
University of Maine at Machias, B
University of Maine at Presque Isle, B
University of New England, MO
University of Southern Maine, MDO
York County Community College, A

Maryland

Baltimore City Community College, A
Bowie State University, BM
Carroll Community College, A
Cecil College, A
Chesapeake College, A
College of Southern Maryland, A
Community College of Baltimore County, A
Coppin State University, M

Frederick Community College, A
Frostburg State University, M
Garrett College, A
Goucher College, MO
Hagerstown Community College, A
Harford Community College, A
Hood College, MO
Johns Hopkins University, MDO
Loyola University Maryland, BMO
Morgan State University, BMD
Mount St. Mary's University, M
Notre Dame of Maryland University, BM
Prince George's Community College, A
St. Mary's College of Maryland, M
Stevenson University, M
Towson University, BM
University of Maryland, Baltimore County, MO
University of Maryland, College Park, MDO
University of Maryland Eastern Shore, BM
University of Maryland University College, MO
Wor-Wic Community College, A

Massachusetts

American International College, MDO
Anna Maria College, BMO
Bay State College, A
Becker College, B
Boston College, MDO
Boston University, MDO
Brandeis University, B
Bridgewater State University, MO
Bunker Hill Community College, A
Cambridge College, MDO
Cape Cod Community College, A
Clark University, BM
Curry College, BMO
Eastern Nazarene College, BMO
Elms College, BMO
Emmanuel College, M
Fitchburg State University, B
Gordon College, MO
Greenfield Community College, A
Hampshire College, B
Harvard University, MD
Lasell College, BM
Lesley University, BMDO
Massachusetts College of Liberal Arts, BMO
Merrimack College, BMO
Mount Holyoke College, B
Northeastern University, MD
Northern Essex Community College, A
Regis College, MD
Salem State University, B
Simmons College, BM
Smith College, BM
Springfield College, BM
Stonehill College, B
Tufts University, BMDO
University of Massachusetts Amherst, BMDO
University of Massachusetts Boston, BMD
University of Massachusetts Dartmouth, MDO
University of Massachusetts Lowell, MDO
Westfield State University, MO
Wheelock College, BM
Worcester State University, MO

Michigan

Adrian College, B
Alma College, B
Andrews University, BMDO
Aquinas College, M
Baker College, AB
Bay Mills Community College, A
Calvin College, M
Central Michigan University, MDO
Cornerstone University, M
Eastern Michigan University, MDO
Ferris State University, M
Finlandia University, B
Gogebic Community College, A
Grand Valley State University, MO
Lake Superior State University, B
Madonna University, M
Marygrove College, BM
Michigan State University, BMDO
Muskegon Community College, A

Northern Michigan University, M
Northwestern Michigan College, A
Oakland University, MDO
Olivet College, M
Saginaw Valley State University, BMO
Schoolcraft College, A
Siena Heights University, MO
Spring Arbor University, M
University of Detroit Mercy, BM
University of Michigan, MD
University of Michigan - Dearborn, BM
University of Michigan - Flint, MDO
Wayne State University, BMDO
Western Michigan University, MDO

Minnesota

Argosy University, Twin Cities, MDO
Augsburg College, BM
Bemidji State University, BM
Bethel University, M
Capella University, MD
Century College, A
The College of St. Scholastica, MO
Concordia College, BM
Concordia University, St. Paul, BMDO
Crown College, B
Gustavus Adolphus College, B
Hamline University, MD
Inver Hills Community College, A
Itasca Community College, A
Macalester College, B
Martin Luther College, M
Minneapolis Community and Technical College, A
Minnesota State University Mankato, BMDO
Minnesota State University Moorhead, MO
North Hennepin Community College, A
St. Catherine University, BM
St. Cloud State University, BMD
Saint Mary's University of Minnesota, BMO
Southwest Minnesota State University, BM
University of Minnesota, Duluth, BMD
University of Minnesota, Twin Cities Campus,
BMDO
University of Northwestern - St. Paul, M
University of St. Thomas, MDO
Vermilion Community College, A
Walden University, MDO
Winona State University, BM

Mississippi

Alcorn State University, MO
Belhaven University, M
Coahoma Community College, A
Copiah-Lincoln Community College, A
Delta State University, MDO
Itawamba Community College, A
Jackson State University, BMDO
Jones County Junior College, A
Millsaps College, B
Mississippi College, MDO
Mississippi Delta Community College, A
Mississippi Gulf Coast Community College, A
Mississippi State University, MDO
Mississippi University for Women, M
Mississippi Valley State University, BM
Northwest Mississippi Community College, A
Southwest Mississippi Community College, A
Tougaloo College, B
University of Mississippi, MDO
University of Southern Mississippi, MDO
William Carey University, MO

Missouri

Avila University, BMO
Central Methodist University, BM
Columbia College, M
Crowder College, A
Drury University, M
East Central College, A
Evangel University, M
Fontbonne University, BM
Hannibal-LaGrange University, BM
Harris-Stowe State University, B
Jefferson College, A
Lindenwood University, BMDO
Maryville University of Saint Louis, MD

Missouri Baptist University, BM
Missouri Southern State University, BM
Missouri Valley College, B
Northwest Missouri State University, BMO
Park University, BM
Rockhurst University, M
Saint Louis University, BMD
Southwest Baptist University, MO
Three Rivers Community College, A
Truman State University, M
University of Central Missouri, BMO
University of Missouri, BMDO
University of Missouri - Kansas City, MDO
University of Missouri - St. Louis, BMDO
Washington University in St. Louis, BMD
Webster University, BMO
William Jewell College, M
William Woods University, B

Montana

Fort Peck Community College, A
Miles Community College, A
Montana State University, MDO
Montana State University Billings, ABMO
Montana State University - Northern, M
University of Great Falls, M
University of Montana, BMDO

Nebraska

Bellevue University, B
Chadron State College, MO
College of Saint Mary, BM
Concordia University, Nebraska, BM
Creighton University, MD
Doane University, M
Hastings College, BM
Midland University, B
Northeast Community College, A
Peru State College, BM
Union College, B
University of Nebraska at Kearney, MO
University of Nebraska at Omaha, MDO
Wayne State College, MO
York College, B

Nevada

Nevada State College, B
Sierra Nevada College, M
University of Nevada, Las Vegas, BMDO
University of Nevada, Reno, BMDO
University of Phoenix - Las Vegas Campus, M

New Hampshire

Franklin Pierce University, B
Great Bay Community College, A
Keene State College, MO
Lakes Region Community College, A
New England College, BMD
Plymouth State University, MO
Rivier University, BMDO
Southern New Hampshire University, BMDO
University of New Hampshire, MDO
White Mountains Community College, A

New Jersey

Bergen Community College, A
Bloomfield College, B
Brookdale Community College, A
Caldwell University, MDO
Centenary College, BM
The College of New Jersey, MO
College of Saint Elizabeth, O
Cumberland County College, A
Drew University, M
Essex County College, A
Fairleigh Dickinson University, College at Florham,
MO
Fairleigh Dickinson University, Metropolitan Campus, MO
Felician University, BMO
Georgian Court University, M
Kean University, M
Monmouth University, BMO
Montclair State University, MDO
New Jersey City University, MD

Rider University, MO
Rowan College at Burlington County, A
Rowan College at Gloucester County, A
Rowan University, BMDO
Rutgers University - New Brunswick, MD
Saint Peter's University, MDO
Salem Community College, A
Seton Hall University, MDO
Stockton University, M
Warren County Community College, A
William Paterson University of New Jersey, M

New Mexico

Clovis Community College, A
Eastern New Mexico University, M
Eastern New Mexico University - Roswell, A
Luna Community College, A
Mesalands Community College, A
National American University (Albuquerque), A
New Mexico Highlands University, M
New Mexico Junior College, A
New Mexico State University, BMDO
New Mexico State University - Alamogordo, A
New Mexico State University - Carlsbad, A
New Mexico State University - Grants, A
Santa Fe Community College, A
University of New Mexico, MDO
University of New Mexico - Gallup, A
University of New Mexico - Taos, A
University of New Mexico - Valencia Campus, A
University of Phoenix - New Mexico Campus, M
University of the Southwest, M
Western New Mexico University, BM

New York

Adelphi University, MDO
Alfred University, M
Bard College, M
Barnard College, B
Binghamton University, State University of New York, MDO
Brooklyn College of the City University of New York, BMO
Canisius College, BMO
City College of the City University of New York, BMO
Colgate University, B
The College at Brockport, State University of New York, MO
College of Mount Saint Vincent, BMO
The College of New Rochelle, BMO
The College of Saint Rose, MO
College of Staten Island of the City University of New York, MO
Concordia College - New York, B
Cornell University, MD
Corning Community College, A
Daemen College, M
Dominican College, B
D'Youville College, MDO
Elmira College, B
Five Towns College, B
Fordham University, BMDO
Genesee Community College, A
Hofstra University, MDO
Hudson Valley Community College, A
Hunter College of the City University of New York, MO
Iona College, M
Kingsborough Community College of the City University of New York, A
Le Moyne College, MO
Lehman College of the City University of New York, M
Long Island University - LIU Brooklyn, MO
Long Island University - LIU Post, MDO
Manhattan College, BMO
Manhattanville College, BMDO
Marist College, M
Medaille College, M
Mercy College, MO
Molloy College, MO
Morrisville State College, A
Mount Saint Mary College, MO
Nazareth College of Rochester, BM
New York Institute of Technology, MO

New York University, MDO
Niagara University, BMDO
Pace University, MO
Queens College of the City University of New York, MO
Roberts Wesleyan College, M
St. Bonaventure University, MO
St. John Fisher College, B
St. John's University, MDO
St. Joseph's College, Long Island Campus, B
St. Joseph's College, New York, BM
St. Lawrence University, MO
St. Thomas Aquinas College, BMO
Sarah Lawrence College, M
Schenectady County Community College, A
Skidmore College, B
State University of New York College at Cortland, MO
State University of New York College at Geneseo, BM
State University of New York College at Oneonta, BMO
State University of New York Empire State College, ABM
State University of New York at Fredonia, BM
State University of New York at New Paltz, BMO
State University of New York at Oswego, BMO
State University of New York at Plattsburgh, B
Syracuse University, BMDO
Touro College, M
University at Albany, State University of New York, MDO
University at Buffalo, the State University of New York, MDO
University of Rochester, MD
Utica College, MO
Vassar College, B
Wagner College, BMO
Wells College, B

North Carolina

Belmont Abbey College, B
Caldwell Community College and Technical Institute, A
Campbell University, BM
Chowan University, BM
College of The Albemarle, A
Duke University, M
East Carolina University, MDO
Elizabeth City State University, M
Elon University, BM
Gardner-Webb University, BMDO
Greensboro College, BM
Guilford College, B
Guilford Technical Community College, A
High Point University, M
Isothermal Community College, A
Lenoir-Rhyne University, M
Livingstone College, B
Mars Hill University, B
Meredith College, M
Methodist University, B
Montreat College, A
North Carolina Agricultural and Technical State University, BM
North Carolina Central University, M
North Carolina State University, BMDO
North Carolina Wesleyan College, B
Pfeiffer University, B
Queens University of Charlotte, M
Salem College, BM
Shaw University, B
University of Mount Olive, A
The University of North Carolina at Chapel Hill, MD
The University of North Carolina at Greensboro, MDO
The University of North Carolina at Pembroke, M
The University of North Carolina Wilmington, MD
Vance-Granville Community College, A
Wake Forest University, M
Western Carolina University, MDO
William Peace University, B
Wingate University, MD
Winston-Salem State University, BM

North Dakota

Dakota College at Bottineau, A
Dickinson State University, B
Mayville State University, B
North Dakota State University, MDO
Sitting Bull College, A
United Tribes Technical College, A
University of Jamestown, M
University of Mary, MD
University of North Dakota, MDO
Valley City State University, BM

Ohio

Antioch University Midwest, M
Ashland University, BMD
Baldwin Wallace University, M
Bluffton University, M
Bowling Green State University, B
Bowling Green State University - Firelands College, AB
Cedarville University, MD
Central State University, B
Cincinnati Christian University, AB
Cleveland State University, MDO
Defiance College, BM
Edison Community College, A
Franciscan University of Steubenville, M
Heidelberg University, BM
Hiram College, B
John Carroll University, BM
Kent State University, BMDO
Kent State University at Salem, A
Kent State University at Stark, M
Kent State University at Tuscarawas, A
Lake Erie College, M
Lorain County Community College, A
Malone University, M
Marietta College, B
Miami University, MDO
Miami University Middletown, A
Mount St. Joseph University, BMO
Mount Vernon Nazarene University, BM
Muskingum University, BM
Ohio Christian University, AB
Ohio Dominican University, BM
Ohio Northern University, B
The Ohio State University, MDO
The Ohio State University - Mansfield Campus, M
The Ohio State University at Marion, M
The Ohio State University - Newark Campus, M
Ohio University, MD
Ohio University - Lancaster, B
Ohio Wesleyan University, B
Otterbein University, BM
Shawnee State University, BM
Sinclair Community College, A
Terra State Community College, A
Tiffin University, BM
Union Institute & University, D
The University of Akron, AM
University of Cincinnati, MDO
University of Cincinnati Blue Ash College, A
The University of Findlay, BM
University of Rio Grande, BM
The University of Toledo, MDO
Urbana University, BM
Ursuline College, M
Walsh University, BM
Washington State Community College, A
Wilmington College, BM
Wittenberg University, BM
Wright State University, BMO
Xavier University, BMD
Youngstown State University, BMD

Oklahoma

Bacone College, AB
Cameron University, M
Connors State College, A
East Central University, M
Family of Faith College, B
Langston University, BM
Northeastern State University, M
Northwestern Oklahoma State University, M
Oklahoma Baptist University, B

Oklahoma City University, BM
Oklahoma State University, MDO
Oral Roberts University, MD
Redlands Community College, A
Southeastern Oklahoma State University, M
Southern Nazarene University, B
Southwestern Christian University, B
Southwestern Oklahoma State University, M
Tulsa Community College, A
University of Central Oklahoma, M
University of Oklahoma, MDO
The University of Tulsa, BM

Oregon

Central Oregon Community College, A
Concordia University, BMD
Corban University, ABM
Eastern Oregon University, ABM
George Fox University, MDO
Klamath Community College, A
Marylhurst University, M
Multnomah University, M
Northwest Christian University, M
Oregon State University, BMD
Oregon State University - Cascades, M
Pacific University, BM
Portland State University, MD
Southern Oregon University, M
Umpqua Community College, A
University of Oregon, BMD
University of Portland, BMD
Warner Pacific College, M
Western Oregon University, M

Pennsylvania

Albright College, M
Alvernia University, M
Arcadia University, BMDO
Bloomsburg University of Pennsylvania, MO
Bucknell University, BM
Butler County Community College, A
Cabrini University, BM
Cairn University, M
California University of Pennsylvania, M
Carlow University, M
Cedar Crest College, BM
Chatham University, M
Chestnut Hill College, MO
Cheyney University of Pennsylvania, MO
Clarion University of Pennsylvania, M
Community College of Beaver County, A
Community College of Philadelphia, A
DeSales University, M
Drexel University, MD
Duquesne University, BMDO
East Stroudsburg University of Pennsylvania, M
Eastern University, MO
Gannon University, MO
Geneva College, M
Gettysburg College, B
Gwynedd Mercy University, M
Haverford College, B
Holy Family University, MD
Indiana University of Pennsylvania, MDO
Juniata College, B
King's College, M
Kutztown University of Pennsylvania, M
La Salle University, MO
Lackawanna College, A
Lancaster Bible College, B
Lehigh Carbon Community College, A
Lehigh University, MDO
Lock Haven University of Pennsylvania, M
Luzerne County Community College, A
Mansfield University of Pennsylvania, BM
Marywood University, M
Mercyhurst North East, A
Mercyhurst University, B
Millersville University of Pennsylvania, M
Misericordia University, M
Moravian College, M
Neumann University, M
Penn State Harrisburg, MDO
Penn State University Park, MDO
Pennsylvania Highlands Community College, A
Point Park University, BM

Robert Morris University, MDO
Rosemont College, BM
Saint Francis University, ABM
Saint Joseph's University, MDO
Saint Vincent College, M
Shippensburg University of Pennsylvania, MO
Slippery Rock University of Pennsylvania, M
Summit University, B
Swarthmore College, B
Temple University, MDO
University of Pennsylvania, MDO
University of Pittsburgh, MD
University of Pittsburgh at Greensburg, B
University of Pittsburgh at Johnstown, B
The University of Scranton, M
Villanova University, M
Washington & Jefferson College, B
Waynesburg University, M
West Chester University of Pennsylvania, MO
Westminster College, MO
Widener University, MD
Wilkes University, BMD
Wilson College, M
York College of Pennsylvania, M

Rhode Island

Brown University, BM
Johnson & Wales University, M
Rhode Island College, D
Roger Williams University, BM
University of Rhode Island, MD

South Carolina

Anderson University, M
Charleston Southern University, M
The Citadel, The Military College of South Carolina, MO
Clemson University, MDO
Coastal Carolina University, MO
Coker College, B
College of Charleston, MO
Columbia College, M
Columbia International University, MDO
Converse College, BMO
Francis Marion University, M
Furman University, BMO
Lander University, M
Limestone College, B
North Greenville University, M
South Carolina State University, M
Southern Wesleyan University, BM
Technical College of the Lowcountry, A
University of South Carolina, MDO
University of South Carolina Upstate, M
Winthrop University, M
Wofford College, B

South Dakota

Augustana University, M
Dakota State University, M
Dakota Wesleyan University, BM
Mount Marty College, B
Northern State University, BM
Sinte Gleska University, AM
South Dakota State University, MD
University of Sioux Falls, BMO
The University of South Dakota, BMDO

Tennessee

Aquinas College, M
Argosy University, Nashville, MDO
Austin Peay State University, MO
Belmont University, BM
Carson-Newman University, BM
Chattanooga State Community College, A
Christian Brothers University, BM
Cumberland University, ABM
Dyersburg State Community College, A
East Tennessee State University, MDO
Freed-Hardeman University, MO
Jackson State Community College, A
Johnson University, M
Lee University, BMO
Lincoln Memorial University, BMDO
Lipscomb University, BMDO
Maryville College, B

Middle Tennessee State University, MDO
Milligan College, BM
Motlow State Community College, A
Pellissippi State Community College, A
Rhodes College, B
Roane State Community College, A
Southern Adventist University, BM
Tennessee State University, BMDO
Tennessee Technological University, BMDO
Tennessee Wesleyan College, BM
Trevecca Nazarene University, MD
Tusculum College, M
Union University, BMDO
University of Memphis, MDO
The University of Tennessee, MDO
The University of Tennessee at Chattanooga, MDO
The University of Tennessee at Martin, M
Vanderbilt University, BMD
Volunteer State Community College, A
Walters State Community College, A
Welch College, B

Texas

Abilene Christian University, MO
Angelo State University, M
Argosy University, Dallas, MD
Arlington Baptist College, BM
Austin College, M
Baylor University, BMDO
Cedar Valley College, A
Cisco College, A
Clarendon College, A
Concordia University Texas, M
Dallas Baptist University, M
Dallas Christian College, B
Del Mar College, A
East Texas Baptist University, BM
Eastfield College, A
Galveston College, A
Hardin-Simmons University, BMD
Houston Baptist University, M
Howard College, A
Huston-Tillotson University, B
Lamar University, MDO
Lee College, A
LeTourneau University, M
Lone Star College - CyFair, A
Lone Star College - Kingwood, A
Lone Star College - Montgomery, A
Lone Star College - North Harris, A
Lone Star College - Tomball, A
Messenger College, B
Midwestern State University, BM
Mountain View College, A
Navarro College, A
Odessa College, A
Our Lady of the Lake University of San Antonio, MD
Palo Alto College, A
Panola College, A
Paris Junior College, A
Paul Quinn College, B
Prairie View A&M University, MD
Rice University, M
St. Mary's University, MO
St. Philip's College, A
Sam Houston State University, MD
Schreiner University, BMO
South Plains College, A
South Texas College, A
Southern Methodist University, MD
Southwest Texas Junior College, A
Southwestern Adventist University, M
Southwestern Assemblies of God University, ABM
Southwestern University, B
Stephen F. Austin State University, MD
Sul Ross State University, MO
Tarleton State University, BMDO
Texas A&M International University, M
Texas A&M University, MD
Texas A&M University - Commerce, MDO
Texas A&M University - Corpus Christi, MD
Texas A&M University - Kingsville, MDO
Texas A&M University - Texarkana, M
Texas Christian University, MDO
Texas Lutheran University, B
Texas Southern University, MD

Texas State University, MDO
Texas Tech University, MD
Texas Wesleyan University, BMD
Texas Woman's University, MD
Trinity University, M
Trinity Valley Community College, A
University of Dallas, B
University of Houston, MD
University of Houston - Clear Lake, MD
University of Houston - Victoria, M
University of the Incarnate Word, MD
University of Mary Hardin-Baylor, MD
University of North Texas, BM
University of Phoenix - Dallas Campus, M
University of Phoenix - Houston Campus, M
University of St. Thomas, BM
The University of Texas at Arlington, MD
The University of Texas at Austin, MD
The University of Texas at El Paso, MD
The University of Texas of the Permian Basin, M
The University of Texas Rio Grande Valley, MD
The University of Texas at San Antonio, B
Wayland Baptist University, M
West Texas A&M University, M

Utah

Argosy University, Salt Lake City, MD
Brigham Young University, BMDO
Snow College, A
Southern Utah University, MO
University of Phoenix - Utah Campus, M
University of Utah, BMD
Utah State University, MDO
Utah Valley University, M
Weber State University, AM
Western Governors University, MO
Westminster College, M

Vermont

Bennington College, BM
Castleton University, MO
College of St. Joseph, M
Community College of Vermont, A
Goddard College, BM
Johnson State College, BM
Lyndon State College, M
Marlboro College, MO
Saint Michael's College, BMO
Sterling College, B
University of Vermont, BMD

Virginia

Argosy University, Washington DC, MDO
Averett University, M
Bluefield College, BM
Central Virginia Community College, A
Christopher Newport University, M
The College of William and Mary, MDO
Dabney S. Lancaster Community College, A
Eastern Mennonite University, M
Eastern Shore Community College, A
Emory & Henry College, M
Ferrum College, B
George Mason University, MDO
Germanna Community College, A
Hampton University, BMDO
Hollins University, M
Liberty University, MDO
Longwood University, M
Mary Baldwin College, M
Marymount University, MD
New River Community College, A
Norfolk State University, M
Old Dominion University, MDO
Paul D. Camp Community College, A
Radford University, MO
Randolph College, M
Regent University, BMDO
Shenandoah University, MDO
Southside Virginia Community College, A
Sweet Briar College, M
Tidewater Community College, A
University of Mary Washington, M
University of Virginia, MDO
Virginia Commonwealth University, MDO
Virginia Highlands Community College, A

Virginia International University, M
Virginia Polytechnic Institute and State University, M
Virginia State University, MDO
Virginia Western Community College, A
Wytheville Community College, A

Washington

Antioch University Seattle, M
Argosy University, Seattle, MD
Central Washington University, BM
City University of Seattle, MO
Eastern Washington University, BM
Everett Community College, A
The Evergreen State College, BM
Gonzaga University, M
Heritage University, BM
Highline College, A
Northwest University, BM
Pacific Lutheran University, M
Saint Martin's University, BM
Seattle Pacific University, B
Seattle University, MDO
Shoreline Community College, A
University of Puget Sound, M
University of Washington, BMD
University of Washington, Bothell, BM
University of Washington, Tacoma, M
Walla Walla University, M
Washington State University, BMD
Washington State University - Vancouver, B
Wenatchee Valley College, A
Western Washington University, M
Whitworth University, BM

West Virginia

Alderson Broaddus University, A
Bethany College, M
Concord University, BM
Fairmont State University, BM
Glenville State College, B
Marshall University, MDO
Ohio Valley University, M
Salem International University, BM
University of Charleston, B
West Liberty University, BM
West Virginia University, MD
West Virginia University at Parkersburg, A
West Virginia Wesleyan College, BM
Wheeling Jesuit University, B

Wisconsin

Alverno College, BM
Beloit College, B
Cardinal Stritch University, MD
Carroll University, BM
Carthage College, MO
Concordia University Wisconsin, BM
Edgewood College, BMDO
Lakeland College, M
Maranatha Baptist University, M
Marian University, MD
Marquette University, MDO
Milwaukee Area Technical College, A
Mount Mary University, BM
Ripon College, B
Silver Lake College of the Holy Family, M
University of Wisconsin - Eau Claire, M
University of Wisconsin - Green Bay, BM
University of Wisconsin - La Crosse, M
University of Wisconsin - Madison, MDO
University of Wisconsin - Milwaukee, BMDO
University of Wisconsin - Oshkosh, BM
University of Wisconsin - Platteville, BM
University of Wisconsin - River Falls, M
University of Wisconsin - Stevens Point, BM
University of Wisconsin - Superior, BM
University of Wisconsin - Whitewater, M
Viterbo University, BMO

Wyoming

Laramie County Community College, A
Western Wyoming Community College, A

U.S. Territories: American Samoa

American Samoa Community College, A

U.S. Territories: Guam

Guam Community College, A
University of Guam, M

U.S. Territories: Northern Mariana Islands

Northern Marianas College, A

U.S. Territories: Puerto Rico

American University of Puerto Rico (Bayamon), M
Bayamón Central University, MO
Caribbean University, D
Inter American University of Puerto Rico, Arecibo Campus, M
Inter American University of Puerto Rico, Barranquitas Campus, M
Inter American University of Puerto Rico, Metropolitan Campus, MD
Inter American University of Puerto Rico, San Germán Campus, B
Pontifical Catholic University of Puerto Rico, ABMD
Universidad Metropolitana, M
Universidad del Turabo, MDO
University of Puerto Rico in Carolina, A
University of Puerto Rico, Río Piedras Campus, MD
University of Puerto Rico in Utuado, AB
University of the Sacred Heart, BMO

U.S. Territories: United States Virgin Islands

University of the Virgin Islands, M

Canada

Alberta

Athabasca University, MO
Concordia University of Edmonton, B
Mount Royal University, B
University of Alberta, B
University of Calgary, B
University of Lethbridge, BM

British Columbia

Simon Fraser University, BMDO
Thompson Rivers University, BM
Trinity Western University, B
The University of British Columbia, BMDO
The University of British Columbia - Okanagan Campus, B
University of Northern British Columbia, M
University of Victoria, BMD

Manitoba

Brandon University, BMO
Providence University College & Theological Seminary, B
Université de Saint-Boniface, M
University of Manitoba, BMD
The University of Winnipeg, B

Maritime Provinces: New Brunswick

Crandall University, B
St. Thomas University, B
Université de Moncton, BM
University of New Brunswick Fredericton, BMD
University of New Brunswick Saint John, B

Maritime Provinces: Nova Scotia

Acadia University, BMD
Cape Breton University, B
Mount Saint Vincent University, BM
St. Francis Xavier University, BM
Université Sainte-Anne, BM

Maritime Provinces: Prince Edward Island

University of Prince Edward Island, BM

Newfoundland and Labrador

Memorial University of Newfoundland, BMDO

Ontario

Brock University, BMD
Lakehead University, BMD
Laurentian University, B
Nipissing University, BMO
Queen's University at Kingston, BMD
Redeemer University College, B
Trent University, B
University of Ottawa, MDO
University of Toronto, BMD
University of Waterloo, B
The University of Western Ontario, BM
University of Windsor, BMD
Wilfrid Laurier University, B
York University, BMD

Quebec

Bishop's University, BMO
Concordia University, BMDO
McGill University, MDO
Télé-université, B
Université Laval, MDO
Université de Montréal, BMDO
Université du Québec en Abitibi-Témiscamingue, BMDO
Université du Québec à Chicoutimi, MD
Université du Québec à Montréal, BMDO
Université du Québec en Outaouais, BMDO
Université du Québec à Rimouski, MDO
Université du Québec à Trois-Rivières, BMD
Université de Sherbrooke, BMO

Saskatchewan

University of Regina, BMDO
University of Saskatchewan, BMDO

EDUCATION/TEACHING OF THE GIFTED AND TALENTED

United States

Alabama

Samford University, M
Troy University, M
The University of Alabama, MO

Arkansas

Arkansas State University, M
University of Arkansas at Little Rock, MO
University of Central Arkansas, O

Colorado

Colorado Mesa University, M
Regis University, O
University of Northern Colorado, M

Connecticut

University of Connecticut, MDO

Delaware

Delaware State University, B
Wilmington University, M

Florida

Barry University, MDO
Carlos Albizu University, Miami Campus, M
Lynn University, M
St. Thomas University, O
University of South Florida, M
Warner University, B

Illinois

Northeastern Illinois University, M

Indiana

Purdue University, M

Kansas

Emporia State University, M
Wichita State University, M

Kentucky

Eastern Kentucky University, B
Morehead State University, M

Louisiana

University of Louisiana at Lafayette, M
University of Louisiana at Monroe, M

Maine

University of Southern Maine, O

Maryland

Johns Hopkins University, MO

Michigan

Grand Valley State University, B

Minnesota

Saint Mary's University of Minnesota, O
University of Minnesota, Twin Cities Campus, O

Mississippi

Mississippi University for Women, M
William Carey University, M

Missouri

Drury University, M
Maryville University of Saint Louis, M
University of Missouri, MD

Montana

University of Great Falls, B

Nebraska

University of Nebraska at Kearney, M

New York

Canisius College, BO
The College of New Rochelle, O
Hofstra University, O
St. Bonaventure University, MO
St. John's University, O
University at Buffalo, the State University of New York, O

North Carolina

Elon University, M
The University of North Carolina at Charlotte, MO

Ohio

Ashland University, M
Bowling Green State University, M
Kent State University, M
The University of Toledo, D
Wright State University, BM
Youngstown State University, M

Oregon

Pacific University, M

Pennsylvania

Millersville University of Pennsylvania, M

South Carolina

Converse College, M

Tennessee

Tennessee Technological University, D

Texas

Hardin-Simmons University, M
Southern Methodist University, M
University of North Texas, M
The University of Texas Rio Grande Valley, M

Virginia

George Mason University, M
James Madison University, M
Liberty University, MO
University of Virginia, M

Washington

Western Washington University, M
Whitworth University, M

West Virginia

West Virginia University, M

Wisconsin

Carthage College, M
University of Wisconsin - Whitewater, M

EDUCATION/TEACHING OF INDIVIDUALS WITH AUTISM

United States

Nevada

Nevada State College, B

Ohio

Wright State University, B

U.S. Territories: Puerto Rico

Inter American University of Puerto Rico, Ponce Campus, B

EDUCATION/TEACHING OF INDIVIDUALS IN EARLY CHILDHOOD SPECIAL EDUCATION PROGRAMS

United States

Arizona

Northland Pioneer College, A
Prescott College, B

Arkansas

Harding University, B

California

Fresno City College, A
Los Angeles Valley College, A
Orange Coast College, A
Palomar College, A
Santa Monica College, A

Delaware

Delaware State University, B

Florida

Daytona State College, B

Illinois

Judson University, B
Lewis University, B
University of Illinois at Urbana - Champaign, B

Kentucky

Eastern Kentucky University, B

Maine

University of Maine at Farmington, B

Maryland

Harford Community College, A

Michigan

Hope College, B

Minnesota

Itasca Community College, A

Missouri

Lindenwood University, B
Missouri Baptist University, B

Nevada

Nevada State College, B

New York

Canisius College, B
Cazenovia College, B
Elmira College, B
Keuka College, B
Roberts Wesleyan College, B
State University of New York College at Geneseo, B
Syracuse University, B

North Carolina

Blue Ridge Community College, A
Mitchell Community College, A

Ohio

Bowling Green State University, B
The University of Akron, B
University of Mount Union, B

Pennsylvania

Clarion University of Pennsylvania, B
Indiana University of Pennsylvania, B
Juniata College, B
Keystone College, B
Lock Haven University of Pennsylvania, B
Shippensburg University of Pennsylvania, B
York College of Pennsylvania, B

South Carolina

York Technical College, A

Tennessee

Motlow State Community College, A

Vermont

University of Vermont, B

Washington

Eastern Washington University, B

Wisconsin

Edgewood College, B
Silver Lake College of the Holy Family, B

U.S. Territories: Puerto Rico

Inter American University of Puerto Rico, Aguadilla
   Campus, B
Inter American University of Puerto Rico, Ponce
   Campus, B

EDUCATION/TEACHING OF IN-DIVIDUALS WITH EMOTIONAL DISTURBANCES

United States

Florida

Broward College, A
South Florida State College, A

Iowa

Morningside College, B

Michigan

Central Michigan University, B
Eastern Michigan University, B
Grand Valley State University, B
Hope College, B
Marygrove College, B
Northern Michigan University, B
Olivet College, B
University of Detroit Mercy, B
Western Michigan University, B

North Carolina

Greensboro College, B

EDUCATION/TEACHING OF IN-DIVIDUALS WITH HEARING IM-PAIRMENTS, INCLUDING DEAFNESS

United States

Florida

Flagler College, B
Florida State College at Jacksonville, A
Hillsborough Community College, A
Miami Dade College, A
North Florida Community College, A

Illinois

MacMurray College, B

Kentucky

Eastern Kentucky University, B

Massachusetts

Boston University, B

Michigan

Eastern Michigan University, B
Grand Valley State University, B
Michigan State University, B

Mississippi

University of Southern Mississippi, B

Nevada

College of Southern Nevada, A
Nevada State College, B

New Jersey

The College of New Jersey, B

New York

Canisius College, B

North Carolina

Barton College, B
The University of North Carolina at Greensboro, B

North Dakota

Minot State University, B

Ohio

Bowling Green State University, B

Oklahoma

University of Science and Arts of Oklahoma, B
The University of Tulsa, B

South Carolina

Converse College, B

Texas

Texas Christian University, B

Utah

Utah Valley University, B

EDUCATION/TEACHING OF IN-DIVIDUALS WITH MENTAL RE-TARDATION

United States

Florida

Broward College, A
South Florida State College, A

Georgia

Brenau University, B

Illinois

Bradley University, B

Indiana

Manchester University, B

Iowa

Morningside College, B

Michigan

Central Michigan University, B
Eastern Michigan University, B
Grand Valley State University, B
Northern Michigan University, B

North Carolina

Greensboro College, B

North Dakota

Minot State University, B
University of Mary, B

Ohio

Bowling Green State University, B
University of Rio Grande, B
Walsh University, B

Wisconsin

Silver Lake College of the Holy Family, B

Canada

Quebec

Université du Québec à Trois-Rivières, B

EDUCATION/TEACHING OF IN-DIVIDUALS WITH MULTIPLE DISABILITIES

United States

Florida

Adventist University of Health Sciences, B

Georgia

Georgia State University, M

Illinois

Bradley University, B
University of Illinois at Urbana - Champaign, BMDO

Indiana

Ball State University, B

Michigan

Grand Valley State University, B

Missouri

Missouri Baptist University, B
Northwest Missouri State University, B

New York

Dominican College, B
Hunter College of the City University of New York,
   M
Syracuse University, M

North Carolina

The University of North Carolina Wilmington, B

Ohio

Bowling Green State University, B
Cleveland State University, M
The University of Akron, B
Walsh University, B
Wright State University, B

Virginia

Norfolk State University, M

West Virginia

West Virginia University, M

EDUCATION/TEACHING OF IN-DIVIDUALS WITH ORTHOPEDIC AND OTHER PHYSICAL HEALTH IMPAIRMENTS

United States

Michigan

Eastern Michigan University, B
Grand Valley State University, B

U.S. Territories: Puerto Rico

University of Puerto Rico in Bayamón, B

EDUCATION/TEACHING OF IN-DIVIDUALS WITH SPECIFIC LEARNING DISABILITIES

United States

Arizona

Prescott College, B

Florida

Bethune-Cookman University, B
Broward College, A
South Florida State College, A

Illinois

Bradley University, B
Judson University, B
Northwestern University, B

Michigan

Aquinas College, B
Cornerstone University, B
Hope College, B
Michigan State University, B
Northern Michigan University, B
University of Detroit Mercy, B
Western Michigan University, B

New York

Canisius College, B
State University of New York at Plattsburgh, B

North Carolina

Appalachian State University, B
Greensboro College, B
Winston-Salem State University, B

Ohio

Baldwin Wallace University, B
Bowling Green State University, B
Malone University, B
Notre Dame College, B
University of Rio Grande, B
Wright State University, B

Oklahoma

Northeastern State University, B

South Carolina

University of South Carolina Upstate, B

West Virginia

West Virginia Wesleyan College, B

Wisconsin

Silver Lake College of the Holy Family, B

EDUCATION/TEACHING OF IN-DIVIDUALS WITH SPEECH OR LANGUAGE IMPAIRMENTS

United States

Alabama

Alabama Agricultural and Mechanical University, B

Georgia

Armstrong State University, B

Louisiana

Louisiana Tech University, B

Massachusetts

Emerson College, B

Michigan

Eastern Michigan University, B

Nebraska

University of Nebraska at Omaha, B

New Mexico

New Mexico State University, B

New York

Brooklyn College of the City University of New York, B
Buffalo State College, State University of New York, B
Elmira College, B
Ithaca College, B
Pace University, B
State University of New York College at Cortland, B

North Dakota

Minot State University, B

Oregon

Chemeketa Community College, A

Texas

Baylor University, B

EDUCATION/TEACHING OF IN-DIVIDUALS WITH VISION IM-PAIRMENTS, INCLUDING BLINDNESS

United States

Florida

Broward College, A
South Florida State College, A

Michigan

Eastern Michigan University, B

New York

St. Francis College, B

Pennsylvania

Kutztown University of Pennsylvania, B

EDUCATION/TEACHING OF IN-DIVIDUALS WHO ARE DEVEL-OPMENTALLY DELAYED

United States

Indiana

Saint Mary-of-the-Woods College, AB

EDUCATIONAL ADMINISTRA-TION AND SUPERVISION

United States

Alabama

Alabama State University, MDO
Auburn University, MDO
Jacksonville State University, MO
Troy University, MO
The University of Alabama, MD
University of Montevallo, MO

Arizona

Argosy University, Phoenix, MDO
Grand Canyon University, M
University of Phoenix - Online Campus, MO
University of Phoenix - Phoenix Campus, M
University of Phoenix - Southern Arizona Campus, M

Arkansas

Arkansas State University, O
Philander Smith College, B
Southern Arkansas University - Magnolia, M
University of Arkansas at Little Rock, MDO
University of Central Arkansas, O

California

Argosy University, Inland Empire, D
Argosy University, Los Angeles, D
Argosy University, Orange County, D
Argosy University, San Diego, D
Argosy University, San Francisco Bay Area, D
Azusa Pacific University, M
California Coast University, MD
California Lutheran University, M
California State University, Bakersfield, M
California State University, Fresno, M
California State University, Fullerton, M
California State University, Long Beach, MD
California State University, Northridge, M
California State University, San Bernardino, M
California State University, San Marcos, M
California State University, Stanislaus, M
Concordia University Irvine, M
Fresno Pacific University, M
Hope International University, M
La Sierra University, MDO
Loyola Marymount University, M
Mills College, MD
National University, M
Notre Dame de Namur University, MO
Pepperdine University, MD
Saint Mary's College of California, MD
San Francisco State University, MO
San Jose State University, MD
Santa Clara University, M
Shasta Bible College, M
Simpson University, M
University of California, Irvine, D
University of California, Riverside, MD
University of La Verne, O
University of the Pacific, MD
University of Phoenix - Bay Area Campus, MD
University of Phoenix - Southern California Campus, MO
University of San Francisco, MD
University of Southern California, D
Whittier College, M

Colorado

Argosy University, Denver, D
University of Colorado Denver, MO
University of Phoenix - Colorado Campus, M
University of Phoenix - Colorado Springs Downtown Campus, MO
Western State Colorado University, M

Connecticut

Post University, M
Sacred Heart University, O
University of Bridgeport, DO
University of Connecticut, DO

Delaware

University of Delaware, M

District of Columbia

The George Washington University, MDO
Howard University, MDO
Trinity Washington University, M
University of Phoenix - Washington D.C. Campus, MD

Florida

Argosy University, Sarasota, D
Argosy University, Tampa, D
Barry University, MD
Florida Agricultural and Mechanical University, MD
Florida Atlantic University, MD
Florida International University, MD
Florida State University, MDO
Keiser University, M
St. Thomas University, MO
University of Florida, D
University of Phoenix - North Florida Campus, M
University of Phoenix - South Florida Campus, M
University of West Florida, D

Georgia

Albany State University, M
Argosy University, Atlanta, D
Georgia Southern University, MD
Georgia State University, MDO
University of Georgia, MDO
University of North Georgia, O

Hawaii

Argosy University, Hawai'i, D
University of Hawaii at Manoa, MD
University of Phoenix - Hawaii Campus, M

Idaho

Idaho State University, MDO

Illinois

Argosy University, Chicago, D
Aurora University, D
Benedictine University, MD
Chicago State University, MD
Concordia University Chicago, MDO
DePaul University, M
Dominican University, M
Governors State University, M
Illinois State University, MD
Lewis University, O
Loyola University Chicago, MDO
McKendree University, M
National Louis University, MO
North Central College, M
Northeastern Illinois University, M
Northern Illinois University, MDO
Robert Morris University Illinois, M
Saint Xavier University, M
Southern Illinois University Carbondale, MD
Southern Illinois University Edwardsville, MO
University of Illinois at Urbana - Champaign, O

Indiana

Ball State University, MDO
Butler University, M
Indiana State University, MDO
Indiana University Bloomington, M
Purdue University, MDO
Purdue University Northwest (Hammond), M
University of Indianapolis, M

Iowa

Clarke University, M
Graceland University, M
Iowa State University of Science and Technology, M
Kaplan University, Davenport Campus, M
St. Ambrose University, M
Upper Iowa University, M

Kansas

Emporia State University, M
Fort Hays State University, MO

Pittsburg State University, O
The University of Kansas, MD
Washburn University, M
Wichita State University, MDO

Kentucky

Bellarmine University, O
Eastern Kentucky University, M
Morehead State University, M
Murray State University, MO
Spalding University, M
Union College, M
University of the Cumberlands, O
University of Louisville, MO
Western Kentucky University, MDO

Louisiana

Grambling State University, D
Louisiana State University and Agricultural & Mechanical College, MDO
Nicholls State University, M
Southeastern Louisiana University, MD
Southern University and Agricultural and Mechanical College, M
University of Holy Cross, M
University of Louisiana at Lafayette, M
Xavier University of Louisiana, M

Maine

University of Southern Maine, O

Maryland

Bowie State University, M
Frostburg State University, M
Johns Hopkins University, MO
Morgan State University, MO
University of Maryland, College Park, MD

Massachusetts

American International College, MO
Bay Path University, M
Boston College, MDO
Bridgewater State University, MO
Cambridge College, MO
Eastern Nazarene College, MO
Fitchburg State University, MO
Massachusetts College of Liberal Arts, M
Merrimack College, M
Northeastern University, MD
Salem State University, M
Suffolk University, MO
University of Massachusetts Lowell, MO
Westfield State University, MO
Worcester State University, MO

Michigan

Andrews University, MDO
Central Michigan University, MO
Eastern Michigan University, MO
Ferris State University, M
Michigan State University, MDO
Northern Michigan University, M
Oakland University, O
Saginaw Valley State University, M
University of Detroit Mercy, M
University of Michigan - Flint, M
Wayne State University, MDO

Minnesota

Argosy University, Twin Cities, DO
St. Cloud State University, MD
Saint Mary's University of Minnesota, O
University of Minnesota, Twin Cities Campus, MD
University of St. Thomas, MDO
Walden University, MDO
Winona State University, M

Mississippi

Delta State University, MO
Jackson State University, MDO
Mississippi College, M
Mississippi State University, MO

Missouri

Lincoln University, MO
Lindenwood University, MDO
Missouri Baptist University, M
Missouri State University, MO
Saint Louis University, MDO
Southeast Missouri State University, MO
Southwest Baptist University, MO
University of Central Missouri, MO
University of Missouri, MDO
University of Missouri - Kansas City, MDO
University of Missouri - St. Louis, MO
William Woods University, MO

Montana

University of Montana, MDO

Nebraska

Chadron State College, MO
Concordia University, Nebraska, M
University of Nebraska at Kearney, MO
University of Nebraska - Lincoln, MDO
University of Nebraska at Omaha, MDO
Wayne State College, MO

Nevada

University of Nevada, Las Vegas, MDO
University of Phoenix - Las Vegas Campus, M

New Hampshire

New England College, MD
Rivier University, M
Southern New Hampshire University, O
University of New Hampshire, MO

New Jersey

Caldwell University, MO
Felician University, MO
Georgian Court University, M
Kean University, M
Monmouth University, M
New Jersey City University, M
Rider University, MO
Rowan University, MO
Rutgers University - New Brunswick, MD
Saint Peter's University, MDO
Seton Hall University, DO

New Mexico

Eastern New Mexico University, M
New Mexico State University, MD
University of Phoenix - New Mexico Campus, M
University of the Southwest, M

New York

Baruch College of the City University of New York, M
Binghamton University, State University of New York, M
Canisius College, BM
City College of the City University of New York, MO
The College at Brockport, State University of New York, O
The College of Saint Rose, MO
Fordham University, MDO
Hunter College of the City University of New York, O
New York University, D
Niagara University, M
Pace University, O
Queens College of the City University of New York, O
St. John's University, DO
St. Lawrence University, MO
State University of New York at New Paltz, MO
State University of New York at Oswego, O
Stony Brook University, State University of New York, MO
University at Albany, State University of New York, MDO
University at Buffalo, the State University of New York, MDO
University of Rochester, D
Yeshiva University, MDO

North Carolina

Appalachian State University, MO
Campbell University, M
East Carolina University, MO
Elizabeth City State University, M
Fayetteville State University, M
Gardner-Webb University, MO
North Carolina Agricultural and Technical State University, M
North Carolina Central University, M
North Carolina State University, MD
The University of North Carolina at Chapel Hill, MD
The University of North Carolina at Charlotte, MO
The University of North Carolina at Greensboro, M
The University of North Carolina at Pembroke, M
The University of North Carolina Wilmington, D
Western Carolina University, M

North Dakota

North Dakota State University, MDO
University of Mary, M

Ohio

Ashland University, M
Baldwin Wallace University, M
Bowling Green State University, MDO
Cleveland State University, MDO
Franciscan University of Steubenville, M
John Carroll University, M
Ohio University, MD
Tiffin University, M
The University of Akron, M
University of Dayton, M
The University of Findlay, M
The University of Toledo, MDO
Ursuline College, M
Wright State University, MO
Xavier University, M
Youngstown State University, MD

Oklahoma

Northeastern State University, M
Oral Roberts University, MD
Southeastern Oklahoma State University, M
Southwestern Oklahoma State University, M
University of Oklahoma, MD

Oregon

Concordia University, M
George Fox University, O
Portland State University, MD
Southern Oregon University, M
University of Portland, M

Pennsylvania

Cairn University, M
California University of Pennsylvania, M
Cheyney University of Pennsylvania, O
Delaware Valley University, M
Drexel University, D
Duquesne University, MO
Eastern University, O
Gannon University, O
Geneva College, M
Gwynedd Mercy University, M
Immaculata University, O
Indiana University of Pennsylvania, DO
Kutztown University of Pennsylvania, M
Marywood University, MD
Mercyhurst University, M
Point Park University, M
Saint Joseph's University, O
Saint Vincent College, M
Shippensburg University of Pennsylvania, M
Slippery Rock University of Pennsylvania, M
Summit University, M
Temple University, M
The University of Scranton, M
Westminster College, MO
Widener University, MD
Wilkes University, D

Rhode Island

Providence College, M

South Carolina

Charleston Southern University, M
The Citadel, The Military College of South Carolina, MO
Clemson University, MO
Columbia College, M
Columbia International University, M
Converse College, O
Furman University, M
South Carolina State University, DO
University of South Carolina, MDO

South Dakota

Dakota Wesleyan University, M
Northern State University, M
Oglala Lakota College, M
South Dakota State University, M
University of Sioux Falls, O
The University of South Dakota, MDO

Tennessee

Argosy University, Nashville, D
Austin Peay State University, O
Bethel University, M
Freed-Hardeman University, M
Lincoln Memorial University, MDO
Lipscomb University, D
Middle Tennessee State University, MO
Tennessee State University, MDO
Union University, O
University of Memphis, MD
The University of Tennessee, MDO
The University of Tennessee at Chattanooga, MO
Vanderbilt University, MD

Texas

Abilene Christian University, O
Angelo State University, MO
Argosy University, Dallas, M
Baylor University, MO
Houston Baptist University, M
Lamar University, M
LeTourneau University, M
Midwestern State University, M
Our Lady of the Lake University of San Antonio, M
Prairie View A&M University, M
Sam Houston State University, MD
Schreiner University, MO
Southwestern Assemblies of God University, M
Sul Ross State University, M
Tarleton State University, MDO
Texas A&M International University, M
Texas A&M University, MD
Texas A&M University - Central Texas, M
Texas A&M University - Corpus Christi, M
Texas A&M University - Kingsville, MD
Texas A&M University - San Antonio, M
Texas A&M University - Texarkana, M
Texas Southern University, MD
Texas Woman's University, M
University of Houston, MD
University of Houston - Clear Lake, M
University of Houston - Victoria, M
University of Mary Hardin-Baylor, MD
The University of Texas at Austin, MD
The University of Texas at El Paso, MD
The University of Texas of the Permian Basin, M
The University of Texas at San Antonio, M
Wayland Baptist University, M
West Texas A&M University, M

Utah

University of Phoenix - Utah Campus, M
University of Utah, M

Vermont

University of Vermont, M

Virginia

Argosy University, Washington DC, D
Averett University, M
George Mason University, M
Hampton University, D
Liberty University, M
Norfolk State University, M

University of Virginia, MDO
Virginia State University, MD

Washington

Argosy University, Seattle, D
Central Washington University, M
City University of Seattle, O
Gonzaga University, M
Heritage University, M
Pacific Lutheran University, M
Saint Martin's University, M
Seattle Pacific University, O
Seattle University, MO
University of Washington, MD
University of Washington, Tacoma, M
Western Washington University, M
Whitworth University, M

West Virginia

Concord University, M
West Virginia University, MD

Wisconsin

Alverno College, M
Concordia University Wisconsin, M
Edgewood College, MO
Silver Lake College of the Holy Family, M
University of Wisconsin - Madison, O
University of Wisconsin - Milwaukee, MDO
University of Wisconsin - Stevens Point, M
University of Wisconsin - Superior, MO
University of Wisconsin - Whitewater, M

U.S. Territories: Guam

University of Guam, M

U.S. Territories: Puerto Rico

Bayamón Central University, M
Caribbean University, M
Inter American University of Puerto Rico, Aguadilla Campus, M
Inter American University of Puerto Rico, Arecibo Campus, M
Inter American University of Puerto Rico, Barranquitas Campus, M
Inter American University of Puerto Rico, Metropolitan Campus, D
Pontifical Catholic University of Puerto Rico, D
Universidad Adventista de las Antillas, M
Universidad Metropolitana, M
Universidad del Turabo, MO
University of Puerto Rico, Río Piedras Campus, MD

Canada

Alberta

University of Alberta, MDO

British Columbia

The University of British Columbia, M

Manitoba

Brandon University, MO
University of Manitoba, M

Maritime Provinces: New Brunswick

Université de Moncton, M

Maritime Provinces: Nova Scotia

St. Francis Xavier University, M

Ontario

The University of Western Ontario, B

Quebec

McGill University, M
Université Laval, MD
Université de Montréal, MDO
Université du Québec à Trois-Rivières, O
Université de Sherbrooke, M

Saskatchewan

University of Regina, M·
University of Saskatchewan, MDO

EDUCATIONAL ASSESSMENT, EVALUATION, AND RESEARCH

United States

Illinois

Blackburn College, B

Pennsylvania

Penn State Altoona, B
Penn State Berks, B
Penn State University Park, B

EDUCATIONAL, INSTRUCTIONAL, AND CURRICULUM SUPERVISION

United States

New York

Canisius College, B

Ohio

Wright State University, B

Texas

Sam Houston State University, B

EDUCATIONAL/INSTRUCTIONAL MEDIA DESIGN

United States

Alabama

Community College of the Air Force, A
Jacksonville State University, B

California

National University, B

Colorado

Pikes Peak Community College, A
Red Rocks Community College, A

Delaware

Wilmington University, B

Illinois

American InterContinental University Online, B
Triton College, A
Western Illinois University, B

Indiana

Ivy Tech Community College - North Central, A

Kentucky

Gateway Community and Technical College, A

Louisiana

Bossier Parish Community College, A

Massachusetts

Bridgewater State University, B

Minnesota

St. Cloud State University, B

Mississippi

Jackson State University, B

New Jersey

Essex County College, A

New York

Canisius College, B

Ohio

Bowling Green State University, B

Oklahoma

Cameron University, AB
University of Central Oklahoma, B

Oregon

Western Oregon University, B

Pennsylvania

Triangle Tech, Pittsburgh, A
Widener University, B

Texas

LeTourneau University, B
Lone Star College - North Harris, A
Midwestern State University, B
Sam Houston State University, B
Tarrant County College District, A
Texas State Technical College, A

Washington

Eastern Washington University, B

U.S. Territories: Puerto Rico

Bayamón Central University, AB
Inter American University of Puerto Rico, Barranquitas Campus, B

Canada

Ontario

The University of Western Ontario, B

EDUCATIONAL LEADERSHIP AND ADMINISTRATION

United States

Alabama

Alabama State University, MDO
Auburn University at Montgomery, O
Community College of the Air Force, A
Jacksonville State University, B
Samford University, MDO
Troy University, MO
The University of Alabama, MDO
The University of Alabama at Birmingham, MDO
University of North Alabama, O
University of South Alabama, M
The University of West Alabama, MO

Alaska

University of Alaska Anchorage, MO

Arizona

Argosy University, Phoenix, M
Arizona State University at the Tempe campus, MD
Glendale Community College, A
Grand Canyon University, D
Northern Arizona University, MDO
Prescott College, M
The University of Arizona, MDO
University of Phoenix - Online Campus, MD
University of Phoenix - Phoenix Campus, M

Arkansas

Arkansas State University, MDO
Arkansas Tech University, MO
Harding University, MO
Henderson State University, MO
John Brown University, M
University of Arkansas, MDO

University of Arkansas at Monticello, M
University of Central Arkansas, MO

California

Argosy University, Inland Empire, MD
Argosy University, Los Angeles, MD
Argosy University, Orange County, MD
Argosy University, San Diego, MD
Argosy University, San Francisco Bay Area, MD
Azusa Pacific University, D
Brandman University, M
California Baptist University, M
California Lutheran University, MD
California State Polytechnic University, Pomona, MD
California State University, Dominguez Hills, M
California State University, East Bay, MD
California State University, Fresno, D
California State University, Fullerton, MD
California State University, Northridge, MD
California State University, Sacramento, M
California State University, San Bernardino, D
California State University, San Marcos, D
California State University, Stanislaus, D
Chapman University, MD
Loyola Marymount University, D
National University, MO
Pepperdine University, D
Point Loma Nazarene University, M
Saint Mary's College of California, M
San Diego State University, M
San Francisco State University, D
Simpson University, M
Soka University of America, M
Sonoma State University, M
Stanford University, M
Trident University International, MD
University of California, Los Angeles, D
University of California, San Diego, D
University of La Verne, MD
University of Phoenix - Bay Area Campus, MD
University of Phoenix - Southern California Campus, M
University of San Diego, MDO
University of San Francisco, B
University of Southern California, D

Colorado

Argosy University, Denver, MD
Colorado Mesa University, M
Colorado State University, MD
Colorado State University - Global Campus, M
Fort Lewis College, MO
Regis University, MO
University of Colorado Colorado Springs, MD
University of Colorado Denver, D
University of Denver, MD
University of Northern Colorado, MDO
Western State Colorado University, M

Connecticut

Central Connecticut State University, MDO
Quinnipiac University, MO
Southern Connecticut State University, MDO
University of Hartford, DO
Western Connecticut State University, D

Delaware

Delaware State University, MD
University of Delaware, MD
Wilmington University, MD

District of Columbia

The Catholic University of America, MD
The George Washington University, MO
Howard University, MDO
University of Phoenix - Washington D.C. Campus, MD

Florida

Argosy University, Sarasota, MDO
Argosy University, Tampa, MDO
Barry University, MDO
Florida Agricultural and Mechanical University, D
Florida Atlantic University, MDO
Florida Gulf Coast University, MDO

Florida International University, MO
Florida State University, MDO
Jacksonville University, M
Keiser University, MDO
Lynn University, MD
Marconi International University, MD
St. Thomas University, D
Southeastern University, M
Stetson University, M
Trinity Baptist College, M
University of Central Florida, MDO
University of Florida, MDO
University of North Florida, MD
University of South Florida, MDO
University of South Florida, St. Petersburg, M
University of South Florida Sarasota-Manatee, M
University of West Florida, MO

Georgia

Albany State University, M
Argosy University, Atlanta, MDO
Augusta University, MO
Berry College, O
Clark Atlanta University, MDO
Columbus State University, MDO
Georgia College & State University, O
Georgia Southern University, MDO
Kennesaw State University, MDO
Mercer University, MDO
University of Georgia, D
University of West Georgia, MO
Valdosta State University, M

Hawaii

Argosy University, Hawai'i, D
Chaminade University of Honolulu, M
University of Hawaii at Manoa, D

Idaho

Boise State University, M
Idaho State University, MDO
Northwest Nazarene University, MDO
University of Idaho, MO

Illinois

American InterContinental University Online, M
Argosy University, Chicago, MDO
Aurora University, M
Benedictine University, M
Bradley University, M
Chicago State University, D
DePaul University, BMD
Eastern Illinois University, MO
Ellis University, M
Elmhurst College, M
Lewis University, MD
McKendree University, M
North Central College, M
Northeastern Illinois University, M
Northern Illinois University, D
Northwestern University, M
Olivet Nazarene University, M
Quincy University, M
Roosevelt University, M
Saint Xavier University, M
Southern Illinois University Edwardsville, D
Trinity International University, M
University of Illinois at Chicago, D
University of Illinois at Springfield, MO
University of Illinois at Urbana - Champaign, MDO
University of St. Francis, MD
Western Illinois University, MDO

Indiana

Butler University, M
Calumet College of Saint Joseph, M
Indiana University Bloomington, MDO
Indiana University Northwest, M
Indiana University - Purdue University Fort Wayne, MO
Indiana University - Purdue University Indianapolis, MO
Indiana Wesleyan University, MO
Oakland City University, D
Valparaiso University, M

Iowa

Iowa State University of Science and Technology, MD
Kaplan University, Davenport Campus, M
Loras College, M
Mount Mercy University, M
The University of Iowa, MDO
University of Northern Iowa, M

Kansas

Benedictine College, M
Emporia State University, M
Kansas State University, MD
Newman University, M
Ottawa University, M
Pittsburg State University, M
Southwestern College, D
The University of Kansas, D
Wichita State University, MD

Kentucky

Asbury University, M
Bellarmine University, MO
Eastern Kentucky University, M
Lindsey Wilson College, M
Morehead State University, MO
Northern Kentucky University, MDO
Spalding University, D
Thomas More College, M
Union College, M
University of the Cumberlands, MDO
University of Kentucky, MDO
University of Louisville, MD

Louisiana

Grambling State University, MDO
Louisiana State University and Agricultural & Mechanical College, MDO
Louisiana State University in Shreveport, M
Louisiana Tech University, MD
McNeese State University, MO
Northwestern State University of Louisiana, MO
Southern University and Agricultural and Mechanical College, M
University of Louisiana at Lafayette, MD
University of Louisiana at Monroe, M
University of New Orleans, MD

Maine

Saint Joseph's College of Maine, M
University of Maine, MDO
University of Maine at Farmington, M
University of New England, MDO
University of Southern Maine, MO

Maryland

Bowie State University, D
Goucher College, MO
Hood College, MO
Johns Hopkins University, MDO
Loyola University Maryland, MO
McDaniel College, M
Morgan State University, D
Notre Dame of Maryland University, MD
Salisbury University, M
Towson University, O
University of Maryland, College Park, MDO
University of Maryland Eastern Shore, D

Massachusetts

Cambridge College, D
Endicott College, D
Framingham State University, M
Gordon College, O
Harvard University, MD
Lesley University, D
Massachusetts College of Liberal Arts, O
Merrimack College, MO
Regis College, D
Simmons College, M
University of Massachusetts Amherst, MDO
University of Massachusetts Dartmouth, D
University of Massachusetts Lowell, D
Wheelock College, M

Michigan

Andrews University, MDO
Calvin College, M
Central Michigan University, MDO
Concordia University Ann Arbor, M
Eastern Michigan University, MDO
Ferris State University, MD
Grand Valley State University, MO
Madonna University, M
Marygrove College, M
Oakland University, MDO
Saginaw Valley State University, MO
Siena Heights University, MO
University of Michigan - Dearborn, MDO
University of Michigan - Flint, DO
Wayne State University, MD
Western Michigan University, MDO

Minnesota

Argosy University, Twin Cities, MDO
Bethel University, D
Capella University, MD
Concordia University, St. Paul, MO
Martin Luther College, M
Minnesota State University Mankato, M
Minnesota State University Moorhead, MO
St. Cloud State University, BM
Saint Mary's University of Minnesota, MD
Southwest Minnesota State University, M
University of Minnesota, Crookston, B
University of Minnesota, Twin Cities Campus, M
University of St. Thomas, MDO
Walden University, MDO
Winona State University, MO

Mississippi

Delta State University, D
Mississippi College, MDO
Mississippi State University, MDO
Mississippi University for Women, M
University of Southern Mississippi, MDO

Missouri

Avila University, B
Columbia College, M
Evangel University, MD
Lincoln University, O
Lindenwood University, DO
Maryville University of Saint Louis, MD
Missouri Baptist University, MO
Northwest Missouri State University, MO
Park University, M
Saint Louis University, MDO
University of Central Missouri, MD
William Woods University, D

Montana

Montana State University, MDO
Rocky Mountain College, M

Nebraska

College of Saint Mary, M
Creighton University, MD
Doane University, M
University of Nebraska at Omaha, MDO

Nevada

Sierra Nevada College, M
University of Nevada, Las Vegas, D
University of Nevada, Reno, MDO

New Hampshire

Keene State College, MO
New England College, MD
Plymouth State University, MO
Rivier University, DO
Southern New Hampshire University, MD
University of New Hampshire, O

New Jersey

Centenary College, M
The College of New Jersey, MO
College of Saint Elizabeth, MD

Fairleigh Dickinson University, College at Florham, M
Fairleigh Dickinson University, Metropolitan Campus, M
Georgian Court University, O
Kean University, MD
Montclair State University, MD
New Jersey City University, M
Ramapo College of New Jersey, M
Rider University, O
Rowan University, MDO
Rutgers University - Camden, M
Seton Hall University, DO
Stockton University, M
Thomas Edison State University, M
William Paterson University of New Jersey, M

New Mexico

New Mexico Highlands University, M
University of New Mexico, MDO
Western New Mexico University, M

New York

Adelphi University, MO
Baruch College of the City University of New York, MO
Binghamton University, State University of New York, O
Brooklyn College of the City University of New York, M
Buffalo State College, State University of New York, O
Canisius College, BMO
The College of New Rochelle, MO
The College of Saint Rose, M
College of Staten Island of the City University of New York, O
D'Youville College, D
Iona College, M
Le Moyne College, MO
Long Island University - LIU Brooklyn, O
Long Island University - LIU Post, O
Manhattan College, MO
Manhattanville College, MDO
Mercy College, MO
New York Institute of Technology, O
New York University, MDO
Niagara University, MDO
Pace University, M
St. Bonaventure University, MO
St. John Fisher College, MD
St. John's University, MDO
St. Thomas Aquinas College, M
State University of New York College at Cortland, O
State University of New York at New Paltz, M
State University of New York at Oswego, O
State University of New York at Plattsburgh, O
Stony Brook University, State University of New York, O
Syracuse University, MDO
Touro College, M
University at Buffalo, the State University of New York, O
University of Rochester, M
Wagner College, MO

North Carolina

Appalachian State University, D
Campbell University, B
East Carolina University, MDO
Gardner-Webb University, D
High Point University, M
Lenoir-Rhyne University, M
Queens University of Charlotte, M
The University of North Carolina at Chapel Hill, D
The University of North Carolina at Charlotte, MDO
The University of North Carolina at Greensboro, MDO
The University of North Carolina Wilmington, MD
Western Carolina University, MDO
Wingate University, MD

North Dakota

University of North Dakota, MDO

Ohio

Ashland University, MD
Baldwin Wallace University, M
Bowling Green State University, D
Cedarville University, M
Kent State University, MDO
Lourdes University, M
Malone University, M
Mount St. Joseph University, M
Ohio Dominican University, M
The Ohio State University, MDO
Union Institute & University, D
University of Cincinnati, MDO
University of Dayton, MDO
University of Mount Union, M
University of Rio Grande, M
Wright State University, BMO
Youngstown State University, D

Oklahoma

Cameron University, M
Northeastern State University, M
Northwestern Oklahoma State University, M
Oklahoma State University, MDO
University of Central Oklahoma, BM
University of Oklahoma, MDO

Oregon

Concordia University, MD
George Fox University, MDO
Lewis & Clark College, DO
Oregon State University, M
Portland State University, MD
University of Portland, M

Pennsylvania

Arcadia University, MDO
Carlow University, M
Chestnut Hill College, MO
Cheyney University of Pennsylvania, MO
Delaware Valley University, M
Drexel University, D
Duquesne University, D
Edinboro University of Pennsylvania, M
Gannon University, DO
Geneva College, M
Holy Family University, MD
Immaculata University, MDO
La Salle University, M
Lehigh University, MDO
Lincoln University, M
Lock Haven University of Pennsylvania, M
Marywood University, MD
Millersville University of Pennsylvania, M
Neumann University, D
Penn State University Park, MD
Point Park University, M
Robert Morris University, MD
Saint Francis University, M
Saint Joseph's University, MDO
Slippery Rock University of Pennsylvania, M
Temple University, MD
University of Pennsylvania, MD
University of Pittsburgh, MD
Villanova University, M
Waynesburg University, M
Widener University, MD
Wilkes University, M
York College of Pennsylvania, M

Rhode Island

Johnson & Wales University, D
Rhode Island College, MO

South Carolina

Bob Jones University, MDO
Clemson University, D
Coastal Carolina University, M
Columbia International University, D
Converse College, MO
Furman University, O
Winthrop University, M

South Dakota

Northern State University, M
South Dakota State University, M
University of Sioux Falls, MO

Tennessee

Argosy University, Nashville, MDO
Austin Peay State University, M
Carson-Newman University, M
Christian Brothers University, M
East Tennessee State University, MDO
Freed-Hardeman University, O
Lee University, MO
Lincoln Memorial University, D
Lipscomb University, MO
Southern Adventist University, M
Tennessee State University, B
Tennessee Technological University, MO
Tennessee Wesleyan College, M
Trevecca Nazarene University, MD
Union University, DO
University of Memphis, M
The University of Tennessee, D
The University of Tennessee at Chattanooga, D
The University of Tennessee at Martin, M
Vanderbilt University, D
Welch College, B

Texas

Abilene Christian University, MO
Argosy University, Dallas, MD
Arlington Baptist College, M
Dallas Baptist University, BM
Hardin-Simmons University, D
Howard Payne University, M
Lamar University, M
LeTourneau University, M
Midwestern State University, B
North American University, M
Prairie View A&M University, MD
St. Mary's University, MO
Sam Houston State University, BMD
Southwestern Adventist University, M
Stephen F. Austin State University, MD
Tarleton State University, BDO
Texas A&M University - Corpus Christi, D
Texas Christian University, MD
Texas State University, MD
Texas Tech University, MD
Trinity University, M
University of Houston, MD
University of Houston - Clear Lake, MD
University of the Incarnate Word, B
University of North Texas, MD
University of St. Thomas, M
The University of Texas at Arlington, MD
The University of Texas at El Paso, MD
The University of Texas Rio Grande Valley, MD
The University of Texas at San Antonio, MD
The University of Texas at Tyler, M
Wayland Baptist University, M

Utah

Argosy University, Salt Lake City, MD
Brigham Young University, MD
University of Utah, MD
Western Governors University, M

Vermont

Castleton University, MO
University of Vermont, MD

Virginia

Argosy University, Washington DC, MDO
The College of William and Mary, MD
George Mason University, MDO
Hampton University, M
James Madison University, M
Liberty University, MDO
Lynchburg College, MD
Norfolk State University, M
Old Dominion University, MDO
Radford University, MO
Regent University, MD
Virginia Commonwealth University, D

Virginia Polytechnic Institute and State University, MDO

Washington

Argosy University, Seattle, MD
Central Washington University, M
City University of Seattle, MD
Eastern Washington University, B
Gonzaga University, D
Pacific Lutheran University, M
Seattle Pacific University, MDO
Seattle University, D
University of Washington, MD
University of Washington, Bothell, M
Walla Walla University, M
Washington State University, MD

West Virginia

American Public University System, M
Concord University, M
Marshall University, MDO
Salem International University, M
West Virginia University, MD
Wheeling Jesuit University, M

Wisconsin

Alverno College, M
Cardinal Stritch University, MD
Carthage College, M
Edgewood College, D
Marian University, MD
Marquette University, MDO
Silver Lake College of the Holy Family, M
University of Wisconsin - Madison, MDO
University of Wisconsin - Oshkosh, M
University of Wisconsin - Whitewater, M
Wisconsin Lutheran College, M

Wyoming

University of Wyoming, MDO

U.S. Territories: Puerto Rico

Inter American University of Puerto Rico, Fajardo Campus, M
Pontifical Catholic University of Puerto Rico, D
Universidad Adventista de las Antillas, M
Universidad del Turabo, D

Canada

Alberta

University of Alberta, MDO
University of Calgary, MD
University of Lethbridge, M

British Columbia

Simon Fraser University, MD
Trinity Western University, MO
The University of British Columbia, D
University of Victoria, MD

Maritime Provinces: Nova Scotia

Acadia University, M
St. Francis Xavier University, M

Maritime Provinces: Prince Edward Island

University of Prince Edward Island, M

Newfoundland and Labrador

Memorial University of Newfoundland, M

Quebec

McGill University, O
Université Laval, O

EDUCATIONAL MEASUREMENT AND EVALUATION

United States

Arizona

Arizona State University at the Tempe campus, D

Arkansas

University of Arkansas, MD

Colorado

University of Colorado Boulder, D
University of Colorado Denver, MD
University of Northern Colorado, MD

Connecticut

Southern Connecticut State University, M
University of Connecticut, MDO

Florida

Florida State University, MDO
University of Florida, MD
University of Miami, MD
University of South Florida, MDO

Georgia

Georgia State University, MD
University of West Georgia, D

Illinois

American InterContinental University Online, M
Loyola University Chicago, MD
University of Illinois at Chicago, M

Indiana

Indiana University Bloomington, D

Iowa

Iowa State University of Science and Technology, M
The University of Iowa, MD
University of Northern Iowa, M

Kansas

The University of Kansas, MD

Kentucky

University of Kentucky, MD

Louisiana

Louisiana State University and Agricultural & Mechanical College, D
McNeese State University, MO
University of Louisiana at Monroe, M

Maine

University of New England, M

Maryland

University of Maryland, College Park, MD

Massachusetts

Boston College, MD
Brandeis University, O
Cambridge College, M
University of Massachusetts Amherst, D

Michigan

Eastern Michigan University, O
Michigan State University, D
Wayne State University, MD
Western Michigan University, MD

Minnesota

University of Minnesota, Twin Cities Campus, MDO
Walden University, MDO

Mississippi

University of Southern Mississippi, MD

Missouri

Missouri State University, O
Missouri Western State University, MO
University of Missouri - St. Louis, MD
Washington University in St. Louis, D

Nebraska

College of Saint Mary, M
University of Nebraska - Lincoln, MD

New Jersey

Montclair State University, O
Rutgers University - New Brunswick, M
Seton Hall University, D

New Mexico

New Mexico State University, M

New York

Syracuse University, MDO
University at Albany, State University of New York, O

North Carolina

North Carolina State University, D
The University of North Carolina at Chapel Hill, MD
The University of North Carolina at Greensboro, D

North Dakota

University of North Dakota, D

Ohio

Kent State University, MD
Ohio University, MD
The University of Toledo, MD

Oklahoma

Southwestern Oklahoma State University, M

Pennsylvania

Duquesne University, M
University of Pennsylvania, MD
University of Pittsburgh, MD
Wilkes University, M

South Carolina

University of South Carolina, MD

Tennessee

Tennessee Technological University, D
University of Memphis, MD
The University of Tennessee, D

Texas

Abilene Christian University, O
Baylor University, D
Houston Baptist University, M
Sul Ross State University, MO
Texas A&M University - San Antonio, M
University of North Texas, M
University of St. Thomas, M
The University of Texas at El Paso, M
The University of Texas Rio Grande Valley, M
Wayland Baptist University, M
West Texas A&M University, M

Utah

Utah State University, D
Western Governors University, M

Virginia

James Madison University, MD
University of Virginia, MD
Virginia Commonwealth University, D
Virginia Polytechnic Institute and State University, D

Washington

University of Washington, M

Wisconsin

University of Wisconsin - Milwaukee, MD

U.S. Territories: Puerto Rico

University of Puerto Rico, Río Piedras Campus, M

Canada

Alberta

University of Calgary, MD

British Columbia

The University of British Columbia, MD
University of Victoria, M

Quebec

Université Laval, MD

EDUCATIONAL MEDIA/IN-STRUCTIONAL TECHNOLOGY

United States

Alabama

Alabama Agricultural and Mechanical University, M
Alabama State University, MO
Auburn University, M
Auburn University at Montgomery, M
Jacksonville State University, M
The University of West Alabama, MO

Alaska

University of Alaska Southeast, M

Arizona

Argosy University, Phoenix, D
Arizona State University at the Tempe campus, MO
Northern Arizona University, MO
University of Phoenix - Online Campus, D

Arkansas

Arkansas Tech University, M
University of Arkansas, M
University of Arkansas at Little Rock, M
University of Central Arkansas, M

California

Argosy University, Orange County, D
Argosy University, San Francisco Bay Area, D
Azusa Pacific University, M
California Baptist University, M
California State Polytechnic University, Pomona, M
California State University, Dominguez Hills, MO
California State University, East Bay, M
California State University, Fullerton, M
California State University, Northridge, M
California State University, Sacramento, M
California State University, San Bernardino, M
California State University, Stanislaus, M
Concordia University Irvine, M
Fresno Pacific University, M
National University, MO
Notre Dame de Namur University, M
Pepperdine University, MD
San Diego State University, MD
San Francisco State University, M
Stanford University, M
Trident University International, D
University of California, Irvine, M
University of San Francisco, M

Colorado

Argosy University, Denver, D
Colorado Christian University, M
Colorado State University - Pueblo, M
Regis University, O
University of Colorado Denver, M
University of Northern Colorado, MD

Connecticut

Central Connecticut State University, M
Eastern Connecticut State University, M
Fairfield University, M
Post University, M

Quinnipiac University, M
Sacred Heart University, O
University of Connecticut, MDO
University of Hartford, M
University of Saint Joseph, M
Western Connecticut State University, M

Delaware

Wilmington University, M

District of Columbia

The George Washington University, MO
University of Phoenix - Washington D.C. Campus, D

Florida

Argosy University, Sarasota, D
Barry University, MDO
Florida Atlantic University, M
Florida Gulf Coast University, M
Florida Institute of Technology, M
Florida International University, MD
Florida State University, MDO
Full Sail University, M
Keiser University, DO
Marconi International University, M
Nova Southeastern University, M
St. Thomas University, MO
University of Central Florida, MDO
University of North Florida, M
University of South Florida, MDO
The University of Tampa, M
University of West Florida, MD

Georgia

Argosy University, Atlanta, D
Georgia College & State University, M
Georgia Southern University, MO
Georgia State University, MD
Kennesaw State University, M
Piedmont College, M
University of Georgia, MDO
University of West Georgia, MO

Hawaii

University of Hawaii at Manoa, MD

Idaho

Boise State University, MDO
Idaho State University, MD

Illinois

American InterContinental University Online, M
Aurora University, M
Chicago State University, M
Concordia University Chicago, M
DeVry University (Downers Grove), M
Ellis University, M
Governors State University, M
Lewis University, M
National Louis University, MO
Northern Illinois University, MD
Northwestern University, MD
Robert Morris University Illinois, M
Saint Xavier University, M
Southern Illinois University Edwardsville, MO
University of St. Francis, O
Western Illinois University, MO

Indiana

Indiana State University, MD
Indiana University Bloomington, MD
Purdue University, MDO
Purdue University Northwest (Hammond), M

Iowa

Clarke University, M
Graceland University, M
Iowa State University of Science and Technology, MD
Kaplan University, Davenport Campus, M
University of Northern Iowa, M

Kansas

Emporia State University, M
Fort Hays State University, M
Kansas State University, M
MidAmerica Nazarene University, M
Ottawa University, M
Pittsburg State University, M
The University of Kansas, MD

Kentucky

Morehead State University, M
University of Kentucky, M
Western Kentucky University, M

Louisiana

Grambling State University, D
Louisiana State University and Agricultural & Mechanical College, M
McNeese State University, MO
Northwestern State University of Louisiana, MO
Southeastern Louisiana University, M
Southern University and Agricultural and Mechanical College, M

Maine

University of Maine, O

Maryland

Frostburg State University, M
Goucher College, MO
Johns Hopkins University, MO
Loyola University Maryland, M
McDaniel College, M
Towson University, MD
University of Maryland, Baltimore County, MO
University of Maryland, College Park, MD

Massachusetts

Bay Path University, M
Bridgewater State University, M
Cambridge College, M
Fitchburg State University, M
Framingham State University, M
Harvard University, MO
Lesley University, O
Massachusetts College of Liberal Arts, M
Salem State University, M
University of Massachusetts Amherst, MDO
University of Massachusetts Boston, MO
Westfield State University, M
Worcester Polytechnic Institute, MD

Michigan

Central Michigan University, MDO
Eastern Michigan University, MO
Grand Valley State University, M
Lawrence Technological University, M
Marygrove College, M
Michigan State University, MD
Oakland University, O
Saginaw Valley State University, M
University of Michigan - Dearborn, M
University of Michigan - Flint, M
Wayne State University, MDO
Western Michigan University, MDO

Minnesota

Argosy University, Twin Cities, D
Capella University, MD
Concordia University, St. Paul, M
Minnesota State University Mankato, MO
St. Cloud State University, M
Saint Mary's University of Minnesota, M
University of Minnesota, Twin Cities Campus, MDO
University of St. Thomas, M
Walden University, MDO

Mississippi

Belhaven University, M
Jackson State University, M
Mississippi State University, MDO
University of Southern Mississippi, MD

Missouri

Avila University, M
Drury University, M
Lindenwood University, M
Missouri Southern State University, M
Missouri State University, M
Northwest Missouri State University, M
Southeast Missouri State University, M
University of Central Missouri, MO
University of Missouri, MDO
Webster University, M
William Woods University, M

Montana

Montana State University Billings, M

Nebraska

Bellevue University, M
University of Nebraska at Kearney, M

Nevada

University of Nevada, Las Vegas, D

New Hampshire

Plymouth State University, M
Southern New Hampshire University, M

New Jersey

College of Saint Elizabeth, O
Fairleigh Dickinson University, College at Florham, O
Fairleigh Dickinson University, Metropolitan Campus, O
Montclair State University, O
New Jersey City University, MD
Ramapo College of New Jersey, M
Rowan University, O
Seton Hall University, M
Stockton University, M
Thomas Edison State University, O

New Mexico

Eastern New Mexico University, M
University of New Mexico, MDO

New York

Adelphi University, MO
Buffalo State College, State University of New York, M
Canisius College, O
College of Mount Saint Vincent, O
The College of Saint Rose, MO
Hofstra University, O
Long Island University - LIU Post, M
Nazareth College of Rochester, M
New York Institute of Technology, MO
New York University, MDO
Pace University, MO
State University of New York College at Oneonta, M
State University of New York College at Potsdam, M
State University of New York Empire State College, M
Stony Brook University, State University of New York, MO
Syracuse University, MO
Touro College, M
University at Albany, State University of New York, M
University at Buffalo, the State University of New York, MO

North Carolina

Appalachian State University, M
East Carolina University, MO
Lenoir-Rhyne University, M
North Carolina Agricultural and Technical State University, M
North Carolina Central University, M
North Carolina State University, MD
The University of North Carolina at Charlotte, M
The University of North Carolina at Greensboro, M
The University of North Carolina Wilmington, M

North Dakota

University of North Dakota, M
Valley City State University, M

Ohio

Ashland University, M
Baldwin Wallace University, M
Bowling Green State University, M
Cleveland State University, D
Franklin University, M
Kent State University, MD
Ohio University, D
Tiffin University, M
University of Dayton, M
The University of Findlay, M
The University of Toledo, MDO
Youngstown State University, M

Oklahoma

Northeastern State University, M
University of Central Oklahoma, M
University of Oklahoma, M

Oregon

Concordia University, M
George Fox University, MO
Northwest Christian University, M
Portland State University, M
Western Oregon University, M

Pennsylvania

Arcadia University, M
Bloomsburg University of Pennsylvania, MO
Carlow University, M
Chestnut Hill College, MO
Delaware Valley University, M
DeSales University, M
Drexel University, MD
Duquesne University, MDO
East Stroudsburg University of Pennsylvania, M
Harrisburg University of Science and Technology, M
Indiana University of Pennsylvania, MD
Kutztown University of Pennsylvania, M
La Salle University, MO
Lehigh University, MDO
Misericordia University, M
Penn State University Park, MDO
Saint Joseph's University, MO
Saint Vincent College, M
University of Pennsylvania, M
Waynesburg University, M
West Chester University of Pennsylvania, O
Widener University, M
Wilkes University, MD

South Carolina

University of South Carolina, M
University of South Carolina Aiken, M

South Dakota

Augustana University, M
Dakota State University, M
Northern State University, M
University of Sioux Falls, M
The University of South Dakota, M

Tennessee

Argosy University, Nashville, MDO
East Tennessee State University, M
Johnson University, M
Lipscomb University, M
Middle Tennessee State University, O
Tennessee Technological University, MO
University of Memphis, MD
The University of Tennessee, MDO
The University of Tennessee at Chattanooga, O

Texas

Abilene Christian University, MO
Lamar University, M
Midwestern State University, M
Our Lady of the Lake University of San Antonio, M
Texas A&M University, M
Texas A&M University - Corpus Christi, M

Texas A&M University - Kingsville, M
Texas A&M University - Texarkana, M
Texas State University, M
Texas Tech University, MD
University of Houston - Clear Lake, M
University of the Incarnate Word, M
The University of Texas at Austin, MD
The University of Texas at San Antonio, MO
Wayland Baptist University, M
West Texas A&M University, M

Utah

Brigham Young University, MD
University of Utah, M
Utah State University, MDO
Utah Valley University, M
Western Governors University, M

Vermont

Marlboro College, MO

Virginia

The College of William and Mary, D
George Mason University, M
James Madison University, M
Liberty University, M
Longwood University, M
Old Dominion University, MD
Radford University, M
University of Virginia, MDO
Virginia Commonwealth University, M
Virginia Polytechnic Institute and State University, M

Washington

Argosy University, Seattle, D
Seattle Pacific University, M
University of Washington, MD

West Virginia

Fairmont State University, M
West Virginia University, MD

Wisconsin

Alverno College, M
Cardinal Stritch University, M
Wisconsin Lutheran College, M

Wyoming

University of Wyoming, MD

U.S. Territories: Puerto Rico

Caribbean University, M
Inter American University of Puerto Rico, Metropolitan Campus, M
University of the Sacred Heart, MO

Canada

Alberta

University of Alberta, M

British Columbia

Simon Fraser University, MD

Maritime Provinces: Nova Scotia

Acadia University, M

Newfoundland and Labrador

Memorial University of Newfoundland, M

Quebec

Concordia University, MDO
Université Laval, MD

EDUCATIONAL POLICY

United States

Alabama

Alabama State University, D

Arizona

Arizona State University at the Tempe campus, D

Arkansas

University of Arkansas, D

California

Stanford University, M
University of Southern California, D

Colorado

University of Colorado Boulder, MD
University of Colorado Denver, D
University of Denver, MD

District of Columbia

The Catholic University of America, D
The George Washington University, MDO
Howard University, MDO

Florida

Florida State University, MDO
University of Florida, D

Georgia

Georgia State University, MDO
University of Georgia, MDO

Hawaii

University of Hawaii at Manoa, D

Illinois

Illinois State University, D
Loyola University Chicago, MD
University of Illinois at Chicago, MD
University of Illinois at Urbana - Champaign, MDO

Indiana

Indiana University Bloomington, MDO

Iowa

The University of Iowa, MDO

Kansas

The University of Kansas, D

Kentucky

University of Kentucky, MD

Maryland

Johns Hopkins University, D
University of Maryland, Baltimore County, M

Massachusetts

Harvard University, M
University of Massachusetts Amherst, D

Michigan

Michigan State University, D
Wayne State University, D

Minnesota

University of Minnesota, Twin Cities Campus, MDO
University of St. Thomas, MO
Walden University, D

New Jersey

Rutgers University - Camden, M
Rutgers University - New Brunswick, D

New York

Cornell University, MD
New York University, M
Niagara University, D
Syracuse University, O
University of Rochester, MD

Ohio

Cleveland State University, D
The Ohio State University, MDO

Pennsylvania

Penn State University Park, MDO
University of Pennsylvania, MD
University of Pittsburgh, D

Tennessee

Vanderbilt University, D

Texas

The University of Texas at Arlington, MD

Virginia

The College of William and Mary, D
Virginia Commonwealth University, D
Virginia Polytechnic Institute and State University, MDO

Washington

University of Washington, MD

Wisconsin

Marquette University, MDO
University of Wisconsin - Madison, MD

Canada

Alberta

University of Alberta, MDO

British Columbia

The University of British Columbia, D

Ontario

The University of Western Ontario, M

EDUCATIONAL PSYCHOLOGY

United States

Alabama

Auburn University, D

Arizona

Northern Arizona University, MDO
The University of Arizona, MDO
University of Phoenix - Southern Arizona Campus, M

California

California Coast University, D
California State University, Long Beach, M
California State University, Northridge, M
Chapman University, M
Holy Names University, MO
La Sierra University, MO
University of California, Davis, D
University of California, Riverside, MD
University of the Pacific, MDO
University of Southern California, D

Colorado

University of Colorado Boulder, MD
University of Colorado Denver, MO
University of Northern Colorado, MD

Connecticut

University of Connecticut, MDO

District of Columbia

The Catholic University of America, D
Howard University, D

Florida

Florida Atlantic University, M
Florida State University, MDO

Georgia

Clark Atlanta University, M
Georgia State University, MD
University of Georgia, MDO

Hawaii

University of Hawaii at Manoa, MD

Illinois

Illinois State University, M
Loyola University Chicago, M
National Louis University, MO
Northern Illinois University, MDO
Southern Illinois University Carbondale, MD
University of Illinois at Chicago, MD
University of Illinois at Urbana - Champaign, MDO

Indiana

Ball State University, MDO
Indiana University Bloomington, MDO
Purdue University, MD

Iowa

The University of Iowa, MD
University of Northern Iowa, M

Kansas

The University of Kansas, MD
Wichita State University, M

Kentucky

University of Kentucky, MDO
University of Louisville, MD

Maine

University of Southern Maine, MO

Massachusetts

American International College, MD
Boston College, MD
Harvard University, M

Michigan

Andrews University, MD
Eastern Michigan University, MO
Michigan State University, D
Wayne State University, MD

Minnesota

Capella University, MD
University of Minnesota, Twin Cities Campus, MDO
Walden University, MD

Mississippi

Mississippi State University, MDO

Missouri

University of Missouri, MDO
University of Missouri - St. Louis, D
Webster University, MO

Nebraska

University of Nebraska - Lincoln, MDO

Nevada

University of Nevada, Las Vegas, MDO
University of Nevada, Reno, MDO

New Jersey

New Jersey City University, MO
Rutgers University - New Brunswick, MD

New Mexico

University of New Mexico, MD

New York

The College of Saint Rose, MO
Fordham University, MDO
New York University, MD
State University of New York College at Oneonta, MO
University at Albany, State University of New York, MDO
University at Buffalo, the State University of New York, MDO

North Carolina

The University of North Carolina at Chapel Hill, MD

Ohio

John Carroll University, M
Kent State University, M
Miami University, MO
The University of Toledo, MD

Oklahoma

Oklahoma State University, MDO
University of Oklahoma, MD

Pennsylvania

Edinboro University of Pennsylvania, M
Immaculata University, MO
Indiana University of Pennsylvania, MO
Penn State University Park, MDO
Temple University, M
Widener University, M

South Carolina

University of South Carolina, MD

South Dakota

The University of South Dakota, MDO

Tennessee

Tennessee Technological University, MO
University of Memphis, MD
The University of Tennessee, MD

Texas

Baylor University, MDO
Texas A&M University, MD
Texas A&M University - Central Texas, M
Texas Tech University, MD
University of Houston, MD
University of the Incarnate Word, M
University of North Texas, MD
The University of Texas at Austin, MD
The University of Texas at El Paso, M
The University of Texas Rio Grande Valley, M

Utah

Brigham Young University, MD
University of Utah, MD

Virginia

George Mason University, MDO
Regent University, D
University of Virginia, MDO
Virginia Commonwealth University, D

Washington

University of Washington, MD
Washington State University, MD

West Virginia

West Virginia University, M

Wisconsin

University of Wisconsin - Madison, MD
University of Wisconsin - Milwaukee, MD

U.S. Territories: Puerto Rico

Pontifical Catholic University of Puerto Rico, M

Canada

Alberta

University of Alberta, MD

British Columbia

Simon Fraser University, MD
University of Victoria, MD

Manitoba

University of Manitoba, M

Maritime Provinces: New Brunswick

Université de Moncton, M

Maritime Provinces: Nova Scotia

Mount Saint Vincent University, M

Newfoundland and Labrador

Memorial University of Newfoundland, M

Ontario

The University of Western Ontario, M

Quebec

McGill University, MD
Université Laval, MD
Université de Montréal, MDO
Université du Québec en Outaouais, M
Université du Québec à Trois-Rivières, MD

Saskatchewan

University of Regina, M
University of Saskatchewan, MDO

EDUCATIONAL STATISTICS AND RESEARCH METHODS

United States

Pennsylvania

Bucknell University, B

ELECTRICAL, ELECTRONIC AND COMMUNICATIONS ENGINEERING TECHNOLOGY/TECHNICIAN

United States

Alabama

Bishop State Community College, A
Calhoun Community College, A
Central Alabama Community College, A
Community College of the Air Force, A
Gadsden State Community College, A
George C. Wallace Community College, A
J. F. Drake State Community and Technical College, A
Jacksonville State University, B
Reid State Technical College, A
Shelton State Community College, A
Southern Union State Community College, A
Troy University, B
Wallace State Community College, A

Alaska

University of Alaska Anchorage, A
University of Alaska Anchorage, Matanuska-Susitna College, A

Arizona

Arizona State University at the Polytechnic campus, B
Arizona Western College, A
Cochise County Community College District, A
Coconino Community College, A
DeVry University (Mesa), A
DeVry University (Phoenix), AB
Mesa Community College, A
Northland Pioneer College, A
Scottsdale Community College, A

Arkansas

Arkansas State University - Beebe, A
East Arkansas Community College, A
National Park College, A
North Arkansas College, A
NorthWest Arkansas Community College, A
University of Arkansas Community College at Hope, A
University of Arkansas at Little Rock, AB

California

Allan Hancock College, A
American River College, A
Bakersfield College, A

California State Polytechnic University, Pomona, B
California State University, Long Beach, B
Cerritos College, A
Citrus College, A
College of San Mateo, A
College of the Sequoias, A
DeVry University (Alhambra), A
DeVry University (Anaheim), A
DeVry University (Bakersfield), A
DeVry University (Fremont), AB
DeVry University (Long Beach), AB
DeVry University (Oxnard), A
DeVry University (Palmdale), A
DeVry University (Pomona), AB
DeVry University (San Diego), A
DeVry University (Sherman Oaks), AB
East Los Angeles College, A
El Camino College, A
Foothill College, A
Glendale Community College, A
Golden West College, A
Las Positas College, A
Los Angeles City College, A
Los Angeles Harbor College, A
Los Angeles Pierce College, A
Los Angeles Southwest College, A
Los Angeles Trade-Technical College, A
Los Medanos College, A
Merced College, A
Mission College, A
Modesto Junior College, A
Moorpark College, A
Mt. San Antonio College, A
Napa Valley College, A
Ohlone College, A
Sacramento City College, A
Saddleback College, A
San Bernardino Valley College, A
San Diego City College, A
San Joaquin Delta College, A
Santa Ana College, A
Santa Barbara City College, A
Santa Rosa Junior College, A
Shasta College, A
Solano Community College, A
Taft College, A
Victor Valley College, A
West Los Angeles College, A
Yuba College, A

Colorado

Aims Community College, A
Colorado Technical University Colorado Springs, AB
DeVry University (Colorado Springs), A
DeVry University (Westminster), AB
Metropolitan State University of Denver, B
Pikes Peak Community College, A
Pueblo Community College, A

Connecticut

Central Connecticut State University, B
Gateway Community College, A
Naugatuck Valley Community College, A
Northwestern Connecticut Community College, A
Three Rivers Community College, A
University of Hartford, AB

Delaware

Delaware State University, B
Delaware Technical & Community College, Jack F. Owens Campus, A
Delaware Technical & Community College, Stanton/Wilmington Campus, A
Delaware Technical & Community College, Terry Campus, A

District of Columbia

University of the District of Columbia, A

Florida

Daytona State College, AB
DeVry University (Miramar), AB
DeVry University (Orlando), AB
Florida Agricultural and Mechanical University, B
Gulf Coast State College, A

Hillsborough Community College, A
Indian River State College, A
Lake-Sumter State College, A
Miami Dade College, AB
Northwest Florida State College, A
Palm Beach State College, A
Pensacola State College, A
St. Johns River State College, A
Seminole State College of Florida, A
South Florida State College, A
State College of Florida Manatee-Sarasota, A

Georgia

Athens Technical College, A
Augusta Technical College, A
Bainbridge State College, A
Central Georgia Technical College, A
Chattahoochee Technical College, A
Columbus Technical College, A
Dalton State College, A
DeVry University (Alpharetta), B
DeVry University (Atlanta), A
DeVry University (Decatur), AB
Fort Valley State University, AB
Georgia Piedmont Technical College, A
Georgia Southern University, B
Gwinnett Technical College, A
Kennesaw State University, B
Lanier Technical College, A
Savannah State University, B
Savannah Technical College, A
South Georgia Technical College, A
Southeastern Technical College, A
Southern Crescent Technical College, A
West Georgia Technical College, A

Hawaii

Hawaii Community College, A
Honolulu Community College, A
Kauai Community College, A

Idaho

Brigham Young University - Idaho, AB
Idaho State University, AB
North Idaho College, A

Illinois

Carl Sandburg College, A
City Colleges of Chicago, Richard J. Daley College,
    A
College of DuPage, A
College of Lake County, A
DeVry University (Addison), B
DeVry University (Chicago), AB
DeVry University (Tinley Park), AB
DeVry University Online, AB
Harper College, A
Heartland Community College, A
Illinois Central College, A
Illinois Valley Community College, A
John A. Logan College, A
Joliet Junior College, A
Kaskaskia College, A
Kishwaukee College, A
Lake Land College, A
Lincoln Land Community College, A
Oakton Community College, A
Prairie State College, A
Rend Lake College, A
Richland Community College, A
Rock Valley College, A
Sauk Valley Community College, A
Shawnee Community College, A
South Suburban College, A
Southeastern Illinois College, A
Southwestern Illinois College, A
Spoon River College, A
Taylor Business Institute, A
Waubonsee Community College, A

Indiana

Indiana State University, B
Indiana University - Purdue University Fort Wayne,
    AB

Indiana University - Purdue University Indianapolis,
    B
Ivy Tech Community College - Bloomington, A
Ivy Tech Community College - Central Indiana, A
Ivy Tech Community College - Columbus, A
Ivy Tech Community College - East Central, A
Ivy Tech Community College - Kokomo, A
Ivy Tech Community College - Lafayette, A
Ivy Tech Community College - North Central, A
Ivy Tech Community College - Northeast, A
Ivy Tech Community College - Northwest, A
Ivy Tech Community College - Richmond, A
Ivy Tech Community College - Southeast, A
Ivy Tech Community College - Southern Indiana, A
Ivy Tech Community College - Southwest, A
Ivy Tech Community College - Wabash Valley, A
Purdue University, AB
Purdue University Northwest (Hammond), B
Purdue University Northwest (Westville), A
Vincennes University, A

Iowa

Clinton Community College, A
Des Moines Area Community College, A
Hamilton Technical College, AB
Hawkeye Community College, A
Indian Hills Community College, A
Iowa Central Community College, A
Iowa Lakes Community College, A
Iowa Western Community College, A
Kirkwood Community College, A
North Iowa Area Community College, A
Northeast Iowa Community College, A
Northwest Iowa Community College, A
Southeastern Community College, A

Kansas

Allen Community College, A
Butler Community College, A
Dodge City Community College, A
Grantham University, AB
Hutchinson Community College, A
Neosho County Community College, A
North Central Kansas Technical College, A
Pittsburg State University, B

Kentucky

Bluegrass Community and Technical College, A
Hopkinsville Community College, A
Jefferson Community and Technical College, A
Madisonville Community College, A
Northern Kentucky University, B
Sullivan College of Technology and Design, A

Louisiana

Delgado Community College, A
ITI Technical College, A
Louisiana Tech University, B
Northwestern State University of Louisiana, AB
Southern University and Agricultural and Mechanical
    College, B
Southern University at Shreveport, A

Maine

Eastern Maine Community College, A
Kennebec Valley Community College, A
Northern Maine Community College, A
Southern Maine Community College, A
University of Maine, B

Maryland

Anne Arundel Community College, A
Baltimore City Community College, A
Capitol Technology University, A
Cecil College, A
Howard Community College, A
Prince George's Community College, A
University of Maryland Eastern Shore, B
Wor-Wic Community College, A

Massachusetts

Benjamin Franklin Institute of Technology, A
Berkshire Community College, A
Fitchburg State University, B
Massachusetts Bay Community College, A

Massasoit Community College, A
Middlesex Community College, A
Northern Essex Community College, A
Quinsigamond Community College, A
Springfield Technical Community College, A
University of Massachusetts Lowell, AB

Michigan

Baker College, AB
Bay de Noc Community College, A
Eastern Michigan University, B
Ferris State University, B
Grand Rapids Community College, A
Henry Ford College, A
Jackson College, A
Kalamazoo Valley Community College, A
Kirtland Community College, A
Lake Superior State University, AB
Lawrence Technological University, A
Macomb Community College, A
Michigan Technological University, B
Monroe County Community College, A
Montcalm Community College, A
Mott Community College, A
Muskegon Community College, A
Northern Michigan University, A
Northwestern Michigan College, A
Oakland Community College, A
St. Clair County Community College, A
Schoolcraft College, A
Wayne County Community College District, A
Wayne State University, B
West Shore Community College, A

Minnesota

Anoka Technical College, A
Dunwoody College of Technology, A
Hennepin Technical College, A
Lake Superior College, A
Minnesota State College - Southeast Technical, A
Minnesota State Community and Technical College,
    A
Minnesota State University Mankato, B
Ridgewater College, A
Rochester Community and Technical College, A
St. Cloud State University, B
St. Cloud Technical & Community College, A
Saint Paul College - A Community & Technical Col-
    lege, A

Mississippi

Copiah-Lincoln Community College, A
East Central Community College, A
East Mississippi Community College, A
Hinds Community College, A
Itawamba Community College, A
Jones County Junior College, A
Meridian Community College, A
Mississippi Delta Community College, A
Mississippi Gulf Coast Community College, A
Northeast Mississippi Community College, A
Northwest Mississippi Community College, A
Pearl River Community College, A
Southwest Mississippi Community College, A
University of Southern Mississippi, B

Missouri

Crowder College, A
DeVry University (Kansas City), AB
Jefferson College, A
Metropolitan Community College - Kansas City, A
Mineral Area College, A
Missouri Western State University, B
Moberly Area Community College, A
North Central Missouri College, A
Ozarks Technical Community College, A
State Technical College of Missouri, A
University of Central Missouri, B

Montana

Miles Community College, A
University of Montana, A

Nebraska

Central Community College - Columbus Campus, A
Central Community College - Grand Island Campus, A
Central Community College - Hastings Campus, A
Metropolitan Community College, A
Southeast Community College, Lincoln Campus, A
Southeast Community College, Milford Campus, A

Nevada

Career College of Northern Nevada, A
College of Southern Nevada, A
DeVry University, A
Great Basin College, A
Nevada State College, B

New Hampshire

Nashua Community College, A
NHTI, Concord's Community College, A
University of New Hampshire at Manchester, B

New Jersey

Brookdale Community College, A
Camden County College, A
County College of Morris, A
DeVry University (North Brunswick), AB
DeVry University (Paramus), AB
Essex County College, A
Fairleigh Dickinson University, Metropolitan Campus, B
Hudson County Community College, A
Mercer County Community College, A
Middlesex County College, A
Passaic County Community College, A
Rowan College at Burlington County, A
Thomas Edison State University, AB

New Mexico

Central New Mexico Community College, A
Doña Ana Community College, A
Luna Community College, A
New Mexico State University - Alamogordo, A
New Mexico State University - Carlsbad, A
Northern New Mexico College, A
San Juan College, A
Santa Fe Community College, A
University of New Mexico - Los Alamos Branch, A

New York

Adirondack Community College, A
Bramson ORT College, A
Bronx Community College of the City University of New York, A
Broome Community College, A
Buffalo State College, State University of New York, B
Cayuga County Community College, A
Clinton Community College, A
College of Staten Island of the City University of New York, A
DeVry College of New York, AB
Dutchess Community College, A
Erie Community College, North Campus, A
Farmingdale State College, B
Fulton-Montgomery Community College, A
Island Drafting and Technical Institute, A
Mohawk Valley Community College, A
Monroe Community College, A
Morrisville State College, A
New York City College of Technology of the City University of New York, AB
Onondaga Community College, A
Queensborough Community College of the City University of New York, A
Rockland Community College, A
Schenectady County Community College, A
State University of New York College of Technology at Alfred, AB
State University of New York College of Technology at Canton, AB
State University of New York College of Technology at Delhi, A
State University of New York Polytechnic Institute, B
Suffolk County Community College, A
Sullivan County Community College, A

Vaughn College of Aeronautics and Technology, B
Westchester Community College, A

North Carolina

Alamance Community College, A
Asheville-Buncombe Technical Community College, A
Beaufort County Community College, A
Bladen Community College, A
Blue Ridge Community College, A
Cape Fear Community College, A
Catawba Valley Community College, A
Central Carolina Community College, A
Central Piedmont Community College, A
Cleveland Community College, A
Craven Community College, A
Davidson County Community College, A
DeVry University, A
Durham Technical Community College, A
Fayetteville Technical Community College, A
Forsyth Technical Community College, A
Gaston College, A
Guilford Technical Community College, A
Haywood Community College, A
Isothermal Community College, A
Mayland Community College, A
Mitchell Community College, A
Nash Community College, A
North Carolina Agricultural and Technical State University, B
Pamlico Community College, A
Pitt Community College, A
Richmond Community College, A
Robeson Community College, A
Rockingham Community College, A
Rowan-Cabarrus Community College, A
Southeastern Community College, A
Southwestern Community College, A
Stanly Community College, A
Surry Community College, A
Tri-County Community College, A
The University of North Carolina at Charlotte, B
Vance-Granville Community College, A
Wake Technical Community College, A
Wayne Community College, A
Western Carolina University, B
Western Piedmont Community College, A
Wilkes Community College, A

North Dakota

Bismarck State College, A

Ohio

Bowling Green State University, B
Bowling Green State University - Firelands College, A
Bryant & Stratton College - Cleveland Campus, AB
Bryant & Stratton College - Eastlake Campus, A
Central Ohio Technical College, A
Cincinnati State Technical and Community College, A
Clark State Community College, A
Cleveland State University, B
Columbus State Community College, A
DeVry University (Columbus), AB
Eastern Gateway Community College, A
Edison Community College, A
ETI Technical College of Niles, A
Fortis College (Centerville), A
Hocking College, A
James A. Rhodes State College, A
Lakeland Community College, A
Lorain County Community College, A
Marion Technical College, A
Miami University Middletown, A
North Central State College, A
Northwest State Community College, A
Owens Community College, A
Sinclair Community College, A
Southern State Community College, A
Terra State Community College, A
The University of Akron, AB
University of Cincinnati, B
University of Dayton, A
Washington State Community College, A
Youngstown State University, AB

Zane State College, A

Oklahoma

Langston University, A
Oklahoma State University, B
Oklahoma State University, Oklahoma City, A
Redlands Community College, A
Rose State College, A
Tulsa Community College, A
Vatterott College (Tulsa), A

Oregon

Blue Mountain Community College, A
Central Oregon Community College, A
Chemeketa Community College, A
Clackamas Community College, A
Columbia Gorge Community College, A
Lane Community College, A
Mt. Hood Community College, A
Oregon Institute of Technology, AB
Portland Community College, A
Rogue Community College, A
Umpqua Community College, A

Pennsylvania

Butler County Community College, A
California University of Pennsylvania, AB
Community College of Allegheny County, A
Community College of Beaver County, A
Delaware County Community College, A
DeVry University (Fort Washington), AB
DeVry University (Philadelphia), A
Erie Institute of Technology, A
Harrisburg Area Community College, A
Johnson College, A
Lehigh Carbon Community College, A
Luzerne County Community College, A
Montgomery County Community College, A
New Castle School of Trades, A
Northampton Community College, A
Penn State Altoona, A
Penn State Berks, A
Penn State Brandywine, A
Penn State DuBois, A
Penn State Erie, The Behrend College, AB
Penn State Fayette, The Eberly Campus, A
Penn State Hazleton, A
Penn State New Kensington, A
Penn State Schuylkill, A
Penn State Shenango, A
Penn State Wilkes-Barre, A
Penn State Worthington Scranton, A
Penn State York, A
Pennsylvania College of Technology, A
Pennsylvania Institute of Technology, A
Pittsburgh Institute of Aeronautics, A
Pittsburgh Technical Institute, A
Thaddeus Stevens College of Technology, A
Triangle Tech, DuBois, A
University of Pittsburgh at Johnstown, B
Westmoreland County Community College, A
Williamson College of the Trades, A
YTI Career Institute - York, A

South Carolina

Aiken Technical College, A
ECPI University (Columbia), A
Florence-Darlington Technical College, A
Greenville Technical College, A
Horry-Georgetown Technical College, A
Midlands Technical College, A
Northeastern Technical College, A
Orangeburg-Calhoun Technical College, A
Piedmont Technical College, A
South Carolina State University, B
Spartanburg Community College, A
Tri-County Technical College, A
Trident Technical College, A
York Technical College, A

South Dakota

Lake Area Technical Institute, A
Oglala Lakota College, A
Sisseton-Wahpeton College, A
South Dakota State University, B

Southeast Technical Institute, A

Tennessee

Chattanooga College - Medical, Dental and Technical Careers, A
Chattanooga State Community College, A
Fountainhead College of Technology, A
Nashville State Community College, A
Northeast State Community College, A
Pellissippi State Community College, A
Southwest Tennessee Community College, A
University of Memphis, B

Texas

Alvin Community College, A
Amarillo College, A
Angelina College, A
Austin Community College District, A
Cisco College, A
Collin County Community College District, A
Del Mar College, A
DeVry University (Austin), B
DeVry University (Irving), AB
Eastfield College, A
El Paso Community College, A
Grayson College, A
Hallmark University, A
Kilgore College, A
Lamar State College - Port Arthur, A
Laredo Community College, A
Lee College, A
LeTourneau University, B
Lone Star College - CyFair, A
Lone Star College - North Harris, A
Lone Star College - Tomball, A
Mountain View College, A
North Central Texas College, A
North Lake College, A
Odessa College, A
Paris Junior College, A
Prairie View A&M University, B
Richland College, A
Sam Houston State University, B
San Antonio College, A
San Jacinto College District, A
South Plains College, A
Tarrant County College District, A
Texarkana College, A
Texas A&M University, B
Texas A&M University - Corpus Christi, B
Texas Southern University, B
Texas State Technical College, A
University of Houston, B
University of North Texas, B
Victoria College, A
Western Technical College (El Paso), A
Wharton County Junior College, A

Utah

Salt Lake Community College, A
Weber State University, AB

Vermont

Vermont Technical College, AB

Virginia

Blue Ridge Community College, A
Dabney S. Lancaster Community College, A
DeVry University (Arlington), B
DeVry University (Chesapeake), A
Eastern Shore Community College, A
ECPI University (Manassas), A
ECPI University (Newport News), A
ECPI University (Richmond), A
ECPI University (Virginia Beach), AB
Hampton University, B
Mountain Empire Community College, A
New River Community College, A
Norfolk State University, B
Northern Virginia Community College, A
Southside Virginia Community College, A
Southwest Virginia Community College, A
Tidewater Community College, A
Virginia Highlands Community College, A
Virginia Western Community College, A

Wytheville Community College, A

Washington

Bates Technical College, A
Central Washington University, B
Clark College, A
Edmonds Community College, A
North Seattle College, A
Olympic College, A
Peninsula College, A
Pierce College at Puyallup, A
Skagit Valley College, A
Spokane Community College, A
Tacoma Community College, A
Yakima Valley Community College, A

West Virginia

Bluefield State College, AB
BridgeValley Community and Technical College (Montgomery), A
Fairmont State University, AB
Mountwest Community & Technical College, A
Pierpont Community & Technical College, A
West Virginia University at Parkersburg, A

Wisconsin

Fox Valley Technical College, A
Gateway Technical College, A
Lakeshore Technical College, A
Madison Area Technical College, A
Mid-State Technical College, A
Milwaukee Area Technical College, A
Northeast Wisconsin Technical College, A
University of Wisconsin - Green Bay, B
Waukesha County Technical College, A
Western Technical College, A

Wyoming

Casper College, A
Western Wyoming Community College, A

U.S. Territories: American Samoa

American Samoa Community College, A

U.S. Territories: Puerto Rico

Huertas Junior College, A
Inter American University of Puerto Rico, Aguadilla Campus, AB
Inter American University of Puerto Rico, San Germán Campus, AB
Universidad del Este, A
Universidad del Turabo, A
University of Puerto Rico in Aguadilla, AB
University of Puerto Rico in Bayamón, B
University of Puerto Rico in Humacao, A

Canada

British Columbia

British Columbia Institute of Technology, AB

Ontario

Lakehead University, B

ELECTRICAL AND ELECTRONIC ENGINEERING TECHNOLOGIES/TECHNICIANS

United States

Alabama

Calhoun Community College, A

Arizona

Embry-Riddle Aeronautical University - Prescott, B

California

Pasadena City College, A

District of Columbia

University of the District of Columbia, B

Florida

Florida Technical College (Orlando), A
Miami Dade College, A

Georgia

Albany Technical College, A

Illinois

Southern Illinois University Carbondale, B

Kentucky

Owensboro Community and Technical College, A
Sullivan College of Technology and Design, A

Maryland

Capitol Technology University, AB

Massachusetts

Benjamin Franklin Institute of Technology, A
Massachusetts Bay Community College, A

Michigan

Lake Superior State University, AB
Lawrence Technological University, A
Northern Michigan University, A
Wayne County Community College District, A
Wayne State University, B

Minnesota

Minnesota State Community and Technical College, A

Missouri

Pinnacle Career Institute (Kansas City), A

New Jersey

Thomas Edison State University, A

New York

Corning Community College, A
Eugenio María de Hostos Community College of the City University of New York, A
Excelsior College, B
Onondaga Community College, A
Rochester Institute of Technology, AB
Vaughn College of Aeronautics and Technology, AB

North Carolina

North Carolina Agricultural and Technical State University, B

North Dakota

Lake Region State College, A
North Dakota State College of Science, A

Ohio

Belmont College, A
Bryant & Stratton College - Eastlake Campus, B
Columbus State Community College, A
ETI Technical College of Niles, A
Kent State University at Trumbull, A
Kent State University at Tuscarawas, A
Miami University Hamilton, A
Terra State Community College, A
Youngstown State University, A

Oklahoma

Eastern Oklahoma State College, A
Vatterott College (Warr Acres), A

Pennsylvania

Penn State Berks, B
Pennsylvania College of Technology, B
Point Park University, AB
Thaddeus Stevens College of Technology, A

South Carolina

York Technical College, A

Texas

LeTourneau University, B

Virginia

Virginia State University, B

West Virginia

Blue Ridge Community and Technical College, A
BridgeValley Community and Technical College
    (South Charleston), A
Pierpont Community & Technical College, A
West Virginia University Institute of Technology, B

Wisconsin

Fox Valley Technical College, A
Moraine Park Technical College, A

Wyoming

Sheridan College, A

U.S. Territories: Puerto Rico

Colegio Universitario de San Juan, A

ELECTRICAL, ELECTRONICS AND COMMUNICATIONS ENGINEERING

United States

Alabama

Alabama Agricultural and Mechanical University, B
Auburn University, B
Remington College - Mobile Campus, A
Tuskegee University, B
The University of Alabama, B
The University of Alabama at Birmingham, B
The University of Alabama in Huntsville, B
University of South Alabama, B

Alaska

University of Alaska Fairbanks, B

Arizona

Arizona State University at the Tempe campus, B
Embry-Riddle Aeronautical University - Prescott, B
Northern Arizona University, B

Arkansas

Arkansas State University, B
Arkansas Tech University, B
Harding University, B
John Brown University, B
University of Arkansas, B

California

California Institute of Technology, B
California Polytechnic State University, San Luis
    Obispo, B
California State Polytechnic University, Pomona, B
California State University, Chico, B
California State University, Fresno, B
California State University, Fullerton, B
California State University, Long Beach, B
California State University, Los Angeles, B
California State University, Northridge, B
California State University, Sacramento, B
Loyola Marymount University, B
National University, B
Northwestern Polytechnic University, B
Pasadena City College, A
San Diego State University, B
San Francisco State University, B
San Jose State University, B
Santa Clara University, B
Southern California Institute of Technology, AB
Stanford University, B
University of California, Berkeley, B
University of California, Davis, B
University of California, Irvine, B
University of California, Los Angeles, B
University of California, Riverside, B
University of California, San Diego, B
University of California, Santa Barbara, B
University of California, Santa Cruz, B

University of the Pacific, B
University of San Diego, B
University of Southern California, B

Colorado

Colorado School of Mines, B
Colorado State University, B
Colorado Technical University Colorado Springs, B
United States Air Force Academy, B
University of Colorado Boulder, B
University of Colorado Colorado Springs, B
University of Colorado Denver, B
University of Denver, B

Connecticut

Fairfield University, B
Trinity College, B
United States Coast Guard Academy, B
University of Bridgeport, B
University of Connecticut, B
University of Hartford, B
University of New Haven, B
Yale University, B

Delaware

Delaware State University, B
University of Delaware, B

District of Columbia

The Catholic University of America, B
The George Washington University, B
Howard University, B
University of the District of Columbia, B

Florida

Broward College, A
Embry-Riddle Aeronautical University - Daytona, B
Florida Agricultural and Mechanical University, B
Florida Atlantic University, B
Florida Institute of Technology, B
Florida International University, B
Jacksonville University, B
Polytechnic University of Puerto Rico, Orlando
    Campus, B
South Florida State College, A
Southern Technical College (Orlando), A
University of Central Florida, B
University of Florida, B
University of Miami, B
University of North Florida, B
University of South Florida, B
University of West Florida, B

Georgia

Georgia Institute of Technology, B
Georgia Southern University, B
Kennesaw State University, B

Hawaii

University of Hawaii at Manoa, B

Idaho

Boise State University, B
Idaho State University, B
University of Idaho, B

Illinois

Bradley University, B
Dominican University, B
Illinois Institute of Technology, B
Northern Illinois University, B
Northwestern University, B
Southern Illinois University Carbondale, B
Southern Illinois University Edwardsville, B
University of Illinois at Chicago, B
University of Illinois at Urbana - Champaign, B

Indiana

Anderson University, B
Indiana Tech, B
Indiana University - Purdue University Fort Wayne,
    B
Indiana University - Purdue University Indianapolis,
    B

Purdue University, B
Purdue University Northwest (Hammond), B
Purdue University Northwest (Westville), B
Rose-Hulman Institute of Technology, B
Trine University, B
University of Evansville, B
University of Notre Dame, B
Valparaiso University, B

Iowa

Dordt College, B
Iowa State University of Science and Technology, B
The University of Iowa, B

Kansas

Allen Community College, A
Kansas State University, B
The University of Kansas, B
Wichita State University, B

Kentucky

Jefferson Community and Technical College, A
University of Kentucky, B
University of Louisville, B
Western Kentucky University, B

Louisiana

Louisiana State University and Agricultural & Me-
    chanical College, B
Louisiana Tech University, B
Southern University and Agricultural and Mechanical
    College, B
Tulane University, B
University of Louisiana at Lafayette, B
University of New Orleans, B

Maine

University of Maine, B
University of Southern Maine, B

Maryland

Anne Arundel Community College, A
Capitol Technology University, B
Carroll Community College, A
College of Southern Maryland, A
Community College of Baltimore County, A
Garrett College, A
Johns Hopkins University, B
Morgan State University, B
United States Naval Academy, B
University of Maryland, College Park, B

Massachusetts

Boston University, B
Eastern Nazarene College, B
Franklin W. Olin College of Engineering, B
Massachusetts Institute of Technology, B
Merrimack College, B
Northeastern University, B
Suffolk University, B
Tufts University, B
University of Massachusetts Amherst, B
University of Massachusetts Boston, B
University of Massachusetts Dartmouth, B
University of Massachusetts Lowell, B
Wentworth Institute of Technology, B
Western New England University, B
Worcester Polytechnic Institute, B

Michigan

Calvin College, B
Central Michigan University, B
Kettering University, B
Lake Superior State University, B
Lawrence Technological University, B
Michigan State University, B
Michigan Technological University, B
Oakland University, B
Saginaw Valley State University, B
University of Detroit Mercy, B
University of Michigan, B
University of Michigan - Dearborn, B
Wayne State University, B
Western Michigan University, B

Minnesota

Minnesota State University Mankato, B
St. Cloud State University, B
University of Minnesota, Duluth, B
University of Minnesota, Twin Cities Campus, B
University of St. Thomas, B

Mississippi

Holmes Community College, A
Jackson State University, B
Mississippi College, B
Mississippi State University, B
University of Mississippi, B

Missouri

Missouri University of Science and Technology, B
Rockhurst University, B
Saint Louis University, B
University of Missouri, B
University of Missouri - Kansas City, B
University of Missouri - St. Louis, B
Washington University in St. Louis, B

Montana

Montana State University, B
Montana Tech of The University of Montana, B

Nebraska

University of Nebraska - Lincoln, B

Nevada

University of Nevada, Las Vegas, B
University of Nevada, Reno, B

New Hampshire

University of New Hampshire, B

New Jersey

The College of New Jersey, B
Fairleigh Dickinson University, Metropolitan Campus, B
New Jersey Institute of Technology, B
Princeton University, B
Rowan University, B
Rutgers University - New Brunswick, B
Stevens Institute of Technology, B

New Mexico

New Mexico Highlands University, B
New Mexico Institute of Mining and Technology, B
New Mexico State University, B
University of New Mexico, B

New York

Binghamton University, State University of New York, B
City College of the City University of New York, B
Clarkson University, B
Columbia University, B
Cooper Union for the Advancement of Science and Art, B
Cornell University, B
Corning Community College, A
Fiorello H. LaGuardia Community College of the City University of New York, A
Hofstra University, B
Hudson Valley Community College, A
Manhattan College, B
New York Institute of Technology, B
New York University, B
Rensselaer Polytechnic Institute, B
Rochester Institute of Technology, B
State University of New York Maritime College, B
State University of New York at New Paltz, B
State University of New York at Oswego, B
State University of New York Polytechnic Institute, B
Stony Brook University, State University of New York, B
Syracuse University, B
Union College, B
United States Military Academy, B
University at Buffalo, the State University of New York, B
University of Rochester, B

North Carolina

Caldwell Community College and Technical Institute, A
Duke University, B
ECPI University (Charlotte), A
North Carolina Agricultural and Technical State University, B
North Carolina State University, B
The University of North Carolina at Charlotte, B
Western Carolina University, B

North Dakota

North Dakota State University, B
University of North Dakota, B

Ohio

Case Western Reserve University, B
Cedarville University, B
Cleveland State University, B
Miami University, B
Mount Vernon Nazarene University, B
Ohio Northern University, B
The Ohio State University, B
Ohio University, B
The University of Akron, B
University of Cincinnati, B
University of Dayton, B
The University of Toledo, B
Wilberforce University, B
Wright State University, B
Youngstown State University, B

Oklahoma

Oklahoma Christian University, B
Oklahoma State University, B
Oral Roberts University, B
University of Central Oklahoma, B
University of Oklahoma, B
The University of Tulsa, B

Oregon

Chemeketa Community College, A
George Fox University, B
Oregon State University, B
Portland State University, B
University of Portland, B

Pennsylvania

Bloomsburg University of Pennsylvania, B
Bucknell University, B
Carnegie Mellon University, B
Drexel University, B
Gannon University, B
Grove City College, B
Lafayette College, B
Lehigh University, B
Penn State Abington, B
Penn State Altoona, B
Penn State Beaver, B
Penn State Berks, B
Penn State Brandywine, B
Penn State DuBois, B
Penn State Erie, The Behrend College, B
Penn State Fayette, The Eberly Campus, B
Penn State Greater Allegheny, B
Penn State Harrisburg, B
Penn State Hazleton, B
Penn State Lehigh Valley, B
Penn State Mont Alto, B
Penn State New Kensington, B
Penn State Schuylkill, B
Penn State Shenango, B
Penn State University Park, B
Penn State Wilkes-Barre, B
Penn State Worthington Scranton, B
Penn State York, B
Shippensburg University of Pennsylvania, B
Temple University, B
University of Pennsylvania, B
University of Pittsburgh, B
The University of Scranton, AB
Ursinus College, B
Villanova University, B
Westminster College, B
Widener University, B

Wilkes University, B
York College of Pennsylvania, B

Rhode Island

Brown University, B
Johnson & Wales University, B
New England Institute of Technology, AB
Roger Williams University, B
University of Rhode Island, B

South Carolina

Benedict College, B
The Citadel, The Military College of South Carolina, B
Clemson University, B
University of South Carolina, B

South Dakota

South Dakota School of Mines and Technology, B
South Dakota State University, B

Tennessee

Christian Brothers University, B
Remington College - Memphis Campus, A
Tennessee State University, B
Tennessee Technological University, B
University of Memphis, B
The University of Tennessee, B
The University of Tennessee at Chattanooga, B
Vanderbilt University, B

Texas

Baylor University, B
Lamar University, B
LeTourneau University, B
Northeast Texas Community College, A
Prairie View A&M University, B
Rice University, B
St. Mary's University, B
Southern Methodist University, B
Texas A&M University, B
Texas A&M University - Kingsville, B
Texas State University, B
Texas Tech University, B
University of Houston, B
University of North Texas, B
The University of Texas at Arlington, B
The University of Texas at Austin, B
The University of Texas at Dallas, B
The University of Texas at El Paso, B
The University of Texas Rio Grande Valley, B
The University of Texas at San Antonio, B
The University of Texas at Tyler, B

Utah

University of Utah, B
Utah State University, B
Weber State University, B

Vermont

Norwich University, B
University of Vermont, B

Virginia

Christopher Newport University, B
George Mason University, B
Hampton University, B
Liberty University, B
Norfolk State University, B
Old Dominion University, B
University of Virginia, B
Virginia Commonwealth University, B
Virginia Military Institute, B
Virginia Polytechnic Institute and State University, B

Washington

Eastern Washington University, B
Gonzaga University, B
Olympic College, A
Seattle Pacific University, B
Seattle University, B
University of Washington, B
University of Washington, Bothell, B
Walla Walla University, B
Washington State University, B

Washington State University - Tri-Cities, B
Washington State University - Vancouver, B
Western Washington University, B

West Virginia

American Public University System, B
Potomac State College of West Virginia University, A
West Virginia University, B
West Virginia University Institute of Technology, B

Wisconsin

Marquette University, B
Milwaukee School of Engineering, B
University of Wisconsin - Madison, B
University of Wisconsin - Milwaukee, B
University of Wisconsin - Platteville, B

Wyoming

University of Wyoming, B

U.S. Territories: Puerto Rico

Caribbean University, B
Huertas Junior College, A
Humacao Community College, A
Inter American University of Puerto Rico, Bayamón
  Campus, B
Polytechnic University of Puerto Rico, B
Universidad del Turabo, B
University of Puerto Rico, Mayagüez Campus, B

Canada

Alberta

University of Calgary, B

British Columbia

Thompson Rivers University, A
The University of British Columbia, B
The University of British Columbia - Okanagan
  Campus, B
University of Victoria, B

Manitoba

University of Manitoba, B

Maritime Provinces: New Brunswick

Université de Moncton, B
University of New Brunswick Fredericton, B

Maritime Provinces: Nova Scotia

Dalhousie University, B

Newfoundland and Labrador

Memorial University of Newfoundland, B

Ontario

Carleton University, B
Lakehead University, B
McMaster University, B
Queen's University at Kingston, B
Royal Military College of Canada, B
Ryerson University, B
University of Ottawa, B
University of Toronto, B
University of Waterloo, B
The University of Western Ontario, B
University of Windsor, B

Quebec

Concordia University, B
Université Laval, B
Université du Québec en Abitibi-Témiscamingue, B
Université du Québec, École de technologie
  supérieure, B
Université du Québec à Trois-Rivières, B
Université de Sherbrooke, B

Saskatchewan

University of Regina, B
University of Saskatchewan, B

ELECTRICAL/ELECTRONICS DRAFTING AND ELECTRICAL/ELECTRONICS CAD/CADD

United States

California

Chabot College, A
Mission College, A
Palomar College, A

Massachusetts

Middlesex Community College, A

Minnesota

Dunwoody College of Technology, A

Texas

Eastfield College, A

ELECTRICAL/ELECTRONICS EQUIPMENT INSTALLATION AND REPAIR

United States

Arizona

Pima Community College, A

Arkansas

University of Arkansas Community College at
  Batesville, A
University of Arkansas - Fort Smith, A

California

Antelope Valley College, A
Barstow Community College, A
Cerro Coso Community College, A
Chabot College, A
City College of San Francisco, A
College of the Redwoods, A
Contra Costa College, A
Cuesta College, A
Diablo Valley College, A
Fresno City College, A
Fullerton College, A
Long Beach City College, A
Los Angeles Valley College, A
Modesto Junior College, A
Orange Coast College, A
San Jose City College, A
Santa Barbara City College, A
Sierra College, A
Southwestern College, A

Florida

Lincoln College of Technology, A

Hawaii

Hawaii Community College, A

Idaho

Lewis-Clark State College, AB

Illinois

College of DuPage, A

Iowa

Iowa Lakes Community College, A

Kansas

Hutchinson Community College, A
Johnson County Community College, A
Northwest Kansas Technical College, A
Pittsburg State University, A

Kentucky

Sullivan College of Technology and Design, A

Louisiana

Delgado Community College, A

Michigan

Macomb Community College, A

Minnesota

Mesabi Range College, A
Riverland Community College, A

Mississippi

Hinds Community College, A

Missouri

State Technical College of Missouri, A

New Hampshire

Lakes Region Community College, A

North Carolina

Cape Fear Community College, A

Pennsylvania

Lincoln Technical Institute (Allentown), A
Pittsburgh Technical Institute, A
Triangle Tech, Greensburg, A

Rhode Island

New England Institute of Technology, A

South Carolina

York Technical College, A

South Dakota

Sinte Gleska University, A
Southeast Technical Institute, A

Tennessee

Southwest Tennessee Community College, A

Texas

St. Philip's College, A

Washington

Wenatchee Valley College, A

Wyoming

Western Wyoming Community College, A

U.S. Territories: Puerto Rico

Colegio Universitario de San Juan, A

Canada

Maritime Provinces: Nova Scotia

Cape Breton University, B

ELECTRICAL/ELECTRONICS MAINTENANCE AND REPAIR TECHNOLOGY

United States

Arizona

Pima Community College, A

Florida

College of Business and Technology - Cutler Bay
  Campus, A
College of Business and Technology - Flagler Cam-
  pus, A
College of Business and Technology - Hialeah Cam-
  pus, A
College of Business and Technology - Miami Gar-
  dens, A
Southern Technical College (Orlando), A

Kentucky

Sullivan College of Technology and Design, AB

Maine

Kennebec Valley Community College, A

Massachusetts

Bunker Hill Community College, A

Missouri

Vatterott College (Saint Charles), A

New Jersey

Bergen Community College, A

New Mexico

Western New Mexico University, A

New York

Mohawk Valley Community College, A

North Carolina

Pitt Community College, A
Wake Technical Community College, A

Pennsylvania

Triangle Tech, Greensburg, A

West Virginia

BridgeValley Community and Technical College
(South Charleston), A

U.S. Territories: Puerto Rico

Colegio Universitario de San Juan, A

ELECTRICAL ENGINEERING

United States

Alabama

Auburn University, MD
Tuskegee University, M
The University of Alabama, MD
The University of Alabama at Birmingham, M
The University of Alabama in Huntsville, MD

Alaska

University of Alaska Fairbanks, M

Arizona

Arizona State University at the Tempe campus,
 MDO
Northern Arizona University, M
The University of Arizona, MD

Arkansas

University of Arkansas, MD

California

California Institute of Technology, MDO
California Polytechnic State University, San Luis
 Obispo, M
California State Polytechnic University, Pomona, M
California State University, Chico, M
California State University, Fresno, M
California State University, Fullerton, M
California State University, Long Beach, M
California State University, Los Angeles, M
California State University, Northridge, M
California State University, Sacramento, M
Northwestern Polytechnic University, M
San Diego State University, M
San Jose State University, M
Santa Clara University, MDO
Stanford University, MD
University of California, Berkeley, MD
University of California, Davis, MD
University of California, Irvine, MD
University of California, Los Angeles, MD
University of California, Merced, MD
University of California, Riverside, MD
University of California, San Diego, MD
University of California, Santa Barbara, MD
University of California, Santa Cruz, MD

University of Southern California, DO

Colorado

Colorado School of Mines, MD
Colorado State University, MD
Colorado Technical University Colorado Springs, M
Colorado Technical University Denver South, M
University of Colorado Boulder, MD
University of Colorado Colorado Springs, M
University of Colorado Denver, MD
University of Denver, MD

Connecticut

Fairfield University, M
University of Bridgeport, M
University of Connecticut, MD
University of New Haven, M
Yale University, MD

Delaware

University of Delaware, MD

District of Columbia

The Catholic University of America, MD
The George Washington University, MDO
Howard University, MD
University of the District of Columbia, M

Florida

Embry-Riddle Aeronautical University - Daytona, M
Florida Agricultural and Mechanical University, MD
Florida Atlantic University, MD
Florida Institute of Technology, MD
Florida International University, MD
Florida State University, MD
University of Central Florida, MDO
University of Florida, MD
University of Miami, MD
University of North Florida, M
University of South Florida, MDO

Georgia

Georgia Institute of Technology, MD
Georgia Southern University, M
Kennesaw State University, M
Mercer University, M

Hawaii

University of Hawaii at Manoa, MD

Idaho

Boise State University, MD
University of Idaho, MD

Illinois

Bradley University, M
DeVry University (Downers Grove), M
Illinois Institute of Technology, MD
Northern Illinois University, M
Northwestern University, MD
Southern Illinois University Carbondale, MD
Southern Illinois University Edwardsville, M
University of Illinois at Urbana - Champaign, MD

Indiana

Indiana University - Purdue University Fort Wayne,
 M
Indiana University - Purdue University Indianapolis,
 MD
Purdue University, MD
Purdue University Northwest (Hammond), M
Rose-Hulman Institute of Technology, M
University of Notre Dame, MD

Iowa

Iowa State University of Science and Technology,
 MD
The University of Iowa, MD

Kansas

Kansas State University, MD
The University of Kansas, MD
Wichita State University, MD

Kentucky

University of Kentucky, MD
University of Louisville, MD

Louisiana

Louisiana State University and Agricultural & Me-
 chanical College, MD
Louisiana Tech University, MD
McNeese State University, M

Maine

University of Maine, MD

Maryland

Capitol Technology University, M
Johns Hopkins University, MDO
Morgan State University, MD
University of Maryland, Baltimore County, MD
University of Maryland, College Park, MD

Massachusetts

Boston University, MD
Massachusetts Institute of Technology, MDO
Northeastern University, MD
Tufts University, MDO
University of Massachusetts Amherst, MD
University of Massachusetts Dartmouth, MDO
University of Massachusetts Lowell, MD
Western New England University, M
Worcester Polytechnic Institute, MDO

Michigan

Grand Valley State University, M
Kettering University, M
Lawrence Technological University, M
Michigan State University, MD
Michigan Technological University, MDO
Oakland University, M
University of Detroit Mercy, MD
University of Michigan, MD
University of Michigan - Dearborn, M
Wayne State University, MD
Western Michigan University, MD

Minnesota

Minnesota State University Mankato, M
St. Cloud State University, M
University of Minnesota, Duluth, M
University of Minnesota, Twin Cities Campus, MD
University of St. Thomas, M

Mississippi

Mississippi State University, MD

Missouri

Missouri University of Science and Technology, MD
University of Missouri, MD
University of Missouri - Kansas City, MD

Montana

Montana State University, MD
Montana Tech of The University of Montana, M

Nebraska

University of Nebraska - Lincoln, MD

Nevada

University of Nevada, Las Vegas, MD
University of Nevada, Reno, MD

New Hampshire

University of New Hampshire, MD

New Jersey

Fairleigh Dickinson University, Metropolitan Cam-
 pus, M
New Jersey Institute of Technology, MD
Princeton University, MD
Rowan University, M
Rutgers University - New Brunswick, MD
Stevens Institute of Technology, MDO

New Mexico

New Mexico Institute of Mining and Technology, M
New Mexico State University, MDO
University of New Mexico, MD

New York

Alfred University, M
Binghamton University, State University of New York, MD
City College of the City University of New York, MD
Clarkson University, MD
Columbia University, MD
Cooper Union for the Advancement of Science and Art, M
Cornell University, MD
Manhattan College, M
New York Institute of Technology, M
New York University, MD
Rensselaer Polytechnic Institute, MD
Rochester Institute of Technology, M
State University of New York at New Paltz, M
Stony Brook University, State University of New York, MD
Syracuse University, MDO
University at Buffalo, the State University of New York, MD
University of Rochester, MD

North Carolina

Duke University, MD
North Carolina Agricultural and Technical State University, MD
North Carolina State University, MD
The University of North Carolina at Charlotte, MD

North Dakota

North Dakota State University, MD
University of North Dakota, M

Ohio

Case Western Reserve University, MD
Cleveland State University, MD
The Ohio State University, MD
Ohio University, MD
The University of Akron, MD
University of Cincinnati, MD
University of Dayton, MD
The University of Toledo, MD
Wright State University, M
Youngstown State University, M

Oklahoma

Oklahoma State University, MD
University of Central Oklahoma, M
University of Oklahoma, MD
The University of Tulsa, MD

Oregon

Oregon Health & Science University, MD
Oregon State University, MD
Portland State University, MD
University of Portland, M

Pennsylvania

Bucknell University, M
Carnegie Mellon University, MD
Drexel University, M
Gannon University, M
Lehigh University, MD
Penn State Harrisburg, M
Penn State University Park, MD
Temple University, MD
University of Pennsylvania, MD
University of Pittsburgh, MD
Villanova University, MO
Widener University, M
Wilkes University, M

Rhode Island

Brown University, MD
University of Rhode Island, MDO

South Carolina

Clemson University, MD
University of South Carolina, MD

South Dakota

South Dakota School of Mines and Technology, M
South Dakota State University, MD

Tennessee

Tennessee State University, M
Tennessee Technological University, M
University of Memphis, MD
The University of Tennessee, MD
The University of Tennessee at Chattanooga, M
Vanderbilt University, MD

Texas

Baylor University, MD
Lamar University, MD
Prairie View A&M University, MD
Rice University, MD
St. Mary's University, M
Southern Methodist University, MD
Texas A&M University, MD
Texas A&M University - Kingsville, M
Texas Tech University, MD
University of Houston, MD
University of North Texas, M
The University of Texas at Arlington, MD
The University of Texas at Austin, MD
The University of Texas at Dallas, MD
The University of Texas at El Paso, MD
The University of Texas Rio Grande Valley, M
The University of Texas at San Antonio, MD
The University of Texas at Tyler, M

Utah

Brigham Young University, MD
University of Utah, MD
Utah State University, MD

Vermont

University of Vermont, MD

Virginia

George Mason University, MDO
Norfolk State University, M
Old Dominion University, MD
University of Virginia, MD
Virginia Commonwealth University, MD
Virginia Polytechnic Institute and State University, MD

Washington

University of Washington, MD
Washington State University, MD

West Virginia

West Virginia University, MD

Wisconsin

Marquette University, MDO
University of Wisconsin - Madison, MD
University of Wisconsin - Milwaukee, M

Wyoming

University of Wyoming, MD

U.S. Territories: Puerto Rico

Polytechnic University of Puerto Rico, M
University of Puerto Rico, Mayagüez Campus, MD

Canada

Alberta

University of Alberta, MD
University of Calgary, MD

British Columbia

The University of British Columbia, MD
University of Victoria, MD

Manitoba

University of Manitoba, MD

Maritime Provinces: New Brunswick

Université de Moncton, M
University of New Brunswick Fredericton, MD

Maritime Provinces: Nova Scotia

Dalhousie University, MD

Newfoundland and Labrador

Memorial University of Newfoundland, MD

Ontario

Carleton University, MD
Lakehead University, M
McMaster University, MD
Queen's University at Kingston, MD
Royal Military College of Canada, MD
University of Ottawa, MD
University of Toronto, MD
University of Waterloo, MD
The University of Western Ontario, MD
University of Windsor, MD

Quebec

Concordia University, MD
École Polytechnique de Montréal, MDO
McGill University, MD
Université Laval, MD
Université du Québec à Trois-Rivières, MD
Université de Sherbrooke, MD

Saskatchewan

University of Saskatchewan, MDO

ELECTRICAL AND POWER TRANSMISSION INSTALLA- TION/INSTALLER

United States

Alaska

University of Alaska Southeast, A

California

APT College, A
Chaffey College, A

Florida

Polk State College, A

Illinois

Southwestern Illinois College, A

Indiana

Ivy Tech Community College - Columbus, A

Kansas

Manhattan Area Technical College, A

Massachusetts

Benjamin Franklin Institute of Technology, A

Michigan

Delta College, A
Lansing Community College, A

Minnesota

Fond du Lac Tribal and Community College, A
Minnesota West Community and Technical College, A

Nevada

College of Southern Nevada, A

New York

State University of New York College of Technology at Alfred, A

State University of New York College of Technology
at Delhi, A

North Carolina

Piedmont Community College, A
Richmond Community College, A

Oklahoma

Oklahoma State University, Oklahoma City, A

Oregon

Clackamas Community College, A
Rogue Community College, A

Pennsylvania

Delaware County Community College, A
Westmoreland County Community College, A

Texas

San Jacinto College District, A

Canada

British Columbia

British Columbia Institute of Technology, A

ELECTRICAL AND POWER TRANSMISSION INSTALLERS

United States

Kansas

Manhattan Area Technical College, A

Minnesota

Minnesota State Community and Technical College -
Wadena, A
Minnesota West Community and Technical College,
A

North Carolina

Martin Community College, A

ELECTRICIAN

United States

Alabama

Bevill State Community College, A
Calhoun Community College, A
George C. Wallace Community College, A
George Corley Wallace State Community College, A
H. Councill Trenholm State Community College, A
J. F. Drake State Community and Technical College,
A
Shelton State Community College, A

Arizona

GateWay Community College, A
Northland Pioneer College, A

California

American River College, A
Antelope Valley College, A
Barstow Community College, A
Chabot College, A
College of San Mateo, A
Palomar College, A
Santiago Canyon College, A

Colorado

Red Rocks Community College, A

Florida

Miami Dade College, A

Idaho

Eastern Idaho Technical College, A

Illinois

Black Hawk College, A
College of Lake County, A
Danville Area Community College, A
Heartland Community College, A
Illinois Valley Community College, A
John Wood Community College, A
Kaskaskia College, A
Prairie State College, A
Rend Lake College, A
Rock Valley College, A
Southwestern Illinois College, A
Waubonsee Community College, A

Indiana

Ivy Tech Community College - Bloomington, A
Ivy Tech Community College - Central Indiana, A
Ivy Tech Community College - East Central, A
Ivy Tech Community College - Kokomo, A
Ivy Tech Community College - Lafayette, A
Ivy Tech Community College - North Central, A
Ivy Tech Community College - Northeast, A
Ivy Tech Community College - Northwest, A
Ivy Tech Community College - Richmond, A
Ivy Tech Community College - Southern Indiana, A
Ivy Tech Community College - Southwest, A
Ivy Tech Community College - Wabash Valley, A

Iowa

Northeast Iowa Community College, A
Western Iowa Tech Community College, A

Kansas

Coffeyville Community College, A
Johnson County Community College, A
North Central Kansas Technical College, A
Northwest Kansas Technical College, A

Kentucky

Bluegrass Community and Technical College, A
Elizabethtown Community and Technical College, A
Owensboro Community and Technical College, A
West Kentucky Community and Technical College, A

Louisiana

Fletcher Technical Community College, A
South Louisiana Community College, A

Maine

Kennebec Valley Community College, A

Maryland

College of Southern Maryland, A

Michigan

Delta College, A
Lansing Community College, A
Oakland Community College, A

Minnesota

Dakota County Technical College, A
Dunwoody College of Technology, A
Lake Superior College, A
Minnesota West Community and Technical College,
A
Northland Community and Technical College, A
Ridgewater College, A
St. Cloud Technical & Community College, A

Mississippi

East Central Community College, A
East Mississippi Community College, A
Hinds Community College, A
Northeast Mississippi Community College, A

Missouri

State Technical College of Missouri, A
Vatterott College (Berkeley), A
Vatterott College (Kansas City), A
Vatterott College (Saint Charles), A
Vatterott College (Sunset Hills), A

Montana

Flathead Valley Community College, A

Nebraska

Central Community College - Hastings Campus, A
Northeast Community College, A

Nevada

College of Southern Nevada, A

New Mexico

Central New Mexico Community College, A
Clovis Community College, A
New Mexico State University - Alamogordo, A

New York

Adirondack Community College, A

North Carolina

Asheville-Buncombe Technical Community College,
A
Cleveland Community College, A
Durham Technical Community College, A
Fayetteville Technical Community College, A
Guilford Technical Community College, A
Haywood Community College, A
McDowell Technical Community College, A
Mitchell Community College, A
Montgomery Community College, A
Nash Community College, A
Piedmont Community College, A
Pitt Community College, A
Randolph Community College, A
Rockingham Community College, A
Rowan-Cabarrus Community College, A
South Piedmont Community College, A
Wake Technical Community College, A
Wilson Community College, A

Ohio

Vatterott College, A

Pennsylvania

Community College of Beaver County, A
Dean Institute of Technology, A
Harrisburg Area Community College, A
Johnson College, A
Luzerne County Community College, A
Northampton Community College, A
Pennsylvania College of Technology, A
Rosedale Technical Institute, A
Triangle Tech, Bethlehem, A
Triangle Tech, Erie, A
Triangle Tech, Pittsburgh, A
Triangle Tech, Sunbury, A

South Dakota

Mitchell Technical Institute, A
Southeast Technical Institute, A
Western Dakota Technical Institute, A

Texas

Brazosport College, A
Grayson College, A
Panola College, A

Utah

Weber State University, A

Virginia

Liberty University, A

Washington

Bates Technical College, A
Bellingham Technical College, A
Walla Walla Community College, A

Wyoming

Western Wyoming Community College, A

U.S. Territories: Puerto Rico

Universidad del Turabo, A

ELECTROCARDIOGRAPH TECHNOLOGY/TECHNICIAN

United States

California

Orange Coast College, A

Delaware

Delaware Technical & Community College, Stanton/Wilmington Campus, A

Oklahoma

Oklahoma State University, Oklahoma City, A

Pennsylvania

Pennsylvania College of Health Sciences, A

Washington

Edmonds Community College, A

ELECTROMECHANICAL AND INSTRUMENTATION AND MAINTENANCE TECHNOLOGIES/TECHNICIANS

United States

California

Chaffey College, A
Cuesta College, A

Colorado

Pueblo Community College, A
Red Rocks Community College, A

Kansas

Cowley County Community College and Area Vocational - Technical School, A

Kentucky

Sullivan College of Technology and Design, AB

Michigan

Northwestern Michigan College, A

New York

Excelsior College, AB

North Carolina

Asheville-Buncombe Technical Community College, A
Cape Fear Community College, A
Catawba Valley Community College, A
Halifax Community College, A
McDowell Technical Community College, A
Mitchell Community College, A
Montgomery Community College, A
Piedmont Community College, A
Pitt Community College, A
Richmond Community College, A
Roanoke-Chowan Community College, A
South Piedmont Community College, A
Wake Technical Community College, A
Wayne Community College, A

Oregon

Chemeketa Community College, A

South Carolina

Greenville Technical College, A

Wisconsin

Northeast Wisconsin Technical College, A

ELECTROMECHANICAL TECHNOLOGY/ELECTROMECHANICAL ENGINEERING TECHNOLOGY

United States

Arizona

Chandler-Gilbert Community College, A
GateWay Community College, A
The Refrigeration School, A

Arkansas

College of the Ouachitas, A
John Brown University, AB
Pulaski Technical College, A

California

Irvine Valley College, A
Los Angeles Harbor College, A

Delaware

Delaware Technical & Community College, Terry Campus, A

Georgia

Georgia Piedmont Technical College, A

Illinois

College of DuPage, A
Lake Land College, A

Iowa

Hawkeye Community College, A
University of Northern Iowa, B

Kentucky

Henderson Community College, A
Maysville Community and Technical College (Maysville), A
Murray State University, B
Southcentral Kentucky Community and Technical College, A

Maine

Central Maine Community College, A

Massachusetts

Bristol Community College, A
Quincy College, A
Quinsigamond Community College, A
Springfield Technical Community College, A

Michigan

Kirtland Community College, A
Lansing Community College, A
Macomb Community College, A
Muskegon Community College, A
Northern Michigan University, A
Oakland Community College, A
Wayne County Community College District, A
Wayne State University, B

Minnesota

Ridgewater College, A

Nebraska

Northeast Community College, A

New Hampshire

Nashua Community College, A

New Jersey

Camden County College, A
Union County College, A

New Mexico

Eastern New Mexico University - Roswell, A

New York

Buffalo State College, State University of New York, B
Excelsior College, AB
New York City College of Technology of the City University of New York, A
Rochester Institute of Technology, B
State University of New York College of Technology at Delhi, A

North Carolina

Blue Ridge Community College, A
Central Piedmont Community College, A
Craven Community College, A
Guilford Technical Community College, A
Haywood Community College, A
Martin Community College, A
Mayland Community College, A
Randolph Community College, A
Richmond Community College, A
South Piedmont Community College, A
Wilkes Community College, A

Ohio

Belmont College, A
Bowling Green State University, B
Bowling Green State University - Firelands College, A
Cincinnati State Technical and Community College, A
Columbus State Community College, A
Edison Community College, A
Miami University Hamilton, B
Miami University Middletown, A
North Central State College, A
Shawnee State University, A
Sinclair Community College, A
Southern State Community College, A
The University of Toledo, B

Pennsylvania

Montgomery County Community College, A
Northampton Community College, A
Pennsylvania College of Technology, A
Westmoreland County Community College, A

Rhode Island

Community College of Rhode Island, A

South Carolina

Denmark Technical College, A
Florence-Darlington Technical College, A

South Dakota

Southeast Technical Institute, A

Tennessee

Motlow State Community College, A

Texas

Angelina College, A
Clarendon College, A
Galveston College, A
Midland College, A
Paris Junior College, A
St. Philip's College, A
Tarrant County College District, A
Texas State Technical College, A
Tyler Junior College, A

Vermont

Vermont Technical College, B

Virginia

ECPI University (Newport News), A
ECPI University (Richmond), A

West Virginia

West Virginia University at Parkersburg, A

Wisconsin

Blackhawk Technical College, A
Chippewa Valley Technical College, A
Fox Valley Technical College, A

Gateway Technical College, A
Lakeshore Technical College, A
Moraine Park Technical College, A
Northcentral Technical College, A
Northeast Wisconsin Technical College, A
Southwest Wisconsin Technical College, A
Western Technical College, A

Canada

Quebec

Université du Québec en Abitibi-Témiscamingue, B

ELECTRONEURODIAGNOSTIC/ ELECTROENCEPHALO- GRAPHIC TECHNOLOGY/ TECHNOLOGIST

United States

California

Orange Coast College, A

Colorado

Community College of Denver, A

Illinois

Lincoln Land Community College, A
Parkland College, A

Iowa

Kirkwood Community College, A
Scott Community College, A

Maryland

Harford Community College, A

Massachusetts

Labouré College, A

Minnesota

Rochester Community and Technical College, A

New Jersey

DeVry University (North Brunswick), A

North Carolina

Catawba Valley Community College, A

Pennsylvania

Community College of Allegheny County, A
Harcum College, A

South Dakota

Southeast Technical Institute, A

Texas

Alvin Community College, A
Collin County Community College District, A
Lone Star College - Kingwood, A

Wisconsin

Western Technical College, A

ELECTRONIC COMMERCE

United States

California

California State University, Fullerton, M

Colorado

University of Phoenix - Colorado Campus, M

Florida

Florida Institute of Technology, M
University of North Florida, M

Georgia

University of Phoenix - Columbus Georgia Campus, M

Illinois

DePaul University, M
Ellis University, M
Lewis University, M
Northwestern University, M

Maryland

Towson University, MO

Michigan

Eastern Michigan University, MO

New Jersey

Fairleigh Dickinson University, Metropolitan Campus, M
Stevens Institute of Technology, M

New Mexico

University of Phoenix - New Mexico Campus, M

New York

New York University, O
University at Buffalo, the State University of New York, O
University of Rochester, M

North Dakota

North Dakota State University, O

Ohio

The University of Akron, M

Oklahoma

Oklahoma Christian University, M

Texas

University of Phoenix - Dallas Campus, M
University of Phoenix - Houston Campus, M
University of Phoenix - San Antonio Campus, M

U.S. Territories: Puerto Rico

Universidad del Este, M

Canada

Maritime Provinces: New Brunswick

University of New Brunswick Saint John, M

Maritime Provinces: Nova Scotia

Dalhousie University, M

Ontario

University of Ottawa, MO

Quebec

HEC Montreal, MO
Université Laval, MO
Université de Montréal, M
Université de Sherbrooke, M

ELECTRONIC MATERIALS

United States

Arkansas

University of Arkansas, MD

Colorado

Colorado School of Mines, M

New Jersey

Princeton University, D

ELEMENTARY EDUCATION AND TEACHING

United States

Alabama

Alabama Agricultural and Mechanical University, BMDO
Alabama Southern Community College, A
Alabama State University, BMO
Athens State University, B
Auburn University, BMDO
Auburn University at Montgomery, BMO
Birmingham-Southern College, B
Concordia College Alabama, B
Faulkner University, B
Huntingdon College, B
Jacksonville State University, BM
Judson College, B
Miles College, B
Oakwood University, B
Samford University, BM
Spring Hill College, BM
Stillman College, B
Troy University, BMO
Tuskegee University, B
The University of Alabama, BMDO
The University of Alabama at Birmingham, BM
The University of Alabama in Huntsville, B
University of Mobile, B
University of Montevallo, BM
University of North Alabama, BMO
University of South Alabama, BM
The University of West Alabama, MO
Wallace State Community College, A

Alaska

Alaska Pacific University, M
University of Alaska Anchorage, B
University of Alaska Anchorage, Kenai Peninsula College, B
University of Alaska Fairbanks, BM
University of Alaska Southeast, ABM
University of Alaska Southeast, Sitka Campus, B

Arizona

Argosy University, Phoenix, D
Arizona Christian University, B
Arizona State University at the Polytechnic campus, B
Arizona State University at the Tempe campus, BM
Arizona State University at the West campus, B
Arizona Western College, A
Central Arizona College, A
Chandler-Gilbert Community College, A
Cochise County Community College District, A
Coconino Community College, A
Diné College, A
Eastern Arizona College, A
GateWay Community College, A
Grand Canyon University, BM
Northcentral University, B
Northern Arizona University, BM
Northland Pioneer College, A
Paradise Valley Community College, A
Phoenix College, A
Pima Community College, A
Prescott College, BM
South Mountain Community College, A
The University of Arizona, BMD
University of Phoenix - Online Campus, MO
University of Phoenix - Phoenix Campus, M
University of Phoenix - Southern Arizona Campus, M

Arkansas

Arkansas Baptist College, B
Arkansas State University, MDO
Arkansas Tech University, BM
Harding University, BM
John Brown University, B
National Park College, A
Southern Arkansas University - Magnolia, M
University of Arkansas, B

University of Arkansas at Little Rock, B
University of the Ozarks, B
Williams Baptist College, B

California

Argosy University, Inland Empire, D
Argosy University, Los Angeles, D
Argosy University, Orange County, D
Argosy University, San Diego, D
Argosy University, San Francisco Bay Area, D
Ashford University, B
Biola University, B
California Lutheran University, D
California State University, Fullerton, M
California State University, Long Beach, M
California State University, Los Angeles, M
California State University, Northridge, M
California State University, Stanislaus, M
Chapman University, M
Cuyamaca College, A
Glendale Community College, A
Hope International University, BM
Humboldt State University, B
Loyola Marymount University, M
The Master's College and Seminary, B
Mills College, M
Mount Saint Mary's University, B
National University, B
Occidental College, M
Orange Coast College, A
Pacific Oaks College, B
Pacific Union College, BM
Point Loma Nazarene University, B
San Diego Christian College, B
San Diego State University, M
San Francisco State University, M
San Jose State University, MO
Stanford University, M
University of California, Irvine, M
University of La Verne, O
University of Phoenix - Bay Area Campus, M
University of Phoenix - Central Valley Campus, M
University of Phoenix - Sacramento Valley Campus, M
University of Phoenix - San Diego Campus, M
University of Phoenix - Southern California Campus, M
University of Redlands, B
University of San Francisco, B
Vanguard University of Southern California, B
Westmont College, B
Whittier College, M
Yuba College, A

Colorado

Adams State University, A
Argosy University, Denver, D
Colorado Christian University, BM
The Colorado College, M
Fort Lewis College, B
Metropolitan State University of Denver, M
Northeastern Junior College, A
Otero Junior College, A
Regis University, B
University of Colorado Denver, M
University of Northern Colorado, B
University of Phoenix - Colorado Campus, M
University of Phoenix - Colorado Springs Downtown Campus, M

Connecticut

Central Connecticut State University, BMO
Eastern Connecticut State University, BM
Fairfield University, MO
Mitchell College, B
Quinnipiac University, M
Sacred Heart University, B
Southern Connecticut State University, BMO
University of Bridgeport, MO
University of Connecticut, BMDO
University of Hartford, BM
Western Connecticut State University, B

Delaware

Delaware State University, B
Delaware Technical & Community College, Jack F. Owens Campus, A
Delaware Technical & Community College, Stanton/Wilmington Campus, A
Delaware Technical & Community College, Terry Campus, A
University of Delaware, B
Wilmington University, BM

District of Columbia

American University, B
The Catholic University of America, B
Gallaudet University, M
The George Washington University, M
Howard University, M
Trinity Washington University, M
University of the District of Columbia, BM
University of Phoenix - Washington D.C. Campus, M

Florida

Argosy University, Sarasota, D
Argosy University, Tampa, D
The Baptist College of Florida, B
Barry University, BMDO
Bethune-Cookman University, B
Broward College, A
Carlos Albizu University, Miami Campus, B
College of Central Florida, A
Daytona State College, B
Edward Waters College, B
Flagler College, B
Florida Agricultural and Mechanical University, BM
Florida Atlantic University, BM
Florida College, B
Florida Gulf Coast University, B
Florida Institute of Technology, M
Florida International University, BM
Florida Memorial University, BM
Florida Southern College, B
Florida SouthWestern State College, B
Florida State University, MDO
Hobe Sound Bible College, B
Jacksonville University, B
Jones College, B
Keiser University, B
Lynn University, B
Miami Dade College, A
Northwest Florida State College, B
Nova Southeastern University, B
Palm Beach Atlantic University, B
Palm Beach State College, A
Pensacola State College, A
Rollins College, BM
Saint Leo University, B
St. Petersburg College, B
St. Thomas University, BM
South Florida State College, AB
Southeastern University, BM
Stetson University, B
Trinity Baptist College, B
Trinity College of Florida, B
University of Central Florida, BMD
University of Florida, BM
University of Miami, B
University of North Florida, BM
University of Phoenix - Central Florida Campus, B
University of Phoenix - North Florida Campus, BM
University of Phoenix - South Florida Campus, BM
University of South Florida, BMDO
University of South Florida, St. Petersburg, M
University of South Florida Sarasota-Manatee, BM
The University of Tampa, B
University of West Florida, BM
Warner University, B

Georgia

Abraham Baldwin Agricultural College, A
Argosy University, Atlanta, D
Bainbridge State College, A
Brenau University, B
Covenant College, B
Dalton State College, AB

Emmanuel College, B
Georgia Southern University, BM
Georgia Southwestern State University, B
Georgia State University, D
Gordon State College, B
Kennesaw State University, BM
Mercer University, B
Paine College, B
Shorter University, B
Toccoa Falls College, B
Truett-McConnell College, B
University of Georgia, MDO
University of Phoenix - Atlanta Campus, B
University of West Georgia, B

Hawaii

Argosy University, Hawai'i, D
Brigham Young University - Hawaii, B
Chaminade University of Honolulu, BM
Hawai'i Pacific University, BM
University of Hawaii at Hilo, B
University of Hawaii at Manoa, B
University of Hawaii - West Oahu, B
University of Phoenix - Hawaii Campus, M

Idaho

Boise State University, B
Brigham Young University - Idaho, B
College of Southern Idaho, A
College of Western Idaho, A
Idaho State University, BM
Lewis-Clark State College, B
North Idaho College, A
Northwest Nazarene University, B
University of Idaho, B

Illinois

Argosy University, Chicago, D
Augustana College, B
Aurora University, BM
Benedictine University, BM
Blackburn College, B
Bradley University, B
Chicago State University, BM
City Colleges of Chicago, Malcolm X College, A
City Colleges of Chicago, Wilbur Wright College, A
Concordia University Chicago, BM
DePaul University, BM
Dominican University, BM
Eastern Illinois University, BM
Elmhurst College, B
Eureka College, B
Governors State University, B
Greenville College, BM
Harper College, A
Illinois College, B
Illinois State University, B
Illinois Valley Community College, A
Illinois Wesleyan University, B
John A. Logan College, A
Judson University, B
Kankakee Community College, A
Knox College, B
Lake Forest College, M
Lewis University, BM
Loyola University Chicago, BM
McKendree University, B
Millikin University, B
Monmouth College, B
Moraine Valley Community College, A
National Louis University, BM
North Central College, B
North Park University, B
Northeastern Illinois University, BM
Northern Illinois University, BMD
Northwestern University, M
Olivet Nazarene University, BM
Parkland College, A
Quincy University, B
Rockford University, BM
Roosevelt University, BM
Saint Xavier University, BM
Sauk Valley Community College, A
Southern Illinois University Carbondale, B
Southern Illinois University Edwardsville, B
Trinity Christian College, B

Trinity International University, B
University of Illinois at Chicago, BM
University of Illinois at Urbana - Champaign, B
University of St. Francis, BM
Western Illinois University, BM
Wheaton College, BM

Indiana

Ancilla College, A
Anderson University, B
Ball State University, BMD
Bethel College, B
Butler University, B
Calumet College of Saint Joseph, B
DePauw University, B
Franklin College, B
Goshen College, B
Grace College, B
Hanover College, B
Holy Cross College, B
Huntington University, B
Indiana State University, B
Indiana Tech, B
Indiana University Bloomington, BMDO
Indiana University East, B
Indiana University Kokomo, B
Indiana University Northwest, BM
Indiana University - Purdue University Fort Wayne, BM
Indiana University - Purdue University Indianapolis, B
Indiana University South Bend, BM
Indiana University Southeast, BM
Indiana Wesleyan University, B
Manchester University, B
Marian University, B
Oakland City University, B
Purdue University, BM
Purdue University Northwest (Hammond), B
Purdue University Northwest (Westville), BM
Saint Joseph's College, B
Saint Mary-of-the-Woods College, AB
Saint Mary's College, B
Trine University, B
University of Evansville, B
University of Indianapolis, BM
University of Saint Francis, B
University of Southern Indiana, BM
Valparaiso University, B
Vincennes University, A

Iowa

Briar Cliff University, B
Buena Vista University, B
Central College, B
Clarke University, B
Coe College, B
Cornell College, B
Dordt College, B
Drake University, B
Emmaus Bible College, B
Faith Baptist Bible College and Theological Seminary, B
Graceland University, B
Grand View University, B
Iowa Lakes Community College, A
Iowa State University of Science and Technology, BM
Iowa Wesleyan University, B
Loras College, B
Luther College, B
Maharishi University of Management, B
Morningside College, B
Mount Mercy University, B
Northwestern College, B
St. Ambrose University, B
Simpson College, B
University of Dubuque, B
The University of Iowa, BM
University of Northern Iowa, BM
Upper Iowa University, B
Waldorf College, B
Wartburg College, B
William Penn University, B

Kansas

Allen Community College, A
Baker University, B
Barclay College, B
Barton County Community College, A
Benedictine College, B
Bethany College, B
Bethel College, B
Central Christian College of Kansas, AB
Cowley County Community College and Area Vocational - Technical School, A
Dodge City Community College, A
Donnelly College, B
Emporia State University, BM
Fort Hays State University, B
Friends University, B
Haskell Indian Nations University, B
Kansas State University, BM
Kansas Wesleyan University, B
Labette Community College, A
MidAmerica Nazarene University, B
Newman University, B
Ottawa University, BM
Pittsburg State University, BM
Pratt Community College, A
Seward County Community College and Area Technical School, A
Southwestern College, B
Sterling College, B
Tabor College, B
The University of Kansas, B
University of Saint Mary, BM
Washburn University, B
Wichita State University, B

Kentucky

Alice Lloyd College, B
Asbury University, B
Bellarmine University, BM
Brescia University, B
Campbellsville University, B
Eastern Kentucky University, BM
Georgetown College, B
Kentucky Christian University, B
Kentucky Mountain Bible College, B
Kentucky State University, B
Kentucky Wesleyan College, B
Lindsey Wilson College, B
Midway University, B
Morehead State University, BM
Murray State University, BMO
Northern Kentucky University, B
Spalding University, BM
Thomas More College, B
Transylvania University, B
Union College, BM
University of the Cumberlands, BM
University of Kentucky, BM
University of Louisville, BM
University of Pikeville, B
Western Kentucky University, BMO

Louisiana

Centenary College of Louisiana, M
Grambling State University, B
Louisiana College, B
Louisiana State University and Agricultural & Mechanical College, BM
Louisiana State University at Alexandria, B
Louisiana State University in Shreveport, B
Louisiana Tech University, B
McNeese State University, BMO
Nicholls State University, BM
Northwestern State University of Louisiana, BMO
Southeastern Louisiana University, BM
Southern University and Agricultural and Mechanical College, BM
Southern University at New Orleans, B
University of Louisiana at Lafayette, B
University of Louisiana at Monroe, BM
University of New Orleans, B
Xavier University of Louisiana, B

Maine

College of the Atlantic, B
Husson University, B
Saint Joseph's College of Maine, B
Thomas College, B
University of Maine, BMDO
University of Maine at Farmington, B
University of Maine at Machias, B
University of Maine at Presque Isle, B
University of New England, B

Maryland

Baltimore City Community College, A
Bowie State University, BM
Carroll Community College, A
Cecil College, A
Chesapeake College, A
College of Southern Maryland, A
Community College of Baltimore County, A
Coppin State University, B
Frederick Community College, A
Frostburg State University, BM
Garrett College, A
Goucher College, BM
Hagerstown Community College, A
Harford Community College, A
Hood College, M
Howard Community College, A
Johns Hopkins University, M
Loyola University Maryland, BMO
McDaniel College, M
Montgomery College, A
Morgan State University, BM
Mount St. Mary's University, B
Notre Dame of Maryland University, B
Prince George's Community College, A
Salisbury University, B
Stevenson University, B
Towson University, BM
University of Maryland, Baltimore County, M
University of Maryland, College Park, B
University of Maryland Eastern Shore, B
Washington Adventist University, B
Wor-Wic Community College, A

Massachusetts

American International College, MO
Anna Maria College, BM
Bay Path University, B
Becker College, B
Boston College, BM
Boston University, B
Brandeis University, M
Bridgewater State University, BM
Cambridge College, M
Clark University, B
Curry College, BM
Eastern Nazarene College, BMO
Elms College, M
Emmanuel College, BM
Endicott College, BM
Fitchburg State University, BM
Framingham State University, BM
Gordon College, B
Hellenic College, B
Lasell College, BM
Lesley University, BM
Massachusetts Bay Community College, A
Merrimack College, BM
Middlesex Community College, A
Northeastern University, M
Northern Essex Community College, A
Quincy College, A
Quinsigamond Community College, A
Regis College, M
Salem State University, BM
Simmons College, BMDO
Smith College, M
Springfield College, B
Springfield Technical Community College, A
Stonehill College, B
Tufts University, BM
University of Massachusetts Amherst, M
Western New England University, BM
Westfield State University, BM

Wheelock College, BM
Worcester State University, BM

Michigan

Adrian College, B
Alma College, B
Alpena Community College, A
Andrews University, BM
Calvin College, B
Central Michigan University, BMD
Concordia University Ann Arbor, B
Cornerstone University, B
Eastern Michigan University, BM
Ferris State University, AB
Gogebic Community College, A
Grace Bible College, B
Grand Rapids Community College, A
Grand Valley State University, BM
Henry Ford College, A
Hope College, B
Kalamazoo Valley Community College, A
Kellogg Community College, A
Kuyper College, B
Lake Michigan College, A
Lake Superior State University, B
Lansing Community College, A
Madonna University, B
Marygrove College, M
Michigan State University, B
Mid Michigan Community College, A
Monroe County Community College, A
Muskegon Community College, A
Northern Michigan University, BM
Oakland University, B
Rochester College, B
Saginaw Valley State University, BM
Siena Heights University, BM
Spring Arbor University, B
University of Detroit Mercy, B
University of Michigan, B
University of Michigan - Dearborn, B
University of Michigan - Flint, B
Washtenaw Community College, A
Wayne County Community College District, A
Wayne State University, BMDO
Western Michigan University, B

Minnesota

Argosy University, Twin Cities, D
Augsburg College, B
Bemidji State University, B
Bethany Lutheran College, B
Bethel University, BM
Capella University, MD
College of Saint Benedict, B
The College of St. Scholastica, B
Concordia College, B
Concordia University, St. Paul, B
Crown College, B
Gustavus Adolphus College, B
Hamline University, B
Martin Luther College, B
Metropolitan State University, B
Minnesota State University Mankato, BMO
Minnesota State University Moorhead, B
Normandale Community College, A
North Central University, B
St. Catherine University, B
St. Cloud State University, B
Saint John's University, B
Saint Mary's University of Minnesota, BMO
Southwest Minnesota State University, B
University of Minnesota, Crookston, B
University of Minnesota, Morris, B
University of Minnesota, Twin Cities Campus, BMD
University of Northwestern - St. Paul, B
University of St. Thomas, M
Vermilion Community College, A
Walden University, MO
Winona State University, B

Mississippi

Alcorn State University, BMO
Belhaven University, BM
Blue Mountain College, BM
Coahoma Community College, A

Copiah-Lincoln Community College, A
Delta State University, BMDO
East Central Community College, A
East Mississippi Community College, A
Holmes Community College, A
Itawamba Community College, A
Jackson State University, BMDO
Mississippi College, BMO
Mississippi Delta Community College, A
Mississippi Gulf Coast Community College, A
Mississippi State University, BMDO
Mississippi University for Women, B
Mississippi Valley State University, BM
Northeast Mississippi Community College, A
Northwest Mississippi Community College, A
Rust College, B
Southwest Mississippi Community College, A
Tougaloo College, B
University of Mississippi, B
University of Southern Mississippi, BMDO
William Carey University, BMO

Missouri

Avila University, B
Baptist Bible College, B
Calvary Bible College and Theological Seminary, B
Central Methodist University, B
College of the Ozarks, B
Crowder College, A
Culver-Stockton College, B
Drury University, BM
Evangel University, B
Fontbonne University, B
Graceland University, B
Hannibal-LaGrange University, B
Harris-Stowe State University, B
Lincoln University, BM
Lindenwood University, B
Maryville University of Saint Louis, BM
Missouri Baptist University, B
Missouri Southern State University, B
Missouri State University, BM
Missouri Valley College, B
Missouri Western State University, B
Northwest Missouri State University, BMO
Ozark Christian College, A
Park University, B
Rockhurst University, B
Saint Louis University, B
Southeast Missouri State University, BM
Southwest Baptist University, B
Three Rivers Community College, A
University of Central Missouri, BM
University of Missouri, BMDO
University of Missouri - Kansas City, B
University of Missouri - St. Louis, BM
Washington University in St. Louis, BM
Webster University, B
Westminster College, B
William Jewell College, B
William Woods University, B

Montana

Aaniiih Nakoda College, A
Blackfeet Community College, A
Carroll College, B
Little Big Horn College, A
Miles Community College, A
Montana State University, B
Montana State University Billings, B
Montana State University - Northern, B
Rocky Mountain College, B
University of Great Falls, B
University of Montana, B
The University of Montana Western, B

Nebraska

Chadron State College, BM
College of Saint Mary, B
Concordia University, Nebraska, BM
Creighton University, BM
Doane University, B
Grace University, B
Hastings College, B
Midland University, B
Northeast Community College, A

Peru State College, B
Union College, B
University of Nebraska at Kearney, BM
University of Nebraska - Lincoln, B
University of Nebraska at Omaha, BM
Wayne State College, BM
Western Nebraska Community College, A
York College, B

Nevada

College of Southern Nevada, A
Great Basin College, AB
Nevada State College, B
Sierra Nevada College, M
Truckee Meadows Community College, A
University of Nevada, Las Vegas, B
University of Nevada, Reno, BM
University of Phoenix - Las Vegas Campus, BM

New Hampshire

Franklin Pierce University, B
Granite State College, B
Keene State College, B
New England College, B
Plymouth State University, BM
Rivier University, BM
Saint Anselm College, B
Southern New Hampshire University, BM
University of New Hampshire, M

New Jersey

Caldwell University, B
Centenary College, B
The College of New Jersey, BM
Felician University, B
Georgian Court University, B
Kean University, B
Monmouth University, M
New Jersey City University, BM
Rider University, BO
Rowan University, BM
Rutgers University - New Brunswick, MD
Saint Peter's University, BMO
Seton Hall University, B
William Paterson University of New Jersey, B

New Mexico

Eastern New Mexico University, BM
New Mexico Highlands University, AB
New Mexico Junior College, A
New Mexico State University, B
New Mexico State University - Grants, A
Northern New Mexico College, A
San Juan College, A
University of New Mexico, BM
University of New Mexico - Gallup, AB
University of Phoenix - New Mexico Campus, M
University of the Southwest, B
Western New Mexico University, BM

New York

Adelphi University, M
Alfred University, B
Boricua College, B
Brooklyn College of the City University of New York, BM
Buffalo State College, State University of New York, BM
Canisius College, BM
City College of the City University of New York, B
College of Mount Saint Vincent, B
The College of New Rochelle, BM
The College of Saint Rose, B
College of Staten Island of the City University of New York, BM
Concordia College - New York, B
Daemen College, B
Dominican College, BM
D'Youville College, BMO
Elmira College, B
Five Towns College, B
Fordham University, BM
Fulton-Montgomery Community College, A
Genesee Community College, A
Hofstra University, BM

Houghton College, B
Hunter College of the City University of New York,
BM
Iona College, B
Ithaca College, M
Keuka College, B
Kingsborough Community College of the City University of New York, A
Le Moyne College, BM
Lehman College of the City University of New York, M
Long Island University - LIU Brooklyn, B
Long Island University - LIU Post, B
Manhattan College, B
Manhattanville College, BM
Medaille College, BM
Medgar Evers College of the City University of New York, B
Mercy College, M
Metropolitan College of New York, M
Molloy College, B
Morrisville State College, A
Mount Saint Mary College, M
Nazareth College of Rochester, BM
New York University, BM
Niagara County Community College, A
Niagara University, BMO
Nyack College, BM
Pace University, BM
Pace University, Pleasantville Campus, B
Queens College of the City University of New York, BMO
The Sage Colleges, B
St. Bonaventure University, B
St. John Fisher College, BMO
St. John's University, BM
St. Joseph's College, Long Island Campus, B
St. Joseph's College, New York, B
St. Thomas Aquinas College, BM
Skidmore College, B
State University of New York College at Cortland, B
State University of New York College at Geneseo, B
State University of New York College at Old Westbury, B
State University of New York College at Oneonta, BM
State University of New York College at Potsdam, BM
State University of New York at Fredonia, B
State University of New York at New Paltz, BM
State University of New York at Oswego, BM
State University of New York at Plattsburgh, BMO
Sullivan County Community College, A
University at Buffalo, the State University of New York, MD
Utica College, B
Wagner College, BM
Wells College, B
Yeshiva University, B
York College of the City University of New York, B

North Carolina

Appalachian State University, BM
Asheville-Buncombe Technical Community College, A
Barton College, BM
Belmont Abbey College, B
Bennett College, B
Campbell University, BM
Catawba College, BM
Chowan University, BM
Cleveland Community College, A
Craven Community College, A
Durham Technical Community College, A
East Carolina University, BMO
Elizabeth City State University, BM
Elon University, BM
Fayetteville State University, BM
Fayetteville Technical Community College, A
Gardner-Webb University, BM
Greensboro College, BM
Guilford College, B
High Point University, BM
Isothermal Community College, A
James Sprunt Community College, A
John Wesley University, B

Lees-McRae College, B
Lenoir Community College, A
Lenoir-Rhyne University, B
Livingstone College, B
Louisburg College, A
Mars Hill University, BM
McDowell Technical Community College, A
Methodist University, B
Mid-Atlantic Christian University, B
Mitchell Community College, A
Montreat College, B
Nash Community College, A
North Carolina Agricultural and Technical State University, BM
North Carolina Central University, BM
North Carolina State University, BM
North Carolina Wesleyan College, B
Pfeiffer University, BM
Piedmont International University, B
Pitt Community College, A
Queens University of Charlotte, BM
Richmond Community College, A
Roanoke-Chowan Community College, A
Rowan-Cabarrus Community College, A
St. Andrews University, B
Salem College, M
Shaw University, B
South Piedmont Community College, A
The University of North Carolina at Chapel Hill, B
The University of North Carolina at Charlotte, BM
The University of North Carolina at Greensboro, BMD
The University of North Carolina at Pembroke, BM
The University of North Carolina Wilmington, BM
Vance-Granville Community College, A
Wayne Community College, A
Western Carolina University, B
Wilson Community College, A
Wingate University, BM
Winston-Salem State University, B

North Dakota

Dickinson State University, B
Mayville State University, B
Minot State University, BM
Turtle Mountain Community College, A
University of Jamestown, B
University of Mary, B
University of North Dakota, BMD
Valley City State University, BM

Ohio

Ashland University, B
Bluffton University, B
Bowling Green State University, B
Defiance College, B
Franciscan University of Steubenville, B
God's Bible School and College, AB
Heidelberg University, B
John Carroll University, B
Lorain County Community College, A
Marietta College, B
Miami University Middletown, A
Notre Dame College, B
The Ohio State University, B
The Ohio State University at Lima, B
The Ohio State University - Mansfield Campus, B
The Ohio State University at Marion, B
The Ohio State University - Newark Campus, B
Ohio University - Zanesville, B
Ohio Wesleyan University, B
Otterbein University, B
Union Institute & University, B
The University of Akron, M
University of Cincinnati, M
University of Cincinnati Clermont College, A
The University of Findlay, B
University of Rio Grande, B
The University of Toledo, D
Urbana University, B
Wilmington College, B
Wright State University, BM
Wright State University - Lake Campus, B
Xavier University, BM
Youngstown State University, B

Oklahoma

Bacone College, B
Cameron University, B
Carl Albert State College, A
East Central University, B
Eastern Oklahoma State College, A
Hillsdale Free Will Baptist College, AB
Langston University, BM
Mid-America Christian University, B
Murray State College, A
Northeastern Oklahoma Agricultural and Mechanical College, A
Northeastern State University, B
Northern Oklahoma College, A
Northwestern Oklahoma State University, BM
Oklahoma Baptist University, B
Oklahoma Christian University, B
Oklahoma City Community College, A
Oklahoma City University, B
Oklahoma Panhandle State University, B
Oklahoma State University, B
Oklahoma Wesleyan University, B
Oral Roberts University, B
Redlands Community College, A
Rogers State University, A
Rose State College, A
St. Gregory's University, B
Seminole State College, A
Southeastern Oklahoma State University, B
Southern Nazarene University, B
Southwestern Oklahoma State University, BM
University of Central Oklahoma, BM
University of Oklahoma, B
University of Science and Arts of Oklahoma, B
The University of Tulsa, BM

Oregon

Concordia University, BM
Corban University, B
Eastern Oregon University, M
George Fox University, B
Lewis & Clark College, M
Linfield College, B
Linn-Benton Community College, A
Marylhurst University, M
Multnomah University, B
Northwest Christian University, B
Oregon State University, M
Pacific University, BM
Portland State University, M
Southern Oregon University, M
Treasure Valley Community College, A
Umpqua Community College, A
University of Portland, B
Warner Pacific College, B

Pennsylvania

Albright College, M
Arcadia University, BMO
Bloomsburg University of Pennsylvania, M
Bryn Athyn College of the New Church, B
Bucknell University, B
Butler County Community College, A
Cabrini University, B
Cairn University, B
California University of Pennsylvania, BM
Cedar Crest College, B
Chatham University, BM
Chestnut Hill College, BMO
Cheyney University of Pennsylvania, M
Clarion University of Pennsylvania, B
DeSales University, B
Drexel University, B
Duquesne University, M
East Stroudsburg University of Pennsylvania, M
Eastern University, O
Edinboro University of Pennsylvania, A
Geneva College, B
Gettysburg College, B
Gwynedd Mercy University, B
Holy Family University, BM
Immaculata University, B
King's College, B
Kutztown University of Pennsylvania, BM
La Roche College, B

Lancaster Bible College, BM
Lock Haven University of Pennsylvania, M
Manor College, A
Mansfield University of Pennsylvania, BM
Marywood University, BM
Mercyhurst University, B
Messiah College, B
Millersville University of Pennsylvania, M
Misericordia University, B
Montgomery County Community College, A
Neumann University, B
Penn State Abington, B
Penn State Altoona, B
Penn State Beaver, B
Penn State Berks, B
Penn State Brandywine, B
Penn State DuBois, B
Penn State Erie, The Behrend College, B
Penn State Fayette, The Eberly Campus, B
Penn State Greater Allegheny, B
Penn State Harrisburg, B
Penn State Hazleton, B
Penn State Lehigh Valley, B
Penn State Mont Alto, B
Penn State New Kensington, B
Penn State Schuylkill, B
Penn State Shenango, B
Penn State University Park, B
Penn State Wilkes-Barre, B
Penn State Worthington Scranton, B
Penn State York, B
Point Park University, B
Reading Area Community College, A
Robert Morris University, B
Rosemont College, BM
Saint Francis University, B
Saint Joseph's University, BMO
Seton Hill University, BMO
Shippensburg University of Pennsylvania, M
Slippery Rock University of Pennsylvania, BM
Summit University, B
Temple University, BMD
Thiel College, B
University of Pennsylvania, BM
University of Pittsburgh, M
University of Pittsburgh at Bradford, B
University of Pittsburgh at Johnstown, B
The University of Scranton, B
Waynesburg University, B
West Chester University of Pennsylvania, O
Westminster College, B
Widener University, BM
Wilkes University, B
Wilson College, ABM

Rhode Island

Brown University, M
Johnson & Wales University, M
Providence College, M
Rhode Island College, BM
Roger Williams University, B
Salve Regina University, B
University of Rhode Island, BM

South Carolina

Anderson University, B
Benedict College, B
Bob Jones University, BM
Charleston Southern University, BM
The Citadel, The Military College of South Carolina, M
Claflin University, B
Clemson University, B
Coastal Carolina University, B
Coker College, B
College of Charleston, BM
Columbia College, BM
Columbia International University, M
Converse College, BM
Erskine College, B
Francis Marion University, BM
Furman University, B
Lander University, B
Limestone College, B
Morris College, B
Newberry College, B

North Greenville University, B
Presbyterian College, B
South Carolina State University, BM
Southern Wesleyan University, B
University of South Carolina, BMD
University of South Carolina Aiken, B
University of South Carolina Beaufort, B
University of South Carolina Upstate, BM
Winthrop University, B

South Dakota

Augustana University, B
Black Hills State University, B
Dakota State University, B
Dakota Wesleyan University, B
Mount Marty College, B
Northern State University, B
Oglala Lakota College, AB
Sinte Gleska University, BM
University of Sioux Falls, B
The University of South Dakota, BM

Tennessee

Aquinas College, B
Argosy University, Nashville, D
Austin Peay State University, MO
Belmont University, B
Bethel University, B
Bryan College, B
Carson-Newman University, BM
Cumberland University, B
East Tennessee State University, M
Freed-Hardeman University, B
Hiwassee College, A
Johnson University, B
Lee University, BM
Lincoln Memorial University, B
Lipscomb University, B
Martin Methodist College, B
Middle Tennessee State University, MO
Nashville State Community College, A
Roane State Community College, A
South College, A
Southern Adventist University, B
Tennessee State University, BM
Tennessee Technological University, BMO
Tennessee Wesleyan College, B
Trevecca Nazarene University, BM
Union University, B
University of Memphis, M
The University of Tennessee, MO
The University of Tennessee at Chattanooga, M
The University of Tennessee at Martin, BM
Vanderbilt University, BM
Welch College, B

Texas

Abilene Christian University, B
Amarillo College, A
Arlington Baptist College, B
Austin College, A
Baylor University, B
Clarendon College, A
Concordia University Texas, B
Dallas Baptist University, BM
Del Mar College, A
East Texas Baptist University, B
Frank Phillips College, A
Grayson College, A
Hill College, A
Howard College, A
Howard Payne University, B
Huston-Tillotson University, B
Jarvis Christian College, B
Kilgore College, A
LeTourneau University, B
McMurry University, B
Navarro College, A
Our Lady of the Lake University of San Antonio, M
Paris Junior College, A
Schreiner University, B
Southwestern Adventist University, B
Southwestern Assemblies of God University, B
Stephen F. Austin State University, M
Sul Ross State University, M
Tarleton State University, B

Texas A&M University - Corpus Christi, M
Texas Christian University, B
Texas College, A
Texas Lutheran University, B
Texas State University, M
Texas Tech University, M
Trinity Valley Community College, A
University of Dallas, B
University of Houston - Downtown, M
University of the Incarnate Word, BM
University of Mary Hardin-Baylor, BD
University of St. Thomas, BM
The University of Texas Rio Grande Valley, M
The University of Texas at San Antonio, B
Wayland Baptist University, BM
West Texas A&M University, B
Wiley College, B

Utah

Dixie State University, B
Snow College, A
Southern Utah University, B
University of Phoenix - Utah Campus, BM
University of Utah, BMD
Utah State University, BM
Utah Valley University, BM
Weber State University, B
Western Governors University, MO
Westminster College, B

Vermont

Castleton University, B
Champlain College, B
College of St. Joseph, BM
Goddard College, B
Green Mountain College, B
Johnson State College, B
Lyndon State College, B
Saint Michael's College, B
University of Vermont, B

Virginia

Argosy University, Washington DC, D
Bluefield College, B
George Mason University, M
Hampton University, BM
James Madison University, M
Liberty University, M
Longwood University, M
Lynchburg College, B
Mary Baldwin College, M
Marymount University, BM
Old Dominion University, M
Regent University, M
University of Mary Washington, M
University of Valley Forge Virginia Campus, B
University of Virginia, MD
Virginia Commonwealth University, M
Virginia Union University, B
Virginia Wesleyan College, B

Washington

Argosy University, Seattle, D
Central Washington University, B
City University of Seattle, BM
Eastern Washington University, M
Gonzaga University, B
Heritage University, B
Northwest University, B
Saint Martin's University, B
University of Puget Sound, M
University of Washington, Tacoma, M
Walla Walla Community College, A
Walla Walla University, B
Washington State University, BM
Washington State University - Tri-Cities, B
Washington State University - Vancouver, B
Western Washington University, BM
Whitworth University, BM

West Virginia

Alderson Broaddus University, B
American Public University System, M
Bethany College, B
Bluefield State College, B

Concord University, B
Davis & Elkins College, B
Fairmont State University, B
Glenville State College, B
Marshall University, BM
Ohio Valley University, B
Potomac State College of West Virginia University, A
Shepherd University, B
University of Charleston, B
West Liberty University, B
West Virginia State University, B
West Virginia University, BM
West Virginia University at Parkersburg, B
West Virginia Wesleyan College, B

Wisconsin

Alverno College, B
Beloit College, B
Cardinal Stritch University, B
Carroll University, B
Carthage College, B
Concordia University Wisconsin, B
Edgewood College, B
Lakeland College, B
Maranatha Baptist University, B
Marian University, B
Marquette University, BO
Ripon College, B
St. Norbert College, B
Silver Lake College of the Holy Family, B
University of Wisconsin - Eau Claire, B
University of Wisconsin - La Crosse, B
University of Wisconsin - Madison, B
University of Wisconsin - Milwaukee, M
University of Wisconsin - Oshkosh, B
University of Wisconsin - Platteville, BM
University of Wisconsin - River Falls, BM
University of Wisconsin - Stevens Point, BM
University of Wisconsin - Superior, B
University of Wisconsin - Whitewater, B
Viterbo University, B
Wisconsin Lutheran College, B

Wyoming

Casper College, A
Central Wyoming College, A
Eastern Wyoming College, A
Northwest College, A
Sheridan College, A
University of Wyoming, B
Western Wyoming Community College, A

U.S. Territories: Guam

University of Guam, B

U.S. Territories: Puerto Rico

American University of Puerto Rico (Bayamon), BM
Bayamón Central University, BM
Caribbean University, BM
Inter American University of Puerto Rico, Aguadilla Campus, BM
Inter American University of Puerto Rico, Arecibo Campus, BM
Inter American University of Puerto Rico, Barranquitas Campus, BM
Inter American University of Puerto Rico, Fajardo Campus, BM
Inter American University of Puerto Rico, Guayama Campus, BM
Inter American University of Puerto Rico, Metropolitan Campus, BM
Inter American University of Puerto Rico, Ponce Campus, BM
Inter American University of Puerto Rico, San Germán Campus, BM
Pontifical Catholic University of Puerto Rico, B
Universidad Adventista de las Antillas, B
Universidad del Este, M
Universidad Metropolitana, BM
Universidad del Turabo, B
University of Puerto Rico in Aguadilla, B
University of Puerto Rico in Arecibo, B
University of Puerto Rico in Humacao, B
University of Puerto Rico in Ponce, B
University of Puerto Rico, Río Piedras Campus, B

University of Puerto Rico in Utuado, B
University of the Sacred Heart, B

U.S. Territories: United States Virgin Islands

University of the Virgin Islands, B

Canada

Alberta

Concordia University of Edmonton, B
The King's University, B
University of Alberta, BMD
University of Calgary, B

British Columbia

Thompson Rivers University, B
Trinity Western University, B
The University of British Columbia, B
University of Northern British Columbia, B
University of Victoria, B

Manitoba

Brandon University, B
University of Manitoba, B
The University of Winnipeg, B

Maritime Provinces: New Brunswick

Kingswood University, B
Université de Moncton, B
University of New Brunswick Fredericton, B

Maritime Provinces: Nova Scotia

Acadia University, B
Mount Saint Vincent University, BM
St. Francis Xavier University, B
Université Sainte-Anne, B

Maritime Provinces: Prince Edward Island

University of Prince Edward Island, B

Newfoundland and Labrador

Memorial University of Newfoundland, B

Ontario

Brock University, B
Lakehead University, B
Queen's University at Kingston, B
Redeemer University College, B
Trent University, B
The University of Western Ontario, B
University of Windsor, B
York University, B

Quebec

Bishop's University, B
Concordia University, B
McGill University, B
Université Laval, B
Université de Montréal, B
Université du Québec en Abitibi-Témiscamingue, B
Université du Québec à Chicoutimi, B
Université du Québec à Montréal, B
Université du Québec en Outaouais, B
Université du Québec à Rimouski, B
Université du Québec à Trois-Rivières, B
Université de Sherbrooke, BMO

Saskatchewan

University of Regina, B

ELEMENTARY AND MIDDLE SCHOOL ADMINISTRATION/ PRINCIPALSHIP

United States

Arkansas

Philander Smith College, B

Kentucky

Berea College, B

North Carolina

Campbell University, B

Ohio

The Ohio State University, B
The Ohio State University at Lima, B
The Ohio State University - Mansfield Campus, B
The Ohio State University at Marion, B
The Ohio State University - Newark Campus, B

South Carolina

Charleston Southern University, B

EMERGENCY CARE ATTENDANT (EMT AMBULANCE)

United States

Arizona

Coconino Community College, A

Delaware

Delaware Technical & Community College, Stanton/Wilmington Campus, A

Illinois

Illinois Eastern Community Colleges, Frontier Community College, A
Trinity College of Nursing and Health Sciences, A
Waubonsee Community College, A

Iowa

Iowa Lakes Community College, A

Kansas

Barton County Community College, A

New Mexico

Clovis Community College, A

New York

Mohawk Valley Community College, A

Virginia

Southside Virginia Community College, A

EMERGENCY MANAGEMENT

United States

Alabama

Auburn University at Montgomery, M
Columbia Southern University, M
Jacksonville State University, MD

Arizona

Arizona State University at the Tempe campus, M
Grand Canyon University, M

Arkansas

Arkansas State University, MO
Arkansas Tech University, M

California

Brandman University, M
California Maritime Academy, M
California State University, Long Beach, M
National University, M
San Diego State University, M
Trident University International, MO

Colorado

University of Colorado Denver, M
University of Denver, MO

Connecticut

University of New Haven, MO

Delaware

University of Delaware, MD

District of Columbia

The George Washington University, M
Georgetown University, M

Florida

Florida Institute of Technology, M
Lynn University, M
Nova Southeastern University, M
University of Central Florida, O
University of Florida, M
University of South Florida, O

Georgia

Georgia State University, MO

Hawaii

University of Hawaii at Manoa, O

Illinois

Benedictine University, M
University of Chicago, M
University of Illinois at Springfield, O

Indiana

Indiana University - Purdue University Indianapolis, O
Trine University, M

Louisiana

Tulane University, M

Massachusetts

Anna Maria College, MO
Boston University, M
Lasell College, M
Massachusetts Maritime Academy, M

Minnesota

Capella University, MD
Walden University, MD

Missouri

Park University, MO

Nebraska

University of Nebraska Medical Center, M

Nevada

University of Nevada, Las Vegas, M

New Jersey

New Jersey Institute of Technology, M
Rutgers University - New Brunswick, O

New York

Adelphi University, O
Excelsior College, M
Fordham University, M
Metropolitan College of New York, M

North Carolina

The University of North Carolina at Charlotte, MO

Ohio

The University of Toledo, O

Oklahoma

Oklahoma State University, MD

Pennsylvania

Drexel University, M
Indiana University of Pennsylvania, M
Millersville University of Pennsylvania, M
Philadelphia University, M
West Chester University of Pennsylvania, O

South Carolina

Lander University, M

Texas

University of North Texas, M

Virginia

George Mason University, O
Liberty University, M
Regent University, M
Virginia Commonwealth University, MO

West Virginia

American Public University System, M

Canada

British Columbia

Royal Roads University, M

Ontario

York University, M

Quebec

Université de Montréal, O

EMERGENCY MEDICAL SERVICES

United States

California

San Diego State University, M

Nebraska

Creighton University, M

Pennsylvania

Drexel University, M

Texas

Baylor University, D

Canada

Ontario

University of Guelph, MD

Quebec

Université Laval, O

EMERGENCY MEDICAL TECHNOLOGY/TECHNICIAN (EMT PARAMEDIC)

United States

Alabama

Bevill State Community College, A
Bishop State Community College, A
Calhoun Community College, A
Columbia Southern University, B
Enterprise State Community College, A
Gadsden State Community College, A
George C. Wallace Community College, A
H. Councill Trenholm State Community College, A
Jefferson State Community College, A
Lurleen B. Wallace Community College, A
Northeast Alabama Community College, A
Northwest-Shoals Community College, A
Southern Union State Community College, A
University of South Alabama, B
The University of West Alabama, A
Wallace State Community College, A

Alaska

University of Alaska Anchorage, A
University of Alaska Anchorage, Kenai Peninsula College, A
University of Alaska Anchorage, Matanuska-Susitna College, A

Arizona

Arizona Western College, A
Central Arizona College, A
Cochise County Community College District, A
Eastern Arizona College, A
Glendale Community College, A
Mohave Community College, A
Northland Pioneer College, A
Paradise Valley Community College, A
Phoenix College, A
Pima Community College, A

Arkansas

Arkansas State University - Mountain Home, A
Arkansas State University - Newport, A
Arkansas Tech University, A
Black River Technical College, A
East Arkansas Community College, A
National Park College, A
North Arkansas College, A
NorthWest Arkansas Community College, A
South Arkansas Community College, A
Southeast Arkansas College, A
University of Arkansas Community College at Batesville, A
University of Arkansas Community College at Hope, A
University of Arkansas for Medical Sciences, AB

California

American River College, A
Bakersfield College, A
Barstow Community College, A
Butte College, A
Cerro Coso Community College, A
City College of San Francisco, A
College of the Siskiyous, A
Columbia College, A
Crafton Hills College, A
East Los Angeles College, A
Foothill College, A
Loma Linda University, B
Los Medanos College, A
Modesto Junior College, A
Mt. San Antonio College, A
Napa Valley College, A
Pacific Union College, A
Palomar College, A
Saddleback College, A
San Diego City College, A
San Diego Miramar College, A
Santa Rosa Junior College, A
Skyline College, A
Southwestern College, A

Colorado

Aims Community College, A
Arapahoe Community College, A
Colorado Mesa University, A
Colorado Mountain College (Leadville), A
Colorado Northwestern Community College, A
Community College of Aurora, A
Lamar Community College, A
Morgan Community College, B
Northeastern Junior College, A
Pikes Peak Community College, A
Pueblo Community College, A
Red Rocks Community College, A
Trinidad State Junior College, A

Connecticut

Capital Community College, A
University of New Haven, AB

Delaware

Delaware Technical & Community College, Jack F. Owens Campus, A

Delaware Technical & Community College, Stanton/Wilmington Campus, A

Delaware Technical & Community College, Terry Campus, A

District of Columbia

The George Washington University, B

Florida

Broward College, A
City College (Fort Lauderdale), A
City College (Miami), A
College of Central Florida, A
Daytona State College, A
Eastern Florida State College, A
Florida Gateway College, A
Florida SouthWestern State College, A
Florida State College at Jacksonville, A
Gulf Coast State College, A
Hillsborough Community College, A
Indian River State College, A
Lake-Sumter State College, A
Miami Dade College, A
Northwest Florida State College, A
Pasco-Hernando State College, A
Pensacola State College, A
Polk State College, A
St. Johns River State College, A
St. Petersburg College, A
Santa Fe College, A
Seminole State College of Florida, A
South Florida State College, A
Southeastern College - West Palm Beach, A
Tallahassee Community College, A
Valencia College, A

Georgia

Athens Technical College, A
Augusta Technical College, A
Columbus Technical College, A
Darton State College, A
Gwinnett Technical College, A
Southern Crescent Technical College, A

Hawaii

Kapiolani Community College, A

Idaho

Brigham Young University - Idaho, B
College of Southern Idaho, A
Idaho State University, A

Illinois

Black Hawk College, A
City Colleges of Chicago, Malcolm X College, A
College of DuPage, A
Concordia University Chicago, B
Harper College, A
Highland Community College, A
Illinois Central College, A
John A. Logan College, A
John Wood Community College, A
Joliet Junior College, A
Kankakee Community College, A
Kaskaskia College, A
Kishwaukee College, A
Lincoln Land Community College, A
McHenry County College, A
Moraine Valley Community College, A
Rend Lake College, A
Southeastern Illinois College, A
Southwestern Illinois College, A
Trinity College of Nursing and Health Sciences, A
Triton College, A

Indiana

Indiana University - Purdue University Indianapolis, A
Ivy Tech Community College - Bloomington, A
Ivy Tech Community College - Columbus, A
Ivy Tech Community College - Kokomo, A
Ivy Tech Community College - North Central, A
Ivy Tech Community College - Richmond, A
Ivy Tech Community College - Southwest, A
Ivy Tech Community College - Wabash Valley, A

Purdue University Northwest (Hammond), A
Saint Joseph's College, A
Vincennes University, A

Iowa

Clinton Community College, A
Hawkeye Community College, A
Indian Hills Community College, A
Iowa Western Community College, A
Kirkwood Community College, A
Mercy College of Health Sciences, A
Muscatine Community College, A
North Iowa Area Community College, A
Northeast Iowa Community College, A
Northwest Iowa Community College, A
Scott Community College, A
Southeastern Community College, A
Western Iowa Tech Community College, A

Kansas

Allen Community College, A
Barton County Community College, A
Coffeyville Community College, A
Cowley County Community College and Area Vocational - Technical School, A
Flint Hills Technical College, A
Garden City Community College, A
Hutchinson Community College, A
Johnson County Community College, A
Kansas City Kansas Community College, A

Kentucky

Eastern Kentucky University, AB
Owensboro Community and Technical College, A
Spalding University, A
Western Kentucky University, A

Louisiana

Bossier Parish Community College, A
Delgado Community College, A
Fletcher Technical Community College, A
South Louisiana Community College, A

Maine

Eastern Maine Community College, A
Kennebec Valley Community College, A
Northern Maine Community College, A
Southern Maine Community College, A

Maryland

Baltimore City Community College, A
Carroll Community College, A
Cecil College, A
Chesapeake College, A
College of Southern Maryland, A
Community College of Baltimore County, A
Frederick Community College, A
Hagerstown Community College, A
Howard Community College, A
Prince George's Community College, A
University of Maryland, Baltimore County, B
Wor-Wic Community College, A

Massachusetts

Anna Maria College, B
Bunker Hill Community College, A
Northern Essex Community College, A
Quinsigamond Community College, A
Springfield College, B

Michigan

Baker College, A
Henry Ford College, A
Jackson College, A
Kalamazoo Valley Community College, A
Kellogg Community College, A
Kirtland Community College, A
Lake Michigan College, A
Lansing Community College, A
Macomb Community College, A
Montcalm Community College, A
Mott Community College, A
North Central Michigan College, A
Oakland Community College, A
St. Clair County Community College, A

Schoolcraft College, A
Wayne County Community College District, A
West Shore Community College, A

Minnesota

Century College, A
Inver Hills Community College, A
Northland Community and Technical College, A
Rochester Community and Technical College, A
St. Cloud Technical & Community College, A
South Central College, A

Mississippi

East Central Community College, A
Hinds Community College, A
Holmes Community College, A
Jones County Junior College, A
Meridian Community College, A
Mississippi Gulf Coast Community College, A
Southwest Mississippi Community College, A

Missouri

Crowder College, A
East Central College, A
IHM Academy of EMS, A
Jefferson College, A
Metropolitan Community College - Kansas City, A
Mineral Area College, A
North Central Missouri College, A
Ozarks Technical Community College, A
St. Charles Community College, A
Southwest Baptist University, A

Montana

Flathead Valley Community College, A
Great Falls College Montana State University, A
Montana State University Billings, A

Nebraska

Creighton University, AB
Northeast Community College, A
Southeast Community College, Lincoln Campus, A

Nevada

College of Southern Nevada, A
Great Basin College, A

New Hampshire

NHTI, Concord's Community College, A

New Jersey

Camden County College, A
Hudson County Community College, A
Union County College, A

New Mexico

Central New Mexico Community College, A
Doña Ana Community College, A
Eastern New Mexico University - Roswell, A
New Mexico Junior College, A
San Juan College, A
University of New Mexico, B

New York

Borough of Manhattan Community College of the City University of New York, A
Broome Community College, A
Dutchess Community College, A
Erie Community College, South Campus, A
Finger Lakes Community College, A
Fiorello H. LaGuardia Community College of the City University of New York, A
Herkimer County Community College, A
Hudson Valley Community College, A
Jefferson Community College, A
Rockland Community College, A
State University of New York College of Agriculture and Technology at Cobleskill, A
Westchester Community College, A

North Carolina

Asheville-Buncombe Technical Community College, A

Caldwell Community College and Technical Institute, A
Cape Fear Community College, A
Catawba Valley Community College, A
Cleveland Community College, A
Coastal Carolina Community College, A
Davidson County Community College, A
Fayetteville Technical Community College, A
Forsyth Technical Community College, A
Gaston College, A
Guilford Technical Community College, A
Lenoir Community College, A
Southwestern Community College, A
Wake Technical Community College, A
Western Carolina University, B

North Dakota

Bismarck State College, A
North Dakota State College of Science, A
Turtle Mountain Community College, A

Ohio

Bowling Green State University, B
Central Ohio Technical College, A
Cincinnati State Technical and Community College, A
Clark State Community College, A
Columbus State Community College, A
Eastern Gateway Community College, A
Hocking College, A
James A. Rhodes State College, A
Kent State University at Trumbull, A
Shawnee State University, A
Sinclair Community College, A
Southern State Community College, A
The University of Akron, A
University of Cincinnati Blue Ash College, A
University of Cincinnati Clermont College, A
Youngstown State University, A

Oklahoma

Oklahoma City Community College, A
Oklahoma State University, Oklahoma City, A
Redlands Community College, A
Rogers State University, A

Oregon

Central Oregon Community College, A
Chemeketa Community College, A
Clackamas Community College, A
Lane Community College, A
Portland Community College, A
Rogue Community College, A
Tillamook Bay Community College, A
Umpqua Community College, A

Pennsylvania

Delaware County Community College, A
Harrisburg Area Community College, A
Lackawanna College, A
Luzerne County Community College, A
Pennsylvania College of Technology, A
Pennsylvania Highlands Community College, A
University of Pittsburgh at Johnstown, A

Rhode Island

New England Institute of Technology, A

South Carolina

Greenville Technical College, A
Technical College of the Lowcountry, A

South Dakota

Lake Area Technical Institute, A
University of Sioux Falls, AB
Western Dakota Technical Institute, A

Tennessee

Dyersburg State Community College, A
Northeast State Community College, A
Roane State Community College, A

Texas

Alvin Community College, A
Amarillo College, A
Angelina College, A
Austin Community College District, A
Brazosport College, A
Brookhaven College, A
Central Texas College, A
Collin County Community College District, A
Del Mar College, A
El Centro College, A
El Paso Community College, A
Galveston College, A
Grayson College, A
Hill College, A
Houston Community College, A
Kilgore College, A
Lamar Institute of Technology, A
Laredo Community College, A
Lee College, A
Lone Star College - CyFair, A
Lone Star College - Montgomery, A
Lone Star College - North Harris, A
Midland College, A
North Central Texas College, A
Northeast Texas Community College, A
Odessa College, A
Paris Junior College, A
San Jacinto College District, A
South Texas College, A
Tarrant County College District, A
Temple College, A
Texarkana College, A
Texas Southmost College, A
Trinity Valley Community College, A
Tyler Junior College, A
The University of Texas Health Science Center at
San Antonio, B
Victoria College, A
Weatherford College, A

Utah

Dixie State University, A
Weber State University, A

Virginia

American National University (Salem), A
Central Virginia Community College, A
J. Sargeant Reynolds Community College, A
Jefferson College of Health Sciences, B
John Tyler Community College, A
Mountain Empire Community College, A
Northern Virginia Community College, A
Patrick Henry Community College, A
Southwest Virginia Community College, A
Thomas Nelson Community College, A

Washington

Central Washington University, B
Clark College, A
Tacoma Community College, A
University of Washington, B

West Virginia

Blue Ridge Community and Technical College, A
Mountwest Community & Technical College, A
Pierpont Community & Technical College, A

Wisconsin

Chippewa Valley Technical College, A
Fox Valley Technical College, A
Gateway Technical College, A
Madison Area Technical College, A
Moraine Park Technical College, A
Northcentral Technical College, A
Waukesha County Technical College, A
Wisconsin Indianhead Technical College, A

Wyoming

Casper College, A
Laramie County Community College, A

U.S. Territories: Puerto Rico

EDP University of Puerto Rico, A
EDP University of Puerto Rico - San Sebastian, A

ENERGY MANAGEMENT AND POLICY

United States

Alabama

Samford University, M

Arizona

University of Phoenix - Online Campus, M
University of Phoenix - Phoenix Campus, M

California

Holy Names University, M
Santa Clara University, O
University of California, Berkeley, MD
University of Phoenix - Bay Area Campus, M
University of Phoenix - Southern California Campus,
M

Colorado

University of Colorado Denver, M

Delaware

University of Delaware, MD

Illinois

Eastern Illinois University, M
University of Illinois at Urbana - Champaign, M

Indiana

Indiana University Bloomington, M

Kansas

Kansas State University, M

Louisiana

Tulane University, M

Maryland

Johns Hopkins University, M

Massachusetts

Boston University, M

Michigan

Michigan Technological University, MD

New Hampshire

Franklin Pierce University, M

New York

New York Institute of Technology, MO
New York University, O
University of Rochester, M

North Carolina

Duke University, M

North Dakota

University of Mary, M

Oklahoma

Oklahoma Baptist University, M
Oklahoma City University, M
The University of Tulsa, M

Pennsylvania

University of Pittsburgh, M
Waynesburg University, M

Texas

Texas Christian University, M

Virginia

George Mason University, M

Canada

Alberta

University of Calgary, MD

ENERGY MANAGEMENT AND SYSTEMS TECHNOLOGY/ TECHNICIAN

United States

Arizona

GateWay Community College, A
The Refrigeration School, A

California

Lassen Community College District, A
Merritt College, A

Colorado

Front Range Community College, A
Red Rocks Community College, A

Delaware

Delaware Technical & Community College, Jack F. Owens Campus, A
Delaware Technical & Community College, Stanton/Wilmington Campus, A
Delaware Technical & Community College, Terry Campus, A

Florida

State College of Florida Manatee-Sarasota, B

Idaho

Idaho State University, AB

Illinois

Danville Area Community College, A
Illinois Central College, A
Illinois Eastern Community Colleges, Wabash Valley College, A
Illinois State University, B
Rock Valley College, A

Indiana

Ivy Tech Community College - East Central, A
Ivy Tech Community College - Southern Indiana, A
Ivy Tech Community College - Southwest, A
Ivy Tech Community College - Wabash Valley, A

Iowa

Hawkeye Community College, A
Iowa Lakes Community College, A
Northeast Iowa Community College, A
Scott Community College, A
Western Iowa Tech Community College, A

Kansas

Pratt Community College, A

Louisiana

South Louisiana Community College, A

Maine

Unity College, B

Massachusetts

Fitchburg State University, B
Mount Wachusett Community College, A
Quinsigamond Community College, A

Michigan

Delta College, A
Ferris State University, B
Henry Ford College, A
Lake Michigan College, A

Lansing Community College, A
Macomb Community College, A
St. Clair County Community College, A

Minnesota

Century College, A
Dakota County Technical College, A
Minnesota West Community and Technical College, A
Northwest Technical College, A
St. Cloud Technical & Community College, A

Missouri

Crowder College, A

Montana

Montana State University Billings, A

Nebraska

Creighton University, B
Northeast Community College, A
Southeast Community College, Milford Campus, A

Nevada

Truckee Meadows Community College, A

New Hampshire

Lakes Region Community College, A

New Jersey

Essex County College, A
Middlesex County College, A
Rowan College at Burlington County, A

New York

Clinton Community College, A
Corning Community College, A
Westchester Community College, A

North Carolina

Lenoir Community College, A
Wayne Community College, A

North Dakota

North Dakota State College of Science, A

Ohio

Cincinnati State Technical and Community College, A
Lakeland Community College, A
Northwest State Community College, A
University of Rio Grande, A

Oregon

Lane Community College, A

Pennsylvania

Community College of Allegheny County, A
Williamson College of the Trades, A

South Dakota

Mitchell Technical Institute, A

Tennessee

Walters State Community College, A

Texas

Houston Community College, A
St. Philip's College, A

Vermont

Vermont Technical College, B

Wisconsin

Fox Valley Technical College, A

Wyoming

Casper College, A
Laramie County Community College, A

ENERGY AND POWER ENGINEERING

United States

Arizona

Arizona State University at the Tempe campus, M

California

San Francisco State University, M
Santa Clara University, MO
Stanford University, MDO

Colorado

University of Colorado Colorado Springs, M

Florida

Florida State University, M

Georgia

Georgia Southern University, M

Illinois

University of Illinois at Urbana - Champaign, M

Iowa

The University of Iowa, MD

Kansas

Kansas State University, M

Massachusetts

Northeastern University, M
University of Massachusetts Lowell, MD
Worcester Polytechnic Institute, M

Michigan

Saginaw Valley State University, M
University of Michigan, M
University of Michigan - Dearborn, M
Wayne State University, MO

New Jersey

New Jersey Institute of Technology, M

New York

Cornell University, MD
New York Institute of Technology, O
Syracuse University, M
University of Rochester, M

North Carolina

Appalachian State University, M
North Carolina Agricultural and Technical State University, MD
The University of North Carolina at Charlotte, MO

Pennsylvania

Carnegie Mellon University, MD
Lehigh University, M

Tennessee

University of Memphis, M
The University of Tennessee, D
The University of Tennessee at Chattanooga, O

Texas

Texas A&M University - Kingsville, D
Texas Tech University, D
University of North Texas, MD

Washington

Washington State University, M

Canada

Alberta

University of Alberta, MD
University of Calgary, MD

ENGINE MACHINIST

United States

California
Glendale Community College, A

Minnesota
Northwest Technical College, A

North Carolina
Tri-County Community College, A

South Dakota
Lake Area Technical Institute, A

ENGINEERING

United States

Alabama
Auburn University, B
Marion Military Institute, A
Oakwood University, B
The University of Alabama in Huntsville, B
Wallace State Community College, A

Alaska
University of Alaska Anchorage, B

Arizona
Arizona State University at the Polytechnic campus, B
Arizona Western College, A
Cochise County Community College District, A

Arkansas
Arkansas State University, B
John Brown University, B

California
Allan Hancock College, A
American River College, A
Bakersfield College, A
Biola University, B
Butte College, A
Cabrillo College, A
California Baptist University, B
California Institute of Technology, B
California National University for Advanced Studies, B
California State Polytechnic University, Pomona, B
California State University, Chico, B
California State University, Long Beach, B
California State University, Los Angeles, B
Cañada College, A
Cerro Coso Community College, A
Chaffey College, A
Citrus College, A
City College of San Francisco, A
Claremont McKenna College, B
College of Marin, A
College of San Mateo, A
College of the Sequoias, A
College of the Siskiyous, A
Contra Costa College, A
Cosumnes River College, A
Cuesta College, A
Cypress College, A
De Anza College, A
East Los Angeles College, A
El Camino College, A
Evergreen Valley College, A
Fresno City College, A
Fullerton College, A
Gavilan College, A
Harvey Mudd College, B
Laney College, A
Long Beach City College, A
Los Angeles City College, A
Los Angeles Southwest College, A

Los Angeles Trade-Technical College, A
Los Angeles Valley College, A
Mills College, B
Modesto Junior College, A
Monterey Peninsula College, A
Moorpark College, A
Napa Valley College, A
Ohlone College, A
Sacramento City College, A
Saddleback College, A
Saint Mary's College of California, B
San Diego Mesa College, A
San Diego State University, B
San Joaquin Delta College, A
San Jose State University, B
Santa Ana College, A
Santa Barbara City College, A
Santa Rosa Junior College, A
Sierra College, A
Southwestern College, A
Stanford University, B
University of California, Davis, B
University of California, Irvine, B
University of California, San Diego, B
Ventura College, A
West Los Angeles College, A

Colorado
Colorado School of Mines, B
Colorado State University - Pueblo, B
United States Air Force Academy, B
University of Colorado Boulder, B
University of Colorado Colorado Springs, B
University of Denver, B

Connecticut
Northwestern Connecticut Community College, A
Quinnipiac University, B
Trinity College, B
Tunxis Community College, A
University of Hartford, B
University of New Haven, B

Delaware
University of Delaware, B

District of Columbia
The Catholic University of America, B
The George Washington University, B

Florida
Barry University, B
Broward College, A
College of Central Florida, A
Daytona State College, AB
Embry-Riddle Aeronautical University - Daytona, B
Florida Institute of Technology, B
Indian River State College, A
Jacksonville University, B
Miami Dade College, A
Pensacola State College, A
St. Thomas University, A
South Florida State College, A
State College of Florida Manatee-Sarasota, A
University of Miami, B

Georgia
Agnes Scott College, B
LaGrange College, B
Mercer University, B
Oglethorpe University, B
Spelman College, B

Hawaii
University of Hawaii at Hilo, B
University of Hawaii at Manoa, B

Idaho
Brigham Young University - Idaho, A
The College of Idaho, B
College of Southern Idaho, A
North Idaho College, A

Illinois
City Colleges of Chicago, Harold Washington College, A
City Colleges of Chicago, Wilbur Wright College, A
College of DuPage, A
College of Lake County, A
Danville Area Community College, A
Dominican University, B
Eastern Illinois University, B
Elgin Community College, A
Harper College, A
Heartland Community College, A
Highland Community College, A
Illinois Central College, A
Illinois Eastern Community Colleges, Frontier Community College, A
Illinois Eastern Community Colleges, Olney Central College, A
Illinois Eastern Community Colleges, Wabash Valley College, A
Illinois Institute of Technology, B
Illinois Valley Community College, A
John A. Logan College, A
Kankakee Community College, A
Kaskaskia College, A
Kishwaukee College, A
Lewis and Clark Community College, A
Lincoln Land Community College, A
McHenry County College, A
McKendree University, B
Moraine Valley Community College, A
North Park University, B
Northwestern University, B
Oakton Community College, A
Olivet Nazarene University, B
Principia College, B
Rend Lake College, A
University of Illinois at Urbana - Champaign, B
Waubonsee Community College, A
Western Illinois University, B
Wheaton College, B

Indiana
Ball State University, B
Bethel College, B
Indiana University Bloomington, B
Indiana University - Purdue University Indianapolis, B
Manchester University, B
Purdue University, B
Purdue University Northwest (Hammond), B
Purdue University Northwest (Westville), A
Rose-Hulman Institute of Technology, B
University of Southern Indiana, B

Iowa
Central College, B
Dordt College, B
Southeastern Community College, A
The University of Iowa, B
Wartburg College, B

Kansas
Allen Community College, A
Benedictine College, B
Central Christian College of Kansas, A
Colby Community College, A
Dodge City Community College, A
Garden City Community College, A
Highland Community College, A
Hutchinson Community College, A
Seward County Community College and Area Technical School, A

Kentucky
Brescia University, A
Eastern Kentucky University, A
Lindsey Wilson College, A
Morehead State University, B

Louisiana
Bossier Parish Community College, A
McNeese State University, B

Maine

Bates College, B
Maine Maritime Academy, B

Maryland

Anne Arundel Community College, A
Baltimore City Community College, A
College of Southern Maryland, A
Community College of Baltimore County, A
Frederick Community College, A
Frostburg State University, B
Hagerstown Community College, A
Harford Community College, A
Howard Community College, A
Johns Hopkins University, B
Loyola University Maryland, B
Montgomery College, A
Morgan State University, B
Prince George's Community College, A
United States Naval Academy, B
University of Maryland, Baltimore County, B
University of Maryland, College Park, B
Washington Adventist University, A

Massachusetts

Berkshire Community College, A
Boston University, B
Bristol Community College, A
Bunker Hill Community College, A
Clark University, B
Eastern Nazarene College, B
Franklin W. Olin College of Engineering, B
Harvard University, B
Holyoke Community College, A
Massachusetts Maritime Academy, B
Northeastern University, B
Springfield Technical Community College, A
Tufts University, B
University of Massachusetts Lowell, B
Wentworth Institute of Technology, B
Worcester Polytechnic Institute, B

Michigan

Albion College, B
Calvin College, B
Ferris State University, A
Grand Rapids Community College, A
Grand Valley State University, B
Henry Ford College, A
Hope College, B
Kalamazoo Valley Community College, A
Lake Superior State University, AB
Lansing Community College, A
Macomb Community College, A
Madonna University, A
Michigan State University, B
Michigan Technological University, B
Northern Michigan University, B
Northwestern Michigan College, A
Saginaw Valley State University, B
St. Clair County Community College, A
Schoolcraft College, A
University of Detroit Mercy, B
University of Michigan, B
University of Michigan - Dearborn, B
Washtenaw Community College, A
Western Michigan University, B

Minnesota

Augsburg College, B
Bethany Lutheran College, B
Central Lakes College, A
Hibbing Community College, A
Itasca Community College, A
Minnesota State Community and Technical College - Moorhead, A
St. Cloud State University, B
University of Northwestern - St. Paul, B
Vermilion Community College, A

Mississippi

Coahoma Community College, A
Copiah-Lincoln Community College, A
East Central Community College, A
East Mississippi Community College, A

Holmes Community College, A
Mississippi State University, B
Northeast Mississippi Community College, A
Southwest Mississippi Community College, A
University of Mississippi, B

Missouri

East-Central College, A
Jefferson College, A
Maryville University of Saint Louis, B
Metropolitan Community College - Kansas City, A
Missouri State University - West Plains, A
Missouri University of Science and Technology, B
Park University, B
St. Charles Community College, A
Saint Louis University, B
University of Missouri - Kansas City, B
Washington University in St. Louis, B

Montana

Miles Community College, A
Montana State University, B
Montana Tech of The University of Montana, B

Nebraska

Northeast Community College, A
Union College, A
University of Nebraska - Lincoln, B

Nevada

Truckee Meadows Community College, A
University of Nevada, Las Vegas, B

New Hampshire

Dartmouth College, B
Saint Anselm College, B
University of New Hampshire, B

New Jersey

Brookdale Community College, A
Essex County College, A
Ocean County College, A
Princeton University, B
Rowan College at Burlington County, A
Rowan College at Gloucester County, A
Rutgers University - Camden, B
Rutgers University - Newark, B
Union County College, A

New Mexico

National American University (Albuquerque), A
New Mexico Highlands University, B
New Mexico Junior College, A
New Mexico Military Institute, A
New Mexico State University - Carlsbad, A
San Juan College, A
Santa Fe Community College, A
Southwestern Indian Polytechnic Institute, A
University of New Mexico - Los Alamos Branch, A

New York

Adirondack Community College, A
Alfred University, B
Binghamton University, State University of New York, B
Borough of Manhattan Community College of the City University of New York, A
Buffalo State College, State University of New York, B
Clarkson University, B
College of Staten Island of the City University of New York, AB
Cooper Union for the Advancement of Science and Art, B
Cornell University, B
Dutchess Community College, A
Erie Community College, North Campus, A
Genesee Community College, A
Jamestown Community College, A
Jefferson Community College, A
Manhattan College, B
Mohawk Valley Community College, A
Morrisville State College, A
Nassau Community College, A
New York University, B

Orange County Community College, A
Queensborough Community College of the City University of New York, A
Rensselaer Polytechnic Institute, B
Rochester Institute of Technology, B
Sarah Lawrence College, B
State University of New York College of Environmental Science and Forestry, B
State University of New York College of Technology at Alfred, A
State University of New York College of Technology at Canton, A
State University of New York at Oswego, B
State University of New York Polytechnic Institute, B
Stony Brook University, State University of New York, B
Suffolk County Community College, A
Tompkins Cortland Community College, A
Ulster County Community College, A
University at Buffalo, the State University of New York, B
University of Rochester, B
Vaughn College of Aeronautics and Technology, B
Wells College, B

North Carolina

Campbell University, A
East Carolina University, B
Elon University, B
North Carolina Agricultural and Technical State University, B
North Carolina State University, B
Pfeiffer University, B
Saint Augustine's University, B
University of North Carolina at Asheville, B
Wake Forest University, B

North Dakota

University of Mary, B

Ohio

Case Western Reserve University, B
Clark State Community College, A
Lorain County Community College, A
Miami University, B
Miami University Middletown, A
Northwest State Community College, A
Ohio Northern University, B
The Ohio State University, B
Ohio Wesleyan University, B
Sinclair Community College, A
Terra State Community College, A
The University of Akron, B
University of Cincinnati, B
Washington State Community College, A
Wright State University, B
Wright State University - Lake Campus, B
Youngstown State University, B

Oklahoma

Cameron University, A
Carl Albert State College, A
East Central University, B
Eastern Oklahoma State College, A
Northeastern Oklahoma Agricultural and Mechanical College, A
Northern Oklahoma College, A
Oklahoma Christian University, B
Oral Roberts University, B
Seminole State College, A
University of Oklahoma, B

Oregon

Central Oregon Community College, A
George Fox University, B
Linn-Benton Community College, A
Oregon State University, B
Umpqua Community College, A
University of Portland, B

Pennsylvania

Butler County Community College, A
Carnegie Mellon University, B
Community College of Philadelphia, A
Delaware County Community College, A

Drexel University, B
Elizabethtown College, B
Geneva College, AB
Gettysburg College, B
Harrisburg Area Community College, A
Lafayette College, B
Lehigh Carbon Community College, A
Lehigh University, B
Messiah College, B
Northampton Community College, A
Penn State Altoona, B
Penn State Berks, B
Penn State University Park, B
Reading Area Community College, A
Robert Morris University, B
Saint Francis University, B
Saint Vincent College, B
Swarthmore College, B
Temple University, B
University of Pennsylvania, B
Valley Forge Military College, A
Waynesburg University, B
Widener University, B
Wilkes University, B
York College of Pennsylvania, B

Rhode Island

Brown University, B
Community College of Rhode Island, A
Roger Williams University, B

South Carolina

Anderson University, B
Bob Jones University, B
Piedmont Technical College, A

Tennessee

Chattanooga State Community College, A
Maryville College, B
Roane State Community College, A
Southern Adventist University, A
Tennessee State University, B
The University of Tennessee at Chattanooga, B
The University of Tennessee at Martin, B

Texas

Abilene Christian University, B
Amarillo College, A
Angelina College, A
Austin Community College District, A
Baylor University, B
Central Texas College, A
Clarendon College, A
Collin County Community College District, A
El Paso Community College, A
Grayson College, A
Hill College, A
LeTourneau University, B
Navarro College, A
Palo Alto College, A
Paris Junior College, A
Richland College, A
San Jacinto College District, A
Schreiner University, B
South Plains College, A
Southwest Texas Junior College, A
Texarkana College, A
Texas Christian University, B
Tyler Junior College, A
University of North Texas, B
Western Texas College, A

Utah

Dixie State University, A
Salt Lake Community College, A
University of Utah, B
Weber State University, AB

Virginia

Central Virginia Community College, A
Danville Community College, A
J. Sargeant Reynolds Community College, A
James Madison University, B
John Tyler Community College, A
New River Community College, A

Norfolk State University, B
Northern Virginia Community College, A
Old Dominion University, B
Thomas Nelson Community College, A
Tidewater Community College, A
University of Virginia, B
The University of Virginia's College at Wise, B
Virginia Western Community College, A

Washington

Everett Community College, A
Gonzaga University, B
Highline College, A
Pacific Lutheran University, B
Seattle Pacific University, B
Seattle University, B
South Seattle College, A
University of Washington, B
Walla Walla University, B

West Virginia

Marshall University, B

Wisconsin

Beloit College, B
Carthage College, B
Milwaukee Area Technical College, A
Milwaukee School of Engineering, B
Northland College, B
University of Wisconsin - Madison, B
University of Wisconsin - Platteville, B

Wyoming

Casper College, A
Central Wyoming College, A
Laramie County Community College, A
Northwest College, A
Sheridan College, A

U.S. Territories: Puerto Rico

Inter American University of Puerto Rico, San
  Germán Campus, B
Polytechnic University of Puerto Rico, B

Canada

Alberta

Mount Royal University, B
University of Alberta, B

British Columbia

British Columbia Institute of Technology, A
Thompson Rivers University, A

Maritime Provinces: New Brunswick

Université de Moncton, B
University of New Brunswick Fredericton, B
University of New Brunswick Saint John, B

Maritime Provinces: Nova Scotia

Cape Breton University, B
Dalhousie University, B
Saint Mary's University, B

Newfoundland and Labrador

Memorial University of Newfoundland, B

Ontario

Carleton University, B
Lakehead University, B
Queen's University at Kingston, B
University of Toronto, B
University of Waterloo, B
The University of Western Ontario, B
University of Windsor, B
York University, B

Quebec

Université Laval, B
Université du Québec en Abitibi-Témiscamingue, B
Université du Québec à Chicoutimi, B
Université du Québec, École de technologie
  supérieure, B

Université du Québec à Rimouski, B

Saskatchewan

University of Regina, B

ENGINEERING AND APPLIED SCIENCES

United States

Alabama

Alabama Agricultural and Mechanical University, MD
Auburn University, MDO
Tuskegee University, MD
The University of Alabama, MD
The University of Alabama at Birmingham, MD
The University of Alabama in Huntsville, MD
University of South Alabama, MD

Alaska

University of Alaska Anchorage, MO
University of Alaska Fairbanks, D

Arizona

Arizona State University at the Tempe campus,
  MDO
Northern Arizona University, MDO
The University of Arizona, MDO

Arkansas

Arkansas State University, M
Arkansas Tech University, M
University of Arkansas, MD

California

California Institute of Technology, MDO
California National University for Advanced Studies,
  M
California Polytechnic State University, San Luis
  Obispo, M
California State University, Chico, M
California State University, East Bay, M
California State University, Fresno, M
California State University, Fullerton, M
California State University, Los Angeles, M
California State University, Northridge, M
California State University, Sacramento, M
Northwestern Polytechnic University, M
San Diego State University, MD
San Francisco State University, M
San Jose State University, M
Santa Clara University, MDO
Stanford University, MDO
University of California, Berkeley, MDO
University of California, Davis, MDO
University of California, Irvine, MD
University of California, Los Angeles, MD
University of California, Merced, D
University of California, Santa Barbara, MD
University of California, Santa Cruz, MD
University of the Pacific, M
University of Southern California, MDO

Colorado

Colorado School of Mines, MDO
Colorado State University, MD
Colorado State University - Pueblo, M
University of Colorado Boulder, MD
University of Colorado Colorado Springs, MD
University of Colorado Denver, MD
University of Denver, MD

Connecticut

Central Connecticut State University, MO
Fairfield University, MO
University of Bridgeport, MD
University of Connecticut, MD
University of Hartford, M
University of New Haven, MO
Yale University, MD

Delaware

University of Delaware, MD

District of Columbia

The Catholic University of America, MDO
The George Washington University, MDO
Howard University, MD
University of the District of Columbia, M

Florida

Florida Agricultural and Mechanical University, MD
Florida Atlantic University, MD
Florida Institute of Technology, MD
Florida International University, MD
Florida State University, MD
University of Central Florida, MDO
University of Florida, MDO
University of Miami, MD
University of South Florida, MD

Georgia

Georgia Institute of Technology, MD
Georgia Southern University, MO
Kennesaw State University, MO
Mercer University, M

Hawaii

University of Hawaii at Manoa, MD

Idaho

Boise State University, MDO
Idaho State University, MDO
University of Idaho, MD

Illinois

Bradley University, M
Eastern Illinois University, MO
Illinois Institute of Technology, MD
Northern Illinois University, M
Northwestern University, MDO
Southern Illinois University Carbondale, MD
Southern Illinois University Edwardsville, M
University of Illinois at Chicago, MD
University of Illinois at Urbana - Champaign, MD

Indiana

Indiana State University, M
Indiana University - Purdue University Fort Wayne, MO
Purdue University, MDO
Purdue University Northwest (Hammond), M
Rose-Hulman Institute of Technology, M
Trine University, M
University of Notre Dame, MD
University of Southern Indiana, M

Iowa

The University of Iowa, MD

Kansas

Kansas State University, MDO
Pittsburg State University, M
The University of Kansas, MD
Wichita State University, MD

Kentucky

University of Kentucky, MD
University of Louisville, MDO

Louisiana

Louisiana State University and Agricultural & Mechanical College, MD
Louisiana Tech University, MD
McNeese State University, MO
Southern University and Agricultural and Mechanical College, M
University of New Orleans, MD

Maine

University of Maine, MD

Maryland

Johns Hopkins University, MDO
Morgan State University, MD
University of Maryland, Baltimore County, MDO
University of Maryland, College Park, M

Massachusetts

Boston University, MD
Harvard University, MD
Massachusetts Institute of Technology, MDO
Merrimack College, M
Northeastern University, MDO
Tufts University, MD
University of Massachusetts Amherst, MD
University of Massachusetts Dartmouth, D
University of Massachusetts Lowell, MDO
Western New England University, MD
Worcester Polytechnic Institute, MDO

Michigan

Central Michigan University, M
Eastern Michigan University, M
Grand Valley State University, M
Lawrence Technological University, MD
Michigan State University, MD
Michigan Technological University, MDO
Oakland University, MD
Saginaw Valley State University, M
University of Detroit Mercy, MD
University of Michigan, MDO
University of Michigan - Dearborn, MD
Wayne State University, MDO
Western Michigan University, MD

Minnesota

St. Cloud State University, M
University of Minnesota, Twin Cities Campus, MDO
University of St. Thomas, MO

Mississippi

Mississippi State University, MD
University of Mississippi, MD

Missouri

Missouri University of Science and Technology, MD
Missouri Western State University, M
University of Missouri, MDO
University of Missouri - Kansas City, MDO
Washington University in St. Louis, MD

Montana

Montana State University, D
Montana Tech of The University of Montana, M

Nebraska

University of Nebraska - Lincoln, MD

Nevada

University of Nevada, Las Vegas, MDO
University of Nevada, Reno, MD

New Hampshire

Dartmouth College, MD

New Jersey

Fairleigh Dickinson University, Metropolitan Campus, M
New Jersey Institute of Technology, MD
Princeton University, MD
Rowan University, M
Stevens Institute of Technology, MDO

New Mexico

New Mexico State University, MDO
University of New Mexico, MDO

New York

Alfred University, MD
Binghamton University, State University of New York, MD
City College of the City University of New York, MD
Clarkson University, MD
Columbia University, MD

Cooper Union for the Advancement of Science and Art, M
Cornell University, MD
Hofstra University, M
Manhattan College, M
New York Institute of Technology, MO
New York University, MDO
Rensselaer Polytechnic Institute, MD
Rochester Institute of Technology, MDO
Stony Brook University, State University of New York, MDO
Syracuse University, MDO
University at Buffalo, the State University of New York, MDO
University of Rochester, MD

North Carolina

Duke University, M
North Carolina Agricultural and Technical State University, MD
North Carolina State University, MD
The University of North Carolina at Charlotte, MDO

North Dakota

North Dakota State University, MD
University of North Dakota, D

Ohio

Case Western Reserve University, MD
Cleveland State University, MD
Kent State University, M
Miami University, M
The Ohio State University, MD
Ohio University, MD
The University of Akron, MD
University of Cincinnati, MD
The University of Toledo, M
Wright State University, MD
Youngstown State University, M

Oklahoma

Oklahoma Christian University, M
Oklahoma State University, MD
University of Central Oklahoma, M
University of Oklahoma, MD
The University of Tulsa, MD

Oregon

Oregon State University, MD
Portland State University, MDO
University of Portland, M

Pennsylvania

Bucknell University, M
Drexel University, MDO
Lehigh University, MD
Penn State Erie, The Behrend College, M
Penn State Harrisburg, MO
Penn State University Park, MD
Robert Morris University, M
Temple University, D
University of Pennsylvania, MDO
University of Pittsburgh, MD
Villanova University, MDO
Widener University, M
Wilkes University, M

Rhode Island

Brown University, MD
University of Rhode Island, MDO

South Carolina

Clemson University, MDO
University of South Carolina, MD

South Dakota

South Dakota School of Mines and Technology, MD
South Dakota State University, MD

Tennessee

Austin Peay State University, M
Christian Brothers University, M
Tennessee State University, MD
Tennessee Technological University, MD

University of Memphis, MD
The University of Tennessee, MD
Vanderbilt University, MD

Texas

Lamar University, MD
LeTourneau University, M
Prairie View A&M University, MD
Rice University, MD
St. Mary's University, M
Southern Methodist University, MD
Texas A&M University - Kingsville, MD
Texas State University, M
Texas Tech University, MD
University of Houston, MD
University of North Texas, M
The University of Texas at Arlington, MD
The University of Texas at Austin, MD
The University of Texas at Dallas, MD
The University of Texas at El Paso, MDO
The University of Texas at San Antonio, MD
West Texas A&M University, M

Utah

Brigham Young University, MD
University of Utah, MD
Utah State University, MDO

Vermont

University of Vermont, MD

Virginia

George Mason University, MDO
James Madison University, M
Liberty University, M
Old Dominion University, MD
University of Virginia, MD
Virginia Commonwealth University, MD
Virginia Polytechnic Institute and State University, MD

Washington

Central Washington University, M
Seattle University, M
University of Washington, MD
Washington State University, MDO

West Virginia

Marshall University, M
West Virginia University, MDO

Wisconsin

Marquette University, MDO
Milwaukee School of Engineering, M
University of Wisconsin - Madison, MD
University of Wisconsin - Milwaukee, MDO
University of Wisconsin - Platteville, M

Wyoming

University of Wyoming, MD

U.S. Territories: Puerto Rico

University of Puerto Rico, Mayagüez Campus, MD

Canada

Alberta

University of Calgary, MD

British Columbia

Simon Fraser University, MD
The University of British Columbia, MD
University of Victoria, MD

Manitoba

University of Manitoba, MD

Maritime Provinces: New Brunswick

Université de Moncton, M
University of New Brunswick Fredericton, MDO

Maritime Provinces: Nova Scotia

Dalhousie University, MD

Newfoundland and Labrador

Memorial University of Newfoundland, MD

Ontario

Carleton University, MD
Lakehead University, M
Laurentian University, MD
McMaster University, MD
Queen's University at Kingston, MD
Royal Military College of Canada, MD
University of Guelph, MD
University of Ottawa, MDO
University of Toronto, MD
University of Waterloo, MD
The University of Western Ontario, MD
University of Windsor, MD

Quebec

Concordia University, MDO
École Polytechnique de Montréal, MDO
McGill University, MDO
Université Laval, MDO
Université du Québec en Abitibi-Témiscamingue, MO
Université du Québec à Chicoutimi, MD
Université du Québec, École de technologie supérieure, MDO
Université du Québec à Rimouski, M
Université de Sherbrooke, MDO

Saskatchewan

University of Regina, MD
University of Saskatchewan, MDO

ENGINEERING DESIGN

United States

Alabama

The University of Alabama at Birmingham, M

California

San Diego State University, M
Santa Clara University, O
Stanford University, M

Illinois

Northwestern University, M

Massachusetts

Worcester Polytechnic Institute, M

New Jersey

Stevens Institute of Technology, M

Pennsylvania

Penn State University Park, M

ENGINEERING/INDUSTRIAL MANAGEMENT

United States

Arizona

Arizona State University at the Tempe campus, B
The University of Arizona, B

Arkansas

John Brown University, B

California

California State University, Long Beach, B
Claremont McKenna College, B
National University, B
Stanford University, B
University of the Pacific, B

Colorado

Fort Lewis College, B

Delaware

Delaware Technical & Community College, Stanton/Wilmington Campus, A

Georgia

Kennesaw State University, B

Illinois

Illinois Institute of Technology, B
University of Illinois at Chicago, B

Indiana

Purdue University Northwest (Hammond), B

Kansas

Grantham University, AB
Kansas State University, B
Pittsburg State University, B
Washburn University, B

Kentucky

Eastern Kentucky University, B
Morehead State University, B

Massachusetts

Worcester Polytechnic Institute, B

Michigan

Eastern Michigan University, B
Lake Superior State University, B
Lawrence Technological University, B
Michigan Technological University, B
Saginaw Valley State University, B
Western Michigan University, B

Missouri

Missouri Southern State University, B
Missouri State University, B
Missouri University of Science and Technology, B

Nevada

College of Southern Nevada, A

New Jersey

Stevens Institute of Technology, B

New York

Clarkson University, B
Columbia University, B
New York Institute of Technology, B
State University of New York College of Technology at Canton, B
United States Merchant Marine Academy, B
United States Military Academy, B

North Carolina

Gaston College, A
Mitchell Community College, A

Ohio

Bowling Green State University, B
Miami University, B
Miami University Hamilton, B
Northwest State Community College, A

Pennsylvania

Grove City College, B
The University of Scranton, B
Widener University, B
Wilkes University, B

Tennessee

Christian Brothers University, B
Middle Tennessee State University, B
The University of Tennessee at Chattanooga, B

Texas

St. Mary's University, B
Texas State University, B
University of the Incarnate Word, B

Utah

LDS Business College, A

Vermont

University of Vermont, B

Virginia

University of Management and Technology, AB

U.S. Territories: Puerto Rico

Universidad del Turabo, B

Canada

Ontario

McMaster University, B

Quebec

Université du Québec à Trois-Rivières, B

ENGINEERING MANAGEMENT

United States

Alabama

The University of Alabama at Birmingham, MD

Alaska

University of Alaska Anchorage, M
University of Alaska Fairbanks, M

Arkansas

Arkansas State University, M

California

California Maritime Academy, M
California National University for Advanced Studies, M
California State Polytechnic University, Pomona, M
California State University, East Bay, M
California State University, Long Beach, M
California State University, Northridge, M
National University, M
Santa Clara University, M
Stanford University, MD
University of California, Berkeley, MD
University of California, Irvine, M
University of Southern California, M

Colorado

Colorado School of Mines, M
University of Colorado Boulder, M
University of Colorado Colorado Springs, MD
University of Denver, M

Connecticut

University of New Haven, MO

District of Columbia

The Catholic University of America, MO
The George Washington University, MDO

Florida

Embry-Riddle Aeronautical University - Worldwide, M
Florida Institute of Technology, M
Polytechnic University of Puerto Rico, Orlando Campus, M
University of South Florida, MD

Georgia

Georgia Southern University, M
Mercer University, M

Idaho

University of Idaho, M

Illinois

Northwestern University, MD
Southern Illinois University Carbondale, M

Indiana

Rose-Hulman Institute of Technology, M
Trine University, M
Valparaiso University, O

Kansas

Kansas State University, M
The University of Kansas, M
Wichita State University, M

Kentucky

University of Louisville, M

Louisiana

McNeese State University, M
University of Louisiana at Lafayette, M
University of New Orleans, M

Maryland

Johns Hopkins University, M
University of Maryland, Baltimore County, MO

Massachusetts

Massachusetts Institute of Technology, M
Merrimack College, M
Northeastern University, MO
Tufts University, M
Western New England University, MD

Michigan

Central Michigan University, MO
Eastern Michigan University, M
Kettering University, M
Lawrence Technological University, M
Oakland University, M
University of Detroit Mercy, M
University of Michigan - Dearborn, M
Wayne State University, MO
Western Michigan University, MD

Minnesota

St. Cloud State University, M
University of Minnesota, Duluth, M
University of St. Thomas, M

Missouri

Missouri University of Science and Technology, MD
University of Missouri - Kansas City, O
Webster University, M

Nebraska

University of Nebraska - Lincoln, M

New Hampshire

Dartmouth College, M

New Jersey

New Jersey Institute of Technology, M
Stevens Institute of Technology, MD

New Mexico

New Mexico Institute of Mining and Technology, M

New York

Clarkson University, M
Cornell University, MD
Rensselaer Polytechnic Institute, MD
Rochester Institute of Technology, M
Syracuse University, M

North Carolina

Duke University, M
The University of North Carolina at Charlotte, MDO

Ohio

Case Western Reserve University, M
University of Dayton, M

Oregon

Portland State University, MD

Pennsylvania

Drexel University, MO
Gannon University, M
Lehigh University, M
Penn State Harrisburg, M
Point Park University, M
Robert Morris University, M
Temple University, MO
Widener University, M
Wilkes University, M

South Carolina

The Citadel, The Military College of South Carolina, M

South Dakota

South Dakota School of Mines and Technology, M

Tennessee

Lipscomb University, M
Middle Tennessee State University, M
The University of Tennessee, MD
The University of Tennessee at Chattanooga, MO

Texas

Dallas Baptist University, M
Lamar University, M
LeTourneau University, M
St. Mary's University, M
Southern Methodist University, MD
Tarleton State University, M
Texas Tech University, M
The University of Texas at Arlington, M
The University of Texas Rio Grande Valley, M

Virginia

Old Dominion University, MD
University of Management and Technology, M
Virginia Polytechnic Institute and State University, M

Washington

Saint Martin's University, M
Washington State University, MO

West Virginia

Marshall University, M

Wisconsin

Marquette University, M
Milwaukee School of Engineering, M
University of Wisconsin - Milwaukee, M

U.S. Territories: Puerto Rico

Polytechnic University of Puerto Rico, M

Canada

Alberta

University of Alberta, M

Maritime Provinces: New Brunswick

University of New Brunswick Fredericton, M

Ontario

University of Ottawa, MO
University of Waterloo, MD

Quebec

Université de Sherbrooke, MO

Saskatchewan

University of Regina, M

ENGINEERING MECHANICS

United States

Colorado

United States Air Force Academy, B

Illinois

University of Illinois at Urbana - Champaign, B

Iowa

Dordt College, B

Maryland

Johns Hopkins University, B

Massachusetts

Worcester Polytechnic Institute, B

Montana

Carroll College, B

New York

Columbia University, B

Pennsylvania

Lehigh University, B

Virginia

Virginia Polytechnic Institute and State University, B

Wisconsin

University of Wisconsin - Madison, B

Canada

Ontario

University of Windsor, B

Quebec

Université du Québec en Abitibi-Témiscamingue, B
Université du Québec à Trois-Rivières, B

ENGINEERING PHYSICS

United States

Alabama

Samford University, B

Arkansas

Arkansas Tech University, B
Henderson State University, B

California

Biola University, B
California Institute of Technology, B
Loyola Marymount University, B
Point Loma Nazarene University, B
Santa Clara University, B
Stanford University, M
University of California, Berkeley, B
University of California, San Diego, BMD
University of the Pacific, B
Westmont College, B
Whittier College, B

Colorado

Adams State University, B
Colorado School of Mines, B
Colorado State University, B
Fort Lewis College, B
University of Colorado Boulder, B

Connecticut

University of Connecticut, B
Yale University, BMD

Delaware

Delaware State University, B

Florida

Embry-Riddle Aeronautical University - Daytona,
  BMD
Jacksonville University, B

Georgia

Morehouse College, B

Idaho

Northwest Nazarene University, B

Illinois

Augustana College, B
Bradley University, B
Illinois Institute of Technology, B
University of Illinois at Chicago, B
University of Illinois at Urbana - Champaign, B

Indiana

Grace College, B
Rose-Hulman Institute of Technology, B
Taylor University, B

Iowa

Loras College, B
Morningside College, B
St. Ambrose University, B
University of Northern Iowa, B

Kansas

Kansas Wesleyan University, B
The University of Kansas, B

Kentucky

Murray State University, B

Louisiana

Louisiana Tech University, D

Maine

University of Maine, BM

Maryland

Morgan State University, B

Massachusetts

Eastern Nazarene College, B
Tufts University, B
University of Massachusetts Boston, B
Worcester Polytechnic Institute, B

Michigan

Eastern Michigan University, B
Kettering University, B
Lansing Community College, A
Michigan Technological University, D
Oakland University, B
University of Michigan, B

Minnesota

Bemidji State University, B
Saint Mary's University of Minnesota, B

Missouri

Saint Louis University, B
Southeast Missouri State University, B

Nebraska

Doane University, B

Nevada

University of Nevada, Reno, B

New Hampshire

Dartmouth College, B

New Jersey

Stevens Institute of Technology, BMDO

New Mexico

New Mexico State University, B

New York

Columbia University, B
Cornell University, BMD
Fordham University, B
New York University, B

Rensselaer Polytechnic Institute, BMD
University at Buffalo, the State University of New
  York, B

North Carolina

Appalachian State University, M
Elon University, B
North Carolina Agricultural and Technical State Uni-
  versity, B

Ohio

Case Western Reserve University, B
John Carroll University, B
Miami University, B
Miami University Hamilton, B
The Ohio State University, B
Wright State University, B
Xavier University, B

Oklahoma

Oral Roberts University, B
Southwestern Oklahoma State University, B
University of Central Oklahoma, BM
University of Oklahoma, BMD
The University of Tulsa, BM

Oregon

Linfield College, B
Oregon State University, B

Pennsylvania

Juniata College, B
Lehigh University, B
Thiel College, B
University of Pittsburgh, B
Westminster College, B

Rhode Island

Brown University, B
Providence College, B

South Dakota

Augustana University, B

Tennessee

Belmont University, B
Christian Brothers University, B
Trevecca Nazarene University, B

Texas

LeTourneau University, B
Stephen F. Austin State University, B
Tarleton State University, B
University of North Texas, B
The University of Texas Rio Grande Valley, B

Virginia

George Mason University, M
Randolph College, B
Randolph-Macon College, B
University of Virginia, MD
Washington and Lee University, B

Washington

Central Washington University, B
Whitworth University, B

Wisconsin

Carroll University, B
University of Wisconsin - Madison, BMD
University of Wisconsin - Platteville, B

Canada

British Columbia

The University of British Columbia, B

Ontario

McMaster University, BMD
Queen's University at Kingston, B
The University of Western Ontario, B

Quebec

École Polytechnique de Montréal, MDO
Université Laval, B

Saskatchewan

University of Saskatchewan, BMD

ENGINEERING-RELATED TECHNOLOGIES

United States

Alaska

University of Alaska Southeast, A

Connecticut

Capital Community College, A
Gateway Community College, A

Maryland

Chesapeake College, A

New York

Rochester Institute of Technology, B
United States Merchant Marine Academy, B

Oklahoma

Tulsa Community College, A

Pennsylvania

Thaddeus Stevens College of Technology, A

ENGINEERING SCIENCE

United States

California

California Polytechnic State University, San Luis
   Obispo, B
National University, A
Sonoma State University, B
University of California, Berkeley, B
University of California, San Diego, B

Colorado

Colorado State University, B
United States Air Force Academy, B

Connecticut

Asnuntuck Community College, A
Capital Community College, A
Manchester Community College, A
Middlesex Community College, A
Naugatuck Valley Community College, A
Norwalk Community College, A
Three Rivers Community College, A
Yale University, B

Florida

Broward College, A
South Florida State College, A
University of Miami, B

Georgia

Emory University, B
Morehouse College, B

Illinois

Benedictine University, B
City Colleges of Chicago, Olive-Harvey College, A
Northwestern University, B
Parkland College, A

Iowa

Wartburg College, B

Louisiana

Tulane University, B

Massachusetts

Bristol Community College, A
Greenfield Community College, A
North Shore Community College, A
Northern Essex Community College, A
Smith College, B
Tufts University, B

Michigan

University of Michigan, B
University of Michigan - Flint, B

Minnesota

Bethel University, B
Concordia University, St. Paul, B
Itasca Community College, A

Mississippi

Jones County Junior College, A

Montana

Carroll College, B

New Jersey

Bergen Community College, A
Camden County College, A
The College of New Jersey, B
County College of Morris, A
Hudson County Community College, A
Mercer County Community College, A
Middlesex County College, A
New Jersey Institute of Technology, B
Raritan Valley Community College, A
Rutgers University - New Brunswick, B

New Mexico

University of New Mexico, B

New York

Broome Community College, A
Corning Community College, A
Finger Lakes Community College, A
Fulton-Montgomery Community College, A
Genesee Community College, A
Hofstra University, B
Hudson Valley Community College, A
Jefferson Community College, A
Kingsborough Community College of the City University of New York, A
Monroe Community College, A
Onondaga Community College, A
Queensborough Community College of the City University of New York, A
Rensselaer Polytechnic Institute, B
Rochester Institute of Technology, A
St. Thomas Aquinas College, B
State University of New York College at Oneonta, B
Suffolk County Community College, A
University of Rochester, B
Westchester Community College, A

Ohio

Muskingum University, B
Ohio Wesleyan University, B
Wright State University, B

Oregon

University of Portland, B

Pennsylvania

Montgomery County Community College, A
Penn State Abington, B
Penn State Altoona, B
Penn State Beaver, B
Penn State Berks, B
Penn State Brandywine, B
Penn State DuBois, B
Penn State Erie, The Behrend College, B
Penn State Fayette, The Eberly Campus, B
Penn State Greater Allegheny, B
Penn State Hazleton, B
Penn State Lehigh Valley, B
Penn State Mont Alto, B
Penn State New Kensington, B

Penn State Schuylkill, B
Penn State Shenango, B
Penn State University Park, B
Penn State Wilkes-Barre, B
Penn State Worthington Scranton, B
Penn State York, B
University of Pittsburgh, B
University of Pittsburgh at Bradford, A

South Carolina

University of South Carolina, B

Tennessee

Belmont University, B
Vanderbilt University, B

Texas

Houston Community College, A
St. Mary's University, B
Trinity University, B

Utah

Southern Utah University, B

Virginia

Sweet Briar College, B

West Virginia

Wheeling Jesuit University, B

Canada

British Columbia

Simon Fraser University, B

Manitoba

University of Manitoba, B

Ontario

University of Toronto, B
The University of Western Ontario, B

ENGINEERING TECHNOLOGIES/TECHNICIANS

United States

Alabama

The University of West Alabama, B

Arizona

Embry-Riddle Aeronautical University - Prescott, B

Arkansas

Arkansas State University, AB
Southern Arkansas University Tech, A

California

Butte College, A
California Maritime Academy, B
Orange Coast College, A

Connecticut

University of Hartford, B

Indiana

Ball State University, B

Kansas

Pittsburg State University, B

Kentucky

Sullivan College of Technology and Design, A

Maryland

Capitol Technology University, B
College of Southern Maryland, A
Community College of Baltimore County, A
Hagerstown Community College, A
Wor-Wic Community College, A

Massachusetts

Bristol Community College, A
Massachusetts Bay Community College, A
Middlesex Community College, A
Quinsigamond Community College, A

Michigan

Mott Community College, A

Mississippi

Holmes Community College, A

Missouri

Missouri Southern State University, A

Nevada

Truckee Meadows Community College, A

New Hampshire

Keene State College, B

New Jersey

Atlantic Cape Community College, A
Camden County College, A
County College of Morris, A
Essex County College, A
Hudson County Community College, A
Middlesex County College, A
Ocean County College, A
Raritan Valley Community College, A
Rowan College at Burlington County, A
Salem Community College, A
Thomas Edison State University, AB

New Mexico

Mesalands Community College, A

New York

Clinton Community College, A
Excelsior College, AB
Morrisville State College, A
New York Institute of Technology, B
State University of New York College of Agriculture
    and Technology at Cobleskill, A
State University of New York College of Technology
    at Canton, A
State University of New York Maritime College, A

North Carolina

East Carolina University, B
Elizabeth City State University, B
Haywood Community College, A
North Carolina Agricultural and Technical State Uni-
    versity, B
The University of North Carolina at Charlotte, B
Western Piedmont Community College, A

Ohio

Bowling Green State University, B
Cincinnati State Technical and Community College,
    A
Clark State Community College, A
Columbus State Community College, A
Northwest State Community College, A
Shawnee State University, B

Oklahoma

Cameron University, B
Carl Albert State College, A
East Central University, B
Northeastern State University, B
Oklahoma City Community College, A
Rogers State University, AB

Pennsylvania

Community College of Allegheny County, A
Harrisburg Area Community College, A
Montgomery County Community College, A
Pennsylvania College of Technology, B
Pennsylvania Highlands Community College, A
South Hills School of Business & Technology
    (Altoona), A

Virginia

Northern Virginia Community College, A
Old Dominion University, B

Washington

Eastern Washington University, B

Wisconsin

Milwaukee Area Technical College, A
Silver Lake College of the Holy Family, B

U.S. Territories: Puerto Rico

University of Puerto Rico in Bayamón, A

Canada

British Columbia

The University of British Columbia, B

ENGINEERING TECHNOLOGY

United States

Alabama

Jefferson State Community College, A
Snead State Community College, A
Tuskegee University, B
University of North Alabama, B
The University of West Alabama, B

Alaska

University of Alaska Anchorage, A

Arizona

Glendale Community College, A
Mesa Community College, A
Penn Foster College, A

Arkansas

East Arkansas Community College, A

California

Allan Hancock College, A
American River College, A
Antelope Valley College, A
Cabrillo College, A
California State Polytechnic University, Pomona, B
California State University, Long Beach, B
Cerro Coso Community College, A
Citrus College, A
City College of San Francisco, A
College of Marin, A
College of San Mateo, A
De Anza College, A
Golden West College, A
Laney College, A
Lassen Community College District, A
Los Angeles Harbor College, A
Modesto Junior College, A
Moorpark College, A
Mt. San Antonio College, A
National University, A
Norco College, A
Pasadena City College, A
San Diego City College, A
San Joaquin Delta College, A
Santa Ana College, A
Santa Barbara City College, A

Colorado

Aims Community College, A
Arapahoe Community College, A
Pueblo Community College, A

Connecticut

Asnuntuck Community College, A
Capital Community College, A
Gateway Community College, A
Middlesex Community College, A
Naugatuck Valley Community College, A
Quinebaug Valley Community College, A

Three Rivers Community College, A
Tunxis Community College, A
University of Hartford, B

Delaware

University of Delaware, B

Florida

College of Central Florida, A
Eastern Florida State College, A
Florida Gateway College, A
Florida State College at Jacksonville, A
Gulf Coast State College, A
Hillsborough Community College, A
Indian River State College, A
Miami Dade College, A
Pensacola State College, A
Polk State College, A
St. Petersburg College, A
South Florida State College, A
University of West Florida, B

Georgia

Berry College, B
Darton State College, A
Georgia Piedmont Technical College, A
Kennesaw State University, B

Hawaii

Honolulu Community College, A

Idaho

Brigham Young University - Idaho, A

Illinois

Illinois State University, B
Morrison Institute of Technology, A
Northern Illinois University, B
Southern Illinois University Carbondale, B
Western Illinois University, B

Indiana

Indiana State University, B
Ivy Tech Community College - Bloomington, A
Ivy Tech Community College - Columbus, A
Ivy Tech Community College - East Central, A
Ivy Tech Community College - Kokomo, A
Ivy Tech Community College - Richmond, A
Ivy Tech Community College - Southern Indiana, A
Ivy Tech Community College - Southwest, A
Ivy Tech Community College - Wabash Valley, A
Vincennes University, A

Iowa

Dordt College, B
Iowa Lakes Community College, A
William Penn University, B

Kansas

Allen Community College, A
Barton County Community College, A
Cowley County Community College and Area Voca-
    tional - Technical School, A
Dodge City Community College, A
Kansas State University, AB
Wichita State University, B

Kentucky

Bluegrass Community and Technical College, A
Brescia University, A
Elizabethtown Community and Technical College, A
Gateway Community and Technical College, A
Jefferson Community and Technical College, A
Maysville Community and Technical College
    (Maysville), A
Maysville Community and Technical College
    (Morehead), A
Morehead State University, AB
Somerset Community College, A
Southcentral Kentucky Community and Technical
    College, A
Sullivan College of Technology and Design, A

Louisiana

Grambling State University, B
Southeastern Louisiana University, B

Maine

Maine Maritime Academy, B
Washington County Community College, A

Maryland

Harford Community College, A
University of Maryland Eastern Shore, B

Massachusetts

Benjamin Franklin Institute of Technology, A
Massachusetts Bay Community College, A
Wentworth Institute of Technology, AB

Michigan

Kalamazoo Valley Community College, A
Lake Superior State University, A
Lawrence Technological University, B
Michigan Technological University, A
Muskegon Community College, A
Southwestern Michigan College, A

Minnesota

Itasca Community College, A
Minnesota State Community and Technical College - Detroit Lakes, A
St. Cloud State University, B

Missouri

Lincoln University, A
Mineral Area College, A
Southeast Missouri State University, B
Three Rivers Community College, A

New Hampshire

Nashua Community College, A
NHTI, Concord's Community College, A

New Jersey

Bergen Community College, A
New Jersey Institute of Technology, B
Rowan College at Gloucester County, A

New Mexico

Eastern New Mexico University, B
New Mexico State University, B
San Juan College, A

New York

Buffalo State College, State University of New York, B
Corning Community College, A
New York Institute of Technology, B
University of Rochester, B
Westchester Community College, A

North Carolina

Central Piedmont Community College, A
Davidson County Community College, A
Lenoir-Rhyne University, B
Western Carolina University, B

North Dakota

Bismarck State College, A

Ohio

Belmont College, A
Cuyahoga Community College, A
Kent State University, B
Kent State University at Tuscarawas, B
Lorain County Community College, A
Marion Technical College, A
Miami University, AB
Miami University Hamilton, B
The University of Toledo, A
Wright State University, A
Wright State University - Lake Campus, A
Youngstown State University, AB

Oklahoma

Oklahoma State University Institute of Technology, A
Oklahoma State University, Oklahoma City, A
Southwestern Oklahoma State University, B

Pennsylvania

Bucks County Community College, A
California University of Pennsylvania, B
Community College of Beaver County, A
Community College of Philadelphia, A
Drexel University, B
Edinboro University of Pennsylvania, A
Luzerne County Community College, A
Pennsylvania Institute of Technology, A
Temple University, B
University of Pittsburgh at Johnstown, B

South Carolina

Midlands Technical College, A
Piedmont Technical College, A
Tri-County Technical College, A
Trident Technical College, A
University of South Carolina Upstate, B

Tennessee

Austin Peay State University, AB
Chattanooga State Community College, A
East Tennessee State University, B
Middle Tennessee State University, B
Northeast State Community College, A
Pellissippi State Community College, A
University of Memphis, B

Texas

Collin County Community College District, A
Midwestern State University, B
North Central Texas College, A
San Antonio College, A
Tarleton State University, B
Texas A&M University, B
Texas State University, B
The University of Texas Rio Grande Valley, B
The University of Texas at Tyler, B
West Texas A&M University, B

Utah

Salt Lake Community College, A
Southern Utah University, B

Virginia

Central Virginia Community College, A
Danville Community College, A
ECPI University (Newport News), A
ECPI University (Richmond), A
ECPI University (Virginia Beach), AB
Lord Fairfax Community College, A
Patrick Henry Community College, A
Rappahannock Community College, A
Virginia Highlands Community College, A

Washington

Columbia Basin College, A
Everett Community College, A
Highline College, A
Olympic College, A
Peninsula College, A
Shoreline Community College, A
South Seattle College, A
Walla Walla Community College, A
Walla Walla University, B

West Virginia

Fairmont State University, AB
Southern West Virginia Community and Technical College, A
West Virginia University Institute of Technology, B

Wisconsin

University of Wisconsin - Stout, B

Wyoming

Western Wyoming Community College, A

ENGLISH

United States

Alabama

Auburn University, MDO
Jacksonville State University, M
Spring Hill College, M
The University of Alabama, MD
The University of Alabama at Birmingham, M
The University of Alabama in Huntsville, MO
University of Montevallo, M
University of North Alabama, M
University of South Alabama, M

Alaska

University of Alaska Anchorage, M
University of Alaska Fairbanks, M

Arizona

Arizona State University at the Tempe campus, MDO
Northern Arizona University, MDO
The University of Arizona, MD

Arkansas

Arkansas State University, MO
Arkansas Tech University, M
University of Arkansas, MD
University of Central Arkansas, M

California

California Baptist University, M
California Polytechnic State University, San Luis Obispo, M
California State Polytechnic University, Pomona, M
California State University, Bakersfield, M
California State University, Chico, M
California State University, Dominguez Hills, MO
California State University, East Bay, M
California State University, Fresno, M
California State University, Fullerton, M
California State University, Long Beach, M
California State University, Los Angeles, M
California State University, Northridge, M
California State University, Sacramento, M
California State University, San Bernardino, M
California State University, San Marcos, M
California State University, Stanislaus, MO
Chapman University, M
Dominican University of California, M
Humboldt State University, M
La Sierra University, M
Loyola Marymount University, M
Mills College, M
Mount Saint Mary's University, M
National University, M
Notre Dame de Namur University, MO
San Diego State University, M
San Francisco State University, MO
San Jose State University, M
Sonoma State University, M
Stanford University, MD
University of California, Berkeley, D
University of California, Davis, MD
University of California, Irvine, MD
University of California, Los Angeles, MD
University of California, Riverside, MD
University of California, San Diego, MD
University of California, Santa Barbara, D
University of California, Santa Cruz, MD
University of Southern California, MD

Colorado

Colorado State University, M
University of Colorado Boulder, MD
University of Colorado Denver, M
University of Denver, MD
University of Northern Colorado, M

Connecticut

Central Connecticut State University, MO
Southern Connecticut State University, M
Trinity College, M

University of Connecticut, MD
Western Connecticut State University, M
Yale University, MD

Delaware

University of Delaware, MD

District of Columbia

The Catholic University of America, MDO
The George Washington University, MD
Georgetown University, M
Howard University, MD

Florida

Florida Atlantic University, M
Florida Gulf Coast University, M
Florida International University, M
Florida State University, MD
University of Central Florida, MDO
University of Florida, MD
University of Miami, MD
University of North Florida, M
University of South Florida, MDO
University of West Florida, M

Georgia

Clark Atlanta University, MD
Emory University, DO
Georgia College & State University, M
Georgia Southern University, M
Georgia State University, MD
University of Georgia, MD
University of West Georgia, M
Valdosta State University, M

Hawaii

University of Hawaii at Manoa, MD

Idaho

Boise State University, M
Idaho State University, MDO
University of Idaho, M

Illinois

Bradley University, M
Chicago State University, M
DePaul University, M
Eastern Illinois University, M
Governors State University, M
Illinois State University, MD
Loyola University Chicago, MD
Northeastern Illinois University, M
Northern Illinois University, MD
Northwestern University, MD
Roosevelt University, M
Southern Illinois University Carbondale, MD
Southern Illinois University Edwardsville, MO
University of Chicago, MD
University of Illinois at Chicago, MD
University of Illinois at Springfield, MO
University of Illinois at Urbana - Champaign, MD
Western Illinois University, MO

Indiana

Ball State University, MD
Butler University, M
Indiana State University, M
Indiana University Bloomington, MD
Indiana University - Purdue University Fort Wayne, MO
Indiana University - Purdue University Indianapolis, MO
Indiana University South Bend, M
Purdue University, MD
Purdue University Northwest (Hammond), M
University of Indianapolis, M
University of Notre Dame, MD
University of Southern Indiana, M
Valparaiso University, MO

Iowa

Iowa State University of Science and Technology, MD
The University of Iowa, MD
University of Northern Iowa, M

Kansas

Emporia State University, M
Fort Hays State University, M
Kansas State University, MO
Pittsburg State University, M
The University of Kansas, MD
Wichita State University, M

Kentucky

Asbury University, M
Eastern Kentucky University, M
Morehead State University, M
Murray State University, M
Northern Kentucky University, MO
University of Kentucky, MD
University of Louisville, MD
Western Kentucky University, M

Louisiana

Grambling State University, M
Louisiana State University and Agricultural & Mechanical College, MD
Louisiana Tech University, MO
McNeese State University, M
Northwestern State University of Louisiana, M
Southeastern Louisiana University, M
Tulane University, MD
University of Louisiana at Lafayette, MD
University of Louisiana at Monroe, M
University of New Orleans, M

Maine

University of Maine, M

Maryland

Bowie State University, M
Johns Hopkins University, D
Morgan State University, MD
Salisbury University, M
University of Maryland, Baltimore County, M
University of Maryland, College Park, MD

Massachusetts

Boston College, MD
Boston University, MD
Brandeis University, MD
Bridgewater State University, M
Clark University, M
Fitchburg State University, MO
Harvard University, DO
Northeastern University, MD
Salem State University, M
Tufts University, MD
University of Massachusetts Amherst, MD
University of Massachusetts Boston, M
Westfield State University, M

Michigan

Andrews University, M
Central Michigan University, M
Eastern Michigan University, MO
Grand Valley State University, M
Marygrove College, M
Michigan State University, MD
Northern Michigan University, MO
Oakland University, M
University of Michigan, MD
University of Michigan - Flint, M
Wayne State University, MD
Western Michigan University, MD

Minnesota

Bemidji State University, M
Minnesota State University Mankato, MO
St. Cloud State University, M
University of Minnesota, Duluth, M
University of Minnesota, Twin Cities Campus, MD
University of St. Thomas, M
Winona State University, M

Mississippi

Jackson State University, M
Mississippi College, M
Mississippi State University, M

University of Mississippi, MD
University of Southern Mississippi, MD

Missouri

Missouri State University, M
Northwest Missouri State University, M
Saint Louis University, MD
Southeast Missouri State University, M
Truman State University, M
University of Central Missouri, M
University of Missouri, MD
University of Missouri - Kansas City, MD
University of Missouri - St. Louis, M
Washington University in St. Louis, MD

Montana

Montana State University, M
University of Montana, M

Nebraska

Creighton University, M
University of Nebraska at Kearney, M
University of Nebraska - Lincoln, MD
University of Nebraska at Omaha, MO

Nevada

University of Nevada, Las Vegas, MD
University of Nevada, Reno, MD

New Hampshire

Rivier University, M
University of New Hampshire, MD

New Jersey

The College of New Jersey, M
Drew University, M
Fairleigh Dickinson University, Metropolitan Campus, M
Monmouth University, M
Montclair State University, M
Princeton University, D
Rutgers University - Camden, M
Rutgers University - New Brunswick, D
Rutgers University - Newark, M
Seton Hall University, M
William Paterson University of New Jersey, M

New Mexico

Eastern New Mexico University, M
New Mexico Highlands University, M
New Mexico State University, MD
University of New Mexico, MD

New York

Binghamton University, State University of New York, MD
Brooklyn College of the City University of New York, M
Buffalo State College, State University of New York, M
City College of the City University of New York, M
The College at Brockport, State University of New York, MO
The College of Saint Rose, M
College of Staten Island of the City University of New York, M
Columbia University, MD
Cornell University, MD
Fordham University, MD
Hofstra University, M
Hunter College of the City University of New York, M
Iona College, M
Lehman College of the City University of New York, M
Mercy College, M
New York University, MD
Queens College of the City University of New York, M
St. Bonaventure University, M
St. John's University, MD
State University of New York College at Cortland, M
State University of New York College at Potsdam, M
State University of New York at New Paltz, M
State University of New York at Oswego, M

Stony Brook University, State University of New
 York, MDO
Syracuse University, MD
University at Albany, State University of New York,
 MD
University at Buffalo, the State University of New
 York, MD
University of Rochester, MD

North Carolina

Appalachian State University, M
Duke University, D
East Carolina University, MDO
Fayetteville State University, M
Gardner-Webb University, M
North Carolina Agricultural and Technical State Uni-
 versity, M
North Carolina Central University, M
North Carolina State University, M
The University of North Carolina at Chapel Hill, MD
The University of North Carolina at Charlotte, MO
The University of North Carolina at Greensboro,
 MDO
The University of North Carolina Wilmington, M
Wake Forest University, M
Western Carolina University, M

North Dakota

North Dakota State University, MD
University of North Dakota, MD

Ohio

Bowling Green State University, MD
Case Western Reserve University, MD
Cleveland State University, M
John Carroll University, M
Kent State University, MDO
Miami University, MD
Ohio Dominican University, M
The Ohio State University, MD
Ohio University, MD
Tiffin University, M
The University of Akron, M
University of Cincinnati, MD
University of Dayton, M
The University of Toledo, MO
Wright State University, M
Xavier University, M
Youngstown State University, M

Oklahoma

Northeastern State University, M
Oklahoma State University, MD
University of Central Oklahoma, M
University of Oklahoma, MD
The University of Tulsa, MD

Oregon

Oregon State University, M
Portland State University, M
University of Oregon, MD

Pennsylvania

Arcadia University, M
Bucknell University, M
Carnegie Mellon University, MD
Duquesne University, MD
Gannon University, M
Indiana University of Pennsylvania, MD
Kutztown University of Pennsylvania, M
La Salle University, MO
Lehigh University, MD
Millersville University of Pennsylvania, M
Penn State University Park, MD
Summit University, M
Temple University, MD
University of Pennsylvania, MD
University of Pittsburgh, MD
Villanova University, M
West Chester University of Pennsylvania, MO

Rhode Island

Brown University, MD
Rhode Island College, MO
University of Rhode Island, MD

South Carolina

Bob Jones University, M
The Citadel, The Military College of South Carolina,
 M
Clemson University, M
College of Charleston, M
Converse College, M
University of South Carolina, MD
Winthrop University, M

South Dakota

South Dakota State University, M
The University of South Dakota, MD

Tennessee

Austin Peay State University, M
Belmont University, M
East Tennessee State University, MO
Lipscomb University, M
Middle Tennessee State University, MD
Sewanee: The University of the South, M
Tennessee Technological University, M
University of Memphis, MDO
The University of Tennessee, MD
The University of Tennessee at Chattanooga, M
Vanderbilt University, MD

Texas

Abilene Christian University, M
Angelo State University, M
Baylor University, MD
Hardin-Simmons University, M
Lamar University, M
Midwestern State University, MD
Our Lady of the Lake University of San Antonio, M
Prairie View A&M University, M
Rice University, MD
St. Mary's University, M
Sam Houston State University, M
Southern Methodist University, MD
Stephen F. Austin State University, M
Sul Ross State University, M
Tarleton State University, M
Texas A&M International University, MD
Texas A&M University, MD
Texas A&M University - Corpus Christi, M
Texas A&M University - Kingsville, M
Texas A&M University - San Antonio, M
Texas A&M University - Texarkana, M
Texas Christian University, MD
Texas Southern University, M
Texas State University, M
Texas Tech University, MD
Texas Woman's University, MD
University of Dallas, M
University of Houston - Clear Lake, M
University of Houston - Downtown, M
University of North Texas, M
The University of Texas at Arlington, MD
The University of Texas at Austin, MD
The University of Texas at Dallas, MD
The University of Texas at El Paso, MDO
The University of Texas of the Permian Basin, M
The University of Texas Rio Grande Valley, M
The University of Texas at San Antonio, MD
The University of Texas at Tyler, M
West Texas A&M University, M

Utah

Brigham Young University, M
University of Utah, MD
Utah State University, M
Weber State University, M

Vermont

Bennington College, M
Middlebury College, M
University of Vermont, M

Virginia

George Mason University, MDO
Hollins University, M
James Madison University, M
Liberty University, M
Lynchburg College, M

Mary Baldwin College, M
Marymount University, M
Old Dominion University, MD
Radford University, M
University of Virginia, MD
Virginia Commonwealth University, M
Virginia Polytechnic Institute and State University, M
Virginia State University, M

Washington

Central Washington University, M
Eastern Washington University, M
Heritage University, M
University of Washington, MD
Washington State University, MD
Western Washington University, M

West Virginia

Marshall University, MO
West Virginia University, MD

Wisconsin

Marquette University, MD
Mount Mary University, M
University of Wisconsin - Eau Claire, M
University of Wisconsin - Madison, MD
University of Wisconsin - Milwaukee, MDO
University of Wisconsin - Oshkosh, M
University of Wisconsin - Stevens Point, M

Wyoming

University of Wyoming, M

U.S. Territories: Guam

University of Guam, M

U.S. Territories: Puerto Rico

Inter American University of Puerto Rico, Metropoli-
 tan Campus, M
University of Puerto Rico, Mayagüez Campus, M
University of Puerto Rico, Río Piedras Campus, MD

Canada

Alberta

University of Alberta, MD
University of Calgary, MD
University of Lethbridge, M

British Columbia

Simon Fraser University, MD
Trinity Western University, M
The University of British Columbia, MD
University of Victoria, MD

Manitoba

University of Manitoba, MD

Maritime Provinces: New Brunswick

University of New Brunswick Fredericton, MD

Maritime Provinces: Nova Scotia

Acadia University, M
Dalhousie University, MD

Newfoundland and Labrador

Memorial University of Newfoundland, MD

Ontario

Brock University, M
Carleton University, MD
Lakehead University, M
McMaster University, MD
Queen's University at Kingston, MD
University of Guelph, M
University of Ottawa, MD
University of Toronto, MD
University of Waterloo, MD
The University of Western Ontario, MD
University of Windsor, M
Wilfrid Laurier University, MD
York University, MD

Quebec

Concordia University, M
McGill University, MD
Université Laval, MD
Université de Montréal, MD

Saskatchewan

University of Regina, M
University of Saskatchewan, MD

ENGLISH EDUCATION

United States

Alabama

Alabama Agricultural and Mechanical University, M
Alabama State University, M
Auburn University, MDO
Auburn University at Montgomery, M
The University of Alabama in Huntsville, M
The University of West Alabama, M

Arizona

Northern Arizona University, M
The University of Arizona, MD
University of Phoenix - Online Campus, M

Arkansas

Arkansas State University, MO
Arkansas Tech University, M
Harding University, M
University of Arkansas at Pine Bluff, M

California

California Baptist University, M
California State University, Northridge, M
Mills College, M
Occidental College, M
San Francisco State University, MO
William Jessup University, M

Colorado

The Colorado College, M
University of Colorado Denver, M

Connecticut

Quinnipiac University, M
University of Connecticut, MDO

District of Columbia

Trinity Washington University, M
University of the District of Columbia, M
University of Phoenix - Washington D.C. Campus, M

Florida

Florida Agricultural and Mechanical University, M
Florida Atlantic University, M
Florida Gulf Coast University, M
Florida International University, M
Florida State University, MDO
University of Central Florida, M
University of Florida, M
University of South Florida, MD
University of South Florida, St. Petersburg, M
University of South Florida Sarasota-Manatee, M

Georgia

Albany State University, M
Clayton State University, M
Columbus State University, MO
Georgia Southern University, M
Georgia State University, M
Kennesaw State University, M
University of Georgia, MDO
University of North Georgia, M
Valdosta State University, M

Hawaii

Chaminade University of Honolulu, M

Illinois

Lake Forest College, M
National Louis University, MO
Southern Illinois University Edwardsville, MO
University of Illinois at Springfield, O
University of St. Francis, M

Indiana

Indiana University - Purdue University Fort Wayne, M
Purdue University, MDO
University of Indianapolis, M

Iowa

The University of Iowa, M
University of Northern Iowa, M

Kansas

Kansas State University, M

Kentucky

Eastern Kentucky University, M
Morehead State University, M
Western Kentucky University, M

Louisiana

Louisiana Tech University, M
Southeastern Louisiana University, M
University of Louisiana at Monroe, M

Maine

University of Maine, M

Maryland

Loyola University Maryland, M
University of Maryland, Baltimore County, M

Massachusetts

Anna Maria College, M
Elms College, M
Fitchburg State University, MO
Framingham State University, M
Smith College, M
Western New England University, M
Worcester State University, M

Michigan

Andrews University, M
Eastern Michigan University, MO
Grand Valley State University, M
University of Michigan, D
Wayne State University, MDO
Western Michigan University, M

Minnesota

Minnesota State University Mankato, M
University of Minnesota, Twin Cities Campus, MD

Mississippi

Delta State University, M
Jackson State University, M
Mississippi College, M
William Carey University, M

Missouri

Northwest Missouri State University, M
University of Missouri, MDO

Montana

University of Montana, M

Nebraska

Chadron State College, M
Wayne State College, M

New Hampshire

Plymouth State University, M
Southern New Hampshire University, M
University of New Hampshire, M

New Jersey

Montclair State University, MO
Rider University, O

Rowan University, O
Rutgers University - New Brunswick, M

New Mexico

New Mexico State University, M
University of New Mexico, MD

New York

Binghamton University, State University of New York, M
Brooklyn College of the City University of New York, M
Buffalo State College, State University of New York, M
City College of the City University of New York, M
The College at Brockport, State University of New York, M
Hofstra University, MD
Hunter College of the City University of New York, M
Iona College, M
Ithaca College, M
Le Moyne College, M
Lehman College of the City University of New York, M
Manhattanville College, M
New York University, MDO
Queens College of the City University of New York, MO
St. John Fisher College, M
State University of New York College at Cortland, M
State University of New York College at Old Westbury, M
State University of New York College at Potsdam, M
State University of New York at New Paltz, M
State University of New York at Plattsburgh, M
Stony Brook University, State University of New York, M
Syracuse University, M
University at Buffalo, the State University of New York, M
Wagner College, M

North Carolina

Appalachian State University, M
East Carolina University, MO
Gardner-Webb University, M
North Carolina Agricultural and Technical State University, M
North Carolina State University, M
The University of North Carolina at Chapel Hill, M
The University of North Carolina at Charlotte, M
The University of North Carolina at Greensboro, M
The University of North Carolina at Pembroke, M

North Dakota

Valley City State University, M

Ohio

Kent State University, M
The University of Toledo, M

Oklahoma

Southwestern Oklahoma State University, M
The University of Tulsa, M

Pennsylvania

Arcadia University, MO
Bloomsburg University of Pennsylvania, M
Chatham University, M
Duquesne University, M
Eastern University, O
Indiana University of Pennsylvania, MD
Kutztown University of Pennsylvania, M
La Salle University, M
Slippery Rock University of Pennsylvania, M
Temple University, M
University of Pennsylvania, MD
University of Pittsburgh, M
Widener University, M
Wilkes University, M

Rhode Island

Brown University, M
Rhode Island College, M

South Carolina

Bob Jones University, M
The Citadel, The Military College of South Carolina, M
Converse College, M
South Carolina State University, M
University of South Carolina, M

Tennessee

Lincoln Memorial University, M
Lipscomb University, O
The University of Tennessee, MO
Vanderbilt University, M

Texas

Our Lady of the Lake University of San Antonio, M
The University of Texas at El Paso, M
Wayland Baptist University, M

Utah

Western Governors University, M

Vermont

College of St. Joseph, M

Virginia

Averett University, M
George Mason University, M
University of Virginia, MD

Washington

University of Washington, MD

Wisconsin

Carthage College, M
University of Wisconsin - Platteville, M

U.S. Territories: Puerto Rico

Caribbean University, M
University of Puerto Rico, Mayagüez Campus, M
University of the Sacred Heart, M

Canada

British Columbia

Simon Fraser University, M
University of Victoria, MD

Manitoba

University of Manitoba, M

ENGLISH/LANGUAGE ARTS TEACHER EDUCATION

United States

Alabama

Auburn University, B
Huntingdon College, B
Judson College, B
Miles College, B
Samford University, B
Spring Hill College, B
Talladega College, B
University of Mobile, B

Arizona

Arizona Christian University, B
Grand Canyon University, B

Arkansas

Arkansas State University, B
Arkansas Tech University, B
Harding University, B
University of Arkansas - Fort Smith, B

California

California State University, Long Beach, B
National University, B
Pepperdine University, B

Simpson University, B
Westmont College, B

Colorado

Adams State University, B
Colorado Christian University, B
Colorado State University, B
Fort Lewis College, B
Western State Colorado University, B

Delaware

Delaware State University, B
University of Delaware, B
Wilmington University, B

District of Columbia

The Catholic University of America, B

Florida

The Baptist College of Florida, B
Barry University, B
Bethune-Cookman University, B
Broward College, A
Flagler College, B
Florida Agricultural and Mechanical University, B
Florida Atlantic University, B
Florida Southern College, B
Florida SouthWestern State College, B
Hobe Sound Bible College, B
Nova Southeastern University, B
Palm Beach Atlantic University, B
South Florida State College, A
Southeastern University, B
State College of Florida Manatee-Sarasota, A
University of Central Florida, B
University of South Florida, B

Georgia

Armstrong State University, B
Brewton-Parker College, B
Columbus State University, B
Covenant College, B
Darton State College, A
Emmanuel College, B
Gordon State College, B
Kennesaw State University, B
Paine College, B
Piedmont College, B
Reinhardt University, B
Toccoa Falls College, B
University of Georgia, B

Hawaii

Brigham Young University - Hawaii, B

Idaho

Boise State University, B
Brigham Young University - Idaho, B
Lewis-Clark State College, B
Northwest Nazarene University, B
University of Idaho, B

Illinois

Augustana College, B
Blackburn College, B
Bradley University, B
Concordia University Chicago, B
Elmhurst College, B
Greenville College, B
John A. Logan College, A
McKendree University, B
Millikin University, B
Saint Xavier University, B
Trinity Christian College, B
University of Illinois at Chicago, B
University of Illinois at Urbana - Champaign, B
University of St. Francis, B

Indiana

Anderson University, B
Bethel College, B
Franklin College, B
Goshen College, B
Grace College, B
Huntington University, B

Indiana University Bloomington, B
Indiana University Northwest, B
Indiana University - Purdue University Fort Wayne, B
Indiana University - Purdue University Indianapolis, B
Indiana University South Bend, B
Indiana University Southeast, B
Indiana Wesleyan University, B
Manchester University, B
Oakland City University, B
Purdue University, B
Taylor University, B
University of Evansville, B
University of Indianapolis, B
University of Saint Francis, B
Valparaiso University, B
Vincennes University, A

Iowa

Buena Vista University, B
Faith Baptist Bible College and Theological Seminary, B
Grand View University, B
Morningside College, B
Northwestern College, B
St. Ambrose University, B
University of Dubuque, B

Kansas

Bethany College, B
Friends University, B
Kansas Wesleyan University, B
MidAmerica Nazarene University, B
Pittsburg State University, B
Southwestern College, B
Tabor College, B
Washburn University, B

Kentucky

Alice Lloyd College, B
Campbellsville University, B
Eastern Kentucky University, B
Kentucky Christian University, B

Louisiana

Grambling State University, B
Louisiana State University in Shreveport, B
Louisiana Tech University, B
Nicholls State University, B
Southeastern Louisiana University, B
Southern University and Agricultural and Mechanical College, B
University of Louisiana at Monroe, B

Maine

Husson University, B
Saint Joseph's College of Maine, B
University of Maine, B
University of Maine at Farmington, B
University of Maine at Machias, B

Maryland

Anne Arundel Community College, A
Carroll Community College, A
Cecil College, A
Hagerstown Community College, A
Harford Community College, A
Montgomery College, A
Washington Adventist University, B

Massachusetts

Anna Maria College, B
Boston University, B
Bridgewater State University, B
Fitchburg State University, B
Merrimack College, B

Michigan

Adrian College, B
Albion College, B
Alma College, B
Aquinas College, B
Central Michigan University, B
Concordia University Ann Arbor, B

Cornerstone University, B
Eastern Michigan University, B
Ferris State University, B
Grand Valley State University, B
Hope College, B
Madonna University, B
Northern Michigan University, B
Rochester College, B
Saginaw Valley State University, B
Spring Arbor University, B
University of Michigan - Flint, B
Western Michigan University, B

Minnesota

Bethel University, B
Crown College, B
Metropolitan State University, B
Minnesota State University Moorhead, B
St. Catherine University, B
Saint Mary's University of Minnesota, B
Southwest Minnesota State University, B
University of Northwestern - St. Paul, B
University of St. Thomas, B
Winona State University, B

Mississippi

Blue Mountain College, B
Coahoma Community College, A
Delta State University, B
Mississippi College, B
Northeast Mississippi Community College, A
Rust College, B
University of Mississippi, B
William Carey University, B

Missouri

College of the Ozarks, B
Culver-Stockton College, B
Hannibal-LaGrange University, B
Lincoln University, B
Missouri State University, B
Missouri Western State University, B
Northwest Missouri State University, B
Saint Louis University, B
Southeast Missouri State University, B
Southwest Baptist University, B
Washington University in St. Louis, B
Webster University, B
William Woods University, B

Montana

Carroll College, B
Montana State University Billings, B
Montana State University - Northern, B
Rocky Mountain College, B
University of Great Falls, B
The University of Montana Western, B

Nebraska

Chadron State College, B
College of Saint Mary, B
Concordia University, Nebraska, B
Hastings College, B
Nebraska Wesleyan University, B
Peru State College, B
Union College, B
Wayne State College, B
York College, B

Nevada

Nevada State College, B

New Hampshire

Colby-Sawyer College, B
Granite State College, B
Keene State College, B
Rivier University, B
Southern New Hampshire University, B

New Jersey

The College of New Jersey, B

New York

Brooklyn College of the City University of New York, B

Buffalo State College, State University of New York, B
Canisius College, B
The College of Saint Rose, B
College of Staten Island of the City University of New York, B
Daemen College, B
Dominican College, B
Elmira College, B
Hofstra University, B
Iona College, B
Ithaca College, B
Keuka College, B
Le Moyne College, B
Long Island University - LIU Brooklyn, B
Long Island University - LIU Post, B
Manhattanville College, B
Marist College, B
Medaille College, B
Nazareth College of Rochester, B
Nyack College, B
Pace University, B
Pace University, Pleasantville Campus, B
Queens College of the City University of New York, B
Roberts Wesleyan College, B
St. Francis College, B
St. John Fisher College, B
St. John's University, B
St. Joseph's College, Long Island Campus, B
St. Joseph's College, New York, B
State University of New York College at Oneonta, B
State University of New York College at Potsdam, B
State University of New York at New Paltz, B
State University of New York at Plattsburgh, B
Syracuse University, B
Utica College, B

North Carolina

Appalachian State University, B
Bennett College, B
East Carolina University, B
Elizabeth City State University, B
Fayetteville State University, B
Gardner-Webb University, B
Greensboro College, B
Louisburg College, A
North Carolina Agricultural and Technical State University, B
Piedmont International University, B
Shaw University, B
The University of North Carolina at Greensboro, B
The University of North Carolina at Pembroke, B
The University of North Carolina Wilmington, B
Western Carolina University, B
Wingate University, B
Winston-Salem State University, B

North Dakota

Mayville State University, B
Minot State University, B
North Dakota State University, B
University of Jamestown, B
University of Mary, B
Valley City State University, B

Ohio

Bowling Green State University, B
Capital University, B
Cedarville University, B
Malone University, B
Miami University, B
Miami University Hamilton, B
Mount Vernon Nazarene University, B
Ohio Dominican University, B
Ohio Northern University, B
The Ohio State University at Lima, B
The Ohio State University - Mansfield Campus, B
The Ohio State University at Marion, B
The Ohio State University - Newark Campus, B
Tiffin University, B
The University of Akron, B
University of Rio Grande, B
Ursuline College, B
Youngstown State University, B

Oklahoma

Cameron University, B
East Central University, B
Northeastern Oklahoma Agricultural and Mechanical College, A
Northeastern State University, B
Northwestern Oklahoma State University, B
Oklahoma Baptist University, B
Oklahoma Christian University, B
Oklahoma City University, B
Oklahoma Wesleyan University, B
Oral Roberts University, B
St. Gregory's University, B
Southeastern Oklahoma State University, B
Southern Nazarene University, B
Southwestern Christian University, B
Southwestern Oklahoma State University, B
University of Central Oklahoma, B
University of Oklahoma, B

Oregon

Concordia University, B
Corban University, B

Pennsylvania

Alvernia University, B
Cabrini University, B
Cairn University, B
Duquesne University, B
Grove City College, B
Holy Family University, B
Juniata College, B
Keystone College, B
La Roche College, B
Lincoln University, B
Marywood University, B
Mercyhurst University, B
Messiah College, B
Misericordia University, B
Point Park University, B
Saint Francis University, B
Seton Hill University, B
Temple University, B
University of Pittsburgh at Johnstown, B
Waynesburg University, B
Widener University, B
York College of Pennsylvania, B

Rhode Island

Providence College, B
Rhode Island College, B
Roger Williams University, B

South Carolina

Anderson University, B
Bob Jones University, B
Charleston Southern University, B
Claflin University, B
Coker College, B
Limestone College, B
Morris College, B
North Greenville University, B
Southern Wesleyan University, B

South Dakota

Dakota State University, B
Dakota Wesleyan University, B
Mount Marty College, B
The University of South Dakota, B

Tennessee

Aquinas College, B
Bryan College, B
King University, B
Lee University, B
LeMoyne-Owen College, B
Lipscomb University, B
Martin Methodist College, B
Maryville College, B
Southern Adventist University, B
Trevecca Nazarene University, B
The University of Tennessee at Chattanooga, B
The University of Tennessee at Martin, B
Welch College, B

Texas

Abilene Christian University, B
Arlington Baptist College, B
Baylor University, B
Dallas Baptist University, B
East Texas Baptist University, B
Hardin-Simmons University, B
Houston Baptist University, B
Howard Payne University, B
LeTourneau University, B
McMurry University, B
Midwestern State University, B
St. Edward's University, B
Schreiner University, B
Southwestern Adventist University, B
Southwestern Assemblies of God University, B
Texas A&M International University, B
Texas Christian University, B
Texas Wesleyan University, B
University of Mary Hardin-Baylor, B
Wayland Baptist University, B

Utah

Dixie State University, B
Southern Utah University, B
Utah Valley University, B
Weber State University, B

Vermont

Goddard College, B
Green Mountain College, B
Johnson State College, B
Lyndon State College, A
University of Vermont, B

Virginia

Averett University, B
Bluefield College, B
Emory & Henry College, B
Virginia Union University, B

Washington

Central Washington University, B
Eastern Washington University, B
Heritage University, B
Northwest University, B
Seattle Pacific University, B
Washington State University, B
Western Washington University, B

West Virginia

Bethany College, B
Glenville State College, B
West Virginia Wesleyan College, B

Wisconsin

Alverno College, B
Carroll University, B
Edgewood College, B
Maranatha Baptist University, B
Marian University, B
Mount Mary University, B
University of Wisconsin - Superior, B
Viterbo University, B
Wisconsin Lutheran College, B

U.S. Territories: Puerto Rico

Bayamón Central University, B
Inter American University of Puerto Rico, San
    Germán Campus, B
Pontifical Catholic University of Puerto Rico, B
Universidad Metropolitana, B
Universidad del Turabo, B
University of Puerto Rico in Aguadilla, B
University of Puerto Rico in Cayey, B
University of Puerto Rico in Utuado, B

Canada

Alberta

University of Alberta, B
University of Lethbridge, B

Ontario

University of Windsor, B
York University, B

Quebec

Bishop's University, B
Université du Québec à Trois-Rivières, B

Saskatchewan

University of Regina, B

ENGLISH LANGUAGE AND LITERATURE

United States

Alabama

Alabama Agricultural and Mechanical University, B
Alabama State University, B
Athens State University, B
Auburn University, B
Auburn University at Montgomery, B
Birmingham-Southern College, B
Faulkner University, B
Huntingdon College, B
Jacksonville State University, B
Judson College, B
Miles College, B
Oakwood University, B
Samford University, B
Spring Hill College, B
Stillman College, B
Talladega College, B
Troy University, B
Tuskegee University, B
The University of Alabama, B
The University of Alabama at Birmingham, B
The University of Alabama in Huntsville, B
University of Mobile, B
University of Montevallo, B
University of North Alabama, B
University of South Alabama, B
The University of West Alabama, B

Alaska

University of Alaska Anchorage, B
University of Alaska Fairbanks, B
University of Alaska Southeast, B

Arizona

Arizona State University at the Polytechnic campus,
    B
Arizona State University at the Tempe campus, B
Arizona State University at the West campus, B
Arizona Western College, A
Cochise County Community College District, A
Eastern Arizona College, A
Mohave Community College, A
Northern Arizona University, B
The University of Arizona, B

Arkansas

Arkansas State University, B
Arkansas Tech University, B
Central Baptist College, B
Harding University, B
Henderson State University, B
Hendrix College, B
John Brown University, B
Lyon College, B
Ouachita Baptist University, B
Philander Smith College, B
Southern Arkansas University - Magnolia, B
University of Arkansas, B
University of Arkansas - Fort Smith, B
University of Arkansas at Little Rock, B
University of Arkansas at Monticello, B
University of Arkansas at Pine Bluff, B
University of Central Arkansas, B
University of the Ozarks, B
Williams Baptist College, B

California

Allan Hancock College, A
American River College, A
Antelope Valley College, A
Ashford University, B
Azusa Pacific University, B
Bakersfield College, A
Berkeley City College, A
Biola University, B
Butte College, A
Cabrillo College, A
California Baptist University, B
California Institute of Technology, B
California Lutheran University, B
California Polytechnic State University, San Luis
    Obispo, B
California State Polytechnic University, Pomona, B
California State University, Bakersfield, B
California State University Channel Islands, B
California State University, Chico, B
California State University, Dominguez Hills, B
California State University, East Bay, B
California State University, Fresno, B
California State University, Fullerton, B
California State University, Long Beach, B
California State University, Los Angeles, B
California State University, Northridge, B
California State University, Sacramento, B
California State University, San Bernardino, B
California State University, San Marcos, B
California State University, Stanislaus, B
Cañada College, A
Cerritos College, A
Chabot College, A
Chaffey College, A
Chapman University, B
Citrus College, A
City College of San Francisco, A
Claremont McKenna College, B
College of Alameda, A
College of the Canyons, A
College of the Desert, A
College of Marin, A
College of San Mateo, A
College of the Sequoias, A
College of the Siskiyous, A
Columbia College, A
Concordia University Irvine, B
Contra Costa College, A
Copper Mountain College, A
Cosumnes River College, A
Crafton Hills College, A
Cuesta College, A
Cuyamaca College, A
De Anza College, A
Diablo Valley College, A
Dominican University of California, B
East Los Angeles College, A
El Camino College, A
Evergreen Valley College, A
Feather River College, A
Folsom Lake College, A
Foothill College, A
Fresno City College, A
Fresno Pacific University, B
Fullerton College, A
Gavilan College, A
Glendale Community College, A
Grossmont College, A
Hartnell College, A
Holy Names University, B
Hope International University, B
Humboldt State University, B
Imperial Valley College, A
Irvine Valley College, A
La Sierra University, B
Long Beach City College, A
Los Angeles City College, A
Los Angeles Mission College, A
Los Angeles Southwest College, A
Los Angeles Valley College, A
Loyola Marymount University, B
The Master's College and Seminary, B
Mendocino College, A
Merritt College, A
Mills College, B

Modesto Junior College, A
Monterey Peninsula College, A
Mount Saint Mary's University, B
Mt. San Antonio College, A
National University, B
Notre Dame de Namur University, B
Occidental College, B
Ohlone College, A
Oxnard College, A
Pacific Union College, B
Palomar College, A
Pepperdine University, B
Pitzer College, B
Point Loma Nazarene University, B
Pomona College, B
Porterville College, A
Reedley College, A
Saint Katherine College, B
Saint Mary's College of California, B
San Bernardino Valley College, A
San Diego Christian College, B
San Diego City College, A
San Diego Mesa College, A
San Diego Miramar College, A
San Diego State University, B
San Diego State University - Imperial Valley Campus, B
San Francisco State University, B
San Joaquin Delta College, A
San Jose City College, A
San Jose State University, B
Santa Ana College, A
Santa Barbara City College, A
Santa Clara University, B
Santa Rosa Junior College, A
Santiago Canyon College, A
Scripps College, B
Sierra College, A
Simpson University, B
Skyline College, A
Solano Community College, A
Sonoma State University, B
Southwestern College, A
Stanford University, B
Taft College, A
University of California, Berkeley, B
University of California, Davis, B
University of California, Irvine, B
University of California, Los Angeles, B
University of California, Merced, B
University of California, Riverside, B
University of California, San Diego, B
University of California, Santa Barbara, B
University of La Verne, B
University of the Pacific, B
University of Redlands, B
University of San Diego, B
University of San Francisco, B
University of Southern California, B
University of the West, B
Vanguard University of Southern California, B
West Los Angeles College, A
West Valley College, A
Westmont College, B
Whittier College, B
William Jessup University, B
Woodland Community College, A
Yuba College, A

Colorado

Adams State University, B
Colorado Christian University, B
The Colorado College, B
Colorado Mesa University, B
Colorado Mountain College (Glenwood Springs), A
Colorado Mountain College (Steamboat Springs), A
Colorado State University, B
Colorado State University - Pueblo, B
Fort Lewis College, B
Metropolitan State University of Denver, B
Naropa University, B
Northeastern Junior College, A
Regis University, B
Trinidad State Junior College, A
United States Air Force Academy, B
University of Colorado Boulder, B

University of Colorado Colorado Springs, B
University of Colorado Denver, B
University of Denver, B
University of Northern Colorado, B
Western State Colorado University, B

Connecticut

Albertus Magnus College, B
Central Connecticut State University, B
Connecticut College, B
Eastern Connecticut State University, B
Fairfield University, B
Northwestern Connecticut Community College, A
Quinnipiac University, B
Sacred Heart University, B
Southern Connecticut State University, B
Trinity College, B
University of Bridgeport, B
University of Connecticut, B
University of Hartford, B
University of New Haven, B
University of Saint Joseph, B
Wesleyan University, B
Western Connecticut State University, B
Yale University, B

Delaware

Delaware State University, B
Goldey-Beacom College, B
University of Delaware, B
Wesley College, B

District of Columbia

The Catholic University of America, B
Gallaudet University, B
The George Washington University, B
Georgetown University, B
Howard University, B
Trinity Washington University, B
University of the District of Columbia, B

Florida

Ave Maria University, B
Barry University, B
Bethune-Cookman University, B
Broward College, A
College of Central Florida, A
Eckerd College, B
Edward Waters College, B
Flagler College, B
Florida Agricultural and Mechanical University, B
Florida Atlantic University, B
Florida Gulf Coast University, B
Florida International University, B
Florida Memorial University, B
Florida State University, B
Indian River State College, A
Jacksonville University, B
Miami Dade College, A
New College of Florida, B
Nova Southeastern University, B
Palm Beach Atlantic University, B
Palm Beach State College, A
Pensacola State College, A
Rollins College, B
Saint Leo University, B
St. Thomas University, B
South Florida State College, A
Southeastern University, B
State College of Florida Manatee-Sarasota, A
Stetson University, B
University of Central Florida, B
University of Florida, B
University of Miami, B
University of North Florida, B
University of South Florida, B
University of South Florida, St. Petersburg, B
University of South Florida Sarasota-Manatee, B
The University of Tampa, B
University of West Florida, B
Warner University, B

Georgia

Abraham Baldwin Agricultural College, A
Agnes Scott College, B

Albany State University, B
Andrew College, A
Armstrong State University, B
Atlanta Metropolitan State College, A
Augusta University, B
Bainbridge State College, A
Berry College, B
Brenau University, B
Brewton-Parker College, B
Clark Atlanta University, B
Clayton State University, B
College of Coastal Georgia, A
Columbus State University, B
Covenant College, B
Dalton State College, AB
Darton State College, A
Emmanuel College, B
Emory University, B
Georgia College & State University, B
Georgia Gwinnett College, B
Georgia Highlands College, A
Georgia Military College, A
Georgia Southern University, B
Georgia Southwestern State University, B
Georgia State University, B
Gordon State College, AB
Kennesaw State University, B
LaGrange College, B
Mercer University, B
Middle Georgia State University, B
Morehouse College, B
Oglethorpe University, B
Paine College, B
Piedmont College, B
Point University, B
Reinhardt University, B
Savannah State University, B
Shorter University, B
South Georgia State College, A
Spelman College, B
Thomas University, B
Toccoa Falls College, B
Truett-McConnell College, B
University of Georgia, B
University of North Georgia, B
University of West Georgia, B
Valdosta State University, B
Wesleyan College, B
Young Harris College, B

Hawaii

Brigham Young University - Hawaii, B
Chaminade University of Honolulu, B
Hawai'i Pacific University, B
University of Hawaii at Hilo, B
University of Hawaii at Manoa, B
University of Hawaii - West Oahu, B

Idaho

Boise State University, B
Brigham Young University - Idaho, B
The College of Idaho, B
College of Southern Idaho, A
College of Western Idaho, A
Idaho State University, B
Lewis-Clark State College, B
North Idaho College, A
Northwest Nazarene University, B
University of Idaho, B

Illinois

Augustana College, B
Aurora University, B
Benedictine University, B
Blackburn College, B
Bradley University, B
Chicago State University, B
City Colleges of Chicago, Wilbur Wright College, A
Concordia University Chicago, B
DePaul University, B
Dominican University, B
East-West University, B
Eastern Illinois University, B
Elmhurst College, B
Eureka College, B
Governors State University, B

Greenville College, B
Harper College, A
Illinois College, B
Illinois State University, B
Illinois Valley Community College, A
John A. Logan College, A
Judson University, B
Kankakee Community College, A
Knox College, B
Lake Forest College, B
Lewis University, B
Lincoln College, A
Loyola University Chicago, B
MacMurray College, B
McKendree University, B
Millikin University, B
Monmouth College, B
Moraine Valley Community College, A
National Louis University, B
North Central College, B
North Park University, B
Northeastern Illinois University, B
Northern Illinois University, B
Northwestern University, B
Olivet Nazarene University, B
Parkland College, A
Principia College, B
Quincy University, B
Rockford University, B
Roosevelt University, B
Saint Xavier University, B
Sauk Valley Community College, A
Southern Illinois University Carbondale, B
Southern Illinois University Edwardsville, B
Spoon River College, A
Trinity Christian College, B
Trinity International University, B
Triton College, A
University of Chicago, B
University of Illinois at Chicago, B
University of Illinois at Springfield, B
University of Illinois at Urbana - Champaign, B
University of St. Francis, B
Western Illinois University, B
Wheaton College, B

Indiana

Ancilla College, A
Anderson University, B
Ball State University, B
Bethel College, B
Butler University, B
Calumet College of Saint Joseph, AB
DePauw University, B
Earlham College, B
Franklin College, B
Goshen College, B
Grace College, B
Hanover College, B
Holy Cross College, B
Huntington University, B
Indiana State University, B
Indiana University Bloomington, B
Indiana University East, B
Indiana University Kokomo, B
Indiana University Northwest, B
Indiana University - Purdue University Fort Wayne, B
Indiana University - Purdue University Indianapolis, B
Indiana University South Bend, B
Indiana University Southeast, B
Indiana Wesleyan University, AB
Manchester University, B
Marian University, B
Oakland City University, B
Purdue University Northwest (Hammond), B
Purdue University Northwest (Westville), B
Saint Joseph's College, B
Saint Mary-of-the-Woods College, B
Saint Mary's College, B
Taylor University, B
University of Evansville, B
University of Indianapolis, B
University of Notre Dame, B
University of Saint Francis, B

University of Southern Indiana, B
Valparaiso University, B
Vincennes University, A
Wabash College, B

Iowa

Briar Cliff University, B
Buena Vista University, B
Central College, B
Clarke University, B
Coe College, B
Cornell College, B
Dordt College, B
Drake University, B
Graceland University, B
Grand View University, B
Grinnell College, B
Iowa State University of Science and Technology, B
Iowa Wesleyan University, B
Loras College, B
Luther College, B
Maharishi University of Management, B
Morningside College, B
Mount Mercy University, B
Northwestern College, B
St. Ambrose University, B
Simpson College, B
University of Dubuque, B
The University of Iowa, B
University of Northern Iowa, B
Upper Iowa University, B
Waldorf College, B
Wartburg College, B
William Penn University, B

Kansas

Baker University, B
Barton County Community College, A
Benedictine College, B
Bethany College, B
Bethel College, B
Butler Community College, A
Central Christian College of Kansas, B
Dodge City Community College, A
Emporia State University, B
Fort Hays State University, B
Friends University, B
Garden City Community College, A
Hutchinson Community College, A
Independence Community College, A
Kansas State University, B
Kansas Wesleyan University, B
Labette Community College, A
McPherson College, B
MidAmerica Nazarene University, B
Newman University, B
Ottawa University, B
Pittsburg State University, B
Pratt Community College, A
Seward County Community College and Area Technical School, A
Sterling College, B
Tabor College, B
The University of Kansas, B
University of Saint Mary, B
Washburn University, B
Wichita State University, B

Kentucky

Alice Lloyd College, B
Asbury University, B
Bellarmine University, B
Berea College, B
Brescia University, B
Campbellsville University, B
Centre College, B
Eastern Kentucky University, B
Georgetown College, B
Kentucky State University, B
Kentucky Wesleyan College, B
Lindsey Wilson College, B
Midway University, B
Morehead State University, B
Murray State University, B
Northern Kentucky University, B
Thomas More College, AB

Transylvania University, B
Union College, B
University of the Cumberlands, B
University of Kentucky, B
University of Louisville, B
University of Pikeville, B
Western Kentucky University, B

Louisiana

Centenary College of Louisiana, B
Dillard University, B
Grambling State University, B
Louisiana College, B
Louisiana State University and Agricultural & Mechanical College, B
Louisiana State University at Alexandria, B
Louisiana State University in Shreveport, B
Louisiana Tech University, B
Loyola University New Orleans, B
McNeese State University, B
Nicholls State University, B
Northwestern State University of Louisiana, B
Southeastern Louisiana University, B
Southern University and Agricultural and Mechanical College, B
Southern University at New Orleans, B
Tulane University, B
University of Holy Cross, B
University of Louisiana at Lafayette, B
University of Louisiana at Monroe, B
University of New Orleans, B
Xavier University of Louisiana, B

Maine

Bates College, B
Bowdoin College, B
Colby College, B
College of the Atlantic, B
Husson University, B
Saint Joseph's College of Maine, B
Thomas College, B
University of Maine, B
University of Maine at Augusta, B
University of Maine at Farmington, B
University of Maine at Fort Kent, B
University of Maine at Machias, B
University of Maine at Presque Isle, B
University of New England, B
University of Southern Maine, B

Maryland

Bowie State University, B
Coppin State University, B
Frostburg State University, B
Goucher College, B
Harford Community College, A
Hood College, B
Johns Hopkins University, B
Loyola University Maryland, B
McDaniel College, B
Morgan State University, B
Mount St. Mary's University, B
Notre Dame of Maryland University, B
St. Mary's College of Maryland, B
Salisbury University, B
Stevenson University, B
Towson University, B
United States Naval Academy, B
University of Baltimore, B
University of Maryland, Baltimore County, B
University of Maryland, College Park, B
University of Maryland Eastern Shore, B
University of Maryland University College, B
Washington Adventist University, B
Washington College, B

Massachusetts

American International College, B
Amherst College, B
Anna Maria College, B
Assumption College, B
Bentley University, B
Boston College, B
Boston University, B
Brandeis University, B
Bridgewater State University, B

Bunker Hill Community College, A
Cape Cod Community College, A
Clark University, B
College of the Holy Cross, B
Curry College, B
Dean College, AB
Eastern Nazarene College, B
Elms College, B
Emmanuel College, B
Endicott College, B
Fitchburg State University, B
Framingham State University, B
Gordon College, B
Greenfield Community College, A
Hampshire College, B
Harvard University, B
Lasell College, B
Lesley University, B
Massachusetts Bay Community College, A
Massachusetts College of Liberal Arts, B
Massachusetts Institute of Technology, B
Merrimack College, B
Mount Holyoke College, B
Mount Ida College, B
Nichols College, B
Northeastern University, B
Pine Manor College, AB
Regis College, B
Roxbury Community College, A
Salem State University, B
Simmons College, B
Smith College, B
Springfield College, B
Stonehill College, B
Suffolk University, B
Tufts University, B
University of Massachusetts Amherst, B
University of Massachusetts Boston, B
University of Massachusetts Dartmouth, B
University of Massachusetts Lowell, B
Wellesley College, B
Western New England University, B
Westfield State University, B
Wheaton College, B
Williams College, B
Worcester State University, B

Michigan

Adrian College, B
Albion College, B
Alma College, B
Alpena Community College, A
Andrews University, B
Aquinas College, B
Calvin College, B
Central Michigan University, B
Concordia University Ann Arbor, B
Eastern Michigan University, B
Grand Rapids Community College, A
Grand Valley State University, B
Hillsdale College, B
Hope College, B
Kalamazoo College, B
Lake Michigan College, A
Lake Superior State University, B
Lansing Community College, A
Lawrence Technological University, B
Madonna University, AB
Marygrove College, B
Michigan State University, B
Michigan Technological University, B
Monroe County Community College, A
Northern Michigan University, B
Northwestern Michigan College, A
Oakland University, B
Olivet College, B
Rochester College, B
Saginaw Valley State University, B
Siena Heights University, B
Spring Arbor University, B
University of Detroit Mercy, B
University of Michigan, B
University of Michigan - Dearborn, B
University of Michigan - Flint, B
Wayne State University, B
Western Michigan University, B

Minnesota

Augsburg College, B
Bemidji State University, B
Bethany Lutheran College, B
Bethel University, B
Carleton College, B
College of Saint Benedict, B
The College of St. Scholastica, B
Concordia College, B
Concordia University, St. Paul, B
Crown College, B
Gustavus Adolphus College, B
Hamline University, B
Macalester College, B
Metropolitan State University, B
Minnesota State University Mankato, B
Minnesota State University Moorhead, B
North Central University, B
St. Catherine University, B
St. Cloud State University, B
Saint John's University, B
Saint Mary's University of Minnesota, B
St. Olaf College, B
Southwest Minnesota State University, B
University of Minnesota, Duluth, B
University of Minnesota, Morris, B
University of Minnesota, Twin Cities Campus, B
University of Northwestern - St. Paul, B
University of St. Thomas, B
Winona State University, B

Mississippi

Alcorn State University, B
Belhaven University, B
Blue Mountain College, B
Copiah-Lincoln Community College, A
Delta State University, B
Itawamba Community College, A
Jackson State University, B
Jones County Junior College, A
Millsaps College, B
Mississippi College, B
Mississippi Delta Community College, A
Mississippi State University, B
Mississippi University for Women, B
Mississippi Valley State University, B
Northeast Mississippi Community College, A
Rust College, B
Southwest Mississippi Community College, A
Tougaloo College, B
University of Mississippi, B
University of Southern Mississippi, B
William Carey University, B

Missouri

Avila University, B
Calvary Bible College and Theological Seminary, B
Central Methodist University, AB
College of the Ozarks, B
Columbia College, B
Cottey College, B
Culver-Stockton College, B
Drury University, B
Evangel University, B
Fontbonne University, B
Hannibal-LaGrange University, AB
Lincoln University, B
Lindenwood University, B
Maryville University of Saint Louis, B
Missouri Baptist University, B
Missouri Southern State University, B
Missouri State University, B
Missouri University of Science and Technology, B
Missouri Valley College, B
Missouri Western State University, B
Northwest Missouri State University, B
Park University, B
Rockhurst University, B
St. Charles Community College, A
Saint Louis University, B
Southeast Missouri State University, B
Southwest Baptist University, B
Stephens College, B
Truman State University, B
University of Central Missouri, B

University of Missouri, B
University of Missouri - Kansas City, B
University of Missouri - St. Louis, B
Washington University in St. Louis, B
Webster University, B
Westminster College, B
William Jewell College, B
William Woods University, B

Montana

Carroll College, AB
Montana State University, B
Montana State University Billings, B
Rocky Mountain College, B
University of Great Falls, B
University of Montana, B
The University of Montana Western, B

Nebraska

Chadron State College, B
College of Saint Mary, B
Concordia University, Nebraska, B
Creighton University, B
Doane University, B
Hastings College, B
Midland University, B
Nebraska Wesleyan University, B
Northeast Community College, A
Peru State College, B
Union College, B
University of Nebraska at Kearney, B
University of Nebraska - Lincoln, B
University of Nebraska at Omaha, B
Wayne State College, B
Western Nebraska Community College, A
York College, B

Nevada

College of Southern Nevada, A
Great Basin College, B
Nevada State College, B
Sierra Nevada College, B
Truckee Meadows Community College, A
University of Nevada, Las Vegas, B
University of Nevada, Reno, B

New Hampshire

Colby-Sawyer College, B
Dartmouth College, B
Franklin Pierce University, B
Granite State College, B
Keene State College, B
Plymouth State University, B
Rivier University, B
Saint Anselm College, B
Southern New Hampshire University, B
University of New Hampshire, B
University of New Hampshire at Manchester, B

New Jersey

Bloomfield College, B
Caldwell University, B
Centenary College, B
The College of New Jersey, B
College of Saint Elizabeth, B
Drew University, B
Fairleigh Dickinson University, College at Florham, B
Fairleigh Dickinson University, Metropolitan Campus, B
Felician University, AB
Georgian Court University, B
Kean University, B
Monmouth University, B
Montclair State University, B
New Jersey City University, B
Passaic County Community College, A
Princeton University, B
Raritan Valley Community College, A
Rider University, B
Rowan College at Burlington County, A
Rowan University, B
Rutgers University - Camden, B
Rutgers University - New Brunswick, B
Rutgers University - Newark, B

Saint Peter's University, B
Seton Hall University, B
Stevens Institute of Technology, B
Stockton University, B
Sussex County Community College, A
Thomas Edison State University, B
William Paterson University of New Jersey, B

New Mexico

Central New Mexico Community College, A
Eastern New Mexico University, B
New Mexico Highlands University, B
New Mexico Junior College, A
New Mexico Military Institute, A
New Mexico State University, B
University of New Mexico, B
University of the Southwest, B
Western New Mexico University, B

New York

Adelphi University, B
Alfred University, B
Bard College, B
Barnard College, B
Baruch College of the City University of New York, B
Binghamton University, State University of New York, B
Borough of Manhattan Community College of the City University of New York, A
Brooklyn College of the City University of New York, B
Buffalo State College, State University of New York, B
Canisius College, B
Cazenovia College, B
City College of the City University of New York, B
Colgate University, B
The College at Brockport, State University of New York, B
College of Mount Saint Vincent, B
The College of New Rochelle, B
The College of Saint Rose, B
College of Staten Island of the City University of New York, B
Columbia University, B
Columbia University, School of General Studies, B
Concordia College - New York, B
Cornell University, B
Daemen College, B
Dominican College, B
D'Youville College, B
Elmira College, B
Fiorello H. LaGuardia Community College of the City University of New York, A
Fordham University, B
Fulton-Montgomery Community College, A
Hamilton College, B
Hartwick College, B
Hilbert College, B
Hobart and William Smith Colleges, B
Hofstra University, B
Houghton College, B
Hunter College of the City University of New York, B
Iona College, B
Ithaca College, B
John Jay College of Criminal Justice of the City University of New York, B
Keuka College, B
Le Moyne College, B
Lehman College of the City University of New York, B
Long Island University - LIU Brooklyn, B
Long Island University - LIU Post, B
Manhattan College, B
Manhattanville College, B
Marist College, B
Marymount Manhattan College, B
Medaille College, B
Mercy College, B
Molloy College, B
Mount Saint Mary College, B
Nazareth College of Rochester, B
New York Institute of Technology, B
New York University, B
Niagara University, B

Nyack College, B
Pace University, B
Pace University, Pleasantville Campus, B
Queens College of the City University of New York, B
Roberts Wesleyan College, B
The Sage Colleges, B
St. Bonaventure University, B
St. Francis College, B
St. John Fisher College, B
St. John's University, B
St. Joseph's College, Long Island Campus, B
St. Joseph's College, New York, B
St. Lawrence University, B
St. Thomas Aquinas College, B
Siena College, B
Skidmore College, B
State University of New York College at Cortland, B
State University of New York College at Geneseo, B
State University of New York College at Oneonta, B
State University of New York College at Potsdam, B
State University of New York Empire State College, AB
State University of New York at Fredonia, B
State University of New York at New Paltz, B
State University of New York at Oswego, B
State University of New York at Plattsburgh, B
Stony Brook University, State University of New York, B
Suffolk County Community College, A
Syracuse University, B
Touro College, B
Union College, B
United States Military Academy, B
University at Albany, State University of New York, B
University at Buffalo, the State University of New York, B
University of Rochester, B
Utica College, B
Vassar College, B
Wagner College, B
Wells College, B
Yeshiva University, B
York College of the City University of New York, B

North Carolina

Appalachian State University, B
Barton College, B
Belmont Abbey College, B
Bennett College, B
Brevard College, B
Campbell University, B
Catawba College, B
Chowan University, B
Davidson College, B
Duke University, B
East Carolina University, B
Elizabeth City State University, B
Elon University, B
Fayetteville State University, B
Gardner-Webb University, B
Greensboro College, B
Guilford College, B
High Point University, B
Johnson C. Smith University, B
Lees-McRae College, B
Lenoir-Rhyne University, B
Livingstone College, B
Louisburg College, A
Mars Hill University, B
Meredith College, B
Methodist University, AB
Montreat College, B
North Carolina Agricultural and Technical State University, B
North Carolina Central University, B
North Carolina State University, B
North Carolina Wesleyan College, B
Pfeiffer University, B
Queens University of Charlotte, B
St. Andrews University, B
Saint Augustine's University, B
Salem College, B
Shaw University, B
University of Mount Olive, B
University of North Carolina at Asheville, B

The University of North Carolina at Chapel Hill, B
The University of North Carolina at Charlotte, B
The University of North Carolina at Greensboro, B
The University of North Carolina at Pembroke, B
The University of North Carolina Wilmington, B
Wake Forest University, B
Warren Wilson College, B
Western Carolina University, B
William Peace University, B
Wingate University, B
Winston-Salem State University, B

North Dakota

Dickinson State University, B
Mayville State University, B
Minot State University, B
North Dakota State University, B
Turtle Mountain Community College, A
University of Jamestown, B
University of Mary, B
University of North Dakota, B
Valley City State University, B

Ohio

Ashland University, B
Baldwin Wallace University, B
Bluffton University, B
Bowling Green State University, B
Capital University, B
Case Western Reserve University, B
Cedarville University, B
Central State University, B
Cleveland State University, B
The College of Wooster, B
Defiance College, B
Denison University, B
Edison Community College, A
Franciscan University of Steubenville, B
Heidelberg University, B
Hiram College, B
John Carroll University, B
Kent State University, B
Kent State University at Ashtabula, B
Kent State University at East Liverpool, B
Kent State University at Geauga, B
Kent State University at Salem, B
Kent State University at Stark, B
Kent State University at Trumbull, B
Kent State University at Tuscarawas, B
Kenyon College, B
Lake Erie College, B
Lourdes University, AB
Malone University, B
Marietta College, B
Miami University, B
Miami University Hamilton, B
Miami University Middletown, A
Mount St. Joseph University, B
Mount Vernon Nazarene University, B
Muskingum University, B
Notre Dame College, B
Oberlin College, B
Ohio Christian University, B
Ohio Dominican University, B
The Ohio State University, B
The Ohio State University at Lima, B
The Ohio State University - Mansfield Campus, B
The Ohio State University at Marion, B
The Ohio State University - Newark Campus, B
Ohio University, B
Ohio Wesleyan University, B
Otterbein University, B
Pontifical College Josephinum, B
Shawnee State University, B
Terra State Community College, A
Tiffin University, B
The University of Akron, B
University of Cincinnati, B
University of Dayton, B
The University of Findlay, B
University of Mount Union, B
University of Rio Grande, B
The University of Toledo, B
Urbana University, B
Ursuline College, B
Walsh University, B

Wilmington College, B
Wittenberg University, B
Wright State University, B
Wright State University - Lake Campus, B
Xavier University, AB
Youngstown State University, B

Oklahoma

Cameron University, B
Carl Albert State College, A
East Central University, B
Hillsdale Free Will Baptist College, A
Langston University, B
Mid-America Christian University, B
Northeastern State University, B
Northwestern Oklahoma State University, B
Oklahoma Christian University, B
Oklahoma City University, B
Oklahoma Panhandle State University, B
Oklahoma State University, B
Oklahoma Wesleyan University, B
Oral Roberts University, B
Redlands Community College, A
Rose State College, A
St. Gregory's University, B
Seminole State College, A
Southeastern Oklahoma State University, B
Southern Nazarene University, B
Southwestern Christian University, B
Southwestern Oklahoma State University, B
University of Central Oklahoma, B
University of Oklahoma, B
University of Science and Arts of Oklahoma, B
The University of Tulsa, B

Oregon

Concordia University, B
Corban University, B
Eastern Oregon University, B
George Fox University, B
Lewis & Clark College, B
Linn-Benton Community College, A
Marylhurst University, B
Multnomah University, B
Northwest Christian University, B
Oregon State University, B
Pacific University, B
Portland State University, B
Reed College, B
Southern Oregon University, B
Umpqua Community College, A
University of Oregon, B
University of Portland, B
Warner Pacific College, B
Western Oregon University, B
Willamette University, B

Pennsylvania

Albright College, B
Allegheny College, B
Alvernia University, B
Arcadia University, B
Bloomsburg University of Pennsylvania, B
Bryn Athyn College of the New Church, B
Bryn Mawr College, B
Bucknell University, B
Bucks County Community College, A
Butler County Community College, A
Cabrini University, B
Cairn University, B
California University of Pennsylvania, B
Carlow University, B
Carnegie Mellon University, B
Cedar Crest College, B
Chatham University, B
Chestnut Hill College, B
Cheyney University of Pennsylvania, B
Clarion University of Pennsylvania, B
Community College of Allegheny County, A
Delaware Valley University, B
DeSales University, B
Dickinson College, B
Drexel University, B
Duquesne University, B
East Stroudsburg University of Pennsylvania, B
Eastern University, B

Edinboro University of Pennsylvania, B
Elizabethtown College, B
Franklin & Marshall College, B
Geneva College, B
Gettysburg College, B
Gwynedd Mercy University, B
Haverford College, B
Holy Family University, B
Immaculata University, AB
Indiana University of Pennsylvania, B
Juniata College, B
King's College, B
Kutztown University of Pennsylvania, B
La Roche College, B
La Salle University, B
Lafayette College, B
Lebanon Valley College, B
Lehigh University, B
Lincoln University, B
Lock Haven University of Pennsylvania, B
Lycoming College, B
Mansfield University of Pennsylvania, B
Marywood University, B
Mercyhurst University, B
Messiah College, B
Millersville University of Pennsylvania, B
Misericordia University, B
Moravian College, B
Mount Aloysius College, B
Muhlenberg College, B
Neumann University, B
Penn State Abington, B
Penn State Altoona, B
Penn State Beaver, B
Penn State Berks, B
Penn State Brandywine, B
Penn State DuBois, B
Penn State Erie, The Behrend College, B
Penn State Fayette, The Eberly Campus, B
Penn State Greater Allegheny, B
Penn State Harrisburg, B
Penn State Hazleton, B
Penn State Lehigh Valley, B
Penn State Mont Alto, B
Penn State New Kensington, B
Penn State Schuylkill, B
Penn State Shenango, B
Penn State University Park, B
Penn State Wilkes-Barre, B
Penn State Worthington Scranton, B
Penn State York, B
Point Park University, B
Robert Morris University, B
Rosemont College, B
Saint Francis University, B
Saint Joseph's University, B
Saint Vincent College, B
Seton Hill University, B
Shippensburg University of Pennsylvania, B
Slippery Rock University of Pennsylvania, B
Susquehanna University, B
Swarthmore College, B
Temple University, B
Thiel College, B
University of Pennsylvania, B
University of Pittsburgh at Bradford, B
University of Pittsburgh at Greensburg, B
University of Pittsburgh at Johnstown, B
The University of Scranton, B
University of Valley Forge, B
Ursinus College, B
Villanova University, B
Washington & Jefferson College, B
Waynesburg University, B
West Chester University of Pennsylvania, B
Westminster College, B
Widener University, B
Wilkes University, B
Wilson College, B
York College of Pennsylvania, B

Rhode Island

Brown University, B
Bryant University, B
Providence College, B
Rhode Island College, B

Roger Williams University, B
Salve Regina University, B
University of Rhode Island, B

South Carolina

Allen University, B
Anderson University, B
Benedict College, B
Bob Jones University, B
Charleston Southern University, B
The Citadel, The Military College of South Carolina, B
Claflin University, B
Clemson University, B
Coastal Carolina University, B
Coker College, B
College of Charleston, B
Columbia College, B
Columbia International University, B
Converse College, B
Erskine College, B
Francis Marion University, B
Furman University, B
Lander University, B
Limestone College, B
Morris College, B
Newberry College, B
North Greenville University, B
Presbyterian College, B
South Carolina State University, B
Southern Wesleyan University, B
University of South Carolina, B
University of South Carolina Aiken, B
University of South Carolina Beaufort, B
University of South Carolina Upstate, B
Winthrop University, B
Wofford College, B

South Dakota

Augustana University, B
Black Hills State University, B
Dakota State University, B
Dakota Wesleyan University, B
Mount Marty College, B
Northern State University, B
Presentation College, A
South Dakota State University, B
University of Sioux Falls, B
The University of South Dakota, B

Tennessee

Aquinas College, B
Austin Peay State University, B
Belmont University, B
Bethel University, B
Bryan College, B
Carson-Newman University, B
Christian Brothers University, B
Cumberland University, B
East Tennessee State University, B
Fisk University, B
Freed-Hardeman University, B
Hiwassee College, A
King University, B
Lane College, B
Lee University, B
LeMoyne-Owen College, B
Lincoln Memorial University, B
Lipscomb University, B
Martin Methodist College, B
Maryville College, B
Middle Tennessee State University, B
Milligan College, B
Nashville State Community College, A
Rhodes College, B
Sewanee: The University of the South, B
Southern Adventist University, B
Tennessee State University, B
Tennessee Technological University, B
Tennessee Wesleyan College, B
Trevecca Nazarene University, B
Tusculum College, B
Union University, B
University of Memphis, B
The University of Tennessee, B
The University of Tennessee at Chattanooga, B

The University of Tennessee at Martin, B
Vanderbilt University, B
Welch College, B

Texas

Abilene Christian University, B
Amarillo College, A
Angelo State University, B
Austin College, B
Baylor University, B
Blinn College, A
Clarendon College, A
Concordia University Texas, B
Dallas Baptist University, B
Del Mar College, A
East Texas Baptist University, B
Frank Phillips College, A
Galveston College, A
Grayson College, A
Hardin-Simmons University, B
Hill College, A
Houston Baptist University, B
Houston Community College, A
Howard College, A
Howard Payne University, B
Huston-Tillotson University, B
Jarvis Christian College, B
Kilgore College, A
Lamar University, B
Lee College, A
LeTourneau University, B
McMurry University, B
Midwestern State University, B
Navarro College, A
Northeast Texas Community College, A
Odessa College, A
Our Lady of the Lake University of San Antonio, B
Palo Alto College, A
Panola College, A
Paris Junior College, A
Prairie View A&M University, B
Rice University, B
St. Edward's University, B
St. Mary's University, B
St. Philip's College, A
Sam Houston State University, B
San Jacinto College District, A
Schreiner University, B
Southern Methodist University, B
Southwestern Adventist University, B
Southwestern Assemblies of God University, AB
Southwestern University, B
Stephen F. Austin State University, B
Sul Ross State University, B
Tarleton State University, B
Texas A&M International University, B
Texas A&M University, B
Texas A&M University - Central Texas, B
Texas A&M University - Commerce, B
Texas A&M University - Corpus Christi, B
Texas A&M University - Kingsville, B
Texas A&M University - San Antonio, B
Texas A&M University - Texarkana, B
Texas Christian University, B
Texas College, B
Texas Lutheran University, B
Texas Southern University, B
Texas State University, B
Texas Tech University, B
Texas Wesleyan University, B
Texas Woman's University, B
Trinity University, B
Trinity Valley Community College, A
University of Dallas, B
University of Houston, B
University of Houston - Clear Lake, B
University of Houston - Downtown, B
University of Houston - Victoria, B
University of the Incarnate Word, B
University of Mary Hardin-Baylor, B
University of North Texas, B
University of St. Thomas, B
The University of Texas at Arlington, B
The University of Texas at Austin, B
The University of Texas at El Paso, B
The University of Texas of the Permian Basin, B

The University of Texas Rio Grande Valley, B
The University of Texas at San Antonio, B
The University of Texas at Tyler, B
Wayland Baptist University, B
West Texas A&M University, B
Wharton County Junior College, A
Wiley College, B

Utah

Dixie State University, B
Salt Lake Community College, A
Southern Utah University, B
University of Utah, B
Utah State University, B
Utah Valley University, AB
Weber State University, B
Westminster College, B

Vermont

Bennington College, B
College of St. Joseph, B
Green Mountain College, B
Johnson State College, B
Lyndon State College, B
Marlboro College, B
Middlebury College, B
Norwich University, B
Saint Michael's College, B
Southern Vermont College, B
University of Vermont, B

Virginia

Averett University, B
Bluefield College, B
Bridgewater College, B
Christopher Newport University, B
The College of William and Mary, B
Eastern Mennonite University, B
Emory & Henry College, B
Ferrum College, B
George Mason University, B
Hampden-Sydney College, B
Hampton University, B
Hollins University, B
James Madison University, B
Liberty University, AB
Longwood University, B
Lynchburg College, B
Mary Baldwin College, B
Marymount University, B
Norfolk State University, B
Old Dominion University, B
Patrick Henry College, B
Radford University, B
Randolph College, B
Randolph-Macon College, B
Regent University, B
Roanoke College, B
Shenandoah University, B
Southern Virginia University, B
Sweet Briar College, B
University of Mary Washington, B
University of Richmond, B
University of Virginia, B
The University of Virginia's College at Wise, B
Virginia Commonwealth University, B
Virginia Military Institute, B
Virginia Polytechnic Institute and State University, B
Virginia State University, B
Virginia Union University, B
Virginia Wesleyan College, B
Washington and Lee University, B

Washington

Central Washington University, B
Eastern Washington University, B
Everett Community College, A
The Evergreen State College, B
Gonzaga University, B
Heritage University, B
Highline College, A
Northwest University, B
Pacific Lutheran University, B
Saint Martin's University, B
Seattle Pacific University, B
Seattle University, B

Skagit Valley College, A
University of Puget Sound, B
University of Washington, B
Walla Walla University, B
Washington State University, B
Washington State University - Tri-Cities, B
Washington State University - Vancouver, B
Western Washington University, B
Whitman College, B
Whitworth University, B

West Virginia

American Public University System, B
Bethany College, B
Concord University, B
Davis & Elkins College, B
Fairmont State University, B
Glenville State College, B
Marshall University, B
Potomac State College of West Virginia University,
    A
Shepherd University, B
University of Charleston, B
West Liberty University, B
West Virginia State University, B
West Virginia University, B
West Virginia Wesleyan College, B
Wheeling Jesuit University, B

Wisconsin

Alverno College, B
Beloit College, B
Cardinal Stritch University, B
Carroll University, B
Carthage College, B
Concordia University Wisconsin, B
Edgewood College, B
Lakeland College, B
Lawrence University, B
Maranatha Baptist University, B
Marian University, B
Marquette University, B
Mount Mary University, B
Northland College, B
Ripon College, B
St. Norbert College, B
Silver Lake College of the Holy Family, B
University of Wisconsin - Eau Claire, B
University of Wisconsin - Green Bay, B
University of Wisconsin - La Crosse, B
University of Wisconsin - Madison, B
University of Wisconsin - Milwaukee, B
University of Wisconsin - Oshkosh, B
University of Wisconsin - Parkside, B
University of Wisconsin - Platteville, B
University of Wisconsin - River Falls, B
University of Wisconsin - Stevens Point, B
University of Wisconsin - Superior, B
University of Wisconsin - Whitewater, B
Viterbo University, B
Wisconsin Lutheran College, B

Wyoming

Casper College, A
Central Wyoming College, A
Eastern Wyoming College, A
Laramie County Community College, A
Northwest College, A
Sheridan College, A
University of Wyoming, B
Western Wyoming Community College, A

U.S. Territories: Guam

University of Guam, B

U.S. Territories: Puerto Rico

Bayamón Central University, B
Inter American University of Puerto Rico, Metropoli-
    tan Campus, B
Inter American University of Puerto Rico, San
    Germán Campus, B
Pontifical Catholic University of Puerto Rico, B
University of Puerto Rico in Cayey, B
University of Puerto Rico, Mayagüez Campus, B
University of Puerto Rico, Río Piedras Campus, B

U.S. Territories: United States Virgin Islands

University of the Virgin Islands, B

Canada

Alberta

Athabasca University, B
Concordia University of Edmonton, B
The King's University, B
Mount Royal University, B
University of Alberta, B
University of Calgary, B
University of Lethbridge, B

British Columbia

Simon Fraser University, B
Thompson Rivers University, B
Trinity Western University, B
The University of British Columbia, B
The University of British Columbia - Okanagan Campus, B
University of the Fraser Valley, B
University of Northern British Columbia, B
University of Victoria, B
Vancouver Island University, B

Manitoba

Booth University College, B
Brandon University, B
University of Manitoba, B
The University of Winnipeg, B

Maritime Provinces: New Brunswick

Crandall University, B
Mount Allison University, B
St. Thomas University, B
Université de Moncton, B
University of New Brunswick Fredericton, B
University of New Brunswick Saint John, B

Maritime Provinces: Nova Scotia

Acadia University, B
Cape Breton University, B
Dalhousie University, B
Mount Saint Vincent University, B
St. Francis Xavier University, B
Saint Mary's University, B
Université Sainte-Anne, B
University of King's College, B

Maritime Provinces: Prince Edward Island

University of Prince Edward Island, B

Newfoundland and Labrador

Memorial University of Newfoundland, B

Ontario

Brock University, B
Carleton University, B
Lakehead University, B
Laurentian University, B
McMaster University, B
Nipissing University, B
Queen's University at Kingston, B
Redeemer University College, B
Royal Military College of Canada, B
Trent University, B
Tyndale University College & Seminary, B
University of Guelph, B
University of Ottawa, B
University of Toronto, B
University of Waterloo, B
The University of Western Ontario, B
University of Windsor, B
Wilfrid Laurier University, B
York University, B

Quebec

Bishop's University, B
Concordia University, B
Université Laval, AB

Université de Montréal, B
Université du Québec à Chicoutimi, B
Université de Sherbrooke, B

Saskatchewan

University of Regina, B
University of Saskatchewan, B

ENGLISH AS A SECOND LANGUAGE

United States

Alabama

The University of Alabama, M
The University of Alabama at Birmingham, M

Arizona

Arizona State University at the Tempe campus, M
Northern Arizona University, MO
The University of Arizona, MD
University of Phoenix - Online Campus, MO

Arkansas

Arkansas Tech University, M
Harding University, M
Henderson State University, O
Southern Arkansas University - Magnolia, M
University of Arkansas at Little Rock, M

California

Azusa Pacific University, M
Biola University, MO
California Baptist University, M
California State University, Chico, M
California State University, Dominguez Hills, O
California State University, East Bay, M
California State University, Fresno, M
California State University, Fullerton, M
California State University, Long Beach, M
California State University, Sacramento, M
California State University, Stanislaus, M
Fresno Pacific University, M
Holy Names University, M
Humboldt State University, M
Notre Dame de Namur University, O
San Diego State University, MO
San Francisco State University, M
San Jose State University, MO
University of California, Berkeley, O
University of California, Los Angeles, MDO
University of California, Riverside, M
University of Phoenix - San Diego Campus, M
University of Phoenix - Southern California Campus, O
University of San Diego, M
University of San Francisco, M
University of Southern California, M

Colorado

Colorado Mesa University, M

Connecticut

Central Connecticut State University, MO
Fairfield University, MO
Post University, M
Sacred Heart University, M
Southern Connecticut State University, M

Delaware

University of Delaware, M
Wilmington University, M

District of Columbia

University of Phoenix - Washington D.C. Campus, M

Florida

Barry University, MO
Carlos Albizu University, Miami Campus, M
Florida Atlantic University, M
Florida International University, M

St. Thomas University, O
University of Central Florida, MDO
University of Florida, O
University of North Florida, M
University of South Florida, MO

Georgia

Columbus State University, O
Kennesaw State University, M

Hawaii

Hawai'i Pacific University, M
University of Hawaii at Manoa, MDO

Idaho

Idaho State University, O
University of Idaho, M

Illinois

Dominican University, M
Lewis University, M
Lincoln Christian University, M
Loyola University Chicago, O
Northeastern Illinois University, M
Quincy University, M
Saint Xavier University, M
Southern Illinois University Carbondale, M
Southern Illinois University Edwardsville, MO
University of Illinois at Chicago, M
University of Illinois at Urbana - Champaign, MD
University of St. Francis, O
Western Illinois University, O
Wheaton College, MO

Indiana

Ball State University, M
Huntington University, M
Indiana State University, MO
Indiana University Bloomington, M
Indiana University - Purdue University Fort Wayne, O
Indiana University - Purdue University Indianapolis, O
Valparaiso University, MO

Iowa

Buena Vista University, M
Iowa State University of Science and Technology, M
The University of Iowa, M
University of Northern Iowa, M

Kansas

Emporia State University, M
MidAmerica Nazarene University, M
Newman University, M

Kentucky

Asbury University, M
Murray State University, M
Western Kentucky University, M

Louisiana

University of Louisiana at Monroe, M

Maine

University of Southern Maine, MO

Maryland

McDaniel College, M
Notre Dame of Maryland University, M
Salisbury University, M
University of Maryland, College Park, M

Massachusetts

Cambridge College, MO
Eastern Nazarene College, O
Elms College, M
Framingham State University, M
Gordon College, O
Lesley University, M
Merrimack College, M
Salem State University, M
Simmons College, MO
University of Massachusetts Amherst, MO

University of Massachusetts Boston, M
Worcester State University, MO

Michigan

Andrews University, M
Central Michigan University, M
Cornerstone University, MO
Eastern Michigan University, MO
Grand Valley State University, M
Madonna University, M
Michigan State University, M
Northern Michigan University, O
Oakland University, O
Wayne State University, DO

Minnesota

Hamline University, M
Minnesota State University Mankato, MO
Minnesota State University Moorhead, M
St. Cloud State University, M
Southwest Minnesota State University, M
University of Minnesota, Twin Cities Campus, M
University of St. Thomas, M
Walden University, MO

Mississippi

Mississippi College, M

Missouri

Avila University, MO
Lindenwood University, M
Missouri Western State University, MO
Northwest Missouri State University, M
Southeast Missouri State University, M
University of Central Missouri, M
University of Missouri - St. Louis, MO

Nebraska

College of Saint Mary, M
University of Nebraska at Kearney, M
University of Nebraska at Omaha, O
Wayne State College, M

Nevada

University of Nevada, Reno, M

New Hampshire

Southern New Hampshire University, M

New Jersey

The College of New Jersey, MO
Kean University, M
Monmouth University, O
Montclair State University, MO
Rider University, O
Rowan University, O
Rutgers University - New Brunswick, M

New Mexico

Eastern New Mexico University, M
University of New Mexico, MD
University of the Southwest, M
Western New Mexico University, M

New York

Adelphi University, MO
Boricua College, M
Canisius College, M
City College of the City University of New York, M
The College of New Rochelle, MO
College of Staten Island of the City University of New York, MO
Fordham University, M
Hofstra University, M
Hunter College of the City University of New York, M
Le Moyne College, M
Lehman College of the City University of New York, M
Long Island University - LIU Brooklyn, M
Manhattanville College, MO
Mercy College, MO
Nazareth College of Rochester, M
New York University, MD

Niagara University, MO
Nyack College, M
Queens College of the City University of New York, M
St. John's University, MO
State University of New York College at Cortland, M
State University of New York at Fredonia, M
State University of New York at New Paltz, MO
Stony Brook University, State University of New York, M
Syracuse University, MO
Touro College, M
University at Buffalo, the State University of New York, MD

North Carolina

East Carolina University, MO
Greensboro College, M
Salem College, M
The University of North Carolina at Chapel Hill, M
The University of North Carolina at Charlotte, M
The University of North Carolina at Greensboro, MO
The University of North Carolina Wilmington, M
Western Carolina University, M

North Dakota

Valley City State University, M

Ohio

Cleveland State University, M
Kent State University, MO
Ohio Dominican University, M
University of Cincinnati, DO
The University of Findlay, M
The University of Toledo, M
Wright State University, M

Oklahoma

Langston University, M
Oklahoma City University, M
University of Central Oklahoma, M

Oregon

Concordia University, M
George Fox University, MO
Multnomah University, M
Pacific University, M
Portland State University, M
University of Portland, M

Pennsylvania

Albright College, M
DeSales University, M
Duquesne University, M
Eastern University, MO
Gannon University, O
Holy Family University, M
Immaculata University, M
Indiana University of Pennsylvania, MD
La Salle University, MO
Lehigh University, O
Messiah College, M
Millersville University of Pennsylvania, M
Penn State University Park, M
Summit University, M
Temple University, M
University of Pennsylvania, MD
University of Pittsburgh, O
West Chester University of Pennsylvania, M
Wilkes University, M

Rhode Island

Brown University, M
Rhode Island College, M

South Carolina

College of Charleston, O
Columbia International University, MO
Furman University, M
University of South Carolina, O

Tennessee

Carson-Newman University, M
Middle Tennessee State University, MO
University of Memphis, MO

The University of Tennessee, MDO

Texas

Dallas Baptist University, M
Houston Baptist University, M
Our Lady of the Lake University of San Antonio, M
Texas A&M University - Kingsville, MD
University of North Texas, M
University of St. Thomas, M
The University of Texas at Arlington, M
The University of Texas at El Paso, O
The University of Texas of the Permian Basin, M
The University of Texas Rio Grande Valley, M
The University of Texas at San Antonio, MO
Wayland Baptist University, M

Utah

Brigham Young University, M
Utah Valley University, M

Vermont

Marlboro College, M
Saint Michael's College, MO

Virginia

George Mason University, M
James Madison University, M
Marymount University, M
Regent University, M
Virginia International University, M

Washington

Central Washington University, M
Eastern Washington University, M
Gonzaga University, M
Heritage University, M
Saint Martin's University, M
Seattle Pacific University, M
Seattle University, MO
University of Washington, M
Washington State University, M

West Virginia

American Public University System, M
West Virginia University, M

Wisconsin

Cardinal Stritch University, M
Edgewood College, M
University of Wisconsin - Milwaukee, O
University of Wisconsin - River Falls, M

U.S. Territories: Guam

University of Guam, M

U.S. Territories: Puerto Rico

Inter American University of Puerto Rico, Arecibo Campus, M
Inter American University of Puerto Rico, Barranquitas Campus, M
Inter American University of Puerto Rico, Metropolitan Campus, M
Inter American University of Puerto Rico, Ponce Campus, M
Inter American University of Puerto Rico, San Germán Campus, M
Pontifical Catholic University of Puerto Rico, M
Universidad del Este, M
Universidad del Turabo, M
University of Puerto Rico, Río Piedras Campus, M

Canada

Alberta

University of Alberta, M

British Columbia

Simon Fraser University, M
Trinity Western University, M
The University of British Columbia, MD

Manitoba

Providence University College & Theological Seminary, MO
University of Manitoba, M

Maritime Provinces: Nova Scotia

Mount Saint Vincent University, M

Ontario

Brock University, M

Quebec

Bishop's University, O
Concordia University, O

ENTERTAINMENT MANAGE-MENT

United States

California

California Intercontinental University, M
California State University, Fullerton, M
California State University, Northridge, M

Colorado

University of Colorado Denver, M

Florida

Full Sail University, M

Illinois

Columbia College Chicago, M

Indiana

Valparaiso University, M

Massachusetts

Berklee College of Music, M

Missouri

Maryville University of Saint Louis, MO

New York

Hofstra University, M
Syracuse University, M

Pennsylvania

Carnegie Mellon University, M

South Carolina

University of South Carolina, M

Texas

University of Dallas, M

ENTOMOLOGY

United States

Alabama

Auburn University, MD

Arizona

The University of Arizona, MD

Arkansas

University of Arkansas, MD

California

University of California, Davis, BMD
University of California, Riverside, BMD

Colorado

Colorado State University, MD

Connecticut

University of Connecticut, MD

Delaware

University of Delaware, BMD

Florida

Broward College, A
South Florida State College, A
University of Florida, BMD

Georgia

University of Georgia, BMD

Hawaii

University of Hawaii at Manoa, MD

Idaho

University of Idaho, MD

Illinois

Illinois State University, M
University of Illinois at Urbana - Champaign, BMD

Indiana

Purdue University, MD

Iowa

Iowa State University of Science and Technology, MD

Kansas

Kansas State University, MD
The University of Kansas, MD

Kentucky

University of Kentucky, MD

Louisiana

Louisiana State University and Agricultural & Mechanical College, MD

Maine

University of Maine, M

Maryland

University of Maryland, College Park, MD

Michigan

Michigan State University, BMD

Minnesota

University of Minnesota, Twin Cities Campus, MD

Mississippi

Mississippi State University, MD

Missouri

University of Missouri, MD

Nebraska

University of Nebraska - Lincoln, BMD

New Jersey

Rutgers University - New Brunswick, MD

New Mexico

New Mexico State University, M

New York

Cornell University, BMD
State University of New York College of Environmental Science and Forestry, MD

North Carolina

North Carolina State University, MD

North Dakota

North Dakota State University, MD
University of North Dakota, MD

Ohio

The Ohio State University, BMD

Oklahoma

Oklahoma State University, BMD

Pennsylvania

Penn State University Park, MD

South Carolina

Clemson University, MD

Tennessee

The University of Tennessee, MD

Texas

Texas A&M University, BMD

Utah

Utah State University, B

Virginia

Virginia Polytechnic Institute and State University, D

Washington

Washington State University, MD

West Virginia

West Virginia University, M

Wisconsin

University of Wisconsin - Madison, BMD

Wyoming

University of Wyoming, MD

Canada

British Columbia

Simon Fraser University, M

Manitoba

University of Manitoba, BMD

Maritime Provinces: New Brunswick

University of New Brunswick Fredericton, B

Newfoundland and Labrador

Memorial University of Newfoundland, B

Ontario

University of Guelph, MD

Quebec

McGill University, MD

ENTREPRENEURIAL AND SMALL BUSINESS OPERA-TIONS

United States

Arizona

Northland Pioneer College, A

Florida

Florida State University, B

Illinois

Loyola University Chicago, B

Massachusetts

Babson College, B

Minnesota

Crown College, B

Nevada

Truckee Meadows Community College, A

New Jersey

Fairleigh Dickinson University, College at Florham, B
Fairleigh Dickinson University, Metropolitan Campus, B

New York

Fashion Institute of Technology, B
New York Institute of Technology, B
State University of New York at Plattsburgh, B

North Dakota

Dakota College at Bottineau, A

Pennsylvania

Penn State University Park, B

Tennessee

Lipscomb University, B

Texas

Virginia College in Austin, A

Utah

LDS Business College, A

U.S. Territories: Puerto Rico

National University College (Bayamón), A

ENTREPRENEURSHIP/ENTRE-PRENEURIAL STUDIES

United States

Alabama

Samford University, B
The University of Alabama in Huntsville, M

Alaska

University of Alaska Anchorage, AB

Arizona

Arizona State University at the Tempe campus, BM
Eastern Arizona College, A
Grand Canyon University, M
The University of Arizona, B

Arkansas

University of Arkansas at Little Rock, O
University of Central Arkansas, B

California

Azusa Pacific University, M
California Baptist University, M
California Intercontinental University, D
California Lutheran University, MO
California State University, Dominguez Hills, B
California State University, East Bay, M
California State University, Fullerton, BM
California State University, San Bernardino, M
Cogswell Polytechnical College, ABM
Cuyamaca College, A
Glendale Community College, A
John Paul the Great Catholic University, B
Loyola Marymount University, B
Menlo College, B
Notre Dame de Namur University, M
Pepperdine University, M
Point Loma Nazarene University, B
Reedley College, A
San Diego State University, M
San Francisco State University, M
Santa Clara University, M
University of San Francisco, BM
University of Southern California, M

Colorado

Aims Community College, A
Colorado Mountain College (Leadville), A
Johnson & Wales University, B
Lamar Community College, A

University of Colorado Boulder, D
University of Colorado Denver, M
Western State Colorado University, B

Connecticut

Fairfield University, MO
Post University, M
Quinnipiac University, B
Three Rivers Community College, A
University of Bridgeport, M
University of Hartford, B

Delaware

Delaware Technical & Community College, Jack F. Owens Campus, A
Delaware Technical & Community College, Terry Campus, A
University of Delaware, M

District of Columbia

American University, M

Florida

Carlos Albizu University, Miami Campus, M
Florida Atlantic University, M
Florida Institute of Technology, M
Fortis College (Winter Park), A
Jacksonville University, B
Lynn University, B
Miami Dade College, A
Northwest Florida State College, A
Rollins College, M
Stetson University, B
Tallahassee Community College, A
University of Central Florida, MO
University of Florida, M
University of Miami, B
University of Phoenix - North Florida Campus, B
University of South Florida, MO
University of South Florida, St. Petersburg, B
The University of Tampa, BM

Georgia

Georgia State University, M
Reinhardt University, B
South University, M

Hawaii

Hawai'i Pacific University, B
University of Hawaii at Manoa, BMO

Idaho

College of Southern Idaho, A
University of Idaho, D

Illinois

Benedictine University, M
Bradley University, B
DePaul University, M
Elgin Community College, A
Ellis University, B
Governors State University, B
Loyola University Chicago, M
Millikin University, B
Northwestern University, M
Trinity Christian College, B
University of Chicago, M
University of Illinois at Chicago, B
University of Illinois at Urbana - Champaign, B
University of St. Francis, B

Indiana

Anderson University, B
Ball State University, B
Butler University, B
Grace College, B
Indiana Wesleyan University, B
Trine University, B
University of Indianapolis, B
University of Notre Dame, B
University of Southern Indiana, B
Valparaiso University, O

Iowa

Buena Vista University, B
Kaplan University, Davenport Campus, M
North Iowa Area Community College, A

Kansas

Cowley County Community College and Area Vocational - Technical School, A
Independence Community College, A
Johnson County Community College, A
Kansas State University, B
Wichita Area Technical College, A
Wichita State University, B

Kentucky

Northern Kentucky University, B
University of Louisville, MD
Western Kentucky University, B

Louisiana

Loyola University New Orleans, M
Southern University at New Orleans, B
Tulane University, M

Maine

College of the Atlantic, B
Husson University, B
University of Maine at Machias, B

Maryland

Anne Arundel Community College, A
Harford Community College, A
University of Baltimore, BM

Massachusetts

Babson College, BM
Bay Path University, M
Bristol Community College, A
Bunker Hill Community College, A
Cambridge College, M
Endicott College, B
Hampshire College, B
Hult International Business School, M
Lasell College, B
Northeastern University, BM
Salem State University, B
Suffolk University, BM
University of Massachusetts Amherst, M
University of Massachusetts Lowell, BMO
Western New England University, B

Michigan

Adrian College, B
Baker College, A
Central Michigan University, B
Cleary University, B
Eastern Michigan University, BMO
Lake Superior State University, B
Montcalm Community College, A
Mott Community College, A
Northern Michigan University, B
Northwood University, Michigan Campus, B
Oakland Community College, A
Oakland University, O
University of Michigan - Flint, B
Western Michigan University, B

Minnesota

Capella University, MD
Crown College, B
Minnesota State Community and Technical College - Detroit Lakes, A
North Hennepin Community College, A
Northland Community and Technical College, A
Saint Mary's University of Minnesota, B
Saint Paul College - A Community & Technical College, A
University of Minnesota, Crookston, B
University of Minnesota, Duluth, B
University of Minnesota, Twin Cities Campus, D
University of St. Thomas, B
Walden University, MD

Mississippi

Jackson State University, B

Missouri

Avila University, B
Lincoln University, M
Lindenwood University, BM
Missouri State University, B
Missouri State University - West Plains, A
Saint Louis University, B
Southeast Missouri State University, M
University of Missouri - Kansas City, D
Washington University in St. Louis, B

Montana

Great Falls College Montana State University, A

Nebraska

Northeast Community College, A
Peru State College, M

Nevada

Sierra Nevada College, B
University of Nevada, Las Vegas, BO

New Hampshire

Dartmouth College, D
Southern New Hampshire University, M

New Jersey

Fairleigh Dickinson University, College at Florham,
BMO
Fairleigh Dickinson University, Metropolitan Campus, MO
Felician University, M
Rider University, B
Rowan University, B
Stevens Institute of Technology, M
Thomas Edison State University, B

New Mexico

Santa Fe Community College, A
University of New Mexico, M

New York

Baruch College of the City University of New York,
M
Binghamton University, State University of New
York, B
Canisius College, B
Clarkson University, B
Columbia University, M
Genesee Community College, A
Herkimer County Community College, A
Hofstra University, B
LIM College, M
Long Island University - LIU Brooklyn, M
Marymount Manhattan College, B
Mercy College, B
Morrisville State College, B
Nassau Community College, A
New York University, MO
Pace University, BM
Pace University, Pleasantville Campus, B
Rensselaer Polytechnic Institute, M
Rochester Institute of Technology, M
Syracuse University, BM
Tompkins Cortland Community College, A
University of Rochester, M

North Carolina

Catawba Valley Community College, A
Cleveland Community College, A
Craven Community College, AB
Duke University, M
Elon University, B
High Point University, B
Lenoir-Rhyne University, BM
Mars Hill University, B
North Carolina State University, M
Richmond Community College, A
South Piedmont Community College, A
The University of North Carolina at Greensboro, B
The University of North Carolina at Pembroke, B

Western Carolina University, BM

North Dakota

United Tribes Technical College, A
University of North Dakota, B

Ohio

Ashland University, B
Baldwin Wallace University, BM
Belmont College, A
Cincinnati State Technical and Community College,
A
Columbus State Community College, A
Franklin University, B
Kent State University, B
Lake Erie College, B
Northwest State Community College, A
Ohio Northern University, B
Southern State Community College, A
University of Dayton, B
University of Rio Grande, M
The University of Toledo, B
Wittenberg University, B
Xavier University, B

Oklahoma

Cameron University, M
East Central University, B
Northeastern State University, B
Oklahoma State University, BMD
Oral Roberts University, M

Oregon

Central Oregon Community College, A
George Fox University, B
University of Portland, M

Pennsylvania

Carnegie Mellon University, BD
Central Penn College, A
Community College of Allegheny County, A
Community College of Beaver County, A
Delaware County Community College, A
Delaware Valley University, M
Drexel University, BM
Duquesne University, B
Eastern University, B
Gannon University, B
Grove City College, B
Harcum College, A
Harrisburg University of Science and Technology, M
Juniata College, B
Lehigh University, M
Mercyhurst University, M
Seton Hill University, BMO
Temple University, BMD
University of Pennsylvania, M
University of Pittsburgh at Bradford, B
Waynesburg University, B
West Chester University of Pennsylvania, O
Wilkes University, BM
York College of Pennsylvania, B

Rhode Island

Bryant University, B
Johnson & Wales University, B
Salve Regina University, M
University of Rhode Island, M

South Carolina

Clemson University, M
Florence-Darlington Technical College, A

South Dakota

South Dakota State University, B
University of Sioux Falls, M

Tennessee

Belmont University, B
East Tennessee State University, O
Lipscomb University, B

Texas

Baylor University, B
Dallas Baptist University, BM
Lamar University, BM
St. Edward's University, B
St. Mary's University, B
Sam Houston State University, B
Southern Methodist University, M
Texas Christian University, B
University of Houston, B
University of Houston - Victoria, M
University of the Incarnate Word, D
University of North Texas, B
The University of Texas at Austin, M
The University of Texas at Dallas, M
The University of Texas Rio Grande Valley, B
The University of Texas at San Antonio, B

Utah

Brigham Young University, B
LDS Business College, A
Salt Lake Community College, A
University of Utah, B

Vermont

Southern Vermont College, B
University of Vermont, B

Virginia

James Madison University, M
Regent University, MDO
Shenandoah University, B
Stratford University (Falls Church), M
Virginia International University, M
Virginia Union University, B

Washington

Edmonds Community College, A
Everett Community College, A
University of Washington, B
Washington State University, B

West Virginia

American Public University System, BM

Wisconsin

Marquette University, BO
Northcentral Technical College, A
Northland College, B
University of Wisconsin - Whitewater, B

Wyoming

Casper College, A
Central Wyoming College, A
Laramie County Community College, A

U.S. Territories: Puerto Rico

Inter American University of Puerto Rico, Aguadilla
Campus, B
Inter American University of Puerto Rico, Barranquitas Campus, AB
Inter American University of Puerto Rico, Bayamón
Campus, B
Inter American University of Puerto Rico, Metropolitan Campus, B
Inter American University of Puerto Rico, Ponce
Campus, B
Inter American University of Puerto Rico, San
Germán Campus, B
Pontifical Catholic University of Puerto Rico, B
University of the Sacred Heart, B

Canada

Alberta

University of Alberta, B

British Columbia

British Columbia Institute of Technology, A
Royal Roads University, B
The University of British Columbia - Okanagan
Campus, B

Maritime Provinces: New Brunswick

University of New Brunswick Fredericton, M

Maritime Provinces: Nova Scotia

Cape Breton University, B
Dalhousie University, B

Ontario

Queen's University at Kingston, M
University of Ottawa, B
University of Waterloo, M
The University of Western Ontario, BM
York University, B

Quebec

HEC Montreal, B
McGill University, BM
Université Laval, O
Université du Québec à Trois-Rivières, B

Saskatchewan

University of Regina, B

ENVIRONMENTAL BIOLOGY

United States

Alabama

Jacksonville State University, B

Arizona

Eastern Arizona College, A

California

California State Polytechnic University, Pomona, B
Humboldt State University, B
The Master's College and Seminary, B
Sonoma State University, M
University of California, Santa Cruz, MD
University of La Verne, B
University of Southern California, M

Colorado

Fort Lewis College, B
Western State Colorado University, B

Florida

University of South Florida, MD
University of West Florida, M

Georgia

Georgia State University, MD

Illinois

Blackburn College, B
Governors State University, M
Greenville College, B

Indiana

Grace College, B
Manchester University, B

Iowa

Northwestern College, B
University of Dubuque, B
William Penn University, B

Kansas

Emporia State University, M
Friends University, B

Kentucky

Midway University, B
University of Louisville, D

Louisiana

Nicholls State University, M
Tulane University, B
University of Louisiana at Lafayette, D

Maine

Colby College, B
College of the Atlantic, B
Unity College, B

Maryland

Hood College, M
McDaniel College, B
Morgan State University, D

Massachusetts

Boston University, B
Bridgewater State University, B
Fitchburg State University, B
Massachusetts Institute of Technology, D
Salem State University, B
University of Massachusetts Amherst, MD

Michigan

Cornerstone University, B
Ferris State University, B
Marygrove College, B
Michigan State University, B

Minnesota

Minnesota State University Mankato, B
St. Cloud State University, B
Saint Mary's University of Minnesota, B

Mississippi

University of Southern Mississippi, M

Missouri

Central Methodist University, B
Lindenwood University, B
Missouri University of Science and Technology, M
Washington University in St. Louis, BD

New Hampshire

Franklin Pierce University, B
Plymouth State University, B

New Jersey

Monmouth University, B
Rutgers University - New Brunswick, MD

New York

Barnard College, B
Colgate University, B
Columbia University, B
Columbia University, School of General Studies, B
Houghton College, B
Iona College, B
Roberts Wesleyan College, B
State University of New York College at Cortland, B
State University of New York College of Environmental Science and Forestry, BMD

North Carolina

Chowan University, B
Wingate University, B

North Dakota

University of North Dakota, MD

Ohio

Heidelberg University, B
Ohio Northern University, B
Ohio University, MD
Otterbein University, B
University of Dayton, B
University of Mount Union, B
Youngstown State University, M

Oklahoma

Southern Nazarene University, B

Pennsylvania

Arcadia University, B
Cedar Crest College, B
Chatham University, M
East Stroudsburg University of Pennsylvania, B
Elizabethtown College, B

Keystone College, B
Philadelphia University, B
University of Pittsburgh at Johnstown, B

Tennessee

Sewanee: The University of the South, B
The University of Tennessee at Martin, B

Texas

Baylor University, M
Texas A&M University, B

Vermont

Bennington College, B
Marlboro College, B

Virginia

Christopher Newport University, B
Hampton University, M
Liberty University, B

Washington

Central Washington University, B

West Virginia

West Virginia University, MD

Wisconsin

Beloit College, B
University of Wisconsin - Madison, MD
Viterbo University, B

Wyoming

Eastern Wyoming College, A

U.S. Territories: Puerto Rico

Inter American University of Puerto Rico, Bayamón Campus, B
Universidad del Turabo, D

Canada

Alberta

University of Alberta, BMD

British Columbia

The University of British Columbia, B

Maritime Provinces: New Brunswick

University of New Brunswick Saint John, B

Maritime Provinces: Nova Scotia

Dalhousie University, M

Newfoundland and Labrador

Memorial University of Newfoundland, B

Ontario

Lakehead University, B
Nipissing University, B
University of Guelph, BMD
University of Windsor, B
York University, B

Quebec

McGill University, B

Saskatchewan

University of Regina, B
University of Saskatchewan, B

ENVIRONMENTAL CONTROL TECHNOLOGIES/TECHNICIANS

United States

Delaware

Delaware State University, B

Florida

Hillsborough Community College, A

Massachusetts

Cape Cod Community College, A
Holyoke Community College, A
Massachusetts Bay Community College, A

Montana

Montana Tech of The University of Montana, A

New Jersey

Middlesex County College, A
Thomas Edison State University, B

New York

Westchester Community College, A

North Dakota

Bismarck State College, A

Ohio

Cincinnati State Technical and Community College, A
Columbus State Community College, A
James A. Rhodes State College, A

South Carolina

Central Carolina Technical College, A

South Dakota

Western Dakota Technical Institute, A

Virginia

Mountain Empire Community College, A
Northern Virginia Community College, A

West Virginia

Davis & Elkins College, B

U.S. Territories: Puerto Rico

University of Puerto Rico in Utuado, B

ENVIRONMENTAL DESIGN/ARCHITECTURE

United States

Alabama

Auburn University, B

Arizona

Arizona State University at the Tempe campus, BD
Scottsdale Community College, A

California

Art Center College of Design, BM
NewSchool of Architecture and Design, B
Otis College of Art and Design, B
San Diego State University, M
University of California, Berkeley, MD
University of California, Irvine, D

Colorado

University of Colorado Boulder, B

Connecticut

Yale University, MD

Florida

Florida Atlantic University, BO

Georgia

University of Georgia, M

Hawaii

University of Hawaii at Manoa, B

Illinois

Olivet Nazarene University, B

Indiana

Ball State University, B

Iowa

Iowa Lakes Community College, A

Kansas

Kansas State University, D

Maine

College of the Atlantic, B

Massachusetts

Boston Architectural College, B
University of Massachusetts Amherst, B

Michigan

Lawrence Technological University, B
Michigan State University, M

Minnesota

University of Minnesota, Twin Cities Campus, B

Missouri

University of Missouri, M
University of Missouri - Kansas City, B

Montana

Montana State University, B

New Jersey

Rutgers University - New Brunswick, B

New Mexico

Central New Mexico Community College, A
University of New Mexico, B

New York

Columbia University, M
Cornell University, BM
Queensborough Community College of the City University of New York, A
State University of New York College of Environmental Science and Forestry, B
Stony Brook University, State University of New York, B
University at Buffalo, the State University of New York, B

North Carolina

North Carolina State University, B

North Dakota

North Dakota State University, B

Ohio

Bowling Green State University, B
Kent State University, M

Oklahoma

University of Oklahoma, B

Pennsylvania

Delaware Valley University, B
Marywood University, B
University of Pennsylvania, B

South Carolina

Clemson University, D

Tennessee

University of Memphis, B

Texas

Texas Tech University, MD
University of Houston, B

Vermont

Bennington College, B
Green Mountain College, B

Virginia

Virginia Polytechnic Institute and State University, D

Washington

Bastyr University, O

U.S. Territories: Puerto Rico

University of Puerto Rico, Río Piedras Campus, B

Canada

Alberta

University of Calgary, MD

Manitoba

University of Manitoba, B

Maritime Provinces: Nova Scotia

Dalhousie University, B

Quebec

Université de Montréal, MDO
Université du Québec à Montréal, B

ENVIRONMENTAL EDUCATION

United States

Alaska

Alaska Pacific University, M

Arizona

Prescott College, M

Colorado

University of Colorado Denver, M

Connecticut

Southern Connecticut State University, MO

Florida

Florida Atlantic University, M
Florida Institute of Technology, M
University of Florida, O

Indiana

Goshen College, M

Minnesota

Hamline University, M
University of Minnesota, Twin Cities Campus, M

New Jersey

Montclair State University, M

New York

Brooklyn College of the City University of New York, M
New York University, M
State University of New York College at Cortland, M

North Carolina

Montreat College, M

Oregon

Concordia University, M
Southern Oregon University, M

Pennsylvania

Arcadia University, MO
Chatham University, M
Slippery Rock University of Pennsylvania, M

Washington

Western Washington University, M

West Virginia

West Virginia University, MD

Wisconsin

Concordia University Wisconsin, M

Canada

British Columbia

Royal Roads University, MO
University of Victoria, D

Quebec

Université du Québec à Montréal, O

ENVIRONMENTAL ENGINEER-ING TECHNOLOGY/ENVIRON-MENTAL TECHNOLOGY

United States

Alabama

Auburn University, MD
Central Alabama Community College, A
James H. Faulkner State Community College, A
Northwest-Shoals Community College, A
The University of Alabama, MD
The University of Alabama at Birmingham, D
The University of Alabama in Huntsville, MD

Alaska

University of Alaska Anchorage, M
University of Alaska Fairbanks, MD

Arizona

Arizona State University at the Tempe campus, MD
Northern Arizona University, M
The University of Arizona, MD

Arkansas

East Arkansas Community College, A
Pulaski Technical College, A
Southern Arkansas University Tech, A
University of Arkansas, M

California

Allan Hancock College, A
Bakersfield College, A
California Institute of Technology, MD
California Polytechnic State University, San Luis Obispo, M
California State University, Fullerton, M
California State University, Long Beach, B
Cuyamaca College, A
Merced College, A
Napa Valley College, A
National University, M
Oxnard College, A
San Diego City College, A
Stanford University, MDO
University of California, Berkeley, MD
University of California, Davis, MDO
University of California, Irvine, MD
University of California, Los Angeles, MD
University of California, Merced, MD
University of California, Riverside, MD
University of Southern California, MD

Colorado

Colorado School of Mines, MD
IntelliTec College (Grand Junction), A
Trinidad State Junior College, A
University of Colorado Boulder, MD
University of Colorado Denver, MD

Connecticut

Naugatuck Valley Community College, A
Three Rivers Community College, A
University of Connecticut, MD
University of New Haven, M
Yale University, MD

Delaware

University of Delaware, MD

District of Columbia

The Catholic University of America, D
The George Washington University, MDO

Florida

Florida Atlantic University, M
Florida International University, M
Florida State University, MD
Miami Dade College, A
Polytechnic University of Puerto Rico, Miami Campus, M
Polytechnic University of Puerto Rico, Orlando Campus, M
University of Central Florida, MD
University of Florida, MDO
University of South Florida, MD

Georgia

Georgia Institute of Technology, MD
Georgia Northwestern Technical College, A
Kennesaw State University, B
Mercer University, M
University of Georgia, M

Hawaii

University of Hawaii at Manoa, MD

Idaho

Idaho State University, M
University of Idaho, M

Illinois

Black Hawk College, A
City Colleges of Chicago, Wilbur Wright College, A
Illinois Institute of Technology, MD
Northwestern University, MD
Southern Illinois University Edwardsville, M
University of Illinois at Urbana - Champaign, MD

Indiana

Rose-Hulman Institute of Technology, M
University of Notre Dame, M

Iowa

Clinton Community College, A
Iowa Lakes Community College, A
Iowa State University of Science and Technology, MD
Muscatine Community College, A
Scott Community College, A
The University of Iowa, MD

Kansas

Kansas State University, MD
The University of Kansas, MD

Kentucky

Bluegrass Community and Technical College, A
University of Louisville, MDO

Louisiana

Louisiana State University and Agricultural & Mechanical College, MD

Maryland

Harford Community College, A
Johns Hopkins University, MDO
University of Maryland, Baltimore County, MD
University of Maryland, College Park, MD
Wor-Wic Community College, A

Massachusetts

Bristol Community College, A
Massachusetts Institute of Technology, MDO
Roxbury Community College, A
Tufts University, BMD
University of Massachusetts Amherst, M
University of Massachusetts Lowell, MDO
Worcester Polytechnic Institute, MDO

Michigan

Baker College, A
Bay de Noc Community College, A

Delta College, A
Lansing Community College, A
Michigan State University, MD
Michigan Technological University, MD
Schoolcraft College, A
University of Detroit Mercy, MD
University of Michigan, MDO

Minnesota

Vermilion Community College, A

Missouri

Crowder College, A
Missouri University of Science and Technology, M
University of Missouri, MD
Washington University in St. Louis, MD

Montana

Montana State University, MD
Montana Tech of The University of Montana, M

Nebraska

University of Nebraska - Lincoln, MD

Nevada

College of Southern Nevada, A
University of Nevada, Las Vegas, MD

New Hampshire

Dartmouth College, MD

New Jersey

Princeton University, MD
Rutgers University - New Brunswick, MD
Stevens Institute of Technology, MDO

New Mexico

New Mexico Institute of Mining and Technology, M

New York

City College of the City University of New York, B
Clarkson University, MD
Columbia University, MD
Cornell University, MD
Erie Community College, North Campus, A
Manhattan College, M
New York City College of Technology of the City University of New York, A
New York Institute of Technology, M
New York University, M
Onondaga Community College, A
Queensborough Community College of the City University of New York, A
Rensselaer Polytechnic Institute, MD
State University of New York College of Environmental Science and Forestry, MD
State University of New York College of Technology at Alfred, A
Syracuse University, M
United States Military Academy, B
University at Buffalo, the State University of New York, MD

North Carolina

Central Piedmont Community College, A
Duke University, MD
North Carolina State University, B
The University of North Carolina at Chapel Hill, MD
The University of North Carolina at Charlotte, D

North Dakota

Dakota College at Bottineau, A
North Dakota State University, MD
University of North Dakota, M

Ohio

Bowling Green State University, B
Cincinnati State Technical and Community College, A
Cleveland State University, MD
Kent State University at Trumbull, A
Ohio University, M
Ohio University - Chillicothe, A
Shawnee State University, B

University of Cincinnati, MD
University of Dayton, M
Youngstown State University, M

Oklahoma

Oklahoma State University, MD
Rose State College, A
University of Oklahoma, MD

Oregon

Oregon Health & Science University, MD
Oregon State University, MD
Portland State University, MD

Pennsylvania

Carnegie Mellon University, MD
Community College of Allegheny County, A
Community College of Beaver County, A
Drexel University, MD
Gannon University, M
Lehigh University, MD
Penn State Harrisburg, M
Penn State University Park, MD
Temple University, M
University of Pittsburgh, MD
Villanova University, MO

Rhode Island

Brown University, B
University of Rhode Island, MD

South Carolina

Clemson University, MD

Tennessee

Middle Tennessee State University, B
Tennessee State University, M
University of Memphis, M
The University of Tennessee, M
Vanderbilt University, MD

Texas

Angelina College, A
Austin Community College District, A
El Paso Community College, A
Lamar University, M
Rice University, MD
Southern Methodist University, MD
Texas A&M University - Kingsville, MD
Texas State Technical College, A
Texas Tech University, MD
The University of Texas at Austin, MD
The University of Texas at El Paso, MD
The University of Texas at San Antonio, MD
The University of Texas at Tyler, M

Utah

Salt Lake Community College, A
University of Utah, MD
Utah State University, MDO

Vermont

Norwich University, M
University of Vermont, MD

Virginia

George Mason University, M
Old Dominion University, MD
Virginia Polytechnic Institute and State University,
   MO

Washington

Clover Park Technical College, A
Shoreline Community College, A
Skagit Valley College, A
University of Washington, MD
Washington State University, MD

West Virginia

Marshall University, M
West Virginia University, MD
West Virginia University at Parkersburg, A

Wisconsin

Marquette University, MDO
University of Wisconsin - Green Bay, B
University of Wisconsin - Madison, MD
University of Wisconsin - Whitewater, B

Wyoming

Sheridan College, A
University of Wyoming, M

U.S. Territories: Puerto Rico

University of Puerto Rico in Aguadilla, B

Canada

Alberta

University of Alberta, MD
University of Calgary, MD

British Columbia

British Columbia Institute of Technology, B
The University of British Columbia, B

Maritime Provinces: New Brunswick

University of New Brunswick Fredericton, MD

Maritime Provinces: Nova Scotia

Dalhousie University, MD

Newfoundland and Labrador

Memorial University of Newfoundland, M

Ontario

Carleton University, MD
Lakehead University, M
Royal Military College of Canada, MD
University of Guelph, BMD
University of Waterloo, MD
The University of Western Ontario, MD
University of Windsor, MD

Quebec

Concordia University, O
École Polytechnique de Montréal, MD
McGill University, MD
Université Laval, M
Université de Sherbrooke, M

Saskatchewan

University of Regina, MD

ENVIRONMENTAL/ENVIRON-
MENTAL HEALTH ENGINEER-
ING

United States

Alabama

The University of Alabama, B

Arizona

Arizona State University at the Polytechnic campus,
   B
Northern Arizona University, B

California

California Polytechnic State University, San Luis
   Obispo, B
Humboldt State University, B
San Diego State University, B
Santa Barbara City College, A
Stanford University, B
University of California, Berkeley, B
University of California, Irvine, B
University of California, Merced, B
University of California, Riverside, B
University of Southern California, B

Colorado

Colorado School of Mines, B
Colorado State University, B
United States Air Force Academy, B
University of Colorado Boulder, B

Connecticut

University of Connecticut, B
Yale University, B

Delaware

University of Delaware, B

District of Columbia

The George Washington University, B

Florida

Florida Gulf Coast University, B
Florida International University, B
South Florida State College, A
University of Central Florida, B
University of Florida, B
University of Miami, B

Georgia

Georgia Institute of Technology, B
Kennesaw State University, B
University of Georgia, B

Illinois

Loyola University Chicago, B
Northwestern University, B
University of Illinois at Urbana - Champaign, B

Indiana

Indiana Tech, B
Purdue University, B
Taylor University, B
University of Notre Dame, B

Louisiana

Louisiana State University and Agricultural & Mechanical College, B
Tulane University, B

Maryland

Johns Hopkins University, B

Massachusetts

Bristol Community College, A
Massachusetts Institute of Technology, B
Suffolk University, B
Tufts University, B
Worcester Polytechnic Institute, B

Michigan

Michigan Technological University, B
University of Michigan, B

Minnesota

University of Minnesota, Twin Cities Campus, B

Missouri

Missouri University of Science and Technology, B

Montana

Montana Tech of The University of Montana, B

Nevada

University of Nevada, Reno, B

New Hampshire

University of New Hampshire, B

New Jersey

New Jersey Institute of Technology, B
Stevens Institute of Technology, B

New Mexico

New Mexico Institute of Mining and Technology, B

New York

Clarkson University, B
Columbia University, B
Cornell University, B
Manhattan College, B
Rensselaer Polytechnic Institute, B
State University of New York College of Environ-
    mental Science and Forestry, B
Syracuse University, B
United States Military Academy, B
University at Buffalo, the State University of New
    York, B

North Carolina

Elon University, B
North Carolina State University, B

North Dakota

University of North Dakota, B

Ohio

Central State University, B
The Ohio State University, B
University of Cincinnati, B

Oklahoma

East Central University, B
Oral Roberts University, B
University of Oklahoma, B

Oregon

Oregon State University, B

Pennsylvania

Bucknell University, B
Drexel University, B
Gannon University, B
Lafayette College, B
Lehigh University, B
Penn State Abington, B
Penn State Altoona, B
Penn State Beaver, B
Penn State Berks, B
Penn State Brandywine, B
Penn State DuBois, B
Penn State Erie, The Behrend College, B
Penn State Fayette, The Eberly Campus, B
Penn State Greater Allegheny, B
Penn State Harrisburg, B
Penn State Hazleton, B
Penn State Lehigh Valley, B
Penn State Mont Alto, B
Penn State New Kensington, B
Penn State Schuylkill, B
Penn State Shenango, B
Penn State University Park, B
Penn State Wilkes-Barre, B
Penn State Worthington Scranton, B
Penn State York, B
Temple University, B
University of Pennsylvania, B
Wilkes University, B

Rhode Island

Roger Williams University, B

South Carolina

Clemson University, B

South Dakota

South Dakota School of Mines and Technology, B

Texas

Rice University, B
Southern Methodist University, B
Tarleton State University, B
Texas A&M University - Kingsville, B
Texas Tech University, B

Utah

Utah State University, B

Vermont

University of Vermont, B

Washington

Seattle University, B

Wisconsin

Marquette University, B
University of Wisconsin - Platteville, B

Wyoming

Central Wyoming College, A

U.S. Territories: Puerto Rico

Polytechnic University of Puerto Rico, B

Canada

British Columbia

British Columbia Institute of Technology, A
University of Northern British Columbia, B

Maritime Provinces: Nova Scotia

Dalhousie University, B

Ontario

Carleton University, B
University of Waterloo, B
The University of Western Ontario, B
University of Windsor, B

Quebec

Université Laval, B

Saskatchewan

University of Regina, B
University of Saskatchewan, B

ENVIRONMENTAL HEALTH

United States

Alabama

Community College of the Air Force, A

Arkansas

University of Arkansas at Little Rock, B

California

California State University, Northridge, B

Colorado

Colorado State University, B

Georgia

University of Georgia, B

Idaho

Boise State University, B
North Idaho College, A

Illinois

Illinois State University, B
University of Illinois at Urbana - Champaign, B

Kentucky

Eastern Kentucky University, B
Western Kentucky University, B

Massachusetts

University of Massachusetts Lowell, B

Michigan

Central Michigan University, B
Oakland University, B

Mississippi

Mississippi Valley State University, B

Missouri

Drury University, B
Missouri Southern State University, B

New York

Queensborough Community College of the City Uni-
    versity of New York, A
State University of New York College of Environ-
    mental Science and Forestry, B
York College of the City University of New York, B

North Carolina

East Carolina University, B
The University of North Carolina at Chapel Hill, B
Western Carolina University, B

Ohio

Bowling Green State University, B
Ohio University, B
Wright State University, B

Oklahoma

East Central University, B

Oregon

Mt. Hood Community College, A
Willamette University, B

South Carolina

Benedict College, B

Tennessee

East Tennessee State University, B
Roane State Community College, A

Texas

Amarillo College, A
Baylor University, B
Texas Southern University, B

Washington

University of Washington, B

U.S. Territories: Puerto Rico

Universidad Metropolitana, B

Canada

Alberta

Concordia University of Edmonton, B

British Columbia

British Columbia Institute of Technology, AB

Saskatchewan

University of Regina, B

ENVIRONMENTAL LAW

United States

California

Chapman University, D
Golden Gate University, M
Stanford University, M

Colorado

University of Colorado Denver, M

District of Columbia

Georgetown University, M

Florida

Florida State University, M
University of Florida, M

Idaho

University of Idaho, D

New Jersey

Montclair State University, O

New York

Pace University, MD

Oklahoma

The University of Tulsa, O

Oregon

Lewis & Clark College, M

Pennsylvania

Lehigh University, O
University of Pittsburgh, M

Texas

Baylor University, D
University of Houston, M

Canada

Alberta

University of Calgary, MO

ENVIRONMENTAL AND OCCU-PATIONAL HEALTH

United States

Alabama

Columbia Southern University, M
The University of Alabama at Birmingham, MD
University of North Alabama, M
University of South Alabama, M

Arkansas

University of Arkansas for Medical Sciences, MO

California

California State University, Northridge, M
Loma Linda University, M
San Diego State University, M
Trident University International, O
University of California, Berkeley, MD
University of California, Los Angeles, MD
University of Southern California, M

Colorado

Colorado State University, MD
University of Colorado Denver, M

Connecticut

University of Connecticut, M
University of New Haven, M
Yale University, MD

District of Columbia

The George Washington University, D

Florida

Embry-Riddle Aeronautical University - Worldwide, M
Florida International University, MD
University of Florida, MD
University of Miami, M
University of South Florida, MDO
University of West Florida, M

Georgia

Emory University, MD
Fort Valley State University, M
Georgia Southern University, MO
Mercer University, M
University of Georgia, M

Idaho

Boise State University, M

Illinois

Lewis University, M
Loyola University Chicago, MO
University of Illinois at Chicago, MD

Indiana

Indiana State University, M
Indiana University Bloomington, MD
Indiana University - Purdue University Indianapolis, M
Purdue University, M
University of Saint Francis, M

Iowa

The University of Iowa, MDO

Kansas

The University of Kansas, M

Kentucky

Eastern Kentucky University, M
Murray State University, M
University of Louisville, MD

Louisiana

Louisiana State University Health Sciences Center, M
Tulane University, MD

Maryland

Johns Hopkins University, D
Towson University, D
University of Maryland, College Park, M

Massachusetts

Anna Maria College, M
Boston University, MD
Harvard University, MD
Tufts University, MD
University of Massachusetts Amherst, MD

Michigan

Oakland University, M
University of Michigan, MD

Minnesota

Capella University, MD
Saint Mary's University of Minnesota, M
University of Minnesota, Twin Cities Campus, MDO

Mississippi

Mississippi Valley State University, M

Missouri

University of Central Missouri, M

Nebraska

University of Nebraska Medical Center, D

Nevada

University of Nevada, Reno, MD

New Hampshire

Keene State College, M

New Jersey

Rutgers University - New Brunswick, MDO

New York

Columbia University, MD
Hunter College of the City University of New York, M
New York University, MD
Rochester Institute of Technology, M
University at Albany, State University of New York, MD

North Carolina

Duke University, O
East Carolina University, MD
North Carolina Agricultural and Technical State University, M
The University of North Carolina at Chapel Hill, MD

Ohio

University of Cincinnati, MD
The University of Toledo, MO

Oklahoma

Northeastern State University, M
Southeastern Oklahoma State University, M
University of Oklahoma Health Sciences Center, MD

Oregon

Oregon State University, MD

Pennsylvania

Gannon University, M
Indiana University of Pennsylvania, MD
Saint Joseph's University, M
Temple University, M
University of Pittsburgh, MDO
West Chester University of Pennsylvania, M

South Carolina

Clemson University, M
University of South Carolina, MD

Tennessee

East Tennessee State University, MD
University of Memphis, M

Texas

The University of Texas at Tyler, M

Washington

University of Washington, MD

West Virginia

West Virginia University, D

Wisconsin

University of Wisconsin - Milwaukee, D
University of Wisconsin - Whitewater, M

U.S. Territories: Puerto Rico

University of Puerto Rico, Medical Sciences Campus, MD
University of the Sacred Heart, M

Canada

Alberta

University of Alberta, M

British Columbia

The University of British Columbia, MD

Ontario

University of Toronto, M

Quebec

McGill University, MD
Université Laval, O
Université de Montréal, M
Université du Québec à Montréal, O

ENVIRONMENTAL POLICY

United States

Alaska

University of Alaska Fairbanks, M

Arizona

Northern Arizona University, M
The University of Arizona, M

California

California State University, Chico, M
San Francisco State University, M

District of Columbia

American University, MO

Florida

Florida Gulf Coast University, M
University of South Florida, MD

University of South Florida, St. Petersburg, M

Georgia

Georgia Institute of Technology, M
Georgia State University, D

Indiana

Indiana University Bloomington, D

Kentucky

Morehead State University, M

Maryland

Johns Hopkins University, MO

Massachusetts

Boston University, M
University of Massachusetts Amherst, MD
University of Massachusetts Lowell, MD

Michigan

Michigan Technological University, MD
University of Michigan, M

New York

Bard College, MO
Columbia University, M
Cornell University, MD
New York University, M
State University of New York College of Environ-
  mental Science and Forestry, MD

North Carolina

Appalachian State University, M
Duke University, D

Ohio

Cleveland State University, M

Pennsylvania

Drexel University, M
Lehigh University, O

Texas

Texas Southern University, MD

Virginia

George Mason University, MD
Virginia Polytechnic Institute and State University, O

West Virginia

American Public University System, M

Wisconsin

University of Wisconsin - Green Bay, M

Canada

Alberta

University of Calgary, MO

Ontario

Wilfrid Laurier University, M

Quebec

Université Laval, M

ENVIRONMENTAL POLICY AND RESOURCE MANAGEMENT

United States

Alabama

Samford University, M
Troy University, M

Alaska

University of Alaska Fairbanks, M

California

California State University, Chico, M
San Francisco State University, M
University of California, Berkeley, MDO
University of California, Santa Barbara, MD

Colorado

Colorado Heights University, M
Naropa University, M
University of Colorado Denver, M
University of Denver, MO
Western State Colorado University, M

Connecticut

Sacred Heart University, M
University of New Haven, M
Yale University, MD

Delaware

University of Delaware, MD
Wesley College, M
Wilmington University, M

District of Columbia

The George Washington University, M

Florida

Polytechnic University of Puerto Rico, Miami Cam-
  pus, M
Polytechnic University of Puerto Rico, Orlando
  Campus, M
University of Miami, D
University of South Florida, O

Hawaii

University of Hawaii at Manoa, MD

Idaho

Boise State University, M
Idaho State University, M
University of Idaho, M

Illinois

Illinois Institute of Technology, M
Southern Illinois University Carbondale, MD
Southern Illinois University Edwardsville, M
University of Chicago, M

Indiana

Indiana University Bloomington, M
Indiana University Northwest, O
Purdue University, MD

Louisiana

Louisiana State University and Agricultural & Mechanical College, M

Maine

University of Maine, D

Maryland

Johns Hopkins University, MO
University of Maryland, Baltimore County, MD
University of Maryland Eastern Shore, M
University of Maryland University College, MO

Massachusetts

Clark University, M
Harvard University, MO
Tufts University, MDO

Michigan

University of Michigan, D

Minnesota

University of Minnesota, Twin Cities Campus, MD

Missouri

Missouri State University, M
Southeast Missouri State University, M
University of Missouri, MD
Webster University, M

Nevada

University of Nevada, Reno, M

New Hampshire

Plymouth State University, M
Southern New Hampshire University, M
University of New Hampshire, M

New Jersey

Kean University, M
Montclair State University, D

New Mexico

University of New Mexico, M

New York

Clarkson University, M
Cornell University, MD
New York Institute of Technology, O
Pace University, M
State University of New York College of Environ-
  mental Science and Forestry, M
Stony Brook University, State University of New
  York, MO
University at Albany, State University of New York,
  M

North Carolina

Duke University, M
The University of North Carolina at Chapel Hill, MD

Ohio

Cleveland State University, M
The Ohio State University, MD
University of Dayton, M
The University of Findlay, M

Oklahoma

Northeastern State University, M

Oregon

Portland State University, M

Pennsylvania

Duquesne University, MO
Indiana University of Pennsylvania, M
Lehigh University, MO
Millersville University of Pennsylvania, M
Penn State University Park, M
Shippensburg University of Pennsylvania, M
Slippery Rock University of Pennsylvania, M

Rhode Island

University of Rhode Island, MD

South Carolina

University of South Carolina, M

Tennessee

Tennessee Technological University, M
The University of Tennessee, MD
Vanderbilt University, MD

Texas

Hardin-Simmons University, M
Rice University, M
St. Edward's University, M
Texas State University, M
Texas Tech University, MD
University of Houston - Clear Lake, M

Utah

Utah State University, MD

Virginia

Virginia Polytechnic Institute and State University, D

Washington

Antioch University Seattle, M
University of Washington, MD

West Virginia

American Public University System, M
West Virginia University, MD

U.S. Territories: Puerto Rico

Inter American University of Puerto Rico, Metropolitan Campus, M
Polytechnic University of Puerto Rico, M
Universidad Metropolitana, M
Universidad del Turabo, M
University of Puerto Rico, Río Piedras Campus, M

Canada

Alberta

University of Alberta, D
University of Calgary, MD

British Columbia

Royal Roads University, MO
Simon Fraser University, MDO

Maritime Provinces: New Brunswick

University of New Brunswick Fredericton, M

Maritime Provinces: Nova Scotia

Dalhousie University, M

Ontario

Trent University, MD
University of Guelph, MD
University of Waterloo, M
Wilfrid Laurier University, MD
York University, MD

Quebec

McGill University, M
Université de Montréal, O
Université du Québec à Chicoutimi, M

ENVIRONMENTAL SCIENCES

United States

Alabama

Auburn University, B
Auburn University at Montgomery, B
Miles College, B
Samford University, B
Troy University, BM
Tuskegee University, M
The University of Alabama, B
The University of Alabama in Huntsville, MD
University of Mobile, B

Alaska

Alaska Pacific University, BM
University of Alaska Anchorage, M
University of Alaska Fairbanks, M

Arizona

Arizona State University at the Tempe campus, D
Arizona State University at the West campus, B
Arizona Western College, A
Coconino Community College, A
Northern Arizona University, BM
The University of Arizona, BMD

Arkansas

Arkansas State University, MD
John Brown University, B
NorthWest Arkansas Community College, A
University of Arkansas, B

California

Biola University, B
Butte College, A
California Baptist University, B
California Institute of Technology, MD
California Lutheran University, B
California State Polytechnic University, Pomona, M

California State University Channel Islands, B
California State University, Chico, M
California State University, Dominguez Hills, M
California State University, East Bay, M
California State University, Fresno, M
California State University, Long Beach, B
California State University, Monterey Bay, B
California State University, Northridge, M
California State University, San Bernardino, M
College of the Desert, A
Columbia College, A
Copper Mountain College, A
Crafton Hills College, A
Humboldt State University, BM
La Sierra University, B
Loyola Marymount University, BM
Mills College, B
National University, B
Ohlone College, A
Pitzer College, B
Point Loma Nazarene University, B
San Diego State University, B
Santa Clara University, B
Scripps College, B
Stanford University, MDO
University of California, Berkeley, MD
University of California, Davis, MD
University of California, Irvine, D
University of California, Los Angeles, BD
University of California, Riverside, BMD
University of California, Santa Barbara, MD
University of San Francisco, B
University of Southern California, B
Whittier College, B
William Jessup University, B

Colorado

The Colorado College, B
Colorado Mesa University, B
Metropolitan State University of Denver, B
Regis University, B
University of Colorado Colorado Springs, M
University of Colorado Denver, M
University of Denver, B

Connecticut

Post University, B
Trinity College, B
University of Connecticut, B
University of New Haven, BMO
Wesleyan University, M
Western Connecticut State University, M
Yale University, MD

Delaware

Delaware State University, B
University of Delaware, B

District of Columbia

American University, B
Howard University, MD
University of the District of Columbia, B

Florida

Ave Maria University, B
Bethune-Cookman University, B
Broward College, A
Flagler College, B
Florida Agricultural and Mechanical University, BMD
Florida Atlantic University, M
Florida Gulf Coast University, M
Florida Institute of Technology, B
Florida International University, M
Florida State College at Jacksonville, A
Florida State University, M
Miami Dade College, A
Nova Southeastern University, BM
South Florida State College, A
Stetson University, B
Tallahassee Community College, A
University of Florida, B
University of South Florida, BMD
University of South Florida, St. Petersburg, BM
University of West Florida, BM

Georgia

Andrew College, A
Berry College, B
Columbus State University, M
Georgia College & State University, B
Georgia Gwinnett College, AB
Gordon State College, A
Kennesaw State University, B
Mercer University, M
Piedmont College, B
University of Georgia, B
Wesleyan College, B

Hawaii

Hawai'i Pacific University, B
University of Hawaii at Hilo, BM
University of Hawaii at Manoa, B

Idaho

Idaho State University, BM
University of Idaho, BMD

Illinois

Benedictine University, B
Blackburn College, B
Bradley University, B
City Colleges of Chicago, Wilbur Wright College, A
Concordia University Chicago, B
DePaul University, B
Dominican University, B
Eureka College, B
Lewis University, B
Loyola University Chicago, B
Monmouth College, B
Northwestern University, B
Southern Illinois University Carbondale, D
Southern Illinois University Edwardsville, BM
Trinity Christian College, B
University of Chicago, M
University of Illinois at Chicago, B
University of Illinois at Springfield, M
University of Illinois at Urbana - Champaign, BMD
University of St. Francis, B
Western Illinois University, D
Wheaton College, B

Indiana

Ball State University, D
Earlham College, B
Goshen College, B
Grace College, B
Indiana University Bloomington, BMDO
Indiana University - Purdue University Indianapolis, B
Martin University, B
Purdue University, B
Taylor University, B
University of Evansville, B
University of Notre Dame, B
University of Saint Francis, AB
Valparaiso University, B

Iowa

Briar Cliff University, B
Buena Vista University, B
Coe College, B
Drake University, B
Iowa State University of Science and Technology, MD
Simpson College, B
University of Dubuque, B
The University of Iowa, B
University of Northern Iowa, B
Upper Iowa University, B
Wartburg College, B

Kansas

Haskell Indian Nations University, B
Kansas State University, D
The University of Kansas, MD
Wichita State University, M

Kentucky

Bellarmine University, B
Murray State University, M

Northern Kentucky University, B
Thomas More College, B

Louisiana

Louisiana State University and Agricultural & Mechanical College, BMD
Loyola University New Orleans, B
McNeese State University, M
Southern University and Agricultural and Mechanical College, M
University of Louisiana at Lafayette, B
University of New Orleans, M

Maine

Colby College, B
Husson University, B
Saint Joseph's College of Maine, B
Unity College, B
University of Maine, BMD
University of Maine at Farmington, B
University of Maine at Presque Isle, B
University of New England, B
University of Southern Maine, B

Maryland

Baltimore City Community College, A
Frostburg State University, B
Harford Community College, A
Hood College, B
Johns Hopkins University, BMO
McDaniel College, B
Salisbury University, B
Stevenson University, B
Towson University, MO
University of Baltimore, B
University of Maryland, Baltimore County, BMD
University of Maryland, College Park, BMD
University of Maryland Eastern Shore, MD
Washington College, B

Massachusetts

Anna Maria College, B
Assumption College, B
Boston University, MD
Curry College, B
Eastern Nazarene College, B
Endicott College, B
Framingham State University, B
Greenfield Community College, A
Harvard University, MD
Massachusetts College of Liberal Arts, B
Massachusetts Institute of Technology, D
Massachusetts Maritime Academy, B
Merrimack College, B
Mount Ida College, B
Northeastern University, B
Quinsigamond Community College, A
Simmons College, B
Stonehill College, B
Suffolk University, B
Tufts University, MD
University of Massachusetts Amherst, B
University of Massachusetts Boston, MD
University of Massachusetts Lowell, BMDO
Westfield State University, B
Wheaton College, B
Williams College, B

Michigan

Adrian College, B
Albion College, B
Calvin College, B
Central Michigan University, B
Keweenaw Bay Ojibwa Community College, A
Lake Michigan College, A
Madonna University, AB
Michigan State University, BMD
Michigan Technological University, B
Northern Michigan University, B
Oakland University, BD
Siena Heights University, B
University of Michigan, MD
University of Michigan - Dearborn, BM
University of Michigan - Flint, B
Wayne State University, B

Minnesota

Anoka-Ramsey Community College, A
Bethel University, B
Fond du Lac Tribal and Community College, A
Minnesota State University Mankato, M
Southwest Minnesota State University, B
University of Minnesota, Duluth, B
University of Minnesota, Twin Cities Campus, B

Mississippi

Jackson State University, MD

Missouri

Central Methodist University, B
Columbia College, B
Drury University, B
Lincoln University, B
Maryville University of Saint Louis, B
Saint Louis University, B
Southeast Missouri State University, BM
Washington University in St. Louis, B
Westminster College, B

Montana

Blackfeet Community College, A
Fort Peck Community College, A
Montana State University, BMD
Rocky Mountain College, B
University of Montana, M
The University of Montana Western, B

Nebraska

Concordia University, Nebraska, B
Creighton University, B

Nevada

Nevada State College, B
Sierra Nevada College, B
Truckee Meadows Community College, A
University of Nevada, Las Vegas, MDO
University of Nevada, Reno, MD

New Hampshire

New England College, B
Southern New Hampshire University, B
University of New Hampshire, B

New Jersey

Fairleigh Dickinson University, Metropolitan Campus, B
Montclair State University, M
New Jersey Institute of Technology, BMD
Ocean County College, A
Ramapo College of New Jersey, B
Rowan College at Burlington County, A
Rutgers University - New Brunswick, BMD
Rutgers University - Newark, MD
Stockton University, M
Thomas Edison State University, AB

New Mexico

Eastern New Mexico University, B
Navajo Technical University, A
New Mexico State University, BMD
University of New Mexico, B

New York

Adelphi University, M
Barnard College, B
Binghamton University, State University of New York, D
Canisius College, B
City College of the City University of New York, D
Clarkson University, BMD
The College at Brockport, State University of New York, BM
College of Staten Island of the City University of New York, M
Columbia University, MD
Columbia University, School of General Studies, B
Cornell University, MD
Corning Community College, A
Erie Community College, North Campus, A

Fiorello H. LaGuardia Community College of the City University of New York, A
Fordham University, B
Hartwick College, B
Hudson Valley Community College, A
Hunter College of the City University of New York, B
Jamestown Community College, A
Keuka College, B
Nazareth College of Rochester, B
New York University, M
Pace University, BM
Pace University, Pleasantville Campus, B
Queens College of the City University of New York, BM
Rensselaer Polytechnic Institute, B
Rochester Institute of Technology, BM
St. Bonaventure University, B
Siena College, B
Skidmore College, B
State University of New York College at Cortland, B
State University of New York College of Environmental Science and Forestry, BMD
State University of New York College of Technology at Alfred, A
United States Military Academy, B
University at Albany, State University of New York, BM
University at Buffalo, the State University of New York, M
University of Rochester, B
Vassar College, B
Westchester Community College, A

North Carolina

Appalachian State University, B
Blue Ridge Community College, A
Brevard College, B
Catawba College, B
Duke University, MD
Elon University, B
Gardner-Webb University, B
North Carolina Agricultural and Technical State University, M
North Carolina State University, B
Pfeiffer University, B
Queens University of Charlotte, B
Roanoke-Chowan Community College, A
The University of North Carolina at Chapel Hill, BMD
The University of North Carolina at Pembroke, B
The University of North Carolina Wilmington, B
Wake Technical Community College, A
Western Carolina University, B
Western Piedmont Community College, A

North Dakota

North Dakota State University, MD
Nueta Hidatsa Sahnish College, A
Sitting Bull College, M
United Tribes Technical College, A

Ohio

Antioch College, B
Ashland University, B
Capital University, B
Cedarville University, B
Cleveland State University, BMD
Heidelberg University, B
Lourdes University, B
Marietta College, B
Miami University, BM
Miami University Hamilton, B
Muskingum University, B
Notre Dame College, B
The Ohio State University, BMD
The Ohio State University Agricultural Technical Institute, A
Otterbein University, B
University of Cincinnati, MD
University of Mount Union, B
The University of Toledo, BMD
Walsh University, B
Wittenberg University, B
Wright State University, MD
Youngstown State University, B

Oklahoma

Oklahoma State University, BMD
Tulsa Community College, A
University of Oklahoma, BMD

Oregon

Linfield College, B
Marylhurst University, B
Oregon Health & Science University, MD
Oregon State University, BMD
Portland State University, MD
University of Oregon, B
Willamette University, B

Pennsylvania

Albright College, B
Allegheny College, B
Bucknell University, B
Bucks County Community College, A
California University of Pennsylvania, B
Carnegie Mellon University, D
Chatham University, B
Chestnut Hill College, B
Cheyney University of Pennsylvania, B
Clarion University of Pennsylvania, B
Dickinson College, B
Drexel University, BMD
Duquesne University, BMO
Eastern University, B
Edinboro University of Pennsylvania, B
Franklin & Marshall College, B
Gannon University, BM
Geneva College, B
Gettysburg College, B
Harrisburg Area Community College, A
Juniata College, B
King's College, B
Kutztown University of Pennsylvania, B
La Salle University, B
Lehigh Carbon Community College, A
Lehigh University, MD
Lincoln University, B
Marywood University, B
Messiah College, B
Montgomery County Community College, A
Moravian College, B
Muhlenberg College, B
Northampton Community College, A
Penn State Harrisburg, MO
Penn State University Park, M
Pennsylvania Highlands Community College, A
Saint Francis University, B
Saint Vincent College, B
Temple University, B
University of Pennsylvania, MD
University of the Sciences, B
The University of Scranton, B
Villanova University, BM
Westminster College, B
Wilson College, B

Rhode Island

Brown University, B
Bryant University, B
Roger Williams University, B
University of Rhode Island, D

South Carolina

Claflin University, B
Clemson University, MD
College of Charleston, M
Lander University, B
University of South Carolina, B
Winthrop University, B
York Technical College, A

South Dakota

Lake Area Technical Institute, A
South Dakota School of Mines and Technology, D
South Dakota State University, B

Tennessee

Belmont University, B
Freed-Hardeman University, B
Lipscomb University, B

Rhodes College, B
Tennessee Technological University, D
The University of Tennessee at Chattanooga, BM
Vanderbilt University, M

Texas

Abilene Christian University, B
Baylor University, BD
Central Texas College, A
Clarendon College, A
Concordia University Texas, B
Dallas Baptist University, B
Hardin-Simmons University, B
Lamar University, B
Midwestern State University, B
Northeast Texas Community College, A
Rice University, MD
St. Mary's University, B
St. Philip's College, A
Sam Houston State University, B
San Jacinto College District, A
Southern Methodist University, BD
Stephen F. Austin State University, BM
Tarleton State University, BM
Texas A&M University, B
Texas A&M University - Commerce, B
Texas A&M University - Corpus Christi, BM
Texas Christian University, BM
Texas State University, B
Texas Tech University, MD
Tyler Junior College, A
University of Houston, B
University of Houston - Clear Lake, BM
University of the Incarnate Word, B
University of North Texas, M
University of St. Thomas, B
The University of Texas at Arlington, BMD
The University of Texas at El Paso, MD
The University of Texas Rio Grande Valley, B
The University of Texas at San Antonio, BMD
Wayland Baptist University, B
West Texas A&M University, BM

Utah

Brigham Young University, BM
University of Utah, M
Utah Valley University, B

Vermont

Bennington College, B
Castleton University, B
Community College of Vermont, A
University of Vermont, B

Virginia

Averett University, B
Bridgewater College, B
Christopher Newport University, M
Emory & Henry College, B
George Mason University, BMD
Longwood University, B
Lynchburg College, B
Randolph College, B
Sweet Briar College, B
University of Virginia, BMD
Virginia Polytechnic Institute and State University, MD

Washington

Central Washington University, B
Eastern Washington University, B
The Evergreen State College, B
Gonzaga University, B
Heritage University, B
Northwest Indian College, AB
Northwest University, B
Seattle University, B
University of Washington, B
University of Washington, Bothell, B
University of Washington, Tacoma, B
Walla Walla University, B
Washington State University, BMD
Washington State University - Tri-Cities, B
Washington State University - Vancouver, B
Western Washington University, BM

West Virginia

Alderson Broaddus University, B
American Public University System, B
Bethany College, B
Concord University, B
Marshall University, BM
West Virginia Wesleyan College, B
Wheeling Jesuit University, B

Wisconsin

Alverno College, B
Carroll University, B
Carthage College, B
Edgewood College, B
St. Norbert College, B
University of Wisconsin - Green Bay, BM
University of Wisconsin - Madison, B
University of Wisconsin - Milwaukee, B
University of Wisconsin - Stout, B
University of Wisconsin - Whitewater, B
Wisconsin Lutheran College, B

Wyoming

Casper College, A
Central Wyoming College, A
Western Wyoming Community College, A

U.S. Territories: Guam

University of Guam, M

U.S. Territories: Puerto Rico

Bayamón Central University, B
Humacao Community College, A
Inter American University of Puerto Rico, Bayamón
   Campus, B
Inter American University of Puerto Rico, Ponce
   Campus, B
Inter American University of Puerto Rico, San
   Germán Campus, BM
Pontifical Catholic University of Puerto Rico, BM
Universidad Metropolitana, B
Universidad del Turabo, MD
University of Puerto Rico, Río Piedras Campus,
   BMD

U.S. Territories: United States Virgin Islands

University of the Virgin Islands, M

Canada

Alberta

Concordia University of Edmonton, B
University of Alberta, BMD
University of Lethbridge, BM

British Columbia

Royal Roads University, B
Simon Fraser University, B
Thompson Rivers University, BM
University of Northern British Columbia, B

Manitoba

University of Manitoba, MD

Maritime Provinces: Nova Scotia

Dalhousie University, BM

Newfoundland and Labrador

Memorial University of Newfoundland, M

Ontario

Laurentian University, M
Queen's University at Kingston, B
Royal Military College of Canada, MD
University of Guelph, BMD
University of Ottawa, B
University of Toronto, MD
University of Waterloo, B
The University of Western Ontario, BMD
University of Windsor, BMD
Wilfrid Laurier University, MD
York University, B

Quebec

Concordia University, B
McGill University, B
Université Laval, M
Université du Québec en Abitibi-Témiscamingue, MD
Université du Québec à Montréal, MDO
Université du Québec à Trois-Rivières, MD
Université de Sherbrooke, MO

Saskatchewan

University of Saskatchewan, BM

ENVIRONMENTAL STUDIES

United States

Alabama

Birmingham-Southern College, B
Columbia Southern University, B
Community College of the Air Force, A
Tuskegee University, B

Alaska

University of Alaska Anchorage, B
University of Alaska Southeast, B

Arizona

Arizona State University at the Tempe campus, BM
Northern Arizona University, B
Prescott College, BM
The University of Arizona, B

Arkansas

Hendrix College, B
John Brown University, B
University of Central Arkansas, B
University of the Ozarks, B

California

California State University, East Bay, B
California State University, Fullerton, M
California State University, Monterey Bay, B
California State University, Sacramento, B
California State University, San Marcos, B
Claremont McKenna College, B
College of the Desert, A
Cosumnes River College, A
De Anza College, A
East Los Angeles College, A
Feather River College, A
Fullerton College, A
Humboldt State University, BM
Las Positas College, A
Merritt College, A
Mills College, B
Napa Valley College, A
National University, B
Occidental College, B
Ohlone College, A
Oxnard College, A
Pacific Union College, B
Pomona College, B
Saddleback College, A
San Bernardino Valley College, A
San Diego State University, B
San Francisco State University, B
San Jose State University, BM
Santa Ana College, A
Santa Barbara City College, A
Santa Clara University, B
Santa Rosa Junior College, A
Sonoma State University, B
Stanford University, B
University of California, Davis, B
University of California, Irvine, B
University of California, San Diego, B
University of California, Santa Barbara, BMD
University of California, Santa Cruz, BD
University of the Pacific, B
University of Redlands, B
University of San Diego, B
University of San Francisco, B

University of Southern California, B
Whittier College, B

Colorado

The Colorado College, B
Colorado Mountain College (Leadville), AB
Fort Lewis College, B
Naropa University, B
Regis University, B
University of Colorado Boulder, BMD
University of Colorado Denver, M
Western State Colorado University, B

Connecticut

Goodwin College, AB
Housatonic Community College, A
Middlesex Community College, A
Mitchell College, B
University of Connecticut, B
University of New Haven, B
Wesleyan University, B
Yale University, B

Delaware

University of Delaware, B
Wesley College, BM

District of Columbia

American University, B
The George Washington University, B
Georgetown University, B
University of the District of Columbia, B

Florida

College of Central Florida, A
Eckerd College, B
Florida Agricultural and Mechanical University, B
Florida Atlantic University, O
Florida International University, BM
Florida Southern College, B
Lynn University, B
New College of Florida, B
Rollins College, B
St. Thomas University, B
The University of Tampa, B

Georgia

Darton State College, A
Emory University, B
Shorter University, B
South University, B
Spelman College, B

Hawaii

Chaminade University of Honolulu, B
Hawai'i Pacific University, B
University of Hawaii at Hilo, B

Idaho

Boise State University, B
The College of Idaho, B

Illinois

Augustana College, B
Elmhurst College, B
Eureka College, B
Harper College, A
Illinois College, B
Illinois Wesleyan University, B
Judson University, B
Knox College, B
Lake Forest College, BM
Loyola University Chicago, B
McKendree University, B
North Park University, B
Northeastern Illinois University, BM
Northern Illinois University, B
Northwestern University, B
Principia College, B
University of Chicago, B
University of Illinois at Springfield, BM

Indiana

Ancilla College, A
DePauw University, B
Earlham College, B
Grace College, B
Indiana University Bloomington, B
Indiana University South Bend, B
Manchester University, B
Taylor University, B
Trine University, B
University of Evansville, B
University of Indianapolis, B
University of Southern Indiana, B

Iowa

Central College, B
Clarke University, B
Coe College, B
Cornell College, B
Dordt College, B
Drake University, B
Iowa Lakes Community College, A
Iowa State University of Science and Technology, B
Luther College, B
Maharishi University of Management, B
University of Dubuque, B
The University of Iowa, B

Kansas

Central Christian College of Kansas, A
Kansas Wesleyan University, B
The University of Kansas, B

Kentucky

Bellarmine University, B
Centre College, B
Eastern Kentucky University, B
Kentucky State University, M
University of Kentucky, B

Louisiana

Louisiana Tech University, B
Loyola University New Orleans, B
Tulane University, B

Maine

Bates College, B
Bowdoin College, B
Colby College, B
College of the Atlantic, BM
Saint Joseph's College of Maine, B
University of Maine at Farmington, B
University of Maine at Fort Kent, B
University of Maine at Machias, B
University of Maine at Presque Isle, B
University of New England, B
University of Southern Maine, B

Maryland

Goucher College, BM
Hood College, B
Howard Community College, A
Johns Hopkins University, B
McDaniel College, B
Mount St. Mary's University, B
St. Mary's College of Maryland, B
Towson University, M
University of Maryland, Baltimore County, B
University of Maryland Eastern Shore, B
Washington College, B

Massachusetts

Amherst College, B
Anna Maria College, B
Bard College at Simon's Rock, B
Berkshire Community College, A
Boston College, B
Brandeis University, B
Bristol Community College, A
Cape Cod Community College, A
Clark University, M
College of the Holy Cross, B
Dean College, A
Eastern Nazarene College, B
Hampshire College, B

Harvard University, B
Lasell College, B
Lesley University, B
Massachusetts College of Liberal Arts, B
Mount Holyoke College, B
Mount Wachusett Community College, A
Northeastern University, B
Smith College, B
Stonehill College, B
Tufts University, BMO
University of Massachusetts Lowell, O
Wellesley College, B
Wheelock College, B
Williams College, B
Worcester Polytechnic Institute, B

Michigan

Adrian College, B
Albion College, B
Aquinas College, M
Calvin College, B
Central Michigan University, B
Henry Ford College, A
Lake Superior State University, B
Marygrove College, B
Michigan State University, B
Olivet College, B
University of Michigan, B
University of Michigan - Dearborn, B
Western Michigan University, B

Minnesota

Augsburg College, B
Bemidji State University, BM
Bethel University, B
Carleton College, B
College of Saint Benedict, B
Concordia College, B
Gustavus Adolphus College, B
Hamline University, B
Itasca Community College, A
Macalester College, B
Minnesota State Community and Technical College, A
Minnesota State University Mankato, B
Minnesota State University Moorhead, B
St. Cloud State University, M
Saint John's University, B
St. Olaf College, B
University of Minnesota, Duluth, B
University of Minnesota, Morris, B
Vermilion Community College, A

Missouri

Columbia College, A
Cottey College, B
Drury University, B
Maryville University of Saint Louis, B
Saint Louis University, B
Southeast Missouri State University, M
University of Central Missouri, M
University of Missouri, B
University of Missouri - Kansas City, B
Washington University in St. Louis, B
Westminster College, B

Montana

Carroll College, B
Montana State University Billings, B
Rocky Mountain College, B
Salish Kootenai College, AB
University of Montana, BM

Nebraska

Concordia University, Nebraska, B
Doane University, B
Midland University, B
University of Nebraska - Lincoln, B

Nevada

University of Nevada, Las Vegas, B

New Hampshire

Colby-Sawyer College, B
Dartmouth College, B

Franklin Pierce University, B
Keene State College, B
Plymouth State University, B
Saint Anselm College, B
Southern New Hampshire University, B
White Mountains Community College, A

New Jersey

Drew University, B
Hudson County Community College, A
Montclair State University, M
Ramapo College of New Jersey, B
Rider University, B
Rowan University, B
Rutgers University - New Brunswick, B
Seton Hall University, B
Stockton University, B
Sussex County Community College, A
Thomas Edison State University, B
Warren County Community College, A
William Paterson University of New Jersey, B

New Mexico

New Mexico Highlands University, B
New Mexico Institute of Mining and Technology, B
New Mexico Junior College, A
Northern New Mexico College, A
Santa Fe Community College, A
University of New Mexico, M
University of New Mexico - Los Alamos Branch, A

New York

Adelphi University, BM
Alfred University, B
Bard College, B
Binghamton University, State University of New York, B
Brooklyn College of the City University of New York, B
Canisius College, B
Cazenovia College, B
City College of the City University of New York, B
Colgate University, B
The College of New Rochelle, B
Columbia-Greene Community College, A
Columbia University, B
Cornell University, MD
Eugene Lang College of Liberal Arts, B
Finger Lakes Community College, A
Fulton-Montgomery Community College, A
Hamilton College, B
Hobart and William Smith Colleges, B
Hofstra University, B
Ithaca College, B
Le Moyne College, B
Manhattanville College, B
Marymount Manhattan College, B
Monroe Community College, A
The New School for Public Engagement, B
New York University, B
Pace University, B
Pace University, Pleasantville Campus, B
Paul Smith's College, AB
Purchase College, State University of New York, B
Queens College of the City University of New York, B
The Sage Colleges, B
St. John's University, B
St. Lawrence University, B
Sarah Lawrence College, B
Siena College, B
Skidmore College, B
State University of New York College of Agriculture and Technology at Cobleskill, AB
State University of New York College at Cortland, B
State University of New York College of Environmental Science and Forestry, BM
State University of New York College at Oneonta, B
State University of New York College at Potsdam, B
State University of New York at Fredonia, B
State University of New York at Plattsburgh, B
Stony Brook University, State University of New York, B
Sullivan County Community College, A
Tompkins Cortland Community College, A
United States Military Academy, B

University of Rochester, BM
Vassar College, B
Wells College, B
Westchester Community College, A

North Carolina

Appalachian State University, B
Brevard College, B
Catawba College, B
Davidson College, B
Duke University, B
Elon University, B
Guilford College, B
Lenoir-Rhyne University, B
Meredith College, B
Montreat College, B
North Carolina Wesleyan College, B
Pamlico Community College, A
Pfeiffer University, B
Queens University of Charlotte, B
Southeastern Community College, A
Southwestern Community College, A
University of Mount Olive, B
University of North Carolina at Asheville, B
The University of North Carolina at Chapel Hill, B
The University of North Carolina Wilmington, BM
Warren Wilson College, B
William Peace University, B

North Dakota

Dickinson State University, AB
Sitting Bull College, A
Turtle Mountain Community College, A
University of North Dakota, B

Ohio

Bowling Green State University, B
Case Western Reserve University, B
Cleveland State University, BMO
Denison University, B
Heidelberg University, B
Hiram College, B
John Carroll University, B
Marietta College, B
Miami University Hamilton, B
Muskingum University, B
Oberlin College, B
Ohio Northern University, B
The Ohio State University, B
Ohio University, BM
Ohio Wesleyan University, B
Stark State College, A
University of Cincinnati, B
University of Cincinnati Clermont College, A
The University of Findlay, B
The University of Toledo, B
Youngstown State University, MO
Zane State College, A

Oklahoma

Oklahoma City University, B
University of Oklahoma, B
The University of Tulsa, B

Oregon

Klamath Community College, A
Lewis & Clark College, B
Linfield College, B
Oregon Institute of Technology, B
Pacific University, B
Portland State University, BM
Reed College, B
Southern Oregon University, B
University of Oregon, BMD
University of Portland, B

Pennsylvania

Allegheny College, B
Bucknell University, B
Chatham University, B
Dickinson College, B
Drexel University, B
Eastern University, B
Franklin & Marshall College, B
Gettysburg College, B

Harrisburg Area Community College, A
Juniata College, B
King's College, B
La Salle University, B
Lackawanna College, A
Lehigh University, B
Lincoln University, B
Mansfield University of Pennsylvania, B
Moravian College, B
Penn State Altoona, B
Penn State University Park, B
Point Park University, M
Robert Morris University, B
Saint Francis University, B
Saint Joseph's University, B
Saint Vincent College, B
Shippensburg University of Pennsylvania, BM
Susquehanna University, B
Temple University, B
Thiel College, B
University of Pennsylvania, BM
University of Pittsburgh at Bradford, B
University of Pittsburgh at Johnstown, B
Ursinus College, B
Villanova University, B
Washington & Jefferson College, B
Waynesburg University, B
Widener University, B

Rhode Island

Brown University, B
Bryant University, B
Salve Regina University, B
University of Rhode Island, B

South Carolina

Clemson University, MD
Furman University, B
Wofford College, B

South Dakota

Black Hills State University, B
Northern State University, B

Tennessee

Lincoln Memorial University, B
Maryville College, B
Sewanee: The University of the South, B
Tennessee Wesleyan College, B
Tusculum College, B
The University of Tennessee at Martin, B

Texas

Austin College, B
Baylor University, BM
Concordia University Texas, B
Huston-Tillotson University, B
Lamar State College - Orange, A
Lamar University, M
Lee College, A
St. Edward's University, B
Southern Methodist University, B
Southwestern University, B
Tarleton State University, B
Texas A&M University, B
Texas State University, M
Trinity University, B
University of St. Thomas, B
The University of Texas at Austin, M

Utah

University of Utah, B
Westminster College, B

Vermont

Bennington College, B
Castleton University, B
Champlain College, B
Goddard College, B
Green Mountain College, BM
Johnson State College, B
Marlboro College, B
Middlebury College, B
Norwich University, B
Saint Michael's College, B

Sterling College, B
University of Vermont, B

Virginia

Christopher Newport University, B
The College of William and Mary, B
Eastern Mennonite University, B
Emory & Henry College, B
Ferrum College, B
Hampton University, B
Hollins University, B
Lynchburg College, B
Randolph College, B
Randolph-Macon College, B
Roanoke College, B
Shenandoah University, B
Sweet Briar College, B
University of Richmond, B
The University of Virginia's College at Wise, B
Virginia Commonwealth University, BM
Virginia Polytechnic Institute and State University, B
Virginia Wesleyan College, B
Washington and Lee University, B

Washington

Central Washington University, B
Everett Community College, A
The Evergreen State College, BM
Gonzaga University, B
Pacific Lutheran University, B
Seattle University, B
University of Washington, B
University of Washington, Bothell, B
University of Washington, Tacoma, B
Walla Walla University, B
Western Washington University, B
Whitman College, B

West Virginia

Shepherd University, B

Wisconsin

Beloit College, B
Carthage College, B
Concordia University Wisconsin, B
Lawrence University, B
Northland College, B
Ripon College, B
University of Wisconsin - Green Bay, B
University of Wisconsin - Madison, B
Wisconsin Lutheran College, B

Wyoming

University of Wyoming, B

U.S. Territories: Puerto Rico

Inter American University of Puerto Rico, San
  Germán Campus, B
Universidad Metropolitana, M

Canada
Alberta

The King's University, B
Mount Royal University, B
University of Alberta, B
University of Calgary, B

British Columbia

Trinity Western University, B
The University of British Columbia, B
The University of British Columbia - Okanagan
  Campus, B
University of Northern British Columbia, BMD
University of Victoria, B

Manitoba

University of Manitoba, B
The University of Winnipeg, B

Maritime Provinces: New Brunswick

Mount Allison University, B
St. Thomas University, B
University of New Brunswick Fredericton, M

Maritime Provinces: Nova Scotia

Acadia University, B
Cape Breton University, B
Dalhousie University, BM
St. Francis Xavier University, B

Newfoundland and Labrador

Memorial University of Newfoundland, B

Ontario

Carleton University, B
Lakehead University, B
McMaster University, B
Nipissing University, B
Redeemer University College, B
Trent University, B
University of Guelph, B
University of Ottawa, B
University of Toronto, B
University of Waterloo, B
The University of Western Ontario, B
University of Windsor, B
Wilfrid Laurier University, B
York University, B

Quebec

Bishop's University, B
Concordia University, MO
Université Laval, BM
Université de Sherbrooke, B

Saskatchewan

University of Regina, B

ENVIRONMENTAL TOXICOLOGY

United States
California

University of California, Davis, B

New York

Clarkson University, B

EPIDEMIOLOGY

United States
Alabama

The University of Alabama at Birmingham, MD

Arizona

The University of Arizona, MD

Arkansas

University of Arkansas for Medical Sciences, MD

California

Loma Linda University, MDO
San Diego State University, MD
Stanford University, MD
University of California, Berkeley, MD
University of California, Davis, MD
University of California, Irvine, MD
University of California, Los Angeles, MD
University of California, San Diego, D
University of Southern California, MD

Colorado

University of Colorado Denver, MD

Connecticut

Yale University, MD

District of Columbia

The George Washington University, M
Georgetown University, MO

Florida

Florida International University, MD
University of Florida, MD
University of Miami, MD
University of South Florida, MDO

Georgia

Emory University, MD
Georgia Southern University, M

Hawaii

University of Hawaii at Manoa, D

Illinois

Northwestern University, D
University of Illinois at Chicago, MD
University of Illinois at Springfield, O

Indiana

Indiana University Bloomington, MD
Indiana University - Purdue University Indianapolis, MD
Purdue University, MD

Iowa

The University of Iowa, MD

Kansas

The University of Kansas, M

Kentucky

University of Kentucky, D
University of Louisville, MD

Louisiana

Louisiana State University Health Sciences Center, MD
Tulane University, MD

Maryland

Johns Hopkins University, MD
University of Maryland, Baltimore County, M
University of Maryland, College Park, MD

Massachusetts

Boston University, MD
Harvard University, MD
Tufts University, MDO
University of Massachusetts Amherst, MD
University of Massachusetts Lowell, MD

Michigan

Michigan State University, MD
University of Michigan, MD

Minnesota

Capella University, D
University of Minnesota, Twin Cities Campus, MD
Walden University, D

Mississippi

University of Southern Mississippi, M

Missouri

Washington University in St. Louis, M

Nebraska

University of Nebraska Medical Center, D

New Jersey

Rutgers University - New Brunswick, MDO
Rutgers University - Newark, O
Thomas Edison State University, O

New Mexico

University of New Mexico, M

New York

Columbia University, MD
Cornell University, MD
Daemen College, M

Hunter College of the City University of New York, M
New York University, D
University at Albany, State University of New York, MD
University at Buffalo, the State University of New York, MD
University of Rochester, BD

North Carolina

North Carolina State University, MD
The University of North Carolina at Chapel Hill, MD

North Dakota

North Dakota State University, M

Ohio

Case Western Reserve University, MD
University of Cincinnati, MD
The University of Toledo, MO

Oklahoma

University of Oklahoma Health Sciences Center, MD

Oregon

Oregon Health & Science University, MO
Oregon State University, M

Pennsylvania

Drexel University, DO
Temple University, M
University of Pennsylvania, M
University of Pittsburgh, MD

Rhode Island

Brown University, MD

South Carolina

Medical University of South Carolina, MD
University of South Carolina, MD

Tennessee

University of Memphis, M

Virginia

George Mason University, M
Virginia Commonwealth University, MD

Washington

University of Washington, MD
Washington State University, MD

Wisconsin

University of Wisconsin - Madison, MD

U.S. Territories: Puerto Rico

University of Puerto Rico, Medical Sciences Campus, M

Canada

Alberta

University of Alberta, M

British Columbia

The University of British Columbia, MD

Maritime Provinces: Nova Scotia

Dalhousie University, M

Maritime Provinces: Prince Edward Island

University of Prince Edward Island, MD

Newfoundland and Labrador

Memorial University of Newfoundland, MDO

Ontario

Queen's University at Kingston, MD
University of Guelph, MD
University of Ottawa, M
University of Toronto, MD

The University of Western Ontario, BMD

Quebec

McGill University, MDO
Université Laval, MD

Saskatchewan

University of Saskatchewan, MD

EQUESTRIAN/EQUINE STUDIES

United States

Alabama

Judson College, B

Arizona

Cochise County Community College District, A
Scottsdale Community College, A
Yavapai College, A

California

Los Angeles Pierce College, A
Sierra College, A
West Hills Community College, A

Colorado

Colorado Northwestern Community College, A
Colorado State University, B
Lamar Community College, A
Northeastern Junior College, A

Connecticut

Post University, B

Florida

College of Central Florida, A

Georgia

Savannah College of Art and Design, B

Idaho

College of Southern Idaho, A

Illinois

Black Hawk College, A
Highland Community College, A

Indiana

Saint Mary-of-the-Woods College, AB

Iowa

Scott Community College, A

Kansas

Allen Community College, A
Dodge City Community College, A

Kentucky

Asbury University, B
Midway University, AB

Massachusetts

Becker College, B
Mount Ida College, B
University of Massachusetts Amherst, A

Missouri

Stephens College, B

Montana

Miles Community College, A
Rocky Mountain College, B
The University of Montana Western, AB

New Jersey

Centenary College, AB
Rutgers University - New Brunswick, B

New York

Cazenovia College, B
Houghton College, B
Morrisville State College, A

North Carolina

Martin Community College, A

North Dakota

North Dakota State University, B

Ohio

Hocking College, A
Lake Erie College, B
The Ohio State University Agricultural Technical Institute, A
Ohio University - Southern Campus, A
Otterbein University, B
The University of Findlay, AB

Oklahoma

Connors State College, A
Redlands Community College, A

Pennsylvania

Delaware Valley University, B
Wilson College, B

Rhode Island

Johnson & Wales University, B

Texas

North Central Texas College, A
West Texas A&M University, B

Virginia

Averett University, B
Emory & Henry College, B

West Virginia

Bethany College, B

Wyoming

Central Wyoming College, A
Laramie County Community College, A
Northwest College, A

ERGONOMICS AND HUMAN FACTORS

United States

Alabama

The University of Alabama, M

Arizona

Arizona State University at the Tempe campus, M

California

California State University, Long Beach, M

District of Columbia

The Catholic University of America, M

Florida

Embry-Riddle Aeronautical University - Daytona, MD
Florida Institute of Technology, MD
University of Miami, MD

Georgia

Georgia Institute of Technology, D

Indiana

Indiana University Bloomington, M
Purdue University, MD

Iowa

The University of Iowa, MD

Massachusetts

Bentley University, M
Tufts University, M
University of Massachusetts Lowell, MDO

Michigan

Michigan Technological University, D

Missouri

Missouri Western State University, M

New York

Cornell University, M
New York University, D

North Carolina

North Carolina State University, D

Ohio

University of Cincinnati, MD
Wright State University, MD

South Carolina

Clemson University, D

Virginia

Old Dominion University, D

Wisconsin

University of Wisconsin - Milwaukee, O

Canada

Quebec

Université de Montréal, O
Université du Québec à Montréal, O

ETHICS

United States

Alabama

Spring Hill College, MO

Arizona

Arizona State University at the Tempe campus, M

Arkansas

John Brown University, M

California

Azusa Pacific University, M
Sonoma State University, M

District of Columbia

American University, M
Georgetown University, M

Florida

University of North Florida, MO

Georgia

Emory University, M
Kennesaw State University, O

Illinois

Loyola University Chicago, M
North Central College, M
Northwestern University, M
University of Chicago, D

Indiana

Valparaiso University, MO

Iowa

Drake University, B

Maine

University of New England, O

Maryland

University of Baltimore, M

Massachusetts

Bridgewater State University, B
New England College of Business and Finance, M
Suffolk University, MO

Michigan

University of Michigan - Flint, B

Minnesota

University of St. Thomas, M

Missouri

University of Missouri, O

Montana

Carroll College, B

New Hampshire

Southern New Hampshire University, M

New Jersey

Stevens Institute of Technology, MO

New York

Columbia University, M
Fordham University, MO
Syracuse University, B

North Carolina

Duke University, M
Southeastern Baptist Theological Seminary, BD
The University of North Carolina at Charlotte, MO

Ohio

Union Institute & University, D
Xavier University, M

Oregon

Oregon State University, M

Pennsylvania

University of Pennsylvania, MD
West Chester University of Pennsylvania, MO

Tennessee

Freed-Hardeman University, M
The University of Tennessee at Chattanooga, O

Texas

St. Edward's University, M
Schreiner University, M
Southern Methodist University, D
Texas State University, M

Vermont

Marlboro College, B

Virginia

George Mason University, M

Washington

University of Washington, Bothell, B

Wisconsin

Marquette University, D

Canada

Ontario

Saint Paul University, B
University of Ottawa, B
The University of Western Ontario, B

Quebec

Université Laval, O
Université du Québec à Chicoutimi, O
Université du Québec à Rimouski, MO
Université de Sherbrooke, O

ETHNIC, CULTURAL MINORITY, AND GENDER STUDIES

United States

California

Cabrillo College, A
California Polytechnic State University, San Luis Obispo, B
California State Polytechnic University, Pomona, B
California State University, Chico, B
California State University, Stanislaus, B
College of Alameda, A
College of Marin, A
College of San Mateo, A
College of the Siskiyous, A
Contra Costa College, A
Cosumnes River College, A
Cypress College, A
Fresno City College, A
Fullerton College, A
Grossmont College, A
Los Angeles Valley College, A
Merritt College, A
Mills College, B
San Diego State University, B
San Jose City College, A
Santa Clara University, B
Southwestern College, A
Stanford University, B
University of California, Berkeley, B
University of California, Irvine, B
University of California, Los Angeles, B
University of Southern California, B

Colorado

The Colorado College, B
University of Colorado Colorado Springs, B
University of Denver, B

Connecticut

Wesleyan University, B
Yale University, B

District of Columbia

American University, B

Georgia

Savannah State University, B

Hawaii

University of Hawaii at Manoa, B

Idaho

Boise State University, B

Illinois

Columbia College Chicago, B
Northeastern Illinois University, B
University of Chicago, B
University of Illinois at Chicago, B

Indiana

Indiana University Bloomington, B
Indiana University South Bend, B

Iowa

Cornell College, B
Grinnell College, B

Kentucky

University of Kentucky, B
Western Kentucky University, B

Massachusetts

Bard College at Simon's Rock, B
Emmanuel College, B
Hampshire College, B
Mount Holyoke College, B
Stonehill College, B
Wellesley College, B
Westfield State University, B
Williams College, B

Michigan

Albion College, B
Central Michigan University, B
Wayne State University, B

Minnesota

Bethel University, B
University of Minnesota, Duluth, B

Missouri

Washington University in St. Louis, B

Nebraska

University of Nebraska - Lincoln, B
University of Nebraska at Omaha, B

New Mexico

New Mexico State University - Alamogordo, A
Santa Fe Community College, A

New York

Columbia University, School of General Studies, B
John Jay College of Criminal Justice of the City University of New York, B
New York University, B
St. Francis College, B
Sarah Lawrence College, B
Skidmore College, B
University at Buffalo, the State University of New York, B

North Carolina

Davidson College, B

Ohio

Bowling Green State University, B
Miami University Hamilton, B
The Ohio State University, B
Xavier University, B

Pennsylvania

Chatham University, B
University of Pittsburgh, B

South Dakota

Dakota Wesleyan University, B

Tennessee

Christian Brothers University, B
Southern Adventist University, B

Texas

University of Houston, B

Utah

University of Utah, B

Vermont

Marlboro College, B
Saint Michael's College, B

Washington

The Evergreen State College, B
University of Washington, B
University of Washington, Tacoma, B
Washington State University, B
Whitman College, B

Wisconsin

Beloit College, B
Lawrence University, B

Canada

Maritime Provinces: New Brunswick

University of New Brunswick Saint John, B

Newfoundland and Labrador

Memorial University of Newfoundland, B

Ontario

Laurentian University, B
The University of Western Ontario, B

Quebec

Université Laval, A

ETHNIC AND CULTURAL STUDIES

United States

Arizona

Arizona State University at the West campus, B
Northern Arizona University, O

California

San Francisco State University, M
University of California, Berkeley, D
University of California, Riverside, D
University of California, San Diego, D
University of San Diego, B
Woodland Community College, A

Colorado

Colorado State University, B
University of Colorado Boulder, BD
University of Colorado Denver, B

Kansas

Kansas State University, B

Minnesota

Metropolitan State University, B
Minnesota State University Mankato, MO
Minnesota State University Moorhead, B
St. Olaf College, B

Nevada

University of Nevada, Las Vegas, MD

New Mexico

University of New Mexico, MD

New York

Cornell University, MD
Sarah Lawrence College, B

North Carolina

The University of North Carolina at Charlotte, M

Oregon

Lewis & Clark College, B
Oregon State University, B
University of Oregon, B
Willamette University, B

Pennsylvania

Messiah College, B

Texas

The University of Texas at Austin, B

Vermont

Goddard College, B

Wisconsin

Edgewood College, B

Canada

Quebec

Université Laval, MD

ETHNOMUSICOLOGY

United States

Arizona

Arizona State University at the Tempe campus, M
The University of Arizona, M

California

San Diego State University, M
University of California, Los Angeles, MD
University of California, Riverside, MD
University of California, Santa Barbara, MD
University of California, Santa Cruz, M

Connecticut

Wesleyan University, MD

Florida

Florida State University, MD
University of Florida, M

Illinois

Northwestern University, M

Indiana

Indiana University Bloomington, MD

Maryland

University of Maryland, College Park, M

Massachusetts

Harvard University, MD
Tufts University, M

New York

New York University, MD
University of Rochester, M

Ohio

Bowling Green State University, M
Kent State University, M

Pennsylvania

University of Pittsburgh, D

Rhode Island

Brown University, D

Texas

University of North Texas, M
The University of Texas at Austin, MD
The University of Texas Rio Grande Valley, M

Virginia

Liberty University, M

Washington

University of Washington, M

Wisconsin

University of Wisconsin - Madison, MD

Canada

Newfoundland and Labrador

Memorial University of Newfoundland, MD

Ontario

Carleton University, M
University of Toronto, MD
York University, M

EUROPEAN HISTORY

United States

Massachusetts

Salem State University, B

New Hampshire

Keene State College, B

Pennsylvania

Gettysburg College, B

South Carolina

Charleston Southern University, B

Texas

Howard Payne University, B

Washington

University of Washington, Tacoma, B

U.S. Territories: Puerto Rico

University of Puerto Rico, Río Piedras Campus, B

Canada

Quebec

McGill University, B

EUROPEAN STUDIES/CIVILIZA-TION

United States

California

Loyola Marymount University, B
Pepperdine University, B
Saint Mary's College of California, B
San Diego State University, B
Scripps College, B
University of California, Irvine, B
University of California, Los Angeles, B

Colorado

Fort Lewis College, B

Delaware

University of Delaware, B

District of Columbia

The George Washington University, B

Florida

New College of Florida, B

Kansas

The University of Kansas, B

Kentucky

Georgetown College, B

Massachusetts

Amherst College, B
Brandeis University, B
Hampshire College, B
Tufts University, B

Michigan

Hillsdale College, B

Minnesota

University of Minnesota, Morris, B

Mississippi

Millsaps College, B

Missouri

University of Missouri, B
Washington University in St. Louis, B
Webster University, B

New Hampshire

University of New Hampshire, B

New Jersey

Rutgers University - New Brunswick, B

New Mexico

University of New Mexico, B

New York

Barnard College, B
Canisius College, B
Hobart and William Smith Colleges, B
New York University, B
Stony Brook University, State University of New York, B
United States Military Academy, B

North Carolina

The University of North Carolina at Chapel Hill, B

Ohio

Bowling Green State University, B
Ohio University, B

Oregon

Portland State University, B

Pennsylvania

Gettysburg College, B
Saint Joseph's University, B

South Carolina

University of South Carolina, B

Tennessee

Belmont University, B
Vanderbilt University, B

Texas

Texas State University, B
Trinity University, B
The University of Texas at Austin, B

Vermont

Bennington College, B
Marlboro College, B
Middlebury College, B
University of Vermont, B

Virginia

Emory & Henry College, B
University of Richmond, B

Washington

Seattle Pacific University, B
University of Washington, B

Wisconsin

Carroll University, B

Canada

Alberta

University of Alberta, B

British Columbia

Trinity Western University, B
The University of British Columbia, B

Maritime Provinces: Nova Scotia

Dalhousie University, B
University of King's College, B

Ontario

Carleton University, B
University of Guelph, B
University of Toronto, B
York University, B

EVOLUTIONARY BIOLOGY

United States

Arizona

Arizona State University at the Tempe campus, D
The University of Arizona, MD

California

Sonoma State University, M
University of California, Irvine, MD
University of California, Los Angeles, MD
University of California, Riverside, MD
University of California, Santa Barbara, MD
University of California, Santa Cruz, MD
University of Southern California, D

Colorado

University of Colorado Boulder, MD
University of Colorado Denver, M
University of Denver, D

Connecticut

Wesleyan University, D
Yale University, BD

Delaware

University of Delaware, MD

Florida

Florida State University, MD
University of Miami, MD
University of South Florida, MD

Georgia

Emory University, D

Hawaii

University of Hawaii at Manoa, MD

Illinois

Illinois State University, M
University of Chicago, D
University of Illinois at Urbana - Champaign, MD

Indiana

Indiana State University, D
Indiana University Bloomington, MD
Purdue University, MD
University of Notre Dame, MD

Iowa

Iowa State University of Science and Technology, MD
The University of Iowa, MD

Kansas

The University of Kansas, MD

Louisiana

Tulane University, BMD
University of Louisiana at Lafayette, D

Maine

College of the Atlantic, B

Maryland

Johns Hopkins University, D
University of Maryland, College Park, MD

Massachusetts

Harvard University, BD
University of Massachusetts Amherst, MD

Michigan

Michigan State University, D
University of Michigan, MD
Wayne State University, D

Minnesota

University of Minnesota, Twin Cities Campus, MD

Missouri

University of Missouri, MD
Washington University in St. Louis, D

Nevada

University of Nevada, Reno, D

New Hampshire

Dartmouth College, BD
University of New Hampshire, D

New Jersey

Montclair State University, M
Princeton University, D
Rutgers University - New Brunswick, BMD

New York

Columbia University, MD
Columbia University, School of General Studies, B
Cornell University, D
Stony Brook University, State University of New York, BMD
University at Albany, State University of New York, D
University at Buffalo, the State University of New York, MDO

North Carolina

The University of North Carolina at Chapel Hill, MD

Ohio

Case Western Reserve University, B
The Ohio State University, MD
Ohio University, MD

Oklahoma

University of Oklahoma, D

Oregon

University of Oregon, MD

Pennsylvania

University of Pittsburgh, D

Rhode Island

Brown University, D

South Carolina

Clemson University, MD
University of South Carolina, MD

Tennessee

The University of Tennessee, MD

Texas

Rice University, BMD
The University of Texas at Austin, D

Vermont

Bennington College, B

West Virginia

West Virginia University, MD

U.S. Territories: Puerto Rico

University of Puerto Rico, Río Piedras Campus, MD

Canada

Alberta

University of Alberta, BMD

Ontario

University of Guelph, MD
University of Toronto, MD

EXECUTIVE ASSISTANT/EXECUTIVE SECRETARY

United States

Arizona

Pima Community College, A

Arkansas

University of Arkansas - Fort Smith, A

Florida

Hillsborough Community College, A
Northwest Florida State College, A
Pensacola State College, A
Santa Fe College, A

Illinois

Danville Area Community College, A
Elgin Community College, A
Illinois Eastern Community Colleges, Frontier Community College, A
Illinois Eastern Community Colleges, Wabash Valley College, A
John A. Logan College, A
John Wood Community College, A
Kaskaskia College, A
Lake Land College, A
Rockford Career College, A
South Suburban College, A
Waubonsee Community College, A

Indiana

Ivy Tech Community College - Bloomington, A
Ivy Tech Community College - Central Indiana, A
Ivy Tech Community College - Columbus, A
Ivy Tech Community College - East Central, A
Ivy Tech Community College - Kokomo, A
Ivy Tech Community College - Lafayette, A
Ivy Tech Community College - North Central, A
Ivy Tech Community College - Northeast, A
Ivy Tech Community College - Northwest, A
Ivy Tech Community College - Richmond, A
Ivy Tech Community College - Southeast, A
Ivy Tech Community College - Southern Indiana, A
Ivy Tech Community College - Southwest, A
Ivy Tech Community College - Wabash Valley, A

Iowa

Hawkeye Community College, A

Kentucky

Ashland Community and Technical College, A
Bluegrass Community and Technical College, A
Elizabethtown Community and Technical College, A
Hopkinsville Community College, A
Maysville Community and Technical College (Maysville), A
Owensboro Community and Technical College, A
Somerset Community College, A
Sullivan University, A

Massachusetts

Cape Cod Community College, A
Quinsigamond Community College, A

Michigan

Henry Ford College, A
Jackson College, A
Kalamazoo Valley Community College, A
Kellogg Community College, A
Northwestern Michigan College, A
St. Clair County Community College, A
Schoolcraft College, A

Minnesota

Dakota County Technical College, A
South Central College, A

Missouri

Crowder College, A
Pinnacle Career Institute (Kansas City), A

Montana

University of Montana, A

New Mexico

Clovis Community College, A

New York

Broome Community College, A
Mildred Elley School, A

North Carolina

Alamance Community College, A
Blue Ridge Community College, A
Brunswick Community College, A
Cape Fear Community College, A
Coastal Carolina Community College, A
Haywood Community College, A
Mayland Community College, A
Mitchell Community College, A
Roanoke-Chowan Community College, A
Stanly Community College, A
Western Piedmont Community College, A
Wilkes Community College, A
Wilson Community College, A

North Dakota

Dakota College at Bottineau, A

Ohio

Bowling Green State University, B
Cincinnati State Technical and Community College,
   A
Edison Community College, A
Fortis College (Ravenna), A
Owens Community College, A
Southern State Community College, A
Terra State Community College, A
University of Cincinnati Blue Ash College, A

Oregon

Chemeketa Community College, A

Pennsylvania

Community College of Beaver County, A
DuBois Business College (DuBois), A
Laurel Business Institute, A
Laurel Technical Institute, A
Luzerne County Community College, A
Thaddeus Stevens College of Technology, A
Westmoreland County Community College, A

Tennessee

Miller-Motte Technical College (Clarksville), A

Texas

Alvin Community College, A
Brookhaven College, A
Cedar Valley College, A
Eastfield College, A
El Centro College, A
Kilgore College, A
Lee College, A
Northeast Texas Community College, A

Virginia

Bryant & Stratton College - Richmond Campus, B
Bryant & Stratton College - Virginia Beach Campus,
   B

Washington

Bellingham Technical College, A
Clark College, A

West Virginia

West Virginia Business College (Nutter Fort), A
West Virginia Northern Community College, A

U.S. Territories: Puerto Rico

Caribbean University, B
Humacao Community College, A
ICPR Junior College - Hato Rey Campus, A
Universidad del Este, A
University of Puerto Rico in Arecibo, B

University of Puerto Rico in Bayamón, B
University of Puerto Rico in Ponce, B
University of Puerto Rico, Río Piedras Campus, B

EXERCISE PHYSIOLOGY

United States

Alabama

Auburn University, B

Arizona

Grand Canyon University, B

California

Biola University, B
California Baptist University, B
Saint Katherine College, B
University of California, Davis, B
University of California, Irvine, B

Colorado

University of Colorado Colorado Springs, B

Delaware

University of Delaware, B

Florida

Ave Maria University, B
Florida Southern College, B
University of Florida, B
University of Miami, B

Idaho

Brigham Young University - Idaho, B

Iowa

Central College, B

Maine

University of Southern Maine, B

Massachusetts

Fitchburg State University, B
Merrimack College, B
Quincy College, A
University of Massachusetts Amherst, B

Minnesota

The College of St. Scholastica, B
University of Minnesota, Twin Cities Campus, B

New York

Brooklyn College of the City University of New York,
   B
Skidmore College, B
State University of New York College at Potsdam, B
University at Buffalo, the State University of New
   York, B

North Carolina

East Carolina University, B
Pfeiffer University, B

Ohio

Baldwin Wallace University, B
Miami University Hamilton, B
Ohio Northern University, B
Ohio University - Eastern, B
University of Dayton, B
The University of Toledo, B

Oregon

Northwest Christian University, B

Pennsylvania

Mercyhurst University, B
Saint Francis University, B
Ursinus College, B

South Carolina

College of Charleston, B

Texas

Baylor University, B

Virginia

Lynchburg College, B
Shenandoah University, B

Washington

Central Washington University, B
Gonzaga University, B
Washington State University - Spokane, B

West Virginia

West Virginia University, B

Wisconsin

Concordia University Wisconsin, B
Marquette University, B

EXERCISE AND SPORTS SCIENCE

United States

Alabama

Auburn University, MD
Auburn University at Montgomery, MO
United States Sports Academy, M
The University of Alabama, MD
The University of Alabama at Birmingham, M
University of North Alabama, M
University of South Alabama, M

Arizona

Arizona State University at the Tempe campus, MD

Arkansas

Arkansas State University, M
University of Arkansas at Little Rock, M

California

California Baptist University, M
California State University, Fresno, M
California State University, Long Beach, M
Humboldt State University, M
Saint Mary's College of California, M
San Diego State University, M
University of California, Davis, M
University of the Pacific, M

Colorado

Colorado State University, MD
University of Northern Colorado, MD

Connecticut

Central Connecticut State University, MO
Sacred Heart University, M
Southern Connecticut State University, M
University of Connecticut, MD

Delaware

Delaware State University, M

District of Columbia

The George Washington University, M
Howard University, M

Florida

Barry University, M
Florida Atlantic University, M
Florida State University, MD
University of Central Florida, MD
University of Florida, MD
University of Miami, MD
University of North Florida, MD
University of South Florida, M
The University of Tampa, M
University of West Florida, M

Georgia

Armstrong State University, M
Columbus State University, M
Georgia College & State University, M
Georgia State University, M
Kennesaw State University, M
Life University, M

Idaho

Boise State University, M

Illinois

Benedictine University, M
Concordia University Chicago, M
Eastern Illinois University, M
Northeastern Illinois University, M
Southern Illinois University Edwardsville, M

Indiana

Ball State University, MD
Indiana University Bloomington, MD
Purdue University, MD

Iowa

Iowa State University of Science and Technology, M
The University of Iowa, MD

Kansas

Wichita State University, M

Kentucky

Morehead State University, M
Murray State University, M
University of Kentucky, MD
University of Louisville, M

Louisiana

Louisiana Tech University, M
McNeese State University, M
University of Louisiana at Monroe, M

Maine

University of Maine, MDO

Maryland

McDaniel College, M

Massachusetts

Northeastern University, M
Smith College, M
Springfield College, MD
University of Massachusetts Boston, MD

Michigan

Central Michigan University, M
Eastern Michigan University, M
Northern Michigan University, M
Oakland University, MO
Wayne State University, MD
Western Michigan University, M

Minnesota

The College of St. Scholastica, M
Concordia University, St. Paul, M
St. Cloud State University, M
University of Minnesota, Twin Cities Campus, MD

Mississippi

Delta State University, M
Mississippi State University, M
University of Mississippi, M

Missouri

Logan University, M
Northwest Missouri State University, M
Southeast Missouri State University, M
University of Missouri, MD

Montana

University of Montana, M

Nebraska

University of Nebraska at Kearney, M
University of Nebraska - Lincoln, M
University of Nebraska at Omaha, D
Wayne State College, M

Nevada

University of Nevada, Las Vegas, M

New Jersey

College of Saint Elizabeth, O
Kean University, M
Montclair State University, MO
Rowan University, M
William Paterson University of New Jersey, M

New Mexico

Eastern New Mexico University, M
New Mexico Highlands University, M
University of New Mexico, MD

New York

Brooklyn College of the City University of New York, M
Ithaca College, M
Long Island University - LIU Brooklyn, M
Manhattanville College, M
Queens College of the City University of New York, M
State University of New York College at Cortland, M
Syracuse University, M
University at Buffalo, the State University of New York, MDO

North Carolina

Appalachian State University, M
East Carolina University, MD
Gardner-Webb University, M
The University of North Carolina at Chapel Hill, M
The University of North Carolina at Charlotte, O
Wake Forest University, M

North Dakota

North Dakota State University, M
University of Mary, M

Ohio

Ashland University, M
Cleveland State University, M
Kent State University, MD
Miami University, M
Ohio University, MD
The University of Akron, M
University of Dayton, M
The University of Toledo, MD

Oklahoma

University of Central Oklahoma, M
University of Oklahoma, MD

Oregon

Oregon State University, MD

Pennsylvania

Bloomsburg University of Pennsylvania, M
California University of Pennsylvania, M
East Stroudsburg University of Pennsylvania, M
Gannon University, M
Indiana University of Pennsylvania, M
Marywood University, M
University of Pittsburgh, MD
West Chester University of Pennsylvania, M

Rhode Island

University of Rhode Island, M

South Carolina

University of South Carolina, MD

South Dakota

The University of South Dakota, M

Tennessee

Austin Peay State University, M
East Tennessee State University, MD
Lipscomb University, M
Middle Tennessee State University, MD
Tennessee State University, M
University of Memphis, M
The University of Tennessee, MD

Texas

Baylor University, M
Midwestern State University, M
Texas State University, M
Texas Tech University, M
Texas Woman's University, MD
University of Houston, M
University of Houston - Clear Lake, M
University of Mary Hardin-Baylor, M
The University of Texas at Arlington, M
The University of Texas at Austin, MD
West Texas A&M University, M

Utah

Brigham Young University, MD
Southern Utah University, M
University of Utah, MD

Virginia

George Mason University, M
James Madison University, M
Liberty University, M
Old Dominion University, M
Virginia Commonwealth University, M
Virginia Polytechnic Institute and State University, MD

Washington

Central Washington University, M
Eastern Washington University, M
Washington State University, M
Western Washington University, M

West Virginia

American Public University System, M
Fairmont State University, M
Marshall University, M
West Virginia University, MD

Wisconsin

University of Wisconsin - La Crosse, M
University of Wisconsin - Whitewater, M

Wyoming

University of Wyoming, M

U.S. Territories: Puerto Rico

Inter American University of Puerto Rico, Metropolitan Campus, M
University of Puerto Rico, Mayagüez Campus, M
University of Puerto Rico, Río Piedras Campus, M

Canada

Alberta

University of Alberta, MD
University of Lethbridge, M

Maritime Provinces: New Brunswick

University of New Brunswick Fredericton, M

Newfoundland and Labrador

Memorial University of Newfoundland, M

Ontario

Lakehead University, M
Queen's University at Kingston, MD

Quebec

Concordia University, M

EXPERIMENTAL PSYCHOLOGY

United States

Alabama

Auburn University, D
The University of Alabama, D

California

California State University, Northridge, M
California State University, San Bernardino, M
San Jose State University, M

Connecticut

University of Connecticut, D
University of Hartford, M

District of Columbia

The Catholic University of America, D
Howard University, D

Florida

Florida Atlantic University, D
Nova Southeastern University, M
University of Central Florida, MD

Idaho

Idaho State University, D

Illinois

Illinois State University, M
Southern Illinois University Carbondale, M

Kentucky

Morehead State University, M
University of Louisville, D
Western Kentucky University, M

Louisiana

McNeese State University, M

Maryland

University of Maryland, College Park, D

Massachusetts

Harvard University, D
Northeastern University, D

Michigan

Central Michigan University, MD

Mississippi

Mississippi State University, M
University of Mississippi, D
University of Southern Mississippi, D

Missouri

Missouri State University, M
Saint Louis University, MD

Montana

University of Montana, D

New Hampshire

Rivier University, M

New Jersey

Fairleigh Dickinson University, Metropolitan Campus, MO
Seton Hall University, M

New Mexico

New Mexico State University, M

New York

Brooklyn College of the City University of New York, M
City College of the City University of New York, D
Cornell University, D
Iona College, M
Rochester Institute of Technology, M

St. John's University, M
Stony Brook University, State University of New York, D
Syracuse University, D

North Carolina

Appalachian State University, M
Duke University, D
North Carolina State University, D

North Dakota

University of North Dakota, D

Ohio

Bowling Green State University, MD
Case Western Reserve University, D
Kent State University, MD
Ohio University, MD
University of Cincinnati, D
The University of Toledo, MD

Oklahoma

University of Central Oklahoma, M

South Carolina

University of South Carolina, MD

Tennessee

Middle Tennessee State University, M
University of Memphis, MD
The University of Tennessee, MD
The University of Tennessee at Chattanooga, M

Texas

Dallas Baptist University, M
Southern Methodist University, M
Texas A&M University - Central Texas, M
Texas Christian University, MD
Texas Tech University, MD
The University of Texas at Arlington, D
The University of Texas at El Paso, M
The University of Texas of the Permian Basin, M
The University of Texas Rio Grande Valley, M

Virginia

The College of William and Mary, M
Old Dominion University, D
Radford University, M

Washington

Central Washington University, M
Eastern Washington University, M
Washington State University, D
Western Washington University, M

Wisconsin

University of Wisconsin - Oshkosh, M

Canada

British Columbia

University of Victoria, MD

Maritime Provinces: New Brunswick

University of New Brunswick Saint John, MD

Newfoundland and Labrador

Memorial University of Newfoundland, MD

Ontario

Lakehead University, M
Laurentian University, M

Quebec

McGill University, MD

Saskatchewan

University of Regina, MD

FACILITIES PLANNING AND MANAGEMENT

United States

California

University of California, Berkeley, O

Connecticut

University of New Haven, M

Kansas

The University of Kansas, O

Massachusetts

Massachusetts Maritime Academy, M
Wentworth Institute of Technology, M

Michigan

Eastern Michigan University, B

Missouri

Missouri State University, B

New York

Cornell University, M
New York City College of Technology of the City University of New York, B
Pratt Institute, M

North Carolina

The University of North Carolina at Charlotte, M

Pennsylvania

Community College of Philadelphia, A

Canada

Quebec

Université Laval, M

FAMILY AND COMMUNITY SERVICES

United States

Arizona

Glendale Community College, A
Phoenix College, A

Arkansas

Harding University, B
John Brown University, B

California

Oxnard College, A
Palomar College, A
Saddleback College, A
University of California, Santa Cruz, B

Florida

University of Florida, B
University of Miami, B

Georgia

Toccoa Falls College, B

Iowa

Iowa State University of Science and Technology, B
University of Northern Iowa, B
William Penn University, B

Kansas

Central Christian College of Kansas, A

Louisiana

Southern University at New Orleans, B

Maine

University of Maine at Machias, B

Maryland

Mount St. Mary's University, B
Stevenson University, B
University of Maryland, College Park, B

Michigan

Andrews University, B
Baker College, A
Michigan State University, B

Missouri

College of the Ozarks, B

North Carolina

East Carolina University, B

Ohio

Bowling Green State University, B
God's Bible School and College, B
Youngstown State University, B

Oklahoma

Connors State College, A
Oklahoma Baptist University, B
Oklahoma Christian University, B

Oregon

Rogue Community College, A

Pennsylvania

La Roche College, B
Messiah College, B
Westmoreland County Community College, A

Tennessee

Union University, B

Texas

Texas Tech University, B

Utah

Snow College, A

Washington

Skagit Valley College, A

Wisconsin

University of Wisconsin - Madison, B

FAMILY AND CONSUMER ECONOMICS AND RELATED SERVICES

United States

Alabama

Alabama Agricultural and Mechanical University, B

California

Allan Hancock College, A
Bakersfield College, A
California State University, Fresno, B
California State University, Sacramento, B
Los Angeles City College, A
Los Angeles Mission College, A
Los Angeles Southwest College, A
Modesto Junior College, A
Monterey Peninsula College, A
Sacramento City College, A
San Bernardino Valley College, A
Santa Ana College, A
West Los Angeles College, A
Yuba College, A

District of Columbia

Howard University, B

Hawaii

University of Hawaii at Manoa, B

Iowa

University of Northern Iowa, B

Louisiana

Louisiana College, B

Maryland

University of Maryland Eastern Shore, B

Michigan

Andrews University, B

Minnesota

Minnesota State University Mankato, B
University of Minnesota, Twin Cities Campus, B

Missouri

University of Missouri, B

Nebraska

University of Nebraska at Kearney, B
University of Nebraska - Lincoln, B

Ohio

Bowling Green State University, B

Tennessee

Carson-Newman University, B
Tennessee State University, B

Utah

Brigham Young University, B
Utah State University, B

Virginia

Virginia State University, B

Washington

Yakima Valley Community College, A

West Virginia

Fairmont State University, B

Wisconsin

University of Wisconsin - Stevens Point, B

U.S. Territories: American Samoa

American Samoa Community College, A

Canada

Maritime Provinces: New Brunswick

Université de Moncton, B

Maritime Provinces: Nova Scotia

Mount Saint Vincent University, B

Maritime Provinces: Prince Edward Island

University of Prince Edward Island, B

FAMILY AND CONSUMER SCIENCES/HOME ECONOMICS TEACHER EDUCATION

United States

Alabama

Jacksonville State University, B
Oakwood University, B

Arkansas

Harding University, B
University of Arkansas at Pine Bluff, B
University of Central Arkansas, B

California

College of the Sequoias, A

Colorado

Colorado State University, B

Florida

South Florida State College, A
State College of Florida Manatee-Sarasota, A

Georgia

Fort Valley State University, B
Georgia Southern University, B
University of Georgia, B

Illinois

Bradley University, B
Northern Illinois University, B

Indiana

Vincennes University, A

Iowa

Iowa State University of Science and Technology, B

Kansas

Pittsburg State University, B

Kentucky

Eastern Kentucky University, B
Western Kentucky University, B

Louisiana

Louisiana Tech University, B

Maryland

University of Maryland Eastern Shore, B

Michigan

Western Michigan University, B

Minnesota

Minnesota State University Mankato, B
St. Catherine University, B

Mississippi

Copiah-Lincoln Community College, A
Itawamba Community College, A
Jones County Junior College, A
Northeast Mississippi Community College, A
Northwest Mississippi Community College, A

Missouri

Fontbonne University, B
Missouri State University, B
Southeast Missouri State University, B

Nebraska

Chadron State College, B
Wayne State College, B

New Mexico

New Mexico State University, B

New York

Queens College of the City University of New York, B
State University of New York College at Oneonta, B
Syracuse University, B

North Carolina

Campbell University, B
East Carolina University, B
North Carolina Agricultural and Technical State University, B

North Dakota

North Dakota State University, B

Ohio

Bowling Green State University, B
The Ohio State University, B

The Ohio State University at Lima, B
Ohio University, B
The University of Akron, B
Youngstown State University, B

Oklahoma

East Central University, B
Langston University, B
University of Central Oklahoma, B

Pennsylvania

Immaculata University, B
Messiah College, B
Seton Hill University, B

South Carolina

Winthrop University, B

South Dakota

South Dakota State University, B

Tennessee

Carson-Newman University, B
Tennessee Technological University, B
The University of Tennessee at Martin, B

Texas

Baylor University, B

Utah

Utah State University, B

Virginia

Hampton University, B
Virginia Polytechnic Institute and State University, B

Washington

Central Washington University, B
Washington State University, B

West Virginia

Fairmont State University, B

Wisconsin

University of Wisconsin - Stevens Point, B
University of Wisconsin - Stout, B

U.S. Territories: Guam

University of Guam, B

U.S. Territories: Puerto Rico

Pontifical Catholic University of Puerto Rico, B

Canada

Alberta

University of Alberta, B

Maritime Provinces: New Brunswick

University of New Brunswick Fredericton, B

Saskatchewan

University of Saskatchewan, B

FAMILY AND CONSUMER SCIENCES/HUMAN SCIENCES

United States

Alabama

Auburn University, B
Jacksonville State University, B
Oakwood University, B
The University of Alabama, B
University of Montevallo, B
University of North Alabama, B

Alaska

University of Alaska Anchorage, A

Arizona

Arizona Western College, A
Mesa Community College, A
Phoenix College, A

Arkansas

Harding University, B
Henderson State University, B
University of Arkansas, BM
University of Arkansas at Pine Bluff, B
University of Central Arkansas, B

California

Antelope Valley College, A
Butte College, A
California State University, East Bay, B
California State University, Fresno, M
California State University, Long Beach, B
California State University, Northridge, BM
Chaffey College, A
College of the Sequoias, A
East Los Angeles College, A
El Camino College, A
Fresno City College, A
Los Angeles City College, A
The Master's College and Seminary, B
Merced College, A
Mt. San Antonio College, A
Ohlone College, A
Orange Coast College, A
Palomar College, A
Saddleback College, A
San Francisco State University, BM
San Joaquin Delta College, A
San Jose City College, A
Shasta College, A
Skyline College, A
Solano Community College, A
University of California, San Diego, B
Yuba College, A

Colorado

Colorado State University, B

Connecticut

University of Saint Joseph, B

Delaware

Delaware State University, B

Florida

College of Central Florida, A
Florida State University, MD
Indian River State College, A
Palm Beach State College, A
University of Florida, M

Georgia

Abraham Baldwin Agricultural College, A
Bainbridge State College, A
University of Georgia, MD

Idaho

Brigham Young University - Idaho, B
Idaho State University, B

Illinois

Bradley University, B
Eastern Illinois University, BM
Illinois State University, BM
Olivet Nazarene University, B
Western Illinois University, B

Indiana

Ball State University, BM
Indiana State University, B
Purdue University, B
Vincennes University, A

Iowa

Iowa Lakes Community College, A
Iowa State University of Science and Technology, BM

Kansas

Allen Community College, A
Garden City Community College, A
Hutchinson Community College, A
Kansas State University, BMDO
Pittsburg State University, B
Pratt Community College, A

Kentucky

Berea College, B
University of Kentucky, B

Louisiana

Louisiana State University and Agricultural & Mechanical College, BMD
Louisiana Tech University, M
Nicholls State University, B
Northwestern State University of Louisiana, B
Southeastern Louisiana University, B
Southern University and Agricultural and Mechanical College, B
University of Louisiana at Monroe, M

Maine

College of the Atlantic, B

Maryland

Morgan State University, B
University of Maryland, College Park, MD
University of Maryland Eastern Shore, B

Massachusetts

Tufts University, MD

Michigan

Great Lakes Christian College, B
Madonna University, B
Western Michigan University, M

Minnesota

Minnesota State University Mankato, B
St. Catherine University, B
University of Northwestern - St. Paul, M
Vermilion Community College, A

Mississippi

Delta State University, B
Itawamba Community College, A
Jones County Junior College, A
Mississippi Delta Community College, A
Mississippi State University, B
Northeast Mississippi Community College, A

Missouri

College of the Ozarks, B
Fontbonne University, BM
Metropolitan Community College - Kansas City, A
Southeast Missouri State University, B
University of Central Missouri, B

Montana

Montana State University, B

Nebraska

Chadron State College, B
University of Nebraska - Lincoln, MD
Wayne State College, B

New Jersey

Montclair State University, B
Rutgers University - New Brunswick, B

New Mexico

Eastern New Mexico University, A
New Mexico Highlands University, B
New Mexico State University, M
University of New Mexico, B

New York

Monroe Community College, A
Queens College of the City University of New York, BM
State University of New York College at Oneonta, B

North Carolina

Appalachian State University, M
Campbell University, B
East Carolina University, M
Meredith College, B
North Carolina Agricultural and Technical State University, B
North Carolina Central University, BM

North Dakota

North Dakota State University, M

Ohio

Bowling Green State University, BM
The Ohio State University, MD
Ohio University, M
Youngstown State University, B

Oklahoma

East Central University, B
Northeastern State University, B
Oklahoma State University, MD
Rose State College, A
University of Central Oklahoma, B

Oregon

Linn-Benton Community College, A

Pennsylvania

Indiana University of Pennsylvania, B
Seton Hill University, B

South Carolina

South Carolina State University, BM

South Dakota

Oglala Lakota College, A
South Dakota State University, M

Tennessee

Carson-Newman University, B
East Tennessee State University, B
Hiwassee College, A
Lipscomb University, B
Tennessee State University, MD
Tennessee Technological University, B
University of Memphis, M
The University of Tennessee at Martin, BM

Texas

Baylor University, B
Hill College, A
Lamar State College - Port Arthur, A
Lamar University, M
Prairie View A&M University, BM
Sam Houston State University, BM
Tarleton State University, B
Texas A&M University - Kingsville, B
Texas Southern University, BM
Texas State University, M
Texas Tech University, B
Texas Woman's University, B
Tyler Junior College, A
University of Houston, M
The University of Texas at Austin, BMD

Utah

Brigham Young University, B
Snow College, A
Southern Utah University, B
Utah State University, M

Virginia

Bridgewater College, B
Liberty University, B
Norfolk State University, B
Southern Virginia University, B

Washington

Central Washington University, B
Seattle Pacific University, B
Washington State University, B

West Virginia

Fairmont State University, B
Marshall University, B
Shepherd University, B

Wisconsin

University of Wisconsin - Madison, MD
University of Wisconsin - Stevens Point, M

Wyoming

University of Wyoming, B

U.S. Territories: Puerto Rico

Pontifical Catholic University of Puerto Rico, B
University of Puerto Rico, Río Piedras Campus, BM

Canada

Alberta

University of Alberta, BMD

British Columbia

The University of British Columbia, B

Manitoba

University of Manitoba, B

Maritime Provinces: Nova Scotia

Mount Saint Vincent University, B

Ontario

The University of Western Ontario, B

FAMILY AND CONSUMER SCIENCES/HUMAN SCIENCES BUSINESS SERVICES

United States

Illinois

University of Illinois at Urbana - Champaign, B

Utah

Brigham Young University, B

FAMILY AND CONSUMER SCIENCES/HUMAN SCIENCES COMMUNICATION

United States

Georgia

University of Georgia, B

FAMILY RESOURCE MANAGEMENT STUDIES

United States

Alabama

The University of Alabama, B

Arizona

Arizona State University at the Tempe campus, B

California

Gavilan College, A

Georgia

University of Georgia, B

Idaho

University of Idaho, B

Iowa

Iowa State University of Science and Technology, B

New Mexico

New Mexico State University, B

Ohio

The Ohio State University, B
The Ohio State University at Lima, B
Ohio University, B

Tennessee

Middle Tennessee State University, B

Texas

Texas Tech University, B

Utah

Brigham Young University, B

FAMILY SYSTEMS

United States

Arkansas

John Brown University, B

California

American River College, A
Grossmont College, A

Connecticut

Goodwin College, AB

Indiana

Anderson University, B

Kentucky

Maysville Community and Technical College (Maysville), A

Maryland

Towson University, B

Michigan

Central Michigan University, B
Spring Arbor University, B
Western Michigan University, B

Mississippi

Mississippi University for Women, B
University of Southern Mississippi, B

North Carolina

Mid-Atlantic Christian University, B

Ohio

Bowling Green State University, B
The University of Akron, B

Oklahoma

University of Central Oklahoma, B

Tennessee

Lipscomb University, B
Southern Adventist University, B

Texas

Lubbock Christian University, B

Utah

Weber State University, B

Washington

Central Washington University, B

FARM/FARM AND RANCH MANAGEMENT

United States

Alabama

Wallace State Community College, A

California

Lassen Community College District, A

Colorado

Lamar Community College, A
Morgan Community College, B
Northeastern Junior College, A

Georgia

Abraham Baldwin Agricultural College, A

Illinois

University of Illinois at Urbana - Champaign, B

Indiana

Purdue University, B

Iowa

Iowa Lakes Community College, A

Kansas

Allen Community College, A
Butler Community College, A
Colby Community College, A
Dodge City Community College, A
Fort Scott Community College, A
Hutchinson Community College, A
Pratt Community College, A

Minnesota

Northland Community and Technical College, A
University of Minnesota, Crookston, B

Mississippi

Copiah-Lincoln Community College, A

Missouri

Crowder College, A
North Central Missouri College, A

Nebraska

Northeast Community College, A

North Dakota

Bismarck State College, A
Sitting Bull College, A

Ohio

Lake Erie College, B
The University of Findlay, B

Oklahoma

Eastern Oklahoma State College, A
Northeastern Oklahoma Agricultural and Mechanical College, A

Oregon

Treasure Valley Community College, A

Rhode Island

Johnson & Wales University, B

Texas

Central Texas College, A
Clarendon College, A
Frank Phillips College, A
North Central Texas College, A
Southwest Texas Junior College, A
Tarleton State University, B
Texas A&M University, B
Texas Christian University, B
Trinity Valley Community College, A
Vernon College, A

Wharton County Junior College, A

Utah

Snow College, A

Wyoming

Eastern Wyoming College, A
Northwest College, A

FASHION/APPAREL DESIGN

United States

Arizona

The Art Institute of Phoenix, B
The Art Institute of Tucson, B
Phoenix College, A
Pima Community College, A

California

Academy of Art University, AB
Academy of Couture Art, AB
Allan Hancock College, A
American River College, A
The Art Institute of California - Hollywood, a campus of Argosy University, AB
The Art Institute of California - Inland Empire, a campus of Argosy University, B
The Art Institute of California - Los Angeles, a campus of Argosy University, B
The Art Institute of California - Orange County, a campus of Argosy University, B
The Art Institute of California - Sacramento, a campus of Argosy University, B
The Art Institute of California - San Diego, a campus of Argosy University, B
The Art Institute of California - San Francisco, a campus of Argosy University, AB
California College of the Arts, B
Cañada College, A
Cerritos College, A
Chaffey College, A
College of the Sequoias, A
Cuesta College, A
El Camino College, A
FIDM/Fashion Institute of Design & Merchandising, Los Angeles Campus, A
FIDM/Fashion Institute of Design & Merchandising, Orange County Campus, A
FIDM/Fashion Institute of Design & Merchandising, San Diego Campus, A
FIDM/Fashion Institute of Design & Merchandising, San Francisco Campus, A
Fullerton College, A
Long Beach City College, A
Los Angeles Trade-Technical College, A
Merced College, A
Moorpark College, A
Orange Coast College, A
Otis College of Art and Design, B
Palomar College, A
Pasadena City College, A
Saddleback College, A
San Diego Mesa College, A
Santa Ana College, A
Santa Monica College, A
Santa Rosa Junior College, A
Ventura College, A
West Valley College, A
Woodbury University, B

Colorado

The Art Institute of Colorado, B
Rocky Mountain College of Art + Design, B

Delaware

University of Delaware, B

District of Columbia

Howard University, B

Florida

The Art Institute of Fort Lauderdale, AB
Jacksonville University, B
Miami International University of Art & Design, AB
Palm Beach State College, A

Georgia

American InterContinental University Atlanta, B
Brenau University, B
Clark Atlanta University, B
Savannah College of Art and Design, B

Hawaii

Honolulu Community College, A
University of Hawaii Maui College, A

Illinois

College of DuPage, A
Columbia College Chicago, B
Dominican University, B
Harper College, A
The Illinois Institute of Art - Chicago, B
The Illinois Institute of Art - Schaumburg, B
School of the Art Institute of Chicago, B

Indiana

The Art Institute of Indianapolis, B
Indiana University Bloomington, B
Purdue University, B

Iowa

Iowa State University of Science and Technology, B

Kansas

Johnson County Community College, A

Maryland

Baltimore City Community College, A
Stevenson University, B
University of Maryland Eastern Shore, B

Massachusetts

Lasell College, B
Massachusetts College of Art and Design, B
Mount Ida College, B

Michigan

Ferris State University, B
Michigan State University, B
Western Michigan University, B

Minnesota

St. Catherine University, B

Mississippi

Itawamba Community College, A

Missouri

Lindenwood University, B
Metropolitan Community College - Kansas City, A
Stephens College, B
Washington University in St. Louis, B

Nevada

The Art Institute of Las Vegas, B

New Jersey

Centenary College, B
Montclair State University, B
Rowan College at Burlington County, A

New Mexico

Santa Fe Community College, A

New York

Buffalo State College, State University of New York, B
Cazenovia College, B
Eugene Lang College of Liberal Arts, B
Fashion Institute of Technology, AB
Genesee Community College, A
Marist College, B
Monroe Community College, A

Nassau Community College, A
Parsons School of Design, AB
Pratt Institute, B
Syracuse University, B
Villa Maria College, B
Wood Tobe - Coburn School, A

North Carolina

The Art Institute of Charlotte, a campus of South
University, A
Meredith College, B

Ohio

Bowling Green State University, B
Columbus College of Art & Design, B
Kent State University, B
University of Cincinnati, B
Ursuline College, B
Virginia Marti College of Art and Design, A

Oklahoma

Clary Sage College, A

Pennsylvania

The Art Institute of Philadelphia, AB
The Art Institute of Pittsburgh, B
Drexel University, B
Harcum College, A
Lehigh Carbon Community College, A
Moore College of Art & Design, B
Philadelphia University, B

South Carolina

The Art Institute of Charleston, a branch of The Art
Institute of Atlanta, B
Bob Jones University, B

Tennessee

Carson-Newman University, B
O'More College of Design, B

Texas

The Art Institute of Austin, a branch of The Art Insti-
tute of Houston, B
The Art Institute of Dallas, a campus of South Uni-
versity, AB
The Art Institute of Houston, B
The Art Institute of San Antonio, a branch of The Art
Institute of Houston, B
Baylor University, B
El Centro College, A
El Paso Community College, A
Houston Community College, A
Texas Tech University, B
Texas Woman's University, B
University of the Incarnate Word, B
University of North Texas, B
Wade College, A

Vermont

Bennington College, B

Virginia

Hampton University, B
Marymount University, B
Virginia Commonwealth University, B

Washington

The Art Institute of Seattle, AB
Seattle Central College, A

Wisconsin

Mount Mary University, B

U.S. Territories: Puerto Rico

EDP University of Puerto Rico, AB
EDP University of Puerto Rico - San Sebastian, A
Escuela de Artes Plasticas y Diseño de Puerto
Rico, B
Pontifical Catholic University of Puerto Rico, A

Universidad del Turabo, A

Canada

Maritime Provinces: Nova Scotia

Dalhousie University, B

Ontario

Ryerson University, B

Quebec

Université du Québec à Montréal, B

FASHION AND FABRIC CON-SULTANT

United States

California

Academy of Art University, AB

Illinois

College of DuPage, A
Harper College, A

FASHION MERCHANDISING

United States

Alabama

Wallace State Community College, A

Arizona

Mesa Community College, A
Penn Foster College, A
Phoenix College, A
Pima Community College, A
Scottsdale Community College, A

Arkansas

Harding University, B

California

Academy of Art University, AB
The Art Institute of California - Orange County, a
campus of Argosy University, B
California State University, Long Beach, B
College of the Sequoias, A
FIDM/Fashion Institute of Design & Merchandising,
Los Angeles Campus, A
FIDM/Fashion Institute of Design & Merchandising,
Orange County Campus, A
FIDM/Fashion Institute of Design & Merchandising,
San Diego Campus, A
FIDM/Fashion Institute of Design & Merchandising,
San Francisco Campus, A
Las Positas College, A
Los Angeles Trade-Technical College, A
Merced College, A
Modesto Junior College, A
Monterey Peninsula College, A
Mt. San Antonio College, A
Pasadena City College, A
Saddleback College, A
San Diego City College, A
San Diego Mesa College, A
San Joaquin Delta College, A
Santa Ana College, A
Santa Rosa Junior College, A
Skyline College, A
Solano Community College, A
Woodbury University, B

Colorado

Johnson & Wales University, B

Connecticut

Gateway Community College, A
University of Bridgeport, AB

Delaware

Delaware State University, B

District of Columbia

University of the District of Columbia, A

Florida

The Art Institute of Fort Lauderdale, B
Indian River State College, A
Johnson & Wales University, B
Lynn University, B
Miami International University of Art & Design, AB
Palm Beach State College, A

Georgia

Abraham Baldwin Agricultural College, A
American InterContinental University Atlanta, B
Brenau University, B
University of Georgia, B

Illinois

College of DuPage, A
Dominican University, B
Harper College, A
The Illinois Institute of Art - Chicago, A
The Illinois Institute of Art - Schaumburg, A
Joliet Junior College, A
Olivet Nazarene University, B
University of Illinois at Urbana - Champaign, B
Western Illinois University, B

Indiana

Harrison College, AB
Vincennes University, A

Iowa

Ellsworth Community College, A
Iowa Lakes Community College, A

Kansas

Johnson County Community College, A

Kentucky

Eastern Kentucky University, B

Louisiana

Louisiana State University and Agricultural & Mechanical College, B

Maryland

Stevenson University, B
University of Maryland Eastern Shore, B

Massachusetts

Bay State College, AB
Fisher College, AB
Lasell College, B
Middlesex Community College, A
Mount Ida College, B
Newbury College, B

Michigan

The Art Institute of Michigan, A
Central Michigan University, B
Eastern Michigan University, B
Grand Rapids Community College, A
Lansing Community College, A
Northwood University, Michigan Campus, B
Western Michigan University, B

Minnesota

Alexandria Technical and Community College, A
Minnesota State Community and Technical College,
A
St. Catherine University, B

Mississippi

Hinds Community College, A
Mississippi Gulf Coast Community College, A
Northeast Mississippi Community College, A
Northwest Mississippi Community College, A
Southwest Mississippi Community College, A

Missouri

Fontbonne University, B
Metropolitan Community College - Kansas City, A
Stevens - The Institute of Business & Arts, AB
Vatterott College (Sunset Hills), A

Montana

University of Montana, B

New Hampshire

Southern New Hampshire University, AB

New Jersey

Berkeley College - Woodland Park Campus, AB
Brookdale Community College, A

New Mexico

Doña Ana Community College, A

New York

Berkeley College - New York City Campus, AB
Berkeley College - White Plains Campus, AB
Buffalo State College, State University of New York,
  B
Fashion Institute of Technology, AB
Genesee Community College, A
Herkimer County Community College, A
Kingsborough Community College of the City University of New York, A
LIM College, AB
Marymount Manhattan College, B
Monroe Community College, A
Nassau Community College, A
New York City College of Technology of the City
  University of New York, A
Parsons School of Design, A
State University of New York College at Oneonta, B

North Carolina

Central Piedmont Community College, A
Johnson & Wales University, B
Mars Hill University, B
Meredith College, B

Ohio

Ashland University, B
Bowling Green State University, B
Kent State University, B
The University of Akron, A
Ursuline College, B
Virginia Marti College of Art and Design, A
Youngstown State University, B

Oklahoma

East Central University, B
University of Central Oklahoma, B

Pennsylvania

The Art Institute of Philadelphia, A
Cheyney University of Pennsylvania, B
Harcum College, A
Immaculata University, AB
Indiana University of Pennsylvania, B
Mercyhurst University, B
Philadelphia University, B

Rhode Island

Johnson & Wales University, B

Tennessee

Carson-Newman University, B
Lipscomb University, B
O'More College of Design, B
Tennessee Technological University, B
The University of Tennessee at Martin, B

Texas

Baylor University, B
Houston Community College, A
Laredo Community College, A
Lee College, A
Sam Houston State University, B
South Plains College, A
Stephen F. Austin State University, B

Tarrant County College District, A
Texas Christian University, B
Texas State University, B
Texas Tech University, B
Texas Woman's University, B
Trinity Valley Community College, A
University of North Texas, B

Utah

Utah State University, B

Virginia

Hampton University, B
Marymount University, B

Washington

Edmonds Community College, A
Pierce College at Fort Steilacoom, A
Spokane Falls Community College, A

Wisconsin

Madison Area Technical College, A
Mount Mary University, B
Western Technical College, A

FASHION MODELING

United States

New York

Fashion Institute of Technology, A

FIBER, TEXTILE AND WEAVING ARTS

United States

California

California College of the Arts, B
California State University, Long Beach, B
Mendocino College, A
Monterey Peninsula College, A

Colorado

Adams State University, B
Colorado State University, B

Georgia

Savannah College of Art and Design, B

Illinois

School of the Art Institute of Chicago, B

Kansas

The University of Kansas, B

Maryland

Maryland Institute College of Art, B

Massachusetts

Massachusetts College of Art and Design, B
University of Massachusetts Dartmouth, B

Michigan

Finlandia University, B
University of Michigan, B

Missouri

College of the Ozarks, B
Kansas City Art Institute, B

New York

Cornell University, B
Syracuse University, B

Ohio

Bowling Green State University, B

Oregon

University of Oregon, B

Pennsylvania

Philadelphia University, B
Temple University, B

Rhode Island

Rhode Island School of Design, B

Washington

Western Washington University, B

Canada

Alberta

Alberta College of Art & Design, B

Maritime Provinces: Nova Scotia

NSCAD University, B

FILIPINO/TAGALOG LANGUAGE AND LITERATURE

United States

Hawaii

University of Hawaii at Manoa, B

FILM/CINEMA STUDIES

United States

Alaska

University of Alaska Fairbanks, B

Arizona

The University of Arizona, B
Yavapai College, A

Arkansas

John Brown University, B
University of Arkansas at Little Rock, B

California

Allan Hancock College, A
Biola University, B
California Baptist University, B
California College of the Arts, B
California State University, Long Beach, B
California State University, Northridge, B
California State University, Sacramento, B
Chapman University, B
Claremont McKenna College, B
College of Marin, A
Columbia College Hollywood, B
Cosumnes River College, A
De Anza College, A
La Sierra University, B
Long Beach City College, A
Los Angeles Film School, A
Moorpark College, A
National University, B
Palomar College, A
Pepperdine University, B
Pitzer College, B
San Francisco State University, B
Santa Barbara City College, A
Santa Monica College, A
Stanford University, B
University of California, Berkeley, B
University of California, Davis, B
University of California, Irvine, B
University of California, Los Angeles, B
University of California, San Diego, B
University of California, Santa Barbara, B
University of California, Santa Cruz, B
University of Southern California, B

Colorado

The Colorado College, B
University of Colorado Boulder, B
University of Denver, B

Connecticut

Connecticut College, B
Quinnipiac University, B
University of Hartford, B
Wesleyan University, B
Yale University, B

District of Columbia

Howard University, B

Florida

Eckerd College, B
Florida State University, B
Full Sail University, B
Jacksonville University, B
Southeastern University, B
The University of Tampa, B

Georgia

Emory University, B
Georgia State University, B
Morehouse College, B
University of Georgia, B

Illinois

Columbia College Chicago, B
Dominican University, B
Judson University, B
Northwestern University, B
School of the Art Institute of Chicago, B
University of Chicago, B
University of Illinois at Urbana - Champaign, B

Indiana

Grace College, B
Huntington University, B
Purdue University, B

Iowa

Coe College, B
The University of Iowa, B

Kansas

Southwestern College, B
The University of Kansas, B

Kentucky

University of Pikeville, B

Louisiana

University of Louisiana at Lafayette, B

Maryland

Johns Hopkins University, B
McDaniel College, B
Stevenson University, B
University of Maryland, College Park, B

Massachusetts

Boston College, B
Brandeis University, B
Clark University, B
Emerson College, B
Mount Holyoke College, B
Northeastern University, B
School of the Museum of Fine Arts, Boston, B
Smith College, B
Tufts University, B
Wellesley College, B
Wheaton College, B

Michigan

Eastern Michigan University, B
Grand Valley State University, B
Oakland Community College, A
Oakland University, B
University of Michigan, B
Wayne State University, B

Minnesota

Augsburg College, B
Carleton College, B
Minnesota State University Moorhead, B
St. Cloud State University, B

Missouri

Stephens College, B
Washington University in St. Louis, B
Webster University, B

Nebraska

University of Nebraska - Lincoln, B

Nevada

University of Nevada, Las Vegas, B

New Hampshire

Dartmouth College, B
Keene State College, B

New Jersey

Bergen Community College, A
Rutgers University - New Brunswick, B

New Mexico

Santa Fe Community College, A
University of New Mexico, B

New York

Bard College, B
Barnard College, B
Brooklyn College of the City University of New York, B
College of Staten Island of the City University of New York, B
Columbia University, B
Columbia University, School of General Studies, B
Cornell University, B
Eugene Lang College of Liberal Arts, B
Fashion Institute of Technology, AB
Hunter College of the City University of New York, B
Ithaca College, B
Marymount Manhattan College, B
New York University, B
Pace University, B
Pace University, Pleasantville Campus, B
Purchase College, State University of New York, B
Queens College of the City University of New York, B
Sarah Lawrence College, B
School of Visual Arts, B
State University of New York at Fredonia, B
University at Buffalo, the State University of New York, B
University of Rochester, B
Vassar College, B
Wells College, B

North Carolina

Saint Augustine's University, B
University of North Carolina School of the Arts, B

Ohio

Baldwin Wallace University, B
Bowling Green State University, B
Denison University, B
Kenyon College, B
The Ohio State University, B
The University of Toledo, B
Wright State University, B

Oklahoma

University of Oklahoma, B
The University of Tulsa, B

Oregon

University of Oregon, B

Pennsylvania

DeSales University, B
Douglas Education Center, A
Lafayette College, B
Muhlenberg College, B

Penn State Abington, B
Penn State Altoona, B
Penn State Beaver, B
Penn State Berks, B
Penn State Brandywine, B
Penn State DuBois, B
Penn State Erie, The Behrend College, B
Penn State Fayette, The Eberly Campus, B
Penn State Greater Allegheny, B
Penn State Hazleton, B
Penn State Lehigh Valley, B
Penn State Mont Alto, B
Penn State New Kensington, B
Penn State Schuylkill, B
Penn State Shenango, B
Penn State University Park, B
Penn State Wilkes-Barre, B
Penn State Worthington Scranton, B
Penn State York, B
Temple University, B
The University of the Arts, B
University of Pennsylvania, B
University of Pittsburgh, B

Rhode Island

Brown University, B
Rhode Island College, B
Roger Williams University, B

Tennessee

Carson-Newman University, B
Memphis College of Art, B
Vanderbilt University, B
Watkins College of Art, Design, & Film, B

Texas

Houston Baptist University, B
KD Conservatory College of Film and Dramatic Arts, A
University of Mary Hardin-Baylor, B

Utah

Brigham Young University, B
University of Utah, B

Vermont

Bennington College, B
Champlain College, B
Marlboro College, B
Middlebury College, B
University of Vermont, B

Virginia

University of Richmond, B

Washington

Central Washington University, B
Eastern Washington University, B
The Evergreen State College, B
Northwest University, B
Seattle University, B
Whitman College, B

Wisconsin

University of Wisconsin - Milwaukee, B

Canada

Alberta

University of Alberta, B
University of Calgary, B

British Columbia

Simon Fraser University, B
The University of British Columbia, B

Manitoba

University of Manitoba, B

Maritime Provinces: Nova Scotia

NSCAD University, B

Ontario

Brock University, B
Carleton University, B
Laurentian University, B
Queen's University at Kingston, B
University of Waterloo, B
The University of Western Ontario, B
University of Windsor, B
Wilfrid Laurier University, B
York University, B

Quebec

Bishop's University, B
Concordia University, B
Université de Montréal, B

Saskatchewan

University of Regina, B

FILM, TELEVISION, AND VIDEO PRODUCTION

United States

Alabama

The University of Alabama, M

Arizona

Arizona State University at the Tempe campus, M

Arkansas

University of Central Arkansas, M

California

Academy of Art University, M
Art Center College of Design, M
The Art Institute of California - San Francisco, a
    campus of Argosy University, M
California College of the Arts, M
California Institute of the Arts, MO
California State University, Fullerton, M
California State University, Northridge, M
Chapman University, M
Loyola Marymount University, M
Mount Saint Mary's University, M
National University, M
New York Film Academy, M
Pepperdine University, M
San Diego State University, M
San Francisco State University, M
San Jose State University, M
Stanford University, M
University of California, Los Angeles, MD
University of California, Santa Barbara, D
University of Southern California, M

Colorado

University of Denver, M
Western State Colorado University, M

Connecticut

Quinnipiac University, M
Sacred Heart University, M

District of Columbia

American University, M
Howard University, M

Florida

Florida Atlantic University, O
Florida State University, M
Miami International University of Art & Design, M
St. Thomas University, M
University of Central Florida, M
University of Miami, M

Georgia

Georgia State University, MD
Savannah College of Art and Design, M

Illinois

Columbia College Chicago, M
DePaul University, M
Northwestern University, MD
School of the Art Institute of Chicago, M

Iowa

The University of Iowa, M

Louisiana

University of New Orleans, M

Maryland

Maryland Institute College of Art, M

Massachusetts

Boston University, M
Massachusetts College of Art and Design, M

Michigan

Central Michigan University, M

Minnesota

Minneapolis College of Art and Design, M

Montana

Montana State University, M
University of Montana, M

Nevada

University of Nevada, Las Vegas, MO

New York

Brooklyn College of the City University of New York,
    M
Columbia University, M
Hofstra University, M
New York University, M
Rochester Institute of Technology, M
School of Visual Arts, M
Syracuse University, M

North Carolina

The University of North Carolina at Greensboro, M
University of North Carolina School of the Arts, M

Ohio

Bowling Green State University, MD
Ohio University, M

Oklahoma

University of Oklahoma, M

Pennsylvania

Carnegie Mellon University, M
Chatham University, M
Drexel University, M
Temple University, M

South Carolina

Bob Jones University, M

Tennessee

Lipscomb University, M
University of Memphis, M

Texas

University of North Texas, M
The University of Texas at Arlington, M
The University of Texas at Austin, M

Utah

Brigham Young University, M
University of Utah, M

Virginia

Hollins University, M
Regent University, M

Wisconsin

University of Wisconsin - Milwaukee, M

U.S. Territories: Puerto Rico

University of the Sacred Heart, MO

Canada

British Columbia

The University of British Columbia, MO
University of Victoria, M

Ontario

Carleton University, M
York University, MD

Quebec

Concordia University, M

Saskatchewan

University of Regina, M

FILM, TELEVISION, AND VIDEO THEORY AND CRITICISM

United States

California

California College of the Arts, M
National University, M
San Francisco State University, M
University of California, Santa Cruz, D
University of Southern California, MD

Connecticut

Yale University, D

Florida

University of Miami, MD
University of South Florida, M

Georgia

Emory University, MO
Savannah College of Art and Design, M

Illinois

DePaul University, M
University of Chicago, D

Indiana

Indiana University Bloomington, D

Iowa

The University of Iowa, MD

Kansas

The University of Kansas, MD

Michigan

Central Michigan University, M
University of Michigan, DO

New York

College of Staten Island of the City University of
    New York, M
Syracuse University, M
University at Buffalo, the State University of New
    York, M

Ohio

Ohio University, M
Tiffin University, M

Pennsylvania

University of Pittsburgh, MDO

Virginia

George Mason University, M
Hollins University, M

Wisconsin

University of Wisconsin - Madison, MD

Canada

British Columbia

The University of British Columbia, MO

Ontario

University of Toronto, MD
Wilfrid Laurier University, MD

Quebec

Concordia University, M
Université Laval, MD
Université de Montréal, MD

FILM/VIDEO AND PHOTO-GRAPHIC ARTS

United States

Alabama

Birmingham-Southern College, B

Arizona

Arizona State University at the Tempe campus, B

California

Mount Saint Mary's University, B
Scripps College, B
Woodbury University, B

Connecticut

Fairfield University, B

Florida

Full Sail University, B

Illinois

School of the Art Institute of Chicago, B
University of Illinois at Chicago, B

Iowa

Coe College, B

Maine

College of the Atlantic, B

Maryland

Maryland Institute College of Art, B

Massachusetts

Greenfield Community College, A
Hampshire College, B
School of the Museum of Fine Arts, Boston, B
Wellesley College, B

Michigan

Northern Michigan University, B
Spring Arbor University, B
Western Michigan University, B

Minnesota

University of Minnesota, Twin Cities Campus, B

Missouri

Calvary Bible College and Theological Seminary, B
Kansas City Art Institute, B

New York

Pratt Institute, B
School of Visual Arts, B
Westchester Community College, A

Ohio

Cleveland State University, B
Columbus College of Art & Design, B

Oklahoma

Oklahoma City University, B

Oregon

Portland State University, B

Pennsylvania

Chatham University, B
La Roche College, B
Saint Joseph's University, B
Swarthmore College, B

Rhode Island

Rhode Island School of Design, B

Tennessee

Nossi College of Art, B

Utah

Brigham Young University, B

Vermont

Marlboro College, B

Virginia

Hollins University, B

Canada

Ontario

Ryerson University, B

FINANCE

United States

Alabama

Alabama Agricultural and Mechanical University, B
Alabama State University, B
Auburn University, B
Auburn University at Montgomery, B
Community College of the Air Force, A
Jacksonville State University, B
Samford University, B
Talladega College, B
Tuskegee University, B
The University of Alabama, B
The University of Alabama at Birmingham, B
The University of Alabama in Huntsville, B
University of Montevallo, B
University of North Alabama, B
University of South Alabama, B
The University of West Alabama, B
Virginia College in Mobile, A
Wallace State Community College, A

Alaska

University of Alaska Anchorage, B

Arizona

Arizona State University at the Tempe campus, B
Mesa Community College, A
Northern Arizona University, B
Penn Foster College, A
Scottsdale Community College, A
The University of Arizona, B
University of Phoenix - Online Campus, B
University of Phoenix - Phoenix Campus, B
University of Phoenix - Southern Arizona Campus, B

Arkansas

Arkansas State University, B
Harding University, B
National Park College, A
NorthWest Arkansas Community College, A
University of Arkansas, B
University of Arkansas at Little Rock, B
University of Central Arkansas, B

California

Bakersfield College, A
California State University, Bakersfield, B
California State University, Dominguez Hills, B
California State University, East Bay, B
California State University, Fresno, B
California State University, Long Beach, B
California State University, Northridge, B
California State University, San Marcos, B
California State University, Stanislaus, B
East Los Angeles College, A
El Camino College, A
Folsom Lake College, A
Golden Gate University, B
La Sierra University, B
Lake Tahoe Community College, A
Laney College, A
Los Angeles City College, A
Los Angeles Mission College, A
Los Angeles Southwest College, A
Loyola Marymount University, B
The Master's College and Seminary, B
Mendocino College, A
Menlo College, B
Merced College, A
Modesto Junior College, A
Mt. San Antonio College, A
National University, B
Pepperdine University, B
Point Loma Nazarene University, B
Porterville College, A
San Bernardino Valley College, A
San Diego City College, A
San Diego State University, B
San Francisco State University, B
San Jose State University, B
Santa Barbara City College, A
Santa Clara University, B
Skyline College, A
Solano Community College, A
University of Phoenix - Sacramento Valley Campus, B
University of San Diego, B
University of San Francisco, B
Vanguard University of Southern California, B

Colorado

Adams State University, B
American Sentinel University, B
Colorado Christian University, B
Colorado Mountain College (Leadville), A
Colorado State University, B
Fort Lewis College, B
Metropolitan State University of Denver, B
Regis University, B
University of Colorado Boulder, B
University of Denver, B
University of Phoenix - Colorado Campus, B
University of Phoenix - Colorado Springs Downtown Campus, B

Connecticut

Albertus Magnus College, B
Central Connecticut State University, B
Eastern Connecticut State University, B
Fairfield University, B
Naugatuck Valley Community College, A
Norwalk Community College, A
Post University, B
Quinnipiac University, B
Sacred Heart University, B
Southern Connecticut State University, B
University of Bridgeport, B
University of Connecticut, B
University of Hartford, B
University of New Haven, B
Western Connecticut State University, B

Delaware

Delaware State University, B
Goldey-Beacom College, B
University of Delaware, B
Wilmington University, B

District of Columbia

American University, B
The Catholic University of America, B
The George Washington University, B
Georgetown University, B
Howard University, B
University of the District of Columbia, B
University of Phoenix - Washington D.C. Campus, B

Florida

Ave Maria University, B
Barry University, B
Broward College, A
Chipola College, A
Florida Atlantic University, B
Florida Gulf Coast University, B
Florida International University, B
Florida State College at Jacksonville, B
Florida State University, B
Indian River State College, A
Jacksonville University, B
Keiser University, B
Miami Dade College, A
Nova Southeastern University, B
Palm Beach Atlantic University, B
Palm Beach State College, A
St. Thomas University, B
Seminole State College of Florida, A
South Florida State College, A
Southeastern University, B
State College of Florida Manatee-Sarasota, A
Stetson University, B
University of Central Florida, B
University of Florida, B
University of Miami, B
University of North Florida, B
University of South Florida, B
University of South Florida, St. Petersburg, B
University of South Florida Sarasota-Manatee, B
The University of Tampa, B
University of West Florida, B
Virginia College in Pensacola, A
Webber International University, B

Georgia

Ashworth College, A
Augusta University, B
Berry College, B
Columbus State University, B
Georgia Southern University, B
Georgia State University, B
Kennesaw State University, B
Mercer University, B
University of Georgia, B
University of North Georgia, B
University of Phoenix - Atlanta Campus, B
University of Phoenix - Augusta Campus, B
University of Phoenix - Columbus Georgia Campus, AB
University of West Georgia, B
Valdosta State University, B

Hawaii

Hawai'i Pacific University, AB
University of Hawaii at Manoa, B
University of Phoenix - Hawaii Campus, B

Idaho

Boise State University, B
Brigham Young University - Idaho, B
Idaho State University, B
Northwest Nazarene University, B
University of Idaho, B

Illinois

Aurora University, B
Benedictine University, B
Bradley University, B
DePaul University, B
Dominican University, B
Eastern Illinois University, B
Ellis University, AB
Elmhurst College, B
Harper College, A
Illinois College, B

Illinois State University, B
Lake Forest College, B
Lewis University, B
Loyola University Chicago, B
McKendree University, B
Morton College, A
North Central College, B
North Park University, B
Northeastern Illinois University, B
Northern Illinois University, B
Quincy University, B
Rockford University, B
Roosevelt University, B
Southern Illinois University Carbondale, B
Spoon River College, A
Trinity Christian College, B
University of Illinois at Chicago, B
University of Illinois at Urbana - Champaign, B
University of St. Francis, B
Western Illinois University, B

Indiana

Anderson University, B
Ball State University, B
Butler University, B
Grace College, B
Harrison College, A
Indiana State University, B
Indiana University - Purdue University Fort Wayne, B
Indiana Wesleyan University, AB
Manchester University, B
Marian University, B
Taylor University, B
University of Evansville, B
University of Notre Dame, B
University of Saint Francis, B
University of Southern Indiana, B
Valparaiso University, B
Vincennes University, A

Iowa

Drake University, B
Iowa Lakes Community College, A
Iowa State University of Science and Technology, B
Kirkwood Community College, A
Loras College, B
Mount Mercy University, B
St. Ambrose University, B
The University of Iowa, B
University of Northern Iowa, B
Wartburg College, B
Western Iowa Tech Community College, A

Kansas

Benedictine College, B
Bethany College, B
Central Christian College of Kansas, A
Dodge City Community College, A
Fort Hays State University, B
Friends University, B
Kansas State University, B
McPherson College, B
Neosho County Community College, A
Pittsburg State University, B
Seward County Community College and Area Technical School, A
Southwestern College, B
The University of Kansas, B
Washburn University, B
Wichita State University, B

Kentucky

Bellarmine University, B
Brescia University, B
Eastern Kentucky University, B
Georgetown College, B
Morehead State University, B
Murray State University, B
Northern Kentucky University, B
University of Kentucky, B
University of Louisville, B
Western Kentucky University, B

Louisiana

Louisiana College, B
Louisiana State University and Agricultural & Mechanical College, B
Louisiana State University in Shreveport, B
Louisiana Tech University, B
Loyola University New Orleans, B
McNeese State University, B
Nicholls State University, B
Southeastern Louisiana University, B
Southern University and Agricultural and Mechanical College, B
Tulane University, B
University of Louisiana at Lafayette, B
University of Louisiana at Monroe, B
University of New Orleans, B

Maine

Husson University, B
Saint Joseph's College of Maine, B
Thomas College, B
University of Maine, B
University of Southern Maine, B

Maryland

Loyola University Maryland, B
Morgan State University, B
Salisbury University, B
University of Baltimore, B
University of Maryland, College Park, B
University of Maryland University College, B

Massachusetts

Babson College, B
Bentley University, B
Boston College, B
Boston University, B
Bridgewater State University, B
Bunker Hill Community College, A
Endicott College, B
Fisher College, B
Fitchburg State University, B
Gordon College, B
Lasell College, B
Merrimack College, B
New England College of Business and Finance, A
Nichols College, B
Northeastern University, B
Northern Essex Community College, A
Salem State University, B
Simmons College, B
Stonehill College, B
Suffolk University, B
University of Massachusetts Amherst, B
University of Massachusetts Dartmouth, B
Western New England University, B

Michigan

Albion College, B
Alma College, B
Central Michigan University, B
Cleary University, B
Cornerstone University, B
Davenport University, AB
Eastern Michigan University, B
Ferris State University, B
Grand Valley State University, B
Hillsdale College, B
Lake Superior State University, B
Macomb Community College, A
Michigan State University, B
Michigan Technological University, B
Monroe County Community College, A
Muskegon Community College, A
Northern Michigan University, B
Northwood University, Michigan Campus, B
Oakland University, B
Olivet College, B
Saginaw Valley State University, B
Spring Arbor University, B
University of Michigan - Dearborn, B
University of Michigan - Flint, B
University of Phoenix - Detroit Campus, B

Walsh College of Accountancy and Business Admin-
istration, B
Wayne State University, B
Western Michigan University, B

Minnesota

Academy College, A
Augsburg College, B
Capella University, B
The College of St. Scholastica, B
Concordia College, B
Concordia University, St. Paul, B
Fond du Lac Tribal and Community College, A
Hamline University, B
Metropolitan State University, B
Minnesota State University Mankato, B
Minnesota State University Moorhead, B
North Hennepin Community College, A
St. Cloud State University, B
Saint Mary's University of Minnesota, B
Southwest Minnesota State University, B
University of Minnesota, Duluth, B
University of Minnesota, Twin Cities Campus, B
University of Northwestern - St. Paul, B
University of St. Thomas, B
Vermilion Community College, A
Winona State University, B

Mississippi

Delta State University, B
Jackson State University, B
Mississippi College, B
Mississippi Gulf Coast Community College, A
Mississippi State University, B
Southwest Mississippi Community College, A
University of Mississippi, B
University of Southern Mississippi, B

Missouri

Avila University, B
Columbia College, B
Culver-Stockton College, B
Drury University, B
Lindenwood University, B
Missouri State University, B
Missouri Western State University, B
Northwest Missouri State University, B
Saint Louis University, B
Southeast Missouri State University, B
Southwest Baptist University, B
University of Central Missouri, B
University of Missouri, B
University of Missouri - St. Louis, B
Washington University in St. Louis, B
Webster University, B

Montana

Carroll College, B
Montana State University Billings, B
University of Montana, B

Nebraska

Creighton University, B
University of Nebraska - Lincoln, B
University of Nebraska at Omaha, B

Nevada

Sierra Nevada College, B
University of Nevada, Las Vegas, B
University of Nevada, Reno, B

New Hampshire

Franklin Pierce University, B
New England College, B
Plymouth State University, B
Rivier University, B
Saint Anselm College, B

New Jersey

Bergen Community College, A
Centenary College, B
Fairleigh Dickinson University, College at Florham,
B
Fairleigh Dickinson University, Metropolitan Cam-
pus, B

Kean University, B
New Jersey City University, B
Passaic County Community College, A
Rider University, B
Rowan University, B
Rutgers University - Camden, B
Rutgers University - New Brunswick, B
Rutgers University - Newark, B
Saint Peter's University, A
Seton Hall University, B
Thomas Edison State University, B
University of Phoenix - Jersey City Campus, B
William Paterson University of New Jersey, B

New Mexico

Doña Ana Community College, A
New Mexico Highlands University, B
New Mexico Junior College, A
New Mexico Military Institute, A
New Mexico State University, B

New York

Adelphi University, B
Alfred University, B
Baruch College of the City University of New York,
B
Binghamton University, State University of New
York, B
Canisius College, B
The College at Brockport, State University of New
York, B
The College of Saint Rose, B
Dominican College, B
Excelsior College, B
Fordham University, B
Fulton-Montgomery Community College, A
Globe Institute of Technology, B
Hofstra University, B
Iona College, B
Ithaca College, B
The King's College, B
Le Moyne College, B
Long Island University - LIU Brooklyn, B
Manhattan College, B
Manhattanville College, B
Marymount Manhattan College, B
Molloy College, B
Nazareth College of Rochester, B
New York Institute of Technology, B
New York University, B
Pace University, B
Pace University, Pleasantville Campus, B
Queens College of the City University of New York,
B
Rochester Institute of Technology, B
Rockland Community College, A
St. Bonaventure University, B
St. John Fisher College, B
St. John's University, B
St. Thomas Aquinas College, B
Siena College, B
State University of New York College at Old
Westbury, B
State University of New York College of Technology
at Canton, B
State University of New York at Fredonia, B
State University of New York at New Paltz, B
State University of New York at Oswego, B
State University of New York at Plattsburgh, B
Syracuse University, B
Touro College, B
Wagner College, B
Westchester Community College, A
Yeshiva University, B

North Carolina

Appalachian State University, B
Central Piedmont Community College, A
East Carolina University, B
Elon University, B
Fayetteville State University, B
Gardner-Webb University, B
High Point University, B
Lenoir-Rhyne University, B
Mars Hill University, B
Methodist University, AB

North Carolina Agricultural and Technical State Uni-
versity, B
Pfeiffer University, B
Queens University of Charlotte, B
The University of North Carolina at Charlotte, B
The University of North Carolina at Greensboro, B
Wake Forest University, B
Western Carolina University, B
Wingate University, B

North Dakota

Dickinson State University, B
Minot State University, B
North Dakota State University, B
University of Mary, B
University of North Dakota, B

Ohio

Ashland University, B
Baldwin Wallace University, B
Bowling Green State University, B
Case Western Reserve University, B
Cedarville University, B
Cleveland State University, B
Cuyahoga Community College, A
Franklin University, AB
Harrison College, A
James A. Rhodes State College, A
John Carroll University, B
Kent State University, B
Lake Erie College, B
Lorain County Community College, A
Malone University, B
Marietta College, B
Miami University, B
Miami University Hamilton, B
Mount Vernon Nazarene University, B
Ohio Dominican University, B
The Ohio State University, B
Ohio University, B
Otterbein University, B
Sinclair Community College, A
Stark State College, A
Tiffin University, B
University of Cincinnati, B
University of Dayton, B
The University of Findlay, AB
University of Mount Union, B
The University of Toledo, B
Walsh University, B
Wittenberg University, B
Wright State University, B
Xavier University, B
Youngstown State University, AB

Oklahoma

Bacone College, B
East Central University, B
Northeastern State University, B
Oklahoma Baptist University, B
Oklahoma Christian University, B
Oklahoma City University, B
Oklahoma State University, B
Oral Roberts University, B
St. Gregory's University, B
Southeastern Oklahoma State University, B
Southern Nazarene University, B
Southwestern Christian University, B
University of Central Oklahoma, B
University of Oklahoma, B
The University of Tulsa, B

Oregon

Corban University, B
George Fox University, B
Linfield College, B
Oregon State University, B
Pacific University, B
Portland State University, B
University of Portland, B

Pennsylvania

Albright College, B
Arcadia University, B
Cabrini University, B

Carnegie Mellon University, B
Cheyney University of Pennsylvania, B
Clarion University of Pennsylvania, B
Community College of Beaver County, A
Community College of Philadelphia, A
DeSales University, B
Drexel University, B
Duquesne University, B
Gannon University, B
Grove City College, B
Holy Family University, B
Immaculata University, B
Indiana University of Pennsylvania, B
Juniata College, B
King's College, B
La Roche College, B
La Salle University, B
Lehigh University, B
Lincoln University, B
Lycoming College, B
Mercyhurst University, B
Penn State Abington, B
Penn State Altoona, B
Penn State Beaver, B
Penn State Berks, B
Penn State Brandywine, B
Penn State DuBois, B
Penn State Erie, The Behrend College, B
Penn State Fayette, The Eberly Campus, B
Penn State Greater Allegheny, B
Penn State Harrisburg, B
Penn State Hazleton, B
Penn State Lehigh Valley, B
Penn State Mont Alto, B
Penn State New Kensington, B
Penn State Schuylkill, B
Penn State Shenango, B
Penn State University Park, B
Penn State Wilkes-Barre, B
Penn State Worthington Scranton, B
Penn State York, B
Philadelphia University, B
Robert Morris University, B
Rosemont College, B
Saint Francis University, B
Saint Joseph's University, B
Saint Vincent College, B
Shippensburg University of Pennsylvania, B
Slippery Rock University of Pennsylvania, B
Susquehanna University, B
Temple University, B
University of Pennsylvania, B
University of Phoenix - Philadelphia Campus, B
University of Pittsburgh, B
University of Pittsburgh at Johnstown, B
The University of Scranton, B
Villanova University, B
Waynesburg University, B
West Chester University of Pennsylvania, B
Wilkes University, B
York College of Pennsylvania, B

Rhode Island

Bryant University, B
Johnson & Wales University, B
Providence College, B
Rhode Island College, B
Roger Williams University, B
Salve Regina University, B
University of Rhode Island, B

South Carolina

Benedict College, B
Charleston Southern University, B
Clemson University, B
Coastal Carolina University, B
College of Charleston, B
Converse College, B
Francis Marion University, B
University of South Carolina, B
Wofford College, B

South Dakota

Dakota State University, B
National American University (Rapid City), B
Northern State University, B

Southeast Technical Institute, A
The University of South Dakota, B

Tennessee

Aquinas College, B
Austin Peay State University, B
Belmont University, B
East Tennessee State University, B
Freed-Hardeman University, B
Hiwassee College, A
King University, B
Lincoln Memorial University, B
Middle Tennessee State University, B
Southern Adventist University, B
Tennessee Technological University, B
Tennessee Wesleyan College, B
Union University, B
University of Memphis, B
The University of Tennessee, B
The University of Tennessee at Martin, B

Texas

Abilene Christian University, B
Angelo State University, B
Austin College, B
Baylor University, B
Cisco College, A
Clarendon College, A
Dallas Baptist University, B
Del Mar College, A
Hardin-Simmons University, B
Houston Baptist University, B
Howard College, A
Howard Payne University, B
Lamar University, B
LeTourneau University, B
Lubbock Christian University, B
McLennan Community College, A
McMurry University, B
Midwestern State University, B
Our Lady of the Lake University of San Antonio, B
Palo Alto College, A
Prairie View A&M University, B
St. Edward's University, B
St. Mary's University, B
Sam Houston State University, B
Schreiner University, B
Southern Methodist University, B
Southwestern Adventist University, B
Stephen F. Austin State University, B
Tarleton State University, B
Texas A&M International University, B
Texas A&M University, B
Texas A&M University - Central Texas, B
Texas A&M University - Commerce, B
Texas A&M University - Corpus Christi, B
Texas A&M University - Kingsville, B
Texas A&M University - San Antonio, B
Texas A&M University - Texarkana, B
Texas Christian University, B
Texas Lutheran University, B
Texas State University, B
Texas Tech University, B
Texas Wesleyan University, B
Texas Woman's University, B
Trinity University, B
Trinity Valley Community College, A
University of Houston, B
University of Houston - Clear Lake, B
University of Houston - Downtown, B
University of Houston - Victoria, B
University of Mary Hardin-Baylor, B
University of North Texas, B
University of Phoenix - Dallas Campus, B
University of Phoenix - Houston Campus, B
University of Phoenix - San Antonio Campus, B
University of St. Thomas, B
The University of Texas at Austin, B
The University of Texas at Dallas, B
The University of Texas at El Paso, B
The University of Texas of the Permian Basin, B
The University of Texas Rio Grande Valley, B
The University of Texas at San Antonio, B
The University of Texas at Tyler, B
West Texas A&M University, B

Utah

Dixie State University, B
Independence University, AB
Salt Lake Community College, A
Southern Utah University, B
University of Phoenix - Utah Campus, B
University of Utah, B
Utah State University, B
Utah Valley University, B
Weber State University, B
Westminster College, B

Virginia

Christopher Newport University, B
The College of William and Mary, B
George Mason University, B
Hampton University, B
James Madison University, B
Old Dominion University, B
Radford University, B
Tidewater Community College, A
Virginia Polytechnic Institute and State University, B
Virginia Union University, B

Washington

Central Washington University, B
Eastern Washington University, B
Gonzaga University, B
Seattle University, B
University of Phoenix - Western Washington Campus, B
University of Washington, B
University of Washington, Tacoma, B
Walla Walla University, B
Washington State University, B
Washington State University - Vancouver, B
Western Washington University, B

West Virginia

Bethany College, B
Fairmont State University, B
Marshall University, B
Mountwest Community & Technical College, A
Pierpont Community & Technical College, A
Southern West Virginia Community and Technical College, A
University of Charleston, B
West Virginia University, B
West Virginia University at Parkersburg, A

Wisconsin

Carroll University, B
Lakeshore Technical College, A
Madison Area Technical College, A
Marian University, B
Marquette University, B
Northeast Wisconsin Technical College, A
Southwest Wisconsin Technical College, A
University of Wisconsin - Eau Claire, B
University of Wisconsin - La Crosse, B
University of Wisconsin - Madison, B
University of Wisconsin - Milwaukee, B
University of Wisconsin - Oshkosh, B
University of Wisconsin - Superior, B
University of Wisconsin - Whitewater, B
Viterbo University, B
Western Technical College, A
Wisconsin Indianhead Technical College, A

Wyoming

University of Wyoming, B

U.S. Territories: Puerto Rico

Bayamón Central University, B
Inter American University of Puerto Rico, Bayamón Campus, B
Inter American University of Puerto Rico, Metropolitan Campus, B
Inter American University of Puerto Rico, Ponce Campus, B
Inter American University of Puerto Rico, San Germán Campus, B
Polytechnic University of Puerto Rico, B
Pontifical Catholic University of Puerto Rico, B
University of Puerto Rico in Aguadilla, B

University of Puerto Rico in Arecibo, B
University of Puerto Rico in Bayamón, B
University of Puerto Rico in Carolina, AB
University of Puerto Rico, Mayagüez Campus, B
University of Puerto Rico in Ponce, B
University of Puerto Rico, Río Piedras Campus, B

Canada

Alberta

University of Alberta, B
University of Calgary, B
University of Lethbridge, B

British Columbia

British Columbia Institute of Technology, A
Thompson Rivers University, B
The University of British Columbia, B
The University of British Columbia - Okanagan
  Campus, B
University of Northern British Columbia, B

Manitoba

University of Manitoba, B

Maritime Provinces: New Brunswick

Université de Moncton, B
University of New Brunswick Fredericton, B

Maritime Provinces: Nova Scotia

Cape Breton University, B
Dalhousie University, B
Saint Mary's University, B

Newfoundland and Labrador

Memorial University of Newfoundland, B

Ontario

Brock University, B
Carleton University, B
Lakehead University, B
Ryerson University, B
University of Guelph, B
University of Ottawa, B
University of Toronto, B
The University of Western Ontario, B
University of Windsor, B
York University, B

Quebec

Bishop's University, B
Concordia University, B
HEC Montreal, B
McGill University, B
Université de Sherbrooke, B

Saskatchewan

University of Regina, B
University of Saskatchewan, B

FINANCE AND BANKING

United States

Alabama

Auburn University, M
Columbia Southern University, M
Troy University, M
The University of Alabama, MD
The University of Alabama at Birmingham, M
The University of Alabama in Huntsville, M
University of North Alabama, M

Alaska

University of Alaska Fairbanks, M

Arizona

Argosy University, Phoenix, M
Arizona State University at the Tempe campus, M
Grand Canyon University, M
The University of Arizona, MD

Western International University, M

California

Argosy University, Inland Empire, M
Argosy University, Los Angeles, M
Argosy University, Orange County, MO
Argosy University, San Diego, M
Argosy University, San Francisco Bay Area, M
Azusa Pacific University, M
California College of the Arts, M
California Intercontinental University, M
California Lutheran University, MO
California State University, East Bay, M
California State University, Fullerton, M
California State University, Los Angeles, M
California State University, San Bernardino, M
Claremont McKenna College, M
Golden Gate University, MO
Holy Names University, M
La Sierra University, M
Lincoln University, MD
National University, M
New Charter University, M
Notre Dame de Namur University, M
Pacific States University, M
Pepperdine University, M
Saint Mary's College of California, M
San Diego State University, M
San Francisco State University, M
Santa Clara University, M
Trident University International, M
University of California, Berkeley, DO
University of California, Los Angeles, D
University of California, Riverside, M
University of California, San Diego, M
University of California, Santa Barbara, D
University of California, Santa Cruz, M
University of La Verne, M
University of San Francisco, M
University of the West, M

Colorado

Argosy University, Denver, M
Aspen University, M
Colorado Heights University, M
Colorado State University, M
Colorado State University - Global Campus, M
Colorado Technical University Colorado Springs, M
Colorado Technical University Denver South, M
Regis University, M
University of Colorado Boulder, D
University of Colorado Denver, M
University of Denver, M

Connecticut

Fairfield University, MO
Post University, M
Sacred Heart University, MDO
University of Bridgeport, M
University of Connecticut, DO
University of New Haven, MO
Yale University, D

Delaware

Goldey-Beacom College, M
University of Delaware, M
Wilmington University, M

District of Columbia

The George Washington University, MD
Georgetown University, MD
Howard University, M

Florida

Argosy University, Sarasota, MO
Argosy University, Tampa, M
Barry University, O
Embry-Riddle Aeronautical University - Daytona, MD
Florida Agricultural and Mechanical University, M
Florida Atlantic University, D
Florida International University, M
Florida National University, M
Florida State University, MD
Jacksonville University, M

Polytechnic University of Puerto Rico, Miami Cam-
  pus, M
Polytechnic University of Puerto Rico, Orlando
  Campus, M
Rollins College, M
Schiller International University, M
University of Florida, MDO
University of Miami, M
University of North Florida, M
University of South Florida, MD
The University of Tampa, M

Georgia

Argosy University, Atlanta, M
Emory University, D
Georgia State University, MD

Hawaii

Argosy University, Hawai'i, MO
Hawai'i Pacific University, M
University of Hawaii at Manoa, MD

Illinois

American InterContinental University Online, M
Argosy University, Chicago, M
Argosy University, Schaumburg, MO
Benedictine University, M
DePaul University, M
DeVry University (Downers Grove), M
Ellis University, M
Illinois Institute of Technology, M
Lewis University, M
Loyola University Chicago, M
North Central College, M
Northeastern Illinois University, M
Northwestern University, MD
Robert Morris University Illinois, M
Saint Xavier University, MO
Southern Illinois University Edwardsville, M
University of Chicago, M
University of Illinois at Chicago, M
University of Illinois at Urbana - Champaign, MD
University of St. Francis, O

Indiana

Indiana University Bloomington, MDO
Indiana University Southeast, M
Purdue University, M
University of Notre Dame, M
Valparaiso University, MO

Iowa

Iowa State University of Science and Technology, M
Kaplan University, Davenport Campus, M
The University of Iowa, MD
Upper Iowa University, M

Kansas

Kansas State University, MO
MidAmerica Nazarene University, M
Newman University, M
Ottawa University, M

Louisiana

Louisiana State University and Agricultural & Me-
  chanical College, MD
Louisiana Tech University, MD
Tulane University, MD
University of New Orleans, M

Maine

University of Maine, M
University of Southern Maine, M

Maryland

Hood College, M
Johns Hopkins University, MO
Loyola University Maryland, M
University of Baltimore, M
University of Maryland University College, MO

Massachusetts

Assumption College, M
Bentley University, M

Boston College, MD
Boston University, M
Brandeis University, MD
Bridgewater State University, M
Clark University, M
Curry College, O
Hult International Business School, M
New England College of Business and Finance, M
Northeastern University, M
Suffolk University, MO
University of Massachusetts Amherst, MD
University of Massachusetts Boston, M
University of Massachusetts Dartmouth, O
University of Massachusetts Lowell, O

Michigan

Andrews University, M
Central Michigan University, M
Cleary University, MO
Davenport University, M
Eastern Michigan University, MO
Michigan State University, MD
Oakland University, MO
University of Michigan - Dearborn, M
University of Michigan - Flint, M
Walsh College of Accountancy and Business Administration, M
Wayne State University, M

Minnesota

Argosy University, Twin Cities, M
Capella University, MD
University of Minnesota, Twin Cities Campus, MD
Walden University, MD

Mississippi

Mississippi College, MO
Mississippi State University, MD

Missouri

American Business & Technology University, M
Avila University, M
Lindenwood University, M
Park University, MO
Saint Louis University, M
Southeast Missouri State University, M
University of Central Missouri, M
University of Missouri, D
University of Missouri - Kansas City, M
Washington University in St. Louis, MD
Webster University, M

Nebraska

Bellevue University, M
University of Nebraska - Lincoln, MD

Nevada

University of Nevada, Reno, M

New Hampshire

Southern New Hampshire University, MO

New Jersey

Fairleigh Dickinson University, College at Florham, MO
Fairleigh Dickinson University, Metropolitan Campus, MO
Monmouth University, M
New Jersey City University, M
Princeton University, M
Rutgers University - Newark, D
Saint Peter's University, M
Seton Hall University, M
Stevens Institute of Technology, M

New Mexico

New Mexico State University, O
University of New Mexico, M

New York

Adelphi University, M
Baruch College of the City University of New York, MD

Binghamton University, State University of New York, MD
Brooklyn College of the City University of New York, M
Columbia University, MD
Cornell University, D
Fordham University, M
Hofstra University, MO
Iona College, MO
Long Island University - LIU Brooklyn, M
Manhattanville College, M
Metropolitan College of New York, M
Mount Saint Mary College, M
New York Institute of Technology, M
New York University, MDO
Niagara University, M
Pace University, M
Rochester Institute of Technology, M
St. John's University, M
St. Thomas Aquinas College, M
State University of New York Polytechnic Institute, M
Stony Brook University, State University of New York, MO
Syracuse University, MD
University at Albany, State University of New York, M
University at Buffalo, the State University of New York, M
University of Rochester, M
Wagner College, M

North Carolina

Duke University, MDO
The University of North Carolina at Chapel Hill, D
The University of North Carolina at Charlotte, MO
The University of North Carolina at Greensboro, O
Wake Forest University, M

Ohio

Case Western Reserve University, M
Cleveland State University, MDO
Kent State University, D
Ohio Dominican University, M
The Ohio State University, M
Ohio University, M
Tiffin University, M
The University of Akron, M
University of Cincinnati, MD
University of Dayton, M
The University of Toledo, M
Wright State University, M
Xavier University, M
Youngstown State University, M

Oklahoma

Northeastern State University, M
Oklahoma Christian University, M
Oklahoma State University, MD
Oral Roberts University, M
The University of Tulsa, M

Oregon

George Fox University, M
Marylhurst University, M
Oregon State University, M
Pacific University, M
Portland State University, M
University of Oregon, D
University of Portland, M

Pennsylvania

Carnegie Mellon University, D
Delaware Valley University, M
DeSales University, M
Drexel University, MD
Duquesne University, M
Gannon University, M
Geneva College, M
Holy Family University, M
La Salle University, MO
Lehigh University, M
Lincoln University, M
Marywood University, M
Penn State Harrisburg, O

Saint Joseph's University, M
Temple University, MD
University of Pennsylvania, MD
University of Pittsburgh, MD
The University of Scranton, M
Villanova University, M
Waynesburg University, M
Wilkes University, M
York College of Pennsylvania, M

Rhode Island

Bryant University, M
Providence College, M
Rhode Island College, O
University of Rhode Island, MD

South Carolina

Charleston Southern University, M
North Greenville University, M

South Dakota

Northern State University, M

Tennessee

Argosy University, Nashville, M
East Tennessee State University, M
King University, M
Lipscomb University, M
Southern Adventist University, M
Tennessee Technological University, M
University of Memphis, D
The University of Tennessee, MD
Vanderbilt University, M

Texas

Argosy University, Dallas, MO
Dallas Baptist University, M
Our Lady of the Lake University of San Antonio, M
St. Edward's University, O
Sam Houston State University, M
Southern Methodist University, M
Southwestern Adventist University, M
Texas A&M International University, M
Texas A&M University, MD
Texas A&M University - Commerce, M
Texas A&M University - San Antonio, M
Texas Christian University, M
Texas State University, M
Texas Tech University, MD
University of Dallas, M
University of Houston, M
University of Houston - Clear Lake, M
University of Houston - Victoria, M
University of North Texas, M
University of St. Thomas, M
The University of Texas at Arlington, MD
The University of Texas at Austin, MD
The University of Texas at Dallas, MD
The University of Texas Rio Grande Valley, D
The University of Texas at San Antonio, MD
West Texas A&M University, M

Utah

Argosy University, Salt Lake City, M
Brigham Young University, M
University of Utah, MD

Vermont

Norwich University, M

Virginia

Argosy University, Washington DC, M
Old Dominion University, MD
University of Virginia, M
Virginia Commonwealth University, M
Virginia International University, M

Washington

Argosy University, Seattle, M
City University of Seattle, MO
Pacific Lutheran University, M
Seattle University, MO
University of Washington, Tacoma, M

West Virginia

American Public University System, M

Wisconsin

Concordia University Wisconsin, M
Edgewood College, M
Lakeland College, M
Marquette University, M
University of Wisconsin - Madison, MD
University of Wisconsin - Whitewater, M

Wyoming

University of Wyoming, M

U.S. Territories: Puerto Rico

Bayamón Central University, M
Inter American University of Puerto Rico, Aguadilla
  Campus, M
Inter American University of Puerto Rico, Arecibo
  Campus, M
Inter American University of Puerto Rico, Bar-
  ranquitas Campus, M
Inter American University of Puerto Rico, Metropoli-
  tan Campus, M
Inter American University of Puerto Rico, Ponce
  Campus, M
Inter American University of Puerto Rico, San
  Germán Campus, M
Pontifical Catholic University of Puerto Rico, M
Universidad Metropolitana, M
University of Puerto Rico, Mayagüez Campus, M
University of Puerto Rico, Río Piedras Campus, MD

Canada

Alberta

University of Alberta, MD
University of Lethbridge, M

British Columbia

Simon Fraser University, M
The University of British Columbia, D
Vancouver Island University, M

Maritime Provinces: Nova Scotia

Dalhousie University, M

Ontario

Queen's University at Kingston, M
University of Ottawa, O
University of Toronto, M
University of Waterloo, M
The University of Western Ontario, M
Wilfrid Laurier University, MD
York University, M

Quebec

Concordia University, M
HEC Montreal, MO
McGill University, M
Télé-université, M
Université Laval, M
Université du Québec à Montréal, O
Université du Québec en Outaouais, MO
Université du Québec à Trois-Rivières, O
Université de Sherbrooke, M

Saskatchewan

University of Saskatchewan, M

FINANCE AND FINANCIAL MANAGEMENT SERVICES

United States

California

National University, B
Saint Mary's College of California, B
San Jose State University, B

Delaware

Goldey-Beacom College, B

Florida

The University of Tampa, B

Georgia

Brenau University, B

Massachusetts

Babson College, B
Bristol Community College, A
Simmons College, B

Michigan

Grace Bible College, B
Olivet College, B

Minnesota

National American University (Bloomington), A
National American University (Brooklyn Center), A

Nebraska

Northeast Community College, A

New York

Columbia University, School of General Studies, B
Hofstra University, B
State University of New York at New Paltz, B

North Dakota

Minot State University, B

Ohio

Columbus State Community College, A

Pennsylvania

Immaculata University, B

Utah

Westminster College, B

Virginia

James Madison University, B
Virginia Commonwealth University, B

Canada

British Columbia

British Columbia Institute of Technology, A

FINANCIAL ENGINEERING

United States

California

University of California, Berkeley, M
University of California, Los Angeles, M

Hawaii

University of Hawaii at Manoa, M

Illinois

University of Illinois at Urbana - Champaign, M

Michigan

University of Michigan, M

New Jersey

Princeton University, MD
Stevens Institute of Technology, M

New York

Baruch College of the City University of New York,
  M
Columbia University, M
New York University, MO
Rensselaer Polytechnic Institute, M

North Carolina

North Carolina State University, M

Oklahoma

The University of Tulsa, M

Pennsylvania

Temple University, M

Canada

Quebec

HEC Montreal, M

FINANCIAL PLANNING AND SERVICES

United States

California

Glendale Community College, A
San Diego State University, B

Connecticut

Capital Community College, A
University of Connecticut, B

Illinois

Triton College, A
University of Illinois at Urbana - Champaign, B

Indiana

Bethel College, B
Purdue University, B

Kansas

Barton County Community College, A
Bethany College, B
Kansas State University, B

Maine

University of Maine at Augusta, B

Maryland

Cecil College, A
Howard Community College, A

Michigan

Central Michigan University, B
Northern Michigan University, B
Olivet College, B
Western Michigan University, B

Minnesota

Minnesota State Community and Technical College,
  A
University of Minnesota, Duluth, B

Missouri

Maryville University of Saint Louis, B

New Jersey

Berkeley College - Woodland Park Campus, AB
Raritan Valley Community College, A
William Paterson University of New Jersey, B

New Mexico

Western New Mexico University, B

New York

Berkeley College - New York City Campus, AB
Broome Community College, A
The College of Saint Rose, B
State University of New York College of Technology
  at Alfred, B

North Dakota

University of Jamestown, B

Ohio

Cincinnati State Technical and Community College, A
Franklin University, B
The University of Akron, B
University of Mount Union, B
Wright State University, B
Youngstown State University, B

Pennsylvania

Marywood University, B
Saint Joseph's University, B
Temple University, B
Widener University, B

Rhode Island

Bryant University, B
Roger Williams University, B

Texas

Baylor University, B
Lubbock Christian University, B
St. Mary's University, B
Southern Methodist University, B

Utah

Brigham Young University, B
Utah Valley University, B

Virginia

Bryant & Stratton College - Virginia Beach Campus, B

Wisconsin

Bryant & Stratton College - Milwaukee Campus, B
University of Wisconsin - Madison, B

Canada

British Columbia

British Columbia Institute of Technology, A

FINE ARTS AND ART STUDIES

United States

Alabama

Birmingham-Southern College, B
Huntingdon College, B
Spring Hill College, MO
The University of Alabama, M

Alaska

University of Alaska Fairbanks, M

Arizona

Arizona State University at the Tempe campus, MD
Southwest University of Visual Arts, M
The University of Arizona, M
Yavapai College, A

Arkansas

University of Arkansas, M
University of Arkansas at Little Rock, M

California

Academy of Art University, ABM
Art Center College of Design, BM
Azusa Pacific University, M
California College of the Arts, M
California Institute of the Arts, MO
California State University, Chico, M
California State University, Fresno, M
California State University, Fullerton, M
California State University, Long Beach, BM
California State University, Los Angeles, M
California State University, Northridge, M
California State University, Sacramento, M
California State University, San Bernardino, M
John F. Kennedy University, M
Mills College, M

Ohlone College, A
Otis College of Art and Design, M
Reedley College, A
San Diego State University, M
San Francisco Art Institute, MO
San Francisco State University, M
San Jose State University, M
Stanford University, MD
University of California, Berkeley, MO
University of California, Davis, M
University of California, Irvine, MD
University of California, Los Angeles, BM
University of California, Riverside, M
University of California, San Diego, MD
University of California, Santa Barbara, M
University of California, Santa Cruz, MD
University of Southern California, MO

Colorado

Adams State University, M
Colorado State University, M
University of Colorado Boulder, M
University of Colorado Denver, M
University of Denver, M
University of Northern Colorado, M

Connecticut

University of Connecticut, M
University of Hartford, BM
Western Connecticut State University, M
Yale University, M

Delaware

University of Delaware, M

District of Columbia

Howard University, M

Florida

Barry University, M
Florida International University, MO
Florida State University, M
Full Sail University, M
Jacksonville University, B
University of Central Florida, M
University of Florida, MD
University of Miami, M
University of South Florida, M

Georgia

Covenant College, B
Georgia Southern University, M
Georgia State University, M
Savannah College of Art and Design, M
University of Georgia, MD

Hawaii

University of Hawaii at Manoa, M

Idaho

Boise State University, M
Idaho State University, M
University of Idaho, M

Illinois

Benedictine University, B
Bradley University, M
Eastern Illinois University, M
Governors State University, M
Illinois State University, M
Lake Forest College, M
Northern Illinois University, M
Northwestern University, M
School of the Art Institute of Chicago, BM
Southern Illinois University Carbondale, M
Southern Illinois University Edwardsville, M
University of Chicago, M
University of Illinois at Chicago, MD
University of Illinois at Urbana - Champaign, M

Indiana

Ball State University, BM
Indiana State University, M
Indiana University Bloomington, MD

Indiana University - Purdue University Indianapolis, M
Indiana Wesleyan University, B
Purdue University, M
University of Indianapolis, M
University of Notre Dame, M
University of Saint Francis, M

Iowa

Grand View University, B
Iowa State University of Science and Technology, M
The University of Iowa, M
University of Northern Iowa, M

Kansas

Fort Hays State University, M
Kansas State University, M
Pittsburg State University, M
The University of Kansas, M
Wichita State University, M

Kentucky

Kentucky Wesleyan College, B
Morehead State University, M
University of Kentucky, M
University of Louisville, M

Louisiana

Louisiana State University and Agricultural & Mechanical College, M
Louisiana Tech University, M
Northwestern State University of Louisiana, M
Tulane University, MD
University of New Orleans, M

Maine

Bowdoin College, B
Maine College of Art, M
University of Maine, M

Maryland

Hood College, B
Loyola University Maryland, B
Maryland Institute College of Art, BMO
Towson University, M
University of Maryland, Baltimore County, B
University of Maryland, College Park, M

Massachusetts

Anna Maria College, BM
Boston University, M
Bunker Hill Community College, A
Framingham State University, M
Hampshire College, B
Lesley University, M
Massachusetts College of Art and Design, MO
Northeastern University, M
Quincy College, A
School of the Museum of Fine Arts, Boston, BMO
Tufts University, M
University of Massachusetts Amherst, M
University of Massachusetts Dartmouth, MO
University of Massachusetts Lowell, B

Michigan

College for Creative Studies, M
Eastern Michigan University, M
Ferris State University, M
Grand Valley State University, B
Madonna University, AB
Michigan State University, M
Northern Michigan University, B
Oakland University, B
Schoolcraft College, A
University of Michigan, BM
University of Michigan - Flint, M
Wayne State University, M

Minnesota

Minneapolis College of Art and Design, MO
Minnesota State University Mankato, M
University of Minnesota, Duluth, M
University of Minnesota, Twin Cities Campus, M

Mississippi

Mississippi College, M
Northeast Mississippi Community College, A
University of Mississippi, M

Missouri

Drury University, M
Fontbonne University, M
Lindenwood University, BM
University of Missouri, M
University of Missouri - Kansas City, MD
Washington University in St. Louis, M
Webster University, M

Montana

Montana State University, M
University of Montana, M

Nebraska

University of Nebraska - Lincoln, M

Nevada

Truckee Meadows Community College, A
University of Nevada, Las Vegas, M
University of Nevada, Reno, M

New Hampshire

New Hampshire Institute of Art, M

New Jersey

County College of Morris, A
Fairleigh Dickinson University, Metropolitan Campus, M
Kean University, M
Monmouth University, B
Montclair State University, M
New Jersey City University, M
Rutgers University - New Brunswick, M
Rutgers University - Newark, B
Salem Community College, A
William Paterson University of New Jersey, M

New Mexico

New Mexico State University, M
University of New Mexico, M

New York

Adelphi University, BM
Bard College, M
Brooklyn College of the City University of New York, M
City College of the City University of New York, M
The College at Brockport, State University of New York, M
The College of Saint Rose, B
Columbia University, M
Cornell University, M
Corning Community College, A
Elmira College, B
Hofstra University, M
Hunter College of the City University of New York, M
Lehman College of the City University of New York, M
Long Island University - LIU Post, BM
Manhattanville College, B
New York Institute of Technology, M
New York University, BMDO
Pratt Institute, BM
Purchase College, State University of New York, BM
Queens College of the City University of New York, M
Rensselaer Polytechnic Institute, MD
Rochester Institute of Technology, MO
St. John's University, B
School of Visual Arts, M
Skidmore College, B
State University of New York at New Paltz, M
State University of New York at Oswego, M
Stony Brook University, State University of New York, M
University at Albany, State University of New York, M

University at Buffalo, the State University of New York, MD
University of Rochester, MD

North Carolina

Duke University, MD
East Carolina University, M
The University of North Carolina at Chapel Hill, M
The University of North Carolina at Greensboro, M
Western Carolina University, M

North Dakota

United Tribes Technical College, A
University of North Dakota, M

Ohio

Antioch University Midwest, M
Bowling Green State University, BM
Cleveland Institute of Art, B
Columbus College of Art & Design, BM
Kent State University, M
Kenyon College, B
Lake Erie College, B
Miami University, M
The Ohio State University, BM
Ohio University, M
Tiffin University, M
The University of Akron, B
University of Cincinnati, M

Oklahoma

Murray State College, A
Oklahoma City University, B
Seminole State College, A
University of Oklahoma, M
The University of Tulsa, M

Oregon

Oregon College of Art & Craft, B
Pacific Northwest College of Art, M
Portland State University, M
University of Oregon, M

Pennsylvania

Allegheny College, B
Butler County Community College, A
Carnegie Mellon University, M
DeSales University, B
Edinboro University of Pennsylvania, M
Indiana University of Pennsylvania, M
La Salle University, O
Marywood University, M
Millersville University of Pennsylvania, M
Moore College of Art & Design, M
Penn State University Park, MDO
Pennsylvania Academy of the Fine Arts, MO
Pennsylvania College of Technology, A
Philadelphia University, M
Saint Francis University, A
Seton Hill University, B
Temple University, M
The University of the Arts, BM
University of Pennsylvania, MO
Ursinus College, B
Widener University, B

Rhode Island

Providence College, B
Rhode Island College, M
Rhode Island School of Design, B

South Carolina

Bob Jones University, M
Clemson University, M
University of South Carolina, M
Winthrop University, M

South Dakota

Sinte Gleska University, AB
The University of South Dakota, M

Tennessee

East Tennessee State University, M
Memphis College of Art, M

University of Memphis, MO
The University of Tennessee, M

Texas

Houston Baptist University, M
Southern Methodist University, M
Stephen F. Austin State University, M
Sul Ross State University, M
Texas A&M University, M
Texas A&M University - Corpus Christi, M
Texas Christian University, M
Texas Southern University, M
Texas Tech University, MD
Texas Woman's University, M
University of Dallas, M
University of Houston, M
University of North Texas, M
The University of Texas at Arlington, M
The University of Texas at Austin, M
The University of Texas at El Paso, M
The University of Texas Rio Grande Valley, M
The University of Texas at San Antonio, M
The University of Texas at Tyler, M
West Texas A&M University, M

Utah

Brigham Young University, M
University of Utah, M
Utah State University, M

Vermont

Johnson State College, M
Marlboro College, B

Virginia

George Mason University, M
Hampden-Sydney College, B
Hollins University, M
James Madison University, M
Liberty University, M
Norfolk State University, M
Radford University, M
University of Mary Washington, B
Virginia Commonwealth University, MD

Washington

Central Washington University, M
Cornish College of the Arts, B
Heritage University, AB
Seattle University, B
University of Washington, BM
Washington State University, M
Washington State University - Vancouver, B

West Virginia

Marshall University, M
West Virginia University, M

Wisconsin

University of Wisconsin - Madison, M
University of Wisconsin - Milwaukee, BM
University of Wisconsin - River Falls, M
University of Wisconsin - Stout, M
University of Wisconsin - Superior, M

U.S. Territories: Guam

University of Guam, BM

U.S. Territories: Puerto Rico

Inter American University of Puerto Rico, San Germán Campus, M
Pontifical Catholic University of Puerto Rico, B
Universidad del Turabo, M

Canada

Alberta

University of Alberta, M
University of Calgary, M
University of Lethbridge, M

British Columbia

Emily Carr University of Art + Design, M
Thompson Rivers University, B

The University of British Columbia, MDO
University of Victoria, M

Maritime Provinces: Nova Scotia

NSCAD University, M

Ontario

University of Guelph, M
University of Waterloo, M
University of Windsor, M
York University, MD

Quebec

Concordia University, M
Université Laval, M
Université du Québec à Chicoutimi, M
Université du Québec à Montréal, M

Saskatchewan

University of Regina, BM
University of Saskatchewan, M

FINE/STUDIO ARTS

United States

Alabama

Auburn University, B
Birmingham-Southern College, B
Huntingdon College, B
Spring Hill College, B
Talladega College, B
The University of Alabama, B

Alaska

University of Alaska Anchorage, B

Arizona

Arizona Western College, A
Chandler-Gilbert Community College, A
Coconino Community College, A
Diné College, A
Northern Arizona University, B
Paradise Valley Community College, A
Phoenix College, A
Prescott College, B
Southwest University of Visual Arts, B
The University of Arizona, B

Arkansas

Harding University, B
Ouachita Baptist University, B
Southern Arkansas University - Magnolia, B
University of Arkansas at Little Rock, B
University of the Ozarks, B
Williams Baptist College, B

California

Academy of Art University, AB
Berkeley City College, A
Biola University, B
California College of the Arts, B
California Institute of the Arts, B
California Polytechnic State University, San Luis
  Obispo, B
California State University, Chico, B
California State University, East Bay, B
California State University, Fullerton, B
California State University, Long Beach, B
California State University, Stanislaus, B
Chapman University, B
Foothill College, A
Humboldt State University, B
John F. Kennedy University, B
La Sierra University, B
Laguna College of Art & Design, B
Loyola Marymount University, B
Mills College, B
Monterey Peninsula College, A
Notre Dame de Namur University, B
Otis College of Art and Design, B
Oxnard College, A
Pacific Union College, B

Pitzer College, B
San Diego Miramar College, A
San Diego State University, B
San Jose State University, B
Santa Barbara City College, A
Santa Clara University, B
Scripps College, B
Skyline College, A
Sonoma State University, B
Stanford University, B
University of California, Davis, B
University of California, Irvine, B
University of California, Riverside, B
University of California, San Diego, B
University of California, Santa Barbara, B
University of the Pacific, B
University of Redlands, B
University of San Francisco, B
University of Southern California, B
Ventura College, A

Colorado

Adams State University, A
The Colorado College, B
Colorado Mountain College (Steamboat Springs), A
Colorado State University, B
Colorado State University - Pueblo, B
Naropa University, B
Northeastern Junior College, A
Rocky Mountain College of Art + Design, B
University of Colorado Boulder, B
University of Colorado Denver, B
University of Northern Colorado, B
Western State Colorado University, B

Connecticut

Albertus Magnus College, B
Connecticut College, B
Eastern Connecticut State University, B
Fairfield University, B
Manchester Community College, A
Middlesex Community College, A
Norwalk Community College, A
Paier College of Art, Inc., B
Southern Connecticut State University, B
Three Rivers Community College, A
Trinity College, B
University of Connecticut, B
University of New Haven, B
Wesleyan University, B

Delaware

Delaware College of Art and Design, A
University of Delaware, B

District of Columbia

American University, B
Gallaudet University, B
The George Washington University, B
Georgetown University, B
Trinity Washington University, B
University of the District of Columbia, B

Florida

Beacon College, AB
Flagler College, B
Florida Agricultural and Mechanical University, B
Florida International University, B
Florida Southern College, B
Florida State University, B
Jacksonville University, B
New College of Florida, B
Nova Southeastern University, B
Palm Beach Atlantic University, B
Ringling College of Art and Design, B
South Florida State College, A
State College of Florida Manatee-Sarasota, A
University of Central Florida, B
University of Florida, B
University of Miami, B
University of North Florida, B
University of South Florida, B
University of West Florida, B

Georgia

Agnes Scott College, B
Brenau University, B
Emory University, B
Piedmont College, B
Shorter University, B
University of Georgia, B
University of North Georgia, B
Wesleyan College, B

Idaho

Brigham Young University - Idaho, B
The College of Idaho, B
University of Idaho, B

Illinois

Benedictine University, B
Bradley University, B
City Colleges of Chicago, Olive-Harvey College, A
Columbia College Chicago, B
Dominican University, B
Elgin Community College, A
Harper College, A
Illinois State University, B
Judson University, B
Kishwaukee College, A
Knox College, B
Lincoln Land Community College, A
Loyola University Chicago, B
McHenry County College, A
Millikin University, B
Morton College, A
Northern Illinois University, B
Prairie State College, A
Principia College, B
Rend Lake College, A
School of the Art Institute of Chicago, B
South Suburban College, A
Southern Illinois University Carbondale, B
Southern Illinois University Edwardsville, B
Southwestern Illinois College, A
Trinity Christian College, B
Triton College, A
University of Illinois at Chicago, B
University of Illinois at Springfield, B
Waubonsee Community College, A
Western Illinois University, B

Indiana

Bethel College, B
DePauw University, B
Huntington University, B
Indiana State University, B
Indiana University Bloomington, B
Indiana University Kokomo, B
Indiana University Northwest, B
Indiana University - Purdue University Fort Wayne,
  B
Indiana University - Purdue University Indianapolis,
  B
Indiana University South Bend, B
Indiana University Southeast, B
Ivy Tech Community College - Bloomington, A
Manchester University, B
Marian University, B
Purdue University, B
Saint Joseph's College, B
University of Indianapolis, B
University of Notre Dame, B
University of Saint Francis, AB

Iowa

Clarke University, B
Coe College, B
Drake University, B
Graceland University, B
Grand View University, B
Grinnell College, B
Iowa Lakes Community College, A
Maharishi University of Management, B
Morningside College, B
St. Ambrose University, B
Simpson College, B
University of Northern Iowa, B

Kansas

Baker University, B
Bethel College, B
Fort Hays State University, B
Kansas State University, B
Pratt Community College, A
Tabor College, B
The University of Kansas, B

Kentucky

Asbury University, B
Bellarmine University, B
Centre College, B
Eastern Kentucky University, B
Georgetown College, B
Kentucky State University, B
Lindsey Wilson College, AB
Morehead State University, B
Murray State University, B
Northern Kentucky University, B
Owensboro Community and Technical College, A
Spalding University, B
Thomas More College, AB
University of the Cumberlands, B
University of Kentucky, B
University of Louisville, B
Western Kentucky University, B

Louisiana

Centenary College of Louisiana, B
Louisiana College, B
Louisiana State University and Agricultural & Mechanical College, B
Loyola University New Orleans, B
Northwestern State University of Louisiana, B
Southern University and Agricultural and Mechanical College, B
Tulane University, B
University of Louisiana at Monroe, B
University of New Orleans, B

Maine

Bowdoin College, B
Colby College, B
Unity College, B
University of Maine, B
University of Maine at Augusta, AB
University of Maine at Presque Isle, B
University of Southern Maine, B

Maryland

Cecil College, A
Frostburg State University, B
Goucher College, B
Harford Community College, A
Maryland Institute College of Art, B
Salisbury University, B
Towson University, B
University of Maryland, Baltimore County, B
University of Maryland, College Park, B

Massachusetts

Amherst College, B
Assumption College, B
Boston College, B
Brandeis University, B
Bridgewater State University, B
Bristol Community College, A
Clark University, B
College of the Holy Cross, B
Curry College, B
Elms College, B
Emmanuel College, B
Endicott College, B
Greenfield Community College, A
Massachusetts College of Art and Design, B
Massasoit Community College, A
Montserrat College of Art, B
Mount Holyoke College, B
Northeastern University, B
School of the Museum of Fine Arts, Boston, B
Smith College, B
Springfield Technical Community College, A
Stonehill College, B
Suffolk University, B

Tufts University, B
University of Massachusetts Amherst, B
Wellesley College, B

Michigan

Albion College, B
Aquinas College, B
Calvin College, B
Central Michigan University, B
College for Creative Studies, B
Delta College, A
Ferris State University, B
Finlandia University, B
Hope College, B
Lansing Community College, A
Marygrove College, B
Saginaw Valley State University, B
University of Michigan - Flint, B
Western Michigan University, B

Minnesota

Anoka-Ramsey Community College, A
Augsburg College, B
Bemidji State University, B
Bethany Lutheran College, B
Bethel University, B
Carleton College, B
Century College, A
College of Saint Benedict, B
Concordia University, St. Paul, B
Hamline University, B
Inver Hills Community College, A
Lake Superior College, A
Minneapolis College of Art and Design, B
Minneapolis Community and Technical College, A
Minnesota State University Mankato, B
Normandale Community College, A
North Hennepin Community College, A
St. Catherine University, B
St. Cloud State University, B
Saint John's University, B
Saint Mary's University of Minnesota, B
University of Minnesota, Duluth, B
University of Minnesota, Morris, B
University of Northwestern - St. Paul, B

Mississippi

East Central Community College, A
Millsaps College, B
Mississippi College, B
University of Mississippi, B
University of Southern Mississippi, B
William Carey University, B

Missouri

College of the Ozarks, B
Culver-Stockton College, B
Drury University, B
East Central College, A
Fontbonne University, B
Lincoln University, B
Lindenwood University, B
Maryville University of Saint Louis, B
Missouri Southern State University, B
Missouri Western State University, B
Park University, B
Saint Louis University, B
Truman State University, B
University of Central Missouri, B
University of Missouri - Kansas City, B
University of Missouri - St. Louis, B
Washington University in St. Louis, B
Webster University, B

Montana

Montana State University, B
University of Great Falls, B

Nebraska

Concordia University, Nebraska, B
Creighton University, B
Union College, B
University of Nebraska - Lincoln, B
University of Nebraska at Omaha, B

Nevada

Sierra Nevada College, B

New Hampshire

Colby-Sawyer College, B
Dartmouth College, B
Franklin Pierce University, B
Keene State College, B
Lakes Region Community College, A
New England College, B
New Hampshire Institute of Art, B
Plymouth State University, B
University of New Hampshire, B

New Jersey

Bergen Community College, A
Brookdale Community College, A
Caldwell University, B
Camden County College, A
The College of New Jersey, B
Cumberland County College, A
Hudson County Community College, A
Kean University, B
Raritan Valley Community College, A
Saint Peter's University, B
Stockton University, B
Sussex County Community College, A
Warren County Community College, A
William Paterson University of New Jersey, B

New Mexico

Clovis Community College, A
Institute of American Indian Arts, AB
New Mexico State University, B
New Mexico State University - Alamogordo, A
Northern New Mexico College, A
Santa Fe University of Art and Design, B
University of New Mexico - Los Alamos Branch, A

New York

Alfred University, B
Bard College, B
Brooklyn College of the City University of New York, B
Buffalo State College, State University of New York, B
Canisius College, B
Cayuga County Community College, A
Cazenovia College, B
The College of New Rochelle, B
College of Staten Island of the City University of New York, B
Columbia University, School of General Studies, B
Cooper Union for the Advancement of Science and Art, B
Cornell University, B
Corning Community College, A
Daemen College, B
Eugene Lang College of Liberal Arts, B
Fashion Institute of Technology, AB
Finger Lakes Community College, A
Fiorello H. LaGuardia Community College of the City University of New York, A
Fulton-Montgomery Community College, A
Genesee Community College, A
Hamilton College, B
Hobart and William Smith Colleges, B
Hofstra University, B
Hudson Valley Community College, A
Hunter College of the City University of New York, B
Ithaca College, B
Jamestown Community College, A
Long Island University - LIU Brooklyn, B
Manhattanville College, B
Marist College, B
Marymount Manhattan College, B
Molloy College, B
Nazareth College of Rochester, B
New York University, B
Niagara County Community College, A
Pace University, B
Parsons School of Design, B
Pratt Institute, AB
Queens College of the City University of New York, B

Queensborough Community College of the City University of New York, A
Rochester Institute of Technology, B
Rockland Community College, A
The Sage Colleges, B
St. Thomas Aquinas College, B
Sarah Lawrence College, B
School of Visual Arts, B
Siena College, B
State University of New York College at Cortland, B
State University of New York College at Oneonta, B
State University of New York College at Potsdam, B
State University of New York at Fredonia, B
Syracuse University, B
Union College, B
University at Buffalo, the State University of New York, B
University of Rochester, B
Vassar College, B
Villa Maria College, A
Wells College, B
Westchester Community College, A

North Carolina

Appalachian State University, B
Barton College, B
Brevard College, B
Caldwell Community College and Technical Institute, A
Campbell University, B
Chowan University, B
East Carolina University, B
Elizabeth City State University, B
Gardner-Webb University, B
High Point University, B
Mars Hill University, B
Meredith College, B
Queens University of Charlotte, B
Salem College, B
Sandhills Community College, A
University of North Carolina at Asheville, B
The University of North Carolina at Chapel Hill, B
The University of North Carolina at Charlotte, B
The University of North Carolina at Greensboro, B
The University of North Carolina at Pembroke, B
The University of North Carolina Wilmington, B
Wake Forest University, B
Western Carolina University, B

North Dakota

University of Jamestown, B

Ohio

Antioch College, B
Ashland University, B
Baldwin Wallace University, B
Bowling Green State University, B
Cedarville University, B
The College of Wooster, B
Denison University, B
Hiram College, B
Kent State University, B
Kenyon College, B
Marietta College, B
Notre Dame College, B
Oberlin College, B
Ohio Northern University, B
The Ohio State University, B
Ohio University, B
Ohio Wesleyan University, B
Shawnee State University, B
Sinclair Community College, A
Terra State Community College, A
The University of Akron, B
University of Cincinnati, B
University of Dayton, B
University of Mount Union, B
Xavier University, B
Youngstown State University, B

Oklahoma

Oklahoma Baptist University, B
Oklahoma City Community College, A
Oklahoma City University, B
Oral Roberts University, B
Tulsa Community College, A

University of Central Oklahoma, B
University of Oklahoma, B
University of Science and Arts of Oklahoma, B
The University of Tulsa, B

Oregon

Lewis & Clark College, B
Linfield College, B
Marylhurst University, B
Pacific Northwest College of Art, B
Reed College, B
University of Oregon, B
Willamette University, B

Pennsylvania

Allegheny College, B
Arcadia University, B
Bloomsburg University of Pennsylvania, B
Bryn Mawr College, B
Bucknell University, B
Carlow University, B
Chatham University, B
Chestnut Hill College, B
Cheyney University of Pennsylvania, B
Community College of Beaver County, A
Delaware County Community College, A
Dickinson College, B
Edinboro University of Pennsylvania, B
Elizabethtown College, B
Franklin & Marshall College, B
Gettysburg College, B
Holy Family University, B
Indiana University of Pennsylvania, B
Juniata College, B
Keystone College, AB
Kutztown University of Pennsylvania, B
Lafayette College, B
Lincoln University, B
Lock Haven University of Pennsylvania, B
Lycoming College, B
Mercyhurst University, B
Messiah College, B
Moore College of Art & Design, B
Muhlenberg College, B
Northampton Community College, A
Pennsylvania Academy of the Fine Arts, B
Pennsylvania College of Art & Design, B
Rosemont College, B
Saint Vincent College, B
Seton Hill University, B
Slippery Rock University of Pennsylvania, B
Susquehanna University, B
Swarthmore College, B
The University of the Arts, B
University of Pennsylvania, B
University of Pittsburgh, B
West Chester University of Pennsylvania, B
Westminster College, B
York College of Pennsylvania, AB

Rhode Island

Brown University, B
Providence College, B
Roger Williams University, B
Salve Regina University, B
University of Rhode Island, B

South Carolina

Bob Jones University, B
Claflin University, B
Coastal Carolina University, B
Coker College, B
College of Charleston, B
Columbia College, B
Converse College, B
Furman University, B
Limestone College, B
North Greenville University, B
Presbyterian College, B
South Carolina State University, B
University of South Carolina, B
University of South Carolina Aiken, B
University of South Carolina Beaufort, B
University of South Carolina Upstate, B
Wofford College, B

South Dakota

Dakota Wesleyan University, B
South Dakota State University, B

Tennessee

Belmont University, B
Christian Brothers University, B
Cumberland University, B
Lee University, B
Lipscomb University, B
Maryville College, B
Memphis College of Art, B
Milligan College, B
Sewanee: The University of the South, B
The University of Tennessee, B
Vanderbilt University, B
Watkins College of Art, Design, & Film, B

Texas

Abilene Christian University, B
Amarillo College, A
Angelo State University, B
Baylor University, B
Central Texas College, A
College of the Mainland, A
Del Mar College, A
Hardin-Simmons University, B
Houston Baptist University, B
Houston Community College, A
Howard Payne University, B
Lamar University, B
McMurry University, B
Rice University, B
Sam Houston State University, B
Southern Methodist University, B
Tarleton State University, B
Texas A&M International University, B
Texas A&M University - Commerce, B
Texas A&M University - Kingsville, B
Texas Christian University, B
Texas Southern University, B
Texas State University, B
University of Dallas, B
University of Houston - Clear Lake, B
University of the Incarnate Word, B
University of Mary Hardin-Baylor, B
University of North Texas, B
University of St. Thomas, B
The University of Texas at Arlington, B
The University of Texas at Austin, B
The University of Texas at El Paso, B
The University of Texas Rio Grande Valley, B
The University of Texas at San Antonio, B
Wayland Baptist University, B
West Texas A&M University, B

Utah

Brigham Young University, B
Southern Utah University, B
Westminster College, B

Vermont

Bennington College, B
Green Mountain College, B
Johnson State College, B
Landmark College, B
Marlboro College, B
Middlebury College, B
University of Vermont, B

Virginia

Bridgewater College, B
Christopher Newport University, B
Emory & Henry College, B
Hampden-Sydney College, B
Liberty University, B
Marymount University, B
Randolph College, B
Randolph-Macon College, B
Sweet Briar College, B
Tidewater Community College, A
University of Richmond, B
Virginia Union University, B
Washington and Lee University, B

Washington

Central Washington University, B
Cornish College of the Arts, B
Eastern Washington University, B
The Evergreen State College, B
Pacific Lutheran University, B
Seattle University, B
Walla Walla University, B
Washington State University, B
Whitman College, B
Whitworth University, B

West Virginia

Alderson Broaddus University, B
Bethany College, B
Concord University, B
West Virginia Wesleyan College, B

Wisconsin

Beloit College, B
Carroll University, B
Carthage College, B
Lawrence University, B
Milwaukee Institute of Art and Design, B
Northland College, B
University of Wisconsin - Oshkosh, B
University of Wisconsin - Stevens Point, B
University of Wisconsin - Superior, B
Viterbo University, B

Wyoming

Casper College, A

U.S. Territories: Puerto Rico

University of Puerto Rico, Mayagüez Campus, B
University of Puerto Rico, Río Piedras Campus, B
University of Puerto Rico in Utuado, B

Canada
Alberta

Alberta College of Art & Design, B
University of Lethbridge, B

British Columbia

Emily Carr University of Art + Design, B
Thompson Rivers University, B
The University of British Columbia, B
University of the Fraser Valley, B
University of Victoria, B

Maritime Provinces: New Brunswick

Mount Allison University, B
Université de Moncton, B

Maritime Provinces: Nova Scotia

Mount Saint Vincent University, B
NSCAD University, B

Ontario

Brock University, B
Nipissing University, B
University of Guelph, B
University of Ottawa, B
University of Waterloo, B
The University of Western Ontario, B
University of Windsor, B
York University, B

Quebec

Bishop's University, B
Concordia University, B
Université Laval, B
Université du Québec en Outaouais, B

Saskatchewan

University of Regina, B
University of Saskatchewan, B

FINNISH AND RELATED LANGUAGES, LITERATURES, AND LINGUISTICS

United States
Washington

University of Washington, B

FIRE PROTECTION

United States
Arizona

Central Arizona College, A

Colorado

Aims Community College, A

Kansas

Kansas City Kansas Community College, A

New Jersey

Sussex County Community College, A

North Carolina

Nash Community College, A

Ohio

The University of Akron, B

Oklahoma

Western Oklahoma State College, A

Washington

Clover Park Technical College, A

Wisconsin

Fox Valley Technical College, A

FIRE PROTECTION ENGINEERING

United States
Connecticut

University of New Haven, MO

Maryland

University of Maryland, College Park, M

Massachusetts

Anna Maria College, M
Worcester Polytechnic Institute, MDO

North Carolina

The University of North Carolina at Charlotte, M

Oklahoma

Oklahoma State University, MD

FIRE PROTECTION AND SAFETY TECHNOLOGY/TECHNICIAN

United States
Alabama

Athens State University, B
Calhoun Community College, A

California

Antelope Valley College, A
College of the Canyons, A

Glendale Community College, A
Hartnell College, A
Oxnard College, A
Palomar College, A
Pasadena City College, A
Victor Valley College, A

Colorado

Aims Community College, A
Colorado Mountain College (Leadville), A
Pikes Peak Community College, A

Connecticut

University of New Haven, AB

Delaware

Delaware State University, B
Delaware Technical & Community College, Stanton/Wilmington Campus, A

Florida

Florida SouthWestern State College, A
Florida State College at Jacksonville, A
Gulf Coast State College, A
Hillsborough Community College, A
Miami Dade College, A
Polk State College, A
Santa Fe College, A
South Florida State College, A

Illinois

College of Lake County, A
Moraine Valley Community College, A

Indiana

Harrison College, A

Iowa

Des Moines Area Community College, A
Kirkwood Community College, A
North Iowa Area Community College, A

Kentucky

Eastern Kentucky University, B
Maysville Community and Technical College (Morehead), A

Louisiana

Delgado Community College, A

Maryland

Anne Arundel Community College, A
Baltimore City Community College, A
Montgomery College, A

Massachusetts

Bristol Community College, A
Bunker Hill Community College, A
Cape Cod Community College, A
Greenfield Community College, A
Mount Wachusett Community College, A
Springfield Technical Community College, A

Michigan

Delta College, A
Macomb Community College, A
Mott Community College, A
Wayne County Community College District, A

Minnesota

Lake Superior College, A
Northland Community and Technical College, A

Missouri

Jefferson College, A

Montana

Montana State University Billings, A

Nevada

Truckee Meadows Community College, A

New Hampshire

Lakes Region Community College, A

New Jersey

Camden County College, A
County College of Morris, A
Middlesex County College, A
Thomas Edison State University, AB
Union County College, A

New Mexico

Eastern New Mexico University - Roswell, A

New York

Jefferson Community College, A
Onondaga Community College, A
Sullivan County Community College, A

North Carolina

Asheville-Buncombe Technical Community College,
   A
Cape Fear Community College, A
Catawba Valley Community College, A
Cleveland Community College, A
Fayetteville Technical Community College, A
Forsyth Technical Community College, A
Gaston College, A
Guilford Technical Community College, A
South Piedmont Community College, A
Wilson Community College, A

Ohio

Belmont College, A
Lakeland Community College, A
The University of Akron, A

Oklahoma

Oklahoma State University, B
Oklahoma State University, Oklahoma City, A

Oregon

Chemeketa Community College, A
Portland Community College, A
Rogue Community College, A
Treasure Valley Community College, A

Pennsylvania

Community College of Allegheny County, A
Delaware County Community College, A
Montgomery County Community College, A
Westmoreland County Community College, A

Texas

Austin Community College District, A
College of the Mainland, A
Collin County Community College District, A
Del Mar College, A
El Paso Community College, A
Houston Community College, A
Lamar Institute of Technology, A
West Texas A&M University, B

Virginia

Jefferson College of Health Sciences, B

Wisconsin

Western Technical College, A

Canada

British Columbia

British Columbia Institute of Technology, A

FIRE SCIENCE/FIREFIGHTING

United States

Alabama

Columbia Southern University, AB
Community College of the Air Force, A
Wallace State Community College, A

Alaska

Ilisagvik College, A
University of Alaska Anchorage, A
University of Alaska Fairbanks, A

Arizona

Arizona Western College, A
Cochise County Community College District, A
Coconino Community College, A
Eastern Arizona College, A
Glendale Community College, A
Mesa Community College, A
Mohave Community College, A
Northland Pioneer College, A
Paradise Valley Community College, A
Phoenix College, A
Pima Community College, A
Yavapai College, A

Arkansas

Black River Technical College, A
National Park College, A
Shorter College, A
Southern Arkansas University Tech, A

California

Allan Hancock College, A
American River College, A
Bakersfield College, A
Barstow Community College, A
Butte College, A
Cabrillo College, A
Cerro Coso Community College, A
Chabot College, A
Chaffey College, A
City College of San Francisco, A
College of the Desert, A
College of San Mateo, A
College of the Sequoias, A
College of the Siskiyous, A
Columbia College, A
Copper Mountain College, A
Cosumnes River College, A
Crafton Hills College, A
East Los Angeles College, A
El Camino College, A
Fresno City College, A
Imperial Valley College, A
Lake Tahoe Community College, A
Las Positas College, A
Long Beach City College, A
Los Angeles Harbor College, A
Los Angeles Valley College, A
Los Medanos College, A
Merced College, A
Mission College, A
Modesto Junior College, A
Monterey Peninsula College, A
Moreno Valley College, A
Mt. San Antonio College, A
Mt. San Jacinto College, A
Oxnard College, A
Porterville College, A
San Diego Miramar College, A
San Joaquin Delta College, A
Santa Ana College, A
Santa Rosa Junior College, A
Shasta College, A
Sierra College, A
Solano Community College, A
Southwestern College, A
University of Antelope Valley, A
Victor Valley College, A
Yuba College, A

Colorado

Community College of Aurora, A
Pueblo Community College, A
Red Rocks Community College, A
Trinidad State Junior College, A

Connecticut

Gateway Community College, A
Norwalk Community College, A
University of New Haven, AB

Delaware

Delaware Technical & Community College,
   Stanton/Wilmington Campus, A

District of Columbia

University of the District of Columbia, A

Florida

Broward College, A
College of Central Florida, A
Daytona State College, A
Eastern Florida State College, A
Embry-Riddle Aeronautical University - Worldwide, B
Florida State College at Jacksonville, A
Indian River State College, A
Keiser University, A
Lake-Sumter State College, A
Miami Dade College, A
Palm Beach State College, A
Polk State College, A
St. Johns River State College, A
St. Petersburg College, A
Seminole State College of Florida, A
State College of Florida Manatee-Sarasota, A
Tallahassee Community College, A
University of Florida, B

Georgia

Augusta Technical College, A
Chattahoochee Technical College, A
Georgia Northwestern Technical College, A
Lanier Technical College, A
Savannah Technical College, A
West Georgia Technical College, A
Wiregrass Georgia Technical College, A

Hawaii

Honolulu Community College, A

Idaho

Eastern Idaho Technical College, A
Idaho State University, AB
Lewis-Clark State College, AB

Illinois

City Colleges of Chicago, Harold Washington Col-
   lege, A
College of DuPage, A
Danville Area Community College, A
Elgin Community College, A
Harper College, A
Illinois Central College, A
Illinois Eastern Community Colleges, Frontier Com-
   munity College, A
John Wood Community College, A
Joliet Junior College, A
Lewis and Clark Community College, A
Lincoln Land Community College, A
McHenry County College, A
Moraine Valley Community College, A
Oakton Community College, A
Prairie State College, A
Richland Community College, A
Rock Valley College, A
Sauk Valley Community College, A
Southeastern Illinois College, A
Southwestern Illinois College, A
Triton College, A
Waubonsee Community College, A

Indiana

Vincennes University, A

Iowa

Hawkeye Community College, A
Kirkwood Community College, A
Northeast Iowa Community College, A
Scott Community College, A
Western Iowa Tech Community College, A

Kansas

Barton County Community College, A
Butler Community College, A
Dodge City Community College, A

Garden City Community College, A
Hutchinson Community College, A
Johnson County Community College, A
Kansas City Kansas Community College, A
Labette Community College, A

Kentucky

Ashland Community and Technical College, A
Bluegrass Community and Technical College, A
Elizabethtown Community and Technical College, A
Gateway Community and Technical College, A
Jefferson Community and Technical College, A
Owensboro Community and Technical College, A
Southcentral Kentucky Community and Technical
    College, A
West Kentucky Community and Technical College, A

Louisiana

Louisiana State University at Eunice, A

Maine

Southern Maine Community College, A

Maryland

Cecil College, A
College of Southern Maryland, A
Frederick Community College, A

Massachusetts

Anna Maria College, B
Berkshire Community College, A
Bristol Community College, A
Massasoit Community College, A
Middlesex Community College, A
North Shore Community College, A

Michigan

Delta College, A
Kalamazoo Valley Community College, A
Lake Superior State University, AB
Lansing Community College, A
Madonna University, AB
Mid Michigan Community College, A
Oakland Community College, A
St. Clair County Community College, A
Schoolcraft College, A
Southwestern Michigan College, A

Minnesota

Hennepin Technical College, A
Northland Community and Technical College, A

Mississippi

Meridian Community College, A

Missouri

Crowder College, A
East Central College, A
Metropolitan Community College - Kansas City, A
Mineral Area College, A
Ozarks Technical Community College, A
St. Charles Community College, A

Montana

Helena College University of Montana, A

Nebraska

Mid-Plains Community College, A
Southeast Community College, Lincoln Campus, A

Nevada

College of Southern Nevada, A

New Hampshire

Lakes Region Community College, A

New Jersey

Mercer County Community College, A
New Jersey City University, B
Passaic County Community College, A
Rowan College at Burlington County, A
Salem Community College, A

New Mexico

Central New Mexico Community College, A
Clovis Community College, A
Doña Ana Community College, A
New Mexico Junior College, A
San Juan College, A

New York

Broome Community College, A
John Jay College of Criminal Justice of the City University of New York, B
Monroe Community College, A
Rockland Community College, A
Schenectady County Community College, A

North Carolina

Central Piedmont Community College, A
Coastal Carolina Community College, A
Davidson County Community College, A

Ohio

Central Ohio Technical College, A
Cincinnati State Technical and Community College, A
Columbus State Community College, A
Cuyahoga Community College, A
Hocking College, A
Lorain County Community College, A
Sinclair Community College, A
Stark State College, A
University of Cincinnati, A

Oklahoma

Oklahoma State University, Oklahoma City, A
Southwestern Oklahoma State University, A

Oregon

Central Oregon Community College, A
Chemeketa Community College, A
Clackamas Community College, A
Clatsop Community College, A
Mt. Hood Community College, A
Southwestern Oregon Community College, A
Treasure Valley Community College, A
Umpqua Community College, A

Pennsylvania

Butler County Community College, A
Community College of Philadelphia, A
Harrisburg Area Community College, A
Luzerne County Community College, A
Northampton Community College, A

Rhode Island

Community College of Rhode Island, A
Providence College, B

South Carolina

Greenville Technical College, A

South Dakota

Western Dakota Technical Institute, A

Tennessee

Chattanooga State Community College, A
Southwest Tennessee Community College, A
Volunteer State Community College, A

Texas

Amarillo College, A
Blinn College, A
Cisco College, A
Collin County Community College District, A
Del Mar College, A
Hill College, A
Laredo Community College, A
Lone Star College - CyFair, A
Lone Star College - Kingwood, A
Lone Star College - Montgomery, A
Midland College, A
Navarro College, A
Odessa College, A
San Antonio College, A
San Jacinto College District, A

South Plains College, A
Southwestern Adventist University, A
Tarrant County College District, A
Tyler Junior College, A
Victoria College, A
Weatherford College, A

Utah

Utah Valley University, AB

Vermont

Vermont Technical College, A

Virginia

Hampton University, B
J. Sargeant Reynolds Community College, A
Southside Virginia Community College, A
Thomas Nelson Community College, A

Washington

Bates Technical College, A
Bellevue College, A
Everett Community College, A
Lower Columbia College, A
Pierce College at Puyallup, A
Skagit Valley College, A
South Puget Sound Community College, A
Spokane Community College, A
Walla Walla Community College, A

West Virginia

American Public University System, A

Wisconsin

Blackhawk Technical College, A
Fox Valley Technical College, A
Madison Area Technical College, A
Milwaukee Area Technical College, A
Waukesha County Technical College, A

Wyoming

Casper College, A
Central Wyoming College, A
Laramie County Community College, A

Canada

Maritime Provinces: New Brunswick

University of New Brunswick Fredericton, B

FIRE SERVICES ADMINISTRATION

United States

Alabama

Chattahoochee Valley Community College, A
Columbia Southern University, B
Jefferson State Community College, A

Arkansas

NorthWest Arkansas Community College, A
Southern Arkansas University Tech, A

California

California State University, Los Angeles, B
Oxnard College, A

Colorado

Colorado State University, B

Connecticut

Capital Community College, A
Naugatuck Valley Community College, A
Three Rivers Community College, A

Delaware

Delaware Technical & Community College,
    Stanton/Wilmington Campus, A

District of Columbia

University of the District of Columbia, B

Florida

Florida State College at Jacksonville, A
St. Thomas University, B

Georgia

Albany State University, B

Illinois

Black Hawk College, A
Lewis University, B
Southern Illinois University Carbondale, B
Western Illinois University, B

Iowa

Waldorf College, B

Kentucky

Eastern Kentucky University, B

Massachusetts

Quinsigamond Community College, A
Salem State University, B

Michigan

Delta College, A

Minnesota

Minnesota State Community and Technical College,
   A

Missouri

Columbia College, A
Lindenwood University, B

Nebraska

University of Nebraska at Omaha, B

New Jersey

Camden County College, A

New York

Dutchess Community College, A
Erie Community College, South Campus, A
Jefferson Community College, A
John Jay College of Criminal Justice of the City Uni-
   versity of New York, B
Mohawk Valley Community College, A

North Carolina

Fayetteville State University, B
The University of North Carolina at Charlotte, B

Ohio

Bowling Green State University, B
University of Cincinnati, B

Oklahoma

Tulsa Community College, A

Oregon

Eastern Oregon University, B
Western Oregon University, B

Pennsylvania

Holy Family University, B
Northampton Community College, A

South Carolina

Technical College of the Lowcountry, A

Texas

Central Texas College, A

Washington

Bellevue College, A
Columbia Basin College, A
Edmonds Community College, A

West Virginia

American Public University System, AB

FISH, GAME AND WILDLIFE MANAGEMENT

United States

Alabama

Auburn University, MD

Arizona

The University of Arizona, MD

Arkansas

Arkansas Tech University, M
University of Arkansas at Pine Bluff, M

California

Humboldt State University, M

Colorado

Colorado State University, MD

Delaware

University of Delaware, M

Florida

University of Florida, MDO
University of Miami, MD

Indiana

Purdue University, MD

Iowa

Iowa State University of Science and Technology,
   MD

Louisiana

Louisiana State University and Agricultural & Mechanical College, MD

Maine

University of Maine, MD

Maryland

Frostburg State University, M
University of Maryland Eastern Shore, M

Massachusetts

University of Massachusetts Amherst, MD

Michigan

Michigan State University, MD

Minnesota

University of Minnesota, Twin Cities Campus, MD

Mississippi

Mississippi State University, MD

Missouri

University of Missouri, MDO

Montana

Montana State University, MD
University of Montana, MD

New Hampshire

University of New Hampshire, M

New Mexico

New Mexico State University, M

New York

Cornell University, MD
State University of New York College of Environmental Science and Forestry, MD

North Carolina

North Carolina State University, MD

North Dakota

University of North Dakota, MD

Ohio

The Ohio State University, MD

Oregon

Oregon State University, MD

Pennsylvania

Penn State University Park, MD

Rhode Island

University of Rhode Island, MD

South Carolina

Clemson University, MD

South Dakota

South Dakota State University, MD

Tennessee

Tennessee Technological University, M
The University of Tennessee, M

Texas

Sul Ross State University, M
Texas A&M University, MD
Texas A&M University - Kingsville, MD
Texas State University, M
Texas Tech University, MD

Utah

Brigham Young University, MD
Utah State University, MD

Virginia

Virginia Polytechnic Institute and State University,
   MD

Washington

University of Washington, MD

West Virginia

American Public University System, M
West Virginia University, M

Wisconsin

University of Wisconsin - Madison, MD

Canada

British Columbia

Simon Fraser University, O

Newfoundland and Labrador

Memorial University of Newfoundland, MO

Quebec

McGill University, MD
Université du Québec à Rimouski, MDO

FISHING AND FISHERIES SCIENCES AND MANAGEMENT

United States

Alaska

University of Alaska Fairbanks, B
University of Alaska Southeast, A
University of Alaska Southeast, Ketchikan Campus,
   A
University of Alaska Southeast, Sitka Campus, A

Arkansas

University of Arkansas at Pine Bluff, B

California
Humboldt State University, B
Monterey Peninsula College, A

Colorado
Colorado State University, B

Delaware
Delaware State University, B

Florida
Florida Keys Community College, A

Georgia
Abraham Baldwin Agricultural College, A

Idaho
North Idaho College, A
University of Idaho, B

Indiana
Purdue University, B

Iowa
Iowa Lakes Community College, A
Iowa State University of Science and Technology, B

Michigan
Lake Superior State University, B
Michigan State University, B

Minnesota
Itasca Community College, A
University of Minnesota, Twin Cities Campus, B
Vermilion Community College, A

Missouri
University of Missouri, B

New York
Finger Lakes Community College, A
State University of New York College of Agriculture and Technology at Cobleskill, A
State University of New York College of Environmental Science and Forestry, B

North Dakota
Dakota College at Bottineau, A

Ohio
Hocking College, A
The Ohio State University, B

Oregon
Central Oregon Community College, A
Mt. Hood Community College, A
Oregon State University, B

Pennsylvania
Mansfield University of Pennsylvania, B

Rhode Island
University of Rhode Island, B

Tennessee
Hiwassee College, A
The University of Tennessee at Martin, B

Texas
Texas A&M University, B

Washington
Bellingham Technical College, A
Peninsula College, A

Canada

British Columbia
The University of British Columbia, B
University of Northern British Columbia, B

Maritime Provinces: New Brunswick
University of New Brunswick Fredericton, B

FLIGHT INSTRUCTOR

United States

Iowa
Iowa Lakes Community College, A

Maine
University of Maine at Augusta, B

North Dakota
University of North Dakota, B

South Dakota
South Dakota State University, B

FLORICULTURE/FLORISTRY OPERATIONS AND MANAGEMENT

United States

California
City College of San Francisco, A
College of San Mateo, A
Cuesta College, A
Long Beach City College, A
Santa Rosa Junior College, A
Southwestern College, A

Illinois
Danville Area Community College, A
Illinois Valley Community College, A

North Dakota
Dakota College at Bottineau, A

Ohio
The Ohio State University Agricultural Technical Institute, A

Pennsylvania
Westmoreland County Community College, A

Virginia
J. Sargeant Reynolds Community College, A

FOLKLORE

United States

California
University of California, Berkeley, M

District of Columbia
The George Washington University, M

Indiana
Indiana University Bloomington, MD

Louisiana
University of Louisiana at Lafayette, M

North Carolina
The University of North Carolina at Chapel Hill, M

Oregon
University of Oregon, M

Pennsylvania
Penn State Harrisburg, O

Texas
The University of Texas at Austin, MD

Utah
Utah State University, M

Virginia
George Mason University, M

Wisconsin
University of Wisconsin - Madison, D

Canada

Alberta
University of Alberta, MD

Newfoundland and Labrador
Memorial University of Newfoundland, MD

FOOD ENGINEERING

United States

Illinois
Illinois Institute of Technology, M

Kansas
Kansas State University, MD

New York
Cornell University, MD
New York University, D

Ohio
The Ohio State University, MD

Canada

Quebec
McGill University, MD

FOOD PREPARATION/PROFESSIONAL COOKING/KITCHEN ASSISTANT

United States

Iowa
Iowa Lakes Community College, A

Kansas
Washburn University, A

FOOD SCIENCE

United States

Alabama
Alabama Agricultural and Mechanical University, B
Auburn University, B
Tuskegee University, B

Arkansas
University of Arkansas, B

California
California Polytechnic State University, San Luis Obispo, B
California State Polytechnic University, Pomona, B
Los Angeles City College, A
Modesto Junior College, A
Saddleback College, A
San Jose State University, B
University of California, Davis, B

Delaware

University of Delaware, B

Florida

Broward College, A
Miami Dade College, A
South Florida State College, A
University of Florida, B

Georgia

University of Georgia, B

Idaho

University of Idaho, B

Illinois

Dominican University, B
University of Illinois at Urbana - Champaign, B

Indiana

Purdue University, B
Vincennes University, A

Iowa

Clarke University, B
Iowa State University of Science and Technology, B

Kansas

Kansas State University, B

Kentucky

University of Kentucky, B

Maine

University of Maine, B

Maryland

University of Maryland, College Park, B

Massachusetts

Framingham State University, B
Greenfield Community College, A
Simmons College, B
University of Massachusetts Amherst, B

Michigan

Michigan State University, B
Western Michigan University, B

Minnesota

Normandale Community College, A
University of Minnesota, Twin Cities Campus, B

Mississippi

Mississippi State University, B

Missouri

Missouri State University - West Plains, A
University of Missouri, B

Nebraska

University of Nebraska - Lincoln, B

New Jersey

Rowan College at Gloucester County, A
Rutgers University - New Brunswick, B

New York

Cornell University, B

North Carolina

Central Piedmont Community College, A
North Carolina Agricultural and Technical State University, B
North Carolina State University, B

North Dakota

North Dakota State University, B

Ohio

Hocking College, A
The Ohio State University, B

Oklahoma

Oklahoma State University, B

Oregon

Mt. Hood Community College, A
Oregon State University, B

Pennsylvania

Delaware Valley University, B
Penn State Abington, B
Penn State Altoona, B
Penn State Beaver, B
Penn State Berks, B
Penn State Brandywine, B
Penn State DuBois, B
Penn State Erie, The Behrend College, B
Penn State Fayette, The Eberly Campus, B
Penn State Greater Allegheny, B
Penn State Hazleton, B
Penn State Lehigh Valley, B
Penn State Mont Alto, B
Penn State New Kensington, B
Penn State Schuylkill, B
Penn State Shenango, B
Penn State University Park, B
Penn State Wilkes-Barre, B
Penn State Worthington Scranton, B
Penn State York, B

South Carolina

Clemson University, B

South Dakota

South Dakota State University, B

Tennessee

The University of Tennessee, B

Texas

Grayson College, A
Texas Tech University, B

Virginia

Virginia Polytechnic Institute and State University, B

Washington

South Seattle College, A
Washington State University, B

Wisconsin

University of Wisconsin - Madison, B
University of Wisconsin - River Falls, B

U.S. Territories: Puerto Rico

University of Puerto Rico in Utuado, A

Canada

British Columbia

The University of British Columbia, B

Manitoba

University of Manitoba, B

Maritime Provinces: Nova Scotia

Acadia University, B
Dalhousie University, B

Newfoundland and Labrador

Memorial University of Newfoundland, B

Ontario

University of Guelph, B

Quebec

Université Laval, B

Saskatchewan

University of Saskatchewan, B

FOOD SCIENCE AND TECH-NOLOGY

United States

Alabama

Alabama Agricultural and Mechanical University, MD
Auburn University, MDO
Tuskegee University, M

Arkansas

University of Arkansas, MD

California

California State University, Fresno, M
California State University, Long Beach, M
Chapman University, M
University of California, Davis, MD
University of Southern California, O

Colorado

Colorado State University, MD

Delaware

University of Delaware, MD

Florida

Florida State University, MD
University of Florida, MD

Georgia

University of Georgia, MD

Hawaii

University of Hawaii at Manoa, M

Idaho

University of Idaho, MD

Illinois

Illinois Institute of Technology, M
University of Illinois at Urbana - Champaign, BMD

Indiana

Purdue University, MD

Iowa

Iowa State University of Science and Technology, MD

Kansas

Kansas State University, MD

Kentucky

University of Kentucky, MD

Louisiana

Louisiana State University and Agricultural & Mechanical College, MD

Maine

University of Maine, MD

Maryland

University of Maryland, College Park, MD
University of Maryland Eastern Shore, MD

Massachusetts

Boston University, M
Framingham State University, M
University of Massachusetts Amherst, MD

Michigan

Michigan State University, MD
Wayne State University, MDO

Minnesota

University of Minnesota, Twin Cities Campus, MD

Mississippi

Mississippi State University, MD
University of Mississippi, M
University of Southern Mississippi, MD

Missouri

University of Missouri, MD

Nebraska

University of Nebraska - Lincoln, MD

New Jersey

Rutgers University - New Brunswick, MD

New Mexico

New Mexico State University, M

New York

Cornell University, MD
New York University, M

North Carolina

Appalachian State University, B
North Carolina State University, MD

North Dakota

North Dakota State University, BMDO

Ohio

The Ohio State University, MD

Oklahoma

Oklahoma State University, MD

Oregon

Oregon State University, MD

Pennsylvania

Drexel University, M
Penn State University Park, MD

Rhode Island

University of Rhode Island, M

South Carolina

Clemson University, MD

South Dakota

South Dakota State University, MD

Tennessee

The University of Tennessee, MD
The University of Tennessee at Martin, M

Texas

Texas A&M University, MD
Texas Tech University, MD
Texas Woman's University, MD

Utah

Brigham Young University, M
Utah State University, MD

Vermont

University of Vermont, MD

Washington

Washington State University, MD

West Virginia

West Virginia University, MD

Wisconsin

University of Wisconsin - Madison, MD
University of Wisconsin - Stout, M

Wyoming

University of Wyoming, M

U.S. Territories: Puerto Rico

University of Puerto Rico, Mayagüez Campus, M

Canada

Alberta

University of Alberta, B

British Columbia

The University of British Columbia, BMD

Manitoba

University of Manitoba, MD

Maritime Provinces: New Brunswick

Université de Moncton, M

Maritime Provinces: Nova Scotia

Dalhousie University, MD

Newfoundland and Labrador

Memorial University of Newfoundland, MD

Ontario

University of Guelph, MD

Quebec

McGill University, MD
Université Laval, MD

Saskatchewan

University of Saskatchewan, MD

FOOD SERVICE, WAITER/WAITRESS, AND DINING ROOM MANAGEMENT/MANAGER

United States

California

Pasadena City College, A

Colorado

Johnson & Wales University, B

Florida

Johnson & Wales University, B

Iowa

Iowa Lakes Community College, A
Iowa Western Community College, A

North Carolina

Johnson & Wales University, B

Pennsylvania

Westmoreland County Community College, A

Utah

LDS Business College, A

West Virginia

Pierpont Community & Technical College, A

FOOD SERVICES MANAGEMENT

United States

Massachusetts

Northeastern University, M

Michigan

Michigan State University, M

New York

Cornell University, MD
New York University, MD
Rochester Institute of Technology, M

Oregon

Marylhurst University, M

FOOD TECHNOLOGY AND PROCESSING

United States

California

Cerritos College, A
Cuesta College, A
Los Angeles City College, A
Mission College, A
Modesto Junior College, A
Saddleback College, A
Victor Valley College, A

Hawaii

Honolulu Community College, A
University of Hawaii Maui College, A

Illinois

Richland Community College, A
University of Illinois at Urbana - Champaign, B

Indiana

Purdue University, B

Iowa

Iowa State University of Science and Technology, B

Mississippi

Copiah-Lincoln Community College, A

New Mexico

New Mexico State University, B

New York

Adirondack Community College, A
Genesee Community College, A
Monroe Community College, A
Westchester Community College, A

North Carolina

Central Piedmont Community College, A
Robeson Community College, A

Ohio

Stark State College, A

Pennsylvania

Butler County Community College, A
Luzerne County Community College, A

Tennessee

Tennessee State University, B

Texas

Tarrant County College District, A

Utah

Brigham Young University, B

Washington

Skagit Valley College, A
South Puget Sound Community College, A
South Seattle College, A
Spokane Community College, A

Wisconsin

Western Technical College, A

Canada

Maritime Provinces: New Brunswick

Université de Moncton, B

FOODS, NUTRITION, AND RE-LATED SERVICES

United States

Alabama

Samford University, B

California

California State University, Long Beach, B
San Diego Mesa College, A

Iowa

Iowa Lakes Community College, A

Michigan

Schoolcraft College, B

Minnesota

University of Minnesota, Twin Cities Campus, B

Utah

Utah State University, B

Canada

Alberta

University of Alberta, B

British Columbia

The University of British Columbia, B

Ontario

University of Guelph, AB

FOODS, NUTRITION, AND WELLNESS STUDIES

United States

Alabama

Auburn University, B
Jacksonville State University, B
Samford University, B
Tuskegee University, B

Alaska

University of Alaska Anchorage, B

Arizona

Arizona State University at the Downtown Phoenix campus, B

Arkansas

University of Arkansas, B
University of Central Arkansas, B

California

Bakersfield College, A
Brandman University, B
Butte College, A
California State University, Fresno, B
California State University, Los Angeles, B
Chaffey College, A
Feather River College, A
Fresno City College, A
Fullerton College, A
Ohlone College, A
Orange Coast College, A

Point Loma Nazarene University, B
Saddleback College, A
San Diego Mesa College, A
Santa Ana College, A

Connecticut

University of Saint Joseph, B

Delaware

Delaware State University, B
University of Delaware, B

District of Columbia

Howard University, B

Florida

Indian River State College, A
Palm Beach State College, A
Pensacola State College, A

Georgia

Fort Valley State University, B
Georgia Southern University, B
Life University, B
University of Georgia, B

Idaho

University of Idaho, B

Illinois

Benedictine University, B
Bradley University, B
Dominican University, B
Northern Illinois University, B
Western Illinois University, B

Indiana

Indiana State University, B

Iowa

Iowa State University of Science and Technology, B
University of Northern Iowa, B
Waldorf College, B

Kentucky

Eastern Kentucky University, B
Murray State University, B
University of Kentucky, B

Louisiana

Bossier Parish Community College, A

Maryland

Morgan State University, B

Massachusetts

Framingham State University, B
North Shore Community College, A

Michigan

Andrews University, B
Madonna University, AB
Wayne State University, B

Minnesota

Leech Lake Tribal College, A
Minnesota State University Mankato, B
St. Catherine University, B

Mississippi

Alcorn State University, B
Northwest Mississippi Community College, A

Missouri

College of the Ozarks, B
Lincoln University, B
University of Missouri, B

Nebraska

University of Nebraska - Lincoln, B

Nevada

Truckee Meadows Community College, A
University of Nevada, Reno, B

New Jersey

Montclair State University, B

New Mexico

Central New Mexico Community College, A
New Mexico State University, B
University of New Mexico, B

New York

Brooklyn College of the City University of New York, B
Hunter College of the City University of New York, B
Ithaca College, B
Lehman College of the City University of New York, B
Morrisville State College, AB
The New School for Public Engagement, B
New York University, B
State University of New York at Plattsburgh, B
Syracuse University, B

North Carolina

North Carolina Agricultural and Technical State University, B
The University of North Carolina at Chapel Hill, B

North Dakota

United Tribes Technical College, A

Ohio

Bluffton University, B
Bowling Green State University, B
The Ohio State University, B
Ohio University, B
Sinclair Community College, A
The University of Akron, B
Youngstown State University, AB

Oklahoma

Carl Albert State College, A
Oklahoma State University, B
University of Central Oklahoma, B

Pennsylvania

Cedar Crest College, B
Indiana University of Pennsylvania, B

South Carolina

South Carolina State University, B

Tennessee

Carson-Newman University, B
Chattanooga State Community College, A
Hiwassee College, A
Huntington College of Health Sciences, A
Middle Tennessee State University, B
Southern Adventist University, A
Tennessee Technological University, B
The University of Tennessee, B

Texas

Prairie View A&M University, B
Sam Houston State University, B
Stephen F. Austin State University, B
Texas A&M University, B
Texas State University, B
Texas Tech University, B
Texas Woman's University, B
The University of Texas at Austin, B

Utah

Snow College, A

Vermont

Goddard College, B

Virginia

James Madison University, B
Radford University, B

Virginia Polytechnic Institute and State University, B

Washington

Bastyr University, B
Seattle Pacific University, B
Washington State University, B

U.S. Territories: Puerto Rico

Universidad del Este, B
University of Puerto Rico, Río Piedras Campus, B

Canada

British Columbia

The University of British Columbia, B

Manitoba

University of Manitoba, B

Maritime Provinces: New Brunswick

Université de Moncton, B

Maritime Provinces: Nova Scotia

Acadia University, B
Mount Saint Vincent University, B
St. Francis Xavier University, B

Maritime Provinces: Prince Edward Island

University of Prince Edward Island, B

Newfoundland and Labrador

Memorial University of Newfoundland, B

Ontario

University of Ottawa, B
University of Toronto, B
The University of Western Ontario, B

Quebec

Université Laval, B
Université de Montréal, B

FOODSERVICE SYSTEMS ADMINISTRATION/MANAGEMENT

United States

Alabama

Bishop State Community College, A

Arizona

Phoenix College, A

California

American River College, A
Long Beach City College, A
Point Loma Nazarene University, B
Santa Barbara City College, A

Connecticut

Lincoln College of New England, A

Florida

Pensacola State College, A

Illinois

Dominican University, B
Harper College, A

Kansas

Flint Hills Technical College, A

Massachusetts

Simmons College, B

Michigan

Mott Community College, A
Northern Michigan University, A
Wayne County Community College District, A

Western Michigan University, B

Nebraska

Northeast Community College, A

New Hampshire

University of New Hampshire, A

New Jersey

Rowan College at Burlington County, A

New York

Morrisville State College, A
Rochester Institute of Technology, B
State University of New York College at Oneonta, B

North Carolina

The University of North Carolina at Greensboro, B

Ohio

The Ohio State University, B
Ohio University, B
Wright State University - Lake Campus, AB

Pennsylvania

Bucks County Community College, A
Butler County Community College, A
Community College of Allegheny County, A

Rhode Island

Johnson & Wales University, B

Tennessee

Lipscomb University, B

Texas

Lamar University, B
Sam Houston State University, B
San Jacinto College District, A

Wisconsin

University of Wisconsin - Stout, B

U.S. Territories: Puerto Rico

Inter American University of Puerto Rico, Aguadilla Campus, A

FOREIGN LANGUAGE TEACHER EDUCATION

United States

Alabama

Auburn University, BM

Arizona

Arizona State University at the Tempe campus, M
Northern Arizona University, M

Arkansas

Arkansas State University, B
Arkansas Tech University, B
Harding University, M
University of Arkansas at Little Rock, M
University of Central Arkansas, M

California

California State University, Sacramento, M
Mills College, M
Occidental College, M
University of California, Irvine, M

Colorado

The Colorado College, M
Colorado State University, M
Colorado State University - Pueblo, M
University of Northern Colorado, M

Connecticut

Central Connecticut State University, MO
Quinnipiac University, M

Southern Connecticut State University, M
University of Connecticut, MDO

Delaware

Delaware State University, M
University of Delaware, M

District of Columbia

The George Washington University, M

Florida

Broward College, A
Florida International University, M
Florida Southern College, B
Florida State University, MDO
South Florida State College, A
State College of Florida Manatee-Sarasota, A
University of Central Florida, B
University of Florida, MD
University of South Florida, BMO

Georgia

Georgia State University, M
Kennesaw State University, M
Piedmont College, B
University of Georgia, BMO

Hawaii

University of Hawaii at Hilo, MD
University of Hawaii at Manoa, MD

Illinois

DePaul University, M
Saint Xavier University, M
University of Illinois at Chicago, M
University of Illinois at Urbana - Champaign, BMD

Indiana

Indiana State University, D
Indiana University Bloomington, BM
Indiana University - Purdue University Indianapolis, M
Manchester University, B
Purdue University, MDO
University of Indianapolis, M
Valparaiso University, B

Iowa

The University of Iowa, MD
University of Northern Iowa, BM

Kentucky

Morehead State University, M
Northern Kentucky University, B
Spalding University, M
University of Kentucky, M
Western Kentucky University, M

Louisiana

University of Louisiana at Monroe, M

Maine

University of Maine, B

Maryland

University of Maryland, Baltimore County, M
University of Maryland, College Park, D

Massachusetts

Boston University, B
Elms College, M
Framingham State University, M
Smith College, M
University of Massachusetts Amherst, M
University of Massachusetts Boston, M
Worcester State University, M

Michigan

Andrews University, M
Calvin College, B
Eastern Michigan University, BMO
Grand Valley State University, B
Michigan State University, D
University of Michigan, M

Wayne State University, MD

Minnesota

Concordia College, BM
University of Minnesota, Duluth, B
University of Minnesota, Twin Cities Campus, M

Mississippi

Mississippi State University, M
University of Mississippi, M
University of Southern Mississippi, M

Missouri

Central Methodist University, B
Southeast Missouri State University, B
University of Missouri, MDO

Nebraska

Concordia University, Nebraska, B
Hastings College, B
University of Nebraska at Kearney, M
University of Nebraska - Lincoln, B
University of Nebraska at Omaha, M
Wayne State College, B

Nevada

University of Nevada, Reno, BM

New Hampshire

Plymouth State University, M
Rivier University, M

New Jersey

Drew University, M
Kean University, M
Rider University, O
Rutgers University - New Brunswick, MD

New York

Binghamton University, State University of New
York, M
Brooklyn College of the City University of New York,
M
Buffalo State College, State University of New York,
B
College of Staten Island of the City University of
New York, B
Columbia University, M
Cornell University, MD
Elmira College, B
Hofstra University, BM
Hunter College of the City University of New York,
M
Iona College, BM
Ithaca College, M
Le Moyne College, M
Long Island University - LIU Post, B
Manhattanville College, M
Nazareth College of Rochester, B
New York University, BM
Pace University, Pleasantville Campus, B
Queens College of the City University of New York,
BMO
St. John Fisher College, M
State University of New York College at Old
Westbury, BM
State University of New York at Plattsburgh, M
Stony Brook University, State University of New
York, M
University at Buffalo, the State University of New
York, MDO
Wagner College, M

North Carolina

Appalachian State University, M
East Carolina University, M
Gardner-Webb University, B
Greensboro College, B
The University of North Carolina at Chapel Hill, M
The University of North Carolina at Charlotte, M
The University of North Carolina at Greensboro, M

Ohio

Ashland University, B
Bowling Green State University, BM
Cleveland State University, M
Miami University, B
Ohio Northern University, B
Ohio Wesleyan University, B
University of Dayton, B
The University of Toledo, M
Youngstown State University, B

Oklahoma

Oral Roberts University, B
University of Oklahoma, B

Oregon

Portland State University, M
Southern Oregon University, M

Pennsylvania

Duquesne University, M
Eastern University, O
Indiana University of Pennsylvania, M
Lincoln University, B
Mercyhurst University, B
Messiah College, B
Penn State Abington, B
Penn State Altoona, B
Penn State Beaver, B
Penn State Berks, B
Penn State Brandywine, B
Penn State DuBois, B
Penn State Erie, The Behrend College, B
Penn State Fayette, The Eberly Campus, B
Penn State Greater Allegheny, B
Penn State Mont Alto, B
Penn State Shenango, B
Penn State University Park, B
Penn State Worthington Scranton, B
Penn State York, B
Saint Francis University, B
Seton Hill University, B
Shippensburg University of Pennsylvania, M
Temple University, B
University of Pittsburgh, M
West Chester University of Pennsylvania, MO

Rhode Island

Providence College, B
Rhode Island College, BM
Roger Williams University, B

South Carolina

College of Charleston, M
University of South Carolina, MD

South Dakota

The University of South Dakota, B

Tennessee

Middle Tennessee State University, M
The University of Tennessee, MO
The University of Tennessee at Chattanooga, B
Vanderbilt University, BM

Texas

Baylor University, B
Howard College, A
Lamar University, M
Texas A&M International University, MD
Texas A&M University - Kingsville, MD
University of Mary Hardin-Baylor, B

Utah

Brigham Young University, M
University of Utah, M

Vermont

Bennington College, M
University of Vermont, BM

Virginia

George Mason University, M
James Madison University, M

University of Virginia, M
Virginia Polytechnic Institute and State University, M
Virginia Wesleyan College, B

Washington

Washington State University, BM

Wisconsin

Carroll University, B
Marquette University, M
University of Wisconsin - Madison, M

U.S. Territories: Puerto Rico

Caribbean University, M
Inter American University of Puerto Rico, Arecibo
Campus, M
Inter American University of Puerto Rico, Bar-
ranquitas Campus, M
Inter American University of Puerto Rico, Metropoli-
tan Campus, M
Universidad del Este, M
University of Puerto Rico, Río Piedras Campus, M
University of the Sacred Heart, M

Canada

Alberta

University of Alberta, B
University of Lethbridge, M

British Columbia

University of Victoria, M

Ontario

University of Windsor, B

Quebec

McGill University, MD
Université de Montréal, B
Université du Québec en Outaouais, O

FOREIGN LANGUAGES AND LITERATURES

United States

Alabama

Auburn University, B
Auburn University at Montgomery, B
Samford University, B
The University of Alabama, B
The University of Alabama at Birmingham, B
The University of Alabama in Huntsville, B
University of Montevallo, B
University of North Alabama, B
University of South Alabama, B

Alaska

University of Alaska Anchorage, B
University of Alaska Fairbanks, B

Arizona

Eastern Arizona College, A
Northern Arizona University, B

Arkansas

Arkansas State University, B
Arkansas Tech University, B
University of Arkansas at Little Rock, B
University of Arkansas at Monticello, B

California

California Polytechnic State University, San Luis
Obispo, B
College of Marin, A
Fresno City College, A
Fullerton College, A
Glendale Community College, A
Long Beach City College, A
Los Angeles Valley College, A
Modesto Junior College, A

Orange Coast College, A
Palomar College, A
Pitzer College, B
Reedley College, A
San Jose City College, A
Scripps College, B
Stanford University, B
University of California, Riverside, B
University of California, San Diego, B
University of California, Santa Cruz, B

Colorado

Colorado State University, B
Colorado State University - Pueblo, B
University of Northern Colorado, B

Connecticut

University of Hartford, B

Delaware

University of Delaware, B

Florida

College of Central Florida, A
South Florida State College, A
University of South Florida, St. Petersburg, B

Georgia

College of Coastal Georgia, B
Covenant College, B
Darton State College, A
Georgia Highlands College, A
Georgia Institute of Technology, B
Gordon State College, A
Piedmont College, B
South Georgia State College, A

Idaho

College of Southern Idaho, A
University of Idaho, B

Illinois

Eastern Illinois University, B
Knox College, B
Principia College, B
Southern Illinois University Carbondale, B
Southern Illinois University Edwardsville, B
Western Illinois University, B

Indiana

Grace College, B
Manchester University, B
Purdue University Northwest (Hammond), B
Vincennes University, A

Iowa

Iowa Lakes Community College, A

Kansas

Benedictine College, B
Emporia State University, B
Hutchinson Community College, A
Independence Community College, A
Kansas State University, B
Wichita State University, B

Louisiana

McNeese State University, B
Tulane University, B
University of Louisiana at Lafayette, B
University of Louisiana at Monroe, B
University of New Orleans, B

Maine

University of Maine, B

Maryland

Frostburg State University, B
Notre Dame of Maryland University, B
St. Mary's College of Maryland, B
Towson University, B
University of Maryland, Baltimore County, B
Washington College, B

Massachusetts

Assumption College, B
Boston University, B
Bunker Hill Community College, A
Framingham State University, B
Gordon College, B
Massachusetts Institute of Technology, B
Stonehill College, B
Suffolk University, B
Tufts University, B
University of Massachusetts Lowell, B

Michigan

Grand Rapids Community College, A
Lake Michigan College, A
Lansing Community College, A
Oakland University, B
Wayne State University, B

Minnesota

University of Minnesota, Twin Cities Campus, B

Mississippi

Delta State University, B
Jackson State University, B
Mississippi State University, B
University of Southern Mississippi, B

Missouri

Central Methodist University, B
Missouri Western State University, B
St. Charles Community College, A
University of Missouri - Kansas City, B
University of Missouri - St. Louis, B
Webster University, B

Montana

Montana State University, B
University of Montana, B

Nebraska

Hastings College, B
Union College, B
University of Nebraska at Omaha, B
Wayne State College, B

Nevada

College of Southern Nevada, A

New Hampshire

Plymouth State University, B

New Jersey

Monmouth University, B
Rutgers University - New Brunswick, B
Saint Peter's University, B
Seton Hall University, B
Stockton University, B
Thomas Edison State University, B

New Mexico

Central New Mexico Community College, A
New Mexico State University, B
University of New Mexico, B

New York

Borough of Manhattan Community College of the
   City University of New York, A
Elmira College, B
Excelsior College, B
Hamilton College, B
Long Island University - LIU Brooklyn, B
Long Island University - LIU Post, B
New York University, B
Pace University, B
State University of New York College at Old
   Westbury, B
Syracuse University, B
Union College, B
Utica College, B

North Carolina

Campbell University, B
East Carolina University, B

Elon University, B
North Carolina State University, B
The University of North Carolina at Chapel Hill, B

Ohio

Kenyon College, B
Lake Erie College, B
University of Dayton, B
Wright State University, B
Youngstown State University, B

Oklahoma

Cameron University, B
Oklahoma City Community College, A

Oregon

Central Oregon Community College, A
Lewis & Clark College, B
Linn-Benton Community College, A

Pennsylvania

Bloomsburg University of Pennsylvania, B
Clarion University of Pennsylvania, B
Community College of Allegheny County, A
Duquesne University, B
Gannon University, B
Juniata College, B
Lock Haven University of Pennsylvania, B
Lycoming College, B
Mercyhurst University, B
Penn State Berks, B
Penn State Lehigh Valley, B
The University of Scranton, B
West Chester University of Pennsylvania, B
Widener University, B

Rhode Island

Roger Williams University, B

South Carolina

The Citadel, The Military College of South Carolina,
   B
Clemson University, B
Francis Marion University, B
Presbyterian College, B
South Carolina State University, B
Winthrop University, B

South Dakota

Augustana University, B

Tennessee

Austin Peay State University, B
East Tennessee State University, B
Middle Tennessee State University, B
Southern Adventist University, B
Union University, B
University of Memphis, B
The University of Tennessee, B
The University of Tennessee at Chattanooga, B

Texas

Central Texas College, A
Hill College, A
Lamar University, B
Panola College, A
Paris Junior College, A
San Jacinto College District, A
Southwestern Assemblies of God University, A
Stephen F. Austin State University, B
Texarkana College, A
Texas A&M University, B
Texas Tech University, B
Tyler Junior College, A
University of Houston, B
The University of Texas at Arlington, B
The University of Texas at San Antonio, B
The University of Texas at Tyler, B

Vermont

Bennington College, B

Virginia

George Mason University, B
James Madison University, B
Longwood University, B
Old Dominion University, B
Radford University, B
Sweet Briar College, B
University of Mary Washington, B
The University of Virginia's College at Wise, B
Virginia Commonwealth University, B

Washington

Everett Community College, A
The Evergreen State College, B
Skagit Valley College, A
University of Puget Sound, B
Washington State University, B
Western Washington University, B

West Virginia

Marshall University, B
West Virginia University, B

Wisconsin

University of Wisconsin - Platteville, B
University of Wisconsin - River Falls, B

Wyoming

Casper College, A
Eastern Wyoming College, A

U.S. Territories: Puerto Rico

University of Puerto Rico, Río Piedras Campus, B

Canada

Alberta

Concordia University of Edmonton, B

Ontario

University of Ottawa, B

Saskatchewan

University of Saskatchewan, B

FOREIGN LANGUAGES, LITERATURES, AND LINGUISTICS

United States

Alaska

University of Alaska Fairbanks, AB

Arizona

Arizona State University at the Tempe campus, B

California

Occidental College, B
Saint Mary's College of California, B
University of California, Berkeley, B
University of California, Los Angeles, B

Connecticut

Yale University, B

Delaware

University of Delaware, B

Georgia

Augusta University, B
Georgia Southern University, B
Kennesaw State University, B
University of West Georgia, B

Hawaii

University of Hawaii at Manoa, B

Illinois

Sauk Valley Community College, A

Indiana

Indiana State University, B
Vincennes University, A

Maryland

Hood College, B

Mississippi

Mississippi College, B

New York

Binghamton University, State University of New York, B
Excelsior College, B
Genesee Community College, A
New York University, B
Purchase College, State University of New York, B
St. Lawrence University, B
United States Military Academy, B

Oklahoma

Tulsa Community College, A

Pennsylvania

Indiana University of Pennsylvania, B

South Carolina

Clemson University, B

South Dakota

Augustana University, B

Tennessee

Nashville State Community College, A

Vermont

Marlboro College, B

Virginia

Averett University, B

Washington

Western Washington University, B

Canada

Alberta

University of Alberta, B
University of Lethbridge, B

FORENSIC NURSING

United States

California

National University, M

Massachusetts

Boston College, M
Fitchburg State University, MO

New Jersey

Monmouth University, MO

Ohio

Cleveland State University, M

Pennsylvania

Duquesne University, MO

FORENSIC PSYCHOLOGY

United States

Arizona

Argosy University, Phoenix, M

California

Argosy University, Inland Empire, M
Argosy University, Los Angeles, M
Argosy University, Orange County, M
Argosy University, San Diego, M
Argosy University, San Francisco Bay Area, M
California Baptist University, M
Holy Names University, MO

Colorado

Argosy University, Denver, M
University of Denver, M

Connecticut

University of New Haven, M

District of Columbia

The George Washington University, O

Florida

Argosy University, Sarasota, M

Georgia

Argosy University, Atlanta, M

Hawaii

Argosy University, Hawai'i, M

Illinois

Argosy University, Chicago, D
Argosy University, Schaumburg, MO

Indiana

Trine University, M

Louisiana

University of Louisiana at Monroe, M

Massachusetts

American International College, M
Cambridge College, M

Minnesota

Argosy University, Twin Cities, MDO
Concordia University, St. Paul, M
Walden University, MD

New Jersey

College of Saint Elizabeth, M
Fairleigh Dickinson University, Metropolitan Campus, M
Montclair State University, O

New York

John Jay College of Criminal Justice of the City University of New York, MD

North Dakota

University of North Dakota, M

Ohio

Tiffin University, M

Oklahoma

University of Central Oklahoma, M

Pennsylvania

Drexel University, D
Immaculata University, O

Rhode Island

Roger Williams University, M

Texas

Argosy University, Dallas, M
Prairie View A&M University, MD
University of Houston - Victoria, M

Utah

Argosy University, Salt Lake City, M

Vermont

Castleton University, M

Virginia

Argosy University, Washington DC, MD
Marymount University, M

FORENSIC SCIENCE AND TECHNOLOGY

United States

Alabama

Alabama State University, M
Jacksonville State University, B
The University of Alabama at Birmingham, M

Arizona

Coconino Community College, A
Embry-Riddle Aeronautical University - Prescott, B
Phoenix College, A

Arkansas

Arkansas State University, A
Arkansas State University - Mountain Home, A
Arkansas State University - Newport, A
Black River Technical College, A
Cossatot Community College of the University of
    Arkansas, A
North Arkansas College, A
Southeast Arkansas College, A
University of Arkansas Community College at Mor-
    rilton, A
University of Arkansas - Fort Smith, A
University of Arkansas at Monticello, A

California

Fresno City College, A
Golden Gate University, M
Grossmont College, A
National University, MO
Palomar College, A
Southwestern College, A
University of California, Davis, M

Colorado

University of Colorado Denver, M

Connecticut

Tunxis Community College, A
University of New Haven, BMO

Delaware

Delaware State University, B

District of Columbia

The George Washington University, MO

Florida

Broward College, A
Florida Atlantic University, M
Florida Gulf Coast University, M
Florida International University, MD
Florida SouthWestern State College, A
Gulf Coast State College, A
Keiser University, B
Lynn University, B
Miami Dade College, A
Pensacola State College, A
Saint Leo University, M
St. Petersburg College, A
South Florida State College, A
University of Central Florida, BM
University of Florida, MO
The University of Tampa, B

Georgia

Albany State University, M
Darton State College, A
Georgia State University, O
Piedmont College, B

Savannah State University, B

Hawaii

Chaminade University of Honolulu, BMO

Idaho

Northwest Nazarene University, B

Illinois

Ellis University, B
Illinois Central College, A
Illinois Valley Community College, A
Kishwaukee College, A
Lewis University, B
Loyola University Chicago, B
Quincy University, B
University of Illinois at Chicago, M
University of St. Francis, O

Indiana

Indiana University - Purdue University Indianapolis,
    BM
Trine University, B

Iowa

Simpson College, B

Kansas

Bethany College, B
Friends University, B
Newman University, B
Washburn University, B
Wichita State University, B

Kentucky

Eastern Kentucky University, B
Thomas More College, B

Louisiana

Louisiana Delta Community College, A

Maine

Husson University, B

Maryland

Carroll Community College, A
Prince George's Community College, A
Stevenson University, M
Towson University, BM
University of Baltimore, B
University of Maryland University College, B

Massachusetts

Bay Path University, BM
Becker College, B
Boston University, M
Eastern Nazarene College, B
Mount Ida College, B
Western New England University, B

Michigan

Lake Michigan College, A
Macomb Community College, A
Madonna University, B
Michigan State University, M
Olivet College, B

Minnesota

Walden University, M

Mississippi

University of Southern Mississippi, BM

Missouri

Columbia College, B
Missouri Western State University, MO
Saint Louis University, B
Webster University, M

Montana

University of Great Falls, B

Nebraska

Nebraska Wesleyan University, M
University of Nebraska - Lincoln, B

New Mexico

Eastern New Mexico University, B
New Mexico Highlands University, B

New York

Borough of Manhattan Community College of the
    City University of New York, A
Buffalo State College, State University of New York,
    B
The College at Brockport, State University of New
    York, M
The College of Saint Rose, B
Farmingdale State College, B
Herkimer County Community College, A
Hilbert College, B
Hofstra University, B
Hudson Valley Community College, A
Iona College, O
John Jay College of Criminal Justice of the City Uni-
    versity of New York, BMD
Long Island University - LIU Post, B
Pace University, BM
Queensborough Community College of the City Uni-
    versity of New York, A
Roberts Wesleyan College, B
The Sage Colleges, B
St. Thomas Aquinas College, B
State University of New York College of Technology
    at Alfred, B
Sullivan County Community College, A
Syracuse University, BM
University at Albany, State University of New York,
    M
Utica College, M

North Carolina

Fayetteville State University, B
Fayetteville Technical Community College, A
Forsyth Technical Community College, A
Gaston College, A
St. Andrews University, B
Saint Augustine's University, B
University of Mount Olive, B
Wayne Community College, A

North Dakota

University of North Dakota, B

Ohio

Cedarville University, B
Central Ohio Technical College, A
Defiance College, B
Miami University, B
Tiffin University, B
The University of Findlay, B
Youngstown State University, B

Oklahoma

University of Central Oklahoma, BM

Pennsylvania

Alvernia University, B
Arcadia University, M
Carlow University, M
Cedar Crest College, BM
Chestnut Hill College, B
Community College of Philadelphia, A
DeSales University, M
Duquesne University, M
Gannon University, B
Keystone College, B
La Salle University, MO
Mercyhurst University, BM
Penn State Altoona, B
Penn State Berks, B
Penn State University Park, B
Point Park University, B
Saint Francis University, B
Seton Hill University, B
The University of Scranton, B
Waynesburg University, B

York College of Pennsylvania, B

Rhode Island

Bryant University, B
Roger Williams University, B
University of Rhode Island, O

South Carolina

Southern Wesleyan University, B

South Dakota

Mount Marty College, B

Tennessee

King University, B

Texas

Grayson College, A
St. Edward's University, B
St. Mary's University, B
Sam Houston State University, BM
Texas A&M University, B
Texas Tech University, M
University of Houston - Victoria, M

Utah

Dixie State University, B
Utah Valley University, B
Weber State University, B

Vermont

Champlain College, M

Virginia

Bluefield College, B
George Mason University, BMO
Liberty University, B
New River Community College, A
Virginia Commonwealth University, BM

Washington

Columbia Basin College, A
Green River College, A
Seattle University, O

West Virginia

American Public University System, BM
Marshall University, M
Potomac State College of West Virginia University,
   A
University of Charleston, M
West Virginia University, BMD
West Virginia University Institute of Technology, B

Wisconsin

Fox Valley Technical College, A
Marian University, B
University of Wisconsin - Platteville, B

Wyoming

Casper College, A

U.S. Territories: American Samoa

American Samoa Community College, A

U.S. Territories: Puerto Rico

Inter American University of Puerto Rico, Aguadilla
   Campus, B
Inter American University of Puerto Rico, Bayamón
   Campus, B
Inter American University of Puerto Rico, Ponce
   Campus, B
Universidad del Turabo, M

Canada

British Columbia

British Columbia Institute of Technology, A

Ontario

University of Toronto, B
University of Windsor, B

Quebec

McGill University, O

FOREST ENGINEERING

United States

Oregon

Oregon State University, B

Canada

Maritime Provinces: New Brunswick

Université de Moncton, B
University of New Brunswick Fredericton, B

FOREST MANAGEMENT/FOREST RESOURCES MANAGEMENT

United States

California

University of California, Berkeley, B

Florida

Broward College, A

Idaho

University of Idaho, B

Maryland

Allegany College of Maryland, A

Michigan

Northwestern Michigan College, A

Minnesota

Vermilion Community College, A

Montana

University of Montana, B

Nebraska

Western Nebraska Community College, A

New York

State University of New York College of Environmental Science and Forestry, B

North Carolina

Haywood Community College, A
North Carolina State University, B

Pennsylvania

Elizabethtown College, B

South Carolina

Clemson University, B

Texas

Stephen F. Austin State University, B

Washington

Whitman College, B

West Virginia

West Virginia University, B

Canada

Alberta

University of Alberta, B

British Columbia

British Columbia Institute of Technology, A
The University of British Columbia, B

Ontario

Lakehead University, B
University of Toronto, B

Quebec

Université Laval, B

FOREST RESOURCES PRODUCTION AND MANAGEMENT

United States

West Virginia

Potomac State College of West Virginia University,
   A

FOREST SCIENCES AND BIOLOGY

United States

Alabama

Auburn University, B

Arizona

Northern Arizona University, B

Colorado

Colorado State University, B

Idaho

University of Idaho, B

Illinois

University of Illinois at Urbana - Champaign, B

Kentucky

University of Kentucky, B

Maine

University of Maine, B

Minnesota

Vermilion Community College, A

New York

State University of New York College of Environmental Science and Forestry, B

Ohio

Ohio Northern University, B

Pennsylvania

Penn State Abington, B
Penn State Altoona, B
Penn State Beaver, B
Penn State Berks, B
Penn State Brandywine, B
Penn State DuBois, B
Penn State Erie, The Behrend College, B
Penn State Fayette, The Eberly Campus, B
Penn State Greater Allegheny, B
Penn State Hazleton, B
Penn State Lehigh Valley, B
Penn State Mont Alto, B
Penn State New Kensington, B
Penn State Schuylkill, B
Penn State Shenango, B
Penn State University Park, B
Penn State Wilkes-Barre, B
Penn State Worthington Scranton, B
Penn State York, B

Tennessee

Sewanee: The University of the South, B

Wisconsin

University of Wisconsin - Madison, B

Canada

Alberta

University of Alberta, B

British Columbia

University of Northern British Columbia, B

Newfoundland and Labrador

Memorial University of Newfoundland, B

FORESTRY

United States

Alabama

Auburn University, MD

Arizona

Eastern Arizona College, A
Northern Arizona University, MD
The University of Arizona, MD

Arkansas

University of Arkansas at Monticello, BM

California

Bakersfield College, A
California Polytechnic State University, San Luis
    Obispo, BM
College of the Redwoods, A
Columbia College, A
Humboldt State University, BM
Modesto Junior College, A
Sierra College, A
University of California, Berkeley, BM

Colorado

Colorado State University, MD

Connecticut

Yale University, MD

Delaware

Delaware State University, B

Florida

College of Central Florida, A
Indian River State College, A
Miami Dade College, A
South Florida State College, A
University of Florida, BMD

Georgia

Abraham Baldwin Agricultural College, A
College of Coastal Georgia, A
Darton State College, A
Georgia Southern University, B
Gordon State College, A
University of Georgia, BMD

Hawaii

Hawaii Community College, A

Idaho

College of Southern Idaho, A
North Idaho College, A

Illinois

Southern Illinois University Carbondale, BM
University of Illinois at Urbana - Champaign, B

Indiana

Purdue University, BMD

Iowa

Iowa Lakes Community College, A
Iowa State University of Science and Technology,
    BMD

Kansas

Allen Community College, A
Barton County Community College, A
Dodge City Community College, A

Kentucky

University of Kentucky, M

Louisiana

Louisiana State University and Agricultural & Me-
    chanical College, MD
Louisiana Tech University, B
Southern University and Agricultural and Mechanical
    College, M

Maine

University of Maine, BMD

Massachusetts

Harvard University, M
University of Massachusetts Amherst, MD

Michigan

Grand Rapids Community College, A
Michigan State University, BMD
Michigan Technological University, BMD

Minnesota

College of Saint Benedict, B
Itasca Community College, A
Saint John's University, B
University of Minnesota, Twin Cities Campus, BMD
Vermilion Community College, A

Mississippi

Copiah-Lincoln Community College, A
East Mississippi Community College, A
Mississippi State University, BMD
Northeast Mississippi Community College, A

Missouri

University of Missouri, BMDO

Montana

Blackfeet Community College, A
Salish Kootenai College, A
University of Montana, BMD

Nevada

University of Nevada, Reno, B

New Hampshire

University of New Hampshire, BM

New Mexico

New Mexico Highlands University, B

New York

Cornell University, MD
Monroe Community College, A
Paul Smith's College, B
State University of New York College of Environ-
    mental Science and Forestry, BMD

North Carolina

Duke University, M
Lenoir-Rhyne University, B
North Carolina State University, MD

Ohio

Hocking College, A
The Ohio State University, BMD

Oklahoma

Eastern Oklahoma State College, A
Northeastern Oklahoma Agricultural and Mechanical
    College, A
Oklahoma State University, MD

Oregon

Central Oregon Community College, A
Oregon State University, MD
Umpqua Community College, A

Pennsylvania

Albright College, B
Penn State University Park, MD

South Carolina

Clemson University, MD

Tennessee

Hiwassee College, A
The University of Tennessee, BM

Texas

Panola College, A
Stephen F. Austin State University, BMD
Texas A&M University, BMD

Utah

Snow College, A
Utah State University, BMD

Vermont

Sterling College, B
University of Vermont, BM

Virginia

Virginia Polytechnic Institute and State University,
    BMD

Washington

Spokane Community College, A
University of Washington, MD

West Virginia

Davis & Elkins College, B
West Virginia University, MD

Wisconsin

Beloit College, B
Northland College, B
University of Wisconsin - Madison, MD
University of Wisconsin - Stevens Point, B

Wyoming

Western Wyoming Community College, A

Canada

Alberta

University of Alberta, MD

British Columbia

The University of British Columbia, BMD

Maritime Provinces: New Brunswick

University of New Brunswick Fredericton, BMD

Ontario

Lakehead University, BMD
University of Toronto, BMD

Quebec

McGill University, MD
Université Laval, BMD
Université du Québec en Abitibi-Témiscamingue, M

FORESTRY TECHNOLOGY/ TECHNICIAN

United States

Alabama

Alabama Southern Community College, A
Lurleen B. Wallace Community College, A

California

El Camino College, A
Modesto Junior College, A
Mt. San Antonio College, A

Georgia

Abraham Baldwin Agricultural College, A
Albany Technical College, A
Coastal Pines Technical College, A
Ogeechee Technical College, A

Illinois

Southeastern Illinois College, A

Maine

University of Maine at Fort Kent, A

Minnesota

Itasca Community College, A
Vermilion Community College, A

Mississippi

Holmes Community College, A
Itawamba Community College, A
Jones County Junior College, A
Northeast Mississippi Community College, A

Montana

Salish Kootenai College, A

New Hampshire

University of New Hampshire, A

New York

Paul Smith's College, A
State University of New York College of Environ-
    mental Science and Forestry, A

North Carolina

Haywood Community College, A
Montgomery Community College, A
Southeastern Community College, A
Wayne Community College, A

Ohio

Hocking College, A

Oregon

Central Oregon Community College, A
Mt. Hood Community College, A

Pennsylvania

Penn State Abington, B
Penn State Altoona, B
Penn State Beaver, B
Penn State Berks, B
Penn State Brandywine, B
Penn State DuBois, B
Penn State Erie, The Behrend College, B
Penn State Fayette, The Eberly Campus, B
Penn State Greater Allegheny, B
Penn State Hazleton, B
Penn State Lehigh Valley, B
Penn State Mont Alto, AB
Penn State New Kensington, B
Penn State Schuylkill, B
Penn State Shenango, B
Penn State Wilkes-Barre, B
Penn State Worthington Scranton, B
Penn State York, B
Pennsylvania College of Technology, A

South Carolina

Horry-Georgetown Technical College, A
York Technical College, A

Virginia

Dabney S. Lancaster Community College, A

Washington

Green River College, A

West Virginia

Glenville State College, A

Canada

British Columbia

British Columbia Institute of Technology, A

FOUNDATIONS AND PHILOSO-PHY OF EDUCATION

United States

Alabama

Spring Hill College, M

Arizona

Northern Arizona University, M

Arkansas

Arkansas State University, M

California

Azusa Pacific University, M
University of California, Riverside, MD

Connecticut

Central Connecticut State University, M
Fairfield University, MO
Southern Connecticut State University, O
University of Connecticut, D

District of Columbia

The George Washington University, O

Florida

Florida Atlantic University, M
Florida State University, MD

Georgia

Georgia State University, MD
University of West Georgia, MO

Hawaii

University of Hawaii at Manoa, MD

Illinois

Chicago State University, M
DePaul University, M
Northern Illinois University, M
Southern Illinois University Edwardsville, M
Western Illinois University, MO

Indiana

Ball State University, D
Indiana University Bloomington, MD
Purdue University, MD

Iowa

Iowa State University of Science and Technology, M
The University of Iowa, MDO

Kansas

The University of Kansas, D

Maryland

University of Maryland, College Park, MDO

Massachusetts

Curry College, M
Harvard University, M

Michigan

Eastern Michigan University, M
Oakland University, M
Wayne State University, MDO

Minnesota

University of Minnesota, Twin Cities Campus, MDO

Missouri

Saint Louis University, MD
Southeast Missouri State University, M

New Jersey

Fairleigh Dickinson University, Metropolitan Cam-
    pus, M
Rutgers University - New Brunswick, MD

New Mexico

University of New Mexico, MD

New York

Binghamton University, State University of New
    York, MDO
Columbia University, M
New York University, MD
Niagara University, M
Syracuse University, MDO
University at Buffalo, the State University of New
    York, D
University of Rochester, D

Ohio

Ashland University, M
Kent State University, MD
University of Cincinnati, MD
The University of Toledo, MD

Oklahoma

Northeastern State University, M

Pennsylvania

Duquesne University, M
Millersville University of Pennsylvania, M
University of Pennsylvania, MD
University of Pittsburgh, MD
Widener University, M

South Carolina

University of South Carolina, D

Tennessee

The University of Tennessee, MD

Texas

University of Houston, MD
University of Houston - Clear Lake, M
The University of Texas of the Permian Basin, M

Utah

Brigham Young University, MD
University of Utah, MD

Washington

Central Washington University, M
University of Washington, MD

Wisconsin

Marquette University, M
University of Wisconsin - Milwaukee, MD

Canada

British Columbia

Simon Fraser University, MD
The University of British Columbia, D
University of Victoria, MD

Manitoba

University of Manitoba, M

Maritime Provinces: Nova Scotia

Mount Saint Vincent University, M

Quebec

McGill University, MD

Saskatchewan

University of Saskatchewan, MDO

FRANCHISING AND FRANCHISE OPERATIONS

United States

Minnesota

St. Catherine University, B

FRENCH LANGUAGE AND LITERATURE

United States

Alabama

Auburn University, B
Jacksonville State University, B
Oakwood University, B
Samford University, B
The University of Alabama, MD
University of North Alabama, B

Alaska

University of Alaska Anchorage, B

Arizona

Arizona State University at the Tempe campus, BM
The University of Arizona, BM

Arkansas

Harding University, B
Hendrix College, B
University of Arkansas, BM
University of Arkansas at Little Rock, B
University of Central Arkansas, B

California

Bakersfield College, A
Cabrillo College, A
California Lutheran University, B
California State University, Chico, B
California State University, East Bay, B
California State University, Fresno, B
California State University, Fullerton, BM
California State University, Long Beach, BM
California State University, Los Angeles, BM
California State University, Northridge, B
California State University, Sacramento, B
California State University, San Bernardino, B
Cerritos College, A
Chabot College, A
Chaffey College, A
Chapman University, B
Citrus College, A
City College of San Francisco, A
Claremont McKenna College, B
College of the Canyons, A
College of the Desert, A
College of Marin, A
College of San Mateo, A
College of the Sequoias, A
Contra Costa College, A
East Los Angeles College, A
Grossmont College, A
Humboldt State University, B
Imperial Valley College, A
Los Angeles City College, A
Los Angeles Valley College, A
Loyola Marymount University, B
Mendocino College, A
Merritt College, A
Mills College, B
Monterey Peninsula College, A
Mount Saint Mary's University, B
Occidental College, B
Palomar College, A
Pepperdine University, B
Point Loma Nazarene University, B
Pomona College, B
Saint Mary's College of California, B
San Bernardino Valley College, A
San Diego Mesa College, A

San Diego State University, B
San Francisco State University, BM
San Jose State University, BM
Santa Barbara City College, A
Santa Clara University, B
Santa Rosa Junior College, A
Scripps College, B
Solano Community College, A
Sonoma State University, B
Southwestern College, A
Stanford University, BMD
University of California, Berkeley, BD
University of California, Davis, BD
University of California, Irvine, BMD
University of California, Los Angeles, BMD
University of California, Riverside, B
University of California, San Diego, B
University of California, Santa Barbara, BD
University of La Verne, B
University of the Pacific, B
University of Redlands, B
University of San Diego, B
University of San Francisco, B
University of Southern California, B
West Los Angeles College, A
West Valley College, A
Westmont College, B
Whittier College, B

Colorado

The Colorado College, B
Colorado State University, B
Regis University, B
University of Colorado Boulder, BMD
University of Colorado Denver, B
University of Denver, B

Connecticut

Central Connecticut State University, BMO
Connecticut College, B
Fairfield University, B
Southern Connecticut State University, B
Trinity College, B
University of Connecticut, BMD
Yale University, BMD

Delaware

Delaware State University, B
University of Delaware, M

District of Columbia

American University, B
The Catholic University of America, B
The George Washington University, B
Georgetown University, B
Howard University, BM

Florida

Barry University, B
Broward College, A
Eckerd College, B
Florida Atlantic University, BM
Florida International University, B
Florida State University, MD
Indian River State College, A
Jacksonville University, B
Miami Dade College, A
New College of Florida, B
Rollins College, B
South Florida State College, A
State College of Florida Manatee-Sarasota, A
Stetson University, B
University of Central Florida, B
University of Florida, BMD
University of Miami, BD
University of South Florida, BM
University of West Florida, B

Georgia

Agnes Scott College, B
Armstrong State University, B
Berry College, B
Clark Atlanta University, B
Columbus State University, B
Emory University, D

Fort Valley State University, B
Georgia College & State University, B
Georgia Southern University, B
Georgia State University, BMO
Mercer University, B
Morehouse College, B
Oglethorpe University, B
Spelman College, B
University of Georgia, BM
University of North Georgia, B
Valdosta State University, B
Wesleyan College, B

Hawaii

University of Hawaii at Manoa, BM

Idaho

Boise State University, B
Idaho State University, B
North Idaho College, A
University of Idaho, B

Illinois

Augustana College, B
Bradley University, B
DePaul University, BM
Dominican University, B
Elmhurst College, B
Illinois College, B
Illinois State University, BM
Illinois Wesleyan University, B
Knox College, B
Lake Forest College, BM
Loyola University Chicago, B
Monmouth College, B
North Central College, B
North Park University, B
Northeastern Illinois University, B
Northern Illinois University, BM
Northwestern University, BDO
Principia College, B
Rockford University, B
Triton College, A
University of Chicago, D
University of Illinois at Chicago, BM
University of Illinois at Urbana - Champaign, BMD
Western Illinois University, B
Wheaton College, B

Indiana

Ball State University, B
Butler University, B
DePauw University, B
Earlham College, B
Franklin College, B
Grace College, B
Hanover College, B
Indiana University Bloomington, BMD
Indiana University Northwest, B
Indiana University - Purdue University Fort Wayne, B
Indiana University - Purdue University Indianapolis, B
Indiana University South Bend, B
Indiana University Southeast, B
Manchester University, B
Marian University, B
Purdue University, BMD
University of Evansville, B
University of Indianapolis, B
University of Notre Dame, BM
University of Southern Indiana, B
Valparaiso University, B
Wabash College, B

Iowa

Central College, B
Coe College, B
Cornell College, B
Grinnell College, B
Iowa State University of Science and Technology, B
Luther College, B
St. Ambrose University, B
Simpson College, B
The University of Iowa, BMD

Wartburg College, B

Kansas

Baker University, B
Benedictine College, B
Fort Hays State University, B
Pittsburg State University, B
The University of Kansas, BMD
Washburn University, B
Wichita State University, B

Kentucky

Asbury University, BM
Berea College, B
Centre College, B
Eastern Kentucky University, B
Georgetown College, B
Morehead State University, B
Murray State University, B
Northern Kentucky University, B
Thomas More College, A
Transylvania University, B
University of the Cumberlands, B
University of Kentucky, B
University of Louisville, BM
Western Kentucky University, BM

Louisiana

Centenary College of Louisiana, B
Louisiana College, B
Louisiana State University and Agricultural & Mechanical College, BMD
Louisiana Tech University, B
Loyola University New Orleans, B
Southern University and Agricultural and Mechanical College, B
Tulane University, BMD
University of Louisiana at Lafayette, MD
Xavier University of Louisiana, B

Maine

Bates College, B
Bowdoin College, B
Colby College, B
University of Maine, B
University of Maine at Fort Kent, B
University of Southern Maine, B

Maryland

Goucher College, B
Hood College, B
Johns Hopkins University, BD
Loyola University Maryland, B
McDaniel College, B
Mount St. Mary's University, B
Notre Dame of Maryland University, B
Salisbury University, B
University of Maryland, College Park, BMD
Washington College, B

Massachusetts

Amherst College, B
Assumption College, B
Bard College at Simon's Rock, B
Boston College, BM
Boston University, BMD
Brandeis University, B
Clark University, B
College of the Holy Cross, B
Gordon College, B
Harvard University, MD
Merrimack College, B
Mount Holyoke College, B
Simmons College, B
Smith College, BM
Stonehill College, B
Suffolk University, B
Tufts University, BM
University of Massachusetts Amherst, BM
University of Massachusetts Boston, B
University of Massachusetts Dartmouth, B
Wellesley College, B
Williams College, B

Michigan

Adrian College, B
Albion College, B
Alma College, B
Andrews University, B
Aquinas College, B
Calvin College, B
Central Michigan University, B
Eastern Michigan University, BM
Grand Valley State University, B
Hillsdale College, B
Hope College, B
Kalamazoo College, B
Lansing Community College, A
Michigan State University, BMD
Northern Michigan University, B
Oakland University, B
Saginaw Valley State University, B
University of Michigan, BD
University of Michigan - Dearborn, B
University of Michigan - Flint, B
Wayne State University, MD
Western Michigan University, B

Minnesota

Augsburg College, B
Carleton College, B
College of Saint Benedict, B
Concordia College, B
Gustavus Adolphus College, B
Macalester College, B
Minnesota State University Mankato, BM
St. Catherine University, B
St. Cloud State University, B
Saint John's University, B
St. Olaf College, B
University of Minnesota, Duluth, B
University of Minnesota, Morris, B
University of Minnesota, Twin Cities Campus, BMD
University of St. Thomas, B

Mississippi

Mississippi College, B
Mississippi State University, M
University of Mississippi, B

Missouri

Drury University, B
Lindenwood University, B
Missouri Southern State University, B
Missouri State University, B
Rockhurst University, B
St. Charles Community College, A
Saint Louis University, BM
Truman State University, B
University of Central Missouri, B
University of Missouri, BMD
University of Missouri - Kansas City, M
Washington University in St. Louis, BMD
Webster University, B
Westminster College, B
William Jewell College, B

Montana

Carroll College, B
University of Montana, BM

Nebraska

Creighton University, B
Doane University, B
Nebraska Wesleyan University, B
Union College, B
University of Nebraska at Kearney, B
University of Nebraska - Lincoln, BMD
Western Nebraska Community College, A

Nevada

University of Nevada, Las Vegas, B
University of Nevada, Reno, BM

New Hampshire

Dartmouth College, B
Keene State College, B
Plymouth State University, B
Saint Anselm College, B

University of New Hampshire, B

New Jersey

Drew University, BM
Fairleigh Dickinson University, College at Florham, B
Fairleigh Dickinson University, Metropolitan Campus, B
Montclair State University, BM
Princeton University, BD
Rider University, BO
Rutgers University - Camden, B
Rutgers University - New Brunswick, BMD
Rutgers University - Newark, B
Seton Hall University, B
William Paterson University of New Jersey, B

New Mexico

New Mexico Military Institute, A
University of New Mexico, BMD

New York

Adelphi University, B
Bard College, B
Barnard College, B
Binghamton University, State University of New York, BM
Brooklyn College of the City University of New York, BM
Buffalo State College, State University of New York, B
Canisius College, B
City College of the City University of New York, B
Colgate University, B
The College at Brockport, State University of New York, B
College of Mount Saint Vincent, B
The College of New Rochelle, B
Columbia University, BMD
Columbia University, School of General Studies, B
Cornell University, BD
Daemen College, B
Fordham University, B
Hamilton College, B
Hartwick College, B
Hobart and William Smith Colleges, B
Hofstra University, BM
Hunter College of the City University of New York, BM
Iona College, B
Ithaca College, B
Le Moyne College, B
Lehman College of the City University of New York, B
Long Island University - LIU Post, B
Manhattan College, B
Manhattanville College, B
Marist College, B
Nazareth College of Rochester, B
New York University, BMDO
Niagara University, B
Purchase College, State University of New York, B
Queens College of the City University of New York, BM
St. Bonaventure University, B
St. John Fisher College, B
St. John's University, B
St. Lawrence University, B
Sarah Lawrence College, B
Siena College, B
Skidmore College, B
State University of New York College at Cortland, B
State University of New York College at Geneseo, B
State University of New York College at Oneonta, B
State University of New York College at Potsdam, B
State University of New York at Fredonia, B
State University of New York at New Paltz, BM
State University of New York at Oswego, B
State University of New York at Plattsburgh, B
Stony Brook University, State University of New York, BM
Syracuse University, BM
Union College, B
United States Military Academy, B
University at Buffalo, the State University of New York, BMDO

University of Rochester, B
Vassar College, B
York College of the City University of New York, B

North Carolina

Campbell University, B
Davidson College, B
Duke University, BD
Elon University, B
Gardner-Webb University, B
Greensboro College, B
Guilford College, B
High Point University, B
Johnson C. Smith University, B
Methodist University, AB
North Carolina Agricultural and Technical State University, B
North Carolina State University, BM
Queens University of Charlotte, B
Salem College, B
University of North Carolina at Asheville, B
The University of North Carolina at Chapel Hill, MD
The University of North Carolina at Charlotte, B
The University of North Carolina at Greensboro, BM
The University of North Carolina Wilmington, B
Wake Forest University, B
Western Carolina University, B

North Dakota

North Dakota State University, B
University of Jamestown, B
University of North Dakota, B

Ohio

Ashland University, B
Baldwin Wallace University, B
Bowling Green State University, BM
Capital University, B
Case Western Reserve University, BM
Cleveland State University, BM
The College of Wooster, B
Denison University, B
Franciscan University of Steubenville, B
Hiram College, B
John Carroll University, B
Kent State University, B
Kenyon College, B
Lake Erie College, B
Miami University, BM
Miami University Hamilton, B
Muskingum University, B
Oberlin College, B
Ohio Northern University, B
The Ohio State University, BMD
Ohio University, BM
Ohio Wesleyan University, B
Otterbein University, B
The University of Akron, B
University of Cincinnati, BMD
University of Dayton, B
University of Mount Union, B
The University of Toledo, BM
Walsh University, B
Wittenberg University, B
Wright State University, B
Xavier University, AB

Oklahoma

Oklahoma City University, B
Oklahoma State University, B
Oral Roberts University, B
University of Central Oklahoma, B
University of Oklahoma, BMD
The University of Tulsa, B

Oregon

Linfield College, B
Oregon State University, B
Pacific University, B
Portland State University, BM
Reed College, B
Southern Oregon University, BM
University of Oregon, BM
Willamette University, B

Pennsylvania

Albright College, B
Allegheny College, B
Arcadia University, B
Bryn Mawr College, B
Bucknell University, B
Cabrini University, B
California University of Pennsylvania, B
Carnegie Mellon University, B
Chestnut Hill College, B
Clarion University of Pennsylvania, B
Dickinson College, B
Eastern University, O
Elizabethtown College, B
Franklin & Marshall College, B
Gettysburg College, B
Grove City College, B
Haverford College, B
Immaculata University, B
Juniata College, B
King's College, B
La Salle University, B
Lafayette College, B
Lebanon Valley College, B
Lehigh University, B
Lincoln University, B
Lycoming College, B
Messiah College, B
Millersville University of Pennsylvania, BM
Moravian College, B
Muhlenberg College, B
Penn State Abington, B
Penn State Altoona, B
Penn State Beaver, B
Penn State Berks, B
Penn State Brandywine, B
Penn State DuBois, B
Penn State Erie, The Behrend College, B
Penn State Fayette, The Eberly Campus, B
Penn State Greater Allegheny, B
Penn State Hazleton, B
Penn State Lehigh Valley, B
Penn State Mont Alto, B
Penn State New Kensington, B
Penn State Schuylkill, B
Penn State Shenango, B
Penn State University Park, BMD
Penn State Wilkes-Barre, B
Penn State Worthington Scranton, B
Penn State York, B
Saint Joseph's University, B
Saint Vincent College, B
Shippensburg University of Pennsylvania, B
Slippery Rock University of Pennsylvania, B
Susquehanna University, B
Swarthmore College, B
Temple University, B
University of Pennsylvania, BMD
University of Pittsburgh, BMD
The University of Scranton, B
Ursinus College, B
Villanova University, B
Washington & Jefferson College, B
West Chester University of Pennsylvania, BMO
Westminster College, B
Widener University, B

Rhode Island

Brown University, BD
Bryant University, B
Providence College, B
Rhode Island College, B
Salve Regina University, B
University of Rhode Island, B

South Carolina

College of Charleston, B
Erskine College, B
Furman University, B
Presbyterian College, B
University of South Carolina, BM
Wofford College, B

South Dakota

Augustana University, B
Northern State University, B
South Dakota State University, B
The University of South Dakota, B

Tennessee

Belmont University, B
King University, B
Lane College, B
Lee University, B
Lipscomb University, B
Middle Tennessee State University, M
Rhodes College, B
Sewanee: The University of the South, B
Southern Adventist University, B
Tennessee State University, B
Tennessee Technological University, B
Tennessee Wesleyan College, B
Union University, B
University of Memphis, M
The University of Tennessee, BMD
The University of Tennessee at Martin, B
Vanderbilt University, BMD

Texas

Austin College, B
Austin Community College District, A
Baylor University, B
Blinn College, A
Lee College, A
Rice University, B
St. Edward's University, B
Sam Houston State University, B
Southern Methodist University, B
Southwestern University, B
Texas A&M University, B
Texas Christian University, B
Texas State University, B
Texas Tech University, B
Trinity University, B
University of Dallas, B
University of Houston, B
University of North Texas, BM
University of St. Thomas, B
The University of Texas at Arlington, BM
The University of Texas at Austin, BMD
The University of Texas at El Paso, B
The University of Texas Rio Grande Valley, B
The University of Texas at San Antonio, B

Utah

Brigham Young University, M
Snow College, A
Southern Utah University, B
University of Utah, BM
Utah State University, B
Weber State University, AB

Vermont

Bennington College, BM
Marlboro College, B
Middlebury College, BMD
Saint Michael's College, B
University of Vermont, BM

Virginia

Bridgewater College, B
Christopher Newport University, B
The College of William and Mary, B
Emory & Henry College, B
George Mason University, M
Hampden-Sydney College, B
Hollins University, B
Lynchburg College, B
Mary Baldwin College, B
Randolph College, B
Randolph-Macon College, B
Roanoke College, B
Sweet Briar College, B
University of Richmond, B
University of Virginia, BMD
The University of Virginia's College at Wise, B
Virginia Polytechnic Institute and State University, B
Virginia Wesleyan College, B

Washington and Lee University, B

Washington

Central Washington University, B
Eastern Washington University, B
Gonzaga University, B
Pacific Lutheran University, B
Seattle University, B
University of Puget Sound, B
University of Washington, BMD
Walla Walla University, B
Washington State University, B
Western Washington University, B
Whitman College, B
Whitworth University, B

West Virginia

Fairmont State University, B
West Virginia University, M
Wheeling Jesuit University, B

Wisconsin

Beloit College, B
Carthage College, B
Edgewood College, B
Lawrence University, B
Marquette University, B
St. Norbert College, B
University of Wisconsin - Eau Claire, B
University of Wisconsin - Green Bay, B
University of Wisconsin - La Crosse, B
University of Wisconsin - Madison, BMDO
University of Wisconsin - Milwaukee, BMO
University of Wisconsin - Oshkosh, B
University of Wisconsin - Stevens Point, B
University of Wisconsin - Whitewater, B

Wyoming

University of Wyoming, BM

U.S. Territories: Puerto Rico

University of Puerto Rico, Mayagüez Campus, B
University of Puerto Rico, Río Piedras Campus, B
University of Puerto Rico in Utuado, B

Canada
Alberta

Athabasca University, B
Concordia University of Edmonton, B
University of Alberta, BMD
University of Calgary, BMD
University of Lethbridge, M

British Columbia

Simon Fraser University, BM
The University of British Columbia, BMD
The University of British Columbia - Okanagan
 Campus, B
University of Victoria, BM

Manitoba

Brandon University, B
University of Manitoba, BMD
The University of Winnipeg, B

Maritime Provinces: New Brunswick

Mount Allison University, B
St. Thomas University, B
Université de Moncton, BMD
University of New Brunswick Fredericton, B
University of New Brunswick Saint John, B

Maritime Provinces: Nova Scotia

Acadia University, B
Cape Breton University, B
Dalhousie University, BMD
Mount Saint Vincent University, B
St. Francis Xavier University, B
Saint Mary's University, B
Université Sainte-Anne, B
University of King's College, B

Maritime Provinces: Prince Edward Island

University of Prince Edward Island, B

Newfoundland and Labrador

Memorial University of Newfoundland, BM

Ontario

Brock University, B
Carleton University, BM
Lakehead University, B
Laurentian University, B
McMaster University, BM
Queen's University at Kingston, BMD
Redeemer University College, B
Royal Military College of Canada, B
Trent University, B
University of Guelph, M
University of Ottawa, BMD
University of Toronto, BMD
University of Waterloo, BMD
The University of Western Ontario, BMD
University of Windsor, B
Wilfrid Laurier University, B
York University, BMD

Quebec

Bishop's University, B
Concordia University, BMO
McGill University, MD
Université Laval, AB
Université de Montréal, BMD
Université du Québec à Chicoutimi, BO
Université du Québec à Rimouski, B
Université du Québec à Trois-Rivières, B
Université de Sherbrooke, BMD

Saskatchewan

University of Regina, BM
University of Saskatchewan, BM

FRENCH LANGUAGE TEACHER EDUCATION

United States
Alabama

Auburn University, B
Talladega College, B

Arkansas

Harding University, B

California

California Lutheran University, B

Colorado

Colorado State University, B

Delaware

Delaware State University, B
University of Delaware, B

District of Columbia

The Catholic University of America, B

Idaho

Boise State University, B

Illinois

Augustana College, B
Bradley University, B
Elmhurst College, B
University of Illinois at Chicago, B
University of Illinois at Urbana - Champaign, B
Western Illinois University, B

Indiana

Franklin College, B
Grace College, B
Indiana University Bloomington, B

Indiana University - Purdue University Fort Wayne,
 B
Indiana University South Bend, B
Manchester University, B
University of Evansville, B
University of Indianapolis, B
Valparaiso University, B

Iowa

The University of Iowa, B

Kansas

Pittsburg State University, B
Washburn University, B

Kentucky

Eastern Kentucky University, B
University of the Cumberlands, B

Louisiana

Louisiana State University in Shreveport, B
Louisiana Tech University, B
Southern University and Agricultural and Mechanical
 College, B
Xavier University of Louisiana, B

Maine

University of Maine, B

Massachusetts

Merrimack College, B

Michigan

Adrian College, B
Albion College, B
Alma College, B
Calvin College, B
Central Michigan University, B
Eastern Michigan University, B
Grand Valley State University, B
Hope College, B
Michigan State University, B
Northern Michigan University, B
University of Michigan - Flint, B
Western Michigan University, B

Minnesota

Concordia College, B
St. Catherine University, B

Missouri

Lindenwood University, B
Missouri State University, B
Missouri Western State University, B
Washington University in St. Louis, B

Nebraska

University of Nebraska - Lincoln, B

New Hampshire

Keene State College, B

New York

Brooklyn College of the City University of New York,
 B
Canisius College, B
Daemen College, B
Elmira College, B
Hofstra University, B
Iona College, B
Ithaca College, B
Le Moyne College, B
Long Island University - LIU Post, B
Manhattanville College, B
Marist College, B
New York University, B
Niagara University, B
Queens College of the City University of New York,
 B
St. John Fisher College, B
State University of New York College at Cortland, B
State University of New York College at Oneonta, B
State University of New York College at Potsdam, B
State University of New York at Plattsburgh, B

North Carolina

Gardner-Webb University, B
North Carolina Agricultural and Technical State University, B
The University of North Carolina at Greensboro, B
The University of North Carolina Wilmington, B

North Dakota

North Dakota State University, B

Ohio

Ashland University, B
Miami University, B
Miami University Hamilton, B
Muskingum University, B
Ohio Northern University, B
Ohio University, B
Ohio Wesleyan University, B
The University of Akron, B
Youngstown State University, B

Oklahoma

University of Central Oklahoma, B

Pennsylvania

Grove City College, B
Holy Family University, B
Juniata College, B
Lincoln University, B
Messiah College, B
Saint Joseph's University, B
Widener University, B

Rhode Island

Providence College, B
Rhode Island College, B
Salve Regina University, B

South Dakota

The University of South Dakota, B

Tennessee

King University, B
Lee University, B
Lipscomb University, B
Southern Adventist University, B
The University of Tennessee at Martin, B

Texas

Austin College, B

Utah

Southern Utah University, B
Weber State University, B

Virginia

Emory & Henry College, B

Washington

Central Washington University, B
Eastern Washington University, B
Washington State University, B
Western Washington University, B

Wisconsin

Edgewood College, B

Canada

Alberta

University of Alberta, B
University of Lethbridge, B

Maritime Provinces: Nova Scotia

Université Sainte-Anne, B

Ontario

University of Toronto, B
University of Waterloo, B
University of Windsor, B

Quebec

Bishop's University, B
Université Laval, B
Université de Montréal, B

Saskatchewan

University of Regina, B

FRENCH STUDIES

United States

California

Mills College, B

Colorado

The Colorado College, B

Connecticut

Wesleyan University, B

District of Columbia

American University, B

Florida

New College of Florida, B
University of North Florida, B

Georgia

Emory University, B

Illinois

North Park University, B

Iowa

Coe College, B

Maine

Bowdoin College, B

Massachusetts

Bard College at Simon's Rock, B
Smith College, B
Suffolk University, B
Wellesley College, B
Wheaton College, B

Minnesota

Carleton College, B

New Hampshire

University of New Hampshire, B

New York

Bard College, B
Barnard College, B
Columbia University, B
Columbia University, School of General Studies, B
Cornell University, B
Fordham University, B
Skidmore College, B
Wagner College, B

Ohio

Case Western Reserve University, B

Oregon

Lewis & Clark College, B
Linfield College, B

Pennsylvania

Moravian College, B
Saint Joseph's University, B
The University of Scranton, B

Rhode Island

Brown University, B
Rhode Island College, B

Virginia

Emory & Henry College, B

Canada

Alberta

University of Alberta, B

British Columbia

University of Victoria, B

Manitoba

The University of Winnipeg, B

Ontario

Brock University, B
University of Guelph, B
University of Waterloo, B
The University of Western Ontario, B
University of Windsor, B
York University, B

FUNERAL DIRECTION/SERVICE

United States

Michigan

Wayne State University, B

FUNERAL SERVICE AND MORTUARY SCIENCE

United States

Alabama

Bishop State Community College, A
Jefferson State Community College, A

Arkansas

Arkansas State University - Mountain Home, A
University of Arkansas Community College at Hope, A

California

American River College, A
Cypress College, A

Colorado

Arapahoe Community College, A

Connecticut

Lincoln College of New England, AB

District of Columbia

University of the District of Columbia, A

Florida

Florida State College at Jacksonville, A
Miami Dade College, A
St. Petersburg College, A

Georgia

Ogeechee Technical College, A

Illinois

City Colleges of Chicago, Malcolm X College, A
Southern Illinois University Carbondale, B
Worsham College of Mortuary Science, A

Indiana

Ivy Tech Community College - Northwest, A
Mid-America College of Funeral Service, A
Vincennes University, A

Iowa

Des Moines Area Community College, A

Kansas

Barton County Community College, A
Kansas City Kansas Community College, A

Louisiana

Delgado Community College, A

Maryland

Community College of Baltimore County, A

Massachusetts

FINE Mortuary College, LLC, A
Mount Ida College, AB

Michigan

Ferris State University, A
Monroe County Community College, A

Minnesota

University of Minnesota, Twin Cities Campus, B

Mississippi

East Mississippi Community College, A
Holmes Community College, A

New Jersey

Mercer County Community College, A

New York

American Academy McAllister Institute of Funeral
    Service, A
Fiorello H. LaGuardia Community College of the
    City University of New York, A
Hudson Valley Community College, A
Nassau Community College, A
St. John's University, B

North Carolina

Fayetteville Technical Community College, A
Randolph Community College, A

Ohio

Cincinnati College of Mortuary Science, AB

Oklahoma

University of Central Oklahoma, B

Oregon

Mt. Hood Community College, A

Pennsylvania

Gannon University, B
Luzerne County Community College, A
Northampton Community College, A
Pittsburgh Institute of Mortuary Science, Incorpo-
    rated, A
Point Park University, B
Thiel College, B

South Carolina

Piedmont Technical College, A

Tennessee

John A. Gupton College, A

Texas

Amarillo College, A
Commonwealth Institute of Funeral Service, A
Dallas Institute of Funeral Service, A
San Antonio College, A

Virginia

John Tyler Community College, A

Wisconsin

Milwaukee Area Technical College, A

FURNITURE DESIGN AND MANUFACTURING

United States

Rhode Island

Rhode Island School of Design, B

Wisconsin

Northcentral Technical College, A

GAME DESIGN AND DEVELOPMENT

United States

Arizona

University of Advancing Technology, M

California

Academy of Art University, M
Shepherd University, M
University of Southern California, M

Connecticut

Sacred Heart University, M

Florida

Full Sail University, M
University of Central Florida, M

Georgia

Savannah College of Art and Design, MO

Illinois

DePaul University, M

Massachusetts

Worcester Polytechnic Institute, M

Michigan

Michigan State University, M

New York

Long Island University - LIU Post, M
New York University, M
Rochester Institute of Technology, M

North Carolina

The University of North Carolina at Charlotte, O

Utah

University of Utah, M

Virginia

Virginia International University, M

West Virginia

West Virginia University, O

Canada

Quebec

Concordia University, O

GAY/LESBIAN STUDIES

United States

California

Mills College, B

Connecticut

Trinity College, B

Massachusetts

Hampshire College, B

New York

Cornell University, B
Sarah Lawrence College, B

Rhode Island

Bryant University, B

Vermont

Bennington College, B
Marlboro College, B

Canada

Ontario

The University of Western Ontario, B

GENDER STUDIES

United States

Arizona

Arizona State University at the Tempe campus, DO
Northern Arizona University, O
The University of Arizona, MDO

California

California State University, Sacramento, M
Dominican University of California, M
San Diego State University, O
University of California, Los Angeles, MD

Colorado

University of Colorado Denver, M

District of Columbia

American University, O
The George Washington University, O

Florida

University of Central Florida, O
University of Florida, MO
University of South Florida, MO

Illinois

Northwestern University, O
Roosevelt University, MO

Indiana

Indiana University Bloomington, D
Indiana University - Purdue University Indianapolis,
    M

Iowa

University of Northern Iowa, M

Maine

University of Maine, M

Massachusetts

Brandeis University, M

Michigan

Central Michigan University, M
Eastern Michigan University, MO
University of Michigan - Flint, M
Wayne State University, D

Minnesota

Minnesota State University Mankato, MO

Mississippi

Delta State University, M

Missouri

University of Missouri - St. Louis, O

New Jersey

The College of New Jersey, O
Rutgers University - New Brunswick, MD

New York

Cornell University, MD
University at Buffalo, the State University of New York, MD

North Carolina

The University of North Carolina at Charlotte, M
The University of North Carolina at Greensboro, MO

Ohio

The Ohio State University, MD
The University of Toledo, O

Oklahoma

University of Oklahoma, O

Oregon

Oregon State University, M

Pennsylvania

Carnegie Mellon University, D

Tennessee

Middle Tennessee State University, O

Virginia

George Mason University, M

Canada

Alberta

University of Lethbridge, M

British Columbia

Simon Fraser University, MD
The University of British Columbia, MD
University of Northern British Columbia, M

Maritime Provinces: Nova Scotia

Saint Mary's University, M

Newfoundland and Labrador

Memorial University of Newfoundland, D

Ontario

Queen's University at Kingston, D
University of Toronto, MD
Wilfrid Laurier University, M
York University, MD

Saskatchewan

University of Saskatchewan, MD

GENE/GENETIC THERAPY

United States

Connecticut

University of Connecticut, B

GENERAL MERCHANDISING, SALES, AND RELATED MARKETING OPERATIONS

United States

California

Orange Coast College, A

Connecticut

University of Hartford, B

Florida

Northwest Florida State College, A

Georgia

Georgia State University, B

Iowa

Iowa Lakes Community College, A

Michigan

Eastern Michigan University, B

Minnesota

Minnesota State Community and Technical College, A

Missouri

Lincoln University, B
Washington University in St. Louis, B

New York

Broome Community College, A
Herkimer County Community College, A
Orange County Community College, A
State University of New York College of Technology at Delhi, A

North Dakota

Lake Region State College, A

South Dakota

Southeast Technical Institute, A

Virginia

Virginia Union University, B

Wisconsin

Northcentral Technical College, A

U.S. Territories: Puerto Rico

American University of Puerto Rico (Bayamon), A
Inter American University of Puerto Rico, Aguadilla Campus, A
Inter American University of Puerto Rico, Ponce Campus, A

Canada

Maritime Provinces: Nova Scotia

Dalhousie University, B

GENERAL OFFICE OCCUPATIONS AND CLERICAL SERVICES

United States

Alaska

Charter College, A

California

Modesto Junior College, A
Reedley College, A
San Joaquin Valley College (Fresno), A
San Joaquin Valley College (Hanford), A
San Joaquin Valley College (Hesperia), A
San Joaquin Valley College (Lancaster), A
San Joaquin Valley College (Ontario), A
San Joaquin Valley College (Salida), A
San Joaquin Valley College (Temecula), A
San Joaquin Valley College - Online, A

Colorado

IBMC College (Fort Collins), A

Iowa

Iowa Lakes Community College, A

Kansas

Cloud County Community College, A
Wichita Area Technical College, A

Kentucky

Gateway Community and Technical College, A

Louisiana

Fletcher Technical Community College, A
ITI Technical College, A

Massachusetts

Massasoit Community College, A
Middlesex Community College, A

Missouri

Jefferson College, A

Montana

Helena College University of Montana, A

Nebraska

Northeast Community College, A
Southeast Community College, Beatrice Campus, A

Nevada

Everest College, A
Great Basin College, A

New Mexico

Clovis Community College, A
Mesalands Community College, A
New Mexico State University - Alamogordo, A
New Mexico State University - Carlsbad, A
New Mexico State University - Grants, A

New York

Corning Community College, A
Jefferson Community College, A
Morrisville State College, A
North Country Community College, A

North Carolina

Alamance Community College, A
Caldwell Community College and Technical Institute, A

North Dakota

Dakota College at Bottineau, A
Sitting Bull College, A
United Tribes Technical College, A

Ohio

Ohio University - Southern Campus, A

Oklahoma

East Central University, B
Oklahoma State University Institute of Technology, A

Pennsylvania

Butler County Community College, A
Laurel Business Institute, A

South Carolina

Bob Jones University, A
York Technical College, A

South Dakota

Sinte Gleska University, A
Southeast Technical Institute, A

Texas

Alvin Community College, A
Del Mar College, A
El Centro College, A
Lone Star College - CyFair, A
Midland College, A
Texas Southmost College, A

Washington

Bellevue College, A
Pierce College at Fort Steilacoom, A

Spokane Falls Community College, A

West Virginia

BridgeValley Community and Technical College (South Charleston), A

U.S. Territories: American Samoa

American Samoa Community College, A

U.S. Territories: Puerto Rico

American University of Puerto Rico (Bayamon), A
ICPR Junior College - Hato Rey Campus, A
Pontifical Catholic University of Puerto Rico, A
University of Puerto Rico in Aguadilla, A
University of Puerto Rico in Cayey, A

GENERAL STUDIES

United States

Alabama

Bevill State Community College, A
Bishop State Community College, A
Calhoun Community College, A
Chattahoochee Valley Community College, A
Columbia Southern University, A
Concordia College Alabama, A
Enterprise State Community College, A
Gadsden State Community College, A
George Corley Wallace State Community College, A
James H. Faulkner State Community College, A
Jefferson Davis Community College, A
Jefferson State Community College, A
Lawson State Community College, A
Lurleen B. Wallace Community College, A
Marion Military Institute, A
Northwest-Shoals Community College, A
Samford University, B
Selma University, B
Shelton State Community College, A
Snead State Community College, A
Southern Union State Community College, A
Spring Hill College, B
Stillman College, B
University of Mobile, AB

Alaska

University of Alaska Southeast, AB
University of Alaska Southeast, Sitka Campus, A

Arizona

Arizona Western College, A
Central Arizona College, A
Chandler-Gilbert Community College, A
Cochise County Community College District, A
Coconino Community College, A
Estrella Mountain Community College, A
GateWay Community College, A
Grand Canyon University, B
Northland Pioneer College, A
Paradise Valley Community College, A
Phoenix College, A
Pima Community College, A
South Mountain Community College, A
University of Phoenix - Online Campus, B

Arkansas

Arkansas Northeastern College, A
Arkansas State University, AB
Arkansas State University - Beebe, A
Arkansas State University - Newport, A
Arkansas Tech University, A
Central Baptist College, A
Cossatot Community College of the University of Arkansas, A
Crowley's Ridge College, A
Harding University, B
Henderson State University, B
John Brown University, AB
North Arkansas College, A
Ouachita Baptist University, A
Rich Mountain Community College, A
South Arkansas Community College, A

Southeast Arkansas College, A
Southern Arkansas University - Magnolia, AB
Southern Arkansas University, A
Southern Arkansas University Tech, A
University of Arkansas Community College at Hope, A
University of Arkansas Community College at Morrilton, A
University of Arkansas - Fort Smith, AB
University of Arkansas at Little Rock, A
University of Arkansas at Monticello, A
University of Central Arkansas, A
University of the Ozarks, B

California

Ashford University, B
Berkeley City College, A
Brandman University, A
California Christian College, A
California Coast University, AB
California State University, San Bernardino, B
California State University, San Marcos, B
Cuyamaca College, A
Gavilan College, A
Hope International University, A
Modesto Junior College, A
National University, AB
Pacific Union College, AB
Pepperdine University, B
Reedley College, A
San Diego State University, B
Sierra College, A
Simpson University, A
Southwestern College, A
Taft College, A
United States University, B
University of the West, B

Colorado

Arapahoe Community College, A
Colorado Christian University, AB
Colorado Mountain College (Leadville), A
Colorado Northwestern Community College, A
Colorado Technical University Colorado Springs, A
Colorado Technical University Online, A
Community College of Aurora, A
Community College of Denver, A
Fort Lewis College, B
Front Range Community College, A
Morgan Community College, A
Pikes Peak Community College, A
Pueblo Community College, A
Red Rocks Community College, A
Trinidad State Junior College, A

Connecticut

Albertus Magnus College, B
Asnuntuck Community College, A
Capital Community College, A
Eastern Connecticut State University, AB
Fairfield University, B
Manchester Community College, A
Naugatuck Valley Community College, A
Norwalk Community College, A
Sacred Heart University, AB
St. Vincent's College, A
Three Rivers Community College, A
University of Bridgeport, AB
University of Connecticut, B
University of Hartford, AB

Delaware

University of Delaware, B
Wilmington University, AB

District of Columbia

The Catholic University of America, B

Florida

Adventist University of Health Sciences, A
Florida Institute of Technology, B
Jacksonville University, B
Miami Dade College, A
New College of Florida, B
Nova Southeastern University, B
Palm Beach Atlantic University, B

South Florida State College, A
Trinity College of Florida, AB
University of Central Florida, B
University of Miami, B
University of South Florida, B
University of South Florida Sarasota-Manatee, AB
Warner University, A

Georgia

Brenau University, B
Brewton-Parker College, AB
Dalton State College, A
Darton State College, A
Georgia Highlands College, A
Georgia Military College, A
Georgia Southern University, B
Gordon State College, A
LaGrange College, B
Point University, A
Savannah State University, B
Shorter University, B
South Georgia State College, A
Toccoa Falls College, AB
University of North Georgia, B
University of Phoenix - Augusta Campus, A

Hawaii

Chaminade University of Honolulu, A
Hawai'i Pacific University, A

Idaho

Boise State University, B
Idaho State University, AB
University of Idaho, B

Illinois

Black Hawk College, A
Chicago State University, B
City Colleges of Chicago, Harold Washington College, A
City Colleges of Chicago, Harry S. Truman College, A
City Colleges of Chicago, Kennedy-King College, A
City Colleges of Chicago, Malcolm X College, A
City Colleges of Chicago, Olive-Harvey College, A
City Colleges of Chicago, Wilbur Wright College, A
Danville Area Community College, A
DePaul University, B
Highland Community College, A
Illinois Central College, A
Illinois Eastern Community Colleges, Frontier Community College, A
Illinois Eastern Community Colleges, Lincoln Trail College, A
Illinois Eastern Community Colleges, Olney Central College, A
Illinois Eastern Community Colleges, Wabash Valley College, A
Illinois State University, B
Illinois Valley Community College, A
John Wood Community College, A
Joliet Junior College, A
Kankakee Community College, A
Kaskaskia College, A
Lake Land College, A
Lewis and Clark Community College, A
Lewis University, B
Lincoln Christian University, AB
Lincoln College, A
Lincoln Land Community College, A
Loyola University Chicago, B
McHenry County College, A
Northwestern University, B
Parkland College, A
Prairie State College, A
Quincy University, B
St. Augustine College, A
Shimer College, B
Southwestern Illinois College, A
Spoon River College, A
University of Illinois at Urbana - Champaign, B
Waubonsee Community College, A

Indiana

Ancilla College, A
Ball State University, AB
Bethel College, AB
Calumet College of Saint Joseph, AB
Indiana Tech, A
Indiana University - Purdue University Fort Wayne, B
Indiana University South Bend, AB
Indiana Wesleyan University, AB
Ivy Tech Community College - Bloomington, A
Ivy Tech Community College - Central Indiana, A
Ivy Tech Community College - Columbus, A
Ivy Tech Community College - East Central, A
Ivy Tech Community College - Kokomo, A
Ivy Tech Community College - Lafayette, A
Ivy Tech Community College - North Central, A
Ivy Tech Community College - Northwest, A
Ivy Tech Community College - Richmond, A
Ivy Tech Community College - Southeast, A
Ivy Tech Community College - Southern Indiana, A
Ivy Tech Community College - Southwest, A
Ivy Tech Community College - Wabash Valley, A
Oakland City University, AB
University of Saint Francis, A

Iowa

Dordt College, B
Iowa Lakes Community College, A

Kansas

Allen Community College, A
Barclay College, A
Barton County Community College, A
Emporia State University, B
Fort Hays State University, AB
Friends University, A
Garden City Community College, A
Grantham University, AB
Hesston College, A
Kansas Wesleyan University, B
Seward County Community College and Area Technical School, A
Southwestern College, AB
Tabor College, B
Wichita State University, B

Kentucky

Asbury University, A
Eastern Kentucky University, AB
Gateway Community and Technical College, A
Kentucky Wesleyan College, B
Maysville Community and Technical College (Morehead), A
Morehead State University, AB
Murray State University, B
Northern Kentucky University, AB
Spalding University, B
University of the Cumberlands, B
University of Kentucky, B
Western Kentucky University, AB

Louisiana

Baton Rouge Community College, A
Bossier Parish Community College, A
Delgado Community College, A
Fletcher Technical Community College, A
Louisiana Delta Community College, A
Louisiana State University at Eunice, A
Louisiana State University in Shreveport, B
Louisiana Tech University, AB
McNeese State University, AB
Nicholls State University, AB
Northwestern State University of Louisiana, AB
Nunez Community College, A
Our Lady of the Lake College, A
River Parishes Community College, A
South Louisiana Community College, A
Southeastern Louisiana University, B
Southern University at New Orleans, B
Southern University at Shreveport, A
Sowela Technical Community College, A
University of Holy Cross, B
University of Louisiana at Lafayette, B
University of Louisiana at Monroe, AB

Maine

Northern Maine Community College, A
Saint Joseph's College of Maine, B
Thomas College, B
University of Maine at Fort Kent, A
University of Maine at Machias, B

Maryland

Baltimore City Community College, A
Carroll Community College, A
Cecil College, A
Chesapeake College, A
Frederick Community College, A
Harford Community College, A
Howard Community College, A

Massachusetts

Anna Maria College, B
Bristol Community College, A
Bunker Hill Community College, A
Dean College, AB
Eastern Nazarene College, B
Fisher College, A
Lasell College, B
Massachusetts Bay Community College, A
Middlesex Community College, A
Mount Wachusett Community College, A
Newbury College, A
Northern Essex Community College, A
Quincy College, A
Quinsigamond Community College, A
Roxbury Community College, A
Salem State University, B
Springfield College, B
University of Massachusetts Amherst, B
Wheelock College, B

Michigan

Alpena Community College, A
Aquinas College, B
Bay Mills Community College, A
Bay de Noc Community College, A
Concordia University Ann Arbor, A
Cornerstone University, B
Delta College, A
Ferris State University, A
Finlandia University, A
Glen Oaks Community College, A
Great Lakes Christian College, A
Henry Ford College, A
Jackson College, A
Kalamazoo Valley Community College, A
Kellogg Community College, A
Kirtland Community College, A
Lake Michigan College, A
Lawrence Technological University, A
Macomb Community College, A
Madonna University, B
Marygrove College, B
Mid Michigan Community College, A
Montcalm Community College, A
Mott Community College, A
North Central Michigan College, A
Northern Michigan University, A
Oakland Community College, A
Saginaw Valley State University, B
Schoolcraft College, A
Siena Heights University, AB
Southwestern Michigan College, A
University of Michigan, B
University of Michigan - Dearborn, B
Washtenaw Community College, A

Minnesota

Concordia University, St. Paul, AB
Crown College, B
Itasca Community College, A
Oak Hills Christian College, A
Rochester Community and Technical College, A
Southwest Minnesota State University, B

Mississippi

Belhaven University, A
Coahoma Community College, A
Delta State University, B

Hinds Community College, A
Holmes Community College, A
University of Mississippi, A
William Carey University, B

Missouri

Columbia College, AB
Crowder College, A
East Central College, A
Lindenwood University, B
Mineral Area College, A
Missouri Baptist University, B
Missouri State University - West Plains, A
National American University (Kansas City), A
St. Charles Community College, A
Saint Louis University, B
Southeast Missouri State University, B
Southwest Baptist University, A
University of Missouri, B
University of Missouri - Kansas City, B

Montana

Blackfeet Community College, A
Fort Peck Community College, A
Helena College University of Montana, A
Montana State University Billings, A
Montana Tech of The University of Montana, B

Nebraska

Northeast Community College, A
Union College, B
University of Nebraska at Kearney, B
University of Nebraska at Omaha, B
Western Nebraska Community College, A
York College, B

Nevada

Great Basin College, A
Truckee Meadows Community College, A
University of Nevada, Reno, B
Western Nevada College, A

New Hampshire

Granite State College, AB
Great Bay Community College, A
Keene State College, B
Lakes Region Community College, A
Nashua Community College, A
NHTI, Concord's Community College, A
River Valley Community College, A
Southern New Hampshire University, B
White Mountains Community College, A

New Jersey

Fairleigh Dickinson University, College at Florham, B
Fairleigh Dickinson University, Metropolitan Campus, B
Monmouth University, A
New Jersey Institute of Technology, B
Ocean County College, A
Rider University, A
University of Phoenix - Jersey City Campus, A

New Mexico

Central New Mexico Community College, A
Clovis Community College, A
Eastern New Mexico University, B
Eastern New Mexico University - Roswell, A
Luna Community College, A
National American University (Albuquerque), A
New Mexico Institute of Mining and Technology, AB
New Mexico State University, B
New Mexico State University - Alamogordo, A
New Mexico State University - Carlsbad, A
St. John's College, B
San Juan College, A
Santa Fe Community College, A
University of New Mexico, B
University of New Mexico - Gallup, AB
University of New Mexico - Los Alamos Branch, A
University of New Mexico - Taos, A
University of the Southwest, B

New York

Alfred University, B
Borough of Manhattan Community College of the City University of New York, A
Buffalo State College, State University of New York, B
Cayuga County Community College, A
The College of Saint Rose, B
Columbia-Greene Community College, A
Cornell University, B
Dutchess Community College, A
Erie Community College, A
Erie Community College, North Campus, A
Erie Community College, South Campus, A
Eugene Lang College of Liberal Arts, B
Genesee Community College, A
Herkimer County Community College, A
Jamestown Community College, A
Medaille College, AB
Mohawk Valley Community College, A
Molloy College, B
Morrisville State College, A
Nassau Community College, A
Niagara County Community College, A
Onondaga Community College, A
Pace University, A
Pace University, Pleasantville Campus, A
Queensborough Community College of the City University of New York, A
Roberts Wesleyan College, B
St. Lawrence University, B
State University of New York College of Technology at Alfred, AB
State University of New York College of Technology at Canton, A
State University of New York College of Technology at Delhi, A
State University of New York Maritime College, B
State University of New York at New Paltz, B
State University of New York Polytechnic Institute, B
Trocaire College, A

North Carolina

Asheville-Buncombe Technical Community College, A
Bladen Community College, A
Blue Ridge Community College, A
Brunswick Community College, A
Cabarrus College of Health Sciences, A
Campbell University, B
Catawba Valley Community College, A
Cleveland Community College, A
Craven Community College, A
East Carolina University, B
Fayetteville Technical Community College, A
Forsyth Technical Community College, A
Gaston College, A
Guilford Technical Community College, A
James Sprunt Community College, A
Martin Community College, A
Mayland Community College, A
McDowell Technical Community College, A
Mitchell Community College, A
Nash Community College, A
Piedmont Community College, A
Pitt Community College, A
Roanoke-Chowan Community College, A
Rockingham Community College, A
Rowan-Cabarrus Community College, A
South Piedmont Community College, A
Wake Technical Community College, A
Warren Wilson College, B
Wilson Community College, A
Winston-Salem State University, B

North Dakota

Dakota College at Bottineau, A
Mayville State University, B
Minot State University, B
Trinity Bible College, B
University of Mary, B
University of North Dakota, B

Ohio

Antioch University Midwest, B
Belmont College, A
Cincinnati State Technical and Community College, A
Franciscan University of Steubenville, A
God's Bible School and College, A
Kent State University, B
Kent State University at Ashtabula, B
Kent State University at East Liverpool, B
Kent State University at Geauga, B
Kent State University at Salem, B
Kent State University at Stark, B
Kent State University at Trumbull, B
Kent State University at Tuscarawas, B
Kettering College, A
Mercy College of Ohio, A
Miami University, A
Miami University Hamilton, A
Mount St. Joseph University, AB
Mount Vernon Nazarene University, A
Ohio Dominican University, AB
Ohio Northern University, B
The Ohio State University, AB
The Ohio State University at Lima, A
The Ohio State University - Mansfield Campus, A
The Ohio State University at Marion, A
The Ohio State University - Newark Campus, A
Ohio Wesleyan University, B
Owens Community College, A
Shawnee State University, AB
Terra State Community College, A
Tiffin University, AB
The University of Akron Wayne College, A
University of Cincinnati Blue Ash College, A
University of Cincinnati Clermont College, A
University of Rio Grande, A
The University of Toledo, AB
Youngstown State University, B

Oklahoma

Bacone College, A
Cameron University, AB
East Central University, B
Hillsdale Free Will Baptist College, A
Murray State College, A
Northeastern Oklahoma Agricultural and Mechanical College, A
Northeastern State University, B
Northwestern Oklahoma State University, B
Oklahoma City Community College, A
Oklahoma Panhandle State University, A
Oklahoma State University, B
Oklahoma State University, Oklahoma City, A
Oklahoma Wesleyan University, AB
Seminole State College, A
Southeastern Oklahoma State University, B
Southern Nazarene University, A
Southwestern Christian University, A
Southwestern Oklahoma State University, A
Southwestern Oklahoma State University at Sayre, A
Tulsa Community College, A
University of Central Oklahoma, B

Oregon

Blue Mountain Community College, A
Chemeketa Community College, A
Clackamas Community College, A
Columbia Gorge Community College, A
Klamath Community College, A
Lane Community College, A
Northwest Christian University, A
Oregon Coast Community College, A
Portland Community College, A
Rogue Community College, A
Tillamook Bay Community College, A

Pennsylvania

Butler County Community College, A
Community College of Allegheny County, A
Community College of Beaver County, A
Delaware County Community College, A
Drexel University, B
Harcum College, A

Harrisburg Area Community College, A
Holy Family University, A
Kutztown University of Pennsylvania, B
La Roche College, B
La Salle University, AB
Lackawanna College, A
Lehigh Carbon Community College, A
Luzerne County Community College, A
Marywood University, B
Misericordia University, B
Mount Aloysius College, A
Northampton Community College, A
Peirce College, A
Pennsylvania Highlands Community College, A
Pennsylvania Institute of Technology, A
Reading Area Community College, A
Seton Hill University, B
Summit University, A
Temple University, AB
Ursinus College, B
Widener University, AB
York College of Pennsylvania, AB

Rhode Island

Community College of Rhode Island, A

South Carolina

Columbia International University, B
North Greenville University, B
Southern Wesleyan University, A

South Dakota

Black Hills State University, A
Dakota State University, A
Mount Marty College, AB
Presentation College, A
Sinte Gleska University, A
South Dakota School of Mines and Technology, A
South Dakota State University, AB

Tennessee

American Baptist College, A
Austin Peay State University, AB
Chattanooga State Community College, A
Christian Brothers University, A
Cleveland State Community College, A
Columbia State Community College, A
Dyersburg State Community College, A
East Tennessee State University, B
Jackson State Community College, A
Lee University, B
Lipscomb University, AB
Motlow State Community College, A
Northeast State Community College, A
Pellissippi State Community College, A
Roane State Community College, A
Southwest Tennessee Community College, A
Trevecca Nazarene University, A
University of Memphis, B
The University of Tennessee at Martin, B
Volunteer State Community College, A
Walters State Community College, A

Texas

Alvin Community College, A
Amarillo College, A
Angelina College, A
Austin College, B
Austin Community College District, A
Brookhaven College, A
Cedar Valley College, A
Central Texas College, A
Clarendon College, A
College of the Mainland, A
Concordia University Texas, A
El Paso Community College, A
Frank Phillips College, A
Galveston College, A
Hill College, A
Houston Community College, A
Howard College, A
Howard Payne University, B
Jarvis Christian College, A
Kilgore College, A
Lamar State College - Port Arthur, A

Lamar University, B
Messenger College, A
Midland College, A
Panola College, A
Paris Junior College, A
Sam Houston State University, B
San Jacinto College District, A
Southwestern Adventist University, AB
Southwestern Assemblies of God University, A
Texas A&M University - Commerce, B
Texas A&M University - Texarkana, B
Texas Christian University, B
Texas College, A
Texas Southern University, B
Texas State University, B
Texas Tech University, B
Texas Woman's University, B
Tyler Junior College, A
University of Mary Hardin-Baylor, B
University of North Texas, B
University of Phoenix - Houston Campus, B
University of St. Thomas, B
The University of Texas at Arlington, B
The University of Texas Rio Grande Valley, B
The University of Texas at San Antonio, B
The University of Texas at Tyler, B
Victoria College, A
Wayland Baptist University, A
West Texas A&M University, B

Utah

Dixie State University, A
Salt Lake Community College, A
Southern Utah University, AB
Utah State University, A
Utah Valley University, A
Weber State University, A

Vermont

Castleton University, A
Champlain College, B
Johnson State College, A
Landmark College, A

Virginia

Eastern Mennonite University, A
Emory & Henry College, B
George Mason University, B
Germanna Community College, A
Hampton University, AB
John Tyler Community College, A
Liberty University, AB
New River Community College, A
Northern Virginia Community College, A
Regent University, A
Shenandoah University, B
Southside Virginia Community College, A
Thomas Nelson Community College, A
University of Management and Technology, AB
University of Valley Forge Virginia Campus, A

Washington

City University of Seattle, AB
Grays Harbor College, A
Northwest University, AB
Seattle Pacific University, B
University of Washington, B
University of Washington, Bothell, B
University of Washington, Tacoma, B
Western Washington University, B

West Virginia

Alderson Broaddus University, A
American Public University System, AB
Blue Ridge Community and Technical College, A
Bluefield State College, B
BridgeValley Community and Technical College (South Charleston), A
Eastern West Virginia Community and Technical College, A
Marshall University, B
Mountwest Community & Technical College, A
Pierpont Community & Technical College, A
Shepherd University, B
University of Charleston, B

West Virginia Northern Community College, A
West Virginia State University, B
West Virginia University, B
West Virginia University Institute of Technology, B
Wheeling Jesuit University, B

Wisconsin

Alverno College, A
Cardinal Stritch University, AM
Concordia University Wisconsin, B
Mount Mary University, B
Northcentral Technical College, A
University of Wisconsin - Stevens Point, B
University of Wisconsin - Superior, A
Viterbo University, A

Wyoming

Casper College, A
Central Wyoming College, A
Eastern Wyoming College, A
Laramie County Community College, A
Northwest College, A
Sheridan College, A
Western Wyoming Community College, A

Canada

Alberta

Ambrose University, B
Athabasca University, B
University of Alberta, B
University of Lethbridge, B

British Columbia

Simon Fraser University, B
Thompson Rivers University, AB
Trinity Western University, B
The University of British Columbia - Okanagan Campus, B
University of the Fraser Valley, AB
University of Northern British Columbia, B

Manitoba

Booth University College, B
Brandon University, B

Maritime Provinces: New Brunswick

Kingswood University, B

Ontario

Lakehead University, B
Ryerson University, B

GENETIC COUNSELING/COUN-SELOR

United States

Alabama

The University of Alabama at Birmingham, M

Arkansas

University of Arkansas for Medical Sciences, M

California

California State University, Stanislaus, M
University of California, Irvine, M

Colorado

University of Colorado Denver, MD

Georgia

Emory University, M

Illinois

Northwestern University, M

Maryland

Johns Hopkins University, M

Massachusetts

Boston University, M
Brandeis University, M

Michigan

University of Michigan, M
Wayne State University, M

Minnesota

University of Minnesota, Twin Cities Campus, M

New York

Sarah Lawrence College, M

North Carolina

The University of North Carolina at Greensboro, M

Ohio

Case Western Reserve University, M
University of Cincinnati, M

Oklahoma

University of Oklahoma Health Sciences Center, M

Pennsylvania

Arcadia University, M
University of Pittsburgh, M

South Carolina

University of South Carolina, M

Texas

The University of Texas Health Science Center at Houston, M

Wisconsin

University of Wisconsin - Madison, MD

Canada

British Columbia

The University of British Columbia, M

Ontario

University of Toronto, M

Quebec

McGill University, M
Université de Montréal, O

GENETICS

United States

Alabama

The University of Alabama at Birmingham, D

Arizona

The University of Arizona, MD

California

California Institute of Technology, D
Stanford University, D
University of California, Davis, BMD
University of California, Irvine, BD
University of California, Riverside, D

Colorado

University of Colorado Boulder, D
University of Colorado Denver, MD

Connecticut

University of Connecticut, MD
Wesleyan University, D
Yale University, D

Delaware

University of Delaware, MD

District of Columbia

The George Washington University, B

Florida

University of Florida, D
University of Miami, MD

Georgia

Emory University, D
University of Georgia, BMD

Hawaii

University of Hawaii at Manoa, MD

Illinois

Illinois State University, MD
University of Chicago, D
University of Illinois at Chicago, D

Indiana

Indiana University Bloomington, D
Purdue University, BMD
University of Notre Dame, MD

Iowa

Iowa State University of Science and Technology,
    BMD
The University of Iowa, MD

Kansas

Kansas State University, MD

Maryland

Johns Hopkins University, MD

Massachusetts

Boston University, D
Brandeis University, D
Harvard University, D
Massachusetts Institute of Technology, D
Tufts University, D
University of Massachusetts Amherst, MD

Michigan

Michigan State University, MD
Wayne State University, D

Minnesota

University of Minnesota, Twin Cities Campus, MD

Mississippi

Mississippi State University, MD

Missouri

University of Missouri, MD
Washington University in St. Louis, MD

Nebraska

University of Nebraska Medical Center, MD

New Hampshire

Dartmouth College, D
University of New Hampshire, BMD

New Jersey

Rutgers University - New Brunswick, MD

New Mexico

New Mexico State University, B
University of New Mexico, MD

New York

Columbia University, MD
Cornell University, D
New York University, M
Stony Brook University, State University of New
    York, D
University at Buffalo, the State University of New
    York, MD
University of Rochester, D

North Carolina

Duke University, D
North Carolina State University, BMD
The University of North Carolina at Chapel Hill, MD

North Dakota

University of North Dakota, MD

Ohio

Case Western Reserve University, D
Kent State University, D
The Ohio State University, MD
Ohio Wesleyan University, B

Oregon

Oregon Health & Science University, D
University of Oregon, D

Pennsylvania

Carnegie Mellon University, D
Cedar Crest College, B
Drexel University, MD
Thomas Jefferson University, D
University of Pennsylvania, D

South Carolina

Clemson University, D
Medical University of South Carolina, D

Tennessee

The University of Tennessee, MD

Texas

The University of Texas Health Science Center at
    Houston, MD
The University of Texas Medical Branch, D

Virginia

Virginia Commonwealth University, MD
Virginia Polytechnic Institute and State University, D

Washington

University of Washington, MD
Washington State University, B

West Virginia

West Virginia University, MD

Wisconsin

Marquette University, MD
University of Wisconsin - Madison, BMD

Wyoming

University of Wyoming, D

U.S. Territories: Puerto Rico

University of Puerto Rico, Río Piedras Campus, MD

Canada

Alberta

University of Alberta, MD
University of Calgary, MD

British Columbia

Thompson Rivers University, B
The University of British Columbia, MD

Ontario

McMaster University, MD
The University of Western Ontario, B

Quebec

McGill University, B
Université de Montréal, O
Université du Québec à Chicoutimi, M

GENOMIC SCIENCES

United States

Alabama

The University of Alabama at Birmingham, D

California

University of California, Riverside, D
University of Southern California, D

Connecticut

University of Connecticut, M
Yale University, D

Georgia

Augusta University, MD
University of Georgia, MD

Illinois

University of Chicago, D

Indiana

Purdue University, D

Maryland

University of Maryland, College Park, D

Massachusetts

Boston University, D
Harvard University, D
Massachusetts Institute of Technology, D

Missouri

Washington University in St. Louis, M

New York

Cornell University, D
New York University, D
University at Buffalo, the State University of New
    York, MD
University of Rochester, D

North Carolina

Duke University, D
North Carolina State University, MD
Wake Forest University, D

North Dakota

North Dakota State University, MD

Ohio

Case Western Reserve University, D
University of Cincinnati, MD
The University of Toledo, M

Pennsylvania

Thomas Jefferson University, D
University of Pennsylvania, D

South Dakota

Black Hills State University, M

Tennessee

The University of Tennessee, MD

Washington

University of Washington, D

West Virginia

West Virginia University, MD

Canada

Quebec

Concordia University, O

GEOCHEMISTRY

United States

California

California Institute of Technology, BMD
California State University, Fullerton, M
University of California, Los Angeles, MD

Colorado

Colorado School of Mines, MD

Connecticut

Yale University, D

Georgia

Georgia State University, D

Hawaii

University of Hawaii at Manoa, MD

Illinois

University of Chicago, D

Indiana

Indiana University Bloomington, MD

Massachusetts

Bridgewater State University, B
Massachusetts Institute of Technology, D

Michigan

Grand Valley State University, B
Western Michigan University, B

Missouri

Missouri University of Science and Technology, MD
Washington University in St. Louis, B

Montana

Montana Tech of The University of Montana, M

Nevada

University of Nevada, Reno, MD

New Mexico

New Mexico Institute of Mining and Technology, MD

New York

Columbia University, B
Cornell University, MD
State University of New York College at Cortland, B
State University of New York College at Geneseo, B
State University of New York at Fredonia, B
State University of New York at New Paltz, B
State University of New York at Oswego, B

Ohio

Bowling Green State University, B
Ohio University, M

Rhode Island

Brown University, B

Texas

The University of Texas at Dallas, MD

Virginia

George Mason University, M

Washington

Whitman College, B

Wisconsin

University of Wisconsin - Milwaukee, D

Canada

Maritime Provinces: New Brunswick

University of New Brunswick Fredericton, B

Ontario

McMaster University, D
University of Waterloo, B

GEODETIC SCIENCES

United States

Ohio

The Ohio State University, MD

Canada

Maritime Provinces: New Brunswick

University of New Brunswick Fredericton, MD

Quebec

Université Laval, MD

GEOGRAPHIC INFORMATION SYSTEMS

United States

Alabama

The University of Alabama, M
University of North Alabama, M

Alaska

University of Alaska Fairbanks, MD

Arizona

Arizona State University at the Tempe campus, MO
Northern Arizona University, MO
The University of Arizona, MO

Arkansas

University of Central Arkansas, MO

California

San Jose State University, O
University of Redlands, M
University of Southern California, MO

Colorado

University of Colorado Denver, M
University of Denver, MO

Connecticut

University of Connecticut, O
University of New Haven, MO

Delaware

Wilmington University, M

Florida

Florida State University, M
University of Florida, MD
University of South Florida, MO

Georgia

Georgia Institute of Technology, M
Georgia State University, O
University of West Georgia, O

Idaho

Idaho State University, M

Illinois

Chicago State University, M
Eastern Illinois University, M
Elmhurst College, M
Western Illinois University, O

Indiana

Indiana University - Purdue University Indianapolis, MO

Iowa

The University of Iowa, MDO

Kentucky

Northern Kentucky University, O

Maine

University of Maine, MDO

Maryland

Johns Hopkins University, MO
Salisbury University, M
University of Maryland, Baltimore County, MO

Massachusetts

Boston University, M
Clark University, M
Northeastern University, M

Michigan

Central Michigan University, M
Eastern Michigan University, MO
Michigan Technological University, M
Western Michigan University, O

Minnesota

Minnesota State University Mankato, O
Saint Mary's University of Minnesota, MO
University of Minnesota, Twin Cities Campus, MD

Missouri

Northwest Missouri State University, MO
Saint Louis University, O
University of Missouri, O

Nebraska

University of Nebraska at Omaha, O

New Hampshire

University of New Hampshire, O

New Jersey

Montclair State University, O

New York

State University of New York College of Environmental Science and Forestry, MD
Stony Brook University, State University of New York, O
University at Buffalo, the State University of New York, M

North Carolina

Appalachian State University, M
East Carolina University, O
Elizabeth City State University, M
North Carolina State University, M
The University of North Carolina at Charlotte, M
The University of North Carolina at Greensboro, O

Ohio

Cleveland State University, MO
The University of Toledo, O

Pennsylvania

Indiana University of Pennsylvania, MO
Millersville University of Pennsylvania, M
University of Pennsylvania, MO
University of Pittsburgh, M
West Chester University of Pennsylvania, O

Tennessee

University of Memphis, O

Texas

Sam Houston State University, MO
Texas State University, MD
The University of Texas at Dallas, MD

Utah

University of Utah, M

Virginia

The College of William and Mary, D
George Mason University, MD
Virginia Commonwealth University, O
Virginia Polytechnic Institute and State University, D

West Virginia

West Virginia University, MD

Wisconsin

University of Wisconsin - Madison, MO
University of Wisconsin - Milwaukee, O

Canada

Alberta

University of Lethbridge, M

Maritime Provinces: Nova Scotia

Acadia University, M

Quebec

Université Laval, M
Université du Québec à Montréal, O

GEOGRAPHY

United States

Alabama

Auburn University, BM
Jacksonville State University, B
Samford University, B
The University of Alabama, BM
University of North Alabama, B
University of South Alabama, B

Alaska

University of Alaska Fairbanks, B

Arizona

Arizona State University at the Tempe campus, BMDO
Northern Arizona University, BMO
The University of Arizona, BMDO

Arkansas

Arkansas Tech University, B
University of Arkansas, BM
University of Central Arkansas, BMO

California

American River College, A
Antelope Valley College, A
Bakersfield College, A
Cabrillo College, A
California State Polytechnic University, Pomona, B
California State University, Chico, B
California State University, Dominguez Hills, B
California State University, East Bay, BM
California State University, Fresno, B
California State University, Fullerton, BM
California State University, Long Beach, BM
California State University, Los Angeles, BM
California State University, Northridge, BM
California State University, Sacramento, B
California State University, San Bernardino, B
California State University, Stanislaus, B
Cañada College, A
Cerritos College, A
Chabot College, A
Chaffey College, A
College of Alameda, A
College of the Canyons, A
College of the Desert, A
College of Marin, A
Columbia College, A
Contra Costa College, A
Cosumnes River College, A
Crafton Hills College, A
Diablo Valley College, A

East Los Angeles College, A
El Camino College, A
Foothill College, A
Fullerton College, A
Grossmont College, A
Humboldt State University, B
Lake Tahoe Community College, A
Los Angeles Mission College, A
Los Angeles Valley College, A
Mt. San Jacinto College, A
Ohlone College, A
Orange Coast College, A
Palomar College, A
Saddleback College, A
San Bernardino Valley College, A
San Diego Mesa College, A
San Diego Miramar College, A
San Diego State University, BMD
San Francisco State University, BM
San Jose State University, BMO
Santa Ana College, A
Santa Barbara City College, A
Santiago Canyon College, A
Sonoma State University, B
Southwestern College, A
University of California, Berkeley, BD
University of California, Davis, MD
University of California, Los Angeles, BMD
University of California, Santa Barbara, BMD
University of Redlands, A
University of Southern California, BMO
West Hills Community College, A
West Los Angeles College, A

Colorado

Adams State University, B
Northeastern Junior College, A
United States Air Force Academy, B
University of Colorado Boulder, BMD
University of Colorado Colorado Springs, BM
University of Colorado Denver, B
University of Denver, BMD
University of Northern Colorado, B

Connecticut

Central Connecticut State University, BM
Southern Connecticut State University, B
University of Connecticut, BMD

Delaware

University of Delaware, BMD

District of Columbia

The George Washington University, BMO

Florida

Broward College, A
Florida Atlantic University, BM
Florida International University, B
Florida State University, BMD
Jacksonville University, B
South Florida State College, A
Stetson University, B
University of Florida, BMD
University of Miami, BM
University of South Florida, BDO

Georgia

Darton State College, A
Georgia College & State University, B
Georgia Southern University, B
Georgia State University, M
Kennesaw State University, B
University of Georgia, BMD
University of West Georgia, B

Hawaii

University of Hawaii at Hilo, B
University of Hawaii at Manoa, BMDO

Idaho

College of Southern Idaho, A
College of Western Idaho, A
University of Idaho, BMD

Illinois

Augustana College, B
Chicago State University, BM
Concordia University Chicago, B
DePaul University, B
Eastern Illinois University, B
Elmhurst College, B
Illinois State University, B
Northeastern Illinois University, BM
Northern Illinois University, BMD
Northwestern University, B
Olivet Nazarene University, B
Southern Illinois University Carbondale, BMD
Southern Illinois University Edwardsville, BM
Triton College, A
University of Chicago, B
University of Illinois at Chicago, M
University of Illinois at Urbana - Champaign, BMD
Western Illinois University, BMO

Indiana

Ball State University, BM
Indiana State University, B
Indiana University Bloomington, BMD
Indiana University - Purdue University Indianapolis, B
Indiana University Southeast, B
Taylor University, B
Valparaiso University, B

Iowa

The University of Iowa, BMDO
University of Northern Iowa, BM

Kansas

Allen Community College, A
Fort Hays State University, BM
Kansas State University, BMDO
Pittsburg State University, B
The University of Kansas, BMD

Kentucky

Eastern Kentucky University, B
Northern Kentucky University, B
University of Kentucky, BMD
University of Louisville, BM
Western Kentucky University, B

Louisiana

Louisiana State University and Agricultural & Mechanical College, BMD
Louisiana Tech University, B
University of New Orleans, M

Maine

University of Maine at Farmington, B

Maryland

Community College of Baltimore County, A
Frostburg State University, B
Johns Hopkins University, BMD
Montgomery College, A
Salisbury University, B
Towson University, BM
University of Maryland, Baltimore County, BMD
University of Maryland, College Park, BMD

Massachusetts

Bard College at Simon's Rock, B
Boston University, BD
Bridgewater State University, B
Clark University, BMD
Fitchburg State University, B
Framingham State University, B
Mount Holyoke College, B
Salem State University, BM
University of Massachusetts Amherst, BM
Worcester State University, B

Michigan

Aquinas College, B
Calvin College, B
Central Michigan University, B
Eastern Michigan University, BO

Grand Valley State University, B
Lake Michigan College, A
Lansing Community College, A
Michigan State University, BMD
Northern Michigan University, B
Western Michigan University, BMDO

Minnesota

Bemidji State University, B
Gustavus Adolphus College, B
Itasca Community College, A
Macalester College, B
Minnesota State University Mankato, BMO
St. Cloud State University, BM
University of Minnesota, Duluth, B
University of Minnesota, Twin Cities Campus, BMD
University of St. Thomas, B
Vermilion Community College, A

Mississippi

Mississippi Delta Community College, A
Mississippi State University, M
University of Southern Mississippi, BMD

Missouri

Missouri Southern State University, B
Missouri State University, BM
Northwest Missouri State University, B
Park University, B
University of Central Missouri, B
University of Missouri, BMO
University of Missouri - Kansas City, B

Montana

University of Montana, BM

Nebraska

Concordia University, Nebraska, B
University of Nebraska at Kearney, B
University of Nebraska - Lincoln, BMD
University of Nebraska at Omaha, BMO
Wayne State College, B
Western Nebraska Community College, A

Nevada

University of Nevada, Reno, BMD

New Hampshire

Dartmouth College, B
Keene State College, B
Plymouth State University, B
University of New Hampshire, B

New Jersey

Montclair State University, B
Rowan University, B
Rutgers University - New Brunswick, BMD
William Paterson University of New Jersey, B

New Mexico

Navajo Technical University, A
New Mexico State University, BM
University of New Mexico, BM

New York

Binghamton University, State University of New York, BM
Buffalo State College, State University of New York, B
Cayuga County Community College, A
City College of the City University of New York, B
Colgate University, B
College of Staten Island of the City University of New York, B
Hofstra University, B
Hunter College of the City University of New York, BMO
Lehman College of the City University of New York, B
Long Island University - LIU Post, B
Sarah Lawrence College, B
State University of New York College at Cortland, B
State University of New York College at Geneseo, B
State University of New York College at Oneonta, B

State University of New York at New Paltz, B
State University of New York at Plattsburgh, B
Syracuse University, BMD
United States Military Academy, B
University at Albany, State University of New York, BM
University at Buffalo, the State University of New York, BMDO
Vassar College, B

North Carolina

Appalachian State University, BM
Chowan University, B
East Carolina University, BMO
Fayetteville State University, B
The University of North Carolina at Chapel Hill, BMD
The University of North Carolina at Charlotte, BMD
The University of North Carolina at Greensboro, BMDO
The University of North Carolina Wilmington, B
Western Carolina University, B

North Dakota

Dickinson State University, B
University of North Dakota, BM

Ohio

Bowling Green State University, B
Central State University, B
Kent State University, BMD
Miami University, BM
Miami University Hamilton, B
Miami University Middletown, A
The Ohio State University, BMD
Ohio University, BM
Ohio Wesleyan University, B
The University of Akron, B
University of Cincinnati, BMD
The University of Toledo, BMDO
Wright State University, AB
Youngstown State University, B

Oklahoma

East Central University, B
Northeastern State University, B
Oklahoma State University, BMD
University of Central Oklahoma, B
University of Oklahoma, BMD

Oregon

Oregon State University, MD
Portland State University, BMD
University of Oregon, BMD
Western Oregon University, B

Pennsylvania

Bucknell University, B
California University of Pennsylvania, B
Edinboro University of Pennsylvania, B
Harrisburg University of Science and Technology, B
Indiana University of Pennsylvania, BM
Kutztown University of Pennsylvania, B
Millersville University of Pennsylvania, B
Penn State Abington, B
Penn State Altoona, B
Penn State Beaver, B
Penn State Berks, B
Penn State Brandywine, B
Penn State DuBois, B
Penn State Erie, The Behrend College, B
Penn State Fayette, The Eberly Campus, B
Penn State Greater Allegheny, B
Penn State Hazleton, B
Penn State Lehigh Valley, B
Penn State Mont Alto, B
Penn State New Kensington, B
Penn State Schuylkill, B
Penn State Shenango, B
Penn State University Park, BMD
Penn State Wilkes-Barre, B
Penn State Worthington Scranton, B
Penn State York, B
Philadelphia University, M
Shippensburg University of Pennsylvania, BM

Slippery Rock University of Pennsylvania, B
Temple University, BMD
University of Pittsburgh at Johnstown, B
Villanova University, B
West Chester University of Pennsylvania, BMO

Rhode Island

Rhode Island College, B

South Carolina

University of South Carolina, BMD

South Dakota

South Dakota State University, BM

Tennessee

East Tennessee State University, B
Nashville State Community College, A
University of Memphis, BM
The University of Tennessee, BMD
The University of Tennessee at Martin, B

Texas

Austin Community College District, A
Del Mar College, A
Sam Houston State University, B
Stephen F. Austin State University, B
Texas A&M University, BMD
Texas Christian University, B
Texas State University, BMD
Texas Tech University, BM
University of Houston - Clear Lake, B
University of North Texas, BM
The University of Texas at Austin, BMD
The University of Texas at Dallas, MD
The University of Texas at El Paso, B
The University of Texas at San Antonio, B
West Texas A&M University, B

Utah

Brigham Young University, B
Snow College, A
University of Utah, MD
Utah State University, BMD
Weber State University, B

Vermont

Castleton University, B
Middlebury College, B
University of Vermont, B

Virginia

Emory & Henry College, B
George Mason University, BMDO
James Madison University, B
Old Dominion University, B
University of Mary Washington, B
University of Richmond, B
Virginia Polytechnic Institute and State University, BM

Washington

Central Washington University, B
Eastern Washington University, B
Green River College, A
Skagit Valley College, A
University of Washington, BMD
Western Washington University, BM

West Virginia

Concord University, BM
Marshall University, BMO
West Virginia University, BMD

Wisconsin

Carthage College, B
University of Wisconsin - Eau Claire, B
University of Wisconsin - La Crosse, B
University of Wisconsin - Madison, BMDO
University of Wisconsin - Milwaukee, BMD
University of Wisconsin - Oshkosh, B
University of Wisconsin - Parkside, B
University of Wisconsin - Platteville, B
University of Wisconsin - River Falls, B

University of Wisconsin - Stevens Point, B
University of Wisconsin - Whitewater, B

Wyoming

University of Wyoming, BM

U.S. Territories: Puerto Rico

University of Puerto Rico, Río Piedras Campus, B

Canada

Alberta

Southern Alberta Institute of Technology, A
University of Alberta, B
University of Calgary, BMD
University of Lethbridge, BM

British Columbia

Simon Fraser University, BMD
Thompson Rivers University, B
Trinity Western University, B
The University of British Columbia, BMD
The University of British Columbia - Okanagan
  Campus, B
University of the Fraser Valley, B
University of Northern British Columbia, B
University of Victoria, BMD
Vancouver Island University, B

Manitoba

Brandon University, B
University of Manitoba, BMD
The University of Winnipeg, B

Maritime Provinces: New Brunswick

Mount Allison University, B
Université de Moncton, B

Maritime Provinces: Nova Scotia

Saint Mary's University, B

Maritime Provinces: Prince Edward Island

University of Prince Edward Island, M

Newfoundland and Labrador

Memorial University of Newfoundland, BMD

Ontario

Brock University, BM
Carleton University, BMD
Lakehead University, B
Laurentian University, B
McMaster University, BMD
Nipissing University, B
Queen's University at Kingston, BMD
Ryerson University, B
Trent University, BMD
University of Guelph, BMD
University of Ottawa, BMD
University of Toronto, BMD
University of Waterloo, BMD
The University of Western Ontario, BMD
Wilfrid Laurier University, BMD
York University, BMD

Quebec

Bishop's University, B
Concordia University, BMO
McGill University, BMD
Université Laval, ABMD
Université de Montréal, BMDO
Université du Québec à Chicoutimi, B
Université du Québec à Montréal, BM
Université du Québec à Rimouski, B
Université du Québec à Trois-Rivières, B
Université de Sherbrooke, MD

Saskatchewan

University of Regina, BMD
University of Saskatchewan, BMD

GEOGRAPHY TEACHER EDUCATION

United States

Delaware

University of Delaware, B

Indiana

Valparaiso University, B

Michigan

Calvin College, B
Grand Valley State University, B
Michigan State University, B
Northern Michigan University, B
Western Michigan University, B

Nebraska

Concordia University, Nebraska, B
Wayne State College, B

North Dakota

Mayville State University, B

Rhode Island

Rhode Island College, B

Tennessee

Cumberland University, B
The University of Tennessee at Martin, B

Utah

Weber State University, B

Canada

Ontario

University of Windsor, B

Quebec

Bishop's University, B
McGill University, B
Université Laval, B
Université de Montréal, B

GEOLOGICAL AND EARTH SCIENCES/GEOSCIENCES

United States

California

California State University, Chico, B
California State University, Dominguez Hills, B
California State University, Fullerton, B
San Jose State University, B
Stanford University, B
University of California, Los Angeles, B

Colorado

Western State Colorado University, B

Connecticut

Yale University, B

Florida

Eckerd College, B
University of Miami, B

Georgia

Georgia Institute of Technology, B

Illinois

University of Illinois at Urbana - Champaign, B

Indiana

Earlham College, B

Iowa

University of Northern Iowa, B

Maryland

Salisbury University, B
Towson University, B

Massachusetts

Boston University, B
Bridgewater State University, B

Minnesota

Minnesota State University Moorhead, B

Nevada

Great Basin College, A

New Jersey

Princeton University, B
Rowan College at Burlington County, A

New York

Cornell University, B
Hamilton College, B
Union College, B
University of Buffalo, the State University of New
  York, B
Utica College, B

Ohio

Cedarville University, B

Oregon

Oregon State University, B

Pennsylvania

Allegheny College, B
Lehigh University, B
Penn State Abington, B
Penn State Altoona, B
Penn State Beaver, B
Penn State Berks, B
Penn State Brandywine, B
Penn State DuBois, B
Penn State Erie, The Behrend College, B
Penn State Fayette, The Eberly Campus, B
Penn State Greater Allegheny, B
Penn State Hazleton, B
Penn State Lehigh Valley, B
Penn State Mont Alto, B
Penn State New Kensington, B
Penn State Schuylkill, B
Penn State Shenango, B
Penn State University Park, B
Penn State Wilkes-Barre, B
Penn State Worthington Scranton, B
Penn State York, B
University of Pittsburgh, B

Rhode Island

University of Rhode Island, B

Texas

Texas A&M University, B
Texas Christian University, B
The University of Texas at Arlington, B

Utah

Brigham Young University, B
University of Utah, B

Virginia

Old Dominion University, B

Washington

Central Washington University, B
University of Washington, B
Western Washington University, B
Whitman College, B

West Virginia

Potomac State College of West Virginia University,
  A

Wyoming
University of Wyoming, B

Canada
Alberta
University of Alberta, B
Ontario
University of Guelph, B

GEOLOGICAL ENGINEERING

United States
Alaska
University of Alaska Anchorage, M
University of Alaska Fairbanks, M

Arizona
Arizona State University at the Tempe campus, MD
The University of Arizona, M

Colorado
Colorado School of Mines, MD

Hawaii
University of Hawaii at Manoa, MD

Idaho
University of Idaho, M

Michigan
Michigan Technological University, MD

Minnesota
University of Minnesota, Twin Cities Campus, M

Missouri
Missouri University of Science and Technology, MD

Montana
Montana Tech of The University of Montana, M

Nevada
University of Nevada, Reno, MD

New Mexico
New Mexico State University, MD

North Dakota
University of North Dakota, M

Ohio
The University of Akron, M

Oklahoma
University of Oklahoma, MD

South Dakota
South Dakota School of Mines and Technology, MD

Utah
University of Utah, MD

Wisconsin
University of Wisconsin - Madison, MD

Canada
British Columbia
The University of British Columbia, MD

Saskatchewan
University of Saskatchewan, MD

GEOLOGICAL/GEOPHYSICAL ENGINEERING

United States
Alaska
University of Alaska Fairbanks, B

California
University of California, Berkeley, B
University of California, Los Angeles, B

Colorado
Colorado School of Mines, B

Massachusetts
Tufts University, B

Michigan
Michigan Technological University, B
University of Michigan, B

Minnesota
University of Minnesota, Twin Cities Campus, B

Mississippi
University of Mississippi, B

Missouri
Missouri University of Science and Technology, B

Montana
Montana Tech of The University of Montana, B

Nevada
University of Nevada, Reno, B

New Jersey
New Jersey Institute of Technology, B
Rutgers University - Newark, B

New York
University of Rochester, B

North Dakota
University of North Dakota, B

South Dakota
South Dakota School of Mines and Technology, B

Texas
The University of Texas at Austin, B

Utah
University of Utah, B

Wisconsin
University of Wisconsin - Madison, B

Canada
Alberta
University of Calgary, B

British Columbia
The University of British Columbia, B

Manitoba
University of Manitoba, B

Maritime Provinces: New Brunswick
University of New Brunswick Fredericton, B

Newfoundland and Labrador
Memorial University of Newfoundland, B

Ontario
Laurentian University, B
Queen's University at Kingston, B
University of Toronto, B

University of Waterloo, B

Quebec
Université Laval, B
Université du Québec à Chicoutimi, B

Saskatchewan
University of Saskatchewan, B

GEOLOGY/EARTH SCIENCE

United States
Alabama
Auburn University, BM
Jacksonville State University, B
The University of Alabama, BMD
University of South Alabama, B

Alaska
Alaska Pacific University, B
University of Alaska Anchorage, B
University of Alaska Fairbanks, BMD

Arizona
Arizona State University at the Tempe campus, BMD
Arizona Western College, A
Eastern Arizona College, A
Northern Arizona University, BM
The University of Arizona, B

Arkansas
Arkansas Tech University, B
University of Arkansas, BM
University of Arkansas at Little Rock, B

California
Antelope Valley College, A
Bakersfield College, A
Cabrillo College, A
California Institute of Technology, BMD
California Lutheran University, B
California Polytechnic State University, San Luis Obispo, B
California State Polytechnic University, Pomona, BM
California State University, Bakersfield, BM
California State University, Chico, BM
California State University, East Bay, BM
California State University, Fresno, BM
California State University, Fullerton, BM
California State University, Long Beach, BM
California State University, Los Angeles, BM
California State University, Northridge, BM
California State University, Sacramento, B
California State University, San Bernardino, B
California State University, Stanislaus, B
Cerritos College, A
Chaffey College, A
College of the Canyons, A
College of the Desert, A
College of Marin, A
College of San Mateo, A
Columbia College, A
Contra Costa College, A
Cosumnes River College, A
Crafton Hills College, A
East Los Angeles College, A
El Camino College, A
Folsom Lake College, A
Fullerton College, A
Grossmont College, A
Hartnell College, A
Humboldt State University, BM
Lake Tahoe Community College, A
Loma Linda University, B
Los Angeles Valley College, A
Monterey Peninsula College, A
Moorpark College, A
National University, B
Occidental College, B
Ohlone College, A
Orange Coast College, A

Palomar College, A
Pomona College, B
Saddleback College, A
San Bernardino Valley College, A
San Diego State University, BM
San Francisco State University, B
San Joaquin Delta College, A
San Jose State University, BM
Santa Ana College, A
Santa Barbara City College, A
Santiago Canyon College, A
Scripps College, B
Sierra College, A
Sonoma State University, B
Southwestern College, A
Stanford University, B
University of California, Berkeley, BMD
University of California, Davis, BMD
University of California, Irvine, B
University of California, Los Angeles, BMD
University of California, Merced, B
University of California, Riverside, BMD
University of California, San Diego, B
University of California, Santa Barbara, B
University of California, Santa Cruz, B
University of the Pacific, B
University of Southern California, B
West Hills Community College, A
West Los Angeles College, A

Colorado

Adams State University, B
The Colorado College, B
Colorado Mesa University, B
Colorado Mountain College (Steamboat Springs), A
Colorado School of Mines, MD
Colorado State University, B
Fort Lewis College, B
Northeastern Junior College, A
University of Colorado Boulder, BMD
University of Northern Colorado, B
Western State Colorado University, B

Connecticut

Central Connecticut State University, B
Southern Connecticut State University, B
University of Connecticut, BMD
Western Connecticut State University, B
Yale University, D

Delaware

University of Delaware, BMD

District of Columbia

The George Washington University, B

Florida

Broward College, A
Florida Atlantic University, BM
Florida International University, B
Florida State University, BMD
Miami Dade College, A
Pensacola State College, A
South Florida State College, A
University of Florida, BMD
University of Miami, B
University of South Florida, BMDO

Georgia

College of Coastal Georgia, A
Columbus State University, B
Georgia Highlands College, A
Georgia Southern University, B
Georgia Southwestern State University, B
Georgia State University, BM
Piedmont College, B
Savannah State University, B
University of Georgia, BMD
University of West Georgia, B
Valdosta State University, B

Hawaii

University of Hawaii at Hilo, B
University of Hawaii at Manoa, BMD

Idaho

Boise State University, BMD
Brigham Young University - Idaho, B
College of Southern Idaho, A
College of Western Idaho, A
Idaho State University, BMO
North Idaho College, A
University of Idaho, BMD

Illinois

Augustana College, B
Concordia University Chicago, B
Eastern Illinois University, B
Illinois State University, B
Northeastern Illinois University, B
Northern Illinois University, BMD
Northwestern University, BD
Olivet Nazarene University, B
Southern Illinois University Carbondale, BMD
Triton College, A
University of Illinois at Chicago, BMD
University of Illinois at Urbana - Champaign, BMD
Western Illinois University, B
Wheaton College, B

Indiana

Ball State University, BM
DePauw University, B
Hanover College, B
Indiana State University, B
Indiana University Bloomington, BMD
Indiana University Northwest, B
Indiana University - Purdue University Fort Wayne, B
Indiana University - Purdue University Indianapolis, BM
Purdue University, B
Taylor University, B
University of Indianapolis, B
University of Southern Indiana, B
Valparaiso University, B
Vincennes University, A

Iowa

Cornell College, B
Iowa Lakes Community College, A
Iowa State University of Science and Technology, BMD
The University of Iowa, B
University of Northern Iowa, B

Kansas

Barton County Community College, A
Emporia State University, B
Fort Hays State University, BM
Kansas State University, BM
The University of Kansas, BMD
Wichita State University, BM

Kentucky

Eastern Kentucky University, BMD
Morehead State University, B
Murray State University, B
Northern Kentucky University, B
University of Kentucky, BMD
Western Kentucky University, BM

Louisiana

Centenary College of Louisiana, B
Louisiana State University and Agricultural & Mechanical College, BMD
Louisiana Tech University, B
Tulane University, B
University of Louisiana at Lafayette, BM
University of New Orleans, B

Maine

Bates College, B
Bowdoin College, B
Colby College, B
University of Maine, BMO
University of Maine at Farmington, B
University of Southern Maine, B

Maryland

Frostburg State University, B
Johns Hopkins University, B
Towson University, B
University of Maryland, College Park, BMD

Massachusetts

Amherst College, B
Boston College, BM
Boston University, B
Bridgewater State University, B
Clark University, B
Framingham State University, B
Harvard University, B
Massachusetts Institute of Technology, BD
Mount Holyoke College, B
Northeastern University, B
Salem State University, B
Smith College, B
Tufts University, B
University of Massachusetts Amherst, B
University of Massachusetts Boston, B
Wellesley College, B
Williams College, B

Michigan

Adrian College, B
Albion College, B
Calvin College, B
Central Michigan University, B
Eastern Michigan University, B
Grand Rapids Community College, A
Grand Valley State University, B
Hope College, B
Lake Michigan College, A
Lake Superior State University, B
Michigan State University, B
Michigan Technological University, BMD
Northern Michigan University, B
University of Michigan, B
University of Michigan - Dearborn, B
Wayne State University, BM
Western Michigan University, B

Minnesota

Bemidji State University, B
Carleton College, B
Gustavus Adolphus College, B
Macalester College, B
Minnesota State University Mankato, B
St. Cloud State University, B
University of Minnesota, Duluth, BMD
University of Minnesota, Morris, B
University of Minnesota, Twin Cities Campus, BMD
University of St. Thomas, B
Vermilion Community College, A

Mississippi

Jackson State University, B
Millsaps College, B
Mississippi State University, BM
University of Mississippi, B
University of Southern Mississippi, BMD

Missouri

Missouri State University, BM
Missouri University of Science and Technology, BMD
Northwest Missouri State University, B
Saint Louis University, B
University of Central Missouri, B
University of Missouri, BMD
University of Missouri - Kansas City, BM
Washington University in St. Louis, B

Montana

Montana State University, B
Montana Tech of The University of Montana, M
Rocky Mountain College, B
University of Montana, BMD

Nebraska

University of Nebraska - Lincoln, B
University of Nebraska at Omaha, B

Nevada

Truckee Meadows Community College, A
University of Nevada, Las Vegas, B
University of Nevada, Reno, BMD

New Hampshire

Dartmouth College, B
Keene State College, B
University of New Hampshire, BM

New Jersey

Kean University, B
Middlesex County College, A
Montclair State University, B
New Jersey City University, B
Rider University, B
Rutgers University - New Brunswick, BMD
Rutgers University - Newark, BM
Stockton University, B
William Paterson University of New Jersey, B

New Mexico

Eastern New Mexico University, B
New Mexico Highlands University, B
New Mexico Institute of Mining and Technology, BMD
New Mexico State University, BM
San Juan College, A
University of New Mexico, B
Western New Mexico University, B

New York

Alfred University, B
Binghamton University, State University of New York, BMD
Brooklyn College of the City University of New York, BMD
Buffalo State College, State University of New York, B
City College of the City University of New York, B
Colgate University, B
The College at Brockport, State University of New York, B
Columbia University, B
Columbia University, School of General Studies, B
Cornell University, MD
Hamilton College, B
Hartwick College, B
Hobart and William Smith Colleges, B
Hofstra University, BM
Lehman College of the City University of New York, B
Long Island University - LIU Post, B
Queens College of the City University of New York, BM
Rensselaer Polytechnic Institute, BMD
St. Lawrence University, B
Skidmore College, B
State University of New York College at Cortland, B
State University of New York College at Geneseo, B
State University of New York College at Oneonta, B
State University of New York College at Potsdam, B
State University of New York at Fredonia, B
State University of New York at New Paltz, B
State University of New York at Oswego, B
State University of New York at Plattsburgh, B
Stony Brook University, State University of New York, B
Syracuse University, BMD
Union College, B
University at Buffalo, the State University of New York, BMD
University of Rochester, BMD
Vassar College, B
York College of the City University of New York, B

North Carolina

Appalachian State University, B
Duke University, BMD
East Carolina University, BMO
Elizabeth City State University, B
Guilford College, B
North Carolina State University, B
The University of North Carolina at Chapel Hill, BMD
The University of North Carolina at Charlotte, B
The University of North Carolina Wilmington, B
Western Carolina University, B

North Dakota

Dickinson State University, B
Minot State University, B
North Dakota State University, B
University of North Dakota, BMD

Ohio

Ashland University, B
Bowling Green State University, BM
Case Western Reserve University, BMD
Cedarville University, B
Central State University, B
The College of Wooster, B
Denison University, B
Edison Community College, A
Kent State University, BMD
Marietta College, B
Miami University, BMD
Miami University Hamilton, B
Muskingum University, B
Oberlin College, B
The Ohio State University, BMD
Ohio University, BM
Ohio Wesleyan University, B
Shawnee State University, B
The University of Akron, BM
University of Cincinnati, BMD
University of Dayton, B
University of Mount Union, B
The University of Toledo, BMD
Wittenberg University, B
Wright State University, ABM
Wright State University - Lake Campus, A
Youngstown State University, B

Oklahoma

Oklahoma State University, BMD
University of Oklahoma, BMD
The University of Tulsa, B

Oregon

Oregon State University, MD
Portland State University, BMD
Southern Oregon University, B
University of Oregon, BMD

Pennsylvania

Allegheny College, B
Bloomsburg University of Pennsylvania, B
Bryn Mawr College, B
Bucknell University, B
California University of Pennsylvania, B
Clarion University of Pennsylvania, B
Dickinson College, B
Drexel University, B
East Stroudsburg University of Pennsylvania, B
Edinboro University of Pennsylvania, B
Franklin & Marshall College, B
Haverford College, B
Indiana University of Pennsylvania, B
Keystone College, B
Kutztown University of Pennsylvania, B
La Salle University, B
Lafayette College, B
Lehigh University, MD
Lock Haven University of Pennsylvania, B
Mercyhurst University, B
Millersville University of Pennsylvania, B
Moravian College, B
Penn State Abington, B
Penn State Altoona, B
Penn State Beaver, B
Penn State Berks, B
Penn State Brandywine, B
Penn State DuBois, B
Penn State Erie, The Behrend College, B
Penn State Fayette, The Eberly Campus, B
Penn State Greater Allegheny, B
Penn State Hazleton, B
Penn State Lehigh Valley, B
Penn State Mont Alto, B
Penn State New Kensington, B
Penn State Schuylkill, B
Penn State Shenango, B
Penn State University Park, B
Penn State Wilkes-Barre, B
Penn State Worthington Scranton, B
Penn State York, B
Shippensburg University of Pennsylvania, B
Slippery Rock University of Pennsylvania, B
Susquehanna University, B
Temple University, BM
University of Pennsylvania, B
University of Pittsburgh, BMD
University of Pittsburgh at Johnstown, B
West Chester University of Pennsylvania, BMO
Wilkes University, B

Rhode Island

Brown University, B
University of Rhode Island, B

South Carolina

Clemson University, B
College of Charleston, B
Furman University, B
University of South Carolina, BMD

South Dakota

South Dakota School of Mines and Technology, BMD
The University of South Dakota, B

Tennessee

Austin Peay State University, B
East Tennessee State University, B
Middle Tennessee State University, B
Sewanee: The University of the South, B
Tennessee Technological University, B
University of Memphis, BMDO
The University of Tennessee, BMD
The University of Tennessee at Chattanooga, B
The University of Tennessee at Martin, B
Vanderbilt University, BM

Texas

Amarillo College, A
Angelo State University, B
Austin Community College District, A
Baylor University, BMD
Central Texas College, A
Del Mar College, A
Grayson College, A
Hardin-Simmons University, B
Hill College, A
Kilgore College, A
Lamar University, B
Lee College, A
Midwestern State University, B
Odessa College, A
Palo Alto College, A
Panola College, A
Rice University, B
St. Philip's College, A
Sam Houston State University, B
San Jacinto College District, A
Southern Methodist University, BMD
Stephen F. Austin State University, BM
Sul Ross State University, BM
Tarleton State University, B
Texas A&M University, BMD
Texas A&M University - Corpus Christi, B
Texas A&M University - Kingsville, B
Texas Christian University, BM
Texas Tech University, B
Trinity University, B
Trinity Valley Community College, A
Tyler Junior College, A
University of Houston, BMD
University of Houston - Downtown, B
The University of Texas at Arlington, BMD
The University of Texas at Austin, BMD
The University of Texas at Dallas, B
The University of Texas at El Paso, BMD
The University of Texas of the Permian Basin, BM
The University of Texas at San Antonio, BM

Wayland Baptist University, B
West Texas A&M University, B

Utah

Brigham Young University, M
Salt Lake Community College, A
Snow College, A
Southern Utah University, B
University of Utah, BMD
Utah State University, BM
Utah Valley University, B
Weber State University, B

Vermont

Castleton University, B
Middlebury College, B
Norwich University, B
University of Vermont, BM

Virginia

The College of William and Mary, B
George Mason University, B
James Madison University, B
Radford University, B
Virginia Polytechnic Institute and State University, B
Virginia Wesleyan College, B
Washington and Lee University, B

Washington

Central Washington University, BM
Eastern Washington University, B
Everett Community College, A
Pacific Lutheran University, B
Skagit Valley College, A
University of Puget Sound, B
University of Washington, BMD
Washington State University, BMD
Washington State University - Vancouver, B
Western Washington University, BM
Whitman College, B

West Virginia

Marshall University, B
Potomac State College of West Virginia University, A
West Virginia University, BMD

Wisconsin

Beloit College, B
Lawrence University, B
Northland College, B
St. Norbert College, B
University of Wisconsin - Eau Claire, B
University of Wisconsin - Green Bay, B
University of Wisconsin - Madison, BMD
University of Wisconsin - Milwaukee, BMD
University of Wisconsin - Oshkosh, B
University of Wisconsin - Parkside, B
University of Wisconsin - River Falls, B
University of Wisconsin - Stevens Point, B

Wyoming

Casper College, A
Central Wyoming College, A
University of Wyoming, BMD
Western Wyoming Community College, A

U.S. Territories: Puerto Rico

University of Puerto Rico, Mayagüez Campus, BM

Canada

Alberta

Mount Royal University, B
University of Alberta, B
University of Calgary, BMD

British Columbia

Thompson Rivers University, A
The University of British Columbia, BMD
University of Victoria, B

Manitoba

Brandon University, B
University of Manitoba, BMD

Maritime Provinces: New Brunswick

Mount Allison University, B
University of New Brunswick Fredericton, BMD
University of New Brunswick Saint John, B

Maritime Provinces: Nova Scotia

Acadia University, BM
Dalhousie University, B
St. Francis Xavier University, BM
Saint Mary's University, B
University of King's College, B

Newfoundland and Labrador

Memorial University of Newfoundland, BMD

Ontario

Brock University, B
Carleton University, B
Lakehead University, BM
Laurentian University, BMD
McMaster University, BMD
Queen's University at Kingston, BMD
University of Ottawa, B
University of Toronto, MD
University of Waterloo, B
The University of Western Ontario, BMD
University of Windsor, B
York University, B

Quebec

McGill University, B
Université Laval, BMD
Université de Montréal, B
Université du Québec à Chicoutimi, B
Université du Québec à Montréal, BM

Saskatchewan

University of Regina, BMD
University of Saskatchewan, BMDO

GEOPHYSICS ENGINEERING

United States

Colorado

Colorado School of Mines, MD

Montana

Montana Tech of The University of Montana, M

GEOPHYSICS AND SEISMOLOGY

United States

Alaska

University of Alaska Fairbanks, MD

California

California Institute of Technology, BMD
California State University, Long Beach, M
Stanford University, BMD
University of California, Berkeley, MD
University of California, Los Angeles, BMD
University of California, Riverside, B
University of California, San Diego, D
University of California, Santa Barbara, B

Colorado

Colorado School of Mines, MD
University of Colorado Boulder, D

Connecticut

Yale University, D

Florida

Florida State University, D
University of Miami, MD

Hawaii

University of Hawaii at Manoa, MD

Idaho

Boise State University, BMD
Idaho State University, M

Illinois

University of Chicago, BD

Indiana

Indiana University Bloomington, M

Louisiana

Louisiana State University and Agricultural & Mechanical College, MD

Massachusetts

Boston College, BM
Boston University, B
Massachusetts Institute of Technology, MD

Michigan

Eastern Michigan University, B
Michigan Technological University, BMD
Western Michigan University, B

Minnesota

University of Minnesota, Twin Cities Campus, MD

Missouri

Missouri University of Science and Technology, BMD
Saint Louis University, D
Washington University in St. Louis, B

Nevada

University of Nevada, Reno, BMD

New Mexico

New Mexico Institute of Mining and Technology, BMD

New York

Cornell University, MD
St. Lawrence University, B
State University of New York College at Geneseo, B
State University of New York at Fredonia, B

Ohio

Bowling Green State University, BM
Ohio University, M
The University of Akron, BM
Wright State University, M

Oklahoma

University of Oklahoma, BMD
The University of Tulsa, B

Oregon

Oregon State University, MD

Rhode Island

Brown University, B

South Carolina

University of South Carolina, B

Tennessee

University of Memphis, M

Texas

Baylor University, BMD
Rice University, BM
Southern Methodist University, BM
Texas A&M University, BMD
University of Houston, BMD
The University of Texas at Austin, B

The University of Texas at Dallas, MD
The University of Texas at El Paso, BM

Utah

University of Utah, BMD

Washington

University of Washington, BMD
Western Washington University, B
Whitman College, B

West Virginia

West Virginia University, MD
West Virginia Wesleyan College, B

Wisconsin

University of Wisconsin - Madison, MD

Wyoming

University of Wyoming, MD

Canada

Alberta

University of Alberta, BMD
University of Calgary, BMD

British Columbia

The University of British Columbia, BMD
University of Victoria, B

Manitoba

University of Manitoba, MD

Maritime Provinces: New Brunswick

University of New Brunswick Fredericton, B

Newfoundland and Labrador

Memorial University of Newfoundland, BMD

Ontario

University of Ottawa, B
University of Waterloo, B
The University of Western Ontario, MD

Quebec

McGill University, B

Saskatchewan

University of Saskatchewan, B

GEOSCIENCES

United States

Alabama

The University of Alabama, M
The University of Alabama in Huntsville, M

Arizona

Arizona State University at the Tempe campus, MD
The University of Arizona, MD

Arkansas

University of Arkansas at Little Rock, O

California

California State University, Chico, M
Loma Linda University, MD
San Francisco State University, M
Stanford University, MDO
University of California, Irvine, MD
University of California, Los Angeles, MD
University of California, San Diego, MD
University of California, Santa Barbara, MD
University of California, Santa Cruz, MD
University of Southern California, MD

Colorado

Colorado State University, MD
University of Northern Colorado, M

Connecticut

Central Connecticut State University, MO
University of New Haven, M
Wesleyan University, M
Western Connecticut State University, M
Yale University, D

Florida

Florida Atlantic University, D
Florida Institute of Technology, M
Florida International University, MD
Florida State University, D
St. Thomas University, O
University of Florida, MD
University of South Florida, MD
University of West Florida, M

Georgia

Georgia Institute of Technology, MD
Georgia State University, MO

Idaho

Idaho State University, MO

Illinois

Northwestern University, D
University of Chicago, D
University of Illinois at Chicago, MD
University of Illinois at Urbana - Champaign, M

Indiana

Indiana University Bloomington, MD
Indiana University - Purdue University Indianapolis,
    MD
Purdue University, MD
University of Notre Dame, MD

Iowa

Iowa State University of Science and Technology,
    MD
The University of Iowa, MD
University of Northern Iowa, M

Kansas

Emporia State University, MO
Fort Hays State University, M

Kentucky

Murray State University, M
Western Kentucky University, M

Louisiana

University of New Orleans, M

Maine

University of Maine, MD

Maryland

Johns Hopkins University, MD

Massachusetts

Boston University, MD
Harvard University, MD
Massachusetts Institute of Technology, MD
University of Massachusetts Amherst, MD

Michigan

Eastern Michigan University, M
Michigan State University, MD
University of Michigan, MD
Western Michigan University, MD

Mississippi

Mississippi State University, MD

Missouri

Missouri State University, M
Saint Louis University, MD
University of Missouri - Kansas City, MD

Washington University in St. Louis, D

Montana

Montana State University, MD
Montana Tech of The University of Montana, M
University of Montana, MD

Nebraska

University of Nebraska - Lincoln, MD

Nevada

University of Nevada, Las Vegas, MD

New Hampshire

Dartmouth College, MD
University of New Hampshire, MD

New Jersey

Montclair State University, M
Princeton University, D

New Mexico

New Mexico Institute of Mining and Technology, MD
University of New Mexico, MD

New York

Brooklyn College of the City University of New York,
    M
City College of the City University of New York, MD
Columbia University, D
Cornell University, MD
Hunter College of the City University of New York,
    M
State University of New York College at Oneonta, M
State University of New York at New Paltz, M
Stony Brook University, State University of New
    York, MD
University at Buffalo, the State University of New
    York, M
University of Rochester, MD

North Carolina

North Carolina Central University, M
North Carolina State University, MD
The University of North Carolina at Charlotte, M
The University of North Carolina Wilmington, M

North Dakota

University of North Dakota, MD

Ohio

Case Western Reserve University, MD
The Ohio State University, MD
The University of Akron, M

Oklahoma

The University of Tulsa, MD

Pennsylvania

Lehigh University, MD
Penn State University Park, MD
University of Pennsylvania, MD
West Chester University of Pennsylvania, M

Rhode Island

Brown University, D
University of Rhode Island, MD

South Carolina

University of South Carolina, MD

South Dakota

South Dakota State University, D

Tennessee

East Tennessee State University, M
Middle Tennessee State University, O

Texas

Baylor University, D
Rice University, MD
Texas Tech University, MD
The University of Texas at Austin, MD

The University of Texas at Dallas, MD

Virginia

George Mason University, MD
Virginia Polytechnic Institute and State University, MD

Canada

Alberta

University of Alberta, MD
University of Calgary, MD

British Columbia

Simon Fraser University, MD
University of Victoria, MD

Maritime Provinces: Nova Scotia

Dalhousie University, MD
St. Francis Xavier University, M

Newfoundland and Labrador

Memorial University of Newfoundland, MD

Ontario

Brock University, M
Carleton University, MD
McMaster University, MD
University of Ottawa, MD
University of Waterloo, MD
The University of Western Ontario, MD
University of Windsor, MD
York University, MD

Quebec

McGill University, MD
Université Laval, MD
Université du Québec à Chicoutimi, M
Université du Québec à Montréal, MDO

GEOTECHNICAL ENGINEERING

United States

Alabama

Auburn University, MD
The University of Alabama in Huntsville, M

California

Stanford University, M
University of California, Berkeley, MD
University of Southern California, M

Colorado

University of Colorado Boulder, MD
University of Colorado Denver, MD

Delaware

University of Delaware, MD

Florida

University of South Florida, MD

Illinois

Illinois Institute of Technology, M
Northwestern University, MD
Southern Illinois University Edwardsville, M
University of Illinois at Urbana - Champaign, B

Iowa

Iowa State University of Science and Technology, MD

Kansas

Kansas State University, MD

Louisiana

Louisiana State University and Agricultural & Mechanical College, MD

Massachusetts

Massachusetts Institute of Technology, D
Tufts University, MD
University of Massachusetts Amherst, M

Missouri

Missouri University of Science and Technology, MD
University of Missouri, MD

New York

Cornell University, MD

Ohio

Ohio University, M
University of Dayton, M

Pennsylvania

Drexel University, MD
Penn State University Park, MD

Texas

The University of Texas at Austin, MD

Vermont

Norwich University, M

Washington

University of Washington, MD

Canada

Alberta

University of Alberta, MD
University of Calgary, MD

Maritime Provinces: New Brunswick

University of New Brunswick Fredericton, MD

Ontario

York University, B

Quebec

École Polytechnique de Montréal, MD
McGill University, MD

GERMAN LANGUAGE AND LITERATURE

United States

Alabama

Auburn University, B
Jacksonville State University, B
Samford University, B
The University of Alabama, M
University of North Alabama, B

Alaska

University of Alaska Anchorage, B

Arizona

Arizona State University at the Tempe campus, BM
The University of Arizona, BMD

Arkansas

Hendrix College, B
University of Arkansas, BM

California

Bakersfield College, A
Cabrillo College, A
California Lutheran University, B
California State University, Chico, B
California State University, Fullerton, M
California State University, Long Beach, BM
Cerritos College, A
Citrus College, A
College of San Mateo, A
El Camino College, A
Grossmont College, A

Los Angeles City College, A
Los Angeles Valley College, A
Monterey Peninsula College, A
Pepperdine University, B
Pomona College, B
Saint Mary's College of California, B
San Bernardino Valley College, A
San Diego State University, B
San Francisco State University, BM
San Jose State University, B
Santa Clara University, B
Scripps College, B
Solano Community College, A
Stanford University, MD
University of California, Berkeley, BD
University of California, Davis, BMD
University of California, Irvine, MD
University of California, Los Angeles, BMD
University of California, San Diego, B
University of California, Santa Barbara, B
University of California, Santa Cruz, B
University of the Pacific, B
University of Redlands, B
West Valley College, A

Colorado

The Colorado College, B
Colorado State University, B
University of Colorado Boulder, M
University of Denver, B

Connecticut

Central Connecticut State University, BO
Connecticut College, B
Fairfield University, B
Southern Connecticut State University, B
Trinity College, B
University of Connecticut, BMD
Yale University, BD

Delaware

Delaware State University, B
University of Delaware, M

District of Columbia

American University, B
The Catholic University of America, B
The George Washington University, B
Georgetown University, BMD
Howard University, B

Florida

Broward College, A
Florida Atlantic University, M
Florida State University, M
Miami Dade College, A
New College of Florida, B
State College of Florida Manatee-Sarasota, A
Stetson University, B
University of Florida, BMD
University of Miami, B
University of South Florida, B

Georgia

Agnes Scott College, B
Berry College, B
Georgia Southern University, B
Georgia State University, BO
Mercer University, B
University of Georgia, BM

Hawaii

University of Hawaii at Manoa, B

Idaho

Boise State University, B
Idaho State University, B
North Idaho College, A

Illinois

Augustana College, B
DePaul University, BM
Elmhurst College, B
Illinois College, B
Illinois State University, BM

Illinois Wesleyan University, B
Knox College, B
North Central College, B
Northern Illinois University, B
Northwestern University, BD
University of Chicago, BMD
University of Illinois at Chicago, MD
University of Illinois at Urbana - Champaign, BMD
Wheaton College, B

Indiana

Ball State University, B
Butler University, B
DePauw University, B
Earlham College, B
Hanover College, B
Indiana University Bloomington, MD
Indiana University - Purdue University Fort Wayne, B
Indiana University - Purdue University Indianapolis, B
Indiana University South Bend, B
Indiana University Southeast, B
Purdue University, BMD
University of Evansville, B
University of Indianapolis, B
University of Notre Dame, B
University of Southern Indiana, B
Valparaiso University, B
Wabash College, B

Iowa

Coe College, B
Cornell College, B
Grinnell College, B
Iowa State University of Science and Technology, B
Luther College, B
Simpson College, B
The University of Iowa, B
Wartburg College, B

Kansas

Baker University, B
Fort Hays State University, B
The University of Kansas, MD
Washburn University, B

Kentucky

Berea College, B
Centre College, B
Murray State University, B
Northern Kentucky University, B
Transylvania University, B
University of Kentucky, BM
Western Kentucky University, BM

Louisiana

Tulane University, B

Maine

Bates College, B
Bowdoin College, B
Colby College, B
University of Maine, B

Maryland

Hood College, B
Johns Hopkins University, BD
Loyola University Maryland, B
McDaniel College, B
Mount St. Mary's University, B
University of Maryland, College Park, BMD
Washington College, B

Massachusetts

Amherst College, B
Bard College at Simon's Rock, B
Boston College, B
Boston University, B
Brandeis University, B
College of the Holy Cross, B
Gordon College, B
Harvard University, BD
Smith College, B
Tufts University, BM

University of Massachusetts Amherst, MD
Wellesley College, B
Wheaton College, B
Williams College, B

Michigan

Adrian College, B
Albion College, B
Alma College, B
Aquinas College, B
Calvin College, B
Central Michigan University, B
Eastern Michigan University, BMO
Hillsdale College, B
Hope College, B
Kalamazoo College, B
Michigan State University, BMD
Oakland University, B
University of Michigan, BMD
Wayne State University, BMD
Western Michigan University, B

Minnesota

Augsburg College, B
Bemidji State University, B
Carleton College, B
College of Saint Benedict, B
Concordia College, B
Gustavus Adolphus College, B
Hamline University, B
Macalester College, B
Minnesota State University Mankato, B
St. Cloud State University, B
Saint John's University, B
St. Olaf College, B
University of Minnesota, Duluth, B
University of Minnesota, Twin Cities Campus, MD
University of St. Thomas, B

Mississippi

Mississippi State University, M
University of Mississippi, B

Missouri

Drury University, B
Missouri Southern State University, B
Missouri State University, B
Saint Louis University, B
Truman State University, B
University of Central Missouri, B
University of Missouri, BM
Washington University in St. Louis, BD
Webster University, B

Montana

University of Montana, BM

Nebraska

Creighton University, B
Doane University, B
Hastings College, B
Nebraska Wesleyan University, B
Union College, B
University of Nebraska at Kearney, B
University of Nebraska - Lincoln, BMD
Western Nebraska Community College, A

Nevada

University of Nevada, Las Vegas, B
University of Nevada, Reno, M

New Hampshire

Dartmouth College, B
University of New Hampshire, B

New Jersey

Drew University, B
Montclair State University, B
Princeton University, BD
Rider University, BO
Rutgers University - Camden, B
Rutgers University - New Brunswick, BMD
Rutgers University - Newark, B

New Mexico

New Mexico Military Institute, A
University of New Mexico, BM

New York

Bard College, B
Barnard College, B
Binghamton University, State University of New York, B
Brooklyn College of the City University of New York, B
Canisius College, B
Colgate University, B
Columbia University, BMD
Columbia University, School of General Studies, B
Cornell University, BMD
Fordham University, B
Hartwick College, B
Hofstra University, B
Hunter College of the City University of New York, B
Ithaca College, B
Nazareth College of Rochester, B
New York University, BMD
Queens College of the City University of New York, B
Sarah Lawrence College, B
Skidmore College, B
State University of New York College at Cortland, B
State University of New York at Oswego, B
Stony Brook University, State University of New York, B
Syracuse University, B
Union College, B
United States Military Academy, B
University at Buffalo, the State University of New York, BMO
University of Rochester, B
Vassar College, B

North Carolina

Davidson College, B
Duke University, BD
Guilford College, B
Lenoir-Rhyne University, B
Methodist University, A
University of North Carolina at Asheville, B
The University of North Carolina at Chapel Hill, MD
The University of North Carolina at Charlotte, B
The University of North Carolina at Greensboro, B
The University of North Carolina Wilmington, B
Wake Forest University, B
Western Carolina University, B

North Dakota

Minot State University, B
University of Jamestown, B
University of North Dakota, B

Ohio

Baldwin Wallace University, B
Bowling Green State University, BM
Case Western Reserve University, B
The College of Wooster, B
Denison University, B
Franciscan University of Steubenville, B
Heidelberg University, B
John Carroll University, B
Kent State University, B
Kenyon College, B
Miami University, B
Miami University Hamilton, B
Muskingum University, B
Oberlin College, B
The Ohio State University, BMD
Ohio University, B
Ohio Wesleyan University, B
University of Cincinnati, BMD
University of Dayton, B
University of Mount Union, B
The University of Toledo, BM
Wittenberg University, B
Wright State University, B
Xavier University, AB

Oklahoma

Oklahoma State University, B
University of Central Oklahoma, B
University of Oklahoma, M
The University of Tulsa, B

Oregon

Linfield College, B
Oregon State University, B
Pacific University, B
Portland State University, BM
Reed College, B
University of Oregon, BMD
Western Oregon University, B
Willamette University, B

Pennsylvania

Allegheny College, B
Bryn Mawr College, B
Bucknell University, B
Carnegie Mellon University, B
Dickinson College, B
Elizabethtown College, B
Franklin & Marshall College, B
Gettysburg College, B
Haverford College, B
Juniata College, B
La Salle University, B
Lafayette College, B
Lebanon Valley College, B
Lehigh University, B
Lycoming College, B
Messiah College, B
Millersville University of Pennsylvania, BM
Moravian College, B
Penn State Abington, B
Penn State Altoona, B
Penn State Beaver, B
Penn State Berks, B
Penn State Brandywine, B
Penn State DuBois, B
Penn State Erie, The Behrend College, B
Penn State Fayette, The Eberly Campus, B
Penn State Greater Allegheny, B
Penn State Hazleton, B
Penn State Lehigh Valley, B
Penn State Mont Alto, B
Penn State New Kensington, B
Penn State Schuylkill, B
Penn State Shenango, B
Penn State University Park, BMD
Penn State Wilkes-Barre, B
Penn State Worthington Scranton, B
Penn State York, B
Saint Joseph's University, B
Susquehanna University, B
Swarthmore College, B
Temple University, B
University of Pennsylvania, BMD
University of Pittsburgh, B
The University of Scranton, B
Ursinus College, B
Washington & Jefferson College, B
West Chester University of Pennsylvania, B

Rhode Island

Brown University, BD
University of Rhode Island, B

South Carolina

College of Charleston, B
Converse College, B
Furman University, B
University of South Carolina, BM
Wofford College, B

South Dakota

Augustana University, B
Northern State University, B
South Dakota State University, B
The University of South Dakota, B

Tennessee

Belmont University, B
Lipscomb University, B

Middle Tennessee State University, M
Rhodes College, B
Sewanee: The University of the South, B
Tennessee Technological University, B
The University of Tennessee, BMD
Vanderbilt University, BMD

Texas

Austin College, B
Austin Community College District, A
Baylor University, B
Blinn College, A
Lee College, A
Rice University, B
Sam Houston State University, B
Southern Methodist University, B
Southwestern University, B
Texas A&M University, B
Texas Christian University, B
Texas State University, B
Texas Tech University, BM
Trinity University, B
University of Dallas, B
University of North Texas, B
The University of Texas at Arlington, B
The University of Texas at Austin, BMD
The University of Texas at El Paso, B

Utah

University of Utah, B
Utah State University, B
Weber State University, AB

Vermont

Middlebury College, BMD
University of Vermont, M

Virginia

Christopher Newport University, B
The College of William and Mary, B
Hampden-Sydney College, B
Randolph-Macon College, B
University of Virginia, BMD
Virginia Polytechnic Institute and State University, B
Virginia Wesleyan College, B
Washington and Lee University, B

Washington

Central Washington University, B
Pacific Lutheran University, B
University of Puget Sound, B
University of Washington, MD
Western Washington University, B
Whitman College, B

Wisconsin

Beloit College, B
Carthage College, B
Concordia University Wisconsin, B
Lakeland College, B
Lawrence University, B
Marquette University, B
St. Norbert College, B
University of Wisconsin - La Crosse, B
University of Wisconsin - Madison, MD
University of Wisconsin - Milwaukee, M
University of Wisconsin - Oshkosh, B
University of Wisconsin - Platteville, B
University of Wisconsin - Stevens Point, B
University of Wisconsin - Whitewater, B
Wisconsin Lutheran College, B

Wyoming

University of Wyoming, BM

Canada

Alberta

University of Alberta, BMD
University of Calgary, BM
University of Lethbridge, BM

British Columbia

The University of British Columbia, BMD
University of Victoria, BM

Manitoba

University of Manitoba, BM
The University of Winnipeg, B

Maritime Provinces: New Brunswick

Mount Allison University, B
University of New Brunswick Fredericton, B
University of New Brunswick Saint John, B

Maritime Provinces: Nova Scotia

Dalhousie University, BM
Mount Saint Vincent University, B
Saint Mary's University, B
University of King's College, B

Maritime Provinces: Prince Edward Island

University of Prince Edward Island, B

Newfoundland and Labrador

Memorial University of Newfoundland, BM

Ontario

Brock University, B
Carleton University, B
McMaster University, B
Queen's University at Kingston, BMD
Trent University, B
University of Ottawa, B
University of Toronto, BMD
University of Waterloo, BMD
The University of Western Ontario, B
University of Windsor, B
York University, B

Quebec

Bishop's University, B
McGill University, MD
Université de Montréal, BMD

Saskatchewan

University of Regina, B
University of Saskatchewan, M

GERMAN LANGUAGE TEACHER EDUCATION

United States

Alabama

Auburn University, B

California

California Lutheran University, B

Colorado

Colorado State University, B

Delaware

Delaware State University, B
University of Delaware, B

District of Columbia

The Catholic University of America, B

Idaho

Boise State University, B

Illinois

Augustana College, B
Elmhurst College, B
University of Illinois at Chicago, B
University of Illinois at Urbana - Champaign, B

Indiana

Indiana University Bloomington, B
Indiana University - Purdue University Fort Wayne, B
Indiana University South Bend, B
University of Evansville, B
Valparaiso University, B

Iowa

The University of Iowa, B

Kansas

Washburn University, B

Michigan

Adrian College, B
Albion College, B
Alma College, B
Calvin College, B
Eastern Michigan University, B
Grand Valley State University, B
Hope College, B
Michigan State University, B
Western Michigan University, B

Minnesota

Concordia College, B

Missouri

Missouri State University, B
Washington University in St. Louis, B

Nebraska

Hastings College, B
University of Nebraska - Lincoln, B

New York

Canisius College, B
Hofstra University, B
Hunter College of the City University of New York, B
Ithaca College, B

North Dakota

Minot State University, B

Ohio

Miami University, B
Miami University Hamilton, B
Muskingum University, B
Ohio Northern University, B
Ohio University, B
Ohio Wesleyan University, B

Oklahoma

University of Central Oklahoma, B

Pennsylvania

Messiah College, B
Saint Joseph's University, B

South Dakota

The University of South Dakota, B

Tennessee

The University of Tennessee at Martin, B

Utah

Weber State University, B

Washington

Western Washington University, B

Wisconsin

Concordia University Wisconsin, B

Canada

Alberta

University of Alberta, B
University of Lethbridge, B

Ontario

University of Windsor, B

GERMAN STUDIES

United States

California

Pomona College, B
Stanford University, B
University of California, Irvine, B
University of California, Riverside, B

Connecticut

Wesleyan University, B

District of Columbia

American University, B

Georgia

Emory University, B

Illinois

University of Illinois at Chicago, B

Iowa

Central College, B
Coe College, B

Massachusetts

Bard College at Simon's Rock, B
Mount Holyoke College, B
Smith College, B
University of Massachusetts Amherst, B
Wellesley College, B
Wheaton College, B

Michigan

Northern Michigan University, B

New York

Bard College, B
Barnard College, B
Columbia University, B
Cornell University, B
Fordham University, B
Hamilton College, B
Ithaca College, B

North Carolina

North Carolina State University, B

Ohio

Case Western Reserve University, B
The College of Wooster, B

Oregon

Lewis & Clark College, B
Linfield College, B

Pennsylvania

Franklin & Marshall College, B
Kutztown University of Pennsylvania, B
Moravian College, B
University of Pittsburgh, B
The University of Scranton, B

Rhode Island

Brown University, B

Virginia

University of Richmond, B

Canada

Alberta

University of Alberta, B

British Columbia

University of Victoria, B

Manitoba

The University of Winnipeg, B

Ontario

Brock University, B
Queen's University at Kingston, B
The University of Western Ontario, B
University of Windsor, B
York University, B

Quebec

McGill University, B
Université de Montréal, B

GERMANIC LANGUAGES, LITERATURES, AND LINGUISTICS

United States

Colorado

University of Colorado Boulder, B

Florida

Jacksonville University, B
New College of Florida, B

Indiana

Indiana University Bloomington, B

Kansas

The University of Kansas, B

Michigan

Calvin College, B
Eastern Michigan University, B
Grand Valley State University, B
Lansing Community College, A

Minnesota

University of Minnesota, Twin Cities Campus, B

Missouri

Washington University in St. Louis, B

New York

Columbia University, School of General Studies, B

Ohio

Ohio Northern University, B

Oklahoma

University of Oklahoma, B

Texas

The University of Texas at San Antonio, B

Washington

University of Washington, B

Wisconsin

University of Wisconsin - Eau Claire, B
University of Wisconsin - Green Bay, B
University of Wisconsin - Madison, B
University of Wisconsin - Milwaukee, B
Wisconsin Lutheran College, B

Canada

Alberta

University of Alberta, B

GERONTOLOGICAL NURSING

United States

Arizona

Arizona State University at the Tempe campus, O
University of Phoenix - Phoenix Campus, O

California

California State University, Stanislaus, M
Loma Linda University, M
Point Loma Nazarene University, M
San Jose State University, M
University of Phoenix - Bay Area Campus, M
University of San Diego, M

Colorado

University of Colorado Colorado Springs, M

Connecticut

Western Connecticut State University, M

Delaware

University of Delaware, MO
Wilmington University, M

Florida

Florida Atlantic University, O
Florida Southern College, M
University of South Florida, MD

Georgia

Armstrong State University, M

Illinois

Rush University, D
Saint Francis Medical Center College of Nursing, M
University of Illinois at Chicago, M

Indiana

Indiana University - Purdue University Fort Wayne, M

Iowa

Allen College, MO

Kansas

The University of Kansas, O

Louisiana

Southern University and Agricultural and Mechanical College, D

Maine

University of Southern Maine, MO

Massachusetts

Boston College, M
Salem State University, M
University of Massachusetts Amherst, D
University of Massachusetts Lowell, MO

Michigan

Oakland University, MO
University of Michigan, M
Wayne State University, M

Minnesota

Capella University, M
St. Catherine University, M
University of Minnesota, Twin Cities Campus, M
Walden University, M

Missouri

Goldfarb School of Nursing at Barnes-Jewish College, M
Maryville University of Saint Louis, M
Research College of Nursing, M
University of Missouri, DO
University of Missouri - Kansas City, D
University of Missouri - St. Louis, O

Nebraska

Creighton University, MD

New Jersey

Felician University, MO
Monmouth University, MO
Seton Hall University, MD

New York

College of Mount Saint Vincent, M
College of Staten Island of the City University of New York, MO
Columbia University, MO
Hunter College of the City University of New York, M
Le Moyne College, MO
Lehman College of the City University of New York, M
Molloy College, MO
Nazareth College of Rochester, M
New York University, DO
University at Buffalo, the State University of New York, D

North Carolina

Duke University, MO
The University of North Carolina at Chapel Hill, M
The University of North Carolina at Greensboro, MO

North Dakota

University of North Dakota, M

Ohio

Case Western Reserve University, M
Kent State University, MD
Mount Carmel College of Nursing, M

Oregon

Oregon Health & Science University, MDO

Pennsylvania

Gwynedd Mercy University, M
La Salle University, MO
University of Pittsburgh, D
West Chester University of Pennsylvania, M
York College of Pennsylvania, M

Rhode Island

University of Rhode Island, M

South Carolina

Medical University of South Carolina, MD

Tennessee

Vanderbilt University, M

Texas

Texas Christian University, M
The University of Texas at Austin, M
The University of Texas Health Science Center at San Antonio, O

Utah

Independence University, M
University of Utah, MO

Virginia

Hampton University, M
James Madison University, M

Washington

Seattle Pacific University, M
Seattle University, M

Wisconsin

Concordia University Wisconsin, M
Marquette University, D
University of Wisconsin - Eau Claire, D
University of Wisconsin - Madison, D

U.S. Territories: Puerto Rico

Caribbean University, M
University of Puerto Rico, Medical Sciences Campus, M

GERONTOLOGY

United States

Arizona

Arizona State University at the Tempe campus, O

Arkansas

Arkansas State University, O
University of Arkansas at Little Rock, O

California

California State University, East Bay, B
California State University, Fullerton, M
California State University, Long Beach, M
California State University, Sacramento, B
El Camino College, A
Mount Saint Mary's University, B
Saddleback College, A
San Diego State University, BM
San Francisco State University, M
San Jose State University, O
University of La Verne, MO
University of Phoenix - Central Valley Campus, M
University of Southern California, BMDO

Colorado

University of Northern Colorado, M
University of Phoenix - Colorado Springs Downtown Campus, M

Connecticut

Gateway Community College, A
Quinnipiac University, B
University of Saint Joseph, O

District of Columbia

University of Phoenix - Washington D.C. Campus, M

Florida

Bethune-Cookman University, B
South Florida State College, A
State College of Florida Manatee-Sarasota, B
University of North Florida, M
University of South Florida, BMDO
University of West Florida, M

Georgia

Georgia State University, MO
University of Georgia, O

Hawaii

University of Hawaii at Manoa, O
University of Phoenix - Hawaii Campus, M

Illinois

City Colleges of Chicago, Wilbur Wright College, A
Concordia University Chicago, M
Eastern Illinois University, M
Northeastern Illinois University, M
University of Illinois at Springfield, M

Indiana

Ball State University, M
Holy Cross College, A
Manchester University, A
Martin University, B
University of Indianapolis, MO
Valparaiso University, MO

Iowa

University of Northern Iowa, B

Kansas

Kansas State University, MO
The University of Kansas, MDO
Wichita State University, BM

Kentucky

Morehead State University, M
Thomas More College, A
University of Kentucky, DO
University of Louisville, M

Louisiana

University of Louisiana at Monroe, MO

Maryland

Anne Arundel Community College, A
McDaniel College, MO
Towson University, BMO
University of Maryland, Baltimore County, MD
University of Maryland University College, B

Massachusetts

North Shore Community College, A
University of Massachusetts Boston, MDO

Michigan

Central Michigan University, O
Eastern Michigan University, O
Madonna University, AB
Siena Heights University, A
Wayne State University, DO

Minnesota

Bethel University, M
Capella University, M
Minnesota State University Mankato, MO
Minnesota State University Moorhead, B
St. Cloud State University, BM

Missouri

Lindenwood University, M
Missouri State University, B
University of Central Missouri, M
University of Missouri, O
University of Missouri - St. Louis, MO
Washington University in St. Louis, MD
Webster University, M

Nebraska

University of Nebraska - Lincoln, D
University of Nebraska at Omaha, BMO

New Hampshire

Lakes Region Community College, A

New Jersey

Thomas Edison State University, B

New York

Adelphi University, O
Alfred University, B
Canisius College, B
The College at Brockport, State University of New York, O
Eugenio María de Hostos Community College of the City University of New York, A
Genesee Community College, A
Ithaca College, B
New York University, D
St. Bonaventure University, B
State University of New York College at Oneonta, B
Utica College, O
York College of the City University of New York, B

North Carolina

Appalachian State University, MO
Barton College, B
East Carolina University, O
Sandhills Community College, A
The University of North Carolina at Charlotte, MO
The University of North Carolina at Greensboro, MO
The University of North Carolina Wilmington, MO
University of Phoenix - Charlotte Campus, M
Winston-Salem State University, B

North Dakota

North Dakota State University, MDO

Ohio

Bowling Green State University, B
Case Western Reserve University, B
John Carroll University, B
Miami University, BMD
Miami University Hamilton, B
Ohio Dominican University, A
Sinclair Community College, A
The University of Akron, D
The University of Toledo, O
Wright State University, B
Youngstown State University, BM

Oklahoma

University of Central Oklahoma, M

Oregon

Oregon Health & Science University, MO
Portland Community College, A
Portland State University, O

Pennsylvania

California University of Pennsylvania, B
Gwynedd Mercy University, B
La Salle University, O
Marywood University, BMD
Saint Joseph's University, M
Slippery Rock University of Pennsylvania, M
Temple University, D

Rhode Island

University of Rhode Island, M

South Carolina

Midlands Technical College, A
University of South Carolina, O

Tennessee

Middle Tennessee State University, O
The University of Tennessee, M

Texas

Texas State University, M
University of North Texas, BM

Utah

University of Utah, MO

Virginia

Virginia Commonwealth University, MDO

Washington

Spokane Falls Community College, A

West Virginia

BridgeValley Community and Technical College (South Charleston), A

Wisconsin

University of Wisconsin - Milwaukee, O
Wisconsin Indianhead Technical College, A

U.S. Territories: Puerto Rico

Pontifical Catholic University of Puerto Rico, B
University of Puerto Rico, Medical Sciences Campus, MO

Canada

British Columbia

Simon Fraser University, MD

Maritime Provinces: New Brunswick

St. Thomas University, B

Maritime Provinces: Nova Scotia

Mount Saint Vincent University, BM

Ontario

Lakehead University, BM
McMaster University, B
York University, B

Quebec

Bishop's University, B
Université Laval, O
Université de Sherbrooke, M

Saskatchewan

University of Regina, BM

GLAZIER

United States

Missouri

Metropolitan Community College - Kansas City, A

GRAPHIC COMMUNICATIONS

United States

Alabama

Bishop State Community College, A
H. Councill Trenholm State Community College, A

Arizona

Arizona State University at the Polytechnic campus, B

California

California Polytechnic State University, San Luis Obispo, B

Colorado

Aims Community College, A

District of Columbia

University of the District of Columbia, A

Florida

Eastern Florida State College, A
Full Sail University, B
Rasmussen College Fort Myers, B
Rasmussen College Land O' Lakes, B
Rasmussen College New Port Richey, B
Rasmussen College Ocala, B
Rasmussen College Tampa/Brandon, B

Georgia

University of Phoenix - Augusta Campus, A

Hawaii

Kapiolani Community College, A

Illinois

Bradley University, B
Illinois State University, B
Prairie State College, A
Rasmussen College Aurora, B
Rasmussen College Mokena/Tinley Park, B
Rasmussen College Rockford, B
Rasmussen College Romeoville/Joliet, B
School of the Art Institute of Chicago, B

Iowa

Grand View University, B
Iowa Lakes Community College, A
Iowa Western Community College, A
Kirkwood Community College, A
University of Northern Iowa, B

Kansas

Fort Scott Community College, A
Hutchinson Community College, A

Kentucky

Murray State University, B
Sullivan College of Technology and Design, AB

Maine

Central Maine Community College, A

Maryland

University of Maryland University College, B

Michigan

Gogebic Community College, A

Minnesota

Rasmussen College Blaine, B
Rasmussen College Bloomington, B
Rasmussen College Brooklyn Park, B
Rasmussen College Eagan, B
Rasmussen College Lake Elmo/Woodbury, B
Rasmussen College Mankato, B
Rasmussen College Moorhead, A
Rasmussen College St. Cloud, B

New Jersey

Middlesex County College, A
University of Phoenix - Jersey City Campus, A

New York

Rochester Institute of Technology, B

North Carolina

Chowan University, B
Piedmont Community College, A

North Dakota

Rasmussen College Fargo, B
University of North Dakota, B

Ohio

Notre Dame College, B
Wright State University - Lake Campus, AB

Oklahoma

Oklahoma City Community College, A
Southern Nazarene University, B

Pennsylvania

Thaddeus Stevens College of Technology, A
Westmoreland County Community College, A

Rhode Island

New England Institute of Technology, AB
Roger Williams University, B

Texas

Sam Houston State University, B
University of Phoenix - Houston Campus, B

Vermont

Castleton University, B

Washington

Clark College, A
Eastern Washington University, B
Walla Walla University, AB

West Virginia

Pierpont Community & Technical College, A

Wisconsin

Carroll University, B
Fox Valley Technical College, A
Milwaukee Area Technical College, A
Northcentral Technical College, A
Rasmussen College Appleton, B
Rasmussen College Green Bay, B
Rasmussen College Wausau, B
University of Wisconsin - Stout, B

Waukesha County Technical College, A

Canada

Maritime Provinces: New Brunswick

University of New Brunswick Saint John, B

Ontario

Ryerson University, B

GRAPHIC DESIGN

United States

Alabama

Auburn University, B
Samford University, B
Spring Hill College, B
Virginia College in Birmingham, A

Arizona

Arizona State University at the Tempe campus, B
The Art Institute of Phoenix, A
The Art Institute of Tucson, A
Glendale Community College, A
Penn Foster College, A
Phoenix College, A
Sessions College for Professional Design, A
Southwest University of Visual Arts, B
Yavapai College, A

Arkansas

Arkansas Tech University, B
Harding University, B
John Brown University, B
Ouachita Baptist University, B
University of Arkansas - Fort Smith, B

California

Academy of Art University, ABM
Art Center College of Design, B
The Art Institute of California - Hollywood, a campus of Argosy University, A
The Art Institute of California - Inland Empire, a campus of Argosy University, AB
The Art Institute of California - Los Angeles, a campus of Argosy University, A
The Art Institute of California - Orange County, a campus of Argosy University, A
The Art Institute of California - Sacramento, a campus of Argosy University, A
The Art Institute of California - San Diego, a campus of Argosy University, AB
The Art Institute of California - San Francisco, a campus of Argosy University, A
Brooks Institute, B
Butte College, A
California College of the Arts, M
California Institute of the Arts, MO
California State Polytechnic University, Pomona, B
California State University, Dominguez Hills, B
California State University, Fresno, B
California State University, Fullerton, M
California State University, Long Beach, B
California State University, Los Angeles, M
California State University, Sacramento, B
Chabot College, A
Chapman University, B
City College of San Francisco, A
College of the Canyons, A
College of the Redwoods, A
College of San Mateo, A
Concordia University Irvine, B
Cosumnes River College, A
Dominican University of California, B
FIDM/Fashion Institute of Design & Merchandising, Los Angeles Campus, AB
FIDM/Fashion Institute of Design & Merchandising, Orange County Campus, A
FIDM/Fashion Institute of Design & Merchandising, San Francisco Campus, A
Foothill College, A

Fresno City College, A
Fullerton College, A
Laguna College of Art & Design, B
Long Beach City College, A
Mt. Sierra College, B
Otis College of Art and Design, M
Pacific Union College, AB
Palomar College, A
Pasadena City College, A
Platt College San Diego, A
Point Loma Nazarene University, B
San Diego State University, BM
San Jose State University, B
Santa Monica College, A
Santa Rosa Junior College, A
Sierra College, A
Southwestern College, A
University of San Francisco, B

Colorado

Adams State University, B
Arapahoe Community College, A
The Art Institute of Colorado, B
Colorado Mesa University, B
Colorado State University, B
Colorado Technical University Colorado Springs, AB
Colorado Technical University Denver South, AB
Community College of Denver, A
Rocky Mountain College of Art + Design, B
University of Denver, B
Western State Colorado University, B

Connecticut

Albertus Magnus College, B
Norwalk Community College, A
Paier College of Art, Inc., B
Three Rivers Community College, A
University of Bridgeport, B
University of Hartford, B
University of New Haven, B
Yale University, M

Delaware

Delaware College of Art and Design, A

District of Columbia

American University, B
University of the District of Columbia, AB

Florida

The Art Institute of Fort Lauderdale, AB
The Art Institute of Tampa, a branch of Miami International University of Art & Design, AB
Broward College, A
College of Business and Technology - Main Campus, A
College of Business and Technology - Miami Gardens, A
Digital Media Arts College, BM
Flagler College, B
Florida Agricultural and Mechanical University, B
Florida Atlantic University, M
Florida Gateway College, A
Florida State University, B
Full Sail University, BM
Jose Maria Vargas University, B
Miami International University of Art & Design, B
Palm Beach Atlantic University, B
Pensacola State College, AB
Ringling College of Art and Design, B
South Florida State College, A
Southern Technical College (Tampa), A
University of Florida, B
University of Miami, BM
The University of Tampa, B

Georgia

Georgia Southern University, BM
Georgia State University, M
Mercer University, B
Savannah College of Art and Design, M

Idaho

Boise State University, B
Northwest Nazarene University, B

Stevens-Henager College (Boise), AB

Illinois

American Academy of Art, B
Augustana College, B
Benedictine University, B
Bradley University, B
Columbia College Chicago, B
DePaul University, B
Elgin Community College, A
Elmhurst College, B
Highland Community College, A
Illinois Central College, A
The Illinois Institute of Art - Chicago, AB
The Illinois Institute of Art - Schaumburg, AB
Illinois State University, M
Illinois Valley Community College, A
John A. Logan College, A
John Wood Community College, A
Judson University, B
Lincoln Land Community College, A
North Central College, B
Oakton Community College, A
Parkland College, A
Quincy University, B
Rend Lake College, A
Robert Morris University Illinois, B
School of the Art Institute of Chicago, BM
Spoon River College, A
Trinity Christian College, B
University of Illinois at Chicago, BM
University of Illinois at Urbana - Champaign, BM
Waubonsee Community College, A
Western Illinois University, O

Indiana

The Art Institute of Indianapolis, AB
Grace College, B
Huntington University, B
Indiana State University, M
Indiana University - Purdue University Fort Wayne,
    B
International Business College (Fort Wayne), AB
International Business College (Indianapolis), A
Ivy Tech Community College - Southwest, A
Marian University, B
University of Notre Dame, M

Iowa

Briar Cliff University, B
Clarke University, B
Dordt College, B
Drake University, B
Grand View University, B
Iowa Lakes Community College, A
Iowa State University of Science and Technology,
    BM
Morningside College, B
Mount Mercy University, B
Northwestern College, B
Simpson College, B

Kansas

Baker University, B
Barton County Community College, A
Cloud County Community College, A
Fort Hays State University, B
Johnson County Community College, A
Kansas Wesleyan University, B
MidAmerica Nazarene University, B
Pittsburg State University, M
Tabor College, B
The University of Kansas, B
Wichita State University, B

Kentucky

Brescia University, B
Kentucky Wesleyan College, B
Morehead State University, M
Sullivan College of Technology and Design, AB

Louisiana

Louisiana State University and Agricultural & Me-
    chanical College, M
Louisiana Tech University, M

Maine

Maine College of Art, B

Maryland

Anne Arundel Community College, A
Harford Community College, A
Maryland Institute College of Art, BMO
University of Baltimore, MD

Massachusetts

Anna Maria College, B
Assumption College, B
Becker College, B
Boston University, BM
Bridgewater State University, B
Bristol Community College, A
Curry College, B
Emmanuel College, B
Endicott College, B
Fitchburg State University, B
Lasell College, B
Massasoit Community College, A
Montserrat College of Art, B
Mount Ida College, B
Newbury College, B
Northeastern University, B
School of the Museum of Fine Arts, Boston, B
Stonehill College, B
Suffolk University, M

Michigan

Alma College, B
The Art Institute of Michigan, AB
Calvin College, B
Central Michigan University, B
College for Creative Studies, B
Ferris State University, AB
Jackson College, A
Kalamazoo Valley Community College, A
Kirtland Community College, A
Lake Michigan College, A
Lansing Community College, A
Lawrence Technological University, B
Madonna University, AB
Michigan State University, B
Mott Community College, A
Northern Michigan University, B
Oakland Community College, A
Oakland University, B
Saginaw Valley State University, B
Siena Heights University, B
Southwestern Michigan College, A
Spring Arbor University, B
University of Michigan, B
Wayne State University, M
Western Michigan University, B

Minnesota

Academy College, A
Augsburg College, B
Bethel University, B
Century College, A
Dakota County Technical College, A
Dunwoody College of Technology, A
Hennepin Technical College, A
Minneapolis Business College, A
Minneapolis College of Art and Design, MO
Minnesota School of Business - Richfield, A
Minnesota School of Business - St. Cloud, A
Minnesota State Community and Technical College,
    A
Minnesota State Community and Technical College -
    Moorhead, A
Minnesota State University Moorhead, B
North Hennepin Community College, A
Rochester Community and Technical College, A
Saint Mary's University of Minnesota, B
University of Minnesota, Duluth, B
University of Minnesota, Twin Cities Campus, B
University of Northwestern - St. Paul, B

Mississippi

Belhaven University, B
Hinds Community College, A
Mississippi College, B

Missouri

College of the Ozarks, B
Columbia College, B
Culver-Stockton College, B
Hickey College, A
Kansas City Art Institute, B
Maryville University of Saint Louis, B
Missouri College, A
Missouri Southern State University, B
Missouri Western State University, B
Park University, B
Stephens College, B
Washington University in St. Louis, B
William Woods University, B

Montana

Montana State University - Northern, AB

Nebraska

Bellevue University, B
Concordia University, Nebraska, B
Creative Center, AB
Creighton University, B
Doane University, B
Northeast Community College, A
Peru State College, B
Union College, AB
University of Nebraska at Omaha, B
Wayne State College, B

Nevada

The Art Institute of Las Vegas, B
University of Nevada, Las Vegas, B

New Hampshire

Colby-Sawyer College, B
Plymouth State University, B
Southern New Hampshire University, B

New Jersey

Bergen Community College, A
Berkeley College - Woodland Park Campus, B
Brookdale Community College, A
Caldwell University, B
Centenary College, B
County College of Morris, A
Montclair State University, B
Rider University, B
Rowan College at Burlington County, A

New Mexico

Eastern New Mexico University - Roswell, A
New Mexico State University - Alamogordo, A
Santa Fe University of Art and Design, B
Western New Mexico University, A

New York

Bryant & Stratton College - Amherst Campus, A
Bryant & Stratton College - Henrietta Campus, A
Bryant & Stratton College - Liverpool Campus, A
Cayuga County Community College, A
City College of the City University of New York, BM
Corning Community College, A
Daemen College, B
Eugene Lang College of Liberal Arts, B
Fashion Institute of Technology, B
Genesee Community College, A
Marymount Manhattan College, B
New York Institute of Technology, M
New York University, M
Parsons School of Design, A
Pratt Institute, ABM
Queens College of the City University of New York,
    B
Rochester Institute of Technology, BM
The Sage Colleges, B
St. John's University, B
St. Thomas Aquinas College, B
School of Visual Arts, BM
State University of New York College of Agriculture
    and Technology at Cobleskill, A
State University of New York College of Technology
    at Alfred, A
State University of New York College of Technology
    at Canton, B

State University of New York at New Paltz, B
Villa Maria College, AB
Wood Tobe - Coburn School, A

North Carolina

Appalachian State University, B
The Art Institute of Charlotte, a campus of South
   University, A
The Art Institute of Raleigh-Durham, a campus of
   South University, A
Campbell University, B
Chowan University, B
East Carolina University, M
Elizabeth City State University, B
Forsyth Technical Community College, A
High Point University, B
King's College, A
Lenoir Community College, A
Lenoir-Rhyne University, B
Mars Hill University, B
Meredith College, B
North Carolina Agricultural and Technical State Uni-
   versity, BM
North Carolina State University, BM
Queens University of Charlotte, B

North Dakota

University of North Dakota, B

Ohio

Antonelli College, A
Art Academy of Cincinnati, A
Baldwin Wallace University, B
Bluffton University, B
Bowling Green State University, M
Bradford School, A
Cedarville University, B
Cleveland Institute of Art, B
Davis College, A
Defiance College, AB
Kent State University, M
Malone University, B
Marietta College, B
Miami University Hamilton, B
Mount St. Joseph University, AB
Mount Vernon Nazarene University, B
Ohio Northern University, B
Ohio University, BM
The University of Akron, B
University of Cincinnati, M
University of Rio Grande, B
Walsh University, B
Wright State University, AB
Wright State University - Lake Campus, A
Xavier University, B
Youngstown State University, B

Oklahoma

East Central University, B
Oklahoma Baptist University, B
Oklahoma State University Institute of Technology, A
Oral Roberts University, B
Southwestern Oklahoma State University, B
University of Central Oklahoma, B

Oregon

The Art Institute of Portland, AB
Chemeketa Community College, A
Pacific Northwest College of Art, B
Portland State University, B

Pennsylvania

Antonelli Institute, A
The Art Institute of Philadelphia, AB
The Art Institute of Pittsburgh, AB
Bradford School, A
Cabrini University, B
California University of Pennsylvania, AB
Chatham University, B
Douglas Education Center, A
Drexel University, B
Harrisburg Area Community College, A
Holy Family University, B
Lehigh Carbon Community College, A
Luzerne County Community College, A

Mansfield University of Pennsylvania, B
Marywood University, BM
Mercyhurst University, B
Moore College of Art & Design, B
Northampton Community College, A
Penn State Abington, B
Penn State Altoona, B
Penn State Beaver, B
Penn State Berks, B
Penn State Brandywine, B
Penn State DuBois, B
Penn State Erie, The Behrend College, B
Penn State Fayette, The Eberly Campus, B
Penn State Greater Allegheny, B
Penn State Hazleton, B
Penn State Lehigh Valley, B
Penn State Mont Alto, B
Penn State New Kensington, B
Penn State Schuylkill, B
Penn State Shenango, B
Penn State University Park, B
Penn State Wilkes-Barre, B
Penn State Worthington Scranton, B
Penn State York, B
Pennsylvania College of Art & Design, B
Philadelphia University, B
Saint Vincent College, B
South Hills School of Business & Technology (State
   College), A
Susquehanna University, B
Temple University, BM
The University of the Arts, B
University of Pennsylvania, O
Waynesburg University, B
Westmoreland County Community College, A

Rhode Island

Rhode Island College, B
Rhode Island School of Design, BM
Salve Regina University, B

South Carolina

Bob Jones University, BM
Coastal Carolina University, B
Coker College, B
Limestone College, B
Newberry College, B
South University, AB

South Dakota

South Dakota State University, B
The University of South Dakota, M

Tennessee

The Art Institute of Tennessee - Nashville, a branch
   of The Art Institute of Atlanta, AB
Carson-Newman University, B
Nossi College of Art, B
O'More College of Design, B
Southern Adventist University, B
University of Memphis, M
The University of Tennessee, M
The University of Tennessee at Martin, B

Texas

Abilene Christian University, B
The Art Institute of Austin, a branch of The Art Insti-
   tute of Houston, A
The Art Institute of Dallas, a campus of South Uni-
   versity, A
The Art Institute of Houston, AB
The Art Institute of San Antonio, a branch of The Art
   Institute of Houston, A
Brookhaven College, A
Cedar Valley College, A
Collin County Community College District, A
Hardin-Simmons University, B
Lamar University, B
Prairie View A&M University, B
St. Edward's University, B
Schreiner University, B
Texas Christian University, B
Texas State Technical College, A
Texas State University, M
University of Houston, B

University of the Incarnate Word, B
University of Mary Hardin-Baylor, B
Wade College, A
Wayland Baptist University, B
West Texas A&M University, B

Utah

Brigham Young University, B
Dixie State University, B
Salt Lake Community College, A
Southern Utah University, B
Stevens-Henager College (West Haven), A
University of Utah, M

Vermont

Castleton University, B
Champlain College, B
Community College of Vermont, A

Virginia

Emory & Henry College, B
George Mason University, M
Liberty University, B
Tidewater Community College, A
Virginia Commonwealth University, B

Washington

The Art Institute of Seattle, AB
Central Washington University, B
Cornish College of the Arts, B
Eastern Washington University, B
Everett Community College, A
Walla Walla University, B

West Virginia

Alderson Broaddus University, B
Concord University, B
West Virginia University, M

Wisconsin

Bryant & Stratton College - Wauwatosa Campus, A
Cardinal Stritch University, BM
Carthage College, B
Concordia University Wisconsin, B
Edgewood College, B
Gateway Technical College, A
Marian University, B
Milwaukee Area Technical College, A
Milwaukee Institute of Art and Design, B
Moraine Park Technical College, A
Mount Mary University, B
Northland College, B
St. Norbert College, B
University of Wisconsin - Stout, B
Waukesha County Technical College, A

Wyoming

Casper College, A
Central Wyoming College, A

U.S. Territories: Guam

University of Guam, M

U.S. Territories: Puerto Rico

Atlantic University College, M
Columbia Centro Universitario (Caguas), A
Inter American University of Puerto Rico, San
   Germán Campus, AM
Universidad del Turabo, B

Canada

Alberta

Alberta College of Art & Design, B

British Columbia

The Art Institute of Vancouver, B
University of the Fraser Valley, A
Vancouver Island University, B

Maritime Provinces: Nova Scotia

NSCAD University, B

Quebec

Université Laval, M

GRAPHIC AND PRINTING EQUIPMENT OPERATOR PRODUCTION

United States

California

City College of San Francisco, A
Fresno City College, A
Fullerton College, A
Golden West College, A
Laney College, A
Mission College, A
Modesto Junior College, A
Moorpark College, A
Palomar College, A
Pasadena City College, A
Riverside City College, A
Sacramento City College, A
San Diego City College, A

Georgia

Georgia Southern University, B

Idaho

Lewis-Clark State College, AB

Illinois

College of DuPage, A
Lake Land College, A
Rock Valley College, A
Western Illinois University, B

Indiana

Vincennes University, A

Iowa

Clinton Community College, A
Iowa Lakes Community College, A

Kansas

Flint Hills Technical College, A

Kentucky

Sullivan College of Technology and Design, A

Maine

Central Maine Community College, A

Michigan

Macomb Community College, A

Minnesota

South Central College, A

Mississippi

Mississippi Delta Community College, A

Missouri

Mineral Area College, A
Moberly Area Community College, A
Ozarks Technical Community College, A

Nebraska

Central Community College - Hastings Campus, A
Metropolitan Community College, A

New Hampshire

Lakes Region Community College, A

New Jersey

Rowan College at Burlington County, A

New York

Erie Community College, South Campus, A
Fulton-Montgomery Community College, A
Monroe Community College, A

Orange County Community College, A

North Carolina

Central Piedmont Community College, A
Chowan University, AB

Ohio

Columbus State Community College, A
Sinclair Community College, A

Oklahoma

Northern Oklahoma College, A
Tulsa Community College, A

Oregon

Chemeketa Community College, A

Pennsylvania

Luzerne County Community College, A

Texas

Central Texas College, A
Eastfield College, A
Tarrant County College District, A

Utah

Dixie State University, A

Virginia

Northern Virginia Community College, A

Washington

Clover Park Technical College, A
Seattle Central College, A
Shoreline Community College, A

West Virginia

Fairmont State University, B

Wisconsin

Madison Area Technical College, A

Wyoming

Northwest College, A

U.S. Territories: Puerto Rico

University of Puerto Rico in Carolina, AB

GREENHOUSE OPERATIONS AND MANAGEMENT

United States

Minnesota

Century College, A
Hennepin Technical College, A
Rochester Community and Technical College, A
University of Minnesota, Crookston, B

North Dakota

Dakota College at Bottineau, A

Ohio

The Ohio State University Agricultural Technical Institute, A

Pennsylvania

Community College of Allegheny County, A

GROUND TRANSPORTATION

United States

Kansas

Johnson County Community College, A

GUNSMITHING/GUNSMITH

United States

Arizona

Yavapai College, A

Colorado

Colorado School of Trades, A
Trinidad State Junior College, A

North Carolina

Fayetteville Technical Community College, A
Lenoir Community College, A
Montgomery Community College, A

Oklahoma

Murray State College, A

HAIR STYLING/STYLIST AND HAIR DESIGN

United States

Colorado

IBMC College (Fort Collins), A

HAZARDOUS MATERIALS MANAGEMENT AND WASTE TECHNOLOGY/TECHNICIAN

United States

Alaska

University of Alaska Fairbanks, M

California

Butte College, A
Fresno City College, A
Fullerton College, A
Humboldt State University, M
Merritt College, A
Palo Verde College, A
Sierra College, A
Southwestern College, A
University of Southern California, M

Colorado

University of Colorado Denver, M

Connecticut

University of New Haven, M

Florida

Pensacola State College, A

Idaho

Idaho State University, M

Kansas

Barton County Community College, A
Kansas City Kansas Community College, A

Massachusetts

Tufts University, MD

Montana

Fort Peck Community College, A

New Jersey

Rutgers University - New Brunswick, MD

New Mexico

New Mexico Institute of Mining and Technology, M

Ohio

Ohio University - Chillicothe, A
The University of Findlay, B

South Carolina

University of South Carolina, MD

Texas

Odessa College, A

Wisconsin

Marquette University, O

HEALTH AIDE

United States

Arizona

Central Arizona College, A

California

National University, A

Colorado

Morgan Community College, B

Indiana

Ivy Tech Community College - Kokomo, A
Ivy Tech Community College - Lafayette, A
Ivy Tech Community College - Wabash Valley, A

Kansas

Allen Community College, A

Nebraska

Northeast Community College, A

Texas

Texarkana College, A

Washington

Edmonds Community College, A

HEALTH AIDES/ATTENDANTS/ ORDERLIES

United States

Kansas

Barton County Community College, A

HEALTH COMMUNICATION

United States

California

Brandman University, M
Chapman University, M
San Diego State University, B
University of Southern California, MD

District of Columbia

The George Washington University, M

Florida

University of Florida, MO

Illinois

DePaul University, M
Southern Illinois University Edwardsville, M

Indiana

Indiana University - Purdue University Indianapolis, MD

Kansas

Kansas State University, M

Louisiana

Tulane University, M

Maryland

Johns Hopkins University, M

Massachusetts

Boston University, M
Emerson College, M
Fitchburg State University, M
Lasell College, MO
Tufts University, MO

Michigan

Cornerstone University, B
Grand Valley State University, B
Michigan State University, M
Wayne State University, O

Missouri

Southeast Missouri State University, B
University of Missouri, M

New York

Cornell University, MD
Stony Brook University, State University of New York, O

North Carolina

East Carolina University, M
The University of North Carolina at Charlotte, M

North Dakota

North Dakota State University, B

Ohio

Ashland University, B
Cleveland State University, O
Ohio University, D
Ohio University - Eastern, B

Pennsylvania

Juniata College, B

Texas

University of Houston, BM

Wisconsin

Marquette University, M

HEALTH EDUCATION

United States

Alabama

Alabama State University, M
Auburn University, MDO
The University of Alabama, MD
The University of Alabama at Birmingham, MD
University of South Alabama, M

Arizona

Arizona State University at the Tempe campus, D
Grand Canyon University, D
University of Phoenix - Online Campus, O

Arkansas

Arkansas State University, O
Harding University, M
University of Arkansas, MD
University of Arkansas at Little Rock, M
University of Arkansas for Medical Sciences, M
University of Central Arkansas, M

California

California State University, Long Beach, M
California State University, Los Angeles, M
California State University, Northridge, M
California State University, San Bernardino, M
California State University, San Marcos, M
John F. Kennedy University, M
Loma Linda University, MD
Mills College, M
San Francisco State University, M
San Jose State University, M
Trident University International, MO
University of San Francisco, M
University of Southern California, M

Colorado

Colorado State University - Pueblo, M
University of Colorado Denver, MD
University of Northern Colorado, M
University of Phoenix - Colorado Springs Downtown Campus, M

Connecticut

Southern Connecticut State University, M

District of Columbia

American University, MO
Howard University, M
University of Phoenix - Washington D.C. Campus, M

Florida

Florida State University, M
Keiser University, M
University of Florida, MDO
University of West Florida, M

Georgia

Albany State University, M
Columbus State University, M
Emory University, MD
Georgia College & State University, M
Georgia Southern University, MD
Georgia State University, M
University of Georgia, MD

Idaho

Idaho State University, M

Illinois

Benedictine University, M
Illinois State University, M
Southern Illinois University Carbondale, MD
Southern Illinois University Edwardsville, MDO
University of Illinois at Chicago, M
University of Illinois at Springfield, O
Western Illinois University, MO

Indiana

Indiana University Bloomington, M
Indiana University - Purdue University Indianapolis, M
Purdue University, MD

Iowa

University of Northern Iowa, M

Kansas

Fort Hays State University, M
The University of Kansas, MDO
Washburn University, M

Kentucky

Eastern Kentucky University, M
Morehead State University, M
Union College, M
University of Louisville, M

Louisiana

Nicholls State University, M
Northwestern State University of Louisiana, M
Southeastern Louisiana University, M
Tulane University, M

Maine

Saint Joseph's College of Maine, M
University of New England, MO

Maryland

Johns Hopkins University, MO
University of Maryland, Baltimore County, M
University of Maryland, College Park, MD

Massachusetts

Brandeis University, D
Cambridge College, MO
Framingham State University, M
Massachusetts College of Liberal Arts, M
Simmons College, O
University of Massachusetts Amherst, MD
Worcester State University, M

Michigan

Eastern Michigan University, MO
University of Michigan, MD
University of Michigan - Flint, M
Wayne State University, MDO
Western Michigan University, DO

Minnesota

Minnesota State University Mankato, MO
Walden University, MD

Mississippi

Alcorn State University, M
Delta State University, M
Jackson State University, M
Mississippi University for Women, M
University of Southern Mississippi, M

Missouri

Logan University, D
Northwest Missouri State University, M
University of Missouri, MD
University of Missouri - Kansas City, M
Washington University in St. Louis, M

Montana

Montana State University, M
University of Montana, M

Nebraska

College of Saint Mary, D
University of Nebraska at Omaha, MD

New Hampshire

Plymouth State University, M

New Jersey

The College of New Jersey, M
Montclair State University, M
New Jersey City University, M
Rutgers University - New Brunswick, MD
Rutgers University - Newark, MD

New Mexico

New Mexico Highlands University, M
University of New Mexico, M

New York

Adelphi University, MO
The College at Brockport, State University of New
York, M
Daemen College, M
Excelsior College, M
Ithaca College, M
Lehman College of the City University of New York,
M
State University of New York College at Cortland, M

North Carolina

East Carolina University, M
North Carolina Agricultural and Technical State University, M
University of Phoenix - Charlotte Campus, M
Wingate University, M

Ohio

Cleveland State University, M
Kent State University, MD
University of Cincinnati, MD

The University of Toledo, MDO
Wright State University, M

Oklahoma

Northeastern State University, M
Oklahoma State University, MDO
University of Oklahoma Health Sciences Center, D

Oregon

Portland State University, M
Western Oregon University, M

Pennsylvania

Arcadia University, M
East Stroudsburg University of Pennsylvania, M
Eastern University, MO
Indiana University of Pennsylvania, M
Marywood University, D
Penn State Harrisburg, M
Pennsylvania College of Health Sciences, M
Saint Francis University, M
Saint Joseph's University, M
Temple University, M
Thomas Jefferson University, DO
University of Pittsburgh, M
West Chester University of Pennsylvania, M
Widener University, MD

Rhode Island

Rhode Island College, MO
University of Rhode Island, M

South Carolina

The Citadel, The Military College of South Carolina,
M
University of South Carolina, MDO

South Dakota

South Dakota State University, M

Tennessee

Austin Peay State University, M
Middle Tennessee State University, M
Tennessee Technological University, M
The University of Tennessee, M

Texas

Baylor University, MD
Prairie View A&M University, M
Texas A&M University, MD
Texas A&M University - Kingsville, M
Texas Southern University, M
Texas State University, M
Texas Woman's University, MD
University of Houston, MD
The University of Texas at Austin, MD
The University of Texas at San Antonio, M
The University of Texas at Tyler, M

Utah

Brigham Young University, M
University of Utah, MD
Utah State University, M

Virginia

James Madison University, M
Longwood University, M
Marymount University, M
Virginia Commonwealth University, M
Virginia State University, D

Washington

Central Washington University, M

West Virginia

Marshall University, M
West Virginia University, D

Wisconsin

Mount Mary University, M
University of Wisconsin - La Crosse, M
University of Wisconsin - Milwaukee, O

Wyoming

University of Wyoming, M

U.S. Territories: Puerto Rico

Inter American University of Puerto Rico, Metropolitan Campus, M
Inter American University of Puerto Rico, San Germán Campus, M
University of Puerto Rico, Medical Sciences Campus, M

Canada

Maritime Provinces: Nova Scotia

Dalhousie University, M

Ontario

University of Waterloo, MD

HEALTH/HEALTH CARE ADMINISTRATION/MANAGEMENT

United States

Alabama

Auburn University, B
Columbia Southern University, B
Community College of the Air Force, A
South University, B
The University of Alabama at Birmingham, B

Arizona

Arizona State University at the Polytechnic campus,
B
Brookline College (Phoenix), AB
CollegeAmerica - Flagstaff, B
GateWay Community College, A
Grand Canyon University, B
Penn Foster College, A
Pima Medical Institute (Mesa), A
Pima Medical Institute (Tucson), A
University of Phoenix - Online Campus, B
University of Phoenix - Phoenix Campus, B
University of Phoenix - Southern Arizona Campus,
B

Arkansas

Harding University, B
National Park College, A

California

Argosy University, Inland Empire, B
Argosy University, Los Angeles, B
Argosy University, Orange County, B
Argosy University, San Diego, B
Argosy University, San Francisco Bay Area, B
Ashford University, B
California Baptist University, B
California Coast University, AB
California College San Diego (San Diego), B
California State University, Dominguez Hills, B
California State University, Long Beach, B
California University of Management and Sciences,
A
Carrington College - Citrus Heights, A
Carrington College - Pleasant Hill, A
Carrington College - Sacramento, A
Carrington College - San Jose, A
Carrington College - San Leandro, A
Concordia University Irvine, B
DeVry University (Alhambra), B
DeVry University (Anaheim), B
DeVry University (Bakersfield), B
DeVry University (Fremont), B
DeVry University (Long Beach), B
DeVry University (Oakland), B
DeVry University (Oxnard), B
DeVry University (Palmdale), B
DeVry University (Pomona), B
DeVry University (San Diego), B
DeVry University (Sherman Oaks), B

Mount Saint Mary's University, A
National University, AB
Pima Medical Institute, A
San Jose State University, B
Simpson University, B
Trident University International, B
University of Antelope Valley, A
University of La Verne, B
University of Phoenix - Bay Area Campus, B
University of Phoenix - Central Valley Campus, B
University of Phoenix - Sacramento Valley Campus, B
University of Phoenix - San Diego Campus, B
West Coast University (North Hollywood), B

Colorado

Adams State University, B
American Sentinel University, B
CollegeAmerica - Denver, B
CollegeAmerica - Fort Collins, B
Colorado Technical University Online, B
DeVry University (Colorado Springs), B
DeVry University (Westminster), B
Metropolitan State University of Denver, B
National American University (Colorado Springs), B
National American University (Denver), AB
Pima Medical Institute (Colorado Springs), A
Pima Medical Institute (Denver), A
Regis University, B
University of Phoenix - Colorado Campus, B

Connecticut

Charter Oak State College, B
St. Vincent's College, B
University of Connecticut, B

Delaware

Goldey-Beacom College, B

District of Columbia

University of the Potomac, B

Florida

Adventist University of Health Sciences, B
Argosy University, Sarasota, B
DeVry University (Jacksonville), B
DeVry University (Miramar), B
DeVry University (Orlando), B
Everest University (Largo), B
Everest University (Orlando), B
Florida Agricultural and Mechanical University, B
Florida Atlantic University, B
Florida International University, B
Florida Southern College, B
Hodges University, B
Indian River State College, B
Millennia Atlantic University, A
Northwest Florida State College, A
Pensacola State College, A
Rasmussen College Fort Myers, B
Rasmussen College Land O' Lakes, B
Rasmussen College New Port Richey, B
Rasmussen College Ocala, B
Rasmussen College Tampa/Brandon, B
Saint Leo University, B
St. Thomas University, B
Santa Fe College, B
South Florida State College, A
South University (Royal Palm Beach), B
South University (Tampa), B
Southern Technical College (Fort Myers), A
Southern Technical College (Tampa), A
State College of Florida Manatee-Sarasota, A
Ultimate Medical Academy Online, A
University of Central Florida, B
University of Miami, B
University of North Florida, B
University of Phoenix - North Florida Campus, B
University of Phoenix - South Florida Campus, B
University of South Florida, B

Georgia

DeVry University (Decatur), B
Middle Georgia State University, B
South University, B

University of Phoenix - Columbus Georgia Campus, B
Valdosta State University, B

Hawaii

Argosy University, Hawai'i, B
University of Hawaii - West Oahu, B
University of Phoenix - Hawaii Campus, B

Idaho

Brigham Young University - Idaho, B
Idaho State University, B
North Idaho College, A
Stevens-Henager College (Boise), B

Illinois

Benedictine University, B
College of DuPage, A
DeVry University (Addison), B
DeVry University (Downers Grove), B
DeVry University (Elgin), B
DeVry University (Naperville), B
DeVry University (Tinley Park), B
DeVry University Online, B
Lewis University, B
Loyola University Chicago, B
Midstate College, B
Rasmussen College Aurora, B
Rasmussen College Mokena/Tinley Park, B
Rasmussen College Rockford, B
Rasmussen College Romeoville/Joliet, B
Southern Illinois University Carbondale, B
University of St. Francis, B
Western Illinois University, B

Indiana

Butler University, B
DeVry University, B
Harrison College, B
Indiana University - Purdue University Fort Wayne, B
Indiana University - Purdue University Indianapolis, B
Saint Mary-of-the-Woods College, B
University of Evansville, B
University of Saint Francis, B
University of Southern Indiana, B
Valparaiso University, B

Iowa

Des Moines Area Community College, A
Iowa Lakes Community College, A
Kaplan University, Des Moines, B
Mercy College of Health Sciences, B
Mount Mercy University, B
Simpson College, B
Upper Iowa University, B

Kansas

Rasmussen College Kansas City/Overland Park, B
Rasmussen College Topeka, B
Southwestern College, B
Washburn University, A
Wichita State University, B

Kentucky

American National University (Louisville), B
Eastern Kentucky University, B
Midway University, B
Thomas More College, B
University of Kentucky, B
Western Kentucky University, B

Louisiana

Dillard University, B
Our Lady of the Lake College, B
University of Louisiana at Lafayette, B

Maine

University of New England, B

Maryland

Frostburg State University, B
Towson University, B

University of Maryland University College, B
Washington Adventist University, B

Massachusetts

Brandeis University, B
Elms College, B
Newbury College, B
Springfield College, B
Stonehill College, B
University of Massachusetts Dartmouth, B

Michigan

Baker College, A
Central Michigan University, B
Cleary University, B
Davenport University, B
Eastern Michigan University, B
Ferris State University, B
Madonna University, B
Oakland Community College, A
South University, B
Spring Arbor University, B
University of Michigan - Dearborn, B
University of Michigan - Flint, B

Minnesota

Capella University, B
Concordia University, St. Paul, B
Globe University - Woodbury, B
Inver Hills Community College, A
Minnesota School of Business - Blaine, B
Minnesota School of Business - Brooklyn Center, B
Minnesota School of Business - Elk River, B
Minnesota School of Business - Plymouth, B
Minnesota School of Business - Richfield, B
Minnesota School of Business - Rochester, B
Minnesota School of Business - St. Cloud, B
Minnesota State University Moorhead, B
National American University (Bloomington), A
National American University (Brooklyn Center), A
Rasmussen College Blaine, B
Rasmussen College Bloomington, B
Rasmussen College Brooklyn Park, B
Rasmussen College Eagan, B
Rasmussen College Lake Elmo/Woodbury, B
Rasmussen College Mankato, B
Rasmussen College Moorhead, B
Rasmussen College St. Cloud, B
University of Minnesota, Crookston, B
University of Minnesota, Duluth, B
University of Minnesota, Twin Cities Campus, B
Walden University, B

Mississippi

Belhaven University, B
Jackson State University, B
Mississippi State University, B

Missouri

Columbia College, B
Harris-Stowe State University, B
Lindenwood University, B
Missouri Baptist University, B
Park University, A
Saint Louis University, B
Southeast Missouri State University, B
Washington University in St. Louis, B

Montana

Montana State University Billings, B
University of Great Falls, B

Nebraska

Creighton University, B
Hastings College, B
Nebraska Methodist College, B
Southeast Community College, Lincoln Campus, A
University of Nebraska at Omaha, B

Nevada

Pima Medical Institute, A
University of Nevada, Las Vegas, B

New Hampshire

Colby-Sawyer College, B
Daniel Webster College, B
Granite State College, B
New England College, B
University of New Hampshire, B

New Jersey

Berkeley College - Woodland Park Campus, AB
Essex County College, A
Saint Peter's University, B

New Mexico

National American University (Albuquerque), AB
Pima Medical Institute (Albuquerque), A
University of Phoenix - New Mexico Campus, B

New York

Berkeley College - New York City Campus, AB
Berkeley College - White Plains Campus, AB
The College of Westchester, B
Dominican College, B
Globe Institute of Technology, B
Iona College, B
Ithaca College, B
Lehman College of the City University of New York, B
Long Island University - LIU Post, B
Plaza College, B
Roberts Wesleyan College, B
State University of New York College of Technology at Canton, B

North Carolina

Appalachian State University, B
Central Piedmont Community College, A
East Carolina University, B
Fayetteville State University, B
Gardner-Webb University, B
Methodist University, AB
Rockingham Community College, A
The University of North Carolina at Chapel Hill, B
Western Carolina University, B
Winston-Salem State University, B

North Dakota

Rasmussen College Fargo, B

Ohio

Baldwin Wallace University, B
Bluffton University, B
Bowling Green State University, B
Brown Mackie College - North Canton, B
Franklin University, B
Harrison College, B
Heidelberg University, B
Kent State University at Trumbull, A
Lourdes University, B
Malone University, B
Mercy College of Ohio, B
Ohio University, B
Ohio University - Eastern, B
South University, B
Terra State Community College, A
Tiffin University, B
The University of Findlay, B
University of Mount Union, B
University of Northwestern Ohio, B
Ursuline College, B
Wilberforce University, B
Wright State University, B

Oklahoma

Community Care College, A
East Central University, B
Langston University, B
Oklahoma State University, Oklahoma City, A
Southwestern Oklahoma State University, B

Oregon

Concordia University, B
Corban University, B
Pioneer Pacific College, AB

Pioneer Pacific College - Eugene/Springfield Branch, A

Pennsylvania

Arcadia University, B
Butler County Community College, A
Carlow University, B
Chestnut Hill College, B
Consolidated School of Business (Lancaster), A
Consolidated School of Business (York), A
Drexel University, B
Elizabethtown College School of Continuing and Professional Studies, AB
Gannon University, B
Harrisburg Area Community College, A
Immaculata University, B
Lebanon Valley College, B
Luzerne County Community College, A
Marywood University, B
Misericordia University, B
Peirce College, B
Penn State Abington, B
Penn State Altoona, B
Penn State Beaver, B
Penn State Berks, B
Penn State Brandywine, B
Penn State DuBois, B
Penn State Erie, The Behrend College, B
Penn State Fayette, The Eberly Campus, B
Penn State Greater Allegheny, B
Penn State Hazleton, B
Penn State Lehigh Valley, B
Penn State Mont Alto, B
Penn State New Kensington, B
Penn State Schuylkill, B
Penn State Shenango, B
Penn State University Park, B
Penn State Wilkes-Barre, B
Penn State Worthington Scranton, B
Penn State York, B
Pennsylvania College of Health Sciences, B
Pennsylvania Institute of Technology, A
Shippensburg University of Pennsylvania, B
University of Pennsylvania, B
University of Phoenix - Philadelphia Campus, B
The University of Scranton, AB
Waynesburg University, B

Rhode Island

New England Institute of Technology, B
Providence College, B
Rhode Island College, B
Roger Williams University, B
Salve Regina University, B
University of Rhode Island, B

South Carolina

Coastal Carolina University, B
Converse College, B
Limestone College, B
South University, B

South Dakota

Augustana University, B
Black Hills State University, B
Globe University - Sioux Falls, B

Tennessee

Baptist College of Health Sciences, B
DeVry University, B
King University, B
Lee University, B
Nashville State Community College, A
Southern Adventist University, B
Tennessee State University, B
Trevecca Nazarene University, B
Virginia College in Chattanooga, A

Texas

Dallas Baptist University, B
LeTourneau University, AB
Our Lady of the Lake University of San Antonio, B
Pima Medical Institute, A
Sam Houston State University, B
South Plains College, A

South University, B
Texas Southern University, B
Texas State University, B
Tyler Junior College, A
University of Houston - Clear Lake, B
The University of Texas at Dallas, B
The University of Texas at El Paso, B

Utah

Argosy University, Salt Lake City, B
Broadview University - West Jordan, B
Independence University, B
Stevens-Henager College (Logan), A
Stevens-Henager College (Orem), A
Stevens-Henager College (Salt Lake City), A
Stevens-Henager College (West Haven), B
University of Phoenix - Utah Campus, B
Weber State University, B

Vermont

Southern Vermont College, B

Virginia

American National University (Salem), B
DeVry University (Chesapeake), B
ECPI University (Newport News), A
ECPI University (Richmond), A
ECPI University (Virginia Beach), AB
James Madison University, B
Jefferson College of Health Sciences, B
Mary Baldwin College, B
Norfolk State University, B
Regent University, B
South University (Glen Allen), B
South University (Virginia Beach), B
Stratford University (Alexandria), B
Stratford University (Falls Church), B
Stratford University (Glen Allen), B
Stratford University (Newport News), B
Stratford University (Virginia Beach), B
Stratford University (Woodbridge), B
University of Management and Technology, B
University of Virginia, B

Washington

Eastern Washington University, B
Pima Medical Institute (Renton), A
Pima Medical Institute (Seattle), A
University of Phoenix - Western Washington Campus, B

West Virginia

Bluefield State College, B
West Virginia University Institute of Technology, B

Wisconsin

Concordia University Wisconsin, B
Globe University - Appleton, B
Globe University - Eau Claire, B
Globe University - Madison East, B
Globe University - Wausau, B
Marian University, B
Rasmussen College Appleton, B
Rasmussen College Green Bay, B
Rasmussen College Wausau, B
University of Wisconsin - Eau Claire, B
Viterbo University, B

U.S. Territories: Puerto Rico

Universidad del Este, B
Universidad Metropolitana, B

Canada

British Columbia

British Columbia Institute of Technology, AB
University of Victoria, B

Ontario

Brock University, B

HEALTH INFORMATICS

United States

Alabama

The University of Alabama at Birmingham, M

Arizona

Grand Canyon University, M
University of Phoenix - Online Campus, MO

Arkansas

Arkansas Tech University, M

California

Golden Gate University, O
National University, M
Trident University International, MO
University of San Diego, M

Colorado

American Sentinel University, M
Regis University, MO

Connecticut

Sacred Heart University, M

District of Columbia

University of Phoenix - Washington D.C. Campus, M

Florida

Barry University, O
Millennia Atlantic University, M
Nova Southeastern University, O
University of Central Florida, M
University of South Florida, MO

Georgia

Augusta University, M
Emory University, M
Georgia State University, M
Kennesaw State University, O

Illinois

Benedictine University, M
DePaul University, M
Northwestern University, D
Southern Illinois University Edwardsville, M
University of Illinois at Chicago, MO
University of Illinois at Urbana - Champaign, MDO

Indiana

Indiana University Bloomington, D
Indiana University - Purdue University Indianapolis, MD

Iowa

The University of Iowa, MDO

Kansas

The University of Kansas, M

Kentucky

Northern Kentucky University, MO

Louisiana

Louisiana Tech University, M

Maryland

Johns Hopkins University, MDO
University of Maryland, Baltimore County, M
University of Maryland University College, MO

Massachusetts

Boston University, MO
Brandeis University, M
Northeastern University, M
University of Massachusetts Lowell, MO

Michigan

University of Michigan, M
University of Michigan - Dearborn, M

Minnesota

Capella University, M
The College of St. Scholastica, MO
Metropolitan State University, O
University of Minnesota, Twin Cities Campus, MD
Walden University, M

Missouri

Logan University, M
Stephens College, O
University of Missouri, MDO

Montana

Montana Tech of The University of Montana, O

New Hampshire

Southern New Hampshire University, M

New Jersey

Stevens Institute of Technology, O

New York

Adelphi University, MO
Brooklyn College of the City University of New York, M
Canisius College, M
Molloy College, M
Roberts Wesleyan College, M
University at Buffalo, the State University of New York, O

North Carolina

East Carolina University, M
The University of North Carolina at Charlotte, MO
University of Phoenix - Charlotte Campus, M

Ohio

The University of Findlay, M

Oregon

Oregon Health & Science University, O

Pennsylvania

Drexel University, M
Temple University, M

South Carolina

University of South Carolina Upstate, M

South Dakota

Dakota State University, M

Tennessee

Lipscomb University, M

Texas

Midwestern State University, M
The University of Texas Health Science Center at Houston, MDO

Virginia

George Mason University, M
Shenandoah University, O
University of Virginia, M
Virginia International University, M

Washington

University of Washington, MD

West Virginia

Marshall University, M

Wisconsin

University of Wisconsin - Milwaukee, MO

U.S. Territories: Puerto Rico

University of Puerto Rico, Medical Sciences Campus, M

Canada

British Columbia

University of Victoria, M

Ontario

University of Toronto, M

HEALTH INFORMATION/MEDICAL RECORDS ADMINISTRATION/ADMINISTRATOR

United States

Alabama

Alabama Southern Community College, A
Alabama State University, B
Enterprise State Community College, A
The University of Alabama at Birmingham, B
Wallace State Community College, A

Alaska

University of Alaska Southeast, A
University of Alaska Southeast, Sitka Campus, A

Arizona

Northland Pioneer College, A

Arkansas

Arkansas Tech University, B
National Park College, A
University of Arkansas for Medical Sciences, B

California

Chabot College, A
Charles R. Drew University of Medicine and Science, A
East Los Angeles College, A
Fresno City College, A
Loma Linda University, B
San Diego Mesa College, A
West Valley College, A

Colorado

Regis University, B

Connecticut

Charter Oak State College, B
Lincoln College of New England, A

Florida

Broward College, A
Daytona State College, A
Florida Agricultural and Mechanical University, B
Florida Gateway College, A
Indian River State College, A
Keiser University, AB
Lake-Sumter State College, A
Miami Dade College, A
Millennia Atlantic University, B
Pensacola State College, A
Rasmussen College Fort Myers, B
Rasmussen College Land O' Lakes, B
Rasmussen College New Port Richey, B
Rasmussen College Ocala, B
Rasmussen College Tampa/Brandon, B
St. Johns River State College, A
St. Petersburg College, A
Santa Fe College, A
South Florida State College, A
University of Central Florida, B

Georgia

Augusta University, B
College of Coastal Georgia, B
Dalton State College, A

Darton State College, A
Georgia Highlands College, A
Gordon State College, B
Middle Georgia State University, B

Idaho

Boise State University, B

Illinois

Chicago State University, B
College of DuPage, A
Illinois Eastern Community Colleges, Lincoln Trail
  College, A
Illinois State University, B
Joliet Junior College, A
Oakton Community College, A
Rasmussen College Aurora, B
Rasmussen College Mokena/Tinley Park, B
Rasmussen College Rockford, B
Rasmussen College Romeoville/Joliet, B
Southeastern Illinois College, A
University of Illinois at Chicago, B

Indiana

Indiana University - Purdue University Indianapolis,
  B
Indiana University Southeast, B

Kansas

Barton County Community College, A
Butler Community College, A
Dodge City Community College, A
Rasmussen College Kansas City/Overland Park, B
Rasmussen College Topeka, B
The University of Kansas, B

Kentucky

Eastern Kentucky University, B
Murray State University, B
Sullivan University, B
Western Kentucky University, B

Louisiana

Louisiana Tech University, B
Southern University at New Orleans, B
Southern University at Shreveport, A
University of Louisiana at Lafayette, B

Maine

University of Maine at Farmington, B

Maryland

Coppin State University, B
Kaplan University, Hagerstown Campus, A
Prince George's Community College, A

Massachusetts

Bunker Hill Community College, A
Labouré College, A
Mount Wachusett Community College, A
Northern Essex Community College, A

Michigan

Davenport University, B
Ferris State University, B
University of Detroit Mercy, B

Minnesota

The College of St. Scholastica, B
Rasmussen College Blaine, B
Rasmussen College Bloomington, B
Rasmussen College Brooklyn Park, B
Rasmussen College Eagan, B
Rasmussen College Lake Elmo/Woodbury, B
Rasmussen College Mankato, B
Rasmussen College Moorhead, B
Rasmussen College St. Cloud, B
Vermilion Community College, A

Mississippi

Holmes Community College, A
Itawamba Community College, A
Mississippi Delta Community College, A
University of Mississippi, B

University of Mississippi Medical Center, B

Missouri

Metropolitan Community College - Kansas City, A
Missouri Western State University, B
Saint Louis University, B
Stephens College, B

Montana

Montana State University Billings, A

Nevada

College of Southern Nevada, A

New Hampshire

Granite State College, B

New Jersey

Camden County College, A
Fairleigh Dickinson University, Metropolitan Campus, B
Georgian Court University, B
Kean University, B
Passaic County Community College, A
Rutgers University - New Brunswick, B
Salem Community College, A

New Mexico

Central New Mexico Community College, A

New York

The College of Westchester, A
Long Island University - LIU Post, B
Medaille College, B
Metropolitan College of New York, B
Monroe Community College, A
Rockland Community College, A
State University of New York Polytechnic Institute, B

North Carolina

Brunswick Community College, A
Central Piedmont Community College, A
Davidson County Community College, A
East Carolina University, B
Edgecombe Community College, A
Forsyth Technical Community College, A
Southwestern Community College, A
Western Carolina University, B

North Dakota

Rasmussen College Fargo, B
Turtle Mountain Community College, A

Ohio

American National University (Youngstown), A
Bowling Green State University, B
Bowling Green State University - Firelands College,
  A
Columbus State Community College, A
Hocking College, A
Miami-Jacobs Career College (Independence), A
The Ohio State University, B
The Ohio State University at Lima, B
Sinclair Community College, A
Stark State College, A
Terra State Community College, A
University of Cincinnati, B
The University of Toledo, B
Ursuline College, B

Oklahoma

East Central University, B
Oklahoma City Community College, A
Southwestern Oklahoma State University, B

Oregon

Portland Community College, A

Pennsylvania

Community College of Philadelphia, A
Duquesne University, B
Laurel Technical Institute, A
Peirce College, B
Pennsylvania College of Technology, B

University of Pittsburgh, B

South Carolina

Florence-Darlington Technical College, A

South Dakota

Dakota State University, B

Tennessee

Daymar College (Clarksville), A
Daymar College (Nashville), A
Nashville State Community College, A
Roane State Community College, A
Tennessee State University, B
Trevecca Nazarene University, B

Texas

Amarillo College, A
El Centro College, A
El Paso Community College, A
Howard College, A
McLennan Community College, A
North Central Texas College, A
South Plains College, A
Tarrant County College District, A
Texas Southern University, B
Texas State University, B
Wharton County Junior College, A

Utah

LDS Business College, A
Weber State University, B

Virginia

ECPI University (Newport News), A
ECPI University (Richmond), A
Marymount University, B
Northern Virginia Community College, A
Stratford University (Alexandria), B
Stratford University (Falls Church), B
Stratford University (Glen Allen), B
Stratford University (Newport News), B
Stratford University (Virginia Beach), B
Stratford University (Woodbridge), B

Washington

Eastern Washington University, B
Shoreline Community College, A
Spokane Community College, A
University of Washington, B

Wisconsin

Rasmussen College Appleton, B
Rasmussen College Green Bay, B
Rasmussen College Wausau, B
University of Wisconsin - Green Bay, B

U.S. Territories: Puerto Rico

Humacao Community College, A

Canada

Maritime Provinces: Nova Scotia

Dalhousie University, B

Ontario

Ryerson University, B

HEALTH INFORMATION/MEDICAL RECORDS TECHNOLOGY/ TECHNICIAN

United States

Alabama

Bishop State Community College, A
Southern Union State Community College, A

Alaska

University of Alaska Southeast, Sitka Campus, A

Arizona

Arizona College, A
Penn Foster College, A
Phoenix College, A
Pima Community College, A

Arkansas

NorthWest Arkansas Community College, A
Ozarka College, A
University of Arkansas for Medical Sciences, A

California

American Career College (Anaheim), A
Brightwood College, Riverside Campus, A
Brightwood College, San Diego Campus, A
Carrington College - Pleasant Hill, A
Charles R. Drew University of Medicine and Science, A
City College of San Francisco, A
Cosumnes River College, A
Cypress College, A
DeVry University (Pomona), A
National University, A
Santa Barbara City College, A

Colorado

Arapahoe Community College, A
Colorado Technical University Denver South, A
DeVry University (Westminster), A
Front Range Community College, A

Connecticut

Lincoln College of New England, A

Florida

College of Business and Technology - Cutler Bay
   Campus, A
College of Central Florida, A
Florida SouthWestern State College, A
Florida State College at Jacksonville, A
Fortis College (Winter Park), A
Hodges University, A
Keiser University, AB
Miami Dade College, A
Millennia Atlantic University, A
Northwest Florida State College, A
Pensacola State College, A
Rasmussen College Fort Myers, A
Rasmussen College Land O' Lakes, A
Rasmussen College New Port Richey, A
Rasmussen College Ocala, A
Rasmussen College Tampa/Brandon, A
Santa Fe College, A
Southern Technical College (Tampa), A
Tallahassee Community College, A
Ultimate Medical Academy Online, A

Georgia

Andrew College, A
Atlanta Technical College, A
Bainbridge State College, A
Columbus Technical College, A
Darton State College, A
DeVry University (Atlanta), A
DeVry University (Decatur), A
Middle Georgia State University, A
Ogeechee Technical College, A
West Georgia Technical College, A

Hawaii

Leeward Community College, A
University of Phoenix - Hawaii Campus, B

Idaho

Boise State University, A
Idaho State University, AB

Illinois

College of DuPage, A
Danville Area Community College, A
DeVry University (Chicago), A
DeVry University Online, A
Highland Community College, A

Illinois Eastern Community Colleges, Frontier Community College, A
John A. Logan College, A
Kaskaskia College, A
Midstate College, A
Moraine Valley Community College, A
Northwestern College - Bridgeview Campus, A
Northwestern College - Chicago Campus, A
Rasmussen College Aurora, A
Rasmussen College Mokena/Tinley Park, A
Rasmussen College Rockford, A
Rasmussen College Romeoville/Joliet, A
Rend Lake College, A
Resurrection University, B
Shawnee Community College, A
Southwestern Illinois College, A
Taylor Business Institute, A
Waubonsee Community College, A

Indiana

Indiana University Northwest, A
Ivy Tech Community College - Central Indiana, A
Ivy Tech Community College - East Central, A
Ivy Tech Community College - Kokomo, A
Ivy Tech Community College - Lafayette, A
Ivy Tech Community College - Wabash Valley, A
Vincennes University, A

Iowa

Kirkwood Community College, A
Northeast Iowa Community College, A
Northwest Iowa Community College, A
Scott Community College, A

Kansas

Hutchinson Community College, A
Rasmussen College Kansas City/Overland Park, A
Rasmussen College Topeka, A
University of Saint Mary, B
Washburn University, A

Kentucky

American National University (Louisville), A
ATA College, A
Daymar College (Bowling Green), A
Jefferson Community and Technical College, A
Sullivan University, A
Western Kentucky University, A

Louisiana

Delgado Community College, A
Louisiana Tech University, A
Southern University at Shreveport, A

Maine

Beal College, A
Kennebec Valley Community College, A
Southern Maine Community College, A
York County Community College, A

Maryland

Anne Arundel Community College, A
Baltimore City Community College, A
Brightwood College, Beltsville Campus, A
Carroll Community College, A
College of Southern Maryland, A
Montgomery College, A

Massachusetts

Fisher College, AB
Quinsigamond Community College, A

Michigan

Baker College, A
Davenport University, AB
Ferris State University, A
Kirtland Community College, A
Northern Michigan University, A
St. Clair County Community College, A
Schoolcraft College, A
Southwestern Michigan College, A

Minnesota

Anoka Technical College, A
Duluth Business University, A
Minnesota State Community and Technical College,
   A
Rasmussen College Blaine, A
Rasmussen College Bloomington, A
Rasmussen College Brooklyn Park, A
Rasmussen College Eagan, A
Rasmussen College Lake Elmo/Woodbury, A
Rasmussen College Mankato, A
Rasmussen College Moorhead, A
Rasmussen College St. Cloud, A
Ridgewater College, A
Rochester Community and Technical College, A
St. Catherine University, A
St. Cloud Technical & Community College, A
Saint Paul College - A Community & Technical College, A

Mississippi

Hinds Community College, A
Southwest Mississippi Community College, A

Missouri

American Business & Technology University, A
Crowder College, A
East Central College, A
Jefferson College, A
Ozarks Technical Community College, A
St. Charles Community College, A
State Fair Community College, A

Montana

Great Falls College Montana State University, A

Nebraska

Central Community College - Hastings Campus, A

Nevada

Brightwood College, Las Vegas Campus, A

New Jersey

Berkeley College - Woodland Park Campus, A
DeVry University (North Brunswick), A
Hudson County Community College, A
Raritan Valley Community College, A
Rowan College at Burlington County, A

New Mexico

Central New Mexico Community College, A
San Juan College, A

New York

ASA College, A
Berkeley College - New York City Campus, A
Berkeley College - White Plains Campus, A
Borough of Manhattan Community College of the
   City University of New York, A
Broome Community College, A
Erie Community College, North Campus, A
Hudson Valley Community College, A
Jamestown Community College, A
Onondaga Community College, A
Plaza College, A
St. John's University, B
State University of New York College of Technology
   at Alfred, A
TCI - College of Technology, A
Trocaire College, A

North Carolina

Catawba Valley Community College, A
Craven Community College, A
DeVry University, A
McDowell Technical Community College, A
Miller-Motte College (Cary), A
Pitt Community College, A
Richmond Community College, A
Southwestern Community College, A

North Dakota

North Dakota State College of Science, A
United Tribes Technical College, A

Williston State College, A

Ohio

American National University (Kettering), A
Bowling Green State University, B
Cincinnati State Technical and Community College, A
Columbus State Community College, A
DeVry University (Columbus), A
DeVry University (Seven Hills), A
Franklin University, B
Mercy College of Ohio, A
Owens Community College, A
Professional Skills Institute, A
Terra State Community College, A
University of Cincinnati Clermont College, A

Oklahoma

Bacone College, A
East Central University, B
Tulsa Community College, A

Oregon

Central Oregon Community College, A

Pennsylvania

Community College of Allegheny County, A
DeVry University (Fort Washington), A
Lehigh Carbon Community College, A
Peirce College, A
Pennsylvania College of Technology, A
Pennsylvania Highlands Community College, A
Pennsylvania Institute of Technology, A
Reading Area Community College, A
South Hills School of Business & Technology (Altoona), A
South Hills School of Business & Technology (State College), A
University of Phoenix - Philadelphia Campus, B

Rhode Island

New England Institute of Technology, A

South Carolina

Greenville Technical College, A
Midlands Technical College, A

South Dakota

Dakota State University, A

Tennessee

Chattanooga State Community College, A
Dyersburg State Community College, A
Fountainhead College of Technology, A
Hiwassee College, A
Volunteer State Community College, A
Walters State Community College, A

Texas

Austin Community College District, A
Blinn College, A
Brightwood College, San Antonio Ingram Campus, A
College of the Mainland, A
Collin County Community College District, A
Del Mar College, A
DeVry University (Irving), A
Houston Community College, A
Howard College, A
Lamar Institute of Technology, A
Lee College, A
Lone Star College - CyFair, A
Lone Star College - North Harris, A
Midland College, A
Panola College, A
Paris Junior College, A
St. Philip's College, A
San Jacinto College District, A
Tyler Junior College, A
Vernon College, A

Utah

Weber State University, A

Washington

Edmonds Community College, A
Tacoma Community College, A

West Virginia

Mountwest Community & Technical College, A
West Virginia Northern Community College, A

Wisconsin

Chippewa Valley Technical College, A
Fox Valley Technical College, A
Gateway Technical College, A
Moraine Park Technical College, A
Northeast Wisconsin Technical College, A
Rasmussen College Appleton, A
Rasmussen College Green Bay, A
Rasmussen College Wausau, A
Waukesha County Technical College, A
Western Technical College, A
Wisconsin Indianhead Technical College, A

U.S. Territories: Puerto Rico

Huertas Junior College, A

HEALTH LAW

United States

California

University of California, San Diego, M

District of Columbia

Georgetown University, M

Illinois

DePaul University, M
Loyola University Chicago, MD
Southern Illinois University Carbondale, M

Massachusetts

Boston University, M
Suffolk University, D

New Jersey

Seton Hall University, MD

New York

Hofstra University, M
Syracuse University, O

Ohio

Cleveland State University, O

Oklahoma

The University of Tulsa, O

Pennsylvania

University of Pittsburgh, M
University of the Sciences, O
Widener University, MD

Texas

Baylor University, D
University of Houston, M

Canada

Quebec

Université de Sherbrooke, MO

HEALTH AND MEDICAL ADMINISTRATIVE SERVICES

United States

Alabama

Virginia College in Mobile, A

Arizona

GateWay Community College, A

California

Carrington College - Pleasant Hill, A
Carrington College - San Leandro, A
National University, A
San Joaquin Valley College (Visalia), A

Florida

Ave Maria University, B
Fortis College (Orange Park), A

Georgia

Brenau University, B
Clayton State University, B

Illinois

National Louis University, B

Iowa

Mount Mercy University, B
North Iowa Area Community College, A

Kansas

Barton County Community College, A
Washburn University, B
Wichita Area Technical College, A

Kentucky

Owensboro Community and Technical College, A

Maryland

University of Baltimore, B

Massachusetts

Northeastern University, B

Michigan

University of Detroit Mercy, B
Western Michigan University, B

Minnesota

Concordia University, St. Paul, B

Mississippi

Hinds Community College, A

Missouri

Concorde Career College, A
Missouri College, A
Missouri Southern State University, B

Nebraska

Bellevue University, B
Northeast Community College, A

New Jersey

Cumberland County College, A

New York

Concordia College - New York, B
State University of New York College of Technology at Canton, B

North Carolina

ECPI University (Greensboro), A

Ohio

Kent State University at Ashtabula, A
Kent State University at Salem, A

Oregon

Eastern Oregon University, B

Pennsylvania

Butler County Community College, A
Community College of Beaver County, A
Pennsylvania College of Technology, B
Westmoreland County Community College, A

South Carolina

ECPI University (Greenville), A
ECPI University (North Charleston), A

Utah

Weber State University, B

West Virginia

Wheeling Jesuit University, B

Wisconsin

Milwaukee Area Technical College, A

U.S. Territories: Puerto Rico

Universidad del Este, B

Canada

British Columbia

British Columbia Institute of Technology, A

HEALTH/MEDICAL PHYSICS

United States

California

California State University, Dominguez Hills, B
California State University, Northridge, B

Nevada

University of Nevada, Las Vegas, B

North Carolina

Cabarrus College of Health Sciences, B

Oregon

Oregon State University, B

Pennsylvania

Bloomsburg University of Pennsylvania, B

Tennessee

Belmont University, B

Canada

Ontario

Ryerson University, B
University of Guelph, B

HEALTH/MEDICAL PREPARA-TORY PROGRAMS

United States

Alabama

South University, B
University of South Alabama, B

Arizona

Arizona State University at the Downtown Phoenix campus, B
Eastern Arizona College, A

Arkansas

Arkansas State University - Beebe, A
Arkansas State University - Newport, A

California

Charles R. Drew University of Medicine and Science, B
College of San Mateo, A
Fullerton College, A
Gavilan College, A
Merritt College, A
Mount Saint Mary's University, A
Southwestern College, A

Florida

College of Central Florida, A
Hodges University, B
Miami Dade College, A
South University (Royal Palm Beach), B
South University (Tampa), B

Georgia

Darton State College, A
Gordon State College, A
Mercer University, B
South Georgia State College, A

Illinois

Aurora University, B
Benedictine University, B
Blackburn College, B
John A. Logan College, A
Northern Illinois University, B

Indiana

Grace College, B

Kentucky

Asbury University, B
Eastern Kentucky University, B

Massachusetts

Eastern Nazarene College, B

Michigan

Cornerstone University, B
Lake Michigan College, A
Madonna University, B
Northern Michigan University, B
Oakland University, B
Saginaw Valley State University, B
South University, B
University of Michigan - Flint, B

Minnesota

St. Cloud State University, B

Mississippi

East Central Community College, A
Northeast Mississippi Community College, A

Missouri

Avila University, B
College of the Ozarks, B
Maryville University of Saint Louis, B
University of Missouri, B

Montana

Fort Peck Community College, A

Nebraska

Chadron State College, B
Northeast Community College, A

New Jersey

Essex County College, A

New York

Hofstra University, B
Ithaca College, B
Le Moyne College, B
Utica College, B

North Carolina

Guilford College, B
Lenoir-Rhyne University, B
Meredith College, B

North Dakota

Valley City State University, B

Ohio

Cleveland State University, B
Edison Community College, A
Kent State University, B
Kent State University at Ashtabula, B
South University, B

University of Cincinnati Blue Ash College, A
The University of Findlay, B

Oklahoma

Connors State College, A
Southern Nazarene University, B
Tulsa Community College, A

Oregon

Oregon State University, B

Pennsylvania

Allegheny College, B
Bloomsburg University of Pennsylvania, B
Drexel University, B
Duquesne University, B
Gannon University, B
Immaculata University, AB
Lock Haven University of Pennsylvania, B
Mercyhurst University, B
Point Park University, B

South Carolina

South University, B

Tennessee

Austin Peay State University, B
Cumberland University, B
Lee University, B
Lipscomb University, B

Texas

Abilene Christian University, B
Baylor University, B

Utah

Weber State University, B

Virginia

Emory & Henry College, B
South University (Glen Allen), B
South University (Virginia Beach), B

Washington

Seattle Pacific University, B
Seattle University, B
Western Washington University, B

West Virginia

Ohio Valley University, A

Wyoming

Eastern Wyoming College, A
Northwest College, A
Western Wyoming Community College, A

Canada

Ontario

University of Waterloo, B

Saskatchewan

University of Regina, B

HEALTH OCCUPATIONS TEACHER EDUCATION

United States

California

National University, B

Oklahoma

University of Central Oklahoma, B

Texas

Baylor University, B
Howard College, A
Midwestern State University, B

Washington

Northwest University, B

HEALTH AND PHYSICAL EDUCATION

United States

Alabama

Jacksonville State University, B
Selma University, B
University of Mobile, B
University of Montevallo, B

Alaska

University of Alaska Anchorage, B

Arizona

Arizona Western College, A
Cochise County Community College District, A
Eastern Arizona College, A

Arkansas

Arkansas State University, B
John Brown University, B
Philander Smith College, B
University of Arkansas, B
University of Arkansas at Monticello, B

California

Antelope Valley College, A
Barstow Community College, A
Biola University, B
Butte College, A
Cabrillo College, A
California Polytechnic State University, San Luis Obispo, B
California State Polytechnic University, Pomona, B
California State University, Chico, B
California State University, Dominguez Hills, B
California State University, Fullerton, B
California State University, Monterey Bay, B
California State University, San Bernardino, B
California State University, San Marcos, B
California State University, Stanislaus, B
Cañada College, A
Cerro Coso Community College, A
Chabot College, A
Chaffey College, A
Citrus College, A
College of the Canyons, A
College of the Desert, A
College of Marin, A
College of the Siskiyous, A
Columbia College, A
Concordia University Irvine, B
Contra Costa College, A
Cosumnes River College, A
Cuesta College, A
Cypress College, A
Feather River College, A
Fullerton College, A
Gavilan College, A
Glendale Community College, A
Grossmont College, A
Hartnell College, A
La Sierra University, B
Lassen Community College District, A
Long Beach City College, A
Los Angeles Valley College, A
The Master's College and Seminary, B
Moreno Valley College, A
Mt. San Antonio College, A
Mt. San Jacinto College, A
Orange Coast College, A
Pacific Union College, B
Pepperdine University, B
Point Loma Nazarene University, B
Reedley College, A
Saint Mary's College of California, B
San Diego State University, B
San Jose State University, B
Santa Monica College, A

Santa Rosa Junior College, A
Sierra College, A
Southwestern College, A
University of San Francisco, B
Vanguard University of Southern California, B
Whittier College, B

Colorado

Arapahoe Community College, A

Delaware

Delaware State University, B
University of Delaware, B

Florida

Florida Agricultural and Mechanical University, B
Jacksonville University, B
Lincoln College of Technology, A
The University of Tampa, B
University of West Florida, B

Georgia

Andrew College, A
College of Coastal Georgia, A
Darton State College, A
Emory University, B
Georgia Southern University, B
Gordon State College, A
Morehouse College, B
University of Georgia, B

Hawaii

Brigham Young University - Hawaii, B
University of Hawaii at Manoa, B

Idaho

Boise State University, B
Northwest Nazarene University, B

Illinois

Blackburn College, B
DePaul University, B
Elgin Community College, A
Elmhurst College, B
Illinois Central College, A
Lincoln College, A
McHenry County College, A
Monmouth College, B
Northern Illinois University, B
Quincy University, B
Robert Morris University Illinois, A
Triton College, A
Waubonsee Community College, A

Indiana

Bethel College, B
Hanover College, B
Marian University, B
Oakland City University, B
Saint Joseph's College, B
Valparaiso University, B
Vincennes University, A

Iowa

Dordt College, B
Grand View University, B
Iowa Lakes Community College, A
Iowa State University of Science and Technology, B
Iowa Wesleyan University, B
Luther College, B
The University of Iowa, B
University of Northern Iowa, B
William Penn University, B

Kansas

Allen Community College, A
Baker University, B
Bethel College, B
Central Christian College of Kansas, AB
Friends University, B
Haskell Indian Nations University, A
Sterling College, B
Tabor College, B
The University of Kansas, B

Kentucky

Asbury University, B
Berea College, B
Morehead State University, B
University of the Cumberlands, B
University of Louisville, B

Louisiana

Louisiana Tech University, B
Northwestern State University of Louisiana, B
University of New Orleans, B

Maine

Husson University, B
University of Southern Maine, B

Maryland

Anne Arundel Community College, A
McDaniel College, B
Washington Adventist University, B

Massachusetts

Holyoke Community College, A
Salem State University, B
University of Massachusetts Boston, B
Westfield State University, B

Michigan

Adrian College, B
Bay Mills Community College, A
Concordia University Ann Arbor, B
Eastern Michigan University, B
Henry Ford College, A
Hillsdale College, B
Lake Michigan College, A
Lansing Community College, A
Northern Michigan University, B
Olivet College, B
Spring Arbor University, B
University of Michigan, B

Minnesota

Concordia College, B
Concordia University, St. Paul, B
Minnesota State University Moorhead, B
North Hennepin Community College, A
St. Catherine University, B
Southwest Minnesota State University, B
University of Northwestern - St. Paul, B

Mississippi

Coahoma Community College, A
East Central Community College, A
East Mississippi Community College, A
Mississippi University for Women, B
University of Southern Mississippi, B
William Carey University, B

Missouri

College of the Ozarks, B
Evangel University, B
Heritage College, A
Missouri Western State University, B
Southeast Missouri State University, B
Southwest Baptist University, B
Truman State University, B

Montana

Carroll College, B
Montana State University Billings, B
Rocky Mountain College, B
University of Great Falls, B
The University of Montana Western, B

Nebraska

Concordia University, Nebraska, B
Doane University, B
Hastings College, B
Northeast Community College, A
Union College, B
Western Nebraska Community College, A

New Hampshire

Keene State College, B
New England College, B
Plymouth State University, B

New Jersey

Monmouth University, B
Raritan Valley Community College, A
Rowan University, B

New Mexico

Central New Mexico Community College, A
Clovis Community College, A
San Juan College, A
Santa Fe Community College, A

New York

Columbia-Greene Community College, A
Corning Community College, A
Erie Community College, A
Erie Community College, North Campus, A
Erie Community College, South Campus, A
Genesee Community College, A
Houghton College, B
Ithaca College, B
Jamestown Community College, A
State University of New York College of Technology
   at Delhi, A
Syracuse University, B

North Carolina

Brevard College, B
Campbell University, B
Catawba College, B
Gardner-Webb University, B
Greensboro College, B
Louisburg College, A
North Carolina Central University, B
The University of North Carolina at Chapel Hill, B
The University of North Carolina at Charlotte, B
The University of North Carolina at Pembroke, B
The University of North Carolina Wilmington, B
Wingate University, B

North Dakota

Dakota College at Bottineau, A
Mayville State University, B
University of Mary, B
Valley City State University, B

Ohio

Baldwin Wallace University, B
Bluffton University, B
Capital University, B
Cleveland State University, B
Miami University, B
The Ohio State University, B
Ohio University, B
Shawnee State University, B
The University of Findlay, B
University of Rio Grande, B
Walsh University, B
Wright State University, B
Youngstown State University, B

Oklahoma

Cameron University, B
Community Care College, A
East Central University, B
Heritage College, A
Oklahoma Baptist University, B
Oklahoma Panhandle State University, B
Oral Roberts University, B
St. Gregory's University, B
Southwestern Christian University, B
University of Science and Arts of Oklahoma, B

Oregon

Central Oregon Community College, A
Eastern Oregon University, B
George Fox University, B
Linfield College, B

Pennsylvania

Community College of Allegheny County, A
Community College of Beaver County, A
Indiana University of Pennsylvania, B
Lincoln University, B
Luzerne County Community College, A
Marywood University, B
Montgomery County Community College, A
Slippery Rock University of Pennsylvania, B
Ursinus College, B
West Chester University of Pennsylvania, B

Rhode Island

Rhode Island College, B

South Carolina

Bob Jones University, B
Charleston Southern University, B
Claflin University, B
South Carolina State University, B
Southern Wesleyan University, B

South Dakota

Black Hills State University, B
South Dakota State University, B

Tennessee

Austin Peay State University, B
Belmont University, B
Bethel University, B
Bryan College, B
East Tennessee State University, B
Freed-Hardeman University, B
Hiwassee College, A
Lee University, B
Lincoln Memorial University, B
Martin Methodist College, B
Maryville College, B
Middle Tennessee State University, B
Milligan College, B
Tennessee Wesleyan College, B
The University of Tennessee at Martin, B
Welch College, B

Texas

Alvin Community College, A
Austin Community College District, A
Baylor University, B
Central Texas College, A
Concordia University Texas, B
Dallas Baptist University, B
East Texas Baptist University, B
Hill College, A
Houston Community College, A
Howard College, A
Howard Payne University, B
Jarvis Christian College, B
Lamar State College - Port Arthur, A
Lubbock Christian University, B
Northeast Texas Community College, A
Paris Junior College, A
Prairie View A&M University, B
Sam Houston State University, B
San Jacinto College District, A
Southwestern Adventist University, B
Tarleton State University, B
Texas A&M International University, B
Texas A&M University - Kingsville, B
Texas Christian University, B
Texas College, B
Tyler Junior College, A
The University of Texas at Austin, B
The University of Texas at Tyler, B
Wayland Baptist University, B
Western Texas College, A

Utah

University of Utah, B
Utah Valley University, AB
Weber State University, B

Vermont

Castleton University, B
Johnson State College, B
Lyndon State College, B

Virginia

Averett University, B
Bridgewater College, B
The College of William and Mary, B
Emory & Henry College, B
Ferrum College, B
James Madison University, B
Liberty University, B
Lynchburg College, B
Randolph College, B

Washington

Eastern Washington University, B
Northwest University, B
Walla Walla University, B
Western Washington University, B

West Virginia

West Virginia State University, B
West Virginia University, B
West Virginia Wesleyan College, B

Wisconsin

Carroll University, B
Concordia University Wisconsin, B
University of Wisconsin - La Crosse, B
University of Wisconsin - Stevens Point, B
University of Wisconsin - Superior, B

Wyoming

Northwest College, A
Sheridan College, A

U.S. Territories: Guam

University of Guam, B

U.S. Territories: Puerto Rico

Pontifical Catholic University of Puerto Rico, B
Universidad Metropolitana, AB
Universidad del Turabo, A

Canada

Alberta

Mount Royal University, B
University of Alberta, B

Ontario

Queen's University at Kingston, B
Redeemer University College, B
University of Ottawa, B
University of Toronto, B
University of Windsor, B
York University, B

Quebec

McGill University, B
Université du Québec à Trois-Rivières, B

Saskatchewan

University of Regina, B

HEALTH AND PHYSICAL EDUCATION/FITNESS

United States

Arizona

Arizona State University at the Downtown Phoenix
   campus, B

Arkansas

John Brown University, B

California

Bryan College, A
California State University, Long Beach, B
Saint Mary's College of California, B

Colorado

Naropa University, B

Georgia

Brewton-Parker College, B
Reinhardt University, B
Valdosta State University, B

Iowa

Coe College, B
Cornell College, B
The University of Iowa, B

Kansas

Bethany College, B
Garden City Community College, A

Maine

University of New England, B

Maryland

College of Southern Maryland, A

Massachusetts

Bridgewater State University, B
Regis College, B

Michigan

Adrian College, B

Minnesota

Concordia College, B
Gustavus Adolphus College, B

Missouri

Avila University, B
Missouri Southern State University, B

Nebraska

Union College, B
Wayne State College, B

New York

Adelphi University, B
Corning Community College, A
Genesee Community College, A
Herkimer County Community College, A
Ithaca College, B
Kingsborough Community College of the City University of New York, A

North Carolina

Campbell University, B
Catawba Valley Community College, A
East Carolina University, B
Fayetteville Technical Community College, A
Greensboro College, B

North Dakota

Mayville State University, B

Ohio

Bowling Green State University, B
Columbus State Community College, A
Mount Vernon Nazarene University, B

Oklahoma

Southern Nazarene University, B
University of Central Oklahoma, B

Oregon

Portland Community College, A

Pennsylvania

Bloomsburg University of Pennsylvania, B
Edinboro University of Pennsylvania, B
Lincoln University, B
Lock Haven University of Pennsylvania, B
Pennsylvania College of Technology, A

South Carolina

Coker College, B
Limestone College, B
North Greenville University, B

South Dakota

South Dakota State University, B

Texas

Midwestern State University, B
Texas Lutheran University, B

Utah

Weber State University, B

Virginia

Averett University, B

Wisconsin

Concordia University Wisconsin, B
University of Wisconsin - Superior, B

U.S. Territories: Puerto Rico

Huertas Junior College, A
University of Puerto Rico in Carolina, A

Canada

Alberta

University of Alberta, B

British Columbia

University of Victoria, B

HEALTH PHYSICS/RADIOLOGICAL HEALTH

United States

Arkansas

University of Arkansas for Medical Sciences, M

California

San Diego State University, M

Connecticut

Quinnipiac University, M

District of Columbia

Georgetown University, M

Georgia

Georgia Institute of Technology, MD

Idaho

Idaho State University, M

Illinois

Illinois Institute of Technology, M

Indiana

Purdue University, MD

Kentucky

University of Kentucky, M

Louisiana

Northwestern State University of Louisiana, M

Massachusetts

University of Massachusetts Lowell, M

Michigan

University of Michigan, MD
Wayne State University, MD

Missouri

University of Missouri, M

Nevada

University of Nevada, Las Vegas, MDO

New Jersey

Rutgers University - Newark, M

North Carolina

East Carolina University, M

Ohio

University of Cincinnati, M

Oklahoma

University of Oklahoma Health Sciences Center, MD

Oregon

Oregon State University, MD

Pennsylvania

Thomas Jefferson University, M

Tennessee

Vanderbilt University, M

Texas

Midwestern State University, M
Texas A&M University, M

Utah

Weber State University, M

Virginia

Virginia Commonwealth University, D

Canada

Alberta

University of Alberta, MD

Ontario

McMaster University, M
University of Toronto, M

Quebec

Université Laval, O

HEALTH PROFESSIONS AND RELATED CLINICAL SCIENCES

United States

Alabama

Athens State University, B
Calhoun Community College, A
Samford University, B
The University of Alabama, B

Alaska

University of Alaska Anchorage, B
University of Alaska Southeast, A
University of Alaska Southeast, Ketchikan Campus, A

Arizona

Diné College, A
Grand Canyon University, B

Arkansas

National Park College, A
Shorter College, A
University of Arkansas at Little Rock, B
University of Central Arkansas, B

California

Azusa Pacific University, B
California State University, East Bay, B
California State University, Fresno, B
California State University, Long Beach, B
California State University, Los Angeles, B

California State University, Sacramento, B
Mendocino College, A
Mission College, A
Ohlone College, A
San Francisco State University, B
Sonoma State University, B
University of California, Santa Cruz, B
West Hills Community College, A

Connecticut

Northwestern Connecticut Community College, A
University of Bridgeport, B
University of Hartford, AB

Delaware

University of Delaware, B

District of Columbia

Georgetown University, B

Florida

Miami Dade College, A
Nova Southeastern University, B
Southeastern College - West Palm Beach, A

Georgia

Armstrong State University, B
Lanier Technical College, A

Idaho

Boise State University, B

Illinois

Bradley University, B
DePaul University, B
Northern Illinois University, B
Spoon River College, A

Indiana

Manchester University, B
Purdue University, B
Saint Mary-of-the-Woods College, B

Iowa

University of Northern Iowa, B

Kansas

Newman University, AB

Kentucky

Gateway Community and Technical College, A

Louisiana

University of Louisiana at Monroe, B

Maine

University of New England, B

Maryland

Allegany College of Maryland, A
Carroll Community College, A
Mount St. Mary's University, B
Towson University, B
University of Maryland, Baltimore County, B

Massachusetts

Berkshire Community College, A
Boston University, B
Curry College, B
Eastern Nazarene College, B
Fisher College, AB
Greenfield Community College, A
MCPHS University, B
Merrimack College, B
North Shore Community College, A
Worcester State University, B

Michigan

Alma College, B
Ferris State University, AB
Glen Oaks Community College, A
Northwestern Michigan College, A
Oakland University, B

Wayne State University, B

Minnesota

Minnesota State University Mankato, B

Mississippi

Coahoma Community College, A
Holmes Community College, A
Northeast Mississippi Community College, A
Southwest Mississippi Community College, A
University of Mississippi, B
William Carey University, B

Missouri

Maryville University of Saint Louis, B
Mineral Area College, A
Missouri Southern State University, B
Stephens College, B
Washington University in St. Louis, B

Nevada

University of Nevada, Reno, B

New Jersey

Essex County College, A
Mercer County Community College, A
Middlesex County College, A
New Jersey City University, B
Saint Peter's University, A
Sussex County Community College, A
Thomas Edison State University, B

New Mexico

New Mexico Junior College, A

New York

Concordia College - New York, B
Corning Community College, A
Elmira College, B
Excelsior College, B
Genesee Community College, A
Herkimer County Community College, A
Long Island University - LIU Brooklyn, B
Long Island University - LIU Post, B
Molloy College, B
Morrisville State College, AB
New York Institute of Technology, B
New York University, A
Onondaga Community College, A
Phillips Beth Israel School of Nursing, A
Queensborough Community College of the City University of New York, A
The Sage Colleges, B
St. Francis College, B
St. John's University, B
St. Joseph's College, Long Island Campus, B
St. Joseph's College, New York, B
State University of New York College at Cortland, B
Touro College, B
Villa Maria College, A

North Carolina

Forsyth Technical Community College, A
Mitchell Community College, A
Piedmont Community College, A
Pitt Community College, A
Queens University of Charlotte, B
Richmond Community College, A
Roanoke-Chowan Community College, A
Saint Augustine's University, B
University of Mount Olive, B
The University of North Carolina Wilmington, B
Wake Technical Community College, A

Ohio

Baldwin Wallace University, B
Belmont College, A
Bowling Green State University, B
Bowling Green State University - Firelands College, A
Cleveland State University, B
Kettering College, B
Lakeland Community College, A
The Ohio State University, B
Ohio University - Chillicothe, A

Ohio University - Southern Campus, A
Terra State Community College, A
University of Cincinnati, B
University of Cincinnati Clermont College, A
Youngstown State University, B

Oklahoma

Carl Albert State College, A
Eastern Oklahoma State College, A
Northeastern State University, B
Southwestern Oklahoma State University, B

Oregon

Corban University, B
Pacific University, B

Pennsylvania

Alvernia University, B
Bucks County Community College, A
Community College of Allegheny County, A
Community College of Philadelphia, A
Gannon University, B
Gettysburg College, B
Gwynedd Mercy University, B
Harcum College, A
Harrisburg Area Community College, A
King's College, B
Lock Haven University of Pennsylvania, AB
Manor College, A
Marywood University, B
Pennsylvania Highlands Community College, A
Point Park University, B
Saint Joseph's University, B
Thomas Jefferson University, B
University of Pennsylvania, B
University of Pittsburgh, B

South Carolina

Clemson University, B
Furman University, B
Midlands Technical College, A

Tennessee

East Tennessee State University, B
King University, B
Maryville College, B
Milligan College, B
Nashville State Community College, A
Southwest Tennessee Community College, A
Tennessee Wesleyan College, B
The University of Tennessee at Martin, B
Volunteer State Community College, A

Texas

Palo Alto College, A
Panola College, A
Southern Methodist University, B
The University of Texas at El Paso, B
The University of Texas at Tyler, B

Utah

LDS Business College, A
Salt Lake Community College, A

Vermont

Castleton University, B
Johnson State College, B
Norwich University, B

Virginia

George Mason University, B
Old Dominion University, B
Randolph College, B

Washington

Bastyr University, B
Edmonds Community College, A
Northwest University, A
Walla Walla University, B

West Virginia

American Public University System, A
Fairmont State University, B
University of Charleston, B

West Liberty University, B
West Virginia State University, B

Wisconsin

Milwaukee Area Technical College, A
University of Wisconsin - Parkside, B
University of Wisconsin - Stevens Point, B

U.S. Territories: Puerto Rico

Caribbean University, AB
Inter American University of Puerto Rico, Ponce
   Campus, B

Canada
British Columbia

British Columbia Institute of Technology, A
The University of British Columbia - Okanagan
   Campus, B

Maritime Provinces: New Brunswick

University of New Brunswick Saint John, B

Maritime Provinces: Nova Scotia

Dalhousie University, B

Ontario

Brock University, B
University of Waterloo, B
The University of Western Ontario, B
Wilfrid Laurier University, B
York University, B

Quebec

Université du Québec à Trois-Rivières, B

HEALTH PROMOTION

United States
Alabama

Auburn University, M
The University of Alabama, MD
The University of Alabama at Birmingham, D
University of North Alabama, M

Arizona

Arizona State University at the Tempe campus, MD

Arkansas

University of Arkansas, MD
University of Arkansas for Medical Sciences, D

California

California Baptist University, M
California State University, Fresno, M
Loma Linda University, MD
National University, MO
San Diego State University, M
Sonoma State University, M
University of Southern California, M

Delaware

University of Delaware, M

District of Columbia

Georgetown University, M

Florida

Florida Atlantic University, M
Florida International University, MD

Georgia

Emory University, M
Georgia College & State University, M
University of Georgia, MD

Idaho

Boise State University, M

Illinois

Benedictine University, M
University of Chicago, MD

Indiana

Ball State University, M
Indiana University Bloomington, M

Iowa

University of Northern Iowa, M

Kansas

Cleveland University - Kansas City, M

Kentucky

Eastern Kentucky University, M
University of Kentucky, MD
University of Louisville, D

Louisiana

McNeese State University, M

Massachusetts

Boston University, D
Bridgewater State University, M
Harvard University, MD
Simmons College, M
Springfield College, M
University of Massachusetts Lowell, D

Michigan

Eastern Michigan University, MO
Oakland University, O
University of Michigan, MD

Minnesota

Walden University, MD

Mississippi

Mississippi State University, M
University of Mississippi, M

Missouri

Lindenwood University, M
University of Missouri, M

Nebraska

Nebraska Methodist College, M
University of Nebraska - Lincoln, M
University of Nebraska Medical Center, D

New Hampshire

Plymouth State University, M

New Jersey

Rowan University, M

New York

Lehman College of the City University of New York,
   M
New York University, M

North Carolina

East Carolina University, M
The University of North Carolina at Chapel Hill, M

Ohio

Kent State University, MD
Mount St. Joseph University, O
Union Institute & University, M
The University of Toledo, MD
Wright State University, M

Oklahoma

University of Central Oklahoma, M
University of Oklahoma, M
University of Oklahoma Health Sciences Center, MD

Oregon

Oregon State University, MD
Portland State University, M

Pennsylvania

Immaculata University, M
University of Pittsburgh, M

South Carolina

University of South Carolina, MDO

Tennessee

Tennessee Technological University, M
The University of Tennessee, M

Texas

Baylor University, D
Texas A&M University, M
University of the Incarnate Word, M

Utah

Brigham Young University, MD
Independence University, M
University of Utah, MD

Vermont

Goddard College, M

Virginia

George Mason University, M
Liberty University, M
Marymount University, M
Old Dominion University, M

West Virginia

Concord University, M
Fairmont State University, M
West Virginia University, MD

Wisconsin

University of Wisconsin - Milwaukee, D
University of Wisconsin - Stevens Point, M

Wyoming

University of Wyoming, M

U.S. Territories: Puerto Rico

Universidad del Turabo, M
University of Puerto Rico, Medical Sciences Campus, O

Canada
Alberta

University of Alberta, MO

Ontario

University of Toronto, M
Wilfrid Laurier University, M

HEALTH PSYCHOLOGY

United States
Alabama

The University of Alabama at Birmingham, M

Arizona

Prescott College, M

California

California Institute of Integral Studies, M
John F. Kennedy University, M
San Diego State University, D

Colorado

University of Colorado Denver, D

Connecticut

Central Connecticut State University, M
Connecticut College, M
University of Connecticut, O

Florida

University of Florida, MD

Georgia

Argosy University, Atlanta, D

Illinois

Argosy University, Chicago, D

Kentucky

Northern Kentucky University, O

Massachusetts

Lesley University, M

Michigan

Central Michigan University, D
University of Michigan - Dearborn, M

Minnesota

Argosy University, Twin Cities, D
Walden University, MD

Missouri

University of Missouri - Kansas City, D

New Jersey

Georgian Court University, M
Rutgers University - New Brunswick, D

New Mexico

University of New Mexico, D

New York

Stony Brook University, State University of New
York, D
Yeshiva University, D

North Carolina

Appalachian State University, M
Duke University, D
East Carolina University, D
The University of North Carolina at Chapel Hill, MD
The University of North Carolina at Charlotte, D

North Dakota

North Dakota State University, D

Oklahoma

Oklahoma State University, MDO

Pennsylvania

Chatham University, M
Drexel University, D
La Salle University, D
University of the Sciences, M

Rhode Island

Rhode Island College, O

Texas

The University of Texas at Arlington, D

Virginia

Argosy University, Washington DC, D
Virginia Commonwealth University, D
Virginia State University, D

Washington

Bastyr University, M

Wisconsin

Viterbo University, M

Canada

British Columbia

The University of British Columbia, MD

HEALTH SERVICES ADMINIS-TRATION

United States

Alabama

Auburn University at Montgomery, O
Columbia Southern University, M
South University, M
Troy University, M
The University of Alabama at Birmingham, MD
The University of Alabama in Huntsville, M
University of North Alabama, M
Virginia College in Birmingham, M
Virginia College in Huntsville, B

Alaska

Alaska Pacific University, M

Arizona

Argosy University, Phoenix, M
Arizona State University at the Downtown Phoenix
campus, B
Arizona State University at the Tempe campus, M
Arizona State University at the West campus, B
Grand Canyon University, M
Northern Arizona University, O
University of Phoenix - Online Campus, MD
University of Phoenix - Phoenix Campus, BM

Arkansas

Arkansas State University, O
Harding University, M
University of Arkansas for Medical Sciences, M

California

Argosy University, Inland Empire, M
Argosy University, Los Angeles, M
Argosy University, Orange County, MO
Argosy University, San Francisco Bay Area, M
Brandman University, M
California Baptist University, M
California Coast University, M
California Intercontinental University, MD
California State University, Bakersfield, M
California State University, Chico, M
California State University, East Bay, M
California State University, Fresno, M
California State University, Long Beach, M
California State University, Los Angeles, M
California State University, Northridge, M
California State University, San Bernardino, M
Chapman University, B
Loma Linda University, M
Mount Saint Mary's University, M
National University, M
New Charter University, M
Point Loma Nazarene University, M
San Diego State University, M
Trident University International, MDO
University of California, Berkeley, D
University of California, Irvine, M
University of California, Los Angeles, MD
University of California, San Diego, M
University of La Verne, M
University of Phoenix - Bay Area Campus, BM
University of Phoenix - Central Valley Campus, M
University of Phoenix - Sacramento Valley Campus,
BM
University of Phoenix - San Diego Campus, B
University of Phoenix - Southern California Campus,
BM
University of San Francisco, BM
University of Southern California, MO

Colorado

American Sentinel University, M
Argosy University, Denver, M
Colorado Heights University, M
Colorado State University - Global Campus, M
Regis University, MO
University of Colorado Denver, M
University of Phoenix - Colorado Campus, M

University of Phoenix - Colorado Springs Downtown
Campus, BM

Connecticut

Post University, M
University of Connecticut, M
University of New Haven, MO
Western Connecticut State University, M
Yale University, MD

Delaware

Goldey-Beacom College, M
Wilmington University, M

District of Columbia

The George Washington University, MO
University of the District of Columbia, B
University of Phoenix - Washington D.C. Campus,
MD

Florida

Argosy University, Sarasota, MO
Argosy University, Tampa, M
Barry University, MO
Belhaven University, B
Broward College, A
Florida Atlantic University, M
Florida Gateway College, A
Florida Institute of Technology, M
Florida International University, M
Florida National University, AB
Hodges University, M
Keiser University, ABM
Saint Leo University, M
St. Petersburg College, B
St. Thomas University, MO
South University (Royal Palm Beach), M
South University (Tampa), M
State College of Florida Manatee-Sarasota, B
University of Central Florida, MO
University of Florida, MD
University of North Florida, M
University of Phoenix - Central Florida Campus, B
University of Phoenix - North Florida Campus, BM
University of Phoenix - South Florida Campus, BM
University of South Florida, MDO

Georgia

Albany State University, M
Argosy University, Atlanta, M
Armstrong State University, MO
Ashworth College, AM
Brenau University, M
Clayton State University, M
Emory University, MD
Georgia Institute of Technology, M
Georgia Southern University, MD
Georgia State University, MD
Kennesaw State University, M
Middle Georgia State University, B
South University, M
University of Georgia, M
University of Phoenix - Atlanta Campus, BM
University of Phoenix - Augusta Campus, ABM
University of Phoenix - Columbus Georgia Campus,
AB
University of West Georgia, O
Valdosta State University, M

Hawaii

Argosy University, Hawai'i, MO
University of Phoenix - Hawaii Campus, BM

Idaho

Boise State University, M
Northwest Nazarene University, M

Illinois

American InterContinental University Online, M
Argosy University, Chicago, M
Argosy University, Schaumburg, MO
Benedictine University, M
DePaul University, M
Ellis University, M
Governors State University, M

Lewis University, M
Loyola University Chicago, MDO
Northwestern University, MD
Robert Morris University Illinois, M
Rush University, MD
Saint Xavier University, MO
Southern Illinois University Carbondale, M
University of Chicago, O
University of Illinois at Chicago, MD
University of Illinois at Urbana - Champaign, BM
University of St. Francis, M
Western Illinois University, O

Indiana

Indiana Tech, M
Indiana University Bloomington, M
Indiana University Kokomo, MO
Indiana University Northwest, BM
Indiana University - Purdue University Fort Wayne, B
Indiana University - Purdue University Indianapolis, BMD
Indiana Wesleyan University, O
University of Evansville, M
University of Saint Francis, M
University of Southern Indiana, M
Valparaiso University, M

Iowa

Kaplan University, Davenport Campus, M
St. Ambrose University, M
The University of Iowa, MD

Kansas

Friends University, M
Grantham University, M
The University of Kansas, MD
University of Saint Mary, M

Kentucky

Eastern Kentucky University, M
University of Kentucky, M
University of Louisville, MD
Western Kentucky University, M

Louisiana

Grambling State University, M
Louisiana State University Health Sciences Center, M
Louisiana State University in Shreveport, M
Loyola University New Orleans, M
McNeese State University, B
Our Lady of the Lake College, M
Tulane University, MD
University of New Orleans, BM

Maine

Husson University, M
Saint Joseph's College of Maine, M
University of Southern Maine, M

Maryland

Johns Hopkins University, MDO
Mount St. Mary's University, M
Stevenson University, M
Towson University, MO
University of Baltimore, M
University of Maryland, Baltimore County, MO
University of Maryland, College Park, MD
University of Maryland University College, MO
Washington Adventist University, M

Massachusetts

Assumption College, MO
Bentley University, B
Boston University, MD
Brandeis University, M
Cambridge College, M
Elms College, M
Framingham State University, M
Harvard University, MD
Lasell College, MO
MCPHS University, M
Quincy College, A
Regis College, M

Suffolk University, M
University of Massachusetts Amherst, MD
University of Massachusetts Lowell, MO
Worcester State University, M

Michigan

Aquinas College, M
Central Michigan University, MDO
Cleary University, M
Davenport University, M
Eastern Michigan University, MO
Grand Valley State University, M
Madonna University, M
Saginaw Valley State University, M
Siena Heights University, M
University of Detroit Mercy, BM
University of Michigan, MD
University of Michigan - Flint, M
University of Phoenix - Detroit Campus, B
Wayne State University, M
Western Michigan University, MO

Minnesota

Argosy University, Twin Cities, M
Capella University, MD
Concordia University, St. Paul, M
Globe University - Woodbury, M
Minnesota State University Moorhead, M
St. Catherine University, M
Saint Mary's University of Minnesota, M
University of Minnesota, Twin Cities Campus, MD
University of St. Thomas, M
Walden University, MD

Mississippi

Belhaven University, M
Delta State University, M
Mississippi College, M
University of Southern Mississippi, M

Missouri

Avila University, M
Goldfarb School of Nursing at Barnes-Jewish College, M
Lindenwood University, M
Missouri State University, M
Park University, MO
Saint Louis University, MD
Southeast Missouri State University, M
Southwest Baptist University, M
University of Missouri, MDO
University of Missouri - St. Louis, O
Webster University, M
William Woods University, M

Montana

Montana State University Billings, M

Nebraska

Bellevue University, M
Nebraska Methodist College, M

Nevada

University of Nevada, Las Vegas, M
University of Phoenix - Las Vegas Campus, B

New Hampshire

Dartmouth College, MD
Franklin Pierce University, MO
New England College, M
Southern New Hampshire University, M

New Jersey

College of Saint Elizabeth, M
Fairleigh Dickinson University, College at Florham, M
Fairleigh Dickinson University, Metropolitan Campus, M
Felician University, M
Kean University, M
New Jersey City University, M
New Jersey Institute of Technology, M
Rider University, B
Rutgers University - Camden, M
Rutgers University - New Brunswick, MD

Rutgers University - Newark, MO
Saint Peter's University, M
Seton Hall University, MDO
University of Phoenix - Jersey City Campus, AB

New Mexico

University of New Mexico, M
University of Phoenix - New Mexico Campus, M

New York

Adelphi University, M
Baruch College of the City University of New York, M
Binghamton University, State University of New York, M
Brooklyn College of the City University of New York, M
The College at Brockport, State University of New York, M
Columbia University, M
Cornell University, MD
Daemen College, M
Dominican College, M
D'Youville College, BMDO
Excelsior College, M
Hilbert College, M
Hofstra University, M
Hunter College of the City University of New York, M
Iona College, MO
Long Island University - LIU Brooklyn, M
Mercy College, M
Metropolitan College of New York, M
Monroe College, B
New York University, MDO
Niagara University, M
Pace University, M
Roberts Wesleyan College, M
Rochester Institute of Technology, MO
St. Joseph's College, Long Island Campus, M
St. Joseph's College, New York, M
Stony Brook University, State University of New York, MDO
Syracuse University, O
University at Albany, State University of New York, MD
University at Buffalo, the State University of New York, M
University of Rochester, M
Utica College, M
Wagner College, M

North Carolina

Duke University, O
Pfeiffer University, M
The University of North Carolina at Chapel Hill, MD
The University of North Carolina at Charlotte, MDO
University of Phoenix - Charlotte Campus, M
Western Carolina University, M
Winston-Salem State University, M

North Dakota

University of Mary, M

Ohio

Baldwin Wallace University, M
Case Western Reserve University, M
Cleveland State University, M
Defiance College, M
Lake Erie College, M
Mount St. Joseph University, D
Ohio Dominican University, M
The Ohio State University, MD
Ohio University, M
Tiffin University, M
The University of Akron, M
The University of Findlay, M
The University of Toledo, MO
Walsh University, O
Wright State University, M
Xavier University, M
Youngstown State University, M

Oklahoma

Northeastern State University, B
Oklahoma Christian University, M
Southern Nazarene University, M
University of Oklahoma, M
University of Oklahoma Health Sciences Center, MD

Oregon

Marylhurst University, M
Oregon Health & Science University, MO
Oregon State University, MD
Pacific University, M
Portland State University, MD
University of Portland, M

Pennsylvania

Carlow University, M
Carnegie Mellon University, M
DeSales University, M
Duquesne University, M
Eastern University, M
Gwynedd Mercy University, M
Harrisburg Area Community College, A
Harrisburg University of Science and Technology, M
Holy Family University, M
Indiana University of Pennsylvania, M
King's College, M
Lebanon Valley College, M
Lehigh University, M
Marywood University, M
Misericordia University, M
Moravian College, M
Mount Aloysius College, M
Penn State Harrisburg, M
Penn State University Park, MD
Pennsylvania College of Health Sciences, M
Robert Morris University, B
Saint Joseph's University, M
Slippery Rock University of Pennsylvania, B
Temple University, M
Thomas Jefferson University, MDO
University of Pennsylvania, MD
University of Phoenix - Philadelphia Campus, B
University of Pittsburgh, MDO
University of the Sciences, MD
The University of Scranton, M
Villanova University, MO
Waynesburg University, M
West Chester University of Pennsylvania, MO
Widener University, M
Wilkes University, M
York College of Pennsylvania, M

Rhode Island

Roger Williams University, M
Salve Regina University, MO
University of Rhode Island, M

South Carolina

Francis Marion University, M
Medical University of South Carolina, MD
South University, M
University of South Carolina, MD

South Dakota

University of Sioux Falls, M
The University of South Dakota, M

Tennessee

Argosy University, Nashville, M
Belhaven University, B
Belmont University, M
East Tennessee State University, O
King University, M
Lipscomb University, M
Southern Adventist University, M
Trevecca Nazarene University, O
University of Memphis, M
The University of Tennessee, M
Vanderbilt University, M

Texas

Argosy University, Dallas, MO
Baylor University, M
Dallas Baptist University, M

Lamar University, M
LeTourneau University, M
Midwestern State University, MO
Our Lady of the Lake University of San Antonio, M
Rice University, M
Texas A&M University, M
Texas A&M University - Corpus Christi, M
Texas A&M University - San Antonio, M
Texas Southern University, M
Texas State University, M
Texas Tech University, M
Texas Woman's University, M
Trinity University, M
University of Dallas, M
University of Houston - Clear Lake, M
University of the Incarnate Word, M
University of North Texas, M
University of Phoenix - Dallas Campus, B
University of Phoenix - Houston Campus, BM
University of Phoenix - San Antonio Campus, BM
The University of Texas at Arlington, M
The University of Texas at Dallas, M
The University of Texas at El Paso, O
The University of Texas at Tyler, M
Wayland Baptist University, M

Utah

Argosy University, Salt Lake City, M
Broadview University - West Jordan, M
Independence University, M
University of Phoenix - Utah Campus, B
University of Utah, MD
Weber State University, M
Western Governors University, M

Vermont

Champlain College, M
Marlboro College, M

Virginia

Argosy University, Washington DC, M
Bryant & Stratton College - Richmond Campus, B
Bryant & Stratton College - Virginia Beach Campus, B
Eastern Mennonite University, M
George Mason University, MD
Liberty University, MO
Marymount University, M
Old Dominion University, M
University of Management and Technology, M
University of Virginia, M
Virginia Commonwealth University, MD
Virginia International University, M

Washington

Argosy University, Seattle, M
University of Phoenix - Western Washington Campus, B
University of Washington, M
University of Washington, Tacoma, B
Washington State University, M

West Virginia

American Public University System, M
Marshall University, M

Wisconsin

Concordia University Wisconsin, M
Herzing University Online, M
Lakeland College, M
Marquette University, M
Milwaukee School of Engineering, M
University of Wisconsin - Oshkosh, M
Viterbo University, M

U.S. Territories: Puerto Rico

Inter American University of Puerto Rico, Ponce Campus, B

University of Puerto Rico, Medical Sciences Campus, M

Canada

Alberta

University of Alberta, M

British Columbia

Royal Roads University, O
Trinity Western University, MO
The University of British Columbia, M

Maritime Provinces: Nova Scotia

Dalhousie University, MD

Ontario

Queen's University at Kingston, M
University of Ottawa, M
University of Toronto, MD
The University of Western Ontario, M

Quebec

McGill University, M
Université de Montréal, MO

Saskatchewan

University of Regina, MO
University of Saskatchewan, M

HEALTH SERVICES/ALLIED HEALTH/HEALTH SCIENCES

United States

Alabama

Alabama Southern Community College, A
Spring Hill College, B

Alaska

Ilisagvik College, A
University of Alaska Anchorage, B
University of Alaska Southeast, Sitka Campus, A

Arkansas

Central Baptist College, B
Hendrix College, B
University of the Ozarks, B

California

Biola University, B
California Baptist University, B
California State University, Chico, B
California State University, Dominguez Hills, B
California State University, Fullerton, B
California State University, Northridge, B
California State University, San Bernardino, B
Columbia College, A
Lincoln University, B
National University, B
Orange Coast College, A
San Diego State University, B
San Jose State University, B
Trident University International, B
University of San Francisco, B
University of Southern California, B

Colorado

Colorado Christian University, B
National American University (Denver), A
University of Colorado Colorado Springs, B
University of Northern Colorado, B

Connecticut

Eastern Connecticut State University, B
Goodwin College, AB
Quinnipiac University, B
University of Hartford, AB

Delaware

Wilmington University, B

Florida

Adventist University of Health Sciences, B
College of Central Florida, A
Florida Agricultural and Mechanical University, B
Florida Gulf Coast University, B
Gulf Coast State College, A
Keiser University, B
Miami Dade College, AB
South Florida State College, A
Stetson University, B
Ultimate Medical Academy Clearwater, A
Ultimate Medical Academy Online, A
Ultimate Medical Academy Tampa, A
University of Central Florida, B
University of Florida, B
University of Miami, B
University of North Florida, B
University of South Florida, B
University of South Florida, St. Petersburg, B
University of West Florida, B

Georgia

Brenau University, B
Columbus State University, B
Georgia Military College, A
Spelman College, B

Hawaii

Hawai'i Pacific University, B

Idaho

Brigham Young University - Idaho, B
The College of Idaho, B
Idaho State University, B

Illinois

Chicago State University, B
DePaul University, B
John A. Logan College, A
McKendree University, B
Wheaton College, B

Indiana

Ancilla College, A
Butler University, B
Valparaiso University, B

Iowa

Graceland University, B
Kaplan University, Des Moines, B
Mercy College of Health Sciences, B
St. Luke's College, B

Kansas

Friends University, B
Garden City Community College, A

Kentucky

Kentucky Wesleyan College, B
Lindsey Wilson College, A
Northern Kentucky University, B
Spalding University, B
University of Kentucky, B
Western Kentucky University, B

Louisiana

Nicholls State University, B
Northwestern State University of Louisiana, B

Maine

Husson University, B
University of Maine at Fort Kent, A
University of New England, B
York County Community College, A

Maryland

Cecil College, A
Towson University, B

Massachusetts

American International College, B
Anna Maria College, B
Bay Path University, B
Boston University, B

Cape Cod Community College, A
Fisher College, AB
Holyoke Community College, A
Lasell College, B
Merrimack College, B
Pine Manor College, A
Quinsigamond Community College, A
Western New England University, B

Michigan

Albion College, B
Madonna University, B
Olivet College, B
Saginaw Valley State University, B
Schoolcraft College, A
University of Michigan - Flint, B

Minnesota

Anoka-Ramsey Community College, A
Century College, A
The College of St. Scholastica, B
Lake Superior College, A
North Hennepin Community College, A
Northland Community and Technical College, A
St. Cloud State University, B
St. Cloud Technical & Community College, A
University of Minnesota, Crookston, B
Walden University, B

Mississippi

University of Southern Mississippi, B

Missouri

College of the Ozarks, B
Cottey College, B
Saint Louis University, B
Southeast Missouri State University, B
University of Missouri - Kansas City, B
Washington University in St. Louis, B

Montana

Aaniiih Nakoda College, A
Carroll College, B

Nebraska

Little Priest Tribal College, A
Union College, B

New Hampshire

Colby-Sawyer College, B
Granite State College, B
White Mountains Community College, A

New Jersey

Berkeley College - Woodland Park Campus, A
Camden County College, A
Essex County College, A
Fairleigh Dickinson University, College at Florham,
  B
Hudson County Community College, A
Middlesex County College, A
Monmouth University, B
Raritan Valley Community College, A
Rider University, B
Rowan College at Burlington County, A
Rowan College at Gloucester County, A
Rutgers University - Newark, B
Stockton University, B
William Paterson University of New Jersey, B

New Mexico

Central New Mexico Community College, A

New York

Albany College of Pharmacy and Health Sciences,
  B
Canisius College, B
Cayuga County Community College, A
The College at Brockport, State University of New
  York, B
Hofstra University, B
Mercy College, B
New York College of Health Professions, AB
Pace University, B

Pace University, Pleasantville Campus, B
Queensborough Community College of the City Uni-
  versity of New York, A
The Sage Colleges, B
State University of New York College of Agriculture
  and Technology at Cobleskill, A
Stony Brook University, State University of New
  York, B

North Carolina

Brevard College, B
Chowan University, B
Greensboro College, B
Pitt Community College, A
Queens University of Charlotte, B
Wake Technical Community College, A

North Dakota

Dakota College at Bottineau, A

Ohio

Aultman College of Nursing and Health Sciences, A
Clark State Community College, A
Heidelberg University, B
Mercy College of Ohio, B
Ohio Dominican University, A
Ohio University - Southern Campus, A
Youngstown State University, B

Oklahoma

Cameron University, A
Carl Albert State College, A
Oklahoma State University Institute of Technology, A
University of Oklahoma Health Sciences Center, B

Oregon

Corban University, B
Klamath Community College, A

Pennsylvania

Alvernia University, B
Cambria-Rowe Business College (Indiana), A
Cambria-Rowe Business College (Johnstown), A
Cheyney University of Pennsylvania, B
Delaware County Community College, A
Gwynedd Mercy University, B
Keystone College, A
Lebanon Valley College, B
Lehigh Carbon Community College, A
Lincoln University, B
Marywood University, B
Mercyhurst University, B
Messiah College, B
Misericordia University, B
Pennsylvania College of Health Sciences, B
Pennsylvania Institute of Technology, A
Reading Area Community College, A
Saint Joseph's University, B
University of the Sciences, B
West Chester University of Pennsylvania, B
Widener University, B

Rhode Island

Rhode Island College, B

Tennessee

Dyersburg State Community College, A
Lee University, B

Texas

Alvin Community College, A
Clarendon College, A
Houston Community College, A
Howard Payne University, A
LeTourneau University, B
Paris Junior College, A
Sam Houston State University, B
Stephen F. Austin State University, B
Texas Southern University, B
Texas Woman's University, B
University of the Incarnate Word, AB
The University of Texas at Dallas, B
The University of Texas Rio Grande Valley, B
West Texas A&M University, B

Utah

Independence University, A
University of Utah, B
Weber State University, AB
Westminster College, B

Virginia

Ferrum College, B

Washington

The Evergreen State College, B
University of Washington, Bothell, B
Whitworth University, B

West Virginia

BridgeValley Community and Technical College
(South Charleston), A

Wyoming

Casper College, A
Northwest College, A
Sheridan College, A
Western Wyoming Community College, A

U.S. Territories: American Samoa

American Samoa Community College, A

U.S. Territories: Puerto Rico

Pontifical Catholic University of Puerto Rico, B
University of Puerto Rico, Medical Sciences Campus, B

Canada

British Columbia

Thompson Rivers University, B

Maritime Provinces: Nova Scotia

Dalhousie University, B

Ontario

University of Ottawa, B
The University of Western Ontario, B
York University, B

HEALTH SERVICES RESEARCH

United States

Alabama

The University of Alabama at Birmingham, MD

Arkansas

University of Arkansas for Medical Sciences, D

California

Stanford University, MD
University of La Verne, M
University of Southern California, D

Colorado

University of Colorado Denver, D

District of Columbia

The George Washington University, M

Florida

Florida Agricultural and Mechanical University, D
University of Florida, D

Georgia

Emory University, M

Idaho

Boise State University, M

Illinois

Northwestern University, D
University of Illinois at Chicago, D

Maryland

Johns Hopkins University, M

Minnesota

University of Minnesota, Twin Cities Campus, MD

Missouri

Washington University in St. Louis, MO

Nebraska

University of Nebraska Medical Center, D

New Hampshire

Dartmouth College, MD

New York

Albany College of Pharmacy and Health Sciences,
M
Clarkson University, M
University of Rochester, D

North Carolina

The University of North Carolina at Charlotte, D
Wake Forest University, M

Ohio

Case Western Reserve University, MD

Pennsylvania

Thomas Jefferson University, MDO
University of Pennsylvania, M

Rhode Island

Brown University, D

South Carolina

Clemson University, MD

Texas

Texas A&M University, D
Texas State University, M

Utah

University of Utah, D

Virginia

Old Dominion University, D
University of Virginia, M
Virginia Commonwealth University, D

Washington

University of Washington, MD

U.S. Territories: Puerto Rico

University of Puerto Rico, Medical Sciences Campus, M

Canada

Alberta

University of Alberta, M

Maritime Provinces: New Brunswick

University of New Brunswick Fredericton, M

Ontario

Lakehead University, M
McMaster University, MD
University of Ottawa, O

HEALTH TEACHER EDUCATION

United States

Alabama

Auburn University, B
Jacksonville State University, B
Troy University, B

The University of Alabama at Birmingham, B

Arkansas

Harding University, B
John Brown University, B

California

Cabrillo College, A
California State University, Stanislaus, B
College of the Sequoias, A
Cosumnes River College, A
National University, B
Trident University International, B
Yuba College, A

Connecticut

Western Connecticut State University, B

Delaware

Delaware State University, B

District of Columbia

University of the District of Columbia, B

Florida

Broward College, A
Palm Beach State College, A
South Florida State College, A
State College of Florida Manatee-Sarasota, A

Georgia

Bainbridge State College, A
Fort Valley State University, B
Georgia Military College, A

Idaho

Idaho State University, B

Illinois

DePaul University, B
Eastern Illinois University, B
Harper College, A
Illinois State University, B
McKendree University, B
Northern Illinois University, B
Southern Illinois University Edwardsville, B
Western Illinois University, B

Indiana

Indiana University Bloomington, B
Purdue University, B
University of Saint Francis, B

Iowa

Graceland University, B
Iowa State University of Science and Technology, B
Iowa Wesleyan University, B
University of Northern Iowa, B
William Penn University, B

Kansas

Central Christian College of Kansas, AB
Kansas Wesleyan University, B
Pratt Community College, A
Seward County Community College and Area Technical School, A
Tabor College, B

Kentucky

Campbellsville University, B
Morehead State University, B
Murray State University, B
Union College, B
University of the Cumberlands, B
University of Kentucky, B

Louisiana

Louisiana College, B

Maine

University of Maine at Farmington, B

Maryland

Howard Community College, A
Morgan State University, B
Prince George's Community College, A
Salisbury University, B
University of Maryland, College Park, B

Massachusetts

Bridgewater State University, B
Springfield College, B

Michigan

Adrian College, B
Alma College, B
Central Michigan University, B
Concordia University Ann Arbor, B
Grand Valley State University, B
Michigan State University, B
Northern Michigan University, B
Olivet College, B
Wayne State University, B
Western Michigan University, B

Minnesota

Augsburg College, B
Bemidji State University, B
Bethel University, B
Concordia College, B
Concordia University, St. Paul, B
Gustavus Adolphus College, B
Minnesota State University Mankato, B
Minnesota State University Moorhead, B
St. Cloud State University, B
Southwest Minnesota State University, B
University of St. Thomas, B
Vermilion Community College, A
Winona State University, B

Mississippi

Copiah-Lincoln Community College, A
Mississippi Delta Community College, A

Missouri

Missouri Baptist University, B
Missouri Valley College, B
Southwest Baptist University, B

Montana

Montana State University Billings, B
Montana State University - Northern, B
Rocky Mountain College, B
University of Great Falls, B
University of Montana, B
The University of Montana Western, B

Nebraska

Concordia University, Nebraska, B
Peru State College, B

Nevada

University of Nevada, Las Vegas, B

New Jersey

Montclair State University, B

New Mexico

New Mexico Highlands University, B
University of New Mexico, B

New York

Brooklyn College of the City University of New York, B
Fulton-Montgomery Community College, A
Hofstra University, B
Houghton College, B
Hunter College of the City University of New York, B
Ithaca College, B
Lehman College of the City University of New York, B
Long Island University - LIU Post, B
State University of New York College at Cortland, B
State University of New York at Oswego, B
York College of the City University of New York, B

North Carolina

East Carolina University, B
Elon University, B
Fayetteville State University, B
Gardner-Webb University, B
North Carolina Central University, B

North Dakota

Mayville State University, B
North Dakota State University, B
Valley City State University, B

Ohio

Bowling Green State University, B
Capital University, B
Defiance College, B
Heidelberg University, B
Kent State University, B
Miami University Hamilton, B
Muskingum University, B
Ohio Wesleyan University, B
Otterbein University, B
The University of Akron, B
University of Cincinnati, B
University of Mount Union, B
University of Rio Grande, B
Urbana University, B
Wilmington College, B
Youngstown State University, B

Oklahoma

Northwestern Oklahoma State University, B
Oral Roberts University, B

Oregon

Linfield College, B
Portland State University, B
Southern Oregon University, B
Umpqua Community College, A

Pennsylvania

East Stroudsburg University of Pennsylvania, B

Rhode Island

Rhode Island College, B

South Dakota

Northern State University, B
South Dakota State University, B
The University of South Dakota, B

Tennessee

Lee University, B
Lincoln Memorial University, B
Maryville College, B
Middle Tennessee State University, B
Tennessee State University, B
Tennessee Technological University, B

Texas

Angelina College, A
Austin Community College District, A
Baylor University, B
Del Mar College, A
Kilgore College, A
Sam Houston State University, B

Utah

Utah State University, B
Utah Valley University, B

Virginia

Averett University, B
Bluefield College, B
George Mason University, B
Hampton University, B
Virginia Commonwealth University, B

Washington

Eastern Washington University, B
Washington State University, B

West Virginia

Concord University, B
University of Charleston, B
West Liberty University, B
West Virginia Wesleyan College, B

Wisconsin

Carroll University, B
University of Wisconsin - La Crosse, B

U.S. Territories: Puerto Rico

Inter American University of Puerto Rico, Barranquitas Campus, B
Inter American University of Puerto Rico, San Germán Campus, B
National University College (Bayamón), B
Pontifical Catholic University of Puerto Rico, B

Canada

Alberta

University of Alberta, B

Maritime Provinces: New Brunswick

University of New Brunswick Fredericton, B

Ontario

University of Toronto, B
University of Windsor, B

Quebec

McGill University, B

Saskatchewan

University of Regina, B

HEALTH UNIT COORDINATOR/ WARD CLERK

United States

Minnesota

Riverland Community College, A

Pennsylvania

Community College of Allegheny County, A

South Dakota

Southeast Technical Institute, A

HEALTH UNIT MANAGER/ WARD SUPERVISOR

United States

North Dakota

University of Mary, B

Pennsylvania

Delaware County Community College, A

Canada

Ontario

Ryerson University, B

HEATING, AIR CONDITIONING AND REFRIGERATION TECHNOLOGY/TECHNICIAN

United States

Alabama

Bevill State Community College, A
Gadsden State Community College, A

George C. Wallace Community College, A
H. Councill Trenholm State Community College, A
J. F. Drake State Community and Technical College, A
Shelton State Community College, A

Arizona

Arizona Automotive Institute, A
Arizona Western College, A
GateWay Community College, A
The Refrigeration School, A

Arkansas

Arkansas State University - Newport, A

California

Antelope Valley College, A
Long Beach City College, A
San Joaquin Valley College (Bakersfield), A
San Joaquin Valley College (Fresno), A
San Joaquin Valley College (Visalia), A

Colorado

Front Range Community College, A
IntelliTec College (Colorado Springs), A

Delaware

Delaware Technical & Community College, Stanton/Wilmington Campus, A

Florida

College of Business and Technology - Flagler Campus, A
College of Business and Technology - Hialeah Campus, A
Lincoln College of Technology, A
Miami Dade College, A

Georgia

Georgia Piedmont Technical College, A
North Georgia Technical College, A
Savannah Technical College, A
South Georgia Technical College, A
Southern Crescent Technical College, A

Illinois

Oakton Community College, A

Iowa

Iowa Lakes Community College, A

Kansas

Johnson County Community College, A
Manhattan Area Technical College, A

Kentucky

Sullivan College of Technology and Design, A

Maine

Kennebec Valley Community College, A

Maryland

Community College of Baltimore County, A

Massachusetts

Massasoit Community College, A
Springfield Technical Community College, A

Michigan

Ferris State University, A
Jackson College, A
Kalamazoo Valley Community College, A
Macomb Community College, A
Mott Community College, A
Northern Michigan University, A
Oakland Community College, A

Minnesota

Dunwoody College of Technology, A
Minnesota State Community and Technical College, A

Mississippi

East Central Community College, A
Northwest Mississippi Community College, A

Missouri

Mineral Area College, A
Vatterott College (Berkeley), AB
Vatterott College (Kansas City), A
Vatterott College (Saint Charles), A
Vatterott College (Sunset Hills), A

New Jersey

Mercer County Community College, A
Raritan Valley Community College, A

New Mexico

New Mexico State University - Carlsbad, A

New York

State University of New York College of Technology at Canton, A
TCI - College of Technology, A

North Carolina

Alamance Community College, A
Martin Community College, A

North Dakota

North Dakota State College of Science, A

Ohio

Clark State Community College, A
Terra State Community College, A
Vatterott College, A

Oklahoma

Oklahoma Technical College, A
Vatterott College (Tulsa), A
Vatterott College (Warr Acres), A

Pennsylvania

Dean Institute of Technology, A
Delaware County Community College, A
New Castle School of Trades, A
Penn Commercial Business and Technical School, A
Pennsylvania College of Technology, A
Triangle Tech, Greensburg, A

Tennessee

Vatterott College (Memphis), A

Texas

Austin Community College District, A
Lamar Institute of Technology, A
Midland College, A
Texas State Technical College, A

Wisconsin

Chippewa Valley Technical College, A
Milwaukee Area Technical College, A
Moraine Park Technical College, A
Northeast Wisconsin Technical College, A

U.S. Territories: Puerto Rico

Humacao Community College, A

HEATING, AIR CONDITIONING, VENTILATION AND REFRIGERATION MAINTENANCE TECHNOLOGY/TECHNICIAN

United States

Alabama

Calhoun Community College, A
George C. Wallace Community College, A
Southern Union State Community College, A
Wallace State Community College, A

Alaska

University of Alaska Anchorage, A
University of Alaska Anchorage, Matanuska-Susitna College, A

Arizona

Arizona Western College, A
GateWay Community College, A
Mohave Community College, A

Arkansas

Pulaski Technical College, A
University of Arkansas Community College at Morrilton, A

California

Antelope Valley College, A
College of the Desert, A
College of San Mateo, A
College of the Sequoias, A
Cypress College, A
El Camino College, A
Fresno City College, A
Laney College, A
Los Angeles Trade-Technical College, A
Los Medanos College, A
Modesto Junior College, A
Mt. San Antonio College, A
Oxnard College, A
Riverside City College, A
San Bernardino Valley College, A
San Joaquin Delta College, A
San Joaquin Valley College (Hesperia), A
San Joaquin Valley College (Lancaster), A
San Joaquin Valley College (Ontario), A
San Joaquin Valley College (Temecula), A
San Jose City College, A

Delaware

Delaware Technical & Community College, Jack F. Owens Campus, A

Florida

College of Business and Technology - Main Campus, A
Indian River State College, A
Miami Dade College, A
Santa Fe College, A

Hawaii

Honolulu Community College, A

Idaho

Lewis-Clark State College, AB
North Idaho College, A

Illinois

City Colleges of Chicago, Kennedy-King College, A
College of DuPage, A
College of Lake County, A
Elgin Community College, A
Harper College, A
Heartland Community College, A
Illinois Central College, A
John A. Logan College, A
Joliet Junior College, A
Kankakee Community College, A
Kaskaskia College, A
Moraine Valley Community College, A
Morton College, A
Sauk Valley Community College, A
Southwestern Illinois College, A
Triton College, A
Waubonsee Community College, A

Indiana

Ivy Tech Community College - Bloomington, A
Ivy Tech Community College - Central Indiana, A
Ivy Tech Community College - Columbus, A
Ivy Tech Community College - East Central, A
Ivy Tech Community College - Kokomo, A
Ivy Tech Community College - Lafayette, A
Ivy Tech Community College - North Central, A
Ivy Tech Community College - Northeast, A

Ivy Tech Community College - Northwest, A
Ivy Tech Community College - Richmond, A
Ivy Tech Community College - Southern Indiana, A
Ivy Tech Community College - Southwest, A
Ivy Tech Community College - Wabash Valley, A

Iowa

Des Moines Area Community College, A
Iowa Lakes Community College, A
North Iowa Area Community College, A
Scott Community College, A
Western Iowa Tech Community College, A

Kansas

Fort Scott Community College, A
Labette Community College, A
Manhattan Area Technical College, A
Northwest Kansas Technical College, A
Seward County Community College and Area Technical School, A
Wichita Area Technical College, A

Kentucky

Big Sandy Community and Technical College, A
Bluegrass Community and Technical College, A

Louisiana

Fletcher Technical Community College, A
Louisiana Delta Community College, A
South Louisiana Community College, A

Maine

Eastern Maine Community College, A
Northern Maine Community College, A
Southern Maine Community College, A

Michigan

Delta College, A
Grand Rapids Community College, A
Kellogg Community College, A
Kirtland Community College, A
Lansing Community College, A
Macomb Community College, A
Mid Michigan Community College, A
Washtenaw Community College, A
Wayne County Community College District, A

Minnesota

Century College, A
Dunwoody College of Technology, A
Hennepin Technical College, A
Minneapolis Community and Technical College, A
Minnesota State College - Southeast Technical, A
Northland Community and Technical College, A
St. Cloud Technical & Community College, A
South Central College, A

Mississippi

Hinds Community College, A
Holmes Community College, A
Northeast Mississippi Community College, A
Northwest Mississippi Community College, A
Southwest Mississippi Community College, A

Missouri

East Central College, A
Jefferson College, A
Ozarks Technical Community College, A
Ranken Technical College, A
State Technical College of Missouri, A

Montana

Montana State University Billings, A

Nebraska

Central Community College - Grand Island Campus, A
Central Community College - Hastings Campus, A
Metropolitan Community College, A
Mid-Plains Community College, A
Northeast Community College, A
Southeast Community College, Milford Campus, A

Nevada

College of Southern Nevada, A
Truckee Meadows Community College, A

New Hampshire

Manchester Community College, A

New Mexico

Central New Mexico Community College, A
Clovis Community College, A
Doña Ana Community College, A
Eastern New Mexico University - Roswell, A

New York

Hudson Valley Community College, A
Mohawk Valley Community College, A
Monroe Community College, A
State University of New York College of Technology at Alfred, A
State University of New York College of Technology at Delhi, A

North Carolina

Asheville-Buncombe Technical Community College, A
Catawba Valley Community College, A
Craven Community College, A
Fayetteville Technical Community College, A
Guilford Technical Community College, A
Johnston Community College, A
Martin Community College, A
Montgomery Community College, A
Pitt Community College, A
Richmond Community College, A
South Piedmont Community College, A
Surry Community College, A
Vance-Granville Community College, A
Wake Technical Community College, A
Wilson Community College, A

North Dakota

Bismarck State College, A
North Dakota State College of Science, A

Ohio

Belmont College, A
Columbus State Community College, A
Fortis College (Ravenna), A
North Central State College, A
University of Northwestern Ohio, A
Washington State Community College, A

Oklahoma

Oklahoma State University Institute of Technology, A

Oregon

Portland Community College, A

Pennsylvania

Butler County Community College, A
Community College of Allegheny County, A
Community College of Beaver County, A
Delaware County Community College, A
Harrisburg Area Community College, A
Johnson College, A
Lehigh Carbon Community College, A
Luzerne County Community College, A
Northampton Community College, A
Pittsburgh Technical Institute, A
Thaddeus Stevens College of Technology, A
Triangle Tech, Greensburg, A
Triangle Tech, Pittsburgh, A
Westmoreland County Community College, A

Rhode Island

New England Institute of Technology, A

South Carolina

Florence-Darlington Technical College, A
Midlands Technical College, A
Piedmont Technical College, A
Spartanburg Community College, A
Tri-County Technical College, A
York Technical College, A

South Dakota

Mitchell Technical Institute, A
Southeast Technical Institute, A
Western Dakota Technical Institute, A

Texas

Amarillo College, A
Brazosport College, A
Cedar Valley College, A
Central Texas College, A
Eastfield College, A
El Paso Community College, A
Galveston College, A
Grayson College, A
Hill College, A
Kilgore College, A
Lamar State College - Port Arthur, A
Lee College, A
Lone Star College - North Harris, A
North Lake College, A
Odessa College, A
Paris Junior College, A
St. Philip's College, A
San Jacinto College District, A
South Plains College, A
South Texas College, A
Tarrant County College District, A
Texarkana College, A
Trinity Valley Community College, A
Tyler Junior College, A
Western Technical College (El Paso), A

Utah

Salt Lake Community College, A

Virginia

Advanced Technology Institute, A
Virginia Highlands Community College, A

Washington

Bates Technical College, A
Bellingham Technical College, A
Clover Park Technical College, A
North Seattle College, A
Renton Technical College, A
Spokane Community College, A
Walla Walla Community College, A
Wenatchee Valley College, A

West Virginia

BridgeValley Community and Technical College (South Charleston), A
West Virginia Northern Community College, A

Wisconsin

Gateway Technical College, A
Western Technical College, A

Wyoming

Laramie County Community College, A

U.S. Territories: Puerto Rico

Huertas Junior College, A

Canada

British Columbia

British Columbia Institute of Technology, A

HEAVY EQUIPMENT MAINTENANCE TECHNOLOGY/TECHNICIAN

United States

Alaska

University of Alaska Anchorage, A

Arizona

Mesa Community College, A

California

Allan Hancock College, A
Los Angeles Trade-Technical College, A

Colorado

Community College of Aurora, A
Trinidad State Junior College, A

Idaho

College of Western Idaho, A
North Idaho College, A

Illinois

Highland Community College, A
Rend Lake College, A

Maine

Eastern Maine Community College, A

Michigan

Ferris State University, AB

Minnesota

Dakota County Technical College, A

Missouri

Metropolitan Community College - Kansas City, A
Ozarks Technical Community College, A
State Technical College of Missouri, A

Montana

University of Montana, A

Nebraska

Metropolitan Community College, A

North Carolina

Beaufort County Community College, A

Ohio

The Ohio State University Agricultural Technical Institute, A

Pennsylvania

Pennsylvania College of Technology, A

Tennessee

Southwest Tennessee Community College, A

Texas

Amarillo College, A
Del Mar College, A
South Texas College, A

Washington

Clover Park Technical College, A
Skagit Valley College, A
South Seattle College, A
Spokane Community College, A
Spokane Falls Community College, A

Wisconsin

Northeast Wisconsin Technical College, A

Wyoming

Western Wyoming Community College, A

Canada

British Columbia

British Columbia Institute of Technology, A

HEAVY/INDUSTRIAL EQUIPMENT MAINTENANCE TECHNOLOGIES

United States

Michigan

Wayne County Community College District, A

Minnesota

Hibbing Community College, A

Mississippi

Coahoma Community College, A

Missouri

East Central College, A
Mineral Area College, A
Ranken Technical College, A

New York

State University of New York College of Technology at Alfred, A

North Carolina

Blue Ridge Community College, A

Washington

Bellingham Technical College, A

HEBREW LANGUAGE AND LITERATURE

United States

California

Los Angeles Valley College, A

District of Columbia

The Catholic University of America, MD

Illinois

University of Illinois at Urbana - Champaign, B

Maryland

Johns Hopkins University, D

Massachusetts

Brandeis University, BM
Harvard University, MD

Michigan

University of Michigan, BMD
Wayne State University, M

Missouri

Washington University in St. Louis, B

New Hampshire

Dartmouth College, B

New York

Baruch College of the City University of New York, B
Binghamton University, State University of New York, B
Brooklyn College of the City University of New York, B
Hofstra University, B
Hunter College of the City University of New York, B
The Jewish Theological Seminary, B
Lehman College of the City University of New York, B
New York University, B
Queens College of the City University of New York, B
Sh'or Yoshuv Rabbinical College, B
Yeshiva University, AB

Ohio

The Ohio State University, B
University of Cincinnati, B

Oregon

Multnomah University, B

Texas

The University of Texas at Austin, B

Utah

Brigham Young University, B
University of Utah, BM

Wisconsin

Concordia University Wisconsin, B
University of Wisconsin - Madison, MD

Canada

Ontario

York University, B

HEBREW STUDIES

United States

Maryland

Towson University, MO

New York

Brooklyn College of the City University of New York, M

Wisconsin

University of Wisconsin - Madison, MD
University of Wisconsin - Milwaukee, M

HEMATOLOGY TECHNOLOGY/TECHNICIAN

United States

Alabama

Community College of the Air Force, A

HERBALISM/HERBALIST

United States

Washington

Bastyr University, B

HIGHER EDUCATION/HIGHER EDUCATION ADMINISTRATION

United States

Alabama

Auburn University, MDO
The University of Alabama, MD

Arizona

Argosy University, Phoenix, MD
Arizona State University at the Tempe campus, M
Grand Canyon University, D
Northern Arizona University, M
The University of Arizona, MD
University of Phoenix - Online Campus, D

Arkansas

John Brown University, M
University of Arkansas, MDO
University of Arkansas at Little Rock, MD

California

Argosy University, Inland Empire, D
Argosy University, Los Angeles, D
Argosy University, Orange County, D
Argosy University, San Diego, D
Argosy University, San Francisco Bay Area, D
Azusa Pacific University, MD
California Baptist University, M
California Lutheran University, D
California State University, Fullerton, M
California State University, Long Beach, M
California State University, Sacramento, M
San Diego State University, M
San Jose State University, MD
Trident University International, MD
University of California, Riverside, MD
University of Phoenix - Bay Area Campus, D
University of San Diego, M
University of Southern California, D

Colorado

Argosy University, Denver, D
University of Northern Colorado, D

Connecticut

University of Connecticut, M
University of New Haven, M

Delaware

University of Delaware, M
Wilmington University, D

District of Columbia

The George Washington University, MDO
University of Phoenix - Washington D.C. Campus, D

Florida

Argosy University, Sarasota, D
Argosy University, Tampa, D
Barry University, MD
Florida Atlantic University, M
Florida International University, D
Florida State University, MDO
University of Central Florida, D
University of Florida, MD
University of Miami, MDO
University of South Florida, MDO

Georgia

Argosy University, Atlanta, D
Columbus State University, M
Georgia Southern University, M
Mercer University, M
University of Georgia, D

Hawaii

Argosy University, Hawai'i, D

Illinois

Argosy University, Chicago, D
Benedictine University, D
Chicago State University, M
Illinois State University, D
Lewis University, M
Loyola University Chicago, MD
McKendree University, M
Northern Illinois University, MD
Robert Morris University Illinois, M
Southern Illinois University Carbondale, M
Southern Illinois University Edwardsville, M
University of St. Francis, M

Indiana

Ball State University, MD
Indiana State University, MD
Indiana University Bloomington, MD
Indiana University - Purdue University Indianapolis, M
Indiana Wesleyan University, M
Purdue University, MD
Taylor University, M

Iowa

Iowa State University of Science and Technology, M
Kaplan University, Davenport Campus, M
The University of Iowa, M
University of Northern Iowa, M
Upper Iowa University, M

Kansas

Pittsburg State University, O
The University of Kansas, MD

Kentucky

Eastern Kentucky University, M
Morehead State University, MO
University of Kentucky, MD
University of Louisville, M
Western Kentucky University, M

Louisiana

Grambling State University, D
Louisiana State University and Agricultural & Mechanical College, D
Louisiana Tech University, D

Maine

University of Maine, MDO
University of Southern Maine, M

Maryland

Morgan State University, MD

Massachusetts

Bay Path University, M
Boston College, MD
Merrimack College, M
Northeastern University, MD
Regis College, D
Salem State University, M
University of Massachusetts Amherst, M

Michigan

Andrews University, MDO
Central Michigan University, DO
Grand Valley State University, M
Lansing Community College, A
Michigan State University, MD
Northern Michigan University, M
Oakland University, O
Siena Heights University, M
Wayne State University, O
Western Michigan University, D

Minnesota

Argosy University, Twin Cities, MD
Bethel University, O
Capella University, MD
Minnesota State University Mankato, M
St. Cloud State University, M
University of Minnesota, Twin Cities Campus, MD
Walden University, MDO

Mississippi

Delta State University, D
Mississippi College, M
Mississippi State University, M
University of Southern Mississippi, MD

Missouri

Maryville University of Saint Louis, D
Missouri State University, M
Saint Louis University, MDO
Southeast Missouri State University, M
University of Missouri, MDO
University of Missouri - Kansas City, D

Montana

Montana State University, MD

Nevada

University of Nevada, Las Vegas, MDO

New Hampshire

New England College, MD
Plymouth State University, DO
University of New Hampshire, O

New Jersey

College of Saint Elizabeth, O
Rowan University, M
Saint Peter's University, D
Seton Hall University, D

New Mexico

University of New Mexico, O

New York

Baruch College of the City University of New York, M
The College of Saint Rose, M
New York University, MD
Stony Brook University, State University of New York, MO
Syracuse University, MD
University at Buffalo, the State University of New York, D
University of Rochester, MD

North Carolina

Appalachian State University, MO
North Carolina State University, MD
The University of North Carolina at Greensboro, MDO
Western Carolina University, M

North Dakota

North Dakota State University, O

Ohio

Bowling Green State University, D
Cleveland State University, D
Kent State University, MDO
Ohio University, MD
Tiffin University, M
Union Institute & University, D
The University of Akron, M
The University of Toledo, MDO
Walsh University, M
Wright State University, MO

Oklahoma

Oklahoma State University, D
Oral Roberts University, D
University of Central Oklahoma, M
University of Oklahoma, MDO

Oregon

George Fox University, M

Pennsylvania

Drexel University, M
Geneva College, M
Indiana University of Pennsylvania, M
Marywood University, MD
Mercyhurst University, M
Messiah College, M
Shippensburg University of Pennsylvania, M
Slippery Rock University of Pennsylvania, M
University of Pennsylvania, MD
University of Pittsburgh, MD
West Chester University of Pennsylvania, O
Wilkes University, D

South Carolina

Clemson University, D
Columbia College, M
Columbia International University, D
University of South Carolina, M

Tennessee

Argosy University, Nashville, D
Johnson University, M
Lincoln Memorial University, D
Union University, D
University of Memphis, D
Vanderbilt University, MD

Texas

Abilene Christian University, M
Angelo State University, M
Argosy University, Dallas, M
Dallas Baptist University, M
Sam Houston State University, M
Texas A&M University - Kingsville, D
Texas Southern University, MD
Texas State University, M
Texas Tech University, MD
University of Houston, M
University of Houston - Victoria, M
University of the Incarnate Word, D
University of Mary Hardin-Baylor, D
University of North Texas, MD
The University of Texas at Arlington, M
The University of Texas at San Antonio, M
Wayland Baptist University, M

Utah

University of Utah, D
Western Governors University, M

Virginia

Argosy University, Washington DC, D
George Mason University, MDO
James Madison University, M
Old Dominion University, MDO
Regent University, D
University of Virginia, MDO
Virginia Polytechnic Institute and State University, M

Washington

Argosy University, Seattle, MD
University of Washington, MD
Western Washington University, M

West Virginia

West Virginia University, M

Wisconsin

University of Wisconsin - La Crosse, M
University of Wisconsin - Madison, M
University of Wisconsin - Milwaukee, O
University of Wisconsin - Whitewater, M

U.S. Territories: Puerto Rico

Inter American University of Puerto Rico, Metropolitan Campus, M

Canada

British Columbia

The University of British Columbia, M

Manitoba

University of Manitoba, M

Quebec

Université de Sherbrooke, MO

HISPANIC-AMERICAN, PUERTO RICAN, AND MEXICAN- AMERI-CAN/CHICANO STUDIES

United States

Arizona

Arizona State University at the Tempe campus, B
The University of Arizona, B

California

California State University, Dominguez Hills, B
California State University, East Bay, B
California State University, Fresno, B
California State University, Fullerton, B
California State University, Long Beach, B
California State University, Los Angeles, B
California State University, Northridge, B
Cerritos College, A

Claremont McKenna College, B
East Los Angeles College, A
Laney College, A
Los Angeles City College, A
Loyola Marymount University, B
Mills College, B
Pepperdine University, B
Pitzer College, B
Pomona College, B
San Diego City College, A
San Diego Mesa College, A
San Diego State University, B
San Francisco State University, B
Santa Ana College, A
Santa Barbara City College, A
Scripps College, B
Solano Community College, A
Sonoma State University, B
Stanford University, B
University of California, Berkeley, B
University of California, Davis, B
University of California, Irvine, B
University of California, Los Angeles, B
University of California, Riverside, B
University of California, Santa Barbara, B
University of California, Santa Cruz, B
University of Southern California, B
Yuba College, A

Colorado

The Colorado College, B
Metropolitan State University of Denver, B
University of Northern Colorado, B

Illinois

City Colleges of Chicago, Wilbur Wright College, A

Louisiana

Tulane University, B

Massachusetts

Boston College, B

Michigan

University of Michigan, B

Minnesota

University of Minnesota, Twin Cities Campus, B

New Hampshire

Dartmouth College, B

New Jersey

Rutgers University - New Brunswick, B
Rutgers University - Newark, B

New Mexico

University of New Mexico, B
Western New Mexico University, B

New York

Brooklyn College of the City University of New York, B
Columbia University, B
Columbia University, School of General Studies, B
Hunter College of the City University of New York, B
State University of New York College at Oneonta, B
University at Albany, State University of New York, B

Ohio

Bowling Green State University, B

Oregon

Lewis & Clark College, B

Pennsylvania

Gettysburg College, B
The University of Scranton, B

Rhode Island

Brown University, B

Tennessee

Vanderbilt University, B

Texas

Our Lady of the Lake University of San Antonio, B
San Jacinto College District, A
Southern Methodist University, B
The University of Texas at El Paso, B
The University of Texas Rio Grande Valley, B
The University of Texas at San Antonio, B

Canada

Alberta

University of Alberta, B

Ontario

McMaster University, B
Trent University, B

Quebec

McGill University, B
Université de Montréal, B

HISPANIC AND LATIN AMERI-CAN LANGUAGES

United States

California

California State University, San Marcos, M
University of California, Berkeley, D
University of California, Los Angeles, D
University of California, Santa Barbara, MD

Colorado

University of Colorado Boulder, D

Connecticut

Central Connecticut State University, M

Illinois

University of Illinois at Chicago, D

Indiana

Indiana University Bloomington, MD

Massachusetts

Boston University, MD
University of Massachusetts Amherst, MD

Michigan

Eastern Michigan University, O
Michigan State University, M

Minnesota

University of Minnesota, Twin Cities Campus, MD

New York

Cornell University, D
Queens College of the City University of New York, M
Stony Brook University, State University of New York, MD

North Carolina

The University of North Carolina at Greensboro, O

Pennsylvania

Indiana University of Pennsylvania, M
University of Pittsburgh, MD

Texas

The University of Texas at Austin, MD

Utah

Brigham Young University, M

Washington

University of Washington, M

Canada

Quebec

Université de Montréal, D

HISPANIC STUDIES

United States

California

California State University, Los Angeles, M
California State University, Northridge, M
California State University, San Marcos, M
San Jose State University, M
University of California, Riverside, MD
University of California, Santa Barbara, D

Florida

St. Thomas University, MO

Illinois

University of Illinois at Chicago, MD

Kentucky

University of Kentucky, MD

Louisiana

Louisiana State University and Agricultural & Mechanical College, M

Michigan

Eastern Michigan University, O
Michigan State University, D

Nevada

University of Nevada, Las Vegas, M

New York

Columbia University, M

North Carolina

The University of North Carolina at Greensboro, O
The University of North Carolina Wilmington, MO

Oregon

Oregon State University, M

Pennsylvania

La Salle University, MO
Villanova University, M

Rhode Island

Brown University, D

Texas

Texas A&M International University, D
Texas A&M University - Kingsville, D
University of Houston, MD
The University of Texas at Austin, M

U.S. Territories: Puerto Rico

Pontifical Catholic University of Puerto Rico, MO
University of Puerto Rico, Mayagüez Campus, M
University of Puerto Rico, Río Piedras Campus, MD

Canada

Alberta

University of Alberta, MD

British Columbia

The University of British Columbia, MD
University of Victoria, M

Ontario

Queen's University at Kingston, M

Quebec

McGill University, MD

HISTOLOGIC TECHNICIAN

United States

Connecticut

Goodwin College, A

Florida

Florida State College at Jacksonville, A
Miami Dade College, A

Georgia

Darton State College, A

Indiana

Indiana University - Purdue University Indianapolis, A

Michigan

Lansing Community College, A
Mott Community College, A
Northern Michigan University, A

Minnesota

North Hennepin Community College, A

Pennsylvania

Pennsylvania Highlands Community College, A

Rhode Island

Community College of Rhode Island, A

Texas

Houston Community College, A
Tarleton State University, A

HISTOLOGIC TECHNOLOGY/ HISTOTECHNOLOGIST

United States

Arizona

Phoenix College, A

Delaware

Delaware Technical & Community College, Stanton/Wilmington Campus, A

Florida

Keiser University, A
Miami Dade College, A

Illinois

Roosevelt University, B

Michigan

Oakland Community College, A
Oakland University, B

Minnesota

Argosy University, Twin Cities, A

Pennsylvania

Harcum College, A

Texas

Argosy University, Dallas, A
Tarleton State University, A

HISTORIC PRESERVATION AND CONSERVATION

United States

Arkansas

Arkansas State University, MD

California

Saint Mary's College of California, B
University of California, Los Angeles, M
University of California, Riverside, M

Colorado

Colorado Mountain College (Leadville), A
University of Colorado Denver, M

Delaware

Delaware State University, BM
University of Delaware, BMD

District of Columbia

The George Washington University, M

Florida

University of Florida, MD

Georgia

Georgia State University, M
Savannah College of Art and Design, BMO
University of Georgia, M

Hawaii

University of Hawaii at Manoa, O

Illinois

School of the Art Institute of Chicago, M

Indiana

Ball State University, M

Kentucky

University of Kentucky, M

Maryland

Goucher College, M
Morgan State University, M
University of Maryland, College Park, MO

Massachusetts

Boston Architectural College, M
Boston University, M
University of Massachusetts Amherst, M

Michigan

Eastern Michigan University, M
Michigan Technological University, D

Minnesota

St. Cloud State University, M

Missouri

Southeast Missouri State University, BO

Montana

Montana Tech of The University of Montana, A

New Hampshire

Plymouth State University, M

New Jersey

Rutgers University - New Brunswick, MO

New Mexico

University of New Mexico, O

New York

Buffalo State College, State University of New York, MO
Columbia University, MO
Cornell University, M

Pratt Institute, M
Syracuse University, O
University at Buffalo, the State University of New York, MO
University of Rochester, M

North Carolina

Piedmont Community College, A
The University of North Carolina at Greensboro, O

Ohio

Cleveland State University, M
Ursuline College, BM

Oregon

University of Oregon, M

Pennsylvania

Penn State Harrisburg, O
University of Pennsylvania, MO

Rhode Island

Roger Williams University, BM
Salve Regina University, B

South Carolina

Clemson University, M
College of Charleston, BM
University of South Carolina, M

Texas

Texas Tech University, M
The University of Texas at Austin, M

Vermont

University of Vermont, M

Virginia

University of Mary Washington, B
Virginia Commonwealth University, O

Washington

University of Washington, O

Wisconsin

University of Wisconsin - Milwaukee, O

HISTORY

United States

Alabama

Alabama State University, B
Athens State University, B
Auburn University, BMDO
Auburn University at Montgomery, B
Birmingham-Southern College, B
Faulkner University, BM
Huntingdon College, B
Jacksonville State University, BM
Judson College, B
Miles College, B
Oakwood University, B
Samford University, B
Spring Hill College, BM
Stillman College, B
Talladega College, B
Troy University, BM
Tuskegee University, B
The University of Alabama, BMD
The University of Alabama at Birmingham, BM
The University of Alabama in Huntsville, BM
University of Mobile, B
University of Montevallo, B
University of North Alabama, BM
University of South Alabama, BM
The University of West Alabama, BM

Alaska

University of Alaska Anchorage, B
University of Alaska Fairbanks, BM
University of Alaska Southeast, B

Arizona

Arizona State University at the Polytechnic campus, B
Arizona State University at the Tempe campus, BMDO
Arizona State University at the West campus, B
Arizona Western College, A
Eastern Arizona College, A
Grand Canyon University, B
Mohave Community College, A
Northern Arizona University, BM
The University of Arizona, BMD

Arkansas

Arkansas State University, BMO
Arkansas Tech University, BM
Central Baptist College, B
Harding University, B
Henderson State University, B
Hendrix College, B
John Brown University, B
Lyon College, B
Ouachita Baptist University, B
Southern Arkansas University - Magnolia, B
University of Arkansas, BMD
University of Arkansas - Fort Smith, B
University of Arkansas at Little Rock, B
University of Arkansas at Monticello, B
University of Arkansas at Pine Bluff, B
University of Central Arkansas, BM
University of the Ozarks, B
Williams Baptist College, B

California

Antelope Valley College, A
Ashford University, B
Azusa Pacific University, B
Bakersfield College, A
Biola University, B
Cabrillo College, A
California Baptist University, B
California Institute of Technology, B
California Lutheran University, B
California Polytechnic State University, San Luis Obispo, BM
California State Polytechnic University, Pomona, BM
California State University, Bakersfield, BM
California State University Channel Islands, B
California State University, Chico, BM
California State University, Dominguez Hills, B
California State University, East Bay, BM
California State University, Fresno, BM
California State University, Fullerton, BM
California State University, Long Beach, BM
California State University, Los Angeles, BM
California State University, Northridge, BM
California State University, Sacramento, B
California State University, San Bernardino, B
California State University, San Marcos, BM
California State University, Stanislaus, BM
Cañada College, A
Cerritos College, A
Chaffey College, A
Chapman University, B
Citrus College, A
Claremont McKenna College, B
College of Alameda, A
College of the Canyons, A
College of the Desert, A
College of Marin, A
College of the Sequoias, A
College of the Siskiyous, A
Concordia University Irvine, B
Contra Costa College, A
Copper Mountain College, A
Cuesta College, A
Cuyamaca College, A
De Anza College, A
Dominican University of California, BM
East Los Angeles College, A
El Camino College, A
Feather River College, A
Foothill College, A
Fresno Pacific University, B
Fullerton College, A

Grossmont College, A
Hartnell College, A
Holy Names University, B
Humboldt State University, B
Irvine Valley College, A
La Sierra University, B
Lassen Community College District, A
Los Angeles City College, A
Los Angeles Mission College, A
Los Angeles Valley College, A
Loyola Marymount University, B
The Master's College and Seminary, B
Mills College, B
MiraCosta College, A
Monterey Peninsula College, A
Mount Saint Mary's University, B
National University, BM
Notre Dame de Namur University, B
Occidental College, B
Ohlone College, A
Orange Coast College, A
Oxnard College, A
Pacific Union College, B
Pasadena City College, A
Pepperdine University, B
Pitzer College, B
Point Loma Nazarene University, B
Pomona College, B
Porterville College, A
Saddleback College, A
Saint Katherine College, B
Saint Mary's College of California, B
San Bernardino Valley College, A
San Diego Christian College, B
San Diego State University, BM
San Diego State University - Imperial Valley Campus, B
San Francisco State University, BM
San Joaquin Delta College, A
San Jose State University, BM
Santa Ana College, A
Santa Barbara City College, A
Santa Clara University, B
Santa Rosa Junior College, A
Santiago Canyon College, A
Scripps College, B
Simpson University, B
Skyline College, A
Solano Community College, A
Sonoma State University, BM
Southwestern College, A
Stanford University, BMD
University of California, Berkeley, BMD
University of California, Davis, BMD
University of California, Irvine, BMD
University of California, Los Angeles, BMD
University of California, Merced, B
University of California, Riverside, BMD
University of California, San Diego, BMD
University of California, Santa Barbara, BD
University of California, Santa Cruz, BMD
University of La Verne, B
University of the Pacific, B
University of Redlands, B
University of San Diego, BM
University of San Francisco, B
University of Southern California, BD
Vanguard University of Southern California, B
West Los Angeles College, A
West Valley College, A
Westmont College, B
Whittier College, B
William Jessup University, B
Woodbury University, B
Woodland Community College, A
Yuba College, A

Colorado

Adams State University, BM
The Colorado College, B
Colorado Mesa University, B
Colorado State University, BM
Colorado State University - Pueblo, B
Fort Lewis College, B
Lamar Community College, A
Metropolitan State University of Denver, B

Northeastern Junior College, A
Otero Junior College, A
Regis University, B
United States Air Force Academy, B
University of Colorado Boulder, BMD
University of Colorado Colorado Springs, BM
University of Colorado Denver, BM
University of Denver, BO
University of Northern Colorado, BM
Western State Colorado University, B

Connecticut

Albertus Magnus College, B
Central Connecticut State University, BMO
Connecticut College, B
Eastern Connecticut State University, B
Fairfield University, B
Quinnipiac University, B
Sacred Heart University, B
Southern Connecticut State University, BM
Trinity College, B
University of Connecticut, BMD
University of Hartford, B
University of New Haven, B
University of Saint Joseph, B
Wesleyan University, B
Western Connecticut State University, BM
Yale University, BMD

Delaware

Delaware State University, B
University of Delaware, BMD
Wesley College, B

District of Columbia

American University, B
The Catholic University of America, BMD
The George Washington University, BMD
Georgetown University, BMD
Howard University, BMD
Trinity Washington University, B
University of the District of Columbia, B

Florida

Ave Maria University, B
Barry University, B
Broward College, A
College of Central Florida, A
Eckerd College, B
Edward Waters College, B
Flagler College, B
Florida Agricultural and Mechanical University, BM
Florida Atlantic University, BMO
Florida College, B
Florida Gulf Coast University, BM
Florida International University, BMD
Florida Southern College, B
Florida State University, BMD
Indian River State College, A
Jacksonville University, B
Miami Dade College, A
New College of Florida, B
Nova Southeastern University, B
Palm Beach Atlantic University, B
Palm Beach State College, A
Pensacola State College, A
Rollins College, B
Saint Leo University, B
St. Thomas University, B
South Florida State College, A
Southeastern University, B
State College of Florida Manatee-Sarasota, A
Stetson University, B
University of Central Florida, BM
University of Florida, BMD
University of Miami, BMD
University of North Florida, BM
University of South Florida, BMD
University of South Florida, St. Petersburg, B
University of South Florida Sarasota-Manatee, B
The University of Tampa, B
University of West Florida, BM
Warner University, B

Georgia

Abraham Baldwin Agricultural College, A
Agnes Scott College, B
Albany State University, B
Andrew College, A
Armstrong State University, BM
Augusta University, B
Bainbridge State College, A
Berry College, B
Brenau University, B
Brewton-Parker College, B
Clark Atlanta University, BMD
Clayton State University, B
College of Coastal Georgia, A
Columbus State University, BM
Covenant College, B
Dalton State College, AB
Darton State College, A
Emory University, BD
Georgia College & State University, BM
Georgia Gwinnett College, B
Georgia Highlands College, A
Georgia Military College, A
Georgia Southern University, BMO
Georgia Southwestern State University, B
Georgia State University, BMD
Gordon State College, AB
Kennesaw State University, B
LaGrange College, B
Mercer University, B
Middle Georgia State University, B
Morehouse College, B
Oglethorpe University, B
Paine College, B
Piedmont College, B
Point University, B
Reinhardt University, B
Savannah State University, B
Shorter University, B
South Georgia State College, A
Spelman College, B
Toccoa Falls College, B
Truett-McConnell College, B
University of Georgia, BMD
University of North Georgia, BM
University of West Georgia, BM
Valdosta State University, BM
Wesleyan College, B
Young Harris College, B

Hawaii

Brigham Young University - Hawaii, B
Chaminade University of Honolulu, B
Hawai'i Pacific University, B
University of Hawaii at Hilo, B
University of Hawaii at Manoa, BMD
University of Hawaii - West Oahu, B

Idaho

Boise State University, BM
Brigham Young University - Idaho, B
The College of Idaho, B
College of Southern Idaho, A
College of Western Idaho, A
Idaho State University, BM
North Idaho College, A
Northwest Nazarene University, B
University of Idaho, BMD

Illinois

Augustana College, B
Aurora University, B
Benedictine University, B
Blackburn College, B
Bradley University, B
Chicago State University, BM
Concordia University Chicago, B
DePaul University, BM
Dominican University, B
Eastern Illinois University, BM
Elmhurst College, B
Eureka College, B
Governors State University, B
Greenville College, B
Harper College, A

Illinois College, B
Illinois State University, BM
Illinois Wesleyan University, B
John A. Logan College, A
Judson University, B
Kankakee Community College, A
Knox College, B
Lake Forest College, BM
Lewis University, B
Lincoln College, A
Loyola University Chicago, BMD
McKendree University, B
Millikin University, B
Monmouth College, B
Moraine Valley Community College, A
North Central College, B
North Park University, B
Northeastern Illinois University, BM
Northern Illinois University, BMD
Northwestern University, BMD
Olivet Nazarene University, B
Parkland College, A
Principia College, B
Quincy University, B
Rockford University, B
Roosevelt University, BM
Saint Xavier University, B
Sauk Valley Community College, A
Southern Illinois University Carbondale, BMD
Southern Illinois University Edwardsville, BM
Spoon River College, A
Trinity Christian College, B
Trinity International University, B
Triton College, A
University of Chicago, BD
University of Illinois at Chicago, BMD
University of Illinois at Springfield, BM
University of Illinois at Urbana - Champaign, BMD
University of St. Francis, B
Western Illinois University, BM
Wheaton College, B

Indiana

Ancilla College, A
Anderson University, B
Ball State University, BM
Bethel College, B
Butler University, BM
DePauw University, B
Earlham College, B
Franklin College, B
Goshen College, B
Grace College, B
Hanover College, B
Holy Cross College, B
Huntington University, B
Indiana State University, BM
Indiana University Bloomington, BMD
Indiana University East, B
Indiana University Kokomo, B
Indiana University Northwest, B
Indiana University - Purdue University Fort Wayne, B
Indiana University - Purdue University Indianapolis, BM
Indiana University South Bend, B
Indiana University Southeast, B
Indiana Wesleyan University, AB
Manchester University, B
Marian University, B
Purdue University, BMD
Purdue University Northwest (Hammond), BM
Purdue University Northwest (Westville), B
Saint Joseph's College, B
Saint Mary's College, B
Taylor University, B
University of Evansville, B
University of Indianapolis, BM
University of Notre Dame, BMD
University of Saint Francis, B
University of Southern Indiana, B
Valparaiso University, BMO
Vincennes University, A
Wabash College, B

Iowa

Briar Cliff University, B
Buena Vista University, B
Central College, B
Clarke University, B
Coe College, B
Cornell College, B
Dordt College, B
Drake University, B
Graceland University, B
Grand View University, B
Grinnell College, B
Iowa Lakes Community College, A
Iowa State University of Science and Technology,
  BMD
Loras College, B
Luther College, B
Morningside College, B
Mount Mercy University, B
Northwestern College, B
St. Ambrose University, B
Simpson College, B
The University of Iowa, BMD
University of Northern Iowa, BM
Waldorf College, B
Wartburg College, B
William Penn University, B

Kansas

Allen Community College, A
Baker University, B
Barton County Community College, A
Benedictine College, B
Bethany College, B
Bethel College, B
Butler Community College, A
Central Christian College of Kansas, AB
Dodge City Community College, A
Emporia State University, BM
Fort Hays State University, BM
Friends University, B
Independence Community College, A
Kansas State University, BMD
Kansas Wesleyan University, B
Labette Community College, A
McPherson College, B
MidAmerica Nazarene University, B
Newman University, B
Ottawa University, B
Pittsburg State University, BM
Pratt Community College, A
Seward County Community College and Area Tech-
  nical School, A
Southwestern College, B
Sterling College, B
Tabor College, B
The University of Kansas, BMD
University of Saint Mary, B
Washburn University, B
Wichita State University, BM

Kentucky

Alice Lloyd College, B
Asbury University, B
Bellarmine University, B
Berea College, B
Brescia University, B
Campbellsville University, B
Centre College, B
Eastern Kentucky University, BM
Georgetown College, B
Kentucky Christian University, B
Kentucky Wesleyan College, B
Lindsey Wilson College, AB
Morehead State University, B
Murray State University, BM
Northern Kentucky University, B
Thomas More College, AB
Transylvania University, B
Union College, B
University of the Cumberlands, B
University of Kentucky, BMD
University of Louisville, BMO
University of Pikeville, B
Western Kentucky University, BM

Louisiana

Centenary College of Louisiana, B
Dillard University, B
Grambling State University, B
Louisiana College, B
Louisiana State University and Agricultural & Me-
  chanical College, BMD
Louisiana State University at Alexandria, B
Louisiana State University in Shreveport, B
Louisiana Tech University, BM
Loyola University New Orleans, B
McNeese State University, B
Nicholls State University, B
Northwestern State University of Louisiana, B
Southeastern Louisiana University, BM
Southern University and Agricultural and Mechanical
  College, BM
Southern University at New Orleans, B
Tulane University, BMD
University of Holy Cross, B
University of Louisiana at Lafayette, BM
University of Louisiana at Monroe, BM
University of New Orleans, BM
Xavier University of Louisiana, B

Maine

Bates College, B
Bowdoin College, B
Colby College, B
Saint Joseph's College of Maine, B
University of Maine, BMD
University of Maine at Farmington, B
University of Maine at Machias, B
University of Maine at Presque Isle, B
University of New England, B
University of Southern Maine, B

Maryland

Bowie State University, B
Coppin State University, B
Frostburg State University, B
Goucher College, B
Harford Community College, A
Hood College, B
Johns Hopkins University, BD
Loyola University Maryland, B
McDaniel College, B
Morgan State University, BMD
Mount St. Mary's University, B
Notre Dame of Maryland University, B
St. Mary's College of Maryland, B
Salisbury University, BM
Stevenson University, B
Towson University, B
United States Naval Academy, B
University of Baltimore, B
University of Maryland, Baltimore County, BM
University of Maryland, College Park, BMD
University of Maryland Eastern Shore, B
University of Maryland University College, B
Washington Adventist University, B
Washington College, B

Massachusetts

American International College, B
Amherst College, B
Anna Maria College, B
Assumption College, B
Bard College at Simon's Rock, B
Bentley University, B
Boston College, BMD
Boston University, BMD
Brandeis University, BMD
Bridgewater State University, B
Bunker Hill Community College, A
Cape Cod Community College, A
Clark University, BMDO
College of the Holy Cross, B
Dean College, AB
Eastern Nazarene College, B
Elms College, B
Emmanuel College, B
Endicott College, B
Fitchburg State University, BMO
Framingham State University, B

Gordon College, B
Hampshire College, B
Harvard University, BD
Lasell College, B
Massachusetts College of Liberal Arts, B
Massachusetts Institute of Technology, B
Merrimack College, B
Mount Holyoke College, B
Northeastern University, BMD
Northern Essex Community College, A
Regis College, B
Salem State University, BM
Simmons College, B
Smith College, BM
Springfield College, B
Stonehill College, B
Suffolk University, B
Tufts University, BMD
University of Massachusetts Amherst, BMD
University of Massachusetts Boston, BM
University of Massachusetts Dartmouth, B
University of Massachusetts Lowell, B
Wellesley College, B
Western New England University, B
Westfield State University, BM
Wheaton College, B
Williams College, B
Worcester Polytechnic Institute, B
Worcester State University, BM

Michigan

Adrian College, B
Albion College, B
Alma College, B
Andrews University, B
Aquinas College, B
Calvin College, B
Central Michigan University, BMO
Concordia University Ann Arbor, B
Cornerstone University, B
Eastern Michigan University, BMO
Ferris State University, B
Grand Valley State University, B
Great Lakes Christian College, B
Hillsdale College, B
Hope College, B
Kalamazoo College, B
Lake Michigan College, A
Lake Superior State University, B
Lansing Community College, A
Madonna University, B
Marygrove College, B
Michigan State University, BMD
Michigan Technological University, B
Northern Michigan University, B
Oakland University, BM
Olivet College, B
Rochester College, B
Saginaw Valley State University, B
Siena Heights University, B
Spring Arbor University, B
University of Detroit Mercy, B
University of Michigan, BDO
University of Michigan - Dearborn, B
University of Michigan - Flint, B
Wayne State University, BMDO
Western Michigan University, BMD

Minnesota

Augsburg College, B
Bemidji State University, B
Bethany Lutheran College, B
Bethel University, B
Carleton College, B
College of Saint Benedict, B
The College of St. Scholastica, B
Concordia College, B
Concordia University, St. Paul, B
Crown College, B
Gustavus Adolphus College, B
Hamline University, B
Macalester College, B
Metropolitan State University, B
Minnesota State University Mankato, BM
Minnesota State University Moorhead, B
St. Catherine University, B

St. Cloud State University, BM
Saint John's University, B
Saint Mary's University of Minnesota, B
St. Olaf College, B
Southwest Minnesota State University, B
University of Minnesota, Duluth, B
University of Minnesota, Morris, B
University of Minnesota, Twin Cities Campus, BMD
University of Northwestern - St. Paul, B
University of St. Thomas, B
Vermilion Community College, A
Winona State University, B

Mississippi

Alcorn State University, B
Belhaven University, B
Blue Mountain College, B
Copiah-Lincoln Community College, A
Delta State University, B
East Mississippi Community College, A
Itawamba Community College, A
Jackson State University, BM
Millsaps College, B
Mississippi College, BM
Mississippi Delta Community College, A
Mississippi State University, BMD
Mississippi University for Women, B
Mississippi Valley State University, B
Northeast Mississippi Community College, A
Southwest Mississippi Community College, A
Tougaloo College, B
University of Mississippi, BMD
University of Southern Mississippi, BMD
William Carey University, B

Missouri

Avila University, B
Calvary Bible College and Theological Seminary, B
Central Methodist University, B
College of the Ozarks, B
Columbia College, B
Culver-Stockton College, B
Drury University, B
Evangel University, B
Fontbonne University, B
Hannibal-LaGrange University, B
Lincoln University, BM
Lindenwood University, B
Maryville University of Saint Louis, B
Missouri Baptist University, B
Missouri Southern State University, B
Missouri State University, BM
Missouri University of Science and Technology, B
Missouri Valley College, B
Missouri Western State University, B
Northwest Missouri State University, BMO
Park University, B
Rockhurst University, B
St. Charles Community College, A
Saint Louis University, BMD
Southeast Missouri State University, BMO
Southwest Baptist University, B
Truman State University, B
University of Central Missouri, BM
University of Missouri, BMD
University of Missouri - Kansas City, BMD
University of Missouri - St. Louis, B
Washington University in St. Louis, BD
Webster University, B
Westminster College, B
William Jewell College, B
William Woods University, B

Montana

Carroll College, B
Montana State University, BMD
Montana State University Billings, B
Rocky Mountain College, B
University of Great Falls, B
University of Montana, BMD
The University of Montana Western, B

Nebraska

Bellevue University, B
Chadron State College, B
Concordia University, Nebraska, B

Creighton University, B
Doane University, B
Hastings College, B
Midland University, B
Nebraska Wesleyan University, BM
Peru State College, B
Union College, B
University of Nebraska at Kearney, BM
University of Nebraska - Lincoln, BMD
University of Nebraska at Omaha, BM
Wayne State College, B
Western Nebraska Community College, A
York College, B

Nevada

College of Southern Nevada, A
Truckee Meadows Community College, A
University of Nevada, Las Vegas, BMD
University of Nevada, Reno, BMD

New Hampshire

Dartmouth College, B
Franklin Pierce University, B
Granite State College, B
Keene State College, B
New England College, B
Plymouth State University, B
Rivier University, B
Saint Anselm College, B
Southern New Hampshire University, B
University of New Hampshire, BMD
University of New Hampshire at Manchester, B

New Jersey

Bergen Community College, A
Bloomfield College, B
Caldwell University, B
Centenary College, B
The College of New Jersey, B
College of Saint Elizabeth, B
Drew University, BMD
Fairleigh Dickinson University, College at Florham, B
Fairleigh Dickinson University, Metropolitan Campus, BM
Felician University, B
Georgian Court University, B
Kean University, B
Monmouth University, BM
Montclair State University, BMO
New Jersey City University, B
New Jersey Institute of Technology, BM
Princeton University, BD
Ramapo College of New Jersey, B
Rider University, B
Rowan College at Burlington County, A
Rowan University, BMO
Rutgers University - Camden, BM
Rutgers University - New Brunswick, BD
Rutgers University - Newark, BM
Saint Peter's University, B
Seton Hall University, BM
Stevens Institute of Technology, B
Stockton University, B
Thomas Edison State University, B
William Paterson University of New Jersey, BM

New Mexico

Central New Mexico Community College, A
Eastern New Mexico University, B
New Mexico Highlands University, BM
New Mexico Junior College, A
New Mexico Military Institute, A
New Mexico State University, BM
University of New Mexico, BMD
University of the Southwest, B
Western New Mexico University, B

New York

Adelphi University, B
Alfred University, B
Bard College, B
Barnard College, B
Baruch College of the City University of New York, B

Binghamton University, State University of New York, BMD
Borough of Manhattan Community College of the City University of New York, A
Bronx Community College of the City University of New York, A
Brooklyn College of the City University of New York, BM
Buffalo State College, State University of New York, BM
Canisius College, B
City College of the City University of New York, BM
Clarkson University, B
Colgate University, B
The College at Brockport, State University of New York, BM
College of Mount Saint Vincent, B
The College of New Rochelle, B
The College of Saint Rose, BM
College of Staten Island of the City University of New York, BM
Columbia University, BMD
Columbia University, School of General Studies, B
Concordia College - New York, B
Cornell University, BMD
Daemen College, B
Dominican College, B
D'Youville College, B
Elmira College, B
Eugene Lang College of Liberal Arts, B
Fordham University, BMD
Fulton-Montgomery Community College, A
Hamilton College, B
Hartwick College, B
Hobart and William Smith Colleges, B
Hofstra University, B
Houghton College, B
Hunter College of the City University of New York, BM
Iona College, BM
Ithaca College, B
The Jewish Theological Seminary, B
John Jay College of Criminal Justice of the City University of New York, B
Keuka College, B
Le Moyne College, B
Lehman College of the City University of New York, BM
Long Island University - LIU Brooklyn, B
Long Island University - LIU Post, B
Manhattan College, B
Manhattanville College, B
Marist College, B
Marymount Manhattan College, B
Mercy College, B
Molloy College, B
Monroe Community College, A
Mount Saint Mary College, B
Nazareth College of Rochester, B
New York University, BMDO
Niagara University, B
Nyack College, B
Pace University, B
Pace University, Pleasantville Campus, B
Purchase College, State University of New York, B
Queens College of the City University of New York, BM
Roberts Wesleyan College, B
The Sage Colleges, B
St. Bonaventure University, B
St. Francis College, B
St. John Fisher College, B
St. John's University, BMD
St. Joseph's College, Long Island Campus, B
St. Joseph's College, New York, B
St. Lawrence University, B
St. Thomas Aquinas College, B
Sarah Lawrence College, BM
Siena College, B
Skidmore College, B
State University of New York College at Cortland, BM
State University of New York College at Geneseo, B
State University of New York College at Old Westbury, B
State University of New York College at Oneonta, B

State University of New York College at Potsdam, B
State University of New York Empire State College, AB
State University of New York at Fredonia, B
State University of New York at New Paltz, B
State University of New York at Oswego, BM
State University of New York at Plattsburgh, B
Stony Brook University, State University of New York, BMD
Syracuse University, BMD
Touro College, B
Union College, B
United States Military Academy, B
University at Albany, State University of New York, BMDO
University at Buffalo, the State University of New York, BMD
University of Rochester, BMD
Utica College, B
Vassar College, B
Wagner College, B
Wells College, B
Yeshiva University, B
York College of the City University of New York, B

North Carolina

Appalachian State University, BM
Barton College, B
Belmont Abbey College, B
Brevard College, B
Campbell University, B
Catawba College, B
Chowan University, B
Davidson College, B
Duke University, BMD
East Carolina University, BM
Elizabeth City State University, B
Elon University, B
Fayetteville State University, BM
Gardner-Webb University, B
Greensboro College, B
Guilford College, B
High Point University, BM
Johnson C. Smith University, B
Lees-McRae College, B
Lenoir-Rhyne University, B
Livingstone College, B
Louisburg College, A
Mars Hill University, B
Meredith College, B
Methodist University, AB
Montreat College, B
North Carolina Agricultural and Technical State University, B
North Carolina Central University, BM
North Carolina State University, BM
North Carolina Wesleyan College, B
Pfeiffer University, B
Queens University of Charlotte, B
Saint Augustine's University, B
Salem College, B
University of Mount Olive, B
University of North Carolina at Asheville, B
The University of North Carolina at Chapel Hill, BMD
The University of North Carolina at Charlotte, BM
The University of North Carolina at Greensboro, BMDO
The University of North Carolina at Pembroke, B
The University of North Carolina Wilmington, BM
Wake Forest University, B
Warren Wilson College, B
Western Carolina University, BM
Wingate University, B
Winston-Salem State University, B

North Dakota

Dakota College at Bottineau, A
Dickinson State University, B
Minot State University, B
North Dakota State University, BMD
Turtle Mountain Community College, A
University of Jamestown, B
University of North Dakota, BMD
Valley City State University, B

Ohio

Antioch College, B
Ashland University, BM
Baldwin Wallace University, B
Bluffton University, B
Bowling Green State University, BMD
Capital University, B
Case Western Reserve University, BMD
Cedarville University, B
Central State University, B
Cleveland State University, BM
The College of Wooster, B
Defiance College, B
Denison University, B
Edison Community College, A
Franciscan University of Steubenville, B
Heidelberg University, B
Hiram College, B
John Carroll University, BM
Kent State University, BMD
Kent State University at Stark, B
Kenyon College, B
Lake Erie College, B
Lorain County Community College, A
Lourdes University, AB
Malone University, B
Marietta College, B
Miami University, BM
Miami University Hamilton, B
Miami University Middletown, A
Mount St. Joseph University, B
Mount Vernon Nazarene University, B
Muskingum University, B
Northwest State Community College, A
Notre Dame College, B
Oberlin College, B
Ohio Christian University, B
Ohio Dominican University, B
Ohio Northern University, B
The Ohio State University, BMD
The Ohio State University at Lima, B
The Ohio State University - Mansfield Campus, B
The Ohio State University at Marion, B
The Ohio State University - Newark Campus, B
Ohio University, BMD
Ohio University - Chillicothe, B
Ohio Wesleyan University, B
Otterbein University, B
Pontifical College Josephinum, B
Shawnee State University, B
Terra State Community College, A
Tiffin University, B
Union Institute & University, M
The University of Akron, BMD
University of Cincinnati, BMD
University of Dayton, B
The University of Findlay, B
University of Mount Union, B
University of Rio Grande, AB
The University of Toledo, BMD
Urbana University, B
Ursuline College, B
Walsh University, B
Wilmington College, B
Wittenberg University, B
Wright State University, ABM
Wright State University - Lake Campus, A
Xavier University, AB
Youngstown State University, BM

Oklahoma

Cameron University, B
Connors State College, A
East Central University, B
Mid-America Christian University, B
Murray State College, A
Northeastern State University, B
Northwestern Oklahoma State University, B
Oklahoma Baptist University, B
Oklahoma Christian University, B
Oklahoma City Community College, A
Oklahoma City University, B
Oklahoma Panhandle State University, B
Oklahoma State University, BMD
Oklahoma State University, Oklahoma City, A
Oklahoma Wesleyan University, AB

Oral Roberts University, B
Rogers State University, AB
Rose State College, A
St. Gregory's University, B
Southeastern Oklahoma State University, B
Southern Nazarene University, B
Southwestern Oklahoma State University, B
University of Central Oklahoma, BM
University of Oklahoma, BMD
University of Science and Arts of Oklahoma, B
The University of Tulsa, BM

Oregon

Corban University, B
Eastern Oregon University, B
George Fox University, B
Lewis & Clark College, B
Linfield College, B
Multnomah University, B
Northwest Christian University, B
Oregon State University, B
Pacific University, B
Portland State University, BM
Reed College, B
Southern Oregon University, B
Umpqua Community College, A
University of Oregon, BMD
University of Portland, B
Warner Pacific University, B
Western Oregon University, B
Willamette University, B

Pennsylvania

Albright College, B
Allegheny College, B
Alvernia University, B
Arcadia University, B
Bloomsburg University of Pennsylvania, B
Bryn Athyn College of the New Church, B
Bryn Mawr College, B
Bucknell University, B
Bucks County Community College, A
Cabrini University, B
California University of Pennsylvania, B
Carlow University, B
Carnegie Mellon University, BD
Cedar Crest College, B
Chatham University, B
Chestnut Hill College, B
Clarion University of Pennsylvania, B
DeSales University, B
Dickinson College, B
Drexel University, B
Duquesne University, BM
East Stroudsburg University of Pennsylvania, BM
Eastern University, B
Edinboro University of Pennsylvania, BM
Elizabethtown College, B
Franklin & Marshall College, B
Gannon University, B
Geneva College, B
Gettysburg College, B
Grove City College, B
Gwynedd Mercy University, B
Haverford College, B
Holy Family University, B
Immaculata University, AB
Indiana University of Pennsylvania, BM
Juniata College, B
King's College, B
Kutztown University of Pennsylvania, B
La Roche College, B
La Salle University, BMO
Lafayette College, B
Lebanon Valley College, B
Lehigh University, BMD
Lincoln University, B
Lock Haven University of Pennsylvania, B
Lycoming College, B
Mansfield University of Pennsylvania, B
Marywood University, B
Mercyhurst University, B
Messiah College, B
Millersville University of Pennsylvania, BM
Misericordia University, B
Moravian College, B

Muhlenberg College, B
Penn State Abington, B
Penn State Altoona, B
Pénn State Beaver, B
Penn State Berks, B
Penn State Brandywine, B
Penn State DuBois, B
Penn State Erie, The Behrend College, B
Penn State Fayette, The Eberly Campus, B
Penn State Greater Allegheny, B
Penn State Hazleton, B
Penn State Lehigh Valley, B
Penn State Mont Alto, B
Penn State New Kensington, B
Penn State Schuylkill, B
Penn State Shenango, B
Penn State University Park, BMD
Penn State Wilkes-Barre, B
Penn State Worthington Scranton, B
Penn State York, B
Point Park University, B
Rosemont College, B
Saint Francis University, B
Saint Joseph's University, B
Saint Vincent College, B
Seton Hill University, B
Shippensburg University of Pennsylvania, BM
Slippery Rock University of Pennsylvania, BM
Susquehanna University, B
Swarthmore College, B
Temple University, BMD
Thiel College, B
University of Pennsylvania, BMD
University of Pittsburgh, BMD
University of Pittsburgh at Bradford, B
University of Pittsburgh at Johnstown, B
University of Pittsburgh at Titusville, A
The University of Scranton, B
Ursinus College, B
Villanova University, BM
Washington & Jefferson College, B
Waynesburg University, B
West Chester University of Pennsylvania, BMO
Westminster College, B
Widener University, B
Wilkes University, B
York College of Pennsylvania, B

Rhode Island

Brown University, BMD
Bryant University, B
Providence College, BM
Rhode Island College, BM
Roger Williams University, B
Salve Regina University, B
University of Rhode Island, BM

South Carolina

Anderson University, B
Benedict College, B
Bob Jones University, BM
Charleston Southern University, B
The Citadel, The Military College of South Carolina,
  BM
Claflin University, B
Clemson University, BM
Coastal Carolina University, B
Coker College, B
College of Charleston, BM
Columbia College, B
Converse College, BM
Erskine College, B
Francis Marion University, B
Furman University, B
Lander University, B
Limestone College, B
Morris College, B
Newberry College, B
North Greenville University, B
Presbyterian College, B
South Carolina State University, B
Southern Wesleyan University, B
University of South Carolina, BMDO
University of South Carolina Aiken, B
University of South Carolina Beaufort, B
University of South Carolina Upstate, B

Winthrop University, BM
Wofford College, B

South Dakota

Augustana University, B
Black Hills State University, B
Dakota Wesleyan University, B
Mount Marty College, B
Northern State University, B
Oglala Lakota College, B
South Dakota State University, B
University of Sioux Falls, B
The University of South Dakota, BM

Tennessee

Aquinas College, B
Austin Peay State University, B
Belmont University, B
Bethel University, B
Bryan College, B
Carson-Newman University, B
Christian Brothers University, B
Cumberland University, B
East Tennessee State University, BMO
Fisk University, B
Freed-Hardeman University, B
Hiwassee College, A
King University, B
Lane College, B
Lee University, B
LeMoyne-Owen College, B
Lincoln Memorial University, B
Lipscomb University, B
Martin Methodist College, B
Maryville College, B
Middle Tennessee State University, BM
Milligan College, B
Nashville State Community College, A
Rhodes College, B
Sewanee: The University of the South, B
Southern Adventist University, B
Tennessee State University, B
Tennessee Technological University, B
Tennessee Wesleyan College, B
Trevecca Nazarene University, B
Tusculum College, B
Union University, B
University of Memphis, BMD
The University of Tennessee, BMD
The University of Tennessee at Chattanooga, B
The University of Tennessee at Martin, B
Vanderbilt University, BMD
Welch College, B

Texas

Abilene Christian University, B
Alvin Community College, A
Amarillo College, A
Angelo State University, B
Austin College, B
Austin Community College District, A
Baylor University, BMD
Blinn College, A
Cisco College, A
Clarendon College, A
Concordia University Texas, B
Dallas Baptist University, B
Del Mar College, A
East Texas Baptist University, B
Frank Phillips College, A
Galveston College, A
Hardin-Simmons University, BM
Hill College, A
Howard College, A
Howard Payne University, B
Huston-Tillotson University, B
Jarvis Christian College, B
Lamar University, BM
Lee College, A
LeTourneau University, B
Lubbock Christian University, B
McMurry University, B
Midwestern State University, BM
Northeast Texas Community College, A
Odessa College, A
Our Lady of the Lake University of San Antonio, B

Palo Alto College, A
Panola College, A
Paris Junior College, A
Paul Quinn College, B
Prairie View A&M University, B
Rice University, BMD
St. Edward's University, B
St. Mary's University, B
St. Philip's College, A
Sam Houston State University, BM
San Jacinto College District, A
Schreiner University, B
Southern Methodist University, BMD
Southwestern Adventist University, B
Southwestern Assemblies of God University, BM
Southwestern University, B
Stephen F. Austin State University, BM
Sul Ross State University, BM
Tarleton State University, BM
Texarkana College, A
Texas A&M International University, BM
Texas A&M University, BMD
Texas A&M University - Central Texas, BM
Texas A&M University - Commerce, B
Texas A&M University - Corpus Christi, BM
Texas A&M University - Kingsville, BM
Texas A&M University - San Antonio, B
Texas A&M University - Texarkana, B
Texas Christian University, BMD
Texas College, B
Texas Lutheran University, B
Texas Southern University, BM
Texas State University, BM
Texas Tech University, BMD
Texas Wesleyan University, B
Texas Woman's University, BM
Trinity University, B
Trinity Valley Community College, A
Tyler Junior College, A
University of Dallas, B
University of Houston, BMD
University of Houston - Clear Lake, BM
University of Houston - Downtown, B
University of Houston - Victoria, B
University of the Incarnate Word, B
University of Mary Hardin-Baylor, B
University of North Texas, BM
University of St. Thomas, B
The University of Texas at Arlington, BMD
The University of Texas at Austin, BMD
The University of Texas at Dallas, BM
The University of Texas at El Paso, BMD
The University of Texas of the Permian Basin, BM
The University of Texas Rio Grande Valley, BM
The University of Texas at San Antonio, BM
The University of Texas at Tyler, BM
Wayland Baptist University, BM
West Texas A&M University, BM
Wiley College, B

Utah

Dixie State University, B
Salt Lake Community College, A
Snow College, A
Southern Utah University, B
University of Utah, BMD
Utah State University, BM
Utah Valley University, AB
Weber State University, B
Westminster College, B

Vermont

Bennington College, B
Castleton University, B
College of St. Joseph, B
Goddard College, B
Green Mountain College, B
Johnson State College, B
Marlboro College, B
Middlebury College, B
Norwich University, BM
Saint Michael's College, B
Southern Vermont College, B
University of Vermont, BM

Virginia

Averett University, BM
Bluefield College, B
Bridgewater College, B
Christendom College, B
Christopher Newport University, B
The College of William and Mary, BMD
Eastern Mennonite University, B
Emory & Henry College, BM
Ferrum College, B
George Mason University, BMD
Hampden-Sydney College, B
Hampton University, B
Hollins University, B
James Madison University, BM
Liberty University, BM
Longwood University, B
Lynchburg College, BM
Mary Baldwin College, B
Marymount University, B
Norfolk State University, B
Old Dominion University, BM
Patrick Henry College, B
Radford University, B
Randolph College, B
Randolph-Macon College, B
Regent University, ABD
Roanoke College, B
Shenandoah University, B
Southern Virginia University, B
Sweet Briar College, B
University of Mary Washington, B
University of Richmond, B
University of Virginia, BMD
The University of Virginia's College at Wise, B
Virginia Commonwealth University, BM
Virginia Military Institute, B
Virginia Polytechnic Institute and State University, BM
Virginia State University, B
Virginia Union University, B
Virginia Wesleyan College, B
Washington and Lee University, B

Washington

Central Washington University, BM
Eastern Washington University, BM
Everett Community College, A
Gonzaga University, B
Northwest University, B
Pacific Lutheran University, B
Saint Martin's University, B
Seattle Pacific University, B
Seattle University, B
Skagit Valley College, A
University of Puget Sound, B
University of Washington, BMD
University of Washington, Tacoma, B
Walla Walla University, B
Washington State University, BMD
Washington State University - Tri-Cities, B
Washington State University - Vancouver, B
Wenatchee Valley College, A
Western Washington University, BM
Whitman College, B
Whitworth University, B

West Virginia

American Public University System, ABM
Bethany College, B
Concord University, B
Davis & Elkins College, B
Fairmont State University, B
Glenville State College, B
Marshall University, BMO
Ohio Valley University, B
Potomac State College of West Virginia University, A
Shepherd University, B
University of Charleston, B
West Liberty University, B
West Virginia State University, B
West Virginia University, BMD
West Virginia University Institute of Technology, B
West Virginia Wesleyan College, B

Wheeling Jesuit University, B

Wisconsin

Alverno College, B
Beloit College, B
Cardinal Stritch University, BM
Carroll University, B
Carthage College, B
Concordia University Wisconsin, B
Edgewood College, B
Lakeland College, B
Lawrence University, B
Marian University, B
Marquette University, BMD
Mount Mary University, B
Northland College, B
Ripon College, B
St. Norbert College, B
Silver Lake College of the Holy Family, B
University of Wisconsin - Eau Claire, BM
University of Wisconsin - Green Bay, B
University of Wisconsin - La Crosse, B
University of Wisconsin - Madison, BMD
University of Wisconsin - Milwaukee, BMD
University of Wisconsin - Oshkosh, B
University of Wisconsin - Parkside, B
University of Wisconsin - Platteville, B
University of Wisconsin - River Falls, B
University of Wisconsin - Stevens Point, BM
University of Wisconsin - Superior, B
University of Wisconsin - Whitewater, B
Viterbo University, B
Wisconsin Lutheran College, B

Wyoming

Casper College, A
Laramie County Community College, A
Northwest College, A
Sheridan College, A
University of Wyoming, BM
Western Wyoming Community College, A

U.S. Territories: Guam

University of Guam, B

U.S. Territories: Puerto Rico

Inter American University of Puerto Rico, Metropolitan Campus, BMD
Inter American University of Puerto Rico, San Germán Campus, B
Pontifical Catholic University of Puerto Rico, BM
Universidad Adventista de las Antillas, B
University of Puerto Rico in Cayey, B
University of Puerto Rico, Mayagüez Campus, B
University of Puerto Rico, Río Piedras Campus, MD
University of Puerto Rico in Utuado, B

Canada

Alberta

Ambrose University, B
Athabasca University, B
Concordia University of Edmonton, B
The King's University, B
Mount Royal University, B
University of Alberta, BMD
University of Calgary, BMD
University of Lethbridge, B

British Columbia

Simon Fraser University, BMD
Thompson Rivers University, B
Trinity Western University, BM
The University of British Columbia, BMD
The University of British Columbia - Okanagan Campus, B
University of the Fraser Valley, B
University of Northern British Columbia, BM
University of Victoria, BMD
Vancouver Island University, B

Manitoba

Brandon University, B
Providence University College & Theological Seminary, B
University of Manitoba, BMD
The University of Winnipeg, BM

Maritime Provinces: New Brunswick

Crandall University, B
Mount Allison University, B
St. Thomas University, B
Université de Moncton, BM
University of New Brunswick Fredericton, BMD
University of New Brunswick Saint John, B

Maritime Provinces: Nova Scotia

Acadia University, B
Cape Breton University, B
Dalhousie University, BMD
Mount Saint Vincent University, B
St. Francis Xavier University, B
Saint Mary's University, BM
Université Sainte-Anne, B
University of King's College, B

Maritime Provinces: Prince Edward Island

University of Prince Edward Island, B

Newfoundland and Labrador

Memorial University of Newfoundland, BMD

Ontario

Brock University, BM
Carleton University, BMD
Lakehead University, BM
Laurentian University, BM
McMaster University, BMD
Nipissing University, B
Queen's University at Kingston, B
Redeemer University College, B
Royal Military College of Canada, B
Trent University, B
Tyndale University College & Seminary, B
University of Guelph, BMD
University of Ottawa, BMD
University of Toronto, BMD
University of Waterloo, BMD
The University of Western Ontario, BMD
University of Windsor, BM
Wilfrid Laurier University, BMD
York University, BMD

Quebec

Bishop's University, B
Concordia University, BMD
McGill University, BMD
Université Laval, BMD
Université de Montréal, BMD
Université du Québec à Chicoutimi, B
Université du Québec à Montréal, BMD
Université du Québec à Rimouski, B
Université du Québec à Trois-Rivières, B
Université de Sherbrooke, BM

Saskatchewan

University of Regina, BM
University of Saskatchewan, BMD

HISTORY OF MEDICINE

United States

Connecticut

Yale University, MD

Minnesota

University of Minnesota, Twin Cities Campus, MD

New Jersey

Rutgers University - New Brunswick, D

Canada

Quebec

McGill University, MD

HISTORY AND PHILOSOPHY OF SCIENCE AND TECHNOLOGY

United States

California

California Institute of Technology, B

Georgia

Georgia Institute of Technology, B

Illinois

University of Chicago, B

Maryland

Johns Hopkins University, B

Massachusetts

Harvard University, B
Worcester Polytechnic Institute, B

New Jersey

Stevens Institute of Technology, B

New York

Bard College, B

North Carolina

Edgecombe Community College, A

Ohio

Case Western Reserve University, B

Oklahoma

University of Oklahoma, B

Pennsylvania

University of Pennsylvania, B
University of Pittsburgh, B

Washington

University of Washington, B

Wisconsin

University of Wisconsin - Madison, B

Canada

Maritime Provinces: Nova Scotia

Dalhousie University, B

Ontario

University of Toronto, B

HISTORY OF SCIENCE AND TECHNOLOGY

United States

Arizona

Arizona State University at the Tempe campus, D

California

University of California, Berkeley, D
University of California, San Diego, D

Connecticut

Yale University, MD

Delaware

University of Delaware, MD

Georgia

Georgia Institute of Technology, MD

Indiana

Indiana University Bloomington, MD
University of Notre Dame, MD

Iowa

Iowa State University of Science and Technology, MD

Maryland

Johns Hopkins University, MD

Massachusetts

Harvard University, MD
Massachusetts Institute of Technology, D

Michigan

Wayne State University, D

Minnesota

University of Minnesota, Twin Cities Campus, MD

New Jersey

Princeton University, D
Rutgers University - New Brunswick, D

New York

Cornell University, MD
Rensselaer Polytechnic Institute, MD

Oklahoma

University of Oklahoma, MD

Oregon

Oregon State University, MD

Pennsylvania

Carnegie Mellon University, D
Drexel University, M
University of Pennsylvania, MD
University of Pittsburgh, MD

Rhode Island

Brown University, D

Virginia

Virginia Polytechnic Institute and State University, MD

West Virginia

West Virginia University, MD

Wisconsin

University of Wisconsin - Madison, MD

Canada

Ontario

University of Toronto, MD

HISTORY TEACHER EDUCATION

United States

Alabama

Auburn University, B
Huntingdon College, B
Samford University, B
Spring Hill College, B
Talladega College, B

University of Mobile, B

Arkansas

University of Arkansas - Fort Smith, B

California

Biola University, B

Colorado

Colorado Christian University, B
Western State Colorado University, B

Delaware

University of Delaware, B

District of Columbia

The Catholic University of America, B

Florida

Florida Southern College, B
Hobe Sound Bible College, B

Georgia

Armstrong State University, B
Brewton-Parker College, B
Covenant College, B
Darton State College, A
Gordon State College, B
Middle Georgia State University, B
Paine College, B
Piedmont College, B
Toccoa Falls College, B

Idaho

Boise State University, B
Brigham Young University - Idaho, B
Northwest Nazarene University, B

Illinois

Augustana College, B
Bradley University, B
Concordia University Chicago, B
Dominican University, B
Elmhurst College, B
Greenville College, B
John A. Logan College, A
McKendree University, B
Saint Xavier University, B
Trinity Christian College, B
University of Illinois at Chicago, B
University of Illinois at Urbana - Champaign, B

Indiana

Indiana University - Purdue University Fort Wayne, B
Manchester University, B
Valparaiso University, B

Iowa

Buena Vista University, B
Dordt College, B
Morningside College, B
St. Ambrose University, B
The University of Iowa, B
Wartburg College, B

Kansas

Central Christian College of Kansas, AB
Friends University, B
Kansas Wesleyan University, B
MidAmerica Nazarene University, B
Pittsburg State University, B
Tabor College, B
Washburn University, B

Kentucky

Campbellsville University, B
Eastern Kentucky University, B

Louisiana

Xavier University of Louisiana, B

Maine

Saint Joseph's College of Maine, B
University of Maine, B
University of Maine at Machias, B

Massachusetts

Eastern Nazarene College, B
Fitchburg State University, B
Merrimack College, B

Michigan

Adrian College, B
Albion College, B
Alma College, B
Calvin College, B
Central Michigan University, B
Cornerstone University, B
Eastern Michigan University, B
Ferris State University, B
Grand Valley State University, B
Hope College, B
Michigan State University, B
Northern Michigan University, B
Rochester College, B
Saginaw Valley State University, B
Spring Arbor University, B
University of Michigan - Flint, B
Western Michigan University, B

Missouri

College of the Ozarks, B
Culver-Stockton College, B
Evangel University, B
Hannibal-LaGrange University, B
Lindenwood University, B
Missouri State University, B
Washington University in St. Louis, B
William Woods University, B

Montana

Carroll College, B
Montana State University Billings, B
Rocky Mountain College, B
University of Great Falls, B
The University of Montana Western, B

Nebraska

Chadron State College, B
Concordia University, Nebraska, B
Hastings College, B
Peru State College, B
Union College, B
Wayne State College, B
York College, B

Nevada

Nevada State College, B

New Hampshire

Keene State College, B

New Jersey

The College of New Jersey, B

New York

College of Staten Island of the City University of New York, B
Dominican College, B
Ithaca College, B
Long Island University - LIU Post, B
Nazareth College of Rochester, B
St. John Fisher College, B
Utica College, B

North Carolina

Appalachian State University, B
Campbell University, B
Elizabeth City State University, B
Gardner-Webb University, B
North Carolina Agricultural and Technical State University, B
Wingate University, B

North Dakota

Mayville State University, B
Minot State University, B
North Dakota State University, B
University of Jamestown, B
University of Mary, B
Valley City State University, B

Ohio

Bowling Green State University, B
Mount Vernon Nazarene University, B
Ohio Northern University, B
Ohio Wesleyan University, B
Tiffin University, B
The University of Akron, B
University of Rio Grande, B

Oklahoma

East Central University, B
Southwestern Christian University, B
Southwestern Oklahoma State University, B
University of Central Oklahoma, B

Pennsylvania

Bucks County Community College, A
Gwynedd Mercy University, B
Holy Family University, B
Saint Francis University, B
Saint Joseph's University, B
University of Pittsburgh at Johnstown, B
Widener University, B

Rhode Island

Providence College, B
Rhode Island College, B
Roger Williams University, B
Salve Regina University, B

South Carolina

Anderson University, B
Charleston Southern University, B
Coker College, B

South Dakota

Dakota Wesleyan University, B
Mount Marty College, B
The University of South Dakota, B

Tennessee

Aquinas College, B
Bryan College, B
Cumberland University, B
King University, B
Lee University, B
Lincoln Memorial University, B
Lipscomb University, B
Martin Methodist College, B
Maryville College, B
Southern Adventist University, B
Trevecca Nazarene University, B
The University of Tennessee at Martin, B
Welch College, B

Texas

Abilene Christian University, B
Dallas Baptist University, B
East Texas Baptist University, B
Hardin-Simmons University, B
Houston Baptist University, B
Howard College, A
Howard Payne University, B
LeTourneau University, B
McMurry University, B
St. Edward's University, B
Schreiner University, B
Texas A&M International University, B
Texas Lutheran University, B
Texas Wesleyan University, B
University of Mary Hardin-Baylor, B

Utah

Southern Utah University, B
Utah Valley University, B
Weber State University, B

Vermont

Johnson State College, B

Virginia

Bluefield College, B
Emory & Henry College, B
Virginia Union University, B

Washington

Central Washington University, B
Washington State University, B
Western Washington University, B

Wisconsin

Carroll University, B
Concordia University Wisconsin, B
Maranatha Baptist University, B
Mount Mary University, B
University of Wisconsin - Superior, B

U.S. Territories: Puerto Rico

Inter American University of Puerto Rico, Metropolitan Campus, B
Inter American University of Puerto Rico, San Germán Campus, B
Pontifical Catholic University of Puerto Rico, B
Universidad Adventista de las Antillas, B
Universidad Metropolitana, B
Universidad del Turabo, B
University of Puerto Rico in Cayey, B
University of Puerto Rico in Utuado, B

Canada

Ontario

University of Windsor, B
York University, B

Quebec

Bishop's University, B
Université Laval, B

HIV/AIDS NURSING

United States

Delaware

University of Delaware, MO

HOLOCAUST AND RELATED STUDIES

United States

New Hampshire

Keene State College, B

Vermont

Marlboro College, B

HOLOCAUST STUDIES

United States

California

Chapman University, M

Massachusetts

Clark University, D

New Jersey

Drew University, O
Kean University, M
Stockton University, M

Pennsylvania

Seton Hill University, O
West Chester University of Pennsylvania, MO

HOME ECONOMICS

United States

Alabama

Alabama Agricultural and Mechanical University, M
The University of Alabama, MD

Arizona

The University of Arizona, MD

Arkansas

University of Central Arkansas, M

California

California State University, Long Beach, M

Indiana

Purdue University, MD

Michigan

Central Michigan University, MO

Missouri

University of Missouri, MDO

Oklahoma

Oklahoma State University, MD
University of Central Oklahoma, M

Tennessee

The University of Tennessee, D

Texas

Stephen F. Austin State University, M
Texas A&M University - Kingsville, M
Texas Tech University, MD

Washington

Central Washington University, M

Canada

Manitoba

University of Manitoba, M

HOME ECONOMICS EDUCATION

United States

Alabama

Alabama Agricultural and Mechanical University, MO

Georgia

University of Georgia, M

Indiana

Purdue University, MDO

Iowa

Iowa State University of Science and Technology, MD

Kentucky

Eastern Kentucky University, M

Louisiana

Louisiana State University and Agricultural & Mechanical College, M

Massachusetts

Cambridge College, M

Montana

Montana State University, M

Nebraska

University of Nebraska - Lincoln, MD
Wayne State College, M

New York

Queens College of the City University of New York, M

South Carolina

South Carolina State University, M

Texas

Texas Tech University, MD

Utah

Utah State University, M

Washington

Central Washington University, M

Canada

British Columbia

The University of British Columbia, M

HOME FURNISHINGS AND EQUIPMENT INSTALLERS

United States

Illinois

Triton College, A

Utah

Brigham Young University, B

HOME HEALTH AIDE/HOME ATTENDANT

United States

California

American River College, A

Kansas

Allen Community College, A
Barton County Community College, A

Pennsylvania

Laurel Business Institute, A

HOMELAND SECURITY

United States

Alabama

Auburn University at Montgomery, M

Arizona

Arizona State University at the Tempe campus, M
University of Phoenix - Online Campus, M
University of Phoenix - Phoenix Campus, M

California

Henley-Putnam University, M
National University, M
University of Phoenix - Southern California Campus, M
University of Southern California, O

Colorado

University of Colorado Denver, M

Connecticut

University of Connecticut, M
University of New Haven, MO

Delaware

Wilmington University, M

District of Columbia

University of the District of Columbia, M

Florida

Keiser University, M
University of Central Florida, O

Georgia

Columbus State University, M

Hawaii

Chaminade University of Honolulu, MO

Illinois

Southern Illinois University Carbondale, M
University of Illinois at Springfield, O

Indiana

Indiana University - Purdue University Indianapolis, O

Iowa

Upper Iowa University, M

Kentucky

Western Kentucky University, M

Louisiana

Northwestern State University of Louisiana, M

Maryland

Johns Hopkins University, O
Towson University, MO

Massachusetts

Endicott College, M
Lasell College, M
Northeastern University, M
University of Massachusetts Lowell, M

Minnesota

Capella University, M
Walden University, MDO

Missouri

Missouri State University, MO

New Jersey

Fairleigh Dickinson University, Metropolitan Campus, M
Georgian Court University, M
Monmouth University, MO
Thomas Edison State University, O

New York

Excelsior College, M
Pace University, M
University at Albany, State University of New York, M

Ohio

Notre Dame College, MO
Tiffin University, M

Oklahoma

University of Oklahoma Health Sciences Center, M

Pennsylvania

Drexel University, M
Penn State University Park, M
Saint Joseph's University, M

Rhode Island

Salve Regina University, MO

Texas

St. Mary's University, M
Sam Houston State University, M
Texas A&M University, O
Wayland Baptist University, M

Virginia

George Mason University, MDO
Regent University, M
University of Management and Technology, M
Virginia Commonwealth University, MO

West Virginia

American Public University System, M

HORSE HUSBANDRY/EQUINE SCIENCE AND MANAGEMENT

United States

Arizona

Yavapai College, A

California

Cosumnes River College, A
Feather River College, A
Santa Rosa Junior College, A

Illinois

Black Hawk College, A

Indiana

Saint Mary-of-the-Woods College, B

Iowa

Ellsworth Community College, A
Kirkwood Community College, A

Kansas

Colby Community College, A

Kentucky

Midway University, B
University of Kentucky, B

Maryland

Cecil College, A

Massachusetts

Becker College, B

Minnesota

Minnesota State Community and Technical College, A
Rochester Community and Technical College, A
University of Minnesota, Crookston, B

Missouri

William Woods University, B

New Hampshire

University of New Hampshire, B

New York

Morrisville State College, B

Ohio

The Ohio State University Agricultural Technical Institute, A
Tiffin University, B

Oklahoma

Oklahoma Panhandle State University, B

Oregon

Linn-Benton Community College, A
Treasure Valley Community College, A

Pennsylvania

Delaware Valley University, AB

Rhode Island

Johnson & Wales University, B

Texas

Clarendon College, A

Utah

Southern Utah University, A

Vermont

Vermont Technical College, B

Virginia

Averett University, B

West Virginia

Potomac State College of West Virginia University, A

Canada

Ontario

University of Guelph, AB

HORTICULTURAL SCIENCE

United States

Alabama

Auburn University, BMD
Wallace State Community College, A

Arizona

Mesa Community College, A

Arkansas

University of Arkansas, M

California

Bakersfield College, A
Butte College, A
California State University, Fresno, B
College of the Sequoias, A
El Camino College, A
Las Positas College, A
Los Angeles Pierce College, A
Modesto Junior College, A
Mt. San Antonio College, A
Reedley College, A
Saddleback College, A
Shasta College, A
University of California, Davis, M
Victor Valley College, A

Colorado

Colorado State University, BMD

Connecticut

Naugatuck Valley Community College, A
University of Connecticut, AB

Delaware

University of Delaware, M

Florida

Broward College, A
Miami Dade College, A
South Florida State College, A
University of Florida, BMD

Georgia

Abraham Baldwin Agricultural College, A
Chattahoochee Technical College, A
Columbus Technical College, A
Gwinnett Technical College, A
North Georgia Technical College, A
South Georgia Technical College, A
Southern Crescent Technical College, A
University of Georgia, MD

Hawaii

University of Hawaii at Hilo, B
University of Hawaii at Manoa, MD
University of Hawaii Maui College, A

Idaho

Brigham Young University - Idaho, B
College of Western Idaho, A
University of Idaho, B

Illinois

City Colleges of Chicago, Richard J. Daley College, A
University of Illinois at Urbana - Champaign, B

Indiana

Purdue University, BMD

Iowa

Iowa State University of Science and Technology, BMD

Kansas

Kansas State University, BMD

Maine

University of Maine, M

Maryland

University of Maryland, College Park, MD

Michigan

Andrews University, A
Michigan State University, BMD

Minnesota

Central Lakes College, A
Century College, A
University of Minnesota, Crookston, B

Mississippi

Jones County Junior College, A
Mississippi Delta Community College, A
Mississippi Gulf Coast Community College, A
Mississippi State University, BMD

Missouri

College of the Ozarks, B
Missouri State University, B
Missouri State University - West Plains, A
Northwest Missouri State University, B
University of Missouri, MD

Montana

Montana State University, B

Nebraska

University of Nebraska - Lincoln, BMD

New Hampshire

University of New Hampshire, B

New Jersey

Cumberland County College, A
Rutgers University - New Brunswick, MD

New Mexico

New Mexico State University, BMD

New York

Cornell University, MD
Morrisville State College, AB

North Carolina

Central Piedmont Community College, A
North Carolina State University, BMDO
Sampson Community College, A
Surry Community College, A

North Dakota

Dakota College at Bottineau, A

Ohio

Clark State Community College, A
The Ohio State University, MD
The Ohio State University Agricultural Technical Institute, A
University of Cincinnati, B

Oklahoma

Eastern Oklahoma State College, A
Oklahoma State University, BMD
Oklahoma State University, Oklahoma City, A

Oregon

Mt. Hood Community College, A
Oregon State University, BMD
Treasure Valley Community College, A

Pennsylvania

Delaware Valley University, B
Luzerne County Community College, A
Penn State Abington, B
Penn State Altoona, B
Penn State Beaver, B
Penn State Berks, B
Penn State Brandywine, B
Penn State DuBois, B
Penn State Erie, The Behrend College, B
Penn State Fayette, The Eberly Campus, B
Penn State Greater Allegheny, B
Penn State Hazleton, B
Penn State Lehigh Valley, B
Penn State Mont Alto, B
Penn State New Kensington, B
Penn State Schuylkill, B
Penn State Shenango, B
Penn State University Park, MD
Penn State Wilkes-Barre, B
Penn State Worthington Scranton, B
Penn State York, B
Temple University, AB
Williamson College of the Trades, A

South Carolina

Clemson University, B
Trident Technical College, A

South Dakota

Southeast Technical Institute, A

Tennessee

Tennessee Technological University, B

Texas

Palo Alto College, A
Richland College, A
Sam Houston State University, B
Stephen F. Austin State University, B
Tarleton State University, B
Tarrant County College District, A
Texas A&M University, MD
Texas A&M University - Kingsville, D
Texas Tech University, M
Trinity Valley Community College, A

Utah

Utah State University, B

Vermont

University of Vermont, BMD

Virginia

Ferrum College, B
Tidewater Community College, A
Virginia Polytechnic Institute and State University, BMD

Washington

South Puget Sound Community College, A
South Seattle College, A
University of Washington, MD
Washington State University, BMD

West Virginia

Potomac State College of West Virginia University, A
West Virginia University, M

Wisconsin

University of Wisconsin - Madison, BMD
University of Wisconsin - Platteville, B
University of Wisconsin - River Falls, B

Wyoming

Sheridan College, A

U.S. Territories: Puerto Rico

University of Puerto Rico, Mayagüez Campus, BM
University of Puerto Rico in Utuado, A

Canada

British Columbia

The University of British Columbia, B

Manitoba

University of Manitoba, MD

Maritime Provinces: Nova Scotia

Dalhousie University, M

Ontario

University of Guelph, AMD

Saskatchewan

University of Saskatchewan, B

HOSPICE NURSING

United States

Michigan

Madonna University, M

HOSPITAL AND HEALTH CARE FACILITIES ADMINISTRATION/ MANAGEMENT

United States

Alabama

The University of Alabama, B

Arizona

Carrington College - Phoenix West, A

California

Cypress College, A

Colorado

CollegeAmerica - Colorado Springs, B

Florida

State College of Florida Manatee-Sarasota, A

Georgia

Clayton State University, B

Hawaii

University of Phoenix - Hawaii Campus, B

Illinois

City Colleges of Chicago, Malcolm X College, A
College of DuPage, A
Governors State University, B
University of St. Francis, B

Kansas

Allen Community College, A
Newman University, B

Louisiana

Bossier Parish Community College, A

Massachusetts

American International College, B

Minnesota

Minnesota West Community and Technical College, A

Missouri

Avila University, B

New Jersey

Thomas Edison State University, B

New York

Ithaca College, B
Metropolitan College of New York, B
New York City College of Technology of the City University of New York, B
St. Joseph's College, Long Island Campus, B
St. Joseph's College, New York, B

Ohio

Tiffin University, B
The University of Toledo, B
Youngstown State University, B

Oklahoma

Langston University, B
University of Oklahoma, B

Pennsylvania

Saint Joseph's University, B

South Dakota

Black Hills State University, B
The University of South Dakota, B

Vermont

Champlain College, B

Virginia

ECPI University (Virginia Beach), B

Wisconsin

University of Wisconsin - Milwaukee, B
Western Technical College, A

Canada

Ontario

York University, B

HOSPITALITY ADMINISTRATION/MANAGEMENT

United States

Alabama

Alabama Agricultural and Mechanical University, M
Auburn University, BO
Columbia Southern University, B
James H. Faulkner State Community College, A
Jefferson State Community College, A
Troy University, M
Tuskegee University, B
The University of Alabama, M
University of South Alabama, B

Arizona

Arizona Western College, A
Coconino Community College, A
Northern Arizona University, B
Penn Foster College, A
Pima Community College, A
Scottsdale Community College, A
University of Phoenix - Phoenix Campus, B

Arkansas

Arkansas Tech University, B
Philander Smith College, B
Pulaski Technical College, A

California

California State Polytechnic University, Pomona, BM
California State University, Dominguez Hills, B
California State University, Fullerton, B
California State University, Long Beach, M
California State University, Northridge, M
College of the Canyons, A
College of the Desert, A
College of the Redwoods, A
Cuesta College, A
Grossmont College, A
MiraCosta College, A
Monterey Peninsula College, A
National University, A
Pasadena City College, A
Reedley College, A
San Diego City College, A
San Diego State University, B
San Francisco State University, B
San Jose State University, B
Southwestern College, A
Trident University International, B
University of Antelope Valley, A
University of Phoenix - Bay Area Campus, B
University of Phoenix - Sacramento Valley Campus, B
University of San Francisco, B

Colorado

Colorado Mesa University, AB
Colorado Mountain College (Leadville), A
Colorado Mountain College (Steamboat Springs), A
Front Range Community College, A
Johnson & Wales University, B
Metropolitan State University of Denver, B
University of Denver, B
University of Phoenix - Colorado Campus, B

Connecticut

Mitchell College, B
Naugatuck Valley Community College, A
Three Rivers Community College, A
University of New Haven, B

Delaware

Delaware State University, B
University of Delaware, BM

District of Columbia

The George Washington University, M
Georgetown University, M
University of the District of Columbia, A

Florida

Beacon College, B
Broward College, A
City College (Gainesville), A
City College (Miami), A
Daytona State College, A
Everglades University (Boca Raton), B
Everglades University (Maitland), B
Everglades University (Sarasota), B
Flagler College, B
Florida Atlantic University, B
Florida International University, BM
Florida National University, A
Florida State University, B
Gulf Coast State College, A
Hillsborough Community College, A
Johnson & Wales University, B
Keiser University, A
Lynn University, BM
Miami Dade College, A
Pensacola State College, A
Saint Leo University, B
St. Petersburg College, A
St. Thomas University, B
Schiller International University, M
South Florida State College, A
University of Central Florida, BMDO

University of South Florida, B
University of South Florida Sarasota-Manatee, BM
University of West Florida, B
Valencia College, A
Webber International University, AB

Georgia

Georgia State University, B
South University, M
University of Phoenix - Atlanta Campus, B
University of Phoenix - Augusta Campus, B
University of Phoenix - Columbus Georgia Campus, AB

Hawaii

Hawai'i Pacific University, M
Kauai Community College, A
University of Phoenix - Hawaii Campus, B

Idaho

Lewis-Clark State College, AB
North Idaho College, A

Illinois

Bradley University, B
College of DuPage, A
DePaul University, BM
Harper College, A
Highland Community College, A
Joliet Junior College, A
Kendall College, B
Lincoln Land Community College, A
Moraine Valley Community College, A
Northwestern College - Bridgeview Campus, A
Roosevelt University, BM
Southern Illinois University Carbondale, B
University of Illinois at Urbana - Champaign, B
Western Illinois University, B

Indiana

Ancilla College, A
Harrison College, B
Indiana University Kokomo, B
Indiana University - Purdue University Fort Wayne, B
Ivy Tech Community College - Bloomington, A
Ivy Tech Community College - Central Indiana, A
Ivy Tech Community College - Columbus, A
Ivy Tech Community College - East Central, A
Ivy Tech Community College - North Central, A
Ivy Tech Community College - Northeast, A
Ivy Tech Community College - Northwest, A
Ivy Tech Community College - Southwest, A
Purdue University, MD
Purdue University Northwest (Hammond), B
Vincennes University, A

Iowa

Des Moines Area Community College, A
Hawkeye Community College, A
Iowa Lakes Community College, A
Iowa State University of Science and Technology, BMD
Kaplan University, Davenport Campus, A
Kirkwood Community College, A
North Iowa Area Community College, A
Scott Community College, A

Kansas

Kansas State University, BMD

Kentucky

Sullivan University, B
University of Kentucky, BM
Western Kentucky University, B

Louisiana

Delgado Community College, A
Northwestern State University of Louisiana, B
Southern University at Shreveport, A
University of Louisiana at Lafayette, B
University of New Orleans, BM

Maine

Husson University, BM

Maryland

Allegany College of Maryland, A
Chesapeake College, A
College of Southern Maryland, A
Morgan State University, B
Stratford University, ABM
Wor-Wic Community College, A

Massachusetts

Berkshire Community College, A
Boston University, B
Bunker Hill Community College, A
Cape Cod Community College, A
Endicott College, BM
Fisher College, B
Greenfield Community College, A
Holyoke Community College, A
Lasell College, BMO
Massachusetts Bay Community College, A
Massasoit Community College, A
Nichols College, B
North Shore Community College, A
Quinsigamond Community College, A
Salem State University, B
University of Massachusetts Amherst, BD

Michigan

Central Michigan University, B
Cleary University, B
Eastern Michigan University, BMO
Ferris State University, B
Grand Valley State University, B
Henry Ford College, A
Lake Michigan College, A
Madonna University, B
Michigan State University, BM
Muskegon Community College, A
North Central Michigan College, A
Northern Michigan University, B

Minnesota

Concordia University, St. Paul, B
Metropolitan State University, B
National American University (Roseville), B
Normandale Community College, A
Saint Paul College - A Community & Technical College, A

Mississippi

Delta State University, B
East Central Community College, A
East Mississippi Community College, A
Hinds Community College, A
Northeast Mississippi Community College, A
Tougaloo College, A
University of Mississippi, B
University of Southern Mississippi, B

Missouri

College of the Ozarks, B
Missouri State University, B
University of Missouri, MD

Montana

Blackfeet Community College, A

Nebraska

University of Nebraska - Lincoln, B

Nevada

College of Southern Nevada, A
University of Nevada, Las Vegas, BMD
University of Phoenix - Las Vegas Campus, B

New Hampshire

Granite State College, B
Lakes Region Community College, A
Southern New Hampshire University, B
University of New Hampshire, B

New Jersey

Bergen Community College, A
County College of Morris, A
Fairleigh Dickinson University, College at Florham, BM
Fairleigh Dickinson University, Metropolitan Campus, BM
Hudson County Community College, A
Montclair State University, B
Rowan College at Burlington County, A
Rutgers University - Camden, B
Stockton University, B
Thomas Edison State University, B
Union County College, A
University of Phoenix - Jersey City Campus, B

New Mexico

Central New Mexico Community College, A
Doña Ana Community College, A
New Mexico State University, B

New York

Adirondack Community College, A
Buffalo State College, State University of New York, B
Cornell University, MD
Corning Community College, A
Genesee Community College, A
Globe Institute of Technology, B
Jefferson Community College, A
Long Island Business Institute, A
Monroe College, ABM
Morrisville State College, AB
New York City College of Technology of the City University of New York, AB
New York University, MO
Niagara County Community College, A
Niagara University, B
Onondaga Community College, A
Paul Smith's College, AB
Rochester Institute of Technology, BM
Rockland Community College, A
St. John's University, B
St. Joseph's College, Long Island Campus, B
St. Joseph's College, New York, B
State University of New York College of Technology at Delhi, B
Sullivan County Community College, A
Syracuse University, B
Trocaire College, A

North Carolina

Appalachian State University, B
Central Piedmont Community College, A
East Carolina University, BM
North Carolina Central University, B
The University of North Carolina at Greensboro, B
Western Carolina University, B

North Dakota

North Dakota State University, B
United Tribes Technical College, A

Ohio

Ashland University, B
Bowling Green State University, B
Cincinnati State Technical and Community College, A
Columbus State Community College, A
Hocking College, A
Kent State University, BM
Kent State University at Ashtabula, B
Lakeland Community College, A
The Ohio State University, B
Terra State Community College, A
Tiffin University, B
The University of Akron, A
The University of Findlay, M
Youngstown State University, AB

Oklahoma

Oklahoma State University, BMD

Oregon

Blue Mountain Community College, A
Chemeketa Community College, A
Mt. Hood Community College, A
Oregon State University, B

Pennsylvania

Butler County Community College, A
Cheyney University of Pennsylvania, B
Drexel University, M
East Stroudsburg University of Pennsylvania, B
Indiana University of Pennsylvania, B
Keystone College, B
Marywood University, B
Mercyhurst North East, A
Mercyhurst University, B
Penn State Abington, B
Penn State Altoona, B
Penn State Beaver, AB
Penn State Berks, AB
Penn State Brandywine, B
Penn State DuBois, B
Penn State Erie, The Behrend College, B
Penn State Fayette, The Eberly Campus, B
Penn State Greater Allegheny, B
Penn State Hazleton, B
Penn State Lehigh Valley, B
Penn State Mont Alto, B
Penn State New Kensington, B
Penn State Schuylkill, B
Penn State Shenango, B
Penn State University Park, BMD
Penn State Wilkes-Barre, B
Penn State Worthington Scranton, B
Penn State York, B
Robert Morris University, B
Seton Hill University, B
Temple University, BMD
University of Phoenix - Philadelphia Campus, B
University of Pittsburgh at Bradford, B
Widener University, B
York College of Pennsylvania, B

Rhode Island

Johnson & Wales University, BM

South Carolina

College of Charleston, B
Technical College of the Lowcountry, A
University of South Carolina, BM
University of South Carolina Beaufort, B

South Dakota

Sisseton-Wahpeton College, A
South Dakota State University, BMD

Tennessee

Belmont University, B
Hiwassee College, B
University of Memphis, B
The University of Tennessee, M

Texas

Austin Community College District, A
Central Texas College, A
Collin County Community College District, A
Dallas Baptist University, B
South Texas College, A
Stephen F. Austin State University, B
Texas Tech University, MD
University of Houston, M
University of North Texas, BM
University of Phoenix - Dallas Campus, B
University of Phoenix - Houston Campus, B
Virginia College in Austin, A

Utah

Provo College, A
Southern Utah University, B
Utah Valley University, AB

Vermont

Champlain College, B
Community College of Vermont, A

Johnson State College, B

Virginia

J. Sargeant Reynolds Community College, A
James Madison University, B
Stratford University (Falls Church), B
Stratford University (Glen Allen), B
Stratford University (Newport News), B
Stratford University (Woodbridge), B
Virginia International University, M
Virginia Polytechnic Institute and State University, MD
Virginia State University, B

Washington

Seattle Central College, A
South Seattle College, A
University of Phoenix - Western Washington Campus, B
Washington State University, B
Washington State University - Global Campus, B
Washington State University - Tri-Cities, B
Washington State University - Vancouver, B

West Virginia

American Public University System, B
Concord University, B
Davis & Elkins College, AB
Mountwest Community & Technical College, A
Potomac State College of West Virginia University, A
West Virginia Northern Community College, A
West Virginia University, B

Wisconsin

Fox Valley Technical College, A
Gateway Technical College, A
Madison Area Technical College, A
Northeast Wisconsin Technical College, A
University of Wisconsin - Stout, B

Wyoming

Casper College, A
Sheridan College, A

U.S. Territories: United States Virgin Islands

University of the Virgin Islands, B

Canada

British Columbia

Royal Roads University, MO

Maritime Provinces: New Brunswick

University of New Brunswick Saint John, B

Maritime Provinces: Nova Scotia

Cape Breton University, B
Mount Saint Vincent University, B

Maritime Provinces: Prince Edward Island

University of Prince Edward Island, B

Ontario

Ryerson University, B
University of Guelph, M

HOSPITALITY AND RECREATION MARKETING OPERATIONS

United States

Alabama

Tuskegee University, B

California

San Diego Mesa College, A

Indiana

Grace College, B

Iowa

Iowa Central Community College, A

Maine

Husson University, B

Michigan

Ferris State University, AB
Muskegon Community College, A

Montana

Flathead Valley Community College, A

New York

Rochester Institute of Technology, B

North Carolina

Methodist University, B

North Dakota

Dakota College at Bottineau, A

Ohio

Ohio Business College (Sandusky), A

Pennsylvania

Luzerne County Community College, A
Montgomery County Community College, A
Saint Joseph's University, B

Wisconsin

Lac Courte Oreilles Ojibwa Community College, A

Canada

Maritime Provinces: Nova Scotia

Cape Breton University, B

Ontario

Tyndale University College & Seminary, B

HOTEL/MOTEL ADMINISTRA-
TION/MANAGEMENT

United States

Alabama

Auburn University, B
Community College of the Air Force, A

Arizona

Central Arizona College, A
Scottsdale Community College, A

California

Bakersfield College, A
California State University, Long Beach, B
Chaffey College, A
City College of San Francisco, A
College of the Canyons, A
Columbia College, A
Cypress College, A
Long Beach City College, A
Monterey Peninsula College, A
Mt. San Antonio College, A
Orange Coast College, A
Oxnard College, A
San Bernardino Valley College, A
San Diego Mesa College, A
Santa Barbara City College, A
Southwestern College, A
University of San Francisco, B

Colorado

Colorado Mountain College (Steamboat Springs), A
Johnson & Wales University, B
University of Denver, B

Connecticut

Gateway Community College, A
Manchester Community College, A
Naugatuck Valley Community College, A
Norwalk Community College, A
University of New Haven, B

Delaware

Delaware Technical & Community College, Stanton/Wilmington Campus, A
Delaware Technical & Community College, Terry Campus, A
University of Delaware, B

District of Columbia

Howard University, B

Florida

Bethune-Cookman University, B
Daytona State College, A
Florida State College at Jacksonville, A
Indian River State College, A
Johnson & Wales University, B
Miami Dade College, A
Palm Beach State College, A
Pensacola State College, A
St. Thomas University, B
Valencia College, A

Georgia

Albany Technical College, A
Athens Technical College, A
Atlanta Technical College, A
Central Georgia Technical College, A
Georgia Southern University, B
Gwinnett Technical College, A
Ogeechee Technical College, A
Savannah Technical College, A

Hawaii

Brigham Young University - Hawaii, B
Hawaii Community College, A
Kapiolani Community College, A
University of Hawaii Maui College, A

Idaho

College of Southern Idaho, A

Illinois

College of DuPage, A
MacCormac College, A
Triton College, A

Indiana

Harrison College, B
Indiana University - Purdue University Fort Wayne, B
International Business College (Fort Wayne), AB
International Business College (Indianapolis), A
Purdue University, B
Vincennes University, A

Iowa

Iowa Lakes Community College, A

Kansas

Butler Community College, A
Cowley County Community College and Area Vocational - Technical School, A
Johnson County Community College, A
Kansas State University, B

Louisiana

Northwest Louisiana Technical College, A
Southern University at Shreveport, A

Maine

Husson University, B
Thomas College, B
University of Maine at Machias, B

Maryland

Anne Arundel Community College, A
Baltimore City Community College, A
Community College of Baltimore County, A
Montgomery College, A
Morgan State University, B
University of Maryland Eastern Shore, B

Massachusetts

Cape Cod Community College, A
Middlesex Community College, A
Mount Ida College, B
Newbury College, B
Northern Essex Community College, A

Michigan

Baker College, A
Ferris State University, AB
Grand Valley State University, B
Lansing Community College, A
Muskegon Community College, A
Northwood University, Michigan Campus, B
Oakland Community College, A

Minnesota

Minneapolis Business College, A
Southwest Minnesota State University, B

Mississippi

Coahoma Community College, A
Mississippi Gulf Coast Community College, A
Northwest Mississippi Community College, A
University of Southern Mississippi, B

Missouri

Ozarks Technical Community College, A
University of Central Missouri, B
University of Missouri, B

Nebraska

Central Community College - Hastings Campus, A

Nevada

College of Southern Nevada, A

New Hampshire

NHTI, Concord's Community College, A

New Jersey

Atlantic Cape Community College, A
Essex County College, A
Mercer County Community College, A
Middlesex County College, A
Passaic County Community College, A
Union County College, A

New York

Broome Community College, A
Bryant & Stratton College - Syracuse Campus, A
Buffalo State College, State University of New York, B
Cornell University, B
Finger Lakes Community College, A
Genesee Community College, A
Keuka College, B
Mohawk Valley Community College, A
Monroe Community College, A
Nassau Community College, A
New York University, B
Niagara University, B
Pace University, B
Paul Smith's College, AB
Rochester Institute of Technology, B
Schenectady County Community College, A
State University of New York College of Agriculture and Technology at Cobleskill, A
State University of New York at Plattsburgh, B
Wood Tobe - Coburn School, A

North Carolina

Asheville-Buncombe Technical Community College, A
Cape Fear Community College, A
Central Piedmont Community College, A

Guilford Technical Community College, A
Johnson & Wales University, B
King's College, A
Nash Community College, A
Sandhills Community College, A
Wake Technical Community College, A
Wilkes Community College, A

Ohio

Ashland University, B
Hocking College, A
The Ohio State University, B
Sinclair Community College, A
The University of Akron, A
The University of Findlay, B

Oklahoma

Carl Albert State College, A
University of Central Oklahoma, B

Oregon

Central Oregon Community College, A
Chemeketa Community College, A
Lane Community College, A
Southern Oregon University, B

Pennsylvania

The Art Institute of Pittsburgh, B
Bradford School, A
Community College of Allegheny County, A
Community College of Philadelphia, A
Delaware County Community College, A
Drexel University, B
Luzerne County Community College, A
Northampton Community College, A
Pittsburgh Technical Institute, A
The Restaurant School at Walnut Hill College, AB
Westmoreland County Community College, A
Widener University, B

Rhode Island

Johnson & Wales University, B

South Carolina

Trident Technical College, A

Tennessee

Pellissippi State Community College, A
South College, A
University of Memphis, B
The University of Tennessee, B

Texas

Del Mar College, A
El Paso Community College, A
Houston Community College, A
Laredo Community College, A
St. Philip's College, A
South Texas College, A
Texas Tech University, B
University of Houston, B
Wiley College, B

Virginia

Hampton University, B
J. Sargeant Reynolds Community College, A
Stratford University (Falls Church), A
Stratford University (Woodbridge), A
Virginia Polytechnic Institute and State University, B

Washington

Highline College, A
Lake Washington Institute of Technology, A
Seattle Central College, A
Skagit Valley College, A
Spokane Community College, A
Yakima Valley Community College, A

West Virginia

Concord University, B

Wisconsin

Mid-State Technical College, A
Milwaukee Area Technical College, A

Moraine Park Technical College, A
Nicolet Area Technical College, A

Wyoming

Central Wyoming College, A

U.S. Territories: Guam

Guam Community College, A

U.S. Territories: Puerto Rico

ICPR Junior College - Hato Rey Campus, A
Inter American University of Puerto Rico, Aguadilla
  Campus, B
Inter American University of Puerto Rico, Fajardo
  Campus, AB
Inter American University of Puerto Rico, Ponce
  Campus, B
Universidad del Este, AB
University of Puerto Rico in Carolina, AB

Canada

British Columbia

Royal Roads University, B
University of Victoria, B

Maritime Provinces: Nova Scotia

Mount Saint Vincent University, B

Ontario

Ryerson University, B
University of Guelph, B

Quebec

Université du Québec à Montréal, B

HOUSING AND HUMAN ENVIRONMENTS

United States

Arkansas

Harding University, B

California

Modesto Junior College, A

Georgia

University of Georgia, B

Iowa

University of Northern Iowa, B

Kentucky

Sullivan College of Technology and Design, A

Minnesota

University of Minnesota, Twin Cities Campus, B

Missouri

Missouri State University, B
University of Missouri, B

Nevada

University of Nevada, Reno, B

Ohio

Ohio University, B
The University of Akron, B

Oklahoma

Oklahoma State University, B

Pennsylvania

Community College of Allegheny County, A

South Carolina

Bob Jones University, B

Utah

Utah State University, B

HUMAN-COMPUTER INTERAC-TION

United States

Florida

Florida Institute of Technology, M

Georgia

Georgia Institute of Technology, M

Illinois

DePaul University, M
University of Illinois at Urbana - Champaign, MDO

Indiana

Indiana University Bloomington, MD
Indiana University - Purdue University Indianapolis,
  MD

Iowa

Iowa State University of Science and Technology,
  MD

Maryland

University of Baltimore, M

Massachusetts

Tufts University, O

New York

Cornell University, MD
Rensselaer Polytechnic Institute, M
Rochester Institute of Technology, M
State University of New York at Oswego, M

Pennsylvania

Carnegie Mellon University, MD

South Carolina

Clemson University, D

Canada

Maritime Provinces: Nova Scotia

Dalhousie University, M

HUMAN DEVELOPMENT

United States

Alabama

Alabama Agricultural and Mechanical University, M
Auburn University, MD
The University of Alabama, M

Arizona

Arizona State University at the Tempe campus, MD
Northern Arizona University, O
The University of Arizona, M

California

Pacific Oaks College, M
University of California, Berkeley, MD
University of California, Davis, D

Colorado

Colorado State University, MD
University of Colorado Denver, M

Connecticut

University of Connecticut, MDO

Delaware

University of Delaware, MD

District of Columbia

The George Washington University, M
Georgetown University, M

Illinois

Argosy University, Chicago, D
Bradley University, M
National Louis University, MO
Northwestern University, D
University of Chicago, D
University of Illinois at Chicago, MD
University of Illinois at Springfield, M
University of Illinois at Urbana - Champaign, MD

Indiana

Purdue University, MD

Iowa

Iowa State University of Science and Technology,
MD

Kansas

Kansas State University, MD

Kentucky

Lindsey Wilson College, M

Maine

University of Maine, MDO

Maryland

Hood College, M
University of Maryland, College Park, MD

Massachusetts

Harvard University, M
Tufts University, MD
Wheelock College, M

Michigan

Central Michigan University, M

Minnesota

Saint Mary's University of Minnesota, M
University of St. Thomas, MD

Mississippi

Mississippi State University, MD

Missouri

Saint Louis University, M
University of Missouri, MD

Montana

Montana State University, M

Nebraska

University of Nebraska - Lincoln, D

Nevada

University of Nevada, Reno, M

New Mexico

University of New Mexico, M

New York

Cornell University, MD
Hofstra University, D
New York University, MDO
St. Lawrence University, MO
University of Rochester, MD

North Carolina

Duke University, D
The University of North Carolina at Greensboro, MD

North Dakota

North Dakota State University, MD

Ohio

Bowling Green State University, M
Kent State University, MD
The Ohio State University, D
University of Dayton, M

Oklahoma

Oklahoma State University, D
University of Central Oklahoma, M

Oregon

Oregon State University, MD

Pennsylvania

Marywood University, D
Penn State University Park, MD
University of Pennsylvania, MD

South Carolina

Clemson University, M

South Dakota

The University of South Dakota, MDO

Tennessee

East Tennessee State University, M
Vanderbilt University, M

Texas

Our Lady of the Lake University of San Antonio, M
Texas Tech University, MD
University of North Texas, M
The University of Texas at Austin, MD

Utah

Brigham Young University, MD
University of Utah, M
Utah State University, MD

Virginia

Virginia Polytechnic Institute and State University,
MD

Washington

University of Washington, M
Washington State University, D

West Virginia

West Virginia University, D

Wisconsin

University of Wisconsin - Madison, MD
University of Wisconsin - Stevens Point, M

Canada

British Columbia

The University of British Columbia, M
University of Victoria, MD

Ontario

Brock University, MD
Laurentian University, M
University of Guelph, MD

HUMAN DEVELOPMENT AND FAMILY STUDIES

United States

Alabama

Auburn University, B
Samford University, B
The University of Alabama, B

Arizona

The University of Arizona, B

Arkansas

Harding University, B
University of Arkansas, B

California

California State University, East Bay, B
California State University, Long Beach, B
California State University, San Bernardino, B
California State University, San Marcos, B
Cuesta College, A
Hope International University, B
Imperial Valley College, A
Ohlone College, A
Pacific Oaks College, B
Saddleback College, A
San Diego Christian College, B
Santiago Canyon College, A
University of California, Davis, B
Vanguard University of Southern California, B

Colorado

Colorado State University, B

Connecticut

Connecticut College, B
Mitchell College, B
University of Connecticut, B

District of Columbia

Trinity Washington University, B
University of the District of Columbia, B

Florida

Eckerd College, B
Florida State University, B
Nova Southeastern University, B

Georgia

Albany Technical College, A
Georgia Southern University, B
LaGrange College, B
University of Georgia, B

Hawaii

Hawai'i Pacific University, B

Idaho

University of Idaho, B

Illinois

City Colleges of Chicago, Olive-Harvey College, A
Northern Illinois University, B
Rockford University, B
University of Illinois at Urbana - Champaign, B

Indiana

Ball State University, B
Indiana State University, B
Purdue University, B
Purdue University Northwest (Hammond), B

Kansas

Kansas State University, B

Kentucky

Eastern Kentucky University, B
Kentucky State University, B
University of Kentucky, B

Louisiana

University of Louisiana at Lafayette, B

Maine

University of Maine, B

Massachusetts

Hellenic College, B
Lesley University, B
Merrimack College, B
Wheelock College, B

Michigan

Concordia University Ann Arbor, B
Cornerstone University, B

Minnesota

Concordia University, St. Paul, B
St. Cloud Technical & Community College, A
Walden University, B

Missouri

Missouri State University, B
Stephens College, B
University of Missouri, B

Nevada

University of Nevada, Reno, B

New Hampshire

University of New Hampshire, B

New Mexico

Central New Mexico Community College, A
Eastern New Mexico University - Roswell, A
New Mexico State University, B
University of New Mexico, B

New York

Binghamton University, State University of New York, B
Cornell University, B
St. Joseph's College, Long Island Campus, B
St. Joseph's College, New York, B
State University of New York at Oswego, B
State University of New York at Plattsburgh, B
Syracuse University, B

North Carolina

The University of North Carolina at Greensboro, B

North Dakota

North Dakota State University, B

Ohio

Antioch University Midwest, B
Bowling Green State University, B
Columbus State Community College, A
Kent State University, B
Kent State University at Salem, B
Kent State University at Stark, B
Miami University, B
Northwest State Community College, A
The Ohio State University, B
Ohio University, B
Youngstown State University, B

Oklahoma

Oklahoma State University, B
Southwestern Christian University, B

Oregon

Oregon State University, B
Oregon State University - Cascades, B
Warner Pacific College, B

Pennsylvania

Bucks County Community College, A
Community College of Allegheny County, A
Indiana University of Pennsylvania, B
Keystone College, B
Penn State Abington, AB
Penn State Altoona, AB
Penn State Beaver, B
Penn State Berks, AB
Penn State Brandywine, AB
Penn State DuBois, AB
Penn State Erie, The Behrend College, AB
Penn State Fayette, The Eberly Campus, AB
Penn State Greater Allegheny, B
Penn State Harrisburg, B
Penn State Hazleton, B
Penn State Lehigh Valley, B
Penn State Mont Alto, AB
Penn State New Kensington, AB
Penn State Schuylkill, AB

Penn State Shenango, AB
Penn State University Park, B
Penn State Wilkes-Barre, B
Penn State Worthington Scranton, AB
Penn State York, AB
Temple University, B
University of Valley Forge, B
Westminster College, B

Rhode Island

University of Rhode Island, B

South Carolina

Benedict College, B
Clemson University, B
Columbia College, B
University of South Carolina Upstate, B

South Dakota

South Dakota State University, B

Tennessee

Freed-Hardeman University, B
University of Memphis, B
The University of Tennessee, B

Texas

Abilene Christian University, B
Amberton University, B
Baylor University, B
Howard Payne University, B
Lamar University, B
Texas A&M University - Kingsville, B
Texas State University, B
Texas Tech University, B
Texas Woman's University, B
University of Houston, B
University of North Texas, B
The University of Texas at Austin, B
The University of Texas of the Permian Basin, B

Utah

Brigham Young University, B
Salt Lake Community College, A
University of Utah, B
Utah State University, AB

Vermont

University of Vermont, B

Virginia

George Mason University, B
Liberty University, B
Virginia Polytechnic Institute and State University, B

Washington

Seattle Pacific University, B
Shoreline Community College, A
Washington State University, B
Washington State University - Global Campus, B
Washington State University - Vancouver, B

West Virginia

American Public University System, B

Wisconsin

University of Wisconsin - Madison, B

Canada

Ontario

University of Guelph, B
University of Waterloo, B

HUMAN GENETICS

United States

California

University of California, Los Angeles, MD

Georgia

Emory University, M

Illinois

University of Chicago, D

Louisiana

Louisiana State University Health Sciences Center, MD
Tulane University, MD

Maryland

Johns Hopkins University, D

Michigan

University of Michigan, MD

Missouri

Washington University in St. Louis, D

New York

Sarah Lawrence College, M

North Carolina

Wake Forest University, D

Ohio

Case Western Reserve University, D

Pennsylvania

University of Pittsburgh, MDO

Tennessee

Vanderbilt University, D

Texas

The University of Texas Health Science Center at Houston, MD

Utah

University of Utah, MD

Virginia

Virginia Commonwealth University, MDO

West Virginia

West Virginia University, MD

Canada

Manitoba

University of Manitoba, MD

Newfoundland and Labrador

Memorial University of Newfoundland, MD

Quebec

McGill University, MD

HUMAN NUTRITION

United States

Colorado

Colorado State University, B
Metropolitan State University of Denver, B

Florida

Broward College, A
State College of Florida Manatee-Sarasota, B

Georgia

Life University, B

Illinois

University of Illinois at Urbana - Champaign, B

Kansas

Kansas State University, B

Kentucky

University of Kentucky, B

New York

Rochester Institute of Technology, B
Syracuse University, B

Ohio

Case Western Reserve University, B
The Ohio State University, B
University of Dayton, B

Oklahoma

University of Central Oklahoma, B

Pennsylvania

Cedar Crest College, B
Penn State Abington, B
Penn State Altoona, B
Penn State Beaver, B
Penn State Berks, B
Penn State Brandywine, B
Penn State DuBois, B
Penn State Erie, The Behrend College, B
Penn State Fayette, The Eberly Campus, B
Penn State Greater Allegheny, B
Penn State Hazleton, B
Penn State Lehigh Valley, B
Penn State Mont Alto, B
Penn State New Kensington, B
Penn State Schuylkill, B
Penn State Shenango, B
Penn State University Park, B
Penn State Wilkes-Barre, B
Penn State Worthington Scranton, B
Penn State York, B

Texas

Baylor University, B
Prairie View A&M University, B
Tarleton State University, B
University of Houston, B

Utah

Southern Utah University, B

Virginia

Bridgewater College, B

Washington

Central Washington University, B
Everett Community College, A
Washington State University, B

Canada

British Columbia

The University of British Columbia, B

Maritime Provinces: Nova Scotia

Cape Breton University, B

Ontario

Ryerson University, B
University of Guelph, B

Quebec

McGill University, B
Université de Montréal, B

HUMAN RESOURCES DEVELOPMENT

United States

Arkansas

University of Arkansas, BMD

California

Antioch University Los Angeles, M
Azusa Pacific University, M
California State University, Sacramento, M
John F. Kennedy University, MO
University of California, Los Angeles, D

Connecticut

University of Bridgeport, M
University of Connecticut, M

District of Columbia

The George Washington University, MDO

Florida

Barry University, MD
Florida International University, MD
Rollins College, M
University of South Florida, O

Illinois

Blackburn College, B
Illinois Institute of Technology, M
National Louis University, M
Northeastern Illinois University, M
Roosevelt University, M
Trinity International University, B

Indiana

Indiana State University, M
Indiana Tech, M

Iowa

Iowa State University of Science and Technology, M

Kansas

Grantham University, BM
Ottawa University, M
Pittsburg State University, M
Southwestern College, B

Kentucky

Kentucky State University, M
Northern Kentucky University, B
University of Louisville, M

Louisiana

Louisiana State University and Agricultural & Mechanical College, MD

Maryland

Bowie State University, M
McDaniel College, M
Towson University, M

Massachusetts

Nichols College, B

Michigan

Oakland University, BM

Minnesota

Minnesota State Community and Technical College - Moorhead, A
University of Minnesota, Twin Cities Campus, MDO
University of St. Thomas, M

Mississippi

Mississippi State University, MDO

Missouri

Park University, AB
University of Missouri - St. Louis, M
Webster University, M
William Woods University, M

Nebraska

University of Nebraska at Omaha, O

Nevada

University of Nevada, Las Vegas, D

New York

The College of New Rochelle, MO
Houghton College, B
New York University, MO
Rochester Institute of Technology, M
Syracuse University, D

North Carolina

North Carolina State University, M
Western Carolina University, M

Ohio

The Ohio State University, B
Xavier University, M

Pennsylvania

Drexel University, M
Indiana University of Pennsylvania, M
La Salle University, MO
Moravian College, M
Penn State University Park, MD
The University of Scranton, M
Villanova University, M

South Carolina

Clemson University, M
Limestone College, B

Tennessee

Lincoln Memorial University, D
The University of Tennessee, M

Texas

Abilene Christian University, M
Amberton University, M
Concordia University Texas, B
LeTourneau University, B
Midwestern State University, BM
Texas A&M University, BMD
University of Houston, BM
The University of Texas at Tyler, BMD

Virginia

Regent University, D
Virginia Commonwealth University, M

Washington

Washington State University - Vancouver, B

Wisconsin

Marquette University, M
University of Wisconsin - Milwaukee, BMO
University of Wisconsin - Stout, M

U.S. Territories: Puerto Rico

Inter American University of Puerto Rico, Metropolitan Campus, M
Inter American University of Puerto Rico, San Germán Campus, M

Canada

Saskatchewan

University of Regina, M

HUMAN RESOURCES MANAGEMENT/PERSONNEL ADMINISTRATION

United States

Alabama

Athens State University, B
Auburn University, B
Auburn University at Montgomery, B
Columbia Southern University, B
Community College of the Air Force, A
Faulkner University, A
Virginia College in Birmingham, A
Virginia College in Mobile, A

Arizona

Northcentral University, B
Penn Foster College, A
The University of Arizona, B
Western International University, B

Arkansas

Central Baptist College, B

California

California Coast University, B
California State University, East Bay, B
California State University, Fresno, B
California State University, Long Beach, B
Golden Gate University, B
Holy Names University, B
La Sierra University, B
San Diego State University, B
San Joaquin Valley College (Visalia), A
San Joaquin Valley College - Online, A
San Jose State University, B
Santa Rosa Junior College, A
Simpson University, B

Colorado

American Sentinel University, B
Colorado Technical University Online, B
Regis University, B

Connecticut

Quinnipiac University, B

Delaware

Delaware State University, B
Delaware Technical & Community College, Terry
    Campus, A
Goldey-Beacom College, B
Wilmington University, B

District of Columbia

The Catholic University of America, B
The George Washington University, B

Florida

Broward College, A
Florida International University, B
Keiser University, B
Millennia Atlantic University, B
Rasmussen College Fort Myers, AB
Rasmussen College Land O' Lakes, AB
Rasmussen College New Port Richey, AB
Rasmussen College Ocala, AB
Rasmussen College Tampa/Brandon, AB
Saint Leo University, B
South Florida State College, A
University of Miami, B
Virginia College in Pensacola, A
Warner University, B

Georgia

Ashworth College, A
Brenau University, B
Georgia Southwestern State University, B

Hawaii

Hawai'i Pacific University, B
University of Hawaii at Manoa, B

Idaho

Idaho State University, B
University of Idaho, B

Illinois

Bradley University, B
Carl Sandburg College, A
DePaul University, B
Ellis University, B
Illinois Eastern Community Colleges, Olney Central
    College, A
Judson University, B
Lewis University, B
Loyola University Chicago, B
McKendree University, B
Moraine Valley Community College, A

North Central College, B
Northeastern Illinois University, B
Northwestern College - Bridgeview Campus, A
Roosevelt University, B
Trinity International University, B
Triton College, A
University of Illinois at Urbana - Champaign, B
University of St. Francis, B
Waubonsee Community College, A
Western Illinois University, B

Indiana

Ball State University, B
Harrison College, AB
Huntington University, B
Indiana State University, B
Purdue University Northwest (Westville), B
Saint Mary-of-the-Woods College, B

Iowa

Briar Cliff University, B
Buena Vista University, B
Hawkeye Community College, A
Iowa Western Community College, A
Mount Mercy University, B
The University of Iowa, B
Western Iowa Tech Community College, A
William Penn University, B

Kansas

Barton County Community College, A
Central Christian College of Kansas, AB
Fort Hays State University, B
Friends University, B
Kansas Wesleyan University, B
Rasmussen College Kansas City/Overland Park, AB
Rasmussen College Topeka, AB
Wichita State University, B

Kentucky

Brescia University, B
Midway University, B
Sullivan University, B

Louisiana

Louisiana Tech University, B
Southwest University, B

Maine

Beal College, A
Saint Joseph's College of Maine, B
Thomas College, B

Maryland

Cecil College, A
Harford Community College, A
University of Baltimore, B
University of Maryland University College, B

Massachusetts

Boston College, B
Fisher College, B
Nichols College, B
Salem State University, B

Michigan

Baker College, AB
Central Michigan University, B
Cleary University, B
Davenport University, B
Ferris State University, B
Lansing Community College, A
Madonna University, B
Michigan State University, B
Oakland University, B
Spring Arbor University, B
University of Michigan - Dearborn, B
University of Michigan - Flint, B

Minnesota

Anoka-Ramsey Community College, A
Capella University, B
Concordia University, St. Paul, B
Metropolitan State University, B

Minnesota State Community and Technical College,
    A
Rasmussen College Blaine, A
Rasmussen College Bloomington, AB
Rasmussen College Brooklyn Park, AB
Rasmussen College Eagan, AB
Rasmussen College Lake Elmo/Woodbury, AB
Rasmussen College Mankato, AB
Rasmussen College Moorhead, AB
Saint Mary's University of Minnesota, B
Saint Paul College - A Community & Technical Col-
    lege, A
University of Minnesota, Duluth, B
University of Minnesota, Twin Cities Campus, B
University of St. Thomas, B
Winona State University, B

Mississippi

Belhaven University, B
University of Southern Mississippi, B
Virginia College in Biloxi, A
Virginia College in Jackson, A

Missouri

Avila University, B
Columbia College, B
Lindenwood University, B
Vatterott College (Sunset Hills), A
Washington University in St. Louis, B
Webster University, B

Montana

Blackfeet Community College, A
Montana State University Billings, A

Nebraska

Bellevue University, B
Hastings College, B
University of Nebraska at Omaha, B

New Hampshire

Granite State College, B
NHTI, Concord's Community College, A

New Jersey

College of Saint Elizabeth, B
Rowan University, B
Rutgers University - New Brunswick, B
Thomas Edison State University, B

New York

Bryant & Stratton College - Amherst Campus, A
Bryant & Stratton College - Buffalo Campus, A
Bryant & Stratton College - Greece Campus, A
Bryant & Stratton College - Henrietta Campus, A
Bryant & Stratton College - Liverpool Campus, A
Bryant & Stratton College - Orchard Park Campus,
    A
Canisius College, B
The College of Saint Rose, B
Dominican College, B
Herkimer County Community College, A
Houghton College, B
Le Moyne College, B
Marymount Manhattan College, B
Nazareth College of Rochester, B
New York Institute of Technology, B
Niagara University, B
Pace University, B
Pace University, Pleasantville Campus, B
Roberts Wesleyan College, B
State University of New York College of Technology
    at Alfred, B
State University of New York at Oswego, B
Trocaire College, A

North Carolina

Asheville-Buncombe Technical Community College,
    A
Barton College, B
Fayetteville Technical Community College, A
Guilford Technical Community College, A
The University of North Carolina at Chapel Hill, B
Wake Technical Community College, A

North Dakota

Rasmussen College Fargo, A
University of North Dakota, B
Valley City State University, B

Ohio

Antioch University Midwest, B
Baldwin Wallace University, B
Bowling Green State University, B
Bryant & Stratton College - Eastlake Campus, A
Clark State Community College, A
Columbus State Community College, A
Edison Community College, A
Franklin University, B
Harrison College, AB
John Carroll University, B
Lake Erie College, B
Lourdes University, B
Northwest State Community College, A
Notre Dame College, B
Ohio Business College (Sandusky), A
Ohio Business College (Sheffield Village), A
The Ohio State University, B
Ohio University, B
Ohio University - Chillicothe, B
Tiffin University, B
The University of Akron, B
The University of Findlay, AB
The University of Toledo, B
Urbana University, AB
Ursuline College, B
Wright State University, B
Xavier University, B
Youngstown State University, B
Zane State College, A

Oklahoma

East Central University, B
Oklahoma Wesleyan University, B
Tulsa Community College, A
University of Central Oklahoma, B

Oregon

Portland State University, B
Umpqua Community College, A

Pennsylvania

Alvernia University, B
Arcadia University, B
Butler County Community College, A
Cabrini University, B
Chestnut Hill College, B
Community College of Allegheny County, A
Community College of Beaver County, A
DeSales University, B
Holy Family University, B
Indiana University of Pennsylvania, B
Juniata College, B
King's College, B
La Salle University, B
Lehigh Carbon Community College, A
Mansfield University of Pennsylvania, B
Mercyhurst University, B
Peirce College, B
Point Park University, B
Saint Francis University, B
Saint Joseph's University, B
Seton Hill University, B
Temple University, B
University of Pennsylvania, B
The University of Scranton, AB
University of Valley Forge, B
Westminster College, B
Westmoreland County Community College, A

Rhode Island

Bryant University, B
Rhode Island College, B

South Carolina

Anderson University, B
Converse College, B
Limestone College, B
York Technical College, A

South Dakota

Black Hills State University, B

Tennessee

Lipscomb University, B
Maryville College, B
Southern Adventist University, B
Tennessee Wesleyan College, B
The University of Tennessee, B
The University of Tennessee at Martin, B

Texas

Amberton University, B
Baylor University, B
Concordia University Texas, B
Lamar University, B
LeTourneau University, B
Our Lady of the Lake University of San Antonio, B
Sam Houston State University, B
Stephen F. Austin State University, B
Tarleton State University, B
Texas A&M University - Central Texas, B
Texas A&M University - Texarkana, B
Texas Woman's University, B
University of the Incarnate Word, B
The University of Texas at San Antonio, B

Utah

Brigham Young University, B
Utah State University, B
Weber State University, B

Virginia

Bryant & Stratton College - Virginia Beach Campus, A
Lynchburg College, B

Washington

Central Washington University, B
Clark College, A
Eastern Washington University, B
Edmonds Community College, A
University of Washington, B
Western Washington University, B

West Virginia

Ohio Valley University, B

Wisconsin

Blackhawk Technical College, A
Cardinal Stritch University, B
Carroll University, B
Chippewa Valley Technical College, A
Fox Valley Technical College, A
Marian University, B
Marquette University, B
Moraine Park Technical College, A
Rasmussen College Appleton, A
Rasmussen College Green Bay, A
Rasmussen College Wausau, A
Silver Lake College of the Holy Family, B
University of Wisconsin - Whitewater, B
Waukesha County Technical College, A
Western Technical College, A
Wisconsin Indianhead Technical College, A

U.S. Territories: Puerto Rico

American University of Puerto Rico (Bayamon), AB
Bayamón Central University, B
Inter American University of Puerto Rico, Aguadilla Campus, B
Inter American University of Puerto Rico, Arecibo Campus, B
Inter American University of Puerto Rico, Barranquitas Campus, B
Inter American University of Puerto Rico, Bayamón Campus, B
Inter American University of Puerto Rico, Fajardo Campus, B
Inter American University of Puerto Rico, Guayama Campus, B
Inter American University of Puerto Rico, Metropolitan Campus, B

Inter American University of Puerto Rico, Ponce Campus, B
Inter American University of Puerto Rico, San Germán Campus, B
Pontifical Catholic University of Puerto Rico, B
Universidad del Este, B
University of Puerto Rico in Aguadilla, B
University of Puerto Rico in Humacao, B
University of Puerto Rico, Mayagüez Campus, B
University of Puerto Rico, Río Piedras Campus, B

Canada

Alberta

Athabasca University, B
Mount Royal University, B
University of Alberta, B
University of Lethbridge, B

British Columbia

British Columbia Institute of Technology, A
Thompson Rivers University, B
The University of British Columbia - Okanagan Campus, B

Maritime Provinces: New Brunswick

University of New Brunswick Fredericton, B

Maritime Provinces: Nova Scotia

Cape Breton University, B
Saint Mary's University, B

Ontario

Brock University, B
Carleton University, B
Lakehead University, B
University of Guelph, B
University of Ottawa, B
University of Waterloo, B
The University of Western Ontario, B
University of Windsor, B
York University, B

Quebec

Bishop's University, B
Concordia University, B
HEC Montreal, B
McGill University, B
Université du Québec à Trois-Rivières, B

Saskatchewan

University of Regina, B
University of Saskatchewan, B

HUMAN RESOURCES MANAGEMENT AND SERVICES

United States

Alabama

Auburn University, D
Columbia Southern University, M
Troy University, M
The University of Alabama in Huntsville, M

Arizona

Grand Canyon University, BM
University of Phoenix - Online Campus, MO
University of Phoenix - Phoenix Campus, MO
University of Phoenix - Southern Arizona Campus, M

California

Azusa Pacific University, M
Brandman University, M
California Coast University, M
California Intercontinental University, M
California State University, East Bay, M
California State University, Sacramento, M
Golden Gate University, MO
La Sierra University, M

Lincoln University, MD
Menlo College, B
National University, M
Notre Dame de Namur University, M
San Diego State University, M
Simpson University, B
Trident University International, M
University of California, Berkeley, O
University of La Verne, M
University of Phoenix - Bay Area Campus, M
University of Phoenix - Central Valley Campus, M
University of Phoenix - Sacramento Valley Campus, M
University of Phoenix - San Diego Campus, M
University of Phoenix - Southern California Campus, M

Colorado

Colorado State University - Global Campus, M
Colorado Technical University Colorado Springs, M
Colorado Technical University Denver South, M
Regis University, O
University of Colorado Denver, M
University of Phoenix - Colorado Campus, M
University of Phoenix - Colorado Springs Downtown Campus, M

Connecticut

Albertus Magnus College, B
Fairfield University, MO
Sacred Heart University, M
University of Bridgeport, M
University of Connecticut, M
University of New Haven, MO

Delaware

Goldey-Beacom College, M
Wilmington University, M

District of Columbia

The Catholic University of America, M
The George Washington University, M
Georgetown University, M
Howard University, M
Trinity Washington University, M
University of Phoenix - Washington D.C. Campus, M

Florida

Barry University, O
Everest University (Largo), M
Everest University (Orlando), M
Everest University (Tampa), M
Florida Institute of Technology, M
Florida International University, M
Florida State University, D
Millennia Atlantic University, M
Polytechnic University of Puerto Rico, Miami Campus, M
Polytechnic University of Puerto Rico, Orlando Campus, M
Rollins College, M
Saint Leo University, M
St. Thomas University, MO
University of Florida, M
University of North Florida, M
University of Phoenix - North Florida Campus, M
University of Phoenix - South Florida Campus, M

Georgia

Albany State University, M
Ashworth College, M
Georgia State University, MD
Savannah State University, M
University of Georgia, M
University of Phoenix - Atlanta Campus, M
University of Phoenix - Augusta Campus, M
University of Phoenix - Columbus Georgia Campus, M

Hawaii

Hawai'i Pacific University, M
University of Hawaii at Manoa, M
University of Phoenix - Hawaii Campus, M

Illinois

American InterContinental University Online, M
Argosy University, Schaumburg, M
Benedictine University, M
DePaul University, M
DeVry University (Downers Grove), M
Lewis University, M
Loyola University Chicago, M
McKendree University, M
National Louis University, M
North Central College, M
Northwestern University, M
Robert Morris University Illinois, M
Roosevelt University, M
University of Chicago, M
University of Illinois at Urbana - Champaign, MDO

Indiana

Indiana Tech, M
Indiana Wesleyan University, MO
Oakland City University, AB
Purdue University, MD

Iowa

Briar Cliff University, M
Iowa Lakes Community College, A
Kaplan University, Davenport Campus, M
Mount Mercy University, M
St. Ambrose University, M
Upper Iowa University, M
William Penn University, B

Kansas

Barton County Community College, A
Ottawa University, M
University of Saint Mary, M

Kentucky

University of Louisville, M

Louisiana

Grambling State University, M

Maine

Thomas College, M

Maryland

Hood College, M

Massachusetts

Assumption College, M
Emmanuel College, MO
Fitchburg State University, M
Framingham State University, M
Lasell College, MO

Michigan

Central Michigan University, MO
Davenport University, M
Eastern Michigan University, MO
Grand Valley State University, B
Marygrove College, M
Michigan State University, MD
Northern Michigan University, M
Oakland University, O
Wayne State University, MD
Western Michigan University, B

Minnesota

Capella University, MD
Concordia University, St. Paul, M
Saint Mary's University of Minnesota, M
University of Minnesota, Twin Cities Campus, M
Walden University, MDO

Mississippi

Belhaven University, M

Missouri

Avila University, M
Lindenwood University, M
Park University, B
University of Missouri - St. Louis, O
Webster University, M

Nebraska

Bellevue University, D
University of Nebraska at Kearney, M

Nevada

University of Phoenix - Las Vegas Campus, M

New Hampshire

Franklin Pierce University, MO
Southern New Hampshire University, O

New Jersey

College of Saint Elizabeth, M
Fairleigh Dickinson University, College at Florham, M
Fairleigh Dickinson University, Metropolitan Campus, MO
Monmouth University, O
Rutgers University - New Brunswick, MD
Rutgers University - Newark, M
Saint Peter's University, M
Stevens Institute of Technology, M
Thomas Edison State University, MO
University of Phoenix - Jersey City Campus, M

New Mexico

New Mexico Highlands University, M
University of New Mexico, M
University of Phoenix - New Mexico Campus, M

New York

Adelphi University, MO
Baruch College of the City University of New York, M
Bryant & Stratton College - Albany Campus, A
Bryant & Stratton College - Amherst Campus, A
Bryant & Stratton College - Buffalo Campus, A
Bryant & Stratton College - Greece Campus, A
Bryant & Stratton College - Henrietta Campus, A
Bryant & Stratton College - Orchard Park Campus, A
Bryant & Stratton College - Syracuse Campus, A
Buffalo State College, State University of New York, O
Columbia University, M
Cornell University, MD
Fordham University, M
Hofstra University, MO
Iona College, O
Long Island University - LIU Brooklyn, M
Manhattanville College, M
Mercy College, M
Nazareth College of Rochester, M
New York Institute of Technology, MO
New York University, MO
Niagara University, BM
Pace University, M
St. Joseph's College, Long Island Campus, M
State University of New York Polytechnic Institute, M
Stony Brook University, State University of New York, MO
University at Albany, State University of New York, M
University at Buffalo, the State University of New York, O

North Carolina

Gaston College, A
North Carolina Agricultural and Technical State University, M
Pitt Community College, A

North Dakota

University of Mary, M

Ohio

Baldwin Wallace University, M
Bryant & Stratton College - Cleveland Campus, A
Bryant & Stratton College - Parma Campus, A
Cleveland State University, M
Columbus State Community College, A
Miami University Hamilton, B
The Ohio State University, MD

Tiffin University, M
The University of Akron, M
University of Mount Union, B

Oklahoma

East Central University, M
Oklahoma Christian University, M
University of Oklahoma, BM

Oregon

George Fox University, M

Pennsylvania

Carlow University, B
Delaware Valley University, M
DeSales University, M
Elizabethtown College School of Continuing and
    Professional Studies, B
Gannon University, M
Holy Family University, M
Immaculata University, B
La Roche College, MO
La Salle University, MO
Lincoln University, M
Mercyhurst University, M
Misericordia University, M
Moravian College, M
Penn State Harrisburg, O
Penn State University Park, M
Robert Morris University, M
Saint Francis University, M
Saint Joseph's University, M
Temple University, M
University of Pittsburgh, BMD
Waynesburg University, M
West Chester University of Pennsylvania, MO
Widener University, BM
Wilkes University, M

Rhode Island

University of Rhode Island, M

South Carolina

Clemson University, M
North Greenville University, M
University of South Carolina, M

South Dakota

The University of South Dakota, M

Tennessee

King University, M
Lipscomb University, M
Middle Tennessee State University, M
Tennessee State University, M
Tennessee Technological University, M

Texas

Amberton University, M
Dallas Baptist University, M
Houston Baptist University, M
Tarleton State University, M
Texas A&M University - Central Texas, M
Texas A&M University - San Antonio, M
Texas State University, M
University of Dallas, M
University of Houston - Clear Lake, M
University of North Texas, M
University of Phoenix - Dallas Campus, M
University of Phoenix - Houston Campus, M
University of Phoenix - San Antonio Campus, M
The University of Texas at Arlington, M
Wayland Baptist University, M

Utah

Brigham Young University, M
University of Phoenix - Utah Campus, M
Utah State University, M

Virginia

Bryant & Stratton College - Richmond Campus, A
George Mason University, M
James Madison University, M
Liberty University, D

Marymount University, MO
Virginia International University, M

Washington

City University of Seattle, O
Seattle Pacific University, M

West Virginia

American Public University System, AM
Marshall University, M
Wheeling Jesuit University, B

Wisconsin

Bryant & Stratton College - Milwaukee Campus, A
Bryant & Stratton College - Wauwatosa Campus, A
Concordia University Wisconsin, M
Herzing University Online, M
Marquette University, M
University of Wisconsin - Madison, MD
University of Wisconsin - Whitewater, M

U.S. Territories: Puerto Rico

Caribbean University, M
Inter American University of Puerto Rico, Aguadilla
    Campus, M
Inter American University of Puerto Rico, Arecibo
    Campus, M
Inter American University of Puerto Rico, Bayamón
    Campus, M
Inter American University of Puerto Rico, Metropoli-
    tan Campus, M
Inter American University of Puerto Rico, Ponce
    Campus, M
Inter American University of Puerto Rico, San
    Germán Campus, MD
Pontifical Catholic University of Puerto Rico, MO
Universidad del Este, M
Universidad Metropolitana, M
Universidad del Turabo, M
University of Puerto Rico, Mayagüez Campus, M
University of Puerto Rico, Río Piedras Campus, M
University of the Sacred Heart, M

Canada

Alberta

Concordia University of Edmonton, B
University of Lethbridge, M

British Columbia

Royal Roads University, MO
The University of British Columbia, B

Ontario

McMaster University, MD
University of Toronto, MD
Wilfrid Laurier University, MD
York University, MD

Quebec

HEC Montreal, M
Université du Québec en Outaouais, B

Saskatchewan

University of Regina, MO

HUMAN SERVICES

United States

Alaska

University of Alaska Anchorage, A
University of Alaska Anchorage, Kenai Peninsula
    College, A
University of Alaska Anchorage, Matanuska-Susitna
    College, A

Arizona

Phoenix College, A
Tohono O'odham Community College, A
University of Phoenix - Phoenix Campus, B

Arkansas

Arkansas Tech University, A
University of Arkansas Community College at Hope,
    A

California

Allan Hancock College, A
American River College, A
Ashford University, B
Bakersfield College, A
Cabrillo College, A
California State University, Dominguez Hills, B
California State University, Fullerton, B
California State University, Monterey Bay, B
California State University, Sacramento, M
California State University, San Bernardino, B
Cañada College, A
Cerritos College, A
Chabot College, A
College of San Mateo, A
College of the Siskiyous, A
Columbia College, A
Contra Costa College, A
Cosumnes River College, A
Cypress College, A
Folsom Lake College, A
Fresno City College, A
Hartnell College, A
Holy Names University, B
Lassen Community College District, A
Long Beach City College, A
Los Angeles City College, A
Mendocino College, A
Merced College, A
Merritt College, A
Modesto Junior College, A
Mount Saint Mary's University, A
National University, MDO
Notre Dame de Namur University, B
Pacific Oaks College, B
Porterville College, A
Riverside City College, A
Sacramento City College, A
Saddleback College, A
San Bernardino Valley College, A
Santa Rosa Junior College, A
Southwestern College, A
University of Phoenix - Bay Area Campus, B
University of Phoenix - Sacramento Valley Campus,
    B
University of Phoenix - San Diego Campus, B
University of Phoenix - Southern California Campus,
    B
Yuba College, A

Colorado

Community College of Denver, A
Metropolitan State University of Denver, B
University of Colorado Colorado Springs, M
University of Phoenix - Colorado Campus, B
University of Phoenix - Colorado Springs Downtown
    Campus, B

Connecticut

Albertus Magnus College, BM
Gateway Community College, A
Goodwin College, A
Housatonic Community College, A
Lincoln College of New England, A
Manchester Community College, A
Middlesex Community College, A
Northwestern Connecticut Community College, A
Norwalk Community College, A
Post University, BM
Quinebaug Valley Community College, A
Quinnipiac University, B
Tunxis Community College, A
University of Bridgeport, BM
University of Hartford, B

Delaware

Delaware Technical & Community College, Jack F.
    Owens Campus, A
Delaware Technical & Community College,
    Stanton/Wilmington Campus, A

Delaware Technical & Community College, Terry
  Campus, A
University of Delaware, B
Wilmington University, M

District of Columbia

The Catholic University of America, A
The George Washington University, B

Florida

Beacon College, AB
Carlos Albizu University, Miami Campus, D
College of Central Florida, A
Daytona State College, A
Indian River State College, A
Miami Dade College, A
Nova Southeastern University, B
Pasco-Hernando State College, A
Rasmussen College Fort Myers, A
Rasmussen College Land O' Lakes, A
Rasmussen College New Port Richey, A
Rasmussen College Ocala, A
Rasmussen College Tampa/Brandon, A
St. Thomas University, B
Southeastern University, BM
Ultimate Medical Academy Online, A
University of South Florida, B

Georgia

Georgia Highlands College, A
Georgia State University, M
Gordon State College, B
Kennesaw State University, B
Mercer University, B
Middle Georgia State University, B
Spelman College, B
Thomas University, M
University of North Georgia, B
University of Phoenix - Augusta Campus, B
University of Phoenix - Columbus Georgia Campus,
  AB
Wesleyan College, B

Hawaii

Hawai'i Pacific University, B
Honolulu Community College, A
University of Hawaii Maui College, A
University of Phoenix - Hawaii Campus, B

Idaho

College of Southern Idaho, A
North Idaho College, A
University of Idaho, M

Illinois

College of DuPage, A
Concordia University Chicago, M
Dominican University, B
Harper College, A
Judson University, B
Lake Land College, A
Lincoln Christian University, B
Loyola University Chicago, B
National Louis University, M
Parkland College, A
Quincy University, B
Rock Valley College, A
Shawnee Community College, A
Southeastern Illinois College, A
University of Illinois at Springfield, MO
University of Illinois at Urbana - Champaign, M

Indiana

Bethel College, AB
Calumet College of Saint Joseph, AB
Indiana Tech, B
Ivy Tech Community College - Bloomington, A
Ivy Tech Community College - Central Indiana, A
Ivy Tech Community College - Columbus, A
Ivy Tech Community College - East Central, A
Ivy Tech Community College - Kokomo, A
Ivy Tech Community College - Lafayette, A
Ivy Tech Community College - North Central, A
Ivy Tech Community College - Northeast, A
Ivy Tech Community College - Northwest, A

Ivy Tech Community College - Richmond, A
Ivy Tech Community College - Southeast, A
Ivy Tech Community College - Southern Indiana, A
Ivy Tech Community College - Southwest, A
Ivy Tech Community College - Wabash Valley, A
Purdue University Northwest (Hammond), M
Saint Mary-of-the-Woods College, B

Iowa

Graceland University, B
Grand View University, B
Iowa Wesleyan University, B
Kaplan University, Des Moines, AB
University of Northern Iowa, M
Upper Iowa University, BM
William Penn University, B

Kansas

Kansas State University, MO
Ottawa University, B
Pratt Community College, A
Rasmussen College Kansas City/Overland Park, A
Rasmussen College Topeka, A
Washburn University, M
Wichita State University, M

Kentucky

Brescia University, A
Hopkinsville Community College, A
Jefferson Community and Technical College, A
Kentucky Wesleyan College, B
Lindsey Wilson College, B
Murray State University, M
Owensboro Community and Technical College, A
University of the Cumberlands, AB

Louisiana

Southern University at Shreveport, A

Maine

Beal College, A
Central Maine Community College, A
University of Maine at Fort Kent, A
University of Maine at Machias, B
York County Community College, A

Maryland

Coppin State University, M
Frederick Community College, A
McDaniel College, M
Towson University, B
University of Baltimore, BM
University of Maryland, Baltimore County, MD

Massachusetts

Anna Maria College, B
Berkshire Community College, A
Brandeis University, M
Bunker Hill Community College, A
Fisher College, B
Fitchburg State University, B
Lasell College, B
Lesley University, B
Massachusetts Bay Community College, A
Massasoit Community College, A
Mount Ida College, B
Mount Wachusett Community College, A
Northeastern University, BM
Northern Essex Community College, A
Quincy College, A
Quinsigamond Community College, A
Springfield College, M
University of Massachusetts Boston, BM
Urban College of Boston, A

Michigan

Andrews University, M
Baker College, A
Cornerstone University, A
Eastern Michigan University, O
Ferris State University, M
Finlandia University, B
Grace Bible College, B
Kellogg Community College, A
Siena Heights University, B

University of Phoenix - Detroit Campus, B
Washtenaw Community College, A
Western Michigan University, DO

Minnesota

Alexandria Technical and Community College, A
Capella University, MD
Century College, A
Fond du Lac Tribal and Community College, A
Inver Hills Community College, A
Itasca Community College, A
Mesabi Range College, A
Metropolitan State University, B
Minneapolis Community and Technical College, A
Minnesota State University Mankato, M
Minnesota State University Moorhead, MO
Minnesota West Community and Technical College,
  A
North Hennepin Community College, A
Pine Technical and Community College, A
Rasmussen College Blaine, A
Rasmussen College Bloomington, A
Rasmussen College Brooklyn Park, A
Rasmussen College Eagan, A
Rasmussen College Lake Elmo/Woodbury, A
Rasmussen College Mankato, A
Rasmussen College Moorhead, A
Rasmussen College St. Cloud, A
Riverland Community College, A
Saint Mary's University of Minnesota, B
South Central College, A
University of Minnesota, Morris, B
University of Northwestern - St. Paul, M
Walden University, BMD

Mississippi

Itawamba Community College, A
Mississippi Gulf Coast Community College, A

Missouri

Columbia College, AB
Drury University, M
Fontbonne University, B
Lindenwood University, M
Metropolitan Community College - Kansas City, A
Missouri Baptist University, B
Missouri Valley College, B
North Central Missouri College, A
Park University, B
St. Charles Community College, A
Southwest Baptist University, B
University of Central Missouri, O
Webster University, M

Montana

Aaniiih Nakoda College, A
Flathead Valley Community College, A
Fort Peck Community College, A
Salish Kootenai College, AB
Stone Child College, A
University of Great Falls, ABM

Nebraska

Bellevue University, M
Doane University, B
Hastings College, B
Metropolitan Community College, A
Midland University, B
Nebraska Indian Community College, A
University of Nebraska at Kearney, M

Nevada

Great Basin College, A
University of Nevada, Las Vegas, B
University of Phoenix - Las Vegas Campus, B

New Hampshire

Granite State College, B
Great Bay Community College, A
Lakes Region Community College, A
Manchester Community College, A
Nashua Community College, A
New England College, M
NHTI, Concord's Community College, A
River Valley Community College, A

White Mountains Community College, A

New Jersey

Atlantic Cape Community College, A
Essex County College, A
Ocean County College, A
Passaic County Community College, A
Rowan College at Burlington County, A
Sussex County Community College, A
Thomas Edison State University, AB
Union County College, A

New Mexico

Eastern New Mexico University, M
New Mexico State University - Alamogordo, A
New Mexico State University - Carlsbad, A
New Mexico State University - Grants, A
Northern New Mexico College, A
University of New Mexico - Taos, A
University of New Mexico - Valencia Campus, A
University of Phoenix - New Mexico Campus, B

New York

Boricua College, BM
Bronx Community College of the City University of
     New York, A
Cazenovia College, AB
Columbia-Greene Community College, A
Corning Community College, A
Dutchess Community College, A
Finger Lakes Community College, A
Fulton-Montgomery Community College, A
Genesee Community College, A
Hilbert College, AB
Hudson Valley Community College, A
Jamestown Community College, A
Jefferson Community College, A
Kingsborough Community College of the City Uni-
     versity of New York, A
Mohawk Valley Community College, A
Monroe Community College, A
Morrisville State College, A
Mount Saint Mary College, B
New York City College of Technology of the City
     University of New York, AB
Niagara County Community College, A
Roberts Wesleyan College, M
Rockland Community College, A
St. Joseph's College, Long Island Campus, B
St. Joseph's College, New York, BM
State University of New York College at Cortland, B
State University of New York College of Technology
     at Alfred, A
Suffolk County Community College, A
Sullivan County Community College, A
Syracuse University, B
TCI - College of Technology, A
Tompkins Cortland Community College, A

North Carolina

Central Piedmont Community College, A
Elon University, B
Forsyth Technical Community College, A
Lees-McRae College, B
Lenoir-Rhyne University, BM
Livingstone College, B
Montreat College, B
Pfeiffer University, B
Queens University of Charlotte, B
Randolph Community College, A
Sandhills Community College, A
Stanly Community College, A
University of Mount Olive, B
Vance-Granville Community College, A
Wingate University, B

North Dakota

Bismarck State College, A
Nueta Hidatsa Sahnish College, A
Rasmussen College Fargo, A
Sitting Bull College, A
Turtle Mountain Community College, A

Ohio

Antioch University Midwest, B
Bowling Green State University - Firelands College,
     A
Central Ohio Technical College, A
Clark State Community College, A
Kent State University, MDO
Lorain County Community College, A
Marion Technical College, A
Ohio Christian University, A
Sinclair Community College, A
Southern State Community College, A
Stark State College, A
Walsh University, A
Wright State University, B
Youngstown State University, M

Oklahoma

East Central University, M
Oklahoma State University, Oklahoma City, A
Southwestern Christian University, B
University of Oklahoma, MO

Oregon

University of Oregon, B

Pennsylvania

Arcadia University, B
Chestnut Hill College, BMO
Community College of Philadelphia, A
Delaware County Community College, A
Elizabethtown College School of Continuing and
     Professional Studies, AB
Geneva College, B
Gwynedd Mercy University, B
Harcum College, A
Harrisburg Area Community College, A
Lackawanna College, A
Lehigh Carbon Community College, A
Lehigh University, M
Lincoln University, BM
Luzerne County Community College, A
Pennsylvania Highlands Community College, A
Rosemont College, M
Seton Hill University, B
University of Phoenix - Philadelphia Campus, B
University of Pittsburgh at Titusville, A
The University of Scranton, AB
University of Valley Forge, A
Waynesburg University, B

South Carolina

Central Carolina Technical College, A
Denmark Technical College, A
Midlands Technical College, A
Piedmont Technical College, A
South Carolina State University, M
Southern Wesleyan University, B
Trident Technical College, A

South Dakota

Black Hills State University, B
Dakota Wesleyan University, B
Lake Area Technical Institute, A
Mitchell Technical Institute, A
Mount Marty College, B
Oglala Lakota College, AB

Tennessee

American Baptist College, B
Bethel University, B
Carson-Newman University, B
East Tennessee State University, B
Hiwassee College, A
Martin Methodist College, B
Tennessee Wesleyan College, B

Texas

Abilene Christian University, MO
Angelina College, A
Austin Community College District, A
Cisco College, A
Hardin-Simmons University, B
LeTourneau University, B
Lone Star College - Montgomery, A

Odessa College, A
St. Mary's University, MD
South Texas College, A
Southwestern Assemblies of God University, B
Texas A&M University - Kingsville, B
Texas Southern University, M
University of North Texas, B
University of Phoenix - Dallas Campus, B
University of Phoenix - Houston Campus, B
University of Phoenix - San Antonio Campus, B
Wayland Baptist University, AB

Utah

University of Phoenix - Utah Campus, B

Vermont

College of St. Joseph, AB
Community College of Vermont, A

Virginia

Liberty University, BM
Southside Virginia Community College, A
Virginia Highlands Community College, A
Virginia Wesleyan College, B

Washington

Central Washington University, B
City University of Seattle, B
Grays Harbor College, A
Highline College, A
Seattle Central College, A
Skagit Valley College, A
University of Phoenix - Western Washington Cam-
     pus, B
Western Washington University, B

West Virginia

Fairmont State University, B
West Virginia University, M

Wisconsin

Concordia University Wisconsin, MD
Madison Area Technical College, A
Marian University, B
Rasmussen College Appleton, A
Rasmussen College Green Bay, A
Rasmussen College Wausau, A
University of Wisconsin - Oshkosh, B
Wisconsin Lutheran College, B

Wyoming

Laramie County Community College, A
Western Wyoming Community College, A

U.S. Territories: American Samoa

American Samoa Community College, A

U.S. Territories: Guam

Guam Community College, A

U.S. Territories: Puerto Rico

Caribbean University, A
Pontifical Catholic University of Puerto Rico, MD
Universidad del Turabo, M

Canada

Alberta

Rocky Mountain College, B

Ontario

Tyndale University College & Seminary, B

Quebec

Université de Montréal, D

HUMANITIES/HUMANISTIC STUDIES

United States

Alabama

Athens State University, B
Faulkner University, B
University of Mobile, B

Alaska

University of Alaska Southeast, AB

Arizona

Cochise County Community College District, A
Harrison Middleton University, ABM
Prescott College, M

Arkansas

Harding University, B
University of Arkansas at Little Rock, B
University of the Ozarks, B

California

Antelope Valley College, A
Ashford University, B
Barstow Community College, A
Biola University, B
Cabrillo College, A
California Institute of Integral Studies, MD
California State Polytechnic University, Pomona, B
California State University, Chico, B
California State University, Dominguez Hills, M
California State University, Monterey Bay, B
California State University, Northridge, B
California State University, Sacramento, B
California State University, San Bernardino, B
Cañada College, A
Cerro Coso Community College, A
Chabot College, A
Chaffey College, A
City College of San Francisco, A
College of Alameda, A
College of the Canyons, A
College of the Desert, A
College of Marin, A
College of the Redwoods, A
College of San Mateo, A
College of the Sequoias, A
College of the Siskiyous, A
Columbia College, A
Concordia University Irvine, B
Contra Costa College, A
Cosumnes River College, A
Crafton Hills College, A
Cuesta College, A
Cypress College, A
De Anza College, A
Diablo Valley College, A
Dominican University of California, BM
Evergreen Valley College, A
Feather River College, A
Fresno City College, A
Fresno Pacific University, B
Fullerton College, A
Golden West College, A
Holy Names University, B
Imperial Valley College, A
Irvine Valley College, A
Lake Tahoe Community College, A
Laney College, A
Lassen Community College District, A
Los Angeles Mission College, A
Los Angeles Southwest College, A
Loyola Marymount University, B
Merced College, A
Merritt College, A
Modesto Junior College, A
Mount Saint Mary's University, M
Mt. San Antonio College, A
Mt. San Jacinto College, A
Napa Valley College, A
Orange Coast College, A
Palo Verde College, A

Palomar College, A
Pasadena City College, A
Sacramento City College, A
Saddleback College, A
San Diego Miramar College, A
San Diego State University, B
San Francisco State University, BM
San Joaquin Delta College, A
San Jose City College, A
San Jose State University, B
Santa Rosa Junior College, A
Scripps College, B
University of California, Irvine, B
University of California, Riverside, B
University of California, Santa Cruz, D
University of San Diego, B
Victor Valley College, A
West Hills Community College, A

Colorado

The Colorado College, M
Colorado Mountain College (Glenwood Springs), A
Colorado Mountain College (Steamboat Springs), A
Fort Lewis College, B
Otero Junior College, A
United States Air Force Academy, B
University of Colorado Boulder, B
University of Colorado Denver, M

Connecticut

Albertus Magnus College, B
Holy Apostles College and Seminary, B
Housatonic Community College, A
University of Bridgeport, B
Wesleyan University, B
Yale University, B

District of Columbia

The George Washington University, B
Georgetown University, M

Florida

Ave Maria University, B
Broward College, A
College of Central Florida, A
Eckerd College, B
Florida Institute of Technology, B
Florida Southern College, B
Florida State University, B
Indian River State College, A
Jacksonville University, B
Johnson University Florida, B
Miami Dade College, A
New College of Florida, B
Nova Southeastern University, B
Rollins College, B
South Florida State College, A
State College of Florida Manatee-Sarasota, A
University of Central Florida, B
University of South Florida, BM
University of West Florida, B

Georgia

Abraham Baldwin Agricultural College, A
Andrew College, A
Emory University, B
Point University, B
Thomas University, B
Wesleyan College, B

Hawaii

Brigham Young University - Hawaii, B
Chaminade University of Honolulu, B
Hawai'i Pacific University, B
University of Hawaii - West Oahu, B

Idaho

Brigham Young University - Idaho, B
Northwest Nazarene University, B

Illinois

Benedictine University, B
Bradley University, B
City Colleges of Chicago, Richard J. Daley College, A

DePaul University, B
Harper College, A
Illinois Institute of Technology, MD
Loyola University Chicago, M
North Central College, B
Northwestern University, B
Quincy University, B
Rockford University, B
Shimer College, B
Trinity International University, B
University of Chicago, BM
University of Illinois at Urbana - Champaign, B

Indiana

Indiana University East, B
Indiana University Kokomo, B
Oakland City University, B
Purdue University, B
Saint Mary-of-the-Woods College, AB
Saint Mary's College, B
Valparaiso University, AB
Wabash College, B

Iowa

Iowa Lakes Community College, A
Northwestern College, B
University of Northern Iowa, B

Kansas

Allen Community College, A
Dodge City Community College, A
Garden City Community College, A
Kansas State University, B
Pratt Community College, A
The University of Kansas, B
Washburn University, A

Kentucky

Eastern Kentucky University, B
Kentucky Christian University, B
Spalding University, B
Thomas More College, AB
University of Louisville, BMD

Louisiana

Our Lady of the Lake College, B
River Parishes Community College, A
University of Holy Cross, B

Maine

University of Southern Maine, B

Maryland

Hood College, M
Towson University, M
Washington College, B

Massachusetts

Anna Maria College, B
Bristol Community College, A
Fisher College, A
Lasell College, B
Lesley University, B
Roxbury Community College, A
Suffolk University, B
University of Massachusetts Amherst, B
Wheelock College, B
Worcester Polytechnic Institute, B

Michigan

Central Michigan University, M
Cornerstone University, B
Lake Michigan College, A
Lansing Community College, A
Lawrence Technological University, B
Michigan State University, B
Michigan Technological University, A
Siena Heights University, B
University of Michigan, B
University of Michigan - Dearborn, B

Minnesota

Bemidji State University, B
College of Saint Benedict, B

The College of St. Scholastica, B
Concordia College, B
Minnesota State University Mankato, B
Saint John's University, B

Mississippi

Belhaven University, B
Southwest Mississippi Community College, A

Missouri

Northwest Missouri State University, B
Saint Louis University, B
Washington University in St. Louis, B
Webster University, B

Nebraska

College of Saint Mary, B
Midland University, B

Nevada

Sierra Nevada College, B

New Hampshire

Plymouth State University, B
University of New Hampshire, B
University of New Hampshire at Manchester, B

New Jersey

Drew University, MDO
Fairleigh Dickinson University, College at Florham, B
Fairleigh Dickinson University, Metropolitan Campus, B
Felician University, B
Georgian Court University, B
Mercer County Community College, A
Montclair State University, B
Passaic County Community College, A
Saint Peter's University, AB
Seton Hall University, B
Stevens Institute of Technology, B
Thomas Edison State University, B

New Mexico

New Mexico Military Institute, A
Santa Fe Community College, A
University of New Mexico, B
Western New Mexico University, B

New York

Adelphi University, B
Bard College, B
Buffalo State College, State University of New York, B
Cayuga County Community College, A
Clarkson University, B
Clinton Community College, A
Colgate University, B
Columbia-Greene Community College, A
Corning Community College, A
Dominican College, B
Dutchess Community College, A
Erie Community College, A
Erie Community College, North Campus, A
Erie Community College, South Campus, A
Finger Lakes Community College, A
Fulton-Montgomery Community College, A
Genesee Community College, A
Herkimer County Community College, A
Hofstra University, D
Houghton College, B
Hunter College of the City University of New York, B
Jamestown Community College, A
Jefferson Community College, A
John Jay College of Criminal Justice of the City University of New York, B
The King's College, B
Long Island University - LIU Brooklyn, AB
Long Island University - LIU Post, B
Marymount Manhattan College, B
Mohawk Valley Community College, A
New York University, BMO
Niagara County Community College, A
Onondaga Community College, A
Orange County Community College, A

Purchase College, State University of New York, B
Roberts Wesleyan College, B
The Sage Colleges, B
St. Lawrence University, B
St. Thomas Aquinas College, B
State University of New York College of Agriculture and Technology at Cobleskill, A
State University of New York College at Old Westbury, B
State University of New York College of Technology at Alfred, A
State University of New York College of Technology at Delhi, A
Suffolk County Community College, A
Tompkins Cortland Community College, A
Touro College, B
Union College, B
United States Military Academy, B
University at Buffalo, the State University of New York, B
Westchester Community College, A

North Carolina

Blue Ridge Community College, A
Chowan University, B
Duke University, M
St. Andrews University, B

North Dakota

Dakota College at Bottineau, A

Ohio

Antioch University Midwest, B
Bowling Green State University, B
Franciscan University of Steubenville, B
John Carroll University, BM
Kent State University, B
Muskingum University, B
The Ohio State University, B
Ohio University, A
Ohio University - Chillicothe, A
Ohio University - Southern Campus, A
Ohio Wesleyan University, B
Pontifical College Josephinum, B
Terra State Community College, A
Tiffin University, M
Union Institute & University, D
The University of Akron, B
University of Rio Grande, B
The University of Toledo, B
Ursuline College, B
Wright State University, M

Oklahoma

Hillsdale Free Will Baptist College, B
Murray State College, A
Oklahoma Baptist University, B
Oklahoma City Community College, A
Oklahoma State University, Oklahoma City, A
Seminole State College, A
University of Central Oklahoma, B
University of Oklahoma, B

Oregon

Central Oregon Community College, A
Concordia University, B
Corban University, B
Marylhurst University, B
Pacific University, B
Portland State University, B
Umpqua Community College, A
University of Oregon, B
Western Oregon University, B
Willamette University, B

Pennsylvania

Arcadia University, M
Bucknell University, B
Bucks County Community College, A
Community College of Allegheny County, A
Community College of Beaver County, A
Drexel University, B
Holy Family University, B
Juniata College, B
Lackawanna College, A

Luzerne County Community College, A
Messiah College, B
Montgomery County Community College, A
Penn State Harrisburg, BMDO
University of Pennsylvania, B
University of Pittsburgh, B
University of Pittsburgh at Bradford, B
University of Pittsburgh at Greensburg, B
University of Pittsburgh at Johnstown, B
University of the Sciences, B
Villanova University, B
Widener University, B

Rhode Island

Providence College, B
Roger Williams University, B
Salve Regina University, MD

South Carolina

Bob Jones University, B
Charleston Southern University, B
Clemson University, D
Coastal Carolina University, B
Columbia International University, B
Wofford College, B

Tennessee

Aquinas College, AB
Lee University, B
LeMoyne-Owen College, B
Lincoln Memorial University, B
Milligan College, B
Tennessee State University, B
The University of Tennessee at Chattanooga, B
Welch College, B

Texas

Baptist University of the Americas, B
Baylor University, B
Brookhaven College, A
Galveston College, A
Lee College, A
Lubbock Christian University, B
Midwestern State University, B
St. Edward's University, M
Sam Houston State University, BMDO
Texarkana College, A
Trinity University, B
University of Dallas, M
University of Houston - Clear Lake, BM
University of Houston - Downtown, B
University of Houston - Victoria, B
The University of Texas at Austin, B
The University of Texas at Dallas, MD
The University of Texas Medical Branch, MD
The University of Texas of the Permian Basin, B
The University of Texas at San Antonio, B

Utah

Brigham Young University, M
Salt Lake Community College, A
Snow College, A
University of Utah, BM
Utah Valley University, A

Vermont

Bennington College, B
Goddard College, B
Johnson State College, B
Marlboro College, B

Virginia

Hollins University, M
John Tyler Community College, A
Old Dominion University, M
University of Richmond, B
Virginia Commonwealth University, MDO
Virginia Polytechnic Institute and State University, MD
Virginia Wesleyan College, B

Washington

Eastern Washington University, B
Everett Community College, A
The Evergreen State College, B

Highline College, A
Seattle University, B
Skagit Valley College, A
University of Washington, B
University of Washington, Bothell, B
University of Washington, Tacoma, B
Walla Walla University, B
Washington State University, B
Washington State University - Global Campus, B
Washington State University - Vancouver, B
Western Washington University, B

West Virginia

American Public University System, M
Bluefield State College, B
Marshall University, BMO

Wisconsin

College of Menominee Nation, A
Concordia University Wisconsin, B
Maranatha Baptist University, B
Northland College, B
St. Norbert College, B
University of Wisconsin - Green Bay, B

Wyoming

Laramie County Community College, A
University of Wyoming, B
Western Wyoming Community College, A

U.S. Territories: Puerto Rico

Universidad del Turabo, B
University of Puerto Rico in Cayey, B
University of Puerto Rico in Utuado, B
University of the Sacred Heart, B

U.S. Territories: United States Virgin Islands

University of the Virgin Islands, B

Canada

Alberta

University of Calgary, B
University of Lethbridge, B

British Columbia

Simon Fraser University, BM
Trinity Western University, BM

Manitoba

Providence University College & Theological Seminary, B

Maritime Provinces: New Brunswick

Mount Allison University, B

Maritime Provinces: Nova Scotia

Mount Saint Vincent University, B

Newfoundland and Labrador

Memorial University of Newfoundland, BM

Ontario

Brock University, B
Carleton University, B
Laurentian University, M
Ryerson University, B
Trent University, B
University of Ottawa, B
University of Toronto, B
York University, BMD

Quebec

Bishop's University, B
Concordia University, BD
McGill University, B

Saskatchewan

Briercrest College, AB
University of Regina, B

HYDRAULICS AND FLUID POWER TECHNOLOGY

United States

Alabama

Auburn University, MD

Colorado

University of Colorado Denver, MD

Maryland

Community College of Baltimore County, A

Minnesota

Hennepin Technical College, A
Minnesota West Community and Technical College, A

Missouri

Missouri University of Science and Technology, MD

Ohio

The Ohio State University Agricultural Technical Institute, A

Pennsylvania

Drexel University, MD

Canada

Quebec

École Polytechnique de Montréal, MD
McGill University, MD

HYDROGEOLOGY

United States

California

California State University, Chico, M

Florida

University of South Florida, O

Hawaii

University of Hawaii at Manoa, MD

Illinois

Illinois State University, M

Indiana

Indiana University Bloomington, MD

Montana

Montana Tech of The University of Montana, M

Nevada

University of Nevada, Reno, MD

North Carolina

East Carolina University, O

Ohio

Ohio University, M

South Carolina

Clemson University, M

Texas

The University of Texas at Dallas, MD

West Virginia

West Virginia University, MD

HYDROLOGY AND WATER RESOURCES SCIENCE

United States

Alabama

Auburn University, MD

Arizona

The University of Arizona, BMD

California

California State University, Bakersfield, M
California State University, Chico, M
Citrus College, A
Humboldt State University, B
Imperial Valley College, A
Los Angeles Trade-Technical College, A
Stanford University, D
University of California, Davis, BMD
University of California, Santa Barbara, B
Ventura College, A

Colorado

Colorado School of Mines, MD
Colorado State University, M
University of Colorado Boulder, MD
University of Colorado Denver, MD

Florida

Indian River State College, A
University of Florida, MD

Idaho

Boise State University, M
College of Southern Idaho, A
Idaho State University, M
University of Idaho, M

Illinois

Illinois State University, M
Southeastern Illinois College, A

Iowa

Iowa Lakes Community College, A

Kansas

Dodge City Community College, A

Kentucky

Murray State University, M

Massachusetts

Massachusetts Institute of Technology, D

Michigan

Lake Superior State University, A
Western Michigan University, B

Minnesota

University of Minnesota, Twin Cities Campus, MD
Vermilion Community College, A

Mississippi

University of Southern Mississippi, M

Missouri

Missouri University of Science and Technology, MD

Nevada

University of Nevada, Reno, MD

New Hampshire

University of New Hampshire, M

New Jersey

Stevens Institute of Technology, M

New Mexico

Doña Ana Community College, A
New Mexico Institute of Mining and Technology, MD

New Mexico State University, M

New York

The College at Brockport, State University of New York, B
Cornell University, MD
Rensselaer Polytechnic Institute, B
State University of New York College of Environmental Science and Forestry, B
State University of New York College at Oneonta, B

Ohio

Heidelberg University, B

Pennsylvania

Drexel University, MD
Temple University, O

Texas

Tarleton State University, B
The University of Texas at Austin, B

Washington

Spokane Community College, A
University of Washington, MD

Wisconsin

Northland College, B
University of Wisconsin - Stevens Point, B

Canada

Alberta

University of Calgary, MD

Maritime Provinces: New Brunswick

University of New Brunswick Fredericton, MD

Maritime Provinces: Nova Scotia

St. Francis Xavier University, B

Ontario

Lakehead University, B
University of Toronto, B

Quebec

McGill University, B

ILLUSTRATION

United States

Arizona

Sessions College for Professional Design, A
Southwest University of Visual Arts, B

Arkansas

John Brown University, B

California

Academy of Art University, ABM
Art Center College of Design, B
California College of the Arts, B
California State University, Fullerton, M
California State University, Long Beach, B
Chabot College, A
Laguna College of Art & Design, B
Mills College, M
San Jose State University, M
University of San Francisco, B

Colorado

Rocky Mountain College of Art + Design, B

Connecticut

Paier College of Art, Inc., B
University of Hartford, B
University of New Haven, B
Western Connecticut State University, M

Delaware

Delaware College of Art and Design, A

Florida

The Art Institute of Fort Lauderdale, B
Ringling College of Art and Design, B

Georgia

The Art Institute of Atlanta, B
Savannah College of Art and Design, BM

Idaho

Boise State University, B

Illinois

American Academy of Art, B
Columbia College Chicago, B
The Illinois Institute of Art - Chicago, B
School of the Art Institute of Chicago, B

Indiana

Grace College, B
Indiana Wesleyan University, B

Kansas

The University of Kansas, B

Maine

Maine College of Art, B

Maryland

Maryland Institute College of Art, BM

Massachusetts

Montserrat College of Art, B
Northeastern University, B
School of the Museum of Fine Arts, Boston, B
University of Massachusetts Dartmouth, B

Michigan

College for Creative Studies, B
Ferris State University, B
Kalamazoo Valley Community College, A
Lawrence Technological University, B
Northern Michigan University, B
University of Michigan, B

Minnesota

Minneapolis College of Art and Design, BM

Missouri

Kansas City Art Institute, B
Washington University in St. Louis, B

New Hampshire

New Hampshire Institute of Art, B

New York

Eugene Lang College of Liberal Arts, B
Fashion Institute of Technology, ABM
Parsons School of Design, B
Pratt Institute, AB
Rochester Institute of Technology, B
St. John's University, B
School of Visual Arts, BM
Syracuse University, BM

North Carolina

East Carolina University, M

Ohio

Art Academy of Cincinnati, B
Cleveland Institute of Art, B
Columbus College of Art & Design, B
Kent State University, M

Oklahoma

Oklahoma State University, Oklahoma City, A

Oregon

Pacific Northwest College of Art, B

Pennsylvania

Arcadia University, B
Douglas Education Center, A
Marywood University, BM
Moore College of Art & Design, B
Pennsylvania College of Art & Design, B
The University of the Arts, B

Rhode Island

Rhode Island School of Design, B

South Carolina

Bob Jones University, M

Tennessee

Nossi College of Art, B

Texas

Collin County Community College District, A

Utah

Brigham Young University, B

Virginia

Hollins University, M
Virginia Commonwealth University, B

Washington

Cornish College of the Arts, B

Canada

Alberta

Alberta College of Art & Design, B

British Columbia

Emily Carr University of Art + Design, B

IMMUNOLOGY

United States

Arizona

The University of Arizona, MD

Arkansas

University of Arkansas for Medical Sciences, D

California

California Institute of Technology, D
Stanford University, D
University of California, Berkeley, D
University of California, Davis, MD
University of California, Los Angeles, MD
University of Southern California, M

Colorado

Colorado State University, MD
University of Colorado Denver, D

Connecticut

Yale University, D

District of Columbia

The George Washington University, D
Georgetown University, MD

Florida

University of Florida, D
University of Miami, D
University of South Florida, M

Georgia

Emory University, D

Illinois

Illinois State University, M
Loyola University Chicago, MD
Rush University, MD
University of Chicago, D

University of Illinois at Chicago, D

Indiana

Indiana University - Purdue University Indianapolis, MD
Purdue University, MD

Iowa

Iowa State University of Science and Technology, MD
The University of Iowa, MD

Kentucky

University of Kentucky, D
University of Louisville, MD

Louisiana

Louisiana State University Health Sciences Center, MD
Tulane University, MD

Maine

University of Southern Maine, M

Maryland

Hood College, M
Johns Hopkins University, MD

Massachusetts

Boston University, D
Massachusetts Institute of Technology, D
Tufts University, D

Michigan

University of Michigan, MD
Wayne State University, MD

Minnesota

University of Minnesota, Duluth, MD
University of Minnesota, Twin Cities Campus, D

Missouri

Saint Louis University, D
University of Missouri, MD
Washington University in St. Louis, D

Montana

Montana State University, MD
University of Montana, D

Nebraska

Creighton University, MD

New Jersey

Rutgers University - New Brunswick, MD
Rutgers University - Newark, D

New York

Cornell University, MD
New York University, D
State University of New York Upstate Medical University, MD
Stony Brook University, State University of New York, D
University at Albany, State University of New York, MD
University at Buffalo, the State University of New York, MD
University of Rochester, MD

North Carolina

Duke University, D
East Carolina University, MD
North Carolina State University, MD
The University of North Carolina at Chapel Hill, MD
Wake Forest University, D

North Dakota

University of North Dakota, MD

Ohio

Case Western Reserve University, MD
University of Cincinnati, MD

The University of Toledo, MD
Wright State University, M

Oklahoma

University of Oklahoma Health Sciences Center, MD

Oregon

Oregon Health & Science University, D

Pennsylvania

Drexel University, MD
Thomas Jefferson University, D
University of Pennsylvania, D
University of Pittsburgh, D

South Carolina

Medical University of South Carolina, MD

South Dakota

The University of South Dakota, MD

Tennessee

Vanderbilt University, MD

Texas

The University of Texas Health Science Center at Houston, MD
The University of Texas Health Science Center at San Antonio, MD
The University of Texas Medical Branch, MD

Virginia

Virginia Commonwealth University, MD

Washington

University of Washington, D
Washington State University, MD

West Virginia

West Virginia University, MD

U.S. Territories: Puerto Rico

Universidad Central del Caribe, M

Canada

Alberta

University of Alberta, MD
University of Calgary, MD

British Columbia

The University of British Columbia, MD

Manitoba

University of Manitoba, MD

Maritime Provinces: Nova Scotia

Dalhousie University, MD

Maritime Provinces: Prince Edward Island

University of Prince Edward Island, MD

Newfoundland and Labrador

Memorial University of Newfoundland, MD

Ontario

McMaster University, MD
Queen's University at Kingston, MD
University of Guelph, MD
University of Ottawa, MD
University of Toronto, MD
The University of Western Ontario, MD

Quebec

McGill University, MD
Université Laval, MD
Université de Montréal, MD
Université de Sherbrooke, MD

Saskatchewan

University of Saskatchewan, MD

INDIAN/NATIVE AMERICAN EDUCATION

United States

Minnesota

The College of St. Scholastica, B

Oklahoma

Northeastern State University, B

Canada

Alberta

University of Alberta, B
University of Lethbridge, B

Ontario

Queen's University at Kingston, B

Saskatchewan

University of Regina, B

INDUSTRIAL DESIGN

United States

Alabama

Auburn University, BM

Arizona

Arizona State University at the Tempe campus, B
GateWay Community College, A

California

Academy of Art University, ABM
Art Center College of Design, BM
The Art Institute of California - Hollywood, a campus of Argosy University, B
The Art Institute of California - Orange County, a campus of Argosy University, B
California College of the Arts, BM
California State University, Long Beach, B
FIDM/Fashion Institute of Design & Merchandising, Los Angeles Campus, B
Las Positas College, A
Mt. San Antonio College, A
NewSchool of Architecture and Design, B
San Francisco State University, BM
San Jose State University, B
Stanford University, B

Colorado

Metropolitan State University of Denver, B

Connecticut

University of Bridgeport, B

Florida

The Art Institute of Fort Lauderdale, B
Florida State University, M

Georgia

Georgia Institute of Technology, BM
Savannah College of Art and Design, BM

Illinois

Columbia College Chicago, B
Rock Valley College, A
University of Illinois at Chicago, B
University of Illinois at Urbana - Champaign, BM

Indiana

Purdue University, B
University of Notre Dame, M

Iowa

Iowa State University of Science and Technology, BM

Kansas

The University of Kansas, B

Louisiana

University of Louisiana at Lafayette, B

Massachusetts

Massachusetts College of Art and Design, B
Wentworth Institute of Technology, B

Michigan

College for Creative Studies, B
Ferris State University, B
Finlandia University, B
Lawrence Technological University, B
University of Michigan, B
Wayne State University, M

New Jersey

Kean University, B
Montclair State University, B
New Jersey Institute of Technology, B

New York

Eugene Lang College of Liberal Arts, B
Fashion Institute of Technology, B
Fiorello H. LaGuardia Community College of the
    City University of New York, A
Parsons School of Design, B
Pratt Institute, BM
Rochester Institute of Technology, BM
Syracuse University, B

North Carolina

Appalachian State University, B
North Carolina State University, BM

Ohio

Cedarville University, B
Cleveland Institute of Art, B
Columbus College of Art & Design, B
The Ohio State University, BM
University of Cincinnati, BM

Oregon

The Art Institute of Portland, B

Pennsylvania

The Art Institute of Philadelphia, B
The Art Institute of Pittsburgh, AB
Carnegie Mellon University, B
Drexel University, B
Luzerne County Community College, A
Pennsylvania College of Technology, B
Philadelphia University, BM
The University of the Arts, BM

Rhode Island

Rhode Island School of Design, BM

South Carolina

Clemson University, B

Texas

University of Houston, B

Utah

Brigham Young University, M
University of Utah, B

Virginia

Virginia Polytechnic Institute and State University, B

Washington

The Art Institute of Seattle, AB
University of Washington, BM
Walla Walla University, B
Western Washington University, B

Wisconsin

Milwaukee Institute of Art and Design, B
University of Wisconsin - Platteville, B
University of Wisconsin - Stout, B

U.S. Territories: Puerto Rico

Escuela de Artes Plasticas y Diseño de Puerto
    Rico, B
Universidad del Turabo, B

Canada

British Columbia

Emily Carr University of Art + Design, B

Ontario

Carleton University, BM

Quebec

Université de Montréal, B

INDUSTRIAL EDUCATION

United States

Alabama

Alabama Agricultural and Mechanical University, M

Florida

Florida Agricultural and Mechanical University, M

Idaho

Idaho State University, M

Kentucky

Eastern Kentucky University, M

Louisiana

Louisiana State University and Agricultural & Me-
    chanical College, M

Minnesota

Capella University, D

Mississippi

Alcorn State University, M
Jackson State University, M

New York

Buffalo State College, State University of New York,
    M
State University of New York at Oswego, M

Pennsylvania

Temple University, M

South Carolina

South Carolina State University, M

Tennessee

Middle Tennessee State University, M

Utah

Utah State University, M

Canada

British Columbia

The University of British Columbia, M

INDUSTRIAL ELECTRONICS
TECHNOLOGY/TECHNICIAN

United States

Alabama

Bevill State Community College, A
J. F. Drake State Community and Technical College,
    A
Lawson State Community College, A
Lurleen B. Wallace Community College, A
Northeast Alabama Community College, A

Northwest-Shoals Community College, A
Shelton State Community College, A
Southern Union State Community College, A

Arizona

Eastern Arizona College, A
Penn Foster College, A

Arkansas

Southeast Arkansas College, A

California

American River College, A
Chabot College, A
Los Angeles Valley College, A
Modesto Junior College, A
Pasadena City College, A
Sierra College, A

Georgia

Dalton State College, A

Idaho

Lewis-Clark State College, AB

Illinois

College of DuPage, A
Danville Area Community College, A
Joliet Junior College, A
Kankakee Community College, A
Lincoln Land Community College, A
Moraine Valley Community College, A

Iowa

Des Moines Area Community College, A
Kirkwood Community College, A
Northwest Iowa Community College, A

Kansas

Northwest Kansas Technical College, A

Kentucky

Bluegrass Community and Technical College, A
Elizabethtown Community and Technical College, A
Sullivan College of Technology and Design, AB

Louisiana

Louisiana Delta Community College, A
South Louisiana Community College, A

Michigan

Ferris State University, A

Minnesota

Central Lakes College, A

Missouri

Ranken Technical College, A

New Mexico

New Mexico State University - Carlsbad, A

North Carolina

Gaston College, A
Lenoir Community College, A
Mayland Community College, A
Wake Technical Community College, A

Ohio

Northwest State Community College, A

Pennsylvania

Johnson College, A
Lackawanna College, A
Lehigh Carbon Community College, A
Northampton Community College, A
Pennsylvania College of Technology, A

South Carolina

Central Carolina Technical College, A
Denmark Technical College, A
Midlands Technical College, A
Spartanburg Community College, A

Technical College of the Lowcountry, A
Tri-County Technical College, A
York Technical College, A

Tennessee

Dyersburg State Community College, A

Texas

Hill College, A
Tyler Junior College, A

Virginia

Lord Fairfax Community College, A
Patrick Henry Community College, A
Thomas Nelson Community College, A

Washington

Bates Technical College, A
Big Bend Community College, A
Wenatchee Valley College, A

Wyoming

Western Wyoming Community College, A

U.S. Territories: Puerto Rico

National University College (Bayamón), A

INDUSTRIAL ENGINEERING

United States

Alabama

Auburn University, B
The University of Alabama in Huntsville, B

Arizona

Arizona State University at the Tempe campus, B
The University of Arizona, B

Arkansas

University of Arkansas, B

California

California Baptist University, B
California Polytechnic State University, San Luis
    Obispo, B
California State Polytechnic University, Pomona, B
California State University, East Bay, B
California State University, Long Beach, B
San Jose State University, B
Santa Barbara City College, A
Stanford University, B
University of San Diego, B
University of Southern California, B

Connecticut

Manchester Community College, A
Quinnipiac University, B
University of Connecticut, B
University of New Haven, B

Florida

Florida Agricultural and Mechanical University, B
South Florida State College, A
University of Central Florida, B
University of Miami, B
University of South Florida, B

Georgia

Georgia Institute of Technology, B

Illinois

Bradley University, B
Northern Illinois University, B
Northwestern University, B
Southern Illinois University Edwardsville, B
University of Illinois at Chicago, B
University of Illinois at Urbana - Champaign, B

Indiana

Indiana Tech, AB
Purdue University, B

Iowa

Iowa State University of Science and Technology, B
St. Ambrose University, B
The University of Iowa, B

Kansas

Kansas State University, B
Wichita State University, B

Kentucky

University of Louisville, B

Louisiana

Louisiana State University and Agricultural & Me-
    chanical College, B
Louisiana Tech University, B

Maryland

Morgan State University, B

Massachusetts

Eastern Nazarene College, B
Northeastern University, B
University of Massachusetts Amherst, B
Western New England University, B
Worcester Polytechnic Institute, B

Michigan

Kettering University, B
Lawrence Technological University, B
Montcalm Community College, A
Oakland University, B
University of Michigan, B
University of Michigan - Dearborn, B
Wayne State University, B
Western Michigan University, B

Minnesota

Central Lakes College, A
St. Cloud State University, B
University of Minnesota, Duluth, B
University of Minnesota, Twin Cities Campus, B

Mississippi

Mississippi State University, B

Missouri

Missouri University of Science and Technology, B
University of Missouri, B

Montana

Montana State University, B

New Jersey

New Jersey Institute of Technology, B
Rutgers University - New Brunswick, B

New Mexico

New Mexico State University, B
Northern New Mexico College, A

New York

Binghamton University, State University of New
    York, B
Columbia University, B
Hofstra University, B
Rensselaer Polytechnic Institute, B
Rochester Institute of Technology, B
State University of New York Maritime College, B
University at Buffalo, the State University of New
    York, B

North Carolina

North Carolina Agricultural and Technical State Uni-
    versity, B
North Carolina State University, B

North Dakota

North Dakota State University, B

Ohio

Kent State University, B
The Ohio State University, B
Ohio University, B
Youngstown State University, B

Oklahoma

Oklahoma State University, B
University of Oklahoma, B

Oregon

Clackamas Community College, A
Oregon State University, B

Pennsylvania

Elizabethtown College, B
Gannon University, B
Lehigh University, B
Penn State Abington, B
Penn State Altoona, B
Penn State Beaver, B
Penn State Berks, B
Penn State Brandywine, B
Penn State DuBois, B
Penn State Erie, The Behrend College, B
Penn State Fayette, The Eberly Campus, B
Penn State Greater Allegheny, B
Penn State Hazleton, B
Penn State Lehigh Valley, B
Penn State Mont Alto, B
Penn State New Kensington, B
Penn State Schuylkill, B
Penn State Shenango, B
Penn State University Park, B
Penn State Wilkes-Barre, B
Penn State Worthington Scranton, B
Penn State York, B
University of Pittsburgh, B

Rhode Island

University of Rhode Island, B

South Carolina

Clemson University, B
Francis Marion University, B
University of South Carolina Aiken, B

South Dakota

South Dakota School of Mines and Technology, B

Tennessee

Nashville State Community College, A
Tennessee State University, B
The University of Tennessee, B

Texas

Lamar University, B
Northeast Texas Community College, A
St. Mary's University, B
Texas A&M University, B
Texas A&M University - Commerce, B
Texas A&M University - Kingsville, B
Texas State University, B
Texas Tech University, B
University of Houston, B
The University of Texas at Arlington, B
The University of Texas at El Paso, B

Vermont

University of Vermont, B

Virginia

Liberty University, B
Virginia Polytechnic Institute and State University, B

Washington

University of Washington, B

West Virginia

West Virginia University, B

Wisconsin

Milwaukee School of Engineering, B
University of Wisconsin - Madison, B
University of Wisconsin - Milwaukee, B
University of Wisconsin - Platteville, B

U.S. Territories: Puerto Rico

Caribbean University, B
Inter American University of Puerto Rico, Bayamón
Campus, B
Polytechnic University of Puerto Rico, B
University of Puerto Rico, Mayagüez Campus, B

Canada

Alberta

University of Calgary, B

Manitoba

University of Manitoba, B

Maritime Provinces: New Brunswick

Université de Moncton, B

Maritime Provinces: Nova Scotia

Dalhousie University, B

Newfoundland and Labrador

Memorial University of Newfoundland, B

Ontario

McMaster University, B
Ryerson University, B
University of Toronto, B
University of Windsor, B

Quebec

Concordia University, B
Université du Québec à Trois-Rivières, B

Saskatchewan

University of Regina, B

INDUSTRIAL HYGIENE

United States

Alabama

The University of Alabama at Birmingham, MD

California

California State University, Northridge, M

Iowa

The University of Iowa, MD

Kentucky

Murray State University, M

Massachusetts

University of Massachusetts Lowell, MD

Michigan

University of Michigan, M

Minnesota

University of Minnesota, Twin Cities Campus, MD

Missouri

University of Central Missouri, M

Montana

Montana Tech of The University of Montana, M

North Carolina

The University of North Carolina at Chapel Hill, MD

Ohio

University of Cincinnati, MD
The University of Toledo, M

South Carolina

University of South Carolina, MD

West Virginia

West Virginia University, M

Wisconsin

University of Wisconsin - Stout, M

U.S. Territories: Puerto Rico

University of Puerto Rico, Medical Sciences Campus, M

INDUSTRIAL AND LABOR RELATIONS

United States

California

University of California, Berkeley, D
University of California, Santa Barbara, D

Connecticut

University of New Haven, M

District of Columbia

Georgetown University, D

Florida

University of Miami, D

Georgia

Georgia State University, D

Illinois

Loyola University Chicago, M
University of Illinois at Urbana - Champaign, MD

Massachusetts

University of Massachusetts Amherst, M

Michigan

Michigan State University, MD
Wayne State University, M

Minnesota

University of Minnesota, Twin Cities Campus, M

New Hampshire

Southern New Hampshire University, M

New Jersey

Rutgers University - New Brunswick, MD

New York

Baruch College of the City University of New York, M
Cornell University, MD
New York Institute of Technology, MO
State University of New York Empire State College, M

Ohio

Cleveland State University, MD
The Ohio State University, D
University of Cincinnati, M

Pennsylvania

Carnegie Mellon University, D
Indiana University of Pennsylvania, M
Penn State University Park, M

Rhode Island

University of Rhode Island, M

West Virginia

West Virginia University, M

Wisconsin

University of Wisconsin - Milwaukee, MO

U.S. Territories: Puerto Rico

Inter American University of Puerto Rico, Metropolitan Campus, M

Canada

Alberta

University of Alberta, D

Newfoundland and Labrador

Memorial University of Newfoundland, M

Ontario

McMaster University, M
Queen's University at Kingston, M
University of Toronto, MD

Quebec

Université Laval, MD
Université de Montréal, MDO
Université du Québec en Outaouais, MDO
Université du Québec à Trois-Rivières, O

INDUSTRIAL/MANAGEMENT ENGINEERING

United States

Alabama

Auburn University, MDO
The University of Alabama in Huntsville, MD

Arizona

Arizona State University at the Tempe campus, MD
The University of Arizona, MD

Arkansas

University of Arkansas, MD

California

California Polytechnic State University, San Luis
Obispo, B
California State University, East Bay, M
California State University, Fresno, M
California State University, Northridge, M
San Jose State University, M
Stanford University, MD
University of California, Berkeley, MD
University of Southern California, MDO

Colorado

Colorado State University - Pueblo, M

Connecticut

University of New Haven, MO

Florida

Florida Agricultural and Mechanical University, MD
Florida State University, MD
University of Central Florida, MDO
University of Florida, MDO
University of Miami, MD
University of South Florida, MDO

Georgia

Georgia Institute of Technology, MD

Illinois

Bradley University, M
Illinois State University, M
Northern Illinois University, M
Northwestern University, MD
Southern Illinois University Edwardsville, M
University of Illinois at Chicago, MD

University of Illinois at Urbana - Champaign, MD

Indiana

Indiana University - Purdue University Fort Wayne, M
Purdue University, MD

Iowa

Iowa State University of Science and Technology, MD
The University of Iowa, MD

Kansas

Kansas State University, MD
Wichita State University, MD

Kentucky

Eastern Kentucky University, M
Morehead State University, M
University of Louisville, MD

Louisiana

Louisiana Tech University, M

Maryland

Morgan State University, MD

Massachusetts

Northeastern University, MD
University of Massachusetts Amherst, MD
University of Massachusetts Dartmouth, MD
University of Massachusetts Lowell, MDO

Michigan

Lawrence Technological University, M
University of Michigan, MD
University of Michigan - Dearborn, M
Wayne State University, MD
Western Michigan University, MD

Minnesota

University of Minnesota, Twin Cities Campus, MD

Mississippi

Mississippi State University, MD

Missouri

University of Missouri, MD

Montana

Montana State University, MD
Montana Tech of The University of Montana, M

Nebraska

University of Nebraska - Lincoln, MD

New Jersey

New Jersey Institute of Technology, MD
Rutgers University - New Brunswick, MD

New Mexico

New Mexico State University, MDO

New York

Binghamton University, State University of New York, MD
Buffalo State College, State University of New York, M
Columbia University, MD
Cornell University, MD
New York University, M
Rensselaer Polytechnic Institute, MD
Rochester Institute of Technology, M
University at Buffalo, the State University of New York, MD

North Carolina

North Carolina Agricultural and Technical State University, MD
North Carolina State University, MD
Western Carolina University, M

North Dakota

North Dakota State University, MD

Ohio

Cleveland State University, MD
The Ohio State University, MD
Ohio University, MD
University of Cincinnati, D
The University of Toledo, MD
Youngstown State University, M

Oklahoma

Oklahoma State University, MD
University of Oklahoma, MD

Oregon

Oregon State University, MD

Pennsylvania

Lehigh University, MD
Penn State University Park, MD
University of Pittsburgh, MD

South Carolina

Clemson University, MD

South Dakota

South Dakota State University, M

Tennessee

University of Memphis, M
The University of Tennessee, MD
The University of Tennessee at Chattanooga, M

Texas

Lamar University, MD
St. Mary's University, M
Texas A&M University, MD
Texas A&M University - Kingsville, M
Texas Southern University, M
Texas State University, M
Texas Tech University, MD
University of Houston, MD
The University of Texas at Arlington, MD
The University of Texas at Austin, MD
The University of Texas at El Paso, MO

Virginia

Virginia Polytechnic Institute and State University, MD

Washington

Central Washington University, M
University of Washington, MD

West Virginia

West Virginia University, MD

Wisconsin

University of Wisconsin - Madison, MD
University of Wisconsin - Milwaukee, M
University of Wisconsin - Stout, M

U.S. Territories: Puerto Rico

University of Puerto Rico, Mayagüez Campus, M

Canada

Manitoba

University of Manitoba, MD

Maritime Provinces: New Brunswick

Université de Moncton, M

Maritime Provinces: Nova Scotia

Dalhousie University, MD

Ontario

University of Toronto, MD
University of Windsor, MD

Quebec

Concordia University, MDO
École Polytechnique de Montréal, MDO
Université Laval, O
Université du Québec à Trois-Rivières, MO

Saskatchewan

University of Regina, MD

INDUSTRIAL AND MANUFAC-TURING MANAGEMENT

United States

Alabama

The University of Alabama, MD

Arkansas

University of Arkansas, M

California

California Polytechnic State University, San Luis Obispo, M
California State University, East Bay, M
Notre Dame de Namur University, M
San Francisco State University, M
San Jose State University, M
University of California, Los Angeles, D

Colorado

Colorado Technical University Colorado Springs, M
Colorado Technical University Denver South, M

Connecticut

Central Connecticut State University, O
University of Bridgeport, M
University of New Haven, MO

District of Columbia

Georgetown University, D

Florida

Polytechnic University of Puerto Rico, Miami Campus, M
Polytechnic University of Puerto Rico, Orlando Campus, M

Illinois

American InterContinental University Online, M
DePaul University, M
Illinois Institute of Technology, M
Northern Illinois University, M
Northwestern University, MD

Indiana

Purdue University, M
University of Southern Indiana, M

Kansas

Kansas State University, M

Massachusetts

Harvard University, D

Michigan

Central Michigan University, M
Oakland University, O
University of Michigan - Flint, M
Wayne State University, MD

Minnesota

University of Minnesota, Twin Cities Campus, D

Missouri

Southeast Missouri State University, M
University of Central Missouri, M

New Hampshire

Southern New Hampshire University, MO

New Jersey

Stevens Institute of Technology, M

New York

Baruch College of the City University of New York, M
Rochester Institute of Technology, M
Syracuse University, D
University of Rochester, M

North Carolina

Duke University, MD
East Carolina University, MO
The University of North Carolina at Charlotte, O
Wake Forest University, M

Ohio

Case Western Reserve University, MD
Cleveland State University, D
University of Cincinnati, D

Oregon

Portland State University, M
University of Portland, M

Pennsylvania

Carnegie Mellon University, MD
Penn State Erie, The Behrend College, M
University of Pittsburgh, M
Wilkes University, M

Tennessee

Tennessee Technological University, M
The University of Tennessee, M

Texas

Texas A&M University - Kingsville, M
University of North Texas, M
The University of Texas at Arlington, M
The University of Texas at Austin, MD
The University of Texas at Tyler, M

Utah

University of Utah, MDO

Virginia

Virginia Commonwealth University, M

Wisconsin

Marquette University, M
Milwaukee School of Engineering, M

U.S. Territories: Puerto Rico

Inter American University of Puerto Rico, Metropolitan Campus, M
Inter American University of Puerto Rico, San Germán Campus, M
Polytechnic University of Puerto Rico, M
University of Puerto Rico, Mayagüez Campus, M
University of Puerto Rico, Río Piedras Campus, M

Canada

Quebec

HEC Montreal, M
McGill University, M

INDUSTRIAL MECHANICS AND MAINTENANCE TECHNOLOGY

United States

Alabama

Calhoun Community College, A
Gadsden State Community College, A
George C. Wallace Community College, A
H. Councill Trenholm State Community College, A
Northeast Alabama Community College, A
Northwest-Shoals Community College, A
Southern Union State Community College, A

The University of West Alabama, A

Alaska

University of Alaska Anchorage, A

Arizona

Eastern Arizona College, A
Northland Pioneer College, A

Arkansas

Arkansas Northeastern College, A
Arkansas State University - Beebe, A
Black River Technical College, A
East Arkansas Community College, A
Southeast Arkansas College, A
University of Arkansas Community College at Morrilton, A
University of Arkansas at Monticello, A

California

San Joaquin Valley College (Lancaster), A
San Joaquin Valley College (Ontario), A

Illinois

College of Lake County, A
Danville Area Community College, A
Elgin Community College, A
Heartland Community College, A
Illinois Eastern Community Colleges, Olney Central College, A
John A. Logan College, A
Joliet Junior College, A
Kaskaskia College, A
Rend Lake College, A
Southwestern Illinois College, A

Indiana

Ivy Tech Community College - East Central, A

Iowa

Des Moines Area Community College, A
Marshalltown Community College, A
Scott Community College, A
Western Iowa Tech Community College, A

Kansas

Johnson County Community College, A
Wichita Area Technical College, A

Kentucky

Bluegrass Community and Technical College, A
Elizabethtown Community and Technical College, A
Somerset Community College, A
Southcentral Kentucky Community and Technical College, A
Sullivan College of Technology and Design, AB

Louisiana

Bossier Parish Community College, A
South Louisiana Community College, A

Maine

Kennebec Valley Community College, A

Michigan

Delta College, A
Henry Ford College, A
Macomb Community College, A
Northern Michigan University, A
Southwestern Michigan College, A

Minnesota

Minnesota State College - Southeast Technical, A
Riverland Community College, A

Mississippi

East Mississippi Community College, A
Northeast Mississippi Community College, A

Missouri

Jefferson College, A

Nebraska

Central Community College - Hastings Campus, A
Northeast Community College, A

New Mexico

Clovis Community College, A
San Juan College, A

North Carolina

Catawba Valley Community College, A

North Dakota

Bismarck State College, A

Ohio

Northwest State Community College, A

Oregon

Chemeketa Community College, A

Pennsylvania

Delaware County Community College, A
Johnson College, A
New Castle School of Trades, A
Pennsylvania College of Technology, A
Reading Area Community College, A
Westmoreland County Community College, A

South Carolina

Aiken Technical College, A
Midlands Technical College, A
York Technical College, A

Tennessee

Dyersburg State Community College, A

Texas

Grayson College, A
Hill College, A
Lamar Institute of Technology, A
North Central Texas College, A
Texarkana College, A

Utah

Snow College, A

Washington

Bellingham Technical College, A
Big Bend Community College, A
Lake Washington Institute of Technology, A
Lower Columbia College, A

Wisconsin

Chippewa Valley Technical College, A
Gateway Technical College, A

Wyoming

Casper College, A
Western Wyoming Community College, A

Canada

British Columbia

British Columbia Institute of Technology, A

INDUSTRIAL AND ORGANIZATIONAL PSYCHOLOGY

United States

Alabama

Auburn University, D
The University of Alabama in Huntsville, M

Arizona

Argosy University, Phoenix, M
Grand Canyon University, D
University of Phoenix - Online Campus, MD

California

Argosy University, Inland Empire, M
California State University, Long Beach, M
California State University, Sacramento, M
California State University, San Bernardino, M
John F. Kennedy University, MO
San Diego State University, M
San Francisco State University, M
San Jose State University, M

Colorado

Argosy University, Denver, M

Connecticut

University of Connecticut, D
University of New Haven, MO

District of Columbia

University of Phoenix - Washington D.C. Campus, D

Florida

Argosy University, Tampa, M
Carlos Albizu University, Miami Campus, M
Florida International University, MD
Keiser University, MD
University of Central Florida, MD
University of South Florida, D
University of West Florida, M

Georgia

Argosy University, Atlanta, M

Illinois

American InterContinental University Online, M
Argosy University, Chicago, M
Argosy University, Schaumburg, M
Elmhurst College, M
Illinois Institute of Technology, D
Illinois State University, M
Roosevelt University, MD
Southern Illinois University Edwardsville, M

Indiana

Indiana University - Purdue University Indianapolis, M
Purdue University, D

Kansas

Emporia State University, M

Kentucky

Eastern Kentucky University, M
Northern Kentucky University, MO
Western Kentucky University, M

Louisiana

Louisiana Tech University, MD

Maryland

University of Maryland, Baltimore County, M
University of Maryland, College Park, MD

Massachusetts

Springfield College, MO

Michigan

Central Michigan University, MD
University of Detroit Mercy, M
Wayne State University, M
Western Michigan University, M

Minnesota

Argosy University, Twin Cities, M
Capella University, MD
Minnesota State University Mankato, M
St. Cloud State University, M
University of Minnesota, Twin Cities Campus, D
Walden University, O

Missouri

Saint Louis University, D
University of Missouri - St. Louis, MD

Nebraska

University of Nebraska at Omaha, M

New Jersey

Fairleigh Dickinson University, College at Florham, M
Kean University, M
Montclair State University, M

New York

Baruch College of the City University of New York, MD
Brooklyn College of the City University of New York, M
Hofstra University, MD
Iona College, M
New York University, M
Touro College, M
University at Albany, State University of New York, MD

North Carolina

Appalachian State University, M
East Carolina University, M
North Carolina State University, D
The University of North Carolina at Charlotte, MD

Ohio

Bowling Green State University, MD
Ohio University, MD
The University of Akron, MD
Wright State University, MD
Xavier University, M

Oklahoma

University of Oklahoma, MD
The University of Tulsa, MD

Pennsylvania

Chatham University, M
Saint Joseph's University, M
Temple University, M
West Chester University of Pennsylvania, M

South Carolina

Clemson University, D

Tennessee

Austin Peay State University, M
Middle Tennessee State University, M
The University of Tennessee, D
The University of Tennessee at Chattanooga, M

Texas

Angelo State University, M
Argosy University, Dallas, M
Lamar University, M
Rice University, MD
St. Mary's University, M
Texas A&M University, D
University of Houston, D
University of the Incarnate Word, M
The University of Texas at Arlington, M

Virginia

George Mason University, MD
Radford University, M

Washington

Seattle Pacific University, MD

Wisconsin

University of Wisconsin - Oshkosh, M

U.S. Territories: Puerto Rico

Bayamón Central University, M
Carlos Albizu University, MD
Inter American University of Puerto Rico, Metropolitan Campus, MD
Pontifical Catholic University of Puerto Rico, D

University of Puerto Rico, Río Piedras Campus, M

Canada

Maritime Provinces: Nova Scotia

Saint Mary's University, M

Ontario

University of Guelph, MD

INDUSTRIAL PRODUCTION TECHNOLOGIES/TECHNICIANS

United States

Alabama

Calhoun Community College, A

Alaska

University of Alaska Fairbanks, A

Arkansas

Arkansas Northeastern College, A

California

Antelope Valley College, A

Delaware

Delaware State University, B

Georgia

Georgia Southern University, B
Kennesaw State University, B
Valdosta State University, B

Indiana

Ivy Tech Community College - Central Indiana, A
Ivy Tech Community College - East Central, A
Ivy Tech Community College - Kokomo, A
Ivy Tech Community College - Lafayette, A
Ivy Tech Community College - North Central, A
Ivy Tech Community College - Northeast, A
Ivy Tech Community College - Richmond, A
Ivy Tech Community College - Southwest, A
Ivy Tech Community College - Wabash Valley, A
Purdue University Northwest (Westville), B

Kansas

Barton County Community College, A
McPherson College, B

Louisiana

Baton Rouge Community College, A
Louisiana Delta Community College, A

Michigan

Ferris State University, B
Henry Ford College, A
Lansing Community College, A
Saginaw Valley State University, B
Southwestern Michigan College, A
Washtenaw Community College, A

Mississippi

Mississippi State University, B

Missouri

Missouri State University, B

Nebraska

Chadron State College, B
Wayne State College, B

New Jersey

Camden County College, A
Essex County College, A
Middlesex County College, A

New York

Broome Community College, A

North Carolina

Edgecombe Community College, A
Guilford Technical Community College, A

North Dakota

Bismarck State College, A

Ohio

Bowling Green State University, B
Kent State University at Trumbull, A
Northwest State Community College, A

Oklahoma

Murray State College, A

Pennsylvania

California University of Pennsylvania, AB
Clarion University of Pennsylvania, A
Community College of Beaver County, A
Millersville University of Pennsylvania, B
Pennsylvania College of Technology, B

South Carolina

Tri-County Technical College, A

Tennessee

Nashville State Community College, A

Texas

Howard College, A
Tarleton State University, B

Virginia

Mountain Empire Community College, A

Washington

Central Washington University, B

U.S. Territories: Puerto Rico

University of Puerto Rico in Arecibo, AB
University of Puerto Rico in Utuado, B

INDUSTRIAL RADIOLOGIC TECHNOLOGY/TECHNICIAN

United States

Alabama

Wallace State Community College, A

Arkansas

National Park College, A

California

Bakersfield College, A
Las Positas College, A
Los Angeles City College, A
Merced College, A
Mt. San Antonio College, A
San Diego Mesa College, A
Yuba College, A

Connecticut

Gateway Community College, A
Middlesex Community College, A

District of Columbia

The George Washington University, A
Howard University, B

Florida

Daytona State College, A
Indian River State College, A
Palm Beach State College, A

Iowa

Briar Cliff University, B
Iowa Central Community College, A
Southeastern Community College, A

Kansas

Cowley County Community College and Area Vocational - Technical School, A
Labette Community College, A
Wichita Area Technical College, A

Louisiana

Our Lady of the Lake College, A
South Louisiana Community College, A

Maryland

University of Maryland Eastern Shore, B

Massachusetts

Northern Essex Community College, A

Michigan

Mid Michigan Community College, A

Mississippi

Copiah-Lincoln Community College, A
Mississippi Gulf Coast Community College, A

New Jersey

Passaic County Community College, A

New Mexico

Doña Ana Community College, A
Northern New Mexico College, A

New York

Monroe Community College, A

North Carolina

Carteret Community College, A
South College - Asheville, A
Vance-Granville Community College, A

Ohio

Cuyahoga Community College, A
Eastern Gateway Community College, A
Lorain County Community College, A
Sinclair Community College, A
Zane State College, A

Oklahoma

Rose State College, A

Oregon

Oregon Institute of Technology, B

Pennsylvania

Widener University, A

South Carolina

Florence-Darlington Technical College, A

Tennessee

Roane State Community College, A

Texas

Amarillo College, A
Blinn College, A
Del Mar College, A
Laredo Community College, A
McLennan Community College, A
Odessa College, A
South Plains College, A
South Texas College, A
Tarrant County College District, A
Tyler Junior College, A
Wharton County Junior College, A

Utah

Salt Lake Community College, A

Virginia

Virginia Highlands Community College, A
Virginia Western Community College, A

Washington

Yakima Valley Community College, A

West Virginia

Southern West Virginia Community and Technical College, A

Wisconsin

Concordia University Wisconsin, B
Madison Area Technical College, A

INDUSTRIAL SAFETY TECHNOLOGY/TECHNICIAN

United States

California

Southwestern College, A

Kentucky

Eastern Kentucky University, B

Minnesota

Northwest Technical College, A
South Central College, A

Oklahoma

Northeastern State University, B

Pennsylvania

Mansfield University of Pennsylvania, B

Texas

University of Houston - Downtown, B
The University of Texas at Tyler, B

Washington

Central Washington University, B

Wisconsin

Fox Valley Technical College, A

INDUSTRIAL TECHNOLOGY/TECHNICIAN

United States

Alabama

Community College of the Air Force, A
Jacksonville State University, B

Alaska

University of Alaska Anchorage, A

Arizona

Arizona Western College, A
Central Arizona College, A
Mesa Community College, A
Northland Pioneer College, A

Arkansas

Arkansas Northeastern College, A
Arkansas Tech University, A
College of the Ouachitas, A
Phillips Community College of the University of Arkansas, A
Pulaski Technical College, A
South Arkansas Community College, A
Southern Arkansas University - Magnolia, AB
Southern Arkansas University Tech, A
University of Arkansas at Pine Bluff, AB

California

Bakersfield College, A
California Polytechnic State University, San Luis Obispo, B
California State University, Fresno, B
California State University, Long Beach, B
California State University, Los Angeles, B
Cerritos College, A
De Anza College, A

Los Angeles Pierce College, A
Los Angeles Trade-Technical College, A
San Diego City College, A
San Joaquin Valley College (Hesperia), A
San Joaquin Valley College (Salida), A
San Joaquin Valley College (Visalia), A
Santa Ana College, A
Santa Barbara City College, A
Yuba College, A

Colorado

Red Rocks Community College, A

Connecticut

Central Connecticut State University, B
Gateway Community College, A
Manchester Community College, A

Florida

Daytona State College, A
Miami Dade College, A
North Florida Community College, A
St. Johns River State College, A
St. Petersburg College, A
Seminole State College of Florida, A

Georgia

Albany Technical College, A
Central Georgia Technical College, A
Columbus Technical College, A
Dalton State College, A
Georgia Piedmont Technical College, A
Lanier Technical College, A
North Georgia Technical College, A
Savannah Technical College, A
South Georgia Technical College, A
Southern Crescent Technical College, A
West Georgia Technical College, A

Idaho

University of Idaho, B

Illinois

Carl Sandburg College, A
College of DuPage, A
Eastern Illinois University, B
Heartland Community College, A
Highland Community College, A
Illinois Central College, A
Illinois Eastern Community Colleges, Wabash Valley
   College, A
Illinois State University, B
Illinois Valley Community College, A
John A. Logan College, A
Lake Land College, A
Lincoln Land Community College, A
Northern Illinois University, B
Parkland College, A
Richland Community College, A
Rock Valley College, A
Southern Illinois University Carbondale, B
Spoon River College, A

Indiana

Ball State University, B
Indiana State University, B
Indiana University - Purdue University Fort Wayne,
   AB
Ivy Tech Community College - Bloomington, A
Ivy Tech Community College - Central Indiana, A
Ivy Tech Community College - Columbus, A
Ivy Tech Community College - East Central, A
Ivy Tech Community College - Kokomo, A
Ivy Tech Community College - Lafayette, A
Ivy Tech Community College - North Central, A
Ivy Tech Community College - Northeast, A
Ivy Tech Community College - Northwest, A
Ivy Tech Community College - Richmond, A
Ivy Tech Community College - Southeast, A
Ivy Tech Community College - Southern Indiana, A
Ivy Tech Community College - Southwest, A
Ivy Tech Community College - Wabash Valley, A
Purdue University Northwest (Hammond), B
Vincennes University, B

Iowa

University of Northern Iowa, B
William Penn University, B

Kansas

Allen Community College, A
Dodge City Community College, A
Fort Hays State University, B
Labette Community College, A
Pittsburg State University, AB
Washburn University, A

Kentucky

Eastern Kentucky University, A
Gateway Community and Technical College, A
Hopkinsville Community College, A
Murray State University, A
Western Kentucky University, B

Louisiana

Bossier Parish Community College, A
Northwestern State University of Louisiana, B
Nunez Community College, A
South Louisiana Community College, A
Southeastern Louisiana University, AB
University of Louisiana at Lafayette, B

Maine

University of Southern Maine, B

Maryland

Hagerstown Community College, A

Massachusetts

Fitchburg State University, B
University of Massachusetts Lowell, B

Michigan

Baker College, B
Eastern Michigan University, B
Ferris State University, B
Grand Rapids Community College, A
Kellogg Community College, A
Lake Michigan College, A
Lake Superior State University, B
Lawrence Technological University, B
Macomb Community College, A
Monroe County Community College, A
Montcalm Community College, A
Muskegon Community College, A
Northern Michigan University, B
Northwestern Michigan College, A
Oakland Community College, A

Minnesota

Bemidji State University, B
Dunwoody College of Technology, B
Northwest Technical College, A
Saint Paul College - A Community & Technical Col-
   lege, A
Vermilion Community College, A

Mississippi

Holmes Community College, A
Jackson State University, B
Mississippi State University, B
Mississippi Valley State University, B
University of Southern Mississippi, B

Missouri

Crowder College, A
Mineral Area College, A
Missouri Southern State University, B
Missouri State University - West Plains, A
Moberly Area Community College, A
Ozarks Technical Community College, A
St. Charles Community College, A
Southeast Missouri State University, B
Three Rivers Community College, A

Montana

Montana State University - Northern, AB

Nebraska

Central Community College - Hastings Campus, A

Nevada

Great Basin College, A
Western Nevada College, A

New Jersey

Cumberland County College, A
Passaic County Community College, A

New Mexico

Eastern New Mexico University - Roswell, A
San Juan College, A

New York

Buffalo State College, State University of New York,
   B
Clinton Community College, A
Erie Community College, North Campus, A
Farmingdale State College, B
Monroe Community College, A

North Carolina

Bladen Community College, A
Central Piedmont Community College, A
East Carolina University, B
Elizabeth City State University, B
Forsyth Technical Community College, A
Nash Community College, A
North Carolina Agricultural and Technical State Uni-
   versity, B
Piedmont Community College, A
Robeson Community College, A
Rowan-Cabarrus Community College, A
Sampson Community College, A
Southeastern Community College, A
Stanly Community College, A
Vance-Granville Community College, A
Wake Technical Community College, A

North Dakota

Bismarck State College, A
University of North Dakota, B

Ohio

Bowling Green State University, B
Bowling Green State University - Firelands College,
   A
Central State University, B
Cincinnati State Technical and Community College,
   A
Clark State Community College, A
Eastern Gateway Community College, A
Edison Community College, A
Hocking College, A
James A. Rhodes State College, A
Kent State University at Trumbull, A
Kent State University at Tuscarawas, A
Lorain County Community College, A
Miami University Middletown, A
The Ohio State University Agricultural Technical In-
   stitute, A
Ohio University, B
Ohio University - Lancaster, A
Owens Community College, A
Sinclair Community College, A
Stark State College, A
University of Dayton, B
University of Rio Grande, AB
Washington State Community College, A
Zane State College, A

Oklahoma

Eastern Oklahoma State College, A
Oklahoma Panhandle State University, AB

Oregon

Blue Mountain Community College, A
Central Oregon Community College, A
Clackamas Community College, A
Mt. Hood Community College, A

Pennsylvania

Bucks County Community College, A
Clarion University of Pennsylvania, B
Community College of Allegheny County, A
Lackawanna College, A
Millersville University of Pennsylvania, AB
Penn State York, A
South Hills School of Business & Technology (State College), A
Westmoreland County Community College, A

Rhode Island

Roger Williams University, B

South Carolina

South Carolina State University, B
Trident Technical College, A

South Dakota

Black Hills State University, B
Southeast Technical Institute, A

Tennessee

Chattanooga State Community College, A
Cleveland State Community College, A
Jackson State Community College, A
Middle Tennessee State University, B
Nashville State Community College, A
Northeast State Community College, A
Southwest Tennessee Community College, A
Tennessee State University, B
Tennessee Technological University, B
Walters State Community College, A

Texas

Frank Phillips College, A
Lamar University, B
Lone Star College - CyFair, A
Lone Star College - North Harris, A
Lone Star College - Tomball, A
Navarro College, A
Northeast Texas Community College, A
Panola College, A
Richland College, A
Sam Houston State University, B
San Antonio College, A
South Texas College, A
Tarleton State University, B
Texas A&M University - Commerce, B
Texas A&M University - Kingsville, B
Texas Southern University, B
Texas Southmost College, A
Texas State University, B
The University of Texas of the Permian Basin, B
The University of Texas at Tyler, B

Vermont

Community College of Vermont, A

Virginia

Blue Ridge Community College, A
Central Virginia Community College, A
Danville Community College, A
John Tyler Community College, A
Mountain Empire Community College, A
Northern Virginia Community College, A
Patrick Henry Community College, A
Paul D. Camp Community College, A
Thomas Nelson Community College, A

Washington

Central Washington University, B
Grays Harbor College, A
Highline College, A
Olympic College, A
Pierce College at Puyallup, A
Shoreline Community College, A
Spokane Community College, A
Western Washington University, B
Yakima Valley Community College, A

West Virginia

Fairmont State University, B
West Virginia University Institute of Technology, B

Wisconsin

Mid-State Technical College, A
Milwaukee Area Technical College, A
University of Wisconsin - Platteville, B

U.S. Territories: Puerto Rico

University of Puerto Rico in Bayamón, A
University of Puerto Rico in Ponce, A

Canada

British Columbia

British Columbia Institute of Technology, A

INFECTIOUS DISEASES

United States

California

University of California, Berkeley, MD

Connecticut

Yale University, D

District of Columbia

The George Washington University, M
Georgetown University, MD

Georgia

University of Georgia, MD

Illinois

Loyola University Chicago, MO

Maryland

Johns Hopkins University, MD

Massachusetts

Tufts University, D

Minnesota

University of Minnesota, Twin Cities Campus, MD

Montana

Montana State University, MD

New Jersey

Rutgers University - Newark, D

New York

Cornell University, MD

North Carolina

North Carolina State University, MD

Pennsylvania

Thomas Jefferson University, O
University of Pittsburgh, MD

Texas

The University of Texas Medical Branch, D

Virginia

George Mason University, M

Canada

Alberta

University of Calgary, MD

Ontario

University of Guelph, MD

Quebec

Université Laval, O

INFORMATION RESOURCES MANAGEMENT/CIO TRAINING

United States

Alabama

Athens State University, B

California

University of California, Irvine, B

Delaware

Wilmington University, B

Florida

Rasmussen College Fort Myers, A
Rasmussen College Land O' Lakes, AB
Rasmussen College New Port Richey, AB
Rasmussen College Ocala, AB
Rasmussen College Tampa/Brandon, AB

Illinois

Lewis University, B

Kansas

Grantham University, B

Maryland

Mount St. Mary's University, B

Michigan

Michigan State University, B
Western Michigan University, B

Minnesota

Metropolitan State University, B

New Jersey

Seton Hall University, B

North Dakota

University of Mary, B

Pennsylvania

Chestnut Hill College, B

Rhode Island

Salve Regina University, B

South Carolina

Southern Wesleyan University, B

Tennessee

Lipscomb University, B

Texas

Abilene Christian University, B
Lubbock Christian University, B

Virginia

ECPI University (Virginia Beach), B

Wisconsin

University of Wisconsin - Eau Claire, B

INFORMATION SCIENCE/STUDIES

United States

Alabama

Alabama State University, B
Auburn University at Montgomery, M
Central Alabama Community College, A
Oakwood University, AB
South University, B
The University of Alabama, MD
The University of Alabama at Birmingham, MD
University of South Alabama, B

Alaska

University of Alaska Anchorage, A

Arizona

Arizona State University at the Tempe campus, M
Cochise County Community College District, A
Eastern Arizona College, A
Northland Pioneer College, A
Rio Salado College, A
Scottsdale Community College, A
The University of Arizona, MD
Yavapai College, A

Arkansas

Arkansas State University - Mountain Home, A
Arkansas Tech University, M
National Park College, A
Ozarka College, A
Rich Mountain Community College, A
University of Arkansas at Little Rock, BMDO

California

Allan Hancock College, A
Bakersfield College, A
California Lutheran University, B
California State University, East Bay, B
California State University, Fullerton, M
California State University, Northridge, B
California State University, Stanislaus, B
Coleman University, M
College of the Sequoias, A
Cuyamaca College, A
De Anza College, A
Humphreys College, AB
Imperial Valley College, A
La Sierra University, B
Laney College, A
Las Positas College, A
Los Angeles Harbor College, A
Los Angeles Trade-Technical College, A
Mendocino College, A
Mission College, A
Monterey Peninsula College, A
Moorpark College, A
National University, B
Notre Dame de Namur University, M
Reedley College, A
Saddleback College, A
San Diego Miramar College, A
San Francisco State University, B
San Jose State University, MD
Santa Ana College, A
Santa Barbara City College, A
University of California, Berkeley, MD
University of California, Irvine, MD
University of California, Los Angeles, MDO
University of California, Merced, MD
University of California, Santa Cruz, B
University of the Pacific, B
University of San Francisco, B
Victor Valley College, A
West Hills Community College, A
West Valley College, A

Colorado

American Sentinel University, AB
Aspen University, MO
Colorado State University, B
Colorado State University - Pueblo, B
Colorado Technical University Colorado Springs, AB
Colorado Technical University Denver South, AB
Lamar Community College, A
National American University (Denver), AB
Regis University, MO
University of Colorado Boulder, B
University of Colorado Denver, D

Connecticut

Albertus Magnus College, B
Central Connecticut State University, M
Eastern Connecticut State University, B
Manchester Community College, A
Northwestern Connecticut Community College, A
Norwalk Community College, A
Quinnipiac University, B

Sacred Heart University, O
Southern Connecticut State University, O
Tunxis Community College, A
University of Hartford, B
University of New Haven, BMO

Delaware

Delaware State University, B
Goldey-Beacom College, AB
University of Delaware, MD

District of Columbia

The Catholic University of America, M
Gallaudet University, B
Howard University, B
University of the District of Columbia, B

Florida

Barry University, BM
Bethune-Cookman University, B
Broward College, A
Edward Waters College, B
Everglades University (Boca Raton), M
Florida Gulf Coast University, M
Florida International University, MD
Florida State University, MDO
Indian River State College, A
Jacksonville University, B
Miami Dade College, A
Nova Southeastern University, MD
Pensacola State College, A
St. Thomas University, B
Seminole State College of Florida, A
South Florida State College, A
South University (Tampa), B
State College of Florida Manatee-Sarasota, A
University of Florida, MD
University of Miami, B
University of Phoenix - North Florida Campus, B
University of South Florida, BMO

Georgia

Albany State University, B
American InterContinental University Atlanta, M
Armstrong State University, BM
Athens Technical College, A
Augusta Technical College, A
Bainbridge State College, A
Brewton-Parker College, B
Central Georgia Technical College, A
Chattahoochee Technical College, A
Clark Atlanta University, M
Clayton State University, B
Coastal Pines Technical College, A
Columbus Technical College, A
Georgia Highlands College, A
Georgia Northwestern Technical College, A
Georgia Piedmont Technical College, A
Georgia Southern University, B
Georgia State University, MDO
Gwinnett Technical College, A
Kennesaw State University, BMO
Lanier Technical College, A
Mercer University, B
Oconee Fall Line Technical College, A
Ogeechee Technical College, A
Reinhardt University, B
Savannah State University, B
South Georgia Technical College, A
South University, B
Southeastern Technical College, A
Southern Regional Technical College, A
University of North Georgia, B
Valdosta State University, BM
West Georgia Technical College, A

Hawaii

Brigham Young University - Hawaii, B
University of Hawaii at Manoa, MDO

Idaho

Boise State University, B
Idaho State University, B

Illinois

American InterContinental University Online, M
Benedictine University, B
Bradley University, BM
DePaul University, BMD
Dominican University, MDO
Elmhurst College, B
Heartland Community College, A
Illinois College, B
Kaskaskia College, A
Lewis University, B
Loyola University Chicago, M
McKendree University, B
Midstate College, A
National Louis University, B
Northwestern University, BM
Olivet Nazarene University, B
Parkland College, A
Quincy University, B
Richland Community College, A
Shawnee Community College, A
Southeastern Illinois College, A
Southern Illinois University Carbondale, B
Spoon River College, A
Triton College, A
University of Illinois at Chicago, B
University of Illinois at Urbana - Champaign, MDO

Indiana

Anderson University, B
Ball State University, M
Goshen College, B
Indiana University Bloomington, MDO
Indiana University - Purdue University Fort Wayne, ABM
Indiana University - Purdue University Indianapolis, M
Ivy Tech Community College - Bloomington, A
Ivy Tech Community College - Central Indiana, A
Ivy Tech Community College - Columbus, A
Ivy Tech Community College - East Central, A
Ivy Tech Community College - Kokomo, A
Ivy Tech Community College - Lafayette, A
Ivy Tech Community College - Richmond, A
Ivy Tech Community College - Southeast, A
Ivy Tech Community College - Southern Indiana, A
Ivy Tech Community College - Southwest, A
Ivy Tech Community College - Wabash Valley, A

Iowa

Central College, B
Grand View University, B
Iowa State University of Science and Technology, M
Luther College, B
Northwestern College, B
Southeastern Community College, A
The University of Iowa, BMDO

Kansas

Allen Community College, A
Barton County Community College, A
Dodge City Community College, A
Emporia State University, B
Fort Hays State University, B
Friends University, B
Kansas State University, BMD
Neosho County Community College, A
Newman University, AB
Ottawa University, B

Kentucky

American National University (Lexington), A
American National University (Louisville), A
Campbellsville University, AB
Madisonville Community College, A
Murray State University, B
Northern Kentucky University, BMO
University of Kentucky, BM

Louisiana

Bossier Parish Community College, A
Grambling State University, B
ITI Technical College, A
Louisiana State University and Agricultural & Mechanical College, M

Louisiana State University in Shreveport, B
Northwestern State University of Louisiana, B
Tulane University, AB

Maine

University of Maine, MDO

Maryland

Capitol Technology University, M
Frostburg State University, B
Harford Community College, A
Hood College, MO
Howard Community College, A
Johns Hopkins University, M
Kaplan University, Hagerstown Campus, A
Morgan State University, B
Notre Dame of Maryland University, B
Prince George's Community College, A
Salisbury University, B
Stevenson University, B
Towson University, BMDO
University of Baltimore, B
University of Maryland, Baltimore County, BMD
University of Maryland, College Park, BMD
University of Maryland University College, BMO
Washington Adventist University, B

Massachusetts

Bentley University, M
Bristol Community College, A
Cape Cod Community College, A
Clark University, M
Harvard University, MD
Massachusetts Institute of Technology, D
North Shore Community College, A
Northeastern University, BM
Roxbury Community College, A
Simmons College, MDO
Suffolk University, B
Tufts University, B
University of Massachusetts Dartmouth, D
University of Massachusetts Lowell, AB
Wentworth Institute of Technology, B
Westfield State University, B
Worcester Polytechnic Institute, B

Michigan

Alpena Community College, A
Andrews University, B
Grand Valley State University, BM
Kirtland Community College, A
Michigan Jewish Institute, AB
Mid Michigan Community College, A
Muskegon Community College, A
South University, B
University of Detroit Mercy, M
University of Michigan, BMD
University of Michigan - Dearborn, M
University of Michigan - Flint, BM
Wayne State University, BMO

Minnesota

Alexandria Technical and Community College, A
Bemidji State University, B
Century College, A
Metropolitan State University, BM
Minnesota State University Mankato, B
Minnesota State University Moorhead, B
National American University (Roseville), AB
St. Catherine University, M
St. Cloud State University, B

Mississippi

Alcorn State University, M
University of Southern Mississippi, MO

Missouri

Harris-Stowe State University, B
Lincoln University, B
Metropolitan Community College - Kansas City, A
Missouri University of Science and Technology, BM
Missouri Western State University, M
National American University (Kansas City), AB
Ozarks Technical Community College, A
University of Central Missouri, M

University of Missouri, MDO
Webster University, B

Montana

University of Great Falls, B
University of Montana, B

Nebraska

Bellevue University, M
Chadron State College, B
Doane University, B
University of Nebraska - Lincoln, D
University of Nebraska at Omaha, BD
Wayne State College, B

Nevada

College of Southern Nevada, A
University of Nevada, Las Vegas, B

New Hampshire

Manchester Community College, A

New Jersey

Essex County College, A
New Jersey Institute of Technology, BMD
Passaic County Community College, A
Ramapo College of New Jersey, B
Rutgers University - New Brunswick, BMD
Rutgers University - Newark, B
Saint Peter's University, AB
Stevens Institute of Technology, MO
Stockton University, B
Union County College, A
Warren County Community College, A

New Mexico

New Mexico Highlands University, B
University of New Mexico - Valencia Campus, A

New York

Adelphi University, B
Baruch College of the City University of New York,
    B
Brooklyn College of the City University of New York,
    BMO
Broome Community College, A
Buffalo State College, State University of New York,
    B
Cayuga County Community College, A
Clarkson University, M
The College at Brockport, State University of New
    York, B
The College of Saint Rose, M
Columbia University, M
Columbia University, School of General Studies, B
Cornell University, D
Dutchess Community College, A
Excelsior College, B
Fordham University, B
Fulton-Montgomery Community College, A
Genesee Community College, A
Jamestown Community College, A
Jefferson Community College, A
Long Island University - LIU Post, BM
Medaille College, B
Medgar Evers College of the City University of New
    York, B
Mercy College, B
Molloy College, B
Monroe College, AB
Monroe Community College, A
Morrisville State College, A
New York City College of Technology of the City
    University of New York, B
Niagara County Community College, A
Niagara University, B
Orange County Community College, A
Pace University, BMDO
Pratt Institute, MO
Queens College of the City University of New York,
    MO
Queensborough Community College of the City Uni-
    versity of New York, A
Rensselaer Polytechnic Institute, M
Rochester Institute of Technology, MD

The Sage Colleges, B
St. John's University, MO
St. Joseph's College, Long Island Campus, B
St. Joseph's College, New York, B
St. Thomas Aquinas College, B
State University of New York College of Agriculture
    and Technology at Cobleskill, A
State University of New York College at Old
    Westbury, B
State University of New York College of Technology
    at Alfred, A
State University of New York College of Technology
    at Canton, A
State University of New York College of Technology
    at Delhi, A
State University of New York at Fredonia, B
State University of New York at Oswego, B
State University of New York Polytechnic Institute,
    BM
Stony Brook University, State University of New
    York, B
Suffolk County Community College, A
Sullivan County Community College, A
Syracuse University, BMD
Tompkins Cortland Community College, A
Touro College, AB
University at Albany, State University of New York,
    BMDO
University at Buffalo, the State University of New
    York, BMO
Westchester Community College, A
York College of the City University of New York, B

North Carolina

Alamance Community College, A
Asheville-Buncombe Technical Community College,
    A
Beaufort County Community College, A
Blue Ridge Community College, A
Brunswick Community College, A
Catawba Valley Community College, A
Central Carolina Community College, A
Chowan University, B
College of The Albemarle, A
Durham Technical Community College, A
East Carolina University, B
Elon University, B
Fayetteville Technical Community College, A
Forsyth Technical Community College, A
Gaston College, A
Guilford Technical Community College, A
Lenoir-Rhyne University, B
Livingstone College, B
Louisburg College, A
Martin Community College, A
Mitchell Community College, A
North Carolina Central University, M
Pitt Community College, A
Roanoke-Chowan Community College, A
Rowan-Cabarrus Community College, A
Sandhills Community College, A
South Piedmont Community College, A
South University, AB
Southwestern Community College, A
Stanly Community College, A
Surry Community College, A
University of Mount Olive, B
The University of North Carolina at Chapel Hill,
    BMDO
The University of North Carolina at Charlotte, MDO
The University of North Carolina at Greensboro, M
Wake Technical Community College, A
Winston-Salem State University, B

North Dakota

Dakota College at Bottineau, A
University of Mary, B

Ohio

Ashland University, B
Belmont College, A
Bowling Green State University, B
Case Western Reserve University, MD
Clark State Community College, A
Cleveland State University, M
Heidelberg University, B

Kent State University, MO
Lorain County Community College, A
Marietta College, B
Miami University Middletown, A
Notre Dame College, B
Ohio Dominican University, B
The Ohio State University, B
Sinclair Community College, A
South University, B
University of Cincinnati, B
University of Cincinnati Clermont College, A
The University of Toledo, B
Wilberforce University, B
Wright State University, B
Youngstown State University, M

Oklahoma

Bacone College, B
Connors State College, A
Murray State College, A
Northern Oklahoma College, A
Northwestern Oklahoma State University, B
Oklahoma Baptist University, B
Oklahoma Christian University, B
Oklahoma State University, D
Oklahoma State University, Oklahoma City, A
Rose State College, A
Southeastern Oklahoma State University, B
Southern Nazarene University, B
University of Oklahoma, BM
The University of Tulsa, B

Oregon

George Fox University, B
Pioneer Pacific College, A
Portland State University, B
University of Oregon, MD

Pennsylvania

Albright College, B
Bucks County Community College, A
Carnegie Mellon University, MD
Clarion University of Pennsylvania, B
DeSales University, M
Drexel University, BMD
Elizabethtown College, B
Elizabethtown College School of Continuing and
    Professional Studies, AB
Gannon University, M
Immaculata University, AB
Lehigh University, M
Mansfield University of Pennsylvania, ABM
Mercyhurst University, B
Montgomery County Community College, A
Penn State Abington, AB
Penn State Altoona, AB
Penn State Beaver, B
Penn State Berks, AB
Penn State Brandywine, B
Penn State DuBois, AB
Penn State Erie, The Behrend College, AB
Penn State Fayette, The Eberly Campus, B
Penn State Greater Allegheny, B
Penn State Harrisburg, B
Penn State Hazleton, A
Penn State Lehigh Valley, AB
Penn State Mont Alto, B
Penn State New Kensington, AB
Penn State Schuylkill, AB
Penn State Shenango, B
Penn State University Park, ABMD
Penn State Wilkes-Barre, B
Penn State Worthington Scranton, B
Penn State York, B
Philadelphia University, B
Robert Morris University, BMD
Saint Joseph's University, B
Slippery Rock University of Pennsylvania, B
Susquehanna University, B
Temple University, MD
Thiel College, B
University of Pennsylvania, MD
University of Pittsburgh, BMDO
University of Pittsburgh at Bradford, A
The University of Scranton, AB
Westminster College, B

Widener University, B
Wilkes University, B

Rhode Island

Johnson & Wales University, B
University of Rhode Island, M

South Carolina

The Citadel, The Military College of South Carolina,
    M
Clemson University, B
Coastal Carolina University, B
College of Charleston, B
Limestone College, B
South University, B
University of South Carolina, BMDO
University of South Carolina Upstate, BM

South Dakota

Dakota State University, BMDO
National American University (Sioux Falls), AB
Sisseton-Wahpeton College, A

Tennessee

Belmont University, B
Carson-Newman University, B
Dyersburg State Community College, A
East Tennessee State University, MO
King University, B
Lipscomb University, B
Nashville State Community College, A
Pellissippi State Community College, A
South College, A
Tennessee Technological University, B
Trevecca Nazarene University, M
Union University, B
The University of Tennessee, MD

Texas

Amarillo College, A
Brookhaven College, A
Del Mar College, A
El Centro College, A
Lamar State College - Orange, A
Laredo Community College, A
Lee College, A
LeTourneau University, B
McLennan Community College, A
Midwestern State University, B
North Central Texas College, A
North Lake College, A
Odessa College, A
Palo Alto College, A
Panola College, A
Paris Junior College, A
Prairie View A&M University, B
St. Mary's University, BM
Sam Houston State University, M
South Texas College, A
South University, B
Southern Methodist University, MD
Tarleton State University, B
Texas A&M International University, B
Texas A&M University - Central Texas, B
Texas A&M University - Commerce, B
Texas Lutheran University, B
Texas Tech University, B
University of Houston, BMD
University of Houston - Clear Lake, M
University of Mary Hardin-Baylor, B
University of North Texas, BM
The University of Texas at Arlington, B
The University of Texas at Austin, MD
The University of Texas at El Paso, BM
The University of Texas of the Permian Basin, B
The University of Texas at San Antonio, MDO
Weatherford College, A

Utah

Brigham Young University, M
Salt Lake Community College, A
Snow College, A
University of Utah, B
Utah State University, B
Utah Valley University, B

Weber State University, B
Western Governors University, M

Vermont

Johnson State College, AB
Marlboro College, MO
Saint Michael's College, B
University of Vermont, B

Virginia

Averett University, B
Christopher Newport University, B
Dabney S. Lancaster Community College, A
ECPI University (Newport News), A
ECPI University (Richmond), A
Ferrum College, B
George Mason University, MDO
Hampton University, B
James Madison University, B
New River Community College, A
Old Dominion University, D
Radford University, B
Rappahannock Community College, A
South University (Glen Allen), B
South University (Virginia Beach), B
Southside Virginia Community College, A
Stratford University (Woodbridge), B
University of Management and Technology, AB
Virginia Commonwealth University, B
Virginia Highlands Community College, A
Virginia Polytechnic Institute and State University, B
Wytheville Community College, A

Washington

Grays Harbor College, A
Pierce College at Puyallup, A
South Puget Sound Community College, A
Spokane Falls Community College, A
University of Washington, MD
University of Washington, Bothell, B

West Virginia

Concord University, B
Davis & Elkins College, B
Eastern West Virginia Community and Technical
    College, A
Glenville State College, B
Marshall University, M
Southern West Virginia Community and Technical
    College, A
West Liberty University, B
West Virginia Wesleyan College, B

Wisconsin

Carroll University, B
Mid-State Technical College, A
Silver Lake College of the Holy Family, B
University of Wisconsin - Green Bay, B
University of Wisconsin - Madison, MD
University of Wisconsin - Milwaukee, BMDO
University of Wisconsin - Parkside, M
University of Wisconsin - Stout, M
University of Wisconsin - Superior, B

Wyoming

Sheridan College, A
Western Wyoming Community College, A

U.S. Territories: Puerto Rico

Atlantic University College, B
Colegio Universitario de San Juan, AB
Inter American University of Puerto Rico, Ponce
    Campus, B
Inter American University of Puerto Rico, San
    Germán Campus, B
Universidad del Turabo, M
University of Puerto Rico, Mayagüez Campus, D
University of Puerto Rico, Río Piedras Campus, M

University of the Sacred Heart, BO

Canada

Alberta

Athabasca University, BM
Mount Royal University, B
Southern Alberta Institute of Technology, A
University of Alberta, BM

British Columbia

British Columbia Institute of Technology, A
Thompson Rivers University, B
The University of British Columbia, MDO

Manitoba

The University of Winnipeg, B

Maritime Provinces: New Brunswick

University of New Brunswick Fredericton, B

Maritime Provinces: Nova Scotia

Cape Breton University, B
Dalhousie University, M
Mount Saint Vincent University, B
St. Francis Xavier University, B

Newfoundland and Labrador

Memorial University of Newfoundland, B

Ontario

Brock University, B
Carleton University, BM
Lakehead University, B
Queen's University at Kingston, MD
University of Ottawa, O
University of Toronto, MD
University of Waterloo, MD
The University of Western Ontario, BMD

Quebec

HEC Montreal, B
McGill University, MDO
Université de Montréal, MD
Université du Québec à Chicoutimi, B
Université du Québec à Trois-Rivières, B
Université de Sherbrooke, BMD

INFORMATION TECHNOLOGY

United States

Alabama

Columbia Southern University, B
University of South Alabama, B

Alaska

Charter College, B

Arizona

Argosy University, Phoenix, AB
Chandler-Gilbert Community College, A
Mohave Community College, A
Rio Salado College, A
University of Phoenix - Phoenix Campus, B
University of Phoenix - Southern Arizona Campus, B
Western International University, B

Arkansas

Arkansas State University - Beebe, A
Arkansas Tech University, AB
Harding University, B

California

Antelope Valley College, A
Argosy University, Inland Empire, AB
Argosy University, Los Angeles, AB
Argosy University, Orange County, AB
Argosy University, San Diego, AB
Argosy University, San Francisco Bay Area, AB

Barstow Community College, A
Bethesda University, B
Brandman University, B
Butte College, A
California Baptist University, B
California Intercontinental University, B
California State University Channel Islands, B
California State University, Chico, B
California State University, Dominguez Hills, B
California State University, Fullerton, B
California State University, Los Angeles, B
California State University, San Bernardino, B
California State University, Stanislaus, B
Cerro Coso Community College, A
Chabot College, A
Chaffey College, A
City College of San Francisco, A
College of Alameda, A
College of the Desert, A
Columbia College, A
Copper Mountain College, A
Cosumnes River College, A
Crafton Hills College, A
Cypress College, A
Evergreen Valley College, A
Fresno City College, A
Fullerton College, A
Golden Gate University, B
Humboldt State University, B
Lassen Community College District, A
Long Beach City College, A
Los Angeles City College, A
Mt. San Jacinto College, A
Palo Verde College, A
Palomar College, A
San Diego State University, B
San Joaquin Valley College - Online, A
San Jose State University, B
Santa Ana College, A
Santa Barbara City College, A
Sierra College, A
Southwestern College, A
Trident University International, B
University of Phoenix - Bay Area Campus, B
University of Phoenix - Sacramento Valley Campus, B
University of Phoenix - San Diego Campus, B
University of Phoenix - Southern California Campus, B
University of San Francisco, B
Vanguard University of Southern California, B

Colorado

American Sentinel University, B
Argosy University, Denver, AB
Colorado Technical University Online, B
National American University (Colorado Springs), B
National American University (Denver), AB
University of Denver, B
University of Phoenix - Colorado Campus, B
University of Phoenix - Colorado Springs Downtown Campus, B

Connecticut

Norwalk Community College, A

District of Columbia

University of the District of Columbia, B

Florida

Argosy University, Sarasota, AB
Argosy University, Tampa, AB
Broward College, B
College of Central Florida, A
Daytona State College, AB
Eastern Florida State College, A
Florida Agricultural and Mechanical University, B
Florida Gateway College, A
Florida International University, B
Florida National University, A
Florida SouthWestern State College, A
Florida State College at Jacksonville, A
Keiser University, AB
Miami Dade College, A
Pasco-Hernando State College, A
Seminole State College of Florida, AB

South University (Royal Palm Beach), B
Southern Technical College (Fort Myers), B
Tallahassee Community College, A
University of Central Florida, B
University of Phoenix - Central Florida Campus, B
University of Phoenix - North Florida Campus, B
University of Phoenix - South Florida Campus, B
University of South Florida, B
University of South Florida Sarasota-Manatee, B
University of West Florida, B

Georgia

American InterContinental University Atlanta, B
Argosy University, Atlanta, AB
Atlanta Technical College, A
Augusta University, B
Clayton State University, B
Columbus State University, B
Georgia Gwinnett College, B
Georgia Military College, A
Georgia Southwestern State University, B
Gordon State College, A
Kennesaw State University, B
Life University, AB
Middle Georgia State University, B
Savannah Technical College, A
University of Phoenix - Atlanta Campus, B
University of Phoenix - Augusta Campus, AB

Hawaii

Argosy University, Hawai'i, AB
Hawaii Community College, A
Kapiolani Community College, A
University of Phoenix - Hawaii Campus, B

Idaho

Boise State University, B
Brigham Young University - Idaho, B
Broadview University - Boise, B

Illinois

American InterContinental University Online, B
Bradley University, B
City Colleges of Chicago, Harold Washington College, A
City Colleges of Chicago, Harry S. Truman College, A
City Colleges of Chicago, Kennedy-King College, A
City Colleges of Chicago, Olive-Harvey College, A
DePaul University, B
Governors State University, B
Heartland Community College, A
Highland Community College, A
Illinois Eastern Community Colleges, Olney Central College, A
Illinois Institute of Technology, B
Illinois State University, B
Illinois Valley Community College, A
John A. Logan College, A
Kishwaukee College, A
Lake Land College, A
Loyola University Chicago, B
McHenry County College, A
McKendree University, B
North Park University, B
Northwestern College - Bridgeview Campus, A
Oakton Community College, A
Prairie State College, A
Robert Morris University Illinois, B
South Suburban College, A
Southwestern Illinois College, A
University of St. Francis, B
Western Illinois University, B

Indiana

Grace College, B
Harrison College, B
Indiana State University, B
Indiana University - Purdue University Fort Wayne, AB
Ivy Tech Community College - Bloomington, A
Ivy Tech Community College - Central Indiana, A
Ivy Tech Community College - Columbus, A
Ivy Tech Community College - East Central, A
Ivy Tech Community College - Kokomo, A

Ivy Tech Community College - Lafayette, A
Ivy Tech Community College - Richmond, A
Ivy Tech Community College - Southeast, A
Ivy Tech Community College - Southern Indiana, A
Ivy Tech Community College - Southwest, A
Ivy Tech Community College - Wabash Valley, A
Purdue University, AB

Iowa

Des Moines Area Community College, A
Iowa Lakes Community College, A
Kaplan University, Cedar Rapids, B
Kaplan University, Davenport Campus, AB
Kaplan University, Des Moines, AB
Kaplan University, Mason City Campus, A
William Penn University, B

Kansas

National American University, A
Ottawa University, B
The University of Kansas, B
University of Saint Mary, B

Kentucky

Jefferson Community and Technical College, A
Kentucky State University, B
Maysville Community and Technical College
   (Morehead), A
Murray State University, B
Northern Kentucky University, B
Southeast Kentucky Community and Technical Col-
   lege, A
Sullivan College of Technology and Design, AB
Sullivan University, B
Thomas More College, AB
Union College, B
Western Kentucky University, B

Louisiana

Delta School of Business and Technology, A
ITI Technical College, A

Maine

University of Maine at Augusta, AB

Maryland

College of Southern Maryland, A
Frederick Community College, A
Frostburg State University, B
Howard Community College, A
Towson University, B
University of Baltimore, B

Massachusetts

Merrimack College, B
Newbury College, B
Simmons College, B
University of Massachusetts Boston, B
Western New England University, B

Michigan

Central Michigan University, B
Ferris State University, AB
Gogebic Community College, A
Lawrence Technological University, B
Monroe County Community College, A
Oakland University, B
Olivet College, B
University of Phoenix - Detroit Campus, B
Walsh College of Accountancy and Business Admin-
   istration, B
West Shore Community College, A

Minnesota

Argosy University, Twin Cities, AB
Capella University, B
Globe University - Minneapolis, B
Globe University - Woodbury, B
Mesabi Range College, A
Minnesota School of Business - Blaine, B
Minnesota School of Business - Brooklyn Center, B
Minnesota School of Business - Elk River, B
Minnesota School of Business - Lakeville, B
Minnesota School of Business - Plymouth, B
Minnesota School of Business - Richfield, B

Minnesota School of Business - Rochester, B
Minnesota School of Business - St. Cloud, B
Minnesota State Community and Technical College -
   Detroit Lakes, A
Minnesota State Community and Technical College -
   Moorhead, A
Minnesota West Community and Technical College,
   A
Southwest Minnesota State University, B

Mississippi

Antonelli College (Hattiesburg), A
Mississippi Gulf Coast Community College, A
Southwest Mississippi Community College, A
Virginia College in Jackson, A

Missouri

American Business & Technology University, A
College of the Ozarks, B
Jefferson College, A
Lindenwood University, B
Metropolitan Community College - Kansas City, A
Missouri Baptist University, B
Missouri State University - West Plains, A
Missouri Western State University, B
Three Rivers Community College, A
University of Missouri - Kansas City, B

Montana

Great Falls College Montana State University, A
University of Great Falls, B
University of Montana, B

Nebraska

Bellevue University, B
Creighton University, B
Kaplan University, Lincoln, B
Kaplan University, Omaha, B
Nebraska Indian Community College, A
University of Nebraska at Omaha, B
Western Nebraska Community College, A

Nevada

University of Phoenix - Las Vegas Campus, B

New Hampshire

Granite State College, B
Plymouth State University, B
Rivier University, B
University of New Hampshire, B
University of New Hampshire at Manchester, B

New Jersey

Bergen Community College, A
Caldwell University, B
Fairleigh Dickinson University, Metropolitan Cam-
   pus, B
Montclair State University, B
New Jersey Institute of Technology, B
Raritan Valley Community College, A
Rowan College at Burlington County, A
Union County College, A
University of Phoenix - Jersey City Campus, AB

New Mexico

Clovis Community College, A
National American University (Albuquerque), AB
Navajo Technical University, A
New Mexico Institute of Mining and Technology, B
New Mexico State University, B
New Mexico State University - Alamogordo, A
University of Phoenix - New Mexico Campus, B

New York

Adirondack Community College, A
Bryant & Stratton College - Albany Campus, A
Bryant & Stratton College - Amherst Campus, A
Bryant & Stratton College - Buffalo Campus, A
Bryant & Stratton College - Greece Campus, A
Bryant & Stratton College - Henrietta Campus, A
Bryant & Stratton College - Liverpool Campus, A
Bryant & Stratton College - Orchard Park Campus,
   A
Bryant & Stratton College - Syracuse Campus, A
The College of Saint Rose, B

Columbia-Greene Community College, A
Cornell University, B
Corning Community College, A
Erie Community College, South Campus, A
Hudson Valley Community College, A
Jamestown Community College, A
Long Island University - LIU Post, B
Monroe College, AB
Monroe Community College, A
Morrisville State College, B
Mount Saint Mary College, B
New York Institute of Technology, B
Queensborough Community College of the City Uni-
   versity of New York, A
Rensselaer Polytechnic Institute, B
Rochester Institute of Technology, B
State University of New York College of Agriculture
   and Technology at Cobleskill, B
State University of New York College of Technology
   at Canton, B
Suffolk County Community College, A
United States Military Academy, B

North Carolina

Asheville-Buncombe Technical Community College,
   A
Bladen Community College, A
Blue Ridge Community College, A
Caldwell Community College and Technical Institute,
   A
Campbell University, B
Carteret Community College, A
Catawba Valley Community College, A
Central Carolina Community College, A
Cleveland Community College, A
College of The Albemarle, A
Craven Community College, A
Durham Technical Community College, A
East Carolina University, B
Fayetteville Technical Community College, A
Forsyth Technical Community College, A
Gaston College, A
Guilford Technical Community College, A
Halifax Community College, A
James Sprunt Community College, A
Johnson C. Smith University, B
Lenoir Community College, A
McDowell Technical Community College, A
Mitchell Community College, A
Montgomery Community College, A
Nash Community College, A
Piedmont Community College, A
Pitt Community College, A
Randolph Community College, A
Richmond Community College, A
Roanoke-Chowan Community College, A
Rockingham Community College, A
Rowan-Cabarrus Community College, A
Sampson Community College, A
South Piedmont Community College, A
Surry Community College, A
Tri-County Community College, A
The University of North Carolina at Pembroke, B
The University of North Carolina Wilmington, B
University of Phoenix - Charlotte Campus, AB
Wake Technical Community College, A
Wayne Community College, A
Western Piedmont Community College, A
Wilson Community College, A
Winston-Salem State University, B

North Dakota

Dakota College at Bottineau, A
University of Jamestown, B

Ohio

American National University (Kettering), A
Bluffton University, B
Bryant & Stratton College - Cleveland Campus, A
Bryant & Stratton College - Eastlake Campus, A
Bryant & Stratton College - Parma Campus, A
Cedarville University, B
Clark State Community College, A
Franklin University, AB
Lorain County Community College, A
Marion Technical College, A

Miami University, B
Ohio University - Chillicothe, B
Owens Community College, A
Sinclair Community College, A
Stark State College, A
Tiffin University, AB
University of Cincinnati, B
University of Rio Grande, B
The University of Toledo, B
Vatterott College, A
Youngstown State University, AB

Oklahoma

Cameron University, AB
Oklahoma State University, B
Oklahoma State University Institute of Technology, A
Oklahoma State University, Oklahoma City, A
University of Central Oklahoma, B
The University of Tulsa, B
Vatterott College (Warr Acres), A

Oregon

Pioneer Pacific College, B

Pennsylvania

Berks Technical Institute, A
Cabrini University, B
Carnegie Mellon University, B
Central Penn College, B
DeSales University, B
Johnson College, A
Juniata College, B
Keystone College, AB
La Roche College, B
La Salle University, B
Laurel Business Institute, A
Lehigh University, B
Lincoln University, B
Mount Aloysius College, B
Peirce College, AB
Penn Commercial Business and Technical School, A
Point Park University, B
Saint Joseph's University, B
Slippery Rock University of Pennsylvania, B
Temple University, B
University of Phoenix - Philadelphia Campus, B
University of Pittsburgh at Titusville, A
Washington & Jefferson College, B

Rhode Island

Bryant University, B
New England Institute of Technology, AB

South Carolina

Bob Jones University, B
Coastal Carolina University, B
Furman University, B
Limestone College, AB

South Dakota

Mount Marty College, B
National American University (Sioux Falls), AB

Tennessee

Argosy University, Nashville, AB
Fountainhead College of Technology, A
LeMoyne-Owen College, B
Lipscomb University, B
Nashville State Community College, A
Northeast State Community College, A
Roane State Community College, A
Southwest Tennessee Community College, A
Trevecca Nazarene University, AB

Texas

Abilene Christian University, B
Argosy University, Dallas, AB
Baylor University, B
Coastal Bend College, A
Del Mar College, A
Galveston College, A
Hallmark University, A
Laredo Community College, A
Lone Star College - CyFair, A
Lone Star College - Montgomery, A

McMurry University, B
Palo Alto College, A
Panola College, A
Stephen F. Austin State University, B
Texas Christian University, B
Tyler Junior College, A
University of Houston - Clear Lake, B
University of North Texas, B
University of Phoenix - Dallas Campus, B
University of Phoenix - Houston Campus, B
University of Phoenix - San Antonio Campus, B
The University of Texas at Dallas, B

Utah

Argosy University, Salt Lake City, AB
Brigham Young University, B
Broadview University - Layton, B
Broadview University - West Jordan, B
Dixie State University, B
LDS Business College, A
Neumont University, B
Salt Lake Community College, A
Southern Utah University, A
University of Phoenix - Utah Campus, B

Vermont

Community College of Vermont, A
Vermont Technical College, AB

Virginia

American National University (Harrisonburg), B
American National University (Salem), AB
Argosy University, Washington DC, AB
Bluefield College, B
Christopher Newport University, B
George Mason University, B
Germanna Community College, A
John Tyler Community College, A
Liberty University, B
Marymount University, B
Northern Virginia Community College, A
Patrick Henry Community College, A
Regent University, AB
Southside Virginia Community College, A
Stratford University (Alexandria), B
Stratford University (Falls Church), B
Stratford University (Glen Allen), B
Stratford University (Newport News), B
Stratford University (Virginia Beach), B
Stratford University (Woodbridge), B
Thomas Nelson Community College, A
Tidewater Community College, A
University of Management and Technology, AB

Washington

Argosy University, Seattle, AB
Central Washington University, B
Everett Community College, A
Northwest Indian College, A
Olympic College, B
University of Phoenix - Western Washington Campus, B
University of Washington, B
University of Washington, Tacoma, B

West Virginia

American Public University System, B
Blue Ridge Community and Technical College, A
Mountwest Community & Technical College, A
West Virginia Junior College - Bridgeport, A
West Virginia Northern Community College, A

Wisconsin

Globe University - Eau Claire, B
Globe University - Green Bay, B
Globe University - La Crosse, B
Globe University - Madison East, B
Globe University - Madison West, B
Globe University - Wausau, B
Marian University, B
Marquette University, B
University of Wisconsin - Stevens Point, B
University of Wisconsin - Whitewater, B

Wyoming

Western Wyoming Community College, A

U.S. Territories: Puerto Rico

EDP University of Puerto Rico - San Sebastian, A
Inter American University of Puerto Rico, Bayamón Campus, B
National University College (Bayamón), AB
Pontifical Catholic University of Puerto Rico, A

Canada

British Columbia

The University of British Columbia - Okanagan Campus, B

Ontario

Ryerson University, B
The University of Western Ontario, B
York University, B

Quebec

Université du Québec, École de technologie supérieure, B
Université de Sherbrooke, B

INORGANIC CHEMISTRY

United States

Alabama

Auburn University, MD

California

California State University, Los Angeles, M

Connecticut

Wesleyan University, D
Yale University, D

District of Columbia

The George Washington University, MD
Georgetown University, D
Howard University, MD

Florida

Florida State University, MD
University of Miami, D

Georgia

University of Georgia, MD

Illinois

Illinois Institute of Technology, M

Indiana

Indiana University Bloomington, D
Purdue University, MD
University of Notre Dame, MD

Iowa

Iowa State University of Science and Technology, MD

Kansas

Kansas State University, M

Kentucky

University of Louisville, MD

Louisiana

Southern University and Agricultural and Mechanical College, M

Maryland

University of Maryland, College Park, MD

Massachusetts

Boston College, D
Brandeis University, MD

Harvard University, D
Massachusetts Institute of Technology, D
Tufts University, MD
University of Massachusetts Lowell, D

Michigan

University of Michigan, D
Wayne State University, D

Mississippi

University of Southern Mississippi, M

Missouri

University of Missouri, MD
University of Missouri - Kansas City, MD

Montana

University of Montana, MD

Nebraska

University of Nebraska - Lincoln, D

New Jersey

Rutgers University - New Brunswick, MD
Rutgers University - Newark, MD
Seton Hall University, MD

New Mexico

Eastern New Mexico University, M

New York

Binghamton University, State University of New
   York, D
Cornell University, D

North Carolina

Wake Forest University, MD

Ohio

Cleveland State University, M
University of Cincinnati, MD
The University of Toledo, MD
Youngstown State University, M

Oregon

Oregon State University, MD

Tennessee

University of Memphis, M
The University of Tennessee, MD
Vanderbilt University, MD

Texas

Rice University, D
The University of Texas at Austin, D

Virginia

Virginia Commonwealth University, MD

West Virginia

West Virginia University, MD

Wisconsin

Marquette University, MD

Canada

Alberta

University of Calgary, MD

Ontario

McMaster University, MD
The University of Western Ontario, B

Quebec

McGill University, B

Saskatchewan

University of Regina, MD

INSTITUTIONAL FOOD WORK-ERS

United States

California

Santa Barbara City College, A

Iowa

Iowa Lakes Community College, A

Michigan

Washtenaw Community College, A

Mississippi

Hinds Community College, A

New Jersey

Atlantic Cape Community College, A

New Mexico

Southwestern Indian Polytechnic Institute, A

North Carolina

James Sprunt Community College, A
Wilkes Community College, A

Texas

El Paso Community College, A
Lamar Institute of Technology, A

INSTRUMENTATION TECHNOL-OGY/TECHNICIAN

United States

Alaska

University of Alaska Anchorage, A

Arkansas

Phillips Community College of the University of Arkansas, A

California

Chaffey College, A

Georgia

Georgia Piedmont Technical College, A

Idaho

Idaho State University, AB

Illinois

Moraine Valley Community College, A

Louisiana

ITI Technical College, A
Louisiana Delta Community College, A
Northwest Louisiana Technical College, A
Sowela Technical Community College, A

Maryland

Hagerstown Community College, A

Michigan

Northern Michigan University, B

Minnesota

Mesabi Range College, A
Ridgewater College, A
St. Cloud Technical & Community College, A

Missouri

Ozarks Technical Community College, A
Ranken Technical College, A

Nevada

Great Basin College, B

New Mexico

San Juan College, A
Southwestern Indian Polytechnic Institute, A

New York

Finger Lakes Community College, A
Monroe Community College, A
Nassau Community College, A

North Carolina

Cape Fear Community College, A
Central Carolina Community College, A

North Dakota

Bismarck State College, A

Ohio

Bowling Green State University, B
Lakeland Community College, A

Oklahoma

Oklahoma State University Institute of Technology, B
Spartan College of Aeronautics and Technology, AB

Pennsylvania

Butler County Community College, A

South Carolina

Orangeburg-Calhoun Technical College, A

Tennessee

Northeast State Community College, A

Texas

Amarillo College, A
Brazosport College, A
Houston Community College, A
Lamar Institute of Technology, A
Lee College, A
San Jacinto College District, A
Texas State Technical College, A

Utah

Salt Lake Community College, A

Virginia

New River Community College, A

Washington

Bellingham Technical College, A
Lower Columbia College, A
Yakima Valley Community College, A

Wisconsin

Mid-State Technical College, A

Wyoming

Western Wyoming Community College, A

U.S. Territories: Puerto Rico

University of Puerto Rico in Bayamón, A
University of Puerto Rico in Carolina, A

INSURANCE

United States

Arizona

Mesa Community College, A

Arkansas

University of Central Arkansas, B

California

California State University, Fullerton, M
Cerritos College, A
College of San Mateo, A
Cypress College, A
Glendale Community College, A
Merced College, A

Palomar College, A
San Diego City College, A
Southwestern College, A

Colorado

University of Colorado Denver, M

Connecticut

University of Connecticut, B
University of Hartford, B

District of Columbia

Gallaudet University, B
Howard University, B

Florida

Broward College, A
Florida State University, MD
South Florida State College, A
University of Florida, D

Georgia

Georgia State University, BMDO
University of Georgia, B

Idaho

Idaho State University, B

Illinois

Bradley University, B
Illinois State University, B
Illinois Wesleyan University, B
Richland Community College, A
University of Illinois at Urbana - Champaign, B

Indiana

Ball State University, B
Butler University, B
Indiana State University, B
Martin University, B
University of Saint Francis, B

Iowa

North Iowa Area Community College, A
William Penn University, B

Louisiana

University of Louisiana at Lafayette, B
University of Louisiana at Monroe, B

Michigan

Northern Michigan University, B
Olivet College, B

Minnesota

University of Minnesota, Twin Cities Campus, B

Mississippi

Delta State University, B
Mississippi State University, B
University of Mississippi, B

Missouri

Missouri State University, B

Montana

Miles Community College, A

New York

Excelsior College, B
Nassau Community College, A
St. John's University, BM

North Carolina

Appalachian State University, B
Central Piedmont Community College, A
Isothermal Community College, A

Ohio

Bowling Green State University, B
Clark State Community College, A
Franklin University, B
Kent State University at Salem, B

Ohio Dominican University, B
Ohio Northern University, B
The Ohio State University, B
University of Cincinnati, B

Oklahoma

University of Central Oklahoma, B

Pennsylvania

Community College of Allegheny County, A
Gannon University, B
Laurel Business Institute, A
Saint Joseph's University, B
Temple University, BD
University of Pennsylvania, BMD

South Carolina

University of South Carolina, B

Texas

Baylor University, B
Southern Methodist University, B
Trinity Valley Community College, A
University of Houston - Downtown, B
University of North Texas, B

Virginia

Virginia Commonwealth University, M

Wisconsin

Madison Area Technical College, A
University of Wisconsin - La Crosse, B
University of Wisconsin - Madison, BMD

U.S. Territories: Puerto Rico

Inter American University of Puerto Rico, Metropolitan Campus, A
Universidad del Este, B

Canada

Alberta

University of Calgary, B

Quebec

McGill University, B
Université Laval, A

INTELLECTUAL PROPERTY LAW

United States

California

Golden Gate University, M
Santa Clara University, M
University of San Francisco, M

Illinois

DePaul University, M

Massachusetts

Boston University, M
Suffolk University, D

New Jersey

Montclair State University, M

New York

Fordham University, M
Yeshiva University, M

Ohio

Case Western Reserve University, M

Pennsylvania

University of Pittsburgh, M

Texas

Baylor University, D
University of Houston, M

Washington

University of Washington, M

INTERCULTURAL/MULTICUL-TURAL AND DIVERSITY STUD-IES

United States

Alabama

University of Mobile, B

California

Biola University, B
Vanguard University of Southern California, B

Colorado

Colorado Heights University, B

Illinois

Judson University, B
Triton College, A

Indiana

Indiana Wesleyan University, B

Massachusetts

Bard College at Simon's Rock, B

Minnesota

Macalester College, B
North Central University, B
St. Catherine University, B

Missouri

Calvary Bible College and Theological Seminary, B
Evangel University, B

New York

Nyack College, AB

North Dakota

Trinity Bible College, B

Oregon

Western Oregon University, B

Pennsylvania

Villanova University, B

South Carolina

Columbia International University, B
Wofford College, B

Tennessee

Trevecca Nazarene University, B

Texas

Baptist University of the Americas, A
University of the Incarnate Word, B

Vermont

Goddard College, B

Washington

The Evergreen State College, B
Northwest University, B

U.S. Territories: Puerto Rico

University of Puerto Rico, Río Piedras Campus, B

Canada

Alberta

Prairie Bible Institute, B
Rocky Mountain College, B

British Columbia

Columbia Bible College, B

Ontario

Wilfrid Laurier University, B

Quebec

Concordia University, B

Saskatchewan

University of Regina, B

INTERDISCIPLINARY STUDIES

United States

Alabama

The University of Alabama, D
The University of Alabama at Birmingham, D
The University of Alabama in Huntsville, MDO
University of South Alabama, MD

Alaska

Alaska Pacific University, M
University of Alaska Anchorage, M
University of Alaska Fairbanks, MD

Arizona

Arizona State University at the Tempe campus, M
Harrison Middleton University, D
The University of Arizona, MD

Arkansas

University of Arkansas, MD
University of Arkansas at Little Rock, M

California

California College of the Arts, M
California Institute of Integral Studies, M
California State University, Bakersfield, M
California State University, East Bay, M
California State University, Long Beach, M
California State University, San Bernardino, M
California State University, Stanislaus, M
Fresno Pacific University, M
Mills College, M
San Diego State University, M
San Jose State University, M
Santa Clara University, M
Sonoma State University, M
University of California, Santa Barbara, D
University of California, Santa Cruz, D

Colorado

University of Colorado Colorado Springs, M

District of Columbia

Georgetown University, M

Florida

Florida Gulf Coast University, M
Florida Institute of Technology, M
Nova Southeastern University, M
University of Central Florida, MO
University of Florida, M
University of South Florida, M

Georgia

Emory University, D

Idaho

Boise State University, M
Idaho State University, M
University of Idaho, M

Illinois

DePaul University, M
University of Chicago, D
University of Illinois at Chicago, D
University of Illinois at Springfield, M
University of Illinois at Urbana - Champaign, D

Indiana

Indiana University Southeast, MO

Iowa

Iowa State University of Science and Technology, M

Kansas

The University of Kansas, MD

Kentucky

University of Louisville, MD
Western Kentucky University, M

Louisiana

Tulane University, D

Maine

University of Maine, MD

Maryland

Frostburg State University, M

Massachusetts

Cambridge College, M
Fitchburg State University, O
Lesley University, M
Massachusetts College of Art and Design, M
Northeastern University, D
Tufts University, D
Worcester Polytechnic Institute, MD

Michigan

Michigan Technological University, MDO
University of Michigan, MD

Minnesota

Minnesota State University Mankato, M
University of Minnesota, Twin Cities Campus, D
Walden University, D

Missouri

University of Missouri, O
University of Missouri - Kansas City, D
University of Missouri - St. Louis, O

Montana

Montana State University Billings, M
Montana Tech of The University of Montana, M
University of Montana, MD

New Jersey

Drew University, MDO
Rutgers University - New Brunswick, D

New Mexico

New Mexico State University, MD
Western New Mexico University, M

New York

Buffalo State College, State University of New York, M
Clarkson University, MD
New York University, M
Niagara University, M
Rensselaer Polytechnic Institute, MD
Rochester Institute of Technology, M
State University of New York at Fredonia, M

North Carolina

Campbell University, M
The University of North Carolina at Charlotte, MDO

Ohio

Bowling Green State University, MD
Hiram College, M
The Ohio State University, MD
Union Institute & University, MD
University of Cincinnati, D
Wright State University, M

Oklahoma

University of Central Oklahoma, M
University of Oklahoma, MD

Oregon

Marylhurst University, M
Oregon State University, M
Southern Oregon University, M
University of Oregon, M

Pennsylvania

DeSales University, M
Lehigh University, MD
Marywood University, D
University of Pittsburgh, D

South Dakota

The University of South Dakota, M

Tennessee

University of Memphis, M
The University of Tennessee at Martin, M

Texas

Amberton University, M
Baylor University, D
Dallas Baptist University, M
Stephen F. Austin State University, M
Texas A&M University - Texarkana, M
Texas State University, M
Texas Tech University, MD
University of Houston - Victoria, M
University of the Incarnate Word, M
University of North Texas, M
The University of Texas at Arlington, M
The University of Texas at Dallas, M
The University of Texas at El Paso, M
The University of Texas Health Science Center at San Antonio, D
The University of Texas Rio Grande Valley, M
The University of Texas at San Antonio, MD
The University of Texas at Tyler, M
Wayland Baptist University, M
West Texas A&M University, M

Vermont

Goddard College, M
University of Vermont, M

Virginia

The College of William and Mary, MD
George Mason University, M
Hollins University, M
Regent University, M
University of Virginia, MD
Virginia Commonwealth University, M
Virginia Polytechnic Institute and State University, MD
Virginia State University, M

Washington

Central Washington University, M
Eastern Washington University, M
University of Washington, Tacoma, M
Washington State University, D

Wisconsin

Marquette University, D
University of Wisconsin - Milwaukee, D

Canada

Alberta

Athabasca University, M

British Columbia

Trinity Western University, M
University of Northern British Columbia, M

Manitoba

University of Manitoba, MD

Maritime Provinces: New Brunswick

University of New Brunswick Fredericton, MD

Maritime Provinces: Nova Scotia

Dalhousie University, D

Ontario

University of Ottawa, DO
The University of Western Ontario, MD
York University, M

Quebec

Concordia University, MD

Saskatchewan

University of Regina, M

INTERIOR ARCHITECTURE

United States

Alabama

Auburn University, B

California

California College of the Arts, B
Woodbury University, B

Connecticut

University of New Haven, B

Florida

College of Central Florida, A

Illinois

School of the Art Institute of Chicago, B

Indiana

Indiana State University, B

Louisiana

Delgado Community College, A
Louisiana State University and Agricultural & Me-
    chanical College, B
Louisiana Tech University, B
University of Louisiana at Lafayette, B

Massachusetts

Boston Architectural College, B

Michigan

Lawrence Technological University, B

Mississippi

Mississippi State University, B
University of Southern Mississippi, B

Missouri

University of Missouri, B

Nebraska

University of Nebraska - Lincoln, B

Nevada

University of Nevada, Las Vegas, B

New York

Syracuse University, B

Ohio

Bowling Green State University, B
Miami University, B
Mount St. Joseph University, B

Oregon

University of Oregon, B

Pennsylvania

Chatham University, B
La Roche College, B
Philadelphia University, B

Rhode Island

Rhode Island School of Design, B

Texas

Sam Houston State University, B
Stephen F. Austin State University, B
Texas Tech University, B
University of Houston, B
University of North Texas, B
The University of Texas at Arlington, B
The University of Texas at San Antonio, B

Wisconsin

Milwaukee Institute of Art and Design, B

INTERIOR DESIGN

United States

Alabama

Auburn University, B
Samford University, B
The University of Alabama, B
Virginia College in Birmingham, AB
Virginia College in Mobile, A
Wallace State Community College, A

Arizona

Arizona State University at the Tempe campus, B
The Art Institute of Phoenix, B
The Art Institute of Tucson, B
Mesa Community College, A
Northern Arizona University, B
Phoenix College, A
Pima Community College, A
Scottsdale Community College, A
Southwest University of Visual Arts, B

Arkansas

Harding University, B
University of Arkansas, B
University of Central Arkansas, B

California

Academy of Art University, ABM
Allan Hancock College, A
American River College, A
Antelope Valley College, A
Art Center College of Design, B
The Art Institute of California - Hollywood, a campus
    of Argosy University, B
The Art Institute of California - Inland Empire, a
    campus of Argosy University, B
The Art Institute of California - Los Angeles, a cam-
    pus of Argosy University, B
The Art Institute of California - Orange County, a
    campus of Argosy University, B
The Art Institute of California - Sacramento, a cam-
    pus of Argosy University, B
The Art Institute of California - San Diego, a cam-
    pus of Argosy University, B
The Art Institute of California - San Francisco, a
    campus of Argosy University, B
Bakersfield College, A
Butte College, A
California State Polytechnic University, Pomona, M
California State University, Fresno, B
California State University, Long Beach, B
California State University, Sacramento, B
Cañada College, A
Chabot College, A
Chaffey College, A
City College of San Francisco, A
College of the Canyons, A

College of Marin, A
College of the Sequoias, A
Cuesta College, A
Design Institute of San Diego, B
El Camino College, A
FIDM/Fashion Institute of Design & Merchandising,
    Los Angeles Campus, AB
FIDM/Fashion Institute of Design & Merchandising,
    Orange County Campus, A
FIDM/Fashion Institute of Design & Merchandising,
    San Francisco Campus, A
Fullerton College, A
Interior Designers Institute, ABM
Las Positas College, A
Long Beach City College, A
Modesto Junior College, A
Monterey Peninsula College, A
Mt. San Antonio College, A
NewSchool of Architecture and Design, B
Ohlone College, A
Orange Coast College, A
Otis College of Art and Design, B
Palomar College, A
Point Loma Nazarene University, B
Saddleback College, A
San Bernardino Valley College, A
San Diego City College, A
San Diego Mesa College, A
San Diego State University, BM
San Francisco State University, B
San Jose State University, B
Santa Barbara City College, A
Santa Monica College, A
Santa Rosa Junior College, A
University of California, Berkeley, O
West Valley College, A

Colorado

Arapahoe Community College, A
The Art Institute of Colorado, B
Colorado State University, B
Front Range Community College, A
Pikes Peak Community College, A
Red Rocks Community College, A
Rocky Mountain College of Art + Design, B

Connecticut

Norwalk Community College, A
Paier College of Art, Inc., B
University of Bridgeport, B

Delaware

Delaware College of Art and Design, A
Delaware Technical & Community College, Terry
    Campus, A

District of Columbia

The George Washington University, M
Howard University, B

Florida

The Art Institute of Fort Lauderdale, AB
The Art Institute of Tampa, a branch of Miami Inter-
    national University of Art & Design, B
Broward College, A
Daytona State College, A
Florida International University, BMO
Florida State College at Jacksonville, A
Florida State University, BM
Indian River State College, A
Miami Dade College, A
Miami International University of Art & Design, B
Palm Beach State College, A
Ringling College of Art and Design, B
Seminole State College of Florida, AB
Southern Technical College (Fort Myers), AB
University of Florida, BMD

Georgia

American InterContinental University Atlanta, B
The Art Institute of Atlanta, B
Brenau University, BM
Georgia Southern University, B
Georgia State University, M
Gwinnett Technical College, A

Lanier Technical College, A
Ogeechee Technical College, A
Savannah College of Art and Design, BM
University of Georgia, MD
Valdosta State University, B

Hawaii

Chaminade University of Honolulu, AB

Idaho

Brigham Young University - Idaho, B
University of Idaho, B

Illinois

College of DuPage, A
Columbia College Chicago, B
Harper College, A
The Illinois Institute of Art - Chicago, B
The Illinois Institute of Art - Schaumburg, B
Joliet Junior College, A
Judson University, B
Robert Morris University Illinois, A
School of the Art Institute of Chicago, M
Southern Illinois University Carbondale, B

Indiana

The Art Institute of Indianapolis, B
Indiana University Bloomington, B
Indiana University - Purdue University Fort Wayne,
   AB
Indiana University - Purdue University Indianapolis,
   AB
Indiana Wesleyan University, B
Ivy Tech Community College - Columbus, A
Ivy Tech Community College - East Central, A
Ivy Tech Community College - North Central, A
Ivy Tech Community College - Southwest, A

Iowa

Hawkeye Community College, A
Iowa State University of Science and Technology,
   BM
Scott Community College, A
University of Northern Iowa, B
Western Iowa Tech Community College, A

Kansas

Fort Hays State University, B
Johnson County Community College, A
Kansas State University, B
McPherson College, B
Wichita Area Technical College, A

Kentucky

Sullivan College of Technology and Design, AB
University of Kentucky, BM

Maryland

Harford Community College, A
Maryland Institute College of Art, B
Montgomery College, A

Massachusetts

Bay Path University, AB
Boston Architectural College, M
Endicott College, BM
Mount Ida College, BM
Newbury College, B
Suffolk University, BM
University of Massachusetts Amherst, M
Wentworth Institute of Technology, B

Michigan

Adrian College, B
The Art Institute of Michigan, AB
Baker College, AB
College for Creative Studies, B
Eastern Michigan University, BM
Ferris State University, B
Henry Ford College, A
Lansing Community College, A
Lawrence Technological University, M
Michigan State University, BM
Oakland Community College, A

Wayne State University, M
Western Michigan University, B

Minnesota

Alexandria Technical and Community College, A
Century College, A
Dakota County Technical College, A
Dunwoody College of Technology, B
University of Minnesota, Twin Cities Campus,
   BMDO

Mississippi

Antonelli College (Hattiesburg), A
Antonelli College (Jackson), A
Mississippi College, B
Northeast Mississippi Community College, A

Missouri

The Art Institute of St. Louis, B
Maryville University of Saint Louis, B
Park University, B
Stevens - The Institute of Business & Arts, AB
University of Central Missouri, B

Montana

Montana State University, A

Nebraska

Metropolitan Community College, A
University of Nebraska - Lincoln, M

Nevada

The Art Institute of Las Vegas, B

New Jersey

Berkeley College - Woodland Park Campus, AB
Brookdale Community College, A
Kean University, B
New Jersey Institute of Technology, B
Raritan Valley Community College, A

New Mexico

Santa Fe Community College, A

New York

Cazenovia College, B
Cornell University, M
Eugene Lang College of Liberal Arts, B
Fashion Institute of Technology, ABM
Marist College, B
Monroe Community College, A
Nassau Community College, A
New York Institute of Technology, B
New York School of Interior Design, ABM
Onondaga Community College, A
Parsons School of Design, AB
Pratt Institute, BM
Rochester Institute of Technology, B
The Sage Colleges, B
School of Visual Arts, B
State University of New York College of Technology
   at Alfred, A
Suffolk County Community College, A
Villa Maria College, AB

North Carolina

Appalachian State University, B
The Art Institute of Charlotte, a campus of South
   University, AB
The Art Institute of Raleigh-Durham, a campus of
   South University, B
Cape Fear Community College, A
Carteret Community College, A
Central Piedmont Community College, A
East Carolina University, B
Forsyth Technical Community College, A
High Point University, B
Living Arts College, B
Meredith College, B
Queens University of Charlotte, BM
Randolph Community College, A
Salem College, B
The University of North Carolina at Greensboro,
   BMO

Western Carolina University, B

North Dakota

North Dakota State University, B

Ohio

Antonelli College, A
Cleveland Institute of Art, B
Columbus College of Art & Design, B
Davis College, A
Kent State University, B
Miami University Hamilton, B
The Ohio State University, BM
Sinclair Community College, A
University of Cincinnati, BM
Virginia Marti College of Art and Design, A

Oklahoma

Clary Sage College, A
Oklahoma Christian University, B
Tulsa Community College, A
University of Central Oklahoma, B
University of Oklahoma, BM

Oregon

The Art Institute of Portland, B
Marylhurst University, B
Oregon State University, B
Portland Community College, A
University of Oregon, M

Pennsylvania

Arcadia University, B
The Art Institute of Philadelphia, AB
The Art Institute of Pittsburgh, B
Chatham University, M
Drexel University, BM
Harcum College, A
Indiana University of Pennsylvania, B
Lehigh Carbon Community College, A
Marywood University, BM
Mercyhurst University, B
Moore College of Art & Design, BM
Northampton Community College, A
Philadelphia University, BM

Rhode Island

New England Institute of Technology, AB
Rhode Island School of Design, M

South Carolina

Anderson University, B
The Art Institute of Charleston, a branch of The Art
   Institute of Atlanta, B
Converse College, B

South Dakota

South Dakota State University, BM

Tennessee

The Art Institute of Tennessee - Nashville, a branch
   of The Art Institute of Atlanta, B
Carson-Newman University, B
East Tennessee State University, B
Middle Tennessee State University, B
O'More College of Design, B
Pellissippi State Community College, A
University of Memphis, M
The University of Tennessee, B
The University of Tennessee at Chattanooga, B
The University of Tennessee at Martin, B
Watkins College of Art, Design, & Film, B

Texas

Abilene Christian University, B
Amarillo College, A
The Art Institute of Austin, a branch of The Art Insti-
   tute of Houston, B
The Art Institute of Dallas, a campus of South Uni-
   versity, B
The Art Institute of Houston, B
The Art Institute of San Antonio, a branch of The Art
   Institute of Houston, B
Baylor University, B

Collin County Community College District, A
El Centro College, A
El Paso Community College, A
Houston Community College, A
Lone Star College - Kingwood, A
San Jacinto College District, A
Texas Christian University, B
Texas State University, B
Texas Tech University, D
University of the Incarnate Word, B
University of North Texas, M
The University of Texas at Austin, BM
Wade College, A

Utah

LDS Business College, A
Utah State University, BM
Weber State University, A

Virginia

The Art Institute of Virginia Beach, a branch of The
    Art Institute of Atlanta, B
The Art Institute of Washington, a branch of The Art
    Institute of Atlanta, B
Hampton University, B
Marymount University, BM
Northern Virginia Community College, A
Tidewater Community College, A
Virginia Commonwealth University, BM
Virginia Polytechnic Institute and State University, B

Washington

The Art Institute of Seattle, AB
Bellevue College, A
Clover Park Technical College, A
Cornish College of the Arts, B
Highline College, A
Seattle Pacific University, B
Spokane Falls Community College, A
Washington State University, BM

West Virginia

Mountwest Community & Technical College, A
University of Charleston, B

Wisconsin

Concordia University Wisconsin, B
Fox Valley Technical College, A
Gateway Technical College, A
Madison Area Technical College, A
Milwaukee Area Technical College, A
Mount Mary University, B
University of Wisconsin - Madison, B
University of Wisconsin - Stevens Point, B
University of Wisconsin - Stout, B
Waukesha County Technical College, A
Western Technical College, A

U.S. Territories: Puerto Rico

EDP University of Puerto Rico, AB
EDP University of Puerto Rico - San Sebastian, A
Polytechnic University of Puerto Rico, B
Universidad del Turabo, B
University of Puerto Rico in Carolina, A

Canada

Alberta

Mount Royal University, B

British Columbia

The Art Institute of Vancouver, B
British Columbia Institute of Technology, A
Thompson Rivers University, B

Manitoba

University of Manitoba, BM

Ontario

Ryerson University, B

Quebec

Université de Montréal, B

INTERMEDIA/MULTIMEDIA

United States

California

Art Center College of Design, B
Biola University, B
Laguna College of Art & Design, B
Mills College, B
Mt. Sierra College, B
Platt College San Diego, AB
San Diego Mesa College, A

Connecticut

Middlesex Community College, A
University of Hartford, B

Florida

Jacksonville University, B

Georgia

Augusta University, B

Illinois

Columbia College Chicago, B
School of the Art Institute of Chicago, B

Indiana

Calumet College of Saint Joseph, B

Iowa

Luther College, B

Maine

Maine College of Art, B
University of Maine at Farmington, B

Maryland

Maryland Institute College of Art, B

Massachusetts

Bard College at Simon's Rock, B
Bristol Community College, A
Emerson College, B
Massachusetts College of Art and Design, B
Montserrat College of Art, B
Northeastern University, B
School of the Museum of Fine Arts, Boston, B
Worcester Polytechnic Institute, B

Minnesota

Academy College, A
Minneapolis College of Art and Design, B

Mississippi

Coahoma Community College, A

Missouri

Missouri State University, B

New Jersey

The College of New Jersey, B
Ramapo College of New Jersey, B

New Mexico

Santa Fe Community College, A

New York

City College of the City University of New York, B
Marist College, B
Purchase College, State University of New York, B
Rochester Institute of Technology, B
State University of New York College of Technology
    at Alfred, B
State University of New York at Fredonia, B

Ohio

Art Academy of Cincinnati, B
The University of Toledo, B

Oklahoma

Oklahoma State University Institute of Technology, A

Oregon

Pacific Northwest College of Art, B

Pennsylvania

Indiana University of Pennsylvania, B
The University of the Arts, B

Utah

Weber State University, B

Vermont

Bennington College, B
Champlain College, B
Marlboro College, B

Washington

The Evergreen State College, B
Western Washington University, B

U.S. Territories: Puerto Rico

University of Puerto Rico, Río Piedras Campus, B

Canada

Alberta

Alberta College of Art & Design, B

Ontario

McMaster University, B

Quebec

Concordia University, B

Saskatchewan

University of Regina, B

INTERNATIONAL AFFAIRS

United States

Alabama

Auburn University at Montgomery, M
Troy University, M

California

Azusa Pacific University, M
California State University, Fresno, M
California State University, Stanislaus, M
Chapman University, M
Concordia University Irvine, M
Pepperdine University, M
San Francisco State University, M
University of California, Berkeley, MD
University of California, San Diego, MD
University of California, Santa Barbara, MD
University of California, Santa Cruz, D
University of the Pacific, D
University of San Diego, M
University of San Francisco, M
University of Southern California, MD

Colorado

Colorado School of Mines, O
University of Colorado Boulder, M
University of Colorado Denver, M
University of Denver, MDO

Connecticut

Central Connecticut State University, M
University of Bridgeport, M
University of Connecticut, M
Yale University, M

Delaware

University of Delaware, MD

District of Columbia

American University, MDO
The Catholic University of America, M
The George Washington University, M

Georgetown University, M

Florida

Embry-Riddle Aeronautical University - Daytona, M
Embry-Riddle Aeronautical University - Worldwide, M
Florida International University, MD
Florida State University, M
University of Florida, M
University of Miami, MD
University of South Florida, MDO

Georgia

Georgia Institute of Technology, MD
Kennesaw State University, M
University of Georgia, MD
University of North Georgia, M

Hawaii

University of Hawaii at Manoa, O

Illinois

DePaul University, M
Northwestern University, MO
University of Chicago, M

Indiana

University of Indianapolis, M

Kansas

Kansas State University, M
The University of Kansas, M

Kentucky

University of Kentucky, M

Maine

University of Maine, M

Maryland

Johns Hopkins University, MDO
Morgan State University, M

Massachusetts

Boston University, M
Brandeis University, M
Harvard University, D
Hult International Business School, M
Lesley University, MO
Northeastern University, M
Tufts University, MD
University of Massachusetts Boston, M

Michigan

Central Michigan University, MO
University of Michigan - Flint, M
Western Michigan University, M

Minnesota

Walden University, D

Missouri

Missouri State University, M
Webster University, M

Nebraska

Creighton University, M

New Hampshire

New England College, M

New Jersey

Fairleigh Dickinson University, Metropolitan Campus, M
Princeton University, MD
Rutgers University - Camden, M
Rutgers University - New Brunswick, MD
Rutgers University - Newark, MD
Seton Hall University, MO

New York

Brooklyn College of the City University of New York, M

City College of the City University of New York, M
Columbia University, M
Cornell University, D
Fordham University, MO
New York University, MO
St. John's University, MO
Syracuse University, M
University of Rochester, MD

North Carolina

Appalachian State University, M
East Carolina University, M
North Carolina State University, M

Ohio

Cleveland State University, M
Ohio University, M

Oklahoma

Oklahoma State University, M
University of Central Oklahoma, M
University of Oklahoma, MO

Oregon

University of Oregon, M

Pennsylvania

Arcadia University, M
Penn State University Park, M
University of Pennsylvania, M
University of Pittsburgh, MDO

Rhode Island

Salve Regina University, MO
University of Rhode Island, M

South Carolina

University of South Carolina, MD

Tennessee

Middle Tennessee State University, M

Texas

Baylor University, M
St. Mary's University, MO
Texas A&M University, MO
Texas State University, M
University of North Texas, M

Utah

University of Utah, MD

Vermont

Norwich University, M

Virginia

George Mason University, M
Liberty University, M
Old Dominion University, MD
Regent University, M
University of Virginia, MD
Virginia International University, M
Virginia Polytechnic Institute and State University, MD

Washington

University of Washington, D

West Virginia

American Public University System, M
West Virginia University, M

Wisconsin

Marquette University, M

Wyoming

University of Wyoming, M

Canada

British Columbia

Simon Fraser University, M
The University of British Columbia, M
University of Northern British Columbia, M

Ontario

Brock University, M
Carleton University, MD
McMaster University, MD
Queen's University at Kingston, D
University of Toronto, M
University of Waterloo, MD
Wilfrid Laurier University, MD
York University, M

Quebec

Université Laval, MD
Université de Montréal, MO

INTERNATIONAL AGRICULTURE

United States

California

University of California, Davis, B

Illinois

University of Illinois at Urbana - Champaign, B

Iowa

Iowa State University of Science and Technology, B

Missouri

University of Missouri, B

New York

Cornell University, B

Texas

Tarleton State University, B

Utah

Utah State University, B

Canada

Maritime Provinces: Nova Scotia

Dalhousie University, B

INTERNATIONAL BUSINESS/ TRADE/COMMERCE

United States

Alabama

Auburn University, B
Auburn University at Montgomery, B
Birmingham-Southern College, B
Samford University, B
Spring Hill College, B
Strayer University - Birmingham Campus, B
Strayer University - Huntsville Campus, B
Troy University, M
University of North Alabama, M

Arizona

Argosy University, Phoenix, MD
Arizona State University at the Tempe campus, M
Arizona State University at the West campus, B
Dunlap-Stone University, B
Embry-Riddle Aeronautical University - Prescott, B

Paradise Valley Community College, A
University of Phoenix - Online Campus, M
University of Phoenix - Phoenix Campus, BM
University of Phoenix - Southern Arizona Campus, M
Western International University, M

Arkansas

Arkansas State University, B
Harding University, BM
John Brown University, BM
University of Arkansas, B
University of Arkansas at Little Rock, B
University of the Ozarks, B

California

Argosy University, Inland Empire, MD
Argosy University, Los Angeles, MD
Argosy University, Orange County, MDO
Argosy University, San Diego, MD
Argosy University, San Francisco Bay Area, MD
Azusa Pacific University, M
Biola University, B
Bristol University, M
California Intercontinental University, MD
California Lutheran University, MO
California State University, Dominguez Hills, B
California State University, East Bay, M
California State University, Fresno, B
California State University, Fullerton, BM
California State University, Long Beach, B
California State University, Los Angeles, M
California State University, San Bernardino, M
California State University, San Marcos, B
California University of Management and Sciences, BM
Cuesta College, A
Dominican University of California, M
Foothill College, A
Fresno Pacific University, B
Fullerton College, A
Glendale Community College, A
Golden Gate University, BM
Grossmont College, A
Hope International University, M
Lincoln University, BM
Long Beach City College, A
Menlo College, B
Monterey Peninsula College, A
Mount Saint Mary's University, B
National University, M
Orange Coast College, A
Pacific States University, MD
Palomar College, A
Pasadena City College, A
Pepperdine University, BM
Saint Mary's College of California, B
San Diego State University, B
San Diego State University - Imperial Valley Campus, B
San Francisco State University, BM
San Jose State University, B
Sonoma State University, M
Southwestern College, A
Trident University International, M
University of California, Berkeley, O
University of California, Los Angeles, MD
University of La Verne, BM
University of Phoenix - Bay Area Campus, BM
University of Phoenix - Central Valley Campus, M
University of Phoenix - Sacramento Valley Campus, BM
University of Phoenix - San Diego Campus, M
University of Phoenix - Southern California Campus, M
University of San Diego, BM
University of San Francisco, BM
University of Southern California, B
University of the West, M
Vanguard University of Southern California, B

Colorado

Adams State University, B
Argosy University, Denver, MD
Colorado Heights University, BM
Colorado State University - Global Campus, M

Colorado Technical University Online, B
Fort Lewis College, B
Johnson & Wales University, B
University of Colorado Denver, M
University of Denver, BM
University of Phoenix - Colorado Campus, M
University of Phoenix - Colorado Springs Downtown Campus, M

Connecticut

Albertus Magnus College, B
Post University, B
Quinnipiac University, B
University of Bridgeport, BM
University of New Haven, MO

Delaware

Goldey-Beacom College, BM
Strayer University - Christiana Campus, B
University of Delaware, B

District of Columbia

The Catholic University of America, B
The George Washington University, BD
Georgetown University, BMD
Howard University, BM
Strayer University - Takoma Park Campus, B
Strayer University - Washington Campus, B
University of the Potomac, AB

Florida

Argosy University, Sarasota, MDO
Argosy University, Tampa, MD
Ave Maria University, B
Barry University, BO
Bethune-Cookman University, B
Broward College, A
Eckerd College, B
Everest University (Largo), M
Everest University (Orlando), M
Everest University (Tampa), M
Everglades University (Boca Raton), B
Everglades University (Maitland), B
Everglades University (Sarasota), B
Florida Atlantic University, BM
Florida Institute of Technology, B
Florida International University, BMD
Florida State University, M
Jacksonville University, B
Keiser University, BMD
Lynn University, BM
Marconi International University, M
Palm Beach Atlantic University, B
Polytechnic University of Puerto Rico, Miami Campus, M
Polytechnic University of Puerto Rico, Orlando Campus, M
Rollins College, BM
St. Petersburg College, B
St. Thomas University, BMO
Schiller International University, ABM
South Florida State College, A
Southeastern University, B
State College of Florida Manatee-Sarasota, B
Stetson University, B
Strayer University - Baymeadows Campus, B
Strayer University - Brickell Campus, B
Strayer University - Coral Springs Campus, B
Strayer University - Doral Campus, B
Strayer University - Fort Lauderdale Campus, B
Strayer University - Maitland Campus, B
Strayer University - Miramar Campus, B
Strayer University - Orlando East Campus, B
Strayer University - Palm Beach Gardens Campus, B
Strayer University - Sand Lake Campus, B
Strayer University - Tampa East Campus, B
Strayer University - Tampa Westshore Campus, B
University of Florida, M
University of Miami, BM
University of North Florida, BM
University of Phoenix - Central Florida Campus, B
University of Phoenix - North Florida Campus, BM
University of Phoenix - South Florida Campus, BM
University of South Florida, B
The University of Tampa, BM

Georgia

American InterContinental University Atlanta, M
Argosy University, Atlanta, MD
Ashworth College, A
Berry College, B
Clayton State University, M
Georgia Institute of Technology, M
Georgia Southern University, B
Georgia State University, M
Kennesaw State University, B
Mercer University, B
Savannah State University, B
Strayer University - Augusta Campus, B
Strayer University - Chamblee Campus, B
Strayer University - Cobb County Campus, B
Strayer University - Columbus Campus, B
Strayer University - Douglasville Campus, B
Strayer University - Lithonia Campus, B
Strayer University - Morrow Campus, B
Strayer University - Roswell Campus, B
Strayer University - Savannah Campus, B
University of Georgia, B
University of Phoenix - Atlanta Campus, BM
University of Phoenix - Augusta Campus, BM
University of Phoenix - Columbus Georgia Campus, ABM
Valdosta State University, B
Wesleyan College, B

Hawaii

Argosy University, Hawai'i, MDO
Brigham Young University - Hawaii, B
Chaminade University of Honolulu, B
Hawai'i Pacific University, BM
Remington College - Honolulu Campus, A
University of Hawaii at Manoa, BMD
University of Phoenix - Hawaii Campus, BM

Idaho

Boise State University, B
The College of Idaho, B
Northwest Nazarene University, B

Illinois

American InterContinental University Online, M
Argosy University, Chicago, MD
Argosy University, Schaumburg, MDO
Augustana College, B
Benedictine University, BM
Bradley University, B
Dominican University, B
Ellis University, M
Elmhurst College, B
Harper College, A
Illinois State University, B
Illinois Wesleyan University, B
Lewis University, BM
Loyola University Chicago, BM
MacCormac College, A
McKendree University, M
Millikin University, B
Monmouth College, B
North Central College, BM
North Park University, B
Northwestern University, M
Olivet Nazarene University, B
Roosevelt University, M
Saint Xavier University, B
Trinity International University, B
Triton College, A
University of Chicago, M
University of St. Francis, B

Indiana

Anderson University, B
Ball State University, B
Bethel College, B
Butler University, B
Indiana Tech, D
Purdue University, M
Taylor University, BM
University of Evansville, B
University of Indianapolis, B
Valparaiso University, BM

Iowa

Buena Vista University, B
Central College, B
Cornell College, B
Drake University, B
Graceland University, B
Iowa State University of Science and Technology, B
Kaplan University, Davenport Campus, M
Mount Mercy University, B
St. Ambrose University, B
Simpson College, B
Upper Iowa University, M
Waldorf College, B
Wartburg College, B

Kansas

Baker University, B
Benedictine College, B
Bethany College, B
Friends University, B
McPherson College, B
MidAmerica Nazarene University, M
Newman University, M
Pittsburg State University, B
Wichita State University, B

Kentucky

Murray State University, B
University of Kentucky, M
University of Louisville, M
Western Kentucky University, B

Louisiana

Dillard University, B
Louisiana State University and Agricultural & Mechanical College, B
Loyola University New Orleans, B
Southwest University, B
Tulane University, M

Maine

Husson University, B
Maine Maritime Academy, BM
Saint Joseph's College of Maine, B
Thomas College, B
University of Maine, M

Maryland

Loyola University Maryland, M
Notre Dame of Maryland University, B
Salisbury University, B
Strayer University - Anne Arundel Campus, B
Strayer University - Owings Mills Campus, B
Strayer University - Prince George's Campus, B
Strayer University - Rockville Campus, B
Strayer University - White Marsh Campus, B
University of Baltimore, BM
University of Maryland, College Park, B
University of Maryland University College, MO

Massachusetts

American International College, B
Assumption College, BM
Babson College, B
Boston University, M
Brandeis University, MD
Bridgewater State University, B
Bunker Hill Community College, A
Clark University, M
Elms College, B
Emerson College, M
Endicott College, B
Hult International Business School, M
Lasell College, B
Massachusetts Bay Community College, A
Massachusetts College of Liberal Arts, B
Massachusetts Maritime Academy, B
Merrimack College, B
Newbury College, B
Nichols College, B
Northeastern University, BM
Roxbury Community College, A
Salem State University, B
Stonehill College, B
Suffolk University, BM

Tufts University, MD
University of Massachusetts Boston, M
University of Massachusetts Dartmouth, O
Western New England University, B

Michigan

Adrian College, B
Aquinas College, B
Central Michigan University, BMO
Cornerstone University, B
Davenport University, B
Eastern Michigan University, BMO
Finlandia University, B
Grand Valley State University, B
Hillsdale College, B
Kuyper College, B
Lake Superior State University, B
Lansing Community College, A
Lawrence Technological University, B
Madonna University, BM
Marygrove College, B
Northwood University, Michigan Campus, B
Oakland University, O
Saginaw Valley State University, B
University of Michigan - Flint, BM
University of Phoenix - Detroit Campus, B
Wayne State University, B

Minnesota

Argosy University, Twin Cities, MD
Augsburg College, B
Concordia College, B
Gustavus Adolphus College, B
Hamline University, B
Metropolitan State University, B
Minnesota State University Mankato, B
National American University (Bloomington), A
National American University (Brooklyn Center), A
St. Catherine University, B
St. Cloud State University, B
Saint Mary's University of Minnesota, BM
University of Minnesota, Twin Cities Campus, B
University of Northwestern - St. Paul, B
University of St. Thomas, B
Walden University, MD

Mississippi

Strayer University - Jackson Campus, B
University of Southern Mississippi, B

Missouri

American Business & Technology University, M
Avila University, BM
College of the Ozarks, B
Columbia College, B
Cottey College, B
Lindenwood University, BM
Maryville University of Saint Louis, B
Northwest Missouri State University, B
Park University, MO
Saint Louis University, BMD
Southeast Missouri State University, BM
University of Missouri, B
Washington University in St. Louis, B
Webster University, M
Westminster College, B

Montana

University of Montana, B

Nebraska

Creighton University, B
Nebraska Wesleyan University, B
Northeast Community College, A
Union College, B
University of Nebraska - Lincoln, B

Nevada

Sierra Nevada College, B
University of Nevada, Las Vegas, B
University of Nevada, Reno, B
University of Phoenix - Las Vegas Campus, BM

New Hampshire

Saint Anselm College, B
Southern New Hampshire University, BO

New Jersey

Bergen Community College, A
Berkeley College - Woodland Park Campus, AB
Caldwell University, B
Fairleigh Dickinson University, College at Florham, MO
Fairleigh Dickinson University, Metropolitan Campus, M
Felician University, B
Georgian Court University, B
Kean University, BM
Monmouth University, B
New Jersey Institute of Technology, B
Ramapo College of New Jersey, B
Raritan Valley Community College, A
Rider University, B
Rutgers University - Newark, D
Saint Peter's University, ABM
Seton Hall University, MO
Stevens Institute of Technology, M
Thomas Edison State University, B
University of Phoenix - Jersey City Campus, BM
William Paterson University of New Jersey, B

New Mexico

New Mexico Highlands University, M
New Mexico State University, B
University of New Mexico, M
University of Phoenix - New Mexico Campus, M
University of the Southwest, B
Western New Mexico University, B

New York

Baruch College of the City University of New York, BMD
Berkeley College - New York City Campus, AB
Binghamton University, State University of New York, B
Brooklyn College of the City University of New York, BM
Canisius College, BM
The College at Brockport, State University of New York, B
Columbia University, M
Concordia College - New York, B
Daemen College, M
Dominican College, B
D'Youville College, BM
Excelsior College, B
Farmingdale State College, B
Fordham University, B
Herkimer County Community College, A
Hilbert College, B
Hofstra University, BMO
Iona College, BMO
Ithaca College, B
LIM College, B
Long Island University - LIU Brooklyn, M
Manhattanville College, M
Marymount Manhattan College, B
Monroe Community College, A
Nazareth College of Rochester, B
New York Institute of Technology, B
New York University, BM
Niagara University, BMO
Pace University, BM
Pace University, Pleasantville Campus, B
Queens College of the City University of New York, B
Rochester Institute of Technology, BM
St. John's University, M
State University of New York Empire State College, M
State University of New York at New Paltz, B
State University of New York at Plattsburgh, B
Tompkins Cortland Community College, A
University at Buffalo, the State University of New York, BM
University of Rochester, M
Utica College, B
Wagner College, M

Westchester Community College, A
Yeshiva University, B

North Carolina

Appalachian State University, B
Campbell University, B
Duke University, MO
Elon University, B
Forsyth Technical Community College, A
Gardner-Webb University, B
High Point University, B
Lenoir-Rhyne University, BM
Miller-Motte College (Cary), A
Pfeiffer University, B
Pitt Community College, A
Salem College, B
Strayer University - Greensboro Campus, B
Strayer University - Huntersville Campus, B
Strayer University - North Charlotte Campus, B
Strayer University - North Raleigh Campus, B
Strayer University - RTP Campus, B
Strayer University - South Charlotte Campus, B
Strayer University - South Raleigh Campus, B
The University of North Carolina at Charlotte, B
The University of North Carolina at Greensboro, B
University of Phoenix - Charlotte Campus, M

North Dakota

Dickinson State University, B
Minot State University, B
University of Jamestown, B

Ohio

Baldwin Wallace University, BM
Bowling Green State University, B
Cedarville University, B
Cleveland State University, BDO
Denison University, B
John Carroll University, B
Lake Erie College, B
Marietta College, B
Mount Vernon Nazarene University, B
Muskingum University, B
Northwest State Community College, A
Ohio Northern University, B
The Ohio State University, B
Ohio University, B
Ohio Wesleyan University, B
Otterbein University, B
Stark State College, A
Tiffin University, BM
The University of Akron, BM
University of Cincinnati, B
University of Dayton, B
The University of Findlay, B
University of Mount Union, B
University of Rio Grande, B
The University of Toledo, BM
Wright State University, BM
Xavier University, BM

Oklahoma

Bacone College, B
East Central University, B
Northeastern State University, B
Oklahoma Baptist University, B
Oklahoma Christian University, M
Oklahoma State University, B
Oral Roberts University, BM
Tulsa Community College, A
University of Central Oklahoma, B
The University of Tulsa, BM

Oregon

George Fox University, B
Linfield College, B
Portland State University, M
Southern Oregon University, M
University of Portland, B

Pennsylvania

Albright College, B
Arcadia University, B
Bucknell University, B
Carnegie Mellon University, B

Chatham University, B
Chestnut Hill College, B
Clarion University of Pennsylvania, B
Delaware Valley University, M
DeSales University, B
Dickinson College, B
Drexel University, B
Duquesne University, B
Eastern University, B
Elizabethtown College, B
Gannon University, B
Gettysburg College, B
Grove City College, B
Harcum College, A
Holy Family University, B
Indiana University of Pennsylvania, B
Juniata College, B
King's College, B
La Roche College, B
La Salle University, BO
Luzerne County Community College, A
Mansfield University of Pennsylvania, B
Marywood University, B
Messiah College, B
Moravian College, B
Neumann University, B
Penn State DuBois, B
Penn State Erie, The Behrend College, B
Penn State Harrisburg, B
Penn State Lehigh Valley, B
Penn State Schuylkill, B
Philadelphia University, B
Rosemont College, B
Saint Francis University, B
Saint Joseph's University, BM
Saint Vincent College, B
Seton Hill University, B
Strayer University - Allentown Campus, B
Strayer University - Center City Campus, B
Strayer University - Delaware County Campus, B
Strayer University - King of Prussia Campus, B
Strayer University - Lower Bucks County Campus, B
Strayer University - Warrendale Campus, B
Susquehanna University, B
Temple University, BMD
Thiel College, B
University of Pennsylvania, BM
University of Phoenix - Philadelphia Campus, B
University of Pittsburgh, BO
The University of Scranton, BM
Villanova University, BM
Washington & Jefferson College, B
Waynesburg University, B
Westminster College, B
Widener University, B
Wilkes University, M

Rhode Island

Bryant University, BM
Johnson & Wales University, B
Providence College, M
Rhode Island College, B
Roger Williams University, B
University of Rhode Island, B

South Carolina

College of Charleston, B
Converse College, B
North Greenville University, B
Strayer University - Charleston Campus, B
Strayer University - Columbia Campus, B
Strayer University - Greenville Campus, B
University of South Carolina, BM

South Dakota

National American University (Rapid City), B
Northern State University, B

Tennessee

Argosy University, Nashville, MD
Belmont University, B
Christian Brothers University, M
Lipscomb University, B
Maryville College, B
Rhodes College, B

Southern Adventist University, B
Strayer University - Knoxville Campus, B
Strayer University - Nashville Campus, B
Strayer University - Shelby Campus, B
Strayer University - Thousand Oaks Campus, B
Tennessee Technological University, BM
Trevecca Nazarene University, B
University of Memphis, B
The University of Tennessee at Martin, B

Texas

Angelo State University, B
Argosy University, Dallas, MDO
Austin College, B
Austin Community College District, A
Baylor University, B
Dallas Baptist University, M
El Paso Community College, A
Hallmark University, M
Houston Baptist University, BM
Houston Community College, A
Laredo Community College, A
Lee College, A
LeTourneau University, B
Midwestern State University, B
Richland College, A
St. Edward's University, B
St. Mary's University, B
Sam Houston State University, B
San Jacinto College District, A
Southwestern Adventist University, B
Stephen F. Austin State University, B
Strayer University - Cedar Hill Campus, B
Strayer University - Irving Campus, B
Strayer University - Katy Campus, B
Strayer University - North Austin Campus, B
Strayer University - Northwest Houston Campus, B
Strayer University - Plano Campus, B
Tarleton State University, B
Texas A&M International University, MD
Texas A&M University - Central Texas, B
Texas A&M University - Corpus Christi, M
Texas A&M University - Kingsville, B
Texas A&M University - San Antonio, M
Texas A&M University - Texarkana, B
Texas Christian University, B
Texas Tech University, B
Trinity University, B
University of Dallas, M
University of Houston - Downtown, B
University of Houston - Victoria, B
University of the Incarnate Word, BM
University of Mary Hardin-Baylor, BM
University of Phoenix - Dallas Campus, BM
University of Phoenix - Houston Campus, BM
University of Phoenix - San Antonio Campus, BM
University of St. Thomas, M
The University of Texas at Arlington, B
The University of Texas at Dallas, BMD
The University of Texas at El Paso, D
The University of Texas Rio Grande Valley, B
The University of Texas at San Antonio, B
Wayland Baptist University, M

Utah

Argosy University, Salt Lake City, MD
University of Phoenix - Utah Campus, M
Westminster College, B

Vermont

Champlain College, B

Virginia

Argosy University, Washington DC, MDO
Eastern Mennonite University, B
Emory & Henry College, B
George Mason University, M
James Madison University, B
Liberty University, MD
Old Dominion University, M
Strayer University - Alexandria Campus, B
Strayer University - Arlington Campus, B
Strayer University - Chesapeake Campus, B
Strayer University - Chesterfield Campus, B
Strayer University - Fredericksburg Campus, B
Strayer University - Henrico Campus, B

Strayer University - Loudoun Campus, B
Strayer University - Manassas Campus, B
Strayer University - Newport News Campus, B
Strayer University - Virginia Beach Campus, B
Strayer University - Woodbridge Campus, B
University of Virginia, M
Virginia International University, M

Washington

Argosy University, Seattle, MD
City University of Seattle, BM
Edmonds Community College, A
Gonzaga University, B
Highline College, A
Northwest University, M
Seattle University, B
Shoreline Community College, A
Spokane Falls Community College, A
University of Phoenix - Western Washington Campus, B
University of Washington, M
Walla Walla University, B
Washington State University, B
Western Washington University, B
Whitworth University, B

West Virginia

American Public University System, M
Davis & Elkins College, B
Marshall University, B
Salem International University, BM
Strayer University - Teays Valley Campus, B

Wisconsin

Alverno College, B
Cardinal Stritch University, B
Concordia University Wisconsin, BM
Lakeland College, B
Marquette University, M
Milwaukee School of Engineering, B
St. Norbert College, B
University of Wisconsin - Eau Claire, B
University of Wisconsin - La Crosse, B
University of Wisconsin - Madison, B
University of Wisconsin - Milwaukee, O
University of Wisconsin - Oshkosh, M
University of Wisconsin - Whitewater, BM
Viterbo University, M

U.S. Territories: Puerto Rico

Inter American University of Puerto Rico, Metropolitan Campus, MD
Inter American University of Puerto Rico, San Germán Campus, D
Polytechnic University of Puerto Rico, M
Pontifical Catholic University of Puerto Rico, BM
Universidad Metropolitana, M
University of Puerto Rico in Humacao, B
University of Puerto Rico, Río Piedras Campus, MD

Canada

Alberta

University of Alberta, BM
University of Lethbridge, BM

British Columbia

British Columbia Institute of Technology, A
Trinity Western University, M
The University of British Columbia, B
University of Northern British Columbia, B
University of Victoria, B
Vancouver Island University, M

Maritime Provinces: New Brunswick

Mount Allison University, B
University of New Brunswick Fredericton, B
University of New Brunswick Saint John, M

Maritime Provinces: Nova Scotia

Dalhousie University, B

Ontario

Brock University, B
Carleton University, B
University of Ottawa, B
University of Waterloo, B
The University of Western Ontario, BM
York University, BM

Quebec

Bishop's University, B
Concordia University, B
HEC Montreal, BM
McGill University, BM
Université Laval, M
Université du Québec en Outaouais, B
Université de Sherbrooke, M

Saskatchewan

University of Regina, BM
University of Saskatchewan, M

INTERNATIONAL AND COMPARATIVE EDUCATION

United States

California

California Baptist University, M
California State University, Dominguez Hills, M
National University, M
Stanford University, MD
University of San Francisco, MD

Connecticut

University of Bridgeport, O

District of Columbia

Gallaudet University, M
The George Washington University, MO

Florida

Florida International University, M
Florida State University, MD

Indiana

Indiana University Bloomington, MD
Valparaiso University, M

Kentucky

Morehead State University, M

Louisiana

Louisiana State University and Agricultural & Mechanical College, MD

Massachusetts

Harvard University, M
University of Massachusetts Amherst, M

Minnesota

University of Minnesota, Twin Cities Campus, MD
Walden University, MDO

Missouri

Avila University, B

New Jersey

The College of New Jersey, MO

New York

New York University, MDO

Ohio

Bowling Green State University, M
Wright State University, M

Pennsylvania

Drexel University, M
Lehigh University, MDO
University of Pennsylvania, M

University of Pittsburgh, MD
Wilkes University, M

Tennessee

Vanderbilt University, M

Virginia

George Mason University, M

Wisconsin

University of Wisconsin - Madison, M

INTERNATIONAL DEVELOPMENT

United States

California

Hope International University, M
Marymount California University, M
University of San Francisco, M

District of Columbia

American University, MO
The George Washington University, M

Florida

University of Florida, MO

Indiana

Indiana University Bloomington, M

Kentucky

Kentucky State University, M

Louisiana

Tulane University, MD

Maryland

Johns Hopkins University, MO

Massachusetts

Clark University, M
Harvard University, M
Tufts University, MD
University of Massachusetts Boston, MD

Michigan

Andrews University, M

Minnesota

Saint Mary's University of Minnesota, M
University of Minnesota, Twin Cities Campus, M
Walden University, M

Mississippi

University of Southern Mississippi, MD

New Hampshire

University of New Hampshire, M

New Jersey

Rutgers University - Camden, M

New Mexico

University of New Mexico, MD

New York

Fordham University, MO
New York University, M

North Carolina

Duke University, M

Ohio

Ohio University, M

Pennsylvania

Eastern University, M
Lehigh University, O

University of Pittsburgh, M

Texas

St. Mary's University, M

Vermont

Norwich University, M

Virginia

Old Dominion University, MD

Canada

Alberta

Athabasca University, M

Maritime Provinces: New Brunswick

University of New Brunswick Fredericton, M

Maritime Provinces: Nova Scotia

Dalhousie University, M
Saint Mary's University, MO

Ontario

University of Guelph, MD
University of Ottawa, M

Quebec

McGill University, M

INTERNATIONAL ECONOMICS

United States

California

University of California, Los Angeles, B
University of California, Santa Cruz, B

Colorado

The Colorado College, B

Connecticut

Yale University, M

District of Columbia

Georgetown University, B
Howard University, B

Florida

University of Miami, MD

Georgia

Georgia State University, B
University of West Georgia, B

Idaho

The College of Idaho, B

Illinois

Rockford University, B

Indiana

Valparaiso University, BM

Maryland

Johns Hopkins University, M

Massachusetts

Fitchburg State University, B

Michigan

Albion College, B
Wayne State University, MD

Minnesota

St. Catherine University, B
University of St. Thomas, B

Missouri

Washington University in St. Louis, B

New Mexico

University of New Mexico, MD

New York

Fordham University, MO
State University of New York at Oswego, B

North Carolina

Elon University, B

Ohio

Cleveland State University, M
John Carroll University, B
Youngstown State University, B

Pennsylvania

Gettysburg College, B
La Salle University, B

Rhode Island

Bryant University, B
Salve Regina University, B

Tennessee

Belmont University, B
Rhodes College, B

Texas

Austin College, B
Texas Christian University, B
Texas Tech University, B
Trinity University, B

Utah

Weber State University, B

Vermont

Marlboro College, B

Virginia

Mary Baldwin College, B
University of Richmond, B

Washington

University of Puget Sound, B

West Virginia

Bethany College, B
West Virginia University, D

Wisconsin

Carthage College, B
Lawrence University, B

Canada

Ontario

Brock University, B
Ryerson University, B
Wilfrid Laurier University, M

Quebec

HEC Montreal, B

INTERNATIONAL FINANCE

United States

District of Columbia

The Catholic University of America, B

Hawaii

Hawai'i Pacific University, B

Massachusetts

Babson College, B

Missouri

Washington University in St. Louis, B

New York

Broome Community College, A

North Carolina

Lenoir-Rhyne University, B

Pennsylvania

Lycoming College, B

Texas

Texas Christian University, B

Utah

Brigham Young University, B

Canada

Quebec

HEC Montreal, B
McGill University, B

INTERNATIONAL/GLOBAL STUDIES

United States

Alabama

Auburn University at Montgomery, B
Samford University, B
University of South Alabama, B

Alaska

University of Alaska Anchorage, B

Arizona

Arizona State University at the Tempe campus, B
The University of Arizona, B

Arkansas

Arkansas Tech University, B
Harding University, B
John Brown University, B
University of Central Arkansas, B

California

California Baptist University, B
Concordia University Irvine, B
Dominican University of California, B
La Sierra University, B
National University, B
Pasadena City College, A
Pepperdine University, B
Pitzer College, B
Point Loma Nazarene University, B
Scripps College, B
University of California, Irvine, B
University of California, Los Angeles, B
University of California, Riverside, B
University of California, Santa Barbara, B
University of La Verne, B
University of Southern California, B
Whittier College, B

Colorado

Colorado Christian University, B
Colorado State University, B
United States Air Force Academy, B
University of Colorado Boulder, B
University of Colorado Denver, B
University of Northern Colorado, B

Connecticut

Albertus Magnus College, B
Central Connecticut State University, B
Sacred Heart University, A
University of New Haven, B
University of Saint Joseph, B

Florida

Flagler College, B
New College of Florida, B
Saint Leo University, B
St. Thomas University, B
University of Central Florida, B
University of Florida, B
University of North Florida, B

Georgia

Andrew College, A
Georgia Institute of Technology, B
Reinhardt University, B

Hawaii

Hawai'i Pacific University, B

Idaho

Brigham Young University - Idaho, B

Illinois

Benedictine University, B
Chicago State University, B
Greenville College, B
Illinois Wesleyan University, B
Knox College, B
McKendree University, B
Monmouth College, B
North Central College, B
North Park University, B
Rockford University, B
University of Illinois at Springfield, B
University of Illinois at Urbana - Champaign, B

Indiana

Hanover College, B
Holy Cross College, A
Manchester University, B
Saint Mary's College, B
Valparaiso University, B

Iowa

Central College, B
Luther College, B
Morningside College, B
The University of Iowa, B

Kansas

Baker University, B
Benedictine College, B
Tabor College, B
The University of Kansas, B

Kentucky

Centre College, B
Eastern Kentucky University, B
Jefferson Community and Technical College, A
Morehead State University, B
Thomas More College, AB
University of Kentucky, B

Louisiana

Louisiana State University and Agricultural & Mechanical College, B
University of New Orleans, B

Maine

Colby College, B
University of Maine at Farmington, B

Maryland

Coppin State University, B
Frostburg State University, B
Hood College, B
Salisbury University, B
University of Baltimore, B
University of Maryland, Baltimore County, B

Massachusetts

Assumption College, B
Bentley University, B
Berkshire Community College, A
Boston College, B
Brandeis University, B

College of the Holy Cross, B
Emmanuel College, B
Endicott College, B
Framingham State University, B
Hampshire College, B
Massachusetts Bay Community College, A
Western New England University, B

Michigan

Adrian College, B
Albion College, B
Hope College, B
Kalamazoo Valley Community College, A
Macomb Community College, A
Michigan State University, B
Oakland Community College, A
Saginaw Valley State University, B
Spring Arbor University, B
University of Michigan, B
Washtenaw Community College, A
Western Michigan University, B

Minnesota

The College of St. Scholastica, B
Concordia College, B
Hamline University, B
Macalester College, B
Minnesota State University Moorhead, B
Saint Mary's University of Minnesota, B
Winona State University, B

Mississippi

Belhaven University, B
Mississippi College, B

Missouri

Culver-Stockton College, B
Maryville University of Saint Louis, B
Missouri State University, B
Missouri Western State University, B
Southeast Missouri State University, B
Webster University, B
Westminster College, B

Nebraska

Concordia University, Nebraska, B
Doane University, B
Nebraska Wesleyan University, B
University of Nebraska - Lincoln, B
University of Nebraska at Omaha, B

Nevada

Sierra Nevada College, B

New Jersey

College of Saint Elizabeth, B
Ocean County College, A
Rowan College at Burlington County, A

New Mexico

University of New Mexico, B

New York

Adelphi University, B
Alfred University, B
Bard College, B
City College of the City University of New York, B
The College of New Rochelle, B
College of Staten Island of the City University of New York, B
Concordia College - New York, B
Davis College, B
Eugene Lang College of Liberal Arts, B
Hofstra University, B
Jamestown Community College, A
Le Moyne College, B
Long Island University - LIU Post, B
Manhattanville College, B
Marymount Manhattan College, B
The New School for Public Engagement, B
New York University, B
Pace University, Pleasantville Campus, B
St. Bonaventure University, B
St. Lawrence University, B
Sarah Lawrence College, B

State University of New York College at Cortland, B
State University of New York College at Potsdam, B
Tompkins Cortland Community College, A
University at Albany, State University of New York, B

North Carolina

Appalachian State University, B
Meredith College, B
North Carolina State University, B
The University of North Carolina at Chapel Hill, B
The University of North Carolina at Charlotte, B
The University of North Carolina Wilmington, B
Warren Wilson College, B
Western Carolina University, B
William Peace University, B

North Dakota

North Dakota State University, B
University of North Dakota, B

Ohio

Baldwin Wallace University, B
Bowling Green State University, B
Case Western Reserve University, B
Cedarville University, B
Kenyon College, B
Malone University, B
Miami University Hamilton, B
The Ohio State University, B
University of Dayton, B

Oklahoma

University of Oklahoma, B

Oregon

George Fox University, B
Oregon State University, B
University of Oregon, B
Willamette University, B

Pennsylvania

Arcadia University, B
Bryn Mawr College, B
Carnegie Mellon University, B
Cedar Crest College, B
Chatham University, B
Chestnut Hill College, B
Drexel University, B
Gannon University, B
Juniata College, B
Lebanon Valley College, B
Lehigh University, B
Mercyhurst University, B
Northampton Community College, A
Point Park University, B
Shippensburg University of Pennsylvania, B
Susquehanna University, B
Temple University, B
University of Pennsylvania, B
Villanova University, B
Washington & Jefferson College, B
Westminster College, B

Rhode Island

Bryant University, B
Providence College, B
Roger Williams University, B
Salve Regina University, B

South Carolina

College of Charleston, B
Columbia International University, B
Presbyterian College, B

South Dakota

South Dakota State University, B
The University of South Dakota, B

Tennessee

Sewanee: The University of the South, B
Tennessee Wesleyan College, B

Texas

Abilene Christian University, B
East Texas Baptist University, B
LeTourneau University, B
Midwestern State University, B
Northwest Vista College, A
St. Edward's University, B
Southern Methodist University, B
Tarleton State University, B
Texas A&M University, B
Texas State University, B
Texas Tech University, B
University of North Texas, B
The University of Texas at Arlington, B
The University of Texas at Austin, B

Utah

Salt Lake Community College, A
University of Utah, B

Vermont

Bennington College, B
Goddard College, B
Marlboro College, B

Virginia

Randolph College, B
Randolph-Macon College, B
Regent University, B

Washington

Everett Community College, A
The Evergreen State College, B
Northwest University, B
Pacific Lutheran University, B
Seattle University, B
University of Washington, Bothell, B
University of Washington, Tacoma, B
Whitman College, B

West Virginia

West Virginia State University, B

Wisconsin

Carroll University, B
Mount Mary University, B
St. Norbert College, B
University of Wisconsin - Madison, B
University of Wisconsin - Milwaukee, B
University of Wisconsin - Platteville, B
University of Wisconsin - River Falls, B
University of Wisconsin - Stevens Point, B
University of Wisconsin - Whitewater, B

Wyoming

Central Wyoming College, A
University of Wyoming, B

Canada

British Columbia

University of Northern British Columbia, B
Vancouver Island University, B

Ontario

University of Ottawa, B
University of Waterloo, B
Wilfrid Laurier University, B

Quebec

Université de Montréal, B

Saskatchewan

Briercrest College, AB
University of Regina, B
University of Saskatchewan, B

INTERNATIONAL MARKETING

United States

Maine

Husson University, B

Minnesota

Saint Paul College - A Community & Technical College, A

New York

Fashion Institute of Technology, B
Pace University, Pleasantville Campus, B

Oklahoma

Oklahoma Baptist University, B
Oral Roberts University, B
Southwestern Christian University, B

Texas

Texas Christian University, B
Texas Southmost College, A

West Virginia

Davis & Elkins College, B

Wisconsin

Waukesha County Technical College, A

INTERNATIONAL PUBLIC HEALTH/INTERNATIONAL HEALTH

United States

Arizona

Arizona State University at the Tempe campus, MDO

California

California Baptist University, B
Loma Linda University, M
San Diego State University, D
Trident University International, MD
University of California, San Diego, D
University of Southern California, BMO

Colorado

University of Colorado Denver, M

Connecticut

Yale University, M

District of Columbia

American University, B
The George Washington University, MD
Georgetown University, M

Florida

University of Florida, MD
University of South Florida, MDO

Georgia

Emory University, M
Mercer University, B

Illinois

Northwestern University, M

Indiana

Bethel College, B

Iowa

The University of Iowa, B

Louisiana

Tulane University, MD

Maryland

Johns Hopkins University, MD

Massachusetts

Boston University, MD
Brandeis University, MD
Harvard University, MD
Tufts University, MD

Michigan

Central Michigan University, O
University of Michigan, M

Minnesota

University of Minnesota, Twin Cities Campus, MD

Missouri

Park University, O
University of Missouri, O
Washington University in St. Louis, M

Nebraska

Union College, B

New York

Cornell University, B
New York University, M
Syracuse University, O

North Carolina

Duke University, M

North Dakota

North Dakota State University, M

Ohio

Cedarville University, M
The University of Toledo, O

Oregon

Oregon State University, M

Pennsylvania

Allegheny College, B
University of Pennsylvania, M

South Carolina

Medical University of South Carolina, M

Virginia

George Mason University, M
Liberty University, M

Washington

University of Washington, MD

Canada

Alberta

University of Alberta, M

British Columbia

Simon Fraser University, O

INTERNATIONAL RELATIONS AND AFFAIRS

United States

Alabama

Samford University, B
Spring Hill College, B
The University of Alabama, B

Arizona

Embry-Riddle Aeronautical University - Prescott, B
Northern Arizona University, B

Arkansas

Hendrix College, B
John Brown University, B
University of Arkansas, B

California

Allan Hancock College, A
American River College, A
Azusa Pacific University, B
Cabrillo College, A
California Lutheran University, B
California State University, Chico, B
California State University, East Bay, B
California State University, Long Beach, B
California State University, Monterey Bay, B
California State University, San Marcos, B
Cañada College, A
Cerritos College, A
Chabot College, A
Claremont McKenna College, B
College of Marin, A
Cuesta College, A
De Anza College, A
Holy Names University, B
Mills College, B
Occidental College, B
Pomona College, B
Saint Mary's College of California, B
San Diego State University, B
San Francisco State University, B
Santa Barbara City College, A
Sonoma State University, B
Stanford University, B
University of California, Davis, B
University of La Verne, B
University of the Pacific, B
University of Redlands, B
University of San Diego, B
University of San Francisco, B
University of Southern California, B

Colorado

University of Denver, B

Connecticut

Connecticut College, B
Fairfield University, B
Quinnipiac University, B
Trinity College, B
University of Bridgeport, B
University of Hartford, B
Yale University, B

Delaware

University of Delaware, B

District of Columbia

American University, B
The George Washington University, B
Georgetown University, B
Trinity Washington University, B

Florida

Barry University, B
Bethune-Cookman University, B
Broward College, A
Eckerd College, B
Florida International University, B
Florida State University, B
Jacksonville University, B
Miami Dade College, A
Nova Southeastern University, B
Rollins College, B
Schiller International University, B
South Florida State College, A
Stetson University, B
University of Miami, B
University of South Florida, B
University of West Florida, B

Georgia

Agnes Scott College, B
Berry College, B
Brenau University, B
Emory University, B
Georgia Institute of Technology, B
Georgia Southern University, B
Kennesaw State University, B
Mercer University, B
Oglethorpe University, B
Spelman College, B
University of Georgia, B
University of North Georgia, B
University of West Georgia, B
Wesleyan College, B

Hawaii

Chaminade University of Honolulu, B
Hawai'i Pacific University, B

Idaho

The College of Idaho, B
Idaho State University, B
Northwest Nazarene University, B
University of Idaho, B

Illinois

Benedictine University, B
Bradley University, B
DePaul University, B
Dominican University, B
Illinois College, B
Illinois Wesleyan University, B
John A. Logan College, A
Knox College, B
Lake Forest College, B
Lewis University, B
Loyola University Chicago, B
McKendree University, B
Northwestern University, B
Roosevelt University, B
Saint Xavier University, B
University of Chicago, B
Wheaton College, B

Indiana

Butler University, B
Indiana University Bloomington, B
Indiana University - Purdue University Indianapolis, B
Indiana University Southeast, B
Indiana Wesleyan University, B
Saint Joseph's College, B
Taylor University, B
University of Evansville, B
University of Indianapolis, B
University of Southern Indiana, B
Valparaiso University, B

Iowa

Cornell College, B
Drake University, B
Graceland University, B
Iowa State University of Science and Technology, B
Loras College, B
Morningside College, B
Mount Mercy University, B
Simpson College, B
Wartburg College, B

Kentucky

Murray State University, B
Northern Kentucky University, B
Western Kentucky University, B

Louisiana

Tulane University, B

Maine

University of Maine, B

Maryland

Goucher College, B
Harford Community College, A
Johns Hopkins University, B
Mount St. Mary's University, B
Notre Dame of Maryland University, B
Towson University, B
Washington College, B

Massachusetts

American International College, B
Boston University, B
Bridgewater State University, B
Clark University, B
Emmanuel College, B
Fitchburg State University, B
Gordon College, B
Greenfield Community College, A
Hampshire College, B
Mount Holyoke College, B
Northeastern University, B
Northern Essex Community College, A
Regis College, B
Simmons College, B
Tufts University, B
Wellesley College, B
Wheaton College, B

Michigan

Adrian College, B
Aquinas College, B
Calvin College, B
Central Michigan University, B
Eastern Michigan University, B
Grand Valley State University, B
Lansing Community College, A
Michigan State University, B
Northern Michigan University, B
Oakland University, B
Saginaw Valley State University, B

Minnesota

Augsburg College, B
Bethel University, B
Carleton College, B
Minnesota State University Mankato, B
St. Catherine University, B
St. Cloud State University, B
University of Minnesota, Duluth, B
University of Minnesota, Twin Cities Campus, B

Mississippi

University of Mississippi, B
University of Southern Mississippi, B

Missouri

Cottey College, B
Drury University, B
Lindenwood University, B
Missouri Southern State University, B
Rockhurst University, B
Saint Louis University, B
Washington University in St. Louis, B
Webster University, B
Westminster College, B
William Jewell College, B

Montana

Carroll College, B

Nebraska

Bellevue University, B
Creighton University, B
Hastings College, B
University of Nebraska at Kearney, B

Nevada

University of Nevada, Reno, B

New Hampshire

Saint Anselm College, B
University of New Hampshire, B

New Jersey

Centenary College, B
The College of New Jersey, B
Drew University, B
Fairleigh Dickinson University, Metropolitan Campus, B
Rider University, B
Seton Hall University, B

New York

Binghamton University, State University of New York, B
Bronx Community College of the City University of New York, A
Canisius College, B
City College of the City University of New York, B
Colgate University, B
The College at Brockport, State University of New York, B
Concordia College - New York, B
Elmira College, B
Fordham University, B
Hamilton College, B
Hobart and William Smith Colleges, B
Iona College, B
Manhattan College, B
Marymount Manhattan College, B
Mercy College, B
Nazareth College of Rochester, B
New York University, B
Niagara University, B
Rochester Institute of Technology, B
The Sage Colleges, B
St. John Fisher College, B
Skidmore College, B
State University of New York College at Cortland, B
State University of New York College at Geneseo, B
State University of New York College at Oneonta, B
State University of New York at New Paltz, B
State University of New York at Oswego, B
Syracuse University, B
United States Military Academy, B
University of Rochester, B
Utica College, B
Vassar College, B
Wagner College, B
Wells College, B

North Carolina

Campbell University, B
Duke University, B
Elon University, B
High Point University, B
Lenoir-Rhyne University, B
Meredith College, B
Methodist University, B
Queens University of Charlotte, B
Salem College, B
Shaw University, B

Ohio

Bowling Green State University, B
Capital University, B
Case Western Reserve University, B
Cleveland State University, B
The College of Wooster, B
Denison University, B
Heidelberg University, B
John Carroll University, B
Kent State University, B
Miami University, B
Muskingum University, B
Ohio Northern University, B
The Ohio State University, B
Ohio University, B
Ohio Wesleyan University, B
Otterbein University, B
Shawnee State University, B
Tiffin University, B
University of Cincinnati, B
University of Mount Union, B
The University of Toledo, B
Walsh University, B
Wittenberg University, B
Wright State University, B
Xavier University, B

Oklahoma

Oklahoma Baptist University, B
Oral Roberts University, B
Southern Nazarene University, B

Oregon

Lewis & Clark College, B
Linfield College, B
Pacific University, B
Portland State University, B
Reed College, B
Southern Oregon University, B
Western Oregon University, B

Pennsylvania

Allegheny College, B
Bucknell University, B
Carnegie Mellon University, B
Chatham University, B
Dickinson College, B
Duquesne University, B
Gettysburg College, B
Harrisburg Area Community College, A
Immaculata University, B
Indiana University of Pennsylvania, B
Juniata College, B
La Roche College, B
La Salle University, B
Lafayette College, B
Lehigh University, B
Lock Haven University of Pennsylvania, B
Muhlenberg College, B
Penn State Abington, B
Penn State Altoona, B
Penn State Beaver, B
Penn State Berks, B
Penn State Brandywine, B
Penn State DuBois, B
Penn State Erie, The Behrend College, B
Penn State Fayette, The Eberly Campus, B
Penn State Greater Allegheny, B
Penn State Hazleton, B
Penn State Lehigh Valley, B
Penn State Mont Alto, B
Penn State New Kensington, B
Penn State Schuylkill, B
Penn State Shenango, B
Penn State University Park, B
Penn State Wilkes-Barre, B
Penn State Worthington Scranton, B
Penn State York, B
Saint Francis University, B
Saint Joseph's University, B
Seton Hill University, B
Temple University, B
University of Pennsylvania, B
The University of Scranton, B
Ursinus College, B
Widener University, B
Wilkes University, B
Wilson College, B
York College of Pennsylvania, B

Rhode Island

Brown University, B
Bryant University, B
Roger Williams University, B

South Carolina

Bob Jones University, B
Francis Marion University, B
Newberry College, B
University of South Carolina, B

South Dakota

Augustana University, B

Tennessee

Belmont University, B
East Tennessee State University, B
Maryville College, B
Middle Tennessee State University, B
Rhodes College, B
University of Memphis, B
The University of Tennessee at Martin, B

Texas

Austin College, B
Baylor University, B
Howard Payne University, B

St. Mary's University, B
Southwestern Adventist University, B
Southwestern University, B
Texas Christian University, B
Texas State University, B
Trinity University, B
University of the Incarnate Word, B
University of St. Thomas, B
The University of Texas at San Antonio, B

Utah

Salt Lake Community College, A

Vermont

Bennington College, B
Marlboro College, B
Middlebury College, B
Norwich University, B
Saint Michael's College, B

Virginia

Bridgewater College, B
The College of William and Mary, B
Ferrum College, B
George Mason University, B
Hampden-Sydney College, B
Hollins University, B
James Madison University, B
Liberty University, B
Lynchburg College, B
Mary Baldwin College, B
Old Dominion University, B
Roanoke College, B
Sweet Briar College, B
University of Mary Washington, B
University of Richmond, B
University of Virginia, B
Virginia Military Institute, B
Virginia Polytechnic Institute and State University, B
Virginia Wesleyan College, B

Washington

Eastern Washington University, B
Gonzaga University, B
Whitworth University, B

West Virginia

American Public University System, B
Bethany College, B
Marshall University, B
West Virginia Wesleyan College, B
Wheeling Jesuit University, B

Wisconsin

Alverno College, B
Beloit College, B
Carroll University, B
Edgewood College, B
Lawrence University, B
St. Norbert College, B
University of Wisconsin - Oshkosh, B
University of Wisconsin - Parkside, B
University of Wisconsin - Stevens Point, B
University of Wisconsin - Superior, B

Wyoming

Casper College, A
Northwest College, A
Western Wyoming Community College, A

Canada

Alberta

University of Calgary, B

British Columbia

Trinity Western University, B
The University of British Columbia, B
The University of British Columbia - Okanagan Campus, B

Maritime Provinces: New Brunswick

Mount Allison University, B
St. Thomas University, B

University of New Brunswick Fredericton, B
University of New Brunswick Saint John, B

Maritime Provinces: Nova Scotia

Dalhousie University, B
Saint Mary's University, B

Ontario

Carleton University, B
Redeemer University College, B
Trent University, B
University of Ottawa, B
University of Toronto, B
University of Waterloo, B
The University of Western Ontario, B
University of Windsor, B
York University, B

Quebec

Bishop's University, B

INTERNATIONAL TRADE

United States

District of Columbia

The George Washington University, M
Georgetown University, D

Michigan

Eastern Michigan University, M

Vermont

Norwich University, M

Washington

University of Washington, O

Wisconsin

Milwaukee School of Engineering, M

U.S. Territories: Puerto Rico

University of Puerto Rico, Río Piedras Campus, MD

Canada

Saskatchewan

University of Saskatchewan, MD

INTERNATIONAL TRADE POLICY

United States

District of Columbia

The George Washington University, M

INTERNET ENGINEERING

United States

California

University of San Francisco, M

Colorado

University of Denver, M

Delaware

Wilmington University, M

Georgia

University of Georgia, M

New Jersey

New Jersey Institute of Technology, M

New York

Hofstra University, M

INTERNET AND INTERACTIVE MULTIMEDIA

United States

Arizona

University of Advancing Technology, M

California

Academy of Art University, M
California State University, East Bay, M
National University, M
San Diego State University, M
University of San Francisco, M
University of Southern California, M

Colorado

Rocky Mountain College of Art + Design, M
University of Denver, M

Connecticut

Fairfield University, O
Quinnipiac University, M
Sacred Heart University, O

Delaware

Wilmington University, M

District of Columbia

Georgetown University, M

Florida

Full Sail University, M
Lynn University, MO
University of Miami, M
University of South Florida, MO

Georgia

Georgia Institute of Technology, MD
Savannah College of Art and Design, MO
University of Georgia, M

Illinois

DePaul University, M
North Central College, M
Northwestern University, M
Western Illinois University, O

Indiana

Indiana University - Purdue University Indianapolis, MD

Kentucky

Lindsey Wilson College, M

Maryland

Towson University, O

Massachusetts

Boston University, M
Northeastern University, M
Worcester Polytechnic Institute, M

Missouri

Lindenwood University, M
University of Missouri, M
Webster University, M

Montana

University of Montana, M

New Hampshire

Southern New Hampshire University, M

New Jersey

Stevens Institute of Technology, O

New Mexico

New Mexico Highlands University, M

New York

Alfred University, M
Brooklyn College of the City University of New York, M
Excelsior College, M
Ithaca College, M
Long Island University - LIU Post, M
New York University, MO
Pace University, M
Pratt Institute, M
Rochester Institute of Technology, O
School of Visual Arts, M
Touro College, M

North Carolina

Elon University, M

Ohio

The Ohio State University, M

Pennsylvania

Duquesne University, MO
Gannon University, M
Kutztown University of Pennsylvania, M
Philadelphia University, M
Robert Morris University, M
University of Pennsylvania, O

Tennessee

Tennessee Technological University, M

Texas

Sam Houston State University, M
University of North Texas, O
The University of Texas at Dallas, MD

Utah

University of Utah, M

Vermont

Marlboro College, MO

Virginia

Virginia Commonwealth University, M
Virginia Polytechnic Institute and State University, M

Wisconsin

Mount Mary University, M

U.S. Territories: Puerto Rico

University of the Sacred Heart, MO

Canada

Quebec

Concordia University, O

INVESTMENT MANAGEMENT

United States

Alaska

Alaska Pacific University, O

California

Lincoln University, MD
Saint Mary's College of California, M
University of San Francisco, M

Colorado

University of Colorado Denver, M

District of Columbia

The George Washington University, M

Florida

Lynn University, M

Illinois

DePaul University, M

Iowa

The University of Iowa, M

Maryland

Johns Hopkins University, O

Massachusetts

Boston University, M

New Hampshire

Southern New Hampshire University, M

New York

Fordham University, M
Hofstra University, MO
Manhattanville College, M
New York University, M
Pace University, M
St. John's University, M

Oklahoma

The University of Tulsa, M

Oregon

Oregon State University, M

Pennsylvania

Marywood University, M

Texas

The University of Texas at Dallas, M

Wisconsin

University of Wisconsin - Madison, D
University of Wisconsin - Milwaukee, O

Canada

Quebec

Concordia University, M

INVESTMENTS AND SECURITIES

United States

Florida

Lynn University, B

Massachusetts

Babson College, B

Nebraska

University of Nebraska - Lincoln, B
University of Nebraska at Omaha, B

New York

Marymount Manhattan College, B

North Dakota

University of North Dakota, B

Rhode Island

Johnson & Wales University, B

IRANIAN/PERSIAN LANGUAGES, LITERATURES, AND LINGUISTICS

United States

California

National University, B

Maryland

University of Maryland, College Park, B

Texas

The University of Texas at Austin, B

Utah

University of Utah, B

IRONWORKING/IRONWORKER

United States

Arizona

GateWay Community College, A

Illinois

Southwestern Illinois College, A

Indiana

Ivy Tech Community College - Lafayette, A
Ivy Tech Community College - North Central, A
Ivy Tech Community College - Northeast, A
Ivy Tech Community College - Northwest, A
Ivy Tech Community College - Southwest, A
Ivy Tech Community College - Wabash Valley, A

ISLAMIC STUDIES

United States

Connecticut

Connecticut College, B

Illinois

DePaul University, B

Massachusetts

Boston College, B
Wellesley College, B

Missouri

Washington University in St. Louis, B

New York

Colgate University, B

Ohio

The Ohio State University, B

Pennsylvania

Swarthmore College, B
Villanova University, B

Texas

The University of Texas at Austin, B

Vermont

Marlboro College, B

Washington

University of Washington, B

Canada

Ontario

The University of Western Ontario, B

ITALIAN LANGUAGE AND LITERATURE

United States

Arizona

Arizona State University at the Tempe campus, B
The University of Arizona, B

California

California State University, Long Beach, B
City College of San Francisco, A
College of the Desert, A
El Camino College, A
Los Angeles Valley College, A
Pepperdine University, B
Saint Mary's College of California, B
San Francisco State University, BM
Santa Clara University, B
Scripps College, B
Stanford University, BMD
University of California, Berkeley, BD
University of California, Davis, B
University of California, Los Angeles, BMD
University of California, San Diego, B
University of Southern California, B
West Valley College, A

Colorado

The Colorado College, B
University of Colorado Boulder, B
University of Denver, B

Connecticut

Central Connecticut State University, BO
Fairfield University, B
Southern Connecticut State University, B
Trinity College, B
University of Connecticut, BMD
Yale University, BD

Delaware

University of Delaware, B

District of Columbia

Georgetown University, B

Florida

Broward College, A
Florida International University, B
Florida State University, M
Miami Dade College, A
University of South Florida, B

Georgia

University of Georgia, B

Illinois

DePaul University, BM
Dominican University, B
Loyola University Chicago, B
Northwestern University, BDO
Triton College, A
University of Chicago, D
University of Illinois at Chicago, B
University of Illinois at Urbana - Champaign, BMD

Indiana

Indiana University Bloomington, BMD
University of Notre Dame, BM

Iowa

The University of Iowa, B

Louisiana

Tulane University, B

Maryland

Johns Hopkins University, BD
University of Maryland, College Park, B

Massachusetts

Boston College, BM
Boston University, B
College of the Holy Cross, B
Harvard University, MD
Mount Holyoke College, B
Smith College, B
Tufts University, B
University of Massachusetts Amherst, BM
University of Massachusetts Boston, B
Wellesley College, B

Michigan

University of Michigan, BD
Wayne State University, M

Minnesota

University of Minnesota, Twin Cities Campus, B

Missouri

Saint Louis University, B
Washington University in St. Louis, B

New Hampshire

Dartmouth College, B
University of New Hampshire, B

New Jersey

Drew University, M
Montclair State University, B
Rutgers University - New Brunswick, BMD
Rutgers University - Newark, B
Seton Hall University, B

New York

Bard College, B
Barnard College, B
Binghamton University, State University of New
   York, BM
Brooklyn College of the City University of New York,
   B
College of Staten Island of the City University of
   New York, B
Columbia University, BMD
Columbia University, School of General Studies, B
Cornell University, BD
Fordham University, B
Hofstra University, B
Hunter College of the City University of New York,
   BM
Iona College, B
Ithaca College, B
Lehman College of the City University of New York,
   B
Long Island University - LIU Post, B
Marist College, B
Nazareth College of Rochester, B
New York University, BMD
Queens College of the City University of New York,
   BM
St. John's University, B
Sarah Lawrence College, B
Stony Brook University, State University of New
   York, BM
Syracuse University, B
University at Buffalo, the State University of New
   York, B
Vassar College, B
York College of the City University of New York, B

North Carolina

Duke University, BD
The University of North Carolina at Chapel Hill, MD

Ohio

Lake Erie College, B
The Ohio State University, BMD
Youngstown State University, B

Oklahoma

University of Oklahoma, B

Oregon

University of Oregon, BM

Pennsylvania

Bryn Mawr College, B
Cabrini University, B
Gettysburg College, B
Haverford College, B
La Salle University, B
Penn State Abington, B
Penn State Altoona, B
Penn State Beaver, B
Penn State Berks, B
Penn State Brandywine, B

Penn State DuBois, B
Penn State Erie, The Behrend College, B
Penn State Fayette, The Eberly Campus, B
Penn State Greater Allegheny, B
Penn State Hazleton, B
Penn State Lehigh Valley, B
Penn State Mont Alto, B
Penn State New Kensington, B
Penn State Schuylkill, B
Penn State Shenango, B
Penn State University Park, B
Penn State Wilkes-Barre, B
Penn State Worthington Scranton, B
Penn State York, B
Saint Joseph's University, B
Susquehanna University, B
Temple University, B
University of Pennsylvania, BMD
University of Pittsburgh, BM
The University of Scranton, B
Villanova University, B

Rhode Island

Brown University, BD
Providence College, B
University of Rhode Island, B

Tennessee

The University of Tennessee, BD

Texas

University of Houston, B
The University of Texas at Austin, BMD

Vermont

Bennington College, B
Middlebury College, BMD

Virginia

University of Virginia, BM

Washington

Gonzaga University, B
University of Washington, BMD

Wisconsin

University of Wisconsin - Madison, BMD
University of Wisconsin - Milwaukee, BMO

Canada

Alberta

University of Alberta, BM

British Columbia

The University of British Columbia, B
University of Victoria, BM

Ontario

Brock University, B
Carleton University, B
Laurentian University, B
University of Ottawa, B
University of Toronto, BMD
The University of Western Ontario, B
University of Windsor, B
York University, B

Quebec

Bishop's University, B
Concordia University, B
McGill University, MD

ITALIAN STUDIES

United States

California

Scripps College, B
University of California, Santa Barbara, B
University of California, Santa Cruz, B

University of San Diego, B

Colorado

The Colorado College, B

Connecticut

Connecticut College, B
Wesleyan University, B

Georgia

Emory University, B

Indiana

Purdue University, B

Louisiana

Tulane University, B

Maine

Bowdoin College, B

Massachusetts

Assumption College, B
Boston University, B
Merrimack College, B
Tufts University, B
Wellesley College, B
Wheaton College, B

New York

Bard College, B
Columbia University, B
Columbia University, School of General Studies, B
Fordham University, B

Ohio

Miami University, B

Pennsylvania

Arcadia University, B
Dickinson College, B
Saint Joseph's University, B
The University of Scranton, B

Rhode Island

Brown University, B

Texas

Southern Methodist University, B

Vermont

University of Vermont, B

Virginia

University of Richmond, B

Canada

Alberta

University of Alberta, B
University of Calgary, B

British Columbia

University of Victoria, B

Manitoba

The University of Winnipeg, B

Maritime Provinces: Nova Scotia

Dalhousie University, B

Ontario

Brock University, B
The University of Western Ontario, B
University of Windsor, B
York University, B

Quebec

McGill University, B
Université de Montréal, B

JAPANESE LANGUAGE AND LITERATURE

United States

Alaska

University of Alaska Anchorage, B
University of Alaska Fairbanks, B

California

California State University, Fullerton, B
California State University, Long Beach, B
California State University, Los Angeles, B
California State University, Monterey Bay, B
Citrus College, A
City College of San Francisco, A
East Los Angeles College, A
El Camino College, A
Foothill College, A
Grossmont College, A
Occidental College, B
Pomona College, B
San Diego State University, B
San Francisco State University, B
San Jose State University, B
Scripps College, B
Stanford University, B
University of California, Berkeley, B
University of California, Davis, B
University of California, Irvine, B
University of California, Los Angeles, B
University of California, San Diego, B
University of California, Santa Barbara, B
University of the Pacific, B
University of San Francisco, B

Colorado

University of Colorado Boulder, B

Connecticut

Trinity College, B
Yale University, B

District of Columbia

Georgetown University, B

Georgia

Emory University, B
University of Georgia, B

Hawaii

University of Hawaii at Hilo, B
University of Hawaii at Manoa, B

Illinois

North Central College, B

Indiana

Ball State University, B
Purdue University, B
University of Notre Dame, B

Iowa

The University of Iowa, B

Kentucky

Murray State University, B
University of Kentucky, B

Maine

Bates College, B

Maryland

University of Maryland, College Park, B

Massachusetts

Boston University, B
Tufts University, B
University of Massachusetts Amherst, B
Wellesley College, B
Williams College, B

Michigan

Calvin College, B
Eastern Michigan University, B
Lansing Community College, A
Michigan State University, B
Oakland University, B
Western Michigan University, B

Minnesota

Gustavus Adolphus College, B
Macalester College, B

Missouri

Washington University in St. Louis, B

Montana

University of Montana, B

New Hampshire

Dartmouth College, B

New York

Bard College, B
Colgate University, B
Hobart and William Smith Colleges, B
Hofstra University, B
Sarah Lawrence College, B
University of Rochester, B
Vassar College, B

North Carolina

The University of North Carolina at Charlotte, B
Wake Forest University, B

Ohio

The Ohio State University, B
The University of Findlay, B
University of Mount Union, B

Oklahoma

University of Oklahoma, B

Oregon

Linfield College, B
Pacific University, B
Portland State University, B
University of Oregon, B

Pennsylvania

Carnegie Mellon University, B
Elizabethtown College, B
Gettysburg College, B
Penn State Abington, B
Penn State Altoona, B
Penn State Beaver, B
Penn State Berks, B
Penn State Brandywine, B
Penn State DuBois, B
Penn State Erie, The Behrend College, B
Penn State Fayette, The Eberly Campus, B
Penn State Greater Allegheny, B
Penn State Hazleton, B
Penn State Lehigh Valley, B
Penn State Mont Alto, B
Penn State New Kensington, B
Penn State Schuylkill, B
Penn State Shenango, B
Penn State University Park, B
Penn State Wilkes-Barre, B
Penn State Worthington Scranton, B
Penn State York, B
Swarthmore College, B
Temple University, B
University of Pittsburgh, B

Texas

Austin Community College District, A

Utah

Snow College, A
University of Utah, B
Weber State University, A

Vermont

Bennington College, B
Middlebury College, B
University of Vermont, B

Washington

Central Washington University, B
University of Puget Sound, B
University of Washington, B
Western Washington University, B

Wisconsin

Beloit College, B
Lawrence University, B
University of Wisconsin - Madison, B

Canada

Alberta

University of Alberta, B

British Columbia

University of Victoria, B

Ontario

McMaster University, B
The University of Western Ontario, B
York University, B

Saskatchewan

University of Regina, B

JAPANESE STUDIES

United States

Arizona

Arizona State University at the Tempe campus, M

California

San Francisco State University, M
Stanford University, MD
University of California, Berkeley, D
University of California, Irvine, MD
University of San Francisco, B

Colorado

University of Colorado Boulder, MD

Hawaii

University of Hawaii at Hilo, B
University of Hawaii at Manoa, MDO

Illinois

DePaul University, M

Indiana

Earlham College, B
Indiana University Bloomington, MD
Purdue University, M

Massachusetts

Harvard University, D
University of Massachusetts Amherst, M

Michigan

Adrian College, B
Eastern Michigan University, O
Hope College, B
Oakland University, B

Minnesota

Gustavus Adolphus College, B

Missouri

Washington University in St. Louis, MD

New York

Columbia University, M
Hofstra University, B

New York University, M
University at Albany, State University of New York, B

Ohio

Case Western Reserve University, B
Kent State University, M
The Ohio State University, MD

Oregon

Linfield College, B
Portland State University, M
University of Oregon, MD
Willamette University, B

Pennsylvania

Gettysburg College, B

Washington

University of Washington, BMD

Wisconsin

University of Wisconsin - Madison, MD
University of Wisconsin - Whitewater, B

Canada

Alberta

University of Alberta, BM

JAZZ/JAZZ STUDIES

United States

California

Santa Rosa Junior College, A
University of Southern California, B

Connecticut

University of Hartford, B

Florida

Florida State University, B
Jacksonville University, B
South Florida State College, A
State College of Florida Manatee-Sarasota, A
University of Miami, B
University of North Florida, B

Illinois

DePaul University, B
North Central College, B
Northwestern University, B
Roosevelt University, B
University of Illinois at Urbana - Champaign, B

Indiana

Butler University, B

Iowa

Drake University, B
Iowa Lakes Community College, A
The University of Iowa, B

Louisiana

Loyola University New Orleans, B

Maine

University of Maine at Augusta, AB

Maryland

Peabody Conservatory of The Johns Hopkins University, B
University of Maryland, Baltimore County, B

Massachusetts

Berklee College of Music, B
New England Conservatory of Music, B

Michigan

Hope College, B
Michigan State University, B
University of Michigan, B
Western Michigan University, B

Minnesota

Minnesota State University Moorhead, B
St. Cloud State University, B

Missouri

University of Missouri - Kansas City, B
Webster University, B

New Jersey

Rutgers University - New Brunswick, B

New York

Bard College, B
City College of the City University of New York, B
Eugene Lang College of Liberal Arts, B
Five Towns College, AB
Hofstra University, B
Ithaca College, B
Manhattan School of Music, B
The New School College of Performing Arts, B
University of Rochester, B

North Carolina

North Carolina Central University, B
The University of North Carolina at Greensboro, B

Ohio

Ashland University, B
Bowling Green State University, B
Capital University, B
Central State University, B
Oberlin College, B
The Ohio State University, B
The University of Akron, B
Youngstown State University, B

Oregon

University of Oregon, B

Pennsylvania

Temple University, B

Rhode Island

Community College of Rhode Island, A

South Carolina

Limestone College, B

Texas

Texas State University, B
University of North Texas, B
The University of Texas at Austin, B

Utah

Brigham Young University, B

Vermont

Bennington College, B
Johnson State College, B

Virginia

Hampton University, B
Liberty University, B
Shenandoah University, B

Washington

Central Washington University, B
Cornish College of the Arts, B
University of Washington, B
Whitman College, B

U.S. Territories: Puerto Rico

Conservatorio de Musica de Puerto Rico, B

Canada

British Columbia

Thompson Rivers University, B

Maritime Provinces: Nova Scotia

St. Francis Xavier University, B

Quebec

Concordia University, B
McGill University, B
Université Laval, A
Université de Montréal, B

JEWELRY/METALSMITHING

United States

Arizona

Arizona State University at the Tempe campus, M

California

Academy of Art University, M
California College of the Arts, M

Georgia

Savannah College of Art and Design, M

Illinois

Illinois State University, M
Southern Illinois University Carbondale, M
University of Illinois at Urbana - Champaign, M

Kansas

The University of Kansas, M

Michigan

Wayne State University, M

New York

City College of the City University of New York, M
Rochester Institute of Technology, M
State University of New York at New Paltz, M
Syracuse University, M

North Carolina

East Carolina University, M

Pennsylvania

Edinboro University of Pennsylvania, M
Temple University, M

Rhode Island

Rhode Island School of Design, M

Virginia

James Madison University, M
Virginia Commonwealth University, M

JEWISH/JUDAIC STUDIES

United States

Arizona

Arizona State University at the Tempe campus, B
The University of Arizona, B

California

American Jewish University, BM
Biola University, MO
California State University, Northridge, B
San Diego State University, B
San Francisco State University, B
Scripps College, B
Touro College Los Angeles, B

University of California, Berkeley, D
University of California, Los Angeles, B
University of California, San Diego, BM
University of Southern California, B

Colorado

University of Colorado Boulder, B

Connecticut

Trinity College, B
University of Connecticut, M
University of Hartford, B
Yale University, B

District of Columbia

American University, B
The George Washington University, B

Florida

Broward College, A
Florida Atlantic University, B
State College of Florida Manatee-Sarasota, A
Talmudic University, B
University of Florida, BM
University of Miami, B

Georgia

Emory University, B

Illinois

DePaul University, B
Hebrew Theological College, B
Telshe Yeshiva - Chicago, O
University of Chicago, B

Indiana

Indiana University Bloomington, BM
Purdue University, B

Louisiana

Tulane University, B

Maryland

Ner Israel Rabbinical College, B
Towson University, M
University of Maryland, College Park, BM

Massachusetts

Brandeis University, MD
Clark University, B
Harvard University, MD
Northeastern University, B
Tufts University, B
University of Massachusetts Amherst, B
Wellesley College, B

Michigan

Michigan Jewish Institute, AB
University of Michigan, BMDO

Minnesota

University of Minnesota, Twin Cities Campus, B

Missouri

Washington University in St. Louis, BM

New Jersey

Rutgers University - New Brunswick, BMO
Seton Hall University, MO

New York

Bard College, B
Barnard College, B
Binghamton University, State University of New York, B
Brooklyn College of the City University of New York, B
Central Yeshiva Tomchei Tmimim-Lubavitch, M
City College of the City University of New York, B
Columbia University, M
Cornell University, MD
Hofstra University, B
Hunter College of the City University of New York, B
The Jewish Theological Seminary, BMD

Lehman College of the City University of New York, B
Mesivta of Eastern Parkway - Yeshiva Zichron Meilech, B
New York University, MD
Queens College of the City University of New York, B
Sh'or Yoshuv Rabbinical College, B
Syracuse University, B
Touro College, M
University at Buffalo, the State University of New York, B
Vassar College, B
Yeshiva University, BMD

North Carolina

Piedmont International University, B

Ohio

Oberlin College, B
The Ohio State University, B

Oklahoma

University of Oklahoma, B

Oregon

University of Oregon, B

Pennsylvania

Dickinson College, B
Gettysburg College, B
Muhlenberg College, B
Penn State Abington, B
Penn State Altoona, B
Penn State Beaver, B
Penn State Berks, B
Penn State Brandywine, B
Penn State DuBois, B
Penn State Erie, The Behrend College, B
Penn State Fayette, The Eberly Campus, B
Penn State Greater Allegheny, B
Penn State Hazleton, B
Penn State Lehigh Valley, B
Penn State Mont Alto, B
Penn State New Kensington, B
Penn State Schuylkill, B
Penn State Shenango, B
Penn State University Park, B
Penn State Wilkes-Barre, B
Penn State Worthington Scranton, B
Penn State York, B
Temple University, B
University of Pennsylvania, B
Yeshiva Beth Moshe, B

Rhode Island

Brown University, B

South Carolina

College of Charleston, B

Tennessee

Vanderbilt University, B

Texas

Criswell College, M
Rice University, D
The University of Texas at Austin, B

Vermont

Bennington College, B
Marlboro College, B

Washington

University of Washington, B

Wisconsin

University of Wisconsin - Madison, B
University of Wisconsin - Milwaukee, B

Canada

Manitoba

University of Manitoba, B

Ontario

Ner Israel Yeshiva College of Toronto, B
The University of Western Ontario, B
York University, B

Quebec

Concordia University, BM
McGill University, BM

JOURNALISM

United States

Alabama

Auburn University, B
Samford University, B
Spring Hill College, B
Stillman College, B
Talladega College, B
Troy University, B
The University of Alabama, BM

Alaska

University of Alaska Anchorage, B
University of Alaska Fairbanks, B

Arizona

Arizona State University at the Downtown Phoenix campus, B
Arizona State University at the Tempe campus, MD
Cochise County Community College District, A
Northern Arizona University, B
Paradise Valley Community College, A
The University of Arizona, BM

Arkansas

Arkansas State University, BM
Arkansas Tech University, BM
Harding University, B
Henderson State University, B
John Brown University, AB
Southern Arkansas University - Magnolia, B
University of Arkansas, BM
University of Arkansas at Little Rock, B
University of Central Arkansas, B

California

Academy of Art University, AB
American River College, A
Ashford University, B
Bakersfield College, A
Biola University, B
Butte College, A
Cabrillo College, A
California Baptist University, B
California Lutheran University, B
California Polytechnic State University, San Luis Obispo, B
California State University, Chico, B
California State University, Dominguez Hills, B
California State University, East Bay, B
California State University, Fresno, BM
California State University, Fullerton, B
California State University, Long Beach, B
California State University, Northridge, BM
California State University, Sacramento, B
Cerritos College, A
Chabot College, A
Citrus College, A
City College of San Francisco, A
College of the Canyons, A
College of the Desert, A
College of San Mateo, A

College of the Sequoias, A
Contra Costa College, A
Cosumnes River College, A
Cuesta College, A
De Anza College, A
East Los Angeles College, A
El Camino College, A
Fullerton College, A
Golden West College, A
Grossmont College, A
Humboldt State University, B
Imperial Valley College, A
Laney College, A
Lassen Community College District, A
Long Beach City College, A
Los Angeles City College, A
Los Angeles Pierce College, A
Los Angeles Valley College, A
Los Medanos College, A
Modesto Junior College, A
Moorpark College, A
Mount Saint Mary's University, B
Mt. San Antonio College, A
National University, ABM
Ohlone College, A
Orange Coast College, A
Palomar College, A
Pepperdine University, B
Point Loma Nazarene University, B
Saddleback College, A
San Bernardino Valley College, A
San Diego City College, A
San Diego State University, B
San Francisco State University, B
San Joaquin Delta College, A
San Jose State University, B
Santa Ana College, A
Santa Monica College, A
Shasta College, A
Skyline College, A
Solano Community College, A
Southwestern College, A
Stanford University, M
Taft College, A
University of California, Berkeley, M
University of California, Irvine, B
University of La Verne, B
University of Southern California, BM
Ventura College, A
West Los Angeles College, A

Colorado

Adams State University, A
Arapahoe Community College, A
Colorado State University, B
Metropolitan State University of Denver, B
Northeastern Junior College, A
University of Colorado Boulder, BMD
University of Denver, B
University of Northern Colorado, B

Connecticut

Central Connecticut State University, B
Housatonic Community College, A
Manchester Community College, A
Quinnipiac University, BM
Sacred Heart University, M
Southern Connecticut State University, B
University of Bridgeport, B
University of Connecticut, B

Delaware

Delaware State University, B

District of Columbia

American University, BM
The George Washington University, B
Georgetown University, M
Howard University, B

Florida

Barry University, B
Broward College, B
College of Central Florida, A
Edward Waters College, B

Flagler College, B
Florida Agricultural and Mechanical University, BM
Florida International University, M
Full Sail University, M
Indian River State College, A
Lynn University, B
Miami Dade College, A
Palm Beach Atlantic University, B
Palm Beach State College, A
Pensacola State College, A
South Florida State College, A
Southeastern University, B
State College of Florida Manatee-Sarasota, A
University of Central Florida, B
University of Florida, BM
University of Miami, BM
University of South Florida, MO
University of South Florida, St. Petersburg, M

Georgia

Abraham Baldwin Agricultural College, A
Darton State College, A
Georgia College & State University, B
Georgia Highlands College, A
Georgia Southern University, B
Georgia State University, B
Kennesaw State University, B
Mercer University, B
Savannah State University, B
South Georgia State College, A
University of Georgia, BMD
University of West Georgia, B

Hawaii

Hawai'i Pacific University, B
University of Hawaii at Manoa, B

Idaho

North Idaho College, A
University of Idaho, B

Illinois

Benedictine University, B
Bradley University, B
City Colleges of Chicago, Wilbur Wright College, A
Columbia College Chicago, BM
Concordia University Chicago, B
DePaul University, BM
Dominican University, B
Eastern Illinois University, B
Illinois State University, B
Illinois Valley Community College, A
John A. Logan College, A
Lewis University, B
Loyola University Chicago, B
North Central College, B
Northern Illinois University, B
Northwestern University, BM
Roosevelt University, BM
School of the Art Institute of Chicago, M
Southern Illinois University Carbondale, BD
University of Illinois at Springfield, M
University of Illinois at Urbana - Champaign, BM
Western Illinois University, B

Indiana

Ball State University, BM
Butler University, B
Franklin College, B
Goshen College, B
Grace College, B
Huntington University, B
Indiana University Bloomington, BMD
Indiana University - Purdue University Indianapolis, B
Indiana University Southeast, B
Indiana Wesleyan University, B
Manchester University, B
University of Southern Indiana, B
Vincennes University, A

Iowa

Dordt College, B
Drake University, B
Grand View University, B

Iowa Central Community College, A
Iowa Lakes Community College, A
Iowa State University of Science and Technology, BM
Mount Mercy University, B
Northwestern College, B
St. Ambrose University, B
Simpson College, B
The University of Iowa, BMD
Wartburg College, B

Kansas

Allen Community College, A
Barton County Community College, A
Benedictine College, B
Butler Community College, A
Cloud County Community College, A
Cowley County Community College and Area Vocational - Technical School, A
Dodge City Community College, A
Fort Hays State University, B
Fort Scott Community College, A
Kansas State University, BM
Seward County Community College and Area Technical School, A
Southwestern College, B
The University of Kansas, BM

Kentucky

Asbury University, B
Campbellsville University, B
Eastern Kentucky University, B
Kentucky State University, B
Murray State University, B
Northern Kentucky University, B
University of the Cumberlands, B
University of Kentucky, B
Western Kentucky University, B

Louisiana

Louisiana College, B
Louisiana Tech University, B
Loyola University New Orleans, B

Maine

Saint Joseph's College of Maine, B
University of Maine, B

Maryland

University of Maryland, College Park, BMD
Washington Adventist University, B

Massachusetts

Boston University, BM
Eastern Nazarene College, B
Emerson College, BM
Harvard University, M
Lasell College, B
Massachusetts College of Liberal Arts, B
Northeastern University, BM
Northern Essex Community College, A
Salem State University, B
Suffolk University, B
University of Massachusetts Amherst, B
Western New England University, B

Michigan

Adrian College, B
Andrews University, B
Central Michigan University, B
Cornerstone University, B
Delta College, A
Eastern Michigan University, B
Grand Rapids Community College, A
Grand Valley State University, B
Madonna University, AB
Michigan State University, BM
Monroe County Community College, A
Oakland University, B
Olivet College, B
Washtenaw Community College, A
Wayne State University, BM
Western Michigan University, B

Minnesota

Bemidji State University, B
Bethel University, B
The College of St. Scholastica, B
Concordia College, B
Concordia University, St. Paul, B
Minnesota State University Mankato, B
Minnesota State University Moorhead, B
North Central University, AB
St. Catherine University, B
St. Cloud State University, B
Saint Mary's University of Minnesota, B
University of Minnesota, Twin Cities Campus, B
University of Northwestern - St. Paul, B
University of St. Thomas, B
Winona State University, B

Mississippi

Copiah-Lincoln Community College, A
Delta State University, B
Itawamba Community College, A
Northeast Mississippi Community College, A
Northwest Mississippi Community College, A
Rust College, B
University of Mississippi, BM
University of Southern Mississippi, B
William Carey University, B

Missouri

Calvary Bible College and Theological Seminary, B
College of the Ozarks, B
Drury University, B
Lincoln University, B
Lindenwood University, BM
Missouri Baptist University, B
Missouri State University, B
University of Central Missouri, B
University of Missouri, BMDO
Washington University in St. Louis, B
Webster University, B

Montana

University of Montana, BM

Nebraska

Creighton University, B
Doane University, B
Hastings College, B
Midland University, B
Northeast Community College, A
University of Nebraska at Kearney, B
University of Nebraska - Lincoln, BM
University of Nebraska at Omaha, B
Western Nebraska Community College, A

Nevada

University of Nevada, Las Vegas, M
University of Nevada, Reno, BM

New Hampshire

Franklin Pierce University, B
Keene State College, B
New England College, B

New Jersey

Bergen Community College, A
The College of New Jersey, B
Montclair State University, B
Rider University, B
Rowan College at Burlington County, A
Rowan University, B
Rutgers University - New Brunswick, B
Rutgers University - Newark, B
Salem Community College, A
Sussex County Community College, A
Thomas Edison State University, B

New Mexico

New Mexico State University, B
University of New Mexico, B

New York

Baruch College of the City University of New York, B

Brooklyn College of the City University of New York, B
Buffalo State College, State University of New York, B
Canisius College, B
Columbia University, MD
Five Towns College, B
Hofstra University, BM
Iona College, B
Ithaca College, B
Kingsborough Community College of the City University of New York, A
Long Island University - LIU Brooklyn, B
Long Island University - LIU Post, B
Marymount Manhattan College, B
Morrisville State College, A
New York University, BMO
Pace University, Pleasantville Campus, B
Purchase College, State University of New York, B
Rochester Institute of Technology, B
St. Bonaventure University, B
St. John's University, B
St. Joseph's College, Long Island Campus, B
St. Joseph's College, New York, B
St. Thomas Aquinas College, B
State University of New York at New Paltz, B
State University of New York at Oswego, B
State University of New York at Plattsburgh, B
Stony Brook University, State University of New York, BMO
Suffolk County Community College, A
Syracuse University, BM
University at Albany, State University of New York, B
Utica College, B
Westchester Community College, A

North Carolina

Appalachian State University, B
Bennett College, B
Campbell University, B
Elon University, B
Gardner-Webb University, B
North Carolina Agricultural and Technical State University, B
Pfeiffer University, B
Queens University of Charlotte, B
Saint Augustine's University, B
The University of North Carolina at Chapel Hill, B

North Dakota

Turtle Mountain Community College, A

Ohio

Ashland University, B
Bowling Green State University, B
Cedarville University, B
Central State University, B
Cincinnati Christian University, B
Cleveland State University, B
Kent State University, BM
Lorain County Community College, A
Marietta College, B
Miami University, B
Miami University Hamilton, B
Mount Vernon Nazarene University, B
Muskingum University, B
Ohio Northern University, B
The Ohio State University, B
Ohio University, BMD
Ohio Wesleyan University, B
Otterbein University, B
Tiffin University, B
The University of Akron, B
University of Cincinnati, B
The University of Findlay, B
Youngstown State University, B

Oklahoma

Bacone College, A
East Central University, B
Eastern Oklahoma State College, A
Langston University, B
Oklahoma Baptist University, B
Oklahoma Christian University, B
Oklahoma State University, B
Rose State College, A

Southern Nazarene University, B
University of Central Oklahoma, B
University of Oklahoma, BMD

Oregon

Corban University, B
George Fox University, B
Mt. Hood Community College, A
Pacific University, B
Umpqua Community College, A
University of Oregon, BMD

Pennsylvania

Bucks County Community College, A
Chatham University, B
Community College of Allegheny County, A
Community College of Beaver County, A
Delaware County Community College, A
Drexel University, M
Duquesne University, B
Edinboro University of Pennsylvania, B
Gannon University, B
Gettysburg College, B
Indiana University of Pennsylvania, B
Lehigh University, B
Lincoln University, B
Luzerne County Community College, A
Messiah College, B
Northampton Community College, A
Penn State Abington, B
Penn State Altoona, B
Penn State Beaver, B
Penn State Berks, B
Penn State Brandywine, B
Penn State DuBois, B
Penn State Erie, The Behrend College, B
Penn State Fayette, The Eberly Campus, B
Penn State Greater Allegheny, B
Penn State Hazleton, B
Penn State Lehigh Valley, B
Penn State Mont Alto, B
Penn State New Kensington, B
Penn State Schuylkill, B
Penn State Shenango, B
Penn State University Park, B
Penn State Wilkes-Barre, B
Penn State Worthington Scranton, B
Penn State York, B
Point Park University, BM
Saint Francis University, B
Seton Hill University, B
Shippensburg University of Pennsylvania, B
Slippery Rock University of Pennsylvania, B
Temple University, BM
University of Pittsburgh at Greensburg, B
University of Pittsburgh at Johnstown, B
Waynesburg University, B
Wilson College, B

Rhode Island

University of Rhode Island, B

South Carolina

Bob Jones University, M
Columbia College, B
North Greenville University, B
University of South Carolina, BMD

South Dakota

Augustana University, B
South Dakota State University, BM

Tennessee

Belmont University, B
Freed-Hardeman University, B
Lee University, B
Southern Adventist University, B
Tennessee Technological University, B
Trevecca Nazarene University, B
Union University, B
University of Memphis, BM
The University of Tennessee, BMD

Texas

Abilene Christian University, B
Amarillo College, A
Angelo State University, BM
Austin Community College District, A
Baylor University, BM
Central Texas College, A
Del Mar College, A
Houston Baptist University, B
Kilgore College, A
Lee College, A
Lubbock Christian University, B
Palo Alto College, A
Panola College, A
Paris Junior College, A
Sam Houston State University, B
San Jacinto College District, A
South Plains College, A
Southern Methodist University, B
Southwestern Adventist University, B
Texarkana College, A
Texas A&M University - Commerce, B
Texas Christian University, BM
Texas Southern University, B
Texas State University, B
Texas Tech University, B
Texas Wesleyan University, B
Trinity Valley Community College, A
University of Houston, B
University of the Incarnate Word, B
University of North Texas, BMO
The University of Texas at Arlington, B
The University of Texas at Austin, BMD
The University of Texas at El Paso, B
West Texas A&M University, B

Utah

Brigham Young University, B
Utah State University, B
Weber State University, B

Vermont

Castleton University, B
Johnson State College, B
Lyndon State College, B

Virginia

Averett University, B
Hampton University, B
Liberty University, B
Norfolk State University, B
Patrick Henry College, B
Radford University, B
Regent University, M
University of Richmond, B
Virginia Commonwealth University, M
Virginia Union University, B
Washington and Lee University, B

Washington

Central Washington University, B
Eastern Washington University, B
Everett Community College, A
Gonzaga University, B
Highline College, A
Seattle University, B
Skagit Valley College, A
University of Washington, B
Walla Walla University, B
Washington State University, B
Western Washington University, B
Whitworth University, B

West Virginia

Alderson Broaddus University, B
Marshall University, BM
Potomac State College of West Virginia University, A
West Virginia University, BMO

Wisconsin

Carroll University, B
Marquette University, BM
University of Wisconsin - Eau Claire, B
University of Wisconsin - Madison, BMD

University of Wisconsin - Oshkosh, B
University of Wisconsin - River Falls, B
University of Wisconsin - Superior, B
University of Wisconsin - Whitewater, B

Wyoming

Casper College, A
Northwest College, A
University of Wyoming, B
Western Wyoming Community College, A

U.S. Territories: Puerto Rico

Bayamón Central University, B
University of Puerto Rico, Río Piedras Campus, BM
University of the Sacred Heart, B

Canada
Alberta

Mount Royal University, B

British Columbia

Thompson Rivers University, B
The University of British Columbia, M

Manitoba

The University of Winnipeg, B

Maritime Provinces: New Brunswick

St. Thomas University, B

Maritime Provinces: Nova Scotia

University of King's College, BM

Ontario

Carleton University, BMD
Ryerson University, B
Trent University, B
University of Ottawa, B
The University of Western Ontario, M
Wilfrid Laurier University, B

Quebec

Concordia University, BO
Université Laval, O

Saskatchewan

University of Regina, BM

JUNIOR HIGH/INTERMEDIATE/ MIDDLE SCHOOL EDUCATION AND TEACHING

United States
Alabama

Jacksonville State University, B

Arkansas

Arkansas Northeastern College, A
Arkansas State University, B
Arkansas State University - Mountain Home, A
Arkansas Tech University, B
Black River Technical College, A
Cossatot Community College of the University of Arkansas, A
Harding University, B
Henderson State University, B
Ouachita Baptist University, B
Ozarka College, A
Rich Mountain Community College, A
Southern Arkansas University - Magnolia, B
Southern Arkansas University Tech, A
University of Arkansas - Fort Smith, B
University of Arkansas at Monticello, B
University of Arkansas at Pine Bluff, B
University of Central Arkansas, B
University of the Ozarks, B

California

Ashford University, B
The Master's College and Seminary, B

Connecticut

Albertus Magnus College, B

Delaware

Delaware State University, B
Delaware Technical & Community College, Jack F. Owens Campus, A
Delaware Technical & Community College, Stanton/Wilmington Campus, A
Delaware Technical & Community College, Terry Campus, A
Wilmington University, B

Florida

Florida Institute of Technology, B
Miami Dade College, A
Saint Leo University, B
South Florida State College, A
University of North Florida, B
University of West Florida, B

Georgia

Albany State University, B
Armstrong State University, B
Augusta University, B
Berry College, B
Brenau University, B
Brewton-Parker College, B
Clayton State University, B
Columbus State University, B
Darton State College, A
Emmanuel College, B
Georgia College & State University, B
Georgia Military College, A
Georgia Southern University, B
Georgia Southwestern State University, B
Gordon State College, A
Kennesaw State University, B
Mercer University, B
Paine College, B
Piedmont College, B
Point University, B
Reinhardt University, B
Shorter University, B
Thomas University, B
Toccoa Falls College, B
Truett-McConnell College, B
University of Georgia, B
University of North Georgia, B
Valdosta State University, B
Young Harris College, B

Illinois

Eastern Illinois University, B
Illinois State University, B
Lewis University, B
McKendree University, B
Southern Illinois University Edwardsville, B
Trinity Christian College, B

Indiana

Bethel College, B
Huntington University, B
Indiana Wesleyan University, B
Manchester University, B

Iowa

Mount Mercy University, B
University of Northern Iowa, B

Kansas

Baker University, B
MidAmerica Nazarene University, B
The University of Kansas, B

Kentucky

Alice Lloyd College, B
Asbury University, B
Bellarmine University, B
Berea College, B

Brescia University, B
Eastern Kentucky University, B
Georgetown College, B
Kentucky Christian University, B
Kentucky Wesleyan College, B
Lindsey Wilson College, B
Midway University, B
Morehead State University, B
Murray State University, B
Northern Kentucky University, B
Spalding University, B
Thomas More College, B
Transylvania University, B
Union College, B
University of the Cumberlands, B
University of Kentucky, B
University of Pikeville, B
Western Kentucky University, B

Louisiana

Louisiana Tech University, B
Nicholls State University, B
Southeastern Louisiana University, B
Southern University and Agricultural and Mechanical
  College, B
University of Louisiana at Lafayette, B
Xavier University of Louisiana, B

Maine

College of the Atlantic, B

Maryland

Stevenson University, B
Towson University, B
University of Maryland, College Park, B

Massachusetts

Anna Maria College, B
Clark University, B
Eastern Nazarene College, B
Fitchburg State University, B
Gordon College, B
Lesley University, B
Merrimack College, B
Salem State University, B

Michigan

Grand Valley State University, B
Lake Superior State University, B
Michigan State University, B

Minnesota

Concordia University, St. Paul, B
St. Cloud State University, B
University of Minnesota, Duluth, B
University of St. Thomas, B

Missouri

Avila University, B
Central Methodist University, B
Evangel University, B
Fontbonne University, B
Harris-Stowe State University, B
Lincoln University, B
Lindenwood University, B
Maryville University of Saint Louis, B
Missouri Baptist University, B
Missouri State University, B
Northwest Missouri State University, B
Rockhurst University, B
Saint Louis University, B
Southeast Missouri State University, B
Southwest Baptist University, B
University of Central Missouri, B
University of Missouri, B
University of Missouri - Kansas City, B
Washington University in St. Louis, B
Webster University, B
Westminster College, B

Montana

University of Great Falls, B

Nebraska

Chadron State College, B
Concordia University, Nebraska, B
Grace University, B
Midland University, B
Nebraska Wesleyan University, B
Peru State College, B
Wayne State College, B
York College, B

New Hampshire

Granite State College, B

New York

Concordia College - New York, B
Ithaca College, B
Manhattan College, B
Medaille College, B
State University of New York College at Cortland, B
State University of New York College at Old
  Westbury, B
State University of New York College at Oneonta, B

North Carolina

Appalachian State University, B
Barton College, B
Campbell University, B
Catawba College, B
East Carolina University, B
Elizabeth City State University, B
Elon University, B
Fayetteville State University, B
Gardner-Webb University, B
Greensboro College, B
High Point University, B
Lenoir-Rhyne University, B
Mars Hill University, B
North Carolina Central University, B
North Carolina State University, B
North Carolina Wesleyan College, B
University of Mount Olive, B
The University of North Carolina at Chapel Hill, B
The University of North Carolina at Charlotte, B
The University of North Carolina at Greensboro, B
The University of North Carolina at Pembroke, B
The University of North Carolina Wilmington, B
Western Carolina University, B
Wingate University, B
Winston-Salem State University, B

North Dakota

University of North Dakota, B

Ohio

Ashland University, B
Baldwin Wallace University, B
Bluffton University, B
Bowling Green State University, B
Capital University, B
Cedarville University, B
Central State University, B
Cleveland State University, B
Kent State University, B
Kent State University at Geauga, B
Kent State University at Stark, B
Lourdes University, B
Malone University, B
Miami University, B
Mount St. Joseph University, B
Mount Vernon Nazarene University, B
Muskingum University, B
Notre Dame College, B
Ohio Christian University, B
Ohio Dominican University, B
Ohio Northern University, B
The Ohio State University, B
The Ohio State University at Lima, B
The Ohio State University - Mansfield Campus, B
The Ohio State University at Marion, B
The Ohio State University - Newark Campus, B
Ohio University - Eastern, B
Ohio University - Lancaster, B
Ohio Wesleyan University, B
Otterbein University, B
The University of Akron, B

University of Cincinnati, B
University of Cincinnati Clermont College, A
University of Dayton, B
University of Mount Union, B
Urbana University, B
Ursuline College, B
Walsh University, B
Wright State University, AB
Wright State University - Lake Campus, B
Xavier University, B
Youngstown State University, B

Oregon

Northwest Christian University, B
Warner Pacific College, B

Pennsylvania

Alvernia University, B
Bloomsburg University of Pennsylvania, B
California University of Pennsylvania, B
Carlow University, B
Clarion University of Pennsylvania, B
Duquesne University, B
Eastern University, B
Edinboro University of Pennsylvania, B
Elizabethtown College, B
Gannon University, B
Gettysburg College, B
Grove City College, B
Indiana University of Pennsylvania, B
Kutztown University of Pennsylvania, B
La Salle University, B
Lock Haven University of Pennsylvania, B
Mercyhurst University, B
Messiah College, B
Millersville University of Pennsylvania, B
Misericordia University, B
Mount Aloysius College, B
Northampton Community College, A
Saint Vincent College, B
Shippensburg University of Pennsylvania, B
Temple University, B
The University of Scranton, B
University of Valley Forge, B
West Chester University of Pennsylvania, B
Wilkes University, B

South Carolina

Bob Jones University, B
Claflin University, B
Coastal Carolina University, B
College of Charleston, B
Columbia College, B
Francis Marion University, B
Newberry College, B
Presbyterian College, B
South Carolina State University, B
University of South Carolina, B
University of South Carolina Aiken, B
University of South Carolina Upstate, B

South Dakota

Black Hills State University, B
Dakota Wesleyan University, B
Sinte Gleska University, B
University of Sioux Falls, B

Tennessee

Belmont University, B
Carson-Newman University, B
Freed-Hardeman University, B
Johnson University, B
Lee University, B
Lipscomb University, B
Nashville State Community College, A
The University of Tennessee at Chattanooga, B

Texas

Alvin Community College, A
Arlington Baptist College, B
Austin College, B
Austin Community College District, A
College of the Mainland, A
Collin County Community College District, A
Concordia University Texas, B

El Paso Community College, A
Grayson College, A
Howard College, A
Lubbock Christian University, B
McMurry University, B
Panola College, A
Schreiner University, B
Tarleton State University, B
Texas Lutheran University, B
Tyler Junior College, A
The University of Texas at San Antonio, B
Wayland Baptist University, B

Vermont

Champlain College, B
Goddard College, B
Johnson State College, B
University of Vermont, B

Virginia

Bluefield College, B
Hampton University, B
Virginia Wesleyan College, B

West Virginia

Bethany College, B
West Virginia Wesleyan College, B

Wisconsin

Alverno College, B
Carroll University, B
Concordia University Wisconsin, B
Lakeland College, B
Marian University, B
Mount Mary University, B

U.S. Territories: Puerto Rico

Bayamón Central University, B

Canada
Manitoba

Brandon University, B

Newfoundland and Labrador

Memorial University of Newfoundland, B

Ontario

The University of Western Ontario, B
York University, B

Saskatchewan

University of Regina, B

JUVENILE CORRECTIONS

United States
Illinois

Danville Area Community College, A
Illinois Central College, A
Illinois Valley Community College, A
Kaskaskia College, A

Michigan

Lansing Community College, A
Oakland University, B

Missouri

Harris-Stowe State University, B
Missouri Southern State University, B

Oklahoma

University of Central Oklahoma, B

Oregon

Chemeketa Community College, A

Texas

Prairie View A&M University, B

KINDERGARTEN/PRESCHOOL EDUCATION AND TEACHING

United States
Alabama

Alabama Agricultural and Mechanical University, B
Alabama Southern Community College, A
Athens State University, B
Jacksonville State University, B
Wallace State Community College, A

Alaska

University of Alaska Anchorage, B

Arizona

Central Arizona College, A
Northland Pioneer College, A
The University of Arizona, B

Arkansas

John Brown University, B
Philander Smith College, B
Shorter College, A
University of Arkansas, B
University of Arkansas at Monticello, B
University of Arkansas at Pine Bluff, B
University of Central Arkansas, B
Williams Baptist College, B

California

Allan Hancock College, A
Ashford University, B
California Polytechnic State University, San Luis Obispo, B
Cerritos College, A
College of the Sequoias, A
El Camino College, A
Humboldt State University, B
Imperial Valley College, A
Lake Tahoe Community College, A
Las Positas College, A
Lassen Community College District, A
Los Angeles Southwest College, A
Los Angeles Valley College, A
Mendocino College, A
Merced College, A
Modesto Junior College, A
Monterey Peninsula College, A
Moorpark College, A
Mount Saint Mary's University, A
Mt. San Antonio College, A
Napa Valley College, A
Ohlone College, A
Pacific Oaks College, B
Patten University, A
Sacramento City College, A
Saddleback College, A
Santa Ana College, A
Santa Barbara City College, A
Shasta College, A
Solano Community College, A
Taft College, A
Victor Valley College, A
West Hills Community College, A
West Valley College, A
Yuba College, A

Colorado

Otero Junior College, A

Connecticut

Eastern Connecticut State University, B
Gateway Community College, A
Manchester Community College, A
Mitchell College, A
Northwestern Connecticut Community College, A
Post University, B
Tunxis Community College, A

Delaware

Delaware State University, B
Delaware Technical & Community College, Jack F. Owens Campus, A
Delaware Technical & Community College, Stanton/Wilmington Campus, A
Delaware Technical & Community College, Terry Campus, A

District of Columbia

Howard University, B
University of the District of Columbia, B

Florida

Barry University, B
Daytona State College, A
Edward Waters College, B
Indian River State College, A
Miami Dade College, A
Palm Beach State College, A
State College of Florida Manatee-Sarasota, A

Georgia

Abraham Baldwin Agricultural College, A
Bainbridge State College, A
Fort Valley State University, B
Georgia State University, B
Piedmont College, B
Thomas University, B
University of Georgia, B

Hawaii

Honolulu Community College, A
Kauai Community College, A

Idaho

Brigham Young University - Idaho, A

Illinois

Columbia College Chicago, B
Eastern Illinois University, B
Elmhurst College, B
Illinois State University, B
John A. Logan College, A
Northern Illinois University, B
Olivet Nazarene University, B
Parkland College, A
Saint Xavier University, B
Spoon River College, A
University of Illinois at Urbana - Champaign, B

Iowa

Iowa Lakes Community College, A
University of Northern Iowa, B
Wartburg College, B

Kansas

Butler Community College, A
Central Christian College of Kansas, AB
Fort Hays State University, B
Hesston College, A
Labette Community College, A
McPherson College, B
Pratt Community College, A

Kentucky

Northern Kentucky University, B

Louisiana

Delgado Community College, A
Louisiana College, B
Louisiana Tech University, B
Nunez Community College, A
Southern University at Shreveport, A

Maine

Northern Maine Community College, A
University of Maine at Farmington, B

Maryland

Bowie State University, B
Howard Community College, A
Prince George's Community College, A
University of Maryland, College Park, B

University of Maryland Eastern Shore, B

Massachusetts

Bristol Community College, A
Cape Cod Community College, A
Eastern Nazarene College, AB
Fisher College, A
Lasell College, B
Lesley University, B
Middlesex Community College, A
North Shore Community College, A
Northern Essex Community College, A
Quinsigamond Community College, A
Roxbury Community College, A
Tufts University, B
Westfield State University, B

Michigan

Alma College, B
Baker College, A
Marygrove College, AB
Michigan State University, B
Siena Heights University, B

Minnesota

Central Lakes College, A
Martin Luther College, B
Minnesota State University Mankato, B
St. Catherine University, B
St. Cloud State University, B
Southwest Minnesota State University, B
University of Minnesota, Crookston, B
University of Minnesota, Duluth, B
University of Minnesota, Twin Cities Campus, B
Vermilion Community College, A

Mississippi

Itawamba Community College, A
Mississippi Gulf Coast Community College, A
Mississippi Valley State University, B
Northeast Mississippi Community College, A

Missouri

Central Methodist University, B
Evangel University, B
Fontbonne University, B
Ozarks Technical Community College, A
University of Missouri, B

Montana

Aaniiih Nakoda College, A
Salish Kootenai College, A
University of Great Falls, AB

Nebraska

Chadron State College, B
Metropolitan Community College, A
Midland University, AB
Peru State College, B
Western Nebraska Community College, A

Nevada

College of Southern Nevada, A
Truckee Meadows Community College, A

New Hampshire

Manchester Community College, A
Nashua Community College, A
NHTI, Concord's Community College, A

New Jersey

County College of Morris, A
Essex County College, A
Kean University, B
New Jersey City University, B
Passaic County Community College, A
Raritan Valley Community College, A

New Mexico

Luna Community College, A
New Mexico Highlands University, B
Santa Fe Community College, A
University of New Mexico - Gallup, A
Western New Mexico University, B

New York

Buffalo State College, State University of New York, B
The College of Saint Rose, B
Finger Lakes Community College, A
Fulton-Montgomery Community College, A
Genesee Community College, A
Hunter College of the City University of New York, B
Long Island University - LIU Post, B
Maria College, A
Nassau Community College, A
St. Thomas Aquinas College, B
State University of New York College of Agriculture and Technology at Cobleskill, B
State University of New York College at Cortland, B
State University of New York College at Oneonta, B
State University of New York at Fredonia, B
Suffolk County Community College, A
Sullivan County Community College, A
Ulster County Community College, A
Wagner College, B

North Carolina

Alamance Community College, A
Beaufort County Community College, A
Catawba College, B
Central Carolina Community College, A
Central Piedmont Community College, A
East Carolina University, B
Elizabeth City State University, B
Greensboro College, B
Isothermal Community College, A
Lees-McRae College, B
Livingstone College, B
Methodist University, B
Mitchell Community College, A
North Carolina Agricultural and Technical State University, B
North Carolina Central University, B
Piedmont International University, AB
Sandhills Community College, A
Shaw University, B
Southeastern Community College, A
The University of North Carolina at Charlotte, B
The University of North Carolina at Pembroke, B
The University of North Carolina Wilmington, B
Vance-Granville Community College, A
Western Carolina University, B
Winston-Salem State University, B

North Dakota

Turtle Mountain Community College, A

Ohio

Ashland University, B
Bluffton University, B
Bowling Green State University, B
Cincinnati Christian University, B
Clark State Community College, A
Cuyahoga Community College, A
John Carroll University, B
Lorain County Community College, A
Miami University, A
Miami University Middletown, A
Northwest State Community College, A
Notre Dame College, B
Ohio Dominican University, B
Ohio Northern University, B
Ohio University - Southern Campus, B
Ohio Wesleyan University, B
Shawnee State University, A
Sinclair Community College, A
Southern State Community College, A
Terra State Community College, A
University of Cincinnati Blue Ash College, A
University of Cincinnati Clermont College, A
University of Rio Grande, A
The University of Toledo, B
Walsh University, B
Washington State Community College, A
Wright State University, B

Oklahoma

Northeastern Oklahoma Agricultural and Mechanical College, A

Northwestern Oklahoma State University, B
Oklahoma Baptist University, B
Oklahoma Christian University, B
Redlands Community College, A
Rose State College, A
Southeastern Oklahoma State University, B
University of Central Oklahoma, B

Oregon

Concordia University, B
Mt. Hood Community College, A
Pacific University, B
Umpqua Community College, A

Pennsylvania

Arcadia University, B
Bucknell University, B
Butler County Community College, A
Cabrini University, B
Cairn University, B
California University of Pennsylvania, AB
Community College of Philadelphia, A
Lincoln University, B
Mansfield University of Pennsylvania, B
Susquehanna University, B
Widener University, B

Rhode Island

Community College of Rhode Island, A

South Carolina

Converse College, B
Erskine College, B
Furman University, B
Orangeburg-Calhoun Technical College, A
Southern Wesleyan University, B
University of South Carolina Upstate, B

South Dakota

Black Hills State University, B
Oglala Lakota College, AB
Sisseton-Wahpeton College, A

Tennessee

Carson-Newman University, B
Cleveland State Community College, A
Lincoln Memorial University, B
Middle Tennessee State University, B
Nashville State Community College, A
Northeast State Community College, A
Roane State Community College, A
Southwest Tennessee Community College, A
Tennessee State University, AB
Tennessee Technological University, B
Union University, B
The University of Tennessee at Martin, B

Texas

Baylor University, B
Cisco College, A
Del Mar College, A
El Paso Community College, A
Grayson College, A
Jarvis Christian College, B
McLennan Community College, A
Odessa College, A
Texas A&M International University, B
Trinity Valley Community College, A

Utah

Snow College, A
Utah State University, B

Vermont

University of Vermont, B

Virginia

Bluefield College, B
Hampton University, B
Norfolk State University, B
Tidewater Community College, A
Virginia Union University, B
Virginia Western Community College, A

Washington

Highline College, A
Pierce College at Puyallup, A
Seattle Central College, A
Shoreline Community College, A
Skagit Valley College, A
South Puget Sound Community College, A
Washington State University, B
Wenatchee Valley College, A
Whatcom Community College, A
Yakima Valley Community College, A

West Virginia

Concord University, B
Glenville State College, B
Marshall University, B
West Liberty University, B
West Virginia Wesleyan College, B

Wisconsin

College of Menominee Nation, A
Concordia University Wisconsin, B
Lakeland College, B
Nicolet Area Technical College, A
Silver Lake College of the Holy Family, B
University of Wisconsin - Oshkosh, B
University of Wisconsin - Stevens Point, B

Wyoming

Casper College, A
Northwest College, A

U.S. Territories: Puerto Rico

Bayamón Central University, B
Inter American University of Puerto Rico, Aguadilla Campus, B
Inter American University of Puerto Rico, Arecibo Campus, B
Inter American University of Puerto Rico, Barranquitas Campus, B
Inter American University of Puerto Rico, Guayama Campus, B
Inter American University of Puerto Rico, Metropolitan Campus, B
Inter American University of Puerto Rico, Ponce Campus, B
Inter American University of Puerto Rico, San Germán Campus, B
National University College (Bayamón), B
Universidad Metropolitana, B

Canada

British Columbia

Summit Pacific College, B
The University of British Columbia, B
University of Victoria, B

Manitoba

Brandon University, B
University of Manitoba, B

Maritime Provinces: New Brunswick

Université de Moncton, B
University of New Brunswick Fredericton, B

Maritime Provinces: Nova Scotia

Mount Saint Vincent University, B

Ontario

University of Windsor, B
York University, B

Quebec

Concordia University, B
Université Laval, B
Université de Montréal, B
Université du Québec en Abitibi-Témiscamingue, B
Université du Québec à Chicoutimi, B
Université du Québec à Montréal, B
Université du Québec en Outaouais, B
Université du Québec à Rimouski, B
Université du Québec à Trois-Rivières, B

Université de Sherbrooke, B

Saskatchewan

University of Regina, B

KINESIOLOGY AND EXERCISE SCIENCE

United States

Alabama

Auburn University at Montgomery, B
Huntingdon College, B
Jacksonville State University, B
Samford University, B
Troy University, B
United States Sports Academy, B
The University of West Alabama, B

Arizona

Arizona State University at the Downtown Phoenix campus, B
Chandler-Gilbert Community College, A
Diné College, A
Glendale Community College, A
Northern Arizona University, B
Paradise Valley Community College, A

Arkansas

Arkansas State University, B
Central Baptist College, B
Harding University, B
John Brown University, B
Ouachita Baptist University, B
Southern Arkansas University - Magnolia, B
University of Central Arkansas, B

California

Antelope Valley College, A
Biola University, B
California Baptist University, B
California Lutheran University, B
California State University, Chico, B
California State University, East Bay, B
California State University, Long Beach, B
California State University, Los Angeles, B
California State University, Northridge, B
California State University, Sacramento, B
California State University, San Marcos, B
Cerritos College, A
Feather River College, A
Humboldt State University, B
La Sierra University, B
The Master's College and Seminary, B
Monterey Peninsula College, A
Notre Dame de Namur University, B
Occidental College, B
Ohlone College, A
Orange Coast College, A
Pacific Union College, B
Palomar College, A
Pepperdine University, B
Point Loma Nazarene University, B
Saint Katherine College, B
Saint Mary's College of California, B
San Diego Christian College, B
San Diego State University, B
San Francisco State University, B
Santa Ana College, A
Santa Barbara City College, A
Santa Rosa Junior College, A
Santiago Canyon College, A
Sonoma State University, B
University of La Verne, B
University of the Pacific, B
University of San Francisco, B
Vanguard University of Southern California, B
Westmont College, B
Whittier College, B
William Jessup University, B

Colorado

Adams State University, B
Colorado Mesa University, B
Colorado State University, B
Colorado State University - Pueblo, B
Regis University, B
University of Northern Colorado, B
Western State Colorado University, B

Connecticut

Norwalk Community College, A
Three Rivers Community College, A

Delaware

Delaware Technical & Community College, Stanton/Wilmington Campus, A
University of Delaware, B

District of Columbia

The George Washington University, B

Florida

Barry University, B
Broward College, A
Florida Atlantic University, B
Florida Gulf Coast University, B
Florida State University, B
Jacksonville University, B
Keiser University, B
Nova Southeastern University, B
South Florida State College, A
Warner University, B

Georgia

Andrew College, A
Augusta University, B
Berry College, B
Columbus State University, B
Emmanuel College, B
Georgia College & State University, B
Georgia Gwinnett College, B
Georgia Southern University, B
Kennesaw State University, B
LaGrange College, B
Life University, B
Point University, B
South Georgia State College, A
Truett-McConnell College, B

Hawaii

Brigham Young University - Hawaii, B
Kapiolani Community College, A
University of Hawaii at Hilo, B
University of Hawaii at Manoa, B

Idaho

Boise State University, B
The College of Idaho, B
Lewis-Clark State College, B
Northwest Nazarene University, B

Illinois

Concordia University Chicago, B
DePaul University, B
Eastern Illinois University, B
Elmhurst College, B
Eureka College, B
Greenville College, B
Illinois State University, B
Lewis and Clark Community College, A
Lewis University, B
McKendree University, B
Monmouth College, B
North Central College, B
North Park University, B
Olivet Nazarene University, B
Prairie State College, A
South Suburban College, A
Southern Illinois University Carbondale, B
Southern Illinois University Edwardsville, B
Trinity Christian College, B
University of Illinois at Chicago, B
University of Illinois at Urbana - Champaign, B
Western Illinois University, B

Indiana

Ancilla College, A
Ball State University, B
Bethel College, B
DePauw University, B
Franklin College, B
Goshen College, B
Grace College, B
Hanover College, B
Huntington University, B
Indiana State University, B
Indiana University Bloomington, B
Indiana University - Purdue University Indianapolis, B
Indiana Wesleyan University, B
Ivy Tech Community College - East Central, A
Ivy Tech Community College - Southern Indiana, A
Manchester University, B
Marian University, B
Purdue University, B
University of Evansville, B
University of Indianapolis, B
University of Southern Indiana, B
Valparaiso University, B

Iowa

Cornell College, B
Dordt College, B
Grand View University, B
Iowa State University of Science and Technology, B
Iowa Wesleyan University, B
Loras College, B
Northwestern College, B
Simpson College, B
The University of Iowa, B
Upper Iowa University, B
William Penn University, B

Kansas

Baker University, B
Barton County Community College, A
Central Christian College of Kansas, AB
Kansas State University, B
Kansas Wesleyan University, B
MidAmerica Nazarene University, B
Ottawa University, B
Pittsburg State University, B
The University of Kansas, B
Wichita State University, B

Kentucky

Bellarmine University, B
Berea College, B
Georgetown College, B
Kentucky Wesleyan College, B
Morehead State University, B
Murray State University, B
Transylvania University, B
Union College, B
Western Kentucky University, B

Louisiana

Louisiana College, B
McNeese State University, B
University of Louisiana at Monroe, B

Maine

Husson University, B
Saint Joseph's College of Maine, B
University of New England, B

Maryland

Carroll Community College, A
Frostburg State University, B
McDaniel College, B
Salisbury University, B
Towson University, B
University of Maryland, College Park, B

Massachusetts

Becker College, B
Bridgewater State University, B
Endicott College, B
Fitchburg State University, B
Gordon College, B

Lasell College, B
Salem State University, B
Simmons College, B
Springfield College, B

Michigan

Adrian College, B
Albion College, B
Alma College, B
Calvin College, B
Central Michigan University, B
Cornerstone University, B
Eastern Michigan University, B
Hillsdale College, B
Hope College, B
Kuyper College, B
Lake Superior State University, B
Michigan State University, B
Michigan Technological University, B
Northern Michigan University, B
Oakland Community College, A
Saginaw Valley State University, B
Spring Arbor University, B
University of Michigan, B
Western Michigan University, B

Minnesota

Augsburg College, B
Bethel University, B
Concordia University, St. Paul, B
Dakota County Technical College, A
Hamline University, B
Minnesota State University Moorhead, B
St. Cloud State University, B
St. Olaf College, B
Southwest Minnesota State University, B
University of Minnesota, Duluth, B
University of Northwestern - St. Paul, B
Winona State University, B

Mississippi

Belhaven University, B
Blue Mountain College, B
Mississippi College, B
University of Mississippi, B

Missouri

Avila University, B
Drury University, B
Hannibal-LaGrange University, B
Lindenwood University, B
Maryville University of Saint Louis, B
Missouri Baptist University, B
Missouri State University, B
Saint Louis University, B
Southwest Baptist University, B
Truman State University, B
Webster University, B
Westminster College, B
William Woods University, B

Montana

Rocky Mountain College, B

Nebraska

Concordia University, Nebraska, B
Creighton University, B
Hastings College, B
Nebraska Wesleyan University, B
Union College, B
University of Nebraska at Omaha, B

Nevada

University of Nevada, Las Vegas, B

New Hampshire

Colby-Sawyer College, B
Manchester Community College, A
Plymouth State University, B
University of New Hampshire, B

New Jersey

Bergen Community College, A
County College of Morris, A
Georgian Court University, B

Montclair State University, B
Raritan Valley Community College, A
Rowan College at Gloucester County, A
Rutgers University - New Brunswick, B
Stockton University, B
William Paterson University of New Jersey, B

New Mexico

New Mexico State University, B
Western New Mexico University, B

New York

Buffalo State College, State University of New York, B
The College at Brockport, State University of New York, B
Ithaca College, B
Long Island University - LIU Brooklyn, B
Mercy College, B
Morrisville State College, B
North Country Community College, A
Queens College of the City University of New York, B
State University of New York College at Cortland, B
Syracuse University, B
United States Military Academy, B

North Carolina

Appalachian State University, B
Brevard College, B
Campbell University, B
Catawba College, B
Chowan University, B
Elon University, B
Greensboro College, B
Guilford College, B
High Point University, B
Lenoir-Rhyne University, B
Mars Hill University, B
Meredith College, B
North Carolina Wesleyan College, B
Queens University of Charlotte, B
Saint Augustine's University, B
Salem College, B
Shaw University, B
The University of North Carolina at Greensboro, B
The University of North Carolina Wilmington, B
Wake Forest University, B
Wingate University, B
Winston-Salem State University, B

North Dakota

North Dakota State University, B
University of Jamestown, B
University of Mary, B
University of North Dakota, B

Ohio

Capital University, B
Cedarville University, B
Clark State Community College, A
Defiance College, B
Kent State University, B
Malone University, B
Miami University, B
Mount Vernon Nazarene University, B
Ohio Dominican University, B
Ohio Northern University, B
The Ohio State University, B
Ohio University, B
University of Dayton, B
University of Mount Union, B
The University of Toledo, B
Walsh University, B
Youngstown State University, B

Oklahoma

East Central University, B
Hillsdale Free Will Baptist College, B
Northeastern State University, B
Oklahoma Baptist University, B
Oklahoma Wesleyan University, B
Oral Roberts University, B
Rose State College, A
St. Gregory's University, B

Southern Nazarene University, B
Southwestern Christian University, B
Southwestern Oklahoma State University, B
University of Central Oklahoma, B
University of Oklahoma, B
The University of Tulsa, B

Oregon

Central Oregon Community College, A
Corban University, B
Linfield College, B
Oregon State University, B
Pacific University, B
Warner Pacific College, B
Western Oregon University, B
Willamette University, B

Pennsylvania

Bucks County Community College, A
Cabrini University, B
Chatham University, B
DeSales University, B
East Stroudsburg University of Pennsylvania, B
Eastern University, B
Gannon University, B
Grove City College, B
Immaculata University, B
King's College, B
Lebanon Valley College, B
Lehigh Carbon Community College, A
Penn State Abington, B
Penn State Altoona, B
Penn State Beaver, B
Penn State Berks, B
Penn State Brandywine, B
Penn State DuBois, B
Penn State Erie, The Behrend College, B
Penn State Fayette, The Eberly Campus, B
Penn State Greater Allegheny, B
Penn State Hazleton, B
Penn State Lehigh Valley, B
Penn State Mont Alto, B
Penn State New Kensington, B
Penn State Schuylkill, B
Penn State Shenango, B
Penn State University Park, B
Penn State Wilkes-Barre, B
Penn State Worthington Scranton, B
Penn State York, B
Seton Hill University, B
Shippensburg University of Pennsylvania, B
Slippery Rock University of Pennsylvania, B
Temple University, B
University of the Sciences, B
The University of Scranton, B
Waynesburg University, B

Rhode Island

University of Rhode Island, B

South Carolina

Anderson University, B
The Citadel, The Military College of South Carolina,
  B
Coastal Carolina University, B
Coker College, B
Lander University, B
University of South Carolina, B
University of South Carolina Aiken, B

South Dakota

Augustana University, B
Dakota State University, B
Dakota Wesleyan University, B
University of Sioux Falls, B

Tennessee

Belmont University, B
Carson-Newman University, B
Freed-Hardeman University, B
Hiwassee College, A
Lee University, B
Lincoln Memorial University, B
Lipscomb University, B
Maryville College, B

Nashville State Community College, A
Southern Adventist University, B
Tennessee Wesleyan College, B
Tusculum College, B
Union University, B
University of Memphis, B
The University of Tennessee, B
The University of Tennessee at Chattanooga, B

Texas

Angelo State University, B
Baylor University, B
Clarendon College, A
Concordia University Texas, B
East Texas Baptist University, B
Hardin-Simmons University, B
Houston Baptist University, B
Huston-Tillotson University, B
Lamar University, B
Lee College, A
LeTourneau University, B
McMurry University, B
North Lake College, A
Our Lady of the Lake University of San Antonio, B
Rice University, B
St. Edward's University, B
St. Mary's University, B
St. Philip's College, A
Sam Houston State University, B
Schreiner University, B
Southwestern Adventist University, AB
Southwestern University, B
Stephen F. Austin State University, B
Tarleton State University, B
Texas A&M International University, B
Texas A&M University, B
Texas A&M University - Commerce, B
Texas A&M University - Corpus Christi, B
Texas A&M University - Kingsville, B
Texas Lutheran University, B
Texas Southern University, B
Texas State University, B
Texas Tech University, B
Texas Wesleyan University, B
Texas Woman's University, B
University of Houston, B
University of Houston - Clear Lake, B
University of the Incarnate Word, B
University of Mary Hardin-Baylor, B
University of North Texas, B
The University of Texas at Arlington, B
The University of Texas at Austin, B
The University of Texas of the Permian Basin, B
The University of Texas Rio Grande Valley, B
The University of Texas at San Antonio, B
The University of Texas at Tyler, B
West Texas A&M University, B

Utah

Brigham Young University, B
Salt Lake Community College, A
Southern Utah University, B
University of Utah, B

Vermont

Castleton University, B
Johnson State College, B
University of Vermont, B

Virginia

Bluefield College, B
Eastern Mennonite University, B
George Mason University, B
Jefferson College of Health Sciences, B
Liberty University, B
Longwood University, B
Norfolk State University, B
Roanoke College, B
University of Virginia, B

Washington

Bastyr University, B
Central Washington University, B
Eastern Washington University, B
Gonzaga University, B

Pacific Lutheran University, B
Seattle Pacific University, B
Seattle University, B
University of Puget Sound, B
Walla Walla University, B
Washington State University, B
Whitworth University, B

West Virginia

Alderson Broaddus University, B
American Public University System, B
Davis & Elkins College, B
Marshall University, B
West Liberty University, B
West Virginia Wesleyan College, B

Wisconsin

Carroll University, B
Lakeland College, B
Marian University, B
University of Wisconsin - Eau Claire, B
University of Wisconsin - La Crosse, B
University of Wisconsin - Madison, B
University of Wisconsin - Milwaukee, B
University of Wisconsin - Parkside, B
University of Wisconsin - Superior, B
Viterbo University, B
Wisconsin Lutheran College, B

Wyoming

Laramie County Community College, A
University of Wyoming, B
Western Wyoming Community College, A

U.S. Territories: Puerto Rico

University of the Sacred Heart, B

Canada

Alberta

University of Calgary, B
University of Lethbridge, B

British Columbia

Simon Fraser University, B
Trinity Western University, B
The University of British Columbia, B
The University of British Columbia - Okanagan
  Campus, B
University of the Fraser Valley, B
University of Victoria, B

Maritime Provinces: New Brunswick

University of New Brunswick Fredericton, B
University of New Brunswick Saint John, B

Maritime Provinces: Nova Scotia

Acadia University, B
Dalhousie University, B
St. Francis Xavier University, B

Newfoundland and Labrador

Memorial University of Newfoundland, B

Ontario

Brock University, B
Lakehead University, B
Laurentian University, B
McMaster University, B
Redeemer University College, B
Trent University, B
University of Guelph, B
University of Ottawa, B
University of Waterloo, B
The University of Western Ontario, B
University of Windsor, B
Wilfrid Laurier University, B

Quebec

Concordia University, B
McGill University, B
Université Laval, B
Université de Montréal, B
Université de Sherbrooke, B

Saskatchewan

University of Regina, B
University of Saskatchewan, B

KINESIOLOGY AND MOVE-MENT STUDIES

United States

Alabama

Auburn University, D
The University of Alabama, MD
The University of Alabama at Birmingham, M
University of North Alabama, M

Arkansas

Southern Arkansas University - Magnolia, M
University of Arkansas, MD
University of Central Arkansas, M

California

California Polytechnic State University, San Luis
    Obispo, M
California State Polytechnic University, Pomona, M
California State University, Chico, M
California State University, Fresno, M
California State University, Long Beach, M
California State University, Los Angeles, M
California State University, Northridge, M
Fresno Pacific University, M
Humboldt State University, M
Saint Mary's College of California, M
San Diego State University, M
San Francisco State University, M
San Jose State University, M
Sonoma State University, M
University of Southern California, MD

Colorado

University of Colorado Boulder, MD

Delaware

University of Delaware, MD

Florida

Barry University, M
University of Florida, MD

Georgia

Georgia College & State University, M
Georgia Southern University, M
Georgia State University, D
University of Georgia, MD

Hawaii

University of Hawaii at Manoa, MD

Idaho

Boise State University, M

Illinois

Eastern Illinois University, M
Northwestern University, D
Southern Illinois University Carbondale, M
Southern Illinois University Edwardsville, M
University of Illinois at Chicago, MD
University of Illinois at Urbana - Champaign, MD
Western Illinois University, M

Indiana

Indiana University Bloomington, MD
Purdue University, MD

Iowa

Iowa State University of Science and Technology,
    MD
University of Northern Iowa, M

Kansas

Kansas State University, MD

Kentucky

University of Kentucky, MD

Louisiana

Louisiana State University and Agricultural & Me-
    chanical College, MD
Southeastern Louisiana University, M

Maine

University of Maine, M

Maryland

Towson University, M
University of Maryland, College Park, MD

Massachusetts

University of Massachusetts Amherst, MD

Michigan

Eastern Michigan University, M
Michigan State University, MD
Michigan Technological University, M
University of Michigan, MD
Wayne State University, MD

Minnesota

University of Minnesota, Twin Cities Campus, MD

Mississippi

Mississippi College, M
Mississippi State University, M
University of Mississippi, D

Missouri

Missouri State University, M
University of Central Missouri, M
Washington University in St. Louis, D

Nevada

University of Nevada, Las Vegas, MD

New Hampshire

University of New Hampshire, MO

New York

Brooklyn College of the City University of New York,
    M
Canisius College, M
Columbia University, D
New York University, M
Sarah Lawrence College, M

North Carolina

East Carolina University, MDO
The University of North Carolina at Chapel Hill, MD
The University of North Carolina at Charlotte, MO
The University of North Carolina at Greensboro, MD
The University of North Carolina at Pembroke, M

North Dakota

University of Mary, M
University of North Dakota, M

Ohio

Bowling Green State University, M
The Ohio State University, MD

Oklahoma

Northeastern State University, M
Southwestern Oklahoma State University, M

Oregon

Oregon State University, MD

Pennsylvania

Penn State University Park, MDO
Temple University, MD
West Chester University of Pennsylvania, MO

South Dakota

The University of South Dakota, M

Tennessee

East Tennessee State University, MO
Tennessee Technological University, M
The University of Tennessee, MD

Texas

Baylor University, D
Dallas Baptist University, M
Hardin-Simmons University, M
Lamar University, M
Sam Houston State University, M
Stephen F. Austin State University, M
Texas A&M University, MD
Texas A&M University - Corpus Christi, M
Texas A&M University - Kingsville, M
Texas A&M University - San Antonio, M
Texas Christian University, M
Texas Woman's University, MD
University of Houston, D
University of the Incarnate Word, M
University of North Texas, M
The University of Texas at Austin, MD
The University of Texas at El Paso, M
The University of Texas of the Permian Basin, M
The University of Texas Rio Grande Valley, M
The University of Texas at San Antonio, M
The University of Texas at Tyler, M

Virginia

James Madison University, M
Old Dominion University, D
University of Virginia, MD

Wisconsin

University of Wisconsin - Madison, MD
University of Wisconsin - Milwaukee, M

Wyoming

University of Wyoming, M

U.S. Territories: Puerto Rico

Inter American University of Puerto Rico, San
    Germán Campus, M
University of Puerto Rico, Mayagüez Campus, M

Canada

Alberta

University of Calgary, MD
University of Lethbridge, M

British Columbia

Simon Fraser University, MD
The University of British Columbia, MD
University of Victoria, M

Manitoba

University of Manitoba, M

Maritime Provinces: Nova Scotia

Dalhousie University, M

Newfoundland and Labrador

Memorial University of Newfoundland, M

Ontario

Lakehead University, M
McMaster University, MD
University of Ottawa, M
University of Toronto, MD
University of Waterloo, MD
The University of Western Ontario, MD
University of Windsor, M
Wilfrid Laurier University, M
York University, MD

Quebec

McGill University, MDO
Université Laval, MD
Université de Montréal, MDO
Université du Québec à Montréal, M
Université de Sherbrooke, M

Saskatchewan

University of Regina, MD
University of Saskatchewan, MDO

KINESIOTHERAPY/ KINESIOTHERAPIST

United States

California

California State University, Long Beach, B

Massachusetts

Boston University, B
Bridgewater State University, B

North Carolina

Shaw University, B

KNOWLEDGE MANAGEMENT

United States

Massachusetts

Framingham State University, B

New York

Syracuse University, B

Pennsylvania

Saint Joseph's University, B

KOREAN LANGUAGE AND LIT-ERATURE

United States

California

University of California, Irvine, B
University of California, Los Angeles, B

Hawaii

University of Hawaii at Manoa, B

Ohio

The Ohio State University, B

Utah

Brigham Young University, B

Washington

University of Washington, B

KOREAN STUDIES

United States

Washington

University of Washington, B

LABOR AND INDUSTRIAL RE-LATIONS

United States

Alabama

Wallace State Community College, A

California

City College of San Francisco, A
El Camino College, A
Laney College, A

Los Angeles Trade-Technical College, A
San Diego City College, A
San Francisco State University, B
San Jose City College, A

Connecticut

University of Bridgeport, B

Indiana

Indiana University - Purdue University Fort Wayne, AB

Iowa

The University of Iowa, B

Massachusetts

University of Massachusetts Boston, B

Michigan

Wayne State University, B

Minnesota

University of Minnesota, Twin Cities Campus, B

New Jersey

Rider University, B
Rutgers University - New Brunswick, B
Seton Hall University, B

New York

Cornell University, B
Ithaca College, B
Kingsborough Community College of the City University of New York, A
New York University, B
State University of New York College at Old Westbury, B
State University of New York College at Potsdam, B
State University of New York Empire State College, AB
State University of New York at Fredonia, B

Ohio

Bowling Green State University, B
Cleveland State University, B
Sinclair Community College, A
Youngstown State University, A

Pennsylvania

Clarion University of Pennsylvania, B
Penn State Abington, B
Penn State Altoona, B
Penn State Beaver, B
Penn State Berks, B
Penn State Brandywine, B
Penn State DuBois, B
Penn State Erie, The Behrend College, B
Penn State Fayette, The Eberly Campus, B
Penn State Greater Allegheny, B
Penn State Hazleton, B
Penn State Lehigh Valley, B
Penn State Mont Alto, B
Penn State New Kensington, B
Penn State Schuylkill, B
Penn State Shenango, B
Penn State University Park, B
Penn State Wilkes-Barre, B
Penn State Worthington Scranton, B
Penn State York, B
Saint Francis University, B

Tennessee

Tennessee Technological University, B

U.S. Territories: Puerto Rico

University of Puerto Rico, Río Piedras Campus, B

Canada

Alberta

Athabasca University, B

Manitoba

University of Manitoba, B

Newfoundland and Labrador

Memorial University of Newfoundland, B

Ontario

Brock University, B
Carleton University, B
Lakehead University, B
McMaster University, B
University of Toronto, B
York University, B

Quebec

McGill University, B
Université Laval, AB
Université de Montréal, B
Université du Québec en Outaouais, B

LABOR STUDIES

United States

California

California State University, Dominguez Hills, B

Connecticut

Eastern Connecticut State University, B

Indiana

Indiana University Bloomington, AB
Indiana University Northwest, AB
Indiana University - Purdue University Indianapolis, AB
Indiana University South Bend, B

Michigan

Eastern Michigan University, B

New Jersey

Bergen Community College, A

New York

Hofstra University, B
Queens College of the City University of New York, B

Vermont

Goddard College, B

Canada

Ontario

University of Windsor, B

LAND USE PLANNING AND MANAGEMENT/DEVELOPMENT

United States

California

California State University, Bakersfield, B

Colorado

Colorado Mountain College (Leadville), A
Metropolitan State University of Denver, B

Florida

Everglades University (Boca Raton), B
Everglades University (Maitland), B
Everglades University (Sarasota), B

Michigan

Central Michigan University, B

Minnesota

Vermilion Community College, A

Montana

Montana State University, B

New York

State University of New York College of Environmental Science and Forestry, B

North Dakota

Dakota College at Bottineau, A

Ohio

Hocking College, A

West Virginia

West Virginia University, B

Wisconsin

University of Wisconsin - River Falls, B

Canada

British Columbia

University of Northern British Columbia, B

Saskatchewan

University of Saskatchewan, B

LANDSCAPE ARCHITECTURE

United States

Alabama

Auburn University, M

Arizona

Arizona State University at the Tempe campus, BM
Southwest University of Visual Arts, B
The University of Arizona, M

Arkansas

University of Arkansas, B

California

Academy of Art University, ABM
California Polytechnic State University, San Luis Obispo, B
California State Polytechnic University, Pomona, BM
Los Angeles Pierce College, A
Merced College, A
Modesto Junior College, A
Mt. San Antonio College, A
Saddleback College, A
San Diego Mesa College, A
University of California, Berkeley, BMO
University of California, Davis, B
West Valley College, A

Colorado

Colorado State University, BMD
University of Colorado Denver, M

Connecticut

University of Connecticut, B

Delaware

University of Delaware, B

Florida

Florida Agricultural and Mechanical University, M
Florida International University, M
University of Florida, BMD

Georgia

University of Georgia, BM

Idaho

University of Idaho, BM

Illinois

Illinois Institute of Technology, MD
University of Illinois at Urbana - Champaign, BMD

Indiana

Ball State University, BM
Purdue University, B

Iowa

Iowa State University of Science and Technology, BM

Kansas

Kansas State University, M

Kentucky

University of Kentucky, B

Louisiana

Louisiana State University and Agricultural & Mechanical College, BM

Maine

College of the Atlantic, B

Maryland

Morgan State University, M
University of Maryland, College Park, BM

Massachusetts

Boston Architectural College, BM
Harvard University, MD
Northeastern University, B
University of Massachusetts Amherst, BM

Michigan

Michigan State University, B
University of Michigan, MD

Minnesota

University of Minnesota, Twin Cities Campus, M

Mississippi

Mississippi State University, BM

Nebraska

University of Nebraska - Lincoln, B

Nevada

Truckee Meadows Community College, A
University of Nevada, Las Vegas, B

New Jersey

Bergen Community College, A
Rutgers University - New Brunswick, B

New Mexico

University of New Mexico, M

New York

City College of the City University of New York, M
Columbia University, M
Cornell University, BM
Monroe Community College, A
Morrisville State College, A
State University of New York College of Environmental Science and Forestry, BM

North Carolina

Caldwell Community College and Technical Institute, A
North Carolina Agricultural and Technical State University, B
North Carolina State University, BM
Wake Technical Community College, A

North Dakota

North Dakota State University, B

Ohio

The Ohio State University, BMD

Oklahoma

Oklahoma State University, BMD
University of Oklahoma, M

Oregon

University of Oregon, BM

Pennsylvania

Chatham University, M
Penn State Brandywine, B
Penn State Lehigh Valley, B
Penn State Schuylkill, B
Penn State University Park, BMD
Penn State Wilkes-Barre, B
Philadelphia University, B
Temple University, BM
University of Pennsylvania, MO

Rhode Island

Rhode Island School of Design, M
University of Rhode Island, B

South Carolina

Clemson University, BM

South Dakota

South Dakota State University, B

Tennessee

The University of Tennessee, M

Texas

Texas A&M University, BMD
Texas Tech University, BM
The University of Texas at Arlington, M
The University of Texas at Austin, M
Western Texas College, A

Utah

Utah State University, BM

Virginia

University of Virginia, M
Virginia Polytechnic Institute and State University, BM

Washington

Bastyr University, O
South Seattle College, A
University of Washington, BM
Washington State University, BM

West Virginia

West Virginia University, B

Wisconsin

University of Wisconsin - Madison, BM

U.S. Territories: Puerto Rico

Polytechnic University of Puerto Rico, M
Universidad del Turabo, B

Canada

British Columbia

The University of British Columbia, BM

Manitoba

University of Manitoba, M

Ontario

University of Guelph, M
University of Toronto, M

Quebec

Université de Montréal, B

LANDSCAPING AND GROUNDSKEEPING

United States

Alabama

James H. Faulkner State Community College, A

California

American River College, A
Antelope Valley College, A
Cabrillo College, A
City College of San Francisco, A
College of Marin, A
College of San Mateo, A
Cuyamaca College, A
Fullerton College, A
Los Angeles Pierce College, A
Merritt College, A
Santa Barbara City College, A
Santa Rosa Junior College, A
Southwestern College, A

Florida

College of Central Florida, A
Miami Dade College, A
Pensacola State College, A
South Florida State College, A
Valencia College, A

Georgia

Abraham Baldwin Agricultural College, A

Illinois

College of DuPage, A
College of Lake County, A
Danville Area Community College, A
Illinois Valley Community College, A
Kishwaukee College, A
Lincoln Land Community College, A
Parkland College, A

Iowa

Hawkeye Community College, A
Iowa Lakes Community College, A
Iowa Western Community College, A
Kirkwood Community College, A

Massachusetts

Springfield Technical Community College, A
University of Massachusetts Amherst, A

Michigan

Andrews University, B
Grand Rapids Community College, A
Lake Michigan College, A
Northwestern Michigan College, A
Oakland Community College, A

Minnesota

Anoka Technical College, A
Century College, A
Dakota County Technical College, A
Hennepin Technical College, A
University of Minnesota, Crookston, B

Mississippi

Hinds Community College, A
Mississippi State University, B
Northeast Mississippi Community College, A

Nebraska

University of Nebraska - Lincoln, B

Nevada

College of Southern Nevada, A

New Mexico

San Juan College, A

New York

State University of New York College of Agriculture
    and Technology at Cobleskill, B
State University of New York College of Technology
    at Delhi, A

North Carolina

Cape Fear Community College, A
North Carolina State University, A
Sandhills Community College, A

North Dakota

Dakota College at Bottineau, A

Ohio

Cincinnati State Technical and Community College,
    A
Clark State Community College, A
The Ohio State University Agricultural Technical In-
    stitute, A
Owens Community College, A

Oklahoma

Oklahoma State University, B

Oregon

Clackamas Community College, A
Portland Community College, A

Pennsylvania

Community College of Allegheny County, A
Penn State Abington, B
Penn State Altoona, B
Penn State Beaver, B
Penn State Berks, B
Penn State Brandywine, B
Penn State DuBois, B
Penn State Erie, The Behrend College, B
Penn State Fayette, The Eberly Campus, B
Penn State Greater Allegheny, B
Penn State Hazleton, B
Penn State Lehigh Valley, B
Penn State Mont Alto, B
Penn State New Kensington, B
Penn State Schuylkill, B
Penn State Shenango, B
Penn State University Park, B
Penn State Wilkes-Barre, B
Penn State Worthington Scranton, B
Penn State York, B
Pennsylvania College of Technology, A
Williamson College of the Trades, A

Tennessee

Tennessee Technological University, B

Vermont

Vermont Technical College, A

Washington

Clark College, A
Clover Park Technical College, A
Edmonds Community College, A
South Seattle College, A
Spokane Community College, A

Wisconsin

Milwaukee Area Technical College, A
Northeast Wisconsin Technical College, A

LANGUAGE INTERPRETATION AND TRANSLATION

United States

Arizona

Pima Community College, A

California

Southwestern College, A

Florida

Indian River State College, A

Hawaii

Kapiolani Community College, A

Indiana

Grace College, B

Iowa

Des Moines Area Community College, A
Northwestern College, B

Kansas

Allen Community College, A

Minnesota

Century College, A

Mississippi

Mississippi College, B

New Jersey

Union County College, A

North Carolina

Cape Fear Community College, A
Cleveland Community College, A

North Dakota

Lake Region State College, A

Ohio

Kent State University, B
Terra State Community College, A

Oklahoma

Oklahoma State University, Oklahoma City, A
Southern Nazarene University, B

Texas

The University of Texas at Arlington, B
The University of Texas Rio Grande Valley, B

Utah

Brigham Young University, B

Vermont

Marlboro College, B

Canada

Maritime Provinces: New Brunswick

Université de Moncton, B

Ontario

Laurentian University, B
University of Ottawa, B
York University, B

Quebec

Concordia University, B
McGill University, B
Université Laval, B
Université de Montréal, B
Université du Québec en Outaouais, B

LASER AND OPTICAL TECHNOLOGY/TECHNICIAN

United States

California

Moorpark College, A
San Jose City College, A

Connecticut

Three Rivers Community College, A

Iowa

Indian Hills Community College, A

Massachusetts

Quinsigamond Community College, A
Springfield Technical Community College, A

New York

Monroe Community College, A
Queensborough Community College of the City University of New York, A

North Carolina

Central Carolina Community College, A

Oregon

Oregon Institute of Technology, B

Tennessee

Roane State Community College, A

Texas

Amarillo College, A
Texas State Technical College, A

U.S. Territories: Puerto Rico

Colegio Universitario de San Juan, A

LATIN AMERICAN STUDIES

United States

Alabama

Samford University, B
The University of Alabama, B

Arizona

Prescott College, B
The University of Arizona, BM

California

California State University, Chico, B
California State University, East Bay, B
California State University, Fullerton, B
California State University, Long Beach, M
California State University, Los Angeles, BM
California State University, Northridge, B
Occidental College, B
Pepperdine University, B
Pomona College, B
Saint Mary's College of California, B
San Diego City College, A
San Diego State University, BM
San Diego State University - Imperial Valley Campus, B
Santa Rosa Junior College, A
Scripps College, B
Stanford University, B
University of California, Berkeley, BM
University of California, Los Angeles, BM
University of California, Riverside, B
University of California, San Diego, BM
University of California, Santa Barbara, M
University of California, Santa Cruz, B
University of San Francisco, B
University of Southern California, D
Whittier College, B

Colorado

University of Denver, B

Connecticut

Connecticut College, B
University of Connecticut, BM
Wesleyan University, B
Yale University, BD

Delaware

University of Delaware, B

District of Columbia

American University, B
The George Washington University, BM
Georgetown University, M

Florida

Broward College, A
Flagler College, B
Florida International University, M
Miami Dade College, A
New College of Florida, B
State College of Florida Manatee-Sarasota, A
University of Central Florida, B
University of Florida, MO
University of Miami, BM
University of South Florida, O

Georgia

Emory University, B
Georgia State University, O

Idaho

University of Idaho, B

Illinois

DePaul University, B
Illinois Wesleyan University, B
Knox College, B
Lake Forest College, B
Northeastern Illinois University, M
University of Chicago, BM
University of Illinois at Chicago, BM
University of Illinois at Urbana - Champaign, BM

Indiana

Earlham College, B
Indiana University Bloomington, M
University of Notre Dame, M

Iowa

Cornell College, B
The University of Iowa, B

Kansas

The University of Kansas, BMO

Kentucky

University of Kentucky, B
University of Louisville, B

Louisiana

Tulane University, BMD

Maine

Bates College, B
Bowdoin College, B
Colby College, B

Maryland

Hood College, B
Johns Hopkins University, B
Washington College, B

Massachusetts

Assumption College, B
Bard College at Simon's Rock, B
Boston University, BM
Brandeis University, B
Hampshire College, B
Smith College, B
Tufts University, B
University of Massachusetts Dartmouth, D
Wellesley College, B

Michigan

Albion College, B
Michigan State University, D
Oakland University, B

Minnesota

Carleton College, B
Gustavus Adolphus College, B
Hamline University, B

Macalester College, B
St. Cloud State University, B
St. Olaf College, B
University of Minnesota, Duluth, B
University of Minnesota, Morris, B

Mississippi

Millsaps College, B

Missouri

Saint Louis University, B
University of Missouri, B
Washington University in St. Louis, B

Nebraska

University of Nebraska - Lincoln, B
University of Nebraska at Omaha, B

Nevada

University of Nevada, Las Vegas, B

New Hampshire

Dartmouth College, B

New Jersey

Rutgers University - New Brunswick, B
Seton Hall University, B
William Paterson University of New Jersey, B

New Mexico

Central New Mexico Community College, A
University of New Mexico, BMD

New York

Adelphi University, B
Bard College, B
Barnard College, B
Binghamton University, State University of New York, B
Boricua College, M
Canisius College, B
City College of the City University of New York, B
Colgate University, B
Columbia University, BMDO
Columbia University, School of General Studies, B
Cornell University, MD
Fordham University, B
Hobart and William Smith Colleges, B
Hofstra University, B
Hunter College of the City University of New York, B
John Jay College of Criminal Justice of the City University of New York, B
Lehman College of the City University of New York, B
New York University, BM
Pace University, B
Queens College of the City University of New York, B
Sarah Lawrence College, B
State University of New York at New Paltz, B
State University of New York at Plattsburgh, B
Syracuse University, B
United States Military Academy, B
University at Albany, State University of New York, BMDO
University at Buffalo, the State University of New York, M
Vassar College, B

North Carolina

Davidson College, B
Duke University, D
The University of North Carolina at Chapel Hill, BO
The University of North Carolina at Charlotte, BM

Ohio

Bowling Green State University, B
Cleveland State University, M
Denison University, B
Miami University, B
Oberlin College, B
The Ohio State University, M
Ohio University, BM
Ohio Wesleyan University, B

Pontifical College Josephinum, B

Oregon

Portland State University, B
University of Oregon, B
Willamette University, B

Pennsylvania

Albright College, B
Bucknell University, B
Dickinson College, B
Gettysburg College, B
Haverford College, B
La Salle University, MO
Penn State Abington, B
Penn State Altoona, B
Penn State Beaver, B
Penn State Berks, B
Penn State Brandywine, B
Penn State DuBois, B
Penn State Erie, The Behrend College, B
Penn State Fayette, The Eberly Campus, B
Penn State Greater Allegheny, B
Penn State Hazleton, B
Penn State Lehigh Valley, B
Penn State Mont Alto, B
Penn State New Kensington, B
Penn State Schuylkill, B
Penn State Shenango, B
Penn State University Park, B
Penn State Wilkes-Barre, B
Penn State Worthington Scranton, B
Penn State York, B
Swarthmore College, B
Temple University, B
University of Pennsylvania, B
University of Pittsburgh, O
Villanova University, B

Rhode Island

Brown University, BMD
Rhode Island College, B

South Carolina

University of South Carolina, B
Wofford College, B

Tennessee

Rhodes College, B
Vanderbilt University, BM

Texas

Baylor University, B
Rice University, B
Southern Methodist University, B
Southwestern University, B
Texas Tech University, B
Trinity University, B
The University of Texas at Austin, BM
The University of Texas at Dallas, M
The University of Texas at El Paso, B

Utah

University of Utah, BM
Westminster College, B

Vermont

Bennington College, B
Marlboro College, B
Middlebury College, B
University of Vermont, B

Virginia

The College of William and Mary, B
George Mason University, B
University of Richmond, B

Washington

Seattle Pacific University, B
University of Washington, B

West Virginia

West Virginia University, M

Wisconsin

Ripon College, B
University of Wisconsin - Eau Claire, B
University of Wisconsin - Madison, MD

Canada
Alberta

University of Alberta, B
University of Calgary, B

British Columbia

Simon Fraser University, MO
The University of British Columbia, B

Ontario

Carleton University, B
McMaster University, B
University of Toronto, B
York University, B

LATIN LANGUAGE AND LITERATURE

United States
Alabama

Samford University, B

California

Saint Mary's College of California, B
Santa Clara University, B
University of California, Berkeley, B
University of California, Los Angeles, B

Connecticut

Yale University, B

District of Columbia

The Catholic University of America, B

Florida

University of Miami, B

Georgia

Emory University, B
Mercer University, B
University of Georgia, B

Illinois

Augustana College, B
Knox College, B
Loyola University Chicago, B
Monmouth College, B
Rockford University, B

Indiana

DePauw University, B
Wabash College, B

Louisiana

Loyola University New Orleans, B
Tulane University, B

Maine

University of Maine, B

Maryland

Loyola University Maryland, B

Massachusetts

Amherst College, B
Boston University, B
Mount Holyoke College, B
Smith College, B
Tufts University, B
Wellesley College, B
Wheaton College, B

Michigan

Hillsdale College, B
Kalamazoo College, B
University of Michigan, B
Western Michigan University, B

Minnesota

Carleton College, B
Concordia College, B
St. Olaf College, B
University of St. Thomas, B

Missouri

Missouri State University, B
University of Missouri, B
Washington University in St. Louis, B

Montana

University of Montana, B

New Hampshire

Dartmouth College, B
University of New Hampshire, B

New Jersey

Montclair State University, B
Rutgers University - New Brunswick, B

New York

Bard College, B
Barnard College, B
Binghamton University, State University of New York, B
Canisius College, B
Colgate University, B
Fordham University, B
Hobart and William Smith Colleges, B
Hofstra University, B
Hunter College of the City University of New York, B
Lehman College of the City University of New York, B
New York University, B
Queens College of the City University of New York, B
Sarah Lawrence College, B

North Carolina

Duke University, B
Wake Forest University, B

Ohio

Bowling Green State University, B
John Carroll University, B
Kenyon College, B
Miami University Hamilton, B
Oberlin College, B
Wright State University, B

Pennsylvania

Bryn Mawr College, B
Duquesne University, B
Franklin & Marshall College, B
Gettysburg College, B
Haverford College, B
Saint Joseph's University, B
Swarthmore College, B
West Chester University of Pennsylvania, B
Westminster College, B

South Carolina

Furman University, B

Tennessee

Sewanee: The University of the South, B

Texas

Austin College, B
Austin Community College District, A
Baylor University, B
Rice University, B
Southwestern University, B
Trinity University, B
The University of Texas at Austin, B

Vermont

Marlboro College, B
University of Vermont, B

Virginia

Hampden-Sydney College, B
Randolph College, B
Randolph-Macon College, B
University of Richmond, B
Virginia Wesleyan College, B

Washington

University of Washington, B
Whitman College, B

Wisconsin

Lawrence University, B
University of Wisconsin - Madison, B

Canada

Alberta

University of Alberta, B

British Columbia

The University of British Columbia, B
University of Victoria, B

Manitoba

University of Manitoba, B
The University of Winnipeg, B

Maritime Provinces: New Brunswick

Mount Allison University, B
University of New Brunswick Fredericton, B

Maritime Provinces: Nova Scotia

Acadia University, B

Newfoundland and Labrador

Memorial University of Newfoundland, B

Ontario

Carleton University, B
University of Ottawa, B
University of Toronto, B
The University of Western Ontario, B
University of Windsor, B
York University, B

LATIN TEACHER EDUCATION

United States

Delaware

University of Delaware, B

Illinois

University of Illinois at Urbana - Champaign, B

Indiana

Indiana University Bloomington, B

Massachusetts

Boston University, B

Michigan

Western Michigan University, B

Minnesota

Concordia College, B

Missouri

Missouri State University, B

Ohio

Miami University, B
Miami University Hamilton, B
Ohio Wesleyan University, B

Pennsylvania

Duquesne University, B

Utah

Brigham Young University, B

LAW ENFORCEMENT

United States

Arizona

University of Phoenix - Phoenix Campus, M

Florida

University of Central Florida, O

Georgia

Albany State University, M

Illinois

Robert Morris University Illinois, M
Western Illinois University, MO

Indiana

Calumet College of Saint Joseph, M

Iowa

Kaplan University, Davenport Campus, M

Kentucky

Eastern Kentucky University, M

Michigan

Michigan State University, M

New Jersey

Saint Peter's University, M

Pennsylvania

Saint Joseph's University, M

Rhode Island

Salve Regina University, MO

West Virginia

West Liberty University, M
West Virginia State University, M

Wisconsin

University of Wisconsin - Milwaukee, M

Canada

Saskatchewan

University of Regina, M

LAW AND LEGAL STUDIES

United States

Alabama

Faulkner University, D
Samford University, BMD
The University of Alabama, MD

Alaska

University of Alaska Southeast, A

Arizona

Arizona State University at the Tempe campus,
   BMD
National Paralegal College, B
The University of Arizona, MD
Western International University, B

Arkansas

Harding University, B
University of Arkansas, MD
University of Arkansas at Little Rock, D

California

Brandman University, B
Chapman University, MD
Claremont McKenna College, B
Cuesta College, A
Golden Gate University, MD
Humphreys College, D
John F. Kennedy University, D
Loyola Marymount University, MD
National University, B
Palomar College, A
Pepperdine University, D
Saddleback College, A
Santa Ana College, A
Santa Barbara City College, A
Santa Clara University, MDO
Scripps College, B
Stanford University, MD
University of California, Berkeley, BMD
University of California, Davis, MD
University of California, Irvine, D
University of California, Los Angeles, MD
University of California, San Diego, M
University of California, Santa Cruz, B
University of La Verne, D
University of the Pacific, MD
University of San Diego, MDO
University of San Francisco, MD
University of Southern California, MD
Whittier College, D

Colorado

Adams State University, B
United States Air Force Academy, B
University of Colorado Boulder, D
University of Denver, BMDO

Connecticut

Post University, AB
Quinnipiac University, BMD
University of Connecticut, D
University of Hartford, AB
University of New Haven, AB
Yale University, MD

Delaware

Goldey-Beacom College, B
Wilmington University, B

District of Columbia

American University, BMD
The Catholic University of America, D
The George Washington University, MD
Georgetown University, MD
Howard University, MD
University of the District of Columbia, BMD

Florida

Barry University, D
Broward College, A
Florida Agricultural and Mechanical University, D
Florida International University, D
Florida National University, B
Florida State University, MD
Keiser University, B
Nova Southeastern University, MD
St. Thomas University, MD
Stetson University, MD
University of Florida, MD
University of Miami, BMDO

Georgia

Brenau University, B
Emory University, MDO
Georgia State University, D
Mercer University, D
University of Georgia, MD

Hawaii

University of Hawaii at Manoa, MDO

Idaho

University of Idaho, D

Illinois

Blackburn College, B
DePaul University, MD
Dominican University, B
Illinois Institute of Technology, MD
Illinois State University, B
Loyola University Chicago, MD
MacCormac College, A
Northern Illinois University, D
Northwestern University, BMD
Southern Illinois University Carbondale, MD
Trinity International University, D
University of Chicago, MD
University of Illinois at Urbana - Champaign, MD

Indiana

Indiana University Bloomington, MDO
Indiana University - Purdue University Indianapolis, MD
Trine University, M
University of Notre Dame, MD
Valparaiso University, MD

Iowa

Drake University, MD
Iowa Lakes Community College, A
Kaplan University, Davenport Campus, BM
The University of Iowa, MD

Kansas

Central Christian College of Kansas, A
Friends University, M
The University of Kansas, D
Washburn University, MD

Kentucky

Kentucky Wesleyan College, B
Morehead State University, B
Northern Kentucky University, D
Thomas More College, B
University of Kentucky, D
University of Louisville, D

Louisiana

Louisiana State University and Agricultural & Mechanical College, MD
Loyola University New Orleans, MD
Southern University and Agricultural and Mechanical College, D
Tulane University, MD

Maine

College of the Atlantic, B
University of Southern Maine, D

Maryland

Carroll Community College, A
College of Southern Maryland, A
Stevenson University, B
University of Baltimore, MD
University of Maryland University College, B

Massachusetts

Amherst College, B
Anna Maria College, B
Bay Path University, B
Boston College, D
Boston University, MD
Bridgewater State University, B
Elms College, B
Hampshire College, B
Harvard University, MD
Lasell College, B
Newbury College, B
Northeastern University, MD
Suffolk University, MD
Tufts University, MD
University of Massachusetts Amherst, B

University of Massachusetts Dartmouth, D
Western New England University, BMD

Michigan

Central Michigan University, B
Macomb Community College, A
Oakland University, B
University of Detroit Mercy, BD
University of Michigan, MD
Wayne State University, MD

Minnesota

Bethany Lutheran College, B
Hamline University, B
University of Minnesota, Twin Cities Campus, MD
University of St. Thomas, MD
Walden University, MD

Mississippi

Mississippi College, DO
University of Mississippi, MD

Missouri

Culver-Stockton College, B
Park University, B
Saint Louis University, BMD
University of Missouri, MD
University of Missouri - Kansas City, MD
Washington University in St. Louis, MD
Webster University, B

Montana

University of Montana, ABD

Nebraska

Bellevue University, B
Creighton University, MDO
Doane University, B
Metropolitan Community College, A
University of Nebraska - Lincoln, MD

Nevada

University of Nevada, Las Vegas, MD

New Hampshire

University of New Hampshire, MDO

New Jersey

Montclair State University, MO
Rutgers University - Camden, D
Rutgers University - Newark, D
Seton Hall University, MD
William Paterson University of New Jersey, B

New Mexico

University of New Mexico, D

New York

Columbia University, MD
Cornell University, MD
Fordham University, MD
Hofstra University, MD
John Jay College of Criminal Justice of the City University of New York, B
Maria College, A
Mercy College, B
Nazareth College of Rochester, B
New York University, MDO
Pace University, MD
St. John Fisher College, B
St. John's University, ABMD
State University of New York at Fredonia, B
Syracuse University, D
Touro College, MD
United States Military Academy, B
University at Buffalo, the State University of New York, MD
Yeshiva University, MD

North Carolina

Campbell University, D
Duke University, MD
Elon University, D
Methodist University, B

North Carolina Central University, D
South College - Asheville, B
The University of North Carolina at Chapel Hill, D
Wake Forest University, MD

North Dakota

University of North Dakota, D

Ohio

Capital University, MD
Case Western Reserve University, MD
Cleveland State University, MDO
Oberlin College, B
Ohio Northern University, MD
The Ohio State University, MD
The University of Akron, MD
University of Cincinnati, D
University of Dayton, MD
The University of Toledo, MD

Oklahoma

Oklahoma City University, MD
University of Central Oklahoma, B
University of Oklahoma, MD
The University of Tulsa, MDO

Oregon

Lewis & Clark College, MD
University of Oregon, MD
Willamette University, MD

Pennsylvania

DeSales University, B
Dickinson College, B
Duquesne University, MD
Harcum College, A
Penn State University Park, MD
Point Park University, B
Saint Joseph's University, BM
Temple University, MD
University of Pennsylvania, MD
University of Pittsburgh, BM
Villanova University, D
Widener University, MD

Rhode Island

Roger Williams University, D

South Carolina

Trident Technical College, A
University of South Carolina, D

South Dakota

The University of South Dakota, D

Tennessee

Belmont University, D
Lincoln Memorial University, D
Lipscomb University, B
University of Memphis, D
The University of Tennessee, D
Vanderbilt University, MD

Texas

Alvin Community College, A
Baylor University, D
Del Mar College, A
Houston Baptist University, B
Lamar State College - Port Arthur, A
Navarro College, A
Palo Alto College, A
St. Mary's University, D
Southern Methodist University, MD
Texas A&M University, D
Texas Southern University, D
Texas Tech University, MD
Texas Wesleyan University, D
University of Houston, MD
The University of Texas at Austin, MD
The University of Texas at Dallas, M
The University of Texas Rio Grande Valley, B
Vernon College, A

Utah

Brigham Young University, MD
University of Utah, MD

Vermont

Champlain College, M

Virginia

The College of William and Mary, MD
Emory & Henry College, B
George Mason University, MD
Liberty University, D
Regent University, MD
University of Richmond, D
University of Virginia, MD
Washington and Lee University, MD

Washington

Gonzaga University, D
Northwest University, B
Seattle University, D
University of Washington, BMD
University of Washington, Tacoma, B

West Virginia

Alderson Broaddus University, B
American Public University System, B
West Virginia University, D

Wisconsin

College of Menominee Nation, A
Marquette University, D
University of Wisconsin - Madison, BMD
University of Wisconsin - Superior, B

Wyoming

University of Wyoming, D

U.S. Territories: Puerto Rico

Pontifical Catholic University of Puerto Rico, BD
University of Puerto Rico, Río Piedras Campus, MD

Canada

Alberta

University of Alberta, MD
University of Calgary, BMDO

British Columbia

The University of British Columbia, MD
University of Victoria, MD

Manitoba

University of Manitoba, M

Maritime Provinces: New Brunswick

Université de Moncton, B
University of New Brunswick Fredericton, B

Maritime Provinces: Nova Scotia

Cape Breton University, B
Dalhousie University, MD

Ontario

Laurentian University, B
Queen's University at Kingston, MD
University of Ottawa, MD
University of Toronto, MD
The University of Western Ontario, MDO
University of Windsor, B
York University, BMD

Quebec

McGill University, BMDO
Université Laval, BMDO
Université de Montréal, BMDO
Université du Québec à Montréal, BO
Université de Sherbrooke, BMDO

Saskatchewan

University of Saskatchewan, MD

LEGAL ADMINISTRATIVE ASSISTANT/SECRETARY

United States

Alabama

Wallace State Community College, A

Arizona

Central Arizona College, A
Northland Pioneer College, A
Yavapai College, A

Arkansas

College of the Ouachitas, A

California

Allan Hancock College, A
Bakersfield College, A
Butte College, A
Cerritos College, A
Chabot College, A
College of the Redwoods, A
Cypress College, A
East Los Angeles College, A
Empire College, A
Fresno City College, A
Fullerton College, A
Glendale Community College, A
Golden West College, A
Lassen Community College District, A
Long Beach City College, A
Los Angeles City College, A
Los Angeles Harbor College, A
Merced College, A
Monterey Peninsula College, A
Mt. San Antonio College, A
Napa Valley College, A
Sacramento City College, A
Saddleback College, A
Sage College, A
San Diego City College, A
San Diego Mesa College, A
Santa Monica College, A
Shasta College, A
Skyline College, A
Solano Community College, A
Southwestern College, A
West Los Angeles College, A
West Valley College, A

Colorado

IBMC College (Fort Collins), A
Otero Junior College, A

Connecticut

Gateway Community College, A
Manchester Community College, A
Middlesex Community College, A

Delaware

Delaware Technical & Community College, Jack F. Owens Campus, A
Delaware Technical & Community College, Terry Campus, A

District of Columbia

University of the District of Columbia, A

Florida

Broward College, A
Miami Dade College, A
Palm Beach State College, A
Pensacola State College, A

Georgia

Georgia Piedmont Technical College, A

Idaho

Lewis-Clark State College, AB
North Idaho College, A

Illinois

Black Hawk College, A
College of DuPage, A
Harper College, A
John Wood Community College, A
Lake Land College, A
Lewis and Clark Community College, A
Lincoln Land Community College, A
MacCormac College, A
Morton College, A
Richland Community College, A
Rockford Career College, A
Sauk Valley Community College, A
Shawnee Community College, A
Southwestern Illinois College, A
Spoon River College, A

Indiana

International Business College (Fort Wayne), AB
International Business College (Indianapolis), A

Iowa

Dordt College, A
Iowa Lakes Community College, A
North Iowa Area Community College, A

Kansas

Cowley County Community College and Area Vocational - Technical School, A
Dodge City Community College, A
Johnson County Community College, A
Labette Community College, A
Washburn University, A

Kentucky

Sullivan University, A

Louisiana

McCann School of Business & Technology (Monroe), A

Maine

Northern Maine Community College, A

Maryland

Howard Community College, A
Kaplan University, Hagerstown Campus, A

Massachusetts

North Shore Community College, A
Roxbury Community College, A

Michigan

Baker College, A
Bay de Noc Community College, A
Kellogg Community College, A
Lake Michigan College, A
Mid Michigan Community College, A
Monroe County Community College, A
Muskegon Community College, A
North Central Michigan College, A
Northwestern Michigan College, A

Minnesota

Alexandria Technical and Community College, A
Anoka Technical College, A
Central Lakes College, A
Dakota County Technical College, A
Hibbing Community College, A
Inver Hills Community College, A
Lake Superior College, A
Minneapolis Business College, A
Minnesota State College - Southeast Technical, A
Minnesota State Community and Technical College, A
Ridgewater College, A
Riverland Community College, A
St. Cloud Technical & Community College, A
South Central College, A

Mississippi

Antonelli College (Hattiesburg), A
Southwest Mississippi Community College, A

Missouri

Crowder College, A
Hickey College, A
Jefferson College, A
Metropolitan Community College - Kansas City, A

Montana

Helena College University of Montana, A
Miles Community College, A
University of Montana, A

Nebraska

Metropolitan Community College, A
Midland University, A

New Mexico

Clovis Community College, A
New Mexico Junior College, A

New York

Fulton-Montgomery Community College, A
Herkimer County Community College, A
Monroe Community College, A
Nassau Community College, A

North Carolina

Alamance Community College, A
Carteret Community College, A
Central Carolina Community College, A
Central Piedmont Community College, A
Cleveland Community College, A
Craven Community College, A
Gaston College, A
King's College, A
Nash Community College, A
Pitt Community College, A
Stanly Community College, A
Vance-Granville Community College, A
Wake Technical Community College, A

North Dakota

Bismarck State College, A

Ohio

Bryant & Stratton College - Cleveland Campus, A
Bryant & Stratton College - Parma Campus, A
Eastern Gateway Community College, A
Fortis College (Ravenna), A
Miami-Jacobs Career College (Independence), A
Miami University Middletown, A
Northwest State Community College, A
Ohio Business College (Sandusky), A
Ohio Business College (Sheffield Village), A
Shawnee State University, A
Sinclair Community College, A
Stark State College, A
Trumbull Business College, A
University of Northwestern Ohio, A
University of Rio Grande, A
Youngstown State University, A

Oklahoma

Oklahoma City Community College, A
Rose State College, A

Oregon

Lane Community College, A
Linn-Benton Community College, A
Mt. Hood Community College, A
Treasure Valley Community College, A
Umpqua Community College, A

Pennsylvania

Bradford School, A
Butler County Community College, A
Cambria-Rowe Business College (Indiana), A
Cambria-Rowe Business College (Johnstown), A
Clarion University of Pennsylvania, A
Community College of Allegheny County, A
Consolidated School of Business (Lancaster), A
Consolidated School of Business (York), A
DuBois Business College (DuBois), A
Laurel Business Institute, A
Laurel Technical Institute, A

McCann School of Business & Technology (Lewisburg), A
Penn Commercial Business and Technical School, A
South Hills School of Business & Technology (Altoona), A

Rhode Island

Community College of Rhode Island, A

South Carolina

Forrest College, A
Piedmont Technical College, A
York Technical College, A

South Dakota

Sinte Gleska University, A

Tennessee

Roane State Community College, A
South College, A

Texas

Alvin Community College, A
Amarillo College, A
Blinn College, A
Del Mar College, A
Eastfield College, A
El Centro College, A
Lamar State College - Port Arthur, A
McLennan Community College, A
Navarro College, A
North Central Texas College, A
North Lake College, A
Northeast Texas Community College, A
Odessa College, A
St. Philip's College, A
San Antonio College, A
South Plains College, A
South Texas College, A
Texas Southmost College, A
Trinity Valley Community College, A
Tyler Junior College, A

Virginia

Bryant & Stratton College - Richmond Campus, A
Dabney S. Lancaster Community College, A

Washington

Bates Technical College, A
Centralia College, A
Clark College, A
Clover Park Technical College, A
Columbia Basin College, A
Edmonds Community College, A
Green River College, A
Highline College, A
Lower Columbia College, A
Renton Technical College, A
South Puget Sound Community College, A
Spokane Community College, A
Walla Walla Community College, A
Wenatchee Valley College, A
Yakima Valley Community College, A

West Virginia

West Virginia Junior College - Charleston, A
West Virginia Junior College - Morgantown, A

Wisconsin

Blackhawk Technical College, A
Milwaukee Area Technical College, A
Moraine Park Technical College, A

Wyoming

Western Wyoming Community College, A

U.S. Territories: Puerto Rico

National University College (Bayamón), A
Universidad del Este, A

LEGAL ASSISTANT/PARALE-GAL

United States

Alabama

Bevill State Community College, A
Calhoun Community College, A
Community College of the Air Force, A
Enterprise State Community College, A
Gadsden State Community College, A
James H. Faulkner State Community College, A
Samford University, B
South University, AB
Virginia College in Birmingham, A
Virginia College in Huntsville, A
Virginia College in Mobile, A
Wallace State Community College, A

Alaska

University of Alaska Fairbanks, A

Arizona

Arizona Western College, A
Brookline College (Phoenix), A
Brookline College (Tucson), A
Mohave Community College, A
National Paralegal College, A
Northland Pioneer College, A
The Paralegal Institute at Brighton College, A
Penn Foster College, A
Phoenix College, A
Pima Community College, A
Yavapai College, A

Arkansas

College of the Ouachitas, A
NorthWest Arkansas Community College, A
Shorter College, A
Southeast Arkansas College, A
University of Arkansas - Fort Smith, A

California

American River College, A
California University of Management and Sciences, A
Cañada College, A
Cerritos College, A
Cerro Coso Community College, A
City College of San Francisco, A
College of the Canyons, A
College of the Redwoods, A
College of the Sequoias, A
Cuesta College, A
Cuyamaca College, A
De Anza College, A
El Camino College, A
Evergreen Valley College, A
Fremont College (Cerritos), A
Fresno City College, A
Fullerton College, A
Humphreys College, B
John F. Kennedy University, B
Merritt College, A
Mt. San Antonio College, A
Mt. San Jacinto College, A
MTI College, A
Napa Valley College, A
National University, AB
Oxnard College, A
Pasadena City College, A
Platt College (Alhambra), A
Platt College (Ontario), A
Saddleback College, A
San Diego City College, A
San Diego Miramar College, A
Santa Rosa Junior College, A
Shasta College, A
Skyline College, A
Southwestern College, A
University of Antelope Valley, A
University of La Verne, B
West Los Angeles College, A

Colorado

Arapahoe Community College, A
Colorado Technical University Online, A
Community College of Denver, A
Everest College (Colorado Springs), A
Everest College (Thornton), A
Front Range Community College, A
IBMC College (Fort Collins), A
Pikes Peak Community College, A

Connecticut

Manchester Community College, A
Naugatuck Valley Community College, A
Northwestern Connecticut Community College, A
Norwalk Community College, A
Quinnipiac University, B
University of Hartford, AB

Delaware

Wesley College, B

Florida

Broward College, A
City College (Altamonte Springs), A
City College (Fort Lauderdale), A
City College (Gainesville), A
City College (Miami), A
College of Central Florida, A
Daytona State College, A
Eastern Florida State College, A
Everest University (Largo), A
Everest University (Orlando), AB
Everest University (Tampa), A
Florida Gulf Coast University, B
Florida Keys Community College, A
Florida National University, A
Florida SouthWestern State College, A
Florida State College at Jacksonville, A
Florida Technical College (DeLand), A
Florida Technical College (Orlando), A
Hillsborough Community College, A
Hodges University, A
Indian River State College, A
Jones College, AB
Keiser University, A
Key College, A
Lake-Sumter State College, A
Lincoln College of Technology, A
Miami Dade College, A
Millennia Atlantic University, AB
Northwest Florida State College, A
Nova Southeastern University, B
Pasco-Hernando State College, A
Pensacola State College, A
Rasmussen College Fort Myers, A
Rasmussen College Land O' Lakes, A
Rasmussen College New Port Richey, A
Rasmussen College Ocala, A
Rasmussen College Tampa/Brandon, A
St. Petersburg College, AB
Santa Fe College, A
Seminole State College of Florida, A
South Florida State College, A
South University (Royal Palm Beach), AB
State College of Florida Manatee-Sarasota, A
Tallahassee Community College, A
University of Central Florida, B
University of West Florida, B
Valencia College, A
Virginia College in Pensacola, A

Georgia

Ashworth College, A
Athens Technical College, A
Atlanta Technical College, A
Central Georgia Technical College, A
Clayton State University, AB
Georgia Military College, A
Georgia Northwestern Technical College, A
Georgia Piedmont Technical College, A
Ogeechee Technical College, A
South Georgia Technical College, A
South University, AB
Southern Crescent Technical College, A
Valdosta State University, B

Hawaii

Kapiolani Community College, A

Idaho

Broadview University - Boise, AB
Eastern Idaho Technical College, A
Idaho State University, AB
Lewis-Clark State College, AB
North Idaho College, A

Illinois

Elgin Community College, A
Ellis University, AB
Harper College, A
Illinois Central College, A
Illinois Eastern Community Colleges, Wabash Valley
  College, A
Illinois State University, B
Kankakee Community College, A
Lewis and Clark Community College, A
Lewis University, B
Loyola University Chicago, B
MacCormac College, A
Midstate College, A
Northwestern College - Bridgeview Campus, A
Northwestern College - Chicago Campus, A
Rasmussen College Aurora, A
Rasmussen College Mokena/Tinley Park, A
Rasmussen College Rockford, A
Rasmussen College Romeoville/Joliet, A
Robert Morris University Illinois, A
Rockford Career College, A
Roosevelt University, B
South Suburban College, A
Southern Illinois University Carbondale, B
Southwestern Illinois College, A

Indiana

Calumet College of Saint Joseph, AB
Harrison College, A
Indiana University - Purdue University Indianapolis,
  B
International Business College (Fort Wayne), AB
International Business College (Indianapolis), A
Ivy Tech Community College - Bloomington, A
Ivy Tech Community College - Central Indiana, A
Ivy Tech Community College - Columbus, A
Ivy Tech Community College - East Central, A
Ivy Tech Community College - Kokomo, A
Ivy Tech Community College - Lafayette, A
Ivy Tech Community College - North Central, A
Ivy Tech Community College - Northeast, A
Ivy Tech Community College - Northwest, A
Ivy Tech Community College - Richmond, A
Ivy Tech Community College - Southeast, A
Ivy Tech Community College - Southern Indiana, A
Ivy Tech Community College - Southwest, A
Ivy Tech Community College - Wabash Valley, A
Marian University, A
Saint Mary-of-the-Woods College, AB
Vincennes University, A

Iowa

Des Moines Area Community College, A
Iowa Lakes Community College, A
Kaplan University, Davenport Campus, AB
Kaplan University, Des Moines, A
Kaplan University, Mason City Campus, A
Kirkwood Community College, A
Western Iowa Tech Community College, A

Kansas

Cloud County Community College, A
Hutchinson Community College, A
Johnson County Community College, A
Kansas City Kansas Community College, A
National American University, A
Newman University, A
Rasmussen College Kansas City/Overland Park, A
Rasmussen College Topeka, A
Washburn University, AB

Kentucky

Beckfield College, AB
Daymar College (Bellevue), A

Daymar College (Bowling Green), A
Daymar College (Owensboro), A
Eastern Kentucky University, AB
Morehead State University, B
Sullivan University, AB
University of Louisville, A
Western Kentucky University, AB

Louisiana

Louisiana State University at Eunice, A
McNeese State University, A
Nunez Community College, A
Southern University at Shreveport, A
Tulane University, A

Maine

Husson University, AB
Kaplan University, South Portland, A

Maryland

Allegany College of Maryland, A
Anne Arundel Community College, A
Baltimore City Community College, A
Chesapeake College, A
Community College of Baltimore County, A
Frederick Community College, A
Harford Community College, A
Kaplan University, Hagerstown Campus, A
Montgomery College, A
Prince George's Community College, A
Stevenson University, B

Massachusetts

Anna Maria College, B
Bay Path University, AB
Boston University, B
Bristol Community College, A
Bunker Hill Community College, A
Elms College, AB
Massachusetts Bay Community College, A
Middlesex Community College, A
Mount Wachusett Community College, A
North Shore Community College, A
Northern Essex Community College, A
Quincy College, A
Suffolk University, AB

Michigan

Davenport University, AB
Delta College, A
Eastern Michigan University, B
Ferris State University, A
Grand Valley State University, B
Henry Ford College, A
Kellogg Community College, A
Lansing Community College, A
Macomb Community College, A
Madonna University, AB
North Central Michigan College, A
Northern Michigan University, B
Oakland Community College, A
South University, B
Wayne County Community College District, A

Minnesota

Alexandria Technical and Community College, A
Globe University - Minneapolis, AB
Globe University - Woodbury, AB
Inver Hills Community College, A
Lake Superior College, A
Minneapolis Business College, A
Minnesota School of Business - Blaine, AB
Minnesota School of Business - Brooklyn Center,
  AB
Minnesota School of Business - Elk River, AB
Minnesota School of Business - Richfield, AB
Minnesota School of Business - Rochester, AB
Minnesota School of Business - St. Cloud, AB
Minnesota State Community and Technical College,
  A
Minnesota State Community and Technical College -
  Detroit Lakes, A
Minnesota State University Moorhead, B
National American University (Bloomington), A
National American University (Brooklyn Center), A

North Hennepin Community College, A
Rasmussen College Blaine, A
Rasmussen College Bloomington, A
Rasmussen College Brooklyn Park, A
Rasmussen College Eagan, A
Rasmussen College Lake Elmo/Woodbury, A
Rasmussen College Mankato, A
Rasmussen College Moorhead, A
Rasmussen College St. Cloud, A
St. Cloud Technical & Community College, A
Winona State University, B

Mississippi

Antonelli College (Jackson), A
Hinds Community College, A
Holmes Community College, A
Mississippi College, B
Mississippi Gulf Coast Community College, A
Mississippi University for Women, B
Northeast Mississippi Community College, A
Northwest Mississippi Community College, A
University of Mississippi, B
University of Southern Mississippi, B
Virginia College in Biloxi, A
Virginia College in Jackson, A

Missouri

Everest College, AB
Hickey College, A
Maryville University of Saint Louis, B
Missouri State University - West Plains, A
Missouri Western State University, A
National American University (Kansas City), AB
Stevens - The Institute of Business & Arts, AB
William Woods University, B

Montana

University of Great Falls, AB
University of Montana, A

Nebraska

Central Community College - Grand Island Campus,
    A
College of Saint Mary, AB
Kaplan University, Lincoln, A
Kaplan University, Omaha, A
Metropolitan Community College, A

Nevada

College of Southern Nevada, A
Truckee Meadows Community College, A

New Hampshire

Nashua Community College, A
NHTI, Concord's Community College, A

New Jersey

Atlantic Cape Community College, A
Bergen Community College, A
Brookdale Community College, A
Camden County College, A
Cumberland County College, A
Essex County College, A
Hudson County Community College, A
Mercer County Community College, A
Middlesex County College, A
Raritan Valley Community College, A
Rowan College at Burlington County, A
Rowan College at Gloucester County, A
Salem Community College, A
Sussex County Community College, A
Union County College, A
Warren County Community College, A

New Mexico

Brookline College, A
Central New Mexico Community College, A
Clovis Community College, A
Doña Ana Community College, A
Eastern New Mexico University - Roswell, A
New Mexico State University - Alamogordo, A
San Juan College, A
Santa Fe Community College, A

New York

Bronx Community College of the City University of
    New York, A
Broome Community College, A
Bryant & Stratton College - Albany Campus, A
Bryant & Stratton College - Amherst Campus, A
Bryant & Stratton College - Henrietta Campus, A
Bryant & Stratton College - Liverpool Campus, A
Daemen College, B
Dutchess Community College, A
Erie Community College, A
Eugenio María de Hostos Community College of the
    City University of New York, A
Finger Lakes Community College, A
Fiorello H. LaGuardia Community College of the
    City University of New York, A
Genesee Community College, A
Herkimer County Community College, A
Hilbert College, AB
Jefferson Community College, A
Maria College, A
Mercy College, B
Mildred Elley - New York City, A
Mildred Elley School, A
Nassau Community College, A
New York Career Institute, A
New York City College of Technology of the City
    University of New York, AB
State University of New York College of Technology
    at Canton, B
Suffolk County Community College, A
Sullivan County Community College, A
TCI - College of Technology, A
Tompkins Cortland Community College, A
Westchester Community College, A

North Carolina

Caldwell Community College and Technical Institute,
    A
Carteret Community College, A
Central Carolina Community College, A
Central Piedmont Community College, A
Coastal Carolina Community College, A
Davidson County Community College, A
Durham Technical Community College, A
Fayetteville Technical Community College, A
Forsyth Technical Community College, A
Gaston College, A
Guilford Technical Community College, A
Halifax Community College, A
Johnston Community College, A
King's College, A
Miller-Motte College (Cary), A
Pitt Community College, A
South College - Asheville, A
South Piedmont Community College, A
Southwestern Community College, A
Surry Community College, A
Western Piedmont Community College, A
Wilson Community College, A

North Dakota

Rasmussen College Fargo, A

Ohio

American National University (Kettering), A
Brown Mackie College - North Canton, B
Bryant & Stratton College - Cleveland Campus, A
Bryant & Stratton College - Eastlake Campus, A
Clark State Community College, A
Columbus State Community College, A
Cuyahoga Community College, A
Edison Community College, A
ETI Technical College of Niles, A
Fortis College (Centerville), A
James A. Rhodes State College, A
Kent State University, B
Kent State University at East Liverpool, A
Kent State University at Trumbull, A
Lake Erie College, B
Lakeland Community College, A
Miami-Jacobs Career College (Independence), A
Mount St. Joseph University, AB
North Central State College, A
Northwest State Community College, A

Shawnee State University, A
Sinclair Community College, A
South University, AB
Stautzenberger College (Brecksville), A
Stautzenberger College (Maumee), A
Tiffin University, B
The University of Akron, A
University of Cincinnati Clermont College, A
University of Northwestern Ohio, A
The University of Toledo, AB
Ursuline College, B
Zane State College, A

Oklahoma

Community Care College, A
East Central University, B
Tulsa Community College, A
Vatterott College (Warr Acres), A

Oregon

Pioneer Pacific College, AB
Portland Community College, A
Sumner College, A

Pennsylvania

Bradford School, A
Central Penn College, A
Community College of Allegheny County, A
Delaware County Community College, A
Fortis Institute (Erie), A
Gannon University, AB
Harrisburg Area Community College, A
Keystone Technical Institute, A
Lackawanna College, A
Lansdale School of Business, A
Lehigh Carbon Community College, A
Luzerne County Community College, A
Manor College, A
McCann School of Business & Technology
    (Lewisburg), A
McCann School of Business & Technology
    (Pottsville), A
Mount Aloysius College, A
Northampton Community College, A
Peirce College, AB
Pennsylvania College of Technology, AB
Pittsburgh Career Institute, A
Westmoreland County Community College, A
Widener University, A

Rhode Island

Community College of Rhode Island, A
Roger Williams University, B

South Carolina

Central Carolina Technical College, A
Florence-Darlington Technical College, A
Forrest College, A
Greenville Technical College, A
Horry-Georgetown Technical College, A
Midlands Technical College, A
Miller-Motte Technical College (North Charleston), A
Orangeburg-Calhoun Technical College, A
South University, AB
Technical College of the Lowcountry, A
Trident Technical College, A

South Dakota

National American University (Rapid City), A
National American University (Sioux Falls), AB
Oglala Lakota College, AB
Western Dakota Technical Institute, A

Tennessee

Brightwood College, Nashville Campus, A
Chattanooga State Community College, A
Daymar College (Clarksville), A
Daymar College (Nashville), A
Miller-Motte Technical College (Clarksville), A
Nashville State Community College, A
Pellissippi State Community College, A
South College, A
Southwest Tennessee Community College, A
The University of Tennessee at Chattanooga, B
Volunteer State Community College, A

Texas

Alvin Community College, A
Angelina College, A
Austin Community College District, A
Brightwood College, Dallas Campus, A
Brightwood College, San Antonio Ingram Campus, A
Center for Advanced Legal Studies, A
Central Texas College, A
Collin County Community College District, A
El Centro College, A
El Paso Community College, A
Houston Community College, A
Kilgore College, A
Lamar State College - Port Arthur, A
Lee College, A
Lone Star College - North Harris, A
McLennan Community College, A
Midland College, A
Navarro College, A
North Central Texas College, A
San Jacinto College District, A
South Texas College, A
South University, B
Stephen F. Austin State University, B
Tarrant County College District, A
Texas A&M University - Commerce, B
Texas Wesleyan University, B
Texas Woman's University, B
Tyler Junior College, A
University of Houston - Clear Lake, B
Virginia College in Austin, A

Utah

Broadview University - Layton, AB
Broadview University - West Jordan, AB
LDS Business College, A
Salt Lake Community College, A
Southern Utah University, A
Utah Valley University, A

Vermont

Champlain College, AB

Virginia

American National University (Harrisonburg), A
American National University (Salem), A
Bryant & Stratton College - Richmond Campus, A
Bryant & Stratton College - Virginia Beach Campus, A
Centura College (Chesapeake), A
Centura College (North Chesterfield), A
Centura College (Virginia Beach), A
Hampton University, B
J. Sargeant Reynolds Community College, A
Mountain Empire Community College, A
New River Community College, A
Patrick Henry Community College, A
Regent University, B
South University (Glen Allen), AB
South University (Virginia Beach), AB
Thomas Nelson Community College, A
Tidewater Community College, A

Washington

Bellingham Technical College, A
Clark College, A
Columbia Basin College, A
Edmonds Community College, A
Highline College, A
Pierce College at Fort Steilacoom, A
Skagit Valley College, A
South Puget Sound Community College, A
Spokane Community College, A
Tacoma Community College, A
Whatcom Community College, A

West Virginia

American Public University System, A
Blue Ridge Community and Technical College, A
BridgeValley Community and Technical College (South Charleston), A
Mountain State College, A
Mountwest Community & Technical College, A
New River Community and Technical College, A
West Virginia Business College (Nutter Fort), A

West Virginia Business College (Wheeling), A
West Virginia Junior College - Morgantown, A
West Virginia Northern Community College, A

Wisconsin

Bryant & Stratton College - Milwaukee Campus, A
Bryant & Stratton College - Wauwatosa Campus, A
Chippewa Valley Technical College, A
Concordia University Wisconsin, B
Fox Valley Technical College, A
Globe University - Appleton, AB
Globe University - Eau Claire, AB
Globe University - Green Bay, AB
Globe University - Madison East, AB
Globe University - Madison West, AB
Globe University - Wausau, AB
Lakeshore Technical College, A
Milwaukee Area Technical College, A
Moraine Park Technical College, A
Northeast Wisconsin Technical College, A
Rasmussen College Appleton, A
Rasmussen College Green Bay, A
Rasmussen College Wausau, A
Western Technical College, A

Wyoming

Casper College, A
Laramie County Community College, A

U.S. Territories: Puerto Rico

Huertas Junior College, A
Universidad del Este, AB

LEGAL AND JUSTICE STUDIES

United States

Alabama

Auburn University at Montgomery, MO

Arizona

Arizona State University at the Tempe campus, MDO
Harrison Middleton University, M
National Paralegal College, M
Prescott College, M

California

Golden Gate University, MD
National University, M
San Francisco State University, M
Stanford University, M
Trident University International, M
University of California, Berkeley, D
University of California, Riverside, D
University of California, San Diego, M
University of San Diego, M

Colorado

University of Denver, MO

District of Columbia

American University, MD
The Catholic University of America, DO
The George Washington University, MDO
University of the District of Columbia, MD

Florida

Hodges University, M
Nova Southeastern University, MD
Saint Leo University, M
University of South Florida, O

Illinois

Governors State University, M
Illinois Institute of Technology, D
Loyola University Chicago, M
Southern Illinois University Carbondale, M
University of Illinois at Springfield, M

Indiana

Valparaiso University, O

Iowa

Kaplan University, Davenport Campus, MO

Kansas

Washburn University, MD

Maryland

University of Baltimore, M

Massachusetts

Boston University, M
Harvard University, D
Northeastern University, MD
University of Massachusetts Lowell, MD

Michigan

Marygrove College, M

Mississippi

Mississippi College, O

Missouri

Webster University, M

Montana

University of Montana, M

Nebraska

University of Nebraska - Lincoln, M

Nevada

University of Nevada, Reno, MD

New Hampshire

Southern New Hampshire University, M
University of New Hampshire, M

New Jersey

Montclair State University, O
Rutgers University - New Brunswick, D

New York

Binghamton University, State University of New York, MD
Columbia University, M
Hofstra University, M
John Jay College of Criminal Justice of the City University of New York, D
New York University, MD
Pace University, M
St. John's University, M
Touro College, M

Ohio

Capital University, M
Case Western Reserve University, M

Oklahoma

Oklahoma City University, M

Pennsylvania

California University of Pennsylvania, M
Temple University, D
University of Pennsylvania, MD
University of Pittsburgh, M

Texas

Prairie View A&M University, MD
Texas State University, M

Utah

Weber State University, M

Vermont

Marlboro College, M

Virginia

Regent University, M

Washington

University of Washington, D

West Virginia

American Public University System, M
University of Charleston, M
West Virginia University, M

U.S. Territories: Puerto Rico

University of the Sacred Heart, M

Canada

Alberta

University of Calgary, MO

British Columbia

Simon Fraser University, M

Ontario

Brock University, M
Carleton University, M
Queen's University at Kingston, MD
University of Windsor, M
Wilfrid Laurier University, D

Quebec

Université Laval, O

LEGAL PROFESSIONS AND STUDIES

United States

Arizona

Northland Pioneer College, A
The University of Arizona, B

California

National University, B

District of Columbia

University of the District of Columbia, A

Florida

City College (Gainesville), A
Hodges University, B

Georgia

Armstrong State University, B
Brenau University, B

Illinois

University of Illinois at Springfield, B

Indiana

Ball State University, B

Louisiana

Tulane University, B

Massachusetts

Bay Path University, B
Bristol Community College, A

Missouri

Maryville University of Saint Louis, B
Missouri Southern State University, B
William Woods University, B

Nebraska

University of Nebraska - Lincoln, B
University of Nebraska at Omaha, B

New Jersey

Berkeley College - Woodland Park Campus, AB
Montclair State University, B
New Jersey Institute of Technology, B
Ramapo College of New Jersey, B

New York

Berkeley College - New York City Campus, AB
St. John's University, B
Syracuse University, B

Oklahoma

The University of Tulsa, B

Pennsylvania

Bucks County Community College, A
California University of Pennsylvania, B
Central Penn College, B
Drexel University, B
Temple University, B
University of Pennsylvania, B

Rhode Island

Roger Williams University, B

LEGAL SUPPORT SERVICES

United States

Illinois

Midstate College, A

New Mexico

Clovis Community College, A

LEISURE STUDIES

United States

Alabama

University of South Alabama, M

Arizona

Prescott College, M

California

California State University, Long Beach, M
San Francisco State University, M

Connecticut

Southern Connecticut State University, M
University of Connecticut, MD

District of Columbia

Howard University, M

Florida

University of West Florida, M

Georgia

University of Georgia, MD

Illinois

University of Illinois at Urbana - Champaign, MD

Indiana

Indiana University Bloomington, D

Iowa

The University of Iowa, MD

Kentucky

Murray State University, M

Missouri

Southeast Missouri State University, M

Nebraska

University of Nebraska at Kearney, M

New York

State University of New York College at Cortland, M

North Carolina

East Carolina University, MO

Ohio

Bowling Green State University, M
The University of Toledo, M

Pennsylvania

Penn State University Park, MD

Tennessee

The University of Tennessee, M

Texas

Texas State University, M

Utah

University of Utah, MD

U.S. Territories: Puerto Rico

Universidad Metropolitana, M

Canada

British Columbia

University of Victoria, M

Maritime Provinces: Nova Scotia

Dalhousie University, M

Ontario

University of Waterloo, MD

Quebec

Université du Québec à Trois-Rivières, MO

LIBERAL ARTS AND SCIENCES STUDIES AND HUMANITIES

United States

Alabama

Alabama Southern Community College, A
Amridge University, AB
Athens State University, B
Auburn University, B
Auburn University at Montgomery, B
Bevill State Community College, A
Calhoun Community College, A
Central Alabama Community College, A
Chattahoochee Valley Community College, A
Enterprise State Community College, A
Faulkner University, AB
Gadsden State Community College, A
George Corley Wallace State Community College, A
James H. Faulkner State Community College, A
Jefferson Davis Community College, A
Jefferson State Community College, A
Lawson State Community College, A
Lurleen B. Wallace Community College, A
Marion Military Institute, A
Northwest-Shoals Community College, A
Selma University, B
Shelton State Community College, A
Southern Union State Community College, A
Troy University, AB
Wallace State Community College, A

Alaska

Alaska Pacific University, B
Ilisagvik College, A
University of Alaska Anchorage, B
University of Alaska Anchorage, Kenai Peninsula College, AB
University of Alaska Anchorage, Matanuska-Susitna College, A
University of Alaska Fairbanks, AB
University of Alaska, Prince William Sound College, A
University of Alaska Southeast, AB

University of Alaska Southeast, Ketchikan Campus, A
University of Alaska Southeast, Sitka Campus, AB

Arizona

Argosy University, Phoenix, B
Arizona Christian University, A
Arizona State University at the Polytechnic campus, B
Central Arizona College, A
Chandler-Gilbert Community College, A
Diné College, A
Eastern Arizona College, A
Estrella Mountain Community College, A
GateWay Community College, A
Mesa Community College, A
Mohave Community College, A
Northern Arizona University, B
Northland Pioneer College, A
Paradise Valley Community College, A
Phoenix College, A
Pima Community College, A
Prescott College, B
South Mountain Community College, A
Tohono O'odham Community College, A
Yavapai College, A

Arkansas

Arkansas Baptist College, AB
Arkansas State University, A
Arkansas State University - Beebe, A
Arkansas State University Mid-South, A
Arkansas State University - Mountain Home, A
Arkansas State University - Newport, A
Black River Technical College, A
Central Baptist College, AB
College of the Ouachitas, A
Cossatot Community College of the University of Arkansas, A
East Arkansas Community College, A
Ecclesia College, A
National Park College, A
North Arkansas College, A
NorthWest Arkansas Community College, A
Ozarka College, A
Phillips Community College of the University of Arkansas, A
Pulaski Technical College, A
Rich Mountain Community College, A
Shorter College, A
Southeast Arkansas College, A
University of Arkansas Community College at Batesville, A
University of Arkansas Community College at Hope, A
University of Arkansas Community College at Morrilton, A
University of Arkansas - Fort Smith, A
University of Arkansas at Little Rock, B
University of Central Arkansas, B
Williams Baptist College, AB

California

Allan Hancock College, A
Allied American University, AB
American Jewish University, B
American River College, A
Antelope Valley College, A
Antioch University Los Angeles, B
Antioch University Santa Barbara, B
Argosy University, Inland Empire, B
Argosy University, Los Angeles, B
Argosy University, Orange County, B
Argosy University, San Diego, B
Argosy University, San Francisco Bay Area, B
Ashford University, AB
Azusa Pacific University, B
Bakersfield College, A
Berkeley City College, A
Biola University, B
Brandman University, B
Butte College, A
California Baptist University, B
California Lutheran University, B
California Polytechnic State University, San Luis Obispo, B

California State Polytechnic University, Pomona, B
California State University, Bakersfield, B
California State University Channel Islands, B
California State University, Chico, B
California State University, Dominguez Hills, B
California State University, East Bay, B
California State University, Fresno, B
California State University, Fullerton, B
California State University, Long Beach, B
California State University, Los Angeles, B
California State University, Monterey Bay, B
California State University, Northridge, B
California State University, Sacramento, B
California State University, San Bernardino, B
California State University, San Marcos, B
California State University, Stanislaus, B
Cañada College, A
Cerritos College, A
Cerro Coso Community College, A
Chabot College, A
Chaffey College, A
Chapman University, B
Citrus College, A
City College of San Francisco, A
Coastline Community College, A
College of Alameda, A
College of the Canyons, A
College of the Desert, A
College of Marin, A
College of the Redwoods, A
College of San Mateo, A
College of the Sequoias, A
College of the Siskiyous, A
Columbia College, A
Community Christian College, A
Concordia University Irvine, AB
Contra Costa College, A
Copper Mountain College, A
Cosumnes River College, A
Crafton Hills College, A
Cuesta College, A
Cuyamaca College, A
Cypress College, A
De Anza College, A
Deep Springs College, A
Diablo Valley College, A
Dominican University of California, B
East Los Angeles College, A
El Camino College, A
Evergreen Valley College, A
Feather River College, A
Folsom Lake College, A
Foothill College, A
Fresno City College, A
Fullerton College, A
Gavilan College, A
Glendale Community College, A
Golden West College, A
Grossmont College, A
Hartnell College, A
Holy Names University, B
Hope International University, B
Humboldt State University, B
Humphreys College, AB
Imperial Valley College, A
Irvine Valley College, A
John F. Kennedy University, B
La Sierra University, B
Lake Tahoe Community College, A
Laney College, A
Las Positas College, A
Lassen Community College District, A
Long Beach City College, A
Los Angeles City College, A
Los Angeles Harbor College, A
Los Angeles Mission College, A
Los Angeles Pierce College, A
Los Angeles Trade-Technical College, A
Los Angeles Valley College, A
Los Medanos College, A
Loyola Marymount University, B
Marymount California University, AB
The Master's College and Seminary, B
Mendocino College, A
Merced College, A
Merritt College, A

MiraCosta College, A
Mission College, A
Monterey Peninsula College, A
Moorpark College, A
Mount Saint Mary's University, AB
Mt. San Jacinto College, A
National University, B
Notre Dame de Namur University, B
Ohlone College, A
Orange Coast College, A
Palo Verde College, A
Palomar College, A
Pasadena City College, A
Patten University, AB
Pepperdine University, B
Point Loma Nazarene University, B
Porterville College, A
Reedley College, A
Rio Hondo College, A
Sacramento City College, A
Saddleback College, A
Saint Mary's College of California, B
San Bernardino Valley College, A
San Diego Christian College, AB
San Diego City College, A
San Diego Mesa College, A
San Diego Miramar College, A
San Diego State University, B
San Diego State University - Imperial Valley Campus, B
San Francisco State University, B
San Joaquin Delta College, A
San Jose City College, A
San Jose State University, B
Santa Ana College, A
Santa Barbara City College, A
Santa Clara University, B
Santa Monica College, A
Santa Rosa Junior College, A
Santiago Canyon College, A
Sierra College, A
Simpson University, B
Skyline College, A
Soka University of America, B
Solano Community College, A
Sonoma State University, B
Southwestern College, A
Taft College, A
Thomas Aquinas College, B
United States University, B
University of California, Los Angeles, B
University of California, Riverside, B
University of California, Santa Barbara, B
University of La Verne, B
University of Redlands, B
University of San Diego, B
University of San Francisco, B
Ventura College, A
Victor Valley College, A
West Hills Community College, A
West Los Angeles College, A
West Valley College, A
Westmont College, B
Whittier College, B

Colorado

Adams State University, AB
Aims Community College, A
Arapahoe Community College, A
Argosy University, Denver, B
Colorado Christian University, B
The Colorado College, B
Colorado Mesa University, AB
Colorado Mountain College (Glenwood Springs), A
Colorado Mountain College (Leadville), A
Colorado Mountain College (Steamboat Springs), A
Colorado Northwestern Community College, A
Colorado State University, B
Colorado State University - Pueblo, B
Community College of Aurora, A
Community College of Denver, A
Fort Lewis College, B
Front Range Community College, A
Lamar Community College, A
Morgan Community College, A
National American University (Colorado Springs), A

Northeastern Junior College, A
Otero Junior College, A
Pikes Peak Community College, A
Pueblo Community College, A
Red Rocks Community College, A
Regis University, B
Trinidad State Junior College, A

Connecticut

Asnuntuck Community College, A
Capital Community College, A
Charter Oak State College, AB
Eastern Connecticut State University, B
Fairfield University, B
Gateway Community College, A
Goodwin College, A
Housatonic Community College, A
Manchester Community College, A
Middlesex Community College, A
Mitchell College, AB
Naugatuck Valley Community College, A
Northwestern Connecticut Community College, A
Norwalk Community College, A
Quinebaug Valley Community College, A
Quinnipiac University, B
Sacred Heart University, B
Southern Connecticut State University, B
Three Rivers Community College, A
Tunxis Community College, A
University of Bridgeport, B
University of Connecticut, B
University of Hartford, AB
University of New Haven, B
Wesleyan University, B
Western Connecticut State University, AB

Delaware

University of Delaware, AB
Wesley College, AB

District of Columbia

American University, AB
The Catholic University of America, B
The George Washington University, B
Georgetown University, B
University of the District of Columbia, A

Florida

Argosy University, Sarasota, B
Argosy University, Tampa, B
Barry University, B
Beacon College, AB
Belhaven University, A
Bethune-Cookman University, B
Broward College, A
Chipola College, A
College of Central Florida, A
Flagler College, B
Florida Agricultural and Mechanical University, A
Florida Atlantic University, AB
Florida College, AB
Florida Gateway College, A
Florida Gulf Coast University, B
Florida International University, B
Florida Keys Community College, A
Florida National University, B
Florida SouthWestern State College, A
Florida State College at Jacksonville, A
Gulf Coast State College, A
Hillsborough Community College, A
Hobe Sound Bible College, AB
Indian River State College, A
Jacksonville University, B
Lake-Sumter State College, A
Miami Dade College, A
New College of Florida, B
North Florida Community College, A
Northwest Florida State College, A
Palm Beach State College, A
Pasco-Hernando State College, A
Pensacola State College, A
Polk State College, A
St. Johns River State College, A
Saint Leo University, A
St. Petersburg College, A
St. Thomas University, B

Santa Fe College, A
Schiller International University, A
Seminole State College of Florida, A
South Florida State College, A
State College of Florida Manatee-Sarasota, A
Tallahassee Community College, A
University of South Florida, St. Petersburg, A
The University of Tampa, B
University of West Florida, A
Valencia College, A

Georgia

Abraham Baldwin Agricultural College, A
Argosy University, Atlanta, A
Armstrong State University, AB
Atlanta Metropolitan State College, A
Augusta University, A
Bainbridge State College, A
Clayton State University, AB
Columbus State University, AB
Dalton State College, A
East Georgia State College, A
Emmanuel College, A
Emory University, B
Emory University, Oxford College, AB
Fort Valley State University, B
Georgia College & State University, B
Georgia Highlands College, A
Gordon State College, A
Life University, B
Middle Georgia State University, AB
Reinhardt University, AB
Savannah State University, A
Shorter University, B
Thomas University, AB
University of Georgia, B
University of North Georgia, A
Valdosta State University, AB

Hawaii

Argosy University, Hawai'i, B
Hawaii Community College, A
Hawai'i Pacific University, B
Hawaii Tokai International College, A
Honolulu Community College, A
Kapiolani Community College, A
Kauai Community College, A
Leeward Community College, A
University of Hawaii at Hilo, B
University of Hawaii at Manoa, B
University of Hawaii Maui College, A
Windward Community College, A

Idaho

Boise State University, A
Brigham Young University - Idaho, AB
College of Southern Idaho, A
College of Western Idaho, A
Lewis-Clark State College, A
New Saint Andrews College, AB
North Idaho College, A
Northwest Nazarene University, B

Illinois

Argosy University, Chicago, B
Argosy University, Schaumburg, B
Augustana College, B
Aurora University, B
Black Hawk College, A
Bradley University, B
Carl Sandburg College, A
Chicago State University, B
City Colleges of Chicago, Harold Washington College, A
City Colleges of Chicago, Harry S. Truman College, A
City Colleges of Chicago, Kennedy-King College, A
City Colleges of Chicago, Malcolm X College, A
City Colleges of Chicago, Olive-Harvey College, A
City Colleges of Chicago, Richard J. Daley College, A
City Colleges of Chicago, Wilbur Wright College, A
College of DuPage, A
College of Lake County, A
Columbia College Chicago, B
Danville Area Community College, A

East-West University, A
Eastern Illinois University, B
Elgin Community College, A
Eureka College, B
Governors State University, B
Greenville College, B
Harper College, A
Heartland Community College, A
Highland Community College, A
Illinois Central College, A
Illinois College, B
Illinois Eastern Community Colleges, Frontier Community College, A
Illinois Eastern Community Colleges, Lincoln Trail College, A
Illinois Eastern Community Colleges, Olney Central College, A
Illinois Eastern Community Colleges, Wabash Valley College, A
Illinois Institute of Technology, B
Illinois State University, B
Illinois Valley Community College, A
Illinois Wesleyan University, B
John A. Logan College, A
John Wood Community College, A
Joliet Junior College, A
Judson University, A
Kaskaskia College, A
Kishwaukee College, A
Lake Land College, A
Lewis and Clark Community College, A
Lewis University, B
Lincoln College - Normal, AB
Lincoln Land Community College, A
Loyola University Chicago, A
MacMurray College, B
McHenry County College, A
Monmouth College, B
Moraine Valley Community College, A
Morton College, A
National Louis University, B
North Central College, B
Northeastern Illinois University, B
Northern Illinois University, B
Northwestern University, B
Oakton Community College, A
Olivet Nazarene University, B
Parkland College, A
Prairie State College, A
Quincy University, AB
Rend Lake College, A
Richland Community College, A
Rock Valley College, A
Roosevelt University, B
St. Augustine College, A
Saint Xavier University, B
Shawnee Community College, A
Shimer College, B
South Suburban College, A
Southern Illinois University Carbondale, B
Southern Illinois University Edwardsville, B
Southwestern Illinois College, A
Spoon River College, A
Trinity International University, B
Triton College, A
University of Chicago, B
University of Illinois at Springfield, B
University of Illinois at Urbana - Champaign, B
University of St. Francis, B
Waubonsee Community College, A
Western Illinois University, B

Indiana

Anderson University, AB
Ball State University, AB
Bethel College, AB
Butler University, B
Calumet College of Saint Joseph, AB
Holy Cross College, AB
Huntington University, B
Indiana State University, B
Indiana University Bloomington, B
Indiana University East, B
Indiana University Kokomo, B
Indiana University Northwest, B

Indiana University - Purdue University Indianapolis, B
Indiana University South Bend, B
Indiana University Southeast, B
Ivy Tech Community College - Bloomington, A
Ivy Tech Community College - Central Indiana, A
Ivy Tech Community College - Columbus, A
Ivy Tech Community College - East Central, A
Ivy Tech Community College - Kokomo, A
Ivy Tech Community College - Lafayette, A
Ivy Tech Community College - North Central, A
Ivy Tech Community College - Northeast, A
Ivy Tech Community College - Northwest, A
Ivy Tech Community College - Richmond, A
Ivy Tech Community College - Southeast, A
Ivy Tech Community College - Southern Indiana, A
Ivy Tech Community College - Southwest, A
Ivy Tech Community College - Wabash Valley, A
Manchester University, B
Marian University, A
Martin University, B
Purdue University Northwest (Hammond), B
Purdue University Northwest (Westville), B
Saint Mary-of-the-Woods College, B
Taylor University, A
Trine University, AB
University of Evansville, B
University of Notre Dame, B
University of Saint Francis, AB
University of Southern Indiana, B
Vincennes University, A

Iowa

Briar Cliff University, A
Clarke University, AB
Clinton Community College, A
Coe College, B
Cornell College, B
Des Moines Area Community College, A
Ellsworth Community College, A
Graceland University, B
Grand View University, B
Hawkeye Community College, A
Indian Hills Community College, A
Iowa Central Community College, A
Iowa Lakes Community College, A
Iowa State University of Science and Technology, B
Iowa Western Community College, A
Kirkwood Community College, A
Loras College, AB
Marshalltown Community College, A
Mercy College of Health Sciences, AB
Muscatine Community College, A
North Iowa Area Community College, A
Northeast Iowa Community College, A
Northwest Iowa Community College, A
Northwestern College, B
Scott Community College, A
Shiloh University, A
Southeastern Community College, A
Southwestern Community College, A
The University of Iowa, B
University of Northern Iowa, B
Upper Iowa University, A
Waldorf College, A
Western Iowa Tech Community College, A
William Penn University, A

Kansas

Barton County Community College, A
Benedictine College, B
Butler Community College, A
Central Christian College of Kansas, B
Cloud County Community College, A
Coffeyville Community College, A
Colby Community College, A
Cowley County Community College and Area Vocational - Technical School, A
Dodge City Community College, A
Donnelly College, A
Fort Hays State University, B
Fort Scott Community College, A
Friends University, B
Garden City Community College, A
Haskell Indian Nations University, A
Hesston College, A

Highland Community College, A
Hutchinson Community College, A
Independence Community College, A
Johnson County Community College, A
Kansas City Kansas Community College, A
Kansas Wesleyan University, B
Labette Community College, A
MidAmerica Nazarene University, A
Neosho County Community College, A
Newman University, AB
Pittsburg State University, B
Pratt Community College, A
Seward County Community College and Area Technical School, A
Southwestern College, B
Tabor College, A
The University of Kansas, B
University of Saint Mary, B
Washburn University, AB
Wichita State University, AB

Kentucky

Ashland Community and Technical College, A
Bellarmine University, B
Bluegrass Community and Technical College, A
Brescia University, AB
Centre College, B
Elizabethtown Community and Technical College, A
Hazard Community and Technical College, A
Henderson Community College, A
Hopkinsville Community College, A
Kentucky State University, AB
Maysville Community and Technical College (Maysville), A
Midway University, B
Murray State University, AB
Northern Kentucky University, AB
Owensboro Community and Technical College, A
Somerset Community College, A
Southeast Kentucky Community and Technical College, A
Spalding University, B
Thomas More College, AB
University of Louisville, B

Louisiana

Baton Rouge Community College, A
Bossier Parish Community College, A
Louisiana College, B
Louisiana Delta Community College, A
Louisiana State University and Agricultural & Mechanical College, B
Louisiana State University at Alexandria, AB
Loyola University New Orleans, B
McNeese State University, B
Northwestern State University of Louisiana, B
Nunez Community College, A
River Parishes Community College, A
Saint Joseph Seminary College, B
Southern University at Shreveport, A
Sowela Technical Community College, A
Tulane University, B

Maine

Central Maine Community College, A
College of the Atlantic, B
Eastern Maine Community College, A
Husson University, B
Kennebec Valley Community College, A
Northern Maine Community College, A
Saint Joseph's College of Maine, B
Southern Maine Community College, A
Thomas College, A
Unity College, A
University of Maine, B
University of Maine at Augusta, AB
University of Maine at Farmington, B
University of Maine at Fort Kent, AB
University of Maine at Presque Isle, AB
University of New England, B
University of Southern Maine, B
York County Community College, A

Maryland

Allegany College of Maryland, A
Anne Arundel Community College, A

Baltimore City Community College, A
Carroll Community College, A
Cecil College, A
Chesapeake College, A
College of Southern Maryland, A
Community College of Baltimore County, A
Coppin State University, B
Frederick Community College, A
Frostburg State University, B
Garrett College, A
Hagerstown Community College, A
Howard Community College, A
Johns Hopkins University, B
Montgomery College, A
Notre Dame of Maryland University, B
Prince George's Community College, A
St. John's College, B
Salisbury University, B
University of Baltimore, B
University of Maryland Eastern Shore, B
University of Maryland University College, AB
Washington Adventist University, B
Washington College, B
Wor-Wic Community College, A

Massachusetts

American International College, AB
Anna Maria College, B
Bard College at Simon's Rock, A
Bay Path University, AB
Becker College, B
Bentley University, B
Berkshire Community College, A
Bristol Community College, A
Cambridge College, B
Cape Cod Community College, A
Curry College, B
Dean College, B
Eastern Nazarene College, B
Elms College, B
Emmanuel College, B
Endicott College, AB
Fisher College, AB
Fitchburg State University, B
Framingham State University, B
Greenfield Community College, A
Hampshire College, B
Harvard University, B
Holyoke Community College, A
Lasell College, B
Lesley University, B
Massachusetts Bay Community College, A
Massachusetts College of Liberal Arts, B
Massachusetts Institute of Technology, B
Massasoit Community College, A
Merrimack College, B
Middlesex Community College, A
Mount Ida College, B
Mount Wachusett Community College, A
North Shore Community College, A
Northern Essex Community College, A
Pine Manor College, A
Quincy College, A
Quinsigamond Community College, A
Regis College, B
Salem State University, B
Springfield Technical Community College, A
Suffolk University, A
Tufts University, B
University of Massachusetts Amherst, B
University of Massachusetts Dartmouth, B
University of Massachusetts Lowell, B
Urban College of Boston, A
Western New England University, AB
Westfield State University, B
Wheelock College, B

Michigan

Albion College, B
Alpena Community College, A
Aquinas College, AB
Bay de Noc Community College, A
Central Michigan University, B
Delta College, A
Ferris State University, A
Finlandia University, B

Grace Bible College, A
Grand Rapids Community College, A
Grand Valley State University, B
Henry Ford College, A
Jackson College, A
Kalamazoo Valley Community College, A
Kellogg Community College, A
Keweenaw Bay Ojibwa Community College, A
Kirtland Community College, A
Kuyper College, A
Lake Michigan College, A
Lake Superior State University, AB
Lansing Community College, A
Macomb Community College, A
Marygrove College, A
Michigan Technological University, B
Mid Michigan Community College, A
Monroe County Community College, A
Montcalm Community College, A
Mott Community College, A
Muskegon Community College, A
North Central Michigan College, A
Northern Michigan University, B
Northwestern Michigan College, A
Oakland Community College, A
Oakland University, B
Olivet College, B
Rochester College, A
Sacred Heart Major Seminary, B
Saginaw Chippewa Tribal College, A
St. Clair County Community College, A
Southwestern Michigan College, A
Spring Arbor University, A
University of Detroit Mercy, B
University of Michigan - Dearborn, B
Washtenaw Community College, A
Wayne County Community College District, A
West Shore Community College, A

Minnesota

Alexandria Technical and Community College, A
Anoka-Ramsey Community College, A
Argosy University, Twin Cities, B
Augsburg College, B
Bemidji State University, AB
Bethany Lutheran College, B
Bethel University, A
Central Lakes College, A
Century College, A
College of Saint Benedict, B
Concordia College, B
Crossroads College, AB
Crown College, B
Fond du Lac Tribal and Community College, A
Hibbing Community College, A
Inver Hills Community College, A
Itasca Community College, A
Lake Superior College, A
Leech Lake Tribal College, A
Mesabi Range College, A
Metropolitan State University, B
Minneapolis Community and Technical College, A
Minnesota State Community and Technical College, A
Minnesota State University Mankato, A
Minnesota State University Moorhead, A
Minnesota West Community and Technical College, A
Normandale Community College, A
North Hennepin Community College, A
Northland Community and Technical College, A
Rainy River Community College, A
Ridgewater College, A
Riverland Community College, A
Rochester Community and Technical College, A
St. Catherine University, A
St. Cloud State University, AB
St. Cloud Technical & Community College, A
Saint John's University, B
St. Olaf College, B
Saint Paul College - A Community & Technical College, A
South Central College, A
University of Northwestern - St. Paul, A
Vermilion Community College, A
Winona State University, A

Mississippi

Alcorn State University, B
Belhaven University, B
Blue Mountain College, B
Copiah-Lincoln Community College, A
East Central Community College, A
East Mississippi Community College, A
Holmes Community College, A
Itawamba Community College, A
Mississippi Delta Community College, A
Mississippi Gulf Coast Community College, A
Mississippi State University, B
Mississippi University for Women, B
Northeast Mississippi Community College, A
Northwest Mississippi Community College, A
Pearl River Community College, A
Southwest Mississippi Community College, A
University of Mississippi, B

Missouri

Columbia College, A
Conception Seminary College, B
Cottey College, B
Crowder College, A
Culver-Stockton College, B
Fontbonne University, B
Hannibal-LaGrange University, B
Harris-Stowe State University, B
Jefferson College, A
Lincoln University, B
Lindenwood University, B
Maryville University of Saint Louis, B
Metropolitan Community College - Kansas City, A
Mineral Area College, A
Missouri Baptist University, B
Missouri Southern State University, B
Moberly Area Community College, A
North Central Missouri College, A
Ozarks Technical Community College, A
Park University, B
St. Charles Community College, A
Saint Louis Christian College, A
St. Louis College of Pharmacy, B
Saint Louis University, B
State Fair Community College, A
Three Rivers Community College, A
University of Missouri - St. Louis, B
Washington University in St. Louis, B
Wentworth Military Academy and College, A
William Jewell College, B
William Woods University, A

Montana

Aaniiih Nakoda College, A
Chief Dull Knife College, A
Dawson Community College, A
Flathead Valley Community College, A
Great Falls College Montana State University, A
Little Big Horn College, A
Miles Community College, A
Montana State University, AB
Montana State University Billings, AB
Montana State University - Northern, B
Montana Tech of The University of Montana, B
Rocky Mountain College, A
Salish Kootenai College, A
Stone Child College, A
University of Montana, B
The University of Montana Western, AB

Nebraska

Central Community College - Columbus Campus, A
Central Community College - Grand Island Campus, A
Central Community College - Hastings Campus, A
College of Saint Mary, B
Grace University, AB
Hastings College, B
Little Priest Tribal College, A
Metropolitan Community College, A
Mid-Plains Community College, A
Midland University, B
Nebraska Indian Community College, A
Northeast Community College, A
Peru State College, B

Southeast Community College, Lincoln Campus, A
Union College, B
University of Nebraska - Lincoln, B
Western Nebraska Community College, A
York College, A

Nevada

College of Southern Nevada, A
Great Basin College, A
Truckee Meadows Community College, A
University of Nevada, Las Vegas, B
Western Nevada College, A

New Hampshire

Colby-Sawyer College, A
Franklin Pierce University, B
Granite State College, B
Great Bay Community College, A
Lakes Region Community College, A
Manchester Community College, A
Nashua Community College, A
New England College, A
NHTI, Concord's Community College, A
Northeast Catholic College, AB
River Valley Community College, A
Rivier University, AB
Saint Anselm College, B
Southern New Hampshire University, B
Thomas More College of Liberal Arts, B
University of New Hampshire at Manchester, A
White Mountains Community College, A

New Jersey

Assumption College for Sisters, A
Atlantic Cape Community College, A
Bergen Community College, A
Brookdale Community College, A
Camden County College, A
Centenary College, A
County College of Morris, A
Cumberland County College, A
Essex County College, A
Fairleigh Dickinson University, Metropolitan Campus, A
Felician University, AB
Hudson County Community College, A
Mercer County Community College, A
Middlesex County College, A
Ocean County College, A
Ramapo College of New Jersey, B
Raritan Valley Community College, A
Rider University, B
Rowan College at Burlington County, A
Rowan College at Gloucester County, A
Rowan University, B
Rutgers University - Camden, B
Rutgers University - New Brunswick, B
Saint Peter's University, B
Salem Community College, A
Seton Hall University, B
Stockton University, B
Sussex County Community College, A
Thomas Edison State University, AB
Union County College, A
Warren County Community College, A
William Paterson University of New Jersey, B

New Mexico

Central New Mexico Community College, A
Clovis Community College, A
Eastern New Mexico University, AB
Eastern New Mexico University - Roswell, A
Luna Community College, A
Mesalands Community College, A
New Mexico Highlands University, B
New Mexico Junior College, A
New Mexico Military Institute, A
New Mexico State University, B
New Mexico State University - Grants, A
St. John's College, B
San Juan College, A
Southwestern Indian Polytechnic Institute, A
University of New Mexico, B
University of New Mexico - Gallup, A
University of New Mexico - Los Alamos Branch, A
University of New Mexico - Taos, A

University of New Mexico - Valencia Campus, A
Western New Mexico University, AB

New York

Adelphi University, A
Adirondack Community College, A
Bard College, A
Baruch College of the City University of New York, B
Boricua College, AB
Borough of Manhattan Community College of the City University of New York, A
Bronx Community College of the City University of New York, A
Broome Community College, A
Buffalo State College, State University of New York, B
Canisius College, B
Cayuga County Community College, A
Cazenovia College, AB
Clarkson University, B
Clinton Community College, A
The College at Brockport, State University of New York, B
College of Mount Saint Vincent, B
The College of New Rochelle, B
The College of Saint Rose, B
College of Staten Island of the City University of New York, A
Columbia-Greene Community College, A
Concordia College - New York, AB
Cornell University, B
Corning Community College, A
Dominican College, A
Dutchess Community College, A
Elmira College, AB
Erie Community College, A
Erie Community College, North Campus, A
Erie Community College, South Campus, A
Eugene Lang College of Liberal Arts, B
Eugenio María de Hostos Community College of the City University of New York, A
Excelsior College, AB
Farmingdale State College, A
Finger Lakes Community College, A
Fiorello H. LaGuardia Community College of the City University of New York, A
Five Towns College, A
Fulton-Montgomery Community College, A
Genesee Community College, A
Herkimer County Community College, A
Hilbert College, A
Hofstra University, B
Houghton College, AB
Hudson Valley Community College, A
Iona College, B
Ithaca College, B
Jamestown Community College, A
Jefferson Community College, A
Keuka College, B
Kingsborough Community College of the City University of New York, A
Long Island University - LIU Brooklyn, AB
Long Island University - LIU Post, AB
Manhattan College, B
Manhattanville College, B
Maria College, A
Marist College, B
Marymount Manhattan College, B
Medaille College, AB
Medgar Evers College of the City University of New York, A
Mercy College, AB
Mohawk Valley Community College, A
Molloy College, AB
Monroe Community College, A
Morrisville State College, A
Nassau Community College, A
The New School for Public Engagement, B
New York City College of Technology of the City University of New York, A
New York University, AB
Niagara County Community College, A
Niagara University, AB
North Country Community College, A
Nyack College, A

Onondaga Community College, A
Orange County Community College, A
Pace University, B
Pace University, Pleasantville Campus, B
Parsons School of Design, B
Paul Smith's College, AB
Purchase College, State University of New York, B
Queensborough Community College of the City University of New York, A
Roberts Wesleyan College, B
Rochester Institute of Technology, B
Rockland Community College, A
The Sage Colleges, B
St. Francis College, AB
St. John Fisher College, B
St. John's University, AB
St. Joseph's College, Long Island Campus, B
St. Joseph's College, New York, B
St. Lawrence University, B
St. Thomas Aquinas College, A
Sarah Lawrence College, B
Schenectady County Community College, A
Skidmore College, B
State University of New York College of Agriculture and Technology at Cobleskill, A
State University of New York College at Oneonta, B
State University of New York College of Technology at Alfred, A
State University of New York College of Technology at Delhi, A
State University of New York at Fredonia, B
State University of New York Maritime College, B
State University of New York at New Paltz, B
State University of New York at Plattsburgh, B
Suffolk County Community College, A
Sullivan County Community College, A
Syracuse University, AB
Tompkins Cortland Community College, A
Touro College, AB
Trocaire College, A
Ulster County Community College, A
Union College, B
University at Albany, State University of New York, B
University of Rochester, B
Utica College, B
Vassar College, B
Villa Maria College, AB
Westchester Community College, A
York College of the City University of New York, B

North Carolina

Alamance Community College, A
Appalachian State University, B
Asheville-Buncombe Technical Community College, A
Barton College, B
Beaufort County Community College, A
Belmont Abbey College, B
Bladen Community College, A
Blue Ridge Community College, A
Brunswick Community College, A
Caldwell Community College and Technical Institute, A
Campbell University, A
Cape Fear Community College, A
Carteret Community College, A
Catawba Valley Community College, A
Central Carolina Community College, A
Central Piedmont Community College, A
Cleveland Community College, A
Coastal Carolina Community College, A
College of The Albemarle, A
Craven Community College, A
Davidson County Community College, A
Durham Technical Community College, A
East Carolina University, B
Edgecombe Community College, A
Elon University, B
Fayetteville Technical Community College, A
Forsyth Technical Community College, A
Gaston College, A
Guilford Technical Community College, A
Halifax Community College, A
Haywood Community College, A
Isothermal Community College, A
James Sprunt Community College, A

Johnson C. Smith University, B
Johnston Community College, A
Lenoir Community College, A
Lenoir-Rhyne University, B
Louisburg College, A
Mars Hill University, B
Martin Community College, A
Mayland Community College, A
McDowell Technical Community College, A
Methodist University, AB
Mitchell Community College, A
Montgomery Community College, A
Montreat College, A
Nash Community College, A
North Carolina Agricultural and Technical State University, B
North Carolina State University, B
North Carolina Wesleyan College, B
Pamlico Community College, A
Piedmont Community College, A
Pitt Community College, A
Randolph Community College, A
Richmond Community College, A
Roanoke-Chowan Community College, A
Rockingham Community College, A
Rowan-Cabarrus Community College, A
Sampson Community College, A
Sandhills Community College, A
Shaw University, B
South Piedmont Community College, A
Southeastern Community College, A
Southwestern Community College, A
Surry Community College, A
Tri-County Community College, A
University of Mount Olive, A
University of North Carolina at Asheville, B
The University of North Carolina at Chapel Hill, B
The University of North Carolina at Greensboro, B
Vance-Granville Community College, A
Wake Technical Community College, A
Wayne Community College, A
Western Carolina University, B
Western Piedmont Community College, A
Wilkes Community College, A
William Peace University, B
Wilson Community College, A
Wingate University, B

North Dakota

Bismarck State College, A
Cankdeska Cikana Community College, A
Dakota College at Bottineau, A
Dickinson State University, AB
Lake Region State College, A
North Dakota State College of Science, A
Nueta Hidatsa Sahnish College, A
Sitting Bull College, A
Trinity Bible College, A
Turtle Mountain Community College, A
Williston State College, A

Ohio

Antioch College, B
Antioch University Midwest, B
Ashland University, B
Bowling Green State University, B
Bowling Green State University - Firelands College, AB
Cedarville University, B
Central Ohio Technical College, A
Chatfield College, A
Cincinnati State Technical and Community College, A
Clark State Community College, A
Cleveland State University, B
Columbus State Community College, A
Cuyahoga Community College, A
Defiance College, B
Edison Community College, A
Kent State University at Ashtabula, AB
Kent State University at East Liverpool, AB
Kent State University at Geauga, AB
Kent State University at Salem, AB
Kent State University at Stark, AB
Kent State University at Trumbull, AB
Kent State University at Tuscarawas, AB

Lakeland Community College, A
Lorain County Community College, A
Lourdes University, A
Malone University, B
Marietta College, AB
Miami University, B
Miami University Middletown, A
Northwest State Community College, A
Ohio Dominican University, B
The Ohio State University - Mansfield Campus, A
The Ohio State University at Marion, A
The Ohio State University - Newark Campus, A
Ohio University, AB
Ohio University - Chillicothe, AB
Ohio University - Eastern, AB
Ohio University - Southern Campus, A
Sinclair Community College, A
Southern State Community College, A
Terra State Community College, A
The University of Akron, AB
The University of Akron Wayne College, A
University of Cincinnati, B
University of Cincinnati Blue Ash College, A
University of Cincinnati Clermont College, A
The University of Toledo, B
Urbana University, AB
Walsh University, AB
Washington State Community College, A
Wilmington College, B
Wittenberg University, B
Wright State University, B
Wright State University - Lake Campus, AB
Xavier University, AB
Youngstown State University, A

Oklahoma

Hillsdale Free Will Baptist College, B
Langston University, B
Mid-America Christian University, A
Northern Oklahoma College, A
Oklahoma Christian University, B
Oklahoma City Community College, A
Oklahoma City University, B
Oklahoma Panhandle State University, B
Oklahoma State University, B
Oral Roberts University, B
Redlands Community College, A
Rogers State University, AB
Rose State College, A
St. Gregory's University, AB
Seminole State College, A
Southwestern Christian University, B
University of Central Oklahoma, B
University of Oklahoma, B
The University of Tulsa, B
Western Oklahoma State College, A

Oregon

Blue Mountain Community College, A
Central Oregon Community College, A
Chemeketa Community College, A
Clackamas Community College, A
Clatsop Community College, A
Columbia Gorge Community College, A
Concordia University, AB
Corban University, B
Eastern Oregon University, B
Gutenberg College, B
Klamath Community College, A
Lane Community College, A
Linn-Benton Community College, A
Mt. Hood Community College, A
Oregon Coast Community College, A
Oregon Institute of Technology, A
Oregon State University, B
Oregon State University - Cascades, B
Pacific University, B
Portland Community College, A
Portland State University, B
Rogue Community College, A
Southern Oregon University, B
Southwestern Oregon Community College, A
Tillamook Bay Community College, A
Umpqua Community College, A
Warner Pacific College, B
Willamette University, B

Pennsylvania

Alvernia University, B
Arcadia University, B
Bryn Athyn College of the New Church, A
Bucks County Community College, A
Cabrini University, B
Cairn University, B
California University of Pennsylvania, AB
Carlow University, B
Carnegie Mellon University, B
Chatham University, B
Chestnut Hill College, AB
Cheyney University of Pennsylvania, B
Clarion University of Pennsylvania, AB
Community College of Allegheny County, A
Community College of Beaver County, A
Community College of Philadelphia, A
Delaware County Community College, A
DeSales University, B
Drexel University, B
Duquesne University, B
Eastern University, A
Gannon University, AB
Gettysburg College, B
Gwynedd Mercy University, A
Immaculata University, A
Indiana University of Pennsylvania, AB
Juniata College, B
Keystone College, A
Kutztown University of Pennsylvania, B
La Roche College, B
Lackawanna College, A
Lehigh Carbon Community College, A
Lock Haven University of Pennsylvania, B
Luzerne County Community College, A
Manor College, A
Mansfield University of Pennsylvania, AB
Mercyhurst North East, A
Montgomery County Community College, A
Mount Aloysius College, AB
Neumann University, AB
Northampton Community College, A
Penn State Abington, AB
Penn State Altoona, AB
Penn State Beaver, AB
Penn State Berks, AB
Penn State Brandywine, AB
Penn State DuBois, AB
Penn State Erie, The Behrend College, AB
Penn State Fayette, The Eberly Campus, AB
Penn State Greater Allegheny, AB
Penn State Harrisburg, A
Penn State Hazleton, A
Penn State Lehigh Valley, AB
Penn State Mont Alto, AB
Penn State New Kensington, AB
Penn State Schuylkill, AB
Penn State Shenango, AB
Penn State University Park, AB
Penn State Wilkes-Barre, AB
Penn State Worthington Scranton, AB
Penn State York, AB
Pennsylvania College of Technology, A
Point Park University, B
Reading Area Community College, A
Rosemont College, B
Saint Joseph's University, AB
Saint Vincent College, B
Shippensburg University of Pennsylvania, B
Temple University, B
Thiel College, A
Thomas Jefferson University, AB
University of Pennsylvania, B
University of Pittsburgh, B
University of Pittsburgh at Bradford, AB
University of Pittsburgh at Titusville, A
The University of Scranton, B
Valley Forge Military College, A
Villanova University, B
West Chester University of Pennsylvania, B
Westmoreland County Community College, A
Wilkes University, B
Wilson College, A

Rhode Island

Bryant University, B
Community College of Rhode Island, A
Providence College, AB
Rhode Island College, B
Roger Williams University, B
Salve Regina University, AB
University of Rhode Island, B

South Carolina

Aiken Technical College, A
Central Carolina Technical College, A
Clinton College, A
Coastal Carolina University, B
Columbia College, B
Columbia International University, B
Denmark Technical College, A
Florence-Darlington Technical College, A
Francis Marion University, B
Greenville Technical College, A
Lander University, B
Limestone College, AB
Midlands Technical College, A
Morris College, B
North Greenville University, B
Northeastern Technical College, A
Orangeburg-Calhoun Technical College, A
Piedmont Technical College, A
Spartanburg Community College, A
Spartanburg Methodist College, A
Technical College of the Lowcountry, A
Tri-County Technical College, A
Trident Technical College, A
University of South Carolina, B
University of South Carolina Aiken, B
University of South Carolina Beaufort, AB
University of South Carolina Lancaster, A
University of South Carolina Salkehatchie, A
University of South Carolina Sumter, A
University of South Carolina Union, A
Williamsburg Technical College, A
York Technical College, A

South Dakota

Augustana University, B
Dakota State University, B
Dakota Wesleyan University, B
Mount Marty College, AB
National American University (Rapid City), A
Northern State University, A
Oglala Lakota College, A
Sinte Gleska University, AB
Sisseton-Wahpeton College, A
South Dakota State University, B
University of Sioux Falls, AB
The University of South Dakota, AB

Tennessee

Argosy University, Nashville, B
Austin Peay State University, B
Belhaven University, A
Belmont University, B
Bryan College, AB
Carson-Newman University, AB
Chattanooga State Community College, A
Christian Brothers University, B
Cleveland State Community College, A
Columbia State Community College, A
Cumberland University, AB
Dyersburg State Community College, A
East Tennessee State University, B
Hiwassee College, A
Jackson State Community College, A
Lincoln Memorial University, B
Martin Methodist College, A
Middle Tennessee State University, B
Motlow State Community College, A
Northeast State Community College, A
Pellissippi State Community College, A
Roane State Community College, A
Southern Adventist University, A
Tennessee State University, B
University of Memphis, B
Volunteer State Community College, A
Walters State Community College, A

Williamson College, A

Texas

Abilene Christian University, B
Alvin Community College, A
Amarillo College, A
Argosy University, Dallas, B
Brazosport College, A
Brookhaven College, A
Central Texas College, A
Clarendon College, A
Coastal Bend College, A
Collin County Community College District, A
Concordia University Texas, AB
Dallas Baptist University, A
Del Mar College, A
Eastfield College, A
El Paso Community College, A
Frank Phillips College, A
Galveston College, A
Grayson College, A
Houston Baptist University, B
Howard Payne University, B
Huston-Tillotson University, A
Jacksonville College, A
Lamar State College - Orange, A
Lamar State College - Port Arthur, A
Laredo Community College, A
Lee College, A
Lone Star College - CyFair, A
McLennan Community College, A
Midwestern State University, AB
Mountain View College, A
North Central Texas College, A
North Lake College, A
Northeast Texas Community College, A
Northwest Vista College, A
Odessa College, A
Palo Alto College, A
Panola College, A
Paris Junior College, A
Ranger College, A
Richland College, A
St. Edward's University, B
St. Philip's College, A
San Antonio College, A
Schreiner University, AB
South Plains College, A
South Texas College, A
Southern Methodist University, B
Southwest Texas Junior College, A
Southwestern Christian University, A
Stephen F. Austin State University, B
Tarleton State University, B
Tarrant County College District, A
Temple College, A
Texarkana College, A
Texas A&M University - Central Texas, B
Texas A&M University - Commerce, B
Texas College, B
Texas Southmost College, A
Texas State University, B
Texas Tech University, B
Texas Wesleyan University, B
Trinity Valley Community College, A
Tyler Junior College, A
University of Houston, B
University of Houston - Victoria, B
University of the Incarnate Word, AB
University of North Texas, B
University of St. Thomas, B
The University of Texas at Austin, B
The University of Texas at Tyler, B
Vernon College, A
Wayland Baptist University, AB
Weatherford College, A
Western Texas College, A

Utah

Argosy University, Salt Lake City, B
Brigham Young University, B
LDS Business College, A
Snow College, A
University of Utah, B
Utah State University, B
Weber State University, B

Vermont

Bennington College, B
Champlain College, B
College of St. Joseph, AB
Community College of Vermont, A
Goddard College, B
Green Mountain College, B
Johnson State College, AB
Landmark College, AB
Marlboro College, B
Middlebury College, B
Southern Vermont College, AB
University of Vermont, B

Virginia

Argosy University, Washington DC, B
Averett University, AB
Blue Ridge Community College, A
Bluefield College, B
Bridgewater College, B
Central Virginia Community College, A
Christendom College, A
Dabney S. Lancaster Community College, A
Danville Community College, A
Eastern Mennonite University, B
Eastern Shore Community College, A
Emory & Henry College, B
Ferrum College, B
George Mason University, B
Germanna Community College, A
J. Sargeant Reynolds Community College, A
James Madison University, B
Liberty University, B
Longwood University, B
Lord Fairfax Community College, A
Marymount University, B
Mountain Empire Community College, A
New River Community College, A
Northern Virginia Community College, A
Patrick Henry College, B
Patrick Henry Community College, A
Paul D. Camp Community College, A
Randolph College, B
Rappahannock Community College, A
Richard Bland College of The College of William and Mary, A
Shenandoah University, B
Southern Virginia University, B
Southside Virginia Community College, A
Southwest Virginia Community College, A
Sweet Briar College, B
Thomas Nelson Community College, A
Tidewater Community College, A
University of Mary Washington, B
University of Virginia, B
The University of Virginia's College at Wise, B
Virginia Highlands Community College, A
Virginia State University, B
Virginia University of Lynchburg, A
Virginia Western Community College, A
Wytheville Community College, A

Washington

Antioch University Seattle, B
Argosy University, Seattle, B
Bellevue College, A
Big Bend Community College, A
Cascadia College, A
Centralia College, A
Clark College, A
Columbia Basin College, A
Edmonds Community College, A
Everett Community College, A
The Evergreen State College, B
Gonzaga University, B
Grays Harbor College, A
Green River College, A
Heritage University, AB
Lower Columbia College, A
North Seattle College, A
Northwest Indian College, A
Northwest University, A
Olympic College, A
Pierce College at Puyallup, A
Seattle Central College, A

Seattle Pacific University, B
Seattle University, B
Shoreline Community College, A
Skagit Valley College, A
South Puget Sound Community College, A
South Seattle College, A
Spokane Community College, A
Spokane Falls Community College, A
Tacoma Community College, A
Walla Walla Community College, A
Washington State University, B
Wenatchee Valley College, A
Western Washington University, B
Whatcom Community College, A
Yakima Valley Community College, A

West Virginia

Blue Ridge Community and Technical College, A
BridgeValley Community and Technical College (Montgomery), A
Eastern West Virginia Community and Technical College, A
Glenville State College, A
Marshall University, B
Mountwest Community & Technical College, A
New River Community and Technical College, A
Ohio Valley University, AB
Potomac State College of West Virginia University, A
Southern West Virginia Community and Technical College, A
West Virginia Northern Community College, A
West Virginia University, B
West Virginia University Institute of Technology, B
West Virginia University at Parkersburg, A
Wheeling Jesuit University, B

Wisconsin

Alverno College, AB
Chippewa Valley Technical College, A
College of Menominee Nation, A
Concordia University Wisconsin, B
Lac Courte Oreilles Ojibwa Community College, A
Madison Area Technical College, A
Marian University, B
Milwaukee Area Technical College, A
Mount Mary University, B
Nicolet Area Technical College, A
University of Wisconsin - Baraboo/Sauk County, A
University of Wisconsin - Barron County, A
University of Wisconsin - Eau Claire, AB
University of Wisconsin - Fond du Lac, A
University of Wisconsin - Fox Valley, A
University of Wisconsin - Green Bay, AB
University of Wisconsin - La Crosse, A
University of Wisconsin - Manitowoc, A
University of Wisconsin - Marathon County, A
University of Wisconsin - Marinette, A
University of Wisconsin - Marshfield/Wood County, A
University of Wisconsin - Milwaukee, B
University of Wisconsin - Oshkosh, AB
University of Wisconsin - Parkside, AB
University of Wisconsin - Platteville, B
University of Wisconsin - Richland, A
University of Wisconsin - River Falls, B
University of Wisconsin - Rock County, A
University of Wisconsin - Sheboygan, A
University of Wisconsin - Stevens Point, A
University of Wisconsin - Superior, A
University of Wisconsin - Washington County, A
University of Wisconsin - Waukesha, AB
University of Wisconsin - Whitewater, AB
Viterbo University, B

Wyoming

Casper College, A
Eastern Wyoming College, A
Northwest College, A
Western Wyoming Community College, A

U.S. Territories: American Samoa

American Samoa Community College, A

U.S. Territories: Guam

Guam Community College, A

U.S. Territories: Northern Mariana Islands

Northern Marianas College, A

U.S. Territories: Puerto Rico

American University of Puerto Rico (Bayamon), A
Pontifical Catholic University of Puerto Rico, B
University of Puerto Rico in Aguadilla, A
University of Puerto Rico in Carolina, A
University of Puerto Rico, Río Piedras Campus, B

Canada

Alberta

Athabasca University, B
University of Alberta, B
University of Lethbridge, B

British Columbia

Okanagan College, A
Simon Fraser University, B
Thompson Rivers University, AB
The University of British Columbia, B
University of the Fraser Valley, A
University of Northern British Columbia, B
University of Victoria, B
Vancouver Island University, B

Manitoba

Brandon University, B
Providence University College & Theological Seminary, B

Maritime Provinces: New Brunswick

Mount Allison University, B
Université de Moncton, B
University of New Brunswick Fredericton, B
University of New Brunswick Saint John, B

Maritime Provinces: Nova Scotia

Mount Saint Vincent University, B
St. Francis Xavier University, B

Ontario

Brock University, B
Lakehead University, B
Laurentian University, B
Nipissing University, B
Trent University, B
Tyndale University College & Seminary, B
University of Waterloo, B
The University of Western Ontario, B
York University, B

Quebec

Bishop's University, B
Télé-université, B

Saskatchewan

University of Regina, B

LIBERAL STUDIES

United States

Alabama

Auburn University at Montgomery, MDO
Faulkner University, M
Jacksonville State University, M
Spring Hill College, MO

Alaska

Alaska Pacific University, M

Arizona

Arizona State University at the Tempe campus, M
Northern Arizona University, M

Arkansas

Arkansas Tech University, M
Henderson State University, M

California

Occidental College, M
San Diego State University, M

Colorado

The Colorado College, M
Regis University, M

Connecticut

Albertus Magnus College, M
Wesleyan University, M

Delaware

University of Delaware, M

District of Columbia

Georgetown University, MD

Florida

Barry University, M
Florida Atlantic University, M
Florida International University, M
Rollins College, M
University of Miami, M
University of South Florida, M
University of South Florida, St. Petersburg, M

Georgia

Clayton State University, M

Illinois

Concordia University Chicago, M
DePaul University, M
Lake Forest College, M
North Central College, M
Northwestern University, M
University of Chicago, M
Western Illinois University, M

Indiana

Indiana University Northwest, M
Indiana University - Purdue University Fort Wayne, M
Indiana University - Purdue University Indianapolis, MDO
Indiana University South Bend, M
University of Southern Indiana, M
Valparaiso University, MO

Kansas

Baker University, M
Fort Hays State University, M
Washburn University, M
Wichita State University, M

Kentucky

Northern Kentucky University, M

Louisiana

Louisiana State University and Agricultural & Mechanical College, M
Louisiana State University in Shreveport, M
Tulane University, M

Maryland

Johns Hopkins University, MO
Loyola University Maryland, M
McDaniel College, M
Notre Dame of Maryland University, M
St. John's College, M
Towson University, M

Massachusetts

Harvard University, M

Michigan

Madonna University, M
Oakland University, M
University of Detroit Mercy, M

Minnesota

Hamline University, M
Metropolitan State University, M
University of Minnesota, Duluth, M

Mississippi

Delta State University, M
Mississippi College, M

New Hampshire

Dartmouth College, M
University of New Hampshire, M

New Jersey

Ramapo College of New Jersey, M
Rutgers University - Camden, M
Thomas Edison State University, M

New Mexico

St. John's College, M

New York

Brooklyn College of the City University of New York, M
The College at Brockport, State University of New York, M
College of Staten Island of the City University of New York, M
Excelsior College, M
Nazareth College of Rochester, M
Queens College of the City University of New York, M
St. John's University, M
State University of New York Empire State College, M
Stony Brook University, State University of New York, M
University at Albany, State University of New York, M
Utica College, M

North Carolina

Duke University, M
North Carolina State University, M
University of North Carolina at Asheville, M
The University of North Carolina at Charlotte, M
The University of North Carolina at Greensboro, M
The University of North Carolina Wilmington, M
Wake Forest University, M

Ohio

Antioch University Midwest, M
Kent State University, M
The University of Toledo, M
Ursuline College, M

Oklahoma

Oklahoma City University, M
University of Oklahoma, MO

Oregon

Reed College, M

Pennsylvania

Alvernia University, M
University of Pennsylvania, M
Villanova University, MO
Widener University, M

South Carolina

Converse College, M
Winthrop University, M

Tennessee

East Tennessee State University, MO
University of Memphis, M
Vanderbilt University, M

Texas

Abilene Christian University, M
Dallas Baptist University, M
Houston Baptist University, M
Rice University, M

St. Edward's University, MO
Southern Methodist University, M
Texas A&M University - Central Texas, M
Texas Christian University, M
University of St. Thomas, M
The University of Texas at El Paso, M

Virginia

Averett University, M
Hollins University, MO
Virginia Polytechnic Institute and State University, O

West Virginia

West Virginia University, M

Wisconsin

St. Norbert College, M
University of Wisconsin - Milwaukee, M

Canada

British Columbia

Simon Fraser University, M

LIBRARY ASSISTANT/TECHNI-CIAN

United States

Arizona

Northland Pioneer College, A

California

Citrus College, A
Long Beach City College, A
Palomar College, A

Colorado

Pueblo Community College, A

Illinois

College of DuPage, A
Illinois Central College, A
Lewis and Clark Community College, A
Waubonsee Community College, A

Indiana

Ivy Tech Community College - Bloomington, A
Ivy Tech Community College - Columbus, A
Ivy Tech Community College - East Central, A
Ivy Tech Community College - Kokomo, A
Ivy Tech Community College - Lafayette, A
Ivy Tech Community College - North Central, A
Ivy Tech Community College - Northeast, A
Ivy Tech Community College - Northwest, A
Ivy Tech Community College - Richmond, A
Ivy Tech Community College - Southeast, A
Ivy Tech Community College - Southern Indiana, A
Ivy Tech Community College - Southwest, A
Ivy Tech Community College - Wabash Valley, A

Maine

University of Maine at Augusta, A

Michigan

Oakland Community College, A

Minnesota

Minneapolis Community and Technical College, A

Nebraska

Central Community College - Hastings Campus, A
Northeast Community College, A

New Mexico

Clovis Community College, A
Northern New Mexico College, A

Ohio

Clark State Community College, A

South Dakota

Western Dakota Technical Institute, A

Washington

Spokane Falls Community College, A

West Virginia

Mountwest Community & Technical College, A

Canada

British Columbia

University of the Fraser Valley, A

LIBRARY SCIENCE

United States

Alabama

The University of Alabama, MD
Wallace State Community College, A

Arizona

Mesa Community College, A
The University of Arizona, MD

Arkansas

Southern Arkansas University - Magnolia, M
University of Central Arkansas, M

California

Azusa Pacific University, MO
Citrus College, A
City College of San Francisco, A
Cuesta College, A
Fresno City College, A
Hartnell College, A
Merced College, A
Pasadena City College, A
Sacramento City College, A
San Jose State University, MD
Santa Ana College, A
University of California, Los Angeles, MDO

Colorado

University of Denver, M
University of Northern Colorado, M

Connecticut

Southern Connecticut State University, BMO

Delaware

Delaware State University, B

District of Columbia

The Catholic University of America, M

Florida

College of Central Florida, A
Florida State University, MDO
Indian River State College, A

Georgia

Valdosta State University, M

Hawaii

University of Hawaii at Manoa, MO

Idaho

College of Southern Idaho, A

Illinois

Chicago State University, M
City Colleges of Chicago, Wilbur Wright College, A
College of DuPage, A
Dominican University, MDO
Olivet Nazarene University, M
University of Illinois at Urbana - Champaign, MDO

Indiana

Indiana University Bloomington, MDO
Indiana University - Purdue University Indianapolis, MO

Iowa

Southwestern Community College, A
The University of Iowa, MD

Kansas

Allen Community College, A

Kentucky

Eastern Kentucky University, M
University of Kentucky, M

Louisiana

Louisiana State University and Agricultural & Mechanical College, M
McNeese State University, O

Maine

University of Maine at Augusta, B

Maryland

McDaniel College, M

Massachusetts

Simmons College, MDO

Michigan

Grand Rapids Community College, A
Wayne State University, MO

Minnesota

St. Catherine University, M
St. Cloud State University, B

Mississippi

Copiah-Lincoln Community College, A
Itawamba Community College, A
University of Southern Mississippi, BMO

Missouri

University of Central Missouri, M
University of Missouri, MDO

Montana

University of Great Falls, B

Nebraska

Chadron State College, B
University of Nebraska at Kearney, M
University of Nebraska at Omaha, B

New Jersey

Rowan University, M
Rutgers University - New Brunswick, MD

New Mexico

Doña Ana Community College, A

New York

Long Island University - LIU Post, O
Pratt Institute, MO
Queens College of the City University of New York, MO
St. John's University, MO
Syracuse University, M
University at Albany, State University of New York, O
University at Buffalo, the State University of New York, MO

North Carolina

Appalachian State University, M
East Carolina University, M
North Carolina Central University, M
The University of North Carolina at Chapel Hill, MDO
The University of North Carolina at Greensboro, M

North Dakota

Valley City State University, M

Ohio

Kent State University, MO
University of Cincinnati Blue Ash College, A
Wright State University, M

Oklahoma

Rose State College, A
University of Central Oklahoma, M
University of Oklahoma, M

Pennsylvania

Clarion University of Pennsylvania, BMO
Drexel University, MDO
Kutztown University of Pennsylvania, BM
Mansfield University of Pennsylvania, M
University of Pittsburgh, MD
Westmoreland County Community College, A

Rhode Island

University of Rhode Island, M

South Carolina

University of South Carolina, MDO

Tennessee

East Tennessee State University, O
Tennessee Technological University, MO
Trevecca Nazarene University, M

Texas

Palo Alto College, A
Sam Houston State University, BM
Texas Woman's University, MD
University of Houston - Clear Lake, M

Virginia

Emory & Henry College, B
Old Dominion University, M

Washington

Highline College, A
University of Washington, MD

West Virginia

Mountwest Community & Technical College, A

Wisconsin

University of Wisconsin - Eau Claire, M
University of Wisconsin - Madison, MD
University of Wisconsin - Milwaukee, MDO
University of Wisconsin - Whitewater, M

U.S. Territories: Puerto Rico

Inter American University of Puerto Rico, Barranquitas Campus, M
Inter American University of Puerto Rico, San Germán Campus, M
Universidad del Turabo, MO
University of Puerto Rico, Río Piedras Campus, MO

Canada

Alberta

University of Alberta, M

British Columbia

The University of British Columbia, MDO

Maritime Provinces: Nova Scotia

Dalhousie University, M

Ontario

The University of Western Ontario, MD

Quebec

McGill University, MDO
Université de Montréal, MD

LIGHTING DESIGN

United States

New York

New York School of Interior Design, M
Rensselaer Polytechnic Institute, MD

Oklahoma

University of Oklahoma, M

Washington

University of Washington, O

LIMNOLOGY

United States

Alaska

University of Alaska Fairbanks, MD

Florida

University of Florida, MD

New York

Cornell University, D

Texas

Baylor University, M

Wisconsin

University of Wisconsin - Madison, MD

LINEWORKER

United States

Arizona

Chandler-Gilbert Community College, A
GateWay Community College, A

Colorado

Trinidad State Junior College, A

Indiana

Ivy Tech Community College - Lafayette, A

Iowa

Northwest Iowa Community College, A

Maine

Kennebec Valley Community College, A

Maryland

College of Southern Maryland, A

Minnesota

Dakota County Technical College, A
Minnesota State Community and Technical College, A
Minnesota West Community and Technical College, A

Missouri

State Technical College of Missouri, A

Nebraska

Northeast Community College, A

New Jersey

Raritan Valley Community College, A

North Carolina

Nash Community College, A

North Dakota

Bismarck State College, A

Pennsylvania

Pennsylvania Highlands Community College, A

South Dakota

Mitchell Technical Institute, A

LINGUISTIC, COMPARATIVE, AND RELATED LANGUAGE STUDIES AND SERVICES

United States

California

University of California, Los Angeles, B
University of California, Santa Barbara, B
University of Southern California, B

Indiana

Indiana University Bloomington, B

Iowa

Iowa State University of Science and Technology, B

Kentucky

University of Kentucky, B

North Carolina

Appalachian State University, B

Utah

Brigham Young University, B

Washington

Northwest University, A

Canada

Alberta

University of Alberta, B

LINGUISTICS

United States

Alabama

The University of Alabama, D

Alaska

University of Alaska Fairbanks, BM

Arizona

Arizona State University at the Tempe campus, MD
Northern Arizona University, D
The University of Arizona, BMD

California

Biola University, BMO
California State University, Dominguez Hills, B
California State University, Fresno, BM
California State University, Fullerton, BM
California State University, Long Beach, M
California State University, Monterey Bay, B
California State University, Northridge, BM
Cañada College, A
National University, M
Pitzer College, B
Pomona College, B
San Diego State University, BMO
San Francisco State University, M
San Jose State University, BMO
Scripps College, B
Stanford University, BMD
University of California, Berkeley, BD
University of California, Davis, BMD
University of California, Los Angeles, MD
University of California, Riverside, B
University of California, San Diego, BD
University of California, Santa Barbara, BD

University of California, Santa Cruz, BMD
University of Southern California, BMD

Colorado

University of Colorado Boulder, BMD
University of Colorado Denver, M

Connecticut

University of Connecticut, BMD
Yale University, BD

Delaware

University of Delaware, BMD

District of Columbia

Gallaudet University, MD
Georgetown University, BMD

Florida

Florida Atlantic University, BM
Florida International University, M
South Florida State College, A
University of Florida, BMDO

Georgia

Emory University, B
Georgia State University, BMD
University of Georgia, BMD

Hawaii

University of Hawaii at Hilo, B
University of Hawaii at Manoa, MD

Illinois

Northeastern Illinois University, M
Northwestern University, BD
Southern Illinois University Carbondale, BM
University of Chicago, BMD
University of Illinois at Chicago, M
University of Illinois at Urbana - Champaign, BMD

Indiana

Ball State University, MD
Indiana State University, M
Indiana University Bloomington, BMD
Purdue University, BMD

Iowa

Central College, B
Iowa State University of Science and Technology, BMD
The University of Iowa, BMD

Kansas

The University of Kansas, BMD

Kentucky

University of Kentucky, B

Louisiana

Tulane University, B

Maine

University of Southern Maine, B

Maryland

University of Maryland, Baltimore County, M
University of Maryland, College Park, BMD

Massachusetts

Bard College at Simon's Rock, B
Boston College, M
Boston University, BMD
Brandeis University, BM
Gordon College, B
Hampshire College, B
Harvard University, BD
Massachusetts Institute of Technology, BD
Northeastern University, B
University of Massachusetts Amherst, BMD
University of Massachusetts Boston, M
Wellesley College, B

Michigan

Calvin College, B
Eastern Michigan University, BMO
Michigan State University, BMD
Oakland University, BMO
University of Michigan, BD
University of Michigan - Flint, B
Wayne State University, BM

Minnesota

Bethel University, B
Carleton College, B
Macalester College, B
University of Minnesota, Duluth, B
University of Minnesota, Twin Cities Campus, BMD

Mississippi

University of Mississippi, B

Missouri

Truman State University, B
University of Missouri, B
Washington University in St. Louis, B

Montana

University of Montana, BM

Nevada

University of Nevada, Las Vegas, B

New Hampshire

Dartmouth College, B
University of New Hampshire, BM

New Jersey

Montclair State University, BMO
Rutgers University - New Brunswick, BD

New Mexico

University of New Mexico, BMD

New York

Binghamton University, State University of New York, B
Brooklyn College of the City University of New York, B
City College of the City University of New York, B
Columbia University, B
Cornell University, BMD
Hofstra University, BMD
Lehman College of the City University of New York, B
New York University, BMD
Queens College of the City University of New York, BM
State University of New York at Oswego, B
Stony Brook University, State University of New York, BMD
Syracuse University, BM
University at Albany, State University of New York, B
University at Buffalo, the State University of New York, BMD
University of Rochester, BM

North Carolina

Duke University, B
East Carolina University, M
Mid-Atlantic Christian University, B
The University of North Carolina at Chapel Hill, BMD

North Dakota

University of North Dakota, M

Ohio

Case Western Reserve University, M
Cedarville University, B
Cleveland State University, BM
Miami University, B
Miami University Hamilton, B
The Ohio State University, BMD
Ohio University, BM
The University of Toledo, B

Oklahoma

University of Oklahoma, B

Oregon

Portland State University, B
Reed College, B
University of Oregon, BMD

Pennsylvania

Bryn Mawr College, B
Bucknell University, B
Carnegie Mellon University, BMD
Penn State University Park, MD
Saint Joseph's University, B
Swarthmore College, B
Temple University, B
University of Pennsylvania, BMD
University of Pittsburgh, BMD
Ursinus College, B

Rhode Island

Brown University, BMD

South Carolina

University of South Carolina, MDO

Tennessee

Carson-Newman University, B
University of Memphis, MD
The University of Tennessee, D

Texas

Baylor University, B
Rice University, BMD
Texas Tech University, M
University of Houston, BM
University of North Texas, BM
The University of Texas at Arlington, BMD
The University of Texas at Austin, BMD
The University of Texas at El Paso, BMO

Utah

Brigham Young University, M
University of Utah, MD

Vermont

Marlboro College, B

Virginia

The College of William and Mary, B
George Mason University, D
Old Dominion University, M
University of Virginia, M
Virginia International University, M

Washington

Seattle Pacific University, B
University of Washington, BMD
Washington State University, B
Western Washington University, B

West Virginia

West Virginia University, M

Wisconsin

Lawrence University, B
University of Wisconsin - Madison, BMD
University of Wisconsin - Milwaukee, BMDO

U.S. Territories: Puerto Rico

University of Puerto Rico, Río Piedras Campus, MD

Canada
Alberta

University of Alberta, BMD
University of Calgary, BMD

British Columbia

Simon Fraser University, BMD
Trinity Western University, BM
The University of British Columbia, BMD

University of Victoria, BMD

Manitoba

University of Manitoba, MD

Maritime Provinces: New Brunswick

Université de Moncton, B
University of New Brunswick Fredericton, B
University of New Brunswick Saint John, B

Maritime Provinces: Nova Scotia

Mount Saint Vincent University, B
University of King's College, B

Newfoundland and Labrador

Memorial University of Newfoundland, BMD

Ontario

Brock University, B
Carleton University, BM
McMaster University, B
Queen's University at Kingston, B
University of Ottawa, BMD
University of Toronto, BMD
The University of Western Ontario, B
York University, BMD

Quebec

Concordia University, BM
McGill University, MD
Université Laval, BMD
Université de Montréal, BMDO
Université du Québec à Chicoutimi, BM
Université du Québec à Montréal, BMD
Université de Sherbrooke, M

Saskatchewan

University of Regina, BM
University of Saskatchewan, B

LIVESTOCK MANAGEMENT

United States

Kansas

Barton County Community College, A
Fort Hays State University, B

Montana

Miles Community College, A

Ohio

The Ohio State University, B
The Ohio State University Agricultural Technical Institute, A

Texas

Tarleton State University, B

LOGIC

United States

Pennsylvania

Carnegie Mellon University, B
University of Pennsylvania, B

Vermont

Marlboro College, B

LOGISTICS AND MATERIALS MANAGEMENT

United States

Alabama

Alabama Agricultural and Mechanical University, M
Athens State University, B
Auburn University, B
Community College of the Air Force, A
The University of Alabama in Huntsville, M

Alaska

University of Alaska Anchorage, ABMO

Arizona

Arizona Western College, A
Cochise County Community College District, A
Pima Community College, A

Arkansas

Arkansas State University, B
Arkansas Tech University, A
University of Arkansas, B

California

California State University, Dominguez Hills, B
California State University, Long Beach, M
Chaffey College, A
FIDM/Fashion Institute of Design & Merchandising, Los Angeles Campus, A
Southwestern College, A
Trident University International, M

Colorado

Colorado Technical University Colorado Springs, M

Connecticut

Central Connecticut State University, O
Goodwin College, A

Florida

Embry-Riddle Aeronautical University - Worldwide, ABM
Florida Gateway College, A
Florida Institute of Technology, BM
Florida State College at Jacksonville, B
Miami Dade College, AB
Polytechnic University of Puerto Rico, Miami Campus, M
St. Thomas University, B
University of North Florida, M

Georgia

Albany State University, B
Athens Technical College, A
Chattahoochee Technical College, A
Clayton State University, B
Georgia College & State University, M
Georgia Institute of Technology, M
Georgia Military College, A
Georgia Southern University, BD
Kennesaw State University, B
South Georgia State College, A

Idaho

Boise State University, B

Illinois

Benedictine University, M
Bradley University, B
City Colleges of Chicago, Olive-Harvey College, A
Elmhurst College, B
University of Illinois at Urbana - Champaign, B
University of St. Francis, BO
Western Illinois University, B

Indiana

Ancilla College, A
Ivy Tech Community College - Bloomington, A
Ivy Tech Community College - Central Indiana, A
Ivy Tech Community College - Columbus, A
Ivy Tech Community College - East Central, A

Ivy Tech Community College - Richmond, A
Ivy Tech Community College - Southeast, A
Ivy Tech Community College - Southern Indiana, A
Ivy Tech Community College - Southwest, A
Ivy Tech Community College - Wabash Valley, A

Iowa

Iowa State University of Science and Technology, B
Kaplan University, Davenport Campus, M
Scott Community College, A

Kansas

Barton County Community College, A
Friends University, M
The University of Kansas, B

Kentucky

Murray State University, B
Sullivan University, A
University of Louisville, O

Louisiana

Southeastern Louisiana University, B

Maine

Maine Maritime Academy, B

Maryland

Cecil College, A
University of Maryland, College Park, B

Massachusetts

Massachusetts Institute of Technology, M
Northeastern University, B
Northern Essex Community College, A

Michigan

Central Michigan University, BMO
Eastern Michigan University, B
Michigan State University, BMD
Western Michigan University, B

Minnesota

Northland Community and Technical College, A
Saint Paul College - A Community & Technical College, A

Mississippi

Hinds Community College, A

Missouri

Missouri Southern State University, B
Missouri State University, B
Park University, AB
University of Missouri - St. Louis, MDO

Nebraska

Central Community College - Hastings Campus, A
University of Nebraska - Lincoln, B

Nevada

Truckee Meadows Community College, A

New Jersey

Bloomfield College, B
Rider University, B
Rutgers University - New Brunswick, B
Rutgers University - Newark, BM
Stevens Institute of Technology, MO

New York

Binghamton University, State University of New York, B
Clarkson University, B
Hofstra University, B
Niagara University, B
Syracuse University, B
United States Merchant Marine Academy, B
University at Buffalo, the State University of New York, M

North Carolina

East Carolina University, M
Fayetteville Technical Community College, A
Forsyth Technical Community College, A
Gaston College, A
Guilford Technical Community College, A
Lenoir Community College, A
Pitt Community College, A
Randolph Community College, A
Rockingham Community College, A
The University of North Carolina at Charlotte, O

North Dakota

North Dakota State University, MD

Ohio

Bowling Green State University, B
Case Western Reserve University, M
Clark State Community College, A
Columbus State Community College, A
Northwest State Community College, A
The Ohio State University, BM
Owens Community College, A
Sinclair Community College, A
Tiffin University, B
The University of Findlay, B
The University of Toledo, B
Wright State University, BM

Oklahoma

Northeastern State University, B

Oregon

Portland State University, B

Pennsylvania

Bloomsburg University of Pennsylvania, B
DeSales University, B
Duquesne University, B
Gannon University, B
Lehigh University, B
Penn State Beaver, B
Penn State Brandywine, B
Penn State Fayette, The Eberly Campus, B
Penn State Greater Allegheny, B
Penn State Hazleton, B
Penn State Lehigh Valley, B
Penn State New Kensington, B
Penn State Schuylkill, B
Penn State Shenango, B
Penn State York, B
Shippensburg University of Pennsylvania, B
Temple University, B
University of Pittsburgh, B
Westmoreland County Community College, A
York College of Pennsylvania, B

Rhode Island

Bryant University, B
University of Rhode Island, B

Tennessee

University of Memphis, B
The University of Tennessee, BMD
The University of Tennessee at Chattanooga, O

Texas

Baylor University, B
Houston Community College, A
Lee College, A
Lone Star College - CyFair, A
Texas A&M University, B
Texas Christian University, B
University of Dallas, M
University of Houston, M
University of North Texas, BMD
The University of Texas at Arlington, M
The University of Texas at Austin, B
The University of Texas at Dallas, B
The University of Texas Rio Grande Valley, B

Utah

Brigham Young University, B
LDS Business College, A

Weber State University, B

Vermont

Norwich University, M

Virginia

George Mason University, MO
Virginia International University, M

Washington

Central Washington University, B
University of Washington, BO

West Virginia

American Public University System, BM

Wisconsin

Fox Valley Technical College, A
Milwaukee Area Technical College, A
Northeast Wisconsin Technical College, A
University of Wisconsin - Stout, B

U.S. Territories: Puerto Rico

Polytechnic University of Puerto Rico, A
Pontifical Catholic University of Puerto Rico, O
Universidad del Turabo, M
University of Puerto Rico in Bayamón, B

Canada

Quebec

Concordia University, B
HEC Montreal, BM
Université du Québec, École de technologie
   supérieure, B

MACHINE SHOP TECHNOL-OGY/ASSISTANT

United States

Alabama

Southern Union State Community College, A

Arizona

Eastern Arizona College, A

California

Modesto Junior College, A
Pasadena City College, A

Colorado

Community College of Denver, A
Pueblo Community College, A
Red Rocks Community College, A

Florida

Daytona State College, A

Illinois

College of Lake County, A

Indiana

Ivy Tech Community College - Central Indiana, A
Ivy Tech Community College - East Central, A
Ivy Tech Community College - Kokomo, A
Ivy Tech Community College - Richmond, A
Ivy Tech Community College - Wabash Valley, A

Kentucky

Bluegrass Community and Technical College, A
Maysville Community and Technical College
   (Maysville), A
Owensboro Community and Technical College, A
West Kentucky Community and Technical College, A

Michigan

Delta College, A
Northwestern Michigan College, A

Minnesota

Northland Community and Technical College, A
Riverland Community College, A

Missouri

Metropolitan Community College - Kansas City, A

New Mexico

San Juan College, A

New York

State University of New York College of Technology
   at Alfred, A

North Carolina

Asheville-Buncombe Technical Community College,
   A
Cape Fear Community College, A
Catawba Valley Community College, A
Craven Community College, A
Durham Technical Community College, A
Fayetteville Technical Community College, A
Forsyth Technical Community College, A
Gaston College, A
Guilford Technical Community College, A
Haywood Community College, A
Lenoir Community College, A
McDowell Technical Community College, A
Mitchell Community College, A
Nash Community College, A
Pitt Community College, A
Randolph Community College, A
Rockingham Community College, A
Wake Technical Community College, A
Wayne Community College, A
Western Piedmont Community College, A

Oregon

Chemeketa Community College, A

Pennsylvania

Butler County Community College, A
Community College of Allegheny County, A
Johnson College, A
Thaddeus Stevens College of Technology, A
Westmoreland County Community College, A

Texas

North Central Texas College, A

Wisconsin

Northeast Wisconsin Technical College, A

MACHINE TOOL TECHNOL-OGY/MACHINIST

United States

Alabama

George C. Wallace Community College, A
H. Councill Trenholm State Community College, A
Shelton State Community College, A
Wallace State Community College, A

Arizona

Pima Community College, A

Arkansas

College of the Ouachitas, A

California

Allan Hancock College, A
Bakersfield College, A
Cerritos College, A
Cerro Coso Community College, A
Chabot College, A
College of Marin, A
College of the Redwoods, A
De Anza College, A
Laney College, A
Long Beach City College, A

Los Angeles Pierce College, A
Los Angeles Valley College, A
Modesto Junior College, A
Mt. San Antonio College, A
Napa Valley College, A
Orange Coast College, A
Reedley College, A
San Bernardino Valley College, A
San Diego City College, A
San Joaquin Delta College, A
San Jose City College, A
Solano Community College, A
Ventura College, A
Yuba College, A

Colorado

Colorado Mesa University, A

Georgia

Columbus Technical College, A
Georgia Piedmont Technical College, A
Gwinnett Technical College, A
Wiregrass Georgia Technical College, A

Idaho

College of Western Idaho, A
Idaho State University, AB
North Idaho College, A

Illinois

City Colleges of Chicago, Wilbur Wright College, A
College of DuPage, A
Elgin Community College, A
Heartland Community College, A
Illinois Eastern Community Colleges, Wabash Valley
   College, A
Southwestern Illinois College, A

Indiana

Ivy Tech Community College - Bloomington, A
Ivy Tech Community College - Central Indiana, A
Ivy Tech Community College - Columbus, A
Ivy Tech Community College - East Central, A
Ivy Tech Community College - Kokomo, A
Ivy Tech Community College - Lafayette, A
Ivy Tech Community College - North Central, A
Ivy Tech Community College - Northeast, A
Ivy Tech Community College - Northwest, A
Ivy Tech Community College - Richmond, A
Ivy Tech Community College - Southern Indiana, A
Ivy Tech Community College - Southwest, A
Ivy Tech Community College - Wabash Valley, A

Iowa

Des Moines Area Community College, A
Hawkeye Community College, A
Indian Hills Community College, A
Iowa Central Community College, A
Iowa Western Community College, A
Kirkwood Community College, A
Muscatine Community College, A
Scott Community College, A
Southeastern Community College, A

Kansas

Cowley County Community College and Area Voca-
   tional - Technical School, A
Hutchinson Community College, A
Wichita Area Technical College, A

Kentucky

Maysville Community and Technical College
   (Morehead), A

Louisiana

Fletcher Technical Community College, A
South Louisiana Community College, A

Maine

Central Maine Community College, A
Eastern Maine Community College, A
Kennebec Valley Community College, A
Southern Maine Community College, A
York County Community College, A

Maryland

Baltimore City Community College, A

Massachusetts

Northern Essex Community College, A

Michigan

Kalamazoo Valley Community College, A
Kellogg Community College, A
Lake Michigan College, A
Lansing Community College, A
Macomb Community College, A
Mid Michigan Community College, A
Muskegon Community College, A
Southwestern Michigan College, A
Wayne County Community College District, A
West Shore Community College, A

Minnesota

Central Lakes College, A
Hennepin Technical College, A
Pine Technical and Community College, A
Ridgewater College, A

Mississippi

East Central Community College, A
Holmes Community College, A
Meridian Community College, A
Northwest Mississippi Community College, A

Missouri

East Central College, A
Jefferson College, A
Mineral Area College, A
Ozarks Technical Community College, A
Ranken Technical College, A
State Fair Community College, A
State Technical College of Missouri, A

Nebraska

Central Community College - Columbus Campus, A
Central Community College - Hastings Campus, A
Southeast Community College, Milford Campus, A

Nevada

Western Nevada College, A

New Hampshire

Nashua Community College, A

New Mexico

Central New Mexico Community College, A
New Mexico Junior College, A

New York

Corning Community College, A

North Carolina

Alamance Community College, A
Blue Ridge Community College, A
Central Piedmont Community College, A
Isothermal Community College, A
Surry Community College, A

North Dakota

North Dakota State College of Science, A

Ohio

Lorain County Community College, A
Northwest State Community College, A
Sinclair Community College, A

Oregon

Clackamas Community College, A
Linn-Benton Community College, A
Portland Community College, A
Southwestern Oregon Community College, A

Pennsylvania

Butler County Community College, A
Community College of Beaver County, A
Delaware County Community College, A
Johnson College, A

New Castle School of Trades, A
Pennsylvania College of Technology, A
Reading Area Community College, A
Westmoreland County Community College, A
Williamson College of the Trades, A

South Carolina

Florence-Darlington Technical College, A
Greenville Technical College, A
Horry-Georgetown Technical College, A
Midlands Technical College, A
Northeastern Technical College, A
Orangeburg-Calhoun Technical College, A
Piedmont Technical College, A
Spartanburg Community College, A
Tri-County Technical College, A
Trident Technical College, A
York Technical College, A

South Dakota

Lake Area Technical Institute, A
Western Dakota Technical Institute, A

Tennessee

Northeast State Community College, A

Texas

Amarillo College, A
Angelina College, A
Brazosport College, A
Del Mar College, A
El Paso Community College, A
Grayson College, A
Lamar Institute of Technology, A
Lee College, A
North Central Texas College, A
Odessa College, A
South Plains College, A
South Texas College, A
Tarrant County College District, A
Vernon College, A

Virginia

New River Community College, A
Virginia Highlands Community College, A
Wytheville Community College, A

Washington

Bates Technical College, A
Bellingham Technical College, A
Clark College, A
Clover Park Technical College, A
Columbia Basin College, A
Green River College, A
Lake Washington Institute of Technology, A
Lower Columbia College, A
Renton Technical College, A
Shoreline Community College, A
South Seattle College, A
Spokane Community College, A

West Virginia

West Virginia University at Parkersburg, A

Wisconsin

Milwaukee Area Technical College, A
Moraine Park Technical College, A
Nicolet Area Technical College, A

Wyoming

Casper College, A
Sheridan College, A

Canada

British Columbia

British Columbia Institute of Technology, A

MANAGEMENT

United States

Alabama

Auburn University, MD
Columbia Southern University, M
Troy University, M
The University of Alabama, MD
The University of Alabama in Huntsville, MO
Virginia College in Birmingham, M

Alaska

University of Alaska Fairbanks, M

Arizona

Argosy University, Phoenix, MD
Grand Canyon University, M
University of Phoenix - Phoenix Campus, M
University of Phoenix - Southern Arizona Campus, M
Western International University, M

Arkansas

University of Arkansas at Little Rock, O

California

Antioch University Los Angeles, M
Argosy University, Inland Empire, MD
Argosy University, Los Angeles, M
Argosy University, Orange County, MDO
Argosy University, San Diego, MD
Argosy University, San Francisco Bay Area, MD
California Baptist University, M
California Coast University, M
California State University, Chico, M
California State University, Fullerton, M
California State University, Los Angeles, M
California State University, Northridge, M
California State University, San Bernardino, M
Golden Gate University, M
Holy Names University, M
La Sierra University, M
New Charter University, M
Notre Dame de Namur University, M
Saint Mary's College of California, M
San Diego State University, M
University of California, Berkeley, O
University of California, San Diego, D
University of La Verne, MO
University of Phoenix - Sacramento Valley Campus, M
University of Phoenix - San Diego Campus, M
University of Phoenix - Southern California Campus, M
University of Redlands, M
University of San Diego, M

Colorado

Argosy University, Denver, MD
University of Colorado Denver, M
University of Phoenix - Colorado Campus, M
University of Phoenix - Colorado Springs Downtown Campus, M

Connecticut

Albertus Magnus College, M
Fairfield University, MO
University of Bridgeport, M
University of Hartford, M
University of Saint Joseph, M

Delaware

Goldey-Beacom College, M
University of Delaware, D

District of Columbia

The Catholic University of America, M
Howard University, M

Florida

Argosy University, Sarasota, MDO
Argosy University, Tampa, MD

Barry University, O
Everest University (Orlando), M
Florida Institute of Technology, M
Hodges University, M
Keiser University, M
Nova Southeastern University, M
Rollins College, M
St. Thomas University, MO
University of Central Florida, MO
University of Florida, MD
University of Miami, M
University of North Florida, M
University of Phoenix - North Florida Campus, M
University of Phoenix - South Florida Campus, M
University of South Florida, M
University of West Florida, M
Webber International University, M

Georgia

Argosy University, Atlanta, MD
Armstrong State University, MO
Ashworth College, M
Georgia Institute of Technology, D
Georgia State University, MD

Hawaii

Argosy University, Hawai'i, MD
University of Phoenix - Hawaii Campus, M

Illinois

American InterContinental University Online, M
Argosy University, Chicago, MD
Argosy University, Schaumburg, MDO
Benedictine University, M
Eastern Illinois University, M
Ellis University, M
Illinois Institute of Technology, D
National Louis University, M
North Central College, M
Northeastern Illinois University, M
Northwestern University, M
Robert Morris University Illinois, M
Saint Xavier University, M
Trinity International University, D

Indiana

Indiana Tech, M
Indiana University Northwest, MO
Indiana Wesleyan University, M
Purdue University, D
Purdue University Northwest (Hammond), M

Iowa

Kaplan University, Davenport Campus, M
The University of Iowa, D

Kansas

Kansas State University, M
Newman University, M
Southwestern College, M
University of Saint Mary, M

Kentucky

Brescia University, M
Northern Kentucky University, M

Louisiana

Southwest University, M

Maine

University of Maine, M
University of Southern Maine, MO

Maryland

Goucher College, M
Johns Hopkins University, M
Notre Dame of Maryland University, M
University of Maryland, College Park, MD
University of Maryland University College, MDO

Massachusetts

Babson College, O
Boston University, MD
Bridgewater State University, M

Cambridge College, M
Clark University, M
Emmanuel College, MO
Harvard University, MD
Lasell College, MO
Massachusetts Institute of Technology, MD
Merrimack College, M
Mount Ida College, M
University of Massachusetts Amherst, MD
University of Massachusetts Dartmouth, O
Worcester Polytechnic Institute, O
Worcester State University, M

Michigan

Aquinas College, M
Central Michigan University, MO
Cornerstone University, M
Eastern Michigan University, M
Ferris State University, M
Kettering University, M
Lawrence Technological University, D
Spring Arbor University, M
University of Detroit Mercy, MO
Walsh College of Accountancy and Business Administration, M

Minnesota

Argosy University, Twin Cities, MD
The College of St. Scholastica, MO
Hamline University, MD
Saint Mary's University of Minnesota, M
Walden University, MDO

Mississippi

Mississippi State University, D

Missouri

Avila University, M
Fontbonne University, M
Lindenwood University, M
Maryville University of Saint Louis, MO
Rockhurst University, MO
University of Missouri, D
University of Missouri - St. Louis, M
Webster University, M
William Woods University, M

Nebraska

University of Nebraska - Lincoln, M

Nevada

University of Nevada, Las Vegas, O
University of Phoenix - Las Vegas Campus, M

New Hampshire

Granite State College, M
New England College, M
Southern New Hampshire University, M

New Jersey

Fairleigh Dickinson University, College at Florham, M
Fairleigh Dickinson University, Metropolitan Campus, MO
Montclair State University, M
New Jersey Institute of Technology, M
Rutgers University - Newark, D
Saint Peter's University, M
Stevens Institute of Technology, M
Thomas Edison State University, M

New Mexico

New Mexico Highlands University, M
University of Phoenix - New Mexico Campus, M

New York

Binghamton University, State University of New York, D
Columbia University, MD
Daemen College, M
Fashion Institute of Technology, M
Hofstra University, MO
Ithaca College, M
Keuka College, M

Long Island University - LIU Brooklyn, M
Long Island University - LIU Post, MO
Marist College, O
Nazareth College of Rochester, M
New York University, M
St. Joseph's College, Long Island Campus, MO
St. Joseph's College, New York, M
St. Thomas Aquinas College, M
State University of New York Empire State College, M
University at Buffalo, the State University of New York, D
University of Rochester, M

North Carolina

Appalachian State University, M
Duke University, M
East Carolina University, O
Montreat College, M
The University of North Carolina at Charlotte, MDO

North Dakota

Minot State University, M

Ohio

Antioch University Midwest, M
Baldwin Wallace University, M
Case Western Reserve University, D
Lake Erie College, M
Mount Vernon Nazarene University, M
Tiffin University, M
The University of Akron, M
University of Cincinnati, D
The University of Toledo, M

Oklahoma

Oklahoma State University, MD
Oral Roberts University, M
Southern Nazarene University, M

Oregon

George Fox University, MD
Marylhurst University, M
University of Oregon, D
Warner Pacific College, M

Pennsylvania

Carnegie Mellon University, M
DeSales University, M
Drexel University, M
Duquesne University, M
Eastern University, M
Gwynedd Mercy University, M
Marywood University, M
Misericordia University, M
Rosemont College, M
Seton Hill University, M
Temple University, M
University of Pennsylvania, MD
The University of Scranton, M
York College of Pennsylvania, M

Rhode Island

Salve Regina University, MO
University of Rhode Island, MD

South Carolina

Charleston Southern University, M
Southern Wesleyan University, M

South Dakota

Oglala Lakota College, M
University of Sioux Falls, M

Tennessee

Argosy University, Nashville, MD
Lipscomb University, M
Middle Tennessee State University, M
Southern Adventist University, M
University of Memphis, D
The University of Tennessee, MD

Texas

Amberton University, M
American InterContinental University Houston, M
Angelo State University, M
Argosy University, Dallas, MD
Dallas Baptist University, M
Houston Baptist University, M
Our Lady of the Lake University of San Antonio, M
Southern Methodist University, M
Southwestern Adventist University, M
Stephen F. Austin State University, M
Texas A&M University, MD
Texas A&M University - Central Texas, M
University of Dallas, M
University of Houston - Victoria, M
University of Mary Hardin-Baylor, M
University of Phoenix - Dallas Campus, M
The University of Texas at Arlington, MD
The University of Texas at Austin, D
The University of Texas at San Antonio, MD
The University of Texas at Tyler, M

Utah

University of Phoenix - Utah Campus, M

Virginia

Argosy University, Washington DC, MD
Liberty University, MD
Marymount University, MO
Old Dominion University, D
University of Management and Technology, MDO
Virginia International University, O

Washington

Argosy University, Seattle, MD
City University of Seattle, M
Seattle Pacific University, M

West Virginia

American Public University System, M

Wisconsin

Concordia University Wisconsin, M
Edgewood College, M
Silver Lake College of the Holy Family, M
University of Wisconsin - Green Bay, M
University of Wisconsin - Madison, M
University of Wisconsin - River Falls, M
University of Wisconsin - Whitewater, M

U.S. Territories: Puerto Rico

Bayamón Central University, M
Inter American University of Puerto Rico, Aguadilla Campus, M
Inter American University of Puerto Rico, San Germán Campus, M
Universidad del Este, M
Universidad del Turabo, MD

Canada

Alberta

Athabasca University, O
University of Alberta, D
University of Calgary, MD
University of Lethbridge, M

British Columbia

Royal Roads University, MO
The University of British Columbia, D

Maritime Provinces: Nova Scotia

Dalhousie University, M

Ontario

Brock University, M
Carleton University, D
Wilfrid Laurier University, MD

Quebec

HEC Montreal, O
McGill University, MO
Université Laval, MDO

Université du Québec à Rimouski, MO
Université de Sherbrooke, O

MANAGEMENT INFORMATION SYSTEMS AND SERVICES

United States
Alabama

Auburn University, BMD
Auburn University at Montgomery, BM
Community College of the Air Force, A
South University, M
Strayer University - Birmingham Campus, B
Strayer University - Huntsville Campus, B
Troy University, M
Tuskegee University, M
The University of Alabama, B
The University of Alabama at Birmingham, BM
The University of Alabama in Huntsville, BMO
University of North Alabama, BM
University of South Alabama, M
The University of West Alabama, B
Virginia College in Birmingham, B

Alaska

University of Alaska Anchorage, B
University of Alaska Southeast, A

Arizona

Argosy University, Phoenix, MD
Arizona State University at the Tempe campus, MD
GateWay Community College, A
Grand Canyon University, M
Northern Arizona University, B
Northland Pioneer College, A
South Mountain Community College, A
The University of Arizona, BM
University of Phoenix - Online Campus, M
University of Phoenix - Phoenix Campus, B
University of Phoenix - Southern Arizona Campus, BM
Western International University, M

Arkansas

Arkansas State University, AO
Arkansas State University Mid-South, A
Arkansas State University - Newport, A
Central Baptist College, B
College of the Ouachitas, A
Cossatot Community College of the University of Arkansas, A
Henderson State University, B
John Brown University, B
Phillips Community College of the University of Arkansas, A
Pulaski Technical College, A
South Arkansas Community College, A
Southeast Arkansas College, A
Strayer University - Little Rock Campus, B
University of Arkansas, BM
University of Arkansas at Little Rock, BMO
University of Arkansas at Monticello, B
University of Central Arkansas, B

California

Argosy University, Inland Empire, MD
Argosy University, Los Angeles, MD
Argosy University, Orange County, MDO
Argosy University, San Diego, MD
Argosy University, San Francisco Bay Area, MD
Azusa Pacific University, B
Biola University, B
California Intercontinental University, BMD
California Lutheran University, MO
California State Polytechnic University, Pomona, M
California State University, East Bay, BM
California State University, Fresno, B
California State University, Fullerton, M
California State University, Long Beach, B
California State University, Los Angeles, M
California State University, Monterey Bay, M
California State University, San Bernardino, M

California University of Management and Sciences, M
Golden Gate University, MO
Laney College, A
Lincoln University, BM
Loyola Marymount University, B
The Master's College and Seminary, B
Menlo College, A
Merced College, A
Modesto Junior College, A
Napa Valley College, A
National University, BM
Pacific States University, M
Point Loma Nazarene University, B
San Diego State University, M
San Francisco State University, M
San Jose State University, M
Santa Clara University, BM
Shasta College, A
Shepherd University, M
Trident University International, BMO
University of California, Berkeley, O
University of California, Los Angeles, D
University of California, Santa Cruz, MD
University of La Verne, M
University of Phoenix - Bay Area Campus, BMD
University of Phoenix - Central Valley Campus, BM
University of Phoenix - Sacramento Valley Campus, BM
University of Phoenix - San Diego Campus, BM
University of Redlands, BM
University of San Francisco, BM
University of the West, M
Victor Valley College, A

Colorado

Adams State University, B
Aims Community College, A
American Sentinel University, BM
Argosy University, Denver, MD
Aspen University, MO
Colorado Christian University, B
Colorado Mesa University, B
Colorado State University, BM
Colorado State University - Global Campus, M
Colorado Technical University Colorado Springs, B
Colorado Technical University Denver South, B
Community College of Aurora, A
Community College of Denver, A
Lamar Community College, A
National American University (Denver), B
Pikes Peak Community College, A
Red Rocks Community College, A
Regis University, O
University of Colorado Boulder, BD
University of Colorado Denver, MD
University of Denver, BM
University of Phoenix - Colorado Campus, BM
University of Phoenix - Colorado Springs Downtown Campus, BM
Western State Colorado University, B

Connecticut

Asnuntuck Community College, A
Capital Community College, A
Central Connecticut State University, B
Fairfield University, BMO
Manchester Community College, A
Post University, B
Quinnipiac University, M
Sacred Heart University, MO
Three Rivers Community College, A
University of Bridgeport, BM
University of Connecticut, B
Western Connecticut State University, B

Delaware

Delaware Technical & Community College, Jack F. Owens Campus, A
Delaware Technical & Community College, Stanton/Wilmington Campus, A
Delaware Technical & Community College, Terry Campus, A
Goldey-Beacom College, BM
Strayer University - Christiana Campus, B
University of Delaware, BMD

Wilmington University, M

District of Columbia

American University, O
The George Washington University, MD
Howard University, M
Strayer University - Takoma Park Campus, B
Strayer University - Washington Campus, B
University of the District of Columbia, B
University of Phoenix - Washington D.C. Campus, BMD

Florida

Argosy University, Sarasota, MDO
Argosy University, Tampa, MD
Barry University, BO
Broward College, A
Florida Agricultural and Mechanical University, M
Florida Atlantic University, BMD
Florida Institute of Technology, BM
Florida International University, BMD
Florida SouthWestern State College, A
Florida State University, MD
Gulf Coast State College, A
Hillsborough Community College, A
Hodges University, M
Jacksonville University, B
Keiser University, BM
Miami Dade College, A
Northwest Florida State College, A
Nova Southeastern University, MD
Pensacola State College, A
Rasmussen College Fort Myers, A
Rasmussen College Land O' Lakes, A
Rasmussen College New Port Richey, A
Rasmussen College Ocala, A
Rasmussen College Tampa/Brandon, A
Santa Fe College, A
Schiller International University, M
South Florida State College, A
South University (Royal Palm Beach), M
South University (Tampa), M
Southeastern University, B
Stetson University, B
Strayer University - Baymeadows Campus, B
Strayer University - Brickell Campus, B
Strayer University - Coral Springs Campus, B
Strayer University - Doral Campus, B
Strayer University - Fort Lauderdale Campus, B
Strayer University - Maitland Campus, B
Strayer University - Miramar Campus, B
Strayer University - Orlando East Campus, B
Strayer University - Palm Beach Gardens Campus, B
Strayer University - Sand Lake Campus, B
Strayer University - Tampa East Campus, B
Strayer University - Tampa Westshore Campus, B
University of Florida, MDO
University of Miami, M
University of North Florida, M
University of Phoenix - Central Florida Campus, B
University of Phoenix - North Florida Campus, BM
University of Phoenix - South Florida Campus, BM
University of South Florida, BMDO
University of South Florida, St. Petersburg, B
The University of Tampa, M
University of West Florida, B

Georgia

Albany State University, B
American InterContinental University Atlanta, M
Argosy University, Atlanta, MD
Augusta University, B
Columbus State University, B
Dalton State College, B
Emory University, D
Georgia College & State University, M
Georgia Institute of Technology, M
Georgia Military College, A
Georgia Southern University, BMO
Georgia State University, MDO
Gwinnett Technical College, A
Interactive College of Technology (Chamblee), A
Mercer University, B
Strayer University - Augusta Campus, B
Strayer University - Chamblee Campus, B

Strayer University - Cobb County Campus, B
Strayer University - Columbus Campus, B
Strayer University - Douglasville Campus, B
Strayer University - Lithonia Campus, B
Strayer University - Morrow Campus, B
Strayer University - Roswell Campus, B
Strayer University - Savannah Campus, B
University of Georgia, BD
University of Phoenix - Atlanta Campus, BM
University of Phoenix - Augusta Campus, BM
University of Phoenix - Columbus Georgia Campus, ABM
University of West Georgia, B

Hawaii

Argosy University, Hawai'i, MDO
Hawai'i Pacific University, BM
University of Hawaii at Manoa, BMDO
University of Phoenix - Hawaii Campus, BM

Idaho

Idaho State University, MO
University of Idaho, B

Illinois

Argosy University, Chicago, MD
Argosy University, Schaumburg, MO
Aurora University, B
Benedictine University, M
Bradley University, B
Carl Sandburg College, A
DePaul University, BM
DeVry University (Downers Grove), M
Ellis University, BM
Elmhurst College, BM
Eureka College, B
Governors State University, BM
Greenville College, B
Illinois College, B
Illinois Institute of Technology, M
Illinois State University, BM
John Wood Community College, A
Lewis University, BM
Loyola University Chicago, BM
Millikin University, B
Moraine Valley Community College, A
National Louis University, B
North Central College, M
Northern Illinois University, BM
Northwestern College - Bridgeview Campus, A
Northwestern University, M
Olivet Nazarene University, B
Rasmussen College Aurora, A
Rasmussen College Mokena/Tinley Park, A
Rasmussen College Rockford, A
Rasmussen College Romeoville/Joliet, A
Robert Morris University Illinois, M
Rockford University, B
Roosevelt University, M
St. Augustine College, A
Southern Illinois University Edwardsville, BM
University of Illinois at Chicago, MD
University of Illinois at Springfield, M
University of Illinois at Urbana - Champaign, B

Indiana

Ball State University, B
Butler University, B
Grace College, B
Harrison College, A
Indiana State University, B
Indiana University Bloomington, M
Indiana University South Bend, M
Purdue University, M
Purdue University Northwest (Hammond), B
Purdue University Northwest (Westville), A
Saint Mary's College, B
University of Notre Dame, B
Valparaiso University, M

Iowa

Briar Cliff University, B
Buena Vista University, B
Dordt College, B
Graceland University, B

Grand View University, B
Iowa State University of Science and Technology, BMD
Kaplan University, Davenport Campus, M
Loras College, B
Luther College, B
Mount Mercy University, B
Simpson College, B
The University of Iowa, B
University of Northern Iowa, B
Upper Iowa University, B

Kansas

Fort Hays State University, B
Friends University, M
Grantham University, M
Manhattan Area Technical College, A
Newman University, BM
Rasmussen College Kansas City/Overland Park, A
Southwestern College, B
The University of Kansas, BM
Wichita State University, B

Kentucky

Eastern Kentucky University, B
Kentucky State University, M
Lindsey Wilson College, A
Morehead State University, ABM
Northern Kentucky University, B
Southeast Kentucky Community and Technical College, A
University of the Cumberlands, B
University of Louisville, B
Western Kentucky University, B

Louisiana

Louisiana State University and Agricultural & Mechanical College, MD
Louisiana Tech University, B
Nicholls State University, B
Northwest Louisiana Technical College, A
South Central Louisiana Technical College, A
Southern University at New Orleans, BM
University of Louisiana at Monroe, B

Maine

Husson University, B
Kaplan University, South Portland, A
Kennebec Valley Community College, A
Thomas College, B
University of Maine, M

Maryland

Allegany College of Maryland, A
Anne Arundel Community College, A
Bowie State University, MO
Capitol Technology University, M
Carroll Community College, A
Cecil College, A
Community College of Baltimore County, A
Garrett College, A
Hagerstown Community College, A
Hood College, M
Johns Hopkins University, MO
Loyola University Maryland, M
Morgan State University, B
Stevenson University, B
Strayer University - Anne Arundel Campus, B
Strayer University - Owings Mills Campus, B
Strayer University - Prince George's Campus, B
Strayer University - Rockville Campus, B
Strayer University - White Marsh Campus, B
Towson University, O
University of Baltimore, BMO
University of Maryland University College, MO

Massachusetts

Anna Maria College, B
Babson College, B
Bay Path University, M
Boston College, B
Boston University, M
Brandeis University, M
Bridgewater State University, B
Clark University, M

Endicott College, M
Massachusetts College of Liberal Arts, B
New England College of Business and Finance, A
Northeastern University, BM
Salem State University, B
University of Massachusetts Boston, M
University of Massachusetts Dartmouth, B
Western New England University, B
Worcester Polytechnic Institute, BM

Michigan

Baker College, B
Calvin College, B
Central Michigan University, BMO
Cleary University, B
Cornerstone University, B
Eastern Michigan University, BMO
Ferris State University, M
Grand Valley State University, M
Kirtland Community College, A
Lake Superior State University, A
Lansing Community College, A
Lawrence Technological University, M
Madonna University, B
Michigan State University, MD
Michigan Technological University, B
Northern Michigan University, B
Northwestern Michigan College, A
Northwood University, Michigan Campus, B
Oakland University, BMO
Spring Arbor University, B
University of Detroit Mercy, BM
University of Michigan - Dearborn, BM
University of Michigan - Flint, M
University of Phoenix - Detroit Campus, B
Walsh College of Accountancy and Business Administration, M
Wayne State University, BO

Minnesota

Academy College, A
Argosy University, Twin Cities, MD
Augsburg College, B
Capella University, MD
The College of St. Scholastica, MO
Globe University - Woodbury, M
Hennepin Technical College, A
Herzing University, B
Lake Superior College, A
Metropolitan State University, BO
Minnesota State University Mankato, MO
National American University (Roseville), AB
Normandale Community College, A
North Hennepin Community College, A
Rasmussen College Blaine, A
Rasmussen College Bloomington, A
Rasmussen College Brooklyn Park, A
Rasmussen College Eagan, A
Rasmussen College Lake Elmo/Woodbury, A
Rasmussen College Mankato, A
Rasmussen College Moorhead, A
Rasmussen College St. Cloud, A
St. Catherine University, B
Saint Paul College - A Community & Technical College, A
University of Minnesota, Twin Cities Campus, MD
University of Northwestern - St. Paul, B
University of St. Thomas, MO
Walden University, MDO
Winona State University, B

Mississippi

Coahoma Community College, A
Delta State University, B
East Mississippi Community College, A
Mississippi Delta Community College, A
Mississippi State University, BMD
Northeast Mississippi Community College, A
Strayer University - Jackson Campus, B
University of Mississippi, B
University of Southern Mississippi, B

Missouri

American Business & Technology University, M
Avila University, BM
Columbia College, B

Drury University, B
Harris-Stowe State University, B
Lindenwood University, MO
Maryville University of Saint Louis, B
Missouri State University, BM
Missouri State University - West Plains, A
Missouri Western State University, M
Northwest Missouri State University, BM
Ozarks Technical Community College, A
Park University, BMO
Saint Louis University, B
State Technical College of Missouri, A
University of Central Missouri, BM
University of Missouri, B
University of Missouri - St. Louis, BM
Webster University, M
Westminster College, B
William Woods University, B

Montana

Montana Tech of The University of Montana, B

Nebraska

Bellevue University, BM
Concordia University, Nebraska, B
Midland University, B
Peru State College, B
University of Nebraska at Kearney, M
University of Nebraska at Omaha, MDO

Nevada

Career College of Northern Nevada, A
Truckee Meadows Community College, A
University of Nevada, Las Vegas, BMO
University of Nevada, Reno, M
University of Phoenix - Las Vegas Campus, BM
Western Nevada College, A

New Hampshire

Daniel Webster College, B
Franklin Pierce University, M
Granite State College, B
Manchester Community College, A
River Valley Community College, A
Rivier University, M
Southern New Hampshire University, MO
University of New Hampshire, M

New Jersey

Atlantic Cape Community College, A
Camden County College, A
County College of Morris, A
Fairleigh Dickinson University, Metropolitan Campus, MO
Felician University, B
Kean University, M
Mercer County Community College, A
Monmouth University, M
New Jersey Institute of Technology, MD
Raritan Valley Community College, A
Rowan College at Burlington County, A
Rowan University, B
Rutgers University - Newark, BD
Saint Peter's University, M
Stevens Institute of Technology, MDO
Strayer University - Cherry Hill Campus, B
Strayer University - Lawrenceville Campus, B
Strayer University - Piscataway Campus, B
Strayer University - Willingboro Campus, B
Thomas Edison State University, B
Union County College, A
University of Phoenix - Jersey City Campus, BM

New Mexico

Clovis Community College, A
Eastern New Mexico University, B
New Mexico Highlands University, B
University of New Mexico, M
University of Phoenix - New Mexico Campus, BM

New York

Adelphi University, M
Baruch College of the City University of New York, MD

Binghamton University, State University of New York, B
Canisius College, B
Clarkson University, B
Daemen College, M
Dominican College, B
Excelsior College, B
Fordham University, BM
Globe Institute of Technology, A
Hofstra University, BMO
Iona College, B
Le Moyne College, B
Long Island University - LIU Brooklyn, M
Long Island University - LIU Post, M
Marist College, MO
Morrisville State College, B
Nassau Community College, A
New York University, MDO
Orange County Community College, A
Pace University, M
Rensselaer Polytechnic Institute, M
Rochester Institute of Technology, BO
St. Bonaventure University, B
St. John's University, BM
State University of New York College at Old Westbury, B
State University of New York at Plattsburgh, B
Stony Brook University, State University of New York, MO
Syracuse University, MDO
Touro College, M
Ulster County Community College, A
University at Albany, State University of New York, M
University at Buffalo, the State University of New York, MO
University of Rochester, M
Yeshiva University, B
York College of the City University of New York, B

North Carolina

Appalachian State University, B
Catawba College, B
East Carolina University, BO
ECPI University (Raleigh), A
Fayetteville State University, B
Gardner-Webb University, B
Haywood Community College, A
Lenoir-Rhyne University, M
Martin Community College, A
Mayland Community College, A
North Carolina Agricultural and Technical State University, B
Pfeiffer University, B
Strayer University - Greensboro Campus, B
Strayer University - Huntersville Campus, B
Strayer University - North Charlotte Campus, B
Strayer University - North Raleigh Campus, B
Strayer University - RTP Campus, B
Strayer University - South Charlotte Campus, B
Strayer University - South Raleigh Campus, B
University of Mount Olive, B
The University of North Carolina at Chapel Hill, D
The University of North Carolina at Charlotte, BO
The University of North Carolina at Greensboro, MDO
The University of North Carolina Wilmington, M
University of Phoenix - Charlotte Campus, M
Wake Forest University, B
Wake Technical Community College, A
Western Carolina University, B
Winston-Salem State University, BM

North Dakota

Lake Region State College, A
Minot State University, BM
North Dakota State University, B
Rasmussen College Fargo, A
University of Jamestown, B
University of Mary, B
Valley City State University, B

Ohio

Bowling Green State University, B
Bowling Green State University - Firelands College, A

Cleveland State University, BMD
Franklin University, B
Lakeland Community College, A
Miami University, B
Miami University Hamilton, A
Miami University Middletown, A
Mount Vernon Nazarene University, B
Ohio Northern University, B
The Ohio State University, BMD
Ohio University, B
Ohio University - Chillicothe, A
Ohio University - Southern Campus, A
Shawnee State University, AB
Tiffin University, B
Trumbull Business College, A
The University of Akron, BM
University of Cincinnati, MD
University of Dayton, B
Ursuline College, B
Wright State University, ABM
Xavier University, B
Youngstown State University, B

Oklahoma

Carl Albert State College, A
East Central University, B
Mid-America Christian University, B
Northeastern State University, B
Oklahoma Baptist University, B
Oklahoma State University, MD
Oral Roberts University, B
Rogers State University, B
Rose State College, A
St. Gregory's University, B
Seminole State College, A
Southeastern Oklahoma State University, M
University of Central Oklahoma, B
University of Oklahoma, BMO
The University of Tulsa, BM

Oregon

Central Oregon Community College, A
Columbia Gorge Community College, A
Corban University, B
George Fox University, B
Lane Community College, A
Linfield College, B
Oregon Institute of Technology, B
Oregon State University, B
Portland Community College, A
Treasure Valley Community College, A
University of Oregon, M

Pennsylvania

Arcadia University, B
Cambria-Rowe Business College (Johnstown), A
Carnegie Mellon University, MD
Central Penn College, M
Community College of Allegheny County, A
Delaware County Community College, A
DeSales University, BM
Drexel University, B
Duquesne University, BM
Elizabethtown College School of Continuing and Professional Studies, B
Gannon University, B
Harrisburg University of Science and Technology, M
Holy Family University, BM
Immaculata University, B
Indiana University of Pennsylvania, B
La Salle University, B
Lackawanna College, A
Marywood University, M
Misericordia University, BM
Montgomery County Community College, A
Mount Aloysius College, A
Penn State Abington, B
Penn State Altoona, B
Penn State Beaver, B
Penn State Berks, B
Penn State Brandywine, B
Penn State DuBois, B
Penn State Erie, The Behrend College, B
Penn State Fayette, The Eberly Campus, B
Penn State Greater Allegheny, B
Penn State Harrisburg, BM

Penn State Hazleton, B
Penn State Lehigh Valley, B
Penn State Mont Alto, B
Penn State New Kensington, B
Penn State Schuylkill, B
Penn State Shenango, B
Penn State University Park, BMD
Penn State Wilkes-Barre, B
Penn State Worthington Scranton, B
Penn State York, B
Philadelphia University, B
Robert Morris University, BMD
Saint Francis University, B
Saint Joseph's University, BM
Seton Hill University, B
Shippensburg University of Pennsylvania, M
Strayer University - Allentown Campus, B
Strayer University - Center City Campus, B
Strayer University - Delaware County Campus, B
Strayer University - King of Prussia Campus, B
Strayer University - Lower Bucks County Campus, B
Strayer University - Warrendale Campus, B
Temple University, BMD
Thiel College, AB
University of Pennsylvania, BMD
University of Phoenix - Philadelphia Campus, B
University of Pittsburgh, BMD
University of Pittsburgh at Titusville, A
The University of Scranton, M
Villanova University, BM
West Chester University of Pennsylvania, O
Widener University, B
Wilson College, A
York College of Pennsylvania, B

Rhode Island

Bryant University, B
New England Institute of Technology, M
Rhode Island College, B
Roger Williams University, B

South Carolina

Charleston Southern University, BM
Claflin University, B
Coastal Carolina University, O
College of Charleston, M
Francis Marion University, B
Newberry College, B
Strayer University - Charleston Campus, B
Strayer University - Columbia Campus, B
Strayer University - Greenville Campus, B

South Dakota

Augustana University, B
Dakota State University, MD
National American University (Sioux Falls), AB
Northern State University, B

Tennessee

Argosy University, Nashville, MD
Belmont University, B
Bethel University, B
Carson-Newman University, B
Chattanooga State Community College, A
Columbia State Community College, A
Jackson State Community College, A
Lee University, B
Middle Tennessee State University, BM
Southern Adventist University, B
Southwest Tennessee Community College, A
Strayer University - Knoxville Campus, B
Strayer University - Nashville Campus, B
Strayer University - Shelby Campus, B
Strayer University - Thousand Oaks Campus, B
Tennessee Technological University, M
Trevecca Nazarene University, MO
University of Memphis, B
The University of Tennessee at Martin, B

Texas

Amberton University, B
Angelo State University, B
Argosy University, Dallas, MDO
Baylor University, BMD

Dallas Baptist University, BM
Del Mar College, A
Hardin-Simmons University, B
Howard Payne University, B
Lamar University, B
McMurry University, B
Midwestern State University, B
Our Lady of the Lake University of San Antonio, M
Panola College, A
Prairie View A&M University, BM
Sam Houston State University, B
San Jacinto College District, A
Schreiner University, B
South University, M
Southern Methodist University, M
Strayer University - Cedar Hill Campus, B
Strayer University - Irving Campus, B
Strayer University - Katy Campus, B
Strayer University - North Austin Campus, B
Strayer University - Northwest Houston Campus, B
Strayer University - Plano Campus, B
Tarleton State University, BM
Texas A&M International University, BMD
Texas A&M University, BM
Texas A&M University - Central Texas, BM
Texas A&M University - Commerce, B
Texas A&M University - Corpus Christi, B
Texas A&M University - Kingsville, B
Texas A&M University - San Antonio, M
Texas A&M University - Texarkana, B
Texas Southern University, BM
Texas State University, M
Texas Tech University, MD
University of Dallas, M
University of Houston, B
University of Houston - Clear Lake, M
University of Houston - Downtown, B
University of Houston - Victoria, M
University of the Incarnate Word, B
University of Mary Hardin-Baylor, BM
University of North Texas, BMD
University of Phoenix - Dallas Campus, BM
University of Phoenix - Houston Campus, BM
University of Phoenix - San Antonio Campus, BM
The University of Texas at Arlington, BMD
The University of Texas at Austin, BMD
The University of Texas at Dallas, BMD
The University of Texas Rio Grande Valley, BM
The University of Texas at San Antonio, B
Wayland Baptist University, M
West Texas A&M University, B

Utah

Argosy University, Salt Lake City, MD
Broadview University - West Jordan, M
Neumont University, B
University of Phoenix - Utah Campus, BM
University of Utah, MDO
Utah State University, MD
Weber State University, AB
Western Governors University, M
Westminster College, B

Vermont

Johnson State College, AB
Norwich University, M

Virginia

Argosy University, Washington DC, MD
Bridgewater College, B
Ferrum College, B
George Mason University, M
James Madison University, M
Liberty University, BM
Marymount University, MO
Northern Virginia Community College, A
Old Dominion University, BM
South University (Virginia Beach), M
Stratford University (Falls Church), M
Strayer University - Alexandria Campus, B
Strayer University - Arlington Campus, B
Strayer University - Chesapeake Campus, B
Strayer University - Chesterfield Campus, B
Strayer University - Fredericksburg Campus, B
Strayer University - Henrico Campus, B
Strayer University - Loudoun Campus, B

Strayer University - Manassas Campus, B
Strayer University - Newport News Campus, B
Strayer University - Virginia Beach Campus, B
Strayer University - Woodbridge Campus, B
University of Management and Technology, MO
Virginia Commonwealth University, MD
Virginia International University, M
Virginia Polytechnic Institute and State University, MO
Virginia State University, B
Virginia Union University, B

Washington

Argosy University, Seattle, MD
Central Washington University, B
City University of Seattle, M
Eastern Washington University, B
Seattle Pacific University, BM
University of Phoenix - Western Washington Campus, B
University of Puget Sound, B
University of Washington, B
Walla Walla University, B
Washington State University, B
Washington State University - Global Campus, B
Washington State University - Vancouver, B
Western Washington University, B
Yakima Valley Community College, A

West Virginia

American Public University System, M
BridgeValley Community and Technical College (Montgomery), A
Davis & Elkins College, AB
Marshall University, B
Strayer University - Teays Valley Campus, B
West Virginia University, B

Wisconsin

Cardinal Stritch University, B
Concordia University Wisconsin, M
Edgewood College, B
Marquette University, M
Milwaukee School of Engineering, B
Rasmussen College Appleton, A
Rasmussen College Green Bay, A
Rasmussen College Wausau, A
University of Wisconsin - Green Bay, B
University of Wisconsin - La Crosse, B
University of Wisconsin - Madison, BD
University of Wisconsin - Milwaukee, B
University of Wisconsin - Oshkosh, B
Viterbo University, B

U.S. Territories: Puerto Rico

Bayamón Central University, AB
Columbia Centro Universitario (Yauco), A
Inter American University of Puerto Rico, Aguadilla Campus, BM
Inter American University of Puerto Rico, Barranquitas Campus, B
Inter American University of Puerto Rico, Fajardo Campus, BM
Inter American University of Puerto Rico, Metropolitan Campus, M
Inter American University of Puerto Rico, Ponce Campus, AB
Inter American University of Puerto Rico, San Germán Campus, M
National University College (Bayamón), B
Polytechnic University of Puerto Rico, M
Pontifical Catholic University of Puerto Rico, BMO
Universidad del Este, BM
Universidad Metropolitana, BM
Universidad del Turabo, B
University of Puerto Rico in Aguadilla, B
University of Puerto Rico, Río Piedras Campus, B
University of the Sacred Heart, M

U.S. Territories: United States Virgin Islands

University of the Virgin Islands, AB

Canada

Alberta

University of Alberta, B
University of Calgary, B
University of Lethbridge, BM

British Columbia

Simon Fraser University, B
Thompson Rivers University, B
The University of British Columbia, BD

Maritime Provinces: Nova Scotia

Dalhousie University, M
Mount Saint Vincent University, B
St. Francis Xavier University, B

Ontario

Carleton University, B
Lakehead University, B
McMaster University, D
University of Ottawa, B
The University of Western Ontario, B
York University, B

Quebec

Bishop's University, B
Concordia University, B
HEC Montreal, BM
McGill University, M
Université Laval, M
Université du Québec à Chicoutimi, B
Université du Québec à Montréal, BM
Université du Québec en Outaouais, B
Université de Sherbrooke, MO

MANAGEMENT SCIENCE

United States

Alabama

Auburn University, B
Tuskegee University, B
The University of Alabama, B

Alaska

University of Alaska Anchorage, A

Arizona

Arizona State University at the Tempe campus, B
University of Phoenix - Online Campus, B
University of Phoenix - Phoenix Campus, B
University of Phoenix - Southern Arizona Campus, B

Arkansas

John Brown University, B
University of Arkansas, B

California

California Coast University, B
California State University, Northridge, B
Glendale Community College, A
National University, B
Point Loma Nazarene University, B
Reedley College, A
Santa Ana College, A
Santiago Canyon College, A
United States University, B
University of California, Merced, B
University of California, San Diego, B
University of Phoenix - Bay Area Campus, B
University of Phoenix - Sacramento Valley Campus, B

Colorado

American Sentinel University, B
University of Phoenix - Colorado Campus, B
University of Phoenix - Colorado Springs Downtown
Campus, B

Connecticut

United States Coast Guard Academy, B

Delaware

Delaware Technical & Community College,
Stanton/Wilmington Campus, A
University of Delaware, B

District of Columbia

The Catholic University of America, B

Florida

Belhaven University, B
Broward College, B
Jacksonville University, B
Keiser University, B
Pensacola State College, A
Saint Leo University, B
South Florida State College, A
Southern Technical College (Tampa), B
University of Florida, B
University of Miami, B
University of Phoenix - Central Florida Campus, B
University of Phoenix - North Florida Campus, B
University of Phoenix - South Florida Campus, B

Georgia

Ashworth College, B
University of Phoenix - Atlanta Campus, B
University of Phoenix - Augusta Campus, B
University of Phoenix - Columbus Georgia Campus,
B

Hawaii

University of Phoenix - Hawaii Campus, B

Idaho

Brigham Young University - Idaho, B

Illinois

Aurora University, B
DePaul University, B
Eastern Illinois University, B
Ellis University, AB
Illinois State University, B
McKendree University, B
National Louis University, B
North Park University, B
Northern Illinois University, B
Quincy University, B
Roosevelt University, B
Sauk Valley Community College, A
Southern Illinois University Carbondale, B
Trinity International University, B
University of Illinois at Chicago, B
University of Illinois at Urbana - Champaign, B
University of St. Francis, B

Indiana

Ball State University, B
Valparaiso University, B

Iowa

Loras College, B
St. Ambrose University, B
The University of Iowa, B

Kentucky

University of Kentucky, B
Western Kentucky University, B

Louisiana

Louisiana State University and Agricultural & Mechanical College, B
Louisiana Tech University, B
McCann School of Business & Technology (Monroe), A
Southwest University, B

Maine

Saint Joseph's College of Maine, B

Maryland

Coppin State University, B
University of Maryland, College Park, B

Massachusetts

American International College, B
Becker College, B
Bridgewater State University, B
Cambridge College, B
Fitchburg State University, B

Michigan

Alma College, B
Grace Bible College, B
Grand Valley State University, B
University of Phoenix - Detroit Campus, B

Minnesota

Hamline University, B
National American University (Bloomington), A
National American University (Brooklyn Center), A

Missouri

Central Methodist University, B
National American University (Kansas City), AB

Montana

Rocky Mountain College, B
University of Great Falls, B

Nevada

Great Basin College, B
Nevada State College, B
University of Phoenix - Las Vegas Campus, B

New Hampshire

Granite State College, B

New Jersey

Bergen Community College, A
Centenary College, B
Rider University, B
Rutgers University - New Brunswick, B
University of Phoenix - Jersey City Campus, B
William Paterson University of New Jersey, B

New Mexico

National American University (Albuquerque), A
University of Phoenix - New Mexico Campus, B
University of the Southwest, B

New York

Manhattan College, B
Siena College, B
State University of New York at Oswego, B
Vaughn College of Aeronautics and Technology, B

North Carolina

Elon University, B
Johnson & Wales University, B
Lenoir-Rhyne University, B
Louisburg College, A
Miller-Motte College (Cary), A
University of Phoenix - Charlotte Campus, B
Wake Forest University, B

North Dakota

Trinity Bible College, B
University of Mary, B

Ohio

Lourdes University, B
Miami University, B
Ohio Northern University, B

Oklahoma

Eastern Oklahoma State College, A
Mid-America Christian University, B
Murray State College, A
Oklahoma Baptist University, B

Oral Roberts University, B
St. Gregory's University, B
Southeastern Oklahoma State University, B

Oregon

Portland State University, B
Tillamook Bay Community College, A

Pennsylvania

Cambria-Rowe Business College (Johnstown), A
Cheyney University of Pennsylvania, B
Duquesne University, B
La Roche College, B
La Salle University, B
Lehigh University, B
Slippery Rock University of Pennsylvania, B
University of Phoenix - Philadelphia Campus, B

Rhode Island

Bryant University, B
Salve Regina University, B

South Carolina

University of South Carolina, B

Tennessee

Belhaven University, B
Belmont University, B
Southern Adventist University, B
University of Memphis, B
The University of Tennessee at Martin, B

Texas

Hardin-Simmons University, B
Southwestern Assemblies of God University, B
Texas A&M University - San Antonio, B
Texas Wesleyan University, B
Trinity University, B
University of Phoenix - Dallas Campus, B
University of Phoenix - Houston Campus, B
University of Phoenix - San Antonio Campus, B
The University of Texas at Dallas, B
The University of Texas at San Antonio, B

Utah

Independence University, B
University of Phoenix - Utah Campus, B

Virginia

Averett University, B
Central Virginia Community College, A
Virginia Polytechnic Institute and State University, B

Washington

Peninsula College, B
University of Phoenix - Western Washington Campus, B
University of Washington, Tacoma, B

Wisconsin

Lakeshore Technical College, A

Wyoming

University of Wyoming, B

Canada

Alberta

Mount Royal University, B
University of Alberta, B

British Columbia

British Columbia Institute of Technology, A
Simon Fraser University, B
University of the Fraser Valley, B

Maritime Provinces: Nova Scotia

Dalhousie University, B

Quebec

HEC Montreal, B
McGill University, B

MANAGEMENT SCIENCES AND QUANTITATIVE METHODS

United States

Arkansas

Arkansas Tech University, B

Georgia

Mercer University, B

Indiana

Indiana State University, B

Iowa

The University of Iowa, B

Minnesota

Southwest Minnesota State University, B

New Jersey

Rutgers University - New Brunswick, B

New York

Canisius College, B
Pace University, B

Ohio

Miami University, B

Pennsylvania

Penn State Lehigh Valley, B
Penn State Schuylkill, B
University of Pennsylvania, B

Virginia

George Mason University, B

U.S. Territories: Puerto Rico

Inter American University of Puerto Rico, Fajardo
   Campus, B

Canada

Quebec

HEC Montreal, B

MANAGEMENT STRATEGY AND POLICY

United States

Arizona

Arizona State University at the Tempe campus, D
The University of Arizona, D
Western International University, M

California

Antioch University Santa Barbara, M
Azusa Pacific University, M
California Miramar University, M
California State University, East Bay, M
Dominican University of California, M
University of California, Los Angeles, D

Colorado

Regis University, M
University of Colorado Denver, M
University of Denver, M

Connecticut

University of New Haven, M

District of Columbia

The George Washington University, MDO

Florida

Florida State University, D
University of South Florida, O
University of West Florida, M

Georgia

Georgia State University, D

Illinois

DePaul University, M
North Central College, M
Northwestern University, MD
Robert Morris University Illinois, M
University of Chicago, M
University of Illinois at Urbana - Champaign, M
University of St. Francis, O

Indiana

Saint Mary-of-the-Woods College, M
Taylor University, M
Valparaiso University, O

Iowa

Mount Mercy University, M
The University of Iowa, M

Kansas

Friends University, M
Grantham University, M

Kentucky

Bellarmine University, M

Louisiana

Tulane University, M

Maryland

Towson University, O

Massachusetts

Bay Path University, M
Bentley University, O
Boston University, M
Brandeis University, M
Harvard University, D
Suffolk University, M
Tufts University, O
University of Massachusetts Amherst, D

Michigan

Davenport University, M
Michigan State University, M
University of Michigan - Dearborn, M

Minnesota

Capella University, MD
University of Minnesota, Twin Cities Campus, D

Missouri

University of Missouri - St. Louis, O

New Hampshire

New England College, M

New Jersey

Stevens Institute of Technology, M

New Mexico

University of New Mexico, M

New York

Hofstra University, M
Manhattanville College, M
New York University, MD
Niagara University, M
Pace University, M
Roberts Wesleyan College, M
St. John's University, M
Syracuse University, D
University of Rochester, M

North Carolina

Duke University, MD
Lenoir-Rhyne University, M
The University of North Carolina at Chapel Hill, D

Ohio

Antioch University Midwest, M
Defiance College, M
Xavier University, M

Oklahoma

Oklahoma Wesleyan University, M

Pennsylvania

Drexel University, D
Gwynedd Mercy University, M
Mercyhurst University, M
Messiah College, M
Neumann University, M
Philadelphia University, M
Saint Joseph's University, M
Temple University, D
University of Pittsburgh, MD
Villanova University, M

Rhode Island

Salve Regina University, MO
University of Rhode Island, M

South Dakota

Black Hills State University, M

Tennessee

Austin Peay State University, M
Freed-Hardeman University, M
Middle Tennessee State University, M
Tennessee State University, M
Tennessee Technological University, M
Vanderbilt University, M

Texas

Amberton University, M
LeTourneau University, M
Southern Methodist University, M
University of Dallas, M
University of North Texas, M
The University of Texas at Dallas, MD

Utah

University of Utah, MDO
Western Governors University, M

Virginia

James Madison University, D
Regent University, D
Virginia Commonwealth University, M

West Virginia

American Public University System, M
University of Charleston, M

Wisconsin

University of Wisconsin - Madison, M

U.S. Territories: Puerto Rico

Universidad del Este, M

Canada

Alberta

University of Calgary, MD
University of Lethbridge, M

British Columbia

The University of British Columbia, D

Ontario

The University of Western Ontario, M

Quebec

HEC Montreal, M
McGill University, M

MANAGEMENT OF TECHNOL-OGY

United States

Alabama

The University of Alabama in Huntsville, O

Arizona

Arizona State University at the Tempe campus, M
University of Advancing Technology, M
University of Phoenix - Online Campus, M
University of Phoenix - Phoenix Campus, M
University of Phoenix - Southern Arizona Campus, M

Arkansas

Harding University, M

California

California Lutheran University, MO
California State University, Los Angeles, M
Coleman University, M
Golden Gate University, O
National University, M
Notre Dame de Namur University, M
Pacific States University, M
University of California, Santa Barbara, M
University of California, Santa Cruz, MD
University of Phoenix - Bay Area Campus, M
University of Phoenix - Central Valley Campus, M
University of Phoenix - Sacramento Valley Campus, M
University of Phoenix - San Diego Campus, M
University of Phoenix - Southern California Campus, M

Colorado

Colorado School of Mines, M
Colorado Technical University Colorado Springs, M
Colorado Technical University Denver South, M
University of Colorado Denver, M
University of Denver, M
University of Phoenix - Colorado Campus, M
University of Phoenix - Colorado Springs Downtown Campus, M

Connecticut

Central Connecticut State University, MO
Fairfield University, M
University of Bridgeport, M

Delaware

University of Delaware, M

District of Columbia

The George Washington University, MD
Georgetown University, M

Florida

Florida Institute of Technology, M
Polytechnic University of Puerto Rico, Orlando Campus, M
Rollins College, M
University of Miami, M
University of South Florida, O

Georgia

Mercer University, M
University of Phoenix - Atlanta Campus, M
University of Phoenix - Augusta Campus, M
University of Phoenix - Columbus Georgia Campus, M

Hawaii

University of Phoenix - Hawaii Campus, M

Idaho

Idaho State University, M
University of Idaho, M

Illinois

DePaul University, M
Illinois State University, M
Lewis University, M
University of Illinois at Urbana - Champaign, M

Indiana

Indiana State University, MD
Purdue University, MD

Iowa

St. Ambrose University, M

Kansas

Kansas State University, M

Kentucky

Murray State University, M
Northern Kentucky University, M
Western Kentucky University, M

Maryland

Johns Hopkins University, MO
Stevenson University, M
Towson University, MO
University of Maryland University College, MO

Massachusetts

Boston University, M
Cambridge College, M
Harvard University, D
Wentworth Institute of Technology, M

Michigan

Eastern Michigan University, D

Minnesota

Capella University, MD
University of Minnesota, Twin Cities Campus, M
University of St. Thomas, MO

Missouri

Southeast Missouri State University, M
University of Central Missouri, MD

Nevada

University of Phoenix - Las Vegas Campus, M

New Jersey

Fairleigh Dickinson University, College at Florham, O
Rutgers University - Newark, D
Seton Hall University, M
Stevens Institute of Technology, MDO
University of Phoenix - Jersey City Campus, M

New Mexico

University of New Mexico, M
University of Phoenix - New Mexico Campus, M

New York

Columbia University, M
Excelsior College, M
Iona College, MO
Marist College, M
New York University, MDO
Rensselaer Polytechnic Institute, MD
State University of New York Polytechnic Institute, M
Stony Brook University, State University of New York, M
University at Albany, State University of New York, M

North Carolina

East Carolina University, D
North Carolina Agricultural and Technical State University, M
North Carolina State University, D
University of Phoenix - Charlotte Campus, M

North Dakota

University of North Dakota, M

Ohio

The University of Akron, M

Oregon

Portland State University, MD
University of Portland, M

Pennsylvania

Harrisburg University of Science and Technology, M
La Salle University, MO
University of Pennsylvania, M

South Dakota

South Dakota School of Mines and Technology, M

Tennessee

Lipscomb University, MO
Trevecca Nazarene University, M

Texas

Dallas Baptist University, M
Texas State University, M
University of Dallas, M
University of Phoenix - Dallas Campus, M
University of Phoenix - Houston Campus, M
University of Phoenix - San Antonio Campus, M
The University of Texas at Dallas, M
The University of Texas at San Antonio, M

Utah

University of Phoenix - Utah Campus, M
Westminster College, M

Vermont

Champlain College, M

Virginia

George Mason University, M
Liberty University, M
Old Dominion University, M
University of Virginia, M

Washington

City University of Seattle, O
University of Washington, M
Washington State University, MO

West Virginia

Marshall University, M

Wisconsin

Herzing University Online, M
Marquette University, M
University of Wisconsin - Madison, M
University of Wisconsin - Whitewater, M

U.S. Territories: Puerto Rico

Polytechnic University of Puerto Rico, M

Canada

Alberta

Athabasca University, M

British Columbia

Simon Fraser University, M

Ontario

Carleton University, M
University of Toronto, M
University of Waterloo, MD
Wilfrid Laurier University, M

Quebec

École Polytechnique de Montréal, M

MANUFACTURING ENGINEERING

United States

Arizona

Arizona State University at the Polytechnic campus, B
Arizona State University at the Tempe campus, M
Central Arizona College, A

California

California Polytechnic State University, San Luis Obispo, B
California State Polytechnic University, Pomona, B
California State University, Northridge, BM
National University, B
University of California, Berkeley, B
University of California, Irvine, MD
University of California, Los Angeles, M
University of Southern California, M

Connecticut

Fairfield University, O

Florida

Broward College, A
Florida State University, MD

Georgia

Georgia Southern University, BO
Savannah College of Art and Design, B

Illinois

Bradley University, BM
Illinois Institute of Technology, M
Northwestern University, B
Southern Illinois University Edwardsville, B
University of Illinois at Urbana - Champaign, B
Western Illinois University, M

Iowa

The University of Iowa, MD

Kansas

Kansas State University, MD
Wichita State University, BMD

Kentucky

Eastern Kentucky University, M
University of Kentucky, M

Maryland

University of Maryland, College Park, MD

Massachusetts

Boston University, BMD
Bristol Community College, A
Massachusetts Institute of Technology, M
Tufts University, O
Western New England University, M
Worcester Polytechnic Institute, MD

Michigan

Grand Valley State University, M
Kettering University, M
Lake Michigan College, A
Lawrence Technological University, MD
Michigan State University, MD
University of Detroit Mercy, B
University of Michigan, MD
University of Michigan - Dearborn, BM
Wayne State University, M
Western Michigan University, M

Minnesota

Minnesota State University Mankato, M
University of St. Thomas, MO

Missouri

Missouri University of Science and Technology, M
University of Missouri, MD

Nebraska

Southeast Community College, Milford Campus, A
University of Nebraska - Lincoln, M

New Jersey

New Jersey Institute of Technology, BM
Stevens Institute of Technology, M

New Mexico

University of New Mexico, M

New York

Cornell University, D
Hofstra University, B
New York University, M
Rochester Institute of Technology, M

North Carolina

Haywood Community College, A
Mitchell Community College, A
North Carolina State University, M

North Dakota

North Dakota State University, BMD

Ohio

Bowling Green State University, M
Central State University, B
Miami University, B
Wright State University, B

Oregon

Oregon Institute of Technology, M
Oregon State University, B
Portland State University, M

Pennsylvania

Lehigh University, M
Penn State Fayette, The Eberly Campus, A
Penn State Greater Allegheny, A
Penn State Hazleton, A
Penn State Wilkes-Barre, A
Penn State York, A
Robert Morris University, B
Villanova University, O

South Carolina

Clemson University, M

Tennessee

East Tennessee State University, MO
Tennessee State University, M

Texas

Southern Methodist University, M
Texas A&M University, M
Texas State University, BM
The University of Texas at El Paso, M
The University of Texas Rio Grande Valley, BM
The University of Texas at San Antonio, M

Utah

Brigham Young University, B

Virginia

Virginia State University, B

Washington

Washington State University, B
Western Washington University, B

Wisconsin

University of Wisconsin - Madison, M
University of Wisconsin - Milwaukee, BM
University of Wisconsin - Stout, BM

U.S. Territories: Puerto Rico

Polytechnic University of Puerto Rico, M

Canada

Alberta

University of Calgary, MD

Manitoba

University of Manitoba, MD

Maritime Provinces: Nova Scotia

Cape Breton University, B

Ontario

University of Toronto, BM
University of Windsor, MD

MANUFACTURING TECHNOLOGY/TECHNICIAN

United States

Alabama

Calhoun Community College, A
Gadsden State Community College, A
H. Councill Trenholm State Community College, A
Lawson State Community College, A

Arizona

Arizona State University at the Polytechnic campus, B
Arizona Western College, A
GateWay Community College, A

Arkansas

Arkansas State University Mid-South, A
East Arkansas Community College, A

California

California State University, Long Beach, B
Cerritos College, A
Chabot College, A
College of the Canyons, A
College of the Redwoods, A
Long Beach City College, A
Los Angeles Valley College, A
San Jose City College, A
Sierra College, A

Colorado

Colorado Mesa University, A
Morgan Community College, AB
Pueblo Community College, A
Red Rocks Community College, A
Trinidad State Junior College, A

Connecticut

Central Connecticut State University, B
Three Rivers Community College, A

Delaware

Delaware Technical & Community College, Stanton/Wilmington Campus, A

Florida

Gulf Coast State College, A
Miami Dade College, A
Northwest Florida State College, A
South Florida State College, A
Tallahassee Community College, A

Georgia

Albany Technical College, A
South Georgia Technical College, A
Southern Crescent Technical College, A

Idaho

College of Southern Idaho, A
Lewis-Clark State College, AB

Illinois

Black Hawk College, A
Bradley University, B
City Colleges of Chicago, Olive-Harvey College, A
College of DuPage, A
Danville Area Community College, A
Illinois Central College, A
Illinois Eastern Community Colleges, Wabash Valley College, A
John Wood Community College, A
Lewis and Clark Community College, A
Moraine Valley Community College, A
Oakton Community College, A
Prairie State College, A
Rend Lake College, A
Southwestern Illinois College, A
Waubonsee Community College, A

Indiana

Ball State University, B
Harrison College, A
Indiana State University, B
Ivy Tech Community College - Bloomington, A
Ivy Tech Community College - Central Indiana, A
Ivy Tech Community College - Columbus, A
Ivy Tech Community College - East Central, A
Ivy Tech Community College - Kokomo, A
Ivy Tech Community College - Lafayette, A
Ivy Tech Community College - Northeast, A
Ivy Tech Community College - Richmond, A
Ivy Tech Community College - Southeast, A
Ivy Tech Community College - Southern Indiana, A
Ivy Tech Community College - Southwest, A
Ivy Tech Community College - Wabash Valley, A
Purdue University, AB
University of Southern Indiana, B
Vincennes University, A

Iowa

Iowa Western Community College, A
Marshalltown Community College, A
North Iowa Area Community College, A
Northwest Iowa Community College, A
Scott Community College, A
University of Northern Iowa, B

Kansas

Flint Hills Technical College, A
Garden City Community College, A
Hutchinson Community College, A
Pittsburg State University, B

Kentucky

Berea College, B
Gateway Community and Technical College, A
Morehead State University, AB
Murray State University, B
Northern Kentucky University, B
Sullivan College of Technology and Design, AB
Western Kentucky University, B

Louisiana

ITI Technical College, A

Massachusetts

Fitchburg State University, B
Quinsigamond Community College, A

Michigan

Alpena Community College, A
Central Michigan University, B
Delta College, A
Eastern Michigan University, B
Kellogg Community College, A
Lawrence Technological University, A
Macomb Community College, A
Oakland Community College, A
St. Clair County Community College, A
Schoolcraft College, A
Wayne County Community College District, A
Wayne State University, B
Western Michigan University, B

Minnesota

Dakota County Technical College, A
Hennepin Technical College, A
Minnesota State Community and Technical College, A
Minnesota West Community and Technical College, A
Normandale Community College, A
Northland Community and Technical College, A
Northwest Technical College, A
Saint Paul College - A Community & Technical College, A

Mississippi

East Mississippi Community College, A
Holmes Community College, A

Missouri

Crowder College, A
Jefferson College, A
Missouri Southern State University, A
Missouri Western State University, AB
State Fair Community College, A
State Technical College of Missouri, A

Nevada

Truckee Meadows Community College, A
Western Nevada College, A

New Jersey

Bergen Community College, A
Essex County College, A
Raritan Valley Community College, A
Thomas Edison State University, AB
Union County College, A

New York

Corning Community College, A
Excelsior College, A
Farmingdale State College, B
Hudson Valley Community College, A
Rochester Institute of Technology, B

North Carolina

East Carolina University, B
Mitchell Community College, A
North Carolina Agricultural and Technical State University, B
Pitt Community College, A
Wake Technical Community College, A
Western Carolina University, B

North Dakota

North Dakota State College of Science, A

Ohio

Bowling Green State University, B
Bowling Green State University - Firelands College, A
Central Ohio Technical College, A
Edison Community College, A
Harrison College, A
Ohio Northern University, B
Owens Community College, A
Terra State Community College, A
The University of Akron, AB
University of Cincinnati Clermont College, A
Wright State University, A

Oklahoma

Southwestern Oklahoma State University, B

Oregon

Central Oregon Community College, A
Clackamas Community College, A
Lane Community College, A
Rogue Community College, A

Pennsylvania

Butler County Community College, A
Edinboro University of Pennsylvania, A
Lehigh Carbon Community College, A
Pennsylvania College of Technology, AB
Westmoreland County Community College, A

Rhode Island

New England Institute of Technology, AB

South Carolina

Spartanburg Community College, A

South Dakota

Lake Area Technical Institute, A

Tennessee

University of Memphis, B

Texas

Houston Community College, A
Midwestern State University, B
Sam Houston State University, B
Tarleton State University, B
Texas A&M University, B
Texas State Technical College, A
Texas State University, B

Utah

Weber State University, AB

Washington

Central Washington University, B
Clark College, A
Everett Community College, A

West Virginia

Mountwest Community & Technical College, A

Wisconsin

Chippewa Valley Technical College, A
Fox Valley Technical College, A
Milwaukee Area Technical College, A
Northcentral Technical College, A
University of Wisconsin - Platteville, B

Wyoming

Casper College, A

U.S. Territories: Puerto Rico

Huertas Junior College, A

MARINE AFFAIRS

United States

California

University of San Diego, M

Delaware

University of Delaware, MD

Florida

Nova Southeastern University, M
University of Miami, M
University of West Florida, M

Louisiana

Louisiana State University and Agricultural & Mechanical College, MD

Maine

University of Maine, M

Massachusetts

University of Massachusetts Dartmouth, MD

New Jersey

Stevens Institute of Technology, M

New York

Stony Brook University, State University of New York, M

Oregon

Oregon State University, M

Rhode Island

University of Rhode Island, MD

Virginia

Old Dominion University, M

Washington

University of Washington, MO

West Virginia

American Public University System, M

Canada

Maritime Provinces: Nova Scotia

Dalhousie University, M

Newfoundland and Labrador

Memorial University of Newfoundland, MDO

Quebec

Université du Québec à Rimouski, MO

MARINE BIOLOGY AND BIOLOGICAL OCEANOGRAPHY

United States

Alabama

Alabama State University, B
Auburn University, B
Jacksonville State University, B
Samford University, B
Spring Hill College, B
Troy University, B
The University of Alabama, B
University of Mobile, B
University of North Alabama, B
The University of West Alabama, B

Alaska

Alaska Pacific University, B
University of Alaska Fairbanks, MD

Arizona

Prescott College, B

California

California State University, Long Beach, B
Humboldt State University, B
San Francisco State University, BM
San Jose State University, B
Sonoma State University, B
University of California, Los Angeles, B
University of California, San Diego, MD
University of California, Santa Barbara, BMD
University of California, Santa Cruz, B
University of San Diego, B
University of Southern California, MD

Colorado

University of Colorado Boulder, MD

Connecticut

University of Connecticut, B
University of New Haven, B

Delaware

University of Delaware, B

Florida

Barry University, B
Broward College, A
Eckerd College, B
Florida Institute of Technology, BM
Florida International University, B
Florida Southern College, B
Jacksonville University, B
New College of Florida, B
Nova Southeastern University, BMD

Rollins College, B
South Florida State College, A
University of Miami, BMD
The University of Tampa, B
University of West Florida, B

Georgia

Savannah State University, AB

Hawaii

Hawai'i Pacific University, B
University of Hawaii at Hilo, BM
University of Hawaii at Manoa, BMD

Illinois

Western Illinois University, O

Kansas

Southwestern College, B

Louisiana

Nicholls State University, M

Maine

College of the Atlantic, B
Maine Maritime Academy, B
Saint Joseph's College of Maine, B
Southern Maine Community College, A
Unity College, B
University of Maine, MD
University of Maine at Machias, B
University of New England, B

Maryland

University of Maryland Eastern Shore, B

Massachusetts

Boston University, B
Northeastern University, BM
Salem State University, B

Minnesota

Bemidji State University, B

Mississippi

University of Southern Mississippi, BM

Missouri

Northwest Missouri State University, B

New Jersey

Fairleigh Dickinson University, College at Florham, B
Fairleigh Dickinson University, Metropolitan Campus, B
Monmouth University, B
Montclair State University, BM
Princeton University, D
Rutgers University - New Brunswick, BMD
Stockton University, B

New York

Stony Brook University, State University of New York, B

North Carolina

The University of North Carolina Wilmington, BMD

Oregon

Oregon Coast Community College, A
University of Oregon, BMD

Pennsylvania

Cheyney University of Pennsylvania, B
East Stroudsburg University of Pennsylvania, B
Gettysburg College, B
Saint Francis University, B
Waynesburg University, B

Rhode Island

Brown University, B
Roger Williams University, B
University of Rhode Island, B

South Carolina

Coastal Carolina University, B
College of Charleston, BM
University of South Carolina, B

Texas

Texas A&M University, B
Texas State University, MD
The University of Texas Rio Grande Valley, B

Virginia

Hampton University, B

Washington

Shoreline Community College, A
Western Washington University, B
Whitman College, B

Wisconsin

Wisconsin Lutheran College, B

U.S. Territories: Guam

University of Guam, M

U.S. Territories: Puerto Rico

University of Puerto Rico in Humacao, B
University of Puerto Rico in Ponce, B

U.S. Territories: United States Virgin Islands

University of the Virgin Islands, B

Canada

British Columbia

The University of British Columbia, B
University of Victoria, B

Maritime Provinces: Nova Scotia

Dalhousie University, B
University of King's College, B

Newfoundland and Labrador

Memorial University of Newfoundland, BMD

Ontario

University of Guelph, B

Quebec

McGill University, B

MARINE ENGINEERING

United States

Michigan

University of Michigan, MDO

New York

United States Merchant Marine Academy, M

MARINE GEOLOGY

United States

Delaware

University of Delaware, MD

Florida

University of Miami, MD

Hawaii

University of Hawaii at Manoa, MD

Massachusetts

Massachusetts Institute of Technology, MD

New York

Cornell University, MD

Washington

University of Washington, MD

MARINE MAINTENANCE/FITTER AND SHIP REPAIR TECHNOLOGY/TECHNICIAN

United States

California

California Maritime Academy, B
Saddleback College, A
Santa Barbara City College, A

Hawaii

Honolulu Community College, A

Idaho

North Idaho College, A

Iowa

Iowa Lakes Community College, A

Louisiana

Fletcher Technical Community College, A

Maine

The Landing School, A
Washington County Community College, A

Minnesota

Minnesota State Community and Technical College, A
Minnesota State Community and Technical College - Detroit Lakes, A

Missouri

State Fair Community College, A

New Hampshire

Lakes Region Community College, A

New York

Kingsborough Community College of the City University of New York, A

North Carolina

Cape Fear Community College, A
College of The Albemarle, A

Rhode Island

New England Institute of Technology, A

Washington

Northwest School of Wooden Boatbuilding, A
Olympic College, A
Seattle Central College, A
Shoreline Community College, A
Skagit Valley College, A

U.S. Territories: Northern Mariana Islands

Northern Marianas College, A

MARINE SCIENCE/MERCHANT MARINE OFFICER

United States

California

Saddleback College, A

Florida

Indian River State College, A
Jacksonville University, B

Maine

Maine Maritime Academy, B

Massachusetts

Massachusetts Maritime Academy, B

Michigan

Northwestern Michigan College, B

New York

State University of New York Maritime College, B
United States Merchant Marine Academy, B

South Carolina

University of South Carolina, B

Texas

San Jacinto College District, A
Texas A&M University, B

Virginia

Hampton University, B

U.S. Territories: American Samoa

American Samoa Community College, A

Canada

Newfoundland and Labrador

Memorial University of Newfoundland, B

MARINE SCIENCES

United States

Alabama

University of South Alabama, MD

Alaska

University of Alaska Fairbanks, MD

California

California State University, East Bay, M
California State University, Fresno, M
California State University, Monterey Bay, M
San Francisco State University, M
San Jose State University, M
University of California, San Diego, M
University of California, Santa Barbara, MD
University of California, Santa Cruz, MD
University of San Diego, M
University of Southern California, MD

Connecticut

University of Connecticut, MD

Delaware

University of Delaware, MD

Florida

Florida Institute of Technology, M
Florida State University, M
Jacksonville University, M
Nova Southeastern University, MO
University of Florida, MD
University of Miami, MD
University of South Florida, MD

Georgia

Savannah State University, M
University of Georgia, MD

Hawaii

Hawai'i Pacific University, M
University of Hawaii at Manoa, O

Maine

University of Maine, MD
University of New England, M

Maryland

University of Maryland, Baltimore County, MD
University of Maryland, College Park, MD
University of Maryland Eastern Shore, MD

Massachusetts

University of Massachusetts Amherst, MD
University of Massachusetts Boston, MD
University of Massachusetts Dartmouth, MD

Michigan

University of Michigan, M

Mississippi

University of Southern Mississippi, MD

New Hampshire

University of New Hampshire, M

New York

Cornell University, MD
Stony Brook University, State University of New York, MD

North Carolina

Duke University, D
North Carolina State University, MD
The University of North Carolina at Chapel Hill, MD
The University of North Carolina Wilmington, MD

Oregon

Oregon State University, M

Rhode Island

University of Rhode Island, MD

South Carolina

Coastal Carolina University, M
College of Charleston, M
Medical University of South Carolina, D
University of South Carolina, MD

Texas

Texas A&M University - Corpus Christi, D
The University of Texas at Austin, MD

Virginia

The College of William and Mary, MD

Washington

Western Washington University, M

Wisconsin

University of Wisconsin - La Crosse, M
University of Wisconsin - Madison, MD

U.S. Territories: Puerto Rico

University of Puerto Rico, Mayagüez Campus, MD

U.S. Territories: United States Virgin Islands

University of the Virgin Islands, M

Canada

British Columbia

The University of British Columbia, MD

Newfoundland and Labrador

Memorial University of Newfoundland, MO

MARINE TRANSPORTATION

United States

California

Orange Coast College, A

Michigan

Northwestern Michigan College, B

New York

United States Merchant Marine Academy, B

MARKETING

United States

Alabama

Alabama Agricultural and Mechanical University, MD
Columbia Southern University, M
The University of Alabama, MD
The University of Alabama at Birmingham, M
The University of Alabama in Huntsville, M

Arizona

Argosy University, Phoenix, MD
Arizona State University at the Tempe campus, MD
Grand Canyon University, M
The University of Arizona, MD
University of Phoenix - Online Campus, MO
University of Phoenix - Phoenix Campus, M
University of Phoenix - Southern Arizona Campus, M
Western International University, M

California

Argosy University, Inland Empire, MD
Argosy University, Los Angeles, MD
Argosy University, Orange County, MDO
Argosy University, San Diego, MD
Argosy University, San Francisco Bay Area, MD
Azusa Pacific University, M
Bristol University, M
California Coast University, M
California Intercontinental University, M
California Lutheran University, MO
California State University, East Bay, M
California State University, Fullerton, M
California State University, Los Angeles, M
California State University, San Bernardino, M
Golden Gate University, MO
Holy Names University, M
Hope International University, M
La Sierra University, M
National University, M
Notre Dame de Namur University, M
San Diego State University, M
San Francisco State University, M
Trident University International, M
University of California, Berkeley, DO
University of California, Los Angeles, D
University of La Verne, M
University of Phoenix - Bay Area Campus, M
University of Phoenix - Central Valley Campus, M
University of Phoenix - Sacramento Valley Campus, M
University of Phoenix - San Diego Campus, M
University of Phoenix - Southern California Campus, M
University of San Francisco, M

Colorado

Argosy University, Denver, MD
Colorado Christian University, B
Colorado Technical University Colorado Springs, M
Colorado Technical University Denver South, M
Regis University, M
University of Colorado Boulder, D
University of Colorado Denver, M
University of Denver, M
University of Phoenix - Colorado Campus, M

University of Phoenix - Colorado Springs Downtown Campus, M

Connecticut

Fairfield University, MO
Post University, M
Sacred Heart University, MO
University of Bridgeport, M
University of Connecticut, MD
University of New Haven, MO
Yale University, D

Delaware

Delaware State University, B
Goldey-Beacom College, M
Wilmington University, M

District of Columbia

The George Washington University, MD
Howard University, M
University of the District of Columbia, B

Florida

Argosy University, Sarasota, MDO
Argosy University, Tampa, MD
Barry University, O
Florida Agricultural and Mechanical University, M
Florida Atlantic University, D
Florida National University, M
Florida State University, MD
Full Sail University, M
Keiser University, MD
Lynn University, M
Polytechnic University of Puerto Rico, Miami Campus, M
Rollins College, M
Saint Leo University, M
University of Florida, MD
University of Miami, M
University of Phoenix - North Florida Campus, M
University of Phoenix - South Florida Campus, M
University of South Florida, BMD
The University of Tampa, M

Georgia

Argosy University, Atlanta, MD
Ashworth College, M
Emory University, D
Georgia State University, MD
University of Phoenix - Atlanta Campus, M
University of Phoenix - Augusta Campus, M
University of Phoenix - Columbus Georgia Campus, M

Hawaii

Argosy University, Hawai'i, MDO
Hawai'i Pacific University, M
University of Hawaii at Manoa, MD
University of Phoenix - Hawaii Campus, M

Illinois

American InterContinental University Online, M
Argosy University, Chicago, MD
Argosy University, Schaumburg, MDO
Benedictine University, M
DePaul University, M
Ellis University, M
Illinois Institute of Technology, M
Lewis University, M
Loyola University Chicago, M
North Central College, M
Northeastern Illinois University, M
Northwestern University, MD
Roosevelt University, M
Saint Xavier University, M
University of Chicago, M

Indiana

Indiana Tech, M
Valparaiso University, O

Iowa

Kaplan University, Davenport Campus, M
Mount Mercy University, B
The University of Iowa, BMD

Kansas

Kansas State University, M
Ottawa University, M
University of Saint Mary, M

Kentucky

University of the Cumberlands, M

Louisiana

Loyola University New Orleans, M
Tulane University, M

Maryland

Hood College, M
Johns Hopkins University, M
Loyola University Maryland, M
Stevenson University, B
University of Baltimore, M

Massachusetts

Assumption College, M
Babson College, B
Bentley University, M
Boston University, M
Brandeis University, M
Clark University, M
Eastern Nazarene College, B
Emerson College, M
Harvard University, D
Hult International Business School, M
Lasell College, MO
Newbury College, B
Simmons College, M
Suffolk University, M
University of Massachusetts Amherst, MD
University of Massachusetts Dartmouth, O
Western New England University, B
Worcester Polytechnic Institute, M

Michigan

Aquinas College, M
Central Michigan University, M
Eastern Michigan University, MO
Michigan State University, MD
Oakland University, O
Saginaw Valley State University, B
University of Michigan - Flint, M
Western Michigan University, B

Minnesota

Argosy University, Twin Cities, MD
Capella University, MD
St. Catherine University, M
Southwest Minnesota State University, M
University of Minnesota, Duluth, M
University of Minnesota, Twin Cities Campus, MD
Walden University, MD

Mississippi

Mississippi State University, MD
University of Mississippi, B
University of Southern Mississippi, B

Missouri

American Business & Technology University, M
Avila University, M
Lindenwood University, M
Maryville University of Saint Louis, MO
Stephens College, B
University of Central Missouri, M
University of Missouri, D
University of Missouri - St. Louis, MO
Washington University in St. Louis, B
Webster University, M
William Woods University, M

Nebraska

University of Nebraska at Kearney, M
University of Nebraska - Lincoln, MD

Nevada

University of Phoenix - Las Vegas Campus, M

New Hampshire

New England College, M
Southern New Hampshire University, MO

New Jersey

Fairleigh Dickinson University, College at Florham, MO
Fairleigh Dickinson University, Metropolitan Campus, MO
Rowan University, O
Rutgers University - Newark, D
Saint Peter's University, M
Seton Hall University, M
University of Phoenix - Jersey City Campus, M

New Mexico

New Mexico State University, D
University of New Mexico, M
University of Phoenix - New Mexico Campus, M

New York

Adelphi University, M
Baruch College of the City University of New York, MD
City College of the City University of New York, M
Columbia University, MD
Cornell University, D
Daemen College, M
Fashion Institute of Technology, M
Fordham University, M
Hofstra University, MO
Iona College, MO
LIM College, M
Long Island University - LIU Brooklyn, M
Manhattanville College, M
Marist College, M
New York Institute of Technology, M
New York University, MD
Niagara University, BM
Pace University, M
Roberts Wesleyan College, M
St. Bonaventure University, M
St. John's University, M
St. Thomas Aquinas College, M
State University of New York at New Paltz, B
State University of New York Polytechnic Institute, M
Stony Brook University, State University of New York, M
Syracuse University, MD
University of Rochester, M
Wagner College, M
Yeshiva University, B

North Carolina

Duke University, MD
The University of North Carolina at Chapel Hill, D
The University of North Carolina at Greensboro, MD
Wake Forest University, M
Western Carolina University, B

North Dakota

Dakota College at Bottineau, A

Ohio

Bowling Green State University, B
Cleveland State University, MDO
Columbus State Community College, A
Franklin University, BM
Kent State University, D
Lourdes University, B
Miami University Hamilton, B
Ohio Northern University, B
The Ohio State University, MD
Tiffin University, M
The University of Akron, M
University of Cincinnati, MD
University of Dayton, M
The University of Toledo, M
Walsh University, M
Wright State University, M
Xavier University, M
Youngstown State University, M

Oklahoma

Oklahoma Christian University, M
Oklahoma State University, MD
Oklahoma Wesleyan University, B
Oral Roberts University, M

Oregon

George Fox University, D
Marylhurst University, M
Oregon State University, M
Tillamook Bay Community College, A
University of Oregon, D
University of Portland, M

Pennsylvania

Carnegie Mellon University, D
DeSales University, M
Drexel University, MD
Duquesne University, BM
Eastern University, B
Gannon University, M
Geneva College, M
La Salle University, MO
Philadelphia University, M
Saint Joseph's University, MO
Temple University, MD
University of Pennsylvania, MD
University of Pittsburgh, M
The University of Scranton, M
Villanova University, M
Wilkes University, M
York College of Pennsylvania, M

Rhode Island

Providence College, M
University of Rhode Island, MD

South Carolina

Newberry College, B

South Dakota

University of Sioux Falls, M

Tennessee

Argosy University, Nashville, MD
East Tennessee State University, MO
King University, M
Southern Adventist University, M
University of Memphis, MD
The University of Tennessee, MD
Vanderbilt University, M

Texas

Argosy University, Dallas, MDO
Dallas Baptist University, M
Our Lady of the Lake University of San Antonio, B
Southern Methodist University, M
Stephen F. Austin State University, M
Texas A&M University, MD
Texas A&M University - Commerce, M
Texas Christian University, M
Texas Tech University, D
University of Dallas, M
University of Houston, D
University of Houston - Victoria, M
University of the Incarnate Word, M
University of North Texas, M
University of Phoenix - Dallas Campus, M
University of Phoenix - Houston Campus, M
University of Phoenix - San Antonio Campus, M
The University of Texas at Arlington, MD
The University of Texas at Austin, MD
The University of Texas at Dallas, MD
The University of Texas Rio Grande Valley, D
The University of Texas at San Antonio, MD

Utah

Argosy University, Salt Lake City, M
LDS Business College, A
University of Phoenix - Utah Campus, M
University of Utah, D

Virginia

Argosy University, Washington DC, MDO
Liberty University, MD
Mary Baldwin College, B
Old Dominion University, D
University of Virginia, M
Virginia Commonwealth University, M
Virginia International University, M

Washington

Argosy University, Seattle, MD
City University of Seattle, MO

West Virginia

American Public University System, M
BridgeValley Community and Technical College (South Charleston), A
West Virginia University, MO

Wisconsin

Concordia University Wisconsin, M
Edgewood College, M
Herzing University Online, M
Marquette University, M
Milwaukee School of Engineering, M
Northeast Wisconsin Technical College, A
University of Wisconsin - Madison, D
University of Wisconsin - Whitewater, M

U.S. Territories: Puerto Rico

Bayamón Central University, M
Inter American University of Puerto Rico, Aguadilla Campus, M
Inter American University of Puerto Rico, Fajardo Campus, M
Inter American University of Puerto Rico, Guayama Campus, M
Inter American University of Puerto Rico, Metropolitan Campus, M
Inter American University of Puerto Rico, Ponce Campus, M
Inter American University of Puerto Rico, San Germán Campus, M
Pontifical Catholic University of Puerto Rico, M
Universidad Metropolitana, M
Universidad del Turabo, M
University of Puerto Rico, Río Piedras Campus, M
University of the Sacred Heart, MO

Canada

Alberta

University of Alberta, D
University of Lethbridge, M

British Columbia

The University of British Columbia, D
Vancouver Island University, M

Maritime Provinces: New Brunswick

University of New Brunswick Fredericton, M

Ontario

Queen's University at Kingston, M
The University of Western Ontario, M
Wilfrid Laurier University, D

Quebec

Concordia University, M
HEC Montreal, M
McGill University, M
Université Laval, M
Université de Sherbrooke, M

Saskatchewan

University of Saskatchewan, M

MARKETING/MARKETING MANAGEMENT

United States

Alabama

Alabama Agricultural and Mechanical University, B
Alabama State University, B
Auburn University, B
Auburn University at Montgomery, B
Columbia Southern University, B
Jacksonville State University, B
Samford University, B
Spring Hill College, B
Talladega College, B
Tuskegee University, B
The University of Alabama, B
The University of Alabama at Birmingham, B
The University of Alabama in Huntsville, B
University of Montevallo, B
University of North Alabama, B
University of South Alabama, B
The University of West Alabama, B
Wallace State Community College, A

Alaska

University of Alaska Anchorage, B

Arizona

Arizona State University at the Tempe campus, B
GateWay Community College, A
Glendale Community College, A
Grand Canyon University, B
Mesa Community College, A
Northcentral University, B
Northern Arizona University, B
Penn Foster College, A
Phoenix College, A
The University of Arizona, B
University of Phoenix - Phoenix Campus, B
University of Phoenix - Southern Arizona Campus, B
Western International University, B

Arkansas

Arkansas Northeastern College, A
Arkansas State University, B
Central Baptist College, B
College of the Ouachitas, A
Harding University, B
John Brown University, B
University of Arkansas, B
University of Arkansas at Little Rock, B
University of Central Arkansas, B
University of the Ozarks, B

California

Azusa Pacific University, B
Bakersfield College, A
Biola University, B
California Baptist University, B
California Coast University, AB
California Lutheran University, B
California State University, Dominguez Hills, B
California State University, East Bay, B
California State University, Fresno, B
California State University, Fullerton, B
California State University, Long Beach, B
California State University, Northridge, B
California State University, Sacramento, B
California State University, San Marcos, B
California State University, Stanislaus, B
Cerritos College, A
College of the Sequoias, A
De Anza College, A
East Los Angeles College, A
El Camino College, A
FIDM/Fashion Institute of Design & Merchandising, Los Angeles Campus, AB
Folsom Lake College, A
Fresno Pacific University, B
Glendale Community College, A
Golden Gate University, B
Golden West College, A

Holy Names University, B
Imperial Valley College, A
La Sierra University, B
Lake Tahoe Community College, A
Laney College, A
Las Positas College, A
Los Angeles City College, A
Los Angeles Southwest College, A
Loyola Marymount University, B
Menlo College, B
Merced College, A
Mission College, A
Modesto Junior College, A
Monterey Peninsula College, A
Moorpark College, A
Mount Saint Mary's University, B
Mt. San Antonio College, A
Napa Valley College, A
National University, B
Norco College, A
Ohlone College, A
Oxnard College, A
Pasadena City College, A
Point Loma Nazarene University, B
Riverside City College, A
San Bernardino Valley College, A
San Diego City College, A
San Diego Mesa College, A
San Diego State University, B
San Francisco State University, B
San Jose State University, B
Santa Ana College, A
Santa Barbara City College, A
Santa Clara University, B
Santiago Canyon College, A
Solano Community College, A
University of La Verne, B
University of Phoenix - Bay Area Campus, B
University of Phoenix - Central Valley Campus, B
University of Phoenix - Sacramento Valley Campus, B
University of Phoenix - San Diego Campus, B
University of San Diego, B
University of San Francisco, B
Vanguard University of Southern California, B
West Los Angeles College, A
West Valley College, A
Woodbury University, B

Colorado

Adams State University, B
Aims Community College, A
American Sentinel University, B
Colorado Christian University, B
Colorado Mountain College (Steamboat Springs), A
Colorado State University, B
Colorado Technical University Online, B
Fort Lewis College, B
Johnson & Wales University, B
Lamar Community College, A
Metropolitan State University of Denver, B
Northeastern Junior College, A
Regis University, B
University of Colorado Boulder, B
University of Denver, B
University of Phoenix - Colorado Campus, B
University of Phoenix - Colorado Springs Downtown Campus, B
Western State Colorado University, B

Connecticut

Albertus Magnus College, B
Central Connecticut State University, B
Fairfield University, B
Manchester Community College, A
Middlesex Community College, A
Naugatuck Valley Community College, A
Norwalk Community College, A
Post University, AB
Quinnipiac University, B
Sacred Heart University, B
Southern Connecticut State University, B
Three Rivers Community College, A
Tunxis Community College, A
University of Bridgeport, B
University of Connecticut, B

University of New Haven, B
Western Connecticut State University, B

Delaware

Delaware State University, B
Delaware Technical & Community College, Jack F. Owens Campus, A
Delaware Technical & Community College, Stanton/Wilmington Campus, A
Delaware Technical & Community College, Terry Campus, A
Goldey-Beacom College, B
University of Delaware, B
Wesley College, B
Wilmington University, B

District of Columbia

The Catholic University of America, B
The George Washington University, B
Georgetown University, B
Howard University, B
University of Phoenix - Washington D.C. Campus, B

Florida

Barry University, B
Broward College, A
College of Central Florida, A
Everest University (Orlando), AB
Florida Atlantic University, B
Florida Gulf Coast University, B
Florida Institute of Technology, B
Florida International University, B
Florida State College at Jacksonville, A
Indian River State College, A
Jacksonville University, B
Johnson & Wales University, B
Keiser University, B
Lynn University, B
Miami Dade College, A
Northwest Florida State College, A
Nova Southeastern University, B
Palm Beach Atlantic University, B
Palm Beach State College, A
Pasco-Hernando State College, A
Rasmussen College Fort Myers, AB
Rasmussen College Land O' Lakes, AB
Rasmussen College New Port Richey, AB
Rasmussen College Ocala, AB
Rasmussen College Tampa/Brandon, AB
St. Johns River State College, A
Saint Leo University, B
St. Thomas University, B
Seminole State College of Florida, A
South Florida State College, A
Southeastern University, B
Southern Technical College (Tampa), A
Stetson University, B
University of Central Florida, B
University of Florida, B
University of Miami, B
University of North Florida, B
University of Phoenix - Central Florida Campus, B
University of Phoenix - North Florida Campus, B
University of Phoenix - South Florida Campus, B
University of South Florida, B
University of South Florida, St. Petersburg, B
University of South Florida Sarasota-Manatee, B
The University of Tampa, B
University of West Florida, B
Webber International University, AB

Georgia

Abraham Baldwin Agricultural College, A
Albany State University, B
Albany Technical College, A
Ashworth College, AB
Athens Technical College, A
Atlanta Technical College, A
Augusta Technical College, A
Augusta University, B
Bainbridge State College, A
Berry College, B
Brenau University, B
Central Georgia Technical College, A
Chattahoochee Technical College, A
Clayton State University, B

Columbus State University, B
Dalton State College, AB
Fort Valley State University, B
Georgia College & State University, B
Georgia Northwestern Technical College, A
Georgia Piedmont Technical College, A
Georgia Southern University, B
Georgia Southwestern State University, B
Georgia State University, B
Gwinnett Technical College, A
Kennesaw State University, B
Lanier Technical College, A
Mercer University, B
Ogeechee Technical College, A
Point University, B
Savannah State University, B
Savannah Technical College, A
South Georgia Technical College, A
Southeastern Technical College, A
Southern Crescent Technical College, A
University of Georgia, B
University of North Georgia, B
University of Phoenix - Atlanta Campus, B
University of Phoenix - Augusta Campus, B
University of Phoenix - Columbus Georgia Campus,
  B
University of West Georgia, B
Valdosta State University, B
West Georgia Technical College, A
Wiregrass Georgia Technical College, A

Hawaii

Chaminade University of Honolulu, B
Hawaii Community College, A
Hawai'i Pacific University, B
Kapiolani Community College, A
University of Hawaii at Manoa, B
University of Hawaii Maui College, A
University of Phoenix - Hawaii Campus, B

Idaho

Boise State University, B
Broadview University - Boise, A
College of Western Idaho, A
Eastern Idaho Technical College, A
Idaho State University, AB
Northwest Nazarene University, B
University of Idaho, B

Illinois

Aurora University, B
Benedictine University, B
Blackburn College, B
Bradley University, B
City Colleges of Chicago, Richard J. Daley College,
  A
City Colleges of Chicago, Wilbur Wright College, A
College of DuPage, A
Columbia College Chicago, B
Concordia University Chicago, B
DePaul University, B
Dominican University, B
Eastern Illinois University, B
Elgin Community College, A
Ellis University, AB
Elmhurst College, B
Greenville College, B
Harper College, A
Illinois State University, B
Illinois Valley Community College, A
Judson University, B
Lake Land College, A
Lewis University, B
Loyola University Chicago, B
MacCormac College, A
MacMurray College, B
McKendree University, B
Millikin University, B
Morton College, A
North Central College, B
North Park University, B
Northeastern Illinois University, B
Northern Illinois University, B
Oakton Community College, A
Olivet Nazarene University, B
Quincy University, B

Rock Valley College, A
Rockford Career College, A
Rockford University, B
Roosevelt University, B
Sauk Valley Community College, A
Southern Illinois University Carbondale, B
Trinity Christian College, B
Trinity International University, B
University of Illinois at Chicago, B
University of Illinois at Urbana - Champaign, B
University of St. Francis, B
Western Illinois University, B

Indiana

Anderson University, B
Ball State University, B
Butler University, B
Goshen College, B
Grace College, B
Harrison College, A
Huntington University, B
Indiana State University, B
Indiana University - Purdue University Fort Wayne,
  B
Indiana Wesleyan University, B
Manchester University, B
Marian University, B
Saint Mary-of-the-Woods College, B
Taylor University, B
Trine University, B
University of Evansville, B
University of Indianapolis, B
University of Notre Dame, B
University of Saint Francis, B
University of Southern Indiana, B
Valparaiso University, B
Vincennes University, A

Iowa

Buena Vista University, B
Des Moines Area Community College, A
Drake University, B
Grand View University, B
Iowa Lakes Community College, A
Iowa State University of Science and Technology, B
Kirkwood Community College, A
Loras College, B
Mount Mercy University, B
St. Ambrose University, B
Simpson College, B
The University of Iowa, B
University of Northern Iowa, B
Upper Iowa University, B
Wartburg College, B

Kansas

Barton County Community College, A
Benedictine College, B
Bethany College, B
Butler Community College, A
Central Christian College of Kansas, A
Cowley County Community College and Area Voca-
  tional - Technical School, A
Dodge City Community College, A
Emporia State University, B
Fort Hays State University, B
Friends University, B
Johnson County Community College, A
Kansas City Kansas Community College, A
Kansas State University, B
Kansas Wesleyan University, B
MidAmerica Nazarene University, B
Neosho County Community College, A
Pittsburg State University, B
Rasmussen College Kansas City/Overland Park, AB
Rasmussen College Topeka, AB
Southwestern College, B
Tabor College, B
The University of Kansas, B
Washburn University, B
Wichita State University, B

Kentucky

Asbury University, B
Campbellsville University, B
Eastern Kentucky University, B

Georgetown College, B
Morehead State University, B
Murray State University, B
Northern Kentucky University, B
Union College, B
University of Kentucky, B
University of Louisville, B
Western Kentucky University, B

Louisiana

Grambling State University, B
Louisiana College, B
Louisiana State University and Agricultural & Me-
  chanical College, B
Louisiana State University in Shreveport, B
Louisiana Tech University, B
Loyola University New Orleans, B
McNeese State University, B
Nicholls State University, B
Southeastern Louisiana University, B
Southern University and Agricultural and Mechanical
  College, B
Southwest University, B
Tulane University, AB
University of Holy Cross, B
University of Louisiana at Lafayette, B
University of Louisiana at Monroe, B
University of New Orleans, B
Xavier University of Louisiana, B

Maine

Husson University, B
Kennebec Valley Community College, A
Saint Joseph's College of Maine, B
Thomas College, B
University of Maine, B
University of Maine at Machias, B
University of Southern Maine, B

Maryland

Allegany College of Maryland, A
Bowie State University, B
Cecil College, A
Harford Community College, A
Kaplan University, Hagerstown Campus, A
Morgan State University, B
Prince George's Community College, A
Salisbury University, B
University of Baltimore, B
University of Maryland, College Park, B
University of Maryland University College, B

Massachusetts

American International College, B
Anna Maria College, B
Assumption College, B
Babson College, B
Bay Path University, B
Becker College, B
Bentley University, B
Boston College, B
Bridgewater State University, B
Bristol Community College, A
Cape Cod Community College, A
Eastern Nazarene College, B
Elms College, B
Emerson College, B
Endicott College, B
Fisher College, B
Fitchburg State University, B
Framingham State University, B
Lasell College, B
Massachusetts College of Liberal Arts, B
Merrimack College, B
New England College of Business and Finance, A
Nichols College, B
North Shore Community College, A
Northeastern University, B
Northern Essex Community College, A
Salem State University, B
Simmons College, B
Springfield Technical Community College, A
Stonehill College, B
Suffolk University, B
University of Massachusetts Amherst, B
University of Massachusetts Dartmouth, B

Western New England University, B

Michigan

Adrian College, B
Alma College, B
Andrews University, B
Baker College, AB
Bay de Noc Community College, A
Central Michigan University, B
Cleary University, AB
Cornerstone University, B
Davenport University, B
Delta College, A
Eastern Michigan University, B
Ferris State University, AB
Grace Bible College, B
Grand Valley State University, B
Hillsdale College, B
Jackson College, A
Kalamazoo Valley Community College, A
Lake Michigan College, A
Lake Superior State University, B
Macomb Community College, A
Madonna University, AB
Marygrove College, B
Michigan State University, B
Michigan Technological University, B
Mid Michigan Community College, A
Monroe County Community College, A
Mott Community College, A
Muskegon Community College, A
Northern Michigan University, B
Northwestern Michigan College, A
Northwood University, Michigan Campus, B
Oakland University, B
Olivet College, B
Rochester College, B
Saginaw Valley State University, B
St. Clair County Community College, A
Schoolcraft College, A
University of Michigan - Dearborn, B
University of Michigan - Flint, B
University of Phoenix - Detroit Campus, B
Walsh College of Accountancy and Business Administration, B
Wayne State University, B
West Shore Community College, A
Western Michigan University, B

Minnesota

Augsburg College, B
Capella University, B
Central Lakes College, A
Century College, A
The College of St. Scholastica, B
Concordia University, St. Paul, B
Dakota County Technical College, A
Globe University - Minneapolis, A
Globe University - Woodbury, A
Hamline University, B
Metropolitan State University, B
Minnesota School of Business - Blaine, A
Minnesota School of Business - Brooklyn Center, A
Minnesota School of Business - Elk River, A
Minnesota School of Business - Lakeville, A
Minnesota School of Business - Plymouth, A
Minnesota School of Business - Richfield, A
Minnesota School of Business - Rochester, A
Minnesota School of Business - St. Cloud, A
Minnesota State Community and Technical College, A
Minnesota State Community and Technical College - Detroit Lakes, A
Minnesota State University Mankato, B
National American University (Bloomington), A
National American University (Brooklyn Center), A
Normandale Community College, A
North Hennepin Community College, A
Northland Community and Technical College, A
Rasmussen College Blaine, A
Rasmussen College Bloomington, AB
Rasmussen College Brooklyn Park, AB
Rasmussen College Eagan, AB
Rasmussen College Lake Elmo/Woodbury, AB
Rasmussen College Mankato, AB
Rasmussen College Moorhead, AB

Rasmussen College St. Cloud, AB
Ridgewater College, A
St. Catherine University, B
St. Cloud State University, B
Saint Mary's University of Minnesota, B
South Central College, A
Southwest Minnesota State University, AB
University of Minnesota, Crookston, B
University of Minnesota, Duluth, B
University of Minnesota, Twin Cities Campus, B
University of Northwestern - St. Paul, B
University of St. Thomas, B
Winona State University, B

Mississippi

Delta State University, B
East Mississippi Community College, A
Hinds Community College, A
Itawamba Community College, A
Jackson State University, B
Meridian Community College, A
Mississippi College, B
Mississippi Gulf Coast Community College, A
Mississippi State University, B
Northeast Mississippi Community College, A
Pearl River Community College, A
Southwest Mississippi Community College, A
University of Mississippi, B
University of Southern Mississippi, B

Missouri

Avila University, B
Calvary Bible College and Theological Seminary, B
College of the Ozarks, B
Columbia College, B
Culver-Stockton College, B
Drury University, B
Evangel University, B
Fontbonne University, B
Hannibal-LaGrange University, B
Lindenwood University, B
Maryville University of Saint Louis, B
Metropolitan Community College - Kansas City, A
Missouri Baptist University, B
Missouri State University, B
Missouri Valley College, B
Missouri Western State University, B
Moberly Area Community College, A
North Central Missouri College, A
Northwest Missouri State University, B
Park University, B
St. Charles Community College, A
Saint Louis University, B
Southeast Missouri State University, B
Southwest Baptist University, B
Three Rivers Community College, A
University of Central Missouri, B
University of Missouri, B
University of Missouri - St. Louis, B
Washington University in St. Louis, B
Webster University, B

Montana

Montana State University, B
Montana State University Billings, B
University of Great Falls, B
University of Montana, B

Nebraska

Central Community College - Columbus Campus, A
Concordia University, Nebraska, B
Creighton University, B
Hastings College, B
Midland University, B
Northeast Community College, A
Peru State College, B
University of Nebraska - Lincoln, B
University of Nebraska at Omaha, B

Nevada

University of Nevada, Las Vegas, B
University of Nevada, Reno, B
University of Phoenix - Las Vegas Campus, B

New Hampshire

Daniel Webster College, B
Franklin Pierce University, B
Granite State College, B
Great Bay Community College, A
Manchester Community College, A
New England College, B
NHTI, Concord's Community College, A
Plymouth State University, B
Rivier University, B
Southern New Hampshire University, AB

New Jersey

Bergen Community College, A
Berkeley College - Woodland Park Campus, B
Brookdale Community College, A
Caldwell University, B
Camden County College, A
Centenary College, B
Fairleigh Dickinson University, College at Florham, B
Fairleigh Dickinson University, Metropolitan Campus, B
Felician University, B
Kean University, B
Middlesex County College, A
Passaic County Community College, A
Raritan Valley Community College, A
Rider University, B
Rowan College at Gloucester County, A
Rowan University, B
Rutgers University - Camden, B
Rutgers University - New Brunswick, B
Rutgers University - Newark, B
Saint Peter's University, AB
Seton Hall University, B
Thomas Edison State University, B
Union County College, A
University of Phoenix - Jersey City Campus, B
William Paterson University of New Jersey, B

New Mexico

New Mexico Highlands University, B
New Mexico Junior College, A
New Mexico State University, B
University of New Mexico - Gallup, A
University of Phoenix - New Mexico Campus, B
Western New Mexico University, B

New York

Adelphi University, B
Adirondack Community College, A
Alfred University, B
Berkeley College - New York City Campus, AB
Berkeley College - White Plains Campus, AB
Binghamton University, State University of New York, B
Bronx Community College of the City University of New York, A
Canisius College, B
The College at Brockport, State University of New York, B
The College of Saint Rose, B
Dominican College, B
Excelsior College, B
Finger Lakes Community College, A
Fordham University, B
Genesee Community College, A
Hofstra University, B
Hudson Valley Community College, A
Iona College, B
Ithaca College, B
Keuka College, B
Kingsborough Community College of the City University of New York, A
Le Moyne College, B
LIM College, B
Manhattan College, B
Manhattanville College, B
Marymount Manhattan College, B
Mercy College, B
Molloy College, B
Monroe Community College, A
Nassau Community College, A
Nazareth College of Rochester, B

New York City College of Technology of the City University of New York, A
New York Institute of Technology, B
New York University, B
Niagara University, B
Pace University, B
Pace University, Pleasantville Campus, B
Roberts Wesleyan College, B
Rochester Institute of Technology, B
Rockland Community College, A
St. Bonaventure University, B
St. John's University, B
St. Joseph's College, Long Island Campus, B
St. Joseph's College, New York, B
St. Thomas Aquinas College, B
Siena College, B
State University of New York College at Old Westbury, B
State University of New York at Fredonia, B
State University of New York at New Paltz, B
State University of New York at Oswego, B
State University of New York at Plattsburgh, B
Suffolk County Community College, A
Sullivan County Community College, A
Syracuse University, B
Westchester Community College, A
Yeshiva University, B
York College of the City University of New York, B

North Carolina

Appalachian State University, B
Asheville-Buncombe Technical Community College, A
Blue Ridge Community College, A
Campbell University, B
Catawba College, B
Central Carolina Community College, A
Central Piedmont Community College, A
Chowan University, B
Cleveland Community College, A
East Carolina University, B
Elon University, B
Fayetteville State University, B
Fayetteville Technical Community College, A
Gardner-Webb University, B
High Point University, B
Isothermal Community College, A
Johnson & Wales University, B
Lenoir Community College, A
Lenoir-Rhyne University, B
Mars Hill University, B
McDowell Technical Community College, A
North Carolina Agricultural and Technical State University, B
North Carolina Wesleyan College, B
Pfeiffer University, B
Pitt Community College, A
Rowan-Cabarrus Community College, A
Southwestern Community College, A
The University of North Carolina at Charlotte, B
University of Phoenix - Charlotte Campus, AB
Western Carolina University, B
Wingate University, B

North Dakota

Dakota College at Bottineau, A
Dickinson State University, B
Minot State University, B
North Dakota State University, B
Rasmussen College Fargo, A
Sitting Bull College, A
Turtle Mountain Community College, A
University of Jamestown, B
University of Mary, B
University of North Dakota, B

Ohio

Ashland University, B
Baldwin Wallace University, B
Bluffton University, B
Bowling Green State University, B
Capital University, B
Case Western Reserve University, B
Cedarville University, B
Cincinnati State Technical and Community College, A

Clark State Community College, A
Cleveland State University, B
Columbus State Community College, A
Cuyahoga Community College, A
Davis College, A
Edison Community College, A
Fortis College (Ravenna), A
Franklin University, B
Harrison College, A
Hocking College, A
James A. Rhodes State College, A
John Carroll University, B
Kent State University, B
Kent State University at Stark, B
Lake Erie College, B
Lakeland Community College, A
Lorain County Community College, A
Malone University, B
Marietta College, B
Marion Technical College, A
Miami University, AB
Miami University Hamilton, A
Miami University Middletown, A
Mount Vernon Nazarene University, B
Northwest State Community College, A
Notre Dame College, B
Ohio Northern University, B
The Ohio State University, B
Ohio University, B
Otterbein University, B
Sinclair Community College, A
Stark State College, A
Terra State Community College, A
Tiffin University, B
The University of Akron, AB
University of Cincinnati, B
University of Dayton, B
The University of Findlay, B
University of Mount Union, B
University of Northwestern Ohio, AB
University of Rio Grande, B
The University of Toledo, B
Urbana University, AB
Ursuline College, B
Walsh University, AB
Washington State Community College, A
Wilberforce University, B
Wilmington College, B
Wittenberg University, B
Wright State University, AB
Xavier University, B
Youngstown State University, AB
Zane State College, A

Oklahoma

Bacone College, B
East Central University, B
Mid-America Christian University, B
Northeastern Oklahoma Agricultural and Mechanical College, A
Northeastern State University, B
Oklahoma Baptist University, B
Oklahoma Christian University, B
Oklahoma City University, B
Oklahoma State University, B
Oral Roberts University, B
St. Gregory's University, B
Southeastern Oklahoma State University, B
Southern Nazarene University, B
Southwestern Christian University, B
Tulsa Community College, A
University of Central Oklahoma, B
University of Oklahoma, B
The University of Tulsa, B

Oregon

Blue Mountain Community College, A
Central Oregon Community College, A
Clackamas Community College, A
Concordia University, B
George Fox University, B
Linfield College, B
Mt. Hood Community College, A
Northwest Christian University, B
Oregon State University, B
Pacific University, B

Pioneer Pacific College - Eugene/Springfield Branch, A
Portland State University, B
Rogue Community College, A
Southern Oregon University, B
Umpqua Community College, A
University of Portland, B

Pennsylvania

Albright College, B
Alvernia University, B
Arcadia University, B
Bucknell University, B
Cabrini University, B
Carnegie Mellon University, B
Central Penn College, A
Chatham University, B
Chestnut Hill College, B
Cheyney University of Pennsylvania, B
Clarion University of Pennsylvania, B
Community College of Allegheny County, A
Community College of Beaver County, A
Delaware Valley University, B
DeSales University, B
Drexel University, B
Duquesne University, B
Elizabethtown College School of Continuing and Professional Studies, B
Fortis Institute (Erie), A
Gannon University, B
Grove City College, B
Holy Family University, B
Immaculata University, B
Indiana University of Pennsylvania, B
Juniata College, B
King's College, B
La Roche College, B
La Salle University, B
Lansdale School of Business, A
Lehigh University, B
Manor College, A
Mansfield University of Pennsylvania, B
Marywood University, B
McCann School of Business & Technology (Hazleton), A
McCann School of Business & Technology (Lewisburg), A
Mercyhurst University, B
Messiah College, B
Neumann University, B
Northampton Community College, A
Penn State Abington, B
Penn State Altoona, B
Penn State Beaver, B
Penn State Berks, B
Penn State Brandywine, B
Penn State DuBois, B
Penn State Erie, The Behrend College, B
Penn State Fayette, The Eberly Campus, B
Penn State Greater Allegheny, B
Penn State Harrisburg, B
Penn State Hazleton, B
Penn State Lehigh Valley, B
Penn State Mont Alto, B
Penn State New Kensington, B
Penn State Schuylkill, B
Penn State Shenango, B
Penn State University Park, B
Penn State Wilkes-Barre, B
Penn State Worthington Scranton, B
Penn State York, B
Philadelphia University, B
Robert Morris University, B
Rosemont College, B
Saint Francis University, B
Saint Joseph's University, B
Saint Vincent College, B
Seton Hill University, B
Shippensburg University of Pennsylvania, B
Slippery Rock University of Pennsylvania, B
South Hills School of Business & Technology (Altoona), A
Susquehanna University, B
Temple University, B
University of Pennsylvania, B
University of Phoenix - Philadelphia Campus, B

University of Pittsburgh, B
The University of Scranton, B
Villanova University, B
Waynesburg University, B
Westminster College, B
Widener University, B
Wilkes University, B
York College of Pennsylvania, B

Rhode Island

Bryant University, B
Community College of Rhode Island, A
Johnson & Wales University, B
Providence College, B
Rhode Island College, B
Roger Williams University, B
Salve Regina University, B
University of Rhode Island, B

South Carolina

Charleston Southern University, B
Claflin University, B
Clemson University, B
Coastal Carolina University, B
College of Charleston, B
Converse College, B
Francis Marion University, B
Limestone College, B
North Greenville University, B
Northeastern Technical College, A
Piedmont Technical College, A
South Carolina State University, B
Trident Technical College, A
University of South Carolina, B

South Dakota

Black Hills State University, B
Dakota State University, B
Globe University - Sioux Falls, A
Lake Area Technical Institute, A
National American University (Rapid City), B
Northern State University, B
Southeast Technical Institute, A
The University of South Dakota, B

Tennessee

Aquinas College, B
Austin Peay State University, B
Belmont University, B
Carson-Newman University, B
East Tennessee State University, B
Freed-Hardeman University, B
Hiwassee College, A
King University, B
Lincoln Memorial University, B
Lipscomb University, B
Maryville College, B
Middle Tennessee State University, B
Southern Adventist University, B
Tennessee Technological University, B
Tennessee Wesleyan College, B
Trevecca Nazarene University, B
Union University, B
University of Memphis, B
The University of Tennessee, B
The University of Tennessee at Martin, B

Texas

Abilene Christian University, B
Alvin Community College, A
Amberton University, B
Angelo State University, B
Austin Community College District, A
Baylor University, B
Brookhaven College, A
Cedar Valley College, A
Central Texas College, A
Cisco College, A
Clarendon College, A
Dallas Baptist University, B
Hardin-Simmons University, B
Houston Baptist University, B
Houston Community College, A
Howard Payne University, B
Lamar University, B

Laredo Community College, A
LeTourneau University, B
Lone Star College - CyFair, A
Lone Star College - Kingwood, A
Lubbock Christian University, B
McMurry University, B
Midwestern State University, B
Navarro College, A
Northwood University, Texas Campus, B
Prairie View A&M University, B
St. Edward's University, B
St. Mary's University, B
Sam Houston State University, B
Schreiner University, B
South Plains College, A
Southern Methodist University, B
Southwestern Adventist University, B
Southwestern Assemblies of God University, B
Stephen F. Austin State University, B
Tarleton State University, B
Tarrant County College District, A
Texarkana College, A
Texas A&M International University, B
Texas A&M University, B
Texas A&M University - Central Texas, B
Texas A&M University - Commerce, B
Texas A&M University - Corpus Christi, B
Texas A&M University - Kingsville, B
Texas A&M University - San Antonio, B
Texas A&M University - Texarkana, B
Texas Christian University, B
Texas Southern University, B
Texas State University, B
Texas Tech University, B
Texas Wesleyan University, B
Texas Woman's University, B
Trinity University, B
Trinity Valley Community College, A
University of Houston, B
University of Houston - Clear Lake, B
University of Houston - Downtown, B
University of Houston - Victoria, B
University of the Incarnate Word, B
University of Mary Hardin-Baylor, B
University of North Texas, B
University of Phoenix - Dallas Campus, B
University of Phoenix - Houston Campus, B
University of Phoenix - San Antonio Campus, B
University of St. Thomas, B
The University of Texas at Arlington, B
The University of Texas at Austin, B
The University of Texas at Dallas, B
The University of Texas at El Paso, B
The University of Texas of the Permian Basin, B
The University of Texas Rio Grande Valley, B
The University of Texas at San Antonio, B
The University of Texas at Tyler, B
West Texas A&M University, B
Western Texas College, A

Utah

Broadview University - Layton, A
Broadview University - West Jordan, A
Independence University, B
Salt Lake Community College, A
Southern Utah University, B
University of Phoenix - Utah Campus, B
University of Utah, B
Utah State University, B
Utah Valley University, B
Weber State University, B
Westminster College, B

Vermont

Castleton University, B
Champlain College, B
Johnson State College, B

Virginia

Averett University, B
Christopher Newport University, B
The College of William and Mary, B
George Mason University, B
Hampton University, B
James Madison University, B
Lynchburg College, B

New River Community College, A
Old Dominion University, B
Radford University, B
Tidewater Community College, A
Virginia Commonwealth University, B
Virginia Polytechnic Institute and State University, B
Virginia State University, B
Virginia Union University, B

Washington

Bellevue College, A
Bellingham Technical College, A
Central Washington University, B
Centralia College, A
Clover Park Technical College, A
Columbia Basin College, A
Eastern Washington University, B
Edmonds Community College, A
Gonzaga University, B
Green River College, A
Northwest University, B
Pierce College at Puyallup, A
Seattle University, B
Shoreline Community College, A
Spokane Community College, A
Spokane Falls Community College, A
University of Phoenix - Western Washington Campus, B
University of Washington, B
University of Washington, Tacoma, B
Walla Walla University, B
Washington State University, B
Washington State University - Vancouver, B
Western Washington University, B
Whitworth University, B
Yakima Valley Community College, A

West Virginia

Alderson Broaddus University, B
American Public University System, B
Bethany College, B
Davis & Elkins College, B
Marshall University, B
Ohio Valley University, B
University of Charleston, B
West Liberty University, B
West Virginia University, B
West Virginia University at Parkersburg, A
West Virginia Wesleyan College, B

Wisconsin

Blackhawk Technical College, A
Carroll University, B
Carthage College, B
Chippewa Valley Technical College, A
Concordia University Wisconsin, B
Fox Valley Technical College, A
Gateway Technical College, A
Globe University - Eau Claire, A
Globe University - Green Bay, A
Globe University - La Crosse, A
Globe University - Madison West, A
Globe University - Wausau, A
Lakeland College, B
Lakeshore Technical College, A
Madison Area Technical College, A
Maranatha Baptist University, B
Marian University, B
Marquette University, B
Mid-State Technical College, A
Milwaukee Area Technical College, A
Moraine Park Technical College, A
Mount Mary University, B
Nicolet Area Technical College, A
Northcentral Technical College, A
Northeast Wisconsin Technical College, A
Rasmussen College Appleton, A
Rasmussen College Green Bay, A
Rasmussen College Wausau, A
Southwest Wisconsin Technical College, A
University of Wisconsin - Eau Claire, B
University of Wisconsin - La Crosse, B
University of Wisconsin - Madison, B
University of Wisconsin - Milwaukee, B
University of Wisconsin - Oshkosh, B
University of Wisconsin - Parkside, B

University of Wisconsin - Superior, B
University of Wisconsin - Whitewater, B
Viterbo University, B
Waukesha County Technical College, A
Western Technical College, A
Wisconsin Indianhead Technical College, A

Wyoming

Casper College, A
University of Wyoming, B
Western Wyoming Community College, A

U.S. Territories: Guam

Guam Community College, A

U.S. Territories: Northern Mariana Islands

Northern Marianas College, A

U.S. Territories: Puerto Rico

Bayamón Central University, B
Caribbean University, B
ICPR Junior College - Hato Rey Campus, A
Inter American University of Puerto Rico, Aguadilla
  Campus, B
Inter American University of Puerto Rico, Arecibo
  Campus, B
Inter American University of Puerto Rico, Bayamón
  Campus, B
Inter American University of Puerto Rico, Fajardo
  Campus, B
Inter American University of Puerto Rico, Metropolitan Campus, B
Inter American University of Puerto Rico, Ponce
  Campus, B
Inter American University of Puerto Rico, San
  Germán Campus, B
Polytechnic University of Puerto Rico, B
Pontifical Catholic University of Puerto Rico, B
Universidad del Este, B
Universidad Metropolitana, AB
Universidad del Turabo, B
University of Puerto Rico in Aguadilla, B
University of Puerto Rico in Arecibo, B
University of Puerto Rico in Bayamón, B
University of Puerto Rico, Mayagüez Campus, B
University of Puerto Rico in Ponce, B
University of Puerto Rico, Río Piedras Campus, B
University of the Sacred Heart, B

U.S. Territories: United States Virgin Islands

University of the Virgin Islands, B

Canada

Alberta

Athabasca University, B
Mount Royal University, B
University of Alberta, B
University of Calgary, B
University of Lethbridge, B

British Columbia

British Columbia Institute of Technology, A
The University of British Columbia, B
The University of British Columbia - Okanagan
  Campus, B
University of Northern British Columbia, B

Maritime Provinces: New Brunswick

Université de Moncton, B
University of New Brunswick Fredericton, B

Maritime Provinces: Nova Scotia

Cape Breton University, B
Dalhousie University, B
Mount Saint Vincent University, B
Saint Mary's University, B

Newfoundland and Labrador

Memorial University of Newfoundland, B

Ontario

Brock University, B
Carleton University, B
Lakehead University, B
Redeemer University College, B
Ryerson University, B
University of Guelph, B
University of Ottawa, B
University of Windsor, B
York University, B

Quebec

Bishop's University, B
Concordia University, B
HEC Montreal, B
McGill University, B
Université de Sherbrooke, B

Saskatchewan

University of Regina, B
University of Saskatchewan, B

MARKETING RESEARCH

United States

Arizona

Penn Foster College, A

California

National University, B
San Diego Mesa College, A

Colorado

University of Colorado Denver, M

Florida

Saint Leo University, M

Illinois

Southern Illinois University Edwardsville, M
University of Illinois at Urbana - Champaign, B

Maine

Husson University, B

Massachusetts

Newbury College, B

Michigan

Michigan State University, M

New Jersey

Bergen Community College, A

New York

Fashion Institute of Technology, B
Hofstra University, M
Ithaca College, B
Pace University, M

North Carolina

Methodist University, B

Ohio

Ashland University, B
Bowling Green State University, B
Ohio Northern University, B

Pennsylvania

Mercyhurst University, B

Texas

The University of Texas at Arlington, M

Wisconsin

Marquette University, M
University of Wisconsin - Madison, M

Canada

Maritime Provinces: Nova Scotia

Mount Saint Vincent University, B

MARRIAGE AND FAMILY THERAPY/COUNSELING

United States

Alabama

Amridge University, MD
University of Mobile, BM
University of Montevallo, M
The University of West Alabama, M

Arizona

Arizona State University at the Tempe campus, M
Grand Canyon University, M
Northcentral University, MDO
University of Phoenix - Phoenix Campus, M

Arkansas

Harding University, M
John Brown University, BM

California

Argosy University, Inland Empire, M
Argosy University, Los Angeles, M
Argosy University, Orange County, M
Argosy University, San Diego, M
Azusa Pacific University, M
Brandman University, M
California Lutheran University, M
California State University, Chico, M
California State University, Dominguez Hills, M
California State University, East Bay, M
California State University, Fresno, M
California State University, Long Beach, M
California State University, Northridge, M
California State University, Sacramento, M
Chapman University, M
Dominican University of California, M
Fresno Pacific University, M
Hope International University, M
Loyola Marymount University, M
National University, M
Notre Dame de Namur University, M
Pacific Oaks College, M
Pepperdine University, M
Saint Mary's College of California, M
San Francisco State University, M
Sonoma State University, M
Southern California Seminary, M
University of La Verne, M
University of Phoenix - Bay Area Campus, M
University of Phoenix - Central Valley Campus, M
University of Phoenix - Southern California Campus,
  M
University of San Francisco, M
University of Southern California, M

Colorado

Argosy University, Denver, MD
Regis University, MO
University of Colorado Denver, M

Connecticut

Central Connecticut State University, M
Fairfield University, MO
University of Saint Joseph, M

Florida

Argosy University, Sarasota, M
Argosy University, Tampa, MD
Barry University, MO
Carlos Albizu University, Miami Campus, M

Florida Atlantic University, O
Florida State University, D
Nova Southeastern University, MD
Palm Beach Atlantic University, M
St. Thomas University, MO
Stetson University, M
University of Central Florida, MO
University of Florida, MDO
University of Miami, M
University of South Florida, MO

Georgia

Argosy University, Atlanta, MDO

Hawaii

Argosy University, Hawai'i, M
Chaminade University of Honolulu, M

Idaho

Idaho State University, M
Northwest Nazarene University, M

Illinois

Argosy University, Chicago, D
Lincoln Christian University, M
Northeastern Illinois University, M
Northwestern University, M
Wheaton College, M

Indiana

Indiana University - Purdue University Fort Wayne,
   M
Indiana Wesleyan University, M
Purdue University, MD
Purdue University Northwest (Hammond), M

Iowa

Mount Mercy University, M
The University of Iowa, D

Kansas

Friends University, M
Kansas State University, MD
Ottawa University, M

Kentucky

Northern Kentucky University, O
University of Louisville, DO
Western Kentucky University, M

Louisiana

University of Holy Cross, M
University of Louisiana at Monroe, MD

Maryland

University of Maryland, College Park, M

Massachusetts

Cambridge College, M
Eastern Nazarene College, M
University of Massachusetts Boston, M

Michigan

Michigan State University, M

Minnesota

Argosy University, Twin Cities, MD
Capella University, M
Minnesota State University Mankato, O
St. Cloud State University, M
Saint Mary's University of Minnesota, MO
University of Minnesota, Twin Cities Campus, MD
University of St. Thomas, O
Walden University, M

Mississippi

Mississippi College, M
University of Southern Mississippi, M

Missouri

Maryville University of Saint Louis, M
Saint Louis University, MDO
Stephens College, M

Nebraska

Grace University, B
University of Nebraska - Lincoln, MD

Nevada

University of Nevada, Las Vegas, M
University of Phoenix - Las Vegas Campus, M

New Hampshire

University of New Hampshire, M

New Jersey

The College of New Jersey, O
Kean University, MO
Seton Hall University, MO

New Mexico

New Mexico State University, M

New York

The College of New Rochelle, M
Hofstra University, M
Iona College, M
Long Island University - LIU Brooklyn, O
Medaille College, M
Mercy College, MO
Nyack College, M
Syracuse University, M
University of Rochester, M

North Carolina

Appalachian State University, M
East Carolina University, MD
Piedmont International University, B
The University of North Carolina at Greensboro, O

North Dakota

North Dakota State University, M

Ohio

The University of Akron, M

Oklahoma

Mid-America Christian University, M
Oklahoma Baptist University, BM
Oklahoma State University, M
Oral Roberts University, M
Southern Nazarene University, M
University of Central Oklahoma, M

Oregon

George Fox University, MO
Lewis & Clark College, M

Pennsylvania

Chatham University, M
Chestnut Hill College, MDO
DeSales University, B
Drexel University, MD
Duquesne University, M
Eastern University, D
Geneva College, M
Kutztown University of Pennsylvania, M
La Salle University, M
Lancaster Bible College, M
Messiah College, M
Seton Hill University, M
Shippensburg University of Pennsylvania, O
Thomas Jefferson University, M

South Carolina

Converse College, M

Tennessee

Johnson University, M
Lee University, M
Lipscomb University, M

Texas

Abilene Christian University, M
Hardin-Simmons University, M
LeTourneau University, M
Our Lady of the Lake University of San Antonio, M

St. Mary's University, MD
Texas A&M University - Central Texas, M
Texas State University, M
Texas Tech University, MD
Texas Wesleyan University, M
Texas Woman's University, MD
University of Houston - Clear Lake, M
University of Mary Hardin-Baylor, M
The University of Texas at Tyler, M

Utah

Argosy University, Salt Lake City, MD
Brigham Young University, MD
Utah State University, M

Virginia

Argosy University, Washington DC, D
Liberty University, M
Regent University, M

Washington

Pacific Lutheran University, M
Seattle Pacific University, MO

Wisconsin

Edgewood College, M
University of Wisconsin - Milwaukee, O
University of Wisconsin - Stout, M

U.S. Territories: Puerto Rico

Bayamón Central University, O

Canada

Manitoba

The University of Winnipeg, MO

Ontario

Saint Paul University, BM
University of Guelph, M

MASON/MASONRY

United States

Arizona

GateWay Community College, A

California

Palomar College, A

Florida

Tallahassee Community College, A

Illinois

Southwestern Illinois College, A

Indiana

Ivy Tech Community College - Central Indiana, A
Ivy Tech Community College - Columbus, A
Ivy Tech Community College - East Central, A
Ivy Tech Community College - Lafayette, A
Ivy Tech Community College - North Central, A
Ivy Tech Community College - Northeast, A
Ivy Tech Community College - Northwest, A
Ivy Tech Community College - Southern Indiana, A
Ivy Tech Community College - Southwest, A
Ivy Tech Community College - Wabash Valley, A

Minnesota

Dakota County Technical College, A

Mississippi

Mississippi Delta Community College, A

Missouri

Metropolitan Community College - Kansas City, A

New York

State University of New York College of Technology
   at Alfred, A

Pennsylvania

Community College of Beaver County, A
Pennsylvania College of Technology, A
Thaddeus Stevens College of Technology, A

MASS COMMUNICATION/ME-DIA STUDIES

United States

Alabama

Auburn University, BM
James H. Faulkner State Community College, A
Miles College, B
Oakwood University, B
Talladega College, B
The University of Alabama, D
University of North Alabama, B

Alaska

University of Alaska Anchorage, B

Arizona

Arizona State University at the Tempe campus, MD

Arkansas

John Brown University, B
Ouachita Baptist University, B
University of Arkansas at Little Rock, M
University of the Ozarks, B

California

American Jewish University, B
California Lutheran University, B
California State University, Bakersfield, B
California State University, East Bay, B
California State University, Fresno, BM
California State University, Fullerton, M
California State University, Long Beach, B
California State University, Northridge, M
California State University, Sacramento, B
California State University, San Marcos, B
Chabot College, A
College of the Desert, A
College of Marin, A
College of the Sequoias, A
College of the Siskiyous, A
De Anza College, A
Fullerton College, A
Glendale Community College, A
Lassen Community College District, A
Los Angeles City College, A
Los Angeles Valley College, A
The Master's College and Seminary, B
Modesto Junior College, A
Monterey Peninsula College, A
Ohlone College, A
Orange Coast College, A
Point Loma Nazarene University, B
Pomona College, B
Sacramento City College, A
San Jose State University, M
Scripps College, B
Sonoma State University, B
University of California, Berkeley, B
University of California, San Diego, B
University of San Francisco, B
Yuba College, A

Colorado

Adams State University, AB
Colorado Mesa University, B
Colorado State University, MD
Colorado State University - Pueblo, B
University of Colorado Boulder, BMD
University of Denver, BM

Connecticut

Middlesex Community College, A
Quinnipiac University, B
University of Bridgeport, B

Delaware

Wesley College, B

District of Columbia

American University, BM
The George Washington University, BMO
Howard University, BMD
University of the District of Columbia, B

Florida

Barry University, B
Bethune-Cookman University, B
Broward College, A
Chipola College, A
Flagler College, B
Florida Gulf Coast University, B
Florida International University, BM
Florida Southern College, B
Florida State College at Jacksonville, B
Jacksonville University, B
Lynn University, BMO
Miami Dade College, A
Palm Beach Atlantic University, B
Palm Beach State College, A
St. Thomas University, B
State College of Florida Manatee-Sarasota, A
University of Florida, MD
University of Miami, B
University of North Florida, B
University of South Florida, BMO
University of South Florida, St. Petersburg, B
University of West Florida, B

Georgia

Albany State University, B
Andrew College, A
Brenau University, B
Emmanuel College, B
Fort Valley State University, B
Georgia Military College, A
Georgia State University, MD
Mercer University, B
Piedmont College, B
University of Georgia, MD
Valdosta State University, B

Hawaii

Hawai'i Pacific University, B

Idaho

Boise State University, B
Idaho State University, B
North Idaho College, A
Northwest Nazarene University, B

Illinois

Augustana College, B
DePaul University, B
Governors State University, B
Greenville College, B
Illinois College, B
Illinois State University, B
Lewis University, B
North Park University, B
Olivet Nazarene University, B
Parkland College, A
Principia College, B
Southern Illinois University Carbondale, M
Southern Illinois University Edwardsville, BM
Spoon River College, A
University of Illinois at Urbana - Champaign, B
University of St. Francis, B

Indiana

Ancilla College, A
DePauw University, B
Hanover College, B
Huntington University, B
Indiana University Bloomington, BD
Indiana University - Purdue University Fort Wayne, B
Indiana Wesleyan University, B
Manchester University, B
Saint Mary-of-the-Woods College, B
University of Southern Indiana, B

Iowa

Briar Cliff University, B
Buena Vista University, B
Dordt College, B
Drake University, B
Grand View University, B
Iowa Central Community College, A
Iowa Lakes Community College, A
Iowa State University of Science and Technology, BM
Loras College, B
University of Dubuque, B
The University of Iowa, BMD
Upper Iowa University, B
Wartburg College, B
William Penn University, B

Kansas

Baker University, B
Benedictine College, B
Bethel College, B
Butler Community College, A
Dodge City Community College, A
Haskell Indian Nations University, A
Kansas State University, M
MidAmerica Nazarene University, B
Newman University, B
Ottawa University, B
Pratt Community College, A
Washburn University, B

Kentucky

Berea College, B
Campbellsville University, B
Lindsey Wilson College, B
Murray State University, M
Spalding University, B
Union College, B

Louisiana

Dillard University, B
Grambling State University, BM
Louisiana College, B
Louisiana State University and Agricultural & Mechanical College, BMD
Louisiana State University at Alexandria, B
Louisiana State University in Shreveport, B
McNeese State University, B
Nicholls State University, B
Southern University and Agricultural and Mechanical College, BM
Tulane University, B
University of Louisiana at Lafayette, BM
University of Louisiana at Monroe, B
Xavier University of Louisiana, B

Maine

Saint Joseph's College of Maine, B
University of Maine, BM
University of Southern Maine, B

Maryland

Bowie State University, B
Frostburg State University, B
Goucher College, B
Harford Community College, A
Morgan State University, B
Towson University, B
University of Maryland, Baltimore County, B
University of Maryland Eastern Shore, B
Washington Adventist University, B

Massachusetts

American International College, B
Anna Maria College, B
Bentley University, B
Boston University, M
Bunker Hill Community College, A
Cape Cod Community College, A
Clark University, B
Dean College, A
Eastern Nazarene College, B
Emerson College, B
Endicott College, B
Fisher College, B

Massachusetts Institute of Technology, B
Massasoit Community College, A
Suffolk University, B
Tufts University, B
Western New England University, B
Worcester State University, B

Michigan

Albion College, B
Andrews University, B
Calvin College, B
Henry Ford College, A
Kuyper College, B
Michigan State University, B
Monroe County Community College, A
Rochester College, B
University of Michigan, D

Minnesota

Bemidji State University, B
Bethel University, B
Concordia University, St. Paul, B
Gustavus Adolphus College, B
Macalester College, B
Minnesota State University Mankato, B
Minnesota State University Moorhead, B
North Central University, AB
Northland Community and Technical College, A
St. Catherine University, B
St. Cloud State University, BM
University of Minnesota, Twin Cities Campus, MD
Vermilion Community College, A
Winona State University, B

Mississippi

Alcorn State University, B
Jackson State University, BM
Mississippi College, B
Mississippi Valley State University, B
Tougaloo College, B
University of Southern Mississippi, MD

Missouri

Calvary Bible College and Theological Seminary, B
Crowder College, A
Culver-Stockton College, B
Lindenwood University, B
Maryville University of Saint Louis, B
Missouri State University, B
Missouri Valley College, B
Stephens College, B
University of Missouri, B
University of Missouri - Kansas City, B
University of Missouri - St. Louis, B
Webster University, B

Nebraska

Hastings College, B
Midland University, B
Northeast Community College, A
University of Nebraska at Kearney, B
University of Nebraska - Lincoln, M
Wayne State College, B

Nevada

University of Nevada, Las Vegas, B

New Hampshire

Colby-Sawyer College, B
Franklin Pierce University, B
New England College, B
University of New Hampshire at Manchester, B

New Jersey

Centenary College, B
Felician University, B
Mercer County Community College, A
Rutgers University - New Brunswick, B
Union County College, A

New Mexico

University of New Mexico, B

New York

Buffalo State College, State University of New York, B
City College of the City University of New York, B
College of Mount Saint Vincent, B
The College of New Rochelle, B
The College of Saint Rose, M
Eugene Lang College of Liberal Arts, B
Finger Lakes Community College, A
Five Towns College, B
Fordham University, B
Fulton-Montgomery Community College, A
Genesee Community College, A
Hobart and William Smith Colleges, B
Hofstra University, B
Hudson Valley Community College, A
Hunter College of the City University of New York, B
Iona College, BMO
Ithaca College, B
Lehman College of the City University of New York, B
Medaille College, B
Mercy College, B
Monroe Community College, A
Mount Saint Mary College, B
Nassau Community College, A
The New School for Public Engagement, B
Niagara County Community College, A
Niagara University, B
Pace University, B
Queens College of the City University of New York, B
Rockland Community College, A
St. Thomas Aquinas College, B
State University of New York College at Oneonta, B
State University of New York at Fredonia, B
State University of New York at Oswego, B
Syracuse University, MD
University at Albany, State University of New York, B
Vassar College, B
Westchester Community College, A

North Carolina

Barton College, B
Campbell University, B
Gardner-Webb University, B
Johnson C. Smith University, B
Meredith College, B
Methodist University, AB
North Carolina Agricultural and Technical State University, B
North Carolina Central University, B
Salem College, B
Shaw University, B
University of North Carolina at Asheville, B
The University of North Carolina at Chapel Hill, BMD
The University of North Carolina at Greensboro, B
The University of North Carolina at Pembroke, B
Winston-Salem State University, B

North Dakota

North Dakota State University, M
University of Jamestown, B
University of Mary, B
Valley City State University, B

Ohio

Ashland University, B
Baldwin Wallace University, B
The College of Wooster, B
Defiance College, B
Denison University, B
Heidelberg University, B
John Carroll University, B
Kent State University, M
Lorain County Community College, A
Miami University, B
Miami University Hamilton, B
Miami University Middletown, A
Sinclair Community College, A
University of Rio Grande, AB
Urbana University, B
Wilberforce University, B
Wilmington College, B

Wright State University, B
Wright State University - Lake Campus, A

Oklahoma

East Central University, B
Langston University, B
Northeastern Oklahoma Agricultural and Mechanical College, A
Northeastern State University, B
Northwestern Oklahoma State University, B
Oklahoma Baptist University, B
Oklahoma Christian University, B
Oklahoma City Community College, A
Oklahoma City University, B
Oklahoma State University, M
University of Oklahoma, MD

Oregon

Linfield College, B
Marylhurst University, B
Pacific University, B
University of Oregon, B
University of Portland, B

Pennsylvania

Allegheny College, B
Arcadia University, B
Bloomsburg University of Pennsylvania, B
Cedar Crest College, B
Central Penn College, B
Chestnut Hill College, B
Drexel University, M
Edinboro University of Pennsylvania, B
Elizabethtown College, B
Elizabethtown College School of Continuing and Professional Studies, AB
Holy Family University, B
Lackawanna College, A
Lock Haven University of Pennsylvania, B
Mansfield University of Pennsylvania, B
Penn State University Park, D
Point Park University, BM
Robert Morris University, B
Saint Francis University, B
Temple University, B
Thiel College, B
University of Pittsburgh, B
University of Pittsburgh at Greensburg, B
University of Pittsburgh at Johnstown, B
Ursinus College, B
Villanova University, B
Widener University, B
Wilson College, B
York College of Pennsylvania, AB

Rhode Island

Bryant University, B
Rhode Island College, B

South Carolina

Benedict College, B
Claflin University, B
Columbia International University, B
Francis Marion University, B
Morris College, B
North Greenville University, B
South Carolina State University, B
Voorhees College, B
Winthrop University, B

South Dakota

Black Hills State University, AB
Oglala Lakota College, A
University of Sioux Falls, B

Tennessee

Austin Peay State University, B
Belmont University, B
Carson-Newman University, B
East Tennessee State University, B
Freed-Hardeman University, B
Johnson University, B
Lincoln Memorial University, B
Lipscomb University, B
Middle Tennessee State University, BM

Southern Adventist University, A
Tennessee State University, B
Trevecca Nazarene University, B
Union University, B
University of Memphis, B
The University of Tennessee at Chattanooga, B

Texas

Amarillo College, A
Austin College, B
Blinn College, A
Clarendon College, A
Concordia University Texas, B
East Texas Baptist University, B
Huston-Tillotson University, B
Lamar State College - Orange, A
LeTourneau University, B
Lubbock Christian University, B
Midwestern State University, B
Paul Quinn College, B
Sam Houston State University, B
South Plains College, A
Southwestern Assemblies of God University, A
Stephen F. Austin State University, BM
Sul Ross State University, B
Texas A&M University - Texarkana, B
Texas Christian University, M
Texas Southern University, B
Texas State University, BM
Texas Tech University, BMD
Texas Wesleyan University, B
University of Houston, BM
University of the Incarnate Word, AB
University of Mary Hardin-Baylor, B
The University of Texas at El Paso, B
The University of Texas Rio Grande Valley, B
The University of Texas at Tyler, B
Wayland Baptist University, B
West Texas A&M University, B
Western Texas College, A
Wiley College, B

Utah

Brigham Young University, M
Dixie State University, B
Salt Lake Community College, A
Snow College, A

Vermont

Castleton University, B
Champlain College, B
Green Mountain College, B
Saint Michael's College, B
Southern Vermont College, B

Virginia

Bluefield College, B
Bridgewater College, B
Emory & Henry College, B
Hampton University, B
Hollins University, B
Virginia Commonwealth University, BM
Virginia State University, B
Virginia Union University, B
Virginia Wesleyan College, B
Wytheville Community College, A

Washington

City University of Seattle, B
The Evergreen State College, B
Gonzaga University, B
Spokane Falls Community College, A
University of Washington, Bothell, B
University of Washington, Tacoma, B
Walla Walla University, B
Washington State University, B
Whitworth University, B

West Virginia

Alderson Broaddus University, B
Concord University, B
University of Charleston, B
West Liberty University, B

Wisconsin

Beloit College, B
Concordia University Wisconsin, B
Marquette University, BM
St. Norbert College, B
University of Wisconsin - Eau Claire, B
University of Wisconsin - Madison, MD
University of Wisconsin - Milwaukee, B
University of Wisconsin - Oshkosh, B
University of Wisconsin - Superior, BM
University of Wisconsin - Whitewater, M
Western Technical College, A

Wyoming

Casper College, A
Laramie County Community College, A

U.S. Territories: Puerto Rico

Pontifical Catholic University of Puerto Rico, B
University of Puerto Rico, Río Piedras Campus, BM
University of the Sacred Heart, B

Canada

Maritime Provinces: New Brunswick

Crandall University, B
Université de Moncton, B

Ontario

Brock University, B
Carleton University, B
University of Toronto, B
The University of Western Ontario, B
Wilfrid Laurier University, B
York University, B

Quebec

Concordia University, B
Télé-université, B
Université Laval, BMD
Université de Montréal, B
Université du Québec à Montréal, B
Université du Québec à Trois-Rivières, B

MASSAGE THERAPY/THERA-PEUTIC MASSAGE

United States

Alabama

Virginia College in Birmingham, A
Virginia College in Huntsville, A

Arizona

Arizona Western College, A
Carrington College - Phoenix North, A
Central Arizona College, A
Chandler-Gilbert Community College, A
Northland Pioneer College, A
Phoenix College, A
Pima Community College, A

California

Bryan College, A
Carrington College - Pleasant Hill, A
San Joaquin Valley College (Salida), A

Colorado

Colorado School of Healing Arts, A
Heritage College, A
IBMC College (Colorado Springs), A
IBMC College (Fort Collins), A
Morgan Community College, B
Trinidad State Junior College, A

Florida

Florida Career College, A
Florida College of Natural Health (Maitland), A
Florida College of Natural Health (Miami), A
Florida College of Natural Health (Pompano Beach), A

Keiser University, A
Miami Dade College, A
Southeastern College - West Palm Beach, A

Idaho

Broadview University - Boise, A
Carrington College - Boise, A
Idaho State University, AB

Illinois

College of DuPage, A
Illinois Valley Community College, A
Joliet Junior College, A
Lewis and Clark Community College, A
Northwestern College - Bridgeview Campus, A
Northwestern College - Chicago Campus, A
Southwestern Illinois College, A

Indiana

Brightwood College, Hammond Campus, A
Harrison College, A
Ivy Tech Community College - Northeast, A
Vincennes University, A

Iowa

Iowa Lakes Community College, A
Muscatine Community College, A
Scott Community College, A

Kentucky

Spencerian College, A

Louisiana

Blue Cliff College - Shreveport, A
McCann School of Business & Technology (Monroe), A

Maryland

College of Southern Maryland, A
Community College of Baltimore County, A

Massachusetts

Springfield Technical Community College, A

Michigan

Oakland Community College, A
St. Clair County Community College, A
Schoolcraft College, A

Minnesota

Duluth Business University, A
Globe University - Woodbury, A
Herzing University, A
Minnesota School of Business - Blaine, A
Minnesota School of Business - Elk River, A
Minnesota School of Business - Lakeville, A
Minnesota School of Business - Plymouth, A
Minnesota School of Business - Rochester, A
Minnesota School of Business - St. Cloud, A
Minnesota State College - Southeast Technical, A
Saint Paul College - A Community & Technical College, A

Mississippi

Antonelli College (Hattiesburg), A
Antonelli College (Jackson), A
Southwest Mississippi Community College, A
Virginia College in Jackson, A

Missouri

Heritage College, A
Midwest Institute (Fenton), A
Midwest Institute (Saint Louis), A
St. Louis College of Health Careers (Saint Louis), A

Nebraska

Myotherapy Institute, A

New Jersey

Camden County College, A

New York

Morrisville State College, A
New York College of Health Professions, AB

Niagara County Community College, A
Queensborough Community College of the City University of New York, A
Swedish Institute, College of Health Sciences, A
Trocaire College, A

North Carolina

Forsyth Technical Community College, A
Gaston College, A
Lenoir Community College, A
Miller-Motte College (Cary), A
Miller-Motte College (Wilmington), A
Pitt Community College, A
South Piedmont Community College, A
Southwestern Community College, A

North Dakota

Williston State College, A

Ohio

Miami-Jacobs Career College (Dayton), A
Ohio College of Massotherapy, A
Owens Community College, A
Stautzenberger College (Maumee), A

Oklahoma

Clary Sage College, A
Heritage College, A

Oregon

Central Oregon Community College, A

Pennsylvania

Butler County Community College, A
Career Training Academy (Lower Burrell), A
Career Training Academy (Monroeville), A
Career Training Academy (Pittsburgh), A
Keystone Technical Institute, A
McCann School of Business & Technology (Pottsville), A

Rhode Island

Community College of Rhode Island, A

South Carolina

Miller-Motte Technical College (North Charleston), A

South Dakota

Globe University - Sioux Falls, A
National American University (Sioux Falls), A

Tennessee

Miller-Motte Technical College (Chattanooga), A
Miller-Motte Technical College (Clarksville), A
Virginia College in Chattanooga, A

Texas

The College of Health Care Professions (Houston), A

Utah

Broadview University - Layton, A
Broadview University - West Jordan, A
Provo College, A

Virginia

Centura College (Chesapeake), A
Centura College (Newport News), A
Centura College (North Chesterfield), A
Centura College (Virginia Beach), A
ECPI University (Newport News), A
ECPI University (Richmond), A
ECPI University (Virginia Beach), A
Miller-Motte Technical College (Lynchburg), A

Washington

Clover Park Technical College, A
Renton Technical College, A

West Virginia

Mountwest Community & Technical College, A

Wisconsin

Globe University - Appleton, A
Globe University - Eau Claire, A
Globe University - Green Bay, A
Globe University - La Crosse, A
Globe University - Madison East, A
Globe University - Madison West, A
Globe University - Wausau, A

Wyoming

Sheridan College, A

U.S. Territories: Puerto Rico

Columbia Centro Universitario (Caguas), A

MATERIALS ENGINEERING

United States

Alabama

Alabama Agricultural and Mechanical University, M
Auburn University, BMD
Tuskegee University, D
The University of Alabama, MD
The University of Alabama at Birmingham, BMD

Arizona

Arizona State University at the Tempe campus, BMD
The University of Arizona, MD

California

California Polytechnic State University, San Luis Obispo, B
California State University, Long Beach, B
California State University, Northridge, M
San Jose State University, BM
Santa Clara University, O
Stanford University, MDO
University of California, Berkeley, MD
University of California, Davis, BMD
University of California, Irvine, BMD
University of California, Los Angeles, BMD
University of California, Merced, B
University of California, Riverside, MD
University of California, Santa Barbara, MD
University of Southern California, M

Colorado

Colorado School of Mines, MD
University of Denver, MD

Connecticut

University of Connecticut, BMD

Delaware

University of Delaware, MD

District of Columbia

The Catholic University of America, M

Florida

Florida International University, MD
Florida State University, MD
South Florida State College, A
University of Central Florida, MD
University of Florida, BMD
University of South Florida, MDO

Georgia

Georgia Institute of Technology, BMD

Idaho

Boise State University, BMD
University of Idaho, B

Illinois

Illinois Institute of Technology, BMD
Northwestern University, BMDO
University of Illinois at Chicago, MD
University of Illinois at Urbana - Champaign, BMD

Indiana

Purdue University, BMD

Iowa

Iowa State University of Science and Technology, BMD
The University of Iowa, MD

Kentucky

University of Kentucky, BMD

Maine

Southern Maine Community College, A

Maryland

Johns Hopkins University, BMD
University of Maryland, College Park, BMD

Massachusetts

Boston University, MD
Massachusetts Institute of Technology, BMDO
University of Massachusetts Lowell, MO
Worcester Polytechnic Institute, BMD

Michigan

Michigan State University, BMD
Michigan Technological University, BMD
Oakland Community College, A
Saginaw Valley State University, M
University of Michigan, BMD

Minnesota

University of Minnesota, Twin Cities Campus, BMD
Winona State University, B

Nebraska

University of Nebraska - Lincoln, MD

Nevada

University of Nevada, Las Vegas, M
University of Nevada, Reno, MD

New Hampshire

Dartmouth College, MD

New Jersey

New Jersey Institute of Technology, MD
Rutgers University - New Brunswick, MD
Stevens Institute of Technology, MD

New Mexico

New Mexico Institute of Mining and Technology, BMD

New York

Alfred University, B
Binghamton University, State University of New York, MD
Clarkson University, D
Columbia University, MD
Cornell University, BMD
Rensselaer Polytechnic Institute, BMD
Rochester Institute of Technology, M
Stony Brook University, State University of New York, MD
University at Albany, State University of New York, B

North Carolina

Duke University, M
North Carolina State University, BMD

Ohio

Case Western Reserve University, BMD
The Ohio State University, BMD
University of Cincinnati, MD
University of Dayton, MD
Wright State University, BM

Pennsylvania

Carnegie Mellon University, MD
Community College of Beaver County, A
Drexel University, BMD
Lehigh University, BMD

Penn State University Park, MD
University of Pennsylvania, BMD
University of Pittsburgh, B

Rhode Island

Brown University, B

South Carolina

Clemson University, BMD

South Dakota

South Dakota School of Mines and Technology, MD

Tennessee

The University of Tennessee, BMD

Texas

Rice University, B
Southern Methodist University, MD
Texas A&M University, MD
Texas State University, D
University of North Texas, B
The University of Texas at Arlington, MD
The University of Texas at Austin, MD
The University of Texas at Dallas, MD
The University of Texas at El Paso, D
The University of Texas at San Antonio, M

Utah

University of Utah, BMD

Virginia

Virginia Polytechnic Institute and State University,
BMD

Washington

University of Washington, BMD
Washington State University, BMD

Wisconsin

Milwaukee Area Technical College, A
University of Wisconsin - Madison, BMD
University of Wisconsin - Milwaukee, BM
Wisconsin Indianhead Technical College, A

Canada

Alberta

University of Alberta, MD

British Columbia

The University of British Columbia, BMD

Maritime Provinces: Nova Scotia

Dalhousie University, MD

Ontario

Carleton University, M
McMaster University, BMD
University of Toronto, BMD
The University of Western Ontario, BMD
University of Windsor, BMD

Quebec

McGill University, BMD

MATERIALS SCIENCES

United States

Alabama

Alabama Agricultural and Mechanical University, D
The University of Alabama, D
The University of Alabama at Birmingham, D
The University of Alabama in Huntsville, MD

Arizona

Arizona State University at the Tempe campus, MD
The University of Arizona, MD

California

California Institute of Technology, MD
Stanford University, MDO
University of California, Berkeley, MD
University of California, Davis, MD
University of California, Irvine, MD
University of California, Los Angeles, MD
University of California, Riverside, MD
University of California, San Diego, MD
University of California, Santa Barbara, MD
University of Southern California, MDO

Colorado

Colorado School of Mines, MD
University of Denver, M

Connecticut

University of Connecticut, MD

Delaware

University of Delaware, MD

District of Columbia

The Catholic University of America, M
The George Washington University, MD
Georgetown University, D

Florida

Florida International University, MD
Florida State University, MD
University of Central Florida, MD
University of Florida, MD
University of South Florida, MDO

Idaho

University of Idaho, D

Illinois

Illinois Institute of Technology, MD
Northwestern University, MDO
School of the Art Institute of Chicago, M
University of Illinois at Urbana - Champaign, MD

Indiana

Indiana University Bloomington, D

Iowa

Iowa State University of Science and Technology,
MD

Kentucky

University of Kentucky, MD

Maryland

Johns Hopkins University, MD
University of Maryland, College Park, MD

Massachusetts

Boston University, MD
Massachusetts Institute of Technology, MDO
Worcester Polytechnic Institute, MD

Michigan

Central Michigan University, D
Michigan State University, MD
University of Michigan, MD
Wayne State University, MDO

Minnesota

University of Minnesota, Twin Cities Campus, MD

Mississippi

Jackson State University, M
University of Mississippi Medical Center, MD

Missouri

Missouri State University, M
Washington University in St. Louis, MD

Montana

Montana Tech of The University of Montana, D

Nebraska

University of Nebraska - Lincoln, D

New Hampshire

Dartmouth College, MD
University of New Hampshire, MD

New Jersey

New Jersey Institute of Technology, MD
Princeton University, D
Rutgers University - New Brunswick, MD

New York

Alfred University, MD
Binghamton University, State University of New
York, MD
Clarkson University, D
Columbia University, MD
Cornell University, MD
Rensselaer Polytechnic Institute, MD
Rochester Institute of Technology, M
State University of New York College of Environ-
mental Science and Forestry, MD
Stony Brook University, State University of New
York, MD
University of Rochester, MD

North Carolina

Duke University, MD
North Carolina State University, MD
The University of North Carolina at Chapel Hill, MD

North Dakota

North Dakota State University, MD

Ohio

Case Western Reserve University, MD
The Ohio State University, MD
University of Cincinnati, MD
The University of Toledo, MD
Wright State University, M

Oregon

Oregon State University, MD

Pennsylvania

Carnegie Mellon University, MD
Lehigh University, MD
Penn State University Park, MD
University of Pennsylvania, MD
University of Pittsburgh, MD

Rhode Island

Brown University, MD

South Carolina

Clemson University, MD

South Dakota

South Dakota School of Mines and Technology, MD

Tennessee

The University of Tennessee, MD
Vanderbilt University, MD

Texas

Rice University, MD
Southern Methodist University, MD
Texas A&M University, MD
Texas State University, MD
The University of Texas at Arlington, MD
The University of Texas at Austin, MD
The University of Texas at Dallas, MD
The University of Texas at El Paso, D

Utah

University of Utah, MD

Vermont

University of Vermont, MD

Virginia

Norfolk State University, M
University of Virginia, MD
Virginia Polytechnic Institute and State University, MD

Washington

University of Washington, MD
Washington State University, MD

Wisconsin

University of Wisconsin - Madison, MD

Canada

Alberta

University of Calgary, MD

British Columbia

The University of British Columbia, MD

Maritime Provinces: New Brunswick

University of New Brunswick Fredericton, MD

Ontario

McMaster University, MD
Royal Military College of Canada, MD
Trent University, M
University of Toronto, MD

MATERNAL AND CHILD HEALTH

United States

Alabama

Troy University, MD
The University of Alabama at Birmingham, MD

California

University of California, Davis, M

Florida

University of South Florida, O

Louisiana

Tulane University, M

Maryland

University of Maryland, College Park, D

Massachusetts

Boston University, MD

Michigan

Oakland University, O

Minnesota

University of Minnesota, Twin Cities Campus, M

New York

Columbia University, MD
Syracuse University, M

North Carolina

East Carolina University, D
The University of North Carolina at Chapel Hill, MD

Ohio

Union Institute & University, B

Washington

University of Washington, M

U.S. Territories: Puerto Rico

University of Puerto Rico, Medical Sciences Campus, M

MATERNAL/CHILD HEALTH AND NEONATAL NURSE/NURSING

United States

Alabama

University of South Alabama, M

California

Point Loma Nazarene University, M

Delaware

University of Delaware, MO

Illinois

Rush University, DO
Saint Francis Medical Center College of Nursing, M
University of Illinois at Chicago, M

Indiana

University of Indianapolis, M

Kentucky

University of Louisville, M

Massachusetts

Boston College, M

Michigan

Wayne State University, MDO

Minnesota

St. Catherine University, M

Mississippi

University of Southern Mississippi, M

Missouri

University of Missouri - Kansas City, M
University of Missouri - St. Louis, M

Nebraska

Creighton University, MDO

New York

Lehman College of the City University of New York, M
Stony Brook University, State University of New York, MDO
University of Rochester, M

North Carolina

Duke University, MO

Ohio

Case Western Reserve University, M

Pennsylvania

University of Pennsylvania, MO
University of Pittsburgh, M

South Carolina

Medical University of South Carolina, MD

Tennessee

Vanderbilt University, M

Texas

Baylor University, M
Hardin-Simmons University, M

U.S. Territories: Puerto Rico

University of Puerto Rico, Medical Sciences Campus, M

Canada

Alberta

University of Alberta, D

MATERNITY NURSING

United States

New York

Stony Brook University, State University of New York, MDO

Ohio

University of Cincinnati, M

Pennsylvania

University of Pennsylvania, M

Texas

The University of Texas at Austin, M

U.S. Territories: Puerto Rico

University of Puerto Rico, Medical Sciences Campus, M

MATHEMATICAL AND COMPUTATIONAL FINANCE

United States

California

University of California, Santa Barbara, D
University of Southern California, M

Connecticut

University of Connecticut, M

District of Columbia

The George Washington University, O

Florida

Florida State University, MD

Georgia

Georgia Institute of Technology, M

Illinois

DePaul University, M
Illinois Institute of Technology, M
University of Chicago, M

Indiana

University of Notre Dame, M

Maryland

Johns Hopkins University, M

Massachusetts

Boston University, D

New Jersey

Monmouth University, M
New Jersey Institute of Technology, M

New York

New York University, M
Rochester Institute of Technology, M

North Carolina

North Carolina State University, M
The University of North Carolina at Charlotte, M

Ohio

University of Dayton, M

Pennsylvania

Carnegie Mellon University, MD

Texas

Rice University, D

Canada

Alberta

University of Alberta, MD

Ontario

University of Toronto, M

Quebec

Université de Montréal, MO

MATHEMATICAL PHYSICS

United States

Colorado

University of Colorado Boulder, D

Indiana

Indiana University Bloomington, D

New Mexico

New Mexico Institute of Mining and Technology, D

Canada

Alberta

University of Alberta, MD

MATHEMATICAL STATISTICS AND PROBABILITY

United States

Florida

University of Miami, B

Indiana

Purdue University, B

Michigan

Albion College, B

New York

Concordia College - New York, B

Pennsylvania

Carnegie Mellon University, B

Canada

Alberta

University of Alberta, B

Ontario

The University of Western Ontario, B

Quebec

Concordia University, B
McGill University, B

MATHEMATICS

United States

Alabama

Alabama Agricultural and Mechanical University, B
Alabama Southern Community College, A
Alabama State University, BM
Athens State University, B
Auburn University, BMD

Auburn University at Montgomery, B
Birmingham-Southern College, B
Huntingdon College, B
Jacksonville State University, BM
Judson College, B
Miles College, B
Oakwood University, B
Samford University, B
Spring Hill College, B
Stillman College, B
Talladega College, B
Troy University, B
Tuskegee University, B
The University of Alabama, BMD
The University of Alabama at Birmingham, BM
The University of Alabama in Huntsville, BMD
University of Mobile, B
University of Montevallo, B
University of North Alabama, B
University of South Alabama, M
The University of West Alabama, B

Alaska

University of Alaska Anchorage, B
University of Alaska Fairbanks, BMDO
University of Alaska Southeast, B

Arizona

Arizona State University at the Tempe campus, BMDO
Arizona Western College, A
Cochise County Community College District, A
Eastern Arizona College, A
Mesa Community College, A
Mohave Community College, A
Northern Arizona University, BMO
Scottsdale Community College, A
The University of Arizona, BMD

Arkansas

Arkansas State University, BM
Arkansas Tech University, B
Harding University, B
Henderson State University, B
Hendrix College, B
John Brown University, B
Lyon College, B
Ouachita Baptist University, B
Philander Smith College, B
Southern Arkansas University - Magnolia, B
University of Arkansas, BMD
University of Arkansas - Fort Smith, B
University of Arkansas at Little Rock, BM
University of Arkansas at Monticello, B
University of Arkansas at Pine Bluff, B
University of Central Arkansas, BM
University of the Ozarks, B

California

American River College, A
Antelope Valley College, A
Azusa Pacific University, B
Bakersfield College, A
Biola University, B
Butte College, A
Cabrillo College, A
California Baptist University, B
California Institute of Technology, BD
California Lutheran University, B
California Polytechnic State University, San Luis Obispo, BM
California State Polytechnic University, Pomona, BM
California State University, Bakersfield, B
California State University Channel Islands, BM
California State University, Chico, B
California State University, Dominguez Hills, B
California State University, East Bay, BM
California State University, Fresno, BM
California State University, Fullerton, BM
California State University, Long Beach, BM
California State University, Los Angeles, BM
California State University, Monterey Bay, B
California State University, Northridge, B
California State University, Sacramento, BM
California State University, San Bernardino, BM
California State University, San Marcos, BM

California State University, Stanislaus, B
Cañada College, A
Cerritos College, A
Chabot College, A
Chaffey College, A
Chapman University, B
Citrus College, A
Claremont McKenna College, B
College of Alameda, A
College of the Canyons, A
College of the Desert, A
College of Marin, A
College of San Mateo, A
College of the Sequoias, A
College of the Siskiyous, A
Columbia College, A
Concordia University Irvine, B
Contra Costa College, A
Copper Mountain College, A
Cosumnes River College, A
Crafton Hills College, A
Cuesta College, A
De Anza College, A
East Los Angeles College, A
El Camino College, A
Feather River College, A
Folsom Lake College, A
Foothill College, A
Fresno City College, A
Fresno Pacific University, B
Fullerton College, A
Gavilan College, A
Glendale Community College, A
Golden West College, A
Grossmont College, A
Hartnell College, A
Harvey Mudd College, B
Humboldt State University, B
Imperial Valley College, A
Irvine Valley College, A
La Sierra University, B
Lake Tahoe Community College, A
Laney College, A
Lassen Community College District, A
Long Beach City College, A
Los Angeles City College, A
Los Angeles Mission College, A
Los Angeles Valley College, A
Los Medanos College, A
Loyola Marymount University, B
The Master's College and Seminary, B
Mendocino College, A
Merced College, A
Merritt College, A
Mills College, B
MiraCosta College, A
Mission College, A
Modesto Junior College, A
Monterey Peninsula College, A
Moorpark College, A
Mount Saint Mary's University, B
Mt. San Antonio College, A
Mt. San Jacinto College, A
National University, B
Occidental College, B
Ohlone College, A
Orange Coast College, A
Oxnard College, A
Pacific Union College, B
Palomar College, A
Pasadena City College, A
Pepperdine University, B
Pitzer College, B
Point Loma Nazarene University, B
Pomona College, B
Porterville College, A
Reedley College, A
Sacramento City College, A
Saddleback College, A
Saint Mary's College of California, B
San Bernardino Valley College, A
San Diego City College, A
San Diego Mesa College, A
San Diego Miramar College, A
San Diego State University, BMD

San Diego State University - Imperial Valley Campus, B
San Francisco State University, BM
San Joaquin Delta College, A
San Jose City College, A
San Jose State University, BM
Santa Ana College, A
Santa Barbara City College, A
Santa Clara University, B
Santa Rosa Junior College, A
Santiago Canyon College, A
Scripps College, B
Sierra College, A
Simpson University, B
Skyline College, A
Solano Community College, A
Sonoma State University, B
Southwestern College, A
Stanford University, BMD
Taft College, A
University of California, Berkeley, BMD
University of California, Davis, BMD
University of California, Irvine, BMD
University of California, Los Angeles, BMD
University of California, Riverside, BMD
University of California, San Diego, BMD
University of California, Santa Barbara, BMD
University of California, Santa Cruz, BMD
University of La Verne, B
University of the Pacific, B
University of Redlands, B
University of San Diego, B
University of San Francisco, B
University of Southern California, BMD
Vanguard University of Southern California, B
Victor Valley College, A
West Hills Community College, A
West Los Angeles College, A
West Valley College, A
Westmont College, B
Whittier College, B
William Jessup University, B
Yuba College, A

Colorado

Adams State University, B
The Colorado College, B
Colorado Mesa University, B
Colorado Mountain College (Glenwood Springs), A
Colorado Mountain College (Steamboat Springs), A
Colorado School of Mines, BMD
Colorado State University, BMD
Colorado State University - Pueblo, B
Fort Lewis College, B
Metropolitan State University of Denver, B
Northeastern Junior College, A
Otero Junior College, A
Regis University, B
United States Air Force Academy, B
University of Colorado Boulder, BMD
University of Colorado Colorado Springs, B
University of Colorado Denver, BMD
University of Denver, BMD
University of Northern Colorado, BMD
Western State Colorado University, B

Connecticut

Albertus Magnus College, B
Central Connecticut State University, BMO
Connecticut College, B
Eastern Connecticut State University, B
Fairfield University, BM
Housatonic Community College, A
Northwestern Connecticut Community College, A
Quinnipiac University, B
Sacred Heart University, B
Southern Connecticut State University, BM
Trinity College, B
University of Bridgeport, B
University of Connecticut, BMD
University of Hartford, B
University of New Haven, B
University of Saint Joseph, B
Wesleyan University, BMD
Western Connecticut State University, BM
Yale University, BMD

Delaware

Delaware State University, BM
University of Delaware, BMD

District of Columbia

American University, B
The Catholic University of America, B
Gallaudet University, B
The George Washington University, BMDO
Georgetown University, BM
Howard University, BMD
Trinity Washington University, B
University of the District of Columbia, B

Florida

Ave Maria University, B
Barry University, B
Bethune-Cookman University, B
Broward College, A
College of Central Florida, A
Eckerd College, B
Edward Waters College, B
Florida Agricultural and Mechanical University, B
Florida Atlantic University, BMD
Florida Gulf Coast University, BM
Florida Institute of Technology, B
Florida International University, BM
Florida Memorial University, B
Florida Southern College, B
Florida State University, BMD
Indian River State College, A
Jacksonville University, B
Lake-Sumter State College, A
Miami Dade College, A
New College of Florida, B
Palm Beach Atlantic University, B
Palm Beach State College, A
Pensacola State College, A
Rollins College, B
Saint Leo University, B
St. Thomas University, B
South Florida State College, A
Southeastern University, B
Stetson University, B
University of Central Florida, BMDO
University of Florida, BMD
University of Miami, BMD
University of North Florida, BM
University of South Florida, BMDO
The University of Tampa, B
University of West Florida, BM

Georgia

Abraham Baldwin Agricultural College, A
Agnes Scott College, B
Albany State University, B
Andrew College, A
Armstrong State University, B
Augusta University, B
Bainbridge State College, A
Berry College, B
Clark Atlanta University, BM
Clayton State University, B
College of Coastal Georgia, AB
Columbus State University, B
Covenant College, B
Dalton State College, AB
Darton State College, A
Emmanuel College, B
Emory University, BMD
Fort Valley State University, B
Georgia College & State University, B
Georgia Gwinnett College, B
Georgia Highlands College, A
Georgia Institute of Technology, MD
Georgia Military College, A
Georgia Southern University, BM
Georgia Southwestern State University, B
Georgia State University, BMD
Gordon State College, AB
Kennesaw State University, B
LaGrange College, B
Mercer University, B
Middle Georgia State University, B
Morehouse College, B

Oglethorpe University, B
Paine College, B
Piedmont College, B
Reinhardt University, B
Savannah State University, B
Shorter University, B
South Georgia State College, A
Spelman College, B
Thomas University, A
University of Georgia, BMD
University of North Georgia, B
University of West Georgia, BM
Valdosta State University, B
Wesleyan College, B
Young Harris College, B

Hawaii

Brigham Young University - Hawaii, B
Hawai'i Pacific University, A
University of Hawaii at Hilo, B
University of Hawaii at Manoa, BMD

Idaho

Boise State University, BM
The College of Idaho, B
College of Southern Idaho, A
Idaho State University, ABMD
Lewis-Clark State College, B
North Idaho College, A
Northwest Nazarene University, B
University of Idaho, BMD

Illinois

Augustana College, B
Aurora University, BM
Benedictine University, B
Blackburn College, B
Bradley University, B
Chicago State University, BM
Concordia University Chicago, B
DePaul University, BM
Dominican University, B
East-West University, B
Eastern Illinois University, BM
Elmhurst College, B
Governors State University, B
Greenville College, B
Harper College, A
Illinois College, B
Illinois State University, BM
Illinois Wesleyan University, B
John A. Logan College, A
Judson University, B
Kankakee Community College, A
Knox College, B
Lake Forest College, B
Lewis University, B
Lincoln College, A
Loyola University Chicago, BM
McKendree University, B
Millikin University, B
Monmouth College, B
Moraine Valley Community College, A
National Louis University, B
North Central College, B
North Park University, B
Northeastern Illinois University, BM
Northern Illinois University, BMD
Northwestern University, BD
Olivet Nazarene University, B
Principia College, B
Quincy University, B
Rockford University, B
Roosevelt University, BM
Saint Xavier University, B
Sauk Valley Community College, A
Southern Illinois University Carbondale, BMD
Southern Illinois University Edwardsville, BM
Spoon River College, A
Trinity Christian College, B
Trinity International University, B
Triton College, A
University of Chicago, BD
University of Illinois at Chicago, BMD
University of Illinois at Springfield, B
University of Illinois at Urbana - Champaign, BMD

University of St. Francis, B
Western Illinois University, BMO
Wheaton College, B

Indiana

Anderson University, B
Ball State University, BM
Bethel College, B
Butler University, B
DePauw University, B
Earlham College, B
Franklin College, B
Goshen College, B
Grace College, B
Hanover College, B
Huntington University, B
Indiana State University, BM
Indiana University Bloomington, BMD
Indiana University East, B
Indiana University Kokomo, B
Indiana University Northwest, B
Indiana University - Purdue University Fort Wayne,
   BMO
Indiana University - Purdue University Indianapolis,
   BMD
Indiana University South Bend, B
Indiana University Southeast, B
Indiana Wesleyan University, AB
Manchester University, B
Marian University, B
Oakland City University, B
Purdue University, BMD
Purdue University Northwest (Hammond), BM
Rose-Hulman Institute of Technology, B
Saint Joseph's College, B
Saint Mary-of-the-Woods College, B
Saint Mary's College, B
Taylor University, B
Trine University, AB
University of Evansville, B
University of Indianapolis, B
University of Notre Dame, BMD
University of Saint Francis, B
University of Southern Indiana, B
Valparaiso University, B
Vincennes University, A
Wabash College, B

Iowa

Briar Cliff University, B
Buena Vista University, B
Central College, B
Clarke University, B
Coe College, B
Cornell College, B
Dordt College, B
Drake University, B
Graceland University, B
Grinnell College, B
Iowa Lakes Community College, A
Iowa State University of Science and Technology,
   BMD
Loras College, B
Luther College, B
Maharishi University of Management, B
Morningside College, B
Mount Mercy University, B
Northwestern College, B
St. Ambrose University, B
Simpson College, B
University of Dubuque, B
The University of Iowa, BMD
University of Northern Iowa, BM
Upper Iowa University, B
Wartburg College, B
William Penn University, B

Kansas

Allen Community College, A
Baker University, B
Barton County Community College, A
Benedictine College, B
Bethany College, B
Bethel College, B
Butler Community College, A
Central Christian College of Kansas, AB

Dodge City Community College, A
Emporia State University, BM
Fort Hays State University, B
Friends University, B
Garden City Community College, A
Highland Community College, A
Hutchinson Community College, A
Independence Community College, A
Kansas State University, BMDO
Kansas Wesleyan University, B
Labette Community College, A
McPherson College, B
MidAmerica Nazarene University, B
Newman University, B
Ottawa University, B
Pittsburg State University, BM
Pratt Community College, A
Seward County Community College and Area Tech-
   nical School, A
Southwestern College, B
Sterling College, B
Tabor College, B
The University of Kansas, BMD
University of Saint Mary, B
Washburn University, B
Wichita State University, BMD

Kentucky

Asbury University, B
Bellarmine University, B
Berea College, B
Campbellsville University, B
Centre College, B
Eastern Kentucky University, BM
Georgetown College, B
Kentucky State University, B
Kentucky Wesleyan College, B
Midway University, B
Morehead State University, B
Murray State University, BM
Northern Kentucky University, B
Thomas More College, AB
Transylvania University, B
Union College, B
University of the Cumberlands, B
University of Kentucky, BMD
University of Louisville, BMD
University of Pikeville, B
Western Kentucky University, BM

Louisiana

Centenary College of Louisiana, B
Dillard University, B
Grambling State University, B
Louisiana College, B
Louisiana State University and Agricultural & Me-
   chanical College, BMD
Louisiana State University at Alexandria, B
Louisiana State University in Shreveport, B
Louisiana Tech University, BMD
Loyola University New Orleans, B
McNeese State University, BM
Nicholls State University, BM
Northwestern State University of Louisiana, B
Southeastern Louisiana University, B
Southern University and Agricultural and Mechanical
   College, BM
Southern University at New Orleans, B
Southern University at Shreveport, A
Tulane University, BMD
University of Louisiana at Lafayette, BMD
University of Louisiana at Monroe, B
University of New Orleans, BM
Xavier University of Louisiana, B

Maine

Bates College, B
Bowdoin College, B
Colby College, B
Saint Joseph's College of Maine, B
University of Maine, B
University of Maine at Farmington, B
University of Maine at Presque Isle, B
University of New England, B
University of Southern Maine, B

Maryland

Anne Arundel Community College, A
Bowie State University, B
Cecil College, A
Coppin State University, B
Frederick Community College, A
Frostburg State University, B
Goucher College, B
Harford Community College, A
Hood College, B
Johns Hopkins University, BD
Loyola University Maryland, B
McDaniel College, B
Morgan State University, BM
Mount St. Mary's University, B
Notre Dame of Maryland University, B
St. Mary's College of Maryland, B
Salisbury University, B
Towson University, B
United States Naval Academy, B
University of Maryland, Baltimore County, B
University of Maryland, College Park, BMD
University of Maryland Eastern Shore, B
Washington Adventist University, B
Washington College, B

Massachusetts

Amherst College, B
Assumption College, B
Bard College at Simon's Rock, B
Bentley University, B
Boston College, BD
Boston University, BMD
Brandeis University, BMDO
Bridgewater State University, B
Bunker Hill Community College, A
Clark University, B
College of the Holy Cross, B
Dean College, A
Eastern Nazarene College, B
Elms College, B
Emmanuel College, B
Endicott College, B
Fitchburg State University, B
Framingham State University, B
Gordon College, B
Hampshire College, B
Harvard University, BD
Holyoke Community College, A
Massachusetts Bay Community College, A
Massachusetts College of Liberal Arts, B
Massachusetts Institute of Technology, BD
Merrimack College, B
Mount Holyoke College, B
Nichols College, B
Northeastern University, BMD
Roxbury Community College, A
Salem State University, BM
Simmons College, B
Smith College, BO
Springfield College, B
Springfield Technical Community College, A
Stonehill College, B
Suffolk University, B
Tufts University, BMD
University of Massachusetts Amherst, BMD
University of Massachusetts Boston, B
University of Massachusetts Dartmouth, B
University of Massachusetts Lowell, BMD
Wellesley College, B
Western New England University, B
Westfield State University, B
Wheaton College, B
Wheelock College, B
Williams College, B
Worcester Polytechnic Institute, BMDO
Worcester State University, B

Michigan

Adrian College, B
Albion College, B
Alma College, B
Alpena Community College, A
Andrews University, B
Aquinas College, B

Calvin College, B
Central Michigan University, BMD
Concordia University Ann Arbor, B
Cornerstone University, B
Eastern Michigan University, BM
Grand Valley State University, B
Hillsdale College, B
Hope College, B
Kalamazoo College, B
Lake Michigan College, A
Lake Superior State University, B
Lansing Community College, A
Lawrence Technological University, B
Macomb Community College, A
Madonna University, B
Marygrove College, B
Michigan State University, BMD
Michigan Technological University, BMD
Mid Michigan Community College, A
Monroe County Community College, A
Northern Michigan University, B
Northwestern Michigan College, A
Oakland University, BM
Olivet College, B
Saginaw Valley State University, B
Siena Heights University, B
Spring Arbor University, B
University of Detroit Mercy, B
University of Michigan, BMD
University of Michigan - Dearborn, B
University of Michigan - Flint, BM
Wayne State University, BMD
Western Michigan University, BMD

Minnesota

Augsburg College, B
Bemidji State University, BM
Bethany Lutheran College, B
Bethel University, B
Carleton College, B
College of Saint Benedict, B
The College of St. Scholastica, B
Concordia College, B
Concordia University, St. Paul, B
Gustavus Adolphus College, B
Hamline University, B
Macalester College, B
Minneapolis Community and Technical College, A
Minnesota State University Mankato, BM
Minnesota State University Moorhead, B
North Hennepin Community College, A
St. Catherine University, B
St. Cloud State University, BM
Saint John's University, B
Saint Mary's University of Minnesota, B
St. Olaf College, B
Southwest Minnesota State University, B
University of Minnesota, Duluth, B
University of Minnesota, Morris, B
University of Minnesota, Twin Cities Campus,
  BMDO
University of Northwestern - St. Paul, B
University of St. Thomas, B
Vermilion Community College, A
Winona State University, B

Mississippi

Alcorn State University, B
Belhaven University, B
Blue Mountain College, B
Coahoma Community College, A
Delta State University, B
East Mississippi Community College, A
Holmes Community College, A
Itawamba Community College, A
Jackson State University, BM
Jones County Junior College, A
Millsaps College, B
Mississippi College, BM
Mississippi Delta Community College, A
Mississippi State University, BMD
Mississippi University for Women, B
Mississippi Valley State University, B
Northeast Mississippi Community College, A
Rust College, B
Tougaloo College, B

University of Mississippi, BMD
University of Southern Mississippi, BMD
William Carey University, B

Missouri

Avila University, B
Calvary Bible College and Theological Seminary, B
Central Methodist University, B
College of the Ozarks, B
Columbia College, B
Crowder College, A
Culver-Stockton College, B
Drury University, B
Evangel University, B
Fontbonne University, B
Hannibal-LaGrange University, B
Harris-Stowe State University, B
Lincoln University, B
Lindenwood University, B
Maryville University of Saint Louis, B
Missouri Baptist University, B
Missouri Southern State University, B
Missouri State University, BM
Missouri University of Science and Technology, MD
Missouri Valley College, B
Missouri Western State University, B
Northwest Missouri State University, BM
Park University, B
Rockhurst University, B
St. Charles Community College, A
Saint Louis University, BMD
Southeast Missouri State University, BM
Southwest Baptist University, B
Truman State University, B
University of Central Missouri, BM
University of Missouri, BMD
University of Missouri - Kansas City, BMD
University of Missouri - St. Louis, BMD
Washington University in St. Louis, BMD
Webster University, B
Westminster College, B
William Jewell College, B
William Woods University, B

Montana

Carroll College, B
Little Big Horn College, A
Montana State University, BMD
Montana State University Billings, B
Montana State University - Northern, B
Montana Tech of The University of Montana, B
Rocky Mountain College, B
University of Great Falls, AB
University of Montana, BMD
The University of Montana Western, B

Nebraska

Chadron State College, B
College of Saint Mary, B
Concordia University, Nebraska, B
Creighton University, AB
Doane University, B
Hastings College, B
Midland University, B
Nebraska Wesleyan University, B
Northeast Community College, A
Peru State College, B
Union College, B
University of Nebraska at Kearney, B
University of Nebraska - Lincoln, BMD
University of Nebraska at Omaha, BM
Wayne State College, B
Western Nebraska Community College, A

Nevada

College of Southern Nevada, A
Nevada State College, A
Truckee Meadows Community College, A
University of Nevada, Las Vegas, BMD
University of Nevada, Reno, BM

New Hampshire

Dartmouth College, BD
Franklin Pierce University, B
Keene State College, B

Plymouth State University, B
Rivier University, BM
Saint Anselm College, B
Southern New Hampshire University, B
University of New Hampshire, BMDO

New Jersey

Bergen Community College, A
Caldwell University, B
Centenary College, B
The College of New Jersey, B
College of Saint Elizabeth, B
Drew University, B
Essex County College, A
Fairleigh Dickinson University, College at Florham,
  B
Fairleigh Dickinson University, Metropolitan Cam-
  pus, BM
Felician University, B
Georgian Court University, B
Kean University, B
Mercer County Community College, A
Monmouth University, B
Montclair State University, BM
New Jersey City University, B
New Jersey Institute of Technology, BD
Passaic County Community College, A
Princeton University, BD
Ramapo College of New Jersey, B
Rider University, B
Rowan College at Burlington County, A
Rowan University, BM
Rutgers University - Camden, BM
Rutgers University - New Brunswick, BMD
Rutgers University - Newark, BD
Saint Peter's University, B
Seton Hall University, B
Stevens Institute of Technology, BMD
Stockton University, B
Thomas Edison State University, AB
Union County College, A
William Paterson University of New Jersey, B

New Mexico

Central New Mexico Community College, A
Eastern New Mexico University, B
New Mexico Highlands University, B
New Mexico Institute of Mining and Technology,
  BMD
New Mexico Junior College, A
New Mexico Military Institute, A
New Mexico State University, BMD
San Juan College, A
University of New Mexico, BMD
Western New Mexico University, B

New York

Adelphi University, B
Alfred University, B
Bard College, B
Barnard College, B
Baruch College of the City University of New York,
  B
Binghamton University, State University of New
  York, BMD
Borough of Manhattan Community College of the
  City University of New York, A
Bronx Community College of the City University of
  New York, A
Brooklyn College of the City University of New York,
  BM
Buffalo State College, State University of New York,
  B
Cayuga County Community College, A
City College of the City University of New York, BM
Clarkson University, BMD
Colgate University, B
The College at Brockport, State University of New
  York, BM
College of Mount Saint Vincent, B
The College of New Rochelle, B
The College of Saint Rose, B
College of Staten Island of the City University of
  New York, B
Columbia University, BMD
Columbia University, School of General Studies, B

Concordia College - New York, B
Cornell University, BD
Corning Community College, A
Daemen College, B
Dominican College, B
D'Youville College, B
Elmira College, B
Eugenio María de Hostos Community College of the City University of New York, A
Excelsior College, B
Finger Lakes Community College, A
Fordham University, B
Fulton-Montgomery Community College, A
Genesee Community College, A
Hamilton College, B
Hartwick College, B
Hobart and William Smith Colleges, B
Hofstra University, B
Houghton College, B
Hunter College of the City University of New York, BM
Iona College, B
Ithaca College, B
Jefferson Community College, A
Keuka College, B
Kingsborough Community College of the City University of New York, A
Le Moyne College, B
Lehman College of the City University of New York, BM
Long Island University - LIU Brooklyn, B
Long Island University - LIU Post, B
Manhattan College, B
Manhattanville College, B
Marist College, B
Medaille College, B
Mercy College, B
Molloy College, B
Monroe Community College, A
Mount Saint Mary College, B
Nassau Community College, A
Nazareth College of Rochester, B
New York University, BMD
Niagara County Community College, A
Niagara University, B
North Country Community College, A
Nyack College, B
Pace University, B
Pace University, Pleasantville Campus, B
Purchase College, State University of New York, B
Queens College of the City University of New York, BM
Rensselaer Polytechnic Institute, BMD
Roberts Wesleyan College, B
Rochester Institute of Technology, BM
Rockland Community College, A
The Sage Colleges, B
St. Bonaventure University, B
St. Francis College, B
St. John Fisher College, B
St. John's University, B
St. Joseph's College, Long Island Campus, B
St. Joseph's College, New York, B
St. Lawrence University, B
St. Thomas Aquinas College, B
Sarah Lawrence College, B
Siena College, B
Skidmore College, B
State University of New York College of Agriculture and Technology at Cobleskill, A
State University of New York College at Cortland, B
State University of New York College at Geneseo, B
State University of New York College at Old Westbury, B
State University of New York College at Oneonta, B
State University of New York College at Potsdam, BM
State University of New York at Fredonia, B
State University of New York at New Paltz, B
State University of New York at Oswego, B
State University of New York at Plattsburgh, B
Stony Brook University, State University of New York, BMD
Suffolk County Community College, A
Sullivan County Community College, A
Syracuse University, BMD

Touro College, B
Union College, B
United States Military Academy, B
University at Albany, State University of New York, BMD
University at Buffalo, the State University of New York, BMD
University of Rochester, BMD
Utica College, B
Vassar College, B
Wagner College, B
Wells College, B
Yeshiva University, BMD
York College of the City University of New York, B

North Carolina

Appalachian State University, BM
Barton College, B
Belmont Abbey College, B
Bennett College, B
Brevard College, B
Campbell University, B
Catawba College, B
Chowan University, B
Davidson College, B
Duke University, BD
East Carolina University, BMO
Elizabeth City State University, BM
Elon University, B
Fayetteville State University, BM
Gardner-Webb University, B
Greensboro College, B
Guilford College, B
High Point University, B
Johnson C. Smith University, B
Lenoir-Rhyne University, B
Livingstone College, B
Louisburg College, A
Mars Hill University, B
Meredith College, B
Methodist University, AB
North Carolina Agricultural and Technical State University, BM
North Carolina Central University, BM
North Carolina State University, BMD
North Carolina Wesleyan College, B
Pfeiffer University, B
Queens University of Charlotte, B
Saint Augustine's University, B
Salem College, B
Sandhills Community College, A
Shaw University, B
University of Mount Olive, B
University of North Carolina at Asheville, B
The University of North Carolina at Chapel Hill, BMD
The University of North Carolina at Charlotte, BMD
The University of North Carolina at Greensboro, BMD
The University of North Carolina at Pembroke, B
The University of North Carolina Wilmington, BMO
Wake Forest University, BM
Warren Wilson College, B
Western Carolina University, BM
Wingate University, B
Winston-Salem State University, B

North Dakota

Dakota College at Bottineau, A
Dickinson State University, B
Mayville State University, B
Minot State University, B
North Dakota State University, BMD
Turtle Mountain Community College, A
University of Jamestown, B
University of Mary, B
University of North Dakota, BM
Valley City State University, B

Ohio

Antioch University Midwest, B
Ashland University, B
Baldwin Wallace University, B
Bluffton University, B
Bowling Green State University, BMD
Capital University, B

Case Western Reserve University, BMD
Cedarville University, B
Central State University, B
Cleveland State University, BM
The College of Wooster, B
Defiance College, B
Denison University, B
Edison Community College, A
Franciscan University of Steubenville, B
Heidelberg University, B
Hiram College, B
John Carroll University, BM
Kent State University, BMD
Kent State University at Stark, B
Kenyon College, B
Lake Erie College, B
Lorain County Community College, A
Malone University, B
Marietta College, B
Miami University, BM
Miami University Hamilton, B
Miami University Middletown, A
Mount St. Joseph University, B
Mount Vernon Nazarene University, B
Muskingum University, B
Notre Dame College, B
Oberlin College, B
Ohio Dominican University, B
Ohio Northern University, B
The Ohio State University, BMD
Ohio University, BMD
Ohio Wesleyan University, B
Otterbein University, B
Shawnee State University, AB
Terra State Community College, A
The University of Akron, BM
University of Cincinnati, BMD
University of Dayton, B
The University of Findlay, B
University of Mount Union, B
University of Rio Grande, AB
The University of Toledo, BMD
Ursuline College, B
Walsh University, B
Washington State Community College, A
Wilmington College, B
Wittenberg University, B
Wright State University, BM
Xavier University, B
Youngstown State University, BM

Oklahoma

Cameron University, B
Carl Albert State College, A
Connors State College, A
East Central University, B
Eastern Oklahoma State College, A
Langston University, B
Mid-America Christian University, B
Murray State College, A
Northeastern State University, B
Northwestern Oklahoma State University, B
Oklahoma Baptist University, B
Oklahoma Christian University, B
Oklahoma City Community College, A
Oklahoma City University, B
Oklahoma Panhandle State University, B
Oklahoma State University, BMD
Oklahoma Wesleyan University, AB
Oral Roberts University, B
Redlands Community College, A
Rose State College, A
St. Gregory's University, B
Seminole State College, A
Southeastern Oklahoma State University, B
Southern Nazarene University, B
Southwestern Oklahoma State University, B
Tulsa Community College, A
University of Central Oklahoma, BM
University of Oklahoma, BMD
University of Science and Arts of Oklahoma, B
The University of Tulsa, BMD

Oregon

Central Oregon Community College, A
Corban University, B

Eastern Oregon University, B
George Fox University, B
Lewis & Clark College, B
Linfield College, B
Linn-Benton Community College, A
Northwest Christian University, B
Oregon State University, BMD
Oregon State University - Cascades, B
Pacific University, B
Portland State University, BMD
Reed College, B
Southern Oregon University, B
Umpqua Community College, A
University of Oregon, BMD
University of Portland, B
Western Oregon University, B
Willamette University, B

Pennsylvania

Albright College, B
Allegheny College, B
Alvernia University, B
Arcadia University, B
Bloomsburg University of Pennsylvania, B
Bryn Mawr College, BMD
Bucknell University, BM
Bucks County Community College, A
Butler County Community College, A
Cabrini University, B
California University of Pennsylvania, B
Carlow University, B
Carnegie Mellon University, BMD
Cedar Crest College, B
Chatham University, B
Chestnut Hill College, B
Cheyney University of Pennsylvania, B
Clarion University of Pennsylvania, B
Community College of Allegheny County, A
Community College of Beaver County, A
DeSales University, B
Dickinson College, B
Drexel University, BMD
Duquesne University, BM
East Stroudsburg University of Pennsylvania, B
Eastern University, B
Edinboro University of Pennsylvania, B
Elizabethtown College, B
Franklin & Marshall College, B
Gannon University, B
Gettysburg College, B
Grove City College, B
Gwynedd Mercy University, B
Harrisburg Area Community College, A
Haverford College, B
Holy Family University, B
Immaculata University, B
Indiana University of Pennsylvania, BM
Juniata College, B
King's College, B
Kutztown University of Pennsylvania, B
La Roche College, B
La Salle University, B
Lafayette College, B
Lebanon Valley College, B
Lehigh Carbon Community College, A
Lehigh University, BMD
Lincoln University, B
Lock Haven University of Pennsylvania, B
Luzerne County Community College, A
Lycoming College, B
Mansfield University of Pennsylvania, B
Marywood University, B
Mercyhurst University, B
Messiah College, B
Millersville University of Pennsylvania, B
Misericordia University, B
Montgomery County Community College, A
Moravian College, B
Muhlenberg College, B
Northampton Community College, A
Penn State Abington, B
Penn State Altoona, B
Penn State Beaver, B
Penn State Berks, B
Penn State Brandywine, B
Penn State DuBois, B

Penn State Erie, The Behrend College, B
Penn State Fayette, The Eberly Campus, B
Penn State Greater Allegheny, B
Penn State Hazleton, B
Penn State Lehigh Valley, B
Penn State Mont Alto, B
Penn State New Kensington, B
Penn State Schuylkill, B
Penn State Shenango, B
Penn State University Park, BMD
Penn State Wilkes-Barre, B
Penn State Worthington Scranton, B
Penn State York, B
Rosemont College, B
Saint Francis University, B
Saint Joseph's University, BMO
Saint Vincent College, B
Seton Hill University, B
Shippensburg University of Pennsylvania, B
Slippery Rock University of Pennsylvania, B
Susquehanna University, B
Swarthmore College, B
Temple University, BMD
Thiel College, B
University of Pennsylvania, BMD
University of Pittsburgh, BMD
University of Pittsburgh at Johnstown, B
The University of Scranton, B
Ursinus College, B
Villanova University, BM
Washington & Jefferson College, B
Waynesburg University, B
West Chester University of Pennsylvania, BMO
Westminster College, B
Widener University, B
Wilkes University, BM
Wilson College, B
York College of Pennsylvania, B

Rhode Island

Brown University, BD
Providence College, B
Rhode Island College, BMO
Roger Williams University, B
Salve Regina University, B
University of Rhode Island, BMD

South Carolina

Allen University, B
Anderson University, B
Benedict College, B
Bob Jones University, B
Charleston Southern University, B
The Citadel, The Military College of South Carolina, B
Claflin University, B
Clemson University, BMD
Coker College, B
College of Charleston, BMO
Columbia College, B
Converse College, B
Erskine College, B
Francis Marion University, B
Furman University, B
Lander University, B
Limestone College, B
Morris College, B
Newberry College, B
North Greenville University, B
Presbyterian College, B
South Carolina State University, B
Southern Wesleyan University, B
University of South Carolina, BMD
University of South Carolina Beaufort, B
University of South Carolina Upstate, B
Winthrop University, B
Wofford College, B

South Dakota

Augustana University, B
Black Hills State University, B
Dakota Wesleyan University, B
Mount Marty College, B
Northern State University, B
South Dakota School of Mines and Technology, B
South Dakota State University, BMD

University of Sioux Falls, B
The University of South Dakota, BM

Tennessee

Austin Peay State University, B
Belmont University, B
Bethel University, B
Bryan College, B
Carson-Newman University, B
Christian Brothers University, B
Cumberland University, B
East Tennessee State University, BMO
Fisk University, B
Freed-Hardeman University, B
King University, B
Lane College, B
Lee University, B
LeMoyne-Owen College, B
Lincoln Memorial University, B
Lipscomb University, B
Maryville College, B
Middle Tennessee State University, BM
Milligan College, B
Nashville State Community College, A
Rhodes College, B
Roane State Community College, A
Sewanee: The University of the South, B
Southern Adventist University, B
Tennessee State University, BM
Tennessee Technological University, BM
Tennessee Wesleyan College, B
Trevecca Nazarene University, AB
Tusculum College, B
Union University, B
University of Memphis, BMD
The University of Tennessee, BMD
The University of Tennessee at Chattanooga, BM
The University of Tennessee at Martin, B
Vanderbilt University, BMD

Texas

Abilene Christian University, B
Alvin Community College, A
Amarillo College, A
Angelina College, A
Angelo State University, B
Austin College, B
Austin Community College District, A
Baylor University, BMD
Blinn College, A
Central Texas College, A
Cisco College, A
Clarendon College, A
College of the Mainland, A
Concordia University Texas, B
Dallas Baptist University, B
Del Mar College, A
East Texas Baptist University, B
Frank Phillips College, A
Galveston College, A
Grayson College, A
Hardin-Simmons University, BM
Hill College, A
Houston Community College, A
Howard College, A
Howard Payne University, B
Huston-Tillotson University, B
Jarvis Christian College, B
Kilgore College, A
Lamar State College - Orange, A
Lamar University, BM
Lee College, A
LeTourneau University, B
Lubbock Christian University, B
McMurry University, B
Midwestern State University, B
Navarro College, A
Northeast Texas Community College, A
Odessa College, A
Our Lady of the Lake University of San Antonio, B
Palo Alto College, A
Panola College, A
Paris Junior College, A
Paul Quinn College, B
Prairie View A&M University, B
Rice University, BD

St. Edward's University, B
St. Mary's University, B
St. Philip's College, A
Sam Houston State University, BM
San Jacinto College District, A
Schreiner University, B
Southern Methodist University, BMD
Southwestern Adventist University, B
Southwestern University, B
Stephen F. Austin State University, BM
Sul Ross State University, B
Tarleton State University, BM
Texarkana College, A
Texas A&M International University, BM
Texas A&M University, BMD
Texas A&M University - Central Texas, BM
Texas A&M University - Commerce, B
Texas A&M University - Corpus Christi, BM
Texas A&M University - Kingsville, BM
Texas A&M University - San Antonio, B
Texas A&M University - Texarkana, B
Texas Christian University, BMD
Texas College, B
Texas Lutheran University, B
Texas Southern University, BM
Texas State University, BM
Texas Tech University, BMD
Texas Wesleyan University, B
Texas Woman's University, BM
Trinity University, B
Trinity Valley Community College, A
Tyler Junior College, A
University of Dallas, B
University of Houston, BMD
University of Houston - Clear Lake, BM
University of Houston - Downtown, B
University of Houston - Victoria, B
University of the Incarnate Word, BM
University of Mary Hardin-Baylor, B
University of North Texas, BM
University of St. Thomas, B
The University of Texas at Arlington, BMD
The University of Texas at Austin, BMD
The University of Texas at Dallas, BMD
The University of Texas at El Paso, BM
The University of Texas of the Permian Basin, B
The University of Texas Rio Grande Valley, BM
The University of Texas at San Antonio, BM
The University of Texas at Tyler, BM
Wayland Baptist University, B
West Texas A&M University, BM
Western Texas College, A
Wharton County Junior College, A
Wiley College, B

Utah

Brigham Young University, MD
Dixie State University, B
Snow College, A
Southern Utah University, B
University of Utah, BMD
Utah State University, BMD
Utah Valley University, AB
Weber State University, B
Westminster College, B

Vermont

Bennington College, B
Castleton University, B
Johnson State College, B
Lyndon State College, B
Marlboro College, B
Middlebury College, B
Norwich University, B
Saint Michael's College, B
University of Vermont, BMD

Virginia

Averett University, B
Bluefield College, B
Bridgewater College, B
Christendom College, B
Christopher Newport University, B
The College of William and Mary, B
Eastern Mennonite University, B
Emory & Henry College, B

Ferrum College, B
George Mason University, BMDO
Hampden-Sydney College, B
Hampton University, B
Hollins University, B
J. Sargeant Reynolds Community College, A
James Madison University, B
Liberty University, B
Longwood University, B
Lynchburg College, B
Mary Baldwin College, B
Marymount University, B
Norfolk State University, B
Old Dominion University, BMD
Radford University, B
Randolph College, B
Randolph-Macon College, B
Regent University, B
Roanoke College, B
Shenandoah University, B
Sweet Briar College, B
University of Mary Washington, B
University of Richmond, B
University of Virginia, BMD
The University of Virginia's College at Wise, B
Virginia Commonwealth University, BM
Virginia Military Institute, B
Virginia Polytechnic Institute and State University, BMD
Virginia State University, BM
Virginia Union University, B
Virginia Wesleyan College, B
Washington and Lee University, B

Washington

Central Washington University, BM
Eastern Washington University, BM
Everett Community College, A
Gonzaga University, B
Heritage University, B
Highline College, A
Northwest University, B
Pacific Lutheran University, B
Saint Martin's University, B
Seattle Pacific University, B
Seattle University, B
Skagit Valley College, A
University of Puget Sound, B
University of Washington, BMD
University of Washington, Bothell, B
Walla Walla University, B
Washington State University, BMD
Washington State University - Tri-Cities, B
Wenatchee Valley College, A
Western Washington University, BM
Whitman College, B
Whitworth University, B

West Virginia

Bethany College, B
Concord University, B
Davis & Elkins College, B
Fairmont State University, B
Marshall University, BM
Potomac State College of West Virginia University, A
Shepherd University, B
West Liberty University, B
West Virginia State University, B
West Virginia University, BMD
West Virginia University Institute of Technology, B
West Virginia Wesleyan College, B
Wheeling Jesuit University, B

Wisconsin

Alverno College, B
Beloit College, B
Cardinal Stritch University, B
Carroll University, B
Carthage College, B
College of Menominee Nation, A
Concordia University Wisconsin, B
Edgewood College, B
Lakeland College, B
Lawrence University, B
Marian University, B

Marquette University, BMD
Mount Mary University, B
Northland College, B
Ripon College, B
St. Norbert College, B
Silver Lake College of the Holy Family, B
University of Wisconsin - Eau Claire, B
University of Wisconsin - Green Bay, B
University of Wisconsin - La Crosse, B
University of Wisconsin - Madison, BD
University of Wisconsin - Milwaukee, BMD
University of Wisconsin - Oshkosh, B
University of Wisconsin - Parkside, B
University of Wisconsin - Platteville, B
University of Wisconsin - River Falls, B
University of Wisconsin - Stevens Point, B
University of Wisconsin - Superior, B
University of Wisconsin - Whitewater, B
Viterbo University, B
Wisconsin Lutheran College, B

Wyoming

Casper College, A
Central Wyoming College, A
Eastern Wyoming College, A
Laramie County Community College, A
Northwest College, A
Sheridan College, A
University of Wyoming, BMD
Western Wyoming Community College, A

U.S. Territories: Guam

University of Guam, B

U.S. Territories: Puerto Rico

Inter American University of Puerto Rico, Bayamón Campus, B
Inter American University of Puerto Rico, Metropolitan Campus, B
Inter American University of Puerto Rico, San Germán Campus, B
Pontifical Catholic University of Puerto Rico, B
University of Puerto Rico in Cayey, B
University of Puerto Rico, Mayagüez Campus, BM
University of Puerto Rico, Río Piedras Campus, BMD

U.S. Territories: United States Virgin Islands

University of the Virgin Islands, B

Canada

Alberta

Concordia University of Edmonton, B
University of Alberta, BMDO
University of Calgary, BMD
University of Lethbridge, BM

British Columbia

Simon Fraser University, BMD
Thompson Rivers University, AB
Trinity Western University, B
The University of British Columbia, BMD
The University of British Columbia - Okanagan Campus, B
University of the Fraser Valley, B
University of Northern British Columbia, BM
University of Victoria, BMD

Manitoba

Brandon University, B
University of Manitoba, BMD
The University of Winnipeg, B

Maritime Provinces: New Brunswick

Mount Allison University, B
St. Thomas University, B
Université de Moncton, BM
University of New Brunswick Fredericton, BMD
University of New Brunswick Saint John, B

Maritime Provinces: Nova Scotia

Acadia University, B
Cape Breton University, B
Dalhousie University, BMD
Mount Saint Vincent University, B
St. Francis Xavier University, B
Saint Mary's University, B
University of King's College, B

Maritime Provinces: Prince Edward Island

University of Prince Edward Island, B

Newfoundland and Labrador

Memorial University of Newfoundland, BMD

Ontario

Brock University, BM
Carleton University, BMD
Lakehead University, BM
Laurentian University, B
McMaster University, BMD
Nipissing University, B
Queen's University at Kingston, BMD
Redeemer University College, B
Royal Military College of Canada, M
Trent University, B
University of Guelph, MD
University of Ottawa, BMD
University of Toronto, MD
University of Waterloo, BMD
The University of Western Ontario, BMD
University of Windsor, BMD
Wilfrid Laurier University, BM
York University, BMD

Quebec

Bishop's University, B
Concordia University, BMD
McGill University, BMD
Université Laval, BMD
Université de Montréal, BMDO
Université du Québec à Chicoutimi, B
Université du Québec à Montréal, BMD
Université du Québec à Rimouski, B
Université du Québec à Trois-Rivières, BM
Université de Sherbrooke, BMD

Saskatchewan

University of Regina, BMD
University of Saskatchewan, BMD

MATHEMATICS AND COMPUTER SCIENCE

United States

Alaska

University of Alaska Anchorage, B

California

Biola University, B
Pepperdine University, B
Saint Mary's College of California, B
Santa Clara University, B
Stanford University, B

Colorado

The Colorado College, B

Delaware

Delaware State University, B

Florida

Palm Beach Atlantic University, B
The University of Tampa, B

Georgia

Emory University, B

Illinois

DePaul University, B
Dominican University, B
Eastern Illinois University, B
Loyola University Chicago, B
University of Illinois at Chicago, B
University of Illinois at Urbana - Champaign, B
University of St. Francis, B

Indiana

Anderson University, B
Grace College, B
Indiana University - Purdue University Fort Wayne, B
Manchester University, B
Purdue University, B
Saint Mary's College, B

Kentucky

Brescia University, B

Maine

Bowdoin College, B

Massachusetts

Massachusetts Institute of Technology, B
Salem State University, B
Springfield College, B
Tufts University, B
University of Massachusetts Dartmouth, B
Wheaton College, B

Michigan

Lake Superior State University, B
Lawrence Technological University, B

Missouri

Crowder College, A
Washington University in St. Louis, B

New York

Hofstra University, B
Ithaca College, B
Rochester Institute of Technology, B
University at Albany, State University of New York, B

North Carolina

Pfeiffer University, B

Ohio

The University of Akron, B

Oregon

Lewis & Clark College, B
Southern Oregon University, B
University of Oregon, B

Pennsylvania

Chestnut Hill College, B
Immaculata University, B
Saint Francis University, B
Temple University, B

Rhode Island

Brown University, B

Tennessee

Bryan College, B
Christian Brothers University, B

Texas

LeTourneau University, B
The University of Texas at Austin, B

Vermont

Bennington College, B
Marlboro College, B

Virginia

Hampden-Sydney College, B

Washington

Western Washington University, B
Whitman College, B

West Virginia

Bethany College, B

Wisconsin

Lawrence University, B

Canada

Alberta

University of Alberta, B

British Columbia

University of Northern British Columbia, B

Manitoba

Brandon University, B

Maritime Provinces: New Brunswick

Mount Allison University, B

Maritime Provinces: Nova Scotia

Mount Saint Vincent University, B

Ontario

Redeemer University College, B
University of Waterloo, B
University of Windsor, B
York University, B

Quebec

McGill University, B
Université Laval, B

Saskatchewan

University of Regina, B

MATHEMATICS AND STATISTICS

United States

California

Saint Mary's College of California, B

Colorado

Western State Colorado University, B

Delaware

Delaware State University, B
Wesley College, B

Indiana

Anderson University, B

Louisiana

Tulane University, B

Massachusetts

Bristol Community College, A

Missouri

University of Missouri - Kansas City, B

New Hampshire

University of New Hampshire, B

New York

Columbia University, School of General Studies, B
Hofstra University, B
New York University, B
Purchase College, State University of New York, B
St. Joseph's College, Long Island Campus, B
St. Joseph's College, New York, B
University of Rochester, B

North Carolina

The University of North Carolina at Charlotte, B

Ohio

Miami University Hamilton, B
Ohio University, B

Pennsylvania

Carnegie Mellon University, B
Lycoming College, B
University of Pittsburgh, B

Vermont

Marlboro College, B

Washington

Seattle Pacific University, B

Canada

Alberta

University of Alberta, B

British Columbia

The University of British Columbia - Okanagan
Campus, B

Saskatchewan

University of Regina, B

MATHEMATICS TEACHER EDUCATION

United States

Alabama

Alabama Agricultural and Mechanical University, MO
Alabama State University, MO
Auburn University, BMDO
Auburn University at Montgomery, M
Huntingdon College, B
Judson College, B
Miles College, B
Spring Hill College, B
Talladega College, B
Troy University, M
The University of Alabama in Huntsville, M
University of Mobile, B
The University of West Alabama, M

Arizona

Arizona Christian University, B
Arizona State University at the Tempe campus, D
Grand Canyon University, B
Northern Arizona University, MO
The University of Arizona, M
University of Phoenix - Online Campus, M

Arkansas

Arkansas State University, BM
Arkansas Tech University, B
Harding University, BM
John Brown University, B
University of Arkansas, M
University of Arkansas - Fort Smith, B
University of Arkansas at Pine Bluff, M
University of Central Arkansas, BM

California

Biola University, B
California Baptist University, B
California Lutheran University, B
California State University, Bakersfield, M
California State University, Chico, M
California State University, Dominguez Hills, M
California State University, East Bay, M
California State University, Fresno, M
California State University, Fullerton, M
California State University, Long Beach, BM
California State University, Northridge, B
California State University, San Bernardino, M

Fresno Pacific University, M
Loyola Marymount University, M
Mills College, M
National University, BMO
Occidental College, M
Pepperdine University, B
San Diego State University, D
San Francisco State University, M
San Jose State University, M
Simpson University, B
University of California, Berkeley, MD
University of California, San Diego, BD
Westmont College, B
William Jessup University, M

Colorado

Adams State University, B
The Colorado College, M
Colorado State University, B
University of Colorado Denver, MD
University of Northern Colorado, MD
Western State Colorado University, B

Connecticut

Quinnipiac University, M
University of Connecticut, MDO
University of Hartford, B

Delaware

Delaware State University, BM
Delaware Technical & Community College, Jack F.
Owens Campus, A
Delaware Technical & Community College,
Stanton/Wilmington Campus, A
Delaware Technical & Community College, Terry
Campus, A
University of Delaware, B
Wilmington University, B

District of Columbia

The Catholic University of America, B
The George Washington University, M
University of the District of Columbia, M
University of Phoenix - Washington D.C. Campus,
M

Florida

Broward College, B
Chipola College, B
Daytona State College, B
Florida Agricultural and Mechanical University, BM
Florida Atlantic University, BM
Florida Institute of Technology, BMDO
Florida International University, M
Florida Southern College, B
Florida SouthWestern State College, B
Florida State University, MDO
Hobe Sound Bible College, B
Indian River State College, B
Miami Dade College, B
Northwest Florida State College, B
Nova Southeastern University, B
Palm Beach Atlantic University, B
St. Petersburg College, B
South Florida State College, A
Southeastern University, B
State College of Florida Manatee-Sarasota, A
University of Central Florida, BMDO
University of Florida, M
University of Miami, D
University of North Florida, B
University of Phoenix - North Florida Campus, M
University of Phoenix - South Florida Campus, M
University of South Florida, BMDO
University of South Florida, St. Petersburg, M

Georgia

Albany State University, M
Armstrong State University, B
Berry College, B
Clark Atlanta University, M
Clayton State University, M
Columbus State University, BMO
Covenant College, B
Darton State College, A

Emmanuel College, B
Georgia Southern University, M
Georgia State University, MD
Gordon State College, B
Kennesaw State University, BM
LaGrange College, B
Middle Georgia State University, B
Paine College, B
Piedmont College, B
Shorter University, B
University of Georgia, BMDO
University of North Georgia, M
University of West Georgia, M

Hawaii

Brigham Young University - Hawaii, B
Chaminade University of Honolulu, M

Idaho

Boise State University, BM
Brigham Young University - Idaho, B
Idaho State University, M
Lewis-Clark State College, B
Northwest Nazarene University, B

Illinois

Augustana College, B
Aurora University, M
Blackburn College, B
Bradley University, B
Concordia University Chicago, B
DePaul University, M
Eastern Illinois University, M
Elmhurst College, B
Greenville College, B
Heartland Community College, A
Highland Community College, A
Illinois Institute of Technology, MD
Illinois State University, D
John A. Logan College, A
Kankakee Community College, A
Kaskaskia College, A
Lake Forest College, M
Lewis University, M
Loyola University Chicago, B
McKendree University, B
Millikin University, B
Moraine Valley Community College, A
National Louis University, MO
Northeastern Illinois University, M
Northwestern University, B
Saint Xavier University, B
Southern Illinois University Edwardsville, M
Southwestern Illinois College, A
Trinity Christian College, B
Triton College, A
University of Illinois at Chicago, BMD
University of Illinois at Urbana - Champaign, BM
University of St. Francis, BM

Indiana

Anderson University, B
Ball State University, M
Bethel College, B
Franklin College, B
Goshen College, B
Grace College, B
Huntington University, B
Indiana University Bloomington, BMD
Indiana University Northwest, B
Indiana University - Purdue University Fort Wayne,
BM
Indiana University - Purdue University Indianapolis,
M
Indiana University South Bend, B
Indiana University Southeast, B
Indiana Wesleyan University, B
Manchester University, B
Oakland City University, B
Purdue University, MDO
Purdue University Northwest (Hammond), M
Taylor University, B
Trine University, B
University of Evansville, B
University of Indianapolis, BM
University of Saint Francis, B

Valparaiso University, B
Vincennes University, AB

Iowa

Buena Vista University, B
Iowa State University of Science and Technology, M
Kaplan University, Davenport Campus, M
Morningside College, B
St. Ambrose University, B
The University of Iowa, BMD
University of Northern Iowa, BM
Wartburg College, B

Kansas

Bethany College, B
Central Christian College of Kansas, A
Friends University, B
Kansas Wesleyan University, B
MidAmerica Nazarene University, B
Pittsburg State University, B
Southwestern College, B
Tabor College, B
Washburn University, B

Kentucky

Alice Lloyd College, B
Asbury University, M
Campbellsville University, B
Eastern Kentucky University, BM
Kentucky Christian University, B
Lindsey Wilson College, B
Morehead State University, M

Louisiana

Grambling State University, BM
Louisiana State University in Shreveport, B
Louisiana Tech University, BM
Nicholls State University, BM
Southern University and Agricultural and Mechanical College, BD
University of Louisiana at Monroe, BM

Maine

Bowdoin College, B
Saint Joseph's College of Maine, B
University of Maine, BMDO
University of Maine at Farmington, B
University of Maine at Machias, B
University of Southern Maine, B

Maryland

Anne Arundel Community College, A
Bowie State University, B
Carroll Community College, A
Chesapeake College, A
Community College of Baltimore County, A
Frederick Community College, A
Harford Community College, A
Hood College, MO
Johns Hopkins University, O
Loyola University Maryland, M
Montgomery College, A
Morgan State University, MD
Salisbury University, M
Stevenson University, M
Towson University, M
University of Maryland, Baltimore County, M
Washington Adventist University, B

Massachusetts

Boston University, B
Bridgewater State University, M
Cambridge College, MO
Fitchburg State University, B
Framingham State University, M
Gordon College, O
Harvard University, M
Lesley University, M
Merrimack College, B
Regis College, B
Salem State University, M
Smith College, M
Tufts University, MD
University of Massachusetts Dartmouth, D

University of Massachusetts Lowell, D
Western New England University, M

Michigan

Adrian College, B
Albion College, B
Alma College, B
Calvin College, B
Central Michigan University, BD
Concordia University Ann Arbor, B
Cornerstone University, B
Eastern Michigan University, B
Ferris State University, B
Grand Valley State University, B
Hope College, B
Madonna University, B
Michigan State University, BMD
Northern Michigan University, B
Oakland University, O
Olivet College, B
Rochester College, B
Saginaw Valley State University, B
Spring Arbor University, B
University of Detroit Mercy, BM
University of Michigan - Dearborn, B
University of Michigan - Flint, B
Wayne State University, MDO
Western Michigan University, BMD

Minnesota

Bemidji State University, M
Bethel University, B
Concordia College, B
Concordia University, St. Paul, B
Gustavus Adolphus College, B
Metropolitan State University, B
Minnesota State University Mankato, M
Minnesota State University Moorhead, B
St. Catherine University, B
Saint Mary's University of Minnesota, B
Southwest Minnesota State University, BM
University of Minnesota, Duluth, B
University of Minnesota, Twin Cities Campus, MD
University of Northwestern - St. Paul, B
University of St. Thomas, BO
Walden University, MO
Winona State University, B

Mississippi

Blue Mountain College, B
Coahoma Community College, A
Delta State University, B
Jackson State University, BM
Mississippi College, M
Northeast Mississippi Community College, A
Northwest Mississippi Community College, A
Rust College, B
University of Mississippi, B
University of Southern Mississippi, MD
William Carey University, B

Missouri

College of the Ozarks, B
Culver-Stockton College, B
Drury University, B
Hannibal-LaGrange University, B
Lincoln University, B
Lindenwood University, B
Missouri State University, BM
Missouri University of Science and Technology, M
Northwest Missouri State University, BM
Saint Louis University, B
Southeast Missouri State University, B
Southwest Baptist University, B
University of Missouri, BMDO
Washington University in St. Louis, B
Webster University, M
William Woods University, B

Montana

Carroll College, B
Montana State University, M
Montana State University Billings, B
Rocky Mountain College, B
University of Great Falls, B

University of Montana, BMD
The University of Montana Western, B

Nebraska

Chadron State College, B
College of Saint Mary, B
Concordia University, Nebraska, B
Hastings College, B
Peru State College, B
Union College, B
University of Nebraska at Kearney, M
University of Nebraska - Lincoln, B
Wayne State College, BM
York College, B

Nevada

Nevada State College, B
University of Nevada, Reno, M

New Hampshire

Keene State College, B
Plymouth State University, BM
Rivier University, B
Southern New Hampshire University, B
University of New Hampshire, B

New Jersey

The College of New Jersey, B
Drew University, M
Felician University, B
Kean University, M
Montclair State University, MDO
New Jersey City University, M
Rider University, O
Rowan University, MO
Rutgers University - Camden, M
Rutgers University - New Brunswick, MD
Saint Peter's University, O

New York

Binghamton University, State University of New York, M
Brooklyn College of the City University of New York, BM
Buffalo State College, State University of New York, BM
Canisius College, B
City College of the City University of New York, BMO
The College at Brockport, State University of New York, M
The College of Saint Rose, B
College of Staten Island of the City University of New York, B
Cornell University, M
Daemen College, B
Dominican College, B
Elmira College, B
Hofstra University, BMD
Hunter College of the City University of New York, BM
Iona College, BM
Ithaca College, BM
Keuka College, B
Le Moyne College, B
Lehman College of the City University of New York, M
Long Island University - LIU Brooklyn, B
Long Island University - LIU Post, B
Manhattanville College, BM
Marist College, B
Medaille College, B
Nazareth College of Rochester, B
New York City College of Technology of the City University of New York, B
New York Institute of Technology, MO
New York University, BM
Niagara University, BM
Nyack College, B
Pace University, B
Pace University, Pleasantville Campus, B
Queens College of the City University of New York, BMO
Roberts Wesleyan College, B
St. Francis College, B

St. John Fisher College, B
St. John's University, B
St. Joseph's College, Long Island Campus, B
St. Joseph's College, New York, B
State University of New York College at Cortland, BM
State University of New York College at Old Westbury, BM
State University of New York College at Oneonta, B
State University of New York College at Potsdam, BM
State University of New York at New Paltz, BM
State University of New York at Plattsburgh, M
Stony Brook University, State University of New York, M
Syracuse University, BMD
Touro College, M
Ulster County Community College, A
University at Buffalo, the State University of New York, MO
Utica College, B
Wagner College, M

North Carolina

Appalachian State University, M
Bennett College, B
Campbell University, B
East Carolina University, BMO
Elizabeth City State University, BM
Fayetteville State University, B
Gardner-Webb University, B
Greensboro College, B
High Point University, M
Louisburg College, A
North Carolina Agricultural and Technical State University, B
North Carolina Central University, M
North Carolina State University, BMD
The University of North Carolina at Chapel Hill, M
The University of North Carolina at Charlotte, M
The University of North Carolina at Greensboro, BM
The University of North Carolina at Pembroke, BM
The University of North Carolina Wilmington, B
Western Carolina University, B
Wingate University, B
Winston-Salem State University, B

North Dakota

Mayville State University, B
Minot State University, BM
North Dakota State University, BMD
University of Jamestown, B
University of Mary, B
Valley City State University, B

Ohio

Bowling Green State University, BM
Capital University, B
Cedarville University, B
Cleveland State University, M
Kent State University, B
Miami University, BM
Miami University Hamilton, B
Mount Vernon Nazarene University, B
Ohio Dominican University, B
Ohio Northern University, B
The Ohio State University, M
Ohio University, D
Ohio Wesleyan University, B
Shawnee State University, B
The University of Akron, B
University of Cincinnati, M
University of Dayton, M
University of Rio Grande, B
The University of Toledo, M
Ursuline College, BM
Walsh University, B
Wright State University, M
Youngstown State University, BM

Oklahoma

Cameron University, B
East Central University, B
Northeastern State University, BM
Northwestern Oklahoma State University, B
Oklahoma Baptist University, B
Oklahoma Christian University, B
Oklahoma State University, MD
Oklahoma Wesleyan University, B
Oral Roberts University, B
St. Gregory's University, B
Southeastern Oklahoma State University, BM
Southern Nazarene University, B
Southwestern Oklahoma State University, BM
University of Central Oklahoma, B
University of Oklahoma, BD
The University of Tulsa, BM

Oregon

Concordia University, BM
Corban University, B
Oregon State University, MD
Portland State University, D
Western Oregon University, M

Pennsylvania

Alvernia University, B
Arcadia University, MO
Bloomsburg University of Pennsylvania, M
Bucks County Community College, A
Cabrini University, B
Cairn University, B
Chatham University, M
Clarion University of Pennsylvania, M
Duquesne University, BM
Eastern University, O
Geneva College, B
Grove City College, B
Gwynedd Mercy University, B
Holy Family University, B
Indiana University of Pennsylvania, M
Juniata College, B
Keystone College, B
Kutztown University of Pennsylvania, M
Lincoln University, B
Marywood University, B
Mercyhurst University, B
Messiah College, B
Millersville University of Pennsylvania, M
Misericordia University, B
Point Park University, B
Saint Francis University, B
Seton Hill University, B
Shippensburg University of Pennsylvania, M
Slippery Rock University of Pennsylvania, M
Summit University, B
Temple University, BM
University of Pittsburgh, MD
University of Pittsburgh at Johnstown, B
Waynesburg University, B
West Chester University of Pennsylvania, M
Widener University, BM
Wilkes University, M
York College of Pennsylvania, B

Rhode Island

Providence College, BM
Rhode Island College, BM
Roger Williams University, B
Salve Regina University, B

South Carolina

Anderson University, B
Bob Jones University, BM
Charleston Southern University, B
The Citadel, The Military College of South Carolina, M
Claflin University, B
Clemson University, BM
Coker College, B
College of Charleston, M
Converse College, M
Limestone College, B
Morris College, B
North Greenville University, B
South Carolina State University, M
Southern Wesleyan University, B
University of South Carolina, M

South Dakota

Black Hills State University, B
Dakota State University, B
Dakota Wesleyan University, B
Mount Marty College, B
The University of South Dakota, B

Tennessee

Bryan College, B
Cumberland University, B
King University, B
Lee University, BM
LeMoyne-Owen College, B
Lincoln Memorial University, B
Lipscomb University, BMO
Maryville College, B
Middle Tennessee State University, MD
Southern Adventist University, B
Tennessee Technological University, MO
Trevecca Nazarene University, B
The University of Tennessee, MO
The University of Tennessee at Chattanooga, BM
The University of Tennessee at Martin, B

Texas

Abilene Christian University, B
Baylor University, B
Dallas Baptist University, B
East Texas Baptist University, B
Hardin-Simmons University, B
Houston Baptist University, B
Howard College, A
Howard Payne University, B
LeTourneau University, B
McMurry University, B
Midwestern State University, B
Our Lady of the Lake University of San Antonio, M
St. Edward's University, B
Schreiner University, B
Stephen F. Austin State University, M
Texas A&M International University, B
Texas Christian University, BM
Texas Lutheran University, B
Texas State University, MD
Texas Wesleyan University, B
Texas Woman's University, M
University of the Incarnate Word, M
University of Mary Hardin-Baylor, B
The University of Texas at Arlington, M
The University of Texas at Dallas, M
The University of Texas at El Paso, M
The University of Texas Rio Grande Valley, M
The University of Texas at San Antonio, M

Utah

Brigham Young University, M
Dixie State University, B
Southern Utah University, B
Utah State University, B
Utah Valley University, BM
Weber State University, B
Western Governors University, BM

Vermont

Castleton University, B
Johnson State College, B
Lyndon State College, B
University of Vermont, BM

Virginia

Averett University, BM
Bluefield College, B
Emory & Henry College, B
George Mason University, M
James Madison University, M
Liberty University, M
Longwood University, M
Radford University, M
Regent University, M
University of Virginia, MD
Virginia Polytechnic Institute and State University, D
Virginia State University, M
Virginia Union University, B

Washington

Central Washington University, B
Eastern Washington University, BM
Heritage University, B
Northwest University, B
Pierce College at Fort Steilacoom, A
Seattle Pacific University, M
Seattle University, B
University of Washington, BMD
University of Washington, Tacoma, M
Walla Walla Community College, A
Washington State University, BMD
Western Washington University, B

West Virginia

Bethany College, B
Davis & Elkins College, B
Glenville State College, B
Ohio Valley University, B
West Virginia University, M
West Virginia Wesleyan College, B

Wisconsin

Carroll University, B
Edgewood College, B
Maranatha Baptist University, B
Marquette University, BM
Mount Mary University, B
University of Wisconsin - Madison, M
University of Wisconsin - Oshkosh, M
University of Wisconsin - River Falls, M
University of Wisconsin - Superior, B
Viterbo University, B

Wyoming

Eastern Wyoming College, A
University of Wyoming, M

U.S. Territories: Puerto Rico

Bayamón Central University, B
Caribbean University, M
Inter American University of Puerto Rico, Arecibo Campus, BM
Inter American University of Puerto Rico, Barranquitas Campus, M
Inter American University of Puerto Rico, Metropolitan Campus, BM
Inter American University of Puerto Rico, Ponce Campus, M
Inter American University of Puerto Rico, San Germán Campus, BM
Pontifical Catholic University of Puerto Rico, B
Universidad Adventista de las Antillas, B
Universidad del Turabo, B
University of Puerto Rico in Cayey, B
University of Puerto Rico, Mayagüez Campus, B
University of Puerto Rico, Río Piedras Campus, M
University of Puerto Rico in Utuado, B
University of the Sacred Heart, M

U.S. Territories: United States Virgin Islands

University of the Virgin Islands, M

Canada

Alberta

University of Alberta, B
University of Lethbridge, B

British Columbia

Simon Fraser University, MD
The University of British Columbia, M
University of Victoria, MD

Maritime Provinces: Nova Scotia

Acadia University, M

Ontario

Brock University, B
University of Waterloo, B
University of Windsor, B
York University, B

Quebec

Bishop's University, B
Concordia University, M
Université Laval, B
Université de Montréal, B
Université du Québec à Trois-Rivières, B

Saskatchewan

University of Regina, B

MEAT CUTTING/MEAT CUTTER

United States

Oklahoma

Eastern Oklahoma State College, A

MECHANIC AND REPAIR TECHNOLOGIES/TECHNICIANS

United States

Arizona

Chandler-Gilbert Community College, A

Colorado

Colorado State University - Pueblo, B

Illinois

Triton College, A

Indiana

Ivy Tech Community College - Bloomington, A
Ivy Tech Community College - Columbus, A
Ivy Tech Community College - Kokomo, A
Ivy Tech Community College - Lafayette, A
Ivy Tech Community College - North Central, A
Ivy Tech Community College - Northwest, A
Ivy Tech Community College - Southwest, A

Kansas

Cloud County Community College, A
Johnson County Community College, A
Washburn University, A

Maine

Washington County Community College, A

Michigan

Macomb Community College, A

Missouri

State Fair Community College, A

New Jersey

Thomas Edison State University, A

New York

Corning Community College, A

Ohio

Ohio Technical College, A

Oklahoma

Oklahoma State University Institute of Technology, A

Pennsylvania

Pennsylvania College of Technology, A

South Carolina

Greenville Technical College, A

Washington

Bates Technical College, A
Centralia College, A

Wyoming

Laramie County Community College, A

U.S. Territories: Puerto Rico

Inter American University of Puerto Rico, Guayama Campus, AB

MECHANICAL DRAFTING AND MECHANICAL DRAFTING CAD/CADD

United States

California

Chaffey College, A
College of the Redwoods, A
Long Beach City College, A
Los Angeles Valley College, A
Sierra College, A

Colorado

IntelliTec College (Colorado Springs), A

Delaware

Delaware Technical & Community College, Jack F. Owens Campus, A

Florida

North Florida Community College, A

Illinois

City Colleges of Chicago, Harry S. Truman College, A
Morrison Institute of Technology, A
Southwestern Illinois College, A

Indiana

Indiana University - Purdue University Indianapolis, B
Lincoln College of Technology, A
Vincennes University, A

Iowa

Des Moines Area Community College, A
Indian Hills Community College, A
Kirkwood Community College, A
Marshalltown Community College, A
North Iowa Area Community College, A
Scott Community College, A
Western Iowa Tech Community College, A

Kansas

Hutchinson Community College, A
Wichita Area Technical College, A

Kentucky

Sullivan College of Technology and Design, A

Michigan

Baker College, A
Lansing Community College, A
Macomb Community College, A
Oakland Community College, A

Minnesota

Alexandria Technical and Community College, A
Anoka Technical College, A
Central Lakes College, A
Globe University - Woodbury, A
Lake Superior College, A
Minnesota State Community and Technical College, A
Minnesota State Community and Technical College - Moorhead, A
Ridgewater College, A
St. Cloud Technical & Community College, A

Missouri

Ozarks Technical Community College, A

New York

Corning Community College, A
Island Drafting and Technical Institute, A

New York City College of Technology of the City University of New York, A
Queensborough Community College of the City University of New York, A

North Carolina

Cleveland Community College, A
Mitchell Community College, A
Stanly Community College, A
Wake Technical Community College, A

Ohio

Edison Community College, A
North Central State College, A

Oregon

Chemeketa Community College, A
Lane Community College, A

Pennsylvania

Butler County Community College, A
Commonwealth Technical Institute, A
Community College of Allegheny County, A
Triangle Tech, Erie, A
Triangle Tech, Greensburg, A
Triangle Tech, Pittsburgh, A
Westmoreland County Community College, A

South Carolina

Florence-Darlington Technical College, A
Greenville Technical College, A
Midlands Technical College, A
Piedmont Technical College, A
Tri-County Technical College, A
York Technical College, A

Texas

Midland College, A

Washington

North Seattle College, A

Wisconsin

Fox Valley Technical College, A
Gateway Technical College, A
Milwaukee Area Technical College, A
Moraine Park Technical College, A
Northcentral Technical College, A
Northeast Wisconsin Technical College, A
Southwest Wisconsin Technical College, A
Waukesha County Technical College, A

Canada

British Columbia

British Columbia Institute of Technology, A

MECHANICAL ENGINEERING

United States

Alabama

Alabama Agricultural and Mechanical University, B
Auburn University, BMD
Tuskegee University, BM
The University of Alabama, BMD
The University of Alabama at Birmingham, BM
The University of Alabama in Huntsville, BMD
University of South Alabama, BM

Alaska

University of Alaska Fairbanks, BM

Arizona

Arizona State University at the Tempe campus, BMD
Embry-Riddle Aeronautical University - Prescott, B
Northern Arizona University, BM
The University of Arizona, BMD

Arkansas

Arkansas State University, B
Arkansas Tech University, B
Harding University, B
John Brown University, B
University of Arkansas, BMD

California

California Baptist University, B
California Institute of Technology, BMDO
California Maritime Academy, B
California Polytechnic State University, San Luis Obispo, BM
California State Polytechnic University, Pomona, BM
California State University, Chico, B
California State University, Fresno, BM
California State University, Fullerton, BM
California State University, Long Beach, BMD
California State University, Los Angeles, BM
California State University, Northridge, BM
California State University, Sacramento, BM
Loyola Marymount University, BM
Pasadena City College, A
San Diego State University, BMD
San Francisco State University, B
San Jose State University, BM
Santa Clara University, BMDO
Stanford University, BMDO
University of California, Berkeley, BMD
University of California, Davis, BMDO
University of California, Irvine, BMD
University of California, Los Angeles, BMD
University of California, Merced, BMD
University of California, Riverside, BMD
University of California, San Diego, BMD
University of California, Santa Barbara, BMD
University of the Pacific, B
University of San Diego, B
University of Southern California, BMDO

Colorado

Colorado School of Mines, BMD
Colorado State University, BMD
United States Air Force Academy, B
University of Colorado Boulder, BMD
University of Colorado Colorado Springs, BM
University of Colorado Denver, BM
University of Denver, BMD

Connecticut

Fairfield University, BM
Quinnipiac University, B
Trinity College, B
United States Coast Guard Academy, B
University of Bridgeport, M
University of Connecticut, BMD
University of Hartford, B
University of New Haven, BM
Yale University, BMD

Delaware

Delaware State University, B
University of Delaware, BMD

District of Columbia

The Catholic University of America, BMD
The George Washington University, BMDO
Howard University, BMD
University of the District of Columbia, B

Florida

Broward College, A
Embry-Riddle Aeronautical University - Daytona, BMD
Florida Agricultural and Mechanical University, BMD
Florida Atlantic University, BMD
Florida Institute of Technology, BMD
Florida International University, BMD
Florida State University, MD
Jacksonville University, B
South Florida State College, A
University of Central Florida, BMD
University of Florida, BMD
University of Miami, BMD
University of North Florida, BM

University of South Florida, BMD

Georgia

Georgia Institute of Technology, BMD
Georgia Southern University, BM
Kennesaw State University, B
Mercer University, M

Hawaii

University of Hawaii at Manoa, BMD

Idaho

Boise State University, BM
Idaho State University, BM
University of Idaho, BMD

Illinois

Bradley University, BM
Illinois Institute of Technology, BMD
Northern Illinois University, BM
Northwestern University, BMD
Southern Illinois University Carbondale, BM
Southern Illinois University Edwardsville, BM
University of Illinois at Chicago, BMD
University of Illinois at Urbana - Champaign, BMD

Indiana

Anderson University, B
Indiana Tech, B
Indiana University - Purdue University Fort Wayne, BM
Indiana University - Purdue University Indianapolis, BMDO
Purdue University, BMDO
Purdue University Northwest (Hammond), BM
Purdue University Northwest (Westville), B
Rose-Hulman Institute of Technology, BM
Trine University, B
University of Evansville, B
University of Indianapolis, B
University of Notre Dame, BMD
Valparaiso University, B

Iowa

Dordt College, B
Iowa State University of Science and Technology, BMD
The University of Iowa, BMD
William Penn University, B

Kansas

Benedictine College, B
Kansas State University, BMD
The University of Kansas, BMD
Wichita State University, BMD

Kentucky

University of Kentucky, BMD
University of Louisville, BMD
Western Kentucky University, B

Louisiana

Louisiana State University and Agricultural & Mechanical College, BMD
Louisiana Tech University, BMD
McNeese State University, MO
Southern University and Agricultural and Mechanical College, B
University of Louisiana at Lafayette, BM
University of New Orleans, BM

Maine

University of Maine, BMD
University of Southern Maine, B

Maryland

Johns Hopkins University, BMD
United States Naval Academy, B
University of Maryland, Baltimore County, BMDO
University of Maryland, College Park, BMD

Massachusetts

Boston University, BMD
Bristol Community College, A

Eastern Nazarene College, B
Franklin W. Olin College of Engineering, B
Massachusetts Institute of Technology, BMDO
Merrimack College, BM
Northeastern University, BMD
Tufts University, BMD
University of Massachusetts Amherst, BMD
University of Massachusetts Dartmouth, BM
University of Massachusetts Lowell, BMD
Wentworth Institute of Technology, B
Western New England University, BM
Worcester Polytechnic Institute, BMDO

Michigan

Andrews University, B
Baker College, B
Calvin College, B
Central Michigan University, B
Grand Valley State University, M
Kettering University, BM
Lake Superior State University, B
Lawrence Technological University, BMD
Michigan State University, BMD
Michigan Technological University, BMDO
Oakland University, BMD
Saginaw Valley State University, B
University of Detroit Mercy, MD
University of Michigan, BMD
University of Michigan - Dearborn, BM
University of Michigan - Flint, B
Wayne State University, BMD
Western Michigan University, BMD

Minnesota

Itasca Community College, A
Minnesota State University Mankato, B
St. Cloud State University, BM
University of Minnesota, Duluth, B
University of Minnesota, Twin Cities Campus, BMD
University of St. Thomas, BM

Mississippi

Mississippi State University, BMD
University of Mississippi, B

Missouri

Missouri University of Science and Technology, BMD
Rockhurst University, B
St. Charles Community College, A
Saint Louis University, B
University of Missouri, BMD
University of Missouri - Kansas City, BM
University of Missouri - St. Louis, B
Washington University in St. Louis, BMD

Montana

Montana State University, BMD

Nebraska

University of Nebraska - Lincoln, BMD

Nevada

University of Nevada, Las Vegas, BMDO
University of Nevada, Reno, BMD

New Hampshire

Daniel Webster College, B
Dartmouth College, MD
University of New Hampshire, BMD

New Jersey

The College of New Jersey, B
New Jersey Institute of Technology, BMD
Princeton University, BMD
Rowan University, BM
Rutgers University - New Brunswick, BMD
Stevens Institute of Technology, BMDO

New Mexico

New Mexico Institute of Mining and Technology, BM
New Mexico State University, BMD
University of New Mexico, BMD

New York

Alfred University, BM
Binghamton University, State University of New York, BMD
Cayuga County Community College, A
City College of the City University of New York, BMD
Clarkson University, BMD
Columbia University, BMD
Cooper Union for the Advancement of Science and Art, BM
Cornell University, BMD
Fiorello H. LaGuardia Community College of the City University of New York, A
Hofstra University, B
Manhattan College, BM
New York Institute of Technology, B
New York University, BMD
Rensselaer Polytechnic Institute, BMD
Rochester Institute of Technology, BM
State University of New York Maritime College, B
State University of New York at New Paltz, B
State University of New York Polytechnic Institute, B
Stony Brook University, State University of New York, BMD
Syracuse University, BMD
Union College, B
United States Military Academy, B
University at Buffalo, the State University of New York, BMD
University of Rochester, BMD

North Carolina

Duke University, BMD
Gaston College, A
North Carolina Agricultural and Technical State University, BMD
North Carolina State University, BMD
The University of North Carolina at Charlotte, BMD

North Dakota

North Dakota State University, BMD
University of Jamestown, B
University of North Dakota, BM

Ohio

Case Western Reserve University, BMD
Cedarville University, B
Cleveland State University, BMD
Miami University, B
Mount Vernon Nazarene University, B
Northwest State Community College, A
Ohio Northern University, B
The Ohio State University, BMD
Ohio University, BMD
The University of Akron, BMD
University of Cincinnati, BMD
University of Dayton, BMD
University of Mount Union, B
The University of Toledo, BMD
Wright State University, BM
Wright State University - Lake Campus, B
Youngstown State University, BM

Oklahoma

Oklahoma Christian University, B
Oklahoma State University, BMD
Oral Roberts University, B
University of Central Oklahoma, BM
University of Oklahoma, BMD
The University of Tulsa, BMD

Oregon

George Fox University, B
Oregon State University, BMD
Portland State University, BMD
University of Portland, BM

Pennsylvania

Bucknell University, BM
Carnegie Mellon University, BMD
Drexel University, BMD
Gannon University, BM
Grove City College, B
Lafayette College, B

Lehigh University, BMD
Penn State Abington, B
Penn State Altoona, B
Penn State Beaver, B
Penn State Berks, B
Penn State Brandywine, B
Penn State DuBois, B
Penn State Erie, The Behrend College, B
Penn State Fayette, The Eberly Campus, B
Penn State Greater Allegheny, B
Penn State Harrisburg, B
Penn State Hazleton, B
Penn State Lehigh Valley, B
Penn State Mont Alto, B
Penn State New Kensington, B
Penn State Schuylkill, B
Penn State Shenango, B
Penn State University Park, BMD
Penn State Wilkes-Barre, B
Penn State Worthington Scranton, B
Penn State York, B
Temple University, BMD
University of Pennsylvania, BMD
University of Pittsburgh, BMD
Ursinus College, B
Villanova University, BMO
Widener University, BM
Wilkes University, BM
York College of Pennsylvania, B

Rhode Island

Brown University, BMD
New England Institute of Technology, AB
Roger Williams University, B
University of Rhode Island, B

South Carolina

The Citadel, The Military College of South Carolina, B
Clemson University, BMD
South Carolina State University, M
University of South Carolina, BMD

South Dakota

South Dakota School of Mines and Technology, BMD
South Dakota State University, BMD

Tennessee

Christian Brothers University, B
Lipscomb University, B
Nashville State Community College, A
Tennessee State University, BM
Tennessee Technological University, BM
University of Memphis, BMD
The University of Tennessee, BMD
The University of Tennessee at Chattanooga, BM
Vanderbilt University, BMD

Texas

Baylor University, BM
Kilgore College, A
Lamar University, BMD
LeTourneau University, B
Lone Star College - North Harris, A
Northeast Texas Community College, A
Prairie View A&M University, B
Rice University, BMD
St. Mary's University, B
Southern Methodist University, BMD
Texas A&M University, BMD
Texas A&M University - Corpus Christi, B
Texas A&M University - Kingsville, BM
Texas Tech University, BMD
University of Houston, BMD
University of North Texas, BMD
The University of Texas at Arlington, BMD
The University of Texas at Austin, BMD
The University of Texas at Dallas, BMD
The University of Texas at El Paso, BMD
The University of Texas of the Permian Basin, B
The University of Texas Rio Grande Valley, BM
The University of Texas at San Antonio, BMD
The University of Texas at Tyler, BM
West Texas A&M University, B

Utah

Brigham Young University, MD
University of Utah, BMD
Utah State University, BMD

Vermont

Norwich University, B
University of Vermont, BMD

Virginia

George Mason University, B
Liberty University, B
Old Dominion University, BMD
University of Virginia, BMD
Virginia Commonwealth University, BMD
Virginia Military Institute, B
Virginia Polytechnic Institute and State University, BMD

Washington

Eastern Washington University, B
Gonzaga University, B
Olympic College, A
Saint Martin's University, BM
Seattle University, B
University of Washington, BMD
University of Washington, Bothell, B
Walla Walla University, B
Washington State University, BMD
Washington State University - Tri-Cities, B
Washington State University - Vancouver, B

West Virginia

Marshall University, BM
Potomac State College of West Virginia University, A
West Virginia University, BMD
West Virginia University Institute of Technology, B

Wisconsin

Marquette University, BMDO
Milwaukee School of Engineering, B
University of Wisconsin - Madison, BMD
University of Wisconsin - Milwaukee, BM
University of Wisconsin - Platteville, B

Wyoming

University of Wyoming, BMD

U.S. Territories: Puerto Rico

Inter American University of Puerto Rico, Bayamón Campus, B
Polytechnic University of Puerto Rico, BM
Universidad del Turabo, B
University of Puerto Rico in Carolina, A
University of Puerto Rico, Mayagüez Campus, BM

Canada
Alberta

University of Alberta, MD
University of Calgary, BMD

British Columbia

Simon Fraser University, MD
The University of British Columbia, BMD
The University of British Columbia - Okanagan Campus, B
University of Victoria, BMD

Manitoba

University of Manitoba, BMD

Maritime Provinces: New Brunswick

Université de Moncton, BM
University of New Brunswick Fredericton, BMD

Maritime Provinces: Nova Scotia

Dalhousie University, MD

Newfoundland and Labrador

Memorial University of Newfoundland, BMD

Ontario

Carleton University, BMD
Lakehead University, B
McMaster University, BMD
Queen's University at Kingston, BMD
Royal Military College of Canada, BMD
Ryerson University, B
University of Guelph, B
University of Ottawa, BMD
University of Toronto, BMD
University of Waterloo, BMD
The University of Western Ontario, BMD
University of Windsor, BMD

Quebec

Concordia University, BMDO
École Polytechnique de Montréal, MDO
McGill University, BMD
Université Laval, BMD
Université du Québec en Abitibi-Témiscamingue, B
Université du Québec, École de technologie supérieure, B
Université du Québec à Trois-Rivières, B
Université de Sherbrooke, BMD

Saskatchewan

University of Saskatchewan, BMD

MECHANICAL ENGINEERING/ MECHANICAL TECHNOLOGY/ TECHNICIAN

United States
Alabama

Alabama Agricultural and Mechanical University, B

Arizona

Arizona State University at the Polytechnic campus, B

Arkansas

University of Arkansas at Little Rock, AB

California

California State University, Long Beach, B
California State University, Sacramento, B
Citrus College, A
Cuesta College, A
Fullerton College, A
Hartnell College, A
Lassen Community College District, A
Long Beach City College, A
San Joaquin Delta College, A
San Jose City College, A

Colorado

Colorado Mesa University, B
Metropolitan State University of Denver, B

Connecticut

Central Connecticut State University, B
Gateway Community College, A
Three Rivers Community College, A
University of Hartford, B

Delaware

Delaware State University, B
Delaware Technical & Community College, Stanton/Wilmington Campus, A

District of Columbia

University of the District of Columbia, B

Georgia

Augusta Technical College, A
Columbus Technical College, A
Georgia Southern University, B
Kennesaw State University, B

Idaho

Brigham Young University - Idaho, A
Idaho State University, AB

Illinois

College of Lake County, A
Illinois Central College, A
Illinois Eastern Community Colleges, Lincoln Trail College, A
Illinois Valley Community College, A
Joliet Junior College, A
Moraine Valley Community College, A
Oakton Community College, A
Prairie State College, A
Triton College, A

Indiana

Indiana University - Purdue University Fort Wayne, AB
Ivy Tech Community College - Lafayette, A
Purdue University, AB
Purdue University Northwest (Hammond), B
Vincennes University, A

Iowa

Southeastern Community College, A

Kansas

Pittsburg State University, B
Wichita Area Technical College, A

Kentucky

Madisonville Community College, A
Sullivan College of Technology and Design, AB

Louisiana

Nicholls State University, B
Southern University at Shreveport, A

Maine

University of Maine, B

Maryland

Hagerstown Community College, A

Massachusetts

Benjamin Franklin Institute of Technology, A
Massachusetts Bay Community College, A
Springfield Technical Community College, A

Michigan

Baker College, A
Central Michigan University, B
Delta College, A
Eastern Michigan University, B
Ferris State University, AB
Kalamazoo Valley Community College, A
Lake Superior State University, AB
Lawrence Technological University, A
Macomb Community College, A
Michigan Technological University, B
Mott Community College, A
Northern Michigan University, B
Wayne State University, B

Minnesota

Rochester Community and Technical College, A

Montana

Montana State University, B

Nevada

College of Southern Nevada, A

New Hampshire

NHTI, Concord's Community College, A
University of New Hampshire at Manchester, B

New Jersey

Camden County College, A
County College of Morris, A
Fairleigh Dickinson University, Metropolitan Campus, B

Middlesex County College, A
Union County College, A

New York

Broome Community College, A
Buffalo State College, State University of New York, B
Cayuga County Community College, A
Corning Community College, A
Erie Community College, North Campus, A
Farmingdale State College, AB
Finger Lakes Community College, A
Jamestown Community College, A
Mohawk Valley Community College, A
Monroe Community College, A
Morrisville State College, A
New York City College of Technology of the City University of New York, AB
Onondaga Community College, A
Queensborough Community College of the City University of New York, A
State University of New York College of Agriculture and Technology at Cobleskill, A
State University of New York College of Technology at Alfred, AB
State University of New York College of Technology at Canton, A
State University of New York Polytechnic Institute, B
Syracuse University, A
United States Military Academy, B
Westchester Community College, A

North Carolina

Alamance Community College, A
Beaufort County Community College, A
Blue Ridge Community College, A
Caldwell Community College and Technical Institute, A
Cape Fear Community College, A
Catawba Valley Community College, A
Central Piedmont Community College, A
Craven Community College, A
Edgecombe Community College, A
Forsyth Technical Community College, A
Gaston College, A
Guilford Technical Community College, A
Haywood Community College, A
Isothermal Community College, A
Mitchell Community College, A
Pitt Community College, A
Richmond Community College, A
South Piedmont Community College, A
The University of North Carolina at Charlotte, B
Wake Technical Community College, A
Wayne Community College, A
Western Piedmont Community College, A
Wilson Community College, A

Ohio

Bowling Green State University, B
Bowling Green State University - Firelands College, A
Central Ohio Technical College, A
Cincinnati State Technical and Community College, A
Clark State Community College, A
Columbus State Community College, A
Eastern Gateway Community College, A
James A. Rhodes State College, A
Kent State University at Trumbull, A
Kent State University at Tuscarawas, A
Lakeland Community College, A
Marion Technical College, A
Miami University, A
Miami University Hamilton, AB
Miami University Middletown, A
North Central State College, A
Northwest State Community College, A
Sinclair Community College, A
Stark State College, A
Terra State Community College, A
The University of Akron, AB
University of Dayton, A
University of Rio Grande, AB
The University of Toledo, B
Washington State Community College, A

Wright State University - Lake Campus, B
Youngstown State University, AB

Oklahoma

Oklahoma State University, B
Oklahoma State University Institute of Technology, A

Oregon

Mt. Hood Community College, A
Oregon Institute of Technology, B
Portland Community College, A

Pennsylvania

Delaware County Community College, A
Harrisburg Area Community College, A
Lehigh Carbon Community College, A
Montgomery County Community College, A
Penn State Altoona, A
Penn State Berks, A
Penn State DuBois, A
Penn State Erie, The Behrend College, AB
Penn State Hazleton, A
Penn State New Kensington, A
Penn State Shenango, A
Penn State York, A
Pennsylvania College of Technology, B
Point Park University, AB
University of Pittsburgh at Johnstown, B
Westmoreland County Community College, A

South Carolina

Greenville Technical College, A
Midlands Technical College, A
Piedmont Technical College, A
South Carolina State University, B
Spartanburg Community College, A
Trident Technical College, A
York Technical College, A

South Dakota

Southeast Technical Institute, A

Tennessee

Pellissippi State Community College, A
Southwest Tennessee Community College, A

Texas

LeTourneau University, B
Midwestern State University, B
Richland College, A
San Antonio College, A
Tarrant County College District, A
Texas A&M University - Corpus Christi, B
Texas State Technical College, A
University of Houston, B
University of North Texas, B

Utah

Weber State University, AB

Vermont

Vermont Technical College, A

Virginia

ECPI University (Newport News), A
ECPI University (Richmond), A
ECPI University (Virginia Beach), A
Virginia State University, B
Virginia Western Community College, A
Wytheville Community College, A

Washington

Bates Technical College, A
Central Washington University, B
Clover Park Technical College, A
Eastern Washington University, B
Shoreline Community College, A
Spokane Community College, A

West Virginia

Bluefield State College, AB
BridgeValley Community and Technical College (Montgomery), A
Fairmont State University, AB

Pierpont Community & Technical College, A
West Virginia University at Parkersburg, A

Wisconsin

Milwaukee Area Technical College, A
University of Wisconsin - Green Bay, B

U.S. Territories: Puerto Rico

Universidad del Turabo, A

Canada

British Columbia

British Columbia Institute of Technology, AB
The University of British Columbia, B

Ontario

Lakehead University, B

Quebec

Université du Québec en Abitibi-Témiscamingue, B

MECHANICAL ENGINEERING RELATED TECHNOLOGIES/ TECHNICIANS

United States

Delaware

Delaware State University, B

Florida

Broward College, A
Florida Keys Community College, A

Illinois

Carl Sandburg College, A

Indiana

Indiana State University, B
Indiana University - Purdue University Indianapolis, B
Purdue University Northwest (Westville), AB

Massachusetts

University of Massachusetts Lowell, AB

Michigan

Glen Oaks Community College, A

New Jersey

Camden County College, A
Middlesex County College, A

New York

Corning Community College, A
Excelsior College, B
Hudson Valley Community College, A
Jefferson Community College, A
Mohawk Valley Community College, A
State University of New York College of Technology at Canton, B
Vaughn College of Aeronautics and Technology, B

North Carolina

Asheville-Buncombe Technical Community College, A
Blue Ridge Community College, A

Ohio

Cleveland State University, B
Terra State Community College, A

Pennsylvania

Community College of Beaver County, A
Pennsylvania College of Technology, B

Texas

LeTourneau University, B

Virginia

Blue Ridge Community College, A
John Tyler Community College, A
Thomas Nelson Community College, A

Wisconsin

Moraine Park Technical College, A

U.S. Territories: Puerto Rico

Polytechnic University of Puerto Rico, A

MECHANICS

United States

Alabama

The University of Alabama, MD

California

California Institute of Technology, MD
San Diego State University, MD
Stanford University, D
University of California, Berkeley, MD
University of California, Merced, D
University of California, San Diego, MD
University of Southern California, M

Colorado

University of Colorado Denver, M

Georgia

Georgia Institute of Technology, MD

Illinois

Northwestern University, MD
Southern Illinois University Carbondale, M
University of Illinois at Urbana - Champaign, MD

Iowa

Iowa State University of Science and Technology,
MD

Louisiana

Louisiana State University and Agricultural & Mechanical College, MD

Maryland

Johns Hopkins University, M
University of Maryland, College Park, MD

Massachusetts

University of Massachusetts Amherst, M
University of Massachusetts Dartmouth, D

Michigan

Michigan State University, MD
Michigan Technological University, MDO

Minnesota

University of Minnesota, Twin Cities Campus, MD

Missouri

Missouri University of Science and Technology, MD

Montana

Montana State University, D

Nebraska

University of Nebraska - Lincoln, MD

New Jersey

Rutgers University - New Brunswick, MD

New Mexico

New Mexico Institute of Mining and Technology, M

New York

Columbia University, MD
Cornell University, MD

Ohio

Ohio University, M
University of Cincinnati, MD
University of Dayton, M

Pennsylvania

Carnegie Mellon University, MD
Drexel University, MD
Lehigh University, MD
Penn State University Park, MD
University of Pennsylvania, MD

Rhode Island

Brown University, MD

Texas

The University of Texas at Austin, MD

Virginia

Virginia Polytechnic Institute and State University,
MD

Wisconsin

University of Wisconsin - Madison, MD
University of Wisconsin - Milwaukee, M

Canada

Alberta

University of Calgary, MD

Maritime Provinces: New Brunswick

University of New Brunswick Fredericton, MD

Quebec

École Polytechnique de Montréal, MD
McGill University, MD

MECHANICS AND REPAIRERS

United States

Idaho

Idaho State University, AB
Lewis-Clark State College, AB

Indiana

Ivy Tech Community College - Bloomington, A
Ivy Tech Community College - Central Indiana, A
Ivy Tech Community College - Columbus, A
Ivy Tech Community College - Kokomo, A
Ivy Tech Community College - Lafayette, A
Ivy Tech Community College - North Central, A
Ivy Tech Community College - Northeast, A
Ivy Tech Community College - Northwest, A
Ivy Tech Community College - Richmond, A
Ivy Tech Community College - Southern Indiana, A
Ivy Tech Community College - Southwest, A
Ivy Tech Community College - Wabash Valley, A

Kansas

Seward County Community College and Area Technical School, A

Kentucky

Owensboro Community and Technical College, A

Michigan

Kalamazoo Valley Community College, A

New York

Corning Community College, A

Oklahoma

Western Oklahoma State College, A

Oregon

Rogue Community College, A

South Carolina

Florence-Darlington Technical College, A

Utah

Utah Valley University, A
Weber State University, A

Wyoming

Western Wyoming Community College, A

MEDIA STUDIES

United States

Alabama

The University of Alabama, M

Arizona

Arizona State University at the Tempe campus, MD

Arkansas

Arkansas State University, M

California

California College of the Arts, M
Pepperdine University, M
San Diego State University, M
San Francisco State University, M
Stanford University, M
University of California, Los Angeles, MD
University of California, Santa Barbara, MD
University of Southern California, MD

Colorado

University of Colorado Boulder, MD

Connecticut

Sacred Heart University, M
Trinity College, M
University of Bridgeport, M

District of Columbia

American University, MD
Georgetown University, M
Howard University, MD

Florida

Digital Media Arts College, M
Florida Atlantic University, M
Florida State University, M
Full Sail University, M
Lynn University, M
University of Florida, M
University of South Florida, M
University of South Florida, St. Petersburg, M

Georgia

Georgia State University, D
Savannah College of Art and Design, M

Illinois

DePaul University, M
Governors State University, M
Northwestern University, MD
Robert Morris University Illinois, M
Southern Illinois University Carbondale, M
Southern Illinois University Edwardsville, O
University of Chicago, D
University of Illinois at Urbana - Champaign, MD

Indiana

Indiana State University, M
Indiana University Bloomington, D
Valparaiso University, MO

Iowa

The University of Iowa, MD

Kansas

The University of Kansas, MD

Kentucky

Northern Kentucky University, O

Louisiana

Louisiana State University and Agricultural & Mechanical College, MD

Maryland

Loyola University Maryland, M
Maryland Institute College of Art, M
University of Maryland, College Park, D

Massachusetts

Boston University, MD
Emerson College, M
Massachusetts College of Art and Design, MO
Massachusetts Institute of Technology, MD

Michigan

Central Michigan University, M
Michigan State University, MD
Saginaw Valley State University, M
University of Michigan, M
Wayne State University, MO

Missouri

Missouri Western State University, M
University of Missouri, M
University of Missouri - Kansas City, M
Webster University, M

Nevada

University of Nevada, Las Vegas, M

New Jersey

Fairleigh Dickinson University, Metropolitan Campus, M
Monmouth University, O
Rowan University, O
Rutgers University - New Brunswick, D

New Mexico

New Mexico Highlands University, M

New York

Brooklyn College of the City University of New York, M
City College of the City University of New York, M
College of Staten Island of the City University of New York, M
Cornell University, MD
Fordham University, M
Hunter College of the City University of New York, M
Metropolitan College of New York, M
New York University, MD
Pace University, M
Pratt Institute, M
Rochester Institute of Technology, M
Syracuse University, M
University at Buffalo, the State University of New York, MDO

North Carolina

Duke University, M
The University of North Carolina at Charlotte, M
The University of North Carolina at Greensboro, M

Ohio

Ohio University, MD

Oregon

University of Oregon, MD

Pennsylvania

Carnegie Mellon University, M
Indiana University of Pennsylvania, D
Kutztown University of Pennsylvania, M
La Salle University, O
Penn State University Park, M
Temple University, M

South Carolina

Bob Jones University, M
University of South Carolina, M

Tennessee

The University of Tennessee, MD

Texas

St. Edward's University, M
The University of Texas at Austin, MD

Vermont

Champlain College, M

Virginia

George Mason University, MD
Norfolk State University, M
Virginia Commonwealth University, D
Virginia State University, M

West Virginia

West Virginia State University, M

Wisconsin

University of Wisconsin - Madison, MD
University of Wisconsin - Milwaukee, MO
University of Wisconsin - Stevens Point, M

Canada

Alberta

University of Lethbridge, M

Ontario

The University of Western Ontario, MD
Wilfrid Laurier University, M

Quebec

Concordia University, M

MEDICAL ADMINISTRATIVE ASSISTANT/SECRETARY

United States

Alabama

Shelton State Community College, A
Wallace State Community College, A

Arizona

Central Arizona College, A
Mesa Community College, A
Scottsdale Community College, A

Arkansas

Arkansas Tech University, A
College of the Ouachitas, A
National Park College, A

California

Berkeley City College, A
Butte College, A
Cabrillo College, A
Carrington College - Sacramento, A
Chaffey College, A
College of Marin, A
Columbia College, A
East Los Angeles College, A
Fresno City College, A
Gavilan College, A
Glendale Community College, A
Lake Tahoe Community College, A
Lassen Community College District, A
Long Beach City College, A
Los Angeles City College, A
Los Angeles Harbor College, A
Merced College, A
Monterey Peninsula College, A
Mt. San Antonio College, A
Ohlone College, A

Palomar College, A
Sacramento City College, A
San Joaquin Valley College (Visalia), A
Shasta College, A
West Los Angeles College, A
West Valley College, A

Colorado

IBMC College (Colorado Springs), A
IBMC College (Fort Collins), A
Otero Junior College, A

Connecticut

Gateway Community College, A
Lincoln College of New England, A
Manchester Community College, A
Middlesex Community College, A
Tunxis Community College, A

Florida

Daytona State College, A
Florida National University, A
Florida Technical College (DeLand), A
Florida Technical College (Orlando), A
Gulf Coast State College, A
Indian River State College, A
Rasmussen College Fort Myers, A
Rasmussen College Land O' Lakes, A
Rasmussen College New Port Richey, A
Rasmussen College Ocala, A
Rasmussen College Tampa/Brandon, A
Ultimate Medical Academy Online, A

Idaho

Broadview University - Boise, A
College of Western Idaho, A
North Idaho College, A

Illinois

City Colleges of Chicago, Richard J. Daley College, A
Danville Area Community College, A
Harper College, A
Illinois Eastern Community Colleges, Olney Central College, A
John A. Logan College, A
Lake Land College, A
Lewis and Clark Community College, A
MacCormac College, A
Morton College, A
Rasmussen College Aurora, A
Rasmussen College Mokena/Tinley Park, A
Rasmussen College Rockford, A
Rasmussen College Romeoville/Joliet, A
Richland Community College, A
Shawnee Community College, A
Spoon River College, A

Iowa

Des Moines Area Community College, A
Hawkeye Community College, A
Iowa Lakes Community College, A
Kaplan University, Des Moines, A
North Iowa Area Community College, A
Western Iowa Tech Community College, A

Kansas

Barton County Community College, A
Butler Community College, A
Dodge City Community College, A
Labette Community College, A
Rasmussen College Kansas City/Overland Park, A

Kentucky

Big Sandy Community and Technical College, A
Bluegrass Community and Technical College, A
Elizabethtown Community and Technical College, A
Hazard Community and Technical College, A
Owensboro Community and Technical College, A
Somerset Community College, A

Louisiana

Blue Cliff College - Shreveport, A

Maine

Kennebec Valley Community College, A
Northern Maine Community College, A

Maryland

Anne Arundel Community College, A
Community College of Baltimore County, A
Frederick Community College, A
Howard Community College, A
Kaplan University, Hagerstown Campus, A

Massachusetts

Bristol Community College, A
Bunker Hill Community College, A
Cape Cod Community College, A
North Shore Community College, A
Northern Essex Community College, A
Quinsigamond Community College, A
Roxbury Community College, A
Springfield Technical Community College, A

Michigan

Baker College, A
Bay de Noc Community College, A
Delta College, A
Grand Rapids Community College, A
Kellogg Community College, A
Kirtland Community College, A
Lake Michigan College, A
Mid Michigan Community College, A
Monroe County Community College, A
Montcalm Community College, A
Muskegon Community College, A
North Central Michigan College, A

Minnesota

Alexandria Technical and Community College, A
Anoka Technical College, A
Central Lakes College, A
Century College, A
Dakota County Technical College, A
Globe University - Woodbury, A
Hennepin Technical College, A
Hibbing Community College, A
Inver Hills Community College, A
Lake Superior College, A
Minnesota School of Business - Blaine, A
Minnesota School of Business - Brooklyn Center, A
Minnesota School of Business - Elk River, A
Minnesota School of Business - Richfield, A
Minnesota School of Business - Rochester, A
Minnesota School of Business - St. Cloud, A
Minnesota State College - Southeast Technical, A
Minnesota State Community and Technical College, A
Minnesota State Community and Technical College - Moorhead, A
Minnesota State Community and Technical College - Wadena, A
Minnesota West Community and Technical College, A
Northland Community and Technical College, A
Northwest Technical College, A
Rasmussen College Blaine, A
Rasmussen College Bloomington, A
Rasmussen College Brooklyn Park, A
Rasmussen College Eagan, A
Rasmussen College Lake Elmo/Woodbury, A
Rasmussen College Mankato, A
Rasmussen College Moorhead, A
Rasmussen College St. Cloud, A
Ridgewater College, A
Riverland Community College, A
Rochester Community and Technical College, A
Vermilion Community College, A

Mississippi

Coahoma Community College, A
East Central Community College, A
East Mississippi Community College, A
Northwest Mississippi Community College, A
Pearl River Community College, A

Missouri

Crowder College, A
Jefferson College, A
Metro Business College (Jefferson City), A
Metropolitan Community College - Kansas City, A
State Fair Community College, A

Montana

Flathead Valley Community College, A
Miles Community College, A
Montana State University Billings, A
University of Montana, A

Nebraska

Midland University, A
Northeast Community College, A

Nevada

Everest College, A

New Hampshire

Manchester Community College, A

New Mexico

New Mexico Junior College, A

New York

Bronx Community College of the City University of New York, A
Bryant & Stratton College - Albany Campus, A
Bryant & Stratton College - Amherst Campus, A
Bryant & Stratton College - Buffalo Campus, A
Bryant & Stratton College - Greece Campus, A
Bryant & Stratton College - Henrietta Campus, A
Bryant & Stratton College - Liverpool Campus, A
Bryant & Stratton College - Orchard Park Campus, A
Bryant & Stratton College - Syracuse Campus, A
Erie Community College, North Campus, A
Fulton-Montgomery Community College, A
Genesee Community College, A
Jefferson Community College, A
Monroe College, A
Morrisville State College, A
Nassau Community College, A

North Carolina

Alamance Community College, A
Central Carolina Community College, A
Central Piedmont Community College, A
Coastal Carolina Community College, A
College of The Albemarle, A
Craven Community College, A
ECPI University (Charlotte), A
Gaston College, A
Halifax Community College, A
Martin Community College, A
Mayland Community College, A
Piedmont Community College, A
Sandhills Community College, A
Stanly Community College, A
Surry Community College, A
Vance-Granville Community College, A
Western Piedmont Community College, A

North Dakota

Bismarck State College, A
Dakota College at Bottineau, A
Dickinson State University, A
Rasmussen College Fargo, A
United Tribes Technical College, A

Ohio

Bryant & Stratton College - Eastlake Campus, A
Bryant & Stratton College - Parma Campus, A
Clark State Community College, A
Davis College, A
Daymar College, A
Eastern Gateway Community College, A
Edison Community College, A
Fortis College (Ravenna), A
Gallipolis Career College, A
Hocking College, A
Marion Technical College, A

Miami-Jacobs Career College (Dayton), A
Miami University Middletown, A
Northwest State Community College, A
Ohio Business College (Sandusky), A
Ohio Business College (Sheffield Village), A
Ohio University - Lancaster, A
Owens Community College, A
Sinclair Community College, A
Stautzenberger College (Maumee), A
Terra State Community College, A
Trumbull Business College, A
University of Cincinnati Blue Ash College, A
University of Northwestern Ohio, A
University of Rio Grande, A
Washington State Community College, A

Oklahoma

Vatterott College (Tulsa), A

Oregon

Blue Mountain Community College, A
Chemeketa Community College, A
Linn-Benton Community College, A
Mt. Hood Community College, A
Treasure Valley Community College, A
Umpqua Community College, A

Pennsylvania

Cambria-Rowe Business College (Johnstown), A
Community College of Allegheny County, A
Community College of Beaver County, A
Consolidated School of Business (Lancaster), A
Consolidated School of Business (York), A
DuBois Business College (DuBois), A
Lackawanna College, A
Laurel Business Institute, A
Laurel Technical Institute, A
Lincoln Technical Institute (Allentown), A
Luzerne County Community College, A
McCann School of Business & Technology (Pottsville), A
Northampton Community College, A
Penn Commercial Business and Technical School, A
Reading Area Community College, A
South Hills School of Business & Technology (Altoona), A
South Hills School of Business & Technology (State College), A

Rhode Island

Community College of Rhode Island, A

South Carolina

ECPI University (Columbia), A
Piedmont Technical College, A
Trident Technical College, A
York Technical College, A

South Dakota

Globe University - Sioux Falls, A
Sinte Gleska University, A

Tennessee

Roane State Community College, A
South College, A

Texas

Alvin Community College, A
Amarillo College, A
Del Mar College, A
Galveston College, A
Hallmark University, A
Lamar State College - Port Arthur, A
McLennan Community College, A
Northeast Texas Community College, A
St. Philip's College, A
South Plains College, A
Texas Southmost College, A
Tyler Junior College, A

Utah

Broadview University - Layton, A
Broadview University - West Jordan, A

Virginia

Dabney S. Lancaster Community College, A
ECPI University (Newport News), A
ECPI University (Richmond), A
Miller-Motte Technical College (Lynchburg), A
New River Community College, A
Wytheville Community College, A

Washington

Carrington College - Spokane, A
Centralia College, A
Clark College, A
Edmonds Community College, A
Green River College, A
Lower Columbia College, A
Pierce College at Fort Steilacoom, A
Renton Technical College, A
Shoreline Community College, A
Skagit Valley College, A
South Puget Sound Community College, A
Spokane Community College, A
Tacoma Community College, A
Walla Walla Community College, A
Wenatchee Valley College, A
Whatcom Community College, A
Yakima Valley Community College, A

West Virginia

BridgeValley Community and Technical College
  (Montgomery), A
Eastern West Virginia Community and Technical
  College, A
West Virginia Business College (Nutter Fort), A

Wisconsin

Blackhawk Technical College, A
Globe University - Appleton, A
Globe University - Eau Claire, A
Globe University - Green Bay, A
Globe University - La Crosse, A
Globe University - Madison East, A
Globe University - Madison West, A
Globe University - Wausau, A
Lakeshore Technical College, A
Madison Area Technical College, A
Milwaukee Area Technical College, A
Nicolet Area Technical College, A
Rasmussen College Appleton, A
Rasmussen College Green Bay, A
Rasmussen College Wausau, A
Western Technical College, A
Wisconsin Indianhead Technical College, A

Wyoming

Western Wyoming Community College, A

U.S. Territories: Puerto Rico

Humacao Community College, A
ICPR Junior College - Hato Rey Campus, A
National University College (Bayamón), A
Universidad del Este, A

Canada

British Columbia

British Columbia Institute of Technology, A

MEDICAL/CLINICAL ASSIS-TANT

United States

Alabama

Chattahoochee Valley Community College, A
George C. Wallace Community College, A
H. Councill Trenholm State Community College, A
J. F. Drake State Community and Technical College,
  A
Northeast Alabama Community College, A
Northwest-Shoals Community College, A
South University, A

Virginia College in Huntsville, A
Wallace State Community College, A

Alaska

University of Alaska Anchorage, A
University of Alaska Fairbanks, A

Arizona

Mohave Community College, A
Penn Foster College, A
Phoenix College, A

Arkansas

Arkansas Tech University, A
Cossatot Community College of the University of
  Arkansas, A
East Arkansas Community College, A

California

Allan Hancock College, A
Antelope Valley College, A
Barstow Community College, A
Cabrillo College, A
California College San Diego (San Diego), A
Cañada College, A
Carrington College - Citrus Heights, A
Carrington College - Pleasant Hill, A
Carrington College - Pomona, A
Carrington College - Sacramento, A
Carrington College - San Jose, A
Carrington College - San Leandro, A
Cerritos College, A
Cerro Coso Community College, A
Chabot College, A
City College of San Francisco, A
College of Marin, A
College of the Redwoods, A
Contra Costa College, A
Cosumnes River College, A
Cuesta College, A
De Anza College, A
East Los Angeles College, A
El Camino College, A
Empire College, A
Fresno City College, A
Lake Tahoe Community College, A
Long Beach City College, A
Merced College, A
MiraCosta College, A
Modesto Junior College, A
Monterey Peninsula College, A
Moreno Valley College, A
Mt. San Jacinto College, A
Ohlone College, A
Orange Coast College, A
Pasadena City College, A
Saddleback College, A
San Diego Mesa College, A
San Joaquin Valley College (Bakersfield), A
San Joaquin Valley College (Fresno), A
San Joaquin Valley College (Hanford), A
San Joaquin Valley College (Hesperia), A
San Joaquin Valley College (Lancaster), A
San Joaquin Valley College (Ontario), A
San Joaquin Valley College (Salida), A
San Joaquin Valley College (Temecula), A
San Joaquin Valley College (Visalia), A
San Joaquin Valley College - Online, A
Santa Ana College, A
Santa Rosa Junior College, A
Shasta College, A
Southwestern College, A
Ventura College, A
West Valley College, A

Colorado

Colorado Mesa University, A
Everest College (Colorado Springs), A
IBMC College (Colorado Springs), A
IBMC College (Fort Collins), A
Morgan Community College, AB
National American University (Denver), A

Connecticut

Capital Community College, A
Goodwin College, A
Lincoln College of New England, A
Northwestern Connecticut Community College, A
Quinebaug Valley Community College, A
St. Vincent's College, A

Delaware

Delaware Technical & Community College, Jack F.
  Owens Campus, A
Delaware Technical & Community College,
  Stanton/Wilmington Campus, A
Delaware Technical & Community College, Terry
  Campus, A

Florida

City College (Altamonte Springs), A
City College (Fort Lauderdale), A
City College (Miami), A
College of Business and Technology - Cutler Bay
  Campus, A
College of Business and Technology - Main Cam-
  pus, A
College of Business and Technology - Miami Gar-
  dens, A
Everest University (Largo), A
Everest University (Orange Park), A
Everest University (Orlando), A
Everest University (Tampa), A
Florida National University, A
Florida Technical College (DeLand), A
Florida Technical College (Orlando), A
Fortis College (Largo), A
Fortis College (Orange Park), A
Fortis College (Winter Park), A
Hodges University, A
Keiser University, A
Meridian College, A
Miami Dade College, A
Rasmussen College Fort Myers, A
Rasmussen College Land O' Lakes, A
Rasmussen College New Port Richey, A
Rasmussen College Ocala, A
Rasmussen College Tampa/Brandon, A
Southeastern College - West Palm Beach, A
Southern Technical College (Fort Myers), A
Southern Technical College (Orlando), A
Southern Technical College (Tampa), A

Georgia

East Georgia State College, A
Georgia Piedmont Technical College, A
Gwinnett Technical College, A
South University, A
Virginia College in Macon, A

Hawaii

Kapiolani Community College, A

Idaho

Brigham Young University - Idaho, A
Broadview University - Boise, A
Carrington College - Boise, A
Eastern Idaho Technical College, A
Idaho State University, AB

Illinois

City Colleges of Chicago, Malcolm X College, A
Fox College, A
Harper College, A
Highland Community College, A
Illinois Eastern Community Colleges, Lincoln Trail
  College, A
Kankakee Community College, A
Midstate College, A
Northwestern College - Bridgeview Campus, A
Northwestern College - Chicago Campus, A
Rasmussen College Aurora, A
Rasmussen College Mokena/Tinley Park, A
Rasmussen College Rockford, A
Rasmussen College Romeoville/Joliet, A
Robert Morris University Illinois, A
Rockford Career College, A
Southwestern Illinois College, A

Indiana

Brightwood College, Hammond Campus, A
Harrison College, A
International Business College (Fort Wayne), AB
International Business College (Indianapolis), A
Ivy Tech Community College - Central Indiana, A
Ivy Tech Community College - Columbus, A
Ivy Tech Community College - East Central, A
Ivy Tech Community College - Kokomo, A
Ivy Tech Community College - Lafayette, A
Ivy Tech Community College - North Central, A
Ivy Tech Community College - Northeast, A
Ivy Tech Community College - Northwest, A
Ivy Tech Community College - Richmond, A
Ivy Tech Community College - Southeast, A
Ivy Tech Community College - Southern Indiana, A
Ivy Tech Community College - Southwest, A
Ivy Tech Community College - Wabash Valley, A

Iowa

Des Moines Area Community College, A
Iowa Central Community College, A
Iowa Lakes Community College, A
Kaplan University, Cedar Rapids, A
Kaplan University, Davenport Campus, A
Kaplan University, Mason City Campus, A
Kirkwood Community College, A
Mercy College of Health Sciences, A
North Iowa Area Community College, A
Palmer College of Chiropractic, A
Southeastern Community College, A
Vatterott College, A
Western Iowa Tech Community College, A

Kansas

Barton County Community College, A
Coffeyville Community College, A
Northwest Kansas Technical College, A
Rasmussen College Kansas City/Overland Park, A
Rasmussen College Topeka, A
Seward County Community College and Area Technical School, A
Wichita Area Technical College, A

Kentucky

American National University (Danville), A
American National University (Florence), A
American National University (Lexington), A
American National University (Louisville), A
American National University (Pikeville), A
American National University (Richmond), A
Bluegrass Community and Technical College, A
Daymar College (Bowling Green), A
Daymar College (Owensboro), A
Henderson Community College, A
Sullivan University, A

Louisiana

Bossier Parish Community College, A
Cameron College, A
McCann School of Business & Technology (Monroe), A
Virginia College in Baton Rouge, A

Maine

Beal College, A
Central Maine Community College, A
Kaplan University, South Portland, A
Kennebec Valley Community College, A
Southern Maine Community College, A
Washington County Community College, A
York County Community College, A

Maryland

Frederick Community College, A
Kaplan University, Hagerstown Campus, A

Massachusetts

Bay State College, A
Massasoit Community College, A
Middlesex Community College, A
Mount Wachusett Community College, A
Salter College (Chicopee), A
Springfield Technical Community College, A

Michigan

Baker College, A
Davenport University, A
Jackson College, A
Kirtland Community College, A
Macomb Community College, A
Mid Michigan Community College, A
Northwestern Michigan College, A
Oakland Community College, A
Southwestern Michigan College, A

Minnesota

Anoka Technical College, A
Argosy University, Twin Cities, A
Dakota County Technical College, A
Duluth Business University, A
Globe University - Woodbury, A
Herzing University, A
Minneapolis Business College, A
Minnesota School of Business - Blaine, A
Minnesota School of Business - Brooklyn Center, A
Minnesota School of Business - Elk River, A
Minnesota School of Business - Lakeville, A
Minnesota School of Business - Richfield, A
Minnesota School of Business - Rochester, A
Minnesota School of Business - St. Cloud, A
Minnesota West Community and Technical College, A
Rasmussen College Blaine, A
Rasmussen College Bloomington, A
Rasmussen College Brooklyn Park, A
Rasmussen College Eagan, A
Rasmussen College Lake Elmo/Woodbury, A
Rasmussen College Mankato, A
Rasmussen College Moorhead, A
Rasmussen College St. Cloud, A
Ridgewater College, A

Mississippi

Antonelli College (Jackson), A
Hinds Community College, A
Northeast Mississippi Community College, A
Virginia College in Biloxi, A

Missouri

Concorde Career College, A
Cox College, A
East Central College, A
Heritage College, A
North Central Missouri College, A
Vatterott College (Berkeley), A
Vatterott College (Kansas City), A
Vatterott College (Saint Charles), A
Vatterott College (Saint Joseph), A
Vatterott College (Springfield), A
Vatterott College (Sunset Hills), A

Montana

Flathead Valley Community College, A
Great Falls College Montana State University, A
Montana State University Billings, A
Montana Tech of The University of Montana, A

Nebraska

Central Community College - Columbus Campus, A
Central Community College - Grand Island Campus, A
Central Community College - Hastings Campus, A
Kaplan University, Lincoln, A
Kaplan University, Omaha, A

Nevada

Career College of Northern Nevada, A

New Hampshire

White Mountains Community College, A

New Jersey

Berkeley College - Woodland Park Campus, A
Hudson County Community College, A
Raritan Valley Community College, A

New Mexico

Clovis Community College, A
Eastern New Mexico University - Roswell, A
New Mexico Junior College, A

New York

ASA College, A
Bramson ORT College, A
Broome Community College, A
Bryant & Stratton College - Albany Campus, A
Bryant & Stratton College - Buffalo Campus, A
Bryant & Stratton College - Greece Campus, A
Bryant & Stratton College - Henrietta Campus, A
Bryant & Stratton College - Liverpool Campus, A
Bryant & Stratton College - Orchard Park Campus, A
Bryant & Stratton College - Syracuse Campus, A
The College of Westchester, A
Columbia-Greene Community College, A
Elmira Business Institute, A
Jamestown Business College, A
Mildred Elley - New York City, A
Mildred Elley School, A
Mohawk Valley Community College, A
Monroe College, A
Niagara County Community College, A
Queensborough Community College of the City University of New York, A
Sullivan County Community College, A
Swedish Institute, College of Health Sciences, A
Trocaire College, A
Wood Tobe - Coburn School, A

North Carolina

Alamance Community College, A
Cabarrus College of Health Sciences, A
Carteret Community College, A
Central Carolina Community College, A
Central Piedmont Community College, A
Cleveland Community College, A
Craven Community College, A
Davidson County Community College, A
ECPI University (Greensboro), A
ECPI University (Raleigh), A
Edgecombe Community College, A
Forsyth Technical Community College, A
Gaston College, A
Guilford Technical Community College, A
Haywood Community College, A
James Sprunt Community College, A
Johnston Community College, A
King's College, A
Lenoir Community College, A
Martin Community College, A
Mayland Community College, A
Miller-Motte College (Cary), A
Mitchell Community College, A
Montgomery Community College, A
Pamlico Community College, A
Piedmont Community College, A
Pitt Community College, A
Randolph Community College, A
Richmond Community College, A
South College - Asheville, A
South Piedmont Community College, A
Stanly Community College, A
Tri-County Community College, A
Vance-Granville Community College, A
Wake Technical Community College, A
Wayne Community College, A
Western Piedmont Community College, A
Wilkes Community College, A

North Dakota

Dakota College at Bottineau, A

Ohio

American National University (Cincinnati), A
American National University (Kettering), A
American National University (Youngstown), A
Belmont College, A
Bradford School, A
Bryant & Stratton College - Eastlake Campus, A
Bryant & Stratton College - Parma Campus, A
Clark State Community College, A

Columbus State Community College, A
Davis College, A
Eastern Gateway Community College, A
Edison Community College, A
ETI Technical College of Niles, A
Fortis College (Centerville), A
Fortis College (Cuyahoga Falls), A
Fortis College (Ravenna), A
Harrison College, A
Hocking College, A
James A. Rhodes State College, A
Miami-Jacobs Career College (Dayton), A
Northwest State Community College, A
Ohio University - Chillicothe, A
Ohio Valley College of Technology, A
Sinclair Community College, A
Southern State Community College, A
Stark State College, A
Stautzenberger College (Brecksville), A
Stautzenberger College (Maumee), A
Terra State Community College, A
The University of Akron, A
University of Cincinnati Blue Ash College, A
University of Northwestern Ohio, A
Youngstown State University, A
Zane State College, A

Oklahoma

Community Care College, A
Oklahoma City Community College, A

Oregon

Central Oregon Community College, A
Linn-Benton Community College, A
Mt. Hood Community College, A
Pioneer Pacific College, A
Pioneer Pacific College - Eugene/Springfield
  Branch, A
Southwestern Oregon Community College, A

Pennsylvania

Berks Technical Institute, A
Bradford School, A
Brightwood Career Institute, Broomall Campus, A
Brightwood Career Institute, Harrisburg Campus, A
Brightwood Career Institute, Pittsburgh Campus, A
Bucks County Community College, A
Career Training Academy (Lower Burrell), A
Career Training Academy (Monroeville), A
Career Training Academy (Pittsburgh), A
Central Penn College, A
Community College of Allegheny County, A
Delaware County Community College, A
Douglas Education Center, A
Harrisburg Area Community College, A
Keystone Technical Institute, A
Lansdale School of Business, A
Laurel Business Institute, A
Laurel Technical Institute, A
Lehigh Carbon Community College, A
McCann School of Business & Technology
  (Lewisburg), A
McCann School of Business & Technology
  (Pottsville), A
Mercyhurst North East, A
Montgomery County Community College, A
Mount Aloysius College, A
Pennsylvania Highlands Community College, A
Pennsylvania Institute of Health and Technology, A
South Hills School of Business & Technology (State
  College), A
Westmoreland County Community College, A
YTI Career Institute - Altoona, A
YTI Career Institute - York, A

Rhode Island

New England Institute of Technology, A

South Carolina

ECPI University (Columbia), A
ECPI University (Greenville), A
ECPI University (North Charleston), A
Forrest College, A
Midlands Technical College, A
Miller-Motte Technical College (North Charleston), A

South University, A
Virginia College in Spartanburg, A
York Technical College, A

South Dakota

Globe University - Sioux Falls, A
Lake Area Technical Institute, A
Mitchell Technical Institute, A
National American University (Sioux Falls), A
Presentation College, A
Western Dakota Technical Institute, A

Tennessee

Concorde Career College, A
Daymar College (Clarksville), A
Daymar College (Nashville), A
Miller-Motte Technical College (Chattanooga), A
Miller-Motte Technical College (Clarksville), A
National College (Bristol), A
National College (Nashville), A
Northeast State Community College, A
South College, A
Southwest Tennessee Community College, A
Vatterott College (Memphis), A

Texas

The College of Health Care Professions (Houston),
  A
El Centro College, A
El Paso Community College, A
Everest College (Arlington), A
Hallmark University, A
Laredo Community College, A
Northeast Texas Community College, A
Panola College, A
San Antonio College, A
San Jacinto College District, A
Vista College, A

Utah

Broadview University - Layton, A
Broadview University - West Jordan, A
LDS Business College, A
Provo College, A
Salt Lake Community College, A
Stevens-Henager College (West Haven), A

Vermont

Community College of Vermont, A

Virginia

American National University (Charlottesville), A
American National University (Danville), A
American National University (Harrisonburg), A
American National University (Lynchburg), A
American National University (Martinsville), A
American National University (Salem), A
Bryant & Stratton College - Richmond Campus, A
Bryant & Stratton College - Virginia Beach Campus,
  A
Central Virginia Community College, A
Centura College (Chesapeake), A
Centura College (Newport News), A
Centura College (North Chesterfield), A
Centura College (Virginia Beach), A
ECPI University (Manassas), A
ECPI University (Virginia Beach), A
Stratford University (Alexandria), A
Stratford University (Falls Church), A
Stratford University (Glen Allen), A
Stratford University (Newport News), A
Stratford University (Virginia Beach), A
Stratford University (Woodbridge), A
Virginia College in Richmond, A

Washington

Big Bend Community College, A
Clark College, A
Columbia Basin College, A
Everett Community College, A
Highline College, A
Lake Washington Institute of Technology, A
Lower Columbia College, A
North Seattle College, A
Olympic College, A

Renton Technical College, A
Skagit Valley College, A
South Puget Sound Community College, A
Wenatchee Valley College, A
Whatcom Community College, A

West Virginia

Blue Ridge Community and Technical College, A
Mountain State College, A
Mountwest Community & Technical College, A
New River Community and Technical College, A
Potomac State College of West Virginia University,
  A
West Virginia Business College (Nutter Fort), A
West Virginia Junior College - Bridgeport, A
West Virginia Junior College - Charleston, A
West Virginia Junior College - Morgantown, A
West Virginia Northern Community College, A

Wisconsin

Bryant & Stratton College - Milwaukee Campus, A
Globe University - Appleton, A
Globe University - Eau Claire, A
Globe University - Green Bay, A
Globe University - La Crosse, A
Globe University - Madison East, A
Globe University - Madison West, A
Globe University - Wausau, A
Lac Courte Oreilles Ojibwa Community College, A
Rasmussen College Appleton, A
Rasmussen College Green Bay, A
Rasmussen College Wausau, A

Wyoming

Western Wyoming Community College, A

U.S. Territories: Guam

Guam Community College, A

U.S. Territories: Puerto Rico

Universidad del Este, A

MEDICAL/HEALTH MANAGE-MENT AND CLINICAL ASSIS-TANT/SPECIALIST

United States

Alabama

Virginia College in Birmingham, B

Arizona

CollegeAmerica - Flagstaff, A

Colorado

Aims Community College, A
CollegeAmerica - Denver, A
National American University (Denver), A

Florida

Florida National University, A

Idaho

Lewis-Clark State College, AB

Indiana

Ivy Tech Community College - Bloomington, A
Ivy Tech Community College - Central Indiana, A
Ivy Tech Community College - Columbus, A
Ivy Tech Community College - East Central, A
Ivy Tech Community College - Lafayette, A
Ivy Tech Community College - Richmond, A
Ivy Tech Community College - Southeast, A
Ivy Tech Community College - Southern Indiana, A
Ivy Tech Community College - Southwest, A
Ivy Tech Community College - Wabash Valley, A

Michigan

Davenport University, B
Henry Ford College, A

New Jersey

Rider University, B

Ohio

Owens Community College, A
Terra State Community College, A

Pennsylvania

Pittsburgh Technical Institute, A

Virginia

Centura College (Chesapeake), A
Centura College (Norfolk), A
Stratford University (Woodbridge), AB

MEDICAL ILLUSTRATION AND INFORMATICS

United States

Georgia

Augusta University, M

Illinois

University of Illinois at Chicago, M

Maryland

Johns Hopkins University, M

New York

Rochester Institute of Technology, M

MEDICAL ILLUSTRATION/MEDICAL ILLUSTRATOR

United States

Iowa

Iowa State University of Science and Technology, B

New York

Rochester Institute of Technology, B

Ohio

Cleveland Institute of Art, B

Pennsylvania

Arcadia University, B

MEDICAL IMAGING

United States

California

University of Southern California, M

Illinois

Illinois Institute of Technology, M

Massachusetts

Boston University, M

New Jersey

Rutgers University - Newark, M

New York

New York University, D

Ohio

Cleveland State University, M
University of Cincinnati, D

South Carolina

Medical University of South Carolina, D

Canada

Ontario

University of Guelph, MD

MEDICAL INFORMATICS

United States

Alabama

University of South Alabama, B

Arizona

Arizona State University at the Tempe campus, MD
The University of Arizona, O
University of Phoenix - Phoenix Campus, O

California

National University, AO
Stanford University, MD
University of California, Davis, M

Colorado

American Sentinel University, B
University of Colorado Denver, M

Florida

Nova Southeastern University, MO

Georgia

Armstrong State University, O

Illinois

Northwestern University, MD
University of Illinois at Urbana - Champaign, MDO

Kansas

The University of Kansas, O

Maryland

Community College of Baltimore County, A
Johns Hopkins University, MDO

Massachusetts

Brandeis University, M
Cambridge College, M
Simmons College, B

Michigan

Grand Valley State University, M
Western Michigan University, B

Minnesota

Capella University, B

Montana

Montana Tech of The University of Montana, AB

Nebraska

University of Nebraska at Omaha, M

New Jersey

Bergen Community College, A
Rutgers University - Newark, MDO

New York

Borough of Manhattan Community College of the City University of New York, A
Columbia University, MD
Excelsior College, MO
Rochester Institute of Technology, M
State University of New York at Plattsburgh, B
Trocaire College, B
University at Buffalo, the State University of New York, O

Ohio

Mount St. Joseph University, B

Oregon

Oregon Health & Science University, MDO

Pennsylvania

Harrisburg Area Community College, A

Tennessee

Dyersburg State Community College, A
Middle Tennessee State University, M
Nashville State Community College, A
The University of Tennessee at Chattanooga, O
Volunteer State Community College, A

Vermont

Champlain College, AB

Virginia

Marymount University, O

Washington

University of Washington, MD

Wisconsin

Milwaukee School of Engineering, M
University of Wisconsin - Milwaukee, D

Canada

Maritime Provinces: Nova Scotia

Dalhousie University, M

Ontario

University of Waterloo, B
The University of Western Ontario, B

MEDICAL INSURANCE CODING SPECIALIST/CODER

United States

Alabama

Columbia Southern University, A
Virginia College in Huntsville, A

Alaska

Charter College, A

California

Bryan College, A
Chabot College, A
National University, A
San Joaquin Valley College - Online, A
Southwestern College, A

Colorado

Colorado Technical University Online, A

Connecticut

Goodwin College, A

Florida

City College (Altamonte Springs), A
City College (Fort Lauderdale), A
City College (Gainesville), A
City College (Miami), A
Everest University (Orange Park), A
Fortis College (Winter Park), A
Southeastern College - West Palm Beach, A

Iowa

Hawkeye Community College, A

Kansas

Barton County Community College, A
Cowley County Community College and Area Vocational - Technical School, A
Grantham University, A

Kentucky

Daymar College (Bellevue), A
Spencerian College, A

Massachusetts

Berkshire Community College, A
Springfield Technical Community College, A

Minnesota

Herzing University, A
Minnesota West Community and Technical College,
A
Northland Community and Technical College, A

Mississippi

Antonelli College (Hattiesburg), A
Antonelli College (Jackson), A

Missouri

Metro Business College (Jefferson City), A
Metro Business College (Rolla), A
Missouri College, A
Vatterott College (Berkeley), A

Montana

Flathead Valley Community College, A
Fort Peck Community College, A

Nebraska

Northeast Community College, A

New Jersey

Salem Community College, A

New York

Elmira Business Institute, A

North Dakota

Dakota College at Bottineau, A
North Dakota State College of Science, A

Ohio

Davis College, A
Terra State Community College, A

Oklahoma

Community Care College, A

Pennsylvania

Bucks County Community College, A
Butler County Community College, A
Career Training Academy (Lower Burrell), A
Career Training Academy (Monroeville), A
Career Training Academy (Pittsburgh), A

South Dakota

Southeast Technical Institute, A

Tennessee

Fountainhead College of Technology, A

Texas

Collin County Community College District, A
Paris Junior College, A

Utah

LDS Business College, A

Virginia

Stratford University (Woodbridge), A

Washington

Columbia Basin College, A
Renton Technical College, A

West Virginia

West Virginia Junior College - Morgantown, A

Wyoming

Laramie County Community College, A

MEDICAL INSURANCE SPECIALIST/MEDICAL BILLER

United States

Alabama

Virginia College in Birmingham, A
Virginia College in Mobile, A

Arizona

Coconino Community College, A

California

Carrington College - Citrus Heights, A
Carrington College - Pleasant Hill, A
Carrington College - Pomona, A
Carrington College - Sacramento, A
Carrington College - San Jose, A
Carrington College - San Leandro, A
Pasadena City College, A
San Joaquin Valley College (Bakersfield), A
San Joaquin Valley College (Hanford), A
San Joaquin Valley College (Hesperia), A

Connecticut

Goodwin College, A

Florida

City College (Altamonte Springs), A
Everest University (Orlando), A
Everest University (Tampa), A
Fortis College (Winter Park), A
Southeastern College - West Palm Beach, A
Southern Technical College (Orlando), A
Ultimate Medical Academy Online, A
Virginia College in Pensacola, A

Idaho

Carrington College - Boise, A

Illinois

Taylor Business Institute, A

Indiana

Harrison College, A

Kentucky

Daymar College (Owensboro), A

Michigan

Jackson College, A

Mississippi

Southwest Mississippi Community College, A

Missouri

Cox College, A
St. Louis College of Health Careers (Saint Louis), A

Ohio

Harrison College, A

Tennessee

Daymar College (Murfreesboro), A

Texas

Virginia College in Austin, A

Virginia

Stratford University (Falls Church), A
Stratford University (Glen Allen), A
Stratford University (Newport News), A
Stratford University (Woodbridge), A

West Virginia

Huntington Junior College, A

Wisconsin

Northcentral Technical College, A
Northeast Wisconsin Technical College, A

MEDICAL MICROBIOLOGY AND BACTERIOLOGY

United States

Alabama

Auburn University, B

California

California Polytechnic State University, San Luis
Obispo, B
Humboldt State University, B
San Francisco State University, B
Sonoma State University, B
University of California, San Diego, B
University of Southern California, D

Colorado

Adams State University, B

Connecticut

Quinnipiac University, B

Delaware

University of Delaware, B

Florida

Florida National University, A
South Florida State College, A
University of Florida, B
University of South Florida, BM

Hawaii

University of Hawaii at Manoa, MD

Kentucky

University of Kentucky, B

Louisiana

Xavier University of Louisiana, B

Massachusetts

Worcester Polytechnic Institute, B

Minnesota

Minnesota State University Mankato, B
University of Minnesota, Duluth, MD
University of Minnesota, Twin Cities Campus, B

Mississippi

Mississippi State University, B

Montana

Montana State University, B
University of Montana, B

Nebraska

Creighton University, MD

New Jersey

Rutgers University - New Brunswick, B

New Mexico

New Mexico State University, B

New York

Wagner College, B

Ohio

Bowling Green State University, B
Ohio Wesleyan University, B

Pennsylvania

Penn State Abington, B
Penn State Altoona, B
Penn State Beaver, B
Penn State Berks, B
Penn State Brandywine, B
Penn State DuBois, B
Penn State Erie, The Behrend College, B
Penn State Fayette, The Eberly Campus, B

Penn State Greater Allegheny, B
Penn State Hazleton, B
Penn State Lehigh Valley, B
Penn State Mont Alto, B
Penn State New Kensington, B
Penn State Schuylkill, B
Penn State Shenango, B
Penn State University Park, B
Penn State Wilkes-Barre, B
Penn State Worthington Scranton, B
Penn State York, B

Texas

The University of Texas at El Paso, B

Utah

Utah State University, B

Vermont

University of Vermont, B

Wisconsin

University of Wisconsin - La Crosse, B
University of Wisconsin - Madison, D
University of Wisconsin - Oshkosh, B

U.S. Territories: Puerto Rico

University of Puerto Rico in Arecibo, B

Canada

Alberta

University of Alberta, MD

British Columbia

The University of British Columbia, B
University of Victoria, B

Manitoba

University of Manitoba, BMD

Maritime Provinces: New Brunswick

University of New Brunswick Fredericton, B

Maritime Provinces: Nova Scotia

Dalhousie University, B
University of King's College, B

Newfoundland and Labrador

Memorial University of Newfoundland, B

Ontario

University of Toronto, B

Quebec

McGill University, B
Université Laval, B
Université de Montréal, B
Université de Sherbrooke, B

Saskatchewan

University of Saskatchewan, B

MEDICAL OFFICE ASSISTANT/ SPECIALIST

United States

Alabama

Virginia College in Birmingham, A

Arizona

Coconino Community College, A
Phoenix College, A

California

Glendale Community College, A
Pasadena City College, A
San Joaquin Valley College (Fresno), A
San Joaquin Valley College (Lancaster), A

San Joaquin Valley College (Ontario), A
San Joaquin Valley College (Salida), A
San Joaquin Valley College (Temecula), A
San Joaquin Valley College (Visalia), A

Colorado

Front Range Community College, A
Morgan Community College, B
Trinidad State Junior College, A

Florida

Broward College, A
Fortis College (Winter Park), A

Hawaii

Remington College - Honolulu Campus, A

Idaho

Lewis-Clark State College, AB

Illinois

Joliet Junior College, A
Kankakee Community College, A
Northwestern College - Bridgeview Campus, A
Sauk Valley Community College, A
Southwestern Illinois College, A

Iowa

Iowa Lakes Community College, A

Kansas

Barton County Community College, A
Johnson County Community College, A
Manhattan Area Technical College, A

Kentucky

ATA College, A
Daymar College (Bellevue), A
Sullivan University, A

Louisiana

Delta School of Business and Technology, A

Maine

Beal College, A

Maryland

Harford Community College, A

Michigan

Alpena Community College, A

Minnesota

Northland Community and Technical College, A
Saint Paul College - A Community & Technical College, A

Missouri

Hickey College, A
Metro Business College (Cape Girardeau), A
Metro Business College (Jefferson City), A
Metro Business College (Rolla), A
Midwest Institute (Saint Louis), A

Montana

Helena College University of Montana, A

New Hampshire

White Mountains Community College, A

New Jersey

Bergen Community College, A

New York

New York Career Institute, A

North Carolina

ECPI University (Charlotte), A
Miller-Motte College (Wilmington), A

North Dakota

Dakota College at Bottineau, A

Ohio

Cincinnati State Technical and Community College, A
Professional Skills Institute, A
Terra State Community College, A

Oklahoma

Vatterott College (Warr Acres), A

Pennsylvania

Butler County Community College, A
Cambria-Rowe Business College (Indiana), A
Commonwealth Technical Institute, A
Penn Commercial Business and Technical School, A
Pittsburgh Technical Institute, A
Westmoreland County Community College, A

South Dakota

Mitchell Technical Institute, A

Texas

Virginia College in Austin, A

Virginia

Patrick Henry Community College, A

West Virginia

West Virginia Junior College - Charleston, A

Wisconsin

Bryant & Stratton College - Wauwatosa Campus, A
Concordia University Wisconsin, B

Wyoming

Central Wyoming College, A
Western Wyoming Community College, A

MEDICAL OFFICE COMPUTER SPECIALIST/ASSISTANT

United States

Colorado

Lamar Community College, A

Iowa

Iowa Lakes Community College, A

Minnesota

Normandale Community College, A
St. Cloud Technical & Community College, A

Mississippi

Mississippi Delta Community College, A

North Carolina

Richmond Community College, A

Oregon

Rogue Community College, A

Wyoming

Western Wyoming Community College, A

MEDICAL OFFICE MANAGE- MENT/ADMINISTRATION

United States

Alabama

Virginia College in Huntsville, A
Virginia College in Mobile, A

Arizona

Carrington College - Mesa, A
Carrington College - Phoenix North, A
Carrington College - Tucson, A

Arkansas

University of Arkansas Community College at Batesville, A
University of Arkansas Community College at Hope, A

California

Carrington College - Sacramento, A
Carrington College - San Jose, A
San Joaquin Valley College - Online, A

Colorado

Aims Community College, A
Pikes Peak Community College, A
Pueblo Community College, A
Red Rocks Community College, A

Connecticut

Norwalk Community College, A

Florida

City College (Gainesville), A
Key College, A
Lincoln College of Technology, A
Meridian College, A

Georgia

Columbus Technical College, A
Dalton State College, A
Georgia Northwestern Technical College, A
Virginia College in Macon, A

Idaho

Carrington College - Boise, A

Illinois

College of Lake County, A

Iowa

Brown Mackie College - Quad Cities, A
Kaplan University, Davenport Campus, A
Kaplan University, Des Moines, A
Vatterott College, A
Western Iowa Tech Community College, A

Kentucky

Beckfield College, A
Brown Mackie College - Hopkinsville, A
Spencerian College - Lexington, A

Louisiana

McCann School of Business & Technology (Monroe), A
Virginia College in Baton Rouge, A

Maryland

Prince George's Community College, A

Massachusetts

Bay State College, A
Salter College (Chicopee), A

Michigan

Henry Ford College, A

Mississippi

Virginia College in Biloxi, A

Missouri

Midwest Institute (Fenton), A
Missouri College, A

New Mexico

Carrington College - Albuquerque, A
Eastern New Mexico University - Roswell, A

New York

ASA College, A
Long Island Business Institute, A
Orange County Community College, A
Queensborough Community College of the City University of New York, A

North Carolina

Beaufort County Community College, A
Caldwell Community College and Technical Institute, A
Cape Fear Community College, A
Catawba Valley Community College, A
Cleveland Community College, A
Craven Community College, A
Durham Technical Community College, A
Fayetteville Technical Community College, A
Forsyth Technical Community College, A
Gaston College, A
Guilford Technical Community College, A
Halifax Community College, A
Johnston Community College, A
Lenoir Community College, A
Nash Community College, A
Piedmont Community College, A
Pitt Community College, A
Randolph Community College, A
Richmond Community College, A
Roanoke-Chowan Community College, A
Rockingham Community College, A
Rowan-Cabarrus Community College, A
South Piedmont Community College, A
Wake Technical Community College, A
Wayne Community College, A
Western Piedmont Community College, A
Wilson Community College, A

Ohio

Belmont College, A
Brown Mackie College - Akron, A
Fortis College (Cuyahoga Falls), A
Ohio Valley College of Technology, A
The University of Akron, A
The University of Akron Wayne College, A

Oregon

Chemeketa Community College, A

Pennsylvania

Douglas Education Center, A
Keystone Technical Institute, A
McCann School of Business & Technology (Lewisburg), A
Mercyhurst North East, A
Pennsylvania Institute of Health and Technology, A
Pennsylvania Institute of Technology, A

South Carolina

Forrest College, A
Virginia College in Spartanburg, A

South Dakota

Presentation College, A

Tennessee

Concorde Career College, A
Virginia College in Chattanooga, A

Texas

Brightwood College, Brownsville Campus, A
Brightwood College, Corpus Christi Campus, A
Brightwood College, McAllen Campus, A
Brightwood College, San Antonio San Pedro Campus, A

Virginia

Virginia College in Richmond, A

Washington

Big Bend Community College, A
Carrington College - Spokane, A

West Virginia

West Virginia Junior College - Bridgeport, A

Wisconsin

Fox Valley Technical College, A
Lac Courte Oreilles Ojibwa Community College, A

MEDICAL PHYSICS

United States

Arizona

The University of Arizona, M

California

University of California, Los Angeles, MD

Colorado

University of Colorado Boulder, D

Florida

Florida Atlantic University, M
University of Florida, MD
University of South Florida, M

Illinois

Rush University, MD
Southern Illinois University Carbondale, M
University of Chicago, D

Indiana

Indiana University Bloomington, M
Purdue University, MD

Kentucky

University of Kentucky, M

Louisiana

Louisiana State University and Agricultural & Mechanical College, M

Massachusetts

Harvard University, D
Massachusetts Institute of Technology, D

Michigan

Oakland University, D
Wayne State University, D

Minnesota

University of Minnesota, Twin Cities Campus, MD

Missouri

University of Missouri, M

New York

Columbia University, M
Hofstra University, M
Stony Brook University, State University of New York, MD

North Carolina

Duke University, MD
East Carolina University, M

Ohio

Cleveland State University, M
University of Cincinnati, M
The University of Toledo, MD
Wright State University, M

Oklahoma

University of Oklahoma Health Sciences Center, MD

Oregon

Oregon State University, MD

Pennsylvania

University of Pennsylvania, M

Tennessee

Vanderbilt University, M

Texas

The University of Texas Health Science Center at Houston, MD
The University of Texas Health Science Center at San Antonio, D

Utah

University of Utah, MD

Virginia

The College of William and Mary, D
Hampton University, MD
Virginia Commonwealth University, MD

Wisconsin

University of Wisconsin - Madison, MD

Canada

Alberta

University of Alberta, MD

British Columbia

University of Victoria, MD

Ontario

McMaster University, MD

Quebec

McGill University, MD

MEDICAL RADIOLOGIC TECHNOLOGY/SCIENCE - RADIATION THERAPIST

United States

Alabama

Community College of the Air Force, A
George C. Wallace Community College, A
Southern Union State Community College, A

Arizona

Carrington College - Phoenix West, A
GateWay Community College, A

Arkansas

Arkansas State University, B
East Arkansas Community College, A
North Arkansas College, A
South Arkansas Community College, A
Southeast Arkansas College, A
University of Arkansas for Medical Sciences, AB
University of Central Arkansas, B

California

Brightwood College, North Hollywood Campus, A
California State University, Long Beach, B
Charles R. Drew University of Medicine and Science, AB
City College of San Francisco, A
Foothill College, A
Loma Linda University, AB
National University, B
Santa Barbara City College, A

Connecticut

Capital Community College, A
Middlesex Community College, A
Naugatuck Valley Community College, A
University of Hartford, B

Florida

Broward College, A
College of Central Florida, A
Eastern Florida State College, A
Florida SouthWestern State College, A
Florida State College at Jacksonville, A
Fortis Institute (Palm Springs), A
Gulf Coast State College, A
Hillsborough Community College, A
Keiser University, A
Miami Dade College, A
Northwest Florida State College, A
Pensacola State College, A
Polk State College, A

Santa Fe College, A
South Florida State College, A
State College of Florida Manatee-Sarasota, A
Tallahassee Community College, A
Valencia College, AB

Georgia

Albany Technical College, A
Armstrong State University, B
Athens Technical College, A
Augusta Technical College, A
Augusta University, B
Central Georgia Technical College, A
Chattahoochee Technical College, A
College of Coastal Georgia, A
Columbus Technical College, A
Gwinnett Technical College, A
Lanier Technical College, A
Southeastern Technical College, A
Southern Crescent Technical College, A
Southern Regional Technical College, A
West Georgia Technical College, A
Wiregrass Georgia Technical College, A

Hawaii

Kapiolani Community College, A

Idaho

Boise State University, B
College of Southern Idaho, A
Idaho State University, AB

Illinois

City Colleges of Chicago, Malcolm X College, A
City Colleges of Chicago, Wilbur Wright College, A
College of DuPage, B
College of Lake County, A
Illinois Eastern Community Colleges, Olney Central College, A
North Central College, B
Parkland College, A
Rend Lake College, A
Roosevelt University, B
Southern Illinois University Carbondale, B
Trinity College of Nursing and Health Sciences, A
University of St. Francis, B

Indiana

Ball State University, B
Indiana University Kokomo, B
Indiana University - Purdue University Fort Wayne, A
Indiana University - Purdue University Indianapolis, B
Indiana University South Bend, B
Ivy Tech Community College - Bloomington, A
Ivy Tech Community College - Central Indiana, A
Ivy Tech Community College - Columbus, A
Ivy Tech Community College - East Central, A
Ivy Tech Community College - Richmond, A
Ivy Tech Community College - Southeast, A
Ivy Tech Community College - Wabash Valley, A
University of Southern Indiana, B
Vincennes University, A

Iowa

Scott Community College, A

Kansas

Hutchinson Community College, A
Newman University, A

Kentucky

Ashland Community and Technical College, A
Bluegrass Community and Technical College, A
Elizabethtown Community and Technical College, A
Hazard Community and Technical College, A
Morehead State University, AB
Somerset Community College, A
Southcentral Kentucky Community and Technical College, A
Southeast Kentucky Community and Technical College, A

Louisiana

Delgado Community College, A
Southern University at Shreveport, A

Maine

Eastern Maine Community College, A

Maryland

Allegany College of Maryland, A
Anne Arundel Community College, A
Chesapeake College, A
Community College of Baltimore County, A
Hagerstown Community College, A
Montgomery College, A
Notre Dame of Maryland University, B
Wor-Wic Community College, A

Massachusetts

Bunker Hill Community College, A
Holyoke Community College, A
Labouré College, A
MCPHS University, B
Middlesex Community College, A
North Shore Community College, A

Michigan

Delta College, A
Ferris State University, A
Grand Valley State University, B
Jackson College, A
Kellogg Community College, A
Lake Michigan College, A
Mott Community College, A
Oakland Community College, A
Oakland University, A
St. Clair County Community College, A
University of Michigan - Flint, B
Washtenaw Community College, A
Wayne State University, B

Minnesota

Argosy University, Twin Cities, A
Dunwoody College of Technology, A
Riverland Community College, A
St. Catherine University, A

Mississippi

Itawamba Community College, A
Mississippi Delta Community College, A
Northeast Mississippi Community College, A

Missouri

Avila University, B
East Central College, A
Missouri Southern State University, A
Saint Louis University, A
Southeast Missouri Hospital College of Nursing and Health Sciences, A
University of Missouri, B

Montana

Flathead Valley Community College, A

Nebraska

Creighton University, B
Northeast Community College, A
Southeast Community College, Lincoln Campus, A
University of Nebraska Medical Center, B

Nevada

College of Southern Nevada, A
Truckee Meadows Community College, A
University of Nevada, Las Vegas, B

New Jersey

Brookdale Community College, A
Cumberland County College, A
Essex County College, A
Fairleigh Dickinson University, College at Florham, B
Mercer County Community College, A
Middlesex County College, A
Passaic County Community College, A
Rowan College at Burlington County, A

Thomas Edison State University, AB
Union County College, A

New Mexico

Northern New Mexico College, A
University of New Mexico, AB

New York

Broome Community College, A
Erie Community College, A
Eugenio María de Hostos Community College of the
City University of New York, A
Fiorello H. LaGuardia Community College of the
City University of New York, A
Long Island University - LIU Post, B
Mohawk Valley Community College, A
Nassau Community College, A
New York City College of Technology of the City
University of New York, AB
Niagara County Community College, A
North Country Community College, A
Orange County Community College, A
St. Francis College, B
State University of New York Upstate Medical Uni-
versity, B

North Carolina

Cape Fear Community College, A
Carolinas College of Health Sciences, A
Catawba Valley Community College, A
Edgecombe Community College, A
Forsyth Technical Community College, A
Pitt Community College, A
Southwestern Community College, A
The University of North Carolina at Chapel Hill, B

North Dakota

Minot State University, B

Ohio

Bowling Green State University, B
Bowling Green State University - Firelands College,
A
Columbus State Community College, A
James A. Rhodes State College, A
Kent State University at Ashtabula, A
Kent State University at Salem, AB
Lakeland Community College, A
Mercy College of Ohio, A
North Central State College, A
The Ohio State University, B
Owens Community College, A
Shawnee State University, A
The University of Akron, A
University of Cincinnati Blue Ash College, A
The University of Findlay, B

Oklahoma

Bacone College, A
Rose State College, A
Southwestern Oklahoma State University, A
Southwestern Oklahoma State University at Sayre,
A
Tulsa Community College, A
University of Oklahoma Health Sciences Center, B
Western Oklahoma State College, A

Oregon

Oregon Health & Science University, B
Portland Community College, A

Pennsylvania

Bloomsburg University of Pennsylvania, B
Clarion University of Pennsylvania, B
Community College of Allegheny County, A
Community College of Beaver County, A
Community College of Philadelphia, A
Drexel University, A
Gwynedd Mercy University, B
Harcum College, A
Johnson College, A
Keystone College, A
La Roche College, AB
Misericordia University, B
Montgomery County Community College, A

Mount Aloysius College, AB
Penn State New Kensington, A
Penn State Schuylkill, A
Pennsylvania College of Health Sciences, A
Pennsylvania College of Technology, A
Pittsburgh Career Institute, A

South Carolina

Aiken Technical College, A
Florence-Darlington Technical College, A
Greenville Technical College, A
Midlands Technical College, A
Orangeburg-Calhoun Technical College, A
Piedmont Technical College, A
Spartanburg Community College, A
Technical College of the Lowcountry, A
York Technical College, A

South Dakota

Mitchell Technical Institute, A
Mount Marty College, B
University of Sioux Falls, B

Tennessee

Baptist College of Health Sciences, B
Belmont University, B
Chattanooga State Community College, A
Columbia State Community College, A
Jackson State Community College, A
Southwest Tennessee Community College, A
Volunteer State Community College, A

Texas

The College of Health Care Professions (Houston),
A
Del Mar College, A
El Centro College, A
El Paso Community College, A
Galveston College, A
Kilgore College, A
Lamar Institute of Technology, A
Lone Star College - CyFair, A
St. Philip's College, A
Texas State University, B

Utah

Salt Lake Community College, A
Weber State University, AB

Vermont

Southern Vermont College, B
University of Vermont, B

Virginia

Averett University, B
Northern Virginia Community College, A

Washington

Bellevue College, A
Bellingham Technical College, A
Carrington College - Spokane, A
Tacoma Community College, A

West Virginia

Alderson Broaddus University, B
Bluefield State College, A
Mountwest Community & Technical College, A
University of Charleston, A
West Virginia Northern Community College, A

Wisconsin

Carroll University, B
Chippewa Valley Technical College, A
Concordia University Wisconsin, B
Milwaukee Area Technical College, A
Moraine Park Technical College, A
Northcentral Technical College, A
Northeast Wisconsin Technical College, A
University of Wisconsin - La Crosse, B
Waukesha County Technical College, A

U.S. Territories: Puerto Rico

Inter American University of Puerto Rico, Aguadilla
Campus, A

Inter American University of Puerto Rico, Ponce
Campus, A
Inter American University of Puerto Rico, San
Germán Campus, A
Universidad Central del Caribe, A
Universidad del Este, B

Canada

British Columbia

British Columbia Institute of Technology, AB
Thompson Rivers University, B

Maritime Provinces: Prince Edward Is-
land

University of Prince Edward Island, B

MEDICAL RECEPTION/RECEP-
TIONIST

United States

Iowa

Iowa Lakes Community College, A

Washington

Edmonds Community College, A

MEDICAL STAFF SERVICES
TECHNOLOGY/TECHNICIAN

United States

Florida

Southern Technical College (Fort Myers), A

Illinois

John Wood Community College, A
Rend Lake College, A

South Carolina

Converse College, B

MEDICAL/SURGICAL NURSING

United States

Illinois

Saint Francis Medical Center College of Nursing,
MDO

New York

Daemen College, O
State University of New York Downstate Medical
Center, MO

Ohio

Ursuline College, M

South Carolina

University of South Carolina, M

Texas

Angelo State University, M

U.S. Territories: Puerto Rico

Pontifical Catholic University of Puerto Rico, M
Universidad Adventista de las Antillas, M

MEDICAL TECHNOLOGY

United States

California

University of California, San Diego, MD

Illinois

Rush University, M

Minnesota

University of Minnesota, Twin Cities Campus, M

Mississippi

University of Southern Mississippi, M

Nebraska

University of Nebraska Medical Center, O

New Jersey

Fairleigh Dickinson University, Metropolitan Campus, M

New York

State University of New York Upstate Medical University, M

Texas

Tarleton State University, M

Utah

University of Utah, M

U.S. Territories: Puerto Rico

Inter American University of Puerto Rico, Metropolitan Campus, M
Pontifical Catholic University of Puerto Rico, O
University of Puerto Rico, Medical Sciences Campus, O

MEDICAL TRANSCRIPTION/ TRANSCRIPTIONIST

United States

Arizona

Central Arizona College, A
GateWay Community College, A
Northland Pioneer College, A

California

Glendale Community College, A
South Coast College, A
Ventura College, A

Illinois

Rockford Career College, A

Iowa

Iowa Lakes Community College, A
Kaplan University, Davenport Campus, A
Southwestern Community College, A

Kansas

Barton County Community College, A
Cowley County Community College and Area Vocational - Technical School, A

Maine

Eastern Maine Community College, A

Massachusetts

Northern Essex Community College, A

Michigan

Jackson College, A
Mid Michigan Community College, A
Oakland Community College, A

Mississippi

Antonelli College (Hattiesburg), A
Antonelli College (Jackson), A

New Jersey

Hudson County Community College, A

New Mexico

New Mexico State University - Carlsbad, A

Ohio

Belmont College, A
University of Cincinnati Blue Ash College, A

Oregon

Chemeketa Community College, A
Treasure Valley Community College, A

Pennsylvania

Fortis Institute (Erie), A
Laurel Business Institute, A

South Dakota

Western Dakota Technical Institute, A

Texas

El Centro College, A

West Virginia

Mountain State College, A
Mountwest Community & Technical College, A

Wisconsin

Lac Courte Oreilles Ojibwa Community College, A

MEDICATION AIDE

United States

Kansas

Barton County Community College, A

MEDICINAL AND PHARMACEUTICAL CHEMISTRY

United States

California

University of California, Irvine, D
University of California, San Diego, B

Connecticut

University of Connecticut, MD

Florida

Florida Agricultural and Mechanical University, MD
University of Florida, MD

Idaho

Idaho State University, D

Indiana

Purdue University, D

Iowa

The University of Iowa, D

Kansas

The University of Kansas, MD

Massachusetts

Worcester Polytechnic Institute, B

Michigan

Michigan Technological University, B
University of Michigan, BD
Wayne State University, D

Minnesota

University of Minnesota, Twin Cities Campus, MD

Montana

University of Montana, MD

New Jersey

New Jersey Institute of Technology, M
Rutgers University - New Brunswick, MD

New York

University at Buffalo, the State University of New York, MD

Ohio

Cleveland State University, M
University of Dayton, B
The University of Toledo, MD

Pennsylvania

Duquesne University, MD
Temple University, MD
University of the Sciences, BMD

Rhode Island

University of Rhode Island, MD

South Carolina

Medical University of South Carolina, D

Tennessee

King University, B

Texas

The University of Texas at Austin, D

Utah

University of Utah, MD

Virginia

Virginia Commonwealth University, M

Washington

University of Washington, D

West Virginia

West Virginia University, MD

Canada

Ontario

University of Guelph, B

MEDIEVAL AND RENAISSANCE STUDIES

United States

Arizona

Arizona State University at the Tempe campus, O

California

California State University, Long Beach, M
Pomona College, B
University of California, Santa Barbara, BD

Connecticut

University of Connecticut, MD
Yale University, MD

District of Columbia

The Catholic University of America, BMDO
Georgetown University, BM

Florida

New College of Florida, B

Georgia

Emory University, B

Illinois

University of Chicago, B

Indiana

Hanover College, B
Indiana University Bloomington, D
Purdue University, B
University of Notre Dame, BMD

Iowa

Cornell College, B
The University of Iowa, B

Louisiana

Tulane University, B

Massachusetts

Harvard University, D
Mount Holyoke College, B
Smith College, B
Wellesley College, B

Michigan

University of Michigan, B

Minnesota

Augsburg College, B
St. Olaf College, B
University of Minnesota, Twin Cities Campus, MD

Nebraska

University of Nebraska - Lincoln, B

New Jersey

Rutgers University - New Brunswick, BD

New York

Bard College, B
Barnard College, B
Binghamton University, State University of New
    York, B
Columbia University, BM
Cornell University, MD
Fordham University, BMO
New York University, B
University at Albany, State University of New York, B
Vassar College, B

North Carolina

Duke University, B

Ohio

Cleveland State University, B
The Ohio State University, B
Ohio Wesleyan University, B

Oregon

University of Oregon, B

Pennsylvania

Dickinson College, B
Penn State Abington, B
Penn State Altoona, B
Penn State Beaver, B
Penn State Berks, B
Penn State Brandywine, B
Penn State DuBois, B
Penn State Erie, The Behrend College, B
Penn State Fayette, The Eberly Campus, B
Penn State Greater Allegheny, B
Penn State Hazleton, B
Penn State Lehigh Valley, B
Penn State Mont Alto, B
Penn State New Kensington, B
Penn State Schuylkill, B
Penn State Shenango, B
Penn State University Park, B
Penn State Wilkes-Barre, B
Penn State Worthington Scranton, B
Penn State York, B
Swarthmore College, B
University of Pittsburgh, O
Ursinus College, B

Rhode Island

Brown University, B

Tennessee

Sewanee: The University of the South, B

Texas

Southern Methodist University, BM

Vermont

Marlboro College, B

Virginia

The College of William and Mary, B
Washington and Lee University, B

Canada

Alberta

University of Calgary, B

British Columbia

University of Victoria, B

Manitoba

University of Manitoba, B

Maritime Provinces: New Brunswick

Mount Allison University, B

Newfoundland and Labrador

Memorial University of Newfoundland, B

Ontario

Carleton University, B
University of Guelph, D
University of Ottawa, B
University of Toronto, MD
University of Waterloo, B
The University of Western Ontario, B
Wilfrid Laurier University, B

Quebec

Université de Montréal, B

Saskatchewan

University of Regina, B
University of Saskatchewan, B

MEDIUM/HEAVY VEHICLE AND TRUCK TECHNOLOGY/TECHNICIAN

United States

Minnesota

Dakota County Technical College, A
Hennepin Technical College, A
St. Cloud Technical & Community College, A

Missouri

State Technical College of Missouri, A

Nebraska

Northeast Community College, A

Ohio

Edison Community College, A

MENTAL HEALTH COUNSELING/COUNSELOR

United States

Alabama

Community College of the Air Force, A
Wallace State Community College, A

Alaska

University of Alaska, Prince William Sound College,
    A

California

Los Angeles City College, A
Mt. San Antonio College, A
Orange Coast College, A
Porterville College, A
San Bernardino Valley College, A

Colorado

Community College of Denver, A

Connecticut

Gateway Community College, A
Housatonic Community College, A
Middlesex Community College, A

Illinois

Illinois Central College, A

Louisiana

Southern University at Shreveport, A

Maryland

Morgan State University, B

Massachusetts

North Shore Community College, A
Northern Essex Community College, A

Michigan

Macomb Community College, A

Minnesota

St. Cloud State University, B

Nebraska

Metropolitan Community College, A

Nevada

Truckee Meadows Community College, A

New Hampshire

NHTI, Concord's Community College, A

New York

Canisius College, B
Iona College, B
Kingsborough Community College of the City University of New York, A
North Country Community College, A

North Carolina

Sandhills Community College, A
Southwestern Community College, A

Ohio

Sinclair Community College, A
Zane State College, A

Oregon

Mt. Hood Community College, A

Pennsylvania

Lackawanna College, A

Rhode Island

Community College of Rhode Island, A

Texas

Alvin Community College, A
Blinn College, A
Del Mar College, A
McLennan Community College, A
South Plains College, A
Tarrant County College District, A

Vermont

Goddard College, B

Virginia

Virginia Western Community College, A

Washington

Pierce College at Puyallup, A

Canada

Manitoba

Brandon University, B

MENTAL AND SOCIAL HEALTH SERVICES AND ALLIED PRO-FESSIONS

United States

Alaska

University of Alaska Fairbanks, A

Kansas

Washburn University, AB

Kentucky

Northern Kentucky University, B

Maine

Kennebec Valley Community College, A
University of Maine at Augusta, AB

Maryland

Baltimore City Community College, A
Chesapeake College, A
College of Southern Maryland, A

Michigan

Bay de Noc Community College, A

New York

Broome Community College, A

North Carolina

Halifax Community College, A
Lenoir Community College, A
Montgomery Community College, A
Piedmont Community College, A
Richmond Community College, A
Roanoke-Chowan Community College, A
South Piedmont Community College, A
Wayne Community College, A
Western Piedmont Community College, A

Ohio

Belmont College, A
Columbus State Community College, A

Pennsylvania

Clarion University of Pennsylvania, AB
Pennsylvania College of Technology, B
Reading Area Community College, A

Rhode Island

Roger Williams University, B

South Dakota

Sinte Gleska University, AB

Virginia

Blue Ridge Community College, A
J. Sargeant Reynolds Community College, A
John Tyler Community College, A
New River Community College, A
Northern Virginia Community College, A
Old Dominion University, B
Southwest Virginia Community College, A
Thomas Nelson Community College, A

Washington

Clover Park Technical College, A
Columbia Basin College, A
Edmonds Community College, A
Lake Washington Institute of Technology, A
Olympic College, A
Tacoma Community College, A

Wisconsin

Milwaukee Area Technical College, A
Northcentral Technical College, A
Southwest Wisconsin Technical College, A

U.S. Territories: Puerto Rico

University of Puerto Rico in Ponce, B

MERCHANDISING AND BUYING OPERATIONS

United States

Illinois

College of DuPage, A

Michigan

Delta College, A

Nebraska

Northeast Community College, A

Ohio

Cuyahoga Community College, A
The University of Akron, A

Texas

North Central Texas College, A

METAL AND JEWELRY ARTS

United States

California

Academy of Art University, AB
Bethesda University, B
California College of the Arts, B
California State University, Long Beach, B
FIDM/Fashion Institute of Design & Merchandising, Los Angeles Campus, A
Monterey Peninsula College, A
Palomar College, A

Colorado

Adams State University, B
Colorado State University, B
Western State Colorado University, B

Georgia

Savannah College of Art and Design, B

Illinois

School of the Art Institute of Chicago, B

Iowa

The University of Iowa, B

Kansas

The University of Kansas, B

Maine

Maine College of Art, B

Massachusetts

Massachusetts College of Art and Design, B
School of the Museum of Fine Arts, Boston, B
University of Massachusetts Dartmouth, B

Michigan

Ferris State University, B
Northern Michigan University, B
University of Michigan, B

Montana

Flathead Valley Community College, A

New Mexico

Santa Fe Community College, A

New York

Fashion Institute of Technology, A
Hofstra University, B
Pratt Institute, B
Rochester Institute of Technology, B
State University of New York at New Paltz, B
Syracuse University, B

North Carolina

College of The Albemarle, A

Ohio

Bowling Green State University, B
Cleveland Institute of Art, B
The University of Akron, B

Oregon

University of Oregon, B

Pennsylvania

Arcadia University, B
Seton Hill University, B
Temple University, B

Rhode Island

Rhode Island College, B
Rhode Island School of Design, B

Texas

Paris Junior College, A
San Antonio College, A

Washington

Central Washington University, B

Canada

Alberta

Alberta College of Art & Design, B

Maritime Provinces: Nova Scotia

NSCAD University, B

METALLURGICAL ENGINEER-ING

United States

Alabama

The University of Alabama, BMD

Colorado

Colorado School of Mines, BMD

Illinois

University of Illinois at Urbana - Champaign, B

Michigan

Michigan Technological University, MD

Missouri

Missouri University of Science and Technology, BMD

Montana

Montana Tech of The University of Montana, BM

Nebraska

University of Nebraska - Lincoln, M

Nevada

University of Nevada, Reno, BMD

Ohio

The Ohio State University, MD

South Dakota

South Dakota School of Mines and Technology, B

Texas

LeTourneau University, B
The University of Texas at El Paso, BMD

Utah

University of Utah, BMD

Canada

British Columbia

The University of British Columbia, BMD

Ontario

Laurentian University, B
University of Toronto, B

Quebec

McGill University, B
Université Laval, BMD

METALLURGICAL TECHNOL-OGY/TECHNICIAN

United States

Alabama

Community College of the Air Force, A

Arkansas

Arkansas Northeastern College, A

Michigan

Macomb Community College, A
Schoolcraft College, A

Oregon

Linn-Benton Community College, A

Pennsylvania

Penn State Altoona, A
Penn State Berks, A
Penn State DuBois, A
Penn State Erie, The Behrend College, A
Penn State Fayette, The Eberly Campus, A
Penn State Hazleton, A
Penn State New Kensington, A
Penn State Schuylkill, A
Penn State Shenango, A
Penn State Wilkes-Barre, A
Penn State York, A

Texas

Kilgore College, A

METALLURGY

United States

Connecticut

University of Connecticut, MD

Canada

British Columbia

The University of British Columbia, MD

METEOROLOGY

United States

Alabama

University of South Alabama, B

Arizona

Northern Arizona University, MD
The University of Arizona, MD

California

San Jose State University, M
University of California, San Diego, M

Colorado

Metropolitan State University of Denver, B

Connecticut

Yale University, D

Florida

Florida Institute of Technology, BM
Florida State University, BMD
University of Miami, BMD

Hawaii

University of Hawaii at Manoa, BMD

Illinois

Western Illinois University, B

Iowa

Iowa State University of Science and Technology, MD

Kentucky

Western Kentucky University, B

Maryland

University of Maryland, College Park, MD

Michigan

Central Michigan University, B

Mississippi

Mississippi State University, M

Missouri

Saint Louis University, MD

New Hampshire

Plymouth State University, M

New Jersey

Rutgers University - New Brunswick, B

North Carolina

North Carolina State University, MD
The University of North Carolina at Charlotte, B

Oklahoma

University of Oklahoma, BMD

Pennsylvania

Millersville University of Pennsylvania, M
Penn State University Park, MD

Texas

Texas A&M University, MD
University of the Incarnate Word, B

Utah

Utah State University, MD

Virginia

Virginia Polytechnic Institute and State University, B

West Virginia

BridgeValley Community and Technical College
(South Charleston), A

Wisconsin

Northland College, B
University of Wisconsin - Milwaukee, B

Canada

Maritime Provinces: Nova Scotia

Dalhousie University, B

Quebec

McGill University, MD
Université du Québec à Montréal, DO

MICROBIOLOGICAL SCIENCES AND IMMUNOLOGY

United States

California

University of California, Los Angeles, B

Canada

Alberta

University of Alberta, B

Maritime Provinces: Nova Scotia

Dalhousie University, B

Quebec

Université de Montréal, B

MICROBIOLOGY

United States

Alabama

Auburn University, B
The University of Alabama, B
The University of Alabama at Birmingham, D

Arizona

Arizona State University at the Tempe campus, BD
Northern Arizona University, B
The University of Arizona, BMD

Arkansas

University of Arkansas for Medical Sciences, D

California

California State University, Chico, B
California State University, Dominguez Hills, B
California State University, Long Beach, BM
California State University, Los Angeles, B
Crafton Hills College, A
Fullerton College, A
Loma Linda University, MD
San Diego State University, BM
San Francisco State University, M
San Jose State University, M
Stanford University, D
University of California, Berkeley, BD
University of California, Davis, BMD
University of California, Irvine, MD
University of California, Los Angeles, MD
University of California, Riverside, MD
University of California, Santa Barbara, B
University of Southern California, M

Colorado

Colorado State University, BMD
University of Colorado Boulder, MD
University of Colorado Denver, MD

Connecticut

University of Connecticut, MD
Yale University, D

Delaware

University of Delaware, MD

District of Columbia

The Catholic University of America, MD
The George Washington University, MD
Georgetown University, MD
Howard University, D

Florida

University of Florida, MD
University of Miami, D
University of South Florida, MD

Georgia

Emory University, D
Georgia State University, MD
University of Georgia, BMD

Hawaii

University of Hawaii at Manoa, BMD

Idaho

Idaho State University, BM
University of Idaho, BMD

Illinois

Illinois Institute of Technology, M
Illinois State University, MD
Loyola University Chicago, MD
Rush University, D
Southern Illinois University Carbondale, BMD
University of Chicago, D
University of Illinois at Chicago, D
University of Illinois at Urbana - Champaign, BMD

Indiana

Indiana University Bloomington, BMD
Indiana University - Purdue University Indianapolis, MD
Purdue University, MD

Iowa

Iowa State University of Science and Technology, BMD
The University of Iowa, BMD
University of Northern Iowa, B

Kansas

Emporia State University, M
Kansas State University, B
The University of Kansas, BMD

Kentucky

University of Kentucky, D
University of Louisville, MD

Louisiana

Louisiana State University and Agricultural & Mechanical College, B
Louisiana State University Health Sciences Center, MD
Tulane University, MD

Maine

University of Maine, BD

Maryland

Hood College, M
Johns Hopkins University, MD
University of Maryland, College Park, B

Massachusetts

Brandeis University, D
Harvard University, D
Massachusetts Institute of Technology, D
Tufts University, D
University of Massachusetts Amherst, BMD

Michigan

Michigan State University, BMD
Northern Michigan University, B
University of Michigan, BMD

University of Michigan - Dearborn, B
Wayne State University, MD

Minnesota

University of Minnesota, Twin Cities Campus, D

Mississippi

University of Mississippi Medical Center, D
University of Southern Mississippi, MD

Missouri

Saint Louis University, D
University of Missouri, MD
Washington University in St. Louis, D

Montana

Montana State University, MD
University of Montana, D

Nebraska

University of Nebraska - Lincoln, B
University of Nebraska Medical Center, MD

New Hampshire

Dartmouth College, D
University of New Hampshire, MD

New Jersey

Rutgers University - New Brunswick, BMD
Rutgers University - Newark, D
Seton Hall University, M

New Mexico

Eastern New Mexico University, M
University of New Mexico, MD

New York

Albany College of Pharmacy and Health Sciences, B
Columbia University, MD
Cornell University, D
New York University, D
State University of New York Upstate Medical University, MD
Stony Brook University, State University of New York, D
University at Buffalo, the State University of New York, MD
University of Rochester, MD
Wagner College, M

North Carolina

Duke University, D
East Carolina University, MD
North Carolina State University, BMD
The University of North Carolina at Chapel Hill, MD
Wake Forest University, D

North Dakota

North Dakota State University, BMD
University of North Dakota, MD

Ohio

Bowling Green State University, B
Case Western Reserve University, D
Miami University, BMD
Miami University Hamilton, B
The Ohio State University, BMD
Ohio University, BMD
The University of Akron, B
University of Cincinnati, MD
Wright State University, M
Youngstown State University, M

Oklahoma

Oklahoma State University, BMD
Southwestern Oklahoma State University, M
University of Oklahoma, BMD
University of Oklahoma Health Sciences Center, MD

Oregon

Oregon Health & Science University, D
Oregon State University, BMD

Pennsylvania

Drexel University, MD
Penn State University Park, MD
Thomas Jefferson University, MD
University of Pennsylvania, D
University of Pittsburgh, BMD
University of the Sciences, B

Rhode Island

University of Rhode Island, BMD

South Carolina

Clemson University, BMD
Medical University of South Carolina, MD

South Dakota

South Dakota State University, BMD
The University of South Dakota, MD

Tennessee

East Tennessee State University, D
The University of Tennessee, MD
Vanderbilt University, MD

Texas

Texas A&M University, BMD
Texas State University, B
Texas Tech University, BM
The University of Texas at Arlington, B
The University of Texas at Austin, D
The University of Texas Health Science Center at Houston, MD
The University of Texas Health Science Center at San Antonio, MD
The University of Texas Medical Branch, MD

Utah

Brigham Young University, BMD
Weber State University, AB

Vermont

University of Vermont, B

Virginia

George Mason University, M
University of Virginia, D
Virginia Commonwealth University, MDO

Washington

Central Washington University, B
University of Washington, BD
Washington State University, B

West Virginia

West Virginia University, MD

Wisconsin

Marquette University, MD
University of Wisconsin - La Crosse, BM
University of Wisconsin - Madison, BD
University of Wisconsin - Milwaukee, B
University of Wisconsin - Oshkosh, M

Wyoming

University of Wyoming, BD

U.S. Territories: Puerto Rico

Humacao Community College, A
Inter American University of Puerto Rico, Aguadilla Campus, B
Inter American University of Puerto Rico, Bayamón Campus, B
Inter American University of Puerto Rico, Metropolitan Campus, BM
Inter American University of Puerto Rico, Ponce Campus, B
Inter American University of Puerto Rico, San Germán Campus, B
Universidad Central del Caribe, M
Universidad del Este, B
University of Puerto Rico in Humacao, B
University of Puerto Rico, Mayagüez Campus, B

University of Puerto Rico, Medical Sciences Campus, MD

Canada

Alberta

University of Alberta, BMD
University of Calgary, MD

British Columbia

The University of British Columbia, MD
The University of British Columbia - Okanagan Campus, B
University of Victoria, MD

Manitoba

University of Manitoba, MD

Maritime Provinces: Nova Scotia

Dalhousie University, MD

Ontario

Queen's University at Kingston, MD
University of Guelph, BMD
University of Ottawa, MD
University of Toronto, B
The University of Western Ontario, MD

Quebec

McGill University, BMD
Université Laval, MD
Université de Montréal, BMD
Université de Sherbrooke, MD

Saskatchewan

University of Saskatchewan, MD

MIDDLE/NEAR EASTERN AND SEMITIC LANGUAGES, LITERATURES, AND LINGUISTICS

United States

Illinois

University of Chicago, B

Michigan

University of Michigan, B
Wayne State University, B

New York

Columbia University, School of General Studies, B

Washington

University of Washington, B

MIDDLE SCHOOL EDUCATION

United States

Alaska

Alaska Pacific University, M

Arizona

The University of Arizona, M
University of Phoenix - Online Campus, M

Arkansas

Arkansas State University, M
Henderson State University, M
University of Arkansas, M
University of Arkansas at Little Rock, M

California

California Lutheran University, D
California State University, Bakersfield, M

Connecticut

Quinnipiac University, M
University of Bridgeport, M

District of Columbia

University of the District of Columbia, M

Florida

University of South Florida, St. Petersburg, M
University of West Florida, M

Georgia

Albany State University, M
Berry College, M
Brenau University, MO
Columbus State University, MO
Emory University, M
Georgia College & State University, M
Georgia Southern University, MO
Georgia Southwestern State University, O
Georgia State University, MD
Kennesaw State University, M
LaGrange College, M
Mercer University, M
Piedmont College, M
University of Georgia, MDO
University of North Georgia, M

Illinois

Chicago State University, M
Eastern Illinois University, M

Indiana

Huntington University, M

Iowa

University of Northern Iowa, M

Kansas

Kansas State University, M
Wichita State University, M

Kentucky

Bellarmine University, M
Morehead State University, M
Murray State University, MO
Spalding University, M
Union College, M
University of the Cumberlands, M
University of Kentucky, M
University of Louisville, M
Western Kentucky University, M

Louisiana

McNeese State University, O
Nicholls State University, M
Northwestern State University of Louisiana, M
University of Louisiana at Monroe, M

Maryland

Goucher College, MO
Hood College, M
Loyola University Maryland, MO
Morgan State University, M
Salisbury University, M

Massachusetts

American International College, MO
Cambridge College, M
Eastern Nazarene College, MO
Fitchburg State University, M
Lesley University, M
Merrimack College, M
Salem State University, M
Simmons College, M
Smith College, M
Tufts University, M
University of Massachusetts Boston, M
University of Massachusetts Dartmouth, MO
Worcester State University, MO

Michigan

Eastern Michigan University, M
Grand Valley State University, M

Saginaw Valley State University, M

Minnesota

Capella University, MD
Walden University, M

Mississippi

Mississippi State University, M

Missouri

Drury University, M
Maryville University of Saint Louis, M
Northwest Missouri State University, M
Southeast Missouri State University, M
University of Missouri - St. Louis, M

New Jersey

Rowan University, O
Saint Peter's University, MO

New York

Brooklyn College of the City University of New York, M
Canisius College, M
City College of the City University of New York, M
The College at Brockport, State University of New York, M
College of Mount Saint Vincent, O
Daemen College, M
Le Moyne College, M
Long Island University - LIU Post, M
Manhattanville College, M
Mount Saint Mary College, M
Nazareth College of Rochester, M
New York Institute of Technology, MO
New York University, M
Niagara University, MO
Roberts Wesleyan College, M
St. Bonaventure University, M
St. John Fisher College, M
St. John's University, O
St. Thomas Aquinas College, M
State University of New York College at Old Westbury, M
State University of New York College at Oneonta, M
State University of New York College at Potsdam, M
State University of New York at Fredonia, M
State University of New York at Oswego, M
Wagner College, M

North Carolina

Appalachian State University, M
Campbell University, M
East Carolina University, M
Fayetteville State University, M
Gardner-Webb University, M
North Carolina Central University, M
North Carolina State University, M
Salem College, M
The University of North Carolina at Charlotte, MD
The University of North Carolina at Greensboro, M
The University of North Carolina at Pembroke, M
The University of North Carolina Wilmington, M
Winston-Salem State University, M

North Dakota

Minot State University, M

Ohio

Cleveland State University, M
John Carroll University, M
Kent State University, M
Mount St. Joseph University, M
The Ohio State University - Newark Campus, M
Ohio University, M
University of Dayton, M
The University of Toledo, M
Ursuline College, M
Wright State University, M
Youngstown State University, M

Oregon

Lewis & Clark College, M
Pacific University, M

Pennsylvania

Bloomsburg University of Pennsylvania, M
Chestnut Hill College, MO
Duquesne University, M
Eastern University, O
Edinboro University of Pennsylvania, M
Holy Family University, M
La Salle University, M
Saint Joseph's University, O
Seton Hill University, MO
Shippensburg University of Pennsylvania, M
Temple University, M
Widener University, M
Wilkes University, M

South Carolina

Clemson University, M
Converse College, M
Winthrop University, M

Tennessee

East Tennessee State University, M
Lee University, M
Middle Tennessee State University, M
Tennessee Technological University, M
University of Memphis, M

Texas

Our Lady of the Lake University of San Antonio, M
University of Houston - Downtown, M

Virginia

Averett University, M
James Madison University, M
Liberty University, MO
Longwood University, M
Mary Baldwin College, M
Old Dominion University, M

Washington

University of Washington, Bothell, M

Wisconsin

University of Wisconsin - Milwaukee, M
University of Wisconsin - Platteville, M

Canada

Maritime Provinces: Nova Scotia

Mount Saint Vincent University, M

MILITARY AND DEFENSE STUDIES

United States

Arizona

Embry-Riddle Aeronautical University - Prescott, M

California

Henley-Putnam University, M

Colorado

University of Colorado Denver, M

District of Columbia

The George Washington University, M

Florida

University of West Florida, M

Hawaii

Hawai'i Pacific University, M

Maryland

Johns Hopkins University, M

Michigan

University of Detroit Mercy, M

Missouri

Columbia College, M
Missouri State University, M

Nebraska

Bellevue University, M

North Carolina

East Carolina University, M

Pennsylvania

University of Pittsburgh, M

Tennessee

Austin Peay State University, M

Vermont

Norwich University, M

Virginia

George Mason University, M
Liberty University, M

West Virginia

American Public University System, M

Canada

Alberta

University of Calgary, MD

Ontario

Royal Military College of Canada, MD

MILITARY STUDIES

United States

Arizona

Cochise County Community College District, A

California

Henley-Putnam University, B

South Carolina

Coastal Carolina University, B

MINERAL ECONOMICS

United States

Colorado

Colorado School of Mines, D

Michigan

Michigan Technological University, M

Texas

The University of Texas at Austin, M

MINERAL/MINING ENGINEERING

United States

Alaska

University of Alaska Fairbanks, M

Arizona

The University of Arizona, MO

Colorado

Colorado School of Mines, MD

Illinois

Southern Illinois University Carbondale, M

Kentucky

University of Kentucky, MD

Michigan

Michigan Technological University, MD

Missouri

Missouri University of Science and Technology, MD

Montana

Montana Tech of The University of Montana, M

Nevada

University of Nevada, Reno, M

New Mexico

New Mexico Institute of Mining and Technology, M

North Dakota

University of North Dakota, M

Pennsylvania

Penn State University Park, MD

South Dakota

South Dakota School of Mines and Technology, M

Texas

The University of Texas at Austin, M

Utah

University of Utah, MD

Virginia

Virginia Polytechnic Institute and State University, MD

West Virginia

West Virginia University, MD

Canada

Alberta

University of Alberta, MD

British Columbia

The University of British Columbia, MD

Maritime Provinces: Nova Scotia

Dalhousie University, MD

Ontario

Laurentian University, MD
Queen's University at Kingston, MD

Quebec

McGill University, MDO
Université Laval, MD
Université du Québec en Abitibi-Témiscamingue, MO

MINERALOGY

United States

Indiana

Indiana University Bloomington, MD

New York

Cornell University, MD

Canada

Quebec

Université du Québec à Chicoutimi, D
Université du Québec à Montréal, D

MINING AND MINERAL ENGI-NEERING

United States

Alaska

University of Alaska Fairbanks, B

Arizona

The University of Arizona, B

Colorado

Colorado School of Mines, B

Illinois

Southern Illinois University Carbondale, B

Kentucky

University of Kentucky, B

Missouri

Missouri University of Science and Technology, B

Montana

Montana Tech of The University of Montana, B

Nevada

University of Nevada, Reno, B

New Mexico

New Mexico Institute of Mining and Technology, B

Pennsylvania

Penn State Abington, B
Penn State Altoona, B
Penn State Beaver, B
Penn State Berks, B
Penn State Brandywine, B
Penn State DuBois, B
Penn State Erie, The Behrend College, B
Penn State Fayette, The Eberly Campus, B
Penn State Greater Allegheny, B
Penn State Hazleton, B
Penn State Lehigh Valley, B
Penn State Mont Alto, B
Penn State New Kensington, B
Penn State Schuylkill, B
Penn State Shenango, B
Penn State University Park, B
Penn State Wilkes-Barre, B
Penn State Worthington Scranton, B
Penn State York, B

South Dakota

South Dakota School of Mines and Technology, B

Utah

University of Utah, B

Virginia

Virginia Polytechnic Institute and State University, B

West Virginia

West Virginia University, B

Canada

British Columbia

The University of British Columbia, B

Ontario

Laurentian University, B
Queen's University at Kingston, B
University of Toronto, B

Quebec

Université Laval, B
Université du Québec en Abitibi-Témiscamingue, B

MINING AND PETROLEUM TECHNOLOGIES/TECHNICIANS

United States

Arizona

Pima Community College, A

U.S. Territories: United States Virgin Islands

University of the Virgin Islands, A

MINING TECHNOLOGY/TECH-NICIAN

United States

Arizona

Eastern Arizona College, A

Illinois

Illinois Eastern Community Colleges, Wabash Valley College, A
Rend Lake College, A
Southeastern Illinois College, A

Nevada

College of Southern Nevada, A

West Virginia

Bluefield State College, B

Wyoming

Casper College, A
Sheridan College, A
Western Wyoming Community College, A

Canada

British Columbia

British Columbia Institute of Technology, A

MISSIONS/MISSIONARY STUD-IES AND MISSIOLOGY

United States

Alabama

Faulkner University, M

Arizona

Arizona Christian University, B

Arkansas

Central Baptist College, B
Harding University, B
Ouachita Baptist University, B

California

Bethesda University, B
Biola University, BM
California Baptist University, B
Fresno Pacific University, M
Hope International University, BM
Simpson University, BM
Vanguard University of Southern California, B

William Jessup University, B

Florida

Belhaven University, AB
Hobe Sound Bible College, AB
Palm Beach Atlantic University, B
Southeastern University, B
Trinity Baptist College, B
Trinity College of Florida, B

Georgia

Georgia Christian University, M
Toccoa Falls College, B
Truett-McConnell College, B

Idaho

Boise Bible College, AB
Northwest Nazarene University, BM

Illinois

Lincoln Christian University, B
Moody Bible Institute, B
Olivet Nazarene University, B
Trinity International University, MD
Wheaton College, MO

Indiana

Anderson University, M
Bethel College, B
Grace College, B
Huntington University, BM
Indiana Wesleyan University, B

Iowa

Dordt College, B
Emmaus Bible College, B
Faith Baptist Bible College and Theological Seminary, AB

Kansas

Central Christian College of Kansas, AB
Manhattan Christian College, AB
MidAmerica Nazarene University, B
Tabor College, B

Kentucky

Asbury University, B
Kentucky Mountain Bible College, B
The Southern Baptist Theological Seminary, BMD
University of the Cumberlands, AB

Michigan

Andrews University, D
Cornerstone University, B
Grace Bible College, B
Kuyper College, B
Rochester College, BM

Minnesota

Concordia University, St. Paul, B
Crossroads College, B
Crown College, B
North Central University, AB
University of Northwestern - St. Paul, B

Missouri

Calvary Bible College and Theological Seminary, B
City Vision University, B
Global University, BM
Southwest Baptist University, B

Nebraska

Grace University, B

New York

Nyack College, MD

North Carolina

Charlotte Christian College and Theological Seminary, ABM
Gardner-Webb University, BMD
Mid-Atlantic Christian University, B
Piedmont International University, AB
Southeastern Baptist Theological Seminary, D

Ohio

Allegheny Wesleyan College, B
Cedarville University, B
God's Bible School and College, AB
Mount Vernon Nazarene University, B
Ohio Christian University, AB

Oklahoma

Hillsdale Free Will Baptist College, AB
Oklahoma Christian University, B
Oklahoma Wesleyan University, B
Oral Roberts University, BMD
Southern Nazarene University, B
Southwestern Christian University, BM

Oregon

Corban University, B
Multnomah University, B
New Hope Christian College, B
Northwest Christian University, B

Pennsylvania

Eastern University, BD
Geneva College, B
Lancaster Bible College, B
Summit University, BMD
University of Valley Forge, B
Villanova University, M

South Carolina

Bob Jones University, B
Columbia International University, MDO
North Greenville University, B

Tennessee

Carson-Newman University, B
Freed-Hardeman University, B
Lee University, B
Lipscomb University, B
Milligan College, M
Southern Adventist University, BM
Welch College, B

Texas

Abilene Christian University, M
Dallas Baptist University, BM
East Texas Baptist University, B
LeTourneau University, B
Lubbock Christian University, B
Messenger College, B
Southwestern Assemblies of God University, M
Wayland Baptist University, B

Virginia

Liberty University, BMD
Regent University, M

Washington

Northwest University, BM

Wisconsin

Concordia University Wisconsin, B
Maranatha Baptist University, B

U.S. Territories: Puerto Rico

Universidad Pentecostal Mizpa, A

Canada

British Columbia

Columbia Bible College, B

Manitoba

Providence University College & Theological Seminary, BMO

Ontario

Emmanuel Bible College, B
Saint Paul University, BM
Tyndale University College & Seminary, MO

Saskatchewan

Briercrest College, B
Horizon College & Seminary, B

MODELING AND SIMULATION

United States

Alabama

The University of Alabama in Huntsville, MDO

Arizona

Arizona State University at the Tempe campus, MD

California

Academy of Art University, M
University of California, San Diego, M
University of Southern California, M

Florida

University of Central Florida, MDO

Georgia

Columbus State University, O

Massachusetts

Worcester Polytechnic Institute, M

New Jersey

Stevens Institute of Technology, M

New York

University at Buffalo, the State University of New York, M

Oregon

Portland State University, O

Pennsylvania

Carnegie Mellon University, M
Philadelphia University, M
University of Pittsburgh, D

Virginia

Old Dominion University, MD
Virginia Commonwealth University, D

Canada

Ontario

Trent University, MD

Quebec

Université Laval, M

MODERN GREEK LANGUAGE AND LITERATURE

United States

California

Fresno City College, A
Saint Mary's College of California, B

Louisiana

Tulane University, B

Massachusetts

Tufts University, B

Michigan

University of Michigan, B

New York

Colgate University, B
Columbia University, B

Lehman College of the City University of New York, B

Ohio

John Carroll University, B
Oberlin College, B
The Ohio State University, B
Wright State University, B

South Carolina

Furman University, B

Wisconsin

Concordia University Wisconsin, B

Canada

Manitoba

University of Manitoba, B
The University of Winnipeg, B

Maritime Provinces: New Brunswick

University of New Brunswick Fredericton, B

Newfoundland and Labrador

Memorial University of Newfoundland, B

Ontario

Carleton University, B
University of Toronto, B
York University, B

MODERN LANGUAGES

United States

California

Citrus College, A
College of the Sequoias, A
Imperial Valley College, A
Saint Mary's College of California, B
San Diego City College, A
Santa Ana College, A
Santiago Canyon College, A
Westmont College, B

Colorado

Metropolitan State University of Denver, B
Otero Junior College, A

Connecticut

Trinity College, B

Florida

Florida Memorial University, B

Illinois

City Colleges of Chicago, Wilbur Wright College, A

Iowa

Cornell College, B

Kansas

Barton County Community College, A

Louisiana

Louisiana College, B

Massachusetts

Clark University, B

Michigan

Alma College, B

Minnesota

Bemidji State University, B
Minnesota State University Mankato, B

Mississippi

Itawamba Community College, A

Missouri

Washington University in St. Louis, B

New Hampshire

Rivier University, B

New Jersey

Saint Peter's University, B

New York

College of Mount Saint Vincent, B
Fordham University, B
Nazareth College of Rochester, B
Purchase College, State University of New York, B
St. Bonaventure University, B
St. Thomas Aquinas College, B
Sarah Lawrence College, B

Ohio

Walsh University, B
Wilmington College, B
Wright State University, B

Oklahoma

Rose State College, A

Oregon

Pacific University, B

Pennsylvania

Gettysburg College, B
Saint Francis University, B
Widener University, B

South Carolina

Presbyterian College, B

Texas

Amarillo College, A
Odessa College, A
Palo Alto College, A
Tyler Junior College, A

Vermont

Marlboro College, B
Saint Michael's College, B

Virginia

The College of William and Mary, B
Hampton University, B
Virginia Military Institute, B

Washington

Walla Walla University, B

West Virginia

Potomac State College of West Virginia University, A

Wisconsin

Beloit College, B

Canada

British Columbia

Trinity Western University, B
University of Victoria, B

Maritime Provinces: New Brunswick

Mount Allison University, B
Université de Moncton, B
University of New Brunswick Fredericton, B

Maritime Provinces: Nova Scotia

Mount Saint Vincent University, B
St. Francis Xavier University, B
Saint Mary's University, B

Ontario

Carleton University, B
Laurentian University, B
McMaster University, B

Trent University, B
University of Ottawa, B
University of Toronto, B
University of Windsor, B
York University, B

Quebec

Bishop's University, B
Université Laval, B
Université de Montréal, B
Université du Québec à Chicoutimi, B

MOLECULAR BIOCHEMISTRY

United States

California

University of California, Davis, B

Connecticut

Wesleyan University, B

New York

Clarkson University, B

South Carolina

Bob Jones University, B

Virginia

University of Richmond, B

Canada

British Columbia

Simon Fraser University, B

MOLECULAR BIOLOGY

United States

Alabama

Auburn University, BD
The University of Alabama at Birmingham, D

Arizona

Arizona State University at the Tempe campus, BD
The University of Arizona, MD

Arkansas

Arkansas State University, MD
University of Arkansas, MD
University of Arkansas for Medical Sciences, MD

California

California Institute of Technology, D
California Lutheran University, B
California State University, Fresno, B
California State University, Sacramento, M
Claremont McKenna College, B
Humboldt State University, B
Pitzer College, B
Pomona College, B
San Diego State University, D
San Francisco State University, BM
San Jose State University, BM
Scripps College, B
Sonoma State University, M
University of California, Berkeley, D
University of California, Davis, MD
University of California, Irvine, MD
University of California, Los Angeles, MD
University of California, Riverside, MD
University of California, San Diego, D
University of California, Santa Barbara, BMD
University of California, Santa Cruz, BMD
University of Southern California, MD

Colorado

Colorado State University, MD
University of Colorado Boulder, MD
University of Colorado Denver, MD
University of Denver, BM

Connecticut

Central Connecticut State University, MO
Connecticut College, B
Quinnipiac University, M
University of Connecticut, M
University of New Haven, MO
Wesleyan University, D
Yale University, BD

Delaware

University of Delaware, MD

District of Columbia

Georgetown University, MD
Howard University, MD

Florida

Florida Institute of Technology, BM
Florida State University, MD
Rollins College, B
Stetson University, B
University of Florida, MD
University of Miami, D
University of South Florida, MD

Georgia

Augusta University, MD
Emory University, D
Georgia State University, MD
University of Georgia, MD

Hawaii

University of Hawaii at Manoa, MD

Idaho

Boise State University, D
University of Idaho, BM

Illinois

Blackburn College, B
Illinois Institute of Technology, MD
Illinois State University, M
Loyola University Chicago, MD
Millikin University, B
Northwestern University, BD
Southern Illinois University Carbondale, MD
University of Chicago, D
University of Illinois at Chicago, D

Indiana

Goshen College, B
Indiana State University, D
Indiana University Bloomington, D
Indiana University - Purdue University Indianapolis, MD
Purdue University, D
University of Notre Dame, MD

Iowa

Coe College, B
Iowa State University of Science and Technology, MD
The University of Iowa, D

Kansas

The University of Kansas, BMD

Kentucky

University of Louisville, MD

Louisiana

Louisiana Tech University, M
Tulane University, BMD

Maine

Colby College, B
University of Maine, BMD

University of Southern Maine, M

Maryland

Hood College, M
Johns Hopkins University, BMD
University of Maryland, Baltimore County, MD
University of Maryland, College Park, D

Massachusetts

Assumption College, B
Boston University, BMD
Brandeis University, MD
Clark University, B
Harvard University, D
Massachusetts Institute of Technology, D
Tufts University, D
Worcester Polytechnic Institute, B

Michigan

Eastern Michigan University, M
Grand Valley State University, M
Lawrence Technological University, B
Michigan State University, MD
Michigan Technological University, D
University of Michigan, BMD
University of Michigan - Flint, B
Wayne State University, MD

Minnesota

University of Minnesota, Duluth, MD
University of Minnesota, Twin Cities Campus, MD

Mississippi

Mississippi State University, MD
University of Southern Mississippi, MD

Missouri

College of the Ozarks, B
Missouri State University, M
Saint Louis University, D
University of Missouri - Kansas City, MD
Washington University in St. Louis, D
William Jewell College, B

Montana

University of Montana, D

Nebraska

University of Nebraska Medical Center, D

Nevada

University of Nevada, Reno, MD

New Hampshire

Dartmouth College, BD

New Jersey

Montclair State University, BMO
Princeton University, BD
Rutgers University - New Brunswick, BMD
Rutgers University - Newark, MD
Seton Hall University, MD

New Mexico

Eastern New Mexico University, M
New Mexico State University, MD
University of New Mexico, MD

New York

Albany College of Pharmacy and Health Sciences, M
Colgate University, B
Columbia University, D
Cornell University, MD
New York University, D
State University of New York Downstate Medical Center, D
State University of New York Upstate Medical University, MD
Stony Brook University, State University of New York, MD
University at Albany, State University of New York, BD

University at Buffalo, the State University of New York, D
University of Rochester, D
Wells College, B
Yeshiva University, B

North Carolina

Appalachian State University, M
Duke University, DO
East Carolina University, MD
The University of North Carolina at Chapel Hill, MD
Wake Forest University, D
Winston-Salem State University, B

North Dakota

North Dakota State University, D
University of North Dakota, BMD

Ohio

Case Western Reserve University, D
The College of Wooster, B
Kent State University, D
Kenyon College, B
Muskingum University, B
Ohio Northern University, B
The Ohio State University, MD
Ohio University, MD
Otterbein University, B
University of Cincinnati, MD
Wright State University, M
Youngstown State University, M

Oklahoma

Oklahoma State University, MD
University of Oklahoma Health Sciences Center, MD

Oregon

Oregon Health & Science University, MD
Oregon State University, D
University of Oregon, D

Pennsylvania

Carnegie Mellon University, D
Chestnut Hill College, B
Clarion University of Pennsylvania, B
Drexel University, MD
Gettysburg College, B
Lehigh University, BMD
Messiah College, B
Penn State University Park, MD
University of Pennsylvania, D
University of Pittsburgh, BD
University of the Sciences, D
The University of Scranton, B
Westminster College, B

Rhode Island

Brown University, BMD
University of Rhode Island, MD

South Carolina

Clemson University, D
Medical University of South Carolina, MD
University of South Carolina, MD

South Dakota

The University of South Dakota, MD

Tennessee

Lipscomb University, M
Middle Tennessee State University, D
Vanderbilt University, BMD

Texas

Southern Methodist University, MD
Texas Woman's University, D
University of North Texas, M
The University of Texas at Austin, D
The University of Texas at Dallas, BMD
The University of Texas Health Science Center at Houston, MD
The University of Texas at San Antonio, D
Wayland Baptist University, B

Utah

Brigham Young University, MD
University of Utah, D

Vermont

Marlboro College, B
University of Vermont, BMD

Virginia

George Mason University, M
Hampton University, B
Virginia Commonwealth University, MD

Washington

University of Puget Sound, B
University of Washington, D
Whitman College, B

West Virginia

West Virginia University, MD

Wisconsin

Alverno College, B
Beloit College, B
Marquette University, MD
University of Wisconsin - Eau Claire, B
University of Wisconsin - La Crosse, M
University of Wisconsin - Madison, BD
University of Wisconsin - Parkside, BM

Wyoming

University of Wyoming, BMD

U.S. Territories: Puerto Rico

Inter American University of Puerto Rico, Metropolitan Campus, M
Universidad Central del Caribe, D
Universidad Metropolitana, B
University of Puerto Rico, Río Piedras Campus, MD

Canada

Alberta

University of Alberta, MD
University of Calgary, BMD
University of Lethbridge, D

British Columbia

Simon Fraser University, BMDO
The University of British Columbia, MD
The University of British Columbia - Okanagan Campus, B

Manitoba

The University of Winnipeg, B

Maritime Provinces: New Brunswick

University of New Brunswick Fredericton, B

Ontario

Lakehead University, B
McMaster University, BMD
Queen's University at Kingston, MD
University of Guelph, BMD
University of Ottawa, MD
University of Toronto, B
York University, B

Quebec

McGill University, B
Université Laval, MD
Université de Montréal, MD

MOLECULAR BIOPHYSICS

United States

Arkansas

University of Arkansas for Medical Sciences, MD

California

California Institute of Technology, MD

Connecticut

Wesleyan University, D
Yale University, D

Florida

Florida State University, D

Illinois

Illinois Institute of Technology, MD
University of Chicago, D

Massachusetts

University of Massachusetts Amherst, D

Missouri

Washington University in St. Louis, D

New Jersey

Rutgers University - New Brunswick, D

New York

New York University, D

North Carolina

Duke University, O

Pennsylvania

Carnegie Mellon University, D
University of Pennsylvania, D
University of Pittsburgh, D

Texas

The University of Texas Medical Branch, MD

MOLECULAR GENETICS

United States

California

University of California, Irvine, MD
University of California, Los Angeles, MD

Colorado

University of Colorado Denver, D

Connecticut

Wesleyan University, D

Florida

University of Florida, M

Georgia

Emory University, D
Georgia State University, MD

Illinois

Illinois State University, M
University of Illinois at Chicago, D

Indiana

Indiana University - Purdue University Indianapolis, MD

Iowa

Iowa State University of Science and Technology, D

Maryland

University of Maryland, College Park, MD

Massachusetts

Harvard University, D

Michigan

Michigan State University, BD
Northern Michigan University, M

Missouri

Washington University in St. Louis, D

New Jersey

Rutgers University - New Brunswick, BMD
Rutgers University - Newark, D

New York

New York University, D
Stony Brook University, State University of New York, D

North Carolina

Duke University, D
Wake Forest University, D

Ohio

The Ohio State University, BMD
University of Cincinnati, MD

Oklahoma

Oklahoma State University, MD

Pennsylvania

University of Pittsburgh, D

Rhode Island

University of Rhode Island, MD

Texas

Texas A&M University, B
The University of Texas Health Science Center at Houston, MD

Vermont

University of Vermont, B

Virginia

University of Virginia, D

Washington

Washington State University, B

Canada

Alberta

University of Alberta, B
University of Calgary, MD

Ontario

University of Guelph, BMD
University of Toronto, MD

MOLECULAR MEDICINE

United States

Alabama

The University of Alabama at Birmingham, D

Arizona

The University of Arizona, MDO

Connecticut

Yale University, D

District of Columbia

The George Washington University, D

Florida

University of South Florida, MD

Georgia

Augusta University, MD

Illinois

University of Chicago, D

Maryland

Johns Hopkins University, D

Massachusetts

Boston University, D

New Hampshire

Dartmouth College, D

New Jersey

Rutgers University - Newark, D

New York

Cornell University, MD
Hofstra University, D

North Carolina

Wake Forest University, MD

Ohio

Case Western Reserve University, D
Cleveland State University, D
University of Cincinnati, D

Pennsylvania

Drexel University, M

Texas

The University of Texas Health Science Center at San Antonio, MD

Washington

University of Washington, D

Canada

Ontario

Queen's University at Kingston, MD

MOLECULAR PATHOGENESIS

United States

Georgia

Emory University, D

Illinois

University of Chicago, D

Missouri

Washington University in St. Louis, D

New Hampshire

Dartmouth College, D

North Dakota

North Dakota State University, D

MOLECULAR PATHOLOGY

United States

Connecticut

Yale University, D

Michigan

University of Michigan, D

New Jersey

Rutgers University - Newark, D

Pennsylvania

University of Pittsburgh, D

Texas

The University of Texas Health Science Center at Houston, MD

MOLECULAR PHARMACOLOGY

United States

California
University of Southern California, MD

Florida
University of South Florida, D

Illinois
Loyola University Chicago, MD

Indiana
Purdue University, D

Massachusetts
Harvard University, D

Nevada
University of Nevada, Reno, D

New Hampshire
Dartmouth College, D

New Jersey
Rutgers University - New Brunswick, MD

New York
New York University, D
University at Buffalo, the State University of New York, D

Pennsylvania
Thomas Jefferson University, D
University of Pittsburgh, D
The University of Scranton, B

Rhode Island
Brown University, MD

South Carolina
Medical University of South Carolina, MD

MOLECULAR PHYSIOLOGY

United States

California
University of California, Los Angeles, D

Connecticut
Yale University, D

Illinois
Loyola University Chicago, D
University of Illinois at Urbana - Champaign, MD

New Jersey
Rutgers University - New Brunswick, MD

New York
Stony Brook University, State University of New York, D

North Carolina
The University of North Carolina at Chapel Hill, D

Ohio
Case Western Reserve University, M

Pennsylvania
Thomas Jefferson University, D
University of Pittsburgh, D

Tennessee
Vanderbilt University, MD

Virginia
University of Virginia, MD

MOLECULAR TOXICOLOGY

United States

California
University of California, Berkeley, D
University of California, Los Angeles, D

Massachusetts
Massachusetts Institute of Technology, D

New York
New York University, D

North Carolina
North Carolina State University, MD

Ohio
University of Cincinnati, MD

MONTESSORI TEACHER EDUCATION

United States

Michigan
Siena Heights University, B

New York
Canisius College, B

Ohio
Xavier University, B

MORTUARY SCIENCE AND EMBALMING/EMBALMER

United States

District of Columbia
University of the District of Columbia, A

Georgia
Gupton-Jones College of Funeral Service, A

Illinois
Carl Sandburg College, A

Michigan
Wayne County Community College District, A

MOTORCYCLE MAINTENANCE AND REPAIR TECHNOLOGY/ TECHNICIAN

United States

Colorado
Red Rocks Community College, A

Iowa
Iowa Lakes Community College, A
Western Iowa Tech Community College, A

Kansas
Fort Scott Community College, A

Missouri
State Technical College of Missouri, A

MOVEMENT AND MIND-BODY THERAPIES AND EDUCATION

United States

Illinois
Moraine Valley Community College, A

Kansas
Highland Community College, A

MOVEMENT THERAPY AND MOVEMENT EDUCATION

United States

Massachusetts
Eastern Nazarene College, B

Texas
Texas Christian University, B

Vermont
University of Vermont, B

Canada

Ontario
Brock University, B

MULTI-/INTERDISCIPLINARY STUDIES

United States

Alabama
Athens State University, B
Bishop State Community College, A
Enterprise State Community College, A
Northwest-Shoals Community College, A
Samford University, B
Southern Union State Community College, A
The University of Alabama in Huntsville, B
University of Montevallo, B
The University of West Alabama, B

Alaska
University of Alaska Fairbanks, AB
University of Alaska Southeast, B

Arizona
Arizona State University at the Downtown Phoenix campus, B
Arizona State University at the Polytechnic campus, B
Arizona State University at the Tempe campus, B
Arizona State University at the West campus, B
Eastern Arizona College, A
Embry-Riddle Aeronautical University - Prescott, B
Grand Canyon University, B
Prescott College, B
South Mountain Community College, A

Arkansas
Arkansas Northeastern College, A
Arkansas State University, B
Arkansas State University Mid-South, A
Arkansas State University - Newport, A
Arkansas Tech University, AB
Black River Technical College, A
Cossatot Community College of the University of Arkansas, A
John Brown University, B
North Arkansas College, A
Rich Mountain Community College, A
Southeast Arkansas College, A
Southern Arkansas University - Magnolia, B
Southern Arkansas University Tech, A

University of Arkansas Community College at
  Batesville, A
University of Arkansas Community College at Hope,
  A
University of Arkansas - Fort Smith, AB
University of Arkansas at Little Rock, B
University of Arkansas at Monticello, AB
University of Central Arkansas, B

California

Ashford University, B
California Baptist University, B
California Institute of Integral Studies, B
California Institute of Technology, B
California Lutheran University, B
California Polytechnic State University, San Luis
  Obispo, B
California State University, Dominguez Hills, B
California State University, Long Beach, B
California State University, Los Angeles, B
California State University, Monterey Bay, B
California State University, San Bernardino, B
California State University, San Marcos, B
California State University, Stanislaus, B
Chaffey College, A
Claremont McKenna College, B
College of the Desert, A
College of the Redwoods, A
Glendale Community College, A
Humboldt State University, B
Loyola Marymount University, B
National University, B
Palo Verde College, A
Pepperdine University, B
Saint Mary's College of California, B
San Diego Christian College, B
San Diego State University, B
San Francisco State University, B
San Jose State University, B
Scripps College, B
Sonoma State University, B
University of California, Berkeley, B
University of California, Davis, B
University of California, Irvine, B
University of California, Los Angeles, B
University of California, Merced, B
University of California, Santa Barbara, B
University of Southern California, B
Woodbury University, B

Colorado

Adams State University, B
The Colorado College, B
Naropa University, B
Regis University, B
University of Colorado Boulder, B
University of Colorado Denver, B
University of Denver, B
University of Northern Colorado, B

Connecticut

Central Connecticut State University, B
Connecticut College, B
University of Connecticut, B
University of Saint Joseph, B
Yale University, B

District of Columbia

American University, B
Georgetown University, B

Florida

Embry-Riddle Aeronautical University - Daytona, B
Florida Institute of Technology, B
Florida International University, B
Florida Southern College, B
Jacksonville University, B
Palm Beach Atlantic University, B
Rollins College, B
South Florida State College, A
University of Florida, B

Georgia

Agnes Scott College, B
Berry College, B

Covenant College, B
Emory University, B
Georgia Institute of Technology, B
Georgia State University, B
Kennesaw State University, B
Mercer University, B
Spelman College, B
Truett-McConnell College, B

Hawaii

Brigham Young University - Hawaii, B

Idaho

Boise State University, B
The College of Idaho, B
Lewis-Clark State College, B
University of Idaho, B

Illinois

Columbia College Chicago, B
Eastern Illinois University, B
Greenville College, B
Illinois Wesleyan University, B
Knox College, B
Lewis University, B
Loyola University Chicago, B
Millikin University, B
National Louis University, B
North Central College, B
Northern Illinois University, B
Northwestern University, B
Robert Morris University Illinois, B
Southern Illinois University Carbondale, B
Triton College, A
University of St. Francis, B
Wheaton College, B

Indiana

Anderson University, B
Ball State University, B
DePauw University, B
Earlham College, B
Indiana State University, B
Indiana University - Purdue University Indianapolis,
  B
Manchester University, B
Taylor University, B
Valparaiso University, B

Iowa

Buena Vista University, B
Central College, B
Cornell College, B
Hawkeye Community College, A
Iowa State University of Science and Technology, B
Iowa Western Community College, A
Luther College, B
Mount Mercy University, B
Muscatine Community College, A
North Iowa Area Community College, A
Scott Community College, A
Western Iowa Tech Community College, A

Kansas

Emporia State University, B
Grantham University, AB
Manhattan Area Technical College, A
Newman University, B
Pittsburg State University, B
University of Saint Mary, B
Washburn University, AB
Wichita State University, B

Kentucky

Ashland Community and Technical College, A
Bellarmine University, B
Berea College, B
Bluegrass Community and Technical College, A
Eastern Kentucky University, B
Georgetown College, B
Hazard Community and Technical College, A
Hopkinsville Community College, A
Kentucky Christian University, B
Kentucky Wesleyan College, B
Midway University, B

Owensboro Community and Technical College, A
Somerset Community College, A
Southcentral Kentucky Community and Technical
  College, A
Thomas More College, B
University of Kentucky, B
University of Pikeville, B
Western Kentucky University, B

Louisiana

Louisiana State University and Agricultural & Me-
  chanical College, B
Northwestern State University of Louisiana, B
Tulane University, B
University of New Orleans, B

Maine

Bates College, B
Bowdoin College, B
Central Maine Community College, A
Colby College, B
Eastern Maine Community College, A
Kennebec Valley Community College, A
University of Maine, B
University of Maine at Farmington, B
Washington County Community College, A
York County Community College, A

Maryland

Anne Arundel Community College, A
Carroll Community College, A
College of Southern Maryland, A
Goucher College, B
Hood College, B
Loyola University Maryland, B
McDaniel College, B
Mount St. Mary's University, B
Notre Dame of Maryland University, B
St. Mary's College of Maryland, B
University of Maryland, Baltimore County, B
University of Maryland, College Park, B
University of Maryland University College, B
Washington College, B

Massachusetts

Boston University, B
Brandeis University, B
Cape Cod Community College, A
Curry College, B
Emmanuel College, B
Hampshire College, B
Lasell College, B
Mount Holyoke College, B
Regis College, B
Simmons College, B
Stonehill College, B
University of Massachusetts Amherst, B
University of Massachusetts Boston, B
University of Massachusetts Dartmouth, B
Wheaton College, B

Michigan

Albion College, B
Cornerstone University, B
Eastern Michigan University, B
Grace Bible College, B
Hope College, B
Kalamazoo College, B
Michigan State University, B
Rochester College, B
Saginaw Valley State University, B
University of Michigan, B
University of Michigan - Dearborn, B
University of Michigan - Flint, B
Western Michigan University, B

Minnesota

Alexandria Technical and Community College, A
Bethel University, B
Century College, A
College of Saint Benedict, B
Hamline University, B
Inver Hills Community College, A
Lake Superior College, A
Macalester College, B

Metropolitan State University, B
Minnesota State College - Southeast Technical, A
Minnesota State University Moorhead, B
Normandale Community College, A
North Hennepin Community College, A
St. Cloud State University, B
Saint John's University, B
University of Minnesota, Crookston, B
University of Minnesota, Duluth, B
University of Minnesota, Morris, B
University of Minnesota, Twin Cities Campus, B
University of Northwestern - St. Paul, B
University of St. Thomas, B

Mississippi

Delta State University, B
Hinds Community College, A
Jackson State University, B
Millsaps College, B
Mississippi State University, B
Mississippi University for Women, B
University of Southern Mississippi, B

Missouri

Calvary Bible College and Theological Seminary, B
Harris-Stowe State University, B
Missouri Baptist University, B
Missouri Western State University, B
Northwest Missouri State University, A
Park University, B
Southeast Missouri State University, B
Stephens College, B
Truman State University, B
University of Missouri - St. Louis, B
Washington University in St. Louis, B
William Jewell College, B

Montana

Carroll College, B
Montana State University Billings, B
Montana Tech of The University of Montana, A
The University of Montana Western, A

Nebraska

Chadron State College, B
Concordia University, Nebraska, B
University of Nebraska at Omaha, B

Nevada

Nevada State College, B
University of Nevada, Las Vegas, B

New Hampshire

Dartmouth College, B
Granite State College, B
Keene State College, B
Plymouth State University, B
Saint Anselm College, B
University of New Hampshire, B

New Jersey

Atlantic Cape Community College, A
Bloomfield College, B
Brookdale Community College, A
Caldwell University, B
The College of New Jersey, B
College of Saint Elizabeth, B
County College of Morris, A
Georgian Court University, B
Monmouth University, B
Montclair State University, B
Princeton University, B
Raritan Valley Community College, A
Rowan University, B
Rutgers University - Camden, B
Rutgers University - New Brunswick, B
Rutgers University - Newark, B
Thomas Edison State University, AB

New Mexico

New Mexico State University - Carlsbad, A
New Mexico State University - Grants, A

New York

Adelphi University, B
Binghamton University, State University of New
  York, B
Buffalo State College, State University of New York,
  B
Clarkson University, B
The College of New Rochelle, B
The Culinary Institute of America, B
D'Youville College, B
Ithaca College, B
Long Island University - LIU Brooklyn, B
Manhattan College, B
Morrisville State College, B
New York Institute of Technology, B
Pace University, B
Queens College of the City University of New York,
  B
St. Lawrence University, B
State University of New York Empire State College,
  AB
Stony Brook University, State University of New
  York, B
Syracuse University, B
University at Albany, State University of New York, B
University at Buffalo, the State University of New
  York, B
University of Rochester, B
Vassar College, B
Yeshiva University, B

North Carolina

Bennett College, B
Brevard College, B
Cabarrus College of Health Sciences, B
Catawba College, B
Davidson College, B
Guilford College, B
High Point University, B
Meredith College, B
The University of North Carolina at Pembroke, B

North Dakota

Bismarck State College, A
North Dakota State College of Science, A
University of North Dakota, B
Williston State College, A

Ohio

Baldwin Wallace University, B
Bluffton University, B
Bowling Green State University, B
Capital University, B
Cincinnati State Technical and Community College,
  A
Cleveland State University, B
The College of Wooster, B
Columbus State Community College, A
Franklin University, B
James A. Rhodes State College, A
Kenyon College, B
Lake Erie College, B
Lourdes University, B
Miami University, A
Miami University Hamilton, B
North Central State College, A
Notre Dame College, B
The Ohio State University, B
Ohio University - Chillicothe, A
Ohio University - Southern Campus, B
Ohio Wesleyan University, B
Otterbein University, B
The University of Akron, AB
University of Cincinnati, B
University of Cincinnati Clermont College, A
Xavier University, B

Oklahoma

Cameron University, B
East Central University, B
Hillsdale Free Will Baptist College, B
Northwestern Oklahoma State University, B
Oklahoma City Community College, A
Oklahoma State University Institute of Technology, A
Rogers State University, B

Southeastern Oklahoma State University, B
Southwestern Oklahoma State University, B
Tulsa Community College, A

Oregon

Marylhurst University, B
Northwest Christian University, B
Portland Community College, A

Pennsylvania

Albright College, B
Allegheny College, B
Arcadia University, B
Bryn Athyn College of the New Church, B
Bryn Mawr College, B
Bucknell University, B
Bucks County Community College, A
Chestnut Hill College, B
Franklin & Marshall College, B
Gannon University, B
Immaculata University, B
Juniata College, B
Lebanon Valley College, B
Lehigh University, B
Lycoming College, B
Mercyhurst University, B
Messiah College, B
Penn State Erie, The Behrend College, B
Penn State Harrisburg, B
Pennsylvania College of Technology, A
Point Park University, B
Robert Morris University, B
Shippensburg University of Pennsylvania, B
Temple University, B
University of Pittsburgh, B
Ursinus College, B
Villanova University, B
Washington & Jefferson College, B
Waynesburg University, B
Westminster College, B
Wilkes University, B

Rhode Island

Providence College, B
Roger Williams University, B

South Carolina

Aiken Technical College, A
College of Charleston, B
Denmark Technical College, A
Florence-Darlington Technical College, A
Greenville Technical College, A
Midlands Technical College, A
Spartanburg Community College, A
Tri-County Technical College, A
Wofford College, B
York Technical College, A

South Dakota

The University of South Dakota, B

Tennessee

Belmont University, B
Bethel University, B
East Tennessee State University, B
Freed-Hardeman University, B
Lane College, B
Lee University, B
Maryville College, B
Middle Tennessee State University, B
Sewanee: The University of the South, B
Southern Adventist University, B
Tennessee Wesleyan College, B
Trevecca Nazarene University, B
Tusculum College, B
University of Memphis, B
The University of Tennessee, B
Vanderbilt University, B

Texas

Abilene Christian University, B
Angelina College, A
Angelo State University, B
Austin College, B
Baylor University, B

Cedar Valley College, A
Dallas Baptist University, B
Dallas Christian College, B
East Texas Baptist University, B
Eastfield College, A
El Paso Community College, A
Howard Payne University, B
Lamar State College - Port Arthur, A
Lamar University, B
LeTourneau University, B
McMurry University, B
Our Lady of the Lake University of San Antonio, B
Prairie View A&M University, B
Rice University, B
Sam Houston State University, B
Southern Methodist University, B
Southwestern Adventist University, B
Stephen F. Austin State University, B
Tarleton State University, B
Texas A&M International University, B
Texas A&M University, B
Texas A&M University - Central Texas, B
Texas A&M University - Commerce, B
Texas A&M University - Kingsville, B
Texas A&M University - Texarkana, B
Texas Southmost College, A
Texas State University, B
Texas Tech University, B
Texas Wesleyan University, B
Texas Woman's University, B
Trinity University, B
University of Houston, B
University of Houston - Clear Lake, B
University of Houston - Downtown, B
University of Houston - Victoria, B
University of North Texas, B
The University of Texas at Arlington, B
The University of Texas at Austin, B
The University of Texas of the Permian Basin, B
The University of Texas Rio Grande Valley, B
The University of Texas at San Antonio, B
The University of Texas at Tyler, B
West Texas A&M University, B

Utah

Dixie State University, B
Southern Utah University, B
Utah State University, B
Utah Valley University, AB

Vermont

Bennington College, B

Virginia

Christopher Newport University, B
The College of William and Mary, B
Eastern Mennonite University, B
Liberty University, AB
Norfolk State University, B
Old Dominion University, B
Radford University, B
University of Mary Washington, B
University of Richmond, B
University of Virginia, B
Virginia Commonwealth University, B
Virginia Union University, B
Virginia Wesleyan College, B
Washington and Lee University, B

Washington

Central Washington University, B
Eastern Washington University, B
The Evergreen State College, B
Heritage University, AB
Northwest Indian College, A
Northwest University, B
Pacific Lutheran University, B
Saint Martin's University, B
University of Washington, Bothell, B
Washington State University, B
Western Washington University, B

West Virginia

Blue Ridge Community and Technical College, A
Eastern West Virginia Community and Technical
  College, A
Glenville State College, B
Mountwest Community & Technical College, A
West Virginia Northern Community College, A
West Virginia University, B
West Virginia University Institute of Technology, B
Wheeling Jesuit University, B

Wisconsin

Alverno College, B
Chippewa Valley Technical College, A
Edgewood College, B
Fox Valley Technical College, A
Marian University, B
Marquette University, B
Moraine Park Technical College, A
Mount Mary University, B
Northcentral Technical College, A
Northeast Wisconsin Technical College, A
Southwest Wisconsin Technical College, A
University of Wisconsin - Green Bay, B
University of Wisconsin - Milwaukee, B
University of Wisconsin - Platteville, B
University of Wisconsin - River Falls, B
University of Wisconsin - Stevens Point, B
University of Wisconsin - Superior, B
University of Wisconsin - Whitewater, B
Viterbo University, B
Waukesha County Technical College, A
Wisconsin Lutheran College, B

Wyoming

University of Wyoming, B

U.S. Territories: Puerto Rico

University of Puerto Rico in Carolina, A

Canada
Alberta

University of Alberta, B
University of Lethbridge, B

British Columbia

Thompson Rivers University, B
University of Northern British Columbia, B

Maritime Provinces: Nova Scotia

Dalhousie University, B
University of King's College, B

Ontario

Ryerson University, B
University of Waterloo, B

Quebec

Université Laval, B

MULTILINGUAL AND MULTI-CULTURAL EDUCATION

United States
Alaska

University of Alaska Fairbanks, M

Arizona

Northern Arizona University, M
The University of Arizona, MDO

California

Azusa Pacific University, M
California State University, Dominguez Hills, M
California State University, Fullerton, M
California State University, Northridge, M
California State University, Sacramento, M
California State University, San Bernardino, M
California State University, Stanislaus, M

Loyola Marymount University, M
San Diego State University, MD
University of California, Riverside, M
University of California, San Diego, M
University of San Francisco, MD
University of Southern California, D

Colorado

Fort Lewis College, B
Regis University, M
University of Colorado Boulder, MD
University of Colorado Denver, M

Connecticut

Fairfield University, MO
Southern Connecticut State University, M
University of Connecticut, MDO

Delaware

University of Delaware, M

District of Columbia

Gallaudet University, O
The George Washington University, MO
Howard University, MD

Florida

Florida Atlantic University, M
Florida International University, M
University of Miami, D
University of West Florida, D

Illinois

Chicago State University, M
DePaul University, M
Northeastern Illinois University, M
Quincy University, M

Indiana

Indiana State University, O
Indiana University Bloomington, MD
Indiana Wesleyan University, B

Maryland

University of Maryland, Baltimore County, MD

Massachusetts

University of Massachusetts Amherst, MO
University of Massachusetts Boston, M

Michigan

Wayne State University, MDO

Minnesota

Minnesota State University Mankato, MO
Saint Mary's University of Minnesota, O
University of Minnesota, Twin Cities Campus, MD
University of St. Thomas, O
Walden University, M

Mississippi

Belhaven University, M

New Jersey

Fairleigh Dickinson University, Metropolitan Campus, M
Kean University, M
Rowan University, O
Rutgers University - New Brunswick, MD

New Mexico

Eastern New Mexico University, M
New Mexico State University, D
University of New Mexico, MD
University of the Southwest, M
Western New Mexico University, M

New York

Brooklyn College of the City University of New York, M
Buffalo State College, State University of New York, M
City College of the City University of New York, M

The College at Brockport, State University of New
    York, MO
College of Mount Saint Vincent, MO
The College of New Rochelle, MO
Fordham University, M
Hofstra University, MD
Hunter College of the City University of New York,
    M
Lehman College of the City University of New York,
    M
Long Island University - LIU Brooklyn, O
Manhattan College, O
New York University, MDO
Queens College of the City University of New York,
    M
St. John's University, MO
State University of New York College at Geneseo,
    M
State University of New York at New Paltz, MO
University at Buffalo, the State University of New
    York, M

North Carolina

The University of North Carolina at Greensboro, D

Ohio

Mount St. Joseph University, M
Ohio University, M
The University of Findlay, BM
Xavier University, M

Oklahoma

Langston University, M

Oregon

George Fox University, M
Western Oregon University, M

Pennsylvania

Eastern University, M
Immaculata University, M
La Salle University, M
University of Pennsylvania, M

Rhode Island

Brown University, M

South Carolina

Columbia International University, M

Tennessee

The University of Tennessee, D
Vanderbilt University, M

Texas

Dallas Baptist University, M
Our Lady of the Lake University of San Antonio, M
Southern Methodist University, M
Sul Ross State University, M
Texas A&M University, M
Texas A&M University - Kingsville, MD
Texas A&M University - San Antonio, M
Texas Southern University, M
Texas State University, M
Texas Tech University, M
University of Houston - Clear Lake, M
University of St. Thomas, BM
The University of Texas at Arlington, M
The University of Texas at Austin, MD
The University of Texas at El Paso, O
The University of Texas Rio Grande Valley, M
The University of Texas at San Antonio, MD

Utah

Utah State University, M

Vermont

Bennington College, M
Goddard College, B

Virginia

George Mason University, M
James Madison University, M

Washington

Heritage University, M
University of Washington, MD

Wisconsin

Edgewood College, M
University of Wisconsin - Milwaukee, D
University of Wisconsin - Whitewater, M

Canada

Alberta

University of Alberta, M
University of Calgary, MD

MUSEOLOGY/MUSEUM STUD-IES

United States

Arizona

Arizona State University at the Tempe campus, M
Northland Pioneer College, A

California

California College of the Arts, M
California State University, Chico, M
California State University, Fullerton, M
John F. Kennedy University, MO
San Francisco Art Institute, M
San Francisco State University, M
University of California, Riverside, M
University of San Francisco, M

Colorado

University of Colorado Boulder, M
University of Denver, M

Connecticut

Trinity College, M

District of Columbia

The George Washington University, MO

Florida

Florida International University, O
Florida State University, MO
University of Florida, M
University of South Florida, O

Georgia

University of West Georgia, O

Hawaii

University of Hawaii at Manoa, O

Illinois

Southern Illinois University Edwardsville, O
University of Illinois at Chicago, M
Western Illinois University, MO

Indiana

Indiana University - Purdue University Indianapolis,
    MO

Iowa

The University of Iowa, B

Kansas

The University of Kansas, MO

Kentucky

University of Louisville, M

Louisiana

Southern University at New Orleans, M

Maine

College of the Atlantic, B

Maryland

Johns Hopkins University, MO
Maryland Institute College of Art, M
Morgan State University, M

Massachusetts

Boston University, O
Harvard University, M
Tufts University, MO

Michigan

University of Michigan - Flint, M

Minnesota

Concordia College, B

Missouri

University of Missouri - St. Louis, MO

New Hampshire

University of New Hampshire, M

New Jersey

Seton Hall University, M

New Mexico

Institute of American Indian Arts, AB
New Mexico State University, O

New York

Bard College, M
City College of the City University of New York, M
Columbia University, M
Fashion Institute of Technology, M
Marist College, M
New York University, MO
Queensborough Community College of the City Uni-
    versity of New York, A
St. John's University, M
State University of New York College at Oneonta, M
Syracuse University, M

North Carolina

The University of North Carolina at Greensboro, O

Ohio

Case Western Reserve University, M
Cleveland State University, M
Walsh University, B
Wright State University, B

Oklahoma

University of Central Oklahoma, M
University of Oklahoma, M
The University of Tulsa, M

Pennsylvania

Juniata College, B
Moore College of Art & Design, B
Penn State Harrisburg, O
The University of the Arts, M

South Carolina

University of South Carolina, MO

Tennessee

Tusculum College, B

Texas

Baylor University, M
Texas Tech University, M
University of North Texas, O

Vermont

Middlebury College, B

Virginia

Randolph College, B
Virginia Commonwealth University, M

Washington

Central Washington University, B
University of Washington, M

Wisconsin

Beloit College, B
University of Wisconsin - Milwaukee, O

Wyoming

Casper College, A

U.S. Territories: Puerto Rico

Caribbean University, M

Canada

British Columbia

The University of British Columbia, M

Ontario

University of Toronto, M

Quebec

Université Laval, O
Université de Montréal, M
Université du Québec à Montréal, M

MUSEUM EDUCATION

United States

District of Columbia

The George Washington University, M

Massachusetts

Tufts University, M

Michigan

Eastern Michigan University, O

New Jersey

Seton Hall University, M

Pennsylvania

The University of the Arts, M

MUSIC

United States

Alabama

Alabama Southern Community College, A
Alabama State University, B
Auburn University, B
Birmingham-Southern College, B
Calhoun Community College, A
Huntingdon College, B
Jacksonville State University, BM
Judson College, B
Oakwood University, B
Samford University, BM
Stillman College, B
Talladega College, B
Troy University, B
The University of Alabama, BMD
The University of Alabama at Birmingham, B
The University of Alabama in Huntsville, B
University of Mobile, B
University of Montevallo, B
University of North Alabama, B
University of South Alabama, BM
Wallace State Community College, A

Alaska

University of Alaska Anchorage, B
University of Alaska Fairbanks, BM

Arizona

Arizona State University at the Tempe campus, BMD
Arizona Western College, A
Cochise County Community College District, A
Eastern Arizona College, A
Mesa Community College, A
Northern Arizona University, BMO
The University of Arizona, BMD

Arkansas

Arkansas State University, BMO
Arkansas Tech University, B
Central Baptist College, B
Harding University, B
Henderson State University, B
Hendrix College, B
John Brown University, B
Lyon College, B
Ouachita Baptist University, B
Southern Arkansas University - Magnolia, B
University of Arkansas, M
University of Arkansas - Fort Smith, B
University of Arkansas at Little Rock, B
University of Arkansas at Monticello, B
University of Arkansas at Pine Bluff, B
University of Central Arkansas, BMO
University of the Ozarks, B
Williams Baptist College, AB

California

Academy of Art University, ABM
Allan Hancock College, A
American River College, A
Antelope Valley College, A
Ashford University, B
Azusa Pacific University, BM
Bakersfield College, A
Bethesda University, B
Biola University, B
Cabrillo College, A
California Baptist University, BM
California Institute of the Arts, MO
California Lutheran University, B
California Polytechnic State University, San Luis Obispo, B
California State Polytechnic University, Pomona, B
California State University, Bakersfield, B
California State University, Chico, B
California State University, Dominguez Hills, B
California State University, East Bay, BM
California State University, Fresno, BM
California State University, Fullerton, BM
California State University, Long Beach, BM
California State University, Los Angeles, BM
California State University, Monterey Bay, B
California State University, Northridge, BM
California State University, Sacramento, BM
California State University, San Bernardino, B
California State University, San Marcos, B
California State University, Stanislaus, B
Cañada College, A
Cerritos College, A
Chabot College, A
Chaffey College, A
Chapman University, B
Citrus College, A
College of the Canyons, A
College of the Desert, A
College of Marin, A
College of San Mateo, A
College of the Sequoias, A
College of the Siskiyous, A
Columbia College, A
Concordia University Irvine, B
Contra Costa College, A
Cosumnes River College, A
Crafton Hills College, A
Cuesta College, A
Cypress College, A
De Anza College, A
Dominican University of California, BM
East Los Angeles College, A
El Camino College, A
Foothill College, A

Fresno City College, A
Fresno Pacific University, B
Fullerton College, A
Gavilan College, A
Glendale Community College, A
Golden West College, A
Grossmont College, A
Hartnell College, A
Holy Names University, BMO
Humboldt State University, B
Imperial Valley College, A
La Sierra University, B
Lake Tahoe Community College, A
Laney College, A
Long Beach City College, A
Los Angeles City College, A
Los Angeles Mission College, A
Los Angeles Pierce College, A
Los Angeles Southwest College, A
Los Angeles Valley College, A
Los Medanos College, A
Loyola Marymount University, B
The Master's College and Seminary, B
Mendocino College, A
Merced College, A
Mills College, BM
MiraCosta College, A
Modesto Junior College, A
Monterey Peninsula College, A
Moorpark College, A
Mount Saint Mary's University, B
Mt. San Antonio College, A
Mt. San Jacinto College, A
Musicians Institute, AB
Napa Valley College, A
Notre Dame de Namur University, B
Occidental College, B
Ohlone College, A
Orange Coast College, A
Pacific Union College, AB
Palomar College, A
Pepperdine University, B
Pitzer College, B
Point Loma Nazarene University, B
Pomona College, B
Porterville College, A
Sacramento City College, A
Saddleback College, A
Saint Katherine College, B
Saint Mary's College of California, B
San Bernardino Valley College, A
San Diego Christian College, B
San Diego City College, A
San Diego Mesa College, A
San Diego State University, BM
San Francisco Conservatory of Music, M
San Francisco State University, BM
San Joaquin Delta College, A
San Jose City College, A
San Jose State University, BM
Santa Ana College, A
Santa Barbara City College, A
Santa Clara University, B
Santa Monica College, A
Santa Rosa Junior College, A
Santiago Canyon College, A
Scripps College, B
Shasta College, A
Shepherd University, M
Sierra College, A
Simpson University, B
Skyline College, A
Solano Community College, A
Sonoma State University, B
Southwestern College, A
Stanford University, BMD
University of California, Berkeley, BD
University of California, Davis, BMD
University of California, Irvine, BM
University of California, Los Angeles, BMD
University of California, Riverside, BMD
University of California, San Diego, BMD
University of California, Santa Barbara, BMD
University of California, Santa Cruz, BMD
University of La Verne, B
University of the Pacific, BM

University of Redlands, BM
University of San Diego, B
University of Southern California, BMDO
Vanguard University of Southern California, B
Ventura College, A
Victor Valley College, A
West Los Angeles College, A
West Valley College, A
Westmont College, B
Whittier College, B
William Jessup University, B
Yuba College, A

Colorado

Adams State University, B
Colorado Christian University, B
The Colorado College, B
Colorado Mesa University, B
Colorado State University, BM
Colorado State University - Pueblo, B
Fort Lewis College, B
Metropolitan State University of Denver, B
Naropa University, B
Northeastern Junior College, A
Regis University, B
University of Colorado Boulder, BMD
University of Colorado Denver, BM
University of Denver, BMO
University of Northern Colorado, BMD
Western State Colorado University, B

Connecticut

Central Connecticut State University, B
Connecticut College, B
Eastern Connecticut State University, B
Fairfield University, B
Manchester Community College, A
Southern Connecticut State University, B
Trinity College, B
University of Bridgeport, B
University of Connecticut, BMDO
University of Hartford, BMDO
University of New Haven, B
Wesleyan University, BMD
Western Connecticut State University, B
Yale University, BMDO

Delaware

Delaware State University, B
University of Delaware, BM

District of Columbia

American University, B
The Catholic University of America, BMDO
The George Washington University, B
Howard University, BM
Trinity Washington University, B
University of the District of Columbia, AB

Florida

Broward College, A
College of Central Florida, A
Eastern Florida State College, A
Eckerd College, B
Florida Agricultural and Mechanical University, B
Florida Atlantic University, BM
Florida College, B
Florida International University, BM
Florida Southern College, B
Florida State University, BMD
Hobe Sound Bible College, A
Indian River State College, A
Jacksonville University, B
Miami Dade College, A
New College of Florida, B
Northwest Florida State College, A
Nova Southeastern University, B
Palm Beach Atlantic University, B
Palm Beach State College, A
Pensacola State College, A
Rollins College, B
St. Petersburg College, A
South Florida State College, A
Southeastern University, B
State College of Florida Manatee-Sarasota, A

Stetson University, B
Trinity Baptist College, B
University of Central Florida, M
University of Florida, BMD
University of Miami, BM
University of South Florida, MD
The University of Tampa, B

Georgia

Abraham Baldwin Agricultural College, A
Agnes Scott College, B
Albany State University, B
Andrew College, A
Armstrong State University, B
Augusta University, B
Berry College, B
Brenau University, B
Clark Atlanta University, B
Clayton State University, AB
Columbus State University, B
Covenant College, B
Darton State College, A
Emmanuel College, B
Emory University, BM
Georgia Christian University, M
Georgia College & State University, B
Georgia Highlands College, A
Georgia Southern University, BM
Georgia Southwestern State University, B
Georgia State University, MDO
Gordon State College, A
Kennesaw State University, B
LaGrange College, B
Mercer University, B
Middle Georgia State University, A
Morehouse College, B
Piedmont College, B
Point University, B
Reinhardt University, BM
Shorter University, B
Spelman College, B
Toccoa Falls College, B
Truett-McConnell College, B
University of Georgia, BMD
University of North Georgia, BM
Valdosta State University, B
Wesleyan College, B
Young Harris College, B

Hawaii

Brigham Young University - Hawaii, B
University of Hawaii at Hilo, B
University of Hawaii at Manoa, BMD

Idaho

Boise State University, BM
Brigham Young University - Idaho, B
The College of Idaho, B
College of Southern Idaho, A
Idaho State University, B
North Idaho College, A
Northwest Nazarene University, B
University of Idaho, BM

Illinois

Augustana College, B
Aurora University, B
Benedictine University, B
Blackburn College, B
Bradley University, B
Carl Sandburg College, A
Chicago State University, B
City Colleges of Chicago, Malcolm X College, A
City Colleges of Chicago, Wilbur Wright College, A
College of Lake County, A
Columbia College Chicago, B
Concordia University Chicago, BM
DePaul University, BMO
Dominican University, B
Eastern Illinois University, BM
Elgin Community College, A
Elmhurst College, B
Greenville College, B
Harper College, A
Illinois College, B
Illinois State University, BMD

Illinois Wesleyan University, B
John A. Logan College, A
Kaskaskia College, A
Knox College, B
Lake Forest College, B
Lewis University, B
Lincoln College, A
Lincoln Land Community College, A
Loyola University Chicago, B
McHenry County College, A
McKendree University, B
Millikin University, B
Monmouth College, B
Moraine Valley Community College, A
Morton College, A
North Central College, B
North Park University, BM
Northeastern Illinois University, BM
Northern Illinois University, BMO
Northwestern University, BMD
Oakton Community College, A
Olivet Nazarene University, B
Principia College, B
Quincy University, B
Rockford University, B
Roosevelt University, BMO
Saint Xavier University, B
Sauk Valley Community College, A
School of the Art Institute of Chicago, B
Southern Illinois University Carbondale, BM
Southern Illinois University Edwardsville, BM
Southwestern Illinois College, A
Trinity Christian College, B
Trinity International University, B
Triton College, A
University of Chicago, BMD
University of Illinois at Chicago, B
University of Illinois at Urbana - Champaign, BMD
University of St. Francis, B
Waubonsee Community College, A
Western Illinois University, BM
Wheaton College, B

Indiana

Ball State University, B
Bethel College, B
Butler University, BM
DePauw University, B
Earlham College, B
Goshen College, B
Hanover College, B
Huntington University, B
Indiana State University, BM
Indiana University Bloomington, BMDO
Indiana University - Purdue University Fort Wayne, B
Indiana University - Purdue University Indianapolis, M
Indiana University South Bend, BM
Indiana University Southeast, B
Manchester University, B
Marian University, AB
Oakland City University, B
Saint Mary-of-the-Woods College, B
Saint Mary's College, B
Taylor University, B
University of Evansville, B
University of Indianapolis, B
University of Notre Dame, B
Valparaiso University, B
Vincennes University, A
Wabash College, B

Iowa

Briar Cliff University, B
Central College, B
Coe College, B
Cornell College, B
Dordt College, B
Drake University, B
Graceland University, B
Grand View University, B
Grinnell College, B
Iowa Lakes Community College, A
Iowa State University of Science and Technology, B
Iowa Wesleyan University, B

Loras College, B
Luther College, B
Morningside College, B
Mount Mercy University, B
Northwestern College, B
St. Ambrose University, B
Simpson College, B
Southwestern Community College, A
The University of Iowa, BMD
University of Northern Iowa, BM
Waldorf College, B
Wartburg College, B

Kansas

Allen Community College, A
Baker University, B
Barton County Community College, A
Benedictine College, B
Bethany College, B
Bethel College, B
Butler Community College, A
Central Christian College of Kansas, AB
Coffeyville Community College, A
Cowley County Community College and Area Vocational - Technical School, A
Dodge City Community College, A
Emporia State University, BM
Fort Hays State University, B
Friends University, B
Independence Community College, A
Kansas State University, BM
Kansas Wesleyan University, B
Labette Community College, A
McPherson College, B
Ottawa University, B
Pittsburg State University, M
Pratt Community College, A
Seward County Community College and Area Technical School, A
Southwestern College, B
Sterling College, B
Tabor College, B
The University of Kansas, BMD
Washburn University, B
Wichita State University, BM

Kentucky

Asbury University, B
Bellarmine University, B
Berea College, B
Campbellsville University, BM
Centre College, B
Eastern Kentucky University, BM
Kentucky State University, B
Morehead State University, B
Murray State University, BM
Northern Kentucky University, B
Thomas More College, A
University of the Cumberlands, B
University of Kentucky, MD
University of Louisville, B
Western Kentucky University, B

Louisiana

Bossier Parish Community College, A
Centenary College of Louisiana, B
Dillard University, B
Grambling State University, B
Louisiana College, B
Louisiana State University and Agricultural & Mechanical College, BMD
Louisiana Tech University, B
Loyola University New Orleans, BM
Nicholls State University, B
Northwestern State University of Louisiana, M
Southeastern Louisiana University, M
Tulane University, BM
University of Louisiana at Lafayette, BM
University of New Orleans, BM
Xavier University of Louisiana, B

Maine

Bates College, B
Bowdoin College, B
Colby College, B
College of the Atlantic, B

University of Maine, BM
University of Maine at Farmington, B
University of Maine at Machias, B
University of Southern Maine, BM

Maryland

Carroll Community College, A
Frostburg State University, B
Goucher College, B
Harford Community College, A
Hood College, B
Howard Community College, A
Johns Hopkins University, BMDO
McDaniel College, B
Morgan State University, BM
Peabody Conservatory of The Johns Hopkins University, B
St. Mary's College of Maryland, B
Salisbury University, B
Towson University, B
University of Maryland, Baltimore County, BO
University of Maryland, College Park, BMD
Washington Adventist University, B
Washington College, B

Massachusetts

Amherst College, B
Anna Maria College, B
Assumption College, B
Bard College at Simon's Rock, B
Berklee College of Music, BM
Boston College, B
Boston University, BMDO
Brandeis University, BMD
Bridgewater State University, B
Bunker Hill Community College, A
Cape Cod Community College, A
Clark University, B
College of the Holy Cross, B
Eastern Nazarene College, B
Elms College, B
Gordon College, B
Hampshire College, B
Harvard University, BMD
Holyoke Community College, A
Massachusetts College of Liberal Arts, B
Massachusetts Institute of Technology, B
Mount Holyoke College, B
New England Conservatory of Music, MDO
Northeastern University, B
Northern Essex Community College, A
Quinsigamond Community College, A
Roxbury Community College, A
Salem State University, B
Simmons College, B
Smith College, B
Tufts University, BM
University of Massachusetts Amherst, MD
University of Massachusetts Boston, B
University of Massachusetts Dartmouth, B
University of Massachusetts Lowell, BM
Wellesley College, B
Westfield State University, B
Wheaton College, B
Williams College, B
Worcester Polytechnic Institute, B

Michigan

Adrian College, B
Albion College, B
Alma College, B
Andrews University, BM
Aquinas College, B
Calvin College, B
Central Michigan University, BM
Concordia University Ann Arbor, B
Cornerstone University, B
Eastern Michigan University, BM
Grace Bible College, B
Grand Rapids Community College, A
Grand Valley State University, B
Henry Ford College, A
Hillsdale College, B
Hope College, B
Kalamazoo College, B
Lake Michigan College, A

Lansing Community College, A
Madonna University, B
Marygrove College, B
Michigan State University, BMD
Northern Michigan University, B
Northwestern Michigan College, A
Oakland University, BMD
Olivet College, B
Rochester College, B
Saginaw Valley State University, B
Spring Arbor University, B
University of Michigan, B
University of Michigan - Flint, B
Wayne State University, BMO
Western Michigan University, BMO

Minnesota

Anoka-Ramsey Community College, A
Augsburg College, B
Bemidji State University, B
Bethany Lutheran College, B
Bethel University, B
Carleton College, B
Century College, A
College of Saint Benedict, B
Concordia College, B
Concordia University, St. Paul, B
Crossroads College, B
Crown College, B
Gustavus Adolphus College, B
Hamline University, B
Macalester College, B
McNally Smith College of Music, B
Minnesota State Community and Technical College, A
Minnesota State University Mankato, BM
Minnesota State University Moorhead, B
Normandale Community College, A
North Central University, AB
North Hennepin Community College, A
St. Catherine University, B
St. Cloud State University, BM
Saint John's University, B
Saint Mary's University of Minnesota, B
St. Olaf College, B
Southwest Minnesota State University, B
University of Minnesota, Duluth, BM
University of Minnesota, Morris, B
University of Minnesota, Twin Cities Campus, BMD
University of Northwestern - St. Paul, B
University of St. Thomas, BM
Vermilion Community College, A
Winona State University, B

Mississippi

Alcorn State University, B
Belhaven University, B
Blue Mountain College, B
Delta State University, B
Itawamba Community College, A
Jones County Junior College, A
Millsaps College, B
Mississippi College, BM
Mississippi Delta Community College, A
Mississippi State University, B
Mississippi University for Women, B
Mississippi Valley State University, B
Northeast Mississippi Community College, A
Rust College, B
Southwest Mississippi Community College, A
Tougaloo College, B
University of Mississippi, BMD
University of Southern Mississippi, BMD
William Carey University, B

Missouri

Avila University, B
Baptist Bible College, AB
Central Methodist University, B
College of the Ozarks, B
Crowder College, A
Culver-Stockton College, B
Drury University, B
East Central College, A
Evangel University, BM
Hannibal-LaGrange University, AB

Lindenwood University, B
Missouri Baptist University, B
Missouri State University, BM
Missouri Valley College, B
Missouri Western State University, B
Northwest Missouri State University, B
Park University, BO
Saint Louis University, B
Southeast Missouri State University, B
Southwest Baptist University, B
Three Rivers Community College, A
Truman State University, BM
University of Central Missouri, BM
University of Missouri, BM
University of Missouri - Kansas City, BMD
University of Missouri - St. Louis, B
Washington University in St. Louis, BMD
Webster University, BM
William Jewell College, B

Montana

Dawson Community College, A
Montana State University, B
Montana State University Billings, B
Rocky Mountain College, B
University of Montana, BM

Nebraska

Chadron State College, B
Concordia University, Nebraska, B
Creighton University, B
Doane University, B
Grace University, AB
Hastings College, B
Midland University, B
Nebraska Wesleyan University, B
Peru State College, B
Union College, B
University of Nebraska at Kearney, B
University of Nebraska - Lincoln, BMD
University of Nebraska at Omaha, BM
Wayne State College, B
York College, B

Nevada

College of Southern Nevada, A
Truckee Meadows Community College, A
University of Nevada, Las Vegas, BMDO
University of Nevada, Reno, BM

New Hampshire

Dartmouth College, BM
Franklin Pierce University, B
Keene State College, B
Plymouth State University, B
University of New Hampshire, BM

New Jersey

Bergen Community College, A
Caldwell University, B
The College of New Jersey, B
College of Saint Elizabeth, B
County College of Morris, A
Drew University, B
Essex County College, A
Felician University, B
Kean University, B
Mercer County Community College, A
Monmouth University, B
Montclair State University, BMO
New Jersey City University, BM
Princeton University, BD
Ramapo College of New Jersey, B
Raritan Valley Community College, A
Rider University, BM
Rowan College at Burlington County, A
Rowan University, BM
Rutgers University - Camden, B
Rutgers University - New Brunswick, BMDO
Rutgers University - Newark, B
Thomas Edison State University, B
William Paterson University of New Jersey, BM

New Mexico

Eastern New Mexico University, B
New Mexico Highlands University, B
New Mexico Junior College, A
New Mexico State University, M
Santa Fe University of Art and Design, B
University of New Mexico, M
Western New Mexico University, B

New York

Adelphi University, B
Adirondack Community College, A
Bard College, BMO
Barnard College, B
Baruch College of the City University of New York, B
Binghamton University, State University of New York, BM
Bronx Community College of the City University of New York, A
Brooklyn College of the City University of New York, BM
Buffalo State College, State University of New York, B
Cayuga County Community College, A
City College of the City University of New York, BM
Colgate University, B
The College of Saint Rose, BM
College of Staten Island of the City University of New York, B
Columbia University, BD
Columbia University, School of General Studies, B
Concordia College - New York, B
Cornell University, BMD
Elmira College, B
Finger Lakes Community College, A
Five Towns College, ABMD
Fordham University, B
Hamilton College, B
Hartwick College, B
Hobart and William Smith Colleges, B
Hofstra University, B
Houghton College, BM
Hunter College of the City University of New York, BM
Ithaca College, BM
Jamestown Community College, A
The Jewish Theological Seminary, B
The Juilliard School, BMDO
Kingsborough Community College of the City University of New York, A
Lehman College of the City University of New York, B
Manhattan School of Music, BMDO
Manhattanville College, B
Molloy College, B
Monroe Community College, A
Nazareth College of Rochester, B
New York University, BMDO
Niagara County Community College, A
Nyack College, AB
Onondaga Community College, A
Purchase College, State University of New York, M
Queens College of the City University of New York, M
Roberts Wesleyan College, B
St. Lawrence University, B
Sarah Lawrence College, B
State University of New York College at Geneseo, B
State University of New York College at Oneonta, B
State University of New York College at Potsdam, BM
State University of New York at Fredonia, B
State University of New York at New Paltz, BM
State University of New York at Oswego, B
State University of New York at Plattsburgh, B
Stony Brook University, State University of New York, B
Suffolk County Community College, A
Syracuse University, B
University at Albany, State University of New York, B
University at Buffalo, the State University of New York, BMDO
University of Rochester, BMD
Vassar College, B
Villa Maria College, B

Wagner College, B
York College of the City University of New York, B

North Carolina

Appalachian State University, M
Bennett College, B
Brevard College, B
Campbell University, B
Catawba College, B
Central Piedmont Community College, A
Chowan University, B
College of The Albemarle, A
Davidson College, B
Duke University, BD
East Carolina University, BMO
Elizabeth City State University, B
Elon University, B
Fayetteville State University, B
Gardner-Webb University, B
Greensboro College, B
Guilford College, B
High Point University, B
Isothermal Community College, A
Johnson C. Smith University, B
Lenoir-Rhyne University, B
Livingstone College, B
Mars Hill University, B
Meredith College, B
Methodist University, AB
North Carolina Agricultural and Technical State University, B
North Carolina Central University, BM
Pfeiffer University, B
Queens University of Charlotte, B
Saint Augustine's University, B
Salem College, B
Sandhills Community College, A
Shaw University, B
Southeastern Community College, A
University of Mount Olive, B
University of North Carolina at Asheville, B
The University of North Carolina at Chapel Hill, BMD
The University of North Carolina at Charlotte, BO
The University of North Carolina at Greensboro, BMD
The University of North Carolina at Pembroke, BM
University of North Carolina School of the Arts, M
The University of North Carolina Wilmington, B
Wake Forest University, B
Western Carolina University, BM
Wingate University, B
Winston-Salem State University, B

North Dakota

Dickinson State University, B
Minot State University, B
North Dakota State University, BMD
University of Jamestown, B
University of North Dakota, BMD
Valley City State University, B

Ohio

Ashland University, B
Baldwin Wallace University, B
Bluffton University, B
Bowling Green State University, BMD
Capital University, BM
Case Western Reserve University, B
Cedarville University, B
Cleveland Institute of Music, B
Cleveland State University, BM
The College of Wooster, B
Denison University, B
Heidelberg University, B
Hiram College, B
Kent State University, BMDO
Kent State University at Stark, B
Kenyon College, B
Lorain County Community College, A
Malone University, B
Marietta College, B
Miami University, B
Miami University Hamilton, B
Mount St. Joseph University, B
Mount Vernon Nazarene University, AB

Muskingum University, B
Oberlin College, BMO
Ohio Northern University, B
The Ohio State University, BMD
Ohio University, MO
Ohio Wesleyan University, B
Otterbein University, B
Sinclair Community College, A
Terra State Community College, A
Tiffin University, B
The University of Akron, BM
University of Cincinnati, BMDO
University of Dayton, B
University of Mount Union, B
University of Rio Grande, AB
The University of Toledo, BMO
Walsh University, B
Wilberforce University, B
Wittenberg University, B
Wright State University, B
Xavier University, B
Youngstown State University, BM

Oklahoma

Cameron University, B
East Central University, B
Eastern Oklahoma State College, A
Hillsdale Free Will Baptist College, A
Langston University, B
Mid-America Christian University, B
Northeastern Oklahoma Agricultural and Mechanical
    College, A
Northeastern State University, B
Northwestern Oklahoma State University, B
Oklahoma Baptist University, B
Oklahoma Christian University, B
Oklahoma City Community College, A
Oklahoma City University, BM
Oklahoma Panhandle State University, B
Oklahoma State University, BM
Oklahoma Wesleyan University, B
Oral Roberts University, B
Rose State College, A
Southeastern Oklahoma State University, B
Southern Nazarene University, B
Southwestern Christian University, B
Southwestern Oklahoma State University, BM
Tulsa Community College, A
University of Central Oklahoma, BM
University of Oklahoma, BMD
University of Science and Arts of Oklahoma, B
The University of Tulsa, B

Oregon

Concordia University, B
Corban University, B
Eastern Oregon University, B
George Fox University, B
Lewis & Clark College, B
Linfield College, B
Marylhurst University, B
Oregon State University, B
Pacific University, B
Portland State University, BM
Reed College, B
Southern Oregon University, B
Umpqua Community College, A
University of Oregon, BMD
University of Portland, B
Warner Pacific College, B
Western Oregon University, BM
Willamette University, B

Pennsylvania

Albright College, B
Allegheny College, B
Bloomsburg University of Pennsylvania, B
Bryn Mawr College, B
Bucknell University, B
Bucks County Community College, A
Cairn University, B
Carnegie Mellon University, BM
Chatham University, B
Chestnut Hill College, B
Cheyney University of Pennsylvania, B
Community College of Allegheny County, A

Community College of Beaver County, A
Community College of Philadelphia, A
Curtis Institute of Music, BM
Dickinson College, B
Duquesne University, BMO
Eastern University, B
Edinboro University of Pennsylvania, B
Elizabethtown College, B
Franklin & Marshall College, B
Geneva College, B
Gettysburg College, B
Grove City College, B
Haverford College, B
Immaculata University, B
Indiana University of Pennsylvania, BM
Kutztown University of Pennsylvania, B
Lafayette College, B
Lehigh University, B
Lincoln University, B
Lock Haven University of Pennsylvania, B
Lycoming College, B
Mansfield University of Pennsylvania, BM
Mercyhurst University, B
Messiah College, B
Millersville University of Pennsylvania, B
Moravian College, B
Muhlenberg College, B
Penn State Altoona, B
Penn State Beaver, B
Penn State Berks, B
Penn State Brandywine, B
Penn State DuBois, B
Penn State Greater Allegheny, B
Penn State Hazleton, B
Penn State Mont Alto, B
Penn State New Kensington, B
Penn State Shenango, B
Penn State University Park, BMDO
Penn State Wilkes-Barre, B
Penn State Worthington Scranton, B
Penn State York, B
Saint Joseph's University, B
Saint Vincent College, B
Seton Hill University, B
Slippery Rock University of Pennsylvania, B
Summit University, B
Susquehanna University, B
Swarthmore College, B
Temple University, BMD
The University of the Arts, M
University of Pennsylvania, BMD
University of Pittsburgh, BMD
University of Valley Forge, M
Washington & Jefferson College, B
West Chester University of Pennsylvania, BM
Westminster College, B
York College of Pennsylvania, AB

Rhode Island

Brown University, BD
Community College of Rhode Island, A
Providence College, B
Rhode Island College, B
Salve Regina University, B
University of Rhode Island, BM

South Carolina

Allen University, B
Anderson University, B
Benedict College, B
Bob Jones University, M
Charleston Southern University, B
Claflin University, B
Coastal Carolina University, B
Coker College, B
College of Charleston, B
Columbia College, B
Converse College, BM
Erskine College, B
Francis Marion University, B
Furman University, B
Lander University, B
Limestone College, B
Newberry College, B
North Greenville University, B
Presbyterian College, B

Southern Wesleyan University, B
University of South Carolina, BMDO
University of South Carolina Upstate, B
Winthrop University, BM

South Dakota

Augustana University, B
Black Hills State University, B
Dakota Wesleyan University, B
Mount Marty College, B
Northern State University, B
South Dakota State University, B
University of Sioux Falls, B
The University of South Dakota, M

Tennessee

Austin Peay State University, BM
Belmont University, BM
Bethel University, B
Bryan College, B
Carson-Newman University, B
Cumberland University, B
East Tennessee State University, B
Fisk University, B
Freed-Hardeman University, B
Hiwassee College, A
King University, B
Lane College, B
Lee University, B
LeMoyne-Owen College, B
Lipscomb University, B
Maryville College, B
Middle Tennessee State University, BM
Milligan College, B
Nashville State Community College, A
Rhodes College, B
Sewanee: The University of the South, B
Southern Adventist University, B
Tennessee State University, B
Tennessee Technological University, B
Tennessee Wesleyan College, B
Trevecca Nazarene University, B
Union University, B
University of Memphis, BMD
The University of Tennessee, BM
The University of Tennessee at Chattanooga, B
The University of Tennessee at Martin, B
Vanderbilt University, B
Welch College, B

Texas

Abilene Christian University, B
Alvin Community College, A
Amarillo College, A
Angelina College, A
Angelo State University, B
Arlington Baptist College, B
Austin College, B
Austin Community College District, A
Baptist University of the Americas, B
Baylor University, BMD
Blinn College, A
Brookhaven College, A
Central Texas College, A
Clarendon College, A
College of the Mainland, A
Collin County Community College District, A
Dallas Baptist University, B
Del Mar College, A
East Texas Baptist University, B
Eastfield College, A
El Paso Community College, A
Galveston College, A
Grayson College, A
Hardin-Simmons University, BM
Hill College, A
Houston Baptist University, B
Howard College, A
Huston-Tillotson University, B
Kilgore College, A
Lamar State College - Port Arthur, A
Lamar University, BM
Lee College, A
Lone Star College - CyFair, A
Lone Star College - Kingwood, A
Lone Star College - Montgomery, A

Lone Star College - North Harris, A
Lone Star College - Tomball, A
Lubbock Christian University, B
McLennan Community College, A
McMurry University, B
Messenger College, B
Midwestern State University, B
Mountain View College, A
Navarro College, A
Northeast Texas Community College, A
Odessa College, A
Our Lady of the Lake University of San Antonio, B
Palo Alto College, A
Panola College, A
Paris Junior College, A
Prairie View A&M University, B
Rice University, BMD
St. Mary's University, B
St. Philip's College, A
Sam Houston State University, BM
San Jacinto College District, A
Schreiner University, B
South Plains College, A
Southern Methodist University, BM
Southwestern Adventist University, B
Southwestern Assemblies of God University, A
Southwestern University, B
Stephen F. Austin State University, BM
Sul Ross State University, B
Tarleton State University, B
Texarkana College, A
Texas A&M International University, B
Texas A&M University, B
Texas A&M University - Commerce, B
Texas A&M University - Corpus Christi, B
Texas A&M University - Kingsville, B
Texas Christian University, BMD
Texas College, B
Texas Lutheran University, B
Texas Southern University, BM
Texas Southmost College, A
Texas State University, BM
Texas Tech University, BMD
Texas Wesleyan University, B
Texas Woman's University, BM
Trinity University, B
Trinity Valley Community College, A
Tyler Junior College, A
University of Houston, BMD
University of the Incarnate Word, B
University of Mary Hardin-Baylor, B
University of North Texas, BMD
University of St. Thomas, B
The University of Texas at Arlington, BM
The University of Texas at Austin, BMD
The University of Texas at El Paso, BM
The University of Texas of the Permian Basin, B
The University of Texas Rio Grande Valley, BM
The University of Texas at San Antonio, BM
The University of Texas at Tyler, B
Wayland Baptist University, B
West Texas A&M University, BM
Wharton County Junior College, A
Wiley College, B

Utah

Brigham Young University, BM
Dixie State University, B
Salt Lake Community College, A
Snow College, AB
Southern Utah University, B
University of Utah, BMD
Utah State University, B
Utah Valley University, AB
Weber State University, B
Westminster College, B

Vermont

Bennington College, BM
Castleton University, B
Johnson State College, B
Marlboro College, B
Middlebury College, B
Saint Michael's College, B
University of Vermont, B

Virginia

Averett University, B
Bluefield College, B
The College of William and Mary, B
Eastern Mennonite University, B
George Mason University, MD
Hampton University, B
Hollins University, B
James Madison University, D
Liberty University, BMD
Lynchburg College, BM
Mary Baldwin College, B
Norfolk State University, BM
Radford University, BM
Randolph-Macon College, B
Roanoke College, B
Shenandoah University, MDO
Southern Virginia University, B
Sweet Briar College, B
Tidewater Community College, A
University of Mary Washington, B
University of Richmond, B
University of Virginia, BMD
Virginia Commonwealth University, M
Virginia Polytechnic Institute and State University, B
Virginia State University, B
Virginia Union University, B
Virginia Wesleyan College, B
Washington and Lee University, B

Washington

Central Washington University, BM
Cornish College of the Arts, B
Eastern Washington University, BM
Everett Community College, A
Gonzaga University, B
Highline College, A
North Seattle College, A
Northwest University, B
Pacific Lutheran University, B
Saint Martin's University, B
Seattle Pacific University, B
Seattle University, B
Shoreline Community College, A
Skagit Valley College, A
Spokane Falls Community College, A
University of Puget Sound, B
University of Washington, BMD
Walla Walla University, B
Washington State University, BM
Wenatchee Valley College, A
Western Washington University, BM
Whitman College, B
Whitworth University, B

West Virginia

Alderson Broaddus University, B
Bethany College, B
Davis & Elkins College, B
Marshall University, M
Shepherd University, B
West Virginia University, BMD
West Virginia Wesleyan College, B

Wisconsin

Alverno College, AB
Cardinal Stritch University, M
Carroll University, B
Carthage College, B
Concordia University Wisconsin, B
Edgewood College, B
Lakeland College, B
Lawrence University, B
Madison Media Institute, A
Marian University, B
Milwaukee Area Technical College, A
Ripon College, B
St. Norbert College, B
Silver Lake College of the Holy Family, B
University of Wisconsin - Eau Claire, B
University of Wisconsin - Green Bay, B
University of Wisconsin - La Crosse, B
University of Wisconsin - Madison, BMD
University of Wisconsin - Milwaukee, BMO
University of Wisconsin - Oshkosh, B

University of Wisconsin - Parkside, B
University of Wisconsin - Platteville, B
University of Wisconsin - River Falls, B
University of Wisconsin - Stevens Point, B
University of Wisconsin - Superior, B
University of Wisconsin - Whitewater, B
Viterbo University, B
Wisconsin Lutheran College, B

Wyoming

Casper College, A
Central Wyoming College, A
Eastern Wyoming College, A
Laramie County Community College, A
Northwest College, A
Sheridan College, A
University of Wyoming, BM
Western Wyoming Community College, A

U.S. Territories: American Samoa

American Samoa Community College, A

U.S. Territories: Puerto Rico

Conservatorio de Musica de Puerto Rico, O
Inter American University of Puerto Rico, San Germán Campus, BM
Pontifical Catholic University of Puerto Rico, B
University of Puerto Rico, Río Piedras Campus, B

Canada

Alberta

Ambrose University, B
Concordia University of Edmonton, B
The King's University, B
University of Alberta, BMD
University of Calgary, BMD
University of Lethbridge, BM

British Columbia

Simon Fraser University, B
Thompson Rivers University, AB
Trinity Western University, B
The University of British Columbia, BMD
University of Victoria, BMD

Manitoba

Brandon University, BM
Providence University College & Theological Seminary, B
University of Manitoba, BM
The University of Winnipeg, B

Maritime Provinces: New Brunswick

Kingswood University, B
Mount Allison University, B
Université de Moncton, B

Maritime Provinces: Nova Scotia

Acadia University, B
Dalhousie University, B
St. Francis Xavier University, B
University of King's College, B

Maritime Provinces: Prince Edward Island

University of Prince Edward Island, B

Newfoundland and Labrador

Memorial University of Newfoundland, BM

Ontario

Brock University, B
Carleton University, B
Lakehead University, B
Laurentian University, B
McMaster University, B
Queen's University at Kingston, B
Redeemer University College, B
University of Guelph, B
University of Ottawa, BMO
University of Toronto, MD
University of Waterloo, B

The University of Western Ontario, BMD
University of Windsor, B
Wilfrid Laurier University, B
York University, BMD

Quebec

Bishop's University, B
Concordia University, BO
McGill University, BMD
Université Laval, BMD
Université de Montréal, BMDO
Université du Québec à Montréal, B

Saskatchewan

University of Regina, BM
University of Saskatchewan, BM

MUSIC HISTORY, LITERATURE, AND THEORY

United States

Alabama

Birmingham-Southern College, B
Chattahoochee Valley Community College, A

Arizona

Arizona State University at the Tempe campus, M

Arkansas

Ouachita Baptist University, B

California

California State University, Fullerton, M
California State University, Long Beach, B
Ohlone College, A
San Francisco State University, M
University of California, Los Angeles, B
University of California, San Diego, B
University of the Pacific, B
University of Redlands, B
University of Southern California, D

Colorado

University of Northern Colorado, MD

Connecticut

University of Connecticut, D
University of Hartford, BM
Yale University, M

Delaware

University of Delaware, B

District of Columbia

American University, B
The Catholic University of America, B

Florida

Florida Atlantic University, M
Florida State University, MD
Jacksonville University, B
New College of Florida, B
South Florida State College, A
University of Florida, MD

Idaho

University of Idaho, B

Illinois

Northwestern University, B
Trinity International University, B
University of Illinois at Urbana - Champaign, B
Wheaton College, B

Indiana

Saint Joseph's College, B

Iowa

University of Northern Iowa, M

Kansas

Central Christian College of Kansas, A
Pittsburg State University, M

Kentucky

University of Kentucky, B
University of Louisville, M

Massachusetts

Boston University, D
Eastern Nazarene College, B
New England Conservatory of Music, B
Tufts University, BM
University of Massachusetts Amherst, M

Michigan

Calvin College, B
University of Michigan, B

Minnesota

St. Cloud State University, B

Mississippi

University of Southern Mississippi, M

Missouri

St. Charles Community College, A
University of Missouri - Kansas City, M
Washington University in St. Louis, B

Nebraska

Hastings College, B
University of Nebraska - Lincoln, M

New Jersey

Rider University, B
Rutgers University - Newark, M

New Mexico

University of New Mexico, M

New York

Concordia College - New York, B
Eugene Lang College of Liberal Arts, B
Five Towns College, D
Hofstra University, B
Long Island University - LIU Post, M
Nazareth College of Rochester, B
St. Bonaventure University, B
Sarah Lawrence College, B
Skidmore College, B
State University of New York at Fredonia, B
Stony Brook University, State University of New
   York, MD
Syracuse University, B
University at Buffalo, the State University of New
   York, M

Ohio

Baldwin Wallace University, B
Bowling Green State University, BM
Case Western Reserve University, MD
The College of Wooster, B
Oberlin College, B
The Ohio State University, B
Ohio University, BM
Otterbein University, B
The University of Akron, BM
University of Cincinnati, BMD
Wright State University, B
Youngstown State University, BM

Pennsylvania

Bucknell University, B
Cairn University, B
Lehigh University, B
Temple University, BM
Ursinus College, B
West Chester University of Pennsylvania, M

South Carolina

Converse College, B
University of South Carolina, M

South Dakota

The University of South Dakota, M

Texas

Baylor University, BM
Rice University, B
Southern Methodist University, M
Texas Christian University, D

Utah

Brigham Young University, B
Snow College, A
University of Utah, M

Vermont

Bennington College, B
Marlboro College, B
University of Vermont, B

Virginia

Bridgewater College, B
Liberty University, B
Randolph College, B

Washington

University of Washington, BMD
Western Washington University, B
Whitman College, B

West Virginia

West Virginia University, M

Wisconsin

University of Wisconsin - Madison, MD
University of Wisconsin - Milwaukee, M

Canada

British Columbia

The University of British Columbia, B
University of Victoria, B

Manitoba

Brandon University, B

Maritime Provinces: New Brunswick

Mount Allison University, B

Maritime Provinces: Nova Scotia

Dalhousie University, B

Newfoundland and Labrador

Memorial University of Newfoundland, B

Ontario

Carleton University, M
McMaster University, B
University of Toronto, B
The University of Western Ontario, B
University of Windsor, B
York University, B

Quebec

McGill University, B
Université du Québec à Montréal, B

Saskatchewan

University of Regina, B

MUSIC PEDAGOGY

United States

Alabama

Samford University, B

California

Holy Names University, B

Illinois

Trinity International University, B
Wheaton College, B

Indiana

Huntington University, B

Maryland

University of Maryland, Baltimore County, B

Massachusetts

Eastern Nazarene College, B

Michigan

Michigan State University, B
Spring Arbor University, B

Minnesota

St. Cloud State University, B

Missouri

Calvary Bible College and Theological Seminary, B

Nebraska

Hastings College, B
Union College, B

North Carolina

Campbell University, B

Oklahoma

University of Oklahoma, B

Oregon

Willamette University, B

Pennsylvania

Temple University, B

South Carolina

Bob Jones University, B

Tennessee

The University of Tennessee at Martin, B

Texas

Baylor University, B

Utah

Brigham Young University, B
Weber State University, B

Virginia

Liberty University, B

Wisconsin

Lawrence University, B
Maranatha Baptist University, B
Viterbo University, B

Canada

Quebec

McGill University, B

MUSIC PERFORMANCE

United States

Alabama

Community College of the Air Force, A
Huntingdon College, B
Samford University, B
Talladega College, B

Alaska

University of Alaska Anchorage, B

Arizona

Arizona State University at the Tempe campus, B
Northern Arizona University, B
The University of Arizona, B

Arkansas

Arkansas State University, B
Henderson State University, B
John Brown University, B
Ouachita Baptist University, B
University of Arkansas, B
University of Central Arkansas, B

California

Biola University, B
California Baptist University, B
California Institute of the Arts, B
California State University, Fullerton, B
California State University, Long Beach, B
California State University, Los Angeles, B
California State University, Stanislaus, B
Chapman University, B
The Colburn School Conservatory of Music, B
Holy Names University, B
Musicians Institute, AB
Notre Dame de Namur University, B
Ohlone College, A
Pacific Union College, B
Point Loma Nazarene University, B
Reedley College, A
San Diego Christian College, B
San Diego State University, B
San Francisco State University, B
San Jose State University, B
University of California, Irvine, B
University of Redlands, B
University of Southern California, B
Vanguard University of Southern California, B

Colorado

Adams State University, B
Colorado Christian University, B
Colorado State University, B
Fort Lewis College, B
Naropa University, B
University of Colorado Boulder, B
University of Denver, B

Connecticut

University of Hartford, B
Western Connecticut State University, B

Delaware

University of Delaware, B

District of Columbia

The Catholic University of America, B

Florida

Bethune-Cookman University, B
Florida Gulf Coast University, B
Florida Southern College, B
Jacksonville University, B
Lynn University, B
Miami Dade College, A
New World School of the Arts, B
Palm Beach Atlantic University, B
South Florida State College, A
Southeastern University, B
State College of Florida Manatee-Sarasota, A
Stetson University, B
University of Central Florida, B
University of Miami, B
University of North Florida, B
University of South Florida, B
The University of Tampa, B
University of West Florida, B

Georgia

Augusta University, B
Brenau University, B
Columbus State University, B
Covenant College, B
Georgia Southern University, B
Georgia State University, B
Kennesaw State University, B
LaGrange College, B
Mercer University, B
Piedmont College, B
Toccoa Falls College, B
University of Georgia, B
University of North Georgia, B
University of West Georgia, B
Valdosta State University, B

Hawaii

Brigham Young University - Hawaii, B

Idaho

Boise State University, B
Idaho State University, B
Northwest Nazarene University, B
University of Idaho, B

Illinois

Augustana College, B
Bradley University, B
Columbia College Chicago, B
Concordia University Chicago, B
DePaul University, B
Elmhurst College, B
Illinois State University, B
Illinois Wesleyan University, B
Judson University, B
Millikin University, B
Northwestern University, B
Olivet Nazarene University, B
Parkland College, A
Rockford University, B
Roosevelt University, B
Saint Xavier University, B
University of Illinois at Urbana - Champaign, B
University of St. Francis, B
Western Illinois University, B
Wheaton College, B

Indiana

Anderson University, B
Bethel College, B
Butler University, B
DePauw University, B
Huntington University, B
Indiana State University, B
Indiana University Bloomington, B
Indiana University - Purdue University Fort Wayne, B
Indiana University South Bend, B
Indiana Wesleyan University, B
Manchester University, B
Marian University, B
Taylor University, B
University of Evansville, B
University of Indianapolis, B
Valparaiso University, B

Iowa

Buena Vista University, B
Clarke University, B
Coe College, B
Dordt College, B
Drake University, B
Morningside College, B
Simpson College, B
The University of Iowa, B
University of Northern Iowa, B
Wartburg College, B
William Penn University, B

Kansas

Butler Community College, A
Central Christian College of Kansas, AB
Fort Hays State University, B
Friends University, B
Kansas Wesleyan University, B
MidAmerica Nazarene University, B
Pittsburg State University, B
Southwestern College, B
Tabor College, B
The University of Kansas, B

Washburn University, B

Kentucky

Kentucky Christian University, B
Kentucky Wesleyan College, B
Transylvania University, B
University of Kentucky, B
Western Kentucky University, B

Louisiana

Dillard University, B
Louisiana State University and Agricultural & Mechanical College, B
Louisiana Tech University, B
Loyola University New Orleans, B
McNeese State University, B
Northwestern State University of Louisiana, B
Southeastern Louisiana University, B
Southern University and Agricultural and Mechanical College, B
Tulane University, B
University of Louisiana at Lafayette, B
University of Louisiana at Monroe, B
Xavier University of Louisiana, B

Maine

University of Maine, B
University of Southern Maine, B

Maryland

Peabody Conservatory of The Johns Hopkins University, B
University of Maryland, Baltimore County, B
University of Maryland, College Park, B
Washington Adventist University, B

Massachusetts

Berklee College of Music, B
Boston University, B
Eastern Nazarene College, B
Gordon College, B
Greenfield Community College, A
New England Conservatory of Music, B
University of Massachusetts Amherst, B
University of Massachusetts Lowell, B

Michigan

Albion College, B
Aquinas College, B
Calvin College, B
Cornerstone University, B
Eastern Michigan University, B
Hope College, B
Lansing Community College, A
Macomb Community College, A
Madonna University, B
Marygrove College, B
Michigan State University, B
Oakland Community College, A
Oakland University, B
University of Michigan, B
University of Michigan - Flint, B
Western Michigan University, B

Minnesota

Augsburg College, B
Bethel University, B
The College of St. Scholastica, B
Concordia College, B
Gustavus Adolphus College, B
Hamline University, B
Minnesota State University Moorhead, B
North Central University, B
St. Cloud State University, B
Saint Mary's University of Minnesota, B
St. Olaf College, B
University of Minnesota, Duluth, B
University of Northwestern - St. Paul, B

Mississippi

Alcorn State University, B
Jackson State University, B
William Carey University, B

Missouri

Avila University, B
Calvary Bible College and Theological Seminary, B
Central Methodist University, B
Missouri Baptist University, B
Missouri Southern State University, B
Missouri State University, B
Truman State University, B
University of Missouri - Kansas City, B
Webster University, B
William Jewell College, B

Montana

Rocky Mountain College, B
University of Montana, B

Nebraska

Hastings College, B
Nebraska Wesleyan University, B
Northeast Community College, A
Peru State College, B
Union College, B
University of Nebraska at Omaha, B

Nevada

Truckee Meadows Community College, A
University of Nevada, Reno, B

New Hampshire

Keene State College, B

New Jersey

Kean University, B
Montclair State University, B
Rowan University, B
Rutgers University - New Brunswick, B
Seton Hall University, B
William Paterson University of New Jersey, B

New Mexico

New Mexico State University, B
University of New Mexico, B

New York

Adirondack Community College, A
Binghamton University, State University of New York, B
Brooklyn College of the City University of New York, B
Canisius College, B
City College of the City University of New York, B
Concordia College - New York, B
Five Towns College, AB
Hofstra University, B
Houghton College, B
Ithaca College, B
The Juilliard School, B
Long Island University - LIU Brooklyn, B
Long Island University - LIU Post, B
Nassau Community College, A
Nazareth College of Rochester, B
The New School College of Performing Arts, B
New York University, B
Nyack College, B
Orange County Community College, A
Queens College of the City University of New York, B
State University of New York College at Potsdam, B
Syracuse University, B
University at Buffalo, the State University of New York, B
University of Rochester, B

North Carolina

Appalachian State University, B
Brevard College, B
Campbell University, B
Catawba College, B
Elon University, B
Gardner-Webb University, B
Greensboro College, B
Lenoir-Rhyne University, B
Mars Hill University, B
Montreat College, B

Salem College, B
The University of North Carolina at Chapel Hill, B
The University of North Carolina at Charlotte, B
The University of North Carolina at Greensboro, B
The University of North Carolina at Pembroke, B
University of North Carolina School of the Arts, B
The University of North Carolina Wilmington, B
Western Carolina University, B

North Dakota

University of Jamestown, B
University of Mary, B
University of North Dakota, B

Ohio

Baldwin Wallace University, B
Bowling Green State University, B
Capital University, B
Cedarville University, B
Central State University, B
Cleveland Institute of Music, B
The College of Wooster, B
Miami University, B
Mount Vernon Nazarene University, B
Ohio Northern University, B
The Ohio State University, B
Ohio University, B
Ohio Wesleyan University, B
Otterbein University, B
Terra State Community College, A
The University of Akron, B
University of Cincinnati, B
University of Dayton, B
University of Mount Union, B
Wright State University, B
Youngstown State University, B

Oklahoma

East Central University, B
Hillsdale Free Will Baptist College, B
Oklahoma Baptist University, B
Oklahoma City University, B
Oral Roberts University, B
Southeastern Oklahoma State University, B
Southern Nazarene University, B
Southwestern Christian University, B
University of Central Oklahoma, AB
The University of Tulsa, B

Oregon

Corban University, B
Marylhurst University, B
Pacific University, B
Portland State University, B
University of Oregon, B
Willamette University, B

Pennsylvania

Allegheny College, B
Bucknell University, B
Carnegie Mellon University, B
Curtis Institute of Music, B
Duquesne University, B
Grove City College, B
Immaculata University, B
Indiana University of Pennsylvania, B
Lebanon Valley College, B
Mansfield University of Pennsylvania, B
Marywood University, B
Mercyhurst University, B
Messiah College, B
Penn State University Park, B
Saint Vincent College, B
Seton Hill University, B
Slippery Rock University of Pennsylvania, B
Susquehanna University, B
Temple University, B
The University of the Arts, B
University of Valley Forge, B
West Chester University of Pennsylvania, B

Rhode Island

Rhode Island College, B

South Carolina

Anderson University, B
Bob Jones University, B
Charleston Southern University, B
Columbia College, B
Converse College, B
Limestone College, B
Newberry College, B
North Greenville University, B

South Dakota

Black Hills State University, B
The University of South Dakota, B

Tennessee

Carson-Newman University, B
Dyersburg State Community College, A
Fisk University, B
Lee University, B
Lipscomb University, B
Maryville College, B
Southern Adventist University, B
Trevecca Nazarene University, AB
Union University, B
The University of Tennessee at Martin, B
Volunteer State Community College, A
Walters State Community College, A
Welch College, B

Texas

Baylor University, B
Cedar Valley College, A
Dallas Baptist University, B
Hardin-Simmons University, B
Houston Community College, A
Howard Payne University, B
Midwestern State University, B
Rice University, B
Sam Houston State University, B
Southern Methodist University, B
Southwestern Adventist University, B
Southwestern Assemblies of God University, B
Texas A&M University - Kingsville, B
Texas Christian University, B
Texas State University, B
Trinity University, B
University of Houston, B
University of the Incarnate Word, B
University of Mary Hardin-Baylor, B
University of North Texas, B
The University of Texas at Arlington, B
The University of Texas at Austin, B
The University of Texas Rio Grande Valley, B
Wayland Baptist University, B
West Texas A&M University, B

Utah

Utah Valley University, B
Weber State University, B

Vermont

Bennington College, B
Castleton University, B
Johnson State College, B
Marlboro College, B
University of Vermont, B

Virginia

Christopher Newport University, B
Emory & Henry College, B
George Mason University, B
James Madison University, B
Liberty University, B
Old Dominion University, B
Randolph College, B
Virginia Commonwealth University, B
Virginia Union University, B

Washington

Central Washington University, B
Gonzaga University, B
University of Puget Sound, B
University of Washington, B
Walla Walla University, B
Washington State University, B

Western Washington University, B
Whitman College, B

West Virginia

Alderson Broaddus University, B
Glenville State College, B

Wisconsin

Cardinal Stritch University, B
Lawrence University, B
Maranatha Baptist University, B
University of Wisconsin - Madison, B
University of Wisconsin - Stevens Point, B
University of Wisconsin - Superior, B
Viterbo University, B

Wyoming

Casper College, A
University of Wyoming, B

U.S. Territories: Puerto Rico

Conservatorio de Musica de Puerto Rico, B
Inter American University of Puerto Rico, Metropolitan Campus, AB

Canada

British Columbia

Thompson Rivers University, B

Manitoba

Brandon University, B

Maritime Provinces: New Brunswick

Mount Allison University, B

Maritime Provinces: Nova Scotia

Dalhousie University, B

Ontario

The University of Western Ontario, B
University of Windsor, B
York University, B

Quebec

Concordia University, B
McGill University, B
Université de Montréal, B

MUSIC TEACHER EDUCATION

United States

Alabama

Alabama Agricultural and Mechanical University, BM
Alabama State University, BM
Auburn University, BMDO
Birmingham-Southern College, B
Huntingdon College, B
Jacksonville State University, B
Judson College, B
Oakwood University, B
Samford University, BM
Talladega College, B
Troy University, M
The University of Alabama, BMDO
University of Mobile, B
University of South Alabama, M

Alaska

University of Alaska Anchorage, B

Arizona

Arizona State University at the Tempe campus, BMD
Northern Arizona University, B
The University of Arizona, BMD

Arkansas

Arkansas State University, BMO
Arkansas Tech University, B

Harding University, B
John Brown University, B
Ouachita Baptist University, B
Southern Arkansas University - Magnolia, B
University of Arkansas - Fort Smith, B
University of Arkansas at Monticello, B
University of Central Arkansas, M
Williams Baptist College, B

California

Ashford University, B
Azusa Pacific University, M
Biola University, B
California Baptist University, BM
California Lutheran University, B
California State University, Fresno, BM
California State University, Fullerton, BM
California State University, Los Angeles, M
California State University, Northridge, M
Chapman University, B
Fresno Pacific University, B
Holy Names University, MO
Humboldt State University, B
La Sierra University, B
The Master's College and Seminary, B
Pacific Union College, B
Pepperdine University, B
Point Loma Nazarene University, B
San Diego State University, BM
San Francisco State University, M
Simpson University, B
Sonoma State University, B
University of the Pacific, BM
University of Redlands, B
University of Southern California, MD
Vanguard University of Southern California, B

Colorado

Adams State University, B
Colorado Christian University, B
The Colorado College, M
Colorado State University, B
Colorado State University - Pueblo, M
Fort Lewis College, B
Metropolitan State University of Denver, B
University of Colorado Boulder, BMD
University of Northern Colorado, BMD
Western State Colorado University, B

Connecticut

Central Connecticut State University, BMO
University of Bridgeport, M
University of Connecticut, BMD
University of Hartford, BMD
Western Connecticut State University, BM

Delaware

Delaware State University, B
University of Delaware, BM

District of Columbia

Howard University, M

Florida

The Baptist College of Florida, B
Bethune-Cookman University, B
Broward College, A
College of Central Florida, A
Florida Agricultural and Mechanical University, B
Florida Atlantic University, BM
Florida International University, M
Florida Memorial University, B
Florida Southern College, B
Florida State University, MD
Hobe Sound Bible College, B
Jacksonville University, B
Miami Dade College, A
Palm Beach Atlantic University, B
Pensacola State College, A
South Florida State College, A
Southeastern University, B
State College of Florida Manatee-Sarasota, A
Stetson University, B
University of Central Florida, B
University of Florida, BMD

University of Miami, BMDO
University of North Florida, B
University of South Florida, BMD
The University of Tampa, B
University of West Florida, B
Warner University, B

Georgia

Albany State University, B
Armstrong State University, B
Augusta University, B
Berry College, B
Brenau University, B
Columbus State University, BMO
Darton State College, A
Emmanuel College, B
Georgia College & State University, BM
Georgia Southern University, B
Georgia State University, MD
Kennesaw State University, B
Mercer University, B
Piedmont College, BM
Reinhardt University, M
Shorter University, B
Toccoa Falls College, B
Truett-McConnell College, B
University of Georgia, BMDO
University of North Georgia, B
University of West Georgia, BM
Young Harris College, B

Hawaii

Brigham Young University - Hawaii, B

Idaho

Boise State University, BM
Brigham Young University - Idaho, B
Idaho State University, B
North Idaho College, A
Northwest Nazarene University, B
University of Idaho, B

Illinois

Augustana College, B
Benedictine University, B
Bradley University, B
Carl Sandburg College, A
Chicago State University, B
College of Lake County, A
Concordia University Chicago, B
DePaul University, BM
Elmhurst College, B
Greenville College, B
Illinois State University, B
Illinois Wesleyan University, B
Lake Forest College, M
McKendree University, BM
Millikin University, B
North Central College, B
North Park University, B
Northern Illinois University, B
Northwestern University, BMD
Olivet Nazarene University, B
Parkland College, A
Quincy University, B
Roosevelt University, BO
Saint Xavier University, BM
Southern Illinois University Edwardsville, MO
Southwestern Illinois College, A
Trinity Christian College, B
Trinity International University, B
University of Illinois at Urbana - Champaign, BMD
University of St. Francis, B
VanderCook College of Music, BM
Wheaton College, B

Indiana

Anderson University, B
Ball State University, BMD
Bethel College, B
Butler University, B
DePauw University, B
Goshen College, B
Huntington University, B
Indiana State University, M

Indiana University Bloomington, B
Indiana University - Purdue University Fort Wayne, B
Indiana University South Bend, B
Indiana Wesleyan University, B
Manchester University, B
Marian University, B
Saint Mary's College, B
Taylor University, B
University of Evansville, B
University of Indianapolis, B
Valparaiso University, B
Vincennes University, A

Iowa

Buena Vista University, B
Central College, B
Clarke University, B
Coe College, B
Cornell College, B
Dordt College, B
Drake University, B
Emmaus Bible College, B
Faith Baptist Bible College and Theological Seminary, B
Graceland University, B
Grand View University, B
Iowa Lakes Community College, A
Iowa State University of Science and Technology, B
Loras College, B
Morningside College, B
Mount Mercy University, B
Northwestern College, B
St. Ambrose University, B
Simpson College, B
The University of Iowa, BMD
University of Northern Iowa, BM
Waldorf College, B
Wartburg College, B

Kansas

Baker University, B
Benedictine College, B
Bethany College, B
Central Christian College of Kansas, AB
Dodge City Community College, A
Emporia State University, B
Fort Hays State University, B
Friends University, B
Kansas State University, B
Kansas Wesleyan University, B
MidAmerica Nazarene University, B
Pittsburg State University, BM
Southwestern College, B
Sterling College, B
Tabor College, B
The University of Kansas, BMD
Washburn University, B
Wichita State University, BM

Kentucky

Asbury University, B
Berea College, B
Campbellsville University, BM
Eastern Kentucky University, BM
Kentucky Wesleyan College, B
Morehead State University, M
Murray State University, M
Northern Kentucky University, B
Transylvania University, B
Union College, M
University of the Cumberlands, B
University of Kentucky, BMD
University of Louisville, BM
Western Kentucky University, M

Louisiana

Louisiana College, B
Louisiana State University and Agricultural & Mechanical College, BD
Louisiana Tech University, B
Loyola University New Orleans, B
McNeese State University, O
Nicholls State University, B
Northwestern State University of Louisiana, B

Southern University and Agricultural and Mechanical College, B
University of Louisiana at Lafayette, M
University of Louisiana at Monroe, M
Xavier University of Louisiana, B

Maine

University of Maine, B
University of Southern Maine, BM

Maryland

Loyola University Maryland, M
Peabody Conservatory of The Johns Hopkins University, B
Towson University, BMO
University of Maryland, Baltimore County, M
University of Maryland, College Park, BMD
University of Maryland Eastern Shore, B
Washington Adventist University, B

Massachusetts

Anna Maria College, B
Berklee College of Music, B
Boston University, BMD
Bridgewater State University, B
Eastern Nazarene College, B
Gordon College, BM
University of Massachusetts Amherst, MD
University of Massachusetts Lowell, M

Michigan

Adrian College, B
Albion College, B
Alma College, B
Andrews University, B
Aquinas College, B
Calvin College, B
Central Michigan University, M
Concordia University Ann Arbor, B
Cornerstone University, B
Eastern Michigan University, B
Grand Rapids Community College, A
Grand Valley State University, B
Hope College, B
Madonna University, B
Michigan State University, BM
Northern Michigan University, B
Oakland University, BD
Olivet College, B
Saginaw Valley State University, B
Spring Arbor University, B
University of Michigan, BMDO
University of Michigan - Flint, B
Western Michigan University, BM

Minnesota

Augsburg College, B
Bemidji State University, B
Bethel University, B
Concordia College, B
Concordia University, St. Paul, B
Crown College, B
Gustavus Adolphus College, B
Minnesota State University Mankato, B
Minnesota State University Moorhead, B
St. Catherine University, B
St. Cloud State University, BM
Saint Mary's University of Minnesota, B
St. Olaf College, B
Southwest Minnesota State University, B
University of Minnesota, Duluth, BM
University of Minnesota, Twin Cities Campus, B
University of Northwestern - St. Paul, B
University of St. Thomas, BM
Winona State University, B

Mississippi

Blue Mountain College, B
Copiah-Lincoln Community College, A
Delta State University, B
East Mississippi Community College, A
Itawamba Community College, A
Jackson State University, BM
Jones County Junior College, A
Mississippi College, BM

Mississippi Delta Community College, A
Mississippi State University, B
Mississippi Valley State University, B
Northeast Mississippi Community College, A
Northwest Mississippi Community College, A
Southwest Mississippi Community College, A
University of Southern Mississippi, BMD
William Carey University, B

Missouri

Baptist Bible College, B
Calvary Bible College and Theological Seminary, B
Central Methodist University, BM
College of the Ozarks, B
Culver-Stockton College, B
Evangel University, BM
Hannibal-LaGrange University, B
Lincoln University, B
Lindenwood University, B
Missouri Baptist University, B
Missouri State University, B
Missouri Western State University, B
Northwest Missouri State University, BM
Southeast Missouri State University, B
Southwest Baptist University, B
University of Central Missouri, B
University of Missouri, BMDO
University of Missouri - Kansas City, BMD
University of Missouri - St. Louis, M
Webster University, BM
William Jewell College, B

Montana

Montana State University, B
Montana State University Billings, B
Rocky Mountain College, B
University of Montana, B
The University of Montana Western, B

Nebraska

Chadron State College, B
Concordia University, Nebraska, B
Grace University, B
Hastings College, B
Midland University, B
Nebraska Wesleyan University, B
Northeast Community College, A
Peru State College, B
Union College, B
University of Nebraska at Kearney, M
University of Nebraska - Lincoln, BMD
University of Nebraska at Omaha, B
Wayne State College, BM
Western Nebraska Community College, A
York College, B

Nevada

University of Nevada, Reno, B

New Hampshire

Keene State College, B
Plymouth State University, BM
Southern New Hampshire University, B

New Jersey

The College of New Jersey, B
Kean University, B
Montclair State University, M
New Jersey City University, BM
Rider University, BM
Rowan University, B
Rutgers University - New Brunswick, BMD

New Mexico

New Mexico State University, BM
University of New Mexico, BM
Western New Mexico University, B

New York

Adelphi University, B
Brooklyn College of the City University of New York, BM
Buffalo State College, State University of New York, B
City College of the City University of New York, B

The College of Saint Rose, BMO
Five Towns College, BMD
Hartwick College, B
Hofstra University, B
Houghton College, B
Hunter College of the City University of New York, M
Ithaca College, BM
Lehman College of the City University of New York, M
Long Island University - LIU Brooklyn, B
Long Island University - LIU Post, BM
Manhattanville College, BM
Molloy College, B
Nazareth College of Rochester, BM
New York University, BMDO
Nyack College, B
Queens College of the City University of New York, BMO
Roberts Wesleyan College, B
State University of New York College at Potsdam, BM
State University of New York at Fredonia, BM
Syracuse University, BM
University at Buffalo, the State University of New York, MO
University of Rochester, BMD

North Carolina

Appalachian State University, BM
Brevard College, B
Campbell University, B
Catawba College, B
Chowan University, B
East Carolina University, BMO
Elon University, B
Fayetteville State University, B
Gardner-Webb University, B
Greensboro College, B
Lenoir-Rhyne University, B
Livingstone College, B
Mars Hill University, B
Meredith College, B
Methodist University, B
North Carolina Agricultural and Technical State University, B
Pfeiffer University, B
Piedmont International University, B
Sandhills Community College, A
The University of North Carolina at Chapel Hill, M
The University of North Carolina at Charlotte, M
The University of North Carolina at Greensboro, BMD
The University of North Carolina at Pembroke, BM
The University of North Carolina Wilmington, B
Western Carolina University, B
Wingate University, B
Winston-Salem State University, B

North Dakota

Dickinson State University, B
Minot State University, B
North Dakota State University, BM
University of Jamestown, B
University of Mary, B
University of North Dakota, BMD
Valley City State University, B

Ohio

Ashland University, B
Baldwin Wallace University, B
Bluffton University, B
Bowling Green State University, BM
Capital University, BM
Case Western Reserve University, BMD
Cedarville University, B
Central State University, B
Cleveland State University, M
The College of Wooster, B
God's Bible School and College, B
Heidelberg University, BM
Kent State University, BMD
Malone University, B
Marietta College, B
Miami University, BM
Miami University Hamilton, B

Mount Vernon Nazarene University, B
Muskingum University, B
Oberlin College, BM
Ohio Christian University, B
Ohio Northern University, B
The Ohio State University, B
Ohio University, M
Ohio Wesleyan University, B
Otterbein University, B
The University of Akron, BM
University of Cincinnati, BM
University of Dayton, BM
University of Mount Union, B
University of Rio Grande, B
The University of Toledo, MO
Wilmington College, B
Wright State University, ABM
Xavier University, B
Youngstown State University, BM

Oklahoma

Cameron University, B
East Central University, B
Langston University, B
Mid-America Christian University, B
Northeastern State University, B
Northwestern Oklahoma State University, B
Oklahoma Baptist University, B
Oklahoma Christian University, B
Oklahoma State University, BM
Oklahoma Wesleyan University, B
Oral Roberts University, B
Southeastern Oklahoma State University, B
Southern Nazarene University, B
Southwestern Oklahoma State University, BM
University of Central Oklahoma, B
University of Oklahoma, BD
The University of Tulsa, B

Oregon

Corban University, B
George Fox University, B
Oregon State University, M
Pacific University, B
Portland State University, M
Umpqua Community College, A
University of Oregon, BMD
Warner Pacific College, B

Pennsylvania

Arcadia University, M
Bucknell University, B
Carnegie Mellon University, M
Chestnut Hill College, B
Clarion University of Pennsylvania, B
Duquesne University, BM
Geneva College, B
Gettysburg College, B
Grove City College, B
Immaculata University, B
Indiana University of Pennsylvania, M
Kutztown University of Pennsylvania, B
Lancaster Bible College, B
Lebanon Valley College, BM
Lincoln University, B
Mansfield University of Pennsylvania, B
Marywood University, BM
Mercyhurst University, B
Messiah College, B
Penn State University Park, BMO
Seton Hill University, B
Summit University, B
Susquehanna University, B
Temple University, BMD
The University of the Arts, M
University of Valley Forge, B
West Chester University of Pennsylvania, MO
Westminster College, B
York College of Pennsylvania, B

Rhode Island

Providence College, B
Rhode Island College, BM
Salve Regina University, B
University of Rhode Island, M

South Carolina

Anderson University, B
Benedict College, B
Bob Jones University, BM
Charleston Southern University, B
Claflin University, B
Coker College, B
College of Charleston, M
Columbia College, B
Converse College, BM
Furman University, B
Limestone College, B
Newberry College, B
North Greenville University, B
Presbyterian College, B
South Carolina State University, B
Southern Wesleyan University, B
University of South Carolina, BMD
University of South Carolina Aiken, B
Winthrop University, BM

South Dakota

Augustana University, B
Dakota Wesleyan University, B
Mount Marty College, B
Northern State University, BM
South Dakota State University, B
University of Sioux Falls, B
The University of South Dakota, BM

Tennessee

Austin Peay State University, M
Belmont University, BM
Bethel University, B
Bryan College, B
Carson-Newman University, B
Cumberland University, B
Fisk University, B
King University, B
Lee University, BM
Lipscomb University, B
Maryville College, B
Milligan College, B
Roane State Community College, A
Southern Adventist University, B
Tennessee State University, M
Tennessee Technological University, BM
Trevecca Nazarene University, B
Union University, B
University of Memphis, MD
The University of Tennessee, M
The University of Tennessee at Chattanooga, BM
The University of Tennessee at Martin, B
Vanderbilt University, B
Welch College, B

Texas

Abilene Christian University, B
Amarillo College, A
Arlington Baptist College, B
Baylor University, B
Dallas Baptist University, B
Del Mar College, A
East Texas Baptist University, B
Hardin-Simmons University, BM
Houston Baptist University, B
Howard College, A
Howard Payne University, B
Jarvis Christian College, B
Lubbock Christian University, B
Midwestern State University, B
Sam Houston State University, B
Schreiner University, B
Southern Methodist University, BM
Southwestern Assemblies of God University, B
Tarleton State University, BM
Texas A&M University - Kingsville, M
Texas Christian University, BMD
Texas Lutheran University, B
Texas State University, M
Texas Tech University, M
Texas Wesleyan University, B
Trinity University, B
University of Houston, D
University of the Incarnate Word, B

University of Mary Hardin-Baylor, B
University of North Texas, MD
University of St. Thomas, B
The University of Texas at Arlington, M
The University of Texas at Austin, MD
The University of Texas at El Paso, M
The University of Texas Rio Grande Valley, M
Wayland Baptist University, B
Wiley College, B

Utah

Brigham Young University, M
Dixie State University, B
Snow College, A
Southern Utah University, B
University of Utah, MD
Utah State University, B
Utah Valley University, B
Weber State University, B

Vermont

Castleton University, B
Johnson State College, B
University of Vermont, B

Virginia

Bluefield College, B
Emory & Henry College, B
George Mason University, MD
Hampton University, BM
James Madison University, M
Liberty University, M
Lynchburg College, B
Norfolk State University, M
Old Dominion University, M
Radford University, M
Shenandoah University, BD
Virginia Commonwealth University, M

Washington

Central Washington University, B
Eastern Washington University, BM
Gonzaga University, B
Northwest University, B
Pacific Lutheran University, B
University of Puget Sound, B
University of Washington, BMD
Walla Walla University, B
Washington State University, B
Wenatchee Valley College, A
Western Washington University, B
Whitworth University, B

West Virginia

Alderson Broaddus University, B
Concord University, B
Davis & Elkins College, B
Fairmont State University, B
Glenville State College, B
West Liberty University, B
West Virginia University, MD
West Virginia Wesleyan College, B

Wisconsin

Alverno College, B
Beloit College, B
Carroll University, B
Carthage College, B
Concordia University Wisconsin, B
Edgewood College, B
Lakeland College, B
Lawrence University, B
Maranatha Baptist University, B
Ripon College, B
St. Norbert College, B
Silver Lake College of the Holy Family, BM
University of Wisconsin - Green Bay, B
University of Wisconsin - Madison, BMD
University of Wisconsin - Milwaukee, BM
University of Wisconsin - Oshkosh, B
University of Wisconsin - River Falls, B
University of Wisconsin - Stevens Point, BM
University of Wisconsin - Superior, B
Viterbo University, B

Wyoming

Casper College, A
Eastern Wyoming College, A
University of Wyoming, BM

U.S. Territories: Puerto Rico

Conservatorio de Musica de Puerto Rico, BM
Inter American University of Puerto Rico, Metropolitan Campus, M
Inter American University of Puerto Rico, San Germán Campus, BM
Pontifical Catholic University of Puerto Rico, B

U.S. Territories: United States Virgin Islands

University of the Virgin Islands, B

Canada

Alberta

University of Alberta, B
University of Lethbridge, B

British Columbia

The University of British Columbia, BM
University of Victoria, BMD

Manitoba

Brandon University, BM

Maritime Provinces: New Brunswick

Université de Moncton, B
University of New Brunswick Fredericton, B

Maritime Provinces: Nova Scotia

Acadia University, B

Maritime Provinces: Prince Edward Island

University of Prince Edward Island, B

Newfoundland and Labrador

Memorial University of Newfoundland, B

Ontario

Brock University, B
McMaster University, B
University of Ottawa, O
University of Toronto, BMD
University of Windsor, B
York University, B

Quebec

Bishop's University, B
McGill University, MD
Université Laval, BMD
Université du Québec à Montréal, B

Saskatchewan

University of Regina, B
University of Saskatchewan, B

MUSIC THEORY AND COMPOSITION

United States

Alabama

Birmingham-Southern College, B
Samford University, B
The University of Alabama, M

Arizona

Arizona State University at the Tempe campus, B
Northern Arizona University, M
The University of Arizona, MD

Arkansas

Ouachita Baptist University, B
University of Central Arkansas, M

California

Biola University, B
California Baptist University, B
California Institute of the Arts, B
California State University, Fullerton, M
California State University, Long Beach, B
Chapman University, B
Ohlone College, A
Pepperdine University, B
Point Loma Nazarene University, B
San Diego State University, M
San Francisco Conservatory of Music, B
Stanford University, D
University of California, Santa Barbara, BMD
University of the Pacific, B
University of Redlands, B
University of Southern California, B

Colorado

Adams State University, B
Colorado State University, B
University of Colorado Boulder, M
University of Denver, B
University of Northern Colorado, MD

Connecticut

University of Connecticut, MD
University of Hartford, M
Western Connecticut State University, B
Yale University, M

Delaware

University of Delaware, B

District of Columbia

The Catholic University of America, B

Florida

Florida State University, BMD
Full Sail University, B
Jacksonville University, B
Lynn University, B
Palm Beach Atlantic University, B
South Florida State College, A
State College of Florida Manatee-Sarasota, A
Stetson University, B
University of Florida, M
University of Miami, BMD
University of South Florida, M

Georgia

Georgia Southern University, B
University of Georgia, B
University of West Georgia, B

Idaho

Boise State University, B
Northwest Nazarene University, B
University of Idaho, B

Illinois

Augustana College, B
Bradley University, B
Columbia College Chicago, B
Concordia University Chicago, B
DePaul University, B
Illinois Wesleyan University, B
Northwestern University, BMD
Olivet Nazarene University, B
Roosevelt University, B
Trinity International University, B
University of Illinois at Urbana - Champaign, B
Wheaton College, B

Indiana

Anderson University, B
Butler University, B
DePauw University, B
Indiana Wesleyan University, B
Manchester University, B
Taylor University, B
Valparaiso University, B

Iowa

Coe College, B
The University of Iowa, B
University of Northern Iowa, B
Wartburg College, B

Kansas

Pittsburg State University, M
The University of Kansas, B

Kentucky

Eastern Kentucky University, M
University of Kentucky, MD
University of Louisville, M

Louisiana

Loyola University New Orleans, B
Tulane University, B

Maryland

University of Maryland, Baltimore County, B

Massachusetts

Berklee College of Music, B
Boston University, BMD
Brandeis University, MD
Eastern Nazarene College, B
Harvard University, MD
New England Conservatory of Music, B
Tufts University, BM
University of Massachusetts Amherst, D

Michigan

Calvin College, B
Central Michigan University, B
Hope College, B
Madonna University, B
Michigan State University, BM
Oakland Community College, A
University of Michigan, BD
Wayne State University, M
Western Michigan University, B

Minnesota

Concordia College, B
McNally Smith College of Music, B
Minnesota State University Moorhead, B
Rochester Community and Technical College, A
St. Cloud State University, B
St. Olaf College, B
University of Minnesota, Duluth, B
University of Northwestern - St. Paul, B

Mississippi

Mississippi College, B
University of Southern Mississippi, M

Missouri

University of Central Missouri, B
University of Missouri - Kansas City, BM
Washington University in St. Louis, B
Webster University, B
William Jewell College, B

Nebraska

Grace University, B
University of Nebraska - Lincoln, M
University of Nebraska at Omaha, B

New Hampshire

Keene State College, B

New Jersey

Montclair State University, M
Rider University, B
Rowan University, B

New Mexico

University of New Mexico, M

New York

Brooklyn College of the City University of New York, B

City College of the City University of New York, B
Cornell University, M
Hofstra University, B
Houghton College, B
Ithaca College, B
Long Island University - LIU Post, M
The New School College of Performing Arts, B
New York University, MDO
Nyack College, B
State University of New York College at Potsdam, B
Stony Brook University, State University of New York, MD
Syracuse University, B
University at Buffalo, the State University of New York, MD
University of Rochester, BMD

North Carolina

Campbell University, B
East Carolina University, M
Gardner-Webb University, B
The University of North Carolina at Greensboro, BM

Ohio

Baldwin Wallace University, B
Bowling Green State University, BM
Capital University, B
Cedarville University, B
Cleveland Institute of Music, B
The College of Wooster, B
Kent State University, MD
Oberlin College, B
Ohio Northern University, B
The Ohio State University, B
Ohio University, BM
The University of Akron, BM
University of Cincinnati, BMD
University of Dayton, B
Youngstown State University, BM

Oklahoma

Oklahoma Baptist University, B
Oklahoma City University, B
Oral Roberts University, B
University of Oklahoma, M
The University of Tulsa, B

Oregon

Lewis & Clark College, B
Marylhurst University, B
University of Oregon, B
Willamette University, B

Pennsylvania

Bucknell University, B
Carnegie Mellon University, B
Curtis Institute of Music, B
Penn State University Park, M
Susquehanna University, B
Temple University, BMD
The University of the Arts, B
University of Pittsburgh, MD
West Chester University of Pennsylvania, M

South Carolina

Newberry College, B
University of South Carolina, M

Tennessee

Belmont University, B
Carson-Newman University, B
Lipscomb University, B
Maryville College, B
Southern Adventist University, B
Trevecca Nazarene University, B
The University of Tennessee, M
Vanderbilt University, B

Texas

Baylor University, BM
Cedar Valley College, A
Dallas Baptist University, B
Hardin-Simmons University, BM
Houston Community College, A
Rice University, BM

Sam Houston State University, B
Southern Methodist University, BM
Texas Christian University, B
Texas State University, M
Trinity University, B
University of Houston, M
University of North Texas, BM
The University of Texas at Austin, BMD
West Texas A&M University, B

Vermont

Bennington College, B
Marlboro College, B

Virginia

Liberty University, B
Norfolk State University, M
Randolph College, B
Shenandoah University, B

Washington

Central Washington University, B
DigiPen Institute of Technology, B
Northwest University, B
University of Washington, B
Washington State University, B
Western Washington University, B
Whitman College, B

West Virginia

West Virginia University, M

Wisconsin

Lawrence University, B
University of Wisconsin - Madison, MD

Canada

British Columbia

The University of British Columbia, B
University of Victoria, B

Manitoba

Brandon University, B

Maritime Provinces: Nova Scotia

Dalhousie University, B

Newfoundland and Labrador

Memorial University of Newfoundland, B

Ontario

The University of Western Ontario, B
University of Windsor, B
York University, B

Quebec

Concordia University, B
McGill University, BMD
Université de Montréal, B

Saskatchewan

University of Regina, BM

MUSIC THERAPY/THERAPIST

United States

Arizona

Arizona State University at the Tempe campus, BM

California

University of the Pacific, BM

Colorado

Colorado State University, B

Florida

Florida State University, BM
South Florida State College, A
University of Miami, BMDO

Georgia

Georgia College & State University, BM
University of Georgia, B

Indiana

Indiana University - Purdue University Fort Wayne, B
Indiana University - Purdue University Indianapolis, M
Saint Mary-of-the-Woods College, BM
University of Evansville, B

Iowa

The University of Iowa, B
Wartburg College, B

Kansas

The University of Kansas, BM

Kentucky

University of Kentucky, M
University of Louisville, B

Louisiana

Loyola University New Orleans, BM

Massachusetts

Anna Maria College, B
Berklee College of Music, B

Michigan

Eastern Michigan University, B
Michigan State University, M
Western Michigan University, BM

Minnesota

Augsburg College, B
University of Minnesota, Twin Cities Campus, B

Mississippi

William Carey University, B

Missouri

Drury University, B
Maryville University of Saint Louis, BM
University of Missouri - Kansas City, BM

New Jersey

Montclair State University, BMO

New York

Molloy College, BM
Nazareth College of Rochester, BM
New York University, M
State University of New York at Fredonia, B
State University of New York at New Paltz, M

North Carolina

Appalachian State University, BM
East Carolina University, M
Queens University of Charlotte, B

North Dakota

University of North Dakota, B

Ohio

Baldwin Wallace University, B
The College of Wooster, B
Ohio University, M
University of Dayton, B

Oregon

Marylhurst University, B
Willamette University, B

Pennsylvania

Drexel University, MO
Duquesne University, B
Elizabethtown College, B
Immaculata University, BM
Marywood University, B
Mercyhurst University, B
Seton Hill University, B

Slippery Rock University of Pennsylvania, B
Temple University, BMD

South Carolina

Charleston Southern University, B
Converse College, B

Texas

Sam Houston State University, B
Southern Methodist University, B
University of the Incarnate Word, B
West Texas A&M University, B

Utah

Utah State University, B

Virginia

Radford University, M
Shenandoah University, B

Washington

Seattle Pacific University, B

Wisconsin

Alverno College, B
Concordia University Wisconsin, B
Edgewood College, B
University of Wisconsin - Oshkosh, B

Canada

British Columbia

Thompson Rivers University, B

Ontario

Wilfrid Laurier University, BM

Quebec

Université du Québec à Montréal, B

MUSICAL INSTRUMENT FABRICATION AND REPAIR

United States

Delaware

Delaware State University, B

Indiana

Indiana University Bloomington, A

Iowa

Western Iowa Tech Community College, A

New York

Queensborough Community College of the City University of New York, A

Washington

Renton Technical College, A

MUSICOLOGY AND ETHNOMUSICOLOGY

United States

Alabama

The University of Alabama, M

Arizona

Northern Arizona University, M
The University of Arizona, M

California

California State University, Los Angeles, M
San Diego State University, M
Stanford University, D
University of California, Davis, D

University of California, Los Angeles, BMD
University of California, Riverside, D
University of California, Santa Barbara, MD
University of Southern California, D

Colorado

University of Colorado Boulder, D
University of Denver, B

Connecticut

University of Connecticut, M

Florida

Florida State University, MD
University of Miami, M

Georgia

Georgia Institute of Technology, MD

Illinois

Northwestern University, BD
University of Illinois at Urbana - Champaign, D

Kansas

The University of Kansas, B

Kentucky

University of Kentucky, MD

Massachusetts

Brandeis University, MD
Harvard University, MD
Tufts University, B

Michigan

Michigan State University, M
University of Michigan, MD

Missouri

University of Missouri - Kansas City, M

New Hampshire

University of New Hampshire, M

New Jersey

Princeton University, D

New York

Brooklyn College of the City University of New York, M
Cornell University, D
University at Buffalo, the State University of New York, D
University of Rochester, D

North Carolina

Duke University, D

Ohio

Bowling Green State University, B
Case Western Reserve University, D
University of Cincinnati, D

Oklahoma

University of Oklahoma, M

Pennsylvania

Temple University, MD
University of Pittsburgh, MD

Rhode Island

Brown University, B
Roger Williams University, B

South Carolina

Converse College, B

Tennessee

East Tennessee State University, B
University of Memphis, MD
The University of Tennessee, M

Texas

Rice University, M
University of North Texas, M
The University of Texas at Austin, MD

Utah

Brigham Young University, M
University of Utah, M

Vermont

Bennington College, B
Marlboro College, B

Virginia

Liberty University, B

Washington

University of Washington, B

Wisconsin

University of Wisconsin - Madison, D

Canada

British Columbia

University of Victoria, MD

Maritime Provinces: Nova Scotia

Dalhousie University, M

Ontario

York University, BM

Quebec

McGill University, MD
Université Laval, MD
Université de Montréal, B

Saskatchewan

University of Regina, M

NAIL TECHNICIAN/SPECIALIST AND MANICURIST

United States

Colorado

IBMC College (Fort Collins), A

Illinois

Lincoln College - Normal, A

NANOTECHNOLOGY

United States

Arizona

Arizona State University at the Tempe campus, M

California

University of California, Riverside, MD
University of California, San Diego, MD

Maryland

Johns Hopkins University, M

New Mexico

University of New Mexico, MD

New York

Cornell University, MD
State University of New York Polytechnic Institute, MD

North Dakota

North Dakota State University, MD

Pennsylvania

Carnegie Mellon University, D
Indiana University of Pennsylvania, M

South Dakota

South Dakota School of Mines and Technology, D

Virginia

The College of William and Mary, D
Virginia Commonwealth University, D

Washington

University of Washington, D

Canada

Alberta

University of Alberta, MD

NATIONAL SECURITY

United States

Alabama

Troy University, M

California

California State University, San Bernardino, M
Henley-Putnam University, D

Connecticut

University of New Haven, MO

District of Columbia

The George Washington University, M
Trinity Washington University, M

Florida

University of Central Florida, D

Kansas

Kansas State University, MD

Massachusetts

Hult International Business School, M

Nebraska

Bellevue University, M

New Jersey

New Jersey City University, MD

New York

New York University, M

Pennsylvania

Drexel University, M
La Salle University, O

Texas

Angelo State University, M
Texas A&M University, O

Virginia

George Mason University, MD
Virginia Polytechnic Institute and State University, O

West Virginia

American Public University System, M

NATURAL RESOURCE ECONOMICS

United States

Michigan

Michigan State University, B

New Hampshire

University of New Hampshire, B

New Mexico

New Mexico State University, B

Ohio

Baldwin Wallace University, B
Malone University, B

Pennsylvania

Juniata College, B

Rhode Island

University of Rhode Island, B

Tennessee

The University of Tennessee, B

Canada

Ontario

University of Guelph, B

Saskatchewan

University of Saskatchewan, B

NATURAL RESOURCES AND CONSERVATION

United States

Alabama

Auburn University, M

Alaska

University of Alaska Fairbanks, BMD
University of Alaska Southeast, B

Arizona

Prescott College, B
The University of Arizona, BMD

Arkansas

University of Arkansas at Monticello, M

California

California Polytechnic State University, San Luis
  Obispo, B
College of the Desert, A
Columbia College, A
Feather River College, A
Humboldt State University, BM
Santa Rosa Junior College, A
University of California, Berkeley, B
University of California, Davis, B

Colorado

Colorado Mountain College (Leadville), A
Colorado Northwestern Community College, A
Colorado State University, B

Connecticut

University of Connecticut, BMD

Delaware

Delaware State University, M
University of Delaware, M

District of Columbia

American University, M

Florida

Everglades University (Boca Raton), B
Everglades University (Maitland), B
Everglades University (Sarasota), B
Florida Gateway College, A
University of Florida, MD

Georgia

University of Georgia, MD

Hawaii

University of Hawaii at Manoa, MD

Idaho

University of Idaho, MD

Illinois

University of Illinois at Urbana - Champaign, BMD

Indiana

Ball State University, BMD
Manchester University, B
Purdue University, BMD
Vincennes University, A

Iowa

Ellsworth Community College, A
Iowa Lakes Community College, A
Iowa State University of Science and Technology,
  MD
Kirkwood Community College, A
Mount Mercy University, B
Muscatine Community College, A
Upper Iowa University, B

Kansas

Haskell Indian Nations University, A

Kentucky

University of Kentucky, B

Louisiana

Louisiana State University and Agricultural & Me-
  chanical College, MD
Louisiana Tech University, B
University of Louisiana at Lafayette, B

Maine

University of Maine, MD

Maryland

Towson University, B
University of Maryland, College Park, BMD
University of Maryland University College, B

Massachusetts

University of Massachusetts Amherst, B

Michigan

Central Michigan University, B
Grand Valley State University, B
Northern Michigan University, B
University of Michigan, B

Minnesota

Central Lakes College, A
Gustavus Adolphus College, B
Itasca Community College, A
University of Minnesota, Crookston, B
Vermilion Community College, A

Mississippi

Mississippi State University, B

Missouri

University of Missouri, BM
Washington University in St. Louis, B

Montana

Montana State University, BM
University of Montana, BM

Nebraska

Nebraska Indian Community College, A
Peru State College, B
University of Nebraska - Lincoln, BMD

Nevada

Truckee Meadows Community College, A
University of Nevada, Reno, B

New Hampshire

University of New Hampshire, BD

New Jersey

Rutgers University - New Brunswick, B

New Mexico

Southwestern Indian Polytechnic Institute, A
University of New Mexico, MD

New York

Cornell University, BMD
Finger Lakes Community College, A
Fulton-Montgomery Community College, A
Morrisville State College, AB
Niagara County Community College, A
State University of New York College of Environ-
  mental Science and Forestry, ABMD
State University of New York College of Technology
  at Canton, B
State University of New York at Plattsburgh, B
Ulster County Community College, A

North Carolina

Duke University, MD
North Carolina State University, BM

North Dakota

Dakota College at Bottineau, A

Ohio

Bowling Green State University, B
Hocking College, A
Kent State University, B
Muskingum University, B
The Ohio State University, BMD

Oklahoma

Murray State College, A
Northeastern State University, M
Oklahoma State University, MD
Southeastern Oklahoma State University, B

Oregon

Central Oregon Community College, A
Oregon State University, M
Treasure Valley Community College, A

Pennsylvania

Penn State Abington, B
Penn State Altoona, B
Penn State Beaver, B
Penn State Berks, B
Penn State Brandywine, B
Penn State DuBois, B
Penn State Erie, The Behrend College, B
Penn State Fayette, The Eberly Campus, B
Penn State Greater Allegheny, B
Penn State Hazleton, B
Penn State Lehigh Valley, B
Penn State Mont Alto, B
Penn State New Kensington, B
Penn State Schuylkill, B
Penn State Shenango, B
Penn State University Park, B
Penn State Wilkes-Barre, B
Penn State Worthington Scranton, B
Penn State York, B

Rhode Island

University of Rhode Island, MD

South Carolina

Clemson University, B

Tennessee

Sewanee: The University of the South, B
Tusculum College, B

Texas

Lubbock Christian University, B
St. Philip's College, A
Texas A&M University, BM
Texas Tech University, B

Utah

Snow College, A
Utah State University, BM

Vermont

Green Mountain College, B
Marlboro College, B
Sterling College, B
University of Vermont, BMD

Virginia

Mountain Empire Community College, A
Virginia Polytechnic Institute and State University, MO

Washington

The Evergreen State College, B
Grays Harbor College, A
Heritage University, A
University of Washington, MD
Walla Walla Community College, A
Washington State University, BMD

Wisconsin

Carroll University, B
College of Menominee Nation, A
Fox Valley Technical College, A
Northland College, B
University of Wisconsin - Platteville, B
University of Wisconsin - River Falls, B
University of Wisconsin - Stevens Point, BM

Wyoming

University of Wyoming, MD

U.S. Territories: American Samoa

American Samoa Community College, A

Canada

Alberta

University of Alberta, BMD

British Columbia

The University of British Columbia, B
University of Northern British Columbia, MD

Maritime Provinces: Nova Scotia

Dalhousie University, M

Ontario

Lakehead University, B
University of Guelph, MD

Quebec

McGill University, MD
Université du Québec à Montréal, O

NATURAL RESOURCES CONSERVATION AND RESEARCH

United States

California

Stanford University, B

Illinois

University of Illinois at Urbana - Champaign, B

Maine

Colby College, B

Massachusetts

Greenfield Community College, A

Michigan

University of Michigan - Flint, B

Nevada

Sierra Nevada College, B

New York

State University of New York College of Agriculture and Technology at Cobleskill, B

Ohio

Miami University, B

Washington

Walla Walla Community College, A

Wisconsin

Northland College, B

NATURAL RESOURCES MANAGEMENT/DEVELOPMENT AND POLICY

United States

Alabama

Auburn University, B
Tuskegee University, B

Alaska

Alaska Pacific University, B
University of Alaska Fairbanks, AM

California

American River College, A
Butte College, A
California Polytechnic State University, San Luis Obispo, M
Cerro Coso Community College, A
Dominican University of California, B
Humboldt State University, B
Reedley College, A
Sacramento City College, A
San Joaquin Delta College, A
Shasta College, A
University of California, Berkeley, BMD
University of La Verne, B
University of San Francisco, M
Ventura College, A

Colorado

Colorado State University, BM
Pikes Peak Community College, A
Trinidad State Junior College, A

Connecticut

University of Connecticut, MD

Delaware

Delaware State University, B
University of Delaware, B

Florida

Everglades University (Boca Raton), B
Everglades University (Maitland), B
Everglades University (Sarasota), B
Pensacola State College, A
St. Petersburg College, B
University of Miami, B

Hawaii

University of Hawaii at Manoa, B

Illinois

College of Lake County, A
University of Illinois at Urbana - Champaign, B

Iowa

Hawkeye Community College, A
Iowa State University of Science and Technology, B

Kansas

Fort Hays State University, B
Hutchinson Community College, A
Kansas State University, B
Tabor College, B

Louisiana

Louisiana State University and Agricultural & Mechanical College, B

Massachusetts

Clark University, B

Michigan

Lake Superior State University, A
Michigan State University, MD
Michigan Technological University, B
University of Michigan, MD

Minnesota

Itasca Community College, A
University of Minnesota, Crookston, B
University of Minnesota, Twin Cities Campus, MD
Vermilion Community College, A

Missouri

Washington University in St. Louis, B

Montana

Aaniiih Nakoda College, A
Blackfeet Community College, A
Rocky Mountain College, B
Salish Kootenai College, A
University of Montana, B

Nebraska

University of Nebraska - Lincoln, BM

Nevada

Great Basin College, AB
University of Nevada, Reno, B

New Hampshire

University of New Hampshire, M

New Jersey

Rutgers University - New Brunswick, B

New Mexico

New Mexico Highlands University, BM

New York

Finger Lakes Community College, A
Marist College, B
Morrisville State College, AB
Paul Smith's College, B
Rochester Institute of Technology, B
State University of New York College of Environmental Science and Forestry, BMD
State University of New York College of Technology at Delhi, A

North Carolina

North Carolina State University, BM
Western Carolina University, B

North Dakota

Cankdeska Cikana Community College, A
North Dakota State University, BMD

Ohio

Bowling Green State University, B
Hocking College, A
Marietta College, B
The Ohio State University, B
The Ohio State University Agricultural Technical Institute, A
Xavier University, B
Zane State College, A

Oklahoma

Bacone College, A
Eastern Oklahoma State College, A

Oregon

Oregon State University, B
Oregon State University - Cascades, B

Pennsylvania

Keystone College, B

Rhode Island

Bryant University, B
University of Rhode Island, BMD

South Carolina

Central Carolina Technical College, A

South Dakota

Oglala Lakota College, A
Sinte Gleska University, A
South Dakota State University, B

Tennessee

The University of Tennessee at Martin, B

Texas

Angelo State University, B
Sul Ross State University, M
Texas A&M University, MD
Texas Tech University, MD
The University of Texas at Austin, M

Vermont

Johnson State College, B
Sterling College, B
University of Vermont, MD

Washington

Central Washington University, M
Spokane Community College, A
University of Washington, MD

West Virginia

Alderson Broaddus University, B
Glenville State College, B
West Virginia University, D

Wisconsin

Lac Courte Oreilles Ojibwa Community College, A
University of Wisconsin - Madison, MD
University of Wisconsin - Stevens Point, B

Wyoming

Northwest College, A

U.S. Territories: Puerto Rico

Universidad Metropolitana, M

Canada

British Columbia

Royal Roads University, B
The University of British Columbia, BMD

Manitoba

University of Manitoba, MD

Maritime Provinces: New Brunswick

University of New Brunswick Saint John, M

Ontario

Laurentian University, D
University of Guelph, AB
The University of Western Ontario, B

Quebec

Université du Québec en Abitibi-Témiscamingue, M

Saskatchewan

University of Saskatchewan, B

NATURAL SCIENCES

United States

Alabama

Athens State University, B
Oakwood University, B

Alaska

University of Alaska Anchorage, B
University of Alaska Fairbanks, A

Arizona

Harrison Middleton University, B
Paradise Valley Community College, A
Phoenix College, A

California

Azusa Pacific University, B
California State University, Dominguez Hills, B
California State University, Fresno, B
California State University, Los Angeles, B
Citrus College, A
Foothill College, A
Fresno Pacific University, AB
Golden West College, A
Humboldt State University, B
Lake Tahoe Community College, A
Lassen Community College District, A
Loyola Marymount University, B
The Master's College and Seminary, B
Merced College, A
Moorpark College, A
National University, B
Ohlone College, A
Pacific Union College, B
Pepperdine University, B
Porterville College, A
Sacramento City College, A
Saddleback College, A
San Joaquin Delta College, A
San Jose State University, B
Santa Rosa Junior College, A
Santiago Canyon College, A
United States University, B
University of La Verne, B
Victor Valley College, A

Colorado

Colorado Mountain College (Glenwood Springs), A
Colorado State University, B
Northeastern Junior College, A

Florida

Miami Dade College, A
New College of Florida, B
St. Petersburg College, A

Georgia

Shorter University, B

Hawaii

Kapiolani Community College, A
Leeward Community College, A
University of Hawaii at Hilo, B

Idaho

Lewis-Clark State College, B

Illinois

Concordia University Chicago, B
Dominican University, B
Judson University, B
Shimer College, B

Indiana

Indiana University East, B
Taylor University, B

Iowa

Central College, B
Dordt College, B
Iowa Lakes Community College, A

Kansas

Benedictine College, B
Bethel College, B
Central Christian College of Kansas, AB
Haskell Indian Nations University, A
Kansas State University, B
McPherson College, B
Tabor College, B
Washburn University, A

Louisiana

Bossier Parish Community College, A

Maine

College of the Atlantic, B

Maryland

Johns Hopkins University, B

Massachusetts

Bard College at Simon's Rock, B
Elms College, B
Lesley University, B
Quincy College, A

Michigan

Calvin College, B
Madonna University, AB
Siena Heights University, B
University of Detroit Mercy, B

Minnesota

Bemidji State University, B
College of Saint Benedict, B
The College of St. Scholastica, B
Concordia College, B
Minnesota State University Mankato, B
St. Cloud State University, B
Saint John's University, B

Missouri

Logan University, B
Park University, B
Washington University in St. Louis, B

Montana

Salish Kootenai College, A

Nebraska

College of Saint Mary, B
Concordia University, Nebraska, B
Doane University, B
Midland University, B
Peru State College, B
University of Nebraska at Omaha, B
York College, B

New Jersey

Felician University, B
Georgian Court University, B
Passaic County Community College, A
Saint Peter's University, B
Thomas Edison State University, B

New York

Colgate University, B
Daemen College, B
Fordham University, B
Hofstra University, B
Houghton College, B
Mount Saint Mary College, B
Roberts Wesleyan College, A
St. Thomas Aquinas College, B
State University of New York College at Geneseo, B
State University of New York College at Potsdam, B

Ohio

Case Western Reserve University, B
Defiance College, B
Lourdes University, A
Xavier University, B

Oklahoma

Oklahoma Baptist University, B
University of Science and Arts of Oklahoma, B

Oregon

Concordia University, B
Umpqua Community College, A
Western Oregon University, B

Pennsylvania

Arcadia University, B
Juniata College, B
Muhlenberg College, B
Saint Vincent College, B
Temple University, B
University of Pennsylvania, B
University of Pittsburgh at Greensburg, B
University of Pittsburgh at Johnstown, B
University of Pittsburgh at Titusville, A

South Dakota

Sisseton-Wahpeton College, A

Tennessee

Christian Brothers University, B

Texas

Amarillo College, A
College of the Mainland, A
Dallas Baptist University, B
Galveston College, A
Lee College, A
Tyler Junior College, A

Vermont

Castleton University, B
Marlboro College, B

Virginia

Virginia Wesleyan College, B

Washington

The Evergreen State College, B
Highline College, A
Skagit Valley College, A
University of Puget Sound, B
University of Washington, B

West Virginia

American Public University System, B

Wisconsin

Carthage College, B
Edgewood College, B
University of Wisconsin - Stevens Point, B

U.S. Territories: Puerto Rico

Bayamón Central University, B
Inter American University of Puerto Rico, San
  Germán Campus, B
Universidad del Este, A
Universidad del Turabo, B
University of Puerto Rico in Cayey, B
University of Puerto Rico, Río Piedras Campus, B
University of Puerto Rico in Utuado, AB

Canada

British Columbia

Trinity Western University, B
University of Northern British Columbia, B

Maritime Provinces: New Brunswick

Mount Allison University, B

Ontario

Lakehead University, B
Trent University, B
York University, B

Quebec

Bishop's University, B
McGill University, B

NATUROPATHIC MEDICINE/ NATUROPATHY

United States

Connecticut

University of Bridgeport, D

Washington

Bastyr University, D

U.S. Territories: Puerto Rico

Universidad del Turabo, D

NAVAL ARCHITECTURE AND MARINE ENGINEERING

United States

Connecticut

United States Coast Guard Academy, B

Louisiana

University of New Orleans, B

Maine

Maine Maritime Academy, B

Maryland

United States Naval Academy, B

Massachusetts

Massachusetts Maritime Academy, B

Michigan

University of Michigan, B

New Jersey

Stevens Institute of Technology, B

New York

State University of New York Maritime College, B
United States Merchant Marine Academy, B
Webb Institute, B

Texas

Texas A&M University, B

Canada

British Columbia

British Columbia Institute of Technology, A

Newfoundland and Labrador

Memorial University of Newfoundland, B

NAVY/MARINE CORPS JROTC/ ROTC

United States

Florida

Jacksonville University, B

Virginia

Hampton University, B

NEAR AND MIDDLE EASTERN LANGUAGES

United States

California

University of California, Los Angeles, MD

Connecticut

Yale University, MD

District of Columbia

The Catholic University of America, MD

Illinois

University of Chicago, D

Indiana

Indiana University Bloomington, MD

Massachusetts

Harvard University, MD

Michigan

University of Michigan, MD

Ohio

The Ohio State University, MD

Oklahoma

Oral Roberts University, M

Texas

The University of Texas at Austin, MD

Utah

University of Utah, MD

NEAR AND MIDDLE EASTERN STUDIES

United States

Arizona

The University of Arizona, BMD

California

California State University, Long Beach, M
Claremont McKenna College, B
Pomona College, B
Scripps College, B
University of California, Berkeley, BMD
University of California, Los Angeles, BMD
University of California, Santa Barbara, B

Connecticut

Yale University, BMD

District of Columbia

American University, B
The Catholic University of America, MD
The George Washington University, BM
Georgetown University, MO

Georgia

Emory University, B

Illinois

University of Chicago, MD
University of Illinois at Urbana - Champaign, M

Kansas

The University of Kansas, MO

Maryland

Hood College, B
Johns Hopkins University, BD
McDaniel College, B

Massachusetts

Brandeis University, BMD
Hampshire College, B
Harvard University, BMD
Mount Holyoke College, B
Smith College, B
Tufts University, B
University of Massachusetts Amherst, B
Wellesley College, B
Williams College, B

Michigan

University of Michigan, BMD
Wayne State University, M

Missouri

Washington University in St. Louis, BM

New Hampshire

Dartmouth College, B

New Jersey

Princeton University, BMD
Rutgers University - New Brunswick, B

New York

Bard College, B
Colgate University, B
Columbia University, BMDO
Columbia University, School of General Studies, B
Cornell University, BMD
Fordham University, B
New York University, BMD
Queens College of the City University of New York, B
Syracuse University, B
United States Military Academy, B

Ohio

Oberlin College, B
The University of Toledo, B

Oregon

Portland State University, B

Pennsylvania

Dickinson College, B
Swarthmore College, B
University of Pennsylvania, MD

Rhode Island

Brown University, BD

South Carolina

Columbia International University, B

Tennessee

University of Memphis, MD

Texas

Rice University, D
Texas State University, B
Trinity University, B
The University of Texas at Austin, BMD

Utah

University of Utah, BMD

Vermont

Marlboro College, B
Middlebury College, B

Virginia

Emory & Henry College, B
George Mason University, M
Liberty University, M
University of Richmond, B
University of Virginia, M

Washington

University of Washington, MD

Wisconsin

University of Wisconsin - Madison, MD

Canada

Ontario

Carleton University, B
University of Toronto, BMD
University of Waterloo, M
The University of Western Ontario, B

Quebec

McGill University, BMDO

NEUROBIOLOGY AND NEUROPHYSIOLOGY

United States

Alabama

The University of Alabama at Birmingham, D

Arkansas

University of Arkansas for Medical Sciences, D

California

California Institute of Technology, D
University of California, Irvine, MD
University of California, Los Angeles, MD
University of Southern California, D

Colorado

University of Colorado Boulder, M
University of Colorado Denver, M

Connecticut

University of Connecticut, MD
Wesleyan University, D
Yale University, D

Georgia

Georgia State University, MD

Illinois

Illinois State University, M
Loyola University Chicago, MD
Northwestern University, MD
University of Chicago, D

Indiana

Indiana University - Purdue University Indianapolis, D
Purdue University, MD

Iowa

The University of Iowa, MD

Kentucky

University of Kentucky, D
University of Louisville, MD

Louisiana

Louisiana State University Health Sciences Center, MD

Massachusetts

Boston University, MD
Brandeis University, D
Harvard University, D
Massachusetts Institute of Technology, D

Michigan

Wayne State University, D

Minnesota

University of Minnesota, Twin Cities Campus, MD

Missouri

University of Missouri, MD

New York

Columbia University, D
Cornell University, D
New York University, D
University at Albany, State University of New York, D
University of Rochester, D

North Carolina

Duke University, D
The University of North Carolina at Chapel Hill, D
Wake Forest University, D

Oklahoma

University of Oklahoma, D

Pennsylvania

Carnegie Mellon University, D

Texas

The University of Texas at Austin, D
The University of Texas at San Antonio, D

Utah

University of Utah, D

Virginia

Virginia Commonwealth University, MD

Washington

University of Washington, D

West Virginia

West Virginia University, D

Wisconsin

University of Wisconsin - Madison, D

Canada

Maritime Provinces: Nova Scotia

Dalhousie University, MD

Ontario

Queen's University at Kingston, MD

Quebec

Université Laval, MD

NEUROSCIENCE

United States

Alabama

The University of Alabama at Birmingham, D

Alaska

University of Alaska Fairbanks, D

Arizona

Argosy University, Phoenix, D
Arizona State University at the Tempe campus, D
The University of Arizona, D

California

California Institute of Technology, MD
University of California, Berkeley, D
University of California, Davis, D
University of California, Irvine, D
University of California, Los Angeles, D
University of California, Riverside, D
University of California, San Diego, D
University of California, Santa Barbara, D
University of Southern California, MD

Colorado

Colorado State University, D
University of Colorado Denver, D

Connecticut

Connecticut College, M
University of Connecticut, D
University of Hartford, M
Yale University, D

Delaware

Delaware State University, MD
University of Delaware, D

District of Columbia

Gallaudet University, D
Georgetown University, D

Florida

Argosy University, Tampa, D
Florida Atlantic University, D
Florida State University, MD
University of Florida, D
University of Miami, D
University of South Florida, MDO

Georgia

Augusta University, MD
Emory University, D
Georgia State University, D
University of Georgia, D

Idaho

University of Idaho, MD

Illinois

Argosy University, Chicago, D
Illinois State University, M
Loyola University Chicago, MD
Northwestern University, D
Rush University, MD
University of Chicago, D
University of Illinois at Chicago, MD
University of Illinois at Urbana - Champaign, D

Indiana

Indiana University Bloomington, D
Purdue University, D

Iowa

Iowa State University of Science and Technology, MD
The University of Iowa, D

Kansas

The University of Kansas, MD

Louisiana

Louisiana State University Health Sciences Center, MD
Tulane University, MD

Maryland

Johns Hopkins University, D
University of Maryland, Baltimore County, D
University of Maryland, College Park, D

Massachusetts

Boston University, D
Brandeis University, MD
Harvard University, D
Massachusetts Institute of Technology, D
Tufts University, D
University of Massachusetts Amherst, MD

Michigan

Central Michigan University, MD
Michigan State University, MD
University of Michigan, D
Wayne State University, D

Minnesota

University of Minnesota, Twin Cities Campus, MD

Mississippi

University of Mississippi Medical Center, D

Missouri

University of Missouri, MD
University of Missouri - St. Louis, MD
Washington University in St. Louis, D

Montana

Montana State University, MD
University of Montana, D

Nebraska

University of Nebraska Medical Center, D

New Hampshire

Dartmouth College, D

New Jersey

Princeton University, D
Rutgers University - New Brunswick, MD
Rutgers University - Newark, D
Seton Hall University, D

New Mexico

University of New Mexico, MD

New York

College of Staten Island of the City University of New York, M
New York University, D
State University of New York Downstate Medical Center, D
State University of New York Upstate Medical University, D
Stony Brook University, State University of New York, MD
University at Albany, State University of New York, MD
University at Buffalo, the State University of New York, MD
University of Rochester, D

North Carolina

Duke University, DO
The University of North Carolina at Chapel Hill, D
Wake Forest University, D

Ohio

Case Western Reserve University, D
Kent State University, D
The Ohio State University, D
Ohio University, MD
University of Cincinnati, D
The University of Toledo, MD

Oklahoma

University of Oklahoma Health Sciences Center, MD

Oregon

Oregon Health & Science University, D
University of Oregon, D

Pennsylvania

Carnegie Mellon University, D
Drexel University, MD
Immaculata University, O
Thomas Jefferson University, D
University of Pennsylvania, D
University of Pittsburgh, D

Rhode Island

Brown University, D

South Carolina

Medical University of South Carolina, MD

South Dakota

The University of South Dakota, MD

Texas

Texas A&M University, D
Texas Christian University, M
The University of Texas at Austin, D
The University of Texas at Dallas, MD

The University of Texas Health Science Center at Houston, MD
The University of Texas Health Science Center at San Antonio, D
The University of Texas Medical Branch, D

Utah

Brigham Young University, MD
University of Utah, D

Vermont

University of Vermont, D

Virginia

George Mason University, MD
University of Virginia, D
Virginia Commonwealth University, MD

Washington

Washington State University, MD

West Virginia

West Virginia University, D

Wisconsin

Marquette University, D
University of Wisconsin - Madison, D

U.S. Territories: Puerto Rico

University of Puerto Rico, Río Piedras Campus, MD

Canada

Alberta

University of Alberta, MD
University of Calgary, MD
University of Lethbridge, MD

British Columbia

The University of British Columbia, MD

Maritime Provinces: Nova Scotia

Dalhousie University, MD

Newfoundland and Labrador

Memorial University of Newfoundland, MD

Ontario

Brock University, MD
Carleton University, M
McMaster University, MD
Queen's University at Kingston, MD
University of Guelph, MD
The University of Western Ontario, MD
Wilfrid Laurier University, MD

Quebec

McGill University, MD
Université de Montréal, MD

NON-PROFIT/PUBLIC/ORGANIZATIONAL MANAGEMENT

United States

Alabama

Auburn University at Montgomery, O
Troy University, M

Arizona

Arizona State University at the Downtown Phoenix campus, B
Arizona State University at the Tempe campus, MO

Arkansas

University of Arkansas at Little Rock, O

California

American Jewish University, M
Antioch University Los Angeles, M

Antioch University Santa Barbara, M
Azusa Pacific University, M
California Baptist University, M
California Lutheran University, M
California State University, Northridge, O
Fresno Pacific University, B
Hope International University, M
Point Loma Nazarene University, BM
San Francisco State University, M
Sonoma State University, O
University of La Verne, MO
University of San Diego, M
University of San Francisco, M
University of Southern California, O
University of the West, M

Colorado

Regis University, MO
University of Colorado Denver, M

Connecticut

Goodwin College, A
Post University, M
University of Connecticut, O

District of Columbia

The George Washington University, O
Trinity Washington University, M

Florida

Carlos Albizu University, Miami Campus, M
Florida Atlantic University, MD
Miami Dade College, A
Polytechnic University of Puerto Rico, Miami Campus, B
University of Central Florida, MO
University of Florida, M
University of North Florida, O
University of South Florida, O
The University of Tampa, M

Georgia

Georgia Southern University, O
Georgia State University, MDO
LaGrange College, B
Toccoa Falls College, B
University of Georgia, MDO

Hawaii

Chaminade University of Honolulu, M

Illinois

Bradley University, M
Concordia University Chicago, B
DePaul University, M
Lewis University, M
North Park University, BM
Trinity International University, B

Indiana

Grace College, B
Huntington University, B
Indiana University Bloomington, MO
Indiana University Northwest, O
Indiana University - Purdue University Indianapolis, O
University of Notre Dame, M

Iowa

University of Northern Iowa, M

Kansas

Donnelly College, B
Friends University, B
MidAmerica Nazarene University, M

Kentucky

Kentucky State University, M
Northern Kentucky University, O
University of Louisville, M

Louisiana

Louisiana State University in Shreveport, M

Maine

Husson University, M

Maryland

Johns Hopkins University, O
Notre Dame of Maryland University, M
University of Maryland, Baltimore County, O

Massachusetts

Assumption College, MO
Bay Path University, M
Brandeis University, M
Cambridge College, M
Lasell College, MO
Northeastern University, M
Simmons College, M
Suffolk University, M
Tufts University, O
Worcester State University, M

Michigan

Central Michigan University, MO
Cleary University, MO
Cornerstone University, B
Eastern Michigan University, MO
Grand Valley State University, M
Great Lakes Christian College, B
University of Michigan - Flint, M
Wayne State University, M
Western Michigan University, O

Minnesota

Capella University, D
Hamline University, M
Metropolitan State University, BM
St. Cloud State University, M
Southwest Minnesota State University, B
University of Minnesota, Twin Cities Campus, B
Walden University, MDO

Missouri

City Vision University, B
Lindenwood University, M
Park University, MO
University of Missouri, O
University of Missouri - St. Louis, MO
Webster University, M
William Jewell College, B

Nevada

University of Nevada, Las Vegas, O

New Hampshire

Granite State College, B
New England College, M
Southern New Hampshire University, O

New Jersey

Bergen Community College, A
Fairleigh Dickinson University, Metropolitan Campus, BO
Kean University, M
Seton Hall University, MO

New York

Baruch College of the City University of New York, M
The College at Brockport, State University of New York, MO
The College of Saint Rose, O
Columbia University, M
Daemen College, M
Fordham University, M
Iona College, O
Mercy College, B
New York University, MO
Pace University, M
University at Albany, State University of New York, MO

North Carolina

High Point University, BM
Lenoir-Rhyne University, B
North Carolina State University, O

Salem College, B
The University of North Carolina at Charlotte, MO
The University of North Carolina at Greensboro, O

Ohio

Case Western Reserve University, MO
Cleveland State University, BMO
John Carroll University, M
Northwest State Community College, A
Tiffin University, B
The University of Toledo, O
Wright State University, B

Oklahoma

Oklahoma State University, O
Oral Roberts University, M
Rogers State University, B
Southwestern Christian University, B
University of Oklahoma, M

Oregon

Corban University, M
Marylhurst University, M
University of Portland, M
Warner Pacific College, M

Pennsylvania

Duquesne University, B
Eastern University, M
Gettysburg College, B
Indiana University of Pennsylvania, D
La Salle University, M
Moravian College, B
Mount Aloysius College, M
Penn State Harrisburg, O
University of Pennsylvania, O
University of Pittsburgh, M
West Chester University of Pennsylvania, MO

Rhode Island

Bryant University, B
Providence College, M
Salve Regina University, O

South Carolina

Columbia International University, B
University of South Carolina Upstate, B

Tennessee

Austin Peay State University, B
East Tennessee State University, M
Lipscomb University, M
Southern Adventist University, BM
Trevecca Nazarene University, B
The University of Tennessee at Chattanooga, MO
Williamson College, B

Texas

Austin College, B
Dallas Baptist University, M
Hardin-Simmons University, B
LeTourneau University, B
Our Lady of the Lake University of San Antonio, M
Texas A&M University, O
University of Houston - Downtown, M
University of North Texas, M

Utah

Brigham Young University, M

Vermont

Marlboro College, M

Virginia

Eastern Mennonite University, M
George Mason University, O
James Madison University, MD
Marymount University, O
Regent University, M
Virginia Commonwealth University, O
Virginia Polytechnic Institute and State University, O

West Virginia

American Public University System, M

Wisconsin

Lakeland College, B
Marquette University, M
University of Wisconsin - Milwaukee, MO

U.S. Territories: Puerto Rico

University of the Sacred Heart, M

Canada

British Columbia

Thompson Rivers University, B
Trinity Western University, MO

Maritime Provinces: Nova Scotia

Dalhousie University, B

Ontario

The University of Western Ontario, B

NORTHERN STUDIES

United States

Alaska

University of Alaska Fairbanks, M

Canada

Manitoba

University of Manitoba, M

NORWEGIAN LANGUAGE AND LITERATURE

United States

Minnesota

St. Olaf College, B

North Dakota

University of North Dakota, B

Utah

Brigham Young University, B

Washington

Pacific Lutheran University, B
University of Washington, B

NUCLEAR ENGINEERING

United States

Arizona

Arizona State University at the Tempe campus, O

California

University of California, Berkeley, BMD

Colorado

Colorado School of Mines, M

Florida

Broward College, A
South Florida State College, A
University of Florida, BMD

Georgia

Georgia Institute of Technology, BMD

Idaho

Idaho State University, BMD
University of Idaho, MD

Illinois

University of Illinois at Urbana - Champaign, BMD

Indiana

Purdue University, BMD

Kansas

Kansas State University, MD

Maryland

United States Naval Academy, B
University of Maryland, College Park, MD

Massachusetts

Massachusetts Institute of Technology, BMDO
University of Massachusetts Lowell, BMD
Worcester Polytechnic Institute, B

Michigan

University of Michigan, BMDO

Minnesota

Itasca Community College, A

Missouri

Missouri University of Science and Technology, BMD
University of Missouri, MDO

Nevada

University of Nevada, Las Vegas, MO

New Mexico

University of New Mexico, BMD

New York

Rensselaer Polytechnic Institute, BMD
United States Military Academy, B

North Carolina

North Carolina State University, BMD

Ohio

The Ohio State University, MD
University of Cincinnati, D

Oregon

Oregon State University, BMD

Pennsylvania

Penn State Abington, B
Penn State Altoona, B
Penn State Beaver, B
Penn State Berks, B
Penn State Brandywine, B
Penn State DuBois, B
Penn State Erie, The Behrend College, B
Penn State Fayette, The Eberly Campus, B
Penn State Greater Allegheny, B
Penn State Hazleton, B
Penn State Lehigh Valley, B
Penn State Mont Alto, B
Penn State New Kensington, B
Penn State Schuylkill, B
Penn State Shenango, B
Penn State University Park, BMD
Penn State Wilkes-Barre, B
Penn State Worthington Scranton, B
Penn State York, B

South Carolina

South Carolina State University, B
University of South Carolina, MD

Tennessee

The University of Tennessee, BMD
The University of Tennessee at Chattanooga, O

Texas

Texas A&M University, BMD

Utah

University of Utah, MD

Virginia

Virginia Commonwealth University, MD
Virginia Polytechnic Institute and State University, MD

Wisconsin

University of Wisconsin - Madison, BMD

Canada

Ontario

McMaster University, D
Royal Military College of Canada, MD

Quebec

École Polytechnique de Montréal, MDO

NUCLEAR ENGINEERING TECHNOLOGY/TECHNICIAN

United States

Arkansas

Arkansas Tech University, A

Delaware

Delaware Technical & Community College, Jack F. Owens Campus, A
Delaware Technical & Community College, Stanton/Wilmington Campus, A

Idaho

Idaho State University, AB

Iowa

Indian Hills Community College, A

Kansas

Flint Hills Technical College, A

Maryland

College of Southern Maryland, A

New Jersey

Thomas Edison State University, AB

New York

United States Military Academy, B

North Dakota

Bismarck State College, A

NUCLEAR AND INDUSTRIAL RADIOLOGIC TECHNOLOGIES/ TECHNICIANS

United States

New York

Manhattan College, B

NUCLEAR MEDICAL TECHNOLOGY/TECHNOLOGIST

United States

Alabama

Community College of the Air Force, A
The University of Alabama at Birmingham, B

Arizona

GateWay Community College, A

Arkansas

University of Arkansas for Medical Sciences, B
University of Central Arkansas, B

California

Charles R. Drew University of Medicine and Science, B
Los Angeles City College, A

Connecticut

Gateway Community College, A

Delaware

Delaware Technical & Community College, Stanton/Wilmington Campus, A

District of Columbia

The George Washington University, A

Florida

Adventist University of Health Sciences, B
Barry University, B
Broward College, A
Gulf Coast State College, A
Hillsborough Community College, A
Keiser University, A
Miami Dade College, A
Santa Fe College, A

Georgia

Augusta University, B
Darton State College, A

Illinois

Benedictine University, B
College of DuPage, A
Lewis University, B
North Central College, B
Roosevelt University, B
Triton College, A
University of St. Francis, B

Indiana

Ball State University, A
Indiana University - Purdue University Indianapolis, B
Vincennes University, A

Iowa

Allen College, B
The University of Iowa, B

Kentucky

Bluegrass Community and Technical College, A
Jefferson Community and Technical College, A

Maine

Maine College of Health Professions, A

Maryland

Frederick Community College, A
Howard Community College, A
Prince George's Community College, A

Massachusetts

MCPHS University, B
Salem State University, B

Michigan

Ferris State University, B
Oakland Community College, A
Oakland University, B

Minnesota

St. Cloud State University, B
Saint Mary's University of Minnesota, B

Missouri

Saint Louis University, B
University of Missouri, B

Nebraska

Peru State College, B
University of Nebraska Medical Center, B

Nevada

University of Nevada, Las Vegas, B

New Jersey

Rowan College at Gloucester County, A
Thomas Edison State University, AB
Union County College, A

New York

Bronx Community College of the City University of New York, A
Manhattan College, B
Molloy College, AB
University at Buffalo, the State University of New York, B

North Carolina

Caldwell Community College and Technical Institute, A
Forsyth Technical Community College, A
Pitt Community College, A

Ohio

Cincinnati State Technical and Community College, A
Columbus State Community College, A
Kettering College, A
Lakeland Community College, A
Lorain County Community College, A
Owens Community College, A
University of Cincinnati, B
University of Cincinnati Blue Ash College, A
The University of Findlay, AB

Oklahoma

East Central University, B
University of Oklahoma Health Sciences Center, B

Pennsylvania

Cedar Crest College, B
Community College of Allegheny County, A
Edinboro University of Pennsylvania, B
Harrisburg Area Community College, A
Indiana University of Pennsylvania, B
Pennsylvania College of Health Sciences, A
Robert Morris University, B
York College of Pennsylvania, B

Rhode Island

Rhode Island College, B

South Carolina

Midlands Technical College, A

South Dakota

Southeast Technical Institute, A

Tennessee

Baptist College of Health Sciences, B

Texas

Amarillo College, A
Del Mar College, A
Galveston College, A
Houston Community College, A
University of the Incarnate Word, B

Utah

Weber State University, B

Vermont

University of Vermont, B

Virginia

Old Dominion University, B

West Virginia

BridgeValley Community and Technical College (South Charleston), A

Wheeling Jesuit University, B

Wisconsin

University of Wisconsin - La Crosse, B

U.S. Territories: Puerto Rico

University of Puerto Rico, Medical Sciences Campus, B

Canada

British Columbia

British Columbia Institute of Technology, A

Maritime Provinces: Nova Scotia

Dalhousie University, B

NUCLEAR/NUCLEAR POWER TECHNOLOGY/TECHNICIAN

United States

Connecticut

Three Rivers Community College, A

Kansas

Allen Community College, A

Missouri

State Technical College of Missouri, A

New Jersey

Salem Community College, A

New York

Excelsior College, A

North Carolina

Cape Fear Community College, A

Ohio

Terra State Community College, A

Texas

Texas State Technical College, A

NUCLEAR PHYSICS

United States

Arkansas

Arkansas Tech University, B

NURSE ANESTHETIST

United States

Alabama

Samford University, M
The University of Alabama at Birmingham, M

Arkansas

Arkansas State University, M

California

California State University, Fullerton, M
National University, M
Samuel Merritt University, MO

Connecticut

Central Connecticut State University, M
Fairfield University, D
Quinnipiac University, D

District of Columbia

Georgetown University, M

Florida

Adventist University of Health Sciences, M
Barry University, M
Florida Gulf Coast University, M
University of Miami, M
University of North Florida, M
University of South Florida, M

Georgia

Augusta University, M

Illinois

Millikin University, D
Rush University, D
Southern Illinois University Edwardsville, D

Kansas

Newman University, M
The University of Kansas, MD

Kentucky

Murray State University, M

Louisiana

Louisiana State University Health Sciences Center, M
Our Lady of the Lake College, M

Maine

University of New England, M

Massachusetts

Boston College, M

Michigan

Oakland University, MO
University of Detroit Mercy, M
University of Michigan - Flint, MD
Wayne State University, MO

Minnesota

Saint Mary's University of Minnesota, M
University of Minnesota, Twin Cities Campus, M

Missouri

Goldfarb School of Nursing at Barnes-Jewish College, M
Missouri State University, M
Webster University, M

Nebraska

Bryan College of Health Sciences, M

New Jersey

Rutgers University - Newark, M

New York

Columbia University, MO
State University of New York Downstate Medical Center, M
University at Buffalo, the State University of New York, D

North Carolina

Duke University, D
The University of North Carolina at Charlotte, MO
The University of North Carolina at Greensboro, MO

North Dakota

University of North Dakota, M

Ohio

Case Western Reserve University, M
Lourdes University, M
Otterbein University, MO
University of Cincinnati, M

Oregon

Oregon Health & Science University, M

Pennsylvania

Bloomsburg University of Pennsylvania, M
Drexel University, M
Gannon University, MO
La Roche College, M
La Salle University, MO
Saint Joseph's University, M
Saint Vincent College, MD
University of Pennsylvania, M
University of Pittsburgh, MD
The University of Scranton, MO
Villanova University, MO
York College of Pennsylvania, M

South Carolina

Medical University of South Carolina, M
University of South Carolina, M

South Dakota

Mount Marty College, M

Tennessee

Lincoln Memorial University, M
Union University, D
The University of Tennessee at Chattanooga, MO

Texas

Texas Christian University, D
Texas Wesleyan University, MD

Utah

Westminster College, M

Virginia

Old Dominion University, M
Virginia Commonwealth University, MD

Washington

Gonzaga University, M

West Virginia

Marshall University, D

Wisconsin

University of Wisconsin - La Crosse, M

U.S. Territories: Puerto Rico

Inter American University of Puerto Rico, Arecibo Campus, M

Canada

British Columbia

The University of British Columbia, MD

NURSE MIDWIFE/NURSING MIDWIFERY

United States

Colorado

University of Colorado Denver, M

District of Columbia

Georgetown University, M

Florida

University of Miami, M

Georgia

Emory University, M

Illinois

University of Illinois at Chicago, M

Indiana

University of Indianapolis, M

Kansas

The University of Kansas, O

Michigan

University of Michigan, M
Wayne State University, M

Minnesota

Bethel University, M
University of Minnesota, Twin Cities Campus, M

New Mexico

National College of Midwifery, MD

New York

Columbia University, M
New York University, MDO
State University of New York Downstate Medical Center, MO
Stony Brook University, State University of New York, MDO

Ohio

Case Western Reserve University, M
University of Cincinnati, M

Oregon

Oregon Health & Science University, MDO

Pennsylvania

DeSales University, M
Philadelphia University, MO
University of Pennsylvania, M

Tennessee

Vanderbilt University, M

Texas

Baylor University, D

Utah

Midwives College of Utah, M

Virginia

James Madison University, M
Old Dominion University, M

Washington

Bastyr University, M
Seattle University, M

West Virginia

West Virginia Wesleyan College, M

Wisconsin

Marquette University, MO

U.S. Territories: Puerto Rico

University of Puerto Rico, Medical Sciences Campus, MO

NURSING

United States

Alabama

Auburn University, M
Auburn University at Montgomery, M
Jacksonville State University, M
Samford University, MD
South University, M
Spring Hill College, MO
Troy University, MDO
The University of Alabama, MD
The University of Alabama at Birmingham, MD
The University of Alabama in Huntsville, MDO
University of Mobile, M
University of North Alabama, M
University of South Alabama, MDO

Alaska

University of Alaska Anchorage, M

Arizona

Arizona State University at the Tempe campus, MDO
Grand Canyon University, MO
Northern Arizona University, MDO
The University of Arizona, MDO
University of Phoenix - Online Campus, MDO
University of Phoenix - Phoenix Campus, MO

Arkansas

Arkansas State University, MDO
Arkansas Tech University, M
University of Arkansas, M
University of Arkansas for Medical Sciences, D
University of Central Arkansas, MO

California

Azusa Pacific University, MD
California Baptist University, MD
California State University, Chico, M
California State University, Dominguez Hills, M
California State University, Fresno, M
California State University, Fullerton, MD
California State University, Long Beach, MD
California State University, Los Angeles, M
California State University, Sacramento, M
California State University, San Bernardino, M
California State University, Stanislaus, M
Fresno Pacific University, M
Holy Names University, MO
Loma Linda University, M
Mount Saint Mary's University, MO
National University, MD
Point Loma Nazarene University, MO
Samuel Merritt University, MDO
San Diego State University, M
San Francisco State University, MO
San Jose State University, MO
Sonoma State University, M
University of California, Irvine, M
University of California, Los Angeles, MD
University of Phoenix - Bay Area Campus, MD
University of Phoenix - Central Valley Campus, M
University of Phoenix - Sacramento Valley Campus, M
University of Phoenix - San Diego Campus, M
University of Phoenix - Southern California Campus, MO
University of San Diego, MD
University of San Francisco, MD
Vanguard University of Southern California, M

Colorado

American Sentinel University, M
Colorado State University - Pueblo, M
Regis University, MD
University of Colorado Colorado Springs, MD
University of Colorado Denver, MD
University of Northern Colorado, MD
University of Phoenix - Colorado Campus, M
University of Phoenix - Colorado Springs Downtown Campus, M

Connecticut

Fairfield University, MD
Quinnipiac University, MD
Sacred Heart University, MDO
Southern Connecticut State University, M
University of Connecticut, MDO
University of Hartford, M
University of Saint Joseph, MD
Western Connecticut State University, MD
Yale University, MDO

Delaware

Delaware State University, M
University of Delaware, MO
Wesley College, M
Wilmington University, MD

District of Columbia

The Catholic University of America, MDO
The George Washington University, MDO
Georgetown University, MD
Howard University, MO
University of Phoenix - Washington D.C. Campus, MD

Florida

Barry University, MDO
Florida Agricultural and Mechanical University, MD
Florida Atlantic University, MDO
Florida International University, MD
Florida Southern College, M
Florida State University, MDO
Jacksonville University, MD
Keiser University, M
Nova Southeastern University, MD
South University (Royal Palm Beach), M
South University (Tampa), M
University of Central Florida, MDO
University of Florida, MD
University of Miami, MD
University of North Florida, MDO
University of Phoenix - North Florida Campus, M
University of Phoenix - South Florida Campus, M
University of South Florida, MD
The University of Tampa, M
University of West Florida, M

Georgia

Albany State University, M
Armstrong State University, M
Augusta University, D
Clayton State University, M
Columbus State University, M
Emory University, MD
Georgia College & State University, MD
Georgia Southern University, D
Georgia State University, MDO
Kennesaw State University, MD
Mercer University, MDO
Piedmont College, M
South University, M
Thomas University, M
University of Phoenix - Atlanta Campus, M
University of Phoenix - Augusta Campus, M
University of Phoenix - Columbus Georgia Campus, M
University of West Georgia, MDO

Hawaii

Hawai'i Pacific University, M
University of Hawaii at Hilo, D
University of Hawaii at Manoa, MDO
University of Phoenix - Hawaii Campus, M

Idaho

Boise State University, MO
Idaho State University, MO

Illinois

Aurora University, M
Benedictine University, M
Blessing-Rieman College of Nursing, M
Bradley University, MO
Chicago State University, M
DePaul University, M
Elmhurst College, M
Governors State University, M
Illinois State University, MDO
Lewis University, MD
Loyola University Chicago, MD
McKendree University, M
Millikin University, MD
North Park University, M
Northern Illinois University, M
Resurrection University, M
Rush University, MDO
Saint Anthony College of Nursing, M
Saint Francis Medical Center College of Nursing, MDO
Saint Xavier University, MO
Southern Illinois University Edwardsville, MDO
University of Illinois at Chicago, MDO

University of St. Francis, MDO

Indiana

Ball State University, MD
Bethel College, M
Goshen College, M
Indiana State University, MD
Indiana University East, M
Indiana University Kokomo, M
Indiana University - Purdue University Fort Wayne, MO
Indiana University - Purdue University Indianapolis, MDO
Indiana University South Bend, M
Indiana Wesleyan University, M
Purdue University Northwest (Hammond), M
University of Indianapolis, MD
University of Saint Francis, MO
University of Southern Indiana, MD
Valparaiso University, MDO

Iowa

Allen College, MDO
Briar Cliff University, M
Clarke University, MDO
Graceland University, MDO
Grand View University, M
Kaplan University, Davenport Campus, M
Mount Mercy University, M
St. Ambrose University, M
The University of Iowa, MD

Kansas

Fort Hays State University, M
Pittsburg State University, M
The University of Kansas, MDO
University of Saint Mary, M
Washburn University, MD
Wichita State University, MD

Kentucky

Bellarmine University, MD
Eastern Kentucky University, M
Kentucky State University, D
Murray State University, M
Northern Kentucky University, MDO
Spalding University, MDO
University of Kentucky, D
University of Louisville, MD
Western Kentucky University, M

Louisiana

Grambling State University, MO
Louisiana State University Health Sciences Center, MD
Loyola University New Orleans, MD
McNeese State University, MO
Nicholls State University, M
Northwestern State University of Louisiana, M
Our Lady of the Lake College, M
Southern University and Agricultural and Mechanical College, MDO
University of Louisiana at Lafayette, M

Maine

Husson University, MO
Saint Joseph's College of Maine, MO
University of Maine, MO
University of Southern Maine, MDO

Maryland

Bowie State University, M
Coppin State University, MO
Frostburg State University, M
Johns Hopkins University, MDO
Morgan State University, M
Salisbury University, MD
Stevenson University, M
Towson University, MO
Washington Adventist University, M

Massachusetts

American International College, M
Boston College, MD
Curry College, M

Elms College, MD
Emmanuel College, MO
Endicott College, MD
Framingham State University, M
MCPHS University, M
Northeastern University, MDO
Regis College, MDO
Salem State University, M
Simmons College, MD
University of Massachusetts Amherst, MD
University of Massachusetts Boston, MD
University of Massachusetts Dartmouth, MD
University of Massachusetts Lowell, MDO

Michigan

Andrews University, MD
Ferris State University, M
Grand Valley State University, MD
Madonna University, M
Michigan State University, MD
Northern Michigan University, MD
Oakland University, MDO
Saginaw Valley State University, M
South University, M
Spring Arbor University, M
University of Michigan, MDO
University of Michigan - Flint, MDO
Wayne State University, DO
Western Michigan University, M

Minnesota

Augsburg College, MD
Bethel University, M
Capella University, MD
The College of St. Scholastica, MO
Metropolitan State University, MD
Minnesota State University Mankato, MD
Minnesota State University Moorhead, M
St. Catherine University, MD
University of Minnesota, Twin Cities Campus, MD
Walden University, MDO
Winona State University, MDO

Mississippi

Alcorn State University, M
Delta State University, MD
Mississippi University for Women, MO
University of Mississippi Medical Center, MD
University of Southern Mississippi, MDO
William Carey University, M

Missouri

Central Methodist University, M
Cox College, M
Goldfarb School of Nursing at Barnes-Jewish College, M
Lindenwood University, M
Maryville University of Saint Louis, MD
Missouri Southern State University, M
Missouri State University, M
Missouri Western State University, MO
Research College of Nursing, M
Saint Louis University, MDO
Southeast Missouri State University, M
University of Central Missouri, M
University of Missouri, MDO
University of Missouri - Kansas City, MD
University of Missouri - St. Louis, MDO
Webster University, M

Nebraska

Clarkson College, MO
College of Saint Mary, M
Creighton University, MDO
Nebraska Methodist College, M
Nebraska Wesleyan University, M
University of Nebraska Medical Center, D

Nevada

University of Nevada, Las Vegas, MDO
University of Nevada, Reno, MD

New Hampshire

Franklin Pierce University, M
Rivier University, M

University of New Hampshire, MDO

New Jersey

The College of New Jersey, MO
College of Saint Elizabeth, M
Fairleigh Dickinson University, Metropolitan Campus, MDO
Felician University, MDO
Kean University, M
Monmouth University, MDO
Ramapo College of New Jersey, M
Rutgers University - Newark, MO
Saint Peter's University, MDO
Seton Hall University, MD
Stockton University, M
Thomas Edison State University, M
William Paterson University of New Jersey, MD

New Mexico

Eastern New Mexico University, M
New Mexico State University, MD
University of New Mexico, MD
University of Phoenix - New Mexico Campus, M

New York

Adelphi University, D
Binghamton University, State University of New York, MDO
College of Mount Saint Vincent, MO
The College of New Rochelle, MO
College of Staten Island of the City University of New York, MDO
Columbia University, MDO
Daemen College, MDO
D'Youville College, MDO
Excelsior College, M
Hunter College of the City University of New York, MO
Keuka College, M
Le Moyne College, MO
Lehman College of the City University of New York, M
Long Island University - LIU Brooklyn, MO
Mercy College, M
Molloy College, MDO
Mount Saint Mary College, MO
Nazareth College of Rochester, M
New York University, MDO
Pace University, MDO
Roberts Wesleyan College, M
St. John Fisher College, MDO
St. Joseph's College, Long Island Campus, M
St. Joseph's College, New York, M
State University of New York Downstate Medical Center, MO
State University of New York Upstate Medical University, MO
Stony Brook University, State University of New York, MDO
University at Buffalo, the State University of New York, MDO
University of Rochester, MD

North Carolina

Duke University, D
East Carolina University, MDO
Gardner-Webb University, MD
Lenoir-Rhyne University, M
Queens University of Charlotte, M
The University of North Carolina at Chapel Hill, MDO
The University of North Carolina at Charlotte, MDO
The University of North Carolina at Greensboro, MDO
The University of North Carolina at Pembroke, M
The University of North Carolina Wilmington, MO
University of Phoenix - Charlotte Campus, M
Western Carolina University, MO
Winston-Salem State University, MD

North Dakota

North Dakota State University, MD
University of Mary, MD
University of North Dakota, MD

Ohio

Capital University, M
Case Western Reserve University, MD
Cleveland State University, MD
Franciscan University of Steubenville, M
Kent State University, MDO
Malone University, M
Mount Carmel College of Nursing, M
Mount St. Joseph University, MD
The Ohio State University, MD
Ohio University, M
Otterbein University, MDO
The University of Akron, MD
University of Cincinnati, MD
The University of Toledo, MDO
Urbana University, MD
Ursuline College, MD
Walsh University, MD
Wright State University, M
Xavier University, MDO
Youngstown State University, M

Oklahoma

Oklahoma Baptist University, M
Oklahoma City University, MD
Southern Nazarene University, M
University of Central Oklahoma, M
University of Oklahoma Health Sciences Center, M

Oregon

Oregon Health & Science University, MDO
University of Portland, MD

Pennsylvania

Bloomsburg University of Pennsylvania, M
Carlow University, D
Cedar Crest College, M
Chatham University, MD
Clarion University of Pennsylvania, MD
DeSales University, MDO
Drexel University, MD
Duquesne University, MDO
Edinboro University of Pennsylvania, MD
Gannon University, D
Gwynedd Mercy University, MD
Holy Family University, M
Immaculata University, M
Indiana University of Pennsylvania, MD
La Roche College, M
La Salle University, MDO
Mansfield University of Pennsylvania, M
Millersville University of Pennsylvania, M
Misericordia University, MD
Moravian College, M
Neumann University, M
Penn State University Park, MD
Robert Morris University, MD
Temple University, MD
Thomas Jefferson University, MD
University of Pennsylvania, MDO
University of Pittsburgh, D
The University of Scranton, MO
Villanova University, MDO
Waynesburg University, MD
West Chester University of Pennsylvania, MDO
Widener University, MDO
Wilkes University, MD
York College of Pennsylvania, MD

Rhode Island

Rhode Island College, M
Salve Regina University, D
University of Rhode Island, MD

South Carolina

Clemson University, MD
Francis Marion University, M
Lander University, M
Medical University of South Carolina, D
South University, M
University of South Carolina, MDO

South Dakota

Mount Marty College, M
South Dakota State University, MD

Tennessee

Aquinas College, M
Austin Peay State University, M
Belmont University, MD
Carson-Newman University, M
East Tennessee State University, MDO
Lincoln Memorial University, M
Middle Tennessee State University, MO
Southern Adventist University, M
Tennessee State University, M
Tennessee Technological University, M
Union University, MDO
University of Memphis, MO
The University of Tennessee, MD
The University of Tennessee at Chattanooga, MDO
Vanderbilt University, MDO

Texas

Abilene Christian University, MO
Baylor University, MD
Hardin-Simmons University, M
Lamar University, M
McMurry University, M
Midwestern State University, M
Our Lady of the Lake University of San Antonio, M
Prairie View A&M University, M
Tarleton State University, M
Texas A&M International University, M
Texas A&M University, M
Texas A&M University - Corpus Christi, M
Texas Christian University, MDO
Texas Woman's University, MD
University of Houston - Victoria, M
University of the Incarnate Word, MD
University of Mary Hardin-Baylor, MO
University of Phoenix - Houston Campus, M
University of Phoenix - San Antonio Campus, M
The University of Texas at Arlington, MD
The University of Texas at Austin, MD
The University of Texas at El Paso, MDO
The University of Texas Health Science Center at Houston, MD
The University of Texas Health Science Center at San Antonio, MDO
The University of Texas Medical Branch, MD
The University of Texas Rio Grande Valley, M
The University of Texas at Tyler, MD
Wayland Baptist University, M
West Texas A&M University, M

Utah

Brigham Young University, M
Independence University, M
University of Phoenix - Utah Campus, M
University of Utah, MD
Utah Valley University, M
Weber State University, M
Westminster College, M

Vermont

Norwich University, M
University of Vermont, MD

Virginia

Eastern Mennonite University, M
George Mason University, MDO
Hampton University, MD
James Madison University, MD
Jefferson College of Health Sciences, M
Liberty University, MD
Lynchburg College, M
Marymount University, MDO
Old Dominion University, MD
Radford University, D
Shenandoah University, MDO
South University (Glen Allen), M
South University (Virginia Beach), M
University of Virginia, MD
Virginia Commonwealth University, MDO

Washington

Gonzaga University, MD
Pacific Lutheran University, MD
Seattle Pacific University, MO
Seattle University, MD

University of Washington, MDO
University of Washington, Bothell, M
University of Washington, Tacoma, M
Washington State University, MDO

West Virginia

Marshall University, M
West Virginia University, MDO
West Virginia Wesleyan College, MO
Wheeling Jesuit University, M

Wisconsin

Alverno College, M
Bellin College, M
Cardinal Stritch University, M
Concordia University Wisconsin, M
Edgewood College, MD
Herzing University Online, M
Marian University, M
Marquette University, MDO
University of Wisconsin - Eau Claire, MD
University of Wisconsin - Madison, D
University of Wisconsin - Milwaukee, MDO
University of Wisconsin - Oshkosh, M
Viterbo University, MD

Wyoming

University of Wyoming, M

U.S. Territories: Puerto Rico

Inter American University of Puerto Rico, Arecibo Campus, M
Pontifical Catholic University of Puerto Rico, M
Universidad Metropolitana, MO
University of Puerto Rico, Medical Sciences Campus, M

Canada

Alberta

Athabasca University, MO
University of Alberta, MD
University of Calgary, MDO
University of Lethbridge, M

British Columbia

Trinity Western University, M
The University of British Columbia, MD
University of Victoria, MD

Manitoba

University of Manitoba, M

Maritime Provinces: New Brunswick

University of New Brunswick Fredericton, M

Maritime Provinces: Nova Scotia

Dalhousie University, MD

Newfoundland and Labrador

Memorial University of Newfoundland, MO

Ontario

Laurentian University, M
McMaster University, MD
Queen's University at Kingston, MDO
University of Ottawa, MDO
University of Toronto, MD
The University of Western Ontario, MD
University of Windsor, M
York University, M

Quebec

McGill University, MDO
Université Laval, MDO
Université de Montréal, MDO
Université du Québec en Outaouais, MO
Université du Québec à Rimouski, MO
Université du Québec à Trois-Rivières, MO

Saskatchewan

University of Regina, M
University of Saskatchewan, M

NURSING ADMINISTRATION

United States

Alabama

Samford University, D
Spring Hill College, MO

Arizona

Arizona State University at the Tempe campus, M

Arkansas

University of Central Arkansas, O

California

California State University, Fullerton, M
Holy Names University, MO
Loma Linda University, M
National University, MO
Samuel Merritt University, M
San Francisco State University, M
San Jose State University, M
Trident University International, D
University of Phoenix - Bay Area Campus, MD
University of San Diego, M
University of San Francisco, MD

Colorado

Regis University, MD
University of Colorado Denver, M

Connecticut

Fairfield University, MD
Quinnipiac University, D
Sacred Heart University, MD
Southern Connecticut State University, M

Delaware

University of Delaware, MO
Wilmington University, M

District of Columbia

The George Washington University, M
University of Phoenix - Washington D.C. Campus, M

Florida

Barry University, MDO
Florida Agricultural and Mechanical University, M
Florida Atlantic University, MO
Florida Southern College, M
Florida State University, MO
University of North Florida, M
University of South Florida, M
University of West Florida, M

Georgia

Augusta University, M
Brenau University, M
Emory University, M
Georgia State University, M
Piedmont College, M

Hawaii

University of Hawaii at Manoa, M

Idaho

Northwest Nazarene University, M

Illinois

Bradley University, M
Lewis University, M
Loyola University Chicago, M
McKendree University, M
Millikin University, M
North Park University, M
Rush University, M
Saint Francis Medical Center College of Nursing, M
Southern Illinois University Edwardsville, MO
University of Illinois at Chicago, O
University of St. Francis, M

Indiana

Indiana State University, M
Indiana University Kokomo, M
Indiana University - Purdue University Fort Wayne, MO
Indiana University - Purdue University Indianapolis, M
Indiana Wesleyan University, M
Purdue University Northwest (Hammond), M
University of Indianapolis, M

Iowa

Allen College, MO
Clarke University, M
Kaplan University, Davenport Campus, M
Mount Mercy University, M

Kansas

Grantham University, M
The University of Kansas, O
University of Saint Mary, M
Washburn University, M

Kentucky

Bellarmine University, M
Spalding University, M

Louisiana

McNeese State University, MO
Nicholls State University, M
Our Lady of the Lake College, M
Southern University and Agricultural and Mechanical College, D

Maine

Saint Joseph's College of Maine, MO
University of Southern Maine, M

Maryland

Bowie State University, M
Frostburg State University, M
Salisbury University, M
Washington Adventist University, M

Massachusetts

American International College, M
Elms College, M
Emmanuel College, M
Framingham State University, M
Northeastern University, M
Salem State University, M
University of Massachusetts Amherst, MD
University of Massachusetts Lowell, D

Michigan

Eastern Michigan University, MO
Ferris State University, M
Grand Valley State University, MD
Madonna University, M
Saginaw Valley State University, M
University of Michigan, M

Minnesota

Bethel University, O
Capella University, M
Metropolitan State University, M
University of Minnesota, Twin Cities Campus, M
Walden University, MDO
Winona State University, M

Missouri

Central Methodist University, M
Cox College, M
Missouri Western State University, MO
Research College of Nursing, M
University of Missouri, D
University of Missouri - Kansas City, M
University of Missouri - St. Louis, M
Webster University, M

Montana

Montana State University, M

Nebraska

Clarkson College, MO
Creighton University, MD
Nebraska Methodist College, M

New Jersey

Felician University, MDO
Kean University, M
Monmouth University, MO
Saint Peter's University, MD
Seton Hall University, M

New Mexico

New Mexico State University, M

New York

Adelphi University, MO
College of Mount Saint Vincent, M
The College of New Rochelle, M
Daemen College, MO
Le Moyne College, MO
Mercy College, M
Molloy College, M
Mount Saint Mary College, M
Pace University, O
Roberts Wesleyan College, M
State University of New York Polytechnic Institute, M
University at Buffalo, the State University of New York, M
University of Rochester, M

North Carolina

Duke University, M
Lenoir-Rhyne University, M
Queens University of Charlotte, M
The University of North Carolina at Chapel Hill, MO
The University of North Carolina at Charlotte, M
The University of North Carolina at Greensboro, M
The University of North Carolina at Pembroke, M

North Dakota

University of Mary, M

Ohio

Capital University, M
Kent State University, M
Lourdes University, M
Mount Carmel College of Nursing, M
Mount St. Joseph University, M
Ohio University, M
Otterbein University, M
University of Cincinnati, M
The University of Toledo, M
Ursuline College, M
Walsh University, M
Wright State University, M

Oklahoma

Oklahoma Wesleyan University, M
Southern Nazarene University, M

Pennsylvania

Bloomsburg University of Pennsylvania, M
Carlow University, M
Cedar Crest College, M
Chatham University, M
DeSales University, D
Drexel University, M
Gannon University, M
Holy Family University, M
Immaculata University, M
Indiana University of Pennsylvania, M
La Roche College, M
La Salle University, MO
Moravian College, M
Pennsylvania College of Health Sciences, M
Saint Joseph's University, M
Temple University, M
University of Pennsylvania, MD
University of Pittsburgh, MD
Villanova University, MO
Waynesburg University, M
York College of Pennsylvania, M

Rhode Island

University of Rhode Island, M

South Carolina

Medical University of South Carolina, M
University of South Carolina, M

Tennessee

Austin Peay State University, M
Middle Tennessee State University, M
Southern Adventist University, M
Tennessee Technological University, M
Union University, D
University of Memphis, M
The University of Tennessee at Chattanooga, M
Vanderbilt University, M

Texas

Abilene Christian University, M
Lamar University, M
Our Lady of the Lake University of San Antonio, M
Prairie View A&M University, M
Texas A&M University - Corpus Christi, M
Texas Christian University, MDO
Texas Woman's University, M
University of Houston - Victoria, M
University of the Incarnate Word, M
University of Mary Hardin-Baylor, M
The University of Texas at Arlington, M
The University of Texas at Austin, M
The University of Texas at El Paso, M
The University of Texas Health Science Center at San Antonio, MD
The University of Texas at Tyler, M

Utah

Independence University, M
Western Governors University, M

Vermont

Norwich University, M

Virginia

Eastern Mennonite University, M
James Madison University, M
Jefferson College of Health Sciences, M
Liberty University, M
Lynchburg College, M
Old Dominion University, MD
University of Virginia, M
Virginia Commonwealth University, M

Washington

Pacific Lutheran University, M
Seattle Pacific University, M
University of Washington, Tacoma, M

West Virginia

West Virginia Wesleyan College, MO

Wisconsin

Herzing University Online, M
Marquette University, D
Milwaukee School of Engineering, M
Mount Mary University, M
University of Wisconsin - Eau Claire, D
University of Wisconsin - Green Bay, M

U.S. Territories: Puerto Rico

Universidad Metropolitana, O

Canada

Alberta

Athabasca University, M

British Columbia

University of Victoria, M

NURSING - ADULT

United States

Alabama

Troy University, MD
University of South Alabama, M

Arkansas

University of Central Arkansas, O

California

California Baptist University, M
Loma Linda University, M
University of San Diego, M

Colorado

University of Colorado Colorado Springs, M
University of Colorado Denver, M

Connecticut

Quinnipiac University, MD
Western Connecticut State University, M

Delaware

University of Delaware, MO
Wilmington University, M

District of Columbia

The George Washington University, MDO

Florida

Florida Atlantic University, O
Florida Southern College, M
South University (Tampa), M
University of Miami, M
University of North Florida, M
University of South Florida, MD

Georgia

Armstrong State University, M
Emory University, M
Georgia State University, MO

Hawaii

University of Hawaii at Manoa, M

Illinois

Lewis University, M
Loyola University Chicago, MO
North Park University, M
Rush University, D
University of Illinois at Chicago, M

Indiana

Indiana University - Purdue University Fort Wayne, M
Purdue University Northwest (Hammond), M

Iowa

Allen College, MO

Kansas

The University of Kansas, O

Kentucky

Spalding University, MO
University of Louisville, M

Louisiana

Louisiana State University Health Sciences Center, M

Maine

University of Southern Maine, MO

Massachusetts

Boston College, M
University of Massachusetts Amherst, D
University of Massachusetts Dartmouth, M

Michigan

Eastern Michigan University, M
Madonna University, M
Oakland University, M
University of Michigan, M
Wayne State University, MDO

Minnesota

St. Catherine University, M
University of Minnesota, Twin Cities Campus, M
Walden University, M
Winona State University, MO

Missouri

Goldfarb School of Nursing at Barnes-Jewish College, M
Maryville University of Saint Louis, M
Research College of Nursing, M
University of Missouri, DO
University of Missouri - Kansas City, MD
University of Missouri - St. Louis, O

Nebraska

Clarkson College, MO
Creighton University, MDO

New Jersey

Felician University, MO
Monmouth University, MO
Rutgers University - Newark, M
Saint Peter's University, MO
Seton Hall University, MD

New York

Adelphi University, MO
College of Mount Saint Vincent, MO
College of Staten Island of the City University of New York, MO
Columbia University, MO
Daemen College, MO
Hunter College of the City University of New York, M
Lehman College of the City University of New York, M
Molloy College, MO
Mount Saint Mary College, MO
New York University, MDO
Stony Brook University, State University of New York, MDO
University at Buffalo, the State University of New York, D

North Carolina

Duke University, MO
The University of North Carolina at Chapel Hill, M
The University of North Carolina at Greensboro, MO

Ohio

Kent State University, M
Mount Carmel College of Nursing, M
University of Cincinnati, M
Wright State University, M

Pennsylvania

Bloomsburg University of Pennsylvania, M
Gwynedd Mercy University, M
La Salle University, MO
Temple University, D
University of Pennsylvania, M
The University of Scranton, M
Villanova University, MO
York College of Pennsylvania, M

South Carolina

Medical University of South Carolina, MD
University of South Carolina, M

Tennessee

Southern Adventist University, M
Vanderbilt University, M

Texas

Angelo State University, M
Texas Christian University, M

Texas Woman's University, M
The University of Texas at Austin, M
The University of Texas Rio Grande Valley, M

Virginia

Hampton University, M
Virginia Commonwealth University, M

Washington

Seattle Pacific University, M
Seattle University, M

Wisconsin

Marian University, M
Marquette University, MDO
University of Wisconsin - Eau Claire, MD
University of Wisconsin - Madison, D
University of Wisconsin - Oshkosh, M

U.S. Territories: Puerto Rico

Universidad del Turabo, MO
University of Puerto Rico, Medical Sciences Campus, M

NURSING - ADVANCED PRACTICE

United States

Alabama

Samford University, M
Troy University, MDO
The University of Alabama in Huntsville, MO

Arizona

Arizona State University at the Tempe campus, O
Grand Canyon University, M
Northern Arizona University, MO
The University of Arizona, MO
University of Phoenix - Online Campus, O
University of Phoenix - Phoenix Campus, MO

Arkansas

University of Central Arkansas, MO

California

California Baptist University, M
California State University, Fresno, M
Fresno Pacific University, M
Holy Names University, MO
Point Loma Nazarene University, M
Samuel Merritt University, MO
San Francisco State University, MO
Sonoma State University, M
United States University, M
University of Phoenix - Sacramento Valley Campus, M
University of Phoenix - Southern California Campus, MO
University of San Diego, M
University of San Francisco, D

Colorado

Regis University, M
University of Colorado Denver, M
University of Northern Colorado, M

Connecticut

Fairfield University, MD
Quinnipiac University, MD
Sacred Heart University, MO
University of Saint Joseph, M

Delaware

University of Delaware, MO
Wilmington University, M

District of Columbia

The George Washington University, MDO
Georgetown University, M
Howard University, O

Florida

Barry University, MO
Florida Atlantic University, MO
Florida State University, D
South University (Royal Palm Beach), M
South University (Tampa), M
University of Miami, M
University of North Florida, O
University of South Florida, MD

Georgia

Albany State University, M
Augusta University, MO
Brenau University, M
Emory University, M
Georgia Southern University, M
Georgia State University, MO
University of North Georgia, M

Hawaii

University of Hawaii at Manoa, M
University of Phoenix - Hawaii Campus, M

Illinois

DePaul University, D
Illinois State University, O
Loyola University Chicago, M
Rush University, D
Saint Francis Medical Center College of Nursing, M
Southern Illinois University Edwardsville, MDO
University of Illinois at Chicago, M
University of St. Francis, MO

Indiana

Indiana State University, M
Indiana University South Bend, M
Purdue University Northwest (Hammond), M
University of Indianapolis, M
University of Saint Francis, MO

Iowa

Allen College, MO
Clarke University, MO
Graceland University, MO

Kentucky

Bellarmine University, M
Eastern Kentucky University, M
Murray State University, M
Spalding University, MO
University of Louisville, M

Louisiana

Grambling State University, O
McNeese State University, MO
Nicholls State University, M
Southern University and Agricultural and Mechanical College, O

Maine

Husson University, MO
Saint Joseph's College of Maine, M
University of Maine, MO
University of Southern Maine, MO

Maryland

Bowie State University, M
Coppin State University, O

Massachusetts

Regis College, O
University of Massachusetts Amherst, D
University of Massachusetts Lowell, M

Michigan

Northern Michigan University, MD
Oakland University, MO
Saginaw Valley State University, MD
University of Detroit Mercy, MO
University of Michigan, M
University of Michigan - Flint, MDO
Wayne State University, D

Minnesota

Augsburg College, MD
Minnesota State University Mankato, M
University of Minnesota, Twin Cities Campus, M
Walden University, M
Winona State University, MO

Mississippi

Delta State University, M
University of Southern Mississippi, MO

Missouri

Cox College, M
Maryville University of Saint Louis, M
Missouri State University, M
Research College of Nursing, M
University of Missouri, D
University of Missouri - Kansas City, MD
University of Missouri - St. Louis, O

Montana

Montana State University, MDO

Nebraska

Clarkson College, MO
Creighton University, MDO

Nevada

University of Nevada, Las Vegas, O

New Hampshire

Rivier University, M
University of New Hampshire, O

New Jersey

Felician University, MO
Monmouth University, MO
Rutgers University - Newark, M

New York

College of Mount Saint Vincent, MO
The College of New Rochelle, MO
College of Staten Island of the City University of New York, D
Columbia University, MO
Dominican College, MD
D'Youville College, MO
Molloy College, MO
Mount Saint Mary College, O
New York University, MDO
Pace University, M
St. John Fisher College, O
State University of New York Downstate Medical Center, MO
State University of New York Polytechnic Institute, MO
State University of New York Upstate Medical University, O
Stony Brook University, State University of New York, MDO
University at Buffalo, the State University of New York, D
University of Rochester, M

North Carolina

Duke University, MO
The University of North Carolina at Chapel Hill, M
The University of North Carolina at Charlotte, MO
The University of North Carolina Wilmington, MO
Winston-Salem State University, M

North Dakota

University of Mary, D
University of North Dakota, M

Ohio

Case Western Reserve University, M
Cedarville University, M
Kent State University, MD
Malone University, M
Mount Carmel College of Nursing, M
Ohio University, M
Otterbein University, MO
The University of Toledo, MO

Wright State University, M

Oregon

Oregon Health & Science University, MDO
University of Portland, D

Pennsylvania

Bloomsburg University of Pennsylvania, M
Carlow University, MO
Clarion University of Pennsylvania, MO
DeSales University, MO
Drexel University, M
Duquesne University, MO
Edinboro University of Pennsylvania, M
Gannon University, MO
Gwynedd Mercy University, M
La Salle University, MDO
Millersville University of Pennsylvania, M
Temple University, D
University of Pennsylvania, MO
University of Pittsburgh, MD
The University of Scranton, MO
Villanova University, MO

Rhode Island

University of Rhode Island, M

South Carolina

Francis Marion University, M
Medical University of South Carolina, MD
University of South Carolina, M

Tennessee

Carson-Newman University, M
East Tennessee State University, D
Lincoln Memorial University, M
Middle Tennessee State University, MO
Southern Adventist University, M
Tennessee State University, M
Tennessee Technological University, M
Union University, D
University of Memphis, M
The University of Tennessee at Chattanooga, MO
Vanderbilt University, M

Texas

Abilene Christian University, M
Baylor University, M
Hardin-Simmons University, M
McMurry University, M
Midwestern State University, M
Prairie View A&M University, M
Texas A&M International University, M
Texas A&M University, M
Texas A&M University - Corpus Christi, M
Texas State University, M
Texas Woman's University, M
University of Houston - Victoria, M
University of Mary Hardin-Baylor, MO
The University of Texas at Arlington, M
The University of Texas at Austin, M
The University of Texas at El Paso, M
The University of Texas Health Science Center at San Antonio, MDO
The University of Texas Rio Grande Valley, M
The University of Texas at Tyler, M
West Texas A&M University, M

Utah

Brigham Young University, M
Westminster College, M

Virginia

James Madison University, M
Liberty University, D
Marymount University, MO
Old Dominion University, MD
Shenandoah University, O
South University (Virginia Beach), M
Virginia Commonwealth University, MO

Washington

Pacific Lutheran University, D
Seattle Pacific University, MO
Seattle University, M

Washington State University, MD

West Virginia

West Virginia Wesleyan College, MO

Wisconsin

Alverno College, M
Bellin College, M
Concordia University Wisconsin, M
Marquette University, O
University of Wisconsin - Eau Claire, MD
University of Wisconsin - Milwaukee, O
University of Wisconsin - Oshkosh, M

U.S. Territories: Puerto Rico

Universidad del Turabo, M
University of Puerto Rico, Medical Sciences Campus, M

Canada

British Columbia

University of Victoria, M

Ontario

Queen's University at Kingston, O

Quebec

McGill University, O

NURSING EDUCATION

United States

Alabama

Auburn University, M
Auburn University at Montgomery, M
Samford University, M
The University of Alabama in Huntsville, O

Arizona

Arizona State University at the Tempe campus, MO
Grand Canyon University, MO
University of Phoenix - Online Campus, M
University of Phoenix - Phoenix Campus, MO

Arkansas

University of Central Arkansas, O

California

Azusa Pacific University, D
California Baptist University, M
California State University, Fresno, M
California State University, Fullerton, M
California State University, Stanislaus, M
Holy Names University, MO
San Jose State University, M
University of Phoenix - Bay Area Campus, M
University of Phoenix - Sacramento Valley Campus, M
University of Phoenix - San Diego Campus, M
University of Phoenix - Southern California Campus, MO

Colorado

Regis University, M
University of Colorado Colorado Springs, M
University of Northern Colorado, MD

Connecticut

Sacred Heart University, M
Southern Connecticut State University, M
University of Hartford, M
University of Saint Joseph, M
Western Connecticut State University, D

District of Columbia

The George Washington University, D
Georgetown University, M
University of Phoenix - Washington D.C. Campus, M

Florida

Barry University, MO
Florida Atlantic University, MO
Florida Southern College, M
Florida State University, MO
Nova Southeastern University, D
South University (Tampa), M
University of Central Florida, O
University of Phoenix - North Florida Campus, M
University of Phoenix - South Florida Campus, M
University of South Florida, MD

Georgia

Albany State University, M
Brenau University, M
Georgia Southern University, O
Piedmont College, M
South University, M
University of North Georgia, M
University of Phoenix - Atlanta Campus, M
University of Phoenix - Augusta Campus, M
University of West Georgia, DO

Hawaii

University of Phoenix - Hawaii Campus, M

Illinois

Bradley University, M
Lewis University, M
McKendree University, M
Millikin University, M
Saint Francis Medical Center College of Nursing, MDO
Southern Illinois University Edwardsville, MO
University of St. Francis, MO

Indiana

Indiana State University, M
Indiana University Kokomo, M
Indiana University - Purdue University Fort Wayne, M
Indiana University - Purdue University Indianapolis, M
Indiana Wesleyan University, M
University of Indianapolis, M
Valparaiso University, MO

Iowa

Clarke University, M
Graceland University, MO
Kaplan University, Davenport Campus, M
Mount Mercy University, M

Kansas

Grantham University, M
University of Saint Mary, M

Kentucky

Bellarmine University, M

Louisiana

McNeese State University, M
Nicholls State University, M
Our Lady of the Lake College, M
Southern University and Agricultural and Mechanical College, D

Maine

Husson University, MO
Saint Joseph's College of Maine, MO
University of Maine, O
University of Southern Maine, M

Maryland

Bowie State University, M
Frostburg State University, M
Salisbury University, M
Towson University, O
Washington Adventist University, M

Massachusetts

American International College, M
Elms College, M
Emmanuel College, M

Framingham State University, M
Regis College, O
Salem State University, M
Worcester State University, M

Michigan

Eastern Michigan University, MO
Ferris State University, M
Grand Valley State University, M
Oakland University, MO
Wayne State University, O

Minnesota

Bethel University, O
Capella University, MD
Metropolitan State University, M
St. Catherine University, M
Walden University, MDO
Winona State University, MO

Mississippi

Delta State University, M

Missouri

Central Methodist University, M
Cox College, M
Goldfarb School of Nursing at Barnes-Jewish College, M
Missouri State University, M
Research College of Nursing, M
University of Missouri - Kansas City, M
Webster University, M

Montana

Montana State University, O

Nebraska

Clarkson College, MO
Nebraska Methodist College, M

Nevada

University of Nevada, Las Vegas, O

New Hampshire

Rivier University, M

New Jersey

Felician University, MO
Monmouth University, MO
Ramapo College of New Jersey, M
Seton Hall University, M
Thomas Edison State University, O

New Mexico

University of Phoenix - New Mexico Campus, M

New York

College of Mount Saint Vincent, O
The College of New Rochelle, O
Daemen College, MO
Excelsior College, M
Le Moyne College, MO
Mercy College, M
Molloy College, M
Mount Saint Mary College, M
New York University, MO
Pace University, MO
Roberts Wesleyan College, M
St. John Fisher College, O
State University of New York College of Technology at Delhi, M
State University of New York Empire State College, M
State University of New York Polytechnic Institute, MO
Stony Brook University, State University of New York, MO

North Carolina

Duke University, M
Lenoir-Rhyne University, M
Queens University of Charlotte, M
The University of North Carolina at Chapel Hill, M
The University of North Carolina at Charlotte, MO

The University of North Carolina at Greensboro, M
The University of North Carolina at Pembroke, M
University of Phoenix - Charlotte Campus, M
Western Carolina University, O
Winston-Salem State University, M

North Dakota

University of Mary, M
University of North Dakota, M

Ohio

Case Western Reserve University, M
Cleveland State University, MD
Kent State University, MO
Lourdes University, M
Mount Carmel College of Nursing, M
Mount St. Joseph University, M
Ohio University, M
Otterbein University, O
The University of Toledo, MO
Ursuline College, M
Walsh University, M

Oklahoma

Northeastern State University, M
Oklahoma Baptist University, M
Oklahoma Wesleyan University, M
Southern Nazarene University, M

Oregon

Oregon Health & Science University, MO
University of Portland, M

Pennsylvania

Carlow University, M
Cedar Crest College, M
Chatham University, M
Clarion University of Pennsylvania, MO
DeSales University, M
Drexel University, M
Duquesne University, M
Edinboro University of Pennsylvania, M
Gwynedd Mercy University, M
Holy Family University, M
Immaculata University, M
Indiana University of Pennsylvania, M
La Roche College, M
La Salle University, O
Messiah College, M
Millersville University of Pennsylvania, M
Moravian College, M
Pennsylvania College of Health Sciences, M
Temple University, M
Villanova University, MO
Waynesburg University, M
West Chester University of Pennsylvania, M
York College of Pennsylvania, M

Rhode Island

University of Rhode Island, M

South Carolina

Francis Marion University, M
Medical University of South Carolina, M

Tennessee

Aquinas College, M
Austin Peay State University, M
Carson-Newman University, M
Middle Tennessee State University, M
Tennessee Technological University, M
Union University, MO
University of Memphis, M
The University of Tennessee at Chattanooga, MO

Texas

Abilene Christian University, M
Angelo State University, M
Lamar University, M
McMurry University, M
Midwestern State University, M
Our Lady of the Lake University of San Antonio, M
Prairie View A&M University, M
Texas A&M University, M
Texas Christian University, M

Texas Woman's University, M
University of Houston - Victoria, M
University of Mary Hardin-Baylor, MDO
The University of Texas at Arlington, M
The University of Texas at Austin, M
The University of Texas at El Paso, MO
The University of Texas Health Science Center at
  San Antonio, MO
The University of Texas at Tyler, M

Utah

University of Phoenix - Utah Campus, M
Western Governors University, M
Westminster College, M

Vermont

Norwich University, M

Virginia

Jefferson College of Health Sciences, M
Liberty University, M
Old Dominion University, M
Shenandoah University, O
Virginia Commonwealth University, M

Washington

Seattle Pacific University, M
University of Washington, Tacoma, M

West Virginia

West Virginia Wesleyan College, MO

Wisconsin

Bellin College, M
Concordia University Wisconsin, M
Herzing University Online, M
Marian University, M
University of Wisconsin - Eau Claire, M

Canada

British Columbia

University of Victoria, M

Maritime Provinces: New Brunswick

University of New Brunswick Fredericton, M

NURSING INFORMATICS

United States

Alabama

Troy University, M

Arizona

University of Phoenix - Phoenix Campus, M

California

National University, MO
University of Phoenix - Bay Area Campus, M
University of Phoenix - Southern California Campus,
  M

District of Columbia

University of Phoenix - Washington D.C. Campus,
  M

Georgia

Georgia State University, M

Illinois

Loyola University Chicago, D

Kansas

Grantham University, M

Michigan

Ferris State University, M

Minnesota

Walden University, MO

New Jersey

Rutgers University - Newark, M

New York

Excelsior College, M
Le Moyne College, MO
New York University, MO

North Carolina

Duke University, MO
The University of North Carolina at Chapel Hill, MO
University of Phoenix - Charlotte Campus, M

Pennsylvania

Waynesburg University, M

Tennessee

Austin Peay State University, M
Tennessee Technological University, M
Vanderbilt University, M

Washington

Seattle Pacific University, M

NUTRITIONAL SCIENCES

United States

Alabama

Alabama Agricultural and Mechanical University, M
Auburn University, BMDO
Tuskegee University, M
The University of Alabama, M
The University of Alabama at Birmingham, MD

Arizona

Arizona State University at the Tempe campus, MD
The University of Arizona, BMD

Arkansas

University of Arkansas for Medical Sciences, M

California

California Baptist University, BM
California State University, Chico, M
California State University, Long Beach, M
California State University, Los Angeles, BM
Chapman University, M
Loma Linda University, MD
Pepperdine University, B
San Diego State University, M
San Jose State University, M
Santa Rosa Junior College, A
University of California, Berkeley, BD
University of California, Davis, BMD

Colorado

Colorado State University, MD
Johnson & Wales University, B
University of Northern Colorado, B

Connecticut

University of Bridgeport, M
University of Connecticut, BMD
University of New Haven, M
University of Saint Joseph, M

Delaware

University of Delaware, BM

District of Columbia

American University, MO
Howard University, MD
University of the District of Columbia, BM

Florida

Broward College, A
Florida International University, MD

Florida State University, MD
Keiser University, B
University of Florida, BMD
University of Miami, M
University of North Florida, M
University of South Florida, MO
The University of Tampa, M

Georgia

Emory University, MD
Georgia Southern University, O
Georgia State University, M
Life University, M
University of Georgia, BMD

Hawaii

University of Hawaii at Manoa, BMD

Idaho

Idaho State University, O

Illinois

Benedictine University, M
Eastern Illinois University, M
Elmhurst College, B
Loyola University Chicago, MO
Northern Illinois University, M
Rush University, M
Southern Illinois University Carbondale, BM
University of Chicago, D
University of Illinois at Chicago, BMD
University of Illinois at Urbana - Champaign, MD

Indiana

Ball State University, M
Indiana University Bloomington, M
Indiana University - Purdue University Indianapolis,
    M
Purdue University, MD
University of Saint Francis, B
University of Southern Indiana, B

Iowa

Iowa State University of Science and Technology,
    BMD

Kansas

Kansas State University, MD
The University of Kansas, MDO

Kentucky

Eastern Kentucky University, M
University of Kentucky, MD

Louisiana

Louisiana State University and Agricultural & Me-
    chanical College, B
Louisiana Tech University, M
McNeese State University, BM
Tulane University, M

Maine

University of Maine, MD

Maryland

Johns Hopkins University, MD
University of Maryland, College Park, MD

Massachusetts

Boston University, BMD
Framingham State University, M
Harvard University, D
Northeastern University, M
Simmons College, MO
Tufts University, MD
University of Massachusetts Amherst, BMD
University of Massachusetts Lowell, BO

Michigan

Andrews University, M
Central Michigan University, M
Eastern Michigan University, M
Michigan State University, BMD
University of Michigan, MD

Wayne State University, MDO

Minnesota

College of Saint Benedict, B
Concordia College, B
Saint John's University, B
University of Minnesota, Twin Cities Campus, BMD

Mississippi

Mississippi State University, MD
University of Mississippi, M
University of Southern Mississippi, MD

Missouri

Logan University, M
Saint Louis University, M
Southeast Missouri State University, M
University of Missouri, MD

Nebraska

University of Nebraska - Lincoln, MD
University of Nebraska Medical Center, O

Nevada

University of Nevada, Las Vegas, B
University of Nevada, Reno, BM

New Hampshire

University of New Hampshire, BMD

New Jersey

College of Saint Elizabeth, MO
Montclair State University, MO
Rutgers University - New Brunswick, BMD
Rutgers University - Newark, MDO

New Mexico

New Mexico State University, M
University of New Mexico, M

New York

Adelphi University, M
Brooklyn College of the City University of New York,
    M
Canisius College, BMO
Columbia University, MD
Cornell University, BMD
D'Youville College, M
Hunter College of the City University of New York,
    M
Lehman College of the City University of New York,
    M
New York Institute of Technology, MO
New York University, BMD
The Sage Colleges, B
State University of New York College at Oneonta, M
Stony Brook University, State University of New
    York, MO
Syracuse University, BM
University at Buffalo, the State University of New
    York, MDO

North Carolina

Appalachian State University, M
East Carolina University, M
Meredith College, MO
North Carolina Agricultural and Technical State Uni-
    versity, M
North Carolina State University, BMD
The University of North Carolina at Chapel Hill, MD
The University of North Carolina at Greensboro,
    BMD

North Dakota

North Dakota State University, M

Ohio

Bowling Green State University, BM
Case Western Reserve University, BMD
Kent State University, M
The Ohio State University, BMD
Ohio University, M
The University of Akron, M
University of Cincinnati, BM

The University of Toledo, M

Oklahoma

Oklahoma State University, MD
Tulsa Community College, A
University of Central Oklahoma, M
University of Oklahoma Health Sciences Center, BM

Oregon

American College of Healthcare Sciences, O
Oregon Health & Science University, MO
Oregon State University, MD

Pennsylvania

Cedar Crest College, O
Drexel University, BM
Immaculata University, M
Indiana University of Pennsylvania, M
La Salle University, B
Marywood University, MO
Penn State University Park, MD
University of Pittsburgh, M
West Chester University of Pennsylvania, M

Rhode Island

Johnson & Wales University, B
University of Rhode Island, MD

South Carolina

Clemson University, M
Winthrop University, M

South Dakota

Sisseton-Wahpeton College, A
South Dakota State University, MD

Tennessee

East Tennessee State University, M
Huntington College of Health Sciences, BMD
Lipscomb University, M
The University of Tennessee, M
The University of Tennessee at Martin, M

Texas

Abilene Christian University, O
Baylor University, M
Sam Houston State University, M
Texas A&M University, MD
Texas State University, M
Texas Tech University, MD
Texas Woman's University, BMD
University of Houston, M
University of the Incarnate Word, BM
The University of Texas at Austin, MD

Utah

Brigham Young University, M
University of Utah, M
Utah State University, MD

Vermont

Goddard College, B
University of Vermont, BMD

Virginia

George Mason University, M
James Madison University, M
Liberty University, M
Virginia Polytechnic Institute and State University,
    MD

Washington

Bastyr University, MO
Central Washington University, BM
University of Washington, MD
Washington State University, BM

West Virginia

Marshall University, M
West Virginia University, M

Wisconsin

Mount Mary University, M
University of Wisconsin - Madison, BMD

University of Wisconsin - Milwaukee, B
University of Wisconsin - Stevens Point, BM
University of Wisconsin - Stout, M

Wyoming

Casper College, A
University of Wyoming, M

U.S. Territories: Puerto Rico

University of Puerto Rico, Medical Sciences Campus, MDO
University of Puerto Rico, Río Piedras Campus, M

Canada

Alberta

University of Alberta, B

British Columbia

The University of British Columbia, MD

Manitoba

University of Manitoba, MD

Maritime Provinces: New Brunswick

Université de Moncton, M

Maritime Provinces: Nova Scotia

Mount Saint Vincent University, BM

Ontario

McMaster University, MD
University of Guelph, BMD
University of Toronto, MD

Quebec

McGill University, BMDO
Université Laval, BMD
Université de Montréal, BMDO

Saskatchewan

University of Saskatchewan, B

OCCUPATIONAL HEALTH AND INDUSTRIAL HYGIENE

United States

California

California State University, Fresno, B

Illinois

Illinois State University, B

Kansas

Seward County Community College and Area Technical School, A

Michigan

Grand Valley State University, B

Montana

Montana Tech of The University of Montana, B

New York

Niagara County Community College, A

North Carolina

North Carolina Agricultural and Technical State University, B

Ohio

Ohio University, B

Oklahoma

University of Central Oklahoma, B

Canada

British Columbia

British Columbia Institute of Technology, A

Ontario

Ryerson University, B

OCCUPATIONAL HEALTH NURSING

United States

Florida

University of South Florida, MD

Illinois

University of Illinois at Chicago, M

Minnesota

University of Minnesota, Twin Cities Campus, MD

New Jersey

Rutgers University - Newark, M

North Carolina

The University of North Carolina at Chapel Hill, M

Ohio

University of Cincinnati, M

U.S. Territories: Puerto Rico

University of the Sacred Heart, M

OCCUPATIONAL SAFETY AND HEALTH TECHNOLOGY/TECHNICIAN

United States

Alabama

Columbia Southern University, AB
Community College of the Air Force, A
Jacksonville State University, B
Wallace State Community College, A

Alaska

University of Alaska Anchorage, A
University of Alaska Anchorage, Kenai Peninsula College, A
University of Alaska Anchorage, Kodiak College, A

Arizona

GateWay Community College, A
Paradise Valley Community College, A

Arkansas

NorthWest Arkansas Community College, A

California

California State University, Fresno, B
Cuyamaca College, A
Las Positas College, A
Mt. San Antonio College, A
San Diego City College, A
San Diego Miramar College, A

Colorado

Trinidad State Junior College, A

Florida

Embry-Riddle Aeronautical University - Daytona, B
Embry-Riddle Aeronautical University - Worldwide, B
Northwest Florida State College, A

Georgia

Coastal Pines Technical College, A
Lanier Technical College, A

Hawaii

Honolulu Community College, A

Indiana

Indiana State University, B
Ivy Tech Community College - Central Indiana, A
Ivy Tech Community College - Northeast, A
Ivy Tech Community College - Northwest, A
Ivy Tech Community College - Wabash Valley, A

Iowa

Clinton Community College, A

Kansas

Pittsburg State University, B

Kentucky

Murray State University, B

Louisiana

Delgado Community College, A
Southeastern Louisiana University, B

Maryland

Anne Arundel Community College, A
Community College of Baltimore County, A

Michigan

Grand Valley State University, B

Mississippi

Southwest Mississippi Community College, A

Missouri

Southwest Baptist University, B
University of Central Missouri, B

New Hampshire

Keene State College, B

New Mexico

San Juan College, A

New York

Rochester Institute of Technology, B

North Carolina

Durham Technical Community College, A

Ohio

Cincinnati State Technical and Community College, A

Oklahoma

Oklahoma State University, Oklahoma City, A
Southeastern Oklahoma State University, B
University of Central Oklahoma, B

Pennsylvania

Indiana University of Pennsylvania, B
Millersville University of Pennsylvania, B
Slippery Rock University of Pennsylvania, B
Westmoreland County Community College, A

Texas

Brazosport College, A
College of the Mainland, A
Del Mar College, A
Houston Community College, A
Kilgore College, A
Lamar Institute of Technology, A
Lamar State College - Port Arthur, A
St. Philip's College, A
San Jacinto College District, A
Texas State Technical College, A
University of Houston - Downtown, B

Washington

Bates Technical College, A
Central Washington University, B

West Virginia

Fairmont State University, AB
Marshall University, B

Wisconsin

University of Wisconsin - Whitewater, B

Wyoming

Central Wyoming College, A

U.S. Territories: Puerto Rico

Bayamón Central University, B

OCCUPATIONAL THERAPIST ASSISTANT

United States

Arizona

Carrington College - Phoenix West, A
Pima Medical Institute (Mesa), A
Pima Medical Institute (Tucson), A

Arkansas

Arkansas State University, A
Arkansas Tech University, A
Pulaski Technical College, A

California

Loma Linda University, A

Colorado

Pima Medical Institute (Denver), A
Pueblo Community College, A

Connecticut

Goodwin College, A
Lincoln College of New England, A
Manchester Community College, A

Delaware

Delaware Technical & Community College, Jack F.
  Owens Campus, A
Delaware Technical & Community College,
  Stanton/Wilmington Campus, A

Florida

Adventist University of Health Sciences, A
Daytona State College, A
Florida State College at Jacksonville, A
Keiser University, A
Polk State College, A
South University (Royal Palm Beach), A
South University (Tampa), A
State College of Florida Manatee-Sarasota, A

Georgia

Augusta Technical College, A
Darton State College, A
Middle Georgia State University, A

Hawaii

Kapiolani Community College, A

Illinois

College of DuPage, A
Fox College, A
Illinois Central College, A
John A. Logan College, A
Kaskaskia College, A
Lewis and Clark Community College, A
Lincoln Land Community College, A
McHenry County College, A
Parkland College, A
Rend Lake College, A
Shawnee Community College, A
South Suburban College, A

Indiana

Ivy Tech Community College - Central Indiana, A
University of Southern Indiana, A

Iowa

Brown Mackie College - Quad Cities, A
Hawkeye Community College, A
Kirkwood Community College, A
Scott Community College, A

Kansas

Newman University, A
Washburn University, A

Kentucky

Brown Mackie College - Hopkinsville, A
Jefferson Community and Technical College, A
Madisonville Community College, A

Louisiana

Bossier Parish Community College, A
Delgado Community College, A
University of Louisiana at Monroe, A

Maine

Kennebec Valley Community College, A

Maryland

Allegany College of Maryland, A
Wor-Wic Community College, A

Massachusetts

Bristol Community College, A
Quinsigamond Community College, A
Springfield Technical Community College, A

Michigan

Baker College, A
Macomb Community College, A
Mott Community College, A
Oakland Community College, A

Minnesota

Anoka Technical College, A
Northland Community and Technical College, A
St. Catherine University, A

Mississippi

Holmes Community College, A

Missouri

Crowder College, A
East Central College, A
Jefferson College, A
Ozarks Technical Community College, A
St. Charles Community College, A
State Fair Community College, A

New Hampshire

River Valley Community College, A

New Jersey

County College of Morris, A
Ocean County College, A
Rutgers University - New Brunswick, A
Rutgers University - Newark, B

New Mexico

Eastern New Mexico University - Roswell, A
San Juan College, A
Western New Mexico University, A

New York

Erie Community College, North Campus, A
Fiorello H. LaGuardia Community College of the
  City University of New York, A
Jamestown Community College, A
Maria College, A
Mercy College, A
Orange County Community College, A

North Carolina

Cabarrus College of Health Sciences, A
Cape Fear Community College, A
Pitt Community College, A
Stanly Community College, A

North Dakota

North Dakota State College of Science, A

Ohio

Brown Mackie College - Akron, A
Cincinnati State Technical and Community College,
  A
James A. Rhodes State College, A
Kent State University at Ashtabula, A
Kent State University at East Liverpool, A
Owens Community College, A

Oklahoma

Murray State College, A
Southwestern Oklahoma State University, A

Pennsylvania

California University of Pennsylvania, A
Community College of Allegheny County, A
Harcum College, A
Lehigh Carbon Community College, A
Mercyhurst North East, A
Penn State Berks, A
Penn State DuBois, A
Penn State Mont Alto, A
Pennsylvania College of Technology, A
Reading Area Community College, A

Rhode Island

Community College of Rhode Island, A
New England Institute of Technology, A

South Carolina

Greenville Technical College, A
Midlands Technical College, A

South Dakota

Lake Area Technical Institute, A

Tennessee

Nashville State Community College, A
Walters State Community College, A

Texas

Austin Community College District, A
Del Mar College, A
Houston Community College, A
Panola College, A
St. Philip's College, A
Tyler Junior College, A
Weatherford College, A

Utah

Salt Lake Community College, A

Virginia

Jefferson College of Health Sciences, A
Virginia College in Richmond, A

Washington

Green River College, A
Pima Medical Institute (Renton), A

West Virginia

University of Charleston, A

Wisconsin

Fox Valley Technical College, A
Wisconsin Indianhead Technical College, A

Wyoming

Casper College, A

U.S. Territories: Puerto Rico

Inter American University of Puerto Rico, Ponce
  Campus, A
University of Puerto Rico in Humacao, A

OCCUPATIONAL THERAPY/ THERAPIST

United States

Alabama

Alabama State University, BM
Oakwood University, A
Tuskegee University, BM
The University of Alabama at Birmingham, MO
University of South Alabama, M
Wallace State Community College, A

Arizona

Carrington College - Phoenix North, A

Arkansas

University of Central Arkansas, M

California

California State University, Dominguez Hills, M
Dominican University of California, BM
Grossmont College, A
Loma Linda University, MD
Monterey Peninsula College, A
Sacramento City College, A
Samuel Merritt University, M
San Jose State University, BM
Santa Ana College, A
Sonoma State University, M
University of Southern California, BMD

Colorado

Colorado State University, MD

Connecticut

Quinnipiac University, BM
Sacred Heart University, BM

District of Columbia

Howard University, B

Florida

Barry University, M
College of Central Florida, A
Florida Agricultural and Mechanical University, M
Florida Gulf Coast University, M
Florida International University, M
Nova Southeastern University, MD
Palm Beach State College, A
South Florida State College, A
South University (Royal Palm Beach), D
State College of Florida Manatee-Sarasota, A
University of Florida, M

Georgia

Andrew College, A
Brenau University, BM
College of Coastal Georgia, A

Idaho

Idaho State University, M

Illinois

Chicago State University, M
City Colleges of Chicago, Wilbur Wright College, A
College of DuPage, A
Elmhurst College, B
Governors State University, M
Illinois College, B
McKendree University, B
Rush University, M
Sauk Valley Community College, A
Southeastern Illinois College, A
University of Illinois at Chicago, MD

Indiana

Indiana State University, M
Indiana University - Purdue University Indianapolis, M
University of Indianapolis, MD
University of Southern Indiana, BM

Iowa

Iowa Central Community College, A
St. Ambrose University, M
Wartburg College, B

Kansas

Barton County Community College, A
The University of Kansas, BMD

Kentucky

Eastern Kentucky University, BM
Spalding University, BM

Louisiana

Louisiana State University Health Sciences Center, M
University of Louisiana at Monroe, M

Maine

Husson University, M
University of New England, BM
University of Southern Maine, M

Maryland

Allegany College of Maryland, A
Community College of Baltimore County, A
Towson University, BM

Massachusetts

American International College, BM
Bay Path University, BM
Boston University, MD
North Shore Community College, A
Salem State University, M
Springfield College, BM
Tufts University, MDO
Worcester State University, BM

Michigan

Baker College, B
Calvin College, B
Eastern Michigan University, BM
Grand Valley State University, BM
Saginaw Valley State University, BM
Wayne State University, M
Western Michigan University, BM

Minnesota

College of Saint Benedict, B
The College of St. Scholastica, M
St. Catherine University, BMD
Saint John's University, B

Mississippi

Coahoma Community College, A
Holmes Community College, A
Northeast Mississippi Community College, A
University of Mississippi Medical Center, M

Missouri

Maryville University of Saint Louis, M
Metropolitan Community College - Kansas City, A
Ozarks Technical Community College, A
Rockhurst University, M
Saint Louis University, BM
University of Missouri, BM
Washington University in St. Louis, MD

Nebraska

College of Saint Mary, M
Creighton University, D

Nevada

Nevada State College, B

New Hampshire

University of New Hampshire, BMO

New Jersey

Kean University, M
Seton Hall University, M
Stockton University, M

New Mexico

University of New Mexico, M
Western New Mexico University, ABM

New York

Columbia University, MD
Dominican College, BM
D'Youville College, BM
Ithaca College, BM
Keuka College, BM
Long Island University - LIU Brooklyn, B
Mercy College, M
Nazareth College of Rochester, B
New York Institute of Technology, M
New York University, MD
Rochester Institute of Technology, M
Rockland Community College, A
State University of New York Downstate Medical Center, B
Stony Brook University, State University of New York, M
Touro College, AM
University at Buffalo, the State University of New York, BM
Utica College, M
York College of the City University of New York, B

North Carolina

Durham Technical Community College, A
East Carolina University, MO
Lenoir-Rhyne University, M
Louisburg College, A
The University of North Carolina at Chapel Hill, MD
Winston-Salem State University, BM

North Dakota

University of Mary, M
University of North Dakota, M

Ohio

Cleveland State University, M
The Ohio State University, M
Shawnee State University, ABM
Sinclair Community College, A
Stark State College, A
The University of Findlay, BM
The University of Toledo, D
Xavier University, BM
Zane State College, A

Oklahoma

Northeastern State University, M
Tulsa Community College, A
University of Oklahoma Health Sciences Center, M

Oregon

Mt. Hood Community College, A
Pacific University, D

Pennsylvania

Alvernia University, M
Brightwood Career Institute, Pittsburgh Campus, A
Chatham University, MD
Duquesne University, BMD
Elizabethtown College, BM
Gannon University, BM
Keystone College, A
Misericordia University, MD
Penn State Mont Alto, B
Philadelphia University, MD
Saint Francis University, BM
Saint Vincent College, B
Temple University, MD
Thomas Jefferson University, MD
University of Pittsburgh, M
University of the Sciences, BMD
The University of Scranton, BM

Rhode Island

New England Institute of Technology, M

South Carolina

Medical University of South Carolina, M
Trident Technical College, A

South Dakota

The University of South Dakota, M

Tennessee

Belmont University, MD
Milligan College, M
Nashville State Community College, A
Roane State Community College, A
Southern Adventist University, A
Tennessee State University, M

Texas

Abilene Christian University, M
Amarillo College, A
Lone Star College - Kingwood, A
Navarro College, A
North Central Texas College, A
South Texas College, A
Texas Woman's University, MD
The University of Texas at El Paso, M
The University of Texas Health Science Center at
  San Antonio, M
The University of Texas Medical Branch, M
The University of Texas Rio Grande Valley, M

Utah

University of Utah, MD

Virginia

James Madison University, M
Jefferson College of Health Sciences, M
Radford University, M
Shenandoah University, M
Virginia Commonwealth University, MD

Washington

Eastern Washington University, BM
University of Puget Sound, MD
University of Washington, M
Yakima Valley Community College, A

West Virginia

West Virginia University, M

Wisconsin

Carthage College, B
Concordia University Wisconsin, BM
Madison Area Technical College, A
Milwaukee Area Technical College, A
Mount Mary University, BMD
University of Wisconsin - La Crosse, M
University of Wisconsin - Madison, MD
University of Wisconsin - Milwaukee, BMO
Western Technical College, A

U.S. Territories: Puerto Rico

University of Puerto Rico, Medical Sciences Campus, M

Canada

Alberta

University of Alberta, MD

British Columbia

The University of British Columbia, M

Manitoba

University of Manitoba, BM

Maritime Provinces: Nova Scotia

Dalhousie University, BM

Ontario

McMaster University, M
Queen's University at Kingston, BM
University of Ottawa, B
University of Toronto, M
The University of Western Ontario, M

Quebec

Université Laval, B
Université de Montréal, BO

OCEAN ENGINEERING

United States

Alaska

University of Alaska Anchorage, O

California

California State University, Long Beach, B
University of California, San Diego, MD

Delaware

University of Delaware, MD

Florida

Broward College, A
Florida Atlantic University, BMD
Florida Institute of Technology, BMD
South Florida State College, A
University of Florida, MD

Hawaii

University of Hawaii at Manoa, MD

Maryland

United States Naval Academy, B

Massachusetts

Massachusetts Institute of Technology, MD

Michigan

Northwestern Michigan College, B
University of Michigan, MDO

New Hampshire

University of New Hampshire, BMDO

New Jersey

Princeton University, D
Stevens Institute of Technology, MD

Rhode Island

University of Rhode Island, BMD

Texas

Texas A&M University, BMD

Virginia

Virginia Polytechnic Institute and State University,
  BM

Canada

Newfoundland and Labrador

Memorial University of Newfoundland, BMD

OCEANOGRAPHY, CHEMICAL AND PHYSICAL

United States

California

Grossmont College, A
Humboldt State University, B
University of California, Los Angeles, MD
University of California, San Diego, MD
University of Southern California, MD

Colorado

University of Colorado Boulder, MD

Connecticut

United States Coast Guard Academy, B
University of Connecticut, MD
Yale University, D

Delaware

University of Delaware, MD

Florida

Florida Institute of Technology, BMD
Florida State University, MD
Nova Southeastern University, MDO
University of Miami, BMD
University of South Florida, MD
University of West Florida, B

Hawaii

Hawai'i Pacific University, B
University of Hawaii at Manoa, MD

Louisiana

Louisiana State University and Agricultural & Mechanical College, BMD

Maine

College of the Atlantic, B
Maine Maritime Academy, B
University of Maine, MD

Maryland

United States Naval Academy, B
University of Maryland, College Park, MD

Massachusetts

Massachusetts Institute of Technology, MD

Michigan

University of Michigan, B

Mississippi

University of Southern Mississippi, B

New Hampshire

University of New Hampshire, M

New Jersey

Princeton University, D
Rider University, B
Rutgers University - New Brunswick, MD

New York

Cornell University, D

North Carolina

Cape Fear Community College, A
Elizabeth City State University, B
North Carolina State University, BMD
The University of North Carolina Wilmington, B

Oregon

Oregon State University, MD

Pennsylvania

Kutztown University of Pennsylvania, B
Millersville University of Pennsylvania, B

Rhode Island

University of Rhode Island, MD

South Carolina

University of South Carolina, B

Texas

Texas A&M University, MD

Virginia

Old Dominion University, MD

Washington

Everett Community College, A
Shoreline Community College, A
University of Washington, BMD

Whitman College, B

Wisconsin
University of Wisconsin - Madison, MD

Canada

British Columbia
The University of British Columbia, BMD
University of Victoria, BMD

Maritime Provinces: Nova Scotia
Dalhousie University, BMD

Newfoundland and Labrador
Memorial University of Newfoundland, BMD

Quebec
McGill University, MD
Université Laval, D
Université du Québec à Rimouski, MD

OFFICE MANAGEMENT AND SUPERVISION

United States

Alabama
Community College of the Air Force, A
Jefferson State Community College, A
Virginia College in Huntsville, A
Virginia College in Mobile, A

Alaska
Ilisagvik College, A

Arkansas
Southern Arkansas University Tech, A

California
Berkeley City College, A
Chabot College, A
Chaffey College, A
College of the Desert, A
College of Marin, A
Cuyamaca College, A
Glendale Community College, A
Los Angeles Valley College, A
MiraCosta College, A
Modesto Junior College, A
National University, B
Point Loma Nazarene University, B
Riverside City College, A
Santa Monica College, A

Colorado
Adams State University, B
Community College of Aurora, A
Community College of Denver, A

Connecticut
Goodwin College, A

Delaware
Delaware Technical & Community College, Jack F. Owens Campus, A
Delaware Technical & Community College, Stanton/Wilmington Campus, A
Delaware Technical & Community College, Terry Campus, A

District of Columbia
University of the District of Columbia, B

Florida
College of Central Florida, A
Eastern Florida State College, A
Florida Gateway College, A
Florida State College at Jacksonville, A
Gulf Coast State College, A
Lake-Sumter State College, A

Miami Dade College, A
Millennia Atlantic University, A
Northwest Florida State College, A
South Florida State College, A
Tallahassee Community College, A
Virginia College in Pensacola, A

Georgia
Clayton State University, B
Dalton State College, A
Emmanuel College, A
Virginia College in Macon, A

Illinois
College of DuPage, A
John A. Logan College, A
John Wood Community College, A
Lake Land College, A
Loyola University Chicago, B
Roosevelt University, B
South Suburban College, A

Indiana
Indiana State University, B
Ivy Tech Community College - Wabash Valley, A
University of Southern Indiana, B

Iowa
Des Moines Area Community College, A
Iowa Lakes Community College, A

Kansas
Seward County Community College and Area Technical School, A

Kentucky
Daymar College (Owensboro), A
Eastern Kentucky University, B
Jefferson Community and Technical College, A
Union College, B

Louisiana
Virginia College in Baton Rouge, A

Maryland
Cecil College, A
Howard Community College, A

Massachusetts
Babson College, B
Massasoit Community College, A
Salter College (Chicopee), A

Michigan
Alpena Community College, A
Eastern Michigan University, B
Lansing Community College, A
Oakland Community College, A
St. Clair County Community College, A
Washtenaw Community College, A
Wayne County Community College District, A

Minnesota
Academy College, A
Alexandria Technical and Community College, A
Anoka Technical College, A
Lake Superior College, A
Northland Community and Technical College, A
Saint Paul College - A Community & Technical College, A

Mississippi
Mississippi Valley State University, B
Northwest Mississippi Community College, A
Virginia College in Biloxi, A
Virginia College in Jackson, A

Missouri
St. Charles Community College, A
Southwest Baptist University, B
University of Central Missouri, B

Montana
Blackfeet Community College, A
Chief Dull Knife College, A

Nebraska
Northeast Community College, A

New Hampshire
White Mountains Community College, A

New Jersey
Rider University, B

New Mexico
Clovis Community College, A
Eastern New Mexico University - Roswell, A
Luna Community College, A

New York
Corning Community College, A
Erie Community College, North Campus, A
Erie Community College, South Campus, A
Globe Institute of Technology, B
Jamestown Business College, A
Jefferson Community College, A
Morrisville State College, AB

North Carolina
Asheville-Buncombe Technical Community College, A
Catawba Valley Community College, A
Cleveland Community College, A
Craven Community College, A
Durham Technical Community College, A
Fayetteville Technical Community College, A
Forsyth Technical Community College, A
Gaston College, A
Guilford Technical Community College, A
Halifax Community College, A
Johnston Community College, A
Lenoir Community College, A
McDowell Technical Community College, A
Miller-Motte College (Cary), A
Mitchell Community College, A
Montgomery Community College, A
Piedmont Community College, A
Pitt Community College, A
Richmond Community College, A
Roanoke-Chowan Community College, A
Rockingham Community College, A
Rowan-Cabarrus Community College, A
Wake Technical Community College, A
Wayne Community College, A
Western Piedmont Community College, A
Wilson Community College, A

North Dakota
Dakota College at Bottineau, A
Valley City State University, B

Ohio
Bowling Green State University, B
Miami University, A
Miami University Hamilton, B
Miami University Middletown, A
Northwest State Community College, A
Owens Community College, A
Shawnee State University, A
Stautzenberger College (Brecksville), A
The University of Akron, A
The University of Akron Wayne College, B

Oklahoma
East Central University, B

Oregon
Chemeketa Community College, A
Clackamas Community College, A
Lane Community College, A
Portland Community College, A
Tillamook Bay Community College, A
Treasure Valley Community College, A

Pennsylvania

Community College of Allegheny County, A
Consolidated School of Business (Lancaster), A
Consolidated School of Business (York), A
Delaware County Community College, A
McCann School of Business & Technology
  (Lewisburg), A

South Carolina

Forrest College, A
Piedmont Technical College, A
University of South Carolina, B
Virginia College in Spartanburg, A

Tennessee

Middle Tennessee State University, B
Pellissippi State Community College, A
Virginia College in Chattanooga, A

Texas

Brookhaven College, A
Lee College, A
Tarleton State University, B
Texas A&M University - Central Texas, B
Virginia College in Austin, A

Virginia

Virginia College in Richmond, A

Washington

Bellevue College, A
Big Bend Community College, A
Centralia College, A
Clover Park Technical College, A
Columbia Basin College, A
Edmonds Community College, A
Grays Harbor College, A
Green River College, A
Peninsula College, A
Renton Technical College, A
Skagit Valley College, A
Tacoma Community College, A
Wenatchee Valley College, A

Wisconsin

Fox Valley Technical College, A
Maranatha Baptist University, AB
Moraine Park Technical College, A
Waukesha County Technical College, A
Western Technical College, A
Wisconsin Indianhead Technical College, A

Wyoming

Eastern Wyoming College, A

U.S. Territories: Guam

Guam Community College, A

U.S. Territories: Puerto Rico

American University of Puerto Rico (Bayamon), B
Inter American University of Puerto Rico, Aguadilla
  Campus, AB
Inter American University of Puerto Rico, Arecibo
  Campus, AB
Inter American University of Puerto Rico, Bar-
  ranquitas Campus, AB
Inter American University of Puerto Rico, Bayamón
  Campus, A
Inter American University of Puerto Rico, Fajardo
  Campus, AB
Inter American University of Puerto Rico, Guayama
  Campus, AB
Inter American University of Puerto Rico, Metropoli-
  tan Campus, B
Inter American University of Puerto Rico, Ponce
  Campus, AB
Inter American University of Puerto Rico, San
  Germán Campus, AB
Pontifical Catholic University of Puerto Rico, B
Universidad Metropolitana, AB
Universidad del Turabo, AB
University of Puerto Rico in Aguadilla, B
University of Puerto Rico in Utuado, B
University of the Sacred Heart, B

ONCOLOGY NURSING

United States

Delaware

University of Delaware, MO

Florida

University of South Florida, MD

Illinois

Loyola University Chicago, MO

Ohio

Case Western Reserve University, M

Pennsylvania

Gwynedd Mercy University, M

U.S. Territories: Puerto Rico

Universidad Metropolitana, O

OPERATIONS MANAGEMENT AND SUPERVISION

United States

Alabama

Auburn University, B
Remington College - Mobile Campus, B

Arizona

Arizona State University at the Polytechnic campus,
  B
The University of Arizona, B
University of Phoenix - Phoenix Campus, B

California

California State University, Dominguez Hills, B
California State University, Long Beach, B
California State University, Stanislaus, B
Golden Gate University, B
San Diego State University, B
University of Phoenix - Bay Area Campus, B
University of Phoenix - Sacramento Valley Campus,
  B

Colorado

Fort Lewis College, B
University of Phoenix - Colorado Campus, B
University of Phoenix - Colorado Springs Downtown
  Campus, B

Connecticut

Goodwin College, B

Delaware

University of Delaware, B

Florida

Florida SouthWestern State College, B
Florida State College at Jacksonville, A
Hillsborough Community College, A
Miami Dade College, A
Northwest Florida State College, A
Polk State College, A
South Florida State College, A

Georgia

Dalton State College, B
Georgia Piedmont Technical College, A
University of Phoenix - Atlanta Campus, B
University of Phoenix - Columbus Georgia Campus,
  AB

Hawaii

Remington College - Honolulu Campus, B
University of Phoenix - Hawaii Campus, B

Idaho

Boise State University, B

Illinois

Governors State University, B
Joliet Junior College, A
Loyola University Chicago, B
McHenry County College, A
Northern Illinois University, B
Oakton Community College, A
Prairie State College, A
University of Illinois at Urbana - Champaign, B

Indiana

Ball State University, B
Indiana University - Purdue University Fort Wayne,
  AB
Indiana University - Purdue University Indianapolis,
  B
Oakland City University, B
Purdue University Northwest (Westville), B
Trine University, B
University of Indianapolis, B
University of Southern Indiana, B

Iowa

Mount Mercy University, B

Kansas

Bethany College, B
Southwestern College, B

Louisiana

Louisiana Tech University, B

Maryland

Capitol Technology University, B

Massachusetts

Babson College, B
Boston College, B
Bunker Hill Community College, A
University of Massachusetts Amherst, B
University of Massachusetts Dartmouth, B
Wentworth Institute of Technology, B

Michigan

Alpena Community College, A
Central Michigan University, B
Ferris State University, B
Macomb Community College, A
Oakland University, B
Saginaw Valley State University, B

Minnesota

Metropolitan State University, B
Minnesota State University Moorhead, B
Northland Community and Technical College, A
University of Minnesota, Crookston, B
University of Minnesota, Twin Cities Campus, B
University of St. Thomas, B

Mississippi

East Mississippi Community College, A

Missouri

Avila University, B
Mineral Area College, A
Washington University in St. Louis, B

Nebraska

University of Nebraska at Kearney, B

Nevada

Great Basin College, A
University of Phoenix - Las Vegas Campus, B

New Hampshire

Granite State College, B
Southern New Hampshire University, B

New Jersey

Thomas Edison State University, B
University of Phoenix - Jersey City Campus, B

New York

Excelsior College, B
Le Moyne College, B
Mohawk Valley Community College, A

North Carolina

Central Carolina Community College, A
Cleveland Community College, A
Durham Technical Community College, A
Fayetteville Technical Community College, A
Lenoir Community College, A
McDowell Technical Community College, A
Mitchell Community College, A
Pitt Community College, A
University of North Carolina at Asheville, B
The University of North Carolina at Charlotte, B
Wayne Community College, A

North Dakota

Bismarck State College, B
University of North Dakota, B

Ohio

Bowling Green State University, B
Cleveland State University, B
Franklin University, B
Miami University, B
The Ohio State University, B
Stark State College, A
Terra State Community College, A
The University of Akron, B
University of Cincinnati, B
University of Dayton, B
The University of Toledo, B
Youngstown State University, B

Oklahoma

Northeastern State University, B
University of Central Oklahoma, B

Oregon

Clackamas Community College, A
Oregon State University, B

Pennsylvania

Carnegie Mellon University, B
Drexel University, B
Edinboro University of Pennsylvania, B
Pennsylvania Highlands Community College, A
University of Pennsylvania, B
University of Phoenix - Philadelphia Campus, B
The University of Scranton, B
Widener University, B

Rhode Island

Rhode Island College, B
Roger Williams University, B

South Dakota

National American University (Rapid City), B
South Dakota State University, B

Tennessee

Chattanooga State Community College, A
Remington College - Memphis Campus, B
Tennessee Technological University, B

Texas

Kilgore College, A
Lamar University, B
Lee College, A
LeTourneau University, B
Sam Houston State University, B
Texas Southern University, B
University of Houston, B
University of North Texas, B
University of Phoenix - Dallas Campus, B
University of Phoenix - Houston Campus, B

Utah

University of Utah, B
Utah State University, B
Utah Valley University, B

Washington

University of Phoenix - Western Washington Campus, B
Washington State University, B
Washington State University - Global Campus, B
Washington State University - Vancouver, B
Western Washington University, B

West Virginia

Blue Ridge Community and Technical College, A

Wisconsin

Chippewa Valley Technical College, A
Marian University, B
Milwaukee Area Technical College, A
Northcentral Technical College, A
Northeast Wisconsin Technical College, A
Southwest Wisconsin Technical College, A
University of Wisconsin - Madison, B
University of Wisconsin - Milwaukee, B
University of Wisconsin - Stout, B
University of Wisconsin - Whitewater, B

U.S. Territories: Puerto Rico

Inter American University of Puerto Rico, Bayamón Campus, B
Inter American University of Puerto Rico, Metropolitan Campus, B
Inter American University of Puerto Rico, Ponce Campus, B
University of Puerto Rico, Río Piedras Campus, B

Canada

Alberta

University of Alberta, B

British Columbia

British Columbia Institute of Technology, A
Thompson Rivers University, B

Maritime Provinces: New Brunswick

Université de Moncton, B

Quebec

Concordia University, B
McGill University, B

Saskatchewan

University of Saskatchewan, B

OPERATIONS RESEARCH

United States

Alabama

The University of Alabama in Huntsville, M

Arkansas

University of Arkansas, M

California

California State University, Fullerton, B
University of California, Berkeley, BMD
University of Southern California, M

Colorado

Colorado School of Mines, D
United States Air Force Academy, B
University of Colorado Boulder, M
University of Colorado Denver, MD

Connecticut

United States Coast Guard Academy, B

Delaware

Delaware Technical & Community College, Stanton/Wilmington Campus, A
University of Delaware, M

District of Columbia

The Catholic University of America, M

Florida

Florida Institute of Technology, M

Georgia

Georgia Institute of Technology, MD
Georgia State University, M

Idaho

Idaho State University, M

Illinois

Southern Illinois University Edwardsville, M
University of Illinois at Chicago, MD
University of Illinois at Urbana - Champaign, B

Indiana

Indiana University - Purdue University Fort Wayne, M

Iowa

Iowa State University of Science and Technology, M
The University of Iowa, MD

Kansas

Kansas State University, M

Maryland

Johns Hopkins University, MD
United States Naval Academy, B

Massachusetts

Babson College, B
Massachusetts Institute of Technology, MD
Northeastern University, M
University of Massachusetts Amherst, MD

Michigan

University of Michigan, MD

Minnesota

Capella University, M

New Jersey

Princeton University, BMD
Rutgers University - New Brunswick, D

New Mexico

New Mexico Institute of Mining and Technology, M

New York

Canisius College, B
Columbia University, BMD
Cornell University, BMD
Long Island University - LIU Brooklyn, B
New York University, B
United States Military Academy, B

North Carolina

North Carolina State University, MD
The University of North Carolina at Chapel Hill, MD

North Dakota

North Dakota State University, M

Ohio

Bowling Green State University, BM
Case Western Reserve University, MD
The Ohio State University, M

Pennsylvania

Carnegie Mellon University, BD

Rhode Island

Bryant University, B

South Carolina

Clemson University, MD

Texas

Southern Methodist University, BMD
Texas Southmost College, A
Texas Tech University, D
The University of Texas at Austin, MD

Virginia

The College of William and Mary, M
George Mason University, MDO
Virginia Commonwealth University, MD

Washington

University of Washington, B

Wisconsin

Milwaukee School of Engineering, B

Canada

British Columbia

Simon Fraser University, MD
The University of British Columbia, M

Maritime Provinces: New Brunswick

University of New Brunswick Fredericton, B

Ontario

Carleton University, B
University of Toronto, B
University of Waterloo, BMD
York University, B

Quebec

École Polytechnique de Montréal, MDO
HEC Montreal, BM
Université du Québec à Trois-Rivières, B

OPHTHALMIC LABORATORY TECHNOLOGY/TECHNICIAN

United States

Alabama

Community College of the Air Force, A

California

Los Angeles City College, A

Connecticut

Middlesex Community College, A

Georgia

Georgia Piedmont Technical College, A

Ohio

Hocking College, A

Washington

Seattle Central College, A
Spokane Community College, A

Canada

Ontario

University of Ottawa, B

OPHTHALMIC AND OPTOMETRIC SUPPORT SERVICES AND ALLIED PROFESSIONS

United States

Indiana

Vincennes University, A

Maine

Saint Joseph's College of Maine, B

Mississippi

Northeast Mississippi Community College, A

Tennessee

Tennessee Wesleyan College, B

OPHTHALMIC TECHNICIAN/TECHNOLOGIST

United States

Arkansas

University of Arkansas for Medical Sciences, B

Colorado

Pima Medical Institute (Denver), A

Florida

Florida State College at Jacksonville, A
Miami Dade College, A

Illinois

Triton College, A

Nevada

College of Southern Nevada, A

Ohio

Lakeland Community College, A

Tennessee

Volunteer State Community College, A

Washington

Renton Technical College, A

U.S. Territories: Puerto Rico

University of Puerto Rico, Medical Sciences Campus, A

OPTICAL TECHNOLOGIES

United States

Alabama

The University of Alabama in Huntsville, M

Florida

University of Central Florida, MD

New Mexico

University of New Mexico, MD

North Carolina

North Carolina Agricultural and Technical State University, MD

Ohio

Cleveland State University, M
University of Dayton, MD

Virginia

Norfolk State University, M

Canada

Quebec

École Polytechnique de Montréal, MD

OPTICIANRY/OPHTHALMIC DISPENSING OPTICIAN

United States

Alabama

Calhoun Community College, A

Connecticut

Goodwin College, A

Florida

Broward College, A
Florida SouthWestern State College, A
Hillsborough Community College, A
Miami Dade College, A

Georgia

Georgia Piedmont Technical College, A
Ogeechee Technical College, A

Massachusetts

Benjamin Franklin Institute of Technology, A

Mississippi

East Mississippi Community College, A

New Jersey

Camden County College, A
Essex County College, A
Raritan Valley Community College, A

New Mexico

Central New Mexico Community College, A
Southwestern Indian Polytechnic Institute, A

New York

Erie Community College, North Campus, A
New York City College of Technology of the City University of New York, A

North Carolina

Durham Technical Community College, A

Ohio

Cuyahoga Community College, A

Rhode Island

Community College of Rhode Island, A

Texas

El Paso Community College, A

Virginia

J. Sargeant Reynolds Community College, A

Wisconsin

Milwaukee Area Technical College, A

OPTICS/OPTICAL SCIENCES

United States

Alabama

Alabama Agricultural and Mechanical University, D
The University of Alabama in Huntsville, MD

Arizona

The University of Arizona, BMD

Colorado

University of Colorado Boulder, D

Delaware

Delaware State University, MD

Florida

University of Central Florida, MD

Indiana

Rose-Hulman Institute of Technology, M

Massachusetts

University of Massachusetts Lowell, M

Michigan

Saginaw Valley State University, B

New Mexico

University of New Mexico, MD

New York

Rochester Institute of Technology, MD
University of Rochester, BMD

North Carolina

Duke University, M
The University of North Carolina at Charlotte, MD

Ohio

Cleveland State University, M
The Ohio State University, BMD

Pennsylvania

Indiana University of Pennsylvania, A

Virginia

The College of William and Mary, D

Washington

Western Washington University, B

OPTOMETRIC TECHNICIAN/ ASSISTANT

United States

Florida

Hillsborough Community College, A

Indiana

Indiana University Bloomington, A

Kansas

Barton County Community College, A

New Jersey

Raritan Valley Community College, A

New York

TCI - College of Technology, A

Oregon

Portland Community College, A

Tennessee

Hiwassee College, A

Texas

El Paso Community College, A
San Jacinto College District, A

U.S. Territories: Puerto Rico

Inter American University of Puerto Rico, Ponce Campus, A

OPTOMETRY

United States

Alabama

The University of Alabama at Birmingham, D

California

University of California, Berkeley, DO

Florida

Nova Southeastern University, MD

Indiana

Indiana University Bloomington, MD

Michigan

Ferris State University, D

Missouri

University of Missouri - St. Louis, D

Ohio

The Ohio State University, MD

Oklahoma

Northeastern State University, D

Oregon

Pacific University, MD

Texas

University of Houston, D
University of the Incarnate Word, D

Canada

Ontario

University of Waterloo, MD

Quebec

Université de Montréal, D

ORAL BIOLOGY

United States

California

University of California, Los Angeles, MD

Florida

University of Florida, D

Georgia

Augusta University, MD

Kentucky

University of Louisville, M

Massachusetts

Boston University, MD

Minnesota

University of Minnesota, Twin Cities Campus, MD

Missouri

University of Missouri - Kansas City, MD

Nevada

University of Nevada, Las Vegas, M

New York

New York University, M
Stony Brook University, State University of New York, MD
University at Buffalo, the State University of New York, D

North Carolina

The University of North Carolina at Chapel Hill, D

Ohio

The Ohio State University, MD
The University of Toledo, M

Pennsylvania

University of Pittsburgh, MD

Canada

Manitoba

University of Manitoba, MD

Quebec

Université de Montréal, M

ORAL AND DENTAL SCIENCES

United States

Alabama

The University of Alabama at Birmingham, M

California

Loma Linda University, MO
University of Southern California, MDO

Florida

University of Florida, MO

Idaho

Idaho State University, O

Illinois

University of Illinois at Chicago, MD

Iowa

The University of Iowa, MDO

Kentucky

University of Kentucky, M

Massachusetts

Boston University, MDO
Harvard University, MDO
Tufts University, MO

Michigan

University of Detroit Mercy, MO
University of Michigan, MD

Minnesota

Metropolitan State University, M
University of Minnesota, Twin Cities Campus, MO

Mississippi

University of Mississippi Medical Center, MD

Missouri

Saint Louis University, M
University of Missouri - Kansas City, DO

Nevada

University of Nevada, Las Vegas, M

New Jersey

Rutgers University - Newark, MO

New York

Columbia University, MDO
New York University, MO
Stony Brook University, State University of New York, O
University at Buffalo, the State University of New York, M
University of Rochester, M

North Carolina

The University of North Carolina at Chapel Hill, MD

Ohio

Case Western Reserve University, MO
The Ohio State University, M

Oregon

Oregon Health & Science University, MO

Pennsylvania

Temple University, MO
University of Pittsburgh, MO

West Virginia

West Virginia University, M

Wisconsin

Marquette University, MO

U.S. Territories: Puerto Rico

University of Puerto Rico, Medical Sciences Campus, O

Canada

British Columbia

The University of British Columbia, MDO

Ontario

University of Toronto, MD
The University of Western Ontario, M

Quebec

Université Laval, MO
Université de Montréal, MO

ORAL PATHOLOGY

United States

New York

Stony Brook University, State University of New York, MD

Ohio

The Ohio State University, M

Pennsylvania

University of Pittsburgh, O

ORGANIC CHEMISTRY

United States

Alabama

Auburn University, D

California

California State University, Los Angeles, M
University of California, Santa Barbara, B

Connecticut

Wesleyan University, D
Yale University, D

District of Columbia

The George Washington University, MD
Georgetown University, D
Howard University, MD

Florida

Florida State University, MD
University of Miami, D

Georgia

Georgia State University, M
University of Georgia, MD

Indiana

Indiana University Bloomington, D
Purdue University, MD
University of Notre Dame, MD

Iowa

Iowa State University of Science and Technology, MD

Kansas

Kansas State University, M

Kentucky

University of Louisville, MD

Louisiana

Southern University and Agricultural and Mechanical College, M

Maryland

University of Maryland, College Park, MD

Massachusetts

Boston College, D
Brandeis University, MD
Harvard University, D
Massachusetts Institute of Technology, D
Tufts University, MD
University of Massachusetts Lowell, D

Michigan

University of Michigan, D
Wayne State University, D

Mississippi

University of Southern Mississippi, M

Missouri

University of Missouri, MD
University of Missouri - Kansas City, MD
University of Missouri - St. Louis, D

Montana

University of Montana, MD

Nebraska

University of Nebraska - Lincoln, D

New Jersey

Rutgers University - New Brunswick, MD
Rutgers University - Newark, MD
Seton Hall University, MD
Stevens Institute of Technology, D

New Mexico

Eastern New Mexico University, M

New York

Binghamton University, State University of New York, D
Cornell University, D
State University of New York College of Environmental Science and Forestry, MD

North Carolina

Wake Forest University, MD

Ohio

Cleveland State University, M
University of Cincinnati, MD
The University of Toledo, MD
Youngstown State University, M

Oregon

Oregon State University, MD

Tennessee

The University of Tennessee, MD
Vanderbilt University, MD

Texas

Rice University, D
The University of Texas at Austin, D

Virginia

Old Dominion University, M
Virginia Commonwealth University, MD

West Virginia

West Virginia University, MD

Wisconsin

Marquette University, MD

Canada

Alberta

University of Calgary, MD

Ontario

Laurentian University, M
McMaster University, MD
The University of Western Ontario, B

Quebec

Concordia University, B
McGill University, B

Saskatchewan

University of Regina, MD

ORGANIZATIONAL BEHAVIOR STUDIES

United States

Alabama

Amridge University, M

Arizona

Arizona State University at the Tempe campus, D
Chandler-Gilbert Community College, A
GateWay Community College, A
Phoenix College, A
University of Phoenix - Phoenix Campus, B
Western International University, M

Arkansas

Central Baptist College, B
John Brown University, B
Philander Smith College, B

California

California Lutheran University, MO
National University, B
Pitzer College, B
Santa Clara University, B
Scripps College, B
Simpson University, B
University of California, Berkeley, D
University of California, Los Angeles, D
University of Phoenix - Bay Area Campus, B
University of Phoenix - Sacramento Valley Campus, B
University of San Francisco, B

Connecticut

Goodwin College, B
University of Hartford, M

Delaware

Wilmington University, B

Florida

Florida Institute of Technology, M
Florida State University, D
Indian River State College, B
Palm Beach Atlantic University, B

Hawaii

University of Hawaii at Manoa, M
University of Phoenix - Hawaii Campus, B

Illinois

Argosy University, Chicago, D
Benedictine University, BM
DePaul University, B
Greenville College, B

Northwestern University, BM
Roosevelt University, B
University of Chicago, M
University of Illinois at Urbana - Champaign, B
University of St. Francis, B

Indiana

Purdue University, D

Iowa

Coe College, B
Waldorf College, B

Kentucky

Midway University, B
Northern Kentucky University, B

Maryland

Towson University, O

Massachusetts

Boston College, D
Harvard University, D
Suffolk University, M

Michigan

University of Michigan, B
Wayne State University, BM

Minnesota

The College of St. Scholastica, B
Concordia University, St. Paul, M

Missouri

Saint Louis University, B

Nebraska

Union College, B
University of Nebraska at Omaha, B

Nevada

University of Phoenix - Las Vegas Campus, B

New Jersey

Fairleigh Dickinson University, College at Florham,
  MO
Rider University, B
University of Phoenix - Jersey City Campus, B

New Mexico

National American University (Albuquerque), B

New York

Baruch College of the City University of New York,
  M
Brooklyn College of the City University of New York,
  M
Cornell University, MD
John Jay College of Criminal Justice of the City Uni-
  versity of New York, D
Manhattan College, B
New York University, MDO
Nyack College, B
Syracuse University, D
United States Military Academy, B
University at Albany, State University of New York,
  MD

North Carolina

High Point University, B
The University of North Carolina at Chapel Hill, D

Ohio

Bluffton University, B
Bowling Green State University, B
Case Western Reserve University, MD
Mount St. Joseph University, B
University of Cincinnati, B
University of Cincinnati Clermont College, A

Oklahoma

Oral Roberts University, B
University of Oklahoma, BM

The University of Tulsa, B

Oregon

Marylhurst University, M

Pennsylvania

Carnegie Mellon University, D
Drexel University, D
Neumann University, B
Penn State Abington, B
Penn State Altoona, B
Penn State Beaver, B
Penn State Berks, B
Penn State Brandywine, B
Penn State DuBois, B
Penn State Erie, The Behrend College, B
Penn State Fayette, The Eberly Campus, B
Penn State Greater Allegheny, B
Penn State Harrisburg, B
Penn State Hazleton, B
Penn State Lehigh Valley, B
Penn State Mont Alto, B
Penn State New Kensington, B
Penn State Schuylkill, B
Penn State Shenango, B
Penn State University Park, B
Penn State Wilkes-Barre, B
Penn State Worthington Scranton, B
Penn State York, B
Robert Morris University, B
Saint Joseph's University, B
University of Phoenix - Philadelphia Campus, B
University of Pittsburgh, MD

Rhode Island

Brown University, B

South Carolina

Anderson University, B
Claflin University, B
Columbia College, O

Texas

University of the Incarnate Word, B
University of North Texas, B
University of Phoenix - Dallas Campus, B
University of Phoenix - Houston Campus, B
The University of Texas at Austin, M

Utah

University of Utah, D

Virginia

Eastern Mennonite University, B
University of Richmond, B

Washington

University of Phoenix - Western Washington Campus, B

Wisconsin

Carroll University, B
Edgewood College, B
Silver Lake College of the Holy Family, M

Canada

Alberta

Athabasca University, B
University of Alberta, B

British Columbia

The University of British Columbia, D

Newfoundland and Labrador

Memorial University of Newfoundland, B

Ontario

The University of Western Ontario, B
Wilfrid Laurier University, MD
York University, B

Quebec

McGill University, B
Université de Sherbrooke, M

ORGANIZATIONAL COMMUNI-CATION

United States

California

Pepperdine University, B

Florida

Florida College, B
Florida Southern College, B
Southeastern University, B

Georgia

Emmanuel College, B
Shorter University, B

Idaho

University of Idaho, B

Illinois

Bradley University, B
Lewis University, B
McKendree University, B
North Central College, B
Roosevelt University, B
University of Illinois at Urbana - Champaign, B

Indiana

Butler University, B
Indiana University - Purdue University Fort Wayne,
  B

Iowa

Buena Vista University, B
St. Ambrose University, B
University of Northern Iowa, B

Kentucky

Murray State University, B
Western Kentucky University, B

Massachusetts

Assumption College, B
Suffolk University, B

Michigan

Albion College, B
Aquinas College, B
Calvin College, B
Western Michigan University, B

Missouri

Missouri State University, B
Northwest Missouri State University, B
Southeast Missouri State University, B

Montana

Montana State University Billings, B

Nebraska

Concordia University, Nebraska, B
Creighton University, A

New Hampshire

Southern New Hampshire University, B

New Jersey

Fairleigh Dickinson University, Metropolitan Campus, B

New York

St. Francis College, B

North Carolina

Pfeiffer University, B

Ohio

Capital University, B
Cleveland State University, B
Franklin University, AB
Ohio Northern University, B
Ohio University - Eastern, B
Ohio University - Lancaster, B
The University of Akron, B
University of Mount Union, B

Oregon

George Fox University, B
Marylhurst University, B

Pennsylvania

Bloomsburg University of Pennsylvania, B
Butler County Community College, A
Temple University, B

Tennessee

Trevecca Nazarene University, B

Texas

Howard Payne University, B
Lubbock Christian University, B

Utah

Brigham Young University, B
Dixie State University, B
Weber State University, B

Washington

Northwest University, B
Washington State University, B

West Virginia

Wheeling Jesuit University, B

Wisconsin

Marian University, B
Viterbo University, B

ORGANIZATIONAL MANAGE-MENT

United States

Alabama

Amridge University, M
Auburn University at Montgomery, M
Columbia Southern University, M
Troy University, M

Arizona

Grand Canyon University, D
University of Phoenix - Online Campus, D
Western International University, M

Arkansas

Harding University, M
University of Central Arkansas, D

California

Antioch University Los Angeles, M
Argosy University, Inland Empire, D
Argosy University, Los Angeles, D
Argosy University, Orange County, D
Argosy University, San Diego, D
Argosy University, San Francisco Bay Area, D
Azusa Pacific University, M
Brandman University, M
California Baptist University, M
California Coast University, D
California College of the Arts, M
California Intercontinental University, M
California State University, East Bay, M
California State University, Fullerton, M
John F. Kennedy University, O
National University, M
Pepperdine University, M
Point Loma Nazarene University, M

Simpson University, M
University of La Verne, MDO
University of Phoenix - Bay Area Campus, D
University of San Francisco, M
University of Southern California, M
Woodbury University, M

Colorado

Argosy University, Denver, D
Colorado State University, M
Colorado State University - Global Campus, M
Regis University, MO
University of Colorado Boulder, D
University of Denver, MO

Connecticut

Albertus Magnus College, M
Eastern Connecticut State University, M
Quinnipiac University, M
University of New Haven, M
Yale University, D

Delaware

Wilmington University, M

District of Columbia

The George Washington University, MO
Trinity Washington University, M
University of Phoenix - Washington D.C. Campus, D

Florida

Argosy University, Sarasota, D
Argosy University, Tampa, D
Carlos Albizu University, Miami Campus, M
Florida Institute of Technology, M
Jacksonville University, M
Keiser University, D
Palm Beach Atlantic University, M

Georgia

Brenau University, M
Columbus State University, M
Emory University, D
Georgia State University, MD
LaGrange College, M
Mercer University, M
South University, M

Hawaii

Argosy University, Hawai'i, D
Hawai'i Pacific University, M
University of Hawaii at Manoa, MD

Idaho

Boise State University, MO

Illinois

Argosy University, Chicago, D
Argosy University, Schaumburg, M
Benedictine University, MD
DePaul University, M
Judson University, M
Lewis University, M
Lincoln Christian University, M
North Central College, M
Northwestern University, MD
Olivet Nazarene University, M
Roosevelt University, MD

Indiana

Indiana Tech, M
Indiana University Bloomington, O
Indiana University - Purdue University Fort Wayne, MO
Indiana University - Purdue University Indianapolis, O
Indiana Wesleyan University, MD

Iowa

Graceland University, D
Grand View University, M
Kaplan University, Davenport Campus, M
St. Ambrose University, M
Upper Iowa University, M

William Penn University, M

Kansas

Baker University, M
Grantham University, M
MidAmerica Nazarene University, M
Newman University, M
The University of Kansas, O

Kentucky

Campbellsville University, M
Midway University, M
Northern Kentucky University, M

Louisiana

Loyola University New Orleans, M
Southwest University, M

Maryland

University of Maryland Eastern Shore, D

Massachusetts

American International College, M
Boston College, D
Boston University, M
Cambridge College, M
Endicott College, M
Nichols College, M
Northeastern University, D
University of Massachusetts Amherst, D
University of Massachusetts Dartmouth, O
Western New England University, M
Worcester Polytechnic Institute, M
Worcester State University, M

Michigan

Aquinas College, M
Cleary University, M
Concordia University Ann Arbor, M
Eastern Michigan University, MO
Siena Heights University, M
South University, M
University of Michigan - Flint, M
Wayne State University, M

Minnesota

Argosy University, Twin Cities, D
Augsburg College, M
Bethel University, M
Capella University, MD
Concordia University, St. Paul, M
St. Catherine University, M
Saint Mary's University of Minnesota, M
University of Northwestern - St. Paul, M
University of St. Thomas, MD
Walden University, MD

Missouri

Avila University, M
Evangel University, M
Maryville University of Saint Louis, M
Saint Louis University, O
Southeast Missouri State University, M
University of Missouri, O
Washington University in St. Louis, M

Nebraska

Bellevue University, M
College of Saint Mary, M
Creighton University, M
Peru State College, M
Wayne State College, M

Nevada

University of Nevada, Las Vegas, D

New Hampshire

Granite State College, M
Southern New Hampshire University, M

New Jersey

College of Saint Elizabeth, M
Fairleigh Dickinson University, College at Florham, O

Rider University, M
Rutgers University - Newark, D
Thomas Edison State University, O

New Mexico

University of New Mexico, M

New York

Concordia College - New York, M
Manhattan College, M
Manhattanville College, M
Medaille College, M
Mercy College, M
New York University, MD
Nyack College, M
Rochester Institute of Technology, O
St. Joseph's College, Long Island Campus, M
State University of New York College at Potsdam, M
Syracuse University, O

North Carolina

Duke University, MD
Gardner-Webb University, D
Lenoir-Rhyne University, M
Pfeiffer University, M
Queens University of Charlotte, M

Ohio

Bluffton University, M
Bowling Green State University, M
Cleveland State University, M
Lourdes University, M
Malone University, M
Mount St. Joseph University, M
Union Institute & University, M
University of Cincinnati, M
The University of Findlay, M

Oklahoma

Mid-America Christian University, M
Oklahoma Christian University, M

Oregon

George Fox University, M
University of Portland, D
Warner Pacific College, M

Pennsylvania

Alvernia University, D
Cabrini University, M
Cairn University, MO
Carlow University, MDO
Central Penn College, M
Duquesne University, M
Eastern University, MD
Gannon University, DO
Geneva College, M
Immaculata University, M
Mansfield University of Pennsylvania, M
Mercyhurst University, MO
Messiah College, MO
Misericordia University, M
Peirce College, M
Point Park University, M
Robert Morris University, M
Saint Joseph's University, M
Shippensburg University of Pennsylvania, M
Summit University, M
University of Pennsylvania, M
Waynesburg University, M
Wilkes University, M

South Carolina

South University, M

South Dakota

The University of South Dakota, M

Tennessee

Lipscomb University, M
Trevecca Nazarene University, M
Vanderbilt University, M

Texas

Dallas Baptist University, M
Our Lady of the Lake University of San Antonio, MD
St. Edward's University, M
University of Dallas, M
University of the Incarnate Word, MD
The University of Texas at San Antonio, D
Wayland Baptist University, M

Vermont

Norwich University, M

Virginia

Argosy University, Washington DC, D
Eastern Mennonite University, M
Emory & Henry College, M
George Mason University, M
James Madison University, D
Regent University, MDO
South University (Virginia Beach), M

Washington

Antioch University Seattle, M
Argosy University, Seattle, D
City University of Seattle, MO
Gonzaga University, M
Northwest University, M
Seattle University, MO

West Virginia

American Public University System, M
University of Charleston, D
West Liberty University, M
Wheeling Jesuit University, M

Wisconsin

Edgewood College, M
Marian University, M
Viterbo University, M

Canada

Alberta

Athabasca University, M
University of Alberta, D

British Columbia

Trinity Western University, MO

Ontario

University of Guelph, M
Wilfrid Laurier University, D

Quebec

Concordia University, M
HEC Montreal, M
Université Laval, M

Saskatchewan

University of Regina, O

ORNAMENTAL HORTICULTURE

United States

Arizona

Mesa Community College, A

Arkansas

University of Arkansas, B

California

Bakersfield College, A
California State University, Fresno, B
College of the Sequoias, A
Cuyamaca College, A
El Camino College, A
Foothill College, A
Golden West College, A
Los Angeles Pierce College, A
Mendocino College, A

Merced College, A
Modesto Junior College, A
Monterey Peninsula College, A
Mt. San Antonio College, A
Saddleback College, A
San Joaquin Delta College, A
Santa Barbara City College, A
Shasta College, A
Solano Community College, A
Southwestern College, A
Victor Valley College, A

District of Columbia

University of the District of Columbia, B

Florida

Miami Dade College, A
Pensacola State College, A

Georgia

Abraham Baldwin Agricultural College, A
Fort Valley State University, B
Gwinnett Technical College, A

Illinois

College of DuPage, A
College of Lake County, A
Kishwaukee College, A
Triton College, A
University of Illinois at Urbana - Champaign, B

Kentucky

Eastern Kentucky University, B

Mississippi

Mississippi Gulf Coast Community College, A

Nebraska

Metropolitan Community College, A

Nevada

College of Southern Nevada, A

New Jersey

Cumberland County College, A
Mercer County Community College, A
Salem Community College, A

New York

Bronx Community College of the City University of
    New York, A
Farmingdale State College, A
Finger Lakes Community College, A
Morrisville State College, B
State University of New York College of Agriculture
    and Technology at Cobleskill, A

North Dakota

Dakota College at Bottineau, A

Ohio

The Ohio State University, B

Oregon

Clackamas Community College, A
Mt. Hood Community College, A

Pennsylvania

Community College of Allegheny County, A
Delaware Valley University, B

Tennessee

Walters State Community College, A

Texas

Howard College, A
Richland College, A
Tarleton State University, B
Texas A&M University, B
Wharton County Junior College, A

Vermont

Vermont Technical College, A

Washington

Spokane Community College, A

Wisconsin

University of Wisconsin - Platteville, B

Canada

British Columbia

University of the Fraser Valley, A

ORTHODONTICS

United States

California

Loma Linda University, MO

Colorado

University of Colorado Denver, M

District of Columbia

Howard University, O

Florida

Jacksonville University, O
University of Florida, MO

Iowa

The University of Iowa, MO

Massachusetts

Boston University, MD
Harvard University, O
Tufts University, O

Michigan

University of Detroit Mercy, MO
University of Michigan, M

Minnesota

University of Minnesota, Twin Cities Campus, M

Missouri

Saint Louis University, M
University of Missouri - Kansas City, O

New Jersey

Rutgers University - Newark, O

New York

Columbia University, MO
New York University, O
Stony Brook University, State University of New York, O
University at Buffalo, the State University of New York, MO

North Carolina

The University of North Carolina at Chapel Hill, M

Ohio

Case Western Reserve University, MO
The Ohio State University, M

Oklahoma

University of Oklahoma Health Sciences Center, M

Oregon

Oregon Health & Science University, MO

Pennsylvania

Seton Hill University, M
Temple University, O
University of Pittsburgh, MO

Washington

University of Washington, MO

West Virginia

West Virginia University, M

Wisconsin

Marquette University, MO

U.S. Territories: Puerto Rico

University of Puerto Rico, Medical Sciences Campus, O

Canada

Alberta

University of Alberta, MD

Manitoba

University of Manitoba, M

Ontario

University of Toronto, M

Quebec

Université de Montréal, M

ORTHOPTICS/ORTHOPTIST

United States

Minnesota

St. Catherine University, B

ORTHOTIST/PROSTHETIST

United States

Alabama

Virginia College in Mobile, A

Florida

St. Petersburg College, B

Michigan

Baker College, A

Minnesota

Century College, A
Concordia University, St. Paul, B

Oklahoma

Oklahoma State University Institute of Technology, A

Washington

Spokane Falls Community College, A
University of Washington, B

OSTEOPATHIC MEDICINE

United States

Florida

Nova Southeastern University, MDO

Indiana

Marian University, D

Kentucky

University of Pikeville, D

Maine

University of New England, D

Michigan

Michigan State University, D

New Jersey

Rowan University, D

New York

New York Institute of Technology, MD

Ohio

Ohio University, D

Tennessee

Lincoln Memorial University, D

Virginia

Liberty University, D

PACIFIC AREA/PACIFIC RIM STUDIES

United States

California

University of San Francisco, M

Hawaii

Brigham Young University - Hawaii, B
University of Hawaii at Manoa, BMO
University of Hawaii - West Oahu, B

Washington

Central Washington University, B

U.S. Territories: Guam

University of Guam, BM

Canada

British Columbia

University of Victoria, BM

PAINTING

United States

Alabama

Birmingham-Southern College, B
The University of Alabama, M

Alaska

University of Alaska Fairbanks, M

Arizona

Arizona State University at the Tempe campus, M
Southwest University of Visual Arts, M

Arkansas

Harding University, B

California

Academy of Art University, M
Biola University, B
California College of the Arts, BM
California State University, East Bay, B
California State University, Long Beach, B
California State University, Los Angeles, M
Cuyamaca College, A
Laguna College of Art & Design, BM
Mills College, M
Otis College of Art and Design, M
San Diego State University, M
San Francisco Art Institute, B
San Jose State University, M
University of San Francisco, B
University of Southern California, M

Colorado

Adams State University, B
Colorado State University, B
University of Colorado Boulder, M

Western State Colorado University, B

Connecticut

University of Hartford, B
University of New Haven, B
Western Connecticut State University, M
Yale University, M

District of Columbia

The George Washington University, M
Howard University, M

Florida

University of Miami, BM

Georgia

Georgia State University, M
Savannah College of Art and Design, BM

Idaho

Northwest Nazarene University, B

Illinois

American Academy of Art, B
Bradley University, BM
Illinois State University, M
Lewis University, B
School of the Art Institute of Chicago, BM
Southern Illinois University Carbondale, M
University of Illinois at Chicago, B
University of Illinois at Urbana - Champaign, BM

Indiana

Indiana State University, M
Indiana University - Purdue University Fort Wayne, B
Indiana Wesleyan University, B
University of Notre Dame, M

Iowa

Coe College, B
Drake University, B
St. Ambrose University, B
The University of Iowa, B

Kansas

Bethany College, B
Kansas Wesleyan University, B
Tabor College, B
The University of Kansas, BM
Wichita State University, M

Louisiana

Louisiana State University and Agricultural & Mechanical College, M

Maine

Maine College of Art, B

Maryland

Maryland Institute College of Art, BM

Massachusetts

Boston University, BM
Massachusetts College of Art and Design, BM
Montserrat College of Art, B
Salem State University, B
School of the Museum of Fine Arts, Boston, B
University of Massachusetts Dartmouth, BO

Michigan

Aquinas College, B
Ferris State University, B
Northern Michigan University, B
Oakland University, B
Wayne State University, M

Minnesota

Minneapolis College of Art and Design, BM

Mississippi

Mississippi College, B

Missouri

College of the Ozarks, B
Columbia College, B
Kansas City Art Institute, B
Washington University in St. Louis, B

New Hampshire

University of New Hampshire, M

New Jersey

Rutgers University - New Brunswick, BM

New York

Brooklyn College of the City University of New York, M
Buffalo State College, State University of New York, B
City College of the City University of New York, M
Columbia University, M
Hofstra University, B
Pratt Institute, ABM
Rochester Institute of Technology, B
Sarah Lawrence College, B
School of Visual Arts, B
State University of New York at New Paltz, BM
Syracuse University, BM

North Carolina

East Carolina University, M

Ohio

Art Academy of Cincinnati, B
Bowling Green State University, B
Cleveland Institute of Art, B
Ohio Northern University, B
Ohio University, M
Youngstown State University, B

Oklahoma

University of Oklahoma, M

Oregon

Pacific Northwest College of Art, B
Portland State University, M
University of Oregon, B

Pennsylvania

Arcadia University, B
Edinboro University of Pennsylvania, M
Luzerne County Community College, A
Marywood University, BM
Pennsylvania Academy of the Fine Arts, MO
Seton Hill University, B
Temple University, BM
The University of the Arts, B

Rhode Island

Providence College, B
Rhode Island College, B
Rhode Island School of Design, BM
Salve Regina University, B

South Dakota

The University of South Dakota, M

Tennessee

Carson-Newman University, B
Memphis College of Art, B
University of Memphis, M
The University of Tennessee, M

Texas

Southern Methodist University, M
Stephen F. Austin State University, M
Sul Ross State University, M
Texas Christian University, BM
University of Dallas, B
University of Houston, BM

Utah

Brigham Young University, B
Dixie State University, B
University of Utah, M

Vermont

Bennington College, B
Johnson State College, M
Marlboro College, B

Virginia

George Mason University, M
James Madison University, M
Virginia Commonwealth University, BM

Washington

Central Washington University, B
University of Washington, BM
Western Washington University, B

West Virginia

West Virginia University, M
West Virginia Wesleyan College, B

Wisconsin

Milwaukee Institute of Art and Design, B

U.S. Territories: Guam

University of Guam, M

U.S. Territories: Puerto Rico

Escuela de Artes Plasticas y Diseño de Puerto Rico, B
Inter American University of Puerto Rico, San Germán Campus, BM
Pontifical Catholic University of Puerto Rico, M
University of Puerto Rico, Río Piedras Campus, B

Canada

Alberta

Alberta College of Art & Design, B
University of Alberta, M

British Columbia

Emily Carr University of Art + Design, B
University of Victoria, M

Maritime Provinces: Nova Scotia

NSCAD University, B

Newfoundland and Labrador

Memorial University of Newfoundland, B

Ontario

University of Windsor, B
York University, B

Quebec

Concordia University, BM

Saskatchewan

University of Regina, BM

PAINTING/PAINTER AND WALL COVERER

United States

Arizona

GateWay Community College, A

Illinois

Southwestern Illinois College, A

Indiana

Ivy Tech Community College - Central Indiana, A
Ivy Tech Community College - East Central, A
Ivy Tech Community College - Lafayette, A
Ivy Tech Community College - North Central, A
Ivy Tech Community College - Northeast, A
Ivy Tech Community College - Northwest, A
Ivy Tech Community College - Southwest, A
Ivy Tech Community College - Wabash Valley, A

PALEONTOLOGY

United States

Connecticut

Yale University, D

Illinois

University of Chicago, D

New Mexico

Mesalands Community College, A

New York

Cornell University, MD

North Carolina

Duke University, D

Ohio

Bowling Green State University, B

Pennsylvania

Mercyhurst University, B

South Dakota

South Dakota School of Mines and Technology, M

Tennessee

East Tennessee State University, M

Texas

The University of Texas at Dallas, MD

West Virginia

West Virginia University, MD

Canada

Alberta

University of Alberta, B

PAPER AND PULP ENGINEERING

United States

Michigan

Western Michigan University, MD

Minnesota

University of Minnesota, Twin Cities Campus, MD

New York

State University of New York College of Environmental Science and Forestry, MDO

North Carolina

North Carolina State University, MD

PARASITOLOGY

United States

Illinois

Illinois State University, M

Indiana

University of Notre Dame, MD

Louisiana

Louisiana State University Health Sciences Center, MD

Tulane University, D

Ohio

Bowling Green State University, B

Washington

University of Washington, D

Canada

Maritime Provinces: Prince Edward Island

University of Prince Edward Island, MD

Quebec

McGill University, MDO

PARKS, RECREATION AND LEISURE FACILITIES MANAGEMENT

United States

Alabama

James H. Faulkner State Community College, A

Arizona

Arizona Western College, A
Northland Pioneer College, A

Arkansas

Arkansas Tech University, B
Henderson State University, B
John Brown University, B
National Park College, A

California

Butte College, A
California State University, Fresno, B
California State University, Sacramento, B
College of the Desert, A
Humboldt State University, B
Modesto Junior College, A
Monterey Peninsula College, A
Mt. San Antonio College, A
Professional Golfers Career College, A
Santa Rosa Junior College, A
West Valley College, A

Colorado

Colorado Mountain College (Leadville), A
Colorado Mountain College (Steamboat Springs), A
Colorado State University, B
Johnson & Wales University, B
University of Northern Colorado, B
Western State Colorado University, B

Connecticut

Northwestern Connecticut Community College, A

Delaware

Delaware State University, B
University of Delaware, B

Florida

Broward College, A
Florida International University, B
Johnson & Wales University, B
South Florida State College, A
Southeastern College - West Palm Beach, A
University of Florida, B
Webber International University, AB

Georgia

Andrew College, A
Augusta Technical College, A
Chattahoochee Technical College, A
College of Coastal Georgia, A
North Georgia Technical College, A
Thomas University, B
University of West Georgia, B

Idaho

Brigham Young University - Idaho, B
University of Idaho, B

Illinois

Chicago State University, B
Eastern Illinois University, B
Illinois State University, B
Moraine Valley Community College, A
University of St. Francis, B
Western Illinois University, B

Indiana

Indiana State University, B
Indiana Tech, AB
Indiana Wesleyan University, B
Trine University, B

Iowa

The University of Iowa, B

Kansas

Allen Community College, A
Kansas State University, B

Kentucky

Asbury University, B
Eastern Kentucky University, B
Union College, B
Western Kentucky University, B

Maine

Husson University, B
University of Maine, B
University of Maine at Machias, B

Massachusetts

Springfield College, B

Michigan

Central Michigan University, B
Eastern Michigan University, B
Ferris State University, B
Gogebic Community College, A
Lake Superior State University, B
Western Michigan University, B

Minnesota

Minnesota State University Mankato, B
University of Minnesota, Crookston, B
Vermilion Community College, A
Winona State University, B

Mississippi

University of Mississippi, B

Missouri

College of the Ozarks, B
Hannibal-LaGrange University, B
Missouri Valley College, B
Missouri Western State University, B
Northwest Missouri State University, B

Nebraska

Hastings College, B

New Hampshire

Franklin Pierce University, B
New England College, B
University of New Hampshire, B

New Jersey

Kean University, B

New Mexico

New Mexico Highlands University, B

New York

Adirondack Community College, A
The College at Brockport, State University of New York, B
Herkimer County Community College, A
Mohawk Valley Community College, A

New York University, B
North Country Community College, A
Paul Smith's College, B
St. Joseph's College, Long Island Campus, B
St. Joseph's College, New York, B
State University of New York College at Cortland, B
Tompkins Cortland Community College, A
Ulster County Community College, A

North Carolina

Appalachian State University, B
Belmont Abbey College, B
Johnson & Wales University, B
Methodist University, B
North Carolina Agricultural and Technical State University, B
North Carolina Central University, B
North Carolina State University, B
Southeastern Community College, A
The University of North Carolina Wilmington, B
Western Carolina University, B
Winston-Salem State University, B

North Dakota

Dakota College at Bottineau, A
University of North Dakota, B

Ohio

Kent State University, B
Zane State College, A

Oklahoma

Eastern Oklahoma State College, A
Oral Roberts University, B
Rose State College, A
Southwestern Oklahoma State University, B

Pennsylvania

Butler County Community College, A
California University of Pennsylvania, B
Cheyney University of Pennsylvania, B
East Stroudsburg University of Pennsylvania, B
Lock Haven University of Pennsylvania, B
Penn State Abington, B
Penn State Altoona, B
Penn State Beaver, B
Penn State Berks, B
Penn State Brandywine, B
Penn State DuBois, B
Penn State Erie, The Behrend College, B
Penn State Fayette, The Eberly Campus, B
Penn State Greater Allegheny, B
Penn State Hazleton, B
Penn State Lehigh Valley, B
Penn State Mont Alto, B
Penn State New Kensington, B
Penn State Schuylkill, B
Penn State Shenango, B
Penn State University Park, B
Penn State Wilkes-Barre, B
Penn State Worthington Scranton, B
Penn State York, B
Slippery Rock University of Pennsylvania, B

Rhode Island

Johnson & Wales University, B

South Carolina

Clemson University, B

South Dakota

Mount Marty College, B
South Dakota State University, B

Tennessee

Middle Tennessee State University, B
Union University, B

Texas

Texas A&M University, B
Texas State University, B
University of North Texas, B
Wayland Baptist University, B
Western Texas College, A

Vermont

Lyndon State College, B
University of Vermont, B

Virginia

Old Dominion University, B

Washington

Central Washington University, B
Eastern Washington University, B
Skagit Valley College, A
Spokane Community College, A

West Virginia

Bethany College, B
Concord University, B
Marshall University, B
Potomac State College of West Virginia University, A
West Virginia State University, B
West Virginia University, B

Wisconsin

Carroll University, B
Southwest Wisconsin Technical College, A
University of Wisconsin - La Crosse, B

Wyoming

Central Wyoming College, A

U.S. Territories: Puerto Rico

University of Puerto Rico, Mayagüez Campus, B

Canada

British Columbia

The University of British Columbia, B
University of Northern British Columbia, B

Ontario

University of Waterloo, B

PARKS, RECREATION, LEISURE AND FITNESS STUDIES

United States

Alabama

Community College of the Air Force, A
Jacksonville State University, B
University of North Alabama, B
University of South Alabama, B

Alaska

Alaska Pacific University, B

Arizona

Arizona State University at the Downtown Phoenix campus, B
Grand Canyon University, B
Northern Arizona University, B
Phoenix College, A

Arkansas

National Park College, A
University of Arkansas, B
University of Arkansas at Pine Bluff, B

California

Allan Hancock College, A
American River College, A
Bakersfield College, A
Biola University, B
California Polytechnic State University, San Luis Obispo, B
California State University, Chico, B
California State University, East Bay, B
California State University, Fresno, B
California State University, Long Beach, B
California State University, Northridge, B

California State University, Sacramento, B
Chabot College, A
College of the Canyons, A
Cuesta College, A
Feather River College, A
Fresno City College, A
Fullerton College, A
Glendale Community College, A
Humboldt State University, B
Merritt College, A
Mt. San Antonio College, A
Palomar College, A
San Bernardino Valley College, A
San Diego City College, A
San Diego State University, B
San Francisco State University, B
San Jose State University, B
Santa Barbara City College, A
Sierra College, A
Simpson University, B
Southwestern College, A
Taft College, A
Ventura College, A

Colorado

Colorado Mountain College (Leadville), A
Fort Lewis College, B
Metropolitan State University of Denver, B
Red Rocks Community College, A
Western State Colorado University, B

Connecticut

Northwestern Connecticut Community College, A
Norwalk Community College, A
Southern Connecticut State University, B

Delaware

Wesley College, B

Florida

Bethune-Cookman University, B
College of Central Florida, A
Florida Keys Community College, A
Miami Dade College, A
St. Petersburg College, A

Georgia

Georgia College & State University, B
Georgia Southern University, B
Shorter University, B
South Georgia State College, A

Idaho

Northwest Nazarene University, B

Illinois

Aurora University, B
Southern Illinois University Carbondale, B
Trinity Christian College, B
University of Illinois at Urbana - Champaign, B

Indiana

Huntington University, B
Indiana University Bloomington, B
Manchester University, B
Vincennes University, A

Iowa

Dordt College, B
Graceland University, B
Iowa Lakes Community College, A
University of Dubuque, B
The University of Iowa, B
University of Northern Iowa, B
Upper Iowa University, B
William Penn University, B

Kansas

Emporia State University, B
Ottawa University, B
Pittsburg State University, B

Kentucky

Campbellsville University, B
Lindsey Wilson College, B

Louisiana

Grambling State University, B

Maine

University of Maine at Machias, B
Washington County Community College, A

Maryland

Community College of Baltimore County, A
Frostburg State University, B
Morgan State University, B

Massachusetts

Bridgewater State University, B
Gordon College, B
Northern Essex Community College, A
Salem State University, B
Springfield College, B

Michigan

Central Michigan University, B
Lake Superior State University, B
Michigan State University, B
Muskegon Community College, A
Northern Michigan University, B
Spring Arbor University, B
Western Michigan University, B

Minnesota

Bemidji State University, B
Minnesota State University Mankato, B
University of Minnesota, Duluth, B
University of Minnesota, Twin Cities Campus, B
Vermilion Community College, A

Mississippi

Alcorn State University, B
Belhaven University, B
University of Southern Mississippi, B

Missouri

Evangel University, B
Lindenwood University, B
Missouri State University, B
Missouri Valley College, B
Southeast Missouri State University, B
Southwest Baptist University, B
University of Central Missouri, B
University of Missouri, B
William Jewell College, B

Montana

University of Montana, B

Nebraska

Chadron State College, B
Midland University, B
University of Nebraska at Kearney, B
University of Nebraska at Omaha, B

Nevada

University of Nevada, Las Vegas, B

New Hampshire

New England College, B
Plymouth State University, B

New Mexico

Eastern New Mexico University, A
New Mexico Highlands University, B
New Mexico Junior College, A
San Juan College, A
Santa Fe Community College, A

New York

Corning Community College, A
Genesee Community College, A
Houghton College, B
Ithaca College, B

Kingsborough Community College of the City University of New York, A
Monroe Community College, A
Niagara County Community College, A
Onondaga Community College, A
St. Thomas Aquinas College, B
State University of New York College at Cortland, B
State University of New York College of Environmental Science and Forestry, B
Sullivan County Community College, A
Tompkins Cortland Community College, A

North Carolina

Brevard College, B
Catawba College, B
East Carolina University, B
Elon University, B
Mars Hill University, B
Montreat College, B
St. Andrews University, B
Shaw University, B
Southeastern Community College, A
Southwestern Community College, A
University of Mount Olive, B
The University of North Carolina at Greensboro, B
Vance-Granville Community College, A
Wingate University, B

North Dakota

Dakota College at Bottineau, A

Ohio

Bowling Green State University, B
Central State University, B
Cincinnati State Technical and Community College, A
Columbus State Community College, A
The Ohio State University, B
Ohio University, B
Zane State College, A

Oklahoma

East Central University, B
Oklahoma Baptist University, B
Oklahoma State University, B
Southeastern Oklahoma State University, B
Southern Nazarene University, A
Southwestern Oklahoma State University, B
University of Central Oklahoma, B

Oregon

Oregon State University, B
Oregon State University - Cascades, B

Pennsylvania

Kutztown University of Pennsylvania, B
Messiah College, B
York College of Pennsylvania, B

Rhode Island

Rhode Island College, B

South Carolina

Benedict College, B
Coker College, B
Limestone College, B
Morris College, B
Newberry College, B
North Greenville University, B
Southern Wesleyan University, B

South Dakota

Black Hills State University, B
The University of South Dakota, B

Tennessee

Cumberland University, B
Maryville College, B
Tennessee State University, B

Texas

Del Mar College, A
Texas A&M University, B

Utah

Brigham Young University, B
Southern Utah University, B
University of Utah, B
Utah State University, B

Vermont

Green Mountain College, B
Johnson State College, B
Lyndon State College, B
Sterling College, B

Virginia

Ferrum College, B
Northern Virginia Community College, A
Radford University, B
Virginia Wesleyan College, B

Washington

Eastern Washington University, B
Green River College, A
Skagit Valley College, A
Western Washington University, B

West Virginia

Davis & Elkins College, B
Shepherd University, B

Wisconsin

Madison Area Technical College, A

Wyoming

Central Wyoming College, A
Northwest College, A

Canada

Alberta

University of Calgary, B

British Columbia

University of Northern British Columbia, B

Manitoba

Providence University College & Theological Seminary, B

Maritime Provinces: New Brunswick

Université de Moncton, B
University of New Brunswick Fredericton, B

Maritime Provinces: Nova Scotia

Dalhousie University, B

Newfoundland and Labrador

Memorial University of Newfoundland, B

Ontario

Brock University, B
Lakehead University, B
Redeemer University College, B
Tyndale University College & Seminary, B
University of Ottawa, B
University of Waterloo, B

Quebec

Concordia University, B
Université du Québec à Montréal, B
Université du Québec à Trois-Rivières, B

PARTS AND WAREHOUSING OPERATIONS AND MAINTENANCE TECHNOLOGY/TECHNICIAN

United States

Colorado

Red Rocks Community College, A

PASTORAL COUNSELING AND SPECIALIZED MINISTRIES

United States

Arkansas

John Brown University, B
Ouachita Baptist University, B

Colorado

Nazarene Bible College, B

Idaho

Boise Bible College, B

Illinois

Judson University, B
Trinity International University, B

Indiana

Crossroads Bible College, B

Kentucky

Brescia University, AB

Michigan

Madonna University, B

Minnesota

Oak Hills Christian College, B
University of Northwestern - St. Paul, B

Missouri

Calvary Bible College and Theological Seminary, B

New York

Davis College, B

Ohio

Malone University, B

Oklahoma

Mid-America Christian University, B
Oklahoma Wesleyan University, B

Oregon

Multnomah University, B

Pennsylvania

Lancaster Bible College, B

Tennessee

Lee University, B
Lipscomb University, B

Texas

College of Biblical Studies - Houston, B

Wisconsin

Maranatha Baptist University, B

Canada

Alberta

Prairie Bible Institute, B

Saskatchewan

Horizon College & Seminary, B

PASTORAL STUDIES/COUNSELING

United States

Alabama

Amridge University, M
Faulkner University, M
Heritage Christian University, M

Oakwood University, AM
Spring Hill College, MO

Arizona

International Baptist College and Seminary, MD

Arkansas

Ecclesia College, B
Harding University, M
John Brown University, B
Ouachita Baptist University, B
Williams Baptist College, B

California

Azusa Pacific University, M
Bethesda University, B
Biola University, BMO
California Baptist University, M
Fresno Pacific University, M
Holy Names University, MO
La Sierra University, M
Life Pacific College, B
Loma Linda University, MO
Loyola Marymount University, M
The Master's College and Seminary, BMD
Patten University, B
Pepperdine University, M
Point Loma Nazarene University, M
San Diego Christian College, B
Santa Clara University, M
Shasta Bible College, M
Simpson University, B
Vanguard University of Southern California, B
William Jessup University, AB

Connecticut

Fairfield University, O

District of Columbia

The Catholic University of America, MDO

Florida

Argosy University, Sarasota, D
Ave Maria University, M
The Baptist College of Florida, B
Barry University, MD
Saint Leo University, M
St. Thomas University, BMDO
Southeastern University, M
Trinity Baptist College, B
Trinity College of Florida, B
University of Fort Lauderdale, M

Georgia

Emmanuel College, B
Emory University, D
Georgia Christian University, D
Luther Rice College & Seminary, MD
Mercer University, M
South University, D

Hawaii

Chaminade University of Honolulu, M

Idaho

Boise Bible College, AB
Northwest Nazarene University, BM

Illinois

Dominican University, B
Greenville College, BM
Judson University, M
Lincoln Christian University, B
Loyola University Chicago, BM
Moody Bible Institute, BMO
Olivet Nazarene University, B
Trinity International University, MD
University of Chicago, M
Wheaton College, M

Indiana

Bethel College, BM
Crossroads Bible College, B
Huntington University, MD

Indiana Wesleyan University, ABM
Marian University, AB
Martin University, M
Saint Joseph's College, B
Saint Mary-of-the-Woods College, O
University of Saint Francis, MO
Valparaiso University, M

Iowa

Faith Baptist Bible College and Theological Seminary, BM
Loras College, M
St. Ambrose University, M
Shiloh University, BM

Kansas

Barclay College, B
Central Christian College of Kansas, AB
Hesston College, A
Manhattan Christian College, B
Newman University, B
Ottawa University, M
Southwestern College, B
University of Saint Mary, B

Kentucky

Campbellsville University, B
Kentucky Christian University, B
Kentucky Mountain Bible College, B
The Southern Baptist Theological Seminary, BMD

Louisiana

Louisiana College, M
New Orleans Baptist Theological Seminary, MD
Xavier University of Louisiana, M

Maine

Husson University, M
Saint Joseph's College of Maine, M

Maryland

Loyola University Maryland, MDO
Maple Springs Baptist Bible College and Seminary, BM

Massachusetts

Anna Maria College, BM
Boston College, MDO
Eastern Nazarene College, B

Michigan

Andrews University, MD
Grace Bible College, B
Kuyper College, B
Madonna University, M
Sacred Heart Major Seminary, M
South University, D
Spring Arbor University, BM

Minnesota

Crown College, B
North Central University, AB
Oak Hills Christian College, B
St. Catherine University, O
Saint John's University, M
University of Northwestern - St. Paul, M
University of St. Thomas, M

Mississippi

Southeastern Baptist College, B

Missouri

Baptist Bible College, BM
Calvary Bible College and Theological Seminary, BM
Global University, MD
Missouri Baptist University, M
Southwest Baptist University, B

Nebraska

Concordia University, Nebraska, BM
Grace University, BM
Nebraska Christian College, B

New Jersey

Georgian Court University, O
Seton Hall University, MO

New York

Davis College, B
Fordham University, MDO
Houghton College, B
Nyack College, MD

North Carolina

Campbell University, M
Carolina Christian College, M
Charlotte Christian College and Theological Seminary, M
Gardner-Webb University, BMD
John Wesley University, B
Piedmont International University, M

Ohio

Cincinnati Christian University, M
Mount St. Joseph University, O
Mount Vernon Nazarene University, B
Notre Dame College, AB
University of Dayton, M
Walsh University, BM
Xavier University, M

Oklahoma

Hillsdale Free Will Baptist College, BM
Mid-America Christian University, M
Oklahoma Christian University, M
Oral Roberts University, BM
St. Gregory's University, B
Southwestern Christian University, BM

Oregon

Corban University, BMDO
George Fox University, BMD
Multnomah University, B
New Hope Christian College, B
Northwest Christian University, B
University of Portland, M
Warner Pacific College, B

Pennsylvania

Cairn University, M
Eastern University, M
Gannon University, MO
La Salle University, MDO
Lancaster Bible College, BMO
Neumann University, MO
Saint Francis University, B
Summit University, BMD
University of Valley Forge, B

South Carolina

Anderson University, M
Bob Jones University, MD
Columbia International University, MDO
North Greenville University, MD
Southern Wesleyan University, M

South Dakota

Mount Marty College, M

Tennessee

Carson-Newman University, M
Freed-Hardeman University, M
Lee University, BM
Lipscomb University, MDO
Milligan College, BMD
Trevecca Nazarene University, M
Union University, D
Welch College, B

Texas

Abilene Christian University, MD
College of Biblical Studies - Houston, B
Criswell College, M
Dallas Baptist University, MD
East Texas Baptist University, BM
Hardin-Simmons University, MD
Houston Baptist University, M

Howard Payne University, M
The King's University, MO
Messenger College, B
Southwestern Assemblies of God University, BM
University of Dallas, M
University of Mary Hardin-Baylor, B
University of St. Thomas, BM
Wayland Baptist University, M

Virginia

Eastern Mennonite University, MO
Hampton University, M
Liberty University, BMD
Marymount University, M
Regent University, MD
University of Valley Forge Virginia Campus, B

Washington

Northwest University, BM
Seattle University, M

West Virginia

Appalachian Bible College, M

Wisconsin

Cardinal Stritch University, M
Concordia University Wisconsin, B
Maranatha Baptist University, BM
Viterbo University, M

U.S. Territories: Puerto Rico

Inter American University of Puerto Rico, Metropolitan Campus, D
Theological University of the Caribbean, B
Universidad Pentecostal Mizpa, AB

Canada

Alberta

Ambrose University, M
Prairie Bible Institute, B
Rocky Mountain College, B

British Columbia

Columbia Bible College, B
Summit Pacific College, B
Trinity Western University, M

Manitoba

Providence University College & Theological Seminary, BMO

Maritime Provinces: New Brunswick

Kingswood University, M

Ontario

Emmanuel Bible College, B
McMaster University, MO
Saint Paul University, MDO
Tyndale University College & Seminary, BM
Wilfrid Laurier University, DO

Saskatchewan

Horizon College & Seminary, B

PATHOBIOLOGY

United States

Alabama

Auburn University, M
The University of Alabama at Birmingham, D

California

University of Southern California, D

Connecticut

University of Connecticut, MD
Yale University, D

Illinois

University of Illinois at Urbana - Champaign, MD

Indiana

Purdue University, MD

Kansas

Kansas State University, MD

Maryland

Johns Hopkins University, D

Michigan

Michigan State University, MD

Missouri

University of Missouri, MD

New York

Columbia University, MD
New York University, D

North Carolina

Wake Forest University, MD

Ohio

The Ohio State University, M
University of Cincinnati, D

Pennsylvania

Drexel University, MD
Penn State University Park, M

Rhode Island

Brown University, MD

South Carolina

Medical University of South Carolina, D

Washington

University of Washington, D

Wyoming

University of Wyoming, M

Canada

Ontario

University of Toronto, MD

PATHOLOGY/EXPERIMENTAL PATHOLOGY

United States

California

Loma Linda University, MD
University of California, Davis, MD
University of California, Irvine, D
University of California, Los Angeles, MD
University of Southern California, MD

Colorado

Colorado State University, MD

Connecticut

Quinnipiac University, M
University of Connecticut, B
Yale University, MD

Florida

University of South Florida, D

Georgia

University of Georgia, MD

Indiana

Indiana University - Purdue University Indianapolis, MD

Purdue University, M

Iowa

Iowa State University of Science and Technology, MD
The University of Iowa, M

Kansas

The University of Kansas, MD

Maryland

Johns Hopkins University, D

Massachusetts

Boston University, D
Harvard University, D
Tufts University, D
University of Massachusetts Lowell, O

Michigan

Michigan State University, MD
University of Michigan, D
Wayne State University, D

Mississippi

University of Mississippi Medical Center, D

Missouri

Saint Louis University, D
University of Missouri, M

Nebraska

University of Nebraska Medical Center, MD

New Jersey

Rutgers University - Newark, D

New Mexico

University of New Mexico, MD

New York

Columbia University, MD
Stony Brook University, State University of New York, D
University at Buffalo, the State University of New York, MD
University of Rochester, D

North Carolina

Duke University, MD
East Carolina University, D
North Carolina State University, MD
The University of North Carolina at Chapel Hill, D

North Dakota

North Dakota State University, D

Ohio

Case Western Reserve University, MD
The Ohio State University, M
University of Cincinnati, D
The University of Toledo, MO

Oklahoma

University of Oklahoma Health Sciences Center, D

Pennsylvania

Penn State Berks, B
University of Pittsburgh, D

South Carolina

Medical University of South Carolina, MD

Tennessee

Vanderbilt University, D

Texas

The University of Texas Medical Branch, D

Utah

University of Utah, D

Vermont

University of Vermont, M

Virginia

University of Virginia, D
Virginia Commonwealth University, D

Washington

University of Washington, D

Wisconsin

University of Wisconsin - Madison, D

Canada

Alberta

University of Alberta, MD
University of Calgary, MD

British Columbia

The University of British Columbia, MD

Manitoba

University of Manitoba, M

Maritime Provinces: Nova Scotia

Dalhousie University, MD

Maritime Provinces: Prince Edward Island

University of Prince Edward Island, MD

Ontario

Queen's University at Kingston, MD
University of Guelph, MDO
The University of Western Ontario, BMD

Quebec

McGill University, MD
Université Laval, O
Université de Montréal, MD

Saskatchewan

University of Saskatchewan, MD

PATHOLOGY/PATHOLOGIST ASSISTANT

United States

Michigan

Wayne State University, B

PEACE STUDIES AND CONFLICT RESOLUTION

United States

California

California State University, Dominguez Hills, B
Chapman University, B
University of California, Berkeley, B

Colorado

Naropa University, B
Regis University, B

Illinois

DePaul University, B

Indiana

Butler University, B
DePauw University, B
Earlham College, B
Goshen College, B
Manchester University, B

Iowa

Wartburg College, B

Maryland

Goucher College, B
Salisbury University, B

Massachusetts

Clark University, B
Hampshire College, B
Tufts University, B
University of Massachusetts Lowell, B
Wellesley College, B

Michigan

Delta College, A

Minnesota

Bethel University, B
College of Saint Benedict, B
The College of St. Scholastica, B
Hamline University, B
Saint John's University, B
University of St. Thomas, B

Missouri

University of Missouri, B

Nebraska

Creighton University, B

New Hampshire

Saint Anselm College, B

New York

Colgate University, B
Manhattan College, B
Nazareth College of Rochester, B
Pace University, B

North Carolina

Guilford College, B
The University of North Carolina at Chapel Hill, B
The University of North Carolina at Greensboro, B

Ohio

John Carroll University, B
Kent State University, B
Ohio Dominican University, B

Oregon

Willamette University, B

Pennsylvania

Gettysburg College, B
Haverford College, B
Juniata College, B
Messiah College, B
Swarthmore College, B
Ursinus College, B

Texas

El Centro College, A

Utah

University of Utah, B

Vermont

Bennington College, B
Goddard College, B
Norwich University, B

Virginia

Eastern Mennonite University, B
George Mason University, B

Washington

Whitworth University, B

Wisconsin

Marquette University, B
University of Wisconsin - Superior, B

Canada

Manitoba

The University of Winnipeg, B

Maritime Provinces: Nova Scotia

Mount Saint Vincent University, B

Ontario

University of Ottawa, B
University of Toronto, B
The University of Western Ontario, B

PEDIATRIC NURSE/NURSING

United States

California

Loma Linda University, M
San Francisco State University, M

Colorado

University of Colorado Denver, M

Delaware

University of Delaware, MO

Florida

University of South Florida, MD

Georgia

Augusta University, MO
Emory University, M
Georgia State University, MO

Illinois

Rush University, DO
University of Illinois at Chicago, M

Kentucky

Spalding University, MO

Massachusetts

Boston College, M

Michigan

University of Michigan, M
Wayne State University, MDO

Minnesota

St. Catherine University, M
University of Minnesota, Twin Cities Campus, M

Missouri

Maryville University of Saint Louis, M
University of Missouri, DO
University of Missouri - Kansas City, MD
University of Missouri - St. Louis, MO

Nebraska

Creighton University, MDO

New Jersey

Seton Hall University, MD

New York

Columbia University, MO
Lehman College of the City University of New York, M
Molloy College, M
New York University, MDO
Stony Brook University, State University of New York, MDO
University of Rochester, M

North Carolina

Duke University, MO
The University of North Carolina at Chapel Hill, M

Ohio

Case Western Reserve University, M
Kent State University, MO
University of Cincinnati, M
The University of Toledo, MO
Wright State University, M

Oregon

Oregon Health & Science University, MDO

Pennsylvania

Drexel University, M
Gwynedd Mercy University, M
University of Pennsylvania, M
University of Pittsburgh, D
Villanova University, MO

South Carolina

University of South Carolina, M

Tennessee

Vanderbilt University, M

Texas

Texas Christian University, M
Texas Woman's University, M
The University of Texas at Austin, M
The University of Texas Health Science Center at San Antonio, O

Virginia

Hampton University, M
Virginia Commonwealth University, M

Wisconsin

Marquette University, MDO
University of Wisconsin - Madison, D

U.S. Territories: Puerto Rico

Caribbean University, M
University of Puerto Rico, Medical Sciences Campus, M

Canada

Ontario

Queen's University at Kingston, M

PEDODONTICS

United States

District of Columbia

Howard University, O

Iowa

The University of Iowa, O

Massachusetts

Boston University, MDO
Tufts University, O

Michigan

University of Michigan, M

New Jersey

Rutgers University - Newark, O

New York

New York University, O

North Carolina

The University of North Carolina at Chapel Hill, M

Ohio

Case Western Reserve University, MO

Oregon

Oregon Health & Science University, O

U.S. Territories: Puerto Rico

University of Puerto Rico, Medical Sciences Campus, O

Canada

Quebec

Université de Montréal, M

PERFORMANCE

United States

Alabama

Samford University, M
The University of Alabama, MD
University of South Alabama, M

Arizona

Arizona State University at the Tempe campus, MD
Northern Arizona University, M
The University of Arizona, MD

Arkansas

Arkansas State University, M
University of Central Arkansas, M

California

California Baptist University, M
California Institute of the Arts, MO
California State University, Fresno, M
California State University, Fullerton, M
California State University, Long Beach, M
California State University, Los Angeles, M
California State University, Northridge, M
Mills College, M
Notre Dame de Namur University, MO
San Diego State University, M
San Francisco Conservatory of Music, M
San Francisco State University, M
University of California, Davis, MD
University of California, Irvine, M
University of California, San Diego, D
University of California, Santa Barbara, MD
University of California, Santa Cruz, M
University of Southern California, MDO

Colorado

University of Colorado Boulder, MD
University of Northern Colorado, MD

Connecticut

University of Connecticut, MD
University of Hartford, MDO

Delaware

University of Delaware, M

Florida

Florida Atlantic University, M
Florida State University, MD
Lynn University, MO
University of Florida, M
University of Miami, MDO
University of South Florida, M

Georgia

Columbus State University, M
Emory University, M
Georgia State University, MDO
Mercer University, M
Reinhardt University, M
Savannah College of Art and Design, M
University of West Georgia, M

Idaho

Boise State University, M

Illinois

DePaul University, MO
Northwestern University, MD
School of the Art Institute of Chicago, M
Southern Illinois University Edwardsville, M

Indiana

Indiana University Bloomington, D

Iowa

University of Northern Iowa, M

Kansas

Pittsburg State University, M

Kentucky

Campbellsville University, M
Eastern Kentucky University, M
Morehead State University, M
University of Kentucky, MD

Louisiana

Loyola University New Orleans, M
Southeastern Louisiana University, M
University of Louisiana at Lafayette, M

Maine

University of Maine, M
University of Southern Maine, M

Maryland

Towson University, M

Massachusetts

Berklee College of Music, M
Boston University, MO
University of Massachusetts Amherst, M

Michigan

Central Michigan University, M
Michigan State University, MD
University of Michigan, MDO
University of Michigan - Flint, M
Wayne State University, M
Western Michigan University, M

Minnesota

McNally Smith College of Music, M
University of Minnesota, Duluth, M
University of St. Thomas, M

Mississippi

Mississippi College, M
University of Southern Mississippi, MD

Missouri

Evangel University, M
Park University, MO
University of Missouri - Kansas City, MD
Webster University, M

Montana

University of Montana, M

Nebraska

University of Nebraska - Lincoln, MD

New Jersey

Montclair State University, MO
New Jersey City University, M
Rider University, M

New Mexico

New Mexico State University, M
University of New Mexico, M

New York

Bard College, MO
Brooklyn College of the City University of New York, M
Cornell University, D
Five Towns College, D
Houghton College, M

Ithaca College, M
Long Island University - LIU Post, M
Manhattan School of Music, MD
New York University, MDO
Pratt Institute, M
State University of New York College at Potsdam, M
Stony Brook University, State University of New York, MD
Syracuse University, M
University at Buffalo, the State University of New York, MO
University of Rochester, MD

North Carolina

Appalachian State University, M
Duke University, D
East Carolina University, MO
The University of North Carolina at Greensboro, MD
University of North Carolina School of the Arts, M

Ohio

Bowling Green State University, M
Case Western Reserve University, MD
Cleveland Institute of Music, MDO
Cleveland State University, M
Kent State University, MO
Miami University, M
Oberlin College, MO
The Ohio State University, M
Ohio University, MO
The University of Akron, M
University of Cincinnati, MDO
The University of Toledo, M
Wright State University, M
Youngstown State University, M

Oklahoma

Oklahoma City University, M
Oklahoma State University, M
Southwestern Oklahoma State University, M
University of Central Oklahoma, M
University of Oklahoma, MD

Oregon

Portland State University, M
Southern Oregon University, M

Pennsylvania

Carnegie Mellon University, M
Indiana University of Pennsylvania, M
Mansfield University of Pennsylvania, M
Messiah College, M
Penn State University Park, MD
Point Park University, M
Temple University, MD
West Chester University of Pennsylvania, MO

Rhode Island

University of Rhode Island, M

South Carolina

Bob Jones University, M
Converse College, M
University of South Carolina, MDO
Winthrop University, M

South Dakota

The University of South Dakota, M

Tennessee

Austin Peay State University, M
Belmont University, M
Lee University, M
The University of Tennessee, M
The University of Tennessee at Chattanooga, M

Texas

Baylor University, M
Hardin-Simmons University, M
Rice University, MD
Southern Methodist University, M
Texas A&M University, M
Texas State University, M
University of Houston, D

University of North Texas, MD
The University of Texas at Arlington, M
The University of Texas at Austin, MD
The University of Texas Rio Grande Valley, M
West Texas A&M University, M

Utah

Brigham Young University, M
University of Utah, MD

Virginia

George Mason University, MDO
Hollins University, M
James Madison University, MD
Norfolk State University, M
Shenandoah University, MD

Washington

Eastern Washington University, M
University of Washington, MD

West Virginia

West Virginia University, MD

Wisconsin

University of Wisconsin - Madison, MD
University of Wisconsin - Milwaukee, MO

Wyoming

University of Wyoming, M

U.S. Territories: Puerto Rico

Conservatorio de Musica de Puerto Rico, O

Canada

British Columbia

University of Victoria, M

Manitoba

Brandon University, M

Newfoundland and Labrador

Memorial University of Newfoundland, M

Ontario

University of Toronto, MD

Quebec

Concordia University, O
McGill University, MD

Saskatchewan

University of Regina, M

PERFUSION TECHNOLOGY/ PERFUSIONIST

United States

Arizona

The University of Arizona, M

Connecticut

Quinnipiac University, M

Illinois

Rush University, M

Nebraska

University of Nebraska Medical Center, M

New York

State University of New York Upstate Medical University, B

Pennsylvania

Carlow University, B

Wisconsin

Milwaukee School of Engineering, M

PERIODONTICS

United States

California

Loma Linda University, M

Colorado

University of Colorado Denver, M

Florida

University of Florida, MO

Iowa

The University of Iowa, MO

Massachusetts

Boston University, MDO
Harvard University, O
Tufts University, O

Michigan

University of Detroit Mercy, MO
University of Michigan, M

Minnesota

University of Minnesota, Twin Cities Campus, M

Missouri

Saint Louis University, M
University of Missouri - Kansas City, O

New York

Columbia University, MO
New York University, O
Stony Brook University, State University of New
  York, O

North Carolina

The University of North Carolina at Chapel Hill, M

Ohio

Case Western Reserve University, MO
The Ohio State University, M

Oklahoma

University of Oklahoma Health Sciences Center, M

Oregon

Oregon Health & Science University, MO

Pennsylvania

Temple University, O
University of Pittsburgh, MO

Canada

British Columbia

The University of British Columbia, O

Manitoba

University of Manitoba, M

Ontario

University of Toronto, M

PERSONAL AND CULINARY SERVICES

United States

Arizona

GateWay Community College, A
Mohave Community College, A

Mississippi

Virginia College in Biloxi, A

Ohio

University of Cincinnati Blue Ash College, A

PETROLEUM ENGINEERING

United States

Alaska

University of Alaska Fairbanks, BM

California

Stanford University, B
University of Southern California, MDO

Colorado

Colorado School of Mines, BMD

Kansas

The University of Kansas, BMD

Louisiana

Louisiana State University and Agricultural & Mechanical College, BMD
University of Louisiana at Lafayette, BM

Missouri

Missouri University of Science and Technology, BMD

Montana

Montana Tech of The University of Montana, BM

New Mexico

New Mexico Institute of Mining and Technology, BMD

North Dakota

University of North Dakota, B

Ohio

Marietta College, B

Oklahoma

University of Oklahoma, BMD
The University of Tulsa, BMD

Pennsylvania

Penn State Abington, B
Penn State Altoona, B
Penn State Beaver, B
Penn State Berks, B
Penn State Brandywine, B
Penn State DuBois, B
Penn State Erie, The Behrend College, B
Penn State Fayette, The Eberly Campus, B
Penn State Greater Allegheny, B
Penn State Hazleton, B
Penn State Lehigh Valley, B
Penn State Mont Alto, B
Penn State New Kensington, B
Penn State Schuylkill, B
Penn State Shenango, B
Penn State University Park, B
Penn State Wilkes-Barre, B
Penn State Worthington Scranton, B
Penn State York, B
Saint Francis University, B
University of Pittsburgh, MD

Texas

Kilgore College, A
Texas A&M University, BMD
Texas A&M University - Kingsville, BM
Texas Tech University, BMD
University of Houston, BM
The University of Texas at Austin, BMD
The University of Texas of the Permian Basin, B

Utah

University of Utah, M

West Virginia

West Virginia University, BMD

Wyoming

University of Wyoming, BMD

Canada

Alberta

Southern Alberta Institute of Technology, A
University of Alberta, MD
University of Calgary, MD

Ontario

University of Toronto, B

Saskatchewan

University of Regina, BMD

PETROLEUM TECHNOLOGY/ TECHNICIAN

United States

Alaska

University of Alaska Anchorage, A

Arkansas

University of Arkansas Community College at Morrilton, A

California

Bakersfield College, A

Illinois

Rend Lake College, A

Louisiana

Bossier Parish Community College, A
Fletcher Technical Community College, A
Nicholls State University, AB

Mississippi

Southwest Mississippi Community College, A

Montana

Montana State University Billings, A

New Mexico

New Mexico Junior College, A

North Dakota

Bismarck State College, A
Williston State College, A

Oklahoma

Oklahoma State University Institute of Technology, A

Pennsylvania

Lackawanna College, A
Mansfield University of Pennsylvania, A
Mercyhurst University, B
University of Pittsburgh at Bradford, A

Texas

Coastal Bend College, A
Houston Community College, A
Panola College, A
South Plains College, A
Western Texas College, A

Canada

British Columbia

British Columbia Institute of Technology, A

Maritime Provinces: Nova Scotia

Cape Breton University, B

PHARMACEUTICAL ADMINIS-TRATION

United States

California

San Diego State University, M
University of Southern California, M

Florida

Florida Agricultural and Mechanical University, M
Nova Southeastern University, D
University of Florida, MD

Georgia

University of Georgia, D

Idaho

Idaho State University, MD

Illinois

University of Illinois at Chicago, MD

Indiana

Purdue University, MO

Michigan

University of Michigan, D

Minnesota

University of Minnesota, Twin Cities Campus, MD

New Jersey

Fairleigh Dickinson University, Metropolitan Campus, MO
New Jersey Institute of Technology, M
Rutgers University - Newark, M

New York

Columbia University, M
St. John's University, M

Ohio

The Ohio State University, MD
The University of Toledo, M

Pennsylvania

Duquesne University, M
Temple University, M
University of the Sciences, M

Texas

University of Houston, MD

Utah

University of Utah, M

Virginia

Virginia Commonwealth University, M

West Virginia

West Virginia University, MD

Wisconsin

University of Wisconsin - Madison, MD

PHARMACEUTICAL ENGINEER-ING

United States

Michigan

University of Michigan, M

New Jersey

New Jersey Institute of Technology, M

PHARMACEUTICAL SCIENCES

United States

Alabama

Auburn University, MD

Arizona

The University of Arizona, MD

California

Chapman University, M
University of the Pacific, MD
University of Southern California, MDO

Colorado

University of Colorado Denver, D

Connecticut

University of Connecticut, MD

Florida

Florida Agricultural and Mechanical University, MD
University of Florida, MD

Georgia

Mercer University, D
University of Georgia, D

Hawaii

University of Hawaii at Hilo, D

Idaho

Idaho State University, MD

Illinois

Rush University, M
University of Illinois at Chicago, MD

Indiana

Butler University, MD
Purdue University, MD

Iowa

The University of Iowa, MD

Kansas

The University of Kansas, M

Kentucky

University of Kentucky, MD

Maryland

Johns Hopkins University, M

Massachusetts

Boston University, MD
MCPHS University, MD
Northeastern University, MD

Michigan

University of Michigan, D
Wayne State University, MD

Minnesota

University of Minnesota, Twin Cities Campus, MD

Missouri

University of Missouri - Kansas City, D

Montana

University of Montana, MD

Nebraska

Creighton University, M
University of Nebraska Medical Center, MD

New Hampshire

Dartmouth College, D

New Jersey

Rowan University, M
Rutgers University - New Brunswick, MD
Stevens Institute of Technology, MO

New Mexico

University of New Mexico, MD

New York

Albany College of Pharmacy and Health Sciences, M
Long Island University - LIU Brooklyn, MD
St. John's University, MD
University at Buffalo, the State University of New York, MD

North Carolina

Campbell University, M
The University of North Carolina at Chapel Hill, MD

North Dakota

North Dakota State University, MD

Ohio

University of Cincinnati, MD
The University of Toledo, M

Oklahoma

University of Oklahoma Health Sciences Center, MD

Oregon

Oregon State University, MD

Pennsylvania

Drexel University, M
Duquesne University, MD
Temple University, MD
University of Pittsburgh, MD
University of the Sciences, MD

Rhode Island

University of Rhode Island, MD

South Carolina

University of South Carolina, MD

South Dakota

South Dakota State University, MD

Tennessee

East Tennessee State University, D

Texas

Texas Southern University, MD
University of Houston, MD
The University of Texas at Austin, MD

Utah

University of Utah, MD

Virginia

Virginia Commonwealth University, MD

Washington

University of Washington, MD

West Virginia

West Virginia University, MD

Wisconsin

University of Wisconsin - Madison, MD

U.S. Territories: Puerto Rico

University of Puerto Rico, Medical Sciences Campus, M

Canada

Alberta

University of Alberta, MD

British Columbia

The University of British Columbia, MD

Manitoba

University of Manitoba, MD

Newfoundland and Labrador

Memorial University of Newfoundland, MD

Ontario

Queen's University at Kingston, MD
University of Toronto, MD

Quebec

Université Laval, MDO
Université de Montréal, MDO

Saskatchewan

University of Saskatchewan, MD

PHARMACEUTICS AND DRUG DESIGN

United States

Indiana

Purdue University, B

Montana

University of Montana, B

Ohio

The Ohio State University, B
The University of Toledo, B

Pennsylvania

Temple University, B
West Chester University of Pennsylvania, B

Rhode Island

University of Rhode Island, B

PHARMACOGNOSY

United States

Illinois

University of Illinois at Chicago, MD

Rhode Island

University of Rhode Island, MD

PHARMACOLOGY

United States

Alabama

Auburn University, M
The University of Alabama at Birmingham, D

Arizona

The University of Arizona, MD

Arkansas

University of Arkansas for Medical Sciences, D

California

Loma Linda University, MD
University of California, Davis, MD
University of California, Los Angeles, MD
University of California, Santa Barbara, BM

Colorado

University of Colorado Denver, D

Connecticut

University of Connecticut, MD
Yale University, D

District of Columbia

Georgetown University, MD
Howard University, MD

Florida

Florida Agricultural and Mechanical University, MD
University of Florida, MD
University of Miami, D
University of South Florida, D

Georgia

Augusta University, MD
Emory University, D
Georgia Southern University, B
University of Georgia, MD

Hawaii

Argosy University, Hawai'i, MO
University of Hawaii at Hilo, M

Idaho

Idaho State University, D

Illinois

Rush University, MD
Southern Illinois University Carbondale, MD
University of Illinois at Chicago, D

Indiana

Indiana University - Purdue University Indianapolis, MD
Purdue University, MD

Iowa

The University of Iowa, MD

Kansas

The University of Kansas, MD

Kentucky

University of Kentucky, D
University of Louisville, MD

Louisiana

Louisiana State University Health Sciences Center, MD
Tulane University, MD

Maryland

Johns Hopkins University, D

Massachusetts

Boston University, MD
MCPHS University, MD
Northeastern University, M
Tufts University, MD

Michigan

Michigan State University, MD
University of Michigan, MD
Wayne State University, D

Minnesota

University of Minnesota, Duluth, MD
University of Minnesota, Twin Cities Campus, MD

Mississippi

University of Mississippi Medical Center, D

Missouri

Saint Louis University, D
University of Missouri, MD
University of Missouri - Kansas City, D

Nebraska

Creighton University, MD
University of Nebraska Medical Center, D

New Hampshire

Dartmouth College, D

New Jersey

Fairleigh Dickinson University, College at Florham, MO
Montclair State University, M
New Jersey Institute of Technology, M
Rutgers University - Newark, DO

New York

Albany College of Pharmacy and Health Sciences, M
Columbia University, MD
Cornell University, MD
State University of New York Upstate Medical University, D
Stony Brook University, State University of New York, BD
University at Buffalo, the State University of New York, MD
University of Rochester, MD

North Carolina

Duke University, D
East Carolina University, D
North Carolina State University, MD
The University of North Carolina at Chapel Hill, D
Wake Forest University, D

North Dakota

University of North Dakota, MD

Ohio

Case Western Reserve University, D
Kent State University, M
The Ohio State University, MD
University of Cincinnati, D
The University of Toledo, MD
Wright State University, M

Oregon

Oregon Health & Science University, D

Pennsylvania

Drexel University, MD
Duquesne University, MD
Thomas Jefferson University, M
University of Pennsylvania, D
University of the Sciences, MD

Rhode Island

University of Rhode Island, MD

South Dakota

The University of South Dakota, MD

Tennessee

East Tennessee State University, D
Maryville College, B
Vanderbilt University, D

Texas

University of Houston, MD
The University of Texas at Austin, D
The University of Texas Health Science Center at San Antonio, D
The University of Texas Medical Branch, MD

Utah

University of Utah, D

Vermont

University of Vermont, M

Virginia

University of Virginia, D
Virginia Commonwealth University, MDO

Washington

University of Washington, D

West Virginia

West Virginia University, MD

Wisconsin

University of Wisconsin - Madison, D

U.S. Territories: Puerto Rico

Universidad Central del Caribe, M
Universidad del Turabo, A
University of Puerto Rico, Medical Sciences Campus, MD

Canada

Alberta

University of Alberta, BMD

British Columbia

The University of British Columbia, BMD

Manitoba

University of Manitoba, MD

Maritime Provinces: Nova Scotia

Dalhousie University, MD

Maritime Provinces: Prince Edward Island

University of Prince Edward Island, MD

Ontario

McMaster University, BMD
Queen's University at Kingston, MD
University of Guelph, MD
University of Ottawa, B
University of Toronto, MD
The University of Western Ontario, B

Quebec

McGill University, MD
Université de Montréal, MD
Université de Sherbrooke, MD

Saskatchewan

University of Saskatchewan, BMD

PHARMACOLOGY AND TOXICOLOGY

United States

District of Columbia

The George Washington University, B

Massachusetts

MCPHS University, B

New York

University at Buffalo, the State University of New York, B

Pennsylvania

University of the Sciences, B

Wisconsin

University of Wisconsin - Madison, B

PHARMACY

United States

Alabama

Auburn University, D
Samford University, BD

Arizona

The University of Arizona, D

Arkansas

Harding University, D
University of Arkansas for Medical Sciences, MD

California

Cerritos College, A
Chapman University, MD
Loma Linda University, D
University of California, San Diego, D
University of the Pacific, BD
University of Southern California, D

Colorado

Regis University, D

Connecticut

University of Connecticut, BD
University of Saint Joseph, D

Delaware

University of Delaware, B

District of Columbia

Howard University, BD

Florida

Broward College, A
Florida Agricultural and Mechanical University, D
Indian River State College, A
Nova Southeastern University, D
Palm Beach Atlantic University, D
South Florida State College, A
University of Florida, MD
University of South Florida, DO

Georgia

Mercer University, D
University of Georgia, MDO

Hawaii

University of Hawaii at Hilo, D

Idaho

The College of Idaho, B
Idaho State University, MD

Illinois

Chicago State University, D
Illinois Institute of Technology, B
Roosevelt University, D
Southern Illinois University Edwardsville, D
University of Illinois at Chicago, MD

Indiana

Butler University, BMD
Manchester University, BD
Purdue University, D

Iowa

Drake University, BD
Iowa Lakes Community College, A
The University of Iowa, BMD

Kansas

Barton County Community College, A
The University of Kansas, B

Kentucky

University of Kentucky, BD

Louisiana

University of Louisiana at Monroe, BD
Xavier University of Louisiana, D

Maine

Husson University, D
University of New England, D

Massachusetts

Eastern Nazarene College, B
MCPHS University, BD
Northeastern University, B
Western New England University, D

Michigan

Ferris State University, D
Mid Michigan Community College, A
University of Michigan, D
Wayne State University, MD

Minnesota

University of Minnesota, Duluth, MD
University of Minnesota, Twin Cities Campus, D

Mississippi

University of Mississippi, MD

Missouri

St. Louis College of Pharmacy, D
University of Missouri - Kansas City, D

Montana

University of Montana, BMD

Nebraska

Creighton University, D
University of Nebraska Medical Center, D

New Jersey

Rutgers University - New Brunswick, MD

New Mexico

University of New Mexico, D

New York

Albany College of Pharmacy and Health Sciences, MD
D'Youville College, D
Long Island University - LIU Brooklyn, BMD
St. John Fisher College, D
St. John's University, B
University at Buffalo, the State University of New York, D

North Carolina

Campbell University, MD
Isothermal Community College, A
Wingate University, D

North Dakota

Turtle Mountain Community College, A

Ohio

Cedarville University, D
Lorain County Community College, A
Ohio Northern University, D
The Ohio State University, BMD
University of Cincinnati, BD
The University of Findlay, D
The University of Toledo, B

Oklahoma

Southwestern Oklahoma State University, D
University of Oklahoma Health Sciences Center, BD

Oregon

Oregon State University, D
Pacific University, D

Pennsylvania

Duquesne University, D
Saint Vincent College, B
Thomas Jefferson University, D

University of Pittsburgh, D
University of the Sciences, BD
Wilkes University, D

Rhode Island

University of Rhode Island, MD

South Carolina

Medical University of South Carolina, D
Presbyterian College, B
South University, D
University of South Carolina, D

South Dakota

South Dakota State University, BD

Tennessee

Belmont University, D
East Tennessee State University, D
Lipscomb University, MD

Texas

Navarro College, A
Texas A&M University, D
Texas Southern University, D
University of Houston, MD
University of the Incarnate Word, D
The University of Texas at Austin, D

Utah

University of Utah, D

Virginia

Hampton University, D
Shenandoah University, D
Virginia Commonwealth University, D

Washington

University of Washington, MD
Washington State University, MD
Washington State University - Spokane, B

West Virginia

Marshall University, D
University of Charleston, D
West Virginia University, MD

Wisconsin

University of Wisconsin - Madison, D

Wyoming

University of Wyoming, D

U.S. Territories: Puerto Rico

University of Puerto Rico, Medical Sciences Campus, MD

Canada

Alberta

University of Alberta, BMD

British Columbia

The University of British Columbia, BMD

Manitoba

University of Manitoba, B

Maritime Provinces: Nova Scotia

Dalhousie University, B

Newfoundland and Labrador

Memorial University of Newfoundland, B

Ontario

University of Toronto, B

Quebec

Université Laval, B
Université de Montréal, B

Saskatchewan

University of Saskatchewan, B

PHARMACY ADMINISTRATION AND PHARMACY POLICY AND REGULATORY AFFAIRS

United States

Iowa

Drake University, B

Michigan

University of Michigan, B

PHARMACY, PHARMACEUTICAL SCIENCES, AND ADMINISTRATION

United States

California

American University of Health Sciences, B

Florida

Virginia College in Pensacola, A

Massachusetts

MCPHS University, B

Mississippi

University of Mississippi, B

New York

Albany College of Pharmacy and Health Sciences, B

North Carolina

Campbell University, B
The University of North Carolina at Chapel Hill, B

North Dakota

North Dakota State University, B

Ohio

Ohio Northern University, B

Pennsylvania

Duquesne University, B
University of the Sciences, B

South Carolina

Francis Marion University, B

U.S. Territories: Puerto Rico

EDP University of Puerto Rico, A
EDP University of Puerto Rico - San Sebastian, A
Universidad del Turabo, A

Canada

Alberta

University of Alberta, B

Maritime Provinces: Nova Scotia

Dalhousie University, B

Quebec

Université Laval, B

PHARMACY TECHNICIAN/AS-SISTANT

United States

Alabama

Community College of the Air Force, A

Arizona

Eastern Arizona College, A
Mohave Community College, A
Pima Community College, A

California

Carrington College - Citrus Heights, A
Carrington College - Pleasant Hill, A
Carrington College - Pomona, A
Carrington College - Sacramento, A
Carrington College - San Jose, A
Carrington College - San Leandro, A
Charles R. Drew University of Medicine and Science, A
Cosumnes River College, A
Foothill College, A
San Joaquin Valley College (Bakersfield), A
San Joaquin Valley College (Fresno), A
San Joaquin Valley College (Hesperia), A
San Joaquin Valley College (Lancaster), A
San Joaquin Valley College (Ontario), A
San Joaquin Valley College (Salida), A
San Joaquin Valley College (Temecula), A
San Joaquin Valley College (Visalia), A
Santa Ana College, A
Santa Rosa Junior College, A

Colorado

Aims Community College, A

Florida

Everest University (Tampa), A
Fortis College (Orange Park), A
Fortis College (Winter Park), A
Miami Dade College, A
Pensacola State College, A
Rasmussen College Fort Myers, A
Rasmussen College Land O' Lakes, A
Rasmussen College New Port Richey, A
Rasmussen College Ocala, A
Rasmussen College Tampa/Brandon, A
Southeastern College - West Palm Beach, A
Tallahassee Community College, A
Ultimate Medical Academy Online, A

Georgia

Abraham Baldwin Agricultural College, A
Albany Technical College, A
Augusta Technical College, A
Columbus Technical College, A
Southern Crescent Technical College, A
West Georgia Technical College, A

Idaho

Carrington College - Boise, A

Illinois

Rasmussen College Aurora, A
Rasmussen College Mokena/Tinley Park, A
Rasmussen College Rockford, A
Rasmussen College Romeoville/Joliet, A
Robert Morris University Illinois, A

Indiana

Vincennes University, A

Iowa

Western Iowa Tech Community College, A

Kansas

Barton County Community College, A
Hutchinson Community College, A
Rasmussen College Kansas City/Overland Park, A
Rasmussen College Topeka, A

Kentucky

Daymar College (Bowling Green), A
Daymar College (Owensboro), A
Sullivan University, A

Louisiana

Bossier Parish Community College, A

Michigan

Baker College, A
Kirtland Community College, A
Oakland Community College, A
Wayne County Community College District, A

Minnesota

Anoka-Ramsey Community College, A
Minnesota State Community and Technical College,
   A
Northland Community and Technical College, A
Rasmussen College Blaine, A
Rasmussen College Bloomington, A
Rasmussen College Brooklyn Park, A
Rasmussen College Eagan, A
Rasmussen College Lake Elmo/Woodbury, A
Rasmussen College Mankato, A
Rasmussen College Moorhead, A
Rasmussen College St. Cloud, A
Riverland Community College, A

Missouri

National American University (Kansas City), A
Vatterott College (Kansas City), A
Vatterott College (Springfield), A

Montana

University of Montana, B

Nebraska

Southeast Community College, Beatrice Campus, A

New Jersey

Salem Community College, A

New York

ASA College, A

North Carolina

Cabarrus College of Health Sciences, A
Fayetteville Technical Community College, A
Guilford Technical Community College, A
Miller-Motte College (Cary), A

North Dakota

North Dakota State College of Science, A

Ohio

American National University (Cincinnati), A
American National University (Kettering), A
American National University (Youngstown), A
University of Northwestern Ohio, A

Oklahoma

Community Care College, A

Oregon

Chemeketa Community College, A

Pennsylvania

Community College of Allegheny County, A
Pennsylvania Institute of Technology, A

South Carolina

Midlands Technical College, A

South Dakota

Western Dakota Technical Institute, A

Tennessee

Concorde Career College, A
Daymar College (Clarksville), A
Daymar College (Nashville), A
Roane State Community College, A

Texas

Alvin Community College, A
Austin Community College District, A
College of the Mainland, A
El Paso Community College, A
Lone Star College - North Harris, A
San Jacinto College District, A
Texarkana College, A
Weatherford College, A

Virginia

J. Sargeant Reynolds Community College, A
Miller-Motte Technical College (Lynchburg), A
Stratford University (Falls Church), A
Stratford University (Glen Allen), A
Stratford University (Newport News), A
Stratford University (Virginia Beach), A
Stratford University (Woodbridge), A

Washington

Clover Park Technical College, A
Edmonds Community College, A
North Seattle College, A
Renton Technical College, A
Tacoma Community College, A

West Virginia

West Virginia Junior College - Bridgeport, A

Wisconsin

Rasmussen College Appleton, A
Rasmussen College Green Bay, A
Rasmussen College Wausau, A

Wyoming

Casper College, A

U.S. Territories: Puerto Rico

Centro de Estudios Multidisciplinarios (Rio Piedras),
   A
Huertas Junior College, A
Humacao Community College, A
Inter American University of Puerto Rico, Aguadilla
   Campus, A
Inter American University of Puerto Rico, Guayama
   Campus, A
National University College (Bayamón), A
Universidad del Este, A
Universidad del Turabo, A

PHILANTHROPIC STUDIES

United States

Indiana

Indiana University - Purdue University Indianapolis,
   MD

Minnesota

Saint Mary's University of Minnesota, M

PHILOSOPHY

United States

Alabama

Auburn University, B
Birmingham-Southern College, B
Samford University, B
Spring Hill College, B
The University of Alabama, B
The University of Alabama at Birmingham, B
The University of Alabama in Huntsville, B
University of South Alabama, B

Alaska

University of Alaska Anchorage, B
University of Alaska Fairbanks, B

Arizona

Arizona State University at the Tempe campus,
   BMD
Arizona Western College, A
Cochise County Community College District, A
Harrison Middleton University, M
Northern Arizona University, B
The University of Arizona, BMD

Arkansas

Arkansas State University, B
Hendrix College, B
Ouachita Baptist University, B
University of Arkansas, BMD
University of Arkansas at Little Rock, B
University of Central Arkansas, B
University of the Ozarks, B

California

Antelope Valley College, A
Azusa Pacific University, B
Bakersfield College, A
Biola University, B
Cabrillo College, A
California Baptist University, B
California Institute of Integral Studies, MD
California Institute of Technology, B
California Lutheran University, B
California Polytechnic State University, San Luis
   Obispo, B
California State Polytechnic University, Pomona, B
California State University, Bakersfield, B
California State University, Chico, B
California State University, Dominguez Hills, B
California State University, East Bay, B
California State University, Fresno, B
California State University, Fullerton, B
California State University, Long Beach, BM
California State University, Los Angeles, BM
California State University, Northridge, B
California State University, Sacramento, B
California State University, San Bernardino, B
California State University, Stanislaus, B
Cañada College, A
Cerritos College, A
Chaffey College, A
Chapman University, B
Claremont McKenna College, B
College of Alameda, A
College of the Canyons, A
College of the Desert, A
Copper Mountain College, A
Crafton Hills College, A
Cypress College, A
De Anza College, A
Dominican University of California, M
East Los Angeles College, A
El Camino College, A
Foothill College, A
Fresno City College, A
Fullerton College, A
Grossmont College, A
Holy Names University, B
Humboldt State University, B
Los Angeles Mission College, A
Los Angeles Valley College, A
Loyola Marymount University, BM
Mills College, B
Monterey Peninsula College, A
Mount Saint Mary's University, B
Notre Dame de Namur University, B
Occidental College, B
Ohlone College, A
Orange Coast College, A
Oxnard College, A
Pepperdine University, B
Pitzer College, B
Point Loma Nazarene University, B
Pomona College, B
Saddleback College, A
Saint Mary's College of California, B
San Bernardino Valley College, A
San Diego Miramar College, A
San Diego State University, BM
San Francisco State University, BM

San Joaquin Delta College, A
San Jose City College, A
San Jose State University, BM
Santa Ana College, A
Santa Barbara City College, A
Santa Clara University, B
Santa Rosa Junior College, A
Santiago Canyon College, A
Scripps College, B
Sierra College, A
Sonoma State University, B
Southwestern College, A
Stanford University, BMD
University of California, Berkeley, BD
University of California, Davis, BMD
University of California, Irvine, BMD
University of California, Los Angeles, BMD
University of California, Riverside, BMD
University of California, San Diego, BD
University of California, Santa Barbara, BD
University of California, Santa Cruz, BMD
University of La Verne, B
University of the Pacific, B
University of Redlands, B
University of San Diego, B
University of San Francisco, B
University of Southern California, BMD
West Los Angeles College, A
Westmont College, B
Whittier College, B
Yuba College, A

Colorado

The Colorado College, B
Colorado State University, BM
Fort Lewis College, B
Metropolitan State University of Denver, B
Northeastern Junior College, A
Regis University, B
United States Air Force Academy, B
University of Colorado Boulder, BMD
University of Colorado Colorado Springs, B
University of Colorado Denver, B
University of Denver, B
University of Northern Colorado, B

Connecticut

Albertus Magnus College, B
Central Connecticut State University, B
Connecticut College, B
Eastern Connecticut State University, B
Fairfield University, B
Holy Apostles College and Seminary, B
Quinnipiac University, B
Sacred Heart University, B
Southern Connecticut State University, B
Trinity College, B
University of Connecticut, BMD
University of Hartford, B
University of Saint Joseph, B
Wesleyan University, B
Yale University, BD

Delaware

Delaware State University, B
University of Delaware, B

District of Columbia

American University, B
The Catholic University of America, BMDO
Gallaudet University, B
The George Washington University, BM
Georgetown University, BMD
Howard University, BM
Trinity Washington University, B

Florida

Ave Maria University, B
Barry University, B
Broward College, A
College of Central Florida, A
Eckerd College, B
Florida Atlantic University, B
Florida Gulf Coast University, B
Florida International University, B

Florida Southern College, B
Florida State University, BMD
Indian River State College, A
Jacksonville University, B
Miami Dade College, A
New College of Florida, B
Nova Southeastern University, B
Palm Beach Atlantic University, B
Palm Beach State College, A
Pensacola State College, A
Rollins College, B
St. John Vianney College Seminary, B
South Florida State College, A
State College of Florida Manatee-Sarasota, A
Stetson University, B
University of Central Florida, B
University of Florida, BMD
University of Miami, BMD
University of North Florida, BMO
University of South Florida, BMD
The University of Tampa, B
University of West Florida, B

Georgia

Agnes Scott College, B
Clark Atlanta University, B
Clayton State University, B
College of Coastal Georgia, A
Covenant College, B
Darton State College, A
Emory University, BDO
Georgia College & State University, B
Georgia Highlands College, A
Georgia Southern University, B
Georgia State University, BM
Kennesaw State University, B
Mercer University, B
Morehouse College, B
Oglethorpe University, B
Paine College, B
Piedmont College, B
South Georgia State College, A
Spelman College, B
Toccoa Falls College, B
University of Georgia, BMD
University of West Georgia, B
Wesleyan College, B

Hawaii

University of Hawaii at Manoa, BMD
University of Hawaii - West Oahu, B

Idaho

Boise State University, B
The College of Idaho, B
Idaho State University, B
Northwest Nazarene University, B
University of Idaho, BM

Illinois

Augustana College, B
Aurora University, B
Benedictine University, B
Bradley University, B
Concordia University Chicago, B
DePaul University, B
Dominican University, B
Eastern Illinois University, B
Elmhurst College, B
Greenville College, B
Harper College, A
Illinois College, B
Illinois State University, B
Illinois Wesleyan University, B
Knox College, B
Lake Forest College, B
Lewis University, B
Lincoln Christian University, B
Loyola University Chicago, BMD
McKendree University, B
Millikin University, B
Monmouth College, B
North Central College, B
North Park University, B
Northeastern Illinois University, B
Northern Illinois University, BM

Northwestern University, BD
Olivet Nazarene University, B
Principia College, B
Rockford University, B
Roosevelt University, B
Saint Xavier University, B
Southern Illinois University Carbondale, BMD
Southern Illinois University Edwardsville, B
Trinity Christian College, B
Trinity International University, B
Triton College, A
University of Chicago, BMD
University of Illinois at Chicago, BMD
University of Illinois at Springfield, B
University of Illinois at Urbana - Champaign, BMD
Western Illinois University, B
Wheaton College, B

Indiana

Ball State University, B
Bethel College, B
Butler University, B
DePauw University, B
Earlham College, B
Franklin College, B
Hanover College, B
Huntington University, B
Indiana State University, B
Indiana University Bloomington, BMD
Indiana University Northwest, B
Indiana University - Purdue University Fort Wayne,
  B
Indiana University - Purdue University Indianapolis,
  BMO
Indiana University South Bend, B
Indiana University Southeast, B
Indiana Wesleyan University, B
Manchester University, B
Marian University, B
Purdue University, BMD
Purdue University Northwest (Hammond), B
Saint Joseph's College, B
Saint Mary's College, B
Taylor University, B
University of Evansville, B
University of Indianapolis, B
University of Notre Dame, BD
University of Saint Francis, B
University of Southern Indiana, B
Valparaiso University, B
Vincennes University, A
Wabash College, B

Iowa

Central College, B
Clarke University, B
Coe College, B
Cornell College, B
Divine Word College, B
Dordt College, B
Drake University, B
Grinnell College, B
Iowa Lakes Community College, A
Iowa State University of Science and Technology, B
Loras College, B
Luther College, B
Morningside College, B
Mount Mercy University, B
Northwestern College, B
St. Ambrose University, B
Simpson College, B
University of Dubuque, B
The University of Iowa, BD
University of Northern Iowa, B
Wartburg College, B

Kansas

Allen Community College, A
Baker University, B
Barton County Community College, A
Benedictine College, B
Bethany College, B
Fort Hays State University, B
Kansas State University, B
Kansas Wesleyan University, B
McPherson College, B

Newman University, B
The University of Kansas, BMD
Washburn University, B
Wichita State University, B

Kentucky

Asbury University, B
Bellarmine University, B
Berea College, B
Centre College, B
Eastern Kentucky University, B
Georgetown College, B
Morehead State University, B
Murray State University, B
Northern Kentucky University, B
The Southern Baptist Theological Seminary, M
Thomas More College, AB
Transylvania University, B
University of Kentucky, BMD
University of Louisville, BM

Louisiana

Centenary College of Louisiana, B
Louisiana College, B
Louisiana State University and Agricultural & Mechanical College, BM
Loyola University New Orleans, B
Tulane University, BMD
University of New Orleans, B
Xavier University of Louisiana, B

Maine

Bates College, B
Bowdoin College, B
Colby College, B
College of the Atlantic, B
Saint Joseph's College of Maine, B
University of Maine, B
University of Southern Maine, B

Maryland

Frostburg State University, B
Goucher College, B
Harford Community College, A
Hood College, B
Johns Hopkins University, BMD
Loyola University Maryland, B
McDaniel College, B
Morgan State University, B
Mount St. Mary's University, BM
Notre Dame of Maryland University, B
St. Mary's College of Maryland, B
Salisbury University, B
Towson University, B
University of Maryland, Baltimore County, B
University of Maryland, College Park, BMD
Washington College, B

Massachusetts

Amherst College, B
Anna Maria College, B
Assumption College, B
Bard College at Simon's Rock, B
Bentley University, B
Boston College, BMD
Boston University, BMD
Brandeis University, BM
Bridgewater State University, B
Clark University, B
College of the Holy Cross, B
Curry College, B
Emmanuel College, B
Gordon College, B
Hampshire College, B
Harvard University, BMD
Massachusetts College of Liberal Arts, B
Massachusetts Institute of Technology, BD
Merrimack College, B
Mount Holyoke College, B
Northeastern University, B
Simmons College, B
Smith College, B
Stonehill College, B
Suffolk University, B
Tufts University, BM

University of Massachusetts Amherst, BMD
University of Massachusetts Boston, B
University of Massachusetts Dartmouth, B
University of Massachusetts Lowell, B
Wellesley College, B
Western New England University, B
Wheaton College, B
Williams College, B
Worcester Polytechnic Institute, B

Michigan

Adrian College, B
Albion College, B
Alma College, B
Aquinas College, B
Calvin College, B
Central Michigan University, B
Concordia University Ann Arbor, B
Eastern Michigan University, BM
Grand Valley State University, B
Hillsdale College, B
Hope College, B
Kalamazoo College, B
Lake Michigan College, A
Lansing Community College, A
Michigan State University, BMD
Northern Michigan University, B
Oakland University, B
Sacred Heart Major Seminary, B
Siena Heights University, B
Spring Arbor University, B
University of Detroit Mercy, B
University of Michigan, BMD
University of Michigan - Dearborn, B
University of Michigan - Flint, B
Wayne State University, BMD
Western Michigan University, BM

Minnesota

Augsburg College, B
Bemidji State University, B
Bethel University, B
Carleton College, B
College of Saint Benedict, B
The College of St. Scholastica, B
Concordia College, B
Gustavus Adolphus College, B
Hamline University, B
Macalester College, B
Metropolitan State University, B
Minneapolis Community and Technical College, A
Minnesota State University Mankato, B
Minnesota State University Moorhead, B
St. Catherine University, B
St. Cloud State University, B
Saint John's University, B
Saint Mary's University of Minnesota, B
St. Olaf College, B
Southwest Minnesota State University, B
University of Minnesota, Duluth, B
University of Minnesota, Morris, B
University of Minnesota, Twin Cities Campus, BMD
University of St. Thomas, B

Mississippi

Belhaven University, B
Delta State University, M
Millsaps College, B
Mississippi State University, B
University of Mississippi, BM
University of Southern Mississippi, B

Missouri

Central Methodist University, B
Columbia College, B
Conception Seminary College, B
Drury University, B
Lindenwood University, B
Missouri State University, B
Missouri University of Science and Technology, B
Missouri Valley College, B
Missouri Western State University, B
Northwest Missouri State University, B
Rockhurst University, B
St. Charles Community College, A
Saint Louis University, BMD

Southeast Missouri State University, B
University of Missouri, BMD
University of Missouri - Kansas City, B
University of Missouri - St. Louis, BM
Washington University in St. Louis, BD
Webster University, B
Westminster College, B
William Jewell College, B

Montana

Carroll College, AB
Montana State University, B
University of Montana, BM

Nebraska

Bellevue University, B
Creighton University, B
Doane University, B
Hastings College, B
Nebraska Wesleyan University, B
St. Gregory the Great Seminary, B
University of Nebraska at Kearney, B
University of Nebraska - Lincoln, BMD
University of Nebraska at Omaha, B

Nevada

Truckee Meadows Community College, A
University of Nevada, Las Vegas, B
University of Nevada, Reno, BM

New Hampshire

Colby-Sawyer College, B
Dartmouth College, B
New England College, B
Plymouth State University, B
Saint Anselm College, B
University of New Hampshire, B

New Jersey

Bergen Community College, A
Bloomfield College, B
The College of New Jersey, B
College of Saint Elizabeth, B
Drew University, B
Fairleigh Dickinson University, College at Florham, B
Fairleigh Dickinson University, Metropolitan Campus, B
Felician University, B
Montclair State University, B
New Jersey City University, B
Princeton University, BD
Rider University, B
Rowan College at Burlington County, A
Rutgers University - Camden, B
Rutgers University - New Brunswick, BD
Rutgers University - Newark, B
Saint Peter's University, B
Seton Hall University, B
Stevens Institute of Technology, B
Thomas Edison State University, B
William Paterson University of New Jersey, B

New Mexico

New Mexico State University, B
University of New Mexico, BMD

New York

Adelphi University, B
Alfred University, B
Bard College, B
Barnard College, B
Baruch College of the City University of New York, B
Binghamton University, State University of New York, BMD
Brooklyn College of the City University of New York, B
Buffalo State College, State University of New York, B
Canisius College, B
City College of the City University of New York, B
Colgate University, B
The College at Brockport, State University of New York, B

College of Mount Saint Vincent, B
The College of New Rochelle, B
College of Staten Island of the City University of
New York, B
Columbia University, BMD
Columbia University, School of General Studies, B
Concordia College - New York, B
Cornell University, BD
D'Youville College, B
Eugene Lang College of Liberal Arts, B
Fiorello H. LaGuardia Community College of the
City University of New York, A
Fordham University, BMD
Hamilton College, B
Hartwick College, B
Hobart and William Smith Colleges, B
Hofstra University, B
Houghton College, B
Hunter College of the City University of New York, B
Iona College, B
Ithaca College, B
The Jewish Theological Seminary, B
John Jay College of Criminal Justice of the City Uni-
versity of New York, B
Le Moyne College, B
Lehman College of the City University of New York,
B
Long Island University - LIU Brooklyn, B
Long Island University - LIU Post, B
Manhattan College, B
Manhattanville College, B
Marist College, B
Molloy College, B
Nazareth College of Rochester, B
New York University, BMD
Niagara University, B
Nyack College, B
Purchase College, State University of New York, B
Queens College of the City University of New York,
B
Rensselaer Polytechnic Institute, B
Rochester Institute of Technology, B
St. Bonaventure University, B
St. Francis College, B
St. John Fisher College, B
St. John's University, B
St. Lawrence University, B
St. Thomas Aquinas College, B
Sarah Lawrence College, B
Siena College, B
Skidmore College, B
State University of New York College at Cortland, B
State University of New York College at Geneseo, B
State University of New York College at Old
Westbury, B
State University of New York College at Oneonta, B
State University of New York College at Potsdam, B
State University of New York at Fredonia, B
State University of New York at New Paltz, B
State University of New York at Oswego, B
State University of New York at Plattsburgh, B
Stony Brook University, State University of New
York, BMDO
Syracuse University, BMD
Union College, B
United States Military Academy, B
University at Albany, State University of New York,
BMD
University at Buffalo, the State University of New
York, BMD
University of Rochester, BMD
Utica College, B
Vassar College, B
Wagner College, B
Wells College, B
Yeshiva University, B
York College of the City University of New York, B

North Carolina

Appalachian State University, B
Chowan University, B
Davidson College, B
Duke University, BD
East Carolina University, B
Elon University, B
Guilford College, B

High Point University, B
Lenoir-Rhyne University, B
Methodist University, A
North Carolina State University, B
Queens University of Charlotte, B
Salem College, B
Southeastern Baptist Theological Seminary, D
University of North Carolina at Asheville, B
The University of North Carolina at Chapel Hill,
BMD
The University of North Carolina at Charlotte, BMO
The University of North Carolina at Greensboro, B
Wake Forest University, B
Warren Wilson College, B
Western Carolina University, B

North Dakota

North Dakota State University, B
University of North Dakota, B

Ohio

Antioch College, B
Ashland University, B
Baldwin Wallace University, B
Bowling Green State University, BMD
Capital University, B
Case Western Reserve University, B
Cleveland State University, BMO
The College of Wooster, B
Denison University, B
Franciscan University of Steubenville, BM
Heidelberg University, B
Hiram College, B
John Carroll University, B
Kent State University, BM
Kenyon College, B
Malone University, B
Marietta College, B
Miami University, BM
Miami University Hamilton, B
Miami University Middletown, A
Mount Vernon Nazarene University, B
Muskingum University, B
Oberlin College, B
Ohio Dominican University, B
Ohio Northern University, B
The Ohio State University, BMD
Ohio University, BM
Ohio Wesleyan University, B
Otterbein University, B
Pontifical College Josephinum, B
The University of Akron, B
University of Cincinnati, BMD
University of Dayton, B
The University of Findlay, B
University of Mount Union, B
The University of Toledo, BM
Urbana University, B
Ursuline College, B
Walsh University, B
Wilmington College, B
Wittenberg University, B
Wright State University, B
Xavier University, B
Youngstown State University, B

Oklahoma

Oklahoma Baptist University, B
Oklahoma City Community College, A
Oklahoma City University, B
Oklahoma State University, BM
St. Gregory's University, B
Southern Nazarene University, B
University of Central Oklahoma, B
University of Oklahoma, BMD
The University of Tulsa, B

Oregon

George Fox University, B
Lewis & Clark College, B
Linfield College, B
Mount Angel Seminary, B
Oregon State University, B
Pacific University, B
Portland State University, B
Reed College, B

University of Oregon, BMD
University of Portland, B
Western Oregon University, B
Willamette University, B

Pennsylvania

Albright College, B
Allegheny College, B
Alvernia University, B
Arcadia University, B
Bloomsburg University of Pennsylvania, B
Bryn Mawr College, B
Bucknell University, B
Cabrini University, B
California University of Pennsylvania, B
Carlow University, B
Carnegie Mellon University, BMD
Clarion University of Pennsylvania, B
DeSales University, B
Dickinson College, B
Drexel University, B
Duquesne University, BMD
East Stroudsburg University of Pennsylvania, B
Eastern University, B
Elizabethtown College, B
Franklin & Marshall College, B
Gannon University, B
Geneva College, B
Gettysburg College, B
Grove City College, B
Gwynedd Mercy University, B
Harrisburg Area Community College, A
Haverford College, B
Indiana University of Pennsylvania, B
Juniata College, B
King's College, B
Kutztown University of Pennsylvania, B
La Salle University, B
Lafayette College, B
Lebanon Valley College, B
Lehigh University, B
Lincoln University, B
Lock Haven University of Pennsylvania, B
Lycoming College, B
Mansfield University of Pennsylvania, B
Marywood University, B
Mercyhurst University, B
Messiah College, B
Millersville University of Pennsylvania, B
Misericordia University, B
Moravian College, B
Muhlenberg College, B
Penn State Abington, B
Penn State Altoona, B
Penn State Beaver, B
Penn State Berks, B
Penn State Brandywine, B
Penn State DuBois, B
Penn State Erie, The Behrend College, B
Penn State Fayette, The Eberly Campus, B
Penn State Greater Allegheny, B
Penn State Hazleton, B
Penn State Lehigh Valley, B
Penn State Mont Alto, B
Penn State New Kensington, B
Penn State Schuylkill, B
Penn State Shenango, B
Penn State University Park, BMD
Penn State Wilkes-Barre, B
Penn State Worthington Scranton, B
Penn State York, B
Rosemont College, B
Saint Charles Borromeo Seminary, Overbrook, B
Saint Francis University, B
Saint Joseph's University, B
Saint Vincent College, B
Slippery Rock University of Pennsylvania, B
Summit University, M
Susquehanna University, B
Swarthmore College, B
Temple University, BMD
Thiel College, B
University of Pennsylvania, BMD
University of Pittsburgh, BMD
The University of Scranton, B
Ursinus College, B

Villanova University, BD
Washington & Jefferson College, B
West Chester University of Pennsylvania, BMO
Westminster College, B
Wilkes University, B
Wilson College, B
York College of Pennsylvania, B

Rhode Island

Brown University, BD
Providence College, B
Rhode Island College, B
Roger Williams University, B
Salve Regina University, B
University of Rhode Island, B

South Carolina

Clemson University, B
Coastal Carolina University, B
College of Charleston, B
Converse College, B
Erskine College, B
Furman University, B
Presbyterian College, B
University of South Carolina, BMD
Wofford College, B

South Dakota

Augustana University, B
Dakota Wesleyan University, B
University of Sioux Falls, B
The University of South Dakota, B

Tennessee

Aquinas College, B
Austin Peay State University, B
Belmont University, B
Carson-Newman University, B
East Tennessee State University, B
Freed-Hardeman University, B
King University, B
Lee University, B
Lipscomb University, B
Martin Methodist College, B
Maryville College, B
Middle Tennessee State University, B
Nashville State Community College, A
Rhodes College, B
Sewanee: The University of the South, B
Union University, B
University of Memphis, BMD
The University of Tennessee, BMD
The University of Tennessee at Martin, B
Vanderbilt University, BMD

Texas

Angelo State University, B
Austin College, B
Austin Community College District, A
Baylor University, BMD
Blinn College, A
Dallas Baptist University, B
Hardin-Simmons University, B
Hill College, A
Houston Baptist University, BM
Howard Payne University, B
Midwestern State University, MD
Palo Alto College, A
Rice University, BMD
St. Edward's University, B
St. Mary's University, B
St. Philip's College, A
Sam Houston State University, B
San Jacinto College District, A
Southern Methodist University, B
Southwestern University, B
Stephen F. Austin State University, B
Texas A&M University, BMD
Texas Christian University, B
Texas Lutheran University, B
Texas State University, BM
Texas Tech University, BM
Trinity University, B
University of Dallas, BMD
University of Houston, BM

University of Houston - Downtown, B
University of the Incarnate Word, B
University of North Texas, BM
University of St. Thomas, BMD
The University of Texas at Arlington, B
The University of Texas at Austin, BD
The University of Texas at Dallas, MD
The University of Texas at El Paso, BM
The University of Texas Rio Grande Valley, B
The University of Texas at San Antonio, BM
Wiley College, B

Utah

Snow College, A
Southern Utah University, B
University of Utah, BMD
Utah State University, B
Utah Valley University, AB
Weber State University, B
Westminster College, B

Vermont

Bennington College, B
Castleton University, B
Green Mountain College, B
Marlboro College, B
Middlebury College, B
Saint Michael's College, B
University of Vermont, B

Virginia

Christendom College, B
Christopher Newport University, B
The College of William and Mary, B
Emory & Henry College, B
Ferrum College, B
George Mason University, BM
Hampden-Sydney College, B
Hollins University, B
Liberty University, BM
Lynchburg College, B
Mary Baldwin College, B
Marymount University, B
Old Dominion University, B
Randolph College, B
Randolph-Macon College, B
Roanoke College, B
Southern Virginia University, B
Sweet Briar College, B
University of Richmond, B
University of Virginia, BMD
Virginia Commonwealth University, B
Virginia Polytechnic Institute and State University, BM
Virginia Wesleyan College, B
Washington and Lee University, B

Washington

Eastern Washington University, B
Everett Community College, A
The Evergreen State College, B
Gonzaga University, BM
Northwest University, B
Pacific Lutheran University, B
Seattle Pacific University, B
Seattle University, B
Skagit Valley College, A
University of Puget Sound, B
University of Washington, BMD
Walla Walla University, B
Washington State University, B
Western Washington University, B
Whitman College, B
Whitworth University, B

West Virginia

American Public University System, B
West Virginia University, B
West Virginia Wesleyan College, B
Wheeling Jesuit University, B

Wisconsin

Alverno College, B
Beloit College, B
Carthage College, B

Lawrence University, B
Marquette University, BMD
Mount Mary University, B
Ripon College, B
St. Norbert College, B
University of Wisconsin - Eau Claire, B
University of Wisconsin - Green Bay, B
University of Wisconsin - La Crosse, B
University of Wisconsin - Madison, BMD
University of Wisconsin - Milwaukee, BM
University of Wisconsin - Oshkosh, B
University of Wisconsin - Parkside, B
University of Wisconsin - Platteville, B
University of Wisconsin - Stevens Point, B
Viterbo University, B
Wisconsin Lutheran College, B

Wyoming

University of Wyoming, BM

U.S. Territories: Guam

University of Guam, B

U.S. Territories: Puerto Rico

Bayamón Central University, B
Pontifical Catholic University of Puerto Rico, B
University of Puerto Rico, Mayagüez Campus, B
University of Puerto Rico, Río Piedras Campus, BM

Canada

Alberta

Concordia University of Edmonton, B
The King's University, B
University of Alberta, BMD
University of Calgary, BMD
University of Lethbridge, BM

British Columbia

Simon Fraser University, BMD
Thompson Rivers University, B
Trinity Western University, BM
The University of British Columbia, BMD
The University of British Columbia - Okanagan Campus, B
University of the Fraser Valley, B
University of Victoria, BM
Vancouver Island University, B

Manitoba

Brandon University, B
University of Manitoba, BM
The University of Winnipeg, B

Maritime Provinces: New Brunswick

Mount Allison University, B
St. Thomas University, B
Université de Moncton, B
University of New Brunswick Fredericton, B
University of New Brunswick Saint John, B

Maritime Provinces: Nova Scotia

Acadia University, BM
Cape Breton University, B
Dalhousie University, BMD
Mount Saint Vincent University, B
St. Francis Xavier University, B
Saint Mary's University, BM
University of King's College, B

Maritime Provinces: Prince Edward Island

University of Prince Edward Island, B

Newfoundland and Labrador

Memorial University of Newfoundland, BM

Ontario

Brock University, BM
Carleton University, BM
Lakehead University, B
Laurentian University, B
McMaster University, BMD

Nipissing University, B
Queen's University at Kingston, BMD
Redeemer University College, B
Saint Paul University, B
Trent University, B
Tyndale University College & Seminary, B
University of Guelph, BMD
University of Ottawa, BMD
University of Toronto, MD
University of Waterloo, BMD
The University of Western Ontario, BMD
University of Windsor, BM
Wilfrid Laurier University, BM
York University, BMD

Quebec

Bishop's University, B
Concordia University, BM
McGill University, BMD
Université Laval, ABMD
Université de Montréal, BMD
Université du Québec à Montréal, BMD
Université du Québec à Trois-Rivières, BMD
Université de Sherbrooke, BMD

Saskatchewan

University of Regina, BM
University of Saskatchewan, BM

PHILOSOPHY AND RELIGIOUS STUDIES

United States

Alabama

Samford University, B
Stillman College, B

Arizona

Harrison Middleton University, B

Arkansas

Hendrix College, B
John Brown University, B
Lyon College, B
Ouachita Baptist University, B
University of the Ozarks, B

California

Holy Names University, B
John F. Kennedy University, B
San Francisco State University, B

Florida

Bethune-Cookman University, B
Florida Agricultural and Mechanical University, B
South Florida State College, A

Georgia

Berry College, B
Covenant College, B

Illinois

Eureka College, B
Quincy University, B

Indiana

Butler University, B
Saint Joseph's College, B
University of Notre Dame, B

Iowa

Buena Vista University, B
Graceland University, B
Iowa Wesleyan University, B

Kansas

Friends University, B
Sterling College, B

Massachusetts

Eastern Nazarene College, B

Mississippi

Millsaps College, B

Missouri

Conception Seminary College, B
Truman State University, B
Washington University in St. Louis, B
William Jewell College, B

Montana

Rocky Mountain College, B

New Jersey

Rowan University, B

New York

Elmira College, B
Roberts Wesleyan College, B
State University of New York at Oswego, B
Syracuse University, B

North Carolina

Barton College, B
Shaw University, B
The University of North Carolina at Pembroke, B
The University of North Carolina Wilmington, B

Ohio

Edison Community College, A
Shawnee State University, B

Pennsylvania

Juniata College, B
Ursinus College, B

South Carolina

Claflin University, B
Newberry College, B
Winthrop University, B

Tennessee

Union University, B
The University of Tennessee at Chattanooga, B

Vermont

Marlboro College, B

Virginia

Bridgewater College, B
Eastern Mennonite University, B
James Madison University, B
Mary Baldwin College, B
Radford University, B
University of Mary Washington, B

Washington

Northwest University, B

West Virginia

West Virginia Wesleyan College, B

Canada

Alberta

University of Alberta, B

PHLEBOTOMY/PHLEBOTOMIST

United States

Arizona

Coconino Community College, A

Colorado

Morgan Community College, B

Florida

Miami Dade College, A

Kansas

Barton County Community College, A

Louisiana

Fletcher Technical Community College, A

Minnesota

Duluth Business University, A
Northland Community and Technical College, A

Pennsylvania

Westmoreland County Community College, A

Virginia

Miller-Motte Technical College (Lynchburg), A
Stratford University (Glen Allen), A
Stratford University (Newport News), A
Stratford University (Woodbridge), A

Washington

Edmonds Community College, A

PHOTOGRAPHIC AND FILM/ VIDEO TECHNOLOGY/TECHNICIAN AND ASSISTANT

United States

Alabama

Calhoun Community College, A

California

Antelope Valley College, A
Chaffey College, A
Cosumnes River College, A
Crafton Hills College, A
Cypress College, A
Fresno City College, A
MiraCosta College, A
Orange Coast College, A
Palomar College, A
Platt College San Diego, B

Colorado

Aims Community College, A

Delaware

Wilmington University, B

Florida

Daytona State College, A
Miami Dade College, A

Maine

Husson University, B

Michigan

Washtenaw Community College, A

Minnesota

Central Lakes College, A
Minneapolis Community and Technical College, A

Mississippi

Hinds Community College, A

New York

Herkimer County Community College, A
Rochester Institute of Technology, B
St. John's University, AB
Suffolk County Community College, A
Tompkins Cortland Community College, A
Villa Maria College, B

North Carolina

Catawba Valley Community College, A
McDowell Technical Community College, A
Randolph Community College, A

Ohio

Brightwood College, Dayton Campus, A
University of Cincinnati Blue Ash College, A

Oklahoma

Oklahoma City Community College, A

Utah

Salt Lake Community College, A

Washington

Bellevue College, A
Olympic College, A

PHOTOGRAPHY

United States

Alabama

The University of Alabama, M

Alaska

University of Alaska Fairbanks, M

Arizona

Northern Arizona University, B
Northland Pioneer College, A
Scottsdale Community College, A
Southwest University of Visual Arts, BM

Arkansas

John Brown University, B

California

Academy of Art University, M
Allan Hancock College, A
American River College, A
Antelope Valley College, A
Art Center College of Design, B
The Art Institute of California - Orange County, a
  campus of Argosy University, A
The Art Institute of California - Sacramento, a cam-
  pus of Argosy University, A
The Art Institute of California - San Diego, a cam-
  pus of Argosy University, A
Bakersfield College, A
Barstow Community College, A
Brooks Institute, BM
Butte College, A
Cabrillo College, A
California Baptist University, B
California College of the Arts, BM
California Institute of the Arts, BMO
California State University, East Bay, B
California State University, Fullerton, M
California State University, Long Beach, B
California State University, Los Angeles, M
California State University, Sacramento, B
Cerritos College, A
Citrus College, A
City College of San Francisco, A
College of the Canyons, A
College of San Mateo, A
Columbia College, A
De Anza College, A
East Los Angeles College, A
El Camino College, A
Foothill College, A
Glendale Community College, A
Grossmont College, A
Hartnell College, A
Laney College, A
Lassen Community College District, A
Los Angeles City College, A
Los Angeles Pierce College, A
Mills College, M
Modesto Junior College, A
Monterey Peninsula College, A
Moorpark College, A
Mt. San Antonio College, A
Mt. San Jacinto College, A
Napa Valley College, A

New York Film Academy, M
Orange Coast College, A
Otis College of Art and Design, BM
Pacific Union College, AB
Pasadena City College, A
Porterville College, A
Saddleback College, A
San Bernardino Valley College, A
San Diego City College, A
San Francisco Art Institute, B
San Joaquin Delta College, A
San Jose City College, A
San Jose State University, M
Santa Ana College, A
Solano Community College, A
Southwestern College, A
University of La Verne, B
University of Southern California, M
Yuba College, A

Colorado

Adams State University, B
Colorado Mountain College (Glenwood Springs), A
Colorado State University, B
Red Rocks Community College, A
University of Colorado Boulder, M
Western State Colorado University, B

Connecticut

Albertus Magnus College, B
Paier College of Art, Inc., AB
University of Hartford, B
Yale University, M

Delaware

Delaware College of Art and Design, A
Delaware Technical & Community College, Terry
  Campus, A

District of Columbia

Gallaudet University, B
The George Washington University, M
Howard University, M

Florida

The Art Institute of Fort Lauderdale, AB
Barry University, BM
Miami Dade College, A
Palm Beach State College, A
Pensacola State College, A
Ringling College of Art and Design, B
St. Petersburg College, A
University of Central Florida, B
University of Miami, BM

Georgia

Georgia State University, M
Gwinnett Technical College, A
Savannah College of Art and Design, BM

Idaho

College of Southern Idaho, A

Illinois

American Academy of Art, B
Bradley University, BM
College of DuPage, A
Columbia College Chicago, BM
Dominican University, B
Illinois State University, M
Judson University, B
School of the Art Institute of Chicago, BM
University of Illinois at Chicago, B
University of Illinois at Urbana - Champaign, BM

Indiana

Grace College, B
Indiana State University, M
Indiana University - Purdue University Fort Wayne,
  B
Indiana Wesleyan University, B
Marian University, B
Purdue University, B
University of Notre Dame, M

Iowa

Coe College, B
Grand View University, B
Iowa Lakes Community College, A
Morningside College, B
The University of Iowa, B

Kansas

Central Christian College of Kansas, A
Kansas Wesleyan University, B

Louisiana

Louisiana State University and Agricultural & Mechanical College, M
Louisiana Tech University, BM

Maine

Maine College of Art, B

Maryland

Cecil College, A
Harford Community College, A
Howard Community College, A
Maryland Institute College of Art, BM

Massachusetts

Bridgewater State University, B
Endicott College, B
Fitchburg State University, B
Lesley University, M
Massachusetts College of Art and Design, BMO
Montserrat College of Art, B
Salem State University, B
School of the Museum of Fine Arts, Boston, B
University of Massachusetts Dartmouth, B

Michigan

Aquinas College, B
College for Creative Studies, B
Cornerstone University, B
Ferris State University, B
Grand Valley State University, B
Lansing Community College, A
Mott Community College, A
Northern Michigan University, B
Oakland Community College, A
Oakland University, B
Wayne State University, M

Minnesota

Dakota County Technical College, A
Hennepin Technical College, A
Minneapolis College of Art and Design, BM

Mississippi

Northeast Mississippi Community College, A

Missouri

Calvary Bible College and Theological Seminary, B
Columbia College, B
Kansas City Art Institute, B
University of Central Missouri, B
Washington University in St. Louis, B

Montana

University of Montana, M

Nebraska

Metropolitan Community College, A

New Hampshire

New Hampshire Institute of Art, BM

New Jersey

County College of Morris, A
Mercer County Community College, A
Rutgers University - New Brunswick, B
Thomas Edison State University, AB

New Mexico

Santa Fe Community College, A
Santa Fe University of Art and Design, B
University of New Mexico, D

New York

Bard College, BM
Brooklyn College of the City University of New York, M
Buffalo State College, State University of New York, B
Cazenovia College, B
Columbia University, M
Cornell University, MD
Eugene Lang College of Liberal Arts, B
Hofstra University, B
Ithaca College, B
Long Island University - LIU Post, B
Marymount Manhattan College, B
Nassau Community College, A
New York University, B
Parsons School of Design, B
Pratt Institute, BM
Purchase College, State University of New York, B
Rochester Institute of Technology, M
Rockland Community College, A
St. John's University, B
Sarah Lawrence College, B
School of Visual Arts, BM
State University of New York at New Paltz, B
Sullivan County Community College, A
Syracuse University, BM
University of Rochester, M
Villa Maria College, AB

North Carolina

The Art Institute of Charlotte, a campus of South University, AB
Carteret Community College, A
East Carolina University, M
Living Arts College, B

North Dakota

Dakota College at Bottineau, A

Ohio

Antonelli College, A
Art Academy of Cincinnati, B
Bowling Green State University, B
Cleveland Institute of Art, B
Columbus College of Art & Design, B
Cuyahoga Community College, A
Ohio University, BM
The University of Akron, B
University of Dayton, B
Youngstown State University, B

Oklahoma

Oklahoma City University, B
Oklahoma State University Institute of Technology, A
University of Central Oklahoma, B
University of Oklahoma, M

Oregon

Pacific Northwest College of Art, B
University of Oregon, B

Pennsylvania

Antonelli Institute, A
Arcadia University, B
Butler County Community College, A
Chatham University, B
Community College of Philadelphia, A
Drexel University, B
Harrisburg Area Community College, A
Luzerne County Community College, A
Marywood University, BM
Moore College of Art & Design, B
Pennsylvania College of Art & Design, B
Point Park University, B
Temple University, BM
The University of the Arts, B

Rhode Island

Providence College, B
Rhode Island College, B
Rhode Island School of Design, BM
Salve Regina University, B

South Carolina

Coker College, B

Tennessee

Carson-Newman University, B
King University, B
Memphis College of Art, B
Nashville State Community College, A
Pellissippi State Community College, A
Southern Adventist University, B
University of Memphis, M
The University of Tennessee, M
Watkins College of Art, Design, & Film, B

Texas

Amarillo College, A
The Art Institute of Dallas, a campus of South University, AB
Lee College, A
Odessa College, A
St. Edward's University, B
Sam Houston State University, B
Southern Methodist University, M
Texas Christian University, BM
Texas State University, B
Tyler Junior College, A
University of Houston, B

Utah

Dixie State University, B
University of Utah, M
Weber State University, B

Vermont

Bennington College, B
Castleton University, B
Goddard College, B
Marlboro College, B

Virginia

The Art Institute of Washington, a branch of The Art Institute of Atlanta, A
Eastern Mennonite University, B
George Mason University, M
Hampton University, B
James Madison University, M
Thomas Nelson Community College, A
Virginia Commonwealth University, BM

Washington

Central Washington University, B
Everett Community College, A
Seattle Central College, A
Seattle University, B
Shoreline Community College, A
University of Washington, BM
Western Washington University, B

Wisconsin

Cardinal Stritch University, B
Carroll University, B
Concordia University Wisconsin, B
Madison Area Technical College, A
Milwaukee Institute of Art and Design, B

Wyoming

Casper College, A
Western Wyoming Community College, A

U.S. Territories: Puerto Rico

Inter American University of Puerto Rico, San Germán Campus, BM
University of Puerto Rico, Río Piedras Campus, B

Canada

Alberta

Alberta College of Art & Design, B

British Columbia

Emily Carr University of Art + Design, B
University of Victoria, M

Maritime Provinces: New Brunswick

Mount Allison University, B

Maritime Provinces: Nova Scotia

NSCAD University, B

Newfoundland and Labrador

Memorial University of Newfoundland, B

Ontario

Ryerson University, B
York University, B

Quebec

Concordia University, B

PHOTOJOURNALISM

United States

California

Brooks Institute, AB
Pasadena City College, A

Florida

University of Miami, B

Illinois

Bradley University, B
Columbia College Chicago, B

Indiana

Vincennes University, A

Kentucky

Western Kentucky University, B

Michigan

Central Michigan University, B

Minnesota

Minnesota State University Moorhead, B

Missouri

University of Missouri, B

Nevada

Sierra Nevada College, B

New York

Rochester Institute of Technology, B
St. John's University, B
Syracuse University, B

North Carolina

Randolph Community College, A

Ohio

Kent State University, B
Ohio University, B

Oklahoma

University of Central Oklahoma, B

Pennsylvania

Point Park University, B

Vermont

Johnson State College, B

Washington

Walla Walla University, B

PHOTONICS

United States

Alabama

The University of Alabama in Huntsville, M

Arkansas

University of Arkansas, MD

California

University of California, San Diego, MD
University of California, Santa Barbara, MD

Florida

University of Central Florida, MD

Massachusetts

Boston University, M

New Jersey

Princeton University, D
Stevens Institute of Technology, MO

New Mexico

University of New Mexico, MD

North Carolina

Duke University, M

Oklahoma

Oklahoma State University, MD

Pennsylvania

Lehigh University, M

PHYSICAL ANTHROPOLOGY

United States

Kansas

Cowley County Community College and Area Vocational - Technical School, A

Washington

University of Washington, B

Canada

Ontario

The University of Western Ontario, B

PHYSICAL CHEMISTRY

United States

Alabama

Auburn University, MD

California

California State University, Los Angeles, M
University of Southern California, D

Connecticut

Yale University, D

District of Columbia

The George Washington University, MD
Howard University, MD

Florida

Florida State University, MD
University of Miami, D

Georgia

Georgia State University, MD
University of Georgia, MD

Indiana

Indiana University Bloomington, D
Purdue University, MD
University of Notre Dame, MD

Iowa

Iowa State University of Science and Technology, MD

Kansas

Kansas State University, M

Kentucky

University of Louisville, MD

Louisiana

Southern University and Agricultural and Mechanical College, M

Maryland

University of Maryland, College Park, MD

Massachusetts

Boston College, D
Brandeis University, MD
Harvard University, D
Massachusetts Institute of Technology, D
Tufts University, MD

Michigan

University of Michigan, D
Wayne State University, D

Mississippi

University of Southern Mississippi, M

Missouri

University of Missouri, MD
University of Missouri - Kansas City, MD

Montana

University of Montana, MD

Nebraska

University of Nebraska - Lincoln, D

New Jersey

Rutgers University - New Brunswick, MD
Rutgers University - Newark, MD
Seton Hall University, MD
Stevens Institute of Technology, D

New Mexico

Eastern New Mexico University, M

New York

Binghamton University, State University of New York, D
Cornell University, D

North Carolina

Wake Forest University, MD

Ohio

Cleveland State University, M
University of Cincinnati, MD
The University of Toledo, MD
Youngstown State University, M

Oregon

Oregon State University, MD

Tennessee

University of Memphis, M
The University of Tennessee, MD
Vanderbilt University, MD

Texas

Rice University, D
The University of Texas at Austin, D

Virginia

Old Dominion University, M
Virginia Commonwealth University, MD

West Virginia

West Virginia University, MD

Wisconsin

Marquette University, MD

Canada

Alberta

University of Calgary, MD

Ontario

Laurentian University, M
McMaster University, MD

PHYSICAL EDUCATION TEACHING AND COACHING

United States

Alabama

Alabama Agricultural and Mechanical University, BM
Alabama Southern Community College, A
Alabama State University, BM
Athens State University, B
Auburn University, BMDO
Auburn University at Montgomery, MO
Faulkner University, B
Huntingdon College, B
Jacksonville State University, BMO
Oakwood University, B
Stillman College, B
Troy University, M
United States Sports Academy, BM
The University of Alabama, BMD
The University of Alabama at Birmingham, BM
University of Mobile, B
University of North Alabama, M
University of South Alabama, BM
The University of West Alabama, BM

Alaska

University of Alaska Anchorage, B

Arizona

Arizona State University at the Tempe campus, M
Grand Canyon University, B

Arkansas

Arkansas State University, BMO
Arkansas Tech University, B
Central Baptist College, B
Cossatot Community College of the University of Arkansas, A
Henderson State University, BM
Ouachita Baptist University, B
Southern Arkansas University - Magnolia, B
University of Arkansas, M
University of Arkansas at Monticello, B
University of Arkansas at Pine Bluff, BM
University of Central Arkansas, B
University of the Ozarks, B
Williams Baptist College, B

California

Allan Hancock College, A
Azusa Pacific University, BM
Bakersfield College, A
Biola University, B
California Baptist University, M
California Lutheran University, B
California State University, Bakersfield, B
California State University, Chico, B
California State University, Dominguez Hills, M
California State University, East Bay, BM
California State University, Fresno, B
California State University, Fullerton, M

California State University, Long Beach, BM
California State University, Los Angeles, M
California State University, Sacramento, M
California State University, Stanislaus, BM
Cerritos College, A
Citrus College, A
College of the Sequoias, A
Concordia University Irvine, M
De Anza College, A
East Los Angeles College, A
El Camino College, A
Foothill College, A
Fresno Pacific University, AB
Humboldt State University, BM
Imperial Valley College, A
Lake Tahoe Community College, A
Lassen Community College District, A
The Master's College and Seminary, B
Mendocino College, A
Merced College, A
Modesto Junior College, A
Monterey Peninsula College, A
National University, B
Pacific Union College, B
Porterville College, A
Sacramento City College, A
Saddleback College, A
San Bernardino Valley College, A
San Diego Christian College, B
San Diego City College, A
San Diego Mesa College, A
San Diego Miramar College, A
San Francisco State University, B
San Joaquin Delta College, A
Santa Barbara City College, A
Skyline College, A
Solano Community College, A
Sonoma State University, BM
Taft College, A
University of San Francisco, B
Vanguard University of Southern California, B
West Hills Community College, A
West Los Angeles College, A
West Valley College, A
Westmont College, B
Yuba College, A

Colorado

Adams State University, BM
Colorado State University - Pueblo, M
Fort Lewis College, B
Northeastern Junior College, A
Trinidad State Junior College, A
University of Northern Colorado, MD
Western State Colorado University, B

Connecticut

Central Connecticut State University, BMO
Eastern Connecticut State University, B
Southern Connecticut State University, M
University of Connecticut, B

Delaware

Delaware State University, B
Wesley College, B

District of Columbia

Gallaudet University, B
Howard University, BM

Florida

Barry University, B
Bethune-Cookman University, B
Broward College, A
College of Central Florida, A
Edward Waters College, B
Florida Agricultural and Mechanical University, BM
Florida International University, BM
Florida Memorial University, B
Florida State University, MDO
Indian River State College, A
Jacksonville University, B
Miami Dade College, A
Nova Southeastern University, B
Palm Beach Atlantic University, B

Palm Beach State College, A
State College of Florida Manatee-Sarasota, A
University of Central Florida, B
University of Florida, M
University of North Florida, B
University of South Florida, BM
University of West Florida, MD
Warner University, B

Georgia

Abraham Baldwin Agricultural College, A
Albany State University, BM
Armstrong State University, B
Augusta University, B
Brewton-Parker College, B
Columbus State University, BM
Fort Valley State University, B
Georgia College & State University, M
Georgia Southern University, B
Georgia Southwestern State University, B
Georgia State University, BM
Kennesaw State University, B
Reinhardt University, B
University of Georgia, MD
University of North Georgia, BM
University of West Georgia, B
Valdosta State University, B

Hawaii

Brigham Young University - Hawaii, B

Idaho

Boise State University, BM
The College of Idaho, B
College of Southern Idaho, A
College of Western Idaho, A
Idaho State University, BM
Lewis-Clark State College, B
Northwest Nazarene University, B
University of Idaho, BM

Illinois

Aurora University, B
Benedictine University, B
Blackburn College, B
Chicago State University, BM
City Colleges of Chicago, Malcolm X College, A
Concordia University Chicago, B
DePaul University, B
Elmhurst College, B
Greenville College, B
Harper College, A
Illinois College, B
Illinois State University, BM
John A. Logan College, A
Judson University, B
McKendree University, B
Millikin University, B
Monmouth College, B
North Central College, B
North Park University, B
Northeastern Illinois University, B
Northern Illinois University, BM
Olivet Nazarene University, B
Quincy University, B
Rockford University, B
Sauk Valley Community College, A
Southern Illinois University Carbondale, M
Southern Illinois University Edwardsville, M
Spoon River College, A
Trinity Christian College, B
Trinity International University, B
University of Illinois at Urbana - Champaign, B
Western Illinois University, B

Indiana

Anderson University, B
Ball State University, BM
Bethel College, B
DePauw University, B
Franklin College, B
Goshen College, B
Huntington University, B
Indiana State University, BM
Indiana Tech, B

Indiana University Bloomington, MD
Indiana University - Purdue University Indianapolis, M
Indiana Wesleyan University, B
Manchester University, B
Marian University, B
Oakland City University, B
Purdue University, BMD
Taylor University, B
Trine University, B
University of Indianapolis, BM
University of Southern Indiana, B
Valparaiso University, B
Vincennes University, A

Iowa

Briar Cliff University, B
Buena Vista University, B
Coe College, B
Cornell College, B
Dordt College, B
Graceland University, B
Grand View University, B
Iowa Lakes Community College, A
Iowa Wesleyan University, B
North Iowa Area Community College, A
Northwestern College, B
Simpson College, B
University of Dubuque, B
University of Northern Iowa, BM
Upper Iowa University, B
Waldorf College, B
Wartburg College, B
William Penn University, B

Kansas

Barton County Community College, A
Benedictine College, B
Bethany College, B
Butler Community College, A
Central Christian College of Kansas, AB
Dodge City Community College, A
Emporia State University, M
Fort Hays State University, BM
Friends University, B
Labette Community College, A
McPherson College, B
MidAmerica Nazarene University, B
Pittsburg State University, BM
Pratt Community College, A
Seward County Community College and Area Technical School, A
Southwestern College, B
Sterling College, B
Tabor College, B
The University of Kansas, BMD
Washburn University, B

Kentucky

Alice Lloyd College, B
Asbury University, B
Campbellsville University, B
Eastern Kentucky University, BM
Kentucky State University, B
Kentucky Wesleyan College, B
Lindsey Wilson College, B
Morehead State University, BM
Murray State University, M
Northern Kentucky University, B
Transylvania University, B
Union College, BM
University of the Cumberlands, B
University of Kentucky, BMD
University of Louisville, M
Western Kentucky University, BM

Louisiana

Grambling State University, B
Louisiana College, B
Louisiana State University and Agricultural & Mechanical College, B
Louisiana Tech University, BM
McNeese State University, B
Nicholls State University, B
Northwestern State University of Louisiana, B
Southeastern Louisiana University, B

Southern University and Agricultural and Mechanical College, B
University of Louisiana at Lafayette, B
University of Louisiana at Monroe, B
Xavier University of Louisiana, B

Maine

Husson University, B
Saint Joseph's College of Maine, B
University of Maine, BM
University of Maine at Presque Isle, B

Maryland

Frostburg State University, B
Goucher College, MO
McDaniel College, M
Morgan State University, B
Prince George's Community College, A
Salisbury University, B
Towson University, B
University of Maryland, College Park, B
University of Maryland Eastern Shore, B

Massachusetts

Boston University, B
Bridgewater State University, BM
Cape Cod Community College, A
Eastern Nazarene College, B
Elms College, B
Endicott College, B
Massachusetts College of Liberal Arts, M
Northern Essex Community College, A
Salem State University, BM
Springfield College, BMDO
Westfield State University, M

Michigan

Adrian College, B
Alma College, B
Aquinas College, B
Calvin College, B
Central Michigan University, B
Concordia University Ann Arbor, B
Cornerstone University, B
Eastern Michigan University, BM
Grand Rapids Community College, A
Grand Valley State University, B
Hope College, B
Madonna University, B
Michigan State University, B
Northern Michigan University, B
Saginaw Valley State University, B
Spring Arbor University, B
Wayne State University, BMDO
Western Michigan University, BM

Minnesota

Augsburg College, B
Bemidji State University, B
Bethel University, B
Concordia College, B
Concordia University, St. Paul, B
Crown College, B
Gustavus Adolphus College, B
Inver Hills Community College, A
Minnesota State University Mankato, BM
Minnesota State University Moorhead, B
North Hennepin Community College, A
St. Catherine University, B
St. Cloud State University, B
Southwest Minnesota State University, B
University of Minnesota, Duluth, B
University of Minnesota, Twin Cities Campus, M
University of Northwestern - St. Paul, B
University of St. Thomas, B
Vermilion Community College, A
Winona State University, B

Mississippi

Alcorn State University, M
Blue Mountain College, B
Coahoma Community College, A
Copiah-Lincoln Community College, A
Delta State University, BM
East Central Community College, A

Itawamba Community College, A
Jackson State University, BM
Jones County Junior College, A
Mississippi College, B
Mississippi Delta Community College, A
Mississippi State University, BM
Mississippi Valley State University, B
Northeast Mississippi Community College, A
Northwest Mississippi Community College, A
Southwest Mississippi Community College, A
University of Southern Mississippi, BMD
William Carey University, B

Missouri

Central Methodist University, B
College of the Ozarks, B
Crowder College, A
Culver-Stockton College, B
Drury University, B
Evangel University, B
Hannibal-LaGrange University, B
Lincoln University, B
Lindenwood University, B
Missouri Baptist University, B
Missouri State University, BM
Missouri Valley College, B
Northwest Missouri State University, BM
Southeast Missouri State University, B
Southwest Baptist University, B
University of Central Missouri, B
University of Missouri - St. Louis, B
Westminster College, B
William Jewell College, B
William Woods University, BM

Montana

Carroll College, B
Miles Community College, A
Montana State University Billings, B
Rocky Mountain College, B
University of Great Falls, B
University of Montana, BM
The University of Montana Western, B

Nebraska

Bellevue University, B
Chadron State College, B
Concordia University, Nebraska, B
Doane University, B
Hastings College, B
Midland University, B
Nebraska Wesleyan University, B
Peru State College, B
Union College, B
University of Nebraska at Kearney, BM
University of Nebraska - Lincoln, B
University of Nebraska at Omaha, MD
Wayne State College, BM
York College, B

New Hampshire

Keene State College, B
New England College, B
Plymouth State University, M
University of New Hampshire, O

New Jersey

The College of New Jersey, BM
Essex County College, A
Kean University, B
Montclair State University, BM
Rowan College at Gloucester County, A
Rowan University, B
William Paterson University of New Jersey, B

New Mexico

Eastern New Mexico University, BM
New Mexico Highlands University, B
New Mexico Junior College, A
New Mexico Military Institute, A
New Mexico State University, B
University of New Mexico, BMD
University of the Southwest, B
Western New Mexico University, B

New York

Adelphi University, BMO
Brooklyn College of the City University of New York, BM
Canisius College, BM
Clinton Community College, A
The College at Brockport, State University of New York, BMO
Dutchess Community College, A
Finger Lakes Community College, A
Fulton-Montgomery Community College, A
Genesee Community College, A
Hofstra University, BD
Houghton College, B
Hudson Valley Community College, A
Hunter College of the City University of New York, B
Ithaca College, BM
Long Island University - LIU Brooklyn, B
Long Island University - LIU Post, B
Manhattan College, B
Monroe Community College, A
Niagara County Community College, A
Queens College of the City University of New York, B
Roberts Wesleyan College, B
The Sage Colleges, B
St. Bonaventure University, B
St. Francis College, B
State University of New York College at Cortland, BM
Stony Brook University, State University of New York, O
Syracuse University, B
York College of the City University of New York, B

North Carolina

Appalachian State University, B
Barton College, B
Campbell University, BM
Catawba College, B
Chowan University, B
East Carolina University, BMDO
Elizabeth City State University, B
Elon University, B
Fayetteville State University, B
Gardner-Webb University, BM
Greensboro College, B
High Point University, B
Lees-McRae College, B
Livingstone College, B
Mars Hill University, B
Meredith College, B
Methodist University, AB
North Carolina Agricultural and Technical State University, M
North Carolina Central University, M
Pfeiffer University, B
Piedmont International University, B
St. Andrews University, B
The University of North Carolina at Chapel Hill, M
The University of North Carolina at Greensboro, B
The University of North Carolina at Pembroke, BM
The University of North Carolina Wilmington, B
Western Carolina University, BM
Wingate University, BM
Winston-Salem State University, B

North Dakota

Dickinson State University, B
Mayville State University, B
Minot State University, B
North Dakota State University, B
Trinity Bible College, B
University of Jamestown, B
University of Mary, BM
Valley City State University, B

Ohio

Ashland University, M
Bowling Green State University, B
Capital University, B
Cedarville University, B
Cleveland State University, M
Defiance College, B
Denison University, B

Heidelberg University, B
John Carroll University, B
Kent State University, B
Lorain County Community College, A
Miami University Hamilton, B
Muskingum University, B
The Ohio State University, BMD
Ohio University, BM
Otterbein University, B
Sinclair Community College, A
The University of Akron, BM
University of Dayton, M
The University of Findlay, B
University of Mount Union, B
University of Rio Grande, ABM
The University of Toledo, M
Walsh University, B
Wilmington College, B
Wright State University, BM
Youngstown State University, B

Oklahoma

Bacone College, B
Carl Albert State College, A
East Central University, B
Eastern Oklahoma State College, A
Hillsdale Free Will Baptist College, A
Langston University, B
Murray State College, A
Northeastern Oklahoma Agricultural and Mechanical
  College, A
Northeastern State University, B
Northwestern Oklahoma State University, B
Oklahoma Baptist University, B
Oklahoma Christian University, B
Oklahoma City University, B
Oklahoma State University, B
Oklahoma Wesleyan University, B
Oral Roberts University, B
Redlands Community College, A
Rose State College, A
Seminole State College, A
Southeastern Oklahoma State University, B
Southern Nazarene University, B
Southwestern Christian University, B
Southwestern Oklahoma State University, B
University of Central Oklahoma, B

Oregon

Concordia University, B
Corban University, B
Linfield College, B
Linn-Benton Community College, A
Southern Oregon University, B
Umpqua Community College, A
Warner Pacific College, B

Pennsylvania

Bucks County Community College, A
Cairn University, B
DeSales University, B
East Stroudsburg University of Pennsylvania, BM
Eastern University, O
Gettysburg College, B
Indiana University of Pennsylvania, M
Lancaster Bible College, B
Luzerne County Community College, A
Marywood University, B
Messiah College, B
Millersville University of Pennsylvania, M
Montgomery County Community College, A
Slippery Rock University of Pennsylvania, BM
Summit University, B
Temple University, MD
University of Pittsburgh, B
University of Pittsburgh at Bradford, B
West Chester University of Pennsylvania, MO

Rhode Island

Rhode Island College, BO
University of Rhode Island, M

South Carolina

Anderson University, B
Charleston Southern University, B

The Citadel, The Military College of South Carolina,
  BM
Coastal Carolina University, B
Coker College, B
College of Charleston, B
Erskine College, B
Lander University, B
Limestone College, B
South Carolina State University, B
Southern Wesleyan University, B
University of South Carolina, BMD
University of South Carolina Upstate, B
Winthrop University, BM

South Dakota

Augustana University, B
Dakota State University, B
Dakota Wesleyan University, B
Northern State University, B
South Dakota State University, M
The University of South Dakota, B

Tennessee

Belmont University, B
Bryan College, B
Carson-Newman University, B
Cumberland University, B
King University, B
Lane College, B
Lincoln Memorial University, B
Lipscomb University, B
Martin Methodist College, B
Maryville College, B
Middle Tennessee State University, M
Roane State Community College, A
Southern Adventist University, B
Tennessee State University, BM
Tennessee Technological University, BM
Trevecca Nazarene University, B
Union University, B
University of Memphis, B
The University of Tennessee at Chattanooga, M
The University of Tennessee at Martin, M
Welch College, B

Texas

Alvin Community College, A
Amarillo College, A
Austin College, B
Baylor University, BMD
Blinn College, A
Cisco College, A
Clarendon College, A
Dallas Baptist University, B
Del Mar College, A
East Texas Baptist University, BM
Galveston College, A
Grayson College, A
Hardin-Simmons University, B
Houston Baptist University, B
Howard College, A
Howard Payne University, B
Huston-Tillotson University, B
Jarvis Christian College, B
Kilgore College, A
Lee College, A
LeTourneau University, B
Lubbock Christian University, B
McLennan Community College, A
McMurry University, B
Navarro College, A
Odessa College, A
Palo Alto College, A
Panola College, A
Paul Quinn College, B
Prairie View A&M University, M
St. Edward's University, B
Sam Houston State University, B
Schreiner University, B
South Plains College, A
Sul Ross State University, BM
Tarleton State University, BM
Texas A&M International University, B
Texas Christian University, B
Texas Lutheran University, B
Texas Southern University, M

Texas State University, M
Texas Woman's University, MD
Trinity Valley Community College, A
Tyler Junior College, A
University of Houston, MD
University of the Incarnate Word, B
University of Mary Hardin-Baylor, B
The University of Texas at Austin, MD
Wayland Baptist University, B
Wharton County Junior College, A
Wiley College, B

Utah

Brigham Young University, M
Snow College, A
Southern Utah University, B
Utah State University, BM
Utah Valley University, B
Weber State University, B

Vermont

Castleton University, B
Johnson State College, B
Lyndon State College, B
Norwich University, B
University of Vermont, B

Virginia

Averett University, M
Bluefield College, B
Eastern Mennonite University, B
Emory & Henry College, B
George Mason University, BM
Hampton University, B
James Madison University, M
Longwood University, M
Old Dominion University, BM
Radford University, B
Roanoke College, B
University of Virginia, MD
Virginia Commonwealth University, MD
Virginia State University, B

Washington

Central Washington University, BM
Eastern Washington University, M
Everett Community College, A
Gonzaga University, B
Skagit Valley College, A
University of Washington, M
Walla Walla University, B
Washington State University, B
Western Washington University, BM
Whitworth University, B

West Virginia

Alderson Broaddus University, B
Bethany College, B
Concord University, B
Davis & Elkins College, B
Fairmont State University, B
Glenville State College, B
Marshall University, B
Ohio Valley University, B
Potomac State College of West Virginia University,
  A
Salem International University, B
West Liberty University, B
West Virginia University, BMD
West Virginia University Institute of Technology, B
West Virginia Wesleyan College, B

Wisconsin

Carroll University, B
Carthage College, B
Concordia University Wisconsin, B
Maranatha Baptist University, B
Ripon College, B
University of Wisconsin - La Crosse, M
University of Wisconsin - Madison, B
University of Wisconsin - Oshkosh, B
University of Wisconsin - Platteville, B
University of Wisconsin - River Falls, B
University of Wisconsin - Stevens Point, B
University of Wisconsin - Superior, B

University of Wisconsin - Whitewater, BM

Wyoming

Casper College, A
Eastern Wyoming College, A
Laramie County Community College, A
University of Wyoming, BM

U.S. Territories: Guam

University of Guam, B

U.S. Territories: Puerto Rico

American University of Puerto Rico (Bayamon), BM
Bayamón Central University, B
Caribbean University, BM
Inter American University of Puerto Rico, Aguadilla
   Campus, B
Inter American University of Puerto Rico, Arecibo
   Campus, B
Inter American University of Puerto Rico, Guayama
   Campus, B
Inter American University of Puerto Rico, Metropoli-
   tan Campus, BM
Inter American University of Puerto Rico, San
   Germán Campus, BM
Pontifical Catholic University of Puerto Rico, B
Universidad del Este, B
Universidad Metropolitana, BM
Universidad del Turabo, BM
University of Puerto Rico in Arecibo, B
University of Puerto Rico in Cayey, B
University of Puerto Rico, Mayagüez Campus, BM
University of Puerto Rico in Utuado, B

Canada

Alberta

University of Alberta, BMD
University of Lethbridge, B

British Columbia

The University of British Columbia, M
University of Victoria, BM
Vancouver Island University, B

Manitoba

University of Manitoba, BM

Maritime Provinces: New Brunswick

Université de Moncton, B
University of New Brunswick Fredericton, BM

Maritime Provinces: Nova Scotia

St. Francis Xavier University, B

Newfoundland and Labrador

Memorial University of Newfoundland, BM

Ontario

Brock University, B
Lakehead University, B
Laurentian University, B
Nipissing University, B
Queen's University at Kingston, B
Redeemer University College, B
University of Toronto, MD
University of Windsor, B
Wilfrid Laurier University, BM
York University, B

Quebec

McGill University, MDO
Université Laval, B
Université de Montréal, BMDO
Université du Québec à Chicoutimi, B
Université du Québec à Montréal, B
Université du Québec à Trois-Rivières, M
Université de Sherbrooke, BMO

Saskatchewan

University of Regina, B
University of Saskatchewan, B

PHYSICAL SCIENCE TECH-NOLOGIES/TECHNICIANS

United States

Delaware

Delaware State University, B

Pennsylvania

Westmoreland County Community College, A

PHYSICAL SCIENCES

United States

Alabama

Auburn University at Montgomery, B
The University of Alabama in Huntsville, B
University of North Alabama, B

Arizona

Arizona State University at the Tempe campus, B
Chandler-Gilbert Community College, A
GateWay Community College, A
Paradise Valley Community College, A
Phoenix College, A
South Mountain Community College, A

Arkansas

Arkansas Tech University, B
John Brown University, B
National Park College, A
University of the Ozarks, B

California

American River College, A
Antelope Valley College, A
Biola University, B
Butte College, A
California State University, East Bay, B
California State University, Sacramento, B
California State University, Stanislaus, B
Cerritos College, A
Chaffey College, A
Citrus College, A
College of Marin, A
College of San Mateo, A
Columbia College, A
Cuesta College, A
El Camino College, A
Feather River College, A
Folsom Lake College, A
Fresno City College, A
Gavilan College, A
Glendale Community College, A
Golden West College, A
Imperial Valley College, A
La Sierra University, B
Lassen Community College District, A
Long Beach City College, A
Los Angeles Mission College, A
The Master's College and Seminary, B
Mendocino College, A
Merced College, A
Mt. San Antonio College, A
Ohlone College, A
Reedley College, A
Sacramento City College, A
Saddleback College, A
San Bernardino Valley College, A
San Diego City College, A
San Diego Mesa College, A
San Diego Miramar College, A
San Diego State University, B
San Francisco State University, B
San Joaquin Delta College, A
San Jose City College, A
Southwestern College, A
Taft College, A
University of California, Davis, B
University of California, Riverside, B
University of the Pacific, B

University of Southern California, B
Ventura College, A
Victor Valley College, A

Colorado

Colorado Mesa University, B
Colorado Mountain College (Steamboat Springs), A
Northeastern Junior College, A

Connecticut

Naugatuck Valley Community College, A
Northwestern Connecticut Community College, A
Wesleyan University, B

Florida

Florida Institute of Technology, B
Miami Dade College, A
Palm Beach State College, A
University of Miami, B

Georgia

Abraham Baldwin Agricultural College, A
Covenant College, B
Wesleyan College, B

Hawaii

Brigham Young University - Hawaii, B

Idaho

North Idaho College, A

Illinois

City Colleges of Chicago, Wilbur Wright College, A
Concordia University Chicago, B
Harper College, A
Olivet Nazarene University, B
Spoon River College, A

Indiana

Anderson University, B
Purdue University Northwest (Hammond), B
Trine University, B
Vincennes University, A

Iowa

Coe College, B
Graceland University, B
Iowa Lakes Community College, A

Kansas

Barton County Community College, A
Dodge City Community College, A
Emporia State University, B
Fort Hays State University, B
Garden City Community College, A
Highland Community College, A
Hutchinson Community College, A
Independence Community College, A
Kansas State University, B
Neosho County Community College, A
Seward County Community College and Area Tech-
   nical School, A
Washburn University, B

Kentucky

Western Kentucky University, B

Louisiana

Northwestern State University of Louisiana, B

Maine

University of Southern Maine, B

Maryland

Howard Community College, A
United States Naval Academy, B
University of Maryland, College Park, B

Massachusetts

Hampshire College, B
Middlesex Community College, A
Roxbury Community College, A
Suffolk University, B
University of Massachusetts Lowell, B

Westfield State University, B
Wheelock College, B
Worcester Polytechnic Institute, B
Worcester State University, B

Michigan

Calvin College, B
Concordia University Ann Arbor, B
Eastern Michigan University, B
Lake Michigan College, A
Lake Superior State University, B
Michigan State University, B
North Central Michigan College, A
Northwestern Michigan College, A
Saginaw Valley State University, B
Wayne State University, B

Minnesota

Bemidji State University, B
Bethany Lutheran College, B
The College of St. Scholastica, B
Minnesota State University Mankato, B
St. Cloud State University, B
Vermilion Community College, A

Mississippi

Jones County Junior College, A
Mississippi University for Women, B
Southwest Mississippi Community College, A

Missouri

Crowder College, A
Ozarks Technical Community College, A

Montana

Montana Tech of The University of Montana, B

Nebraska

Chadron State College, B
Concordia University, Nebraska, B
Doane University, B
Midland University, B

Nevada

Western Nevada College, A

New Jersey

Middlesex County College, A
Rowan University, B

New Mexico

New Mexico Institute of Mining and Technology, B
San Juan College, A
Santa Fe Community College, A
University of New Mexico - Gallup, A
University of New Mexico - Los Alamos Branch, A
University of New Mexico - Taos, A
Western New Mexico University, B

New York

Borough of Manhattan Community College of the
    City University of New York, A
Colgate University, B
College of Staten Island of the City University of
    New York, A
Fulton-Montgomery Community College, A
Hudson Valley Community College, A
Morrisville State College, B
New York City College of Technology of the City
    University of New York, A
Queensborough Community College of the City Uni-
    versity of New York, A
Roberts Wesleyan College, A
Rochester Institute of Technology, B
St. John's University, B
State University of New York Empire State College,
    AB
Stony Brook University, State University of New
    York, B
Union College, B
United States Military Academy, B
Yeshiva University, B

North Carolina

Chowan University, B
The University of North Carolina at Chapel Hill, B

North Dakota

Dakota College at Bottineau, A
Minot State University, B
University of North Dakota, B

Ohio

Bowling Green State University, B
Defiance College, B
Mount Vernon Nazarene University, B
Otterbein University, B
University of Dayton, B
University of Rio Grande, B
Washington State Community College, A
Wright State University, B
Wright State University - Lake Campus, B
Xavier University, B
Youngstown State University, B

Oklahoma

Carl Albert State College, A
Eastern Oklahoma State College, A
Hillsdale Free Will Baptist College, A
Oklahoma Wesleyan University, AB
Redlands Community College, A
Seminole State College, A
Southern Nazarene University, B
Tulsa Community College, A

Oregon

Central Oregon Community College, A
Umpqua Community College, A
Warner Pacific College, B

Pennsylvania

Butler County Community College, A
California University of Pennsylvania, B
Harrisburg Area Community College, A
Juniata College, B
Lehigh Carbon Community College, A
Lincoln University, B
Montgomery County Community College, A
Muhlenberg College, B
Penn State Erie, The Behrend College, B
Reading Area Community College, A
Saint Vincent College, B
University of Pittsburgh, B
University of Pittsburgh at Bradford, B
Villanova University, B

South Dakota

Black Hills State University, B
Dakota State University, B

Tennessee

Roane State Community College, A

Texas

Alvin Community College, A
Amarillo College, A
Austin Community College District, A
Midwestern State University, B
Navarro College, A
Paris Junior College, A
Sam Houston State University, B
San Jacinto College District, A
Southwestern University, B
Texas A&M International University, B
Trinity Valley Community College, A
The University of Texas Rio Grande Valley, B
Wiley College, B

Utah

Salt Lake Community College, A
Snow College, A
Southern Utah University, B
University of Utah, B
Utah Valley University, A

Vermont

Bennington College, B
Lyndon State College, B
Saint Michael's College, B

Virginia

George Mason University, B
Hampton University, B
University of Mary Washington, B

Washington

Bellevue College, A
Centralia College, A
The Evergreen State College, B
Green River College, A
Northwest Indian College, A
Olympic College, A
Pierce College at Fort Steilacoom, A
Seattle Pacific University, B
Seattle University, B
Tacoma Community College, A
Washington State University, B
Wenatchee Valley College, A

West Virginia

Bethany College, B

Wisconsin

Ripon College, B
University of Wisconsin - Superior, B

Wyoming

Central Wyoming College, A
University of Wyoming, B

U.S. Territories: Puerto Rico

University of Puerto Rico, Mayagüez Campus, B

Canada

Alberta

University of Alberta, B

British Columbia

University of the Fraser Valley, A

Maritime Provinces: Nova Scotia

St. Francis Xavier University, B

Ontario

Brock University, B
McMaster University, B
Trent University, B
University of Guelph, B
University of Ottawa, B
York University, B

Quebec

Université du Québec à Chicoutimi, B

PHYSICAL AND THEORETICAL CHEMISTRY

United States

Texas

LeTourneau University, B
Rice University, B

Canada

Ontario

The University of Western Ontario, B

PHYSICAL THERAPIST ASSIS-TANT

United States

Alabama

Bishop State Community College, A
Community College of the Air Force, A
George C. Wallace Community College, A
Jefferson State Community College, A
South University, A

Arizona

Brookline College (Phoenix), A
Carrington College - Mesa, A
GateWay Community College, A
Mohave Community College, A
Pima Medical Institute (Mesa), A
Pima Medical Institute (Tucson), A

Arkansas

Arkansas State University, A
Arkansas Tech University, A
South Arkansas Community College, A

California

Carrington College - Pleasant Hill, A
Loma Linda University, A
Ohlone College, A
Sacramento City College, A
San Diego Mesa College, A

Colorado

Arapahoe Community College, A
Morgan Community College, A
Pima Medical Institute (Denver), A
Pueblo Community College, A

Connecticut

Capital Community College, A
Manchester Community College, A
Naugatuck Valley Community College, A

Delaware

Delaware Technical & Community College, Jack F. Owens Campus, A
Delaware Technical & Community College, Stanton/Wilmington Campus, A

Florida

College of Central Florida, A
Florida Gateway College, A
Florida SouthWestern State College, A
Florida State College at Jacksonville, A
Gulf Coast State College, A
Indian River State College, A
Keiser University, A
Miami Dade College, A
Pensacola State College, A
Polk State College, A
St. Petersburg College, A
South University (Royal Palm Beach), A
South University (Tampa), A
State College of Florida Manatee-Sarasota, A

Georgia

Darton State College, A
Gwinnett Technical College, A
South University, A

Hawaii

Kapiolani Community College, A

Idaho

Carrington College - Boise, A
Idaho State University, AB

Illinois

Black Hawk College, A
College of DuPage, A
Elgin Community College, A
Fox College, A
Illinois Central College, A

Kankakee Community College, A
Kaskaskia College, A
Lake Land College, A
Oakton Community College, A
Southern Illinois University Carbondale, A
Southwestern Illinois College, A

Indiana

Ivy Tech Community College - East Central, A
Ivy Tech Community College - Kokomo, A
Ivy Tech Community College - Southern Indiana, A
University of Evansville, A
University of Indianapolis, A
University of Saint Francis, A
Vincennes University, A

Iowa

Hawkeye Community College, A
Kirkwood Community College, A
Mercy College of Health Sciences, A
Muscatine Community College, A
North Iowa Area Community College, A
Scott Community College, A
Western Iowa Tech Community College, A

Kansas

Barton County Community College, A
Colby Community College, A
Hutchinson Community College, A
Seward County Community College and Area Technical School, A
Washburn University, A

Kentucky

Hazard Community and Technical College, A
Jefferson Community and Technical College, A
Madisonville Community College, A
Somerset Community College, A
Southeast Kentucky Community and Technical College, A
West Kentucky Community and Technical College, A

Louisiana

Bossier Parish Community College, A
Delgado Community College, A
Louisiana College, A
Our Lady of the Lake College, A
Southern University at Shreveport, A

Maine

Kennebec Valley Community College, A
University of Maine at Presque Isle, A

Maryland

Allegany College of Maryland, A
Anne Arundel Community College, A
Baltimore City Community College, A
Carroll Community College, A
College of Southern Maryland, A
Howard Community College, A
Montgomery College, A
Wor-Wic Community College, A

Massachusetts

Bay State College, A
Berkshire Community College, A
Mount Wachusett Community College, A
North Shore Community College, A
Quincy College, A
Springfield Technical Community College, A

Michigan

Baker College, A
Delta College, A
Finlandia University, A
Henry Ford College, A
Kellogg Community College, A
Macomb Community College, A
Mott Community College, A
Oakland Community College, A
South University, A

Minnesota

Anoka-Ramsey Community College, A
Lake Superior College, A
Northland Community and Technical College, A
St. Catherine University, A

Mississippi

Hinds Community College, A

Missouri

Jefferson College, A
Missouri Western State University, A
Ozarks Technical Community College, A
State Fair Community College, A
State Technical College of Missouri, A

Montana

Great Falls College Montana State University, A

Nebraska

Nebraska Methodist College, A
Northeast Community College, A
Southeast Community College, Lincoln Campus, A
Union College, B
Western Nebraska Community College, A

Nevada

Carrington College - Las Vegas, A
College of Southern Nevada, A
Pima Medical Institute, A

New Hampshire

River Valley Community College, A

New Jersey

Essex County College, A
Mercer County Community College, A
Union County College, A

New Mexico

Carrington College - Albuquerque, A
Pima Medical Institute (Albuquerque), A
San Juan College, A

New York

Broome Community College, A
Fiorello H. LaGuardia Community College of the City University of New York, A
Genesee Community College, A
Kingsborough Community College of the City University of New York, A
Nassau Community College, A
Niagara County Community College, A
Onondaga Community College, A
Orange County Community College, A
State University of New York College of Technology at Canton, A
Villa Maria College, A

North Carolina

Caldwell Community College and Technical Institute, A
Craven Community College, A
Fayetteville Technical Community College, A
Guilford Technical Community College, A
Martin Community College, A
Randolph Community College, A
South College - Asheville, A
South University, A
Southwestern Community College, A
Stanly Community College, A

Ohio

Bradford School, A
Clark State Community College, A
Edison Community College, A
Hocking College, A
Kent State University at Ashtabula, A
Kent State University at East Liverpool, A
Lorain County Community College, A
Marion Technical College, A
North Central State College, A
Owens Community College, A
Professional Skills Institute, A

Shawnee State University, A
South University, A
University of Cincinnati Clermont College, A
Zane State College, A

Oklahoma

Carl Albert State College, A
Murray State College, A
Northeastern Oklahoma Agricultural and Mechanical College, A
Southwestern Oklahoma State University, A
Tulsa Community College, A

Pennsylvania

Butler County Community College, A
California University of Pennsylvania, A
Community College of Allegheny County, A
Harcum College, A
Lehigh Carbon Community College, A
Mercyhurst North East, A
Mount Aloysius College, A
Penn State DuBois, A
Penn State Hazleton, A
Penn State Mont Alto, A
Penn State Shenango, A
Pennsylvania Institute of Technology, A
Reading Area Community College, A
University of Pittsburgh at Titusville, A

Rhode Island

Community College of Rhode Island, A
New England Institute of Technology, A

South Carolina

Greenville Technical College, A
Midlands Technical College, A
Technical College of the Lowcountry, A
York Technical College, A

South Dakota

Lake Area Technical Institute, A

Tennessee

Chattanooga State Community College, A
Jackson State Community College, A
South College, A
Southwest Tennessee Community College, A
Volunteer State Community College, A
Walters State Community College, A

Texas

Austin Community College District, A
Blinn College, A
El Paso Community College, A
Houston Community College, A
Kilgore College, A
Lone Star College - Montgomery, A
Northeast Texas Community College, A
St. Philip's College, A
San Jacinto College District, A
South University, A
Tyler Junior College, A
Victoria College, A
Weatherford College, A

Utah

Dixie State University, A
Provo College, A
Salt Lake Community College, A

Virginia

ECPI University (Virginia Beach), A
Jefferson College of Health Sciences, A
South University (Glen Allen), A
South University (Virginia Beach), A

Washington

Green River College, A
Olympic College, A
Pima Medical Institute (Seattle), A
Spokane Falls Community College, A
Whatcom Community College, A

West Virginia

Blue Ridge Community and Technical College, A
Mountwest Community & Technical College, A

Wisconsin

Blackhawk Technical College, A
Chippewa Valley Technical College, A
Gateway Technical College, A
Nicolet Area Technical College, A
Northeast Wisconsin Technical College, A
Waukesha County Technical College, A
Western Technical College, A

Wyoming

Laramie County Community College, A

U.S. Territories: Puerto Rico

EDP University of Puerto Rico, A
EDP University of Puerto Rico - San Sebastian, A
Inter American University of Puerto Rico, Ponce Campus, A
University of Puerto Rico in Humacao, A
University of Puerto Rico in Ponce, A

PHYSICAL THERAPY/THERA-PIST

United States

Alabama

Alabama State University, D
Oakwood University, A
The University of Alabama at Birmingham, D
University of South Alabama, D
Wallace State Community College, A

Arizona

Northern Arizona University, D

Arkansas

Arkansas State University, D
Harding University, D
NorthWest Arkansas Community College, A
University of Central Arkansas, D

California

Allan Hancock College, A
Azusa Pacific University, D
Biola University, B
California State University, Fresno, BMD
California State University, Long Beach, D
California State University, Northridge, M
Cerritos College, A
Chapman University, D
De Anza College, A
Humboldt State University, M
Loma Linda University, MD
Monterey Peninsula College, A
Mount Saint Mary's University, D
Ohlone College, A
Samuel Merritt University, D
San Diego State University, D
San Francisco State University, D
Sonoma State University, M
University of the Pacific, MD
University of Southern California, D
Vanguard University of Southern California, B

Colorado

Regis University, D
University of Colorado Denver, D

Connecticut

Housatonic Community College, A
Quinnipiac University, BD
Sacred Heart University, BDO
University of Connecticut, D
University of Hartford, BMD

Delaware

University of Delaware, D

District of Columbia

The George Washington University, D
Howard University, B

Florida

Broward College, A
College of Central Florida, A
Daytona State College, A
Florida Agricultural and Mechanical University, D
Florida Gulf Coast University, MD
Florida International University, D
Indian River State College, A
Nova Southeastern University, D
Palm Beach State College, A
Seminole State College of Florida, A
State College of Florida Manatee-Sarasota, A
University of Central Florida, D
University of Florida, D
University of Miami, D
University of North Florida, MD
University of South Florida, D

Georgia

Andrew College, A
Armstrong State University, BD
Athens Technical College, A
College of Coastal Georgia, A
Emory University, D
Georgia State University, D
Gwinnett Technical College, A
Mercer University, D
University of North Georgia, D

Idaho

Idaho State University, D
Northwest Nazarene University, B

Illinois

Bradley University, D
Chicago State University, B
Dominican University, B
Elmhurst College, B
Governors State University, MD
Loyola University Chicago, B
Morton College, A
Northern Illinois University, BMD
Northwestern University, D
Rush University, M
University of Illinois at Chicago, MD

Indiana

Indiana State University, D
Indiana University - Purdue University Indianapolis, D
University of Evansville, D
University of Indianapolis, MD

Iowa

Clarke University, D
Clinton Community College, A
Indian Hills Community College, A
Iowa Central Community College, A
St. Ambrose University, D
Scott Community College, A
The University of Iowa, MD

Kansas

Allen Community College, A
Barton County Community College, A
Butler Community College, A
Dodge City Community College, A
The University of Kansas, D
University of Saint Mary, D
Wichita State University, D

Kentucky

Bellarmine University, BD
University of Kentucky, D
Western Kentucky University, D

Louisiana

Bossier Parish Community College, A
Louisiana State University Health Sciences Center, D

Maine

Husson University, D
University of New England, D

Maryland

Chesapeake College, A
University of Maryland Eastern Shore, BD

Massachusetts

American International College, BD
Boston University, D
Eastern Nazarene College, B
Northeastern University, BD
Simmons College, BD
Springfield College, BD
University of Massachusetts Lowell, D

Michigan

Andrews University, BD
Central Michigan University, D
Grand Valley State University, BD
Mid Michigan Community College, A
Monroe County Community College, A
Oakland University, MDO
University of Michigan - Flint, DO
Wayne State University, D

Minnesota

College of Saint Benedict, B
The College of St. Scholastica, D
Concordia University, St. Paul, D
Gustavus Adolphus College, B
St. Catherine University, D
St. Cloud State University, B
Saint John's University, B
University of Minnesota, Morris, B
University of Minnesota, Twin Cities Campus, MD

Mississippi

Coahoma Community College, A
East Mississippi Community College, A
Holmes Community College, A
Northeast Mississippi Community College, A
University of Mississippi Medical Center, M

Missouri

Maryville University of Saint Louis, BD
Metropolitan Community College - Kansas City, A
Missouri State University, D
Rockhurst University, D
Saint Louis University, MD
Southwest Baptist University, D
University of Missouri, MD
Washington University in St. Louis, D

Montana

University of Montana, BD

Nebraska

Clarkson College, A
Creighton University, D
University of Nebraska Medical Center, D
Western Nebraska Community College, A

Nevada

University of Nevada, Las Vegas, D

New Hampshire

Franklin Pierce University, D
Manchester Community College, A

New Jersey

Rutgers University - Camden, D
Rutgers University - Newark, D
Seton Hall University, D
Stockton University, D

New Mexico

University of New Mexico, D

New York

Clarkson University, D
College of Staten Island of the City University of New York, D
Columbia University, D
Daemen College, DO
Dominican College, MD
D'Youville College, BDO
Genesee Community College, A
Herkimer County Community College, A
Ithaca College, BD
Kingsborough Community College of the City University of New York, A
Long Island University - LIU Brooklyn, D
Mercy College, D
Mount Saint Mary College, B
Nazareth College of Rochester, BMD
New York Institute of Technology, D
New York University, MDO
State University of New York College of Environmental Science and Forestry, B
State University of New York Downstate Medical Center, B
State University of New York Upstate Medical University, D
Stony Brook University, State University of New York, D
Suffolk County Community College, A
Touro College, AD
University at Buffalo, the State University of New York, D
Utica College, D

North Carolina

Campbell University, M
Central Piedmont Community College, A
Duke University, D
East Carolina University, D
Elon University, D
Louisburg College, A
Nash Community College, A
Southwestern Community College, A
The University of North Carolina at Chapel Hill, MD
Western Carolina University, MD
Winston-Salem State University, D

North Dakota

Turtle Mountain Community College, A
University of Jamestown, D
University of Mary, D
University of North Dakota, MD

Ohio

Bowling Green State University, B
Clark State Community College, A
Cleveland State University, D
James A. Rhodes State College, A
Mount St. Joseph University, D
Muskingum University, B
The Ohio State University, D
Ohio University, D
Sinclair Community College, A
Stark State College, A
The University of Akron, B
University of Dayton, D
The University of Findlay, BD
The University of Toledo, MD
Walsh University, D
Youngstown State University, D

Oklahoma

Langston University, BD
Rose State College, A
University of Oklahoma Health Sciences Center, M

Oregon

Central Oregon Community College, A
George Fox University, D
Mt. Hood Community College, A
Pacific University, MD

Pennsylvania

Arcadia University, D
Chatham University, D
DeSales University, D

Drexel University, MDO
Duquesne University, BD
Gannon University, D
Keystone College, B
Lebanon Valley College, D
Misericordia University, D
Neumann University, D
Saint Francis University, BD
Saint Vincent College, B
Slippery Rock University of Pennsylvania, D
Temple University, D
Thomas Jefferson University, D
University of Pittsburgh, D
University of the Sciences, BD
The University of Scranton, BD
Widener University, MD

Rhode Island

University of Rhode Island, D

South Carolina

Medical University of South Carolina, D
Trident Technical College, A

South Dakota

The University of South Dakota, D

Tennessee

Belmont University, D
East Tennessee State University, D
Hiwassee College, A
Roane State Community College, A
Southern Adventist University, A
Tennessee State University, BD
The University of Tennessee at Chattanooga, BD

Texas

Amarillo College, A
Angelo State University, D
Baylor University, D
Clarendon College, A
Hardin-Simmons University, D
Hill College, A
Kilgore College, A
Laredo Community College, A
McLennan Community College, A
Odessa College, A
South Plains College, A
Tarleton State University, B
Tarrant County College District, A
Texas State University, D
Texas Woman's University, D
The University of Texas at El Paso, D
The University of Texas Health Science Center at San Antonio, D
The University of Texas Medical Branch, MD
Wharton County Junior College, A

Utah

University of Utah, D

Vermont

University of Vermont, D

Virginia

Hampton University, BD
Lynchburg College, D
Marymount University, D
Northern Virginia Community College, A
Old Dominion University, D
Radford University, D
Shenandoah University, D
Virginia Commonwealth University, D
Virginia Highlands Community College, A
Wytheville Community College, A

Washington

Eastern Washington University, D
University of Puget Sound, D
University of Washington, D

West Virginia

Marshall University, D
West Virginia University, D

Wheeling Jesuit University, D

Wisconsin

Carroll University, MD
Concordia University Wisconsin, BMD
Marquette University, D
Milwaukee Area Technical College, A
University of Wisconsin - La Crosse, D
University of Wisconsin - Milwaukee, D

U.S. Territories: Puerto Rico

University of Puerto Rico, Medical Sciences Campus, M

Canada

Alberta

University of Alberta, MD

British Columbia

Thompson Rivers University, B

Manitoba

University of Manitoba, BM

Maritime Provinces: Nova Scotia

Dalhousie University, BM

Ontario

McMaster University, M
Queen's University at Kingston, BM
University of Ottawa, B
University of Toronto, M
The University of Western Ontario, MO

Quebec

Concordia University, B
Université Laval, B
Université de Montréal, B

PHYSICIAN ASSISTANT

United States

Alabama

The University of Alabama at Birmingham, M
University of South Alabama, M

Arizona

Northern Arizona University, M

Arkansas

Harding University, M
University of Arkansas for Medical Sciences, M

California

Charles R. Drew University of Medicine and Science, B
Foothill College, A
Loma Linda University, M
Moreno Valley College, A
Samuel Merritt University, M
San Joaquin Valley College (Visalia), A
University of Southern California, M

Colorado

University of Colorado Denver, M

Connecticut

Quinnipiac University, BM
University of Bridgeport, M
Yale University, M

District of Columbia

The George Washington University, BM
Howard University, B

Florida

Barry University, M
Keiser University, M
Miami Dade College, A

Nova Southeastern University, M
South University (Tampa), M
State College of Florida Manatee-Sarasota, A
University of Florida, M

Georgia

Andrew College, A
College of Coastal Georgia, A
Emory University, M
Georgia Highlands College, A
Mercer University, M
South University, M

Idaho

Idaho State University, M

Illinois

City Colleges of Chicago, Malcolm X College, A
Elmhurst College, B
Rush University, M
Southern Illinois University Carbondale, BM
University of St. Francis, M

Indiana

Butler University, BM
Indiana State University, M
University of Saint Francis, M

Iowa

The University of Iowa, M

Kansas

Barton County Community College, A
Central Christian College of Kansas, A
Seward County Community College and Area Technical School, A
Wichita State University, M

Kentucky

University of the Cumberlands, M
University of Kentucky, BM

Louisiana

Louisiana State University Health Sciences Center, M
Our Lady of the Lake College, M

Maine

Saint Joseph's College of Maine, B
University of New England, M

Maryland

Towson University, M

Massachusetts

Bay Path University, M
Boston University, M
MCPHS University, M
Northeastern University, M
Springfield College, BM
Tufts University, M

Michigan

Central Michigan University, M
Eastern Michigan University, M
Grand Valley State University, BM
University of Detroit Mercy, M
Wayne County Community College District, A
Wayne State University, M
Western Michigan University, M

Minnesota

Augsburg College, M
Bethel University, M
St. Catherine University, M

Missouri

Missouri State University, M
Saint Louis University, M
University of Missouri - Kansas City, M

Montana

Rocky Mountain College, M

Nebraska

Peru State College, B
Union College, BM
University of Nebraska Medical Center, M

New Hampshire

Franklin Pierce University, M

New Jersey

Monmouth University, M
Rutgers University - Newark, M
Seton Hall University, M

New Mexico

University of New Mexico, M

New York

Clarkson University, M
Daemen College, BM
D'Youville College, BM
Hofstra University, M
Le Moyne College, M
Long Island University - LIU Brooklyn, B
Mercy College, M
New York Institute of Technology, M
Pace University, M
Rochester Institute of Technology, B
St. Francis College, B
St. John's University, B
State University of New York Downstate Medical Center, B
Stony Brook University, State University of New York, M
Touro College, BM
Wagner College, B
York College of the City University of New York, B

North Carolina

Campbell University, M
Duke University, M
East Carolina University, M
Elon University, M
Gardner-Webb University, M
Lenoir-Rhyne University, M
Methodist University, BM
Salem College, B

North Dakota

University of North Dakota, M

Ohio

Baldwin Wallace University, M
Case Western Reserve University, M
Cleveland State University, BM
Cuyahoga Community College, A
Kettering College, ABM
Marietta College, M
Ohio Dominican University, M
University of Dayton, M
The University of Findlay, M
University of Mount Union, M
The University of Toledo, M

Oklahoma

University of Oklahoma Health Sciences Center, M

Oregon

Oregon Health & Science University, M
Pacific University, M

Pennsylvania

Arcadia University, M
Chatham University, M
DeSales University, BM
Drexel University, M
Duquesne University, BM
Gannon University, BM
King's College, M
Lock Haven University of Pennsylvania, M
Marywood University, M
Mercyhurst University, M
Pennsylvania College of Technology, B
Philadelphia University, BM
Saint Francis University, BM

Saint Vincent College, B
Seton Hill University, BM
Thomas Jefferson University, M
University of Pittsburgh, M
University of the Sciences, BM

Rhode Island

Johnson & Wales University, M

South Carolina

Medical University of South Carolina, M

South Dakota

The University of South Dakota, BM

Tennessee

Bethel University, BM
Christian Brothers University, M
South College, M
Trevecca Nazarene University, M

Texas

The University of Texas Health Science Center at
  San Antonio, M
The University of Texas Medical Branch, M

Utah

University of Utah, M

Virginia

James Madison University, M
Jefferson College of Health Sciences, M
Shenandoah University, M

Washington

University of Washington, B

West Virginia

Alderson Broaddus University, M
Pierpont Community & Technical College, A
University of Charleston, M

Wisconsin

Carroll University, M
Marquette University, M
University of Wisconsin - La Crosse, M

PHYSICS

United States

Alabama

Alabama Agricultural and Mechanical University,
  BMD
Alabama State University, B
Auburn University, BMD
Birmingham-Southern College, B
Jacksonville State University, B
Miles College, B
Samford University, B
Troy University, B
Tuskegee University, B
The University of Alabama, BMD
The University of Alabama at Birmingham, BMD
The University of Alabama in Huntsville, BMD
University of North Alabama, B
University of South Alabama, B

Alaska

University of Alaska Fairbanks, BMD

Arizona

Arizona State University at the Tempe campus,
  BMD
Arizona Western College, A
Cochise County Community College District, A
Eastern Arizona College, A
Embry-Riddle Aeronautical University - Prescott, B
Northern Arizona University, BM
The University of Arizona, BMD

Arkansas

Arkansas State University, B
Arkansas Tech University, B
Harding University, B
Henderson State University, B
Hendrix College, B
Ouachita Baptist University, B
Southern Arkansas University - Magnolia, B
University of Arkansas, BMD
University of Arkansas at Little Rock, B
University of Arkansas at Pine Bluff, B
University of Central Arkansas, B

California

Allan Hancock College, A
Antelope Valley College, A
Azusa Pacific University, B
Bakersfield College, A
Biola University, B
Butte College, A
Cabrillo College, A
California Institute of Technology, BD
California Lutheran University, B
California Polytechnic State University, San Luis
  Obispo, B
California State Polytechnic University, Pomona, B
California State University, Bakersfield, B
California State University, Chico, B
California State University, Dominguez Hills, B
California State University, East Bay, B
California State University, Fresno, BM
California State University, Fullerton, BM
California State University, Long Beach, BM
California State University, Los Angeles, BM
California State University, Northridge, BM
California State University, Sacramento, B
California State University, San Bernardino, B
California State University, San Marcos, B
California State University, Stanislaus, B
Cañada College, A
Cerritos College, A
Chaffey College, A
Claremont McKenna College, B
College of the Canyons, A
College of the Desert, A
College of Marin, A
College of San Mateo, A
College of the Siskiyous, A
Concordia University Irvine, B
Contra Costa College, A
Cosumnes River College, A
Crafton Hills College, A
Cuesta College, A
Cuyamaca College, A
De Anza College, A
El Camino College, A
Foothill College, A
Fullerton College, A
Grossmont College, A
Hartnell College, A
Harvey Mudd College, B
Humboldt State University, B
La Sierra University, B
Los Angeles City College, A
Los Angeles Harbor College, A
Los Angeles Valley College, A
Loyola Marymount University, B
Monterey Peninsula College, A
Occidental College, B
Ohlone College, A
Orange Coast College, A
Pacific Union College, B
Pepperdine University, B
Pitzer College, B
Point Loma Nazarene University, B
Pomona College, B
Saddleback College, A
Saint Mary's College of California, B
San Bernardino Valley College, A
San Diego Mesa College, A
San Diego Miramar College, A
San Diego State University, BM
San Francisco State University, BM
San Jose State University, BM
Santa Ana College, A
Santa Barbara City College, A

Santa Clara University, B
Santa Rosa Junior College, A
Santiago Canyon College, A
Scripps College, B
Sierra College, A
Skyline College, A
Solano Community College, A
Sonoma State University, B
Southwestern College, A
Stanford University, BD
University of California, Berkeley, BD
University of California, Davis, BMD
University of California, Irvine, BMD
University of California, Los Angeles, BMD
University of California, Merced, BMD
University of California, Riverside, BMD
University of California, San Diego, BD
University of California, Santa Barbara, BD
University of California, Santa Cruz, BMD
University of La Verne, B
University of the Pacific, B
University of Redlands, B
University of San Diego, B
University of San Francisco, B
University of Southern California, BMD
West Hills Community College, A
West Los Angeles College, A
West Valley College, A
Westmont College, B
Whittier College, B

Colorado

Adams State University, B
The Colorado College, B
Colorado Mesa University, B
Colorado School of Mines, MD
Colorado State University, BMD
Colorado State University - Pueblo, B
Fort Lewis College, B
Metropolitan State University of Denver, B
Regis University, B
United States Air Force Academy, B
University of Colorado Boulder, BMD
University of Colorado Colorado Springs, B
University of Colorado Denver, B
University of Denver, BMD
University of Northern Colorado, B
Western State Colorado University, B

Connecticut

Central Connecticut State University, BMO
Connecticut College, B
Fairfield University, B
Southern Connecticut State University, B
Trinity College, B
University of Connecticut, BMD
University of Hartford, B
Wesleyan University, BD
Yale University, BD

Delaware

Delaware State University, BMD
University of Delaware, BMD

District of Columbia

American University, B
The Catholic University of America, BMD
The George Washington University, BMD
Georgetown University, B
Howard University, BMD
University of the District of Columbia, B

Florida

Ave Maria University, B
Broward College, A
College of Central Florida, A
Eckerd College, B
Embry-Riddle Aeronautical University - Daytona, B
Florida Agricultural and Mechanical University, BMD
Florida Atlantic University, BMD
Florida Institute of Technology, B
Florida International University, BMD
Florida State University, BMD
Indian River State College, A
Jacksonville University, B

Miami Dade College, A
New College of Florida, B
Pensacola State College, A
Rollins College, B
St. Thomas University, B
South Florida State College, A
State College of Florida Manatee-Sarasota, A
Stetson University, B
University of Central Florida, BMD
University of Florida, BMD
University of Miami, BMD
University of North Florida, B
University of South Florida, BMD
University of West Florida, B

Georgia

Agnes Scott College, B
Armstrong State University, B
Augusta University, B
Berry College, B
Clark Atlanta University, BM
College of Coastal Georgia, A
Covenant College, B
Dalton State College, A
Darton State College, A
Emory University, BD
Georgia College & State University, B
Georgia Highlands College, A
Georgia Institute of Technology, BMD
Georgia Southern University, B
Georgia State University, BMD
Gordon State College, A
Kennesaw State University, BM
Mercer University, B
Morehouse College, B
Oglethorpe University, B
Paine College, B
Piedmont College, B
South Georgia State College, A
Spelman College, B
University of Georgia, BMD
University of North Georgia, B
University of West Georgia, B
Valdosta State University, B

Hawaii

University of Hawaii at Manoa, BMD

Idaho

Boise State University, B
Brigham Young University - Idaho, B
The College of Idaho, B
College of Southern Idaho, A
Idaho State University, ABMD
North Idaho College, A
Northwest Nazarene University, B
University of Idaho, BMD

Illinois

Augustana College, B
Benedictine University, B
Bradley University, B
Chicago State University, B
DePaul University, BM
Eastern Illinois University, B
Elmhurst College, B
Greenville College, B
Illinois College, B
Illinois Institute of Technology, BMD
Illinois State University, B
Illinois Wesleyan University, B
John A. Logan College, A
Kankakee Community College, A
Knox College, B
Lake Forest College, B
Lewis University, B
Loyola University Chicago, B
Millikin University, B
Monmouth College, B
Moraine Valley Community College, A
North Central College, B
North Park University, B
Northeastern Illinois University, B
Northern Illinois University, BMD
Northwestern University, BD
Principia College, B

Sauk Valley Community College, A
Southern Illinois University Carbondale, BMD
Southern Illinois University Edwardsville, B
Spoon River College, A
Triton College, A
University of Chicago, BMD
University of Illinois at Chicago, BMD
University of Illinois at Urbana - Champaign, BMD
Western Illinois University, BM
Wheaton College, B

Indiana

Anderson University, B
Ball State University, BM
Butler University, B
DePauw University, B
Earlham College, B
Goshen College, B
Hanover College, B
Indiana State University, B
Indiana University Bloomington, BMD
Indiana University - Purdue University Fort Wayne, B
Indiana University - Purdue University Indianapolis, BMD
Indiana University South Bend, B
Indiana University Southeast, B
Manchester University, B
Purdue University, BMD
Purdue University Northwest (Hammond), B
Rose-Hulman Institute of Technology, B
Taylor University, B
University of Evansville, B
University of Indianapolis, B
University of Notre Dame, BMD
Valparaiso University, B
Wabash College, B

Iowa

Buena Vista University, B
Central College, B
Coe College, B
Cornell College, B
Dordt College, B
Drake University, B
Grinnell College, B
Iowa State University of Science and Technology, BMD
Luther College, B
Morningside College, B
Simpson College, B
The University of Iowa, BMD
University of Northern Iowa, BM
Wartburg College, B

Kansas

Allen Community College, A
Baker University, B
Barton County Community College, A
Benedictine College, B
Butler Community College, A
Dodge City Community College, A
Emporia State University, B
Fort Hays State University, B
Kansas State University, BMD
MidAmerica Nazarene University, B
Pittsburg State University, BM
The University of Kansas, BMD
Washburn University, B
Wichita State University, B

Kentucky

Bellarmine University, B
Berea College, B
Centre College, B
Eastern Kentucky University, B
Georgetown College, B
Kentucky Wesleyan College, B
Morehead State University, B
Murray State University, B
Northern Kentucky University, B
Thomas More College, AB
Transylvania University, B
University of the Cumberlands, B
University of Kentucky, BMD
University of Louisville, BMD

Western Kentucky University, BM

Louisiana

Dillard University, B
Louisiana College, B
Louisiana State University and Agricultural & Mechanical College, BMD
Louisiana State University in Shreveport, B
Louisiana Tech University, BMD
Loyola University New Orleans, B
Southeastern Louisiana University, B
Southern University and Agricultural and Mechanical College, BM
Tulane University, BD
University of Louisiana at Lafayette, BM
University of New Orleans, BMD
Xavier University of Louisiana, B

Maine

Bates College, B
Bowdoin College, B
Colby College, B
University of Maine, BMD
University of Southern Maine, B

Maryland

Cecil College, A
Frostburg State University, B
Goucher College, B
Harford Community College, A
Johns Hopkins University, BD
Loyola University Maryland, B
McDaniel College, B
Morgan State University, B
Notre Dame of Maryland University, B
St. Mary's College of Maryland, B
Salisbury University, B
Towson University, B
United States Naval Academy, B
University of Maryland, Baltimore County, BMD
University of Maryland, College Park, BMD
Washington College, B

Massachusetts

Amherst College, B
Bard College at Simon's Rock, B
Boston College, BMD
Boston University, BMD
Brandeis University, BMD
Bridgewater State University, B
Bunker Hill Community College, A
Clark University, BD
College of the Holy Cross, B
Eastern Nazarene College, B
Gordon College, B
Hampshire College, B
Harvard University, BD
Holyoke Community College, A
Massachusetts College of Liberal Arts, B
Massachusetts Institute of Technology, BMD
Merrimack College, B
Mount Holyoke College, B
Northeastern University, BMD
Simmons College, B
Smith College, B
Springfield Technical Community College, A
Stonehill College, B
Suffolk University, B
Tufts University, BMD
University of Massachusetts Amherst, BMD
University of Massachusetts Boston, B
University of Massachusetts Dartmouth, BM
University of Massachusetts Lowell, BMD
Wellesley College, B
Wheaton College, B
Williams College, B
Worcester Polytechnic Institute, BMD

Michigan

Adrian College, B
Albion College, B
Alma College, B
Andrews University, B
Aquinas College, B
Calvin College, B

Central Michigan University, BMD
Eastern Michigan University, BM
Grand Valley State University, B
Hillsdale College, B
Hope College, B
Kalamazoo College, B
Kettering University, B
Lake Michigan College, A
Lawrence Technological University, B
Michigan State University, BMD
Michigan Technological University, BMD
Northern Michigan University, B
Oakland University, BMD
Saginaw Valley State University, B
Spring Arbor University, B
University of Michigan, BD
University of Michigan - Dearborn, B
University of Michigan - Flint, B
Wayne State University, BMD
Western Michigan University, BMD

Minnesota

Augsburg College, B
Bemidji State University, B
Bethel University, B
Carleton College, B
College of Saint Benedict, B
Concordia College, B
Gustavus Adolphus College, B
Hamline University, B
Macalester College, B
Minnesota State University Mankato, BM
Minnesota State University Moorhead, B
St. Catherine University, B
St. Cloud State University, B
Saint John's University, B
Saint Mary's University of Minnesota, B
St. Olaf College, B
University of Minnesota, Duluth, BM
University of Minnesota, Morris, B
University of Minnesota, Twin Cities Campus, BMD
University of St. Thomas, B
Vermilion Community College, A
Winona State University, B

Mississippi

Jackson State University, B
Millsaps College, B
Mississippi College, B
Mississippi State University, BMD
Northeast Mississippi Community College, A
Tougaloo College, B
University of Mississippi, BMD
University of Southern Mississippi, BMD

Missouri

Central Methodist University, B
Drury University, B
Lincoln University, B
Missouri Southern State University, B
Missouri State University, BM
Missouri University of Science and Technology, BMD
Rockhurst University, B
Saint Louis University, B
Southeast Missouri State University, B
Truman State University, B
University of Central Missouri, B
University of Missouri, BMD
University of Missouri - Kansas City, BMD
University of Missouri - St. Louis, BMD
Washington University in St. Louis, BD
Westminster College, B
William Jewell College, B

Montana

Carroll College, B
Montana State University, BMD
University of Montana, B

Nebraska

Chadron State College, B
Concordia University, Nebraska, B
Creighton University, BM
Doane University, B

Hastings College, B
Nebraska Wesleyan University, B
Northeast Community College, A
Union College, B
University of Nebraska at Kearney, B
University of Nebraska - Lincoln, BMD
Western Nebraska Community College, A

Nevada

Truckee Meadows Community College, A
University of Nevada, Las Vegas, BMD
University of Nevada, Reno, BMD

New Hampshire

Dartmouth College, BMD
Saint Anselm College, B
University of New Hampshire, BMD

New Jersey

Bergen Community College, A
The College of New Jersey, B
Drew University, BM
Fairleigh Dickinson University, Metropolitan Campus, B
Mercer County Community College, A
Montclair State University, B
New Jersey City University, B
New Jersey Institute of Technology, B
Princeton University, BD
Ramapo College of New Jersey, B
Rowan College at Burlington County, A
Rowan University, B
Rutgers University - Camden, B
Rutgers University - New Brunswick, BMD
Rutgers University - Newark, B
Saint Peter's University, B
Seton Hall University, B
Stevens Institute of Technology, BMDO
Stockton University, B

New Mexico

Central New Mexico Community College, A
New Mexico Highlands University, B
New Mexico Institute of Mining and Technology, BMD
New Mexico Military Institute, A
New Mexico State University, BMD
San Juan College, A
University of New Mexico, BMD

New York

Adelphi University, B
Alfred University, B
Bard College, B
Barnard College, B
Binghamton University, State University of New York, BMD
Brooklyn College of the City University of New York, BM
Buffalo State College, State University of New York, B
Canisius College, B
City College of the City University of New York, BMD
Clarkson University, BMD
Colgate University, B
The College at Brockport, State University of New York, B
College of Staten Island of the City University of New York, B
Columbia University, BMD
Columbia University, School of General Studies, B
Cornell University, BMD
Finger Lakes Community College, A
Fordham University, B
Hamilton College, B
Hartwick College, B
Hobart and William Smith Colleges, B
Hofstra University, B
Houghton College, B
Hunter College of the City University of New York, BMD
Iona College, B
Ithaca College, B

Kingsborough Community College of the City University of New York, A
Le Moyne College, B
Lehman College of the City University of New York, B
Long Island University - LIU Post, B
Manhattan College, B
Monroe Community College, A
New York University, BMD
Pace University, Pleasantville Campus, B
Purchase College, State University of New York, B
Queens College of the City University of New York, BMD
Rensselaer Polytechnic Institute, BMD
Roberts Wesleyan College, B
St. Bonaventure University, B
St. John Fisher College, B
St. John's University, B
St. Lawrence University, B
Sarah Lawrence College, B
Siena College, B
Skidmore College, B
State University of New York College at Cortland, B
State University of New York College at Geneseo, B
State University of New York College at Oneonta, B
State University of New York College at Potsdam, B
State University of New York at Fredonia, B
State University of New York at New Paltz, B
State University of New York at Oswego, B
State University of New York at Plattsburgh, B
Stony Brook University, State University of New York, BMD
Syracuse University, BMD
Union College, B
United States Military Academy, B
University at Albany, State University of New York, BMD
University at Buffalo, the State University of New York, BMD
University of Rochester, BMD
Utica College, B
Vassar College, B
Wagner College, B
Wells College, B
Yeshiva University, B
York College of the City University of New York, B

North Carolina

Appalachian State University, B
Davidson College, B
Duke University, BD
East Carolina University, BMD
Elizabeth City State University, B
Elon University, B
Guilford College, B
High Point University, B
Lenoir-Rhyne University, B
Louisburg College, A
North Carolina Agricultural and Technical State University, BM
North Carolina Central University, BM
North Carolina State University, BMD
University of North Carolina at Asheville, B
The University of North Carolina at Chapel Hill, BMD
The University of North Carolina at Charlotte, B
The University of North Carolina at Greensboro, B
The University of North Carolina at Pembroke, B
The University of North Carolina Wilmington, B
Wake Forest University, BMD

North Dakota

Minot State University, B
North Dakota State University, BMD
University of North Dakota, BMD

Ohio

Ashland University, B
Baldwin Wallace University, B
Bluffton University, B
Bowling Green State University, BM
Case Western Reserve University, BMD
Cedarville University, B
Cleveland State University, BM
The College of Wooster, B
Denison University, B

Hiram College, B
John Carroll University, B
Kent State University, BMD
Kenyon College, B
Lorain County Community College, A
Marietta College, B
Miami University, BM
Miami University Hamilton, B
Miami University Middletown, A
Muskingum University, B
Oberlin College, B
Ohio Northern University, B
The Ohio State University, BMD
Ohio University, BMD
Ohio Wesleyan University, B
Otterbein University, B
Terra State Community College, A
The University of Akron, BM
University of Cincinnati, BMD
University of Dayton, B
University of Mount Union, B
The University of Toledo, BMD
Wittenberg University, B
Wright State University, BM
Xavier University, B
Youngstown State University, B

Oklahoma

Cameron University, B
Connors State College, A
East Central University, B
Oklahoma Baptist University, B
Oklahoma City Community College, A
Oklahoma City University, B
Oklahoma State University, BMD
Oklahoma State University, Oklahoma City, A
Oral Roberts University, B
Rogers State University, A
Rose State College, A
Southern Nazarene University, B
University of Central Oklahoma, B
University of Oklahoma, BMD
University of Science and Arts of Oklahoma, B
The University of Tulsa, BMD

Oregon

Lewis & Clark College, B
Linfield College, B
Linn-Benton Community College, A
Oregon State University, BMD
Pacific University, B
Portland State University, BMD
Reed College, B
University of Oregon, BMD
University of Portland, B
Willamette University, B

Pennsylvania

Albright College, B
Allegheny College, B
Arcadia University, B
Bloomsburg University of Pennsylvania, B
Bryn Mawr College, BMD
Bucknell University, B
California University of Pennsylvania, B
Carnegie Mellon University, BMD
Chatham University, B
Clarion University of Pennsylvania, B
Community College of Allegheny County, A
Community College of Beaver County, A
Dickinson College, B
Drexel University, BMD
Duquesne University, B
East Stroudsburg University of Pennsylvania, BM
Edinboro University of Pennsylvania, B
Elizabethtown College, B
Franklin & Marshall College, B
Geneva College, B
Gettysburg College, B
Grove City College, B
Haverford College, B
Indiana University of Pennsylvania, BM
Juniata College, B
King's College, B
Kutztown University of Pennsylvania, B
Lafayette College, B

Lebanon Valley College, B
Lehigh University, BMD
Lincoln University, B
Lock Haven University of Pennsylvania, B
Lycoming College, B
Messiah College, B
Millersville University of Pennsylvania, B
Moravian College, B
Muhlenberg College, B
Northampton Community College, A
Penn State Abington, B
Penn State Altoona, B
Penn State Beaver, B
Penn State Berks, B
Penn State Brandywine, B
Penn State DuBois, B
Penn State Erie, The Behrend College, B
Penn State Fayette, The Eberly Campus, B
Penn State Greater Allegheny, B
Penn State Hazleton, B
Penn State Lehigh Valley, B
Penn State Mont Alto, B
Penn State New Kensington, B
Penn State Schuylkill, B
Penn State Shenango, B
Penn State University Park, BMD
Penn State Wilkes-Barre, B
Penn State Worthington Scranton, B
Penn State York, B
Saint Joseph's University, B
Saint Vincent College, B
Shippensburg University of Pennsylvania, B
Slippery Rock University of Pennsylvania, B
Susquehanna University, B
Swarthmore College, B
Temple University, BMD
Thiel College, B
University of Pennsylvania, BMD
University of Pittsburgh, BMD
University of the Sciences, B
The University of Scranton, B
Ursinus College, B
Villanova University, B
Washington & Jefferson College, B
West Chester University of Pennsylvania, B
Westminster College, B
Widener University, B
Wilkes University, B
York College of Pennsylvania, A

Rhode Island

Brown University, BMD
Rhode Island College, B
University of Rhode Island, BMD

South Carolina

Benedict College, B
Bob Jones University, B
The Citadel, The Military College of South Carolina, B
Clemson University, BMD
Coastal Carolina University, B
College of Charleston, B
Erskine College, B
Francis Marion University, B
Furman University, B
Presbyterian College, B
South Carolina State University, B
University of South Carolina, BMD
Wofford College, B

South Dakota

Augustana University, B
South Dakota School of Mines and Technology, BMD
South Dakota State University, BM
The University of South Dakota, BMD

Tennessee

Austin Peay State University, B
Belmont University, B
Carson-Newman University, B
Christian Brothers University, B
East Tennessee State University, B
Fisk University, BM
King University, B

Lane College, B
Lipscomb University, B
Middle Tennessee State University, B
Nashville State Community College, A
Rhodes College, B
Sewanee: The University of the South, B
Southern Adventist University, B
Tennessee State University, B
Tennessee Technological University, B
Trevecca Nazarene University, B
Union University, B
University of Memphis, BM
The University of Tennessee, BMD
The University of Tennessee at Chattanooga, B
Vanderbilt University, BMD

Texas

Abilene Christian University, B
Amarillo College, A
Angelina College, A
Angelo State University, B
Austin College, B
Austin Community College District, A
Baylor University, BMD
Blinn College, A
Del Mar College, A
Frank Phillips College, A
Grayson College, A
Hardin-Simmons University, B
Hill College, A
Houston Baptist University, B
Houston Community College, A
Kilgore College, A
Lamar University, B
Lee College, A
McMurry University, B
Midwestern State University, B
Navarro College, A
Northeast Texas Community College, A
Odessa College, A
Palo Alto College, A
Panola College, A
Paris Junior College, A
Prairie View A&M University, B
Rice University, BMD
St. Mary's University, B
Sam Houston State University, B
San Jacinto College District, A
Southern Methodist University, BMD
Southwestern University, B
Stephen F. Austin State University, BM
Tarleton State University, B
Texarkana College, A
Texas A&M University, BMD
Texas A&M University - Central Texas, B
Texas A&M University - Commerce, B
Texas A&M University - Kingsville, B
Texas Christian University, BMD
Texas Lutheran University, B
Texas Southern University, B
Texas State University, BM
Texas Tech University, BMD
Trinity University, B
Tyler Junior College, A
University of Dallas, B
University of Houston, BMD
University of Houston - Clear Lake, BM
University of North Texas, B
The University of Texas at Arlington, BMD
The University of Texas at Austin, BMD
The University of Texas at Dallas, BMD
The University of Texas at El Paso, BM
The University of Texas Rio Grande Valley, B
The University of Texas at San Antonio, BMD
West Texas A&M University, B
Wiley College, B

Utah

Brigham Young University, BMD
Salt Lake Community College, A
Snow College, A
University of Utah, BMD
Utah State University, BMD
Utah Valley University, AB
Weber State University, B
Westminster College, B

Vermont

Bennington College, B
Marlboro College, B
Middlebury College, B
Norwich University, B
Saint Michael's College, B
University of Vermont, BM

Virginia

Bridgewater College, B
Christopher Newport University, BM
The College of William and Mary, BMD
Emory & Henry College, B
George Mason University, BMDO
Hampden-Sydney College, B
Hampton University, BMD
Hollins University, B
James Madison University, B
Longwood University, B
Lynchburg College, B
Mary Baldwin College, B
Norfolk State University, B
Old Dominion University, BMD
Radford University, B
Randolph College, B
Randolph-Macon College, B
Roanoke College, B
Sweet Briar College, B
University of Mary Washington, B
University of Richmond, B
University of Virginia, BMD
Virginia Commonwealth University, BM
Virginia Military Institute, B
Virginia Polytechnic Institute and State University,
    BMD
Washington and Lee University, B

Washington

Central Washington University, B
Eastern Washington University, B
Everett Community College, A
Gonzaga University, B
Pacific Lutheran University, B
Seattle Pacific University, B
Seattle University, B
University of Puget Sound, B
University of Washington, BMD
Walla Walla University, B
Washington State University, BMD
Western Washington University, B
Whitman College, B
Whitworth University, B

West Virginia

Marshall University, BM
Potomac State College of West Virginia University,
    A
West Virginia University, BMD
West Virginia Wesleyan College, B
Wheeling Jesuit University, B

Wisconsin

Beloit College, B
Carroll University, B
Carthage College, B
Edgewood College, B
Lawrence University, B
Marquette University, B
St. Norbert College, B
University of Wisconsin - Eau Claire, B
University of Wisconsin - La Crosse, B
University of Wisconsin - Madison, BMD
University of Wisconsin - Milwaukee, BMD
University of Wisconsin - Oshkosh, B
University of Wisconsin - Parkside, AB
University of Wisconsin - River Falls, B
University of Wisconsin - Stevens Point, B
University of Wisconsin - Whitewater, B
Wisconsin Lutheran College, B

Wyoming

Casper College, A
Northwest College, A
University of Wyoming, B

U.S. Territories: Puerto Rico

Pontifical Catholic University of Puerto Rico, B
University of Puerto Rico in Humacao, B
University of Puerto Rico, Mayagüez Campus, BM
University of Puerto Rico, Río Piedras Campus,
    BMD
University of Puerto Rico in Utuado, B

U.S. Territories: United States Virgin Islands

University of the Virgin Islands, A

Canada

Alberta

University of Alberta, BMD
University of Calgary, BMD
University of Lethbridge, BM

British Columbia

Simon Fraser University, BMD
Thompson Rivers University, AB
The University of British Columbia, BMD
The University of British Columbia - Okanagan
    Campus, B
University of the Fraser Valley, B
University of Northern British Columbia, B
University of Victoria, BMD

Manitoba

Brandon University, B
University of Manitoba, BMD
The University of Winnipeg, B

Maritime Provinces: New Brunswick

Mount Allison University, B
Université de Moncton, BM
University of New Brunswick Fredericton, BMD
University of New Brunswick Saint John, B

Maritime Provinces: Nova Scotia

Acadia University, B
Dalhousie University, BMD
St. Francis Xavier University, BM
Saint Mary's University, B
University of King's College, B

Maritime Provinces: Prince Edward Island

University of Prince Edward Island, B

Newfoundland and Labrador

Memorial University of Newfoundland, BMD

Ontario

Brock University, BM
Carleton University, BMD
Lakehead University, BM
Laurentian University, B
McMaster University, BD
Queen's University at Kingston, BMD
Royal Military College of Canada, BM
Ryerson University, B
Trent University, BM
University of Guelph, BMD
University of Ottawa, BMD
University of Toronto, MD
University of Waterloo, BMD
The University of Western Ontario, BMD
University of Windsor, BMD
Wilfrid Laurier University, B
York University, BMD

Quebec

Bishop's University, B
Concordia University, BMD
McGill University, BMD
Université Laval, BMD
Université de Montréal, BMD
Université du Québec à Chicoutimi, B
Université du Québec à Montréal, B
Université du Québec à Trois-Rivières, BMD
Université de Sherbrooke, BMD

Saskatchewan

University of Regina, BMD
University of Saskatchewan, BMD

PHYSICS TEACHER EDUCATION

United States

Alabama

Auburn University, B

Arkansas

Arkansas State University, B

California

University of California, San Diego, B

Colorado

Colorado State University, B

Delaware

Delaware State University, B
University of Delaware, B

Florida

Broward College, A
Florida Institute of Technology, B
Miami Dade College, B
State College of Florida Manatee-Sarasota, A

Hawaii

Brigham Young University - Hawaii, B

Idaho

Brigham Young University - Idaho, B

Illinois

Augustana College, B
Bradley University, B
Elmhurst College, B
Greenville College, B
University of Illinois at Chicago, B
University of Illinois at Urbana - Champaign, B

Indiana

Anderson University, B
Ball State University, B
Goshen College, B
Indiana University Bloomington, B
Indiana University - Purdue University Fort Wayne,
    B
Indiana University South Bend, B
Manchester University, B
University of Evansville, B
Valparaiso University, B

Iowa

Buena Vista University, B
Morningside College, B

Kansas

Kansas Wesleyan University, B
Pittsburg State University, B

Kentucky

Eastern Kentucky University, B

Louisiana

Louisiana State University in Shreveport, B
Louisiana Tech University, B
Southern University and Agricultural and Mechanical
    College, B

Maine

University of Maine at Farmington, B

Maryland

Anne Arundel Community College, A
Chesapeake College, A

Community College of Baltimore County, A
Harford Community College, A
Montgomery College, A
University of Maryland, Baltimore County, B

Massachusetts

Eastern Nazarene College, B
Merrimack College, B

Michigan

Adrian College, B
Albion College, B
Alma College, B
Central Michigan University, B
Eastern Michigan University, B
Grand Valley State University, B
Hope College, B
Madonna University, B
Michigan State University, B
Northern Michigan University, B
Saginaw Valley State University, B
Western Michigan University, B

Minnesota

Concordia College, B
Gustavus Adolphus College, B
Minnesota State University Moorhead, B
Saint Mary's University of Minnesota, B
University of St. Thomas, B
Winona State University, B

Missouri

Central Methodist University, B
Lincoln University, B
Missouri State University, B
University of Central Missouri, B
University of Missouri, B
Washington University in St. Louis, B

Nebraska

Chadron State College, B
Concordia University, Nebraska, B
Hastings College, B
Union College, B
University of Nebraska - Lincoln, B

New Jersey

The College of New Jersey, B

New York

Brooklyn College of the City University of New York,
   B
Canisius College, B
City College of the City University of New York, B
College of Staten Island of the City University of
   New York, B
Hofstra University, B
Ithaca College, B
Le Moyne College, B
Queens College of the City University of New York,
   B
Roberts Wesleyan College, B
St. John Fisher College, B
St. John's University, B
State University of New York College at Cortland, B
State University of New York College at Oneonta, B
State University of New York College at Potsdam, B
State University of New York at New Paltz, B
Syracuse University, B
Utica College, B

North Carolina

North Carolina Agricultural and Technical State University, B

North Dakota

Minot State University, B
North Dakota State University, B

Ohio

Bowling Green State University, B
Cedarville University, B
Miami University Hamilton, B
Mount Vernon Nazarene University, B

Ohio Northern University, B
Ohio Wesleyan University, B
University of Rio Grande, B
Xavier University, B

Oklahoma

East Central University, B
University of Central Oklahoma, B

Pennsylvania

Grove City College, B
Juniata College, B
Messiah College, B
Saint Joseph's University, B
Saint Vincent College, B

Rhode Island

Providence College, B
Rhode Island College, B

South Dakota

The University of South Dakota, B

Tennessee

King University, B
Lipscomb University, B
Southern Adventist University, B
Trevecca Nazarene University, B

Texas

Abilene Christian University, B
Howard College, A
Southwestern Adventist University, B

Utah

Utah State University, B
Weber State University, B

Virginia

Emory & Henry College, B

Washington

Eastern Washington University, B
Seattle University, B
Washington State University, B

Canada
Alberta

University of Alberta, B

Ontario

University of Waterloo, B
University of Windsor, B
York University, B

Quebec

Bishop's University, B

Saskatchewan

University of Regina, B

PHYSIOLOGY

United States
Alabama

Community College of the Air Force, A

Arizona

The University of Arizona, BMD

Arkansas

University of Arkansas for Medical Sciences, MD

California

California State University, Long Beach, B
California State University, San Marcos, B
Crafton Hills College, A
Loma Linda University, MD

San Francisco State University, M
San Jose State University, M
Stanford University, D
University of California, Berkeley, MD
University of California, Davis, MD
University of California, Irvine, D
University of California, Los Angeles, BMD
University of California, Santa Barbara, B
University of Southern California, M

Colorado

University of Colorado Boulder, BMD
University of Colorado Denver, D

Connecticut

University of Connecticut, MD
Yale University, D

Delaware

University of Delaware, MD

District of Columbia

Georgetown University, MD
Howard University, D

Florida

University of Florida, MD
University of Miami, D
University of South Florida, MD

Georgia

Augusta University, MD
Georgia Institute of Technology, MD
Georgia State University, MD
University of Georgia, MD

Hawaii

University of Hawaii at Manoa, MD

Illinois

Illinois State University, MD
Loyola University Chicago, M
Northwestern University, M
Rush University, D
Southern Illinois University Carbondale, BMD
University of Illinois at Chicago, MD
University of Illinois at Urbana - Champaign, BMD

Indiana

Ball State University, M
Indiana State University, D
Purdue University, MD
University of Notre Dame, MD

Iowa

The University of Iowa, MD

Kansas

Kansas State University, D
The University of Kansas, MD

Kentucky

University of Kentucky, D
University of Louisville, MD

Louisiana

Louisiana State University Health Sciences Center,
   MD
Tulane University, MD

Maryland

Johns Hopkins University, D
Salisbury University, M

Massachusetts

Boston University, MD
Emmanuel College, B
Harvard University, D
University of Massachusetts Amherst, MD

Michigan

Eastern Michigan University, M
Michigan State University, BMD

Northern Michigan University, B
University of Michigan, MD
Wayne State University, MD
Western Michigan University, M

Minnesota

University of Minnesota, Duluth, MD
University of Minnesota, Twin Cities Campus, BD

Mississippi

University of Mississippi Medical Center, D

Missouri

Saint Louis University, D
University of Missouri, MD

Nebraska

University of Nebraska Medical Center, MD

Nevada

University of Nevada, Reno, D

New Hampshire

Dartmouth College, D

New Jersey

Montclair State University, M
Rutgers University - New Brunswick, MD
Rutgers University - Newark, D

New Mexico

University of New Mexico, MD

New York

Columbia University, MD
Cornell University, MD
New York University, D
State University of New York Upstate Medical University, MD
Stony Brook University, State University of New York, D
University at Buffalo, the State University of New York, MD
University of Rochester, MD

North Carolina

East Carolina University, D
North Carolina State University, MD
Wake Forest University, D

North Dakota

University of North Dakota, MD

Ohio

Case Western Reserve University, MD
Kent State University, MD
Ohio University, MD
University of Cincinnati, D
Wright State University, M
Youngstown State University, M

Oklahoma

Oklahoma Baptist University, B
Oklahoma State University, B
University of Oklahoma Health Sciences Center, MD

Oregon

Oregon Health & Science University, D
University of Oregon, BMD

Pennsylvania

Penn State University Park, MD
University of Pennsylvania, D

Rhode Island

Brown University, MD

South Dakota

The University of South Dakota, MD

Tennessee

East Tennessee State University, D
The University of Tennessee, MD

Texas

Southern Methodist University, M
The University of Texas Medical Branch, MD

Utah

Brigham Young University, BMD
University of Utah, D

Virginia

University of Virginia, D
Virginia Commonwealth University, MDO

Washington

Seattle Pacific University, B
University of Washington, BD

West Virginia

West Virginia University, MD

Wisconsin

Marquette University, BMD
University of Wisconsin - La Crosse, M
University of Wisconsin - Madison, MD

Wyoming

University of Wyoming, BMD

U.S. Territories: Puerto Rico

Universidad Central del Caribe, M
University of Puerto Rico, Medical Sciences Campus, MD

Canada

Alberta

University of Alberta, BMD
University of Calgary, MD

British Columbia

The University of British Columbia, B

Manitoba

University of Manitoba, MD

Maritime Provinces: Nova Scotia

Dalhousie University, MD

Maritime Provinces: Prince Edward Island

University of Prince Edward Island, MD

Ontario

McMaster University, MD
Queen's University at Kingston, MD
University of Guelph, MD
University of Ottawa, B
University of Toronto, MD
The University of Western Ontario, BMD

Quebec

McGill University, BMD
Université Laval, MD
Université de Montréal, MD
Université de Sherbrooke, MD

Saskatchewan

University of Saskatchewan, BMD

PIANO AND ORGAN

United States

Alabama

Birmingham-Southern College, B
Samford University, B

Arizona

Grand Canyon University, B

Arkansas

Ouachita Baptist University, B

California

California Baptist University, B
Chapman University, B
The Colburn School Conservatory of Music, B
The Master's College and Seminary, B
Point Loma Nazarene University, B
San Francisco Conservatory of Music, B
University of the Pacific, B
University of Redlands, B
University of Southern California, B

Delaware

University of Delaware, B

District of Columbia

The Catholic University of America, B

Florida

Barry University, B
Jacksonville University, B
Palm Beach Atlantic University, B
Southeastern University, B
Stetson University, B
University of Miami, B

Georgia

Shorter University, B

Hawaii

Brigham Young University - Hawaii, B

Illinois

Illinois Wesleyan University, B
Northwestern University, B
Roosevelt University, B

Indiana

Indiana University - Purdue University Fort Wayne, B
Valparaiso University, B

Iowa

Dordt College, B
Drake University, B
Iowa Lakes Community College, A
The University of Iowa, B

Kansas

The University of Kansas, B

Kentucky

Campbellsville University, B

Louisiana

Louisiana College, B
Xavier University of Louisiana, B

Maryland

Peabody Conservatory of The Johns Hopkins University, B

Massachusetts

Anna Maria College, B
Berklee College of Music, B
Eastern Nazarene College, B
New England Conservatory of Music, B

Michigan

Andrews University, B
Hope College, B
Madonna University, B
Oakland University, B
Spring Arbor University, B
Western Michigan University, B

Minnesota

McNally Smith College of Music, AB
St. Cloud State University, B
University of Northwestern - St. Paul, B

Mississippi

East Central Community College, A
Itawamba Community College, A
Mississippi College, B

Missouri

Calvary Bible College and Theological Seminary, B
College of the Ozarks, B

Nebraska

Grace University, B
Hastings College, B
University of Nebraska at Omaha, B

New Jersey

Rider University, B

New York

Houghton College, B
Ithaca College, B
Manhattan School of Music, B
The New School College of Performing Arts, B
New York University, B
Nyack College, B
Roberts Wesleyan College, B
State University of New York at Fredonia, B
Syracuse University, B

North Carolina

Campbell University, B

Ohio

Ashland University, B
Baldwin Wallace University, B
Bowling Green State University, B
Capital University, B
Cedarville University, B
Cincinnati Christian University, B
Heidelberg University, B
Oberlin College, B
The Ohio State University, B
Ohio University, B
Otterbein University, B
The University of Akron, B
University of Cincinnati, B
Youngstown State University, B

Oklahoma

East Central University, B
Hillsdale Free Will Baptist College, B
Oklahoma City University, B
Oral Roberts University, B
University of Central Oklahoma, B
The University of Tulsa, B

Oregon

Willamette University, B

Pennsylvania

Summit University, B

South Carolina

Bob Jones University, B
Coker College, B
Columbia College, B
Converse College, B
Furman University, B

Tennessee

Carson-Newman University, B
Lipscomb University, B
Maryville College, B
Union University, B
The University of Tennessee at Martin, B
Vanderbilt University, B

Texas

Abilene Christian University, B
Dallas Baptist University, B
East Texas Baptist University, B
Hardin-Simmons University, B
Houston Baptist University, B
Howard Payne University, B
Southern Methodist University, B

Texas Christian University, B

Utah

Brigham Young University, B
Weber State University, B

Virginia

Liberty University, B
Shenandoah University, B

Washington

Central Washington University, B
Cornish College of the Arts, B
University of Washington, B
Walla Walla University, B
Whitworth University, B

Wisconsin

Lawrence University, B

U.S. Territories: Puerto Rico

Conservatorio de Musica de Puerto Rico, B

Canada

Alberta

University of Alberta, B

British Columbia

The University of British Columbia, B
University of Victoria, B

Maritime Provinces: New Brunswick

Mount Allison University, B

Maritime Provinces: Nova Scotia

Acadia University, B

Newfoundland and Labrador

Memorial University of Newfoundland, B

Ontario

The University of Western Ontario, B
York University, B

Quebec

McGill University, B

PIPEFITTING/PIPEFITTER AND SPRINKLER FITTER

United States

Arizona

GateWay Community College, A

California

Bakersfield College, A
Los Angeles Trade-Technical College, A

Florida

Miami Dade College, A

Illinois

Black Hawk College, A
Southwestern Illinois College, A

Indiana

Ivy Tech Community College - Bloomington, A
Ivy Tech Community College - Central Indiana, A
Ivy Tech Community College - Columbus, A
Ivy Tech Community College - East Central, A
Ivy Tech Community College - Lafayette, A
Ivy Tech Community College - North Central, A
Ivy Tech Community College - Northeast, A
Ivy Tech Community College - Northwest, A
Ivy Tech Community College - Richmond, A
Ivy Tech Community College - Southern Indiana, A
Ivy Tech Community College - Southwest, A
Ivy Tech Community College - Wabash Valley, A

Maine

Northern Maine Community College, A

Michigan

Delta College, A
Kellogg Community College, A
Oakland Community College, A
Washtenaw Community College, A

New York

State University of New York College of Technology
at Delhi, A

Rhode Island

New England Institute of Technology, A

Texas

Brazosport College, A

Canada

British Columbia

British Columbia Institute of Technology, A

PLANETARY ASTRONOMY AND SCIENCE

United States

Alabama

Alabama Agricultural and Mechanical University, D

Arizona

Arizona State University at the Tempe campus, D
The University of Arizona, MD

Arkansas

University of Arkansas, MD

California

California Institute of Technology, BMD
University of California, Los Angeles, MD
University of California, Santa Cruz, MD

Connecticut

Western Connecticut State University, M
Yale University, D

Florida

Florida Institute of Technology, B
St. Thomas University, O

Hawaii

University of Hawaii at Manoa, MD

Illinois

University of Chicago, D

Maryland

University of Maryland, Baltimore County, M

Massachusetts

Harvard University, MD
Massachusetts Institute of Technology, D

Michigan

University of Michigan, MD

Missouri

Washington University in St. Louis, D

New Mexico

University of New Mexico, MD

New York

Cornell University, D

North Dakota

University of North Dakota, M

Pennsylvania

University of Pittsburgh, MD
West Chester University of Pennsylvania, O

Texas

University of Houston, M

Virginia

Hampton University, MD

West Virginia

American Public University System, M

Canada

Ontario

University of Waterloo, B
The University of Western Ontario, B
York University, MD

Quebec

McGill University, BMD

PLANT BIOLOGY

United States

Arizona

Arizona State University at the Tempe campus, M

California

University of California, Berkeley, D
University of California, Davis, MD
University of California, Riverside, MD

Connecticut

University of Connecticut, MD
Yale University, D

Florida

Florida State University, MD
University of Florida, MD

Georgia

University of Georgia, MD

Illinois

Illinois State University, M
Northwestern University, MD
Southern Illinois University Carbondale, MD
University of Illinois at Urbana - Champaign, MD

Indiana

Indiana University Bloomington, MD

Iowa

Iowa State University of Science and Technology, MD

Maryland

University of Maryland, College Park, MD

Massachusetts

University of Massachusetts Amherst, MD

Michigan

Michigan State University, MD

Minnesota

University of Minnesota, Twin Cities Campus, MD

Missouri

University of Missouri, MD
Washington University in St. Louis, D

New Hampshire

University of New Hampshire, MD

New Jersey

Rutgers University - New Brunswick, MD

New York

Cornell University, MD
New York University, D

North Carolina

North Carolina State University, MD

Ohio

Ohio University, MD

Pennsylvania

Penn State University Park, MD

South Carolina

Clemson University, MD

Texas

The University of Texas at Austin, MD

Vermont

University of Vermont, MD

Canada

Alberta

University of Alberta, MD

Quebec

Université Laval, MD

PLANT GENETICS

United States

Indiana

Purdue University, B

PLANT MOLECULAR BIOLOGY

United States

California

University of California, Riverside, D

Connecticut

University of Connecticut, MD

Florida

University of Florida, MD

Illinois

Illinois State University, M
University of Illinois at Urbana - Champaign, B

Massachusetts

University of Massachusetts Amherst, MD

Michigan

Michigan Technological University, MD

New Jersey

Rutgers University - New Brunswick, MD

New York

Cornell University, MD

PLANT NURSERY OPERATIONS AND MANAGEMENT

United States

California

American River College, A
City College of San Francisco, A
College of Marin, A
College of San Mateo, A
Cosumnes River College, A
Cuyamaca College, A
Fullerton College, A
Merritt College, A
MiraCosta College, A
Modesto Junior College, A
Southwestern College, A

Colorado

Colorado State University, B

Florida

Miami Dade College, A

Illinois

Joliet Junior College, A

Ohio

The Ohio State University Agricultural Technical Institute, A

Pennsylvania

Community College of Allegheny County, A

Washington

Edmonds Community College, A

Canada

Maritime Provinces: Nova Scotia

Dalhousie University, A

PLANT PATHOLOGY/ PHYTOPATHOLOGY

United States

Alabama

Auburn University, MD

Arizona

The University of Arizona, MD

Arkansas

University of Arkansas, M

California

University of California, Davis, MD
University of California, Riverside, MD

Colorado

Colorado State University, MD

Florida

University of Florida, MD

Georgia

University of Georgia, MD

Hawaii

University of Hawaii at Manoa, MD

Indiana

Purdue University, MD

Iowa

Iowa State University of Science and Technology, MD

Kansas
Kansas State University, MD

Kentucky
University of Kentucky, MD

Louisiana
Louisiana State University and Agricultural & Mechanical College, MD

Maine
University of Maine, M

Michigan
Michigan State University, MD

Minnesota
University of Minnesota, Twin Cities Campus, MD

Mississippi
Mississippi State University, MD

Montana
Montana State University, M

New Jersey
Rutgers University - New Brunswick, MD

New Mexico
New Mexico State University, BM

New York
Cornell University, MD
State University of New York College of Environmental Science and Forestry, MD

North Carolina
North Carolina State University, MD

North Dakota
North Dakota State University, MD

Ohio
The Ohio State University, BMD

Oklahoma
Oklahoma State University, MD

Pennsylvania
Penn State University Park, MD

Tennessee
The University of Tennessee, MD

Texas
Texas A&M University, MD

Virginia
Virginia Polytechnic Institute and State University, D

Washington
Washington State University, MD

West Virginia
West Virginia University, M

Wisconsin
University of Wisconsin - Madison, BMD

Canada

Maritime Provinces: Nova Scotia
Dalhousie University, M

Ontario
University of Guelph, MD

PLANT PHYSIOLOGY

United States

Indiana
Purdue University, D

Massachusetts
University of Massachusetts Amherst, MD

New York
Cornell University, MD

Tennessee
The University of Tennessee, MD

Virginia
Virginia Polytechnic Institute and State University, D

Canada

Manitoba
University of Manitoba, MD

Maritime Provinces: Nova Scotia
Dalhousie University, M

PLANT PROTECTION AND INTEGRATED PEST MANAGEMENT

United States

California
California State Polytechnic University, Pomona, B
Los Angeles Pierce College, A

Delaware
University of Delaware, B

Hawaii
University of Hawaii at Manoa, B

Illinois
University of Illinois at Urbana - Champaign, B

Iowa
Iowa State University of Science and Technology, B

Mississippi
Hinds Community College, A

Texas
West Texas A&M University, B

Washington
Washington State University, B

U.S. Territories: Puerto Rico
University of Puerto Rico, Mayagüez Campus, B
University of Puerto Rico in Utuado, A

Canada

Maritime Provinces: Nova Scotia
Dalhousie University, A

PLANT SCIENCES

United States

Alabama
Alabama Agricultural and Mechanical University, MD
Auburn University, B
Tuskegee University, BM

Arizona
The University of Arizona, BMD

Arkansas
Arkansas State University, B
University of Arkansas, D

California
California State University, Fresno, BM
Reedley College, A
University of California, Riverside, MD
University of California, Santa Cruz, B
Ventura College, A

Colorado
Colorado State University, MD

Connecticut
University of Connecticut, MD

Delaware
Delaware State University, M
University of Delaware, BMD

Florida
South Florida State College, A
University of Florida, BD

Georgia
University of Georgia, MD

Hawaii
Leeward Community College, A
University of Hawaii at Manoa, BMD

Idaho
University of Idaho, MD

Illinois
Illinois State University, M
Rend Lake College, A
Southern Illinois University Carbondale, BM

Indiana
Purdue University, D

Iowa
Iowa State University of Science and Technology, MD

Kansas
Kansas State University, M

Kentucky
University of Kentucky, MD

Louisiana
Louisiana State University and Agricultural & Mechanical College, B
Louisiana Tech University, B

Maine
University of Maine, D

Massachusetts
University of Massachusetts Amherst, BMD

Michigan
Michigan State University, MD

Minnesota
University of Minnesota, Crookston, B
University of Minnesota, Twin Cities Campus, BMD

Mississippi
Mississippi State University, MD
Northwest Mississippi Community College, A

Missouri
Missouri State University, M
University of Missouri, BMD

Montana

Montana State University, BMD

New Jersey

Mercer County Community College, A
Rutgers University - New Brunswick, B

New Mexico

New Mexico State University, M

New York

Cornell University, BMD
Lehman College of the City University of New York, D
State University of New York College of Agriculture and Technology at Cobleskill, AB
State University of New York College of Environmental Science and Forestry, BMD

North Carolina

North Carolina Agricultural and Technical State University, M

North Dakota

North Dakota State University, MD

Ohio

The Ohio State University, BD

Oklahoma

Oklahoma State University, MD

Pennsylvania

Penn State University Park, BMD

South Carolina

Clemson University, MD

South Dakota

South Dakota State University, MD

Tennessee

Middle Tennessee State University, B
Tennessee State University, M
The University of Tennessee, BM

Texas

Texas A&M University, MD
Texas A&M University - Kingsville, M
Texas Tech University, BMD
West Texas A&M University, M

Utah

Brigham Young University, MD
Utah State University, BMD

Vermont

Sterling College, B
University of Vermont, BMD

Washington

Washington State University, B
Washington State University - Tri-Cities, B

West Virginia

West Virginia University, BD

Wisconsin

University of Wisconsin - Madison, MD

Canada

British Columbia

The University of British Columbia, MD

Manitoba

University of Manitoba, MD

Maritime Provinces: Nova Scotia

Dalhousie University, B

Ontario

Lakehead University, B
University of Guelph, B

Quebec

McGill University, MDO

Saskatchewan

University of Saskatchewan, MD

PLASMA AND HIGH-TEMPERATURE PHYSICS

United States

Colorado

University of Colorado Boulder, MD

New Jersey

Princeton University, D

West Virginia

West Virginia University, MD

PLASTICS ENGINEERING TECHNOLOGY/TECHNICIAN

United States

California

Cerritos College, A

Connecticut

Quinebaug Valley Community College, A

Florida

Daytona State College, A

Georgia

West Georgia Technical College, A

Illinois

College of DuPage, A

Kansas

Pittsburg State University, B
Wichita Area Technical College, A

Massachusetts

Mount Wachusett Community College, A

Michigan

Eastern Michigan University, B
Ferris State University, AB
Grand Rapids Community College, A
Macomb Community College, A

Minnesota

Hennepin Technical College, A

North Carolina

Davidson County Community College, A
Isothermal Community College, A
Wake Technical Community College, A

Ohio

Cincinnati State Technical and Community College, A
Lorain County Community College, A
Northwest State Community College, A
Shawnee State University, AB
Sinclair Community College, A
Terra State Community College, A

Pennsylvania

Penn State Erie, The Behrend College, A
Pennsylvania College of Technology, AB

Texas

El Paso Community College, A
South Texas College, A

Utah

Weber State University, B

Wisconsin

Milwaukee Area Technical College, A

Canada

British Columbia

British Columbia Institute of Technology, A

PLATEMAKER/IMAGER

United States

Arkansas

Phillips Community College of the University of Arkansas, A

Illinois

Illinois Central College, A

PLAYWRITING AND SCREENWRITING

United States

California

Academy of Art University, B
Chapman University, B
Loyola Marymount University, B
Pacific Union College, A
University of Southern California, B

Florida

Broward College, A

Georgia

Emory University, B

Illinois

Columbia College Chicago, B
DePaul University, B
Judson University, B

Massachusetts

Emerson College, B

Minnesota

Metropolitan State University, B
Minneapolis Community and Technical College, A

New York

Marymount Manhattan College, B
Purchase College, State University of New York, B

Ohio

Ohio University, B

Pennsylvania

Drexel University, B
Point Park University, B
The University of the Arts, B

Utah

Brigham Young University, B

Vermont

Bennington College, B

Washington

Central Washington University, B

Wyoming

Northwest College, A

Canada

Ontario

York University, B

Quebec

Concordia University, B
Université de Montréal, B

PLUMBING TECHNOLOGY/ PLUMBER

United States

Arizona

Arizona Western College, A
GateWay Community College, A

California

College of San Mateo, A

Florida

Miami Dade College, A

Iowa

Northeast Iowa Community College, A

Maine

Southern Maine Community College, A

Michigan

Delta College, A
Macomb Community College, A

Minnesota

Minnesota State Community and Technical College, A
Minnesota State Community and Technical College - Moorhead, A
Minnesota West Community and Technical College, A
Northland Community and Technical College, A
St. Cloud Technical & Community College, A

Mississippi

Hinds Community College, A

Missouri

Vatterott College (Berkeley), A
Vatterott College (Kansas City), A

Montana

Montana State University - Northern, A

New Mexico

Central New Mexico Community College, A

Pennsylvania

Community College of Beaver County, A
Luzerne County Community College, A
Thaddeus Stevens College of Technology, A

South Carolina

York Technical College, A

South Dakota

Sinte Gleska University, A
Southeast Technical Institute, A

PODIATRIC MEDICINE

United States

Florida

Barry University, D

Ohio

Kent State University, D

Pennsylvania

Temple University, D

POLISH LANGUAGE AND LITERATURE

United States

Illinois

University of Illinois at Chicago, B

Michigan

University of Michigan, B

Pennsylvania

University of Pittsburgh, B

Wisconsin

University of Wisconsin - Madison, B

POLITICAL COMMUNICATION

United States

Florida

Florida Southern College, B

Massachusetts

Emerson College, B
Suffolk University, B

Nebraska

Nebraska Wesleyan University, B

Utah

Weber State University, B

Virginia

Regent University, B

Washington

University of Washington, B

Canada

Maritime Provinces: New Brunswick

St. Thomas University, B

Quebec

Université de Montréal, B

POLITICAL SCIENCE AND GOVERNMENT

United States

Alabama

Alabama Agricultural and Mechanical University, B
Alabama State University, B
Athens State University, B
Auburn University, BMDO
Auburn University at Montgomery, BMDO
Birmingham-Southern College, B
Huntingdon College, B
Jacksonville State University, BM

Miles College, B
Samford University, B
Spring Hill College, B
Troy University, B
Tuskegee University, B
The University of Alabama, BMD
The University of Alabama at Birmingham, B
The University of Alabama in Huntsville, B
University of Mobile, B
University of Montevallo, B
University of North Alabama, B
University of South Alabama, B

Alaska

University of Alaska Anchorage, B
University of Alaska Fairbanks, B

Arizona

Arizona State University at the Polytechnic campus, B
Arizona State University at the Tempe campus, BMD
Arizona State University at the West campus, B
Arizona Western College, A
Eastern Arizona College, A
Northern Arizona University, BMDO
Pima Community College, A
The University of Arizona, BMD

Arkansas

Arkansas State University, BMO
Arkansas Tech University, B
Harding University, B
Henderson State University, B
Hendrix College, B
John Brown University, B
Lyon College, B
Ouachita Baptist University, B
Philander Smith College, B
Southern Arkansas University - Magnolia, B
University of Arkansas, BM
University of Arkansas - Fort Smith, B
University of Arkansas at Little Rock, B
University of Arkansas at Monticello, B
University of Arkansas at Pine Bluff, B
University of Central Arkansas, B
University of the Ozarks, B

California

American Jewish University, B
Antelope Valley College, A
Azusa Pacific University, B
Bakersfield College, A
Biola University, B
Cabrillo College, A
California Baptist University, B
California Institute of Technology, B
California Lutheran University, B
California Polytechnic State University, San Luis Obispo, BM
California State Polytechnic University, Pomona, B
California State University, Bakersfield, B
California State University Channel Islands, B
California State University, Chico, BM
California State University, Dominguez Hills, B
California State University, East Bay, B
California State University, Fresno, B
California State University, Fullerton, BM
California State University, Long Beach, BM
California State University, Los Angeles, BM
California State University, Northridge, BM
California State University, Sacramento, BM
California State University, San Bernardino, B
California State University, San Marcos, B
California State University, Stanislaus, B
Cañada College, A
Cerritos College, A
Chaffey College, A
Chapman University, B
Claremont McKenna College, B
College of Alameda, A
College of the Canyons, A
College of the Desert, A
College of Marin, A
College of the Siskiyous, A
Concordia University Irvine, B

Contra Costa College, A
Copper Mountain College, A
Crafton Hills College, A
Cuesta College, A
De Anza College, A
Diablo Valley College, A
Dominican University of California, BM
East Los Angeles College, A
El Camino College, A
Feather River College, A
Foothill College, A
Fullerton College, A
Grossmont College, A
Humboldt State University, B
Los Angeles Valley College, A
Loyola Marymount University, B
The Master's College and Seminary, B
Merced College, A
Mills College, B
Monterey Peninsula College, A
Mount Saint Mary's University, B
National University, B
Notre Dame de Namur University, B
Occidental College, B
Orange Coast College, A
Oxnard College, A
Pepperdine University, BM
Pitzer College, B
Point Loma Nazarene University, B
Pomona College, B
Saddleback College, A
Saint Mary's College of California, B
San Bernardino Valley College, A
San Diego Christian College, B
San Diego City College, A
San Diego State University, BM
San Francisco State University, BM
San Joaquin Delta College, A
San Jose State University, B
Santa Ana College, A
Santa Barbara City College, A
Santa Clara University, B
Santa Rosa Junior College, A
Santiago Canyon College, A
Scripps College, B
Skyline College, A
Solano Community College, A
Sonoma State University, BMO
Southwestern College, A
Stanford University, BMD
University of California, Berkeley, BD
University of California, Davis, BMD
University of California, Irvine, BD
University of California, Los Angeles, BMD
University of California, Merced, B
University of California, Riverside, BMD
University of California, San Diego, BD
University of California, Santa Barbara, BMD
University of California, Santa Cruz, BD
University of La Verne, B
University of the Pacific, B
University of Redlands, B
University of San Diego, B
University of San Francisco, B
University of Southern California, BMD
Vanguard University of Southern California, B
West Los Angeles College, A
Westmont College, B
Whittier College, B
William Jessup University, B

Colorado

Adams State University, A
Colorado Christian University, B
The Colorado College, B
Colorado Mesa University, B
Colorado State University, BMD
Colorado State University - Pueblo, B
Fort Lewis College, B
Metropolitan State University of Denver, B
Northeastern Junior College, A
Otero Junior College, A
Regis University, B
United States Air Force Academy, B
University of Colorado Boulder, BMD
University of Colorado Colorado Springs, B

University of Colorado Denver, BM
University of Denver, B
University of Northern Colorado, B
Western State Colorado University, B

Connecticut

Albertus Magnus College, B
Central Connecticut State University, B
Connecticut College, B
Eastern Connecticut State University, B
Fairfield University, B
Quinnipiac University, B
Sacred Heart University, B
Southern Connecticut State University, BM
Trinity College, B
United States Coast Guard Academy, B
University of Connecticut, BMD
University of Hartford, B
University of New Haven, B
Wesleyan University, B
Western Connecticut State University, B
Yale University, BD

Delaware

Delaware State University, B
University of Delaware, BMD
Wesley College, B
Wilmington University, B

District of Columbia

American University, BMO
The Catholic University of America, BMD
The George Washington University, BMD
Georgetown University, BMD
Howard University, BMD
Trinity Washington University, B
University of the District of Columbia, B

Florida

Barry University, B
Bethune-Cookman University, B
Broward College, A
Eckerd College, B
Flagler College, B
Florida Agricultural and Mechanical University, BM
Florida Atlantic University, BM
Florida Gulf Coast University, B
Florida International University, BMD
Florida Memorial University, B
Florida Southern College, B
Florida State University, BMD
Indian River State College, A
Jacksonville University, B
Keiser University, B
Lynn University, B
Miami Dade College, A
New College of Florida, B
Nova Southeastern University, B
Palm Beach Atlantic University, B
Palm Beach State College, A
Rollins College, B
Saint Leo University, B
St. Thomas University, B
South Florida State College, A
Stetson University, B
University of Central Florida, BMD
University of Florida, BMDO
University of Miami, BM
University of North Florida, B
University of South Florida, BMDO
University of South Florida, St. Petersburg, B
The University of Tampa, B
University of West Florida, BM

Georgia

Abraham Baldwin Agricultural College, A
Agnes Scott College, B
Albany State University, B
Armstrong State University, B
Augusta University, BM
Bainbridge State College, A
Berry College, B
Brewton-Parker College, B
Clark Atlanta University, BMD
Clayton State University, B

College of Coastal Georgia, A
Columbus State University, B
Dalton State College, A
Darton State College, A
Emory University, BD
Fort Valley State University, B
Georgia College & State University, B
Georgia Gwinnett College, B
Georgia Highlands College, A
Georgia Military College, A
Georgia Southern University, B
Georgia Southwestern State University, B
Georgia State University, BMD
Gordon State College, A
Kennesaw State University, B
LaGrange College, B
Mercer University, B
Middle Georgia State University, A
Morehouse College, B
Oglethorpe University, B
Piedmont College, B
Reinhardt University, B
Savannah State University, B
South Georgia State College, A
Spelman College, B
Thomas University, B
University of Georgia, BMD
University of North Georgia, B
University of West Georgia, B
Valdosta State University, B
Wesleyan College, B
Young Harris College, B

Hawaii

Brigham Young University - Hawaii, B
Hawai'i Pacific University, B
University of Hawaii at Manoa, BMD
University of Hawaii - West Oahu, B

Idaho

Boise State University, B
Brigham Young University - Idaho, B
The College of Idaho, B
College of Southern Idaho, A
College of Western Idaho, A
Idaho State University, BMD
North Idaho College, A
Northwest Nazarene University, B
University of Idaho, BMD

Illinois

Augustana College, B
Aurora University, B
Benedictine University, B
Blackburn College, B
Bradley University, B
Chicago State University, B
Concordia University Chicago, B
DePaul University, B
Dominican University, B
Eastern Illinois University, BM
Elmhurst College, B
Governors State University, BM
Illinois College, B
Illinois Institute of Technology, B
Illinois State University, BM
Illinois Wesleyan University, B
John A. Logan College, A
Kankakee Community College, A
Knox College, B
Lake Forest College, B
Lewis University, B
Loyola University Chicago, BMD
McKendree University, B
Millikin University, B
Monmouth College, B
Moraine Valley Community College, A
National Louis University, B
North Central College, B
North Park University, B
Northeastern Illinois University, BM
Northern Illinois University, BMD
Northwestern University, BD
Olivet Nazarene University, B
Principia College, B
Quincy University, B

Rockford University, B
Roosevelt University, BM
Saint Xavier University, B
Sauk Valley Community College, A
Southern Illinois University Carbondale, BMD
Southern Illinois University Edwardsville, B
Spoon River College, A
Triton College, A
University of Chicago, BD
University of Illinois at Chicago, BMD
University of Illinois at Springfield, BM
University of Illinois at Urbana - Champaign, BMD
University of St. Francis, B
Western Illinois University, BM
Wheaton College, B

Indiana

Anderson University, B
Ball State University, BM
Bethel College, B
Butler University, B
DePauw University, B
Earlham College, B
Franklin College, B
Grace College, B
Hanover College, B
Holy Cross College, A
Huntington University, B
Indiana State University, B
Indiana University Bloomington, BMD
Indiana University East, B
Indiana University Northwest, B
Indiana University - Purdue University Fort Wayne, B
Indiana University - Purdue University Indianapolis, BMO
Indiana University South Bend, B
Indiana University Southeast, B
Indiana Wesleyan University, B
Manchester University, B
Marian University, B
Purdue University, BMD
Purdue University Northwest (Hammond), B
Saint Joseph's College, B
Saint Mary's College, B
Taylor University, B
University of Evansville, B
University of Indianapolis, B
University of Notre Dame, BD
University of Saint Francis, B
University of Southern Indiana, B
Valparaiso University, B
Vincennes University, A
Wabash College, B

Iowa

Briar Cliff University, B
Buena Vista University, B
Central College, B
Coe College, B
Cornell College, B
Dordt College, B
Drake University, B
Grand View University, B
Grinnell College, B
Iowa Lakes Community College, A
Iowa State University of Science and Technology, BM
Kaplan University, Davenport Campus, M
Loras College, B
Luther College, B
Morningside College, B
Mount Mercy University, B
Northwestern College, B
St. Ambrose University, B
Simpson College, B
The University of Iowa, BD
University of Northern Iowa, B
Wartburg College, B
William Penn University, B

Kansas

Allen Community College, A
Barton County Community College, A
Benedictine College, B
Bethany College, B

Butler Community College, A
Dodge City Community College, A
Emporia State University, B
Fort Hays State University, B
Friends University, B
Kansas State University, BM
Pittsburg State University, B
Seward County Community College and Area Technical School, A
The University of Kansas, BMD
University of Saint Mary, B
Washburn University, B
Wichita State University, B

Kentucky

Asbury University, B
Bellarmine University, B
Berea College, B
Brescia University, B
Campbellsville University, B
Centre College, B
Eastern Kentucky University, BM
Georgetown College, B
Kentucky State University, B
Kentucky Wesleyan College, B
Morehead State University, B
Murray State University, B
Northern Kentucky University, B
Thomas More College, AB
Transylvania University, B
University of the Cumberlands, B
University of Kentucky, BMD
University of Louisville, BM
Western Kentucky University, BM

Louisiana

Centenary College of Louisiana, B
Dillard University, B
Grambling State University, BM
Louisiana State University and Agricultural & Mechanical College, BMD
Louisiana Tech University, B
Loyola University New Orleans, B
McNeese State University, B
Nicholls State University, B
Southeastern Louisiana University, B
Southern University and Agricultural and Mechanical College, BM
Tulane University, BD
University of Louisiana at Lafayette, B
University of Louisiana at Monroe, B
University of New Orleans, BMD
Xavier University of Louisiana, B

Maine

Bates College, B
Bowdoin College, B
Colby College, B
Saint Joseph's College of Maine, B
University of Maine, B
University of Maine at Farmington, B
University of Maine at Presque Isle, B
University of New England, B
University of Southern Maine, B

Maryland

Bowie State University, B
Frederick Community College, A
Frostburg State University, B
Goucher College, B
Harford Community College, A
Hood College, B
Johns Hopkins University, BMDO
Loyola University Maryland, B
McDaniel College, B
Morgan State University, B
Mount St. Mary's University, B
Notre Dame of Maryland University, B
St. Mary's College of Maryland, B
Salisbury University, B
Towson University, B
United States Naval Academy, B
University of Baltimore, B
University of Maryland, Baltimore County, B
University of Maryland, College Park, BD
University of Maryland University College, B

Washington Adventist University, B
Washington College, B

Massachusetts

American International College, B
Amherst College, B
Anna Maria College, B
Assumption College, B
Bard College at Simon's Rock, B
Boston College, BMD
Boston University, BMD
Brandeis University, BMD
Bridgewater State University, B
Cape Cod Community College, A
Clark University, B
College of the Holy Cross, B
Emmanuel College, B
Endicott College, B
Fitchburg State University, B
Framingham State University, B
Gordon College, B
Hampshire College, B
Harvard University, BMD
Hult International Business School, M
Massachusetts College of Liberal Arts, B
Massachusetts Institute of Technology, BMD
Merrimack College, B
Mount Holyoke College, B
Northeastern University, BMD
Northern Essex Community College, A
Pine Manor College, B
Regis College, B
Salem State University, B
Simmons College, B
Smith College, B
Stonehill College, B
Suffolk University, BMO
Tufts University, B
University of Massachusetts Amherst, BMD
University of Massachusetts Boston, B
University of Massachusetts Dartmouth, B
University of Massachusetts Lowell, B
Wellesley College, B
Western New England University, B
Westfield State University, B
Wheaton College, B
Wheelock College, B
Williams College, B

Michigan

Adrian College, B
Albion College, B
Alma College, B
Andrews University, B
Aquinas College, B
Calvin College, B
Central Michigan University, BM
Eastern Michigan University, B
Ferris State University, B
Grand Valley State University, B
Hillsdale College, BMD
Hope College, B
Kalamazoo College, B
Lake Michigan College, A
Lake Superior State University, B
Lansing Community College, A
Marygrove College, B
Michigan State University, BMD
Northern Michigan University, B
Oakland University, B
Saginaw Valley State University, B
Spring Arbor University, B
University of Detroit Mercy, B
University of Michigan, BD
University of Michigan - Dearborn, B
University of Michigan - Flint, BM
Wayne State University, BMD
Western Michigan University, BMD

Minnesota

Augsburg College, B
Bemidji State University, B
Bethel University, B
Carleton College, B
College of Saint Benedict, B
Concordia College, B

Gustavus Adolphus College, B
Hamline University, B
Macalester College, B
Minnesota State University Mankato, B
Minnesota State University Moorhead, B
St. Catherine University, B
St. Cloud State University, B
Saint John's University, B
Saint Mary's University of Minnesota, B
St. Olaf College, B
Southwest Minnesota State University, B
University of Minnesota, Duluth, B
University of Minnesota, Morris, B
University of Minnesota, Twin Cities Campus, BD
University of St. Thomas, B
Vermilion Community College, A
Winona State University, B

Mississippi

Alcorn State University, B
Belhaven University, B
Delta State University, B
Itawamba Community College, A
Jackson State University, BM
Millsaps College, B
Mississippi College, BM
Mississippi Delta Community College, A
Mississippi State University, BMD
Mississippi University for Women, B
Northeast Mississippi Community College, A
Rust College, B
Tougaloo College, B
University of Mississippi, BMD
University of Southern Mississippi, BMD

Missouri

Avila University, B
Calvary Bible College and Theological Seminary, B
Central Methodist University, B
Columbia College, B
Culver-Stockton College, B
Drury University, B
Evangel University, B
Harris-Stowe State University, B
Lincoln University, B
Lindenwood University, B
Missouri Southern State University, B
Missouri State University, BMO
Missouri Valley College, B
Missouri Western State University, B
Northwest Missouri State University, B
Park University, B
Rockhurst University, B
St. Charles Community College, A
Saint Louis University, BM
Southeast Missouri State University, B
Southwest Baptist University, B
Truman State University, B
University of Central Missouri, B
University of Missouri, BMD
University of Missouri - Kansas City, BM
University of Missouri - St. Louis, BMD
Washington University in St. Louis, BMD
Webster University, B
Westminster College, B
William Jewell College, B

Montana

Carroll College, B
Montana State University, B
Rocky Mountain College, B
University of Great Falls, B
University of Montana, M

Nebraska

Creighton University, B
Doane University, B
Hastings College, B
Nebraska Wesleyan University, B
University of Nebraska at Kearney, B
University of Nebraska - Lincoln, BMDO
University of Nebraska at Omaha, BMO
Wayne State College, B
Western Nebraska Community College, A

Nevada

University of Nevada, Las Vegas, BMD
University of Nevada, Reno, BMD

New Hampshire

Dartmouth College, B
Franklin Pierce University, B
Keene State College, B
New England College, B
Plymouth State University, B
Rivier University, B
Saint Anselm College, B
Southern New Hampshire University, B
University of New Hampshire, BMO
University of New Hampshire at Manchester, B

New Jersey

Bergen Community College, A
Bloomfield College, B
Caldwell University, B
Centenary College, B
The College of New Jersey, B
Drew University, B
Fairleigh Dickinson University, College at Florham, B
Fairleigh Dickinson University, Metropolitan Campus, BM
Felician University, B
Kean University, B
Monmouth University, B
Montclair State University, BMO
New Jersey City University, B
Princeton University, BD
Ramapo College of New Jersey, B
Rider University, B
Rowan University, B
Rutgers University - Camden, B
Rutgers University - New Brunswick, BMD
Rutgers University - Newark, BM
Saint Peter's University, B
Salem Community College, A
Seton Hall University, B
Stockton University, B
Thomas Edison State University, B
William Paterson University of New Jersey, B

New Mexico

Central New Mexico Community College, A
Eastern New Mexico University, B
New Mexico Highlands University, BM
New Mexico State University, BM
University of New Mexico, BMD

New York

Adelphi University, B
Alfred University, B
Bard College, B
Barnard College, B
Baruch College of the City University of New York, B
Binghamton University, State University of New York, BMD
Brooklyn College of the City University of New York, BM
Buffalo State College, State University of New York, B
Canisius College, B
City College of the City University of New York, B
Clarkson University, B
Colgate University, B
The College at Brockport, State University of New York, B
The College of New Rochelle, B
The College of Saint Rose, BM
College of Staten Island of the City University of New York, B
Columbia University, BMD
Columbia University, School of General Studies, B
Cornell University, BD
Daemen College, B
Elmira College, B
Eugene Lang College of Liberal Arts, B
Excelsior College, B
Finger Lakes Community College, A
Fordham University, BM

Hamilton College, B
Hartwick College, B
Hilbert College, B
Hobart and William Smith Colleges, B
Hofstra University, B
Houghton College, B
Hunter College of the City University of New York, B
Iona College, B
Ithaca College, B
John Jay College of Criminal Justice of the City University of New York, B
Le Moyne College, B
Lehman College of the City University of New York, B
Long Island University - LIU Brooklyn, B
Long Island University - LIU Post, B
Manhattan College, B
Manhattanville College, B
Marist College, B
Marymount Manhattan College, B
Mercy College, B
Molloy College, B
Monroe Community College, A
Mount Saint Mary College, B
Nazareth College of Rochester, B
New York Institute of Technology, B
New York University, BMD
Niagara University, B
Pace University, B
Pace University, Pleasantville Campus, B
Purchase College, State University of New York, B
Queens College of the City University of New York, B
Rochester Institute of Technology, B
The Sage Colleges, B
St. Bonaventure University, B
St. Francis College, B
St. John Fisher College, B
St. John's University, BMO
St. Joseph's College, Long Island Campus, B
St. Joseph's College, New York, B
St. Lawrence University, B
Sarah Lawrence College, B
Siena College, B
Skidmore College, B
State University of New York College at Cortland, B
State University of New York College at Geneseo, B
State University of New York College at Oneonta, B
State University of New York at Fredonia, B
State University of New York at New Paltz, B
State University of New York at Oswego, B
State University of New York at Plattsburgh, B
Stony Brook University, State University of New York, BMD
Syracuse University, BMDO
Touro College, B
Union College, B
United States Military Academy, B
University at Albany, State University of New York, BMD
University at Buffalo, the State University of New York, BMD
University of Rochester, BD
Utica College, B
Vassar College, B
Wagner College, B
Wells College, B
Yeshiva University, B
York College of the City University of New York, B

North Carolina

Appalachian State University, BM
Barton College, B
Bennett College, B
Campbell University, B
Catawba College, B
Chowan University, B
Davidson College, B
Duke University, BMD
East Carolina University, BMO
Elizabeth City State University, B
Elon University, B
Fayetteville State University, BM
Gardner-Webb University, B
Greensboro College, B
Guilford College, B

High Point University, B
Johnson C. Smith University, B
Lenoir-Rhyne University, B
Livingstone College, B
Louisburg College, A
Mars Hill University, B
Meredith College, B
Methodist University, AB
North Carolina Agricultural and Technical State University, B
North Carolina Central University, B
North Carolina State University, B
North Carolina Wesleyan College, B
Pfeiffer University, B
Queens University of Charlotte, B
Saint Augustine's University, B
Shaw University, B
University of North Carolina at Asheville, B
The University of North Carolina at Chapel Hill, BMD
The University of North Carolina at Charlotte, BM
The University of North Carolina at Greensboro, BMO
The University of North Carolina at Pembroke, B
The University of North Carolina Wilmington, B
Wake Forest University, B
Western Carolina University, B
William Peace University, B
Wingate University, B
Winston-Salem State University, B

North Dakota

Dickinson State University, B
North Dakota State University, B
University of Jamestown, B
University of North Dakota, B

Ohio

Ashland University, BM
Baldwin Wallace University, B
Bowling Green State University, B
Capital University, B
Case Western Reserve University, BMD
Cedarville University, B
Central State University, B
Cleveland State University, B
The College of Wooster, B
Denison University, B
Franciscan University of Steubenville, B
Heidelberg University, B
Hiram College, B
John Carroll University, B
Kent State University, BMD
Kenyon College, B
Lake Erie College, B
Lorain County Community College, A
Malone University, B
Marietta College, B
Miami University, BM
Miami University Hamilton, B
Miami University Middletown, A
Mount Vernon Nazarene University, B
Muskingum University, B
Notre Dame College, B
Oberlin College, B
Ohio Christian University, B
Ohio Dominican University, B
Ohio Northern University, B
The Ohio State University, BD
The Ohio State University - Newark Campus, B
Ohio University, BM
Ohio Wesleyan University, B
Otterbein University, B
The University of Akron, BM
University of Cincinnati, BMD
University of Dayton, B
The University of Findlay, B
University of Mount Union, B
University of Rio Grande, B
The University of Toledo, BM
Ursuline College, B
Walsh University, B
Wilberforce University, B
Wilmington College, B
Wittenberg University, B
Wright State University, B

Xavier University, AB
Youngstown State University, B

Oklahoma

Cameron University, B
East Central University, B
Northeastern State University, B
Northwestern Oklahoma State University, B
Oklahoma Baptist University, B
Oklahoma City Community College, A
Oklahoma City University, B
Oklahoma State University, BMD
Oral Roberts University, B
Rose State College, A
St. Gregory's University, B
Southeastern Oklahoma State University, B
Southwestern Oklahoma State University, B
University of Central Oklahoma, BM
University of Oklahoma, BMD
University of Science and Arts of Oklahoma, B
The University of Tulsa, B

Oregon

George Fox University, B
Lewis & Clark College, B
Linfield College, B
Oregon State University, B
Pacific University, B
Portland State University, BMD
Reed College, B
Southern Oregon University, B
Umpqua Community College, A
University of Oregon, BMD
University of Portland, B
Western Oregon University, B
Willamette University, B

Pennsylvania

Albright College, B
Allegheny College, B
Alvernia University, B
Arcadia University, B
Bloomsburg University of Pennsylvania, B
Bryn Mawr College, B
Bucknell University, B
Cabrini University, B
California University of Pennsylvania, B
Carlow University, B
Cedar Crest College, B
Chatham University, B
Chestnut Hill College, B
Cheyney University of Pennsylvania, B
Clarion University of Pennsylvania, B
DeSales University, B
Dickinson College, B
Drexel University, B
Duquesne University, B
East Stroudsburg University of Pennsylvania, BM
Eastern University, B
Edinboro University of Pennsylvania, B
Elizabethtown College, B
Franklin & Marshall College, B
Gannon University, B
Geneva College, B
Gettysburg College, B
Grove City College, B
Haverford College, B
Holy Family University, B
Immaculata University, AB
Indiana University of Pennsylvania, B
Juniata College, B
King's College, B
Kutztown University of Pennsylvania, B
La Roche College, B
La Salle University, B
Lafayette College, B
Lebanon Valley College, B
Lehigh University, BM
Lincoln University, B
Lock Haven University of Pennsylvania, B
Lycoming College, B
Mansfield University of Pennsylvania, B
Mercyhurst University, B
Messiah College, B
Millersville University of Pennsylvania, B
Moravian College, B

Muhlenberg College, B
Neumann University, B
Penn State Abington, B
Penn State Altoona, B
Penn State Beaver, B
Penn State Berks, B
Penn State Brandywine, B
Penn State DuBois, B
Penn State Erie, The Behrend College, B
Penn State Fayette, The Eberly Campus, B
Penn State Greater Allegheny, B
Penn State Hazleton, B
Penn State Lehigh Valley, B
Penn State Mont Alto, B
Penn State New Kensington, B
Penn State Schuylkill, B
Penn State Shenango, B
Penn State University Park, BMD
Penn State Wilkes-Barre, B
Penn State Worthington Scranton, B
Penn State York, B
Point Park University, B
Rosemont College, B
Saint Francis University, B
Saint Joseph's University, B
Saint Vincent College, B
Seton Hill University, B
Shippensburg University of Pennsylvania, B
Slippery Rock University of Pennsylvania, B
Susquehanna University, B
Swarthmore College, B
Temple University, BMD
Thiel College, B
University of Pennsylvania, BMDO
University of Pittsburgh, BMD
University of Pittsburgh at Bradford, B
University of Pittsburgh at Greensburg, B
University of Pittsburgh at Johnstown, B
The University of Scranton, B
Ursinus College, B
Villanova University, BM
Washington & Jefferson College, B
West Chester University of Pennsylvania, B
Westminster College, B
Widener University, B
Wilkes University, B
York College of Pennsylvania, B

Rhode Island

Brown University, BD
Bryant University, B
Providence College, B
Rhode Island College, B
Roger Williams University, B
Salve Regina University, B
University of Rhode Island, BM

South Carolina

Benedict College, B
Charleston Southern University, B
The Citadel, The Military College of South Carolina, B
Claflin University, B
Clemson University, B
Coastal Carolina University, B
Coker College, B
College of Charleston, B
Columbia College, B
Converse College, BM
Erskine College, B
Francis Marion University, B
Furman University, B
Lander University, B
Morris College, B
Newberry College, B
Presbyterian College, B
South Carolina State University, B
University of South Carolina, BMD
University of South Carolina Aiken, B
University of South Carolina Upstate, B
Winthrop University, B
Wofford College, B

South Dakota

Augustana University, B
Black Hills State University, B

Northern State University, B
South Dakota State University, B
University of Sioux Falls, B
The University of South Dakota, BMD

Tennessee

Austin Peay State University, B
Belmont University, B
Bryan College, B
Carson-Newman University, B
Cumberland University, B
East Tennessee State University, BMO
Fisk University, B
Freed-Hardeman University, B
King University, B
Lee University, B
LeMoyne-Owen College, B
Lipscomb University, B
Martin Methodist College, B
Maryville College, B
Middle Tennessee State University, BM
Milligan College, B
Nashville State Community College, A
Rhodes College, B
Sewanee: The University of the South, B
Tennessee State University, B
Tennessee Technological University, B
Trevecca Nazarene University, B
Union University, B
University of Memphis, BM
The University of Tennessee, BMD
The University of Tennessee at Chattanooga, B
The University of Tennessee at Martin, B
Vanderbilt University, BMD

Texas

Abilene Christian University, B
Angelo State University, B
Austin College, B
Austin Community College District, A
Baylor University, BMD
Dallas Baptist University, B
Del Mar College, A
East Texas Baptist University, B
Hardin-Simmons University, B
Hill College, A
Houston Baptist University, B
Howard Payne University, B
Huston-Tillotson University, B
Lamar University, BM
Lee College, A
McMurry University, B
Midwestern State University, BM
Northeast Texas Community College, A
Odessa College, A
Our Lady of the Lake University of San Antonio, B
Paris Junior College, A
Prairie View A&M University, B
Rice University, BD
St. Edward's University, B
St. Mary's University, BM
St. Philip's College, A
Sam Houston State University, BM
San Jacinto College District, A
Schreiner University, B
Southern Methodist University, B
Southwestern University, B
Stephen F. Austin State University, B
Sul Ross State University, BM
Tarleton State University, BM
Texarkana College, A
Texas A&M International University, BM
Texas A&M University, BMD
Texas A&M University - Central Texas, BM
Texas A&M University - Commerce, B
Texas A&M University - Corpus Christi, B
Texas A&M University - Kingsville, BM
Texas A&M University - San Antonio, B
Texas A&M University - Texarkana, B
Texas Christian University, B
Texas College, B
Texas Lutheran University, B
Texas Southern University, B
Texas State University, BM
Texas Tech University, BMD
Texas Wesleyan University, B

Texas Woman's University, BM
Trinity University, B
Trinity Valley Community College, A
Tyler Junior College, A
University of Dallas, BMD
University of Houston, BMD
University of Houston - Downtown, B
University of the Incarnate Word, B
University of Mary Hardin-Baylor, B
University of North Texas, BM
University of St. Thomas, B
The University of Texas at Arlington, BM
The University of Texas at Austin, BMD
The University of Texas at Dallas, BMD
The University of Texas at El Paso, BM
The University of Texas of the Permian Basin, BM
The University of Texas Rio Grande Valley, B
The University of Texas at San Antonio, BM
The University of Texas at Tyler, BM
West Texas A&M University, B

Utah

Brigham Young University, M
Salt Lake Community College, A
Snow College, A
Southern Utah University, B
University of Utah, BMD
Utah State University, BM
Utah Valley University, B
Weber State University, B
Westminster College, B

Vermont

Bennington College, B
Goddard College, B
Johnson State College, B
Marlboro College, B
Middlebury College, B
Norwich University, B
Saint Michael's College, B
Southern Vermont College, B
University of Vermont, B

Virginia

Averett University, B
Bridgewater College, B
Christendom College, B
Christopher Newport University, B
The College of William and Mary, B
Emory & Henry College, B
Ferrum College, B
George Mason University, BMD
Hampden-Sydney College, B
Hampton University, B
Hollins University, B
James Madison University, BM
Liberty University, ABM
Longwood University, B
Lynchburg College, B
Mary Baldwin College, B
Marymount University, B
Norfolk State University, B
Old Dominion University, B
Patrick Henry College, B
Radford University, B
Randolph College, B
Randolph-Macon College, B
Regent University, M
Roanoke College, B
Shenandoah University, B
Sweet Briar College, B
University of Mary Washington, B
University of Richmond, B
University of Virginia, BMD
The University of Virginia's College at Wise, B
Virginia Commonwealth University, BMDO
Virginia Polytechnic Institute and State University, BM
Virginia State University, B
Virginia Union University, B
Virginia Wesleyan College, B
Washington and Lee University, B

Washington

Central Washington University, B
Eastern Washington University, B

Everett Community College, A
The Evergreen State College, B
Gonzaga University, B
Northwest University, B
Pacific Lutheran University, B
Saint Martin's University, B
Seattle Pacific University, B
Seattle University, B
Skagit Valley College, A
University of Puget Sound, B
University of Washington, BMD
Washington State University, BMDO
Washington State University - Vancouver, B
Western Washington University, BM
Whitman College, B
Whitworth University, B

West Virginia

Alderson Broaddus University, B
American Public University System, BM
Bethany College, B
Concord University, B
Davis & Elkins College, B
Fairmont State University, B
Marshall University, BM
Potomac State College of West Virginia University, A
Shepherd University, B
University of Charleston, B
West Liberty University, B
West Virginia State University, B
West Virginia University, BMD
West Virginia University Institute of Technology, B
West Virginia Wesleyan College, B

Wisconsin

Alverno College, B
Beloit College, B
Cardinal Stritch University, B
Carroll University, B
Carthage College, B
Concordia University Wisconsin, B
Edgewood College, B
Lawrence University, B
Marquette University, BM
Ripon College, B
St. Norbert College, B
University of Wisconsin - Eau Claire, B
University of Wisconsin - Green Bay, B
University of Wisconsin - La Crosse, B
University of Wisconsin - Madison, BD
University of Wisconsin - Milwaukee, BMD
University of Wisconsin - Oshkosh, B
University of Wisconsin - Parkside, B
University of Wisconsin - Platteville, B
University of Wisconsin - River Falls, B
University of Wisconsin - Stevens Point, B
University of Wisconsin - Superior, B
University of Wisconsin - Whitewater, B

Wyoming

Casper College, A
Laramie County Community College, A
Northwest College, A
University of Wyoming, BM
Western Wyoming Community College, A

U.S. Territories: American Samoa

American Samoa Community College, A

U.S. Territories: Guam

University of Guam, B

U.S. Territories: Puerto Rico

Inter American University of Puerto Rico, Fajardo Campus, A
Inter American University of Puerto Rico, San Germán Campus, B
Pontifical Catholic University of Puerto Rico, B
Universidad del Este, B
University of Puerto Rico, Mayagüez Campus, B
University of Puerto Rico, Río Piedras Campus, B

University of Puerto Rico in Utuado, B

Canada

Alberta

Athabasca University, B
Concordia University of Edmonton, B
University of Alberta, BMD
University of Calgary, BMD
University of Lethbridge, BM

British Columbia

Simon Fraser University, BMD
Thompson Rivers University, B
Trinity Western University, B
The University of British Columbia, BMD
The University of British Columbia - Okanagan
   Campus, B
University of the Fraser Valley, B
University of Northern British Columbia, BM
University of Victoria, BMD

Manitoba

Brandon University, B
University of Manitoba, BM
The University of Winnipeg, B

Maritime Provinces: New Brunswick

Mount Allison University, B
St. Thomas University, B
Université de Moncton, B
University of New Brunswick Fredericton, BM
University of New Brunswick Saint John, B

Maritime Provinces: Nova Scotia

Acadia University, BM
Cape Breton University, B
Dalhousie University, BMD
Mount Saint Vincent University, B
St. Francis Xavier University, B
Saint Mary's University, B
University of King's College, B

Maritime Provinces: Prince Edward Island

University of Prince Edward Island, B

Newfoundland and Labrador

Memorial University of Newfoundland, BM

Ontario

Brock University, BM
Carleton University, BMD
Lakehead University, B
Laurentian University, B
McMaster University, BMD
Queen's University at Kingston, BMD
Redeemer University College, B
Ryerson University, B
Trent University, B
University of Guelph, BM
University of Ottawa, BMD
University of Toronto, BMD
University of Waterloo, BMD
The University of Western Ontario, BMD
University of Windsor, BM
Wilfrid Laurier University, BMD
York University, BMD

Quebec

Bishop's University, B
Concordia University, BD
McGill University, BMD
Université Laval, ABMD
Université de Montréal, BMD
Université du Québec à Chicoutimi, B
Université du Québec à Montréal, BMD

Saskatchewan

University of Regina, BM
University of Saskatchewan, BM

POLYMER CHEMISTRY

United States

Kansas

Pittsburg State University, B

New York

State University of New York College of Environmental Science and Forestry, B

Ohio

The University of Akron, B

Wisconsin

University of Wisconsin - Stevens Point, B

POLYMER/PLASTICS ENGINEERING

United States

Alabama

Auburn University, BMD

California

California Polytechnic State University, San Luis
   Obispo, M

Connecticut

University of Connecticut, MD

Illinois

University of Illinois at Urbana - Champaign, B

Kansas

Pittsburg State University, M

Massachusetts

University of Massachusetts Amherst, MD
University of Massachusetts Lowell, BMDO

Michigan

Eastern Michigan University, M
Wayne State University, O

Mississippi

University of Southern Mississippi, BMD

Missouri

University of Missouri - Kansas City, MD

New Jersey

Stevens Institute of Technology, DO

New York

Cornell University, MD

North Carolina

North Carolina State University, D

North Dakota

North Dakota State University, MD

Ohio

Case Western Reserve University, BMD
The University of Akron, BMD

Oregon

Central Oregon Community College, A

Pennsylvania

Carnegie Mellon University, M
Lehigh University, MD
Penn State Erie, The Behrend College, B

Tennessee

The University of Tennessee, MD

Virginia

The College of William and Mary, D

Washington

Western Washington University, B

Wisconsin

University of Wisconsin - Madison, M
University of Wisconsin - Stout, B

POPULATION STUDIES

United States

Massachusetts

Harvard University, MD

New York

Cornell University, MD
New York University, D

Pennsylvania

University of Pennsylvania, MD

Canada

Ontario

University of Guelph, MD

Quebec

Université de Montréal, MD

PORTUGUESE LANGUAGE AND LITERATURE

United States

California

University of California, Los Angeles, BM
University of California, Santa Barbara, BMD

Connecticut

Yale University, BD

District of Columbia

Georgetown University, B

Florida

Broward College, A
Florida International University, B
Miami Dade College, A
University of Florida, B

Georgia

Emory University, DO

Illinois

Northwestern University, D
University of Illinois at Urbana - Champaign, BMD

Indiana

Indiana University Bloomington, BMD

Iowa

The University of Iowa, B

Louisiana

Tulane University, BMD

Maryland

University of Maryland, College Park, MD

Massachusetts

Harvard University, MD
Smith College, B
University of Massachusetts Amherst, BMD
University of Massachusetts Dartmouth, BMD

Michigan

Michigan State University, MD

Minnesota

University of Minnesota, Twin Cities Campus, MD

New Jersey

Princeton University, D
Rutgers University - New Brunswick, B

New Mexico

University of New Mexico, BMD

New York

Brooklyn College of the City University of New York,
B
New York University, MD
United States Military Academy, B

North Carolina

The University of North Carolina at Chapel Hill, MD

Ohio

The Ohio State University, BMD

Rhode Island

Rhode Island College, B

Tennessee

The University of Tennessee, D
Vanderbilt University, MD

Texas

The University of Texas at Austin, BMD

Utah

Brigham Young University, M

Washington

University of Washington, M

Wisconsin

University of Wisconsin - Madison, BMD

Canada

Ontario

University of Toronto, BMD

POULTRY SCIENCE

United States

Alabama

Auburn University, BMD
Tuskegee University, BM
Wallace State Community College, A

Arkansas

University of Arkansas, BMD

California

Modesto Junior College, A

Delaware

Delaware State University, B
Delaware Technical & Community College, Jack F.
Owens Campus, A

Georgia

Abraham Baldwin Agricultural College, A
University of Georgia, BMD

Maryland

University of Maryland Eastern Shore, B

Mississippi

Hinds Community College, A
Mississippi State University, BMD

Northwest Mississippi Community College, A

New York

State University of New York College of Agriculture
and Technology at Cobleskill, A

North Carolina

North Carolina State University, BMD
Sampson Community College, A
Surry Community College, A

Texas

Stephen F. Austin State University, B
Texas A&M University, BMD

Virginia

Virginia Polytechnic Institute and State University,
BMD

Wisconsin

University of Wisconsin - Madison, B

Canada

Ontario

University of Guelph, MD

PRE-DENTISTRY STUDIES

United States

Alabama

Alabama Southern Community College, A
Auburn University, B
Birmingham-Southern College, B

Arkansas

Ouachita Baptist University, B
Williams Baptist College, B

California

California State University, East Bay, B
Chapman University, B
Sonoma State University, B
University of San Francisco, B
Westmont College, B

Connecticut

Albertus Magnus College, B
Quinnipiac University, B
University of Bridgeport, B

District of Columbia

American University, B
The George Washington University, B

Florida

Barry University, B
Florida Southern College, B
Jacksonville University, B
Pensacola State College, A
St. Thomas University, B
Stetson University, B

Georgia

Andrew College, A
College of Coastal Georgia, A
Darton State College, A
Georgia Southern University, B
Oglethorpe University, B
Young Harris College, B

Idaho

Boise State University, B
Northwest Nazarene University, B

Illinois

Bradley University, B
Concordia University Chicago, B
Elmhurst College, B
Illinois College, B

MacMurray College, B
McKendree University, B
Millikin University, B
North Central College, B
North Park University, B
Rockford University, B
University of Illinois at Chicago, B
University of St. Francis, B

Indiana

Anderson University, B
Ball State University, B
Indiana University - Purdue University Fort Wayne,
B
Indiana Wesleyan University, B
Manchester University, B
University of Indianapolis, B
Vincennes University, A

Iowa

Coe College, B
Dordt College, B
Drake University, B
Graceland University, B
Iowa Lakes Community College, A
Iowa State University of Science and Technology, B
Iowa Wesleyan University, B
Mount Mercy University, B
Simpson College, B
The University of Iowa, B
Upper Iowa University, B
William Penn University, B

Kansas

Allen Community College, A
Barton County Community College, A
Central Christian College of Kansas, B
Kansas Wesleyan University, B
Newman University, B
Tabor College, B
Washburn University, B

Kentucky

Campbellsville University, B
Lindsey Wilson College, B

Maine

Saint Joseph's College of Maine, B

Maryland

Morgan State University, B
University of Maryland, College Park, B
University of Maryland Eastern Shore, B
Washington Adventist University, B
Washington College, B

Massachusetts

Boston University, B
Clark University, B
Eastern Nazarene College, B
University of Massachusetts Amherst, B

Michigan

Alma College, B
Calvin College, B
Grand Valley State University, B
Lake Michigan College, A
Lake Superior State University, B
Madonna University, B
Northern Michigan University, B
Saginaw Valley State University, B

Minnesota

College of Saint Benedict, B
Gustavus Adolphus College, B
Hamline University, B
Minnesota State University Mankato, B
St. Catherine University, B
St. Cloud State University, B
Saint John's University, B
Southwest Minnesota State University, B
University of Minnesota, Morris, B

Mississippi

Coahoma Community College, A
East Central Community College, A
Holmes Community College, A
Northeast Mississippi Community College, A

Missouri

Evangel University, B
Lindenwood University, B
Maryville University of Saint Louis, B
Missouri Valley College, B
University of Central Missouri, B
Washington University in St. Louis, B

Nebraska

Concordia University, Nebraska, B
Hastings College, B
Midland University, B
Northeast Community College, A
Peru State College, B
Union College, B
University of Nebraska - Lincoln, B
Western Nebraska Community College, A

New Hampshire

Franklin Pierce University, B
Rivier University, B
Saint Anselm College, B

New Jersey

Rutgers University - New Brunswick, B
Stevens Institute of Technology, B

New York

Buffalo State College, State University of New York, B
City College of the City University of New York, B
College of Mount Saint Vincent, B
Elmira College, B
Fordham University, B
Hobart and William Smith Colleges, B
Hofstra University, B
Houghton College, B
Keuka College, B
Le Moyne College, B
Nazareth College of Rochester, B
Niagara University, B
Roberts Wesleyan College, B
Rochester Institute of Technology, B
State University of New York College at Cortland, B
State University of New York College of Environmental Science and Forestry, B
State University of New York College at Geneseo, B
State University of New York College at Oneonta, B
State University of New York at Oswego, B
Syracuse University, B
Utica College, B
Wagner College, B
Wells College, B

North Carolina

Campbell University, B
Gardner-Webb University, B
Methodist University, B

North Dakota

Dickinson State University, B
Mayville State University, B
Valley City State University, B

Ohio

Ashland University, B
Baldwin Wallace University, B
Bowling Green State University, B
Defiance College, B
Heidelberg University, B
John Carroll University, B
Mount Vernon Nazarene University, B
Muskingum University, B
Ohio Northern University, B
The Ohio State University, B
Ohio Wesleyan University, B
Otterbein University, B
University of Dayton, B

University of Rio Grande, B
Urbana University, B
Walsh University, B
Wilmington College, B
Youngstown State University, B

Oklahoma

Northwestern Oklahoma State University, B

Oregon

Pacific University, B
University of Portland, B

Pennsylvania

Allegheny College, B
Arcadia University, B
Cedar Crest College, B
Gettysburg College, B
King's College, B
Lehigh University, B
Mercyhurst University, B
Saint Francis University, B
Susquehanna University, B
Thiel College, B
University of Pittsburgh at Johnstown, B
Waynesburg University, B
Westminster College, B
Widener University, B

Rhode Island

Rhode Island College, B

South Carolina

Clemson University, B
Furman University, B
Limestone College, B
Wofford College, B

South Dakota

Augustana University, B
Northern State University, B
University of Sioux Falls, B

Tennessee

Cumberland University, B
Hiwassee College, A
Lipscomb University, B
Tennessee Technological University, B
Union University, B
The University of Tennessee at Martin, B

Texas

Abilene Christian University, B
Austin Community College District, A
Clarendon College, A
Hill College, A
Kilgore College, A
Midwestern State University, B
Panola College, A
St. Philip's College, A
Tarleton State University, B
Texas Wesleyan University, B
Trinity University, B
University of Dallas, B
Wiley College, B

Utah

Utah State University, B
Weber State University, B

Vermont

Saint Michael's College, B

Virginia

Hampton University, B
Virginia Wesleyan College, B

Washington

Walla Walla University, B
Whitworth University, B

West Virginia

Bethany College, B
Davis & Elkins College, B

Potomac State College of West Virginia University, A
West Liberty University, B
West Virginia Wesleyan College, B

Wisconsin

Carroll University, B
Carthage College, B
Concordia University Wisconsin, A
Lawrence University, B
Ripon College, B
University of Wisconsin - Oshkosh, B
University of Wisconsin - Parkside, B
Viterbo University, B

Wyoming

Casper College, A
Eastern Wyoming College, A
Western Wyoming Community College, A

Canada

British Columbia

Trinity Western University, B
University of Victoria, B

Manitoba

Brandon University, B
University of Manitoba, B
The University of Winnipeg, B

Maritime Provinces: New Brunswick

Mount Allison University, B
University of New Brunswick Fredericton, B

Maritime Provinces: Nova Scotia

Acadia University, B
Dalhousie University, B
St. Francis Xavier University, B

Maritime Provinces: Prince Edward Island

University of Prince Edward Island, B

Ontario

University of Windsor, B
York University, B

Quebec

Université Laval, B
Université de Montréal, B

Saskatchewan

University of Regina, B

PRE-LAW STUDIES

United States

Alabama

Alabama Southern Community College, A
Auburn University, B
Birmingham-Southern College, B
Talladega College, B

Arizona

Northern Arizona University, B

Arkansas

Ouachita Baptist University, B
Williams Baptist College, B

California

Ashford University, B
Azusa Pacific University, B
Biola University, B
California State University, Dominguez Hills, B
California State University, Fresno, B
Foothill College, A
Fresno Pacific University, B
The Master's College and Seminary, B

National University, B
Notre Dame de Namur University, B
Pacific Union College, B
Sonoma State University, B
University of California, Santa Cruz, B
Vanguard University of Southern California, B
Westmont College, B
Whittier College, B

Colorado

Colorado Christian University, B
Western State Colorado University, B

Connecticut

Albertus Magnus College, B
Quinnipiac University, B
University of Bridgeport, B

District of Columbia

The George Washington University, B

Florida

Barry University, B
College of Central Florida, A
Florida Institute of Technology, B
Florida National University, A
Florida Southern College, B
Jacksonville University, B
Nova Southeastern University, B
Palm Beach Atlantic University, B
Pensacola State College, A
St. Thomas University, B
Stetson University, B
Webber International University, B

Georgia

Andrew College, A
Darton State College, A
Emmanuel College, B
Oglethorpe University, B
Young Harris College, B

Idaho

College of Southern Idaho, A
Northwest Nazarene University, B

Illinois

Aurora University, B
Concordia University Chicago, B
Dominican University, B
Elmhurst College, B
Illinois College, B
John A. Logan College, A
Judson University, B
MacMurray College, B
McKendree University, B
Millikin University, B
North Central College, B
North Park University, B
Rockford University, B
University of Illinois at Urbana - Champaign, B
University of St. Francis, B

Indiana

Anderson University, B
Huntington University, B
Indiana Tech, B
Indiana Wesleyan University, B
Manchester University, B
Trine University, B
University of Indianapolis, B

Iowa

Coe College, B
Dordt College, B
Drake University, B
Grand View University, B
Iowa Lakes Community College, A
Iowa State University of Science and Technology, B
Mount Mercy University, B
Simpson College, B
The University of Iowa, B
William Penn University, B

Kansas

Allen Community College, A
Barton County Community College, A
Central Christian College of Kansas, AB
Fort Hays State University, B
Garden City Community College, A
Kansas Wesleyan University, B
Newman University, B
Seward County Community College and Area Technical School, A
Tabor College, B
Washburn University, B

Kentucky

Campbellsville University, B
Lindsey Wilson College, B
Thomas More College, A

Louisiana

Louisiana College, B
Xavier University of Louisiana, B

Maryland

Anne Arundel Community College, A
Morgan State University, B
University of Baltimore, B
University of Maryland, College Park, B
University of Maryland Eastern Shore, B
Washington Adventist University, B
Washington College, B

Massachusetts

Babson College, B
Becker College, B
Clark University, B
Eastern Nazarene College, B
Massachusetts College of Liberal Arts, B
Smith College, B

Michigan

Adrian College, B
Alma College, B
Andrews University, B
Calvin College, B
Ferris State University, A
Lake Michigan College, A
Lake Superior State University, B
Madonna University, B
Michigan State University, B
Northern Michigan University, B
Saginaw Valley State University, B
Siena Heights University, B

Minnesota

Bemidji State University, B
College of Saint Benedict, B
Crown College, B
Gustavus Adolphus College, B
Hamline University, B
Minnesota State University Mankato, B
St. Catherine University, B
St. Cloud State University, B
Saint John's University, B
Southwest Minnesota State University, B
University of Minnesota, Morris, B

Mississippi

Coahoma Community College, A
East Mississippi Community College, A
Holmes Community College, A
Northeast Mississippi Community College, A

Missouri

Evangel University, B
Fontbonne University, B
Lindenwood University, B
Missouri Valley College, B
Westminster College, B

Montana

University of Montana, B

Nebraska

Concordia University, Nebraska, B
Hastings College, B
Midland University, B
Northeast Community College, A
Peru State College, B
Union College, B
Western Nebraska Community College, A

New Hampshire

Franklin Pierce University, B
New England College, B
Rivier University, B
Saint Anselm College, B

New Jersey

Rutgers University - New Brunswick, B
Stevens Institute of Technology, B

New Mexico

Central New Mexico Community College, A
Navajo Technical University, A
Western New Mexico University, B

New York

Bard College, B
Binghamton University, State University of New York, B
Buffalo State College, State University of New York, B
City College of the City University of New York, B
College of Mount Saint Vincent, B
The College of New Rochelle, B
The College of Saint Rose, B
Concordia College - New York, B
Dominican College, B
Elmira College, B
Fordham University, B
Hartwick College, B
Hobart and William Smith Colleges, B
Hofstra University, B
Houghton College, B
Ithaca College, B
Keuka College, B
Le Moyne College, B
Nazareth College of Rochester, B
Niagara University, B
Rensselaer Polytechnic Institute, B
Roberts Wesleyan College, B
Rochester Institute of Technology, B
Sarah Lawrence College, B
State University of New York College at Cortland, B
State University of New York College of Environmental Science and Forestry, B
State University of New York College at Geneseo, B
State University of New York College at Oneonta, B
State University of New York at Fredonia, B
State University of New York at Oswego, B
Syracuse University, B
Utica College, B
Wagner College, B
Wells College, B

North Carolina

Campbell University, B
Catawba College, B
Chowan University, B
Gardner-Webb University, B
Louisburg College, A
Mars Hill University, B
Methodist University, B
Pfeiffer University, B
William Peace University, B
Wingate University, B

North Dakota

Dickinson State University, B
Mayville State University, B
Valley City State University, B

Ohio

Ashland University, B
Bowling Green State University, B
Cedarville University, B
Defiance College, B

Heidelberg University, B
John Carroll University, B
Mount Vernon Nazarene University, B
Muskingum University, B
Notre Dame College, B
Ohio Northern University, B
Ohio Wesleyan University, B
Otterbein University, B
University of Cincinnati Blue Ash College, A
University of Cincinnati Clermont College, A
The University of Findlay, B
University of Rio Grande, B
Urbana University, B
Wilmington College, B
Youngstown State University, B

Oklahoma

Carl Albert State College, A
Connors State College, A
Northwestern Oklahoma State University, B
Oklahoma Christian University, B
Oklahoma City University, B
Oklahoma Wesleyan University, B

Oregon

Central Oregon Community College, A
Corban University, B
Southern Oregon University, B
University of Portland, B
Warner Pacific College, B

Pennsylvania

Albright College, B
Allegheny College, B
Arcadia University, B
Cedar Crest College, B
DeSales University, B
Gettysburg College, B
Keystone College, B
King's College, B
Mansfield University of Pennsylvania, B
Saint Francis University, B
Seton Hill University, B
Susquehanna University, B
Thiel College, B
University of Pittsburgh at Greensburg, B
University of Pittsburgh at Johnstown, B
Waynesburg University, B
Westminster College, B

Rhode Island

Bryant University, B
Rhode Island College, B

South Carolina

Furman University, B
Limestone College, B
Wofford College, B

South Dakota

Augustana University, B
National American University (Rapid City), B
Northern State University, B
University of Sioux Falls, B

Tennessee

Cumberland University, B
Hiwassee College, A
King University, B
Lincoln Memorial University, B
Lipscomb University, B
Nashville State Community College, A
Tennessee Technological University, B
Union University, B

Texas

Abilene Christian University, B
Angelina College, A
Baylor University, B
Clarendon College, A
Hill College, A
Howard Payne University, B
Kilgore College, A
Midwestern State University, B
Panola College, A

Paris Junior College, A
St. Philip's College, A
Trinity University, B
University of Dallas, B
Virginia College in Austin, A
Wayland Baptist University, AB
West Texas A&M University, B
Western Texas College, A
Wiley College, B

Utah

Utah State University, B
Weber State University, B

Vermont

Bennington College, B
Champlain College, B
Marlboro College, B
Saint Michael's College, B

Virginia

Emory & Henry College, B
Hampton University, B

Washington

Pacific Lutheran University, B
Walla Walla University, B
Whitworth University, B

West Virginia

Bethany College, B
Davis & Elkins College, B
Potomac State College of West Virginia University, A
West Liberty University, B
West Virginia Wesleyan College, B

Wisconsin

Carthage College, B
Concordia University Wisconsin, B
Lawrence University, B
Ripon College, B
University of Wisconsin - Oshkosh, B
University of Wisconsin - Superior, B
Viterbo University, B

Wyoming

Casper College, A
Central Wyoming College, A
Laramie County Community College, A
Western Wyoming Community College, A

U.S. Territories: American Samoa

American Samoa Community College, A

U.S. Territories: Puerto Rico

Pontifical Catholic University of Puerto Rico, B

Canada

British Columbia

University of Victoria, B

Manitoba

Brandon University, B
University of Manitoba, B
The University of Winnipeg, B

Maritime Provinces: New Brunswick

Mount Allison University, B
University of New Brunswick Fredericton, B

Maritime Provinces: Nova Scotia

Acadia University, B
Dalhousie University, B
St. Francis Xavier University, B

Ontario

Carleton University, B
Lakehead University, B
University of Windsor, B
York University, B

Quebec

Université Laval, B
Université de Montréal, B

Saskatchewan

University of Regina, B

PRE-MEDICINE/PRE-MEDICAL STUDIES

United States

Alabama

Alabama Southern Community College, A
Auburn University, B
Birmingham-Southern College, B
Samford University, B

Alaska

Alaska Pacific University, B

Arizona

Arizona State University at the Downtown Phoenix campus, B
Eastern Arizona College, A

Arkansas

Ouachita Baptist University, B
University of Arkansas, B
Williams Baptist College, B

California

Ashford University, B
California State University, East Bay, B
Chapman University, B
Fresno Pacific University, B
The Master's College and Seminary, B
Notre Dame de Namur University, B
Sonoma State University, B
University of California, Santa Cruz, B
University of San Francisco, B
Vanguard University of Southern California, B
Westmont College, B
Whittier College, B

Colorado

Colorado Christian University, B

Connecticut

Albertus Magnus College, B
Quinnipiac University, B
University of Bridgeport, B
University of Hartford, B

District of Columbia

American University, B
The George Washington University, B

Florida

Barry University, B
Broward College, A
College of Central Florida, A
Florida Southern College, B
Jacksonville University, B
Pensacola State College, A
St. Thomas University, B
Southeastern University, B
Stetson University, B

Georgia

Andrew College, A
College of Coastal Georgia, A
Darton State College, A
Georgia Southern University, B
Mercer University, B
Oglethorpe University, B
Young Harris College, B

Hawaii

Hawai'i Pacific University, B

Idaho

Boise State University, B
Northwest Nazarene University, B

Illinois

Augustana College, B
Bradley University, B
City Colleges of Chicago, Malcolm X College, A
Concordia University Chicago, B
Dominican University, B
Elmhurst College, B
Illinois College, B
MacMurray College, B
McKendree University, B
Millikin University, B
North Central College, B
North Park University, B
Northwestern University, B
Rockford University, B
Sauk Valley Community College, A
Trinity International University, B
University of St. Francis, B

Indiana

Anderson University, B
Ball State University, B
Earlham College, B
Holy Cross College, B
Huntington University, B
Indiana University - Purdue University Fort Wayne, B
Indiana University - Purdue University Indianapolis, B
Indiana Wesleyan University, B
Manchester University, B
Trine University, B
University of Indianapolis, B
University of Notre Dame, B
Vincennes University, A

Iowa

Coe College, B
Dordt College, B
Drake University, B
Graceland University, B
Iowa Lakes Community College, A
Iowa State University of Science and Technology, B
Iowa Wesleyan University, B
Mercy College of Health Sciences, B
Mount Mercy University, B
Simpson College, B
The University of Iowa, B
Upper Iowa University, B
William Penn University, B

Kansas

Allen Community College, A
Barton County Community College, A
Central Christian College of Kansas, B
Garden City Community College, A
Kansas Wesleyan University, B
Newman University, B
Seward County Community College and Area Technical School, A
Tabor College, B
Washburn University, B

Kentucky

Campbellsville University, B
Lindsey Wilson College, B

Louisiana

Xavier University of Louisiana, B

Maine

Saint Joseph's College of Maine, B
University of Maine at Machias, B
University of New England, B

Maryland

Howard Community College, A
Morgan State University, B
University of Maryland Eastern Shore, B
Washington Adventist University, B

Washington College, B

Massachusetts

Bard College at Simon's Rock, B
Clark University, B
Eastern Nazarene College, B
Massachusetts College of Liberal Arts, B
MCPHS University, B
Smith College, B
Springfield Technical Community College, A
University of Massachusetts Amherst, B

Michigan

Adrian College, B
Alma College, B
Andrews University, B
Calvin College, B
Concordia University Ann Arbor, B
Grand Valley State University, B
Lake Michigan College, A
Lansing Community College, A
Madonna University, B
Michigan State University, B
Northern Michigan University, B
Saginaw Valley State University, B

Minnesota

Bemidji State University, B
College of Saint Benedict, B
Gustavus Adolphus College, B
Hamline University, B
Minnesota State University Mankato, B
Rochester Community and Technical College, A
St. Catherine University, B
St. Cloud State University, B
Saint John's University, B
Southwest Minnesota State University, B
University of Minnesota, Morris, B

Mississippi

Coahoma Community College, A
East Central Community College, A
East Mississippi Community College, A
Holmes Community College, A
Northeast Mississippi Community College, A

Missouri

Avila University, B
Evangel University, B
Lindenwood University, B
Maryville University of Saint Louis, B
Missouri Valley College, B
University of Central Missouri, B
Washington University in St. Louis, B

Montana

University of Montana, B

Nebraska

Concordia University, Nebraska, B
Hastings College, B
Midland University, B
Northeast Community College, A
Peru State College, B
Union College, B
University of Nebraska - Lincoln, B
Western Nebraska Community College, A

Nevada

Nevada State College, B

New Hampshire

Franklin Pierce University, B
Rivier University, B
Saint Anselm College, B

New Jersey

Rutgers University - New Brunswick, B
Stevens Institute of Technology, B

New Mexico

Mesalands Community College, A
San Juan College, A

New York

Bard College, B
Binghamton University, State University of New York, B
Buffalo State College, State University of New York, B
City College of the City University of New York, B
College of Mount Saint Vincent, B
The College of New Rochelle, B
Elmira College, B
Fordham University, B
Hartwick College, B
Hobart and William Smith Colleges, B
Hofstra University, B
Houghton College, B
Ithaca College, B
Keuka College, B
Le Moyne College, B
Nazareth College of Rochester, B
Niagara University, B
Rensselaer Polytechnic Institute, B
Roberts Wesleyan College, B
Rochester Institute of Technology, B
St. Thomas Aquinas College, B
Sarah Lawrence College, B
State University of New York College at Cortland, B
State University of New York College of Environmental Science and Forestry, B
State University of New York College at Geneseo, B
State University of New York College at Oneonta, B
State University of New York at Fredonia, B
State University of New York at Oswego, B
Syracuse University, B
Utica College, B
Wagner College, B
Wells College, B

North Carolina

Campbell University, B
Catawba College, B
Chowan University, B
Gardner-Webb University, B
Lenoir-Rhyne University, B
Louisburg College, A
Mars Hill University, B
Methodist University, B
North Carolina Wesleyan College, B
Pfeiffer University, B
St. Andrews University, B
Wingate University, B

North Dakota

Dakota College at Bottineau, A
Dickinson State University, B
Mayville State University, B
Valley City State University, B

Ohio

Ashland University, B
Baldwin Wallace University, B
Bluffton University, B
Bowling Green State University, B
Defiance College, B
Heidelberg University, B
John Carroll University, B
Kettering College, B
Miami University, B
Mount Vernon Nazarene University, B
Muskingum University, B
Notre Dame College, B
Ohio Northern University, B
Ohio Wesleyan University, B
Otterbein University, B
The University of Akron, B
University of Dayton, B
The University of Findlay, B
University of Rio Grande, B
Urbana University, B
Walsh University, B
Wilmington College, B
Wright State University, B
Youngstown State University, B

Oklahoma

Eastern Oklahoma State College, A
Northeastern Oklahoma Agricultural and Mechanical
  College, A
Northwestern Oklahoma State University, B
Oklahoma City University, B

Oregon

Central Oregon Community College, A
Concordia University, B
Oregon Institute of Technology, B
Pacific University, B
Southern Oregon University, B
University of Portland, B
Warner Pacific College, B

Pennsylvania

Allegheny College, B
Arcadia University, B
Cedar Crest College, B
Gettysburg College, B
Immaculata University, B
Keystone College, B
King's College, B
La Salle University, B
Lehigh University, B
Penn State Abington, B
Penn State Altoona, B
Penn State Beaver, B
Penn State Berks, B
Penn State Brandywine, B
Penn State DuBois, B
Penn State Erie, The Behrend College, B
Penn State Fayette, The Eberly Campus, B
Penn State Greater Allegheny, B
Penn State Hazleton, B
Penn State Lehigh Valley, B
Penn State Mont Alto, B
Penn State New Kensington, B
Penn State Schuylkill, B
Penn State Shenango, B
Penn State University Park, B
Penn State Wilkes-Barre, B
Penn State Worthington Scranton, B
Penn State York, B
Philadelphia University, B
Saint Francis University, B
Slippery Rock University of Pennsylvania, B
Susquehanna University, B
Thiel College, B
University of Pittsburgh at Johnstown, B
Waynesburg University, B
West Chester University of Pennsylvania, B
Westminster College, B
Widener University, B

Rhode Island

Bryant University, B
Rhode Island College, B

South Carolina

Bob Jones University, B
Clemson University, B
Furman University, B
Limestone College, B
Southern Wesleyan University, B
Wofford College, B

South Dakota

Augustana University, B
Northern State University, B
University of Sioux Falls, B

Tennessee

Cumberland University, B
Hiwassee College, A
King University, B
Lincoln Memorial University, B
Lipscomb University, B
Nashville State Community College, A
Tennessee Technological University, B
Union University, B
The University of Tennessee at Martin, B

Texas

Abilene Christian University, B
Angelina College, A
Austin Community College District, A
Clarendon College, A
Hill College, A
Kilgore College, A
Midwestern State University, B
Paris Junior College, A
St. Philip's College, A
Tarleton State University, B
Texas Lutheran University, B
Trinity University, B
University of Dallas, B
Western Texas College, A
Wiley College, B

Utah

Utah State University, B
Weber State University, B

Vermont

Bennington College, B
Johnson State College, B
Marlboro College, B
Saint Michael's College, B

Virginia

Averett University, B
Hampton University, B
Virginia Wesleyan College, B

Washington

Pacific Lutheran University, B
Walla Walla University, B
Washington State University, B
Whitworth University, B

West Virginia

Bethany College, B
Concord University, B
Davis & Elkins College, B
Potomac State College of West Virginia University,
  A
West Liberty University, B
West Virginia Wesleyan College, B

Wisconsin

Carroll University, B
Carthage College, B
Concordia University Wisconsin, A
Lawrence University, B
Ripon College, B
University of Wisconsin - Milwaukee, B
University of Wisconsin - Oshkosh, B
University of Wisconsin - Parkside, B
Viterbo University, B

Wyoming

Casper College, A
Eastern Wyoming College, A
Western Wyoming Community College, A

U.S. Territories: Puerto Rico

Caribbean University, B
Pontifical Catholic University of Puerto Rico, B
University of Puerto Rico, Mayagüez Campus, B

Canada

British Columbia

Trinity Western University, B
University of Victoria, B

Manitoba

Brandon University, B
University of Manitoba, B
The University of Winnipeg, B

Maritime Provinces: New Brunswick

Mount Allison University, B
University of New Brunswick Fredericton, B

Maritime Provinces: Nova Scotia

Acadia University, B
Dalhousie University, B
St. Francis Xavier University, B

Maritime Provinces: Prince Edward Island

University of Prince Edward Island, B

Newfoundland and Labrador

Memorial University of Newfoundland, B

Ontario

University of Windsor, B
York University, B

Quebec

Université Laval, B
Université de Montréal, B
Université de Sherbrooke, B

Saskatchewan

University of Regina, B

PRE-NURSING STUDIES

United States

Arizona

Arizona State University at the Downtown Phoenix
  campus, B
Arizona Western College, A

Arkansas

Ouachita Baptist University, B

California

Biola University, B
California State University, Fullerton, B
National University, AB

Delaware

Delaware State University, B

Florida

Jacksonville University, B
Pensacola State College, A
St. Thomas University, B

Georgia

Andrew College, A
Berry College, B
Georgia Military College, A
Reinhardt University, A

Idaho

The College of Idaho, B

Illinois

Lincoln Christian University, A
Lincoln College, A
Trinity International University, B

Iowa

Iowa Lakes Community College, A
Simpson College, B
The University of Iowa, B

Kansas

Garden City Community College, A
Tabor College, B

Kentucky

Eastern Kentucky University, B

Massachusetts

Eastern Nazarene College, B

Michigan

Bay de Noc Community College, A
Madonna University, B
Southwestern Michigan College, A
University of Michigan - Flint, B

Minnesota

University of Northwestern - St. Paul, B

Mississippi

East Central Community College, A
Holmes Community College, A

Missouri

Lindenwood University, B
Missouri Baptist University, B
Missouri Valley College, B

Montana

Blackfeet Community College, A

Nebraska

Concordia University, Nebraska, B
Peru State College, B

New Mexico

Eastern New Mexico University, A

New York

Houghton College, B
State University of New York College at Geneseo, B

North Carolina

Mars Hill University, B

North Dakota

Cankdeska Cikana Community College, A
Dakota College at Bottineau, A

Ohio

Cedarville University, B
Cleveland State University, B
Edison Community College, A
Wright State University, B

Oklahoma

Northeastern Oklahoma Agricultural and Mechanical
    College, A
Oklahoma City University, B
Oklahoma State University, Oklahoma City, A
Tulsa Community College, A

Pennsylvania

Allegheny College, B
Gettysburg College, B
Harcum College, A
Keystone College, A
La Salle University, B

South Carolina

Limestone College, B

Tennessee

Hiwassee College, A
Lipscomb University, B
Nashville State Community College, A
Tennessee Wesleyan College, B

Texas

Baylor University, B
Hardin-Simmons University, B
Hill College, A
McMurry University, B
Paris Junior College, A
St. Philip's College, A
Tyler Junior College, A

Utah

Brigham Young University, B

Virginia

Averett University, B

Washington

Central Washington University, B
Seattle University, B

West Virginia

Potomac State College of West Virginia University,
    A

Wisconsin

College of Menominee Nation, A
Concordia University Wisconsin, A

Wyoming

Western Wyoming Community College, A

Canada

Manitoba

The University of Winnipeg, B

PRE-PHARMACY STUDIES

United States

Alabama

Alabama Southern Community College, A
Auburn University, B

Arizona

Eastern Arizona College, A

Arkansas

Ouachita Baptist University, B

California

Westmont College, B

Florida

Barry University, B
College of Central Florida, A
Pensacola State College, A
State College of Florida Manatee-Sarasota, A

Georgia

Andrew College, A
College of Coastal Georgia, A
Dalton State College, A
Darton State College, A
Emmanuel College, B
Georgia Highlands College, A
Georgia Southern University, B
Gordon State College, A
Young Harris College, B

Idaho

College of Southern Idaho, A
Northwest Nazarene University, B

Illinois

Benedictine University, B
City Colleges of Chicago, Malcolm X College, A
Dominican University, B
Elmhurst College, B
John A. Logan College, A
Millikin University, B
University of St. Francis, B

Indiana

Butler University, B
Huntington University, B
Indiana University - Purdue University Indianapolis,
    B
Manchester University, B
Vincennes University, A

Iowa

Dordt College, B
Iowa Lakes Community College, A
Simpson College, B
The University of Iowa, B

Kansas

Allen Community College, A
Central Christian College of Kansas, B
Dodge City Community College, A
Garden City Community College, A
Seward County Community College and Area Tech-
    nical School, A
Tabor College, B
Washburn University, B

Kentucky

Lindsey Wilson College, B

Maine

Husson University, B
Saint Joseph's College of Maine, B
University of New England, B

Maryland

Howard Community College, A

Massachusetts

Anna Maria College, B
Eastern Nazarene College, B
Quinsigamond Community College, A

Michigan

Calvin College, B
Ferris State University, A
Henry Ford College, A
Lake Michigan College, A
Madonna University, A
Northern Michigan University, B
Schoolcraft College, A

Minnesota

College of Saint Benedict, B
Hamline University, B
St. Cloud State University, B
Saint John's University, B
University of Minnesota, Morris, B

Mississippi

Coahoma Community College, A
East Central Community College, A
Holmes Community College, A
Northeast Mississippi Community College, A

Missouri

Missouri Valley College, B
St. Charles Community College, A
University of Central Missouri, B
Washington University in St. Louis, B

Montana

University of Montana, B

Nebraska

Concordia University, Nebraska, B
Northeast Community College, A
Peru State College, B
University of Nebraska - Lincoln, B
Western Nebraska Community College, A

New York

Houghton College, B
Le Moyne College, B
Monroe Community College, A
Roberts Wesleyan College, B

North Carolina

Campbell University, B
Gardner-Webb University, B
Louisburg College, A
Wingate University, B

North Dakota

Mayville State University, B
Valley City State University, B

Ohio

Ashland University, B
Baldwin Wallace University, B

Mount Vernon Nazarene University, B
Muskingum University, B
University of Cincinnati Blue Ash College, A
University of Cincinnati Clermont College, A
Walsh University, B
Youngstown State University, B

Oklahoma

Rose State College, A
Tulsa Community College, A
University of Central Oklahoma, B

Oregon

Central Oregon Community College, A

Pennsylvania

Allegheny College, B
Edinboro University of Pennsylvania, A
Gettysburg College, B
Keystone College, A
King's College, B
Luzerne County Community College, A
Slippery Rock University of Pennsylvania, B

South Carolina

Clemson University, B
Limestone College, B

South Dakota

Augustana University, B

Tennessee

Bethel University, B
Cumberland University, B
Hiwassee College, A
King University, B
Lipscomb University, B
Union University, B
The University of Tennessee at Martin, B

Texas

Amarillo College, A
Angelina College, A
Austin Community College District, A
Hill College, A
Kilgore College, A
Midwestern State University, B
Panola College, A
Paris Junior College, A
St. Philip's College, A
Tarleton State University, B

Utah

Weber State University, B

Vermont

Saint Michael's College, B

Virginia

Emory & Henry College, B

West Virginia

Potomac State College of West Virginia University,
   A
University of Charleston, B
West Virginia Wesleyan College, B

Wisconsin

Carroll University, B
University of Wisconsin - Parkside, B
Viterbo University, B

Wyoming

Casper College, A
Eastern Wyoming College, A
Laramie County Community College, A
Northwest College, A
Western Wyoming Community College, A

Canada

British Columbia

Trinity Western University, B

Manitoba

The University of Winnipeg, B

Maritime Provinces: New Brunswick

Mount Allison University, B

Maritime Provinces: Nova Scotia

Dalhousie University, B

Ontario

University of Windsor, B
York University, B

Quebec

Université Laval, B
Université de Montréal, B

Saskatchewan

University of Regina, B

PRE-THEOLOGY/PRE-MINISTE-RIAL STUDIES

United States

Arkansas

John Brown University, B

California

Point Loma Nazarene University, B
Westmont College, B

Colorado

Nazarene Bible College, A

Florida

Ave Maria University, B
Southeastern University, B
Trinity College of Florida, B

Georgia

Andrew College, A
Point University, B
Shorter University, B

Illinois

Concordia University Chicago, B
Trinity International University, B

Indiana

Manchester University, B
University of Indianapolis, B

Iowa

Emmaus Bible College, B
Simpson College, B

Kansas

Central Christian College of Kansas, B
Tabor College, B
Washburn University, B

Massachusetts

Eastern Nazarene College, B

Michigan

Adrian College, B
Alma College, B
Calvin College, B
Concordia University Ann Arbor, B
Kuyper College, B

Minnesota

College of Saint Benedict, B
Crossroads College, B
Martin Luther College, B
Saint John's University, B
University of Northwestern - St. Paul, B

Nebraska

Concordia University, Nebraska, B
Doane University, B
Grace University, B

New York

Concordia College - New York, B
Nyack College, B

North Carolina

Mid-Atlantic Christian University, B

Ohio

Ashland University, B
Ohio Northern University, B
Ohio Wesleyan University, B
University of Rio Grande, B

Oklahoma

Oral Roberts University, B

Oregon

Concordia University, B
Corban University, B

Pennsylvania

Geneva College, B
Summit University, B
Waynesburg University, B

South Carolina

Columbia International University, B

South Dakota

Augustana University, B

Tennessee

Hiwassee College, A
King University, B
Lee University, B
Tennessee Wesleyan College, B
Williamson College, B

Texas

University of Dallas, B

Virginia

Eastern Mennonite University, A

West Virginia

Alderson Broaddus University, B
Bethany College, B

U.S. Territories: Puerto Rico

Theological University of the Caribbean, A

Canada

Alberta

Concordia University of Edmonton, B

British Columbia

Columbia Bible College, B

Maritime Provinces: New Brunswick

Mount Allison University, B

PRE-VETERINARY STUDIES

United States

Alabama

Alabama Southern Community College, A
Auburn University, B

Arizona

The University of Arizona, B

Arkansas

Ouachita Baptist University, B

California

California State University, East Bay, B
Chapman University, B
Sonoma State University, B
University of San Francisco, B
Westmont College, B

Connecticut

Albertus Magnus College, B
Quinnipiac University, B
University of Bridgeport, B

Delaware

Delaware State University, B
University of Delaware, B

District of Columbia

American University, B

Florida

Barry University, B
Broward College, A
College of Central Florida, A
Florida Southern College, B
Jacksonville University, B
Pensacola State College, A
Stetson University, B

Georgia

Andrew College, A
College of Coastal Georgia, A
Darton State College, A
Georgia Southern University, B
Oglethorpe University, B
Young Harris College, B

Idaho

Boise State University, B
Northwest Nazarene University, B

Illinois

Bradley University, B
Elmhurst College, B
Illinois College, B
MacMurray College, B
McKendree University, B
Millikin University, B
North Central College, B
North Park University, B
Rockford University, B
University of Illinois at Chicago, B
University of Illinois at Urbana - Champaign, B
University of St. Francis, B

Indiana

Anderson University, B
Indiana University - Purdue University Fort Wayne,
    B
Indiana University - Purdue University Indianapolis,
    B
Indiana Wesleyan University, B
Manchester University, B
Purdue University Northwest (Hammond), B
University of Indianapolis, B
Vincennes University, A

Iowa

Coe College, B
Dordt College, B
Drake University, B
Iowa Lakes Community College, A
Iowa State University of Science and Technology, B
Iowa Wesleyan University, B
Mount Mercy University, B
Simpson College, B
The University of Iowa, B
Upper Iowa University, B

Kansas

Allen Community College, A
Barton County Community College, A

Central Christian College of Kansas, B
Garden City Community College, A
Kansas Wesleyan University, B
Newman University, B
Seward County Community College and Area Tech-
    nical School, A
Tabor College, B
Washburn University, B

Kentucky

Campbellsville University, B
Lindsey Wilson College, B

Maine

College of the Atlantic, B
Saint Joseph's College of Maine, B

Maryland

University of Maryland, College Park, B
Washington Adventist University, B
Washington College, B

Massachusetts

Becker College, B
Clark University, B
Eastern Nazarene College, B
University of Massachusetts Amherst, B

Michigan

Adrian College, B
Alma College, B
Andrews University, B
Calvin College, B
Grand Valley State University, B
Lake Michigan College, A
Madonna University, B
Michigan State University, B
Northern Michigan University, B

Minnesota

Bemidji State University, B
College of Saint Benedict, B
Gustavus Adolphus College, B
Hamline University, B
Minnesota State University Mankato, B
St. Catherine University, B
St. Cloud State University, B
Saint John's University, B
Southwest Minnesota State University, B
University of Minnesota, Crookston, B
University of Minnesota, Morris, B

Mississippi

East Central Community College, A
East Mississippi Community College, A
Holmes Community College, A
Northeast Mississippi Community College, A

Missouri

Evangel University, B
Lindenwood University, B
Maryville University of Saint Louis, B
Missouri Valley College, B
Northwest Missouri State University, B
University of Central Missouri, B
Washington University in St. Louis, B

Montana

Montana State University, B

Nebraska

Concordia University, Nebraska, B
Hastings College, B
Midland University, B
Northeast Community College, A
Peru State College, B
University of Nebraska - Lincoln, B
Western Nebraska Community College, A

Nevada

College of Southern Nevada, A
University of Nevada, Reno, B

New Hampshire

Franklin Pierce University, B
Rivier University, B

New Mexico

Western New Mexico University, B

New York

Binghamton University, State University of New
    York, B
Buffalo State College, State University of New York,
    B
City College of the City University of New York, B
Concordia College - New York, B
Elmira College, B
Fordham University, B
Hartwick College, B
Hobart and William Smith Colleges, B
Hofstra University, B
Houghton College, B
Keuka College, B
Le Moyne College, B
Mercy College, B
Nazareth College of Rochester, B
Niagara University, B
Roberts Wesleyan College, B
Rochester Institute of Technology, B
State University of New York College of Environ-
    mental Science and Forestry, B
State University of New York College at Geneseo, B
State University of New York College at Oneonta, B
State University of New York College of Technology
    at Canton, B
State University of New York at Fredonia, B
State University of New York at Oswego, B
Syracuse University, B
Utica College, B
Wells College, B

North Carolina

Campbell University, B
Gardner-Webb University, B
Louisburg College, A
Mars Hill University, B
Methodist University, B
St. Andrews University, B
Wingate University, B

North Dakota

Dakota College at Bottineau, A
Dickinson State University, B
Mayville State University, B
Valley City State University, B

Ohio

Ashland University, B
Baldwin Wallace University, B
Defiance College, B
Heidelberg University, B
John Carroll University, B
Mount Vernon Nazarene University, B
Muskingum University, B
Ohio Northern University, B
Ohio Wesleyan University, B
Otterbein University, B
The University of Findlay, B
University of Rio Grande, B
Urbana University, B
Walsh University, B
Wilmington College, B
Youngstown State University, B

Oklahoma

Northeastern Oklahoma Agricultural and Mechanical
    College, A

Oregon

Pacific University, B
Warner Pacific College, B

Pennsylvania

Allegheny College, B
Arcadia University, B
Cedar Crest College, B

Gettysburg College, B
King's College, B
Mercyhurst University, B
Penn State University Park, B
Saint Francis University, B
Susquehanna University, B
Thiel College, B
University of Pittsburgh at Johnstown, B
Waynesburg University, B
Westminster College, B
Widener University, B

Rhode Island

Rhode Island College, B

South Carolina

Clemson University, B
Furman University, B
Limestone College, B
Wofford College, B

South Dakota

Augustana University, B
University of Sioux Falls, B

Tennessee

Cumberland University, B
Hiwassee College, A
King University, B
Lincoln Memorial University, B
Lipscomb University, B
Tennessee Technological University, B
The University of Tennessee at Martin, B

Texas

Abilene Christian University, B
Angelina College, A
Austin Community College District, A
Hill College, A
Kilgore College, A
Lubbock Christian University, B
Midwestern State University, B
Panola College, A
Tarleton State University, B
Trinity University, B

Utah

Utah State University, B
Weber State University, B

Vermont

Marlboro College, B
Saint Michael's College, B

Virginia

Emory & Henry College, B
Hampton University, B
Virginia Wesleyan College, B

Washington

Walla Walla University, B
Whitworth University, B

West Virginia

Bethany College, B
Concord University, B
Davis & Elkins College, B
Potomac State College of West Virginia University, A
West Virginia Wesleyan College, B

Wisconsin

Carroll University, B
Carthage College, B
Lawrence University, B
Ripon College, B
University of Wisconsin - Oshkosh, B
University of Wisconsin - Parkside, B
Viterbo University, B

Wyoming

Casper College, A
Eastern Wyoming College, A

Western Wyoming Community College, A

Canada

Alberta

University of Alberta, B

British Columbia

Trinity Western University, B
The University of British Columbia, B
University of Victoria, B

Manitoba

Brandon University, B
University of Manitoba, B
The University of Winnipeg, B

Maritime Provinces: New Brunswick

Mount Allison University, B
University of New Brunswick Fredericton, B

Maritime Provinces: Nova Scotia

Acadia University, B
Dalhousie University, B
St. Francis Xavier University, B

Maritime Provinces: Prince Edward Island

University of Prince Edward Island, B

Ontario

York University, B

Quebec

Université de Montréal, B

Saskatchewan

University of Regina, B

PRECISION METAL WORKING

United States

Alabama

Shelton State Community College, A

California

Reedley College, A

Michigan

Delta College, A
Oakland Community College, A

Montana

Montana Tech of The University of Montana, A

Ohio

Northwest State Community College, A

South Dakota

Western Dakota Technical Institute, A

PRECISION PRODUCTION

United States

Kansas

Wichita Area Technical College, A

Michigan

Delta College, A
Lake Michigan College, A
Mott Community College, A
Washtenaw Community College, A

Missouri

East Central College, A
Jefferson College, A

Mineral Area College, A
St. Charles Community College, A

New Jersey

Salem Community College, A

North Carolina

Haywood Community College, A
Western Piedmont Community College, A

South Carolina

Midlands Technical College, A

Wisconsin

Western Technical College, A

Wyoming

Sheridan College, A

PRECISION PRODUCTION TRADES

United States

Illinois

College of DuPage, A

Kentucky

Owensboro Community and Technical College, A

Missouri

Mineral Area College, A

Pennsylvania

Butler County Community College, A
Johnson College, A

South Carolina

Midlands Technical College, A

PRECISION SYSTEMS MAINTENANCE AND REPAIR TECHNOLOGIES

Canada

British Columbia

British Columbia Institute of Technology, A

PREPRESS/DESKTOP PUBLISHING AND DIGITAL IMAGING DESIGN

United States

Arizona

Coconino Community College, A

California

Antelope Valley College, A
Cabrillo College, A
California Baptist University, B
College of San Mateo, A
Gavilan College, A
Long Beach City College, A
Palomar College, A
Pasadena City College, A
Platt College San Diego, A

Delaware

Wilmington University, B

Hawaii

Leeward Community College, A

Illinois

College of DuPage, A
Kankakee Community College, A
Lake Land College, A
Northwestern College - Bridgeview Campus, A
Southwestern Illinois College, A

Iowa

Des Moines Area Community College, A
Hawkeye Community College, A
Iowa Lakes Community College, A
North Iowa Area Community College, A
Northeast Iowa Community College, A
Western Iowa Tech Community College, A

Kansas

Kansas City Kansas Community College, A
Northwest Kansas Technical College, A

Kentucky

Sullivan College of Technology and Design, AB

Louisiana

South Louisiana Community College, A

Minnesota

Dunwoody College of Technology, A
Hennepin Technical College, A
Ridgewater College, A
Saint Mary's University of Minnesota, B

New Jersey

Camden County College, A

New York

Rochester Institute of Technology, B

North Carolina

Chowan University, B

Ohio

Art Academy of Cincinnati, B
Cincinnati State Technical and Community College,
   A
Terra State Community College, A

Oregon

Umpqua Community College, A

Pennsylvania

La Salle University, B

Rhode Island

New England Institute of Technology, AB

South Dakota

Southeast Technical Institute, A

Tennessee

O'More College of Design, B

Texas

Alvin Community College, A
Houston Community College, A
Howard College, A
Lee College, A

Washington

Clover Park Technical College, A
Edmonds Community College, A

Wisconsin

Northeast Wisconsin Technical College, A

Wyoming

Northwest College, A

U.S. Territories: Puerto Rico

EDP University of Puerto Rico, B

PRINTING MANAGEMENT

United States

Kansas

Pittsburg State University, B

Kentucky

Eastern Kentucky University, B

Michigan

Ferris State University, B

Minnesota

University of Minnesota, Duluth, B

Missouri

College of the Ozarks, B

New York

Rochester Institute of Technology, B

Wisconsin

Carroll University, B

PRINTING PRESS OPERATOR

United States

Illinois

Lake Land College, A

Minnesota

Dunwoody College of Technology, A

West Virginia

BridgeValley Community and Technical College
   (Montgomery), A

PRINTMAKING

United States

Alabama

Birmingham-Southern College, B
The University of Alabama, M

Alaska

University of Alaska Fairbanks, M

Arizona

Arizona State University at the Tempe campus, M

California

Academy of Art University, M
California College of the Arts, BM
California State University, East Bay, B
California State University, Long Beach, B
De Anza College, A
Laguna College of Art & Design, B
San Diego State University, M
San Francisco Art Institute, B
Sonoma State University, B
University of San Francisco, B

Colorado

Adams State University, B
University of Colorado Boulder, M
Western State Colorado University, B

Connecticut

University of Hartford, B
Yale University, M

Florida

University of Miami, BM

Georgia

Georgia State University, M
Savannah College of Art and Design, BM

Idaho

Northwest Nazarene University, B

Illinois

Bradley University, BM
Illinois State University, M
School of the Art Institute of Chicago, BM

Indiana

Indiana State University, M
Indiana University - Purdue University Fort Wayne,
   B
Indiana University - Purdue University Indianapolis,
   M
Indiana Wesleyan University, B
University of Notre Dame, M

Iowa

Drake University, B
The University of Iowa, B

Kansas

The University of Kansas, BM
Wichita State University, M

Louisiana

Louisiana State University and Agricultural & Mechanical College, M

Maine

Maine College of Art, B

Maryland

Maryland Institute College of Art, B

Massachusetts

Massachusetts College of Art and Design, B
Montserrat College of Art, B
Salem State University, B
School of the Museum of Fine Arts, Boston, B
University of Massachusetts Dartmouth, O

Michigan

Aquinas College, B
Northern Michigan University, B
University of Michigan, B
Wayne State University, M

Minnesota

Minneapolis College of Art and Design, B

Missouri

Columbia College, B
Kansas City Art Institute, B
Washington University in St. Louis, B

New Jersey

Rutgers University - New Brunswick, B

New Mexico

Santa Fe Community College, A

New York

Brooklyn College of the City University of New York,
   M
Buffalo State College, State University of New York,
   B
City College of the City University of New York, M
Columbia University, M
Pratt Institute, BM
Purchase College, State University of New York, B
Rochester Institute of Technology, O
Sarah Lawrence College, B
School of Visual Arts, B
State University of New York at New Paltz, BM
Syracuse University, BM

North Carolina

East Carolina University, M

Ohio

Art Academy of Cincinnati, B
Bowling Green State University, B
Cleveland Institute of Art, B
Ohio Northern University, B
Ohio University, BM
Youngstown State University, B

Oklahoma

University of Oklahoma, M

Oregon

Pacific Northwest College of Art, B
Portland State University, M
University of Oregon, B

Pennsylvania

Edinboro University of Pennsylvania, M
Marywood University, M
Pennsylvania Academy of the Fine Arts, MO
Seton Hill University, B
Temple University, BM
The University of the Arts, BM

Rhode Island

Rhode Island College, B
Rhode Island School of Design, BM

South Dakota

The University of South Dakota, M

Tennessee

University of Memphis, M
The University of Tennessee, M

Texas

Southern Methodist University, M
Texas Christian University, B
University of Dallas, B
The University of Texas at El Paso, B

Utah

Brigham Young University, B
University of Utah, M

Vermont

Bennington College, B
Johnson State College, M

Virginia

George Mason University, M
Virginia Commonwealth University, M

Washington

Western Washington University, B

West Virginia

West Virginia University, M

Wisconsin

Milwaukee Institute of Art and Design, B

U.S. Territories: Puerto Rico

Escuela de Artes Plasticas y Diseño de Puerto
  Rico, B
Inter American University of Puerto Rico, San
  Germán Campus, BM

Canada

Alberta

Alberta College of Art & Design, B
University of Alberta, BM

British Columbia

Emily Carr University of Art + Design, B

Maritime Provinces: New Brunswick

Mount Allison University, B

Maritime Provinces: Nova Scotia

NSCAD University, B

Newfoundland and Labrador

Memorial University of Newfoundland, B

Ontario

University of Windsor, B
York University, B

Quebec

Concordia University, B

Saskatchewan

University of Regina, B

PROJECT MANAGEMENT

United States

Alabama

The University of Alabama in Huntsville, M
University of North Alabama, M

Alaska

University of Alaska Anchorage, M

Arizona

University of Phoenix - Online Campus, MO
University of Phoenix - Phoenix Campus, M

California

California Intercontinental University, M
National University, MO
Trident University International, M
University of California, Berkeley, O
University of Phoenix - Bay Area Campus, M
University of Phoenix - Southern California Campus,
  M

Colorado

Aspen University, MO
Colorado Christian University, M
Colorado State University - Global Campus, M
Colorado Technical University Colorado Springs, M
Colorado Technical University Denver South, M
Regis University, O
University of Denver, MO

Connecticut

Post University, M

District of Columbia

American University, O
The George Washington University, MO

Florida

Embry-Riddle Aeronautical University - Worldwide,
  M
Florida Institute of Technology, M
Polytechnic University of Puerto Rico, Miami Cam-
  pus, M
Saint Leo University, M

Georgia

Brenau University, M

Illinois

American InterContinental University Online, M
DeVry University (Downers Grove), M
Ellis University, M
Lewis University, M
Northwestern University, MD
Saint Xavier University, MO
Southern Illinois University Edwardsville, M

Iowa

Kaplan University, Davenport Campus, M

Kansas

Grantham University, M
The University of Kansas, M

Massachusetts

Boston University, MO
Brandeis University, M
Lasell College, MO
Northeastern University, M

Michigan

Ferris State University, M
University of Michigan - Dearborn, M

Minnesota

Capella University, MD
Metropolitan State University, O
Saint Mary's University of Minnesota, MO
Walden University, MDO

Mississippi

Mississippi State University, M

Missouri

American Business & Technology University, M
Avila University, M
Maryville University of Saint Louis, MO

Montana

Montana Tech of The University of Montana, M

Nebraska

Bellevue University, M
University of Nebraska at Omaha, O

New Hampshire

Granite State College, M
New England College, M
Southern New Hampshire University, MO

New Jersey

Stevens Institute of Technology, MO

New York

New York University, O
Rochester Institute of Technology, O

North Carolina

Western Carolina University, M

North Dakota

University of Mary, M

Ohio

Wright State University, M

Oklahoma

Oklahoma Christian University, M
University of Oklahoma, M

Pennsylvania

Carlow University, M
DeSales University, M
Drexel University, M
Harrisburg University of Science and Technology, M
Lehigh University, M
Mount Aloysius College, M
Penn State Erie, The Behrend College, M
Robert Morris University, M

South Carolina

The Citadel, The Military College of South Carolina,
  M
Winthrop University, MO

Tennessee

Christian Brothers University, O
King University, M
Trevecca Nazarene University, O
The University of Tennessee at Chattanooga, O

Texas

Amberton University, M
Dallas Baptist University, M
Sam Houston State University, M
Texas A&M University - San Antonio, M
University of Dallas, M

University of Houston, M
The University of Texas at Dallas, M
Wayland Baptist University, M

Vermont

Marlboro College, MO
Norwich University, M

Virginia

George Mason University, M
Liberty University, MD
Marymount University, O
University of Management and Technology, MO
Virginia International University, M

Washington

City University of Seattle, MO
Northwest University, M

West Virginia

American Public University System, M

Wisconsin

Herzing University Online, M
Lakeland College, M
University of Wisconsin - Platteville, M
University of Wisconsin - Stout, M
Viterbo University, M

U.S. Territories: Puerto Rico

Universidad del Turabo, M

Canada

Alberta

Athabasca University, MO
University of Calgary, MD

British Columbia

Royal Roads University, O

Ontario

Queen's University at Kingston, M
University of Ottawa, O

Quebec

Université du Québec en Abitibi-Témiscamingue, MO
Université du Québec à Chicoutimi, M
Université du Québec à Montréal, MO
Université du Québec en Outaouais, MO
Université du Québec à Rimouski, MO

Saskatchewan

University of Regina, O

PSYCHIATRIC/MENTAL HEALTH NURSE/NURSING

United States

Arizona

Arizona State University at the Tempe campus, O

Arkansas

Southern Arkansas University - Magnolia, M

California

Point Loma Nazarene University, M
University of San Diego, M
University of San Francisco, D

Colorado

University of Colorado Denver, M

Connecticut

Fairfield University, MD
University of Saint Joseph, M

Delaware

University of Delaware, MO

Georgia

Georgia State University, MO

Illinois

Rush University, D
Saint Francis Medical Center College of Nursing, M
University of St. Francis, MO

Iowa

Allen College, O

Kansas

The University of Kansas, O

Kentucky

University of Louisville, M

Louisiana

McNeese State University, MO
Nicholls State University, M

Maine

Husson University, MO
University of Southern Maine, O

Massachusetts

Boston College, M
Northeastern University, M
University of Massachusetts Lowell, MO

Michigan

University of Michigan - Flint, O
Wayne State University, MDO

Minnesota

University of Minnesota, Twin Cities Campus, M

Mississippi

University of Southern Mississippi, O

Missouri

University of Missouri, D

Montana

Montana State University, MD

New Hampshire

Rivier University, M

New Jersey

Monmouth University, MO

New York

Columbia University, MO
Hunter College of the City University of New York, MO
Molloy College, M
New York University, MDO
Stony Brook University, State University of New York, MDO
University at Buffalo, the State University of New York, D
University of Rochester, M

North Carolina

The University of North Carolina at Chapel Hill, MO

North Dakota

University of North Dakota, M

Ohio

Case Western Reserve University, M
Kent State University, M
University of Cincinnati, M

Oregon

Oregon Health & Science University, MO

Pennsylvania

Drexel University, M
University of Pennsylvania, M
University of Pittsburgh, D

Rhode Island

University of Rhode Island, M

South Carolina

University of South Carolina, MO

Tennessee

Lincoln Memorial University, M
Vanderbilt University, M

Texas

Midwestern State University, M
The University of Texas at Austin, M
The University of Texas Health Science Center at San Antonio, O

Virginia

Hampton University, M
University of Virginia, M
Virginia Commonwealth University, M

Washington

Seattle University, M
Washington State University, MD

West Virginia

West Virginia Wesleyan College, M

Wisconsin

Alverno College, M
University of Wisconsin - Madison, D

U.S. Territories: Puerto Rico

Pontifical Catholic University of Puerto Rico, M
University of Puerto Rico, Medical Sciences Campus, M

PSYCHIATRIC/MENTAL HEALTH SERVICES TECHNICIAN

United States

Alabama

Columbia Southern University, B

Alaska

University of Alaska Anchorage, AB

California

Cuesta College, A
Cypress College, A
Yuba College, A

Colorado

Pikes Peak Community College, A
Pueblo Community College, A

Connecticut

Asnuntuck Community College, A
Naugatuck Valley Community College, A
Three Rivers Community College, A

Florida

City College (Altamonte Springs), A
Hillsborough Community College, A

Idaho

College of Southern Idaho, A

Illinois

Illinois Central College, A

Indiana

Indiana University - Purdue University Fort Wayne, B
Ivy Tech Community College - Bloomington, A
Ivy Tech Community College - Central Indiana, A
Ivy Tech Community College - Columbus, A
Ivy Tech Community College - Lafayette, A
Ivy Tech Community College - Northeast, A
Ivy Tech Community College - Northwest, A
Ivy Tech Community College - Richmond, A
Ivy Tech Community College - Southeast, A
Ivy Tech Community College - Southern Indiana, A
Ivy Tech Community College - Southwest, A

Maine

University of Maine at Augusta, AB

Maryland

Allegany College of Maryland, A
Anne Arundel Community College, A
Community College of Baltimore County, A
Hagerstown Community College, A
Montgomery College, A

Massachusetts

Middlesex Community College, A

Michigan

Lake Superior State University, A
Wayne County Community College District, A

Minnesota

Rochester Community and Technical College, A

New York

Fiorello H. LaGuardia Community College of the
City University of New York, A
Kingsborough Community College of the City University of New York, A

North Carolina

Edgecombe Community College, A
Guilford Technical Community College, A
Roanoke-Chowan Community College, A
Western Piedmont Community College, A
Wilkes Community College, A

North Dakota

North Dakota State College of Science, A
Williston State College, A

Ohio

North Central State College, A

Pennsylvania

Community College of Allegheny County, A
Montgomery County Community College, A
Pennsylvania College of Technology, A

Texas

Alvin Community College, A
Eastfield College, A
El Paso Community College, A
Houston Community College, A

Virginia

Blue Ridge Community College, A

Washington

Pierce College at Fort Steilacoom, A

Wisconsin

Gateway Technical College, A
Waukesha County Technical College, A
Wisconsin Indianhead Technical College, A

PSYCHOANALYSIS AND PSYCHOTHERAPY

United States

Arizona

Prescott College, M

Colorado

Naropa University, M

Illinois

Argosy University, Chicago, D

New York

New York University, O

Pennsylvania

Immaculata University, O

Virginia

Regent University, M

PSYCHOLOGY

United States

Alabama

Alabama Agricultural and Mechanical University,
BMO
Alabama State University, B
Athens State University, B
Auburn University, BMD
Auburn University at Montgomery, BM
Birmingham-Southern College, B
Huntingdon College, B
Jacksonville State University, BM
Judson College, B
Oakwood University, B
Samford University, B
South University, B
Spring Hill College, B
Stillman College, B
Talladega College, B
Troy University, B
Tuskegee University, B
The University of Alabama, BD
The University of Alabama at Birmingham, BMD
The University of Alabama in Huntsville, BM
University of Mobile, B
University of Montevallo, B
University of North Alabama, B
University of South Alabama, B
The University of West Alabama, B

Alaska

Alaska Pacific University, B
University of Alaska Anchorage, BMD
University of Alaska Anchorage, Kenai Peninsula
College, B
University of Alaska Fairbanks, BD

Arizona

Argosy University, Phoenix, ABMD
Arizona Christian University, B
Arizona State University at the Tempe campus,
BMD
Arizona State University at the West campus, B
Arizona Western College, A
Chandler-Gilbert Community College, A
Cochise County Community College District, A
Coconino Community College, A
Eastern Arizona College, A
Grand Canyon University, BD
Mohave Community College, A
Northcentral University, BMDO
Northern Arizona University, BM
Pima Community College, A
Prescott College, B
The University of Arizona, BMD
University of Phoenix - Online Campus, M

University of Phoenix - Phoenix Campus, BM
University of Phoenix - Southern Arizona Campus,
M

Arkansas

Arkansas State University, B
Arkansas Tech University, BM
Central Baptist College, B
Cossatot Community College of the University of
Arkansas, A
Harding University, B
Henderson State University, B
Hendrix College, B
John Brown University, B
Lyon College, B
Ouachita Baptist University, B
Philander Smith College, B
Southern Arkansas University - Magnolia, B
University of Arkansas, BMD
University of Arkansas - Fort Smith, B
University of Arkansas at Little Rock, BM
University of Arkansas at Monticello, B
University of Arkansas at Pine Bluff, B
University of Central Arkansas, BMDO
University of the Ozarks, B
Williams Baptist College, B

California

Alliant International University - San Diego, B
American Jewish University, B
American River College, A
Antioch University Los Angeles, M
Argosy University, Inland Empire, ABMD
Argosy University, Los Angeles, ABMD
Argosy University, Orange County, ABMD
Argosy University, San Diego, ABMD
Argosy University, San Francisco Bay Area, ABMD
Ashford University, B
Azusa Pacific University, BMD
Bakersfield College, A
Berkeley City College, A
Biola University, BD
Brandman University, BM
Cabrillo College, A
California Baptist University, B
California Coast University, ABM
California Institute of Integral Studies, MD
California Lutheran University, BMD
California Polytechnic State University, San Luis
Obispo, BM
California State Polytechnic University, Pomona, BM
California State University, Bakersfield, B
California State University Channel Islands, B
California State University, Chico, BM
California State University, Dominguez Hills, BM
California State University, East Bay, B
California State University, Fresno, BM
California State University, Fullerton, BM
California State University, Long Beach, BM
California State University, Los Angeles, BM
California State University, Monterey Bay, B
California State University, Northridge, BM
California State University, Sacramento, BM
California State University, San Bernardino, BM
California State University, San Marcos, BM
California State University, Stanislaus, BM
Cañada College, A
Cerritos College, A
Chabot College, A
Chaffey College, A
Chapman University, B
Citrus College, A
Claremont McKenna College, B
College of Alameda, A
College of the Canyons, A
College of the Desert, A
College of Marin, A
College of the Siskiyous, A
Concordia University Irvine, B
Contra Costa College, A
Copper Mountain College, A
Crafton Hills College, A
Cuesta College, A
Cypress College, A
De Anza College, A
Diablo Valley College, A

Dominican University of California, B
East Los Angeles College, A
El Camino College, A
Evergreen Valley College, A
Folsom Lake College, A
Foothill College, A
Fresno Pacific University, AB
Fullerton College, A
Golden Gate University, MO
Hartnell College, A
Holy Names University, B
Hope International University, B
Humboldt State University, BM
Imperial Valley College, A
John F. Kennedy University, BMDO
La Sierra University, B
Lake Tahoe Community College, A
Lassen Community College District, A
Loma Linda University, D
Los Angeles City College, A
Los Angeles Mission College, A
Los Angeles Valley College, A
Los Medanos College, A
Loyola Marymount University, B
Marymount California University, B
Mendocino College, A
Menlo College, B
Mills College, B
MiraCosta College, A
Monterey Peninsula College, A
Mount Saint Mary's University, B
National University, BM
Notre Dame de Namur University, BM
Occidental College, B
Ohlone College, A
Orange Coast College, A
Oxnard College, A
Pacific Union College, B
Palo Alto University, BMD
Palomar College, A
Pasadena City College, A
Pepperdine University, BMD
Pitzer College, B
Point Loma Nazarene University, B
Pomona College, B
Sacramento City College, A
Saddleback College, A
Saint Mary's College of California, B
San Bernardino Valley College, A
San Diego Christian College, B
San Diego City College, A
San Diego Mesa College, A
San Diego Miramar College, A
San Diego State University, BMD
San Diego State University - Imperial Valley Campus, B
San Francisco State University, BMO
San Joaquin Delta College, A
San Jose City College, A
San Jose State University, BM
Santa Ana College, A
Santa Barbara City College, A
Santa Clara University, B
Santa Rosa Junior College, A
Santiago Canyon College, A
Scripps College, B
Sierra College, A
Simpson University, B
Skyline College, A
Solano Community College, A
Sonoma State University, B
Southern California Seminary, D
Southwestern College, A
Stanford University, BD
Touro College Los Angeles, B
University of California, Berkeley, BD
University of California, Davis, BD
University of California, Irvine, BD
University of California, Los Angeles, BMD
University of California, Merced, BMD
University of California, Riverside, BMD
University of California, San Diego, BD
University of California, Santa Barbara, BD
University of California, Santa Cruz, BD
University of La Verne, BMD
University of the Pacific, BM

University of Phoenix - Bay Area Campus, B
University of Phoenix - Sacramento Valley Campus, B
University of Phoenix - Southern California Campus, M
University of Redlands, B
University of San Diego, B
University of San Francisco, B
University of Southern California, BMD
University of the West, BM
Vanguard University of Southern California, B
West Hills Community College, A
West Los Angeles College, A
West Valley College, A
Westmont College, B
Whittier College, B
William Jessup University, B
Woodbury University, B
Woodland Community College, A
Yuba College, A

Colorado

Adams State University, B
Argosy University, Denver, ABMD
Colorado Christian University, B
The Colorado College, B
Colorado Mesa University, B
Colorado Mountain College (Glenwood Springs), A
Colorado State University, BMD
Colorado State University - Pueblo, B
Fort Lewis College, B
Metropolitan State University of Denver, B
Naropa University, B
Northeastern Junior College, A
Otero Junior College, A
Regis University, B
Trinidad State Junior College, A
University of Colorado Boulder, BMD
University of Colorado Colorado Springs, BMD
University of Colorado Denver, B
University of Denver, BMD
University of Northern Colorado, BMD
University of Phoenix - Colorado Campus, B
University of Phoenix - Colorado Springs Downtown Campus, B
Western State Colorado University, B

Connecticut

Albertus Magnus College, B
Central Connecticut State University, BM
Charter Oak State College, B
Connecticut College, BM
Eastern Connecticut State University, B
Fairfield University, B
Mitchell College, B
Norwalk Community College, A
Post University, B
Quinnipiac University, B
Sacred Heart University, B
Southern Connecticut State University, BM
Trinity College, B
University of Bridgeport, B
University of Connecticut, BMDO
University of Hartford, BMD
University of New Haven, B
University of Saint Joseph, B
Wesleyan University, B
Western Connecticut State University, B
Yale University, BD

Delaware

Delaware State University, B
Goldey-Beacom College, B
University of Delaware, BD
Wesley College, B
Wilmington University, B

District of Columbia

American University, B
The Catholic University of America, BMD
Gallaudet University, B
The George Washington University, BMDO
Georgetown University, BD
Howard University, BMD
Trinity Washington University, B
University of the District of Columbia, B

University of Phoenix - Washington D.C. Campus, MD

Florida

Argosy University, Sarasota, ABMD
Argosy University, Tampa, ABMD
Ave Maria University, B
Barry University, BMO
Beacon College, AB
Bethune-Cookman University, B
Broward College, A
Carlos Albizu University, Miami Campus, BMD
College of Central Florida, A
Eckerd College, B
Edward Waters College, B
Flagler College, B
Florida Agricultural and Mechanical University, BM
Florida Atlantic University, BMD
Florida Gulf Coast University, B
Florida Institute of Technology, BMD
Florida International University, BMD
Florida Memorial University, B
Florida National University, B
Florida Southern College, B
Florida State University, BMD
Indian River State College, A
Jacksonville University, B
Keiser University, BMD
Lynn University, B
Miami Dade College, A
New College of Florida, B
Nova Southeastern University, BMDO
Palm Beach Atlantic University, B
Palm Beach State College, A
Pensacola State College, A
Rollins College, B
Saint Leo University, B
St. Thomas University, B
South Florida State College, A
South University (Royal Palm Beach), B
South University (Tampa), B
Southeastern University, B
State College of Florida Manatee-Sarasota, A
Stetson University, B
Trinity College of Florida, B
University of Central Florida, BMD
University of Florida, BMD
University of Miami, BMD
University of North Florida, BM
University of South Florida, BD
University of South Florida, St. Petersburg, BM
University of South Florida Sarasota-Manatee, B
The University of Tampa, B
University of West Florida, BM
Warner University, B

Georgia

Abraham Baldwin Agricultural College, A
Agnes Scott College, B
Albany State University, B
Andrew College, A
Argosy University, Atlanta, ABMDO
Armstrong State University, B
Ashworth College, A
Augusta University, BM
Bainbridge State College, A
Berry College, B
Brenau University, M
Brewton-Parker College, B
Clark Atlanta University, B
Clayton State University, M
College of Coastal Georgia, AB
Columbus State University, B
Covenant College, B
Dalton State College, A
Darton State College, A
Emmanuel College, B
Emory University, BD
Fort Valley State University, B
Georgia Gwinnett College, B
Georgia Highlands College, A
Georgia Institute of Technology, MD
Georgia Military College, A
Georgia Southern University, BMD
Georgia Southwestern State University, B
Georgia State University, BD

Gordon State College, A
Kennesaw State University, B
LaGrange College, B
Life University, AB
Mercer University, B
Middle Georgia State University, B
Morehouse College, B
Oglethorpe University, B
Paine College, B
Piedmont College, B
Point University, AB
Reinhardt University, B
Shorter University, B
South Georgia State College, A
South University, B
Spelman College, B
Thomas University, B
Truett-McConnell College, B
University of Georgia, BMD
University of North Georgia, B
University of Phoenix - Atlanta Campus, B
University of Phoenix - Augusta Campus, B
University of Phoenix - Columbus Georgia Campus,
   AB
University of West Georgia, BMDO
Valdosta State University, BMO
Wesleyan College, B
Young Harris College, B

Hawaii

Argosy University, Hawai'i, ABMDO
Brigham Young University - Hawaii, B
Chaminade University of Honolulu, B
Hawai'i Pacific University, B
University of Hawaii at Manoa, BMDO
University of Hawaii - West Oahu, B
University of Phoenix - Hawaii Campus, B

Idaho

Boise State University, B
Brigham Young University - Idaho, B
The College of Idaho, B
College of Southern Idaho, A
College of Western Idaho, A
Idaho State University, BD
Lewis-Clark State College, B
North Idaho College, A
Northwest Nazarene University, B
University of Idaho, BM

Illinois

Argosy University, Chicago, BMD
Argosy University, Schaumburg, BMO
Augustana College, B
Aurora University, B
Benedictine University, B
Blackburn College, B
Bradley University, B
Chicago State University, B
Concordia University Chicago, BM
DePaul University, BM
Dominican University, B
Eastern Illinois University, BMO
Elmhurst College, B
Governors State University, BM
Greenville College, B
Harper College, A
Illinois College, B
Illinois Institute of Technology, BMD
Illinois State University, BMDO
Illinois Wesleyan University, B
John A. Logan College, A
Judson University, B
Kankakee Community College, A
Knox College, B
Lake Forest College, B
Lewis University, B
Lincoln Christian University, B
Loyola University Chicago, BMD
MacMurray College, B
McKendree University, B
Millikin University, B
Monmouth College, B
Moraine Valley Community College, A
National Louis University, BMDO
North Central College, B

North Park University, B
Northeastern Illinois University, B
Northern Illinois University, BMD
Northwestern University, BD
Olivet Nazarene University, B
Quincy University, B
Rockford University, B
Roosevelt University, BMD
Saint Xavier University, B
Sauk Valley Community College, A
Southern Illinois University Carbondale, BMD
Southern Illinois University Edwardsville, BMO
Spoon River College, A
Trinity Christian College, B
Trinity International University, B
Triton College, A
University of Chicago, BD
University of Illinois at Chicago, BMD
University of Illinois at Springfield, B
University of Illinois at Urbana - Champaign, BMD
University of St. Francis, B
Western Illinois University, BMO
Wheaton College, BMD

Indiana

Anderson University, B
Ball State University, BM
Bethel College, B
Butler University, B
Calumet College of Saint Joseph, AB
DePauw University, B
Earlham College, B
Franklin College, B
Goshen College, B
Grace College, B
Hanover College, B
Holy Cross College, B
Huntington University, B
Indiana State University, BMD
Indiana Tech, B
Indiana University Bloomington, BD
Indiana University East, B
Indiana University Kokomo, B
Indiana University Northwest, B
Indiana University - Purdue University Fort Wayne,
   B
Indiana University - Purdue University Indianapolis,
   BMD
Indiana University South Bend, B
Indiana University Southeast, B
Indiana Wesleyan University, B
Manchester University, B
Marian University, B
Martin University, BM
Oakland City University, B
Purdue University, BD
Purdue University Northwest (Hammond), B
Purdue University Northwest (Westville), B
Saint Joseph's College, B
Saint Mary-of-the-Woods College, B
Saint Mary's College, B
Taylor University, B
Trine University, B
University of Evansville, B
University of Indianapolis, BMD
University of Notre Dame, BD
University of Saint Francis, MO
University of Southern Indiana, B
Valparaiso University, BM
Vincennes University, A
Wabash College, B

Iowa

Briar Cliff University, B
Buena Vista University, B
Central College, B
Clarke University, B
Coe College, B
Cornell College, B
Dordt College, B
Drake University, B
Graceland University, B
Grand View University, B
Grinnell College, B
Iowa Lakes Community College, A

Iowa State University of Science and Technology,
   BD
Iowa Wesleyan University, B
Loras College, B
Luther College, B
Morningside College, B
Northwestern College, B
St. Ambrose University, B
Simpson College, B
University of Dubuque, B
The University of Iowa, BMDO
University of Northern Iowa, BM
Upper Iowa University, B
Waldorf College, B
Wartburg College, B
William Penn University, B

Kansas

Allen Community College, A
Baker University, B
Barclay College, B
Barton County Community College, A
Benedictine College, B
Bethany College, B
Bethel College, B
Butler Community College, A
Central Christian College of Kansas, AB
Coffeyville Community College, A
Dodge City Community College, A
Emporia State University, BM
Fort Hays State University, BMO
Friends University, B
Garden City Community College, A
Highland Community College, A
Hutchinson Community College, A
Kansas State University, BMD
Kansas Wesleyan University, B
McPherson College, B
MidAmerica Nazarene University, B
Newman University, B
Ottawa University, B
Pittsburg State University, BM
Pratt Community College, A
Seward County Community College and Area Tech-
   nical School, A
Southwestern College, B
Tabor College, B
The University of Kansas, BMD
University of Saint Mary, BM
Washburn University, BM
Wichita State University, BD

Kentucky

Asbury University, B
Bellarmine University, B
Berea College, B
Brescia University, B
Campbellsville University, B
Centre College, B
Eastern Kentucky University, BMO
Georgetown College, B
Kentucky Christian University, B
Kentucky State University, B
Kentucky Wesleyan College, B
Lindsey Wilson College, B
Midway University, B
Morehead State University, BM
Murray State University, BM
Northern Kentucky University, B
Spalding University, BMD
Thomas More College, AB
Transylvania University, B
Union College, BM
University of the Cumberlands, AB
University of Kentucky, BMD
University of Louisville, BD
University of Pikeville, B
Western Kentucky University, BMO

Louisiana

Centenary College of Louisiana, B
Dillard University, B
Grambling State University, B
Louisiana College, B

Louisiana State University and Agricultural & Mechanical College, BMD
Louisiana State University at Alexandria, B
Louisiana State University in Shreveport, B
Louisiana Tech University, BMD
McNeese State University, BM
Nicholls State University, B
Northwestern State University of Louisiana, BM
Southeastern Louisiana University, BM
Southern University and Agricultural and Mechanical College, BM
Southern University at New Orleans, B
Tulane University, BMD
University of Louisiana at Lafayette, BM
University of Louisiana at Monroe, BM
University of New Orleans, BMD
Xavier University of Louisiana, B

Maine

Bates College, B
Bowdoin College, B
Colby College, B
College of the Atlantic, B
Husson University, B
Saint Joseph's College of Maine, B
Thomas College, B
University of Maine, BMD
University of Maine at Farmington, B
University of Maine at Machias, B
University of Maine at Presque Isle, B
University of New England, B
University of Southern Maine, B

Maryland

Bowie State University, B
Carroll Community College, A
Coppin State University, B
Frederick Community College, A
Frostburg State University, BM
Goucher College, B
Harford Community College, A
Hood College, BMO
Johns Hopkins University, BD
Loyola University Maryland, BMDO
McDaniel College, B
Morgan State University, BMD
Mount St. Mary's University, B
Notre Dame of Maryland University, B
St. Mary's College of Maryland, B
Salisbury University, B
Stevenson University, B
Towson University, B
University of Baltimore, B
University of Maryland, Baltimore County, BMD
University of Maryland, College Park, BMD
University of Maryland University College, B
Washington Adventist University, B
Washington College, B

Massachusetts

American International College, BM
Amherst College, B
Anna Maria College, B
Assumption College, BM
Bard College at Simon's Rock, B
Bay Path University, B
Becker College, B
Boston College, BMD
Boston University, BMD
Brandeis University, BMD
Bridgewater State University, BM
Bunker Hill Community College, A
Cambridge College, BM
Cape Cod Community College, A
Clark University, B
College of the Holy Cross, B
Curry College, B
Dean College, AB
Eastern Nazarene College, B
Elms College, B
Emmanuel College, B
Endicott College, B
Fisher College, AB
Fitchburg State University, B
Framingham State University, BM
Gordon College, B

Hampshire College, B
Harvard University, BD
Lasell College, B
Lesley University, MDO
Massachusetts College of Liberal Arts, B
Merrimack College, B
Mount Holyoke College, BM
Mount Ida College, B
Newbury College, B
Nichols College, B
Northeastern University, B
Northern Essex Community College, A
Pine Manor College, B
Quinsigamond Community College, A
Regis College, B
Salem State University, BMO
Simmons College, B
Smith College, B
Springfield College, B
Stonehill College, B
Suffolk University, BMDO
Tufts University, BMD
University of Massachusetts Amherst, BMD
University of Massachusetts Boston, B
University of Massachusetts Dartmouth, BMO
University of Massachusetts Lowell, BM
Wellesley College, B
Western New England University, B
Westfield State University, BM
Wheaton College, B
Williams College, B
Worcester State University, B

Michigan

Adrian College, B
Albion College, B
Alma College, B
Andrews University, BMDO
Aquinas College, B
Calvin College, B
Central Michigan University, BMDO
Concordia University Ann Arbor, B
Cornerstone University, B
Eastern Michigan University, BMD
Ferris State University, AB
Gogebic Community College, A
Grand Valley State University, B
Hillsdale College, B
Hope College, B
Kalamazoo College, B
Lake Michigan College, A
Lake Superior State University, B
Lansing Community College, A
Lawrence Technological University, B
Madonna University, BM
Marygrove College, B
Michigan State University, BMD
Michigan Technological University, B
Mid Michigan Community College, A
Monroe County Community College, A
Northern Michigan University, BMO
Oakland University, B
Olivet College, B
Rochester College, B
Saginaw Valley State University, B
Siena Heights University, AB
South University, B
Spring Arbor University, B
University of Detroit Mercy, BMDO
University of Michigan, D
University of Michigan - Dearborn, B
University of Michigan - Flint, B
Wayne State University, BMD
Western Michigan University, BMD

Minnesota

Argosy University, Twin Cities, ABMDO
Augsburg College, B
Bemidji State University, B
Bethany Lutheran College, B
Bethel University, B
Capella University, BMD
Carleton College, B
College of Saint Benedict, B
The College of St. Scholastica, B
Concordia College, B

Concordia University, St. Paul, B
Crown College, B
Gustavus Adolphus College, B
Hamline University, B
Itasca Community College, A
Macalester College, B
Metropolitan State University, BM
Minnesota State University Mankato, BMD
Minnesota State University Moorhead, B
North Central University, AB
St. Catherine University, B
St. Cloud State University, BMD
Saint John's University, B
Saint Mary's University of Minnesota, B
St. Olaf College, B
Southwest Minnesota State University, B
University of Minnesota, Duluth, B
University of Minnesota, Morris, B
University of Minnesota, Twin Cities Campus, BD
University of Northwestern - St. Paul, B
University of St. Thomas, BMDO
Vermilion Community College, A
Walden University, BMDO
Winona State University, B

Mississippi

Alcorn State University, B
Belhaven University, B
Blue Mountain College, B
Coahoma Community College, A
Delta State University, B
East Central Community College, A
Holmes Community College, A
Itawamba Community College, A
Jackson State University, BD
Millsaps College, B
Mississippi College, B
Mississippi State University, BMD
Mississippi University for Women, B
Northeast Mississippi Community College, A
Tougaloo College, B
University of Mississippi, B
University of Southern Mississippi, BMD
William Carey University, BM

Missouri

Avila University, BM
Central Methodist University, AB
College of the Ozarks, B
Columbia College, B
Cottey College, B
Crowder College, A
Culver-Stockton College, B
Drury University, B
Evangel University, BM
Fontbonne University, B
Hannibal-LaGrange University, B
Lincoln University, B
Lindenwood University, B
Maryville University of Saint Louis, B
Missouri Baptist University, B
Missouri Southern State University, B
Missouri State University, BM
Missouri University of Science and Technology, B
Missouri Valley College, B
Missouri Western State University, B
Northwest Missouri State University, BM
Park University, B
Rockhurst University, B
St. Charles Community College, A
Saint Louis University, BMD
Southeast Missouri State University, B
Southwest Baptist University, B
Stephens College, B
Truman State University, B
University of Central Missouri, BM
University of Missouri, BMD
University of Missouri - Kansas City, BMD
University of Missouri - St. Louis, BMDO
Washington University in St. Louis, BD
Webster University, BM
Westminster College, B
William Jewell College, B
William Woods University, B

Montana

Aaniiih Nakoda College, A
Carroll College, B
Fort Peck Community College, A
Montana State University, BM
Montana State University Billings, ABM
Rocky Mountain College, B
University of Great Falls, B
University of Montana, BMDO
The University of Montana Western, B

Nebraska

Bellevue University, B
Chadron State College, B
College of Saint Mary, B
Concordia University, Nebraska, B
Creighton University, B
Doane University, B
Grace University, B
Hastings College, B
Midland University, B
Nebraska Wesleyan University, B
Northeast Community College, A
Peru State College, B
Union College, B
University of Nebraska at Kearney, B
University of Nebraska - Lincoln, BMD
University of Nebraska at Omaha, BMDO
Wayne State College, B
Western Nebraska Community College, A
York College, B

Nevada

Nevada State College, B
Sierra Nevada College, B
Truckee Meadows Community College, A
University of Nevada, Las Vegas, BMD
University of Nevada, Reno, BMD
University of Phoenix - Las Vegas Campus, B

New Hampshire

Colby-Sawyer College, B
Daniel Webster College, B
Dartmouth College, BD
Franklin Pierce University, B
Granite State College, B
Keene State College, B
New England College, AB
Plymouth State University, B
Rivier University, BM
Saint Anselm College, B
Southern New Hampshire University, BMO
University of New Hampshire, BD
University of New Hampshire at Manchester, B

New Jersey

Bergen Community College, A
Bloomfield College, B
Caldwell University, B
Centenary College, B
The College of New Jersey, B
College of Saint Elizabeth, BMO
Drew University, B
Fairleigh Dickinson University, College at Florham,
   BMO
Fairleigh Dickinson University, Metropolitan Cam-
   pus, BMDO
Felician University, B
Georgian Court University, B
Kean University, BM
Monmouth University, BMO
Montclair State University, BM
New Jersey City University, B
Passaic County Community College, A
Princeton University, BD
Ramapo College of New Jersey, B
Rider University, B
Rowan College at Burlington County, A
Rowan University, BMO
Rutgers University - Camden, BM
Rutgers University - New Brunswick, BD
Rutgers University - Newark, BD
Saint Peter's University, B
Salem Community College, A
Seton Hall University, BMDO

Stockton University, B
Thomas Edison State University, B
University of Phoenix - Jersey City Campus, BM
William Paterson University of New Jersey, B

New Mexico

Central New Mexico Community College, A
Clovis Community College, A
Eastern New Mexico University, AB
New Mexico Highlands University, BM
New Mexico Institute of Mining and Technology, B
New Mexico State University, BMD
San Juan College, A
Santa Fe Community College, A
University of New Mexico, BD
University of the Southwest, B
Western New Mexico University, B

New York

Adelphi University, BMD
Alfred University, B
Bard College, B
Barnard College, B
Baruch College of the City University of New York,
   B
Binghamton University, State University of New
   York, BD
Bronx Community College of the City University of
   New York, A
Brooklyn College of the City University of New York,
   BMD
Buffalo State College, State University of New York,
   B
Canisius College, B
Cayuga County Community College, A
Cazenovia College, B
City College of the City University of New York,
   BMD
Clarkson University, B
Colgate University, B
The College at Brockport, State University of New
   York, BM
College of Mount Saint Vincent, B
The College of New Rochelle, B
The College of Saint Rose, B
College of Staten Island of the City University of
   New York, B
Columbia University, BD
Columbia University, School of General Studies, B
Concordia College - New York, B
Cornell University, BD
Daemen College, B
Dominican College, B
D'Youville College, B
Elmira College, B
Eugene Lang College of Liberal Arts, B
Excelsior College, B
Finger Lakes Community College, A
Fiorello H. LaGuardia Community College of the
   City University of New York, A
Fordham University, BMD
Fulton-Montgomery Community College, A
Genesee Community College, A
Hamilton College, B
Hartwick College, B
Hilbert College, B
Hobart and William Smith Colleges, B
Hofstra University, BMD
Houghton College, B
Hunter College of the City University of New York,
   BM
Iona College, BMO
Ithaca College, B
Keuka College, B
Le Moyne College, B
Lehman College of the City University of New York,
   B
Long Island University - LIU Brooklyn, B
Long Island University - LIU Post, B
Manhattan College, B
Manhattanville College, B
Maria College, B
Marist College, BMO
Marymount Manhattan College, B
Medaille College, BMD

Medgar Evers College of the City University of New
   York, B
Mercy College, BM
Molloy College, B
Morrisville State College, A
Mount Saint Mary College, B
Nazareth College of Rochester, B
The New School for Public Engagement, B
New York Institute of Technology, B
New York University, BMDO
Niagara University, B
Nyack College, B
Pace University, BM
Pace University, Pleasantville Campus, B
Purchase College, State University of New York, B
Queens College of the City University of New York,
   BM
Rensselaer Polytechnic Institute, B
Roberts Wesleyan College, B
Rochester Institute of Technology, BMO
The Sage Colleges, B
St. Bonaventure University, B
St. Francis College, B
St. John Fisher College, B
St. John's University, BMD
St. Joseph's College, Long Island Campus, B
St. Joseph's College, New York, B
St. Lawrence University, B
St. Thomas Aquinas College, B
Sarah Lawrence College, B
Siena College, B
Skidmore College, B
State University of New York College of Agriculture
   and Technology at Cobleskill, B
State University of New York College at Cortland, B
State University of New York College at Geneseo, B
State University of New York College at Old
   Westbury, B
State University of New York College at Oneonta, B
State University of New York College at Potsdam, B
State University of New York Empire State College,
   AB
State University of New York at Fredonia, B
State University of New York at New Paltz, BMO
State University of New York at Oswego, B
State University of New York at Plattsburgh, BMO
State University of New York Polytechnic Institute, B
Stony Brook University, State University of New
   York, BMD
Sullivan County Community College, A
Syracuse University, B
Touro College, BM
Union College, B
University at Albany, State University of New York,
   BMD
University at Buffalo, the State University of New
   York, BMD
University of Rochester, BD
Utica College, B
Vassar College, B
Wagner College, B
Wells College, B
Yeshiva University, BMD
York College of the City University of New York, B

North Carolina

Appalachian State University, BM
Barton College, B
Belmont Abbey College, B
Bennett College, B
Brevard College, B
Campbell University, B
Catawba College, B
Chowan University, B
Davidson College, B
Duke University, BD
East Carolina University, B
Elizabeth City State University, B
Elon University, B
Fayetteville State University, BM
Gardner-Webb University, BM
Greensboro College, B
Guilford College, B
High Point University, B
John Wesley University, B
Johnson C. Smith University, B

Lees-McRae College, B
Lenoir-Rhyne University, B
Livingstone College, B
Louisburg College, A
Mars Hill University, B
Meredith College, B
Methodist University, AB
North Carolina Agricultural and Technical State University, B
North Carolina Central University, BM
North Carolina State University, BD
North Carolina Wesleyan College, B
Pfeiffer University, B
Queens University of Charlotte, B
St. Andrews University, B
Saint Augustine's University, B
Salem College, B
Shaw University, B
South University, B
Southeastern Baptist Theological Seminary, M
University of Mount Olive, B
University of North Carolina at Asheville, B
The University of North Carolina at Chapel Hill, BD
The University of North Carolina at Charlotte, BMDO
The University of North Carolina at Greensboro, BMD
The University of North Carolina at Pembroke, B
The University of North Carolina Wilmington, BM
Wake Forest University, BM
Warren Wilson College, B
Western Carolina University, BM
William Peace University, B
Wingate University, B
Winston-Salem State University, B

North Dakota

Dakota College at Bottineau, A
Dickinson State University, B
Mayville State University, B
Minot State University, B
North Dakota State University, BMD
University of Jamestown, B
University of Mary, B
University of North Dakota, BMD
Valley City State University, B

Ohio

Antioch College, B
Antioch University Midwest, M
Ashland University, B
Baldwin Wallace University, B
Bluffton University, B
Bowling Green State University, BMD
Capital University, B
Case Western Reserve University, BMD
Cedarville University, B
Central State University, B
Cincinnati Christian University, AB
Cleveland State University, BMDO
The College of Wooster, B
Defiance College, B
Denison University, B
Edison Community College, A
Franciscan University of Steubenville, B
Heidelberg University, B
Hiram College, B
John Carroll University, B
Kent State University, BMD
Kent State University at Ashtabula, B
Kent State University at East Liverpool, B
Kent State University at Geauga, B
Kent State University at Salem, B
Kent State University at Stark, B
Kent State University at Trumbull, B
Kent State University at Tuscarawas, B
Kenyon College, B
Lake Erie College, B
Lorain County Community College, A
Lourdes University, B
Malone University, B
Marietta College, BM
Miami University, BMD
Miami University Hamilton, B
Miami University Middletown, A
Mount St. Joseph University, B

Mount Vernon Nazarene University, B
Muskingum University, B
Notre Dame College, B
Oberlin College, B
Ohio Christian University, B
Ohio Dominican University, B
Ohio Northern University, B
The Ohio State University, BD
The Ohio State University at Lima, B
The Ohio State University - Mansfield Campus, B
The Ohio State University at Marion, B
The Ohio State University - Newark Campus, B
Ohio University, BMD
Ohio Wesleyan University, B
Otterbein University, B
Shawnee State University, B
South University, B
Terra State Community College, A
Tiffin University, BM
Union Institute & University, BMD
The University of Akron, BMD
University of Cincinnati, BD
University of Cincinnati Blue Ash College, A
University of Cincinnati Clermont College, A
University of Dayton, B
The University of Findlay, B
University of Mount Union, B
University of Rio Grande, A
The University of Toledo, BMD
Urbana University, B
Ursuline College, B
Walsh University, B
Wilberforce University, B
Wilmington College, B
Wittenberg University, B
Wright State University, ABMD
Wright State University - Lake Campus, AB
Xavier University, ABMD
Youngstown State University, BM

Oklahoma

Cameron University, BM
Connors State College, A
East Central University, BM
Eastern Oklahoma State College, A
Hillsdale Free Will Baptist College, AB
Langston University, B
Murray State College, A
Northeastern Oklahoma Agricultural and Mechanical College, A
Northeastern State University, BM
Northwestern Oklahoma State University, B
Oklahoma Baptist University, B
Oklahoma Christian University, B
Oklahoma City Community College, A
Oklahoma City University, B
Oklahoma Panhandle State University, B
Oklahoma State University, BMD
Oklahoma State University, Oklahoma City, A
Oklahoma Wesleyan University, B
Oral Roberts University, B
Redlands Community College, A
Rose State College, A
St. Gregory's University, B
Seminole State College, A
Southeastern Oklahoma State University, B
Southern Nazarene University, BM
Southwestern Oklahoma State University, B
University of Central Oklahoma, BM
University of Oklahoma, BMD
University of Science and Arts of Oklahoma, B
The University of Tulsa, BMD

Oregon

Concordia University, B
Corban University, B
Eastern Oregon University, B
George Fox University, B
Lewis & Clark College, BM
Linfield College, B
Marylhurst University, B
Multnomah University, B
Northwest Christian University, B
Oregon State University, B
Oregon State University - Cascades, B
Pacific University, BMD

Portland State University, BMD
Reed College, B
Southern Oregon University, BM
Umpqua Community College, A
University of Oregon, BMD
University of Portland, B
Warner Pacific College, B
Western Oregon University, B
Willamette University, B

Pennsylvania

Albright College, B
Allegheny College, B
Alvernia University, B
Arcadia University, BM
Bloomsburg University of Pennsylvania, B
Bryn Athyn College of the New Church, B
Bryn Mawr College, B
Bucknell University, BM
Bucks County Community College, A
Butler County Community College, A
Cabrini University, B
Cairn University, B
California University of Pennsylvania, B
Carlow University, B
Carnegie Mellon University, BD
Cedar Crest College, B
Chatham University, B
Chestnut Hill College, BMDO
Cheyney University of Pennsylvania, B
Clarion University of Pennsylvania, B
Community College of Allegheny County, A
Community College of Beaver County, A
Community College of Philadelphia, A
Delaware County Community College, A
DeSales University, B
Dickinson College, B
Drexel University, BMD
Duquesne University, BD
East Stroudsburg University of Pennsylvania, B
Eastern University, B
Edinboro University of Pennsylvania, B
Elizabethtown College, B
Franklin & Marshall College, B
Gannon University, B
Geneva College, BM
Gettysburg College, B
Grove City College, B
Gwynedd Mercy University, B
Harrisburg Area Community College, A
Haverford College, B
Holy Family University, B
Immaculata University, BMDO
Indiana University of Pennsylvania, BMD
Juniata College, B
Keystone College, B
King's College, B
Kutztown University of Pennsylvania, B
La Roche College, B
La Salle University, BMD
Lafayette College, B
Lebanon Valley College, B
Lehigh Carbon Community College, A
Lehigh University, BMD
Lock Haven University of Pennsylvania, B
Lycoming College, B
Manor College, A
Mansfield University of Pennsylvania, BM
Marywood University, BM
Mercyhurst University, B
Messiah College, B
Millersville University of Pennsylvania, BM
Misericordia University, B
Montgomery County Community College, A
Moravian College, B
Mount Aloysius College, BM
Muhlenberg College, AB
Neumann University, B
Penn State Abington, B
Penn State Altoona, B
Penn State Beaver, B
Penn State Berks, B
Penn State Brandywine, B
Penn State DuBois, B
Penn State Erie, The Behrend College, B
Penn State Fayette, The Eberly Campus, B

Penn State Greater Allegheny, B
Penn State Harrisburg, BMDO
Penn State Hazleton, B
Penn State Lehigh Valley, B
Penn State Mont Alto, B
Penn State New Kensington, B
Penn State Schuylkill, B
Penn State Shenango, B
Penn State University Park, BMD
Penn State Wilkes-Barre, B
Penn State Worthington Scranton, B
Penn State York, B
Pennsylvania Highlands Community College, A
Philadelphia University, B
Point Park University, B
Reading Area Community College, A
Robert Morris University, B
Rosemont College, B
Saint Francis University, B
Saint Joseph's University, BM
Saint Vincent College, B
Seton Hill University, B
Shippensburg University of Pennsylvania, BM
Slippery Rock University of Pennsylvania, B
Summit University, B
Susquehanna University, B
Swarthmore College, B
Temple University, BD
Thiel College, B
University of Pennsylvania, BD
University of Phoenix - Philadelphia Campus, B
University of Pittsburgh, BMD
University of Pittsburgh at Bradford, B
University of Pittsburgh at Greensburg, B
University of Pittsburgh at Johnstown, B
University of Pittsburgh at Titusville, A
University of the Sciences, B
The University of Scranton, B
University of Valley Forge, B
Ursinus College, B
Villanova University, BM
Washington & Jefferson College, B
Waynesburg University, B
West Chester University of Pennsylvania, BMO
Westminster College, B
Widener University, B
Wilkes University, B
Wilson College, B
York College of Pennsylvania, B

Rhode Island

Brown University, BD
Bryant University, B
Providence College, B
Rhode Island College, BMO
Roger Williams University, B
Salve Regina University, B
University of Rhode Island, BD

South Carolina

Anderson University, B
Benedict College, B
Charleston Southern University, B
The Citadel, The Military College of South Carolina, BMO
Claflin University, B
Clemson University, BD
Coastal Carolina University, B
Coker College, B
College of Charleston, B
Columbia College, B
Columbia International University, B
Converse College, B
Erskine College, B
Francis Marion University, BMO
Furman University, B
Lander University, B
Limestone College, B
Newberry College, B
North Greenville University, B
Presbyterian College, B
South Carolina State University, B
South University, B
Southern Wesleyan University, B
University of South Carolina, MD
University of South Carolina Aiken, B

University of South Carolina Beaufort, B
University of South Carolina Upstate, B
Winthrop University, BMO
Wofford College, B

South Dakota

Augustana University, B
Black Hills State University, B
Dakota Wesleyan University, B
Mount Marty College, B
Northern State University, B
Presentation College, B
South Dakota State University, B
University of Sioux Falls, B
The University of South Dakota, BMD

Tennessee

Aquinas College, B
Argosy University, Nashville, ABMD
Austin Peay State University, BM
Belmont University, B
Bethel University, B
Bryan College, B
Carson-Newman University, B
Christian Brothers University, B
Cumberland University, B
East Tennessee State University, BD
Fisk University, BM
Freed-Hardeman University, B
Hiwassee College, A
King University, B
Lee University, B
Lincoln Memorial University, B
Lipscomb University, BM
Martin Methodist College, B
Maryville College, B
Middle Tennessee State University, BMO
Milligan College, B
Nashville State Community College, A
Rhodes College, B
Sewanee: The University of the South, B
Southern Adventist University, BM
Tennessee State University, BMD
Tennessee Technological University, B
Tennessee Wesleyan College, B
Trevecca Nazarene University, B
Tusculum College, B
Union University, B
University of Memphis, BMDO
The University of Tennessee, BMD
The University of Tennessee at Chattanooga, BM
The University of Tennessee at Martin, B
Vanderbilt University, BM

Texas

Abilene Christian University, BM
Alvin Community College, A
Amarillo College, A
Angelina College, A
Angelo State University, BM
Argosy University, Dallas, ABMD
Austin College, B
Austin Community College District, A
Baylor University, BMD
Blinn College, A
Cisco College, A
Clarendon College, A
Dallas Baptist University, B
Dallas Christian College, B
Del Mar College, A
East Texas Baptist University, B
Frank Phillips College, A
Grayson College, A
Hardin-Simmons University, BM
Hill College, A
Houston Baptist University, BM
Howard College, A
Howard Payne University, B
Huston-Tillotson University, B
Kilgore College, A
Lamar University, BM
Lee College, A
LeTourneau University, BM
Lubbock Christian University, B
McMurry University, B
Midwestern State University, B

Navarro College, A
Northeast Texas Community College, A
Odessa College, A
Our Lady of the Lake University of San Antonio, BMD
Palo Alto College, A
Panola College, A
Paris Junior College, A
Prairie View A&M University, B
Rice University, BMD
St. Edward's University, B
St. Mary's University, B
St. Philip's College, A
Sam Houston State University, BMDO
San Antonio College, A
San Jacinto College District, A
Schreiner University, B
South University, B
Southern Methodist University, BD
Southwestern Adventist University, B
Southwestern Assemblies of God University, A
Southwestern University, B
Stephen F. Austin State University, BM
Sul Ross State University, BM
Tarleton State University, B
Texas A&M International University, BM
Texas A&M University, BMD
Texas A&M University - Central Texas, B
Texas A&M University - Commerce, B
Texas A&M University - Corpus Christi, BM
Texas A&M University - Kingsville, BMD
Texas A&M University - Texarkana, BM
Texas Christian University, BMD
Texas Lutheran University, B
Texas Southern University, BM
Texas State University, BM
Texas Tech University, BMD
Texas Wesleyan University, B
Texas Woman's University, BMDO
Trinity University, B
Trinity Valley Community College, A
Tyler Junior College, A
University of Dallas, BM
University of Houston, BMD
University of Houston - Clear Lake, BM
University of Houston - Downtown, B
University of Houston - Victoria, BM
University of the Incarnate Word, BM
University of Mary Hardin-Baylor, B
University of North Texas, BMO
University of Phoenix - Dallas Campus, B
University of Phoenix - Houston Campus, B
University of St. Thomas, B
The University of Texas at Arlington, BMD
The University of Texas at Austin, BD
The University of Texas at Dallas, BMD
The University of Texas at El Paso, BMD
The University of Texas of the Permian Basin, BM
The University of Texas Rio Grande Valley, BM
The University of Texas at San Antonio, BMD
The University of Texas at Tyler, BM
Wayland Baptist University, B
West Texas A&M University, BM

Utah

Argosy University, Salt Lake City, ABMD
Brigham Young University, MD
Dixie State University, B
Salt Lake Community College, A
Southern Utah University, B
University of Phoenix - Utah Campus, B
University of Utah, BD
Utah State University, BMD
Utah Valley University, AB
Weber State University, B
Westminster College, B

Vermont

Bennington College, B
Castleton University, BM
Champlain College, B
College of St. Joseph, BM
Goddard College, B
Green Mountain College, B
Johnson State College, B
Lyndon State College, B

Marlboro College, B
Middlebury College, B
Norwich University, B
Saint Michael's College, B
Southern Vermont College, B
University of Vermont, BD

Virginia

Argosy University, Washington DC, ABMD
Averett University, B
Bluefield College, B
Bridgewater College, B
Christopher Newport University, B
The College of William and Mary, B
Eastern Mennonite University, B
Emory & Henry College, B
Ferrum College, B
George Mason University, BMDO
Hampden-Sydney College, B
Hampton University, BM
Hollins University, B
James Madison University, BM
Liberty University, AB
Longwood University, B
Lynchburg College, B
Mary Baldwin College, B
Marymount University, B
Norfolk State University, BMD
Old Dominion University, BMD
Radford University, BM
Randolph College, B
Randolph-Macon College, B
Regent University, AB
Roanoke College, B
Shenandoah University, B
South University (Glen Allen), B
South University (Virginia Beach), B
Sweet Briar College, B
University of Mary Washington, B
University of Richmond, B
University of Valley Forge Virginia Campus, B
University of Virginia, BMD
The University of Virginia's College at Wise, B
Virginia Commonwealth University, BD
Virginia Military Institute, B
Virginia Polytechnic Institute and State University, BMD
Virginia State University, BMD
Virginia Union University, B
Virginia Wesleyan College, B
Washington and Lee University, B

Washington

Antioch University Seattle, MD
Argosy University, Seattle, ABMDO
Bastyr University, B
Central Washington University, BM
City University of Seattle, B
Eastern Washington University, BM
Everett Community College, A
The Evergreen State College, B
Gonzaga University, B
Heritage University, B
Highline College, A
Northwest University, BMD
Pacific Lutheran University, B
Saint Martin's University, B
Seattle Pacific University, B
Seattle University, BM
Skagit Valley College, A
University of Phoenix - Western Washington Campus, B
University of Puget Sound, B
University of Washington, BD
University of Washington, Tacoma, B
Walla Walla University, B
Washington State University, BMD
Washington State University - Global Campus, B
Washington State University - Tri-Cities, B
Washington State University - Vancouver, B
Western Washington University, BM
Whitman College, B
Whitworth University, B

West Virginia

Alderson Broaddus University, B
American Public University System, BM
Bethany College, B
Concord University, B
Davis & Elkins College, B
Fairmont State University, B
Marshall University, BMDO
Ohio Valley University, B
Potomac State College of West Virginia University, A
Shepherd University, B
University of Charleston, B
West Liberty University, B
West Virginia State University, B
West Virginia University, BMD
West Virginia University Institute of Technology, B
West Virginia Wesleyan College, B
Wheeling Jesuit University, B

Wisconsin

Alverno College, B
Beloit College, B
Cardinal Stritch University, BM
Carroll University, B
Carthage College, B
Concordia University Wisconsin, BM
Edgewood College, B
Lakeland College, B
Lawrence University, B
Marian University, B
Marquette University, BD
Mount Mary University, B
Northland College, B
Ripon College, B
St. Norbert College, B
Silver Lake College of the Holy Family, B
University of Wisconsin - Eau Claire, BMO
University of Wisconsin - Green Bay, B
University of Wisconsin - La Crosse, BMO
University of Wisconsin - Madison, BD
University of Wisconsin - Milwaukee, BMD
University of Wisconsin - Oshkosh, BM
University of Wisconsin - Parkside, B
University of Wisconsin - Platteville, B
University of Wisconsin - River Falls, B
University of Wisconsin - Stevens Point, B
University of Wisconsin - Stout, B
University of Wisconsin - Superior, B
University of Wisconsin - Whitewater, BMO
Viterbo University, B
Wisconsin Lutheran College, B

Wyoming

Casper College, A
Central Wyoming College, A
Laramie County Community College, A
Northwest College, A
Sheridan College, A
University of Wyoming, BMD
Western Wyoming Community College, A

U.S. Territories: Guam

University of Guam, B

U.S. Territories: Puerto Rico

Bayamón Central University, B
Carlos Albizu University, BMD
Inter American University of Puerto Rico, Aguadilla Campus, B
Inter American University of Puerto Rico, Fajardo Campus, B
Inter American University of Puerto Rico, Metropolitan Campus, BMD
Inter American University of Puerto Rico, Ponce Campus, B
Inter American University of Puerto Rico, San Germán Campus, BMD
Pontifical Catholic University of Puerto Rico, BD
Universidad Adventista de las Antillas, B
Universidad del Este, B
Universidad Metropolitana, B
Universidad del Turabo, B
University of Puerto Rico in Cayey, B
University of Puerto Rico, Mayagüez Campus, B

University of Puerto Rico in Ponce, B
University of Puerto Rico, Río Piedras Campus, BMD
University of Puerto Rico in Utuado, B
University of the Sacred Heart, B

U.S. Territories: United States Virgin Islands

University of the Virgin Islands, B

Canada

Alberta

Athabasca University, B
Concordia University of Edmonton, B
The King's University, B
Mount Royal University, B
University of Alberta, BMD
University of Calgary, BMD
University of Lethbridge, BM

British Columbia

Simon Fraser University, BMD
Thompson Rivers University, B
Trinity Western University, B
The University of British Columbia, BMD
The University of British Columbia - Okanagan Campus, B
University of the Fraser Valley, B
University of Northern British Columbia, BMD
University of Victoria, BMD
Vancouver Island University, B

Manitoba

Booth University College, B
Brandon University, B
University of Manitoba, BMD
The University of Winnipeg, B

Maritime Provinces: New Brunswick

Crandall University, B
Mount Allison University, B
St. Thomas University, B
Université de Moncton, B
University of New Brunswick Fredericton, BMD
University of New Brunswick Saint John, BMD

Maritime Provinces: Nova Scotia

Acadia University, BM
Cape Breton University, B
Dalhousie University, BMD
Mount Saint Vincent University, B
St. Francis Xavier University, B
Saint Mary's University, BMD
University of King's College, B

Maritime Provinces: Prince Edward Island

University of Prince Edward Island, B

Newfoundland and Labrador

Memorial University of Newfoundland, BMD

Ontario

Brock University, BMD
Carleton University, BMD
Lakehead University, BMD
Laurentian University, BM
McMaster University, BMD
Nipissing University, B
Queen's University at Kingston, BMD
Redeemer University College, B
Royal Military College of Canada, B
Ryerson University, B
Trent University, B
Tyndale University College & Seminary, B
University of Guelph, BMD
University of Ottawa, BD
University of Toronto, MD
University of Waterloo, BMD
The University of Western Ontario, BMD
University of Windsor, BMD
Wilfrid Laurier University, BMD
York University, BMD

Quebec

Bishop's University, B
Concordia University, BMD
McGill University, BMD
Université Laval, BD
Université de Montréal, BMD
Université du Québec en Abitibi-Témiscamingue, B
Université du Québec à Chicoutimi, B
Université du Québec à Montréal, BD
Université du Québec en Outaouais, B
Université du Québec à Trois-Rivières, BDO
Université de Sherbrooke, BM

Saskatchewan

University of Regina, BMD
University of Saskatchewan, BMD

PSYCHOLOGY TEACHER EDUCATION

United States

California

California Lutheran University, B

Delaware

University of Delaware, B

Idaho

Boise State University, B

Illinois

Bradley University, B

Indiana

Valparaiso University, B

Kansas

Central Christian College of Kansas, A
Pittsburg State University, B

Kentucky

Campbellsville University, B

Michigan

Albion College, B
Alma College, B
Concordia University Ann Arbor, B
University of Michigan - Flint, B

Montana

Rocky Mountain College, B

Nebraska

Concordia University, Nebraska, B
Wayne State College, B
York College, B

Ohio

Ohio Wesleyan University, B

Pennsylvania

Widener University, B

Tennessee

Cumberland University, B
Lee University, B

Utah

Brigham Young University, B
Weber State University, B

Wisconsin

Carroll University, B

PUBLIC ADMINISTRATION

United States

Alabama

Auburn University, BMDO
Auburn University at Montgomery, MDO
Samford University, B
South University, M
Talladega College, B
Troy University, M
The University of Alabama, M
The University of Alabama at Birmingham, M
University of South Alabama, M

Alaska

University of Alaska Anchorage, BM
University of Alaska Southeast, M

Arizona

Argosy University, Phoenix, M
Arizona State University at the Tempe campus, MD
Grand Canyon University, M
Northern Arizona University, BMO
Rio Salado College, A
Scottsdale Community College, A
The University of Arizona, BMD
University of Phoenix - Online Campus, M
University of Phoenix - Phoenix Campus, BM
Western International University, M

Arkansas

Arkansas State University, M
Harding University, B
Henderson State University, B
National Park College, A
Southern Arkansas University - Magnolia, M
University of Arkansas, B
University of Arkansas at Little Rock, M
University of Central Arkansas, B

California

Argosy University, Inland Empire, M
Argosy University, Los Angeles, M
Argosy University, Orange County, MO
Argosy University, San Diego, M
Argosy University, San Francisco Bay Area, M
Azusa Pacific University, M
Biola University, B
Brandman University, M
California Baptist University, BM
California Lutheran University, BM
California Miramar University, B
California State Polytechnic University, Pomona, M
California State University, Bakersfield, BM
California State University, Chico, BM
California State University, Dominguez Hills, BM
California State University, East Bay, BM
California State University, Fresno, BM
California State University, Fullerton, BM
California State University, Long Beach, M
California State University, Los Angeles, M
California State University, Northridge, M
California State University, Sacramento, M
California State University, San Bernardino, M
California State University, Stanislaus, M
Citrus College, A
East Los Angeles College, A
Golden Gate University, M
Los Angeles City College, A
National University, BM
New Charter University, M
Notre Dame de Namur University, M
Palomar College, A
Pepperdine University, M
San Diego State University, BM
San Diego State University - Imperial Valley Campus, B
San Francisco State University, M
San Jose State University, M
Santiago Canyon College, A
Solano Community College, A
Sonoma State University, M
Southwestern College, A

Trident University International, M
University of La Verne, BMD
University of Phoenix - Bay Area Campus, BM
University of Phoenix - Central Valley Campus, M
University of Phoenix - Sacramento Valley Campus, BM
University of Phoenix - San Diego Campus, M
University of Phoenix - Southern California Campus, BM
University of San Francisco, BM
University of Southern California, MO

Colorado

Argosy University, Denver, M
Colorado Mesa University, B
Regis University, B
University of Colorado Colorado Springs, M
University of Colorado Denver, MD
University of Phoenix - Colorado Campus, M
University of Phoenix - Colorado Springs Downtown Campus, BM

Connecticut

Fairfield University, M
Housatonic Community College, A
Post University, M
University of Connecticut, MO
University of New Haven, BMO

Delaware

University of Delaware, M
Wilmington University, M

District of Columbia

Gallaudet University, M
The George Washington University, MD
Howard University, M
University of the District of Columbia, M
University of Phoenix - Washington D.C. Campus, BM

Florida

Argosy University, Sarasota, MO
Argosy University, Tampa, M
Barry University, M
Broward College, A
Edward Waters College, B
Everglades University (Boca Raton), B
Everglades University (Maitland), B
Everglades University (Sarasota), B
Flagler College, B
Florida Agricultural and Mechanical University, M
Florida Atlantic University, BMD
Florida Gulf Coast University, M
Florida Institute of Technology, M
Florida International University, BMD
Florida Memorial University, B
Florida National University, A
Florida State University, MDO
Keiser University, B
Miami Dade College, A
Northwest Florida State College, A
Nova Southeastern University, BM
St. Thomas University, BMO
South Florida State College, A
South University (Royal Palm Beach), M
Southern Technical College (Fort Myers), B
State College of Florida Manatee-Sarasota, A
University of Central Florida, BMO
University of North Florida, MO
University of Phoenix - North Florida Campus, M
University of Phoenix - South Florida Campus, M
University of South Florida, O
University of West Florida, M

Georgia

Albany State University, M
Clark Atlanta University, M
Columbus State University, M
Georgia College & State University, M
Georgia Southern University, M
Georgia State University, M
Kennesaw State University, M
Savannah State University, M
South University, M

University of Georgia, MD
University of North Georgia, M
University of Phoenix - Atlanta Campus, BM
University of Phoenix - Augusta Campus, BM
University of Phoenix - Columbus Georgia Campus, BM
University of West Georgia, MO

Hawaii

Hawai'i Pacific University, B
University of Hawaii at Manoa, MO
University of Hawaii - West Oahu, B
University of Phoenix - Hawaii Campus, BM

Idaho

Boise State University, MO
Idaho State University, M
University of Idaho, M

Illinois

Argosy University, Chicago, M
Argosy University, Schaumburg, M
Augustana College, B
Blackburn College, B
DePaul University, M
DeVry University (Downers Grove), M
Governors State University, M
Illinois Institute of Technology, M
Lewis University, B
Northern Illinois University, M
Northwestern University, M
Roosevelt University, BM
Southern Illinois University Carbondale, M
Southern Illinois University Edwardsville, M
University of Illinois at Chicago, MD
University of Illinois at Springfield, MDO

Indiana

Ball State University, M
Indiana State University, M
Indiana University Bloomington, BMDO
Indiana University Kokomo, BMO
Indiana University Northwest, BM
Indiana University - Purdue University Fort Wayne, B
Indiana University - Purdue University Indianapolis, BO
Trine University, M
University of Evansville, M
University of Southern Indiana, M

Iowa

Buena Vista University, B
Drake University, M
Iowa State University of Science and Technology, M
University of Northern Iowa, B
Upper Iowa University, BM

Kansas

Barton County Community College, A
Kansas State University, M
The University of Kansas, BMD
Washburn University, B
Wichita State University, M

Kentucky

Eastern Kentucky University, M
Kentucky State University, BM
Morehead State University, M
Murray State University, B
Northern Kentucky University, MO
University of Kentucky, MD
University of Louisville, M
Western Kentucky University, M

Louisiana

Grambling State University, M
Louisiana College, B
Louisiana State University and Agricultural & Mechanical College, MD
Southern University and Agricultural and Mechanical College, M
Southern University at New Orleans, B
Southern University at Shreveport, A
University of New Orleans, M

Maine

University of Maine at Augusta, AB
University of Maine at Fort Kent, B
University of Maine at Machias, B

Maryland

Bowie State University, M
Hood College, M
Johns Hopkins University, BM
University of Baltimore, MD
University of Maryland, College Park, M
University of Maryland University College, B
Washington Adventist University, M

Massachusetts

Anna Maria College, M
Bridgewater State University, M
Clark University, MO
Fisher College, B
Framingham State University, M
Harvard University, M
Northeastern University, M
Suffolk University, MO
Tufts University, O
University of Massachusetts Amherst, M
University of Massachusetts Dartmouth, O

Michigan

Calvin College, B
Central Michigan University, MO
Eastern Michigan University, BMO
Ferris State University, A
Grand Valley State University, BM
Northern Michigan University, BM
Oakland University, BM
Saginaw Valley State University, BM
Siena Heights University, B
University of Michigan - Dearborn, M
University of Michigan - Flint, BM
University of Phoenix - Detroit Campus, B
Wayne State University, BM
Western Michigan University, MDO

Minnesota

Argosy University, Twin Cities, M
Capella University, MD
Hamline University, MD
Metropolitan State University, BM
Minneapolis Community and Technical College, A
Minnesota State University Mankato, BM
St. Cloud State University, B
Southwest Minnesota State University, B
University of St. Thomas, B
Walden University, BMDO
Winona State University, B

Mississippi

Belhaven University, M
Itawamba Community College, A
Jackson State University, MD
Millsaps College, B
Mississippi State University, MD
Mississippi University for Women, B
Mississippi Valley State University, B

Missouri

Central Methodist University, AB
Columbia College, B
Evangel University, B
Lincoln University, BM
Lindenwood University, BM
Missouri State University, BM
Missouri Valley College, B
Northwest Missouri State University, B
Park University, BM
Saint Louis University, M
Southeast Missouri State University, M
University of Missouri, O
University of Missouri - Kansas City, MD
University of Missouri - St. Louis, BMO
Webster University, M

Montana

Montana State University, M
Montana State University Billings, M

University of Montana, M

Nebraska

Bellevue University, M
Doane University, B
Hastings College, B
University of Nebraska at Omaha, BMDO

Nevada

University of Nevada, Las Vegas, BMO
University of Nevada, Reno, M
University of Phoenix - Las Vegas Campus, BM

New Hampshire

Plymouth State University, B
Southern New Hampshire University, B
University of New Hampshire, M

New Jersey

College of Saint Elizabeth, M
County College of Morris, A
Fairleigh Dickinson University, College at Florham, M
Fairleigh Dickinson University, Metropolitan Campus, MO
Kean University, BM
Passaic County Community College, A
Rutgers University - Camden, M
Rutgers University - Newark, MD
Saint Peter's University, M
Seton Hall University, MO
Thomas Edison State University, BM
University of Phoenix - Jersey City Campus, BM

New Mexico

Mesalands Community College, A
Navajo Technical University, A
University of New Mexico, M
Western New Mexico University, B

New York

Adelphi University, O
Alfred University, B
Baruch College of the City University of New York, BM
Binghamton University, State University of New York, M
City College of the City University of New York, M
The College at Brockport, State University of New York, MO
The College of New Rochelle, M
Columbia University, M
Eugenio María de Hostos Community College of the City University of New York, A
Excelsior College, M
Hilbert College, M
Hudson Valley Community College, A
John Jay College of Criminal Justice of the City University of New York, BM
Long Island University - LIU Brooklyn, M
Long Island University - LIU Post, BM
Marist College, M
Metropolitan College of New York, BM
New York University, BMDO
Pace University, M
St. John's University, BO
Syracuse University, BMDO
University at Albany, State University of New York, MDO
Wagner College, B
Westchester Community College, A

North Carolina

Appalachian State University, M
Campbell University, B
Catawba College, B
East Carolina University, MO
Elon University, B
Fayetteville Technical Community College, A
Lenoir Community College, A
North Carolina Central University, M
North Carolina State University, MD
Shaw University, B
The University of North Carolina at Chapel Hill, M
The University of North Carolina at Charlotte, MO

The University of North Carolina at Pembroke, BM
The University of North Carolina Wilmington, MO

North Dakota

Cankdeska Cikana Community College, A
University of North Dakota, M

Ohio

Baldwin Wallace University, B
Bowling Green State University, BM
Capital University, B
Cedarville University, B
Cleveland State University, BMDO
Franklin University, B
Heidelberg University, B
John Carroll University, B
Kent State University, M
Miami University, B
Miami University Hamilton, B
Notre Dame College, B
Ohio Dominican University, M
The Ohio State University, BM
Ohio University, M
Ohio Wesleyan University, B
Sinclair Community College, A
The University of Akron, M
University of Dayton, M
The University of Findlay, M
The University of Toledo, MO
Wright State University, M

Oklahoma

Mid-America Christian University, M
Rogers State University, B
University of Central Oklahoma, BM
University of Oklahoma, BM

Oregon

Portland State University, M
University of Oregon, B
Western Oregon University, B
Willamette University, B

Pennsylvania

Carnegie Mellon University, M
Cheyney University of Pennsylvania, M
Duquesne University, MO
Elizabethtown College School of Continuing and
    Professional Studies, B
Gannon University, M
Harrisburg University of Science and Technology, M
Kutztown University of Pennsylvania, BM
La Salle University, B
Lehigh Carbon Community College, A
Lincoln University, B
Marywood University, M
Penn State Harrisburg, MDO
Point Park University, AB
Saint Francis University, B
Shippensburg University of Pennsylvania, BM
University of Pennsylvania, MO
University of Phoenix - Philadelphia Campus, B
University of Pittsburgh, BMD
Villanova University, M
Waynesburg University, B
West Chester University of Pennsylvania, MO
Widener University, M

Rhode Island

Rhode Island College, BM
Roger Williams University, BM
University of Rhode Island, M

South Carolina

Clemson University, M
College of Charleston, M
University of South Carolina, M

South Dakota

Northern State University, B
The University of South Dakota, MD

Tennessee

Cumberland University, M
East Tennessee State University, MO

Lipscomb University, B
Tennessee State University, BMD
University of Memphis, M
The University of Tennessee, BM
The University of Tennessee at Chattanooga, MO
The University of Tennessee at Martin, B

Texas

Argosy University, Dallas, MO
Baylor University, BM
Central Texas College, A
Del Mar College, A
Houston Community College, A
Lamar Institute of Technology, A
Lamar University, M
Midwestern State University, B
St. Mary's University, MO
Sam Houston State University, BM
San Antonio College, A
Stephen F. Austin State University, BM
Texas A&M International University, M
Texas A&M University, M
Texas A&M University - Corpus Christi, M
Texas Southern University, BM
Texas State University, BM
Texas Tech University, M
Tyler Junior College, A
University of Houston, M
University of Houston - Clear Lake, B
University of North Texas, M
University of Phoenix - Dallas Campus, BM
University of Phoenix - Houston Campus, BM
University of Phoenix - San Antonio Campus, M
The University of Texas at Arlington, M
The University of Texas at Austin, M
The University of Texas at Dallas, B
The University of Texas Rio Grande Valley, BM
The University of Texas at San Antonio, BM
The University of Texas at Tyler, M
West Texas A&M University, B

Utah

Argosy University, Salt Lake City, M
Brigham Young University, M
Southern Utah University, M
University of Utah, MD

Vermont

Norwich University, M
University of Vermont, M

Virginia

Argosy University, Washington DC, M
George Mason University, BMDO
James Madison University, BM
Liberty University, M
Old Dominion University, MD
Regent University, BM
Thomas Nelson Community College, A
University of Management and Technology, MO
Virginia Commonwealth University, MO
Virginia International University, M
Virginia Polytechnic Institute and State University,
    MDO

Washington

Argosy University, Seattle, M
Eastern Washington University, BM
The Evergreen State College, BM
Seattle University, BM
University of Phoenix - Western Washington Cam-
    pus, B
University of Washington, M

West Virginia

American Public University System, M
Marshall University, M
West Virginia University, M

Wisconsin

Concordia University Wisconsin, M
Marquette University, MO
Silver Lake College of the Holy Family, B
University of Wisconsin - Green Bay, B
University of Wisconsin - La Crosse, B

University of Wisconsin - Milwaukee, M
University of Wisconsin - Oshkosh, M
University of Wisconsin - Stevens Point, B
University of Wisconsin - Whitewater, B

Wyoming

Laramie County Community College, A
University of Wyoming, M

U.S. Territories: Guam

University of Guam, BM

U.S. Territories: Northern Mariana Is-
lands

Northern Marianas College, A

U.S. Territories: Puerto Rico

Bayamón Central University, B
Pontifical Catholic University of Puerto Rico, BM
Universidad del Turabo, AB
University of Puerto Rico, Río Piedras Campus, M

U.S. Territories: United States Virgin
Islands

University of the Virgin Islands, M

Canada

Alberta

Athabasca University, B
University of Lethbridge, B

British Columbia

University of Victoria, BMD

Manitoba

University of Manitoba, BM
The University of Winnipeg, M

Maritime Provinces: New Brunswick

Université de Moncton, M
University of New Brunswick Fredericton, M

Maritime Provinces: Nova Scotia

Dalhousie University, MO

Ontario

Brock University, B
Carleton University, BMD
McMaster University, M
Ryerson University, B
University of Guelph, BM
University of Ottawa, BO
University of Toronto, B
The University of Western Ontario, B
York University, BM

Quebec

Concordia University, BMD
Université du Québec à Montréal, M
Université de Sherbrooke, M

Saskatchewan

University of Regina, MO
University of Saskatchewan, B

PUBLIC ADMINISTRATION AND
SOCIAL SERVICE PROFES-
SIONS

United States

Alabama

Jacksonville State University, B
Troy University, B

Arizona

Prescott College, B
University of Phoenix - Southern Arizona Campus,
    B

California

College of Alameda, A
Grossmont College, A
San Diego State University, B
Southwestern College, A
University of Phoenix - Central Valley Campus, B
University of Phoenix - Sacramento Valley Campus, B

Colorado

University of Phoenix - Colorado Campus, B

Delaware

Delaware State University, B

Georgia

College of Coastal Georgia, B

Hawaii

University of Phoenix - Hawaii Campus, B

Illinois

John A. Logan College, A
National Louis University, B
Northeastern Illinois University, B

Kentucky

Thomas More College, A

Massachusetts

Cape Cod Community College, A
Lasell College, B

Michigan

University of Detroit Mercy, B

Nevada

University of Phoenix - Las Vegas Campus, B

New Jersey

Rutgers University - Newark, B

New Mexico

University of Phoenix - New Mexico Campus, B

New York

Metropolitan College of New York, A
New York University, B
Onondaga Community College, A
Schenectady County Community College, A
State University of New York Empire State College, B
Ulster County Community College, A

Ohio

The University of Akron, A

Oklahoma

Oklahoma State University, Oklahoma City, A

Pennsylvania

Point Park University, A

South Carolina

Columbia College, B

South Dakota

Dakota Wesleyan University, B

Tennessee

Cleveland State Community College, A
Milligan College, B
Trevecca Nazarene University, B

Utah

University of Phoenix - Utah Campus, B

Virginia

Emory & Henry College, B

Washington

The Evergreen State College, B

PUBLIC AFFAIRS

United States

Alabama

The University of Alabama in Huntsville, M

Arizona

Arizona State University at the Tempe campus, MD

Arkansas

University of Arkansas at Little Rock, MO

California

Notre Dame de Namur University, M
University of San Francisco, M

Colorado

University of Colorado Colorado Springs, M
University of Colorado Denver, MD

District of Columbia

American University, M
The George Washington University, MO

Florida

Florida International University, D
University of Central Florida, MDO
University of Florida, M
University of South Florida, O

Indiana

Indiana University Bloomington, MDO
Indiana University Northwest, MO
Indiana University - Purdue University Indianapolis, MO
Indiana University South Bend, M

Kentucky

Murray State University, M
University of Louisville, D

Maryland

University of Baltimore, MD

Massachusetts

University of Massachusetts Boston, M

Michigan

Western Michigan University, MDO

Minnesota

University of Minnesota, Twin Cities Campus, M

Mississippi

Jackson State University, MD

Missouri

Park University, M
University of Missouri, MDO
University of Missouri - Kansas City, MD

Nevada

University of Nevada, Las Vegas, D

New Jersey

Princeton University, MD

New Mexico

New Mexico Highlands University, M

New York

Cornell University, M
Metropolitan College of New York, M

North Carolina

The University of North Carolina at Greensboro, M
Western Carolina University, M

Ohio

Cleveland State University, D
The Ohio State University, MD

Oregon

Portland State University, D

Pennsylvania

Indiana University of Pennsylvania, M
Penn State Harrisburg, MDO
West Chester University of Pennsylvania, MO

South Carolina

Clemson University, D

Texas

Texas A&M University, MO
The University of Texas at Arlington, D
The University of Texas at Austin, MD
The University of Texas at Dallas, MD
The University of Texas Rio Grande Valley, M

Virginia

George Mason University, M
Virginia Commonwealth University, MDO
Virginia Polytechnic Institute and State University, MDO

Washington

University of Washington, MD
Washington State University, MDO

Wisconsin

University of Wisconsin - Madison, M

Canada

Ontario

McMaster University, M
University of Waterloo, M
York University, M

Quebec

Concordia University, O

Saskatchewan

University of Saskatchewan, MD

PUBLIC/APPLIED HISTORY AND ARCHIVAL ADMINISTRATION

United States

Arkansas

Arkansas Tech University, B

Indiana

Goshen College, B

Massachusetts

Salem State University, B

Michigan

Central Michigan University, B
Western Michigan University, B

North Dakota

North Dakota State University, B

Ohio

Baldwin Wallace University, B
Wright State University, B

Pennsylvania

Cairn University, B

Rhode Island

Rhode Island College, B

Texas

McMurry University, B

Virginia

Emory & Henry College, B

Canada

Quebec

Concordia University, B

PUBLIC FINANCE

United States

Maine

Husson University, B

Rhode Island

Johnson & Wales University, B

PUBLIC HEALTH

United States

Alabama

Auburn University at Montgomery, O
The University of Alabama at Birmingham, MD

Alaska

University of Alaska Anchorage, M

Arizona

Argosy University, Phoenix, M
Arizona State University at the Tempe campus, O
Grand Canyon University, M
Northern Arizona University, O
The University of Arizona, MD

Arkansas

University of Arkansas for Medical Sciences, MDO

California

Argosy University, Inland Empire, M
Argosy University, Los Angeles, M
Argosy University, Orange County, M
Argosy University, San Diego, M
Argosy University, San Francisco Bay Area, M
Berkeley City College, A
California Baptist University, M
California State University, Fresno, M
California State University, Fullerton, M
California State University, Northridge, M
California State University, San Bernardino, M
Charles R. Drew University of Medicine and Science, M
Loma Linda University, MDO
National University, M
San Diego State University, MD
San Francisco State University, M
San Jose State University, MO
Trident University International, MDO
University of California, Berkeley, BMD
University of California, Irvine, BMD
University of California, Los Angeles, MD
University of California, San Diego, D
University of San Francisco, M
University of Southern California, MD

Colorado

Argosy University, Denver, M
University of Colorado Denver, MD
University of Northern Colorado, M

Connecticut

Southern Connecticut State University, M
Yale University, MD

District of Columbia

The George Washington University, MD
Georgetown University, M
Howard University, M
Trinity Washington University, M

Florida

Argosy University, Sarasota, M
Argosy University, Tampa, M
Florida Agricultural and Mechanical University, MD
Florida International University, MD
Florida State University, M
Nova Southeastern University, M
University of Florida, MDO
University of Miami, MD
University of North Florida, MO
University of South Florida, MDO
University of West Florida, M

Georgia

Argosy University, Atlanta, M
Armstrong State University, M
Augusta University, M
Emory University, MD
Fort Valley State University, M
Georgia Southern University, MD
Georgia State University, MDO
Mercer University, M
University of Georgia, D

Hawaii

Argosy University, Hawai'i, M
University of Hawaii at Manoa, MD

Idaho

Boise State University, MO
Idaho State University, M

Illinois

Argosy University, Chicago, M
Argosy University, Schaumburg, M
Benedictine University, M
Chicago State University, M
DePaul University, M
Elmhurst College, M
Loyola University Chicago, M
Northern Illinois University, M
Northwestern University, M
University of Illinois at Chicago, MD
University of Illinois at Springfield, MO
University of Illinois at Urbana - Champaign, BM

Indiana

Indiana University Bloomington, BMD
Indiana University - Purdue University Indianapolis, MD
Purdue University, MD
University of Indianapolis, M
Valparaiso University, M

Iowa

Allen College, MO
The University of Iowa, MDO

Kansas

Kansas State University, MDO
The University of Kansas, M

Kentucky

University of Kentucky, MD
University of Louisville, D
Western Kentucky University, M

Louisiana

Louisiana State University Health Sciences Center, MD
Louisiana State University in Shreveport, M
Tulane University, MDO

Maine

University of New England, MO
University of Southern Maine, MO

Maryland

Johns Hopkins University, MD
Morgan State University, MD
University of Maryland, College Park, BMD

Massachusetts

Boston University, MD
Hampshire College, B
Harvard University, MD
Northeastern University, M
Tufts University, MDO
University of Massachusetts Amherst, MD
University of Massachusetts Lowell, O

Michigan

Davenport University, M
Grand Valley State University, M
Michigan State University, M
University of Michigan, MD
University of Michigan - Flint, BM
Wayne State University, MO

Minnesota

Argosy University, Twin Cities, M
St. Catherine University, M
University of Minnesota, Twin Cities Campus, MDO
Walden University, MD

Mississippi

University of Southern Mississippi, M

Missouri

Missouri State University, M
Saint Louis University, D
University of Missouri, MO
Washington University in St. Louis, MD

Montana

University of Montana, MO

Nevada

University of Nevada, Las Vegas, MD
University of Nevada, Reno, MD

New Hampshire

Dartmouth College, M
University of New Hampshire, MO

New Jersey

Montclair State University, M
Rutgers University - Camden, MO
Rutgers University - New Brunswick, MD
Rutgers University - Newark, MO
Stockton University, B

New Mexico

New Mexico State University, MO
University of New Mexico, M

New York

Adelphi University, MO
Brooklyn College of the City University of New York, M
Columbia University, MD
Daemen College, M
Excelsior College, M
Hofstra University, M
Hunter College of the City University of New York, M
Monroe College, M
New York University, MD
St. John's University, M
Sarah Lawrence College, M
State University of New York Downstate Medical Center, M
Stony Brook University, State University of New York, MO
Syracuse University, MO
University at Albany, State University of New York, MD
University at Buffalo, the State University of New York, M
University of Rochester, M

North Carolina

East Carolina University, M
Lenoir-Rhyne University, M
The University of North Carolina at Chapel Hill, MD
The University of North Carolina at Charlotte, M

North Dakota

North Dakota State University, MD
University of North Dakota, M

Ohio

Bowling Green State University, M
Case Western Reserve University, M
Cleveland State University, M
Lourdes University, B
The Ohio State University, MD
Ohio University, M
The University of Akron, M
The University of Toledo, MO
Wright State University, M

Oklahoma

University of Oklahoma Health Sciences Center, MD

Oregon

Oregon State University, MD
Portland State University, MDO

Pennsylvania

Arcadia University, M
Drexel University, MDO
Franklin & Marshall College, B
La Salle University, M
Temple University, MD
Thomas Jefferson University, MO
University of Pennsylvania, M
University of Pittsburgh, MDO
University of the Sciences, M
West Chester University of Pennsylvania, MO

Rhode Island

Brown University, M

South Carolina

University of South Carolina, BM

Tennessee

Argosy University, Nashville, M
Austin Peay State University, M
East Tennessee State University, MDO
Tennessee State University, M
University of Memphis, M
The University of Tennessee, M
Vanderbilt University, M

Texas

Argosy University, Dallas, M
Texas A&M University, MD
The University of Texas Health Science Center at Houston, MDO
The University of Texas Medical Branch, M

Utah

Argosy University, Salt Lake City, M
Independence University, M
Salt Lake Community College, A
University of Utah, MD
Utah State University, B
Westminster College, M

Virginia

Argosy University, Washington DC, M
George Mason University, MO
Shenandoah University, B
University of Virginia, M
Virginia Commonwealth University, M
Virginia Polytechnic Institute and State University, M

Washington

Argosy University, Seattle, M
University of Washington, M

West Virginia

American Public University System, M
Marshall University, M
West Virginia University, MD

Wisconsin

University of Wisconsin - Milwaukee, MDO
Western Technical College, A

Canada

Alberta

Concordia University of Edmonton, B
University of Alberta, MD

British Columbia

Simon Fraser University, M
The University of British Columbia, MD

Ontario

Laurentian University, D
Queen's University at Kingston, M
University of Ottawa, D
University of Toronto, MD
University of Waterloo, M

Quebec

Université de Montréal, DO

PUBLIC HEALTH EDUCATION AND PROMOTION

United States

Arizona

Arizona State University at the Downtown Phoenix campus, B

Arkansas

University of Arkansas, B

California

Berkeley City College, A
California Baptist University, B
California State University, Long Beach, B

District of Columbia

American University, B

Georgia

Georgia Southern University, B
Kennesaw State University, B
University of Georgia, B

Idaho

College of Southern Idaho, A

Illinois

Chicago State University, B
Western Illinois University, B

Indiana

Purdue University, B

Iowa

The University of Iowa, B

Kentucky

Eastern Kentucky University, B

Louisiana

Louisiana State University in Shreveport, B
Southeastern Louisiana University, B

Massachusetts

Simmons College, B

Michigan

Central Michigan University, B

Minnesota

University of Minnesota, Duluth, B
University of St. Thomas, B

Mississippi

Mississippi University for Women, B

Montana

Montana State University - Northern, B

New Hampshire

Colby-Sawyer College, B
Plymouth State University, B

New Jersey

Thomas Edison State University, B

New Mexico

New Mexico State University, B

New York

Borough of Manhattan Community College of the City University of New York, A
Ithaca College, B
State University of New York College of Technology at Canton, B

North Carolina

Appalachian State University, B
Barton College, B
East Carolina University, B
North Carolina Central University, B
Queens University of Charlotte, B
The University of North Carolina at Charlotte, B
The University of North Carolina at Greensboro, B
The University of North Carolina Wilmington, B

Ohio

Malone University, B
University of Cincinnati Blue Ash College, A
University of Mount Union, B
The University of Toledo, B

Oklahoma

Oklahoma State University, B
University of Central Oklahoma, B

Pennsylvania

Northampton Community College, A
Temple University, B
The University of Scranton, B

South Carolina

Coastal Carolina University, B
College of Charleston, B
University of South Carolina Beaufort, B

Texas

Texas State University, B
University of North Texas, B
The University of Texas at Austin, B

Utah

University of Utah, B
Weber State University, B

Virginia

Liberty University, B
Lynchburg College, B
Marymount University, B

Washington

Central Washington University, B
Eastern Washington University, B
Walla Walla University, B

Wisconsin

University of Wisconsin - La Crosse, B

U.S. Territories: Puerto Rico

Inter American University of Puerto Rico, Ponce Campus, B

University of Puerto Rico, Medical Sciences Campus, B

Canada

Maritime Provinces: Nova Scotia

Dalhousie University, B

Ontario

Laurentian University, B

PUBLIC HEALTH (MPH, DPH)

United States

Alabama

Samford University, B

Alaska

University of Alaska Anchorage, B
University of Alaska Fairbanks, A
University of Alaska Southeast, A

Arizona

Arizona State University at the Downtown Phoenix campus, B
Northern Arizona University, B
The University of Arizona, B

Arkansas

University of Arkansas, B

California

California State University, Long Beach, B
Dominican University of California, B
National University, B
Santa Clara University, B
Trident University International, B
University of California, Merced, B

Colorado

Fort Lewis College, B
University of Colorado Denver, B

Connecticut

Southern Connecticut State University, B
University of Saint Joseph, B

Delaware

Delaware State University, B

District of Columbia

American University, B

Florida

University of Miami, B
University of South Florida, B
The University of Tampa, B

Georgia

Agnes Scott College, B
Mercer University, B

Hawaii

University of Hawaii at Manoa, B

Illinois

Augustana College, B

Indiana

Indiana University - Purdue University Indianapolis, B
University of Evansville, B
Valparaiso University, B

Iowa

Allen College, B

Kentucky

University of the Cumberlands, B
University of Kentucky, B
University of Louisville, B

Louisiana

Dillard University, B

Maine

University of New England, B

Maryland

Anne Arundel Community College, A
Johns Hopkins University, B

Massachusetts

American International College, B
Northern Essex Community College, A
Regis College, B
Tufts University, B
University of Massachusetts Amherst, B
University of Massachusetts Lowell, B

Michigan

Alma College, B
Calvin College, B
Wayne State University, B

Minnesota

Minnesota State University Mankato, B
Walden University, B

Mississippi

University of Southern Mississippi, B

Missouri

Missouri Western State University, B
Saint Louis University, B

Nebraska

University of Nebraska at Omaha, B

Nevada

University of Nevada, Las Vegas, B

New Hampshire

Colby-Sawyer College, B
Franklin Pierce University, B

New Jersey

The College of New Jersey, B
County College of Morris, A
Montclair State University, B
Rutgers University - New Brunswick, B
William Paterson University of New Jersey, B

New York

The College of Saint Rose, B
Hunter College of the City University of New York, B
Long Island University - LIU Brooklyn, B
Monroe College, B
New York University, B
State University of New York College at Old Westbury, B
Syracuse University, B
University at Albany, State University of New York, B
University of Rochester, B

North Carolina

Elon University, B
The University of North Carolina at Charlotte, B

Ohio

Baldwin Wallace University, B
Bluffton University, B
Kent State University, B
Kent State University at Trumbull, B
The Ohio State University, B
Ohio University, B
Youngstown State University, B

Oklahoma

Langston University, B

Oregon

Oregon State University, B
Portland State University, B

Pennsylvania

Drexel University, B
Gannon University, B
Keystone College, B
La Salle University, B
Mercyhurst University, B
Saint Francis University, B
Slippery Rock University of Pennsylvania, B
West Chester University of Pennsylvania, B

Rhode Island

Roger Williams University, B

South Carolina

Benedict College, B

Tennessee

East Tennessee State University, B

Texas

Sam Houston State University, B
Texas A&M University, B
The University of Texas at Austin, B
The University of Texas at San Antonio, B

Utah

Westminster College, B

Washington

Central Washington University, B
University of Washington, B

West Virginia

American Public University System, AB
Marshall University, B
West Virginia University, B

Wisconsin

Carroll University, B

U.S. Territories: Puerto Rico

Universidad del Turabo, B

Canada

Alberta

University of Lethbridge, B

Maritime Provinces: Nova Scotia

Cape Breton University, B

Ontario

Brock University, B
Ryerson University, B
York University, B

PUBLIC HISTORY

United States

Arizona

Arizona State University at the Tempe campus, M

Arkansas

University of Arkansas at Little Rock, M

California

California State University, East Bay, M
California State University, Sacramento, MD
University of California, Santa Barbara, D

Colorado

University of Colorado Denver, M

Florida

Florida State University, M
University of West Florida, M

Georgia

Armstrong State University, M
Georgia College & State University, M
Georgia State University, M
University of West Georgia, O

Illinois

Eastern Illinois University, M
Loyola University Chicago, M
University of Illinois at Springfield, M

Indiana

Indiana University - Purdue University Indianapolis, M

Iowa

University of Northern Iowa, M

Kentucky

Northern Kentucky University, M
University of Louisville, O

Maryland

University of Maryland, Baltimore County, D

Massachusetts

Northeastern University, M

Missouri

Southeast Missouri State University, M

New Jersey

Rutgers University - Camden, M

New York

New York University, O
St. John's University, M
University at Albany, State University of New York, O

North Carolina

East Carolina University, M
North Carolina State University, M

Pennsylvania

Duquesne University, M
Indiana University of Pennsylvania, M
La Salle University, M
Lehigh University, M
Shippensburg University of Pennsylvania, M

South Carolina

University of South Carolina, MO

Tennessee

Middle Tennessee State University, D

Texas

The University of Texas at Austin, D

Virginia

George Mason University, D

West Virginia

American Public University System, M

PUBLIC POLICY ANALYSIS

United States

Alabama

Auburn University at Montgomery, D

Arizona

Arizona State University at the Downtown Phoenix campus, B

Arizona State University at the Tempe campus, M
The University of Arizona, D

Arkansas

University of Arkansas, D

California

California Lutheran University, M
California State University, East Bay, M
California State University, Long Beach, M
California State University, Sacramento, M
Mills College, BM
Pepperdine University, M
Pomona College, B
San Francisco State University, M
Scripps College, B
Stanford University, B
University of California, Berkeley, MD
University of California, Los Angeles, M
University of California, Riverside, B
University of California, San Diego, M
University of the Pacific, M
University of Redlands, B
University of Southern California, MDO

Colorado

University of Colorado Boulder, M
University of Denver, BM

Connecticut

Trinity College, BM
University of Saint Joseph, B

Delaware

University of Delaware, BMD

District of Columbia

The George Washington University, BMD
Georgetown University, M

Florida

Florida State University, MDO
Jacksonville University, B
New College of Florida, B
Southeastern University, B
University of South Florida, M

Georgia

Albany State University, M
Georgia Institute of Technology, BMD
Georgia State University, BM
University of Georgia, MD

Hawaii

University of Hawaii at Manoa, O

Idaho

Boise State University, MO

Illinois

DePaul University, BM
Loyola University Chicago, M
National Louis University, M
Northwestern University, BMD
Olivet Nazarene University, B
University of Chicago, BMD

Indiana

Indiana University Bloomington, MD
Indiana University - Purdue University Fort Wayne, BMO
Indiana Wesleyan University, B

Iowa

University of Northern Iowa, M

Kentucky

Morehead State University, BM
University of Kentucky, MD
University of Louisville, M

Louisiana

Southern University and Agricultural and Mechanical College, D

Maine

College of the Atlantic, B
University of Southern Maine, M

Maryland

Johns Hopkins University, BM
St. Mary's College of Maryland, B
University of Maryland, Baltimore County, MD
University of Maryland, College Park, MD

Massachusetts

Anna Maria College, B
Bentley University, B
Brandeis University, M
Hampshire College, B
Harvard University, MD
Massachusetts College of Liberal Arts, B
Northeastern University, MD
Simmons College, M
Suffolk University, BMO
Tufts University, M
University of Massachusetts Amherst, M
University of Massachusetts Boston, MD
University of Massachusetts Dartmouth, MO

Michigan

Albion College, B
Eastern Michigan University, O
Michigan State University, B
University of Michigan, BMD
University of Michigan - Dearborn, M
Wayne State University, M

Minnesota

Concordia University, St. Paul, B
St. Cloud State University, B
University of Minnesota, Twin Cities Campus, M
Walden University, MDO

Mississippi

Jackson State University, MD
Mississippi State University, MD
University of Mississippi, B

Missouri

Lincoln University, M
Saint Louis University, MDO
University of Missouri, O
University of Missouri - St. Louis, MO
Washington University in St. Louis, M

Nebraska

University of Nebraska - Lincoln, O

New Hampshire

New England College, M

New Jersey

Monmouth University, M
Princeton University, BMD
Rutgers University - Camden, M
Rutgers University - New Brunswick, MD
Rutgers University - Newark, MO
Saint Peter's University, AB
Seton Hall University, M
William Paterson University of New Jersey, M

New York

Baruch College of the City University of New York, M
Brooklyn College of the City University of New York, M
Columbia University, M
Cornell University, BMD
Hamilton College, B
Hobart and William Smith Colleges, B
John Jay College of Criminal Justice of the City University of New York, D
New York University, M
Rochester Institute of Technology, BM
The Sage Colleges, B
Sarah Lawrence College, B
State University of New York Empire State College, M

Stony Brook University, State University of New York, M
University at Albany, State University of New York, BMDO
University of Rochester, M
Wagner College, B

North Carolina

Duke University, BMD
Elon University, B
The University of North Carolina at Chapel Hill, BD
The University of North Carolina at Charlotte, DO

Ohio

Cleveland State University, M
Muskingum University, B
The Ohio State University, D
Union Institute & University, MD

Oklahoma

University of Oklahoma, M

Oregon

Oregon State University, MD
Portland State University, D
University of Oregon, M

Pennsylvania

Carnegie Mellon University, BMD
Chatham University, B
Dickinson College, B
Duquesne University, MO
Eastern University, M
Penn State Harrisburg, BO
Saint Vincent College, B
Susquehanna University, B
University of Pennsylvania, BMD
University of Pittsburgh, MD
University of Pittsburgh at Greensburg, B

Rhode Island

Brown University, M
Bryant University, B
University of Rhode Island, BM

South Carolina

Clemson University, DO

South Dakota

Dakota Wesleyan University, B
The University of South Dakota, M

Tennessee

Trevecca Nazarene University, B
University of Memphis, M
Vanderbilt University, B

Texas

Baylor University, M
Del Mar College, A
Howard Payne University, B
Rice University, B
St. Mary's University, O
Southern Methodist University, B
The University of Texas at Austin, D
The University of Texas at Dallas, BM
The University of Texas Rio Grande Valley, M

Utah

Brigham Young University, B
University of Utah, M

Vermont

Bennington College, B
Norwich University, M

Virginia

The College of William and Mary, BM
George Mason University, MD
Liberty University, M
Longwood University, M
University of Virginia, BM
Virginia Commonwealth University, D

Virginia Polytechnic Institute and State University, BM

Washington

Central Washington University, B
University of Washington, D
University of Washington, Bothell, M
Washington State University, B
Washington State University - Vancouver, B

West Virginia

American Public University System, M
West Virginia University, MD

U.S. Territories: Puerto Rico

Universidad del Este, M
University of Puerto Rico, Río Piedras Campus, M

Canada

Alberta

Mount Royal University, B

British Columbia

Simon Fraser University, M

Maritime Provinces: New Brunswick

University of New Brunswick Fredericton, M

Ontario

Brock University, M
Carleton University, D
McMaster University, MD
Queen's University at Kingston, M
University of Guelph, M
Wilfrid Laurier University, M
York University, BM

Quebec

Concordia University, MD
Université de Montréal, O

Saskatchewan

University of Regina, MDO
University of Saskatchewan, MD

PUBLIC RELATIONS, ADVERTISING, AND APPLIED COMMUNICATION

United States

Alabama

Spring Hill College, B

Arizona

Northern Arizona University, B

Arkansas

Arkansas State University, B
John Brown University, AB
University of Central Arkansas, B

California

California Lutheran University, B
Pepperdine University, B

Colorado

Metropolitan State University of Denver, B

Florida

The University of Tampa, B

Illinois

Bradley University, B
DePaul University, B
Harper College, A
Loyola University Chicago, B

Indiana

Butler University, B
Grace College, B

Iowa

Buena Vista University, B

Maine

Thomas College, B
University of Maine at Presque Isle, A

Michigan

Northern Michigan University, B
Spring Arbor University, B
Western Michigan University, B

Minnesota

The College of St. Scholastica, B
Saint Mary's University of Minnesota, B

Missouri

College of the Ozarks, B
Columbia College, B
Missouri Western State University, B

New York

Morrisville State College, B
Rochester Institute of Technology, B
St. John's University, B

North Carolina

Campbell University, B

Ohio

Marietta College, B
Notre Dame College, B
Ohio Northern University, B

Oklahoma

Oklahoma City University, B
Oklahoma State University, B

Pennsylvania

Community College of Beaver County, A
Duquesne University, B
Marywood University, B

Tennessee

Belmont University, B
Lipscomb University, B

Texas

Abilene Christian University, B

Utah

Brigham Young University, B
LDS Business College, A
Weber State University, B

Vermont

Johnson State College, B
University of Vermont, B

Virginia

Virginia State University, B

Washington

Washington State University, B

Wisconsin

Carroll University, B

U.S. Territories: Puerto Rico

Universidad Metropolitana, B

Canada

British Columbia

Royal Roads University, B

PUBLIC RELATIONS/IMAGE MANAGEMENT

United States

Alabama

Auburn University, B
Community College of the Air Force, A
South University, B
The University of Alabama, B

Arizona

Glendale Community College, A

Arkansas

Harding University, B
John Brown University, AB

California

Biola University, B
California Lutheran University, B
California State University, Dominguez Hills, B
California State University, East Bay, B
California State University, Fresno, B
California State University, Fullerton, B
California State University, Long Beach, B
Chapman University, B
Cosumnes River College, A
Long Beach City College, A
Los Angeles City College, A
The Master's College and Seminary, B
San Diego State University, B
San Jose State University, B
University of Southern California, B

Connecticut

Quinnipiac University, B

Delaware

Delaware State University, B

Florida

Barry University, B
Florida Agricultural and Mechanical University, B
Palm Beach Atlantic University, B
South Florida State College, A
University of Florida, B
University of Miami, B

Georgia

Georgia Southern University, B
South University, B
University of Georgia, B

Hawaii

Hawai'i Pacific University, B

Idaho

University of Idaho, B

Illinois

Bradley University, B
Columbia College Chicago, B
Dominican University, B
Greenville College, B
Illinois State University, B
Lewis University, B
Monmouth College, B
Roosevelt University, B

Indiana

Huntington University, B
Indiana Wesleyan University, B
Taylor University, B
Vincennes University, A

Iowa

Coe College, B
Drake University, B
Iowa State University of Science and Technology, B
Loras College, B
Mount Mercy University, B

Northwestern College, B
St. Ambrose University, B
University of Northern Iowa, B
Wartburg College, B
William Penn University, B

Kansas

Fort Hays State University, B
McPherson College, B

Kentucky

Eastern Kentucky University, B
Murray State University, B
Northern Kentucky University, B
Western Kentucky University, B

Louisiana

University of Louisiana at Lafayette, B

Maine

Saint Joseph's College of Maine, B

Maryland

Bowie State University, B
Hood College, B

Massachusetts

Cape Cod Community College, A
Emerson College, B
Lasell College, B
Salem State University, B
Suffolk University, B
Western New England University, B

Michigan

Andrews University, B
Central Michigan University, B
Cornerstone University, B
Eastern Michigan University, B
Ferris State University, B
Northern Michigan University, B
Wayne State University, B

Minnesota

Minnesota State University Mankato, B
Minnesota State University Moorhead, B
St. Cloud State University, B
University of Northwestern - St. Paul, B

Mississippi

Mississippi College, B

Missouri

Avila University, B
Crowder College, A
Missouri Baptist University, B
Stephens College, B
University of Central Missouri, B
Webster University, B

Montana

Carroll College, B
Montana State University Billings, B

Nebraska

Hastings College, B

New Hampshire

Keene State College, B
New England College, B

New Jersey

Brookdale Community College, A
Rider University, B
Rowan University, B

New York

Buffalo State College, State University of New York, B
Hofstra University, B
Iona College, B
Ithaca College, B
Long Island University - LIU Post, B
Mount Saint Mary College, B

Rochester Institute of Technology, B
State University of New York at Oswego, B
Syracuse University, B
Utica College, B

North Carolina

Appalachian State University, B
North Carolina Agricultural and Technical State University, B
Pfeiffer University, B

North Dakota

Bismarck State College, A
North Dakota State University, B

Ohio

Baldwin Wallace University, B
Bowling Green State University, B
Capital University, B
Cleveland State University, B
Franklin University, AB
Heidelberg University, B
Kent State University, B
Miami University, B
Mount Vernon Nazarene University, B
Ohio University - Zanesville, B
Otterbein University, B
Tiffin University, B
The University of Akron, B
The University of Findlay, B
University of Rio Grande, B
Ursuline College, B
Xavier University, AB

Oklahoma

Oklahoma Christian University, B
University of Central Oklahoma, B

Oregon

University of Oregon, B

Pennsylvania

Chatham University, B
La Salle University, B
Mansfield University of Pennsylvania, B
Point Park University, B
Saint Francis University, B
Slippery Rock University of Pennsylvania, B
University of Pittsburgh at Bradford, B
Westminster College, B
York College of Pennsylvania, B

Rhode Island

Johnson & Wales University, B
University of Rhode Island, B

South Carolina

University of South Carolina, B

Tennessee

Belmont University, B
Freed-Hardeman University, B
Lee University, B
Lipscomb University, B
Middle Tennessee State University, B
Southern Adventist University, B
Union University, B
The University of Tennessee, B

Texas

Amarillo College, A
Southern Methodist University, B
Texas Christian University, B
Texas State University, B
Texas Tech University, B
University of Houston, B
The University of Texas at Arlington, B
The University of Texas at Austin, B

Utah

Weber State University, B

Vermont

Castleton University, B
Champlain College, B

Virginia

Hampton University, B
South University (Virginia Beach), B

Washington

Central Washington University, B
Gonzaga University, B
Walla Walla University, B
Washington State University, B

West Virginia

Alderson Broaddus University, B
West Virginia Wesleyan College, B

Wisconsin

Carroll University, B
Marquette University, B

U.S. Territories: Puerto Rico

Inter American University of Puerto Rico, Ponce
  Campus, B
Pontifical Catholic University of Puerto Rico, B
University of Puerto Rico, Río Piedras Campus, B

Canada

Alberta

Mount Royal University, B

Maritime Provinces: Nova Scotia

Mount Saint Vincent University, B

Ontario

University of Ottawa, B
University of Toronto, B

PUBLISHING

United States

Arizona

Arizona State University at the Tempe campus, O

District of Columbia

The George Washington University, M

Illinois

DePaul University, M
North Central College, M
Northwestern University, M

Iowa

Graceland University, B

Maryland

University of Baltimore, M

Massachusetts

Emerson College, BM

Missouri

University of Missouri, B

New Jersey

Rowan University, O

New York

New York University, M
Pace University, MO
Rochester Institute of Technology, B

Pennsylvania

Carnegie Mellon University, M
Drexel University, M
Rosemont College, M

Rhode Island

Brown University, D

Texas

Sam Houston State University, M
University of Houston - Victoria, M

Canada

British Columbia

Simon Fraser University, M

PURCHASING, PROCURE-MENT/ACQUISITIONS AND CONTRACTS MANAGEMENT

United States

Alabama

Athens State University, B
Community College of the Air Force, A
The University of Alabama in Huntsville, B

Arizona

Arizona State University at the Tempe campus, B

California

California State University, East Bay, B
De Anza College, A

District of Columbia

University of the District of Columbia, B
University of the Potomac, B

Florida

Northwest Florida State College, B

Illinois

University of Illinois at Urbana - Champaign, B

Maryland

Cecil College, A

Michigan

Central Michigan University, B

Ohio

Columbus State Community College, A
Miami University Hamilton, A

South Carolina

Greenville Technical College, A

Tennessee

Trevecca Nazarene University, A

Texas

University of Houston - Downtown, B

Washington

Shoreline Community College, A

QUALITY CONTROL AND SAFETY TECHNOLOGIES/ TECHNICIANS

United States

Colorado

Community College of Denver, A

Indiana

Ivy Tech Community College - Lafayette, A
Ivy Tech Community College - Wabash Valley, A

Kentucky

Elizabethtown Community and Technical College, A

Michigan

Macomb Community College, A
Madonna University, AB

Minnesota

Pine Technical and Community College, A

New Mexico

Eastern New Mexico University - Roswell, A

Ohio

Cuyahoga Community College, A

Oklahoma

University of Central Oklahoma, B

Washington

Clover Park Technical College, A

QUALITY CONTROL TECHNOL-OGY/TECHNICIAN

United States

Arizona

Mesa Community College, A

Arkansas

Arkansas State University - Beebe, A

California

California National University for Advanced Studies,
  B
California State University, Dominguez Hills, B
California State University, Long Beach, B
Los Angeles Pierce College, A
Los Angeles Southwest College, A
Mt. San Antonio College, A
San Jose State University, B
Santa Ana College, A

Connecticut

Goodwin College, A

Illinois

Heartland Community College, A
Illinois Eastern Community Colleges, Frontier Com-
  munity College, A
Illinois Eastern Community Colleges, Lincoln Trail
  College, A
Rock Valley College, A

Indiana

Ivy Tech Community College - Lafayette, A

Michigan

Grand Rapids Community College, A
Macomb Community College, A

Missouri

Metropolitan Community College - Kansas City, A

Nebraska

Central Community College - Columbus Campus, A
Central Community College - Hastings Campus, A
Southeast Community College, Milford Campus, A

New York

Broome Community College, A
Monroe Community College, A

North Carolina

Central Carolina Community College, A

Ohio

Bowling Green State University, B
Columbus State Community College, A

James A. Rhodes State College, A
Lakeland Community College, A
Lorain County Community College, A
Sinclair Community College, A

Oklahoma

Spartan College of Aeronautics and Technology, AB

Pennsylvania

Community College of Allegheny County, A
Northampton Community College, A

South Carolina

Aiken Technical College, A

Texas

Tarleton State University, B
Tarrant County College District, A

Utah

Salt Lake Community College, A
Weber State University, A

Washington

South Seattle College, A

Wisconsin

Lakeshore Technical College, A
Mid-State Technical College, A
Northeast Wisconsin Technical College, A

U.S. Territories: Puerto Rico

Universidad del Turabo, A
University of Puerto Rico in Aguadilla, B
University of Puerto Rico in Utuado, B

QUALITY MANAGEMENT

United States

Alabama

The University of Alabama, M

California

California Intercontinental University, M
California State University, Dominguez Hills, M
San Jose State University, M
Trident University International, MO

Florida

Florida Institute of Technology, M

Illinois

Northwestern University, M

Indiana

Calumet College of Saint Joseph, M

Iowa

Mount Mercy University, M
Upper Iowa University, M

Massachusetts

Regis College, M
University of Massachusetts Boston, MO

Michigan

Eastern Michigan University, MO
Madonna University, M

New Hampshire

Southern New Hampshire University, O

New Jersey

Rutgers University - New Brunswick, M
Stevens Institute of Technology, O

New York

Hofstra University, M

North Carolina

East Carolina University, M

Pennsylvania

Penn State Erie, The Behrend College, M

Tennessee

The University of Tennessee at Chattanooga, O

Wisconsin

Marian University, M
University of Wisconsin - Stout, M

U.S. Territories: Puerto Rico

Universidad del Turabo, M

QUANTITATIVE ANALYSIS

United States

Alabama

The University of Alabama at Birmingham, M

California

San Francisco State University, M
University of California, Santa Barbara, D
University of Southern California, D

Colorado

University of Colorado Denver, M

Connecticut

University of Connecticut, O

Florida

University of Florida, D

Illinois

Northwestern University, M

Indiana

Purdue University, MD

Iowa

The University of Iowa, M

Maryland

University of Maryland, College Park, MD

Minnesota

University of Minnesota, Twin Cities Campus, O

New Jersey

Rutgers University - Newark, M

New Mexico

University of New Mexico, D

New York

Baruch College of the City University of New York, M
Columbia University, M
Cornell University, MD
Hofstra University, M
St. John's University, M
Syracuse University, D
University at Buffalo, the State University of New York, M

North Carolina

Duke University, MD

Ohio

University of Cincinnati, MD

Oregon

University of Oregon, M

Pennsylvania

Drexel University, MD
La Salle University, MO
Lehigh University, M

Texas

University of North Texas, M
The University of Texas at Arlington, MD
The University of Texas at Austin, M

Virginia

Virginia Commonwealth University, M
Virginia Polytechnic Institute and State University, O

U.S. Territories: Puerto Rico

University of Puerto Rico, Río Piedras Campus, M

Canada

British Columbia

The University of British Columbia, MD

RABBINICAL STUDIES

United States

Florida

Talmudic University, B

New York

Central Yeshiva Tomchei Tmimim-Lubavitch, B
Ohr Somayach/Joseph Tanenbaum Educational Center, B
Rabbinical Academy Mesivta Rabbi Chaim Berlin, B
Sh'or Yoshuv Rabbinical College, B
Talmudical Seminary Oholei Torah, B

Pennsylvania

Talmudical Yeshiva of Philadelphia, B

Canada

Quebec

Université Laval, AB

RADIATION BIOLOGY/ RADIOBIOLOGY

United States

Alabama

Auburn University, M

Colorado

Colorado State University, MD

District of Columbia

Georgetown University, M

Iowa

The University of Iowa, M

Massachusetts

Suffolk University, B

Oklahoma

University of Oklahoma Health Sciences Center, MD

Tennessee

Austin Peay State University, M

Canada

Quebec

Université de Sherbrooke, MD

RADIATION PROTECTION/ HEALTH PHYSICS TECHNICIAN

United States

Florida

Cambridge Institute of Allied Health and Technology, A
Keiser University, A

Illinois

Lewis University, B

Indiana

Indiana University - Purdue University Indianapolis, B

New Jersey

Thomas Edison State University, AB

South Carolina

Aiken Technical College, A
Spartanburg Community College, A

Texas

Lone Star College - CyFair, A

RADIO AND TELEVISION

United States

Alabama

Auburn University, B
Troy University, B
The University of Alabama, B
University of Montevallo, B

Arizona

Northern Arizona University, B

Arkansas

John Brown University, B
University of Arkansas at Little Rock, B

California

Biola University, B
Butte College, A
California State University, Fresno, B
California State University, Fullerton, B
California State University, Long Beach, B
California State University, Los Angeles, B
California State University, Monterey Bay, B
Chabot College, A
Chaffey College, A
College of San Mateo, A
Columbia College Hollywood, B
Cosumnes River College, A
Cuesta College, A
De Anza College, A
Fullerton College, A
Glendale Community College, A
Golden West College, A
Grossmont College, A
Laney College, A
Lassen Community College District, A
Long Beach City College, A
Los Angeles City College, A
Los Angeles Southwest College, A
Los Angeles Valley College, A
The Master's College and Seminary, B
Modesto Junior College, A
Mt. San Antonio College, A
Napa Valley College, A
Ohlone College, A
Oxnard College, A
Palomar College, A
Pasadena City College, A
Pepperdine University, B
Saddleback College, A
San Bernardino Valley College, A
San Diego City College, A
San Diego State University, B
San Francisco State University, B
San Jose State University, B
Santa Monica College, A
Southwestern College, A
Vanguard University of Southern California, B

Colorado

Aims Community College, A

Delaware

Delaware State University, B

District of Columbia

The George Washington University, B
Howard University, B

Florida

Barry University, B
Broward College, A
City College (Fort Lauderdale), A
Daytona State College, A
Miami Dade College, A
South Florida State College, A
Southeastern University, B
State College of Florida Manatee-Sarasota, A
University of Central Florida, B
University of Florida, B
University of Miami, B

Georgia

Georgia Southern University, B
Savannah College of Art and Design, B

Illinois

Bradley University, B
Chicago State University, B
City Colleges of Chicago, Kennedy-King College, A
Columbia College Chicago, B
Illinois Eastern Community Colleges, Wabash Valley College, A
Lake Land College, A
Lewis and Clark Community College, A
Lewis University, B
North Central College, B
Northwestern University, B
Parkland College, A
Southern Illinois University Carbondale, B
Western Illinois University, B

Indiana

Ball State University, B
Butler University, B
University of Southern Indiana, B

Iowa

Drake University, B
Iowa Central Community College, A
Iowa Lakes Community College, A
St. Ambrose University, B
Wartburg College, B
William Penn University, B

Kansas

Colby Community College, A
Dodge City Community College, A
Southwestern College, B

Kentucky

American National University (Lexington), A
Eastern Kentucky University, B
Murray State University, B
University of Kentucky, B
Western Kentucky University, B

Massachusetts

Eastern Nazarene College, B
Emerson College, B
Lasell College, B

Michigan

Cornerstone University, B
Delta College, A
Grand Valley State University, B

Lawrence Technological University, A
Wayne State University, B

Minnesota

Bemidji State University, B
St. Cloud State University, B
Southwest Minnesota State University, B
University of Northwestern - St. Paul, AB

Mississippi

Coahoma Community College, A
Northeast Mississippi Community College, A
Northwest Mississippi Community College, A

Missouri

Evangel University, B
Missouri Baptist University, B
University of Central Missouri, B
University of Missouri, B

Montana

University of Montana, B

Nebraska

Hastings College, B

New Hampshire

Franklin Pierce University, B

New Jersey

Montclair State University, B
Rider University, B
Rowan University, B

New York

Brooklyn College of the City University of New York, B
Buffalo State College, State University of New York, B
Genesee Community College, A
Hofstra University, B
Iona College, B
Ithaca College, B
Marist College, B
Onondaga Community College, A
St. Francis College, B
State University of New York at Fredonia, B
Sullivan County Community College, A
Syracuse University, B

North Carolina

Appalachian State University, B
Central Carolina Community College, A
Elon University, B
Isothermal Community College, A
North Carolina Agricultural and Technical State University, B

North Dakota

Minot State University, B

Ohio

Ashland University, B
Bowling Green State University, B
Kent State University, B
Marietta College, B
Ohio Northern University, B
Ohio University, B
Ohio University - Zanesville, A
Otterbein University, B
The University of Akron, B
University of Cincinnati, B
University of Dayton, B
Washington State Community College, A
Xavier University, AB
Youngstown State University, B

Oklahoma

Oklahoma Christian University, B
University of Central Oklahoma, B

Oregon

Mt. Hood Community College, A
Pacific University, B

Pennsylvania

Point Park University, B
Temple University, B
University of Pittsburgh at Bradford, B
Waynesburg University, B

South Dakota

University of Sioux Falls, B

Tennessee

Union University, B

Texas

Alvin Community College, A
Amarillo College, A
Austin Community College District, A
Central Texas College, A
Del Mar College, A
Lee College, A
Sam Houston State University, B
San Antonio College, A
Texas A&M University - Commerce, B
Texas Southern University, B
Texas State University, B
Texas Tech University, B
Texas Wesleyan University, B
Tyler Junior College, A
University of Houston, B
University of the Incarnate Word, B
University of North Texas, B
The University of Texas at Arlington, B
The University of Texas at Austin, B
Western Texas College, A

Utah

Weber State University, B

Vermont

Castleton University, B
Lyndon State College, B

Virginia

Virginia Western Community College, A

Washington

Gonzaga University, B
Walla Walla University, B

Wisconsin

University of Wisconsin - Oshkosh, B
University of Wisconsin - Superior, B

Wyoming

Central Wyoming College, A
Northwest College, A

U.S. Territories: Puerto Rico

Pontifical Catholic University of Puerto Rico, B

Canada

Ontario

Ryerson University, B
The University of Western Ontario, B

RADIO AND TELEVISION BROADCASTING TECHNOL-OGY/TECHNICIAN

United States

Alabama

Alabama Agricultural and Mechanical University, B

Arizona

Arizona Western College, A
South Mountain Community College, A

California

Ohlone College, A
Pasadena City College, A

Colorado

Aims Community College, A
Pikes Peak Community College, A

Connecticut

Lincoln College of New England, A

Delaware

Wilmington University, B

Florida

Miami Dade College, A
State College of Florida Manatee-Sarasota, A

Hawaii

Leeward Community College, A

Idaho

Northwest Nazarene University, B

Illinois

Lincoln College, A
Parkland College, A
Waubonsee Community College, A

Indiana

Vincennes University, A

Iowa

Iowa Lakes Community College, A
Iowa Western Community College, A
Kirkwood Community College, A
Marshalltown Community College, A

Kansas

Cloud County Community College, A
Hutchinson Community College, A

Maryland

Towson University, B

Massachusetts

Emerson College, B
Mount Wachusett Community College, A
Roxbury Community College, A
Springfield Technical Community College, A
Suffolk University, B

Michigan

Ferris State University, B
Lansing Community College, A
Oakland Community College, A
Schoolcraft College, A

Mississippi

Hinds Community College, A
Northwest Mississippi Community College, A

Missouri

College of the Ozarks, B
Mineral Area College, A
Ozarks Technical Community College, A

Nebraska

Central Community College - Hastings Campus, A
Northeast Community College, A

New Jersey

Bergen Community College, A
Brookdale Community College, A
Camden County College, A
Mercer County Community College, A

New Mexico

Santa Fe Community College, A

New York

Adirondack Community College, A
Borough of Manhattan Community College of the
   City University of New York, A
Genesee Community College, A
Long Island University - LIU Post, B
New York Institute of Technology, B
New York University, B
Tompkins Cortland Community College, A

North Carolina

Cleveland Community College, A
Gardner-Webb University, B
Gaston College, A
Wilkes Community College, A

Ohio

International College of Broadcasting, A
Ohio University - Southern Campus, A

Pennsylvania

Gannon University, B
La Salle University, B
Lehigh Carbon Community College, A
Luzerne County Community College, A
Mercyhurst North East, A
Northampton Community College, A
Westmoreland County Community College, A

Rhode Island

New England Institute of Technology, A

South Carolina

Tri-County Technical College, A
York Technical College, A

Texas

Cedar Valley College, A
Houston Community College, A
San Jacinto College District, A

Utah

Salt Lake Community College, A

Vermont

Lyndon State College, A

Washington

Bates Technical College, A
Clover Park Technical College, A

Wisconsin

Milwaukee Area Technical College, A

Wyoming

Northwest College, A

U.S. Territories: Puerto Rico

Universidad del Turabo, B
University of Puerto Rico in Arecibo, AB
University of Puerto Rico in Utuado, B

Canada

British Columbia

British Columbia Institute of Technology, A

RADIO, TELEVISION, AND DIGI-TAL COMMUNICATION

United States

Alabama

Spring Hill College, B

Arizona

University of Advancing Technology, B

Arkansas

Arkansas State University, B
John Brown University, B

California

American River College, A
San Francisco State University, B
Santiago Canyon College, A

Georgia

Clark Atlanta University, B

Iowa

Drake University, B
William Penn University, B

Kentucky

Asbury University, B

Maryland

Towson University, B

Massachusetts

Emerson College, B

Michigan

Central Michigan University, B
Lawrence Technological University, A
Madonna University, AB

New Jersey

Seton Hall University, B

New York

Cayuga County Community College, A
Genesee Community College, A
Hofstra University, B
State University of New York College of Agriculture
   and Technology at Cobleskill, B
Sullivan County Community College, A

North Carolina

Campbell University, B
Western Carolina University, B

North Dakota

North Dakota State University, B

Ohio

Ashland University, B
The University of Akron, B

Oklahoma

Rogers State University, B

Pennsylvania

Keystone College, AB
Montgomery County Community College, A
Pennsylvania Highlands Community College, A

South Dakota

Mitchell Technical Institute, A

Texas

Dallas Baptist University, B
Texas Christian University, B

Utah

Brigham Young University, B

Washington

Washington State University, B

Wisconsin

Fox Valley Technical College, A
Marquette University, B

RADIOLOGIC TECHNOLOGY/ SCIENCE - RADIOGRAPHER

United States

Alabama

Gadsden State Community College, A
George C. Wallace Community College, A
H. Councill Trenholm State Community College, A
Jefferson State Community College, A
University of South Alabama, B

Alaska

University of Alaska Anchorage, A

Arizona

Arizona Western College, A
Carrington College - Phoenix North, A
GateWay Community College, A
Pima Community College, A
Pima Medical Institute (Mesa), A
Pima Medical Institute (Tucson), A

Arkansas

Henderson State University, B
National Park College, A
University of Arkansas - Fort Smith, AB

California

Antelope Valley College, A
Cabrillo College, A
Cañada College, A
Chaffey College, A
City College of San Francisco, A
Contra Costa College, A
Crafton Hills College, A
Cypress College, A
Foothill College, A
Fresno City College, A
Long Beach City College, A
Los Angeles City College, A
Merritt College, A
National University, B
Pasadena City College, A
Pima Medical Institute, A
Santa Rosa Junior College, A

Colorado

Aims Community College, A
Colorado Mesa University, AB
Community College of Denver, A
Pima Medical Institute (Denver), A
Pueblo Community College, A
Red Rocks Community College, A

Connecticut

Quinnipiac University, B
St. Vincent's College, AB

Delaware

Delaware Technical & Community College, Jack F.
   Owens Campus, A
Delaware Technical & Community College,
   Stanton/Wilmington Campus, A

District of Columbia

The George Washington University, B

Florida

Adventist University of Health Sciences, AB
Cambridge Institute of Allied Health and Technology,
   A
Florida National University, A
Miami Dade College, A
Pasco-Hernando State College, A
St. Johns River State College, A
St. Petersburg College, A
State College of Florida Manatee-Sarasota, A

Georgia

Andrew College, A
Dalton State College, A
Gordon State College, A

Idaho

Lewis-Clark State College, A

Illinois

Black Hawk College, A
Carl Sandburg College, A
Danville Area Community College, A
Elgin Community College, A
Harper College, A
Heartland Community College, A
Illinois Central College, A
John Wood Community College, A
Joliet Junior College, A
Kankakee Community College, A
Kaskaskia College, A
Kishwaukee College, A
Lewis University, B
Lincoln Land Community College, A
Moraine Valley Community College, A
Northwestern College - Chicago Campus, A
Sauk Valley Community College, A
South Suburban College, A
Southwestern Illinois College, A
Trinity College of Nursing and Health Sciences, A
Triton College, A
University of St. Francis, B

Indiana

Indiana University Kokomo, A
Indiana University Northwest, AB
Indiana University - Purdue University Indianapolis,
   A
Indiana University South Bend, A
University of Saint Francis, A

Iowa

Allen College, A
Indian Hills Community College, A
Mercy College of Health Sciences, A
Northeast Iowa Community College, A
Northwest Iowa Community College, A
St. Luke's College, A
The University of Iowa, B

Kansas

Barton County Community College, A
Fort Hays State University, AB
Friends University, B
Hutchinson Community College, A
Newman University, A
Washburn University, A

Kentucky

Jefferson Community and Technical College, A
Madisonville Community College, A
Northern Kentucky University, B
Owensboro Community and Technical College, A
Spencerian College, AB
Spencerian College - Lexington, A

Louisiana

Fortis College, A
Louisiana State University at Alexandria, A
Louisiana State University at Eunice, A
McCann School of Business & Technology (Mon-
   roe), A
McNeese State University, B
Northwestern State University of Louisiana, B
Southern University at Shreveport, A
University of Louisiana at Monroe, B

Maine

Kennebec Valley Community College, A
Maine College of Health Professions, A
Southern Maine Community College, A

Maryland

Prince George's Community College, A

Massachusetts

Massachusetts Bay Community College, A
Massasoit Community College, A
MCPHS University, B
Northern Essex Community College, A

Quinsigamond Community College, A
Regis College, AB
Springfield Technical Community College, A

Michigan

Baker College, A
Henry Ford College, A
Lake Michigan College, A
Lansing Community College, A
Northern Michigan University, AB
Oakland University, B

Minnesota

Argosy University, Twin Cities, A
Century College, A
Lake Superior College, A
Minnesota State College - Southeast Technical, A
Minnesota State Community and Technical College,
   A
Minnesota State Community and Technical College -
   Detroit Lakes, A
Minnesota West Community and Technical College,
   A
Northland Community and Technical College, A
Ridgewater College, A
Rochester Community and Technical College, A

Mississippi

Hinds Community College, A
University of Mississippi, B

Missouri

Cox College, AB
Jefferson College, A
Missouri State University, B
Northwest Missouri State University, B
State Fair Community College, A
University of Missouri, B

Montana

Great Falls College Montana State University, A
Montana Tech of The University of Montana, A
University of Montana, A

Nebraska

Clarkson College, A
Nebraska Methodist College, AB
University of Nebraska Medical Center, B
Western Nebraska Community College, A

Nevada

Brightwood College, Las Vegas Campus, A
Great Basin College, A
Pima Medical Institute, A

New Jersey

Bergen Community College, A
County College of Morris, A
Fairleigh Dickinson University, Metropolitan Cam-
   pus, A
Hudson County Community College, A
Union County College, A

New Mexico

Central New Mexico Community College, A
Pima Medical Institute (Albuquerque), A

New York

Adirondack Community College, A
Hudson Valley Community College, A
Manhattan College, B
St. John's University, B
State University of New York College of Technology
   at Alfred, A
State University of New York Upstate Medical Uni-
   versity, B
Trocaire College, B

North Carolina

Asheville-Buncombe Technical Community College,
   A
Caldwell Community College and Technical Institute,
   A
Carolinas College of Health Sciences, A

Catawba Valley Community College, A
Cleveland Community College, A
Fayetteville Technical Community College, A
Forsyth Technical Community College, A
Lenoir Community College, A
Pitt Community College, A
Randolph Community College, A
Rowan-Cabarrus Community College, A
Sandhills Community College, A
Wake Technical Community College, A

North Dakota

North Dakota State University, B
University of Jamestown, B
University of Mary, B

Ohio

Aultman College of Nursing and Health Sciences, A
Central Ohio Technical College, A
Kettering College, AB
Marion Technical College, A
The Ohio State University, B
Sinclair Community College, A
University of Rio Grande, A
Xavier University, A

Oklahoma

Oklahoma State University, Oklahoma City, A
University of Oklahoma Health Sciences Center, B

Oregon

Central Oregon Community College, A
Oregon Institute of Technology, B

Pennsylvania

Alvernia University, A
Butler County Community College, A
Gannon University, A
Gwynedd Mercy University, B
Harrisburg Area Community College, A
Holy Family University, AB
Keystone College, A
Mansfield University of Pennsylvania, A
Montgomery County Community College, A
Northampton Community College, A
Pennsylvania College of Health Sciences, A
Pennsylvania Highlands Community College, A
University of Pittsburgh at Bradford, B
Westmoreland County Community College, A
Widener University, AB
York College of Pennsylvania, B

Rhode Island

Community College of Rhode Island, A
Rhode Island College, B

South Carolina

York Technical College, A

South Dakota

Mitchell Technical Institute, A
Presentation College, AB

Tennessee

Baptist College of Health Sciences, B
Fortis Institute (Cookeville), A
South College, A

Texas

Amarillo College, A
Austin Community College District, A
Brookhaven College, A
El Centro College, A
El Paso Community College, A
Galveston College, A
Grayson College, A
Houston Community College, A
Howard College, A
Kilgore College, A
Laredo Community College, A
Paris Junior College, A
Pima Medical Institute, A
San Jacinto College District, A
Tyler Junior College, A

Weatherford College, A

Utah

Dixie State University, A
Weber State University, AB

Vermont

Champlain College, A
College of St. Joseph, AB

Virginia

Central Virginia Community College, A
ECPI University (Virginia Beach), A
Southwest Virginia Community College, A
Virginia Commonwealth University, B
Virginia Western Community College, A

Washington

Clark College, A
Pima Medical Institute (Seattle), A
Wenatchee Valley College, A

West Virginia

Bluefield State College, B
Marshall University, B
University of Charleston, B

Wisconsin

Lakeshore Technical College, A
Marian University, B
Mount Mary University, B
Western Technical College, A

Wyoming

Casper College, A
Laramie County Community College, A

U.S. Territories: Puerto Rico

Inter American University of Puerto Rico, Aguadilla
   Campus, B
Inter American University of Puerto Rico, Bar-
   ranquitas Campus, AB
Inter American University of Puerto Rico, Ponce
   Campus, B
Inter American University of Puerto Rico, San
   Germán Campus, B
Universidad Central del Caribe, B
Universidad del Este, A
University of Puerto Rico, Medical Sciences Cam-
   pus, A

Canada

Maritime Provinces: New Brunswick

Université de Moncton, B

Maritime Provinces: Nova Scotia

Dalhousie University, B

Ontario

University of Toronto, B

RANGE SCIENCE AND MAN-AGEMENT

United States

Arizona

The University of Arizona, MD

California

Humboldt State University, B
University of California, Berkeley, M

Colorado

Colorado State University, BMD

Idaho

University of Idaho, B

Kansas

Fort Hays State University, B
Kansas State University, MD

Minnesota

Vermilion Community College, A

Montana

Montana State University, MD

Nebraska

Chadron State College, B
University of Nebraska - Lincoln, B

Nevada

University of Nevada, Reno, B

New Mexico

New Mexico State University, BMD

North Dakota

North Dakota State University, B

Oregon

Oregon State University, BMD
Treasure Valley Community College, A

South Dakota

South Dakota State University, B

Texas

Sul Ross State University, BM
Tarleton State University, B
Texas A&M University, BMD
Texas A&M University - Kingsville, M
Trinity Valley Community College, A

Utah

Snow College, A
Utah State University, BMD

Wyoming

Casper College, A
Central Wyoming College, A
Eastern Wyoming College, A
Northwest College, A
Sheridan College, A
University of Wyoming, BMD

Canada

Alberta

University of Alberta, B

READING TEACHER EDUCA-TION

United States

Alabama

Alabama Agricultural and Mechanical University, D
Alabama State University, M
Auburn University, DO
Jacksonville State University, M
Troy University, M
The University of Alabama at Birmingham, M
The University of Alabama in Huntsville, M
University of South Alabama, M

Arizona

The University of Arizona, MDO
University of Phoenix - Online Campus, M
University of Phoenix - Phoenix Campus, M

Arkansas

Arkansas State University, MO
Harding University, BM
Henderson State University, M
Southern Arkansas University - Magnolia, M
University of Arkansas at Little Rock, MDO

University of Central Arkansas, M

California

California Baptist University, M
California State University, East Bay, M
California State University, Fresno, M
California State University, Fullerton, M
California State University, Los Angeles, M
California State University, Northridge, M
California State University, Sacramento, M
California State University, San Bernardino, M
California State University, San Marcos, M
California State University, Stanislaus, M
Fresno Pacific University, MO
Laney College, A
Loyola Marymount University, M
National University, MO
Saint Mary's College of California, M
San Diego State University, M
San Francisco State University, MO
San Jose State University, O
Sonoma State University, M
Trident University International, M
University of California, Riverside, M
University of La Verne, MO
University of San Diego, M
University of San Francisco, M

Colorado

Regis University, MO
University of Colorado Denver, M
University of Northern Colorado, M
Western State Colorado University, M

Connecticut

Central Connecticut State University, MO
Eastern Connecticut State University, M
Sacred Heart University, O
Southern Connecticut State University, MO
University of Bridgeport, MO
University of Connecticut, MDO
University of Saint Joseph, M
Western Connecticut State University, M

Delaware

Delaware State University, M
Wilmington University, M

District of Columbia

The George Washington University, O
Trinity Washington University, M

Florida

Barry University, MO
Florida Atlantic University, M
Florida Gulf Coast University, M
Florida International University, MD
Florida Memorial University, M
Florida State University, MDO
St. Thomas University, MO
University of Central Florida, MO
University of Florida, M
University of Miami, D
University of North Florida, M
University of South Florida, MDO
University of South Florida, St. Petersburg, M
University of West Florida, M

Georgia

Armstrong State University, O
Berry College, M
Georgia College & State University, M
Georgia Southern University, MO
Georgia State University, MD
Kennesaw State University, M
Mercer University, M
University of Georgia, MDO
University of West Georgia, M

Idaho

Boise State University, M
Idaho State University, M

Illinois

Aurora University, M
Benedictine University, M
Chicago State University, M
Concordia University Chicago, BM
DePaul University, M
Dominican University, M
Governors State University, M
Illinois State University, M
Judson University, MD
Lewis University, M
Loyola University Chicago, MO
McKendree University, M
National Louis University, MO
Northeastern Illinois University, M
Northern Illinois University, MD
Olivet Nazarene University, M
Quincy University, M
Rockford University, M
Roosevelt University, M
Saint Xavier University, M
Southern Illinois University Edwardsville, MO
University of St. Francis, M
Western Illinois University, M

Indiana

Indiana University Bloomington, MDO
Indiana University - Purdue University Indianapolis, O
Purdue University, MDO

Iowa

Clarke University, M
Dordt College, B
Graceland University, M
Iowa Wesleyan University, B
Kaplan University, Davenport Campus, M
Mount Mercy University, M
University of Northern Iowa, BM
Upper Iowa University, B
William Penn University, B

Kansas

Emporia State University, M
Kansas State University, M
Newman University, M
Pittsburg State University, M
Washburn University, M

Kentucky

Asbury University, M
Bellarmine University, M
Georgetown College, M
Morehead State University, M
Murray State University, MO
Union College, M
University of the Cumberlands, M
University of Kentucky, M
Western Kentucky University, M

Louisiana

Grambling State University, M
McNeese State University, MO
Northwestern State University of Louisiana, O
Southeastern Louisiana University, M
University of Louisiana at Monroe, M

Maine

University of Maine, DO
University of New England, MO
University of Southern Maine, MO

Maryland

Bowie State University, M
Coppin State University, M
Frostburg State University, M
Goucher College, MO
Hood College, M
Johns Hopkins University, M
Loyola University Maryland, MO
McDaniel College, M
Salisbury University, MD
Towson University, MO
University of Maryland, College Park, MDO

Massachusetts

American International College, MO
Boston College, MO
Bridgewater State University, MO
Cambridge College, M
Curry College, MO
Eastern Nazarene College, MO
Elms College, M
Endicott College, M
Framingham State University, M
Gordon College, O
Harvard University, M
Lesley University, MO
Massachusetts College of Liberal Arts, M
Merrimack College, O
Regis College, M
Salem State University, M
Simmons College, MO
University of Massachusetts Amherst, MD
University of Massachusetts Lowell, MDO
Westfield State University, M
Wheelock College, M
Worcester State University, MO

Michigan

Aquinas College, B
Calvin College, M
Central Michigan University, M
Eastern Michigan University, BM
Ferris State University, M
Grand Valley State University, BM
Madonna University, M
Marygrove College, M
Michigan State University, BM
Northern Michigan University, M
Oakland University, MDO
Saginaw Valley State University, M
Siena Heights University, M
Spring Arbor University, M
University of Michigan - Flint, M
Wayne State University, MDO
Western Michigan University, MD

Minnesota

Bethel University, MO
Capella University, MD
Concordia University, St. Paul, MO
Hamline University, M
St. Cloud State University, B
Saint Mary's University of Minnesota, MO
Southwest Minnesota State University, M
University of Minnesota, Twin Cities Campus, MD
University of St. Thomas, MO
Walden University, MDO

Mississippi

Belhaven University, M
Blue Mountain College, M
Mississippi State University, D
Mississippi University for Women, M

Missouri

Drury University, M
Evangel University, M
Hannibal-LaGrange University, M
Maryville University of Saint Louis, M
Missouri State University, M
Northwest Missouri State University, M
Park University, M
University of Central Missouri, BM
University of Missouri, MDO
University of Missouri - Kansas City, MO
University of Missouri - St. Louis, M
Webster University, M

Montana

Montana State University Billings, M
University of Great Falls, B
University of Montana, B

Nebraska

Concordia University, Nebraska, BM
University of Nebraska at Kearney, M
University of Nebraska at Omaha, M
York College, B

Nevada

University of Nevada, Reno, MD

New Hampshire

Plymouth State University, M
Rivier University, M
Southern New Hampshire University, M

New Jersey

Caldwell University, MO
The College of New Jersey, MO
Fairleigh Dickinson University, College at Florham, O
Fairleigh Dickinson University, Metropolitan Campus, O
Kean University, M
Montclair State University, M
New Jersey City University, M
Rider University, MO
Rowan University, MO
Rutgers University - New Brunswick, MD
Saint Peter's University, M
William Paterson University of New Jersey, M

New Mexico

Eastern New Mexico University, M
University of New Mexico, MD
Western New Mexico University, M

New York

Adelphi University, M
Alfred University, M
Binghamton University, State University of New York, M
Buffalo State College, State University of New York, M
Canisius College, BMO
City College of the City University of New York, M
The College at Brockport, State University of New York, M
The College of New Rochelle, M
The College of Saint Rose, M
Fordham University, MO
Le Moyne College, M
Lehman College of the City University of New York, M
Long Island University - LIU Post, M
Manhattanville College, M
Medaille College, M
Mercy College, MO
Mount Saint Mary College, MO
Nazareth College of Rochester, M
New York University, M
Niagara University, M
Pace University, MO
Queens College of the City University of New York, M
Roberts Wesleyan College, M
St. Bonaventure University, M
St. John Fisher College, M
St. John's University, MDO
St. Joseph's College, Long Island Campus, M
St. Joseph's College, New York, M
St. Thomas Aquinas College, MO
State University of New York College at Cortland, BM
State University of New York College at Geneseo, M
State University of New York College at Oneonta, BM
State University of New York College at Potsdam, M
State University of New York at Fredonia, M
State University of New York at New Paltz, M
State University of New York at Oswego, M
State University of New York at Plattsburgh, M
Syracuse University, M
Touro College, M
University at Albany, State University of New York, MDO
University at Buffalo, the State University of New York, MO
Wagner College, M

North Carolina

Appalachian State University, M
East Carolina University, M
North Carolina Agricultural and Technical State University, M
Queens University of Charlotte, M
Salem College, M
The University of North Carolina at Chapel Hill, MD
The University of North Carolina at Charlotte, M
The University of North Carolina at Greensboro, M
The University of North Carolina at Pembroke, BM
The University of North Carolina Wilmington, M
Wingate University, B

North Dakota

University of Mary, M
University of North Dakota, M

Ohio

Ashland University, M
Baldwin Wallace University, M
Bowling Green State University, MO
Kent State University, M
Lourdes University, M
Mount St. Joseph University, MO
Notre Dame College, M
Ohio University, M
The University of Akron, M
University of Cincinnati, MDO
University of Dayton, M
The University of Findlay, M
Ursuline College, M
Wilmington College, M
Wright State University, B
Xavier University, M
Youngstown State University, M

Oklahoma

East Central University, B
Northeastern State University, M
Northwestern Oklahoma State University, M
Southeastern Oklahoma State University, M
University of Central Oklahoma, BM
University of Oklahoma Health Sciences Center, O

Oregon

Concordia University, M
George Fox University, M
Portland State University, M
Southern Oregon University, M
University of Portland, M

Pennsylvania

Arcadia University, MO
Bloomsburg University of Pennsylvania, M
California University of Pennsylvania, M
Chestnut Hill College, MO
Clarion University of Pennsylvania, M
Duquesne University, M
East Stroudsburg University of Pennsylvania, M
Eastern University, MO
Edinboro University of Pennsylvania, MO
Gannon University, MO
Geneva College, M
Holy Family University, M
Indiana University of Pennsylvania, MO
Kutztown University of Pennsylvania, M
La Salle University, MO
Lincoln University, M
Marywood University, M
Millersville University of Pennsylvania, M
Misericordia University, M
Penn State Harrisburg, M
Saint Francis University, M
Saint Joseph's University, MO
Shippensburg University of Pennsylvania, M
Slippery Rock University of Pennsylvania, M
Summit University, M
University of Pennsylvania, M
University of Pittsburgh, MD
The University of Scranton, M
West Chester University of Pennsylvania, MO
Westminster College, MO
Widener University, MD
Wilkes University, M

York College of Pennsylvania, M

Rhode Island

Providence College, M
Rhode Island College, M
University of Rhode Island, M

South Carolina

The Citadel, The Military College of South Carolina, M
Clemson University, M
Converse College, O
Furman University, M
University of South Carolina, MD
Winthrop University, M

South Dakota

Augustana University, M
University of Sioux Falls, M

Tennessee

Austin Peay State University, M
East Tennessee State University, M
Lipscomb University, MO
Middle Tennessee State University, MD
Southern Adventist University, M
Tennessee State University, B
Tennessee Technological University, MDO
University of Memphis, MD
The University of Tennessee, MDO
Vanderbilt University, M

Texas

Baylor University, B
Dallas Baptist University, M
Hardin-Simmons University, M
Houston Baptist University, M
Howard College, A
Midwestern State University, BM
Our Lady of the Lake University of San Antonio, M
Sam Houston State University, BMD
Southern Methodist University, M
Southwestern Adventist University, M
Sul Ross State University, MO
Texas A&M International University, B
Texas A&M University - Corpus Christi, M
Texas A&M University - Kingsville, M
Texas A&M University - San Antonio, M
Texas Christian University, M
Texas State University, M
Texas Tech University, M
Texas Wesleyan University, B
Texas Woman's University, MD
University of Houston - Clear Lake, M
University of St. Thomas, M
The University of Texas at Austin, MD
The University of Texas at El Paso, M
The University of Texas of the Permian Basin, M
The University of Texas Rio Grande Valley, M
The University of Texas at San Antonio, MD
The University of Texas at Tyler, M
West Texas A&M University, M

Utah

Brigham Young University, M
University of Utah, MD

Vermont

Castleton University, MO
College of St. Joseph, M
Goddard College, B
Johnson State College, M
Lyndon State College, BM
Saint Michael's College, M

Virginia

Averett University, M
Emory & Henry College, M
George Mason University, M
James Madison University, M
Liberty University, M
Longwood University, M
Lynchburg College, M
Old Dominion University, MD
Radford University, M

Regent University, M
University of Virginia, D
Virginia Commonwealth University, MO

Washington

Central Washington University, M
City University of Seattle, M
Eastern Washington University, BM
Heritage University, M
Saint Martin's University, M
Seattle Pacific University, M
Seattle University, MO
University of Washington, D
Walla Walla University, M
Washington State University, BM

West Virginia

American Public University System, M
Concord University, M
Fairmont State University, M
Marshall University, MO
West Virginia University, M

Wisconsin

Alverno College, M
Cardinal Stritch University, M
Carthage College, MO
Concordia University Wisconsin, M
Edgewood College, M
Marquette University, MO
University of Wisconsin - Eau Claire, M
University of Wisconsin - Milwaukee, M
University of Wisconsin - Oshkosh, M
University of Wisconsin - River Falls, M
University of Wisconsin - Stevens Point, M
University of Wisconsin - Superior, M
University of Wisconsin - Whitewater, M

U.S. Territories: Guam

University of Guam, M

Canada

British Columbia

Simon Fraser University, D
The University of British Columbia, MD
University of Victoria, MD

Maritime Provinces: Nova Scotia

Mount Saint Vincent University, BM

REAL ESTATE

United States

Alabama

Auburn University, M
Calhoun Community College, A
Wallace State Community College, A

Arizona

Arizona State University at the Tempe campus, M
Mesa Community College, A
Scottsdale Community College, A

California

American River College, A
Antelope Valley College, A
Bakersfield College, A
Butte College, A
Cabrillo College, A
California State University, Dominguez Hills, B
California State University, East Bay, B
California State University, Fresno, B
California State University, Sacramento, M
Cerritos College, A
Chabot College, A
Citrus College, A
City College of San Francisco, A
College of the Canyons, A
College of Marin, A

College of San Mateo, A
College of the Sequoias, A
Contra Costa College, A
Cosumnes River College, A
Cuesta College, A
Cuyamaca College, A
De Anza College, A
East Los Angeles College, A
El Camino College, A
Folsom Lake College, A
Foothill College, A
Fresno City College, A
Fullerton College, A
Gavilan College, A
Glendale Community College, A
Golden West College, A
Hartnell College, A
Lake Tahoe Community College, A
Las Positas College, A
Lassen Community College District, A
Long Beach City College, A
Los Angeles City College, A
Los Angeles Harbor College, A
Los Angeles Pierce College, A
Los Angeles Southwest College, A
Los Angeles Trade-Technical College, A
Los Angeles Valley College, A
Los Medanos College, A
Mendocino College, A
Menlo College, B
Merced College, A
Merritt College, A
MiraCosta College, A
Mission College, A
Modesto Junior College, A
Monterey Peninsula College, A
Mt. San Antonio College, A
Mt. San Jacinto College, A
Napa Valley College, A
National University, A
Norco College, A
Ohlone College, A
Orange Coast College, A
Pacific States University, M
Palomar College, A
Riverside City College, A
Sacramento City College, A
Saddleback College, A
San Bernardino Valley College, A
San Diego City College, A
San Diego Mesa College, A
San Diego State University, B
San Jose City College, A
Santa Ana College, A
Santa Barbara City College, A
Santa Rosa Junior College, A
Santiago Canyon College, A
Shasta College, A
Sierra College, A
Southwestern College, A
University of California, Berkeley, D
University of San Diego, BM
University of Southern California, BM
Ventura College, A
Victor Valley College, A
West Los Angeles College, A

Colorado

Colorado Mountain College (Steamboat Springs), A
Colorado State University, B
Colorado Technical University Online, B
Red Rocks Community College, A
University of Denver, BM

Connecticut

University of Connecticut, B

District of Columbia

The George Washington University, O
Georgetown University, M

Florida

Broward College, A
Florida Atlantic University, B
Florida International University, BM
Florida State College at Jacksonville, A

Miami Dade College, A
South Florida State College, A
University of Central Florida, B
University of Florida, BMDO
University of Miami, BM
University of South Florida, M

Georgia

Georgia State University, BMDO
University of Georgia, B
University of West Georgia, B

Hawaii

University of Hawaii at Manoa, M

Idaho

College of Southern Idaho, A

Illinois

College of DuPage, A
DePaul University, BM
Illinois Central College, A
Morton College, A
Northwestern College - Bridgeview Campus, A
Northwestern University, M
Oakton Community College, A
Roosevelt University, MO
Southeastern Illinois College, A
University of Illinois at Chicago, M
University of Illinois at Urbana - Champaign, B

Iowa

Iowa Lakes Community College, A
University of Northern Iowa, B

Kansas

Dodge City Community College, A

Kentucky

Jefferson Community and Technical College, A
Madisonville Community College, A

Maryland

Johns Hopkins University, M
University of Baltimore, B
University of Maryland, College Park, M

Massachusetts

Brandeis University, M
Bristol Community College, A
Massachusetts Institute of Technology, M
Northern Essex Community College, A

Michigan

Central Michigan University, B
Lansing Community College, A

Minnesota

Dakota County Technical College, A
Minnesota State University Mankato, B
St. Cloud State University, B
University of St. Thomas, BM

Mississippi

Hinds Community College, A
Mississippi State University, B
University of Mississippi, B

Missouri

University of Missouri, B
University of Missouri - Kansas City, M

Nebraska

Northeast Community College, A
University of Nebraska at Omaha, B

Nevada

University of Nevada, Las Vegas, B

New Hampshire

NHTI, Concord's Community College, A

New Jersey

Monmouth University, M
Rutgers University - Newark, M
Thomas Edison State University, B

New Mexico

New Mexico Junior College, A
University of New Mexico - Valencia Campus, A

New York

Baruch College of the City University of New York, BM
Columbia University, M
Cornell University, M
Nassau Community College, A
New York University, BMO
Syracuse University, B
University at Buffalo, the State University of New York, M

North Carolina

Central Piedmont Community College, A
Isothermal Community College, A
The University of North Carolina at Charlotte, MO

Ohio

Belmont College, A
Bowling Green State University, B
Cincinnati State Technical and Community College, A
Cleveland State University, MO
Columbus State Community College, A
Cuyahoga Community College, A
Eastern Gateway Community College, A
Hondros College, A
Lorain County Community College, A
Miami University Hamilton, A
Miami University Middletown, A
The Ohio State University, B
Sinclair Community College, A
Terra State Community College, A
The University of Akron, B
University of Cincinnati, B
University of Cincinnati Blue Ash College, A

Oklahoma

University of Central Oklahoma, B

Oregon

Marylhurst University, BM
Portland State University, BM

Pennsylvania

Clarion University of Pennsylvania, B
Community College of Allegheny County, A
Drexel University, BM
Harrisburg Area Community College, A
Luzerne County Community College, A
Montgomery County Community College, A
Saint Francis University, A
Temple University, B
University of Pennsylvania, BMD
Villanova University, BM
Westmoreland County Community College, A

South Carolina

Clemson University, M
University of South Carolina, B

Tennessee

University of Memphis, M

Texas

Amarillo College, A
Austin Community College District, A
Baylor University, BD
Blinn College, A
Cedar Valley College, A
Cisco College, A
Collin County Community College District, A
Del Mar College, A
El Paso Community College, A
Houston Community College, A
Lamar Institute of Technology, A

Lamar State College - Orange, A
Laredo Community College, A
McLennan Community College, A
North Central Texas College, A
North Lake College, A
Richland College, A
San Antonio College, A
San Jacinto College District, A
South Plains College, A
Southern Methodist University, BM
Texarkana College, A
Texas A&M University, M
Texas Christian University, B
Trinity Valley Community College, A
University of North Texas, B
The University of Texas at Arlington, BMD
The University of Texas at El Paso, B
The University of Texas at San Antonio, B

Utah

University of Utah, M

Virginia

George Mason University, M
Longwood University, M
Tidewater Community College, A
Virginia Commonwealth University, BMO
Virginia Polytechnic Institute and State University, B

Washington

Bellevue College, A
North Seattle College, A
Spokane Falls Community College, A
Washington State University, B

West Virginia

American Public University System, A

Wisconsin

Madison Area Technical College, A
Marquette University, BM
Milwaukee Area Technical College, A
Nicolet Area Technical College, A
University of Wisconsin - Madison, BMD
University of Wisconsin - Milwaukee, BO
University of Wisconsin - Stout, B
Waukesha County Technical College, A

U.S. Territories: Puerto Rico

Inter American University of Puerto Rico, Metropolitan Campus, B

Canada

British Columbia

British Columbia Institute of Technology, A
The University of British Columbia, B

Ontario

University of Guelph, B

RECEPTIONIST

United States

Iowa

Iowa Lakes Community College, A

Massachusetts

Bristol Community College, A

Montana

University of Montana, A

North Dakota

Dakota College at Bottineau, A

RECORDING ARTS TECHNOL- OGY/TECHNICIAN

United States

Arizona

Glendale Community College, A
Paradise Valley Community College, A
Phoenix College, A

California

The Art Institute of California - Hollywood, a campus of Argosy University, AB
The Art Institute of California - Inland Empire, a campus of Argosy University, AB
The Art Institute of California - Los Angeles, a campus of Argosy University, AB
The Art Institute of California - San Diego, a campus of Argosy University, AB
The Art Institute of California - San Francisco, a campus of Argosy University, B
Chaffey College, A
Citrus College, A
Fresno City College, A
Fullerton College, A
Long Beach City College, A
Los Angeles Film School, A
Loyola Marymount University, B
MiraCosta College, A
Orange Coast College, A

Colorado

Aims Community College, A
The Art Institute of Colorado, B

District of Columbia

American University, B

Florida

The Art Institute of Fort Lauderdale, B
Full Sail University, B
Miami Dade College, A
Miami International University of Art & Design, B

Georgia

The Art Institute of Atlanta, B
Savannah College of Art and Design, B

Illinois

Columbia College Chicago, B
Greenville College, B
The Illinois Institute of Art - Chicago, B
The Illinois Institute of Art - Schaumburg, B
Tribeca Flashpoint College, A

Indiana

Butler University, B
Indiana University Bloomington, AB
Vincennes University, A

Iowa

Western Iowa Tech Community College, A

Kansas

Kansas City Kansas Community College, A

Louisiana

Bossier Parish Community College, A

Maine

Husson University, B

Maryland

Peabody Conservatory of The Johns Hopkins University, B

Massachusetts

Berklee College of Music, B
Springfield Technical Community College, A

Michigan

The Art Institute of Michigan, B
Grand Rapids Community College, A
Michigan Technological University, B
Schoolcraft College, A

Minnesota

Hennepin Technical College, A
The Institute of Production and Recording, A
Minneapolis Community and Technical College, A
Ridgewater College, A

Nebraska

Northeast Community College, A

Nevada

The Art Institute of Las Vegas, B

New Jersey

Union County College, A

New York

Finger Lakes Community College, A
Fiorello H. LaGuardia Community College of the City University of New York, A
Five Towns College, B
Ithaca College, B
Queensborough Community College of the City University of New York, A
State University of New York at Fredonia, B

North Carolina

Elon University, B
Guilford Technical Community College, A
Living Arts College, B

North Dakota

Bismarck State College, A

Ohio

Malone University, B

Pennsylvania

The Art Institute of Philadelphia, B
Community College of Philadelphia, A
Lehigh Carbon Community College, A
Montgomery County Community College, A
York College of Pennsylvania, B

Rhode Island

New England Institute of Technology, B

Tennessee

The Art Institute of Tennessee - Nashville, a branch of The Art Institute of Atlanta, B
Belmont University, B

Texas

The Art Institute of Austin, a branch of The Art Institute of Houston, B
The Art Institute of Dallas, a campus of South University, B
The Art Institute of Houston, B
Northwest Vista College, A
South Plains College, A
Texas State University, B

Utah

Broadview Entertainment Arts University, A

Virginia

The Art Institute of Washington, a branch of The Art Institute of Atlanta, B

Washington

The Art Institute of Seattle, AB
Northwest University, B
Shoreline Community College, A

Wisconsin

Madison Media Institute, A

U.S. Territories: Puerto Rico

Columbia Centro Universitario (Caguas), A

RECREATION AND PARK MANAGEMENT

United States

Arkansas

University of Arkansas, MD

California

California State University, Chico, M
California State University, East Bay, M
California State University, Long Beach, M
California State University, Northridge, M
California State University, Sacramento, M
San Francisco State University, M
San Jose State University, M

Colorado

Colorado State University, MD

Connecticut

Southern Connecticut State University, M

Florida

Florida International University, M
Florida State University, MDO
University of Florida, MD

Georgia

Georgia College & State University, M

Idaho

University of Idaho, M

Illinois

Aurora University, M
Southern Illinois University Carbondale, M
Western Illinois University, M

Indiana

Indiana State University, MD
Indiana University Bloomington, MD
Purdue University, MD

Iowa

The University of Iowa, D

Kentucky

Eastern Kentucky University, M
Western Kentucky University, M

Maryland

Frostburg State University, M

Massachusetts

Springfield College, M

Michigan

Central Michigan University, M
Michigan State University, MD

Minnesota

Winona State University, M

Mississippi

Delta State University, M
University of Mississippi, M

Missouri

Northwest Missouri State University, M
University of Missouri, M

Montana

University of Montana, M

Nebraska

University of Nebraska at Kearney, M
University of Nebraska at Omaha, MD

New Hampshire

New England College, M
University of New Hampshire, M

New York

Iona College, O
Lehman College of the City University of New York, M
State University of New York College at Cortland, M

North Carolina

East Carolina University, MO
North Carolina Central University, M
North Carolina State University, MD
The University of North Carolina at Greensboro, M

Ohio

Bowling Green State University, M
Kent State University, M
Ohio University, M
The University of Toledo, MD
Wright State University, M

Oklahoma

Southwestern Oklahoma State University, M

Pennsylvania

Penn State University Park, MD
Slippery Rock University of Pennsylvania, M

Rhode Island

University of Rhode Island, M

South Carolina

Clemson University, MD

South Dakota

South Dakota State University, M

Tennessee

Middle Tennessee State University, M
Southern Adventist University, M
The University of Tennessee, M

Texas

Hardin-Simmons University, M
Texas A&M University, MD
Texas State University, M

Utah

University of Utah, MD
Utah State University, MD

Virginia

George Mason University, M
Liberty University, M
Virginia Commonwealth University, M

Washington

Eastern Washington University, M

West Virginia

West Virginia University, M

Wisconsin

University of Wisconsin - La Crosse, M

U.S. Territories: Puerto Rico

Universidad Metropolitana, M

Canada

Alberta

University of Alberta, MD

Manitoba

University of Manitoba, M

Maritime Provinces: New Brunswick

University of New Brunswick Fredericton, M

Maritime Provinces: Nova Scotia

Acadia University, M

Ontario

University of Waterloo, MD

REGIONAL STUDIES (U.S., CANADIAN, FOREIGN)

United States

Arizona

Prescott College, B

Arkansas

Arkansas Tech University, A

Colorado

The Colorado College, B

Georgia

Mercer University, B

Mississippi

University of Mississippi, B

Missouri

Washington University in St. Louis, B

New York

Columbia University, School of General Studies, B
Houghton College, B

Canada

Quebec

McGill University, B

Saskatchewan

University of Regina, B
University of Saskatchewan, B

REHABILITATION COUNSELING

United States

Alabama

Alabama Agricultural and Mechanical University, M
Alabama State University, M
Auburn University, MD
Troy University, M

Arizona

The University of Arizona, MD

Arkansas

Arkansas State University, M
University of Arkansas, MD
University of Arkansas at Little Rock, MO

California

California State University, Fresno, M
California State University, Los Angeles, M
California State University, San Bernardino, M
San Diego State University, M
San Francisco State University, M

Colorado

University of Northern Colorado, MD

Connecticut

Central Connecticut State University, MO

District of Columbia

The George Washington University, M
University of the District of Columbia, M

Florida

Barry University, MO
Florida Atlantic University, M
Florida International University, M
University of North Florida, M
University of South Florida, MO

Georgia

Fort Valley State University, M
Georgia State University, M
Mercer University, M
Thomas University, M

Idaho

University of Idaho, M

Illinois

Illinois Institute of Technology, MD
Northeastern Illinois University, M

Indiana

University of Saint Francis, MO

Iowa

The University of Iowa, MD

Kansas

Emporia State University, M
The University of Kansas, D

Kentucky

University of Kentucky, MD

Louisiana

Louisiana State University Health Sciences Center, M
Southern University and Agricultural and Mechanical College, M
University of Louisiana at Lafayette, M

Maine

University of Southern Maine, M

Maryland

Coppin State University, M
University of Maryland, College Park, M
University of Maryland Eastern Shore, M

Massachusetts

Assumption College, MO
Springfield College, M
University of Massachusetts Boston, M

Michigan

Michigan State University, MD
Wayne State University, M
Western Michigan University, M

Minnesota

Minnesota State University Mankato, M
St. Cloud State University, M

Mississippi

Jackson State University, M
Mississippi State University, M

Missouri

Maryville University of Saint Louis, M

Montana

Montana State University Billings, M

New Jersey

Rutgers University - Newark, MD

New York

Hofstra University, MO
Hunter College of the City University of New York, M
St. Bonaventure University, M
University at Buffalo, the State University of New York, MO

North Carolina

East Carolina University, MDO
The University of North Carolina at Chapel Hill, M
Winston-Salem State University, M

Ohio

Bowling Green State University, M
Kent State University, M
Ohio University, M
Wilberforce University, M
Wright State University, M

Oklahoma

East Central University, M
Langston University, M

Oregon

Western Oregon University, M

Pennsylvania

Edinboro University of Pennsylvania, M
The University of Scranton, M

Rhode Island

Salve Regina University, MO

South Carolina

University of South Carolina, MO

Tennessee

University of Memphis, M
The University of Tennessee, M

Texas

University of North Texas, O
The University of Texas at Austin, MD
The University of Texas at El Paso, M
The University of Texas Rio Grande Valley, MD

Utah

Utah State University, M

Virginia

Virginia Commonwealth University, MO

Washington

Western Washington University, M

West Virginia

West Virginia University, M

Wisconsin

University of Wisconsin - Madison, MD
University of Wisconsin - Stout, M

U.S. Territories: Puerto Rico

Bayamón Central University, M
Pontifical Catholic University of Puerto Rico, M
University of Puerto Rico, Río Piedras Campus, M

REHABILITATION SCIENCES

United States

Alabama

Alabama State University, M
The University of Alabama at Birmingham, D

Colorado

University of Colorado Denver, D

Florida

University of Florida, D

Illinois

Northwestern University, D
University of Illinois at Urbana - Champaign, M

Indiana

Indiana University - Purdue University Indianapolis, MD

Iowa

The University of Iowa, MD

Kansas

The University of Kansas, D

Kentucky

University of Kentucky, D

Maryland

University of Maryland Eastern Shore, M

Massachusetts

Boston University, D
Lasell College, M

Michigan

Central Michigan University, MD
Western Michigan University, M

Missouri

Logan University, M
Washington University in St. Louis, D

New York

New York University, D
University at Buffalo, the State University of New York, MDO

North Carolina

Appalachian State University, M
East Carolina University, MDO

Ohio

The Ohio State University, D
University of Cincinnati, D

Oklahoma

University of Oklahoma Health Sciences Center, M

Pennsylvania

California University of Pennsylvania, M
Clarion University of Pennsylvania, M
Duquesne University, MD
East Stroudsburg University of Pennsylvania, M
Temple University, MD
University of Pittsburgh, MD

South Carolina

Medical University of South Carolina, D
University of South Carolina, O

Texas

The University of Texas Medical Branch, D

Utah

University of Utah, D

Virginia

George Mason University, DO
Virginia Commonwealth University, D

Washington

University of Washington, D

Wisconsin

Concordia University Wisconsin, M
Marquette University, MD

University of Wisconsin - La Crosse, M

Canada

Alberta

University of Alberta, D

British Columbia

The University of British Columbia, MD

Manitoba

University of Manitoba, MD

Ontario

McMaster University, MD
Queen's University at Kingston, MD
University of Ottawa, M
University of Toronto, MD

Quebec

McGill University, MDO
Université de Montréal, O

REHABILITATION AND THERA-PEUTIC PROFESSIONS

United States

Alabama

Alabama State University, B
Troy University, B

Arizona

Prescott College, B

Arkansas

University of Arkansas at Pine Bluff, B

California

California State University, Los Angeles, B
National University, A

Colorado

Heritage College, A

Georgia

Thomas University, B

Illinois

Southern Illinois University Carbondale, B

Iowa

Iowa Lakes Community College, A

Louisiana

Southern University and Agricultural and Mechanical College, B

Maryland

University of Maryland Eastern Shore, B

Massachusetts

Assumption College, B
Boston University, B
Springfield College, B
University of Massachusetts Lowell, B

Michigan

Baker College, B

Montana

Montana State University Billings, B

Nebraska

College of Saint Mary, B

New Jersey

Camden County College, A
Middlesex County College, A

Ocean County College, A
Rutgers University - New Brunswick, AB
Rutgers University - Newark, AB
Union County College, A

New York

Hilbert College, B
Ithaca College, B
Nassau Community College, A
Orange County Community College, A

Ohio

Columbus State Community College, A
North Central State College, A
Wilberforce University, B

Pennsylvania

East Stroudsburg University of Pennsylvania, B
Lock Haven University of Pennsylvania, B
Penn State Abington, B
Penn State Altoona, B
Penn State Beaver, B
Penn State Berks, B
Penn State Brandywine, B
Penn State DuBois, B
Penn State Erie, The Behrend College, B
Penn State Fayette, The Eberly Campus, B
Penn State Greater Allegheny, B
Penn State Hazleton, B
Penn State Lehigh Valley, B
Penn State Mont Alto, B
Penn State New Kensington, B
Penn State Schuylkill, B
Penn State Shenango, B
Penn State University Park, B
Penn State Wilkes-Barre, B
Penn State Worthington Scranton, B
Penn State York, B

Wyoming

Central Wyoming College, A

Canada

Manitoba

University of Manitoba, B

Ontario

University of Waterloo, B
York University, B

Quebec

Université de Montréal, B

RELIABILITY ENGINEERING

United States

Arizona

Arizona State University at the Tempe campus, M

Maryland

University of Maryland, College Park, MD

Tennessee

The University of Tennessee, M

RELIGION/RELIGIOUS STUDIES

United States

Alabama

Amridge University, D
Athens State University, B
Birmingham-Southern College, B
Heritage Christian University, M
Huntingdon College, B
Judson College, B
Miles College, B

Oakwood University, A
Samford University, B
Spring Hill College, B
The University of Alabama, B
University of Mobile, B
Wallace State Community College, A

Arizona

Arizona State University at the Tempe campus,
    BMD
Grand Canyon University, B
Harrison Middleton University, M
The University of Arizona, B

Arkansas

Arkansas Baptist College, AB
Hendrix College, B
John Brown University, B
Philander Smith College, B
University of Central Arkansas, B
University of the Ozarks, B
Williams Baptist College, B

California

Ashford University, B
Azusa Pacific University, B
Bethesda University, M
Biola University, BMO
California Institute of Integral Studies, MD
California Lutheran University, B
California State University, Bakersfield, B
California State University, East Bay, B
California State University, Fresno, B
California State University, Fullerton, B
California State University, Long Beach, BM
California State University, Northridge, B
California State University, Sacramento, B
Cerritos College, A
Chaffey College, A
Chapman University, B
Claremont McKenna College, B
Concordia University Irvine, BM
Crafton Hills College, A
Dominican University of California, BM
Fullerton College, A
Holy Names University, BMO
Hope International University, BM
Humboldt State University, B
La Sierra University, BM
Loma Linda University, M
The Master's College and Seminary, B
Mount Saint Mary's University, BM
Notre Dame de Namur University, B
Occidental College, B
Orange Coast College, A
Pacific Union College, B
Pepperdine University, BM
Pitzer College, B
Point Loma Nazarene University, M
Pomona College, B
Saint Mary's College of California, B
San Bernardino Valley College, A
San Diego State University, B
San Joaquin Delta College, A
San Jose State University, B
Santa Clara University, B
Santa Rosa Junior College, A
Scripps College, B
Southern California Seminary, M
Stanford University, BD
University of California, Berkeley, BD
University of California, Davis, B
University of California, Irvine, B
University of California, Los Angeles, B
University of California, Riverside, BD
University of California, San Diego, B
University of California, Santa Barbara, BMD
University of La Verne, B
University of the Pacific, B
University of Redlands, B
University of San Diego, B
University of San Francisco, B
University of Southern California, B
University of the West, BMD
Vanguard University of Southern California, BM
Westmont College, B

Whittier College, B

Colorado

Colorado Christian University, B
The Colorado College, B
Naropa University, BM
Regis University, B
University of Colorado Boulder, BM
University of Denver, BMD

Connecticut

Albertus Magnus College, B
Connecticut College, B
Fairfield University, B
Holy Apostles College and Seminary, AB
Sacred Heart University, BM
Trinity College, B
University of Bridgeport, B
University of Saint Joseph, B
Wesleyan University, B
Yale University, BD

District of Columbia

The Catholic University of America, BMDO
The George Washington University, BM
Georgetown University, M
Trinity Washington University, B

Florida

Ave Maria University, B
Broward College, A
College of Central Florida, A
Eckerd College, B
Florida International University, BM
Florida Memorial University, B
Florida Southern College, B
Florida State University, MD
New College of Florida, B
Palm Beach State College, A
Rollins College, B
Saint Leo University, B
St. Thomas University, B
South Florida State College, A
State College of Florida Manatee-Sarasota, A
Stetson University, B
University of Central Florida, B
University of Florida, BMD
University of Miami, B
University of North Florida, B
University of South Florida, BMD

Georgia

Agnes Scott College, B
Beulah Heights University, ABM
Brewton-Parker College, AB
Clark Atlanta University, B
Emory University, BD
Georgia State University, BM
LaGrange College, B
Luther Rice College & Seminary, M
Morehouse College, B
Paine College, B
Piedmont College, B
Reinhardt University, B
Shorter University, B
Spelman College, B
University of Georgia, BM
Wesleyan College, B
Young Harris College, B

Hawaii

Chaminade University of Honolulu, B
University of Hawaii at Manoa, BM

Idaho

The College of Idaho, B
New Saint Andrews College, O
Northwest Nazarene University, BM

Illinois

Augustana College, B
Aurora University, B
Bradley University, B
Concordia University Chicago, BM
DePaul University, B

Greenville College, B
Illinois College, B
Illinois Wesleyan University, B
Lake Forest College, B
Lewis University, B
McKendree University, B
Monmouth College, B
North Central College, B
Northwestern University, BMD
Olivet Nazarene University, BM
Principia College, B
Saint Xavier University, B
University of Chicago, MD
University of Illinois at Urbana - Champaign, BM
Western Illinois University, B

Indiana

Ancilla College, A
Anderson University, B
Ball State University, B
Butler University, B
Calumet College of Saint Joseph, AB
DePauw University, B
Earlham College, B
Franklin College, B
Goshen College, B
Huntington University, AB
Indiana University Bloomington, BMD
Indiana University - Purdue University Indianapolis,
    B
Manchester University, B
Martin University, B
Oakland City University, AB
Purdue University, B
Saint Mary's College, B
University of Indianapolis, B
University of Notre Dame, M
Wabash College, B

Iowa

Central College, B
Clarke University, B
Coe College, B
Cornell College, B
Dordt College, B
Drake University, B
Faith Baptist Bible College and Theological Semi-
    nary, M
Graceland University, BM
Grand View University, B
Grinnell College, B
Iowa State University of Science and Technology, B
Loras College, B
Luther College, B
Morningside College, B
Mount Mercy University, B
Northwestern College, B
Simpson College, B
University of Dubuque, B
The University of Iowa, BMD
University of Northern Iowa, B
Wartburg College, B

Kansas

Allen Community College, A
Baker University, B
Barton County Community College, A
Bethany College, B
Bethel College, B
Central Christian College of Kansas, AB
Cowley County Community College and Area Voca-
    tional - Technical School, A
Kansas Wesleyan University, B
Manhattan Christian College, B
MidAmerica Nazarene University, B
Ottawa University, B
Tabor College, B
The University of Kansas, BM
Washburn University, B

Kentucky

Bellarmine University, M
Berea College, B
Campbellsville University, B
Centre College, B
Georgetown College, B

Kentucky Christian University, M
Kentucky Wesleyan College, B
The Southern Baptist Theological Seminary, M
Thomas More College, AB
Transylvania University, B
Union College, B
University of the Cumberlands, M
University of Pikeville, B
Western Kentucky University, B

Louisiana

Centenary College of Louisiana, B
Louisiana College, B
Loyola University New Orleans, B
New Orleans Baptist Theological Seminary, AB
Tulane University, B

Maine

Bates College, B
Bowdoin College, B
Colby College, B
Saint Joseph's College of Maine, B

Maryland

Goucher College, B
Hood College, B
Loyola University Maryland, B
McDaniel College, B
Morgan State University, B
Notre Dame of Maryland University, B
St. Mary's College of Maryland, B
Towson University, B
Washington Adventist University, M

Massachusetts

Amherst College, B
Boston University, BMD
College of the Holy Cross, B
Eastern Nazarene College, B
Elms College, BM
Emmanuel College, B
Hampshire College, B
Harvard University, BD
Hellenic College, B
Merrimack College, B
Mount Holyoke College, B
Northeastern University, B
Smith College, B
Stonehill College, B
Tufts University, B
Wellesley College, B
Wheaton College, B
Williams College, B

Michigan

Adrian College, B
Albion College, B
Alma College, B
Andrews University, B
Aquinas College, B
Calvin College, B
Central Michigan University, B
Concordia University Ann Arbor, B
Hillsdale College, B
Hope College, B
Kalamazoo College, B
Lansing Community College, A
Madonna University, AB
Marygrove College, B
Michigan State University, B
Siena Heights University, B
Spring Arbor University, B
University of Detroit Mercy, BM
University of Michigan, BMD
Western Michigan University, BMO

Minnesota

Augsburg College, B
Bemidji State University, B
Bethany Lutheran College, B
Carleton College, B
The College of St. Scholastica, B
Concordia College, B
Gustavus Adolphus College, B
Hamline University, B

Macalester College, B
North Central University, B
St. Olaf College, B
University of Minnesota, Twin Cities Campus, BM
University of St. Thomas, BM

Mississippi

Delta State University, M
Millsaps College, B
Tougaloo College, AB
University of Mississippi, B
University of Southern Mississippi, B
William Carey University, B

Missouri

Avila University, B
Central Christian College of the Bible, B
Central Methodist University, B
Culver-Stockton College, B
Drury University, B
Fontbonne University, B
Global University, A
Missouri State University, BM
Missouri Valley College, B
Southwest Baptist University, B
University of Missouri, BM
Washington University in St. Louis, BM
Webster University, B
Westminster College, B
William Jewell College, B

Montana

University of Great Falls, B

Nebraska

Doane University, B
Hastings College, B
Midland University, B
Nebraska Christian College, B
Nebraska Wesleyan University, B
University of Nebraska at Omaha, B
York College, B

New Hampshire

Dartmouth College, B

New Jersey

Bergen Community College, A
Bloomfield College, B
Drew University, B
Felician University, B
Georgian Court University, B
Montclair State University, B
Princeton University, BD
Rabbinical College of America, B
Rutgers University - New Brunswick, BMO
Saint Peter's University, B
Seton Hall University, BMO
Thomas Edison State University, B

New Mexico

Eastern New Mexico University, B
University of New Mexico, B

New York

Bard College, B
Barnard College, B
Baruch College of the City University of New York,
    B
Brooklyn College of the City University of New York,
    B
Canisius College, B
Colgate University, B
College of Mount Saint Vincent, B
The College of New Rochelle, B
Columbia University, BMD
Columbia University, School of General Studies, B
Concordia College - New York, AB
Cornell University, BMD
Daemen College, B
Fordham University, BMDO
Hamilton College, B
Hartwick College, B
Hobart and William Smith Colleges, B
Hofstra University, B

Houghton College, B
Hunter College of the City University of New York, B
Iona College, B
The Jewish Theological Seminary, BMD
The King's College, B
Le Moyne College, B
Manhattan College, B
Manhattanville College, B
Marist College, B
Medgar Evers College of the City University of New York, B
Molloy College, B
Nazareth College of Rochester, B
New York University, BMO
Niagara University, B
Nyack College, BM
Queens College of the City University of New York, B
Roberts Wesleyan College, B
St. Bonaventure University, M
St. Francis College, B
St. John Fisher College, B
St. Lawrence University, B
St. Thomas Aquinas College, B
Sarah Lawrence College, B
Siena College, B
Skidmore College, B
State University of New York College at Old Westbury, B
Stony Brook University, State University of New York, B
Syracuse University, BMD
Union College, B
University at Albany, State University of New York, B
University of Rochester, B
Vassar College, B
Yeshiva Derech Chaim, D

North Carolina

Appalachian State University, B
Brevard College, B
Campbell University, B
Catawba College, B
Charlotte Christian College and Theological Seminary, M
Chowan University, B
Davidson College, B
Duke University, BMD
Elon University, B
Gardner-Webb University, B
Greensboro College, B
Guilford College, B
High Point University, B
Lees-McRae College, B
Lenoir-Rhyne University, B
Mars Hill University, B
Meredith College, B
Methodist University, B
North Carolina State University, B
North Carolina Wesleyan College, B
Pfeiffer University, B
Queens University of Charlotte, B
Salem College, B
University of Mount Olive, B
University of North Carolina at Asheville, B
The University of North Carolina at Chapel Hill, BMD
The University of North Carolina at Charlotte, BM
The University of North Carolina at Greensboro, B
Wake Forest University, BM
Warren Wilson College, B
Wingate University, B

North Dakota

University of Jamestown, B
University of Mary, B
University of North Dakota, B

Ohio

Ashland University, B
Baldwin Wallace University, B
Capital University, B
Case Western Reserve University, B
Cincinnati Christian University, M
Cleveland State University, B
The College of Wooster, B

Defiance College, B
Denison University, B
Heidelberg University, B
Hiram College, B
John Carroll University, BM
Kenyon College, B
Lourdes University, AB
Miami University, B
Mount St. Joseph University, BM
Mount Vernon Nazarene University, AB
Muskingum University, B
Oberlin College, B
Ohio Northern University, B
The Ohio State University, B
Ohio University, B
Ohio Wesleyan University, B
Otterbein University, B
University of Dayton, B
The University of Findlay, B
University of Mount Union, B
The University of Toledo, B
Urbana University, B
Ursuline College, B
Wilmington College, B
Wittenberg University, B
Wright State University, B
Xavier University, AB
Youngstown State University, B

Oklahoma

Oklahoma Baptist University, B
Oklahoma Christian University, B
Oklahoma City University, BM
Oklahoma Wesleyan University, B
Southwestern Christian University, B
University of Oklahoma, B
The University of Tulsa, B

Oregon

Concordia University, B
Corban University, AB
Lewis & Clark College, B
Linfield College, B
Oregon State University, B
Portland State University, B
Reed College, B
University of Oregon, B
Warner Pacific College, B
Willamette University, B

Pennsylvania

Albright College, B
Allegheny College, B
Alvernia University, B
Bryn Athyn College of the New Church, BM
Bryn Mawr College, B
Bucknell University, B
Cabrini University, B
Cairn University, BM
Dickinson College, B
Elizabethtown College School of Continuing and Professional Studies, B
Franklin & Marshall College, B
Gettysburg College, B
Grove City College, B
Haverford College, B
Holy Family University, B
Indiana University of Pennsylvania, B
Juniata College, B
La Roche College, B
La Salle University, BMDO
Lafayette College, B
Lebanon Valley College, B
Lehigh University, B
Lincoln University, B
Lycoming College, B
Marywood University, B
Mercyhurst University, B
Moravian College, B
Muhlenberg College, B
Penn State Abington, B
Penn State Altoona, B
Penn State Beaver, B
Penn State Berks, B
Penn State Brandywine, B
Penn State DuBois, B

Penn State Erie, The Behrend College, B
Penn State Fayette, The Eberly Campus, B
Penn State Greater Allegheny, B
Penn State Hazleton, B
Penn State Lehigh Valley, B
Penn State Mont Alto, B
Penn State New Kensington, B
Penn State Schuylkill, B
Penn State Shenango, B
Penn State Wilkes-Barre, B
Penn State Worthington Scranton, B
Penn State York, B
Rosemont College, B
Saint Charles Borromeo Seminary, Overbrook, M
Saint Francis University, B
Saint Joseph's University, B
Seton Hill University, B
Summit University, M
Susquehanna University, B
Swarthmore College, B
Temple University, BMD
Thiel College, B
University of Pennsylvania, BD
University of Pittsburgh, B
The University of Scranton, B
University of Valley Forge, M
Ursinus College, B
Villanova University, B
Westminster College, B
Wilson College, B

Rhode Island

Brown University, BD
Mater Ecclesiae College, B
Providence College, M
Salve Regina University, BM

South Carolina

Allen University, B
Anderson University, B
Bob Jones University, M
Charleston Southern University, B
Clinton College, A
College of Charleston, B
Columbia College, B
Converse College, B
Erskine College, B
Furman University, B
Newberry College, B
Presbyterian College, B
Southern Wesleyan University, B
Spartanburg Methodist College, A
University of South Carolina, BM
Wofford College, B

South Dakota

Augustana University, B
Mount Marty College, AB
Presentation College, A

Tennessee

Belmont University, B
Carson-Newman University, B
Christian Brothers University, M
King University, B
Lane College, B
Lee University, M
Maryville College, B
Milligan College, MD
Rhodes College, B
Sewanee: The University of the South, B
Southern Adventist University, ABM
Tennessee Wesleyan College, B
Trevecca Nazarene University, BM
Union University, BMD
The University of Tennessee, BM
Vanderbilt University, BMD

Texas

Abilene Christian University, M
Amarillo College, A
Arlington Baptist College, B
Austin College, B
Baptist University of the Americas, B
Baylor University, BMD

Criswell College, AB
Dallas Baptist University, M
East Texas Baptist University, BM
Hardin-Simmons University, M
Hill College, A
Jarvis Christian College, AB
Kilgore College, A
Messenger College, B
Our Lady of the Lake University of San Antonio, B
Paul Quinn College, B
Rice University, BD
Schreiner University, B
Southern Methodist University, BMD
Southwestern Adventist University, B
Southwestern Assemblies of God University, M
Southwestern University, B
Texas Christian University, B
Texas College, B
Texas Wesleyan University, B
Trinity University, B
Trinity Valley Community College, A
University of Houston, B
University of the Incarnate Word, BM
University of North Texas, B
University of St. Thomas, M
The University of Texas at Austin, B
The University of Texas at Tyler, B
Wayland Baptist University, M
Wiley College, B

Utah

University of Utah, B

Vermont

Goddard College, B
Marlboro College, B
Middlebury College, B
Saint Michael's College, B
University of Vermont, B

Virginia

Averett University, B
Bluefield College, B
The College of William and Mary, B
Eastern Mennonite University, M
Emory & Henry College, B
Ferrum College, B
George Mason University, BM
Hampden-Sydney College, B
Hampton University, B
Hollins University, B
Liberty University, ABMD
Lynchburg College, B
Mary Baldwin College, B
Marymount University, B
Randolph College, B
Randolph-Macon College, B
Regent University, D
Roanoke College, B
Shenandoah University, B
Sweet Briar College, B
University of Richmond, B
University of Virginia, BMD
Virginia Commonwealth University, B
Virginia University of Lynchburg, BM
Virginia Wesleyan College, B
Washington and Lee University, B

Washington

Central Washington University, B
The Evergreen State College, B
Gonzaga University, B
Northwest University, AB
Pacific Lutheran University, B
Saint Martin's University, B
Seattle University, B
University of Puget Sound, B
University of Washington, BMD
Walla Walla University, B
Washington State University, B
Whitman College, B
Whitworth University, B

West Virginia

American Public University System, B
Bethany College, B
Davis & Elkins College, B
Ohio Valley University, B
West Virginia Wesleyan College, B

Wisconsin

Alverno College, B
Beloit College, B
Cardinal Stritch University, BM
Carroll University, B
Carthage College, B
Concordia University Wisconsin, B
Edgewood College, B
Lakeland College, B
Lawrence University, B
Maranatha Baptist University, M
Northland College, B
Ripon College, B
St. Norbert College, B
University of Wisconsin - Eau Claire, B
University of Wisconsin - Madison, B
University of Wisconsin - Milwaukee, B
University of Wisconsin - Oshkosh, B
Viterbo University, B
Wisconsin Lutheran College, B

Wyoming

Laramie County Community College, A
University of Wyoming, B

U.S. Territories: Guam

Pacific Islands University, AB

U.S. Territories: Puerto Rico

Bayamón Central University, B

Canada

Alberta

Ambrose University, O
Concordia University of Edmonton, BM
Prairie Bible Institute, A
University of Alberta, B
University of Calgary, BMD
University of Lethbridge, BM

British Columbia

Columbia Bible College, B
Trinity Western University, B
The University of British Columbia, BMD

Manitoba

Booth University College, B
Brandon University, B
Providence University College & Theological Seminary, B
University of Manitoba, BMD
The University of Winnipeg, BM

Maritime Provinces: New Brunswick

Crandall University, B
Kingswood University, B
Mount Allison University, B
St. Thomas University, B

Maritime Provinces: Nova Scotia

Cape Breton University, B
Dalhousie University, B
Mount Saint Vincent University, B
St. Francis Xavier University, B
Saint Mary's University, BM
University of King's College, B

Maritime Provinces: Prince Edward Island

University of Prince Edward Island, B

Newfoundland and Labrador

Memorial University of Newfoundland, BM

Ontario

Carleton University, B
Laurentian University, B
McMaster University, BMD
Queen's University at Kingston, BM
Redeemer University College, B
Saint Paul University, B
University of Ottawa, BMD
University of Toronto, MD
University of Waterloo, BD
The University of Western Ontario, B
Wilfrid Laurier University, BMD
York University, B

Quebec

Bishop's University, B
Concordia University, BMD
McGill University, BMD
Université Laval, MD
Université de Montréal, BMD
Université du Québec à Montréal, BMD
Université du Québec à Rimouski, B
Université de Sherbrooke, M

Saskatchewan

Briercrest College, B
University of Regina, BM
University of Saskatchewan, BM

RELIGIOUS EDUCATION

United States

Alabama

Oakwood University, B

Arkansas

Harding University, B
Williams Baptist College, B

California

Azusa Pacific University, M
Bethesda University, B
Biola University, BMD
Concordia University Irvine, B
La Sierra University, M
Loyola Marymount University, M
The Master's College and Seminary, B
Shasta Bible College, M
Simpson University, B
University of San Francisco, MD
Vanguard University of Southern California, B
William Jessup University, B

Colorado

Nazarene Bible College, AB

Florida

Florida College, B
Johnson University Florida, B
Talmudic University, B

Georgia

Toccoa Falls College, B

Idaho

Boise Bible College, AB
Northwest Nazarene University, B

Illinois

Concordia University Chicago, BM
Loyola University Chicago, BM
Moody Bible Institute, B
Olivet Nazarene University, B
Trinity International University, D
Wheaton College, BM

Indiana

Crossroads Bible College, B
Indiana Wesleyan University, B
Marian University, AB
Taylor University, B

Iowa

Faith Baptist Bible College and Theological Seminary, B
Northwestern College, B

Kansas

Barclay College, B
Benedictine College, B
Manhattan Christian College, AB
Sterling College, B

Kentucky

Asbury University, B
Campbellsville University, B
Kentucky Mountain Bible College, B
Lindsey Wilson College, B

Louisiana

Louisiana College, B
Loyola University New Orleans, B
New Orleans Baptist Theological Seminary, MD

Maryland

Maple Springs Baptist Bible College and Seminary, M
Towson University, MO
Washington Adventist University, B

Massachusetts

Boston College, MDO
Brandeis University, M
Eastern Nazarene College, B
Northeastern University, D

Michigan

Andrews University, BMDO
Concordia University Ann Arbor, B
Great Lakes Christian College, B
Kuyper College, AB
Rochester College, M

Minnesota

Concordia University, St. Paul, B
Crossroads College, B
Crown College, B
Oak Hills Christian College, B
Saint Mary's University of Minnesota, BM
University of St. Thomas, M

Missouri

Baptist Bible College, B
Global University, BM
Hannibal-LaGrange University, B
Midwest University, B
Ozark Christian College, B
Saint Louis Christian College, B
Southwest Baptist University, B

Nebraska

Concordia University, Nebraska, BM
Grace University, B
York College, B

New Jersey

Felician University, MO
Georgian Court University, O

New York

Concordia College - New York, B
Fordham University, MDO
Houghton College, B
The Jewish Theological Seminary, BMD
Rabbinical College Bobover Yeshiva B'nei Zion, B
Yeshiva Gedolah Imrei Yosef D'Spinka, B
Yeshiva University, MDO

North Carolina

Apex School of Theology, A
Belmont Abbey College, B
Carolina Christian College, M
Gardner-Webb University, BM
Heritage Bible College, AB
Methodist University, A
Pfeiffer University, BM

Piedmont International University, AB
Southeastern Baptist Theological Seminary, M

Ohio

Allegheny Wesleyan College, B
Ashland University, B
Cedarville University, B
Cincinnati Christian University, AB
Defiance College, B
Franciscan University of Steubenville, B
John Carroll University, B
Malone University, B
Mount Vernon Nazarene University, B
Ohio Northern University, B
Tri-State Bible College, B
University of Dayton, B
Walsh University, M
Xavier University, M

Oklahoma

Hillsdale Free Will Baptist College, AB
Oklahoma Christian University, B
Oral Roberts University, BM
Southern Nazarene University, B
Southwestern Christian University, B

Oregon

Concordia University, B
Corban University, B
George Fox University, M
Multnomah University, B
New Hope Christian College, B

Pennsylvania

La Salle University, O
Lancaster Bible College, B
Messiah College, B
Summit University, BM
Thiel College, B
University of Valley Forge, B
Westminster College, B

South Carolina

Columbia College, B
Columbia International University, BM
Morris College, B
Presbyterian College, B

Tennessee

Bryan College, B
Lee University, B
Martin Methodist College, B
Milligan College, M
Southern Adventist University, BM
Welch College, B

Texas

Concordia University Texas, B
Dallas Baptist University, ABM
Howard Payne University, B
Messenger College, B
Southwestern Assemblies of God University, M
University of St. Thomas, M
Wayland Baptist University, B

Utah

Brigham Young University, M

Virginia

Liberty University, M
Regent University, D
University of Valley Forge Virginia Campus, B

Washington

Northwest University, B
Seattle Pacific University, B

West Virginia

Davis & Elkins College, B

Wisconsin

Edgewood College, B

U.S. Territories: Puerto Rico

Inter American University of Puerto Rico, Fajardo Campus, B
Inter American University of Puerto Rico, Metropolitan Campus, D
Pontifical Catholic University of Puerto Rico, M
Theological University of the Caribbean, B
Universidad Adventista de las Antillas, B

Canada

British Columbia

Summit Pacific College, B

Manitoba

Providence University College & Theological Seminary, BMO

Maritime Provinces: New Brunswick

Kingswood University, B

Ontario

Emmanuel Bible College, B
Heritage College and Seminary, B
Master's College and Seminary, B
McMaster University, B
Tyndale University College & Seminary, B

Quebec

McGill University, B
Université du Québec à Chicoutimi, B
Université du Québec à Montréal, B
Université du Québec à Rimouski, B

RELIGIOUS/SACRED MUSIC

United States

Alabama

Samford University, B
University of Mobile, B

Arizona

Arizona Christian University, B

Arkansas

Central Baptist College, B
John Brown University, B
Ouachita Baptist University, B
Williams Baptist College, B

California

Hope International University, B
The Master's College and Seminary, B
Patten University, B
Point Loma Nazarene University, B
San Diego Christian College, B

Colorado

Nazarene Bible College, AB

Connecticut

University of Hartford, B

Florida

Ave Maria University, B
Jacksonville University, B
Southeastern University, B
Warner University, B

Georgia

Emmanuel College, B
Shorter University, B

Idaho

Northwest Nazarene University, B

Illinois

Concordia University Chicago, B
Greenville College, B

Judson University, B
Moody Bible Institute, B
North Park University, B
Olivet Nazarene University, B
Quincy University, B
Trinity International University, B

Indiana

Anderson University, B
Huntington University, B
Indiana Wesleyan University, AB
Marian University, B
Oakland City University, B

Iowa

Drake University, B
Faith Baptist Bible College and Theological Seminary, B
Wartburg College, B

Kansas

Barclay College, B
Central Christian College of Kansas, AB
Manhattan Christian College, AB

Kentucky

Asbury University, B
Campbellsville University, B
Kentucky Christian University, B
Kentucky Mountain Bible College, B
Kentucky Wesleyan College, B
University of the Cumberlands, B

Louisiana

Louisiana College, B
New Orleans Baptist Theological Seminary, AB

Massachusetts

Eastern Nazarene College, B

Michigan

Aquinas College, B
Calvin College, B
Concordia University Ann Arbor, B
Great Lakes Christian College, B
Kuyper College, B
Madonna University, B

Minnesota

Bethany Lutheran College, B
Concordia University, St. Paul, B
Crossroads College, B
Crown College, B
Gustavus Adolphus College, B
North Central University, AB
St. Olaf College, B

Mississippi

Blue Mountain College, B
Southeastern Baptist College, A
William Carey University, B

Missouri

Calvary Bible College and Theological Seminary, AB
College of the Ozarks, B
Evangel University, B
Lincoln University, B
Midwest University, B
Missouri Baptist University, B
Ozark Christian College, B
Saint Louis Christian College, B
William Jewell College, B

Nebraska

Concordia University, Nebraska, B
Grace University, B
Nebraska Christian College, AB

New Jersey

Rider University, B

New York

Concordia College - New York, B
Nyack College, B

North Carolina

Gardner-Webb University, B
Lenoir-Rhyne University, B
Pfeiffer University, B
Piedmont International University, B

North Dakota

University of Mary, B

Ohio

Bowling Green State University, B
Cincinnati Christian University, AB
Franciscan University of Steubenville, B
God's Bible School and College, A
Malone University, B
Mount Vernon Nazarene University, AB
Ohio Christian University, AB

Oklahoma

East Central University, B
Hillsdale Free Will Baptist College, AB
Mid-America Christian University, B
Oklahoma Baptist University, B
Oklahoma City University, B
Oklahoma Wesleyan University, B
Oral Roberts University, B
Southern Nazarene University, B
Southwestern Christian University, B

Oregon

Corban University, B
Multnomah University, B
New Hope Christian College, B
Northwest Christian University, B

Pennsylvania

Lancaster Bible College, B
Seton Hill University, B
Summit University, B
University of Valley Forge, B
Westminster College, B

South Carolina

Anderson University, B
Charleston Southern University, B
Columbia International University, B
Furman University, B
North Greenville University, B
Southern Wesleyan University, B

Tennessee

Bethel University, B
Carson-Newman University, B
Johnson University, B
Lee University, B
Martin Methodist College, B
Trevecca Nazarene University, AB
Union University, B
Welch College, B

Texas

Baylor University, B
Concordia University Texas, B
Dallas Baptist University, AB
East Texas Baptist University, B
Hardin-Simmons University, B
Howard Payne University, B
Messenger College, B
Southwestern Assemblies of God University, B
Texas Christian University, B
University of Mary Hardin-Baylor, B
Wayland Baptist University, B

Virginia

Bluefield College, B
Liberty University, B
Shenandoah University, B

Washington

Northwest University, B

Wisconsin

Concordia University Wisconsin, B
Maranatha Baptist University, B

Canada
Alberta

University of Alberta, B
Vanguard College, B

British Columbia

Summit Pacific College, B

Ontario

Emmanuel Bible College, B
Heritage College and Seminary, B

Quebec

McGill University, B

Saskatchewan

Briercrest College, AB
Horizon College & Seminary, B

REPRODUCTIVE BIOLOGY

United States
Hawaii

University of Hawaii at Manoa, MD

Massachusetts

Tufts University, D

New Jersey

Rutgers University - New Brunswick, MD

New York

Cornell University, MD

West Virginia

West Virginia University, MD

Wyoming

University of Wyoming, MD

Canada
British Columbia

The University of British Columbia, MD

Ontario

Queen's University at Kingston, MD

Saskatchewan

University of Saskatchewan, MD

RESORT MANAGEMENT

United States
California

Cerro Coso Community College, A
College of the Desert, A

Florida

Florida Gulf Coast University, B

Nevada

Sierra Nevada College, B

New Hampshire

White Mountains Community College, A

New York

Finger Lakes Community College, A
Morrisville State College, B

Rochester Institute of Technology, B
State University of New York College of Technology
    at Delhi, A

Pennsylvania

Lehigh Carbon Community College, A

South Carolina

Coastal Carolina University, B

Texas

Virginia College in Austin, A

Vermont

Green Mountain College, B

Wisconsin

Lakeland College, B

RESOURCE MANAGEMENT

United States

Colorado

Colorado State University, MD

New Hampshire

University of New Hampshire, M

New York

State University of New York College of Environ-
    mental Science and Forestry, MD

West Virginia

West Virginia University, D

RESPIRATORY CARE THERAPY/THERAPIST

United States

Alabama

Calhoun Community College, A
George C. Wallace Community College, A
Shelton State Community College, A
The University of Alabama at Birmingham, B
University of South Alabama, B
Wallace State Community College, A

Arizona

Carrington College - Mesa, A
Carrington College - Phoenix North, A
Cochise County Community College District, A
GateWay Community College, A
Pima Community College, A

Arkansas

Arkansas State University - Mountain Home, A
NorthWest Arkansas Community College, A
Pulaski Technical College, A
Southeast Arkansas College, A
University of Arkansas for Medical Sciences, A

California

American River College, A
Antelope Valley College, A
Butte College, A
Concorde Career College (Garden Grove), A
Concorde Career College (North Hollywood), A
Concorde Career College (San Diego), A
Crafton Hills College, A
East Los Angeles College, A
El Camino College, A
Foothill College, A
Fresno City College, A
Grossmont College, A
Loma Linda University, AB
Los Angeles Valley College, A
Modesto Junior College, A

Mt. San Antonio College, A
Napa Valley College, A
Ohlone College, A
Orange Coast College, A
San Joaquin Valley College (Bakersfield), A
San Joaquin Valley College (Ontario), A
San Joaquin Valley College (Temecula), A
San Joaquin Valley College (Visalia), A
Santa Monica College, A
Skyline College, A
Victor Valley College, A

Colorado

Pueblo Community College, A

Connecticut

Goodwin College, A
Manchester Community College, A
Naugatuck Valley Community College, A
Norwalk Community College, A
University of Hartford, B

District of Columbia

University of the District of Columbia, A

Florida

Broward College, A
Daytona State College, A
Florida Agricultural and Mechanical University, B
Florida SouthWestern State College, AB
Florida State College at Jacksonville, A
Gulf Coast State College, A
Hillsborough Community College, A
Indian River State College, A
Keiser University, A
Miami Dade College, A
Nova Southeastern University, B
Polk State College, A
St. Johns River State College, A
St. Petersburg College, A
Santa Fe College, A
Seminole State College of Florida, A
South Florida State College, A
State College of Florida Manatee-Sarasota, A
Tallahassee Community College, A
Valencia College, A

Georgia

Armstrong State University, B
Athens Technical College, A
Augusta Technical College, A
Augusta University, B
College of Coastal Georgia, A
Darton State College, A
Georgia State University, B
Gwinnett Technical College, A
Middle Georgia State University, AB
Southern Regional Technical College, A

Hawaii

Kapiolani Community College, A

Idaho

Boise State University, AB
Idaho State University, A
Stevens-Henager College (Boise), AB

Illinois

City Colleges of Chicago, Malcolm X College, A
City Colleges of Chicago, Olive-Harvey College, A
College of DuPage, A
Illinois Central College, A
Kankakee Community College, A
Kaskaskia College, A
Lincoln Land Community College, A
Moraine Valley Community College, A
Parkland College, A
Rock Valley College, A
St. Augustine College, A
Southwestern Illinois College, A
Trinity College of Nursing and Health Sciences, A
Triton College, A

Indiana

Ball State University, B
Indiana University - Purdue University Indianapolis,
    B
Ivy Tech Community College - Bloomington, A
Ivy Tech Community College - Central Indiana, A
Ivy Tech Community College - Lafayette, A
Ivy Tech Community College - Northeast, A
Ivy Tech Community College - Northwest, A
Ivy Tech Community College - Richmond, A
Ivy Tech Community College - Southern Indiana, A
Ivy Tech Community College - Wabash Valley, A
University of Indianapolis, B
University of Southern Indiana, A

Iowa

Clinton Community College, A
Des Moines Area Community College, A
Hawkeye Community College, A
Kirkwood Community College, A
Northeast Iowa Community College, A
St. Luke's College, A
Scott Community College, A
Southeastern Community College, A

Kansas

Barton County Community College, A
Dodge City Community College, A
Hutchinson Community College, A
Johnson County Community College, A
Kansas City Kansas Community College, A
Labette Community College, A
Newman University, A
Seward County Community College and Area Tech-
    nical School, A
The University of Kansas, B
Washburn University, A

Kentucky

Bellarmine University, B
Bluegrass Community and Technical College, A
Elizabethtown Community and Technical College, A
Jefferson Community and Technical College, A
Madisonville Community College, A
Maysville Community and Technical College
    (Maysville), A
Maysville Community and Technical College
    (Morehead), A
Morehead State University, A
Northern Kentucky University, B
Somerset Community College, A
Southeast Kentucky Community and Technical Col-
    lege, A
Spencerian College, A
West Kentucky Community and Technical College, A

Louisiana

Bossier Parish Community College, A
Delgado Community College, A
Louisiana State University at Eunice, A
Southern University at Shreveport, A

Maine

Kennebec Valley Community College, A
Southern Maine Community College, A

Maryland

Allegany College of Maryland, A
Baltimore City Community College, A
Community College of Baltimore County, A
Frederick Community College, A
Prince George's Community College, A
Salisbury University, B

Massachusetts

Berkshire Community College, A
Massasoit Community College, A
North Shore Community College, A
Northern Essex Community College, A
Quinsigamond Community College, A
Springfield Technical Community College, A

Michigan

Delta College, A
Ferris State University, A
Henry Ford College, A
Kalamazoo Valley Community College, A
Macomb Community College, A
Monroe County Community College, A
Mott Community College, A
Northern Michigan University, B
Oakland Community College, A

Minnesota

Concordia University, St. Paul, B
Lake Superior College, A
Northland Community and Technical College, A
St. Catherine University, B
Saint Paul College - A Community & Technical College, A

Mississippi

Coahoma Community College, A
Hinds Community College, A
Itawamba Community College, A
Meridian Community College, A
Mississippi Gulf Coast Community College, A
Northeast Mississippi Community College, A
Northwest Mississippi Community College, A
Pearl River Community College, A

Missouri

Concorde Career College, A
East Central College, A
Metropolitan Community College - Kansas City, A
Missouri Southern State University, A
Missouri State University, B
Ozarks Technical Community College, A
University of Missouri, B

Montana

Great Falls College Montana State University, A
University of Montana, A

Nebraska

Metropolitan Community College, A
Midland University, AB
Nebraska Methodist College, AB
Southeast Community College, Lincoln Campus, A

Nevada

College of Southern Nevada, A

New Hampshire

River Valley Community College, A

New Jersey

Atlantic Cape Community College, A
Bergen Community College, A
Brookdale Community College, A
County College of Morris, A
Cumberland County College, A
Fairleigh Dickinson University, College at Florham, B
Hudson County Community College, A
Mercer County Community College, A
Middlesex County College, A
Ocean County College, A
Passaic County Community College, A
Raritan Valley Community College, A
Rowan College at Burlington County, A
Rowan College at Gloucester County, A
Rutgers University - New Brunswick, A
Rutgers University - Newark, B
Salem Community College, A
Thomas Edison State University, AB
Union County College, A

New Mexico

Central New Mexico Community College, A
Doña Ana Community College, A
Eastern New Mexico University - Roswell, A
San Juan College, A
Santa Fe Community College, A

New York

Canisius College, B
Erie Community College, North Campus, A
Genesee Community College, A
Hudson Valley Community College, A
Long Island University - LIU Brooklyn, B
Mohawk Valley Community College, A
Molloy College, A
Nassau Community College, A
Rockland Community College, A
State University of New York Upstate Medical University, B
Stony Brook University, State University of New York, B
Sullivan County Community College, A
Westchester Community College, A

North Carolina

Carteret Community College, A
Catawba Valley Community College, A
Central Piedmont Community College, A
Durham Technical Community College, A
Edgecombe Community College, A
Fayetteville Technical Community College, A
Pitt Community College, A
Robeson Community College, A
Rockingham Community College, A
Sandhills Community College, A
Southwestern Community College, A
Stanly Community College, A
The University of North Carolina at Charlotte, B

North Dakota

North Dakota State University, B
University of Mary, B

Ohio

Bowling Green State University, B
Bowling Green State University - Firelands College, AB
Columbus State Community College, A
Cuyahoga Community College, A
Eastern Gateway Community College, A
James A. Rhodes State College, A
Kent State University at Ashtabula, AB
Kettering College, AB
Lakeland Community College, A
North Central State College, A
The Ohio State University, B
Shawnee State University, A
Sinclair Community College, A
Southern State Community College, A
Stark State College, A
The University of Akron, B
University of Cincinnati, B
University of Cincinnati Clermont College, A
The University of Toledo, B
Youngstown State University, B

Oklahoma

Oklahoma City Community College, A
Rose State College, A
Tulsa Community College, A

Oregon

Lane Community College, A
Mt. Hood Community College, A

Pennsylvania

Brightwood Career Institute, Philadelphia Mills Campus, A
Clarion University of Pennsylvania, A
Community College of Allegheny County, A
Community College of Philadelphia, A
Delaware County Community College, A
Gannon University, AB
Gwynedd Mercy University, AB
Harrisburg Area Community College, A
Indiana University of Pennsylvania, B
Luzerne County Community College, A
Mansfield University of Pennsylvania, A
Mercyhurst North East, A
Pennsylvania College of Health Sciences, A
Reading Area Community College, A
Thaddeus Stevens College of Technology, A

University of Pittsburgh at Johnstown, A
York College of Pennsylvania, AB
YTI Career Institute - Altoona, A

Rhode Island

Community College of Rhode Island, A

South Carolina

Florence-Darlington Technical College, A
Greenville Technical College, A
Midlands Technical College, A
Orangeburg-Calhoun Technical College, A
Piedmont Technical College, A
Spartanburg Community College, A
Trident Technical College, A

South Dakota

Dakota State University, AB

Tennessee

Baptist College of Health Sciences, B
Chattanooga State Community College, A
Columbia State Community College, A
Concorde Career College, A
Roane State Community College, A
Tennessee State University, B
Volunteer State Community College, A
Walters State Community College, A

Texas

Alvin Community College, A
Amarillo College, A
Angelina College, A
Collin County Community College District, A
Del Mar College, A
El Centro College, A
El Paso Community College, A
Houston Community College, A
Howard College, A
Lamar Institute of Technology, A
Lone Star College - Kingwood, A
McLennan Community College, A
Midland College, A
Midwestern State University, B
St. Philip's College, A
San Jacinto College District, A
South Plains College, A
Tarrant County College District, A
Temple College, A
Texas Southern University, B
Texas Southmost College, A
Texas State University, B
Tyler Junior College, A
The University of Texas Health Science Center at San Antonio, B
The University of Texas Medical Branch, B
Victoria College, A
Weatherford College, A

Utah

Dixie State University, A
Independence University, AB
Stevens-Henager College (Logan), A
Stevens-Henager College (Orem), A
Stevens-Henager College (Salt Lake City), A
Weber State University, AB

Vermont

Vermont Technical College, A

Virginia

Central Virginia Community College, A
J. Sargeant Reynolds Community College, A
Jefferson College of Health Sciences, A
Mountain Empire Community College, A
Northern Virginia Community College, A
Shenandoah University, B
Southside Virginia Community College, A

Washington

Highline College, A
Seattle Central College, A
Spokane Community College, A
Tacoma Community College, A

West Virginia

BridgeValley Community and Technical College (Montgomery), A
Marshall University, B
Mountwest Community & Technical College, A
West Virginia Northern Community College, A
Wheeling Jesuit University, B

Wisconsin

Cardinal Stritch University, B
Chippewa Valley Technical College, A
Madison Area Technical College, A
Mid-State Technical College, A
Milwaukee Area Technical College, A
Moraine Park Technical College, A
Northeast Wisconsin Technical College, A
Western Technical College, A

Wyoming

Casper College, A

U.S. Territories: Puerto Rico

Centro de Estudios Multidisciplinarios (Rio Piedras), A
Huertas Junior College, A
Inter American University of Puerto Rico, Guayama Campus, A
Universidad Adventista de las Antillas, AB
Universidad Metropolitana, AB
Universidad del Turabo, A

Canada

British Columbia

Thompson Rivers University, B

Maritime Provinces: Nova Scotia

Dalhousie University, B

Ontario

University of Waterloo, B

RESPIRATORY THERAPY TECHNICIAN/ASSISTANT

United States

Arizona

Carrington College - Mesa, A
Carrington College - Phoenix West, A
Pima Medical Institute (Mesa), A
Pima Medical Institute (Tucson), A

California

American Career College (Anaheim), A
American Career College (Los Angeles), A
Brightwood College, Modesto Campus, A
California College San Diego (San Diego), AB
Carrington College - Pleasant Hill, A
Pima Medical Institute, A
San Joaquin Valley College (Rancho Cordova), A

Colorado

Pima Medical Institute (Denver), A

Delaware

Delaware Technical & Community College, Jack F. Owens Campus, A
Delaware Technical & Community College, Stanton/Wilmington Campus, A

District of Columbia

University of the District of Columbia, A

Florida

Florida National University, A
Florida SouthWestern State College, A
Keiser University, A
Miami Dade College, A

Georgia

Augusta Technical College, A
Coastal Pines Technical College, A
Columbus Technical College, A
Dalton State College, A
Georgia Highlands College, A
Georgia Northwestern Technical College, A
Southeastern Technical College, A
Southern Crescent Technical College, A

Kansas

Hutchinson Community College, A
Kansas City Kansas Community College, A

Kentucky

Ashland Community and Technical College, A
Southcentral Kentucky Community and Technical College, A

Louisiana

McCann School of Business & Technology (Monroe), A

Massachusetts

Bunker Hill Community College, A
Northern Essex Community College, A

Michigan

Northern Michigan University, A

Missouri

Mineral Area College, A
Missouri State University - West Plains, A

Nevada

Carrington College - Las Vegas, A
Pima Medical Institute, A

New Mexico

Pima Medical Institute (Albuquerque), A

New York

Borough of Manhattan Community College of the City University of New York, A

Rhode Island

Rhode Island College, B

South Carolina

Tri-County Technical College, A

Texas

Pima Medical Institute, A

Washington

Pima Medical Institute (Renton), A

Canada

Maritime Provinces: Nova Scotia

Dalhousie University, B

RESTAURANT, CULINARY, AND CATERING MANAGEMENT/ MANAGER

United States

Arizona

The Art Institute of Phoenix, B
Northland Pioneer College, A
Pima Community College, A

Arkansas

Arkansas Tech University, A

California

American River College, A
The Art Institute of California - Hollywood, a campus of Argosy University, B
The Art Institute of California - Inland Empire, a campus of Argosy University, B
The Art Institute of California - Los Angeles, a campus of Argosy University, B
The Art Institute of California - Orange County, a campus of Argosy University, B
The Art Institute of California - Sacramento, a campus of Argosy University, B
The Art Institute of California - San Diego, a campus of Argosy University, B
The Art Institute of California - San Francisco, a campus of Argosy University, B
Chaffey College, A
City College of San Francisco, A
College of the Canyons, A
Columbia College, A
Cosumnes River College, A
Cypress College, A
Fresno City College, A
Grossmont College, A
Long Beach City College, A
MiraCosta College, A
Orange Coast College, A
Southwestern College, A

Colorado

The Art Institute of Colorado, B
Colorado Mountain College (Steamboat Springs), A

Delaware

Delaware Technical & Community College, Stanton/Wilmington Campus, A

Florida

The Art Institute of Fort Lauderdale, B
The Art Institute of Tampa, a branch of Miami International University of Art & Design, B
Broward College, A
College of Central Florida, A
Florida State College at Jacksonville, A
Gulf Coast State College, A
Hillsborough Community College, A
Johnson & Wales University, B
Lincoln College of Technology, AB
Lincoln Culinary Institute, A
Miami Dade College, A
Pensacola State College, A
St. Petersburg College, A

Georgia

The Art Institute of Atlanta, AB

Hawaii

University of Hawaii - West Oahu, B

Illinois

City Colleges of Chicago, Malcolm X College, A
College of DuPage, A
College of Lake County, A
Elgin Community College, A
The Illinois Institute of Art - Chicago, AB
The Illinois Institute of Art - Schaumburg, AB
John Wood Community College, A
McHenry County College, A
Moraine Valley Community College, A
Southwestern Illinois College, A
University of Illinois at Urbana - Champaign, B

Indiana

The Art Institute of Indianapolis, B
Vincennes University, A

Iowa

Iowa Lakes Community College, A
Kirkwood Community College, A

Kansas

Johnson County Community College, A

Maine

Eastern Maine Community College, A

Maryland

Stratford University, A

Michigan

The Art Institute of Michigan, B
Ferris State University, A
Grand Rapids Community College, A

Minnesota

Hibbing Community College, A

Missouri

The Art Institute of St. Louis, B

Nebraska

Central Community College - Hastings Campus, A
Southeast Community College, Lincoln Campus, A

Nevada

The Art Institute of Las Vegas, B

New Jersey

Bergen Community College, A
Raritan Valley Community College, A

New York

Mohawk Valley Community College, A
Morrisville State College, A
State University of New York College of Agriculture
and Technology at Cobleskill, A
State University of New York College of Technology
at Delhi, AB

North Carolina

The Art Institute of Charlotte, a campus of South
University, AB
The Art Institute of Raleigh-Durham, a campus of
South University, B
Johnson & Wales University, B
Nash Community College, A

Ohio

Bowling Green State University, B
Cincinnati State Technical and Community College,
A
Cuyahoga Community College, A
Lakeland Community College, A

Oregon

The Art Institute of Portland, B
Lane Community College, A
Linn-Benton Community College, A
Southwestern Oregon Community College, A

Pennsylvania

The Art Institute of Philadelphia, B
The Art Institute of Pittsburgh, B
Community College of Allegheny County, A
JNA Institute of Culinary Arts, A
Pennsylvania College of Technology, B
Reading Area Community College, A
Westmoreland County Community College, A

Rhode Island

Johnson & Wales University, B

South Carolina

The Art Institute of Charleston, a branch of The Art
Institute of Atlanta, AB

Tennessee

The Art Institute of Tennessee - Nashville, a branch
of The Art Institute of Atlanta, B

Texas

The Art Institute of Austin, a branch of The Art Institute of Houston, AB
The Art Institute of Dallas, a campus of South University, AB
The Art Institute of Houston, AB

The Art Institute of San Antonio, a branch of The Art
Institute of Houston, AB
Culinary Institute LeNotre, A
San Jacinto College District, A

Utah

LDS Business College, A

Vermont

New England Culinary Institute, AB

Virginia

The Art Institute of Virginia Beach, a branch of The
Art Institute of Atlanta, B
The Art Institute of Washington, a branch of The Art
Institute of Atlanta, B

Washington

The Art Institute of Seattle, B

West Virginia

Blue Ridge Community and Technical College, A

Wisconsin

Milwaukee Area Technical College, A
Southwest Wisconsin Technical College, A
Waukesha County Technical College, A

U.S. Territories: Guam

Guam Community College, A

U.S. Territories: Puerto Rico

Universidad del Este, B

RESTAURANT/FOOD SER-
VICES MANAGEMENT

United States

Alabama

The University of Alabama, B

Alaska

University of Alaska Anchorage, B

California

Glendale Community College, A
Oxnard College, A
Santa Rosa Junior College, A
University of San Francisco, B

Colorado

Colorado State University, B
Johnson & Wales University, B

Connecticut

Naugatuck Valley Community College, A
Norwalk Community College, A

Florida

Broward College, A
Hillsborough Community College, A
Miami Dade College, A
University of Central Florida, B
Valencia College, A

Georgia

Kennesaw State University, B

Illinois

Triton College, A

Iowa

Iowa Lakes Community College, A

Maryland

Stratford University, AB

Massachusetts

Quinsigamond Community College, A

Michigan

Oakland Community College, A

Minnesota

Minneapolis Community and Technical College, A
South Central College, A
Southwest Minnesota State University, B

Missouri

College of the Ozarks, B
University of Missouri, B

Nevada

College of Southern Nevada, A
University of Nevada, Las Vegas, B

New Hampshire

Lakes Region Community College, A

New Jersey

Rowan College at Burlington County, A

New York

The Culinary Institute of America, B
Erie Community College, North Campus, A
Fiorello H. LaGuardia Community College of the
City University of New York, A
Morrisville State College, AB
Niagara University, B
Rochester Institute of Technology, B
Schenectady County Community College, A

North Carolina

Johnson & Wales University, B

Ohio

The Ohio State University, B
Owens Community College, A
The University of Akron, A
Wright State University, B

Pennsylvania

Messiah College, B
Northampton Community College, A
Pennsylvania College of Technology, A
The Restaurant School at Walnut Hill College, AB

Tennessee

L'Ecole Culinaire - Memphis, A

Texas

Central Texas College, A
St. Philip's College, A

Utah

LDS Business College, A

Virginia

Culinary Institute of Virginia, B
ECPI University (Virginia Beach), B
J. Sargeant Reynolds Community College, A
Stratford University (Alexandria), B
Stratford University (Falls Church), AB
Stratford University (Glen Allen), B
Stratford University (Newport News), AB
Stratford University (Virginia Beach), B
Stratford University (Woodbridge), AB

Washington

Central Washington University, B

RETAILING AND RETAIL OP-
ERATIONS

United States

California

American River College, A
Butte College, A
Cañada College, A
Chabot College, A

Chaffey College, A
College of San Mateo, A
Crafton Hills College, A
Cypress College, A
Evergreen Valley College, A
Fresno City College, A
Grossmont College, A

Colorado

Arapahoe Community College, A

Illinois

Black Hawk College, A
College of DuPage, A
Elgin Community College, A
Illinois Central College, A
Moraine Valley Community College, A

Indiana

International Business College (Fort Wayne), AB

Iowa

Iowa Lakes Community College, A
Western Iowa Tech Community College, A

Kansas

Fort Scott Community College, A
Garden City Community College, A
Hutchinson Community College, A

Massachusetts

Fisher College, B

Michigan

Delta College, A

Minnesota

Capella University, B
Minnesota State College - Southeast Technical, A
Rochester Community and Technical College, A
University of Minnesota, Twin Cities Campus, B

Missouri

Stevens - The Institute of Business & Arts, AB

New Jersey

Rowan College at Burlington County, A

New York

Nassau Community College, A
Wood Tobe - Coburn School, A

North Carolina

Alamance Community College, A
Blue Ridge Community College, A

Ohio

Bowling Green State University, B
University of Cincinnati Blue Ash College, A

Oklahoma

University of Central Oklahoma, B

Oregon

Blue Mountain Community College, A
Central Oregon Community College, A
Clackamas Community College, A

Pennsylvania

Bradford School, A
Bucks County Community College, A
Community College of Allegheny County, A
Delaware County Community College, A

South Carolina

University of South Carolina, B

Texas

Lamar University, B
North Central Texas College, A

Utah

Weber State University, A

Washington

Bates Technical College, A
Central Washington University, B
Clark College, A

West Virginia

American Public University System, AB

Wisconsin

Northeast Wisconsin Technical College, A
University of Wisconsin - Madison, B
Western Technical College, A

Wyoming

Casper College, A

Canada

Alberta

University of Alberta, B

Ontario

Ryerson University, B

RHETORIC

United States

Alabama

The University of Alabama, MD
The University of Alabama at Birmingham, M

Arizona

Arizona State University at the Tempe campus, D
Northern Arizona University, M
The University of Arizona, MD

Arkansas

University of Arkansas at Little Rock, M

California

California State University, Dominguez Hills, O
California State University, Northridge, M
California State University, Stanislaus, M
National University, M
San Diego State University, M
University of California, Berkeley, D
University of Southern California, D

Colorado

University of Colorado Denver, M

District of Columbia

The Catholic University of America, O

Florida

Florida Atlantic University, M
Florida State University, MD
University of South Florida, MD

Georgia

Georgia State University, MD
Valdosta State University, M

Idaho

Idaho State University, M

Illinois

DePaul University, M
Northwestern University, D
Southern Illinois University Carbondale, MD

Indiana

Ball State University, M
Indiana University Bloomington, D

Iowa

Iowa State University of Science and Technology, MD
The University of Iowa, MD

Kentucky

Northern Kentucky University, O
University of Louisville, MD

Louisiana

University of Louisiana at Lafayette, MD

Maryland

Salisbury University, M

Massachusetts

University of Massachusetts Amherst, D

Michigan

Michigan State University, MD
Michigan Technological University, MD
University of Michigan - Flint, M

Missouri

Missouri Western State University, M

Nebraska

University of Nebraska - Lincoln, MD

New Jersey

Monmouth University, M
Rowan University, O

New Mexico

New Mexico Highlands University, M
New Mexico State University, MD

New York

Hofstra University, M
Rensselaer Polytechnic Institute, MD
Syracuse University, MD

North Carolina

East Carolina University, MD
North Carolina State University, D
The University of North Carolina at Charlotte, M
The University of North Carolina at Greensboro, D

North Dakota

North Dakota State University, D

Ohio

Bowling Green State University, D
Kent State University, D
Ohio University, D
The University of Findlay, M
Wright State University, M

Pennsylvania

Carnegie Mellon University, MD
Duquesne University, MD

South Carolina

Bob Jones University, M
Clemson University, D

Tennessee

The University of Tennessee at Chattanooga, MO

Texas

Abilene Christian University, M
Texas Christian University, D
Texas State University, M
Texas Tech University, D
Texas Woman's University, D
University of Houston - Downtown, M
The University of Texas at El Paso, MD
The University of Texas Rio Grande Valley, M

Utah

Brigham Young University, M
University of Utah, MD

Virginia

George Mason University, D
James Madison University, M
Virginia Commonwealth University, M

Virginia Polytechnic Institute and State University, D

Washington

Eastern Washington University, M

Wisconsin

University of Wisconsin - Madison, MD
University of Wisconsin - Milwaukee, DO

ROBOTICS TECHNOLOGY/ TECHNICIAN

United States

Arizona

University of Advancing Technology, B

California

Yuba College, A

Florida

Daytona State College, A

Idaho

Idaho State University, AB

Illinois

College of DuPage, A
Illinois Central College, A
Kaskaskia College, A
McHenry County College, A

Indiana

Indiana State University, B
Indiana University - Purdue University Indianapolis, B
Ivy Tech Community College - Columbus, A
Ivy Tech Community College - Lafayette, A
Ivy Tech Community College - North Central, A
Ivy Tech Community College - Northeast, A
Ivy Tech Community College - Richmond, A
Ivy Tech Community College - Southwest, A
Vincennes University, A

Kansas

Wichita Area Technical College, A

Kentucky

Sullivan College of Technology and Design, AB

Louisiana

Southern University at Shreveport, A

Michigan

Kirtland Community College, A
Lake Superior State University, B
Macomb Community College, A
Oakland Community College, A
Washtenaw Community College, A

Minnesota

Central Lakes College, A
Dunwoody College of Technology, A
Minnesota West Community and Technical College, A

Mississippi

Alcorn State University, B

New York

Sarah Lawrence College, B

North Carolina

Wake Technical Community College, A

Ohio

James A. Rhodes State College, A
Terra State Community College, A
University of Rio Grande, AB

Pennsylvania

Butler County Community College, A
California University of Pennsylvania, A
Community College of Allegheny County, A
Delaware County Community College, A
Pennsylvania College of Technology, A

South Dakota

Lake Area Technical Institute, A

Texas

Texas State Technical College, A

Utah

Utah Valley University, A

Wyoming

Casper College, A

Canada

British Columbia

British Columbia Institute of Technology, A

ROMANCE LANGUAGES, LIT- ERATURES, AND LINGUISTICS

United States

Alabama

The University of Alabama, MD

California

Loyola Marymount University, B
Pomona College, B
San Diego State University, M
University of California, Berkeley, D

Connecticut

Wesleyan University, B

Florida

University of Miami, D

Georgia

Clark Atlanta University, MD
Emory University, B
University of Georgia, BMD

Illinois

Northern Illinois University, M
Rockford University, B
University of Chicago, BMD
University of Illinois at Chicago, B
University of Illinois at Urbana - Champaign, D

Indiana

DePauw University, B
University of Notre Dame, BM

Louisiana

University of New Orleans, M

Maine

Bowdoin College, B
University of Maine, B

Maryland

Hood College, B
Johns Hopkins University, BD
University of Maryland, College Park, B

Massachusetts

Boston University, MD
Harvard University, B
Merrimack College, B
Mount Holyoke College, B
Tufts University, B

Michigan

Michigan State University, MD
University of Michigan, B
University of Michigan - Flint, B
Wayne State University, M

Minnesota

Carleton College, B

Missouri

Truman State University, B
University of Missouri, MD
University of Missouri - Kansas City, M
Washington University in St. Louis, BMD
William Jewell College, B

Nevada

University of Nevada, Las Vegas, B

New Hampshire

Dartmouth College, B

New York

City College of the City University of New York, B
Colgate University, B
Columbia University, MD
Cornell University, MD
Hunter College of the City University of New York, BM
New York University, M
Queens College of the City University of New York, M
St. Thomas Aquinas College, B
Stony Brook University, State University of New York, M
University at Buffalo, the State University of New York, MD

North Carolina

Appalachian State University, M
North Carolina Agricultural and Technical State University, B
Queens University of Charlotte, B
The University of North Carolina at Chapel Hill, BMD

Ohio

Oberlin College, B
University of Cincinnati, MD

Oregon

University of Oregon, BMD

Pennsylvania

Bryn Mawr College, B
Gettysburg College, B
Haverford College, B
University of Pennsylvania, BMD

Tennessee

Vanderbilt University, B

Texas

Texas Tech University, M
The University of Texas at Austin, D

Virginia

University of Virginia, MD
Washington and Lee University, B

Washington

Highline College, A
University of Washington, B

West Virginia

Wheeling Jesuit University, B

Wisconsin

Beloit College, B
Ripon College, B

Canada

Alberta

University of Alberta, B
University of Lethbridge, B

British Columbia

The University of British Columbia, B
University of Victoria, B

Maritime Provinces: New Brunswick

Mount Allison University, B
University of New Brunswick Fredericton, B

Ontario

University of Toronto, B
York University, B

ROOFER

United States

Arizona

Penn Foster College, A

California

Chabot College, A

RURAL PLANNING AND STUDIES

United States

Alaska

University of Alaska Fairbanks, M

California

California State University, Chico, M

Iowa

Iowa State University of Science and Technology, D

Montana

University of Montana, M

North Carolina

East Carolina University, M

Wyoming

University of Wyoming, M

Canada

Manitoba

Brandon University, MO

Maritime Provinces: Nova Scotia

Dalhousie University, M

Ontario

University of Guelph, MD

Quebec

Université Laval, O

RURAL SOCIOLOGY

United States

Alabama

Auburn University, M

Iowa

Iowa State University of Science and Technology, MD

Missouri

University of Missouri, MD

Montana

University of Montana, M

New York

Cornell University, MD

Ohio

The Ohio State University, MD

Pennsylvania

Penn State University Park, MDO

Wisconsin

University of Wisconsin - Madison, M

Canada

Alberta

University of Alberta, MD

RUSSIAN LANGUAGE AND LITERATURE

United States

Alaska

University of Alaska Anchorage, B

Arizona

Arizona State University at the Tempe campus, B
The University of Arizona, BM

California

El Camino College, A
Pomona College, B
San Diego State University, B
Scripps College, B
University of California, Berkeley, D
University of California, Davis, B
University of California, Los Angeles, B
University of California, San Diego, B
University of Southern California, B

Colorado

University of Denver, B

Connecticut

Trinity College, B
Yale University, BD

District of Columbia

American University, B
The George Washington University, B
Georgetown University, B
Howard University, B

Florida

New College of Florida, B
University of Florida, B
University of South Florida, B

Georgia

Emory University, B
University of Georgia, B

Hawaii

University of Hawaii at Manoa, B

Idaho

Idaho State University, A

Illinois

University of Illinois at Chicago, B
University of Illinois at Urbana - Champaign, B

Indiana

Purdue University, B
University of Notre Dame, B

Iowa

Cornell College, B
Grinnell College, B
Luther College, B
The University of Iowa, B

Kentucky

University of Kentucky, B

Louisiana

Tulane University, B

Maine

Bowdoin College, B

Maryland

Goucher College, B
University of Maryland, College Park, B

Massachusetts

Amherst College, B
Boston College, BM
Boston University, B
Brandeis University, B
College of the Holy Cross, B
Harvard University, D
Smith College, B
Tufts University, B
Wellesley College, B
Wheaton College, B
Williams College, B

Michigan

Michigan State University, B
University of Michigan, BM

Minnesota

Carleton College, B
Gustavus Adolphus College, B
Macalester College, B
St. Olaf College, B
University of Minnesota, Twin Cities Campus, B

Missouri

Saint Louis University, B
Truman State University, B
University of Missouri, BM

Montana

University of Montana, B

Nebraska

University of Nebraska - Lincoln, B

New Hampshire

Dartmouth College, B
University of New Hampshire, B

New Jersey

Princeton University, D
Rutgers University - New Brunswick, B

New York

Bard College, B
Barnard College, B
Brooklyn College of the City University of New York, B
Colgate University, B
Columbia University, BM
Columbia University, School of General Studies, B
Cornell University, B
Hofstra University, B
Hunter College of the City University of New York, B
Lehman College of the City University of New York, B

New York University, BM
Queens College of the City University of New York, B
Sarah Lawrence College, B
Syracuse University, B
United States Military Academy, B
University of Rochester, B
Vassar College, B

North Carolina

Duke University, B
The University of North Carolina at Chapel Hill, MD
Wake Forest University, B

Ohio

Bowling Green State University, B
Kent State University, BM
Miami University Hamilton, B
Oberlin College, B
The Ohio State University, B
Ohio University, B

Oklahoma

Oklahoma State University, B
University of Oklahoma, B

Oregon

Portland State University, B
Reed College, B
University of Oregon, M
Willamette University, B

Pennsylvania

Bryn Mawr College, B
Bucknell University, B
Carnegie Mellon University, B
Dickinson College, B
Haverford College, B
Juniata College, B
La Salle University, B
Penn State Abington, B
Penn State Altoona, B
Penn State Beaver, B
Penn State Berks, B
Penn State Brandywine, B
Penn State DuBois, B
Penn State Erie, The Behrend College, B
Penn State Fayette, The Eberly Campus, B
Penn State Greater Allegheny, B
Penn State Hazleton, B
Penn State Lehigh Valley, B
Penn State Mont Alto, B
Penn State New Kensington, B
Penn State Schuylkill, B
Penn State Shenango, B
Penn State University Park, BM
Penn State Wilkes-Barre, B
Penn State Worthington Scranton, B
Penn State York, B
Swarthmore College, B
University of Pennsylvania, B
University of Pittsburgh, B
West Chester University of Pennsylvania, B

Rhode Island

Brown University, M

South Carolina

University of South Carolina, B

Tennessee

Sewanee: The University of the South, B
The University of Tennessee, BD
Vanderbilt University, B

Texas

Austin Community College District, A
Baylor University, B
Texas A&M University, B
Trinity University, B
The University of Texas at Arlington, B
The University of Texas at Austin, B

Utah

University of Utah, B

Vermont

Middlebury College, BMD
University of Vermont, B

Virginia

Virginia Polytechnic Institute and State University, B

Washington

Central Washington University, B
Seattle Pacific University, B
University of Washington, BMD

Wisconsin

Beloit College, B
Lawrence University, B
University of Wisconsin - Madison, B
University of Wisconsin - Milwaukee, B

Wyoming

University of Wyoming, B

Canada

Alberta

University of Alberta, B
University of Calgary, B

British Columbia

The University of British Columbia, B
University of Victoria, B

Manitoba

University of Manitoba, B

Maritime Provinces: New Brunswick

University of New Brunswick Fredericton, B

Maritime Provinces: Nova Scotia

Dalhousie University, B
University of King's College, B

Newfoundland and Labrador

Memorial University of Newfoundland, B

Ontario

Carleton University, B
McMaster University, B
University of Ottawa, B
University of Toronto, B
University of Waterloo, BM
York University, B

Quebec

McGill University, MD

Saskatchewan

University of Saskatchewan, B

RUSSIAN STUDIES

United States

Alaska

University of Alaska Fairbanks, B

California

Scripps College, B
University of California, Los Angeles, B
University of California, Riverside, B
University of California, San Diego, B
University of California, Santa Cruz, B

Colorado

The Colorado College, B
University of Colorado Boulder, B

Connecticut

Wesleyan University, B
Yale University, B

Delaware

University of Delaware, B

District of Columbia

American University, B
The George Washington University, B

Florida

State College of Florida Manatee-Sarasota, A
Stetson University, B

Georgia

Emory University, B

Illinois

University of Chicago, B
University of Illinois at Urbana - Champaign, B

Indiana

DePauw University, B

Iowa

Cornell College, B
The University of Iowa, B

Kansas

The University of Kansas, B

Louisiana

Tulane University, B

Maine

Colby College, B

Maryland

University of Maryland, College Park, B

Massachusetts

Boston College, B
Mount Holyoke College, B
Smith College, B
Tufts University, B
University of Massachusetts Amherst, B
Wellesley College, B
Wheaton College, B

Michigan

Grand Valley State University, B
University of Michigan, B

Minnesota

Carleton College, B
Gustavus Adolphus College, B
St. Olaf College, B

Missouri

University of Missouri, B
Washington University in St. Louis, B

Montana

University of Montana, B

New Hampshire

Dartmouth College, B

New Mexico

University of New Mexico, B

New York

Bard College, B
Colgate University, B
Columbia University, B
Columbia University, School of General Studies, B
Hamilton College, B
Hobart and William Smith Colleges, B
Syracuse University, B
United States Military Academy, B
University of Rochester, B

Ohio

Bowling Green State University, B
The College of Wooster, B
Kent State University, B
Oberlin College, B

Oklahoma

The University of Tulsa, B

Oregon

University of Oregon, B

Pennsylvania

Carnegie Mellon University, B
Lafayette College, B
Muhlenberg College, B

Rhode Island

Brown University, B

Tennessee

Rhodes College, B

Texas

Texas Tech University, B
The University of Texas at Austin, B

Vermont

Middlebury College, B
University of Vermont, B

Virginia

George Mason University, B
University of Richmond, B
Washington and Lee University, B

Wisconsin

Lawrence University, B

Canada

British Columbia

The University of British Columbia, B
University of Victoria, B

Manitoba

University of Manitoba, B

Maritime Provinces: Nova Scotia

Dalhousie University, B

Ontario

Carleton University, B
McMaster University, B
University of Toronto, B
University of Waterloo, B
York University, B

SACRED MUSIC

United States

Alabama

Samford University, M
The University of Alabama, M

California

Bethesda University, M
Hope International University, M
University of Southern California, MD

Florida

The Baptist College of Florida, M
University of Florida, M

Georgia

Mercer University, M

Illinois

Concordia University Chicago, M

Indiana

Saint Joseph's College, MO

Kentucky

Campbellsville University, M
University of Kentucky, M

Louisiana

New Orleans Baptist Theological Seminary, MD

Minnesota

Saint John's University, M

Missouri

Webster University, M

New Jersey

Rider University, M

New York

The Jewish Theological Seminary, M

North Carolina

Charlotte Christian College and Theological Seminary, M
East Carolina University, M
Southeastern Baptist Theological Seminary, M

South Carolina

Bob Jones University, M

Tennessee

Belmont University, M
Lee University, M

Texas

Baylor University, MD
Dallas Baptist University, M
Hardin-Simmons University, M
The University of Texas at Austin, M

Virginia

Liberty University, MD
Shenandoah University, MO

Wisconsin

Concordia University Wisconsin, M

SAFETY ENGINEERING

United States

Alabama

The University of Alabama at Birmingham, M

Arizona

Embry-Riddle Aeronautical University - Prescott, M

California

University of Southern California, MO

Florida

Florida Institute of Technology, M

Indiana

Indiana University Bloomington, M

Kentucky

Murray State University, M

Minnesota

University of Minnesota, Duluth, M

New Jersey

New Jersey Institute of Technology, M

New York

Rochester Institute of Technology, M

West Virginia

West Virginia University, M

SALES, DISTRIBUTION AND MARKETING OPERATIONS

United States

Alabama

Gadsden State Community College, A
Tuskegee University, B

Arkansas

Harding University, B
Phillips Community College of the University of Arkansas, A
Rich Mountain Community College, A

California

American River College, A
Antelope Valley College, A
Butte College, A
Chabot College, A
City College of San Francisco, A
College of the Canyons, A
College of San Mateo, A
Cosumnes River College, A
Cuesta College, A
Cypress College, A
Fresno City College, A
Fullerton College, A
Long Beach City College, A
Los Angeles Valley College, A
MiraCosta College, A
Orange Coast College, A
San Jose City College, A
Santa Ana College, A
Santa Barbara City College, A
Santa Monica College, A
Sierra College, A
Southwestern College, A

Connecticut

Quinnipiac University, B

Georgia

Dalton State College, AB
Kennesaw State University, B

Illinois

College of DuPage, A
Harper College, A
McKendree University, B
Oakton Community College, A
University of Illinois at Urbana - Champaign, B

Iowa

Des Moines Area Community College, A
Hawkeye Community College, A
Iowa Lakes Community College, A
Iowa Western Community College, A
Marshalltown Community College, A
North Iowa Area Community College, A
Northeast Iowa Community College, A
Western Iowa Tech Community College, A

Kansas

Johnson County Community College, A

Kentucky

Sullivan University, A

Maine

Husson University, B

Massachusetts

Babson College, B
Bentley University, B
Greenfield Community College, A

Michigan

Baker College, A
Lansing Community College, A
North Central Michigan College, A

Minnesota

Academy College, A
Alexandria Technical and Community College, A
Anoka-Ramsey Community College, A
Metropolitan State University, B
Minnesota State College - Southeast Technical, A
Northland Community and Technical College, A
Northwest Technical College, A
Ridgewater College, A
St. Catherine University, B
St. Cloud State University, A
St. Cloud Technical & Community College, A
University of Minnesota, Twin Cities Campus, B

Missouri

Avila University, B

Montana

Miles Community College, A

Nevada

College of Southern Nevada, A

New Jersey

Rowan College at Burlington County, A

New Mexico

University of New Mexico - Los Alamos Branch, A

New York

Long Island University - LIU Brooklyn, B
New York University, B
State University of New York College of Technology
   at Alfred, A
Syracuse University, B

Ohio

Bowling Green State University, B
Cuyahoga Community College, A
Owens Community College, A
The University of Akron, B
The University of Findlay, AB

Oklahoma

University of Central Oklahoma, B

Pennsylvania

Harrisburg Area Community College, A
Johnson College, A
Montgomery County Community College, A
Seton Hill University, B
University of Pennsylvania, B
West Chester University of Pennsylvania, B
Westmoreland County Community College, A

South Carolina

Aiken Technical College, A
Central Carolina Technical College, A
Florence-Darlington Technical College, A
Greenville Technical College, A
Midlands Technical College, A

South Dakota

Black Hills State University, B

Tennessee

Middle Tennessee State University, B
Pellissippi State Community College, A
Southern Adventist University, AB
University of Memphis, B

Texas

Baylor University, B
North Central Texas College, A
Sam Houston State University, B
Texas A&M University, B
University of Houston, B
University of the Incarnate Word, B

Virginia

Hampton University, B

Wisconsin

Lac Courte Oreilles Ojibwa Community College, A
University of Wisconsin - Stout, B
University of Wisconsin - Superior, B
Western Technical College, A

U.S. Territories: Guam

Guam Community College, A

U.S. Territories: Puerto Rico

American University of Puerto Rico (Bayamon), B
Inter American University of Puerto Rico, Aguadilla
   Campus, A
Universidad Metropolitana, AB

Canada

Ontario

Brock University, B
Ryerson University, B
York University, B

Quebec

HEC Montreal, B

SALES AND MARKETING OPERATIONS/MARKETING AND DISTRIBUTION TEACHER EDUCATION

United States

Florida

Broward College, A

Illinois

Parkland College, A

Kansas

Central Christian College of Kansas, A

Michigan

Eastern Michigan University, B
Western Michigan University, B

Mississippi

Northwest Mississippi Community College, A

New Mexico

Eastern New Mexico University, B

New York

State University of New York at Oswego, B

North Carolina

Fayetteville State University, B
Louisburg College, A
North Carolina State University, B

Ohio

Bowling Green State University, B
Wright State University, AB

Tennessee

Middle Tennessee State University, B

Utah

Utah State University, B

Washington

Central Washington University, B

Wisconsin

University of Wisconsin - Stout, B

SALON/BEAUTY SALON MANAGEMENT/MANAGER

United States

Alabama

J. F. Drake State Community and Technical College,
   A
Northwest-Shoals Community College, A

Florida

Lincoln College of Technology, A
Southeastern College - West Palm Beach, A

Michigan

Delta College, A
Mott Community College, A
Oakland Community College, A
Schoolcraft College, A

Mississippi

Virginia College in Jackson, A

Utah

LDS Business College, A

SANSKRIT AND CLASSICAL INDIAN LANGUAGES, LITERATURES, AND LINGUISTICS

United States

Iowa

The University of Iowa, B

Massachusetts

Harvard University, B

SCANDINAVIAN LANGUAGES, LITERATURES, AND LINGUISTICS

United States

California

University of California, Berkeley, BD
University of California, Los Angeles, BM

Illinois

Augustana College, B
North Park University, B

Iowa

Luther College, B

Massachusetts

Harvard University, D
University of Massachusetts Amherst, MD

Minnesota

Gustavus Adolphus College, B
University of Minnesota, Twin Cities Campus, MD

New York

Cornell University, MD

Texas

The University of Texas at Austin, B

Washington

University of Washington, MD

Wisconsin

University of Wisconsin - Madison, MD

Canada

Alberta

University of Alberta, B

SCANDINAVIAN STUDIES

United States

California

University of California, Los Angeles, B

District of Columbia

American University, B

Illinois

North Park University, B

Minnesota

Concordia College, B
Gustavus Adolphus College, B

Washington

Pacific Lutheran University, B
University of Washington, B

Wisconsin

University of Wisconsin - Madison, B

SCHOOL LIBRARIAN/SCHOOL LIBRARY MEDIA SPECIALIST

United States

Minnesota

The College of St. Scholastica,.B

Montana

University of Great Falls, B

Nebraska

Chadron State College, B
University of Nebraska at Omaha, B

Oklahoma

East Central University, B

SCHOOL NURSING

United States

Illinois

University of Illinois at Chicago, M

Massachusetts

Cambridge College, M

New Jersey

Felician University, MO
Kean University, M
Monmouth University, MO
Rowan University, O
Seton Hall University, M

Ohio

Wright State University, M

Pennsylvania

Eastern University, O
La Salle University, O
Saint Joseph's University, M
West Chester University of Pennsylvania, O

Virginia

Eastern Mennonite University, M

SCHOOL PSYCHOLOGY

United States

Alabama

Alabama Agricultural and Mechanical University, M
Troy University, MO
University of North Alabama, M
The University of West Alabama, MO

Arizona

Argosy University, Phoenix, MD
Northern Arizona University, DO
The University of Arizona, DO

Arkansas

Arkansas State University, M
University of Central Arkansas, MDO

California

Azusa Pacific University, M
California Baptist University, M
California State University, East Bay, M
California State University, Los Angeles, M
California State University, Northridge, M
California State University, Sacramento, M
Chapman University, MDO
Fresno Pacific University, M
Humboldt State University, M
La Sierra University, O
Loyola Marymount University, M
National University, M
San Diego State University, M
San Francisco State University, O
University of California, Riverside, D
University of California, Santa Barbara, DO
University of La Verne, M
University of the Pacific, MDO

Colorado

University of Colorado Denver, MO
University of Denver, O
University of Northern Colorado, DO
University of Phoenix - Colorado Campus, M
University of Phoenix - Colorado Springs Downtown Campus, M

Connecticut

Central Connecticut State University, M
Fairfield University, MO
Southern Connecticut State University, MO
University of Connecticut, MDO
University of Hartford, M

Delaware

University of Delaware, MO

District of Columbia

Gallaudet University, O
Howard University, MD

Florida

Argosy University, Sarasota, M
Barry University, MO
Carlos Albizu University, Miami Campus, M
Florida International University, MO
Florida State University, D
Nova Southeastern University, M
University of Central Florida, O
University of Florida, MDO
University of South Florida, DO

Georgia

Georgia Southern University, MO
Georgia State University, MDO
Mercer University, M

Hawaii

Argosy University, Hawai'i, M
Chaminade University of Honolulu, M

Idaho

Idaho State University, MO
Northwest Nazarene University, M

Illinois

DePaul University, M
Eastern Illinois University, O
Illinois State University, DO
Loyola University Chicago, DO
National Louis University, MO
Quincy University, M
Southern Illinois University Edwardsville, O
Western Illinois University, O

Indiana

Ball State University, MDO
Indiana State University, DO
Indiana University Bloomington, MDO
Purdue University Northwest (Hammond), M

Iowa

The University of Iowa, DO
University of Northern Iowa, MO

Kansas

Emporia State University, MO
Fort Hays State University, O
Ottawa University, M
Pittsburg State University, O
The University of Kansas, DO
Wichita State University, O

Kentucky

Eastern Kentucky University, O
Union College, M
University of Kentucky, DO
Western Kentucky University, O

Louisiana

Louisiana State University and Agricultural & Mechanical College, MD
Louisiana State University in Shreveport, O
McNeese State University, M
Nicholls State University, MO

Maine

Husson University, M
University of Southern Maine, MD

Maryland

Towson University, O
University of Maryland, College Park, MD

Massachusetts

Assumption College, MO
Cambridge College, M
Lesley University, M
Northeastern University, DO
Suffolk University, O
Tufts University, MO
University of Massachusetts Amherst, MDO
University of Massachusetts Boston, MD
Worcester State University, O

Michigan

Andrews University, MO
Central Michigan University, DO
Grand Valley State University, MO
Michigan State University, MDO
University of Detroit Mercy, D
Wayne State University, MD

Minnesota

Capella University, MD
Minnesota State University Mankato, D
Minnesota State University Moorhead, MO
University of Minnesota, Twin Cities Campus, MDO

Mississippi

Mississippi State University, DO
University of Southern Mississippi, D

Missouri

Evangel University, M
Lindenwood University, M
University of Missouri, MDO
University of Missouri - St. Louis, O

Montana

Montana State University, M
University of Montana, MDO

Nebraska

University of Nebraska at Kearney, MO
University of Nebraska - Lincoln, MDO
University of Nebraska at Omaha, MO

Nevada

University of Phoenix - Las Vegas Campus, M

New Hampshire

Keene State College, MO
Plymouth State University, MO

New Jersey

Caldwell University, MO
Fairleigh Dickinson University, Metropolitan Campus, MD
Georgian Court University, MO
Kean University, MDO
New Jersey City University, O
Rider University, O
Rowan University, MO
Rutgers University - New Brunswick, MD
Seton Hall University, M

New Mexico

New Mexico State University, O

New York

Adelphi University, M
Alfred University, MDO
Brooklyn College of the City University of New York, MO
Canisius College, M
The College of New Rochelle, M
The College of Saint Rose, MO
Fordham University, DO
Hofstra University, D
Iona College, M
Marist College, MO
Mercy College, M
Niagara University, MO
Pace University, MD
Queens College of the City University of New York, MO
Rochester Institute of Technology, MO
St. John's University, MD
State University of New York at Plattsburgh, MO
Syracuse University, MDO
Touro College, M
University at Albany, State University of New York, DO
Yeshiva University, D

North Carolina

Appalachian State University, M
Gardner-Webb University, M
Lenoir-Rhyne University, M
North Carolina State University, D
The University of North Carolina at Chapel Hill, MD
The University of North Carolina at Greensboro, O
Western Carolina University, M

North Dakota

Minot State University, O
University of Mary, M

Ohio

Bowling Green State University, MO
Heidelberg University, M
Kent State University, MDO

The University of Akron, MD
University of Cincinnati, DO
University of Dayton, MO
The University of Toledo, MO
Youngstown State University, M

Oklahoma

Southwestern Oklahoma State University, M
University of Central Oklahoma, M

Oregon

George Fox University, O
Lewis & Clark College, MO
Oregon State University - Cascades, M

Pennsylvania

Arcadia University, M
California University of Pennsylvania, M
Duquesne University, MDO
Eastern University, MO
Edinboro University of Pennsylvania, MO
Immaculata University, M
Indiana University of Pennsylvania, DO
Lehigh University, DO
Millersville University of Pennsylvania, M
Penn State University Park, MDO
Slippery Rock University of Pennsylvania, M
Temple University, MDO

Rhode Island

Rhode Island College, O
University of Rhode Island, MD

South Carolina

The Citadel, The Military College of South Carolina, O
Francis Marion University, MO
University of South Carolina, D

South Dakota

The University of South Dakota, DO

Tennessee

Middle Tennessee State University, M
Tennessee State University, MD
Tennessee Technological University, MO
University of Memphis, MDO
The University of Tennessee, DO
The University of Tennessee at Chattanooga, O

Texas

Abilene Christian University, O
Argosy University, Dallas, M
Baylor University, O
Our Lady of the Lake University of San Antonio, M
Sam Houston State University, O
Stephen F. Austin State University, M
Tarleton State University, M
Texas A&M University, D
Texas A&M University - Central Texas, O
Texas State University, O
Texas Woman's University, DO
Trinity University, M
University of Houston - Clear Lake, M
University of Houston - Victoria, M
The University of Texas at Austin, MD
The University of Texas Rio Grande Valley, M
The University of Texas at San Antonio, MO
The University of Texas at Tyler, M

Utah

Brigham Young University, O
University of Phoenix - Utah Campus, M
University of Utah, MD
Utah State University, M

Vermont

College of St. Joseph, M

Virginia

The College of William and Mary, MO
George Mason University, MO
James Madison University, MDO
Lynchburg College, M

Radford University, O
University of Virginia, D

Washington

Central Washington University, M
Eastern Washington University, M
Seattle University, M
University of Washington, M

West Virginia

American Public University System, M
Marshall University, O

Wisconsin

University of Wisconsin - Eau Claire, MO
University of Wisconsin - La Crosse, MO
University of Wisconsin - Milwaukee, DO
University of Wisconsin - River Falls, MO
University of Wisconsin - Stout, MO
University of Wisconsin - Superior, O
University of Wisconsin - Whitewater, MO

U.S. Territories: Puerto Rico

Inter American University of Puerto Rico, Metropolitan Campus, MD
Inter American University of Puerto Rico, San Germán Campus, MD

Canada

Alberta

University of Alberta, MD
University of Calgary, MD

British Columbia

The University of British Columbia, MDO

Manitoba

University of Manitoba, M

Maritime Provinces: Nova Scotia

Mount Saint Vincent University, M

Quebec

McGill University, MDO

SCIENCE TEACHER EDUCATION/GENERAL SCIENCE TEACHER EDUCATION

United States

Alabama

Alabama Agricultural and Mechanical University, MO
Alabama State University, MO
Auburn University, BMDO
Auburn University at Montgomery, M
Huntingdon College, B
Judson College, B
Oakwood University, B
Talladega College, B
Troy University, M
The University of Alabama in Huntsville, M
University of South Alabama, M
The University of West Alabama, M

Arizona

Arizona Christian University, B
Harrison Middleton University, M
Northern Arizona University, MO
University of Phoenix - Online Campus, M

Arkansas

Arkansas State University, MO
Arkansas Tech University, B
Harding University, B
Ouachita Baptist University, B
University of Arkansas at Pine Bluff, M
University of Central Arkansas, B

California

Ashford University, B
Biola University, BMO
California Baptist University, M
California Lutheran University, B
California State University, Bakersfield, M
California State University, Dominguez Hills, M
California State University, Fullerton, M
California State University, Long Beach, M
California State University, Northridge, M
California State University, San Bernardino, M
Fresno Pacific University, M
The Master's College and Seminary, B
Mills College, M
Occidental College, M
San Diego State University, D
San Jose State University, M
University of California, Berkeley, MD
University of California, San Diego, D

Colorado

Adams State University, B
The Colorado College, M
Colorado State University, B
University of Colorado Denver, MD
University of Northern Colorado, MD
Western State Colorado University, B

Connecticut

Central Connecticut State University, MO
Eastern Connecticut State University, M
Quinnipiac University, M
Southern Connecticut State University, MO
University of Connecticut, BMD
University of New Haven, M

Delaware

Delaware State University, BM
Wilmington University, B

District of Columbia

The George Washington University, M

Florida

Broward College, B
Chipola College, B
Florida Agricultural and Mechanical University, BM
Florida Atlantic University, BM
Florida Institute of Technology, BMDO
Florida International University, M
Florida SouthWestern State College, B
Florida State University, MDO
Hobe Sound Bible College, B
Indian River State College, B
Miami Dade College, B
Northwest Florida State College, B
St. Petersburg College, B
South Florida State College, A
Southeastern University, B
State College of Florida Manatee-Sarasota, A
University of Central Florida, BMDO
University of Florida, M
University of Miami, D
University of North Florida, B
University of South Florida, BMD
University of South Florida, St. Petersburg, M
University of West Florida, MD
Warner University, B

Georgia

Albany State University, BM
Armstrong State University, B
Brewton-Parker College, B
Clark Atlanta University, M
Columbus State University, BMO
Covenant College, B
Darton State College, A
Georgia State University, MD
Piedmont College, B
University of Georgia, BMDO

Hawaii

Brigham Young University - Hawaii, B
Chaminade University of Honolulu, M

Idaho

Boise State University, M
Lewis-Clark State College, B

Illinois

Aurora University, M
Benedictine University, M
Bradley University, B
Concordia University Chicago, B
DePaul University, M
Eastern Illinois University, B
Illinois Institute of Technology, MD
Lake Forest College, M
Lewis University, M
Loyola University Chicago, B
McKendree University, B
Moraine Valley Community College, A
National Louis University, MO
Olivet Nazarene University, B
Saint Xavier University, M
Southern Illinois University Edwardsville, B
University of Chicago, D
University of Illinois at Chicago, D
University of Illinois at Urbana - Champaign, BM
University of St. Francis, BM

Indiana

Ball State University, BMD
Bethel College, B
Goshen College, B
Huntington University, B
Indiana State University, BM
Indiana Tech, M
Indiana University Bloomington, MD
Indiana University - Purdue University Fort Wayne, B
Indiana University South Bend, B
Indiana Wesleyan University, B
Manchester University, B
Purdue University, MDO
Purdue University Northwest (Hammond), M
Taylor University, B
Trine University, B
University of Indianapolis, BM
University of Notre Dame, B
Valparaiso University, B
Vincennes University, AB

Iowa

Buena Vista University, B
Coe College, B
Dordt College, B
Graceland University, B
Iowa Central Community College, A
Iowa Lakes Community College, A
Iowa State University of Science and Technology, M
Kaplan University, Davenport Campus, M
Morningside College, B
Mount Mercy University, B
The University of Iowa, BM
University of Northern Iowa, BM
Upper Iowa University, B
William Penn University, B

Kansas

Central Christian College of Kansas, A
Fort Hays State University, M
Tabor College, B

Kentucky

Alice Lloyd College, B
Asbury University, M
Campbellsville University, B
Eastern Kentucky University, M
Morehead State University, M
Union College, M
University of Kentucky, B

Louisiana

Grambling State University, M
Louisiana College, B
Louisiana Tech University, M
McNeese State University, M
Nicholls State University, B

Southern University and Agricultural and Mechanical College, BD
University of Louisiana at Monroe, M
Xavier University of Louisiana, B

Maine

College of the Atlantic, B
University of Maine, BMDO
University of Maine at Machias, B

Maryland

Bowie State University, B
Hood College, M
Loyola University Maryland, M
Morgan State University, MD
Notre Dame of Maryland University, B
Stevenson University, M
University of Maryland, Baltimore County, M

Massachusetts

Boston College, M
Boston University, B
Bridgewater State University, M
Cambridge College, M
Eastern Nazarene College, B
Elms College, M
Fitchburg State University, MO
Lesley University, M
Merrimack College, B
Salem State University, M
Smith College, M
Tufts University, MD
University of Massachusetts Amherst, O
University of Massachusetts Lowell, D

Michigan

Adrian College, B
Albion College, B
Alma College, B
Andrews University, BM
Aquinas College, B
Calvin College, B
Central Michigan University, BM
Concordia University Ann Arbor, B
Cornerstone University, B
Eastern Michigan University, BM
Grand Valley State University, B
Hope College, B
Lawrence Technological University, M
Madonna University, B
Michigan State University, BM
Michigan Technological University, M
Northern Michigan University, BM
Olivet College, B
Rochester College, B
Saginaw Valley State University, BM
University of Michigan - Dearborn, BM
University of Michigan - Flint, B
Wayne State University, MDO
Western Michigan University, BMDO

Minnesota

Bemidji State University, B
Crown College, B
Hamline University, M
Minnesota State University Mankato, BM
St. Cloud State University, B
University of Minnesota, Duluth, B
University of Minnesota, Twin Cities Campus, MD
University of St. Thomas, B
Vermilion Community College, A
Walden University, MO
Winona State University, B

Mississippi

Itawamba Community College, A
Jackson State University, M
Jones County Junior College, A
Mississippi College, M
Mississippi Delta Community College, A
Mississippi State University, M
Northeast Mississippi Community College, A
Northwest Mississippi Community College, A
University of Mississippi, B
University of Southern Mississippi, MD

Missouri

Central Methodist University, B
Evangel University, B
Hannibal-LaGrange University, B
Lindenwood University, B
Missouri Baptist University, B
Missouri State University, BM
Missouri Valley College, B
Northwest Missouri State University, BM
Saint Louis University, B
Southeast Missouri State University, B
Southwest Baptist University, B
University of Missouri, BMDO
Washington University in St. Louis, B
Webster University, B

Montana

Montana State University, B
Montana State University Billings, B
Montana State University - Northern, B
Rocky Mountain College, B
University of Great Falls, B
University of Montana, B
The University of Montana Western, B

Nebraska

Chadron State College, B
College of Saint Mary, B
Concordia University, Nebraska, B
Doane University, B
Hastings College, B
Midland University, B
Nebraska Wesleyan University, B
Peru State College, B
Union College, B
University of Nebraska at Kearney, M
University of Nebraska - Lincoln, B
Wayne State College, BM
York College, B

Nevada

Nevada State College, B
University of Nevada, Las Vegas, B

New Hampshire

Keene State College, B
Plymouth State University, BM
Southern New Hampshire University, B
University of New Hampshire, D

New Jersey

Drew University, M
Fairleigh Dickinson University, Metropolitan Campus, M
Kean University, M
Montclair State University, M
Rider University, BO
Rowan University, M
Rutgers University - New Brunswick, MD

New Mexico

New Mexico Highlands University, B
New Mexico Institute of Mining and Technology, M
University of New Mexico, O
Western New Mexico University, B

New York

Alfred University, B
Binghamton University, State University of New York, M
Brooklyn College of the City University of New York, M
Buffalo State College, State University of New York, BM
Canisius College, B
City College of the City University of New York, BM
The College at Brockport, State University of New York, MO
Columbia University, M
Concordia College - New York, B
Hofstra University, BMD
Hunter College of the City University of New York, BM
Iona College, M
Ithaca College, BM

Le Moyne College, B
Lehman College of the City University of New York, M
Manhattanville College, M
New York Institute of Technology, MO
New York University, BM
Niagara University, BM
Pace University, M
Queens College of the City University of New York, MO
State University of New York College at Cortland, BM
State University of New York College at Old Westbury, BM
State University of New York College at Oneonta, B
State University of New York College at Potsdam, M
State University of New York at Fredonia, B
State University of New York at New Paltz, BM
State University of New York at Oswego, B
State University of New York at Plattsburgh, M
Stony Brook University, State University of New York, MD
Syracuse University, MD
Touro College, M
Ulster County Community College, A
University at Buffalo, the State University of New York, MO
Wagner College, M

North Carolina

Appalachian State University, M
Campbell University, B
Catawba College, B
East Carolina University, BMO
Elizabeth City State University, M
Elon University, B
Greensboro College, B
Mars Hill University, B
Methodist University, B
North Carolina Agricultural and Technical State University, BM
North Carolina State University, BMD
Pfeiffer University, B
Sandhills Community College, A
The University of North Carolina at Chapel Hill, M
The University of North Carolina at Greensboro, M
The University of North Carolina at Pembroke, BM
Western Carolina University, B

North Dakota

Dickinson State University, B
Minot State University, BM
North Dakota State University, BMD
University of North Dakota, B
Valley City State University, B

Ohio

Ashland University, B
Bowling Green State University, BM
Capital University, B
Cedarville University, B
Cleveland State University, M
Defiance College, B
Heidelberg University, B
John Carroll University, M
Kent State University, B
Malone University, B
Miami University, B
Miami University Hamilton, B
Mount Vernon Nazarene University, B
Ohio Northern University, B
Ohio University, M
Otterbein University, B
Shawnee State University, B
Tiffin University, B
The University of Akron, B
University of Cincinnati, M
University of Dayton, B
The University of Findlay, BM
University of Rio Grande, B
The University of Toledo, M
Ursuline College, BM
Walsh University, B
Wilmington College, B
Wright State University, ABM
Xavier University, B

Youngstown State University, BM

Oklahoma

East Central University, B
Northeastern State University, BM
Northwestern Oklahoma State University, B
Oklahoma Baptist University, B
Oklahoma Christian University, B
Oklahoma Wesleyan University, B
Oral Roberts University, B
Southeastern Oklahoma State University, B
Southern Nazarene University, B
Southwestern Oklahoma State University, BM
University of Central Oklahoma, B
University of Oklahoma, B
The University of Tulsa, M

Oregon

Concordia University, BM
Oregon State University, MD
Pacific University, M
Portland State University, M
Warner Pacific College, B
Western Oregon University, M

Pennsylvania

Arcadia University, BMO
Bloomsburg University of Pennsylvania, M
Chatham University, M
Clarion University of Pennsylvania, M
Duquesne University, M
East Stroudsburg University of Pennsylvania, M
Eastern University, O
Elizabethtown College, B
Gettysburg College, B
Juniata College, B
Kutztown University of Pennsylvania, M
Lebanon Valley College, M
Marywood University, B
Mercyhurst University, B
Saint Francis University, B
Shippensburg University of Pennsylvania, M
Slippery Rock University of Pennsylvania, M
Summit University, B
Temple University, BM
University of Pennsylvania, MO
University of Pittsburgh, MD
University of Pittsburgh at Johnstown, B
Waynesburg University, B
West Chester University of Pennsylvania, O
Widener University, BM
Wilkes University, M
York College of Pennsylvania, B

Rhode Island

Brown University, M
Rhode Island College, B

South Carolina

Bob Jones University, B
Charleston Southern University, B
The Citadel, The Military College of South Carolina, M
Clemson University, BM
College of Charleston, M
Converse College, M
South Carolina State University, M
Southern Wesleyan University, B
University of South Carolina, M

South Dakota

Black Hills State University, B
University of Sioux Falls, B
The University of South Dakota, B

Tennessee

LeMoyne-Owen College, B
Lincoln Memorial University, B
Martin Methodist College, B
Middle Tennessee State University, MD
Tennessee Technological University, MO
Union University, B
The University of Tennessee, MO
The University of Tennessee at Chattanooga, B
The University of Tennessee at Martin, B

Vanderbilt University, M

Texas

Abilene Christian University, B
Baylor University, B
Dallas Baptist University, B
Hardin-Simmons University, BMD
Houston Baptist University, B
LeTourneau University, B
Midwestern State University, B
Our Lady of the Lake University of San Antonio, M
Ranger College, A
Rice University, M
San Jacinto College District, A
Tarleton State University, B
Texas A&M International University, B
Texas Christian University, BM
Texas State University, M
Texas Tech University, M
University of Mary Hardin-Baylor, B
The University of Texas at Dallas, M
The University of Texas at El Paso, M
The University of Texas Rio Grande Valley, M
Wayland Baptist University, BM

Utah

Brigham Young University, BM
Dixie State University, B
Snow College, A
Southern Utah University, B
University of Utah, MD
Utah State University, B
Utah Valley University, B
Weber State University, B
Western Governors University, BM

Vermont

Castleton University, B
Lyndon State College, BM
University of Vermont, BM

Virginia

Averett University, M
Bluefield College, B
George Mason University, M
Lynchburg College, M
University of Virginia, MD

Washington

Central Washington University, B
Eastern Washington University, B
Heritage University, BM
Seattle Pacific University, M
University of Washington, MD
University of Washington, Tacoma, M
Washington State University, B
Western Washington University, BM

West Virginia

Fairmont State University, B
Glenville State College, B
University of Charleston, B

Wisconsin

Alverno College, BM
Carroll University, B
Carthage College, M
Concordia University Wisconsin, B
Edgewood College, B
Lakeland College, B
Maranatha Baptist University, B
Marian University, B
Mount Mary University, B
Northland College, B
University of Wisconsin - Eau Claire, B
University of Wisconsin - La Crosse, B
University of Wisconsin - Madison, M
University of Wisconsin - Platteville, B
University of Wisconsin - River Falls, M
University of Wisconsin - Stevens Point, M
University of Wisconsin - Stout, B
University of Wisconsin - Superior, B
Viterbo University, B
Wisconsin Lutheran College, M

Wyoming

University of Wyoming, M

U.S. Territories: Puerto Rico

American University of Puerto Rico (Bayamon), M
Bayamón Central University, B
Caribbean University, M
Inter American University of Puerto Rico, Arecibo Campus, M
Inter American University of Puerto Rico, Barranquitas Campus, M
Inter American University of Puerto Rico, Metropolitan Campus, BM
Inter American University of Puerto Rico, Ponce Campus, M
Inter American University of Puerto Rico, San Germán Campus, BM
Pontifical Catholic University of Puerto Rico, B
Universidad del Turabo, B
University of Puerto Rico in Cayey, B
University of Puerto Rico, Río Piedras Campus, M
University of Puerto Rico in Utuado, B

Canada

Alberta

University of Alberta, B
University of Lethbridge, B

British Columbia

The University of British Columbia, BM
University of Victoria, MD

Manitoba

University of Manitoba, B

Maritime Provinces: New Brunswick

University of New Brunswick Fredericton, B

Maritime Provinces: Nova Scotia

Acadia University, M

Newfoundland and Labrador

Memorial University of Newfoundland, B

Ontario

Brock University, B
Lakehead University, B
Laurentian University, O
Queen's University at Kingston, B
University of Toronto, B
University of Windsor, B
York University, B

Quebec

Bishop's University, B
Université Laval, B
Université du Québec à Chicoutimi, B
Université du Québec à Montréal, B
Université du Québec à Rimouski, B

Saskatchewan

University of Regina, B

SCIENCE TECHNOLOGIES/ TECHNICIANS

United States

Alaska

University of Alaska Fairbanks, A
University of Alaska Southeast, A

Arizona

Arizona State University at the Downtown Phoenix campus, B
Arizona State University at the Polytechnic campus, B
Northern Arizona University, B
The University of Arizona, B

California

College of the Redwoods, A
Victor Valley College, A

Colorado

Aims Community College, A
Arapahoe Community College, A
Community College of Aurora, A
Community College of Denver, A
Front Range Community College, A
Morgan Community College, A
Pueblo Community College, A
Red Rocks Community College, A
Trinidad State Junior College, A

Delaware

Delaware Technical & Community College, Stanton/Wilmington Campus, A

Louisiana

Baton Rouge Community College, A

Maryland

Baltimore City Community College, A

Massachusetts

Bridgewater State University, B

Michigan

Madonna University, AB
Oakland Community College, A

Montana

Fort Peck Community College, A

New Jersey

Kean University, B

New York

Cayuga County Community College, A
Maria College, A
Schenectady County Community College, A
State University of New York College of Agriculture and Technology at Cobleskill, A
Sullivan County Community College, A

North Carolina

North Carolina State University, B

North Dakota

Dakota College at Bottineau, A
Nueta Hidatsa Sahnish College, A

Ohio

Bowling Green State University, B
University of Cincinnati Blue Ash College, A
University of Cincinnati Clermont College, A

Oregon

Klamath Community College, A
Willamette University, B

Pennsylvania

Community College of Allegheny County, A
Delaware County Community College, A
Reading Area Community College, A

Tennessee

Cleveland State Community College, A
Columbia State Community College, A
Jackson State Community College, A
Pellissippi State Community College, A

Washington

Cascadia College, A

West Virginia

Blue Ridge Community and Technical College, A
Eastern West Virginia Community and Technical College, A
Mountwest Community & Technical College, A
New River Community and Technical College, A
Ohio Valley University, A

West Virginia Northern Community College, A

Wisconsin

University of Wisconsin - Stout, B

Canada

British Columbia

British Columbia Institute of Technology, A

SCIENCE, TECHNOLOGY AND SOCIETY

United States

Alaska

University of Alaska Anchorage, B

Arizona

Arizona State University at the Polytechnic campus, B

Arkansas

Southeast Arkansas College, A

California

California State Polytechnic University, Pomona, B
Claremont McKenna College, B
Pitzer College, B
Pomona College, B
Scripps College, B
Stanford University, B

Connecticut

Wesleyan University, B

District of Columbia

Georgetown University, B

Georgia

Georgia Institute of Technology, B

Illinois

Northwestern University, B

Indiana

Butler University, B

Kansas

Seward County Community College and Area Technical School, A

Maine

Colby College, B

Massachusetts

Massachusetts Institute of Technology, B
Tufts University, B
Worcester Polytechnic Institute, B

Michigan

Eastern Michigan University, B

Missouri

Washington University in St. Louis, B

Nevada

Truckee Meadows Community College, A

New Jersey

New Jersey Institute of Technology, B
Rutgers University - Newark, B

New York

Cornell University, B
Farmingdale State College, B
Morrisville State College, B
Rensselaer Polytechnic Institute, B
Sarah Lawrence College, B
Vassar College, B

North Carolina

North Carolina State University, B

Pennsylvania

Lehigh University, B
Penn State University Park, B

Tennessee

Vanderbilt University, B

Texas

Angelina College, A
Texas Tech University, B

Virginia

James Madison University, B

Washington

Heritage University, B
University of Puget Sound, B
University of Washington, Bothell, B

Canada

Alberta

University of Alberta, B

Maritime Provinces: New Brunswick

St. Thomas University, B

Maritime Provinces: Nova Scotia

Dalhousie University, B
University of King's College, B

Ontario

University of Windsor, B
York University, B

Quebec

Université du Québec à Montréal, B

SCULPTURE

United States

Alabama

Birmingham-Southern College, B
The University of Alabama, M

Alaska

University of Alaska Fairbanks, M

Arizona

Arizona State University at the Tempe campus, M

California

Academy of Art University, M
Biola University, B
California College of the Arts, BM
California State University, East Bay, B
California State University, Fullerton, M
California State University, Long Beach, B
Chabot College, A
Cuesta College, A
De Anza College, A
Evergreen Valley College, A
Grossmont College, A
Laguna College of Art & Design, B
Long Beach City College, A
Los Angeles Valley College, A
Mills College, M
Monterey Peninsula College, A
Otis College of Art and Design, BM
Palomar College, A
San Diego State University, M
San Francisco Art Institute, B
Sonoma State University, B
University of Southern California, M

Colorado

Colorado State University, B
University of Colorado Boulder, M
Western State Colorado University, B

Connecticut

University of Hartford, B
University of New Haven, B
Yale University, M

District of Columbia

The George Washington University, M
Howard University, M

Florida

University of Miami, BM

Georgia

Georgia State University, M
Savannah College of Art and Design, BM

Idaho

Northwest Nazarene University, B

Illinois

Bradley University, BM
Dominican University, B
Illinois State University, M
School of the Art Institute of Chicago, BM
University of Illinois at Urbana - Champaign, BM

Indiana

Indiana State University, M
Indiana University - Purdue University Fort Wayne, B
Indiana University - Purdue University Indianapolis, M
University of Notre Dame, M

Iowa

Drake University, B
The University of Iowa, B

Kansas

Bethany College, B
The University of Kansas, BM
Wichita State University, M

Louisiana

Louisiana State University and Agricultural & Mechanical College, M

Maine

Maine College of Art, B

Maryland

Maryland Institute College of Art, BM

Massachusetts

Boston University, BM
Massachusetts College of Art and Design, B
Montserrat College of Art, B
Salem State University, B
School of the Museum of Fine Arts, Boston, B
University of Massachusetts Dartmouth, BO

Michigan

Aquinas College, B
Ferris State University, B
Northern Michigan University, B
University of Michigan, B
Wayne State University, M

Minnesota

Minneapolis College of Art and Design, BM
Minnesota State University Mankato, B
St. Cloud State University, B

Mississippi

Mississippi College, B

Missouri

Kansas City Art Institute, B
Washington University in St. Louis, B

New Jersey

Mercer County Community College, A
Rutgers University - New Brunswick, BM
Salem Community College, A

New Mexico

Mesalands Community College, A
Santa Fe Community College, A

New York

Alfred University, M
Brooklyn College of the City University of New York, M
Buffalo State College, State University of New York, B
City College of the City University of New York, M
Columbia University, M
Pratt Institute, BM
Rochester Institute of Technology, B
Sarah Lawrence College, B
School of Visual Arts, B
State University of New York at New Paltz, BM
Syracuse University, BM

North Carolina

East Carolina University, M

Ohio

Art Academy of Cincinnati, B
Bowling Green State University, B
Cleveland Institute of Art, B
Ohio Northern University, B
Ohio University, BM
The University of Akron, B

Oklahoma

University of Oklahoma, M

Oregon

Pacific Northwest College of Art, B
Portland State University, BM
University of Oregon, B

Pennsylvania

Edinboro University of Pennsylvania, M
Marywood University, BM
Pennsylvania Academy of the Fine Arts, MO
Seton Hill University, B
Temple University, BM
The University of the Arts, B

Rhode Island

Providence College, B
Rhode Island College, B
Rhode Island School of Design, BM

South Dakota

The University of South Dakota, M

Tennessee

The University of Tennessee, M

Texas

Southern Methodist University, M
Stephen F. Austin State University, M
Sul Ross State University, M
Texas Christian University, BM
University of Dallas, B
University of Houston, B
The University of Texas at El Paso, B

Utah

Brigham Young University, B
Dixie State University, B
University of Utah, M

Vermont

Bennington College, B
Johnson State College, M

Marlboro College, B

Virginia

George Mason University, M
Virginia Commonwealth University, BM

Washington

Central Washington University, B
University of Washington, B
Western Washington University, B

West Virginia

West Virginia University, M

Wisconsin

Milwaukee Institute of Art and Design, B

U.S. Territories: Puerto Rico

Escuela de Artes Plasticas y Diseño de Puerto Rico, B
Inter American University of Puerto Rico, San Germán Campus, BM
University of Puerto Rico, Río Piedras Campus, B

Canada

Alberta

Alberta College of Art & Design, B
University of Alberta, M

British Columbia

Emily Carr University of Art + Design, B
University of Victoria, M

Maritime Provinces: New Brunswick

Mount Allison University, B

Maritime Provinces: Nova Scotia

NSCAD University, B

Newfoundland and Labrador

Memorial University of Newfoundland, B

Ontario

University of Windsor, B
York University, B

Quebec

Concordia University, BM

Saskatchewan

University of Regina, BM

SECONDARY EDUCATION AND TEACHING

United States

Alabama

Alabama Agricultural and Mechanical University, BMO
Alabama Southern Community College, A
Alabama State University, BMO
Auburn University, BMDO
Auburn University at Montgomery, MO
Birmingham-Southern College, B
Jacksonville State University, BM
Miles College, B
Samford University, M
Spring Hill College, BM
Troy University, BM
The University of Alabama, BMDO
The University of Alabama at Birmingham, BM
The University of Alabama in Huntsville, B
University of Montevallo, M
University of North Alabama, BMO
University of South Alabama, BM
The University of West Alabama, M

Alaska

University of Alaska Anchorage, B
University of Alaska Fairbanks, BM
University of Alaska Southeast, M

Arizona

Argosy University, Phoenix, D
Arizona Christian University, B
Arizona State University at the Polytechnic campus, B
Arizona State University at the Tempe campus, BM
Arizona State University at the West campus, B
Arizona Western College, A
Eastern Arizona College, A
Grand Canyon University, BM
Northcentral University, B
Northern Arizona University, M
Prescott College, BM
The University of Arizona, MD
University of Phoenix - Online Campus, MO
University of Phoenix - Phoenix Campus, M
University of Phoenix - Southern Arizona Campus, M

Arkansas

Arkansas Baptist College, B
Central Baptist College, B
Harding University, BM
John Brown University, BM
Ouachita Baptist University, B
Southern Arkansas University - Magnolia, M
University of Arkansas, MO
University of Arkansas at Little Rock, M
University of Arkansas at Pine Bluff, BM
University of the Ozarks, B

California

Argosy University, Inland Empire, D
Argosy University, Los Angeles, D
Argosy University, Orange County, D
Argosy University, San Diego, D
Argosy University, San Francisco Bay Area, D
Ashford University, B
Biola University, B
California State University, Bakersfield, M
California State University, Fullerton, M
California State University, Long Beach, M
California State University, Los Angeles, M
California State University, Northridge, M
California State University, Stanislaus, M
Chapman University, M
Hope International University, M
Humboldt State University, B
Loyola Marymount University, M
The Master's College and Seminary, B
Mills College, M
Mount Saint Mary's University, B
National University, B
Occidental College, M
Pacific Union College, M
San Diego Christian College, B
San Diego State University, M
San Francisco State University, MO
San Jose State University, O
Stanford University, M
University of California, Irvine, M
University of La Verne, O
University of Phoenix - Bay Area Campus, M
University of Phoenix - Central Valley Campus, M
University of Phoenix - Sacramento Valley Campus, M
University of Phoenix - San Diego Campus, M
University of Phoenix - Southern California Campus, M
University of Redlands, B
University of San Francisco, B
Vanguard University of Southern California, B
Westmont College, B
Whittier College, M

Colorado

The Colorado College, M
Fort Lewis College, B
University of Colorado Denver, M
University of Phoenix - Colorado Campus, M

University of Phoenix - Colorado Springs Downtown Campus, M

Connecticut

Albertus Magnus College, B
Central Connecticut State University, M
Eastern Connecticut State University, M
Fairfield University, M
Quinnipiac University, M
Southern Connecticut State University, B
University of Bridgeport, MO
University of Connecticut, MDO
University of Hartford, B
Western Connecticut State University, B

Delaware

Delaware State University, B
Wilmington University, M

District of Columbia

American University, B
The Catholic University of America, BM
Gallaudet University, M
The George Washington University, M
Howard University, M
Trinity Washington University, M
University of the District of Columbia, M
University of Phoenix - Washington D.C. Campus, M

Florida

Argosy University, Sarasota, D
Argosy University, Tampa, D
Chipola College, B
College of Central Florida, A
Daytona State College, B
Edward Waters College, B
Florida Agricultural and Mechanical University, M
Florida Gulf Coast University, B
Florida Memorial University, B
Florida State University, M
Jacksonville University, B
Nova Southeastern University, B
Saint Leo University, B
St. Thomas University, B
South Florida State College, A
Trinity Baptist College, B
University of North Florida, BM
University of Phoenix - North Florida Campus, M
University of Phoenix - South Florida Campus, M
University of South Florida, MDO
The University of Tampa, B
University of West Florida, M
Warner University, B

Georgia

Argosy University, Atlanta, D
Armstrong State University, M
Berry College, BM
Brenau University, M
Brewton-Parker College, B
Columbus State University, MO
Emory University, M
Georgia College & State University, MO
Georgia Military College, A
Georgia Southern University, MO
Georgia State University, MD
Gordon State College, A
Kennesaw State University, M
LaGrange College, M
Mercer University, M
Piedmont College, BM
Thomas University, B
Toccoa Falls College, B
University of North Georgia, M
University of West Georgia, M
Young Harris College, B

Hawaii

Argosy University, Hawai'i, D
Brigham Young University - Hawaii, B
Chaminade University of Honolulu, BM
Hawai'i Pacific University, B
University of Hawaii at Manoa, B
University of Phoenix - Hawaii Campus, M

Idaho

Idaho State University, BM
Northwest Nazarene University, B
University of Idaho, B

Illinois

Argosy University, Chicago, D
Aurora University, B
Benedictine University, M
Blackburn College, B
Chicago State University, M
City Colleges of Chicago, Malcolm X College, A
Concordia University Chicago, BM
DePaul University, BM
Dominican University, B
Elmhurst College, B
Greenville College, M
Illinois College, B
John A. Logan College, A
Judson University, B
Kankakee Community College, A
Knox College, B
Lake Forest College, M
Lewis University, BM
Loyola University Chicago, BM
McKendree University, B
National Louis University, M
North Central College, B
North Park University, B
Northeastern Illinois University, M
Northern Illinois University, D
Northwestern University, BM
Olivet Nazarene University, M
Parkland College, A
Rockford University, BM
Roosevelt University, M
Saint Xavier University, M
Sauk Valley Community College, A
Trinity International University, B
University of Illinois at Chicago, M
University of Illinois at Urbana - Champaign, B
University of St. Francis, M
Wheaton College, BM

Indiana

Ancilla College, A
Ball State University, M
Bethel College, B
Butler University, B
Goshen College, B
Huntington University, B
Indiana University Bloomington, BMD
Indiana University East, B
Indiana University Kokomo, B
Indiana University Northwest, BM
Indiana University - Purdue University Fort Wayne, BM
Indiana University South Bend, BM
Indiana University Southeast, BM
Indiana Wesleyan University, B
Manchester University, B
Marian University, B
Purdue University Northwest (Westville), B
Taylor University, B
Trine University, B
University of Indianapolis, BM
University of Southern Indiana, M
Valparaiso University, B
Vincennes University, A

Iowa

Briar Cliff University, B
Clarke University, B
Coe College, B
Cornell College, B
Dordt College, B
Drake University, B
Emmaus Bible College, B
Graceland University, B
Grand View University, B
Iowa State University of Science and Technology, B
Kaplan University, Davenport Campus, M
Maharishi University of Management, B
Mount Mercy University, B
Northwestern College, B

St. Ambrose University, B
Simpson College, B
University of Dubuque, B
The University of Iowa, M
University of Northern Iowa, M
Waldorf College, B
Wartburg College, B
William Penn University, B

Kansas

Allen Community College, A
Baker University, B
Barton County Community College, A
Benedictine College, B
Central Christian College of Kansas, AB
Emporia State University, B
Kansas State University, B
Kansas Wesleyan University, B
MidAmerica Nazarene University, B
Newman University, B
Pittsburg State University, M
Tabor College, B
The University of Kansas, B
Wichita State University, BM

Kentucky

Alice Lloyd College, B
Bellarmine University, BM
Campbellsville University, B
Eastern Kentucky University, M
Lindsey Wilson College, B
Midway University, B
Morehead State University, M
Murray State University, MO
Northern Kentucky University, B
Spalding University, BM
Thomas More College, B
Union College, M
University of the Cumberlands, BM
University of Kentucky, M
University of Louisville, M
Western Kentucky University, MO

Louisiana

Centenary College of Louisiana, M
Grambling State University, B
Louisiana College, B
Louisiana State University and Agricultural & Mechanical College, M
McNeese State University, BMO
Nicholls State University, M
Northwestern State University of Louisiana, BMO
Southern University and Agricultural and Mechanical College, BM
University of Louisiana at Lafayette, B
University of Louisiana at Monroe, BM
University of New Orleans, B
Xavier University of Louisiana, B

Maine

College of the Atlantic, B
Husson University, B
Thomas College, B
Unity College, B
University of Maine, BMDO
University of Maine at Farmington, B
University of Maine at Presque Isle, B

Maryland

Bowie State University, BM
Cecil College, A
Frostburg State University, M
Goucher College, M
Hood College, M
Howard Community College, A
Johns Hopkins University, M
Loyola University Maryland, MO
McDaniel College, M
Morgan State University, BM
Salisbury University, M
Towson University, M
University of Maryland, Baltimore County, M
University of Maryland, College Park, BMDO

Massachusetts

American International College, MO
Anna Maria College, B
Boston College, BM
Brandeis University, M
Bridgewater State University, M
Clark University, B
Eastern Nazarene College, BMO
Elms College, M
Emmanuel College, BM
Endicott College, BM
Fitchburg State University, BM
Gordon College, B
Lasell College, B
Lesley University, BM
Merrimack College, BM
Northeastern University, M
Salem State University, BM
Simmons College, BM
Smith College, M
Springfield College, BM
Springfield Technical Community College, A
Tufts University, M
University of Massachusetts Amherst, M
University of Massachusetts Dartmouth, MO
Western New England University, B
Westfield State University, M
Worcester State University, MO

Michigan

Adrian College, B
Alma College, B
Alpena Community College, A
Andrews University, BM
Calvin College, B
Central Michigan University, MD
Concordia University Ann Arbor, B
Eastern Michigan University, M
Ferris State University, A
Gogebic Community College, A
Grace Bible College, B
Grand Rapids Community College, A
Grand Valley State University, BM
Henry Ford College, A
Kuyper College, B
Lake Michigan College, A
Lake Superior State University, B
Lansing Community College, A
Marygrove College, M
Michigan State University, B
Mid Michigan Community College, A
Northern Michigan University, BM
Oakland University, M
Rochester College, B
Saginaw Valley State University, M
Siena Heights University, BM
Spring Arbor University, B
University of Detroit Mercy, B
University of Michigan, B
University of Michigan - Dearborn, B
Washtenaw Community College, A
Wayne State University, BMDO

Minnesota

Argosy University, Twin Cities, D
Augsburg College, B
Bemidji State University, B
Bethel University, M
College of Saint Benedict, B
Concordia University, St. Paul, B
Gustavus Adolphus College, B
Hamline University, B
Minnesota State University Mankato, BMO
North Central University, B
St. Catherine University, B
St. Cloud State University, B
Saint John's University, B
Saint Mary's University of Minnesota, MO
University of Minnesota, Morris, B

Mississippi

Alcorn State University, M
Belhaven University, M
Coahoma Community College, A
Delta State University, M

East Central Community College, A
East Mississippi Community College, A
Jackson State University, MO
Mississippi College, M
Mississippi State University, BMDO
Tougaloo College, B
William Carey University, M

Missouri

Calvary Bible College and Theological Seminary, B
Central Methodist University, B
Drury University, M
Evangel University, BM
Fontbonne University, B
Hannibal-LaGrange University, B
Harris-Stowe State University, B
Lincoln University, MO
Maryville University of Saint Louis, M
Missouri Baptist University, B
Missouri Southern State University, B
Missouri State University, BM
Missouri University of Science and Technology, B
Missouri Valley College, B
Northwest Missouri State University, MO
Rockhurst University, B
Southeast Missouri State University, M
University of Central Missouri, B
University of Missouri, B
University of Missouri - Kansas City, B
University of Missouri - St. Louis, BM
Washington University in St. Louis, BM
Webster University, B
Westminster College, B
William Jewell College, B
William Woods University, B

Montana

Carroll College, B
Montana State University Billings, B
Rocky Mountain College, B
University of Great Falls, BM
University of Montana, B
The University of Montana Western, B

Nebraska

Chadron State College, M
College of Saint Mary, B
Concordia University, Nebraska, BM
Creighton University, BM
Grace University, B
Hastings College, B
Midland University, B
Northeast Community College, A
Peru State College, B
University of Nebraska at Kearney, M
University of Nebraska at Omaha, BMO
Western Nebraska Community College, A
York College, B

Nevada

Great Basin College, B
Nevada State College, B
Sierra Nevada College, M
University of Nevada, Las Vegas, B
University of Nevada, Reno, M

New Hampshire

Franklin Pierce University, B
Granite State College, B
Keene State College, B
New England College, B
Plymouth State University, M
Rivier University, B
Saint Anselm College, B
Southern New Hampshire University, M
University of New Hampshire, M

New Jersey

Caldwell University, B
Centenary College, B
The College of New Jersey, BM
Felician University, B
Monmouth University, BM
New Jersey City University, M
Rider University, B

Rowan University, M
Saint Peter's University, MO
Seton Hall University, B
William Paterson University of New Jersey, BM

New Mexico

Eastern New Mexico University, M
New Mexico State University, B
San Juan College, A
University of New Mexico, BM
University of Phoenix - New Mexico Campus, M
University of the Southwest, B
Western New Mexico University, BM

New York

Adelphi University, M
Alfred University, B
Binghamton University, State University of New York, M
Brooklyn College of the City University of New York, M
Buffalo State College, State University of New York, B
Canisius College, BM
Cazenovia College, B
City College of the City University of New York, BMO
Colgate University, M
The College of Saint Rose, BM
College of Staten Island of the City University of New York, M
Cornell University, M
Dominican College, B
D'Youville College, BMO
Elmira College, B
Fordham University, BM
Hofstra University, BMO
Houghton College, B
Hunter College of the City University of New York, BM
Iona College, B
Ithaca College, BM
Keuka College, B
Le Moyne College, BM
Long Island University - LIU Post, O
Manhattanville College, BM
Medaille College, BM
Mercy College, M
Molloy College, B
Mount Saint Mary College, BM
Nazareth College of Rochester, B
New York Institute of Technology, MO
New York University, M
Niagara University, BMO
Queens College of the City University of New York, MO
Roberts Wesleyan College, M
Rochester Institute of Technology, M
St. Bonaventure University, M
St. John's University, MO
St. Thomas Aquinas College, BM
State University of New York College at Cortland, BM
State University of New York College at Geneseo, M
State University of New York College at Old Westbury, B
State University of New York College at Oneonta, BM
State University of New York College at Potsdam, M
State University of New York at Fredonia, BM
State University of New York at New Paltz, MO
State University of New York at Oswego, BM
State University of New York at Plattsburgh, M
Syracuse University, M
Utica College, B
Wagner College, BM
Wells College, B
York College of the City University of New York, B

North Carolina

Campbell University, BM
Elon University, B
Fayetteville State University, M
Gardner-Webb University, B
Greensboro College, B

Guilford College, B
High Point University, BM
Mars Hill University, B
Methodist University, B
North Carolina Agricultural and Technical State University, BM
North Carolina State University, M
Salem College, M
University of Mount Olive, B
The University of North Carolina at Chapel Hill, M
The University of North Carolina at Charlotte, MD
The University of North Carolina at Greensboro, B
Wake Forest University, M

North Dakota

Dickinson State University, B
University of North Dakota, BD
Valley City State University, B

Ohio

Ashland University, B
Central State University, B
Defiance College, BM
God's Bible School and College, B
Heidelberg University, B
John Carroll University, BM
Kent State University, M
Lake Erie College, B
Lourdes University, B
Marietta College, B
Mount St. Joseph University, M
Ohio University, BM
Ohio University - Chillicothe, AB
Ohio Wesleyan University, B
Otterbein University, B
Union Institute & University, B
University of Cincinnati, BMD
University of Cincinnati Blue Ash College, A
University of Cincinnati Clermont College, A
University of Dayton, BM
The University of Findlay, B
University of Rio Grande, B
The University of Toledo, BMD
Urbana University, B
Walsh University, B
Wilmington College, B
Wright State University, BM
Xavier University, M
Youngstown State University, BM

Oklahoma

Carl Albert State College, A
Eastern Oklahoma State College, A
Hillsdale Free Will Baptist College, B
Langston University, B
Mid-America Christian University, B
Northwestern Oklahoma State University, BM
Oklahoma Christian University, B
Oklahoma City University, B
Oklahoma State University, B
Rogers State University, A
Southwestern Oklahoma State University, M
University of Central Oklahoma, BM
The University of Tulsa, M

Oregon

Concordia University, BM
Corban University, B
Eastern Oregon University, M
George Fox University, M
Lewis & Clark College, M
Northwest Christian University, B
Pacific University, BM
Portland State University, M
Southern Oregon University, M
University of Portland, B
Warner Pacific College, B
Western Oregon University, BM

Pennsylvania

Albright College, B
Arcadia University, BMO
Bloomsburg University of Pennsylvania, M
Bucknell University, B
California University of Pennsylvania, M

Carlow University, M
Cedar Crest College, B
Chatham University, M
Chestnut Hill College, MO
Delaware Valley University, B
DeSales University, B
Drexel University, B
Duquesne University, M
East Stroudsburg University of Pennsylvania, M
Eastern University, O
Edinboro University of Pennsylvania, M
Gettysburg College, B
Gwynedd Mercy University, B
Harrisburg Area Community College, A
Holy Family University, M
Immaculata University, O
Kutztown University of Pennsylvania, BM
La Salle University, BM
Lancaster Bible College, M
Lincoln University, B
Lock Haven University of Pennsylvania, B
Mansfield University of Pennsylvania, BM
Marywood University, M
Mercyhurst University, BM
Montgomery County Community College, A
Mount Aloysius College, B
Northampton Community College, A
Penn State Abington, B
Penn State Altoona, B
Penn State Beaver, B
Penn State Berks, B
Penn State Brandywine, B
Penn State DuBois, B
Penn State Erie, The Behrend College, B
Penn State Fayette, The Eberly Campus, B
Penn State Greater Allegheny, B
Penn State Hazleton, B
Penn State Lehigh Valley, B
Penn State Mont Alto, B
Penn State New Kensington, B
Penn State Schuylkill, B
Penn State Shenango, B
Penn State University Park, B
Penn State Wilkes-Barre, B
Penn State Worthington Scranton, B
Penn State York, B
Reading Area Community College, A
Saint Francis University, B
Saint Joseph's University, BMO
Slippery Rock University of Pennsylvania, BM
Summit University, B
Susquehanna University, B
Temple University, BM
Thiel College, B
University of Pennsylvania, M
University of Pittsburgh, MD
University of Pittsburgh at Bradford, B
University of Pittsburgh at Johnstown, B
The University of Scranton, BM
University of Valley Forge, B
Villanova University, BM
Waynesburg University, B
West Chester University of Pennsylvania, MO
Wilkes University, M
Wilson College, M

Rhode Island

Brown University, M
Johnson & Wales University, M
Providence College, M
Rhode Island College, BM
Roger Williams University, B
Salve Regina University, B
University of Rhode Island, BM

South Carolina

Bob Jones University, M
Charleston Southern University, B
The Citadel, The Military College of South Carolina, BM
Clemson University, BM
College of Charleston, B
Converse College, BM
Francis Marion University, M
Furman University, B
Lander University, B

South Carolina State University, M
University of South Carolina, MD
University of South Carolina Aiken, B
University of South Carolina Upstate, B
Winthrop University, M

South Dakota

Augustana University, B
Black Hills State University, B
Dakota Wesleyan University, M
Mount Marty College, B
Northern State University, B
Presentation College, B
Sinte Gleska University, B
University of Sioux Falls, B
The University of South Dakota, BM

Tennessee

Argosy University, Nashville, D
Austin Peay State University, MO
Belmont University, B
Carson-Newman University, BM
Cumberland University, B
East Tennessee State University, M
Freed-Hardeman University, B
Hiwassee College, A
Lee University, M
Lincoln Memorial University, B
Middle Tennessee State University, M
Nashville State Community College, A
Tennessee Technological University, BMO
Tennessee Wesleyan College, B
Trevecca Nazarene University, M
Union University, B
University of Memphis, M
The University of Tennessee, M
The University of Tennessee at Chattanooga, BM
The University of Tennessee at Martin, M
Vanderbilt University, BM
Welch College, B

Texas

Abilene Christian University, B
Alvin Community College, A
Austin College, B
Austin Community College District, A
Baylor University, B
Brookhaven College, A
Clarendon College, A
College of the Mainland, A
Collin County Community College District, A
Concordia University Texas, B
Dallas Baptist University, M
Frank Phillips College, A
Grayson College, A
Hill College, A
Houston Community College, A
Howard College, A
Huston-Tillotson University, B
Jarvis Christian College, B
LeTourneau University, B
Lubbock Christian University, B
McMurry University, B
Midwestern State University, B
Our Lady of the Lake University of San Antonio, M
Paris Junior College, A
Sam Houston State University, B
San Jacinto College District, A
Southwestern Assemblies of God University, BM
Stephen F. Austin State University, MD
Sul Ross State University, M
Tarleton State University, BO
Texas A&M University - Corpus Christi, M
Texas Christian University, B
Texas Southern University, M
Texas State University, M
Texas Tech University, M
Tyler Junior College, A
University of Dallas, B
University of Houston - Downtown, M
University of the Incarnate Word, M
University of Mary Hardin-Baylor, D
University of St. Thomas, BM
The University of Texas Rio Grande Valley, M
Wayland Baptist University, M
West Texas A&M University, B

Western Texas College, A

Utah

Dixie State University, B
University of Phoenix - Utah Campus, M
University of Utah, MD
Utah State University, BM

Vermont

Castleton University, B
Champlain College, B
College of St. Joseph, BM
Johnson State College, BM
Saint Michael's College, B
University of Vermont, B

Virginia

Argosy University, Washington DC, D
Bluefield College, B
George Mason University, M
Hampton University, BM
James Madison University, M
Liberty University, M
Marymount University, M
Norfolk State University, M
Old Dominion University, M
Virginia Commonwealth University, MO
Virginia Polytechnic Institute and State University, B
Virginia Wesleyan College, B

Washington

Argosy University, Seattle, D
Eastern Washington University, M
Gonzaga University, B
Northwest University, B
Seattle Pacific University, M
University of Puget Sound, M
University of Washington, Bothell, M
Washington State University, BM
Western Washington University, M
Whitworth University, BM

West Virginia

Alderson Broaddus University, B
American Public University System, M
Concord University, B
Fairmont State University, B
Glenville State College, B
Marshall University, BM
Ohio Valley University, B
Potomac State College of West Virginia University, A
Salem International University, B
Shepherd University, B
West Liberty University, B
West Virginia State University, B
West Virginia University, M
West Virginia Wesleyan College, B

Wisconsin

Beloit College, B
Cardinal Stritch University, B
Carthage College, B
Concordia University Wisconsin, B
Lakeland College, B
Lawrence University, B
Marian University, B
Marquette University, BO
Northland College, B
Ripon College, B
University of Wisconsin - Eau Claire, M
University of Wisconsin - Milwaukee, M
University of Wisconsin - Oshkosh, B
University of Wisconsin - Platteville, BM
University of Wisconsin - Stevens Point, BM
Wisconsin Lutheran College, B

Wyoming

Central Wyoming College, A
Eastern Wyoming College, A
Northwest College, A
Sheridan College, A
University of Wyoming, B
Western Wyoming Community College, A

U.S. Territories: Guam

University of Guam, BM

U.S. Territories: Puerto Rico

Caribbean University, B
Inter American University of Puerto Rico, San Germán Campus, B
Polytechnic University of Puerto Rico, B
Universidad Adventista de las Antillas, B
Universidad Metropolitana, BM
University of Puerto Rico, Río Piedras Campus, B
University of the Sacred Heart, B

Canada

Alberta

The King's University, B
University of Alberta, MD
University of Calgary, B

British Columbia

Trinity Western University, B
The University of British Columbia, B
University of Northern British Columbia, B
University of Victoria, B

Manitoba

University of Manitoba, B
The University of Winnipeg, B

Maritime Provinces: New Brunswick

Université de Moncton, B
University of New Brunswick Fredericton, B

Maritime Provinces: Nova Scotia

Acadia University, B
Mount Saint Vincent University, B
St. Francis Xavier University, B
Université Sainte-Anne, B

Maritime Provinces: Prince Edward Island

University of Prince Edward Island, B

Newfoundland and Labrador

Memorial University of Newfoundland, B

Ontario

Brock University, B
Lakehead University, B
Trent University, B
The University of Western Ontario, B
University of Windsor, B
York University, B

Quebec

Bishop's University, B
Université Laval, B
Université de Montréal, B
Université du Québec en Abitibi-Témiscamingue, B
Université du Québec à Chicoutimi, B
Université du Québec à Montréal, B
Université du Québec en Outaouais, B
Université du Québec à Rimouski, B
Université du Québec à Trois-Rivières, B
Université de Sherbrooke, B

Saskatchewan

University of Regina, B
University of Saskatchewan, B

SECONDARY SCHOOL ADMINISTRATION/PRINCIPALSHIP

United States

Mississippi

Holmes Community College, A

North Carolina

The University of North Carolina at Pembroke, B

South Carolina

Charleston Southern University, B

SECURITIES SERVICES ADMINISTRATION/MANAGEMENT

United States

Alabama

The University of Alabama in Huntsville, MO
Virginia College in Birmingham, M

Arizona

University of Phoenix - Online Campus, M

California

Henley-Putnam University, B
University of Phoenix - Bay Area Campus, M

Colorado

Colorado Technical University Denver South, M
University of Denver, MO

District of Columbia

The George Washington University, M

Florida

Webber International University, BM

Indiana

Vincennes University, A

Iowa

Kaplan University, Davenport Campus, M
Western Iowa Tech Community College, A

Kansas

Southwestern College, BM
Washburn University, B

Kentucky

Eastern Kentucky University, M

Massachusetts

Anna Maria College, M
Quincy College, A

Michigan

University of Detroit Mercy, M

Mississippi

Mississippi College, B

Missouri

Saint Louis University, B
Webster University, M

Nebraska

Bellevue University, M

New Jersey

New Jersey City University, MD

New York

Excelsior College, MO
John Jay College of Criminal Justice of the City University of New York, BM
St. John's University, B
TCI - College of Technology, A

North Carolina

East Carolina University, O

Pennsylvania

Carnegie Mellon University, M
Central Penn College, B
Mercyhurst University, MO

Tennessee

Pellissippi State Community College, A

Texas

University of Houston - Downtown, M

West Virginia

American Public University System, BM

SECURITY AND LOSS PRE-VENTION SERVICES

United States

Alabama

Community College of the Air Force, A

California

Carrington College - Pleasant Hill, A
Carrington College - San Jose, A
Carrington College - San Leandro, A
Citrus College, A
Grossmont College, A
National University, B

Florida

Miami Dade College, A
Tallahassee Community College, A

Georgia

Ashworth College, A

Illinois

Illinois Central College, A
Lewis University, B

Indiana

Vincennes University, A

Kansas

Highland Community College, A

Massachusetts

Anna Maria College, B

Michigan

Delta College, A
Northern Michigan University, B

New Jersey

Union County College, A

New York

Farmingdale State College, B
John Jay College of Criminal Justice of the City University of New York, A

Ohio

Miami-Jacobs Career College (Independence), A

Oklahoma

Eastern Oklahoma State College, A

Pennsylvania

Community College of Beaver County, A

Rhode Island

Johnson & Wales University, B

Texas

Hill College, A

SECURITY AND PROTECTIVE SERVICES

United States

Alabama

Chattahoochee Valley Community College, A

Arizona

Glendale Community College, A
University of Phoenix - Online Campus, AB

Arkansas

NorthWest Arkansas Community College, A
Southeast Arkansas College, A

California

San Joaquin Valley College (Bakersfield), A
University of Phoenix - Southern California Campus, B

Colorado

Pikes Peak Community College, A
Red Rocks Community College, A
University of Phoenix - Colorado Springs Downtown Campus, B

Connecticut

Goodwin College, A
Mitchell College, B

Florida

Florida Atlantic University, B
Florida SouthWestern State College, B
Florida State College at Jacksonville, B
Miami Dade College, B
St. Petersburg College, AB

Georgia

Savannah State University, B
University of Phoenix - Atlanta Campus, B
University of Phoenix - Augusta Campus, B

Hawaii

University of Phoenix - Hawaii Campus, B

Idaho

Idaho State University, AB

Illinois

Lewis University, B
Western Illinois University, B

Kansas

Barton County Community College, A
Washburn University, B

Kentucky

Midway University, B

Louisiana

Baton Rouge Community College, A

Massachusetts

Massachusetts Maritime Academy, B

Michigan

Concordia University Ann Arbor, B
Eastern Michigan University, B
Lake Superior State University, AB
Madonna University, B
Schoolcraft College, A
University of Phoenix - Detroit Campus, B

Minnesota

Capella University, B
Century College, A
Northland Community and Technical College, A

Nevada

University of Phoenix - Las Vegas Campus, B

New Jersey

Ocean County College, A
Thomas Edison State University, B
University of Phoenix - Jersey City Campus, B

New York

Onondaga Community College, A
Roberts Wesleyan College, B

North Dakota

North Dakota State University, B

Ohio

Franklin University, B
Lakeland Community College, A
Owens Community College, A
Tiffin University, B

Oklahoma

Northwestern Oklahoma State University, B

Oregon

Portland Community College, A

Pennsylvania

Butler County Community College, A
Neumann University, B
Penn State Altoona, B
Penn State Berks, B
Penn State University Park, B
Pittsburgh Technical Institute, A
Point Park University, B
University of Phoenix - Philadelphia Campus, B
Westmoreland County Community College, A

Texas

El Paso Community College, A
University of Phoenix - Dallas Campus, B
University of Phoenix - Houston Campus, B

Virginia

Northern Virginia Community College, A
Virginia Commonwealth University, B

Washington

Clover Park Technical College, A
University of Phoenix - Western Washington Campus, B

Wisconsin

Marian University, B

Wyoming

Central Wyoming College, A
Laramie County Community College, A

SELLING SKILLS AND SALES OPERATIONS

United States

California

College of San Mateo, A
Cypress College, A
Santa Barbara City College, A
Santa Monica College, A

Florida

Northwest Florida State College, A

Illinois

Bradley University, B
Carl Sandburg College, A
College of DuPage, A
College of Lake County, A
Danville Area Community College, A
Illinois Valley Community College, A
John A. Logan College, A
John Wood Community College, A
Joliet Junior College, A
McHenry County College, A

Southwestern Illinois College, A
Triton College, A

Indiana

Ball State University, B
Purdue University, B

Iowa

Ellsworth Community College, A
Iowa Lakes Community College, A

Michigan

Lansing Community College, A

Minnesota

Minnesota State College - Southeast Technical, A
Ridgewater College, A
St. Catherine University, B

Nebraska

Bellevue University, B

New Jersey

William Paterson University of New Jersey, B

North Carolina

High Point University, B

Ohio

Cuyahoga Community College, A
Hondros College, A
The University of Akron, A

Oklahoma

University of Central Oklahoma, B

Pennsylvania

Butler County Community College, A

Tennessee

University of Memphis, B

Utah

Weber State University, B

Washington

Clark College, A

U.S. Territories: Puerto Rico

Inter American University of Puerto Rico, San
  Germán Campus, A

SEMITIC LANGUAGES, LITERATURES, AND LINGUISTICS

United States

California

Pepperdine University, B

Indiana

Indiana University Bloomington, B

Pennsylvania

University of Pennsylvania, B

Texas

The University of Texas at Austin, B

SHEET METAL TECHNOLOGY/ SHEETWORKING

United States

Arizona

Coconino Community College, A
GateWay Community College, A

California

American River College, A
Chabot College, A
Long Beach City College, A
Palomar College, A
Santiago Canyon College, A

Florida

Miami Dade College, A

Illinois

Rock Valley College, A
Shawnee Community College, A
Southwestern Illinois College, A

Indiana

Ivy Tech Community College - Central Indiana, A
Ivy Tech Community College - Lafayette, A
Ivy Tech Community College - North Central, A
Ivy Tech Community College - Northeast, A
Ivy Tech Community College - Northwest, A
Ivy Tech Community College - Southern Indiana, A
Ivy Tech Community College - Southwest, A
Ivy Tech Community College - Wabash Valley, A
Vincennes University, A

Iowa

Kirkwood Community College, A

Michigan

Delta College, A
Macomb Community College, A

Minnesota

Lake Superior College, A

Montana

Montana State University Billings, A

Ohio

Terra State Community College, A

Pennsylvania

Community College of Allegheny County, A
Thaddeus Stevens College of Technology, A

Canada

British Columbia

British Columbia Institute of Technology, A

SIGN LANGUAGE INTERPRETATION AND TRANSLATION

United States

Alabama

Troy University, B

Arizona

Coconino Community College, A
Phoenix College, A

Arkansas

University of Arkansas at Little Rock, AB

California

American River College, A
Antelope Valley College, A
Berkeley City College, A
College of the Canyons, A
College of the Sequoias, A
Golden West College, A
Los Angeles Pierce College, A
Los Angeles Southwest College, A
Mt. San Antonio College, A
Ohlone College, A
Palomar College, A
Riverside City College, A

Colorado

Front Range Community College, A
Pikes Peak Community College, A
University of Northern Colorado, B

Connecticut

Northwestern Connecticut Community College, A

District of Columbia

Gallaudet University, B

Florida

Miami Dade College, A
University of North Florida, B

Georgia

Valdosta State University, B

Idaho

Idaho State University, B

Illinois

Columbia College Chicago, B
Illinois Central College, A
John A. Logan College, A
MacMurray College, B
Quincy University, B
Southwestern Illinois College, A
Waubonsee Community College, A

Indiana

Bethel College, B
Goshen College, B
Indiana University - Purdue University Indianapolis,
  B

Iowa

Iowa Western Community College, A
Kirkwood Community College, A
Scott Community College, A

Kansas

Johnson County Community College, A

Kentucky

Eastern Kentucky University, B
University of Louisville, B

Louisiana

Delgado Community College, A

Maryland

Community College of Baltimore County, A

Massachusetts

Framingham State University, B
Northern Essex Community College, A

Michigan

Lansing Community College, A
Madonna University, B
Mott Community College, A
Oakland Community College, A

Minnesota

Minnesota State Community and Technical College -
  Moorhead, A
North Central University, AB
St. Catherine University, A
Saint Paul College - A Community & Technical College, A

Mississippi

Hinds Community College, A

Missouri

Ozark Christian College, B
William Woods University, B

Nebraska

Nebraska Christian College, B

New Hampshire

University of New Hampshire, B
University of New Hampshire at Manchester, B

New Jersey

Camden County College, A
Ocean County College, A
Rowan College at Burlington County, A
Union County College, A

New Mexico

Clovis Community College, A
Eastern New Mexico University - Roswell, A
Santa Fe Community College, A
University of New Mexico, B

New York

Mohawk Valley Community College, A
Rochester Institute of Technology, B
Suffolk County Community College, A

North Carolina

Blue Ridge Community College, A
Central Piedmont Community College, A
Western Piedmont Community College, A
Wilson Community College, A

Ohio

Cincinnati Christian University, A
Cincinnati State Technical and Community College, A
Columbus State Community College, A
Kent State University, B
Lakeland Community College, A
Sinclair Community College, A
University of Cincinnati, B
Wright State University, B

Oklahoma

Oklahoma State University, Oklahoma City, A
Tulsa Community College, A

Oregon

Western Oregon University, B

Pennsylvania

Bloomsburg University of Pennsylvania, B
Community College of Allegheny County, A
Community College of Philadelphia, A
Mount Aloysius College, AB

South Dakota

Augustana University, B

Tennessee

Maryville College, B
Nashville State Community College, A

Texas

Austin Community College District, A
Collin County Community College District, A
Del Mar College, A
Eastfield College, A
El Paso Community College, A
Houston Community College, A
Howard College, A
Lone Star College - CyFair, A
Lone Star College - North Harris, A
McLennan Community College, A
Tarrant County College District, A
Tyler Junior College, A

Utah

Salt Lake Community College, A

Virginia

J. Sargeant Reynolds Community College, A

Washington

Seattle Central College, A
Spokane Falls Community College, A

Wisconsin

Milwaukee Area Technical College, A
Northcentral Technical College, A

U.S. Territories: Puerto Rico

Universidad del Turabo, B

Canada

Ontario

York University, B

SLAVIC, BALTIC, AND ALBANIAN LANGUAGES, LITERATURES, AND LINGUISTICS

United States

New Jersey

Rutgers University - Newark, B

SLAVIC LANGUAGES, LITERATURES, AND LINGUISTICS

United States

California

Grossmont College, A
Stanford University, BD
University of California, Berkeley, BD
University of California, Los Angeles, BMD
University of California, Santa Barbara, B
University of Southern California, MD

Connecticut

Yale University, D

Florida

Florida State University, M

Illinois

Northwestern University, BD
University of Chicago, B
University of Illinois at Chicago, BMD
University of Illinois at Urbana - Champaign, BMD

Indiana

Indiana University Bloomington, BMD

Kansas

The University of Kansas, BMD

Massachusetts

Boston College, B
Harvard University, BD

Michigan

University of Michigan, MD
Wayne State University, B

New Jersey

Princeton University, BD

New York

Columbia University, BMD
Columbia University, School of General Studies, B
Cornell University, MD
New York University, M

North Carolina

Duke University, BMO
The University of North Carolina at Chapel Hill, MD

Ohio

The Ohio State University, MD

Pennsylvania

University of Pittsburgh, BMD

Rhode Island

Brown University, MD

Texas

The University of Texas at Austin, MD

Utah

Brigham Young University, D

Virginia

University of Virginia, BMD

Washington

University of Washington, BMD

Wisconsin

University of Wisconsin - Madison, MD
University of Wisconsin - Milwaukee, M

Canada

Alberta

University of Alberta, BMD

British Columbia

The University of British Columbia, B
University of Victoria, B

Manitoba

University of Manitoba, BM

Ontario

University of Toronto, BMD

SLAVIC STUDIES

United States

Connecticut

Connecticut College, B

Illinois

Northwestern University, B

New York

Barnard College, B
Columbia University, School of General Studies, B

Texas

Baylor University, B

Wisconsin

Lawrence University, B

Canada

Ontario

University of Ottawa, B
University of Waterloo, B

SMALL BUSINESS ADMINISTRATION/MANAGEMENT

United States

Alaska

University of Alaska Anchorage, A

Arizona

Northland Pioneer College, A

California

American River College, A
Antelope Valley College, A
Butte College, A
Cañada College, A
Cerritos College, A
Cerro Coso Community College, A
Chabot College, A
College of the Canyons, A
Cosumnes River College, A
Cypress College, A
Fullerton College, A
Lincoln University, B
MiraCosta College, A
San Jose City College, A
Sierra College, A

Colorado

Adams State University, B
Colorado Northwestern Community College, A

Florida

Florida Institute of Technology, B
Florida Southern College, B

Georgia

Brenau University, B

Idaho

Lewis-Clark State College, AB

Illinois

Black Hawk College, A
Bradley University, B
Harper College, A
Moraine Valley Community College, A
North Central College, B
South Suburban College, A
Southwestern Illinois College, A
Waubonsee Community College, A

Indiana

Huntington University, B

Iowa

Iowa Lakes Community College, A

Kansas

Independence Community College, A

Maine

Husson University, B

Massachusetts

Anna Maria College, B
Babson College, B
Springfield Technical Community College, A

Michigan

Bay de Noc Community College, A
Delta College, A
Northern Michigan University, B
Schoolcraft College, A

Missouri

Avila University, B
Missouri College, A

Montana

Blackfeet Community College, A
Flathead Valley Community College, A
Helena College University of Montana, A
Miles Community College, A
Rocky Mountain College, B

Nebraska

University of Nebraska at Omaha, B

New Jersey

Middlesex County College, A
Raritan Valley Community College, A

New York

Borough of Manhattan Community College of the
   City University of New York, A
Hilbert College, B

North Carolina

Chowan University, B

North Dakota

Dakota College at Bottineau, A

Ohio

Ohio Wesleyan University, B
The University of Akron, A

Oregon

Blue Mountain Community College, A

Pennsylvania

Arcadia University, B
Bucks County Community College, A
Community College of Beaver County, A
Saint Joseph's University, B
The University of Scranton, B

Tennessee

Carson-Newman University, B

Virginia

J. Sargeant Reynolds Community College, A

Wisconsin

Carroll University, B

U.S. Territories: Puerto Rico

Pontifical Catholic University of Puerto Rico, B

Canada

Maritime Provinces: Nova Scotia

Dalhousie University, B

SMALL ENGINE MECHANICS AND REPAIR TECHNOLOGY/ TECHNICIAN

United States

California

City College of San Francisco, A
Los Medanos College, A
Southwestern College, A

Idaho

College of Western Idaho, A

Iowa

Iowa Lakes Community College, A

Montana

University of Montana, A

North Dakota

North Dakota State College of Science, A

South Dakota

Mitchell Technical Institute, A

Washington

Bates Technical College, A

Canada

British Columbia

British Columbia Institute of Technology, A

SOCIAL AND PHILOSOPHICAL FOUNDATIONS OF EDUCATION

United States

California

Hope International University, B
National University, B

Illinois

Northwestern University, B

Kentucky

Transylvania University, B

Missouri

Washington University in St. Louis, B

New York

Eugene Lang College of Liberal Arts, B

Pennsylvania

Dickinson College, B

Vermont

Goddard College, B

Washington

Eastern Washington University, B

SOCIAL PSYCHOLOGY

United States

Arizona

Arizona State University at the Tempe campus, D

California

San Francisco State University, M
University of Southern California, D

Colorado

Naropa University, M
University of Denver, D

Connecticut

Connecticut College, M
University of Connecticut, MD
Yale University, D

Delaware

University of Delaware, D

District of Columbia

The George Washington University, D
Howard University, D

Florida

Florida State University, D

Illinois

Loyola University Chicago, MD
Northwestern University, D

Indiana

Ball State University, M
Indiana University Bloomington, D

Iowa

Iowa State University of Science and Technology, D

Kansas

The University of Kansas, M

Maine

Husson University, M

Maryland

University of Maryland, College Park, D

Massachusetts

Brandeis University, D
Clark University, D
Harvard University, D
University of Massachusetts Amherst, MD
University of Massachusetts Lowell, M

Michigan

University of Michigan, D
Wayne State University, D

Minnesota

University of Minnesota, Twin Cities Campus, D
Walden University, MD

Missouri

Washington University in St. Louis, D

Nebraska

University of Nebraska - Lincoln, D

Nevada

University of Nevada, Reno, D

New Jersey

Rutgers University - New Brunswick, D
Rutgers University - Newark, D

New Mexico

New Mexico State University, D

New York

Brooklyn College of the City University of New York, M
Cornell University, MD
New York University, D
Stony Brook University, State University of New York, D
Syracuse University, D
University at Albany, State University of New York, D
University of Rochester, D

North Carolina

The University of North Carolina at Chapel Hill, D
The University of North Carolina at Charlotte, M
The University of North Carolina at Greensboro, MD

North Dakota

North Dakota State University, D

Ohio

Bowling Green State University, M
The Ohio State University, D

Oregon

University of Oregon, MD

Pennsylvania

Carnegie Mellon University, D

Texas

Texas A&M University, D
Texas Christian University, M
University of Houston, D

Virginia

Virginia Commonwealth University, D

Washington

University of Washington, D

Wisconsin

University of Wisconsin - Madison, D

U.S. Territories: Puerto Rico

University of Puerto Rico, Río Piedras Campus, M

Canada

British Columbia

The University of British Columbia, MD
University of Victoria, MD

Newfoundland and Labrador

Memorial University of Newfoundland, M

Ontario

Brock University, MD
Queen's University at Kingston, MD
University of Guelph, MD
University of Windsor, MD
Wilfrid Laurier University, MD

Quebec

Université du Québec à Rimouski, M

SOCIAL SCIENCE TEACHER EDUCATION

United States

Alabama

Auburn University, B
Judson College, B
University of Mobile, B

Arkansas

Arkansas State University, B
Henderson State University, B

California

Biola University, B
California Lutheran University, B
Pacific Union College, B
Simpson University, B
Westmont College, B

Colorado

Western State Colorado University, B

Delaware

University of Delaware, B
Wilmington University, B

Florida

Flagler College, B
Florida Agricultural and Mechanical University, B
Florida Atlantic University, B
Florida Southern College, B
South Florida State College, A
Southeastern University, B
University of Central Florida, B
University of South Florida, B
Warner University, B

Georgia

Emmanuel College, B

Hawaii

Brigham Young University - Hawaii, B

Idaho

Boise State University, B
Lewis-Clark State College, B

Illinois

Blackburn College, B
Bradley University, B
Concordia University Chicago, B
Eastern Illinois University, B
Knox College, B
McKendree University, B
Millikin University, B
University of Illinois at Urbana - Champaign, B

Indiana

Manchester University, B
Valparaiso University, B

Iowa

Buena Vista University, B
Dordt College, B
St. Ambrose University, B
University of Northern Iowa, B
Upper Iowa University, B
Wartburg College, B
William Penn University, B

Kansas

Central Christian College of Kansas, A
Emporia State University, B
Tabor College, B

Kentucky

Campbellsville University, B
Lindsey Wilson College, B

Maine

University of Maine at Farmington, B
University of Maine at Machias, B

Maryland

Mount St. Mary's University, B

Michigan

Eastern Michigan University, B
Michigan State University, B
Northern Michigan University, B
Saginaw Valley State University, B
University of Detroit Mercy, B
Western Michigan University, B

Minnesota

Saint Mary's University of Minnesota, B
Winona State University, B

Mississippi

Blue Mountain College, B
Coahoma Community College, A
Delta State University, B
Jackson State University, B
Northwest Mississippi Community College, A
Rust College, B

Missouri

Central Methodist University, B
Lincoln University, B
Lindenwood University, B
Northwest Missouri State University, B
Saint Louis University, B
Southwest Baptist University, B
Washington University in St. Louis, B

Montana

Carroll College, B
Montana State University, AB
Montana State University Billings, B
Montana State University - Northern, B
University of Great Falls, B
University of Montana, B

Nebraska

College of Saint Mary, B
Concordia University, Nebraska, B
Grace University, B
Hastings College, B
Nebraska Wesleyan University, B
Peru State College, B
Union College, B
University of Nebraska - Lincoln, B
Wayne State College, B
York College, B

New York

Dominican College, B
Medaille College, B
State University of New York College at Oneonta, B
Utica College, B

North Carolina

Chowan University, B
Fayetteville State University, B
Gardner-Webb University, B
Louisburg College, A
The University of North Carolina at Greensboro, B

North Dakota

Mayville State University, B
Minot State University, B
University of Mary, B
University of North Dakota, B
Valley City State University, B

Ohio

Bowling Green State University, B
Ohio Dominican University, B
Shawnee State University, B
University of Rio Grande, B
Youngstown State University, B

Oregon

Corban University, B

Pennsylvania

Holy Family University, B
Mansfield University of Pennsylvania, B
Marywood University, B
Mercyhurst University, B

Rhode Island

Rhode Island College, B

South Dakota

The University of South Dakota, B

Texas

Baylor University, B
Howard College, A

Utah

Brigham Young University, B
Dixie State University, B
Southern Utah University, B
University of Utah, B
Weber State University, B
Western Governors University, B

Vermont

Johnson State College, B
Lyndon State College, B

Washington

Central Washington University, B
Eastern Washington University, B
Western Washington University, B

Wisconsin

Carroll University, B
University of Wisconsin - Superior, B

U.S. Territories: Puerto Rico

University of Puerto Rico in Cayey, B

Canada

Alberta

University of Alberta, B

Ontario

York University, B

SOCIAL SCIENCES

United States

Alabama

Alabama Southern Community College, A
Athens State University, B
Faulkner University, B

Miles College, B
Oakwood University, B
Spring Hill College, B
Troy University, BM
The University of Alabama at Birmingham, B
University of Mobile, B
University of Montevallo, B
University of North Alabama, B

Alaska

University of Alaska Southeast, B
University of Alaska Southeast, Sitka Campus, B

Arizona

Arizona State University at the West campus, B
Arizona Western College, A
Cochise County Community College District, A
Diné College, A
Harrison Middleton University, BM
Northern Arizona University, B
Prescott College, B

Arkansas

Harding University, B
Shorter College, A
Southern Arkansas University - Magnolia, B
University of Arkansas at Monticello, B
University of Arkansas at Pine Bluff, B

California

Allan Hancock College, A
American River College, A
Antelope Valley College, A
Ashford University, B
Azusa Pacific University, B
Barstow Community College, A
Berkeley City College, A
Biola University, B
Brandman University, B
Butte College, A
Cabrillo College, A
California Institute of Technology, MD
California Lutheran University, B
California Polytechnic State University, San Luis
  Obispo, B
California State University, Chico, M
California State University, Los Angeles, B
California State University, Monterey Bay, B
California State University, Sacramento, B
California State University, San Bernardino, BM
California State University, San Marcos, B
California State University, Stanislaus, B
Cerro Coso Community College, A
Chabot College, A
Chaffey College, A
Citrus College, A
City College of San Francisco, A
College of Alameda, A
College of the Canyons, A
College of the Desert, A
College of Marin, A
College of San Mateo, A
College of the Sequoias, A
College of the Siskiyous, A
Copper Mountain College, A
Cosumnes River College, A
Crafton Hills College, A
De Anza College, A
Feather River College, A
Folsom Lake College, A
Foothill College, A
Fresno City College, A
Gavilan College, A
Glendale Community College, A
Hartnell College, A
Hope International University, B
Humboldt State University, BM
Imperial Valley College, A
Irvine Valley College, A
Lake Tahoe Community College, A
Laney College, A
Lassen Community College District, A
Long Beach City College, A
Los Angeles Mission College, A
Los Angeles Southwest College, A
Mendocino College, A

Merced College, A
Merritt College, A
Mission College, A
Modesto Junior College, A
Mount Saint Mary's University, B
Mt. San Antonio College, A
Mt. San Jacinto College, A
National University, B
Notre Dame de Namur University, B
Ohlone College, A
Orange Coast College, A
Palomar College, A
Point Loma Nazarene University, B
Porterville College, A
Reedley College, A
Sacramento City College, A
Saddleback College, A
Saint Mary's College of California, B
San Diego City College, A
San Diego Mesa College, A
San Diego Miramar College, A
San Diego State University, B
San Diego State University - Imperial Valley Cam-
  pus, B
San Joaquin Delta College, A
San Jose City College, A
San Jose State University, B
Santa Ana College, A
Santa Rosa Junior College, A
Santiago Canyon College, A
Sierra College, A
Skyline College, A
Solano Community College, A
Taft College, A
University of California, Berkeley, B
University of California, Irvine, B
University of California, Merced, MD
University of California, Santa Barbara, D
University of California, Santa Cruz, D
University of La Verne, B
University of the Pacific, B
University of Southern California, B
Victor Valley College, A
West Hills Community College, A
West Valley College, A
Westmont College, B
Whittier College, B
Yuba College, A

Colorado

Colorado Christian University, B
Colorado Mesa University, B
Colorado Mountain College (Glenwood Springs), A
Colorado Mountain College (Steamboat Springs), A
Colorado State University - Pueblo, B
Northeastern Junior College, A
Otero Junior College, A
Regis University, B
United States Air Force Academy, B
University of Denver, B
University of Northern Colorado, B

Connecticut

Albertus Magnus College, B
Central Connecticut State University, B
Holy Apostles College and Seminary, B
Housatonic Community College, A
Northwestern Connecticut Community College, A
Quinnipiac University, B
University of Bridgeport, B
Wesleyan University, B
Western Connecticut State University, B
Yale University, M

District of Columbia

American University, B
Georgetown University, B

Florida

Broward College, A
College of Central Florida, A
Edward Waters College, B
Florida Agricultural and Mechanical University, M
Florida Atlantic University, B
Florida Southern College, B
Florida State University, B

Indian River State College, A
Jacksonville University, B
Miami Dade College, A
New College of Florida, B
Palm Beach State College, A
South Florida State College, A
State College of Florida Manatee-Sarasota, A
Stetson University, B
University of Central Florida, B
University of Florida, M
University of South Florida, B
University of South Florida, St. Petersburg, B
University of South Florida Sarasota-Manatee, B
University of West Florida, B

Georgia

Abraham Baldwin Agricultural College, A
Andrew College, A
Berry College, B
Brewton-Parker College, B
Covenant College, B
Fort Valley State University, B
Piedmont College, B
Point University, B
Shorter University, B
Thomas University, B
University of North Georgia, B
Wesleyan College, B

Hawaii

Chaminade University of Honolulu, B
Hawai'i Pacific University, B
University of Hawaii - West Oahu, B

Idaho

Boise State University, B
The College of Idaho, B
College of Southern Idaho, A
Lewis-Clark State College, B
North Idaho College, A

Illinois

Benedictine University, B
DePaul University, B
Governors State University, B
Illinois Institute of Technology, B
McKendree University, B
National Louis University, B
North Central College, B
Northwestern University, B
Olivet Nazarene University, B
Rockford University, B
Roosevelt University, B
Saint Xavier University, B
Shimer College, B
Southern Illinois University Carbondale, B
Spoon River College, A
Trinity International University, B
University of Chicago, BMD
University of Illinois at Springfield, M

Indiana

Ball State University, B
Bethel College, B
Calumet College of Saint Joseph, B
Indiana University Bloomington, D
Indiana University - Purdue University Indianapolis, M
Manchester University, B
Oakland City University, B
Trine University, AB
University of Southern Indiana, AB
Valparaiso University, AB

Iowa

Central College, B
Divine Word College, AB
Dordt College, B
Iowa Lakes Community College, A
University of Northern Iowa, M
Upper Iowa University, B

Kansas

Benedictine College, B
Central Christian College of Kansas, AB

Dodge City Community College, A
Emporia State University, B
Garden City Community College, A
Highland Community College, A
Hutchinson Community College, A
Independence Community College, A
Kansas State University, B
Labette Community College, A
Pratt Community College, A

Kentucky

Asbury University, B
Brescia University, B
Campbellsville University, ABM
Kentucky State University, B
Morehead State University, B
Northern Kentucky University, B
Spalding University, B
Western Kentucky University, B

Louisiana

Loyola University New Orleans, B
Southern University and Agricultural and Mechanical College, M
University of Holy Cross, B

Maine

University of Maine at Augusta, B
University of Maine at Fort Kent, B
University of Maine at Presque Isle, B
University of New England, B
University of Southern Maine, B

Maryland

Coppin State University, B
Frostburg State University, B
Howard Community College, A
Johns Hopkins University, BD
Loyola University Maryland, B
Towson University, BM
University of Maryland, Baltimore County, D
University of Maryland Eastern Shore, B
University of Maryland University College, B

Massachusetts

American International College, B
Anna Maria College, B
Bard College at Simon's Rock, B
Boston University, B
Bristol Community College, A
Curry College, B
Greenfield Community College, A
Harvard University, B
Lesley University, B
Massachusetts Bay Community College, A
Massachusetts Institute of Technology, D
Mount Holyoke College, B
Roxbury Community College, A
University of Massachusetts Amherst, B
University of Massachusetts Boston, B
Williams College, B
Worcester Polytechnic Institute, BD

Michigan

Adrian College, B
Andrews University, B
Aquinas College, B
Bay Mills Community College, A
Calvin College, B
Central Michigan University, B
Concordia University Ann Arbor, B
Eastern Michigan University, BMO
Grand Valley State University, B
Kalamazoo College, B
Lake Superior State University, B
Lansing Community College, A
Marygrove College, B
Michigan State University, B
Michigan Technological University, B
Northwestern Michigan College, A
Olivet College, B
Siena Heights University, B
Spring Arbor University, B
University of Detroit Mercy, B
University of Michigan, BD

University of Michigan - Dearborn, B
University of Michigan - Flint, BM

Minnesota

Bemidji State University, B
Bethany Lutheran College, B
Bethel University, B
College of Saint Benedict, B
The College of St. Scholastica, B
Gustavus Adolphus College, B
Hamline University, B
Metropolitan State University, B
Minnesota State University Mankato, B
St. Catherine University, B
St. Cloud State University, B
Saint John's University, B
University of Minnesota, Morris, B
University of St. Thomas, B

Mississippi

Belhaven University, B
Coahoma Community College, A
Delta State University, B
East Mississippi Community College, A
Itawamba Community College, A
Mississippi College, M
Mississippi University for Women, B
Rust College, B
Southwest Mississippi Community College, A
William Carey University, B

Missouri

Fontbonne University, B
Missouri Baptist University, B
Southeast Missouri State University, B
Washington University in St. Louis, B

Montana

University of Great Falls, B
University of Montana, B

Nebraska

Bellevue University, B
College of Saint Mary, B
Doane University, B
Midland University, B
Northeast Community College, A
Peru State College, B
Union College, B
Wayne State College, B

Nevada

College of Southern Nevada, A
Great Basin College, B
University of Nevada, Las Vegas, B

New Hampshire

Colby-Sawyer College, B
Granite State College, B
Keene State College, B
Plymouth State University, B
Southern New Hampshire University, B

New Jersey

Bergen Community College, A
Brookdale Community College, A
Caldwell University, B
Essex County College, A
Monmouth University, B
Montclair State University, M
Ramapo College of New Jersey, B
Rowan College at Burlington County, A
Rutgers University - New Brunswick, B
Saint Peter's University, AB
Thomas Edison State University, B
Warren County Community College, A

New Mexico

Eastern New Mexico University, B
New Mexico Highlands University, B
New Mexico Military Institute, A
University of the Southwest, B
Western New Mexico University, B

New York

Adelphi University, B
Binghamton University, State University of New York, B
Canisius College, B
Cazenovia College, B
Clarkson University, B
Clinton Community College, A
Colgate University, B
College of Mount Saint Vincent, B
College of Staten Island of the City University of New York, B
Columbia University, M
Concordia College - New York, B
Corning Community College, A
Dominican College, B
Elmira College, B
Finger Lakes Community College, A
Fulton-Montgomery Community College, A
Genesee Community College, A
Hilbert College, B
Ithaca College, B
John Jay College of Criminal Justice of the City University of New York, B
Keuka College, B
Long Island University - LIU Brooklyn, AB
Long Island University - LIU Post, B
Manhattanville College, B
Marymount Manhattan College, A
Mercy College, B
Monroe Community College, A
Mount Saint Mary College, B
Nazareth College of Rochester, B
New York University, BM
Niagara County Community College, A
Niagara University, B
Pace University, B
Pace University, Pleasantville Campus, B
Purchase College, State University of New York, B
Queens College of the City University of New York, M
The Sage Colleges, B
St. John's University, B
St. Joseph's College, Long Island Campus, B
St. Joseph's College, New York, B
St. Lawrence University, B
St. Thomas Aquinas College, B
Sarah Lawrence College, B
Skidmore College, B
State University of New York College at Old Westbury, B
State University of New York Empire State College, AB
State University of New York Polytechnic Institute, B
Suffolk County Community College, A
Syracuse University, MD
Touro College, B
Union College, B
University at Buffalo, the State University of New York, B
University of Rochester, B
Utica College, B
Westchester Community College, A

North Carolina

Campbell University, B
Gardner-Webb University, B
Johnson C. Smith University, B
Livingstone College, B
Mars Hill University, B
Montreat College, B
North Carolina Agricultural and Technical State University, B
Pfeiffer University, B
St. Andrews University, B
The University of North Carolina at Charlotte, M
Warren Wilson College, B
Winston-Salem State University, B

North Dakota

Dakota College at Bottineau, A
Dickinson State University, B
Mayville State University, B
Minot State University, B
North Dakota State University, BM

Turtle Mountain Community College, A
University of Mary, B
University of North Dakota, B
Valley City State University, B

Ohio

Ashland University, B
Bluffton University, B
Bowling Green State University, B
Cleveland State University, B
Defiance College, B
Franklin University, B
Lake Erie College, B
Lorain County Community College, A
Miami University Middletown, A
The Ohio State University, MD
Ohio University, M
Ohio University - Zanesville, A
Shawnee State University, AB
Terra State Community College, A
The University of Akron, B
University of Cincinnati Clermont College, A
University of Rio Grande, B
Wilmington College, B
Wright State University, B

Oklahoma

Carl Albert State College, A
Eastern Oklahoma State College, A
Hillsdale Free Will Baptist College, A
Mid-America Christian University, B
Northeastern Oklahoma Agricultural and Mechanical College, A
Northwestern Oklahoma State University, B
Oklahoma Baptist University, B
Oklahoma Panhandle State University, B
Oklahoma Wesleyan University, B
Redlands Community College, A
Rogers State University, AB
St. Gregory's University, AB
Seminole State College, A
Southwestern Christian University, B
Tulsa Community College, A

Oregon

Central Oregon Community College, A
Concordia University, B
Corban University, B
Eastern Oregon University, B
Marylhurst University, B
Oregon State University, B
Oregon State University - Cascades, B
Portland State University, B
Southern Oregon University, B
Umpqua Community College, A
University of Oregon, B
Warner Pacific College, B
Western Oregon University, B

Pennsylvania

Bloomsburg University of Pennsylvania, B
California University of Pennsylvania, BM
Carnegie Mellon University, D
Cheyney University of Pennsylvania, B
Clarion University of Pennsylvania, B
Community College of Allegheny County, A
Community College of Beaver County, A
Edinboro University of Pennsylvania, BM
Elizabethtown College, B
Gettysburg College, B
Harrisburg Area Community College, A
Indiana University of Pennsylvania, B
Keystone College, B
Kutztown University of Pennsylvania, B
La Salle University, B
Lock Haven University of Pennsylvania, B
Luzerne County Community College, A
Mansfield University of Pennsylvania, B
Marywood University, B
Mercyhurst University, B
Millersville University of Pennsylvania, B
Misericordia University, B
Montgomery County Community College, A
Mount Aloysius College, B
Muhlenberg College, B
Reading Area Community College, A

Robert Morris University, B
Rosemont College, B
University of Pennsylvania, B
University of Pittsburgh, B
University of Pittsburgh at Bradford, B
University of Pittsburgh at Greensburg, B
University of Pittsburgh at Johnstown, B
Ursinus College, B
Waynesburg University, B
Widener University, B
Wilson College, B

Rhode Island

Providence College, B
Roger Williams University, B
University of Rhode Island, B

South Carolina

Allen University, B
Charleston Southern University, B
The Citadel, The Military College of South Carolina, M
Clemson University, D
South Carolina State University, B
Southern Wesleyan University, B
University of South Carolina Beaufort, B

South Dakota

Black Hills State University, B
University of Sioux Falls, A

Tennessee

Cumberland University, B
LeMoyne-Owen College, B
Roane State Community College, A
University of Memphis, M
The University of Tennessee at Chattanooga, B
Vanderbilt University, B

Texas

Amarillo College, A
Central Texas College, A
Clarendon College, A
Concordia University Texas, AB
Galveston College, A
Howard College, A
Howard Payne University, B
Kilgore College, A
Lamar State College - Orange, A
Lamar State College - Port Arthur, A
Laredo Community College, A
Midwestern State University, B
Navarro College, A
Odessa College, A
Our Lady of the Lake University of San Antonio, B
Paris Junior College, A
St. Edward's University, M
San Jacinto College District, A
Southwestern Adventist University, B
Southwestern Assemblies of God University, A
Sul Ross State University, B
Texarkana College, A
Texas A&M International University, BM
Texas A&M University - San Antonio, B
Tyler Junior College, A
University of Dallas, B
University of Houston - Downtown, B
University of North Texas, B
The University of Texas Rio Grande Valley, B
The University of Texas at San Antonio, B
The University of Texas at Tyler, BM
Wayland Baptist University, AB
West Texas A&M University, B
Western Texas College, A
Wiley College, B

Utah

University of Utah, B
Westminster College, B

Vermont

Bennington College, B
Castleton University, B
Community College of Vermont, A
Lyndon State College, B

Marlboro College, B

Virginia

Eastern Mennonite University, B
Ferrum College, B
George Mason University, DO
Hampton University, B
Hollins University, M
J. Sargeant Reynolds Community College, A
Liberty University, B
Mary Baldwin College, B
Northern Virginia Community College, A
Radford University, B
Thomas Nelson Community College, A
Virginia Wesleyan College, B

Washington

Central Washington University, B
The Evergreen State College, B
Heritage University, A
Highline College, A
Skagit Valley College, A
University of Washington, BM
University of Washington, Tacoma, B
Washington State University, B
Washington State University - Global Campus, B
Washington State University - Tri-Cities, B
Washington State University - Vancouver, B
Whitman College, B

West Virginia

Bluefield State College, B
Davis & Elkins College, A
West Liberty University, B

Wisconsin

Alverno College, B
Carthage College, B
Edgewood College, B
Mount Mary University, B
University of Wisconsin - Green Bay, B
University of Wisconsin - Parkside, A
University of Wisconsin - Platteville, B
University of Wisconsin - River Falls, B
University of Wisconsin - Stevens Point, B
University of Wisconsin - Stout, B
University of Wisconsin - Superior, B
University of Wisconsin - Whitewater, B
Viterbo University, B
Wisconsin Lutheran College, B

Wyoming

Central Wyoming College, A
Eastern Wyoming College, A
Laramie County Community College, A
Northwest College, A
University of Wyoming, B
Western Wyoming Community College, A

U.S. Territories: Puerto Rico

Universidad del Turabo, AB
University of Puerto Rico in Arecibo, B
University of Puerto Rico in Carolina, A
University of Puerto Rico in Cayey, B
University of Puerto Rico in Humacao, B
University of Puerto Rico, Mayagüez Campus, B
University of Puerto Rico in Ponce, A
University of Puerto Rico, Río Piedras Campus, B
University of Puerto Rico in Utuado, AB
University of the Sacred Heart, B

U.S. Territories: United States Virgin Islands

University of the Virgin Islands, B

Canada

Alberta

Concordia University of Edmonton, B
The King's University, B
University of Alberta, B
University of Lethbridge, B

British Columbia

Simon Fraser University, B
The University of British Columbia, B

Manitoba

Providence University College & Theological Seminary, B

Maritime Provinces: New Brunswick

Université de Moncton, B

Maritime Provinces: Nova Scotia

Mount Saint Vincent University, B

Newfoundland and Labrador

Memorial University of Newfoundland, B

Ontario

Brock University, B
Royal Military College of Canada, B
Trent University, B
University of Ottawa, B
University of Toronto, MD
University of Waterloo, B
The University of Western Ontario, B
University of Windsor, B
Wilfrid Laurier University, M
York University, B

Quebec

Bishop's University, B
Concordia University, B
Université de Montréal, B
Université du Québec en Abitibi-Témiscamingue, B
Université du Québec à Chicoutimi, B
Université du Québec en Outaouais, B

Saskatchewan

Briercrest College, A
University of Regina, BM

SOCIAL STUDIES TEACHER EDUCATION

United States

Alabama

Alabama Agricultural and Mechanical University, M
Alabama State University, MO
Auburn University, MDO
Auburn University at Montgomery, M
Huntingdon College, B
Spring Hill College, BM
Troy University, M
The University of Alabama in Huntsville, M
The University of West Alabama, M

Arizona

Arizona Christian University, B

Arkansas

Arkansas State University, MO
Arkansas Tech University, B
Harding University, BM
John Brown University, B
Ouachita Baptist University, B
University of Arkansas at Pine Bluff, M
University of Central Arkansas, B

California

Biola University, B
California State University, Chico, M
California State University, East Bay, M
California State University, Fresno, M
Mills College, M
Occidental College, M
University of California, Santa Cruz, M

Colorado

Adams State University, B
The Colorado College, M

Colorado State University, B
University of Northern Colorado, B

Connecticut

Quinnipiac University, M
University of Connecticut, MDO

Delaware

University of Delaware, B

District of Columbia

Trinity Washington University, M
University of the District of Columbia, M

Florida

The Baptist College of Florida, B
Bethune-Cookman University, B
Broward College, A
Florida Agricultural and Mechanical University, M
Florida Atlantic University, M
Florida International University, M
Florida State University, MDO
Nova Southeastern University, B
St. Thomas University, B
State College of Florida Manatee-Sarasota, A
University of Central Florida, MD
University of Florida, M
University of South Florida, M
University of West Florida, D

Georgia

Columbus State University, BMO
Georgia Southern University, M
Georgia State University, MD
Kennesaw State University, B
LaGrange College, B
University of Georgia, BMDO
University of North Georgia, M

Hawaii

Chaminade University of Honolulu, M

Idaho

Brigham Young University - Idaho, B

Illinois

Bradley University, B
John A. Logan College, A
Lake Forest College, M
Lewis University, M
University of Illinois at Chicago, D
University of Illinois at Urbana - Champaign, B
University of St. Francis, BM

Indiana

Anderson University, B
Ball State University, B
Bethel College, B
Franklin College, B
Goshen College, B
Grace College, B
Huntington University, B
Indiana State University, B
Indiana University Bloomington, BMD
Indiana University Northwest, B
Indiana University - Purdue University Fort Wayne, B
Indiana University - Purdue University Indianapolis, B
Indiana University South Bend, B
Indiana University Southeast, B
Indiana Wesleyan University, B
Manchester University, B
Oakland City University, B
Purdue University, BMDO
Saint Mary-of-the-Woods College, B
Taylor University, B
Trine University, B
University of Evansville, B
University of Indianapolis, BM
University of Saint Francis, B

Iowa

Dordt College, B
The University of Iowa, BMD

Kansas

Bethany College, B
Central Christian College of Kansas, AB
Emporia State University, M
MidAmerica Nazarene University, B

Kentucky

Alice Lloyd College, B
Asbury University, M
Campbellsville University, B
Eastern Kentucky University, M
Kentucky Christian University, B
Morehead State University, M
Union College, B
University of the Cumberlands, B
University of Kentucky, B

Louisiana

Grambling State University, BM
Louisiana State University in Shreveport, B
Louisiana Tech University, BM
Nicholls State University, B
Southeastern Louisiana University, B
Southern University and Agricultural and Mechanical
 College, B
University of Louisiana at Monroe, BM
Xavier University of Louisiana, B

Maine

University of Maine, BM

Maryland

University of Maryland, Baltimore County, M

Massachusetts

Boston University, B
Bridgewater State University, M
Cambridge College, M
Fitchburg State University, MO
Framingham State University, M
Merrimack College, B
Smith College, M
Worcester State University, M

Michigan

Adrian College, B
Alma College, B
Andrews University, M
Aquinas College, B
Calvin College, B
Central Michigan University, B
Concordia University Ann Arbor, B
Cornerstone University, B
Eastern Michigan University, B
Grand Valley State University, B
Hope College, B
Madonna University, B
Michigan State University, BM
Northern Michigan University, B
Rochester College, B
Siena Heights University, B
Spring Arbor University, B
University of Detroit Mercy, B
University of Michigan - Dearborn, B
University of Michigan - Flint, B
Wayne State University, MDO
Western Michigan University, B

Minnesota

Bethel University, B
Concordia College, B
Concordia University, St. Paul, B
Crown College, B
Gustavus Adolphus College, B
Metropolitan State University, B
Minnesota State University Mankato, BM
Minnesota State University Moorhead, B
St. Catherine University, B
St. Olaf College, B
University of Minnesota, Duluth, B

University of Minnesota, Twin Cities Campus, MD
University of Northwestern - St. Paul, B
University of St. Thomas, B

Mississippi

Delta State University, M
Mississippi College, BM
Northeast Mississippi Community College, A
Northwest Mississippi Community College, A
University of Mississippi, B
University of Southern Mississippi, O
William Carey University, BM

Missouri

Missouri State University, M
Northwest Missouri State University, M
Southeast Missouri State University, B
University of Missouri, BMDO
Washington University in St. Louis, B
Webster University, M

Montana

Carroll College, B
Rocky Mountain College, B
University of Great Falls, B

Nebraska

Chadron State College, BM
Hastings College, B
Wayne State College, M
York College, B

New Hampshire

Granite State College, B
Keene State College, B
Plymouth State University, BM
Rivier University, BM
Southern New Hampshire University, B

New Jersey

Drew University, M
Rider University, O
Rutgers University - New Brunswick, MD

New York

Binghamton University, State University of New
 York, M
Brooklyn College of the City University of New York,
 BM
Buffalo State College, State University of New York,
 BM
Canisius College, B
City College of the City University of New York, BO
The College at Brockport, State University of New
 York, M
The College of Saint Rose, B
Daemen College, B
Elmira College, B
Hofstra University, BMD
Hunter College of the City University of New York,
 M
Iona College, BM
Ithaca College, BM
Keuka College, B
Le Moyne College, BM
Lehman College of the City University of New York,
 M
Long Island University - LIU Brooklyn, B
Long Island University - LIU Post, B
Manhattanville College, BM
Marist College, B
Nazareth College of Rochester, B
New York University, BMO
Niagara University, B
Nyack College, B
Pace University, B
Pace University, Pleasantville Campus, B
Queens College of the City University of New York,
 BMO
Roberts Wesleyan College, B
St. Francis College, B
St. John Fisher College, BM
St. John's University, B
St. Joseph's College, Long Island Campus, B
St. Joseph's College, New York, B

State University of New York College at Cortland,
 BM
State University of New York College at Old
 Westbury, BM
State University of New York College at Potsdam,
 BM
State University of New York at New Paltz, BM
State University of New York at Plattsburgh, M
Stony Brook University, State University of New
 York, M
Syracuse University, BM
Ulster County Community College, A
University at Buffalo, the State University of New
 York, MO
Utica College, B
Wagner College, M

North Carolina

Appalachian State University, M
Barton College, B
Campbell University, B
East Carolina University, BM
Fayetteville State University, M
Greensboro College, B
North Carolina State University, M
Pfeiffer University, B
The University of North Carolina at Chapel Hill, M
The University of North Carolina at Charlotte, M
The University of North Carolina at Greensboro, BM
The University of North Carolina at Pembroke, BM
Western Carolina University, B
Winston-Salem State University, B

North Dakota

North Dakota State University, BM

Ohio

Bowling Green State University, B
Capital University, B
Cedarville University, B
Cleveland State University, B
Kent State University, B
Malone University, B
Miami University, B
Miami University Hamilton, B
Mount Vernon Nazarene University, B
Ohio Northern University, B
Ohio University, D
Ohio Wesleyan University, B
The University of Akron, B
University of Cincinnati, M
The University of Toledo, M
Ursuline College, BM
Youngstown State University, B

Oklahoma

Cameron University, B
East Central University, B
Northeastern State University, B
Oklahoma Baptist University, B
Oklahoma Christian University, B
Oklahoma Wesleyan University, B
Oral Roberts University, B
St. Gregory's University, B
Southeastern Oklahoma State University, B
Southern Nazarene University, B
Southwestern Oklahoma State University, M
University of Central Oklahoma, B
University of Oklahoma, B

Oregon

Concordia University, B
Corban University, B
Portland State University, M
Warner Pacific College, B
Western Oregon University, M

Pennsylvania

Alvernia University, B
Arcadia University, M
Bloomsburg University of Pennsylvania, M
Cabrini University, B
Cairn University, B
Chatham University, M
Duquesne University, BM

East Stroudsburg University of Pennsylvania, M
Eastern University, O
Gannon University, B
Grove City College, B
Holy Family University, B
Juniata College, B
Keystone College, B
Kutztown University of Pennsylvania, M
La Salle University, MO
Mansfield University of Pennsylvania, B
Messiah College, B
Misericordia University, B
Penn State Harrisburg, B
Saint Francis University, B
Slippery Rock University of Pennsylvania, M
Summit University, B
Temple University, BM
University of Pittsburgh, M
University of Pittsburgh at Johnstown, B
Waynesburg University, B
Widener University, BM
Wilkes University, M
York College of Pennsylvania, B

Rhode Island

Brown University, M
Rhode Island College, M

South Carolina

Bob Jones University, BM
Charleston Southern University, B
The Citadel, The Military College of South Carolina,
   M
Converse College, M
Erskine College, B
Morris College, B
North Greenville University, B
South Carolina State University, M
University of South Carolina, M

South Dakota

Augustana University, B

Tennessee

Lee University, M
LeMoyne-Owen College, B
Maryville College, B
The University of Tennessee, MO
The University of Tennessee at Chattanooga, B

Texas

Abilene Christian University, B
Baylor University, B
East Texas Baptist University, B
Hardin-Simmons University, B
Houston Baptist University, B
Howard College, A
Howard Payne University, B
Huston-Tillotson University, B
LeTourneau University, B
Midwestern State University, B
St. Edward's University, B
Southwestern Adventist University, B
Southwestern Assemblies of God University, B
Texas A&M International University, B
Texas Christian University, B
Texas Lutheran University, B
Wayland Baptist University, BM

Utah

Utah State University, B
Weber State University, B
Western Governors University, MO

Vermont

Castleton University, B
College of St. Joseph, M
Green Mountain College, B
Johnson State College, B
University of Vermont, B

Virginia

Averett University, BM
Bluefield College, B
George Mason University, M

University of Virginia, MD
Virginia Polytechnic Institute and State University, D
Virginia Wesleyan College, B

Washington

Eastern Washington University, B
Northwest University, B
University of Washington, MD
Washington State University, B
Western Washington University, B

West Virginia

American Public University System, M
Concord University, M
Glenville State College, B
University of Charleston, B

Wisconsin

Alverno College, B
Carroll University, B
Carthage College, M
Maranatha Baptist University, B
Marian University, B
Mount Mary University, B
Northland College, B
University of Wisconsin - Eau Claire, B
University of Wisconsin - La Crosse, B
University of Wisconsin - River Falls, M
University of Wisconsin - Superior, B
Viterbo University, B

Wyoming

Casper College, A

U.S. Territories: Puerto Rico

Caribbean University, M
Inter American University of Puerto Rico, Arecibo
   Campus, M
Inter American University of Puerto Rico, Bar-
   ranquitas Campus, BM
Inter American University of Puerto Rico, Fajardo
   Campus, B
Inter American University of Puerto Rico, Metropoli-
   tan Campus, BM
Inter American University of Puerto Rico, Ponce
   Campus, M
Inter American University of Puerto Rico, San
   Germán Campus, B
Pontifical Catholic University of Puerto Rico, B
Universidad Adventista de las Antillas, B
University of Puerto Rico in Cayey, B
University of Puerto Rico, Río Piedras Campus, M

Canada

Alberta

University of Alberta, B
University of Lethbridge, B

British Columbia

The University of British Columbia, M
University of Victoria, MD

Maritime Provinces: Nova Scotia

Acadia University, M

Ontario

York University, B

Saskatchewan

University of Regina, B

SOCIAL WORK

United States

Alabama

Alabama Agricultural and Mechanical University, BM
Auburn University, B
Community College of the Air Force, A
Jacksonville State University, B
Judson College, B

Lawson State Community College, A
Miles College, B
Oakwood University, B
Talladega College, B
Troy University, BM
Tuskegee University, B
The University of Alabama, BMD
The University of Alabama at Birmingham, B
University of Montevallo, B
University of North Alabama, B
University of South Alabama, B

Alaska

University of Alaska Anchorage, BMO
University of Alaska Fairbanks, B

Arizona

Arizona State University at the Downtown Phoenix
   campus, B
Arizona State University at the Tempe campus,
   MDO
Chandler-Gilbert Community College, A
Cochise County Community College District, A
Diné College, A
Northern Arizona University, B
Pima Community College, A

Arkansas

Arkansas Baptist College, B
Arkansas State University, BMO
Central Baptist College, B
Harding University, B
Henderson State University, B
Philander Smith College, B
Phillips Community College of the University of Ar-
   kansas, A
Shorter College, A
Southern Arkansas University - Magnolia, B
University of Arkansas, BM
University of Arkansas at Little Rock, BM
University of Arkansas at Monticello, B
University of Arkansas at Pine Bluff, B

California

American Jewish University, M
Azusa Pacific University, BM
Berkeley City College, A
Biola University, B
Brandman University, B
California State University, Bakersfield, M
California State University, Chico, M
California State University, Dominguez Hills, M
California State University, East Bay, BM
California State University, Fresno, BM
California State University, Fullerton, M
California State University, Long Beach, BM
California State University, Los Angeles, BM
California State University, Monterey Bay, M
California State University, Northridge, M
California State University, Sacramento, BM
California State University, San Bernardino, BM
California State University, San Marcos, M
California State University, Stanislaus, M
Chapman University, B
East Los Angeles College, A
El Camino College, A
Fresno Pacific University, B
Humboldt State University, BM
La Sierra University, B
Loma Linda University, MD
Mount Saint Mary's University, B
Pacific Union College, B
Point Loma Nazarene University, B
Sacramento City College, A
San Diego City College, A
San Diego State University, BM
San Francisco State University, BM
San Jose State University, BMO
University of California, Berkeley, BMD
University of California, Los Angeles, MD
University of Southern California, MD
Whittier College, B

Colorado

Adams State University, B
Colorado Mesa University, B
Colorado State University, BMD
Colorado State University - Pueblo, B
Metropolitan State University of Denver, BM
University of Denver, MDO

Connecticut

Albertus Magnus College, B
Capital Community College, A
Central Connecticut State University, B
Eastern Connecticut State University, B
Manchester Community College, A
Quinnipiac University, M
Sacred Heart University, B
Southern Connecticut State University, BM
University of Saint Joseph, B
Western Connecticut State University, B

Delaware

Delaware State University, BM

District of Columbia

The Catholic University of America, BMD
Gallaudet University, M
Howard University, BMD
University of the District of Columbia, B

Florida

Barry University, MD
Belhaven University, B
Broward College, A
Chipola College, A
College of Central Florida, A
Edward Waters College, B
Florida Agricultural and Mechanical University, BM
Florida Atlantic University, BMD
Florida Gulf Coast University, BM
Florida International University, BMD
Florida State University, BMD
Indian River State College, A
Miami Dade College, A
Palm Beach State College, A
Saint Leo University, BM
South Florida State College, A
Southeastern University, B
State College of Florida Manatee-Sarasota, A
University of Central Florida, BMO
University of North Florida, B
University of South Florida, BMDO
University of West Florida, BM
Warner University, B

Georgia

Abraham Baldwin Agricultural College, A
Albany State University, BM
Andrew College, A
Augusta University, B
Clark Atlanta University, BMD
Dalton State College, B
Darton State College, A
Fort Valley State University, B
Georgia Military College, A
Georgia State University, BMO
Gordon State College, A
Kennesaw State University, M
Middle Georgia State University, A
Oglethorpe University, B
Savannah State University, BM
Thomas University, B
University of Georgia, BMDO
Valdosta State University, M
West Georgia Technical College, A

Hawaii

Brigham Young University - Hawaii, B
Hawai'i Pacific University, BM
University of Hawaii at Manoa, BMD

Idaho

Boise State University, BM
Brigham Young University - Idaho, B
Idaho State University, B
Lewis-Clark State College, B

Northwest Nazarene University, BM

Illinois

Aurora University, BMD
Bradley University, B
Chicago State University, M
City Colleges of Chicago, Harold Washington College, A
City Colleges of Chicago, Kennedy-King College, A
College of Lake County, A
Concordia University Chicago, B
DePaul University, M
Dominican University, M
Elgin Community College, A
Governors State University, BM
Greenville College, B
Illinois Eastern Community Colleges, Wabash Valley College, A
Illinois State University, BM
Illinois Valley Community College, A
John A. Logan College, A
Lake Land College, A
Lewis University, B
Loyola University Chicago, BMDO
MacMurray College, B
McKendree University, B
Millikin University, B
Northeastern Illinois University, B
Oakton Community College, A
Olivet Nazarene University, B
Rockford University, B
St. Augustine College, B
Sauk Valley Community College, A
Shawnee Community College, A
South Suburban College, A
Southern Illinois University Carbondale, BM
Southern Illinois University Edwardsville, BM
Southwestern Illinois College, A
Trinity Christian College, B
University of Chicago, MD
University of Illinois at Chicago, BMDO
University of Illinois at Springfield, B
University of Illinois at Urbana - Champaign, MD
University of St. Francis, BMO
Waubonsee Community College, A
Western Illinois University, B

Indiana

Anderson University, B
Ball State University, B
Goshen College, B
Huntington University, B
Indiana State University, BM
Indiana University Bloomington, B
Indiana University East, BM
Indiana University Northwest, BM
Indiana University - Purdue University Indianapolis, BMDO
Indiana University South Bend, BM
Indiana Wesleyan University, B
Manchester University, B
Purdue University Northwest (Westville), B
Saint Mary's College, B
Taylor University, B
University of Indianapolis, B
University of Saint Francis, B
University of Southern Indiana, BM
Valparaiso University, B
Vincennes University, A

Iowa

Briar Cliff University, B
Buena Vista University, B
Clarke University, BM
Dordt College, B
Graceland University, B
Iowa Central Community College, A
Iowa Lakes Community College, A
Kirkwood Community College, A
Loras College, B
Luther College, B
Mount Mercy University, B
Northeast Iowa Community College, A
Northwestern College, B
St. Ambrose University, M
The University of Iowa, BMD

University of Northern Iowa, BM
Wartburg College, B

Kansas

Allen Community College, A
Barton County Community College, A
Bethel College, B
Central Christian College of Kansas, A
Cowley County Community College and Area Vocational - Technical School, A
Dodge City Community College, A
Fort Hays State University, B
Garden City Community College, A
Haskell Indian Nations University, A
Kansas State University, B
Newman University, M
Pittsburg State University, B
Pratt Community College, A
Tabor College, B
The University of Kansas, BMD
Washburn University, BM
Wichita State University, BM

Kentucky

Asbury University, BM
Big Sandy Community and Technical College, A
Brescia University, B
Campbellsville University, BM
Eastern Kentucky University, B
Elizabethtown Community and Technical College, A
Henderson Community College, A
Hopkinsville Community College, A
Kentucky Christian University, B
Kentucky State University, B
Morehead State University, B
Murray State University, B
Northern Kentucky University, BM
Spalding University, BM
Union College, B
University of Kentucky, BMD
University of Louisville, BMDO
University of Pikeville, B
Western Kentucky University, BM

Louisiana

Grambling State University, BM
Louisiana College, B
Louisiana State University and Agricultural & Mechanical College, MD
Northwestern State University of Louisiana, B
Southeastern Louisiana University, B
Southern University and Agricultural and Mechanical College, B
Southern University at New Orleans, BM
Tulane University, MD
University of Louisiana at Monroe, B

Maine

Saint Joseph's College of Maine, B
University of Maine, BMO
University of Maine at Presque Isle, B
University of New England, BM
University of Southern Maine, BM

Maryland

Bowie State University, B
Coppin State University, B
Frostburg State University, B
Harford Community College, A
Hood College, B
McDaniel College, B
Morgan State University, BMD
Salisbury University, BM
University of Maryland, Baltimore County, B
University of Maryland Eastern Shore, B

Massachusetts

Anna Maria College, B
Assumption College, O
Boston College, MD
Boston University, MD
Bridgewater State University, BM
Bristol Community College, A
Eastern Nazarene College, B
Elms College, B

Gordon College, B
Holyoke Community College, A
Regis College, B
Salem State University, BM
Simmons College, BMD
Smith College, MD
Springfield College, MO
Western New England University, B
Westfield State University, B
Wheelock College, BM

Michigan

Adrian College, B
Andrews University, BM
Calvin College, B
Central Michigan University, B
Cornerstone University, B
Eastern Michigan University, BM
Ferris State University, AB
Gogebic Community College, A
Grand Valley State University, BM
Hope College, B
Kuyper College, B
Madonna University, B
Marygrove College, B
Michigan State University, BMD
Monroe County Community College, A
Northern Michigan University, B
Oakland University, B
Saginaw Valley State University, B
Siena Heights University, B
Southwestern Michigan College, A
Spring Arbor University, B
University of Detroit Mercy, B
University of Michigan, MD
University of Michigan - Flint, B
Wayne County Community College District, A
Wayne State University, BMDO
Western Michigan University, BM

Minnesota

Augsburg College, BM
Bemidji State University, B
Bethel University, B
Capella University, D
The College of St. Scholastica, BM
Concordia College, B
Metropolitan State University, B
Minnesota State University Mankato, BM
Minnesota State University Moorhead, B
North Central University, B
St. Catherine University, BMD
St. Cloud State University, BM
St. Olaf College, B
Southwest Minnesota State University, B
University of Minnesota, Duluth, BM
University of Minnesota, Twin Cities Campus, MD
University of St. Thomas, BM
Walden University, MD
Winona State University, B

Mississippi

Alcorn State University, B
Belhaven University, B
Coahoma Community College, A
Delta State University, B
Itawamba Community College, A
Jackson State University, BMD
Mississippi College, B
Mississippi Delta Community College, A
Mississippi State University, B
Mississippi Valley State University, B
Northeast Mississippi Community College, A
Rust College, B
University of Mississippi, BM
University of Southern Mississippi, BM

Missouri

Avila University, B
College of the Ozarks, B
Evangel University, B
Fontbonne University, B
Hannibal-LaGrange University, B
Lincoln University, B
Lindenwood University, B
Missouri Southern State University, B

Missouri State University, BM
Missouri Western State University, B
Park University, BM
St. Charles Community College, A
Saint Louis University, BM
Southeast Missouri State University, B
Southwest Baptist University, B
University of Central Missouri, B
University of Missouri, BMDO
University of Missouri - Kansas City, M
University of Missouri - St. Louis, BMO
Washington University in St. Louis, MDO
William Woods University, B

Montana

University of Montana, BM

Nebraska

Chadron State College, B
Creighton University, B
Nebraska Indian Community College, A
Nebraska Wesleyan University, B
Union College, B
University of Nebraska at Kearney, B
University of Nebraska at Omaha, BM
Western Nebraska Community College, A
York College, B

Nevada

Great Basin College, B
University of Nevada, Las Vegas, BM
University of Nevada, Reno, BM

New Hampshire

Franklin Pierce University, B
Nashua Community College, A
Plymouth State University, B
Saint Anselm College, B
University of New Hampshire, BMO

New Jersey

Bergen Community College, A
Brookdale Community College, A
Camden County College, A
Centenary College, B
Cumberland County College, A
Essex County College, A
Georgian Court University, B
Hudson County Community College, A
Kean University, M
Monmouth University, BMO
Ramapo College of New Jersey, B
Rutgers University - Camden, B
Rutgers University - New Brunswick, BMD
Rutgers University - Newark, B
Salem Community College, A
Seton Hall University, B
Stockton University, BM

New Mexico

Eastern New Mexico University - Roswell, A
Mesalands Community College, A
New Mexico Highlands University, M
New Mexico State University, BM
New Mexico State University - Grants, A
San Juan College, A
Santa Fe Community College, A
Western New Mexico University, BM

New York

Adelphi University, BMD
Binghamton University, State University of New York, M
Buffalo State College, State University of New York, B
The College at Brockport, State University of New York, BMO
The College of New Rochelle, B
The College of Saint Rose, B
College of Staten Island of the City University of New York, BM
Columbia University, MD
Concordia College - New York, B
Cornell University, D
Daemen College, BM

Dominican College, B
Fordham University, BMD
Genesee Community College, A
Hunter College of the City University of New York, MD
Iona College, B
Keuka College, B
Lehman College of the City University of New York, B
Long Island University - LIU Brooklyn, B
Long Island University - LIU Post, B
Marist College, B
Medgar Evers College of the City University of New York, B
Mercy College, B
Molloy College, B
Mount Saint Mary College, B
Nazareth College of Rochester, BM
New York University, BMD
Niagara University, B
Nyack College, B
Roberts Wesleyan College, BM
Siena College, B
Skidmore College, B
State University of New York College of Agriculture and Technology at Cobleskill, A
State University of New York College at Cortland, B
State University of New York at Fredonia, B
State University of New York at Plattsburgh, B
Stony Brook University, State University of New York, BMD
Syracuse University, BM
Touro College, M
University at Albany, State University of New York, BMD
University at Buffalo, the State University of New York, MD
Yeshiva University, MD
York College of the City University of New York, B

North Carolina

Appalachian State University, BM
Barton College, B
Bennett College, B
Campbell University, B
Central Carolina Community College, A
Central Piedmont Community College, A
East Carolina University, BMO
Elizabeth City State University, B
Fayetteville State University, BM
Johnson C. Smith University, B
Livingstone College, B
Louisburg College, A
Mars Hill University, B
Meredith College, B
Methodist University, AB
North Carolina Agricultural and Technical State University, BM
North Carolina Central University, B
North Carolina State University, BM
Shaw University, B
The University of North Carolina at Chapel Hill, MD
The University of North Carolina at Charlotte, BM
The University of North Carolina at Greensboro, BM
The University of North Carolina at Pembroke, BM
The University of North Carolina Wilmington, BM
Warren Wilson College, B
Western Carolina University, BM

North Dakota

Dickinson State University, B
Minot State University, B
Sitting Bull College, A
Turtle Mountain Community College, A
University of Mary, B
University of North Dakota, BM

Ohio

Ashland University, B
Bluffton University, B
Bowling Green State University, B
Bowling Green State University - Firelands College, AB
Capital University, B
Case Western Reserve University, MD
Cedarville University, B

Central State University, B
Clark State Community College, A
Cleveland State University, BM
Defiance College, B
Edison Community College, A
Franciscan University of Steubenville, B
James A. Rhodes State College, A
Lakeland Community College, A
Lorain County Community College, A
Lourdes University, B
Malone University, B
Marion Technical College, A
Miami University, B
Miami University Hamilton, B
Miami University Middletown, A
Mount St. Joseph University, B
Mount Vernon Nazarene University, B
Northwest State Community College, A
Ohio Dominican University, B
The Ohio State University, BMD
The Ohio State University at Lima, M
The Ohio State University - Mansfield Campus, M
The Ohio State University - Newark Campus, M
Ohio University, BM
Terra State Community College, A
Union Institute & University, B
The University of Akron, ABM
The University of Akron Wayne College, AB
University of Cincinnati, BM
University of Cincinnati Blue Ash College, A
University of Cincinnati Clermont College, A
The University of Findlay, B
University of Rio Grande, AB
The University of Toledo, BMO
Ursuline College, B
Washington State Community College, A
Wilberforce University, B
Wilmington College, B
Wright State University, AB
Wright State University - Lake Campus, A
Xavier University, B
Youngstown State University, AB
Zane State College, A

Oklahoma

Connors State College, A
East Central University, B
Northeastern State University, B
Northwestern Oklahoma State University, B
Oral Roberts University, B
Tulsa Community College, A
University of Oklahoma, BM

Oregon

Blue Mountain Community College, A
Chemeketa Community College, A
Clackamas Community College, A
Concordia University, B
George Fox University, BM
Pacific University, BM
Portland State University, BMD
Rogue Community College, A
Umpqua Community College, A
University of Portland, B
Warner Pacific College, B

Pennsylvania

Alvernia University, B
Bloomsburg University of Pennsylvania, B
Bryn Mawr College, MD
Butler County Community College, A
Cabrini University, B
Cairn University, B
California University of Pennsylvania, BM
Carlow University, B
Cedar Crest College, B
Chatham University, B
Community College of Allegheny County, A
Eastern University, B
Edinboro University of Pennsylvania, ABM
Elizabethtown College, B
Elizabethtown College School of Continuing and
  Professional Studies, A
Gannon University, B
Harrisburg Area Community College, A
Immaculata University, B

Juniata College, B
Kutztown University of Pennsylvania, BM
La Salle University, B
Lancaster Bible College, B
Lehigh Carbon Community College, A
Lock Haven University of Pennsylvania, B
Mansfield University of Pennsylvania, B
Marywood University, BMD
Mercyhurst University, B
Messiah College, B
Millersville University of Pennsylvania, BM
Misericordia University, B
Neumann University, B
Northampton Community College, A
Reading Area Community College, A
Saint Francis University, B
Seton Hill University, B
Shippensburg University of Pennsylvania, BM
Slippery Rock University of Pennsylvania, B
Temple University, BMO
University of Pennsylvania, MD
University of Pittsburgh, BMDO
University of Valley Forge, B
West Chester University of Pennsylvania, BM
Widener University, BMD

Rhode Island

Community College of Rhode Island, A
Providence College, B
Rhode Island College, BM
Salve Regina University, B

South Carolina

Benedict College, B
Coker College, B
Columbia College, B
Florence-Darlington Technical College, A
Limestone College, B
Piedmont Technical College, A
South Carolina State University, B
University of South Carolina, BMD
Winthrop University, BM

South Dakota

Northern State University, A
Oglala Lakota College, AB
Presentation College, B
University of Sioux Falls, B
The University of South Dakota, BM

Tennessee

Austin Peay State University, BM
Belhaven University, B
Belmont University, B
East Tennessee State University, BM
Freed-Hardeman University, B
King University, B
LeMoyne-Owen College, B
Lincoln Memorial University, B
Lipscomb University, B
Middle Tennessee State University, BM
Milligan College, B
Nashville State Community College, A
Southern Adventist University, BM
Tennessee State University, BM
Tennessee Technological University, B
Trevecca Nazarene University, B
Union University, BM
University of Memphis, B
The University of Tennessee, BMD
The University of Tennessee at Chattanooga, B
The University of Tennessee at Martin, B

Texas

Abilene Christian University, BM
Amarillo College, A
Angelina College, A
Angelo State University, B
Austin Community College District, A
Baylor University, BMD
Clarendon College, A
Del Mar College, A
Eastfield College, A
El Paso Community College, A
Galveston College, A

Hardin-Simmons University, B
Howard Payne University, B
Jarvis Christian College, B
Lamar University, B
Lubbock Christian University, B
Midwestern State University, B
Northeast Texas Community College, A
Our Lady of the Lake University of San Antonio, BM
Paris Junior College, A
Prairie View A&M University, B
St. Edward's University, B
St. Philip's College, A
South Plains College, A
Southwestern Assemblies of God University, B
Stephen F. Austin State University, BM
Tarleton State University, B
Texas A&M University - Central Texas, B
Texas A&M University - Commerce, B
Texas A&M University - Kingsville, B
Texas Christian University, BM
Texas College, B
Texas Southern University, B
Texas Southmost College, A
Texas State University, BM
Texas Tech University, BM
Texas Woman's University, B
Tyler Junior College, A
University of Houston, MD
University of Houston - Clear Lake, B
University of Houston - Downtown, B
University of Mary Hardin-Baylor, B
University of North Texas, B
The University of Texas at Arlington, BMD
The University of Texas at Austin, BMD
The University of Texas at El Paso, BM
The University of Texas of the Permian Basin, B
The University of Texas Rio Grande Valley, BM
The University of Texas at San Antonio, M
West Texas A&M University, BM
Wiley College, B

Utah

Brigham Young University, M
Salt Lake Community College, A
University of Utah, BMD
Utah State University, B
Utah Valley University, B
Weber State University, B

Vermont

Castleton University, B
Champlain College, B
University of Vermont, BM

Virginia

Christopher Newport University, B
Eastern Mennonite University, B
Ferrum College, B
George Mason University, BM
Hampton University, B
James Madison University, B
Longwood University, B
Mary Baldwin College, B
Norfolk State University, BMD
Radford University, BM
Virginia Commonwealth University, BMD
Virginia State University, B
Virginia Union University, B
Virginia Wesleyan College, B

Washington

Eastern Washington University, BM
Heritage University, B
Pacific Lutheran University, B
Saint Martin's University, B
Seattle University, B
Spokane Falls Community College, A
University of Washington, BMD
University of Washington, Tacoma, BM
Walla Walla University, BM

West Virginia

Bethany College, B
Concord University, B
Marshall University, B

Potomac State College of West Virginia University, A
Shepherd University, B
West Liberty University, B
West Virginia Northern Community College, A
West Virginia State University, B
West Virginia University, BM
West Virginia University at Parkersburg, A

Wisconsin

Carthage College, B
College of Menominee Nation, A
Concordia University Wisconsin, B
Lac Courte Oreilles Ojibwa Community College, A
Marian University, B
Marquette University, B
Mount Mary University, B
University of Wisconsin - Eau Claire, B
University of Wisconsin - Green Bay, BM
University of Wisconsin - Madison, BMD
University of Wisconsin - Milwaukee, BMDO
University of Wisconsin - Oshkosh, BM
University of Wisconsin - River Falls, B
University of Wisconsin - Superior, B
University of Wisconsin - Whitewater, B
Viterbo University, B

Wyoming

Casper College, A
University of Wyoming, BM
Western Wyoming Community College, A

U.S. Territories: Guam

University of Guam, BM

U.S. Territories: Puerto Rico

Bayamón Central University, B
Caribbean University, B
Inter American University of Puerto Rico, Aguadilla Campus, B
Inter American University of Puerto Rico, Arecibo Campus, B
Inter American University of Puerto Rico, Fajardo Campus, B
Inter American University of Puerto Rico, Metropolitan Campus, BM
Pontifical Catholic University of Puerto Rico, BM
Universidad del Este, BM
Universidad Metropolitana, B
Universidad del Turabo, B
University of Puerto Rico in Humacao, B
University of Puerto Rico, Río Piedras Campus, BMD
University of Puerto Rico in Utuado, B
University of the Sacred Heart, B

U.S. Territories: United States Virgin Islands

University of the Virgin Islands, B

Canada

Alberta

University of Calgary, BMDO

British Columbia

Thompson Rivers University, BM
The University of British Columbia, BMD
The University of British Columbia - Okanagan Campus, B
University of the Fraser Valley, ABM
University of Northern British Columbia, BM
University of Victoria, BM

Manitoba

Booth University College, B
Université de Saint-Boniface, B
University of Manitoba, BMD

Maritime Provinces: New Brunswick

St. Thomas University, B
Université de Moncton, BM

Maritime Provinces: Nova Scotia

Dalhousie University, BM

Newfoundland and Labrador

Memorial University of Newfoundland, BM

Ontario

Carleton University, BM
Lakehead University, BM
Laurentian University, BM
McMaster University, BM
Redeemer University College, B
Ryerson University, B
Trent University, B
University of Ottawa, BM
University of Toronto, MD
University of Waterloo, B
The University of Western Ontario, B
University of Windsor, BM
Wilfrid Laurier University, MD
York University, BMD

Quebec

McGill University, BMDO
Université Laval, BMD
Université de Montréal, BMDO
Université du Québec en Abitibi-Témiscamingue, BM
Université du Québec à Chicoutimi, B
Université du Québec à Montréal, BM
Université du Québec en Outaouais, BM
Université de Sherbrooke, BM

Saskatchewan

University of Regina, BMD

SOCIOBIOLOGY

United States

California

University of California, Davis, D

SOCIOLOGY

United States

Alabama

Alabama Agricultural and Mechanical University, B
Athens State University, B
Auburn University, BM
Auburn University at Montgomery, BM
Birmingham-Southern College, B
Jacksonville State University, B
Samford University, B
Spring Hill College, B
Talladega College, B
Troy University, B
Tuskegee University, B
The University of Alabama, B
The University of Alabama at Birmingham, BMD
The University of Alabama in Huntsville, B
University of Mobile, B
University of Montevallo, B
University of North Alabama, B
University of South Alabama, B
The University of West Alabama, B

Alaska

University of Alaska Anchorage, B
University of Alaska Fairbanks, B

Arizona

Arizona State University at the Tempe campus, BMD
Arizona State University at the West campus, B
Coconino Community College, A
Eastern Arizona College, A
Grand Canyon University, B
Mohave Community College, A

Northern Arizona University, BM
Pima Community College, A
The University of Arizona, BD

Arkansas

Arkansas State University, BMO
Arkansas Tech University, B
Henderson State University, B
Hendrix College, B
Ouachita Baptist University, B
Philander Smith College, B
University of Arkansas, BM
University of Arkansas at Little Rock, B
University of Arkansas at Pine Bluff, B
University of Central Arkansas, B
University of the Ozarks, B

California

Antelope Valley College, A
Azusa Pacific University, B
Bakersfield College, A
Berkeley City College, A
Biola University, B
Brandman University, B
Cabrillo College, A
California Baptist University, B
California Lutheran University, B
California Polytechnic State University, San Luis Obispo, B
California State Polytechnic University, Pomona, B
California State University, Bakersfield, BM
California State University Channel Islands, B
California State University, Dominguez Hills, BMO
California State University, East Bay, B
California State University, Fresno, B
California State University, Fullerton, BM
California State University, Long Beach, B
California State University, Los Angeles, BM
California State University, Northridge, BM
California State University, Sacramento, BM
California State University, San Bernardino, B
California State University, San Marcos, BM
California State University, Stanislaus, B
Cañada College, A
Cerritos College, A
Chaffey College, A
Chapman University, B
Citrus College, A
College of Alameda, A
College of the Canyons, A
College of the Desert, A
College of the Sequoias, A
Contra Costa College, A
Crafton Hills College, A
Cuesta College, A
Cypress College, A
De Anza College, A
East Los Angeles College, A
El Camino College, A
Feather River College, A
Foothill College, A
Fresno City College, A
Fresno Pacific University, A
Fullerton College, A
Holy Names University, B
Humboldt State University, BM
La Sierra University, B
Los Angeles City College, A
Los Angeles Mission College, A
Los Angeles Valley College, A
Los Medanos College, A
Loyola Marymount University, B
Mills College, B
MiraCosta College, A
Monterey Peninsula College, A
Mount Saint Mary's University, B
National University, B
Notre Dame de Namur University, B
Occidental College, B
Ohlone College, A
Orange Coast College, A
Oxnard College, A
Palomar College, A
Pasadena City College, A
Pepperdine University, B
Pitzer College, B

Point Loma Nazarene University, B
Pomona College, B
Saddleback College, A
Saint Mary's College of California, B
San Bernardino Valley College, A
San Diego City College, A
San Diego Mesa College, A
San Diego Miramar College, A
San Diego State University, BM
San Francisco State University, B
San Joaquin Delta College, A
San Jose State University, BM
Santa Ana College, A
Santa Barbara City College, A
Santa Clara University, B
Santa Rosa Junior College, A
Santiago Canyon College, A
Scripps College, B
Skyline College, A
Sonoma State University, B
Southwestern College, A
Stanford University, BD
University of California, Berkeley, BD
University of California, Davis, BMD
University of California, Irvine, BD
University of California, Los Angeles, BMD
University of California, Merced, B
University of California, Riverside, BMD
University of California, San Diego, BD
University of California, Santa Barbara, BD
University of California, Santa Cruz, BD
University of La Verne, B
University of the Pacific, B
University of Redlands, B
University of San Diego, B
University of San Francisco, B
University of Southern California, BD
Vanguard University of Southern California, B
West Los Angeles College, A
West Valley College, A
Westmont College, B
Whittier College, B
Woodland Community College, A

Colorado

The Colorado College, B
Colorado Mesa University, B
Colorado State University, BMD
Colorado State University - Pueblo, B
Fort Lewis College, B
Metropolitan State University of Denver, B
Northeastern Junior College, A
Regis University, B
University of Colorado Boulder, BD
University of Colorado Colorado Springs, BM
University of Colorado Denver, BM
University of Denver, B
University of Northern Colorado, BM
Western State Colorado University, B

Connecticut

Albertus Magnus College, B
Central Connecticut State University, B
Connecticut College, B
Eastern Connecticut State University, B
Post University, B
Quinnipiac University, B
Sacred Heart University, B
Southern Connecticut State University, BM
Trinity College, B
University of Connecticut, BMD
University of Hartford, B
Wesleyan University, B
Western Connecticut State University, B
Yale University, BD

Delaware

Delaware State University, B
University of Delaware, BMD

District of Columbia

American University, B
The Catholic University of America, BM
Gallaudet University, B
The George Washington University, BM
Georgetown University, B

Howard University, BMD
Trinity Washington University, B
University of the District of Columbia, B

Florida

Barry University, B
Bethune-Cookman University, B
Broward College, A
College of Central Florida, A
Eckerd College, B
Edward Waters College, B
Flagler College, B
Florida Agricultural and Mechanical University, B
Florida Atlantic University, BM
Florida Gulf Coast University, B
Florida International University, BMD
Florida Memorial University, B
Florida State University, BMD
Indian River State College, A
Jacksonville University, B
Miami Dade College, A
New College of Florida, B
Nova Southeastern University, B
Pensacola State College, A
Rollins College, B
Saint Leo University, B
South Florida State College, A
Stetson University, B
University of Central Florida, BMD
University of Florida, BMD
University of Miami, BMD
University of North Florida, B
University of South Florida, BMD
The University of Tampa, B
University of West Florida, BM

Georgia

Abraham Baldwin Agricultural College, A
Agnes Scott College, B
Albany State University, B
Andrew College, A
Augusta University, B
Bainbridge State College, A
Brewton-Parker College, B
Clark Atlanta University, BM
Clayton State University, B
College of Coastal Georgia, A
Columbus State University, B
Covenant College, B
Darton State College, A
Emory University, BD
Fort Valley State University, B
Georgia College & State University, B
Georgia Highlands College, A
Georgia Military College, A
Georgia Southern University, BM
Georgia Southwestern State University, B
Georgia State University, BMD
Gordon State College, A
Kennesaw State University, B
LaGrange College, B
Mercer University, B
Middle Georgia State University, A
Morehouse College, B
Oglethorpe University, B
Paine College, B
Piedmont College, B
Point University, B
Reinhardt University, B
Savannah State University, B
Shorter University, B
South Georgia State College, A
Spelman College, B
Thomas University, B
University of Georgia, BMD
University of North Georgia, B
University of West Georgia, BMO
Valdosta State University, M

Hawaii

Hawai'i Pacific University, B
University of Hawaii at Manoa, BMD
University of Hawaii - West Oahu, B

Idaho

Boise State University, B
Brigham Young University - Idaho, B
College of Southern Idaho, A
College of Western Idaho, A
Idaho State University, BM
North Idaho College, A
University of Idaho, B

Illinois

Augustana College, B
Aurora University, B
Benedictine University, B
Bradley University, B
Chicago State University, B
Concordia University Chicago, B
DePaul University, BM
Dominican University, B
Eastern Illinois University, B
Elmhurst College, B
Greenville College, B
Illinois College, B
Illinois Institute of Technology, B
Illinois State University, BM
Illinois Wesleyan University, B
John A. Logan College, A
Judson University, B
Kankakee Community College, A
Knox College, B
Lake Forest College, B
Lewis University, B
Loyola University Chicago, BMD
McKendree University, B
Millikin University, B
Monmouth College, B
Moraine Valley Community College, A
North Central College, B
North Park University, B
Northeastern Illinois University, B
Northern Illinois University, BM
Northwestern University, BD
Olivet Nazarene University, B
Rockford University, B
Roosevelt University, BM
Saint Xavier University, B
Sauk Valley Community College, A
Southern Illinois University Carbondale, BMD
Southern Illinois University Edwardsville, BM
Spoon River College, A
Triton College, A
University of Chicago, BD
University of Illinois at Chicago, BMD
University of Illinois at Urbana - Champaign, BMD
Western Illinois University, BM
Wheaton College, B

Indiana

Anderson University, B
Ball State University, BM
Bethel College, B
Butler University, B
DePauw University, B
Earlham College, B
Franklin College, B
Goshen College, B
Grace College, B
Hanover College, B
Holy Cross College, A
Huntington University, B
Indiana University Bloomington, BMD
Indiana University East, B
Indiana University Kokomo, B
Indiana University Northwest, B
Indiana University - Purdue University Fort Wayne, BM
Indiana University - Purdue University Indianapolis, BM
Indiana University South Bend, B
Indiana University Southeast, B
Indiana Wesleyan University, B
Manchester University, B
Marian University, B
Martin University, B
Purdue University, BMD
Purdue University Northwest (Hammond), B

Saint Joseph's College, B
Saint Mary's College, B
Taylor University, B
University of Evansville, B
University of Indianapolis, BM
University of Notre Dame, BD
University of Saint Francis, B
University of Southern Indiana, B
Valparaiso University, B
Vincennes University, A

Iowa

Buena Vista University, B
Central College, B
Coe College, B
Cornell College, B
Dordt College, B
Drake University, B
Grinnell College, B
Iowa Central Community College, A
Iowa Lakes Community College, A
Iowa State University of Science and Technology,
  BMD
Loras College, B
Luther College, B
Mount Mercy University, B
Northwestern College, B
St. Ambrose University, B
Simpson College, B
University of Dubuque, B
The University of Iowa, BMD
University of Northern Iowa, B
Upper Iowa University, B
Wartburg College, B
William Penn University, B

Kansas

Allen Community College, A
Baker University, B
Barton County Community College, A
Benedictine College, B
Bethany College, B
Butler Community College, A
Central Christian College of Kansas, AB
Emporia State University, B
Fort Hays State University, B
Friends University, B
Kansas State University, BMD
Kansas Wesleyan University, B
McPherson College, B
MidAmerica Nazarene University, B
Newman University, B
Ottawa University, B
Pittsburg State University, B
Pratt Community College, A
The University of Kansas, BMD
Washburn University, B
Wichita State University, BM

Kentucky

Asbury University, B
Bellarmine University, B
Berea College, B
Campbellsville University, B
Eastern Kentucky University, B
Georgetown College, B
Kentucky Wesleyan College, B
Morehead State University, BM
Murray State University, B
Northern Kentucky University, B
Thomas More College, AB
Transylvania University, B
Union College, B
University of Kentucky, BMD
University of Louisville, BMD
University of Pikeville, B
Western Kentucky University, BM

Louisiana

Centenary College of Louisiana, B
Dillard University, B
Grambling State University, B
Louisiana State University and Agricultural & Me-
  chanical College, BMD
Louisiana State University in Shreveport, B
Louisiana Tech University, B

Loyola University New Orleans, B
McNeese State University, B
Nicholls State University, B
Southeastern Louisiana University, BM
Southern University and Agricultural and Mechanical
  College, B
Southern University at New Orleans, B
Southern University at Shreveport, A
Tulane University, BD
University of Louisiana at Lafayette, B
University of Louisiana at Monroe, B
University of New Orleans, BM
Xavier University of Louisiana, B

Maine

Bates College, B
Bowdoin College, B
Colby College, B
Saint Joseph's College of Maine, B
University of Maine, B
University of New England, B
University of Southern Maine, B

Maryland

Bowie State University, B
Frostburg State University, B
Goucher College, B
Harford Community College, A
Hood College, B
Johns Hopkins University, BMD
Loyola University Maryland, B
McDaniel College, B
Morgan State University, BM
Mount St. Mary's University, B
St. Mary's College of Maryland, B
Salisbury University, B
University of Maryland, Baltimore County, BM
University of Maryland, College Park, BMD
University of Maryland Eastern Shore, B
Washington College, B

Massachusetts

American International College, B
Amherst College, B
Anna Maria College, B
Assumption College, B
Boston College, BMD
Boston University, BMD
Brandeis University, BMD
Bridgewater State University, B
Bunker Hill Community College, A
Clark University, B
College of the Holy Cross, B
Curry College, B
Dean College, AB
Eastern Nazarene College, B
Elms College, B
Emmanuel College, B
Fitchburg State University, B
Framingham State University, B
Gordon College, B
Hampshire College, B
Harvard University, BD
Lasell College, B
Massachusetts College of Liberal Arts, B
Merrimack College, B
Mount Holyoke College, B
Northeastern University, BMD
Salem State University, B
Simmons College, B
Smith College, B
Springfield College, B
Stonehill College, B
Suffolk University, B
Tufts University, B
University of Massachusetts Amherst, BMD
University of Massachusetts Boston, BMD
University of Massachusetts Dartmouth, B
University of Massachusetts Lowell, BMO
Wellesley College, B
Western New England University, B
Westfield State University, B
Wheaton College, B
Williams College, B
Worcester State University, B

Michigan

Adrian College, B
Albion College, B
Alma College, B
Andrews University, B
Aquinas College, B
Calvin College, B
Central Michigan University, B
Eastern Michigan University, BM
Ferris State University, B
Grand Valley State University, B
Hillsdale College, B
Hope College, B
Lake Michigan College, A
Lake Superior State University, B
Lansing Community College, A
Madonna University, B
Michigan State University, BMD
Mid Michigan Community College, A
Northern Michigan University, B
Oakland University, B
Olivet College, B
Saginaw Valley State University, B
Spring Arbor University, B
University of Detroit Mercy, B
University of Michigan, BD
University of Michigan - Dearborn, B
University of Michigan - Flint, B
Wayne State University, BMD
Western Michigan University, BMD

Minnesota

Augsburg College, B
Bemidji State University, B
Bethany Lutheran College, B
Carleton College, B
College of Saint Benedict, B
Concordia College, B
Concordia University, St. Paul, B
Gustavus Adolphus College, B
Hamline University, B
Macalester College, B
Minnesota State University Mankato, BM
Minnesota State University Moorhead, B
St. Catherine University, B
St. Cloud State University, B
Saint John's University, B
Saint Mary's University of Minnesota, B
Southwest Minnesota State University, B
University of Minnesota, Duluth, BM
University of Minnesota, Morris, B
University of Minnesota, Twin Cities Campus, BMD
University of St. Thomas, B
Vermilion Community College, A
Winona State University, B

Mississippi

Alcorn State University, B
Itawamba Community College, A
Jackson State University, BM
Mississippi College, B
Mississippi State University, BMD
Mississippi Valley State University, B
Northeast Mississippi Community College, A
Rust College, B
Tougaloo College, B
University of Mississippi, BM
University of Southern Mississippi, B

Missouri

Avila University, B
Central Methodist University, B
College of the Ozarks, B
Columbia College, B
Drury University, B
Evangel University, B
Fontbonne University, B
Hannibal-LaGrange University, B
Harris-Stowe State University, B
Lincoln University, BM
Lindenwood University, B
Maryville University of Saint Louis, B
Missouri Southern State University, B
Missouri State University, B
Missouri Valley College, B

Missouri Western State University, B
Northwest Missouri State University, B
Park University, B
St. Charles Community College, A
Saint Louis University, B
Southwest Baptist University, B
Truman State University, B
University of Central Missouri, BM
University of Missouri, BMD
University of Missouri - Kansas City, BM
University of Missouri - St. Louis, B
Webster University, B
Westminster College, B

Montana

Carroll College, B
Montana State University, B
Montana State University Billings, AB
Rocky Mountain College, B
University of Great Falls, B
University of Montana, BM

Nebraska

Bellevue University, B
Concordia University, Nebraska, B
Creighton University, B
Doane University, B
Hastings College, B
Midland University, B
Nebraska Wesleyan University, B
University of Nebraska at Kearney, B
University of Nebraska - Lincoln, BMD
University of Nebraska at Omaha, M
Wayne State College, B
Western Nebraska Community College, A

Nevada

College of Southern Nevada, A
University of Nevada, Las Vegas, BMD
University of Nevada, Reno, BM

New Hampshire

Colby-Sawyer College, B
Dartmouth College, B
Franklin Pierce University, B
Keene State College, B
New England College, AB
Rivier University, B
Saint Anselm College, B
University of New Hampshire, BMD

New Jersey

Bergen Community College, A
Bloomfield College, B
Caldwell University, B
Centenary College, B
The College of New Jersey, B
College of Saint Elizabeth, B
Drew University, B
Fairleigh Dickinson University, College at Florham, B
Fairleigh Dickinson University, Metropolitan Campus, B
Kean University, BM
Monmouth University, B
Montclair State University, B
New Jersey City University, B
Princeton University, BD
Ramapo College of New Jersey, B
Rider University, B
Rowan College at Burlington County, A
Rowan University, B
Rutgers University - Camden, B
Rutgers University - New Brunswick, BMD
Rutgers University - Newark, B
Saint Peter's University, B
Salem Community College, A
Seton Hall University, B
Stockton University, B
Thomas Edison State University, B
William Paterson University of New Jersey, BM

New Mexico

Central New Mexico Community College, A
Eastern New Mexico University, B

New Mexico Highlands University, M
New Mexico State University, BM
University of New Mexico, BMD
Western New Mexico University, B

New York

Adelphi University, B
Alfred University, B
Bard College, B
Barnard College, B
Baruch College of the City University of New York, B
Binghamton University, State University of New York, BMD
Borough of Manhattan Community College of the City University of New York, A
Brooklyn College of the City University of New York, BMD
Buffalo State College, State University of New York, B
Canisius College, B
City College of the City University of New York, BM
Clarkson University, B
Colgate University, B
The College at Brockport, State University of New York, B
College of Mount Saint Vincent, B
The College of New Rochelle, B
Columbia University, BMD
Columbia University, School of General Studies, B
Concordia College - New York, B
Cornell University, BMD
D'Youville College, B
Eugene Lang College of Liberal Arts, B
Excelsior College, B
Finger Lakes Community College, A
Fordham University, B
Hamilton College, B
Hartwick College, B
Hobart and William Smith Colleges, B
Hofstra University, B
Houghton College, B
Hunter College of the City University of New York, BM
Iona College, B
Ithaca College, B
John Jay College of Criminal Justice of the City University of New York, B
Keuka College, B
Le Moyne College, B
Lehman College of the City University of New York, B
Long Island University - LIU Brooklyn, B
Long Island University - LIU Post, B
Manhattan College, B
Manhattanville College, B
Marymount Manhattan College, B
Mercy College, B
Molloy College, B
Mount Saint Mary College, B
Nazareth College of Rochester, B
New York Institute of Technology, B
New York University, BMD
Niagara University, B
Nyack College, B
Purchase College, State University of New York, B
Queens College of the City University of New York, BM
The Sage Colleges, B
St. Bonaventure University, B
St. Francis College, B
St. John Fisher College, B
St. John's University, BM
St. Joseph's College, Long Island Campus, B
St. Joseph's College, New York, B
St. Lawrence University, B
Sarah Lawrence College, B
Siena College, B
Skidmore College, B
State University of New York College at Cortland, B
State University of New York College at Geneseo, B
State University of New York College at Old Westbury, B
State University of New York College at Oneonta, B
State University of New York College at Potsdam, B
State University of New York at Fredonia, B

State University of New York at New Paltz, B
State University of New York at Oswego, B
State University of New York at Plattsburgh, B
State University of New York Polytechnic Institute, B
Stony Brook University, State University of New York, BMD
Syracuse University, BD
Touro College, B
Union College, B
United States Military Academy, B
University at Albany, State University of New York, BMDO
University at Buffalo, the State University of New York, BMD
Utica College, B
Vassar College, B
Wagner College, B
Wells College, B
Yeshiva University, B
York College of the City University of New York, B

North Carolina

Appalachian State University, BMO
Catawba College, B
Chowan University, B
Davidson College, B
Duke University, BMD
East Carolina University, BM
Elizabeth City State University, B
Elon University, B
Fayetteville State University, BM
Gardner-Webb University, B
Greensboro College, B
Guilford College, B
High Point University, B
Lenoir-Rhyne University, B
Livingstone College, B
Louisburg College, A
Mars Hill University, B
Meredith College, B
Methodist University, AB
North Carolina Agricultural and Technical State University, B
North Carolina Central University, M
North Carolina State University, BMD
North Carolina Wesleyan College, B
Pfeiffer University, B
Queens University of Charlotte, B
Saint Augustine's University, B
Salem College, B
Shaw University, B
University of North Carolina at Asheville, B
The University of North Carolina at Chapel Hill, BMD
The University of North Carolina at Charlotte, BM
The University of North Carolina at Greensboro, BM
The University of North Carolina at Pembroke, B
The University of North Carolina Wilmington, BM
Wake Forest University, B
Warren Wilson College, B
Western Carolina University, B
Wingate University, B
Winston-Salem State University, B

North Dakota

Minot State University, B
North Dakota State University, BM
University of North Dakota, BM

Ohio

Ashland University, B
Baldwin Wallace University, B
Bowling Green State University, BMD
Capital University, B
Case Western Reserve University, BMD
Central State University, B
Cleveland State University, BM
The College of Wooster, B
Denison University, B
Franciscan University of Steubenville, B
Hiram College, B
John Carroll University, B
Kent State University, BMD
Kent State University at Ashtabula, B
Kent State University at Stark, B
Kenyon College, B

Lorain County Community College, A
Lourdes University, AB
Miami University, B
Miami University Hamilton, B
Miami University Middletown, A
Mount St. Joseph University, B
Muskingum University, B
Oberlin College, B
Ohio Dominican University, B
Ohio Northern University, B
The Ohio State University, BD
The Ohio State University - Mansfield Campus, B
The Ohio State University at Marion, B
The Ohio State University - Newark Campus, B
Ohio University, BM
Ohio Wesleyan University, B
Otterbein University, B
Shawnee State University, B
The University of Akron, BMD
University of Cincinnati, BMD
University of Dayton, B
The University of Findlay, B
University of Mount Union, B
University of Rio Grande, AB
The University of Toledo, BM
Urbana University, B
Ursuline College, B
Walsh University, B
Wilberforce University, B
Wittenberg University, B
Wright State University, AB
Wright State University - Lake Campus, A
Xavier University, AB
Youngstown State University, B

Oklahoma

Bacone College, A
Cameron University, B
Connors State College, A
East Central University, B
Langston University, B
Northeastern State University, B
Northwestern Oklahoma State University, B
Oklahoma Baptist University, B
Oklahoma City Community College, A
Oklahoma City University, BM
Oklahoma State University, BMD
Rose State College, A
Southeastern Oklahoma State University, B
Southern Nazarene University, B
University of Central Oklahoma, BM
University of Oklahoma, BMD
University of Science and Arts of Oklahoma, B
The University of Tulsa, B

Oregon

George Fox University, B
Linfield College, B
Oregon State University, B
Pacific University, B
Portland State University, BMD
Reed College, B
Southern Oregon University, B
Umpqua Community College, A
University of Oregon, BMD
University of Portland, B
Western Oregon University, B
Willamette University, B

Pennsylvania

Albright College, B
Arcadia University, B
Bloomsburg University of Pennsylvania, B
Bryn Mawr College, B
Bucknell University, B
Cabrini University, B
Carlow University, B
Chestnut Hill College, B
Cheyney University of Pennsylvania, B
Clarion University of Pennsylvania, B
Community College of Allegheny County, A
Community College of Beaver County, A
Delaware County Community College, A
Dickinson College, B
Drexel University, B
Duquesne University, B

East Stroudsburg University of Pennsylvania, B
Eastern University, B
Edinboro University of Pennsylvania, B
Elizabethtown College, B
Franklin & Marshall College, B
Geneva College, B
Gettysburg College, B
Grove City College, B
Gwynedd Mercy University, B
Haverford College, B
Holy Family University, B
Immaculata University, B
Indiana University of Pennsylvania, BM
Juniata College, B
King's College, B
Kutztown University of Pennsylvania, B
La Roche College, B
La Salle University, B
Lafayette College, B
Lebanon Valley College, B
Lehigh University, BM
Lincoln University, B
Lock Haven University of Pennsylvania, B
Lycoming College, B
Marywood University, B
Mercyhurst University, B
Messiah College, B
Millersville University of Pennsylvania, B
Moravian College, B
Muhlenberg College, B
Penn State Abington, B
Penn State Altoona, B
Penn State Beaver, B
Penn State Berks, B
Penn State Brandywine, B
Penn State DuBois, B
Penn State Erie, The Behrend College, B
Penn State Fayette, The Eberly Campus, B
Penn State Greater Allegheny, B
Penn State Harrisburg, B
Penn State Hazleton, B
Penn State Lehigh Valley, B
Penn State Mont Alto, B
Penn State New Kensington, B
Penn State Schuylkill, B
Penn State Shenango, B
Penn State University Park, BMD
Penn State Wilkes-Barre, B
Penn State Worthington Scranton, B
Penn State York, B
Rosemont College, B
Saint Francis University, B
Saint Joseph's University, B
Saint Vincent College, B
Seton Hill University, B
Shippensburg University of Pennsylvania, BM
Susquehanna University, B
Temple University, BMD
Thiel College, B
University of Pennsylvania, BMD
University of Pittsburgh, BMD
University of Pittsburgh at Bradford, B
University of Pittsburgh at Johnstown, B
The University of Scranton, AB
Ursinus College, B
Villanova University, B
Washington & Jefferson College, B
Waynesburg University, B
West Chester University of Pennsylvania, B
Westminster College, B
Widener University, B
Wilkes University, B
Wilson College, B
York College of Pennsylvania, B

Rhode Island

Brown University, BMD
Bryant University, B
Providence College, B
Rhode Island College, B
Roger Williams University, B
Salve Regina University, B
University of Rhode Island, B

South Carolina

Benedict College, B
Charleston Southern University, B
Claflin University, B
Clemson University, BM
Coastal Carolina University, B
Coker College, B
College of Charleston, B
Converse College, B
Francis Marion University, B
Furman University, B
Lander University, B
Morris College, B
Newberry College, B
Presbyterian College, B
South Carolina State University, B
University of South Carolina, BMD
University of South Carolina Aiken, B
University of South Carolina Beaufort, B
University of South Carolina Upstate, B
Voorhees College, B
Winthrop University, B
Wofford College, B

South Dakota

Augustana University, B
Black Hills State University, B
Northern State University, B
South Dakota State University, BMD
University of Sioux Falls, B
The University of South Dakota, B

Tennessee

Austin Peay State University, B
Belmont University, B
Bethel University, B
Carson-Newman University, B
Cumberland University, B
East Tennessee State University, BM
Fisk University, B
Hiwassee College, A
Lane College, B
Lee University, B
LeMoyne-Owen College, B
Maryville College, B
Middle Tennessee State University, BM
Milligan College, B
Nashville State Community College, A
Tennessee State University, B
Tennessee Technological University, B
Tennessee Wesleyan College, B
Trevecca Nazarene University, B
Union University, B
University of Memphis, BM
The University of Tennessee, BMD
The University of Tennessee at Martin, B
Vanderbilt University, BMD

Texas

Abilene Christian University, B
Alvin Community College, A
Angelo State University, B
Austin College, B
Austin Community College District, A
Baylor University, BMD
Clarendon College, A
Dallas Baptist University, B
Del Mar College, A
East Texas Baptist University, B
Frank Phillips College, A
Grayson College, A
Hardin-Simmons University, B
Hill College, A
Howard College, A
Howard Payne University, B
Huston-Tillotson University, B
Jarvis Christian College, B
Lamar University, B
Lee College, A
McMurry University, B
Midwestern State University, B
Navarro College, A
Northeast Texas Community College, A
Odessa College, A
Our Lady of the Lake University of San Antonio, B

Palo Alto College, A
Panola College, A
Paris Junior College, A
Prairie View A&M University, BM
Rice University, BD
St. Edward's University, B
St. Mary's University, B
St. Philip's College, A
Sam Houston State University, BM
San Jacinto College District, A
Southern Methodist University, B
Southwestern University, B
Stephen F. Austin State University, B
Tarleton State University, B
Texas A&M International University, B
Texas A&M University, BMD
Texas A&M University - Central Texas, B
Texas A&M University - Commerce, B
Texas A&M University - Corpus Christi, B
Texas A&M University - Kingsville, BM
Texas A&M University - San Antonio, B
Texas Christian University, B
Texas College, B
Texas Lutheran University, B
Texas Southern University, BM
Texas State University, BM
Texas Tech University, BM
Texas Wesleyan University, B
Texas Woman's University, BMD
Trinity University, B
Trinity Valley Community College, A
Tyler Junior College, A
University of Houston, BM
University of Houston - Clear Lake, BM
University of Houston - Downtown, B
University of the Incarnate Word, B
University of Mary Hardin-Baylor, B
University of North Texas, BM
The University of Texas at Arlington, BM
The University of Texas at Austin, BMD
The University of Texas at Dallas, BMD
The University of Texas at El Paso, BMO
The University of Texas of the Permian Basin, B
The University of Texas Rio Grande Valley, BM
The University of Texas at San Antonio, BM
The University of Texas at Tyler, M
Wayland Baptist University, B
West Texas A&M University, B
Wiley College, B

Utah

Brigham Young University, M
Dixie State University, B
Salt Lake Community College, A
Snow College, A
Southern Utah University, B
University of Utah, BMD
Utah State University, BMD
Weber State University, B
Westminster College, B

Vermont

Bennington College, B
Castleton University, B
Goddard College, B
Johnson State College, B
Marlboro College, B
Middlebury College, B
Saint Michael's College, B
University of Vermont, B

Virginia

Averett University, B
Bridgewater College, B
Christopher Newport University, B
The College of William and Mary, B
Emory & Henry College, B
George Mason University, BMD
Hampton University, B
Hollins University, B
James Madison University, B
Longwood University, B
Lynchburg College, B
Mary Baldwin College, B
Marymount University, B
Norfolk State University, B

Old Dominion University, BM
Radford University, B
Randolph College, B
Randolph-Macon College, B
Roanoke College, B
Shenandoah University, B
Sweet Briar College, B
University of Mary Washington, B
University of Richmond, B
University of Virginia, BMD
The University of Virginia's College at Wise, B
Virginia Commonwealth University, BMO
Virginia Polytechnic Institute and State University,
   BMD
Virginia State University, B
Virginia University of Lynchburg, B
Virginia Wesleyan College, B
Washington and Lee University, B

Washington

Central Washington University, B
Eastern Washington University, B
Everett Community College, A
The Evergreen State College, B
Gonzaga University, B
Pacific Lutheran University, B
Seattle Pacific University, B
Seattle University, B
Skagit Valley College, A
University of Puget Sound, B
University of Washington, BMD
Walla Walla University, B
Washington State University, BMD
Washington State University - Vancouver, B
Wenatchee Valley College, A
Western Washington University, B
Whitman College, B
Whitworth University, B

West Virginia

American Public University System, B
Concord University, B
Davis & Elkins College, B
Fairmont State University, B
Marshall University, BM
Potomac State College of West Virginia University,
   A
Shepherd University, B
West Liberty University, B
West Virginia State University, B
West Virginia University, BM
West Virginia Wesleyan College, B

Wisconsin

Alverno College, B
Beloit College, B
Cardinal Stritch University, B
Carroll University, B
Carthage College, B
Edgewood College, B
Lakeland College, B
Marquette University, B
Northland College, B
Ripon College, B
St. Norbert College, B
University of Wisconsin - Eau Claire, B
University of Wisconsin - La Crosse, B
University of Wisconsin - Madison, BMD
University of Wisconsin - Milwaukee, BM
University of Wisconsin - Oshkosh, B
University of Wisconsin - Parkside, B
University of Wisconsin - River Falls, B
University of Wisconsin - Stevens Point, B
University of Wisconsin - Superior, B
University of Wisconsin - Whitewater, B
Viterbo University, B

Wyoming

Casper College, A
Laramie County Community College, A
Northwest College, A
University of Wyoming, BM
Western Wyoming Community College, A

U.S. Territories: Guam

University of Guam, B

U.S. Territories: Puerto Rico

Inter American University of Puerto Rico, Metropoli-
   tan Campus, B
Inter American University of Puerto Rico, Ponce
   Campus, B
Inter American University of Puerto Rico, San
   Germán Campus, B
Pontifical Catholic University of Puerto Rico, B
Universidad del Turabo, B
University of Puerto Rico in Cayey, B
University of Puerto Rico, Mayagüez Campus, B
University of Puerto Rico, Río Piedras Campus, BM
University of Puerto Rico in Utuado, B

Canada

Alberta

Athabasca University, B
Concordia University of Edmonton, B
The King's University, B
Mount Royal University, B
University of Alberta, BMD
University of Calgary, BMD
University of Lethbridge, BM

British Columbia

Simon Fraser University, BMD
Thompson Rivers University, B
Trinity Western University, B
The University of British Columbia, BMD
The University of British Columbia - Okanagan
   Campus, B
University of the Fraser Valley, B
University of Victoria, BMD
Vancouver Island University, B

Manitoba

Brandon University, B
University of Manitoba, BMD
The University of Winnipeg, B

Maritime Provinces: New Brunswick

Crandall University, B
Mount Allison University, B
St. Thomas University, B
Université de Moncton, B
University of New Brunswick Fredericton, BMD
University of New Brunswick Saint John, B

Maritime Provinces: Nova Scotia

Acadia University, BM
Cape Breton University, B
Dalhousie University, BMD
Mount Saint Vincent University, B
St. Francis Xavier University, B
Saint Mary's University, B
University of King's College, B

Maritime Provinces: Prince Edward Island

University of Prince Edward Island, B

Newfoundland and Labrador

Memorial University of Newfoundland, BMD

Ontario

Brock University, BM
Carleton University, BMD
Lakehead University, BM
Laurentian University, BM
McMaster University, BMD
Nipissing University, B
Queen's University at Kingston, BMD
Redeemer University College, B
Ryerson University, B
Trent University, B
University of Guelph, BMD
University of Ottawa, BM
University of Toronto, BMD
University of Waterloo, BMD

The University of Western Ontario, BMD
University of Windsor, BMD
Wilfrid Laurier University, BM
York University, BMD

Quebec

Bishop's University, B
Concordia University, BM
McGill University, BMDO
Université Laval, BMD
Université de Montréal, BMD
Université du Québec à Montréal, BMD
Université du Québec en Outaouais, B
Université du Québec à Rimouski, B

Saskatchewan

University of Regina, BM
University of Saskatchewan, BMD

SOFTWARE ENGINEERING

United States

Alabama

Auburn University, MD
Jacksonville State University, M
The University of Alabama in Huntsville, MO

Arizona

Arizona State University at the Tempe campus, M

California

California State University, Fullerton, M
California State University, Northridge, M
California State University, Sacramento, M
National University, M
San Jose State University, M
Santa Clara University, O
University of Southern California, M

Colorado

Colorado Technical University Colorado Springs, M
Colorado Technical University Denver South, M
Regis University, MO
University of Colorado Colorado Springs, M
University of Denver, M

Connecticut

Fairfield University, M
University of Connecticut, MD
University of New Haven, M

Florida

Embry-Riddle Aeronautical University - Daytona, M
Florida Agricultural and Mechanical University, M
Florida Institute of Technology, M
Nova Southeastern University, M
University of North Florida, M
University of West Florida, M

Georgia

Kennesaw State University, MO
Mercer University, M

Illinois

DePaul University, M
Illinois Institute of Technology, M
Loyola University Chicago, M
Northwestern University, M

Indiana

Rose-Hulman Institute of Technology, M

Kentucky

Northern Kentucky University, O

Maine

University of Southern Maine, O

Maryland

Loyola University Maryland, M
Towson University, O

Massachusetts

Brandeis University, M

Michigan

Grand Valley State University, M
Oakland University, M
University of Detroit Mercy, M
University of Michigan - Dearborn, M

Minnesota

University of Minnesota, Twin Cities Campus, M
University of St. Thomas, MO

Missouri

University of Missouri - Kansas City, M

Nebraska

University of Nebraska at Omaha, O

New Hampshire

University of New Hampshire, O

New Jersey

Monmouth University, MO
New Jersey Institute of Technology, M
Stevens Institute of Technology, MO

New York

Marist College, M
New York University, O
Pace University, MO
Rochester Institute of Technology, M
Stony Brook University, State University of New York, O

North Carolina

East Carolina University, M

North Dakota

North Dakota State University, MDO

Ohio

Bowling Green State University, M
Cleveland State University, M

Oregon

Portland State University, M

Pennsylvania

Carnegie Mellon University, MD
Drexel University, M
Gannon University, M
The University of Scranton, M
Villanova University, M

South Carolina

University of South Carolina, M
Winthrop University, MO

Tennessee

Tennessee Technological University, M

Texas

St. Mary's University, M
Southern Methodist University, MD
Texas State University, M
Texas Tech University, M
University of Houston - Clear Lake, M
The University of Texas at Arlington, MD
The University of Texas at Dallas, MD
The University of Texas at El Paso, M

Utah

University of Utah, MO

Virginia

George Mason University, M
Stratford University (Falls Church), M
University of Management and Technology, M
Virginia International University, M
Virginia Polytechnic Institute and State University, O

Washington

Seattle University, M
University of Washington, Bothell, M
University of Washington, Tacoma, M

West Virginia

American Public University System, M
West Virginia University, M

Wisconsin

Carroll University, M
University of Wisconsin - La Crosse, M

Canada

Alberta

University of Calgary, M

British Columbia

The University of British Columbia, M

Ontario

McMaster University, MD
Royal Military College of Canada, MD
University of Waterloo, M

Quebec

Concordia University, MDO
Université Laval, O

Saskatchewan

University of Regina, M

SOIL CHEMISTRY AND PHYSICS

United States

Tennessee

The University of Tennessee, B

SOIL SCIENCE AND AGRONOMY

United States

California

California Polytechnic State University, San Luis Obispo, B
University of California, Davis, B

Colorado

Colorado State University, B

Florida

South Florida State College, A
University of Florida, B

Georgia

University of Georgia, B

Indiana

Purdue University, B

Iowa

Iowa Lakes Community College, A

Michigan

Michigan State University, B

Minnesota

Vermilion Community College, A

Nebraska

University of Nebraska - Lincoln, B

New Mexico

New Mexico State University, B

North Dakota

North Dakota State University, B

Ohio

The Ohio State University Agricultural Technical Institute, A

Oklahoma

Oklahoma State University, B

Oregon

Treasure Valley Community College, A

Pennsylvania

Penn State Abington, B
Penn State Altoona, B
Penn State Beaver, B
Penn State Berks, B
Penn State Brandywine, B
Penn State DuBois, B
Penn State Erie, The Behrend College, B
Penn State Fayette, The Eberly Campus, B
Penn State Greater Allegheny, B
Penn State Hazleton, B
Penn State Lehigh Valley, B
Penn State Mont Alto, B
Penn State New Kensington, B
Penn State Schuylkill, B
Penn State Shenango, B
Penn State Wilkes-Barre, B
Penn State Worthington Scranton, B
Penn State York, B

Tennessee

The University of Tennessee at Martin, B

Utah

Snow College, A
Utah State University, B

Washington

Washington State University, B

Wisconsin

University of Wisconsin - Madison, B
University of Wisconsin - Stevens Point, B

U.S. Territories: Puerto Rico

University of Puerto Rico, Mayagüez Campus, B

Canada

British Columbia

The University of British Columbia, B

Saskatchewan

University of Saskatchewan, B

SOIL SCIENCES

United States

Hawaii

University of Hawaii at Manoa, B

North Carolina

North Carolina State University, B

South Carolina

Clemson University, B

Utah

Brigham Young University, B

Canada

Alberta

University of Alberta, B

SOLAR ENERGY TECHNOLOGY/TECHNICIAN

United States

Arizona

Arizona Western College, A
Coconino Community College, A

Missouri

Crowder College, A

New Mexico

San Juan College, A

Oregon

Treasure Valley Community College, A

Pennsylvania

Community College of Allegheny County, A
Pennsylvania College of Technology, A

Texas

Texas State Technical College, A

Wisconsin

Lac Courte Oreilles Ojibwa Community College, A

SOLID STATE AND LOW-TEMPERATURE PHYSICS

United States

New Jersey

Rowan University, B

SOMATIC BODYWORK

United States

Vermont

Goddard College, B

SOMATIC BODYWORK AND RELATED THERAPEUTIC SERVICES

United States

Vermont

Goddard College, B

SOUTH ASIAN LANGUAGES, LITERATURES, AND LINGUISTICS

United States

Connecticut

Yale University, B

Illinois

Northwestern University, B
University of Chicago, B

Washington

University of Washington, B

Canada

British Columbia

The University of British Columbia, B

SOUTH ASIAN STUDIES

United States

Illinois

University of Chicago, B

Indiana

Indiana University Bloomington, B

Massachusetts

Hampshire College, B
Mount Holyoke College, B

Missouri

University of Missouri, B

New York

Binghamton University, State University of New York, B
Columbia University, School of General Studies, B

Pennsylvania

Gettysburg College, B
University of Pennsylvania, B

Rhode Island

Brown University, B

Vermont

Middlebury College, B

Washington

University of Washington, B

Canada

British Columbia

The University of British Columbia, B

Manitoba

University of Manitoba, B

Ontario

University of Toronto, B

Quebec

Concordia University, B

SOUTH AND SOUTHEAST ASIAN STUDIES

United States

California

University of California, Berkeley, M
University of California, Riverside, M

Hawaii

University of Hawaii at Manoa, O

Illinois

University of Chicago, MD
University of Illinois at Urbana - Champaign, M

Iowa

The University of Iowa, M

Maryland

Johns Hopkins University, M

Massachusetts

Harvard University, M

Michigan

University of Michigan, MO

New York

Columbia University, MO
Cornell University, MD

Ohio

Ohio University, M

Pennsylvania

University of Pennsylvania, MD

Virginia

University of Virginia, M

Washington

University of Washington, M

Wisconsin

University of Wisconsin - Madison, MD

SOUTHEAST ASIAN LAN-GUAGES, LITERATURES, AND LINGUISTICS

United States

Massachusetts

Harvard University, B

SOUTHEAST ASIAN STUDIES

United States

California

University of California, Berkeley, B
University of California, Los Angeles, B

Massachusetts

Tufts University, B

Washington

University of Washington, B

SPANISH AND IBERIAN STUD-IES

United States

California

Loma Linda University, A

Connecticut

Wesleyan University, B

Indiana

Wabash College, B

Iowa

Coe College, B

Maine

Bowdoin College, B

New York

Bard College, B
Fordham University, B
New York University, B

Texas

Austin College, B

Virginia

Emory & Henry College, B

Canada

Manitoba

The University of Winnipeg, B

Ontario

The University of Western Ontario, B
York University, B

Quebec

McGill University, B

SPANISH LANGUAGE AND LIT-ERATURE

United States

Alabama

Auburn University, BM
Auburn University at Montgomery, B
Birmingham-Southern College, B
Jacksonville State University, B
Judson College, B
Oakwood University, B
Samford University, B
Spring Hill College, B
Troy University, B
The University of Alabama, BMD
University of North Alabama, B

Alaska

University of Alaska Anchorage, B

Arizona

Arizona State University at the Tempe campus, BMD
Arizona State University at the West campus, B
Arizona Western College, A
Northern Arizona University, BM
The University of Arizona, BMD

Arkansas

Harding University, B
Henderson State University, B
Hendrix College, B
John Brown University, B
Lyon College, B
Ouachita Baptist University, B
Southern Arkansas University - Magnolia, B
University of Arkansas, BM
University of Arkansas - Fort Smith, B
University of Arkansas at Little Rock, B
University of Central Arkansas, B
University of the Ozarks, B

California

Allan Hancock College, A
Azusa Pacific University, B
Bakersfield College, A
Berkeley City College, A
Biola University, B
Cabrillo College, A
California Baptist University, B
California Lutheran University, B
California State Polytechnic University, Pomona, B
California State University, Bakersfield, BM
California State University Channel Islands, B
California State University, Dominguez Hills, B
California State University, East Bay, B
California State University, Fresno, BM

California State University, Fullerton, BM
California State University, Long Beach, BM
California State University, Los Angeles, BM
California State University, Monterey Bay, B
California State University, Northridge, BM
California State University, Sacramento, B
California State University, San Bernardino, BM
California State University, San Marcos, BM
California State University, Stanislaus, B
Cañada College, A
Cerritos College, A
Chabot College, A
Chaffey College, A
Chapman University, B
Citrus College, A
City College of San Francisco, A
Claremont McKenna College, B
College of Alameda, A
College of the Canyons, A
College of the Desert, A
College of Marin, A
College of San Mateo, A
College of the Sequoias, A
College of the Siskiyous, A
Contra Costa College, A
Copper Mountain College, A
Cosumnes River College, A
Crafton Hills College, A
De Anza College, A
East Los Angeles College, A
El Camino College, A
Foothill College, A
Fresno City College, A
Fresno Pacific University, AB
Gavilan College, A
Grossmont College, A
Hartnell College, A
Holy Names University, B
Humboldt State University, B
Imperial Valley College, A
La Sierra University, B
Lake Tahoe Community College, A
Long Beach City College, A
Los Angeles City College, A
Los Angeles Mission College, A
Los Angeles Southwest College, A
Los Angeles Valley College, A
Loyola Marymount University, B
Mendocino College, A
Merritt College, A
Mills College, B
Modesto Junior College, A
Monterey Peninsula College, A
Mount Saint Mary's University, B
National University, B
Occidental College, B
Ohlone College, A
Orange Coast College, A
Oxnard College, A
Pacific Union College, B
Pasadena City College, A
Pepperdine University, B
Pitzer College, B
Point Loma Nazarene University, B
Pomona College, B
Saint Mary's College of California, B
San Bernardino Valley College, A
San Diego Mesa College, A
San Diego Miramar College, A
San Diego State University, BM
San Diego State University - Imperial Valley Campus, B
San Francisco State University, BM
San Jose State University, BM
Santa Barbara City College, A
Santa Clara University, B
Santa Rosa Junior College, A
Scripps College, B
Simpson University, B
Solano Community College, A
Sonoma State University, B
Southwestern College, A
Stanford University, BMD
United States University, B
University of California, Berkeley, BD
University of California, Davis, BMD

University of California, Irvine, BMD
University of California, Los Angeles, BM
University of California, Riverside, BMD
University of California, San Diego, B
University of California, Santa Barbara, BMD
University of California, Santa Cruz, B
University of La Verne, B
University of the Pacific, B
University of Redlands, B
University of San Diego, B
University of San Francisco, B
University of Southern California, BD
West Los Angeles College, A
West Valley College, A
Westmont College, B
Whittier College, B

Colorado

Adams State University, B
The Colorado College, B
Colorado Mesa University, B
Colorado State University, B
Fort Lewis College, B
Regis University, B
University of Colorado Boulder, BMD
University of Colorado Colorado Springs, B
University of Colorado Denver, BM
University of Denver, B
University of Northern Colorado, BM
Western State Colorado University, B

Connecticut

Albertus Magnus College, B
Central Connecticut State University, BMO
Connecticut College, B
Eastern Connecticut State University, B
Fairfield University, B
Quinnipiac University, B
Sacred Heart University, B
Southern Connecticut State University, B
Trinity College, B
University of Connecticut, BMD
University of Saint Joseph, B
Western Connecticut State University, B
Yale University, BD

Delaware

Delaware State University, B
University of Delaware, BM

District of Columbia

American University, B
The Catholic University of America, BMD
Gallaudet University, B
The George Washington University, B
Georgetown University, BMD
Howard University, BM
University of the District of Columbia, B

Florida

Barry University, B
Broward College, A
Eckerd College, B
Flagler College, B
Florida Atlantic University, BM
Florida Gulf Coast University, B
Florida International University, BMD
Florida Southern College, B
Florida State University, MD
Indian River State College, A
Jacksonville University, B
Miami Dade College, A
New College of Florida, B
Rollins College, B
South Florida State College, A
State College of Florida Manatee-Sarasota, A
Stetson University, B
University of Central Florida, BM
University of Florida, BMD
University of Miami, BMD
University of North Florida, B
University of South Florida, BM
The University of Tampa, B
University of West Florida, B

Georgia

Agnes Scott College, B
Albany State University, B
Armstrong State University, B
Berry College, B
Clark Atlanta University, B
Columbus State University, B
Emory University, BDO
Georgia College & State University, B
Georgia Southern University, M
Georgia State University, BMO
LaGrange College, B
Mercer University, B
Morehouse College, B
Oglethorpe University, B
Piedmont College, B
Shorter University, B
Spelman College, B
University of Georgia, BM
University of North Georgia, B
Valdosta State University, B
Wesleyan College, B
Young Harris College, B

Hawaii

University of Hawaii at Manoa, BM

Idaho

Boise State University, B
The College of Idaho, B
Idaho State University, B
North Idaho College, A
Northwest Nazarene University, B
University of Idaho, B

Illinois

Augustana College, B
Aurora University, B
Benedictine University, B
Blackburn College, B
Bradley University, B
Chicago State University, B
Concordia University Chicago, B
DePaul University, BM
Dominican University, B
Elmhurst College, B
Greenville College, B
Illinois College, B
Illinois State University, BM
Illinois Wesleyan University, B
Knox College, B
Lake Forest College, BM
Lewis University, B
Loyola University Chicago, BM
McKendree University, B
Millikin University, B
Monmouth College, B
North Central College, B
North Park University, B
Northeastern Illinois University, B
Northern Illinois University, BM
Northwestern University, BD
Olivet Nazarene University, B
Principia College, B
Rockford University, B
Roosevelt University, M
Saint Xavier University, BM
Trinity Christian College, B
Triton College, A
University of Chicago, D
University of Illinois at Chicago, BMD
University of Illinois at Urbana - Champaign, BMD
Western Illinois University, B
Wheaton College, B

Indiana

Anderson University, B
Ball State University, B
Butler University, B
DePauw University, B
Earlham College, B
Franklin College, B
Goshen College, B
Grace College, B
Hanover College, B

Holy Cross College, A
Indiana State University, M
Indiana University Bloomington, BMD
Indiana University Northwest, B
Indiana University - Purdue University Fort Wayne, B
Indiana University - Purdue University Indianapolis, B
Indiana University South Bend, B
Indiana University Southeast, B
Indiana Wesleyan University, B
Manchester University, B
Marian University, B
Purdue University, MD
Saint Mary's College, B
Taylor University, B
University of Evansville, B
University of Indianapolis, B
University of Notre Dame, BM
University of Southern Indiana, B
Valparaiso University, B
Wabash College, B

Iowa

Briar Cliff University, B
Buena Vista University, B
Central College, B
Clarke University, B
Coe College, B
Cornell College, B
Dordt College, B
Graceland University, B
Grand View University, B
Grinnell College, B
Iowa Lakes Community College, A
Iowa State University of Science and Technology, B
Loras College, B
Luther College, B
Morningside College, B
Northwestern College, B
St. Ambrose University, B
Simpson College, B
The University of Iowa, BMD
University of Northern Iowa, BM
Wartburg College, B

Kansas

Baker University, B
Benedictine College, B
Fort Hays State University, B
Friends University, B
McPherson College, B
MidAmerica Nazarene University, B
Pittsburg State University, B
The University of Kansas, BMD
Washburn University, B
Wichita State University, M

Kentucky

Asbury University, BM
Bellarmine University, B
Berea College, B
Brescia University, B
Centre College, B
Eastern Kentucky University, B
Georgetown College, B
Kentucky State University, B
Kentucky Wesleyan College, B
Morehead State University, B
Murray State University, B
Northern Kentucky University, B
Thomas More College, AB
Transylvania University, B
University of the Cumberlands, B
University of Kentucky, BM
University of Louisville, BM
University of Pikeville, B
Western Kentucky University, BM

Louisiana

Louisiana College, B
Louisiana State University and Agricultural & Mechanical College, B
Louisiana Tech University, B
Loyola University New Orleans, B
Southeastern Louisiana University, B

Southern University and Agricultural and Mechanical
  College, B
Tulane University, BMD
Xavier University of Louisiana, B

Maine

Bates College, B
Bowdoin College, B
Colby College, B
University of Maine, B

Maryland

Goucher College, B
Hood College, B
Johns Hopkins University, BD
Loyola University Maryland, B
McDaniel College, B
Mount St. Mary's University, B
Notre Dame of Maryland University, B
Salisbury University, B
University of Maryland, College Park, BMD
Washington College, B

Massachusetts

Amherst College, B
Anna Maria College, B
Assumption College, B
Bard College at Simon's Rock, B
Bentley University, B
Boston College, BM
Boston University, B
Brandeis University, B
Bridgewater State University, B
Clark University, B
College of the Holy Cross, B
Elms College, B
Emmanuel College, B
Framingham State University, BM
Gordon College, B
Harvard University, MD
Merrimack College, B
Mount Holyoke College, B
Northeastern University, B
Regis College, B
Salem State University, BM
Simmons College, B
Smith College, B
Stonehill College, B
Suffolk University, B
Tufts University, B
University of Massachusetts Amherst, BMD
University of Massachusetts Boston, B
University of Massachusetts Dartmouth, B
Wellesley College, B
Westfield State University, B
Williams College, B
Worcester State University, BM

Michigan

Adrian College, B
Albion College, B
Alma College, B
Andrews University, B
Aquinas College, B
Calvin College, B
Central Michigan University, BM
Cornerstone University, B
Eastern Michigan University, BM
Grand Valley State University, B
Hillsdale College, B
Hope College, B
Kalamazoo College, B
Lake Superior State University, B
Lansing Community College, A
Madonna University, B
Michigan State University, BMD
Northern Michigan University, B
Oakland University, B
Saginaw Valley State University, B
Siena Heights University, B
Spring Arbor University, B
University of Michigan, BD
University of Michigan - Dearborn, B
University of Michigan - Flint, B
Wayne State University, MD
Western Michigan University, BMD

Minnesota

Augsburg College, B
Bemidji State University, B
Bethel University, B
Carleton College, B
College of Saint Benedict, B
The College of St. Scholastica, B
Concordia College, B
Gustavus Adolphus College, B
Hamline University, B
Macalester College, B
Minnesota State University Mankato, BM
Minnesota State University Moorhead, B
St. Catherine University, B
St. Cloud State University, B
Saint John's University, B
Saint Mary's University of Minnesota, B
St. Olaf College, B
Southwest Minnesota State University, B
University of Minnesota, Duluth, B
University of Minnesota, Morris, B
University of Minnesota, Twin Cities Campus, BMD
University of Northwestern - St. Paul, B
University of St. Thomas, B
Winona State University, B

Mississippi

Blue Mountain College, B
Millsaps College, B
Mississippi College, B
Mississippi State University, M
Mississippi University for Women, B
University of Mississippi, B

Missouri

College of the Ozarks, B
Drury University, B
Evangel University, B
Lincoln University, B
Lindenwood University, B
Missouri Southern State University, B
Missouri State University, B
Northwest Missouri State University, B
Park University, B
Rockhurst University, B
St. Charles Community College, A
Saint Louis University, BM
Southwest Baptist University, B
Truman State University, B
University of Central Missouri, B
University of Missouri, BMD
University of Missouri - Kansas City, M
Washington University in St. Louis, BMD
Webster University, B
Westminster College, B
William Jewell College, B

Montana

Carroll College, B
Montana State University Billings, B
University of Montana, BM

Nebraska

Chadron State College, B
Concordia University, Nebraska, B
Creighton University, B
Doane University, B
Hastings College, B
Nebraska Wesleyan University, B
Union College, B
University of Nebraska at Kearney, B
University of Nebraska - Lincoln, BMD
Wayne State College, B
Western Nebraska Community College, A

Nevada

University of Nevada, Las Vegas, B
University of Nevada, Reno, BM

New Hampshire

Dartmouth College, B
Keene State College, B
Plymouth State University, B
Rivier University, B
Saint Anselm College, B

University of New Hampshire, BM

New Jersey

Caldwell University, B
The College of New Jersey, B
College of Saint Elizabeth, B
Drew University, BM
Fairleigh Dickinson University, College at Florham,
  B
Fairleigh Dickinson University, Metropolitan Cam-
  pus, B
Georgian Court University, B
Kean University, BM
Montclair State University, BM
New Jersey City University, B
Princeton University, BD
Ramapo College of New Jersey, B
Rider University, BO
Rowan University, B
Rutgers University - Camden, B
Rutgers University - New Brunswick, BMD
Rutgers University - Newark, B
Saint Peter's University, B
Seton Hall University, B
William Paterson University of New Jersey, B

New Mexico

Eastern New Mexico University, B
New Mexico Highlands University, B
New Mexico Military Institute, A
New Mexico State University, M
Santa Fe Community College, A
University of New Mexico, BMD
Western New Mexico University, B

New York

Adelphi University, B
Alfred University, B
Bard College, B
Barnard College, B
Baruch College of the City University of New York,
  B
Binghamton University, State University of New
  York, BM
Brooklyn College of the City University of New York,
  BM
Buffalo State College, State University of New York,
  B
Canisius College, B
City College of the City University of New York, BM
Colgate University, B
The College at Brockport, State University of New
  York, B
College of Mount Saint Vincent, B
The College of New Rochelle, B
College of Staten Island of the City University of
  New York, B
Columbia University, BD
Cornell University, BD
Daemen College, B
Dominican College, B
Fiorello H. LaGuardia Community College of the
  City University of New York, A
Fordham University, B
Hartwick College, B
Hobart and William Smith Colleges, B
Hofstra University, B
Houghton College, B
Hunter College of the City University of New York,
  BM
Iona College, BM
Ithaca College, B
John Jay College of Criminal Justice of the City Uni-
  versity of New York, B
Le Moyne College, B
Lehman College of the City University of New York,
  BM
Long Island University - LIU Brooklyn, B
Long Island University - LIU Post, B
Manhattan College, B
Manhattanville College, B
Marist College, B
Mercy College, B
Mount Saint Mary College, B
Nazareth College of Rochester, B
New York University, BMD

Niagara University, B
Pace University, B
Pace University, Pleasantville Campus, B
Purchase College, State University of New York, B
Queens College of the City University of New York,
    BM
Roberts Wesleyan College, B
St. Bonaventure University, B
St. Francis College, B
St. John Fisher College, B
St. John's University, BM
St. Joseph's College, Long Island Campus, B
St. Joseph's College, New York, B
St. Lawrence University, B
St. Thomas Aquinas College, B
Sarah Lawrence College, B
Siena College, B
Skidmore College, B
State University of New York College at Cortland, B
State University of New York College at Geneseo, B
State University of New York College at Old
    Westbury, B
State University of New York College at Oneonta, B
State University of New York College at Potsdam, B
State University of New York at Fredonia, B
State University of New York at New Paltz, BM
State University of New York at Oswego, B
State University of New York at Plattsburgh, B
Stony Brook University, State University of New
    York, B
Syracuse University, BM
Union College, B
United States Military Academy, B
University at Albany, State University of New York,
    BMD
University at Buffalo, the State University of New
    York, BMDO
University of Rochester, B
Vassar College, B
Wagner College, B
Wells College, B
York College of the City University of New York, B

North Carolina

Barton College, B
Campbell University, B
Catawba College, B
Davidson College, B
Duke University, BD
Elon University, B
Fayetteville State University, B
Gardner-Webb University, B
Greensboro College, B
Guilford College, B
High Point University, B
Johnson C. Smith University, B
Lenoir-Rhyne University, B
Mars Hill University, B
Meredith College, B
Methodist University, AB
North Carolina Central University, B
North Carolina State University, BM
Queens University of Charlotte, B
Salem College, B
University of North Carolina at Asheville, B
The University of North Carolina at Chapel Hill, MD
The University of North Carolina at Charlotte, BMO
The University of North Carolina at Greensboro,
    BMO
The University of North Carolina at Pembroke, B
The University of North Carolina Wilmington, BM
Wake Forest University, B
Warren Wilson College, B
Western Carolina University, B
Winston-Salem State University, B

North Dakota

Dickinson State University, B
Minot State University, B
North Dakota State University, B
University of Jamestown, B
University of North Dakota, B
Valley City State University, B

Ohio

Ashland University, B
Baldwin Wallace University, B
Bluffton University, B
Bowling Green State University, BM
Capital University, B
Case Western Reserve University, B
Cedarville University, B
Cleveland State University, BM
The College of Wooster, B
Denison University, B
Franciscan University of Steubenville, B
Heidelberg University, B
Hiram College, B
John Carroll University, B
Kent State University, B
Kenyon College, B
Lake Erie College, B
Marietta College, B
Miami University, B
Miami University Hamilton, B
Miami University Middletown, A
Mount Vernon Nazarene University, B
Muskingum University, B
Oberlin College, B
Ohio Northern University, B
The Ohio State University, BMD
Ohio University, BM
Ohio Wesleyan University, B
Otterbein University, B
The University of Akron, BM
University of Cincinnati, BMD
University of Dayton, B
The University of Findlay, B
University of Mount Union, B
The University of Toledo, BM
Walsh University, B
Wilmington College, B
Wittenberg University, B
Wright State University, B
Xavier University, AB
Youngstown State University, B

Oklahoma

Northeastern State University, B
Northwestern Oklahoma State University, B
Oklahoma Baptist University, B
Oklahoma Christian University, B
Oklahoma City University, B
Oklahoma State University, B
Oral Roberts University, B
Southeastern Oklahoma State University, B
Southern Nazarene University, B
Southwestern Oklahoma State University, B
University of Central Oklahoma, B
University of Oklahoma, BMD
The University of Tulsa, B

Oregon

George Fox University, B
Linfield College, B
Oregon State University, B
Pacific University, B
Portland State University, BM
Reed College, B
Southern Oregon University, BM
University of Oregon, BM
University of Portland, B
Western Oregon University, B
Willamette University, B

Pennsylvania

Albright College, B
Allegheny College, B
Arcadia University, B
Bryn Mawr College, B
Bucknell University, B
Cabrini University, B
California University of Pennsylvania, B
Carnegie Mellon University, B
Chestnut Hill College, B
Clarion University of Pennsylvania, B
DeSales University, B
Dickinson College, B
Duquesne University, B

East Stroudsburg University of Pennsylvania, B
Eastern University, BO
Elizabethtown College, B
Franklin & Marshall College, B
Gettysburg College, B
Grove City College, B
Haverford College, B
Immaculata University, AB
Indiana University of Pennsylvania, B
Juniata College, B
King's College, B
Kutztown University of Pennsylvania, B
La Salle University, B
Lafayette College, B
Lebanon Valley College, B
Lehigh University, B
Lincoln University, B
Lock Haven University of Pennsylvania, B
Lycoming College, B
Marywood University, B
Messiah College, B
Millersville University of Pennsylvania, BM
Moravian College, B
Muhlenberg College, B
Penn State Abington, B
Penn State Altoona, B
Penn State Beaver, B
Penn State Berks, B
Penn State Brandywine, B
Penn State DuBois, B
Penn State Erie, The Behrend College, B
Penn State Fayette, The Eberly Campus, B
Penn State Greater Allegheny, B
Penn State Hazleton, B
Penn State Lehigh Valley, B
Penn State Mont Alto, B
Penn State New Kensington, B
Penn State Schuylkill, B
Penn State Shenango, B
Penn State University Park, BMD
Penn State Wilkes-Barre, B
Penn State Worthington Scranton, B
Penn State York, B
Rosemont College, B
Saint Francis University, B
Saint Joseph's University, B
Saint Vincent College, B
Seton Hill University, B
Shippensburg University of Pennsylvania, B
Slippery Rock University of Pennsylvania, B
Susquehanna University, B
Swarthmore College, B
Temple University, BMD
University of Pennsylvania, BMD
University of Pittsburgh, BMD
University of Pittsburgh at Greensburg, B
The University of Scranton, B
Ursinus College, B
Villanova University, B
Washington & Jefferson College, B
West Chester University of Pennsylvania, BMO
Westminster College, B
Widener University, B
Wilkes University, B
Wilson College, B
York College of Pennsylvania, B

Rhode Island

Brown University, B
Bryant University, B
Providence College, B
Rhode Island College, B
Salve Regina University, B
University of Rhode Island, BM

South Carolina

Anderson University, B
Bob Jones University, B
Charleston Southern University, B
Clemson University, B
Coastal Carolina University, B
College of Charleston, B
Columbia College, B
Converse College, B
Erskine College, B
Furman University, B

Lander University, B
Newberry College, B
North Greenville University, B
Presbyterian College, B
University of South Carolina, BM
University of South Carolina Beaufort, B
University of South Carolina Upstate, B
Winthrop University, M
Wofford College, B

South Dakota

Augustana University, B
Black Hills State University, B
Northern State University, B
South Dakota State University, B
The University of South Dakota, B

Tennessee

Belmont University, B
Bryan College, B
Carson-Newman University, B
Fisk University, B
Freed-Hardeman University, B
King University, B
Lee University, B
Lipscomb University, B
Maryville College, B
Middle Tennessee State University, M
Rhodes College, B
Sewanee: The University of the South, B
Southern Adventist University, B
Tennessee State University, B
Tennessee Technological University, B
Tennessee Wesleyan College, B
Union University, B
The University of Tennessee, BMD
The University of Tennessee at Martin, B
Vanderbilt University, BMD

Texas

Abilene Christian University, B
Angelo State University, B
Austin College, B
Austin Community College District, A
Baptist University of the Americas, B
Baylor University, BM
Blinn College, A
East Texas Baptist University, B
Grayson College, A
Hardin-Simmons University, B
Houston Baptist University, B
Howard College, A
Howard Payne University, B
Lee College, A
McMurry University, B
Midwestern State University, B
Northeast Texas Community College, A
Our Lady of the Lake University of San Antonio, B
Prairie View A&M University, B
Rice University, B
St. Edward's University, B
St. Mary's University, B
St. Philip's College, A
Sam Houston State University, BM
Southern Methodist University, B
Southwestern University, B
Sul Ross State University, B
Tarleton State University, B
Texas A&M International University, B
Texas A&M University, BMD
Texas A&M University - Commerce, B
Texas A&M University - Corpus Christi, B
Texas A&M University - Kingsville, BM
Texas Christian University, B
Texas Lutheran University, B
Texas Southern University, B
Texas Southmost College, A
Texas State University, BM
Texas Tech University, BD
Texas Wesleyan University, B
Trinity University, B
Trinity Valley Community College, A
University of Dallas, B
University of Houston, BMD
University of Houston - Downtown, B
University of the Incarnate Word, B

University of Mary Hardin-Baylor, B
University of North Texas, BM
University of St. Thomas, B
The University of Texas at Arlington, BM
The University of Texas at Austin, BMD
The University of Texas at El Paso, BM
The University of Texas of the Permian Basin, BM
The University of Texas Rio Grande Valley, BM
The University of Texas at San Antonio, BM
The University of Texas at Tyler, B
Wayland Baptist University, B
West Texas A&M University, B
Wharton County Junior College, A

Utah

Brigham Young University, M
Dixie State University, B
Snow College, A
Southern Utah University, B
University of Utah, BMD
Utah State University, B
Utah Valley University, B
Weber State University, AB

Vermont

Bennington College, BM
Castleton University, B
Marlboro College, B
Middlebury College, BMD
Saint Michael's College, B
University of Vermont, B

Virginia

Bridgewater College, B
Christopher Newport University, B
Eastern Mennonite University, B
Emory & Henry College, B
Ferrum College, B
Hampden-Sydney College, B
Hollins University, B
Liberty University, B
Lynchburg College, B
Mary Baldwin College, B
Randolph College, B
Randolph-Macon College, B
Roanoke College, B
Shenandoah University, B
Southern Virginia University, B
Sweet Briar College, B
University of Richmond, B
University of Virginia, BMD
The University of Virginia's College at Wise, B
Virginia Polytechnic Institute and State University, B
Virginia Wesleyan College, B
Washington and Lee University, B

Washington

Central Washington University, B
Eastern Washington University, B
Gonzaga University, B
Seattle University, B
Skagit Valley College, A
University of Puget Sound, B
University of Washington, BM
Walla Walla University, B
Washington State University, B
Western Washington University, B
Whitman College, B
Whitworth University, B

West Virginia

Bethany College, B
Davis & Elkins College, B
Marshall University, M
Shepherd University, B
West Virginia University, M
Wheeling Jesuit University, B

Wisconsin

Beloit College, B
Cardinal Stritch University, B
Carroll University, B
Carthage College, B
Concordia University Wisconsin, B
Edgewood College, B

Lakeland College, B
Lawrence University, B
Marian University, B
Marquette University, BM
Mount Mary University, B
Ripon College, B
St. Norbert College, B
University of Wisconsin - Eau Claire, B
University of Wisconsin - Green Bay, B
University of Wisconsin - La Crosse, B
University of Wisconsin - Madison, BMD
University of Wisconsin - Milwaukee, BMO
University of Wisconsin - Oshkosh, B
University of Wisconsin - Parkside, B
University of Wisconsin - Platteville, B
University of Wisconsin - Stevens Point, B
University of Wisconsin - Whitewater, B
Viterbo University, B
Wisconsin Lutheran College, B

Wyoming

Laramie County Community College, A
Northwest College, A
University of Wyoming, BM
Western Wyoming Community College, A

U.S. Territories: Puerto Rico

Inter American University of Puerto Rico, Metropolitan Campus, BM
Inter American University of Puerto Rico, Ponce Campus, M
Pontifical Catholic University of Puerto Rico, BO
Universidad Adventista de las Antillas, B
University of Puerto Rico in Cayey, B
University of Puerto Rico, Mayagüez Campus, B
University of Puerto Rico, Río Piedras Campus, B
University of Puerto Rico in Utuado, B

Canada

Alberta

Mount Royal University, B
University of Alberta, B
University of Calgary, BMD
University of Lethbridge, M

British Columbia

The University of British Columbia, B
The University of British Columbia - Okanagan Campus, B
University of Victoria, B

Manitoba

University of Manitoba, B

Maritime Provinces: New Brunswick

Mount Allison University, B
St. Thomas University, B
University of New Brunswick Fredericton, B
University of New Brunswick Saint John, B

Maritime Provinces: Nova Scotia

Dalhousie University, B
Mount Saint Vincent University, B
University of King's College, B

Maritime Provinces: Prince Edward Island

University of Prince Edward Island, B

Newfoundland and Labrador

Memorial University of Newfoundland, B

Ontario

Brock University, B
Carleton University, B
Laurentian University, B
Queen's University at Kingston, BM
University of Guelph, B
University of Ottawa, BMD
University of Toronto, BMD
University of Waterloo, B
The University of Western Ontario, BMD
University of Windsor, B

Wilfrid Laurier University, B
York University, B

Quebec

Bishop's University, B
Concordia University, B
Université Laval, BMD
Université de Montréal, M

Saskatchewan

University of Regina, B
University of Saskatchewan, B

SPANISH LANGUAGE TEACHER EDUCATION

United States

Alabama

Auburn University, B
Spring Hill College, B

Arkansas

Harding University, B
University of Arkansas - Fort Smith, B

California

California Lutheran University, B

Colorado

Adams State University, B
Colorado State University, B
Western State Colorado University, B

Delaware

Delaware State University, B
University of Delaware, B

District of Columbia

The Catholic University of America, B

Georgia

Georgia Southern University, B
Piedmont College, B

Idaho

Boise State University, B
Brigham Young University - Idaho, B
Northwest Nazarene University, B

Illinois

Augustana College, B
Bradley University, B
Elmhurst College, B
Greenville College, B
Lewis University, B
Saint Xavier University, B
Trinity Christian College, B
University of Illinois at Chicago, B
University of Illinois at Urbana - Champaign, B
Western Illinois University, B

Indiana

Anderson University, B
Franklin College, B
Goshen College, B
Grace College, B
Indiana University Bloomington, B
Indiana University - Purdue University Fort Wayne, B
Indiana University - Purdue University Indianapolis, B
Indiana University South Bend, B
Indiana Wesleyan University, B
Manchester University, B
Taylor University, B
University of Evansville, B
University of Indianapolis, B
Valparaiso University, B

Iowa

Buena Vista University, B
Dordt College, B
Morningside College, B
St. Ambrose University, B
The University of Iowa, B

Kansas

Friends University, B
MidAmerica Nazarene University, B
Pittsburg State University, B
Washburn University, B

Kentucky

Eastern Kentucky University, B
Kentucky Wesleyan College, B
University of the Cumberlands, B

Louisiana

Southern University and Agricultural and Mechanical College, B
Xavier University of Louisiana, B

Maine

University of Maine, B

Maryland

Anne Arundel Community College, A
Carroll Community College, A
Community College of Baltimore County, A
Frederick Community College, A
Harford Community College, A
Montgomery College, A

Massachusetts

Merrimack College, B
Salem State University, B

Michigan

Adrian College, B
Albion College, B
Alma College, B
Calvin College, B
Central Michigan University, B
Cornerstone University, B
Eastern Michigan University, B
Grand Valley State University, B
Hope College, B
Michigan State University, B
Northern Michigan University, B
Saginaw Valley State University, B
University of Michigan - Flint, B
Western Michigan University, B

Minnesota

Bethel University, B
Concordia College, B
Minnesota State University Moorhead, B
St. Catherine University, B
Saint Mary's University of Minnesota, B
Southwest Minnesota State University, B
Winona State University, B

Mississippi

Blue Mountain College, B

Missouri

College of the Ozarks, B
Evangel University, B
Lindenwood University, B
Missouri Western State University, B
Northwest Missouri State University, B
Washington University in St. Louis, B

Montana

Carroll College, B
Montana State University Billings, B

Nebraska

Chadron State College, B
College of Saint Mary, B
Concordia University, Nebraska, B
Hastings College, B
University of Nebraska - Lincoln, B

Nevada

University of Nevada, Las Vegas, B

New Hampshire

Keene State College, B

New York

Brooklyn College of the City University of New York, B
Canisius College, B
College of Staten Island of the City University of New York, B
Daemen College, B
Elmira College, B
Hofstra University, B
Iona College, B
Ithaca College, B
Le Moyne College, B
Long Island University - LIU Brooklyn, B
Long Island University - LIU Post, B
Manhattanville College, B
Marist College, B
New York University, B
Niagara University, B
Pace University, B
Queens College of the City University of New York, B
Roberts Wesleyan College, B
St. John Fisher College, B
St. John's University, B
St. Joseph's College, Long Island Campus, B
St. Joseph's College, New York, B
State University of New York College at Cortland, B
State University of New York College at Old Westbury, B
State University of New York College at Oneonta, B
State University of New York College at Potsdam, B
State University of New York at New Paltz, B
Syracuse University, B
Ulster County Community College, A

North Carolina

Campbell University, B
Fayetteville State University, B
Gardner-Webb University, B
Greensboro College, B
North Carolina Agricultural and Technical State University, B
The University of North Carolina at Greensboro, B
The University of North Carolina Wilmington, B
Western Carolina University, B
Winston-Salem State University, B

North Dakota

Minot State University, B
North Dakota State University, B
Valley City State University, B

Ohio

Ashland University, B
Cedarville University, B
Miami University, B
Miami University Hamilton, B
Mount Vernon Nazarene University, B
Muskingum University, B
Notre Dame College, B
Ohio Northern University, B
Ohio University, B
Ohio Wesleyan University, B
The University of Akron, B
Youngstown State University, B

Oklahoma

East Central University, B
Northeastern State University, B
Oklahoma Baptist University, B
Oral Roberts University, B
Southeastern Oklahoma State University, B
University of Central Oklahoma, B

Pennsylvania

Duquesne University, B
Grove City College, B
Holy Family University, B
Marywood University, B

Messiah College, B
Saint Joseph's University, B
Widener University, B
York College of Pennsylvania, B

Rhode Island

Providence College, B
Rhode Island College, B
Salve Regina University, B

South Carolina

Bob Jones University, B
Charleston Southern University, B
North Greenville University, B

South Dakota

The University of South Dakota, B

Tennessee

Bryan College, B
King University, B
Lee University, B
Lipscomb University, B
Maryville College, B
The University of Tennessee at Martin, B

Texas

Abilene Christian University, B
Baylor University, B
East Texas Baptist University, B
Hardin-Simmons University, B
Houston Baptist University, B
Howard Payne University, B
Lubbock Christian University, B
McMurry University, B
Our Lady of the Lake University of San Antonio, B
St. Edward's University, B
Texas A&M International University, B
Texas Wesleyan University, B
University of Mary Hardin-Baylor, B

Utah

Southern Utah University, B
Utah Valley University, B
Weber State University, B

Washington

Central Washington University, B
Eastern Washington University, B
Washington State University, B
Western Washington University, B

Wisconsin

Carroll University, B
Concordia University Wisconsin, B
Edgewood College, B
Marian University, B
Mount Mary University, B
Viterbo University, B

U.S. Territories: Puerto Rico

Bayamón Central University, B
Inter American University of Puerto Rico, Aguadilla Campus, B
Inter American University of Puerto Rico, Arecibo Campus, B
Inter American University of Puerto Rico, Barranquitas Campus, B
Inter American University of Puerto Rico, Fajardo Campus, B
Inter American University of Puerto Rico, Metropolitan Campus, B
Inter American University of Puerto Rico, San Germán Campus, B
Pontifical Catholic University of Puerto Rico, B
Universidad Metropolitana, B
University of Puerto Rico in Cayey, B
University of Puerto Rico in Utuado, B

Canada

Alberta

University of Alberta, B

Quebec

Bishop's University, B

SPECIAL EDUCATION AND TEACHING

United States

Alabama

Alabama Agricultural and Mechanical University, BMO
Alabama Southern Community College, A
Alabama State University, BM
Athens State University, B
Auburn University, BMD
Auburn University at Montgomery, BMO
Jacksonville State University, BM
Samford University, M
The University of Alabama, BMDO
The University of Alabama at Birmingham, M
University of North Alabama, M
University of South Alabama, BMO
The University of West Alabama, BMO

Alaska

University of Alaska Anchorage, MO
University of Alaska Fairbanks, M
University of Alaska Southeast, Sitka Campus, B

Arizona

Arizona State University at the Polytechnic campus, B
Arizona State University at the Tempe campus, BMO
Arizona State University at the West campus, B
Grand Canyon University, BM
Northern Arizona University, BM
Prescott College, M
The University of Arizona, BMD
University of Phoenix - Online Campus, MO
University of Phoenix - Phoenix Campus, M
University of Phoenix - Southern Arizona Campus, MO

Arkansas

Arkansas State University, BM
Harding University, M
Henderson State University, M
John Brown University, B
University of Arkansas, BM
University of Arkansas at Little Rock, MO
University of Arkansas at Pine Bluff, B
University of Central Arkansas, MO

California

Azusa Pacific University, M
Biola University, MO
Brandman University, M
California Baptist University, M
California Lutheran University, M
California State Polytechnic University, Pomona, M
California State University, Bakersfield, M
California State University, Chico, M
California State University, Dominguez Hills, M
California State University, East Bay, M
California State University, Fresno, M
California State University, Fullerton, M
California State University, Long Beach, M
California State University, Los Angeles, MD
California State University, Northridge, M
California State University, Sacramento, M
California State University, San Marcos, M
California State University, Stanislaus, M
Chapman University, MO
Dominican University of California, M
Fresno Pacific University, M
Holy Names University, MO
Long Beach City College, A
Loyola Marymount University, M
National University, BMO
Notre Dame de Namur University, MO
Pacific Oaks College, BM
Point Loma Nazarene University, M

Saint Mary's College of California, M
San Diego State University, M
San Francisco State University, MDO
San Jose State University, BM
Sonoma State University, MO
University of California, Berkeley, D
University of California, Los Angeles, D
University of California, Riverside, MD
University of La Verne, MO
University of the Pacific, BM
University of Phoenix - Bay Area Campus, M
University of San Diego, M
University of San Francisco, MD

Colorado

Adams State University, BM
Colorado Christian University, BM
Colorado Mesa University, M
Colorado State University - Pueblo, M
Metropolitan State University of Denver, BM
Regis University, O
University of Colorado Colorado Springs, M
University of Colorado Denver, MD
University of Northern Colorado, BMD

Connecticut

Central Connecticut State University, MO
Fairfield University, MO
Southern Connecticut State University, BM
University of Connecticut, BMDO
University of Hartford, B
University of Saint Joseph, BMO
Western Connecticut State University, M

Delaware

Delaware State University, BM
University of Delaware, B
Wilmington University, M

District of Columbia

The Catholic University of America, M
Gallaudet University, MDO
The George Washington University, MDO
Howard University, M
Trinity Washington University, M
University of the District of Columbia, B
University of Phoenix - Washington D.C. Campus, M

Florida

Barry University, BMDO
Broward College, AB
Carlos Albizu University, Miami Campus, BM
College of Central Florida, A
Flagler College, B
Florida Atlantic University, BMD
Florida Gulf Coast University, BM
Florida International University, BMD
Florida Memorial University, M
Florida State University, MDO
Indian River State College, B
Jacksonville University, B
Lynn University, M
Miami Dade College, AB
Pensacola State College, A
St. Petersburg College, B
St. Thomas University, M
South Florida State College, A
Southeastern University, B
Trinity Baptist College, BM
University of Central Florida, MDO
University of Florida, BMDO
University of Miami, MDO
University of North Florida, BM
University of South Florida, BMDO
University of West Florida, BM
Warner University, B

Georgia

Albany State University, BM
Armstrong State University, BM
Augusta University, B
Brenau University, M
Clark Atlanta University, M
Columbus State University, BMO

Darton State College, A
Georgia College & State University, BMO
Georgia Gwinnett College, B
Georgia Southern University, BMO
Georgia Southwestern State University, BM
Georgia State University, MD
Kennesaw State University, M
Piedmont College, M
University of Georgia, BMDO
University of North Georgia, B
University of West Georgia, BMO
Valdosta State University, BMO

Hawaii

Brigham Young University - Hawaii, B
Chaminade University of Honolulu, BM
University of Hawaii at Manoa, BMD
University of Phoenix - Hawaii Campus, M

Idaho

Boise State University, BM
Idaho State University, BMO
University of Idaho, BM

Illinois

Aurora University, BM
Benedictine University, BM
Chicago State University, M
Concordia University Chicago, B
DePaul University, BM
Dominican University, M
Eastern Illinois University, BM
Elmhurst College, BM
Governors State University, M
Greenville College, B
Highland Community College, A
Illinois State University, BMD
John A. Logan College, A
Kankakee Community College, A
Lewis University, BM
Lincoln Land Community College, A
Loyola University Chicago, BMO
MacMurray College, B
McHenry County College, A
McKendree University, M
Moraine Valley Community College, A
National Louis University, MO
Northeastern Illinois University, BM
Northern Illinois University, M
Quincy University, BMO
Rend Lake College, A
Rockford University, BM
Roosevelt University, BM
Saint Xavier University, M
Sauk Valley Community College, A
Southern Illinois University Carbondale, BM
Southern Illinois University Edwardsville, BMO
Trinity Christian College, B
University of Illinois at Chicago, MD
University of Illinois at Urbana - Champaign, BMDO
University of St. Francis, BM
Western Illinois University, BM

Indiana

Ball State University, MDO
Goshen College, B
Grace College, B
Huntington University, B
Indiana State University, B
Indiana University Bloomington, BDO
Indiana University - Purdue University Fort Wayne, MO
Indiana University - Purdue University Indianapolis, MO
Indiana University South Bend, BM
Indiana University Southeast, B
Indiana Wesleyan University, B
Manchester University, B
Marian University, B
Oakland City University, B
Purdue University, BMDO
Purdue University Northwest (Hammond), M
Saint Mary-of-the-Woods College, B
University of Evansville, B
University of Saint Francis, BMO
University of Southern Indiana, B

Vincennes University, AB

Iowa

Buena Vista University, B
Clarke University, M
Graceland University, M
Iowa State University of Science and Technology, MD
Kaplan University, Davenport Campus, M
Loras College, M
Morningside College, BM
Mount Mercy University, M
St. Ambrose University, M
The University of Iowa, MD
University of Northern Iowa, BM
William Penn University, B

Kansas

Benedictine College, B
Emporia State University, M
Fort Hays State University, M
Kansas State University, MD
Kansas Wesleyan University, B
McPherson College, B
MidAmerica Nazarene University, M
Ottawa University, M
Pittsburg State University, M
Southwestern College, M
The University of Kansas, MD
University of Saint Mary, M
Washburn University, M
Wichita State University, M

Kentucky

Asbury University, BM
Bellarmine University, BM
Brescia University, B
Campbellsville University, M
Eastern Kentucky University, BM
Georgetown College, M
Kentucky State University, M
Midway University, B
Morehead State University, BM
Murray State University, BM
Northern Kentucky University, BO
Spalding University, BM
Union College, M
University of the Cumberlands, BMO
University of Kentucky, BMD
University of Louisville, M
Western Kentucky University, BM

Louisiana

Grambling State University, M
Louisiana College, B
Louisiana Tech University, BM
McNeese State University, MO
Northwestern State University of Louisiana, MO
Southeastern Louisiana University, M
Southern University and Agricultural and Mechanical College, BMD
University of Louisiana at Monroe, M
University of New Orleans, MD

Maine

Saint Joseph's College of Maine, B
University of Maine, M
University of Maine at Farmington, B
University of Maine at Presque Isle, A
University of New England, B
University of Southern Maine, MO

Maryland

Bowie State University, BM
Coppin State University, BM
Frostburg State University, M
Goucher College, BMO
Harford Community College, A
Hood College, BM
Johns Hopkins University, MO
Loyola University Maryland, BMO
McDaniel College, M
Towson University, BMO
University of Maryland, College Park, B
University of Maryland Eastern Shore, BM

Washington Adventist University, B

Massachusetts

American International College, MO
Assumption College, MO
Bay Path University, MO
Boston College, MO
Boston University, B
Bridgewater State University, BM
Cambridge College, MO
Curry College, BM
Eastern Nazarene College, BMO
Elms College, M
Endicott College, MD
Fitchburg State University, BM
Framingham State University, M
Lasell College, M
Lesley University, BMO
Massachusetts College of Liberal Arts, M
Merrimack College, BM
Northeastern University, M
Regis College, M
Salem State University, M
Simmons College, BMO
Smith College, M
Springfield College, M
University of Massachusetts Amherst, MDO
University of Massachusetts Boston, M
Westfield State University, BM
Wheelock College, BM
Worcester State University, MO

Michigan

Andrews University, M
Calvin College, BM
Central Michigan University, MO
Eastern Michigan University, MO
Ferris State University, M
Grand Valley State University, BM
Henry Ford College, A
Madonna University, M
Michigan State University, BMD
Northern Michigan University, BM
Oakland University, MO
Saginaw Valley State University, BM
Siena Heights University, M
Spring Arbor University, BM
University of Detroit Mercy, BM
University of Michigan - Dearborn, M
University of Michigan - Flint, M
Wayne State University, BMDO
Western Michigan University, MD

Minnesota

Augsburg College, B
Bemidji State University, M
Bethel University, MO
Capella University, MD
Concordia University, St. Paul, MO
Martin Luther College, M
Minnesota State University Mankato, MO
Minnesota State University Moorhead, BM
Normandale Community College, A
St. Cloud State University, BM
Saint Mary's University of Minnesota, MO
Southwest Minnesota State University, BM
University of Minnesota, Twin Cities Campus, BMDO
University of St. Thomas, MO
Walden University, MDO
Winona State University, BM

Mississippi

Alcorn State University, M
Delta State University, M
Jackson State University, BMO
Mississippi College, M
Mississippi State University, BMDO
Northeast Mississippi Community College, A
University of Mississippi, B
University of Southern Mississippi, BMDO
William Carey University, M

Missouri

Avila University, B
Drury University, M
Evangel University, B
Fontbonne University, BM
Lincoln University, BM
Lindenwood University, B
Missouri State University, BM
Missouri Valley College, B
Missouri Western State University, MO
Northwest Missouri State University, M
Saint Louis University, M
Southeast Missouri State University, BM
University of Central Missouri, BM
University of Missouri, BMD
University of Missouri - Kansas City, M
University of Missouri - St. Louis, MO
Washington University in St. Louis, M
Webster University, BM
William Woods University, B

Montana

Miles Community College, A
Montana State University Billings, ABM
University of Great Falls, B

Nebraska

Chadron State College, B
Concordia University, Nebraska, B
Creighton University, M
Doane University, B
Hastings College, B
Nebraska Wesleyan University, B
Peru State College, B
University of Nebraska at Kearney, BM
University of Nebraska - Lincoln, BMDO
University of Nebraska at Omaha, BM
Wayne State College, BM
York College, B

Nevada

College of Southern Nevada, A
Nevada State College, B
University of Nevada, Las Vegas, BD
University of Nevada, Reno, MD

New Hampshire

Franklin Pierce University, M
Keene State College, M
New England College, BM
Plymouth State University, M
Rivier University, BM
Southern New Hampshire University, BM
University of New Hampshire, M

New Jersey

Caldwell University, MO
Centenary College, BM
The College of New Jersey, BMO
College of Saint Elizabeth, M
Fairleigh Dickinson University, Metropolitan Campus, MO
Felician University, B
Kean University, BM
Monmouth University, BMO
Montclair State University, MD
New Jersey City University, BM
Rider University, MO
Rowan College at Gloucester County, A
Rowan University, BMO
Rutgers University - New Brunswick, MD
Saint Peter's University, MO
Seton Hall University, BM
William Paterson University of New Jersey, BM

New Mexico

Eastern New Mexico University, BM
New Mexico Highlands University, BM
New Mexico State University, BMDO
San Juan College, A
University of New Mexico, BMDO
University of the Southwest, BM
Western New Mexico University, BM

New York

Adelphi University, MO
Binghamton University, State University of New York, M
Brooklyn College of the City University of New York, MO
Buffalo State College, State University of New York, BM
Canisius College, BM
City College of the City University of New York, MO
The College of New Rochelle, BM
The College of Saint Rose, BM
College of Staten Island of the City University of New York, MO
Concordia College - New York, M
Daemen College, BM
Dominican College, BM
D'Youville College, M
Fordham University, MO
Hofstra University, MDO
Houghton College, B
Hunter College of the City University of New York, M
Iona College, M
Keuka College, B
Le Moyne College, BM
Lehman College of the City University of New York, M
Long Island University - LIU Post, MO
Manhattan College, BMO
Manhattanville College, M
Medaille College, BM
Medgar Evers College of the City University of New York, B
Metropolitan College of New York, M
Mount Saint Mary College, M
Nazareth College of Rochester, B
New York University, BM
Niagara University, BMO
Nyack College, M
Pace University, BM
Pace University, Pleasantville Campus, B
Queens College of the City University of New York, M
Roberts Wesleyan College, BM
Rochester Institute of Technology, M
St. Bonaventure University, BMO
St. John Fisher College, BMO
St. John's University, BMO
St. Joseph's College, Long Island Campus, BM
St. Joseph's College, New York, BM
St. Thomas Aquinas College, BMO
State University of New York College at Cortland, M
State University of New York College at Geneseo, B
State University of New York College at Old Westbury, B
State University of New York College at Oneonta, M
State University of New York College at Potsdam, M
State University of New York at New Paltz, M
State University of New York at Oswego, M
State University of New York at Plattsburgh, BM
Syracuse University, MD
Touro College, BM
University at Albany, State University of New York, MD
University at Buffalo, the State University of New York, D
Wagner College, M

North Carolina

Appalachian State University, M
Barton College, B
Bennett College, B
Brunswick Community College, A
Catawba College, B
Craven Community College, A
East Carolina University, BMO
Elizabeth City State University, B
Elon University, BM
Greensboro College, BM
High Point University, BM
Louisburg College, A
Mars Hill University, B
McDowell Technical Community College, A
Methodist University, B
Nash Community College, A

North Carolina Agricultural and Technical State University, B
North Carolina Central University, M
North Carolina State University, M
North Carolina Wesleyan College, B
Pfeiffer University, B
Roanoke-Chowan Community College, A
Salem College, M
The University of North Carolina at Charlotte, BMDO
The University of North Carolina at Greensboro, BMDO
The University of North Carolina at Pembroke, B
The University of North Carolina Wilmington, BM
Western Carolina University, B
Winston-Salem State University, BM

North Dakota

Mayville State University, B
Minot State University, ABM
University of Mary, M
University of North Dakota, MD

Ohio

Ashland University, BM
Baldwin Wallace University, M
Bluffton University, B
Bowling Green State University, BM
Capital University, B
Cedarville University, B
Central State University, B
Cleveland State University, BM
Defiance College, M
Heidelberg University, B
John Carroll University, B
Kent State University, BMDO
Lake Erie College, B
Malone University, M
Miami University, B
Miami University Hamilton, B
Mount St. Joseph University, BO
Mount Vernon Nazarene University, B
Muskingum University, B
Notre Dame College, M
Ohio Dominican University, B
The Ohio State University, BD
Ohio University, BM
Shawnee State University, B
Union Institute & University, B
The University of Akron, BM
University of Cincinnati, BMDO
University of Cincinnati Clermont College, A
University of Dayton, BM
The University of Findlay, B
University of Mount Union, B
University of Rio Grande, M
The University of Toledo, BMD
Ursuline College, BM
Walsh University, B
Wilmington College, B
Wright State University, BM
Xavier University, BM
Youngstown State University, BM

Oklahoma

East Central University, B
Langston University, B
Northwestern Oklahoma State University, B
Oklahoma Baptist University, B
Oklahoma City University, B
Oral Roberts University, B
Southeastern Oklahoma State University, B
Southwestern Oklahoma State University, BM
University of Central Oklahoma, BM
University of Oklahoma, BMD
University of Oklahoma Health Sciences Center, M

Oregon

Concordia University, M
George Fox University, M
Lewis & Clark College, M
Pacific University, M
Portland Community College, A
Southern Oregon University, M
University of Portland, M
Western Oregon University, M

Pennsylvania

Albright College, M
Arcadia University, MDO
Bloomsburg University of Pennsylvania, BMO
Cabrini University, B
California University of Pennsylvania, BM
Carlow University, M
Chatham University, M
Chestnut Hill College, MO
Cheyney University of Pennsylvania, BM
Clarion University of Pennsylvania, BM
DeSales University, M
Drexel University, M
Duquesne University, M
East Stroudsburg University of Pennsylvania, M
Eastern University, MO
Edinboro University of Pennsylvania, ABMO
Gannon University, O
Geneva College, BM
Grove City College, B
Gwynedd Mercy University, BM
Holy Family University, BM
Immaculata University, O
Indiana University of Pennsylvania, M
Kutztown University of Pennsylvania, B
La Salle University, MO
Lancaster Bible College, M
Lebanon Valley College, B
Lehigh Carbon Community College, A
Lehigh University, MD
Mansfield University of Pennsylvania, BM
Marywood University, BM
Mercyhurst University, BM
Messiah College, M
Millersville University of Pennsylvania, BM
Misericordia University, M
Penn State Abington, B
Penn State Altoona, B
Penn State Beaver, B
Penn State Berks, B
Penn State Brandywine, B
Penn State DuBois, B
Penn State Erie, The Behrend College, B
Penn State Fayette, The Eberly Campus, B
Penn State Greater Allegheny, B
Penn State Hazleton, B
Penn State Lehigh Valley, B
Penn State Mont Alto, B
Penn State New Kensington, B
Penn State Schuylkill, B
Penn State Shenango, B
Penn State University Park, BMDO
Penn State Wilkes-Barre, B
Penn State Worthington Scranton, B
Penn State York, B
Point Park University, M
Saint Francis University, B
Saint Joseph's University, BMO
Saint Vincent College, M
Seton Hill University, MO
Shippensburg University of Pennsylvania, M
Slippery Rock University of Pennsylvania, BM
Temple University, M
University of Pittsburgh, MD
Waynesburg University, BM
West Chester University of Pennsylvania, BMO
Widener University, BM
Wilkes University, M

Rhode Island

Community College of Rhode Island, A
Johnson & Wales University, M
Providence College, BM
Rhode Island College, BMO
Salve Regina University, B
University of Rhode Island, M

South Carolina

Anderson University, B
Bob Jones University, M
Clemson University, BM
Coastal Carolina University, B
College of Charleston, BM
Columbia College, B
Converse College, BM

Erskine College, B
Francis Marion University, M
Furman University, BM
Lander University, B
South Carolina State University, BM
Southern Wesleyan University, B
University of South Carolina, MD
University of South Carolina Aiken, B
University of South Carolina Upstate, M
Winthrop University, BM

South Dakota

Augustana University, BM
Black Hills State University, B
Dakota State University, B
Dakota Wesleyan University, B
Mount Marty College, B
Northern State University, B
Oglala Lakota College, B
Sinte Gleska University, AB
The University of South Dakota, BM

Tennessee

Austin Peay State University, BM
Belmont University, M
Bethel University, B
Carson-Newman University, B
Christian Brothers University, B
Cumberland University, B
East Tennessee State University, BM
Fisk University, B
Freed-Hardeman University, BM
Lee University, BM
LeMoyne-Owen College, B
Lipscomb University, BM
Middle Tennessee State University, BM
Nashville State Community College, A
Tennessee State University, BM
Tennessee Technological University, BMO
Trevecca Nazarene University, BM
Tusculum College, B
Union University, B
University of Memphis, BMD
The University of Tennessee, BMO
The University of Tennessee at Chattanooga, BM
The University of Tennessee at Martin, BM
Vanderbilt University, BM

Texas

Angelo State University, M
Baylor University, BD
Dallas Baptist University, M
Hill College, A
Houston Baptist University, B
Howard College, A
Lamar University, MD
Midwestern State University, BM
Our Lady of the Lake University of San Antonio, BM
Prairie View A&M University, M
St. Edward's University, B
Sam Houston State University, BMD
Southern Methodist University, M
Stephen F. Austin State University, M
Tarleton State University, O
Texas A&M International University, BM
Texas A&M University, M
Texas A&M University - Corpus Christi, M
Texas A&M University - Kingsville, M
Texas A&M University - San Antonio, M
Texas A&M University - Texarkana, M
Texas Christian University, BM
Texas State University, M
Texas Tech University, MD
Texas Woman's University, MD
University of Houston, M
University of Houston - Victoria, M
University of North Texas, M
University of St. Thomas, M
The University of Texas at Austin, MD
The University of Texas at El Paso, M
The University of Texas Health Science Center at San Antonio, M
The University of Texas of the Permian Basin, M
The University of Texas Rio Grande Valley, M
The University of Texas at San Antonio, BM
The University of Texas at Tyler, M

Wayland Baptist University, M
West Texas A&M University, M
Wiley College, B

Utah

Brigham Young University, BMDO
University of Phoenix - Utah Campus, M
University of Utah, BMD
Utah State University, BMDO
Weber State University, B
Western Governors University, M
Westminster College, B

Vermont

Castleton University, BMO
College of St. Joseph, M
Johnson State College, M
Lyndon State College, BM
Saint Michael's College, MO
University of Vermont, M

Virginia

Averett University, M
George Mason University, MDO
Hampton University, B
James Madison University, M
Liberty University, M
Longwood University, M
Lynchburg College, M
Marymount University, BM
Norfolk State University, M
Northern Virginia Community College, A
Old Dominion University, MD
Radford University, MO
Randolph College, M
Regent University, MDO
University of Virginia, MDO
Virginia Commonwealth University, MDO
Virginia Union University, B
Virginia Wesleyan College, B

Washington

Central Washington University, BM
City University of Seattle, BM
Eastern Washington University, BM
Gonzaga University, BM
Heritage University, BM
Saint Martin's University, BM
Seattle Pacific University, B
Seattle University, MO
University of Washington, MD
University of Washington, Tacoma, M
Walla Walla University, M
Washington State University, BMD
Western Washington University, B
Whitworth University, BM

West Virginia

American Public University System, M
Concord University, BM
Fairmont State University, BM
Glenville State College, B
Marshall University, M
West Virginia University, MD
West Virginia Wesleyan College, B

Wisconsin

Alverno College, M
Cardinal Stritch University, M
Carthage College, B
Concordia University Wisconsin, M
Edgewood College, MO
Silver Lake College of the Holy Family, M
University of Wisconsin - Eau Claire, BM
University of Wisconsin - Madison, BMD
University of Wisconsin - Milwaukee, BMDO
University of Wisconsin - Oshkosh, M
University of Wisconsin - Stevens Point, BM
University of Wisconsin - Stout, B
University of Wisconsin - Superior, BM
University of Wisconsin - Whitewater, BM
Wisconsin Lutheran College, B

Wyoming

University of Wyoming, BMDO

U.S. Territories: Guam

University of Guam, BM

U.S. Territories: Puerto Rico

American University of Puerto Rico (Bayamon), BM
Bayamón Central University, BM
Caribbean University, BM
Inter American University of Puerto Rico, Arecibo Campus, B
Inter American University of Puerto Rico, Barranquitas Campus, ABM
Inter American University of Puerto Rico, Fajardo Campus, BM
Inter American University of Puerto Rico, Metropolitan Campus, BM
Inter American University of Puerto Rico, Ponce Campus, B
Inter American University of Puerto Rico, San Germán Campus, BM
Pontifical Catholic University of Puerto Rico, B
Universidad del Este, BM
Universidad Metropolitana, BM
Universidad del Turabo, BM
University of Puerto Rico in Cayey, B
University of Puerto Rico, Medical Sciences Campus, O
University of Puerto Rico, Río Piedras Campus, M

Canada

Alberta

University of Alberta, MD
University of Lethbridge, B

British Columbia

The University of British Columbia, BMDO
University of Victoria, BM

Manitoba

Brandon University, MO
University of Manitoba, M

Maritime Provinces: New Brunswick

University of New Brunswick Fredericton, B

Maritime Provinces: Nova Scotia

Acadia University, M
Mount Saint Vincent University, M

Newfoundland and Labrador

Memorial University of Newfoundland, B

Ontario

The University of Western Ontario, M
University of Windsor, B
York University, B

Quebec

Université de Montréal, B
Université du Québec en Abitibi-Témiscamingue, B
Université du Québec à Chicoutimi, B
Université du Québec à Montréal, B
Université du Québec en Outaouais, B
Université du Québec à Rimouski, B
Université de Sherbrooke, BMO

Saskatchewan

University of Saskatchewan, MDO

SPECIAL PRODUCTS MARKETING OPERATIONS

United States

Alabama

Wallace State Community College, A

Arizona

Scottsdale Community College, A

California

Cuyamaca College, A
El Camino College, A
Los Angeles City College, A
Merced College, A
Mission College, A
Modesto Junior College, A
Saddleback College, A
San Diego City College, A

Connecticut

Gateway Community College, A

Florida

Indian River State College, A
Palm Beach State College, A

Illinois

Dominican University, B

Maryland

University of Maryland Eastern Shore, B

Michigan

Muskegon Community College, A

Minnesota

Northland Community and Technical College, A
Vermilion Community College, A

Mississippi

Copiah-Lincoln Community College, A

Missouri

Metropolitan Community College - Kansas City, A
State Fair Community College, A

New Mexico

Western New Mexico University, B

New York

Buffalo State College, State University of New York, B
Fashion Institute of Technology, B
Monroe Community College, A
Rochester Institute of Technology, B
Tompkins Cortland Community College, A

North Carolina

Central Piedmont Community College, A

Ohio

Sinclair Community College, A

Pennsylvania

Saint Joseph's University, B

Texas

Del Mar College, A
El Centro College, A
South Plains College, A
Stephen F. Austin State University, B
University of North Texas, B

Washington

Central Washington University, B
South Seattle College, A
Yakima Valley Community College, A

West Virginia

Concord University, B

Canada

Maritime Provinces: Nova Scotia

Mount Saint Vincent University, B

SPECIALIZED MERCHANDISING, SALES, AND MARKETING OPERATIONS

United States

Massachusetts

Bay State College, A

New Jersey

Middlesex County College, A

New York

Fashion Institute of Technology, B

North Carolina

High Point University, B

Pennsylvania

Saint Joseph's University, B

Texas

Baylor University, B
Wade College, A

SPEECH AND INTERPERSONAL COMMUNICATION

United States

Alabama

The University of Alabama, M

Arkansas

Arkansas State University, MO
University of Arkansas at Little Rock, M

California

California State University, Fullerton, M
University of California, Santa Barbara, D

Colorado

Colorado State University, M
University of Denver, MD

Georgia

Georgia State University, M
University of Georgia, MD

Idaho

Idaho State University, M

Illinois

Eastern Illinois University, M
Northwestern University, MD
Southern Illinois University Carbondale, MD
Southern Illinois University Edwardsville, M

Indiana

Ball State University, M
Indiana University Bloomington, MD

Iowa

The University of Iowa, MD

Louisiana

University of Louisiana at Monroe, M

Maryland

University of Maryland, College Park, MD

Mississippi

University of Southern Mississippi, MD

Missouri

Washington University in St. Louis, D

Nebraska

University of Nebraska - Lincoln, MD

New Jersey

Seton Hall University, M

New York

Brooklyn College of the City University of New York, MD
Rensselaer Polytechnic Institute, MD

North Carolina

Wake Forest University, M

North Dakota

North Dakota State University, M

Ohio

Bowling Green State University, MD
Ohio University, MD

Oregon

Portland State University, MO

South Carolina

Bob Jones University, M

Tennessee

The University of Tennessee, MD

Texas

Texas Christian University, M
University of Houston, M

Virginia

Old Dominion University, M

Wisconsin

Marquette University, M
University of Wisconsin - Madison, MD
University of Wisconsin - Stevens Point, M
University of Wisconsin - Superior, M

SPEECH-LANGUAGE PATHOLOGY/PATHOLOGIST

United States

Alabama

University of Montevallo, B

Arkansas

Harding University, B

California

Biola University, B
San Diego State University, B

District of Columbia

University of the District of Columbia, B

Florida

Nova Southeastern University, B

Georgia

University of West Georgia, B
Valdosta State University, B

Illinois

College of DuPage, A
Northwestern University, B
Parkland College, A
Saint Xavier University, B
Trinity Christian College, B

Iowa

University of Northern Iowa, B

Louisiana

Xavier University of Louisiana, B

Maryland

Loyola University Maryland, B
Towson University, B

Massachusetts

Elms College, A
Emerson College, B

Michigan

Eastern Michigan University, B
Northern Michigan University, B

Minnesota

Minnesota State University Moorhead, B
St. Cloud State University, B

Mississippi

Jackson State University, B
Mississippi University for Women, B

Missouri

Rockhurst University, B
University of Central Missouri, B

Nebraska

University of Nebraska - Lincoln, B

Nevada

Nevada State College, B
University of Nevada, Reno, B

New York

Brooklyn College of the City University of New York, B
Lehman College of the City University of New York, B
Marymount Manhattan College, B
Molloy College, B
Nazareth College of Rochester, B

North Carolina

Wilkes Community College, A

North Dakota

Lake Region State College, A
Williston State College, A

Ohio

Cleveland State University, B
Miami University Hamilton, B
The University of Toledo, B

Oklahoma

Oklahoma State University, B
University of Central Oklahoma, B
University of Oklahoma Health Sciences Center, B
University of Science and Arts of Oklahoma, B

Pennsylvania

Clarion University of Pennsylvania, B
Duquesne University, B
Edinboro University of Pennsylvania, B
Geneva College, B

South Carolina

Columbia College, B

Tennessee

Southern Adventist University, A

Texas

Abilene Christian University, B
Texas Christian University, B

Virginia

James Madison University, B

Washington

Eastern Washington University, B

West Virginia

Marshall University, B

U.S. Territories: Puerto Rico

Inter American University of Puerto Rico, Aguadilla Campus, B
Inter American University of Puerto Rico, Fajardo Campus, B
Inter American University of Puerto Rico, Ponce Campus, B
Universidad Metropolitana, B
Universidad del Turabo, B

SPEECH AND RHETORICAL STUDIES

United States

California

California State University, Northridge, M
San Francisco State University, M
San Jose State University, M

Hawaii

University of Hawaii at Manoa, M

Illinois

Northeastern Illinois University, M

Louisiana

Louisiana Tech University, MD

Nevada

University of Nevada, Reno, M

New York

Brooklyn College of the City University of New York, M
New York University, MD

South Carolina

Bob Jones University, M
University of South Carolina, M

SPEECH TEACHER EDUCATION

United States

Arkansas

Arkansas Tech University, B
Harding University, B

Colorado

Colorado State University, B

Georgia

Darton State College, A

Idaho

Boise State University, B

Illinois

Bradley University, B
McKendree University, B

Indiana

Anderson University, B
Indiana University - Purdue University Fort Wayne, B
University of Indianapolis, B

Iowa

Buena Vista University, B
Dordt College, B
Northwestern College, B
St. Ambrose University, B
The University of Iowa, B
University of Northern Iowa, B
Wartburg College, B

Kansas

Central Christian College of Kansas, A
Friends University, B
Kansas Wesleyan University, B
Pratt Community College, A
Southwestern College, B

Kentucky

University of the Cumberlands, B

Louisiana

Louisiana Tech University, B

Michigan

Albion College, B
Central Michigan University, B
Cornerstone University, B
Olivet College, B
Saginaw Valley State University, B
University of Michigan - Flint, B

Minnesota

Bemidji State University, B
St. Catherine University, B
St. Cloud State University, B
Southwest Minnesota State University, B
University of St. Thomas, B

Mississippi

Northwest Mississippi Community College, A
William Carey University, B

Missouri

Culver-Stockton College, B
Evangel University, B
Southwest Baptist University, B
William Jewell College, B

Montana

Carroll College, B

Nebraska

Hastings College, B
Midland University, B
Wayne State College, B
York College, B

New York

Brooklyn College of the City University of New York, B

North Dakota

Dickinson State University, B

Ohio

Bowling Green State University, B
Capital University, B
University of Rio Grande, B

Oklahoma

East Central University, B
Oklahoma City University, B
Southern Nazarene University, B

Pennsylvania

Summit University, B

South Dakota

Augustana University, B
The University of South Dakota, B

Tennessee

Lee University, B
Trevecca Nazarene University, B

Texas

Austin College, B
Dallas Baptist University, B
East Texas Baptist University, B
Hardin-Simmons University, B
Houston Baptist University, B
Howard College, A
Howard Payne University, B

San Antonio College, A
University of Mary Hardin-Baylor, B

Utah

Brigham Young University, B

Washington

Northwest University, B
Western Washington University, B

Canada

Alberta

University of Alberta, B

Ontario

University of Windsor, B
York University, B

SPORT AND FITNESS ADMIN-ISTRATION/MANAGEMENT

United States

Alabama

Athens State University, B
Faulkner University, B
Huntingdon College, B
Jacksonville State University, B
Samford University, B
Troy University, BM
United States Sports Academy, BMD
The University of Alabama, M

Arizona

Arizona State University at the Downtown Phoenix campus, B
Arizona Western College, A
Grand Canyon University, B

Arkansas

Arkansas State University, BM
Ecclesia College, B
Harding University, B
Henderson State University, M
John Brown University, B
University of Arkansas, MD
University of Arkansas at Little Rock, M

California

American River College, A
Bristol University, M
California Baptist University, M
California State University, Long Beach, M
California University of Management and Sciences, BM
Cañada College, A
Cerritos College, A
Chabot College, A
Concordia University Irvine, M
Fresno Pacific University, B
Fullerton College, A
Glendale Community College, A
Holy Names University, M
Menlo College, B
National University, AM
Pepperdine University, B
Saint Mary's College of California, BM
San Diego State University, M
Sonoma State University, M
University of San Francisco, M

Colorado

Colorado Mesa University, B
Fort Lewis College, B
Johnson & Wales University, B
University of Colorado Denver, M
University of Northern Colorado, MD
Western State Colorado University, B

Connecticut

Albertus Magnus College, B
Eastern Connecticut State University, B
Mitchell College, B
Post University, B
Three Rivers Community College, A
University of Connecticut, B
University of New Haven, BMO

Delaware

Delaware State University, B
Goldey-Beacom College, B
University of Delaware, B
Wilmington University, B

District of Columbia

The George Washington University, M
Georgetown University, M
Howard University, M

Florida

Barry University, BM
Flagler College, B
Florida Agricultural and Mechanical University, M
Florida Atlantic University, M
Florida Institute of Technology, B
Florida International University, M
Florida Southern College, B
Florida State University, MDO
Jacksonville University, BM
Johnson & Wales University, B
Keiser University, A
Lake-Sumter State College, A
Lynn University, BM
Nova Southeastern University, B
Saint Leo University, BM
St. Thomas University, BM
Southeastern University, B
Stetson University, B
University of Central Florida, M
University of Florida, BMD
University of Miami, BM
University of North Florida, BM
University of South Florida, M
The University of Tampa, B
Webber International University, ABM

Georgia

Andrew College, A
Brenau University, B
Clayton State University, B
Emmanuel College, B
Georgia Southern University, BM
Georgia State University, M
Kennesaw State University, B
Reinhardt University, B
Toccoa Falls College, B

Idaho

The College of Idaho, B

Illinois

Aurora University, B
Blackburn College, B
Columbia College Chicago, B
Concordia University Chicago, B
DePaul University, M
Elmhurst College, B
Greenville College, B
Illinois Eastern Community Colleges, Frontier Community College, A
Illinois Eastern Community Colleges, Lincoln Trail College, A
Illinois Eastern Community Colleges, Wabash Valley College, A
Judson University, B
Lewis University, BM
Lincoln College - Normal, B
MacMurray College, B
McKendree University, B
Millikin University, B
North Central College, BM
Northern Illinois University, M
Northwestern University, M
Olivet Nazarene University, B

Quincy University, B
Robert Morris University Illinois, M
Rock Valley College, A
Rockford University, B
Southern Illinois University Carbondale, B
University of Illinois at Urbana - Champaign, B
Western Illinois University, M

Indiana

Ball State University, B
Bethel College, B
Grace College, B
Huntington University, B
Indiana State University, MD
Indiana Tech, B
Indiana University Bloomington, MD
Indiana Wesleyan University, B
Manchester University, B
Marian University, B
Purdue University, MD
Saint Joseph's College, B
Taylor University, B
Trine University, B
University of Indianapolis, BM
University of Southern Indiana, B
Valparaiso University, BM
Vincennes University, A

Iowa

Buena Vista University, B
Clarke University, B
Des Moines Area Community College, A
Dordt College, B
Grand View University, B
Iowa Lakes Community College, A
Loras College, B
North Iowa Area Community College, A
Northwestern College, B
St. Ambrose University, B
Simpson College, B
The University of Iowa, BD
University of Northern Iowa, M
Waldorf College, B
Wartburg College, B
William Penn University, B

Kansas

Baker University, B
Barton County Community College, A
Bethany College, B
Central Christian College of Kansas, AB
Friends University, B
Hutchinson Community College, A
Kansas Wesleyan University, BM
MidAmerica Nazarene University, B
Southwestern College, B
Tabor College, B
The University of Kansas, B
University of Saint Mary, B
Wichita State University, M

Kentucky

Alice Lloyd College, B
Asbury University, B
Bellarmine University, B
Eastern Kentucky University, BM
Georgetown College, B
Kentucky Wesleyan College, B
Midway University, B
Morehead State University, BM
Northern Kentucky University, B
Thomas More College, B
Union College, B
University of the Cumberlands, B
University of Louisville, BM
Western Kentucky University, M

Louisiana

Grambling State University, M
Louisiana State University and Agricultural & Mechanical College, B
Southeastern Louisiana University, B

Maine

Husson University, B
Saint Joseph's College of Maine, B
Thomas College, B
University of New England, B

Maryland

Coppin State University, B
Garrett College, A
Howard Community College, A
Morgan State University, B
Mount St. Mary's University, B
Towson University, B

Massachusetts

American International College, B
Anna Maria College, B
Becker College, B
Bridgewater State University, B
Bunker Hill Community College, A
Dean College, B
Eastern Nazarene College, B
Elms College, B
Emmanuel College, B
Endicott College, BM
Fisher College, B
Fitchburg State University, B
Holyoke Community College, A
Lasell College, BMO
Merrimack College, B
Mount Ida College, B
Newbury College, B
Nichols College, B
Northern Essex Community College, A
Salem State University, B
Springfield College, BM
Springfield Technical Community College, A
University of Massachusetts Amherst, BMD
Western New England University, BM

Michigan

Adrian College, B
Calvin College, B
Central Michigan University, BM
Cleary University, B
Cornerstone University, B
Davenport University, B
Delta College, A
Eastern Michigan University, BM
Hillsdale College, B
Lake Superior State University, B
Madonna University, B
Michigan Technological University, B
Northern Michigan University, B
Northwood University, Michigan Campus, B
Olivet College, B
Rochester College, B
Saginaw Valley State University, B
Siena Heights University, B
Southwestern Michigan College, A
Spring Arbor University, B
University of Michigan, BM
Wayne State University, M
Western Michigan University, BM

Minnesota

Bemidji State University, B
Concordia University, St. Paul, BM
Crown College, B
Hamline University, B
Minnesota State University Mankato, B
North Central University, B
St. Cloud State University, M
University of Minnesota, Crookston, B
University of Minnesota, Twin Cities Campus, MD
Winona State University, M

Mississippi

Alcorn State University, B
Belhaven University, BM
Mississippi College, B
Mississippi State University, M
University of Southern Mississippi, BM

Missouri

Central Methodist University, B
Columbia College, B
Culver-Stockton College, B
Fontbonne University, B
Lindenwood University, BM
Maryville University of Saint Louis, BMO
Missouri Baptist University, B
Missouri State University, M
Missouri Valley College, B
Missouri Western State University, M
Rockhurst University, B
Southeast Missouri State University, BM
Southwest Baptist University, B
Westminster College, B
William Woods University, B

Montana

Montana State University, B
Montana State University Billings, B
Rocky Mountain College, B

Nebraska

Concordia University, Nebraska, B
Hastings College, B
Nebraska Wesleyan University, B
Union College, B
University of Nebraska at Kearney, BM
Wayne State College, BM
York College, B

Nevada

University of Nevada, Las Vegas, B

New Hampshire

Colby-Sawyer College, B
Daniel Webster College, B
Franklin Pierce University, BM
New England College, BM
NHTI, Concord's Community College, A
Plymouth State University, B
Southern New Hampshire University, BMO

New Jersey

Camden County College, A
Centenary College, B
Fairleigh Dickinson University, College at Florham, M
Fairleigh Dickinson University, Metropolitan Campus, M
Montclair State University, M
Rider University, B
Salem Community College, A
Seton Hall University, BM
Union County College, A
William Paterson University of New Jersey, B

New Mexico

Eastern New Mexico University, M
New Mexico Highlands University, M
New Mexico Military Institute, A
University of New Mexico, MD
University of the Southwest, M

New York

Adelphi University, BM
Adirondack Community College, A
Brooklyn College of the City University of New York, M
Canisius College, BM
Cayuga County Community College, A
Cazenovia College, B
The College at Brockport, State University of New York, BM
Columbia University, M
Concordia College - New York, B
Farmingdale State College, B
Globe Institute of Technology, B
Hilbert College, B
Hofstra University, M
Iona College, O
Ithaca College, B
Jefferson Community College, A
Kingsborough Community College of the City University of New York, A

Long Island University - LIU Brooklyn, B
Manhattanville College, M
Medaille College, B
Morrisville State College, A
New York University, MO
Niagara County Community College, A
Niagara University, B
St. Bonaventure University, B
St. John Fisher College, B
St. John's University, BM
St. Thomas Aquinas College, B
State University of New York College at Cortland, M
State University of New York College of Technology
    at Alfred, A
State University of New York College of Technology
    at Delhi, A
State University of New York at Oswego, B
Sullivan County Community College, A
Syracuse University, BM
Tompkins Cortland Community College, A

North Carolina

Barton College, B
Belmont Abbey College, B
Campbell University, B
Catawba College, B
Chowan University, B
East Carolina University, MO
Elon University, B
Gardner-Webb University, B
Greensboro College, B
Guilford College, B
Johnson C. Smith University, B
Johnson & Wales University, B
Lees-McRae College, B
Lenoir-Rhyne University, B
Livingstone College, B
Louisburg College, A
Mars Hill University, B
Methodist University, B
North Carolina Agricultural and Technical State Uni-
    versity, B
North Carolina Central University, M
North Carolina State University, BM
Pfeiffer University, B
Queens University of Charlotte, B
The University of North Carolina at Chapel Hill, M
Western Carolina University, B
Wingate University, BM
Winston-Salem State University, B

North Dakota

Minot State University, B
North Dakota State University, B
University of Jamestown, B
University of Mary, BM

Ohio

Ashland University, M
Baldwin Wallace University, B
Bluffton University, B
Bowling Green State University, BM
Cedarville University, B
Cleveland State University, BM
Columbus State Community College, A
Defiance College, BM
Kent State University, BM
Lake Erie College, B
Lorain County Community College, A
Malone University, B .
Marietta College, B
Miami University, B
Mount St. Joseph University, B
Mount Vernon Nazarene University, AB
Notre Dame College, B
Ohio Dominican University, BM
Ohio Northern University, B
The Ohio State University, B
Ohio University, M
Otterbein University, B
Shawnee State University, B
Tiffin University, BM
The University of Akron, B
University of Cincinnati, B
University of Cincinnati Clermont College, A
University of Dayton, B

The University of Findlay, B
University of Mount Union, B
Wilmington College, B
Wittenberg University, B
Xavier University, BM

Oklahoma

Oklahoma Baptist University, B
Oklahoma Christian University, B
Rogers State University, B
Southern Nazarene University, BM
Southwestern Christian University, B
Tulsa Community College, A
The University of Tulsa, B

Oregon

Central Oregon Community College, A
Concordia University, B
Corban University, B
Lane Community College, A
University of Oregon, M

Pennsylvania

Alvernia University, B
Bucks County Community College, A
Butler County Community College, A
California University of Pennsylvania, BM
DeSales University, B
Drexel University, BM
East Stroudsburg University of Pennsylvania, M
Gannon University, B
Geneva College, B
Harcum College, A
Holy Family University, B
Indiana University of Pennsylvania, M
Keystone College, B
Lehigh Carbon Community College, A
Lock Haven University of Pennsylvania, BM
Manor College, A
Mercyhurst North East, A
Mercyhurst University, M
Messiah College, BM
Millersville University of Pennsylvania, M
Misericordia University, BM
Neumann University, BM
Northampton Community College, A
Pennsylvania College of Technology, B
Robert Morris University, BM
Seton Hill University, BM
Slippery Rock University of Pennsylvania, B
Temple University, BD
University of Pittsburgh at Bradford, B
University of Valley Forge, B
Westminster College, B
Widener University, B
York College of Pennsylvania, B

Rhode Island

Johnson & Wales University, B

South Carolina

The Citadel, The Military College of South Carolina,
    B
Claflin University, B
Coastal Carolina University, B
Coker College, BM
Erskine College, B
Limestone College, B
North Greenville University, B
University of South Carolina, BM
Winthrop University, B

South Dakota

Augustana University, BM
Black Hills State University, B
Dakota Wesleyan University, B
Northern State University, BM

Tennessee

Belmont University, M
East Tennessee State University, BM
King University, B
Lipscomb University, BM
Martin Methodist College, B
Southern Adventist University, B

Tennessee State University, M
Tennessee Technological University, M
Tennessee Wesleyan College, B
Trevecca Nazarene University, B
Tusculum College, B
Union University, B
University of Memphis, B
The University of Tennessee, BM

Texas

Abilene Christian University, B
Angelo State University, M
Baylor University, M
Dallas Baptist University, B
Hardin-Simmons University, BM
Howard Payne University, B
Lamar University, B
LeTourneau University, B
Lubbock Christian University, B
Midwestern State University, BM
Rice University, B
Sam Houston State University, M
Schreiner University, B
Southern Methodist University, BM
Southwestern Adventist University, AB
Southwestern Assemblies of God University, B
Texas A&M University, BM
Texas A&M University - Commerce, B
Texas Lutheran University, B
Texas Southern University, B
Texas State University, B
Texas Tech University, B
Texas Woman's University, MD
University of Dallas, M
University of Houston, B
University of the Incarnate Word, BM
University of Mary Hardin-Baylor, BM
The University of Texas at Austin, B
Wayland Baptist University, B
West Texas A&M University, M

Utah

Salt Lake Community College, A

Vermont

Castleton University, B
Johnson State College, B
Lyndon State College, B
Southern Vermont College, B

Virginia

Averett University, B
Eastern Mennonite University, B
Emory & Henry College, B
Ferrum College, B
George Mason University, M
Hampton University, BM
Liberty University, BMO
Lynchburg College, B
Old Dominion University, M
Roanoke College, B
Shenandoah University, B

Washington

Central Washington University, M
Clark College, A
Eastern Washington University, M
Gonzaga University, BM
Lake Washington Institute of Technology, A
Seattle Pacific University, B
Seattle University, M
Spokane Falls Community College, A
Walla Walla University, B
Washington State University, BM

West Virginia

Alderson Broaddus University, B
American Public University System, B
Bethany College, B
Davis & Elkins College, B
Glenville State College, B
Marshall University, M
Salem International University, B
University of Charleston, B
West Virginia University, MD

West Virginia Wesleyan College, B

Wisconsin

Cardinal Stritch University, BM
Carthage College, B
Concordia University Wisconsin, B
Maranatha Baptist University, B
Marian University, B
Marquette University, M
University of Wisconsin - Parkside, B
Viterbo University, B

U.S. Territories: Puerto Rico

Inter American University of Puerto Rico, Metropolitan Campus, B
Universidad del Turabo, B

Canada

Alberta

Mount Royal University, B
University of Alberta, M

British Columbia

Trinity Western University, B
University of Victoria, B

Maritime Provinces: New Brunswick

Université de Moncton, B
University of New Brunswick Fredericton, M

Maritime Provinces: Nova Scotia

Cape Breton University, B

Ontario

Brock University, B
Laurentian University, B
The University of Western Ontario, B
University of Windsor, B
York University, B

Saskatchewan

University of Regina, B

SPORT PSYCHOLOGY

United States

Arizona

Argosy University, Phoenix, MD

California

Argosy University, Inland Empire, M
Argosy University, Orange County, M
Argosy University, San Francisco Bay Area, M
California State University, Fresno, M
California State University, Long Beach, M
John F. Kennedy University, M
National University, M

Colorado

University of Denver, M

Connecticut

Southern Connecticut State University, M

Florida

Barry University, M
Florida State University, MD

Georgia

Argosy University, Atlanta, M

Illinois

Argosy University, Schaumburg, M
Southern Illinois University Edwardsville, M

Indiana

Purdue University, MD

Massachusetts

Springfield College, MO

Minnesota

Capella University, M

New Jersey

Seton Hall University, M

Ohio

Cleveland State University, M

Oregon

Oregon State University, D

Pennsylvania

California University of Pennsylvania, M
Chatham University, M
Lock Haven University of Pennsylvania, M

Rhode Island

University of Rhode Island, M

Texas

The University of Texas at Austin, M

West Virginia

West Virginia University, D

Canada

Newfoundland and Labrador

Memorial University of Newfoundland, M

Ontario

Queen's University at Kingston, M

SPORTS MEDICINE

United States

Alabama

United States Sports Academy, M

California

California State University, Long Beach, M

Florida

University of Florida, M
University of Miami, M

Georgia

Armstrong State University, MO
Georgia State University, M

Michigan

Eastern Michigan University, MO

Tennessee

The University of Tennessee, MD

Virginia

Shenandoah University, O

STATISTICS

United States

Alabama

Auburn University, M

Alaska

University of Alaska Fairbanks, MDO

Arizona

Arizona State University at the Tempe campus, MDO

Arizona State University at the West campus, B
Northern Arizona University, M
The University of Arizona, MD

Arkansas

University of Arkansas, M

California

California Baptist University, B
California Polytechnic State University, San Luis Obispo, B
California State University, East Bay, BM
California State University, Fullerton, B
California State University, Long Beach, B
San Diego State University, BM
San Francisco State University, B
San Jose State University, M
Sonoma State University, B
Stanford University, MD
University of California, Berkeley, BMD
University of California, Davis, BMD
University of California, Irvine, MD
University of California, Los Angeles, BMD
University of California, Riverside, BMD
University of California, San Diego, MD
University of California, Santa Barbara, BMD
University of California, Santa Cruz, MD
University of Southern California, M

Colorado

Colorado School of Mines, B
Colorado State University, BMD
University of Colorado Denver, MD
University of Denver, M

Connecticut

Central Connecticut State University, MO
University of Connecticut, BMD
Yale University, BMD

Delaware

University of Delaware, BM

District of Columbia

American University, B
The George Washington University, BMDO
Georgetown University, M
Trinity Washington University, B

Florida

Broward College, A
College of Central Florida, A
Florida Atlantic University, M
Florida International University, BM
Florida State University, BMD
South Florida State College, A
State College of Florida Manatee-Sarasota, A
University of Central Florida, BMO
University of Florida, BMD
University of North Florida, BM
University of South Florida, BMD

Georgia

Georgia Institute of Technology, M
Georgia State University, MD
University of Georgia, BMD

Idaho

Idaho State University, B
University of Idaho, M

Illinois

Loyola University Chicago, BM
Northern Illinois University, M
Northwestern University, BMD
Southern Illinois University Edwardsville, M
University of Chicago, BMD
University of Illinois at Chicago, BMD
University of Illinois at Urbana - Champaign, BMD

Indiana

Ball State University, M
Indiana University Bloomington, BMD

Indiana University - Purdue University Fort Wayne, B
Indiana University - Purdue University Indianapolis, D
Purdue University, MD
Saint Mary's College, B
University of Notre Dame, MD

Iowa

Dordt College, B
Iowa State University of Science and Technology, BMD
The University of Iowa, BMD

Kansas

Kansas State University, BMDO
The University of Kansas, MDO

Kentucky

Eastern Kentucky University, B
Murray State University, M
Northern Kentucky University, B
University of Kentucky, MD

Louisiana

Louisiana State University and Agricultural & Mechanical College, M
Louisiana Tech University, MD
McNeese State University, M
Tulane University, M
Xavier University of Louisiana, B

Maine

University of Southern Maine, MO

Maryland

Johns Hopkins University, MD
Loyola University Maryland, B
University of Maryland, Baltimore County, BMD
University of Maryland, College Park, MD

Massachusetts

Amherst College, B
Harvard University, BMD
Mount Holyoke College, B
University of Massachusetts Amherst, MD
Williams College, B

Michigan

Central Michigan University, B
Eastern Michigan University, B
Grand Valley State University, B
Michigan State University, BMD
Michigan Technological University, B
Oakland University, BO
University of Michigan, BMD
Wayne State University, MD
Western Michigan University, BMDO

Minnesota

Minnesota State University Mankato, M
St. Cloud State University, B
University of Minnesota, Duluth, B
University of Minnesota, Morris, B
University of Minnesota, Twin Cities Campus, BMD
Winona State University, B

Mississippi

Jackson State University, B
Mississippi State University, MD

Missouri

Missouri University of Science and Technology, D
University of Missouri, BMD
University of Missouri - Kansas City, MD
Washington University in St. Louis, BMD

Montana

Montana State University, BMD
Montana Tech of The University of Montana, B
University of Montana, B

Nebraska

University of Nebraska - Lincoln, MD

New Hampshire

University of New Hampshire, B

New Jersey

Montclair State University, M
Rutgers University - New Brunswick, BMD
Stevens Institute of Technology, MO

New Mexico

New Mexico Institute of Mining and Technology, M
University of New Mexico, BMD

New York

Barnard College, B
Baruch College of the City University of New York, BM
Columbia University, BMD
Columbia University, School of General Studies, B
Cornell University, BMD
Hunter College of the City University of New York, BM
New York University, MD
Rochester Institute of Technology, BO
St. John Fisher College, B
St. Lawrence University, B
State University of New York College at Oneonta, B
Stony Brook University, State University of New York, MDO
University at Buffalo, the State University of New York, B
University of Rochester, BMD

North Carolina

Duke University, MD
East Carolina University, MO
Elon University, B
North Carolina State University, BMD
The University of North Carolina at Chapel Hill, MD
The University of North Carolina at Charlotte, MO
The University of North Carolina Wilmington, BMO

North Dakota

North Dakota State University, BMDO

Ohio

Bowling Green State University, BMD
Case Western Reserve University, BMD
Miami University, BM
Miami University Hamilton, B
Ohio Northern University, B
The Ohio State University, MD
Ohio Wesleyan University, B
The University of Akron, B
University of Cincinnati, MD
The University of Toledo, MD
Wright State University, B
Youngstown State University, M

Oklahoma

Oklahoma State University, BMD
University of Central Oklahoma, BM

Oregon

Oregon State University, MD
Portland State University, M
Reed College, B

Pennsylvania

Carnegie Mellon University, BMD
Lehigh University, B
Penn State Abington, B
Penn State Altoona, B
Penn State Beaver, B
Penn State Berks, B
Penn State Brandywine, B
Penn State DuBois, B
Penn State Erie, The Behrend College, B
Penn State Fayette, The Eberly Campus, B
Penn State Greater Allegheny, B
Penn State Hazleton, B
Penn State Lehigh Valley, B
Penn State Mont Alto, B
Penn State New Kensington, B
Penn State Schuylkill, B

Penn State Shenango, B
Penn State University Park, BMD
Penn State Wilkes-Barre, B
Penn State Worthington Scranton, B
Penn State York, B
Slippery Rock University of Pennsylvania, B
Temple University, MD
University of Pennsylvania, BMD
University of Pittsburgh, BMD

Rhode Island

Bryant University, B
University of Rhode Island, MDO

South Carolina

Clemson University, MD
University of South Carolina, BMDO

South Dakota

South Dakota State University, MD

Tennessee

University of Memphis, M
The University of Tennessee, BMD
The University of Tennessee at Martin, B

Texas

Baylor University, BMD
LeTourneau University, B
Rice University, BMD
Sam Houston State University, M
Southern Methodist University, BMD
Stephen F. Austin State University, M
Texas A&M University, MD
Texas A&M University - Kingsville, M
Texas Tech University, MD
University of Houston - Clear Lake, M
University of the Incarnate Word, M
The University of Texas at Austin, MD
The University of Texas at Dallas, MD
The University of Texas at El Paso, BM
The University of Texas at San Antonio, BMD

Utah

Brigham Young University, M
University of Utah, M
Utah State University, BM

Vermont

Marlboro College, B
University of Vermont, BM

Virginia

George Mason University, MDO
Hampton University, M
University of Virginia, MD
Virginia Commonwealth University, MD
Virginia Polytechnic Institute and State University, BMD

Washington

University of Washington, BMD

West Virginia

West Virginia University, M

Wisconsin

University of Wisconsin - Madison, BMD

Wyoming

Casper College, A
Eastern Wyoming College, A
University of Wyoming, BMD

U.S. Territories: Puerto Rico

University of Puerto Rico, Mayagüez Campus, M

Canada

Alberta

University of Alberta, MDO
University of Calgary, BMD

British Columbia

Simon Fraser University, BMD
The University of British Columbia, BMD
The University of British Columbia - Okanagan
  Campus, B
University of Victoria, BMD

Manitoba

University of Manitoba, BMD
The University of Winnipeg, B

Maritime Provinces: New Brunswick

University of New Brunswick Fredericton, BMD
University of New Brunswick Saint John, B

Maritime Provinces: Nova Scotia

Acadia University, M
Dalhousie University, BMD
Mount Saint Vincent University, B
University of King's College, B

Newfoundland and Labrador

Memorial University of Newfoundland, BMD

Ontario

Brock University, BM
Carleton University, B
McMaster University, BM
Queen's University at Kingston, BMD
University of Guelph, MD
University of Ottawa, BMD
University of Toronto, MD
University of Waterloo, BMD
The University of Western Ontario, BMD
University of Windsor, MD
York University, BMD

Quebec

Concordia University, B
McGill University, BMD
Université Laval, BM
Université de Montréal, BMDO

Saskatchewan

University of Regina, BMD
University of Saskatchewan, BMD

STRUCTURAL BIOLOGY

United States

Alabama

The University of Alabama at Birmingham, D

California

Stanford University, D

Connecticut

University of Connecticut, MD

Florida

Florida State University, MD

Illinois

Illinois State University, M
Northwestern University, D

Iowa

Iowa State University of Science and Technology,
  MD

Louisiana

Tulane University, MD

Massachusetts

Harvard University, D
Massachusetts Institute of Technology, D

Michigan

Michigan State University, D

Minnesota

University of Minnesota, Twin Cities Campus, D

New York

Columbia University, D
Cornell University, MD
New York University, D
Stony Brook University, State University of New
  York, D
Syracuse University, D
University at Albany, State University of New York,
  MD
University at Buffalo, the State University of New
  York, MD
University of Rochester, D

North Carolina

Duke University, O

Pennsylvania

Carnegie Mellon University, D
Thomas Jefferson University, D
University of Pittsburgh, D

Texas

The University of Texas Health Science Center at
  San Antonio, MD
The University of Texas Medical Branch, D

Washington

University of Washington, D

STRUCTURAL ENGINEERING

United States

Alabama

Auburn University, MD
The University of Alabama in Huntsville, M

California

California State University, Northridge, M
Stanford University, M
University of California, Berkeley, MD
University of California, San Diego, BMD
University of Southern California, B

Colorado

University of Colorado Boulder, MD
University of Colorado Denver, MD

Delaware

University of Delaware, MD

Florida

University of Central Florida, BO
University of South Florida, MD

Illinois

Illinois Institute of Technology, M
Northwestern University, MD
Southern Illinois University Edwardsville, M
University of Illinois at Urbana - Champaign, B

Iowa

Iowa State University of Science and Technology,
  MD

Kansas

Kansas State University, MD

Louisiana

Louisiana State University and Agricultural & Mechanical College, MD

Massachusetts

Bristol Community College, A
Massachusetts Institute of Technology, D
Tufts University, MD
University of Massachusetts Amherst, M

Michigan

University of Michigan, M
Western Michigan University, B

Missouri

University of Missouri, MD

Nevada

College of Southern Nevada, A

New Jersey

Stevens Institute of Technology, MO

New York

Cornell University, MD
University at Buffalo, the State University of New
  York, BMD

North Dakota

University of North Dakota, M

Ohio

Ohio University, M
University of Dayton, M

Pennsylvania

Drexel University, M
Harrisburg Area Community College, A
Penn State Harrisburg, BO

Tennessee

University of Memphis, M

Texas

Southern Methodist University, D
The University of Texas at Tyler, M

Vermont

Norwich University, M

Virginia

George Mason University, M

Washington

University of Washington, MD

Wisconsin

Marquette University, MD
Moraine Park Technical College, A

Canada

Alberta

University of Alberta, MD
University of Calgary, MD

Maritime Provinces: New Brunswick

University of New Brunswick Fredericton, MD

Quebec

École Polytechnique de Montréal, MD
McGill University, MD

STUDENT PERSONNEL SER-VICES

United States

Arizona

Northern Arizona University, M

Arkansas

Arkansas State University, MO
Arkansas Tech University, M
University of Arkansas at Little Rock, M
University of Central Arkansas, M

California

Azusa Pacific University, M
California State University, Bakersfield, M
California State University, Long Beach, M
Fresno Pacific University, MO
San Jose State University, M
University of Southern California, M

Colorado

Colorado State University, M
University of Northern Colorado, D

Connecticut

University of Bridgeport, M

District of Columbia

The George Washington University, MO

Florida

Nova Southeastern University, M
University of Central Florida, M
University of Florida, M
University of South Florida, M
University of West Florida, M

Georgia

University of Georgia, MD

Illinois

DePaul University, M
Eastern Illinois University, M
Illinois State University, M
Lewis University, M
Southern Illinois University Edwardsville, M
Western Illinois University, M

Indiana

Indiana State University, M
Indiana University - Purdue University Indianapolis, M

Iowa

Iowa State University of Science and Technology, M
Kaplan University, Davenport Campus, M
The University of Iowa, MD
University of Northern Iowa, M

Kansas

Kansas State University, M

Kentucky

University of the Cumberlands, O
University of Louisville, MD
Western Kentucky University, M

Louisiana

Grambling State University, D
Northwestern State University of Louisiana, M

Maryland

University of Maryland, College Park, MDO

Massachusetts

Merrimack College, M
Springfield College, M

Michigan

Central Michigan University, M
Northern Michigan University, M

Minnesota

Minnesota State University Mankato, MDO
St. Cloud State University, M
University of Minnesota, Twin Cities Campus, MDO
University of St. Thomas, MO

Mississippi

Mississippi State University, MD
University of Southern Mississippi, M

Missouri

Missouri State University, M
Saint Louis University, M

University of Central Missouri, M

Nebraska

University of Nebraska at Kearney, M

New Jersey

College of Saint Elizabeth, O
Monmouth University, M
Rutgers University - New Brunswick, M
Seton Hall University, M

New York

Binghamton University, State University of New York, M
Buffalo State College, State University of New York, M
Canisius College, M
The College of Saint Rose, M
Manhattan College, O
New York University, M
State University of New York at Plattsburgh, M
Syracuse University, M
University of Rochester, M

North Carolina

Appalachian State University, M

North Dakota

University of Mary, M

Ohio

Ashland University, M
Bowling Green State University, M
Kent State University, M
Ohio University, M
University of Dayton, M
Walsh University, M

Oklahoma

University of Central Oklahoma, M

Oregon

Oregon State University, M

Pennsylvania

Bloomsburg University of Pennsylvania, M
Bucknell University, M
Indiana University of Pennsylvania, M
Messiah College, M
Shippensburg University of Pennsylvania, M
Slippery Rock University of Pennsylvania, M
West Chester University of Pennsylvania, O

Rhode Island

University of Rhode Island, M

South Carolina

Bob Jones University, MO
The Citadel, The Military College of South Carolina, M
Clemson University, M
University of South Carolina, M

Tennessee

Lee University, M
The University of Tennessee, M

Texas

St. Edward's University, M
Texas State University, M

Utah

University of Utah, M

Virginia

Hampton University, M
Liberty University, M
Regent University, M
University of Virginia, M
Virginia Commonwealth University, M
Virginia Polytechnic Institute and State University, M

Wisconsin

Concordia University Wisconsin, M
Marquette University, M
University of Wisconsin - La Crosse, M

Wyoming

University of Wyoming, M

Canada

Manitoba

Providence University College & Theological Seminary, M

SUBSTANCE ABUSE/ADDICTION COUNSELING

United States

Alabama

Gadsden State Community College, A
Troy University, M

Arizona

Grand Canyon University, M
Mohave Community College, A
Pima Community College, A
Rio Salado College, A

Arkansas

Arkansas State University, O
University of Arkansas at Pine Bluff, M
University of Central Arkansas, B

California

American River College, A
Butte College, A
Charles R. Drew University of Medicine and Science, A
College of the Desert, A
College of San Mateo, A
College of the Siskiyous, A
Fresno City College, A
Glendale Community College, A
Hartnell College, A
Lassen Community College District, A
Long Beach City College, A
Mendocino College, A
Merritt College, A
Modesto Junior College, A
Mt. San Jacinto College, A
National University, A
Oxnard College, A
Palomar College, A
Saddleback College, A
San Jose City College, A
University of California, Berkeley, O
Yuba College, A

Connecticut

Fairfield University, O
Gateway Community College, A
Housatonic Community College, A
Middlesex Community College, A
Naugatuck Valley Community College, A
Northwestern Connecticut Community College, A
Post University, M
Quinebaug Valley Community College, A

Delaware

Delaware Technical & Community College, Stanton/Wilmington Campus, A
Delaware Technical & Community College, Terry Campus, A

District of Columbia

The George Washington University, M

Florida

City College (Gainesville), A
Florida SouthWestern State College, A

Miami Dade College, A
Palm Beach Atlantic University, M
St. Petersburg College, A
University of South Florida, M

Hawaii

Argosy University, Hawai'i, O

Idaho

Northwest Nazarene University, M

Illinois

Carl Sandburg College, A
City Colleges of Chicago, Harold Washington College, A
City Colleges of Chicago, Kennedy-King College, A
College of DuPage, A
College of Lake County, A
Governors State University, M
Illinois Central College, A
Moraine Valley Community College, A
Oakton Community College, A
St. Augustine College, A
Triton College, A
University of Illinois at Springfield, MO
University of St. Francis, B

Indiana

Indiana University Northwest, M
Indiana University - Purdue University Fort Wayne, B
Indiana University - Purdue University Indianapolis, D
Indiana Wesleyan University, ABM
Martin University, B

Iowa

Southeastern Community College, A

Kansas

Butler Community College, A
Colby Community College, A
Garden City Community College, A
Kansas City Kansas Community College, A
Kansas Wesleyan University, B
Newman University, B
Washburn University, ABM

Kentucky

University of Louisville, M

Louisiana

McNeese State University, M
Northwestern State University of Louisiana, B

Maine

Beal College, A
University of Southern Maine, O

Maryland

Anne Arundel Community College, A
Community College of Baltimore County, A
Coppin State University, M
Howard Community College, A
Johns Hopkins University, D
Wor-Wic Community College, A

Massachusetts

Cambridge College, MO
North Shore Community College, A
Springfield College, M

Michigan

University of Detroit Mercy, BMO

Minnesota

Capella University, MD
Century College, A
Mesabi Range College, A
Metropolitan State University, B
Minneapolis Community and Technical College, A
North Central University, B
St. Cloud State University, B
Saint Mary's University of Minnesota, O

Walden University, MD

Missouri

City Vision University, B
Maryville University of Saint Louis, M

Montana

Dawson Community College, A
Flathead Valley Community College, A
University of Great Falls, AB

Nevada

University of Nevada, Las Vegas, O

New Hampshire

Keene State College, B
NHTI, Concord's Community College, A

New Jersey

Camden County College, A
The College of New Jersey, MO
Kean University, M
Monmouth University, M
Montclair State University, O

New York

Adirondack Community College, A
Broome Community College, A
Corning Community College, A
Erie Community College, A
Finger Lakes Community College, A
Genesee Community College, A
Hudson Valley Community College, A
Mohawk Valley Community College, A
New York Institute of Technology, O
Pace University, MD
Stony Brook University, State University of New York, M
Suffolk County Community College, A
Syracuse University, O
Tompkins Cortland Community College, A
Westchester Community College, A

North Carolina

Chowan University, B
East Carolina University, MDO
Guilford Technical Community College, A
Lenoir-Rhyne University, M
Pitt Community College, A
Sandhills Community College, A
Southwestern Community College, A
The University of North Carolina at Charlotte, O
Wake Technical Community College, A
Western Piedmont Community College, A

North Dakota

Minot State University, B
University of Mary, BM

Ohio

Cleveland State University, O
Ohio Christian University, B
Southern State Community College, A
Tiffin University, B
University of Cincinnati, B

Oklahoma

Northeastern State University, M
Oklahoma State University, Oklahoma City, A
University of Central Oklahoma, M
University of Oklahoma, M

Oregon

Central Oregon Community College, A
Chemeketa Community College, A
Lewis & Clark College, A
Portland Community College, A
Tillamook Bay Community College, A
Treasure Valley Community College, A

Pennsylvania

Alvernia University, B
Carlow University, MO
Chestnut Hill College, MO

Community College of Allegheny County, A
Drexel University, B
Slippery Rock University of Pennsylvania, M
Waynesburg University, M

Rhode Island

Community College of Rhode Island, A
Salve Regina University, O

South Dakota

Sinte Gleska University, B
Sisseton-Wahpeton College, A
The University of South Dakota, BMO

Texas

Alvin Community College, A
Amarillo College, A
Angelina College, A
Austin Community College District, A
Eastfield College, A
El Paso Community College, A
Grayson College, A
Howard College, A
Lamar State College - Port Arthur, A
Lee College, A
Midland College, A
Odessa College, A
Texarkana College, A
Tyler Junior College, A

Vermont

College of St. Joseph, BM
Johnson State College, M

Virginia

J. Sargeant Reynolds Community College, A
Liberty University, M

Washington

Clark College, A
Columbia Basin College, A
Edmonds Community College, A
Lower Columbia College, A
Northwest Indian College, A
Olympic College, A
Peninsula College, A
Pierce College at Fort Steilacoom, A
Pierce College at Puyallup, A
Seattle Central College, A
Spokane Falls Community College, A
Wenatchee Valley College, A
Yakima Valley Community College, A

West Virginia

Mountain State College, A

Wisconsin

Chippewa Valley Technical College, A
College of Menominee Nation, A
Fox Valley Technical College, A
Lac Courte Oreilles Ojibwa Community College, A
Moraine Park Technical College, A
Northcentral Technical College, A
Viterbo University, BM

Wyoming

Casper College, A

U.S. Territories: Puerto Rico

Universidad Central del Caribe, M

Canada

Alberta

University of Lethbridge, BM

SUPERINTENDENCY AND EDUCATIONAL SYSTEM ADMINISTRATION

United States

Iowa

Dordt College, B

SUPPLY CHAIN MANAGEMENT

United States

Alabama

Alabama Agricultural and Mechanical University, M
The University of Alabama in Huntsville, MO

Arizona

Arizona State University at the Tempe campus, MD

California

California State University, East Bay, M
California State University, San Bernardino, M
Golden Gate University, O
University of La Verne, M
University of San Diego, MO
University of Southern California, MO

Connecticut

Central Connecticut State University, O
Quinnipiac University, M

District of Columbia

Howard University, M

Florida

Embry-Riddle Aeronautical University - Worldwide, M
Florida Institute of Technology, M
Polytechnic University of Puerto Rico, Miami Campus, M
University of Florida, O

Georgia

Clayton State University, M
Georgia Southern University, D

Illinois

Elmhurst College, M
Loyola University Chicago, M
Western Illinois University, O

Iowa

Kaplan University, Davenport Campus, M
The University of Iowa, M

Kansas

Friends University, M
Kansas State University, M

Kentucky

University of Louisville, O

Maine

Maine Maritime Academy, M

Maryland

Towson University, MO

Massachusetts

Suffolk University, M
University of Massachusetts Dartmouth, O
University of Massachusetts Lowell, O

Michigan

Eastern Michigan University, MO
Michigan State University, MD
University of Michigan, M
University of Michigan - Dearborn, M

Minnesota

Capella University, MD
University of Minnesota, Twin Cities Campus, M
Walden University, D

Missouri

Lindenwood University, M
University of Missouri - St. Louis, DO
Washington University in St. Louis, M

New Hampshire

Southern New Hampshire University, MO

New Jersey

Rutgers University - Newark, D
Seton Hall University, M

New York

Rensselaer Polytechnic Institute, M
Syracuse University, MD

North Carolina

North Carolina Agricultural and Technical State University, M
North Carolina State University, M
The University of North Carolina at Charlotte, O
The University of North Carolina at Greensboro, O

Ohio

Case Western Reserve University, MD
The University of Akron, M
Wright State University, M

Oregon

Oregon State University, M
Portland State University, M

Pennsylvania

Delaware Valley University, M
Moravian College, M
Penn State University Park, M

Rhode Island

Bryant University, M
University of Rhode Island, M

Tennessee

University of Memphis, D
The University of Tennessee at Chattanooga, O

Texas

Texas A&M University - San Antonio, M
Texas Christian University, M
University of Dallas, M
University of Houston, M
University of North Texas, M
The University of Texas at Austin, MD
The University of Texas at Dallas, M

Vermont

Norwich University, M

Wisconsin

Marquette University, M
University of Wisconsin - Madison, M
University of Wisconsin - Stout, M
University of Wisconsin - Whitewater, M

Canada

Ontario

Wilfrid Laurier University, MD

Quebec

HEC Montreal, MO

SURGICAL NURSING

United States

U.S. Territories: Puerto Rico

Inter American University of Puerto Rico, Arecibo Campus, M

SURGICAL TECHNOLOGY/ TECHNOLOGIST

United States

Alabama

Calhoun Community College, A
Community College of the Air Force, A
James H. Faulkner State Community College, A
Virginia College in Birmingham, A
Virginia College in Mobile, A

Arizona

GateWay Community College, A
Mohave Community College, A

Arkansas

North Arkansas College, A
Southeast Arkansas College, A
University of Arkansas - Fort Smith, A
University of Arkansas for Medical Sciences, A

California

American Career College (Anaheim), A
American Career College (Los Angeles), A
American Career College (Ontario), A
Carrington College - Citrus Heights, A
Carrington College - San Jose, A
Fresno City College, A
MiraCosta College, A
San Joaquin Valley College (Bakersfield), A
San Joaquin Valley College (Fresno), A
Skyline College, A
Southwestern College, A

Colorado

Aims Community College, A
Colorado Technical University Colorado Springs, A
Colorado Technical University Denver South, A
Everest College (Thornton), A
Pueblo Community College, A

Connecticut

Manchester Community College, A

Florida

Fortis College (Orange Park), A
Gulf Coast State College, A
Keiser University, A
Northwest Florida State College, A
Southeastern College - West Palm Beach, A
Southern Technical College (Fort Myers), A
Southern Technical College (Tampa), A
Tallahassee Community College, A
Virginia College in Pensacola, A

Georgia

Athens Technical College, A
Augusta Technical College, A
Coastal Pines Technical College, A
Columbus Technical College, A
Georgia Northwestern Technical College, A
Georgia Piedmont Technical College, A
Lanier Technical College, A
Savannah Technical College, A
Southern Crescent Technical College, A
Southern Regional Technical College, A
Virginia College in Macon, A

Idaho

College of Southern Idaho, A
College of Western Idaho, A
Eastern Idaho Technical College, A

Stevens-Henager College (Boise), A

Illinois

City Colleges of Chicago, Malcolm X College, A
College of DuPage, A
Illinois Central College, A
Lincoln Land Community College, A
Parkland College, A
Richland Community College, A
Robert Morris University Illinois, A
Rock Valley College, A
Southeastern Illinois College, A
Trinity College of Nursing and Health Sciences, A

Indiana

Harrison College, A
Ivy Tech Community College - Central Indiana, A
Ivy Tech Community College - Columbus, A
Ivy Tech Community College - East Central, A
Ivy Tech Community College - Kokomo, A
Ivy Tech Community College - Lafayette, A
Ivy Tech Community College - Northwest, A
Ivy Tech Community College - Southwest, A
Ivy Tech Community College - Wabash Valley, A
University of Saint Francis, A
Vincennes University, A

Iowa

Iowa Lakes Community College, A
Kirkwood Community College, A
Mercy College of Health Sciences, A
Western Iowa Tech Community College, A

Kansas

Hutchinson Community College, A
Seward County Community College and Area Technical School, A
Washburn University, A
Wichita Area Technical College, A

Kentucky

American National University (Florence), A
American National University (Lexington), A
American National University (Louisville), A
Bluegrass Community and Technical College, A
Jefferson Community and Technical College, A
Owensboro Community and Technical College, A
Somerset Community College, A
Spencerian College, A
West Kentucky Community and Technical College, A

Louisiana

McCann School of Business & Technology (Monroe), A
South Louisiana Community College, A
Southern University at Shreveport, A
Virginia College in Baton Rouge, A

Maine

Eastern Maine Community College, A
Southern Maine Community College, A

Maryland

Anne Arundel Community College, A
Baltimore City Community College, A
Frederick Community College, A
Montgomery College, A

Massachusetts

Springfield Technical Community College, A

Michigan

Baker College, A
Delta College, A
Henry Ford College, A
Kalamazoo Valley Community College, A
Kirtland Community College, A
Lansing Community College, A
Macomb Community College, A
Northern Michigan University, A
Oakland Community College, A
Wayne County Community College District, A

Minnesota

Anoka Technical College, A
Lake Superior College, A
Minnesota West Community and Technical College, A
Northland Community and Technical College, A
Rasmussen College Brooklyn Park, A
Rasmussen College St. Cloud, A
Rochester Community and Technical College, A
St. Cloud Technical & Community College, A

Mississippi

East Central Community College, A
Hinds Community College, A
Holmes Community College, A
Virginia College in Biloxi, A
Virginia College in Jackson, A

Missouri

Lincoln University, A

Montana

Flathead Valley Community College, A
Great Falls College Montana State University, A
Montana State University Billings, A
University of Montana, A

Nebraska

Metropolitan Community College, A
Nebraska Methodist College, A
Northeast Community College, A
Southeast Community College, Lincoln Campus, A

New Hampshire

Great Bay Community College, A

New Jersey

Berkeley College - Woodland Park Campus, A

New Mexico

Central New Mexico Community College, A
San Juan College, A

New York

Nassau Community College, A
Niagara County Community College, A
Swedish Institute, College of Health Sciences, A
Trocaire College, A

North Carolina

Asheville-Buncombe Technical Community College, A
Blue Ridge Community College, A
Cabarrus College of Health Sciences, A
Cape Fear Community College, A
Coastal Carolina Community College, A
Fayetteville Technical Community College, A
Guilford Technical Community College, A
Miller-Motte College (Cary), A
Miller-Motte College (Wilmington), A
Sandhills Community College, A
Wilson Community College, A

North Dakota

Bismarck State College, A

Ohio

American National University (Cincinnati), A
American National University (Kettering), A
American National University (Youngstown), A
Brown Mackie College - North Canton, A
Central Ohio Technical College, A
Cincinnati State Technical and Community College, A
Columbus State Community College, A
Cuyahoga Community College, A
Lakeland Community College, A
Lorain County Community College, A
Miami-Jacobs Career College (Dayton), A
Owens Community College, A
Sinclair Community College, A
The University of Akron, A
University of Cincinnati Clermont College, A

Oklahoma

Community Care College, A
Heritage College, A
Oklahoma City Community College, A
Tulsa Community College, A

Oregon

Mt. Hood Community College, A

Pennsylvania

Community College of Allegheny County, A
Delaware County Community College, A
Harrisburg Area Community College, A
Lackawanna College, A
Luzerne County Community College, A
McCann School of Business & Technology (Lewisburg), A
McCann School of Business & Technology (Pottsville), A
Montgomery County Community College, A
Mount Aloysius College, A
Pennsylvania College of Health Sciences, A
Pennsylvania College of Technology, A
Pittsburgh Technical Institute, A
University of Pittsburgh at Johnstown, A

Rhode Island

New England Institute of Technology, A

South Carolina

Central Carolina Technical College, A
Midlands Technical College, A
Miller-Motte Technical College (North Charleston), A
York Technical College, A

South Dakota

Presentation College, A
Southeast Technical Institute, A
Western Dakota Technical Institute, A

Tennessee

Concorde Career College, A
Miller-Motte Technical College (Chattanooga), A
Miller-Motte Technical College (Clarksville), A
Northeast State Community College, A
Walters State Community College, A

Texas

Austin Community College District, A
The College of Health Care Professions (Houston), A
Collin County Community College District, A
El Centro College, A
El Paso Community College, A
Kilgore College, A
Lamar State College - Port Arthur, A
Lone Star College - Tomball, A
Paris Junior College, A
San Jacinto College District, A
South Plains College, A
Tarrant County College District, A
Trinity Valley Community College, A
Tyler Junior College, A
Virginia College in Austin, A

Utah

Stevens-Henager College (West Haven), A

Virginia

American National University (Danville), A
American National University (Harrisonburg), A
ECPI University (Manassas), A
ECPI University (Virginia Beach), A
Miller-Motte Technical College (Lynchburg), A
Sentara College of Health Sciences, A
Virginia College in Richmond, A

Washington

Bellingham Technical College, A
Clover Park Technical College, A
Columbia Basin College, A
Renton Technical College, A
Spokane Community College, A

West Virginia

BridgeValley Community and Technical College
  (Montgomery), A
West Virginia Northern Community College, A

Wisconsin

Gateway Technical College, A
Milwaukee Area Technical College, A
Moraine Park Technical College, A
Waukesha County Technical College, A
Western Technical College, A

Wyoming

Laramie County Community College, A

SURVEY METHODOLOGY

United States

Maryland

University of Maryland, College Park, MD

Michigan

University of Michigan, MDO

Nebraska

University of Nebraska - Lincoln, MD

SURVEY TECHNOLOGY/SUR-VEYING

United States

Alabama

Troy University, B

Alaska

University of Alaska Anchorage, AB

Arizona

Phoenix College, A

Arkansas

University of Arkansas Community College at Morrilton, A
University of Arkansas at Monticello, AB

California

Bakersfield College, A
College of the Canyons, A
Cuyamaca College, A
Mt. San Antonio College, A
Sacramento City College, A
Santa Rosa Junior College, A
Santiago Canyon College, A

Colorado

Metropolitan State University of Denver, B

Delaware

Delaware Technical & Community College, Jack F.
  Owens Campus, A
Delaware Technical & Community College,
  Stanton/Wilmington Campus, A

Florida

Everglades University (Boca Raton), B
Everglades University (Maitland), B
Everglades University (Sarasota), B
Indian River State College, A
Palm Beach State College, A
South Florida State College, A
University of Florida, B

Georgia

Kennesaw State University, B

Idaho

Idaho State University, B

Illinois

Moraine Valley Community College, A
Morrison Institute of Technology, A
Triton College, A
Waubonsee Community College, A

Indiana

Purdue University Northwest (Hammond), B
Vincennes University, A

Kentucky

Big Sandy Community and Technical College, A

Louisiana

Nicholls State University, B
South Louisiana Community College, A

Maine

University of Maine, B

Maryland

Community College of Baltimore County, A

Michigan

Ferris State University, AB
Lansing Community College, A
Macomb Community College, A

Minnesota

Saint Paul College - A Community & Technical College, A

Montana

Flathead Valley Community College, A

Nevada

College of Southern Nevada, A
Great Basin College, B

New Jersey

Middlesex County College, A

New Mexico

New Mexico State University, B
Santa Fe Community College, A

New York

Mohawk Valley Community College, A
Paul Smith's College, A
State University of New York College of Environ-
  mental Science and Forestry, A
State University of New York College of Technology
  at Alfred, AB

North Carolina

Asheville-Buncombe Technical Community College,
  A
Central Piedmont Community College, A
Fayetteville Technical Community College, A
Guilford Technical Community College, A
Sandhills Community College, A
Wake Technical Community College, A
Western Piedmont Community College, A

North Dakota

Bismarck State College, A

Ohio

The Ohio State University, B
Sinclair Community College, A
Stark State College, A
The University of Akron, AB

Oklahoma

Oklahoma State University, Oklahoma City, A

Oregon

Clackamas Community College, A
Oregon Institute of Technology, B

Pennsylvania

Penn State Wilkes-Barre, AB
Pennsylvania College of Technology, A

South Carolina

South Carolina State University, B

South Dakota

Southeast Technical Institute, A

Tennessee

East Tennessee State University, B

Texas

Austin Community College District, A
Texas State Technical College, A
Tyler Junior College, A

Utah

Salt Lake Community College, A
Utah Valley University, AB

Washington

Bates Technical College, A
Bellingham Technical College, A
Clark College, A
Renton Technical College, A

West Virginia

Glenville State College, A

Wisconsin

Gateway Technical College, A
Nicolet Area Technical College, A

Wyoming

Sheridan College, A

U.S. Territories: Guam

Guam Community College, A

U.S. Territories: Puerto Rico

Polytechnic University of Puerto Rico, AB
University of Puerto Rico, Mayagüez Campus, B

Canada

British Columbia

British Columbia Institute of Technology, AB

Maritime Provinces: New Brunswick

University of New Brunswick Fredericton, B

Quebec

Université Laval, B

SURVEYING ENGINEERING

United States

Florida

Florida Atlantic University, B

Iowa

Des Moines Area Community College, A
Kirkwood Community College, A

Michigan

Ferris State University, B
Michigan Technological University, B

New Mexico

Central New Mexico Community College, A

North Carolina

North Carolina Agricultural and Technical State University, B

Rhode Island

Community College of Rhode Island, A

Canada

Maritime Provinces: New Brunswick

University of New Brunswick Fredericton, MD

SUSTAINABILITY MANAGEMENT

United States

Arizona

Argosy University, Phoenix, MD

California

Argosy University, Inland Empire, MD
Argosy University, Los Angeles, M
Argosy University, Orange County, MD
Argosy University, San Francisco Bay Area, MD
Dominican University of California, M
National University, M
Point Loma Nazarene University, M
San Francisco State University, M
University of California, Berkeley, O

Colorado

Argosy University, Denver, MD
Colorado State University, M
University of Colorado Denver, M

Florida

Argosy University, Sarasota, MDO
Argosy University, Tampa, MD
University of South Florida, M

Georgia

South University, M

Hawaii

Argosy University, Hawai'i, MD

Illinois

Argosy University, Chicago, MD
Argosy University, Schaumburg, M
DePaul University, M
Illinois Institute of Technology, M

Indiana

Indiana University Bloomington, M
University of Saint Francis, M
Valparaiso University, O

Iowa

Maharishi University of Management, M

Maine

University of Maine, M
University of Southern Maine, M

Massachusetts

Brandeis University, M
Clark University, M

Michigan

Aquinas College, M
Cleary University, MO

Minnesota

Argosy University, Twin Cities, MD

New Hampshire

Franklin Pierce University, M
Southern New Hampshire University, M
University of New Hampshire, O

New Jersey

Fairleigh Dickinson University, College at Florham,
  O

New York

Bard College, M
Baruch College of the City University of New York,
  M
Columbia University, M
Rochester Institute of Technology, MD
State University of New York College of Environmental Science and Forestry, M

Ohio

Baldwin Wallace University, M
Case Western Reserve University, D

Oklahoma

Oklahoma State University, O

Oregon

Oregon State University, MD
University of Portland, M

Pennsylvania

Chatham University, M
Duquesne University, M

Tennessee

Lipscomb University, M

Texas

Argosy University, Dallas, MDO

Utah

Argosy University, Salt Lake City, MD

Vermont

Goddard College, M
Marlboro College, M

Virginia

Argosy University, Washington DC, MD
George Mason University, M

Washington

Argosy University, Seattle, MD
City University of Seattle, O
Seattle Pacific University, M

Wisconsin

Edgewood College, M
University of Wisconsin - Green Bay, M
University of Wisconsin - Stout, M
University of Wisconsin - Superior, M

Canada

Saskatchewan

University of Saskatchewan, M

SUSTAINABLE DEVELOPMENT

United States

Alaska

University of Alaska Fairbanks, D

Arizona

Arizona State University at the Tempe campus,
  MDO
Northern Arizona University, M

California

Antioch University Los Angeles, M
California State University, Stanislaus, M
Stanford University, M
University of California, Berkeley, O
University of California, Santa Barbara, MD
University of Southern California, O

Colorado

University of Colorado Denver, MD

Connecticut

University of Connecticut, M

District of Columbia

American University, M

Florida

Florida Atlantic University, O
University of Florida, M
University of South Florida, MO

Georgia

Emory University, M
Savannah College of Art and Design, M
University of Georgia, M

Hawaii

Hawai'i Pacific University, M

Illinois

DePaul University, M
Eastern Illinois University, M
Judson University, M
Western Illinois University, O

Iowa

Iowa State University of Science and Technology,
  MD

Maryland

University of Maryland, College Park, M

Massachusetts

Boston Architectural College, M
Brandeis University, M
Clark University, M
Lesley University, M
University of Massachusetts Amherst, M
University of Massachusetts Lowell, O

Michigan

University of Michigan, M
Wayne State University, O

Minnesota

Minneapolis College of Art and Design, O
Walden University, MD

Mississippi

Mississippi State University, MD

New Jersey

Montclair State University, M
Ramapo College of New Jersey, M

New York

City College of the City University of New York, M
Clarkson University, MD
Columbia University, M
Cornell University, MD
Fashion Institute of Technology, M
Hofstra University, M
New York School of Interior Design, M
New York University, M
Pace University, M
Pratt Institute, M
Rochester Institute of Technology, MD
State University of New York College of Environmental Science and Forestry, MD

North Carolina

Appalachian State University, M
Lenoir-Rhyne University, M

Ohio

Cleveland State University, M
Xavier University, M

Oklahoma

University of Oklahoma, MD

Pennsylvania

Carnegie Mellon University, M
Penn State University Park, M
Philadelphia University, M
Temple University, M
West Chester University of Pennsylvania, O

Tennessee

Lipscomb University, MO

Texas

St. Edward's University, M
Southern Methodist University, M
Texas A&M University - Kingsville, D
Texas State University, M
Texas Tech University, M
The University of Texas at Arlington, M
The University of Texas at Austin, M

Washington

University of Washington, MD

West Virginia

West Virginia University, D

Wisconsin

University of Wisconsin - Madison, M

Canada

Alberta

University of Calgary, M

Maritime Provinces: New Brunswick

University of New Brunswick Fredericton, M

Maritime Provinces: Nova Scotia

Acadia University, M

Ontario

The University of Western Ontario, M

Quebec

HEC Montreal, O

SWEDISH LANGUAGE AND LITERATURE

United States

Utah

Brigham Young University, B

Washington

University of Washington, B

SYSTEM ADMINISTRATION/ADMINISTRATOR

United States

Arizona

Rio Salado College, A

California

American River College, A
Butte College, A
Cabrillo College, A
Cañada College, A
Chabot College, A
City College of San Francisco, A
College of San Mateo, A
Cosumnes River College, A
Cuesta College, A
Gavilan College, A
Long Beach City College, A
Los Angeles City College, A
Ohlone College, A

Santa Barbara City College, A
Sierra College, A
Southwestern College, A

Colorado

National American University (Colorado Springs), B
National American University (Denver), AB
Regis University, B

Connecticut

Quinebaug Valley Community College, A

Florida

Broward College, A
Florida National University, A
Florida SouthWestern State College, A
Florida State College at Jacksonville, A
Gulf Coast State College, A
Miami Dade College, A
Palm Beach State College, A
Polk State College, A
Seminole State College of Florida, A
South Florida State College, A
Southern Technical College (Tampa), A

Idaho

College of Western Idaho, A

Illinois

Heartland Community College, A
Illinois Valley Community College, A
Kaskaskia College, A
Kishwaukee College, A
Parkland College, A
Southwestern Illinois College, A

Indiana

Harrison College, A
Ivy Tech Community College - Bloomington, A
Ivy Tech Community College - Central Indiana, A
Ivy Tech Community College - East Central, A
Ivy Tech Community College - Kokomo, A
Ivy Tech Community College - Richmond, A
Ivy Tech Community College - Southeast, A
Ivy Tech Community College - Southern Indiana, A
Ivy Tech Community College - Southwest, A
Ivy Tech Community College - Wabash Valley, A

Iowa

Dordt College, B
Kirkwood Community College, A
North Iowa Area Community College, A

Kansas

Manhattan Area Technical College, A

Kentucky

Sullivan College of Technology and Design, AB

Louisiana

Louisiana Delta Community College, A

Maine

Central Maine Community College, A
York County Community College, A

Massachusetts

Massachusetts Bay Community College, A
Simmons College, B

Michigan

Michigan Technological University, B
Wayne County Community College District, A

Minnesota

Academy College, A
Inver Hills Community College, A
Lake Superior College, A
Minneapolis Community and Technical College, A
Minnesota State Community and Technical College - Wadena, A
Ridgewater College, A
Rochester Community and Technical College, A
St. Cloud Technical & Community College, A

Mississippi

Southwest Mississippi Community College, A

Missouri

Metropolitan Community College - Kansas City, A
Missouri College, A
Vatterott College (Berkeley), AB
Vatterott College (Kansas City), A
Vatterott College (Sunset Hills), AB

Montana

University of Great Falls, B

Nebraska

Bellevue University, B
Central Community College - Grand Island Campus, A
Southeast Community College, Lincoln Campus, A
Southeast Community College, Milford Campus, A

New Jersey

Bergen Community College, A
Brookdale Community College, A

New Mexico

Clovis Community College, A
National American University (Albuquerque), B

New York

The College of Westchester, A
Corning Community College, A
Genesee Community College, A
Hudson Valley Community College, A
Island Drafting and Technical Institute, A
Rochester Institute of Technology, B
Rockland Community College, A

North Carolina

Sampson Community College, A
Stanly Community College, A

North Dakota

Dakota College at Bottineau, A

Ohio

Cincinnati State Technical and Community College, A
Northwest State Community College, A
Sinclair Community College, A
Vatterott College, A
Walsh University, B

Oregon

Linn-Benton Community College, A

Pennsylvania

Berks Technical Institute, A
Bucks County Community College, A
Butler County Community College, A
Laurel Business Institute, A
Montgomery County Community College, A
Pittsburgh Technical Institute, A

South Dakota

Mitchell Technical Institute, A

Tennessee

Martin Methodist College, B
Vatterott College (Memphis), A

Texas

Collin County Community College District, A
Del Mar College, A
Eastfield College, A
Houston Community College, A
San Antonio College, A
Texas State Technical College, A

Vermont

Champlain College, B

Washington

Edmonds Community College, A

Wisconsin

Western Technical College, A

U.S. Territories: Puerto Rico

Universidad del Este, B

SYSTEM MANAGEMENT

United States

Florida

Florida Institute of Technology, M

Indiana

Rose-Hulman Institute of Technology, M

Mississippi

University of Mississippi, M

Nebraska

University of Nebraska - Lincoln, M

New York

Fordham University, M
New York University, M

Ohio

Kent State University, D

U.S. Territories: Puerto Rico

Universidad del Turabo, D

SYSTEM, NETWORKING, AND LAN/WAN MANAGEMENT/MAN-AGER

United States

Alaska

Charter College, A

California

MTI College, A

Colorado

National American University (Denver), AB

Florida

College of Business and Technology - Main Campus, A
St. Johns River State College, A

Georgia

University of Phoenix - Augusta Campus, A

Hawaii

University of Hawaii - West Oahu, B

Illinois

Moraine Valley Community College, A

Iowa

Iowa Lakes Community College, A

Kansas

Cloud County Community College, A

Michigan

Baker College, A
North Central Michigan College, A
Northern Michigan University, B
Wayne County Community College District, A

Minnesota

Academy College, A
Capella University, B

Mississippi

Alcorn State University, B

Missouri

Metropolitan Community College - Kansas City, A
Mineral Area College, A
Vatterott College (Kansas City), A
Vatterott College (Springfield), A

Montana

University of Great Falls, B

New Jersey

University of Phoenix - Jersey City Campus, A

New Mexico

National American University (Albuquerque), B
Southwestern Indian Polytechnic Institute, A

New York

Bryant & Stratton College - Albany Campus, A
Bryant & Stratton College - Amherst Campus, A
Bryant & Stratton College - Buffalo Campus, A
Bryant & Stratton College - Greece Campus, A
Bryant & Stratton College - Henrietta Campus, A
Bryant & Stratton College - Liverpool Campus, A
Morrisville State College, B
Rochester Institute of Technology, B
State University of New York College of Technology at Alfred, B

North Carolina

Blue Ridge Community College, A
Craven Community College, A
Durham Technical Community College, A
Gaston College, A
Guilford Technical Community College, A
Miller-Motte College (Cary), A
Nash Community College, A
Pitt Community College, A
Rowan-Cabarrus Community College, A
Southwestern Community College, A

North Dakota

Williston State College, A

Ohio

Belmont College, A
Bryant & Stratton College - Cleveland Campus, A
Bryant & Stratton College - Eastlake Campus, A
Bryant & Stratton College - Parma Campus, A

Oklahoma

Oklahoma City Community College, A
Southern Nazarene University, B

Pennsylvania

Community College of Beaver County, A
McCann School of Business & Technology (Lewisburg), A

South Dakota

Dakota State University, AB
National American University (Rapid City), B

Tennessee

Pellissippi State Community College, A

Texas

Central Texas College, A
Collin County Community College District, A
El Paso Community College, A
Hallmark University, B
Hill College, A
Lone Star College - Tomball, A
Midland College, A
Paris Junior College, A
St. Philip's College, A
Temple College, A
Texas A&M University, B
Texas State Technical College, A
Tyler Junior College, A

Utah

LDS Business College, A
Stevens-Henager College (Logan), A
Stevens-Henager College (Orem), A
Stevens-Henager College (Salt Lake City), A

Vermont

Champlain College, B

Virginia

Bryant & Stratton College - Richmond Campus, A
Bryant & Stratton College - Virginia Beach Campus, A
Stratford University (Falls Church), A

Washington

Central Washington University, B

West Virginia

Blue Ridge Community and Technical College, A

Wisconsin

Bryant & Stratton College - Milwaukee Campus, A

SYSTEMATIC BIOLOGY/BIO-LOGICAL SYSTEMATICS

United States

California

Stanford University, D
University of California, Irvine, D
University of California, Merced, MD
University of California, San Diego, D

District of Columbia

The George Washington University, D

Illinois

Northwestern University, D
University of Chicago, D

Indiana

Purdue University, D

Massachusetts

Harvard University, D
Massachusetts Institute of Technology, D

Michigan

Michigan State University, D

Missouri

Washington University in St. Louis, D

New Hampshire

Dartmouth College, D

New Jersey

Rutgers University - New Brunswick, D

Pennsylvania

University of Pittsburgh, D

Virginia

Virginia Commonwealth University, D

Canada

Ontario

University of Toronto, MD

SYSTEMS ENGINEERING

United States

Alabama

Auburn University, MDO
The University of Alabama in Huntsville, M
University of South Alabama, D

Arizona

Arizona State University at the Tempe campus, M
The University of Arizona, BMD
Western International University, M

Arkansas

University of Arkansas at Little Rock, BMDO

California

California Institute of Technology, MD
California State University, Fullerton, M
California State University, Northridge, M
Loyola Marymount University, M
National University, M
San Jose State University, M
Stanford University, B
University of California, Merced, MD
University of California, Santa Cruz, B
University of Southern California, MDO

Colorado

Colorado State University - Pueblo, M
Colorado Technical University Colorado Springs, M
Colorado Technical University Denver South, M
Regis University, M
University of Colorado Colorado Springs, M

Connecticut

University of New Haven, M

Delaware

Delaware State University, B

District of Columbia

The George Washington University, BMDO
Georgetown University, M

Florida

Broward College, A
Embry-Riddle Aeronautical University - Daytona, MD
Embry-Riddle Aeronautical University - Worldwide, M
Florida Institute of Technology, MD
South Florida State College, A
University of Florida, BMDO
University of South Florida, O

Georgia

Georgia Institute of Technology, M
Georgia Southern University, M
Kennesaw State University, BMO

Illinois

University of Illinois at Urbana - Champaign, MD

Indiana

Indiana University - Purdue University Fort Wayne, M
Rose-Hulman Institute of Technology, M
Taylor University, B

Iowa

Iowa State University of Science and Technology, M

Maine

Maine Maritime Academy, B

Maryland

Johns Hopkins University, MO
United States Naval Academy, B
University of Maryland, Baltimore County, MO
University of Maryland, College Park, M

Massachusetts

Boston University, MD
Eastern Nazarene College, B
Massachusetts Institute of Technology, MD
Massachusetts Maritime Academy, B
Northeastern University, M
University of Massachusetts Dartmouth, MD
Worcester Polytechnic Institute, MO

Michigan

Ferris State University, B
Oakland University, MD
University of Michigan - Dearborn, MD
Wayne State University, O

Minnesota

University of St. Thomas, M

Mississippi

Mississippi State University, MD

Missouri

Missouri University of Science and Technology, MD
Washington University in St. Louis, B

Nebraska

University of Nebraska at Omaha, O

New Jersey

Rutgers University - New Brunswick, MD
Stevens Institute of Technology, BMDO

New Mexico

New Mexico Institute of Mining and Technology, M
New Mexico State University, O
University of New Mexico, MD

New York

Cornell University, M
New York University, M
Rensselaer Polytechnic Institute, MD
Rochester Institute of Technology, BMD
Stony Brook University, State University of New York, M
Syracuse University, O
United States Military Academy, B

North Carolina

North Carolina Agricultural and Technical State University, MD
The University of North Carolina at Charlotte, BMDO

Ohio

American National University (Cincinnati), A
Case Western Reserve University, BD
The Ohio State University, MD
Ohio University, M

Pennsylvania

Carnegie Mellon University, M
Harrisburg University of Science and Technology, M
Lehigh University, MD
University of Pennsylvania, BMD

Rhode Island

Johnson & Wales University, B
Providence College, B

Tennessee

Belmont University, B
National College (Nashville), A
Tennessee State University, MD

Texas

Southern Methodist University, MD
Texas A&M International University, B
Texas A&M University - Kingsville, D
Texas Tech University, M
University of Houston - Clear Lake, M
The University of Texas at Arlington, M
The University of Texas at Dallas, M
The University of Texas at El Paso, MO

The University of Texas Rio Grande Valley, M

Utah

University of Utah, MO

Virginia

American National University (Danville), A
George Mason University, BMDO
Old Dominion University, MD
University of Virginia, BMD
Virginia Polytechnic Institute and State University, MD

Wisconsin

University of Wisconsin - Madison, MD

Wyoming

University of Wyoming, B

Canada

Alberta

University of Alberta, MD

British Columbia

Simon Fraser University, MD

Ontario

Carleton University, BM
University of Waterloo, BMD

Quebec

Concordia University, MO

Saskatchewan

University of Regina, MD

SYSTEMS SCIENCE AND THEORY

United States

Arizona

Arizona State University at the Tempe campus, MD

California

John F. Kennedy University, B
Stanford University, B

Connecticut

Yale University, B

Illinois

Eastern Illinois University, O

Louisiana

Louisiana State University and Agricultural & Mechanical College, M
Louisiana State University in Shreveport, M

Maryland

Hood College, M

Massachusetts

Boston University, B
Worcester Polytechnic Institute, MDO

Michigan

Oakland University, M

Missouri

Washington University in St. Louis, B

New Jersey

Fairleigh Dickinson University, Metropolitan Campus, M
New Jersey Institute of Technology, M
Stevens Institute of Technology, MD

New York

Binghamton University, State University of New York, MD
Syracuse University, B
United States Military Academy, B

Ohio

Miami University, M
Miami University Middletown, A

Oregon

Portland State University, MDO

Pennsylvania

Carnegie Mellon University, B

Texas

Southern Methodist University, MD

Virginia

James Madison University, B

West Virginia

Marshall University, B

Wyoming

University of Wyoming, B

Canada

Ontario

Carleton University, M
University of Ottawa, MO

TALMUDIC STUDIES

United States

California

Yeshiva Ohr Elchonon Chabad/West Coast Talmudical Seminary, B

Colorado

Yeshiva Toras Chaim Talmudical Seminary, B

Connecticut

Bais Binyomin Academy, B

Florida

Talmudic University, B
Yeshiva Gedolah Rabbinical College, B

Illinois

Telshe Yeshiva - Chicago, B

Michigan

Michigan Jewish Institute, A
Yeshiva Beth Yehuda - Yeshiva Gedolah of Greater Detroit, B

New Jersey

Rabbi Jacob Joseph School, B
Talmudical Academy of New Jersey, B

New York

Beis Medrash Heichal Dovid, B
Beth Hatalmud Rabbinical College, B
The Jewish Theological Seminary, B
Kehilath Yakov Rabbinical Seminary, B
Machzikei Hadath Rabbinical College, B
Mesivta Torah Vodaath Rabbinical Seminary, B
Mesivtha Tifereth Jerusalem of America, B
Mirrer Yeshiva, B
Rabbinical College Beth Shraga, B
Rabbinical College Bobover Yeshiva B'nei Zion, B
Rabbinical College Ch'san Sofer, B
Rabbinical College of Long Island, B
Talmudical Institute of Upstate New York, B
Torah Temimah Talmudical Seminary, B
United Talmudical Seminary, B

U.T.A. Mesivta of Kiryas Joel, B
Yeshiva Derech Chaim, B
Yeshiva D'Monsey Rabbinical College, B
Yeshiva Karlin Stolin Rabbinical Institute, B
Yeshiva and Kolel Bais Medrash Elyon, B
Yeshiva Shaar Hatorah Talmudic Research Institute, B
Yeshiva Shaarei Torah of Rockland, B
Yeshiva of the Telshe Alumni, B
Yeshivas Novominsk, B
Yeshivat Mikdash Melech, B
Yeshivath Zichron Moshe, B

TAXATION

United States

Alabama

Troy University, MO
The University of Alabama, M
The University of Alabama in Huntsville, M

Arizona

National Paralegal College, M

California

California Miramar University, M
California Polytechnic State University, San Luis Obispo, M
California State University, Fullerton, M
California State University, Los Angeles, M
California State University, Northridge, M
Chapman University, MD
Golden Gate University, MO
Loyola Marymount University, M
San Jose State University, M
University of San Diego, MO
University of San Francisco, M
University of Southern California, M

Colorado

University of Colorado Denver, M
University of Denver, M

Connecticut

Fairfield University, MO
University of Hartford, MO
University of New Haven, MO

Delaware

Goldey-Beacom College, M

District of Columbia

Georgetown University, M

Florida

Florida Atlantic University, M
Florida Gulf Coast University, M
Florida International University, M
Florida State University, M
Nova Southeastern University, M
St. Thomas University, M
University of Central Florida, M
University of Florida, MD
University of Miami, M
University of South Florida, M

Georgia

Georgia State University, M
University of Phoenix - Augusta Campus, B

Hawaii

University of Hawaii at Manoa, M

Idaho

Boise State University, M

Illinois

DePaul University, M
Illinois Institute of Technology, M
Loyola University Chicago, M
Northern Illinois University, M

Northwestern University, M
Southern Illinois University Edwardsville, M
University of Illinois at Urbana - Champaign, M

Indiana

University of Notre Dame, M

Kentucky

Northern Kentucky University, O

Louisiana

University of New Orleans, M

Maryland

University of Baltimore, M

Massachusetts

American International College, M
Bentley University, M
Boston University, M
Northeastern University, M
Suffolk University, M

Michigan

Grand Valley State University, BM
Michigan State University, M
University of Michigan, M
Walsh College of Accountancy and Business Administration, M
Wayne State University, M

Minnesota

University of Minnesota, Twin Cities Campus, M

Mississippi

Mississippi State University, M
University of Mississippi, M

Missouri

Fontbonne University, B
University of Missouri, O
University of Missouri - Kansas City, M

New Hampshire

Southern New Hampshire University, M

New Jersey

Fairleigh Dickinson University, College at Florham, MO
Fairleigh Dickinson University, Metropolitan Campus, M
Seton Hall University, O

New Mexico

University of New Mexico, M

New York

Baruch College of the City University of New York, M
Canisius College, B
Fordham University, M
Hofstra University, MO
Long Island University - LIU Brooklyn, M
New York University, MO
Pace University, M
St. John's University, M
State University of New York College at Old Westbury, M
University at Albany, State University of New York, M

North Carolina

Appalachian State University, M
Wake Forest University, M

Ohio

Capital University, M
Cleveland State University, M
The University of Akron, M
University of Cincinnati, M

Oklahoma

The University of Tulsa, M

Pennsylvania

Philadelphia University, M
Robert Morris University, M
Temple University, M
Villanova University, M
Widener University, M

Rhode Island

Bryant University, M

Texas

Southern Methodist University, M
Texas Christian University, M
Texas Tech University, M
University of Houston, M
The University of Texas at Arlington, M

Utah

Weber State University, M

Washington

University of Washington, M

Wisconsin

University of Wisconsin - Madison, M
University of Wisconsin - Milwaukee, O

U.S. Territories: Puerto Rico

University of the Sacred Heart, M

Canada

British Columbia

British Columbia Institute of Technology, A

Ontario

University of Waterloo, M

Quebec

HEC Montreal, MO
McGill University, B
Université de Montréal, M
Université de Sherbrooke, MO

TEACHER ASSISTANT/AIDE

United States

Arizona

Mesa Community College, A
Northland Pioneer College, A
Phoenix College, A

California

Antelope Valley College, A
Chaffey College, A
City College of San Francisco, A
Cypress College, A
Fresno City College, A
Hartnell College, A
Los Angeles City College, A
Los Angeles Southwest College, A
Merced College, A
Moorpark College, A
National University, A
Saddleback College, A
San Diego City College, A
Victor Valley College, A

Colorado

Community College of Denver, A

Connecticut

Manchester Community College, A

Florida

Indian River State College, A
Miami Dade College, A

Georgia

University of Phoenix - Augusta Campus, A

Hawaii

Kapiolani Community College, A

Idaho

College of Southern Idaho, A

Illinois

Blackburn College, B
City Colleges of Chicago, Malcolm X College, A
Danville Area Community College, A
Heartland Community College, A
Highland Community College, A
Illinois Central College, A
Illinois Eastern Community Colleges, Lincoln Trail
    College, A
Illinois Valley Community College, A
John A. Logan College, A
Joliet Junior College, A
Kankakee Community College, A
Kaskaskia College, A
Kishwaukee College, A
Lincoln Land Community College, A
Moraine Valley Community College, A
Prairie State College, A
Southwestern Illinois College, A
Waubonsee Community College, A

Indiana

Saint Mary-of-the-Woods College, A
Valparaiso University, A
Vincennes University, A

Iowa

Dordt College, A
Western Iowa Tech Community College, A

Kansas

Cloud County Community College, A
Fort Scott Community College, A
Highland Community College, A
Neosho County Community College, A

Kentucky

Bluegrass Community and Technical College, A
Elizabethtown Community and Technical College, A
Gateway Community and Technical College, A
Somerset Community College, A

Louisiana

Southern University at Shreveport, A

Maine

Eastern Maine Community College, A
University of Maine at Presque Isle, A
Washington County Community College, A

Maryland

Harford Community College, A

Massachusetts

Massasoit Community College, A

Michigan

Lansing Community College, A
Montcalm Community College, A

Minnesota

Century College, A
Northland Community and Technical College, A
Ridgewater College, A
Rochester Community and Technical College, A
St. Cloud Technical & Community College, A

Missouri

St. Charles Community College, A
State Fair Community College, A

Montana

Fort Peck Community College, A
The University of Montana Western, A

New Hampshire

NHTI, Concord's Community College, A

New Jersey

Brookdale Community College, A
Mercer County Community College, A
Middlesex County College, A

New Mexico

Clovis Community College, A
New Mexico State University - Carlsbad, A
New Mexico State University - Grants, A
Western New Mexico University, A

New York

Borough of Manhattan Community College of the
    City University of New York, A
Eugenio María de Hostos Community College of the
    City University of New York, A
Fiorello H. LaGuardia Community College of the
    City University of New York, A
Fulton-Montgomery Community College, A
Genesee Community College, A
Jamestown Community College, A
Jefferson Community College, A
Kingsborough Community College of the City Uni-
    versity of New York, A
Schenectady County Community College, A
State University of New York College of Agriculture
    and Technology at Cobleskill, A

North Carolina

Alamance Community College, A
Blue Ridge Community College, A
Brunswick Community College, A
Carteret Community College, A
College of The Albemarle, A
Durham Technical Community College, A
Haywood Community College, A
Isothermal Community College, A
Mitchell Community College, A
Southeastern Community College, A
Vance-Granville Community College, A

North Dakota

Dakota College at Bottineau, A
Sitting Bull College, A

Ohio

North Central State College, A
Northwest State Community College, A
Southern State Community College, A
The University of Akron Wayne College, A

Oklahoma

East Central University, B

Oregon

Linn-Benton Community College, A
Portland Community College, A

Pennsylvania

Community College of Beaver County, A
Lehigh Carbon Community College, A
Montgomery County Community College, A
Northampton Community College, A

Tennessee

Johnson University, A

Texas

Angelina College, A
El Centro College, A
Hill College, A
Odessa College, A
St. Philip's College, A
Southwest Texas Junior College, A
University of Phoenix - Houston Campus, B

Utah

Salt Lake Community College, A

Vermont

Community College of Vermont, A

Virginia

Eastern Mennonite University, A
Patrick Henry Community College, A

Washington

Clover Park Technical College, A
Green River College, A
Pierce College at Fort Steilacoom, A
Shoreline Community College, A
Tacoma Community College, A

Wisconsin

Alverno College, A
Gateway Technical College, A
Moraine Park Technical College, A
Northcentral Technical College, A
Northeast Wisconsin Technical College, A
Waukesha County Technical College, A

Wyoming

Central Wyoming College, A

TEACHER EDUCATION, MULTIPLE LEVELS

United States

Alabama

Birmingham-Southern College, B
Samford University, B
Troy University, B
University of North Alabama, B
The University of West Alabama, B

Arizona

International Baptist College and Seminary, B

Arkansas

Arkansas State University Mid-South, A
Arkansas State University - Mountain Home, A
Arkansas State University - Newport, A
Harding University, B
North Arkansas College, A
Southern Arkansas University Tech, A
University of Arkansas Community College at Hope, A
University of Arkansas Community College at Morrilton, A

California

Biola University, B
San Diego Christian College, B

Colorado

Adams State University, B

Delaware

Delaware Technical & Community College, Jack F. Owens Campus, A
Delaware Technical & Community College, Stanton/Wilmington Campus, A
Delaware Technical & Community College, Terry Campus, A

Florida

Florida Southern College, B
University of South Florida, St. Petersburg, B

Georgia

College of Coastal Georgia, AB
Piedmont College, B
South Georgia State College, A
Spelman College, B

Illinois

Concordia University Chicago, B
DePaul University, B
Dominican University, B

Illinois College, B
Kishwaukee College, A
McKendree University, B
Quincy University, B
Trinity International University, B
University of Illinois at Urbana - Champaign, B

Indiana

Crossroads Bible College, B
Indiana Wesleyan University, B
Manchester University, B
Saint Mary-of-the-Woods College, B

Iowa

Dordt College, B
Northwestern College, B

Kansas

Pratt Community College, A

Kentucky

Spalding University, B
University of Louisville, B
Western Kentucky University, B

Louisiana

University of Holy Cross, B
University of Louisiana at Lafayette, B

Maine

University of Maine at Fort Kent, B

Maryland

Frostburg State University, B

Massachusetts

Assumption College, B
Eastern Nazarene College, B
Merrimack College, B

Michigan

Adrian College, B
Finlandia University, B
Lake Superior State University, B
Mid Michigan Community College, A
University of Michigan - Flint, B

Minnesota

The College of St. Scholastica, B
Hamline University, B
Itasca Community College, A
Martin Luther College, B
Minneapolis Community and Technical College, A
St. Cloud State University, AB
University of Minnesota, Duluth, B

Missouri

Lindenwood University, B
Missouri Baptist University, B
Washington University in St. Louis, B
William Jewell College, B

Montana

University of Great Falls, B
The University of Montana Western, B

Nebraska

College of Saint Mary, B
Concordia University, Nebraska, B
Grace University, B
Midland University, B
University of Nebraska - Lincoln, B
York College, B

New Hampshire

New England College, B

New Jersey

Camden County College, A
College of Saint Elizabeth, B
Felician University, B
Stockton University, B

New Mexico

Central New Mexico Community College, A
University of the Southwest, B

New York

Canisius College, B
Cayuga County Community College, A
Columbia University, B
Genesee Community College, A
Hofstra University, B
Ithaca College, B
Manhattan College, B
Molloy College, B
Mount Saint Mary College, B
Nyack College, B
Onondaga Community College, A
Westchester Community College, A

North Carolina

Campbell University, B
Gardner-Webb University, B
Louisburg College, A
Methodist University, B
Saint Augustine's University, B
Wake Forest University, B

North Dakota

Dickinson State University, B

Ohio

Bowling Green State University, B
Central State University, B
John Carroll University, B
Miami University Hamilton, B
Ohio Dominican University, B
Ohio Northern University, B
Ohio Wesleyan University, B
Shawnee State University, B
University of Rio Grande, B
Wright State University, B

Oklahoma

Oklahoma State University Institute of Technology, A

Pennsylvania

Community College of Beaver County, A
Delaware County Community College, A
Gannon University, B
Geneva College, B
Summit University, B

South Carolina

College of Charleston, B
Columbia International University, B

South Dakota

Augustana University, B
Dakota Wesleyan University, B

Tennessee

Austin Peay State University, B
Tennessee Wesleyan College, B
University of Memphis, B
The University of Tennessee at Martin, B

Texas

Brookhaven College, A
Houston Community College, A
Huston-Tillotson University, B
Midland College, A
North American University, B
Northeast Texas Community College, A
Paris Junior College, A
Tarleton State University, B
Texas A&M University - Central Texas, B
Texas Lutheran University, B
Tyler Junior College, A
Wayland Baptist University, B

Utah

Utah State University, B
Western Governors University, B

Vermont

Goddard College, B

Virginia

Averett University, B
Emory & Henry College, B
Virginia Union University, B
Virginia Wesleyan College, B

Washington

Eastern Washington University, B
Heritage University, B
Walla Walla University, B
Washington State University, B

West Virginia

West Virginia Wesleyan College, B

Wisconsin

Concordia University Wisconsin, B
Mount Mary University, B
Northland College, B

Wyoming

Western Wyoming Community College, A

U.S. Territories: Puerto Rico

Universidad Metropolitana, B
University of Puerto Rico in Bayamón, B

Canada

Manitoba

Université de Saint-Boniface, B

Maritime Provinces: New Brunswick

Crandall University, B

Ontario

Queen's University at Kingston, B
Redeemer University College, B
University of Windsor, B
York University, B

Saskatchewan

University of Saskatchewan, B

TEACHER EDUCATION AND PROFESSIONAL DEVELOPMENT, SPECIFIC LEVELS AND METHODS

United States

Arkansas

John Brown University, B

Delaware

Delaware State University, B

Florida

Ave Maria University, B
Miami Dade College, A

Hawaii

Leeward Community College, A

Illinois

Columbia College Chicago, B

Maryland

Harford Community College, A

Massachusetts

Anna Maria College, B
Boston University, B
Cape Cod Community College, A
Eastern Nazarene College, B

Minnesota

St. Cloud State University, B

Missouri

Jefferson College, A
Washington University in St. Louis, B

New Jersey

Rowan University, B

New York

Concordia College - New York, B
Corning Community College, A

North Carolina

Appalachian State University, B

Ohio

Wright State University, B
Xavier University, B

Pennsylvania

Cairn University, B
Community College of Allegheny County, A
Immaculata University, B
Manor College, A

South Carolina

Anderson University, B

Utah

Brigham Young University, B
Weber State University, B

Virginia

Emory & Henry College, B
Lynchburg College, B

Washington

Western Washington University, B

U.S. Territories: Puerto Rico

Bayamón Central University, B
Inter American University of Puerto Rico, Metropolitan Campus, B
Inter American University of Puerto Rico, San Germán Campus, B

TEACHER EDUCATION AND PROFESSIONAL DEVELOPMENT, SPECIFIC SUBJECT AREAS

United States

California

National University, A

Florida

Florida Institute of Technology, B

Georgia

Piedmont College, B

Illinois

Columbia College Chicago, B

Indiana

Indiana University Bloomington, B
Taylor University, B

Iowa

Graceland University, B

Kansas

Pittsburg State University, B

Kentucky

Eastern Kentucky University, B
Murray State University, B
University of Kentucky, B

Louisiana

Louisiana Tech University, B

Maryland

Harford Community College, A

Massachusetts

Eastern Nazarene College, B

Michigan

Eastern Michigan University, B
Madonna University, B
Northern Michigan University, B

Minnesota

Augsburg College, B
University of Minnesota, Duluth, B

Mississippi

Mississippi State University, B

Missouri

Avila University, B
Missouri State University, B
Missouri Western State University, B
Northwest Missouri State University, B
St. Charles Community College, A
State Fair Community College, A
William Woods University, B

Nebraska

Concordia University, Nebraska, B
Union College, B
University of Nebraska - Lincoln, B
Wayne State College, B

New Hampshire

Plymouth State University, B

North Carolina

Appalachian State University, B
Gardner-Webb University, B
The University of North Carolina Wilmington, B

North Dakota

Minot State University, B

Ohio

Bowling Green State University, B
Wright State University, B

Oklahoma

University of Central Oklahoma, B

Pennsylvania

Cairn University, B
Community College of Allegheny County, A
Marywood University, B
Penn State University Park, A
Point Park University, B

Texas

Baylor University, B

Utah

Brigham Young University, B
Utah State University, B
Weber State University, B

Virginia

Averett University, B
Old Dominion University, B

Washington

Western Washington University, B

Wisconsin

University of Wisconsin - Eau Claire, B
University of Wisconsin - Stout, B

U.S. Territories: Puerto Rico

Bayamón Central University, B

Canada

Alberta

University of Lethbridge, B

Ontario

University of Ottawa, B

Saskatchewan

University of Regina, B

TEACHING ASSISTANTS/AIDES

United States

Arizona

Northland Pioneer College, A

Colorado

Community College of Denver, A

Ohio

Terra State Community College, A

TEACHING ENGLISH OR FRENCH AS A SECOND OR FOREIGN LANGUAGE

Canada

Ontario

University of Ottawa, B

TEACHING ENGLISH AS A SECOND OR FOREIGN LANGUAGE/ESL LANGUAGE INSTRUCTOR

United States

Arizona

Grand Canyon University, B

California

California State University, Stanislaus, B

District of Columbia

American University, B
The Catholic University of America, B

Georgia

Gordon State College, A

Hawaii

Brigham Young University - Hawaii, B
Hawai'i Pacific University, B
University of Hawaii at Manoa, B

Indiana

Goshen College, B
Huntington University, B
Indiana Wesleyan University, B

Iowa

University of Northern Iowa, B

Maryland

Salisbury University, B

Massachusetts

Simmons College, B

Michigan

Calvin College, B
Cornerstone University, A

Minnesota

Augsburg College, B
Bethel University, B
Concordia University, St. Paul, B
Crown College, B
Minnesota State University Moorhead, B
University of Northwestern - St. Paul, B
Winona State University, B

Montana

Carroll College, B
University of Montana, B

Nebraska

Concordia University, Nebraska, B
Doane University, B
Union College, A

New Hampshire

Granite State College, B

New York

Davis College, B
Houghton College, B
Le Moyne College, B
Niagara University, B
Nyack College, B
Queens College of the City University of New York, B

North Carolina

Gardner-Webb University, B

Ohio

Kent State University, B
The University of Findlay, B
Wright State University, B

Oklahoma

Eastern Oklahoma State College, A
Langston University, B
Oklahoma Christian University, B
Oklahoma City University, B

Oregon

Multnomah University, B

Pennsylvania

Saint Joseph's University, B

Tennessee

Lee University, B
Maryville College, B
Southern Adventist University, B
Union University, B

Texas

Tarleton State University, B
The University of Texas at San Antonio, B

Utah

Brigham Young University, B

Virginia

Liberty University, B

Washington

Eastern Washington University, B
Northwest University, B
Washington State University, B

Wisconsin

Concordia University Wisconsin, B
University of Wisconsin - Oshkosh, B
University of Wisconsin - River Falls, B

U.S. Territories: Guam

University of Guam, B

U.S. Territories: Puerto Rico

Bayamón Central University, B
Inter American University of Puerto Rico, Aguadilla Campus, B
Inter American University of Puerto Rico, Arecibo Campus, B
Inter American University of Puerto Rico, Barranquitas Campus, B
Inter American University of Puerto Rico, Fajardo Campus, B
Inter American University of Puerto Rico, Guayama Campus, B
Inter American University of Puerto Rico, Metropolitan Campus, B
Inter American University of Puerto Rico, Ponce Campus, B
Inter American University of Puerto Rico, San Germán Campus, B
Universidad del Este, B
University of Puerto Rico in Humacao, B

Canada

British Columbia

The University of British Columbia, B
University of Victoria, B

Manitoba

Providence University College & Theological Seminary, B

Maritime Provinces: New Brunswick

University of New Brunswick Fredericton, B
University of New Brunswick Saint John, B

Ontario

Brock University, B
Carleton University, B
York University, B

Quebec

Concordia University, B
Université Laval, B
Université du Québec à Chicoutimi, B
Université du Québec à Montréal, B

Saskatchewan

Briercrest College, B

TEACHING FRENCH AS A SECOND OR FOREIGN LANGUAGE

United States

Michigan

Saginaw Valley State University, B

North Carolina

Campbell University, B

Canada

Alberta

University of Alberta, B

Ontario

University of Toronto, B
University of Windsor, B

Quebec

Bishop's University, B
McGill University, B
Université Laval, B

TECHNICAL AND BUSINESS WRITING

United States

Alabama

The University of Alabama in Huntsville, O

Arkansas

University of Arkansas at Little Rock, M

Colorado

Colorado State University, M

Illinois

Illinois Institute of Technology, MD

Louisiana

Louisiana Tech University, MO

Maryland

Johns Hopkins University, MO

Massachusetts

Fitchburg State University, M
Massachusetts Institute of Technology, M

Minnesota

Metropolitan State University, M

North Carolina

The University of North Carolina at Greensboro, O

Pennsylvania

Carnegie Mellon University, M
Drexel University, M
University of the Sciences, MO

Texas

Texas Tech University, MD

Virginia

James Madison University, M

Canada

Ontario

Laurentian University, O
University of Waterloo, M

TECHNICAL COMMUNICATION

United States

Alabama

Auburn University, MDO

Colorado

Colorado State University, MD

Florida

University of South Florida, O

Idaho

Boise State University, M

Illinois

North Central College, M

Massachusetts

Harvard University, M
Northeastern University, M

Michigan

Eastern Michigan University, MO
Lawrence Technological University, M
Michigan Technological University, MD

Minnesota

Minnesota State University Mankato, MO

Missouri

Missouri Western State University, M

Montana

Montana Tech of The University of Montana, M

Nebraska

University of Nebraska at Omaha, O

New Jersey

New Jersey Institute of Technology, M

New York

Rensselaer Polytechnic Institute, M

North Carolina

East Carolina University, M
North Carolina State University, M
The University of North Carolina at Charlotte, O

Ohio

Bowling Green State University, M

Pennsylvania

Drexel University, M

Texas

Texas State University, M
University of Houston - Downtown, M

Washington

Eastern Washington University, M
University of Washington, MD

Wisconsin

University of Wisconsin - Milwaukee, O
University of Wisconsin - Stout, M

TECHNICAL TEACHER EDUCATION

United States

Alabama

Athens State University, B
Auburn University, B

Arkansas

University of Arkansas, B

California

College of the Siskiyous, A

Idaho

University of Idaho, B

Illinois

Eastern Illinois University, B
University of Illinois at Urbana - Champaign, B

Kentucky

University of Kentucky, B
Western Kentucky University, A

Michigan

Ferris State University, B

Missouri

East Central College, A
Mineral Area College, A
Moberly Area Community College, A
State Fair Community College, A
University of Missouri, B

Montana

Montana State University, B

North Dakota

Valley City State University, B

Ohio

Bowling Green State University, B
The Ohio State University, B
The University of Akron, B
Wright State University, B

Oklahoma

Oklahoma State University, B

Oregon

Chemeketa Community College, A

South Carolina

Tri-County Technical College, A

Texas

Howard College, A

Utah

Utah State University, B

Vermont

Castleton University, B

Washington

Central Washington University, B

West Virginia

West Virginia University Institute of Technology, B

Wisconsin

University of Wisconsin - Stout, B

Canada

Ontario

Queen's University at Kingston, B

Quebec

Université Laval, B

Saskatchewan

University of Saskatchewan, B

TECHNICAL THEATRE/THEATRE DESIGN AND TECHNOLOGY

United States

Alaska

University of Alaska Anchorage, B
University of Alaska Fairbanks, B

Arizona

The University of Arizona, B

California

American River College, A
Biola University, B
California Institute of the Arts, B
Foothill College, A
Fresno City College, A
Gavilan College, A
Glendale Community College, A
Grossmont College, A
Long Beach City College, A
Los Angeles Valley College, A
MiraCosta College, A
Ohlone College, A
Pasadena City College, A
Pepperdine University, B
Santa Barbara City College, A
University of Southern California, B
Vanguard University of Southern California, B

Colorado

Red Rocks Community College, A
Western State Colorado University, B

Connecticut

University of Connecticut, B

Florida

Broward College, A
Florida Southern College, B
Florida State College at Jacksonville, A
Miami Dade College, A
University of Miami, B

Georgia

Piedmont College, B
Savannah College of Art and Design, B
University of North Georgia, B

Illinois

Columbia College Chicago, B
DePaul University, B
Illinois Wesleyan University, B
Millikin University, B
North Central College, B

Indiana

Huntington University, B
Purdue University, B
Vincennes University, A

Iowa

Coe College, B

Kansas

Southwestern College, B
The University of Kansas, B

Maine

Husson University, B

Maryland

Carroll Community College, A
Harford Community College, A
Howard Community College, A

Massachusetts

Bard College at Simon's Rock, B
Boston University, B
Emerson College, B
Fitchburg State University, B
Salem State University, B

Michigan

Lansing Community College, A
Michigan Technological University, B
Oakland University, B
University of Michigan, B
University of Michigan - Flint, B
Western Michigan University, B

Minnesota

Normandale Community College, A

Missouri

College of the Ozarks, B
Lindenwood University, B
Stephens College, B

Montana

Rocky Mountain College, B

Nebraska

Doane University, B

Nevada

University of Nevada, Las Vegas, B

New Hampshire

Keene State College, B

New Jersey

Bergen Community College, A
Centenary College, B
Kean University, B
New Jersey Institute of Technology, B

New Mexico

San Juan College, A
Santa Fe University of Art and Design, B
University of New Mexico, B

New York

Binghamton University, State University of New
    York, B
Genesee Community College, A
Ithaca College, B
Marymount Manhattan College, B
Nassau Community College, A
Nazareth College of Rochester, B
New York City College of Technology of the City
    University of New York, B
Purchase College, State University of New York, B
Syracuse University, B

North Carolina

Elon University, B
Greensboro College, B
University of North Carolina School of the Arts, B

Ohio

Ashland University, B
Baldwin Wallace University, B
Ohio Northern University, B
University of Cincinnati, B
University of Rio Grande, A
Wright State University, B

Oklahoma

Oklahoma City University, B
Oral Roberts University, B
University of Central Oklahoma, B

Pennsylvania

Penn State Abington, B
Penn State Altoona, B
Penn State Beaver, B
Penn State Berks, B
Penn State Brandywine, B
Penn State DuBois, B
Penn State Erie, The Behrend College, B
Penn State Fayette, The Eberly Campus, B
Penn State Greater Allegheny, B
Penn State Hazleton, B
Penn State Lehigh Valley, B
Penn State Mont Alto, B
Penn State New Kensington, B
Penn State Schuylkill, B
Penn State Shenango, B
Penn State University Park, B
Penn State Wilkes-Barre, B
Penn State Worthington Scranton, B
Penn State York, B
Seton Hill University, B
Slippery Rock University of Pennsylvania, B
The University of the Arts, B

Rhode Island

Rhode Island College, B

South Carolina

Coker College, B

Tennessee

Belmont University, B
Freed-Hardeman University, B
Lipscomb University, B

Texas

Baylor University, B
Texas Christian University, B
Trinity University, B

Utah

Brigham Young University, B
Dixie State University, B
Utah Valley University, A

Vermont

Bennington College, B
Johnson State College, A

Virginia

Shenandoah University, B

Washington

Central Washington University, B
Cornish College of the Arts, B

West Virginia

Bethany College, B
Davis & Elkins College, B

Wyoming

Casper College, A
Central Wyoming College, A
Western Wyoming Community College, A

Canada

Alberta

University of Alberta, B
University of Lethbridge, B

Newfoundland and Labrador

Memorial University of Newfoundland, B

Ontario

Ryerson University, B
The University of Western Ontario, B

Quebec

Concordia University, B

Saskatchewan

University of Regina, B

TECHNOLOGY AND PUBLIC POLICY

United States

Arizona

Arizona State University at the Tempe campus, M

District of Columbia

The George Washington University, MO

Massachusetts

Massachusetts Institute of Technology, MD

Michigan

Eastern Michigan University, M

Minnesota

St. Cloud State University, M
University of Minnesota, Twin Cities Campus, M

New York

Rensselaer Polytechnic Institute, MD
Rochester Institute of Technology, M
Stony Brook University, State University of New
    York, D

Pennsylvania

Carnegie Mellon University, D

Texas

The University of Texas at Austin, M

TECHNOLOGY TEACHER EDUCATION/INDUSTRIAL ARTS TEACHER EDUCATION

United States

Arizona

Eastern Arizona College, A

Arkansas

University of the Ozarks, B

California

Cerritos College, A
Fresno City College, A
Fullerton College, A

Colorado

Colorado State University, B

Connecticut

Central Connecticut State University, B

Florida

St. Petersburg College, B
State College of Florida Manatee-Sarasota, A

Georgia

Georgia Southern University, B

Illinois

Chicago State University, B
Illinois State University, B

Indiana

Ball State University, B
Indiana State University, B
Purdue University, B

Iowa

Iowa Lakes Community College, A
University of Northern Iowa, B

Kansas

Allen Community College, A
Cowley County Community College and Area Vocational - Technical School, A
Pittsburg State University, B

Kentucky

Berea College, B

Massachusetts

Fitchburg State University, B
Westfield State University, B

Michigan

Delta College, A
Eastern Michigan University, B
Western Michigan University, B

Minnesota

Bemidji State University, B
St. Cloud State University, B

Mississippi

Jackson State University, B

Missouri

Lindenwood University, B
Southeast Missouri State University, B

Montana

Montana State University - Northern, B
The University of Montana Western, B

Nebraska

Chadron State College, B
Union College, B
Wayne State College, B

New Jersey

The College of New Jersey, B

New Mexico

Central New Mexico Community College, A
New Mexico Highlands University, B
University of New Mexico, B

New York

Buffalo State College, State University of New York, B
New York City College of Technology of the City University of New York, B
State University of New York at Oswego, B

North Carolina

North Carolina Agricultural and Technical State University, B
North Carolina State University, B

North Dakota

Valley City State University, B

Ohio

Bowling Green State University, B
Ohio Northern University, B
The Ohio State University, B

Oklahoma

Eastern Oklahoma State College, A

Rhode Island

Rhode Island College, B

South Carolina

South Carolina State University, B

Tennessee

Middle Tennessee State University, B
Roane State Community College, A

Texas

Wayland Baptist University, B

Utah

Southern Utah University, B
Utah State University, B

Washington

Western Washington University, B

Wisconsin

University of Wisconsin - Platteville, B
University of Wisconsin - Stout, B
Viterbo University, B

Wyoming

Casper College, A
University of Wyoming, B

Canada

Alberta

University of Alberta, B

TELECOMMUNICATIONS

United States

Arkansas

University of Arkansas, M

California

California Miramar University, M
National University, M
University of California, San Diego, MD
University of California, Santa Cruz, M
University of Southern California, MO

Colorado

University of Colorado Boulder, M
University of Denver, M

Connecticut

Fairfield University, O

District of Columbia

The George Washington University, M

Florida

Florida International University, M
University of Florida, M

Hawaii

University of Hawaii at Manoa, O

Illinois

Illinois Institute of Technology, M
Roosevelt University, M

Indiana

Ball State University, M
Indiana University Bloomington, M

Louisiana

University of Louisiana at Lafayette, M

Maryland

Johns Hopkins University, M
University of Maryland, College Park, M

Massachusetts

Boston University, M
Northeastern University, M
University of Massachusetts Dartmouth, O

Michigan

Michigan State University, M

Minnesota

Saint Mary's University of Minnesota, M

Missouri

University of Missouri - Kansas City, MD

New Hampshire

Franklin Pierce University, O

New Jersey

New Jersey Institute of Technology, M
Stevens Institute of Technology, M

New York

Pace University, MO
State University of New York Polytechnic Institute, M
Syracuse University, M

North Carolina

The University of North Carolina at Chapel Hill, M

Ohio

Ohio University, M

Oklahoma

University of Oklahoma, M

Pennsylvania

Drexel University, M
University of Pittsburgh, MDO

Texas

Southern Methodist University, M
University of Houston, M
The University of Texas at Dallas, MD

Virginia

George Mason University, M
Stratford University (Falls Church), M

U.S. Territories: Puerto Rico

Universidad del Turabo, M

Canada

Alberta

University of Alberta, MD

TELECOMMUNICATIONS MANAGEMENT

United States

Alaska

Alaska Pacific University, M

California

California Miramar University, M
San Diego State University, M

Colorado

University of Colorado Boulder, M

Kentucky

Murray State University, M

Maryland

Capitol Technology University, M

Massachusetts

Boston University, M

New Jersey

Stevens Institute of Technology, MDO

New York

New York University, O
Syracuse University, MO

North Carolina

East Carolina University, M

Oklahoma

Oklahoma State University, M

Pennsylvania

Carnegie Mellon University, M

Wisconsin

University of Wisconsin - Stout, M

Canada

Quebec

Concordia University, O

TELECOMMUNICATIONS TECHNOLOGY/TECHNICIAN

United States

California

APT College, A
California State University, East Bay, B
Columbia College Hollywood, AB
Los Angeles City College, A
Moorpark College, A
Napa Valley College, A
San Bernardino Valley College, A
San Diego City College, A
Santa Ana College, A
Skyline College, A
Solano Community College, A

Colorado

Arapahoe Community College, A

Florida

Miami Dade College, A
Pensacola State College, A
Seminole State College of Florida, A

Georgia

Georgia Piedmont Technical College, A
Kennesaw State University, B

Illinois

Illinois Eastern Community Colleges, Lincoln Trail
College, A
Lake Land College, A

Indiana

Ivy Tech Community College - Lafayette, A
Ivy Tech Community College - North Central, A
Ivy Tech Community College - Northwest, A
Ivy Tech Community College - Southern Indiana, A
Ivy Tech Community College - Southwest, A

Iowa

Iowa Central Community College, A
Kirkwood Community College, A
Western Iowa Tech Community College, A

Maine

Eastern Maine Community College, A

Maryland

Howard Community College, A
Morgan State University, B

Massachusetts

Massasoit Community College, A
Northern Essex Community College, A
Quinsigamond Community College, A
Springfield Technical Community College, A

Minnesota

Minnesota State Community and Technical College,
A
Ridgewater College, A
South Central College, A

Mississippi

Hinds Community College, A
Meridian Community College, A
Northwest Mississippi Community College, A

New Jersey

County College of Morris, A
Union County College, A

New York

Canisius College, B
Cayuga County Community College, A
Erie Community College, South Campus, A
Farmingdale State College, B
Hudson Valley Community College, A
Monroe Community College, A
New York City College of Technology of the City
University of New York, AB
Pace University, AB
Pace University, Pleasantville Campus, B
Queensborough Community College of the City University of New York, A
Rochester Institute of Technology, B
St. John's University, B

North Carolina

Central Carolina Community College, A
Guilford Technical Community College, A
Haywood Community College, A
Wake Technical Community College, A

Oklahoma

Carl Albert State College, A
Spartan College of Aeronautics and Technology, AB

Oregon

Pacific University, B

Pennsylvania

Delaware County Community College, A
Penn State DuBois, A
Penn State Fayette, The Eberly Campus, A
Penn State Hazleton, A
Penn State New Kensington, A
Penn State Schuylkill, A
Penn State Shenango, A
Penn State Wilkes-Barre, A
Penn State York, A

South Carolina

Trident Technical College, A

South Dakota

Mitchell Technical Institute, A

Texas

Amarillo College, A
Central Texas College, A
Collin County Community College District, A
Lee College, A
St. Philip's College, A
South Plains College, A
Texas State Technical College, A

Utah

Salt Lake Community College, A

Virginia

ECPI University (Glen Allen), A
ECPI University (Newport News), A
ECPI University (Richmond), A
ECPI University (Virginia Beach), A

Washington

Clark College, A
Clover Park Technical College, A
North Seattle College, A
Skagit Valley College, A

U.S. Territories: Puerto Rico

Colegio Universitario de San Juan, A
University of the Sacred Heart, B

TERATOLOGY

United States

West Virginia

West Virginia University, MD

TEXTILE DESIGN

United States

Arizona

Arizona State University at the Tempe campus, M

California

Academy of Art University, M
California College of the Arts, M
California State University, Los Angeles, M
University of California, Davis, M

Georgia

Savannah College of Art and Design, M

Illinois

Illinois State University, M
School of the Art Institute of Chicago, MO

Kansas

The University of Kansas, M

Massachusetts

Massachusetts College of Art and Design, M

Michigan

Wayne State University, M

Minnesota

University of Minnesota, Twin Cities Campus, MDO

Missouri

Lindenwood University, M

New York

Cornell University, MD
LIM College, M

North Carolina

East Carolina University, M
The University of North Carolina at Greensboro, MD

Ohio

University of Cincinnati, M

Pennsylvania

Drexel University, M
Philadelphia University, M
Temple University, M

Rhode Island

Rhode Island School of Design, M

Texas

University of North Texas, M

TEXTILE SCIENCE

United States

Michigan

Michigan State University, B

Nebraska

University of Nebraska - Lincoln, B

TEXTILE SCIENCES AND ENGINEERING

United States

Alabama

Auburn University, B

Georgia

Georgia Institute of Technology, B

Massachusetts

University of Massachusetts Dartmouth, M

New York

Cornell University, MD

North Carolina

North Carolina State University, BMD

Pennsylvania

Philadelphia University, BMD

Texas

The University of Texas at Austin, M

THANATOLOGY

United States

Maryland

Hood College, MO

New York

Brooklyn College of the City University of New York, M
The College of New Rochelle, O

THEATER

United States

Alabama

The University of Alabama, M

Arizona

Arizona State University at the Tempe campus, MD
The University of Arizona, M

Arkansas

University of Arkansas, M

California

Academy of Art University, M
California Institute of the Arts, MO
California State University, Fullerton, M
California State University, Long Beach, M
California State University, Los Angeles, M
California State University, Northridge, M
California State University, San Bernardino, M
San Diego State University, M
San Francisco State University, M
San Jose State University, M
Stanford University, D
University of California, Berkeley, D
University of California, Davis, MD
University of California, Irvine, MD
University of California, Los Angeles, MD
University of California, San Diego, MD
University of California, Santa Barbara, MD
University of California, Santa Cruz, O
University of San Diego, M
University of Southern California, M

Colorado

Naropa University, M
University of Colorado Boulder, MD

Connecticut

University of Connecticut, M
Yale University, MDO

Delaware

University of Delaware, M

District of Columbia

The Catholic University of America, M
The George Washington University, MO

Florida

Florida Atlantic University, M
Florida State University, MD
University of Central Florida, M
University of Florida, M

Georgia

Columbus State University, M
Savannah College of Art and Design, M
University of Georgia, MD

Hawaii

University of Hawaii at Manoa, MD

Idaho

Idaho State University, M
University of Idaho, M

Illinois

DePaul University, M
Illinois State University, M
Northern Illinois University, M
Northwestern University, MD
Roosevelt University, M
Southern Illinois University Carbondale, MD

University of Illinois at Urbana - Champaign, MD
Western Illinois University, M

Indiana

Indiana University Bloomington, MD
Purdue University, M

Iowa

The University of Iowa, M

Kansas

Kansas State University, M
Pittsburg State University, M
The University of Kansas, MD

Kentucky

University of the Cumberlands, M
University of Louisville, M

Louisiana

Louisiana State University and Agricultural & Mechanical College, MD
Louisiana Tech University, M
Tulane University, M
University of New Orleans, M

Maryland

Towson University, M
University of Maryland, Baltimore County, M
University of Maryland, College Park, MD

Massachusetts

Boston University, MO
Brandeis University, M
Emerson College, M
Smith College, M
Tufts University, MD
University of Massachusetts Amherst, M

Michigan

Eastern Michigan University, M
Michigan State University, M
Northern Michigan University, M
University of Michigan, MD
Wayne State University, M

Minnesota

Minnesota State University Mankato, M
University of Minnesota, Twin Cities Campus, MD

Mississippi

University of Southern Mississippi, M

Missouri

Fontbonne University, M
Lindenwood University, M
Missouri State University, M
University of Central Missouri, M
University of Missouri, MD
University of Missouri - Kansas City, M
Washington University in St. Louis, M

Montana

University of Montana, M

Nebraska

University of Nebraska - Lincoln, M
University of Nebraska at Omaha, M

Nevada

University of Nevada, Las Vegas, M

New Jersey

Drew University, M
Montclair State University, M
Rowan University, M
Rutgers University - New Brunswick, M

New Mexico

University of New Mexico, M

New York

Binghamton University, State University of New York, M
Brooklyn College of the City University of New York, M
Columbia University, MD
Cornell University, D
Fordham University, M
Hunter College of the City University of New York, M
Long Island University - LIU Post, M
New York University, MD
Pace University, M
Purchase College, State University of New York, M
Sarah Lawrence College, M
Stony Brook University, State University of New York, M
University at Buffalo, the State University of New York, MD

North Carolina

The University of North Carolina at Chapel Hill, M
The University of North Carolina at Charlotte, M
The University of North Carolina at Greensboro, M
University of North Carolina School of the Arts, M

North Dakota

University of North Dakota, M

Ohio

Bowling Green State University, MD
Case Western Reserve University, M
Kent State University, M
Miami University, M
The Ohio State University, MD
Ohio University, M
The University of Akron, M
University of Cincinnati, MD

Oklahoma

Oklahoma City University, M
Oklahoma State University, M
University of Oklahoma, M

Oregon

Portland State University, M
Southern Oregon University, M
University of Oregon, MD
University of Portland, M

Pennsylvania

Arcadia University, M
Carnegie Mellon University, M
Penn State University Park, M
Point Park University, M
Temple University, M
University of Pittsburgh, MD
Villanova University, M

Rhode Island

Brown University, MD

South Carolina

Bob Jones University, M
University of South Carolina, M

South Dakota

The University of South Dakota, M

Tennessee

University of Memphis, M
The University of Tennessee, M

Texas

Baylor University, M
Southern Methodist University, M
Texas State University, M
Texas Tech University, M
Texas Woman's University, M
University of Houston, M
The University of Texas at Austin, MD
The University of Texas Rio Grande Valley, MO

Utah

Brigham Young University, M
Utah State University, M

Virginia

Averett University, M
Hollins University, MO
Mary Baldwin College, M
Regent University, M
University of Virginia, M
Virginia Commonwealth University, M
Virginia Polytechnic Institute and State University, M

Washington

Central Washington University, M
University of Washington, MD

West Virginia

West Virginia University, M

Wisconsin

University of Wisconsin - Madison, MD
University of Wisconsin - Milwaukee, M
University of Wisconsin - Superior, M

Canada

Alberta

University of Alberta, M
University of Calgary, M
University of Lethbridge, M

British Columbia

The University of British Columbia, MD
University of Victoria, M

Ontario

University of Guelph, M
University of Ottawa, M
University of Toronto, MD
York University, MD

Quebec

Université Laval, MD
Université de Sherbrooke, M

Saskatchewan

University of Saskatchewan, M

THEATRE LITERATURE, HISTORY AND CRITICISM

United States

California

Saint Mary's College of California, B

Connecticut

Albertus Magnus College, B
University of Connecticut, B

Georgia

Clark Atlanta University, B

Illinois

DePaul University, B
Northwestern University, B
University of Illinois at Urbana - Champaign, B

Iowa

Buena Vista University, B

Maine

Bowdoin College, B

Massachusetts

Salem State University, B
Suffolk University, B
Tufts University, B

Michigan

Western Michigan University, B

Missouri

Washington University in St. Louis, B

New York

Marymount Manhattan College, B

Vermont

Bennington College, B
Marlboro College, B

Virginia

Averett University, B

Washington

University of Washington, B

West Virginia

West Virginia University, B

Canada

Maritime Provinces: Nova Scotia

Dalhousie University, B

Newfoundland and Labrador

Memorial University of Newfoundland, B

THEOLOGICAL AND MINISTERIAL STUDIES

United States

Arkansas

John Brown University, B

California

California Christian College, AB
Hope International University, B
Horizon University, B

Florida

Trinity College of Florida, B

Illinois

Lincoln Christian University, AB

Indiana

Huntington University, B
Saint Mary-of-the-Woods College, B

Kansas

Manhattan Christian College, AB

Maryland

Faith Theological Seminary, B

Michigan

Cornerstone University, B

Minnesota

Concordia University, St. Paul, B
University of Northwestern - St. Paul, B

Nebraska

Union College, B

Ohio

God's Bible School and College, B

Oklahoma

Bacone College, A
Oklahoma Wesleyan University, B

Pennsylvania

Summit University, B

South Carolina

Bob Jones University, AB

Tennessee

Williamson College, B

Texas

Hardin-Simmons University, B
Howard Payne University, B
Lubbock Christian University, B
Messenger College, B

Wisconsin

Marquette University, B

Canada

Alberta

Prairie Bible Institute, B

Quebec

Concordia University, B

Saskatchewan

Horizon College & Seminary, B

THEOLOGY AND RELIGIOUS VOCATIONS

United States

Alabama

Amridge University, MD
Faulkner University, M
Samford University, MD
Spring Hill College, MO

Arizona

International Baptist College and Seminary, M

Arkansas

Ouachita Baptist University, B

California

American Jewish University, M
Azusa Pacific University, MD
Bethesda University, M
Biola University, MDO
California Institute of Integral Studies, M
California Lutheran University, MDO
Concordia University Irvine, M
Fresno Pacific University, M
John Paul the Great Catholic University, M
Loyola Marymount University, M
The Master's College and Seminary, MD
Pepperdine University, M
Santa Clara University, MDO
Shepherd University, MD
Simpson University, B
Southern California Seminary, MD
University of the West, M
Vanguard University of Southern California, M

Colorado

Naropa University, M
University of Denver, D

Connecticut

Holy Apostles College and Seminary, MO
Yale University, M

District of Columbia

The Catholic University of America, MDO
Georgetown University, D
Howard University, MD

Florida

Ave Maria University, BMD
The Baptist College of Florida, M
Barry University, MD

Bethune-Cookman University, M
Hobe Sound Bible College, B
Palm Beach Atlantic University, M
St. Thomas University, D
Southeastern University, AB
Talmudic University, M

Georgia

Emory University, MD
Georgia Christian University, MD
Luther Rice College & Seminary, MD
Mercer University, MD

Hawaii

Chaminade University of Honolulu, M

Idaho

New Saint Andrews College, MO
Northwest Nazarene University, M

Illinois

Lincoln Christian University, M
Loyola University Chicago, MDO
Moody Bible Institute, MO
Olivet Nazarene University, M
Trinity Christian College, B
Trinity International University, MDO
University of Chicago, D
Wheaton College, MD

Indiana

Ancilla College, A
Anderson University, AMD
Bethel College, M
Indiana Wesleyan University, M
Oakland City University, MD
Saint Mary-of-the-Woods College, MO
University of Notre Dame, MD
University of Saint Francis, M
Valparaiso University, MO

Iowa

Faith Baptist Bible College and Theological Seminary, M
Graceland University, M
Loras College, M
Shiloh University, M
University of Dubuque, MD

Kansas

Barclay College, M
Newman University, BM
Southwestern College, M

Kentucky

Campbellsville University, M
Kentucky Christian University, M
Kentucky Mountain Bible College, B
The Southern Baptist Theological Seminary, MD

Louisiana

Louisiana College, M
Loyola University New Orleans, MO
New Orleans Baptist Theological Seminary, MD
Xavier University of Louisiana, M

Maryland

Faith Theological Seminary, MD
Loyola University Maryland, M
Maple Springs Baptist Bible College and Seminary, MDO
Mount St. Mary's University, M
Ner Israel Rabbinical College, MDO

Massachusetts

Boston College, MDO
Boston University, MD
Eastern Nazarene College, B
Harvard University, M

Michigan

Andrews University, MDO
Madonna University, M
Sacred Heart Major Seminary, M

Spring Arbor University, M

Minnesota

Crossroads College, B
Crown College, M
St. Catherine University, MO
Saint John's University, M
University of Northwestern - St. Paul, M
University of St. Thomas, M

Missouri

Baptist Bible College, M
Calvary Bible College and Theological Seminary, M
Global University, MD
Missouri Baptist University, B
Saint Louis University, MD

Nebraska

Creighton University, M
Grace University, M

New Jersey

College of Saint Elizabeth, M
Drew University, MDO
Georgian Court University, MO
Seton Hall University, MO

New York

Central Yeshiva Tomchei Tmimim-Lubavitch, M
Concordia College - New York, B
Fordham University, MD
The Jewish Theological Seminary, MDO
Machzikei Hadath Rabbinical College, O
Nyack College, MD
Rabbinical Academy Mesivta Rabbi Chaim Berlin, O
St. John's University, M
Yeshiva Karlin Stolin Rabbinical Institute, O
Yeshivath Zichron Moshe, O

North Carolina

Apex School of Theology, MD
Campbell University, MD
Charlotte Christian College and Theological Seminary, M
Duke University, MD
Gardner-Webb University, MD
Lenoir-Rhyne University, MD
Pfeiffer University, M
Piedmont International University, MD
Shaw University, M
Southeastern Baptist Theological Seminary, MD

Ohio

Cedarville University, B
Cincinnati Christian University, M
Franciscan University of Steubenville, M
Lourdes University, M
Malone University, M
Mount St. Joseph University, MO
Mount Vernon Nazarene University, M
Ohio Dominican University, M
Pontifical College Josephinum, M
Tri-State Bible College, M
University of Dayton, MD
Ursuline College, M
Walsh University, M
Xavier University, M

Oklahoma

Oklahoma Christian University, M
Oklahoma Wesleyan University, BM
Oral Roberts University, MD
Southern Nazarene University, B

Oregon

Corban University, MDO
George Fox University, MDO
Marylhurst University, M
Mount Angel Seminary, M
Multnomah University, MD

Pennsylvania

Bryn Athyn College of the New Church, M
Cairn University, M

Duquesne University, MD
Eastern University, MD
Gannon University, O
La Salle University, MDO
Lancaster Bible College, MDO
Saint Charles Borromeo Seminary, Overbrook, M
Summit University, BMD
Thiel College, B
The University of Scranton, M
University of Valley Forge, ABM
Villanova University, M
Yeshiva Beth Moshe, O

Rhode Island

Providence College, M

South Carolina

Bob Jones University, MDO
Columbia International University, MDO

Tennessee

Belmont University, B
Carson-Newman University, M
Freed-Hardeman University, M
Johnson University, M
Lee University, BM
Lipscomb University, MDO
Mid-America Baptist Theological Seminary, MD
Milligan College, MD
Sewanee: The University of the South, MD
Southern Adventist University, M
Trevecca Nazarene University, ABM
Union University, B
Vanderbilt University, M
Williamson College, B

Texas

Abilene Christian University, BM
Arlington Baptist College, BM
Austin Graduate School of Theology, M
Baptist Missionary Association Theological Seminary, M
Baylor University, MD
Criswell College, M
Dallas Baptist University, BM
Hardin-Simmons University, MD
Houston Baptist University, M
Howard Payne University, M
The King's University, MDO
LeTourneau University, B
Lubbock Christian University, M
St. Mary's University, MO
Southern Methodist University, MD
Southwestern Assemblies of God University, M
University of Dallas, M
University of St. Thomas, BM
Wayland Baptist University, M

Virginia

Christendom College, M
Eastern Mennonite University, MO
Liberty University, MDO
Regent University, MD
Virginia Union University, MD

Washington

Northwest University, BM
Seattle Pacific University, MO
Seattle University, MO
Whitworth University, M

Wisconsin

Lakeland College, M
Maranatha Baptist University, M
Marquette University, MD
St. Norbert College, M

U.S. Territories: Puerto Rico

Inter American University of Puerto Rico, Metropolitan Campus, D

Pontifical Catholic University of Puerto Rico, M

Canada

Alberta

Ambrose University, MO
Concordia University of Edmonton, BM
Prairie Bible Institute, B

British Columbia

Trinity Western University, MD

Manitoba

Providence University College & Theological Seminary, MDO
The University of Winnipeg, MO

Maritime Provinces: New Brunswick

Kingswood University, M

Maritime Provinces: Nova Scotia

Acadia University, MD
Saint Mary's University, M

Ontario

Heritage College and Seminary, MO
Master's College and Seminary, B
McMaster University, MDO
Queen's University at Kingston, MO
Saint Paul University, MDO
Tyndale University College & Seminary, MO
Wilfrid Laurier University, MDO

Quebec

Concordia University, M
McGill University, MD
Université Laval, MD
Université de Montréal, MDO
Université du Québec à Chicoutimi, MD
Université de Sherbrooke, MDO

Saskatchewan

Horizon College & Seminary, B

THEOLOGY/THEOLOGICAL STUDIES

United States

Alabama

Oakwood University, B

Arkansas

John Brown University, B
Ouachita Baptist University, B
Williams Baptist College, AB

California

Azusa Pacific University, B
Biola University, B
Concordia University Irvine, B
Life Pacific College, B
Loyola Marymount University, B
The Master's College and Seminary, B
Pacific Union College, B
Saint Katherine College, B
Saint Mary's College of California, B
University of San Francisco, B
Vanguard University of Southern California, B
William Jessup University, AB

Colorado

Colorado Christian University, B

District of Columbia

Georgetown University, B

Florida

Ave Maria University, B
Barry University, B
Palm Beach Atlantic University, B

St. John Vianney College Seminary, B
St. Thomas University, B

Georgia

Brewton-Parker College, B

Idaho

Northwest Nazarene University, B

Illinois

Benedictine University, B
Concordia University Chicago, B
Dominican University, B
Elmhurst College, B
Loyola University Chicago, B
Moody Bible Institute, B
Olivet Nazarene University, B
Trinity Christian College, B
University of Chicago, B
University of St. Francis, B

Indiana

Anderson University, B
Hanover College, B
Holy Cross College, B
Huntington University, B
Indiana Wesleyan University, B
Marian University, AB
University of Notre Dame, B
University of Saint Francis, B
Valparaiso University, B

Iowa

Briar Cliff University, AB
Dordt College, B
St. Ambrose University, B
University of Dubuque, B

Kansas

Benedictine College, B
Central Christian College of Kansas, A
Manhattan Christian College, B
MidAmerica Nazarene University, B
Newman University, B
University of Saint Mary, B

Kentucky

Bellarmine University, B
Brescia University, B
Kentucky Mountain Bible College, B

Louisiana

Louisiana College, B
University of Holy Cross, B
Xavier University of Louisiana, B

Maine

Saint Joseph's College of Maine, B

Maryland

Mount St. Mary's University, B
Washington Adventist University, B
Yeshiva College of the Nation's Capital, B

Massachusetts

Anna Maria College, B
Assumption College, B
Boston College, B
Eastern Nazarene College, B
Hellenic College, B

Michigan

Andrews University, B
Calvin College, B
Grace Bible College, B
Kuyper College, B
Sacred Heart Major Seminary, A
Spring Arbor University, B

Minnesota

College of Saint Benedict, B
Concordia University, St. Paul, B
Crossroads College, B
Crown College, B

Martin Luther College, B
St. Catherine University, B
Saint John's University, B
Saint Mary's University of Minnesota, B

Mississippi

Northeast Mississippi Community College, A

Missouri

Calvary Bible College and Theological Seminary, AB
Global University, B
Missouri Baptist University, A
Ozark Christian College, AB
Rockhurst University, B
Saint Louis Christian College, B
Saint Louis University, B
Southwest Baptist University, B

Montana

Carroll College, B
University of Great Falls, B

Nebraska

College of Saint Mary, B
Concordia University, Nebraska, B
Creighton University, AB
Nebraska Christian College, B
Union College, B

New Hampshire

Saint Anselm College, B

New Jersey

Assumption College for Sisters, A
Caldwell University, B
College of Saint Elizabeth, B
Saint Peter's University, B
Seton Hall University, B

New Mexico

University of the Southwest, B

New York

Bard College, B
Fordham University, B
Holy Trinity Orthodox Seminary, B
Houghton College, B
Ohr Hameir Theological Seminary, B
Rabbinical Academy Mesivta Rabbi Chaim Berlin, B
Rabbinical College of Ohr Shimon Yisroel, B
Rabbinical Seminary of America, B
St. Bonaventure University, B
St. John's University, B
Yeshiva and Kollel Harbotzas Torah, B
Yeshiva of Nitra Rabbinical College, B
Yeshivath Viznitz, B

North Carolina

Apex School of Theology, B
Belmont Abbey College, B
John Wesley University, B
Piedmont International University, AB

North Dakota

University of Mary, B

Ohio

Franciscan University of Steubenville, AB
Mount Vernon Nazarene University, B
Notre Dame College, B
Ohio Dominican University, AB
Rabbinical College of Telshe, B
Walsh University, B

Oklahoma

Hillsdale Free Will Baptist College, B
Oklahoma Wesleyan University, B
Oral Roberts University, B
St. Gregory's University, B
Southern Nazarene University, B
Southwestern Christian University, B

Oregon

Concordia University, B
Multnomah University, B
University of Portland, B
Warner Pacific College, B

Pennsylvania

Carlow University, B
DeSales University, B
Duquesne University, B
Eastern University, B
Gannon University, B
Immaculata University, AB
King's College, B
Saint Vincent College, B
Talmudical Yeshiva of Philadelphia, B
University of Valley Forge, B

Rhode Island

Providence College, B

South Carolina

Morris College, B

Tennessee

American Baptist College, B
Aquinas College, B
Lee University, B
Martin Methodist College, B
Mid-America Baptist Theological Seminary, A
Southern Adventist University, B
Union University, B

Texas

Baptist Missionary Association Theological Seminary, AB
Hardin-Simmons University, B
Howard Payne University, B
The King's University, AB
St. Edward's University, B
St. Mary's University, B
Southwestern Adventist University, B
Southwestern Assemblies of God University, B
Texas Lutheran University, B
University of Dallas, B
University of St. Thomas, B

Virginia

Bluefield College, B
Christendom College, B
Eastern Mennonite University, B

Washington

Pacific Lutheran University, B
Seattle Pacific University, B
Walla Walla University, B
Whitworth University, B

West Virginia

Appalachian Bible College, AB

Wisconsin

Concordia University Wisconsin, B
Marian University, B
Marquette University, B
Mount Mary University, B
Silver Lake College of the Holy Family, B

U.S. Territories: Puerto Rico

Universidad Adventista de las Antillas, B
Universidad Pentecostal Mizpa, AB

Canada

Alberta

Ambrose University, B
The King's University, B
Prairie Bible Institute, B
Rocky Mountain College, B
Vanguard College, B

British Columbia

Summit Pacific College, B

Manitoba

Providence University College & Theological Seminary, B
The University of Winnipeg, B

Ontario

Emmanuel Bible College, B
Heritage College and Seminary, B
Master's College and Seminary, B
Ner Israel Yeshiva College of Toronto, B
Queen's University at Kingston, B
Redeemer University College, B
Saint Paul University, B
The University of Western Ontario, B

Quebec

Concordia University, B
McGill University, B
Université Laval, AB
Université de Montréal, B
Université du Québec à Chicoutimi, B
Université du Québec à Rimouski, B
Université du Québec à Trois-Rivières, B

Saskatchewan

Briercrest College, B
Horizon College & Seminary, B

THEORETICAL CHEMISTRY

United States

Connecticut

Wesleyan University, D
Yale University, D

District of Columbia

Georgetown University, D

New York

Cornell University, D

Pennsylvania

Carnegie Mellon University, D

Tennessee

The University of Tennessee, D
Vanderbilt University, M

West Virginia

West Virginia University, MD

Canada

Alberta

University of Calgary, MD

Ontario

Laurentian University, M

Saskatchewan

University of Regina, MD

THEORETICAL AND MATHEMATICAL PHYSICS

United States

California

Chapman University, B

New York

University at Buffalo, the State University of New York, B

Pennsylvania

Carnegie Mellon University, B

West Virginia

Bethany College, B

Wisconsin

Viterbo University, B

Canada

Ontario

University of Guelph, B
University of Ottawa, B
The University of Western Ontario, B

THEORETICAL PHYSICS

United States

Delaware

Delaware State University, D

Georgia

Emory University, D

Massachusetts

Harvard University, D

New Jersey

Rutgers University - New Brunswick, MD

New York

Cornell University, MD

West Virginia

West Virginia University, MD

Canada

British Columbia

University of Victoria, MD

THERAPEUTIC RECREATION

United States

California

Loyola Marymount University, M

Colorado

Naropa University, M

Florida

Florida International University, M
University of Florida, M

Indiana

Indiana University Bloomington, M

Iowa

The University of Iowa, M

Louisiana

Southern University and Agricultural and Mechanical
College, M

New Hampshire

University of New Hampshire, M

New York

State University of New York College at Cortland, M

North Carolina

North Carolina Central University, M
The University of North Carolina at Greensboro, M

Pennsylvania

Temple University, M

Tennessee

The University of Tennessee, M

Texas

Texas State University, M

Wisconsin

University of Wisconsin - La Crosse, M
University of Wisconsin - Milwaukee, O

THERAPEUTIC RECREATION/ RECREATIONAL THERAPY

United States

California

California State University, East Bay, B
Santa Barbara City College, A

Colorado

Colorado Mountain College (Glenwood Springs), A

Connecticut

Northwestern Connecticut Community College, A

Florida

Broward College, A

Indiana

Indiana Tech, B

Iowa

The University of Iowa, B

Louisiana

Southern University and Agricultural and Mechanical
College, B

Maine

Unity College, B
University of Southern Maine, B

Massachusetts

Springfield College, B

Michigan

Calvin College, B
Central Michigan University, B
Eastern Michigan University, B
Grand Valley State University, B

Minnesota

Minnesota State University Mankato, B
Ridgewater College, A
St. Cloud State University, B

New York

Ithaca College, B
St. Thomas Aquinas College, B
State University of New York College at Cortland, B
Utica College, B

North Carolina

Catawba College, B
East Carolina University, B
St. Andrews University, B
Shaw University, B
The University of North Carolina Wilmington, B
Western Carolina University, B
Western Piedmont Community College, A
Winston-Salem State University, B

Ohio

North Central State College, A
The University of Toledo, B

Pennsylvania

Community College of Allegheny County, A
Lincoln University, B
Slippery Rock University of Pennsylvania, B

Temple University, B

Texas

Austin Community College District, A

Utah

Brigham Young University, B

Virginia

Hampton University, B
Longwood University, B

Washington

Eastern Washington University, B

Wisconsin

University of Wisconsin - La Crosse, B
University of Wisconsin - Milwaukee, B

Canada

Maritime Provinces: Nova Scotia

Dalhousie University, B

Ontario

University of Waterloo, B

Quebec

Concordia University, B

THERAPIES--DANCE, DRAMA, AND MUSIC

United States

Massachusetts

Lesley University, M

TOOL AND DIE TECHNOLOGY/ TECHNICIAN

United States

Alabama

Bevill State Community College, A
Calhoun Community College, A
Gadsden State Community College, A
George C. Wallace Community College, A
George Corley Wallace State Community College, A
J. F. Drake State Community and Technical College,
   A
Shelton State Community College, A

California

Ventura College, A

Illinois

John A. Logan College, A
Rock Valley College, A

Indiana

Ivy Tech Community College - Bloomington, A
Ivy Tech Community College - Central Indiana, A
Ivy Tech Community College - Columbus, A
Ivy Tech Community College - East Central, A
Ivy Tech Community College - Kokomo, A
Ivy Tech Community College - Lafayette, A
Ivy Tech Community College - North Central, A
Ivy Tech Community College - Northeast, A
Ivy Tech Community College - Northwest, A
Ivy Tech Community College - Richmond, A
Ivy Tech Community College - Southern Indiana, A
Ivy Tech Community College - Southwest, A
Ivy Tech Community College - Wabash Valley, A
Vincennes University, A

Iowa

Des Moines Area Community College, A
Marshalltown Community College, A
North Iowa Area Community College, A

Michigan

Delta College, A
Ferris State University, A
Macomb Community College, A

Minnesota

Dunwoody College of Technology, A
Hennepin Technical College, A
Ridgewater College, A

Mississippi

Northeast Mississippi Community College, A

North Carolina

Craven Community College, A
Wake Technical Community College, A

Ohio

North Central State College, A

Utah

Utah State University, B

TOURISM PROMOTION OPERATIONS

United States

Illinois

College of DuPage, A

Minnesota

St. Cloud State University, A

New York

Genesee Community College, A
Jefferson Community College, A

North Carolina

Blue Ridge Community College, A

Ohio

Bowling Green State University, B

Pennsylvania

Community College of Allegheny County, A

Canada

Maritime Provinces: Nova Scotia

Cape Breton University, B

TOURISM AND TRAVEL SERVICES MANAGEMENT

United States

Arizona

Arizona State University at the Downtown Phoenix campus, B

California

Butte College, A
Los Angeles City College, A
Los Medanos College, A
Saddleback College, A
San Diego City College, A
San Diego Mesa College, A
Santa Ana College, A
Santiago Canyon College, A
West Los Angeles College, A

Colorado

Colorado Mountain College (Steamboat Springs), A
Fort Lewis College, B

Delaware

Delaware State University, B

Florida

Broward College, A
Daytona State College, A
Johnson & Wales University, B
Miami Dade College, A
St. Thomas University, B
Schiller International University, B

Georgia

Albany Technical College, A
Athens Technical College, A
Atlanta Technical College, A
Central Georgia Technical College, A
Gwinnett Technical College, A
Ogeechee Technical College, A
Savannah Technical College, A

Hawaii

Brigham Young University - Hawaii, B
Hawai'i Pacific University, B
Kapiolani Community College, A
University of Hawaii at Manoa, B

Illinois

College of DuPage, A
John A. Logan College, A
MacCormac College, A
Moraine Valley Community College, A
Northwestern College - Bridgeview Campus, A

Indiana

Indiana University - Purdue University Indianapolis, B

Kansas

Fort Hays State University, B

Louisiana

Southern University at Shreveport, A
University of Holy Cross, B

Maine

Kaplan University, South Portland, A
University of Maine at Machias, B

Massachusetts

Bunker Hill Community College, A
Fisher College, B
North Shore Community College, A
Northern Essex Community College, A
Salem State University, B

Michigan

Lansing Community College, A

Minnesota

Dakota County Technical College, A
St. Cloud State University, B

Mississippi

Hinds Community College, A

Missouri

Stevens - The Institute of Business & Arts, A

Nebraska

Midland University, A

Nevada

College of Southern Nevada, A

New Hampshire

Great Bay Community College, A
NHTI, Concord's Community College, A
Plymouth State University, B

New York

Adirondack Community College, A
Bryant & Stratton College - Syracuse Campus, A
Finger Lakes Community College, A
Fiorello H. LaGuardia Community College of the City University of New York, A
Genesee Community College, A
Kingsborough Community College of the City University of New York, A
Monroe Community College, A
Morrisville State College, A
Niagara County Community College, A
Niagara University, B
Rockland Community College, A
Sullivan County Community College, A

North Carolina

Blue Ridge Community College, A
Central Piedmont Community College, A

Ohio

Bowling Green State University, B
Columbus State Community College, A
Hocking College, A
Lakeland Community College, A
Lorain County Community College, A
Sinclair Community College, A
University of Northwestern Ohio, A
Zane State College, A

Oklahoma

Northeastern State University, B

Oregon

Chemeketa Community College, A
Mt. Hood Community College, A
Oregon State University - Cascades, B

Pennsylvania

Bucks County Community College, A
Consolidated School of Business (York), A
Luzerne County Community College, A
Westmoreland County Community College, A

Rhode Island

Johnson & Wales University, B

South Carolina

University of South Carolina, B

South Dakota

Black Hills State University, AB

Texas

Amarillo College, A
Austin Community College District, A
El Paso Community College, A
Houston Community College, A
Texas A&M University, B
The University of Texas at San Antonio, B

Vermont

Johnson State College, B

Virginia

George Mason University, B

Washington

Central Washington University, B
Highline College, A
Yakima Valley Community College, A

West Virginia

Concord University, B

Wisconsin

Madison Area Technical College, A

U.S. Territories: Guam

Guam Community College, A

U.S. Territories: Puerto Rico

ICPR Junior College - Hato Rey Campus, A
Pontifical Catholic University of Puerto Rico, B
University of Puerto Rico in Carolina, B
University of the Sacred Heart, B

Canada

Alberta

University of Calgary, B

British Columbia

British Columbia Institute of Technology, A
Thompson Rivers University, B

Maritime Provinces: Nova Scotia

Cape Breton University, B
Mount Saint Vincent University, B

Ontario

Brock University, B
University of Guelph, B

TOURISM AND TRAVEL SERVICES MARKETING OPERATIONS

United States

California

City College of San Francisco, A
Cypress College, A
Long Beach City College, A
Orange Coast College, A
San Diego Mesa College, A
Southwestern College, A

Illinois

College of DuPage, A

Massachusetts

Bay State College, A

Michigan

Western Michigan University, B

Missouri

University of Central Missouri, B

New York

Herkimer County Community College, A
Morrisville State College, A
Rochester Institute of Technology, B
State University of New York College of Agriculture and Technology at Cobleskill, A
State University of New York College of Technology at Delhi, A

Ohio

Ohio University - Southern Campus, A

Pennsylvania

Community College of Beaver County, A
Luzerne County Community College, A
Montgomery County Community College, A

Rhode Island

Johnson & Wales University, B

Virginia

American National University (Salem), A

Washington

Edmonds Community College, A

Wisconsin

Milwaukee Area Technical College, A

U.S. Territories: Puerto Rico

Huertas Junior College, A
University of the Sacred Heart, B

Canada

Maritime Provinces: Nova Scotia

Mount Saint Vincent University, B

TOXICOLOGY

United States

Alabama

The University of Alabama at Birmingham, MD
University of South Alabama, M

Arkansas

University of Arkansas for Medical Sciences, M

California

San Diego State University, M
University of California, Berkeley, B
University of California, Davis, MD
University of California, Irvine, MD
University of California, Los Angeles, D
University of California, Riverside, MD
University of California, Santa Cruz, MD
University of Southern California, MD

Colorado

University of Colorado Denver, D

Connecticut

University of Connecticut, MD

District of Columbia

The George Washington University, M

Florida

Florida Agricultural and Mechanical University, MD
University of Florida, MO

Illinois

University of Illinois at Chicago, M

Indiana

Indiana University Bloomington, M
Indiana University - Purdue University Indianapolis, MD
Purdue University, MD

Iowa

Iowa State University of Science and Technology, MD
The University of Iowa, MD

Kansas

The University of Kansas, MD

Kentucky

University of Kentucky, MD
University of Louisville, MD

Louisiana

Louisiana State University and Agricultural & Mechanical College, M
University of Louisiana at Monroe, BD

Maryland

Johns Hopkins University, D
University of Maryland Eastern Shore, MD

Massachusetts

Massachusetts Institute of Technology, MD

Michigan

Eastern Michigan University, B
Michigan State University, MD
University of Michigan, MD

Wayne State University, MD

Minnesota

University of Minnesota, Duluth, MD
University of Minnesota, Twin Cities Campus, MD

Mississippi

University of Mississippi Medical Center, D

Missouri

University of Missouri - Kansas City, D

Montana

University of Montana, MD

Nebraska

University of Nebraska - Lincoln, MD
University of Nebraska Medical Center, D

New Hampshire

Dartmouth College, D

New Jersey

Rutgers University - New Brunswick, MD

New Mexico

University of New Mexico, MD

New York

Columbia University, MD
Cornell University, MD
Nazareth College of Rochester, B
New York University, MD
St. John's University, BM
University at Albany, State University of New York, MD
University at Buffalo, the State University of New York, MD
University of Rochester, D

North Carolina

Duke University, O
North Carolina State University, MD
The University of North Carolina at Chapel Hill, MD

Ohio

Ashland University, B
Wright State University, M

Oregon

Oregon State University, MD

Pennsylvania

Penn State Beaver, B
Penn State Berks, B
Penn State DuBois, B
Penn State Fayette, The Eberly Campus, B
Penn State Greater Allegheny, B
Penn State Hazleton, B
Penn State Mont Alto, B
Penn State New Kensington, B
Penn State Shenango, B
Penn State University Park, B
Penn State Wilkes-Barre, B
Penn State York, B
University of the Sciences, MD

Rhode Island

University of Rhode Island, MD

South Carolina

Medical University of South Carolina, D

Texas

Prairie View A&M University, M
Texas Southern University, MD
Texas Tech University, MD
The University of Texas at Austin, D
The University of Texas Health Science Center at San Antonio, M
The University of Texas Medical Branch, D

Utah

University of Utah, D
Utah State University, MD

Virginia

Virginia Commonwealth University, MDO

Washington

University of Washington, MD

West Virginia

West Virginia University, MD

Wisconsin

University of Wisconsin - Madison, MD

U.S. Territories: Puerto Rico

University of Puerto Rico, Medical Sciences Campus, MD

Canada

British Columbia

Simon Fraser University, M

Maritime Provinces: Prince Edward Island

University of Prince Edward Island, MD

Ontario

Queen's University at Kingston, MD
University of Guelph, BMD
University of Toronto, B
The University of Western Ontario, B

Quebec

Université de Montréal, O

Saskatchewan

University of Saskatchewan, BMDO

TRADE AND INDUSTRIAL TEACHER EDUCATION

United States

Alabama

Auburn University, B

Arkansas

National Park College, A

California

California State University, Long Beach, B
California State University, San Bernardino, B
East Los Angeles College, A
Victor Valley College, A

Delaware

Delaware State University, B

District of Columbia

University of the District of Columbia, B

Florida

Broward College, A
Florida Agricultural and Mechanical University, B
South Florida State College, A
State College of Florida Manatee-Sarasota, A
University of Central Florida, B
University of West Florida, B

Georgia

Darton State College, A
Valdosta State University, B

Illinois

Southern Illinois University Carbondale, B

Indiana

Indiana State University, B

Iowa

Iowa Lakes Community College, A
Southeastern Community College, A
Upper Iowa University, B

Kansas

Neosho County Community College, A
Pratt Community College, A

Kentucky

Eastern Kentucky University, AB
Murray State University, AB
University of Louisville, B
Western Kentucky University, B

Maine

University of Southern Maine, B

Massachusetts

Fitchburg State University, B
Quinsigamond Community College, A

Michigan

Western Michigan University, B

Minnesota

Bemidji State University, B

Mississippi

Copiah-Lincoln Community College, A
Itawamba Community College, A

Missouri

Lindenwood University, B

Nebraska

University of Nebraska - Lincoln, B

New Mexico

New Mexico Junior College, A
Western New Mexico University, B

New York

Buffalo State College, State University of New York, B
State University of New York at Oswego, B

North Carolina

Isothermal Community College, A
Lenoir Community College, A
North Carolina Agricultural and Technical State University, B
Southwestern Community College, A

North Dakota

Turtle Mountain Community College, A

Ohio

Bowling Green State University, B
The University of Toledo, B

Oklahoma

University of Central Oklahoma, B

Pennsylvania

Indiana University of Pennsylvania, B
Temple University, B

Texas

Del Mar College, A
Howard College, A
Palo Alto College, A
Wayland Baptist University, B

Virginia

ECPI University (Newport News), A
ECPI University (Richmond), A
Norfolk State University, B
Virginia State University, B

Washington

Central Washington University, B
South Seattle College, A

Wyoming

University of Wyoming, B

U.S. Territories: Puerto Rico

Universidad del Turabo, B

Canada

Alberta

University of Alberta, B

British Columbia

British Columbia Institute of Technology, A

Newfoundland and Labrador

Memorial University of Newfoundland, B

Quebec

Université du Québec à Chicoutimi, B
Université du Québec à Montréal, B
Université du Québec à Rimouski, B

Saskatchewan

University of Saskatchewan, B

TRANSCULTURAL NURSING

United States

Minnesota

Augsburg College, MD

New Jersey

Rutgers University - Newark, D

TRANSLATION AND INTERPRETATION

United States

Arizona

Arizona State University at the Tempe campus, O

California

University of California, Santa Barbara, D

Colorado

University of Denver, O

Delaware

University of Delaware, M

District of Columbia

Gallaudet University, MD

Florida

University of North Florida, M

Georgia

Georgia State University, O

Illinois

University of Illinois at Urbana - Champaign, M

Michigan

Marygrove College, O

New Jersey

Drew University, M
Montclair State University, O
Rutgers University - New Brunswick, M

New York

Binghamton University, State University of New York, DO
Columbia University, M
New York University, M
University of Rochester, MO

North Carolina

The University of North Carolina at Charlotte, O

Ohio

Kent State University, MD

Pennsylvania

La Salle University, MO

Texas

Texas A&M International University, M

Wisconsin

University of Wisconsin - Milwaukee, O

U.S. Territories: Puerto Rico

University of Puerto Rico, Río Piedras Campus, MO

Canada

Ontario

University of Ottawa, MD
York University, M

Quebec

Concordia University, O
Université Laval, MO
Université de Montréal, MDO

TRANSLATIONAL BIOLOGY

United States

California

University of California, Irvine, M

Iowa

The University of Iowa, MD

New Jersey

Rutgers University - New Brunswick, M

Texas

The University of Texas at San Antonio, D

TRANSPERSONAL AND HU-MANISTIC PSYCHOLOGY

United States

California

John F. Kennedy University, M

Colorado

Naropa University, M

Washington

Seattle University, M

TRANSPORTATION AND HIGH-WAY ENGINEERING

United States

Alabama

Auburn University, MD
The University of Alabama in Huntsville, M

Arizona

Arizona State University at the Tempe campus, O

Arkansas

University of Arkansas, M

California

Art Center College of Design, M
University of California, Berkeley, MD
University of California, Davis, MD
University of California, Irvine, MD
University of Southern California, MO

Colorado

University of Colorado Denver, MD

Delaware

University of Delaware, MD

Florida

University of Central Florida, O
University of South Florida, MDO

Illinois

Illinois Institute of Technology, M
Northwestern University, MD
Southern Illinois University Edwardsville, M

Iowa

Iowa State University of Science and Technology, MD

Kansas

Kansas State University, MD

Louisiana

Louisiana State University and Agricultural & Mechanical College, MD

Maryland

Morgan State University, M

Massachusetts

Massachusetts Institute of Technology, D
University of Massachusetts Amherst, M

Michigan

College for Creative Studies, M

Missouri

University of Missouri, M

Nevada

University of Nevada, Las Vegas, M

New Jersey

New Jersey Institute of Technology, MD

New York

Cornell University, MD
New York University, MD
Rensselaer Polytechnic Institute, MD

Ohio

Ohio University, M
University of Dayton, M
The University of Toledo, A

Tennessee

University of Memphis, M

Texas

Texas Southern University, M
The University of Texas at Tyler, M

Virginia

George Mason University, MD
Virginia Polytechnic Institute and State University, O

Washington

University of Washington, MD

West Virginia

Marshall University, M

Wisconsin

Gateway Technical College, A
Marquette University, MDO

Canada

Alberta

University of Calgary, MD

British Columbia

British Columbia Institute of Technology, A

Maritime Provinces: New Brunswick

University of New Brunswick Fredericton, MD

Ontario

University of Toronto, B

Quebec

École Polytechnique de Montréal, MD

TRANSPORTATION AND MATE-RIALS MOVING

United States

Arizona

Cochise County Community College District, A

California

Los Angeles Trade-Technical College, A
Mt. San Antonio College, A
Sacramento City College, A
San Diego City College, A
San Diego Miramar College, A
Southwestern College, A
West Hills Community College, A

Illinois

City Colleges of Chicago, Richard J. Daley College, A
College of DuPage, A
Lewis University, B

Maine

Maine Maritime Academy, B

Maryland

Cecil College, A

Michigan

Baker College, A
Muskegon Community College, A

Nebraska

Mid-Plains Community College, A

New York

Nassau Community College, A
Niagara University, B
Schenectady County Community College, A
United States Merchant Marine Academy, B

North Carolina

Central Piedmont Community College, A

Ohio

Sinclair Community College, A

Tennessee

Tennessee State University, B

Virginia

Northern Virginia Community College, A

Washington

Highline College, A

Canada

British Columbia

The University of British Columbia, B

TRANSPORTATION/TRANS-PORTATION MANAGEMENT

United States

California

California Maritime Academy, M
San Jose State University, M
University of California, Davis, MD
University of California, Santa Barbara, D

Florida

Embry-Riddle Aeronautical University - Worldwide, B
Florida Institute of Technology, M
Florida State College at Jacksonville, A
Gulf Coast State College, A
Polk State College, A
South Florida State College, A
University of North Florida, B

Indiana

Ivy Tech Community College - Central Indiana, A

Iowa

Iowa State University of Science and Technology, M

Louisiana

University of New Orleans, M

Maine

Maine Maritime Academy, M

Maryland

Cecil College, A
Hagerstown Community College, A
Morgan State University, M

Massachusetts

Bridgewater State University, B

New Jersey

New Jersey Institute of Technology, MD

New York

New York University, M
State University of New York Maritime College, M

North Carolina

North Carolina Agricultural and Technical State University, B

North Dakota

North Dakota State University, MD

Ohio

Wright State University, B

Pennsylvania

Temple University, M
University of Pennsylvania, B

Tennessee

The University of Tennessee, MD

Texas

Del Mar College, A
LeTourneau University, B
Texas A&M University, B
Texas Southern University, M

Virginia

George Mason University, MO

Washington

University of Washington, O

West Virginia

American Public University System, M

Wisconsin

University of Wisconsin - Superior, B

U.S. Territories: Puerto Rico

Pontifical Catholic University of Puerto Rico, O

Canada

British Columbia

The University of British Columbia, D

Quebec

McGill University, BM

TRAVEL AND TOURISM

United States

Arizona

Arizona State University at the Tempe campus, MDO

California

California State University, East Bay, M
California State University, Fullerton, M
California State University, Northridge, M
San Francisco State University, M

District of Columbia

The George Washington University, MO

Florida

Florida Atlantic University, O
Schiller International University, M
University of Central Florida, M
University of Florida, MD
University of South Florida, M

Georgia

Savannah College of Art and Design, M

Hawaii

University of Hawaii at Manoa, M

Illinois

Western Illinois University, M

Indiana

Indiana University Bloomington, M
Purdue University, MD

Louisiana

University of New Orleans, M

Massachusetts

Endicott College, M
Lasell College, MO
University of Massachusetts Amherst, D

Michigan

Eastern Michigan University, M

Minnesota

University of Minnesota, Twin Cities Campus, MD

New York

New York University, MO
Rochester Institute of Technology, M
Syracuse University, M

North Carolina

East Carolina University, M
North Carolina State University, MD

Ohio

Kent State University, M

Pennsylvania

Penn State University Park, MD
Temple University, MD

South Carolina

Clemson University, MD
University of South Carolina, M

Tennessee

The University of Tennessee, M

Texas

University of North Texas, M

Virginia

Liberty University, M
Virginia Polytechnic Institute and State University, MD

Canada

British Columbia

Royal Roads University, MO

Ontario

University of Waterloo, M

Quebec

Université du Québec à Trois-Rivières, MO

TRUCK AND BUS DRIVER/COMMERCIAL VEHICLE OPERATION

United States

Arizona

Mohave Community College, A

Illinois

Spoon River College, A

Iowa

Scott Community College, A

Minnesota

Northland Community and Technical College, A

Nebraska

Central Community College - Hastings Campus, A

TURF AND TURFGRASS MANAGEMENT

United States

Arizona

Northland Pioneer College, A

California

College of the Desert, A
Cuyamaca College, A
Mt. San Jacinto College, A
Southwestern College, A

Delaware

Delaware Technical & Community College, Jack F. Owens Campus, A

Florida

Florida SouthWestern State College, A

Georgia

North Georgia Technical College, A
University of Georgia, B

Illinois

College of Lake County, A
Danville Area Community College, A
Joliet Junior College, A

Iowa

Iowa Lakes Community College, A
Kirkwood Community College, A

Massachusetts

University of Massachusetts Amherst, AB

Michigan

Lake Michigan College, A
Northwestern Michigan College, A

Minnesota

Rochester Community and Technical College, A
University of Minnesota, Crookston, B

Missouri

Ozarks Technical Community College, A
State Technical College of Missouri, A

Nebraska

University of Nebraska - Lincoln, B

New Jersey

Rutgers University - New Brunswick, B

New Mexico

New Mexico State University, B

North Carolina

Brunswick Community College, A
Catawba Valley Community College, A
Guilford Technical Community College, A
North Carolina State University, AB
Sandhills Community College, A
Wayne Community College, A

North Dakota

North Dakota State University, B

Ohio

Cincinnati State Technical and Community College, A
The Ohio State University, B
The Ohio State University Agricultural Technical Institute, A

Oklahoma

Oklahoma State University, Oklahoma City, A

Pennsylvania

Community College of Allegheny County, A
Delaware Valley University, B
Penn State Abington, B
Penn State Altoona, B
Penn State Beaver, B
Penn State Berks, B
Penn State Brandywine, B
Penn State DuBois, B
Penn State Erie, The Behrend College, B
Penn State Fayette, The Eberly Campus, B
Penn State Greater Allegheny, B
Penn State Hazleton, B
Penn State Lehigh Valley, B
Penn State Mont Alto, B
Penn State New Kensington, B
Penn State Schuylkill, B
Penn State Shenango, B
Penn State University Park, B
Penn State Wilkes-Barre, B
Penn State Worthington Scranton, B
Penn State York, B

Westmoreland County Community College, A
Williamson College of the Trades, A

South Carolina

Clemson University, B

South Dakota

Southeast Technical Institute, A

Tennessee

Tennessee Technological University, B

Texas

Houston Community College, A
Texas A&M University, B
Texas State Technical College, A
Western Texas College, A

Washington

Clover Park Technical College, A
Walla Walla Community College, A

Canada

Ontario

University of Guelph, A

TURKISH LANGUAGE AND LITERATURE

United States

Texas

The University of Texas at Austin, B

Utah

University of Utah, B

UKRAINE STUDIES

Canada

Alberta

University of Alberta, B

UKRAINIAN LANGUAGE AND LITERATURE

Canada

Alberta

University of Alberta, B

Saskatchewan

University of Saskatchewan, B

URAL-ALTAIC AND CENTRAL ASIAN STUDIES

United States

Indiana

Indiana University Bloomington, B

URBAN DESIGN

United States

Arizona

Arizona State University at the Tempe campus, M

California

University of California, Berkeley, MD
University of California, Los Angeles, MD

Colorado

University of Colorado Denver, MD

Florida

University of Miami, M

Georgia

Georgia Institute of Technology, M
Savannah College of Art and Design, M

Illinois

DePaul University, M
Judson University, M

Indiana

Ball State University, M

Massachusetts

Harvard University, M

Michigan

Lawrence Technological University, M
University of Michigan, M

Missouri

Washington University in St. Louis, M

New Mexico

University of New Mexico, O

New York

City College of the City University of New York, M
Cornell University, M
Hofstra University, M
New York Institute of Technology, M
Pratt Institute, M
State University of New York College of Environmental Science and Forestry, M
University at Buffalo, the State University of New York, MDO

North Carolina

The University of North Carolina at Charlotte, M

Ohio

Kent State University, M

Pennsylvania

Carnegie Mellon University, M
Temple University, MD
University of Pennsylvania, O

Texas

Prairie View A&M University, M
Rice University, M
The University of Texas at Austin, M

Washington

University of Washington, MDO

Canada

Ontario

University of Toronto, MD

URBAN EDUCATION AND LEADERSHIP

United States

California

Holy Names University, M
Loyola Marymount University, M
University of San Francisco, M
University of Southern California, D

Delaware

University of Delaware, B

Florida

Florida International University, M

Georgia

Georgia State University, M

Illinois

Northeastern Illinois University, M
University of Chicago, M
University of Illinois at Chicago, D

Maryland

Johns Hopkins University, O
Morgan State University, D

Michigan

Marygrove College, M
University of Michigan - Dearborn, D

Nebraska

University of Nebraska at Omaha, O

New Jersey

The College of New Jersey, B
New Jersey City University, M

New York

College of Mount Saint Vincent, M
Long Island University - LIU Brooklyn, MO
Manhattanville College, M

Ohio

Cleveland State University, D

Oklahoma

Langston University, M

Pennsylvania

Alvernia University, M
Cheyney University of Pennsylvania, M
Temple University, M
University of Pennsylvania, M

Rhode Island

Brown University, M
Providence College, M

Tennessee

Vanderbilt University, M

Texas

University of Houston - Downtown, M

Virginia

Norfolk State University, M
Virginia Commonwealth University, D

Wisconsin

Cardinal Stritch University, M
University of Wisconsin - Milwaukee, BMD

URBAN FORESTRY

United States

California

University of California, Davis, B

Illinois

University of Illinois at Urbana - Champaign, B

Louisiana

Southern University and Agricultural and Mechanical College, B

Minnesota

Hennepin Technical College, A
University of Minnesota, Crookston, B

North Dakota

Dakota College at Bottineau, A

Ohio

Kent State University at Trumbull, A

Canada

Quebec

Université Laval, B

URBAN PLANNING

United States

Arizona

Arizona State University at the Tempe campus, MDO
The University of Arizona, M

California

University of California, Los Angeles, MD
University of Southern California, MDO

Indiana

Ball State University, M

Kentucky

University of Louisville, M

Massachusetts

Harvard University, MD

Michigan

Wayne State University, MO

Minnesota

Minnesota State University Mankato, MO

New York

Columbia University, MD
Hunter College of the City University of New York, M
New York University, M

Ohio

Cleveland State University, MO

Pennsylvania

University of Pittsburgh, M

Texas

Texas State University, M
The University of Texas at Arlington, D

Utah

University of Utah, MD

West Virginia

West Virginia University, M

Wisconsin

University of Wisconsin - Milwaukee, MO

Canada

Quebec

Université de Montréal, M

URBAN AND REGIONAL PLAN-NING

United States

Alabama

Alabama Agricultural and Mechanical University, M
Auburn University, M
The University of Alabama, M
University of North Alabama, M

Arizona

Arizona State University at the Tempe campus, MDO
Northern Arizona University, MO

Arkansas

University of Central Arkansas, M

California

California Polytechnic State University, San Luis Obispo, M
California State Polytechnic University, Pomona, M
California State University, Chico, M
San Diego State University, M
San Jose State University, MO
University of California, Berkeley, MD
University of California, Davis, M
University of California, Irvine, MD
University of Southern California, D

Colorado

University of Colorado Denver, MD

Connecticut

University of New Haven, M

District of Columbia

The Catholic University of America, M
Georgetown University, M

Florida

Florida Atlantic University, MO
Florida State University, MD
University of Central Florida, M
University of Florida, MD
University of South Florida, MO

Georgia

Georgia Institute of Technology, MD
Georgia State University, MDO
Savannah State University, M

Hawaii

University of Hawaii at Manoa, MDO

Idaho

Northwest Nazarene University, M
University of Idaho, M

Illinois

Loyola University Chicago, M
University of Illinois at Chicago, MD
University of Illinois at Urbana - Champaign, MD

Iowa

Iowa State University of Science and Technology, M
The University of Iowa, M

Kansas

Kansas State University, M
The University of Kansas, M

Kentucky

Eastern Kentucky University, M

Louisiana

University of New Orleans, M

Maine

University of Southern Maine, MO

Maryland

Morgan State University, M
University of Maryland, College Park, MD

Massachusetts

Boston University, M
Clark University, M
Lesley University, M
Massachusetts Institute of Technology, MD
University of Massachusetts Amherst, MD
University of Massachusetts Lowell, MO

Michigan

Eastern Michigan University, MO
Michigan State University, M
University of Michigan, MD

Minnesota

University of Minnesota, Twin Cities Campus, M

Mississippi

Delta State University, M
Jackson State University, MD

Missouri

Missouri State University, M

Nebraska

University of Nebraska - Lincoln, M

New Hampshire

University of New Hampshire, M

New Jersey

Rutgers University - New Brunswick, MD

New Mexico

University of New Mexico, M

New York

Cornell University, MD
New York University, M
Pratt Institute, M
State University of New York College of Environ-
    mental Science and Forestry, M
Syracuse University, O
University at Albany, State University of New York,
    M
University at Buffalo, the State University of New
    York, MDO

North Carolina

East Carolina University, M
The University of North Carolina at Chapel Hill, MD
The University of North Carolina at Charlotte, O

North Dakota

North Dakota State University, M

Ohio

Cleveland State University, M
The Ohio State University, MD
University of Cincinnati, M
The University of Toledo, MDO

Oklahoma

University of Oklahoma, M

Oregon

Portland State University, M
University of Oregon, M

Pennsylvania

Eastern University, M
Indiana University of Pennsylvania, M
Philadelphia University, M
Temple University, M
University of Pennsylvania, MDO
West Chester University of Pennsylvania, MO

South Carolina

Clemson University, M
College of Charleston, O

Tennessee

East Tennessee State University, MO
University of Memphis, M
Vanderbilt University, M

Texas

Texas A&M University, MD
Texas Southern University, MD
The University of Texas at Arlington, M
The University of Texas at Austin, MD
The University of Texas at San Antonio, M

Utah

Utah State University, M

Virginia

University of Virginia, M
Virginia Commonwealth University, MO
Virginia Polytechnic Institute and State University, M

Washington

Eastern Washington University, M
Northwest University, M
University of Washington, MD

West Virginia

West Virginia University, MD

Wisconsin

University of Wisconsin - Madison, MD

U.S. Territories: Puerto Rico

University of Puerto Rico, Río Piedras Campus, M

Canada

British Columbia

The University of British Columbia, MD

Manitoba

University of Manitoba, M

Maritime Provinces: New Brunswick

University of New Brunswick Fredericton, M

Maritime Provinces: Nova Scotia

Dalhousie University, M

Ontario

Queen's University at Kingston, M
University of Toronto, MD
University of Waterloo, MD

Quebec

Concordia University, O
McGill University, MD
Université Laval, MD
Université de Montréal, O
Université du Québec en Outaouais, M
Université du Québec à Rimouski, MDO

URBAN STUDIES/AFFAIRS

United States

Arizona

Arizona State University at the Downtown Phoenix
    campus, B
Arizona State University at the Tempe campus, D

California

Antioch University Los Angeles, B
Azusa Pacific University, M
California State University, Dominguez Hills, B
California State University, Northridge, B
California State University, Stanislaus, B

Loyola Marymount University, B
San Diego State University, B
San Francisco State University, B
Stanford University, B
University of California, Berkeley, B
University of California, Irvine, BMD
University of California, San Diego, B
University of San Francisco, M

Connecticut

Albertus Magnus College, B
Trinity College, B
University of Connecticut, B

Delaware

Delaware State University, B
University of Delaware, MD

District of Columbia

University of the District of Columbia, B

Florida

Florida Memorial University, B
New College of Florida, B

Georgia

Morehouse College, B
Oglethorpe University, B
Savannah State University, M

Illinois

DePaul University, B
Elmhurst College, B
Loyola University Chicago, M
Moody Bible Institute, MO
Northeastern Illinois University, B
Northwestern University, B
University of Illinois at Chicago, B
Wheaton College, B

Kentucky

University of Louisville, D

Louisiana

Dillard University, B
University of New Orleans, BMD

Maryland

Coppin State University, B
Towson University, B
University of Maryland, Baltimore County, MD

Massachusetts

Boston University, BM
Hampshire College, B
Massachusetts Institute of Technology, MD
Northeastern University, M
Tufts University, BM
Worcester State University, B

Michigan

Aquinas College, B
Eastern Michigan University, M
Wayne State University, BM

Minnesota

Augsburg College, B
Minnesota State University Mankato, BMO
North Central University, B
St. Cloud State University, B
University of Minnesota, Duluth, B
University of Minnesota, Twin Cities Campus, B

Mississippi

Jackson State University, B

Missouri

Harris-Stowe State University, B
Saint Louis University, BM
University of Missouri - Kansas City, B
Washington University in St. Louis, B

Nebraska

University of Nebraska at Omaha, B

New Jersey

New Jersey City University, BM
New Jersey Institute of Technology, D
Rutgers University - Camden, B
Rutgers University - New Brunswick, B
Rutgers University - Newark, MD
Saint Peter's University, AB

New York

Barnard College, B
Brooklyn College of the City University of New York, M
Buffalo State College, State University of New York, B
Canisius College, B
College of Mount Saint Vincent, B
Columbia University, B
Columbia University, School of General Studies, B
Eugene Lang College of Liberal Arts, B
Fordham University, BM
Hobart and William Smith Colleges, B
Hunter College of the City University of New York, BM
Le Moyne College, M
Manhattan College, B
Metropolitan College of New York, B
The New School for Public Engagement, B
New York Institute of Technology, B
New York University, BM
Parsons School of Design, B
Purchase College, State University of New York, B
Queens College of the City University of New York, BM
University at Albany, State University of New York, BO
Vassar College, B

North Dakota

North Dakota State University, M

Ohio

Cleveland State University, BMDO
The College of Wooster, B
Lorain County Community College, A
Ohio University, B
Ohio Wesleyan University, B
University of Cincinnati, B
The University of Toledo, B
Wright State University, BM

Oklahoma

University of Oklahoma, M

Oregon

Portland State University, BMD
Warner Pacific College, B

Pennsylvania

Albright College, B
Bryn Mawr College, B
Eastern University, M
Haverford College, B
Temple University, MD
University of Pennsylvania, B
University of Pittsburgh, B

Rhode Island

Brown University, B

South Carolina

College of Charleston, B
Furman University, B

Tennessee

Lipscomb University, B
Rhodes College, B

Texas

Trinity University, B
The University of Texas at Arlington, M
The University of Texas at Austin, B

Utah

University of Utah, B

Virginia

Norfolk State University, M
Old Dominion University, D
Virginia Commonwealth University, B
Virginia Polytechnic Institute and State University, MDO

Washington

University of Washington, Tacoma, B

Wisconsin

University of Wisconsin - Green Bay, B
University of Wisconsin - Milwaukee, MD
University of Wisconsin - Oshkosh, B

Canada

Alberta

University of Calgary, B
University of Lethbridge, BM

British Columbia

Simon Fraser University, MO
The University of British Columbia, B

Manitoba

The University of Winnipeg, B

Ontario

Carleton University, B
Ryerson University, B
The University of Western Ontario, B
York University, B

Quebec

Concordia University, BM
McGill University, B
Université de Montréal, B
Université du Québec à Montréal, BMD

VEHICLE MAINTENANCE AND REPAIR TECHNOLOGIES

United States

Arkansas

Arkansas State University - Beebe, A

California

Victor Valley College, A

Kansas

McPherson College, B

Minnesota

Northland Community and Technical College, A

New Mexico

Central New Mexico Community College, A

New York

Corning Community College, A
State University of New York College of Technology at Alfred, A

North Carolina

Guilford Technical Community College, A

North Dakota

North Dakota State College of Science, A

Pennsylvania

Pennco Tech, A

South Dakota

Western Dakota Technical Institute, A

Utah

LDS Business College, A

Virginia

Northern Virginia Community College, A

Washington

Clover Park Technical College, A

Canada

British Columbia

British Columbia Institute of Technology, A

VEHICLE AND VEHICLE PARTS AND ACCESSORIES MARKETING OPERATIONS

United States

Michigan

Northwood University, Michigan Campus, B

Nebraska

Central Community College - Hastings Campus, A

Pennsylvania

Pennsylvania College of Technology, A

VETERINARY/ANIMAL HEALTH TECHNOLOGY/TECHNICIAN AND VETERINARY ASSISTANT

United States

Alabama

Jefferson State Community College, A

Arizona

Penn Foster College, A
Pima Community College, A
Pima Medical Institute (Mesa), A
Pima Medical Institute (Tucson), A

California

California University of Management and Sciences, A
Carrington College - Citrus Heights, A
Carrington College - Pleasant Hill, A
Carrington College - Pomona, A
Carrington College - Sacramento, A
Carrington College - San Jose, A
Carrington College - San Leandro, A
Carrington College - Stockton, A
Cosumnes River College, A
Foothill College, A
Hartnell College, A
Los Angeles Pierce College, A
Pima Medical Institute, A
San Diego Mesa College, A
San Joaquin Valley College (Fresno), A
Yuba College, A

Colorado

Bel - Rea Institute of Animal Technology, A
Colorado Mountain College (Glenwood Springs), A
Community College of Denver, A
Front Range Community College, A
Pima Medical Institute (Colorado Springs), A

Connecticut

Northwestern Connecticut Community College, A

Delaware

Delaware Technical & Community College, Jack F. Owens Campus, A

Florida

College of Central Florida, A
Eastern Florida State College, A
Florida Gateway College, A

Hillsborough Community College, A
Miami Dade College, A
Pensacola State College, A
St. Petersburg College, AB

Georgia

Athens Technical College, A
Central Georgia Technical College, A
Fort Valley State University, A
Gwinnett Technical College, A
Ogeechee Technical College, A

Idaho

Brigham Young University - Idaho, A
Broadview University - Boise, A
College of Southern Idaho, A

Illinois

Fox College, A
John A. Logan College, A
Joliet Junior College, A
Kaskaskia College, A
Parkland College, A
Rend Lake College, A
Shawnee Community College, A
Vet Tech Institute at Fox College, A

Indiana

Harrison College, A
International Business College (Fort Wayne), A
International Business College (Indianapolis), A
Purdue University, AB
Vet Tech Institute at International Business College
  (Fort Wayne), A
Vet Tech Institute at International Business College
  (Indianapolis), A

Iowa

Des Moines Area Community College, A
Iowa Western Community College, A
Kirkwood Community College, A
Western Iowa Tech Community College, A

Kansas

Colby Community College, A
Independence Community College, A

Kentucky

Morehead State University, AB
Murray State University, B
Owensboro Community and Technical College, A

Louisiana

Northwestern State University of Louisiana, A

Maine

University of Maine at Augusta, AB
York County Community College, A

Maryland

Community College of Baltimore County, A

Massachusetts

Becker College, AB
Holyoke Community College, A
Mount Ida College, AB
North Shore Community College, A

Michigan

Baker College, A
Lansing Community College, A
Macomb Community College, A
Michigan State University, B
Oakland Community College, A
Wayne County Community College District, A

Minnesota

Argosy University, Twin Cities, A
Duluth Business University, A
Globe University - Woodbury, AB
Minnesota School of Business - Blaine, A
Minnesota School of Business - Elk River, A
Minnesota School of Business - Lakeville, A
Minnesota School Of Business - Plymouth, AB

Minnesota School of Business - Rochester, A
Minnesota School of Business - St. Cloud, A
Ridgewater College, A
Rochester Community and Technical College, A

Mississippi

Hinds Community College, A
Mississippi State University, B

Missouri

Crowder College, A
Hickey College, A
Jefferson College, A
Vet Tech Institute at Hickey College, A

Nebraska

Nebraska College of Technical Agriculture, A
Northeast Community College, A
University of Nebraska - Lincoln, B

Nevada

Pima Medical Institute, A
Truckee Meadows Community College, A

New Hampshire

Great Bay Community College, A
University of New Hampshire, A

New Jersey

Bergen Community College, A
Camden County College, A
Thomas Edison State University, AB

New Mexico

Central New Mexico Community College, A
Eastern New Mexico University - Roswell, A
Navajo Technical University, A
San Juan College, A

New York

Fiorello H. LaGuardia Community College of the
  City University of New York, A
Genesee Community College, A
Medaille College, AB
State University of New York College of Technology
  at Alfred, A
State University of New York College of Technology
  at Canton, AB
State University of New York College of Technology
  at Delhi, AB
Ulster County Community College, A
Westchester Community College, A

North Carolina

Asheville-Buncombe Technical Community College,
  A
Central Carolina Community College, A
Gaston College, A

North Dakota

North Dakota State University, B
Turtle Mountain Community College, A

Ohio

Bradford School, A
Brown Mackie College - Akron, A
Brown Mackie College - North Canton, A
Columbus State Community College, A
Cuyahoga Community College, A
Kent State University at Tuscarawas, A
Stautzenberger College (Brecksville), A
Stautzenberger College (Maumee), A
University of Cincinnati Blue Ash College, A
Vet Tech Institute at Bradford School, A

Oklahoma

Community Care College, A
Murray State College, A
Oklahoma State University, Oklahoma City, A
Tulsa Community College, A

Oregon

Portland Community College, A

Pennsylvania

Harcum College, A
Johnson College, A
Lehigh Carbon Community College, A
Manor College, A
Northampton Community College, A
Vet Tech Institute, A
Wilson College, B

Rhode Island

New England Institute of Technology, A

South Carolina

Tri-County Technical College, A
Trident Technical College, A

South Dakota

Globe University - Sioux Falls, A
National American University (Rapid City), A

Tennessee

Chattanooga State Community College, A
Columbia State Community College, A
Lincoln Memorial University, A
Volunteer State Community College, A

Texas

Austin Community College District, A
Cedar Valley College, A
Lone Star College - Tomball, A
Texas A&M University - Kingsville, B
Vet Tech Institute of Houston, A

Utah

Brigham Young University, B
Broadview University - Layton, A
Broadview University - West Jordan, A

Vermont

Vermont Technical College, A

Virginia

Blue Ridge Community College, A

Washington

Pierce College at Fort Steilacoom, A
Pierce College at Puyallup, A
Pima Medical Institute (Renton), A
Pima Medical Institute (Seattle), A
Yakima Valley Community College, A

Wisconsin

Gateway Technical College, A
Globe University - Appleton, A
Globe University - Eau Claire, A
Globe University - Green Bay, A
Globe University - La Crosse, A
Globe University - Madison East, AB
Globe University - Madison West, A
Globe University - Wausau, A
Madison Area Technical College, A

Wyoming

Eastern Wyoming College, A
Northwest College, A

U.S. Territories: Puerto Rico

Universidad del Turabo, A
University of Puerto Rico in Arecibo, A
University of Puerto Rico, Medical Sciences Cam-
  pus, B

Canada

Maritime Provinces: Nova Scotia

Dalhousie University, A

Ontario

University of Guelph, A

VETERINARY MEDICINE

United States

Alabama

Auburn University, D
Tuskegee University, MD

California

University of California, Davis, D

Colorado

Colorado State University, D

Florida

University of Florida, D

Georgia

University of Georgia, MD

Illinois

University of Illinois at Urbana - Champaign, D

Indiana

Purdue University, D

Iowa

Iowa State University of Science and Technology, M

Kansas

Kansas State University, D

Louisiana

Louisiana State University and Agricultural & Mechanical College, D

Maryland

University of Maryland, College Park, D

Massachusetts

Tufts University, MD

Michigan

Michigan State University, D

Minnesota

University of Minnesota, Twin Cities Campus, D

Mississippi

Mississippi State University, D

Missouri

University of Missouri, D

New York

Cornell University, D

North Carolina

North Carolina State University, MD

Oklahoma

Oklahoma State University, D

Oregon

Oregon State University, D

Pennsylvania

University of Pennsylvania, D

Tennessee

The University of Tennessee, D

Texas

Texas A&M University, MD

Virginia

Virginia Polytechnic Institute and State University, D

Washington

Washington State University, D

Wisconsin

University of Wisconsin - Madison, MD

Canada

Maritime Provinces: Prince Edward Island

University of Prince Edward Island, D

Ontario

University of Guelph, MD

Quebec

Université de Montréal, D

Saskatchewan

University of Saskatchewan, MD

VETERINARY SCIENCES

United States

Alabama

Auburn University, MD
Tuskegee University, MD

California

University of California, Davis, MO

Colorado

Colorado State University, MD

Florida

University of Florida, MDO

Georgia

University of Georgia, M

Idaho

University of Idaho, MD

Illinois

University of Illinois at Urbana - Champaign, MD

Indiana

Purdue University, MD

Iowa

Iowa State University of Science and Technology, MD

Kansas

Kansas State University, MO

Kentucky

University of Kentucky, MD
University of Louisville, O

Louisiana

Louisiana State University and Agricultural & Mechanical College, MD

Maryland

University of Maryland, College Park, MD

Michigan

Michigan State University, MD

Minnesota

University of Minnesota, Twin Cities Campus, MD

Mississippi

Mississippi State University, MD

Missouri

University of Missouri, MD

Nebraska

University of Nebraska - Lincoln, MD

North Carolina

North Carolina State University, MD

North Dakota

North Dakota State University, MD

Ohio

The Ohio State University, MD

Oklahoma

Oklahoma State University, MD

Oregon

Oregon State University, MD

Pennsylvania

Drexel University, M

South Carolina

Clemson University, MD

South Dakota

South Dakota State University, MD

Texas

Texas A&M University, MD

Utah

Utah State University, MD

Virginia

Virginia Polytechnic Institute and State University, MD

Washington

University of Washington, M
Washington State University, MD

Wisconsin

University of Wisconsin - Madison, MD

Canada

Maritime Provinces: Prince Edward Island

University of Prince Edward Island, MD

Ontario

University of Guelph, MDO

Quebec

Université de Montréal, MD

Saskatchewan

University of Saskatchewan, MD

VIOLIN, VIOLA, GUITAR AND OTHER STRINGED INSTRUMENTS

United States

California

The Colburn School Conservatory of Music, B
San Francisco Conservatory of Music, B
University of Southern California, B

Florida

Stetson University, B

Illinois

Northwestern University, B
Roosevelt University, B

Iowa

The University of Iowa, B

Kansas

The University of Kansas, B

Louisiana

Xavier University of Louisiana, B

Maryland

Peabody Conservatory of The Johns Hopkins University, B

Massachusetts

Berklee College of Music, B
Eastern Nazarene College, B
New England Conservatory of Music, B

Michigan

Hope College, B

Minnesota

McNally Smith College of Music, AB
St. Cloud State University, B
University of Northwestern - St. Paul, B

Nebraska

Hastings College, B
University of Nebraska at Omaha, B

New York

Houghton College, B
Manhattan School of Music, B
The New School College of Performing Arts, B
State University of New York at Fredonia, B
Syracuse University, B

Ohio

Heidelberg University, B
Oberlin College, B
Otterbein University, B
The University of Akron, B
Youngstown State University, B

Oklahoma

Oklahoma City University, B
University of Central Oklahoma, B

Oregon

Willamette University, B

Pennsylvania

Carnegie Mellon University, B

South Carolina

Converse College, B

Tennessee

Vanderbilt University, B

Texas

Hardin-Simmons University, B
Texas Christian University, B

Utah

Brigham Young University, B

Virginia

Liberty University, B

Washington

Central Washington University, B
Cornish College of the Arts, B
Seattle University, B
University of Washington, B

Wisconsin

Lawrence University, B

U.S. Territories: Puerto Rico

Conservatorio de Musica de Puerto Rico, B

Canada

British Columbia

The University of British Columbia, B

Maritime Provinces: New Brunswick

Mount Allison University, B

Maritime Provinces: Nova Scotia

Acadia University, B

Newfoundland and Labrador

Memorial University of Newfoundland, B

Ontario

The University of Western Ontario, B

Quebec

McGill University, B

VIROLOGY

United States

Connecticut

Yale University, D

Illinois

Rush University, MD

Indiana

Purdue University, D

Iowa

The University of Iowa, MD

Minnesota

University of Minnesota, Twin Cities Campus, D

New Jersey

Rutgers University - New Brunswick, MD

Ohio

Case Western Reserve University, D

Pennsylvania

University of Pennsylvania, D
University of Pittsburgh, D

Texas

The University of Texas Health Science Center at Houston, MD
The University of Texas Medical Branch, D

Canada

Maritime Provinces: Prince Edward Island

University of Prince Edward Island, MD

Ontario

McMaster University, MD

Quebec

Université de Montréal, D

VISION SCIENCE/PHYSIOLOGICAL OPTICS

United States

Alabama

The University of Alabama at Birmingham, MD

California

University of California, Berkeley, MD

Indiana

Indiana University Bloomington, B

Massachusetts

University of Massachusetts Boston, M

Oregon

Pacific University, MD

Pennsylvania

University of Pittsburgh, MD

Rhode Island

Providence College, B

Texas

University of Houston, MD
University of the Incarnate Word, B

Canada

Alberta

University of Alberta, MD

Ontario

University of Guelph, MD
University of Waterloo, MD

Quebec

Université de Montréal, MO

VISUAL AND PERFORMING ARTS

United States

Alabama

Samford University, B

Arizona

Arizona State University at the Tempe campus, B
Arizona State University at the West campus, B
Chandler-Gilbert Community College, A
Coconino Community College, A
Paradise Valley Community College, A
Phoenix College, A
Pima Community College, A
Prescott College, B
The University of Arizona, B

California

American Musical and Dramatic Academy, Los Angeles, B
Antelope Valley College, A
Ashford University, B
California Baptist University, B
California Institute of the Arts, B
California State University Channel Islands, B
California State University, San Marcos, B
Cerritos College, A
Cerro Coso Community College, A
Chaffey College, A
Citrus College, A
Crafton Hills College, A
Cypress College, A
Feather River College, A
Gavilan College, A
Grossmont College, A
Long Beach City College, A
Mt. San Antonio College, A
Mt. San Jacinto College, A
Occidental College, B
Point Loma Nazarene University, B
Saint Mary's College of California, B
San Francisco Art Institute, B
San Jose State University, B
Sierra College, A

University of California, Davis, B
University of California, Irvine, B
University of California, Los Angeles, B
University of San Francisco, B
University of Southern California, B

Colorado

Naropa University, B
University of Colorado Colorado Springs, B
Western State Colorado University, B

Connecticut

University of New Haven, B

Florida

The Baptist College of Florida, B
Eckerd College, B
Jacksonville University, B
Northwest Florida State College, A
University of South Florida, B
University of South Florida, St. Petersburg, B

Georgia

Andrew College, A
Emory University, B
Kennesaw State University, B
LaGrange College, B
Savannah State University, B

Illinois

Blackburn College, B
Illinois State University, B
Illinois Wesleyan University, B
Kankakee Community College, A
Millikin University, B
Moraine Valley Community College, A
Northwestern University, B
School of the Art Institute of Chicago, B
University of Chicago, B
University of St. Francis, B

Iowa

Iowa State University of Science and Technology, B
Northwestern College, B

Kansas

Garden City Community College, A
Highland Community College, A
Hutchinson Community College, A
Kansas Wesleyan University, B
Seward County Community College and Area Technical School, A
University of Saint Mary, B
Wichita State University, B

Kentucky

Union College, B

Louisiana

Bossier Parish Community College, A
Centenary College of Louisiana, B
Grambling State University, B
University of Louisiana at Lafayette, B

Maine

Maine College of Art, B
University of Maine at Farmington, B
University of Maine at Machias, B

Maryland

Community College of Baltimore County, A
Maryland Institute College of Art, B
University of Baltimore, B

Massachusetts

Bard College at Simon's Rock, B
Berkshire Community College, A
Cape Cod Community College, A
Emerson College, B
Endicott College, B
Harvard University, B
Massachusetts College of Liberal Arts, B
Pine Manor College, AB
Roxbury Community College, A

School of the Museum of Fine Arts, Boston, B
Stonehill College, B
Suffolk University, B
Wheelock College, B
Worcester State University, B

Michigan

Michigan Technological University, B
Mott Community College, A
Spring Arbor University, B
University of Michigan, B

Minnesota

St. Cloud State University, B

Mississippi

Blue Mountain College, B
Coahoma Community College, A
Delta State University, B
Jackson State University, B
Mississippi State University, B
Mississippi University for Women, B
University of Southern Mississippi, B

Missouri

Missouri State University, B
Southeast Missouri State University, B

Nebraska

Concordia University, Nebraska, B

New Hampshire

NHTI, Concord's Community College, A

New Jersey

Bloomfield College, B
Fairleigh Dickinson University, College at Florham, B
Fairleigh Dickinson University, Metropolitan Campus, B
Middlesex County College, A
Ocean County College, A
Ramapo College of New Jersey, B
Rutgers University - New Brunswick, B
Saint Peter's University, B
Seton Hall University, B
Stockton University, B

New Mexico

New Mexico Highlands University, B
New Mexico State University, B

New York

Adelphi University, B
Barnard College, B
Borough of Manhattan Community College of the City University of New York, A
Cazenovia College, B
Columbia University, B
Columbia University, School of General Studies, B
Dutchess Community College, A
Fiorello H. LaGuardia Community College of the City University of New York, A
Herkimer County Community College, A
Ithaca College, B
Long Island University - LIU Brooklyn, B
Manhattanville College, B
Nassau Community College, A
New York University, B
Purchase College, State University of New York, B
Queensborough Community College of the City University of New York, A
Rensselaer Polytechnic Institute, B
The Sage Colleges, B
St. Bonaventure University, B
Schenectady County Community College, A
State University of New York College at Geneseo, B
State University of New York College at Old Westbury, B
State University of New York at New Paltz, B
Ulster County Community College, A
Vassar College, B

North Carolina

Bennett College, B
Chowan University, B
Fayetteville State University, B
Johnson C. Smith University, B
Lees-McRae College, B
Saint Augustine's University, B
University of Mount Olive, B

Ohio

Antioch College, B
Baldwin Wallace University, B
Bluffton University, B
Kent State University, B
Kent State University at Stark, B
Ohio Northern University, B
University of Cincinnati, B
University of Mount Union, B
University of Rio Grande, B
Wittenberg University, B
Youngstown State University, B

Oklahoma

Cameron University, B
Oklahoma City University, B
Rogers State University, B
St. Gregory's University, B

Oregon

Oregon State University, B
Oregon State University - Cascades, B
Rogue Community College, A

Pennsylvania

Bucknell University, B
Bucks County Community College, A
Cheyney University of Pennsylvania, B
Community College of Allegheny County, A
Drexel University, B
East Stroudsburg University of Pennsylvania, B
Gannon University, B
Gettysburg College, B
Harrisburg Area Community College, A
Indiana University of Pennsylvania, B
Neumann University, B
Penn State Abington, B
Penn State Altoona, B
Penn State Beaver, B
Penn State Berks, B
Penn State Brandywine, B
Penn State DuBois, B
Penn State Erie, The Behrend College, B
Penn State Fayette, The Eberly Campus, B
Penn State Greater Allegheny, B
Penn State Hazleton, B
Penn State Lehigh Valley, B
Penn State Mont Alto, B
Penn State New Kensington, B
Penn State Schuylkill, B
Penn State Shenango, B
Penn State University Park, B
Penn State Wilkes-Barre, B
Penn State Worthington Scranton, B
Penn State York, B
Saint Joseph's University, B
Seton Hill University, B
Temple University, B
University of Pennsylvania, B
University of Pittsburgh at Greensburg, B
Waynesburg University, B

Rhode Island

Brown University, B

South Carolina

Clemson University, B
Spartanburg Methodist College, A

South Dakota

The University of South Dakota, B

Tennessee

Cumberland University, B
King University, B

Tennessee Wesleyan College, B
Tusculum College, B
The University of Tennessee at Martin, B

Texas

Amarillo College, A
Austin College, B
Frank Phillips College, A
Lee College, A
Rice University, B
Texas Southern University, B
University of Houston - Downtown, B
The University of Texas at Austin, B
The University of Texas at Dallas, B

Utah

Brigham Young University, B
University of Utah, B

Vermont

Bennington College, B
Champlain College, B
Johnson State College, B
Marlboro College, B

Virginia

Ferrum College, B
George Mason University, B
John Tyler Community College, A
Longwood University, B
Northern Virginia Community College, A
Thomas Nelson Community College, A
University of Mary Washington, B
Virginia State University, B
Virginia Union University, B
Virginia Wesleyan College, B

Washington

The Evergreen State College, B
University of Washington, B
University of Washington, Bothell, B
Western Washington University, B

Wisconsin

Cardinal Stritch University, B
University of Wisconsin - Green Bay, B
University of Wisconsin - Superior, B

Wyoming

Northwest College, A
Western Wyoming Community College, A

U.S. Territories: Puerto Rico

Inter American University of Puerto Rico, San
   Germán Campus, B
University of Puerto Rico, Río Piedras Campus, B
University of Puerto Rico in Utuado, B
University of the Sacred Heart, B

Canada

Alberta

Concordia University of Edmonton, B
University of Alberta, B
University of Lethbridge, B

British Columbia

Simon Fraser University, B
The University of British Columbia, B
The University of British Columbia - Okanagan
   Campus, B

Ontario

University of Toronto, B
University of Windsor, B
York University, B

Quebec

Concordia University, B

Saskatchewan

University of Regina, B
University of Saskatchewan, B

VITICULTURE AND ENOLOGY

United States

California

California State University, Fresno, M
University of California, Davis, MD

VOCATIONAL REHABILITATION COUNSELING/COUNSELOR

United States

Florida

South Florida State College, A
State College of Florida Manatee-Sarasota, A

Illinois

University of Illinois at Urbana - Champaign, B

Kansas

Emporia State University, B

Louisiana

Southern University and Agricultural and Mechanical
   College, B

Missouri

Maryville University of Saint Louis, B

North Carolina

East Carolina University, B
Winston-Salem State University, B

Ohio

Bowling Green State University, B
Wright State University, B

Oklahoma

East Central University, B

Washington

Edmonds Community College, A
Spokane Falls Community College, A

Wisconsin

University of Wisconsin - Madison, B
University of Wisconsin - Stout, B

VOCATIONAL AND TECHNICAL EDUCATION

United States

Arizona

Northern Arizona University, MO
University of Phoenix - Phoenix Campus, M

Arkansas

University of Arkansas, MD

California

California Baptist University, M
California State University, Sacramento, M
California State University, San Bernardino, M

Colorado

Colorado State University, MD

Connecticut

Central Connecticut State University, MO

Delaware

Wilmington University, M

District of Columbia

The George Washington University, O

Florida

Florida Agricultural and Mechanical University, M
University of Central Florida, M
University of South Florida, MDO
University of West Florida, M

Georgia

University of Georgia, MDO

Idaho

Idaho State University, M
University of Idaho, M

Illinois

Chicago State University, M
Southern Illinois University Carbondale, MD

Indiana

Ball State University, M
Indiana State University, M
Purdue University, MDO

Iowa

Iowa State University of Science and Technology,
   MD
University of Northern Iowa, MD

Kansas

Pittsburg State University, MO

Kentucky

Morehead State University, M
Murray State University, M

Louisiana

Louisiana State University and Agricultural & Mechanical College, MD

Maine

University of New England, MO

Maryland

University of Maryland Eastern Shore, M

Massachusetts

Fitchburg State University, M
Westfield State University, MO

Michigan

Wayne State University, MDO
Western Michigan University, M

Minnesota

University of Minnesota, Twin Cities Campus, MO

Mississippi

Alcorn State University, M

Missouri

University of Central Missouri, M
University of Missouri, MDO

Montana

Montana State University, M

Nebraska

University of Nebraska - Lincoln, M
Wayne State College, M

New Mexico

Eastern New Mexico University, M

New York

Buffalo State College, State University of New York,
   M
Niagara University, M
State University of New York at Oswego, M

North Carolina

Appalachian State University, M
East Carolina University, M

North Carolina Agricultural and Technical State University, M

North Dakota

North Dakota State University, D
Valley City State University, M

Ohio

Bowling Green State University, M
Kent State University, M
The University of Toledo, MO
Wright State University, M

Oregon

Concordia University, M

Pennsylvania

California University of Pennsylvania, M
Clarion University of Pennsylvania, M
Indiana University of Pennsylvania, M
Millersville University of Pennsylvania, M
Penn State University Park, MDO
Temple University, M

Texas

Texas State University, M
University of North Texas, M
The University of Texas at Tyler, MD

Virginia

James Madison University, M
Old Dominion University, MD
Virginia Polytechnic Institute and State University, MDO

Washington

Central Washington University, M
Washington State University, D

West Virginia

Marshall University, M

Wisconsin

University of Wisconsin - Stout, MDO

U.S. Territories: Puerto Rico

Inter American University of Puerto Rico, Metropolitan Campus, M

Canada

British Columbia

University of Victoria, D

VOICE AND OPERA

United States

Alabama

Birmingham-Southern College, B
Samford University, B
Talladega College, B
University of Mobile, B

Arizona

Arizona Christian University, B

Arkansas

Ouachita Baptist University, B

California

Biola University, B
California Baptist University, B
California State University, Long Beach, B
Chapman University, B
The Master's College and Seminary, B
Notre Dame de Namur University, B
Point Loma Nazarene University, B
Reedley College, A
San Francisco Conservatory of Music, B
University of the Pacific, B

University of Redlands, B
University of Southern California, B

Delaware

Delaware State University, B
University of Delaware, B

District of Columbia

The Catholic University of America, B

Florida

Barry University, B
Jacksonville University, B
Palm Beach Atlantic University, B
Southeastern University, B
Stetson University, B
University of Miami, B

Georgia

Shorter University, B

Hawaii

Brigham Young University - Hawaii, B

Illinois

Bradley University, B
Illinois Wesleyan University, B
Northwestern University, B
Roosevelt University, B
University of Illinois at Urbana - Champaign, B

Indiana

Indiana University - Purdue University Fort Wayne, B
Valparaiso University, B

Iowa

Dordt College, B
Drake University, B
Iowa Lakes Community College, A
The University of Iowa, B

Kansas

MidAmerica Nazarene University, B
The University of Kansas, B

Kentucky

Campbellsville University, B

Louisiana

Louisiana College, B
Loyola University New Orleans, B

Maryland

Peabody Conservatory of The Johns Hopkins University, B

Massachusetts

Anna Maria College, B
Berklee College of Music, B
Boston University, B
Eastern Nazarene College, B
New England Conservatory of Music, B

Michigan

Andrews University, B
Calvin College, B
Hope College, B
Madonna University, B
Oakland Community College, A
Oakland University, B
Western Michigan University, B

Minnesota

McNally Smith College of Music, AB
Minnesota State University Mankato, B
St. Cloud State University, B
University of Northwestern - St. Paul, B

Mississippi

East Central Community College, A
Jones County Junior College, A
Mississippi College, B

Missouri

Calvary Bible College and Theological Seminary, B
Washington University in St. Louis, B

Nebraska

Grace University, B
Hastings College, B
Peru State College, B
University of Nebraska at Omaha, B

New Jersey

Rider University, B

New York

Houghton College, B
Ithaca College, B
Long Island University - LIU Post, B
Manhattan School of Music, B
The New School College of Performing Arts, B
Nyack College, B
Roberts Wesleyan College, B
State University of New York at Fredonia, B
Syracuse University, B

Ohio

Baldwin Wallace University, B
Bowling Green State University, B
Capital University, B
Cincinnati Christian University, B
Heidelberg University, B
Oberlin College, B
The Ohio State University, B
Ohio University, B
Otterbein University, B
The University of Akron, B
University of Cincinnati, B
Youngstown State University, B

Oklahoma

East Central University, B
Oklahoma Baptist University, B
Oklahoma Christian University, B
Oklahoma City University, B
Oral Roberts University, B
University of Central Oklahoma, B
The University of Tulsa, B

Oregon

Willamette University, B

Pennsylvania

Bucknell University, B
Carnegie Mellon University, B

South Carolina

Bob Jones University, B
Coker College, B
Columbia College, B
Converse College, B
Furman University, B

South Dakota

Black Hills State University, B
Northern State University, B

Tennessee

Belmont University, B
Carson-Newman University, B
Lipscomb University, B
Maryville College, B
Union University, B
The University of Tennessee at Martin, B
Vanderbilt University, B

Texas

Abilene Christian University, B
Alvin Community College, A
Dallas Baptist University, B
Del Mar College, A
East Texas Baptist University, B
Hardin-Simmons University, B
Houston Baptist University, B
Howard Payne University, B
Navarro College, A

Southern Methodist University, B
Texas Christian University, B
Trinity University, B

Utah

Brigham Young University, B
Weber State University, B

Vermont

Bennington College, B

Virginia

Liberty University, B

Washington

Central Washington University, B
Cornish College of the Arts, B
University of Washington, B
Whitworth University, B

Wisconsin

Lawrence University, B

U.S. Territories: Puerto Rico

Conservatorio de Musica de Puerto Rico, B

Canada
Alberta

University of Alberta, B

British Columbia

The University of British Columbia, B
University of Victoria, B

Manitoba

Brandon University, B

Maritime Provinces: New Brunswick

Mount Allison University, B

Maritime Provinces: Nova Scotia

Acadia University, B

Newfoundland and Labrador

Memorial University of Newfoundland, B

Ontario

The University of Western Ontario, B
York University, B

Quebec

McGill University, B
Université de Montréal, B

WATCHMAKING AND JEWELRYMAKING

United States
North Carolina

Haywood Community College, A

Texas

Austin Community College District, A
Paris Junior College, A

Washington

North Seattle College, A

WATER QUALITY AND WASTE-WATER TREATMENT MANAGEMENT AND RECYCLING TECHNOLOGY/TECHNICIAN

United States
Arizona

Arizona Western College, A
GateWay Community College, A

California

Citrus College, A
College of the Canyons, A
Hartnell College, A
Mt. San Jacinto College, A
Palomar College, A
Santiago Canyon College, A

Colorado

Colorado Mesa University, A
Red Rocks Community College, A

Delaware

Delaware Technical & Community College, Jack F. Owens Campus, A

Georgia

Ogeechee Technical College, A

Idaho

College of Southern Idaho, A

Iowa

Kirkwood Community College, A

Kansas

Fort Scott Community College, A

Kentucky

Western Kentucky University, A

Massachusetts

Bristol Community College, A

Michigan

Bay de Noc Community College, A
Delta College, A
Lake Superior State University, A

Minnesota

St. Cloud Technical & Community College, A
Vermilion Community College, A

Nevada

College of Southern Nevada, A

New Mexico

Santa Fe Community College, A

North Carolina

Blue Ridge Community College, A

Oregon

Clackamas Community College, A
Linn-Benton Community College, A

Pennsylvania

Thaddeus Stevens College of Technology, A

South Carolina

York Technical College, A

Texas

Northwest Vista College, A

Virginia

Virginia Polytechnic Institute and State University, B

Wisconsin

Milwaukee Area Technical College, A
Moraine Park Technical College, A

WATER RESOURCES

United States
Alaska

University of Alaska Fairbanks, M

Arizona

The University of Arizona, MD

California

California State University, Monterey Bay, M
Humboldt State University, M
University of California, Riverside, MD
University of the Pacific, D
University of Southern California, M

Colorado

Colorado State University, M
University of Colorado Denver, M

District of Columbia

University of the District of Columbia, M

Florida

University of Florida, MD

Georgia

Albany State University, M

Idaho

University of Idaho, MD

Maine

University of Maine, MD

Massachusetts

University of Massachusetts Amherst, MD

Michigan

Eastern Michigan University, MO

Minnesota

University of Minnesota, Twin Cities Campus, MD

Missouri

Missouri University of Science and Technology, MD
University of Missouri, MD

Nevada

University of Nevada, Las Vegas, M

New Hampshire

University of New Hampshire, M

New Jersey

Rutgers University - New Brunswick, MD

New Mexico

New Mexico State University, MD
University of New Mexico, M

New York

Cornell University, MD
State University of New York College of Environmental Science and Forestry, M

Oregon

Oregon State University, MD

Utah

Utah State University, MD

Wisconsin

Marquette University, O
University of Wisconsin - Madison, M
University of Wisconsin - Milwaukee, MD

Wyoming

University of Wyoming, MD

Canada
Alberta

University of Calgary, MD

British Columbia

The University of British Columbia, M

Maritime Provinces: New Brunswick

University of New Brunswick Fredericton, MD

Maritime Provinces: Nova Scotia

Dalhousie University, M

WATER RESOURCES ENGINEERING

United States

Alabama

The University of Alabama in Huntsville, M

California

Santa Ana College, A
University of California, Berkeley, MD

Colorado

University of Colorado Boulder, MD

Connecticut

University of New Haven, M

Delaware

University of Delaware, MD

Florida

University of South Florida, MDO

Idaho

University of Idaho, MD

Illinois

University of Illinois at Urbana - Champaign, B

Indiana

Indiana University Bloomington, M

Kansas

Kansas State University, MD

Louisiana

Louisiana State University and Agricultural & Mechanical College, MD

Massachusetts

Bristol Community College, A
Tufts University, MD
University of Massachusetts Amherst, M

Missouri

University of Missouri, MD

Montana

Helena College University of Montana, A

Nevada

University of Nevada, Reno, B

New Jersey

Stevens Institute of Technology, M

New Mexico

New Mexico Institute of Mining and Technology, M

New York

Cornell University, MD
State University of New York College of Environmental Science and Forestry, BMD

Ohio

Central State University, B
Ohio University, M
University of Dayton, M

Oregon

Oregon State University, MD

Pennsylvania

Carnegie Mellon University, M
Villanova University, MO

Tennessee

University of Memphis, M

Texas

Southern Methodist University, D
The University of Texas at Austin, MD
The University of Texas at Tyler, M

Utah

Utah State University, MD

Vermont

Norwich University, M

Virginia

George Mason University, M

Washington

University of Washington, MD

Wisconsin

Gateway Technical College, A
Marquette University, O

Canada

Alberta

University of Alberta, MD

Ontario

University of Guelph, BMD

Quebec

McGill University, MD

WATER, WETLANDS, AND MARINE RESOURCES MANAGEMENT

United States

Colorado

Colorado State University, B
Western State Colorado University, B

Florida

Florida Gulf Coast University, B
South Florida State College, A

Iowa

Iowa Lakes Community College, A

Minnesota

University of Minnesota, Crookston, B

Texas

Texas A&M University, B
Texas State University, B

WEB/MULTIMEDIA MANAGEMENT AND WEBMASTER

United States

Alabama

Virginia College in Birmingham, A
Virginia College in Huntsville, B

Arizona

Rio Salado College, A

Arkansas

Arkansas State University Mid-South, A

California

Fresno City College, A
Glendale Community College, A
Grossmont College, A
Los Angeles City College, A
MiraCosta College, A
Pepperdine University, B
San Jose City College, A
Southwestern College, A

Colorado

American Sentinel University, B
Red Rocks Community College, A

Florida

Florida Career College, A
St. Petersburg College, A
Seminole State College of Florida, A

Georgia

Georgia College & State University, B

Idaho

Lewis-Clark State College, AB

Illinois

Illinois Central College, A
Joliet Junior College, A
Kaskaskia College, A
Moraine Valley Community College, A
Quincy University, B
Southwestern Illinois College, A
University of St. Francis, B

Indiana

Indiana Tech, AB
Vincennes University, A

Iowa

University of Dubuque, B

Massachusetts

Northern Essex Community College, A

Michigan

Delta College, A
Kalamazoo Valley Community College, A
Monroe County Community College, A
Northern Michigan University, B
St. Clair County Community College, A
Wayne County Community College District, A

Minnesota

Academy College, A
Riverland Community College, A

Mississippi

Southwest Mississippi Community College, A

Missouri

Metropolitan Community College - Kansas City, A

Montana

Flathead Valley Community College, A
Montana Tech of The University of Montana, A
University of Great Falls, B

Nebraska

Bellevue University, B
Grace University, B

New Hampshire

River Valley Community College, A

New Jersey

Bergen Community College, A

New Mexico

Clovis Community College, A

New York

Morrisville State College, B
Rochester Institute of Technology, B
State University of New York College of Technology at Alfred, B

North Carolina

Nash Community College, A
Sandhills Community College, A
Stanly Community College, A

Ohio

Antonelli College, A
Sinclair Community College, A
Stark State College, A

Oregon

Clackamas Community College, A

Pennsylvania

Community College of Beaver County, A
Delaware County Community College, A
DuBois Business College (DuBois), A
Lansdale School of Business, A
Montgomery County Community College, A

Rhode Island

Community College of Rhode Island, A

South Carolina

Limestone College, B
Trident Technical College, A

Tennessee

Trevecca Nazarene University, B

Texas

Del Mar College, A
Howard College, A
Temple College, A

Utah

Neumont University, B

Virginia

ECPI University (Virginia Beach), AB

Washington

Clark College, A
Columbia Basin College, A
Edmonds Community College, A
Walla Walla Community College, A

West Virginia

American Public University System, AB
West Virginia Junior College - Charleston, A

Wisconsin

Fox Valley Technical College, A
Gateway Technical College, A
Northeast Wisconsin Technical College, A

Wyoming

Casper College, A
Western Wyoming Community College, A

WEB PAGE, DIGITAL/MULTIME-DIA AND INFORMATION RE-SOURCES DESIGN

United States

Alabama

Virginia College in Birmingham, A

Arizona

The Art Institute of Phoenix, B
The Art Institute of Tucson, B
DeVry University (Phoenix), AB
GateWay Community College, A

Glendale Community College, A
Paradise Valley Community College, A
Phoenix College, A
Rio Salado College, A
Sessions College for Professional Design, A
University of Advancing Technology, B
The University of Arizona, B

Arkansas

Harding University, B

California

Academy of Art University, AB
The Art Institute of California - Hollywood, a campus of Argosy University, AB
The Art Institute of California - Inland Empire, a campus of Argosy University, B
The Art Institute of California - Los Angeles, a campus of Argosy University, AB
The Art Institute of California - Orange County, a campus of Argosy University, AB
The Art Institute of California - Sacramento, a campus of Argosy University, AB
The Art Institute of California - San Diego, a campus of Argosy University, B
The Art Institute of California - San Francisco, a campus of Argosy University, AB
Azusa Pacific University, B
Berkeley City College, A
Cabrillo College, A
Cerro Coso Community College, A
Chaffey College, A
College of San Mateo, A
College of the Sequoias, A
DeVry University (Alhambra), AB
DeVry University (Anaheim), AB
DeVry University (Bakersfield), AB
DeVry University (Fremont), AB
DeVry University (Long Beach), AB
DeVry University (Oakland), AB
DeVry University (Oxnard), AB
DeVry University (Palmdale), AB
DeVry University (Pomona), AB
DeVry University (San Diego), AB
DeVry University (Sherman Oaks), AB
Hartnell College, A
Los Angeles City College, A
National University, B
Oxnard College, A
Palomar College, A
Platt College San Diego, B
San Jose City College, A
Santa Clara University, B
Sierra College, A
Southwestern College, A

Colorado

The Art Institute of Colorado, AB
DeVry University (Colorado Springs), AB
DeVry University (Westminster), AB
National American University (Denver), AB
Pueblo Community College, A
Red Rocks Community College, A

Connecticut

Norwalk Community College, A
Quinnipiac University, B

Delaware

Wilmington University, A

Florida

The Art Institute of Fort Lauderdale, AB
The Art Institute of Tampa, a branch of Miami International University of Art & Design, B
DeVry University (Jacksonville), AB
DeVry University (Miramar), AB
DeVry University (Orlando), AB
Florida National University, A
Florida SouthWestern State College, A
Florida State College at Jacksonville, A
Florida Technical College (DeLand), A
Florida Technical College (Orlando), A
Full Sail University, B
Gulf Coast State College, A

Miami Dade College, A
Miami International University of Art & Design, B
Palm Beach State College, A
Pasco-Hernando State College, A
Polk State College, A
Rasmussen College Fort Myers, AB
Rasmussen College Land O' Lakes, AB
Rasmussen College New Port Richey, AB
Rasmussen College Ocala, AB
Rasmussen College Tampa/Brandon, AB
St. Petersburg College, A
Seminole State College of Florida, A
Tallahassee Community College, A

Georgia

The Art Institute of Atlanta, AB
Central Georgia Technical College, A
Chattahoochee Technical College, A
Columbus Technical College, A
DeVry University (Alpharetta), AB
DeVry University (Decatur), AB
DeVry University (Duluth), AB
Georgia Northwestern Technical College, A
Lanier Technical College, A
North Georgia Technical College, A
Southeastern Technical College, A
Southern Crescent Technical College, A
West Georgia Technical College, A
Wiregrass Georgia Technical College, A

Idaho

Brigham Young University - Idaho, A
College of Southern Idaho, A
College of Western Idaho, A
Eastern Idaho Technical College, A

Illinois

American Academy of Art, B
City Colleges of Chicago, Olive-Harvey College, A
Columbia College Chicago, B
DePaul University, B
DeVry University (Addison), AB
DeVry University (Chicago), AB
DeVry University (Gurnee), AB
DeVry University (Tinley Park), AB
DeVry University Online, AB
Harper College, A
Heartland Community College, A
Highland Community College, A
Illinois Central College, A
The Illinois Institute of Art - Schaumburg, AB
Lewis and Clark Community College, A
Northwestern College - Bridgeview Campus, A
Parkland College, A
Rasmussen College Aurora, A
Rasmussen College Mokena/Tinley Park, A
Rasmussen College Rockford, B
Rasmussen College Romeoville/Joliet, A
School of the Art Institute of Chicago, B
Spoon River College, A
Tribeca Flashpoint College, A
Waubonsee Community College, A

Indiana

The Art Institute of Indianapolis, B
DeVry University, AB
Grace College, B
Harrison College, B
Indiana Wesleyan University, B

Iowa

Hawkeye Community College, A
Iowa Wesleyan University, B
Kirkwood Community College, A
North Iowa Area Community College, A
Southwestern Community College, A
University of Dubuque, B
Western Iowa Tech Community College, A

Kansas

Cloud County Community College, A
Hutchinson Community College, A
Independence Community College, A
Johnson County Community College, A
Rasmussen College Kansas City/Overland Park, AB

Rasmussen College Topeka, AB

Kentucky

Sullivan College of Technology and Design, AB
Thomas More College, A

Louisiana

South Louisiana Community College, A

Maryland

Cecil College, A
Hagerstown Community College, A
Montgomery College, A

Massachusetts

Bunker Hill Community College, A
Cape Cod Community College, A
Hampshire College, B
Lasell College, B
Middlesex Community College, A
Mount Wachusett Community College, A
North Shore Community College, A
Northern Essex Community College, A
Quinsigamond Community College, A

Michigan

The Art Institute of Michigan, AB
Baker College, A
Kalamazoo Valley Community College, A
Kellogg Community College, A
Lansing Community College, A
Monroe County Community College, A
Schoolcraft College, A
Washtenaw Community College, A

Minnesota

Academy College, A
Century College, A
Dakota County Technical College, A
Dunwoody College of Technology, A
Hennepin Technical College, A
Lake Superior College, A
Mesabi Range College, A
Minneapolis Community and Technical College, A
Minnesota State College - Southeast Technical, A
Minnesota State Community and Technical College, A
Minnesota State Community and Technical College - Detroit Lakes, A
Rasmussen College Blaine, A
Rasmussen College Bloomington, AB
Rasmussen College Brooklyn Park, AB
Rasmussen College Eagan, AB
Rasmussen College Lake Elmo/Woodbury, AB
Rasmussen College Mankato, AB
Rasmussen College Moorhead, AB
Rasmussen College St. Cloud, AB
Ridgewater College, A
Riverland Community College, A
Rochester Community and Technical College, A

Missouri

American Business & Technology University, A
The Art Institute of St. Louis, AB
DeVry University (Kansas City), AB
Lindenwood University, B
Metropolitan Community College - Kansas City, A
Northwest Missouri State University, B
State Fair Community College, A
Vatterott College (Berkeley), A
Vatterott College (Kansas City), A
Vatterott College (Sunset Hills), A
William Jewell College, B

Montana

Miles Community College, A
University of Great Falls, B

Nevada

The Art Institute of Las Vegas, B
College of Southern Nevada, A
DeVry University, AB

New Jersey

County College of Morris, A
DeVry University (North Brunswick), AB
DeVry University (Paramus), AB
Raritan Valley Community College, A

New Mexico

National American University (Albuquerque), B

New York

Borough of Manhattan Community College of the City University of New York, A
Bryant & Stratton College - Liverpool Campus, A
The College of Saint Rose, B
The College of Westchester, A
Corning Community College, A
Genesee Community College, A
Hudson Valley Community College, A
Iona College, B
Mohawk Valley Community College, A
Morrisville State College, B
New York City College of Technology of the City University of New York, B
Niagara County Community College, A
Rochester Institute of Technology, B

North Carolina

The Art Institute of Charlotte, a campus of South University, B
The Art Institute of Raleigh-Durham, a campus of South University, B
ECPI University (Greensboro), A
Living Arts College, B
Stanly Community College, A
University of North Carolina at Asheville, B

North Dakota

Bismarck State College, A
North Dakota State College of Science, A
Rasmussen College Fargo, A

Ohio

American National University (Cincinnati), A
American National University (Kettering), A
Belmont College, A
Cedarville University, B
Central Ohio Technical College, A
DeVry University (Columbus), AB
DeVry University (Seven Hills), AB
Franklin University, B
North Central State College, A
Northwest State Community College, A
Ohio Business College (Sheffield Village), A
Stark State College, A
Stautzenberger College (Maumee), A
Terra State Community College, A
University of Mount Union, B
Walsh University, B
Zane State College, A

Oklahoma

DeVry University, AB
Oklahoma State University, Oklahoma City, A

Oregon

The Art Institute of Portland, B

Pennsylvania

The Art Institute of Philadelphia, AB
The Art Institute of Pittsburgh, AB
Bucks County Community College, A
Butler County Community College, A
Delaware County Community College, A
DeVry University (Fort Washington), AB
DeVry University (King of Prussia), AB
DeVry University (Philadelphia), AB
Drexel University, B
Duquesne University, B
Harrisburg Area Community College, A
Juniata College, B
Lansdale School of Business, A
Laurel Business Institute, A
Lehigh Carbon Community College, A
Mercyhurst University, B

Northampton Community College, A
Pennsylvania College of Technology, B
Pittsburgh Technical Institute, A
Reading Area Community College, A
Thiel College, B
The University of the Arts, B
Westmoreland County Community College, A

Rhode Island

Johnson & Wales University, B
New England Institute of Technology, AB

South Carolina

The Art Institute of Charleston, a branch of The Art Institute of Atlanta, AB
ECPI University (Greenville), A
Limestone College, AB
Trident Technical College, A

South Dakota

Dakota Wesleyan University, B
National American University (Sioux Falls), B

Tennessee

Chattanooga State Community College, A
DeVry University, AB
Dyersburg State Community College, A
Lipscomb University, B
Motlow State Community College, A
Pellissippi State Community College, A
Tennessee Technological University, B
Trevecca Nazarene University, B
Walters State Community College, A

Texas

The Art Institute of Austin, a branch of The Art Institute of Houston, AB
The Art Institute of Dallas, a campus of South University, B
The Art Institute of Houston, AB
The Art Institute of San Antonio, a branch of The Art Institute of Houston, AB
College of the Mainland, A
Collin County Community College District, A
Del Mar College, A
DeVry University (Austin), AB
DeVry University (Irving), AB
DeVry University (San Antonio), AB
El Centro College, A
Northwest Vista College, A
San Antonio College, A
Texas State Technical College, A

Utah

LDS Business College, A
Neumont University, B
Utah Valley University, AB

Vermont

Champlain College, AB

Virginia

American National University (Salem), A
The Art Institute of Virginia Beach, a branch of The Art Institute of Atlanta, AB
The Art Institute of Washington, a branch of The Art Institute of Atlanta, AB
DeVry University (Arlington), AB
DeVry University (Chesapeake), AB
DeVry University (Manassas), AB
ECPI University (Glen Allen), A
ECPI University (Manassas), A
ECPI University (Richmond), A
J. Sargeant Reynolds Community College, A
Southern Virginia University, B
Stratford University (Woodbridge), A

Washington

The Art Institute of Seattle, A
Bellevue College, A
Central Washington University, B
Clover Park Technical College, A
Columbia Basin College, A
Edmonds Community College, A
Everett Community College, A

Highline College, A
Peninsula College, A
University of Washington, Bothell, B
Walla Walla University, B

Wisconsin

Blackhawk Technical College, A
Madison Media Institute, A
Rasmussen College Appleton, A
Rasmussen College Green Bay, A
Rasmussen College Wausau, A
University of Wisconsin - Stevens Point, B
Wisconsin Indianhead Technical College, A

Wyoming

Casper College, A
Western Wyoming Community College, A

U.S. Territories: Puerto Rico

Atlantic University College, B
Universidad del Turabo, A

Canada

British Columbia

Emily Carr University of Art + Design, B

Quebec

Bishop's University, B
Concordia University, B

WELDING TECHNOLOGY/ WELDER

United States

Alabama

George C. Wallace Community College, A
Shelton State Community College, A
Southern Union State Community College, A
Wallace State Community College, A

Alaska

University of Alaska Anchorage, A
University of Alaska Anchorage, Kodiak College, A

Arizona

Cochise County Community College District, A
Eastern Arizona College, A
Mohave Community College, A
Northland Pioneer College, A
Pima Community College, A

Arkansas

Arkansas State University - Mountain Home, A
Phillips Community College of the University of Arkansas, A

California

Allan Hancock College, A
American River College, A
Antelope Valley College, A
Bakersfield College, A
Barstow Community College, A
Butte College, A
Cerritos College, A
Cerro Coso Community College, A
Chabot College, A
College of the Canyons, A
College of San Mateo, A
College of the Sequoias, A
College of the Siskiyous, A
Cuesta College, A
El Camino College, A
Fresno City College, A
Glendale Community College, A
Hartnell College, A
Imperial Valley College, A
Laney College, A
Las Positas College, A
Lassen Community College District, A

Long Beach City College, A
Los Angeles Pierce College, A
Los Angeles Trade-Technical College, A
Los Medanos College, A
Modesto Junior College, A
Mt. San Antonio College, A
Napa Valley College, A
Orange Coast College, A
Palomar College, A
Pasadena City College, A
Porterville College, A
Reedley College, A
Riverside City College, A
San Bernardino Valley College, A
San Diego City College, A
Santa Ana College, A
Shasta College, A
Solano Community College, A
Ventura College, A
Victor Valley College, A
West Hills Community College, A
Yuba College, A

Colorado

Aims Community College, A
Community College of Denver, A
Front Range Community College, A
Morgan Community College, AB
Pikes Peak Community College, A
Pueblo Community College, A
Red Rocks Community College, A
Trinidad State Junior College, A

Florida

Northwest Florida State College, A
Tallahassee Community College, A

Georgia

Bainbridge State College, A

Hawaii

Hawaii Community College, A
Honolulu Community College, A
University of Hawaii Maui College, A

Idaho

Brigham Young University - Idaho, AB
College of Southern Idaho, A
Eastern Idaho Technical College, A
Idaho State University, AB
Lewis-Clark State College, AB
North Idaho College, A

Illinois

College of DuPage, A
Heartland Community College, A
Highland Community College, A
Illinois Central College, A
Kankakee Community College, A
Kaskaskia College, A
Rend Lake College, A
Rock Valley College, A
Shawnee Community College, A
Southeastern Illinois College, A
Southwestern Illinois College, A
Triton College, A
Waubonsee Community College, A

Iowa

Iowa Central Community College, A
Iowa Lakes Community College, A
Kirkwood Community College, A
North Iowa Area Community College, A
Scott Community College, A
Southeastern Community College, A
Western Iowa Tech Community College, A

Kansas

Butler Community College, A
Coffeyville Community College, A
Cowley County Community College and Area Vocational - Technical School, A
Dodge City Community College, A
Garden City Community College, A
Hutchinson Community College, A

Johnson County Community College, A
Manhattan Area Technical College, A
Neosho County Community College, A
Northwest Kansas Technical College, A
Pratt Community College, A
Wichita Area Technical College, A

Kentucky

Bluegrass Community and Technical College, A
Elizabethtown Community and Technical College, A
Jefferson Community and Technical College, A
Maysville Community and Technical College (Maysville), A

Louisiana

South Louisiana Community College, A

Maine

Beal College, A
Eastern Maine Community College, A
Kennebec Valley Community College, A

Michigan

Delta College, A
Ferris State University, A
Grand Rapids Community College, A
Kalamazoo Valley Community College, A
Kellogg Community College, A
Kirtland Community College, A
Lansing Community College, A
Macomb Community College, A
Monroe County Community College, A
Montcalm Community College, A
Muskegon Community College, A
Oakland Community College, A
Schoolcraft College, A
Washtenaw Community College, A
Wayne County Community College District, A
West Shore Community College, A

Minnesota

Anoka Technical College, A
Central Lakes College, A
Dunwoody College of Technology, A
Northland Community and Technical College, A
Ridgewater College, A

Mississippi

Coahoma Community College, A
East Mississippi Community College, A
Mississippi Gulf Coast Community College, A
Southwest Mississippi Community College, A

Missouri

Crowder College, A
East Central College, A
Jefferson College, A
Moberly Area Community College, A
Ozarks Technical Community College, A
St. Charles Community College, A
State Technical College of Missouri, A
Vatterott College (Berkeley), A

Montana

Dawson Community College, A
Flathead Valley Community College, A
Great Falls College Montana State University, A
Helena College University of Montana, A
University of Montana, A

Nebraska

Central Community College - Columbus Campus, A
Central Community College - Grand Island Campus, A
Central Community College - Hastings Campus, A
Metropolitan Community College, A
Mid-Plains Community College, A
Northeast Community College, A
Southeast Community College, Lincoln Campus, A

Nevada

Great Basin College, A
Truckee Meadows Community College, A
Western Nevada College, A

New Hampshire

Manchester Community College, A
White Mountains Community College, A

New Mexico

Central New Mexico Community College, A
Clovis Community College, A
Doña Ana Community College, A
Eastern New Mexico University - Roswell, A
New Mexico Junior College, A
New Mexico State University - Carlsbad, A
San Juan College, A
University of New Mexico - Gallup, A
Western New Mexico University, A

New York

Jamestown Community College, A
Mohawk Valley Community College, A
State University of New York College of Technology
  at Alfred, A
State University of New York College of Technology
  at Delhi, A

North Carolina

Alamance Community College, A
Asheville-Buncombe Technical Community College,
  A
Beaufort County Community College, A
Bladen Community College, A
Blue Ridge Community College, A
Catawba Valley Community College, A
Central Piedmont Community College, A
Craven Community College, A
Halifax Community College, A
Haywood Community College, A
Isothermal Community College, A
Lenoir Community College, A
Nash Community College, A
Pitt Community College, A
Southeastern Community College, A
Tri-County Community College, A
Vance-Granville Community College, A
Western Piedmont Community College, A

North Dakota

Bismarck State College, A
North Dakota State College of Science, A
Williston State College, A

Ohio

Belmont College, A
The Ohio State University, B
Ohio Technical College, A
Owens Community College, A
Terra State Community College, A

Oklahoma

Oklahoma Technical College, A
Tulsa Welding School, A

Oregon

Chemeketa Community College, A
Clackamas Community College, A
Lane Community College, A
Linn-Benton Community College, A
Portland Community College, A
Rogue Community College, A
Southwestern Oregon Community College, A
Treasure Valley Community College, A

Pennsylvania

Community College of Allegheny County, A
Community College of Beaver County, A
Pennsylvania College of Technology, A
Pennsylvania Highlands Community College, A
Pittsburgh Technical Institute, A
Thaddeus Stevens College of Technology, A
Triangle Tech, DuBois, A
Triangle Tech, Sunbury, A
Westmoreland County Community College, A

South Carolina

York Technical College, A

South Dakota

Lake Area Technical Institute, A
Southeast Technical Institute, A

Tennessee

Northeast State Community College, A

Texas

Angelina College, A
Austin Community College District, A
Brazosport College, A
Central Texas College, A
Cisco College, A
Coastal Bend College, A
Del Mar College, A
Galveston College, A
Grayson College, A
Hill College, A
Kilgore College, A
Lamar Institute of Technology, A
Lee College, A
Lone Star College - CyFair, A
Lone Star College - North Harris, A
Midland College, A
Mountain View College, A
North Central Texas College, A
Northeast Texas Community College, A
Odessa College, A
Panola College, A
Paris Junior College, A
Ranger College, A
St. Philip's College, A
San Jacinto College District, A
South Plains College, A
Tarrant County College District, A
Texarkana College, A
Trinity Valley Community College, A
Tyler Junior College, A
Western Texas College, A

Utah

Salt Lake Community College, A
Weber State University, AB

Virginia

Liberty University, A
New River Community College, A

Washington

Bellingham Technical College, A
Big Bend Community College, A
Centralia College, A
Clark College, A
Columbia Basin College, A
Everett Community College, A
Grays Harbor College, A
Green River College, A
Lower Columbia College, A
Olympic College, A
Renton Technical College, A
Skagit Valley College, A
South Puget Sound Community College, A
South Seattle College, A
Spokane Community College, A
Spokane Falls Community College, A
Walla Walla Community College, A

West Virginia

Southern West Virginia Community and Technical
  College, A
West Virginia University at Parkersburg, A

Wisconsin

Fox Valley Technical College, A
Madison Area Technical College, A
Milwaukee Area Technical College, A
Nicolet Area Technical College, A

Wyoming

Casper College, A
Central Wyoming College, A
Eastern Wyoming College, A
Northwest College, A
Sheridan College, A

Western Wyoming Community College, A

U.S. Territories: American Samoa

American Samoa Community College, A

Canada

British Columbia

British Columbia Institute of Technology, A

WELL DRILLING/DRILLER

United States

Mississippi

Southwest Mississippi Community College, A

Pennsylvania

Westmoreland County Community College, A

WESTERN EUROPEAN STUDIES

United States

California

California State University, Long Beach, M
San Diego State University, M

Colorado

University of Colorado Denver, M

Connecticut

University of Connecticut, M

District of Columbia

American University, O
The Catholic University of America, M
The George Washington University, M
Georgetown University, M

Georgia

Armstrong State University, M
Georgia College & State University, M

Illinois

Illinois Wesleyan University, B
University of Illinois at Urbana - Champaign, M

Indiana

Indiana University Bloomington, M

Maine

Bates College, B
University of Maine, M

Massachusetts

Boston College, M
Tufts University, B

Michigan

Central Michigan University, O
Wayne State University, D

Mississippi

Mississippi State University, MD

Nebraska

Creighton University, M

Nevada

University of Nevada, Reno, D

New Jersey

Monmouth University, M

New York

Columbia University, MO
Cornell University, MD
New York University, M
University of Rochester, MD

North Carolina

East Carolina University, M

Oregon

Willamette University, B

Pennsylvania

La Salle University, O
University of Pittsburgh, O

Rhode Island

Brown University, MD

Texas

Baylor University, D

Washington

Seattle University, B

West Virginia

American Public University System, M

Canada

Ontario

Carleton University, O
University of Guelph, M

WILDLIFE BIOLOGY

United States

Arizona

Eastern Arizona College, A

Colorado

Adams State University, B
Colorado State University, B

Idaho

North Idaho College, A

Iowa

Iowa Lakes Community College, A

Kansas

Central Christian College of Kansas, A
Dodge City Community College, A
Friends University, B
Kansas State University, B
Pratt Community College, A

Maine

College of the Atlantic, B
Unity College, B

Maryland

Frostburg State University, B

Michigan

University of Michigan - Flint, B

Minnesota

St. Cloud State University, B
Vermilion Community College, A

New York

State University of New York College of Environmental Science and Forestry, B

North Carolina

Lees-McRae College, B

Ohio

Ohio University, B

Pennsylvania

Keystone College, B

Texas

Texas State University, B
West Texas A&M University, B

Vermont

University of Vermont, B

Virginia

Liberty University, B

Wyoming

University of Wyoming, B

Canada

British Columbia

University of Northern British Columbia, B

Maritime Provinces: New Brunswick

University of New Brunswick Fredericton, B

Ontario

University of Guelph, B

Quebec

McGill University, B

WILDLIFE AND WILDLANDS SCIENCE AND MANAGEMENT

United States

Alabama

Auburn University, B

Alaska

University of Alaska Fairbanks, B

Arkansas

Arkansas State University, B
Arkansas Tech University, B
University of Arkansas at Monticello, B

California

Feather River College, A
Humboldt State University, B
Monterey Peninsula College, A
Moorpark College, A
Mt. San Antonio College, A

Colorado

Front Range Community College, A

Delaware

Delaware State University, B
University of Delaware, B

Florida

University of Florida, B

Georgia

Abraham Baldwin Agricultural College, A
College of Coastal Georgia, A
Ogeechee Technical College, A
University of Georgia, B

Idaho

North Idaho College, A
University of Idaho, B

Illinois

Shawnee Community College, A
Southeastern Illinois College, A

University of Illinois at Urbana - Champaign, B

Iowa

Iowa Lakes Community College, A

Kansas

Barton County Community College, A
Fort Hays State University, B

Kentucky

Eastern Kentucky University, B
Murray State University, B

Louisiana

McNeese State University, B

Maine

Unity College, B
University of Maine, B

Maryland

Frostburg State University, B
Garrett College, A

Michigan

Lake Superior State University, B
Michigan State University, B
Michigan Technological University, B

Minnesota

Itasca Community College, A
Vermilion Community College, A

Mississippi

Holmes Community College, A
Mississippi State University, B

Missouri

College of the Ozarks, B
Missouri State University, B
Missouri Western State University, B
Northwest Missouri State University, B
University of Missouri, B

Montana

Flathead Valley Community College, A
Montana State University, B
University of Montana, B

Nebraska

Peru State College, B

Nevada

University of Nevada, Reno, B

New Hampshire

University of New Hampshire, B

New Mexico

Eastern New Mexico University, B
New Mexico State University, B
Western New Mexico University, B

New York

State University of New York College of Agriculture
and Technology at Cobleskill, AB
State University of New York College of Environmental Science and Forestry, B

North Carolina

Haywood Community College, A

North Dakota

Dakota College at Bottineau, A
Valley City State University, B

Ohio

Hocking College, A
The Ohio State University, B

Oklahoma

Eastern Oklahoma State College, A

Oregon

Oregon State University, B
Treasure Valley Community College, A

Pennsylvania

Delaware Valley University, B
Juniata College, B
Penn State DuBois, A

Rhode Island

University of Rhode Island, B

South Dakota

Dakota Wesleyan University, B
South Dakota State University, B

Tennessee

Hiwassee College, A
Lincoln Memorial University, B
Tennessee Technological University, B
The University of Tennessee, B
The University of Tennessee at Martin, B

Texas

Stephen F. Austin State University, B
Sul Ross State University, B
Tarleton State University, B
Texas A&M University, B
Texas A&M University - Commerce, B
Texas A&M University - Kingsville, B

Utah

Utah State University, B

Vermont

Sterling College, B

Washington

Spokane Community College, A
Washington State University, B

West Virginia

Potomac State College of West Virginia University,
  A
West Virginia University, B

Wisconsin

University of Wisconsin - Madison, B
University of Wisconsin - Stevens Point, B

Wyoming

Casper College, A
Eastern Wyoming College, A
Laramie County Community College, A
Western Wyoming Community College, A

U.S. Territories: Puerto Rico

University of Puerto Rico in Humacao, B

Canada

Alberta

University of Alberta, B

British Columbia

British Columbia Institute of Technology, A
The University of British Columbia, B
University of Northern British Columbia, B

Maritime Provinces: New Brunswick

University of New Brunswick Fredericton, B

WOMEN'S HEALTH NURSING

United States

California

California State University, Fullerton, M
San Francisco State University, M

Colorado

University of Colorado Denver, M

Delaware

University of Delaware, MO

Georgia

Emory University, M
Georgia State University, MO

Illinois

Loyola University Chicago, MO
University of Illinois at Chicago, M

Indiana

Indiana University - Purdue University Fort Wayne,
  M
University of Indianapolis, M

Massachusetts

Boston College, M

Michigan

Wayne State University, M

Minnesota

University of Minnesota, Twin Cities Campus, M

Missouri

University of Missouri - Kansas City, MD

New Jersey

Rutgers University - Newark, M

New York

Stony Brook University, State University of New
  York, MDO

North Carolina

Duke University, MO

Ohio

Case Western Reserve University, M
Kent State University, MO
University of Cincinnati, M

Pennsylvania

Drexel University, M
University of Pennsylvania, M

South Carolina

University of South Carolina, M

Tennessee

Vanderbilt University, M

Texas

Texas Woman's University, M

Virginia

Hampton University, M
Old Dominion University, M
Virginia Commonwealth University, M

Canada

Ontario

Queen's University at Kingston, M

WOMEN'S STUDIES

United States

Alabama

The University of Alabama, M

Arizona

Arizona State University at the Tempe campus, B
Arizona State University at the West campus, B

Northern Arizona University, BO
Prescott College, B
The University of Arizona, BMDO

California

Cabrillo College, A
California Institute of Integral Studies, MD
California State University, Fresno, B
California State University, Fullerton, B
California State University, Long Beach, B
California State University, Northridge, B
California State University, San Marcos, B
Cerritos College, A
Dominican University of California, BM
Foothill College, A
Fresno City College, A
Loyola Marymount University, B
Monterey Peninsula College, A
Palomar College, A
Pitzer College, B
Pomona College, B
Sacramento City College, A
Saddleback College, A
Saint Mary's College of California, B
San Diego State University, BM
San Francisco State University, BM
Santa Ana College, A
Santa Clara University, B
Santa Monica College, A
Santa Rosa Junior College, A
Santiago Canyon College, A
Scripps College, B
Sierra College, A
Sonoma State University, B
Southwestern College, A
Stanford University, B
University of California, Berkeley, B
University of California, Davis, B
University of California, Riverside, B
University of California, San Diego, B
University of California, Santa Barbara, BMD
University of California, Santa Cruz, B
West Valley College, A
Yuba College, A

Colorado

The Colorado College, B
Fort Lewis College, B
Regis University, B
University of Colorado Boulder, B
University of Colorado Denver, M

Connecticut

Connecticut College, B
Eastern Connecticut State University, B
Sacred Heart University, B
Southern Connecticut State University, M
Trinity College, B
University of Connecticut, B
University of Hartford, B
University of Saint Joseph, B
Yale University, B

Delaware

University of Delaware, B

District of Columbia

American University, BO
The George Washington University, MO
Georgetown University, B
Trinity Washington University, B

Florida

Broward College, A
Eckerd College, B
Florida Atlantic University, MO
Florida International University, B
State College of Florida Manatee-Sarasota, A
University of Florida, BMO
University of Miami, B
University of South Florida, BM

Georgia

Agnes Scott College, B
Armstrong State University, B

Clark Atlanta University, MD
Emory University, BDO
Georgia State University, BMO
Spelman College, B
University of Georgia, BO
Wesleyan College, B

Hawaii

University of Hawaii at Manoa, BO

Illinois

Augustana College, B
Benedictine University, M
Concordia University Chicago, B
DePaul University, BM
Dominican University, B
Illinois Wesleyan University, B
Knox College, B
Loyola University Chicago, B
Northeastern Illinois University, B
Northwestern University, B
Roosevelt University, MO
Triton College, A
University of Illinois at Chicago, B
University of Illinois at Urbana - Champaign, B
Western Illinois University, B

Indiana

Ball State University, B
Butler University, B
DePauw University, B
Earlham College, B
Indiana University - Purdue University Fort Wayne,
  AB
Manchester University, B
Purdue University, B
Saint Mary's College, B

Iowa

Coe College, B
Cornell College, B
Iowa State University of Science and Technology, B
Luther College, B
The University of Iowa, BO
University of Northern Iowa, M

Kansas

Kansas State University, BO
The University of Kansas, B
Wichita State University, B

Kentucky

Berea College, B
University of Louisville, BMO

Louisiana

Tulane University, B

Maine

Bates College, B
Bowdoin College, B
Colby College, B
University of Maine, B
University of Southern Maine, B

Maryland

Goucher College, B
Towson University, BMO
University of Maryland, Baltimore County, BO
University of Maryland, College Park, BMD

Massachusetts

Amherst College, B
Brandeis University, BM
Clark University, B
Greenfield Community College, A
Hampshire College, B
Harvard University, B
Lesley University, M
Merrimack College, B
Simmons College, B
Smith College, BO
Tufts University, B
University of Massachusetts Amherst, B

University of Massachusetts Boston, B
University of Massachusetts Dartmouth, B
Wellesley College, B
Wheaton College, B
Williams College, B

Michigan

Adrian College, B
Albion College, B
Central Michigan University, B
Eastern Michigan University, BMO
Grand Valley State University, B
Hope College, B
Kalamazoo College, B
Michigan State University, B
Oakland University, B
University of Michigan, BDO
University of Michigan - Dearborn, B
Western Michigan University, B

Minnesota

Augsburg College, B
Carleton College, B
College of Saint Benedict, B
Gustavus Adolphus College, B
Hamline University, B
Macalester College, B
Metropolitan State University, B
Minnesota State University Mankato, BMO
Minnesota State University Moorhead, B
St. Catherine University, B
Saint John's University, B
St. Olaf College, B
University of Minnesota, Duluth, B
University of Minnesota, Morris, B
University of Minnesota, Twin Cities Campus, BD
University of St. Thomas, B

Mississippi

Mississippi University for Women, B

Missouri

Saint Louis University, B
Washington University in St. Louis, B
Webster University, B

Montana

University of Montana, B

Nebraska

University of Nebraska - Lincoln, B

Nevada

University of Nevada, Las Vegas, B
University of Nevada, Reno, B

New Hampshire

Dartmouth College, B
Keene State College, B
University of New Hampshire, B

New Jersey

Bergen Community College, A
The College of New Jersey, B
College of Saint Elizabeth, B
Drew University, B
Montclair State University, B
New Jersey City University, B
Rutgers University - New Brunswick, BMD
Rutgers University - Newark, B
William Paterson University of New Jersey, B

New Mexico

New Mexico State University, B
University of New Mexico, BO

New York

Barnard College, B
Brooklyn College of the City University of New York,
  B
Canisius College, B
City College of the City University of New York, B
Colgate University, B

The College at Brockport, State University of New
  York, B
The College of New Rochelle, B
Columbia University, B
Columbia University, School of General Studies, B
Cornell University, D
Fordham University, B
Hamilton College, B
Hobart and William Smith Colleges, B
Hofstra University, B
Hunter College of the City University of New York, B
The Jewish Theological Seminary, BM
Nazareth College of Rochester, B
Pace University, B
Purchase College, State University of New York, B
Queens College of the City University of New York,
  B
St. Bonaventure University, B
Sarah Lawrence College, BM
State University of New York College at Potsdam, B
State University of New York at Fredonia, B
State University of New York at New Paltz, B
State University of New York at Oswego, B
State University of New York at Plattsburgh, B
Stony Brook University, State University of New
  York, BO
Suffolk County Community College, A
Syracuse University, B
University at Albany, State University of New York,
  BM
University of Rochester, B
Vassar College, B
Wells College, B

North Carolina

Appalachian State University, B
Duke University, B
Guilford College, B
North Carolina State University, B
Salem College, B
Southeastern Baptist Theological Seminary, M
University of North Carolina at Asheville, B
The University of North Carolina at Chapel Hill, B
The University of North Carolina at Charlotte, O
The University of North Carolina at Greensboro,
  BMO
Warren Wilson College, B

North Dakota

North Dakota State University, B

Ohio

Bowling Green State University, B
Case Western Reserve University, B
Cleveland State University, B
The College of Wooster, B
Denison University, B
Kenyon College, B
Miami University, B
Oberlin College, B
The Ohio State University, BMD
Ohio University, B
Ohio Wesleyan University, B
University of Cincinnati, BMO
University of Dayton, B
The University of Toledo, BO
Wright State University, B

Oklahoma

University of Oklahoma, BO
The University of Tulsa, B

Oregon

Oregon State University, BM
Portland State University, B
University of Oregon, B
Willamette University, B

Pennsylvania

Albright College, B
Bucknell University, B
Cabrini University, B
Carnegie Mellon University, D
Chatham University, BM
Dickinson College, B

Duquesne University, B
Gettysburg College, B
Lafayette College, B
Lehigh University, B
Penn State Abington, B
Penn State Altoona, B
Penn State Beaver, B
Penn State Berks, B
Penn State Brandywine, B
Penn State DuBois, B
Penn State Erie, The Behrend College, B
Penn State Fayette, The Eberly Campus, B
Penn State Greater Allegheny, B
Penn State Hazleton, B
Penn State Lehigh Valley, B
Penn State Mont Alto, B
Penn State New Kensington, B
Penn State Schuylkill, B
Penn State Shenango, B
Penn State University Park, B
Penn State Wilkes-Barre, B
Penn State Worthington Scranton, B
Penn State York, B
Swarthmore College, B
Temple University, B
University of Pennsylvania, B
University of Pittsburgh, BO
The University of Scranton, B
Villanova University, B
West Chester University of Pennsylvania, B

Rhode Island

Brown University, B
Bryant University, B
Providence College, B
Rhode Island College, B
University of Rhode Island, B

South Carolina

Clemson University, B
College of Charleston, B
University of South Carolina, BO

Tennessee

East Tennessee State University, B
Middle Tennessee State University, O
Sewanee: The University of the South, B
Vanderbilt University, B

Texas

Austin College, B
Rice University, B
Southwestern University, B
Texas A&M University, B
Texas Woman's University, MD
University of Houston - Clear Lake, B
The University of Texas at Austin, B
The University of Texas at San Antonio, B

Utah

University of Utah, B

Vermont

Bennington College, B
Castleton University, B
Goddard College, B
Marlboro College, B
Middlebury College, B
University of Vermont, B

Virginia

The College of William and Mary, B
George Mason University, M
Hollins University, B
Old Dominion University, B
Randolph-Macon College, B
University of Richmond, B
Virginia Commonwealth University, B
Virginia Wesleyan College, B

Washington

Eastern Washington University, B
Pacific Lutheran University, B
Seattle University, B
University of Washington, BD

Washington State University, B

Wisconsin

Alverno College, B
Northland College, B
University of Wisconsin - Eau Claire, B
University of Wisconsin - La Crosse, B
University of Wisconsin - Madison, BMD
University of Wisconsin - Milwaukee, BM
University of Wisconsin - Whitewater, B

Wyoming

Casper College, A
University of Wyoming, B

U.S. Territories: Puerto Rico

Inter American University of Puerto Rico, Metropolitan Campus, M

Canada

Alberta

Athabasca University, B
University of Alberta, B
University of Calgary, B
University of Lethbridge, BM

British Columbia

Simon Fraser University, BMD
The University of British Columbia, B
University of Northern British Columbia, B
University of Victoria, B
Vancouver Island University, B

Manitoba

University of Manitoba, B
The University of Winnipeg, B

Maritime Provinces: New Brunswick

St. Thomas University, B

Maritime Provinces: Nova Scotia

Dalhousie University, B
Mount Saint Vincent University, BM
St. Francis Xavier University, B
Saint Mary's University, BM
University of King's College, B

Newfoundland and Labrador

Memorial University of Newfoundland, BM

Ontario

Brock University, B
Carleton University, B
Lakehead University, BM
Laurentian University, B
McMaster University, B
Nipissing University, B
Queen's University at Kingston, BMD
Trent University, B
University of Ottawa, BM
University of Toronto, BMD
University of Waterloo, B
The University of Western Ontario, B
University of Windsor, B
Wilfrid Laurier University, B
York University, BMD

Quebec

Bishop's University, B
Concordia University, B
Université Laval, O

Saskatchewan

University of Regina, BM
University of Saskatchewan, BMD

WOOD SCIENCE AND WOOD PRODUCTS/PULP AND PAPER TECHNOLOGY

United States

California

Bakersfield College, A
Laney College, A

Georgia

Ogeechee Technical College, A

Idaho

University of Idaho, B

Indiana

Purdue University, B

Maine

Kennebec Valley Community College, A
University of Maine, B

New York

Morrisville State College, A
State University of New York College of Environmental Science and Forestry, B

North Carolina

Haywood Community College, A
North Carolina State University, B

Oregon

Oregon State University, B

Virginia

Dabney S. Lancaster Community College, A

West Virginia

Potomac State College of West Virginia University, A
West Virginia University, B

Wisconsin

University of Wisconsin - Stevens Point, B

Canada

British Columbia

The University of British Columbia, B

Ontario

University of Toronto, B

Quebec

Université Laval, B

WOODWORKING

United States

Colorado

Red Rocks Community College, A

Indiana

Vincennes University, A

Michigan

North Central Michigan College, A

New Mexico

Santa Fe Community College, A

New York

Rochester Institute of Technology, B

North Carolina

Haywood Community College, A

WORD PROCESSING

United States

California

College of the Sequoias, A
Los Angeles City College, A
Modesto Junior College, A
Santa Ana College, A
Yuba College, A

Connecticut

Gateway Community College, A
Quinebaug Valley Community College, A

Florida

Palm Beach State College, A
Seminole State College of Florida, A

Illinois

Richland Community College, A

Iowa

Iowa Lakes Community College, A

Kansas

Pratt Community College, A

Michigan

Kellogg Community College, A
Monroe County Community College, A

Minnesota

Riverland Community College, A

Mississippi

Mississippi Gulf Coast Community College, A

Missouri

Three Rivers Community College, A

New Mexico

New Mexico State University - Carlsbad, A

North Carolina

Sampson Community College, A
Stanly Community College, A

Ohio

ETI Technical College of Niles, A
Lorain County Community College, A
Sinclair Community College, A
Stark State College, A

Pennsylvania

Laurel Business Institute, A

Texas

Del Mar College, A
Eastfield College, A
Galveston College, A
North Central Texas College, A
San Antonio College, A

Wyoming

Western Wyoming Community College, A

WORK AND FAMILY STUDIES

United States

Ohio

Miami University Hamilton, B

Utah

Brigham Young University, B

WRITING

United States

Alabama

The University of Alabama, M
The University of Alabama at Birmingham, M

Alaska

University of Alaska Anchorage, M
University of Alaska Fairbanks, M

Arizona

Arizona State University at the Tempe campus, M
Northern Arizona University, MO
The University of Arizona, M

Arkansas

University of Arkansas, M
University of Arkansas at Little Rock, M
University of Central Arkansas, M

California

Academy of Art University, M
Antioch University Los Angeles, MO
California College of the Arts, M
California Institute of the Arts, MO
California Institute of Integral Studies, M
California State University, East Bay, M
California State University, Fresno, M
California State University, Long Beach, M
California State University, Northridge, M
California State University, Sacramento, M
California State University, San Bernardino, M
California State University, San Marcos, M
California State University, Stanislaus, M
Chapman University, M
Dominican University of California, M
Holy Names University, M
La Sierra University, M
Loyola Marymount University, M
Mills College, M
Mount Saint Mary's University, M
National University, M
Otis College of Art and Design, M
Pepperdine University, M
Saint Mary's College of California, M
San Diego State University, M
San Francisco State University, M
Sonoma State University, M
University of California, Berkeley, O
University of California, Davis, M
University of California, Irvine, M
University of California, Riverside, M
University of California, San Diego, M
University of California, Santa Barbara, D
University of California, Santa Cruz, M
University of San Francisco, M
University of Southern California, MD

Colorado

Colorado State University, M
Naropa University, M
University of Colorado Boulder, M
University of Colorado Denver, M
University of Denver, D
Western State Colorado University, M

Connecticut

Albertus Magnus College, M
Fairfield University, M
Trinity College, M
Western Connecticut State University, M
Yale University, MO

Florida

Florida Atlantic University, M
Florida International University, M
Florida State University, MD
Full Sail University, M
Nova Southeastern University, M
University of Florida, M
University of Miami, M
University of North Florida, M
University of South Florida, MO
The University of Tampa, M
University of West Florida, M

Georgia

Armstrong State University, MO
Georgia College & State University, M
Georgia State University, MD
Kennesaw State University, M
Savannah College of Art and Design, M
University of Georgia, MD

Idaho

Boise State University, M
University of Idaho, M

Illinois

Chicago State University, M
Columbia College Chicago, M
DePaul University, M
Illinois State University, M
Lake Forest College, M
National Louis University, MO
North Central College, M
Northeastern Illinois University, M
Northwestern University, M
Roosevelt University, M
School of the Art Institute of Chicago, MO
Southern Illinois University Carbondale, M
Southern Illinois University Edwardsville, M
University of Chicago, M
University of Illinois at Urbana - Champaign, M
Western Illinois University, O

Indiana

Ball State University, MD
Butler University, M
Indiana State University, M
Indiana University Bloomington, M
Indiana University - Purdue University Indianapolis, O
Purdue University, M
University of Notre Dame, M

Iowa

Iowa State University of Science and Technology, M
The University of Iowa, M
University of Northern Iowa, M

Kansas

The University of Kansas, M
Wichita State University, M

Kentucky

Asbury University, M
Eastern Kentucky University, M
Murray State University, M
Northern Kentucky University, O
Spalding University, M
University of Louisville, M
Western Kentucky University, M

Louisiana

Louisiana State University and Agricultural & Mechanical College, M
McNeese State University, M
Southeastern Louisiana University, M
University of Louisiana at Lafayette, MD

Maine

University of Southern Maine, M

Maryland

Goucher College, M
Johns Hopkins University, MO
Towson University, M
University of Baltimore, M
University of Maryland, College Park, MD

Massachusetts

Bay Path University, M
Boston University, MD
Emerson College, M
Lesley University, M

Massachusetts Institute of Technology, M
Regis College, MO
University of Massachusetts Amherst, M
University of Massachusetts Boston, M
University of Massachusetts Dartmouth, MO
Western New England University, M

Michigan

Central Michigan University, M
Eastern Michigan University, MO
Michigan State University, MD
Northern Michigan University, M
University of Michigan, M
University of Michigan - Flint, M
Wayne State University, MD
Western Michigan University, MD

Minnesota

Hamline University, M
Minnesota State University Mankato, M

Missouri

Lindenwood University, M
Missouri Western State University, M
Park University, O
Southeast Missouri State University, M
University of Missouri - Kansas City, M
Washington University in St. Louis, M

Montana

University of Montana, M

Nebraska

Creighton University, M
University of Nebraska at Kearney, M
University of Nebraska - Lincoln, MD
University of Nebraska at Omaha, MO

Nevada

University of Nevada, Las Vegas, M

New Hampshire

New England College, M
New Hampshire Institute of Art, M
Rivier University, M
Southern New Hampshire University, M

New Jersey

Drew University, M
Fairleigh Dickinson University, College at Florham,
    M
Kean University, M
Monmouth University, M
Montclair State University, O
Rowan University, MO
Rutgers University - Camden, M
Rutgers University - New Brunswick, M
Rutgers University - Newark, M
William Paterson University of New Jersey, M

New Mexico

Institute of American Indian Arts, M
New Mexico Highlands University, M
New Mexico State University, M
University of New Mexico, M

New York

Adelphi University, M
Binghamton University, State University of New
    York, M
Brooklyn College of the City University of New York,
    M
City College of the City University of New York, M
The College at Brockport, State University of New
    York, MO
Columbia University, M
Cornell University, M
Hofstra University, M
Hunter College of the City University of New York,
    M
Manhattanville College, M
New York University, M
Pratt Institute, M

Queens College of the City University of New York,
    M
St. Joseph's College, New York, M
Sarah Lawrence College, M
School of Visual Arts, M
Stony Brook University, State University of New
    York, MO
Syracuse University, MD

North Carolina

East Carolina University, MD
Lenoir-Rhyne University, M
North Carolina State University, M
Queens University of Charlotte, M
The University of North Carolina at Greensboro, M
The University of North Carolina Wilmington, M
Warren Wilson College, M

North Dakota

North Dakota State University, D

Ohio

Antioch University Midwest, M
Ashland University, M
Bowling Green State University, MD
Cleveland State University, M
Kent State University, M
Tiffin University, M
Union Institute & University, M
The University of Akron, M
The University of Findlay, M
The University of Toledo, O
Wright State University, M

Oklahoma

Oklahoma State University, M
University of Central Oklahoma, M
University of Oklahoma, M

Oregon

Oregon State University, M
Pacific University, M
University of Oregon, M

Pennsylvania

Carlow University, M
Carnegie Mellon University, M
Cedar Crest College, M
Chatham University, M
Penn State Harrisburg, O
Rosemont College, M
Saint Joseph's University, M
Seton Hill University, MO
Temple University, M
University of Pennsylvania, MD
University of Pittsburgh, M
Wilkes University, M

Rhode Island

Brown University, M
Rhode Island College, MO

South Carolina

Clemson University, M
Coastal Carolina University, M
University of South Carolina, M

Tennessee

Sewanee: The University of the South, M
University of Memphis, MD
The University of Tennessee at Chattanooga, MO
Vanderbilt University, M

Texas

Abilene Christian University, M
Our Lady of the Lake University of San Antonio, M
Sam Houston State University, M
Texas State University, M
University of Houston, MD
University of Houston - Victoria, M
University of North Texas, M
The University of Texas at Austin, M
The University of Texas at El Paso, MO
The University of Texas Rio Grande Valley, M

Utah

Brigham Young University, M
University of Utah, MD
Utah State University, M
Westminster College, M

Vermont

Bennington College, M
Goddard College, M

Virginia

George Mason University, MD
Hollins University, MO
James Madison University, M
Old Dominion University, M
Regent University, M
University of Virginia, M
Virginia Commonwealth University, M
Virginia Polytechnic Institute and State University,
    MD

Washington

Eastern Washington University, M
Pacific Lutheran University, M
Seattle Pacific University, M
University of Washington, M
University of Washington, Bothell, M

West Virginia

West Virginia University, M
West Virginia Wesleyan College, M

Wisconsin

Mount Mary University, M
University of Wisconsin - Eau Claire, M
University of Wisconsin - Madison, M
University of Wisconsin - Milwaukee, DO

Wyoming

University of Wyoming, M

U.S. Territories: Puerto Rico

University of the Sacred Heart, MO

Canada

British Columbia

The University of British Columbia, M
University of Victoria, M

Maritime Provinces: Nova Scotia

University of King's College, M

Ontario

University of Toronto, M
University of Windsor, M

Quebec

Concordia University, M

Saskatchewan

University of Regina, M

YOUTH MINISTRY

United States

Arizona

Arizona Christian University, B

Arkansas

Harding University, B
John Brown University, B

California

Hope International University, B
Simpson University, B
Vanguard University of Southern California, B
William Jessup University, B

Colorado

Colorado Christian University, B

Florida

Florida Southern College, B
Trinity College of Florida, B

Georgia

Toccoa Falls College, B

Idaho

Boise Bible College, B

Illinois

Greenville College, B
Judson University, B
Lincoln Christian University, B
North Park University, B
Olivet Nazarene University, B
Trinity International University, B

Indiana

Anderson University, B
Crossroads Bible College, B
Grace College, B
Huntington University, B
Indiana Wesleyan University, B
University of Indianapolis, B

Iowa

Dordt College, B
Emmaus Bible College, B

Kansas

Central Christian College of Kansas, AB
Hesston College, A
Manhattan Christian College, B
MidAmerica Nazarene University, B
Southwestern College, B
Tabor College, B

Kentucky

Asbury University, B
Kentucky Mountain Bible College, B
The Southern Baptist Theological Seminary, B

Louisiana

New Orleans Baptist Theological Seminary, A

Massachusetts

Eastern Nazarene College, B

Michigan

Andrews University, B
Cornerstone University, B
Grace Bible College, B
Great Lakes Christian College, B
Kuyper College, B
Rochester College, B
Spring Arbor University, B

Minnesota

Augsburg College, B
Crossroads College, B
Crown College, B
North Central University, B
Oak Hills Christian College, B
University of Northwestern - St. Paul, B

Missouri

Calvary Bible College and Theological Seminary, AB

Nebraska

Grace University, B

New York

Davis College, B
Nyack College, B

North Carolina

Mid-Atlantic Christian University, B
Pfeiffer University, B
Piedmont International University, AB

North Dakota

Trinity Bible College, B

Ohio

Bluffton University, B
Cedarville University, B
Malone University, B
Mount Vernon Nazarene University, B
Ohio Christian University, B
Ohio Dominican University, B
Ohio Northern University, B

Oklahoma

Hillsdale Free Will Baptist College, B
Southern Nazarene University, B
Southwestern Christian University, B

Oregon

Corban University, B
Multnomah University, B
New Hope Christian College, B
Northwest Christian University, B

Pennsylvania

Cairn University, B
Eastern University, B
Geneva College, B
Lancaster Bible College, B
Summit University, B
University of Valley Forge, AB

South Carolina

Charleston Southern University, B
Columbia International University, B
North Greenville University, B

South Dakota

University of Sioux Falls, B

Tennessee

Carson-Newman University, B
Freed-Hardeman University, B
King University, B
Lee University, B
Lipscomb University, B
Trevecca Nazarene University, B

Texas

East Texas Baptist University, B
Howard Payne University, B
LeTourneau University, B
Lubbock Christian University, B
Messenger College, B
Southwestern Assemblies of God University, B

Virginia

University of Valley Forge Virginia Campus, B

Washington

Northwest University, B

Wisconsin

Concordia University Wisconsin, B
Maranatha Baptist University, B

Canada

Alberta

Prairie Bible Institute, AB
Rocky Mountain College, B

Manitoba

Providence University College & Theological Seminary, B

Ontario

Emmanuel Bible College, B
Master's College and Seminary, B
Redeemer University College, B

Saskatchewan

Briercrest College, B
Horizon College & Seminary, B

YOUTH SERVICES/ADMINISTRATION

United States

Alabama

Samford University, B

Arizona

Pima Community College, A

Kentucky

Murray State University, B

Massachusetts

Wheelock College, B

New Jersey

Montclair State University, B

Oklahoma

Southwestern Christian University, B

Rhode Island

Rhode Island College, B

South Carolina

Midlands Technical College, A

Canada

British Columbia

Thompson Rivers University, B
University of Northern British Columbia, B

Ontario

The University of Western Ontario, B

ZOOLOGY/ANIMAL BIOLOGY

United States

Alabama

Auburn University, BM

California

California State University, Long Beach, B
Cerritos College, B
El Camino College, A
Humboldt State University, B
San Bernardino Valley College, A
San Diego State University, B
San Francisco State University, B
Sonoma State University, B
University of California, Davis, BM
University of California, Santa Barbara, B

Colorado

Colorado State University, BMD

Connecticut

University of Connecticut, MD

Florida

Broward College, A
Palm Beach State College, A
South Florida State College, A
University of Florida, BMD

Georgia

Fort Valley State University, B

Hawaii

University of Hawaii at Manoa, BMD

Idaho

North Idaho College, A

Illinois

Illinois State University, MD
Olivet Nazarene University, B
Southern Illinois University Carbondale, BMD
University of Chicago, D
University of Illinois at Urbana - Champaign, MD
Western Illinois University, O

Indiana

Indiana University Bloomington, MD

Kansas

Central Christian College of Kansas, AB
Emporia State University, M
Garden City Community College, A

Kentucky

Kentucky Wesleyan College, B

Maine

College of the Atlantic, B
University of Maine, BMD

Michigan

Andrews University, B
Michigan State University, BMD
Northern Michigan University, B

Montana

University of Montana, BMD

New Hampshire

University of New Hampshire, BMD

New Jersey

Rutgers University - Newark, B

New Mexico

Eastern New Mexico University, M
Western New Mexico University, B

New York

Canisius College, BM
Cornell University, D
State University of New York College of Environ-
    mental Science and Forestry, B
State University of New York at Oswego, B

North Carolina

Mars Hill University, B
North Carolina State University, BMD

North Dakota

Dakota College at Bottineau, A
North Dakota State University, BMD
University of North Dakota, MD

Ohio

Kent State University, B
Malone University, B
Miami University, B
Miami University Hamilton, B
Miami University Middletown, A
The Ohio State University, B
Ohio University, B
Ohio Wesleyan University, B
The University of Akron, B

Oklahoma

Oklahoma State University, B
University of Oklahoma, B

Oregon

Oregon State University, BMD

Pennsylvania

Delaware Valley University, B

Texas

Texas A&M University, B
Texas Tech University, BMD
The University of Texas at El Paso, B

Utah

Snow College, A
Utah State University, B
Weber State University, B

Vermont

Bennington College, B
University of Vermont, B

Virginia

Liberty University, B

Washington

The Evergreen State College, B
Washington State University, B

Wisconsin

University of Wisconsin - Madison, BMD
University of Wisconsin - Oshkosh, M

Wyoming

University of Wyoming, BMD

Canada

Alberta

University of Alberta, B
University of Calgary, B

British Columbia

Thompson Rivers University, B
The University of British Columbia, BMD
The University of British Columbia - Okanagan
    Campus, B
University of Victoria, B

Manitoba

Brandon University, B
University of Manitoba, BMD

Maritime Provinces: New Brunswick

University of New Brunswick Fredericton, B

Maritime Provinces: Nova Scotia

Dalhousie University, B

Newfoundland and Labrador

Memorial University of Newfoundland, B

Ontario

University of Guelph, BMD
University of Toronto, B

Quebec

McGill University, B